S0-BIW-498

REFERENCE ENCYCLOPEDIA

WITHDRAWN

OF THE
AMERICAN INDIAN

23RD EDITION

BARRY T. KLEIN

REFERENCE ENCYCLOPEIA OF THE AMERICAN INDIAN

23rd Edition

Copyright © 2018

TODD PUBLICATIONS
Delray Beach, Florida 33446
(561) 910-0440
E-mail: toddpub@yahoo.com

All Rights Reserved
No part of this book may be reproduced in any form
Without permission in writing from the publisher

While every effort has been made to ensure the reliability of the
Information presented in this publication, Todd Publications
Does not guarantee the accuracy of the data contained herein.
Todd accepts no payments for listings; and inclusion in the publication
of any organization, institution, publication, or individual
does not imply endorsement by the editor or publisher

ISBN 978-0-873400-459

Table of Contents

Section Two:

Canadian Section:

Section Three:

Section Four:

Introduction

According to figures released by the 2015 U.S. Census, there are approximately three million American Indians & Alaska Natives and two million mixed-race Native Americans in the United States. The ten states with the largest American Indian & Alaska Native alone or in-combination population in 2015 were California (800,000), Oklahoma (550,000), Arizona (370,000), Texas (300,000), New York (250,000), New Mexico (220,000), Washington (170,000), North Carolina (150,000), Florida (100,000), and Michigan (75,000). Alaska has approximately 100,000 Eskimos and Aleuts. The largest number of people who identified with an American Indian tribal grouping, either alone or in combination, identified as Cherokee (819,000). The Navajo tribal grouping had the largest number of individuals who identified with one tribal grouping and no other race (287,000). Among the largest American Indian tribal groupings, Blackfeet had the highest proportion that reported more than one tribal grouping or race. Almost 75% of Blackfeet individuals reported an additional race and/or tribal grouping. The largest Native tribal grouping, either alone or in combination, was Yup'ik (34,000), followed by Inupiat (33,000). Yup'ik also had the greatest number of people who identified with one tribal grouping and no other race (29,000). Among all Alaska Native tribal groupings, Tlingit-Haida had the highest proportion who reported more than one tribal grouping or race. 42% of Tlingit-Haida individuals reported an additional race and/or tribal grouping.

Population figures have been increasing at a rate of more than 50% per decade since 1960. There is no one Federal or tribal definition that establishes a person's identity as Native American. Government Agencies use different criteria for determining who is a Native American. Similarly, tribal groups have varying requirements for determining tribal membership.

There are more than 300 Federal Indian reservations and 567 federally recognized tribes in the United States including about 200 Alaska Native village groups. An Indian reservation is an area of land reserved for Indian use. The name comes from the early days of Indian-white relations when Indian tribes relinquished land through treaties, reserving a portion for their own use. Congressional acts, Executive orders, and agreements have also created reservations. Many reservations today, however, have some non-Indian residents and non-Indian landowners. Tribe among the North American Indians originally meant a body of persons bound together by blood ties who were socially, politically, and religiously organized, and who lived together, occupying a definite territory and speaking a common language or dialect. With the relegation of Indians to reservations, the word tribe developed a number of different meanings. Today, it can be a distinct group within an Indian village or community, a large number of communities, several different groups or villages speaking different languages but sharing a common government, or a widely scattered number of villages with a common language but no common government. According to a 2010 estimate by the DOI's Office of Indian Affairs, about 1.5 million Indians live on or adjacent to reservations. The remaining 3.5 million Native Americans and Alaska Natives reside in cities and suburbs across the country.

A special U.S. Senate committee charged with investigating fraud and mismanagement in the Office of Indian Affairs has recommended adoption of what it calls "A New Federalism,"" in which the federal government would abolish the BIA and transfer annual federal appropriations directly to tribal governments. The committee said new agreements are needed between the federal governments and the tribes "that both allow American Indians to run their own affairs and pledge permanent federal support for tribal governments." These new agreements would not affect any existing treaty rights or alter the legal status of tribal governments. An Office of Federal-Tribal Relations (OFTR) would be created within the executive office of the President. The OFTR would be responsible for negotiating and overseeing implementation of formal agreements with federally recognized Indian tribes. "The agreements will allow any tribe that so chooses to exit the current bureaucracy of federal Indian programs and to receive and use at its own discretion a proportional share of the federal Indian budget." The committee proposes that funding be allocated to tribal governments based solely on population figures. The special committee also recommended that each House of Congress create a permanent full committee on Indian affairs, with additional staff specifically assigned to perform oversight and investigations.

The U.S., upon ratification of an agreement by both a tribe and the federal government, would provide the tribe with an annual Tribal Self-Governance Grant (TSGG), equaling its fair share of the current federal Indian budget. The size of the grant would be proportional to the population base of the tribe. Each grant would be supplemented by an annual cost-of-living allowance. Equally important, there would be a transfer from the Department of the Interior's Office of Indian Affairs and Indian Health Service and any other federal agency with Indian-related programs to the contracting tribes, such assets as necessary for the tribe to carry out their new responsibilities under the agreement.

This 23rd Edition of Reference Encyclopedia of the American Indian is divided into four main sections. The first section contains source listings. Each listing gives address, phone number, contact and, in most cases, a brief description of activities and pertinent information. Listings are arranged either alphabetically or alpha-geographically. At the beginning of each section there is an explanatory note detailing the type of sources listed and the manner in which they are arranged. The length of each listing reflects the amount of material received from each source. Material has been researched directly from questionnaires or has been gathered from other reliable sources. For further information on any listed source, it is suggested that the reader write to the address or call the number given in the listing. The second section is solely Canadian listings; the third section of the book is a bibliography of approximately 10,000 in-print books. Listed alphabetically, each book gives basic bibliographic information. The alphabetical section is broken down into a subject categories section with corresponding titles listed for each category. A publishers index is provided at the end giving the publishers' addresses and phone numbers. The fourth section contains approximately 3,000 listings of which there are more than 1,500 biographical sketches of prominent Native Americans involved in Indian Affairs, education, healthcare, business, the arts and professions, as well as non-Indians active in Indian affairs, history, art, anthropology, archaeology, etc., and the many fields to which the subject of the American Indian is related.

All changes and additions to the listings in this book should be directed to me at the address given at the bottom of the title page.

Barry Klein
Editor

REFERENCE ENCYCLOPEDIA OF THE AMERICAN INDIAN

There are 567 federally recognized American Indian tribal nations & communities. These groups are entitled to U.S. legal protections of tribal self-government & rights to tribally owned land. Included are about 200 Alaskan Native groups & 200 state recognized & non-recognized Indian communities that have not signed treaties, or that have not had regular legal relations with the U.S. Government. The U.S. Department of the Interior, Office of Indian Affairs is the agency that identifies & recognizes Indian tribal entities for establishing & maintaining federal government-to-government relations with Native Americans. Those tribal nations, bands & groups that are recognized by the agency are listed below, with the agency or area office of jurisdiction indicated.

This section lists tribal nations & communities and their governing bodies that handle tribal affairs. Arranged alphabetically within states.

ALABAMA

THE POARCH BAND OF CREEK INDIANS
5811 Jack Springs Rd. • Atmore, AL 36502
(251) 368-9136 Fax 368-4502/1026; Website: www.pci-nsn.gov
Stephanie A. Bryan, Chairperson; E-mail: sbryan@pci-nsn.gov
Robert McGhee, Vice Chair; E-mail: rmcghee@pci-nsn.gov
Eddie Tullis, Treasurer; Charlotte Meckel, Secretary
Edie Jackson, Tribal Administrator
Councilmembers: Arthur Mothershed, Keith Martin, Sandy Hollinger, Dewitt Carter, Garvis Sells,
Eddie Jackson, Tribal Administrator; E-mail: ejackson@pci-nsn.gov
Kelli Ramer, Tribal Council Office Director (368-9136 ext. 2110)
E-mail: kramer@pci-nsn.gov
Debra Strickland, Legislative Cordinator (251) 368-9136 ext. 2935
E-mail: dstrickland@pci-nsn.gov
Edie Jackson, Health & Elder Services Division Director
E-mail: ejackson@pci-nsn.gov
Karla S. Martin, Community Services Division Director
E-mail: ksmartin@pci-nsn.gov
Sandra Hiebert, Education Director; E-mail: shiebert@pci-nsn.gov
Daniel McGhee, Tribal Gaming Commission Administrator
E-mail: dmcghee@pci-nsn.gov
Mindy N. Jackson, Cultural Director; E-mail: mjackson@pci-nsn.gov
Brandy Chunn, Museum Coordinator; E-mail: bchunn@pci-nsn.gov
Deidra Suwanee Dees, Director/Tribal Archivist
E-mail: ddees@pci-nsn.gov
James T. Martin, CIEDA President & CEO
Gayle Johnson, Editor, Poarch Creek News
E-mail: gjohnson@pci-nsn.gov
Sharon Delmar, Public Relations Tribal Liaison
E-mail: sdelmar@pci-nsn.gov
Tribe served: Creek. *Enrolled members*: 3,000 (1,000 members live in the vicinity of Poarch, eight miles northwest of Atmore, in rural Escambia County, 57 miles east of Mobile.) The Tribe operates a variety of economic enterprises that employ hundreds of area residents. *Resources*: Creek Indian Enterprises Development Authority (CIEDA); Museum, Gift Shop. *Activities*: Annual Thanksgiving Powwow. *Facilities*: Poarch Creek Indian Gaming manages three gaming facilities in Alabama, including: the Wind Creek Casino & Hotel in Atmore; Creek Casino Wetumpka; and, Creek Casino Montgomery. The Poarch Band of Creek Indians is an active partner in the state of Alabama, contributing to economic, educational, social and cultural projects benefiting both tribal members & residents of these local communities & neighboring towns. Publications: Monthly newsletter; Tribal press releases. Choctaw Agency. Eastern Regional Office.

ALASKA

NATIVE VILLAGE OF AFOGNAK
323 Carolyn St., Kodiak, AK 99615
(907) 486-6357 Fax 486-6529
Website: www.afognak.org; E-mail: tribe@afognak.org
Loretta Nelson, Chairperson (expires 2016)
Meagan Christiansen, Vice Chairperson (expires 2017)
Melissa Borton, Tribal Adminstrator; Nancy Nelson, Program Administrator
Kari Sherod, Alutiiq Language Program Manager
Denise Malutin, Cultural Programs Coordinator
Afognak Native Corporation: (907) 486-6014 Fax 486-2514
(907) 222-9500 Fax 222-9501; Website: www.afognak.com
Greg Hambright, President/CEO; Denise May, Chairperson
Loretta Nelson, Vice-Chairperson; Janice Stiller, Secretary
Programs: Ag'waneq Language Program; Social Services; Environmental.
Resources: Heritage Library; Alutiiq Museum. West-Central Alaska Agency.

AGDAAGUX TRIBE OF KING COVE
P.O. Box 249, King Cove, AK 99612
(907) 497-2648 Fax 497-2803
Etta Kuzakin, President; E-mail: atc@arctic.net
West-Central Alaska Agency

NATIVE VILLAGE OF AKHIOK
P.O. Box 5030, Akhiok, AK 99615
(907) 836-2312 Fax 836-2345; Donene Amodo, President
Tribe: Eskimo. *In residence*: 90. West-Central Alaska Agency.

AKIACHAK NATIVE COMMUNITY
P.O. Box 70, Akiachak, AK 99551
(907) 825-4626 Fax 825-4029
Phillip Peters, Sr., President; E-mail: akiachak@aitc.org
Tribe: Yup'ik Eskimo. *In residence*: 500. *Area*: 115,600 acres.
Cooperatively manage community library with school district.
West-Central Alaska Agency.

AKIAK NATIVE COMMUNITY
P.O. Box 52127, Akiak, AK 99552
(907) 765-7112 Fax 765-7512
Ivan M. Ivan, Sr., Chief; E-mail: akiak@aol.com
Tribe: Eskimo. In residence: 225. West-Central Alaska Agency.

NATIVE VILLAGE OF AKUTAN
Akutan Traditional Council, P.O. Box 89, Akutan, AK 99553
(907) 698-2300 Fax 698-2301; Joe Bereskin, President
Tribe: Eskimo. Self-Gov: Aleutian/Pribilof Islands Association
West-Central Alaska Agency.

NATIVE VILLAGE OF ALAKANUK
P.O. Box 149, Alakanuk, AK 99554
(907) 238-3419 Fax 238-3429
Ben Phillip, President; E-mail: Clarence@avcp.org
Tribe: Eskimo. Self-Gov: Association of Village Council President.
West-Central Alaska Agency

ALATNA NATIVE VILLAGE
P.O. Box 70, Allakaket, Alatna, AK 99720
(907) 968-2261 Fax 968-2305; Sam Harding, First Chief
E-mail: alatnatribe@yahoo.com
Self-Gov: Tanana Chiefs. Fairbanks Agency.

NATIVE VILLAGE OF ALEKNAGIK
P.O. Box 115, Aleknagik, AK 99555
(907) 842-2080 Fax 842-2081
Website: www.aleknagiktraditionalcouncil.com
Margie Aloysius, President; George Tinker, Vice President
Allen Ilutsik, Village Administrator
E-mail: aleknagiktraditional@yahoo.com
Self-Gov: Bristol Bay Native Association, Inc. *Tribe*: Athapascan.
In residence: 175. West-Central Alaska Agency.

ALEUT COMMUNITY OF SAINT PAUL ISLAND
P.O. Box 86, St. Paul Island, AK 99660
(907) 546-3200 Fax 546-3254; Amos Philemonoff, President
E-mail: president@tgspi.com
Tribe: Aleut. Self-Gov: Aleutian/Pribilof Islands Association.
West-Central Alaska Agency.

ALGAACIQ NATIVE VILLAGE
P.O. Box 48, St. Mary's, AK 99658
(907) 438-2932 Fax 438-2227; Moses Paukan, Sr., President
Self-Gov: Association of Village Council Presidents
Tribe: Eskimo. *In residence*: 125. West-Central Alaska Agency.

ALLAKAKET VILLAGE
P.O. Box 30, Allakaket, AK 99720
(907) 968-2237 Fax 968-2233; Simon Pollock, First Chief
E-mail: alakaketepa@yahoo.com
Self-Gov: Tanana Chiefs. *Tribe*: Athapascan. *In residence*: 120.
Fairbanks Agency.

NATIVE VILLAGE OF AMBLER
P.O. Box 47, Ambler, AK 99786
(907) 445-2238 Fax 445-2257; Katherine Cleveland, First Chief
E-mail: tribemanager@iivisaappaat.org
Self-Gov: Maniilaq Consortium. Fairbanks Agency.

VILLAGE OF ANAKTUVUK PASS
P.O. Box 21157, Anaktuvuk Pass, AK 99721
(907) 661-2575 Fax 661-2576
Charles Hugo, President; E-mail: akp@inupiatgov.com
Tribe: Eskimo. *In residence*: 100. Fairbanks Agency.

YUPIIT OF ANDREAFSKI
P.O. Box 88, St. Mary's, AK 99658
(907) 438-2312 Fax 438-2512; George Beans, Sr., President
E-mail: yupiit.of.andreafki@gmail.com
Tribe: Yupiit. *Membership*: 150. *Publication*: Andreafsky Tribal Newsletter.
Activities: Meetings are held 1st Wednesday of each month. West-Central
Alaska Agency.

ANGOON COMMUNITY ASSOCIATION
P.O. Box 328, Angoon, AK 99820
(907) 788-3411 Fax 788-3412; Frank Sharp, President
E-mail: rjack@ccthita.org
Self-Gov: Central Council of Tlingit-Haida. West-Central Alaska Agency

VILLAGE OF ANIAK
P.O. Box 349, Aniak, AK 99557
(907) 675-4349 Fax 675-4513; Wayne Morgan, President
E-mail: aniaktribe@yahoo.com
Tribe: Eskimo. In residence: 150. West-Central Alaska Agency.

ANVIK VILLAGE
P.O. Box 10, Anvik, AK 99558
(907) 663-6322 Fax (866) 524-5035; Website: www.anviktribalcouncil.com
Carl Jerue, Jr., First Chief; E-mail: carljerue@yahoo.com
Robert Walker, Second Chief; E-mail: anch47_jump@yahoo.com
Self-Gov: Tanana Chiefs. *Tribe*: Eskimo. *In residence*: 150. Fairbanks Agency.

ASA'CARSARMIUT TRIBE
P.O. Box 32249, Mountain Village, AK 99632
(907) 591-2814 Fax 591-2811; James C. Landlord, First Chief
Tribe: Eskimo. *In residence*: 275. West-Central Alaska Agency.

NATIVE VILLAGE OF ATKA
P.O. Box 47030, Atka, AK 99547
(907) 839-2229 Fax 839-2269
Mark Snigaroff, President; E-mail: atkaira@gci.net
Self-Gov: Aleutian/Pribilof Islands Association. West-Central Alaska Agency.

VILLAGE OF ATMAUTLUAK
P.O. Box 6568, Atmautluak, AK 99559
(907) 553-5610 Fax 553-5216; Nicholai O. Pavilla, President
E-mail: atmautluaktc@hughes.net
West-Central Alaska Agency.

NATIVE VILLAGE OF ATQASUK
P.O. Box 91108, Atqasuk, AK 99791
(907) 633-2575 Fax 633-2576; Elizabeth Bordeaux, President
E-mail: jkakpik@hotmail.com. Fairbanks Agency.

NATIVE VILLAGE OF BARROW
Inupiat Traditional Government, P.O. Box 1130, Barrow, AK 99723
(907) 852-4411 Fax 852-8844; Thomas Olemaun, President
Website: www.nvbarrow.net; E-mail: toleaun@nvbarrow.net
Tribe: Inupiat. *In residence*: 3,000. Fairbanks Field Office.

BEAVER VILLAGE COUNCIL
P.O. Box 24029, Beaver, AK 99724
(907) 628-6126 Fax 628-6815; Rhonda Pitka, Chief
Self-Gov: Tanana Chiefs. *Tribes*: Eskimo, Athapascan, Indian.
In residence: 150. Fairbanks Agency.

NATIVE VILLAGE OF BELKOFSKY
P.O. Box 57, King Cove, AK 99612
(907) 497-3122 Fax 497-3123
James Kenezuroff, President; E-mail: kcbtc@arctic.net
Self-Gov: Aleutian/Pribilof Islands Association, Inc.
Tribe: Aleut. *In residence*: 200. West-Central Alaska Agency.

NATIVE VILLAGE OF BILL MOORE'S SLOUGH
P.O. Box 20288 • Kotlik, AK 99620
(907) 899-4232 Fax 899-4461; Cheryl Sinka, Chairperson
E-mail: rbmsroads@yahoo.com
Self-Gov: Assn of Village Council PresidentsWest-Central Alaska Agency.

BIRCH CREEK TRIBAL COUNCIL
P.O. Box 71372, Fort Yukon, AK 99701
(907) 221-2211 Fax 221-2312; Ernest E. James, First Chief
E-mail: e_itta@hotmail.com
Self-Gov: Tanana Chiefs. Fairbanks Agency.

NATIVE VILLAGE OF BREVIG MISSION
P.O. Box 85039, Brevig Mission, AK 99785
(907) 642-4301 Fax 642-2099; E-mail: tc.kts@kawerak.org
Stewart R. Tocktoo, President
Self-Gov: Kawerak. Fairbanks Agency.

NATIVE VILLAGE OF BUCKLAND (IRA)
P.O. Box 67, Buckland, AK 99727
(907) 494-2171 Fax 494-2192; Percy Ballot, Sr., President
E-mail: tribeclerk@nunachiak.org
Self-Gov: Maniilaq Consortium. Fairbanks Agency.

NATIVE VILLAGE OF CANTWELL
P.O. Box 94, Cantwell, AK 99729
(907) 768-2591 Fax 768-1111; Rene Nicklie, President
E-mail: hallvc@mtaonlin.net
Self-Gov: Copper River Native Association, Inc.
Tribe: Athapascan. West-Central Alaska Agency.

CENTRAL COUNCIL OF TLINGIT & HAIDA INDIAN TRIBES OF ALASKA
320 W. Willoughby Ave., Suite 300, Juneau, AK 99801
(800) 344-1432; (907) 586-1432 Fax 586-8970; Website: www.ccthita.org;
Richard J. Peterson (Tlingit), President; E-mail: rpeterson@ccthita.org
Corrine Garza, COO, Tribal Opeations; Theresa Velton, CFO-Finance
Richard Peterson, 1st V.P.; E-mail: richard@kasan.org
Tribes: Tlingit & Haida. *Population served*: 29,000.

CHALKYITSIK VILLAGE
P.O. Box 57, Chalkyitsik, AK 99788
(907) 848-8117 Fax 848-8986; Stephanie Herbert First Chief
E-mail: ta_cvc@hotmail.com
Self-Gov: Tanana Chiefs. Fairbanks Agency.

CHEESH-NA TRIBAL COUNCIL
P.O. Box 241, Gakona, AK 99586
(907) 822-3503 Fax 822-5179
Larry Sinyon, President; E-mail: wjustin@cheeshna.org
West-Central Alaska Agency

VILLAGE OF CHEFORNAK
P.O. Box 110, Chefornak, AK 99561
(907) 867-8850 Fax 867-8711; Alexie Flynn, President
E-mail: cyf_tcoffice@yahoo.com
Self-Gov: Association of Village Council Presidents
Tribe: Eskimo. *In residence*: 175. West-Central Alaska Agency.

NATIVE VILLAGE OF CHENEGA (aka Chanega)
623 Cato St., P.O. Box 8079, Chenega Bay, AK 99574
(907) 573-5132 Fax 573-5120
E-mail: s.angiaik@nativevillageofchanega.com
Larry Evanoff, Chairperson
Self-Gov: Chugachmiut, Inc. West-Central Alaska Agency.

CHEVAK NATIVE VILLAGE
P.O. Box 140, Chevak, AK 99563
(907) 858-7428 Fax 858-7812; James Ayuluk, First Chief
E-mail: chevaktc@gmail.com
Self-Gov: Association of Village Council Presidents
Tribe: Eskimo. *In residence*: 400. West-Central Alaska Agency.

CHICKALOON VILLAGE - ATHABASCAN NATION
P.O. Box 1105, Chickaloon, AK 99674
(907) 745-0749 Fax 745-0709; Website: www.chickaloon.org
E-mail: cvadmin@chickaloon.org; Gary Harrison, Chief & Chair
Rick Harrison, Vice Chair; Jennifer Harrison, Executive Director
Maintains school. *Publication*: "Traditional Stories About Values"
by Katherine Wade. West-Central Alaska Agency.

CHIGNIK BAY TRIBAL COUNCIL
P.O. Box 50, Chignik, AK 99564
(907) 749-2445 Fax 749-2423
E-mail: cbaytc@aol.com; Roderick Carlson, President
Self-Gov: Bristol Bay Native Association, Inc.
Tribe: Eskimo. *In residence*: 385. West-Central Alaska Agency.

NATIVE VILLAGE OF CHIGNIK LAGOON
P.O. Box 09, Chignik Lagoon, AK 99565
 (907) 840-2281 Fax 840-2217
 Clemens Grunert, Jr., President; E-mail: clagoon@gci.net
Self-Gov: Bristol Bay Native Association, Inc.
Tribe: Eskimo. West-Central Alaska Field Office.

CHIGNIK LAKE VILLAGE COUNCIL
P.O. Box 33, Chignik Lake, AK 99548
 (907) 845-2212 Fax 845-2217; John Lind, President
 E-mail: chignicklakecouncil@gmail.com
Self-Gov: Bristol Bay Native Association, Inc.
Tribe: Eskimo. West-Central Alaska Agency.

CHILKAT INDIAN VILLAGE (KLUKWAN)
HC 60 Box 2207 • Haines, AK 99827
 (907) 767-5505 Fax 767-5518
 Website: www.chilkatindianvillage.org
 E-mail: klukwan@chilkat-nsn.gov; Kimberley Strong, President
West-Central Alaska Agency.

CHILKOOT INDIAN ASSOCIATION (IRA)
P.O. Box 490, Haines, AK 99827
 (907) 766-2323 Fax 766-2365
 Website: www.chilkatindianvillage.org
 Mr. Leslie B. Katzeek, President
 E-mail: lkatzeek@chilkoot-nsn.gov
Self-Gov: Central Council of Tlingit-Haida
Tribe: Chilkoot. West-Central Alaska Agency.

CHINIK ESKIMO COMMUNITY (aka Golovin)
P.O. Box 62020, Golovin, AK 99762
 (907) 779-2214 Fax 779-2829; Irene A. Navarro, President
 E-mail: inavarro@kawerak.org
Self-Gov: Kawerak. *Tribe*: Eskimo. *In residence*: 140. Fairbanks Agency.

NATIVE VILLAGE OF CHISTOCHINA
P.O. Box 241, Gakona, AK 99586
 (907) 822-3503 Fax 822-5179; Karen Eskilda, President
Tribe: Athapascan. West-Central Alaska Agency.

CHITINA TRADITIONAL INDIAN VILLAGE
P.O. Box 31, Chitina, AK 99566
 (907) 823-2215 Fax 823-2233; Website: www.chitinanative.com
 Rose Tyone, President; E-mail: nativevillageofchitina@yahoo.com
West-Central Alaska Agency. Maintains a Community Health Center.
Resources: Chitina Native Corporation.

NATIVE VILLAGE OF CHUATHBALUK (Russian Mission, Kuskokwim)
P.O. Box CHU, Chuathbaluk, AK 99557
 (907) 467-4313 Fax 467-4113; Jerry Peterson, Chairperson
 E-mail: chuathtradcouncil@gmail.com
West-Central Alaska Field Office.

CHULOONAWICK NATIVE VILLAGE
P.O. Box 245, Chuloonawick, AK 99581
 (907) 949-1345 Fax 949-1346
 Michael A. Jimmy, President; E-mail: coffice@starband.net
West-Central Alaska Agency.

CIRCLE NATIVE COMMUNITY (IRA)
P.O. Box 89, Circle, AK 99733
 (907) 733-2822 Fax 773-2823
Solomon John, 1st Chief; E-mail: angela@arcticrg.com
Self-Gov: Tanana Chiefs. *Tribe*: Athapascan. *In residence*: 115.
Fairbanks Agency.

VILLAGE OF CLARK'S POINT
P.O. Box 90, Clark's Point, AK 99569
 (907) 236-1435 Fax 236-1428; Betty Gardiner, President
 E-mail: sharonclark3225@yahoo.com
Self-Gov: Bristol Bay Native Association, Inc.
West-Central Alaska Agency.

COOK INLET TRIBAL COUNCIL, INC.
3600 San Jeronimo Dr. • Anchorage, AK 99508
 (877) 985-5900; (907) 793-3378 Fax 793-3602
 Website: www.citci.com; Gloria O'Neil, President/CEO
Purpose: Provide social, educational & employment services to 12,000
Alaska Natives & Native Americans living in Cook Inlet region.
Established 1983.

NATIVE VILLAGE OF NOME COUNCIL
200 W. 5th Ave., P.O. Box 1090, Nome, AK 99762
 (907) 443-7649 Fax 443-5965; Shane Smithhisler, Chairman
 Website: www.kawerak.org; E-mail: cou@kawerak.org
Self-Gov: Kawerak. Alaska Regional Office.

CRAIG COMMUNITY ASSOCIATION
1330 Craig/Klawock Hwy., P.O. Box 828, Craig, AK 99921
 (907) 826-3996 Fax 826-3997; Clinton E. Cook, President
 E-mail: tribal.admin@craigtribe.org
Self-Gov: Central Council of Tlingit-Haida. West-Central Alaska Agency.

NATIVE VILLAGE OF CROOKED CREEK
P.O. Box 69, Crooked Creek, AK 99575
 (907) 432-2200 Fax 432-2201; Julie Zaukar President
 Website: iditacom.org; E-mail: bbcc@starband.net
Self-Gov: Kuskokwim Native Association. *Tribe*: Athapascan.
West-Central Alaska Agency.

CURYUNG TRIBAL COUNCIL
531 D St., P.O. Box 216, Dillingham, AK 99576
 (907) 842-2384 Fax 842-4510; E-mail: dorothy@curyungtribe.com
 Thomas Tilden, 1st Chief; Joyce Armstrong, 2nd Chief
Self-Gov: Bristol Bay Native Association, Inc. *Tribes*: Athapascan & Indian.
In residence: 450. West-Central Alaska Agency.

NATIVE VILLAGE OF DEERING
P.O. Box 36089, Deering, AK 99736
 (907) 363-2138 Fax 363-2107; Website: www.ipnatchiaq,org
 Kevin Mooto, President; E-mail: tribeadmin@ipnatchiaq.org
Self-Gov: Maniilaq Consortium. *Tribe*: Eskimo. In residence: 250.
Fairbanks Agency.

NATIVE VILLAGE OF DIOMEDE (IRA) (aka Inalik)
P.O. Box 7079, Diomede, AK 99762
 (907) 686-2175 Fax 686-2203
 Robert F. Soolook, President; E-mail: fozenna@kawerak.org
Self-Gov: Kawerak. Fairbanks Agency.

VILLAGE OF DOT LAKE
P.O. Box 2279, Dot Lake, AK 99737
 (907) 882-2695 Fax 882-5558; Roberta Hamilton, President
 E-mail: karla.champagne@tananachiefs.org
Self-Gov: Tanana Chiefs. Fairbanks Agency.

DOUGLAS INDIAN ASSOCIATION
811 W. 12th St. • Juneau, AK 99801
 (907) 364-2916 Fax 364-2917; Clarence Laiti, President
 E-mail: emorrison-dia@gci.net
West-Central Alaska Agency.

NATIVE VILLAGE OF EAGLE (IRA)
P.O. Box 19, Eagle, AK 99738
 (907) 547-2281 Fax 571-2318; E-mail: eagle.village@yahoo.com
 Bertha Ulzi, First Chief
Self-Gov: Tanana Chiefs. *Tribes*: Eskimo & Indian. Fairbanks Agency.

EDZENO NATIVE VILLAGE COUNCIL
P.O. Box 9105, Nikolai, AK 99691
 (907) 293-2311 Fax 293-2481; Nick Alexia, First Chief
 E-mail: nickalexia@hotmail.com
Self Gov: Tanana Chiefs. *Tribes*: Athapascans & Indian.
In residence: 145. Fairbanks Agency.

NATIVE VILLAGE OF EEK
P.O. Box 89, Eek, AK 99578
 (907) 536-5128 Fax 536-5418; E-mail: etcgov@yahoo.com
 Annie M. Pete, President
Self-Gov: Association of Village Council Presidents
Tribe: Eskimo. *In residence*: 190. West-Central Alaska Agency.

EGEGIK VILLAGE
289 Airport Rd., P.O. Box 29, Egegik, AK 99579
 (907) 233-2211 Fax 233-2312; Kevin Deigh, First Chief
 E-mail: egegiktribeoffice@yahoo.com
Self-Gov: Bristol Bay Native Association, Inc. *Tribes*: Eskimo & Indian.
In residence: 140. West-Central Alaska Field Office.

EKLUTNA NATIVE VILLAGE
26339 Eklutna Village Rd., Chugiak, AK 99567
 (907) 688-6020 Fax 688-6021; Website: www.eklutna-nsn.gov

Lee Stephan, President/First Chief; E-mail: president@eklutna-nsn.gov
Maria Coleman, Vice President; Marlene Johnson, Tribal Administrator
E-mail: administrator@eklutna-nsn.gov
Tribe: Athapascan. West-Central Alaska Agency.

NATIVE VILLAGE OF EKUK
P.O. Box 530, Dillingham, AK 99576
(907) 842-3842 Fax 842-3843; Robert Heyano, President
E-mail: evc@ekukvc.net
Self-Gov: Bristol Bay Native Association, Inc. West-Central Alaska Agency.

NATIVE VILLAGE OF EKWOK
P.O. Box 1388, Ekwok, AK 99580
(907) 464-3336 Fax 424-7739; Website: www.bbna.com
E-mail: king2rick@yahoo.com; Luki Akelkok, Sr., President
Self-Gov: Bristol Bay Native Association, Inc. West-Central Alaska Agency.

NATIVE VILLAGE OF ELIM
P.O. Box 39070, Elim, AK 99739
(907) 890-3737 Fax 890-3738; Website: www.kawerak.org
E-mail: eli.tc@kawerak.org; Robert A. Keith, President
Self-Gov: Kawerak. *Tribe*: Eskimo. *In residence*: 225. Fairbanks Agency.

EMMONAK VILLAGE
P.O. Box 126, Emmonak, AK 99581
(907) 949-1720 Fax 949-1384; Gretchen Kameroff, President
E-mail: emktribal@hughes.net
Self-Gov: Association of Village Council Presidents
West-Central Alaska Agency.

EVANSVILLE VILLAGE (aka Bettles Field)
P.O. Box 26087, Bettles Field, AK 99726
(907) 692-5005 Fax 692-5006; Frank Thompson, Chief
E-mailevansvillealaska@gmail.com
Self-Gov: Tanana Chiefs. *Tribes*: Eskimo & Indian. *In residence*: 65.
Fairbanks Agency.

NATIVE VILLAGE OF EYAK
P.O. Box 1388, Cordova, AK 99574
(907) 424-7738 Fax 424-7739; Darrell Olsen, Chairperson
Website: www.nveyak.org; E-mail: reyna@eyak-nsn.gov
Self-Gov: Chugachmuit, Inc. West-Central Alaska Agency.

NATIVE VILLAGE OF FALSE PASS
P.O. Box 29, False Pass, AK 99583
(907) 548-2227 Fax 548-2256; E-mail: falsepasstribe@gmail.com
Carleen Hoblet, President; West-Central Alaska Agency.

NATIVE VILLAGE OF FORT YUKON (IRA)
Gwichyaa Zhee Gwichi'in Tribal Government
P.O. Box 126, Fort Yukon, AK 99740
(907) 662-2581 Fax 662-2222; Website: www.fortyukon.org
E-mail: dorene.mahler@fortyukon.org; Nancy James, First Chief
Self-Gov: Tanana Chiefs. *Tribes*: Athapascan & Indian. *In residence*: 600.
Fairbanks Agency.

NATIVE VILLAGE OF GAKONA
P.O. Box 102, Gakona, AK 99586
(907) 822-5777 Fax 822-5997; Website: www.nvgkonavc.com
Darin Gene, President; E-mail: gakonavc@cviinternet.net
Self-Gov: Copper River Native Association, Inc. West-Central Alaska Agency.

GALENA VILLAGE (aka LOUDEN VILLAGE)
100 Tiger Hwy., Galena, AK 99741
(907) 656-1711 Fax 656-1716; Jenny Pelkola, 1st Chief
E-mail: estherwarner@hotmail.com
Self Gov: Tanana Chiefs. Fairbanks Agency.

NATIVE VILLAGE OF GAMBELL
P.O. Box 90, Gambell, AK 99742
(907) 985-5346 Fax 985-5014; Eddie Ungott, President
E-mail: nvg_gm@yahoo.com; Self Gov: Gambell. Fairbanks Agency.

NATIVE VILLAGE OF GEORGETOWN
5313 Arctic Blvd., Suite 104, Anchorage, AK 99518
(907) 274-2195 Fax 274-2196; Traci Maczynski, President
Website: www.georgetowntc.com
E-mail: will.hartman@georgetowntc.com

NATIVE VILLAGE OF GOODNEWS BAY
P.O. Box 3, Goodnews Bay, AK 99589

(907) 967-8929 Fax 967-8330; George Bright, President
E-mail: goodnews907@hotmail.com
Self-Gov: Assn of Village Council Presidents. West-Central Alaska Agency.

ORGANIZED VILLAGE OF GRAYLING (IRA)
General Delivery, Grayling, AK 99590
(907) 453-5116 Fax 453-5146; Gabriel H. Nicholi, Chief
Self-Gov: Tanana Chiefs. Fairbanks Agency.

GULKANA VILLAGE COUNCIL
P.O. Box 254, Gakona, AK 99586
(907) 822-4545 Fax 822-3976; Eileen Ewan, President
Website: www.gulkanacouncil.org; E-mail: admin@gulkanacouncil.org
Self Gov: Copper River Native Assn. *Tribe*: Athapascan.
West-Central Alaska Agency.

GWICH'IN ARCTIC VILLAGE
P.O. Box 22079, Arctic Village, AK 99722
(907) 587-5923 Fax 587-5128; Jonathon John, President
E-mail: nativemovement@hotmail.com.
Tribe: Athapascan. Fairbanks Agency.

NATIVE VILLAGE OF HAMILTON
P.O. Box 20248, Kotlik, AK 99620
(907) 899-4252 Fax 899-4202; George A.E. Williams, President
E-mail: toripurple@yahoo.com
Self-Gov: Assn of Village Council Presidents.
West-Central Alaska Agency.

MENDAS CHA-AG TRIBE OF HEALY LAKE
P.O. Box 74090, Fairbanks, AK 99706
(907) 479-0638 Fax 479-0639; JoAnn Polston, President
E-mail: jpolstonhltc@live.com; Self-Gov: Tanana Chiefs.
Fairbanks Agency.

HOLY CROSS VILLAGE
P.O. Box 89, Holy Cross, AK 99602
(907) 476-7124 Fax 476-7132; Alfred J. Demientieff, Jr., First Chief
Website: www.holycrosstribe.org; E-mail: info@holycrosstribe.org
Self-Gov: Tanana Chiefs. *Tribes*: Eskimo & Athapascan.
In residence: 225. Fairbanks Agency.

HOONAH INDIAN ASSOCIATION (IRA)
P.O. Box 602, Hoonah, AK 99829
(907) 945-3545 Fax 945-3703; Frank Wright, Jr., President
E-mail: rstarbard@hiatribe.org
Self-Gov: Central Council of Tlingit-Haida. West-Central Alaska Agency.

NATIVE VILLAGE OF HOOPER BAY
P.O. Box 69, Hooper Bay, AK 99604
(907) 758-4915 Fax 758-4066; Edgar Hoelscher, Chief
E-mail: nvhpb@yahoo.com
Tribe: Eskimo. In residence: 450. Self-Gov: Association of Village Council
Presidents. West-Central Alaska Agency.

HUGHES VILLAGE
P.O. Box 45029, Hughes, AK 99745
(907) 899-2239 Fax 889-2252; Wilmer Beetus, First Chief
E-mail: janet.bifelt@tananachiefs.org
Tribe: Athapascan. Self Gov: Tanana Chiefs. Fairbanks Agency.

HUSLIA VILLAGE COUNCIL
P.O. Box 70, Huslia, AK 99746
(907) 829-2294 Fax 829-2214; Norman Carl Burgett, First Chief
E-mail: Eileen.jackson@hotmail.com
Tribe: Huslia Athabascan. *Activities*: Owns & operates Athabasca Cultural
Journeys, tourism project located at P.O. Box 10, Huslia, AK 99746 (800) 423-
0094. Self-Gov: Tanana Chiefs. Fairbanks Agency.

HYDABURG COOPERATIVE ASSOCIATION
P.O. Box 349, Hydaburg, AK 99922
(907) 285-3666 Fax 285-3541; Sidney Edenshaw, President
Website: http://hydaburgtribe.org; E-mail: hcatribe@gmail.com
Self-Gov: Central Council of Tlingit-Haida. West-Central Alaska Agency.

IGIUGIG VILLAGE
P.O. Box 4008, Iguigig, AK 99613
(907) 533-3211 Fax 533-3217; AlexAnna Salmon, President
E-mail: igiugig@starband.net
Self-Gov: Bristol Bay Native Association, Inc.
West-Central Alaska Agency.

VILLAGE OF ILIAMNA
P.O. Box 286, Iliamna, AK 99606
(907) 571-1246 Fax 571-1256; Thomas Hedlund, President
E-mail: ilivc@iliamnave.org
Tribes: Athapascan and Indian. West-Central Alaska Agency.

INUPIAT COMMUNITY OF THE ARCTIC SLOPE
P.O. Box 934, Barrow, AK 99723
(907) 852-4227 Fax 852-4246; George Edwardson, President
Website: www.inupiatgov.com; E-mail: kimlem@gci.net.
Fairbanks Agency.

IQURMIUT TRADITIONAL COUNCIL
P.O. Box 09, Russian Mission, AK 99657
(907) 584-5511 Fax 584-5593; Wassily Alexie, President
E-mail: iqurmiut71@yahoo.com
Tribe: Iqurmiut (Eskimo). West-Central Alaska Agency.

IVANOF BAY VILLAGE
P.O. Box 500, Perryville, AK 99648
(907) 552-2263 Fax 552-2363; Edgar John Shangan, President
Webste: www.ivanoffbaytribe.org; E-mail: Nicole@ivanoffbaytribe.org
Self-Gov: Bristol Bay Native Association, Inc. West-Central Alaska Agency.

KAGUYAK VILLAGE
P.O. Box 5078, Akhiok, AK 99615
(907) 836-2231 Fax 836-2345; Phyllis Amodo, President
E-mailpamodo_98@yahoo.com. West-Central Alaska Agency.

ORGANIZED VILLAGE OF KAKE (IRA)
P.O. Box 316, Kake, AK 99830
(907) 785-6471 Fax 785-4902; Casimero A. Aceveda, President
E-mailgewilliams@kakefirstnation.org; Self Gov: Kake.
Attraction: Keex Kwaan Pulltabs/Bingo. West-Central Alaska Agency.

KAKTOVIK VILLAGE (aka BARTER ISLAND)
P.O. Box 130, Kaktovik, AK 99747
(907) 640-2042 Fax 640-2044; Edward Rexford, President
E-mail: nvkaktovik@starband.net. Fairbanks Agency.

NATIVE VILLAGE OF KALSKAG
P.O. Box 50, Kalskag, AK 99607
(907) 471-2207 Fax 471-2399; Julia F. Dorris, President
E-mail: kalskagtribal@yahoo.com
Self-Gov: Association of Village Council Presidents
Tribe: Eskimo. *In residence*: 225. West-Central Alaska Agency.

NATIVE VILLAGE OF KALTAG
P.O. Box 129, Kaltag, AK 99748
(907) 534-2224 Fax 534-2299; Justin Esmailka, First Chief
Self-Gov: Tanana Chiefs. Fairbanks Agency.

NATIVE VILLAGE OF KANATAK
P.O. Box 872231, Wasilla, AK 99654
(907) 357-5991 Fax 357-5992; Henry F. Forshey, President
Website: www.kanatak.org; E-mail: ktcpresident@yahoo.com
Self-Gov: Bristol Bay Native Association, Inc. *Tribe*: Kanatak.
Goal: To improve living conditions of tribal members and to
protect & preserve our culture. West-Central Alaska Agency.

NATIVE VILLAGE OF KARLUK
P.O. Box 22, Karluk, AK 99608
(907) 241-2218 Fax 241-2208
Alicia L. Reft, President; E-mail: a96lynn@aol.com
Tribe: Aleut. In residence: 225. West-Central Alaska Agency.

ORGANIZED VILLAGE OF KASAAN
P.O. Box 26, Kasaan, AK 99950
(907) 542-2230 Fax 542-3006; Ronald Leighton, President
Website: www.kasan.org; E-mail: sam@kasan.org
Self-Gov: Central Council of Tlingit-Haida. West-Central Alaska Agency.

NATIVE VILLAGE OF KASIGLUK
P.O. Box 19, Kasigluk, AK 99609
(907) 477-6405 Fax 477-6212; Kathleen Brink, President
E-mail: kasigluk.admin@gmail.com
Tribe: Eskimo. *In residence*: 175. West-Central Alaska Agency.

KENAITZE INDIAN TRIBE
150 N. Willow St., P.O. Box 988 • Kenai, AK 99611
(907) 335-7200 Fax 335-7239; Website: www.kenaitze.org

Rosalie Tepp, Chairperson; E-mail: rtepp@kenaitze.org
Jaylene Peterson-Nyren, Executive Director; E-mail: jaylene@kenaitze.org
Aexandra "Sasha" Lindgren, Director of Tribal Government Affairs
E-mail: alindgren@kenaitze.org
M. Scott Moon, Communications Specialist; E-mail: smoon@kenaitze.org
Serve more than 1,750 Alaska Natives on the Kenai Peninsula. After three
years of litigation, the Kenaitze Tribe recently won a landmark Federal Court
decision restoring the Kenaitze Indian Tribal members the right to enjoy their
traditional & customary subsistence fishing rights on the Kenai Peninsula.
Those rights had been denied for 40 years by the State of Alaska. *Resources*:
Dena'ina Wellness Center; Early Childhood Center. *Publication*: Newsletter.
West-Central Alaska Agency.

KETCHIKAN INDIAN COMMUNITY
2960 Tongass Ave., Ketchikan, AK 99901
(907) 228-9313 Fax 225-5158; Website: www.kictribe.org
Irene Dundas, President (617-6220); E-mail: idundas@kictribe.org
Joe Reeves, Vice President (617-8850); E-mail: jreeves@kictribe.org
Ken Truitt, Treasurer (253) 304-4645; E-mail: ktruitt@kictribe.org
Gloria Burns, Secretary (617-5901); E-mail: gburns@kictribe.org
Facilities: Health & Dental Clinics; Deer Mountain Tribal Hatchery
& Eagle Center; Child Care Center. West-Central Alaska Agency.

NATIVE VILLAGE OF KIANA
P.O. Box 69, Kiana, AK 99749
(907) 475-2109 Fax 475-2180; Crystal Johnson, President
E-mail: tribedirector@katyaaq.org. Self-Gov: Maniilaq Consortium.
Tribe: Eskimo. *In residence*: 220. Fairbanks Agency.

KING ISLAND NATIVE COMMUNITY (IRA)
P.O. Box 682, Nome, AK 99762
(907) 443-2209 Fax 443-8049
Megan Avlanna-Stimpfle, Acting Chief
Self-Gov: Kawerak. Fairbanks Agency.

KING SALMON TRIBE
P.O. Box 68, King Salmon, AK 99613
(907) 246-3553 Fax 246-3449; Ralph Angasan, Sr., President
E-mail: kstvc@starband.net. West-Central Alaska Agency.

NATIVE VILLAGE OF KIPNUK
P.O. Box 57, Kipnuk, AK 99614
(907) 896-5515 Fax 896-5240; Daniel Jimmy, Sr., President
E-mail: ktc99614@yahoo.com. West-Central Alaska Agency.

NATIVE VILLAGE OF KIVALINA (IRA)
51 Berry St., P.O. Box 50051 • Kivalina, AK 99750
(907) 645-2153 Fax 645-2193; Millie Hawley, President
E-mail: tribeadminkivaliniq.org. Self-Gov: Maniilaq Consortium
Tribe: Inupiat of Kivalina. In residence: 360. *Council members*: Fred Swan
& Oscar Sage, Sr. *Activities*: New Years Day traditional; Fairbanks Agency.

KLAWOCK COOPERATIVE ASSOCIATION
P.O. Box 430 • Klawock, AK 99925
(907) 755-2265 Fax 755-8800; Archie W. Demmert III, President
E-mail: kcamngr@aptalaska.net
Self-Gov: Central Council of Tlingit-Haida. West-Central Alaska Agency.

NATIVE VILLAGE OF KLUTI-KAAH (aka COPPER CENTER)
P.O. Box 68 • Copper Center, AK 99573
(907) 822-5541 Fax 822-5130; John Craig, President
E-mail: nvkkadmin@cvinternet.net
Self-Gov: Copper River Native Association, Inc.
Tribe: Athapascan. *In residence*: 115. West-Central Alaska Agency.

KNIK TRIBAL COUNCIL
901 W. Commercial Dr. • Wasilla, AK 99687
(907) 373-7991 Fax 373-2161; Michael Tucker, President
Website: www.kniktribalcouncil.org
E-mail: kniktribe@matonline.net
West-Central Alaska Agency.

NATIVE VILLAGE OF KOBUK
P.O. Box 51039 • Kobuk, AK 99751
(907) 948-2203 Fax 948-2123; Johnetta Horner President
Email: tribeadmin@laugvik.org
Self-Gov: Maniilaq Consortium. *Tribe*: Eskimo. Fairbanks Agency.

KOKHANOK VILLAGE
P.O. Box 1007 • Kokhanok, AK 99606
(907) 282-2202 Fax 282-2264; Peducia Andrew, President

E-mail: kokhanokvc@yahoo.com
Self-Gov: Bristol Bay Native Assn, Inc.
Tribe: Aleut. West-Central Alaska Agency.

NATIVE VILLAGE OF KOLIGANEK
P.O. Box 5057 • Koliganek, AK 99576
(907) 596-3434 Fax 596-3462; Herman Nelson, Sr., President
E-mail: nancylarson87@yahoo.com
Self-Gov: Association of Village Council Presidents
Tribe: Aleut. West-Central Alaska Agency.

NATIVE VILLAGE OF KONGIGANAK
P.O. Box 5069, Kongiganak, AK 99559
(907) 557-5226 Fax 557-5224; Joseph Joseph, President
E-mail: kongtribe@gmail.com
Self-Gov: Assn of Village Council Presidents.
West-Central Alaska Agency.

VILLAGE OF KOTLIK
P.O. Box 20210, Kotlik, AK 99620
(907) 899-4326 Fax 899-4790; Laurencia Mike, President
E-mail: pakaran@avcp.org
Self-Gov: Assn of Village Council Presidents
Tribe: Eskimo. West-Central Alaska Agency.

NATIVE VILLAGE OF KOTZEBUE (IRA)
600 Fifth Ave., P.O. Box 296, Kotzebue, AK 99752
(800) 442-3467; (907) 442-3467 Fax 442-2162
Website: www.kotzebueira.org; E-mail: kotzebueeira@gmail.com
Chester Ballot, President; E-mail: clballot@otz.net
Tom Okleasik, Executive Director
E-mail: executive.director@qira.org
Martin Shroyer, Chairperson; E-mail: mshroyer@otz.net
Self-Gov: Maniilaq Consortium. *Tribe*: Eskimo. In residence: 1,900.
Activities: Northwest Alaska Native Trade Fair. Fairbanks Agency.

NATIVE VILLAGE OF KOYUK (IRA)
P.O. Box 53030, Koyuk, AK 99753
(907) 963-3651 Fax 963-2353; Lola Hannon, President
E-mail: tc.kka@kawerak.org
Self-Gov: Kawerak. *Tribe*: Eskimo. *In residence*: 190. Fairbanks Agency.

KOYUKUK NATIVE VILLAGE
P.O. Box 109, Koyukuk, AK 99754
(907) 927-2253 Fax 927-2220; Leo Lolnitz, 1st Chief
Self-Gov: Tanana Chiefs. *Tribe*: Athapascan. *In residence*: 115.
Fairbanks Agency.

ORGANIZED VILLAGE OF KWETHLUK (IRA)
P.O. Box 130, Kwethluk, AK 99621
(907) 757-6714 Fax 757-6328; Tonya Epchook, President
E-mail: kwethlukira@gmail.com
Tribe: Eskimo. *In residence*: 350. West-Central Alaska Agency.

NATIVE VILLAGE OF KWIGILLINGOK
P.O. Box 90, Kwigillingok, AK 99622
(907) 588-8114 Fax 588-8429; Fred P. Phillip, President
E-mail: kwktribal@yahoo.com
Self-Gov: Association of Village Council Presidents
Tribe: Eskimo. *In residence*: 350. West-Central Alaska Agency.

NATIVE VILLAGE OF KWINHAGAK (IRA)
P.O. Box 149, Quinhagak, AK 99655
(907) 556-8165 Fax 556-8166
Joshua Cleveland, President
Website: www.kwinhagak.com; E-mail: jmark.nvk@gmail.com
Self-Gov: Association of Village Council Presidents. *Tribe*: Yup'ik Eskimo.
In residence: 600. *Total acreage*: 120,000. West-Central Alaska Agency.

NATIVE VILLAGE OF LARSEN BAY
P.O. Box 50, Larsen Bay, AK 99624
(907) 847-2207 Fax 847-2307; Chad Aga, President
E-mail: mvcirr@gmail.com; E-mail: larsenbaytribe@gmail.com.
Tribe: Eskimo. Anchorage Agency.

LEVELOCK VILLAGE
P.O. Box 70, Levelock, AK 99625
(907) 287-3030 Fax 287-3032; Alexander Tallekpalek, President
E-mail: levelockak@gci.net
Self-Gov: Bristol Bay Native Association.
Tribe: Aleut. West-Central Alaska Agency.

LIME VILLAGE
P.O. Box LVD, Lime Village, McGrath, AK 99627
(907) 526-5236 Fax 526-5235; Jennifer John, President
E-mail: limevillage@gmail.com; West-Central Alaska Agency.

VILLAGE OF LOWER KALSKAG
P.O. Box 27, Lower Kalskag, AK 99626
(907) 471-2379 Fax 471-2378; Phyllis E. Evan, President
E-mail: klaskagtribal@yahoo.com
Tribe: Eskimo. *In residence*: 175. West-Central Alaska Agency.

MANLEY HOT SPRINGS VILLAGE
P.O. Box 105, Manley Hot Springs, AK 99756
(907) 672-3177 Fax 672-3200; E-mail: mvcirr@gmail.com
Raymond P. Woods, Chief
Self-Gov: Tanana Chiefs. Fairbanks Agency.

MANOKOTAK VILLAGE
P.O. Box 169, Manokotak, AK 99628
(907) 289-2067 Fax 289-1235
Ray Shawn Tugatuk, President
E-mail: kmo_villagecouncil@yahoo.com.
Self-Gov: Bristol Bay Native Assn, Inc.
Tribes: Eskimo and Indian. In residence: 190.
West-Central Alaska Agency.

NATIVE VILLAGE OF MARSHALL (aka Fortuna Ledge)
110 Poltes Ave., P.O. Box 110, Marshall, AK 99585
(907) 679-6302 Fax 679-6187; Nicholai Duny, President
E-mail: john_andrewmlltc@gci.net
Tribe: Eskimo. In residence: 120. West-Central Alaska Agency.

NATIVE VILLAGE OF MARY'S IGLOO
P.O. Box 546, Teller, AK 99778
(907) 642-3731 Fax 642-2189
E-mail: cablowaluk@kawerak.org; Lucy H. Oquilluk, President
Self-Gov: Kawerak. Fairbanks Agency.

McGRATH NATIVE VILLAGE
P.O. Box 134, McGrath, AK 99627
(907) 524-3024 Fax 524-3899
E-mail: tmd1ak@yahoo.com; Alice Dale, 1st Chief
Self-Gov: Tanana Chiefs. *Tribes*: Athapascan, Indian & Eskimo.
In residence: 125. Fairbanks Agency.

NATIVE VILLAGE OF MEKORYUK
100 Chase Rd., P.O. Box 66, Mekoryuk, AK 99630
(907) 827-8828 Fax 827-8133; Albert R. Williams, President
E-mail: nativevillage.mekoryukira@yahoo.com
Tribe: Eskimo. *In residence*: 225. West-Central Alaska Agency.

MENTASTA LAKE TRADITIONAL COUNCIL
P.O. Box 6019, Mentasta Lake, AK 99780
(907) 291-2319 Fax 291-2305; Teddy Sanford, First Chief
E-mail: mentastatraditionalcouncil@yahoo.com.
West-Central Alaska Agency

METLAKATLA INDIAN COMMUNITY, ANNETTE USLAND RESERVE
8th & Milton, P.O. Box 8, Metlakatla, AK 99926
(907) 886-4441 Fax 886-3338; Audrey M.L. Hudson, Mayor
Website: www.metlakatla.com; Northwest Regional Office.
Tribe: Tsimshean. *Attraction*: Metlakatla Bingo Hall. Head Start Program.

NATIVE VILLAGE OF MINTO
P.O. Box 58026, Minto, AK 99758
(907) 798-7112 Fax 798-7627; Clifford Charlie, Chief
E-mail: mintovillagecouncil@hotmail.com
Self Gov: Tanana Chiefs; *Tribes*: Athapascan & Indian.
In residence: 225. Fairbanks Agency.

NAKNEK NATIVE VILLAGE
P.O. Box 210, Naknek, AK 99633
(907) 246-4210 Fax 246-3563; Linda Halverson, President
E-mail: nnvcpresident@gmail.com. Self-Gov: Bristol Bay Native Assn, Inc.
Tribes: Aleut & Indian. Anchorage Agency.

NATIVE VILLAGE OF NANWALEK (aka ENGLISH BAY)
100 Nikita St., P.O. Box 8028, Nanwalek, AK 99603
(907) 281-2274 Fax 281-2252; John W. Kvasnikoff, Chief
E-mail: nanwalek@yahoo.com. Self-Gov: Chugachmiut, Inc.
Tribe: Eskimo. *In residence*: 115. West-Central Alaska Agency.

NATIVE VILLAGE OF NAPAIMUTE
2920 Hogan Bay Circle • Anchorage, AK 99515
  (907) 543-2887 Fax 543-2892; Devron Hellings, President
  Website: www.napaimute.org; E-mail: napaimute@gci.net
Self-Gov: Assn of Village Council Presidents. West-Central Alaska Agency.

NATIVE VILLAGE OF NAPAKIAK
1083 Mission Rd., P.O. Box 34069, Napakiak, AK 99634
  (907) 589-2135 Fax 589-2136; Jacob Black, President
  E-mail: naparyyaraq@hughes.net
Self-Gov: Association of Village Council Presidents
Tribe: Eskimo. *In residence*: 200. West-Central Alaska Agency.

NATIVE VILLAGE OF NAPASKIAK
P.O. Box 6009, Napaskiak, AK 99559
  (907) 737-7364 Fax 737-7039
  E-mail: fjenkins@napaskiak.org; Steven Maxie, Jr., President
Self-Gov: Association of Village Council Presidents
Tribe: Eskimo. *In residence*: 175. West-Central Alaska Agency.

NATIVE VILLAGE OF NELSON LAGOON TRIBAL COUNCIL
P.O. Box 913, Nelson Lagoon, AK 99571
  (907) 989-2204 Fax 989-2233; Paul E. Gundersen President
  E-mail: jjgundel125@aol.com
Self-Gov: Aleutian/Pribilof Islands Assn, Inc. West-Central Alaska Agency.

NENANA TRADITIONAL COUNCIL
P.O. Box 356, Nenana, AK 99760
  (907) 832-5461 Fax 832-1077; Donald Charlie, 1st Chief
  E-mail: nenananativecouncil@gmail.com
Self-Gov: Tanana Chiefs; *Tribes*: Athapascan & Indian. *In residence*: 175.
Fairbanks Agency.

NEW KOLIGANEK VILLAGE COUNCIL
P.O. Box 5057, Koliganek, AK 99576
  (907) 596-3434 Fax 596-3462; Herman Nelson, Sr., President
  E-mail: newkgkvc@hotmail.com
Tribes: Athapascan & Indian. *In residence*: 205.
Councilmembers: Gust Tunguing, Sr., Gust Tunguing, Jr., Blunka Ishnook, Jr.,
  Betty Lee & Edward Kapatak. West-Central Alaska Agency.

NEW STUYAHOK VILLAGE
P.O. Box 49, New Stuyahok, AK 99636
  (907) 693-3173 Fax 693-3179
  E-mail: newstutribe@hotmail.com; Peter Christopher, Sr., President
Self-Gov: Bristol Bay Native Association, Inc.
Tribe: Athapascan. In residence: 140. West-Central Alaska Agency.

NEWHALEN VILLAGE
P.O. Box 207, Iliamna, AK 99606
  (907) 571-1410 Fax 571-1537; Henry Olympic, President
  E-mail: newhalentribal@yahoo.com
Self-Gov: Bristol Bay Native Association, Inc. *Tribes*: Aleut & Indian.
West-Central Alaska Field Office.

NEWTOK TRADITIONAL COUNCIL
P.O. Box 5565, Newtok, AK 99559
  (907) 237-2314 Fax 237-2428; Paul Charles, President.
  E-mail: Stanley_tomm2003@yahoo.com
West-Central Alaska Agency.

NATIVE VILLAGE OF NIGHTMUTE
P.O. Box 90021, Nightmute, AK 99690
  (907) 647-6215 Fax 647-6112; Simeon Tulik, President
  E-mail: negtemiut_tribe@live.com
Tribe: Eskimo. West-Central Alaska Agency.

NATIVE VILLAGE OF NIKOLSKI
P.O. Box 105, Nikolski, AK 99638
  (907) 576-2225 Fax 576-2205; Arnold Dushkin, President
  E-mail: nvnikolski@hotmail.com
Self-Gov: Aleutian/Pribilof Islands Assn, Inc. West-Central Alaska Agency.

NINILCHIK TRADITIONAL COUNCIL
15910 Sterling Hwy., P.O. Box 39070, Ninilchik, AK 99639
  (907) 567-3313 Fax 567-3308; Richard G. Encelewski, President
  Website: www.ninilchiktribe-nsn.gov; E-mail: ntc@ninilchiktribe-nsn.gov
  Richard 'Greg' Encelewski, President; William 'Dean' Kvasnikoff, Vice Pres.
  Lorita Linder, Secretary/Treasurer; Kenny Odman, Director
  Sara Jackinski & Kaitlyn Nolan, Council members
Tribe: Kenaitse. *In residence*: 120. West-Central Alaska Field Office.

NATIVE VILLAGE OF NOATAK
1 Swamp St., P.O. Box 89, Noatak, AK 99761
  (907) 485-2173 Fax 485-2137; Vernon Adams, Sr., President
  E-mail: tribeadmin@nautaaq.org
Self-Gov: Maniilaq Consortium *Tribes*: Eskimo and Indian.
In residence: 550. Fairbanks Field Office.

NOME ESKIMO COMMUNITY
P.O. Box 1090, Nome, AK 99762
  (907) 443-2246 Fax 443-3539; Shane Smithhisler, President
  Website: www.nnecalaska.org; E-mail: nomeeskimo@gci.net
  Self-Gov: Kawerak. *Tribes*: Eskimo and Indian. *In residence*: 1,750.
Fairbanks Field Office.

NONDALTON VILLAGE
P.O. Box 49, Nondalton, AK 99640
  (907) 294-2220 Fax 294-2234; William Evanoff, President
  E-mail: nondaltontribe@yahoo.com
Tribe: Athapascan. *In residence*: 175. West-Central Alaska Field Office.

NATIVE VILLAGE OF NOORVIK
P.O. Box 209, Noorvik, AK 99763
  (907) 636-2144 Fax 636-2284; Wilbur Horwarth, Sr., President
  E-mailtribemanager@nuurvik.org. Self-Gov: Maniilaq Consortium
Tribe: Eskimo. *In residence*: 450. Nome Agency.

NORTHWAY VILLAGE
P.O. Box 516, Northway, AK 99764
  (907) 778-2287 Fax 778-2220; Gerald Albert, President
  E-mail: alaskabee40@yahoo.com
Tribe: Athapascan. *In residence*: 150. Fairbanks Field Office.

NATIVE VILLAGE OF NUIQSUT
P.O. Box 89169, Nuiqsut, AK 99789
  (907) 480-3010 Fax 480-3009; Samuel Kanaknana, President
  E-mail: native.village@astacalaska.net
Tribe: Athapascan. *In residence*: 125. Fairbanks Field Office.

NULATO VILLAGE
P.O. Box 65049, Nulato, AK 99765
  (907) 898-2339 Fax 898-2207; Michael J. Stickman, First Chief
  E-mail: nulatotribe@yahoo.com
Tribe: Athapascan. *In residence*: 250. Fairbanks Agency.

NUNAKAUYARMUIT TRIBE
P.O. Box 37048, Toksook Bay, AK 99637
  (907) 427-7114 Fax 427-7714; Simeon John, President
  E-mail: nunnakauyaktc@hotmail.com
Tribe: Eskimo. West-Central Alaska Agency.

NATIVE VILLAGE OF NUNAM IQUA
P.O. Box 27, Sheldon's Point, AK 99666
  (907) 498-4184 Fax 498-4185; Edward J. Adams, President
  E-mail: nunamtribe@gmail.com
Self-Gov: Assn of Village Council Presidents. West-Central Alaska Agency.

NATIVE VILLAGE OF NUNAPITCHUK (IRA)
P.O. Box 130, Nunapitchuk, AK 99641
  (907) 527-5705 Fax 527-5711; Wassillie Pleasant, President
  E-mail: tribaladmin@yupik.org
Self-Gov: Association of Village Council Presidents
Tribe: Eskimo. *In residence*: 200. West-Central Alaska Agency.

VILLAGE OF OHOGAMIUT
P.O. Box 49, Marshall, AK 99585
  (907) 679-6517 Fax 679-6516
  Darlene Isaac, President; E-mail: admin@ohogtc.org
West-Central Alaska Agency.

NATIVE VILLAGE OF OLD HARBOR
P.O. Box 62, Old Harbor, AK 99643
  (907) 286-2215 Fax 286-2277; Website: www.aldharbortribal.org
  Stella M. Krumrey, President; Melissa Berns, Vice President
  Bobbi Anne Barnowsky, Tribal Administrator
  E-mail: tribal.administration@ohtcmail.org
Tribe: Alutiiq Eskimo. *In residence*: 200. West-Central Alaska Agency.

ORUTSARARMUIT TRADITIONAL NATIVE COUNCIL
P.O. Box 927, Bethel, AK 99559
  (907) 543-2608 Fax 543-2639; Walter Jim, Chairperson
  Population served: Bethel Native Corporation Shareholders.

Programs: Social Services; Vocational Training; Higher Education grants; Energy Assistance; Housing Improvement; among others. West-Central Alaska Agency.

OSCARVILLE TRADITIONAL COUNCIL
P.O. Box 6129, Oscarville, AK 99559
  (907) 737-7099 Fax 737-7428
  Nicholai Stevens, President; E-mail: mstevens@avcp.org
Self-Gov: Association of Village Council Presidents
Tribes: Indian and Eskimo. West-Central Alaska Agency.

NATIVE VILLLAGE OF OUZINKIE
P.O. Box 130, Ouzinkie, AK 99644
  (907) 680-2259 Fax 680-2214; Robert Boskofsky, Sr., President
  E-mail: jillboskofsky977@yahoo.com West-Central Alaska Agency.

NATIVE VILLAGE OF PAIMIUT
P.O. Box 230, Hooper Bay, AK 99604
  (907) 758-4002 Fax 758-4024; Albert Simon, Sr., President
  E-mail: hnapoleon@paimiut.org. West-Central Alaska Agency.

NATIVE VILLAGE OF PAULOFF HARBOR
P.O. Box 97, Sand Point, AK 99661
  (907) 383-6075 Fax 383-6094; Willliam Dushkin, Sr., President
  E-mail: pauloff@arctic.net. West-Central Alaska Agency.

PEDRO BAY VILLAGE
P.O. Box 47020, Pedro Bay, AK 99647
  (907) 850-2225 Fax 850-2221; Keith Jensen, President
  Website: www.pedrobay.com; E-mail: villagecouncil@pedrobay.com
Tribe: Athapascan. West-Central Alaska Agency.

NATIVE VILLAGE OF PERRYVILLE (IRA)
P.O. Box 101, Perryville, AK 99648
  (907) 853-2203 Fax 853-2230; Gerald B. Kosbruk, President
  E-mailnvproads@hotmail.com
Self-Gov: Bristol Bay Native Association, Inc.
Tribe: Eskimo. *In residence*: 175. West-Central Alaska Agency.

PETERSBURG INDIAN ASSOCIATION (IRA)
P.O. Box 1418, Petersburg, AK 99833
  (907) 772-3636 Fax 772-3637; Barry Morrison, President
  E-mail: barrymorrison@piatribe.org
Self-Gov: Central Council of Tlingit-Haida. West-Central Alaska Agency.

PILOT POINT TRIBAL COUNCIL
P.O. Box 109, Pilot Point, AK 99766
  (907) 797-2330 Fax 797-2332; Jack Schaefer, President
  E-mail: peggy.frankson@tikigaq.org
Self-Gov: Bristol Bay Native Association, Inc. West-Central Alaska Agency.

PILOT STATION TRADITIONAL COUNCIL
P.O. Box 5119, Pilot Station, AK 99650
  (907) 549-3373 Fax 549-3301; Rex J. Nick, President
  E-mail: mpkelly_963@hotmail.com
Self-Gov: Association of Village Council Presidents
Tribe: Eskimo. West-Central Alaska Agency.

NATIVE VILLAGE OF PITKA'S POINT
P.O. Box 127, St. Mary's, AK 99658
  (907) 438-2833 Fax 438-2569; Ruth Riley, President
  E-mail: pitkaspoint@yahoo.com
Tribe: Eskimo. West-Central Alaska Agency.

PLATINUM TRADITIONAL VILLAGE
P.O. Box 8, Platinum, AK 99651
  (907) 979-8220 Fax 979-8178; Norman Small, President
  E-mail: ptutribal@hotmail.com
Tribe: Eskimo. West-Central Alaska Agency.

NATIVE VILLAGE OF POINT HOPE (IRA)
P.O. Box 109, Point Hope, AK 99766
  (907) 368-2330 Fax 368-2332; James Nash, President
Tribe: Eskimo. *In residence*: 385. Fairbanks Agency.

NATIVE VILLAGE OF POINT LAY (IRA)
P.O. Box 59031, Point Lay, AK 99759
  (907) 833-2575 Fax 833-2528; Marie Tracey, President
  E-mail: pointlay@inupiatgov.com
Tribe: Eskimo. *In residence*: 125. Fairbanks Agency.

NATIVE VILLAGE OF PORT GRAHAM
P.O. Box 5510, Port Graham, AK 99603
  (907) 284-2227 Fax 284-2222; Patrick N. Norman, 1st Chief
  E-mail: pnormanvc@hotmail.com. Self-Gov: Chugachmiut, Inc.
Tribe: Eskimo. *In residence*: 115. West-Central Alaska Agency.

NATIVE VILLAGE OF PORT HEIDEN
P.O. Box 49007, Port Heiden, AK 99549
  (907) 837-2296 Fax 837-2297; John Christensen, Jr., President
  E-mail: john.christensen@hotmail.com
Self-Gov: Bristol Bay Native Association, Inc. West-Central Alaska Agency.

NATIVE VILLAGE OF PORT LIONS
P.O. Box 69, Port Lions, AK 99550
  (907) 454-2234 Fax 454-2434; Denise May, President
  E-mail: nvop132@starband.net; E-mail: portlions@aitc.org
West-Central Alaska Agency.

PORTAGE CREEK VILLAGE
1327 E. 72nd Ave., Unit B, Anchorage, AK 99515
  (907) 277-1105 Fax 277-1104; Maryanne Johnson, President
  E-mail: ciugtaq@yahoo.com
Self-Gov: Bristol Bay Native Association, Inc. West-Central Alaska Agency.

QAGAN TAYAGUNGIN TRIBE OF SAND POINT VILLAGE
P.O. Box 447, Sand Point, AK 99661
  (907) 383-5616 Fax 383-5814; David O. Osterback, President
  Website: www.qttribe.org; E-mail: qttadmin@arctic.net
Tribe: Qagun Tayagungin (Aleut).
Self-Gov: Aleutian/Pribilof Islands Assn, Inc. West-Central Alaska Agency.

QAWALANGIN TRIBE OF UNALASKA
P.O. Box 334, Unalaska, AK 99685
  (907) 581-2920 Fax 581-3644; Thomas Robinson, Sr., President
  E-mail: robin.qawalangin@gmail.com
Self-Gov: Aleutian/Pribilof Islands Assn, Inc. West-Central Alaska Agency.

RAMPART VILLAGE
P.O. Box 29, Rampart, AK 99767
  (907) 358-3312 Fax 358-3115; Floyd Green, President
  E-mail: rvcirr@gmail.com
Self-Gov: Tanana Chiefs Conference
Tribe: Athapascan. *In residence*: 140. Fairbanks Agency.

VILLAGE OF RED DEVIL
P.O. Box 61, Red Devil, AK 99656
  (907) 447-3223 Fax 447-3224; Mary Willis, President
Self-Gov: Assn of Village Council Presidents.
West-Central Alaska Agency.

RUBY TRIBAL COUNCIL
P.O. Box 210, Ruby, AK 99768
  (907) 468-4479 Fax 468-4474; Patrick McCarty, First Chief
  E-mail: rubynativecouncil@hotmail.com
Self-Gov: Tanana Chiefs, *Tribe*: Athapascan. *In residence*: 150.
Fairbanks Agency.

SAINT GEORGE TRADITIONAL COUNCIL
P.O. Box 940, St. George Island, AK 99591
  (907) 859-2205 Fax 859-2242; Christopher Merculief, President
  E-mail: cmerculief@yahoo.com
Self-Gov: Aleutian/Pribilof Islands Assn, Inc.
West-Central Alaska Agency.

NATIVE VILLAGE OF ST. MICHAEL
P.O. Box 59050, St. Michael, AK 99659
  (907) 923-2304 Fax 923-2406
  Theresa Kobuk, President
Self-Gov: Kawerak. Fairbanks Agency.

VILLAGE OF SALAMATOFF
P.O. Box 2682, Kenai, AK 99611
  (907) 283-7864 Fax 283-6470
  Chris Monfor, President; E-mail: snainc@alaska.net
West-Central Alaska Agency.

NATIVE VILLAGE OF SAVOONGA
P.O. Box 120, Savoonga, AK 99785
  (907) 984-6414 Fax 984-6027; Delbert Pungowiyi, President
  E-mail: stoolie@kawerak.org. Self-Gov: Kawerak
Tribe: Eskimo. *In residence*: 330. Fairbanks Agency.

ORGANIZED VILLAGE OF SAXMAN (IRA)
Route 2, Box 2 - Saxman, Ketchikan, AK 99901
(907) 247-2502 Fax 247-2504; Lee Wallace, President
E-mail: saxmanira@kpunet.net
Self-Gov: Central Council of Tlingit-Haida. West-Central Alaska Agency.

SCAMMON BAY TRADITIONAL COUNCIL
P.O. Box 110, Scammon Bay, AK 99662
(907) 558-5425 Fax 558-5134; George Smith, President
E-mail: admin@marayamiut.org
Self-Gov: Assn of Village Council Presidents.
West-Central Alaska Agency.

NATIVE VILLAGE OF SELAWIK
59 N. Tundra St., Selawik, AK 99770
(907) 484-2165 Fax 484-2226; Diana Ramoth, President
E-mail: tribeadmin@akuligaq.org
Self-Gov: Maniilaq Consortium. Fairbanks Agency.

SELDOVIA VILLAGE TRIBE
Drawer L, Seldovia, AK 99663
(907) 234-7898 Fax 234-7865; Crystal Collier, President
Website: www.svt.org; E-mail: svt@svt.org
Don Kashevaroff, President. West-Central Alaska Agency.

SHAGELUK NATIVE VILLAGE (IRA)
P.O. Box 109, Shageluk, AK 99665
(907) 473-8239 Fax 473-8295; Roger Hamilton, Jr., Chief
E-mail: shageluktribe@gmail.com
Self-Gov: Tanana Chiefs. Tribe: Athapascan. In residence: 150.
Fairbanks Agency.

NATIVE VILLAGE OF SHAKTOOLIK
P.O. Box 100, Shaktoolik, AK 99771
(907) 955-3701 Fax 955-2352; Matilda Harvey, President
E-mail: ksagoonick@kawerak.org
Self-Gov: Kawerak. Fairbanks Agency.

NATIVE VILLAGE OF SHISHMAREF
P.O. Box 72110, Shishmaref, AK 99772
(907) 649-3821 Fax 649-2104; Johnson Eningowuk, President
E-mail: tc.shh@kawerak.org
Self-Gov: Kawerak. Tribe: Eskimo. In residence: 200. Fairbanks Agency.

NATIVE VILLAGE OF SHUNGNAK (IRA)
P.O. Box 64, Shungnak, AK 99773
(907) 437-2163 Fax 437-2183; Billy Lee, President
E-mail: tribeclerk@issingnak.org. Self-Gov: Maniilaq Consortium.
Tribe: Eskimo. In residence: 200. Fairbanks Agency.

SITKA TRIBE OF ALASKA
456 Katlian St., Sitka, AK 99835
(907) 747-3207 Fax 747-4915; Website: www.sitkatribe.org
Kathy Hope Erickson, Chairperson
E-mail: lawrence.widmark@sitkatribe-nsn.gov
Tribe: Sitka. West-Central Alaska Agency.

SKAGWAY VILLAGE
P.O. Box 1157, Skagway, AK 99840
(907) 983-4068 Fax 983-3068; Jamie Bricker, Chair/President
E-mail: dcommander@skagwaytraditional.org
Self-Gov: Central Council of Tlingit-Haida. West-Central Alaska Agency.

VILLAGE OF SLEETMUTE
P.O. Box 109, Sleetmute, AK 99668
(907) 449-4263 Fax 449-4265; Sandra Greger, President
E-mail: traditional.council@sleetmute.net
Self-Gov: Association of Village Council Presidents
Tribes: Athapascan & Indian. In residence: 175. West-Central Alaska Agency.

VILLAGE OF SOLOMON
P.O. Box 2053, Nome, AK 99762
(907) 443-4985 Fax 443-5189; Kirsten Timbers, President
E-mail: tc.sol@kawerak.org. Self-Gov: Kawerak. Fairbanks Agency.

NATIVE VILLAGE OF SOUTH NAKNEK
P.O. Box 70029, South Naknek, AK 99670
(907) 246-8614 Fax 246-8613; Donald F. Nielsen, President
Website: www.southnaknek.info; E-mail: lorianne_n@hotmail.com
Self-Gov: Bristol Bay Native Association, Inc. West-Central Alaska Agency.

STEBBINS COMMUNITY ASSOCIATION
P.O. Box 71002 • Stebbins, AK 99671
(907) 934-3561 Fax 934-3560; Anna Nashoanak, President
E-mail: Stebbins_ira@yahoo.com
Self-Gov: Kawerak. Tribe: Eskimo. In residence: 175. Fairbanks Agency.

NATIVE VILLAGE OF STEVENS (IRA)
P.O. Box 74012 • Stevens Village, AK 99774
(907) 478-7228 Fax 478-7229; Michael E. Simon, President
E-mail: haroldsimon907@gmail.com. Self-Gov: Tanana Chiefs.
Tribe: Athapascan. In residence: 125. Fairbanks Agency.

VILLAGE OF STONY RIVER
P.O. Box SRV • Stony River, AK 99557
(907) 537-3253 Fax 537-3254; Mary L. Willis, President
E-mail: stoney.river@yahoo.com
Self-Gov: Assn of Village Council Presidents. West-Central Alaska Agency.

SUN'AQ TRIBE OF KODIAK
312 W. Marine Way, Kodiak, AK 99615
(907) 486-4449 Fax 486-3361; Frank Peterson, Chairperson
Website: www.sunaq.org; E-mail: ceo@sunaq.org
West-Central Alaska Agency.

TAKOTNA VILLAGE
P.O. Box TYC • Takotna, AK 99675
(907) 298-2212 Fax 298-2314; Vera Lynn Goods, Chief
E-mail: klzall@yahoo.com
Self-Gov: Tanana Chiefs. Tribes: Eskimo & Indian. Fairbanks Agency.

NATIVE VILLAGE OF TANACROSS
P.O. Box 76009 • Tanacross, AK 99776
(907) 883-5024 Fax 883-4497; Herbie Demit, President
Website: www.nativevillageoftanacross.com
E-mail:tanacrossvillagecouncil@yahoo.com. Self-Gov: Tanana Chiefs.
Tribe: Athapascan. In residence: 150. Fairbanks Agency.

NATIVE VILLAGE OF TANANA
P.O. Box 130 • Tanana, AK 99777
(907) 366-7160 Fax 366-7195; Curtis Sommer, President
E-mail:tananatribalcouncil@hotmail.com
Self-Gov: Tanana IRA Native Council
Tribes: Athapascan & Indian. In residence: 225. Fairbanks Agency.

TANGIRNAQ NATIVE VILLAGE (aka Woody Island Tribal)
3449 East Rezanof Dr., Kodiak, AK 99615
(800) 478-5721 ext. 9872; (907) 486-9872 Fax 486-4829
Gordon Pullar, Jr., President; E-mail: gordon.pullar@kanaweb.org
Website: www.woodyisland.com; E-mail: info@woodyisland.com
Mitch Gregoroff, Vice President. West-Central Alaska Agency.

NATIVE VILLAGE OF TATITLEK
P.O. Box 171 • Tatitlek, AK 99677
(907) 325-2311 Fax 325-2298; David Totemoff, President
E-mail: totemoffdavid@yahoo.com
Self-Gov: Chugachmiut, Inc. Tribe: Aleut. In residence: 150.
West-Central Alaska Agency.

NATIVE VILLAGE OF TAZLINA
P.O. Box 87 • Glenallen, AK 99588
(907) 822-4375 Fax 822-5865; Gloria Stickwan, President
E-mail: tazlina@cvinternet.net
Self-Gov: Copper River Native Assn, Inc. West-Central Alaska Agency.

TELIDA NATIVE VILLAGE COUNCIL
P.O. Box 9104 • Nikolai, AK 99691
(907) 293-2440 Fax 293-2641; Bernie Gregory, First Chief
E-mail: kuskoyim@aol.com
Self-Gov: Tanana Chiefs. Fairbanks Agency.

TELLER TRADITIONAL COUNCIL
P.O. Box 567 • Teller, AK 99778
(907) 642-3381 Fax 642-2072; Jenny Lee, President
E-mail: cisbaell@kawerak.org
Self-Gov: Kawerak. Tribe: Eskimo. In residence: 200. Fairbanks Agency.

NATIVE VILLAGE OF TETLIN (IRA)
P.O. Box 797, Tok, AK 99780
(907) 324-2130 Fax 324-2131; Michael Sam, President
E-mail: tetlinvillagecouncil@gmail.com. Self-Gov: Tanana Chiefs
Tribe: Athapascan. In residence: 125. Fairbanks Agency

CENTRAL COUNCIL OF TLINGIT & HAIDA INDIAN TRIBES OF ALASKA
320 W. Willoughby Ave. #300 • Juneau, AK 99801
(907) 586-1432 Fax 586-8970; Richard J. Peterson, President
Website: www.ccthita.org; E-mail: rpeterson@ccthita.org
West-Central Alaska Agency.

TRADITIONAL VILLAGE OF TOGIAK
P.O. Box 310 • Togiak, AK 99678
(907) 493-5003 Fax 493-5005; Jimmy Coopchiak, President
E-mail: tuyuruak@starband.net
Self-Gov: Bristol Bay Native Association, Inc.
Tribe: Eskimo. *In residence*: 175. West-Central Alaska Agency.

TULUKSAK NATIVE COMMUNITY (IRA)
P.O. Box 95 • Tuluksak, AK 99679
(907) 695-6420 Fax 695-6932; Noah C. Alexie, President
E-mail: tuluksak@aitc.org
Tribe: Eskimo. *In residence*: 200. West-Central Alaska Agency.

NATIVE VILLAGE OF TUNTUTULIAK
P.O. Box 8086 • Tuntutuliak, AK 99680
(907) 256-2128 Fax 256-2080; Alice Fitka, President
E-mail: pparila@tuntutuliaktc.org
Self-Gov: Association of Village Council Presidents
Tribe: Eskimo. *In residence*: 120. West-Central Alaska Agency.

NATIVE VILLAGE OF TUNUNAK (IRA)
P.O. Box 77 • Tununak, AK 99681
(907) 652-6527 Fax 652-6011; George B. Hooper, Jr., President
E-mail: tribe2work@yahoo.com. Self-Gov: Assn of Village Council Presidents.
West-Central Alaska Agency.

TWIN HILLS VILLAGE COUNCIL
P.O. Box TWA • Twin Hills, AK 99576
(907) 525-4821 Fax 525-4822; Arthur Sharp, President
E-mail: william15@starband.net
Self-Gov: Bristol Bay Native Assn, Inc. West-Central Alaska Agency.

NATIVE VILLAGE OF TYONEK (IRA)
P.O. Box 82009 • Tyonek, AK 99682
(907) 583-2111 Fax 583-2442; Arthur M. Standifer, President
Tribe: Athapascan. *In residence*: 200. West-Central Alaska Agency.

UGASHIK TRADITIONAL VILLAGE COUNCIL
206 E. Fireweed Ln #204 • Anchorage, AK 99503
(907) 338-7611 Fax 338-7659; Fred Matsuno, President
E-mail: ugashikoffice4@alaska.net. *Tribes*: Eskimo and Indian.
Self-Gov: Bristol Bay Native Association, Inc. West-Central Alaska Agency.

UMKUMIUT NATIVE VILLAGE
P.O. Box 90062 • Nightmute, AK 99690
(907) 647-6145 Fax 647-6146; Jay Dull, Sr., President
E-mail: umkumiut@yahoo.com. West-Central Alaska Agency.

NATIVE VILLAGE OF UNALAKLEET (IRA)
270 Main St., P.O. Box 270 • Unalakleet, AK 99684
(907) 624-3622 Fax 624-3621; Jacob Ivanoff, President
Website: www.unalakleet.net; E-mail: middyj@nsedc.com
Self-Gov: Kawerak. *Tribes*: Eskimo & Indian. *In residence*: 870. *Total acreage*: 258. *Council members*: Paul Katchatag, Ruth Blatchford, Eleanor Bahr. *Activities*: Operates a clinic. *Publication*: Unalit Newsletter. Fairbanks Agency.

NATIVE VILLAGE OF UNGA
P.O. Box 508 • Sand Point, AK 99661
(907) 383-2415 Fax 383-5553; John A. Foster, President
Website: www.ungatribe.org; E-mail: ungatribe@arctic.net
Self-Gov: Aleutian/Pribilof Islands Assn, Inc. West-Central Alaska Agency.

VILLAGE OF VENETIE (IRA)
P.O. Box 81119 • Venetie, AK 99781
(907) 849-8165 Fax 849-8097; Steve D. Frank, First Chief
E-mail: venetievillagecouncil@yahoo.com
Tribe: Athapascan. *In residence*: 125. Fairbanks Agency.

VILLAGE OF WAINWRIGHT
P.O. Box 22 • Wainwright, AK 99783
(907) 763-2726 Fax 763-2536; Howard Patkotak, President
E-mail: hpatkotak@ain.olgoonik.com
Tribe: Eskimo. *In residence*: 335. Fairbanks Agency.

NATIVE VILLAGE OF WALES (IRA)
P.O. Box 549 • Wales, AK 99783
(907) 664-3062 Fax 664-3062; Anna Oxereok, President
Website: www.kawerak.org; E-mail: tc.waa@kawerak.org
Tribe: Eskimo. *In residence*: 225. Fairbanks Agency.

NATIVE VILLAGE OF WHITE MOUNTAIN
P.O. Box 84090 • White Mountain, AK 99784
(907) 638-3651 Fax 638-3652; Lincoln M. Simon, Jr., President
E-mail: dbarr@kawerak.org; Self-Gov: Kawerak
Tribes: Eskimo & Indian. *In residence*: 200. Fairbanks Agency.

WRANGELL COOPERATIVE ASSOCIATION (IRA)
P.O. Box 868 • Wrangell, AK 99929
(907) 874-4304 Fax 874-4305; Richard J. Oliver, President
E-mail wcatribe@gmail.com
Self-Gov: Central Council of Tlingit-Haida. West-Central Alaska Agency.

YAKUTAT TLINGIT TRIBE
P.O. Box 418 • Yakutat, AK 99689
(907) 784-3238 Fax 784-3595; Victoria L. Demmert, President
Self Gov: Yakutat Tlingit Tribe. *Tribes*: Tlingit & Haida.
West-Central Alaska Agency.

ARIZONA

AK-CHIN INDIAN COMMUNITY
Maricopa Reservation, 42507 W. Peters & Nall Rd. • Maricopa, AZ 85138
(520) 568-1000 Fax 568-4566; Website: www.ak-chin.nsn.us
Robert Miguel Chairperson; Gabriel Lopez, Vice Chairperson
Councilmembers: Delia M. Carlyle, Alvin Antone, Ann Marie Antone
Raychel Peters, Ak-Chin O'odham Runner Editor
(520) 568-1375 Fax 568-1376
Tribes: Ak-Chin (Papago & Pima). *Enrolled members*: 775. *In residence*: 450. *Area*: 21,500 acres. *Location*: 58 miles south of Phoenix in the northwestern part of Pinal County. *Facilities*: Ak Chin Community Library & Education Center. *Enterprises*: Ak-Chin Farms Enterprise; Industrial Park. *Attractions*: Harrah's Ak-Chin Casino & Resort; Ak Chin Him Dak Eco-Museum. Community Events: Annual Him-Dak Celebration in April; Native American Recognition Day in November; St. Francis of Assisi Feast in October; Masik Ta:S (Ak-Chn birthday) in December. *Publication*: O'odham Runner, bi-monthly newspaper; E-mail: runner@ak-chin.nsn.us. Pima Agency.

COCOPAH INDIAN TRIBE
Cocopah Reservation, 14515 S. Veterans Dr. • Somerton, AZ 85350
(928) 627-2102 Fax 627-3173; Website: www.cocopah.com
Sherry Cordova, Chairperson; J. Deal Begay, Jr., Vice Chairperson
Lilia Tafoya, Executive Secretary; E-mail: cocotcsec@cocopah.com
Councilmembers: Marvin Sharkey, Jr., Rosa J. Long, Edmund Domingues
Veronica Menta, Tribal Administrator; E-mail: mentav@cocopah.com
E-mail: administrator@cocopah.com
Wynnie Ortega, Education Coordinator (627-4973 Fax 627-4979)
E-mail: cocoed@cocopah.com
Leo Maxwell, THMP Director (627-2681 Fax 627-2929)
E-mail: cocothmp@cocopah.com
Lynetta Thomas, Cocopah Community Center Coordinator
(627-5658 Fax 627-3173) E-mail: thomasl@cocopah.com
Jill McCormick, Cultural Resources Manager (627-4849 Fax 627-3173)
E-mail: culturalres@cocoph.com
Wynnie Ortega, Education Director (627-4973 Fax 627-4979)
E-mail: cocoed@cocopah.com
Kathleen Bartosh, Museum Director (627-1992 Fax 627-2280)
E-mail: museum@cocopah.com
Jonathan Athens, Director/Public Relations; E-mail: athensj@cocopah.com
Tribe served: Cocopah. *Enrolled members*: 1,000. *In residence*: 550. *Area*: 6,500 acres; located 13 miles south of Yuma, AZ, along the Colorado River. *Facilities*: Community Center; Cocopah Museum & Cultural Center; Fort Yuma Health Center. *Attractions*: Cocopah Casino & Cocoph Resort & Conference Center (928) 726-8066; Cocopah RV & Golf Resort. Fort Yuma Agency.

COLORADO RIVER INDIAN TRIBES
Colorado River Indian Reservation
26600 Mohave Rd. • Parker, AZ 85344
(928) 669-9211 Fax 669-1391
Website: www.crit-nsn.gov; E-mail: feedback@critonline.com
Dennis Patch, Chairperson; Keith Moses, Vice Chairperson
Amelia Flores, Secretary; Valerie Welsh-Tahbo, Treasurer
Councilmembers: Johnny Hill, Jr., Granthum Stevens, Johnson "J.D." Fisher, Herman "TJ" Laffoon, Jr., Robert "Bobby" Page
Dennis Patch, Education Dept. Director (669-8831)

Daniel Barbara, Health & Social Services Director (669-6577 Fax 669-8881)
Gilford D. Harper, Library/Archives Director (69-1332 Fax 669-8262)
Tribes: Mohave, Chemehuevi, Hopi, and Navajo. *Tribal enrollment*: 3,500. *In residence*: 1,000. *Area*: 300,000 acres located along the Colorado River in Arizona and southeast California. *Programs*: Fish & Game, Education, Health & Social Services, Recreation, Housing. *Resources*: Tribal Museum & Library; Old Mohave Presbyterian Church, National Historic Site. *Attractions*: BlueWater Resort/Casino; lodging & camping; Colorado River; archaeological excavations and ruins of La Paz, a former gold mining town. *Activities*: National Indian Day, Mohave Day, All-Indian Rodeo, 4th of July Celebration; Annual Thanksgiving & Christmas Program. *Publication*: CRIT Newsletter, quarterly. Manataba Messenger. Head Start Program. Colorado River Agency.

FORT McDOWELL YAVAPAI NATION
Fort McDowell Yavapai Reservation
P.O. Box 17779 • Fountain Hills, AZ 85269
(480) 789-7000 Fax 837-1630; Website: www.fmyn.org
Bernadine Burnette, President; E-mail: bburnette@ftmcdowell.org
Pansy Thomas, Vice President; E-mail: pthomas@ftmcdowell.org
Selena Castaneda, Secretary; E-mail: scastaneda@ftmcdowell.org
Pamela Mott, Treasurer; E-mail: pmott@ftmcdowell.org
Councilmembers: Paul Russell & Gerald Doka
Nimrod Thomas, Administrative Manager
Phillip Dorchester, General Manager (789-7000)
 E-mail: pdorchester@ftmcdowell.org
Jacquelyn McCalvin, Librarian (789-7848)
 E-mail: jmccalvin@ftmcdowell.org
Bill Myhr, Education Division Director
 E-mail: bmyhr@ftmcdowell.org
Karen Ray, Cultural Development Manager
 E-mail: kray@ftmcdowell.org
Kerry Passey, Acting Cief Judge (789-7604)
Tribes: Yavapai. *Tribal enrollment*: 950. *In residence*: 550. *Area*: 40 sq. miles; 24,680 acres located twenty miles northeast of Phoenix on the Verde River. *Attractions*: Fort McDowell Casino; WeKoPa Golf Club; Fort McDowell Adventures (a Western theme outdoor venue); RV Park; Radisson Fort McDowell Resort & Conference Center; Radisson Poco Diablo Resort in Sedona; Roosevelt Dam & Reservoir; Bartlett Reservoir. *Events*: Annual Native American Fine Arts Show; monthly Native American Arts, Crafts & Jewelry Show; Annual Gathering of the Pai's Festival; annual Spring Rodeo. Salt River Field Office.

GILA RIVER INDIAN COMMUNITY
Gila River Reservation, P.O. Box 97 • Sacaton, AZ 85147
(520) 562-9840/1 Fax 562-9849
Website: www.gilariver.org; E-mail: info@gilariver.org
Stephen Roe Lewis, Governor; E-mail: executive.mail@gric.nsn.us
Monica Lynn Antone, Lt. Governor; Robert Keller, Treasurer
Linus Everling, General Counsel
June Shorthair, Communications & Public Affairs Director
Pamela Thompson, Community Manager
Ann Manuel, Acting Director of Community Services
Councilmembers: (562-9720 Fax 562-9729)
Arzie Hogg, District 1; E-mail: arzie.hogg@gilariver-nsn.gov
Joey Whitman, District 1; E-mail: joey.whitman@gilariver-nsn.gov
Carol A. Schurz, District 2; E-mail: carol.schurz@gilariver-nsn.gov
Carolyn Williams, District 3; E-mail: Carolyn.williams@gilariver-nsn.gov
Rodney Jackson, District 3; E-mail: Rodney.jackson@gilariver-nsn.gov
Barney B. Enos, Jr., District 4; E-mail: barney.enos@gilariver-nsn.gov
Pamela Johnson, District 4; E-mail: Pamela.jjohnson@gilariver-nsn.gov
Jennifer Allison, District 4; E-mail: Jennifer.allison@gilariver-nsn.gov
Nada Celaya, District 4; E-mail: nada.celeya@gilariver-nsn.gov
Janice Stewart, District 5; E-mail: Janice.stewart@gilariver-nsn.gov
Franklin Pablo, Sr., District 5; E-mail: franklin.pablosr@gilariver-nsn.gov
Robert Stone, District 5; E-mail: Robert.stone@gilariver-nsn.gov
Marlin Dixon, District 5; E-mail: marlin.dixon@gilariver-nsn.gov
Charles Goldtooth, District 6; E-mail: charles.goldtooth@gilariver-nsn.gov
Anthony Villareal, Sr., District 6; E-mail: anthony.villarealsr@gilariver-nsn.gov
Terrance Evans, District 6; E-mail: terrance.evans@gilariver-nsn.gov
Devin C. Redbird, District 7; E-mail: devin.redbird@gilariver-nsn.gov
Huhugam Heritage Center: 21359 S. Maricopa Rd., Suite 5041,
 Chandler, AZ 85226 (520) 796-3500; Website: www.grichhc.org
Mario Molina, Education Director (562-3662 ext. 236)
 E-mail: Mario.molina@gric.nsn.us
Laverne Dallas, Health Director; E-mail: laverne.dallas@gric.nsn.us
Roberto A. Jackson, GRIN Managing Editor (562-9715 Fax 562-9712)
 E-mail: Roberto.jackson@gric.nsn.us; grin@gric.nsn.us
Tribes: Pima-Maricopa. *In residence*: 9,750. *Area*: 370,000 acres. *Program*: Head Start. *Resources*: Huhugam Heritage Center; owns & operates the Vee Quiva Casino, Wild Horse Pass Casino & the Lone Butte Casino. *Publication*: Gila River Indian News (GRIN). Pima Agency.

HAVASUPAI TRIBE
Havasupai Reservation, P.O. Box 10 • Supai, AZ 86435
(928) 448-2731 Fax 448-2551
Website: www.havasupai-nsn.gov; E-mail: info@havasupai-nsn.gov
Don E. Watahomigie, Chairperson; E-mail: htchair@havasupai-nsn.gov
Edmond Tilousi, Vice Chair; E-mail: htvchair@havasupai-nsn.gov
Councilmembers: Eva Kissoon, Shelton Manakaja, Mathew Putesoy, Sr., Carletta Tilousi, Thomas Siyuja, Sr.
Tribe: Havasupai. *Enrolled members*: 640. *In residence*: 450. *Area*: 188,000 acres. Located in Coconino County; Havasu (Cataract) Canyon within the Grand Canyon. *Resources*: Trading Post; tribal Lodge; tribal museum offering tribal crafts & displays; photographs. *Programs*: Education; Health; Head Start. *Events*: Annual Peach Festival, 2nd weekend in August. Truxton Canon Field Office.

HOPI TRIBE
Hopi Reservation, P.O. Box 123 • Kykotsmovi, AZ 86039
(928) 734-2441 Fax 734-6665
Website: www.hopi-nsn.gov; E-mail: hopicouncil@hopi.nsn.us
Herman G. Honanie, Chairperson
Alfred Lomahquahu, Jr., Vice Chair
Theresa Lomakema, Council Secretary
Robert Sumatzkuku, Treasurer
Alfonso Sakeva, Sergeant-At-Arms
Neva Poneoma, Legislative Secretary (734-3133)
 E-mail: nponeoma@hopi.nsn.us
Councilmembers:
Village of Upper Moencopi: LeRoy Shingoitewa, Bruce Fredericks, Wayne Kuwanhyoima, Michael Elmer
Village of Bakabi: Ruth Kewanimptewa, Clifford Qotsaquahu, Lamar Keevama
Village of Kykotsmovi: Antone Honanie, Jack Harding, Jr., Nada Talayumptewa, David Talayumptewa
Village of Sipaulavi: Norene Kootswatewa, Anita Bahnimptewa, Rosa Honanie
Village of Mishongovi: Craig Andrews, Emma Anderson, Pansy K. Edmo, Rolanda Yoyletsdewa
First Mesa Consolidated Villages: Albert T. Sinquah, Wallace Youvella, Sr., Dale Sinquah, Celestino Youvella
Lorencita Joshweseoma, MPH, Director of Health & Human Services
Tribes: Hopi & Tewa. *In residence*: 8,500. *Area*: 1,565,376 acres.
Resources: Hopi Cultural Center; Hopi Wellness Center; arts & crafts shops; tribal museum; motels & restaurants. *Publication*: Navajo Hopi Observer; Hopi Tutuveni (bimonthly tribal newspaper). Head Start Program. Hopi Agency.

HUALAPAI TRIBAL NATION
Hualapai Reservation, P.O. Box 179 • Peach Springs, AZ 86434
(888) 769-2221; (928) 769-2216 Fax 769-2343
Website: www.hualapai-nsn.gov
Damon R. Clarke, Chairperson (2016-2020)
 E-mail: damon.clarke@hualapai-nsn.gov
Philbert Watahomigie, Sr., Vice Chairperson (2016-2020)
 E-mail: pwatahomigie@hualapai-nsn.gov
Councilmembers:
William Clay Bravo; E-mail: william.bravo@hualapai-nsn.gov
Stewart M. Crozier; E-mail: stewart.crozier@hualapai-nsn.gov
Shelton Scott Crozier; E-mail: sscrozier2001@yahoo.com
Carrie Imus; E-mail: cimus@frontiernet.net
Marietta Jean Pagilawa; E-mail: jpagilawa@hualapai-nsn.gov
Shawna Havatone; E-mail: Shawna.havatone@hualapai-nsn.gov
Emma Tapija; E-mail: emma.tapija@hualapai-nsn.gov
Lucille J. Watahomigie, Director of Education
 E-mail: hualapaieducationdepartment@gmail.com
April Havatone, Court Administrator; E-mail: ahavatone@hualapai-nsn.gov
Tribe: Hualapai. *Enrolled members*: 1,535. *In residence*: 1,620. *Area*: 995,000 acres. *Programs*: Loretta Jackson-Kelly, Director of Historic Preservation; Lucille J. Watahomigie, Education Director; Sandra L.Y. Irwin, Health Director; James B. Navenma, Housing Director. *Resources*: Native American Research Center for Health (NARCH), Terri Hutchins, Project Coordinator. The project is currently operating a youth Internet radio station: EPCH through the KIDSTAR radio network at www.kidstar.org. The project is also working to set up a Hualapai community radio station, KBAJ. *Publication*: GAMYU, newsletter. *Attraction*: The Grand Canyon. Truxton Canon Field Office.

KAIBAB BAND OF PAIUTE INDIANS
Tribal Administration Bldg., #1 North Pipe Spring Rd. • Fredonia, AZ 86022
(928) 643-7245 Fax (888) 939-3777
Website: www.kaibabpaiute-nsn.gov
E-mail: info@kaibabpaiute-nsn.gov
Roland Maldonado, Chairperson; (643-8301)
 E-mail: rolandm@kaibabpaiute-nsn.gov

Carmen Bradley, Vice Chairperson; (435) 899-5555
  E-mail: Bradley@fredonia.net
Yolanda Rogers, Treasurer; E-mail: yrogers@kaibabpaiute-nsn.gov
Councilmembers: Carlos Bulletts, Elwin John, Lawanda Hill, Manuel Savala
Amanda Bundy, Education Director (643-6025 Fax 286-8311)
  E-mail: abundy@kaibabpaiute-nsn.gov
Dennis Day, Southern Paiute Consortium Director (643-8330)
Tribe: Paiute. *In residence*: 250. *Area*: 120,840 acres located in Arizona & Utah. *Programs*: Education; Human Services; Human Resources; Housing; Environmental; Wildlife. *Facilities*: Tribe Library (643-6004). *Attractions*: Pipe Springs National Monument Visitor Center & Cultural Museum. *Activities*: Kaibab Paiute Heritage Day Celebration. Southern Paiute Field Station.

THE NAVAJO (DINE) NATION
100 Parkway, P.O. Box 7440 • Window Rock, AZ 86515
(928) 871-7000 Fax 871-4025
Website: www.navajo-nsn.gov; E-mail: info@nnopvp.org
Russell Begaye, President (871-7915)
  E-mail: russellbegaye@navajo-nsn.gov
Francelia Johnson, Presidential Scheduler (871-7915)
  E-mail: fjhnson@navajo-nsn.gov
Jonathan Nez, Vice President; (871-7001)
  E-mail: jonathannez@navajo-nsn.gov
Christopher Bahe, VP Scheduler (871-7001)
  E-mail: cbahe@navajo-nsn.gov
Councilmembers: George Apachito; Lorenzo Bates; Elmer P. Begay; Mel R. Begay; Nelson S. BeGaye; Russell Begaye; Katherine Benally; Joshua Lavar Butler, Lorenzo Curley; Charles Damon II; Jonathan Hale; Kenneth Maryboy; Jonathan Nez; Leonard H. Pete; Walter Phelps; Alton Joe Shepherd; Danny Simpson; Roscoe D. Smith; David L. Tom; Duane Tsinigine; Leonard Tsosie; Dwight Witherspoon; Edmund Yazzie.
Robert Joe, Chief Operations Officer (810-8505)
  E-mail: rjoe@navajo-nsn.gov
Chaity Sam, Chief Operations Officer Scheduler (810-8505)
  E-mail: cksam@navajo-nsn.gov
Mihio Manus, Communications Director (871-7728)
  E-mail: mmanus@navajo-nsn.gov
Arbin Mitchell, Chief of Staff
  E-mail: arbinmitchell@navajo-nsn.gov
Leonard Chee, Western Agency Lisiason (871-7917)
  E-mail: leonardchee@navajo-nsn.gov
Nina Chester, Northern Agency Lisiason (871-7204)
  E-mail: ninnachester@navajo-nsn.gov
Yvonne Kee-Billison, Fort Defiance Agency Liaison (871-7244)
  E-mail: yvonnekeebillison@navajo-nsn.gov
Angela Cody, Former Bennett Freeze Area Liaison (380-2977)
  E-mail: acody@navajo-nsn.gov
Mark Freeland, Eastern Agency/State of NM Liaison (871-6028)
  E-mail: m.freeland@navajo-nsn.gov
James Davis, Council Liaison (871-7025)
  E-mail: jjdavisjr@navajo-nsn.gov
Nikola Toledo, Federal Government Budget Liaison (871-7005)
  E-mail: mtoledo@navajo-nsn.gov
Karis N. Begaye, Legal Counsel (871-7004)
  E-mail: knbegaye@navajo-nsn.gov
Mihio Manus, Public Information Officer (871-7728)
  E-mail: mmanus@navajo-nsn.gov
Nicole Q. Macias, Senior Public Information Officer (871-6361)
  E-mail: nqmacias@navajo-nsn.gov
Michele Crank, Special Projects (871-7916)
  E-mail: mjcrank@navajo-nsn.gov
Peterson Zah, Navajo Nation Ambassador (871-7244)
  E-mail: pzah@navajo-nsn.gov
Lorenzo Bates, Nation Speaker (871-7160 Fax 871-7255)
Ethel Branch, Attorney General, Department of Justice
  E-mail: ebranch@nndoj.org (871-6345)
Allen Sloan, Acting Chief Justice
Dominic Beyal, Executive Director, Office of Management & Budget
Wenona Benally, Executive Director, Navajo-Hopi Land Commission
  E-mail: wbenally@navajo-nsn.gov (871-6441)
Andrew Tah, Superintendent, Department of Dine' Education
Virgil Brown, Executive Director, Division of General Services
  E-mail: virgilbrownjr@navajo-nsn.gov (871-6311)

Terrelene Massey, Executive Director, Division of Social Services
  E-mail: tmassey@navajo-nsn.gov (871-6556)
Carl Smith, Executive Director, Division of Community Development
  E-mail: carlsmith@navajodot.org (371-8300)
Tommy Lewis, Supt. of Schools, Dept. of Dine Education
  E-mail: tomylewis@nndode.org (871-7475)
Dr. Gloria Segay, Division Director, Department of Health

  E-mail: Gloria.segay@nndoh.org (871-6350)
Crystal J. Deschinny, Executive Director, Division of Economic Development
  E-mail: cdeschinny@navajo-nsn.gov (871-6544)
Dr. Donald Benn, Executive Director, Navajo EPA
  E-mail: donbenn@navajo-nsn.gov (871-7692)
Bidtah Becker, Executive Director, Division of Natural Resources
  E-mail: bidtahnbecker@navajo-nsn.gov (871-6592)
Paulene Thomas, Acting Executive Director, Gaming Regulatory Office
  E-mail: paulenethomas@navajo-nsn.gov (871-6712)
Tribe: Navajo of Arizona, New Mexico & Utah. Nation covers 27,000 square miles and more than a dozen national monuments, tribal parks & historic sites. *In residence*: 185,000. *Area*: 16 million acres located in northern Arizona, northwest New Mexico, and southern Utah. *Attractions*: Navajo Nation Fair (September); summer & winter ceremonials (each week); Office of Navajo Veterans Affairs: P.O. Box 430; (602) 871-6597 Ext. 6598. Museum & library. *Head Start Program*: Division of Child Development, Box 260, Fort Defiance, AZ 86505 (602) 729-5360. Navajo Tourism, (www.discovernavajo.com) P.O. Box 663, Window Rock, AZ 86515 (928) 810-8501 Fax 810-8500; eNewsletter. *Publications*: The Navajo Times, newspaper (website: www.navajotimes.com). Discover Navajo: The Official Navajo Nation Visitor Guide. Museum. Library. Navajo Area Office.

Navajo Nation Washington Office:
750 First St. NE #1010 • Washington, DC 20002
  (202) 682-7390 Fax 682-7391; Website: www.nnwo.org
  E-mail: info@nnwo.org; E-mail: nnwo750@yahoo.com
Jackson Brossy, Executive Director; (202) 775-0393
  E-mail: jbrossy@nnwo.org
Percy Anderson, Office Liaison
Publications: Navajo Nation Washington Office Newsletter, quarterly; The Legislative News, bi-monthly updates on congressional legislation, news & information in the U.S. Senate, U.S. House of Representatives, White House, and federal agencies.

PASCUA YAQUI TRIBE
7474 S. Camino De Oeste • Tucson, AZ 85746
(520) 883-5000 Fax 883-5014; Website: www.pascuayaqui-nsn.gov
Robert Valencia, Chairperson
  E-mail: robert.valencia@pascuayaqui-nsn.gov
Peter Yucupicio, Vice Chairperson
  E-mail: peter.yucupicio@pascuayaqui-nsn.gov
Raymundo Baltazar, Treasurer
Mary Jane Buenamea, Secretary
Councilmembers: Cruzita Armenta, Hermina Frias, Francisco Valencia, David Ramirez, Rosa Soto Alvarez, Antonio Campoy, Francisco Munoz
Veronica Gastello, Education Director (883-5049)
  E-mail: veronica.gastello@pascuayaqui-nsn.gov
Alfred Urbina, Attorney General (883-5106)
Tribe: Pascua Yaqui. *Area*: 250 acres. *Facilities*: Radio Station, KPYT-LP 100.3 FM; Dr. Fernando Escalante Tribal Library/Resource Center. *Programs*: Health Services; Head Start. *Attractions*: Casino of the Sun & Casino Del Sol; Anselmo Valencia Tori Amphitheater; Bingo Hall. *Enterprises*: Yaqui Enterprises. *Publication*: Yaqui Times. Salt River Field Office.

QUECHAN TRIBE
Fort Yuma Indian Reservation, P.O. Box 1899 • Yuma, AZ 85366
(760) 572-0213 Fax 572-2102; Website: www.itcaonline.com
Keeny Escalanti, Sr., President; Virgil S. Smith, Vice President
Councilmembers: Jordan Joaquin, Lorainne E. White, Aaron Brown, Mark William Whiye II, Marsha E. Hill
Ora Lee Durand-Valisto, Higher Education/Vocational Training Director
  E-mail: o.durand@quechantribe.com
Barbara Levy, language Coordinator
Chase Choate, Environmental Director
Brian Golding, Sr., Economic Development Director
Claudette C. White, Chief Judge (760) 572-5552
Tribe: Fort Yuma-Quechan. *Tribal enrollment*: 2,475. *Area*: 45,000 acres located along both sides of the Colorado River near Yuma, Arizona. The reservation borders the states of AZ, CA, Baja California & Mexico. *Facilities*: Heritage Center. *Attractions*: Quechan Paradise Casino & Resort. Located in Arizona & California. Fort Yuma Field Office.

SALT RIVER PIMA-MARICOPA INDIAN COMMUNITY
10005 East Osborn Rd. • Scottsdale, AZ 85256
(480) 362-7400 Fax 362-7575; Website: www.srpmic-nsn.gov
Delbert Ray, President; Martin Harvier, Vice President
Council members: District I – Salt River: Jenelle Howard, Archie Kashoya, Thomas Largo, Sr., Ricardo Leonard, David Antone
District II – Lehi: Michael Dallas, Deanna Scabby
Kierstin Anderson, Tribal Managing Attorney (362-5670)
  E-mail: kierstin.anderson@srpmic-nsn.gov

Tribes: Pima & Maricopa. *Enrolled members*: 6,000+. *Area*: 52,600 acres; 19,000 acres as a natural preserve and 12,000 acres are under cultivation in a variety of crops, located east of Scottsdale & north of Mesa in Salt River Valley, adjacent to Phoenix. Departments: Economic Development; History & Culture. *Programs*: Head Start; Community Development Dept.; Salt River Development Co. (www.srdeco.com) *Attraction*: Casino Arizona. *Activities*: Annual Walk for O'odham & Piipaash (March); Annual Honor the Child Powwow (July); SRPMIC Earth Day Fair; Early Childhood Education Parade (May); Red Mountain Powwow (November). *Facilities*: Three Community Education Centers; Early Childhood Education Center; Salt River Elementary School (K-6) & Salt River High School (7-12). *Resources*: Hoo Hoogam Ki Museum; Salt River Library. *Publication*: Au-Authm Action News, monthly tribal newspaper. Dodie Manuel, Managing Editor (362-7731). Salt River Agency.

SAN CARLOS APACHE TRIBE
1 San Carlos Ave., P.O. Box 0 • San Carlos, AZ 85550
(928) 475-2361 Fax 475-2567; Website: www.sancarlosapache.com
Terry Rambler, Chairperson; Tao Etpison, Vice Chairperson
Council members: *Bylas District*: Hugh Moses, Jr., Jonathan Kitcheyan & Alicia Cadmus; *Gilson Wash District*: Simon Hooke & Tao Etpison; *Peridot District*: Frederick Ferreaira, Jr. & Wendsler Nosie; *Seven Mile*: Bernadette Goode & Mitchell Hoffman
Herb Stevens, Cultural Center Director (475-2894)
Tribe: San Carlos Apache. *In residence*: 10,800. *Area*: 1,835,000 acres. *Resources*: Cultural Center (475-2894) located on Hwy. 70 with a display of artifacts of the Apaches in the early 1800's & modern artwork in basketry, beadwork, traditional clothing/attire with an information center; Hospital Service Unit HIS; Wellness Center; Apache Nation Business Center & Chamber of Commerce; San Carlos Training Institute. *Activities*: Annual Red Paint Powwow & Indian Market; Apache Tribal Fair (November); Indian Roundup (May & November); Self-Governance. *Attractions*: Apache Gold Casino Resort; Coolidge Dam; Tonto National Forest. *Publication*: San Carlos Apache Moccasin newspaper featuring news about the San Carlos Apache people and its tribal government. *Program*: Head Start. San Carlos Agency.

SAN JUAN SOUTHERN PAIUTE TRIBE
P.O. Box 1989 • Tuba City, AZ 86045
(928) 283-4589 Fax 283-5761; Website: www.itcaonline.com
Carlene Yellowhair, President (283-4762 Fax 283-4758)
E-mail: cyellow_sjspt.president@outlook.com
Candelora Lehi, Administrative Officer
Councilmembers: Henry Whiskers, Clyde Whiskers, Mabel Lehi, Grace Lehi, Camilia Younker
Tribes: Paiute-Navajo. *Population served*: 275. *Activities*: Annual powwow 3rd week of June. *Publications*: Sands to the Mountains (Bunte & Franklin); The Paiute Indians of North America. Southern Paiute Field Office. Library.

TOHONO O'ODHAM NATION
Sells Reservation, P.O. Box 837 • Sells, AZ 85634
(520) 383-2028 Fax 383-3379; Website: www.tonation-nsn.gov
Edward D. Manuel, Chairperson; Verlon M. Jose, Vice Chairperson
Timothy Joaquin (Gu Achi,) Legislative Chairperson
Lucinda Allen (Sif Oidak), Legislative Vice Chairperson
Legislative Council:
Baboquivari District: Veronica J. Harey, Chairperson; Vernon Smith; Frances Miguel, Reps.
Chukaut Kuk District: Marla Kay Henry, Chairperson; Billman Lopez; Ethel Garcia, Reps.
Gu Achi District: Camillus Lopez, Chairperson; Loretta Lewis, Rep.
Gu Vo District: Geneva S. Ramon, Chairperson; Grace Manuel; Pamela Anghill, Reps.
Hickiwan District: Delma Garcia, Chairperson Louis Lopez; Sandra Ortega, Reps.
Pisinemo District: Stanley Cruz, Chairperson; Chester Antone & Monica K. Morgan, Reps.
San Lucy District: Albert Manuel, Jr., Chairperson; Diana Manuel; Jana Montana, Reps.
San Xavier District: Austin Nunez, Chairperson; Olivia Villegas-Liston, Hilarlon Campus, Reps
Schuk Toak District: Phyllis Juan, Chairperson; Anthony Francisco, Jr. & Quintin Lopez, Reps.
Sells District: Evelyn Juan-Manuel Barbara Havier & Arthur Wilson, Reps.
Sif Oidak District: Rita A. Wilson, Chairperson; Mary Lopez, Rep.
Violet Lui-Frank, Chief Judge
Walter Marcus, Larry Yazzie & Donald Harvey, Judges
Tribe: Tohono O'odham. *Tribal enrollment*: 28,000 *In residence*: 13,500. *Reservations served*: Sells, San Xavier, and Gila Bend. *Area*: 2.7 million acres. Located 25 miles west of Tucson. *Government*: Legislative Branch consists of two representatives each from 12 districts. *Resources*: Tohono O'odham Community College; five recreation centers; health center; six Head Start

preschools; KOHN Radio - 91.9 FM. *Programs*: Health & Human Services; Higher Education; Early Childhood Development; Vocational Rehabilitation; Natural Resources; Planning and Economic Development; Housing; Public Safety & Environmental Protection; Gaming; Employment and Training; Youth Council; Senior Services. *Attractions*: San Xavier Mission Del Bac; Baboquivari Mountain Park; Desert Diamond Casino & Golden Hasan Casino. *Events*: Annual Powwow/Rodeo. *Publication*: Tohono O'odham News. Papago Agency.

TONTO APACHE TRIBE
Tonto Apache Reservation 30 • Payson, AZ 85541
(928) 474-5000 Fax 474-9125; Website: www.itcaonline.com
Jeri DeCola, Chairperson; Calvin Johnson, Vice Chairperson
Councilmembers: Lucinda Flores, Hunter Doka, Charlie Lopez
Walt Nader, Tribal Administrator
Calvin Johnson, Economic Development Director
Ronnie McDaniel, Chief Judge
Tribe: Tonto Apache. *Enrolled members*: 110. *In residence*: 140. *Area*: 325 acres. Located in northwestern Gila County, 95 miles northeast of Phoenix. *Attractions*: Mazatzal Casino; The Paysonglo Lodge. *Publication*: Payson Roundup, tribal newspaper. Truxton Canon Agency.

WHITE MOUNTAIN APACHE TRIBE
Fort Apache Indian Reservation
201 E. Walnut St., P.O. Box 700 • Whiteriver, AZ 85941
(928) 338-4346 Fax 338-1514; Website: www.wmat.nsn.us
Ronnie Lupe, Chairperson; E-mail: rlupe@wmat.us
Kasey Velasquez, Vice Chairperson
Councilmembers: Arnold Beach & Tony Alsenay, District 1
Colleen Faden, District 2; Floyd Walker, District 3
Alvena Alekay Bush, Jerome Kasey III, District 4
Jim Palmer, Jr. & Fred Soto, Tribal Attorneys
Carol Gatewood-Kasey, Chief Judge; Candace Kane, Associate Judge
Tribe: White Mountain Apache. *Enrolled members*: 12,000. *In residence*: 2,500. *Area*: 1,664,872 acres. *Resources*: Hon-Dah Home Center; White Mountain Apache Cultural Center & Museum. *Programs*: Education; Health & Social Services; Human Resources; Wildlife & Outdoor Recreation; Head Start. *Attractions*: Hon-Dah Resort Casino; Sunrise Park Ski Resort. *Events*: Annual Hon-Dah Powwow; annual Tribal Fair & Rodeo. *Publication*: Fort Apache Scout, biweekly newspaper. Fort Apache Agency.

YAVAPAI-APACHE NATION
Camp Verde Reservation, 2400 W. Datsi St. • Camp Verde, AZ 85941
(928) 567-3649 Fax 567-1082; Website: www.yavapai-apache.org
Jane Russell Winiecki, Chairperson; Larry Jackson, Sr., Vice Chairperson
E-mail: tlewis@yan-tribe.org (567-1021)
Karla Reimer, Tribal Secretary; E-mail: kreimer@yan-tribe.org
Council Members: Annette Mendez, Dave Kinsey, Jr., Nancy Guzman, Monica Marquez, Mamie Fox, Lorna Hazelwood, Robin Hazelwood
Don Decker, Director of Public Relations; E-mail: ddecker@yan-tribe.org
Tribe: Yavapai-Apache. *Enrolled members*: 2,300. *In residence*: 600. *Area*: 1,600 acres. The Yavapai-Apache Nation is located in the Verde Valley and is comprised of five (5) tribal communities: Tunlii, Middle Verde, Rimrock, Camp Verde and Clarkdale. *Programs*: Wellness; UNITY Youth Council; Alcohol & Substance Abuse; Health & Human Services; Higher Education; Economic Development; Senior; Elder & Disabled Advocacy; Language & Media; Gaming Commission; Land & Water; Tourism *Resources*: Medical Center; Yavapai-Apache Cultural Resource Center; The Montessori Children's House. *Attractions*: Cliff Castle Casino; The Lodge & Conference Center at Cliff Castle; Distant Drums RV Park. *Publication*: Gah'Navah / Ya ti' newspaper. Truxton Canon Agency.

YAVAPAI-PRESCOTT INDIAN TRIBE
530 E. Merritt St. • Prescott, AZ 86301
(928) 445-8790 Fax 778-9445; Website: www.ypit.com
Ernest Jones, Sr., President; E-mail: ejones@ypit.com
Robert Ogo, Vice President; Lorna Galeano, Secretary-Treasurer
Councilmembers: Calvin Hunter, Jr., Sheila Salazar
Tribe: Yavapai. *Enrolled members*: 160. *Area*: 1,402 acres. *Special program*: Powwow; 10-K. *Facilities*: Owns & operates Bucky's Casino, Yavapai Casino; Prescott Resort & Conference Center; and Sundog Business Park located on Hwy. 89N. *Publication*: Viola Jimulla, The Indian Chieftess. Library. Truxton Canon Agency.

CALIFORNIA

AGUA CALIENTE BAND OF CAHUILLA INDIANS
5401 Dinah Shore Dr.• Palm Springs, CA 92262
(800) 790-3398; (760) 699-6800 Fax 699-6863
Website: www.aguacaliente.org
E-mail: tribalgovernment@aguacaliente.net

Jeff L. Grubbe, Chairperson; E-mail: jgrubbe@aguacaliente.net
Larry N. Olinger, Vice Chairperson
Vincent Gonzales, III, Secretary/Treasurer
Councilmembers: Anthony W. Purnel & Reid D. Milanovich
Alva Johnson, Executive Director of Government Affairs
Tom Davis, Chief Planning & Development Officer
 E-mail: tdavis@aguacaliente-nsn.gov
Alva Johnson, Director of Government Affairs & Public Relations
Margaret Park, Director of Planning & Natural Resources
Tribe: Agua Caliente Band of Cahuilla Indians. *In residence*: 250. *Area*: 52,000 acres of which 6,700 acres lie within the Palm Springs city limits. The area includes the Palm, Murray, Andreas, Tahquitz & Chino Canyons. *Programs*: Tribal Family Services; Child Development; Cultural Preservation; Housing; Planning & Development; Scholarship; Enrollment. *Resources*: Cultural Museum on 8.5 acres which holds permanent & changing exhibitions, a Research Library, Education Center, and a 150-seat Theater; affiliated with the Smithsonian Institution. *Activities*: Spa Resort Casino; Agua Caliente Casino; Indian Canyons Golf Resort. Palm Springs Agency.

ALTURAS RANCHERIA
P.O. Box 340 • Alturas, CA 96101
 (530) 233-5571 Fax 233-4165; Phillip Del Rosa, Chairperson
Tribe: Achomawi (Pit River). *Enrolled members*: 15. *Area*: 20 acres, near Alturas, California, in Modoc County. *Attractions*: Desert Rose Casino. Northern California Agency.

AUGUSTINE BAND OF CAHUILLA INDIANS
P.O. Box 846 • Coachella, CA 92236
 (760) 398-4722 Fax 369-7161; Website: www.augustinetribe.org
Amanda Vance, Chairperson
William Vance, Vice Chairperson/Treasurer
Ronnie Vance, Secretary
Tribe: Cahuilla. *Enrolled members*: 10. *Area*: 500 acres. *Attraction*: Augustine Casino. *Projects*: In December 2008, the Augustine Band of Cahuilla Indians made history and established itself as a leader in Indian Country in the area of renewable energy. The Tribe was the first tribe in Southern California to develop a major solar energy project approved by the United States Bureau of Indian Affairs (BIA). The Tribe installed a 1.1 megawatt photovoltaic plant on its reservation. The plant, located on the Augustine Solar Energy Park, produces enough energy to power a significant percentage of the total energy needs of the Tribe's business operations. In a few short years the project will not only pay for itself, but will also start earning a profit. The solar energy project represents a major step in achieving the Tribe's dual goals of becoming self-sufficient, and protecting the Earth's natural resources. Southern California Agency.

BARONA BAND OF MISSION INDIANS
Barona Reservation, 1095 Barona Rd. • Lakeside, CA 92040
 (619) 443-6612 Fax 443-0681
 Website https://www.barona-nsn.gov/
 E-mail: counciloffice@barona-nsn.gov
Edwin "Thorpe" Romero, Chairperson
Raymond Welch, Vice Chairperson
Councilmembers: Adam Reyes, Melissa Donayre, Bonnie LaChappa,
Manuel Navarro, Michael "Tony" Rodriguez
Laurie Egan-Hedley, Cultural Center & Museum Director/Curator
 E-mail: museum@baronamuseum.org; E-mail: lhedley@barona-nsn.gov
Kevin Van Wanseele, Gaming Commission Chairperson
Katy Duperry, Librarian/Archivist; E-mail: kduperry@barona-nsn.gov
Tribe: Ipai-Tiai Diegueno (Barona Band of Mission Indians). *In residence*: 536. *Area*: 5,664 acres. *Programs*: Barona Valley Environmental Sustainability Program; Gaming. *Resources*: Barona Cultural Center & Museum; Casino; Barona Indian Charter School. *Attraction*: Barona Resort & Casino. *Activities*: Annual Powwow on Labor Day Weekend; Annual Traditional Gathering in mid-August. Southern California Agency.

BENTON PAIUTE - UTU UTU GWAITU PAIUTE TRIBE
Benton Paiute Reservation
25669 Highway 6 PMBI • Benton, CA 93512
 (760) 933-2321 Fax 933-2412
 Website: www.bentonpaiutereservation.org
 E-mail: bentonpaiutetribe118@gmail.com
Tina Braithwaite, Chairperson
 E-mail: t.braithwaite@bentonpaiutereservation.org
Shane Saulque, Vice Chairperson
 E-mail: s.saulque@bentonpaiutereservation.org
Richard Eric Dearmore, Secretary/Treasurer
 E-mail: e.dearmore@bentonpaiutereservation.org
Councilmembers: Cecil Rambeau &Tahvooche Saulque Chavez
 E-mail: tahvoochesaulque@yahoo.com

Joseph Saulque, Director of Arbitration; E-mail: pokaneabe@gmail.com
Tribe: Utu Utu Gwaitu Paiute. *In residence*: 75. *Area*: 160 acres located in Mono County, in Blind Springs Valley three miles from Benton Hot Springs. *Activity*: Annual Meeting. Newsletter. Central California Agency.

BERRY CREEK RANCHERIA OF MAIDU INDIANS OF CALIFORNIA
5 Tyme Way • Oroville, CA 95966
 (530) 534-3859 Fax 534-1151
James Edwards, Chairperson
 E-mail: jedwards@berrycreekrancheria.com
Tribe: Tyme Maidu. Enrolled members: 304. In residence: 140. Area: 66 acres. *Attraction*: Operates Gold Country Casino & Hotel (see Casino section). *Publication*: Monthly tribal newsletter. Tribal Council. Central California Agency.

BIG LAGOON RANCHERIA
708 9th St. • Arcada, CA 95521
 (707) 826-2079 Fax 826-0459
Virgil Moorehead, Chairperson; E-mail: vmoorehead@earthlink.net
Tribes: Yurok & Tolowa. *Enrolled members*: 24. *In residence*: 12. *Area*: 9 acres located 30 miles north of Eureka. Operates the Barstow Casino & Resort in Barstow, California, with Los Coyotes Band of Cahuilla & Cupeno Indians. Northern California Agency.

BIG PINE PAIUTE TRIBE OF THE OWENS VALLEY
825 S. Main St., P.O. Box 700 • Big Pine, CA 93513
 (760) 938-2003 Fax 938-2942; Website: www.bigpinepaiute.org
 E-mail: info@bigpinepaiute.org
Genevieve Jones "Gina", Chairperson
James Rambeau, Sr., Vice Chair; E-mail: j.rambeau@bigpinepaiute.org
Rena Tibbetts, Secretary; E-mail: r.tibbetts @bigpinepaiute.org
Katie Rico-Moose, Treasurer; E-mail: k.moose @bigpinepaiute.org
Roseanne Moose, Member-at-Large & Vice Chair of the
 Big Pine Development Corporation; E-mail: r.moose@bigpinepaiute.org
Jill Paydon, Tribal AdmInistrator; E-mail: j.paydon@bigpinepaiute.org
Cheryl Levine, Indian Education Center Director
 E-mail: c.levine@bigpinepaiute.org
Jacqueline "Danielle" Gutirrez, Tribal Historic Preservation Officer
 E-mail: d.guierrez@bigpinepaiute.org
Sally Manning, Environmental Director
 E-mail: s.manning@bigpinepaiute.org
Tribes: Paiute & Shoshone. *Enrolled members*: 600. *In residence*: 400. *Area*: 300 acres located in Inyo County. *Departments*: Education, Environmental, Housing, Tribal Historic Preservation Office; Economic Development, Human Resources. Publication: Tribal newsletter. Central California Agency.

BIG SANDY RANCHERIA BAND OF WESTERN MONO INDIANS
37387 Auberry Mission Rd., P.O. Box 337 • Auberry, CA 93602
 (559) 374-0066 Fax 855-4129/4640
 Website: www.bigsandyrancheria.com
Elizabeth D. Kipp, Chairperson; E-mail: lkipp@bsrnation.com
Miles Baty, Vice Chairperson; E-mail: mbaty@bsrnation.com
Patricia Soto, Treasurer; E-mail: psoto@bsrnation.com
Regina Riley, Secretary; E-mail: griley@bsrnation.com
Sharon Baty Simpson, Member-at-Large
Tom Rizzo, Tribal Administrator; E-mail: trizzo@bsrnation.com
Johanna Leal, Head Start Director; E-mail: jleal@bsrnation.com
Norelva Alarcon, Family Activities Director
 E-mail: nalarcon@bsrnation.com
Mark Powless, Mafrlene Johnson & Rudy Gonzales, Gaming Commissioners
 E-mail: mpowless@bsrgaming.com; E-mail: mjohnson@bsrgaming.com
 E-mail: rgonnzales@bsrgaming.com
Tribe: Mono. *In residence*: 65. *Area*: 8 acres. *Attraction*: Mono Wind Casino & Resort (www.monowind.com). *Publication*: "Smoke Signals' Newsletter. Central California Agency.

BIG VALLEY BAND OF POMO INDIANS
Big Valley Rancheria, 2726 Mission Rancheria Rd. • Lakeport, CA 95453
 (707) 263-3924 Fax 533-2941; Website: www.bvrancheria.com
 E-mail: administrator@big-valley.net
Anthony Jack, Chairperson; E-mail: ajack@big-valley.net
Michael Gomez, Vice Chairperson
Carla Rodriguez, Treasurer; Vivian McCloud, Secretary
Ben Ray, III, Tribal Administrator
Nancy Hernandez, Social Services Director/ICWA Coordinator
Elizabeth Howe, Economic Development Director
Tribe: Pomo & Pit River. *Enrollment*: 225. *Attraction*: Konocti Vista Casino, Hotel & RV Park located in Lake County, California on Clear Lake. Website: www.kvcasino.com. *Publication*: Rancheria Newsletter. Central California Agency.

BISHOP PAIUTE TRIBE

Bishop Reservation, 50 N. Tu Su Lane • Bishop, CA 93514
(760) 873-3584 Fax 873-4143; Website: www.bishoppaiutetribe.com
Brian Poncho, Interim Chairperson & Vice Chairperson (937-0084)
  E-mail: deston.rogers@bishoppaiute.org
Earleen Williams, Secretary/Treasurer
  E-mail: gertrude.brown@bishoppaiute.org
Bill Vega & Jeff Romero, Councilmembers
Valerie Spoonhunter, Interim Tribal Administrator (873-3584 ext. 222)
  E-mail: valerie.spoonhunter@bishoppaiute.org
Shawn Bengochia, Education Director (873-5740)
  E-mail: shawn.bengochia@bishoppaiute.org
Tribes: Paiute & Shoshone. *Enrolled members*: 2,000. *Area*: 875 acres located at the foot of the Eastern Sierra Nevada Mountains in Bishop. *Resources*: Culture Center & Museum; *Programs*: Toiyabe Indian Health Project; career development; housing; education center (teaching of the Paiute language); headstart & daycare; elders program. *Attractions*: Paiute Palace Casino; annual Powwow in July. *Memberships*: Intertribal Council of California; National Congress of American Indians; California Indian Manpower Consortium; California National Indian Gaming Association. *Publication*: Bishop Tribal (BITC) Newsletter, bimonthly. Central California Agency.

BLUE LAKE RANCHERIA

428 Chartin Rd., P.O. Box 428 • Blue Lake, CA 95525
(707) 668-5101 Fax 668-4272
Website: www.bluelakerancheria-nsn.gov
E-mail: info@bluelakerancheria-nsn.gov
Claudia Brundin, Chairperson
Arla Ramsey, Vice Chairperson & Tribal Administrator
Art Ramsey, Secretary/Treasurer
Diane Holliday & Dorothy McKinnon, Members-at-Large
Tribes: Wiyot, Yurok, Cherokee, Warm Springs, Black Foot, Towala. *In residence*: 53. *Area*: 91 acres. *Programs*: Education; Child & Elderly Health & Welfare; Sovereignty & Self-Government; Economic Development; Environmental; Public Safety. *Attractions*: Blue Lake Casino. Northern California Field Office.

BRIDGEPORT INDIAN COLONY

355 Sage Brush Dr., P.O. Box 37 • Bridgeport, CA 93517
(760) 932-7083 Fax 932-7846
Website: www.bridgeportindiancolony.com
John Glazier, Chairperson; Thomas Crawford, Vice Chair
David Rambeau, Secretary; E-mail: secretary@bridgeportindiancolony.com
Leon Draper, Administrator; E-mail: admin@bridgeportindiancolony.com
Dana Christensen & Ervin Lent, Council Members-at-large
Deb Dyer, Finance Director; E-mail: finance@bridgeportindiancolony.com
Tribes: Miwok, Mono, Paiute, Shoshone & Washoe. *In residence*: 120. Central California Agency.

BUENA VISTA RANCHERIA OF ME-WUK INDIANS

1418 20th St., Suite 200 • Sacramento, CA 95811
(916) 491-0011 Fax 491-0012
Website: www.buenavistatribe.com; E-mail: info@buenavistatribe.com
Rhonda L. Morningstar Pope, Chairperson
Denean Swenson, Tribal Administrator
Mike DeSpain, Environmental Resources Director
Penny Arciniaga, Tribal Member Services
Arnold Samuel, General Counsel
Tribe: Me-Wuk. *Area*: 67.5 acres located near Ione, Calif. *Resources*: Child Development Center; Environmental Resources Dept. *Attractions*: Buena Vista Casino; Fall Festival. Central California Agency.

CABAZON BAND OF MISSION INDIANS

84-245 Indio Spring Dr. • Indio, CA 92201
(760) 342-2593 Fax 347-7880
Douglas Welmas, Chairperson; Brenda Soulliere, 1st Vice Chair
Charles Welmas, 2nd Vice Chair; Mark Nichols, CEO; Duff Wenz, COO
Judy Stapp, Cultural Affairs Director
Patrick Schoonover, Legal Affairs Director
Greg Cervantes, Public Affairs Director; Joan Kite, Public Information Officer
Tribe: Cahuilla. *Enrolled members*: 40. *Total acreage*: 1,700 acres located in Coachella Valley, Riverside County. *Resources*: Cahuilla Child Development Center; Cabazon Cultural Museum; Cabazon Tribal Reference Library. *Attractions*: Fantasy Springs Casino & Resort (See Casino section); Indio Powwows (Spring & Thanksgiving). *Publications*: Cabazon Circle Newsletter; Code of Cabazon Band of Mission Indians, and Return of the Buffalo - The Explosion of Indian Gaming. Southern California Agency.

CAHUILLA BAND OF INDIANS

52701 Hwy. 371, Suite B-1 P.O. Box 391760 • Anza, CA 92539
(951) 763-5549 Fax 763-2808
Website: www.cahuilla.net; E-mail: tribalcouncil@cahuilla.net
Daniel Salgado, Sr., Chairperson; E-mail: chairman@cahuilla.net
Andrea Candelaria, Vice Chairperson, Roberta Leash, Secretary
Adrian Salgado, Sr. & Erica Calloway, Council members
Jay Baczkowski, Tribal Administrator
Andreas Heredia, Cultural Director
  E-mail: culturaldirector@cahuilla.net
Jayne Lieera, Economic Development Chair
  E-mail: edc@cahuilla.net
Luther Salgado, Jr., Environmental Director
Tribe: Cahuilla. *Enrolled members*: 325. *In residence*: 175. *Area*: 18,880 acres. Located in a rural Southern California area of Riverside County, adjacent to township of Anza, CA. *Attractions*: Cahuilla Casino; Cahuilla Travel website; Cahuilla Smoke Shop. Scholarships available for higher education. Southern California Agency.

CAMPO KUMEYAAY NATION

36190 Church Rd., Suite 1 • Campo, CA 91906
(619) 478-9046 Fax 478-5818
Website: www.campo-nsn.gov; E-mail: info@campo-nsn.gov
Ralph Goff, Chairperson; E-mail: rgoff@campo-nsn.gov
Harry Paul Cuero, Vice Chairperson; E-mail: hcuero@campo-nsn.gov
Marcus Cuero, Treasurer; Annah Ceballos, Secretary
Committee members: Brian Connolly, Steven Cuero & Vanessa Parkhurst
Debbie Cuero, Education Director; E-mail: dcuero@campo-nsn.gov
Tribe served: Kumeyaay Diegueno. *In residence*: 350. *Area*: 15,336 acres. *Departments*: Education; Gaming; Economic Development; Muht Hei, Inc.; Shu;luuk Wind Project. Southern Indian Health Council. *Attractions*: Golden Acorn Casino. Southern California Agency.

NORTHERN PAIUTE TRIBE OF CEDARVILLE RANCHERIA

300 West 1st St. • Alturas, CA 96101
(530) 233-3969 Fax 233-4776
Website: www.cedarvillerancheria.net; E-mail: cedranch@citlink.net
Melissa Davis, Chairperson; Lacy DeGarmo, Secretary
Tribe: Paiute. *Enrolled members*: 30. *Area*: 19 acres. *Facilities*: Strong Family Health Center; Community Center, Cedarville. Northern California Field Office.

CHEMEHUEVI INDIAN TRIBE

1990 Palo Verde Dr., P.O. Box 1976 • Havasu Lake, CA 92363
(760) 858-4219 Fax 858-5400
Website: www.chemehuevi.net; E-mail: chemehuevit@cit-nsn.gov
Charles F. Wood, Chairperson; E-mail: chairman@cit-nsn.gov
Glenn H. Lodge, Vice Chairperson; E-mail: vice.chair@cit-nsn.gov
June Leivas, Secretary/Treasurer; E-mail: sec.treas@cit-nsn.gov
Councilmembers: Conkie Hoover, Matthew Leivas, Edward C. "Butch" Ochoa, Sierra Pencile, Edward D. "Tito' Smith, Steven Escobar
Donna Ellsworth, Tribal Administrator; E-mail: administrator@cit-nsn.gov
Matthew Levias, Sr., Director of the Cultural Center (858-1115 fax 858-5400)
Anna Ochoa, Archivist; Email: cultural@cit-nsn.gov
Dusty R. Bacon, Education Director; E-mail: citeddirector@gmail.com
Les Marston & David Dehnert, Tribal Attorneys (707) 462-6846
  E-mail: marston1@pacbell.net; E-mail: ddehnert@ca.rr.com
Tribe: Chemehuevi. *In residence*: 135. *Area*: 32,000 acres of trust land. *Resources*: Cultural Center; Community Center. *Programs*: Education; Health; Environmental; Housing; Child Welfare; Water; Head Start. *Attractions*: Havasu Landing Resort & Casino; Nuwuvi Days Celebration/June; Indian Days/September. *Publications*: Newsletter. In CA & AZ. Colorado River Agency.

CHER-AE HEIGHTS INDIAN COMMUNITY OF THE TRINIDAD RANCHERIA

P.O. Box 630 • Trinidad, CA 95570
(707) 677-0211 Fax 677-3921; Website: www.trinidad-rancheria.org
Garth Sundberg, Chairperson; Zack Brown, Vice Chairperson
James Brown, Council Seat #1; Fred Sundberg, Sr., Council Seat #2
Trina Mathewson, Secretary/Treasurer
Jacque Hostler-Carmesin, CEO; Amy Atkins, Executive Manager
Angela Higley, CFO; Michael Hostler, Tribal Council Coordinator
Dessa Gunning, Librarian; Lisa Ladanyi, Human Resources Director
Rachel Sundberg, Library Administrator & Cultural Resources Coordinator/
  Tribal Historic Preservation Officer; Jonas Savage, Environmental Director
Tribes: Yurok, Hupa, Wiyot, Tolowa. *Population*: 75. *Area*: 91.5 acres. *Programs*: Education; Social Services; Cultural Resources; Environmental; Technology. *Resources*: Tribal Library. *Attraction*: Cher-Ae Heights Casino. Northern California Field Office.

CHICKEN RANCH BAND OF ME-WUK INDIANS

16955 Nelson Rd., P.O. Box 1159 • Jamestown, CA 95327
(209) 984-4806 Fax 984-5606; Melissa Powell, Chairperson
Tribe: Sierra Miwok. *Enrolled members*: 11. *Area*: 2.85 acres located in Tuolumne County. *Attraction*: Chicken Ranch Bingo & Casino. Central California Agency.

CLOVERDALE RANCHERIA OF POMO INDIANS
555 S. Cloverdale Blvd., Suite A • Cloverdale, CA 95425
(707) 894-5775 Fax 894-5727
Website: www.cloverdalerancheria.com
E-mail: info@cloverdalerancheria.com
Patricia Hermosillo, Chairperson; Silver Galleto, Vice Chairperson
Vickey Macias, Tribal Treasurer; Maria Elliott, Secretary
Sandra Roope, Tribal Representative
Tribe: Pomo. *Enrollment*: 500. *Area*: 27.5 acres.
Attraction: Resort & Casino. Central California Agency.

COLD SPRINGS TRIBE OF MONO INDIANS
P.O. Box 209 • Tollhouse, CA 93667
(559) 855-5043 Fax 855-4445; E-mail: csrancheria@netptc.net
Website: www.coldspringsrancheria.com
Jeffery Lee, Chairperson; E-mail: csrancheiajeff@netptc.net
Judy Ratchford, Vice Chairperson; E-mail: csrancheriajudy@netptc.net
Blossom Hunter, Sec./Treasurer; E-mail: csrancheriablossom@netptc.net
Councilmembers: Sheila Edd, Irene Marquez, Rachel Lewis
Tribe: Mono. *In residence*: 270. *Area*: 155 acres located in central California
about 30 miles east of Fresno in the foothills. Central California Agency.

COLUSA INDIAN COMMUNITY
3730 Hwy. 45 • Colusa, CA 95932
(530) 458-8231 Fax 458-4186
Website: www.colusa-nsn.gov; E-mail: cicc@colusa-nsn.gov
Daniel Gomez, Chair; Laurie Costa, Director of Colusa Wellness Center
Tribe: Cachil DeHe Band of Wintun Indians. *Enrolled members*: 84. *In
residence*: 55. *Area*: 290 acres. *Programs*: Health Clinic; Wellness Center;
Preschool; Economic Development; Farming; Learning Center; Language
Preservation. In 2004, the Colusa Indian Community Council published the first
edition of the Cachil Dehe Band of Wintun Indians language book. The project
was a collaborative effort by elders and the University of California, Berkeley
linguistics department for future generations. Although the publication of this
book was an initial step towards the restoration of our native language, this
project and others are still in their infancy and will continue to expand to
include additional words on CD and DVD tutorials for all members to use.
Attraction: Colusa Casino Resort (www.colusacasino.com). Central California
Agency.

CORTINA BAND OF WINTUN INDIANS
570 6th St., P.O. Box 1630 • Williams, CA 95987
(530) 473-3274 Fax 473-3301
Charlie Wright, Chairperson; Connie Gomez, Secretary
Tribe: Wintun. *In residence*: 90. *Area*: 640 acres. Central California Agency.

COYOTE VALLEY BAND OF POMO INDIANS
7601 N. State St., P.O. Box 39 • Redwood Valley, CA 95470
(707) 485-8723 Fax 485-1247
Website: www.coyotevalleytribe.org
Hiram O. Campbell, Sr., Tribal Chief
Michael Hunter Chairperson; Patrick Naredo, Vice Chairperson
Candace Gonzalez, Secretary; Kelli Jaynes, Treasurer
Councilmembers: Melinda Hunter & John Feliz, Sr.
Ghazal Mahdavian, Tribal Administrator
Bryant Herrera, Education Director
Melinda Hunter, Health & Human Services Director
Eddie F. Knight, Tribal Historian; Richard H. Campbell, Chief General Council
Tribe served: Pomo. *Enrolled members*: 317. *In residence*: 170. *Area*: 70 acres
located in Redwood Valley, Mendocino County. *Programs*: Education; Health;
Housing; Environmental. *Attraction*: Coyote Valley Shodakai Casino (Website:
www.coyotevalleycasino.com). Central California Agency.

CUYAPAIPE BAND OF KUMEYAAY INDIANS
Cuyapaipe Reservation, 4054 Willows Rd. • Alpine, CA 91903
(619) 455-6315 Fax 445-9126; E-mail: info@kumeyaay.com
Robert Pinto, Sr., Chairperson
Tribe: Ewiiaapaayp Band of Kumeyaay Indians - Diegueno.
Enrolled members: 30. *Area*: 4,156 acres. Southern California Agency.

DRY CREEK RANCHERIA BAND OF POMO INDIANS
3250 Hwy. 128 E, P.O. Box 607 • Geyserville, CA 95441
(707) 431-4090 Fax 857-3794
Website: www.drycreekrancheria.com
Chris Wright, Chairperson; Betty Arterberry, Vice Chairperson
Margie Rojes, Secretary/Treasurer; Steve Smith, HR Director
Members-at-Large: Jim Silva & Tieraney Giron
Tribe: Pomo. *Population*: 150. *Area*: 75 acres. *Programs*: Education; Cultural;
Environment; Housing, Human Resources; Support Services; Dry Creek
Gaming Commission (522-4280). *Attraction*: River Rock Casino (website:
www.riverrockcasino.com). Central California Agency.

ELEM INDIAN COLONY OF POMO INDIANS
Sulphur Bank of Pomo Indians, 16170 Main St., Suite 1
P.O. Box 757 • Lower Lake, CA 95457
(707) 994-3400 Fax 998-2993; Website: www.elemindiancolony.org
E-mail: elem.admin@elemindiancolony.org
Agustin Garcia, Chairperson; E-mail: a.garcia@elemindiancolony.org
April Popaditch, Vice Chairperson
E-mail: a.popaditch@elemindiancolony.org
Sarah Brown Garcia, Secretary/Treasurer
E-mail: s.garcia@elemindiancolony.org
Members At Large: Shane Woods-John & Penny Moranda
Tribe: Elem Band of Pomo Indians. *In residence*: 55. *Population*: 165.
Central California Agency.

ELK VALLEY RANCHERIA
2332 Howland Hill Rd. • Crescent City, CA 95531
(866) 464-4680; (707) 464-4680 Fax 465-6372
Website: www.elk-valley.com
Dale A. Miller, Chairperson; E-mail: dmiller@elk-valley.com
Rock Warner, Vice-Chairperson; E-mail: rwarner@elk-valley.com
Christina Jones, Secretary; E-mail: cjones@elk-valley.com
Jennifer Akins, Treasurer; jakins@elk-valley.com
Councilmembers: John D. Green, Linda Martin, Doug Mattz,
Heidi Valadao, LaWanda Quinnell
Wanda Green, Librarian
Tribes served: Tolowa/Yurok. *Area*: 400 acres. *Attractions*: Elk Valley Casino;
Hiouchi RV Resort; Del Norte Golf Course; Tsunami Bowling Center
Resources: Museum & Library. *Publication*: Tribal newsletter. Northern
California Agency.

ENTERPRISE RANCHERIA BAND OF MAIDU INDIANS
2133 Monte Vista Ave. • Oroville, CA 95966
(855) 891-0307; (530) 532-9214 Fax 532-1768
Website: www.enterpriserancheria.org; E-mail: info@enterpriserancheria.org
Glenda Nelson, Chairperson; E-mail: glendan@enterpriserancheria.org
Greg Borene, Vice Chairperson; E-mail: gregb@enterpriserancheria.org
Cindy Smith, Secretary; E-mail: cindys@enterpriserancheria.org
Councilmembers: Arthur Angle, Donna Rodriguez & Crystal Gilbert
Thomas Lozano, Treasurer; E-mail: thomasl@enterpriserancheria.org
Creig Marcus, Tribal Administrator; E-mail: creigm@enterpriserancheria.org
Donna Rodriguez, Education Chair; E-mail: donnar@enterpriserancheria.org
Tribe: Maidu. *Area*: 40 acres. *Programs*: Emergency Services; Elders &
Disabled; Human Services; Health; Education; Cultural; Housing; Employment.
Publication: Bi-monthly tribal newsletter. Central California Agency.

FORT BIDWELL PAIUTE INDIAN COMMUNITY
130 Me-Thee-UH Rd., P.O. Box 129 • Fort Bidwell, CA 96112
(530) 279-6252 Fax 279-2233; Bernold Pollard, Chairperson
Tribe: Paiute. *In residence*: 110. *Area*: 3,335 acres. *Activity*: Powwows.
Northern California Field Office.

FORT INDEPENDENCE PAIUTE TRIBE
Fort Independence Indian Reservation
P.O. Box 67 • Independence, CA 93526
(760) 878-5160 Fax 878-2311; Website: www.fortindependence.com
Norm Wilder, Chairperson; Karma Henry, Vice Chairperson
Stephanie Arman, Secretary/Treasurer; Carl Dahlberg, Tribal Administrative
Priscilla Naylor, Tribal Historic Preseervation Officer
Tribe: Paiute. *Enrolled members*: 136. *In residence*: 70. *Area*: 360 acres.
Program: Air Quality Program. *Attraction*: Winnedumah Winns Casino; RV
Campground. *Publication*: Quarterly newsletter. Central California Agency.

FORT MOJAVE INDIAN TRIBE
Fort Mojave Reservation, 500 Merriman Ave. • Needles, CA 92363
(760) 629-4591 Fax 629-5767; Website: www.mojaveindiantribe.com
Timothy Williams, Chairperson; Shan Lewis, Vice Chairperson
Colleen Garcia, Secretary
Councilmembers: Martha McCord, Norvin McCord, Nichole Garcia,
Johnny Hemmers
Neil Flores, Chief Magistrate; Kelly Hills, Court Administrator
Dee Howard, Tribal Administrator; E-mail: deborahhoward@fortmojave.com
Fort Mojave Education Department, P.O. Box 7066, Mohave Valley, AZ 86446
(928) 346-1121 Fax 346-1123. E-mail: tribaled1@ftmojave.com
Tribe: Mojave. *In residence*: 1,120. *Area*: 42,000 acres. Located in California,
Arizona, and Nevada. *Attractions*: Operates the Avi Resort & Casino, Crossing
Casino & Spirit Mountain Casino; Mojave Resort Golf. *Resources*: Ava Ich Asiit
Tribal Library (P.O. Box 5499, Mohave Valley, AZ 86446 (928) 346-2665 Fax
346-2666). *Activities*: Annual Ward Valley Spiritual Gathering, in February;
Annual Avi Kwa Ame Powwow, in February; Annual Mojave Indian Days in
October. *School*: Aha MacCav High School. *Publication*: Ech-Kah-Nav-Cha
Newsletter. Colorado River Agency.

FEDERATED INDIANS OF GRATON RANCHERIA
6400 Redwood Dr., Suite 300 • Rohnert Park, CA 94928
(707) 566-2288 Fax 566-2291
Website: www.gratonrancheria.com; E-mail: coastmiwok@aol.com
Greg Sarris, Chairperson; E-mail: gsarris@gratonrancheria.com
Lorelle W.B. Ross, Vice Chairperson
Gene Buvelot, Treasurer; Melissa Elgin, Secretary
Councilmembers: Robert Stafford, Jr., Lawrence Stafford & Lynn Silva
Laura Bento, Education & Employment Coordinator
    E-mail: lbento@gratonrancheria.com
Briana Albini, Environmental Coordinator & Cultural Director
Laura Bento, Education & Employment Coordinator (586-6100 ext. 617)
Lara Walker, Wellnes & Justice Director (586-6110)
Tribal Youth Mentorship Program; E-mail: lwalker@gratonrancheria.com
Gillian Hayes, Director of Planning & Development
Tribes: Coast Miwok & Southern Pomo. *Population served*: 1,000. *Facilities*:
Graton Tribal Library (library@gratonrancheria.com). *Programs*: Education &
Employment; Sacred Sites Preservation & Protection, Elder Services; Housing,
Environmental & Cultural Preservation; Wellness & Justice Services; Economic
Development. *Attraction*: Graton Resort & Casino www.gratonresortcasino.com
Central California Agency.

GREENVILLE RANCHERIA
1405 Montgomery Rd. • Red Bluff, CA 96080
(530) 528-8600 Fax 527-7488
Website: www.greenvillerancheria.com
Kyle Self, Chairperson; Crystal Rios, Vice Chairperson
Rachel Radcliff, Secretary/Treasurer
Guadalupe Luna & Debra Self, Tribal Repsresentatives
Tribe: Maidu. *Population served*: 2,000. *Area*: Located three miles east of
Greenville in the Indian Valley in the Sierra Nevada Mountains of Northern
California. *Facilities*: Tribal Health Center. *Programs*: Medical, Social Services,
Cultural-NAGPRA, Housing, Indian Child Welfare, Mental Health, Substance
Abuse, Employment, Environmental. *Resources*: Medical-Dental Clinics
located at 410 Main St., Greenville & at 1425 Montgomery, Red Bluff, CA
96080. *Publication*: Monthly newsletter. Central California Agency.

GRINDSTONE INDIAN RANCHERIA OF WINTUN-WAILAKI INDIANS
3600 County Road 305 #13A • Elk Grove, CA 95758
P.O. Box 63 • Elk Creek, CA 95939
(530) 968-5365 Fax 968-5366
Ronald Kirk, Chairperson
Tribe: Wintun-Wailaki. *Enrolled members*: 162. *In residence*: 98. *Area*: 120
acres. Central California Agency.

GUIDIVILLE RANCHERIA OF CALIFORNIA
P.O. Box 339 • Talmadge, CA 95481
(707) 462-3682 Fax 462-9183
Merlene Sanchez, Chairperson
Tribe: Pomo. *Population*: 100. *Area*: 44 acres. Northern California Agency.

HABEMATOLEL POMO OF UPPER LAKE RANCHERIA
375 E. Hwy. 20, P.O. Box 516 • Upper Lake, CA 95485
(877) 543-5102; (707) 275-0737 Fax 275-0757
Website: www.upperlakepomo.com
E-mail: tribaladmin@upperlakepomo.com
Sherry Treppa, Chairperson (2008-present); (275-9050 ext. 201)
    E-mail streppa@hpultribe-nsn.gov
Angelina Arroyo, Vice Chairperson; (275-9050 ext. 202)
Iris Picton, Secretary; E-mail: ecsecretary@gmail.com
Kimberly Roni Cobarrubia, Treasurer (275-9050 ext. 203)
    E-mail: Kimberly.marcks@yahoo.com
Aimee Jackson, Tracey Treppa, Sam Icay, *Members-at-Large*
Tribe: Habermatolel Pomo of Upper Lake. *Enrolled members*: 203. *Area*: 11
acres. *Programs*: Gaming, Health & Human Services, Housing. *Attraction*:
Running Creek Casino. Central California Agency.

HOOPA VALLEY TRIBE
P.O. Box 1348 • Hoopa, CA 95546
(530) 625-4211 Fax 625-4594
Ryan P. Jackson, Chairperson; E-mail: chairman.jackson@gmail.com
Oscar "Tyke" Billings, Agency Field District & Vice Chairperson
    E-mail: oscar.billings@hoopa-nsn.gov
Diana McCovey-Ferris, Norton Field Distrit Rep.
    E-mail: diana.mccovey.ferris@gmail.com
Edward Guyer II, Soctish-Chenone District Rep.
Gary Risling, Bald Hill Dirict Rep.
Joseph LeMieux, Campbell Field District Rep.
    E-mail: cbfdistrict@gmail.com
Leilani Pole, Hostler-Matilton District Rep.
    E-mail: leilani.pole@hoopa-nsn.gov

Vivienna Orcutt, Mesket Field District Rep.
    E-mail: vivienna.orcutt@hoopa-nsn.gov
Oscar Tyke Billings, Agency Field District Rep.
    E-mail: Oscar.billings@hoopa-nsn.gov
Viva Campbell, Executive Secretary
Billy Carpenter, Sergeant at Arms
Erika Chase, Interim Director of Hoopa Tribal Education Association
    (530) 625-4413
Leslie Jackson, Tribal Archives Director
Suzanne Burcell, Director of Hoopa College Success Program
    E-mail: Suzanne.burcell@humboldt.edu
Jolene Gates, Director of Hoopa Career & Technical Education Program
    E-mail: jgates@hoopa-nsn.gov
Tribe: Hoopa. *In residence*: 2,200. *Area*: 86,042 acres. *Location*: Located
along Trinity River, 35 miles northeast of Eureka, California. *Programs*:
Education; Health; Human Services; Natural Resources; Fisheries & Forestry;
Environmental; Head Start. *Resources*: Hoopa Tribal Museum; Kim Yerton
Memorial Library; KIDE 91.3 FM. *Attraction*: Lucky Bear Casino & Bingo.
Publication: Hoopa People Newspaper, Two Rivers Tribune, weekly news.
Northern California Agency.

HOPLAND BAND OF POMO INDIANS
3000 Shanel Rd. • Hopland, CA 95449
(707) 472-2100 Fax 744-1506
Website: www.hoplandtribe.com; Email: info@hoplandtribe.com
Joe San Diego, Chairperson; E-mail: joe2@hoplandtribe.com
Sonny J. Elliott, Sr., Vice Chairperson; E-mail: sjelliott@hoplandtribe.com
Suzanna Romero, Secretary; E-mail: sromero@hoplandtribe.com
Shawn Padi, Teasurer; E-mail: spadi@hoplandtribe.com
Councilmembers: David Steele, Lyesha Miller, Bernadette Mora
Bernadette Mora, Tribal Administrator; E-mail: bmora@hoplandtribe.com
Jacqueline Sanchez, Education Director; E-mail: jsanchez@hoplandtribe.com
Katie Williams-Elliott, Education Coordinator
    E-mail: kwilliams-elliott@hoplandtribe.com
Kathy Littlebear, Health Director; E-mail: klittlebear@hoplandtribe.com
Terri McCartney, EPA Director; E-mail: tmccartney@hoplandtribe.com
Tribe: Sho-ka-wah Band of Pomo Indians. *In residence*: 150. *Area*: 2,070
acres. *Programs*: Education; Health & Social Services; EPA Environmental.
Resources: Early Childhood Development School (3-5 years-old); *Attraction*:
Hopland Shokawah Casino. *Publication*: Jah-Noo, bimonthly newsletter.
Central California Agency.

INAJA-COSMIT BAND OF INDIANS
Inaja-Cosmit Reservation, 2005 S. Escondido Blvd. • Escondido, CA 92025
(760) 737-7628 Fax 747-8568; Rebecca M. Osuna, Chairperson
Tribe: Kumeyaay Diegueno. *In residence*: 15. *Area*: 852 acres.
Southern California Agency.

IONE BAND OF MIWOK INDIANS
9252 Bush St. #3, P.O. Box 699 • Plymouth, CA 95669
(209) 245-5800 Fax 245-3112; Website: www.ionemiwok.org
E-mail: administrator@ionnemiwok.org
Yvonne Miller, Chairperson; Glen Villa, Sr. Vice Chairperson
Sandra Waters, Treasurer; Glen Villa, Jr., Secretary
Tribe: Miwok. *Enrollment*: 700. *Area*: 228 acres. *Programs*: Cultural Heritage;
Social Services; Healthcare; Housing; Environmental; Economic Development;
Education, Human Resources. *Attractions*: Planning a casino. *Publication*:
Newsletter. Central California Agency.

JACKSON RANCHERIA BAND OF MIWUK INDIANS
P.O. Box 1090 • Jackson, CA 95642
(209) 223-1935 Fax 223-5366
Adam Dalton, Chairperson; Earl Dalton, Vice Chairperson
Derik Dalton, Secretary/Treasurer
Robert Dalton & Dennis Dalton, Council Reps
Tribe: Miwuk. Area: 330 acres. *Activities*: Jackson Rancheria Casino (Website:
www.jacksoncasino.com) & Hotel; RV Park. Central California Agency.

JAMUL INDIAN VILLAGE
14191 Hwy. 94, P.O. Box 612 • Jamul, CA 91935
(619) 669-4785 Fax 669-4817; Raymond Hunter, Chairperson
Erica M. Pinto, Chairperson; E-mail: empinto747@yahoo.com
Kenneth Meza, Vice Chairperson; Lisa M. Cumper, Secretary/Treasurer
Councilmembers: Michael Hunter, Christopher Pinto, Carlene Chamberlain
Tribe: Kumeyaay Diegueno. *In residence*: Unoccupied. *Area*: 6.4 acres.
Attractions: A $360 million casino is scheduled to open in Jamul Indian
Village in 2016. Southern California Agency.

KARUK TRIBE OF CALIFORNIA
64236 Second Ave., P.O. Box 1016 • Happy Camp, CA 96039
(800) 505-2785; (530) 493-1600 Fax 493-5322; Website: www.karuk.us

Russell Attebery, Chairperson; E-mail: rattebery@karuk.us
Robert Super, Vice Chairperson; E-mail: rjsuper@karuk.us
Michael Thom, Secretary/Treasurer; E-mail: mthom@karuk.us
Sonny Davis & Arch Super (Yreka); Alvis Johnson, Jody Waddell (Happy
 Camp); Joshua Saxon & Renee Stauffer (Orleans), *Councilmembers*
Alan Merrill, Education Coordinator; E-mail: amerrill@karuk.us
Bari Talley, Library & People's Center Coordinator; E-mail: btalley@karuk.us
Tribe: Karuk. *Enrolled members*: 3,555. *Facility*: Panamnik Library & Computer
Center - The Karuk's People's Center (P.O. Box 426, Orleans, CA 95556 (530)
627-3081). *Programs*: Education; Community Services & Development; Health;
Child & Family Services; Language; Natural Resources; Head Start.
Resources: Karuk People's Center; Karuk Tribal Libraries. The Mission of the
Karuk People's Center: As the museum & cultural center of the Karuk Tribe,
the Karuk People's Center is devoted to the preservation, promotion &
celebration of Karuk history, language, traditions & living culture. *Attraction*:
Karuk Casino (in preparation in Yreka). *Activities*: Karuk Men & Youth Culture
Class; Spring Basket Weavers Gathering; annual powwow. *Publication*:
Quarterly Newsletter. Northern California Field Office.

KASHIA BAND OF POMO INDIANS OF STEWARTS POINT RANCHERIA
1420 GuernevilleRd. Suite I • Santa Rosa, CA 95403
 (707) 591-0580 Fax 591-0583; Website: www.stewartspoint.org
Reno Keoni Franklin, Chairperson; Glenda Jacob McGill, Vice Chair
Tara Antone, Secretary; Angelique Lane, Treasurer
Councilmembers: Marlene Adam, Dino Franklin, Elayne Muro
Vaughn Pena, Tribal Administrator
 E-mail: vaughn@stewartspoint.org
Tribe: Kashia Pomo. *In residence*: 100. *Tribal enrollment*: 860. *Area*: 40 acres.
The majority of Tribal members residing in Sonoma, Mendocino, Lake and
Napa Counties which is the service area for the Kashia Pomo Indians of the
Rancheria. *Publication*: Quarterly newsletter. Central California Agency.

LA JOLLA BAND OF LUISENO INDIANS
22000 Highway 76 • Pauma Valley, CA 92061
 (760) 742-3771 Fax 742-1704
Website: www.lajollaindians.com
Thomas Rodriguez, Chairperson; Mark Lofton, Vice Chairperson
Adam Geisler, Secretary; Cody Schlater, Treasurer
Wiliam C. Nelson II, Councilmember
Tribe: Luiseno. *In residence*: 390. *Enrolled members*: 700. *Area*: 10,000 acres
located off State Hwy 76, 25 miles east of Escondido and 60 miles northeast of
San Diego. *Attractions*: La Jolla Indian Campground; Resort & Casino are
planned. Southern California Agency.

LA POSTA BAND OF MISSION INDIANS
8½ Crestwood Rd., P.O. Box 1120 • Boulevard, CA 91905
 (619) 478-2113 Fax 478-2125
Gwendolyn Parada, Chairperson
David LaChappa, Vice Chairperson
Eric LaChappa, Secretary/Treasurer
Councilmembers: Richard Estrada & Victor Estrada
Tribe: Kumeyaay Diegueno. *Enrolled members*: 18. *Area*: 3,471 acres located
off Hwy. 8 East 40 iles from El Cajon. *Resources*: La Posta in the Union
Tribune. *Attraction*: Resort & Casino. Southern California Agency.

CAHTO TRIBE OF THE LAYTONVILLE RANCHERIA
300 Cahto Dr., P.O. Box 1239 • Laytonville, CA 95454
 (707) 984-6197 Fax 984-6201; Website: www.cahto.org
Aimie R. Lucas, Chairperson; E-mail: chairman@cahto.org.
Corey James, Vice Chairperson; E-mail: vice-chair@cahto.org
Kendra Campbell, Secretary/Treasurer; Karen Wilson, Member-at-Large
Paula Britton, Tribal Administrator; E-mail: ta@cahto.org
Joseph Wiseman, Chief Judge
Tribe: Cahto-Pomo. *In residence*: 250. *Area*: 202 acres located two miles west
of the town of Laytonville. *Programs*: Social Services; Housing; Environmental;
Human Resources; Veterans. *Attraction*: Red Fox Casino. Central California
Agency.

LONE PINE PAIUTE-SHOSHONE TRIBE
Lone Pine Paiute-Shoshone Reservation
975 Teya Rd., P.O. Box 747 • Lone Pine, CA 93545
 (760) 876-1034 Fax 876-8302
Website: www.lppsr.org; E-mail: administrator@lppsr.org
Mary Wuester, Chairperson; E-mail: chair@lppsr.org
Richard Button, Vice Chairperson; E-mail: vicechair@lppsr.org
Janet Hansen, Treasurer; E-mail: treasurer@lppsr.org
Loretta Howard, Trustee; E-mail: trustee@lppsr.org
Tribes: Paiute, Shoshone. *Enrolled members*: 350. *Area*: 237 acres
located 200 miles north of Los Angeles and 60 miles south of Bishop.
Program: Environmental. Central California Agency.

LOS COYOTES BAND OF CAHUILLA & CUPENO INDIANS
2300 Camino San Ignacio, P.O. Box 189 • Warner Springs, CA 92086
 (760) 782-0711 Fax 782-2701
Website: www.loscoyotestribe.com
Shane Chapparosa, Chairperson; Ray Chapparosa, Vice Chairperson
Councilmembers: Edward Norte, Lynn Chapparosa, Janet Dillman,
Milton Cambell, Aaron Saubel
John Parada, Environmental Director
Tribes: Cahuilla, Cupeno. *In residence*: 70. *Enrolled members*: 290.
Area: 24,762 acres located 50 miles east of San Diego. *Attractions*:
Barstow Casino & Resort. Southern California Agency.

LOWER LAKE RANCHERIA KOI NATION
P.O. Box 3162 • Santa Rosa, CA 95402
 (707) 575-5586 Fax 575-5506; Website: www.koination.com
Darin Beltran, Chairperson; Drake Beltran, Vice Chairperson
Dino Beltran, Treasurer; Judy Morgan Faber, Secretary
Tribe: Koi-Pomo. *Enrolled members*: 50. *Program*: Economic Development.
Central California Agency.

LYTTON BAND OF POMO INDIANS
437 Aviation Blvd. • Santa Rosa, CA 95403
 (707) 575-5917 Fax 575-6974; Marjorie Mejia, Chairperson
Tribe: Pomo. *Enrolled members*: 250. *Resources*: Education Center, Child
Care Center. *Attraction*: Casino San Pablo. Central California Agency.

MANCHESTER BAND OF POMO INDIANS OF MANCHESTER RANCHERIA
24 Mamie Laiwa Dr., P.O. Box 623 • Point Arena, CA 95468
 (707) 882-2788 Fax 882-3417; Jaime Cobarubba, Chairperson
Tribe: Pomo. *Population*: 212. *Area*: 364 acres located near the towns of
Manchester & Point Arena in Mendocino County. Central California Agency.

MANZANITA BAND OF THE KUMEYAAY NATION
Manzanita Reservation, P.O. Box 1302 • Boulevard, CA 91905
 (619) 766-4930 Fax 766-4957; Angela Elliott Santos, Acting Chairperson
Tribe: Kumeyaay Diegueno. *Enrolled members*: 70. *In residence*: 22. *Area*:
3,580 acres located in the western part of the Carrizo Desert. *Resources*:
Mountain Empire School; Manzanita Center/Library. *Programs*: Manzanita
Language; Economic Development Project. Southern California Agency.

MECHOOPDA MAIDU INDIANS OF CHICO RANCHERIA
125 Mission Ranch Blvd. • Chico, CA 95926
 (888) 472-9118; (530) 899-8922 Fax 899-8517
Website: www.mechoopda-nsn.gov; E-mail: mit@mechoopda-nsn.gov
Dennis Ramirez, Chairperson; Sandra Knight, Vice-Chairperson
Robyn Forristel, Treasurer; Roberta Lewis, Secretary
Paulita Hopper, Kyle McHenry & Cassy Wilson, Councilmembers
Inder Wadhwa, Executive Director of Northern Valley Indian Health
Tribe: Maidu. *Facilities*: Mechoopda Community Center. *Programs*: Education;
Health; Housing; Economic Development; Child Welfare; Tribal Youth;
Environmental Protection; Cultural. *Attraction*: Casino Entertainment Project.

MESA GRANDE BAND OF MISSION INDIANS
Mesa Grande Reservation, 27000 Black Canyon Rd.
P.O. Box 270 • Santa Ysabel, CA 92070
 (760) 782-3818 Fax 782-0795
Website: www.mesagrandeband-nsn.gov
E-mail: mgbomi@mesagrandeband-nsn.gov
Virgil Oyos, Chairperson; Curtis La Chusa, Vice Chairperson
Gina Dominguez, Secretary/Treasurer
Councilmembers: Tony Gumatoatoa, Jesse Morales & Michael Dominguez
Tribe: Kumeyaay Diegueno. *Enrolled members*: 75. *Area*: 1,820 acres.
Programs: Education; Youth/Child Welfare; Buffalo Project. Mesa Grande
Library. Southern California Agency.

MIDDLETOWN RANCHERIA BAND OF POMO INDIANS
22223 Hwy. 29, P.O. Box 1035 • Middletown, CA 95461
 (707) 987-3670 Fax 987-9091
Website: www.middletownrancheria-nsn.gov
Jose Simon, III, Chairperson; Sally Peterson, Vice Chairperson
Pamela Reyes-Gutierrez, Secretary; Paula Beltran, Treasurer
Carlos Negrete, Tribal Representative
Tribe: Pomo. *Population*: 75. *Area*: 109 acres.
Attraction: Twin Pine Casino & Hotel. Website: www.twinpine.com
Central California Agency.

MOORETOWN RANCHERIA OF MAIDU NDIANS
1 Alverda Dr. • Oroville, CA 95966
 (530) 533-3625 Fax 533-3680
Gary Archuleta, Chairperson; Melvin Jackson, Vice Chairperson
Vickie Ruggle, Secretary; Ruben Aeista, Treasurer

Councilmembers: Martinn D. Archuleta, Gregory Osbrn, Claude Taylor, Jr.
Tribes: Concow-Maidu. *Area*: 35 acres in trust; 20 acres in fee land.
Attractions: The Feather Falls Casino & Lodge; School. Library.
Central California Agency.

MORONGO BAND OF CAHUILLA INDIANS
12700 Pumarra Rd. • Banning, CA 92220
(951) 849-4697 Fax 849-4425; Website: www.morongonation.org
Robert Martin, Chairperson; Mary Ann Andreas, Vice Chairperson
Councilmembers: Damon Sandoval, James Siva, Brian Lugo,
Anne Robinson, John Muncy
Sajeed (Titu) Asghar, Chief Executive Officer
G. Michael Milhiser, Chief Administrative Officer
Steven Garwood, Chief Financial Officer
Kimberly A. Cluff, General Counsel
Tribe: Cahuilla. *In residence*: 375. *Population*: 750. *Area*: 35,250 acres.
Resources: The Morongo Resource Center; Morongo School; The Center for
Advanced Studies. *Programs*: Education; Tribal Scholarship Program; Cultural;
Social Services; Housing; Tribal Operations; Environmental Protection;
Emergency Services; Human Resources; Planning & Construction. *Attractions*:
Morongo Casino, Resort & Spa; Thunder & Lightning Powwow. *Resources*:
Morongo Community Library. Southern California Agency.

NORTH FORK RANCHERIA OF MONO INDIANS
33143 Road 222, P.O. Box 929 • North Fork, CA 93643
(559) 877-2461/5530 Fax 877-2467
Website: www.northforkrancheria-nsn.gov
E-mail: nfrancheria@nfr-nsn.gov
Gary Walker, Chairperson; E-mail: gwalker@nfr-nsn.gov
Judy Elaine Fink, Vice Chairperson; E-mail: efink@nfr-nsn.gov
Katrina Guitierez, Secretary; E-mail: kguitierez@nfr-nsn.gov
Maryann McGovran, Treasurer; E-mail: mmcgovran@nfr-nsn.gov
Ed Polkerhorn, Councilmember; E-mail: epolkerhorn@nfr-nsn.gov
Tribe: Mono. *In residence*: 1,800. *Area*: 305 acres in Madera County.
Resources: Community Center; Library. *Programs*: Housing Authority, Tribal
Environmental Protection Department, Temporary Assistance for Needy
Families. *Attraction*: Planning a casino & resort. *Published works*: "Nu Qwah
Neum," quarterly newsletter. Central California Agency.

PALA BAND OF MISSION INDIANS
12196 Pala Mission Rd., P.O. Box 50 • Pala, CA 92059
(760) 891-3500 Fax 742-1411
Website: www.palatribe.com; E-mail: cupa@palatribe.com
Robert H. Smith, Chairperson; Howard Maxcy, Vice Chairperson
Theressa Villa, Secretary; Theresa J. Nieto, Treasurer
Councilmembers: Dion Perez & Sheila Lopez,
Tribe served: Luiseno-Cupa. *In residence*: 395. *Population*: 1,575. *Area*:
12,333 acres. *Resources*: Pala Rez Radio 91.3 FM; Cupa Cultural Center;
Pala Learning Center; Little Feathers Preschool; Pala Child Care Center; Cupa
Day (May); Museum; Pala Library. *Programs*: Social Services, Economic
Development, Environment, Housing. *Attractions*: Pala Casino Resort & Spa;
Pala Avocado Grove; annual powwow. *Publication*: Pala Mumalki, newsletter.
Southern California Agency.

PASKENTA BAND OF NOMLAKI INDIANS
P.O. Box 709 • Corning, CA 96021, CA 95963
(530) 528-3538 Fax 865-1870; Website: www.paskenta-nsn.gov
Andrew Alejandre, Chairperson; E-mail: aalejandre@paskenta.org
Latisha Miller, Vice Chairperson; E-mail: lmiller@paskenta.org
Ambrosia Rico, Treasurer; E-mail: arico@paskenta.org
Natasha Magana, Member-at-Large; E-mail: nmagana@paskenta.org
Ines Crosby, Tribal Administrator
Tribe: Nomlaki; Central Wintun. *Enrolled members*: 240. *Area*: 2,000 acres
near Corning, California Located in Tehama & Glenn Counties. *Attraction*:
Rolling Hills Casino. Central California Agency.

PAUMA BAND OF LUISENO INDIANS
1010 Reservation Rd., P.O. Box 369 • Pauma Valley, CA 92061
(760) 742-1289 Fax 742-3422; Website: www.paumatribe.com
Temet A. Aguilar, Chairperson; Christobol Devers, Vice Chairperson
Robert Quisquis, Secretary/Treasurer; Dale Brush, Member-at-Large
Tribe: Pauma Band of Luiseno. *Population served*: 186. *Area*: 5,826 acres.
Program: Johnson-O'Malley. *Resources*: Pauma Center; Pauma Library.
Attraction: Casino Pauma; Hotel & Spa; Memorial Celebration. *Publication*:
Pauma News. Southern California Agency.

PECHANGA BAND OF LUISENO INDIANS
P.O. Box 1477 • Temecula, CA 92593
(951) 676-2768 Fax 695-1778; Website: www.pechanga-nsn.gov
Mark A. Macarro, Chairperson; E-mail: lburke@pechanga-nsn.gov
Robyn Delfino, Treasurer; Louise Burke, Secretary

Councilmembers: Robert "RJ" Munoa, Corrina Garbani Sanchez, Marc Luker,
Raymond Basquez, Jr., Catalina R. Chacon, Russell "Butch" Murphy
Raymond Magee, Gaming Commission Chair
Lindsey Fletcher (Luiseno), Associate General Counsel
Tribe served: Luiseno. *In residence*: 186. *Population*: 450. *Area*: 5,826 acres.
Attractions: Pechanga Resort & Casino. *Activities*: Annual Pechanga Powwow,
July 4th weekend. *Publication*: Indian Gaming newsletter (Internet)
Website: www.pechanga.net. Southern California Agency.

PICAYUNE RANCHERIA OF THE CHUKCHANSI INDIANS
46575 Road 417 • Coarsegold, CA 93614
(559) 683-6633 Fax 683-0599
Website: www.chukchansi.net; E-mail: prci.info@chukchansi.net
Claudia Gonzales, Chairperson; E-mail: cgonzales@tcouncil.com
Nakomis Hernandez, Vice Chairperson
 E-mail: nhernandez@tcouncil.com
Thomas Walker, Secretary; E-mail: twalker@tcouncil.com
Dixie Jackson, Treasurer; E-mail: twalker@tcouncil.com
Melvin Espe, Secretary; E-mail: mespe@tcouncil.com
Harold Hammond, Dora Jones, Morris Reid, *Members-at-Large*
Tribe: Chukchansi. *In residence*: 65. *Area*: 235 acres located from the San
Joaquin River to the south to Yosemite National Park to the north, North Fork
to the east to Chowchilla to the west. *Programs*: Gaming; Economic
Development; Community Grant Program. *Attractions*: Chukchansi Gold
Resort & Casino; Powwow, 1st weekend in October. Pre-school. *Publication*:
Newsletter. Central California Agency.

PINOLEVILLE POMO NATION
367 N. State St., Suite 204 • Ukiah, CA 95482
(707) 463-1454 Fax 463-6601; Leona Williams, Chairperson
Angela James, Vice Chair & Director of Tribal Historic Preservation Office
Theresa Williams, Secretary; Karen Pena, Treasurer
Councilmembers: Lisa Goodwin, Monica Brown, Lydia Carretero
David Edmunds, Environmental Director
 E-mail: david.s.edmunds@gmail.com
Tribe: Pomo. *Enrolled members*: 305. *Area*: 100 acres *Location*: Off Orr
Springs Rd. north of Ukiah. *Programs*: Self-Governance; Social Services;
Economic Development; Environmental; Housing; Head Start; Community
Health; Vocational Rehabilitation. *Resources*: Pinoleville Tribal Library.
Attractions: Casino/Hotel in development. Central California Agency.

PIT RIVER TRIBE
3670 Park Ave. • Burney, CA 96013
(530) 335-5421 Fax 335-3140; Website: www.pitrivertribe.org
Mickey Gemmill, Jr., Chairperson
Lawrence Cantrell, Vice Chairperson
Faith Santillan, Tribal Secretary
Charles White, Tribal Adminisrator (335-5421)
Councilmembers: Melvin Elmore, Delores Raglin, Gwen Wolfin, Faith
 Santillian, Vernon Ward, Shawnna Harrison, Raquel Preston, Will George,
 Randy Quinn, Irvin Brown, Ray Alvarez, Ben Gomez, Richard Wilson
Vernon Ward, Social Srrvices Director
Tribe: Pit River (consists of eleven autonomous bands in several locations
organized as one tribe). *Enrolled members*: 1,800. *Area*: 9,242 acres.
Programs: Solid Waste & Recycling; Environmental; Social Services.
Attraction: Pit River Casino. Northern California Field Office.

POTTER VALLEY TRIBE OF POMO INDIANS
2251 S. State St. • Ukiah, CA 95482
(707) 462-1213 Fax 462-1240; Website: www.pottervalleytribe.com
E-mail: pvtsecretary@pottervalleytribe.com
Salvador Rosales, Chairperson & Administrator
Rosemary Rahmaoui, Tribal Secretary & Assistant Administrator
Losario Rosales, Treasurer; Gerrilyn Reeves, Secretary
Kathy Redhorse Stallworth, CFO
Gregg Young, Environmental Director
Tribe: Pomo. *Facilities*: Community Center; Library. Central California Agency.

QUARTZ VALLEY INDIAN RESERVATION
13601 Quartz Valley Rd., P.O. Box 24 • Fort Jones, CA 96032
(530) 468-5907 Fax 468-5908; Website: www.qvir.com
Frieda Bennett, Chairperson; E-mail: tribalchairman@qvir-nsn.gov
Sherrie Williams, Vice Chairperson; E-mail: tribalvice@qvir-nsn.gov
Lisa Carle, Secretary; E-mail: tribalsecretary@qvir-nsn.gov
Joselyn Kelley, Treasurer; E-mail: tribaltreasurer@qvir-nsn.gov
Mike Slizewski, Administrator; E-mail: mike.slizewski@qvir-nsn.gov
Alondra Bailey, Board Member #1; E-mail: board1@qvir-nsn.gov
Timothy Bennett, Board Member #2; E-mail: board2@qvir-nsn.gov
Charlene Henry, Member-at-Large; E-mail: mem2@qvir-nsn.gov
Isaiah Wiliams, Member-at-Large; E-mail: mem3@qvir-nsn.gov
Frieda Bennett, Education Director; E-mail: frieda.bennett@qvir-nsn.gov

Kyle Nelson, Health Clinic Project Coordinator (530) 468-4470 ext. 304)
E-mail: kyle.nelson@qvir-nsn.gov
Crystal Robinson, Environmental Director
E-mail: crystal.robinson@qvir-nsn.gov
Tribes: Karuk & Shasta. *Membership*: 250. *Area*: Legal boundaries encompass 640 acres in Quartz Valley - all tribal land was lost to the termination process. *Programs*: Education; Annual Culture Camp; Modoc Lassen Indian Housing Authority; Environmental; Human Resources; Social Services. *Resources*: Library. *Publication*: Quartz Valley Indian News, newsletter. Northern California Field Office.

QUECHAN INDIAN TRIBE

Fort Yuma Indian Reservation, 350 Picacho Rd. • Winterhaven, CA 92283
P.O. Box 1899 • Yuma, AZ 85366
(760) 572-0213 Fax 572-2102
Keeny Escalanti, Sr., President; Virgil S. Smith, Vice President
Councilmembers: Jordan Joaquin, Aaron Brown, Lorainne E. White,
Mark William White II, Marsha E. Hil, Virgil Smith
Claudette C. White, Chief Judge; E-mail: tribal.court@quechantribe.com
Tribe: Quechan. *Tribal enrollment*: 2,475. *Area*: 45,000 acres. *Attractions*: Paradise Casino & Bingo Hall; Quechan Heritage Center & Hotel. Located in Arizona & California. Fort Yuma Field Office.

RAMONA BAND OF CAHUILLA INDIANS

56310 Hwy. 371, Suite B, P.O. Box 391670 • Anza, CA 92539
(951) 763-4105 Fax 763-4325; Website: www.ramona-nsn.gov
Joseph Hamilton, Chairperson; E-mail: jhamilton@ramonatribe.com
Manuel Hamilton, Vice Chairperson; E-mail: mhamilton@ramonatribe.com
Susan Reckker, Tribal Administrator; E-mail: sreckker@ramonatribe.com
John Gomez, Cultural Resource Manager; E-mail: jgomez@ramonatribe.com
Reginald Agunwah, EPA Coordinator; E-mail: ragunwah@ramonatribe.com
Tribe: Cahuilla. *Area*: 560 acres located 27 miles southeast of Hemet, off Hwy. 74. *Program*: Eco Tourism Project leading to the Eco-Tourism Cultural Resort. Southern California Agency.

REDDING RANCHERIA

2000 Redding Rancheria Rd. • Redding, CA 96001
(800) 479-8979; (530) 225-8979 Fax 241-1879
Website: www.redding-rancheria.com
Jack Potter, Jr., Chairperson; Jason Hayward, Jr., Vice Chairperson
Jeremy Hayward, Treasurer; Glen Hayward, Secretary
Councilmembers: Jason Hart, Don Mennewr, Leon Benner
Patty Spaulding, 1st Alt. Councilperson
Michelle Hayward, 2nd Alt. Councilperson
Hope Wilkes, 3rd Alt. Councilperson
Tracy Edwards, Tribal CEO; Stacey Carman, COO; Tamra Olson, CFO
Tribes: Pit River, Wintun, Yana. *Area*: 31 acres. *Resources*: Indian Health Clinic; Health Fair. *Programs*: Community Services; Cultural Resources; Education; Gaming; Human Resources; Health; Head Start; Child Care. *Attractions*: Win-River Casino; Stillwater Powwow. *Publications*: Redding Rancheria Times (newsletter); Redding Rancheria Indian Health Service (newsletter). Library. Northern California Agency.

REDWOOD VALLEY BAND OF POMO INDIANS

Redwood Valley Reservation, 3250 Road I • Redwood Valley, CA 95470
(707) 485-0361 Fax 485-5726
Elizabeth Hansen, Chairperson
Tribe: Little River Band of Pomo Indians. *Location*: Northeast of Redwood Valley in Mendocino County, California. Central California Agency.

RESIGHINI RANCHERIA COAST INDIAN COMMUNITY

156 Klamath Beach Rd., P.O. Box 529 • Klamath, CA 95548
(707) 482-2431 Fax 482-3425; Website: www.resighinirancheria.com
Rick Dowd, Chairperson; E-mail: rickdowd7@gmail.com
Donald D. Valenzuela, Vice Chairperson & Tribal Manager
E-mail: valenzuela.don@gmail.com
Gary Dowd, Secretary; Marilyn Lunsford, Treasurer
Kathy Dowd, Councilperson & Administrative Secretary
E-mail: kathydowd6@gmail.com
Tribe: Yurok. *Enrolled members*: 110. *In residence*: 40. *Area*: 230 acres. *Programs*: Social Services; Housing; Environmental; Ecological Restoration. *Attraction*: Gold Bear Casino. Northern California Agency.

RINCON BAND OF LUISENO INDIANS

1 West Tribal Rd., P.O. Box 68 • Valley Center, CA 92082
(760) 749-1051 Fax 749-8901; Website: www.rincontribe.org
Bo Mazzetti, Chairperson; E-mail: bomazzetti@aol.com
Tishmall Turner, Vice Chairperson
Councilmembers: Alfonso Kolb, Sr., Steve Stallings, Laurie Gonzalez
Faith Price, *Council Liaison*

Tribe served: Luiseno. *Population*: 1,495. In residence: 150. *Area*: 3,918 acres. *Resources*: Rincon Indian Education Center; Rincon Museum/Library; All Tribes American Indian Charter School. *Programs*: Head Start; Language & Literacy; Tutorial; Day Care. *Attraction*: Harrah's Rincon Casino & Resort. Southern California Agency.

ROBINSON RANCHERIA OF POMO INDIANS

1545 East Hwy. 20, P.O. Box 428 • Nice, CA 95453
(707) 275-0527 Fax 275-0235; Website: www.robinsonrancheria.org
E-mail: robinsonrancheria@robinsonrancheria.org
E.J. Crandell, Chairperson; E-mail: ej@rrrc.com
Jaime Campanero, Vice Chairperson; E-mail: jcampanero@rrrc.com
Colleen Duncan Pete, Secretary/Treasurer; E-mail: cpete@rrrc.com
Members-at-Large: Charlene J. Duncan, Jaime Blancas Boggs, Nathan Solorio
Candace Lowe, Tribal Administrator
Tribe: Pomo. *Resources*: Environmental Center; Child Care Center. *Programs*: Education; Health Care; Economic Development; Youth Prevention Services; Child Welfare; Child Care; Environmental; Elders Program. *Attraction*: Robinson Rancheria Resort & Casino (website: www.rrrc.com). Central California Agency.

BEAR RIVER BAND OF ROHNERVILLE RANCHERIA

27 Bear River Dr. • Loleta, CA 95551
(707) 733-1900 Fax 733-1972; Website: www.brb-nsn.gov
Barry Brenard, Chairperson; E-mail: barrybrenard@brb-nsn.gov
Dakota McGinnis, Vice Chairperson & Economic Development Director
E-mail: dakotamcginnis@brb-nsn.gov
Aileen Meyer, Secretary & Education Director
E-mail: aileenmeyer@brb-nsn.gov
Wendell Freeman, Treasurer; E-mail: wendellfreeman@brb-nsn.gov
Members-at-Large: John McGinnis, Edwin Smith, Delmar Keisner,
Matthew Mattson, Executive Director of Tribal Government Operations
E-mail: matthewmattson@brb-nsn.gov
Teresa McGinnis, Communications Director
E-mail: tmcginnis@brb-nsn.gov
Liana Whiteley, Social Services Director; E-mail: lianawhiteley@brb-nsn.gov
Tribes served: Wiyot, Mattole. *Area*: 62 acres. Due to the newness of the Rohnerville Rancheria as a federally recognized Indian Tribe, services the Tribe currently provides to its members are limited. It is the direction of the Tribe to secure grants to develop and expand programs such as education, health, social services, housing, employment, economic development and cultural rejuvenation. *Enterprises*: Bear River Casino-Hotel Resort; Bear River Tobacco Traders. *Resources*: Library. Northern California Agency.

ROUND VALLEY INDIAN TRIBES

77826 Covelo Rd. • Covelo, CA 95428
(707) 983-6126 Fax 983-6128
Website: www.rvit.org; E-mail: administrator@rvit.org
James Russ, President; E-mail: president@council.rvit.org
Carlino Bettega, Vice President; E-mail: vicepresident@council.rvit.org
Lewis Whipple, Secretary; E-mail: secretary@council.rvit.org
Douglas Hutt, Jr., Treasurer; E-mail: treasurer@council.rvit.org
Carlos Rabano, Sergeant-At-Arms; E-mail: crabano@council.rvit.org
Councilmembers: Douglas Lincoln, Jr. & Cora Lee Simmons
E-mail: dlincoln@council.rvit.org; clsimmons@council.rvit.org
Tribes: Wailaki, Yuki, Nomlacki, Pomo, Concow, Pit River, Little Lake. *In residence*: 1,300. *Area*: 33,000 acres one mile north of Covelo. *Programs*: Child Care, Domestic Violence; Child Welfare; Senior Care; Health & Housing; Environmental; Vocational Training; Head Start. *Resources*: Health Center, Career Center, Education Center, Senior Center; Tribal Library. *Attractions*: Hidden Oaks Casino; California Indian Days (annually, 3rd weekend in Sept.); All Indian Rodeo Spring & Fall Festivals. *Publication*: Poekan Tribal Newsletter/ Newspaper. Central California Agency.

SAN MANUEL BAND OF MISSION INDIANS

26569 Community Center Rd. • Highland, CA 92346
(909) 864-8933 Fax 864-3370; Website: www.sanmanuel-nsn.gov
Lynn Valbuena, Chairperson; Anthony Lee, Chief Judge
Tribe: Serrano. *Enrolled members*: 200. *In residence*: 55. *Area*: 820 acres located in San Bernardino County. *Resources*: California Native American Day (4th Friday of September) (www.nativeamericanday.org); Summer Academy; Learning Resource Center. *Programs*: California Indian Cultural Awareness Conference; Education-Tutoring; Serrano Language Revitalization Project; Economic Development; Health Services; Public Safety; Planning & Development. *Attraction*: Indian Bingo & Casino website: www.sanmanuel.com Southern California Agency.

SAN PASQUAL BAND OF MISSION INDIANS

24458 N. Lake Wohlford Rd., P.O. Box 365 • Valley Center, CA 92082
(760) 749-3200 Fax 749-3876
Website: www.sanpasqualbandofmissionindians.org

Allen E. Lawson, Chairperson
Victoria Diaz, Vice Chairperson
Tilda Green, Secretary/Treasurer
Councilmembers: Steven Cope & David L. Tolar, Jr.
Mark Schultz, Chief Operating Officer
Lorraine Orosco, Education Dept. Executive Director
Justin Quis Quis, Chairperson of Gaming Commission
Tribe: Kumeyaay Diegueno. *Enrolled members*: 950. *In residence*: 752. *Area*: 1,379 acres. *Facilities*: Cultural Center. *Programs*: Education; Environmental; Economic Development; Indian Health; Land & Housing. *Attraction*: Valley View Casino & Hotel. Southern California Agency.

TACHI-YOKUT TRIBE OF THE SANTA ROSA RANCHERIA
16835 Alkali Dr., P.O. Box 8 • Lemoore, CA 93245
(559) 924-1278 Fax 925-2931; Website: www.tachi-yokut-nsn.gov
Ruben Barrios, Chairperson; E-mail: rbarrios@tachi-yokut-nsn.gov
Elmer Thomas, Vice Chairperson; E-mail: ethomas@tachi-yokut-nsn.gov
Rafaela Dieter, Secretary; Dena Baga, Treasurer
Elaine Jeff & Patricia Davis, Delegates
Janice Cuara, Tribal Administrator; E-mail: jcuara@tachi-yokut.com
Aurora Cuara, Education Director; Raymond Jeff, Tribal Historian
Lalo Franco, Cultural Director
Ambar Castillo, Social Services Director; Larry Sisco, Gaming Chairperson
Dan Decker & Cher Stewart, *Tribal attorneys*
Tribe: Tachi Yokut. *In residence*: 135. *Population served*: 300. *Area*: 170 acres. *Programs*: Social Services; Education; Cultural; Environmental; Child Welfare; Elders; Housing; Gaming. *Attraction*: Tachi Palace Casino & Resort (website: www.tachipalace.com). Central California Agency.

SANTA ROSA BAND OF CAHUILLA INDIANS
65200 Highway 74, Mountain Center, CA 92561
P.O. Box 391820 • Anza, CA 92539
(951) 659-2700 Fax 659-2228
Website: www.santarosacahuilla-nsn.gov
Steven Estrada, Chairperson (2016-present)
John Marcus (2006-present), Vice Chairperson
Alexis Rubalcava-Alto, Secretary; Lovina Saul, Treasurer
Councilmembers: Mayme Modesto, Jeanian Espinoza, Gabriella Rubalcava
Tribe: Cahuilla. *Enrolled members*: 110. *In residence*: 70. *Area*: 11,000 acres. Located in Riverside County, between Palm Springs & Anza. Southern California Agency.

SANTA YNEZ BAND OF CHUMASH INDIANS
100 Via Juana Lane, P.O. Box 517 • Santa Ynez, CA 93460
(805) 688-7997 Fax 686-9578
Website: www.santaynezchumash.org
E-mail: info@santaynezchumash.org
Kenneth Kahn, Chairperson; Paul Armenta, Vice Chairperson
Maxine Littlejohn, Secretary-Treasurer
Committeemembers: Gary Pace & Mike Lopez
Niki Sandoval, Education Director
 E-mail: nsandoval@santaynezchumash.org
Ron Sisson, Health Clinic Executive Director
Cecilia Ramos, MD, Medical Director
Guy Markham, DDS, Dental Director
Kelly Schmandt Ferguson, Environmental Director
Tribe: Chumash (Santa Ynez Band). *In residence*: 100. *Population*: 200. *Area*: 126 acres. *Programs*: Chumash Indians Foundation (E-mail: vsandoval@sychumashfoundation.org); Chumash Language; Education; Environmental; Culture; Health; Gaming. *Resources*: Health Clinic; Elders Council (P.O. Box 365 (805) 688-8446 Fax 693-1768. *Attractions*: Chumash Casino & Resort; annual powwow in September; Southern California Agency.

IIPAY NATION OF SANTA YSABEL
Schoolhouse Canyon Rd., P.O. Box 130 • Santa Ysabel, CA 92070
(760) 765-0845 Fax 765-2545
Website: www.iipaynation-nsn.gov
E-mail: info@iipaynation-nsn.gov
Virgil Perez, Chairperson; Paul Gonzalez, Vice Chair
Bonnie Osuna, Legislator Speaker
Legislators: Brandie Taylor, Misty Taylor, Sunni Dominguez,
 Stanley Rodriguez, Michael Baay, Anthony Baay
David Vialpando, Gaming Commission Chairperson
 Karen Vigneault, Librarian (765-2903)
Tribe: Iipay Nation of Santa Ysabel. *Population*: 900. *In residence*: 305. *Area*: 15,527 acres. *Location*: Hwy. 79, in North San Diego County near Lake Henshaw between the towns of Santa Ysabel & Warner Springs. *Programs*: Youth; Literacy; Head Start. *Resources*: Resource Center; Tribal Library. *Attraction*: Santa Ysabel Resort & Casino (website: www.santaysabelresortandcasino.com). Southern California Agency.

CALIFORNIA VALLEY MIWOK TRIBE
Sheep Ranch Rancheria, 4620 Shippee Lane • Stockton, CA 95212
Mail: 2140 Shattuck Ave. #602 • Berkeley, CA 94704
(209) 931-4567 Fax 931-4333
Website: www.californiavalleymiwok.us
E-mail: office@cvmt.net or administration@californiavalleymiwok.com
Silvia Burley, Chairperson; E-mail: sburley@cvmt.net
Anjelica Paulk, Vice Chairperson; E-mail: jelica@cvmt.net
Rashel Reznor, Secretary/Treasurer & ICWA Coordinator
Daveen Williams, Cultural Arts & Crafts Coordinator
 & Health & Human Resources Manager
Tiger Paulk, Economic Development Director
Yakima K. Dixie, Hereditary Spokesperson
Velma WhiteBear, Executive Director; Chadd Everone, Deputy
Tribe: California Valley Me-Wuk. *Programs*: Health & Human Resources; Cultural Preservation; Indian Child Welfare; Water Resources; Enrollment. Central California Agency.

SCOTTS VALLEY BAND OF POMO INDIANS
2727 Systron Dr., Suite 100 • Concord, CA 94518
(925) 363-4778 Fax 363-5295; Website: www.sv-nsn.gov
1005 Parallel Dr. • Lakeport, CA 95453
 (707) 263-3348; Gabriel Ray, Chairperson;
 Website: www.svtribaltanf.org; E-mail: info@svtribaltanf.org
Sara Hicks, Executive Director; E-mail: sara.hicks@sv-nsn.gov

SHERWOOD VALLEY RANCHERIA BAND OF POMO INDIANS
190 Sherwood Hill Dr. • Willits, CA 95490
(707) 459-9690 Fax 459-6936
Website: www.sherwoodvalleybandofpomo.com
E-mail: info@sherwoodvalleyband.com
Mike Knight, Chairperson; E-mail: svrchairman@yahoo.com
Melanie Rafanan, Vice Chairperson
 E-mail: mcrafanan@sbcglobal.net
Karen Sheherd, Secretary; Tracy Wright, Treasurer
Carol Cook, Parliamentarian
Councilmembers: Buffey Wright & Yvonne Quintero
 Sharol L. McDade, Tribal Administrator
 E-mail: svradministrator@sbcglobal.net
Carmen Ochoa, Tribal Services Manager
Stan Horstman, Health Serices Manager
Tribe: Pomo. *Enrolled members*: 450. *In residence*: 180. *Area*: 356 acres located in Mendocino County, near Willits on Hwy. 101. *Attractions*: Black Bart Casino; Sherwood Valley Pomo Casino. Central California Agency.

SHINGLE SPRINGS BAND OF MIWOK INDIANS
Shingle Springs Rancheria, 5168 Honpie Rd. • Placerville, CA 95667
Mailing address: P.O. Box 1340 • Shingle Springs, CA 95682
(530) 698-1400 Fax 676-8033
Website: www.shinglespringsrancheria.com
E-mail: info@ssband.org
Nicholas H. Fonseca, Chairperson; E-mail: nfonseca@ssband.org
Hermo Olanio, Vice Chairperson; E-mail: holanio@ssband.org
Councilmembers: Regina Cuellar, MalissaTayaba, Brian Fonseca,
 Yvonne "Bernie" Gonzales, Allan Campbell
Ernest Vargas, Tribal Administrator; E-mail: evargas@ssband.org
Christine Williams, Chief Judge (698-1446)
AmyAnn Taylor, Attorney General (387-4194)
 E-mail: ataylor@ssband.org
Daniel Fonseca, Director of Cultural Resources (306-3069)
 E-mail: dfonseca@ssband.org
Barbara Silva, Librarian; E-mail: bsilva@ssband.org
Tribe: Miwok. *In residence*: 141. *Area*: 160 acres. *Programs*: Cultural Resources; Environmental; Gaming; Human Resources. *Resources*: Health & Wellness Center; Tribal Library. *Attraction*: Red Hawk Casino; annual "Big Time" powwow last weekend in August. Central California Agency.

SOBOBA BAND OF LUISENO INDIANS
23906 Soboba Rd., P.O. Box 487 • San Jacinto, CA 92583
(951) 654-2765/5544 Fax 654-4198; Website: www.soboba-nsn.gov
Scott Cozart, Chairperson; E-mail: scozart@soboba-nsn.gov
Isaiah Vivanco, Vice Chairperson; E-mail: ivivanco@soboba-nsn.gov
Monica Herrera, Secretary; Kelli Hurtado, Treasurer
Rose Salgado Sergeant-at Arms
Dione Kitchen, Executive Assistant to the Tribal Council
 E-mail: dkitchen@soboba-nsn.gov
Joseph Ontiveros, Cultural Resource Director
 E-mail: jontiveros@soboba-nsn.gov
Carrie Lynn Garcia, Culture Program Manager (951) 654-5544
Nancy Currie, Tribal Family Services Director

Celeste Hughes, Gaming Commissioner
E-mail: chughes@soboba-nsn.gov
David J. Montoya III (Ohkay Owingeh Pueblo), In-House Tribal Attorney
Tribe: Luiseno. *Enrolled members*: 1200. *Area*: 7,000 acres located at the foothills of the San Jacinto Mountains. *Resources*: Soboba Cultural Center & Research Library; Pre-school; Noli Indian School (Grades 6-12); Soboba Clinic; Sports Complex. *Programs*: Tribal Family Services (487-0283); *Attractions*: Soboba Casino; The Oaks Retreat (website: www.theoaksat soboba.com); Country Club; annual Soboba (golf) Classic; annual powwow in September. *Publication*: Family Services monthly newsletter. Southern California Agency.

SUSANVILLE INDIAN RANCHERIA
745 Joaquin St. • Susanville, CA 96130
(530) 257-4923 Fax 260-0098; Website: www.sir-nsn.gov
Deana Bovee, Chairperson; Arian Hart, Vice Chairperson
Aaron Dixon, Sr., Secretary/Treasurer
Councilmembers: Aaron Brazzanovich, Jr., District 1
Robert Joseph, District 2
Tina Sanchez (On-Trust Land), At-Large Representative
Marvena Harris (Lassen County), At-Large Representative
Anna Pasqua, Education Director (252-1658)
E-mail: SIR_Ed_director@frontier.com
Donna Clark, Language Program Coordinator
E-mail: d_clark@frontier.com
Meredith Gosejohan, Natural Resources Director
E-mail: nrd_director@frontier.com
Tribes: Paiute, Maidu, Pit River & Washoe. *In residence*: 438. *Area*: 1,341 acres. *Programs*: Education, Child Care/Welfare, Housing, Environment, Gaming Commission; Natural Resources; Economic Development. *Resources*: Health Center; Library in Education Center. *Attraction*: Diamond Mountain Casino & Hotel. *Publication*: Tribal Newsletter. Northern California Field Office.

SYCUAN BAND OF KUMEYAAY NATION
1 Kwaaypaay Court • El Cajon, CA 92019
(619) 445-2613 Fax 445-0238; Website: www.sycuantribe.org
Cody J. Martinez, Chairperson; Henry R. Murphy, Vice Chairperson
Charlene Worrell, Secretary; LaShunna Davidson, Treasurer
Councilmembers: Xusha Brown, Alanna Sandoval, Joshua Muse
Nubia Ford, Education Director (619) 659-5897
E-mail: nford@sycuan-nsn.gov
Tribe: Kumeyaay Diegueno. *In residence*: 33. *Area*: 632 acres. *Programs*: Education; Development Corporation; Gaming Commission; Human Resources; Fire/Police. *Programs*: Child Care; Preschool & After School Programs; Language. *Resources*: Medical/Dental Center; Kumeyaay Community College; Kumeyaay Language Institute; Sycuan Institute on Tribal Gaming at San Diego State University. *Attractions*: Sycuan Casino & Resort (www.sycuan.com); Golf Academy; annual powwow in Sept. Southern California Agency.

TABLE MOUNTAIN RANCHERIA
Sky Harbor Rd., P.O. Box 410 • Friant, CA 93626
(559) 822-2587 Fax 822-2693; Leanne Walker-Grant, Chairperson
Tribe: Mono-Chuckchansi Band of Yokuts & Monache. *Enrolled members*: 34.
In residence: 11. *Area*: 61 acres located in Fresno County. *Attraction*: Table Mountain Casino (website: www.tmcasino.com). Central California Agency.

TIMBISHA SHOSHONE TRIBE
621 West Line St. #109, P.O. Box 1779 • Bishop, CA 93515
(760) 872-3614 Fax 872-3670; Website: www.timbisha.com
George Gholson, Chairperson (258-5620)
E-mail: george@timbisha.com
White Dove Kennedy, Vice Chairperson (258-5918)
E-mail: whitedove@timbisha.com
Ellie Jackson, Secretary/Treasurer (872-3614)
E-mail: ellie.jackson@timbisha.com
Councilmembers:
Earl Frank III (258-5919); E-mail: earl.frank@timbisha.com
Dora Jones (775-258-5551); E-mail: dora.jones@timbisha.com
Mervin Hess, Tribal Administrator; E-mail: mhess @timbisha.com
Tribe: Timbisha Shoshone. *Area*: 7,700 acres. *Resources*: Photo Galleries.
Programs: Economic & Community Development; Natural & Cultural Resources; Housing; Health & Social Services; Environmental. *Publication*: "The Timbisha Shoshone Tribe & Their Living Valley" by the Timbisha Historical Preservation Committee. Central California Agency.

TOLOWA TRIBE OF THE SMITH RIVER RANCHERIA
140 Rowdy Creek Rd. • Smith River, CA 95567
(707) 487-9255 Fax 487-0930; Website: www.tolowa-nsn.gov
Scott D. Sullivan, Chairperson; E-mail: scott.sullivan@tolowa.com
Denise Padgette, Vice Chairperson; E-mail: dpadgette@tolowa.com
Jeri Thompson, Secretary; E-mail: jeri.thompson@tolowa.com

Leon McCallum, Treasurer; E-mail: leann.babcock@tolowa.com
Councilmembers: Marvin Richards, Dr. Joseph Giovannetti, Kara Brundin
Ronda Ritchie, Interim COO; E-mail: ronda.ritchie@tolowa.com
Virginia Young, Operations Manager; E-mail: virginia.young@tolowa.com
Nita Rolfe, Project Coordinator (487-9255); E-mail: nrolfe@tolowa.com
Richard Blake, Presiding Judge; Devon White, Tribal Court Administrator
Pyuwa Bommelyn, Culture Department Director
Laura Valley, Gaming Commission Director
Tribe: Tolowa. *In residence*: 175. *Area*: 161 acres. *Programs*: Tribal Heritage Preservation; Housing; Natural Resources; Gaming; Human Resources; Economic Development; Enrollment. *Attraction*: The Lucky 7 Casino. *Publication*: Dee-ni' Nuu-wee-ya', Tribal newsletter. Northern California Agency.

TORRES MARTINEZ DESERT CAHUILLA INDIANS
66-725 Martinez St. • Thermal, CA 92274
(760) 397-0300 Fax 397-3925; Website: www.torresmartinez.org
E-mail: tmchair@torresmartinez.org
Thomas Tortez, Chairperson; E-mail: tmttortez@torresmartinez.org
Desiree Franco, Vice Chairperson; E-mail: tmdfranco@torresmartinez.org
Altrena Santillanes, Secretary; E-mail: tmssantillanes@torresmartinez.org
Tina Jimenez, Treasurer; E-mail: tmtjimenez@torresmartinez.org
Councilmembers: Frank Durgin, Jr., Elesha Duro, Beverlyann Cedeno (Proxy)
Tribe: Cahuilla. *In residence*: 90. *Area*: 25,000 acres. *Resources*: Education/Library Center. *Programs*: Education; TANF (Temporary Assistance for Needy Families). *Attraction*: Red Earth Casino. Southern California Agency.

TULE RIVER INDIAN TRIBE
Tule River Reservation, P.O. Box 589 • Porterville, CA 93258
(559) 781-4271 Fax 791-2121
Website: www.tulerivertribe-nsn.gov
Neil Peyron, Chairperson
E-mail: neil.peyron@tulerivertribe-nsn.gov
Ryan Garfield, Vice Chairperson
E-mail: ryan.garfield@tulerivertribe-nsn.gov
Gary Santos, Treasurer; Wendy Correa, Secretary
Councilmembers: Joey Garfield, Heather Teran , Duane M. Garfield, Sr.,
Charles Dabney, Kenneth McDarment
Victor Silvas, Tribal Administrator (781-4271 ext. 1039)
Dr. Jerry Livesey, Education Director (784-6135)
Charles Farmer, Human Resources Director
Charmaine McDarment, General Counsel
Tribe: Yokut. *In residence*: 550. *Area*: 54,000 acres. *Resources*: Child Care Center; Health Center; Education Center. *Programs*: TANF; Alcoholism; Child Welfare; Education; Environmental; Forestry; Human Resources; Housing; Health & Recreation. *Attractions*: Eagle Mountain Casino (559) 788-6223 www.eaglemtncasino.com); annual powwow. *Enterprises*: Tule River Aero Industries www.tuleriveraero.com. Eagle Feather Trading Post. Central California Agency.

TUOLUMNE BAND OF ME-WUK INDIANS
Tuolumne Reservation, 19595 Mi-Wu St.
P.O. Box 699 • Tuolumne, CA 95379
(209) 928-5300 Fax 928-1677; E-mail: tmtc@mlode.com
Kevin A. Day, Chairperson; Jon Otterson, Executive Director
Jackie Campidonica, Administrative Supervisor
Marta Mantzourania, Enrollment Specialist
Reba Fuller, Government Affairs & Administrative Specialist
Tribe: Me-Wuk (Miwok). *Enrolled members*: 285. *Area*: 325 acres. *Programs*: Education; Planning & Development; Cultural; Language Preservation; Health & Safety; Social Services; Gaming; Human Resources. *Resources*: Health Centers in Tuolumne & Sonora, CA (928-5400) www.tmwihc.com); Economic Development Authority (928-9391). *Attraction*: Black Oak Casino & Hotel (website: blackoakcasino.com). Central California Agency.

TWENTY-NINE PALMS BAND OF LUISENO MISSION INDIANS
46-200 Harrison St. • Coachella, CA 92236
(760) 863-2444 Fax 863-2449; Darrell Mike, Chairperson
Tribes: Luiseno & Chemuevi. Unoccupied. *Area*: 402 acres located in San Bernardino Co. *Attractions*: Spotlight 29 Casino; Tortoise Rock Casino Website: www.29palmstribe.com. Southern California Agency.

UNITED AUBURN INDIAN COMMUNITY OF THE AUBURN RANCHERIA
10720 Indian Hill Rd. • Auburn, CA 95603
(530) 883-2390 Fax 883-2380
Gene Whitehouse, Chairperson; John Williams, Vice Chairperson
Calvin Moman, Secretary; Jason Camp, Treasurer
Gabe Cayton, Councilmember
Tribes: Miwok & Maidu. Located in the Sierra Nevada foothills in Aurbrn, CA.
Programs: Education; Health; Economic Development; Environmental Protection; Community Development. *Attraction*: Thunder Valley Casino. *Publication*: Newsletter. Central California Agency.

VIEJAS BAND OF KUMEYAAY INDIANS

Viejas Reservation, 1 Viejas Grade Rd. • Alpine, CA 91901
(619) 445-3810 Fax 445-5337; E-mail: community@viejas.com
Website: www.viejasbandofkumeyaay.org
  Robert J. Welch, Jr., Chairperson; E-mail: apico@viejas-nsn.gov
  Victor E. Woods, Vice Chairperson
  Rene Curo, Secretary; Samuel Q. Brown, Treasurer
Councilmembers: Adrian M. Brown, Kevin Carriizosa, Gabriel TeSam
Tribe: Kumeyaay Diegueno. *In residence*: 195. *Area*: 1,600 acres. *Resources*:
Viejas Indian School; Borrego Springs Bank, N.A.; Viejas Outlet Center.
Attractions: Viejas Casino (www.viejas.com); Viejas Entertainment &
Production; Ma-Tar-Awa Recreational Vehicle Park. *Publications*: The
Kumeyaay Way, tribal quarterly magazine. Southern California Agency.

WASHOE TRIBE OF NEVADA & CALIFORNIA

Alpine Washoe Reservation, 96A Washoe Blvd. • Woodfords, CA 96120
(530) 694-2170 Fax 694-1890; Website: www.washoetribe.us
  Neil Mortimer, Chairperson; (775) 265-8600
    E-mail: neil.mortimer@washoetribe.us
  Mahlon Machado, Vice Chairperson (775) 265-8600
    E-mail: mahlon.machado@washoetribe.us
  Jeremy Steele, Secretary-Treasurer
    E-mail: Jeremy.steele@washoetribe.us
Tribe: Washoe. *In residence*: 350. *Area*: 80 Acres. *Resources*: Indian
Education Center; Western Nevada Agency. Headquarters located in
Gardnerville, NV.

WILTON RANCHERIA

9728 Kent St. • Elk Grove, CA 95624
(916) 683-6000 Fax 683-6015
Website: www.wiltonrancheria-nsn.gov
E-mail: tribaloffice@wiltonrancheria-nsn.gov
  Raymond Hitchcock, Chairperson
    E-mail: rhitchcock@wiltonrancheria-nsn.gov
  Cammeron Hodson, Vice Chairperson
    E-mail: chodson@wiltonrancheria-nsn.gov
  Jesus Tarango & Elizabeth Singh, Tribal Council Spokespersons
Councilmembers: Mark Andrews, Annette Williams, David Andrews,
  Joseph Rangel
Tribe: Wintun. *Area*: 100 acres. Central California Agency.

WIYOT TRIBE OF THE TABLE BLUFF RANCHERIA

1000 Wiyot Dr. • Loleta, CA 95551
(800) 388-7633; (707) 733-5055 Fax 733-5601
Website: www.wiyot.com; Ted Hernandez, Chairperson
  Brian Mead, Vice Chairperson & Tribal Administrator
  Leona Wilkinson, Secretary; Michelle Hernandez, Treasurer
Councilmembers: Vincent DiMarzo & Ardith Huber, Cheryl Seidner
  Tom Torma, Cultural Director; Sarah Vevoda, Social Services Director
  Stephen Kullmann, Natural Resources Director
Tribe: Wiyot. *In residence*: 218. Area: 102 acres. *Resources*: Community
Center; Heritage Center; Library/Archives. *Programs*: Cultural; Social Services;
Environmental; Human Resources; Language; Historic Preservation.
Publication: Monthly newsletter. Northern California Field Office.

YOCHA DEHE WINTUN NATION

Rumsey Rancheria, P.O. Box 18 • Brooks, CA 95606
(530) 796-3400 Fax 796-2143
Website: www.yochadehe.org; E-mail: info@yochadehe-nsn.gov
  Leland Kinter, Chairperson; Anthony Roberts, Treasurer
  James Kinter, Secretary/Cultural Renewal Chair
Councilmembers: Matthew Lowell, Jr. & Mia Durham
  Sarah Martinez, Director of Education
  Mia Durham, Health & Wellness Committee Chair
Tribe: Yocha Dehe Wintun. *Population served*: 50. *Area*: 67 acres. Community
Council. *Programs*: Health & Wellness; Cultural Rene-wal; Language Learning;
Land & Resources. *Resources*: Yocha Dehe Wintun Academy; Tribal College;
Yocha Dehe Library. *Attraction*: Cache Creek Casino Resort; Central California
Agency.

THE YUROK TRIBE

190 Klamath Blvd., P.O. Box 1027 • Klamath, CA 95548
(707) 482-1350 Fax 482-1377
Website: www.yuroktribe.org; E-mail: tara@yuroktribe.nsn.us
  Thomas P. O'Rourke, Sr., Chairperson
    E-mail: torourke@yuroktribe.nsn.us
  David Gensaw, Vice Chairperson; E-mail: dgensaw@yuroktribe.nsn.us
  Troy Ralstin, Executive Director; E-mail: tralstin@yuroktribe.nsn.us
  Earl Jackson, Deputy Executive Director
    E-mail: ejackson@yuroktribe.nsn.us
Councilmembers: Larry Hendrix, Orick District; Jack Mattz, North District;

Lana McCovey, South District; Ryan Ray, Requa District; Joe James,
East District; Thomas Wilson, Weitchpec District; Mindy Natt, Pecwan District
Jeremiah Swain, Executive Secretary; E-mail: jswain@yuroktribe.nsn.us
Jim McQuillen, Education Department Director
  E-mail: jmcquillen@yuroktribe.nsn.us
Tanya Sangrey, Economic Development Corp. Director
  E-mail: tsangrey@yuroktribe.nsn.us
Rhonda Wright, Legal Secretary; (707) 482-1350 ext. 1408
  E-mail: rwright@yuroktribe.nsn.us
Abby Abinanti, Chief Judge
Weitchpec Office: Hwy 96 • Weitchpec, CA 95546
(530) 625-4130 Fax 625-4148
Eureka/Cutten Office: 3969 Walnut Dr. • Cutten, CA 95501
(707) 444-0433 Fax 444-0104
Tribe: Yurok. *Area*: 5,400 acres. *Programs*: Culture & Repatriation; Child Care;
Housing; Economic Development; Education (Yurok Language); Environ-
mental; Social Services; Vocational Rehabilitation; Natural Resources (Water-
shed Restoration); Fisheries & Forestry; Public Safety. *Attractions*: Requa
Resort (camping); Fishing. *Publication*: Yurok Today, quarterly newsletter.
California Field Office.

COLORADO

SOUTHERN UTE INDIAN TRIBE

356 Ouray Dr., P.O. Box 737 • Ignacio, CO 81137
(970) 563-0100 Fax 563-0396; Website www.southernute-nsn.gov
  Clement Frost, Chairperson; Mel Baker, Vice Chairperson
Councilmembers: *Alex Cloud,* Adam Red, Mel Baker,
  Kevin Frost, Amy Barry, Lorelei Cloud
  Ramona Y. Eagle & Andrew Frost, Executive Officer
  Jeff Fingert, Chief Financial Officer
  Loren Sekayumptewa, Tribal Services Dept. Director
  Lena Atencio, Natural Resources Department Director (563-0125)
  Latitia Taylor, Education Department Director (563-0237)
  Carole Veloso, Health Center Director (563-4581)
  Edna J. Frost, Tribal Information Services Director
  Edward Box III, Culture Department Director (563-2984)
  Chantel Cloud, Chief Judge; Lorelyn Hall, Legal Department Director
Tribe: Southern Ute. *In residence*: 1,300. *Area*: 307,000 acres located along
the Colorado--New Mexico border. *Programs*: Tribal Services; Health Services;
Legal; Education; Housing; Natural Resources; Wildlife Management; Finance;
Justice & Regulatory; Management Information Systems; Construction &
Project Management; Diabetes Program; Community Action; Head Start
Program: P.O. Box 400 (303) 563-4566. Cheryl Clay, Director - comprehensive
early childhood development services to about 100 children and their families
in the reservation area. *Resources*: SunUte Community Center; Health Center;
Southern Ute Indian Montessori Academy; Southern Ute Museum & Cultural
Center; Library; KSUT, Tribal radio station. *Attractions*: Sky Ute Casino &
Resort; Sky Ute Fairgrounds; Sun Ute Community Center; annual Sun Dance,
Bear Dance & Ute Fair Powwow. *Publication*: "Ute Drum," newspaper.
Southern Ute Agency.

UTE MOUNTAIN UTE TRIBE

Ute Mountain Reservation
124 Mike Wash Rd., P.O. Box 109 • Towaoc, CO 81334
(800) 847-5485; (970) 565-3751 Fax 564-5709
Website: www.utemountainutetribe.com
  Harold Cuthair, Chairperson; E-mail: hcuthair@utemountain.org
  Juanita Plentyholes, Vice Chair; E-mail: jplentyholes@utemountain.org
  Colleen Cuthair, Treasurer; E-mail: ccuthair@utemountain.org
  Elaine Cantsee, Secretary; E-mail: ecantsee@utemountain.org
Councilmembers: Marissa Box, Prisllena Rabbit, DeAnne House
Tribe: Ute Mountain Ute - the Weeinuche Band of Utes, one of the seven
original Ute bands that inhabited the entire state of Colorado. *Enrolled
members*: 1,500. *In residence*: 1,750. *Area*: 553,000 acres. Located in
Colorado, New Mexico, & Utah. *Programs*: Environmental. *Attractions*: Ute
Mountain Casino, Hotel & Resort; RV Park; Tribal Park; Visitor Center &
Museum; Pottery Factory. Ute Mountain Field Office.

CONNECTICUT

MASHANTUCKET (WESTERN) PEQUOT TRIBAL NATION

2 Matts Path, P.O. Box 3060 • Mashantucket, CT 06338
(860) 396-6100 Fax 396-6540; Website: www.mashantucket.com
  Rodney A. Butler, Chairperson; Richard E. Sebastian, Vice Chairperson
  Crystal M. Whiple, Secretary; Jean M. Swift, Treasurer
Councilmembers: Roy Calebut-Ingram, Daniel Menihan, Merrill "Marvin" Reels
Elders council: Joyce Walker, Chair; Gary Carter, Vice Chair
  Anthony Sebastian, Secretary/Treasurer
  Anthony Kulla, Pequot Times Editor

Tribe: Mashantucket Pequot. *Area*: 1,250 acres (trust). *Populatin*: 350. *Resources*: Tribal Health Services (P.O. Box 3260, Mashantucket, CT (312-8000); Museum & Research Center (P.O. Box 3180, Mashantucket, CT (800) 411-9671); Library & Archives; www.pequotmuseum.org. *Departments*: Pequot Health Care; Education; Child Protective Services; Cultural Resources, Natural Resources Protection, Public Affairs, Public Safety, Tribal Business Advisory Board; Tribal Court; Planning & Community Development. *Attractions*: Foxwoods Resort & Casino; MGM Grand at Foxwoods; Lake of Isles; The Spa at Norwich Inn; Great Cedar Hotel; Two Trees Inn. *Publications*: The Pequot Times, monthly tribal newspaper; book, "The Pequots in Southern New England: The Fall and Rise of an American Indian Nation." Gift Shop. Eastern Regional Office.

THE MOHEGAN TRIBE
13 Crow Hill Rd. • Uncasville, CT 06382
(860) 862-6100 Fax 862-6115
Kevin P. Brown (*Red Eagle*), Chairperson
 E-mail: kbrown@moheganmail.com
James Gessner, Jr., Vice Chairperson
Kathy Regan-Pyne, Corresponding Secretary
Cheryl A. Todd, Recording Secretary; E-mail: ctodd@moheganmail.com
Thayne D. Hutchins, Jr., Treasurer; Mark F. Brown, Ambassordor
Bruce (*Two Dogs*) Bozsum, Ambassador
William Quidgeon, Jr., Joseph William Smith, Councilors
Council of Elders: (862-6150)
Laurence J. Roberge, Chairperson & Justice
Charlie (*Two Bears*) Strickland, Vice Chairperson & Justice
Beth (*Elizabeth*) Regan (*Morning Deer*), Secretary & Justice
Marie Pineault, Treasurer & Justice of the Peace
Stephanie (*Morning Fire*) Mugford Fielding, Elder & Justice
Sharon "Accomac" Maynard, Elder & Justice
Bill Gucfa, Elder & Justice
Christopher Harris (*Painted Turtle*), Elder & Justice
Traditional Leaders: Marilyn "Lynn" Malerba, Lifetime Chief
Melissa Tantaquidgeon Zobel, Medicine Woman & Tribal Historian
Tribe: Mohegan. *Acres*: 244 acres. *Location*: On the Thames River in Uncasville (land taken into Trust). The state returned the 116-acre Fort Shantok State Park to the tribe for which the tribe paid $3 million. Shantok, which overlooks the Thames River, is the site of the Mohegans' only active burial ground. *Programs*: Land Preservation & Planning; Environmental Protection; Public Works & Safety; Education; Health & Human Services; Cultural & Community Programs; Governmental Affairs & Public Relations; Gaming; Housing; Educational Outreach; Cultural Outreach; Tribal Publications. *Resources*: Archaeological Field School; Community & Government Center; Energy, Environment, Economics & Education Center; Archaeological Field School. *Attractions*: Mohegan Sun Casino (website: www.mohegansun.com); annual Wigwam Festival (3rd weekend in August). *Publications*: The Native Americans of Connecticut: Holding On & Moving Forward – a teacher resource guide (free downloading available); NiYaYo (newspaper) free of charge by subscription. Lesson plans & books & videos are available for purchase on the website. Eastern Regional Office.

FLORIDA

BIG CYPRESS RESERVATION
c/o Seminole Tribe, 6300 Stirling Rd. • Hollywood, FL 33024
 (800) 683-7800; (954) 966-6300
Manuel Tiger, Big Cypress Representative
Tribe: Miccosukee Seminole. *In residence*: 450. *Area*: 42,700 acres located in southern Florida. *Resources*: Ah-Tah-Thi-Ki Museum; Billie Swamp Safari.

BRIGHTON RESERVATION
c/o Seminole Tribe, 6300 Stirling Rd. • Hollywood, FL 33024
 (800) 683-7800; Andrew J. Bowers, Jr., Brighton Representative
Tribe: Cow Creek. *In residence*: 570. *Area*: 35,800 acres located in south-central Florida.

MICCOSUKEE INDIAN TRIBE OF FLORIDA
Box 440021, Tamiami Sta. • Miami, FL 33144
 (305) 223-8380 Fax 223-1011; Website: www.miccosukee.com
Billy Cypress, Chairperson; Roy Cypress, Jr., Assistant Chairperson
Gabriel Osceola, Secretary; Jerry Cypress, Treasurer
William Osceola, Lawmaker
Tribe: Creek. *In residence*: 640. *Area*: 333 acres located on Tamiami Trail, 40 miles west of Miami. *Resources*: Day Care Center; Senior Center; Health Clinic. *Programs*: Head Start; Social Service; Vocational & Higher Education. *Attractions*: Miccosukee Indian Village & Museum; Resort & Casino (www.miccosukeeresort.com); Golf & Country Club; Miccosukee Indian Arts Festival. Eastern Regional Office.

SEMINOLE TRIBE OF FLORIDA
6300 Stirling Rd. • Hollywood, FL 33024
 (800) 683-7800; (954) 966-6300 Fax 967-3486
Website: www.semtribe.com; E-mail: comments@semtribe.com
Marcellus W. Osceola, Jr., Chairperson & V.P. of STOF, Inc.
Mitchell Cypress, Vice Chairperson & President, STOF, Inc.
Christopher Osceola, Hollywood Representative
Andrew J. Bowers, Jr., Brighton/Tampa Representative
Cicero Osceola, Big Cypress/Immokalee Representative
Connie Whidden, Health Director (962-2009)
Camellia Osceola, Editor-in-Chief, Seminole Tribune
 E-mail: camelliaosceola@semtribe.com (985-5701 ext. 10735)
Brett Daly, Tribune Senior Editor; E-mail: brettdaly@semtribe.com
Board of Directors:
Mitchell Cypress, Presiednt, STOF, Inc.
Marcellus W. Osceola, Jr., Vice President, STOF, Inc.
Gordon Wareham, Hollywood Representative
Joe Frank, Big Cypress Representative
Larry Howard, Brighton Representative
Tribal Court: 6300 Stirling Rd., Suite 320, Hollywood, FL 33024
Website: www. tribalcourt@semtribe.com
 (800) 683-7800; (954) 966-6300 Fax 967-3438
Willie Johns, Chief Justice (Brighton Reservation)
Amy Johns, Associate Justice (Brighton Reservation)
Moses Jumper, Jr., Associate Justice (Big Cypress Reservation)
Tribe: Seminole. *In residence*: 500. *Population served*: 12,450. *Area*: 480 acres. Located on U.S. 441, in Hollywood, FL in the Fort Lauderdale--Miami area. Maintains six non-contiguous reservations (most of any tribe in North America): Hollywood, Big Cypress, Brighton, Fort Pierce, Immokalee & Tampa. *Department & Divisions*: Native Learning Center (NLC) which offers tuition-free courses & training to Native Americans & Indigenous people with an emphasis on the educational needs of Tribal members and their communities; Environmental; Health & Housing; Aviation. *Attractions*: Seminole Hard Rock Hotel & Casino Hollywood; the Seminole Okalee Indian Village & the Ah-Tah-Thi-Ki Museum at Okalee Village located on the Big Cypress Reservation (the Seminole Indian Village features typical village life & customs, Native arts & crafts, and native animal exhibits; owns & operates casinos in Brighton, Immokalee, Coconut Creek, & Tampa; Indian ceremonials held in mid-July. Museum & Library. *Publication*: "Seminole Tribune," tribal newspaper. Tribal council. Head Start Program. Seminole Agency.

IDAHO

COEUR D'ALENE TRIBE
850 A St., P.O. Box 408 • Plummer, ID 83851
 (208) 686-1800 Fax 686-1182; Website: www.cdatribe-nsn.gov
Chief James Allan, Chairperson
Ernest Stensgar, Vice Chairperson
Donnie Sczenski, Secretary/Treasurer
Councilmembers:
Leta L. Campbell, Charlotte Nilson, Margaret SiJohn,
Cynthia "Cindy" Williams
Chris Meyer, Director of Education (686-5013)
 E-mail: cmeyer@cdatribe-nsn.gov
Audra Vincent, Language Program Director
Robert Matt, Administrative Director
Helo Hancock, Legislative Director (686-0752)
Heather Keen, Public Relations Director (686-2023)
 E-mail: hkeen@cdatribe-nsn.gov
Eva White, Chief Judge (686-1777)
Matthew Stensgar, Gaming Director (665-6920)
 E-mail: mwstensgar@cdatribe-nsn.gov
Jennifer L. Fletcher, Editor - "Council Fires"
Tribe: Coeur D'Alene (Skitswish) (Schitsu'umsh). *Enrolled members*: 1,955. *In residence*: 950. *Area*: 345,000 acres located about 33 miles south of Coeur D'Alene, Idaho. *Departments*: Education; Cultural; Social Services; Law Enforcement; Language; Natural Resources; Information Technology; Veterans; Justice. *Resources*: Wellness Center - Benewah Medical Center; Tribal School. *Attractions*: The Coeur D'Alene Casino/Hotel. *Publication*: Council Fires, tribal newspaper. Coeur d'Alene Tribe BIA Field Office.

KOOTENAI TRIBE OF IDAHO
P.O. Box 1269 • Bonners Ferry, ID 83805
 (208) 267-3519 Fax 267-2960; Website: www.kootenai.org
Gary Aitken, Jr., Chairperson
Councilmembers:
Duane E. Saunders, Jennifer Porter, Amethyst Aitken,
Kym Cooper, Ronald Abraham, Velma Bahe
Mathias David, Tribal Elder

Tribe: Kootenai. In residence: 150. *Area*: 2,680 acres located in Boundary County, near Mirror Lake and the Canadian border. *Programs*: Kootenai Valley Resource Initiative; Fish & Wildlife; Environment. *Resources*: Health Clinic. *Attractions*: Twin Rivers Canyon Resort, 40-acre RV Park & Campground; Kootenai River Inn & Casino. Northern Idaho Agency.

NEZ PERCE TRIBE
100 Main St., P.O. Box 305 • Lapwai, ID 83540
(208) 843-7342/7389 Fax 843-7354/7343
Website: www.nezperce.org; E-mail: nptec@nezperce.org
Mary Jane Miles, Chairperson; E-mail: maryjanem@nezperce.org
McCoy Oatman, Vice Chairperson; E-mail: mccoyo@nezperce.org
Casey Mitchell, Secretary; Shannon Wheeler, Treasurer
Elizabeth Arthur-Attao, Asst. Secretary/Treasurer
Councilmembers: Samuel N. Penney, Arthur Broncheau, Quintin Ellenwood
Bill Picard, Chaplain
Gary Dorr, General Council Chairperson
 E-mail: garydorrgc@nezperce.org
Edion Whiteplume, Vice Chairperson
 E-mail: edonw@nezperce.org
Shirley Allman, General Council Secretary
 E-mail: shirleya.generalcouncil@nezperce.org
Tribe: Nez Perce. *In residence*: 2,200. *Area*: 92,685 acres located a few miles from the city of Lewiston in Nez Perce, Lewis, Clearwater & Idaho Counties. *Commissions*: Fish & Wildlife; Tribal Gaming; Tribal Employment Rights; Tribal Enterprise Board. *Resources*: Lapwai (Ni-Mii-Puu) Health Center; Satellite (Kamiah) Health Center; Tribal Court. *Programs*: Social Services; Child Protection; Safety; Housing; Human Resources; Natural Resources; Land Enterprise; Gaming; Head Start. *Attractions*: Nez Perce Tribal Gaming Enterprise operates two casinos, the Clearwater River Casino in Lewiston, and It'Se-Ye-Ye Bingo & Casino in Kamiah; Epehtes Powwow, in late March; Esskahpo Powwow, in June; Lookingglass Powwow, in August; Festival of Nations (last weekend - September). Northern Idaho Agency.

NORTHWESTERN BAND OF THE SHOSHONE NATION
Pocatello Tribal Office: 505 Pershing Ave. #200 • Pocatello, ID 83201
(208) 478-5712 Fax 478-5713
Brigham Tribal Office: 707 N. Main St. • Brigham City, UT 84302
(800) 310-8241; (435) 734-2286 Fax 734-0424
Website: www.nwbshoshone.com
Shane Warner, Chairperson/CEO (Pocatello Office)
 E-mail: swarner@nwbshoshone.com
Darren Parry, Vice Chairperson (Brigham City Office)
 E-mail: dparry@arrowpoint.us
Dennis Alex, Secretary (Pocatello Office)
 E-mail: banner02@gmail.com
Byron Timbimboo, Treasurer (Brigham City Office)
 E-mail: wood-da@msn.com
Councilmembers: Jeffrey Parry (Brigham City) E-mail: jparry@tope.us
Cale Worley (Brigham City) E-mail: cworley@nwbshoshone.com
Jason S. Walker (Pocatello) E-mail: jwalker@nwbshoshone.com
Tribe: Shoshone. Located in Idaho & Utah. *Programs*: Education; Health; Housing; Enrollment; Cultural & Natural Resources; Environment. *Resources*: Economic Development Corporation - Two locations: Brigham Tribal Office and at 1177 E. South Temple, Salt Lake City, UT 84102 (877) 777-2327. Through the Intermountain Tribal Alliance (ITA), the tribe has developed a Community Development Financial Institution (CDFT) that has created a venture capital fund to develop tribal companies that implement Harvard Project on American Indian Economic Development for corporate governance principles. Fort Hall Agency.

SHOSHONE-BANNOCK TRIBES
Fort Hall Indian Reservation, P.O. Box 306 • Fort Hall, ID 83203
(208) 478-3721 Fax 2478-3730
Website: www.shoshonebannocktribes.com
Nathan Small, Chairperson; E-mail: nsmall@sbtribes.com
Darrell Shay, Vice Chairperson; E-mail: dshay@sbtribes.com
Marcus Coby, Secretary; E-mail: mcoby@sbtribes.com
Tino Batt, Treasurer; E-mail: tbatt@sbtribes.com
Ladd Edmo, Sergeant-At-Arms; E-mail: ledmo@sbtribes.com
Councilmembers: Darrell Dixey & Donna Bollinger
Angelo Gonzales, Executive Director
Laverne Beech, Manager of Public Affairs
William Bacon & Brandelle Whitworth, General Counsel
Monte Gray, Tribal Attorney
Lori Edmo-Suppah, Editor-Sho-Ban News
Tribes: Shoshone-Bannock. *Enrolled members*: 5,820. *In residence*: 5,760 (1,825 non-Indians). *Area*: 523,917 acres located near Pocatello, Idaho, east and south of the Snake River. *Resources*: Tribal Museum & Library (237-9791); Early Childhood Development Center; Trading Post; Tribal Enterprise Farm; Tribal Bison Herd. Programs/Departments: Human Services; Education,

Employment & Training (EET) Program; Language & Cultural Preservation program; Elderly Nutrition Program; Energy Resource Management Program; Fish & Gaming Department; Gaming Commission; Housing Authority. *Attractions*: Bannock Peak Casino; Fort Hall Casino; High Stakes Bingo; RV Park; American Falls; annual Shoshone-Bannock Indian Festival held in August; Fishing & Hunting in the "Bottoms area of Reservation. *Publication*: Sho-Ban News. Head Start Program. Fort Hall Agency.

IOWA

OMAHA TRIBE
P.O. Box 368 • Macy, NE 68039
(402) 837-5391 Fax 837-5308; Website: www.omaha-nsn.gov
Mike Wolfe, Chairperson
Tribe: Omaha. Located in Iowa & Nebraska. Winnebago Agency.
See listing under Nebraska.

SAC & FOX TRIBE OF THE MISSISSIPPI IN IOWA/MESKWAKI NATION
349 Meskwaki Rd. • Tama, IA 52339
(641) 484-4678 Fax 484-5424; Website: www.sacandfoxnation-nsn.gov
Troy Wanatee, Chairperson; Alvin Wild Cat, Vice Chairperson
Lavern Jefferson, Treasurer; Jason Davenport, Secretary
March Runner, Executive Director; Lisa LaCroix, Education Director
Councilmembers:
Jarvis Bear, Education Liaison; Troy Wanatee, Health Liaison;
Jason Davenport, Agriculture Liaison; Gerald Sanache, Homes Liaison
Tribe: Meskwaki Sac & Fox. *Enrolled members*: 1,400. *Area*: 8,000+ acres. *Departments*: Health Services (Diabetes Program); Family Services; Economic Development; Higher Education; Language Preservation; Housing; Natural Resources; Sac & Fox Gaming Commission. *Resources*: Meskwaki Settlement School,;Tribal Museum; Con-vention Center; Wellness Center; Senior Center; Meskwaki Trading Post. *Attractions*: Meskwaki Bingo Casino Hotel; annual Powwow. *Publication*: Meskwaki Nation Times. Midwest Regional Office.

WINNEBAGO TRIBE OF NEBRASKA
100 Bluff St., P.O. Box 687 • Winnebago, NE 68071
(402) 878-3103 Fax 878-2963; Website: www.winnebagotribe.com
Frank White, Chairperson (878-3110)
 E-mail: frank.white@winnebagotribe.com
Vince Bass, Vice Chairperson (878-3102)
 E-mail: vince.bass@winnebagotribe.com
Victoria Kitcheyan, Treasurer; Kenny Mallory, Secetary
Councilmembers: Darla LaPoint, James Snow, Coly Brown,
Curtis St. Cyr, Isaac Smith
Tribe: Winnebago. Located in Nebraska & Iowa (off-reservation lands in Iowa.) Winnebago Agency. See listing under Nebraska.

KANSAS

IOWA TRIBE OF KANSAS & NEBRASKA
3345 A. Thrasher Rd. • White Cloud, KS 66094
(785) 595-3212 Fax 595-5171
Website: www.iowatribeofkansasandnebraska.com
Timothy Rhodd, Chairperson; E-mail: trhodd@iowas.org
Alan Kelley, Vice Chairperson; E-mail: akelley@iowas.org
Tony Fee, Secretary; E-mail: tony.fee@iowas.org
Kelli Cheek, Treasurer & Higher Education Program Director
 E-mail: kcheek@iowas.org
Robbie Craig, Councilmember; E-mail: rcraig@iowas.org
Becky Parker, Community Health Representative
Montie Deer, Appellate Judge; Charles H. Tripp, Judge
Tribe: Ioway. *Enrolled members*: 1,700. *In residence*: 800. *Area*: 7,000 acres. *Resources*: Native American Heritage Museum in Highland, KS; Ioway Cultural Institute; Ioway; Wellness Center; Senior Center; Day Care Center; Ioway Virtual Library & Bookstore. *Programs*: Family Services; Fish & Wildlife; Health. *Attraction*: Casino White Cloud; annual Powwow. *Publication*: Ioway News. Movie: Lost Nation: The Ioway. Located in Kansas & Nebraska. Horton Field Office.

KICKAPOO TRIBE IN KANSAS
824 111th Dr. • Horton, KS 66439
(877) 864-2746; (785) 486-2131 Fax 486-2801
Lester Randall, Chairperson; E-mail: lester.randall@ktik-nsn.gov
Fred Thomas, Vice Chairperson; E-mail: fred.thomas@ktik-nsn.gov
Russell Bradley, Treasurer; Carla Ramirez-Cavin, Secretary
Councilmembers: Bernadette Thomas, Jason Thomas, Tina Wahwasuck-Keo
Jolene Walters, Health Director; E-mail: Jolene.walters@ihs.gov
Nora Pemma Parker, Education Director; E-mail: nora.parker@ktik-nsn.gov
Amelia Holmes, Legal Attorney; E-mail: amelia.holmes@ktik-nsn.gov
Eric S. Sheets, Environmental Director; E-mail: eric.sheets@ktik-nsn.gov

Tribe: Kickapoo. *Enrolled members*: 1,675. *In residence*: 600. *Resources*: Kickapoo Health Center; DPP Wellness Center; Senior Citizens Center; Kickapoo Judicial Center; Kickapoo Nation School. *Programs*: Education; Human Resources; Social Services; Senior Citizens; Health; Environmental; Head Start. *Attractions*: Trading Post; annual Powwow. *Publication*: Plum Creek News. Horton Field Office.

PRAIRIE BAND POTAWATOMI NATION
16281 Q Road • Mayetta, KS 66509
(877) 715-6789; (785) 966-4000 Fax 966-4002
Website: www.pbpindiantribe.com; E-mail: info@pbpnation.org
Liana Onnen, Chairperson; E-mail: lianao@pbpnation.org
Zach Pahmahmie, Vice Chairperson; E-mail: zachp@pbpnation.org
Camilla Chouteau, Secretary; E-mail: camillac@pbpnation.org
Councilmembers: Warren Wahweotten, Thomas M. Wabnum, Juanita Jessepe
 Peggy Houston, Tribal Operations Manager (966-3900)
 Suzanne Heck, Newspaper Editor (966-3920)
 E-mail: michellesimon@pbpnation.org
 Gary Mitchell, Gaming Commissioner (966-3048)
Tribe: Prairie Band Potawatomi. *Enrolled members*: 5,000. *Resources*: Health Center (966-8200). *Programs*: Community Services; Education; Health & Wellness, Diabetes; Economic Development; Human Resources; Housing; Education & Children's; Child Welfare; Youth; Vocational. *Attractions*: Prairie Band Casino & Resort; annual Powwow in June. *Publication*: Potawatomi News, bimonthly newspaper. Horton Field Office.

SAC & FOX NATION OF MISSOURI IN KANSAS & NEBRASKA
305 N. Main St. • Reserve, KS 66434
(785) 742-7471 Fax 742-3785; Website: www.sacandfoxks.com
Tiauna Carnes, Chairperson (742-0053)
 E-mail: tcarnes@sacandfoxcasino.com
James Jensen, Vice Chairperson; E-mail: jjensen@sacandfoxcasino.com
Rita Bahr, Secretary; E-mail: rbahr@sacandfoxcasino.com
Bridgette Robidoux, Treasurer; E-mail: brobidoux@sacandfoxcasino.com
Victoria Ramos, Councilmember; E-mail: vramos@sacandfoxcasino.com
Kevin Burnison, Executive Director; E-mail: kburnison@sacandfoxcasino.com
Ralph Simon, Chief Justice; Chris Halbert, Tribal Attorney
Tribe: Sac & Fox of Missouri in Kansas & Nebraska. *Resources*: Health & Dental Clinic; Tribal Museum; Library. *Programs*: Health Services; Education & Enrollment; Alcohol & Substance Abuse; Environmental Protection; Gaming Commission; Housing; Social Services; Wildlife Management; Youth. *Attraction*: Sac & Fox Casino, located in Powhattan, Kansas; annual Powwow, last week in August; Trading Post. Horton Field Office.

SHAWNEE TRIBE
P.O. Box 860114 • Shawnee, KS 66286 (913) 284-6635
P.O. Box 189 • Miami, OK 74355 (918) 542-2441 Fax 542-2922
Website: www.shawnee-tribe.com
Ron Sparkman, Chief; Jodi Hayes, Tribal Administrator
(See Miami, Oklahoma office)

LOUISIANA

SOVEREIGN NATION OF THE CHITIMACHA
155 Chitimacha Loop, P.O. Box 661 • Charenton, LA 70523
(866) 936-2654; (337) 923-4973 Fax 923-6848
Website: www.chitimacha.gov; E-mail: info@chitimacha.gov
Melissa Darden, Chairperson; E-mail: melissa.darden@chitimacha.gov
April C. Wyatt, Vice Chairperson; E-mail: april.wyatt@chitimacha.gov
Jackie Junca, Secretary/Treasurer
Councilpersons-At-Large: Jacob Darden & John Paul Darden
Jules M. Darden, Chief Administrative Officer (923-4973)
 E-mail: administration@chitimacha.gov
Kimberly S. Walden, Cultural Director/Historic Preservation Officer
 E-mail: cultureinfo@chitimacha.gov; E-mail: thpo@chitimacha.gov
Brian Headley, Director of Development (923-4000)
 E-mail: brian@chitimacha.gov
Bruce Burgess, President, Board of Education (923-4973)
 E-mail: bruce@chitimacha.gov
Karen Matthews, Director of Health & Human Services (923-9955)
 E-mail: karen@chitimacha.gov
Tanya Rosamond, Principal of Tribal School (923-9960)
 E-mail: schoolinfo@chitimacha.gov
Tribe: Chitimacha. *Enrolled members*: 950. *In residence*: 350. *Area*: 260 acres. *Resources*: Chitimacha Tribal School; Museum & Library. *Programs*: Scholarships; Health. *Attractions*: Cypress Bayou Casino; Chitimacha Tribal Fair (Fourth of July Weekend). *Publication*: Tribal Newsletter; The Chitimacha People, by Herbert T. Hoover (part of the tribal series). Eastern Regional Office.

COUSHATTA TRIBE OF LOUISIANA
1940 C.C. Bel Rd., P.O. Box 818 • Elton, LA 70532
(337) 584-2261 Fax 584-2998; Website: www.koasatiheritage.org
Kevin Sickey, Chairperson; David Sickey, Vice Chairperson
Jerold Poncho, Secretary/Treasurer
Pratt Doucet & Wayne Wilson, Council Members At-Large
Tribe: Coushatta. *In residence*: 295. *Area*: 154 acres. *Resources*: Tribal Preschool; Community, Health & Learning Centers; Cultural Heritage Center. *Project*: Koasati Language Project. *Programs*: Education; Housing Improvement; Youth Conservation Corp., Environmental Health Services; Public Safety; Economic Development; Private School; Adult Vocational Training; Mental Health Counseling. *Attractions*: Coushatta Casino Resort; Longleaf Pine Needle Basket Weaving. Eastern Regional Office.

JENA BAND OF CHOCTAW INDIANS
P.O. Box 14 • Jena, LA 71342
(318) 992-2717 Fax 992-8244
Website: www.jenachoctaw.org; E-mail: info@jenachoctaw.org
Cheryl Smith, Principal Chief; E-mail: csmith@jenachoctaw.org
Councilmembers: Christy Murphy, Libby Rogers, Lisa Norris, Lillie Williamson
 Mona Maxwell, Director of Social Services (992-0136)
 Carrie Fisher, Inter-Tribal Council Representative (992-0495)
 Kellye Smith, Health Director (992-2763)
 E-mail: ksmith@jenachoctaw.org
 Alina Shively, Tribal Historic Preservation Officer (992-1205)
 Julie R. Wilkerson, Tribal Attorney (419-8434)
 E-mail: jwilkerson@jenachoctaw.org
Tribe: Choctaw. *Enrolled members*: 241. *Programs*: Education; Health & Social Services; Housing; Transportation. Eastern Regional Office

TUNICA-BILOXI TRIBE OF LOUISIANA
150 Melacon Rd. • Marksville, LA 71351
(318) 253-9767 Fax 253-9791; Website: www.tunicabiloxi.org
Joey P. Barbry, Chairperson
Marshall Ray Sampson, Sr., Vice Chairperson
Beverly Chapman-Rachal, Secretary-Treasurer
Leslie Fontenot, Council Administrator
Council members: Brenda Lintinger, Alejos Lopez, Jr., Harold Pierite, Sr.
 Earl Barbry, Jr.,
 Lois Henry, Education Director; E-mail: lshenry@yahoo.com
 Marshall Pierite, Social Services Director
 Benjamin Clyde Bennett, Jr., Tribal Judge
 Earl Barbry, Jr., Director - Tribal Museum & Cultural Resources Center
 E-mail: earlii@tunica.org
 Rudy Wambsgans, Gaming Commission Chairperson
Tribe: Tunica-Biloxi. *Enrolled members*: 648. *Resources*: Tunica-Biloxi Cultural & Educational Resources Center; Tribal Museum; Gaming-Economic Development Corporation. *Programs*: Education; Health; Social Services; Trust; Housing; Employment. *Attractions*: Grand Casino Avoyelles; Paragon Casino Resort; annual Powwow (www.tunicapowwow.org); Trading Post. *Publication*: Newsletter. Eastern Area Office.

MAINE

AROOSTOOK BAND OF MICMACS
7 Northern Rd., P.O. Box 772 • Presque Island, ME 04769
(800) 355-1435; (207) 764-1972 Fax 764-7667
Website: www.micmac-nsn.gov; E-mail: tribalcouncil@micmac-nsn.gov
Edward Peter Paul, Tribal Chief (2017-21)
 E-mail: epeterpaul@micmac-nsn.gov
Richard Silliboy, Vice Chief (2017-21)
 E-mail: rsilliboy@micmac-nsn.gov
Fred Getchell, Treasurer (2015-19)
 E-mail: jmorey@micmac-nsn.gov
Sheila McCormack (2015-19), Secretary
 E-mail: smccorack@micmac-nsn.gov
Council members: Brandon Getchell, Christina Donnelly, Theresa Cochran, Teresitia Hamel, Dora Dow
 Dena Winslow, Tribal Planner; E-mail: dwinslow@micmac-nsn.gov
 Nichole Francis, Education Director; E-mail: nfrancis@micmac-nsn.gov
Tribe: Micmac. *Enrolled members*: 1,250. Total Micmac population is about 15,000, most live in Canada. About 1,000 Micmacs live in Maine and are the most traditional Indians in the eastern U.S. The Micmac Nation, today, is composed of seven districts with 29 bands and a population of approximately 30 thousand. The Micmac language is an Algonquin one, related to that of the Micmacs' southern neighbors, the Maliseets, Passamaquoddy, Penobscot & Abenaki. All these northeastern tribes are culturally & linguistically related. Collectively, this group is called the "Wabanaki", which means "People of the Daybreak", or "Dawn land People" (wabun meaning "light" or "white", aki meaning "earth"). Like other tribes of Maine, the Micmac, continue to produce

a variety of traditional baskets made of splint ash wood, birch bark and split cedar. The Micmac are recognized as excellent producers of porcupine quill on birch bark boxes and wooden flowers of strips of maple, cedar and white birch. On November 26, 1991 after complex legal maneuvering and political lobbying the Aroostook Band of Micmacs finally achieved Federal Recognition with the passage of the Aroostook Band of Micmacs Settlement Act. This act provided the Community with acknowledgment of its tribal status in the United States. The Aroostook Band of Micmacs have succeeded in rejuvenating a part of the Micmac Nation. *Programs*: Health & Housing; Head Start. *Resources*: Tribal Museum. Eastern Regional Office.

HOULTON BAND OF MALISEET INDIANS
88 Bell Rd. • Littleton, ME 04730
(800) 545-8524; (207) 532-4273 Fax 532-2660
Website: www.maliseets.com
 Clarissa Sabattis, Tribal Chief; E-mail: tribal.chief@maliseets.com
Councilmembers: Tony Tomah, Gloria Tomah, Suzanne Desiderio,
Susanna Wright, David Lindsay, Linda Raymond
Michelle Barrows, Health Department (532-2240 ext. 123
Amber Wire, Education Director (532-4273 x210
 E-mail: edu.director@maliseets.com
Susanna Wright, Social Services & Child Welfare Director (532-7260)
 E-mail: ssdir@maliseets.com
Tribe: Maliseet. *Population served*: 300. *Programs*: Education & Language; Social Services; Health; Domestic Violence; Housing; Indian Child Welfare; Youth; Natural Resources; Head Start. Resources: Cultural Community Education Center. *Attraction*: Maliseet Recognition Day, October 10. Eastern Regional Office.

PASSAMAQUODDY TRIBE – INDIAN TOWNSHIP
Indian Township, P.O. Box 301 • Princeton, ME 04668
(207) 796-2301 Fax 796-2420; Website: www.passamaquoddy.com
William J. Nicholas, Chief; Leslie Nicholas I, Vice Chief
Matthew Dana II, Tribal Representative
Councilmembers: Aaron Dana, Wade Lola, Alexander Nicholas I,
 Nipawset Sabattus, Joseph Socobasin
Nora Deschaine, Education Director (796-6102 Fax 796-5256)
Donald Soctomah, Cultural Resources Director (796-5533)
Tribe: Passamaquoddy. *Enrolled members*: 3,370 (including Pleasant Point). *In residence*: 1,365. Area: 200,000 acres. Indian communities at Peter Dana Point & The Strip. *Programs*: Health-Wellness Center; Education; Social Services; Economic Development; Environment; Housing; Fish & Wildlife; Fire & Rescue. *Resources*: Wellness Center; Tribal Museum. *Publication*: Newsletter. Eastern Regional Office. The Passamaquoddy Tribe, having two locations, is represented by the Joint Tribal Council which consists of the individual Tribal Councils of Indian Township, in Princeton, and at the the Pleasant Point Reservation (Sipayik) in Perry, Maine. The boundary cuts through the middle of Passamaquoddy Tribes homeland. The Passamaquoddy have occupied this watershed region for at least the past 600+ generations (12,000+ years). This new USA-Canada boundary line was created about 200 years ago & was imposed on the Passamaquoddy by the Jay Treaty of 1794. (Aboriginal Rights for the good stuff)...Interestingly, in 1974, the Jay Treaty was revisited when a group of eight Wabanaki (including Mi'kmaq, Maliseet, Passamaquoddy & Penobscot tribes people) challenged US immigration officials and committed an "illegal" border crossing.

PASSAMAQUODDY TRIBE – PLEASANT POINT
9 Sakom Rd., P.O. Box 343 • Perry, ME 04667
(207) 853-2600 Fax 853-6039; Website: www.wabanaki.com
Reubin Clayton Cleaves, Governor (Sakom); Kenneth Poynter, Lt. Governor
Ralph Dana, Sakom-Chief; Elizabeth (Maggie) Dana, Vice Sakom-Chief
Councilmembers:
 Darren Paul, Philip Bassett, Adam Bailey, Newell Lewey, Maria Dana
 Kenneth Poynter, Tribal Manager
 Christine Downing, Newsletter Administrator/Manager
 Edward Nicholas, Tribal Court Administrator/Manager
Tribe: Passamaquoddy. *In residence*: 2,005. *Area*: 141,000 acres. *Resources*: Beatrice Rafferty School; Waponahki Museum & Resource Center. *Programs*: Health; Education; Public Safety; Human Services; Youth & Recreation; Housing; Fish & Game; Elderly; Environmental. *Attractions*: Annual Indian Day Ceremonies - 2nd weekend in August; Artists & Crafts; Tribal TV - a closed circuit community access cable system. *Publica-tions*: Sipayik Bare Bones Newsletter; publications. Eastern Regional Office.

PENOBSCOT INDIAN NATION
12 Wabanaki Way • Indian Island, ME 04468
(877) 736-6272; (207) 817-7776 Fax 817-7482
Website: www.penobscotnation.org
Kirk Francis, Chief (817-7350); Bill Thompson (817-7350), Vice Chief
Mary Settles, Administrative Secretary
Councilmembers: Ronald Bear, Pamela Cunningham, Robert Dana,
Lee Ann Francis, Christopher Francis, Yvonne Francis-Ferland,
Miles Francis, Charlene Virgilio, Beth Sockbeson, Maulian Smith,
Cheryl Francis, John Neptune
Theodore Bear, Mitchell, Tribal State Representative (827-0392)
Benjamin Huerth, MD, Medical Director
Candi Ewer, Education & Career Services Director (817-7348)
Carlene Miller, Learning Center Supervisor (817-7345)
Carol Dana, Penobscot Language Master; Gabe Paul, Language Instructor
Joshua Woodbury, Language Resource Coordinator
James E. Francis, Sr., Cultural & Historic Preservation Director
Chris Sockalexis, Tribal Historic Preservation Officer
John Banks, Natural Resources Department Director
Lisa Morin, Tribal Court Director (817-7328)
Eric M. Mehnert, Chief Judge (817-7329)
Mark Chavaree, Legal Department Director (817-7324)
Tribe: Penobscot. *Enrolled members*: 2,365. *In residence*: 1,150. *Area*: 4,400 acres located on Indian Island. *Departments*: Penobscot Nation Cultural & Historic Preservation; Education & Career Services; Housing Authority; Human Resources, Natural Resources, Trust Services, Human Services, Boys & Girls Club, Higher Education. *Resources*: Health Center; Day Care Center; Kateri Center; Indian Island School; Penobscot Museum; Enterprises; Assisted Living Center. *Attraction*: Penobscot High Stakes Bingo. *Publication*: Penobscot News. Eastern Regional Office.

MASSACHUSETTS

WAMPANOAG TRIBE OF GAY HEAD (AQUINNAH)
20 Black Brook Rd. • Aquinnah, MA 02535
(508) 645-9265 Fax 645-3790; Website: www.wampanoagtribe.net
Cheryl Andrews-Maltais, Chairperson
Richard Randolph, Vice Chairperson & Aid to Tribal Government
Stephanie White, Treasurer; Eleanor Hebert, Secretary
Councilmembers: Keith Marden, Jonathan Perry, Leigh Vanderhoop,
Jay Smalley, Kristina Hook, Steven Craddock
F. Ryan Malonson, Honorary Seat – Tribal Chief
Jason Baird, Honorary Seat – Tribal Medicine Man
Judith Graham-Robey, Tribal Administrator
Grace Reeves, Gladys Widdiss, Elder Councilmembers
Renee Lopes-Pocknett, Education Director
F. Ryan Malonson, Acting Health Director
Bettina Washington, Tribal Historic Preservation Officer
Bret Stearns, Natural Resources Director
Cheryl Andrews-Maltais, Chairperson, Aquinnah Wampanoag Gaming Corp.
Tribe: Aquinnah Wampanoag. *Enrolled members*: 1,200. *In residence*: 270; *off island residence*, 850. *Area*: 485 acres on the southwest corner of Martha's Vineyard Island in the town of Gay Head. *Resources*: Aquinnah Cultural Center. *Programs*: Health; Housing; Human Services; Education; Cultural Resource Protection; Natural Resources; Economic Development; Environmental Laboratory. *Attractions*: Aquinnah Gaming. Eastern Area Office.

MICHIGAN

BAY MILLS INDIAN COMMUNITY
12140 W. Lakeshore Dr. • Brimley, MI 49715
(906) 248-3241 Fax 248-3283/5492
Website: www.baymills.org; www.4baymills.com
Levi Carrick, Sr., Chairperson; Randy Touchtone, Vice Chairperson
Albert Bertram, Treasurer; Stacey Walden, Secretary
Arlen Kuzmik, Council Member; Bryan Newland, Chief Judge
Amy Perron, Social Services Director (248-8303)
Vicki Newland, Gaming Commission Administrator
Tribe: Chippewa (Bay Mills & Sault Ste. Marie Bands.) *Enrolled members*: 1,582. *In residence*: 475. *Area*: 3,494 acres. *Resources*: Ellen Marshall Memorial Health Center; Bay Mills Community College; Ojibwe Charter School; Tribal Court. *Programs*: Conservation; Housing; Food & Energy Assistance; Human Resources; Enrollment; Gaming; Boys & Girls Club. *Attraction*: Bay Mills Resort & Casino, & Kings Club Casino, both in Brimley, Mich. *Publication*: Bay Mills News, newspaper. Executive Council. Michigan Field Office.

GRAND TRAVERSE BAND OF OTTAWA & CHIPPEWA INDIANS
2605 N. West Bay Shore Dr. • Peshawbestown, MI 49682
(866) 534-7750; (231) 534-7750 Fax 534-7568
Website: www.gtbindians.org
Thurlow "Sam" McClellan, Chairperson (534-7129)
 E-mail: thurlow.mcclellan@gtbindians.com
Kimberly Vargo, Vice Chairperson (534-7564)
 E-mail: Kimberly.vargo@gtbindians.com
David Arroyo, Treasurer; E-mail: david.arroyo@gtbindians.com
Jane Rohl, Secretary (534-7694)

Councilmembers: Tom Shomin, Percy Bird, Jr., Mark Wilson
Mary Pelcher, Tribal Manager (534-7750)
 E-mail: mary.pelcher@gtbindians.com
Tanya S. Wanageshik, Chief Judge; (534-7041)
Mary Roberts, Chief Appellate Judge
Dave Spinniken, Newsletter Editor (534-7366)
 E-mail: dave.spinniken@gtbindians.com
Tribes: Ottawa (mostly), some Chippewa. *Enrolled members*: 4,000. *Area*: 2,370 acres. *Programs*: Education; Community Services; Healthcare; Natural Resources; Public Safety; Family & Behavioral Services; Head Start; Human Resources; Environmental Services. *Resources*: Eyaawing Museum & Cultural Center; Benodjenh Center; Peshawbestown Community Center; Economic Development Corporation (EDC) (800) 392-8257; (231) 534-8402. *Attractions*: Grand Traverse Resort & Spa (800) 236-1577; (231) 534-6000; Leelanau Sands Casino in Suttons Bay, & Turtle Creek Casino in Williamsburg, Michigan; annual "Peshawbestown Powwow" held 3rd weekend in August; Health Fair Friday before powwow; active Elder's group; annual Education Banquet; Fall Festival; operates tribal school & library. *Publication*: GTB News, monthly newsletter. Michigan Field Office.

HANNAHVILLE INDIAN COMMUNITY
N14911 Hannahville B-1 Rd. • Wilson, MI 49896
(906) 466-2342 Fax 466-2933; Website: www.hannahville.net
Kenneth Meshigaud, Chairperson
Elaine Meshigaud, Vice Chairperson
Tammy Meshigaud, Secretary; Lisa Little, Treasurer
Councilmembers: Earl Meshigaud, Robin Halfaday, John Meshigaud,
 D. Joe Sagataw, Charlotte Harris, Jeremy Brunette, Tonto Wandahsega
 Jesse Wandahsega, Amanda Hess, Noreena Meshigaud-Dwyer
 Lois Tovar (1st Alt.), Richard Meshigaud (2nd At.)
Susie Meshigaud, Cultural Committee Chair & HHS Director
Anna Larson, Higher Education Director
Brad Madalinski, Gaming Commission Chairperson (723-2046)
Tribe: Potawatomi. *Enrolled members*: 670. *In residence*: 395. *Area*: 2,850 acres. *Resources*: Hannahville Potawatomi Virtual Museum; Hannahville Indian School (website: www.hannahvilleschool.net); Potawatomi Heritage Center for Culture, Language & History www.potawatomilanguage.org) Earl Meshigaud, Director. *Programs*: Environmental; Adult Education; FACE; Public School Academy. *Attractions*: Island Resort & Casino (800-682-6040; www.islandresortandcasino.com); Annual Great Lakes Area Traditional Pow Wow in June. *Publication*: Hannahville Happenings, tribal newsletter. Michigan Field Office.

NOTTAWASEPPI HURON BAND OF POTAWATOMI
Pine Creek Indian Reservation, 2221 - 1 1/2 Mile Rd. • Fulton, MI 49052
(269) 729-5151 Fax 729-5920
Website: www.nhbpi.com; E-mail: jhenckel@nhbpi.com
Jamie Stuck, Chairperson; E-mail: jstuck@nhbpi.com
Dorie Rios, Vice Chairperson; E-mail: dorier@nhbpi.com
Christine Lanning, Secretary; E-mail: clanning@nhbpi.com
Jeff Chivis, Treasurer; E-mail: jeff.chivis@nhbpi.com
Robyn Burlingham, Tribal Council/FDA Coordinator
 E-mail: rburlingham@nhbpi.com
Dane Turner, Chief Executive Officer (704-8493)
 E-mail: dane.turner@nhbpi.com
Homer A. Mandoka, Sergeant-at-Arms; E-mail: hmandoka@nhbpi.com
Rosalind Johnston, Health & Human Services Direector (704-8344)
Gregory Smith, Chief Justice
Melissa L. Pope, Chief Judge (729-5151)
Holly L. Curtis, Tribal Court Administrator (704-8395)
 E-mail: fjacko@nhbpi.com
Bill Brooks, Chief Legal Officer (704-8372); E-mail: bbrooks@nhbpi.com
Heather Chapman, Senior Staff Attorney (704-8429)
 E-mail: hchapman@nhbpi.com
Dan Green, Chief Planning Officer; E-mail: dgreen@nhbpi.com
Fred Jacko, Jr., CHPO Director & Tribal Historic Preservation
 E-mail: fjacko@nhbpi.com(704-8407)
Mon-ee Zapata, Cultural Specialist (704-8353)
 E-mail: mzapata@nhbpi.com
Michelle Simms, EPS Education Specialist (704-8357)
 E-mail: michelle.simms@nhbpi.com
Andrea Rainer, Higher Education Specialist (704-8356)
 E-mail: arainer@nhbpi.com
John Rodwan, Environmental Director; E-mail: jrodwan@nhbpi.com
Judi Henckel, Director of Communications & PR (704-8361)
 E-mail: jhenckel@nhbpi.com
Tribe: Potawatomi. *In residence*: 600. *Area*: 120 acres located in Calhoun County's Athens Township. *Resources*: Tribal Community Outreach Center. *Programs*: Health & Human Services; Education; Enrollment; Housing; Language Restoration Project; Environmental; Human Resources; Elders; Potawatomi Language & Culture (www.neaseno.org); Gaming Commission.

Attractions: FireKeepers Hotel & Casino. *Publication*: Turtle Press, newsletter. Michigan Field Office.

KEWEENAW BAY INDIAN COMMUNITY
L'Anse Reservation, 16429 Beartown Rd. • Baraga, MI 49908
(906) 353-6623 Fax 353-7540; Website: www.kbic-nsn.gov
Warren Chris Swartz, Jr., President
Jennifer Misegan, Vice President
Susan J. LaFernier, Secretary
Toni J. Minton, Assistant Secretary
Doreen G. Blaker, Treasurer
Larry J. Denomie III, Chief Executive Officer
Councilmembers: Mike LaFernier, Sr., Robert R.D. Curtis, Jr.,
 Gary F. Loonsfoot, Jr., Rodney Loonsfoot, Fred Dakota,
 Randall Haataja, Elizabeth D. Mayo
 Lynn Haataja, Gaming Commission Executive Director (353-4225)
 Gary Loonsfoot, Jr., Tribal Historic Preservation Officer &
 Language Coordinator; E-mail: gloonsfoot@kbic-nsn.gov
Mary Bergerson, Lbrary Director (353-8163)
Tribe: Lake Superior Band of Chippewa Indians (Keewenah Bay, L'Anse & Ontonagan Bands.) *In residence*: 950. *Area*: 10,000 acres. *Programs*: Culture Committee; Employment; Education; Health & Human Service. *Resources*: Donald A. LaPointe Health & Education Center; Ojibwa Community College (www.kbocc.org); Family Learning Center; Ojibwa Community Library. *Attractions*: Ojibwa Casino Resort, Baraga; Big Bucks Bingo; Ojibwa Casino, Marquette; annual Maawanji'ding Powwow. *Publication*: Wiikwedong Dazhi-Ojibwe, monthly tribal newsletter (www.newsletter@kbic-nsn.gov). Michigan Field Office.

LAC VIEUX DESERT BAND OF LAKE SUPERIOR CHIPPEWA INDIANS
P.O. Box 249 • Watersmeet, MI 49969
(906) 358-4577 Fax 358-4785; Website: www.lvdtribal.com
James Williams, Jr., Chairperson
Giiwegiizhigookway Martin, Vice Chairperson
Susan McGeshick, Treasurer; Gertrude McGeshick, Secretary
Councilmembers: Henry Smith, Michelle Hazen, Mitchell McGeshick
 Michael Hazen, Jr., Tyrone McGeshick
 Richard Williams, Education Director; Mark Esqueda, Tribal Judge
 Dee Dee McGeshick, Social Services Director (358-4940)
Tribe: Chippewa (Lac Vieux Desert Band). *Area*: 1,269 acres. *Resources*: Health Clinic; Museum; Library. *Attraction*: Lac Vieux Desert Resort & Casino Complex; annual Powwow in August. Michigan Field Office.

LITTLE RIVER BAND OF OTTAWA INDIANS
2608 Government Center Dr. • Manistee, MI 49660
(888) 723-8288; (231) 723-8288 Fax 398-2961
Website https://lrboi-nsn.gov/; E-mail: comments@lrboi-nsn.gov
Larry Romanelli, Tribal Ogema; E-mail: lromanelli@lrboi-nsn.gov
Mary Thomas, Executive Assistant (398-6824)
Joseph Riley II, Speaker; (398-6854) E-mail: jriley@lrboi-nsn.gov
Sandy Lewis, Recorder (398-6869) E-mail: smlewis@lrboi-nsn.gov
Councilmembers: Ron Pete, Jamie Friedel, Ron Wittenberg, Diane Lonn,
 Frankie Medacco, Shannon Crampton, Gary DiPiazza
 Angela Eagle, Public Affairs Officer (398-6840)
 E-mail: aeagle@lrboi-nsn.gov
Don MacDonald, Tribal Health Clinic Director
Yvonne Parsons, Education Program Coordinator
 E-mail: yparsons@lrboi-nsn.gov
Jonnie "Jay" Sam II, Historic Preservation Director (398-6893)
Dave Corey, Gaming Commissioner
Deb Miller, Court Administrator; E-mail: dmiller@lrboi-nsn.gov
Tribe: Ottawa. *Commissions*: Gaming; Health. *Departments*: Education; Grants; Historic Preservation; Natural Resources; Planning; Public Affairs; Public Safety; Utility. *Resources*: Health Clinic; Justice Center *Attractions*: Little River Casino. *Publication*: Rapid River News, weekly; Little River Currents, tribal newsletter. Michigan Field Office.

LITTLE TRAVERSE BAY BANDS OF ODAWA INDIANS
7500 Odawa Circle • Harbor Springs, MI 49740
(866) 652-5822; (231) 242-1418 Fax 242-1411
Website: www.ltbbodawa-nsn.gov
E-mail: tribalcouncil@ltbbodawa-nsn.gov
Regina Gasco Bentley, Chairperson (838-2081)
 E-mail: tribalchair@ltbbodawa-nsn.gov
Stella Kay, Vice Chairperson
Marci R. Reyes, Treasurer; Julie Shananaquet, Secretary
Aaron Otto, Legislative Leader; E-mail: aotto@ltbbodawa-nsn.gov
Alan Proctor, Interim Tribal Administrator (242-1421)
 E-mail: aproctor@ltbbodawa-nsn.gov
Councilmembers: Frank Bernard, Beatrice A. Law, David Harrington,
 Emily Proctor, Dexter McNamara, Michael J. Naganashe

Annette VandeCar, Communications Coordinator (242-1427)
James Bransky, General Counsel (242-1407)
Sharon Sierzputowski, Health Director (242-1610)
Tribe: Odawa. *Area*: 336 sq. miles. *Programs*: Language, Housing, Health, Education, Natural Resources; Enrollment; Technology Training; Gaming; Economic Development. *Resources*: Cultural Library. *Attractions*: Odawa Casino Resort in Petoskey, Michigan; annual Odawa Homecoming Powwow in August. *Publication*: Odawa Trails, monthly newsletter. Michigan Field Office.

MATCH-E-BE-NASH-SHE-WISH BAND OF POTTAWATOMI INDIANS

Gun lake Tribe, 2872 Mission Dr. • Dorr, MI 49344
(269) 397-1780 Fax 397-1781; Website: www.mbpi.org
Scott Sprague (Bradley District), Chairperson
Ed Pigeon (Salem District), Vice Chairperson
Jeff Martin (Salem District), Secretary
Bob Peters (Bradley District), Treasurer
Councilmembers-At-Large: Jodie Palmer, Phyllis Davis, Jennie Pearl Heeren
John Shagonaby, Chief Executive Officer
P.O. Box 90, Dorr, MI 49323 (681-0498)
Dawn Krauss, Tribal Administrator (681-9510)
Jennie Pearl Heeren, Education Director
Kelly Wesaw, Health & Human Services Director
Michael Pigeon, Language/Culture Coordinator (397-1660)
Kara Wilson, Tribal Librarian
Melissa Brown, Housing Coordinator
Elizabeth Binoniemi-Smith, Environmental Director
Amanda Sprague, Tribal Court Administrator (397-1630)
Michael D. Petoskey, Tribal Court Chief Judge (397-1630)
Tribe: Pottawatomi. *Area*: 147 acres. *Programs*: Language & Culture; Health & Human Services; Education; Finance; Enrollment; Environmental. *Attraction*: Gun Lake Casino in Bradley, Mich. Michigan Field Office.

POKAGON BAND OF POTAWATOMI INDIANS

58620 Sink Rd., Box 180 • Dowagiac, MI 49047
(800) 517-0777; (269) 782-6323 Fax 782-9625
Website: www.pokagonband-nsn.gov
John Warren, Chairperson; E-mail: john.warren@pokagonband-nsn.gov
Robert Moody, Jr., Vice Chair; E-mail: bob.moody@pokagonband-nsn.gov
Mark Parrish, Secretary; Eugene Magnuson, Treasurer
Councilmembers: Roger Rader, Matt Wesaw, Steve Winchester, Becky Price, Alex Wesaw, Andy Jackson, Judy Winchester (Elders Rep.)
Elders council: Stanley Morseau, Chairperson; Maxine Margiotta, Vice Chair, Judy Augusta, Secretary; Clarence White, Treasurer
Catherine Ford, Member-At-Large.
Jason M. Wesaw, Government Manager (782-8998)
E-mail: jason.m.wesaw@pokagonband-nsn.gov
Anita Grivins, Finance Director (462-4206)
E-mail: anita.grivins@pokagonband-nsn.gov
Paige Risser, Director of Communications (462-4283)
E-mail: paige.risser@pokagonband-nsn.gov
Sam Morseau, Education Director (782-0887)
E-mail: sam.morseau@pokagonband-nsn.gov
Mark Pompey, MSW, Director of Social Services (462-4277)
E-mail: mark.pompey@pokagonband-nsn.gov
Marcus Winchester, Director of Language & Culture (462-4224)
E-mail: marcus.winchester@pokagonband-nsn.gov
Samantha R. Smith, Trial Librarian (478-4841)
E-mail: Samantha.smith@pokagonband-nsn.gov
Tribe: Potawatomi. *Enrolled members*: 3,634. *Resources*: Wellness Center; Community Center; Council Lodge; Elders Hall; Tribal Library. *Programs*: Social Services; Health Services; Education; Department of Language & Culture; Natural Resources; Information Technology; Housing & Facilities; Human Resources; Historic Preservation. *Attractions*: Four Winds Casino Resort; annual powwow; Campgrounds. *Publication*: Pokegnek Yajdanawa - "The Pakogan's Tell It" - Tribal Newsletter. Head Start. Michigan Field Office.

SAGINAW CHIPPEWA INDIAN TRIBE

Isabella Reservation, 7070 E. Broadway • Mount Pleasant, MI 48858
(989) 775-4000 Fax 775-4131; Website: www.sagchip.org
Frank Cloutier, Chief (District 3)
Brent Jackson, Sub-Chief (District 1)
Gayle Ruhl, Treasurer (District 1)
Michelle Colwell, Secretary (District 1)
Ronnie Ekdahl, Sergeant-at-Arms (Dstrict 1)
Diana Quigno-Grundahl, Chaplain (District 1)
District 1 Council Reps.: Lindy Hunt, Candace Benzinger, Kenny Sprague, Amanda Oldman, Tim Davis
District 2 Rep.: Ronald Nelson
District 3 Rep.: Frank Cloutier, At-Large
Erik Rodriguez, Interim Public Relations Director
E-mail: erodriguez@sagchip.org

Marcella Hadden, Public Relations Manager
E-mail: mahadden@sagchip.org
Charmaine Shawana, Tribal Historic Preservation Officer
Shannon Martin, Director-Ziibiwing Center; E-mail: smartin@sagchip.org
Clinton Pelcher, Jr., Director of 7th Generation Program
Patrick M. Shannon, Chief Judge
Tribe: Saginaw-Chippewa. *In residence*: 450. *Area*: 1,125 acres. *Resources*: Nimke Clinic; Nimkee Fitness; Elijah Elk Cultural Center; The Ziibiwing Center of Anishinabe Culture & Lifeways (6650 E. Broadway) (775-4750 Fax 775-4770); Saginaw Chippewa Tribal College; Native Direct (online products); Migizi Economic Development Co. (775-4000); Tribal Library. *Programs*: Child & Family Services; Education; Health; Housing; Anishinabe Language Revitalization; Human Resources; Information Technology; 7th Generation Program/Elijah Elk Cultural Center. *Attractions*: Soaring Eagle Casino & Resort & Saganing Eagles Landing Casino (888) 7-EAGLE-7; Eagle Bay Marina (846-6065); The Green Suites (Golf); annual Powwow; Annual Great Lakes All Anishnabe Elders Invitational Golf Tournament. *Publication*: Tribal Observer, monthly newspaper. Michigan Field Office.

SAULT STE. MARIE TRIBE OF CHIPPEWA INDIANS

523 Ashmun St., Sault Ste. Marie, MI 49783
(800) 793-0660; (906) 635-6050 Fax 635-4969
Website: www.saulttribe.com
Aaron A. Payment, Chairperson
E-mail: aaronpayment@saulttribe.net
Cathy Abramson, Unit I Director (322-3823)
Dennis McKelvie, Unit I Director, Treasurer (643-6981)
E-mail: dmckelvie@saulttribe.net
Kimberly Gravelle, Unit I Director (440-4407)
DJ Hoffman, Unit I Director (440-1334)
E-mail: djhoffman@saulttribe.net
Jennifer McLeod, Unit I Director (440-9762)
E-mail: jmcleod@saulttribe.net
Catherine Hollowell, Unit II Director (430-5551)
E-mail: chollowell@saulttribe.net
Lana Causley, Unit II Director (484-2954)
E-mail: lcausley@saulttribe.net
Keith Massaway, Director, Unit III (643-6981)
E-mail: kmassaway@saulttribe.net
Bridgett Sorenson, Unit III Director, Secretary (430-0536)
E-mail: bsorenson@saulttribe.net
Denise Chase, Unit IV Director, Vice Chairperson (341-6783)
E-mail: dchase@saulttribe.net
Darcy Morrow, Unit IV Director (203-6699)
E-mail: dmorrow@saulttribe.net
Rita Glyptis, Unit V Director (450-7299)
Angeline Boulley, Education Director (635-6050)
Jackie Minton, Cultural Bldgs. Coordinator
E-mail: jminton@saulttribe.net
Jocelyn K. Fabry, Chief Judge (635-4963)
Tribe: Sault Ste. Marie Chippewa. *Reservations served*: St. Ignace, Manistique, Munising, Michigan. *Enrolled members*: 40,000. *In residence*: 2,500. *Area*: 242 acres. *Resources*: Michigan Indian Press; Health & Human Services Building; JKL Bahweting School. *Programs*: Community & Family Services; Elderly; Language; Culture; Education; Early Childhood; Youth Education & Activities; Health; Employment; Housing; Natural Resources; Recreation; Enrollment. *Attractions*: Kewadin Casinos in Sault Ste. Marie, St. Ignace, Manistique, Christmas & Hessel, MI.; Greektown Casino in Detroit, MI; Tribal Powwows (two each summer, July 4th (Sault Ste. Marie), and the first week in August (St. Ignace.) *Publication*: "Win Awenwen Nisasotowen," Sault Tribe Newspaper. Michigan Field Office.

MINNESOTA

BOIS FORTE BAND OF OJIBWE

Bois Forte Reservation, 5344 Lakeshore Dr.
P.O. Box 16 • Nett Lake, MN 55772
(800) 221-8129; (218) 757-3261 Fax 757-3312
Vermillion office: 1610 Farm Rd. South • Tower, MN 55790
(218) 753-4905 Fax 753-4055; Website: www.boisforte.com
Cathy Chavers, Chairperson; E-mail: cchavers@boisforte-nsn.gov
David Morrison, Sr., Secretary-Treasurer
E-mail: david.morrison@boisforte-nsn.gov
Travis Morrison, District I Rep. E-mail: travis.morrison@boisforte-nsn.gov
Brandon Benner, District I Rep. E-mail: bbenner@boisforte-nsn.gov
Ray Toutloff, District II Representative; E-mail: ray.toutloff@boisforte-nsn.gov
Donna Hoffer, Health & Human Services Director
E-mail: donna.hoffer@boisforte-nsn.gov
Billie Mason, Commissioner of Education; E-mail: bmason@boisforte-nsn.gov
Wendy L. Thompson, Judicial Services Director (757-3462)

Louise Isham, Editor-Bois Forte News; E-mail lisham@boisforte-nsn.gov
Terri Drift-Hill, Director of Communications; E-mail: thill@boisforte-nsn.gov
Bev Miller, Executive Director-Heritage Museum Program (753-6017)
Tribe: Ojibwe (Chippewa-Deer Creek). *In residence*: 1,250. *Area*: 41,750 acres. *Programs*: Health; Education & Training; Head Start; Gaming; Elders; Human Services; Business Development. *Resources*: Heritage Center (753-6017 Fax 753-6026). *Attractions*: Dakota Futures, Inc.; Fortune Bay Resort Casino; annual Sah-Gii-Bah-Gah Powwow in June; Lake Vermillion Powwow in June. *Publication*: Bois Forte News. A component reservation of the Minnesota Chippewa Tribe. Minneapolis Office.

BAND OF LAKE SUPERIOR CHIPPEWA
Fond du Lac Reservation, 1720 Big Lake Rd. • Cloquet, MN 55720
(218) 879-4593 Fax 879-4146; Website: www.fdlrez.com
Kevin DuPuis, Chairperson; E-mail: kevindupuis@fdlrez.com
Ferdinand Martineau, Jr., Secretary/Treasurer
Vanessa L. Northrup, District I Cloquet Representative
Bruce M. Savage, District II Sawyer Representative
Roger M. Smith, Sr., District III Brookston Representative
Gary S. Frazer, Executive Director
Vern Zacher, Tribal College Chairperson
Hon. Suzanne Ojibway Townsen, Chief Judge
Thomas Howes, Natural Resources Program Manager;
 Language Advisory Committee Chairperson
Janis A. Fairbanks, Anishinaabemowin Coordinator
Jeff Savage, Cultural Center & Museum Director (878-7582)
Mike Rabideaux, Education Supt.; Kellie Powless, Librarian
Tribe: Lake Superior (Ojibwe) Chippewa. *In residence*: 1,750. *Area*: 100,000 acres. *Programs*: Community Services; Social Services; Education (878-7242); Human Resources; Natural Resources; Head Start. *Resources*: Cultural Museum (878-7582); Community Center; Library; Tribal College; Fond du Lac Ojibway School (Library); Radio 89.1 WGZS FM. *Attractions*: Black Bear Casino Resort, Fond-De-Luth Casino; Golf Course; Ni-mi-win Powwow; Mash-ka-wisen Pow-Wow. *Publication*: Nahgahchiwanong Dibahjimowinnan, online monthy tribal news-letter. Component Reservation of the Minnesota Chippewa Tribe. Minneapolis Office.

GRAND PORTAGE BAND OF LAKE SUPERIOR CHIPPEWA
Grand Portage Reservation, P.O. Box 428 • Grand Portage, MN 55605
(218) 475-2277 Fax 475-2284; Website: www.maiba.org
Norman DesChampe, Chairperson; E-mail: norman@grandportage.com
John Morrin, Vice Chairperson; April McCormick, Secretary/Treasurer
Janice Marie Spry & Arvid Dahl, *Councilmembers*
Tribe: Ojibwe (Chippewa). *Enrolled members*: 260. *In residence*: 518. *Area*: 43,836 acres located near Lake Superior, adjacent to the Canadian border. *Resources*: National Monument Heritage Center; Health Clinic; Elderly Nutrition Center. *Programs*: Community Services; Gaming; Food Distribution; Education; Health & Human Services; Elderly; Head Start. *Attractions*: Grand Portage National Monument; Grand Portage Heritage Centeer; Grand Portage Lodge & Casino, Website:www.grandportage.com; Grand Portage Trading Post. Component reservation of Minnesota Ojibwe (Chippewa) Tribe. Minneapolis Office.

LEECH LAKE BAND OF OJIBWE
Leech Lake Reservation, 6530 U.S. Hwy. #2 NW
190 Sailstar Dr. NW • Cass Lake, MN 56633
(800) 442-3909; (218) 335-8200 Fax 335-8309
Website: www.llojibwe.org
Faron Jackson, Sr., Chairperson
Arthur LaRose, Secretary/Treasurer
Robert Aitken, Executive Director
Penny DeVault, District I Rep; Steve White, District II Rep.
Leroy Staples Fairbanks III, District III Rep.
Paul W. Day, Chief Judge
Tribe: Minnesota Ojibwe (Mississippi & Pillanger Bands.) *In residence*: 5,200. *Area*: 27,760 acres. *Programs*: Education; Health & Human Services; Employment & Training; Housing; Legal Services (website: www.alslegal.org); Human Resources, Economic Development, Head Start. *Resources*: Chief Bug-O-Nay-Ge-Shig School; Leech Lake Tribal College; *Attractions*: Palace Casino & Bingo; White Oak Casino; Northern Lights Casino; Bingo; five annual Powwows: Spring, Fourth of July, Labor Day, Veterans Day, and Winter. *Publications*: DeBahJiMon, monthly newspaper; Leech Lake Reservation Fact Sheet. Component reservation of Minnesota Chippewa Tribe. Minneapolis Office.

LOWER SIOUX INDIAN COMMUNITY
39527 Reservation Hwy. 1, P.O. Box 308 • Morton, MN 56270
(507) 697-6185 Fax 697-8617; Website: www.lowersioux.com
Brian Pendleton, President; E-mail: brian.pendleton@lowersioux.com
Robert Larsen, Vice President; E-mail: robert.larsen@lowersioux.com
Grace Goldtooth, Treasurer; E-mail: grace.goldtooth@lowersioux.com

Earl Pendleton, Secretary; E-mail: earl.pendleton@lowersioux.com
Gary Prescott, Tribal Secretary; E-mail: gary.prescott@lowersioux.com
Darin Prescott, Director of Community Health & Social Services & Clinic CEO
 E-mail: darin.prescott@lowersioux.com
Tribe: Mdewakanton Sioux. *Enrolled members*: 930. *In residence*: 982. *Area*: 1,743 acres. *Programs*: Health, Chemical Dependency & Mental Health; Economic Development, Finance, Enrollment, Employment, Housing, Environment, Recreation, Mental Health, Historic Preservation, Social Services. *Attractions*: Jackpot Junction Casino Hotel; Dacotah Ridge Golf Course; annual Lower Sioux Wacipi (powwow). *Publication*: Witechi Wi - Hard Moon, monthly tribal newsletter. Midwest Regional Office.

MILLE LACS BAND OF OJIBWE
43408 Oodena Dr. • Onamia, MN 56359
(320) 532-4181 Fax 532-7505; Website: www.millelacsojibwe.org
Melanie Benjamin, Chief Executive (532-7486)
Carolyn Shaw-Beaulieu, Secretary/Treasurer
Sandra L. Blake, District I Representative
David "Niib" Aubid, District II Representative
Harry Davis, District III Representatives
Todd Matha, Solicitor General
Legislative Staff: Stacey Thunder, Legislative Counsel;
Caryn Day, Legislative Communications Liaison;
Katie Draper, Director of Government Affairs (515-0846)
 E-mail: katie.draper@millelacsband.com
Joseph Nayquonabe, Jr., Commissioner of Corporate Affairs
Shelly Diaz, Commissioner of Administration (532-7480)
Todd Matha, Solicitor General
Rick St. Germaine, Commissioner of Education (630-0674)
Jocelyn Shingobe, Executive Director, Dept. of Education
Rebecca St. Germaine, Commissioner of Health & Human Services
Bradley Harrington, Commissioner of Natural Resources (532-7439)
John Gerdener, Commissioner of Finance
Percy Benjamin, Commissioner of Community Development (532-7508)
Tribe: Ojibwe (Chippewa). *Enrolled members*: 4,000+. *In residence*: 950. *Area*: 61,000 acres in Mille Lacs, Pine, Crow Wing, and Atkin counties. About 3,500 acres are held in trust for the Bands, and the Band owns about 3,000 acres. *Resources*: Mille Lacs Indian Museum; Mille Lacs Corporate Ventures. *Runs two schools*: Nay Ah Shing Abinoojiiyag School, grades K-4; and The Nay Ah Shing Upper School, grades 5-12; Minisinaakwaang Leadership Academy; Pine Grove Leadership Academy; Boys & Girls Club; Library located in the Nay Ah Shing Upper School. *Programs*: Education; Health & Human Services; Economic Development; Natural Resources; Housing; Family Violence Prevention; Head Start; Scholarships; Community Youth Services; Corporate Commission. *Attractions*: Grand Casino Mille Lacs, Grand Casino Hinckley; Annual Grand Celebration Powwow & Rodeo in Hinckley; Annual Powwow in Mille Lacs. *Publications*: Ojibwe Inaajimowin, monthly band newspaper; The Woodland Voice, quarterly newsletter; Mille Lacs Progress, bi-annual newspaper; Baswewe "Echo", songbook & cassette - 25 original songs in Ojibwe. A component reservation of Minnesota Ojibwe Tribe; publications. Minneapolis Office.

MINNESOTA CHIPPEWA TRIBE
P.O. Box 217 • Cass Lake, MN 56633
(218) 335-8581 Fax 335-8496
Website: www.mnchippewatribe.org; E-mail: jbruce@mnchippewatribe.org
Kevin R. Dupuis, President (Fond du Lac Reservation Chairperson)()
Ferdinand W. Martineau, Jr., Vice President
 (Fond du Lac Reservation Secretary/Treasurer)
Melanie Benjamin, Secretary (Mille Lacs Reservation Chief Executive)
David C. Morrison, Treasurer (Bois Forte Reservation Secretary/Treasurer)
Executive Committee:
Gary Frazer, Executive Director; E-mail: gfrazer@mnchippewatribe.org
Norman W. Deschampe (Grand Portage Reservation Chairperson)
Dennis. B. Morrison (Grand Portage), Ferdinand Narineau, Jr. (Fond du Lac),
 Carolyn M. Shaw-Beaulieu (Mille Lacs), Kevin Leecy (Bois Forte),
 Faron Jackson, Sr. (Leech Lake), Arthur LaRose (Leech Lake),
 Terrance Tibbetts (White Earth), Tara Mason (White Earth)
Joel Smith, Director of Administration; E-mail: jsmith@mnchippewatribe.org
Tribe: Chippewa (Ojibwe/Anishnabe). *Reservations*: Nett Lake, Fond du Lac, Grand Portage, Leech Lake, Mille Lacs, & White Earth. Minneapolis Office.

PRAIRIE ISLAND INDIAN COMMUNITY
5636 Sturgeon Lake Rd. • Welch, MN 55089
(800) 554-5473; (651) 385-4124 Fax 385-4180
Website: www.prairieisland.org
Shelley Buck, President; E-mail: rjohnson@piic.org
Lucy Taylor, Vice President; E-mail: ltaylor@piic.org
Edward Buck, Secretary; Johnny Johnson, Treasurer
Audrey Bennett, Asst. Secretary/Treasurer
Marv Ray, Tribal Administrator

Paul Dressen, Education Director (385-4153)
 E-mail: paul.dressen@piic.org
Mary Wells, CHS Administrator (385-4187); E-mail: mary.wells@piic.org
Blake Johnson, Government Relations; E-mail: blake.johnson@piic.org
Clay Tix, Gaming Executive Director; E-mail: clay.tix@piic.org
B.J. Jones, Chief Judge (385-4161)
Jessie Seim, General Counsel; E-mail: jessie.seim@piic.org
Tribe: Mdewakanton Sioux. *In residence*: 135. *Area*: 534 acres located off Highway 61 & Hwy. 316 in Welch. *Programs*: Family Services, Employment, Wellness, Economic Development, Education, Enrollment, Gaming, Veterans Memorial Buffalo Project. *Resources*: Wellness Center; Prairie Island Learning Center. *Attractions*: Treasure Island Resort & Casino; summer & winter Prairie Island Powwows. *Publication*: Bimonthly newsletter; book, "Transformation of an Island" - historical perspective of the community. Midwest Regional Office.

RED LAKE BAND OF OJIBWE INDIANS

24200 Council St., P.O. Box 550 • Red Lake, MN 56671
(866) 311-9758; (218) 679-3341 Fax 679-3378
Website: www.redlakenation.org
Darrell G. Seki, Sr., Chairperson
Donald Cook, Secretary; Annette Johnson, Treasurer
Gary Nelson & Glenda Martin, Ponemah Reps
Allen Pemberton & Julius Thunder, Redby Reps
Robert Smith & Roman Stately, Red Lake Reps
Robert Reynolds & Richard Barrett, Little Rock Reps
Hereditary Chiefs: Gerald Spears, Greeting Spear, Alexander Gillepsie, Jr.
 Henry Sutton, George W. King & James Loud
Tribe: Red Lake Band of Ojibwe (Chippewa). *Enrolled members*: 11,425. *In residence*: 2,850. *Area*: 820,000 acres located along lower Red Lake, 30 miles north of Bemidji, Minnesota. *Programs*: Social Service, Education, Health, Economic Development, Head Start. *Resources*: Red Lake Elementary & High Schools. *Attraction*: Three casinos - Seven Clans Casino in Red Lake, Thief River Falls, Warroad, MN. *Publication*: Red Lake Net News. Red Lake Agency.

SHAKOPEE MDEWAKANTON SIOUX (DAKOTA) COMMUNITY

2330 Sioux Trail, NW • Prior Lake, MN 55372
(952) 445-8900 Fax 445-8906
Website: www.shakopeedakota.org; E-mail: info@shakopeedakota.org
Charlie Vig, Chairperson; E-mail: charlie.vig@shakopeedakota.org
Keith B. Anderson, Vice Chairperson
 E-mail: keith.anderson@shakopeedakota.org
Freedom Brewer, Secretary-Treasurer
 E-mail: freedom.brewer@shakopeedakota.org
Bill Rudnicki, Tribal Administrator
 E-mail: bill.rudnicki@shakopeedakota.org
James Lien, Health Administrator
 E-mail: james.lien@shakopeedakota.org
Joanna Bryant, Wellness Administrator (233-2961)
 E-mail: joanna.bryant@shakopeedakota.org
Nancy Martin, Family & Children's Services (496-6192)
 E-mail: nancy.martin@shakopeedakota.org
Leonard Wabasha, Cultural Resources Director
 E-mail: culturalresources@shakopeedakota.org
Beth Tepper, Education Director
 E-mail: beth.tepper@shakopeedakota.org
Deborah Peterson, Librarian (403-5550)
 E-mail: Deborah.peterson@shakopeedakota.org
Tribe: Mdewakanton Sioux. *In residence*: 110. *Area*: 3,361 acres. *Programs*: Family & Children's Services, Education, Health, Cultural, Land & Natural Resources. *Resources*: Library; Cultural Center planned. *Attractions*: Mystic Lake Casino Hotel; Little Six Casino; The Meadows at Mystic Lake; Dakotah! Sport & Fitness; Playworks; Dakotah Meadows RV Park; Mystic Lake Mall of America Store; annual Wacipi Powwow in August. *Publication*: Newsletter. Midwest Regional Office.

UPPER SIOUX COMMUNITY OF MINNESOTA

Pezihutazizi Oyate, P.O. Box 147 • Granite Falls, MN 56241
(320) 564-2360 Fax 564-3264
Website: www.uppersiouxcommunity-nsn.gov
Kevin Jensvold, Chairperson; Marisa Anywaush, Vice Chairperson
Tremayne Blue, Secretary; Sharon Odegard, Treasurer
Sharon Pazi Zea, Member-at-Large
Candice Hamilton, Health Services Director
Jared Wagner, Environmental Specialist (564-3853)
Laurie Blue-Pooler, Tribal Programs Director
Jim Hiedeman, Social Services Director; Lenor Scheffler, Tribal Judge
Tribe: Dakota. *Enrolled members*: 485. *In residence*: 225. *Area*: 1,440 acres. *Programs*: Health, Social Services; Telecommunication Project. *Resources*: Dakota Wicohan, a cultural resource center. *Attractions*: Prairie's Edge Casino Resort; Prairie View RV Park & Campground. *Publication*: Dakota Tiwahe. Midwest Regional Office.

WHITE EARTH NATION

P.O. Box 418 • White Earth, MN 56591
(218) 983-3285 Fax 983-3641; Website: www.whiteearth.com
Terrence "Terry" Tibbetts, Chairperson
Tara Mason, Secretary-Treasurer
Steven "Punky" Clark, District I Representative
Kathy Goodwin, District II Representative
Eugene "Umsey" Tibbetts, District III Representative
Community council contacts:
 White Earth (Ogema) Charles Hanks, Jr., Chair (983-4159)
 Pine Point (Ponsford) Mike Swan, Chair (573-2154)
 Rice Lake (Bagley); George Auginaush, Chair (694-2795)
 Elbow Lake (Waubun) Pat Cobb, Chair (473-2216)
 Mahnomen (MN) Mary Gagnon, Chair (935-2588)
 Naytahwaush (MN) Deanne Fox, Secretary
 Calloway (MN) Terri Boyer, Vice Chair (375-2951)
 Cass Lake (MN) Joe Holstein (335-8572)
 Iron Range (Grand Rapids) Al Donnell (256-8713)
 Urban-Minneapolis/St. Paul Area, Bonni Boudreau (952) 594-0403)
 Joan LaVoy, Education Director (983-3285)
 E-mail: joan.lavoy@whiteearth.com
 Pat Butler, Health Director (983-3286)
 Christie Haverkamp, Tribal Gaming Manager (935-2148)
 E-mail: christieh@whiteearth.com
Tribe: Ojibwe (Chippewa). *Enrolled members*: 28,000. *Area*: 27,560 acres. *Programs*: Education, Health, Housing, Human Resources, Human Services, Natural Resources, Public Safety, Child Care, Public Works, Head Start. *Resources*: Pine Point IHS Clinic (Ponsford, MN); White Earth IHS Clinic (Ogema, MN); White Earth Community College. *Attractions*: Shooting Star Casino in Mahnomen, Minnesota; annual White Earth Celebration & Powwow in June. *Publication*: "Anishinaabeg Today," newsletter; Pine Point News; Moccasin Telegrah Online Newsletter. Member of the six reservation Minnesota Chippewa Tribe. Minneapolis Office.

MISSISSIPPI

MISSISSIPPI BAND OF CHOCTAW INDIANS

101 Industrial Rd. • Choctaw, MS 39350
(601) 656-5251 Fax 656-1992
Website: www.choctaw.org; E-mail: info@choctaw.org
Phyllis J. Anderson, Tribal Chief (Red Water)
Hilda Nickey, Vice Chief (Conehatta)
Richard Isaac, Secretary/Treasurer (Red Water)
Berdie Steve, Committee System Coordinator (Bogue Homa)
Lola Parkerson, Education (Pearl River)
Davita McClelland, Congressional & Governmental Affairs (Bogue Chitto)
Councilmembers: (17 members in eight communities)
Bogue Chitto: Sammy Clemmons, Jr., Roderick Bell, Davita McClelland
Conchatta: Randy Anderson, Tarina Anderson
Crystal Ridge: Chris Eaves
Pearl River: Lola Parkerson, Deborah Martin, Barry McMillan
Red Water: Sharon Johnson
Standing Pine: Loriann Ahshapanek, Dorothy Wilson
Tucker: Wilma Simpson-McMillan (Tucker); Dorothy Wilson (Tucker)
Tribe: Mississippi Band of Choctaws. *Membership*: 10,000. *In residence*: 5,500. *Area*: 35,000 acres located in nine east central Mississippi counties centering on eight distinct Indian communities. *Programs*: Education - operates six grammar schools, a middle school, and a high school; Adult Education Program; Head Start; Health Care - tribe manages a 43 bed hospital; Choctaw Housing Authority - manages over 500 housing units; Language; Arts & Crafts. Cultural Resources: Chahta Immi Cultural Center; Choctaw Museum & Library. *Economic Resources*: Chahta Enterprise; Choctaw Electronics Enterprise; Choctaw Manufacturing Enterprise; Choctaw Greetings Enterprise; First American Printing & Direct Mail Enterprise; Choctaw Residential Center Enterprise; Choctaw Shopping Enterprise; Choctaw-Creek Technologies; Chata Development Co.; Choctaw Transit Authority. Tribal enterprises employ approximately 1,800 workers and generates over $75 million in annual sales. *Attractions*: Silver Star Hotel & Casino, Golden Moon Hotel & Casino; Dancing Rabbit Golf Club, Geyser Falls Water Theme Park, and Clearwater Keys. Communication: tribe operates local TV station WHTV on Cable 5; annual Choctaw Indian Fair (July); Choctaw Indian Princess. *Publications*: Choctaw Community News, monthly newspaper. Choctaw Agency.

MISSOURI

EASTERN SHAWNEE TRIBE OF OKLAHOMA

127 W. Oneida St., P.O. Box 350 • Seneca, MO 64865
(866) 674-3786; (918) 666-2435 Fax 666-2186
1080 S. Bluejacket Rd. • Wyandotte, OK 74370
(866) 666-3489; (918) 666-5151 Fax 666-3325

Website: https://www.estoo-nsn.gov
Glenna J. Wallace, Chief; Jack Ross, 2nd Chief
Judy Brown, Secretary; Cheryl Barnes, Treasurer
Larry Kropp, 1st Council; Shawn Daugherty, 2nd Council
Wanda Stovall, 3rd Council; Frank Miller, Chief of Staff
Tribe: Eastern Shawnee. *Enrolled members*: 2,950. *In residence*: 400. *Area*: 210 acres located in Missouri & Oklahoma. *Resources*: Bearskin Healthcare & Wellness Center; eastern Shawnee Library; traditional Indian beading classes. *Programs*: Education; Social Services; Aging; Health; Housing; Cultural Preservation; Children & Family Services; Gaming. *Attractions*: Bordertown Casino; Indigo Sky Casino. *Publication*: "Shooting Star," tribal newsletter. Miami Agency.

MONTANA

BLACKFEET NATION
Blackfeet Reservation, 1 Agency Square • Browning, MT 59417
(406) 338-7521 Fax 338-7530
Website: www.blackfeetnation.com; E-mail: btbc@3rivers.net
Harry Barnes, Chairperson; Terry J. Tatsey, Vice Chairperson
Tyson T. Running Wolf, Secretary
Councilmembers: Timothy Davis, Carl D. Kipp, Iliff "Scott" Kipp, Sr., Joe McKay, Roland Kennerly, Jr., Nelse St. Goddard
Tribe: Blackfeet. *Enrolled members*: 15,560. *In residence*: 7,000. *Area*: 1.5 million acres located west of Glacier National Park, south of the Canadian border. *Resources*: Arts & Culture Center; Blackfeet Community College (www.bfcc.edu); Blackfeet National Bank; Piegan Institute (Darrell Robes Kipp, co-founder & director); Blackfeet Nation Store. *Programs*: Head Start. *Attractions*: Lodgepole Gallery & Tipi Village (www.blackfeetculturecamp.com), Museum of the Plains Indian; Annual Blackfeet Medicine Lodge Ceremonial & Sun Dance in July. *Publication*: Tribal Council Reports, bimonthly. Blackfeet Agency.

CROW NATION (APSAALOOKE NATION)
Crow Indian Reservation
Baacheeitche Ave., P.O. Box 129 • Crow Agency, MT 59022
(406) 638-3708 Fax 638-3881; Website: www.crow-nsn.gov
Darrin N. Old Coyote, Chairperson
Carlson Goes Ahead, Vice Chairperson
R. Knute Old Crow, Secretary; Shawn Backbone, Vice Secretary
Dr. Luke Enemy Hunter, Chief Executive Officer
Oliver Half, Chief Operations Officer; E-mail: oliver.half@crow-nsn.gov
Cedric Blackeagle, Senior Policy Advisor
 E-mail: cedric.blackeagle@crow-nsn.gov
Birdena Real Bird, Director of Education (638-3712)
Jacquelyn Stewart, Health & Human Services Director
Channis Whiteman, Director of Economic Development
Calvin Herrera, Natural Resources Director
Eric Birdingound, Speaker of the House
Leroy Not Afraid, Chief Judge
Legislature:
Arrow Creek-Pryor District:
 Lawrence DeCrane, Johnny Demontiney, Bryce Hugs
Black Lodge District:
 Bryson Rogers, Gregory Three Irons, Frank White Clay
Center Lodge-Reno District:
 Eric Birdinground, Shawn Real Bird, Paul J. Hill
Mighty Few-Wyola District:
 Brandon Good Luck, Gordon Real Bird, Jr., Harold Male Bear Stone
Valley of the Chiefs-Lodge Grass District:
 Tyson Gros Ventre, Thomas Yellowtail, Victor C. Nomee
Valley of the Giveaways-Big Horn District:
 Patrick Alden, Eugene Deputy, Paul Spotted Horse
Tribe: Crow. *Enrolled members*: 13,100. *In residence*: 8,243. *Area*: 2.2 million acres located in southeastern Montana in Big Horn County, 15 miles southeast of Hardin, Montana. Occupies a total of 408,444 acres of trust land. *Programs*: Education, Social Services; Gaming; Head Start. *Resources*: Little Bighorn College; Library. *Attractions*: Custer Battlefield National Monument & Museum; Apsaalooke Nights Casino; Bighorn Casino; annual Crow Fair & Rodeo Celebration, 3rd weekend in August; powwow at New Years; Crow Native Days. *Publication*: The Crow Briefs, monthly tribal newsbrief. Crow Central Education Commission, P.O. Box 249 (406) 638-2697. Crow Agency.

CONFEDERATED SALISH & KOOTENAI TRIBES
Flathead Indian Reservation
42487 Complex Blvd., P.O. Box 278 • Pablo, MT 59855
(888) 835-8766; (406) 675-2700 Fax 675-2806
Website: www.cskt.org; E-mail: info@cskt.org
E-mail: csktcouncil@cskt.org
Vernon Finley (Polson), Chairperson

Leonard Twoteeth (Elmo), Vice Chairperson
Troy Felsman (Arlee), Secretary; Anita Matt (Dixon), Treasurer
Councilmembers: Leonard Gray (Hot Springs), Dennis Clairmont (Pablo), Ron Trahan (St. Ignatius), Patty Stevens (St. Ignatius), Shelly Fyant (Arlee), Carole Lankford (Ronan)
Robert McDonald, Communications Director (675-2700 ext. 1222)
 E-mail: robertmc@cskt.org
Tribes: Bitterroot Salish, the Pend d'Oreille & Kootenai. *Enrolled members*: 7,000. *In residence*: 4,500. *Area*: 1.317 million acres, of which more than 790,000 acres are owned & managed by the tribes and its members. *Resources*: The Peoples Center Museum & Gift Shop; Salish & Kootenai College; Two Eagle River School. *Programs*: Education; Cultural Preservation; Health & Wellness; Early Childhood Services; Housing; Environmental Protection; Employment & Job Training; Fish, Wildlife & Recreation; Water Management; Natural Resources; Head Start. *Attractions*: Gray Wolf Peak Casino; Kwataqnuk Resort Casino; 4th of July Celebration in Arlee, & Standing Arrow Powwow in Elmo. *Publications*: Charkoosta News, weekly tribal newspaper; Flathead Nation Good Medicine Newsletter - CSKT-Tribal Health, P.O. Box 880, St. Ignatius, MT 59865 (406) 745-3525 Fax 745-4231. Flathead Agency.

FORT BELKNAP INDIAN COMMUNITY
Fort Belknap Agency, 656 Agency Main St., RR 1 Box 66 • Harlem, MT 59526
(406) 353-2205 Fax 353-4541; Website: www.ftbelknap.org
Mark L. Azure, President (353-8303)
George Horse Capture, Jr., Vice President (353-8472)
Benita Plain Feather, Secretary-Treasurer (353-8304)
Loren "Bum" Stiffarm, Chief Administrative Officer (353-8448)
Tracy R. King, Health Dept. Manager (353-3160)
Elizabeth Beaumont, News Editor (353-2878)
Charlotte Lamebull, Chief Finance Officer
Ina Nez Perce, Environmental Protection Manager
Don Sollars, Chief Judge
Councilmembers: Ronald "Fudd" Stffarm (Mountain Gros Ventre); Franklin "Randy" Perez (Assiniboine-At-Large); David Crasco (Mountain Assiniboine); Gerald "Manny" Healy (River Assiniboine); Curtis Horn (Assiniboine Representative-At-Large); Phillip V. Shortman (Gros Ventre-At-Large); Alvin "Jim" Kennedy (Gros Ventre Representative-At-Large); Patricia "Patty" Quisno (River Gros Ventre)
Tribes: Gros Ventre & Assiniboine. *Enrolled members*: 7,000. *In residence*: 2,500. *Area*: 675,602 acres. Located in north central Montana, 35 miles east of Havre. *Resources*: Head Start Center; Senior Citizens Center; Fort Belknap College (2-year institution of higher education). *Programs*: Health; Education; Social Services; Environmental; Head Start Program - Alma Young, Director (353-2827). *Attractions*: Mid-Winter Fair (February); Milk River Indian Days (3rd weekend of July); Hays X-Mas Powwow; Hays Fair & Radio (July); Hays Powwow (July); Chief Joseph Celebration (October). *Publications*: Fort Belknap News (353-8503); Circle Speaker (environmental newsletter); Hays newsletter (Hays community newsletter). Fort Belknap Agency.

FORT PECK ASSINIBOINE & SIOUX TRIBES
501 Medicine Bear Rd., P.O. Box 1027 • Poplar, MT 59255
(406) 768-2300/5155 Fax 768-5478
Website: www.fortpecktribes.org; E-mail: info@fortpecktribes.net
Floyd Azure, Chairperson; E-mail: fazure@fortpecktribes.net
Charles Headdress, Vice Chair; E-mail: cheaddress@fortpecktribes.net
Jestin Dupree, Sergeant-at-Arms; E-mail: jdupree@fortpecktribes.net
Tribal Executive Board:
 Stacey Summers; Grant Stafne; Terry Rattling Thunder; Lonnie Headdress; Pearl Hopkins; Anthony Shields; Roxanne Gourneau; Thomas Christian; Dana Buckles; Leonard Bighorn Crowbelt; Marva Chapman-Firemoon; Edward Bauer
Tribe: Assiniboine & Sioux. *Enrolled members*: 11,800. *In residence*: 6,000. *Area*: 981,144 acres. Located 40 miles west of the North Dakota border and 50 miles south of the Canadian border north of the Missouri River. *Facilities*: Culture Center & Museum; Fort Peck Community College; Tribal Library. *Programs*: Education; Health; Cultural Resources; Water Resources; Environmental Protection; Economic Development; Human Resources; Head Start. *Media*: 96.9 FM radio. *Publication*: Monthly newsletter. Fort Peck Agency.

NORTHERN CHEYENNE TRIBE
Northern Cheyenne Reservation
P.O. Box 128 • Lame Deer, MT 59043
(406) 477-6284 Fax 477-6210
Website: www.cheyennenation.com
Lawrence Jace Killsback, President
Conrad Fisher, Vice President
Melissa Lonebear, Secretary
Tamara Ontiveros, Treasurer
Leo Killsback, Tribal Report Editor

Ashland District Reps:
Waylon Rogers; E-mail: waylon.rogers@cheyennenation.com
Joe Fox, Jr.; E-mail: joe.fox@cheyennenation.com
Birney District Reps:
Ernest Littlemouth; E-mail: ernest.littlemouth@cheyennenation.com
Busby District Reps:
Dana Eaglefeathers; E-mail: dana.eaglefeathers@cheyennenation.com
Sheldon King; E-mail: Sheldon.king@cheyennenation.com
Lame Deer District Reps:
Merlin Sioux; E-mail: merlin.sioux@cheyennenation.com
Benji Headswift; E-mail: benji.headswift@cheyennenation.com
Vernon Small; E-mail: vernon.small@cheyennenation.com
William Rowland; E-mail: william.rowland@cheyennenation.com
Muddy District Rep:
Debra Charette; E-mail: debra.charette@cheyennenation.com
Hon. Roni Rae Brady, Chief Judge (477-8340 Fax 477-6111)
Tribe: Northern Cheyenne. *Enrolled members*: 10,050. *In residence*: 4,868. *Area*: 444,000 acres. Located in southeastern Montana. *Districts*: General: P.O. Box 628, Lame Deer, MT 59043, Tim Lamewoman, Chair; Ashland: P.O. Box 340, Ashland, MT 59003 (406) 784-2267, Virgil Fisher, Chair; Birney: P.O. Box 845, Lame Deer, MT 59043 (406) 477-6419, Vacant, Chair; Busby: P.O. Box 1087, Lame Deer, MT 59043 (406) 477-4507, Dolly Rockroads, Chair; Lame Deer: P.O. Box 401, Lame Deer, MT 59043 (406) 477-3054, Kristina Quaempts-Redbird, Chair; Muddy: P.O. Box 1306, Lame Deer, MT 59043 (406) 477-8900, Vacant, Chair. *Resources*: Northern Cheyenne Arts & Crafts Center; Tribal school. *Programs*: Welness; Education; Water Quality; Transit; Head Start. *Attractions*: 4th of July Pow Wow; Sand Creek Massacre National Historic Site; Ceremonial Grounds; Education & Cultural Centers. *Publication*: Tribal Report. Northern Cheyenne Agency.

CHIPPEWA-CREE INDIAN TRIBE
Rocky Boy's Reservation, RR1 Box 544 • Box Elder, MT 59521
(406) 395-4478/5705 Fax 395-4497/5702
Website: www.chippewacree.org
Harlan Baker, Chairperson
Ted Whitford, Acting Vice Chairperson
Councilmembers: Joe Demonntiney, Calvin Jilot, Jody LaMere,
Beau Mitchell, Ted Russette, Daryl Wright
Running Wolf-Bitz, Chief Judge
Tribes: Chippewa & Cree. *Enrolled members*: 6,177. *In residence*: 3,500. *Area*: 122,532 acres located in Bear Paw Mountains, north central Montana. *Resources*: Health Center; Stone Child College. *Programs*: Education, Health; Cultural; Social Services; Housing; Natural Resources; Senior Citizens; Water Resources; Head Start. *Attraction*: Bear Paw Casino; Northern Winz Casino; Powwow; Rodeo. *Publication*: Rocky Boy Tribal Newsletter. Rocky Boy's Agency.

NEBRASKA

OMAHA TRIBE
Omaha Reservation, 101 Main St., P.O. Box 368 • Macy, NE 68039
(402) 837-5391 Fax 837-5308; Website: www.omaha-nsn.gov
Mike Wolfe, Chairperson; Orville Cayou, Vice Chairperson
Clifford Wolfe, Jr., Secretary; Alan Harlan, Treasurer
Councilmembers:
Jeff Miller, Jr., Rodney Morris, Jessica Webster-Valentino
Marisa Cummings, Chief of Tribal Operations
E-mail: mcummings@omahatribe.com
Mick Scarmon, Chief Judge (837-4045)
Tribe: Omaha. *Enrolled members*: 5,500. *In residence*: 3,225. *Area*: 29,150 acres located in Nebraska & Iowa. *Resources*: Carl T. Curtis Health Education Center; Wellness Center. *Programs*: Alcohol Abuse; Environmental Protection; Child Welfare; Senior Citizens; Higher Eduation; Employment; Head Start. *Attractions*: Blackbird Bend Casino; Lucky 77 Casino. Winnebago Agency.

PONCA TRIBE OF NEBRASKA
252 Spruce Ave., P.O. Box 288 • Niobrara, NE 68760
(402) 857-3391 Fax 857-3736
Website: www.poncatribe-ne.org; E-mail: info@poncatribe-ne.org
Larry Wright, Jr., Chairperson (402) 540-7122
E-mail: ldwrightjr@gmail.com
Patrick Lamoureux (District 1), Vice Chairperson (712) 899-8563
E-mail: poncapatrick@gmail.com
Candace Bossard (District 4), Secretary (402) 857-3391
James LaPointe (District 3), Treasurer (02) 310-1997
Councilmembers: Phil Wendzillo & Patrick Lamoreux (District 1)
Crystal Howell (District 2) (402) 301-9396
E-mail: crystalhowell27@yahoo.com
Steve Laravie, Sr. (District 3), (402) 309-6151
E-mail: stevelaravie81@yahoo.com

Alex Taylor (District 4) (402) 750-2045
E-mail: alextaylor@gmail.com
Thomas Wright II, Executive Director of Tribal Affairs (371-8834)
E-mail: twright@poncatribe-ne.org
Jacob Olsufka, Director of Finance (734-5275)
E-mail: jolsufka@poncatribe-ne.org
Larry Voegele, CEO Tribal Health Programs (734-5275)
E-mail: lvoegele@poncatribe-ne.org
Pat Eichberger, Director of Education (371-7564)
E-mail: pate@poncatribe-ne.org
Randy Teboe, Clture Director (857-3519)
E-mail: rteboe@poncatribe-ne.org
Tribe: Ponca. *Enrolled members*: 2,500. Located in Nebraska & South Dakota. *Programs*: Culture; Education; Environmental; Health; Human Resources; Social Services; Buffalo. *Facilities*: Tribal Museum & Library; Health & Wellness Center; Ponca Hills Clinic. *Publication*: PTN Newsletter. Winnebago Agency. *Preamble of Ponca Constitution*: "We, the members of the Ponca Tribe of Nebraska, in order to restore, preserve & protect all rights aboriginally held by our people & their descendants, promote peace, prosperity, happiness, and the general welfare of the members of our Tribe and our posterity, to exercise home rule, to assert our inherent sovereignty, to protect our right of self-government, to conserve custom, to improve our social order, to protect our rights as individuals, to promote our economic welfare, to promote domestic tranquility, to promote business enterprises both cooperative & individual, to promote educational opportunities for all Ponca people, to consolidate our land holdings by purchase, exchange, transfer, gift, or otherwise, ordain & establish this Constitution in accordance with our inherent sovereignty, and all previous aboriginal rights of our members and Treaties previously entered into with the United States of America."

SANTEE SIOUX NATION
425 Frazier Ave. N., Suite 2 • Niobrara, NE 68760
(402) 857-2302 Fax 857-2307
Website: www.santeedakota.org
Roger Trudell, Chairperson & Health Director
E-mail: rtrudell@santeedakota.org
David Henry, Vice Chairperson
E-mail: davidhenry00@yahoo.com
Stuart Redwing, Tribal Secretary
Frank Whipple, Treasurer; E-mail: franklinwhipple@yahoo.com
District Representatives:
Marion Brandt, Hobu Creek District
Don LaPointe, Jr., Santee District
Darlene Blue Bird, Howe Creek District,
Larry "Ike" Denny, Bazile Creek District
Dewayne Whipple, Trial Historian & Musem Curator (857-2772)
Rick Thomas, Director-Tribal Historic Preservation Office (640-9561)
Tessa Avery, Director-Economic Development Office (857-3338)
Lee Ickles, Business Operations Manager (857-3330)
James Trudell, Tribal Planning (667-2922)
Tribe: Santee Sioux. *Enrolled members*: 2,500. *In residence*: 603. *Area*: 9.449 acres. *Resources*: Tribal Museum; Nebraska Indian Community College. *Programs*: Social Services; Higher Education; Human Resources; Health; Head Start. *Attractions*: Ohiyo Casino; Diamond B Trout Resort & Restaurant. Winnebago Agency.

WINNEBAGO TRIBE OF NEBRASKA
100 Bluff St., P.O. Box 687 • Winnebago, NE 68071
(402) 878-2272 Fax 878-2963; Website: www.winnebagotribe.com
Frank White, Chairperson (878-3110)
E-mail: frank.white@winnebagotribe.com
Vince Bass, Vice Chairperson (878-3102)
E-mail: vince.bass@winnebagotribe.com
Victoria Kitcheyan, Treasurer; Kenny Mallory, Secetary
Councilmembers: Darla LaPoint, James Snow, Coly Brown,
Curtis St. Cyr, Isaac Smith
Carol Snow, Chief Administrative Officer (878-3101)
Patrice Bass, Education Director (878-2631)
E-mail: patrice.bass@winnebagotribe.com
Mona Zuffante, Health Director (878-2294)
E-mail: mona.zuffante@winnebagotribe.com
Joseph Painter, EPD Manager (878-4060)
E-mail: joseph.painter@winnebagotribe.com
David Lee Smith, Tribal Historian & Director - Museum/Research Center
(878-3313)
Lance Morgan, President & CEO of Ho-Chunk, Inc. (878-2809)
Tribe: Ho-Chunk. *Enrolled members*: 5,000. *In residence*: 2,600. *Area*: 120,000 acres located in Nebraska & Iowa (off-reservation lands in Iowa.) *Resources*: Winnebago Hospital; Little Priest Tribal College; St. Augustine's Indian Mission; Senior Center; Angel Decora Memorial Museum & Research Center; Blackhawk Center; Little Bear Day Care Center; Nursing Home; Little Priest

Tribal College (878-2380); St. Augustine's Indian Mission; Winnebago Public Schools. *Programs*: Education; Environmental Protection; Head Start. *Enterprises*: Ho-Chunk, Inc. (the economic development corporation for the tribe); Woodland Trails Art & Retail; Tribal Bison Project. *Attrac-tions*: WinnaVegas Casino; Iron Horse Bar & Casino; Native Star Casino; Wildlife & Parks; Bison Project; Annual Winnebago Powwow. *Publication*: Winnebago Indian News. Winnebago Agency.

NEVADA

DUCKWATER SHOSHONE TRIBE
Duckwater Reservation, P.O. Box 140068 • Duckwater, NV 89314
(775) 863-0227 Fax 863-0301; Website: www.duckwatertribe.org
Rodney Mike, Chairperson
Kathy Adams-Blackeye, Vice Chairperson
Lili Ann Pete, Secretary
Councilmembers: Lorin Watson & Paul Walker, Jr.
Gonnie Mendez, Tribal Manager; E-mail: gonnie_mendez@yahoo.com
Margie Nuttall, Education Division Manager; E-mail: Margaret.nuttall@bie.edu
Alfreda Walker, Division of Health & Human Services Manager (863-0222)
 E-mail: alfreda.walker@ihs.gov
Tribe: Shoshone. *In residence*: 150. *Area*: 3,815 acres. *Activities*: Duckwater Festival; operates Duckwater Shoshone Elementary School (K-8th grade). *Publication*: Duckwater Tribal newsletter. Eastern Nevada Agency.

ELY SHOSHONE TRIBE
16 Shoshone Circle • Ely, NV 89301
(775) 289-4888 Fax 289-3833
Alvin S. Marques, Chairperson; Victor McQueen, Jr., Vice Chairperson
LeWayne McQueen, Secretary/Treasurer
Councilmembers Christine Stones & Geraldine Rice
Sandra Barela, Tribal Coordinator; Luana McQueen, Education Director
Christa Mike, Health Director; Boyd Graham, Language Coordinator
Tribe: Lemhi Shoshone. *Enrolled members*: 500. *In residence*: 250. *Area*: 111 acres. *Publication*: Ely Times (www.elynews.com). Eastern Nevada Agency.

FALLON PAIUTE-SHOSHONE TRIBE
565 Rio Vista Rd. • Fallon, NV 89406
(775) 423-6075 Fax 423-5202; Website: www.fpst.org
Len George, Chairperson; E-mail: chairman@fpst.org
Yvonee Mori, Vice Chairperson; E-mail: vicechairman@fpst.org
Laura Ijames, Secretary; E-mail: secretary@fpst.org
Jon Pishion, Treasurer; E-mail: fbctreasurer@fpst.org
Councilmembers: Steve Austin, Gayle Miles & Michelle Bowers
Sheri Hunter, Tribal Administrator
 E-mail: tribaladministrator@fpst.org
Felicia Siyuja, Education Director
 E-mail: educationdirector@fpst.org
Bill Kockenmeister, Chief Tribal Judge
Joe Herman, Health Director; Donna Cossette, Cultural Coordinator
Ermert Nihoa, Numa News Editor; E-mail: tribalnews@fpst.org
Brenda Hooper, Librarian (423-8065) Email: library@fpst.org
Tribes: Paiute & Shoshone. *In residence*: 700. *Area*: 8,200 acres. *Programs*: Education; Health Services; Youth & Family Services; Environmental; Economic Development; Tribal Resources; Housing; Social Services; Fallon Tribal Development Corp. *Resources*: Tribal library; Image Gallery. *Activities*: Nevada Indian Days, Rodeo & Powwow, 3rd weekend in July. *Publication*: "Numa News," monthly tribal newsletter. Western Nevada Agency.

FORT McDERMITT PAIUTE & SHOSHONE TRIBE
8955 Mission Rd., P.O. Box 457 • McDermitt, NV 89421
(775) 532-8259 Fax 532-8487
Billy Bell, Chairperson; Ione Crutcher, Secretary
Tribes: Paiute & Shoshone. *Enrolled members*: 710. In residence: 315.
Area: 35,000 acres located in Nevada & Oregon. Western Nevada Agency.

LAS VEGAS PAIUTE TRIBE
1 Paiute Dr. • Las Vegas, NV 89106
(702) 386-3926 Fax 383-4019; Website: www.lvpaiutetribe.com
Benny Tso, Chairperson; Chris Spottedeagle, Vice Chairperson
Councilmembers: Deryn Pete, Debra Faria, Kevin Mike, Marla Pete, Curtis Anderson
Tribe: Paiute. *Enrolled members*: 125. *Area*: 3,850 acres. *Resources*: Child Development Center; Las Vegas Paiute Golf Resort located at Snow Mountain; Snow Mountain Smoke shop; Las Vegas Paiute Tribal Smoke shop. *Programs*: Education; Health & Human Services; *Programs*: Tribal Scholarship Program - hosts annual tribal Golf Scholarship Tournament each September; annual Snow Mountain Powwow held on Memorial Day Weekend. Southern Paiute Field Station.

LOVELOCK PAIUTE TRIBE
Fort Bidwell Reservation, P.O. Box 878 • Lovelock, NV 89419
(775) 273-7861 Fax 273-3802; Website: www.lovelockpaiutetribe.com
Victor Mann, Chairperson; E-mail: vmann@lovelockpaiutetribe.com
Richard Happy, Vice Chair; E-mail: rhappy@lovelockpaiutetribe.com
Sherry Sandusky, Secretary; E-mail: ssandusky@lovelockpaiutetribe.com
Doug Osbourne, Tribal Administrator & Councilmember (273-7861)
Ernest Moose, Councilmember; Bill Kockenmeister, Presiding Judge
Debbie George, Johnson O'Malley Program Contact (273-1204)
 E-mail: dgeorge@lovelockpaiutetribe.com
Jeanette Smith, Community Health Representative (273-7861)
Fran Machado, Director of Social & Human Services (273-5081)
 E-mail: fmachado@lovelockpaiutetribe.com
Tribe: Paiute. *In residence*: 175. *Area*: 20 acres. *Programs*: Health Services; Environmental; Social & Human Services; Tribal Elders; Johnson O'Malley; Housing. *Publication*: Tribal newsletter. Western Nevada Agency.

MOAPA BAND OF PAIUTE INDIANS
1 Lincoln St., P.O. Box 340 • Moapa, NV 89025
(702) 865-2787 Fax 865-2875; Website: https://www.moapapaiutes.com/
Darren Daboda, Chairperson; E-mail: chair.mbop@mvdsl.com
Vickie Simmons, Vice Chairperson; Tyler Samson, Council Secretary
Councilmembers: Leslie Bradley, Greg Anderson, Delaine Bow
Ewell Longhorn, Tribal Administrator; E-mail: admin.mbop@mvdsl.com
Ural Begay, Cultural Committee Chair; E-mail: uscott125@yahoo.com
Tribe: Moapa Band of Paiute Indians (Southern Paiute). *In residence*: 295.
Area: 72,000 acres located at exit 75 on I-15, 30 miles north of Las Vegas. *Resources*: Tribal Store. *Programs*: Education; Health; Social Services; Cultural; Human Resources; Housing; Farming; Head Start. *Events*: Annual Southern Paiute Veterans Powwow in November. Southern Paiute Field Office.

PYRAMID LAKE PAIUTE TRIBE
208 Capitol Hill, P.O. Box 256 • Nixon, NV 89424
(775) 574-1000 Fax 574-1008; Website: http://plpt.nsn.us
Vinton Hawley, Chairperson; E-mail: vhawley@plpt.nsn.us
Alan Mandell, Vice Chairperson; E-mail: amandell@plpt.nsn.us
Brenda Henry, Secretary; E-mail: bhenry@plpt.nsn.us
Della John, Tribal Executive Officer; E-mail: djohn@plpt.nsn.us
Councilmembers: Leona Collins, Bonnie Akaka-Smith, Genevieve John, John Guerrero, Brian Wadsworth, Mervin Wright, Jr.
Shannon Mandell, Museum Director
Anthony Sampson, Higher Education Program Director
 E-mail: asampson@plpt.nsn.us
Tribe: Paiute. *Enrolled members*: 2,253. *In residence*: 850. *Area*: 475,000 acres located 35 miles northeast of Reno. Pyramid Lake covers 112,000 acres. *Resources*: Library; Museum; Numaga Senior Center. *Programs*: Johnson O'Malley; Higher Education; Health Services; Child Care; Human Resources; Language/Cultural; Environmental; Economic Development; Water Resources. *Attraction*: Sacred Visions Powwow. *Publication*: PLPT Newspaper. Western Nevada Agency.

RENO-SPARKS INDIAN COLONY
98 Colony Rd. • Reno, NV 89502
(775) 329-2936 Fax 954-9175/329-8710
Website: www.rsic.org; E-mail: smontooth@rsic.org
Arlan D. Melendez, Chairperson; E-mail: amelendez@rsic.org
Daryl "Doug" Gardipe, Vice Chairperson; E-mail: dgardipe@rsic.org
Robin Eagle, Secretary; Verna Nuno, Treasurer
Councilmembers: Theresa Coffman, Shawna Kirsten, Jody McCloud, Jackie Quoetone
Alicia Wadsworth, Executive Secretary; E-mail: awadsworth@rsic.org
Andrea Johnson-Harper, Tribal Health Center Director (329-5162)
 E-mail: ajohnsonharper@rsic.org
San San Tin, Education Manager; E-mail: stin@rsic.org
Cordelia Able-Johnson, Community Health Coordinator (329-5162 ext. 1920)
 E-mail: cable-johnson@rsic.org
Steve Moran, Director of Economic Development
 E-mail: smoran@rsic.org (785-1366 ext. 5403)
Joyce Melendez, Tribal Archivist; E-mail: archives@rsic.org (329-8802)
Victoria Oldenburg, Senior Staff Attorney; E-mail: voldenburg@rsic.org
Joseph J. Van Walraven, Chief Tribal Judge (785-8775)
Stacey Montooth, PR/Community Information Officer (329-2936)
 E-mail: smontooth@rsic.org
Adriana Gutierez, Librarian; E-mail: agutierrez@rsic.org
Tribes: Washoe & Paiute. *Enrolled members*: 980. *Area*: 1,988 acres; 28 acres in downtown Reno and the remaining 1,960 in Hungry Valley, 19 miles north of Reno. *Resources*: Health Center; Senior Center. *Programs*: Health & Human Services; Education; Economic Development; Community Services; Public Works, Public Safety; Senior Citizens; Human Resources. *Attraction*: Annual Numaga Powwow. *Publication*: Tribal newsletter. Western Nevada Agency.

SHOSHONE-PAIUTE TRIBES
Duck Valley Indian Reservation, P.O. Box 219 • Owyhee, NV 89832
(208) 759-3100 Fax 759-3103; Website: www.shopaitribes.org
Theodore "Ted" Howard, Chairperson; E-mail: howard.tedl@shopai.org
Buster Gibson, Vice Chairperson; E-mail: gibson.buster@shopai.org
Angele SaBori, Executive Secretary; E-mail: smith.angele@shopai.org
James "Rudy" Blossom, Secretary; E-mail: blossom.james@shopai.org
James Gibson, Treasurer; E-mail: gibson.jim@shopai.org
Councilmembers: Teresa Manuelito, Arnold Thomas, Yvonne Powers
Pete Putra, Tribal Administrator; E-mail: putra.pete@shopai.org
Steve Dean, Project Coordinator; E-mail: dean.steve@shopai.org
Ted Howard, Cultural Resources Director (759-3100 ext. 1243)
Email howard.ted@shopai.org
Laura Hull-Teller, Enrollment Director; E-mail: hulteller.laura@shopai.org
Shane Darrington, Chief Tribal Judge (775) 757-2741
Yvonne Power, Shopai News Editor; E-mail: shopainews@shopai.org
Tribes: Shoshone & Paiute. *Enrolled members:* 2,300. *Area:* 290,000 acres, located in Nevada & Idaho. *Departments & Programs:* Education; Health Facility; Cultural; Environmental Protection; Human Resources; Tribal Enrollment; Land/Natural Resources. *Publication:* Shopai News. See listing under Nevada for more information. Eastern Nevada Field Office

SUMMIT LAKE PAIUTE TRIBE
1001 Rock Blvd. • Sparks, NV 89431
(800) 335-7978; (775) 827-9670 Fax 827-9678
Website: www.summitlaketribe.org
Page Linton, Chairperson; E-mail: page.linton@summitlaketribe.org
Randi DeSoto, Vice Chairperson (622-7520)
E-mail: randi.desoto@summitlaketribe.org
Eugene Mace, Secretary/Treasurer
E-mail: Eugene.mace@summitlaketribe.org
Councilmembers: Jerry Barr & Thalia Dick
William Cowan, Natural Resources Dept. Director
E-mail: william.cowan@summitlaketribe.org
Tribe: Paiute. *Area:* 12,573 acres. *Programs:* Education; Social Services; Health; Environmental. *Publication:* Tribal newsletter. Western Nevada Agency.

TE-MOAK BAND OF WESTERN SHOSHONE INDIANS OF NEVADA
525 Sunset St. • Elko, NV 89801
(775) 738-9251 Fax 738-2345; Website: www.temoaktribe.com
Lydia Johnson (Battle Mountain), Chairperson
Davis Gonzales (Elko), Vice Chairperson
Councilmembers: Steve Brady (Wells); David Decker (Elko Chair);
Leta Jim (Wells Chair); Edith Smartt (South Fork Chair)
Florine Maine (Battle Mountain); Gerald Temoke (Elko);
Alice Tybo (South Fork),
Tribe: Te-Moak Band of Western Shoshone. *Area:* 15,000 acres. Headquarters serving four district Shoshone colonies in Nevada: Battle Mountain Colony, Elko Colony, South Fork Colony, & Wells Colony. *Programs:* Health-Diabetes; Social Services; Housing. *Attractions:* Elko Band Powwow. *Publication:* Te-Moak Tribal Newspaper. Eastern Nevada Agency.

TE-MOAK BAND OF WESTERN SHOSHONE INDIANS
Battle Mountain Band Colony
37 Mountain View Dr. • Battle Mountain, NV 89820
(775) 635-2004 Fax 635-8016
Lydia Johnson, Chairperson; Florine Maine, Vice Chairperson
Tribe: Te-Moak Band of Western Shoshone. A constituent band of the Te-Moak Tribe of Western Shoshone Indians. *Enrolled members:* 516. *In residence:* 165. *Area:* 683 acres. *Resources:* Senior Citizen's Center; Library. Eastern Nevada Agency.

TE-MOAK TRIBE OF WESTERN SHOSHONE INDIANS OF NEVADA
Elko Band Colony, 1850 Silver Eagle P.O. Box 748 • Elko, NV 89801
(775) 738-8889 Fax 753-5439
David Decker, Chairperson; Davis Gonzales, Vice Chairperson
Tribe: Te-Moak Band of Western Shoshone. *Enrolled members:* 1,143. *Area:* 193 acres located in the high desert of northeastern Nevada near the Humboldt River. *Resources:* Community Center; Health Clinic; Child Care Center. Eastern Nevada Field Office.

TE-MOAK TRIBE OF WESTERN SHOSHONE INDIANS
South Fork Reservation, 21 Lee Unit-13 • Spring Creek, NV 89815
(775) 744-4273 Fax 744-4523; Website: www.southforkbandcouncil.org
E-mail: sforkcouncil.adm@gmail.com
Website: www.temoaktribe.com/southfork.shtml
Tyler Reynolds, Chairperson; Edith Smartt, Vice Chairperson
Councilmembers: Alice Tybo, Brandon Reynolds, Dalles Smales,
Gilbert Temoke
Tribe: Te-Moak Band of Western Shoshone. A constituent band of the

Te-Moak Tribe of Western Shoshone Indians. *Enrolled members:* 260. *In residence:* 120. *Area:* 13,049 acres, 28 miles south of the city of Elko. *Programs:* Economic Development; Fisheries; Agriculture & Livestock. Eastern Nevada Field Office.

TE-MOAK TRIBE OF WESTERN SHOSHONE INDIANS
Wells Indian Band Colony, P.O. Box 809 • Wells, NV 89835
(775) 752-3045 Fax 752-0569
Website: www.temoaktribe.com/wells.shtml
E-mail: wellsbandmf@yahoo.com
Casey Franco, Chairperson; Steve Brady, Vice Chairperson
Councilmembers: Cael Healey, Ervin Bobb, Charlotte Healey, Harvey Healey
Tribe: Te-Moak Tribe of Western Shoshone. A constituent band of the Te-Moak Tribe of Western Shoshone Indians. *Enrolled members:* 177. *In residence:* 34. *Area:* 80 acres located in northeastern Nevada, just west of the city of Wells, in Elko County. *Attractions:* Gift & smoke shops; annual powwow. Community Center. Eastern Nevada Field Office.

WALKER RIVER PAIUTE TRIBE
1022 Hospital Rd., P.O. Box 220 • Schurz, NV 89427
(775) 773-2306 Fax 773-2585; Website: www.wrpt.us
Bobby D. Sanchez, Chairperson; Amber Torres, Vice Chairperson
Gina Wachsmuth, Secretary; Marlene Begay, Treasurer
Councilmembers: Genia Williams, Standard Frank, Jr., Sharon Williams
Ken Richardson, Heath Director (773-2205)
Leslie Williams, Economic Development Coordinator (773-2306)
Tribe: Paiute. *In residence:* 900. *Area:* 325,000 acres in Schurz, Mineral County, and in Churchill & Lyon Counties. *Resources:* Tribal Health Center. *Attraction:* Annual Pinenut Festival in September. Western Nevada Agency.

WASHOE TRIBE OF NEVADA & CALIFORNIA
919 U.S. Hwy. 395 South • Gardnerville, NV 89410
(800) 76-WASHOE; (775) 265-8600 Fax 265-6240
Website: www.washoetribe.us
Neil Mortimer, Chairperson; E-mail: neil.mortimer@washoetribe.us
Mahlon Machado, Vice Chair; E-mail: mahlon.machado@washoetribe.us
Jeremy Steele, Acting Secretary/Treasurer
E-mail: Jeremy.steele@washoetribe.us
Cheron Watchman, Tribal Administrator
Off Reservation representatives:
Jeremy Steele & Mahlon Machado (350-7903)
Constance Barnes, Education Director (775) 782-6320)
Tribe: Washoe. *In residence:* 1,480. *Area:* 4,300 acres; plus over 60,000 acres of ten noncontiguous parcels & numerous public domain allotments. *Colonies served:* Dresslerville, Woodfords, Carson Colony & Stewart Colony. *Resources:* Library & Archives at Stewart Colony; Washoe Cultural Resource Center at Lake Tahoe; Health Center. *Programs:* Education; Social Services; Environmental; Health; Housing; Language; Historic Preservation; Human Resources; Law Enforcement; Senior Citizens; Head Start. *Attractions:* Native American Arts Festival in July; Annual Tribal Picnic. *Publication:* Tribal Talk, monthly tribal newsletter; Off-Rez Report, quarterly. Western Nevada Agency.

WASHOE TRIBE OF THE CARSON COLONY
2900 S. Curry St., P.O. Box 3269 • Carson City, NV 89703
(775) 883-6459 Fax 883-6467; Website: www.washoetribe.us
Gary Nevers, Chairperson; Chad Malone, Vice Chairperson
Ellen Fillmore, Secretary-Treasurer
Eleanor Muscott & Tyler Rupert, Councilmembers
Tribe: Washoe. A component Band of the Washoe Tribe. *Area:* 150 acres. *Publication:* Off-Reservation News. Western Nevada Agency.

WASHOE TRIBE OF THE DRESSLERVILLE COLONY
1585 Watasheamu • Gardnerville, NV 89460
(775) 265-5645 Fax 265-6240; Website: www.washoetribe.us
Rueben Vasquez, Chairperson
E-mail: reuben.vasquez@washoetribe.us
William Smokey, Vice Chairperson
E-mail: william.smokey@washoetribe.us
Councilmembers: Elivia McDonals, Willie Smokey, Julllie Barr
Tribe: Washoe. A component Band of the Washoe Tribe. *Area:* 40 acres. Western Nevada Agency.

WASHOE TRIBE OF THE STEWART COMMUNITY
465 Clear Creek • Carson City, NV 89701
(775) 883-7794 or 883-5679; Website: www.washoetribe.us
Jacqueline Steele, Chairperson; Stan Smokey, Vice Chairperson
Darrell D. Kizer, Secretary-Treasurer
Dorothy McCloud & Richard Burchett, Councilmembers
Tribe: Washoe. A component Band of the Washoe Tribe. Western Nevada Agency.

WASHOE TRIBE OF THE WOODFORDS COMMUNITY
Alpine Washoe Reservation, 96A Washoe Blvd. • Woodfords, CA 96120
(530) 694-2170 Fax 694-1890; Website: www.washoetribe.us
Irvin Jim, Chairperson; Deirdre Jones-Flood, Vice Chairperson
Geoff Ellis, Councilmember
Tribe: Washoe. A component Band of the Washoe Tribe of Nevada
& California. Western Nevada Agency. See listing under California.

WINNEMUCCA INDIAN COLONY
1985 hanson St. • Winnemucca, NV 89445
Mailing address: 200 S. Virginia St., 8th Fl • Reno, NV 89501
(702) 722-3833; Website: www.winnemuccaindiancolony.weebly.com
Thomas Wasson, Chairperson
Councilmembers: Misty Morning Dawn Rojo-Alvarez, Eric Magiera,
Judy Rojo, Katherine Hasbrouck,
Tribe: Paiute. *In residence*: 110. *Area*: 350 acres. Western Nevada Agency.

YERINGTON PAIUTE TRIBE
171 Campbell Lane • Yerington, NV 89447
(775) 463-3301 Fax 463-2416
Laurie Thom, Chairperson; E-mail: chairman@ypt-nsn.gov
Albert Roberts, Vice Chairperson; Shelley Cunningham, Secretary
Councilmembers: Linda Howard, Delmar Stevens, Elwood Emm,
Cassie Roberts, Nate Landa
Deborah Dunn, Tribal Manager
Sandra-Mae Pickens, Judge; James Van Winkle, Chief Justice
Lorna L. Conway, Newsletter Editor
Tribe: Paiute. *In residence*: 430. *Area*: 24,000 acres. *Resources*: Community Center; Health & Wellness Center; Library. *Programs*: Health, Education, Head Start, Human Resources, Child-care. *Publication*: Newsletter. Western Nevada Agency.

YOMBA SHOSHONE TRIBE
HC 61 Box 6275 • Austin, NV 89310
(775) 964-2463 Fax 964-2443; Website: www.yombatribe.org
Darryl Brady, Chairperson; Ronald Snooks, Vice Chairperson
Kenny Smith, Secretary/Treasurer
Councilmembers: Randy Brady, Chris Dyer, Daniel Hooper
Judy Camarillo, Administrator; E-mail: admin@yombatribe.org
Tribe: Western Shoshone. *Enrolled members*: 186. *In residence*: 114.
Area: 4,681 acres. Western Nevada Agency.

NEW MEXICO

PUEBLO OF ACOMA
P.O. Box 309 • Acomita, NM 87034
(505) 552-6604 Fax 552-7204; Website: www.puebloofacoma.org
Kurt Riley, Governor; Raymond J. Concho, Jr., 1st Lt. Governor
Christopher J. Garcia, 2nd Lt. Governor; Marcus Leno, Tribal Secretary
Elliott Sanchez, Jr., Tribal Interpreter; Michael S. Lewis, Head Councilperson
Councilmembers: Harold M. Chino, Head Councilperson
Derek C. Valdo, Ernest M. Vallo, Timothy J. Chavez, Brian Torivio,
Robert T. Garcia, Barney Chino, Garcia Chino, Edmund Seymour,
Rex Salvador, Harold Felipe, Ted Martinez, Joseph Castillo
Stanley Holder, Executive Director of Education
Tonita Sarracino, Health & Wellness Director
Donalyn Sarracino, Social Services Program Director
Michael Torivio, Gaming Commission Chairperson
Tribe: Acoma Pueblo. *In residence*: 3,000. *Area*: 431,664 acres located 50 miles west of Albuquerque. *Resources*: Sky City Cultural Center; Haak'u Museum; Sky City Travel Center & RV Park; Acoma Community School; Senior Center; Acoma Learning Center; Public Library & Computer Center. *Programs*: Health & Wellness; Education; Historic Preservation; Housing; Human Resources; Indian Child Welfare; Language Retention; Realty & Natural Resources; Environmental Protection; Head Start. *Attraction*: Sky City Casino & Hotel. *Activities*: Acoma Cattle Growers Association; Annual Feast of San Estevan at Old Acoma on Sept. 2nd of every year; Annual Native American Arts & Crafts Show; Acoma Big Game Hunts; Acoma Land & Cattle. *Publication*: "Acoma: Pueblo in the Sky," by Ward Alan Minge. Southern Pueblos Agency.

PUEBLO OF COCHITI
255 Cochiti St., P.O. Box 70 • Cochiti, NM 87072
(505) 465-2244 Fax 465-1135; Website: www.pueblodecochiti.org
Leroy Arquero, Governor
Tribe: Cochiiti Pueblo. *In residence*: 530. *Area*: 53,779 acres located in Sandoval County, 55 miles north of Albuquerque near U.S. 85 on the west bank of the Rio Grande River. *Attractions*: Golf Course, Farm Enterprise. Southern Pueblos Agency.

PUEBLO OF ISLETA
Tribal Rd. 40, Bldg. 117-A, P.O. Box 1270 • Isleta, NM 87022
(505) 869-3111 Fax 869-7596; Website: www.isletapueblo.com
Eddie Paul Torres, Sr., Governor
Antonio Chewiwi, 1st Lt. Governor
Isidor Abeita, 2nd Lt. Governor
Frank E. Lujan, Tribal Council President
Douglas Jiron, Vice President; Edward Calabaza, Secretary
Councilmembers:
Fernando Abeita, Juan Rey Abeita, Michael Allen Lente, Verna Teller
Daniel Waseta, Director - Dept. of Cultural & Historic Preservation
Lawrence Lucero, Chief Judge
Nathaniel Lujan, Newsltter Editor
Tribe: Isleta Pueblo. *In residence*: 3,500. *Area*: 209,000 acres located 13 miles south of Albuquerque. *Resources*: Health Center; Public Library (869-8119). *Programs*: Social Services; Higher Education; Head Start. *Attractions*: Isleta Resort & Casino; Isleta Eagle Golf Course; Islleta Lakes & RV Park. *Publication*: Isleta Pueblo News, newsletter. Southern Pueblos Agency.

PUEBLO OF JEMEZ (WALATOWA)
4471 Hwy. 4, P.O. Box 280 • Jemez Pueblo, NM 87024
(575) 834-7359 Fax 834-7331; Website: www.jemezpueblo.org
Joseph A. Toya, Governor
William Waquie, 1st Lt. Governor
Jonathan Romero, 2nd Lt. Governor
Benny Shendo, Jr., Tribal Administrator
Lynn Toledo, Executive Assistant; E-mail: ltoledo@jemezpueblo.org
Maria K. Clark, Health & Human Services Director
Kevin Shendo, Director-Dept. of Education Director (834-9102)
 E-mail: shendo@jemezpueblo.org
Tribe: Jemez Pueblo. *Enrolled members*: 3,400. *In residence*: 2,000. *Area*: 89,000 acres located 55 miles northwest of Albuquerque. *Resources*: Walatowa Visitor Center & Museum; Senior Center. *Programs*: Health & Human Services; Housing; Education; Human Resources; Public Safety; Resource Protection; Towa Arts & Crafts. Southern Pueblos Agency.

JICARILLA APACHE NATION
P.O. Box 507 • Dulce, NM 87528
(505) 759-3242 Fax 759-3005
Ty Vicenti, President; Ernest Petago, Vice Chairperson
Councilmembers: Philbert Vigil, Martin Perea, William E. Muniz, Bilford Vicenti,
Adrian Notsinneh, Lillian Veneno, Wainwright Velarde, Leon Reval
Cordell TeCube, Environmental Departrment Director
Tribe served: Jicarilla Apache. *In residence*: 2,600. *Area*: 742,303 acres located about two miles northwest of Albuquerque. *Programs*: Cultural Affairs Office - Language Revitalization, Cultural Education, Historic Preservation; Health & Human Services; Education & Recreation; Environmental Protection; Public Safety; Community Development; Natural Resources; Employment & Training. *Attractions*: Apache Nugget Casino and the Wild Horse Casino; Annual Little Beaver Powwow & Rodeo, 3rd weekend in July; Game & Fish. *Publication*: Jicarilla News. Gift Shop. Jicarilla Agency.

PUEBLO OF LAGUNA
P.O. Box 194 • Laguna, NM 87026
(505) 552-6654 Fax 552-6941; Website: www.lagunapueblo-nsn.gov
Virgil A. Siow, Governor; Wilfred Herrera, Jr., 1st Lt. Governor
Marvin Trujillo, Jr., 2nd Lt. Governor; Patrick Pruitt, Head Fiscale
Ryan Riley, 1st Fiscale; Filbert Antonio, 2nd Fiscale
Frank Cerno, Jr., Secretary; David A. Martinez, Treasurer
Alvin D. Martin, Tribal Interpreter
Jaye Chissoe, Administrative Services Director
 E-mail: info.asd@lagunapueblo-nsn.gov
Jim Hooper, Jr., Chief of Operations; Bruce Fox, Presiding Judge
Janice Kowemy, Director/Librarian
Annette Nunez, Newspaper Editor
Tribe: Laguna Pueblo. *In residence*: 4,250. *Area*: 420,000 acres located 40 miles west of Albuquerque, on U.S. 66. *Resources*: Laguna Schools; Laguna Education Foundation; Laguna Public Library. *Programs*: Education; Head Start. *Attractions*: Dancing Eagle Casino; Route 66 Casino; Laguna Feast Days. *Publication*: Kukadze'eta Towncrier, community news. Laguna Agency.

MESCALERO APACHE TRIBE
101 Central Ave., P.O. Box 227 • Mescalero, NM 88340
(575) 464-4494 Fax 464-9191
Website: http://mescaleroapachetribe.com
Danny Breuninger, President; Gabe Aguilar, Vice President
Kenny Blazer, Secretary; Marilyn Blaylock, Treasurer
Ben Martinez, Tribal Administrator; Crystal Garcia, Executive Secretary
Councilmembers: Pamela Morgan, Helen Klinekole, LeClaire Gayton,
Christie LaPaz, Jr., Caroline Valdez, Pascal Enjady
Gregory Mendez, Tribal Community Service Chairperson

Freddy Kaydahzinne, Tribal Cultural Affairs Chairperson
Elaina Via, Government Affairs Liaison
Kelton Starr, Education Office Director
Vincent Knight, Chief Judge; Leonard Kanesewah III, Associate Judge
Francine Kanseah & Hazel Spottedbird, Alternate Judges
Tribe served: Mescalero Apache. *Enrolled members*: 4,000+. *In residence*: 2,750. *Area*: 460,173 acres located 30 miles northeast of Alamagordo, New Mexico. *Programs*: Education; Cultural Affairs; Housing; Social Services; Human Services; Senior Citizens; Head Start. *Attractions*: Mescalero Apache Cultural Center & Museum; Inn of the Mountain Gods Resort & Casino; Ski Apache Ski Resort; Mescalero Big Game Hunting; Mescalero Tribal Fish Hatchery. Enterprises: Casino Apache Travel Center; Mescalero Apache Telecom. *Publication*: Apache Scout, monthly newsletter. Mescalero Agency.

PUEBLO OF NAMBE

15A NP 102 West • Santa Fe, NM 87506
(505) 455-4400 Fax 455-2038; Website: www.nambepueblo.org
E-mail: info@nambepueblo.org
Phillip A. Perez, Governor; Arnold J. Garcia, Lt. Governor
Donald Avila, Warchief; Clarance Sanchez, Lt. Warchief
Tribe: Nambe Pueblo. *Enrolled membes*: 575. *In residence*: 1,600. *Area*: 19,000 acres located five miles east of Pojoaque, New Mexico, on Hwy. 285. *Resources*: Wellness Center, Senior Center. *Programs*: Domestic Violence; Substance Abuse; Child Welfare; Community Health; Education; Environmental; SenNorthern Pueblos Agency.

OHKAY OWINGEH (SAN JUAN PUEBLO)

Popay St., State Rd. 74, P.O. Box 1099 • San Juan Pueblo, NM 87566
(505) 852-4400 Fax 852-4820; Peter Garcia, Jr., Governor
Matthew Martinez, 1st Lt. Governor; Daniel Maes, 2nd Lt. Governor
Elena Arrellano, Tribal Librarian; E-mail: elenasanjuanpueblo@yahoo.com
Tribe: Ohkay Owingeh Pueblo. *Enrolled members*: 6,750. *In residence*: 3,500. *Area*: 12,000 acres located five miles north of Espanola, near Hwy. 64. *Resources*: Indian Pueblo Cultural Center; Ohkay Owingeh Community School; Library. *Programs*: Education; Johnson O'Malley; Head Start. *Attractions*: OhKay Casino (website: www.ohkay.com) RV Park; Fishing tournaments. Northern Pueblos Agency.

PUEBLO OF PICURIS

P.O. Box 127 • Penasco, NM 87553
(575) 587-2519 Fax 587-1071
Craig Quanchello, Governor; Wayne Yazza, Jr., Lt. Governor
E-mail: tribalsecretary@picurispueblo.com
Tribe: Picuris Pueblo. *Enrolled members*: 1,900. *In residence*: 100. *Area*: 1,500 acres located east of the Rio Grande River, 20 miles south of Taos, New Mexico. *Resources*: Poeh Cultural Center; Guided Tours; Picuris Pueblo Museum. *Program*: Bison Program. *Attractions*: San Lorenzo Feast Day; The High Country Tri-Cultural Arts & Crafts Fair (first weekend in July). Northern Pueblos Agency.

PUEBLO OF POJOAQUE

78 Cities of Gold Rd. • Santa Fe, NM 87506
(505) 455-3334 Fax 455-0174/5065
Website: www.poehcenter.com; E-mail: info@poehcenter.com
Joseph M. Talachy, Governor; Jenelle Roybal, Lt. Governor
George Rivera, Executive Director of Poeh Cultural Center
Vernon Lujan, Museum Director; Melissa Talachy, Museum Curator
Tribe: Pojoaque Pueblo. *In residence*: 200. *Area*: 11,500 acres. *Resources*: The Poeh Cultural Center & Museum. *Attractions*: Buffalo Thunder Resort & Casino; Annual Feast Day (December). Northern Pueblos Agency.

RAMAH NAVAJO CHAPTER

HCR62, Box 13 • Ramah, NM 87321
(505) 775-7142 Fax 775-7141
Website: www.ramah.navajochapters.org
E-mail: ramah@navajochapters.org
David Jose, President; Jamie Henio, Vice President
Dixie M. Begay, Secretary/Treasurer
Norman M. Begay, Council Delegate
Brenda L. Yazzie, Community Services Coordinator
Tribe: Navajo. Ramah-Navajo Agency.

PUEBLO OF SAN FELIPE

P.O. Box 4339 • San Felipe Pueblo, NM 87001
(575) 867-3381 Fax 867-3383
Ronald Tenorio, Governor; E-mail: gov.rtenorio@sfpueblo.com
Delbert Sanchez, Lt. Governor; Bruce Garcia, Administrator
Tribe: San Felipe Pueblo. *Enrolled members*: 2,200+. *In residence*: 3,250. *Area*: 49,000 acres located 25 miles north of Albuquerque, off U.S. 85. *Programs*: Education; Social Services; Gaming; Head Start. *Attractions*: San Felipe Casino Hollywood; annual Feast of St. Philip on May 1. Southern Pueblos Agency.

PUEBLO OF SAN ILDEFONSO

2 Tunyo Ope, Rt. 5, Box 315-A • Santa Fe, NM 87501
(505) 455-2273 Fax 455-7351
James R. Mountain, Governor
E-mail: governor@sanipueblo.org
F. Wayne Martinez, Lt. Governor; E-mail: wmartinez.tc@outlook.com
Irene Tse-Pe, Secetary; E-mail: itsepe.tc@outlook.com
Councilmembers: Glenda Fred-Weahkee, Thelma Gonzales, Donald Pena, Terrence Garcia, Perry Martinez, Chris Moquino, Leon Roybal, Tim Martinez
Robert J. Little, Council attorney
E-mail: robertlyttle@yahoo.com
Darren Stand, Tribal Admin. (455-4148)
E-mail: dstand@sanipueblo.org
Marcel Povijua, Tribal Services Director (455-4160)
E-mail: mmpovijua@sanipueblo.org
Tribe: San Ildefonso Tewa. *In residence*: 600. *Area*: 26,000 acres located 20 miles northwest of Santa Fe, off Hwy. 285. *Attractions*: Sandia Resort & Casino; Bien Mur Indian Market; Annual Feast Day (January 23); small museum & library. Northern Pueblos Agency.

PUEBLO OF SANDIA

481 Sandia Loop • Bernalillo, NM 87004
(505) 867-3317 Fax 867-9235; Website: www.sandiapueblo.nsn.us
Malcolm Montoya, Governor; Lawrence Gutierrez, Lt. Governor
Jose A. Sanchez, Warchief; J. Domingo Otero, Lt. Warchief
Tunte Vigil, Gaming Commissioner
Tribe: Pueblo. *In residence*: 490. *Area*: 22,870 acres located 14 miles north of Albuquerque, on US 85. *Resources*: Health Center; Learning Resource Center; Tribal Public Library. *Attractions*: Bien Mur Indian Market & Travel Center; Sandia Resort/Casino; Los Amigos Roundup. Southern Pueblos Agency

TAMAYA (SANTA ANA) PUEBLO

2 Dove Rd. • Pueblo of Santa Ana, NM 87004
(505) 867-3301 Fax 867-3395; Website: www.santaana-nsn.gov
Lawrence Montoya, Governor; Robert Ortiz, Tribal Administrator
Tribe: Tamaya Pueblo. *Enrolled members*: 550. *Area*: 73,000 acres near Jemez Creek, eight miles from Bernalillo. *Resources*: Day Care Center; Public Library. *Programs*: Education; Health; Language & Culture; Community Development; Natural Resources; Summer; Gaming; Human Resources; Social Services. *Attractions*: Santa Ana Star Casino; Santa Ana Golf Course; Pueblo Feast Days. Southern Pueblos Agency.

PUEBLO OF SANTA CLARA

1 Kee St., P.O. Box 580 • Espanola, NM 87532
(505) 753-7330 Fax 753-5375
J. Michael Chavarria, Governor; John Shije, Lt. Governor
Tribe: Pueblo. *In residence*: 2,350. *Area*: 45,744 acres located 25 miles northwest of Santa Fe. *Resources*: Small library. *Activities*: Annual Feasts, June & August. *Publication*: Monthly newsletter. Northern Pueblos Agency.

KEWA PUEBLO (SANTO DOMINGO)

P.O. Box 99 • Santo Domingo Pueblo, NM 87052
(505) 465-2214 Fax 465-2688
Brian Coriz, Governor; Esquipula Tenorio, Lt. Governor
Oneida Cate, Social Services Manager
Kathleen Pacheco, Court Coordinator; Cynthia Aguilar, Librarian
Tribe: Kewa Pueblo. *In residence*: 2,700. *Area*: 70,000 acres located in Sandoval County, ten miles east of the Rio Grande River. *Program*: Head Start. Southern Pueblos Agency.

PUEBLO OF TAOS

1075 Veteran's Highway, P.O. Box 1846 • Taos, NM 87571
(575) 758-9593 Fax 758-460; Website: www.taospueblo.com
Luis Romero, Governor; E-mail: governor@taospueblo.com
Tribe: Taos Pueblo. *In residence*: 1,900. *Area*: 99,000 acres.
Attraction: Taos Mountain Casino. Northern Pueblos Agency.

PUEBLO OF TESUQUE

Rt. 42, Box 360-T • Santa Fe, NM 87501
(505) 955-7732 Fax 982-2331
Mark Mitchell, Governor; Travis Vigil, Lt. Governor
Tribe: Pueblo. *In residence*: 325. *Area*: 17,000 acres located ten miles north of Santa Fe. Tribal Council. Northern Pueblos Agency.

PUEBLO OF ZIA

135 Capitol Square Dr. • Zia Pueblo, NM 87053
(505) 867-3304 Fax 867-3308
Carl B. Schildt, Governor; Jerome Lucero, Lt. Governor
Tribe: Zia Pueblo. *In residence*: 650. *Area*: 112,000 acres located 16 miles northwest of Bernalillo. *Resources*: Cultural Center/Library. Southern Pueblos Agency.

PUEBLO OF ZUNI
1203B State Hwy 53, P.O. Box 339 • Zuni, NM 87327
(505) 782-7000 Fax 782-7202; Website: www.ashiwi.org
Val Panteah, Governor (2015-present); Birdena Sanchez, Lt. Governor
Councilmembers: Virginia Chavez, Carlton Bowekaty, Audrey Simplico,
Eric Bobelu
Samuel Crowfoot (Blackfoot), Chief Tribal Judge (782-7123)
Tribe: Zuni (Ashiwi). *Total population*: 18,700. *Area*: 463,000 acres. Located 150 miles west of Albuquerque and 40 miles south of Gallup, NM, on the Arizona border. *Population served*: 7,100. *Resources*: Zuni Wellness Center; Zuni Youth Center; A:shiwi A:wan Museum & Heritage Center; Education & Career Development Center; Home Health Care; Youth Center; Senior Citizen Center; Zuni Recovery Center; Zuni Public Library. *Programs*: Community Corrections; Natural Resources; Education & Career Development; Environmental Protection; Housing & Development; Tribal Records & Archives; Head Start. *Tribal Enterprises*: Pueblo of Zuni Arts & Crafts; Forest Products & Services; Zuni Rental; Cultural Resources (E-mail: zcre@zcre.net); Zuni Skies Unlimited; Zuni Technologies; ZEE Inc. Media: KSHI (90.9 FM) Radio Station. *Publication*: A:shiwi News. Zuni Agency.

NEW YORK

CAYUGA NATION
2540 SR-89, P.O. Box 803 • Seneca Falls, NY 13148
(315) 568-0750 Fax 568-0752; Website: www.cayuganation-nsn.gov
Clint Halftown (Heron Clan), Federal Representative
Tim Twoguns (Turtle Clan), Alternate Federal Representative
Representatives: Gary Wheeler (Turtle Clan), Donald Jimerson (Bear Clan), Michael Barringer (Wolf Clan)
Tribe: Cayuga (member of Six Nations). *Enrolled members*: 500 in New York. *In residence*: 150. *Area*: 824 acres. *Programs*: Housing. Eastern Regional Office.

OIL SPRINGS CORNERS RESERVATION
P.O. Box 146 • Kill Buck, NY 14748
Tribe served: Seneca. *Area*: 640 acres. Located near
Cuba Lake in Allegheny County. Eastern Regional Office.

ONEIDA INDIAN NATION
2037 Dream Catcher Plaza • Oneida, NY 13421
(800) 685-6115; (315) 829-8900 Fax 829-8958
Website: www.oneidaindiannation.com; E-mail: info@oneida-nation.org
Ray Halbritter (Wolf Clan), Nation Representative
Kim Jacobs (Wolf Clan), Nation Clerk
Representatives: Chuck Fougnier & Keller George, Wolf Clan
Beulah Green (Turtle Clan), Clan Mother
Dale Rood & Clint Hill, Turtle Clan
Brian Patterson & Pete John, Bear Clan
Kenneth Deane, Government Programs Officer (829-8212)
Dan Smith, Public Affairs; E-mail: oneidanationnews@oneida-nation.org
Tribe: Oneida (member of Six Nations). *Enrolled members*: 1,000. *In residence*: 500. *Area*: 1,700 acres located three miles south of the city of Oneida in Madison County in Central New York. *Resources*: Health Center; Education Resource Center Incentive/Scholarships; Children & Elders Center; Museum-Shako:wi Cultural Center (829-8801) located at 5 Territory Rd.; Nation library (part of the Education Resource Center); operates convenience stores & marinas. *Programs*: Elders Program; Education; Health Services; Recreation & Youth Programs; Dept. of Communications. *Attractions*: Turning Stone Resort & Casino (361-7711) in Verona, NY; Yellow Brick Road Casino (366-9400) in Chittenango, NY; traditional ceremonies held in Council House throughout the year. *Publications*: Indian Country Today (newspaper); Oneida Nation News; The Insider, employee information. Eastern Regional Office.

ONONDAGA INDIAN NATION
3951 Route 11 • Nedrow, NY 13120
(315) 492-1922 Fax 469-4717
Website: www.onondaganation.org
E-mail: admin@onondaganation.org
Irving Powless, Jr., Chief; Oren Lyons, Traditional Chief & Faithkeeper
Tribes: Onondaga, Oneida & Cayuga (member of Six Nations – Haudenosaunee, People of the Long House). *In residence*: 1,500. *Area*: 7,300 acres located near Nedrow, six miles south of Syracuse. *Attractions*: Ceremonies in longhouse. Eastern Regional Office.

SAINT REGIS MOHAWK TRIBE
412 State Route 37 • Akwesasne, NY 13655
(518) 358-2272 Fax 358-3203; Website: www.srmt-nsn.gov
E-mail: communcations@srmt-nsn.gov
Michael Conners (*Karoniahtens*) (2017-20), Chief
Beverly Cook (*Kiohawlton*) (2016-19), Chief

Eric Thompson, (*Tehoroniathe*) (2015-18), Chief (2015-18), Chief
Sub-Chiefs: Shelley Jacobs (2016-19), Agnes Jacobs (2017-20),
Cheryl Jacobs (2015-18)
David T. Staddon, Director of Public Information
Peter J. Herne, Tribal Judge; Betty Roundpoint, Tribal Clerk
Steven B. Cook, Director of Economic Development
David Trout Staddon, Editor of Monthly Newsletter
Tribe: St. Regis Mohawk (member of Six Nations). *In residence*: 6,500. *Area*: 14,640 acres located in Franklin County on Rt. 37. Straddles the Canadian border; portion lies within Quebec & Ontario. *Programs*: Education; Cultural; Environment; Human Services; Indian Health Service; Office for the Aging. *Resources*: Museum; Library; St. Regis Mohawk School. *Attractions*: Akwesasne Mohawk Casino (www.mohawkcasino.com); Mohawk Bingo Palace & Class II Casino. *Publication*: SRMT Kawenni:ios, monthly newsletter. Eastern Regional Office.

SENECA NATION OF INDIANS
Websites: www.sni.org; www.senecanation.com;
www.honorindiantreaties.org
Todd Gates, President; Maurice A. John, Sr., Treasurer
Allegany: 90 Ohiyo Way • Salamanca, NY 14779 (716) 945-1790
Allegany Councilors:
Tina Abrams, Arlene C. Bova, Ricky Armstrong, Sr., William Canella,
Mike Williams, Stephen Gordon, Al E. George
Cattaraugus: 12837 Rte. 438 • Irving, NY 14081
(716) 532-4900 Fax 532-6272
Cattaraugus Councilors:
Linda Doxtator, Jeffrey Gill, Ross John, Sr., Presley M.C. Redeye,
Rick Jimerson, Liona LeRoy, Keith White, Sr., John Williams, Jr.
Rena Phearsdorf, Higher Education Program Coordinator
Tribe: Seneca (member of Six Nations). *Reservations*: Allegany (40,500 acres) & Cattaraugus (21,600 acres). Population: 7,200. *In residence*: 4,000. *Departments*: Early Childhood Learning; Archives; Community Planning & Development; Economic Development & Tourism; Education - Head Start Program; Employ-ment/Training; Environmental Protection; Health; Housing; Human Resources; Senior Advocate Services; Tribal Historic Preservation. *Resources*: Allegany Community Center; Cattaraugus Community Center; Buffalo Native Resource Center; Seneca-Iroquois National Museum in Salamanca; Seneca Nation Library (branches for both Allegany & Cattaraugus Reservation). *Attractions*: Seneca Allegany Casino & Hotel (in Salamanca); Seneca Niagara Casino & Hotel (in Niagara Falls); Seneca Buffalo Creek (in downtown Buffalo); Seneca Sports Arena (at the Cattaraugus Reservation); Seneca Fall Festival (2nd weekend in September); Allegany Indian Fair (late August); Spring & Christmas Bazaars. *Publication*: Tribal Newsletter. Eastern Regional Office.

SHINNECOCK TRIBE
P.O. Box 5006 • Southampton, NY 11968
(631) 283-6143 Fax 283-0751
Website: www.shinnecocknation.com
E-mail: sination@optonline.net; E-mail: nationsvoice@shinnecock.org
Daniel Collins, Chairperson; Bradden Smith, Vice Chairperson
Bryan Polite, Secretary of Council; Taobi Silva, Treasurer
Nichol Dennis-Banks, Secretary of General Council
Eugene E. Cuffee, Sachem; Lucille Bosley, Sunksqua
James W. Eleazer & Donald Williams, Council of Elders Co-Chairs
Beverly Jensen, Director of Communications (204-9301 Fax 822-1270)
Tribe: Shinnecock. *Enrolled members*: 1,300. *In residence*: 615. *Area*: 1,200 acres. Located in Suffolk County, NY, near Southampton. *Facilities*: Health Clinic; Cultural Center & Museum; Shellfish Hatcheries; Environment Center. *Programs*: Education; Health; Economic Development; Youth Council; Environmental; Gaming. *Attractions*: Annual Labor Day Powwow; Feast of the Moon of the Flowers (June); Nunnowa (Shinnecock Thanksgiving-one week before National Thanksgiving); plans have been made for a casino. *Publication*: Nation News. Video: "Our Land, Our Future." (ten minute feature explores the Tribe's history, cultural heritage & ongoing quest for economic self-sufficiency.

TONAWANDA BAND OF SENECA INDIANS
7027 Meadville Rd. • Basom, NY 14013
(716) 542-4244 Fax 542-4008; Roger Hill, Chief
Tribe: Tonawanda Seneca (member of Six Nations). *Enrolled members*: 1,200. *In residence*: 700. *Area*: 7,549 acres located on Route 267, near Batavia, NY and just west of Basom, NY. Council of Chiefs. Eastern Regional Office.

TUSCARORA INDIAN NATION
2006 Mt. Hope Rd. • Lewiston, NY 14092
(716) 297-1148 Fax 297-7355; Website: www.tuscaroras.com
Leo R. Henry, Chief (716) 622-7061
Kenneth Patterson, Stuart Patterson, Neil Patterson, Sr.
& Neil Patterson, Jr., Chief's Council

Tribe: Tuscarora (member of Six Nations). *Enrolled members*: 1,500. *In residence*: 1,155. *Area*: 5,700 acres located in Niagara County near Sanborn & Lewiston on Upper Mountain Rd. *Attractions*: Tuscarora Field Day 2nd Saturday of July & Tuscarora Community Fair in October. Eastern Regional Office.

UNKECHAUG (POOSPATUCK) INDIAN NATION
P.O. Box 86 • Mastic, NY 11950
(631) 281-6464 Fax 281-5859
Harry B. Wallace, Principal Chief
Mary Treadwell, Treasurer; Wanda Edwards, Secretary
David Hunt, Keeper of the Records
Junie Langhorn & Kenneth L. Morin, Jr., Trustees
Tribe: Unkechaug (Poospatuck). *Enrolled members*: 450. *In residence*: 275. *Area*: 56 acres located on the Forge River near Moriches Bay, Long Island, NY. *Special programs*: Maintains the Unkechaug Nation Cultural School, established in 1995, teaches children language, history, songs & dances. Tribal members have also re-established the tradition of making wampum using both ancient & modern techniques. *Attractions*: Strawberry Festival in June; Corn Festival in August; Mid-Winter Social in January; Poospatuck Smoke Shop; Giftshop. *Publication*: My People the Unkechaug, by Donald Treadwell (Lone Otter). Eastern Area Office.

NORTH CAROLINA

EASTERN BAND OF CHEROKEE INDIANS
88 Council House Loop Rd., Qualla Boundary
P.O. Box 455 • Cherokee, NC 28719
(800) 438-1601 (828) 497-7000 Fax 497-7007/8196
Website: https://ebci.com/ E-mail: josiowle@nc-cherokee.com
Mitchell A. Hicks, Principal Chief (359-7002)
  Address: P.O. Box 1927, Cherokee, NY 28719
Bill Taylor (Wolfetown), Chairperson; Brandon Jones, Vice Chair
Councilmembers: B. Ensley, Anita Lossiah, Richard French, Teresa McCoy, Robert "Bo" Crowe, Adam Wachacha, Marie Junaluska, Tommye Saunooke, Albert D. Rose, Travis Smith
Tribe: Eastern Band of Cherokee. *Enrolled members*: 14,000. *In residence*: 10,800. *Area*: 56,572 acres located 50 miles west of Asheville, North Carolina. *Resources*: Operates School & Hospital. *Programs*: Community Services; Health; Education; Housing; Timber & Natural Resources; Enrollment; Planning Board; Social Services. *Attractions*: Replica of an Oconaluftee Indian Village; Museum of the Cherokee; Qualla Arts & Crafts Cooperative; Casino. *Special activity*: Annual Cherokee Fall Festival. Cherokee Agency.

NORTH DAKOTA

MHA NATION - THREE AFFILIATED TRIBES
Mandan, Hidatsa & Arikara Nation - Fort Berthold Reservation
404 Frontage Rd. • New Town, ND 58763
(701) 627-4781 Fax 627-3503
Website: www.mhanation.com; E-mail: info@mhanation.com
Mark N. Fox (Hidatsa), Chairperson
  E-mail: chairmanfox@mhanation.com
Randy Phelan (Mandan), Vice Chairperson
  E-mail: rphelan@mhanation.com
Fred Fox (White Shield), Executive Secretary
  E-mail: ffox@mhanation.com
Mervin Packineau (Parshall/Lucky Mound), Treasurer
  E-mail: mpackineau@mhanation.com
Councilmembers: Frank Grady (Four Bears), Cory Spotted Bear (Twin Buttes), Monica Mayer (New Town/Little Shell)
Al Nygard Chief Executive Officer
 E-mail: alnygard@mhanation.com
Frank Grady, Health & Human Resource Committee Chairperson
Cory Spotted Bear, Chairperson-Education Committee
Monica Mayer, Chairperson-Economic Development Committee
Randy Phelan, Chairperson-Natural Resources Committee
Fred Fox, Chairperson-Judicial Committee/Human Resources
Tribes: Three Affiliated Tribes - Mandan, Hidatsa, Arikara. *Enrolled members*: 12,000. *In residence*: 4,000. *Area*: 980,000 acres located four miles west of New Town, ND, above Garrison Dam on the Missouri River, southwest of Minot, North Dakota. *Programs*: Economic Development; Education; Energy; Judicial Committee Human Resources; Health; Natural Resources; Head Start. *Resources*: Operates schools at Mandaree, White Shield & Twin Buttes, ND; Museum at 4-Bears complex, New Town, ND; Library at Fort Berthold Community College. *Attractions*: 4 Bears Casino & Lodge; Community Pow-Wows through the summer months. *Publication*: Mandan, Hidatsa & Arikara Times, tribal newspaper. Fort Berthold Agency.

SPIRIT LAKE TRIBE
P.O. Box 359 • Fort Totten, ND 58335
(701) 766-4221 Fax 766-4126
Website: www.spiritlakenation.com
Myra Pearson, Chairperson; Douglas Yankton, Sr., Vice Chairperson
Lonna Jackson-Street, Tribal Secretary/Treasurer
Councilmembers:
Kim Three Irons, Fort Totten District Rep.
Douglas Yankton, Sr., Crow Hill District Rep.
Alberta Redfox, Woodlake District Rep.
Duane Jackson, Sr., Mission District Rep.
Joseph Vetch, Chief Judge; William D. Cavanugh, Associate Judge
Tracy Charboneau, Health Program Manager
Tribe: Sisseton-Wahpeton Sioux. *Enrolled members*: 7,250. *In residence*: 2,069, enrolled members, and 350 other Indians & 900 non-Indians. *Area*: 245,141 acres, about 405 square miles primarily in Benson County along the Sheyenne River. *Resources*: Health Center; Sioux Manufacturing Corp. *Programs*: Health; Early Childhood; Healthy Start; Head Start; Enrollment; Senior Services; Food Distribution; Victim Assistance; Water Resource Management; Vocational Rehabilitation; Fish & Wildlife; Environmental Protection. *Attractions*: Spirit Lake Casino & Lodge; annual Fort Totten Days Powwow (July). Fort Totten Agency.

STANDING ROCK SIOUX TRIBE
Standing Rock Reservation
Bldg. 1, N. Standing Rock Ave., P.O. Box D • Fort Yates, ND 58538
(701) 854-8500 Fax 854-7299; Website: www.standingrock.org
Dave Archambault II, Chairperson
Jesse B.J. McLaughlin, Vice Chairperson
Adele White, Secretary
Jon Eagle, Sr., Tribal Historic Preservation Officer
Councilmembers At-Large: Paul Archambault, Chad Harrison, Charles Walker, Mike Faith, Dana Yellow Fat, Kory McLaughlin
District Representatives:
Joe White Mountain, Jr. (Bear Soldier District)
Cody Two Bears (Cannon Ball District)
Frank White Bull (Kenel District)
James D. Dunn (Long Soldier District)
Samuel "Ben" Harrison (Porcupine District)
Caroline Thompson (Rock Creek District)
Robert Taken Alive (Little Eagle District)
Duane Claymore (Wakpala District)
Tribe: Sioux. *In residence*: 9,000 (4,300 Yankton Sioux in North Dakota, and 4,700 Teton Sioux in South Dakota.) *Area*: 306,000 acres (ND); 540,000 acres (SD) located 60 miles south of Bismarck, N.D., in North & South Dakota. *Resources*: United Tribes Technical College. *Programs*: Child Care & Welfare; Historic Preservation; Water Resources; Elderly Protection; Environmental Health; Food Distribution; Tobacco Prevention; Head Start. *Attraction*: Grand River Casino in Mobridge, SD. Standing Rock Agency.

TRENTON INDIAN SERVICE AREA (TISA)
Board of Directors, P.O. Box 210 • Trenton, ND 58853
(701) 774-0461 Fax 774-8003
Henry "Chig" LaDue, Chairperson; E-mail: tisachair@nccray.net;
Tribe: Turtle Mountain Chippewa. *Enrolled members*: 2,000. *Total population*: 3,000. *Area*: 6,700 acres, bounded on the north by the Canadian border and on the west by the Fort Peck Indian Reservation in Montana. *Attraction*: Trenton Indian Service Area Days each July. Turtle Mountain Agency.

TURTLE MOUNTAIN BAND OF CHIPPEWA INDIANS
4180 Hwy. 281, P.O. Box 900 • Belcourt, ND 58316
(701) 477-2600 Fax 477-6836; Website: www.tmbci.org
Richard McCloud, Chairperson
Elmer Davis, Jr. (District III Council Rep.), Vice Chairperson
Jolean Peltier, Tribal Secretary
William Falcon & Todd Falcon, District I Council Reps.
Elaine Lee & Gordon Falcon, District II Council Reps
Duane Rabbe, Jr. & Clay Moran, District III Council Reps
Carson Belgarde & Ted Henry, District IV Council Reps
Tribe: Chippewa. *Enrolled members*: 30,000+. *In residence*: 10,750. *Area*: 35,579 acres located west of the Canadian border. *Resources*: Turtle Mountain Community College; Ojibwa Indian School; Indian Health Service Hospital. *Programs*: Education; Child Care & Welfare; Community Health; Alcohol & Drug Prevention; Natural Resources; Human Resources; Senior Citizens; Environmental Protection; Enrollment; Employment & Training; Tourism & Recreation; Planning & Economic Development; Scholarships; Head Start. *Attraction*: Sky Dancer Hotel & Casino. Turtle Mountain Agency.

OKLAHOMA
**NOTE: There are no reservations in Oklahoma.
Instead, holdings by the various Oklahoma Indian tribes.**

ABSENTEE-SHAWNEE TRIBE
2025 S. Gordon Cooper Dr. • Shawnee, OK 74801
(405) 275-4030 Fax 275-5637
Website: www.astribe.com; E-mail: info@astribe.com
Edwina Butler-Wolfe, Governor; Isaac Gibson, Lt. Governor
John Raymond Johnson, Secretary; Leah Bates, Treasurer
Anthony Johnson, Representative
Henryetta Ellis, Director of Cultural Preservation
Tresha Spoon, Director of Education; E-mail: tresham@astribe.com
Tribe: Absentee-Shawnee. *Enrolled members*: 3,400. *In residence*: 1,500. *Area*: 33 acres. *Resources*: Cultural Center, Child Development Center, Little Axe Health Center, Li-Si-Wi-Nwi Medical Clinic; Shawnee Clinic, Wills Clinic; Shawnee Pharmacy; Gift Shop. *Programs*: Community Health & Prevention, Diabetes & Wellness; Education, After School Program; Gaming; Historic Preservation; Language; Housing; Elders Services; Counseling Services; Domestic Violence; Employment; Environmental Health & Engineering, Cultural Preservation, Social Service; scholarship awards. *Attraction*: Thunderbird Casino. *Publication*: The Absentee-Shawnee News, monthly newsletter. Shawnee Agency.

ALABAMA QUASSARTE TRIBAL TOWN
101 E. Broadway • Wetumka, OK 74883
(405) 452-3987 Fax 452-3968; Tarpie Yargee, Chief
Website: www.alabama-quassarte.org
Tribes: Alabama & Quassarte. *Enrolled members*: 380. *Area*: 878 acres. *Facility*: Library. *Programs*: Health, Education, Social Services, Economic Development. *Activities*: Annual Retreat, 3rd weekend in Sept. *Publication*: Newsletter. Okmulgee Agency.

THE APACHE TRIBE OF OKLAHOMA
511 E. Colorado St., P.O. Box 1330 • Anadarko, OK 73005
(800) 246-2942; (405) 247-9493 Fax 247-2686
Website: www.apachetribe.org
Lymon Guy, Chairperson; E-mail: chairman@apachetribe.org
Christopher Chalepah, Vice Chairperson
Yolanda Reyna, Secretry/Treasurer
Carmela Fowler & Bobby Jay, Committee Members
Ponce Leon, Tribal Administrator
Kim Pendarvis, Social Services Director
Tribe: Kiowa Apache. *Enrolled members*: 2,300. *In residence*: 550.
Attraction: Gold River Bingo & Casino. Anadarko Agency.

CADDO NATION
P.O. Box 487 • Binger, OK 73009
(405) 656-2344 Fax 656-2892; Website: www.caddonation-nsn.gov
Tamara Francis-Fourkiller, Chairperson; E-mail: tffourkiller.cn@gmail.com
Carol Ross, Vice Chairperson; E-mail: cross@caddonation.org
Phillip Martin, Secretary; E-mail: pmartin@caddonation.org
Marilyn McDonald, Treasurer; E-mail: mmcdonald@caddonation.org
Vacant, Anadarko Representative
Marilyn Threlkeld, Binger Rep.; E-mail: tthrelkeld@caddonation.org
Maureen "Mo" Owings, Ft. Cobb Rep.; E-mail: mowings@caddonation.org
Jennifer Wilson, OKC Rep.; E-mail: jwilson@caddonation.org
Tribe: Caddo. *Enrolled members*: 5,367. *Facilities*: Caddo Heritage Museum & Library - sponsors workshops on cultural traditions. *Resources*: Hasinai Center; Museum. *Programs*: Social Services; Child Care & Welfare; Alcohol/ Drug Abuse; Aging & Elderly Nutrition; Community Health; Education; Environmental; Child Welfare; Historic Preservation; Housing & Employment; Head Start. *Attractions*: Traditional dances held throughout the year including the annual Clara Brown Dance (mid-September), Murrow Family Dance (June) & Hasinai Youth Camp (June), Annual Dance (November). *Publication*: Caddo Nation News, monthly newsletter. Anadarko Agency.

CHEROKEE NATION OF OKLAHOMA
22361 Bald Hill Rd. (74464), P.O. Box 948 • Tahlequah, OK 74465
(800) 256-0671; (918) 456-0671 Fax 458-5580
Website: www.cherokee.org; E-mail: council-public@cherokee.org
Bill John Baker, Principal Chief
 E-mail: bill-baker@cherokee.org
S. Joe Crittenden, Deputy Principal Chief
E-mail: joe-crittenden@cherokee.org
Chuck Hoskin, Jr., Secretary of State
Todd Hembree, Attorney General
Lisa Fields, Court Administrator
Washington, DC office: 126 C St., NW • Washington, DC 20001
(202) 393-7007 (website: www.cnwo.org)

District Councilmembers: E-mail: council-public@cherokee.org
Rex Jordan, District 1 (Hulbert) 918-772-3240
 E-mail: rex-jordan@cherokee.org
Joe Byrd, District 2 (Tahlequah) 918-316-9463
 E-mail: joe-byrd@cherokee.org
David Walkingstick, District 3 (Tahlequah) 918-456-4256
 E-mail: david-walkingstick@cherokee.org
Don Garvin, District 4 (Muskogee) 918-616-3961
 E-mail: don-garvin@cherokee.org
David Thornton, District 5 (Vian) 918-773-6067
 E-mail: david-thornton@cherokee.org
Bryan Warner, District 6 (Sallisaw) 918-570-9731
 E-mail: bryan-warner@cherokee.org
Frankie Hargis, District 7 (Stilwell) 918-316-9454
 E-mail: Frankie-hargis@cherokee.org
Shawn Crittenden, District 8 (Stilwell) 918-506-9757
 E-mail: shawn-crittenden@cherokee.org
Curtis G. Snell, District 9 (Rose) 918-868-2800
 E-mail: Curtis-snell@cherokee.org
Harley Buzzard, District 10 (Eucha) 918-253-8665
 E-mail: Harley-buzzard@cherokee.org
Victoria Vazquez, District 11 (Welch) 918-323-2980
Dick Lay, District 12 (Ochelata) 918-822-2981
 E-mail: dick-lay@cherokee.org
Buel Anglen, District 13 (Claremore) 918-527-6803
 E-mail: buel-anglen@cherokee.org
Keith-Austin, District 14 (Claremore) 918-508-9116
 E-mail: keith-austin@cherokee.org
Janees Taylor, District 15 (Pryor) 918-525-2086
 E-mail: janees-taylor@cherokee.org
Jack D. Baker & Wanda Hatfield, Council Members-At-Large
Tribe: Cherokee of Oklahoma. *Enrolled members*: 317,000. *Resources*: Cherokee Heritage Center; Cherokee Nation Business Enterprises; Cherokee Nation Radio Show, "Cherokee Voices, Cherokee Sounds" 102.1 FM on Sundays from 8-9 a.m. with host Dennis Sixkiller. *Programs*: Education; Health & Wellness; Cultural; Language; Child Care Services; Children, Youth & Family Services; Human Resources; Housing; Natural Resources; Employment; Head Start. *Attraction*: Casino. Eastern Oklahoma Regional Office.

CHEYENNE & ARAPAHO TRIBES
100 Red Moon Circle P.O. Box 38 • Concho, OK 73022
(800) 247-4612; (405) 422-7430 Fax 422-7417/7424/8227
Website: www.c-a-tribes.org; Eddie Hamilton, Governor
Cornell Sankey, Lt. Governor; Ida Hoffman, Chief of Staff
Robert Wilson, Chief Executive Policy Analyst
Kay Mackety, Treasury Director
Teresa Dorsett, Executive Director of Administration
Lisa Martin, Tribal Council Coordinator
Robert Wilson, Chief Executive Policy Analyst
Nikki Factor-Navarro, Social Services Director
Carrie Whitlow, Education Director
Nicholas Barton, Dept.of Health Executive Director
Chester Whiteman, Director of Economic Development
William Tallbear, Housing Director
Tony Choate, Executive Officer – Media Relations
 E-mail: tony.choate@chickasaw.net
Rosemary Stephens, Editor-in-Chief "Tribal Tribune" & Public Information
Officer; E-mail: rmstephens@c-a-tribes.org (422-7446)
Tribes: Cheyenne & Arapaho. *Enrolled members*: 11,000. Cheyenne & Arapaho *in residence*: 5,000. *Other Indian population*: 5,000. *Tribal Trust Property Area*: 10,200 acres; *Individual Trust Property Area*: 70,000 acres. *Resources*: Tribal College. *Programs*: Education; Social Services; Community Health; Culture; Diabetes Wellness & Fitness; Substance Abuse; Elderly Care; Food Distribution; Indian Child Welfare; Information Technology; Planning & Economic Development; Crisis Assistance; Housing. *Activities*: Annual Summerfest in August. *Attractions*: Lucky Star Casino's: Clinton & Concho; Feather Warrior Casino's: Canton & Watonga. *Publication*: Tribal Tribune, monthly newsletter. Concho Field Office.

CHICKASAW NATION
801 N. Mississippi, P.O. Box 1548 • Ada, OK 74821
(580) 436-7280 Fax 436-4287; Website: www.chickasaw.net
Bill Anoatubby, Governor; Jefferson Keel, Lt. Governor
Mark Holmes Colbert, Chief Justice
Pat Woods, Director of Operations/Administrator
The Chickasaw Tribal Legislature, P.O. Box 2669 • Ada, OK 74821
(580) 436-7280/1460 Fax 436-4287
District Legislative Representatives:
 Pontotoc District: Toby Perkins, Nancy Elliott, Katie Case,
  Dean McManus, Lisa Billy

Pickens District: David Woerz, Connie Barker, Linda Briggs, Shana Tate Hammond, David Woerz
Panola District: Beth Alexander
Tishomingo District: Scott Wood, Timothy Colbert, Steven Woods
Tribe: Chickasaw. *Enrolled members*: 38,000 in U.S.; 12,000+ in residence. *Area*: 7,648 square miles inside boundary; 2,000+ acres owned by the Chickasaw Nation. *Programs*: Cultural; Education; Health; Social Services; Youth & Family Services; Housing; Head Start. *Resources*: Medical Center; Chickasaw Cultural Center; Chickasaw Foundation; Chickasaw Outpost; Carter Seminary in Ardmore, Chickasaw Council House Museum in Tishomingo; Tribal Museum & Library in Ada; Chickasaw Press; McSwain Theatre (owned & operated by the Chickasaw Nation); Chickasaw TVKCNP 89.5 FM (Chickasaw Community Radio). *Attractions*: WinStar World Casino & Hotel; Chickasaw Festival & Annual Meeting in Tishomingo, OK in the Fall; Chickasaw Nation Industries, Deryl Wright, President/CEO. *Publications*: Chickasaw Times, monthly tribal newspaper; Chickasaw Dictionary. Chickasaw Agency.

CHOCTAW NATION OF OKLAHOMA
529 N. 16th St., P.O. Box 1210 • Durant, OK 74702
(800) 522-6170; (580) 924-8280 Fax 924-1150
Website: www.choctawnation.com
Gary Batton, Chief; E-mail: gbatton@choctawnation.com
Jack Austin, Jr., Assistant Chief
Judy Allen, Senior Executive Officer of Tribal Relations
 E-mail: jallen@choctawnation.com
District Councilmembers:
 Thomas Williston, District 1 - Rt. 2, Box 554, Idabel, OK 74745
 (580) 212-4776; E-mail: twilliston@choctawnation.com
 Tony Ward, District 2 - 603 N. Bock St. 259, Broken Bow, OK 74728
 (580) 380-6729; E-mail: tward@choctawnation.com
 Kenny Bryant, District 3 - Rt. 1, Box 5060, Talhina, OK 74571
 (918) 567-3473
 Delton Cox, District 4 – P.O. Box 29, Pocola, OK 74902 (918) 436-1884
 Ron Perry, District 5 – Stigler, OK 74902 (918) 967-2616
 E-mail: rperry@choctawnation.com
 Joe Coley, District 6 – P.O. Box 661, Willburton, OK 74578
 (918) 465-0189; E-mail: jcoley@choctawnation.com
 Jack Austin, District 7 – P.O. Box 725, Clayton, OK 74536
 (918) 569-4804; E-mail: jaustin@choctawnation.com
 Perry Thompson, District 8 – Rt. E, Box 846, Hugo, OK 74743
 (580) 326-9466; E-mail: pthompson@choctawnation.com
 Ted Dosh, District 9 – 28752 DR 70 E, Bennington, OK 74723
 (580) 847-2536; Email: tdosh@choctawnation.com
 Anthony Dillard, District 10 – 1182 S. Nix Rd., Caney, OK 74533
 (580) 775-4723; E-mail: adillard@choctawnation.com
 Bob Pate, District 11 – P.O. Box 1695, McAlester, OK 74502
 (918) 426-7647; E-mail: bpate@choctawnation.com
 James Frazier, District 12 – P.O. Box 134, Coalgate, OK 74538
 (580) 927-2727; E-mail: jfrazier@choctawnation.com
Judy Allen, Tribal Relations; E-mail: jallen@choctawnation.com
Teresa Jackson, Health Services Senior Executive Officer
 E-mail: tjackson@choctawnation.com
Brad Mallett, Senior Executive Office – Division of Legal & Compliance
 E-mail: bmallett@choctawnation.com
Theresa Jackson, Member Services Senor Executive Officer
 E-mail: tjackson@choctawnation.com
Jim Parrish, Director of Education/School Programs
 E-mail: jparrish@choctawnation.com
Joy Culbreath, Executive Director of Education
 E-mail: jculbreath@choctawnation.com
Sue Folsom, Executive Director - Cultural Resources, Museum,
 Labor Day Festival; E-mail: suefolsom@choctawnation.com
Kay Jackson, Director of Cultural Events
 E-mail: kjackson@choctawnation.com
Kevin Gwin, Director of Special Projects
 E-mail: kgwin@choctawnation.com
Pam Waugh, Tvshka Homma Project Coordinator
Seth Fairchild, Executive Director of Chahta Foundation
Thomas Kanuch, Senior Executive Officer of Commerce
Billy Hamilton, Business Resource Center Program Director
Ian Thompson, Director of Historic Preservation Dept.
 E-mail: ithompson@choctawnation.com
Regina Green, Museum Director (918) 569-4465
 E-mail: rgreen@choctawnation.com
Lisa Reed, Executive Director of Public Relations (800) 522-6170 Ext. 2245
 P.O. Box 1210, Durant, OK 74702
 E-mail: lisareed@choctawnation.com
Tribe: Choctaw. *Enrolled members*: 191,500, (third largest tribe by population in U.S.). Located within ten and a half counties in southeastern Oklahoma. *Resources*: Chahta Foundation; Choctaw Nation Museum at Tvshka Homma; Native American Business Resource Center; Wheelock Academy Museum at

former Wheelock Campus in Millerton, OK; Jones Academy (residential boarding school, K-12; School of Choctaw Language Business Resource Center; Choctaw Bookstore. *Programs*: Community & Social Services; Language; Health; Education; STAR (Success Through Academic Recognition); Historic Preservation; Housing; Financial; Communication; Senior Heritage Resource; Head Start. *Attractions*: Choctaw Casino Resort Hotel; annual commemorative "Trail of Tears" Walk, Skullyville, OK; annual 4-day Labor Day Festival, at tribal capital, Tushka Homma, OK; Choctaw Cinema; Veterans Ceremony, Nov. 11th each year at Tushka Homma. *Publications*: "Bishinik," monthly newspaper; children's books; history book; dictionary; language curriculum: Choctaw definer; annual calendar. Talihina Field Office.

CITIZEN POTAWATOMI NATION
1601 S. Gordon Cooper Dr. • Shawnee, OK 74801
(800) 880-9880; (405) 275-3121 Fax 275-0198
Website: www.potawatomi.org
John A. Barrett, Jr., Chairperson
 E-mail: rbarrett@potawatomi.org
Linda Capps, Vice Chairperso
 E-mail: lcapps@potawatomi.org
D. Wayne Trousdale, Secretary-Treasurer
 E-mail: dtrousdale@potawatomi.org
District Representatives:
 Roy Slavin, District 1; Eva Marie Carney, District 2
 Robert Whistler, District 3; John Boursaw, District 4
 Gene Lambert, District 5; Rande Payne, District 6
 Mark Johnson, District 7; Dave Carney, District 8
 Paul Wesselhoft, District 9; David Joe Barrett, District 10
 Lisa Kraft, District 11; Paul Schmidlkofer, District 12
 Bobbie Bowden, District 13
 Tesia Zientek, Administrator/Education Director
 E-mail: tesia.zientek@potawatomi.org
 E-mail: college@potawatomi.org
 Michael Dodson, Public Information Director
 Angela Renee Riley, Chief Justice; Philip D. Lujan, Chief District Judge
Tribe: Citizen Band Potawatomi. *Enrolled members*: 8,500 in Oklahoma; 25,500, nationwide. *Area*: 300 acres (in trust). *Resources*: Tribal Museum; Archives & Library; Historic Preservation Office; Child Development Center; Cultural Heritage Center; Gathering of Potawatomi Nations. *Programs*: Women, Infants, and Children (WIC) programs; Nutrition; Human Resources; Health; Social Services; Tribal Heritage Project - digital recordings by tribal members of family histories, with photos & historical documents & recordings; Language; Veterans Historical Project - digital audio/video; Family Reunion Festival - last weekend in June each year to re-establish family/tribal ties & culture unique to CPN; Inter-Tribal Powwow - each October (competitive powwow). *Attractions*: FireLake Grand Casino; Trading Post. *Publications*: How-Ni-Kan, tribal newsletter; Grandfather, Tell Me A Story (oral history book). Under jurisdiction of Southern Plains Regional Office.

THE COMANCHE NATION
584 NW Bingo Rd. (73507), P.O. Box 908 • Lawton, OK 73502
(877) 492-4988; (580) 492-3240 Fax 492-3796
Website: www.comanchenation.com
William Nelson, Sr., Chairperson
 E-mail: williamn@comanchenation.com
Susan Cothern, Vice Chairperson
 E-mail: susanc@comanchenation.com
Jerry Tahsequah, Secretary/Treasurer
Business Committee: No. 1, Johnny Poahway; No. 2, Eddie Ahdosy;
 No. 3, Ron Redelk; No. 4, Clyde Narconey
 Jimmy Arterberry, Tribal Administrator
 E-mail: administration@comanchenation.com
 Delores Twohatchet, Higher Education Director
 Jolene Schonchin, Public Information Officer
 E-mail: pio@comanchenation.com
Tribe: Comanche. *Enrolled members*: 16,400; *In residence*: 7,765 residing in & around Lawton & southwest Oklahoma. *Resources*: Comanhe Nation College; Comanche National Museum & Cultural Center; Outreach Centers; Community Centers; Tourism Center. *Programs*: Health; Higher Education; Historic Preservation Office; Native American Graves Protection & Repatriation Act Office; Language Immersion Program (See Comanche Language & Cultural Preservation Committee Website: www.comanchelanguage.org); Social Services; Cultural; Student Services; Food Distribution; Economic Development; Child Welfare, Development & Support. *Activities*: Comanche Nation Fair, in early October; Powwows. *Attractions*: Casinos: Comanche Nation Casino, Comanche Red River Casino, Comanche Spur Casino, Comanche Star Casino. Water Park. *Publication*: The Comanche Nation News E-mail: Comanche_news@yahoo.com; Language Newsletter. Anadarko Agency.

DELAWARE TRIBE OF INDIANS

5100 Tuxedo Blvd. • Bartlesville, OK 74006
(918) 337-6590 Fax 337-6591; Website: www.delawaretribe.org
E-mail: tribe@delawaretribe.org
Chester "Chet" Brooks, Chief (337-6593)
 E-mail: cbrooks@delawaretribe.org
Bonnie Jo Griffith, Assistant Chief
 E-mail: bgriffith@delawaretribe.org
Charles Randall, Secretary; E-mail: crandall@delawaretribe.org
Councilmembers: Larry Joe Brooks, Benita Shea, Nate Young IV,
 Dr. Nicky Kay Michael
Allan Barnes, Tribal Manager (337-6573)
 E-mail: abarnes@delawaretribe.org
Don Mason, Chief Judge
Anita Mathis, Cultural Resources Director (337-6595)
 E-mail: amathis@delawaretribe.org
Dr. Brice Obemeyer, Historic Preservation Director (335-7026)
 E-mail: bobermeyer@delawaretribe.org
Curtis Zunigha, Family & Children Services Director (879-2189)
 E-mail: czunigha@delawaretribe.org
Nancy Sumpter, Wellness Center Coordinator (337-6586)
 E-mail: nsumpter@delawaretribe.org
Mike Taylor, Enironmental Director (337-6584)
 E-mail: mtaylor@delawaretribe.org
Greg Brown, Delaware Indian News Editor (286-5476)
 E-mail: gbrown@delawaretribe.org
Trust Board:
Chester "Chet" Brooks, Chairperson
Roger Stewart, Secretary; E-mail: rstewart@delawaretribe.org
John Sumpter, Treasurer; E-mail: longwalkerlongwalk@sbcglobal.net
Larry Joe Brooks, Homer Scott, Mary Jo Peterson, Members
Tribe: Lenni Lenape. *Project*: Lenape Talking Dictionary - the official online talking dictionary for the Delaware Tribe's native language, Lenape. This project is ongoing & where possible, includes full translations, usage examples, & audio recordings of Lenape words & phrases - E-mail: lenapelang@aol.com. *Resources*: Community Wellness Center. *Programs*: Community Services; Health; Educational Assistance; Cultural & Historic Preservation; Language Revitalization; Housing; Elders' Services. *Attractions*: Casino Oklahoma; Annual Delaware Powwow in May. *Publication*: Delaware Indian News. Eastern Oklahoma Regional Office.

THE DELAWARE NATION

31064 State Hwy. 281, P.O. Box 825 • Anadarko, OK 73005
(405) 247-2448 Fax 247-9393; Website: www.delawarenation.com
E-mail: info@delawarenation.com
Deborah Dotson, President
 E-mail: ddotson@delawarenation.com
Michael McLane, Vice President
 E-mail: mmclane@delawarenation.com
Sue Stone, Secretary; Matt Watkins, Treasurer
Terry Williams, Councilmember
 E-mail: twilliams@delawarenation.com
Janice Maddox, Tribal Administrator
 E-mail: jmaddox@delawarenation.com
Nekole Alligood, Director of NAGPRA
 Email: nalligood@delawarenation.com
Sonnie Allen, Director of Cultural Preservation
 E-mail: sallen@delawarenation.com
Janelle Archita, Finance Director
 E-mail: jarchita@delawarenation.com
Heather Cozard, Social Services Director
 E-mail: hcozard@delawarenation.com
Kyle Harris, Public Relations Director
 E-mail: kharris@delawarenation.com
Jenna Craft, Government Relations Director
 E-mail: jcraft@delawarenation.com
Tribe: Delaware. *Population served*: 950. *Area*: 2,400 acres held jointly with the Wichita & Caddo Tribes. *Programs*: Aging; Environmental, Family & Social Services, Housing, Cultural Preservation, Vocational Rehabilitation. Resources: Museum & Library. *Attractions*: Gift shop; Casino in development. *Publications*: Cooley's Traditional Stories of the Delaware, and Turtle Tales: Oral Traditions of the Delaware of Western Oklahoma, both edited by Duane Hale. Anadarko Agency.

EASTERN SHAWNEE TRIBE OF OKLAHOMA

10080 S. Bluejacket Rd. • Wyandotte, OK 74370
(866) 666-3489; (918) 666-5151 Fax 666-3325
Website https://www.estoo-nsn.gov; E-mail: chief@estoo.net
Glenna J. Wallace, Chief (2006-present); (666-2435)
Jack Ross, 2nd Chief
Committeemembers: Larry Kropp, 1st Council; Shawn Daugherty, 2nd Council;

Wanda Stovall, 3rd Council
 Judy Brown, Secretary; Cheryl Barnes, Treasurer
Tribe: Eastern Shawnee. Bluejacket Complex, West Seneca, MO (see listing under MO). *Enrolled members*: 2,700. Located in Missouri & Oklahoma. *Resources*: Bearskin Healthcare & Wellness Center; Museum; Captain Library. *Programs*: Education; Cultural Preservation; Children & Family Services; Health & Social Services; Suicide Prevention; Agency on Aging; Environmental Protection; Land Management; Natural Resources; Human Resources; Gaming. *Resources*: Wellness Center; George J. Captain Library. *Attraction*: Bordertown Bingo & Casino; Indigo Sky Casino; RV Park. *Publication*: The Shooting Star, newsletter. Miami Agency.

FORT SILL APACHE TRIBE

Oklahoma office: 43187 US Hwy. 281
Route 2, Box 121 • Apache, OK 73507
(877) 826-0726; (580) 588-2298 Fax 588-3133
New Mexico office: 20885 Frontage Rd. • Deming, NM 88030
(575) 544-0073 Fax 544-0224; Website: www.fortsillapache-nsn.gov
Jeff Haozous, Chairperson (2002-present)
Lori Gooday Ware, Vice Chairperson
Leland Michael Darrow, Secretary-Treasurer
Committeemembers: Jeanette Mann, Loretta Buckner, Robin Isom,
Tribe: Fort Sill Chiricahua Warm Springs Apache. *Enrolled members*: 650. *Resources*: Fort Sill Apache Industries. *Programs*: Language; Environmental & Energy. *Attraction*: Fort Sill Apache Casino in Lawton, OK. Anadarko Agency.

IOWA NATION OF OKLAHOMA

3560 West 76th Rd., Rt. 1, Box 721 • Perkins, OK 74059
(888) 336-4692; (405) 547-2402 Fax 547-1032
Website: www.iowanation.org
Business Committee:
Bobby Walkup, Chairperson; E-mail: bwalkup@iowanation.org
Edgar B. Kent, Jr., Vice Chair; E-mail: ekent@iowanation.org
Chalis Cox, Secretary; E-mail: ccox@iowanation.org
Judith Shores, Treasurer; E-mail: jshores@iowanation.org
Eagleboy McClellan, Councilperson; E-mail: emcclellan@iowanation.org
Administration:
Renee Hagler, Tribal Administrator; E-mail: rhagler@iowanation.org
Kelly Myers, Gaming Commission Chairperson
Linda Bigsoldier, CEO Tribal Enterprises
Sam Caruso, Tribal Representative; Linda Shipley, Attorney General
Sandy Tharp-Thee, Librarian; E-mail: stharp@iowanation.org
Tribe: Iowa. All tribes living within the jurisdiction. *Enrolled members*: 500. *Resources*: Library; Health Clinic. *Programs*: Social Services; Higher Education; Early Childhood Development; Child Protection Services; Tribal Assistance; Law Enforcement; Direct Employment Assistance; Gaming; Human Resources; Enrollment; Economic Development; Substance Abuse; Environmental. *Attractions*: Cimarron Casino; RV Park; Bah-Kho-Je Gallery; Smokeshop; annual powwow in late June. *Publication*: Bah-Kho-Je Journal, tribal newsletter. Shawnee Agency.

THE KAW NATION

698 Grandview Dr., P.O. Box 50 • Kaw City, OK 74641
(866) 404-5297; (580) 269-2552 Fax 269-2301
Website: www.kawnation.com
Jacque Secondine Hensley, Chairperson
Lynn Dunson, Vice Chairperson; Terry Pepper, Secretary
Councilmembers: Erin Kekahbah, Tahagena "Gena" Warren
Cheri Dunn, Cruz Maldonado
Terri Humble, Director of Self-Governance
 E-mail: thumble@kawnation.com
Donna Villa, Cultural Committee President
Jeff Washko, Kaw Enterprise Development Director
Crystal Douglas, Kanza Museum Director
 E-mail: crystal_douglas@kawnation.com
Lauren Murray, Librarian & Kanza News Editor
 E-mail: lmurray@kawnation.com
Valerie Devol, Attorney General
Tribe: Kaw. *Enrolled members*: 3,125. *Area*: 1,400 acres in Oklahoma & Kansas. *Facilities*: Kaw City, Newkirk, Ponca City, Braman, Chilocco. *Resources*: Kanza Health & Wellness Center; White Eagle Health Clinic; Pawnee Health Center; Osage Health Clinic; Kanza Museum; Kaw Nation Library & Learning Center. *Programs/Departments*: Diabetes Awareness; Cultural Preservation; Educational & Social Services; Child Welfare & Support Services; Community Development; Domestic Violence; Women's Health; Housing Authority; Human Resources; Food Services; Emergency Management; Youth; Kaw Language; Environmental; Academic Scholarships; Self-Governance. *Attractions*: SouthWind Casino/ Bingo; Kaw City SouthWind Casino; Braman SouthWind Casino; annual Intertribal Powwow (2nd Thursday August); Smoke Shop. *Publication*: Kanza News, quarterly newsletter. Pawnee Agency.

KIALEGEE TRIBAL TOWN
627 E. Hwy. 9, P.O. Box 332 • Wetumka, OK74883
(405) 452-3262 Fax 452-3413; Website: http://kialegeetribal.webstarts.com
Tiger Hobia, Mekko/Town King; E-mail: tiger.hobia@kialegeetribe.net
Thomas Givens, First Warrior; E-mail: thomas.givens@kialegeetribe.net
Lynelle Shatswel, Secretary; Agnes Givens, Treasurer
Della Sherill, Lois Harjo, Justina Yargee, Advisors
Henry Harjo, EPA Director; E-mail: henry.harjo@kialegeeetribe.net
Beth Peterson, EDA Board Chairperson
Ardeena Angela, Program Director
　E-mail: ardeena.angela@kialegeetribe.net
Martha Givens, Health Board Chairperson
June Fixico, Education Board Chairperson
Tribe: Muscogee Creek. *Enrolled members*: 440.
Publication: Newsletter. Okmulgee Agency.

KICKAPOO TRIBE OF OKLAHOMA
P.O. Box 70 • McLoud, OK 74851
(405) 964-2075 Fax 964-4265
Website: www.kickapootribeofoklahoma.com
David Pacheco, Jr., Chairperson; E-mail: dpacheco@okkt.net
Nathan Gonzales, Vice Chairperson; E-mail: ngonzales@okkt.net
Patricia Gonzales, Secretary
　E-mail: patriciagnzales@kickapootribeofoklahma.com
George Lopez, Treasurer; E-mail: glopez@okkt.net
Janetta Mahtapene, Councilperson; E-mail: janetta.mahtapene@okkt.net
Kristen Wilson, Executive Director
　E-mail: kwilson@kickapootribeofoklahoma.com
Tonia George, Director of Education
　E-mail: tgeorge@kickapootribeofoklahoma.com
David James, Director of Social Services; E-mail: david.james@okkt.net
Greg Bigler, Attorney General; E-mail: gdbigler@swbell.net
Tribe: Kickapoo. *Enrolled members*: 2,000 in Oklahoma & 500 in Kansas.
Programs: Education; Human Resources; Environmental; Social Services;
Nutrition; Child Welfare; Kickapoo Language; Scholarship; Tribal Youth;
Gaming; Head Start. *Attraction*: Kickapoo Casino. Shawnee Agency.

KIOWA TRIBE OF OKLAHOMA
100 Kiowa Way, P.O. Box 369 • Carnegie, OK 73015
(855) 228-9975; (580) 654-2300 Fax 654-8412
Website https://www.kiowatribe.org; E-mail: kbo@kiowatribe.org
Matthew M. Komalty, Chairperson
Charles Domebo Eisenberger, Vice Chairperson
Rhonda J. Ahhaitty, Secretary; Renee M. Plata, Treasurer
Councilmembers: Dave Geimausaddle, Anita L. Onco Johnson,
Thomas Kaulaity, Ronald C. Poolaw, Sr. , Modina M. Waters,
Ben Lucero Hovakah-Wolf
Ewell Longhorn, Executive Director; E-mail: admin@kiowatribe.org
David Bearshield, Executive Secretary; E-mail: dbearshield@kiowatribe.org
James E. Nelson, Jr., Higher Education Director (654-7007)
　E-mail: highered@kiowatribe.org
Amie Tah-Bone, Museum Director; E-mail: museum@kiowatribe.org
Keith Vasquez, Public Relations Officer
Tribe: Kiowa. *Enrolled members*: 11,500. *Facilities*: Indian City USA; Red
Buffalo Hall; Kiowa Museum. *Programs*: Community Health; Teen Suicide
Prevention; Alcohol & Drug Abuse; Kiowa Culture Preservation Authority
(KCPA); Indian Child Welfare; Child Care; Aging; Environmental; NAGPRA;
Higher Education; Job Placement & Training; Enrollment; Transit Program;
Social Services; Food Distribution; Head Start. *Attractions*: Kiowa Casino;
Kiowa Voices Radio Show on 98.5 FM; Kiowa Tribe Live Video Channel; Gift
Shop. *Publication*: Kiowa Newsletter, monthly newspaper. Anadarko Agency.

MIAMI TRIBE OF OKLAHOMA
3410 P St., NW, P.O. Box 1326 • Miami, OK 74355
(918) 541-1300 Fax 542-7260; Website: www.miamination.com
Douglas G. Lankford, Chief; Dustin Olds, Second Chief
Donya Williams, Secretary-Treasurer
Tera Hatley, First Councilperson; Scott Willard, Second Councilperson
Gloria Steed, Education Director; Administrative Executive Officer
David Efird, Tribal Grievance Committee Chairperson
Misty Ellison, Director of Leonard Learning Center
William Chase, Tribal Finance Officer
Julie Olds, Cultural Resources Officer & Tribal Newspaper Editor (541-2180)
　E-mail: jolds@maimination.com
Barbara Mullin, Tribal Programs Officer
Dustin Olds, Natural Resources Officer
Diane Hunter, Tribal Historic Preservation Officer (541-8966)
Jerry Lankford, Gaming Commission Chairperson
Robin Lasg, Tribal Attorney/Gaming Commissioner
Charles Tripp, District Court Judge
Jewel Cunningham Tribal Ambassador & Princess

Tribe: Miami. *Enrolled members*: 3,800+. *Resources*: Leonard Learning Center
(preschool); Library; Nutrition Center; Miami Nation Enterprises. *Programs*:
Community Services; Social Services; Child Care & Welfare; Education (The
Yaamia Project that maintains a liaison between the Miami Tribe of Oklahoma
and Miami University, Ohio); Economic Development; Employment & Training;
Cultural Resources; Historic Preservation; Natural Resources; Housing;
Elder's; Gaming. *Attractions*: Winter Gathering (first Saturday in January);
Annual National Gathering (last week of May, 1st week in June); language
camp, family day. *Publication*: "Atotankiki Myaamiaki," Miami Nation
Newspaper. Miami Agency.

MODOC TRIBE OF OKLAHOMA
22 N. Eight Tribes Trail • Miami, OK 74354
(918) 542-1190 Fax 542-5415
Website: www.modoctribe.net; E-mail: modoctribe@cableone.net
Bill G. Follis, Chief & Tribal Administrator
Judy Cobb, Second Chief; Ramona Rosiere, Secretary/Treasurer
Phil Follis, 1st Councilperson; Theodore McCullum, 2nd Councilperson
Troy LittleAxe, Assistant Tribal Administrator & Tribal Attorney
Jack Shadwick, Tribal Registrar Historian & Education Director
John Ballard, Tribal Planner (542-6117)
Tribe: Modoc. *Resources*: Tribal Archives & Library; Video Training Center/IT;
Modoc Smoke Shop; Bison Range. *Programs*: Health & Wellness; Education;
Social Services; Child Care Development; Children & Family Services; Women
Against Violence; Housing, Recycling & Environmental. *Attraction*: Bison
Range; Smoke Shop. Miami Agency.

MUSCOGEE (CREEK) NATION OF OKLAHOMA
P.O. Box 158 • Okmulgee, OK 74447
(800) 482-1979; (918) 756-1410 Fax 756-6812
(918) 732-7605 Fax 756-2911/1434 Website: www.mcnnc.com
James Floyd, Principal Chief; Louis Hicks, 2nd Chief
Charles "Bo" Colbert, Chief of Staff (732-7625)
Judy Haumpy, Tribal Administrator (732-7620)
　E-mail: jhaumpy@mcn-nsn.gov
John Blue, Acting Secretary of the Nation
Neenah Tiger, Secretary of Commnity & Human Services
Thomas Yahola, Speaker; David Hill, Sgt.-At-Arms
Kevin Dellinger, Attorney General
Greg Anderson, Secretary of Education, Employment & Training
Johnnie Greene, Chairperson-Health, Education & Welfare
Darrell Proctor, Chairperson-Land, Natural Resources & Cultural Preservation
Robert Hufft, Chairperson-Business, Finance & Justice
Shoneen Alexander-Ross, Acting Secretary of Health
Dr. Wayne Johnson, Department of Education & Training
Buddy York, Gaming Commissioner
Brad Fox, Housing; Bill S. Fife, Commerce
Cherrah Giles, Community & Human Services; Jeff Fife, Interior.
Neely Tsoodle, Mvskoke Media Director
National Council members: P.O. Box 158, Okmulgee, OK 74447
Creek District: David Hill, Seat A; Dode W. Barnett, Seat B;
Muskogee District: Pete Beaver, Seat A; Joyce C. Deere, Seat B
McIntosh District: Darrell Proctor, Seat A; Adam Jones III, Seat B;
Okfuskee District: Randall Hicks, Seat A; Mitch Jack, Seat B
Okmulgee District: Del Beaver, Seat A; James Jennings, Seat B;
Tukvptce District: Rufus Scott, Seat A; Thomas Yahola, Seat B
Tulsa District: Robert Hufft, Seat A, 2nd Speaker; Lucien Tiger III, Seat B
Wagoner/Roger/Mayes District: Johnnie Greene, Seat A;
　Mark Randolph, Seat B
Tribe: Muscogee Creek. *Enrolled members*: 71,000. *Area*: 6,000 acres located
in an eight county area in northeastern Oklahoma--bounded on the north at
Admiral Street in the city of Tulsa, and on the south by the Canadian River.
Resources: Claremore Indian Hospital; College of Muscogee Nation; Creek
Council House Museum; Library; Mvskoke Radio KOKL 1240. *Programs*:
Health Centers (Eufaula Indian Health Center; Koweta Indian Health Center;
Sapulpa Indian Health Center; Okmulgee Indian Health Center; Tulsa Indian
Health Resource Center); Education; Cultural; Housing; Child Care; Children &
Family Services; Communications; Senior Services; Economic Development;
Tourism; Head Start. *Attractions*: Green Corn, Creek Festival, & Creek Rodeo.
Publication: Muscogee Nation News & Media Alert. Okmulgee Field Station.

THE OSAGE NATION
627 Grandview, P.O. Box 1449 • Pawhuska, OK 74056
(800) 320-8742; (918) 287-5555/5632 Fax 287-5562/9
Website: www.osagenation-nsn.gov
E-mail: ootc@osagenation-nsn.gov
Geoffrey Standing Bear, Principal Chief
Raymond Red Corn, Assistant Principal Chief
Deirdre Bigheart, Director of Operations
Debbie Atterberry, Sr. Executive Advisor
Chris White, Executive Director Government Affairs

Linda LaZelle, Communications Officer
Patrick Lewis, Sgt. at Arms; Vann Bighorse, Cultural Director
Angela Pratt, Speaker of the Congress (287-5691)
  E-mail: apratt@osagecongress-nsn.gov
Alice Buffalohead, 2nd Speaker of the Congress
  E-mail: abuffalohead@osagecongress-nsn.gov
Congress members: Shannon Edwards, John Maker, Archie Mason,
James Norris, Ron Shaw, MD, William "Kugee" Supernaw, Joe Tillman,
R.J. Walker, Maria Whitehorn
Ida Doyle, Director of Education
  E-mail: idoyle@osagenation-nsn.gov
Hallie Winter, Curator/Museum Director (287-5222)
  E-mail: hwinter@osagenation-nsn.gov
Herman M. Lookout, Language Director
  E-mail: langinfo@osagenation-nsn.gov
Everett Waler, Chairperson of the Minerals Council
Charles Lohah, Nation Chief Justice
Holli Wells, Attorney General
Mark Simms, Gaming Enterprise Board Chairperson
Tribe: Osage. Enrolled members: 6,000. Resources: Wah Zha Zhi Cultural Center; Early Learning Center; Osage Museum; Wah Zha Zhi Press. Resources: Pawhuska & Fairfax Language Centers. Programs: Education; Health & Wellness; Housing; Social Services; Food Distribution; Childcare & Child Support Services; Language; Diabetes Health; Language; Mineral Council; Human Resources; Environmental; Gaming Enterprise; Employment; Head Start. Attraction: Osage Million Dollar Elm Casino. Publication: Newsletter. Osage Agency.

OTOE-MISSOURIA TRIBE
8151 Hwy. 177 • Red Rock, OK 74651
  (877) 692-6863; (580) 723-4466 Fax 723-4273
  Website: www.omtribe.org; E-mail: info@omtribe.org
  John R. Shotton, Chairperson; E-mail: jshotton@omtribe.org
  Ted Grant, Vice Chairperson; E-mail: tgrant@omtribe.org
  Darrell Kihega, Secretary; E-mail: dkihega@omtribe.org
  Courtney Burgess, Treasurer; E-mail: cburgess@omtribe.org
Councilmembers:
  Wesley J. Hudson, First Member; E-mail: whudson@omtribe.org
  Melanie Harader, Second Member; E-mail: mharader@omtribe.org
  Alvin Moore, Sr., Third Member; E-mail: amoore@omtribe.org
  Michael Gawhega, Executive Director of Administration
    E-mail: mgawhega@omtribe.org
  Gloree Tah, Education Director; E-mail: gtah@omtribe.org
  Ada Mehojah, Director of Social Services; E-mail: amehojah@omtribe.org
  Heather Payne, Public Information Officer; E-mail: hpayne@omtribe.org
  Sky Campbell, Language Department Director; E-mail: sky@omtribe.org
Tribe: Otoe-Missouria. Enrolled members: 1,440. Area: 20,700 acres. Resources: Tribal Museum & Library; Development Authority - 923 N. Robinson, #500, Oklahoma City, OK 73112 (405) 235-4700. Programs: Otoe language; Employment & Training; Social Services; Substance Abuse; Enrollment; Elders; Child Care & Welfare; Health/Diabetes; Housing; Environmental. Attractions: 7 Clans Paradise Casino; First Council Casino & Hotel; Council Bluff Event Center; annual Otoe-Missouria Summer Encampment in July. Pawnee Agency.

OTTAWA TRIBE OF OKLAHOMA
13 S. 69 A, P.O. Box 110 • Miami, OK 74355
  (918) 540-1536 Fax 542-3214; Website: www.ottawatribe.org
  E-mail: adawetribe@sbcglobal.net; E-mail: adawe.oto@gmail.com
  Ethel E. Cook, Chief; Suzy Crawford, Second Chief
  Teresa Smith, Secretary-Treasurer
  Margie Ross, Tribal Administrator
  John Charles Dawes, First Councilperson
  Rhonda Dixon Hayworth, Librarian (542-6162)
Tribe: Ottawa. Enrolled members: 2,500. Resources: Adawe Community Center; Archives Library; Ottawa University. Programs: Community Health; Education; Social Services; Environmental; Child Care. Attraction: High Winds Casino. Publication: Adawe News. Miami Agency.

PAWNEE NATION OF OKLAHOMA
881 Little Dee Dr., P.O. Box 470 • Pawnee, OK 74058
  (918) 762-3621 Fax 762-6446
  Website: www.pawneenation.org
  W. Bruce Pratt, President; Darrell Wildcat, Vice President
  Phammie N. Littlesun, Secretary; M. Angela Thompson, Treasurer
Councilmembers:
  Sammye Adson, 1st Council Seat; Dawna Hare, 2nd Seat
  Adrian Spottedhorsechief, 3rd Seat; Liana Chapman Teter, 4th Seat
  Andrew Knife Chief, Executive Office Director
  Muriel Robedeaux, Administrative Director
    E-mail: mrobedeaux@pawneenation.org

Dorna Riding-in-Battese, Education Division Director (762-3227)
Tiffany Frietze, Health & Community Services Director
  E-mail: tfrietze@pawneenation.org
Herb Adson, Cultural Resources Director (762-3227)
John Michael Knife Chief, Tribal Historic Preservation Officer
Brian Kirk, Planning Director; E-mail: bkirk@pawneenation.org
Dianne Barker Harrold, Chief Judge; Bob D. Buchanan, Chief Justice
Justices: Mark EchoHawk, Gregory Smith, Chad Harsha, Angel Smith
  E-mail: skanuho@pawneenation.org (762-3011)
Toni Hill, Communications Manager
The Nasharo Counci:
  Warren Pratt, Jr., Head Nasharo Chief/Skidi
  Pat Leading Fox, 1st Chief Skidi; Francis Morris, 1st Chief Pitahawirata
  Morgan LittlleSun, 1st Chief Kitkehahki
  Ralph Haymond, 2nd Chief Kitkehahki; Matt Reed, 2nd Chief Chaui
  Lester Sun Eagle, Nasharo Secretary/Pitahawirata
  Jimmy Horn, Nasharo Treasurer/1st Chief Chaui
Tribe: Pawnee. Enrolled members: 2,500. Resources: Pawnee Nation College. Programs: Education & Training "Te-Tu-Koo" Resources: (762-2541 Fax 762-4643); Cultural Preservation; Health & Community Services (Diabetes); Law Enforcement; Planning & Tribal Development; Natural Resources & Safety; Gaming. Attractions: Trading Post Casino; Chilocco Casino & Plaza Casino are planned. Publication: Chaticks si Chaticks, bimonthly newspaper. Pawnee Agency.

PEORIA TRIBE OF OKLAHOMA
118 S. Eight Tribes Trail, P.O. Box 1527 • Miami, OK 74355
  (800) 259-9987; (918) 540-2535 Fax 540-2538
  Website: www.peoriatribe.com
  John P. Froman, Chief & Tribal Administrator (540-4155)
  E-mail: jfroman@peoriatribe.com
  Jason Dollarhide, 2nd Chief (542-1873)
  Tonya Mathews, Secretary (533-8379)
  E-mail: stand74354@gmail.com
  Aaron Wayne Blalock, Treasurer
  Carolyn Ritchey, 1st Council member (541-7597)
  Craig Harper, 2nd Council member (964-0075)
  E-mail: craig@procomrestoration.com
  Alan Goforth, 3rd Council member (542-7408)
  Donna Fitzgibbon, Kevin Dawes & Shelly Downs,
  Cultural/Language Committee/Powwow
  Donna Fitzgibbon, Education Chairperson
  E-mail: dfitzgibbon@peoriatribe.com
  Barbara Stacy, Community Health Representative
  E-mail: bstacy@peoriatribe.com
  M. Annette Black, Housing/Social Services
  Hank Downum, Economic Development
  E-mail: hdownum@peoriatribe.com
  Jason Dollarhide, Chairperson, Repatriation/NAGPRA Committee
  Jim Dixon, Environmental Director; E-mail: jdixon@peoriatribe.com
  Tonya R. Mathews, Executive Director, Gaming Commission (919-3508)
  E-mail: tmathews@peoriatribe.com
Tribe: Peoria. Resources: Inter-Tribal Substance Abuse Prevention & Treatment Center; Library; Trading Post. Programs: Education; Health; Child Care; Child Care Development; Culture & Language; Enrollment; Housing & Social Services; Environmental; Repatriation, NAGPRA; Economic Develop-ment. Attractions: Buffalo Run Casino; Annual Stomp Peoria Dance; Peoria Powwow; Trading Post. Publication: Toni-We-Kee-Toh, quarterly news. Miami Agency.

PONCA TRIBE OF INDIANS OF OKLAHOMA
20 White Eagle Dr. • Ponca City, OK 74601
  (580) 762-8104 Fax 762-2743; Website: www.ponca.com
  Earl "Trey" S. Howe, III, Chairperson; E-mail: thowe@ponca.com
  Scotty Simpson, Jr., Vice Chairperson; E-mail: ssimpson@ponca.com
  Paula Mendoza, Secretary/Treasurer; E-mail: pmendoza@ponca.com
Committeemembers: Steve Pensoneau, Pete Buffalohead,
  Oliver LittleCook, Jimmie Sherron
  Bennett Arkekata, Tribal Administrator
  Sarah J. Allen-Nelsen, Education/Training Department Director (763-0120)
Tribe: Ponca. Enrolled members: 3,580. In residence: 3,000. Resources: Wellness Center; Social Development Center; Ponca Library. Programs: Pona Tribal Language; Family Services; Health; Transit; Education; Environmental Protection; Youth; Family Services; Senior Citizens; Child Welfare; Food Distribution. Attractions: Two Rivers Casino; White Eagle Park; Fancy Dance Casino Chilocco; Smoke Shop; Bingo Hall. Under Pawnee Agency.

THE QUAPAW TRIBE OF INDIANS
5681 S. 630 Rd., P.O. Box 765 • Quapaw, OK 74363
  (888) OGAHPAH; (918) 542-1853 Fax 542-4694
  Website: www.quapawtribe.com
  John L. Berrey, Chairperson; E-mail: jberrey@ogahpah.com

Thomas Mathews, Vice Chairperson
  E-mail: crawfish74354@yahoo.com
Tamara Smiley-Reeves, Secretary/Treasurer
  E-mail: tsmiley@quapawtribe.com
Susie Attocknie, Chairperson – Social Services & Education Committee
Ardina Moore, Chairperson – Cultural Committee & Language Preservation
Councilmembers: T.C. Bear, Zachary Turley, Ranny McWatters,
  Marilyn Waters
Donna Mercer, Tribal Administrator; E-mail: dmercer@quapawtribe.com
Krista Pierce, Education Director; E-mail: kpierce@quapawtribe.com
Jami Rodgers, Commnity Health Rep.; E-mail: jrodgers@quapawtribe.com
Patti Rice, Social Services Director; E-mail: price@quapawtribe.com
Patty Billings, Library Director; E-mail: pbillings@quapawtribe.com
Carol Feathers, Tribal Court Admin; E-mail: cfeathers@quapawtribe.com
Jon Douthitt, Tribal Judge
Anna McKinnen, Public Relations Director
  E-mail: amckibben@quapawtribe.com
Tribe: Quapaw. *Enrolled members*: 1,450. *Area*: 13,000+ acres. *Facilities*: OGahPah Learning Center; Quapaw Tribal Museum; Library. *Programs*: Education; Housing; Community Health; Social Services; Family Services; Substance Abuse; Environmental. *Activities*: Annual powwow held on July 4. *Attraction*: Quapaw Casino; Downstream Casino Resort; Eagle Creek Golf Club. *Publication*: Quapaw Tribal News, quarterly newsletter. Miami Agency.

SAC & FOX NATION OF OKLAHOMA
920883 S. Hwy. 99 Bldg. A • Stroud, OK 74079
  (918) 968-3526 Fax 968-1142; Website: www.sacandfoxnation-nsn.gov
Kay Rhoads, Principal Chief; E-mail: chief@sacandfoxnation-nsn.gov
Jacklyn King, 2nd Chief; E-mail: secondchief@sacandfoxnation-nsn.gov
Mary F. McCormick, Secretary; E-mail: secretary@sacandfoxnation-nsn.gov
Jared King, Treasurer; E-mail: treasurer@sacandfoxnation-nsn.gov
Robert Williamson, Committee Member
  E-mail: cmember@sacandfoxnation-nsn.gov
Ken Johnson, Managing Editor of Sac & Fox News
  E-mail: newspaper@sacandfoxnation-nsn.gov
Tribe: Sac & Fox. *Enrolled members*: 3,000+. *Area*: 800 acres. *Resources*: Black Hawk Health Clinic; Sac & Fox National Public Library. *Programs*: Education; Cultural; Sac & Fox Language; Food Distribution; Indian Child Welfare; Social Services; Housing; Health Services; Human Resources; Environmental Services; NAGPRA. *Activities*: Powwow & Rodeo. *Attractions*: Sac & Fox Nation Casino in Shawnee; RV Park; Smoke Shop. *Publications*: Sac & Fox News, monthly newspaper; Sac & Fox Nation Welcomes You to Capitol (historical & tourism brochure); Sac & Fox Court: Justice for a Nation (court brochure). Pawnee Agency.

SEMINOLE NATION OF OKLAHOMA
P.O. Box 1498 • Wewoka, OK 74884
  (405) 257-7205 Fax 257-7209; Website: www.sno-nsn.gov
Leonard M. Harjo, Principal Chief; Lewis Johnson, Assistant Chief
Alvina Coker, General Council Secretary (257-7276)
  E-mail: coker.a@sno-nsn.gov
General Council members:
The General Council consists of 28 representatives, two from each
  of the twelve bands and two each from the Freedman Bands
Caesar Bruner Band: Anthony Conley & LaEtta Osborne-Sampson
Ceyha Band: John Narcomey & Rosanna Jones
Dosar Barkus Band: Kevin Hardeman & Kent Dindy
Eufaula Band: Nancy Fixico, & Ida Gonzales
Fusutche Band: Kelly Davis & David Narcomey
Hecete Band: Patricia Kishketon & Sterling Springer
Hvteyicvlke Band: Nanette Hazelwood & Karen Fullbright
Mekusukey Band: Jennifer Horne & Sena Yesslith
Nurcup Harjo Band: Marilyn Moore & Lottie Coodie
Ocese Band: Susie Harjo & Abraham Farani
Rewalke Band: Emman Spain & Wayne Shaw
Tallahassee Band: Kathryn McCoy & Charlie Hill
Tom Palmer Band: Dewayne Miller & Fannie Harjo
Tusekia Harjo Band: Cheri Hardeman & Ralph Coker
Ashley Noey, Administrator Services Coordinator
Kelly Gaines Stoner, William Wantland, Joe Taylor, Supreme Court Justices
Natalie Harjo, Historic Preservation/Cultural Resources
Jerome Harrison, Director of Health Resources
Clara Keawphalouk, Director of Higher Education Staff
Willis Deatherage, Chairperson of the Gaming Commission
  E-mail: willisdeatherage@hughes.net
Jeremy Larney, SNGA Commissioner; E-mail: jlarney@sngaok.com
Tribe: Seminole. *Enrolled members*: 18,800; 5,350 live in Seminole County; and 13,550 live within the state of Oaklahoma. *Area*: Located in the town of Wewoka, Oklahoma, about 30 miles southeast of the town of Shawnee. The tribe owns 372 acres of federal trust land and 53 acres of fee simple land. An additional 35,443 allotted acres supplement the tribal land base. *Resources*:

Museum; Indian Health Clinic; Seminole Nation Communications Dept.; Seminole Nation Radio Show on KWSH 1260 AM each Tuesday at 11 a.m; Seminole Nation Gaming Agency (www.snga.ok.com). *Programs*: Alcohol Substance Abuse; Social Services; Indian Child Welfare; Transit; Enrollment; Alcohol Substance Abuse & Prevention; Domestic Violence; Food Distribution; Community Health; Food Distribution; Housing; Environmental Protection; Human Resources; Career Development; Head Start. *Attractions*: Seminole Nation Casino; River Mist Casino; Trading Post Casino; Trading Post. *Publication*: Cokv Tvlvme, monthly newspaper. Wewoka Agency.

SENECA-CAYUGA TRIBE OF OKLAHOMA
23701 South 655 Road • Grove, OK 74344
  (866) 787-5452; (918) 787-5452 Fax 787-5521
  Website: www.sctribe.com; E-mail: senecanet@gmail.com
William L. Fisher, Chief; E-mail: wfisher@sctribe.com
Jerry Crow, Second Chief; E-mail: jcrow@sctribe.com
Sarah S. Channing, Secretary-Treasurer
  E-mail: schanning@sctribe.com
General Council members:
Sallie Whte, 1st Councilperson; E-mail: salliew@sctribe.com
Lisa Spano, 2nd Councilperson; E-mail: lspano@sctribe.com
Calvin Cassady, 3rd Councilperson; E-mail: ccassady@sctribe.com
Geneva Fletcher, 4th Councilperson; E-mail: gfletcher@sctribe.com
Curt Lawrence, Executive Director; E-mail: clawrence@sctribe.com
Shawn Stovall, Community Health Rep. & Wellness Director
Lori Beaty, Chief Financial Officer; E-mail: lbeaty@sctribe.com
Carol Brown, HR & Education Manager
  E-mail: cbrown@sctribe.com
William Tarrant, Cultural Director
Micco Emarthla, National Historic Preservation Officer
Mark Westfall, Indian Child Welfare Program
  E-mail: mwestfall@sctribe.com
Danielle Brashear, Gaming Commissioner
Joanna Hadley, Casino General Manager (786-8528)
Raylene Hackler, Librarian - Career Resources
  E-mail: rhackler@sctribe.com
Rick Dubois, Environmental Program Director
Betty King-Dry, Family Services Manager
Hoyit Bacon, Director of Economic Development
  E-mail: hbacon@sctribe.com
Tribes: Seneca & Cayuga. *Enrolled members*: 4,400. *In residence*: 2,000. *Resources*: Wellness Center; Career Resources Bldg. *Programs*: Education; Substance Abuse; Community Health; Housing; Child Welfare; Economic Development; Public Safety; Environmental; Human Resources. *Attraction*: Grand Lake Casino & Resort. *Publication*: Gah-Yah-Tont, tribal newsletter. Miami Agency.

THE SHAWNEE TRIBE
29 S. Hwy 69A, P.O. Box 189 • Miami, OK 74355
  (918) 542-2441 Fax 542-2922
P.O. Box 860114 • Shawnee, KS 66018 (913) 284-6635
  Website: www.shawnee-tribe.com
  E-mail: shawneetribe@shawnee-tribe.com
Ron Sparkman, Chief; E-mail: rondede1@gmail.com
Ben Barnes, 2nd Chief; E-mail: benbarnes@gmail.com
Carolyn Foster, Secretary
  E-mail: Carolyn.smith1960@yahoo.com
Roy D. Baldridge, Treasurer; E-mail: ckrtstr@yahoo.com
Jodi Hayes, Tribal Administrator
Councilmembers: Carolyn Smith, Diana McLean, Roberta Coombes,
  Joel Barnes, Herbert Adams, Corey Winesburg, Scott Secondine
  Greg Pitcher, Economic Development Director
  Tena Both, Director of Children's & Family Services
  Rosanna Sheppard, Director of Environment & Natural Resources
Tribe: Shawnee. *Area*: 210,000 acres in Oklahoma & Kansas. *Resources*: Shawnee Tribe Development Corp.; Library for historical & genealogical research. *Programs*: Child Care & Development; Children & Family Services; Historic Preservation; Housing; Environmental Protection; Economic Development; Energy Assistance; Social Services. *Attractions*: Annual Powwow in August or September each year; Gift Shop & Gallery. *Publication*: Shawnee Journal, quarterly newsletter. Miami Agency.

THLOPTHLOCCO CREEK TRIBAL TOWN
P.O. Box 188 • Okemah, OK 74859
  (918) 560-6198 Fax 623-0045; Website: www.tttown.org
Ryan Morrow, Town King; Celesta Johnson, Secretary
Max Trickey, Treasurer; Brent Brown, Warrior
Business Committee Advisers: Janna Dickey, Tracy Hill, Ron Barnett,
  Barbara Canard-Welborn, Tonya Walker
  Mary Zuni Chalan, Executive Director; Sharon Taylor, Librarian
  Suzette Trickey, Gaming Commission Chairperson

Tribe: Muskogee Creek. *Enrolled members*: 1,500. *In residence*: 845. *Area*: 2,300 acres located in east-central Oklahoma in the town of Clearview about five miles north of Weleetka, Okemah, OK. The Tribal Town is part of the Creek Nation of Oklahoma that owns over 6,000 acres of federal trust lands. *Attractions*: Creek Nation Casino Okemah; Golden Pony Casino. *Publication*: Drum Beat newsletter. Okmulgee Agency.

TONKAWA TRIBE OF OKLAHOMA
1 Rush Buffalo Rd. • Tonkawa, OK 74653
(580) 628-2561 Fax 628-2279
Website: www.tonkawatribe.com
Russell Martin, President
Patrick E. Waldroup, Vice President
Racheal N. Starr, Secretary/Treasurer
Joshua D. Waffle, Tribal Administrator
Diana Allen, Director of Finance
Mary Starr, Community Health Representative
Leroy P. Enloe, Wellness center Coordinator
Lisa Norman, Education Program Coordinator
Walter I. Hare, Executive Director-Programs & Services
Christine Baker, Gaming Commission Executive
Douglas Revard, Chief Judge
Tribe: Tonkawa. *Enrolled members*: 500. *In residence*: 550. *Area*: 1,232 acres located in Kay County, in northern Oklahoma on the west bank of the Chikaskia River, 2.5 miles southeast of the town of Tonkawa. *Resources*: Community Center; Tribal Museum & Library. *Programs*: Education; Health/Diabetes; Alcohol & Substance Abuse; Indian Child Welfare; Human Resources; Child Care; Housing; Environmental. *Attraction*: Native Lights Casino. *Publication*: Tonkawa Tribal News. Pawnee Agency.

UNITED KEETOOWAH BAND OF CHEROKEE INDIANS IN OKLAHOMA
P.O. Box 746 • Tahlequah, OK 74465
(918) 431-1818 Fax 431-1873; Website: www.ukb-nsn.gov
E-mail: ukbnews@unitedkeetoowahband.org
Joe Bunch, Chief; Joyce Fourkiller-Hawk, Secretary
Ellie Mae Worley, Treasurer
Sammy Still, Editor of Gaduwa Cherokee News, Public Information Officer
District Representatives:
Eddie Sacks, Canadian District; Clifford Wofford, Cooweescoowee District;
Jerry Hansen, Delaware District; Tom Duncan, Flint District;
William Christie, Goingsnake District; Peggy Girty, Illinois District;
Barry Dotson, Seqyouah District; Charles Smoke, Saline District;
Anile Locust, Tahlequah District
Tribe: Keetoowah Cherokee. *Enrolled members*: 7,700. *Resources*: Language, History & Culture Department; Child Development Center; Wellness Center; Keetoowah Cherokee Clinic; John Hair Cultural Center & Museum; Higher Education; Elder Nutrition Center; Library. *Programs*: Education; Health & Family Services; Housing; Human Resources; Indian Child Care & Welfare; Elder Nutrition & Assistance; Environmental; Language, History & Cultural; Economic Development; Natural Resources; Enrollment; Victim Assistance; Gaming. *Enterprise*: Keetoowah Construction, Inc. (453-9162). *Attractions*: Keetoowah Cherokee Casino; annual Keetoowah Cherokee Celebration (1st Saturday in Oct.); Gift Shop *Publication*: Gaduwa Cherokee News (456-8698). Eastern OK Regional Office.

WICHITA & AFFILIATED TRIBES
P.O. Box 729 • Anadarko, OK 73005
(405) 247-2425 Fax 247-2430; Website: www.wichitatribe.com
Terri Parton, President; Jesse E. Jones, Vice President
Myles Stephenson, Jr., Secretary; Vanessa Vance, Treasurer
James Nelson, Jr., Administrator; Edward Wakinney, Finance Director
E-mail: ed.wakinney@wichitatribe.com
Councilmembers: Shirley Davilla, Nahuseah Mandujano, Matt Robinson
Marland Toyekoyah, Tribal Administrator
E-mail: marland.toyekoyah@wichitatribe.com
Fran Harrison, Health Services Administration Director
Yolanda Walker, Education Director
E-mail: yolanda.walker@wichitatribe.com
Sandra Wilson, Gaming Commission Chairperson
E-mail: wgcbusiness@wichitagc.com
Jason Prince, WDEP Director
E-mail: jason.prince@wichitatribe.com
Tribes: Wichita, Waco, Keechi, Tawakonie. *Enrolled members*: 2,500. *Resources*: Museum & Library. *Programs*: Education; Health; Culture & Language; Family & Children Services; Social Services; Food Distribution; Housing; Employment; Transportation; Gaming; Economic Development; Enrollment; Food Distribution; Environmental; Senior Nutrition. *Attractions*: Casino (in construction). Publication Monthly newsletter. Gift Shop. Anadarko Agency.

WYANDOTTE NATION OF OKLAHOMA
64700 E. Hwy. 60, P.O. Box 250 • Wyandotte, OK 74370
(800) 256-2539; (918) 678-2297 Fax 678-2944
Website: www.wyandotte-nation.org
Billy Friend, Chief; Norman Hilderbrand, Second Chief
Councilmembers: Ramona Reid, Vivian Fink, Juanita McQuistion, Eric Lofland
Dana Butterfield, Director of Family Services (678-6319)
Tammy Charles, Librarian
Tribe: Wendat, Wyandotte. *Enrolled members*: 500. *Resources*: Wyandotte Elementary School; Bearskin Health & Wellness Center. *Programs*: Education; Family Services; Environmental Protection; Human Resources; Elderly Services; Housing. *Attractions*: Wyandotte Nation Casino; The Lucky Turtle Casino; Cultural Days; annual Meeting & Powwow. *Publication*: The Turtle Speaks, newsletter. Miami Agency.

EUCHEE (YUCHI) TRIBE OF INDIANS
P.O. Box 10 • Sapulpa, OK 74067
(918) 224-3065 Fax 224-3140
Andrew Skeeter, Chairperson; Don Cahwee, Vice Chairperson
Clinton Sag, At-Large Representative
Steve Brown, Secretary & Polecat Representative
Amy Yargee & Esther Yarge, Sand Creek Representatives
Phillip Wilson & Felix Brown, Duck Creek Representatives
Tribe: Euchee. *Resources*: Indian Health Centers. *Program*: Language.
Publication: The Euchee Sun, newsletter

OREGON

BURNS PAIUTE TRIBE
Burns Paiute Indian Colony, 100 Pasigo St. • Burns, OR 97720
(541) 573-1910 Fax 573-2012
Website: www.burnspaiute-nsn.gov; E-mail: bpt.council@gmail.com
Joe DeLaRosa, Chairperson; Dean Adams, Vice Chairperson
Tracy Kennedy, Secretary; Jarvis Kennedy, Sergeant-at-Arms
Councilmembers: Lucas Samor, Shayla Barney, Cecil Dick
Anna DeBoard, Tribal General Manager
Kenton Dick, Tribal Planner (573-5562)
Twila Teeman, Health Serrvices Director (573-8049)
Carla Teeman, Social Services Specialist (573-8043)
Jason Kesling, Natural Resources Director (573-8087)
Linda Beaver, Court Administraor (573-8072)
Angela Smartt, Gaming Commissioner
E-mail: bptgra2@gmail.com (573-1500)
Kerry Opie, Education Specialist; E-mail: Kerry.opie@burnspaiute-nsn.gov
Tribe: Paiute. *Enrolled members*: 410. *In residence*: 250. *Area*: 11,944 acres located in Harney Basin, Harney County. *Resources*: Wadatika Health Center. *Programs*: Education; Health; Social Services; Cultural Resources & Preservation; Indian Child Care & Welfare; Food Distribution; Gaming; Environmental Protection; Transporta-tion; Housing; Human Resources; Natural Resources; Fish & Wildlife. Activities: Annual Powwow. *Attractions*: The Old Camp Casino; RV Park. *Publication*: Tu'Kwa Hone, weekly newsletter. Warm Springs Agency.

CONFEDERATED TRIBES OF COOS, LOWER UMPQUA & SUISLAW INDIANS
1245 Fulton Ave. • Coos Bay, OR 97420
(888) 280-0726; (541) 888-9577 Fax 888-0302
Website: www.ctclusi.org; E-mail: bgarcia@ctclusi.org
Warren Brainard, Chief (297-1655); E-mail: wbrainard@ctclusa.org
Mark Ingersoll, Chairperson (290-4610); E-mail: mingersoll@ctclusi.org
Teresa Spangler, Vice Chair (808-48828); Email: tspangler@ctclusi.org
Councilmembers:
Doc Slyter (Position 1) (808-7625); E-mail: dslyter@ctclusi.org
Beverly Bowen (Position 2) (290-4531); E-mail: bbowen@ctclusi.org
Mark Ingersoll (Position 3) (290-4610); E-mail: mingersoll@ctclusi.org
Tara Bowen (Position 4) (808-7394); E-mail: tbowen@ctclusi.org
Teresa Spangler (Position 5); Email: tspangler@ctclusi.org
Arron McNutt, Position 6) (297-1183); E-mail: amcnutt@ctclusi.org
Alexis Barry, Tribal CEO (888-9577); E-mail: abarry@ctclusi.org
Angela Bowen, Director-Education (888-1317); E-mail: abowen@ctclusi.org
Vicki Faciane, Health & Human Services Administrator
E-mail: vfaciane@ctclusa.org (888-7515)
Jesse Beers, Cultural Director (888-1319); E-mail: jbeers@ctclusi.org
Vicki Faciane, HHS Director (888-7515)
Tribes: Lower Umpqua & Suislaw. *Programs*: Education; Health Services; Culture; Family & Employment Services; Childcare & Welfare; Housing; Human Resources; Natural Resources; Gaming; Enrollment. *Enterprises*: Blue Earth Services & Technology. *Attractions*: Three Rivers Casino & Hote; Ocean Dunes Golf Coursel. *Publication*: Newsletter. Siletz Field Office.

CONFEREDATED TRIBES OF GRAND RONDE

9615 Grand Ronde Rd. • Grand Ronde, OR 97347
(800) 422-0232; (503) 879-5211 Fax 879-5964
Website: www.grandronde.org; E-mail: info@grandronde.org
Reynold L. Leno, Chairperson; Cheryle Kennedy, Vice Chairperson
Jon George, Secretary; E-mail: tribalcouncil@grandronde.org
Councilmembers: Jack Giffin, Jr., Chris Mercier, Tonya Gleason-Shepek,
 Denise Harvey, Kathleen George, Brenda Tuomi
Siobhan Taylor, Public Affairs Director
  E-mail: publicaffairs@grandronde.org
Dean Rhoades, Editor of Smoke Signals
  E-mail: news@grandronde.org
Dave Fullerton, Director of Social Services (503) 879-2034
Leslie Riggs, Education Manager (879-2284)
  E-mail: leslie.riggs@grandronde.org
  E-mail: education@grandronde.org
Portland Office: 4445 S.W. Barbur Blvd., Portland, OR 97239
(503) 235-4230 Fax 239-8047
  E-mail: portland@grandronde.org
Eugene Office: 221 W. 10th Ave., Eugene, OR 97401
(541) 484-7085 Fax 484-7097; E-mail: eugene@grandronde.org
Tribes: Five Confederated *Tribes*: Rogue River, Chasta, Molalla, Umpqua &
Kalapuya. *Area*: Located in northwest Oregon. *Enrolled members*: 5,100. *In
residence*: 650. *Resources*: Health & Wellness Center (879-2236). Library.
Programs: Health & Wellness; Social Services; Cultural; Human Resources;
Elderly; Gaming. *Attractions*: Spirit Mountain Casino; Restoration Celebration
in November; Annual powwow in August; Marcellus Norwest Memorial
Veterans Powwow in July; Education Honor & Recognition Celebration in
May/June. *Publication*: Smoke Signals, bi-weekly tribal newsletter. Satellite
offices in Portland & Eugene, OR. Siletz Field Office.

COQUILLE INDIAN TRIBE

3050 Tremont St., P.O. Box 783 • North Bend, OR 97459
(800) 622-5869; (541) 756-0904 Fax 888-2418
Website: www.coquilletribe.org; E-mail: cit@coquilletribe.org
E-mail: tribalcouncil@coquilletribe.org
Donald Ivy, Chief; E-mail: donivy@coquilletribe.org
Brenda Meade, Chairperson; E-mail: brendameade@coquilletribe.org
Kippy Robbins, Vice Chairperson; E-mail: kippyrobbins@coquilletribe.org
Joan Metcalf, Secretary/Treasurer; E-mail: joanmetclaf@coquilletribe.org
Councilmembers: Linda Mecum, Eric Metcalf
Mark Johnston, Interim Executive Administrative Director
  E-mail: markjohnston@coquilletribe.org
Kelle Little, Community Health Center Administrator
  E-mail: kellelittle@coquilletribe.org
Bridgett Wheeler, Culture, Education & Library Director (756-0904)
  E-mail: bridgettwheeler@coquilletribe.org
Kassandra Rippee, Tribal Historic Preservation Officer
  E-mail: kassandrarippee@coquilletribe.org
Denise Stuntzer, Wellness Coordinator
  E-mail: wellness@coquilletribe.org
Donald Owen Costello, Chief Judge
Terry Springer, Gaming Commissioner
  E-mail: terryspringer@coquilletribe.org
Todd Tripp, Director of Planning & Community Services
  E-mail: toddtripp@coquilletribe.org
Chris Tanner, Librarian; E-mail: christanner@coquilletribe.org
Clark Walworth, Communications Officer
  E-mail: clarkwalworth@coquilletribe.org
Tribes: Upper & Lower Coquilles. *Enrolled members*: 650. *Area*: 5,410 acres
Coquille Forest, and 1,045 acre Empire Reservation, located on the southern
coast of Oregon, primarily in Coos County. *Resources*: Community Center;
Community Health Center; CIT Library. *Programs*: Education; Health;
Diabetes; Human Resources; Planning, Realty & Community Services;
Housing, GIS; Gaming. *Enterprises*: Coquille Economic Development Corp.
(CEDCO) (756-0662) E-mail: info@cedco.net. *Attractions*: The Mill Casino;
annual Restoration Celebration & Salmon Bake, last weekend in June; Mid-
Winter Gathering; Cultural Preservation Conference. *Publications*: K'Wen
'inish-ha, "Tribal Tidbits" monthly tribal newsletter; "Changing Landscapes,"
annual publication of the proceedings of the tribe's Cultural Preservation
Conference. Siletz Agency.

COW CREEK BAND OF UMPQUA TRIBE OF INDIANS

2371 NE Stevens, Suite 100 • Roseburg, OR 97470
(800) 929-8229; (541) 672-9405 Fax 673-0432
Website: www.cowcreek.com; E-mail: info@cowcreek.com
Dan Courtney, Chairperson; Gary Jackson, Vice Chairperson
Robert VanNorman, Treasurer; Yvonne Dumont-McCafferty, Secretary
Carol McKinney, Tribal Representative
Board members: Luann Urban, Steve Jackson, Jessica Bochart, Tom Fox,
 George T. Rondeau, Gerald Rainville, Robert Estabrook

Kathie Olson, Executive Director; Dr. Sharon Stanphill, Health Director
 Carma Mornarich & Lois Schlegek, Program Officers
Tribe: Umpqua. *Resources*: The Cow Creek Foundation; The Cow Creek
Health & Wellness Center (541) 839-1347. *Programs*: Umpqua Indian
Development; Health Services; Tribal Career Development Program; Diabetes
Prevention; Nutrition & Weight Loss; Natural Resources; Education; Employ-
ment. *Enterprise*: Umpqua Indian Development Corporation; The Cow Creek
Foundation. *Attraction*: Seven Feathers Hotel & Casino Resort. Siletz Agency.

FORT McDERMITT RESERVATION

Tribes: Paiute & Shoshone. Located in Oregon & Nevada. See listing in NV.

CONFEDERATED TRIBES OF SILETZ INDIANS

201 SE Swan Ave., P.O. Box 549 • Siletz, OR 97380
(800) 922-1399; (541) 444-2532 Fax 673-0432
Website: www.ctsi.nsn.us
Delores Pigsley, Chairperson; E-mail: dpigsley@msn.com
Alfred "Bud" Lane III, Vice Chairperson; E-mail: budl@ctsi.nsn.us
Robert Kentta, Treasurer; E-mail: rkentta@ctsi.nsn.us
Sharon Edenfield, Secretary; E-mail: sharone@ctsi.nsn.us
Councilmembers: Joe Lane, Lillie Butler, Reggie Butler, Sr.,
 Loraine Butler, Gloria Ingle
Brenda Bremner, Tribal General Manager (444-2532)
Sharon Edenfield, Administrative Manager; E-mail: sharone@ctsi.nsn.us
Pamela Barlow-Lind, Tribal Planner; E-mail: pamelal@ctsi.nsn.us
Marci Muschamp, Interm Health Director; E-mail: marcim@ctsi.nsn.us
Cathern Tufts, Staff Attorney; E-mail: cathernt@ctsi.nsn.us
Tribes: Siletz – many Confederated Tribes, representing ten different
languages. *Enrolled members*: 5,100. *In residence*: 800. *Population served*:
2,800. *Area*: 3,666 acres of timberlands in Lincoln County located on the
northcentral Oregon coast, as well as several parcels of land purchased by the
Tribe, totalliing 16,000 acres. *Resources*: New Health Care Clinic; Cultural
Center; Museum & Archive; Tenas Illahee Child Care Center; Gaming –
Lincoln City, OR; Tribal Business Corp. *Programs*: Housing & Development;
Education Healthcare; Employment & Social Services; Language; Gaming;
Head Start. *Attractions*: Chinook Winds Casino Resort; RV Park; Memorial Day
& Restoration Day Celebrations in May & November; August Powwow, 2nd
weekend. *Publication*: Siletz News. Siletz Agency.

CONFEDERATED TRIBES OF THE UMATILLA INDIAN RESERVATION

Nixyaawii Governance Center, 46411 Timine Way • Pendleton, OR 97801
(541) 429-7379; (541) 276-3165 Fax 276-3095
Website: www.umatilla.nsn.us; E-mail: info@ctuir.org
Alan Crawford, General Council Chairperson (429-7378)
  E-mail: generalcouncil@ctuir.org
Kyle McGuire, General Council Vice Chairperson
  E-mail: kylemcguire@ctuir.org
Jiselle Halfmoon, General Council Secretary
  E-mail: jisellehalfmoon@ctuir.org
Thomas Morning Owl, General Council Interpreter
  E-mail: thomasmorningowl@ctuir.org; E-mail: bot@ctuir.org
Gary Burke, Board of Trustees Chairperson
Jeremy Wolf, Board of Trustees Vice Chairperson
Rosenda Shippentower, Board of Trustees Treasurer
David Close, Board of Trustees Secretary
Dave Tovey, Executive Director-Administration
  E-mail: oed@ctuir.org
Debra Croswell, Deputy Executive Director
Cristina Ferea, Indian Education Coordinator
  E-mail: education@ctuir.org
Maureen Minthorn, Gaming Commissioner
Naomi Stacy, Office of Legal Counsel Director (429-7400)
Brent Leonhard, Tribal Attorney; E-mail: legalcounsel@ctuir.org
Chuck Sams, Communications Director; E-mail: communications@ctuir.org
Bill Tovey, Economic & Community Development Director
  E-mail: economicdevelopment@ctuir.org
Eric Quaempts, Natural Resources Director
  E-mail: naturalresources@ctuir.org
Ramona Halcomb, Education Director (276-8120)
  E-mail: education@ctuir.org
Board of Trustees members:
 Woodrow Star, Justin Quaempts, Armand Minthorn, Woodrow Star,
 Aaron Ashley
Tribes: Umatilla, Cayuse, Walla Walla. *Enrolled members*: 2,800. *In residence*:
1,750. *Area*: 95,273 acres located in Umatilla County, adjacent to Pendleton
and west of Umatilla National Forest. *Facilities*: Yellowhawk Tribal Health
Center; Tamastslikt Cultural Institute; KCUW 101.1 FM, tribal radio station.
Programs: Education; Health; Children & Family Services; Public Works &
Safety; Economic & Community Development; Natural Resources. *Attractions*:
Wildhorse Resort & Casino. *Publication*: Confederated Umatilla Journal (CUJ)
Newspaper. Umatilla Agency.

CONFEDERATED TRIBES OF THE WARM SPRINGS RESERVATION
1233 Veterans St. • Warm Springs, OR 97761
(541) 553-1161 Fax 553-1924
Austin Greene, Jr., Chairperson
Evaline Patt, Vice Chairperson; E-mail: epatt@wstribes.org
Michele Stacona, Secretary-Treasurer/CEO
Alyssa Macy, Chief Operations Officer
Delvis Heath, Warm Springs Chief; E-mail: delvis.heath@wstribes.org
Joe Moses, Paiute Chief; E-mail: joe.moses@wstribes.org
Alfred Smith, Jr., Wasco Chief & Agency District Rep.
Delvis Heath, Sr., Hereditary Chief
Joseph Moses, Paiute Chief; E-mail: josephmoses@wstribes.org
Adele Waheneka, Tribal Secretary
Simnasho Dist. Reps: Ron Suppah, Raymond Tsumpti, Charles Calico
Agency District Reps: Carina Miller, Alfred Smith & Valerie Switzler
Seekseekqua District Reps: Lee Tom, Brigette McConville
Agency District Reps: Carina Miller, Valerie Switzler
Lynn Davis, Director of Administrative Services
Louie Pitt, Governmental Affairs/Planning Director
 E-mail: lpitt@wstribes.org
Janice Clements, Health & Welfare Chairperson
Caroline Cruz, Health & Human Services General Manager
Deanie Smith, Education Chairperson
Lepha Smith, Culture & Heritage Chairperson
Dave McMechan, Editor - Spilyay Tymoo (553-1338)
Tribes: Warm Springs, Wasco, Paiute, Walla Walla, Waco. *Enrolled members:* 4,000. *In residence:* 2,750. *Area:* 563,916 acres located in Jefferson & Wasco Counties, east of the Cascade Mountains. The Wasco bands on the Columbia River were the eastern-most group of Chinookan-speaking Indians. Although they were principally fishermen, their frequent contact with other Indians throughout the region provided for abundant trade. Roots and beads were available from other Chinookan bands such as the Clackamas. Game, clothing & horses came from trade with Sahaptin bands such as the neighboring Warm Springs and the more distant Nez Perce. In exchange for these goods, the Wasco traded root bread, salmon meal, and bear grass. The Warm Springs bands that lived along the Columbia's tributaries spoke Sahaptin. Unlike the Wascoes, the Warm Springs bands moved between winter and summer villages, and depended more on game, roots and berries. However, salmon was also an important staple for the Warm Springs bands and, like the Wascoes, they built elaborate scaffolding over waterfalls which allowed them to harvest fish with long-handled dip nets. Contact between the Warm Springs bands & the Wascoes was frequent and, although they spoke different languages and observed different customs, they could converse & traded heavily. The Paiutes lived in southeastern Oregon & spoke a Shoshonean dialect. The lifestyle of the Paiutes was considerably different from that of the Wasco and Warm Springs bands. Their high-plains existence required that they migrate further and more frequently for game, and fish was not an important part of their diet. The Paiute language was foreign to the Wasco & Warm Springs bands, & commerce among them was infrequent. In early times, contact between them often resulted in skirmishes. Although Paiute territories historically included a large area from southeastern Oregon into Nevada, Idaho, & western Utah, the Paiute bands that eventually settled at Warm Springs lived in the area of Lake, Harney, and Malheur counties in Oregon. *Resources:* Community Wellness Center; The Museum at Warm Springs; KWSO 91.9 FM radio (553-1968). *Programs:* Language; Social & Family Services; Culture & Heritage; Fish & Wildlife; Health & Welfare; Public Safety; Legal Services; Housing; Natural Resources; Economic Development; Land Use Planning; Agriculture; Timber; Water Board; Education; Head Start. *Attractions:* Kah-Nee-Ta High Desert Resort & Casino. *Publication:* Spilyay Tymoo Newspaper (www.wsnews.org). Warm Springs Agency.

KLAMATH TRIBES OF OREGON
501 Chiloquin Blvd., P.O. Box 436 • Chiloquin, OR 97624
(800) 524-9787; (541) 783-2219 Fax 783-2029
Website: www.klamathtribes.org
Don Gentry, Chairperson; E-mail: don.gentry@klamathtribes.com
Gail Hatcher, Vice Chairperson; E-mail: gail.hatcher@klamathtribes.com
Roberta Frost, Secretary; E-mail: Roberta.frost@klamathtribes.com
Brandi Hatcher, Treasurer; E-mail: brandi.hatcher@klamathtribes.com
Councilmembers: Jeannie M. McNair, Steve Weiser, Perry Chocktoot, Devery M. Saluskin II, David M. Ochoa, Kathleen Hatcher-Mitchell
George Lopez, Tribal Administration General Manager
Julie Bettles, Director of Education & Employment
Rhonda Kruhler, Public Information/News Manager
 E-mail: rhonda.kruhler@klamathtribes.com
Jeremy A. Brave-Heart, Tribal Chief Judge
Tribes: Klamath, Modoc, Yahooskin. *Enrolled members:* 3,500. *Resources:* Tribal Wellness Center. *Programs:* Education; Health & Family Services; Social Services; Community Services; Employment; Alcohol & Substance Abuse; Natural Resources; Planning & Enterprise; Cultural & Heritage; Housing.

Attractions: Kla-Mo-Ya Casino; annual Restoration Celebration, held the 4th weekend in August; Captain Jack Memorial Day Rodeo & Powwow; annual New Year's Eve Sobriety Celebrations; annual Return of C'waam Ceremony. *Publication:* Klamath News, monthly newspaper. Northwest Regional Office.

RHODE ISLAND

NARRAGANSETT INDIAN TRIBE
Administration Bldg., 4533 S. County Trail
P.O. Box 268 • Charleston, RI 02813
(401) 364-1100 Fax 364-1104
Website: www.narragansettindiannation.org
E-mail: narragansettindian@gmail.com
Matthew Thomas (*Seventh Hawk*), Chief Sachem
Lloyd G. Wilcox (*Running Wolf*), Elder Medicineman
John Brown, Medicineman; John Mahoney, Tribal Secretary
Councilmembers:
Casssius Spears, Jr., 1st Council; John Pompey, 2nd Council
Betty Johnson, Mary Brown, Walter Babcock, Lonny Brown,
Yvonne Simonds Lamphere
Anthony Dean Stanton, Director of Administration
Jacqueline A. Stanton, Educaton Director
Tribe: Narragansett. *Enrolled members:* 2,500. *Area:* 1,800 acres. *Resources:* Narragansett Indian Health Center; Child Care Center. *Programs:* Education; Health & Human Services; Child Care & Welfare; Adult Vocational Training; Community Planning & Natural Resources; Housing; Historic Preservation (P.O. Box 700, Wyoming, RI 02898 - 401-539-1190). *Attraction:* Annual Tribal Elder's Day in May. *Publication:* Newsletter. Eastern Regional Office.

SOUTH CAROLINA

CATAWBA INDIAN NATION
996 Avenue of the Nations • Rock Hill, SC 29730
(803) 366-4792 Fax 366-0629
Website: www.catawbaindian.net; E-mail: info@catawbaindian.net
Bill Harris, Chief; Jason Harris, Assistant Chief
Rod Beck, Secretary/Treasurer
Councilmembers: Sammy Beck & Dean Canty
Elizabeth Harris, Tribal Administrator
 E-mail: Elizabeth.harris@catawbaindian.net,
Linda Love, Social Services Director
 E-mail: linda.love@catawbaindian.net
Elizabeth Harris, Community Planner
Jackie Canty, Economic Development Director
 E-mail: Jackie.canty@catawbaindian.net
Darin Steen, Environmental Services Director
 E-mail: darin.steen@catawbaindian.net
Denise Williams, Rights Protection Director
Tribe: Catawba. *Enrolled members:* 2,800. *Resources:* Technology Achievement Center; Cultural Center; Catawba Service Unit - The Clinic; Senior Center; ISWA Development Corp. *Programs:* Social Services; Economic Development; Real Estate & Other Rights Protection; Tribal Planning & Development; Housing; Environmental; Head Start. *Attraction:* Bingo Hall in York County. *Publication:* Community News, newsletter. Eastern Area Office.

SOUTH DAKOTA

CHEYENNE RIVER SIOUX TRIBE
2001 Main St., P.O. Box 590 • Eagle Butte, SD 57625
(605) 964-4155 Fax 964-4151; Website: www.sioux.org
Harold C. Frazier, Chairperson
Bob Chasing Hawk Vice Chairperson (964-6685)
Ev Ann White Feather, Tribal Secretary (964-8311)
Benita Clark, Treasurer (964-4426)
Kenneth Little Thunder, Administrative Officer (964-4155)
Tribal Council Representatives: (605) 964-6685 Fax 964-6680
District 1: Bernita in the Woods & Bryce in the Woods
District 2: Ted "Buddy" Knife, Jr.
District 3: Edward Widow, John Kessler
District 4: Mark Knight, Kevin C. Keckler, Jim Pearman
 Merrie Miller White Bull,
District 5: Robert Chasing Hawk, Raymond Uses the Knife,
 Derek Bartlett, Ryman Le Beau
District 6: Tartar Ward, Tuffy Thompson
Todd Ward, Sargeant at Arms
Steve Vance, Historic Preservation Officer (964-7554)
 E-mail: stevev.crstpres@outlook.com
Kurt Spilker, Tribal Attorney (964-6682)
 E-mail: kurt.spiker@crst-nsn.gov

Tribe: Cheyenne River Sioux. *In residence*: 5,500. *Area*: 3 million+ acres located in Dewey & Zeibach Counties. *Resources*: Cheyenne River Health Center; HV Johnston Cultural Center; Oglala Lakota College; Cheyenne River Community College Center; Presentation College - Lakota College; Cheyenne Eagle Butte School; Takini School; Tiospaye Topa School; Dupree School; Timber Lake School. *Programs*: Human Services; Health Education, Diabetes; Education; Head Start; Employment; Counseling; Cultural Preservation, Language; Environmental Protection; Economic Development; Housing; Vocational Rehabilitation. *Attraction*: Bingo Hall. *Publication*: CRST Newsletter, monthly; Archive Tribal News. Cheyenne River Agency.

CROW CREEK SIOUX TRIBE

100 Drifting Goose Rd., P.O. Box 50 • Fort Thompson, SD 57339
(605) 245-2221 Fax 245-2470; Roxanne Sazue, Chairperson
Councilmembers:
Roland Hawk, Tina Grey Owl, Francine Middletent, Fort Thompson District
Jamie Fallis, Big Bend District; Gilbert Ray Pickner, Crow Creek District
Silas Blaine, Tribal Schools Superintendent
Tribe: Crow Creek Sioux. *Enrolled members*: 3,550. *In residence*: 1,830. *Area*: 125,600 acres located in parts of Buffalo, Hughes, and Hyde counties on the east bank of the Missouri River in central South Dakota. *Resources*: Native American Telecom-Crow Creek; Crow Creek Tribal School. *Programs*: Health & Human Services; Education; Head Start. *Attraction*: Lode Star Casino. Crow Creek Agency.

FLANDREAU SANTEE SIOUX TRIBE

603 W. Broad Ave., P.O. Box 283 • Flandreau, SD 57028
(605) 997-3891 Fax 997-3878; Website: www.santeesioux.com
Anthony Reider, President; E-mail: president@fsst.org
Andrew Weston, Vice President
Gordon Jones, Jr., Secretary; Ryan Kills-a-Hundred, Treasurer
Jean Paul Roy, Trustee I; David Killsahundred, Trustee II
Mike Weston, Trustee III, Jason Armstrong, Trustee IV
John Peebles & Seth Pearman, Tribal Attorneys
Justin Taylor, Health Administrator (997-2642)
Sherman Marshall, Tribal Judge
Tribe: Santee Sioux. *In residence*: 715. *Area*: 5,000 acres. *Resources*: Tribal Wellness Center; Agnes Ross Educational Center; Grace Moore Senior Center; Smith Publishing (located in Dell Rapids, SD). *Programs*: Education; Health, Social Services; Counseling; Natural Resources; Senior Citizens; Housing. *Attractions*: Royal River Casino & Hotel; annual powwow in July. *Publication*: Monthly Tribal Newsletter. Great Plains Regional Office.

LOWER BRULE SIOUX TRIBE (KUL WICASA OYATE)

187 Oyate Circle, P.O. Box 187 • Lower Brule, SD 57548
(605) 473-5561 Fax 473-5606; Website: www.lbst.org
Boyd Gourneau, Chairperson; E-mail: chairman@lbst.org
Tribe: Sicangu Lower Brule Sioux. *Enrolled members*: 2,500. *In residence*: 1,310. Total area: 221,646. Tribal owned area: 132,800 acres located in central South Dakota, 58 miles southeast of Fort Pierre on historic Hwy. 1806 (the Native American Scenic Byway) and 15 miles north of Reliance, at exit 248 on I-90. *Resources*: Akta Lakota Museum. *Programs*: Head Start. *Attractions*: Buffalo Interpretive Center located at 29349 Hwy. 1806 in Fort Pierre; Buffalo & Elk Preserves maintaining about 300 bison & 200 elk in three ranges of approximately 6200 acres; Big Bend Landmark & Narrows Interpretive Area; Golden Buffalo Casino & Resort; Powwows; Annual Fair & Rodeo, 2nd weekend in August. Lower Brule Agency.

OGLALA (LAKOTAH) SIOUX TRIBE

Pine Ridge Reservation, W. Hwy 18, Red Cloud Bldg.
107 West Main St., P.O. Box 2070 • Pine Ridge, SD 57770
(605) 867-5821/2470 Fax 867-1788; E-mail: ostoyate@gmail.com
Website: www.oglalalakotanation.info
Executive Committee:
Troy "Scott" Weston, President; E-mail: tsweston@gwtc.net
Darla Black, Vice President; (867-4009) E-mail: darla@oglala.org
Donna Salomon, Secretary; (867-8468) E-mail: donnas@oglala.org
Mason Big Crow, Treasurer; E-mail: mason@oglala.org
James Red Willow, 5th Member (867-8439)
Abraham Tobacco, Sergeant-At-Arms (454-0093)
Eagle Nest District: P.O. Box 289, Wanblee, SD 57577
Council Representatives: Jim Meeks (454-2399)
Blaine Little Thunder (462-5058) E-mail: blainlt@goldenwest.net
LaCreek District: P.O. Box 681, Martin, SD 57551
Council Representatives:
Cora White Horse; (685-1097) E-mail: cora.whitehorse@gmail.com
Craig Dillon (685-1004) E-mail: cdillon@hotmail.com
Medicine Root District: P.O. Box 496, Kyle, SD 57752 (455-1141)
Council Representatives:
Stanley Little Whiteman; E-mail: s.lwm52@hotmail.com
Austin Watkins (455-1141) E-mail: Austin@oglala.org

Chauncey Wilson (455-1000) E-mail: wilsonrodeo@goldenwest.net
Oglala District: *Council Representatives*:
P.O. Box 289, Oglala, SD 57764 (867-5617)
Stephanie Leasure; E-mail: star.stef13@gmail.com
Valentina Merdanian; E-mail: vmerdanian@gmail.com
Pass Creek District: *Council Representatives*:
P.O. Box 560, Allen, SD 57714 (455-2540)
Lydia Bear Killer; E-mail: lydiabearkiller@gmail.com
James Cross (455-1118) E-mail: jamescross0810@gmail.com
Pine Ridge Village: P.O. Box 748, Pine Ridge, SD 57770 (867-5635)
Council Representatives:
Richard Greenwald (867-2158); E-mail: richard_greenwald@yahoo.com
Ella "John" Carlow (441-0114); E-mail: ejcarlow@hotmail.com
Robin Tapio (867-5749); E-mail: supertap_46@yahoo.com
Porcupine District: P.O. Box 217, Porcupine, SD 57772 (867-5728)
Phillip Good Crow (455-2387) E-mail: pgoodcrow@yahoo.com
David Pourier (455-2837) E-mail: pourierdavid@yahoo.com
Wakpamni District: P.O. Box 1993, Pine Ridge, SD 57770 (867-5287)
Council Representatives:
Jackie Siers (407-8914) E-mail: jackier62@hotmail.com
Sonia Little Hawk-Weston (867-1920) E-mail: soniaw@gwtc.net
Wounded Knee District: P.O. Box 133, Manderso, SD 57756 (867-5428)
Council Representatives:
Collins "CJ" Clifford (407-1246) E-mail: cliffordcj@yahoo.com
Lisa Jumping Eagle-Deleon (407-2650) E-mail: lrowland_ost@hotmail.com
Dr. Richard Zephier, Executive Director (407-8429)
E-mail: rzephier@oglala.org
CJ Clifford, Tribe Education Committee Chair
Caroline Bettelyoun, Coordinator (454-4984)
Sonia Little Hawk-Westonn, Health & Human Services Chair
James Cross, Economic & Business Development Chair
Floyd Brings Plenty, Finance Committee Chair (454-4988)
Tribe: Oglala Sioux. *Enrolled members*: 38,332. In residence: 19,639. *Total Area*: @2 million acres, 1,771,196 acres (SD) & 90,000 acres (Nebraska). *Tribally owned*: 706,340 acres located 60 miles east of the Black Hills, extending into Nebraska. *Resources*: Akta Lakota Museum & Cultural Center (www.aktalakota.org) located in Chamberlain, SD: The Lakota Fund (605) 455-2500 (see Association section). *Programs*: Health & Human Services; Diabetes Prevention; Higher Education; Head Start; Child Care & Development; Economic Development; Home Improvement; Human Resources; Job Place-ment & Training; Johnson O'Malley; Meals for the Elderly; Land & Natural Resources; Transportation; Veteran's' Vocational Rehabilitation; Water Maintenance & Conservation; Energy; Environmental Protection; Food Distribution. Attraction: Prairie Wind Casino; annual Oglala Sioux Sun Dance (August); Wounded Knee Battlefield (15 miles northeast of Pine Ridge); Badlands National Monument. Pine Ridge Agency.

PONCA TRIBE OF NEBRASKA

Located in Nebraska and South Dakota. See listing under Nebraska.

ROSEBUD SIOUX TRIBE

Rosebud Reservation, **11 Legion Ave.,** P.O. Box 430 • Rosebud, SD 57570
(888) 747-2381; (605) 747-2381 Fax 747-2905
Website https://www.rosebudsiouxtribe-nsn.gov/
E-mail: council@rst-nsn.gov
William "Willie" Kindle, President; Scott Herman, Vice President
Julie Peneaux, Secretary; Wayne Boyd, Treasurer
Ed Clairmont, Sergeant-at-Arms
Wayne Bear Shield, General Operations Director
Community Council Representatives:
Edward "Sonny" Farmer, Jr. (319-0913), Antelope Community
Richard Charging Hawk (462-6741), Black Pipe Community
Charles I. White Pipe, Jr. (828-6043) Bull Creek Community
Arnetta Brave (828-3064), Butte Creek Community
Arlene R. Black Bear (319-1587), Corn Creek Community
Rita Means, Grass Mountain Community
Royal Yellow Hawk (319-1496), He Dog Community
Robert Rattling Leaf (828-6577), Horse Creek Community
Shizue LaPointe (842-1227), Ideal Community
Wayne Frederick (828-1266), Okreek Community
Brian Dillion (319-0204), Parmelee Community
Patricia Douville (840-8283), Ring Thunder Community
Richard "Tuffy" Lunderman (319-1028), Rosebud Community
Kathleen Wooden Knife (747-2057), Soldier Creek Community
Lila Kills In Sight (747-5217), Spring Creek Community
Michael Boltz, Sr. (747-2538), St. Francis Community
James Leader Charge (319-1359), Swift Bear Community
Richard "Smokey" Whipple (828-0846), Two-Strike Community
Lester Kills The Enemy (319-1462), Upper Cut Meat Community
Tribe: Sicangu Oyate - Rosebud Lakota Sioux. *Enrolled members*: 27,000. *In residence*: 22,000. *Area*: 964,778 acres located in south-central South Dakota,

adjoining the Nebraska State line. *Resources*: St. Francis Mission; Sioux Indian Museum; Tribal Land Enterprises; Youth Advocacy Center; Rosebud Elementary School; St. Francis Indian School; Sinte Gleska University; Day Care Center. *Programs*: Education; Head Start; Health; Diabetes Prevention; Alcohol & Substance Abuse; Elderly; Enrollment; Social Services; Child & Family Services; Child Care Development; Forestry; Natural Resources; Economic Development; Food Distribution; Environmental (Wind Farm Project). *Attractions*: Rosebud Casino; Crazy Horse Canyon Park (tribe-operated); annual Rosebud Fair & Rodeo, 4th weekend in August; Mud Races. *Publication*: Sicangu Sun Times, Bi-weekly tribal newspaper. Rosebud Agency.

SISSETON WAHPETON OYATE
Lake Traverse Reservation, 100 Veterans Memorial Dr.
12554 BIA Hwy. 711, P.O. Box 509 • Agency Village, SD 57262
 (605) 698-3911 Fax 742-0265
 Website: www.swo-nsn.gov; E-mail: webadmin@swo-nsn.gov
 David Flute, Chairperson; E-mail: chairman@swo-nsn.gov
 Floyd Kirk, Jr., Vice Chairperson; E-mail: swovicechair@swo-nsn.gov
 Crystal Heminger, Secretary; E-mail: swosecretary@swo-nsn.gov
District Council members:
Big Coulee District: E-mail: bcrep@swo-nsn.gov
 David Spider, Chairperson (228-9561)
 Lynn Halbert, District Vice Chairperson (268-3035)
 Ann German, District Coordinator (938-4475)
Buffalo Lake District: E-mail: blrep@swo-nsn.gov
 Louie Johnson, District Chairperson (951-4960)
 John Lincoln, Vice Chairperson (924-0563)
Enemy Swim District: E-mail: esrep@swo-nsn.gov
 David Gill, District Chairperson
 Tim Peters, District Vice Chairperson (237-2928)
Lake Traverse District; E-mail: ltrep@swo-nsn.gov
 Darwin James, District Chairperson (268-3743)
 Jacky White, District Vice Chairperson (268-0726)
 Francis Crawford, Tribal Council Representative
Long Hollow District; E-mail: lhrep@swo-nsn.gov
 Robin Quinn, District Chairperson (268-0977)
 Darrell Quinn, Jr., District Vice Chairperson (237-9392)
 Val Keoke, District Coordinator (698-4005)
Old Agency District; E-mail: oarep@swo-nsn.gov
 Jesse Larsen, District Chairperson (924-1635)
 E-mail: oadchairperson@venturecomm.net
 Cherilyn Marks, District Vice Chairperson (268-2024)
 E-mail: oadvicechairperson@venturecomm.net
 Seava Sartwell, District Coordinator (698-4013)
 E-mail: oadcoordinator@venturecomm.net
Heipa/Veblen District; E-mail: hvrep@swo-nsn.gov
 Karen White, District Chairperson (268-0661)
 Alan Amos White, District Vice Chairperson (742-0636)
 Renae Lufkins, District Coordinator (738-2324)
 E-mail: heipadistrict2016@gmail.com
 Audrey German, Community Health Education Program Manager (742-3651)
 E-mail: audrey.german@ihs.gov
 Sara Decoteau, Health Center Program Manager (742-3697)
 E-mail: sara.decoteau@ihs.gov
 Janell Williams, Higher Ediucation Program Director (742-0150)
 E-mail: janellb@swo-nsn.gov
 Dr. Sherry Johnson, Education Director
 Debra Flute, Esq., SWO Attorney
 E-mail: debraf@swo-nsn.gov
 Shaun Eastman, Esq., SWO Attorney
 E-mail: shaune@swo-nsn.gov
 Megan LaFromboise, JD; E-mail: meganl@swo-nsn.gov
Tribe: Sisseton-Wahpeton Oyate. *Enrolled members*: 13,872. *In residence*: 12,300. *Area*: 250,000 acres located in South & North Dakota (only a minor portion in North Dakota.) *Resources*: Woodrow Wilson Keeble Memorial Health Care Center; Tiospa Zina Tribal School; Sisseton-Wahpeton College. *Project*: New Tribal Administration Building (under construction). *Programs*: Higher Education; Health & Human Services; Family Services; Child Protection & Support; Youth Services; Housing; Veteran Services; Elderly Services; Legal Services; Natural Resources; Fish & Wildlife; Historic Preservation; Head Start. *Enterprise*: Dakota Western Corporation. *Attraction*: Dakota Sioux Casino, Dakota Connection Casino; annual powwow. *Publication*: Sota Iya Ye Yapi, weekly newspaper. Sisseton Agency.

YANKTON SIOUX TRIBE
P.O. Box 1153 • Wagner, SD 57380
 (605) 384-3641/3804 Fax 384-5687
 Website: www.yanktonsiouxtribe.net
 Robert Flying Hawk, Chairperson
 E-mail: robertflyinghawk@gmail.com
 Jody Zephier, Vice Chairperson; E-mail: zephierj@yahoo.com

 Glenford "Sam" Sully, Secretary; Leo O'Connor, Treasurer
Councilmembers: Gregory Cournoyer, Jr., Jason Cooke,
 Roseanne Wade, Diane Merrick, Mona Wright
 Richard Sully, Tribal Health Educator (384-3641)
 E-mail: rsullycouncil2002@yahoo.com
 William Roller, Tribal Librarian
Tribe: Yankton Sioux. *Enrolled members in residence*: 3,500. *Area*: 40,000 acres. *Resources*: Ihanktonwan Community College. *Programs*: Health; Child Care; Human Resources; Head Start. *Attractions*: Fort Randall Casino & Hotel. Yankton Agency.

TEXAS

ALABAMA-COUSHATTA TRIBE OF TEXAS
571 State Park Rd. 56 • Livingston, TX 77351
 (936) 563-1100 Fax 563-1131
 Website: www.alabama-coushatta.com
 E-mail: information@actribe.org
 Colabe III Clem F. Sylestine, Principal Chief
 Skalaaba Herbert Johnson, Sr., Second Chief
 Jo Ann Battise, Chairperson
 Ronnie Thomas, Vice Chairperson
 Nita Battise, Secretary/Treasurer
 Stephanie Williams, Tribal Administrator (563-1101)
 E-mail: williams.stephanie@actribe.org
 Tina Battise, Deputy Administrator
 E-mail: battise.tina@actribe.org
Councilmembers: David Battise, Obrey Alec, Rolannd Poncho,
 Maynard Williams, Johnny Stafford
 Janie Rhinesmith, Education Director (563-1280)
 E-mail: acedu@actribe.org
 Sharon Miller, Public Information Officer (563-1100)
 E-mail: information@actribe.org
Tribe: Alabama-Coushatta of Texas. *Enrolled members*: 1,150. *Area*: 9,700 acres. *Resources*: Chief Kina Health Clinic (563-2058/9); Library. *Programs*: Health, Diabetes Education; WIA Employment & Training; Head Start (563-1300); Richard Cordes, Social Services Director (563-5215); Janie Rhinesmith, Education Director (563-1280); Youth; Environmental (Cecilia Flores, Specialist); Youth; Employment/Training; Enrollment. *Attractions*: Annual Powwow 1st weekend in June. *Publication*: Tribal newsletter. Southern Plains Regional Office.

KICKAPOO TRADITIONAL TRIBE OF TEXAS
HC 1 Box 9700 • Eagle Pass, TX 78852
 (830) 773-2105 Fax 757-9228
 Juan Garza, Jr., Chairperson
Tribe: Kickapoo. *Enrolled members*: 3,000. *In residence*: 425. *Area*: 120 acres on the Rio Grande River just south of Eagle Pass. *Programs*: Education; Health; Cultural; Economic Development; Gaming; Environmental; Housing; Social Services. *Attraction*: Kickapoo Lucky Eagle Casino. Under jurisdiction of Southern Plains Regional Office.

YSLETA DEL SUR PUEBLO
117 S. Old Pueblo Rd. • El Paso, TX 79907
P.O. Box 17579 • El Paso, TX 79917
 (915) 859-8053 Fax 859-4252
 Website: www.ysletadelsurpueblo.org
 Carlos Hisa, Governor; Christopher Gomez, Lt. Governor
Council Captains: Raul Willy Almazar III, Benjamin Paiz,
 Capt. Sergio Loera, Jr., Rene Lopez
Tribe: Tigua. *Enrolled members*: 1,702. *Area*: 2,700 acres, within the city limits of El Paso & City of Socorro. *Resources*: Community Health Center; Recreation & Wellness Center; Cultural Center. *Programs*: Health & Human Services; Diabetes Prevention; Education; Housing; Economic Development; Empowerment; Day Care. *Enterprises*: Tigua, Inc.; Speaking Rock Entertainment Center. *Publication*: Tigua News. Southern Pueblos Agency.

UTAH

CONFEDERATED TRIBES OF THE GOSHUTE INDIAN RESERVATION
195 Tribal Center Rd., P.O. Box 6104 • Ibapah, UT 84034
 (435) 234-1138 Fax 234-1162; E-mail: goshutetribe@yahoo.com
 Virgil W. Johnson, Chairperson; E-mail: virgilwjohnson@yahoo.com
 Madeline Greymountain, Vice Chairperson
Councilmembers: Amos Murphy, Richard Henriod, Lavar Tom
 Jeanine Hooper, Social Services Program Coordinator
 Christine Steele, Acting Health Director
 Elvira Murphy, Education Director (234-1140)
Tribe: Goshute. *Enrolled members*: 450. *In residence*: 200. *Area*: 112,870 acres located in White Pine County in East Central Nevada and in Juab &

Toole Counties in West Central Utah. *Programs*: Education; Health; Diabetes Prevention; Social Services; Housing; Environmental; Elderly Food Service; Alcohol & Substance Abuse; Violence Against Women. *Attraction*: Annual powwow. *Publication*: Newsletter. Eastern Nevada Field Office.

NORTHWESTERN BAND OF SHOSHONE NATION
Brigham Office: 707 N. Main St. • Brigham City, UT 84302
(800) 310-8241; (435) 734-2286 Fax 734-0424
  Website: www.nwbshoshone.com
Pocatello Office: 505 Pershing Ave., Suite 200,
  Pocatello (Blackfoot) ID 83201
(208) 478-5712 Fax 478-5713
Shane Warner, Chairperson/CEO (Pocatello Office)
  E-mail: swarner@nwbshoshone-nsn.gov
Darren Parry, Vice Chairperson (Brigham City Office)
  E-mail: dparry@nwbshoshone-nsn.gov
Dennis Alex, Secretary (Brigham City Office)
  E-mail: gdavis@nwbshoshone.com
Byron Timbimboo, Treasurer (Brigham City Office)
  E-mail: btimbimboo@nwbshoshone-nsn.gov
Jeffrey Parry (Brigham City), Larry Neaman (Pocatello),
  Shane Warner (Pocatello), Councilmembers
Tribe: Shoshone. Located in Idaho & Utah. *Programs*: Education; Health; Housing; Cultural & Natural Resources; Environment. *Resources*: Economic Development Corporation - Two locations: Brigham Tribal Office and at 1177 E. South Temple, Salt Lake City, UT 84102 (877) 777-2327. Through the Intermountain Tribal Alliance (ITA), the Tribe has developed a Community Development Financial Institution (CDFT) that has created a venture capital fund to develop tribal companies that implement Harvard Project on American Indian Economic Development for corporate governance principles. Fort Hall Agency.

PAIUTE INDIAN TRIBE OF UTAH
440 N. Paiute Dr. • Cedar City, UT 84720
(435) 586-1112 Fax 867-2659
  Website: www.utahpaiutes.org
Tamra Borchardt-Slayton Chairperson
  E-mail: tamiborchardt@gmail.cm
Cedar Band: P.O. Box 235, Cedar City, UT 84721
  (435) 586-9433 Fax 586-5915; Mertin Bow, Chairperson
Indian Peaks Band: 940 W. 526 S., Cedar City, UT 84721
  Tamra Borchardt-Slayton, Chairperson
Kanosh Band: P.O. Box 116, Kanosh, UT 84637
  Corrina Bow, Chairperson (383-3283)
Koosharem Band: P.O. Box 205, Richfield, UT 84701
  (435) 893-8432 Fax 896-8607; LaTosha Mayo, Chairperson
Shivwits Band: 6060 W. 3650 N., Ivins, UT 84765
  Website: www.shivwits.org; Patrick Charles, Chairperson
Colette Cox, Education Director
Gaylord Robb, Economic Development Director
  E-mail: Gaylord.robb@ihs.gov
Tribe: Paiute. *Enrolled members*: 850. *Area*: 35,000 acres in ten separate land parcels in Southwestern Utah. *Resources*: Library. *Programs*: Cultural Resources; Education; Health; Community Services; Housing; Behavioral Care; Human Resources; Economic Development. *Attractions*: Paiute Restoration Gathering & Powwow in June. *Publication*: Tribal newsletter. Southern Paiute Agency.

SKULL VALLEY BAND OF GOSHUTE INDIANS
Skull Valley Reservation, P.O. Box 448 • Grantsville, UT 84029
(435) 882-4532 Fax 882-4889
Candace Bear, Chairperson; (831-4079)
  E-mail: candaceb@svgoshutes.com
Tribe: Skull Valley Goshute. *Enrolled members*: 135. *Area*: 18,000 acres located 45 miles southwest of Salt Lake City. *Resources*: Library & cultural center currently being developed. Uintah & Ouray Agency.

UTE INDIAN TRIBE
The Uintah & Ouray Indian Reservation
910 South 7500 East, P.O. Box 190 • Fort Duchesne, UT 84026
(435) 722-5141 Fax 722-2374
  Website: www.utetribe.com; E-mail: utetribe@utetribe.com
Luke Duncan, Chairperson & Uncomphgre Band Rep.
  E-mail: luked@utetribe.com
Edred Secakuku, Vice Chairperson & Whiteriver Band Rep.
Deneen Kane, Secretary; Patty Marks, Tribal Attorney
Business Committee members:
  Stewart Pike (Uncomphgre Band Rep.); Tony Small (Uncomphgre Band
  Rep.); Bruce Ignacio (Uintah Band Rep.); Ronald Wopsock (Uintah Band
  Rep.); Cummings J. Vanderhoop (WhiteriverBand Rep.)
Tribe: Northern Ute. *Enrolled members*: 3,050. *In residence*: 2,200. *Area*: 4.5 million acres overseeing about 1.3 million acres of trust land. The second

largest Indian reservation in the U.S. is located in the Uintah Basin in northeast Utah, approximately 150 miles east of Salt Lake City on US Hwy. 40. *Resources*: Red Pine Treatment Center. *Programs*: Education-Head Start; Cultural; Community Services; Health; Senior; Public Safety; Housing; Energy & Minerals; Fish & Wildlife. *Attraction*: Annual Thanksgiving Pow-Wow. *Publication*: Ute Bulletin. Uintah & Ouray Agency.

VIRGINIA

UNITED CHEROKEE INDIAN TRIBE OF VIRGINIA
P.O. Box 1104 • Madison Heights, VA 24572
(434) 847-4104 Fax 847-3200
  Website: www.ucitova.org; E-mail: ucitova@aol.com
Samuel H. Penn, Sr. (*Mountain Wolf*), Chief
Samuel H. Penn *Leaping Wolf*), Vice Chief
Shelby W. Penn (*Quiet Fire*), Secretary
Kenneth M. Penn, Sr. (*Red Man*), Treasurer
Ollie Spencer, Sr., Brian O. Wood, Bernetta Chambers-Penn,
  Norma Wood Wilson, Diane McCoy, Robert C. McCoy, Jr., Councilmembers
Tribe: Cherokee Tribe of Virginia. *Enrolled members*: 150. *Resources*: Library. *Attractions*: Traditional Cherokee holidays, festivals, and ceremonies. Eastern Area Office.

PAMUNKEY INDIAN TRIBE
1054 Pocahontas Trail. • King William, VA 23086
(804) 843-3526; Website: www.pamunkey.net
  E-mail: pamunkeytrc@gmail.com
Robert Gray, Chief; G. Bradby Brown, Assistant Chief/Councimember
Councilmembers: Warren Cook, Walter Hill, Jr., Ivy Hill, Layne Cook,
  Tim Langston, Gordon Atkinson
Tribe: Pamunkey. *Enrolled members*: 200. *In residence*: 100. *Area*: 1,250 acres. *Resources*: Pamunkey Indian Museum & Photo Gallery; Museum Shop.

WASHINGTON

CONFEDERATED TRIBES OF THE CHEHALIS RESERVATION
420 Howanut Rd., P.O. Box 536 • Oakville, WA 98568
(360) 273-5911 Fax 273-5914; Website: www.chehalistribe.org
Don Secena, Chairperson; Jessie Goddard, Vice Chairperson
Shoni Pannkuk, Treasurer; David Burnett, Secretary
Leroy Boyd, Sr., 5th Council Member
Jeff Warnke, Office of Government & Public Relations
Richard Bellon, Tribal Administration General Manager
Racheal Mendez, Director of Higher Education (709-1698)
John Shortman, Jr., K-12 Education Coordinator
Dianne "DeDe" Devlin, Cultural Coordinator (709-1671)
Fred Shortman, Communications Coordinator
  E-mail: fshortman@chehalistribe.org
Lloyd Commander, Head Start Director
Tribe: Chehalis. *Enrolled members*: 535. *In residence*: 765. *Area*: 4,225 acres located in the southeastern corner of Grays Harbor County bordering Thurston County, southeast of Oakville. *Resources*: Wellness Center; Community Center; Medical & Dental Clinic. *Programs*: Education; Health; Public Safety; Family Services; Gaming; Housing; Natural Resources; Head Start. *Attractions*: Lucky Eagle Casino & Bingo; Eagles Landing Hotel; Great Wolf Lodge. *Publication*: Chehalis Tribal Newsletter. Olympic Peninsula Agency.

CONFEDERATED TRIBES OF THE COLVILLE RESERVATION
1 Colville St., P.O. Box 150 • Nespelem, WA 99155
(509) 634-2212 Fax 634-4116; Website: https://www.cct-cbc.com
Francis Somday, Executive Director of Administration
  E-mail: francis.somday@colvilletribes.com
Michael Marchand, Chairperson (Omak District Rep.)
  E-mail: michael.marchand@colvilletribes.com
Edwin Marchand, Vice Chairperson (Omak District Rep.)
  E-mail edwin.marchand@colvilletribes.com
Bessie Simpson, Secretary (Inchlium District Rep)
  E-mail: Bessie.simpson.cbc@colvilletribes.com
Councilmembers & Committee Chairs:
Andy Joseph, Jr., Nespelem District Rep. (634-2209)
  E-mail: andy.joseph@colvilletribes.com
  Chair, Human Services Committee
Ricky Gabriel, Nespelem District Rep. (634-2207)
  Email: ricky.gabriel@colvilletribes.com
William Womer, Nespelem District Rep. (634-2252)
  Email: william.womer.cbc@colvilletribes.com
  Chair, Community Development Committee
Jack Ferguson, Keller District Rep. (634-2215)
  E-mail: jack.ferguson@colvilletribes.com
  Chair, Management & Budget Committee

Susie Allen, Inchelium District Rep. (634-2210)
  E-mail: susie.allen.cbc@colvilletribes.com
Georgia Simpson, Inchelium District Rep. (634-2208)
  E-mail: georgia.simpson.cbc@colvilletribes.com
Joel Boyd, Inchelium District Rep. (634-2219)
  E-mail: joel.boyd.cbc@colvilletribes.com
  Chair for Law & Justice
Sheilah Cleveland, Nespelem District #2 Rep. (634-2208)
  E-mail: sheilah.cleveland.cbc@colvilletribes.com
  Chair, Law & Justice Committee
Rodney Cawston, Nespelem District Rep. (634-2205)
  E-mail: Rodney.cawston.cbc@colvilletribes.com
  Chair for Natural Resources
Joseph Somday, Keller District Rep. (634-2214)
  E-mail: joseph.somday@colvilletribes.com
  Chair, Natural Resource Committee
Larry Allen, Inchelium District Rep. (634-2216)
  E-mail: jack.ferguson@colvilletribes.com
  Chair, Education & Employment
Norma Sanchez, Omak District Rep. (634-2206)
  E-mail: norma.sanchez@colvilletribes.com
  Tribal Government Chair
Edwin Marchand, Omak District Rep. (634-2212)
  E-mail: edwin.marchand@colvilletribes.com
Melissa Louis, Omak District Rep. (634-2211)
  E-mail: Melissa.louis.cbc@colvilletribes.com

Tribes: Confederated Tribes (Colville, Okanogan, Lakes, San Poil, Methow, Nespelem, Entiat, Wenatchee, Moses, Nez Perce, Palouse.) *Enrolled members*: 6,600. *In residence*: 3,750. *Area*: 1,087,271 acres located in Okanogan & Ferry Counties. *Four districts*: Inchelium, Keller, Nespelem, and Omak. *Resources*: Community Health Centers; Colville Tribal Enterprise Corporation; Library. *Programs*: Health Services; Employment & Training; Natural Resources; Public Works/Housing; Education/Head Start; Gaming. *Attractions*: Owns & operates three casinos - Coulee Dam Casino; Mill Bay Casino, Okanogan Casino/Bingo; Grand Coulee Dam; Old Fort Okanogan; Burial Place of Nez Perce, Chief Joseph; July 4th Powwow; annual Salmon Feast in September. *Publication*: Tribal Tribune. Colville Agency.

COWLITZ INDIAN TRIBE
1055 9th Ave., Suite B, P.O. Box 2547 • Longview, WA 98632
(360) 577-8140 Fax 577-7432; Website: www.cowlitz.org
William "Bill" Iyall, Chairperson; E-mail: wiyall@cowlitz.org
Philip Harju, Vice Chairperson & Tribal Attorney
  E-mail: pharju@cowlitz.org
Nancy Osborne, Secretary; Dan Meyer, Treasurer
Carolee Morris, Tribal Administrator
Steve Kutz, Director of Health & Human Services (575-8277)
  E-mail: skutz.health@cowlitz.org
Nathan Reynolds, Interim Director of Cultural Department
  E-mail: culture@cowlitz.org
Christine Myers, Tribal Planner
Carolyn Medeiros, Cowlitz Project Coordinator
  E-mail: cjmfox1@aol.com
Councilmembers: Mike Iyall, Karissa Lowe, Lenny Bridges, Debbie Hassler, Katherine Iyall-Vasquez, Steve Kutz, Randy Russell, Patty Kinswa-Gaiser, Cassandra Sellards-Reck, John O'Brien, Carolee Morris, Taylor Aalvik, Celine Cloquet, Cathy Raphael, Jerry Iyall, Tim Van Mechelen, Christine Hawkins, Rourke Monohon.
Tribe: Cowlitz. *Area*: Located in Cowlitz County. *Programs*: Housing, Education, Health; Child Welfare; Cultural; Natural Resources; Economic Development. *Attractions*: The Cowlitz Casino; annual Powwow. *Publication*: Tribal News.

HOH TRIBE
Hoh River Indian Reservation
2464 Lower Hoh Rd., P.O. Box 2196 • Forks, WA 98331
(360) 374-6582 Fax 374-5426; Website: http://www.hohtribe-nsn.org
Maria Lopez, Chairperson; (374-3271)
  E-mail: marial@hohtribe-nsn.org
Melvinjohn Ashue, Vice Chairperson (808-8658)
  E-mail: melvinjohn.ashue@hohtribe-nsn.org
Lisa Martinez, Secretary (780-2004)
  E-mail: lisa.martinez@hohtribe-nsn.org
Rosetta Hernandez, Treasurer (374-2005)
  E-mail: rosetta.hernandez@hohtribe-nsn.org
Councilmembers: Derek Benally, Enrique Barragan, Bobbyjoe Ashue
Vacant, Executive Director (374-6501)
Pat O'Brien, Chief Financial Officer (860-9039)
Leann Easton, Tribal Attorney
Dawn Gomez, Health Clinic Director (374-4280)
Tara Sexton, Family Services Director (374-5037)

Tribe: Hoh. *In residence*: 75. *Area*: 900 acres located at Cape Flattery in Jefferson County. *Resources*: Chief Klia Wellness Center & Hoh Tribe Health Clinic; Food Bank Nutrition Center; Peninsula College Longhouse. *Programs*: Social Services; Housing; Natural Resources; Cultural Resources; Tribal Arts; Language; Emergency Management; Fisheries. *Publication*: Chala-at Newsletter. Olympic Peninsula Agency.

JAMESTOWN S'KLALLAM TRIBE
1033 Old Blyn Hwy. • Sequim, WA 98382
(360) 683-1109 Fax 681-4643
Website: www.jamestowntribe.org; E-mail: info@jamestowntribe.org
William Ron Allen, Chairperson (1977-present) & CEO (1982-present)
  (681-4621); E-mail: rallen@jamestowntribe.org
Liz Mueller, Vice Chairperson (681-4628)
  E-mail: lmueller@jamestowntribe.org
Annette Nesse, Chief Operations Officer
  E-mail: anesse@jamestowntribe.org
Lisa M. Barrell, Secretary (681-3418)
  E-mail: heatherjohnsonjock@yahoo.com
Theresa R. Lehman, Treasurer (457-5772)
  E-mail: lehman1949@hotmail.com
Kurt Grinnell, Council Member (461-1229)
  E-mail: k_grinnell@msn.com
Rob Welch, Social & Community Services Director
  E-mail: rwelch@jamestowntribe.org
Brent Simcosky, Health Director
  E-mail: bsimcosky@jamestowntribe.org
Janet Duncan, Culture Committee Chair
  E-mail: jduncan@jamestowntribe.org
Leanne Jenkins, Tribal Planning Director
  E-mail: ljenkins@jamestowntribe.org
Jack Grinnell, Chair- Economic Development Authority
Jeff Allen, Gaming Commission Chair
  E-mail: jallen@jamestowntribe.org
Bonnie Roos, Tribal Libarian (582-5783)
  E-mail: library@jamestowntribe.org
  E-mail: broos@jamestowntribe.org
Rochelle Blankenship, Executive Director of Tribal Gaming
  Email: rblankenship@jamestowntribe.org
Tribe: Jamestown Band of S'Klallam Indians. *Enrolled members*: 564. *In residence*: None. *Area*: 20 acres in Clallam County. *Resources*: Family Health & Dental Clinics; Dental Clinic; Health & Wellness Center; Northwest Native Expressions Art Gallery; Tribal Library. *Programs*: Health; Social & Community Services; Cultural Resources; Gaming; Natural Resources; Economic Development. *Attractions*: Seven Cedars Casino; Tse-whit-zen Ancient Indian Village in Port Angeles Harbor; annual tribal picnic. *Publication*: Jamestown Tribal News. Olympic Peninsula Agency.

KALISPEL TRIBE
P.O. Box 39 • Usk, WA 99180
(509) 445-1147 Fax 455-1705
Website: www.kalispeltribe.com; E-mail: info@kalispeltribe.com
Glen Nenema, Chairperson; Raymond Pierre III, Vice Chairperson
Darren Holmes, Secretary
Betty Jo Piengkham & Curt Holmes, Councilmembers
Anna Armstrong, Director of Education (447-7141)
Lisa Guzman, Health Care Administrator (789-7612)
Dr. Rajeev Rajendra, Camas Center Clinic
Francis Cullooyah, Culture Program Director
Jessie Fountain, Language Coordinator
Shantel Nydegger, Tribal Gaming Executive Director (481-6162)
Deanne Osterman, Executive Director of Natural Resources
  Email: dosterman@knrd.org
Anita Dupris, Chief Justice of Trbal Court of Appeals
Milton Nomee, Traditional Chief Judge
David Bonga, Senior Tribal Attorney (789-7601)
Lorraine Paralange, Tribal Attorney (789-7603)
Tribe: Kalispel. *Enrolled members*: 450. *In residence*: 250. *Area*: Located in Pend Oreille County. *Resources*: Camus Center for Community Wellness; Camas Learning Center; Camas Early Learning Center; Camas Center Clinic; Kalispel Tribal Economic Authority (KTEA); Agricultural Enterprise; Library. *Programs*: Social Services; Health; Camas Education Program; Culture-Language Program; Behavioral Health; Natural Resources; Agricultural Program; Day Care; Recreation & Fitness; Gaming. *Attractions*: Northern Quest Resort & Casino; Bufallo herd; annual Powwow. Spokane Agency.

LOWER KLALLAM TRIBE
2851 Lower Elwha Rd. • Port Angeles, WA 98362
(360) 452-8471 Fax 452-3428; Website: www.elwha.org
Frances G. Charles, Chairperson
Russell N. Hepfer, Vice Chairperson

Anthony Charles, Secrertary/Treasurer
Councilmembers: Joseph A. Turrey, Steve Robideau
Jessica Egnew, Education Director
 E-mail: Jessica.egnew@elwha.nsn.us
Kevin Collins, Counseling Administrator (452-4599)
Suzie Bennett, Heritage Training Center Manager (417-8545)
Tribe: Lower Elwha Band of Klallam Indians. *Enrolled members*: 470. *Area*: 430 acres located in Clallam County. *Resources*: Tribal Center; Health Clinic; Heritage Training Center (417-8545); Tribal Library. *Programs*: Substance Abuse; Klallam Language; Health; Housing; Elders; Environmental; Hatchery-Fisheries; Head Start; Child Care; Higher Adult-Vocational Education. *Attraction*: Elwha River Casino. Olympic Peninsula Agency.

LUMMI NATION
2616 Kwina Rd. • Bellingham, WA 98226
 (360) 384-1489 Fax 380-1850; Website: www.lummi-nsn.org
 Tim Ballew, Chairperson; Johnny Felix, Vice Chairperson
 Celina Phair, Treasure; Steven Toby, Secretary
Councilmembers: Rita Jefferson, Jeremiah Julius, Nickolaus Lewis, Travis Brockle, Henry Cagey, Victor Johnson, Lawrence Solomon
Tribe: Lummi. *Enrolled members*: 3,300. *Area*: 12 acres (tribally-owned); 8,000 acres (allotted) including tidelands located in Whatcom County. *Resources*: Lummi Tribal Health Center; San Juan Cable Channel 2; Employment Training Center; Lummi Schelangen Dept. - Culture & Language; Library/Archives; Lummi Nation School, K-12; Northwest Indian College. *Programs*: Health & Human Services; Education; Employment & Training; Culture & Language; Housing; Natural Resources; Head Start. *Attractions*: Silver Reef Hotel, Casino & Spa; annual Lummi Stommish Water Festival in June. *Publication*: Squol Quol newspaper, a bi-weekly community newsletter. Puget Sound Agency.

MAKAH TRIBE
141 Resort Dr., P.O. Box 115 • Neah Bay, WA 98357
 (360) 645-3235 Fax 645-2788
 Website: www.makah.com; E-mail: makah@centurytel.net
 Nate Tyler, Chairperson; Greig Arnold, Vice Chairperson
 JoDeah Haupt-Richards, Secretary (645-3235)
 E-mail: jodean.haupt-richards@makah.com
 Leah Neuneker, Treasurer; Bud Denny, Director of Economic Development
Councilmembers: Maria Tolliver & Patrick DePoe
 Brittany Olson, General Manager; E-mail: brittany.olson@makah.com
Tribe: Makah. *Enrolled members*: 1,200. *Area*: 28,000 acres located on the Pacific Ocean & Straits of Juan De Fuca in Clallam County. *Resources*: Makah Cultural & Research Center - Museum & Library (E-mail: makahmuseum@centurytenet); two Youth Centers; School; Makah Business Enterprises. *Programs*: Education; Language; Historic Preservation; Senior Citizens; Head Start. *Attractions*: Hobuck Beach Campgrounds & Resort; Museum Store; annual Makah Days Celebration in Aug.; Treaty Day. *Publication*: Monthly newsletter. Olympic Peninsula Agency.

MUCKLESHOOT INDIAN TRIBE
39015 - 172nd St. SE • Auburn, WA 98092
 (253) 939-3311 Fax 939-5311; Website: www.muckleshoot.nsn.us
 Virginia Cross, Chairperson; Anita Mitchell, Vice Chairperson
 Jeremy James, Secretary; Jaison Elkins, Treasurer
Councilmembers: Louie Ungaro, John Daniels, Jr., Jessica Garcia-Jones
 Mike Jerry, Sr., Kerri Marquez
 Randy Doucet, Chief Judge
 Warren Oliver, Executive Director of Gaming
Tribe: Muckleshoot. *In residence*: 3,300. *Area*: 1,959 acres located in King County. *Resources*: Muckleshoot Tribal School; Muckleshoot Tribal College. *Programs*: Education; Health & Wellness; Community Services; Human Resources; Community Development; Housing; Recreation; Head Start. *Attractions*: White River Amphitheatre; Muckleshoot Casino, Muckleshoot Casino II; Muckleshoot Bingo; Salish Lodge; Emerald Downs Racetrack. *Activities*: Muckleshoot Powwow; First Salmon Ceremony. *Publication*: Muckleshoot Monthly (939-3311). Puget Sound Agency.

NISQUALLY INDIAN TRIBE
Nisqually Reservation. 4820 She-Nah-Num Dr. SE • Olympia, WA 98513
 (360) 456-5221 Fax 438-8889; Website: www.nisqually-nsn.gov
 Farron McCloud, Chairperson; E-mail: mccloud.farron@nisqually-nsn.gov
 Chris Olin, Vice Chairperson; E-mail: olin.chris@nisqually-nsn.gov
 Sheila McCloud, Secretary; E-mail: mccloud.sheila@nisqually-nsn.gov
 Julie Palm, Treasurer; E-mail: palm.julie@nisqually-nsn.gov
Councilmembers:
 Brian McCloud 5th Council; E-mail: mccloud.brian@nisqually-nsn.gov
 Hanford McCloud, 6th Council; E-mail: mccloud.hanford@nisqually-nsn.gov
 Wilie Frank III, 7th Council; E-mail: frank.willie@nisqually-nsn.gov
 John Simmons, Tribal CEO; E-mail: simmons.john@nisqually-nsn.gov
 Marie McDonald, Interim Community Services Director
 E-mail: mcdonald.marie@nisqually-nsn.gov

Marlene Mercado, Judicial Services Director
 E-mail: mercado.marlene@nisqually-nsn.gov
Leona Colegrove, Director of Legal Department
 E-mail: colegrove.leona@nisqually-nsn.gov
Lynette Brown, Court Administrator
 E-mail: brown.lynette@nisqually-nsn.gov
Linda McCloud, Education Director
 E-mail: mccloud.linda@nisqually-nsn.gov
Samantha Phillips, Health Services Director
Leslee Youckton, Newsletter Editor
 E-mail: youckton.leslee@nisqually-nsn.gov
Tribe: Nisqually. *Enrolled members*: 600. *In residence*: 5,800. *Area*: 5,000 acres located in Thurston & Pierce Counties. *Resources*: Youth & Community Center; Tribal Library. *Programs*: Education; Social Services; Health Services; Culture; Natural Resources; Economic Development; Head Start. *Attractions*: Red Wind Casino. *Publication*: Nisqually Tribal News. Puget Sound Agency.

NOOKSACK INDIAN TRIBE
5016 Deming Rd., P.O. Box 157 • Deming, WA 98244
 (360) 592-5176/5164 Fax 592-2125/4506
 Website: www.nooksacktribe.org; E-mail: nooksack@nooksack-nsn.gov
 Bob Kelly, Chairperson (592-5164); Rick D. George, Vice Chairperson
 Agripina Smith, Treasurer; Nadene Rapada, Secretary
Councilmembers: Bob Solomon, Katherine Canete, Lona Johnson, Roy Bailey
 Lona Johnson (newsletter editor)
 Patrick Check, Tribal Administrator
 Brock Hochsprung, Chief Financial Officer
 Raquel Montoya-Lewis, Chief Judge (306-5125)
 Donia Edwards, Education & Head Start Director (966-2043)
 Lona Johnson, Health Department Director (966-2106)
 George D. Swanaset, Jr., Cultural Resources Dept. Director
 E-mail: george.swanasetjr@nooksack-nsn.gov
 Nadeen Jimmy, Social Services Director (592-5176)
 E-mail: njimmy@nooksack-nsn.gov
Tribe: Nooksack. *Enrolled members*: 2,000. *In residence*: 750. *Area*: 2,906 acres located 17 miles east of Bellingham in Whatcom County. *Resources*: Health Clinic. *Programs*: Education; Cultural Resources; Health; Social Services; Child Welfare; Elders; Youth & Family; Housing; Natural Resources; Environmental Protection; Employment; Head Start. *Attractions*: Nooksack River Casino; Northwood Casino; annual Nooksack Days Powwow in September. *Publication*: Snee Nee Chum, quarterly tribal newsletter. Puget Sound Agency.

PORT GAMBLE S'KLALLAM TRIBE
31912 Little Boston Rd. NE • Kingston, WA 98346
 (360) 297-2646 Fax 297-7097
 Website: www.pgst.nsn.us; E-mail: info@pgst.nsn.us
 Jeromy C. Sullivan, Chairperson; Chris Tom, Vice Chairperson
 Renee Veregge, Council I; Kyle Carpenter, Council II, Lena Tunkara, Council III, & Talia DeCoteau, Council IV
 Dallas DeGuire, Director of Administration
 Laurie Mattson, Director of Tribal Services
 Marjorie Zarate, Chief Executive Officer
 Betty DeCoteau, Chief Financial Officer; E-mail: betty@pgst.nsn.us
 Marie Hebert, Cultural Resources Director (297-6359)
 Juanita Holtyn, Career & Education Director
 Jaclyn Haight, Early Childhood Education Program Director (297-6262)
 E-mail: jhaight@pgst.nsn.us
 Edward Fox, Health Services Director (297-9661)
 Noel Higa, Director of Economic Development
 Paul McCollum, Natural Resources Director (297-4792)
 Rogina Beckwith & Steven Moe, Tribal Attorneys
Tribe: Port Gamble S'Klallam. *Enrolled members*: 1,250. *In residence*: 650, with another 150 tribal members residing adjacent to the reservation. *Area*: 1,341 acres located in the northern end of the Kitsap Peninsula in Kitsap County in Washington State. Reservation land is held in trust for the tribe. *Resources*: House of Knowledge; Little Boston Library; Wellness Center; Career & Education Center. *Programs*: Education; Cultural; Housing; Social Services; Economic Development; Natural Resources; Head Start. *Attractions*: The Point Casino & Bingo. *Publication*: S'Klallam Monthly Tribal Newspaper. Puget Sound Field Office.

THE PUYALLUP TRIBE OF INDIANS
Puyallup Reservation, 3009 E. Portland Ave. • Tacoma, WA 98404
 (253) 573-7801 Fax 573-7944; Website: www.puyallup-tribe.com
 Bill Sterud, Chairperson; Lawrence W. LaPoint, Vice Chairperson
 Sheri Davis, Administrative Executive Officer
Councilmembers: David Bean, James Rideout, Sylvia Miller, Tim Reynon, Annette Bryan
 Carol Ann Hawks, Puyallup Tribal Archivist
 William Veliz, Executive Director of Tribal Services

Jody Brooks, Commnity/Family Services Program (573-7920)
Joyce Tobolski, Higher Education Program Manager (573-7918)
Darwin Long Fox, Chief Judge (680-5585)
John Weymer, Tribal News Publisher
Tribes: Puyallup, Nisqually, Muckleshoot, Skwawksnamish, & Steilacoom. *Enrolled members*: 3,850. *Population served*: 6,500. *Area*: 33 acres located in Pierce County. *Resources*: Tribal Health Authority; Chief Leschi Schools; Grandview Early Learning Center. *Programs*: Child Support; Indian Child Welfare; Children Services; Community Domestic Violence Advocacy; Community Family Services; Crisis Assistance; Design & Construction Management; Educational Incentives; Elder Tribal Member Medical Assistance; Elder Care Services; Emergency Assistance; Energy Assistance; Enrollment; Fisheries; Higher Education; Historic Preservation; Language; Law Enforcement; Legal; Natural Resources; Environmental Protection; Wildlife; Public Safety; Housing. *Attractions*: Emerald Queen Casino & Hotel; Emerald Queen Hotel & Casino at Fife; Chinook Landing Marina; annual Powwow. *Publication*: Puyallup Tribal News. Puget Sound Agency.

QUILEUTE NATION
90 Main St., P.O. Box 279 • LaPush, WA 98350
(360) 374-6163 Fax 374-6311; Website: www.quileutenation.org
Charles Woodruff, Chairperson
    E-mail: chas.woodruff@quileutenation.org
Tony Foster, Vice Chairperson
    E-mail: tony.foster@quileutenation.org
James Jackson, Secretary
    E-mail: james.jackson@quileutenation.org
Naomi Jacobson, Treasurer
    E-mail: naomi.jacobson@quileutenation.org
Crystal Lyons, Treasurer
    E-mail: crystal.lyons@quileutenation.org
Doug Woodruff, Member-at-Large
    E-mail: doug.woodruff@quileutenation.org
Gerald Smith, General Manager (374-7412)
    E-mail: Gerald.smith@quileutenation.org
Leona Colgrove, Chief Judge (374-4305)
Nicole Earls, Human Services Director (374-3353)
    E-mail: nicole.earls@quileutenation.org
Andrew Shogren, Health Clinic Director (374-4318)
Mel Moon, Natural Resources Director (374-3133)
    E-mail: mel.moon@quileutenation.org
Jackie Jacobs, Executive Secretary & Tribal Publicist (388-9200)
    E-mail: Jackie.jacobs@quileutenation.org
Emily Foster, Talking Raven Editor (374-7760)
    E-mail: emily.foster@quileutenation.org
Mark Jacobson, Principal/Superintendent (374-5609)
    E-mail: info@quileutetribalschool.org
Tribe: Quileute. *Enrolled members*: 720. *In residence*: 350. *Area*: 640 acres located on the Pacific Ocean in Clallam County. *Resources*: Health Clinic; Senior Center; Quileute Tribal School, K-8. *Programs*: Human Services; Education; Natural Resources; Housing; Head Start. *Attractions*: Quileute Casino; Quileute Days (July); Elders Week Celebration (May). *Publication*: The Talking Raven, monthly tribal news; The Quileute of La Push (book). Olympic Peninsula Agency.

QUINAULT INDIAN NATION
1214 Aalis Dr., P.O. Box 189 • Taholah, WA 98587
(888) 616-8211; (360) 276-8211 Fax 276-4191
Website: www.quinaultindiannation.com
Fawn R. Sharp, President
    E-mail: fsharp@quinault.org
Tyson Johnston, Vice Chairperson
    E-mail: tjohnston@quinault.org
Latosha Underwood, Secretary
    E-mail: lunderwood@quinault.org
Larry Ralston, Treasurer
    E-mail: lralston@quinault.org
Council members:
Gina James, 1st Councilperson
Chet Tweed, 2nd Councilperson
Pierre Augare, 3rd Councilperson
Noreen Underwood, 4th Councilperson
Dawneen Delecruz, 5th Councilperson
Clarinda "Pies" Underwood, 6th Councilperson & Newsletter Editor
Thomas Obi, 7th Councilperson
Robert Martin, Tribal Operations
Debi Martin, Administrator; Ray Dodge, Legal Counsel
Leilani Jones-Chubby, Museum/Cultural Center
Justine James, Culture Affairs Manager
Amelia Delacruz, Department of Social Services Manager (276-4405)

Tribe: Quinault. *Enrolled members*: 2,400. *Area*: 136,456 acres located 40 miles north of Hoguiam, on Pacific Ocean in Grays Harbor County. *Resources*: Roger Saux Health Center; Quinault Museum & Library. *Programs*: Education; Social Service; Chemical Dependency; Nutrition; Head Start. *Attractions*: Quinault Beach Resort & Casino; Indian Village; annual celebration in July. *Publications*: Nugguam, tribal newspaper; Business Directory. Olympic Peninsula Agency.

SAMISH INDIAN NATION
2918 Commercial Ave., P.O. Box 217 • Anacortes, WA 98221
(877) 711-8896; (360) 293-6404 Fax 299-0790
Website https://www.samishtribe.nsn.us/
E-mail: samishtribe@samishtribe.nsn.us
Thomas Wooten, Chairperson; Tim King, Vice Chairperson;
Leslie Eastwood, Tribal General Manager
Dana Matthews, Secretary; Tamara Rogers, Treasurer
Councilmembers: Jenna Burnett, Dave Blackinton, Gary D. Hatch
Leslie Eastwood, Tribal General Manager
Rosie Cayou-James, Cultural Outreach Manager
Jason Ticknor, Archives Manager
Joanne Liantonio, Health Administrator
Michelle Johnson, Social Services Director
Tanya Portwine, Longhouse Director
Zam De Shields, Planning Director
Todd Woodard, Natural Resources Director
Michelle Johnson, Language Project Specialist
Tribe served: Samish. *Location*: Skagit County. *Resources*: Samish Early Learning Center; Samish Gallery of Native Arts. *Programs*: Education; Social Services; Health & Human Services; Chemical Dependency Wellness; Archives; Cultural Resources; Employment; Natural Resources; Housing; Vocational Rehabiliation; Elders; Indian Child Welfare; Head Start/Child Care. *Attractions*: Fidalgo Bay Resort & RV Park. *Publication*: Samish News. Puget Sound Agency.

SAUK-SUIATTLE INDIAN TRIBE
5318 Chief Brown Lane • Darrington, WA 98241
(360) 436-0131 Fax 436-1511; Website: www.sauk-suiattle.com
Norma A. Joseph, Chairperson; M. Kevin Lenon, Vice Chairperson
Karen Misanes, Treasurer; Patrick Roberts, Secretary
Councilmembers: Sonja Metcalf, Cammie Carrigan, Benjamin Joseph
Tribe: Sauk-Suiattle. *Enrolled members*: 215. *Area*: 23 acres located in Skagit County. *Programs*: Daycare Preschool; Jobs; Public Safety; Housing; Health & Social Services; Natural Resources; Elders Food. *Attractions*: Annual Yo-Buch Days (July); Annual Sauk-Suiattle Powwow (August); Annual Huckleberry Festival (September); Library. Puget Sound Agency.

SHOALWATER BAY INDIAN TRIBE
2373 Old Tokeland Rd., P.O. Box 130 • Tokeland, WA 98590
(800) 633-5218; (360) 267-6766 Fax 267-6778
Website: www.shoalwaterbay-nsn.gov
Charlene Nelson, Chairperson; (267-8101)
    E-mail: cnelson@shoalwaterbay-nsn.gov
Jennifer Taylor, Vice Chairperson; (267-8189)
    E-mail: jtaylor@shoalwaterbay-nsn.gov
Lynn Clark, Secretary & Court Administrator
    lclark@shoalwaterbay-nsn.gov
Joel Blake, Treasurer; E-mail: jblake@shoalwater-nsn.gov
Dennis Julnes, Member-at-Large; (267-8350)
    E-mail: djulnes@shoalwaterbay-nsn.gov
Michael Rogers, Tribal Administrator/CEO
Tony A. Johnson, Education Program Manager
Kim Zillyet-Harris, Health Clinic Director
Tanya Brown, Community Health Representative
Earl Davis, Heritage & Cultural Coordinator
Steve Spencer, Natural Resources Director
James Anderson, Gaming Commission Chair (267-8213)
    E-mail: janderson@shoalwaterbay-nsn.gov
Linda R. Rose, Library Manager (267-8190)
    E-mail: lrose@shoalwaterbay-nsn.gov
Tribe: Shoalwater Bay. *In residence*: 100. *Area*: 355 acres located in Pacific County, near Tokeland. *Resources*: Wellness Center; Tribal Community Library; Willapa Bay Enterprise. *Programs*: Education; Cultural; Recreation & Fitness; Environmental; Indian Child Welfare; Human Resources; Tribal Gaming. *Attractions*: Shoalwater Bay Casino & RV Park; Willapa Bay Enterprises; annual Powwow in July; Annual Health Fair in May. *Publication*: Newsletter. Olympic Peninsula Agency.

SKOKOMISH TRIBAL NATION
80 N. Tribal Center Rd. • Skokomish, WA 98584
(360) 426-4232 Fax 877-5943; Website: www.skokomish.org
Charles "Guy" Miller, Chairperson; E-mail: gmiller@skokomish.org

Terri Twiddy-Butler, Vice Chairperson; E-mail: tbutler@skokomish.org
Alex Gouley, Secretary; E-mail: agouley@skokomish.org
Councilmembers`: Tim "Wiggs" LeClair, Annette Smith, Tom Strong
Winona Plant, General Council President; E-mail: wplant@skokomish.org
Yvonne Oberly, Tribal Manager & CEO; E-mail: yoberly@skokomish.org
Tom Strong, Deputy Tribal Manager; E-mail: tstrong@skokomish.org
Kris Miller, Cultural Resources Director; E-mail: kmiller@skokomish.org
Jackie Smith, Archivist; E-mail: jsmith@skokomish.org
Antonio Sandifer, Education Director; E-mail: asandifer@skokomish.org
Ed Fox, Health Department Director; E-mail: efox@skokomish.org
Cheri Cook, Learning Center Coordinator; E-mail: ccook@skokomish.org
Yvonne Oberly, Chief Executive Officer; E-mail: yoberly@skokomish.org
Mark Warren, Editor of Sounder, monthly newspaper
  E-mail: sounder@skokomish.org
Tribe: Skokomish. Enrolled members: 1,000. In residence: 350. Area: 6,300 acres located in Mason County. Resources: Health Center; Tribal Enterprises; Museum & Library. Programs: Health; Cultural & Historic Preservation; Domestic Violence; Gaming; Head Start. Attractions: Snoqualmie Casino; Bird Watching Tours; 1st Plant Ceremony (April); 1st Salmon Ceremony (August); 1st Elk Ceremony (October). Publication: Portrait of a Tribe: An Intro to the Skokomish; The Sounder, monthly newspaper; In the Loop, daily newsletter. Olympic Peninsula Agency.

SNOQUALMIE INDIAN TRIBE
8130 Railroad Ave., P.O. Box 969 • Snoqualmie, WA 98065
  (888) 348-3323; (425) 888-6551 Fax 888-6727
  Website: www.snoqualmietribe.us
  Nathan "Pat" Barker, Andy de los Angeles, Chiefs
  Sunny Clear, Chairperson; E-mail: sunny@snoqualmietribe.us
  Jolene Williams, Vice Chairperson; E-mail: sharon@snoqualmietribe.us
  Alisa Burley, Secretary; E-mail: alisa@snoqualmietribe.us
  Suzanne Sailto, Treasurer
  Katherine Barker, Lifetime Council Member/Historian
  E-mail: qwhaltsa@snoqualmienation.com
Councilmembers: Lois Sweet Dorman, Michael Ross, Richard Zambrano,
  Bob de los Angeles, Steve de los Angeles, Daniel Willoughby
  Wes Willoughby, Council Alternate
  Jake Repin, Tribal Administrator & Operations Officer
  E-mail: jake@snoqualmienation.com
  Jaime Martin, Government Affairs & Special Projects Officer
  E-mail: jlamb@snoqualmietribe.us
  Jaime Martin, Communications & Public Relations Officer
  E-mail: jaime.martin@snoqualmietribe.us
  Kellie Kvasnnikoff, Chief Information Officer
  E-mail: cio@snoqualmienation.com
  Steve Mullen-Moses, Director of Archaeology/Historic Preservation
  E-mail: steve@snoqualmienation.com
  Adam Osbekoff, Cultural Resource Outreach Specialist
  E-mail: adam@snoqualmietribe.us
  Cindy Spiry, Environmental & Natural Resources Director (292-3734)
  E-mail: cindy@snoqualmietribe.us
  Megan Cotton, Gaming Commission Chairperson
Tribe: Snoqualmie Coast Salish. Enrolled members: 650. Resources: Raging River Recovery Center. Programs: Health & Social Services; Education; Indian Child Welfare; Behavioral Health; Gaming; Cultural; Historic Preservation; Environmental; Transportation; Enrollment; Emergency Management; Sports & Recreation. Attractions: Snoqualmie Casino; Snoqualmie Falls; Arts & Crafts Store. Puget Sound Field Office.

SPOKANE TRIBE OF INDIANS
6195 Ford-Wellpinit Rd., P.O. Box 100 • Wellpinit, WA 99040
  (509) 458-6500 Fax 458-6552; Website: www.spokanetribe.com
  Carol Evans, Chairperson; E-mail: carole@spokanetribe.com
  David Browneagle, Vice Chairperson
  E-mail: david.browneagle@spokanetribe.com
  Greg Abrahamson, Secretary; E-mail: grega@spokanetribe.com
Councilmembers: Glenn Ford & Danny Kieffer
  Brea Franco, Education Program Manager (458-8005)
  E-mail: brea.franco@spokanetribe.com
  Bob Brisbois, Tribal Health & Fitness Director
  E-mail: bob.brisbois@spokanetribe.com
  Mike Tedesco, Planning & Economic Development Director (458-6502)
  E-mail: tedesco@spokanetribe.com
  Jamie Sijohn, Public Relations Director (458-6586)
  Monica Peone, Rawhide Press Editor (458-6587)
  E-mail: rawhide@spokanetribe.com
  Jessie Stensgar, Health Educator (258-4517)
Tribe: Spokane. Enrolled members: 2,500. In residence: 1,200. Area: 159,000 acres located in the southwest corner of Stevens County, 50 miles northwest of Spokane, Wash. Resources: Tribal Hatchery; Spokane Tribal College. Programs: Health & Human Services; Cultural; Spokane Language; Food

Distribution; Housing, Senior Services; Natural Resources. Attractions: Snoqualmie Casino; Two Rivers Casino in Davenport, WA; Double Eagle Casino; Grand Coulee Dam; Old Fort Spokane; Tsimshian Mission (1838); annual Heritage Day Celebration; annual Labor Day powwow. Publication: Rawhide Press, tribal newspaper. Spokane Agency.

SQUAXIN ISLAND TRIBE
Squaxin Island Reservation, 10 SE Squaxin Lane • Shelton, WA 98584
  (877) 386-3649; (360) 426-9781 Fax 426-6577
  Website: www.squaxinisland.org
  Arnold Cooper, Chairman; E-mail: acooper@squaxin.us
  Charlene Krise, Vice Chairperson; E-mail: ckrise@squaxin.us
  Steven Dorland, Secretary; Vickie Kruger, Treasurer
Councilmembers: Vince Henry, Bev Hawks & David Whitener, Jr.
  Charlene Krise, Museum Director; E-mail: ckrise@squaxin.us
  Stephanie Tompkins, NWITC Director
  E-mail: stompkins@squaxin.us
  Rhonda Foster, Cultural Resources Director (432-3850)
  E-mail: rfoster@squaxin.us
  Liz Yeahquo, Librarian: E-mail: eyeahquo@squaxin.us
Tribes: Squaxin Island, Nisqually, Steilacoom, et al. Enrolled members: 1,000. Area: Located in Mason County. Resources: Museum, Library & Research Center; Learning Center; Northwest Indian Treatment Center (NWITC); Ethnic Heritage Art Gallery; Island Enterprises, Inc. Programs: Tobacco Cessation; Community Development; Health & Human Services; Cultural Resources; Natural Resources, Environmental Protection; Human Resources; Elders. Attraction: Little Creek Casino Resort. Publication: Klah-Che-Min Newsletter; Daily Scoop by e-mail. Olympic Peninsula Agency.

STILLAGUAMISH TRIBE OF INDIANS
3310 Smokey Point Dr., P.O. Box 277 • Arlington, WA 98223
  (360) 652-7362 Fax 659-3113; Website: www.stillaguamish.com
  Shawn Yanity, Chairperson; Eric White, Vice Chairperson
  Trisha Pecor, Secretary; Nicholas Smith, Treasurer
Councilmembers: Tara Smith & Stacy White
  John Miller, Executive Director of Administration (652-7362)
  E-mail: johnmiller@stillaguamish.com
  Edward Wurtz, Legal Dept. Director (572-3033)
  E-mail: ewurtz@stillaguamish.com
  LeAnne Gillett, Education Director
  E-mail: lgillett@stillaguamish.com
  Shelly Summers & Victoria Yeager, Health Services Co-Directors (435-9338)
  E-mail: ssummers@stillaguamish.com; vyeager@stillaguamish.com
  Tara Boser, Cultural Resources Director
  E-mail: tboser@stillaguamish.com
  Jeremy Smith, Gaming Commissioner; E-mail: jsmith@stillaguamish.com
Tribe: Stillaguamish. Enrolled members: 250 with a service population of about 1,500. Area: 76 acres located in northern Snohomish County near Arlington between the Cascade Mountains & Puget Sound. Resources: Wellness Clinic. Programs: Health; Family Resources; Education; Cultural Resources; Economic Development; Human Resources; Natural Resources; Transportation; Bison; Fisheries. Attractions: Angel of the Winds Casino; Festival of the River & Powwow. Publication: Stillaguamish News, quarterly tribal newsletter. Puget Sound Agency.

THE SUQUAMISH TRIBE
Port Madison Indian Reservation
18490 Suquamish Way, P.O. Box 498 • Suquamish, WA 98392
  (360) 598-3311 Fax 598-3135; Website https://suquamish.nsn.us
  Leonard Foresman, Tribal Chairperson & Foundation President
  E-mail: lforesman@suquamish.nsn.us
  Bardow Lewis, Vice Chairperson
  E-mail: blewis@suquamish.nsn.us
E-mail: wgeorge@suquamish.nsn.us
  Nigel Lawrence, Secretary; Robin Sigo, Treasurer
Councilmembers: Rich Purser, Sammy Mabe, Luther "Jay" Mills, Jr.
  Wayne George, Executive Director & Editor-in-Chief of Suquamish News
  Serene Williams, Librarian (394-8691) E-mail: sgeorge@suquamish.nsn.us
  15838 Sandy Hook Rd., Poulsbo, WA 98370
Tribe: Suquamish. Enrolled members: 950. In residence: 500. Area: 8,000 acres located in Kitsap County. Resources: Wellness Center; Suquamish Foundation (www.suquamishfoundation.org); Suquamish Museum & Cultural Center; Early Learning Center; Photographic Archives & Oral History Collection; Library. Programs: Education; Wellness; Health & Human Services; Community Development; Youth Services; Elders; Child Welfare. Attractions: Clearwater Casino & Resort; Totem Poles throughout the Reservation; Chief Seattle Day (annual traditional tribal celebration held in August). Publications: Dsub'Wub' Siatsub, Suquamish News (tribal newsletter); A Guide to Oral History in the Native American Community; Suquamish Tribal Photographic Archives Project: A Case Study; Suquamish Today; & The Eyes of Chief Seattle (exhibit catalog). Puget Sound Agency.

SWINOMISH INDIAN TRIBAL COMMUNITY

11404 Moorage Way, P.O. Box 817 • LaConnor, WA 98257
(360) 466-7314 Fax 466-5309; Website: www.swinomish.org
M. Brian Cladoosby, Chairperson; Brian Porter, Vice Chairperson
Sophie Bailey, Secretary; Barbara James, Treasurer
Senators: Glen Edwards (Gaming Chair), Steve Edwards,
Chester Cayou, Jr. (Cultural Chair); Brian Wilbur, Kevin Paul,
Joseph Williams, Leon John
Tracy James, Education Director (466-7320)
  E-mail: trjames@swinomish.nsn.us
Allan Olson, General Manager (466-7221); Mark Pouley, Chief Judge
Steve LeCuyer, Legal Director & Tribal Attorney (466-7220)
  E-mail: slecuyer@swinomish.nsn.us
Brian Wilbur, Health, Education & Social Services Chair
Mark Pouley, Chief Judge/Court Administrator
Debra Lekanof, Intergovernmental Affairs Liaison
  E-mail: dlekanof@swinomish.nsn.us
Michael M. Vendiola, Kee Yoks Editor (466-7258)
Tribes: Swinomish, Samish, Lower Skagit, and Kikiallus. *Enrolled members*: 790. *Area*: 7,000 acres located in Skagit County. *Resources*: Northwest Indian College; Swinomish Community Library. *Programs*: Education; Lushootseed Language & Culture; Alcohol & Substance Abuse; Health & Fitness; Social Services; Human Resources; Senior Services; Environment; Enrollment; Emergency Management; Domestic Violence; Planning & Community Development; Gaming; Fisheries; Hunting & Wildlife. *Attractions*: Swinomish Northern Lights Casino; RV Park & Camping; "Treaty Day Celebration" (January); "All My Relations Pow Wow" (June); First Salmon Ceremony. *Publication*: Kee Yoks Newsletter; "A Gathering of Wisdoms." Puget Sound Agency.

TULALIP TRIBES

6406 Marine Dr. • Tulalip, WA 98271
(800) 869-8287; (360) 651-4000 Fax 651-4032
Website: https://www.tulaliptribes-nsn.gov
Marie Zackuse Chairperson; Teri Gobin, Vice Chairperson
Les Parks, Treasurer; Theresa Sheldon, Secretary
Councilmembers: Bonnie Juneau, Jared Parks, Melvin Sheldon, Jr.
Misty Napeahi, General Manager
Ron Whitener, Chief Judge; Gary F. Bass, Associate Judge
Francesca Hillery, Public Affairs Officer
  E-mail: fhillery@tulaliptribes-nsn.gov
Tribes: Tulalip (Snohomish, Snoqualmie, Skagit, Suiattle, Samish, and allied bands). *Enrolled members*: 4,000. *In residence*: 2,500. *Area*: 22,000 acres located in Snohomish County. *Resources*: Health Clinic; Tulalip Lushootseed Language Dept.; Heritage School; Education Center; Hibulb Cultural Center & Natural History Preserve; Museum; Library; Veteran's Center. *Programs*: Education; Community Services & Development; Family & Youth Services; Elders/Senior Services; Health & Safety; Environment; Economic Development; Human Resources; Cultural; Language (Lushootseed); Natural Resources; Recreation; Higher Education - Evergreen State College Tribal Reservation Based Community Determined Program; *Attractions*: Quil Ceda Casino & Nightclub & Quil Ceda Village; Tulalip Resort Casino; Bingo. *Publication*: Tulalip News. Puget Sound Agency.

UPPER SKAGIT TRIBE

25944 Community Plaza • Sedro Woolley, WA 98284
(360) 854-7090 Fax 856-7004
Website: https://upperskagit.nsopw.gov
Jennifer Washington, Chairperson
  E-mail: jenniferw@upperskagit.com
Scott Schuyler, Natural Resources Director
Tribe: Upper Skagit. *Enrolled members*: 540. *In residence*: 250. *Area*: 110 acres located in Skagit County. *Attractions*: Skagit Valley Casino & Resort. Puget Sound Agency.

YAKAMA NATION

401 Fort Rd., P.O. Box 151 • Toppenish, WA 98948
(509) 865-5121 Fax 865-5528; Website: www.yakamanation-nsn.gov
JoDe L. Goudy, Chairperson & Public Relations/Media Committee
Delano Saluskin Vice Chairperson
Athena Sanchey-Yallup, Secretary; Gerald Lewis, Assistant Secretary
Asa Washines, Sargent-at-Arms & Chair of Legislative Committee
Councilmembers: Edwin Lewis, Virgil Lewis, Raymond Smartlowit,
Frank Mespile, Vivian Babs George, Lottie Sam, George Selam
Esther Moses-Hyipeer, Leland Bill
Davis Washines, General Council Chairperson
Larena Sohappy, General Council Vice Chairperson
Ned Tillequots, Jr., Secretary/Treasurer
Gerald Lewis, Cultural Committee Chairperson
Tribes: Confederated Tribes & Bands of the Yakama Nation. *Enrolled members*: 9,000. *Area*: 1,377,030 acres located in Yakima & Klickitat Counties in south-central Washington State along the Cascade Mountain Range.

Resources: Cultural Heritage Center; Yakama Nation Museum & Library; Yakama Nation Radio KYNR 1490 AM; Tribal Enterprises. *Programs*: Education; Health; Cultural; Economic Development; Multimedia Services; Enrollment; Youth; Employment; Housing; Veteran's; Timber, Fish & Wildlife; Cultural; Environmental; Head Start; Gaming; Tourism. *Attractions*: Yakama Nation Legends Casino; All-Indian Rodeo (June); Annual Powwow (July); Huckleberry Feast (August). *Publication*: Yakama Nation Review. Yakama Agency.

WISCONSIN

THE BAD RIVER BAND OF LAKE SUPERIOR CHIPPEWA TRIBE

The Bad River Reservation, Chief Blackbird Center
7282 Maple St., P.O. Box 39 • Odanah, WI 54861
(715) 682-7111 Fax 682-7118; Website: www.badriver-nsn.gov
Robert Blanchard Chairperson; Michael Berlin, Vice Chairperson
Etta Burns, Treasurer; Rae Ann Maday, Secretary
Councilmembers: Barbara Smart, Bonnie Greene, Dylan Jennings
Stephanie Julian, Education Director
  E-mail: educationdirector@badriver-nsn.gov@yahoo.com
Isabelle Kappeler, Health Board Chair; Norma Soulier, Librarian
Tribe: Bad River Band of Lake Superior Band of (Ojibwe) Chippewa. *Enrolled members*: 7,100. *In residence*: 1,500. *Area*: 125,000 acres located on Lake Superior, southeast of Duluth, Minnesota. *Resources*: Library. *Programs*: Social & Family Services; Education; Healthcare; Human Resources; Natural Resources; Housing & Realty; Planning & Development; Enrollment; Emergency Response; Head Start; Gaming; Tourism. *Attractions*: Bad River Lodge, Casino & Convention Center (682-7121); www.badriver.com; Annual Minomin Wild Rice Powwow in August. Great Lakes Agency.

FOREST COUNTY POTAWATOMI COMMUNITY

5415 Everybody's Rd., P.O. Box 340 • Crandon, WI 54520
(800) 960-5479; (715) 478-7200 Fax 478-4714/7277
Website: www.fcpotawatomi-nsn.gov
Harold "Gus" Frank, Chairperson; Hartford Shegonee, Vice Chairperson
Lorna Shawano, Secretary; Richard Gouge III, Treasurer
Councilmembers: James Crawford, & Nate Gilpin
Tom Boelter, Education Director (478-7355)
Nate Guldan, Land & Natural Resources Division Director (478-7222)
Eugene L. White-Fish, Chief Judge (478-7255)
Kaye Garcia, Foundation Executive Director (847-7720)
  E-mail: kaye.garcia@fcpotawatomi-nsn.gov
Tribe: Forest County Potawatomi. *Enrolled members*: 1,250. *In residence*: 450. *Area*: 10,000 acres. *Resources*: Health & Wellness Center; FCP Cultural Center, Library & Museum; Potawatomi Business Development Corp0ration; Forest County Potawatomi Foundation. *Programs*: Education; Child Care & Support; Domestic Violence Center; Economic Support; Elderly; Emergency Management; Enrollment. *Attractions*: Potawatomi Carter Casino & Hotel (Wabeno); Potawatomi (Milwaukee) Bingo & Casino; Indian Springs Lodge. *Publication*: Potawatomi Traveling Times (PTT News), monthly newspaper. Great Lakes Agency.

HO-CHUNK NATION

9814 Airport Rd., P.O. Box 667 • Black River Falls, WI 54615
(800) 294-9343; (715) 284-9343 Fax 284-3172
Website: www.ho-chunknation.com
Wilfred Cleveland, President
  E-mail: wilfrid.cleveland@ho-chunk.com
Douglas Greengrass, Vice President
  E-mail: douglas.greengrass@ho-chunk.com
Sarah Funmaker, Executive Secretary
  E-mail: sarah.funmaker@ho-chunk.com
Kelly Jo Funmaker, Executive Administration Officer
  E-mail: Kelly.jo.funmaker@ho-chunk.com
Karena M. Thundercloud, Executive Director of Administration
  E-mail: karena.thundercloud@ho-chunk.com
Joy Thompson, General Council Administrator
  E-mail: joy.thompson@ho-chunk.com
Jeriah Rave, Executive Compliance Officer
  E-mail: jeriah.rave@ho-chunk.com
Nehomah Thundercloud, Executive Director – Department of Education
  E-mail: education.intake@ho-chunk.com
Woody White, Culture & Community Education Project Manager
Collin Price, Public Relations Officer
  E-mail: Collin.price@ho-chunk.com
Michelle Ramberg, Public Relations Specialist
  E-mail: michelle.ramberg@ho-chunk.com
John Swimmer (Cherokee), General Council Attorney
  E-mail: john.swimmer@ho-chunk.com
Legislature: (13 Reps from 5 Districts)
Karena Thundercloud & Hinu Smith (District 1)

Kristin WhiteEagle, Carly Lincoln, Andrea Estabo (District 2)
Kathy DeCamp & Lawrence Walker, Jr. (District 3)
Shelby Visintin (District 4)
Matthew Mullen, Kathyleen Lone Tree-Whiterabbit, Forest Whiterabbit, Robert TwoBears (District 5)
Tribe served: Ho-Chunk (Winnebago). *Enrolled members*: 7,253. *In residence*: 5,100. *Area*: 4,100 acres. *Resources*: Wellness Center; Health Care Clinics; Community Center; Bluewing Cultural Center (P.O. Box 670, Tomah, WI 54660 (608) 374-1264 Fax 374-1251). *Programs*: Social Services; Youth Services; Elderly Services; Cultural Resources; Education - Head Start Centers; Gaming; Food Distribution; Housing; Indian Child Welfare; Alcohol & Drug Abuse; Mental Health Services; Language. *Attractions*: Ho-Chunk Casino, Bingo & Hotel (Wisconsin Dells-Baraboo, WI); Majestic Pines Casino, Bingo & Hotel (Black River Falls, WI); Rainbow Casino, Nekoosa, WI); Whitetail Crossing Casino (Tomah, WI); DeJope Gaming (Madison, WI); Bison Project (33502 Sand Lane, Muscoda, WI 53373 (608) 739-3568). Great Lakes Agency.

LAC COURTE OREILLES BAND OF OJIBWE
13394 W. Trapania Rd. • Hayward, WI 54843
(715) 634-8934 Fax 634-4797; Website: www.lco-nsn.gov
Michael "Mic" Isham, Chairperson; E-mail: micisham@yahoo.com
Russell "Rusty" Barber, Vice Chairperson; E-mail: rbarber@lco-nsn.gov
Norma Ross, Secretary/Treasurer; E-mail: nross@lco-nsn.gov
Donald Carley, Gary Clause, Larry Kagigebi, *Council*
Kim Strand, Business Executive Director; E-mail: kstrand@lco-nsn.gov
Kim Beaudin, Chair of Health Board; Gregg Duffek, Health Center Director
Tribe: Lac Courte Oreilles Band of Ojibwe (Lake Superior Chippewa). *Enrolled members*: 2,200. *Area*: 70,000 acres located within Sawyer County. *Resources*: WOJB 88.9 FM Radio (www.wojb.org); K-12 School System; LCO Community College; Casino Convention Center; Cultural Center & Museum/Library; Halfway House; Boys & Girls Club; Indian Child Welfare; Child Care; Oakwood Haven for Child & Domestic Abuse. *Programs*: Natural & Cultural Resources; Health Services; Alcohol & Drug Abuse Prevention; Housing/Home; Family & Child Education; Family Preservation & Support; Food Distribution; Nutrition Education; Employment; Transportation; Environmental-Historic Preservation; Social Services; Education - Head Start; Child Development. *Attractions*: Grindstone Creek Casino; Annual Contest Powwow, May/June; Annual Honor Earth Powwow, 3rd weekend July; Annual Veterans Day Powwow, Nov. 11th; Annual New Years Eve Sobriety Powwow, Dec. 31st. *Publication*: LCO Ojibwe Early Childhood Curriculum. Great Lakes Agency.

LAC DU FLAMBEAU BAND OF LAKE SUPERIOR CHIPPEWA INDIANS OJIBWAY NATION OF WISCONSIN
418 Little Pine Rd., P.O. Box 67 • Lac du Flambeau, WI 54538
(715) 588-3303 Fax 588-7930; Website: www.ldftribe.com
Henry "Butch" St. Germaine, President; Mike Allen, Sr., Vice President
Jamie Allen, Secretary; Melinda Young, Treasurer
Councilmembers: Eric Chapman, Alice Soulier, George Thompson Charles Burgess, Betty Jo Graveen; Frank Mitchell, John Johnson
Joseph Wildcat, Sr., Tribal Adminstrator (588-4264)
Ashley M. Maki, Education Director; E-mail: amaki@ldftribe.com
AJ Ernst, Director of Health & Human Services Department (588-1511) E-mail: ajernst@ldftribe.com
Melinda Young, Tribal Historic Preservation Officer
Brent McFarland, Director of Business & Economic Development E-mail: bmcfarland@ldftribe.com
Garold Smith, Chief Judge (588-4200)
R. Terry Hoyt, Tribal Attorney (588-4239)
Tribe: Lac du Flambeau Band of Lake Superior Chippewa Indians. *Enrolled members*: 3,000. *In residence*: 2,400. *Native American population*: 1,420. *Area*: 144 square miles. *Resources*: Peter Christensen Health Center & Dental Clinic; George W. Brown, Jr. Ojibwe Museum & Cultural Center Library (P.O. Box 804 (588-3333); Woodland Indian Art Center; Northwoods NiiJii Enterprise Community, Inc. *Programs*: Social Services; Health & Wellness; Education; Ojibwe Language; Energy; Natural Resources; Human Resources; Gaming; E-mail: info@lacduflambeauchamber.com; Economic Support; Historic Preservation; Planning & Development; Head Start. *Attractions*: Lake of the Torches Resort Casino; Lac du Flambeau Indian Bowl Powwows (summers); annual Bear River Powwow; Weekly Powwow INDIANSows; 4th of July Powwow; Art shows; Craft workshops. *Publication*: Reflections of Lac du Flambeau (book); Gikendaasowin LDF News, monthly newsletter; Youth News, monthly newsletter. Under jurisidiction of Great Lakes Agency.

MENOMINEE INDIAN TRIBE OF WISCONSIN
W2908 Tribal Office Loop Rd., P.O. Box 910, Keshena, WI 54135
(715) 799-5100 Fax 799-3373; Website: www.menominee-nsn.gov
Gary Besaw, Chairperson (995-5114); E-mail: gbesaw@mitw.org
Ruth Waupoose, Vice Chairperson; Craig Corn, Secretary
Gary Besaw & Laurie Boivin, Legislators
Jonathan Wilber, Tribal Administrator (799-5154) E-mail: jwilber@mitw.org

Lauurie Boivin, Governmental Affairs Committee Chairperson
Craig Corn, Budget & Finance Committee Chairperson
Crystal Chevalier, Community Development Director (799-5155)
Shannon Chapman, Education Director; (799-5110) E-mail: smchapman@mitw.org
Carol Corn, Social Services Director; E-mail: ccorn@mitw.org
Mark Caskey, Wellness Director; E-mail: markc@mtclinic.net
Myrna Warrington, Health & Family Committee Chairperson
Jerry Waukau, Health Clinic Director; E-mail: jerryw@mtclinic.net
Susan Blodgett, Community Resource Center Director (799-5137) E-mail sblodgett@mitw.org
Joey Awonohopay, Menominee Language & Culture Commission Director E-mail: jawonohopay@mitw.org (799-4849)
David Grignon, Historic Preservation Director (799-5258) E-mail: dgrignon@mitw.org
Michael Wilber, Library Director; E-mail: mwilber@mail.nfls.lib.wi.us
Lindzey Spice, Tribal Attorney (799-5194); E-mail: lspice@mitw.org
Lynette Miller, Tribal Gaming Commission Executive Director E-mail: lmiller@mitw.org (799-5610)
Stephan Tourtillott-Grochowski, Supreme Court Chief Justice (799-3348)
Devan Erdmann, Nation News Editor; (799-5167) E-mail: derdmann@mitw.org
Tribe: Menominee. *Enrolled members*: 8,700. *In residence*: 3,750. *Area*: 233,800 acres located off Hwy. 47, 55 Tribal Office Loop Rd. *Resources*: Health Clinics; Cultural Museum; Library; Menominee Tribal School in Neopit, WI; College of the Menominee Nation in Keshena & Green Bay; Wilma M. Peters Judicial Center. *Programs*: Health Services; Social Services; Language & Culture; Human Resources; Food Distribution; Aging; Youth; Head Start; Hunting & Fishing. *Attractions*: Menominee Casino-Bingo-Hotel (800) 343-7778 Fax (715) 799-1313; Annual Powwow, 1st weekend in August; Restoration Day, Dec. 22nd. *Publication*: "Menominee Nation News," twice monthly. Midwest Regional Office

ONEIDA NATION OF WISCONSIN
N7210 Seminary Rd., P.O. Box 365, Oneida, WI 54155
(800) 236-2214; (920) 869-2214 Fax 869-2194
Website: www.oneida-nsn.gov; E-mail: jhouse1@oneidanation.org
Tehassi Hill, Chairperson (869-4420); E-mail: rhill7@oneidanation.org
Dawn Moon-Kopetsky, Senior Policy Advisor (869-4427)
Brandon Stevens, Vice Chair (869-4378) E-mail: bstevens@oneidanation.org
Lisa Summers, Secretary (869-4478) E-mail: lsummer2@oneidanation.org
Trish King, Treasurer (869-4462); E-mail: tking@oneidanation.org
Councilmembers:
Kirby Metoxen (869-4441); E-mail: kmetox@oneidanation.org
Ernie Stevens III (869-4382); E-mail: esteven4@oneidanation.org
Jennifer Webster (869-4457); E-mail: jwebste1@oneidanation.org
Daniel Guzman King (869-4366); E-mail: dguzman@oneidanation.org
David P.Jordan (869-4483); E-mail: djordan1@oneidanation.org
Rita Lara, Oneida Museum Director; Eric Doxtator, Museum Educator
Louis Williams, Library Manager; E-mail: lwilliam@oneidanation.org
Raeann Skenandore, Court Administrator (497-5800)
Tribe: Oneida. *In residence*: 2,700 (tribal roll: 3,800). *Area*: 2,600 acres. *Resources*: Oneida Nation Museum; Oneida Community Library; Oneida Nation Elementary/High School. *Programs*: Health & Wellness; Environ-mental Health & Safety; Language & Cultural Heritage; Social Services; Children & Family Services; Elder Services; Education & Training; Fitness & Recreation; Arts; Recreation; Veterans; Head Start. *Attractions*: Oneida Casino and the Oneida Radisson Inn-Green Bay; Oneida Powwow (4th of July week-end). *Publication*: Kalihwisaks (bi-weekly) newspaper. Great Lakes Agency.

RED CLIFF BAND OF LAKE SUPERIOR CHIPPEWA (OJIBWE)
88385 Pike Rd., Hwy. 13 • Bayfield, WI 54814
(715) 779-3700 Fax 779-3704; Website: www.redcliff-nsn.gov
Richard "Rick" Peterson, Chairperson
Nathan Gordon, Vice Chairperson
Johanna Wilson, Treasurer; Mercie Gordon, Secretary
Councilmembers: Jean Gordon, Antone Basina, Daniel Duffy
Carolyn Lee Charette-Gouge, Nicholas DePerry
Krystle Topping, Director of Education (ext. 4258)
Patricia Deragon-Navarro, Health Administrator (779-3707) E-mail: pderagon-nav@redcliff-nsn.gov
Tribe: Ojibwe - Red Cliff Band of Lake Superior Chippewa. *Enrolled members*: 6,879. *In residence*: 1,266. *Area*: 7,311 acres, extending over Lake Superior about 25 miles northwest of Ashland, Wisconsin. *Resources*: Community Health Center; Bayfield School. *Programs*: Education; Health; Social Services; Alcohol & Drug Abuse; Housing; Natural Resources; Ojibwe Language & Heritage Preservation; Elderly. *Attractions*: Isle Vista Casino; Legendary Waters Resort & Casino; annual powwow in July. *Publications*: Divisional Newsletters: Health & Education. Great Lakes Agency.

ST. CROIX CHIPPEWA INDIANS OF WISCONSIN
24663 Angeline Ave. • Webster, WI 54893
(800) 236-2195; (715) 349-2195 Fax 349-5768
Website: www.stcciw.com
Lewis Taylor (Sand Lake Representative), Chairperson
Crystal Peterson (Danbury Community Representative), Vice Chairperson
Stuart Bearheart (Maple Plain Community Represenattive), Sec-Treasurer
Jay Emery (Sand Lake Community Representative), Councilmember
Carmen Bugg (Round Lake Community Representative), Councilmember
Francis Songetay, Tribal Administrator; Judy Warmanen, Newspaper Editor
Karen Washington, Education Director (ext. 5303)
 E-mail: karenw@stcroixtribalcenter.com
Sarah Cormell, Health Director
 E-mail: sarahc@stcroixtribalcenter.com
Wanda McFaggen, Director/Tribal Historic Preservation Officer
 E-mail: wandam@stcroixtribalcenter.com
Marjorie Eagleman & Steve Fowler, Cultural Coordinators (ext. 5117)
 E-mail: marjoriee@stcroixtribalcenter.com
 E-mail: stevef@stcroixtribalcenter.com
Jeff Cormell, General Counsel (ext. 5118)
 E-mail: jeffc@stcroiixtriibalcenter.com
Shayna Gray, Legal Department Manager (ext. 5138)
 E-mail: shaynag@stcroixtribalcenter.com
Crystal Mihaly, Chief Judge (ext.5109)
 E-mail: cmihaly@stcroixtribalcenter.com
Tribe: St. Croix Chippewa. *Enrolled members*: 1,100. *Area*: 3,000 acres. *Resources*: Tribal Behavioral Health Clinic; St. Croix Chippewa Enterprises, 24670 State Rd. 35/70, Suite 700, Siren, WI 54872 (800-236-2195). *Programs*: Education; Health; Culture; Environmental Services/Natural Resources; Economic Development; Employment; Head Start. *Attractions*: St. Croix Casino & Hotel; annual St. Croix Casino Golf Tournament; annual St. Croix Wild Rice Powwow. *Publication*: The Vision, bi-monthly newspaper. Great Lakes Agency.

SOKAOGON CHIPPEWA COMMUNITY
Mole Lake Band of Lake Superior Chippewa
3051 Sand Lake Rd. • Crandon, WI 54520
(715) 478-7500 Fax 478-5275
Website: www.sokaogonchippewa.com
Chris McGeshick, Chairperson; Arlyn Ackley, Jr., Vice Chairperson
Vickie Ackley, Treasurer; Myra Jane VanZile, Secretary
Sarah M. McGeshick #1 & Ronald W. Quade. #2, *Councilmembers*
Dean VanZile, Higher Education & Education Director (478-3830)
Paulette Smith, Health Director (478-5180)
Amanda VanZile, Family Services Department Director (478-3265)
 E-mail: Amanda.vanzile@scc-nsn.gov
Tribe: Mole Lake Chippewa. *Enrolled members*: 450. *Area*: 1,700 acres. *Resources*: Community Health Center. *Programs*: Education; Health; Youth Council; Elderly; Family Services; Employment; Housing; Economic Development. *Attractions*: Mole Lake Casino & Bingo; annual powwow. *Publication*: Mole Lake monthly newspaper. Great Lakes Agency.

STOCKBRIDGE-MUNSEE COMMUNITY BAND OF MOHICAN INDIANS
N8476 Mo He Con Nuck Rd., P.O. Box 70 • Bowler, WI 54416
(715) 793-4111 Fax 793-1307; Website: www.mohican-nsn.gov
E-mail: tribal.council@mohican-nsn.gov
Shannon Holsey, President (793-4387)
 E-mail: shannon.holsey@mohican-nsn.gov
Dr. Jolene Bowman, Vice Chairperson (793-4060)
 E-mail: jolene.bowman@mohican-nsn.gov
Jerilyn Johnson, Secretary (793-4387)
 E-mail: jerilyn.johnson@mohican-nsn.gov
Janet Miller, Treasurer (793-4881)
Jeff Vele, Mohican News (793-4389)
 E-mail: mohican.news@mohican.com

Councilmembers: Chad Miller, Jeremy Mohawk, Scott Vele, Sterling Schreiber
Linda Mohawk-Katchenago, Tribal Administrator (793-4355)
 E-mail: linda.katchenago@mohican-nsn.gov
Jolene Bowman, Director of Education
Nancy Miller-Korth, Health Director
Nathalee Kristiansen, Library/Museum Manager
 E-mail: nathalee.kristiansen@mohican-nsn.gov
Bridget Swanke (793-4868), Senior Counsel
 E-mail: bridget.swanke@mohican-nsn.gov
Dennis Puzz (793-4367), General Counsel
 E-mail: dennis.puzz@mohican-nsn.gov
Ken Davids, Darcy Malone, Tony Granquist, Gaming Commissioners
Tribe: Stockbridge-Munsee Band of Mohicans. *Enrolled members*: 1,500. *In residence*: 900. *Area*: Towns of Bartelme & Red Springs...64,000 acres (17,000 in trust). *Resources*: Health & Wellness Center; Arvid E. Miller Library & Museum. *Programs*: Education; Health & Wellness; Family Services; Lenape Mohican Language; Culture; Employment; Economic Support. *Activities*: Runs Veterans Annual Powwow, 2nd weekend in August. *Attraction*: North Star Mohican Casino. *Publication*: "Mohican News", biweekly. Great Lakes Agency.

WYOMING

NORTHERN ARAPAHO TRIBE
Wind River Indian Reservation, P.O. Box 396 • Fort Washakie, WY 82514
(307) 332-6120 Fax 332-7543; Website: www.northernarapaho.com
 E-mail: northernarapaho@msn.com
Roy B. Borwn, Chairperson; Lee Spoonhunter, Co-Chairperson
Councilmembers: Norman P. Willow, Sr., Stephen M. Fast Horse,
 Clarinda C. Thunder, Anthony A. Addison, Sr.
Tribes: Arapaho & Shoshone. *In residence*: 7,500 (combines Arapaho & Shoshone). *Enrolled members*: 4,850 (Arapaho). *Area*: 2.2 million acres located in east-central Wyoming between the scenic Wind River Range & Owl Creek Mountains. *Resources*: White Buffalo Recovery Center (Youth Programs); Library; Business Development Corporation; Wind River Tribal College; Central Wyoming College. *Programs*: Social Services; Education; Sky People Higher Education; Language/Cultural; Health & Wellness (Diabetes); Housing; Economic Development; Child Care; Food Distribution; Head Start - Karen King, Director. *Attractions*: Wind River Casino; Arapahoe Ranch; annual powwow. *Publications*: Hei'towoot News or Wind River News; Social Service Directory; handbooks & pamphlets. Wind River Agency.

EASTERN SHOSHONE TRIBE
Wind River Indian Reservation, 14 N. Fork Rd.
P.O. Box 538 • Fort Washakie, WY 82514
 (307) 332-3532 Fax 332-3055; Website: www.easternshoshone.org
Clinton Wagon, Chairperson; E-mail: cdwagon@e-shoshone.com
Vernon Hill, Co-Chairperson; E-mail: vhill@e-shoshone.com
Shawna Harris, Executive Secretary
Councilmembers: Robert "Nick" Harris, Jodi McAdams, Karen Lacroix,
 Leslie Shakespeare
Edward Wadda, Eastern Shoshone Liaison
Tribes: Shoshone & Arapaho. *In residence*: 7,500 (combined Shoshone & Arapaho). *Enrolled members*: 2,650 (Shoshone). *Area*: 2.2 million acres located in east-central Wyoming between the scenic Wind River Range & Owl Creek Mountains. *Resources*: Tribal Cultural Center; Museum & Archives; White Buffalo Recovery Center (Youth Programs); Library; Business Development Corporation; Wind River Tribal College; Central Wyoming College. *Programs*: Social Services; Education; Language/Cultural; Health & Wellness (Diabetes); Housing; Economic Development; Child Care & Welfare; Food Distribution; Senior; Head Start - Karen King; Gaming. *Attraction*: Shoshone Rose Casino; Indian Days, annual powwow; Eastern Shoshone Tribal Fair; Wind River Music Festival; Shoshone Stampede Rodeo; Crowheart Big Wind Celebration & Crowheart Traditional Powwow & Rodeo. *Publications*: Shoshone Times, tribal newsletter; Wind River News; Social Service Directory; handbooks & pamphlets. Wind River Agency.

OTHER INDIAN TRIBES & GROUPS

This section lists Indian tribes, groups & bands that represent the interests of its members, They are, in most cases, landless, recognized by various states, but not yet federally recognized.

ALABAMA

CHER-O-CREEK INTRA TRIBAL INDIANS
1315 Northfield Circle • Dothan, AL 36302 (334) 596-4866
  Violet Parker Hamilton, Principal Chief; E-mail: vlt_hamilton@yahoo.com

CHEROKEE TRIBE OF NORTHEAST ALABAMA
P.O. Box 66 • Huntsville, AL 35811 (256) 426-6344
  Website: www.cherokeetribeofnortheastalabama.com
  Stanley Long, Principal Chief; E-mail: stan.long11@gmail.com
  Mary Slaton, First Vice Chief; E-mail: firstvicechief_mary@yahoo.com
  Rita Skelton, 2nd Vice-Chief; Council Chairperson
  Betty Baker, Treasure; E-mail: bettynsteve7@att.net
  Bomba Little Easter, Historian & Cultural Advisor
  E-mail: 4easter@comcast.net
Tribal Councilors: Ollis Brown, Jr., Maybelle Blackbear, Janie Tatro, Valerie McCay, Audrey Lemley, Skip Adams, Danny Skillman. *Publication*: Misty Mountain News, quarterly newspaper.

ECHOTA CHEROKEE TRIBE OF ALABAMA
630 County Road 1281, P.O. Box 768 • Falkville, AL 35622
(256) 734-7337 Fax 734-7373
  Website: www.echotacherokeetribe.homestead.com
  E-mail: echotacherokeetribe4@yahoo.com
  Stanley "Lame Bear" Trimm, Chief
  Charlotte S. Hallmark, Vice Chief; John Berryhill, Chairperson
  Nancy Massey, Secretary; Sue Warren, Treasurer
  Cherokee Brasher, Councilman-at-Large
Serves Cherokees in the Maylene region.

MA-CHIS LOWER CREEK INDIAN TRIBE OF ALABAMA
64 Private Rd. 1312 • Elba, AL 36323 (334) 897-2950
  Website: www.machistribe.net; E-mail: machis@centurytel.net
  James C. Wright, Chief; E-mail: chiefjames@centurytel.net
Purpose: To promote economic development & long-term financial vianility of Machis Nation and to achieve economic self sufficiency.

MOWA BAND OF CHOCTAW INDIANS
1080 W. Red Fox Rd. • Mt. Vernon, AL 36560
  (251) 829-5500 Fax 829-632; Website: www.mowa-choctaw.com
  Lebaron Byrd, Chief
  Kesler Weaver, Council Chairperson; Samuel Hill, Tribal Judge
Tribe: Choctaw. *In Residence*: 3,600. *Area*: 300 acres. *Geographic Boundaries*: North Mobile County & South Washington County, along the banks of the Mobile & Tombigbee Rivers. *Washington County Council Members*: Verma Reed, Donell Orso, Cleve Reed, Addie Odom; *Mobile County Council Members*: John A. Byrd, Sr., Alex Hopkins, Sr., Claudette Snow, Cherry Smith. *Facilities*: Museum & Cultural Center; operates two Indian schools. Program: Language & Culture. *Events*: Annual powwow, 3rd weekend in June; Cultural Festival - last weekend in September. Mowa Choctaw Dancers. *Publication*: "Chata" quarterly newsletter. Choctaw Agency.

PIQUA SHAWNEE TRIBE
3412 Wellford Circle • Birmingham, AL 35226
  Website: www.piquashawnee.com; E-mail: piquashawnee@gmail.com
  Gary Hunt (*Medicine Hawk*), Principal Chief; E-mail: okema@live.com
  Duane Everhart, Second Chief, Newsletter; Rodney Phillips, Treasurer
  Jan Fraz, Secretary; Anita Penington, Tribal Mother
  Don Rankin, Ceremonial Keeper & State Representative
  Ken Tankersley, NAGPRA Tribal Representative
  Barbara Lehmann, Senior Advisor to the Chief & Preservation Officer
Enrolled members: 300. Recognized tribe of the State of Alabama.

STAR CLAN OF MUSCOGEE CREEKS
242 County Road 2254 • Troy, AL 36079
  (334) 399-3612; C. Scott Sanders, Chief
  E-mail: osahwv@charter.net

UNITED CHEROKEE ANI-YUN-WIYA NATION
P.O. Box 754 • Guntersville, AL 35976 (256) 582-2333
  Website: www.ucan-online.org; E-mail: ucanonline@bellsouth.net
  Gina Williamson, Principal Chief; E-mail: stilwtrs@bellsouth.net
Publication: Native Pride newsletter

ARIZONA

BARRIO PASCUA
San Ignacio Yaqui Council, Inc.
2256 North Calle Central • Tucson, AZ 85705

GUADALUPE ORGANIZATIONS
8810 South 56th St. • Guadalupe, AZ 85705

SAN IGNACIO YAQUI COUNCIL
785 W. Sahuaro St. • Tucson, AZ 85705
  (520) 884-8527

SAN JUAN NORTHERN PAIUTE
P.O. Box 2656 • Tuba City, AZ 86045

ARKANSAS

OUACHITA INDIANS OF ARKANSAS & AMERICA
Revived Ouachita Indian Grand Council
Story, AR (no address since last edition)
  Chief John "Lone Elk" Woodall, Grand Head Chief
  Cletus "Songbird" Jones, Grand Head Vice Chief
Tribe: Ouachita Indians of Arkansas & America. *Programs*: Health, Social Service, Housing, Employment and Education in Indian traditions & customs; & environmental concerns of Mother Earth. *Activities*: Annual Native American Indian Powwow and Crafts Fair; personal appearances of Chief Lone Elk and members for school children and organizations. Organized 1981.

CALIFORNIA

ACJACHMEN NATION (JUANENO BAND OF MISSION INDIANS)
31411 La Matanza St. , San Juan Capistrano, CA 92675
  (949) 488-3484 Fax 488-3294
  Website: www.juaneno.com; E-mail: info@juaneno.com
  Teresa M. Romero, Chair; Anthony Vaughn, Vice Chairperson
  Kim Olivares Leone, Secretary/Treasurer
  Ruthie A. Stoffel, Member at Large; Wick Lobo, Newsletter Editor
Tribe: Juaneno Band of Mission Indians. *Publication*: Cuel Atah, Monthly Tribal Newsletter

ALEXANDER VALLEY MISHEWAL WAPPO
1037 Kings St. #D • Santa Rosa, CA 95404

AMAH BAND OF MUTSUN-OHLONE/COSTANOAN TRIBE OF SANTA CLARA CO.
789 Canada Rd. • Woodside, CA 94062
  (415) 851-7747; Irene Zwierlein, Contact

**AMERICAN INDIAN COUNCIL OF MARIPOSA CO.
(a.k.a. YOSEMITE)**
P.O. Box 1200 • Mariposa, CA 95338
  (209) 966-4296

ANTELOPE VALLEY PAIUTE TRIBE
P.O. Box 119 • Coleville, CA 96107

ATAHUN SHOSHONES OF SAN JUAN CAPISTRANO
2352 Bahia Dr. • La Jolla, CA 92037

BIG MEADOWS LODGE TRIBE
P.O. Box 362 • Chester, CA 96020

BO-CAH AMA COUNCIL
P.O. Box 1387 • Mendocino, CA 95460
Tribe: Coastal Pomo

BUTTE TRIBAL COUNCIL
3300 Spencer Ave. • Oroville, CA95965

CAWIS-CALIFORNIA KAWEAH TRIBE
23514 Archibald Ave. • Carson, CA 90745
  Timothy A. Rodda, Chief

CENTRAL CALIFORNIA INDIAN TRIBAL COUNCIL
1425 S. Center St. • Stockton, CA 95206 (209) 466-0201

CHEROKEES OF NORTHERN CENTRAL VALLEY
P.O. Box 160963 • Sacramento, CA 95816
  Website: www.ncentralvalleyca.cherokee.org

E-mail: ncentralvalleyca@cherokee.org
Sari Clark, Secretary; Mike Webb, Treasurer
Bruce West, Alternate Secretary/Membership Coordinator
Shirley Rowland, Historian/Events Coordinator; E-mail: sdr1934@att.net
Jennifer Trantham, Community Relations & Media
Publication: Newsletter.

CHILULA TRIBE
P.O. Box 724 • Eureka, CA 95502

CHOINUMNI TRIBE
4233 W. Sierra Madre • Fresno, CA 93722
(209) 233-9781; Mae Davidian, Contact

CHUKCHANSI YOKOTCH TRIBE
P.O. Box 329 • Raymond, CA 93653

CHUKCHANSI YOKOTCH TRIBE OF MARIPOSA
4962 Watt Rd. • Mariposa, CA 95338-9743
(209) 742-7060; Lynda Appling, Contact

COASTAL BAND OF CHUMASH NATION
610 Del Monte Ave. • Santa Barbara, CA 93101

COSTANOAN/MUTSUN INDIANS OF CALIFORNIA
P.O. Box 28 • Hollister, CA 95024
Website: www.indiancanyon.org

COSTANOAN OHLONE INDIANS
922 N. Lassen Ave. • Ontario, CA 91764

COSTANOAN RUMSEN CARMEL TRIBE
244 East 1st St. • Pomona, CA 91766
(909) 623-7889 Fax 629-6081
Website: www.costanoanrumsen.org; E-mail: rumsen@aol.com
Tony Cerda, Chairperson; Gloria Castro, Vice Chairperson
Francine Chacon, Secretary; Juan Casados, Treasurer
Tribe: Costanoan (Ohlone) Rumsen-Carmel. *Facilities*: Wellness Center.
Activities: Annual Ohlone Gathering & Powwow in April.

DUNLAP BAND OF MONO INDIANS
P.O. Box 126 • Dunlap, CA 93621

ESSELEN TRIBE OF MONTEREY COUNTY
38655 Tassajara Rd. • Carmel Valley, CA 93924
(408) 659-2153; Jim Barker, Tom Little Bear Nason, Contacts

FERNANDENO/TATAVIAM BAND OF MISSION INDIANS
1019 Second St. #1 • San Fernando, CA 91340
(818) 837-0794 Fax 837-0796; Website: www.tataviam-nsn.us
Rudy Ortega, Jr., President; Darlene Villasenor, Vice President
Mark Villasenor, Secretary; Elisa Ornelas, Treasurer
Tribal Senate: David Ortega, Michael Ortega, Steve Ortega, Arturo Pleitez,
Cathy Salas, Francine Salas, Raymond Salas
Council of Elders: Alan Salazar, Ted Garcia, Kathy Ann Flores,
Bernice Frances Cooke, Beverly Folkes

GABRIELINO/TONGVA TRIBE
SAN GABRIEL BAND OF MISSION INDIANS
1999 Avenue of the Stars, Suite 1100 • Los Angeles, CA 90067
(310) 587-2203 Fax 587-2281; Website: www.gabrielinotribe.org
E-mail: info@gabrielinotribe.org
Bernie Acuna, Chairperson (428-5690
Tribal councilpersons:
Charles Alvarez, Councilperson (403-6048)
E-mail: calvarez@gabrielinotribe.org
Linda Candelaria, Councilperson (626) 676-1184
E-mail: lcandelaria1@gabrielinotribe.org
Vincent Holguin, Councilperson; Jerry Maldonado, Councilperson
Casino Projects:: Inglewood Casino Resort Proposal;
Garden Grove Casino Resort Proposal

HAYFORK BAND OF NOR-EL-MUK WINTU INDIANS
P.O. Box 673 • Hayfork, CA 96041 (916) 628-5175
Raymond Patton, Contact

INDIAN CANYON MUTSUN BAND OF COSTANOAN INDIANS
P.O. Box 28, Hollister, CA 95024
Website: www.indiancanyon.org; Ann-Marie Sayers, Chairperson
Land recently revived to trust. *Program*: Costanoan Indian Research.

KERN VALLEY INDIAN COMMUNITY
P.O. Box 226 • Lake Isabella, CA 93240 (916) 731-4561
Donna Begay, Chairperson; Harold Williams, Chairperson

KONKOW VALLEY BAND OF MAIDU 1185 18th St. • Oroville, CA 95965
Website: www.maidu.com; Thaddeus Cason, Chairperson
Holly Nielsen, Treasurer; Kate Hedges, Secretary
Tony Salaruzo & Pete Moak, Councilmembers
Tribe: Maidu. Maintains a Cultural Preservation Association.

LIKELY RANCHERIA
P.O. Drawer 1570 • Burney, CA 96013
(916) 335-5421; *Tribe*: Pit River.

MELOCHUNDUM BAND OF TOLOWA INDIANS
P.O. Box 388 • Fort Dick, CA 95538

MONO LAKE INDIAN COMMUNITY
P.O. Box 237 • Lee Vining, CA 93541
Jerry Andrews, Contact

MONO TRIBAL COUNCIL AT DUNLAP
P.O. Box 344 • Dunlap, CA 93621 (209) 338-2842
Dock & Florence Dick, Contacts; *Tribe*: Mono.

MONTGOMERY CREEK RANCHERIA
P.O. Drawer 1570 • Burney, CA 96013
(619) 335-5421 *Tribe*: Pit River.

MUWEKMA OHLONE TRIBE OF THE SAN FRANCISCO BAY AREA
2574 Seaboard Ave. • San Jose, CA 95131
(408) 383-9318, 205-9714 Fax (510) 581-94
Website: www.muwekma.org; E-mail: muwekma@muwekma.org
Rosemary Cambra, Chairperson; E-mail: rcambra@muwekma.org
Monica V. Arellano, Vice Chairperson; E-mail: marellano@muwekma.org
Karl Thompson, Treasurer; Norma Sanchez, Tribal Administrator
Alan Leventhal, Tribal Ethno-Historian
Councilmembers: Hank Alvarez (Elder), Gloria E. Arellano, JoAnn Brose
(Elder), Robert Martinez, Jr., Richard Massiatt, Sheila Guzman -Schmidt, Carol
Sullivan (Elder), Faye Thompson-Frei (Elder).

NOR-EL-MUK WINTU INDIANS
P.O. Box 3027 • Weaverville, CA 96093-3027
(916) 628-5175

NORTH FORK BAND OF MONO INDIANS
P.O. Box 49 • North Fork, CA 93643 (209) 299-3729
Website: www.northforkrancheria.com; Ron Goode, Contact

OAKBROOK CHUMASH PEOPLE
3290 Long Ranch Pkwy. • Thousand Oaks, CA 91362
Paul Varela, Contact

OHLONE/COSTANOAN MUWEKMA TRIBE
San Jose, CA area (408) 441-6473
Website: www.muwekma.org; E-mail: web@muwekma.org
Rosemary Cambra, Chairperson; *Tribal members*: 400.

OHLONE/COSTANOAN ESSELEN NATION
P.O. Box 1301 • Monterey, CA 93942 (408) 455-8315
Website: www.ohlonecostanoanesselennation.com
Louise J. Miranda Ramirez, Chairperson
Christianne Najera, Vice Chairperson
Charlotte Diaz-Gomez, Tribal Administrator
Tribe: Ohlone/Costanoan Esselen. *Activities*: Annual tribal gathering

PAJARO VALLEY OHLONE INDIAN COUNCIL
110 Dick Phelps Rd. • Watsonville, CA 95076
(408) 728-8471; Patrick Orozco, Contact

PINOLEVILLE POMO INDIANS
367 N. State St., Suite 204 • Ukiah, CA 95482
(707) 463-1454; Website: www.pinoleville.org

PLUMAS COUNTY INDIANS, INC.
P.O.Box 102, Taylorsville, CA 95947
Tommy Merino, Contact

ROARING CREEK RANCHERIA
Montgomery Creek • Shasta, CA 96065
Tribe: Pit River

SALINAN TRIBE OF MONTEREY COUNTY
P.O. Box 2166 • Concord, CA 93930
(800) 997-8999; Robert Duckworth, Contact

SAN LUIS REY BAND OF MISSION INDIANS
Mission Indians Bands Paralegal Consortium
360 N. Midway, Suite 301 • Escondido, CA 92027
(619) 741-1996; Carmen Mojado, Contact

SHASTA NATION
P.O. Box 1054, Yreka, CA 96097
(916) 842-5654 Roy Hall, Jr., Contact

SHEEP RANCH RANCHERIA
Sheep Ranch, CA 95250
Tribe served: Me-Wuk.

SHIVWITS BAND OF PAIUTES
Located near Santa Clara, CA

TEHATCHAPI TRIBE
219 East H St., Tehatchapi, CA 93561

TENA COUNCIL
located near Greenfield, CA
(408) 659-5812; Teresa Candelaria, Chair

THREE RIVERS INDIAN LODGE
13505 Union Rd., Manteca, CA (209) 858-2421

TEJON INDIAN TRIBE
1731 Hasti Acres Dr., Suite 108 • Bakersfield, CA 93309
(661) 834-8566 Fax 834-8564
Kathryn Montes-Morgan, Chairperson

TOLOWA NATION
P.O. Box 213, Fort Dick, CA 95538
(707) 464-7332 • Charlene Storr, Contact

TSNUNGWE TRIBE
P.O. Box 373, Salyer, CA95563
(916) 629-3356; John Ammon, Contact

UNITED LUMBEE NATION OF N.C. & AMERICA
P.O. Box 115, Ravendale, CA 96123
(530) 249-5651 Fax (916) 244-4459
Debbie "Grandmother Wolf" Valenta, Chief
Tribe served: United Lumbee Nation. Council Elders: Elmer "Shorty" Gray, Benton Screaming Eagle Bailey, Gary Bear Paw Ledbetter, Patty Flaming Star Ledbetter, and Helyn Burnt Willow Taylor. Pow-wow. *Publications*: United Lumbee Nation Times, 3x/year newspaper. Northern California Agency.

MAIDU SUMMIT CONSORTIUM & CONSERVANCY
289 Main St. Chester, CA 96020
(916) 258-2299 Fax 258-2300; Website: www.maidusummit.org
Kenneth Holbrook, Executive Director
E-mail: director@maidusummit.org
Lorena Gorbet, Secretary/Treasurer (375-0779
Our nine original member organizations once included: Greenville Rancheria, Maidu Cultural Development Group, Maiduk Weye, Mountain Maidu Historical Preservation Association, Roundhouse Council, Susanville Indian Rancheria, Tasmam Koyom Foundation, Tsi-Akim Maidu, and the United Maidu Nation.

WADATKUHT BAND OF NORTHERN PAIUTES
Honey Lake Valley, P.O. Box 541 • Susanville, CA 96134

WASHOE/PAIUTE OF ANTELOPE VALLEY
P.O. Box 52 • Coleville, CA 96079

WINTU TRIBE OF N. CALIFORNIA
P.O. Box 71036, Project City, CA 96079
(916) 878-4428 • Gene Malone, Contact

WINTU TRIBE OF SASHTA COUNTY
7480 Dr Creek Rd., Redding, CA 96003

WUKCHUMNI COUNCIL
Clovis, CA (209) 323-9817
Martha Tapleras, Contact

YOKAYO POMO RANCHERIA
1114 Helen Ave., Ukiah, CA 95482
Doreen Mitchell, Chairperson

COLORADO

BAHANTEC KAWEAH TRIBE OF COLORADO
105 So. 8th Ave. • Brighton, CO 80601
Alvin Martinez, Chief

MUNSEE THAMES RIVER DELAWARE TRIBAL COUNCIL
Manitou Springs, CO

CONNECTICUT

PAUGUSETT INDIAN NATION
Golden Hill Indian Reservation, Stanavage Rd., Colchester, CT
General Delivery • Trumbull, CT 06611 (203) 377-4410
Big Eagle (Aurelius H. Piper, Sr.), Tribal Chief
Quiet Hawk (Aurelius H. Piper, Jr.), Council Chief
Tribe served: Paugusett Indian Nation. *In residence*: 5. *Population served*: 80. *Area*: 1/4 acre, 1 house; 107 acres in Colchester, CT. Program: Sweatlodge; White Buffalo Society. *Publications*: Quarter Acre of Heartache, and Red Man in Red Square. Eastern Regional Office.

EASTERN PEQUOT TRIBAL NATION
640 Lantern Hill Rd., P.O. Box 370 • North Stonington, CT 06359
(860) 535-1868 Fax 535-8026; E-mail: eptn1683@yahoo.com
Katherine Sebastian-Dring, Chairperson
Brenda Geer, Vice Chairperson
Lynn Powers, Secretary; Joseph Perry, Treasurer
James A. Cunha, Jr., (Chief Growling Bear)
Roy Sebastian, Chief Hockeo "Running Deer"
Lynn Powers, Recording Secretary; Joseph Perry, Treasurer
Councillors:
Tyrone Gambrell, Larry Pemberton,, La'Tasha Maddox, Joanne Silva Njoka
Ambassadors:
Agnes Cunha "White Dove" & Marcia Flowers "Dreaming Spirits"
Tribe: Paucatuck Eastern Pequot. *In residence*: 115. *Area*: 225 acres. *Activities*: Harvest Moon Powwow every Columbus Day weekend in October. Library (for use by tribal members only). *Publications*: Powwow books at annual pow-wow, and "The Pequot Tribe," by Allison Lassieur.

SCHAGHTICOKE TRIBAL NATION
101 Elizabeth St., 2nd Fl. • Derby, CT 06418
(203) 736-0782 Fax 736-0875
Website: www.schaghticoke.com; E-mail: stn1699@yahoo.com
Richard L. Velky, Chief; E-mail: chiefvelkystn@aol.com
Charles Kilson, Vice Chief; Betty Kaladish, Secretary
Joseph Velky, Jr., Treasurer
Councilmembers: Linda Kilson, Frederick Parmalee, Dean Pomeroy, Tony Crone, Colette Kimball
Tribe: Schaghticoke. *Tribal members*: 300. *Area*: 400 acres.
Located in Kent, CT. Eastern Area Office.

DELAWARE

LENAPE INDIAN TRIBE OF DELAWARE
4164 N. Dupont Hwy., Suite 6, Dover, DE 19901
(302) 730-4601; Website: www.lenapeindiantribeofdelaware.com
Dennis J. Coker, Principal Chief; Lisa Coker Hurd, Assistant Chief
Minnie Bowen, Secretary; Marian A. Coker, Treasurer
Councilmembers: Carla Coker, Theo Braunsill, Terry Sammons

NANTICOKE INDIAN ASSOCIATION
27073 John J. Williams Hwy. Millsboro, DE 19966
(302) 945-3400; Website: www.nanticokeindians.org
E-mail: info@nanticokeindians.org
Natosha N. Carmine, Chief
Isaac Jackson, Assistant Chief
Christine Hudson, Treasurer; Leslie Wilson, Secretary
Councilmembers: Kyle Harmon, Bonnie G. Hall, Ashley Wright
Terry Johnson, Brett Jackson, Chris Zakrociemski
Tribe: Nanticoke. *Programs*: JTPA, Indian Elders (CHEER).
Description: State recognized tribe. *Activities*: Nanticoke Indian Center; Operates Indian Museum (April-December); annual powwow in September.

FLORIDA

THE APALACHICOLA BAND OF CREEK INDIANS
c/o Mary Blount, Chairwoman
104 West 4th Ave. • Tallahassee, FL 32303

CREEKS EAST OF THE MISSISSIPPI
c/o Thomley, 7701 Ennon School Rd. • Walnut Hill, FL 32568
(904) 587-2116

ECHOTA CHEROKEE TRIBE OF FLORIDA
P.O. Box 325 • Sneads, FL 32460 (904) 593-5176

FLORIDA TRIBE OF EASTERN CREEK INDIANS
P.O. Box 3028 • Bruce, FL 32455
(850) 835-2078 Fax 835-5691
John C.B. Thomas, Chairperson
Kenneth McKenzie, Vice-Chairperson; Andrew Ramsey, Chief
Tribe: Eastern Creek. *Ceremonies*: Pine Arbor Tribal Town; Berry, Green Corn, Little Green Corn, Harvest. The Museum (Blountstown, FL); Library. *Publication*: The Florida Muskogee (Creek) News.

NORTH BAY CLAN OF LOWER CREEK MUSCOGEE TRIBE
P.O. Box 687, Lynn Haven, FL 32444
(904) 265-3345; Lonzo Woods, Chief

OCKLEHUVA BAND OF SEMINOLE-YAMASEE
P.O. Box 521 • Orange Springs, FL 32812 (904) 546-1386

TOPACHULA TRIBAL COUNCIL
Pine Arbor Tribal Town, @ Tallahassee

TUSCOLA UNITED CHEROKEE TRIBE OF FLORIDA & ALABAMA
P.O. Box 49, Geneva, FL 32732

GEORGIA

CANE BREAK BAND OF EASTERN CHEROKEES
Rte. 3, Box 750 • Dahlonega, GA 30533 (706) 864-6010

GEORGIA TRIBE OF EASTERN CHEROKEE
aka GEORGIA CHEROKEE INDIANS
P.O. Box 1915 • Cumming, GA 30028
(770) 888-9856; Website: www.georgiatribeofeasterncherokee.com
Lucien Lamar Sneed, Director

LOWER MUSKOGEE CREEK TRIBE-EAST OF THE MISSISSIPPI
Tama Reservation • Cairo, GA

AMERICAN CHEROKEE CONFEDERACY
619 Pine Cone Rd. • Albany, GA 31705-6906
(229) 787-5722; Website: www.acconfederacy.org
E-mail: info@acconfederacy.org
William Rattlesnale Jackson, Principal Chief
Michael Black Hawk Willeford, Principal Vice Chief
William R. Robertson, Tribal Attorney
David Wind Walker Willeford, Orator/Parliamentor
Activities: Special Chiefs of Council meeting in March; annual meeting for membership in September. Indian library. *Publication*: Quarterly newsletter.

TENNESSEE RIVER BAND OF CHICKAMAUGA CHEROKEE
address unknown (located near Flintstone, GA)
David Q. Brown, Raven, Chairperson; Robert T. Murray, Chief
Tribes: Metis Cherokee of TN, GA, and AL.
Publication: Voices of the Council Fire, newsletter.

IDAHO

DELAWARES OF IDAHO TRIBE
P.O. Box 4912 • Boise, ID 83712
(208) 368-0839 Fax 686-8813

KUTEXO KAWEAH TRIBE OF IDAHO
1311 E. Commercial St. • Weiser, ID 86672-2452
J.K. Jones, Councilperson

INDIANA

INDIANA MIAMI COUNCIL
641 Buchanan St., Huntington, IN 46750

MIAMI NATION OF INDIANS OF INDIANA
80 W. 6th St., P.O. Box 41 • Peru, IN 46970
(800) 253-3578; (765) 473-9631 Fax 472-4162
Website: www.miamiindians.org
E-mail: miamiindians@sbcglobal.net
Brian "Blue Jay" Buchanan, Chief
John Dunnagan, Vice Chief-Tribal Historian, Chair-NAGPRA Committee
Sarah E. Siders, Secretary; Allen Dunnagen, Treasurer
John Morringer, Gary Rex Siders, David O. Marks, Jr., Jackie Williams, Rachelle Mongosa, Marilyn Rumsey, Alice C. Bowyer, Patricia Hrybyk, Carl T. Lavoncher II, Shane D. Fox, Tim White, Clyde Hayslett, Jr., Rick Marks, Council members
Tribe: Miami of Indiana. *Departments*: Education Committee; Community Food Pantry. *Resources*: Crane's Nest Store, official tribal store. Attraction: Maimi Indian Bingo. *Publication*: "Cry of the Crane," quarterly newsletter. Not yet federally recognized as of date of publication.

UPPER KISPOKO BAND OF SHAWNEE
@ Kokomo, IN 46901

WEA INDIAN TRIBE OF INDIANA, INC.
2417 Village Rd. • Charleston, IL 61920
Website: www.weaindiantribe.com
E-mail: weastrong@sbcglobal.net
Terry Stuff, Sr., Chief
Brenda (Mahkoonsahkwa) Lindley, Administrator

KANSAS

DELAWARE-MUNCIE TRIBE
P.O. Box 274, Pomona, KS 66076

KAWEAH INDIAN NATION OF AMERICA
P.O. Box 48003 • Wichita, KS 67201
1602 E. Central • Wichita, KS 67214 (316) 303-1275
Chief Thunderbird IV Webber, Grand Chief
Debra Flynn, Secretary of State
Donald Gilbert, Chief Financial Officer
5301 E. Butte St., Mesa, AZ 85205 (480) 654-1118
Tribe: Kaweah Shoshone. *Publications*: "Kaweah Indian News."
Publications: Kaweah/Itza History; Itza Language Dictionary.

SWAN CREEK & BLACK RIVER CHIPPEWAS
519 Willow St., Ottawa, KS 66067

WYANDOT NATION OF KANSAS
P.O. Box 171755 • Kansas City, KS 66117
Website: www.wyandot.org

LOUISIANA
(State Recognized)

ADAI CADDO TRIBE
4500 Hwy. 485 • Robeline, LA 71469
(318) 472-8680 Fax 472-8684
Website: www.aidiindiannation.com
Rufus Davis, Chairperson. State recognized in 1993.

BILOXI-CHITIMACHA-CHOCTAW OF LOUISIANA
Louisiana State Recognized Tribes of Lafourche & Terribonne Parishes
Biloxi-Chitimacha Confederation of Muskogees
P.O. Box 856 • Zachary, LA 70791 (225) 359-2476
Website: www.biloxi-chitimacha.com
Randy P. Verdun, Confederation Chairperson
Ernest Dardar, Vice Chairperson
Tribal Communities: Grand Caillou/Dulac Band of Biloxi-Chitimachas
114 Retreat Dr. • Bourg, LA 70343 (985) 594-6593
Marlene V. Foret, Tribal Chairperson
Isle de Jean Charles Band of Biloxi-Chitimachas
100 Dennis St. • Montegut, LA 70377 (985) 594-3725
Albert P. Naquin, Tribal Chief
Bayou Lafourche Band of Biloxi-Chitimacha
P.O. Box 856 • Zachary, LA 70791 (225) 359-2476
Randy P. Verdun, Tribal Chief
E-mail: chiefrandyverdun@biloxi-chitimacha.com

CHOCTAW-APACHE TRIBE OF EBARB
P.O. Box 1428, Zwolle, LA 71486
(318) 645-2588 Fax 645-2589
Website: www.choctaw-apache.org; E-mail: achoctaw@yahoo.com

Thomas Rivers, Chief/Chairperson; Amelia Rivers, Vice Chairperson
Alexis Hubbard, Secretary; Susie Sepulvado, Treasurer
Kallie Walraven, Elvis Procell, Nancy Sanchez, Reggie Ezernack,
Veronica Brown, Joanne Sepeda, *Councilmembers*
Tribe: Choctaw & Lipan Apache. *In residence*: 900. *Location*: West Central
Sabine Parish. *Programs*: Vocational Rehabilitation. *Activities*: Annual Pow-
wow, last weekend in May. Maintains school - only officially recognized "Indian
School" in the state of Louisiana. State recognized in 1978.

CLIFTON CHOCTAW INDIANS
1312 Clifton Rd. • Gardner, LA 71447
 (318) 793-4253 Fax 793-4211; Myrtlene Vega, Chairperson
State recognized in 1978.

FOUR WINDS TRIBE
La Cherokee Confederacy, P.O. Box 118 • Merryville, LA 70653
 (337) 825-8641 Fax 537-1697; Website: www.fourwindstribellc.com
Jackie Womack, Principal Chief. State recognized in 1997.

POINTE AU CHIEN INDIAN TRIBE
P.O. Box 416 • Montegut, LA 70377
 (985) 594-6250
Charles Verdin, Chairperson; Donald Dardar, 2nd Chairperson
 E-mail: verdin1504@yahoo.com; State recognized 2004.

UNITED HOUMA NATION
20986 Hwy. 1 • Golden Meadow, LA 70357
 (985) 475-6640 Fax 475-7109
 Website: www.unitedhoumanation.org
 E-mail: info@unitedhoumanation.org
Thomas Dardar, Jr. (District 6), Principal Chief
 E-mail: thomas.dardar@unitedhoumanation.org
August Crappel (District 8), Vice Principal Chief
 E-mail: august.crappel@unitedhoumanation.org
Monique Verdin (District 7), Secretary
 E-mail: monique.verdin@unitedhoumanation.org
Maryal Mewherter (District 6), Treasurer
 E-mail: maryal.mewherter@unitedhoumanation.org
Adam Crappel (District 1); Lora Ann Chaisson (District 2)
Pierre Solet (District 3), Parliamentarin
John Silver (District 4); Monique Verdin (District 7)
Donny Verdin (District 10); Michael Dardar, Sr. (District 11)
Kevin Billiot, ITCLA Executive Director; E-mail: kbilliot@itcla.com
Lacy Vito, Community Outreach Coordinator
 E-mail: lacy.vito@unitedhoumanation.org
Lanor Curole, Youth Development Director
 E-mail: lanor.curole@unitedhoumanation.org
Tribe: Houma. *Enrolled members*: 17,000. *Area*: 4,570 sq. miles. Located in
southeast Louisiana, including Terrebonne, Lafourche, St. Mary's, Jefferson
Parishes. *Programs*: Cultural Revitalization; Education; Health, Vocational
Rehabilitation; Emergency Preparedness. *Resources*: Inter-Tribal Council of
Louisiana (ITCLA)' KUHN 88.9 FM (Nation owned). *Activities*: Annual
Powwow. No corporate land base.

MARYLAND

ACCOHANNOCK INDIAN TRIBE
Box 404 • Marion, MD 21838
 (410) 623-2660; E-mail: accohannock@verizon.net
Sewell Fitzhugh, Contact

THE PISCATAWAY CONOY CONFEDERACY & SUBTRIBES
P.O. Box 1484, La Plata, MD 20646 (301) 609-7625
 Ms. Mervin Savoy, Tribal Chair

PISCATAWAY INDIAN NATION
P.O. Box 131 • Accokeek, MD 20607 (301) 932-0808
 Billy "Red Wing" Tayac, Contact

POCOMOKE INDIAN NATION
P.O. Box 687 • Mount Airy, MD 21771
 Website: www.pocomoke-indian-nation.org
 John Howard, Contact

THE YOUGHIOGHENY BAND OF SHAWNEE
6110 Melvern Dr. • Bethesda, MD 20851
 (301) 530-5281

MASSACHUSETTS

COWASUCK BAND OF THE PENNACOOK-ABENAKI PEOPLE
c/o Cowass North America, Inc., P.O. Box 52 • Alton, NH 03809
 (603) 776-1090 Fax 776-1091
 Website: www.cowasuck.org; E-mail: cowasuck@tds.net
 Paul W. Pouliot, Chief & President; E-mail: paulp@cowasuck.org
 Denise Pouliot, Treasurer; E-mail: denisep@cowasuck.org
Councilmembers: Arlene Andresen, Robert Pease, Jr., Rene Blanchette,
 Doris Nickles, Gail Demers
Tribe: Cowasuck Abenaki. *Facilities*: Library & Museum. *Programs*:
Educational & Cultural; Social Services; Religious Services; Environemntal.
Publication: Aln8bak News, quarterly newsletter.

MASHPEE WAMPANOAG INDIAN TRIBE
483 Great Neck Rd., South, P.O. Box 1048 • Mashpee, MA 02649
 (508) 477-0208 Fax 477-1218
 Website: www.mashpeewampanoagtribe.com
 Cedric Cromwell, Chairperson; Jessie 'little doe' Baird, Vice Chairperson
 Robert Hendricks, Treasurer; Marie Stone, Secretary
Councilmembers: Yvonne Avant, Cheryl Frye-Cromwell, Robert Dias, Carlton
 Hendricks, Charles Foster, Edwina Johnson-Graham, Winona Pocknett
 Nitana Hicks Greendeer, Education Director
 Unique A. Lopes, Human Services Director
 E-mail: unique.lopes@mwtribe.com
 Brian Harris, Economic Development Committee Chairperson
 Steve Heime, Health Advisory Committee Chairperson
Maintains tribal museum. Holds annual powwow in July.

NEW ENGLAND COASTAL SCHAGTICOKE INDIAN ASSOCIATION
P.O. Box 551 • Avon, MA 02322
 (617) 961-1346; Laurence "Swift Tide" Shanks, Chief

NIPMUC NATION
Grafton/Hassanamisco Reservation
25 Main St. • South Grafton, MA 01560
 (774) 317-9138 Fax 317-9138
 Website: www.nipmucnation.org; E-mail: info@nipmucnation.org
 Walters Vickers, Chief Natachaman
 Frances Richardson Garnett, Chairperson
 Rae Gould, Tribal Historic Preservation Officer
State-recognized; waiting for federal recognition.
Museum & Cultural Center being planned for Worcester, Mass.

MICHIGAN

BURT LAKE BAND OF OTTAWA & CHIPPEWA INDIANS
P.O. Box 206 • Brutus, MI 49716 (616) 529-6113
 Website: www.burtlakeband.org; E-mail: crcaee@yahoo.com
 Curtis P. Chambers, Chairperson
 Augustine Kiogima, Jr., Vice Chairperson
 Bruce R. Hamlin, Secretary; David Massey, Treasurer

CHAC KAWEAH TRIBE OF MICHIGAN
328 So. First • Ishpeming, MI 49849
 Nick Valenti, Chief

GRAND RIVER BANDS OF OTTAWA INDIANS
1316 Front Ave., P.O. Box 2937 • Grand Rapids, MI 49501
 (616) 458-8759 Fax 458-9039; Website: www.grboi.com
 E-mail: grbottawa@yahoo.com; Ron Yob, Chairperson
State recognized. *Publication*: Riverbends newsletter

LAKE SUPERIOR CHIPPEWA OF MARQUETTE TRIBAL COUNCIL
P.O. Box 1071 • Marquette, MI 49855 (906) 249-3969

LES CHENEAUX TRIBE
P.O Box 267 • Hessel, MI49862 (906) 484-3574

NASHDO KAWEAH TRIBE OF MICHIGAN
P.O. Box 295 • Republic, MI 49879
 Valerie Jandreau, Chief

NORTHERN MICHIGAN OTTAWA TRIBE
1391 Terrace St. • Muskegon, MI 49441

POTAWATOMI INDIAN TRIBE OF INDIANA & MICHIGAN
Route 6, Box 526 • Dowagiac, MI 49047

MISSOURI

CHICKAMAUGA CHEROKEE NATION, MO/AR WHITE RIVER BAND
106 S. Calhoun Ave. • Ash, MO 65604
(417) 751-3422

CHICKAMAUGA CHEROKEE NATION
RT. 2, Box2029 • Fair Play, MO 65649
(417) 654-4003

CHICKAMAUGA CHEROKEE NATION
P.O. Box 95 • Rockport, MO 65279 (314) 698-2097

KAHOLE KAWEAH TRIBE OF MISSOURI
104 Sherill St. • Licking, MO 65542
Russell Rodda, Chief

NORTHERN CHEROKEE NATION OF THE OLD LOUISIANA TERRITORY
PMB242, 3305 Clark Lane • Columbia, MO 65202
(573) 885-1070 Fax 885-7903; Website: www.ncnolt.net
E-mail: ncnoltnation@gmail.com
Ken DesCombes, (Grey Elk), Chief; Kristina DesCombes, Secretary
Tribe: Northern Cherokee. *Activities*: Annual Cultural Gathering
in September. *Publication*: Norhern Cherokee Newspaper.

MONTANA

BLACKFOOT NATION
Spirit Talk Culture Institute, P.O. Box 477 • East Glacier, MT 59434
(406) 338-2882
Long Standing Bear, Chief; E-mail: longstandingbearchief@yahoo.com
Publications: Spirit Talk News (published six issues/year); The Piikani Sun,
periodic book. Publishes books under Spirit Talk Press.

LITTLE SHELL TRIBE OF CHIPPEWA INDIANS OF MONTANA
625 Central Ave. W, Suite 100 • Great Falls, MT 59404
(406) 315-2400 Fax 315-2401
Website: www.montanalittleshelltribe.org
Gerald Gray, Chairperson; E-mail: ggray@gng.net
Clarence Sivertsen, 1st Vice Chairperson
Leona Kienenberger, 2nd Vice Chairperson
Colleen Hill, Secetary/Treasurer
Council members: Richard Parenteau, Don Davis, Shawn Gilbert
Tribe: Chippewa. *Activities*: Metis Celebration & Powwow.
Publication: Tribal Newsletter.

SWAN CREEK & BLACK RIVER CHIPPEWA
Dixon, MT

NEBRASKA

SOUTHERN CHEROKEE
P.O. Box 3913 • Omaha, NE 68103
(402) 620-9596; Website: www.southerncherokee.com.
E-mail: southerncherokeegov@southerncherokee.com
Carl Hudson, Principal Chief

NEW JERSEY

THE NANTICOKE LENNI-LENAPE TRIBAL NATION
18 E. Commerce St., P.O. Box 544 • Bridgeton, NJ 08302
(856) 455-6910 Fax 455-5338
Website: www.nanticoke-lenape.info
E-mail: contact@nanticoke-lenape.info
Mark M. Gould, Chairperson; Lew Pierce, Co-Chairperson
Tribe: Nanticoke Lenni-Lenape. *Facilities*: Cultural Center; Museum & Library.
Programs: Job training & employment; drug/alcohol/cigarette abuse; AIDS
education; elders/senior services; referral service. *Activities*: Cultural-dancing,
singing & drumming; annual powwow in June.

CHEROKEE NATION OF NEW JERSEY
1164 Stuyvesant Ave. • Irvington, NJ 07111
(973) 489-1368; Carl Watson Longbow, Principal Chief
Katherine Buffalo Woman Ferrante, Chief Assistant
Edward Sunwolf, Chief Speaker
Activities: Actively involved with the habitat & environmental matters of Mother
Earth. *Programs*: Performances for senior citizens & schools. Maintains mini
museum, library and trading post.

NATIVE DELAWARE INDIANS
c/o New Jersey Indian Office
300 Main St., Suite 3F • Orange, NJ 07050
(201) 675-0694

POWHATAN RENAPE NATION - RANKOKUS RESERVATION
P.O. Box 225 • Rancocas, NJ 08073
(609) 261-4747 Fax 261-7313; Website: www.powhatan.org
Michael Adams, Chairperson; Chief Nemattanew (Roy Crazy Horse)
Location: Located near Mt. Holly, NJ, the reservation consists of the Powhatan
ancestral village with a conference center, heritage museum & art gallery,
library, gift shop, & nature trails. *Programs*: Crafts - Indian artists demonstrate
their skills; cultural; audio-visual presentations; and classes & meetings in
Powhatan language and traditions are held. *Activities*: Annual Arts Festival.

RAMAPOUGH LENAPE INDIAN NATION
Ramapough Lenape Indian Center, 189 Stag Hill Rd. • Mahwah, NJ 07430
P.O. Box 103 • Hillburn, NY 10931 (201) 529-5750; (201) 529-1171
Website: www.ramapoughlenapenation.org
Dwaine C. Perry (Deer Clan) (Sachem Maqua), Chief
Vincent Mann (Eagle Spirit), Turtle Clan Chief
Tanya Van Dunk, Tribal Recording Secretary
Debbie DeFreese (Deer Clan), Chief
Johny Bragg (Patterson Band), Chief
Floyd Hicks (Waywayanda Band), Chief
Rich Logan (Marten Band), Chief
Wallace E. Dennison III, Tribal Administrator
Michael Mann, President of Board; Francine Mann, Tribal Project Director
Enrolled members: 5,000. *Location*: In Mahwah, NJ, 27 miles northwest of
New York City in Bergen County. *Facilities*: Woodlands Online Library.
Programs: Cultural, lecture program; Language;

NEW MEXICO

PUEBLO OF SAN JUAN DE GUADALUPE
Piro/Manso/Tiwa Indian Tribal Council
4048 Callede Estrellas • Las Cruces, NM 88012
(505) 647-5372; Edward R. Roybal II, Governor
Carlos Sanchez, Lt. Governor
Andrew Roybal, 1st War Captain
Tribes: Piro, Manso & Tiwa. *Enrolled members*: 220. *Location*: A non-federally
recognized tribe situated within an urban city near the Rio Grande River in the
Mesilla Valley in southern New Mexico. *Population served*: 350. *Project*:
Establishing a tribal cultural center. *Activities*: Tribal religious ceremonies and
feast days occur four times a year in March, June, September & December.
State recognized. Federal recognition is pending.

TIWA INDIAN TRIBE
4028 San Ysidro Rd. • San Ysidro, NM 88005
a.k.a. San Juan de Guadalupe Tiwa

CHIRICAHUA APACHE NDE NATION
P.O. Box 1240 • San Carlos, NM 85550
Website: www.chiricahuaapache.org
E-mail: info@chiricahuaapache.org
(505) 299-2276; (575) 534-1379; (928) 475-2579
Edward (Two Moons) Chavez, President
Robert Van Fleet, Administration
William C. Bradford, Attorney General
Joe Saenz, Secretary of State
E-mail: jsaenz@chiricahuaapache.org
Charles Vargas, CEO BSS – Director
E-mail: cvargas@chiricahuaapache.org
Joseph & Gloria Beltrran, Head Elders Council

NEW YORK

ABENAKI INDIAN VILLAGE
Lake George, NY 12845

MONTAUK INDIAN TRIBE
Hempstead Dr. • Sag Harbor, NY 11963

NORTH CAROLINA

THE ALGONQUIAN INDIANS OF NORTH CAROLINA, INC.
1205 Newport Ave. • Elizabeth City, NC 27909
(757) 477-3589; Website: www.ncalgonquians.com
Marilyn Berry Morrison, Contact

Roanoke-Hatteras & Mattamuskeet Indian Tribes. *Activities*: Annual American Indian Cultural Festival & Powwow, in August.

CHEROKEE INDIANS OF HOKE CITY
Rt. 1, Box 129-C, Lumber Bridge, NC 28357 (919) 975-0222

CHEROKEE INDIANS OF ROBESON & ADJOINING COUNTIES
Rte. 2, P.O. Box 272-A, Red Springs, NC 28377

CHEROKEE-POWHATTAN INDIAN ASSOCIATION
P.O. Box 3265, Roxboro, NC 27573 (919) 599-6448

COHARIE INDIAN TRIBE
Coharie Intra-Tribal Council, 7531 N. US Hwy. 421, Clinton, NC 28328
(910) 564-6909 Fax 564-2701; Website: www.coharietribe.org
E-mail: coharie_chief@yahoo.com
Rev. Wilbert Ammons, Chief; Nadine Wright, Chairperson
Elizabeth A. Maynor, Tribal Administrator
Tribe: Coharie. *Enrolled members*: 2,520. *In residence*: 2,100. *Programs*: Health & Drug; Housing; Economic Development; Senior Citizens.
Activities: Annual Coharie Indian Cultural Powwow in early September.

HALIWA-SAPONI INDIAN TRIBE
39021 NC Hwy.561, P.O. Box 99, Hollister, NC 27844
(252) 586-4017 Fax 586-3918
Website: www.haliwa-saponi.com
E-mail: info@haliwa-saponi.com
Dr. Brucie O. Richardson, Chief; Jeff Anstead, Vice Chief
Rev. Michael Richardson, Chairperson
Alfred Richardson, Vice Chairperson
Rev. John Lee, Treasurer
Councilmembers: Dudley Lynch, Roena Daniel, Donzell Mills,
Earl Evans, Ladonna D. Richardson, Rydell Richardson
Alfred R. Richardson, Tribal Administrator
Barry Richardson, NC Commission of Indian Affairs Rep.
Ruth Ealing, NC Commission of Indian Affairs Rep.
Tribe: Haliwa-Saponi. *Enrolled members*: 3,800. *In residence*: 2,700. *Facilities*: Library & museum. *Programs*: Education; Health; Housing; Economic Development. *Activities*: Annual Powwow (3rd Saturday in April).

HATTADARE INDIAN TRIBE
Rte. 1, Box 85-B, Bunnlevel, NC 28323 (919) 893-2512

LUMBEE TRIBE OF NORTH CAROLINA
6984 NC Hwy. 711, P.O. Box 2709 • Pembroke, NC 28372
(800) 659-6585; (919) 521-7861 Fax 521-7790
Website: www.lumbeetribe.com
Harvey Godwin, Jr., Chairperson
E-mail: hgodwin@lumbeetribe.com
Tony Hunt, Tribal Administrator
District 1: Gaddy, Rowland, Orrum, Sterlings, Whitehouse, & Thompson
 Representative LaKishia Spaulding Sweat
District 2: Back Swamp, Fairmont & Smyrna
 Representative Terry Hunt
 Representative Janie Oxendine McFarland
District 3: Lumberton and West Howellsville
 Representative Lesaundri Hunt
 Representative Al Locklear
District 4: Red Springs and Philadelphus
 Representative Jonathan Locklear
District 5: Oxendine & Prospect
 Representative Jarrod Lowery
 Representative Bobby Oxendine
District 6: Raft Swamp and North Pembroke
 Representative Douglas Locklear Jr.
 Representative Larry Townsend
District 7: South Pembroke and Union
 Representative Reginald Oxendine Jr.
 Representative Jan Lowery
 Representative Bill James Brewington
District 8: Burnt Swamp
 Representative Daniel Jones
District 9: Saddletree
 Representative Anita Hammonds Blanks
District 10: Shannon, Rennert, & South St. Pauls
 Representative Janet Locklear
District 11: Hoke County
 Representative Frank Cooper
District 12: Scotland County, Maxton, and Alfordsville
 Representative Shelley Strickland
 Representative Areatha Patterson

District 13: Cumberland County, Parkton, Lumber Bridge, & North St. Pauls
 Representative William Maiden
District 14: East Howellsville, Wisharts, and Britts
 Representative Barbara Lowery
Belinda Brewer, Housing Coordinator & Council Assistant
 E-mail: bbrewer@lumbeetribe.com; Amanda Strickland, Tribal Liaison
Tammy Maynor, Director of Governmental Affairs
Alex Baker, Public Relations Manager
Rodney Nichols, Chief Judge
Tribe: Lumbee. The Lumbee Tribal Council is comprised of 21 members elected from 14 districts. *Enrolled members*: 55,000. Resides primarily in Robeson, Hoke, Cumberland & Scotland counties of North Carolina. *Resources*: Health Clinic. *Programs*: Education; Health; Vocational Rehabilitation; Rehabilitation; Housing & Home Ownership; Youth; Volunteer; Elder Services.

MEHERRIN INDIAN TRIBE
P.O. Box 274, Ahoskie, NC 27910
(252) 398-3321 Fax 396-0334; Website: www.meherrintribe.com
Wayne Brown, Principal Chief; E-mail: chiefbrownmeherrin@yahoo.com
Dr. Aaron Winston, Chairperson; Dr. Terry Hall, Treasurer
Councilmembers: A.R. Chavis, Jr., Warren Hall, Devonna Mountain, Douglas Patterson, Marcus Robbins,
Tribe: Meherrin. Area: 46.9 acres. *Activities*: Annual powwow in October; Family & Friends Day in May; Festivals; Thanksgiving Celebration. *Publication*: Quarterly newsletter for tribal members.

NEW RIVER TRIBE OF METIS
P.O. Box 126, Laurel Springs, NC 28644
Wayne (Guardian Bear) Rodgers, Chief; Mary Nichols, Vice-Chief
Brian Hampton, Peace Chief; Sally Meachum, Sec/Treas.
Activities: Annual powwow, Homecoming Festival; Teaching Weekends, Medicine Weekends; Red Fox Warrior Society; Phoenix Rising Women's Society. Developing funding for the Western North Carolina Center for Metis Education & presently providing a speakers bureau making presentations at schools & businesss. *Publication*: "The Drumbeat," tribal information journal.

NORTHERN TSALAGI INDIAN TRIBE OF SOUTHWEST VIRGINIA
1813 Chandler St. • Burlington, NC 27217 (919) 584-4834

OCCANEECHI BAND OF SAPONI NATION (OBSN)
Tribal grounds: 4902 Dailey Story Rd. • Burlington, NC 27217
Mailing address: P.O. Box 356 • Mebane, NC 27302
(336) 421-1317 Fax 304-3724
Website: www.obsn.org; E-mail: obsntribe@gmail.com
William A. "Tony" Hayes, Tribal Chairperson
Sharn M. Jeffries, Vice Chairperson
Vickie Jeffries, Tribal Administrator (Treasurer & Secretary)
 E-mail: vickiejeffries@yahoo.com
Council members: Keshia Enoch, Calvetta Watlington, Beverly Payne,
 Tammy Hayes-Hill, John "Blackfeather" Jeffries
Tribe: Occaneechi Saponi. *Mission*: The preserve, protect & promotie their tribal history, culture & traditions; providing social, economic & educational resources, opportunities & services that will contribute to the well being of the tribal community.

SOUTHERN BAND TUSCARORA INDIAN TRIBE
832 US 13N • Windsor, NC 27983
(252) 794-4559 or (540) 287-5280
Website: www.southernbandtuscarora.com
Emory Thomas (Deer Clan), Chief
Robert Armstrong (Eel Clan), Chief
Timothy Lowery (Sand Turtle Clan(, Chief
Eli Cherry (Snipe Clan), Chief
Chief David Striking Wolf Miller (Wolf Clan Rep.)
Pamela Miller Thomas (Wolf/Deer Clan), Secretary
Grand Council: Marilyn Dreamwalker Mejorado (Bear Clan Rep.);
 Pamela Earth Woman Thomas (Deer Clan Rep.);

WACCAMAW SIOUAN TRIBE
7239 Old Lake Rd., P.O. Box 69, Bolton, NC 28423
(910) 655-8778 Fax 655-8779; E-mail: siouan@aol.com
Website: www.waccamaw-siouan.com
Lacy Wayne Freeman, Chief
Matthew Blanks, Chairperson
 E-mail: matthew.blanks@waccamaw-siouan.com
LaSandra Young, Vice Chairperson
 E-mail: lasandra.young@waccamaw-siouan.com
Eric Graham, Secretary; E-mail: eric.graham@waccamaw-siouan.com
Darren Freeman, Treasurer
 E-mail: darren.freeman@waccamaw-siouan.com

Councilmembers: Terry Mitchell, Ervin Freeman, Elwood Patrick
Tribe: Waccamaw Siouan. *Area*: Located 37 miles west of Wilmington, NC. *Facilities*: Child Care Center. *Programs*: Education; Health; Housing; Child Care; Youth (Drum Circle). *Attractions*: Annual Fall Powwow.

WUTEXO KAWEAH TRIBE OF N.C.
106 Fox Chase Village • New Bern, NC 28562
  Darlene Debardelben, Chief

NORTH DAKOTA

CHRISTIAN PEMBINA CHIPPEWA INDIANS
P.O. Box 727, Dunseith, ND 58329

LITTLE SHELL BAND OF CHIPPEWA
Dunseith, ND 58329

OHIO

ALLEGHENNY TRIBAL COUNCIL
Canton, OH Sakim, Chief (lifetime)
Tribe: Alleghenny Lenape. *Membership*: 17,000 (nationwide).
Activities: Annual Festival in June; crafts, dancing & medicine ceremonies.

SHAWNEE NATION UNITED REMNANT BAND
P.O. Box 162 • Dayton, OH 45401

THE TALLIGE CHEROKEE NATION
P.O. Box 339 • Lucasville, OH 45648
  (740) 259-9153; Website: www.tallige.com

OKLAHOMA

SOUTHERN CHEROKEE INDIANS
16178 E 243rd St. S. • Webbers Falls, OK 74470
  (918) 464-2777; Website: www.southerncherokeeok.com
  E-mail: principalchief@southerncherokeeok.com
  Andrew D. Light, Chief

OREGON

CHETCO TRIBE
564 Fern St., Brookings, OR 97415
  (541) 439-4841; Nancy Dupaquier, Contact

TCHINOUK INDIANS (CHINOOK)
5621 Altamont Dr., Klamath Falls, OR 97601

PUERTO RICO

TAINO NATION OF THE ANTILLES
P.O. Box 883 • New York, NY 10025-0883
  (212) 866-4573 (718) 287-4853
  Pedro Guanikeyu Torres, Principal Chief
Governed by Council of Chiefs. *Goal*: Reclaim right to aboriginal identity, restore tribal government, acquire lands at home for tribal purposes, restore culture, language, customs, traditions & heritage. *Activities*: The Wanakan, Inc. Cultural Center located at 252 E. 4th St., New York, NY 10009 (212) 844-0097 and (718) 485-0467. Assists the Taino people in cultural reconstruction & overseas presentations of indigenous music, song, and dance. *Publication*: Taino Nation News, bi-monthly newsletter in Spanish and English.

SOUTH CAROLINA

THE BEAVER CREEK INDIANS OF ORANGEBURG COUNTY
230 Pine St. NW, P.O. Box 699 • Salley, SC 29137
  (803) 258-1900; Website: www.beavercreekindians.org
  Louie Chavis, Chief; Keith D. Grice, Vice Chief
  Velma Grice, Treasurer; Daniel Bolin, Sr., Chairperson
  Kathleen Chavis, Secretary
Councilmembers: Wanda Ammons, Arthur Chavis, Ronnie Chavis,
  Judy Collins, Julia Reynolds, Katie Walling
Council of Elders: Kenny Adams, Chief; Annis Williams, Tribal Mother;
  Elizabeth Gleaton, Betty Walling, Betty Cassidy, Robert Williams

CHALOKLOWA CHICKASAW INDIAN PEOPLE
501 Tanner Lane • Hemingway, SC 29554
  (843) 380-1481
  Vernon Tanner, Chief; Joe Tanner, Vice Chief

EASTERN CHEROKEE, SOUTHERN IROQUOIS & UNITED TRIBES OF SC
P.O. Box 7062 • Columbia, SC 29202
  (803) 397-3938; Website: www.cherokeeofsouthcarolina.com

EDISTO NATCHEZ KUSSO TRIBE OF SOUTH CAROLINA
215 Indigo Rd. • Ridgeville, SC 29472
  (843) 871-6740; Matthew Creel, Chief

LOWER CHEROKEE NATION OF SOUTH CAROLINA
3688 Warrior Creek Church Rd. • Gray Court, SC 29645
  Gene Norris, Chief; Mary Louise Worthy, Vice Chief
Area: 4.2 acres. *Facilities*: Museum; Cherokee Living Village.
Activities: Annual pow-wow.

NATCHEZ TRIBE OF SOUTH CAROLINA
79 Bluff Rd. • Columbia, SC29201
  (803) 988-1074; Samuel Earl Davis, Chief

SANTEE INDIAN ORGANIZATION
675 Bayview St. • Holly Hill, SC 29059
  Oscar Pratt, Sr., Chief; T.L. Scott, Vice-Chief

WACCAMAW INDIAN PEOPLE
5691 Bluewater Rd. • Aynor, SC 29511
  (843) 358-6877 Fax 347-0312
  Website: www.waccamawindians.us
  E-mail: waccamawchief@gmail.com
  Harold D. Hatcher, Chief
  Susan Hayes-Hatcher, 2nd Chief
  Reba McCaffrey, Treasurer
  Jennifer Michelle Hatcher, Secretary
    E-mail: Jennifer.hatcher@gmail.com
  Scott Beaver, Chief of Council; Homer Johnson, Jeanie Wright, Richia Powell,
Council members: Neal Richard, Robert Benton, Dalton Hatcher
  Doug Hatcher, Administrato; E-mail: superterran@gmail.com
Tribe: Waccamaw. Organized in 1992 under the laws of the state of South Carolina. *Area*: 20 acres located in the Dog Bluff community near Aynor, SC. *Facility*: The Education & Cultural Center. *Activities*: Programs in traditional crafts, spirituality, traditional medicines, foods, as well as children's programs; Sweat Lodges; Annual Pauwau (powwow) November. *Publication*: Newsletter.

TENNESSEE

ETOWAH CHEROKEE NATION
150 9th Ave. N • Cleveland, TN 37203
  Hugh Gibbs, Chief
Tribes: Upper towns, Cherokee & descendants. *In residence*: 150. Total acreage: 1.5 Historic-Council grounds area. Historic home range - Upper towns-Ohio River Valley to Tennessee River Valley; contemporary home range - Tennessee & tributaries River Valleys. *Activities*: School/public presentations; 7 Cherokee ceremonials. Museum & Library specializing in Upper towns material. *Publications*: My People The Cherokee by Hu Gibbs.

TEXAS

APALACHICOLA BAND OF CREEK INDIANS
113 N. First St. • Mabank, TX (903) 880-0240
  Mary Sixwomen Blount, Tribal Administrator
  E-mail: sixwomen@yahoo.com

LIPAN APACHE TRIBE OF TEXAS
P.O. Box 5218 • McAllen, TX 78502
  (361) 215-5121 or 985-1381
  Website: www.lipanapache.org; E-mail: contact@lipanapache.org
  Bernard F. Barcena, Jr., Chairperso; E-mail: bbarcena@lipanapache.org
  Robert Soto, Vice Chairperson, Newsletter Editor; E-mail: robtsoto@aol.com
  Juan S. Garcia, Secretary; E-mail: jsgarcia@lipanapache.org
  Erika Sauseda, Teasurer
  Oscar Rodriguez, Tribal Administrator; E-mail: Oscar@lipanapache.org
  Ric Canty, Records Director/Councilmember
  Joel Cabral, Council Advisor; E-mail: jcabral@lipanapache.org
  Raquel Monday, Bilingual Communications Lisiaon & Council Advisor
  David Diaz, Council Advisor; E-mail: ddiaz@lipanapache.org
Council members: Tom Castillo, Rudy Ramirez, Pedro Salinas Flores,
  Marvey Garcia, Jose Gonzalez
Tribe: Lipan Apache. *Facilities*: Museum & Cultural Center. *Programs*: Education; Health; Cultural; Language Preservation; Employment & Housing. *Activities*: Annual powwow. *Publication*: Desert Wind, newsletter.

WHITE MESA COMMUNITY
P.O. Box 7096 • White Mesa, UT 84511
(970) 564-5602
Elayne Cantsee, Council Rep. E-mail: eatcitty@utemountain.org

VERMONT

ABENAKI NATION OF MISSISQUOIA
100 Grand Ave. • Swanton, VT 05488
(802) 868-6255
Lawrence Moose Lampman, Chief
Eugene Rich, Co-Chairperson; John Vincelette, Secretary
Councilmembers: Michael Farrell, John Churchill, Crystal Lampman,
William Brotherton
Tribe: St. Francis/Sokoki Band of Abenakis of Vermont. *Enrolled members*:
1,700. *Attractions*: Abenaki Tribal Museum. *Activities*: Annual Heritage Day
Celebration.

VIRGINIA

CHICKAHOMINY INDIANS, EASTERN DIVISION
2895 Mt. Pleasant Rd. • Providence Forge, VA 23140
(804) 966-7815 or 966-7815;
Website: www.cied.org; E-mail: chief@cied.org
Gene "Pathfollower" Adkins, Chief; Gerald A. Stewart, Assistant Chief
Matthew Chippawa Adkins, Treasurer; Joanne C. Howard, Secretary
Council members: Joseph Adkins, Darrell Adkins, Scott Holmes,
Doris Austin, Norman K. Hogge
Enrolled members: 150. Located in New Kent County, 25 miles east of
Richmond. *Activities*: Annual Chickahominy Fall Festival & Powwow the 3rd
weekend of September.

THE UPPER MATTAPONI INDIAN TRIBE
1467 Mattaponi Reservation Circle • West Point, VA 23181
(804) 769-4508 Fax 769-0294; Website: www.uppermattaponi.org
Webster "Little Eagle" Custalow, Chief
Carl "Lone Eagle" Custalow, Vice Chief
Tribe: Mattaponi. Tribal enrollment: 450. *In residence*: 75. *Area*; 150 acres
located in King William County along the Mattaponi River off Rt. 30 at Rt. 626.
Facilities: Sharon Indian School; Mattaponi Fish Hatchery & Marine Science
Center; operates a museum, trading post and craft shop.

MONACAN INDIAN NATION
P.O. Box 1136 • Madison Heights, VA 24572
(434) 946-0389 Fax 946-0390
Website: www.monacannation.com; E-mail: mnation538@aol.com
Dean Branham, Chief; Pam Thompson, Assistant Chief
Diane Shields, Treasurer; Teresa Pollak, Secretary
Councilmembers: Lou Branham, Santina Knight, Sherry Branham Williams,
Rhonda Simpson, Russell Drysdale
Tribe: Monacan. *Tribal rolls*: 1,700. In residence: 500. Total acreage: 110
acres located on Bear Mountain, 10 miles northwest of Lynchburg, VA.
Facilities: Monacan Ancestral Museum; Giftshop; Bear Mountain Indian
Mission School - a National Historic Landmark. *Activities*: Annual Monacan
Powwow; Homecoming Festival; Scholarship Auction; Land Recovery Project.
Publication: Monacan News, bimonthly. Received state recognition in 1989.

NANSEMOND INDIAN TRIBE
P.O. Box 6558 • Portsmouth, VA 23703
(757) 986-3354; Website: www.nansemond.org
Barry W. Bass, Chief; Sandy McCready, Secretary
Tribe: Nansemond. *Population*: 300. The area of Reeds Ferry & Chuckatuck in
Suffolk was the original preserve of the Nansemonds. Today members are
stretched across Norfolk, Chesapeake, Virginia Beach, & Portsmouth.
Councilmembers: Alvin L. Bond; Kenneth P. Bass, Sr. (Iron Horse); Barry W.
Bass (Big Buck); Charles T. Bond; Gary F. Bond (Red Hawk). *Facilities*:
Museum. *Publication*: Tribal News.

NOTTOWAY INDIAN TRIBE OF VIRGINIA
P.O. Box 246 • Capron, VA 23829
(434) 658-4454; Website: www.nottowayindians.org
E-mail: nottowayofva@aol.com
Lynette Allston, Chairperson & Chief
William Wright, Vice Chairperson & War Chief
Councilmembers: Archie Elliott (Assistant Chief), Edwin Dukes, Vivian Lucas,
Beth Roach, Leroy Hardy, Sidney Turner, Edward Branch
Received State Recognition on February 26, 2010. Many Nottoway Indian
Tribe of Virginia Tribal members live in the communities throughout
Southampton County. Annual powwow in September.

RAPPAHANNOCK TRIBE
5036 Indian Neck Rd. • Indian Neck, VA 23148
(804) 769-0260; Website: www.rappahannocktribe.org
E-mail: info@rappahannocktribe.org
G. Anne Richardson, Chief
Tribe: Rappahannock. *Enrolled members*: 750. Located in King & Queen
County. *Facilities*: Tribal Cultural Center. *Activities*: Rappahannock Tribal Pow-
Wow; Dancers.

UPPER MATTAPONI INDIAN TRIBE
13383 King William Rd., P.O. Box 174 • King William, VA 23086
(804) 769-0041; Website: www.uppermattaponi.org
Kenneth Adams, Chief
Tribe: Upper Mattaponi. *Area*: 32 acres located in King William County. A new
cultural village site is being developed on Rt. 30, known as the Pamunkey-
Mattaponi Trail. *Facilities*: Sharon Indian School. *Activities*: Annual Tribal
powwow last weekend in May.

WASHINGTON

CHINOOK NATION
3 E. Park St., P.O. Box 368 • Bay Center, WA 98527
(360) 875-6670 Fax 875-6680
Website: www.chinooknation.org; E-mail: office@chinooknation.org
Tony Johnson, Chairperson & Cultural Committee Chair
Sam Robinson, Vice Chairperson; Peggy Disney, Secretary/Treasurer
Council members: Devon Abing, Gary Johnson, Jessica Porter, Jane Pulliam,
Gina Rife, Jeremy Wekell (Health & Social Services Committee Chair)
Enrolled members: 2,304. Located in Pacific County, WA and Klamath County,
OR. Does not yet have a permanent reservation.

DUWAMISH TRIBE OF INDIANS
4705 W. Marginal Way SW • Seattle, WA 98106
(206) 431-1582; Website: www.duwamishtribe.org
E-mail: dts@qwestoffice.net
Cecile A. Hansen, Chairperson (lifetime term)
Cindy Williams, Secretary
James Rasmussen, Jolene Williams, Mary Jane Holmes,
William Conklin, Sr., Barbara Droettboom, Council members
Tribe: Duwamish. *Enrolled members*: 572. *Area*: Located in King County,
Seattle metro area. *Facilities*: Longhouse & Cultural Center; The Longhouse
Gallery & Gift Shop. *Activities*: Duwamish Language & Dance Group; annual
meeting in June; river restoration; fundraising events. *Publications*: Tribal
newsletter; Washington's "Landless" Tribes: Our Quest for Federal Tribal
Recognition.

KIKIALLUS INDIAN NATION
3933 Bagley Ave. N. • Seattle, WA 98103
Website: www.kikiakkusnation.org
E-mail: kikiallusnation@gmail.com
Paul Lavan, Chief; Located in King County

MARIETTA BAND OF NOOKSACK TRIBE
1827 Marine Dr. • Bellingham, WA 98226
Robert Davis, Jr., Chairperson

SNOHOMISH TRIBE OF INDIANS
9792 Edmonds Way #267 • Edmonds, WA 98020
(425) 744-1855; Website: www.snohomishtribe.com
E-mail: secretary@snohomishtribe.com
Michael C. Evans, Chairperson
E-mail: chair@snohomishtribe.com
Becky Porter, Vice Chairperson
E-mail: vicechair@snohomishtribe.com
Carol Turner, Secretary; Sue Van Senus, Treasurer
Councilmembers: Sharon Medica (Position 1); Salima Worthington
(Position 2); Kimber Van Senus (Position 3); Pamela Bond (Position 4);
Katie Wright (Position 5); Tessa Evans-Campbell (Position 6);
Dottie Burton (Alternate Position).
Tribe: Snohomish. *Programs*: Governance Leadership Development. *Activities*:
Annual Canoe Activity Project for tribal youth; Annual September Gathering;
Annual Treaty Celebration in January. *Publications*: Quarterly newsletter; "The
Snohomish Sound," in-house cookbook of tribal members' family recipes.
Located in Skagit County.

SNOQUALMIE INDIAN TRIBE
P.O. Box 969 • Snoqualmie, WA 98065
(425) 888-6551; Website: www.snoqualmietribe.us
E-mail: pr@snoqualmietribe.us
Andy de los Angeles, Nathan Barker, Jerry Enick, Chiefs

Carolyn Lubenau, Chairperson; Sharon Frelinger, Vice Chairperson
Alisa Burley, Secretary; Richard Zambrano, Treasurer
Jerry Lamb, General Manager; Katherine Barker, Lifetime Elder
Councilmembers: Bob de los Angeles, Steve de los Angeles, Michael Ross,
Suzanne Sailto, Jolene Williams, Daniel Willoughby
Council Alternatives: Kaina Mullen & Wes Willoughby
Located in Kings County.

STEILACOOM TRIBE
1515 Lafayette St., P.O. Box 88419 • Steilacoom, WA 98388
(253) 584-6308; E-mail: steilacoomtribe@mmsn.com
Danny K. Marshall, Chairperson; Ken DittBenner, Vice Chairperson
Bonnie Marshall, Secretary; Lacie Deck, Treasurer
Councilmembers: Steve Thomas, Dawn Hardison-Stevens, Melissa Marshall,
Percy Hicks, Linda Ross
Tribes: Steilacoom; with Sastuck, Spanaway, Tlithlow & Segwallitchu bands.
Location: Located in Pierce County. As of May 1994, this tribe did not yet have
a permanent reservation. *Enrolled members*: 665. *Facilities*: Tribal Cultural
Center & Museum.

WISCONSIN

BROTHERTOWN INDIAN NATION
P.O. Box 2206 • Fond du Lac, WI 54936
(920) 929-9964 Fax 929-9965
Website: www.brothertownindians.org
E-mail: office@brothertownindians.org
Bob Fowler, Vice Chairperson
David Hankwitz, Secretary; Michelle Wood, Treasurer
Council members: Skip Blanc & Roger Straw
Tribe: Brothertown. *Enrolled members*: 3,100. *Programs*: Archaeological
Project; Brothertown Circle; Crafts. *Activities*: Annual picnic in July; annual
Homecoming Powwows selling crafts in October. Archives held at Adams
House, Fond du Lac Historical Society, WI. *Publications*: "The Brotherton
Indian Nation of Wisconsin: A Brief History", brochure; "A Man Called
Sampson," by Will & Rudi Ottery; "Families of Ettink & Welch," by Joan
Waldvogel.

FEDERALLY RECOGNIZED TRIBES & BANDS

ABSENTEE-SHAWNEE TRIBE OF INDIANS OF OKLAHOMA

ALABAMA-COUSHATTA TRIBES OF TEXAS

ALASKAN NATIVES
Aleuts, Eskimos, and Indians (Athapascans)

APACHE
Apache Tribe of Oklahoma, Camp Verde Reservation, Arizona
Fort Apache Reservation (White Mountain), Arizona
Fort Sill Apache Tribe of Oklahoma
Fort McDowell Reservation, Arizona
Jicarilla Apache Reservation, New Mexico
Mescalero Apache Reservation, New Mexico
San Carlos Reservation, Arizona
Tonto Apache Tribe of Arizona

ARAPAHOE
Arapahoe Tribe of Oklahoma
Wind River Reservation, Wyoming

ASSINIBOINE-SIOUX
Fort Belknap Reservation, Montana
Fort Peck Reservation, Montana

BANNOCK (SHOSHONE-BANNOCK)
Fort Hall Reservation, Idaho

BLACKFEET
Blackfeet Reservation, Montana

CABAZON BAND OF MISSION INDIANS, CALIFORNIA

CADDO
Caddo Nation of Oklahoma

CAHTO INDIAN TRIBE OF THE LAYTONVILLE RANCHERIA, CALIFORNIA

CAHUILLA MISSION INDIANS
Agua Calienta Band, California, Augustine Reservation, California
Cahuilla Reservation, California, Morongo Reservation, California
Ramona Reservation, California
Santa Rosa Reservation, California, Torres Martinez Reservation, California

CALIFORNIA VALLEY MIWOK TRIBE, CALIFORNIA

CATAWBA INDIAN NATION

CAYUGA
Cayuga Nation of New York, Cayuga Tribe of Oklahoma

CHEHALIS
Confederated Tribes of the Chehalis Reservation, Washington

CHEMEHUEVI
Chemehuevi Reservation, California

CHEROKEE
Cherokee Nation of Oklahoma
Eastern Band of Cherokee, North Carolina
United Keetoowah Band of Cherokee Indians, Oklahoma
United Cherokee of Alabama
Echota Cherokee of Alabama
Cherokees of Northeast Alabama
Cherokees of Southeast Alabama
Cherokees of Jackson City, Alabama
Southeastern Cherokee Confederacy, Georgia (ST)
Georgia Tribe of Cherokees, Georgia
Cherokee Tribe of Robeson & Adjoining Counties, North Carolina
Cherokee Indians of Hoke County, North Carolina
Northwest Wolf Band of South Eastern Cherokee Confederacy, OR
Red Clay Inter-Tribal Band of the South Eastern Cherokee
  Confederacy, TennesseeCherokee Tribe of Virginia

CHEYENNE
Cheyenne Tribe of Oklahoma, Northern Cheyenne Tribe of Montana

CHICKASAW
Chickasaw Nation of Oklahoma

CHIPPEWA
Bay Mills Reservation (Sault Ste. Marie Band), Michigan
Grande Traverse Band of Chippewa, Michigan
Isabella Reservation (Saginaw Chippewa), Michigan
L'Anse Reservation, Michigan
Lake Superior Band of Chippewa:
  Bad River Reservation, Wisconsin
  Lac Courte Oreilles Reservation, Wisconsin
  Lac du Flambeau Reservation, Wisconsin
  Red Cliff Reservation, Wisconsin
Minnesota Chippewa Tribe (six reservations):
  Nett Lake (Boise Forte) Reservation, Fond du Lac Reservation
  Grand Portage Reservation, Leech Lake Reservation
  Mill Lac Reservation, White Earth Reservation
Red Lake Reservation, Minnesota
Rocky Boy's Reservation, Montana
Sault Ste. Marie Reservation, Michigan
St. Croix Reservation, Wisconsin
Sokoagon Chippewa Community (Mole Lake Band), Wisconsin
Turtle Mountain Reservation, North Dakota

CHITIMACHA
Chitimacha Tribe of Louisiana

CHOCTAW
Choctaw Nation of Oklahoma
Mississippi Band of Choctaw, Mississippi

COCOPAH
Cocopah Tribe of Arizona

COEUR D' ALENE
Coeur D' Alene Reservation, Idaho

COLORADO RIVER INDIAN TRIBES
Colorado River Reservation, Arizona & California

COMANCHE
Comanche Nation of Oklahoma

**CONFEDERATED SALISH & KOOTENAI TRIBES
OF THE FLATHEAD RESERVATION, MONTANA**

**CONFEDERATED TRIBES OF THE
CHEHALIS RESERVATION, WASHINGTON**

**CONFEDERATED TRIBES OF THE
COLVILLE RESERVATION, WASHINGTON**

**CONFEDERATED TRIBES OF THE COOS,
LOWER UMPQUA & SIUSLAW INDIANS OF OREGON**

**CONFEDERATED TRIBES OF THE GOSHUTE RESERVATION,
NEVADA & UTAH**

**CONFEDERATED TRIBES OF THE GRANDE RONDE
COMMUNITY OF OREGON**

CONFEDERATED TRIBES OF THE SILETZ RESERVATION, OREGON

CONFEDERATED TRIBES OF THE UMATILLA RESERVATION, OREGON

**CONFEDERATED TRIBES OF THE WARM SPRINGS RESERVATION,
OREGON**

**CONFEDERATED TRIBES & BANDS OF THE YAKAMA NATION,
WASHINGTON**

COQUILLE TRIBE OF OREGON

COUSHATTA
Coushatta Tribe of Louisiana

CREE
Cree Indians of Rocky Boy's Reservation, Montana

CREEK
Alabama-Quassarte Tribal Town of the Creek Nation, Oklahoma
Creek Nation of Oklahoma
Kialegee Tribal Town of the Creek Nation, Oklahoma
Thlopthlocco Tribal Town of the Creek Nation, Oklahoma

CROW
Crow Tribe of Montana

DELAWARE
Delaware Tribes of Western Oklahoma

DIEGUENO (MISSION INDIANS)
Barona Reservation, California, Campo Reservation, California
Capitan Grande Reservation, California, Cuyapaipe Reservation, California
Inaga and Cosmit Reservations, California, LaPosta Reservation, California
Manzanita Reservation, California, Mesa Grande Reservation, California
San Pasqual Reservation, California, Santa Ysabel, Reservation, California
Sycuan Reservation, California, Viejas Reservtion, California

GOSHUTE
Confederated Tribes of the Goshute Reservation, Nevada and Utah
Skull Valley Band of the Goshute Indians of Utah

GROS VENTRE
Fort Belknap Reservation, Montana

HAVASUPAI
Havasupai Tribe of Arizona

HO-CHUNK (WINNEBAGO)
Ho-Chunk (Winnebago) Tribe of Wisconsin

HOH
Hoh Reservation, Washington

HOOPA
Hoopa Valley Reservation, California

HOPI
Hopi Tribe of Arizona

HUALAPAI
Hualapai Reservation, Arizona

IOWA
Iowa Tribe of Oklahoma; Iowa Reservation, Nebraska and Kansas

KALISPEL
Kalispel Reservation, Washington

KAROK
Karok Tribe of California

KAW
Kaw Indian Tribe of Oklahoma

KICKAPOO
Kickapoo Reservation, Kansas; Kickapoo Tribe of Oklahoma

KIOWA
Kiowa Tribe of Oklahoma

KLALLAM
Jamestown Band of Klallam Indians, Washington
Lower Elwha Reservation, Washington
Port Gamble Reservation, Washington

KOOTENAI
Kootenai Tribe of Idaho

**LOS COYOTES BAND OF CAHUILLA & CUPENO INDIANS
OF THE LOS COYOTES RESERVATION, CALIFORNIA**

LUISENO (MISSION INDIANS)
La Jolla Reservation, California, Pala Reservation, California
Pauma and Yuima Reservation, California
Pechanga Reservation, California, Rincon Reservation, California
Soboba Reservation, California, Twenty-Nine Palms Reservation, California

LUMMI
Lummi Reservation, Washington

MAIDU
Berry Creek Rancheria, California, Enterprise Rancheria, California
Susanville Indian Rancheria, California

MAKAH
Makah Reservation, Washington

MARICOPA
Gila River Reservation, Arizona; Salt River Reservation, Arizona

ME-WUK (MIWOK)
Jackson Rancheria, California
Shingle Springs Band of Me-Wuk Indians of California
Trinidad Rancheria (Cher-Ae Heights Indian Community), California
Tuolumne Band of Me-Wuk Indians of California

MENOMINEE
Menominee Reservation, Wisconsin

MIAMI
Miami Tribe of Oklahoma; Table Bluff Rancheria of California

MICCOSUKEE
Miccosukkee Tribe of Florida

MODOC
Modoc Tribe of Oklahoma

MOHAVE
Fort McDowell Reservation, Arizona

MOHAWK
St. Regis Band of Mohawk, New York

MONO
Cold Springs Rancheria, California

MUCKLESHOOT
Muckleshoot Reservation, Washington

NAVAJO
Navajo Reservation, Arizona, New Mexico and Utah

NEZ PERCE
Nez Perce Reservation, Idaho

NISQUALLY
Nisqually Reservation, Washington

NOOKSACK
Nooksack Indian Tribe of Washington

OMAHA
Omaha Tribe of Nebraska

ONEIDA
Oneida Nation of New York; Oneida Tribe of Wisconsin

ONONDAGA
Onondaga Nation of New York

OSAGE
Osage Tribe of Oklahoma

OTOE-MISSOURIA
Otoe-Missouria of Oklahoma

OTTAWA
Grande Traverse Band, Michigan, Ottawa Tribe of Oklahoma

PAIUTE
Big Pine Reservation, California, Bishop Colony, California
Bridgeport Indian Colony, California, Burns Paiute Indian Colony, Oregon
Cedarville Rancheria, California, Duck Valley Reservation, Nevada
Fallon Reservation and Colony, Nevada, Fort Bidwell Reservation, California
Fort Independence Reservation, California
Fort McDermitt Reservation, Nevada, Kaibab Reservation, Arizona
Las Vegas Indian Colony, Nevada, Lone Pine Reservation, California
Lovelock Indian Colony, Nevada, Moapa River Indian Reservation, Nevada
Pyramid Lake Reservation, Nevada, Summit Lake Reservation, Nevada
Utah: Cedar City, Indian Peaks, Kanosh, Koosharen and Shivwite
Utu Utu Gwaitu Paiute Tribe of the Benton Paiute Reservation, California
Walker River Reservation, Nevada, Winnemucca Indian Colony, Nevada
Yerington Colony and Campbell Ranch, Nevada

PASQUA YAQUI
Pascua Yaqui Tribe of Arizona

PASSAMAQUODDY
Passamaquoddy Tribe of Maine

PAWNEE
Pawnee Indian Tribe of Oklahoma

PENOBSCOT
Penobscot Tribe of Maine

PEORIA
Peoria Tribe of Oklahoma

PIT RIVER
Alturas Indian Rancheria, California, Big Bend Rancheria, California
Lookout Rancheria, California, Montgomery Creek Rancheria, California
Roaring Creek Rancheria, California, Susanville Indian Rancheria, California
XL Ranch Reservation, California

POMO
Cloverdale Rancheria, California
Coyote Valley Band, California
Dry Creek Rancheria, California
Hopland Rancheria (Hopland Band), California
Manchester--Point Arena Rancheria (Manchester Band), California
Middletown Rancheria, California
Robinson Rancheria. California
Sherwood Valley Rancheria, California
Stewarts Point Rancheria (Kashia Band), California
Sulphur Bank Rancheria (Elem Indian Colony), California
Upper Lake Band, California

PONCA
Ponca Tribe of Nebraska; Ponca Tribe of Oklahoma

POTAWATOMI
Citizen Band Potawatomi Indians of Oklahoma

Forest County Potawatomi Community of Wisconsin
Hannahville Indian Community of Michigan
Prairie Band of Potawatomi of Kansas

PUEBLO (NEW MEXICO)
Pueblo of Acoma, Pueblo of Cochiti
Pueblo of Jemez, Pueblo of Ildefonso
Pueblo of Isleta, Pueblo of Laguna
Pueblo of Nambe, Pueblo of Picuris
Pueblo of Pojoaque
Pueblo of San Felipe, Pueblo of San Juan,
Pueblo of Sandia
Pueblo of Santa Ana, Pueblo of Santa Clara
Pueblo of Santo Domingo
Pueblo of Taos
Pueblo of Tesuque
Pueblo of Zia
Zuni Reservation (Zuni Tribe)

PUYALLUP
Puyallup Reservation, Washington

QUAPAW
Quapaw Tribe of Oklahoma

QUECHAN
Fort Yuma Reservation (Yuma), California

QUILEUTE
Quileute Reservation, Washington

QUINAULT
Quinault Reservation, Washington

RENO-SPARKS INDIAN COLONY, NEVADA

RESIGHINI RANCHERIA, CALIFORNIA

ROUND VALLEY INDIAN TRIBES OF ROUND VALLEY RESERVATION, CALIFORNIA (FORMERLY THE COVELO INDIAN COMMUNITY)

SAC & FOX NATION OF OKLAHOMA

SAC & FOX TRIBE OF THE MISSISSIPPI IN IOWA

SAC & FOX OF THE MISSOURI IN KANSAS & NEBRASKA

SAGINAW CHIPPEWA INDIAN TRIBE OF MICHIGAN SALISH & KOOTENAI
Flathead Reservation (Confederated Tribes), Montana

SAMISH INDIAN TRIBE, WASHINGON

SAN MANUAL BAND OF SERRANO MISSION INDIANS OF THE SAN MANUAL RESERVATION, CALIFORNIA

SAN JUAN SOUTHERN PAIUTE TRIBE OF ARIZONA

SANTA YNEZ CHUMASH MISSION INDIANS OF THESANTA YNEZ RESERVATION, CALIFORNIA

SANTEE SIOUX NATION, NEBRAKSA

SAUK-SUIATTLE
Sauk-Suiattle Tribe of Washington

SEMINOLE
Seminole Nation of Oklahoma
Seminole Tribe of Florida

SENECA
Seneca-Cayuga Tribe of Oklahoma
Seneca Nation of New York
Tonawanda Band, New York

SHAWNEE
Absentee Shawnee of Oklahoma
Eastern Shawnee Tribe of Oklahoma

SHOALWATER
Shoalwater Bay Reservation, Washington

SHOSHONE
Battle Mountain Colony (Te-Moak Band), Nevada
Big Pines Band (Owens Valley), California
Duck Valley Reservation, Nevada, Duckwater Reservation, Nevada
Elko Colony (Te-Moak Band), Nevada, Ely Indian Colony, Nevada
Fallon Reservation and Colony, Nevada, Fort McDermitt Reservation, Nevada
Lone Pine Reservation, California, Northwestern Band, Utah
South Fork Colony, Nevada, Wind River Reservation, Wyoming
Yomba Shoshone Tribe of Nevada

SIOUX
Cheyenne River Reservation, South Dakota
Crow Creek Reservation, South Dakota
Devils Lake Reservation, North Dakota
Flandreau Santee Sioux Reservation, South Dakota
Fort Peck Reservation (Assiniboine & Sioux), South Dakota
Lower Brule Sioux Reservation, South Dakota
Lower Sioux Community (Mdewakanton), Minnesota
Pine Ridge Reservation (Oglala), South Dakota
Prairie Island Reservation (Mdewakanton), Minnesota
Rosebud Reservation, South Dakota
Shakopee Mdewakanton Sioux Community, Minnesota
Sisseton-Wahpeton Sioux Reservation, South Dakota
Standing Rock Reservation, North and South Dakota
Upper Sioux Reservation, Minnesota
Yankton Sioux Tribe of South Dakota

SKAGIT
Upper Skagit Indian Tribe of Washington

SKOKOMISH
Skokomish Reservation, Washington

SMITH RIVER
Big Lagoon Rancheria, California

SPOKANE
Spokane Tribe of Washington

SQUAXIN ISLAND
Squaxin Island Reservation, Washington

STILLAGUAMISH
Stillaguamish Tribe of Washington

STOCKBRIDGE-MUNSEE
Stockbridge-Munsee Community of Mohican Indians, Wisconsin

SWINOMISH
Swinomish Reservation, Washington

SUQUAMISH
Port Madison Reservation, Washington

TACHE
Santa Rosa Rancheria, California

THREE AFFILIATED TRIBES (GROSS VENTRE, HIDATSA, MANDAN)
Three Affiliated Tribes of Fort Berthold, North Dakota

TOHONO O'ODHAM - PIMA/PAPAGO
Ak Chin Indian Community of the Maricopa Indian Reservation, Arizona
Gila Bend Reservation, Arizona; Gila River Reservation, Arizona
Salt River Reservation, Arizona; San Xavier Reservation, Arizona
Sells Reservation, Arizona

TOLOWA
Cher-Ae Heights Community, Trinidad Rancheria, California

TONKAWA
Tonawa Tribe of Oklahoma

TULALIP
Tule River Reservation, California

TUSCARORA
Tuscarora Nation of New York

UMATILLA
Confederated Tribes of the Umatilla Reservation, Oregon

UTE
Southern Ute Reservation, Colorado
Uintah and Ouray Reservation, Utah
Ute Mountain Reservation, Colorado, Utah and New Mexico

WARM SPRINGS
Confederated Tribes of the Warm Springs Reservation
(Walla Walla and Cayuga), Oregon

WASHOE
Carson Colony, Nevada
Dresslerville Rancheria, Nevada
Reno-Sparks Indian Colony, Nevada
Susanville Indian Rancheria, California
Washoe Rancheria, Nevada

WICHITA
Wichita Tribe of Oklahoma

WINNEBAGO
Winnebago Tribe of Nebraska

WINTUN
Colusa Rancheria (Cachil DeHe Band), California
Cortina Indian Rancheria, California
Grindstone Indian Rancheria (Wintun-Wailaki), California
Rumsey Indian Rancheria, California

WYANDOTTE
Wyandotte Tribe of Oklahoma

YAKAMA
Yakama Reservation (Confederated Tribes), Washington

YAVAPAI
Camp Verde Reservation, Arizona
Yavapai-Prescott Tribe of Arizona

YOKUT
Santa Rosa Rancheria, California
Table Mountain Rancheria, California

YUROK
Berry Creek Reservation, California
Hoopa Valley Reservation, California
Trinidad Rancheria (Cher-Ae Heights), California

This section is an alpha-geographical listing of government agencies - regional & state, concerned with American Indian affairs. The principal federal agency in this area is the Office of Indian Affairs of the U.S. Department of the Interior. Listings describe the activities of the office, with a directory of the Central (Washington, DC) Office.

OFFICE OF ASSISTANT SECRETARY – INDIAN AFFAIRS
U.S. DEPARTMENT OF THE INTERIOR (DOI)

1849 C St., NW, MS-3642-MIB • WASHINGTON, DC 20240-0001
(202) 208-7163 Fax 208-5320
Website: www.doi.gov; E-mail: feedback@ios.doi.gov
Ryan Zinke, U.S. Secretary of the Interior
Michael S. Black (Oglala Sioux), Acting Asst. Secretary - Indian Affairs
3611-MIB (202) 208-3710 Fax 501-1516
Ann Marie Bledsoe Downes (Winnebago), Deputy Assistant Secretary – Indian Affairs
Clint Hastings, Advisor to the Assistant Secretary – Indian Affairs
Anthony "Morgan" Rodman, Executive Director, White House Council On Native American Affairs
Mr. Lynn Polacca, Deputy Regional Director of Trust Services
Sarah Walters, Chief of Staff to the Assistant Secretary
Cheryl Andrews-Maltais, Policy Advisor to the Assistant Secretary
Tana Fitzpatrick & Miles Janssen, Counselors to the Assistant Secretary
R. Lee Fleming, Director, Office of Federal Acknowledgement
George Bearpaw, Director, Office of Budget Management
Ann Marie Bledsoe Downs, Acting Director, Bureau of Indian Education

Bureau of Indian Affairs (BIA)

1849 C St., NW, MS-4606-MIB • Washington, DC 20240
(202) 208-5116 Fax 208-6334
Michael S. Black, BIA Director – Bureau of Indian Affairs
Debrah McBride, Special Assistant to the Director, BIA
Michael R. Smith, Deputy Bureau Director – Field Operations
Starr Penland, Special Assistant to the Deputy Director, BIA, Field Operations
Hankie P. Ortiz (Kiowa), Deputy Bureau Director - Indian Services
MS 4511-MIB (202) 513-7640 Fax 208-5113
Spike Bighorn, Associate Deputy Bureau Director, Indian Services
Darren A. Cruzan, Deputy Bureau Director, Justice Services
Helen Riggs, Deputy Bureau Director, Trust Services
MS 4618-MIB (208-5831 Fax 208-5015)
Faline Haven, Associate Deputy Bureau Director – Trust Services

Office of the Chief Financial Officer (OCFO) Indian Affairs

12220 Sunrise Valley Dr., Reston, VA 20191
(703) 390-6485 Fax 390-6304; James Schock, Chief Financial Officer
The office is headed by the Chief Financial Officer (CFO) and Deputy Chief Financial Officer (DCFO) who serve as the principal financial management advisors to the Assistant Secretary-Indian Affairs and other senior Indian Affairs officials. It is comprised of the following four divisions: Acquisitions and Property Management; Financial Systems; Accounting Operations; Financial Reporting and Analysis. Located in Reston, VA, the CFO is the primary conduit to the Department's financial management community. The CFO also serves as head of the contracting activity, the senior Indian Affairs acquisition official, the audit liaison officer, and the management control coordinator for Indian Affairs. The OCFO is responsible for all aspects of financial management, including loan and construction accounting; power and irrigation billings and collections; acquisitions & grants; & property & space management activities. The OCFO prepares Indian Affairs financial statements and is the primary liaison with the Department's Office of Inspector General. The OCFO ensures financial management is consistent with requirements of the Chief Financial Officers Act, Government Performance and Results Act, Office of Management and Budget guidance, Department of the Treasury, General Accounting Office, and Federal Accounting Standards Advisory Board.

Office of Congressional & Legislative Affairs – Indian Affairs (OCLA-IA)

MS 3648-MIB 1849 C St., NW, Washington, DC 20240
(202) 208-5706 Fax 208-4623; Darren Pete, Director
Congressional & Legislative Affairs oversee & coordinate the legislative planning and congressional relations activities for Indian Affairs. The office provides legislative research & assistance in developing, drafting, & analyzing proposed legislation. These activities are coordinated with the Office of the Secretary to ensure consistency of Departmental communications with Congress. Legislative research and assistance are provided to program offices in developing & drafting legislation, preparing testimony, & providing legislative histories on various issues. The Office responds to requests for information from congressional staff, the Department, other Federal Agencies, Tribal leadership, members and organizations, law firms, and the public at large, on various issues concerning American Indians & Alaska Natives. Congressional correspondence is coordinated through this office.

Office of Indian Energy & Economic Development (IEED)

1951 Constitution Ave, NW, Rm. 20-SIB, Washington, DC 20245
(202) 219-0740 Fax 208-4564
Jack Stevens, Acting Director; (202) 208-6764
E-mail: jack.stevens@bia.gov
Purpose: to help Indian communities gain economic self-sufficiency through the development of their energy & mineral resources, application of established business practices, & co-sponsorship of innovative training programs. The office is made up of three Divisions: **Division of Energy and Mineral Development** - Assists tribes with the exploration, development, and management of their energy and mineral resources with the ultimate goal of creating jobs & sustainable tribal economies. **Division of Economic Development** - Assists tribes in creating an environment for economic progress through training, business planning, & expert consultation. **Division of Capital Investment** - Manages the Indian Loan Guaranty Program to facilitate access to capital and loan financing for Indians.

Office of Indian Gaming (OIG)

MS 3657-MIB 1849 C St., NW, Washington, DC 20240
(202) 219-4066 Fax 273-3153; Paula L. Hart, Director
The Office is under the supervision of the Deputy Assistant Secretary-Indian Affairs Economic Development and Policy, is responsible for implementing those gaming-related activities assigned to the Bureau of Indian Affairs by the Indian Gaming Regulatory Act and other Federal laws. The office develops policies and procedures for review & approval of: tribal/state compacts; per capita distributions of gaming revenues; and requests to take land into trust for purpose of conducting gaming. Work is coordinated with the National Indian Gaming Commission and with state, local, & tribal governments that may be impacted by gaming proposals.

Office of Information Management Technology

12220 Sunrise Valley Dr., Reston, VA 20191
(703) 390-6500 ext. 6501 Fax 390-6737
Joseph J. Austin, Associate Chief Information Officer
Office of Information Management Technology (OIMT) is responsible for the planning, acquisition, utilization, architecture, security, operations, & management of information resources & Information Technology (IT) for all Indian Affairs, i.e., Office of the Assistant Secretary and the Bureaus of Indian Affairs and Indian Education. This includes leading Indian Affairs strategic IT planning to improve the use of information & information processing resources, developing policies promoting program and the effective use of information technology and resources throughout Indian Affairs in consultation with Indian Affairs Program Directors, & developing effective working relationships with internal IA program customers and OIMT organizations in the Department. The office supervises field and Central Office staff, providing management and oversight of all Indian Affairs information resources and technology; provides direction & oversight for Indian Affairs information system security activities; E-Government activities, the development & implementation of the Indian Affairs IT policies on the creation and disposition of information & systems; & ensures standardized technology & information resource functions within Indian Affairs to achieve continuity of information technology & resource accountability throughout the organization. Six divisions are under the direction of and assist the ACIO in carrying out the OIMT responsibilities and functions.

Office of Public Affairs (OPA)

MS-3658-MIB, 1849 C St., NW, Washington, DC 20240
(202) 208-3710 Fax 501-1516; E-mail: feedback@bia.gov
Nedra Darling, Director
The Office supports the Office of the Assistant Secretary-Indian Affairs, the Bureau of Indian Affairs and the Bureau of Indian Education by providing information on secretarial decisions & actions to news media and other entities interested in Indian Affairs via news releases, media relations, and the Indian Affairs website. It is the primary contact within Indian Affairs for journalists, writers, researchers and the public seeking general information about IA bureaus, offices, programs & activities; American Indians and Alaska Natives; federally recognized tribes; federal Indian laws and policies; and the history of federal-tribal relations as they relate to Indian Affairs.

Office of Regulatory Affairs & Collaborative Action (RACA)

1001 Indian School Rd. NW, Suite 312, Albuquerque, NM 87104
(505) 563-3805 Fax 563-3811; Elizabeth Appel, Director
The Office of Regulatory Affairs & Collaborative Action (RACA), formerly known as the Office of Regulatory Management (ORM), is responsible for a broad range of regulatory functions that involve collaboration with all Indian Affairs (IA) bureaus, offices, tribal partners and other stakeholders,

Office of Self-Governance (OSG)
1951 Constitution Ave, NW, MS-355G SIB, Washington, DC 20245
(202) 219-0240 Fax 219-1404
Sharee Freeman, Director
The Office is responsible for implementation of the Tribal Self Governance Act of 1994, including development and implementation of regulations, policies, & guidance in support of self-governance initiatives. The staff negotiates annual funding agreements with eligible tribes & consortia, coordinates the collection of budget & performance data from self-governance tribes, and resolves issues that are identified in financial & program audits of self-governance operations. The Office works with tribal governments to protect and support tribal sovereignty within a Government-to-Government partnership and to advocate for the transfer of Federal programmatic authorities and resources to tribal governments in accordance with tribal self-governance statutes & policies. Included in the Appendices is a table illustrating tribal participation in Self-Governance. The staff works with self-governance tribes to implement & resolve issues or problems associated with self-governance agreements. Self-governance tribes represent nearly 40 percent of all federally recognized tribes nationwide. The Office provides financial management, budgeting, accounting and contracting services for an estimated $400 million in funds annually that are allocated or awarded to self-governance tribes, including reprogramming within Operation of Indian Programs (OIP) and transfers from other Federal programs.

Office of the Special Trustee for American Indians (OST)
1849 C St., NW, MS-4141-MIB • WASHINGTON, DC 20240-0001
(202) 208-7163 Fax 208-5320
Vincent G. Logan (Osage), Special Trustee for American Indians
Jerry Gidner, Principal Deputy Special Trustee
Established by the American Indian Trust Fund Management Reform Act of 1994 (Public Law 103-412), OST was created to improve the accountability and management of Indian funds held in trust by the federal government. As trustee, DOI has the primary fiduciary responsibility to manage both tribal trust funds and Individual Indian Money (IIM) accounts. The purpose of OST is to provide oversight, reform and coordination of the policies, procedures, systems and practices used by various agencies to manage Indian trust assets. This effort is integrally related to DOI's goal of meeting its responsibilities to American Indians. The goals of OST include: to protect and preserve Indian trust assets and collect and accurately account for income due beneficiaries; to obtain agreement with all tribal and individual Indian account holders on the balances in their trust accounts in a manner that is fair to both the Indian community and the general public, does not impair or impede reform efforts, and does not result in reductions in Indian programs; and to provide timely and responsive customer services to account holders.

Office of Indian Education Programs
500 Gold Ave. SW Rm. 7C, P.O. Box 769, Albuquerque, NM 87103

Alaska Liaison Officer: (202) 208-5819

Law Enforcement Services: MS: 4560-MIB.
(208) 5787 Fax 208-6170; (208-3485); (208) 5039;
Central Office, Albuquerque, P.O. Box 66 • Albuquerque, NM 87103
(505) 248-7939 Fax 248-7905
Indian Police Academy, 1300 W. Richey • Artesia, NM 88210
(505) 748-8151 Fax 748-8162
Drug Enforcement Section (748-8148).

INDIAN ARTS & CRAFTS BOARD
U.S. Dept. of the Interior, 1849 C. St., NW MS 2058-MIB
WASHINGTON, DC 20240 (888) 278-3253
(202) 208-3773 Fax 208-5196; Website: www.iacb.doi.gov

The following are federal offices that direct special programs for Indians and related other federal and congressional offices.

EXECUTIVE BRANCH

White House Council on Native American Affairs
1849 C St., NW, MS-4146-MIB • WASHINGTON, DC 20240-0001
Sally Jewell, Chairperson
Anthony "Morgan" Rodman, Executive Director
 E-mail: anthony.rodman@bia.gov
Jodi Gillette, Senior Policy Advisor for Native American Affairs
Advisory Council on Historic Preservation (ACHP)
Office of Native American Affairs
 Valerie Hauser, Director; E-mail: vhauser@achp.gov
 William Dancing Feather, Program Analyst
 E-mail: wdancingfeather@achp.gov
 Rae Gould, Program Analyst; E-mail: rgould@achp.gov

Office of Intergovernmental Affairs, Old Executive Office Bldg., Rm. 122
17th & Pennsylvania Ave., NW • Washington, DC 20503
(202) 456-2896 Fax 456-7015.

U.S. Department of Agriculture
14th and Independence Ave., SW • Washington, DC 20250
 Linda Cronin, Acting Director-Office of Tribal Relations
 E-mail: linda.cronin@wdc.usda..gov
 Fred Clark, Director-Office of Tribal Relations-Forest Service
 E-mail: fclark@fs.fed.us
Native American Programs - Office of Intergovernmental Affairs, Rm. 102-A, Administration Bldg. (202) 720-3805; Equal Opportunity Specialist, Indian Affairs, Rm. 2305, Auditor's Bldg. (202) 720-7370; Liaison for Indian Assistance, Rural Development Staff, Soil Conservation Service, Rm. 6103, South Bldg., P.O. Box 2890, Washington, DC 20013 (202) 720-7690.

Denali Commission
 Joel Neimeyer, Federal Co-Chair; E-mail: jneimeyer@denali.gov

U.S. Department of Commerce - U.S. Small Business Administration
Office of Intergovernmental Affairs • Washington, DC 20230
(202) 401-3059
 Star Wilbraham, Senior Advisor; E-mail: star.wilbraham@sba.gov

Bureau of the Census, Federal Center • Suitland, MD 20233
Liaison for American Indians & Alaska Natives
(301) 763-2607 Fax 763-3862
 Dee Alexander, Tribal Affairs Coordinator
 E-mail: dee.a.alexander@census.gov

U.S. Department of Defense
 Lisa Morales, Senior Tribal Liaison/Tribal Nations Program Manager
 U.S. Army Corps of Engineers

U.S. Department of Education - Office of Indian Education
Rm. 3E205, LBJ Bldg. 6, 400 Maryland Ave., SW • Washington, DC 20202
(202) 260-3774 Fax 260-7779
 Website: www.2.ed.gov; E-mail: indian.education@ed.gov
 Joyce A. Silverthorne, Director (401-0767)
 Bernard Garcia, Formula Group Leader (260-1454)
 John Cheek, Discretionary Team Leader (401-0274)
Enrichment Program; Indian Fellowship Program (202) 401-1916; Indian Gifted & Talented Pilot Program (202) 401-1916; & Planning, Pilot, & Demonstration Program. Office of the Assistant Secretary for Elementary & Secondary Education (202) 401-1342; Office of Special Education & Rehabilitative Services, 330 C St., SW, Rm. 4072, Switzer Bldg., Washington, DC 20202 (202) 732-1353, Fax (202) 732-3897

U.S. Department of Energy - Office of Indian Energy Policy & Programs
 Christopher C. Deschene, Director; E-mail: chris.deschene@hq.doe.gov

U.S. Environmental Protection Agency
American Indian Environmental Office
1200 Pennsylvania Ave., NW; MS: 4104M • Washington, DC 20460
(202) 564-0303 Fax 564-0298; Website: www.epa.gov/owindian
 Felicia Wright, Acting Director; E-mail: wright.felicia@epa.gov

U.S. Department of Health & Human Services
Administration for Native Americans (ANA)
Humphrey Bldg. Rm. 615 F, 200 Independence Ave., SW
Washington, DC 20201 (202) 690-7000; (202) 690-7776
 Stacey Ecoffey, Principal Advisor for Tribal Affairs,
 Office of Intergovernmental & External Affairs
 E-mail: Stacey.ecoffey@hhs.gov
Intra-Departmental Council on Indian Affairs (202) 690-6546
American Indian, Alaskan Native & Native Hawaiian Programs
330 Independence Ave., SW • Washington, DC 20201
(202) 619-2957 or 619-0641
Indian Health Service, Room 5A-55, Parklawn Bldg.
5600 Fishers Lane • Rockville, MD 20857 (301) 443-1083

Head Start Bureau, American Indian Program Branch
Room 2116, 330 C St., SW, Washington, DC 20202 (202) 205-8457

U.S. Department of Homeland Security (DHS)
 David Munro, Director – Tribal Government Affairs
 E-mail: david.munro@hq.dhs.gov

U.S. Dept. of Housing & Urban Development (HUD)
Office of Native American Programs (ONAP)
1999 Broadway, Suite 3390 • Denver, CO 80202

(303) 675-1600 Fax 675-1660
Heidi J. Frechette, Deputy Assistant Secretary for native American Programs
E-mail: Heidi.j.freshette@hud.gov
Native American Home Loans Section 184 K Program: Eligible for all registered tribal members regardless of degree of Indian blood. To assist Native American Indians as well as Alaska Native families get financing to buy homes in Native American societies. Native American borrowers that qualify for section 184 mortgages could buy a home with low down payment, no monthly mortgage assurance and flexible underwriting.

U.S. Dept. of the Interior-National Park Service
American Indian Liaison Office
1849 C St., NW, Rm. 3410 • Washington, DC 20240
(202) 208-5475/5476

U.S. Department of Justice - Office of Tribal Justice (OTJ)
950 Pennsylvania Ave., NW • Washington, DC 20530
(202) 514-8812 Fax 514-9078
Website: www.justice.gov/otj; E-mail: otj@usdoj.gov
Tracy Toulou (Colville), Director
Gina Allery (Anishinnabe), Deputy Director
Marcia Good, Senior Counsel to the Director
Joshua Ederheimer, Senior Advisor
Jeanne Jacobs, Chief of Staff
Dawn S. Baum (Mole Lake Chippewa/Menominee), Attorney Advisor
Environment & Natural Resources Division
Indian Claims Section & Indian Resources Section
(202) 514-2701 Fax 514-0557
The OTJ is the primary point of contact for the Dept. of Justice with federally recognized Native American tribes, and advises the Department on legal & policy matters pertaining to Native Americans. The mission of the Office of Tribal Justice (OTJ) shall be to provide a principal point of contact within the Department of Justice to listen to the concerns of Indian Tribes and to communicate the Department's policies to the Tribes and the public; to promote internal uniformity of Department of Justice policies and litigation positions relating to Indian county; and to coordinate with other Federal agencies and with State and local governments on their initiatives in Indian country.

U.S. Department of Labor
Division of Indian & Native American Programs
Employment & Training Administration
200 Constitution Ave., NW • Washington, DC 20210
(202) 693-4650 Fax 693-4674
Tom Dowd, Deputy Director – Office of Federal Contract
Compliance Programs; E-mail: dowd.tom@dol.gov
Athena Brown, Program Chief – Division of Indian & Native American Programs – Employment & Training Administration
E-mail: brown.athena@dol.gov

U.S. Department of Transportation
400 7th St., SW • Washington, DC 20590 (202) 366-1111
American Indian Nations, National Highway Traffic Safety Administration
(817) 334-4300
Robert W. Sparrow, Jr., Designated Federal Official, Tribal Transportation
Self-Governance Program; E-mail: Robert.sparrow@dot.gov

U.S. Department of Treasury
William G. Norton, Senior Advisor on Tribal Affairs
Point of Contact for Tribal Consultation
E-mail: William.norton@treasury.gov

Department of Veterans Affairs (VA)
Stephanie Birdwell, Director – Office of Tribal Government Relations
E-mail: Stephanie.birdwell@va.gov

LEGISLATIVE BRANCH - U.S. CONGRESS - SENATE

U.S. Senate Committee on Indian Affairs
838 Hart Office Bldg. • Washington, DC 20510
(202) 224-2251 Fax 228-2589 (Repub), 224-5429 (Dem.)
Website: www.indian.senate.gov
John Barrasco (WY-R), Majority Chairperson
Jon Tester (WY-D), Minority Chairperson
Mike Andrews, Majority Staff Director & Chief Counsel
Rhonda Harjo, Majority Deputy Chief Counsel
Brandon Ashley, Majority Senior Policy Advisor
Jacqueline Bisille, Majority Policy Advisor
Emily Newman & John Simermeyer, Majority Counselors

Anthony Walters, Minority Staff Director & Chief Counsel
Jake Schellinger, Minority Counsel
Jim Eismeier, Administrator Director
David Stuart, Director of Information Technology
Committee members:
Republicans: John Barrasso (WY); John McCain (AZ); Lisa Murkowski (AK); John Hoeven (ND); Michael Crapo (ID); James Lankkford (OK); Steve Daines (MT); Jerry Moran (KS)
Democrats: Jon Tester (MT); Heidi Heitkamp (ND); Al Franken (MN); Tom Udall (NM); Brian Schatz (HI); Maria Cantwell (WA)

HOUSE OF REPRESENTATIVES

House Subcommittee on Indian & Alaska Native Affairs
1522 Longworth House Office Bldg.
New Jersey & Independence Ave., SE • Washington, DC 20515
(202) 226-7736 Fax 226-0522; House Native American Caucus
Republicans: Don Young (AK), Chairperson; Dan Benishek (MI); Paul Gosar (AZ); Doug LaMalfa (CA); Jeff Denham (CA); Paul Cook (CA); Amata Coleman Radweagen, Vice Chair (American Somoa, At-Large)
Democrats: Raul Ruiz (CA), Ranking Member; Madeleine Bordallo (Guam), At-Large; Gregorio Sablan (Northern Mariana Islands); Pedro Pierluisi (Puerto Rico), At-Large; Norma Torres (CA); Raul Grijalva (AZ)

OFFICE OF INDIAN AFFAIRS - REGIONAL OFFICES

ALASKA REGIONAL OFFICE
Bureau of Indian Affairs, 3601 C St., Suite 1100
ANCHORAGE, AK 99503-5947
(800) 645-8465; (907) 271-1828 Fax 271-1349
Kathy Cline, Acting Regional Director; E-mail: kathy.cline@bia.gov
Except for the Annette Island Reserve, which falls under the Northwest Region, the entire state of Alaska falls under the Alaska Region. The nearly 80,000 tribal members that make up the 229 tribes under the Alaska Region jurisdiction stretch from Ketchikan in the Southeast Panhandle to Barrow on the Arctic Ocean and from Eagle on the Yukon Territory border to Atka in the Aleutian Island Chain. *Activities*: Annual BIA Tribal Providers Conference.

EASTERN OKLAHOMA REGIONAL OFFICE
Bureau of Indian Affairs, 3100 W. Peak Blvd.
P.O. Box 8002 • MUSKOGEE, OK 74401
(918) 781-4608 Fax 781-4604
Eddie Streater, Acting Regional Director
E-mail: eddie.streater@bia.gov
Jessie Durham, Deputy Regional Director

EASTERN REGIONAL OFFICE
Bureau of Indian Affairs
545 Marriott Dr., #700 • NASHVILLE, TN 37214
(615) 564-6500 Fax 564-6701
E-mail: eastern.inquiries@bia.gov
Bruce Maytubby, Regional Director
Johnna Blackhair, Deputy Regional Director, Trust Services
Serves as the representative for the Director, with the responsibility to work toward strengthening intergovernmental assistance to all the federally recognized tribes under the jurisdiction of the Eastern Regional Office. The Eastern Region has a Deputy Regional Director who works directly under the Regional Director.

GREAT PLAINS REGIONAL OFFICE
Bureau of Indian Affairs, 115 4th Ave., SE • ABERDEEN, SD 57401
(888) 703-5487; (605) 226-7343 Fax 226-7446
Timothy L. LaPointe, Regional Director
E-mail: timothy.lapointe@bia.gov
Danelle Daugherty, Deputy Regional Director - Indian Services
E-mail: ddaugherty@bia.gov
Provides program direction and supervision to 12 Agencies encompassing 16 federally recognized Tribes. The Great Plains Regional Director is responsible for the direction & oversight of Bureau responsibilities & activities as they pertain to the mission and goals of the Department of Interior and the Bureau of Indian Affairs. This includes the protection of trust assets through effective natural resources management & strengthening tribal governments while enhancing economic development & protecting & preserving tribal sovereignty to enhancing the quality of life standards throughout the communities we serve. The Great Plains Region is under the direction of the Regional Director, who reports to the Director, Bureau of Indian Affairs, through the Deputy Bureau Director, Field Operations. The Office of the Regional Director provides program direction & supervision to 12 Agencies encompassing 16 federally recognized Tribes.

MIDWEST REGIONAL OFFICE

Bureau of Indian Affairs, Norman Pointe II Bldg.
5600 W. American Blvd., Suite 500 • BLOOMINGTON, MN 55347
  (612) 713-4400 Fax 713-4401
  Scott Sufficool, Acting Regional Director
  E-mail: scott.sufficool@bia.gov
Serves 35 tribal governments & reservations and has a jurisdiction that covers approximately 4.6 million acres located within the states of Iowa, Michigan, Minnesota and Wisconsin. There are also three agencies and one agency/field office within the region that are, the Michigan Agency located in Sault Ste. Marie, Michigan; the Minnesota Agency located in Bemidji, Minnesota; and the Great Lakes Agency located in Ashland, Wisconsin. The agency/field office is the Red Lake Agency located in Red Lake, Minnesota. Of these, the Great Lakes, Minnesota & Michigan agencies are multi-tribe agencies while the Red Lake Agency serves only the Red Lake Tribe and Red Lake Reservation. In addition to the agencies and the agency/field office, seven tribes are provided direct services by the Regional Office.

NAVAJO REGIONAL OFFICE

Bureau of Indian Affairs, P.O. Box 1060 • GALLUP, NM 87305
  (505) 863-8314 Fax 863-8324
  Sharon A. Pinto, Regional Director; E-mail: Sharon.pinto@bia.gov
  Pearl Chamberlin, Acting Deputy Regional Director-Trust Services
  E-mail: pchamberlin@bia.gov
Mission: To enhance the quality of life, facilitate economic opportunity, carry out the responsibility to protect & improve the trust assets of the Navajo Nation and individual Indians. The Office is committed to provide high quality services to our customers in a timely and professional manner; to have a challenging and dynamic organization that is flexible in addressing the changing needs of our customers; to have employees who are committed, knowledgeable and empowered; to strive for excellence while fostering cooperation, coordination, and consultation in support of Indian self-determination and tribal sovereignty.

NORTHWEST REGIONAL OFFICE

Bureau of Indian Affairs, 911 NE 11th Ave. • PORTLAND, OR 97232
  (503) 231-6702 Fax 231-6791
  Stanley M. Speaks, Regional Director; E-mail: Stanley.speaks@bia.gov
  Twyla Stange, Deputy Regional Director, Indian Services
  E-mail: tstange@bia.gov
  Bodie Shaw, Deputy Regional Director, Trust Services
Has jurisdiction over 15 agencies & field stations located in the states of Washington, Oregon, Idaho, Montana, and southeastern Alaska. There are approximately 94,150 Indian people 45 federally recognized tribes living on or near reservations, which exceed five million acres in total size.

PACIFIC REGIONAL OFFICE

Bureau of Indian Affairs, 2800 Cottage Way • SACRAMENTO, CA 95825
  (916) 978-6000 Fax 978-6099
  Amy Dutschke, Regional Director; E-mail: amy.dutschke@bia.gov
  Kevin Bearquiver, Deputy Regional Director, Trust Services
  E-mail: kevin.bearquiver@bia.gov
  Dale Risling, Deputy Regional Director, Indian Services
  E-mail: dale.risling@bia.gov
Mission: To work toward strengthening intergovernmental assistance to the 104 Federally recognized Tribes in the Region's service area and improving interagency & intergovernmental cooperation & coordination within the Region. The Pacific Regional Office is under the direction of the Regional Director who is responsible to the Director, (BIA), for all non-education related Bureau programs, functions, & activities assigned to the Region. The Regional Director represents the Bureau in dealings with other governmental entities & serves as the representative of the Director, (BIA), with responsibility to work toward strengthening intergovernmental assistance to the 104 Federally recognized Tribes in the Region's service area and improving interagency and intergovernmental cooperation and coordination within the Region. The Office of the Regional Director provides program direction & supervision to four agencies responsible for formulation and promulgating Region applications of national policies; for monitoring and evaluating operating programs and offices to ensure program effectiveness, efficiency, and conformance with established policies; & for obtaining adequate technical advice and assistance to support field operations.

ROCKY MOUNTAIN REGIONAL OFFICE

Bureau of Indian Affairs, 2021 4th Ave. North • BILLINGS, MT 59101
  (406) 247-7943 Fax 247-7976
  Darryl LaCounte, Regional Director; E-mail: darryl.lacounte@bia.gov
  John Anevski, Acting Deputy Regional Director, Indian Services
  Email: john.anevski@bia.gov
The Rocky Mountain Regional Office (RMRO) is under the direction of the Regional Director, who is responsible to the Director, Bureau of Indian Affairs, through the Deputy Bureau Director, Field Operations. The Regional Director represents the RMRO in dealing with other governmental and tribal entities.

The RMRO's mission is to provide services to American Indian Tribes, Individual American Indians and other Agencies, effectively managing and protecting the Trust Resources, enhancing the quality of life and supporting Tribal Sovereignty, while actively promoting Self-Determination, and Economic Development opportunities.

SOUTHERN PLAINS REGIONAL OFFICE

Bureau of Indian Affairs, W.C.D. Office Complex
P.O. Box 368 • ANADARKO, OK 73005
  (405) 247-6673 Fax 247-5611
  Dan Deerinwater, Regional Director
  E-mail: dan.deerinwater@bia.gov
  Terry Bruner, Deputy Regional Director, Indian Services
  E-mail: terry.bruner@bia.gov
  Bruce Maytubby, Deputy Regional Director, Trust Services
  E-mail: bruce.maytubby@bia.gov
The Southern Plains Region is under the direction of the Regional Director, who is responsible to the Director, Bureau of Indian Affairs, through the Deputy Bureau Director, Field Operations. The Regional Director represents the Southern Plains Region in dealing with other governmental entities and tribal entities. The Regional Director serves as the representative for the Director of the Bureau of Indian Affairs with the responsibility to work toward strengthening intergovernmental assistance to all the Federally recognized tribes under the jurisdiction of the Southern Plains Regional Office. The Southern Plains Region has two (2) Deputy Regional Directors, who work directly under the Regional Director.

SOUTHWEST REGIONAL OFFICE

Bureau of Indian Affairs
1001 Indian School Rd., NW • ALBUQUERQUE, NM 87125
  (505) 563-3103 Fax 563-3101
  William T. Walker, Regional Director; E-mail: William.walker@bia.gov
  Gregory Mehojah, Deputy Regional Director, Indian & Trust Services
  Email: gregory.mehojah@bia.gov
The Southwest Region is under the direction of the Regional Director, who is responsible to the Director, Bureau of Indian Affairs, through the Deputy Bureau Director, Field Operations. The Regional Director represents the Southwest Region in dealing with other governmental entities & tribal entities. The Regional Director serves as the representative for the Secretary of the Interior with the responsibility to work toward strengthening intergovernmental assistance to all the Federally recognized tribes under the jurisdiction of the Southwest Regional Office. The Southwest Region has one Deputy Regional Director, who works directly under the Regional Director.

WESTERN REGIONAL OFFICE

Bureau of Indian Affairs
2600 N. Central Ave., 4th Fl. • PHOENIX, AZ 85004
  (602) 379-6789 Fax 379-3168
  Bryan Bowker, Regional Director; E-mail: bryan.bowker@bia.gov
  Carolyn Richards, Acting Deputy Regional Director, Indian Services
  E-mail: Carolyn.richards@bia.gov
  Rodney McVey, Acting Deputy Regional Director, Trust Services
  E-mail: rodney.mcvey@bia.gov
Serves approximately 143,000 American Indian people enrolled in 42 tribes. It is responsible for 12,950,000 acres primarily in the states of Arizona (excluding the Navajo Region), Nevada & Utah. Portions are also in California, Oregon and Idaho. Thirteen Indian agencies & Irrigation Project are Western Regional Office partners. Region's tribes include the O'odham, Yaqui, Yuman and Pai Tribes of Arizona's low and mid deserts and Grand Canyon, Apache of the mid-deserts & mountain forests. The Hopi live on Arizona's Colorado Plateau mesas. Nevada has many bands & tribes of Shoshone & Paiute people. The many tribes & bands of Ute people inspired the state of Utah's name.

STATE AGENCY OFFICES

ALASKA

FAIRBANKS AGENCY

Bureau of Indian Affairs, 101 12th Ave., Rm. 166 • FAIRBANKS, AK 99701
  (800) 822-3596; (907) 456-0222 Fax 456-0225
  Kathy Cline, Superintendent; E-mail: kathy.cline@bia.gov

JUNEAU OFFICE

Bureau of Indian Affairs
P.O. Box 21647, 709 West 9th St. • ANCHORAGE, AK 99802
  (800) 645-8397; (907) 586-7177 Fax 586-7252

METLAKATLA AGENCY

Bureau of Indian Affairs, P.O. Box 450 • METLAKATLA, AK 99926
  (907) 886-3791 Fax 886-7738

ARIZONA

CHINLE AGENCY
Bureau of Indian Affairs, Navajo Rt. 7, Bldg. 136-C
P.O. Box 7H • CHINLE, AZ 86503
  (928) 674-5100 Fax 674-5112
  Sharon Pinto, Regional Director; E-mail: Sharon.pinto@bia.gov
Serves the Navajo people within the central region of the Navajo Nation. CNA has a total population of 27,823. CNA has a total of 1,363,423 acres. The Chinle Navajo Agency (CNA) provides quality services to the Navajo Indian people within the central region of the Navajo Nation. The central region is in the State of Arizona. The Chinle Agency is comprised of both Indian and Trust services programs. The Agency Trust services programs are: Natural Resources and Real Estate Services. Trust services programs are under the general supervision of the Regional Program Divisions, whom report to the Deputy Regional Director, Trust Services. The Indian services programs are Transportation and Safety programs which are under the general supervision of the Regional Program Divisions, whom report to the Deputy Regional Director, Indian Services. The Agency Office is located in Chinle, Arizona.

FORT DEFIANCE AGENCY
Bureau of Indian Affairs, Blue Canyon Rd., BIA Bldg. #40
P.O. Box 7H • FORT DEFIANCE, AZ 86504
  (928) 729-7218 Fax 729-7213
  Sharon Pinto, Regional Director; E-mail: Sharon.pinto@bia.gov
Serves the Navajo Indian people within the southern region of Navajo Nation. According to the 2010 U.S. Census, FDA has a total population of 43,138. FDA has a total of 3,211,317 acres. The Fort Defiance Agency (FDA) provides quality services to the Navajo Indian people within the southern region of the Navajo Nation. The southern region is comprised of the States of Arizona and New Mexico. The Fort Defiance Agency provides both Indian and Trust services programs. The Agency Trust services programs are: Natural Resources and Real Estate Services. Trust services programs are under the general supervision of the Regional Program Divisions, whom report to the Deputy Regional Director, Trust Services. The Indian services programs are Transportation and Safety programs and are under the general supervision of the Regional Program Divisions, whom report to the Deputy Regional Director, Indian Services. The Agency Office is located in Fort Defiance, Arizona.

HOPI AGENCY
Bureau of Indian Affairs
100 Main St., P.O. Box 158 • KEAMS CANYON, AZ 86034
  (928) 738-2228 Fax 738-5522
  Wendell Honanie, Supt.; E-mail: wendell.honanie@bia.gov
Serves the Hopi Tribe (928) 734-3100.

COLORADO RIVER AGENCY
Bureau of Indian Affairs, 12124 - 1st Ave. • PARKER, AZ 85344
  (928) 669-7111 Fax 669-7187
  Kellie Youngbear, Supt.; E-mail: kellie.youngbear@bia.gov
Serves Chemehuevi, Colorado River & Ft Mojave Tribes.

PIMA AGENCY
Bureau of Indian Affairs
104 N. Main St., P.O. Box 8 • SACATON, AZ 85247
  (520) 562-3326 Fax 562-3543
  Cecilia Martinez, Supt.; E-mail: cecilia.martinez@bia.gov
Serves the Ak Chin Indian Community and the Gila River Indian Community.

SAN CARLOS AGENCY
Bureau of Indian Affairs, P.O. Box 209 • SAN CARLOS, AZ 85550
  (928) 475-2321 Fax 475-2783
Serves the San Carlos Apache Reservation.

SALT RIVER AGENCY
Bureau of Indian Affairs
10000 E. McDowell Rd. • SCOTTSDALE, AZ 85256
  (480) 421-0807 Fax 421-0808
  George Patton, Supt.; E-mail: george.patton@bia.gov
Serves the Fort McDowell Yavapai Tribe, the Pascua Yaqui Tribe, and the Salt River Pima-Maricopa Indian Community.

PAPAGO AGENCY
Bureau of Indian Affairs, P.O. Box 490 • SELLS, AZ 85634
  (520) 383-3286 Fax 383-2087
  Nina Siquieros, Supt.; E-mail: nina.siquieros@bia.gov
Serves the Tohono O'odham Nation.

WESTERN NAVAJO AGENCY
Bureau of Indian Affairs, East Hwy. 160 & Warrior Dr.
P.O. Box 127 • TUBA CITY, AZ 86045
  (928) 283-2252 Fax 283-2215
  Sharon Pinto, Regional Director; E-mail: Sharon.pinto@bia.gov
Serves the Navajo Indian people within the western region of Navajo Nation. The Western Navajo Agency (WNA) provides quality services to the Navajo Indian people within the western region of the Navajo Nation. The western region encompasses Utah & Arizona. The Western Navajo Agency is comprised of both Indian & Trust services programs. The Agency Trust services programs are: Natural Resources and Real Estate Services. Trust services programs are under the general supervision of the Regional Program Divisions, whom report to the Deputy Regional Director, Trust Services. The Indian services programs are Transportation & Safety programs and are under the general supervision of the Regional Program Divisions, whom report to the Deputy Regional Director, Indian Services.

TRUXTON CANON AGENCY
Bureau of Indian Affairs, P.O. Box 37 • VALENTINE, AZ 86434
  (928) 769-2286 Fax 769-2444
  James Williams, Supt.; E-mail: james.williams@bia.gov
Tribes served: Havasupai, Hualapai, Tonto Apache, Yavapai-Apache, and Yavapai-Prescott.

FORT APACHE AGENCY
Bureau of Indian Affairs, P.O. Box 560 • WHITERIVER, AZ 85941
  (928) 338-5303 Fax 338-5383
  Nona Tuchawena, Supt.; E-mail: nona.tuchawena@bia.gov
Serves the White Mountain Apache Tribe (928) 338-5353.

FORT YUMA AGENCY
Bureau of Indian Affairs, 256 South 2nd Ave., Suite D • YUMA, AZ 85366
  (928) 782-1202 Fax 782-1266
  Irene Herder, Supt.; E-mail: Irene.herder@bia.gov
Serves the Cocopah & Quechan Tribes.

CALIFORNIA

PALM SPRINGS AGENCY
Bureau of Indian Affairs, 3700A Tachevah Dr., Suite 201
P.O. Box 2245 • PALM SPRINGS, CA 92262
  (760) 416-2133 Fax 416-2687
  Ollie Beyal, Supt.; E-mail: Ollie.beyal@bia.gov
Serves the Agua Caliente Tribe.

NORTHERN CALIFORNIA AGENCY
Bureau of Indian Affairs
364 Knollcrest Dr., Suite 105 • REDDING, CA 96002
  (530) 223-7960 Fax 223-5167
Serves the Indian communities within a seven county area of No. California.

SOUTHERN CALIFORNIA AGENCY
Bureau of Indian Affairs
1451 Research Park Dr. #100 • RIVERSIDE, CA 92507
  (951) 276-6624 Fax 276-6642
  Robert Eben, Supt.; E-mail: robert.eben@bia.gov
Serves the Indian communities within a four county area of So. California.

CENTRAL CALIFORNIA AGENCY
Bureau of Indian Affairs
650 Capital Mall, Suite 8-500 • SACRAMENTO, CA 95815
  (916) 930-3680 Fax 930-3780
  Troy Burdick, Supt.; E-mail: troy.burdick@bia.gov
Serves the Indian communities of the 21 county area of Central California.

COLORADO

SOUTHERN UTE AGENCY
Bureau of Indian Affairs, P.O. Box 315 • IGNACIO 81137
  (970) 563-4511 Fax 563-9321
  Priscilla Bancroft, Supt.; E-mail: Priscilla.bancroft@bia.gov
Serves the Southern Ute Tribe with approximately 1,375 members.

UTE MOUNTAIN UTE AGENCY
Bureau of Indian Affairs, 440 Sunset Blvd., Phillip Coyote Memorial Hall
P.O. Box KK • TOWAOC, CO 81334
  (970) 565-8473 Fax 565-8906
  Priscilla Bancroft, Supt.; E-mail: priscilla.bancroft@bia.gov
Serves the Ute Mountain Ute Tribe; approximately 2,000 members.

FLORIDA

SEMINOLE AGENCY
Bureau of Indian Affairs
6100 Hollywood Blvd., #206 • HOLLYWOOD, FL 33024
(954) 983-1537 Fax 983-5018; E-mail: eastern.inquiries@bia.gov
Serves the Seminole Nation of Florida and the Miccosukee Tribe.

IDAHO

FORT HALL AGENCY
Bureau of Indian Affairs, P.O. Box 220 • FORT HALL, ID 83203
(208) 238-2301 Fax 237-0466
Randy Thompson, Supt.; E-mail: randy.thompson@bia.gov
Serves the Shoshone-Bannock Tribes of the Fort Hall Reservation,
and the Northwest Band of Shoshone Nation of Utah (Washakie).

NORTHERN IDAHO AGENCY
Bureau of Indian Affairs, P.O. Box 277 • LAPWAI, ID 83540
(208) 843-9410 Fax 843-9440
Serves the Kootenai Tribe of Idaho and the Nez Perce Tribe.

COEUR D'ALENE AGENCY
925 A St., P.O. Box 287 • PLUMMER, ID 83851
(208) 686-1887 Fax 686-1903. Serves the Coeur d'Alene Tribe.

KANSAS

HORTON AGENCY
Bureau of Indian Affairs, P.O. Box 31 • HORTON 66439
(785) 486-2161 Fax 486-2515
Antoinette G. Houle, Supt.; E-mail: antoinette.houle@bia.gov
Serves the Iowa, Kickapoo of Kansas, Prairie Band Potawatomi
and the Sac & Fox Tribe of Missouri.

MICHIGAN

MICHIGAN AGENCY
Bureau of Indian Affairs, 2845 Ashmun St. • SAULT STE. MARIE, MI 49783
(906) 632-6809 Fax 632-0689
Jason D. Oberle, Supt.; E-mail: jason.oberle@bia.gov
Serves the Federally recognized Michigan & Indiana tribes.
The Michigan Agency of the Bureau of Indian Affairs is located in the city of
Sault Ste. Marie, Michigan. The Agency Office is headed by the Supt. who
reports to the Midwest Regional Director. The Superintendent is the leader of
the work groups that provide advice on administrative and program matters.
The work groups also advise and assist the federally recognized Michigan
tribes. The Michigan Agency serves tribal governments, tribal organizations
and reservations located within the states of Michigan and Indiana.

MINNESOTA

MINNESOTA AGENCY
Bureau of Indian Affairs, Federal Bldg., Rm. 418
522 Minnesota Ave., NW • BEMIDJI, MN 56601
(218) 751-2011 Fax 751-4367
Patricia Olby, Supt.; E-mail: patty.olby@bia.gov
Teresa Estes, Deputy Supt. – Trust Services
E-mail: teresa.estes@bia.gov
Serves the Minnesota Chippewa Tribe, and its six member Bands: Bois Forte,
Fond du Lac, Grand Portage, Leech Lake, White Earth, and Mille Lacs, located
in the northern & central regions of Minnesota. The Minnesota Agency serves
as the headquarters from which the Bureau's responsibility to Federally
recognized tribes are carried out. The Agency has primary & full responsibility
for the government-to-government relationship to the Minnesota Chippewa
Tribe, and its six member Bands (Bois Forte, Fond du Lac, Grand Portage,
Leech Lake, White Earth, and Mille Lacs), which are located in the northern
and central regions of Minnesota. The Office of the Superintendent is charged
with the authority and responsibility for the daily management of the varied
programs & inherent federal responsibilities associated with the management
of Agency resources. The office provides overall program planning; staffing;
execution & coordination of Bureau programs administered on behalf of the six
Federally recognized tribes within its jurisdiction. Assistance is provided to
tribes in contract administration, real estate services, forest management, tribal
government, program administration, self-determination/self-governance
services, road construction, delivery of direct services and fulfillment of the
Federal Government's trust responsibilities.

RED LAKE AGENCY/FIELD OFFICE
Bureau of Indian Affairs, c/o Red Lake Dept. of Natural Resources (DNR)
P.O. Box 279, Red Lake, MN 56671
(218) 679-3341 Fax 679-3378
Located in North-Central Minnesota, the Red Lake Reservation is home to the
Red Lake Band of Chippewa Indians. In January 1997, the Red Lake tribe
entered into a self-governance compact with the federal government thereby
allowing the Red Lake tribe to manage certain trust and Indian services
programs previously being managed by the BIA. One of these trust programs,
Forestry, was included in the compact that allowed for management of the
program by the tribe. As such, one "residual" Forestry position was
established at Red Lake to oversee the governments trust responsibility to the
tribe, and this Forester position still exists today at the Red Lake Agency.

MISSISSIPPI

CHOCTAW AGENCY
Bureau of Indian Affairs, 421 Powell St. • PHILADELPHIA, MS 39350
(601) 656-1521 Fax 656-2350
Rheta Harjo, Superintendent
Serves the Mississippi Band of Choctaw Indians.

MONTANA

ROCKY BOY'S FIELD OFFICE
Bureau of Indian Affairs, RR 1, Box 542 • BOX ELDER, MT 59521
(406) 395-4476 Fax 395-4382
Mamie Charette, Field Rep.; E-mail: mamie.charette@bia.gov
Serves the Chippewa Cree Reservation located in north central Montana
near Havre, Montana. The agency provides direct services in the Executive
Direction area only with one field representative on site to administer the
residual federal functions.

BLACKFEET AGENCY
Bureau of Indian Affairs
531 Boundary St., P.O. Box 880 • BROWNING, MT 59417
(406) 338-7544 Fax 338-2968
Thedis Crowe, Supt.; E-mail: thedis.crowe@bia.gov
Lisa R. Bullshoe, Fiduciary Trust Officer (338-4358)
Serves the Blackfeet Reservation located in north central Montana
with approximately 16,000 enrolled tribal members. The agency provides direct
services in the following program areas: Executive Direction & Administration,
Facilities Management, Social Services, Agriculture, Forestry, Trust Services,
Probate, Irrigation, Lease Compliance, Dam Maintenance & Real Estate
Services.

CROW AGENCY
Bureau of Indian Affairs
Weaver Dr., BIA Bldg. #2, P.O. Box 69 • CROW AGENCY, MT 59022
(406) 638-2672 Fax 638-2380
Vianna M. Stewart, Supt.; E-mail: vianna.stewart@bia.gov
Serves the Crow Reservation located in southeastern Montana
with approximately 12,000 enrolled tribal members. The agency provides direct
services in the following program areas: Executive Direction & Administration,
Facilities Management, Social Services, Agriculture, Forestry, Trust Services,
Probate, Irrigation, Real Estate Services, Wildland Fire Preparedness &
Suppression and Other Aid to Tribal Government.

FORT BELKNAP AGENCY
Bureau of Indian Affairs, 158 Tribal Way, Suite B • HARLEM, MT 59526
(406) 353-2901 Fax 353-4206
Susan Messerly, Supt.; E-mail: susan.messerly@bia.gov
Serves the Fort Belknap Reservation located in north central Montana near
Havre, Montana with approximately 6,500 Gros Ventre & Assiniboine enrolled
tribal members. The agency provides direct services in the following program
areas: Executive Direction & Administration, Facilities Management,
Agriculture, Forestry, Trust Services, Probate, Irrigation, & Real Estate
Services.

NORTHERN CHEYENNE AGENCY
Bureau of Indian Affairs, P.O. Box 40 • LAME DEER, MT 59043
(406) 477-8242 Fax 477-6636
Michael Addy, Supt.; E-mail: Michael.addy@bia.gov
Serves the Northern Cheyenne Reservation with approximately 9,300 enrolled
tribal members. The agency provides direct services in the following program
areas: Executive Direction & Administration, Facilities Management, Social
Services, Natural Resources, Agriculture, Rights Protection, Trust Services,
Probate, and Real Estate Services.

FLATHEAD AGENCY
Bureau of Indian Affairs, P.O. Box 40 • PABLO, MT 59855
  (406) 675-2700 Fax 675-2805
  Ernest "Bud" Moran, Supt.
Serves the Confederated Salish & Kootenai Tribes.

FORT PECK AGENCY
Bureau of Indian Affairs, P.O. Box 637 • POPLAR, MT 59255
  (406) 768-5312 Fax 768-3405
  Howard Bemer, Supt.; E-mail: howard.bemer@bia.gov
Serves the Fort Peck Reservation located in northeastern Montana near Wolfpoint, MT, with about 12,000 Assiniboine & Sioux enrolled tribal members. The agency provides direct services in the following program areas: Executive Direction & Administration, Facilities Management, Social Services, Trust Services, Probate, Irrigation, Real Estate Appraisals, Tribal Management & Development and Real Estate Services.

NEBRASKA

WINNEBAGO AGENCY
Bureau of Indian Affairs, P.O. Box 18 • WINNEBAGO, NE 68071
  (402) 878-2502 Fax 878-2943; Ernest F. Pourier, Acting Supt.
Serves the Omaha Tribe of Nebraska (5,450 members); Santee Sioux Nation (2,665 members); and the Winnebago Tribe of Nebraska (4,200 members). The Winnebago Agency is located in Winnebago, Nebraska in the Northeast corner of Nebraska that is 20 miles south of Sioux City, IA and 80 miles north of Omaha, NE. The Agency serves the Omaha, Santee Sioux Nation and Winnebago Tribes. Winnebago Agency does recognize Tribal sovereignty, efforts to achieve self-determination and self-sufficiency but also recognizes our Trust responsibility to protect and preserve tribal resources. Total trust acreage at Winnebago Agency is over 65,000 & 700 leases being processed. These 700 leases attribute to $3,000,000 being paid to our beneficiaries. Winnebago Agency Fire Program received a National Award-Hazardous Fuel Treatment Program. The Agency provides services to the Omaha Tribe of Nebraska with a reservation population of 2476 Tribal members. Enrolled in the Omaha Tribe are over 5427 members with trust acreage of 27,828. Santee Sioux Tribe of Nebraska with a reservation population of 670 Tribal members. Enrolled in the Santee Sioux Tribe are over 2662 members, and total trust acreage on the reservation of 10,198. The Winnebago Tribe of Nebraska has a service population of 1637 people and 4192 Tribal enrolled members. Total Trust Acreage is 27,637 acres.

NEVADA

WESTERN NEVADA AGENCY
Bureau of Indian Affairs
311 E. Washington St. • CARSON CITY, NV 89701
  (775) 887-3500 Fax 887-3531
Serves the Indian tribes in Western Nevada.

EASTERN NEVADA AGENCY
Bureau of Indian Affairs, 1555 Shoshone Circle • ELKO, NV 89801
  (775) 738-5165 Fax 738-4710
  Joseph McDade, Supt.; E-mail: joseph.mcdade@bia.gov
Serves the tribes in Eastern Nevada.

NEW MEXICO

SOUTHERN PUEBLOS AGENCY
Bureau of Indian Affairs, 1001 Indian School Rd., NW
P.O. Box 26567 • ALBUQUERQUE, NM 87125
  (505) 563-3600 Fax 563-3068
  John Antonio, Supt.; E-mail: john.antonio@bia.gov
Serves the following ten Federally recognized tribes: Pueblo of Acoma, Pueblo of Cochiti, Pueblo of Isleta, Pueblo of Jemez, Pueblo of San Felipe, Pueblo of Sandia, Pueblo of Santa Ana, Pueblo of Santo Domingo, Ysleta del Sur Pueblo, and Pueblo of Zia. A total population of about 26,350 members.

EASTERN NAVAJO AGENCY
Bureau of Indian Affairs, Chaco Blvd. & Code Talker, Bldg. #222
P.O. Box 328 • CROWNPOINT, NM 87313
  (505) 786-6032 Fax 786-6111
  Lester Tsosie, Supt.; E-mail: lester.tsosie@bia.gov
Serves the Navajo Indian people within the eastern region of the Navajo Nation. According to the 2010 U.S. Census, ENA has a total population of 33,216. ENA has a total of 1,039,210 acre. *Service programs*: Transportation & Safety. *Trust services*: Natural Resources, Real Estate, and Probate & Real Estate.

JICARILLA AGENCY
Bureau of Indian Affairs, P.O. Box 167 • DULCE, NM 87528
  (575) 759-3951 Fax 759-3948
Serves the Jicarilla Apache Nation with approximately 3,400 members.

NORTHERN PUEBLOS AGENCY
Bureau of Indian Affairs, P.O. Box 4269 • ESPANOLA, NM 87533
  (505) 753-1400 Fax 753-1404
  Raymond Fry, Superintendent; E-mail: raymond.fry@bia.gov
Serves six Federally recognized tribes: Pueblo of Nambe, Pueblo of Pojoaque, Pueblo of San Ildefonso, Ohkay Owingeh, Pueblo of Santa Clara; also, two Self-Governance tribes: Pueblo Taos, & Pueblo Tesuque, 10,300 members.

LAGUNA AGENCY
Bureau of Indian Affairs, P.O. Box 1448 • LAGUNA, NM 87026
  (505) 552-6001 Fax 552-7497
  Marianna Begay, Administrator
Serves the Pueblo of Laguna with approximately 7,825 members.

MESCALERO AGENCY
Bureau of Indian Affairs
590 Sage Ave., P.O. Box 189 • MESCALERO, NM 88340
  (575) 464-4423 Fax 464-4215
  Charles Riley, Supt.; E-mail: charles.riley@bia.gov
Serves the Mescalero Apache Tribe with approximately 4,000 members.

RAMAH-NAVAJO AGENCY
Bureau of Indian Affairs, HC-61, Box 14 • RAMAH, NM 87321
  (505) 775-3235 Fax 775-3387
  Eileen Garcia, Acting Supt.; E-mail: eileen.garcia@bia.gov
Serves the Ramah Navajo Chapter of the Navajo Nation with 2,500 members.

SHIPROCK AGENCY
Bureau of Indian Affairs, Nataani Nez Complex Bldg. 169, 2nd Fl.
North Hwy. 491, P.O. Box 3538 • SHIPROCK, NM 87420
  (505) 368-3300 Fax 368-3312
  Sharon Pinto, Regional Director; E-mail: Sharon.pinto@bia.gov
Serves Navajo Indian people within northeastern region of the Navajo Nation. The Shiprock Navajo Agency (SNA) provides quality services to the Navajo Indian people within the northeastern portion of the Navajo Nation. The northeastern portion encompasses the Four Corners Region that includes Utah, Arizona and New Mexico. Shiprock Navajo Agency is comprised of both Indian and Trust services programs. The Agency Trust services programs are: Natural Resources, Real Estate Services, and Probate and Estate Services. Trust services programs are under the general supervision of the Regional Program Divisions, whom report to the Deputy Regional Director, Trust Services. The Indian services programs are Transportation & Safety programs and are under the general supervision of the Regional Program Divisions, whom report to the Deputy Regional Director, Indian Services.

ZUNI AGENCY
Bureau of Indian Affairs
1203B State Hwy. 53, P.O. Box 369 • ZUNI, NM 87327
  (505) 782-7271 Fax 782-7229
  Clayton Seoutewa, Supt.; E-mail: clayton.seoutewa@bia.gov
Serves the Zuni tribe of approximately 8,430 members who reside on the reservation.

NORTH CAROLINA

CHEROKEE AGENCY
Bureau of Indian Affairs, Hwy. 441 North • CHEROKEE, NC 28719
  (828) 497-9131 Fax 497-6715
Serves the Eastern Band of Cherokee Nation and several New York Tribes, including Cayuga Nation, Oneida Nation, Seneca Nation of Indians, St. Regis Mohawk Tribe, Tonawanda Band of Seneca Indians, and Tuscarora Nation.

NORTH DAKOTA

TURTLE MOUNTAIN AGENCY
Bureau of Indian Affairs
BIA Road #7, P.O. Box 60 • BELCOURT, ND 58316
  (701) 477-3191 Fax 477-6628
  David "Mike" Kepln, Acting Supt.
Serves the Turtle Mountain Band of Chippewa with approximately 30,100 enrolled tribal members. The Turtle Mountain Agency is located in the community of Belcourt, North Dakota, which is geographically located in the far north central part of the State, approximately 10 miles southeast of the International Peace Garden. The land base of the reservation is entirely within

Rolette County, measuring 12 miles long by 6 miles wide. When the Federal Government issued allotments to tribal members, the land approved by Congress was insufficient to meet the allotments needs of the Tribe. As a result, Congress authorized members of the Band to take allotments on the Public Domain in Montana, South Dakota and North Dakota. Today, the land holdings of the Turtle Mountain Band of Chippewa & individual tribal members stand at approximately 79,176 acres with an equal amount located in Montana and South Dakota. The agency is staffed with approximately 50 employees, the vast majority being tribal members.

FORT TOTTEN AGENCY
Bureau of Indian Affairs
816 3rd Ave. North, P.O. Box 270 • FORT TOTTEN, ND 58335
(701) 766-4545 Fax 766-4117
Monte Lebeau, Supt.; E-mail: monte.lebeau@bia.gov
Serves the Spirit Lake Tribe. Fort Totten, North Dakota is located 180 miles due north of Aberdeen, South Dakota, and provides services to the Spirit Lake Sioux Tribe with an enrollment population of 6,700 members. Tribal Council consists of 6 elected officials including 4 council members for each of the four districts within the reservation, a Tribal Chair & Secretary – Treasurer. Eligible voters participate in elections every 4 years with a primary in April and the general election in May. 4,500 members reside on or near the Spirit Lake Nation. The Spirit Lake Reservation is comprised of 383 square miles containing 245,120 acres of which 67,479 acres are held in trust as follows: Tribal 34,382 Individual 33,097

STANDING ROCK AGENCY
Bureau of Indian Affairs, P.O. Box E • FORT YATES, ND 58538
(701) 854-3433 Fax 854-7184
Sheila White Mountain, Supt.; E-mail: Sheila.whitemountain@bia.gov
Serves the Standing Rock Sioux Tribe with almost 15,600 members.
Standing Rock Agency, formerly known and established in 1868 as Grand River Agency on the banks of the Grand River (South Dakota) and relocated upstream in 1874 & renamed, Standing Rock Agency (Ft. Yates, North Dakota), is the Field Office for the Bureau of Indian Affairs providing Trust Services and Indian Services to the Standing Rock Sioux Tribe. The Agency is located in Fort Yates, North Dakota (former U.S. Army Military Post). The Standing Rock Sioux Indian Reservation straddles North and South Dakota and encompasses all of Sioux County in North and all of Corson County, and small parcels in Ziebach and Perkins Counties in South Dakota.

FORT BERTHOLD AGENCY
Bureau of Indian Affairs, P.O. Box 370 • NEW TOWN, ND 58763
(701) 627-4707 Fax 627-3601
Kayla Danks, Supt.; E-mail: kayla.danks@bia.gov
Serves the Three Affiliated Tribes with approximately 10,250 members.
The Agency is located in New Town, North Dakota in central North Dakota on the Missouri River system. The Agency serves the Three Affiliated Tribes, the Arikara, Hidatsa and Mandan Tribes. Enrollment is 10,249 and approximately 4,053 members reside on the reservation. The Trust acreage managed by the Bureau of Indian Affairs is 343,000 allotted and 80,000 Tribal acres. The total reservation is 980,000 acres.

OKLAHOMA

CHICKASAW AGENCY
Bureau of Indian Affairs
2015 Lonnie Abbott Blvd., P.O. Box 2240 • ADA, OK 74821
(580) 436-0784 Fax 436-3215
Stephanie A. Large, Supt.; E-mail: stephanie.large@bia.gov
Serves the Indian people in the 11.5 counties under the Agency's jurisdiction. Works with the Chickasaw Nation in the development of plans to each goals established jointly by the Nation and the Bureau.

ANADARKO AGENCY
Bureau of Indian Affairs, Hwy. 281 N. & Parker McKenzie Rd.
P.O. Box 309 • ANADARKO, OK 73005
(405) 247-6677 Fax 247-3942
George Beatty, Supt.; E-mail: robin.phillips@bia.gov
Serves the following tribes: Kiowa, Comanche, Apache, Wichita & Affiliated Tribes, Caddo, Delaware, and Fort Sill Apache Tribes. 29,000 members.

CHEROKEE AGENCY
Tahlequah Field Office (Cherokee Nation)
Cherokee Nation W.W. Keeler Tribal Complex
17675 S Muskogee Ave, Room 112 • Tahlequah OK 74464
Mailing address: PO Box 440 • Tahlequah OK 74465
(918) 453-5715 Fax 458-9598

Muskogee/Eastern Oklahoma Field Office (BIA)
Eastern Oklahoma Regional Office (BIA)
3100 W. Peak Blvd, • Muskogee OK 74401
Mailing Address: PO Box 2699 • Muskogee, OK 74402
(918) 781-4675 Fax 781-4679

CONCHO AGENCY
Bureau of Indian Affairs
1635 East Hwy. 66, P.O. Box 68 • EL RENO, OK 73005
(405) 262-7481 Fax 262-3140
Betty Tippeconnie, Supt.
Serves two Federally-recognized tribes, the Cheyenne & Arapaho Tribes with approximately 11,500 resident members.

MIAMI AGENCY
Bureau of Indian Affairs
34 "A" St., NE (2nd Fl.), P.O. Box 391 • MIAMI, OK 74355
(918) 542-3396 Fax 542-7202
Paul Yates, Superintendent; E-mail: paul.yates@bia.gov
Rhonda Loftin, Deputy Supt. - Trust Services
Serves nine Federally recognized tribes: Eastern Shawnee Tribe of Oklahoma; Miami Tribe of Oklahoma; Modoc Tribe of Oklahoma; Ottawa Tribe of Oklahoma; Peoria Tribe of Indians of Oklahoma; Quapaw Tribe of Indians; Seneca-Cayuga Tribe of Oklahoma; Shawnee Tribe; and Wyandotte Nation.

OKMULGEE AGENCY
Bureau of Indian Affairs - Muscogee (Creek) Nation Complex
P.O. Box 8002 • MUSKOGEE, OK 74402
(918) 781-4608 Fax 781-4604
Carla Norman, Supt.; E-mail: carla.norman@bia.gov
Serves four Federally recognized Tribes: Alabama-Quassarte Tribal own, Kialegee Tribal Town, Muscogee (Creek) Nation, & Thlopthlocco Tribal Town.

TALIHINA AGENCY
Bureau of Indian Affairs, c/o Eastern Oklahoma Regional Office
P.O. Box 8002 • MUSKOGEE, OK 74402
(918) 781-4682 Fax 781-4604; Cristy Hammons, Tribal Liaison
Serves the Choctaw Nation of Oklahoma covering 10.5 counties located in southeastern Oklahoma.

OSAGE AGENCY
Bureau of Indian Affairs
813 Grandview, P.O. Box 1539 • PAWHUSKA, OK 74056
(918) 287-5700 Fax 287-4320
Robin Phillips, Superintendent; E-mail: robin.phillips@bia.gov
Richard Winlock, Deputy Superintendent; E-mail: richard.winlock@bia.gov
Provides services to the Osage Nation & Osage Mineral Estate.

PAWNEE AGENCY
Bureau of Indian Affairs, 850 Agency Rd., P.O. Box 440 • PAWNEE, OK 74058
(918) 762-2585 Fax 762-3201
Robin Bellmard, Supt.; E-mail: robin.bellmard@bia.gov
Serves approximately 7,200 tribal members within the four tribes under the jurisdiction: Otoe-Missouria, Pawnee, Tonkawa & Ponca Tribes.

WEWOKA AGENCY
Bureau of Indian Affairs, P.O. Box 1540 • SEMINOLE, OK 74818
(405) 303-2701 Fax 303-2091
Ramona Ellis, Supt.; E-mail: ramona.ellis@bia.gov
Serves the Seminole Nation of Oklahoma and its tribal members residing in Seminole County, Oklahoma.

SHAWNEE FIELD OFFICE
Bureau of Indian Affairs, 640 W. Independence • SHAWNEE, OK 74801
(405) 273-0317 Fax 273-0072
Manages the realty & agriculture functions for the approximately 500 enrolled members of the Kickapoo Tribe of Oklahoma.

OREGON

UMATILLA AGENCY
Bureau of Indian Affairs, P.O. Box 520 • PENDLETON, OR 97801
(541) 278-3786 Fax 278-3791
Michael Jackson, Supt.; E-mail: michael.jackson@bia.gov
Serves the Confederated Tribes of the Umatilla Indian Reservation.

SILETZ AGENCY
Bureau of Indian Affairs, P.O. Box 569 • SILETZ, OR 97380
(541) 444-2679 Fax 444-2243
Stanley Speaks, Regional Director (contact)

Serves the following tribes: Confederated Tribes of Coos, Lower Umpqua & Siuslaw Indians, Confederated Tribes of the Grand Ronde Community of Oregon; Coquille Tribe of Oregon; Cow Creek Band of Umpqua Indians of Oregon, & the Confederated Tribes of Siletz Reservation

WARM SPRINGS AGENCY
Bureau of Indian Affairs, P.O. Box 1239 • WARM SPRINGS, OR 97761
(541) 553-2411 Fax 553-2426
John Halliday, Supt.; E-mail: john.halliday@bia.gov
Serves the following tribes: Burns Paiute, Confederated Tribes of the Warm Springs Reservation, and the Klamath Indian Tribe.

SOUTH DAKOTA

CHEYENNE RIVER AGENCY
Bureau of Indian Affairs, P.O. Box 325 • EAGLE BUTTE, SD 57625
(605) 964-6611 Fax 964-4060
Gregg Bourland, Supt.; E-mail: gregg.bourland@bia.gov
James E. Murray, Fiduciary Trust Officer (605) 964-7707 Fax 964-7706
Serves the Cheyenne River Sioux Tribe, an unincorporated Tribe consisting predominantly of the Minneconjou, SiHaSapa, Oohenumpa, & Itazipco bands of the Lakota or Great Sioux Nation. The reservation consists of 1,450,644 trust acres in Ziebach and Dewey County in central South Dakota; in addition to Meade, Stanley, Haakon, Perkins, and Lawrence Counties. The Tribe also owns 480 acres of fee land in Crook County, Wyoming. The current tribal enrollment is 15,993 with about 70% living on the reservation. Governing body is a Chair, Vice-Chair, Secretary, Treasurer and 15 council members.

CROW CREEK AGENCY
Bureau of Indian Affairs, P.O. Box 139 • FORT THOMPSON, SD 57339
(605) 245-2311 Fax 245-2343
Patrick F. Duffy, Supt.; E-mail: patrick.duffy@bia.gov
Serves the Crow Creek Sioux Tribe located along the eastern shore of the Missouri River in Central South Dakota. The reservation covers an area of more than 295,000 acres within its exterior boundaries. The trust land base is 125,000 acres. Estimated tribal enrollment is more than 3,500 members. The Crow Creek Sioux Reservation is divided geographically into three districts/communities: Ft. Thompson, Crow Creek, & Big Bend, with Ft. Thompson being the largest community and also serving as the tribal headquarters. Crow Creek Agency works with the Crow Creek Sioux Tribe within the government-to-government framework to address needs of the tribe & its members. Major programs operated by the Agency include Real Estate Services, Natural Resources, Wildland Fire, Probate, Transportation, & Human Services.

LOWER BRULE AGENCY
Bureau of Indian Affairs, 190 Oyate Circle • LOWER BRULE, SD 57548
(605) 473-5512 Fax 473-5491
James Two Bulls, Supt.; E-mail: james.twobulls@bia.gov
Serves the Lower Brule Sioux Tribe. The Lower Brule Agency is located at Lower Brule, South Dakota, and services the Lower Brule Sioux Tribe and Reservation. The reservation covers 404 square miles in Lyman and Stanley counties in central South Dakota, bounded on the northeast and east by the Missouri River, which was closed by the Big Bend Dam in 1963. On the east and north side of the reservoir, Lake Sharpe, is the Crow Creek Reservation. The Lower Brule Reservation population is 1,664 and tribal membership is 3,410. The Lower Brule Sioux Tribe is the largest employer on the reservation, operating many BIA and IHS programs, the Golden Buffalo Casino & Motel, Tribal Farm, propane plant, popcorn processing plant, a construction company, and hunting enterprise.

PINE RIDGE AGENCY
Bureau of Indian Affairs
Hwy. 18, Main St., Bldg. 159, P.O. Box 1203 • PINE RIDGE, SD 57770
(605) 867-5125 Fax 867-1141
Cleve Her Many Horses, Supt.; E-mail: cleve.hermanyhorses@bia.gov
Serves the Oglala Sioux Tribe with almost 47,000 members.
The Pine Ridge Indian Reservation consists of approximately 2.1 million acres and it is located in the southwest portion of the state and occupies areas in Shannon, Jackson, and Bennett counties. *Critical Activities/Services Provided to Tribe*: The trust services provided by the Agency include Real Estate Services, Fire Management, Social Services, Land Operations, Probate & Estate Services, & Facilities Management. The non-trust services include Executive Direction/Administrative Services. There are 53 Agency employees.

ROSEBUD AGENCY
Bureau of Indian Affairs, P.O. Box 550 • ROSEBUD, SD 57570
(605) 747-2224 Fax 747-2805
LeeAnn Beardt, Supt.; E-mail: leeann.beardt@bia.gov
Serves the Rosebud Sioux Tribe with approximately 24,220 members.
SISSETON AGENCY

Bureau of Indian Affairs, P.O. Box 688 • AGENCY VILLAGE, SD 57262
(605) 698-3001 Fax 698-7784
Russell Hawkins, Supt.; E-mail: russell.hawkins@bia.gov
Serves the Sisseton Wahpeton Oyate with approximately 12,400 members. The Sisseton Agency serves 108,589 acres of trust land for the Sisseton-Wahpeton Oyate. The Sisseton- Wahpeton Oyate is the tenth largest employer in the state of South Dakota. The Sisseton-Wahpeton Oyate operates three casinos; one in North Dakota and two in South Dakota.

YANKTON AGENCY
Bureau of Indian Affairs
29775 S. Main St., P.O. Box 577 • WAGNER, SD 57380
(605) 384-3651 Fax 384-3876; Benjiman Kitto, Supt.
Serves the Yankton Sioux Tribe with approximately 11,600 members; and the Ponca Tribe of Nebraska with about 2,800 members.

UTAH

UINTAH & OURAY AGENCY
Bureau of Indian Affairs, P.O. Box 130 • FORT DUCHESNE, UT 84026
(435) 722-4300 Fax 722-2323
Lelilah Duncan, Supt.; E-mail: lelilah.duncan@bia.gov

SOUTHERN PAIUTE AGENCY
Bureau of Indian Affairs, P.O. Box 720 • ST. GEORGE, UT 84771
(435) 674-9720 Fax 674-9714
James Williams, Supt.; E-mail: james.williams@bia.gov
Serves the Kaibab Paiute, Las Vegas Tribes, Moapa Tribe, Paiute Indian Tribe of Utah, and the San Juan Southern Paiute Tribe.

WASHINGTON

OLYMPIC PENINSULA AGENCY
Bureau of Indian Affairs, P.O. Box 48 • ABERDEEN, WA 98550
(360) 533-9100 Fax 533-9141
Gregory K. Masten, Acting Supt.; E-mail: gregory.masten@bia.gov
Tribes served: Confederated Tribes of the Chehalis Reservation, Cowlitz Indian Tribe, Hoh Indian Tribe, Jamestown S'Klallam Tribe, Lower Elwha Tribal Community, Quileute Tribe, Shoalwater Bay Tribe, Skokomish Indian Tribe, Squaxin Island Tribe.

PUGET SOUND AGENCY
Bureau of Indian Affairs, 2707 Colby Ave., #1101 • EVERETT, WA 98201
(425) 258-2651 Fax 258-1254
Tribes served: Lummi, Muckelshoot, Nisqually, Nooksack, Port Gamble S'Klallam, Puyallup, Samish, Sauk-Suiattle, Snoqualmie, Stillaguamish, Swinomish, Suquamish, Tulalip, and Upper Skagit Indian Tribe.

MAKAH AGENCY
Bureau of Indian Affairs, P.O. Box 115 • NEAH BAY, WA 98357
(360) 645-3198 Fax 645-3199
Serves the Makah Indian Tribe (360) 645-2201.

COLVILLE AGENCY
Bureau of Indian Affairs, P.O. Box 111 • NESPELEM, WA 99155
(509) 634-2316 Fax 634-2355
Debra Wulff, Supt.; E-mail: debra.wulff@bia.gov
Serves the Confederated Tribes of the Colville Reservation.

TAHOLAH AGENCY
Bureau of Indian Affairs, P.O. Box 39 • TAHOLAH, WA 98587
(360) 276-4850 Fax 276-4853.
Gregory K. Masten, Supt.; E-mail: gregory.masten@bia.gov
Serves the Quinault Tribe.

YAKAMA AGENCY
Bureau of Indian Affairs, P.O. Box 632 • TOPPENISH, WA 98948
(509) 865-2255 Fax 865-3636
David L. Shaw, Supt.; E-mail: david.shaw@bia.gov
Serves the Confederated Tribes & Bands of the Yakama Nation.

WAPATO IRRIGATION PROJECT
Bureau of Indian Affairs, P.O. Box 220 • WAPATO, WA 98951
(509) 877-3155 Fax 877-3478

SPOKANE AGENCY
Bureau of Indian Affairs, P.O. Box 389 • WELLPINIT, WA 99040
(509) 258-4561 Fax 258-7542
Marcella Teters, Supt.; E-mail: marcella.teters@bia.gov
Serves the Kalispel Indian Community and the Spokane Tribe.

WISCONSIN

GREAT LAKES AGENCY
Bureau of Indian Affairs, 916 W. Lake Shore Dr. • ASHLAND, WI 54806
 (800) 495-4655; (715) 682-4527 Fax 682-8897
 Kimberly Bouchard, Supt.; E-mail: Kimberly.bouchard@bia.gov
Serves ten Federally recognized tribes in Wisconsin including
six Bands of Lake Superior Chippewa, and four additional tribes.
The Great Lakes Agency was established in 1894 at La Pointe on Madeline
Island in the Chequamegon Bay of Lake Superior-the largest fresh water lake
in the world. In 1943 the Agency was moved to Ashland, Wisconsin on the
southern shore of Chequamegon Bay. Until the mid 1970's the Agency
provided direct services to all the tribes located in the States of Wisconsin and
Michigan. Today, the Agency continues to serve as the headquarters from
which the Bureau's responsibilities to Federally recognized tribes are carried
out. The Agency has primary responsibility for the government-to-government
relationship for ten of the eleven Federally recognized tribes in Wisconsin
including six Bands of Lake Superior Chippewa, and four additional tribes.

WYOMING

WIND RIVER AGENCY
Bureau of Indian Affairs, P.O. Box 158 • FORT WASHAKIE, WY 82514
 (307) 332-7810 Fax 332-4578
 Norma Gourneau, Supt.; E-mail: norma.gourneau@bia.gov
Serves The Wind River Reservation in southwestern Wyoming near Lander,
Wyoming; more than 3,900 Eastern Shoshone and 8,600 Northern Arapahoe
enrolled tribal members. The agency provides direct services in the following
program areas: Executive Direction & Administration, Facilities Management,
Agriculture, Forestry, Trust Services, Probate, Irrigation & Real Estate
Services.

This section lists national associations, societies, and organizations active in Indian affairs; also, state & regional associations. Listings arranged alphabetically.

ADMINISTRATION FOR CHILDREN & FAMILIES (ACF)
ADMINISTRATION FOR NATIVE AMERICANS (ANA)
ACF Native American Affairs Advisory Council (NAAAC)
U.S. Department of Health & Human Services
330 C St., SW • Washington, DC 20201
 (202) 401-9246 Fax 401-1022
 Website: www.acf.hhs.gov/program-topics/native-americans/tribes
 E-mail: anacomments@acf.hhs.gov
 Lillian Sparks Robinson (Rosebud/Oglala Lakota), Commissioner (2010-)
 E-mail: lillian.sparks-robinson@acf.hhs.gov
 Kimberly Romine, Deputy Commissioner (202) 205-5603
 E-mail: kimberly.romine@acf.hhs.gov
Purpose: To promote the goal of self-sufficiency by providing discretionary grant funding for community based projects, and training/technical assistance to eligible tribes & native organizations. Established 1974.

ADMINISTRATION ON AGING (AoA)
Office for American Indians, Alaskan Native & Native Hawaiian Programs
One Massachusetts Ave.• Washington, DC 20201
 (202) 357-0148; Website: www.olderindians.aoa.gov
 Cynthia LaCounte, Project Manager
 E-mail: cynthia.lacounte@aoa.hhs.gov
Purpose: Title VI is to promote the delivery of supportive & nutrition services to American Indians & Alaska Natives that are comparable to services offered to other older people under the Title III program. *Contractor*: Kauffman & Associates (KAI) - under contract with the AoA, KAI will provide services: Training & Technical Assistance; Logistic Support to the Federal Interagency Task Force on Old Indians; Coordination of Trainings; Research & Technical Support (website, newsletter, and databases).

ADOPT-A-NATIVE-ELDER PROGRAM
P.O. Box 3401 • Park City, UT 84060
 (435) 649-0535 Fax 649-8136; Website: www.anelder.org
 E-mail: mail@anelder.org; Linda Myers, Founder
Purpose: To assist traditional Dine (Navajo) Elders, in the Native tradition of the Giveaway, in maintaining their traditional spiritual & cultural lifestyles. The program supports over 350 traditional Elders who live in the northern portion of Arizona & southern Utah. *Activities*: Food, clothes and medical assistance programs focus on helping the Elders live on the land in the ways of The People, as they have for thousands of years. Hundreds of people from all over the U.S. and a few foreign countries have joined in the Spirit of the Giveaway. Annual Navajo Rug Show & Sale in November. *Publication*: ANE Newsletter.

THE AFFILIATED TRIBES OF NORTHWEST INDIANS (ATNI)
6636 NE Sandy Blvd. • Portland, OR 97213
 (503) 249-5770 Fax 249-5773
 Website: www.atnitribes.org; E-mail: atni@atnitribes.org
 Terri Parr W, Executive Director (509) 209-2417
 E-mail: tparrw@atnitribes.org
 Patricia Whitefoot, Education Chairperson
 E-mail: pwhitefoot@toppenish.wednet.edu
Executive Board Members:
 Fawn Sharp (Quinault), President (360) 276-8211
 E-mail: fsharp@quinault.org
 Melvin R. Sheldon, Jr. (Tulalip), 1st VP (360) 716-4300
 E-mail: melsheldon@tulaliptribes-nsn.gov
 Theresa Sheldon (Tulalip), 2nd VP (425) 508-6556
 E-mail: tsheldon@tulaliptribes-nsn.gov
 Andy Joseph, Jr. (Colville), 3rd VP (509) 631-4406
 E-mail: andy.joseph@colvilletribes.com
 Jeannie Louie (Coeur d'Alene), Secretary (208) 686-7156
 E-mail: jlouie@cdatribe-nsn.gov
 Alfred M. Nmee (Cooeur d'Alene), Assistant Secretary (208) 686-1009
 E-mail: amnomee@cdatribe-nsn.gov
 Sharon Goudy (Yakama), Treasurer (509) 865-7156
 E-mail: sgoudy@ynce.com
Description: 57 Northwest tribal governments from Oregon, Washington, Idaho, Northern California, Southeast Alaska, and Western Montana. *Purpose*: Dedicated to promoting tribal self-determination & sovereignty. *Programs*: Culture & Elders; Education; Indian Child Welfare; Gaming; Housing; Law & Justice; Natural Resources, Energy; Economic Development. *Activities*: Annual Conference; Energy Conference; National Tribal Summit. *Resources*: ATNI Economic Development Corp., 18230 Frost Rd., Dallas, OR 97338 (503) 917-0550 Fax 623-4714; Mike Marchand (Colville), President. E-mail: atni_vp1@hotmail.com; Amber Schultz-Oliver, Executive Director. E-mail: amber@atniedc.com. *Publication*: ATNI News.

AMERICAN ACADEMY OF PEDIATRICS
Native American Child Health
141 Northwest Point Blvd. • Elk Grove Village, IL 60007
 (800) 433-9016 ext. 4739; (847) 981-4739
 Website: www.aap.org/nach; E-mail: indianhealth@aap.org
Faculty: Tammy Keller & Ronald David Freeman, DMD (dental health)
Purpose: To provide leadership in the development of medical policies & initiatives which promote the health of Native American children, particularly urban Indians and/or geographically isolated. **The International Meeting on Indigenous Child Health** (IMICH), held every two years (The 7th meeting to be held from March 31 to April 2, 2017, Denver, Colorado), focuses on innovative clinical care models & community-based public health approaches for children & youth in First Nations, Inuit, Métis, American Indian, Alaska Native and other Indigenous communities around the world. Co-hosted by the Canadian Paediatric Society & the American Academy of Pediatrics, this meeting brings together health care providers and researchers working with children, youth and families in American Indian, Alaska Native, First Nations, Inuit, Métis & other Indigenous communities. Participants share model programs & research, learn about prevalent health problems, and acquire practical skills for use in community settings. Opportunities to share knowledge & support one another's efforts, to network & develop partnerships are built into the program. *Activities*: Conducts pediatric consultation visits & continuing medical education presentations to chosen areas within the Indian Health Service (IHS); strengthen ties with Indian tribes, especially those responsible for their own health care; survey IHS sites to determine pediatric locum tenens opportunities & share this information with interested pediatricians; presents an annual Native American Child Health Advocacy award to individuals who have made a significant contribution to improving the health of Native American children. *Publications*: Catalogue available. Library. Established 1965.

AMERICAN ANTHROPOLOGICAL ASSOCIATION (AAA)
ASSOCIATION OF INDIGENOUS ANTROPOLOGISTS
2200 Wilson Blvd., Suite 600 • Arlington, VA 22201
 (703) 528-1902 Fax 528-354; Website: www.aaanet.org/sections/aia
 Richard Meyers, President; E-mail: Richard.meyers@sdstate.edu
 Valerie Lambert (Choctaw), Past President; E-mail: vlambert@unc.edu
 Jason Younker (Coquille), Past President; E-mail: jyounker@uoregon.edu
 Terry "Scott Ketchum, Secretary/Treasurer
Purpose: To advance anthropological study relating to indigenous peoples, both past & present; to provide a network for the support & encouragement of Indigenous study; to encourage professional work that will benefit the discipline. *Activities*: Sponsors visiting lecturers, congressional fellowship & departmental services programs. Maintains speaker's bureau, consultants' bureau & placement service. Sponsors competitions; bestows awards; conducts research programs & compiles statistics. Conducts symposia & publishes a quarterly journal, "American Ethnologist," a periodic Monograph Series, a monthly newsletter, "Unit News in Anthropology Newsletter; Proceedings, The Development of Political Organization in Native North America. Annual conference. *Publications*: American Anthropologist, quarterly journal; Anthropology & Education, quarterly journal; Anthropology Newsletter, 9x per year; Cultural Anthropology, quarterly journal; Guide to Departments of Anthropology, annual; periodic monograph series. Established 1902.

AMERICAN ANTIQUARIAN SOCIETY
185 Salisbury St. • Worcester, MA 01609
 (508) 755-5221 Fax 753-3311; Website: www.americanantiquarian.org
 E-mail: library@americanantiquarian.org
 Ellen S. Dunlap, President (471-2161)
 E-mail: edunlap@mwa.org; Thomas G. Knoles, Librarian
Description: A national research library of American history, literature & culture through 1876. *Membership*: 570. *Purpose*: To collect, preserve & encourage serious study of the materials of American history & life through 1876. Library. Newsletter. Established 1812.

AMERICAN FRIENDS SERVICE COMMITTEE
Native American/Native Peoples Program
1501 Cherry St. • Philadelphia, PA 19102
 (215) 241-7125 Fax 241-7119
 Website: www.afsc.org; E-mail: afscinfo@afsc.org
 Shan Cretin, General Secretary (215) 241-7104
Description: One of the corporate expressions of Quaker faith & practice. *Purpose*: To conduct programs with U.S. communities on the problem of minority group housing, employment & denial of legal rights. Established 1917.

AMERICAN HISTORICAL ASSOCIATION
400 A St., SE • Washington, D.C. 20003
 (202) 544-2422 Fax 544-8307
 Website: www.historians.org; E-mail: info@historians.org
 Jim Grossman, Executive Director (ext. 999)
 E-mail: jgrossman@historians.org

Julia Brookins, Special Projects Coordinator (ext. 119)
E-mail: jbrookins@historians.org
Amanda Moniz, Program Coordinator
Membership: 15,000. Professional historians, educators, and others interested in promoting historical studies and collecting, preserving historical manuscripts. *Publications*: American Indians and the Study of U.S. History, by Ned Blackhawk (pamphlet, $7); American Historical Review, 5/yr. Library. Established 1884.

AMERICAN INDIAN & ALASKA NATIVE LUTHERAN ASSOCIATION
Evangelical Lutheran Church in America (ELCA)
8765 W. Higgins Rd. • Chicago, IL 60631
(800) 638-3522; (773) 380-2700 Fax 380-1465
Elizabeth Gaskins, President; Mark Allred, Program Director
Description: Consists of a nine-member board of American Indians & Alaskan Natives. Acts as an advocate & consultant to Lutheran churches on behalf of the needs of Indian communities. Supports American Indian & Alaskan native rights. Supersedes the National Indian Lutheran Board (founded 1970). Biennial conference. Established 1987.

AMERICAN INDIAN / ALASKA NATIVE SOCIAL WORK EDUCATORS ASSOCIATION
465 Breckenridge St. • Buffalo, NY 14213-1634
Membership: Indian social workers concerned with the social welfare of Indian people. *Purpose*: To meet the unique needs of Indians according to their customs, traditions, life style & values. Established 1970.

AMERICAN INDIAN & ALASKA NATIVE TOURISM ASSOCIATION
(AIANTA) 2401 12th St., NW • Albuquerque, NM 87104
(505) 724-3592 Fax 212-7023
Website: www.aianta.org; E-mail: info@aianta.org
Camille L. Ferguson (Tlingit of Sitka Tribe), Executive Director
Sherrie Bowman (Laguna Pueblo), Office & Administrative Manager
E-mail: sbowman@aianta.org
Rachel Cromer-Howard, Public Relations & Media Specialist
E-mail: rcromer@aianta.org
Gail E. Chehak (Klamath), American Indian Tourism Conference Fundraiser
gchehak@aianta.org
Sherry L. Rupert (Paiute/Washoe), Vice President, Nevada Indian Territory
Rachel Moreno (Sitka), Secretary/Alaska Region Representative
Jackie Yellowtail (Crow), Treasurer, Plains Region Representative
James Surveyor (Hopi), At-Large Representative
LaDonna Brave Bull Allard (Standing Rock Sioux), At-Large Representative
Regional Reps: Tony Azure (Santee Sioux of Nebraska), Alaska Region; Michele Crank (Dine), Southwest Region; Leslie Johnson (Puyallup), Pacific Region; Janee Doxtator (Oneida), Eastern Region; Kirby Metoxen (Oneida-Wisconsin), Midwest Region; William Lowe (Muscogee Creek), Plains Region; Aimee D. Awonohopay (St. Croix Chippewa), Midwest Region; Rowena M. Akana (Hawaiian), Pacific Region
Description: A nonprofit association of Native American tribes & tribal businesses from six regions: Eastern, Plains, Midwest, Southwest, Pacific Northwest, & Alaska. *Mission*: To define, introduce, grow & sustain American Indian, Alaska Native & Native Hawaiian tourism that honors & sustains tribal traditions & values. *Purpose*: To promote Indian Country tourism; to serve as the voice & resource for its constituents in marketing tourism, providing training & educational resources to tribal members, and serving as liaison between Indian country & governmental & private entities for the development, growth, & sustenance of Indian tourism. *Activities*: Publications; Annual conference & report; brochure. Established 1999.

AMERICAN INDIAN ARTISTS, INC. (AMERINDA)
288 E. 10th St. • New York, NY 10009
(212) 598-0968 Fax 598-0125
Website: www.amerinda.org; E-mail: amerinda@amerinda.org
David Bunn Martine, Chairperson
Diane Fraher (Osage/Cherokee), Founder & Director
Lloyd E. Oxendine (Lumbee), Native American Arts Consultant
Steve Elm, Editor of Talking Stick
Purpose: American Indian Artists works to empower Native Americans, break down barriers, & foster understanding & appreciation for Native culture. Through a variety of arts programs, productions & services to artists, AMERINDA supports Native artists who embody the traditional practices & values that define Indian culture. AMERINDA also promotes the indigenous perspective in the arts to a wide audience through mainstream art forms-- visual, performing, literacy & media arts. *Book*: Sovereign Bones: New Native American Writing by Eric Gansworth (Onondaga). *Video*: "The Reawakening," the first independent feature film produced by Native people and American Indian Artists, Inc. in 2003 set on the Onondaga Nation and in New York City. A character-driven dramatic film of contemporary Native American tradition & culture, based on the themes of personal redemption and the power of love.

Written & directed by Diane Fraher (Osage). *Publication*: "Talking Stick," Native Arts Quarterly. Established in 1987.

AMERICAN INDIAN ARTS COUNCIL, INC.
725 Preston Forest Shopping Center, Suite B • Dallas, TX 75230
(214) 891-9640; E-mail: aiac@flash.net
Ms. Joel C. Olson, President; Pat Peterson, Executive Director
Purpose: To increase the awareness of the American Indian community; to enhance the quality of life by making American Indian art & cultural activities accessible to both the art community & the community-at-large; to educate the public, thereby enhancing an appreciation of the tribal heritage, art, culture, history, traditions, & contributions of American Indians to our culturally diverse community; to foster, promote, & showcase American Indian visual & performing arts. Opened the "Native Arts Center & Gallery" in December 2006 (214) 265-0071. *Activities*: sponsor & produce an annual American Indian Art Festival & Market (Fall); create and sustain an Academic Scholarship Fund for Native American students enrolled in institutions of higher learning; develop a Museum of American Indian Arts & Culture; community exhibits; Cultural Presenters Program; Speakers Bureau. *Publication*: Quarterly newsletter; general information brochure & special event advertising supplement. Resource library.

AMERICAN INDIAN BUSINESS LEADERS (AIBL)
Gallagher Business Bldg. #366 • Missoula, MT 59812
(877) 245-2425; (406) 243-2298 Fax 243-2086
Website: www.aibl.org; E-mail: info@aibl.org
Prairie Bighorn, Executive Director; E-mail: prairie.bighorn@aibl.org
Kyla Phalin-Two Bulls, Membership Coordinator
Sara Montgomery, Great Lakes Director
Dave Archambault, Mary Ellen Turmell,, Dr. Joe McDonald, Larry Gianchetta, John Turnell, Don Meyer, Dr. Ron Sheffield, Chad Barber, Board of Directors
Regional office: Great Lakes Regional American Indian Business Leaders
Fond du Lac Tribal & Community College, 2101 14th St., Cloquet, MN 55720
(218) 879-0874 Fax 879-0814
Purpose: To support & promote the education & development of future American Indian business leaders. *Programs*: Indigi-Biz Camp; Financial Literacy. *Activities*: Annual National Leadership Conference in April. *Publications*: "The Indian Business Owner's Guide"; Quarterly newsletter.

AMERICAN INDIAN CANCER FOUNDATION
615 First Ave. NE, Suite 125 • Minneapolis, MN 55413
(612) 314-4848 Fax 314-4840
Website: www.aicaf.org; E-mail: info@aicaf.org
Website: www.americanindiancancer.org
Michael A. Goze (Ho-Chunk), Chairperson
Kristine Rhodes (Anishinaabe), Executive Director
E-mail: krhodes@aicaf.org
Neely Snyder (Anishinaabe), Operations Manager
E-mail: nsnyder@aicaf.org
David Perdue, MD, MSPH (Chickasaw), Medical Director
Amanda Dionne (Northern Cheyenne/Turtle Mountain Ojibwe, Outreach Coordinator; E-mail: adionne@aicaf.org
Laura Keyes), Anishinaabe) & Joy Rivers (Haudenosaunee), Community Health Workers
Mission: To eliminate the disparities American Indians & Alaska Natives face in cancer prevention, early detection, and access to quality cancer & survivor support. Established 2010.

AMERICAN INDIAN CHILDREN'S HUNGER FUND
P.O. Box 724 • Laveen, AZ 85339
(623) 376-0727 Fax 376-0732
Website: www.americanindianchildren.org
Don Aime (Blessed Cloud), Director; E-mail: daime0642@aol.com
Description: A health & welfare organization that focuses on the survival of North & Central American Indian children & implements programs that provide food, clothing & spiritual education to them & their families.

AMERICAN INDIAN COLLEGE FUND
8333 Greenwood Blvd. • Denver, CO 80221
(800) 776-3863; (303) 426-8900 Fax 426-1200
Website: www.collegefund.org; E-Mail: info@collegefund.org
Cheryl Crazy Bull (Sicangu Lakota), President & CEO
Tammy Miller-Carlson, CFO; NancyJo Houk, VP of Resource Development
Tanksi Clairmont (Sicangu Lakota/Sisseton-Wahpeton Dakota) Tribal College & University Program Administrator
Tarajean Yazzie-Mintz (Navajo) & David Sanders, Program Officers
Bridget Skenadore (Dine), Native Arts & Culture Projects Coordinator
Dina Horwedel, Esq., Director of Public Education & Communication
E-mail: dhorwedel@collegefund.org
Elmer Guy, Board Chairperson, President, Navajo Technical College

Cynthia Lindquist, 1st Vice Chairperson
President, Cankdeska Cikana Community College
Laurel Vermillion, 2nd Vice Chairperson, President, Sitting Bull College
David M. Gipp, Trustee Emeritus
Purpose: To raise scholarship funds for American Indian students at qualified tribal colleges & universities & to generate broad awareness of those institutions and the Fund itself. The Fund also raises money & resources for other needs at the schools, including capital projects, operations, endowments, & program initiatives. *Program*: Wakanjeya "Sacred Little Ones" early childhood education initiative. *Activities*: Disbursements made directly to tribal colleges, public education campaign, product sales including Pendleton blankets, college tours & other special events. *Publication*: Annual report. Established 1989.

AMERICAN INDIAN DANCE THEATRE

(323) 463-1914; Hanay Geiogamah (Kiowa/Delaware), Director
Description: The group has 20 dancers, representing various tribes across the country, including Zuni, Ute, Apache, Cheyenne & Creek. They perform dances of different tribes touring the U.S. & Europe. In 2006, the theatre joined a multicultural consortium called the "Cultural Roundtable" at the Los Angeles Theatre Center created to bringing multicultural theatre to audiences in venues in downtown Los Angeles, *Facilities*: Gallery; Archives of Performances, *Videos*: American Indian Dance Theatre. Vol. 1, Finding the Circle (WNET/Thirteen; Tatge/Lasseau Productions, 1989); Vol. 2, Dances for the New Generations (PBS TV, 1993) & CDs. Established 1987.

AMERICAN INDIAN DEVELOPMENT ASSOCIATES (AIDA)

2401 12th St. NW #212 • Albuquerque, NM 87104
(505) 842-1122/1964 Fax 842-9652
Website: www.aidainc.net; E-mail: info@aidainc.net
Purpose: To support tribal self-determination through education, health, justice & community development. Scholarships available. *Activities*: Provides professional services to support Indian tribes, federal & state agencies & community groups. *Services*: Tribal Justice Systems Development; Community Development; Health & Wellness; Conference Planning; Research & Evaluation; Training & Technical Assistance.

AMERICAN INDIAN DISABILITY TECHNICAL ASSISTANCE CENTER

(AIDTAC) Center for Excellence in Disability Education, Research & Services
University of Montana Rural Institute, 52 Corbin Hall • Missoula, MT 59812
(406) 243-5467; Julie Clay, Coordinator
Project: American Indian Disability Legislation: "Toward the Development of a Process that Respects Sovereignty & Cultural Diversity." *Goal*: To develop & test methods for fostering the adoption of disability legislation by American Indian tribes consistent with principles established within the American With Disabilities Act & are respectful of tribal sovereignty & cultural diversity. Established 2000.

AMERICAN INDIAN EDUCATION FUND (AIEF)

P.O. Box 27491 • Albuquerque, NM 87125
(800) 881-8694 (donor information)
Website: www.nrcprograms.org; E-mail: info@aiefprogram.org
Paula Long Fox, Chairperson
Program Office: 1310 E. Riverview Dr. • Phoenix, AZ 85034
(866) 866-8642 Fax (602) 340-8050
Rafael Tapia, Program Director; E-mail: rtapia@nativepartnership.org
A program member group of the National Relief Charities. *Mission*: To give American Indian students the tools & opportunities to learn; to help Native American people improve the quality of their lives by providing opportunities for them to bring about positive changes in their communities. *Programs*: Purchasing school supplies, curriculum materials, supporting student incentive programs, funding repair of structural deterioration in schools & awarding grants to American Indian students for tuition & living expenses; scholarships; challenge grants. *Publication*: Quarterly newsletter. Established 1997.

AMERICAN INDIAN ENVIRONMENTAL OFFICE (AIEO)

Office of International & Tribal Affairs (OITA)
U.S. Environmental Protection Agency
1200 Pennsylvania Ave., NW, MC: 2690M • Washington, DC 20460
(202) 564-0303 Fax 564-0298
Website: www.epa.gov/tp; E-mail: oiiainternet-comments@epa.gov
Jane Nishida, OITA Principal Deputy Assistant Administrator
JoAnn K. Chase (Eastern Cherokee), Director; (564-0303)
E-mail: chase.joann@epa.gov
Andrew Baca, Acting Deputy Director (566-0815)
E-mail: baca.andrew@epa.gov
Jeff Besougloff, Senior Advisor, Law & Policy Program (564-0292)
E-mail: besougloff.jeff@epa.gov
Dona Harris, Acting Senior Advisor (564-6633)
E-mail: harris.dona@epa.gov

Luke Jones, Senior Advisor, Tribal Capacity Development
(564-4013); E-mail: jones.luke@epa.gov
Program: Tribal ecoAmbassador Program. *Activities*: Provides information on the respective roles of tribes & EPA in protecting human health and the environment in Indian country. *Publication*: Newsletter.

AMERICAN INDIAN FILM INSTITUTE

333 Valencia St. #322 • San Francisco, CA 94103
(415) 554-0525 Fax 554-0542
Michael Smith (Sioux), Founder & President
Linda Lilly & Tami Wasson, Marketing Team
Description: A non-profit media arts center *Mission*: To encourage Native filmmakers; to develop Indian & non-Indian audiences for this work; to advocate for authentic visual & work-force representations of Indians in the media; to open up opportunities for Native Americans to enter the workforce of the creative economy. *Programs*: Tribal Touring (taking Native films & filmmakers on the road); Summer Projects. *Activities*: Digital Training Workshops; Community Film Festival; American Indian Film Festival; Annual Silver Star Powwow & Indian Market. Established 1975.

AMERICAN INDIAN GRADUATE CENTER

3701 San Mateo Blvd. NE • Albuquerque, NM 87110
(800) 628-1920; (505) 881-4584 Fax 884-0427
Website: www.aigcs.org
Angelique Albert (Confederated Salish & Kootenai), Executive Director
E-mail: angelique@aigcs.org
Joan Currier, Chief Operating Officer
E-mail: joan@aigcs.org
Erin Griego, Executive Assistant
E-mail: erin@aigcs.org
Marveline Vallo Gabbard (Pueblo of Acoma), Program Associate
for Scholarships & Programs; E-mail: marveline@aigcs.org
Josh Lucio (Zuni), Program Associate for Scholarships & Programs
E-mail: josh@aigcs.org
Christa Moya (Dine'), Director of Financial Aid/Student Services
E-mail: christa@aigcs.org
Sara LaBarge (Menominee), Director of Scholarship Operations
E-mail: sara@aigcs.org
Michael L. Bates (Cherokee), Academic Advisor
E-mail: michael@aigcs.org
Gabriel M. Bell (Cheyenne & Arapaho), Coordinator of Student Services
Holly Cok Macarro (Red Lake Band Ojibwe), Board President
Joel M. Frank, Sr. (Seminole of Florida), Vice President
Steve Stallings (Rincon Band Luiseno); Secretary-Treasurer:
Purpose: To help open doors to graduate education for American Indian & Alaska Native college graduates by providing educational assistance. *Programs*: Graduate Fellowship & Special Programs; Outreach & Student Services. *Activities*: Has awarded more than 10,000 fellowships to qualified Native American & Alaska Native students (from federally recognized tribes) pursuing Master's, doctoral & professional degrees in all fields of study. *Publication*: Biannual magazine. Established 1969.

AMERICAN INDIAN HEALTH & MANAGEMENT POLICY (AIHMP)

P.O. Box 42535 • Phoenix, AZ 85080
(602) 999-5391 Fax 926-2321; Website: www.aihmp.com
David Tonemah (Kiowa), President
Carlyle Begay (Navajo), Vice President of Business Development
Lee Olitzky & Darryl Tonemah, Consultants
Description: An Indian-owned consulting company, dedicated to improving healthcare services for American Indians by bridging the gap between patients & health services.

AMERICAN INDIAN HERITAGE FOUNDATION

P.O. Box 750 • Pigeon Forge, TN 37868
Website: www.indians.org
Princess Pale Moon (Cherokee/Ojibwa), President/Chairperson
Donors: 25,000+. Corporate & individual donors. *Purpose*: To inform & educate non-Indians concerning the culture & heritage of the American Indian; to be responsive to the felt needs of Indian people both at the tribal & urban levels; to introduce a positive Indian presence into every strata of society where it is appropriate; and to initiate creative programs to actively share the diverse Indian culture in many creative ways. The website provides a Resource Directory comprised of the following categories: Tribal Directory, American Indian Articles, Indigenous Peoples' Literature, www.Indians.org Store. *Facilities*: Museum & Library. Gift store. *Activities/Programs*: American Indian Student Eagle Awards Program; Emergency Relief Distribution Program; Outstanding Achievement Youth Role Model Program; sponsors the National Miss Indian USA Pageant & Scholarship Program; & promotes the National American Indian Heritage Month. *Publication*: Occasional bulletins. Established 1973.

AMERICAN INDIAN HIGHER EDUCATION CONSORTIUM (AIHEC)
121 Oronoco St. • Alexandria, VA 22314
(703) 838-0400 Fax 838-0388
Website: www.aihec.org; E-mail: info@aihec.org
Carrie L. Billy, President & CEO; E-mail: cbilly@aihec.org
Meg Goetz, Vice President for Advocacy; E-mail: mgoetz@aihec.org
Tina Cooper, Vice President of Finance & Administration
 E-mail: tcooper@aihec.org
Alex Grandon, Program Coordinator; E-mail: agrandon@aihec.org
Deborah His Horse is Thunder, Program Director
 E-mail: dhishorseisthunder@aihec.org
Cynthia Lindquist (Cankdeska Cikana Community College), Chair
Laurel Vermillion (Sitting Bull College), Vice Chairperson
Robert Martin (Institute of American Indian Arts), Secretary
Michael Parish (Bay Mills Community College), Treasurer
David Yarlott, Jr. (Little Big Horn College), Member-at-Large
Rachel Marchbans, Journal Publisher
 E-mail: rachael@tribalcollegejournal.org
Purpose: To promote higher education opportunities for this nation's 37 tribal colleges. *Programs*: American Indian Measures for Success (AIMS); AIHEC Portals - Science, Technology, Engineering, Mathematics (STEM) Portal; First Americans Land-grant College Organization & Network (FALCON) Portal; Indigenous Evaluation Resource center Portal; Staff Support for Student Services (ATPN-TRIO); Tribal Colleges & Universities Library Association Project. *Activities*: Represents 37 tribally-controlled colleges in the U.S. to the Congress, federal agencies, and other national organizations, in an effort to acquire funds, support programs, and growth; to build a satellite network linking the 37 tribal colleges; technical assistance; research. *Publications*: Tribal College Journal, quarterly. Library. Established 1978.

THE AMERICAN INDIAN HORSE REGISTRY (AIHR)
9028 State Park Rd. • Lockhart, TX 78644
(512) 398-6642; Website: www.indianhorse.com
 Nanci Falley, President; E-mail: aihrnanci@gmail.com
Membership: 1,200. Persons who own or desire to own American Indian horses. *Purpose*: To collect, record, and preserve the pedigrees of American Indian horses. *Activities*: National Indian Horse Show each September; awards programs for members. Maintains Indian Horse Hall of Fame Museum. *Publications*: American Indian Horse Studbook, annual; quarterly newsletter. Library. Established 1961.

AMERICAN INDIAN LAW ALLIANCE
P.O. Box 3036 • Hoboken, NJ 07030
 Website: www.ailanyc.org; E-mail: aila@ailanyc.org
Tonya Gonnella Frichner (Onondaga), Esq. (Onondaga), Emeritus Founder
Betty Lyons (Onondaga), President & Executive Director
Murielle Borst-Tarrant, Chief of Staff
Roger Drew, Research & Policy Advisor
June Lorenzo, International Legal Advisor
Steve Newcomb (Shawnee/Lenape), International Research Coordinator
Description: An indigenous, non-profit organization that works with Indigenous nations, communities & organizations in their struggle for sovereignty, human rights & social justice for their people. *Purpose*: To advocate for the survival of Native cultures, individuals & nations with the emphasis of our advocacy in the law. *Activities/Programs*: Research & technical support for traditional original Native governments on national & international levels; legal services project for individuals in New York City with specific legal problems. Established 1989.

AMERICAN INDIAN LAW CENTER, INC.
P.O. Box 4456, 1117 Stanford, N.E. • Albuquerque, NM 87196
(505) 277-5462 Fax 277-1035
Website: www.ailc-inc.org; E-mail: begay@law.unm.edu
Helen B. Padilla (Isleta Pueblo), Esq., Director
 E-mail: padilla@ailc-inc.org
Heidi Nesbitt, Assistant Director & PLSI Director
 E-mail: nesbitt@ailc-inc.org
Francine M. Jaramillo (Isleta Pueblo), Senior Policy Analyst
 E-mail: Jaramillo@ailc-inc.org
Valerie S. Begay, Court Clerk & Office Administrator
 E-mail: begay@ailc-inc.org
Anthony Lee, Esq., Staff Attorney
Melanie P. Fritzsche, Esq., Staff Attorney
 E-mail: fritzsche@ailc-inc.org
Philip S. Deloria, Board President
 E-mail: deloria@law.unm.edu
Helen B. Padilla (Isleta Pueblo), Secretary
Benjamin Hanley (Navajo), Treasurer
Charles Trimble (Oglala Lakota) & Mark Trahant (Shoshone-Bannock),
 Board Members
Heidi Nesbitt, Director of the Pre-Law Summer Institute
 E-mail: nesbitt@law.unm.edu

Description: Staff of 12 Indian law graduates and attorneys; located at the University of New Mexico, School of Law. *Purpose*: To provide training & technical assistance to Native Americans and First Nation communities; to render services, primarily research & training, of a broad legal & governmental nature; and to assist tribes in making legal decisions when assistance is necessary. *Programs*: The Pre-Law Summer Institute (PLSI) for American Indians & Alaska Natives. Helped found & currently provides staff support to the Commission on State-Tribal Relations; provides individualized training for tribal judges & tribal prosecutors; administers the Special Scholarship Program in Law for American Indians through which students receive admission advice, financial assistance, tutorial aid, and job placement services; provides assistance to Alaskan natives; sponsors conferences & seminars. *Resources*: American Indian Prevention Resource Center; OU Native American Studies Department; OU Native American Law Program. *Curriculum*: Nee-Kon'-Nah Time – curriculum of prevention activities designed for use with 3 to 5 year old children in American Indian head start & preschool programs. *Video & Presentation Kit*: Remembering What We Know," a 12-minute movie for informing & stimulating discussions with high school & young adult age groups. *Publications*: American Indian Law Newsletter, bimonthly; cultural curriculum lessons and workshop proceedings; manuals for tribal judges & prosecutors, and on Indian criminal court procedures. Library. Established 1967.

AMERICAN INDIAN LAWYER TRAINING PROGRAM, INC.
1002 W. Vine St. • Stockton, CA 95203
(209) 460-0924 Fax 460-0934
Website: www.indianlawreporter.org
 Richard Trudell (Santee Sioux), Executive Director
Purpose: To strengthen & enhance the development of tribal institutions by providing programs & services that improve access to the vast & complex legal developments that affect Indian tribes & their members; promotes communication & cooperation among & between members of the Indian legal community; and develop the skills of members of the Indian legal community. *Projects*: Indian attorney fellowship program; summer internships; law associate program; tribal court advocate training project; and working seminars and conferences. *Publication*: The Indian Law Reporter, monthly newsletter; Indian Tribes As Sovereign Governments: A Sourcebook on Federal-Tribal History, Law, and Policy, Second Edition, 228 pp. $25.

AMERICAN INDIAN LIBERATION CRUSADE, INC.
4009 S. Halldale Ave. • Los Angeles, CA 90062
(323) 299-1810; Basil M. Gaynor, President
Membership: 4,000. *Purpose*: To transform the negative stereotypical thinking of both Indians & White people, while facilitating self-sufficiency & self-determination for the American Indian. *Activities*: Support ministry to Indian churches & organizations on the Indian Reservations across the nation. Assist with relief, education, emergency situations, and provide a network of talents & resources; sends Indian children to summer Bible Camp; maintain a radio broadcast making known the needs & hopes of the First Americans. *Publication*: "The Indian Crusader," quarterly newsletter; "The Four Directions'; "A Warrior's Greatest Honor" & other publications. Established 1952.

AMERICAN INDIAN LIBRARY ASSOCIATION (AILA)
Website: www.ailanet.org; E-mail: ailawebsite@gmail.com
Heather Devine-Hardy (Eastern Shawnee), Executive Director
Omar Poler (Sokaogon Chippewa), President (2016-17)
Naomi Bishop (Pima-Maricopa), VP & President Elect (2018-19)
Aaron LaFromboise (Blackfeet), Secretary
Liana Juliano, Treasurer
Patricia Cutright (Lakota), Jessica Humphries (Metis), 2016-18;
 Ofelia "Liz" Zepeda (Tohono O'odham), 2016-18, Members-at-Large
George Gottschalk, Editor-Newsletter
Purpose: To promote the development, maintenance, & improvement of libraries, library systems, and cultural & information services on reservations and in communities of Native Americans & Native Alaskans. *Publication*: AILA Newsletter, quarterly, $10/year-individuals, $25/year-organizations; $5/year students. Annual conference program during American Library Association annual conference in June. Established 1979.

AMERICAN INDIAN MOVEMENT
P.O. Box 13521 • Minneapolis, MN 55414
(612) 721-3914 Fax 721-7826
Website: www.aimovement.org; E-mail: aimggc@att.net
 Clyde H. Belcourt (Ojibwa), Co-Founder & Director
 William Means (Oglala Lakota), Council Member
Membership: 5,000. Primary objective is to encourage self-determination among American Indians and to establish international recognition of American Indian treaty rights. *Activities*: Founded Heart of the Earth Survival School which enrolls 600 students from preschool to adult programs; The AIM Media Project - AIM Radio; maintains historical archives & speakers' bureau; conducts research; Online Store. *Publication*: Survival News, quarterly. Annual meeting. Established 1968.

AMERICAN INDIAN POLICY CENTER
1463 Hewitt Ave. • St. Paul, MN 55104
  (651) 644-1728; Website: www.americanindianpolicycenter.org
  John Poupart (Lac du Flambeau Anishinaabe), President
The American Indian Policy Center Blog was revived in 2015, as a non-profit to write about thoughts pertaining to the Indian community. It was born out of a lot of discussions among the founding group of writers, other bloggers, and professionals. What was needed, in the view of the founders, was a media for the thoughts pertaining to American Indians and the wider community to discuss the issues of Indian life--a place for diverse and divergent voices and perspectives. Today the Center Blog focuses on research, policy development and education on critical Indian issues. We encourage forums on significant issues of public policy, from primary education to preservation of treaty rights. We also encourage expanding research on Indian issues using a unique model of Reality-Based Research. *Activities*: Sponsors two annual forums on significant issues of public policy. Published works: To Build a Bridge, An Introduction to Working With American Indian Communities, a manual, $12 per copy. Established 1992.

AMERICAN INDIAN RESEARCH OPPORTUNITIES (AIRO)
Montana State University, 312 Roberts Hall
P.O. Box 1763820 • Bozeman, MT 59717
  (406) 994-6723 Fax 994-5559; Website: www.montana.edu/wwwai
  Amy Stix, Director (994-5567); E-mail: amy.stix@coe.montana.edu
Description: A consortium of Montana's seven tribal colleges (Blackfeet Community College, Chief Dull Knife College, Fort Belknap College Fort Peck Community College, Little Big Horn College, Salish Kootenai College; Stone Child College) & Montana State University-Bozeman (MSU). *Faculty/Staff*: Kimberly McKeehan & Jennifer Woodcock, Admin. Associates. *Purpose*: To provide opportunities for American Indian students in career fields where they are significantly underrepresented. An advisory board consists of representatives from the seven tribal colleges & MSU. *Programs*: BRIDGES - Bridging Tribal Colleges to MSU; Montana Apprenticeship Program (MAP), a minority biomedical research support program (MBRS), and a minority access-to-research careers program; Summer Research.

AMERICAN INDIAN RESOURCES INSTITUTE
319 MacArthur Blvd. • Oakland, CA 94610
  (510) 834-9333; Richard Trudell, Executive Director
Purpose: To design & implement programs to promote tribal sovereignty & self-determination through provision of training resources to Indian attorneys, law students, & advocates committed to serving the legal needs of Indian people. *Program*: American Indian Lawyer Training Program. Established 1973.

AMERICAN INDIAN RIGHTS & RESOURCES ORGANIZATION (AIRRO)
41801 Corte Valentine • Temecula, CA 92592
  (951) 694-6264; Website: www.airro.org
  John Gomez, Jr., President; Carla Foreman Maslin, Chairperson
  John A. Gomez, Sr., Vice Chairperson
Description: A California non-profit dedicated to human & civil rights. *Purpose*: To educate & assist all individuals regarding basic human & civil rights issues in Indian Country; to educate the public to basic injustices and effect change; and to provide all individuals with equal rights & protection. *Activities*: Annual membership meeting. *Publication*: Newsletter.

AMERICAN INDIAN RITUAL OBJECT REPATRIATION FOUNDATION
463 E. 57th St. • New York, NY 10128
  (212) 980-9441 Fax 421-2746
  Website: www.repatriationfoundation.org
  Elizabeth Sackler, PhD, Founder/President
Purpose: An intercultural organization committed to assisting in the return of ceremonial objects to American Indian Nations and to educating the public about the importance of repatriation. *Activities*: Assist in the repatriation of ceremonial objects by acting as a liaison between collectors, dealers, auction houses & Native representatives; provide collectors who currently possess ritual objects with information about the cultural significance of the object; locate & contact American Indian individuals needed to authenticate and/or escort home sacred objects identified for repatriation; provide information about federal and other repatriation policies; sponsor workshops addressing the repatriation process and the significance of sacred material culture to American Indian communities; collect information regarding repatriation activities. *Publications*: Biannual newsletter; "Mending the Circle: A Native American Repatriation Guide." News & Notes. Established 1992.

AMERICAN INDIAN SCIENCE & ENGINEERING SOCIETY (AISES)
Headquarters: 2305 Renard SE, Suite 200, P.O. Box 9828
Albuquerque, NM 87119 (505) 765-1052 Fax 765-5608
Colorado Field Office: 1225 Ken Pratt Blvd., Suite 206, Longmont, CO 80501
  (720) 552-6123 Fax 526-6940
  Website: www.aises.org; E-mail: info@aises.org

  Sarah Echohawk (Pawnee), Chief Executive Officer (Colorado Field Office)
    (720) 552-6123 ext. 104; E-mail: sechohawk@aises.org
  Kyle Coulon (Onondaga), Program & Development Officer
    (720) 552-6123 ext. 108 (Colorado Field Office)
  Katherine Cristiano, Events Officer (Colorado Field Office)
    (720) 552-6123 ext. 103; E-mail: kcristiano@aises.org
  Kathy DeerInWater (Cherokee), Director of Special Projects & Research
    (720) 552-6123 ext. 107; E-mail: kdeerinwater@aises.org
  Kellie-Jewett-Fernandez (Cheyenne River Sioux), Director of Programs/
    Resource Development; E-mail: kjfernandez@aises.org
Membership: 1,500. American Indian & non-Indian students & professionals in science, technology, & engineering fields. *Purpose*: To provide training & educational opportunities to American Indian college students & tribal leaders; to increase the number of American Indian & Alaskan Natives in engineering, science & other related technology disciplines; seeks to motivate & encourage students to pursue graduate studies in science, engineering & technology; and the ultimate goal is to serve as a catalyst for the advancement of American Indians to become more self-reliant members of society. *Facilities*: American Indian Science & Education Center; AISES Environmental Institute - camp for about 35 kids, ages 11-17, for 1-2 week sessions to experience nature and to put together the best of modern science with traditional American Indian values & teachings. Located in Pike Mountain National Forest, about 50 miles southwest of Denver; American Indian Development Foundation - to encourage Native American Indian students to pursue their educational goals. Library. *Activities*: Conducts teacher-training programs; sponsors internships nationwide & specially designed workshops; curriculum materials development; conducts research and community-affiliated programs; sponsors scholarship; maintains speakers bureau & job placement service. *Bestows Awards*: The annual Professional Awards; Leadership Awards; Leadership Conference Awards; AISES Chapter Awards; Scholarships. *Publications*: Journal, biennial; Winds of Change, quarterly magazine published AISES & The Pohly Co. (617) 816-0707; E-mail: kenglish@pohlyco.com; Science Education Newsletter, quarterly; Annual Report. Annual National Conference in November. Established 1977.

AMERICAN INDIAN SCOUTING ASSOCIATION (AISA)
Website: www.amerindscouting.org
  Gene Karr (Mississippi Choctaw), Chairperson
  Claire Manning (Shoshone Paiute), Chair-Elect
  Pam Voelz (Menominee), Chef Financial Officer
  John Martin (Cherokee), Chief Elder
Description: The American Indian Relationship Committee of the Boy Scouts of America was established in 1956. A joint venture with the Boy Scouts & Girl Scouts of America. *Purpose*: To help adults as well as troop leaders to develop their talents through Scouting to better serve American Indian youth. To help youths of all tribes & cultures learn by association to appreciate the wide differences of people of Indian heritage. *Activities*: AISA conducts an Annual Seminar hosted by a local tribe or American Indian community. *Awards*: Indian Youth Awards; Joseph T. Provost Award; Francis X. Guardipee Award. Established 1975.

AMERICAN INDIAN SEARCH (AIS)
813 Harbor Blvd. #223 • West Sacramento, CA 95691
  (916) 273-9440; Website: www.americanindiansearch.com
  Joseph Brown Thunder, Founder
"Directory of American Indian Businesses & Groups": A directory that allows users and businesses the chance to find one another and establish business connections. The mission for AIS is "keeping tribal dollars in tribal communities." AIS allows American Indian businesses & groups an opportunity to list their group on a centralized web page. Basic listings are free and include business name, address, contact info & e-mail. Established 2006.

AMERICAN INDIAN SOURCING (AIS)
245 E. 19th St., Suite 11R • New York, NY 10003
  Jerry Ashton, President (212) 982-2151
Montana office: 2200 Rebich Lane, Dillon, MT 59725
  Frank Odasz, Exec. VP/Operations (406) 683-6270
Description: An outsource & consulting firm in the field of procurement, contact centers, & American Indian centered economic development throughout the U.S. It's staff & consultancy board is comprised of both Native and non-Native businessmen, educators, artists & job development specialists. *Purpose*: To bring business opportunities to "First Americans" and stave the flow of jobs leaving the U.S.; to expand Native American business opportunities on or nearby their reservations & villages which is vital to the preservation of Native culture & people.

AMERICAN INDIAN STUDIES RESEARCH INSTITUTE (AISRI)
Indiana University, 422 N. Indiana Ave. • Bloomington, IN 47408
  (812) 855-4086 Fax 855-7529
  Website: www.indiana.edu/~aisri; E-mail: aisri@indiana.edu

Raymond J. DeMallie & Douglas R. Parks, Co-Directors
E-mail: demallie@indiana.edu; drparks@indiana.edu
Sally Anderson, Linguistics & Lexicographer
Jon Bowman, Director, CDEL
Dennis Christafferson, Project Manager
Purpose: To serve as an interdisciplinary research center for projects focusing on the Native peoples of the Americas. The Institute was founded in part on the premise that language, culture & history are inextricably interrelated. Current projects focus on Plains Indian languages, cultures & history, and include software development that enhances linguistic documentation, analysis & publication. *Faculty*: Serafin M. Coronel-Molina, Ray DeMallie, Brian Gilley, Jason Baird Jackson, Philip S. LeSourd, Douglas R. Parks, Laura L. Scheiber, Christina Snyder, Daniel Frank Susiak. *Research Associates*: Carolyn R. Anderson, Rani-Henrik Andersson, Robert E. Bieder, John Enrico, Francis Flavin, Gregory Fields, Kellie Jean Hogue, Thomas Kavanagh, Paul Kroeber, Joanna Cohan Scherer, Wallace Hooper. *Publications*: Newsletter; Anthropological Linguistics journal; Studies in the Native Languages of the Americas (monograph series); Sources of American Indian Oral Literature (monograph series); Studies in the Anthropology of North American Indians (monograph series). Established 1985.

AMERICAN INDIAN VETERANS MEMORIAL ORGANIZATION
P.O. Box 7367 • Phoenix, AZ 85011
(480) 861-5880; Susan Ware Larson, President
Melissa Kohl, Treasurer; Loren Tapahe, Secretary
Mission: To build a memorial dedicated to all American Indian veterans and to provide a place for all to go and honor those who have served. Dennis Numkena, Hopi artist & military veteran, designed the memorial to capture the spirit of the eagle and to incorporate the four elements of creation spirituality: fire, water, earth and air. These elements of ceremony will allow the bringing of the warriors spirits home. Established 1996.

AMERICAN INDIAN YOUTH RUNNING STRONG
8301 Richmond Hwy. #200 • Alexandria, VA 22309
(888) 491-9859; (703) 317-9881 Fax 317-9690
Website: www.indianyouth.org; E-mail: info@indianyouth.org
Katsi Cook (Akwesasne Mohawk), Executive Director
James O'Brien, Esq., Chairperson
Emil Her Many Horses (Oglala Lakota), Treasurer
Billy Mills (Oglala Lakota), National Spokesperson
Purpose: To help American Indian people meet their immediate survival needs - food, water & shelter - while implementing & supporting programs designed to create opportunities for self-sufficiency & self-esteem, particularly for tribal youth. *Programs*: Long-term development programs such as organic gardening, housing, water resource development, nutrition, healthcare & youth programs. *Publications*: Quarterly newsletter; reports. Established 1986.

AMERICAN INDIANS IN FILM & TELEVISION
65 N. Allen Ave. #105 • Pasadena, CA 91106
(818) 578-0344; Website: www.facebook.com/americanindians
Sonny Skyhawk (Sicangu Lakota), CEO & Founder
Established 1980.

AMERICANS FOR INDIAN OPPORTUNITY (AIO)
1001 Marquette Ave. NW • Albuquerque, NM 87102
(505) 842-8677 Fax 842-8658; Website: www.aio.org
LaDonna Harris (Comanche), Founder/President
Eddie Tullis (Poarch Creek), Vice President
Ivan Posey (Eastern Shoshone), Co-Vice President
Laura Harris (Comanche), Executive Director
E-mail: lharris@aio.org
Roland Cheeku (Zuni), Senior Fellow & Archivist
Shawna Sunrise (Santo Domingo Pueblo/Dine'), Communications & Social Media Coordinator
Description: Americans for Indian Opportunity catalyzes & facilitates culturally appropriate initiatives & opportunities that enrich the cultural, political and economic lives of Indigenous peoples. *Purpose*: AIO draws upon traditional Indigenous values to foster enlightened & responsible leadership, inspires stakeholder-driven solutions, & convenes visionary leaders to probe contemporary issues & address challenges of the new century. *Projects*: AIO's acclaimed initiative, "The American Indian Ambassadors Program," is a Native American community capacity-building, leadership development effort that AIO has been operating since 1993. The program is designed to engage early to mid-career Native American professionals strengthen, within an Indigenous cultural context, their ability to improve the well-being & growth of their communities. In addition, AIO projects & initiatives include: partnering with Indigenous communities worldwide through the newly formed international organization, the Advancement of Global Indigeneity, an outgrowth of a partnership with the Advancement of Maori Opportunity (AMO), New Zealand; developing solutions through consensus building methodology, as a developer and facilitator of the

Indigenous Leadership Interactive System (ILIS™); enhancing intergovernmental relations & acting as a resource & facilitation center. *Awards*: The Eugene Crawford Memorial Peace Pipe Award; The Taos Blue Lake Spirit of Indigeneity Award; *Publication*: The Ambassador: Newsletter of "The American Indian Ambassadors Program; Annual Report; e-News. Established 1970.

AMERIND FOUNDATION, INC.
2100 N. Amerind Rd., P.O. Box 400 • Dragoon, AZ 85609-0400
(520) 586-3666 Fax 586-4679
Website: www.amerind.org; E-mail: amerind@amerind.org
Christine Szuter, Executive Director
E-mail: cszuter@amerind.org
Annie larkin, Associate Curator of Public Programs
E-mail: alarkin@amerind.org
Eric Kaldahl, Chief Curator & Deputy Director
E-mail: ekaldahl@amerind.org
Deni Mitchell, Director of Museum Services
E-mail: deni@amerind.org
Sally Newland, Librarian; E-mail: libros@amerind.org
Description: A nonprofit archaeological research institution & museum specializing in Native American cultures of the Americas. *Facilities*: Amerind Museum, Research Center, Library, and Art Gallery; Museum store. *Programs*: School Programs; Seminar Programs. *Activities*: Archaeological field research in the Greater Southwest; Semiannual meetings in May & November; events, workshops & tours. *Publications*: Amerind Quarterly; Amerind Technical Reports; New World Studies Series (UNM Press); Amerind Studies in Archaeology Series (UA Press) on the archaeology of the Southwest & Northern Mexico. Established 1937.

AMERIND RISK MANAGEMENT CORP.
502 Cedar Dr. • Santa Ana Pueblo, NM 87004
(800) 352-3496 Fax (800) 388-7475; (505) 404-5000 Fax 404-5001
Website: www.amerind-corp.org
Derek Valdo (Acoma), Chief Executive Officer
Dennis McCann, Chief Operating Officer
Geoffrey C. Blackwell (Muscogee (Creek)), Chief Strategy Officer & General Counsel
Greg Borene (Maidu), Chairperson
Description: The only 100% Native American owned & operated insurance provider in Indian Country. Incudes a consortium of tribes & tribal housing authorities throughout the U.S. working together to protect themselves & their tribal families from disasters. Represented by nine regions with each region electing a representative to serve on the Board of Directors. *Activities*: Provides risk management consulting services & insurance products to Native American & Alaska Native Housing Authorities, Tribal Designated Housing Entities, Tribal organizations and their tribal members. The primary focus has been the management of a risk sharing pool providing property & casualty protection for Indian housing, currently 220 members representing more than 400 tribes. Annual Conference & Trade Fair.

ANTIQUE TRIBAL ART DEALERS ASSOCIATION (ATADA)
215 Sierra SE • Albuquerque, NM 87108
Website: www.atada.org
David Ezziddine, Executive Director & Secretary
(505) 984-3216 Fax 986-0765
John Molloy, President; Peter Carl, Vice President
(212) 249-3020; E-mail: info@johnmolloygallery.com
Steve Begner, Treasurer (505) 823-4560
Barry Walsh, Education Committee Chair
(978) 544-0231; E-mail: rbauver@hughes.net
W. Roger Fry, Legal Committee Co-chair
E-mail: wfry@rendigs.com (513) 381-9200
Len Weakley, Legal Committee Co-chair (513) 381-9265
Description: Established to set ethical & professional standards for the trade and to provide education for the public. Members pledge to act as honest brokers, to guarantee authenticity and to provide the buying public with the available information on the age, source, integrity and collection history of the objects that they sell. *Activities*: Gallery & Directory. *Publications*: ATADA News; Native American Art & the Law, A Collector's Guide (ATADA Foundation, 2010).

THE APPLESEED FOUNDATION - TRIBAL PARTNERSHIP PROGRAM
727 15th St. NW • Washington, DC 20005
(202) 347-7960 Fax 347-7961
Website: www.appleseednetwork.org
Bert Brandenburg, President
E-mail: bbrandenburg@appleseednetwork.org
Purpose: To assist Native Americans by matching pro-bono counsel from several top firms with individual tribes & Native American organizations throughout the country. Founded 1993.

THE ARCHAEOLOGICAL CONSERVANCY
1717 Girard Blvd. NE • Albuquerque, NM 87106
  (505) 266-1540; Website: www.archaeologicalconservancy.org
  Gordon P. Wilson, Chairperson
  Jim Walker, Southwest Regional Director; E-mail: tacsw@nm.net
620 3rd St., Suite 300 • Lincoln, CA 95648 (530) 592-9797 (916) 424-6240
  Cory D. Wilkins, Western Regional Director; E-mail: tac-west@comcast.net
3620 N. High St., Suite 307 • Columbus, OH 43214 (614) 267-1100
  Paul Gardner, Midwest Regional Director; E-mail: tac-midwest@sbcglobal.net
8 East 2nd St., Suite 101 • Frederick, MD 21701 (301) 682-6359
  Andy Stout, Eastern Regional Director; E-mail: tac_east@verizon.net
P.O. Box 270 • Marks, MS 38646 (662) 326-6465
  Jessica Crawford, Southeast Regional Director
  E-mail: tacsoutheast@cableone.net
Membership: 17,000. People interested in preserving prehistoric & historic sites for interpretive or research purposes. *Purpose*: To acquire for permanent preservation the ruins of past American cultures, primarily those of American Indians. *Publication*: "American Archaeology" (quarterly). Established 1980.

ARCHAEOLOGICAL INSTITUTE OF AMERICA (AIA)
656 Beacon St., 6th Floor • Boston, MA 02215
  (617) 353-9361 Fax 353-6550; Website: www.archaeological.org
  Ann Benbow, Executive Director; E-mail: abenbow@aia.bu.edu
  Kevin Quinlan, COO/Publisher; E-mail: kquinlan@aia.bu.edu
Membership: 11,000. Educational & scientific society of archaeologists & others interested in archaeological study & research. *Activities*: Workshops; Archaeological Fairs; Conferences; Annual Meeting. *Publications*: Newsletter; Archaeology Magazine, bimonthly; Dig Magazine, bimonthly (children's magazine); American Journal of Archaeology, quarterly; Archaeological Fieldwork Opportunities Bulletin, annual. Annual meeting. Established 1879.

ASSOCIATION FOR THE STUDY OF AMERICAN INDIAN LITERATURES (ASAIL)
775 New York Ave. • Brooklyn, NY 11203
  Website: www.asail.org
  Jill Doerfler, President; E-mail: doerflj@d.umn.edu
  Chadwick Allen, SAIL Editor (Ohio State University)
  Robert Nelson, Historian (University of Richmond (VA)
Membership: Primarily academic, and those involved one way or another with the study of or creation of Native American literatures (oral as well as print, old time as well as contemporary). *Mission*: To promote the study, criticism, and research of American Indian written & oral literary traditions. An affiliate of Modern Language Assn. *Publication*: Studies in American Indian Literatures, quarterly scholarly journal focusing exclusively on American Indian literatures.

ASSOCIATION OF AMERICAN INDIAN & ALASKA NATIVE PROFESSORS
University of Wisconsin-Milwaukee, P.O. Box 413 • Milwaukee, WI 53201
  (414) 229-6251; Michael Wilson, Contact; E-mail: Michael@uwm.edu
Purpose: To continue the process of communication between and among current & potential members; to stimulate research in Indian/Alaska Native issues in all disciplines; to promote American Indian/Alaska Native intellectualism. *Database*: Nativeprofs-list@uwm.edu – A listserv for and about the American Indian & Alaska Native Professoriate's 300+ members from more than 100 colleges & universities. *Activities*: Annual conference. Established 1993.

ASSOCIATION OF AMERICAN INDIAN PHYSICIANS (AAIP)
1225 Sovereign Row #103 • Oklahoma City, OK 73108
  (405) 946-7072 Fax 946-7651
  Website: www.aaip.com; E-mail: admin@aaip.com
  Ron Shaw, MD (Osage), Board President (2016-17)
  Gerald Hill, MD (Klamath/Paiute), Past President (2015-16)
  Andrew Haputa, MD (Cherokee), Past President (2014-15)
  Adrian Begay MD (Navajo-Dine'), Past President (2013-14)
  Polly Olsen (Yakama), Executive Director; E-mail: polsen@aaip.com
  John Stafford (Muscogee (Creek)), Program Director
  E-mail: jstafford@aaip.com
  Gary Lankford (Cherokee), Program Director; E-mail: glankford@aaip.com
  Alex Springer (Seminole of Oklahoma), Communications Manager
  E-mail: aspringer@aaip.com
Membership: 350+ physicians (MD/DO) of 1/8 American Indian descent or more. *Purpose*: To pursue excellence in Native American healthcare by promoting education in the medical disciplines, honoring traditional healing principles & restoring the balance of mind, body & spirit; to encourage & recruit American Indians into the health professions; to provide a forum for the interchange of ideas & information of mutual interest between physicians; to make recommendations to government agencies regarding the health of American Indians & Alaska Natives; to enter into contracts with these agencies to provide consultation and other expert opinions regarding health care of American Indians & Alaska Natives. *Program*: The National Native American Youth Initiative - A Health, Biomedical Research, & Policy Development

Program for Native American high school students between the ages of 16 & 18. To motivate them to remain in the academic pipeline and to pursue a career in the health professions and/or biomedical research; & prepare students for admission to college & professional schools. *Activities*: Seeks scholarship funds for Indian professional students; conducts seminars for students interested in health careers; Annual meeting in August. *Publications*: Quarterly AAIP newsletter; American Indian Health Careers Handbook. Annual conference. Established 1971.

ASSOCIATION OF COMMUNITY TRIBAL SCHOOLS (ACTS)
220 Omaha St., P.O. Box 1518 • Mission, SD 57555
  (605) 838-0424 (phone & fax); Website: www.acts-tribal.org
  Roger C. Bordeaux (Rosebud Lakota), Executive Director
  Tom Miller (Potawatomi), Board President
Membership: American Indian controlled schools organized under the Indian Self-Determination Education Assistance Act & Tribally Controlled Schools Act. *Mission*: To assist Community Tribal Schools towards their mission of ensuring that when students complete their schools they are prepared for lifelong learning & that these students will strengthen & perpetuate traditional tribal societies. *Goals*: To provide tribal specific accreditation; to provide timely communication to member schools; to publish one yearly manual for member schools; to represent member schools at congressional hearings, etc.; to provide an ACTS webpage to circulate information. *Publication*: Quarterly newsletter. Established 1982.

ASSOCIATION OF NATIVE AMERICAN MEDICAL STUDENTS (ANAMS)
1225 Sovereign Row #103 • Oklahoma City, OK 73159
  (405) 946-7072 Fax 946-7651; Website: www.anamstudents.org
  Aaron Robinson (Menominee), Presient (2016-17)
  Paul Blackcloud (Hunkpapa Lakota), Past President (2015-16)
  Ryan Wilson (Inupiaq), Past President (2014-15)
  Michelle Huyser (Navajo-Dine') Past President (2013-14)
Membership: 100; Student organization representing Native American graduate health profession students throughout the U.S. & Canada. Comprised of Native American students enrolled in medical school or in allied health professions. *Purpose*: To aid its members in the successful completion of their graduate health professions curricula; to provide a forum for the interchange of ideas & information between Native American graduate health profession students; to make recommendations to governmental & other organizations regarding the health & education of Native Americans; to encourage the recruitment & retention of Native Americans in medicine. *Publication*: AIDS Regional Directory: Resources in Indian Country. Established 1975.

ASSOCIATION OF TRIBAL ARCHIVES, LIBRARIES, & MUSEUMS (ATALM) 6308 Harden Dr. • Oklahoma City, OK 73118
  (405) 522-3515; Website: www.atalm.org
  Susan Feller, President & CEO; (405) 401-8293)
  E-mail: susan@atalm.org
  Melissa Brodt, Project Director (405) 401-9657
  E-mail: melissa@atalm.org
  Walter Echo-Hawk, Board Chair
Description: A non-profit organization that maintains a network of support for indigenous programs, provides culturally relevant programming & services, encourages collaboration among tribal & non-tribal cultural institutions, and articulates contemporary issues related to developing & sustaining the cultural sovereignty of Native Nations. *Programs*: Annual Guardians of Culture & Lifeways International Awards. *Activities*: Annual Conference in October. *Publications*: Reports. Established 2007.

ASSOCIATION ON AMERICAN INDIAN AFFAIRS
966 Hungerford Dr., Suite 12-B • Rockville, MD 20850
  (240) 314-7155 Fax 314-7159
  Website: https://www.indian-affairs.org
  E-mail: general.aaia@indian-affairs.org
  Kimberly A. Dutcher (Navajo-Dine'), Executive Director
Board members: Faith Roessel (Navajo), President
  Alfred R. Ketzler, Sr. (Athabascan), Vice President
  Brad Keeler (Cherokee), Treasurer; Frank Ettawageshik (Odawa), Secretary
Field office: P.O. Box 8 • Hollister, NC 27844
  (252) 467-8918 Fax (877) 755-4720
AAIA Language Program: P.O. Box 509 • Agency Village, SD 57262
  (605) 698-4400 ext. 367 Fax 698-7067
  Tammy DeCoteau (Sisseton-Wahpeton Oyate), Director
Membership: 30,000. *Mission*: To promote the health, education, & welfare of children & youth; sustaining & perpetuating tribal languages & cultures; protecting tribal sovereignty, religions & natural resources; advocating for tribal constitutional, legal, human rights. *Programs*: Religious Freedom; Repatriation; Language Preservation; Health-Diabetes Prevention; Scholarships; Youth Programs/Summer Camps; Indian Child Welfare; Federal Acknowledgement. Aids Indian tribes in mobilizing all available resources--federal, state & private-- for a coordinated attack on the problems of poverty & injustice, and protects

the constitutional & treaty rights of Native peoples, as well as their special aboriginal rights. *Scholarships*: The Adolph Van Pelt Scholarship; the Sequoyah Graduate Scholarship; David Risling Emergency Aid Scholarship; Florence Young Memorial Scholarship; The Displaced Homemaker Scholarship; The Elizabeth & Sherman Asche Memorial Scholarship to graduate & undergraduate students pursuing a major in public health, preferably with an emphasis in Diabetes; and the Allogan Slagle Scholarship for students from tribes that are not federally recognition. *Publications*: Indian Affairs, Biannual newsletter; 1996 Proceedings of the National Sacred Sites Caucus. Archives are held at Princeton University Mudd Library. Established 1922.

NOTAH BEGAY III FOUNDATION

290 Prairie Star Rd. • Santa Ana Pueblo, NM 87004
(505) 867-0775 Fax 867-0776
Website: www.nb3foundation.org; E-mail: info@nb3f.org
Notah Begay III (Navajo/San Felipe Pueblo), Founder
  Website: www.notah.com
Justin Huenemann (Dine'), President & CEO
Clint Begay (Dine'/San Felipe & Isleta Pueblos), Program Director
Sean McCabe (Dine'), Board Chairperson
James Meggesto (Onondaga), Vice Chairperson
Cathy Newby (Dine'), Treasurer
Purpose: To create sustainable programs designed by Native Americans for Native American youth that will promote good health & leadership development. To help tribal nations build the capacity to design & sustain effective sports, wellness & youth development programs for Native American youth. Established 2005.

BLACK NATIVE AMERICAN ASSOCIATION (BNAA)

(843) 476-3634; Don 'Little Cloud' Davenport (Seminole), Founder
Zenobia Embry-Nimmer (Cherokee), Co-founder
Richard 'Rip' Harris (Creek/Choctaw), Co-founder
Bonita Roxie Aleja Sizemore
  (Poarch Creek/Seminole/Choctaw/Cherokee)
Description: An intertribal group of people with African-American and Native American heritage that organized in late summer 1992 in the Oakland-San Francisco Bay Area. Membership includes indigenous peoples from all over the world. *Activities*: Speakers Bureau; national powwow; tribal ceremonies; native languages; drum classes; referral services.

BOWMAN PERFORMANCE CONSULTING, LLC

271 River Pine Dr., Shawano, WI 54166
(715) 526-9240 Fax 526-6028
Website: www.bpcwi.com; E-mail: info@bpcwi.com
Nicole R. Bowman-Farrell (Mohican/Munsee), President & Founder
  E-mail: nbowman@bpcwi.com
Linda Sue Warner (Comanche), Senior Project Manager
  E-mail: lwarner@bpcwi.com
Martin Reinhardt (Mohican/Munsee), Senior Level Project Consultant
Karen Washinawatok (Menominee), Cultural Resource & Research Specialist
Purpose: BPC is the only certified Native American professional consulting & scientific research and evaluation firm in the country. Provides business, educational, professional development & training consulting services working within tribal communities as well as bridging tribal & non-tribal groups on policy, research, strategic planning, and evaluation topics.

BUREAU OF CATHOLIC INDIAN MISSIONS

2021 H St., NW • Washington, DC 20006
(877) 237-1605; (202) 331-8542 Fax 331-8544
Website: www.blackandindianmission.org
Father Maurice Henry Sands, Executive Director
Purpose: The support of Catholic Indian missions, parishes, schools, centers, and activities; the advocacy for national legislation for the benefit of all American Indian tribes, pueblos, nations. *Activities*: Archives--located in the library at Marquette University, Milwaukee, Wisconsin; participation in the Tekakwitha Conference; testimony to congressional committees on legislation affecting Indian groups; presentations on Indian issues to organizations; grants to Catholic Indian organizations through the diocese in which they are located. *Publications*: Native Scholar, annual magazine; The Sentinel, quarterly newsletter. Established 1874.

CATCHING THE DREAM

8200 Mountain Rd., NE #203 • Albuquerque, NM 87110
(505) 262-2351 Fax 262-0534
Website: www.catchingthedream.org; E-mail: nscholarsh@aol.com
Dean Chavers (Lumbee), Director & Board member
  E-mail: ctd4deanchavers@aol.com
Joy Noll, Business Manager

James Lujan (Taos Pueblo), Board President
  E-mail: jlujantaos@yahoo.com
Darrell F. Jeanotte (Turtle Mountain Chippewa), Vice President
  E-mail: jeanotte@dakota2k.net
Gloria Hale (Navajo), Treasurer
Jodie Palmer (Potawatomi), Secretary
  E-mail: jodie.palmer@wmich.edu
Membership: 600. Native Americans and others working to ensure that Native American college students prepare adequately for college, enroll, graduate, & return to their tribes as doctors, nurses, teachers, engineers, business entrepreneurs, dentists, & computer programmers. Also advocates for school improvement for reservation schools. *Programs*: Operates six grant programs for school improvement - The Reading Award Program; The Native Educator Scholarship Program; The Golden Star Attendance (GSA) Program; The Supplemental Literacy Grant; Numerous Awards. Holds an annual Exemplary Institute featuring successful Indian education program; seminars & conferences. *Publications*: Newsletter; annual report in September. Publishes books on Indian education, exemplary programs, proposal writing, & management: The National Indian Grant Directory; How to Write Winning Proposals; Racism in Indian Country; Research in Indian Education; Deconstructing the Myths; Indian Students & College Preparation; Indian Teachers & Indian Control; The Secret of No Face; Exemplary Programs in Indian Education; Basics of Fundraising. Established 1987.

CENTER FOR AMERICAN INDIAN ECONOMIC DEVELOPMENT (CAIED)

W.A. Franke College of Business, Alliance Bank Business Outreach Center
Box 15066, Northern Arizona University • Flagstaff, AZ 86011
(928) 523-7320 Fax 523-5990
Website: www.cba.nau.edu/caied; E-mail: caied@nau.edu
N. Levi Esquerra (Chemehuevi), Director; E-mail: levi.esquerra@nau.edu
Gwen Cody, Program Coordinator; E-mail: gwen.cody@nau.edu
Crystal Cree, Coordinator; E-mail: crystal.cree@nau.edu
Description: Acts as an information & resource center for the 22 tribal nations & communities located in Arizona. *Program*: Native American Hospitality Leadership Program. *Activities*: Maintains a database library offering current information on Arizona tribes; services include technical assistance, business consulting & training; Tribal Leadership Summit & Conferences. *Publication*: Doing Business on Arizona Indian Lands, CD-ROM, $49.95. Established 1985.

CENTER FOR AMERICAN INDIAN HEALTH

Johns Hopkins Bloomberg School of Public Health
621 N. Washington St. • Baltimore, MD 21205
(410) 955-6931 Fax 955-2010; Website: www.jhsph.edu/caih
Allison Barlow, Director; E-mail: abarlow@jhsph.edu
Shannon Archuleta & Anna Beach, Administrative Coordinators (Whiteriver)
Kendrea Begay, Research Program Supervisor (Chinle, AZ)
  E-mail: kbegay@jhsph.edu
Mathuram Santosham, MD, MPH, Director Emeritus
  E-mail: msantosh@jhsph.edu
Faculty: Albuquerque Office: Nicole Neault, MPH, Kristen Speakman, MPH; *Gallup Office*: Jim Campbell, MD, Dan VanDeRiet, MD, Raymond Reid, MD; *Whiteriver Office*: Laura Brown, MD, Kathleen Norton, MEd
Mission: To work in partnership with tribes to research, design, implement, and evaluate interventions to raise the health & wellbeing of American Indians to the highest possible level. *Facilities & Personnel*: The placement within the Johns Hopkins Medical Institutions allows the Center to draw on vast intellectual resources & multi-disciplined approaches to address tribes' priority health & social problems. The Center currently operates 11 health stations on the Navajo (AZ/NM), White Mountain Apache (AZ), and Wind River (WY) Reservations, whose combined populations represent about one-fourth of American Indians living on reservations in the U.S. Over the past five years, the Center has conducted additional projects with tribes in North Carolina, California, South Dakota, Alaska, Michigan, Wisconsin, and Oklahoma. More than half of the Center's 70-person staff is American Indian, including an American Indian physician, more than 30 Native outreach workers, and four field-based project coordinators. *Programs*: All programs are crafted to increase the skill and capacity of tribes. Each initiative includes a training and employment component to ensure that indigenous workers carry out the work. For the NATIVEVISION program (www.nativevision.org), the Center provides ongoing technical expertise to Native communities to support all aspects of the planning, design, implementation & evaluation of NATIVEVISION programs. Johns Hopkins employs local program coordinators to oversee the day-to-day operations of the NATIVEVISION on the reservations involved. *Activities*: Operates an annual Sports Camp that is helped funded by the NFL (National Football league) Players Association (www.nflpa.org). It also helps with the management of the camp by recruiting pro athletes from various sports to adopt and routinely visit the NATIVE VISION communities across the America. The Nick Lowery (ex-NFL player) Foundation (www.nicklowery.com) assists with youth development strategies, as well as recruitment of athletes & Native American role models, & development of financial resources. Established 1991.

CENTER FOR INDIAN COMMUNITY DEVELOPMENT (CICD)
Humboldt State University, 1 Harpst St. • Arcata, CA 95521
(707) 826-3711 Fax 826-5258
 Website: www.humboldt.edu/cicd; E-mail: crc@humboldt.edu
Zo Devine, Associate Director; Nancy J. Busler, Administrative Coordinator
Description: Collection covers community economic & organizational development, assessment of local needs for archaeological research, regeneration of American Indian languages & literatures and the application of computer systems to publication of Indian languages. *Purpose*: To provide services to American Indian communities in Northern California. *Resources*: Library; Goudi'ni Native American Arts Gallery; Indian Teacher & Education Personnel Program (ITEPP); Indian Natural Resource, Science & Engineering Program (INSREP); Native American Forum (used for events, speakers, meetings). *Programs*: The American Indian Language Program; publishes textbooks & instructional material in and about Hupa, Karuk, Tolowa, Yurok, and other Indian languages; Native American Forum. *Publications*: Now You're Speaking Karuk, 2nd Ed.; Now You're Speaking Tolowa; Now You're Speaking Hupa: The Hupa People, Their Language, 2nd revised Ed.; Environmental Protection, Native American Lands: A Cultural Approach to Integrated Environmental Studies; Hupa Language Dictionaries; The Evolution of Tribal Governments & Constitutions. Established 1966.

CENTER FOR INDIGENOUS ARTS & CULTURES
Division of Southwest Learning Centers, Inc.
P.O. Box 2626 • Santa Fe, NM 87504-8627
(505) 473-5375 Fax 466-5375
 Website: www.indianartbooks.com; E-mail: indians@nets.com
Gregory Schaaf, PhD, Director; Angie Van Schaaf, Assistant Director
Purpose: To provide services to American Indians and communities, as well as providing educational materials for the general public. CIAC Press is a non-profit publishing company that produces books, videotapes, CDs and other forms of media. Monthly seminars are offered related to American Indian art & cultural activities. CIAC will help any American Indian artist develop their biography free of charge. *Activities/Programs*: "The American Indian Art Series," is a planned 20-vol. series featuring American Indian artist biographical profiles grouped by art form. Five volumes are now available: Vol. 1 - Hopi-Tewa Pottery: 500 Artist Biographies, $50; Vol. 2 - Pueblo Indian Pottery: 750 Artist Biographies, Limited Ed., $250; Vol. 3 - American Indian Textiles: 2,000 Artist Biographies, $65; Vol. 4 - Southern Pueblo Pottery: 2,000 Artist Biographies, $65; Vol. 5 - American Indian Jewelry I: 1,200 Artist Biographies, $65; Vol. 6 - American Indian Baskets I: 1,500 Artist Biographies, $65; Vol. 7 – Hopi Katsina: 1,600 Artist Biographies, $65; Vol. 8 – American Indian Jewelry II: A-L: 1,800 Artist Biographies, $70; Vol. 9 – American Indian Jewelry III: M-Z: 2,100 Artist Biographies, $70; Vol. 10 – Artists of Indian Market: 1922 to the present. Future volumes will profile sculptors, bead-workers, doll-makers, musical instrument makers, clothing designers and more. The last three volumes will be the Native artists of Mexico, Central & South America. Once completed the series will embrace over 30,000 artists throughout the Western Hemisphere. Features a small museum with over 3,000 objects in the collection. There is a small library & archives featuring over 100,000 documents. *Publications*: Beyond the "American Indian Art Series," CIAC also distributes other works by Dr. Gregory Schaaf. Established 1972.

CENTER FOR INDIGENOUS PEOPLES STUDIES (CIPS)
California State University, San Bernardino
5500 University Pkwy. • San Bernardino, CA 92407
 (909) 537-5000; Website: www.cips.csueb.edu
James V. Fenelon, Director; Thomas Long, Associate Director
Purpose: To study American Indians & local, national & international indigenous peoples. The Center conducts research, facilitates curricular & instructional programs, coordinates academic activities & interacts on at least four levels of indigenous peoples, contributing to the development of knowledge & advancement of related social issues.

THE CENTER FOR THE STUDY OF AMERICAN INDIAN LAW & POLICY
Native American Law Program, University of Oklahoma
College of Law, 300 Timberdell Rd. • Norman, OK 73019
 (405) 325-4676 Fax 325-6282
 Lindsay Robertson, Faculty Director; E-mail: lrobertson@ou.edu
Joint Degree Program: J.D. & Master in American Indian Studies. *Native American Resources*: American Indian Law Review; Native American Constitution & Law Digitization Project - Cooperative effort by the Law Center and the National Indian Law Library (NILL) of the Native American Rights Fund, and Native American tribes providing access to the Constitution, Tribal Codes, and other legal documents. Native American Law Student Association (NALSA). NALSA Moot Court Competition.

CENTER FOR THE STUDY OF ETHNICITY & RACE
Columbia University, 422 Hamilton Hall, M.C. 2880
1130 Amsterdam Ave. • New York, NY 10027
(212) 854-0507

 Website: www.cser.columbia.edu; E-mail: cser@columbia.edu
Josephine Caputo, Coordinator; E-mail: jc2768@columbia.edu
Frances Negron-Muntaner, Director; E-mail: fn2103@columbia.edu
Teresa Aguayo, Assistant Director (854-0510)
 E-mail: ta2015@columbia.edu
John Gamber, English Faculty
Mission: To support & promote the innovative thinking about race, ethnicity, indigeneity and other categories of difference to better understand their role & impact in modern society. *Activities*: Conferences, seminars, exhibits, film screenings, & lectures. The CSER has become the home of Native American/Indigenous Studies as an area of specialization.

CENTER FOR THE STUDY OF THE FIRST AMERICANS
Department of Anthropology, Texas A&M University
4352 TAMU • College Station, TX 77843-4352
(979) 845-4046 Fax 845-4070
 Website: csfa.tamu.edu; E-mail: csfa@tamu.edu
Michael Waters, Director
Ted Goebel, Associate Director; E-mail: goebel@tamu.edu
Mission: To develop new knowledge regarding Paleo-American origins, human dispersal, settlement, & cultural & biological development that occurred during the Pleistocene; to train students who will go on to continue First Americans research; to disseminate the results of academic research about the first Americans to the general public through our publications. *Publications*: Mammoth Trumpet, a quarterly news magazine providing articles about the First Americans; Current Research in the Pleistocene (available, 28 back issues...discontinued in 2012); The Simon Clovis Cache (book, including photos & line drawings of 32 artifacts in the Herrett collection); numerous other books, including: Who Were the First Americans? New Perspectives on the First Americans; Ice Age Peoples of North America, available from Texas A&M U. Press.

**CENTER FOR THE STUDY OF LEADERSHIP
IN AMERICAN INDIAN EDUCATION**
College of Education - Education Policy Studies Dept.
Pennsylvania State University, 302A Rackley Bldg.
University Park, PA 16802 (814) 865-1489
 Felicia Wilkins Turner, Interim Director
Program: American Indian Leadership Program (AILP). *Purpose*: To conduct research & outreach that helps inform the public & improve the education of American Indians & Alaska Natives at the local, state, tribal, national & international levels. *Goal*: To serve as clearinghouse on American Indian/Alaska Native education, research, policy, and practice. *Activities*: To train qualified leaders for service to Indian nations by providing graduate degrees in educational administration & certification credentials of principals & superintendents. Fellowships. Library. Established 2010.

CENTER FOR WORLD INDIGENOUS STUDIES
PMB 214, 1001 Cooper Point Rd. SW, Suite 140 • Olympia, WA 98502
(360) 529-4896 Fax (253) 276-0084; Website: www.cwis.org
 Rudolph C. Ryser (Cowlitz), Chairperson
 Director; Ku Kalakahua (Hawaiian), Director;
 John Schertow, Director; Gregg Wilkinson, Director
 Jennifer Rubis, Treasurer; Russell Jim (Yakama), Secretary
 Gordon Pllar (Aleut), Sharon H. Eluska (Navajo), Randy Scott (Tlingit),
 Rossalee Tizya (Vandu Kutchin), et al., Founding Advisory Board
Description: A non-profit research & education organization. Goal: To establish cooperation between nations & to democratize international relations between nations & between nations & states. *Facilities*: Center for Traditional Medicine; Chief George Manuel Library; Forum for Global Exchange. *Programs*: Certificate Program; Masters Degree program; Internships; Associate Scholars Program; American Indian Caregiver Study; Media Center (offers related audio & video, books & maps); CWIS Store; Consultation Services. Multimedia Course: A Comprehensive Evidenced-Based Course for Practitioners & Families Living with Diabetes - Books: Preventing & Treating Diabetes, Naturally: The Native Way; Health Wellness & Pride (free download). *Resources*: Fourth World Institute; Center for Traditional Medicine; Forum for Global Exchange; Daykeeper Press; The Chief George Manuel Memorial Library. *Video*: Polarity Therapy Protocol: Treatment for Diabetes (free download). *Audios*: Salish Food Gathering Preparation & Preserving Methods for Health (free); Oolichan Oil: Elixir of the Sea (free download); Relaxation & Guided Imagery for Diabetes (free download). PowerPoint: Traditional Medicine & Culinary Pedagogy (free download). *Publications*: Fourth World Journal; Publication & distribution of literature written & voiced by leading contributors from Fourth World Nations.

CENTER OF AMERICAN INDIAN & MINORITY HEALTH (CAIMH)
Duluth Campus: Duluth School of Medicine
University of Minnesota, Room 182-SMed
1035 University Dr. • Duluth, MN 55812-2487
(218) 726-7235 Fax 726-8948

Twin Cities Campus: University of Minnesota, Rm. D604 Mayo Memorial Bldg.
420 Delaware St. SE • Minneapolis, MN 55455 (612) 624-0465 Fax 624-0473
  Website: www.caimh.umn.edu; E-mail: caimh@d.umn.edu
  Mary J. Owen, MD, Director; E-mail: mjowen@d.umn.edu
  Anna Wirta Kosobuski (Bois Forte Ojibwe), Associate Director
    E-mail: awirta1@d.umn.edu
Purpose: To offer today's American Indian students a pathway to achieve a successful career in health or science related careers. *Programs*: Summer Programs; Health Careers Opportunities Program (HCOP); Native Americans Into Medicine (NAM). Established 1987.

CENTERS FOR AMERICAN INDIAN & ALASKA NATIVE HEALTH
American Indian & Alaska Native Programs
University of Colorado Health Sciences Center
Nighthorse Campbell Native Health Bldg.
13055 E. 17th Ave., MS: F800 • Aurora, CO 80045
  (303) 724-1414 Fax 724-1474
  E-mail: caianh.webmaster@ucdenver.edu
  Judith Albino, Professor & President Emerita
    E-mail: Judith.albino@ucdenver.edu
  Spero M. Manson, Director; E-mail: spero.manson@ucdenver.edu
  Terry Batliner, DDS, Associate Director; E-mail: terry.batliner@ucdenver.edu
  Doug Novins, Associate Director; E-mail: douglas.novins@ucdenver.edu
  Lori Trullinger, Center Administrator; E-mail: lori.trullinger@ucdenver.edu
  Erin Swyers, Project Manager; E-mail: erin.swyers@ucdenver.edu
Mission: To promote the health & wellbeing of American Indians & Alaska Native Health. The Center has 4 major program functions: Research, research training, information dissemination, & technical assistance. *Projects & Centers*: Center for Excellence in Eliminating Health Disparities; Center for Native Oral Health Resources; Circles of Care Evaluation Technical Assistance Center; Head Start Research Center; Native Elder Research Center; Resource Center for Minority Aging Research; Project EXPORT; REACH; Special Diabetes Program for Indians Competitive Grant Program Coordinating Center; Trial Early Childhood Research Center. Publications. Journal.

CHEROKEE INDIAN TRIBE ONLINE RECORDS
  Website: www.nanations.com
  Website: www.accessgenealogy.com/native
  Website: www.cherokeeheritage.org
  Website: www.archives.gov
  Website: www.kindredtrails.com
Purpose: Provides individual & family heritage charts for Cherokees nationally. The charge is $25 to search 43 records, 7 of them are of the Cherokee in the Civil War. The fee is for all the information on the records from 1817-1924.

CHEROKEE LANGUAGE & CULTURE
3639 S. Fir Blvd. • Broken Bow, OK 74011
  (918) 893-1581; Website: www.cherokeemadeeasy.com
  Prentice & Willena Robinson, Owners; E-mail: prenticewillena@aol.com
Purpose: To keep the Cherokee language and history alive & as accurate as possible. *Programs*: Lectures on language and history. *Publications*: Book & tapes - Cherokee Made Easy. Study course - workbook & tape (language study); hymns/history book; Your Name in Cherokee book; picture associated Syllable Flash Cards; national award winning videos on Cherokee history & Native American artists. Established 1974.

THE CHEROKEE NATION FOUNDATION
800 S. Muskogee • Tahlequah, OK 74464
  (918) 207-0950; Website: www.cherokeenationfoundation.org
  E-mail: contact@cherokeenationfoundation.org
  Janice Randall (Cherokee) Executive Director
Mission: To provides educational assistance to more than 300,000 Cherokee citizens while helping to revitalize the Cherokee language.

CHEROKEE NATIONAL HISTORICAL SOCIETY
Cherokee Heritage Center, P.O. Box 515 • Tahlequah, OK 74465
  (888) 999-6007; (918) 456-6007 Fax 456-6165
  Website: www.cherokeeheritage.org
  Candessa Tehee, (Cherokee), Executive Director
  Callie Chunestudy (Cherokee), Museum Curator
  Gina Burnett, Outreach Coordinator
  Noel Grayson, Village Supervisor
  Tonia Weavel, Education Director
Description: Persons & organizations interested in preserving the history & traditions of the Cherokee Indian Nation. *Purpose*: To interest the public in Cherokee history; to mark locations of historic significance to the Cherokees. Resources: Cherokee Heritage Center; Cherokee Village; Trail of Tears Exhibit. *Activities/Programs*: Sponsors educational, charitable, & benevolent activities for Cherokees and their descendants; operated Cherokee Heritage Center, which includes the Cherokee National Museum, and Cherokee Arboretum and Herb Garden; maintains a "living" Indian Village, circa 1700-50

and a Rural Cherokee Museum Village, circa 1875-90; annually presents the Trail of Tears, an outdoor symphonic drama; maintains Cherokee Hall of Fame for persons of Cherokee descent; also maintains the Ho-Chee-Nee Trail of Tears Memorial Chapel; annual Trail of Tears Art Show; lecture series on Cherokee history and culture. *Publications*: The Columns, 4/year newsletter; Trail of Tears Drama Program, annual. Library.

CHICKASAW FOUNDATION
110 West 12th St. • Ada, OK 74821
  (580) 421-9030; Website: www.chickasawfoundation.org
    Email: chickasawfoundation@chickasaw.net
  Johnna R. Walker (Chickasaw), Executive Director
  Tracie Carter, Special Projects Coordinatoor
  Deanna Hartley-Kelso, Chairperson; Lisa John, Vice Chairperson
  Matthew Chestnut, Treasurer; Bill Lance, Secretary
Board Members: Tina M. Cooper; Dr. Judy Gooforth Parker,
  Kirk Perry; John Fryrear
Mission: To preserve, promote & protect Chickasaw culture & development, from historic preservation to healthcare. Offers a variety of scholarships, providing educational assistance for students who demonstrate excellence in academics, community service, dedication to Native American and a commitment to learning. Deadline to apply is June 1st.

CHRISTIAN HOPE INDIAN ESKIMO FELLOWSHIP (CHIEF)
1644 E. Campo Bello Dr. • Phoenix, AZ 85022
  (602) 482-0828 Fax 482-0860; Website: www.chief.org
  E-mail: info@chief.org; Rev. Tom Claus, Founder & President Emeritus
Description: A network of Native ministries & churches, including AmerTribes (website: www.amertribes.org). *Mission*: To disciple & equip a strong Native American leadership for the development of the indigenous church throughout North, Central & South America. Established 1975.

CIRCLE FOR AMERICAN INDIAN REHABILITATION (CAIR)
Interwork Institute, College of Education, San Diego State University
3950 Camino del Rio North • San Diego, CA 92108
  (619) 594-6163 Fax 594-4208
  Website: www.interwork.sdsu.edu/centers.html
  Jim E. Warne (Oglala Lakota), Director
    E-mail: jwarne@interwork.sdsu.edu
Purpose: To provide high standards of continuing education, training, & technical assistance. Hosts the American Indian Advisory Council Website. *Programs*: American Indian Vocational Rehabilitation Programs. Publication: CANAR Newsletter

CLAN STAR, INC.
732 Tsali Blvd., P.O. Box 1630 • Cherokee, NC 28719
  (888) 636-4748; (828) 497-5507 Fax 497-5688
  Website: www.clanstar.org
  Terri Henry (Eastern Cherokee), Founder & Principal Director
  Jacqueline Agtuca, J.D., Public Policy Director
Description: The mission of Clan Star is devoted to improving justice to strengthen the sovereignty of Indigenous women through legal, legislative and policy initiatives, and, education and awareness. Clan Star provides technical assistance, training and consultation to Indian Tribes and organizations in the development of public policy strategies addressing violence against women. CSI is a technical assistance provider to recipients of the OVW's Tribal Domestic Violence & Sexual Assault Coalitions grant program. Technical assistance is designed to increase organizational capacity to address the unmet needs of American Indian and Alaska Native women by supporting the development of the leadership and/or organizational membership to effect social change and systemic reform in response to violence against Indian women. Clan Star's technical assistance has specialized focus on the intersection of federal, tribal and state laws as those laws impact American Indian victims of domestic violence and sexual assault. Established 2001.

COMANCHE LANGUAGE & CULTURAL PRESERVATION COMMITTEE
1375 N.E. Cline Rd. • Elgin, OK 73538-3086
  (877) 492-4988; (580) 492-5126 Fax 492-5119
  Website: www.comanchelanguage.org
  E-mail: clcpc@comanchelanguage.org
  Winifred "Bud" (Yackeschi) Walters (Comanche), President
  Billie Kreger (Comanche), Vice President
  Barbara Goodin (Comanche), Secretary/Treasurer
Purpose: To revive the Comanche language into a "living language" once again; to foster a cooperative relationship among federal, state & tribal agencies, schools, parents and others for the preservation & promotion of the Comanche language & culture; to change the direction of the Comanche language -- from near extinction -- and to take our language into the future. *Activities*: Developed Comanche dictionary, flash cards, picture dictionary, language lessons, hymn book & college work books; administered immersion programs, children's camps, community language classes, & language

workshops; provide teachers for daycare & pre-schools; certified two speakers to teach in the Comanche Nation College. *Publications*: Quarterly language newsletter; Comanche dictionary, picture dictionary, flash cards, hymnbook, language lessons; cassettes & CDs. Established 1993.

CONSORTIA OF ADMINISTRATORS FOR NATIVE AMERICAN REHABILITATION, INC. (CANAR)
1775 Eye St., NW Suite 1150 • Washington, DC 20006
  (202) 587-2741 Fax (877) 260-8098
  Website: www.canar.org; E-mail: info@canar.org
  Lou Adams, Training Director
  Cinda Hughes, Legislative Affairs Coordinator
  E-mail: chughes@canar.org
Administrative Office: P.O. Box 45928 • Rio Rancho, NM 87174
  (505) 350-4258 Fax (877) 260-8098
  Lyle Cook (Cheyenne River Sioux), Board President
  E-mail: ability@lakotanetwork.com
  Lanor Curole (United Houma), Vice President
  E-mail: lanor.curole@unitedhoumanation.org
  Peggy Venable (Lower Muskogee Creek), Treasurer
  E-mail: mvr4@rose.net
  Celeste Hunt (Lumbee), Secretary; E-mail: chunt@lumbeetribe.com
Description: Works to advance & improve rehabilitation services for Native Americans. *Mission*: To serve as an avenue for collaboration & cooperation between administrators of rehabilitation projects serving Native American persons with disabilities; to increase & enhance the quality of services, resulting in positive outcomes for Native American persons with disabilities. *Program*: TVR CIRCLE (Trial Vocational Rehabilitation – Continuous Improvement of Rehabilitation Counselors, Leaders & Educators). *Activities*: Conferences & Training. *Publication*: Newsletter.

COUNCIL OF ENERGY RESOURCE TRIBES (CERT)
8200 S. Quebec St. #509 • Centennial, CO 80112
  (303) 345-5632 Fax 682-9743; Website: www.certredearth.com
  Clint LeBeau (Cheyenne River Sioux), Program Manager
Membership: 57. American Indian tribes owning energy resources. *Purpose*: To promote the general welfare of members through the protection, conservation, control & prudent management of their oil, coal, natural gas, uranium, and other resources. *Activities*: Provides on-site, technical assistance to tribes in energy resource management; conducts programs to enhance tribal planning & management capacities; sponsors workshops. Established 1975.

COUNCIL OF INDIAN NATIONS
P.O. Box 1800 • Apache Junction, AZ 85217
  (800) 811-6955; (540) 825-2605
  Website: www.nrcprograms.org; E-mail: info@cinprograms.org
  Lovena B. Lee, Chairperson; Lisa Begay, Program Coordinator
Purpose: To help Native American people improve the quality of their lives by providing opportunities for them to bring about positive changes in their communities. *Activities/Programs*: A non-profit organization that develops self-help programs & emergency relief services for Native Americans on reservations in the Southwest. Services include: emergency food distribution, clothing & shoe distributions, winterization of homes, school supplies, holiday dinners, gifts & stockings for children at Christmas & Easter, baby baskets for new mothers and incentive programs for seniors, adult volunteers & children. *Publication*: Quarterly newsletter. Established 1995.

COUNCIL ON NATIVE AMERICAN FARMING & RANCHING (CNAFR)
Office of Tribal Relations, U.S. Department of Agriculture
Rm. 500-A Whitten Bldg., 1400 Independence Ave. SW
Washington, DC 20250 (202) 205-2249 Fax 720-1058
  Leslie Wheelock, Director; E-mail: leslie.wheelock@osec.usda.gov
John Lowery, Tribal Relations Manager; E-mail: john.lowery@osec.usda.gov
The Office of Tribal Relations is the lead Agency that works with all USDA Mission Areas to stay advised and involved in the formal process of consultation with Tribal governments. The Office of Tribal Relations also works with the Office of Intergovernmental and External Affairs, the Office of General Counsel, the Senior Policy Team, and other key offices working across USDA. OTR also works with counterparts in other Federal agencies to achieve these goals.

CRAZY HORSE MEMORIAL FOUNDATION
12151 Avenue of the Chiefs • Crazy Horse, SD 57730
  (605) 673-4681 Fax 673-2185
  Website: www.crazyhorsememorial.org
  E-mail: memorial@crazyhorse.org
  Ruth Ziolkowski, Chief Executive Officer
  Dr. Laurie Becvar, President & Chief Operating Officer
  John Rozell, Chairperson; Bill Colson, Vice Chairperson
  Jadwiga Ziolkowski, Executive V.P./Secretary; Warren Harming, Treasurer

Purpose: To carve a mountain (Thunderhead Mountain) into the memorial statue of the Sioux Chief Crazy Horse, astride his pony, pointing to the lands of his people (563' high and 641' long.) Carved from Thunderhead Mountains in South Dakota by sculptor Korczak Ziolkowski, 1908-1982; and to build and maintain a university, museum, & medical center for Native Americans. *Activities*: Operates the Indian Museum of North America & Crazy Horse Memorial; offers scholarships to Native Americans. *Publications*: News from Crazy Horse Memorial, quarterly newsletter; Korczak: Storyteller in Stone (biography); Crazy Horse & Korczak; and Korczak, Saga of Sitting Bull's Bones and Crazy Horse Memorial 40th Anniversary Booklet. Library. Annual meeting. Established 1948.

THE CULTURAL CONSERVANCY (TCC)
1016 Lincoln Blvd., 1st Floor, P.O. Box 29044 • San Francisco, CA 94129
  (415) 561-6594 Fax 561-6482; Website: www.nativeland.org
  Melissa Kaye Nelson (Turtle Mountain Chippewa), President &
   Executive Director (1993-present)
  Nicola Wagenberg (Colombian), V.P. & Program Director for TCC
  Kaylena Bray (Seneca), Foodways Director
Purpose: To protect & restore indigenous cultures, empowering them in the direct application of their traditional knowledge & practices on their ancestral lands. Established 1985.

CULTURAL SURVIVAL
2067 Massachusetts Ave. • Cambridge, MA 02140
  (617) 441-5400 Fax 441-5417; Website: www.culturalsurvival.org
  E-mail: culturalsurvival@culturalsurvival.org
  Suzanne Benally (Navajo/Santa Clara Tewa), Executive Director
   E-mail: sbenally@cs.org
  Mark Camp, Deputy Executive Director; E-mail: mcamp@cs.org
  Sarah Fuller, President & Chairperson; Duane Champagne, Vice Chair
Description: International advocate for the human rights of indigenous peoples. Promotes the rights, voices & visions of indigenous peoples. *Programs*: Endangered Languages; Community Radio; Global Response; Bazaars. *Education & Outreach*: Internships; Cultural Survival Bazaar; Secondary School Program. *Special Projects*: Black Mesa Weavers for Life & Land; Indigenous Action Network; Ethnosphere Initiative. *Publications*: Cultural Survival Quarterly (newsletter); Cultural Survival Weekly Indigenous News; Cultural Survival Voices; World Indigenous News, free e-publication.

DINE POLICY INSTITUTE
Dine College, P.O. Box 96 • Tsaile, AZ 86556
  (928) 724-6942 Fax 724-6837
  Website: www.dinecollege.edu/institutes/dpi/
  Moroni Benally (Navajo), Director (724-6942)
   E-mail: mtbenally@dinecollege.edu
  Michael Parrish, Policy Analyst (724-6945)
   E-mail: mparrish@dinecollege.edu
Mission: Research organization for facilitating, analyzing issues, and educating to protect the sovereignty & cultural integrity of the Dine' (Navajo). *Program*: Advisory Circle - A panel of traditional knowledge holders (elders & medicine people) and Navajo scholars. *Activities*: Annual conference, workshops & seminars; internship program.

DISCOVER NATIVE AMERICA
2461 SW 85th Ter. • Fort Lauderdale, FL 33324
  (954) 370-3900 Fax 370-3999
  Website: www.discovernativeamerica.com
  Lee Tiger (Florida Seminole), Founder
Description: A website designed to give the world one convenient site to learn about the history & culture of the American Indian tribes of the U.S. *Mission*: To educate the general public regarding American Indian history & culture; to encourage communication among Indian tribes; to provide information on tribal activities & cultural events; to share information with native peoples & others throughout the world.

THE EDUCATION FOR PARENTS OF INDIAN CHILDREN WITH SPECIAL NEEDS (EPICS) PROJECT
Southwest Communication Resources, Inc.
1600 San Pedro Dr. NE • Albuquerque, NM 87110
  (888) 499-2070; (505) 767-6630 Fax 767-6631
  Website: www.epicsproject.org; E-mail: info@swcr.org
  Liz Martin (Navajo), Board President; Dale Vicente (Acoma) VP
  Alvino Sandoval (Navajo), Interim Executive Director & Program Manager
  Judy Wiley (Apache), NAPTAC Project Manager
  Brooke Garcia & Joseph Garcia (Navajo), Training Specialists
Purpose: To provide services to parents of children with special needs & professionals who serve them. EPICS conducts workshops & provides individual assistance to parents. The staff provides input to state & national advisory boards on issues affecting Indian families that have children with special needs. *Publication*: Newsletter. Library. Established 1985.

THE FALMOUTH INSTITUTE, INC.
3702 Pender Dr. #300 • Fairfax, VA 22030
  (800) 992-4489; (703) 352-2250 Fax 352-2323
  Website: www.falmouthinstitute.com
  E-mail: information@falmouthinstitute.com
  Richard Phelps, Chief Executive Officer
  Brenda Brainard (Confederated Coos, Lower Umpqua & Suislaw),
    Director - NATIVES Indian Education Program
Purpose: To provide quality training, technical assistance, and consulting to the American Indian & Alaska native communities. *Activities/programs*: Training programs & workshops - quarterly brochure. *Scholarships*: Awarded to an American Indian who is a member of a federally recognized tribe and is a high school senior accepted to an accredited college. *Publications*: American Indian Report, monthly online magazine; Native American Law Digest, monthly; various course manuals. Library. Established 1985.

FEDERAL BAR ASSOCIATION - INDIAN LAW SECTION
1220 N. Fillmore St., Suite 444 • Arlington, VA 22201
  (571) 481-9100 Fax 481-9090; E-mail: fba@fedbar.org
  Website: www.fedbar.org/sections/indian-law-section
  Tracy Toulou, Chairperson; E-mail: tracy.toulou2@usdoj.gov
  Kristen Carpenter, Deputy Chair
    E-mail: kristen.carpenter@colorado.edu
  Ann Tweeedy (Muckleshoot), Secretary
    E-mail: ann.tweedy@muckleshoot.nsn.us
  Helen Padilla, Treasurer; E-mail: padilla@law.unm.edu
Committees include: Indian Law Development, Public Education, Tribal Justice, and Newsletter. *Purpose*: To participate as amicus in important Indian law cases, comment on developing Indian legislation, and offer expertise & advice to developing tribal court systems. *Activities*: Annual Indian Law Conference in the Fall. The Conference is an aggregate of lawyers, law students, law professors, and federal, state, and tribal personnel - Indians and non-Indians - serving as speakers and listeners. It focuses on putting in perspective the court decisions & legislative action and analyzing how they impact the exercise of tribal sovereignty and other Indian rights. Makes available for purchase the proceedings of Indian Law conferences. Offers a limited number of partial scholarships to individuals from law schools, public interest and other organizations unable to allocate funds for the full conference registration fee. *Publication*: Federal Indian Law Newsletter. Dues: $5. Indian Law Section. Established 1990.

FEDERATION OF INDIAN SERVICE EMPLOYEES
1218 Lomas Blvd. NW • Albuquerque, NM 87102
  (505) 243-4088 Fax 243-4098; Website: www.fiseheadquarters.org
  Sue Parton, President (414-6891); E-mail: sparton@fise-aft.org
  Jim Gertner, Vice President; E-mail: jgertner@fise-aft.org
  Janelle Horse, Secretary/Treasurer; E-mail: jhorse@fise-aft.org
  Connie Weldon-Montero, BIE Rep; Tony Rowe, BIA Rep.
Membership: 750 professional educators employed in federal schools operated by the Bureau of Indian Affairs in the Albuquerque-Navajo areas. *Purpose*: To meet the unique needs & interests of teachers within the BIA's Office of Indian Education Programs, an affiliate of the American Federation of Teachers. Supports programs & projects that will improve the entire educational program in BIA schools. *Publication*: Newsletter. Annual meeting. Established 1967.

FIRST NATIONS DEVELOPMENT INSTITUTE
2432 Main St., 2nd Floor • Longmont, CO 80501
  (303) 774-7836 Fax 774-7841
  Website: www.firstnations.org; E-mail: info@firstnations.org
  Michael E. Roberts (Tlingit), President; Raymond Foxworth, VP Grantmaking
  Jackie Francke (Navajo-Dine'), VP Programs & Administration
  Sarah Dewees, Sr. Director of Research, Policy & Asset-Building Programs
  Catherine Bryan (Navajo), Senior Program Officer
  Autumn Romero (Chippewa Cree), Program Coordinator
  Randy Blauvelt, Senior Communications Officer (774-7836)
  B. Thomas Vigil, Chairperson of the Board
Purpose: To assist American Indian tribes & communities obtain economic self-sufficiency through the promotion of culturally appropriate economic development activities & efforts. *Programs*: The Eagle Staff Fund provides grants for reservation-based economic development projects to tribes & Native nonprofits; The First Nations Oweesta Program re-lends capital to reservation-based micro-enterprise loan funds, revolving loan funds, and Native owned banks & credit unions. In addition to these two programs, First Nations also engages in various research-oriented projects through its Strengthening Native American Philanthropy programs. *Research programs*: Native Assets Research Center; The Census Information Center. *Publications*: Research publications; Annual Reports; Conference Reports; Technical Reports; Speeches & articles; CRA Manual; Investment Series; et al. Annual board meeting. Established 1980. *Field Office*: 2217 Princess Anne St., Suite 111-1, Fredericksburg, VA 22401 (540) 371-5615 Fax 371-3505; Laura Smith, Office Manager.

FIRST NATIONS FILM & VIDEO FESTIVAL, INC.
  Website: www.fnfvf.org; (847) 863-8693
  Ernest M. Whiteman III (Northern Arapaho), Director
    E-mail: ernest-3@fnfvf.org
Description: A full three-day festival showcasing the latest in Native American-produced films & videos. *Purpose*: To provide an appropriate venue for Native American film & video makers of all skill levels; advocates for and celebrates the works of Native American film & video that break racial stereotypes & promotes awareness of contemporary Native American issues & society. Established 1990.

FIRST NATIONS OWEESTA CORPORATION
2432 Main St. • Longmont, CO 80501
Field office: 1010 9th St., Suite 4F • Rapid City, SD 57701
  (605) 342-3770 Fax 342-3771
  Website: www.oweesta.org; E-mail: info@oweesta.org
  Chrystal Cornelius (Oneida/Ojibwe), Executive Director
    E-mail: chrystel@oweesta.org
  Krystal Langholz, Chief Operating Officer
    E-mail: krystal@oweesta.org
  Chasity Savage, Chief External Relations Officer
    E-mail: chasity@oweesta.org
  Lanalle Smith (Navajo), Program Manager
  Michael Roberts (Tlingit), President
  Marguerite Smith, Vice Chairperson
Mission: Supports economic growth in Native American communities through the creation, development and capitalization of Community Development Financial Institutions. *Activities*: Training & technical assistance; lending & capitalization; research, policy & advocacy.

FIRST PEOPLES FUND
P.O. Box 2977 • Rapid City, SD 57709
  (605) 348-0324 Fax 348-6594; Website: www.firstpeoplesfund.org
  Lori Pourier (Oglala Lakota), President; E-mail: lori@firstpeoplesfund.org
  Jessica Miller, Program Manager; E-mail: Jessica@firstpeoplesfund.org
  Brandie McDonald (Chickasaw/Choctaw), Program Manager
    E-mail: brandie@firstpeoplesfund.org
  Sheila White Horse (Sicangu Lakota), Operations Manager
  Sherry Salway Black (Oglala Lakota), Chairperson
  David Cournoyer (Sicangu Lakota), Secretary/Treasurer
Purpose: To honor & support the creative community-centered First People's artists through grant programs & awards. *Programs*: Grants; professional development workshops. *Publication*: E-Spirit Newsletter. Established 1995.

FIRST PEOPLES: NEW DIRECTIONS IN INDIGENOUS STUDIES
Main Library Bldg., 5th Fl., 1510 E. University Blvd. Tucson, AZ 85721
  (520) 628-8484; Website: www.firstpeoplesnewdirections.org
  Natasha Varner, Program Coordinator
In 2009, the Andrew W. Mellon Foundation awarded four university presses: University of Arizona Press, University of Minnesota Press, University of North Carolina Press, and Oregon State University Press; a collaborative grant that establishes an innovative partnership that supports the publication of 40 books over four years by junior authors whose publications will contribute to the development of the field of Indigenous Studies. Established 2009.

FIRST PEOPLES WORLDWIDE
857 Leeland Rd. • Fredericksburg, VA 22405
  (540) 899-6545 Fax 899-6501; Website: www.firstpeoples.org
  Rebecca Adamson (Eastern Cherokee), Founder & President
  Jacqueline Tiller (Tlingit/Filipino), Administrative Manager
  Stephanie Conduff (Cherokee), Communications Manager
Description: Indigenous-led organization providing funding directly to Indigenous communities. *Purpose*: To focus on funding local development projects in Indigenous communities all over the world while creating bridges between our communities & corporations, governments, academics, NGOs & investors in their regions.

FOURTH WORLD CENTER FOR THE STUDY
OF INDIGENOUS LAW & POLITICS
University of Colorado, College of Liberal Arts & Sciences
CB 190, P.O. Box 173364 • Denver, CO 80217
  (303) 556-2850 Fax 556-6041
  Glenn T. Morris, Executive Director
Purpose: Seeks to promote peaceful change through dissemination of information & ideas; to provide resources & services that focus on the legal & political issues faced by indigenous populations. *Resources*: Features a library, periodicals, audio & visual equipment, & news file archives on current development issues surrounding the "Fourth World," and will soon offer a certificate program in this area. *Activities*: Develops academic courses, compiles & publishes literature & documentation, and presents a public forum & arbitration in the political arena. *Publication*: Forth World Bulletin.

FRIENDS COMMITTEE ON NATIONAL LEGISLATION
245 Second St., NE • Washington, DC 20002
(800) 630-1330; (202) 547-6000 Fax 547-6019
Website: www.fcnl.org
Ruth Flower, Director of Native American Advocacy Program
Description: A Quaker lobbying organization seeking to impact public policy and the Congress on issues of concern, among which are Native American rights including the upholding of treaty rights, the self-determination of Indian communities, & the Federal trusteeship responsibility. FCNL has specifically advocated, along with tribes and Indian organizations, on land & water rights. Federal Indian programs, health care, education, economic development, fishing rights, and self-determination. *Publication*: Indian Report, quarterly newsletter. Established 1943.

FUTURES FOR CHILDREN
9600 Tennyson St. NE • Albuquerque, NM 87122
(800) 545-6843; (505) 821-2828 Fax 821-4141
Website: www.futures-for-children.org
Mary Anne Larsen, Chairperson-Board of Directors
Teresa C. Gomez (Isleta Pueblo), President/CEO
Don Massey, COO & CEO of American Indian Store
Herbert Manheimer (Navajo), Director of Program Field Staff
Debby De La Rosa (Jicarilla Apache), Director - Program Administrator
Eric Manolito (Navajo), Senior Regional Coordinator
MaDnna Analla (Laguna Pueblo), Senior Regional Coordinator
Vincente Silva, Director of Program Support/Information Technology
Winona Gishal (Navajo), Regional Coordinator
Josalyn Williams, Regional Coordinator
Purpose: To improve the quality of education for American Indian children through mentoring & training; to build relationships which provide educational encouragement & cross cultural learning. *Programs*: Friendship/Mentorship - encourages American Indian children to stay in school & graduate through one-to-one mentoring; Youth Leadership - trains American Indian students to be leaders & critical thinkers; Families in Action - increases family involvement in children's academic studies. *Publication*: "Storyteller" newsletter.

GATHERING OF NATIONS
3301 Coors Blvd. NW #R300 • Albuquerque, NM 87120
(505) 836-2810 Fax 839-0475
Website: www.gatheringofnations.com
Derek Mathews, Director
Purpose: To promote the traditions & culture of the American Indian, in the most positive manor possible; to dispel stereotypes created about the American Indian; to provide Indian people the opportunity to participate, practice, teach, and exchange tribal traditions & costumes among all the tribes; and to enlighten the non-Indian about the history & culture of America's first inhabitants. Does not offer scholarships. *Activities*: Academic support for Indian students in college; development instructional materials on Indian history & culture for elementary & secondary schools; sponsors periodic song, dance, and Miss Indian World competitions; bestows awards. Annual powwow, 4th weekend in April (North America's biggest powwow, the largest annual gathering of Native Americans in the world). *Publications*: Newsletter; Annual magazine; program book; Video Lesson Plans - Elementary & Secondary Schools. Established 1984.

GOVERNOR'S INTERSTATE INDIAN COUNCIL, INC. (GIIC)
302 East Dakota Ave. • Pierre, SD 57501
(605) 773-3415
JR LaPlante (Cheyenne River Lakota), President
Chris Howell, Vice President; Ninlau Simmons, Secretary
Sherry L. Rupert, Treasurer
Goals: To promote & protect the various interests, welfare and wellbeing of Indian People of the U.S., and in particular those Indian residents within the various participating states of the GIIC. *Mission*: To promote & enhance government-to-government relations between the tribes & states; respect & recognize individual sovereignty of the tribes and the states; support the preservation of traditional Indian culture, language and values; and encourage socioeconomic development aimed at tribal self-sufficiency. *Activities*: Annual General Assembly; annual conference & business meeting, hosted by a member state. Began 1947.

GREAT PLAINS INDIAN GAMING ASSOCIATION (GPIGA)
855 Basin Ave. • Bismarck, ND 58504
(701) 255-9275 Fax 255-9281; E-mail: gpiga@gpiga.com
J. Kurt Luger, Executive Director
Purpose: To bring together & provide information and services to all the 24 federally recognized Tribal Nations in the Great Plains region, including the states of North & South Dakota, Nebraska, Iowa, Kansas, Wyoming & Montana, who are operating gaming enterprises; also, to develop common strategies & positions concerning issue affecting all gaming tribes, and to promote tribal economic development and its positive impacts within the Great

Plains. *Activities*: Annual Great Plains/Midwest Indian Gaming Trade Show & Conference. Established 1997.

GEORGE BIRD GRINNELL AMERICAN INDIAN FUND
P.O. Box 59033 • Potomac, MD 20859
(301) 424-2440 Fax 424-8281
Dr. Paula Mintzies, Executive Director
Purpose: Provides support to organizations that improve educational opportunities for American Indians; expand cultural, recreational and social services available to Native children & their families; empower American Indian children, families, communities & nations; promotes understanding of and respect for American Indian nations. *Programs*: Operates two scholarship awards: 'Schuyler M. Meyer, Jr. Award' & the 'Al Qoyawayma Award'; supports 'Circle of Life Essay Program'; provides financial support to other organizations as well as established programs; e.g. learning programs in partnership with other organizations. Established 1988.

HARVARD PROJECT ON AMERICAN INDIAN ECONOMIC DEVELOPMENT
Harvard University, Kennedy School of Government
79 JFK St. • Cambridge, MA 02138
(617) 495-1480 Fax 496-3900
Website: www.hpaied.org; E-mail: hpaied@hks.harvard.edu
Stephen Cornell, Udall Center-U. of AZ, Co-director & NNI Faculty Chair
Joseph P. Kalt, Co-director & Ford Foundation Professor Emeritus
Nicole Grenier, Programs Coordinator
Miriam R. Jorgensen, Research Director & Native Nations Institute
Megan Moana Hill (Oneida of Wisc.), Honoring Nations' Director
Manley A. Begay, Jr. (Dine'), Co-director & Faculty Chair of
   Native Nations Institute
Regis Pecos (Cochiti), Chair of Honoring Nations Board of Governors
Oren R. Lyons (Onondaga), Honoring Nations' Chairperson Emeritus
Purpose: To understand & foster the conditions under which sustained, self-determined social & economic development is achieved among American Indian nations. A systematic, comparative study of social & economic development on American Indian reservations. *Programs & Partnerships*: Honoring Nations (An Awards Program that identifies, celebrates, & shares outstanding examples of Tribal Governance); Native Nations Institute (NNI); Harvard University Native American Program; The Education Initiative (educational resources for Indigenous self-governance); Advisory Services. *Activities*: Research, advisory services executive education & the administration of a tribal governance awards program in all of its activities. *Publications & Research*: Books, Reports, Case Studies; Occasional Papers on Native Affairs; Article & Chapter Reprints; Testimony & Speeches; Field Reports; Teaching Cases; Tools & Data.

INDIAN ARTS & CRAFTS ASSOCIATION (IACA)
4010 Carlisle NE, Suite C • Albuquerque, NM 87107
(505) 265-9149 Fax 265-8251; Website: www.iaca.com
Kathi Ouellet, President (Retail Representative)
   E-mail: trader@rivertradingpost.com
Georgia Fischel, Vice President (Retail Rep.)
Dawn Dark Mountain (Oneida of Wisconsin), Artist Rep., Santa Fe, NM
Jacque Foutz, Wholesale Rep., Kirtland, NM
Membership: 700. Indian crafts people & artists, museums, retailers, wholesalers & collectors. *Purpose*: To promote, preserve, & protect the handmade creations of the Native American Indian. *Activities*: Semiannual wholesale markets for retailers only; marketing information; educational seminars; Native American Art; Artist of the Year Prints. *Award*: Artist of the Year Award, annually, $1,500. *Publications*: Monthly newsletter; annual directory; brochures for point-of-purchase distribution. Semiannual wholesale trade shows. Library. Established 1974.

INDIAN ARTS & CRAFTS BOARD - HEADQUARTERS
U.S. Department of the Interior
1849 C St., NW - MS #2528-MIB • Washington, DC 20240
(888) ART-FAKE; (202) 208-3773 Fax 208-5196
Website: www.doi.gov/iacb; Meridith Z. Stanton, Director
Harvey Pratt (Cheyenne Arapaho), Board Chairperson
Rose Fosdick (Nome Esimo), Board Vice Chairperson
Description: The Indian Arts & Crafts Board was created by Congress in 1935 to promote American Indian & Alaska Native economic development through the expansion of the Indian arts & crafts market. In support of this mission, the Board: implements the Indian Arts & Crafts Act of 1990, Public Law 101-644; increases the participation of Native Americans in the growing $1 billion a year Native American fine arts & crafts business; assists emerging artists entering the market; & assists Native American cultural leaders who are developing institutional frameworks for supporting the evolution & preservation of tribal cultural activities. The Board operates three museums: the Museum of the Plains Indian in Browning, MT; the Sioux Indian Museum in Rapid City, SD; and the Southern Plains Indian Museum in Anadarko, OK. *Mission*: To

promote the economic development of federally recognized American Indians & Alaska Natives through the expansion of the Indian arts & crafts market; to provide professional business advice, information on the Act and related marketing issues, fundraising assistance, and promotional opportunities to Native American artists, craftspeople, and cultural organizations of federally recognized tribes. *Publications*: Source Directory: American Indian & Alaska Native Owned and Operated Arts & Crafts Businesses (serves as a marketing link between about 180 Native American owned & operated arts & crafts enterprises and over 40,000 consumers); The Indian Arts & Crafts Act brochure and "Know the Law" brochure.

INDIAN HEALTH SERVICE (IHS)
U.S. Dept. of Health & Human Services
The Reyes Bldg., 801 Thompson Ave. #400 • Rockville, MD 20852
(301) 443-3593; Website: https://ihs.gov
Mary L. Smith (Cherokee), Principal Deputy Director
Christopher Mandregan, Jr. (Aleut), Acting Deputy Director
Elizabeth A. Fowler (Comanche), Deputy Director for Mgmt. Operations
RADM Sarah Linde, MD, Chief Medical Officer
RADM Sandra Pattea (Yavapai/Hopi), Deputy Director
 of Intergovernmental Affairs
RADM Richie K. Grinnell (Sac & Fox of Missouri), Deputy Director
 for Field Operations
Goals: To raise the status of health of American Indians to the highest levels possible. *Programs*: Provides a full range of curative, preventive, & rehabilitative services for approximately 2.5 million eligible American Indians & Alaskan Natives. *Publication*: Trends in Indian Health, annual. Established 1955. See IHS section for names & locations of facilities.

INDIAN LAND TENURE FOUNDATION
151 E. County Rd. B2 • Little Canada, MN 55117
(651) 766-8999 Fax 766-0012
Website: www.iltf.org; E-mail: info@indianlandtenure.org
Chris Stainbrook (Oglala Lakota), President
Erick Giles (Muscogee Creek), NICC Program Director
Jim Wabindato Little River Band Ottawa), Program/Development Officer
Grant McGinnis & Alex Buffalohead (Sisseton Waheton Oyate),
 Communication Officers
John E. Sirois (Okanagan/Wenatchi), Chairperson
Staci Emm (Yerington Paiute), Vice Chairperson
William Tovey (Umatilla), Secretary/Treasurer
Purpose: To educate every Indian landowner about Indian land management, ownership & transference issues; to use Indian land to help Indian people discover & maintain their culture; to increase economic assets of Indian landowners; to reform the legal mechanisms related to recapturing the physical, cultural & economic assets for Indian people & strengthening sovereignty of Indian land; to support activities and raise funds to carry out goals related to Indian land tenure. *Programs*: National Indian Carbon Coalition (NICC); grants-education, cultural awareness, economic opportunity.

INDIAN LAW & ORDER COMMISSION
UCLA American Indian Studies Center
3220 Campbell Hall, Box 951548 • Los Angeles, CA 90095
Website: www.aisc.ucla.edu/iloc; E-mail: iloc@aisc.ucla.edu
Troy A. Eid, JD, Chairperson;
Affie Ellis, Tom Gede, JD, Carole Goldberg, Stephanie Herseth-Sandlin,
 Jefferson Keel, EarlRalph Pomeroy III, Theresa Pouly,
 Ted Quasula (Hualapai), Commissioners
The Tribal Law & Order Act (TLOA), signed into law by President Obama, makes federal agencies more accountable for servicing Indian land. TLOA also provides greater freedom for tribes to design and run their own criminal justice systems. TLOA created the Indian Law & Order Commission, an independent, all-volunteer advisory group, to help with securing equal justice for Native Americans living and working on Indian lands. The purpose of this website is to provide updates, news, and resources related to the Commission's activities. The Commission wrote and published its final report & recommendations to the President & Congress of the U.S. in a report entitled, "A Roadmap for Making Native America Safer," reflects comprehensive assessments of criminal justice systems servicing Native American & Alaska Native communities.

INDIAN LAW RESOURCE CENTER
602 N. Ewing St. • Helena MT 59601-3603
(406) 449-2006 Fax 449-2031
Website: www.indianlaw.org; E-mail: mt@indianlaw.org
Robert "Tim" Coulter (Potawatomi), Board President & Executive Director
Jana L. Walker (Cherokee/Shawnee/Delaware), Senior Attorney
Marilyn Richardson (Chippewa), Assistant to the Director
Ginny Underwood (Comanche/Kiowa), Communications Director
Lisa Myaya, Development Director; Chris T. Foley (Cherokee), Attorney
Susan M. Masten (Yurok), Board Chairperson

Norma Bixby (Northern Cheyenne) & Terri Henry (Cherokee), Chairwomen
Melanie Benjamin (Mille lacs Ojibwe), Treasurer
Lucy Rain Simpson (Navajo), Secretary
District Office: 601 E Street, SE • Washington, DC 20003
(202) 547-2800 Fax 547-2803 E-mail: dcoffice@indianlaw.org
Armstrong A. Wiggins, Director of the DC office
Leonardo A. Crippa (Kolla-Argentina), Senior Attorney
Karla E. General (Mohawk), & Gretchen Gordon, Staff Attorneys
Purpose: To provide a legal, educational & research service for American Indians & other Indian tribes & nations & other indigenous peoples in the Western Hemisphere; seeks to enable Indian people to survive as distinct peoples with unique living cultures; to combat discrimination & injustice in the law; & protection of the environment. *Activities*: Engages in human rights advocacy on behalf of Indians at the U.N.; & offers free legal help to tribes. *Publications*: Indian Rights-Human Rights (handbook); Indigenous Notes (e-newsletter); annual report, articles & reprints. Established 1978.

INDIAN LIFE MINISTRIES
Intertribal Christian Communications
P.O. Box 32 • Pembina, ND 58271
(800) 665-9275; (204) 661-9333 Fax 661-3982
Website: www.indianlife.org; E-mail: ilm@indianlife.org
Tim Nielsen, General Director
Headquarters address: 188 Henderson Hwy, Winnipeg, Manitoba, Canada R2L 1L6. *Purpose*: To publish & distribute culturally & spiritually relevant literature for Native North Americans. *Publication*: Indian Life: Christian Media for Native North Americans.

INDIAN RIGHTS ASSOCIATION
1717 Arch St. • Philadelphia, PA 19103
(215) 665-4523 Fax 977-8612; Timothy C. Scheve, Director
Membership: 700. Consists of those interested in protection of the legal & human rights of American Indians & promotion of their welfare. *Publications*: Indian Truth, bimonthly newsletter (presently inactive). Annual Meeting. Established 1882.

INDIAN YOUTH OF AMERICA
P.O. Box 2786 • Sioux City, IA 51106
(712) 252-3230 Fax 252-3712
Website: www.indianyouthofamerica.org
Patricia Trudell Gordon, Executive Director
 E-mail: pgordon206@aol.com
Purpose: To improve the lives of Indian children; to inform families, social service agencies, and courts on the rights of Indian people under the Indian Child Welfare Act. *Program*: The American Indian Child Service Program-- attempts to prevent the distressful effects brought on by the breakup of Indian families. *Facility*: Resource Center. *Activities*: Conducts summer camp for Indian children ages 10-14; distributes information through its Resource Center and has a college scholarship program. Locally, staff provides referrals, advocacy & consultation services to Native American families & children; sponsors an afterschool program for children ages 8-13; also holds meetings & annual Substance Abuse & Indian Child Welfare Act workshops. Established 1978.

INDIANS INTO MEDICINE (INMED)
University of North Dakota School of Medicine & Health Sciences
UNDSMHS. Room 2101, 501 N. Columbia Rd. Stop 9037
Grand Forks, ND 58202 (701) 777-3037 Fax 777-3277
Web site: www.med.und.edu/inmed/; E-mail: inmed@med.und.edu
Eugene L. DeLorme, JD, Director
 E-mail: Eugene.delorme@med.und.edu
Kathleen Fredericks, College Coordinator (3464)
 E-mail: Kathleen.fredericks@med.und.edu
Naomi Bender, Program Coordinator (3279)
 E-mail: Naomi.bender@med.und.edu
Purpose: To assist American Indian students preparing for health careers; provide summer academic enrichment sessions at the junior high, high school, college & pre-medical levels; provide academic year support for college & professional students; to increase the awareness of and interest in health care professions among young American Indians. *Services*: Referral & counseling services; tutoring; financial aid; minority medical education program (for college students); and Med Prep (for students preparing for medical school). The INMED director is a coordinator for Indian Health Service scholarships; provides short-term emergency loans to participating students. *Activities*: Educational conferences. *Publications*: Indians Into Medicine (recruitment book); Healthy Games & Teasers (activity book); Good Medicine for Our People (coloring book); Serpent, Staff & Drum (quarterly newsletter). Library-The INMED Learning Resource Center includes a variety of books and journals to assist students in their courses and in preparing for health careers entrance exams; distributes recruitment publications. Established 1973.

INDIANZ.COM
Noble Savage Media, LLC & Ho-Chunk, Inc.
1000 Industrial Parkway • Winnebago, NE 68071
(800) 296-4170; (402) 878-2400 Fax 878-2771
Website: www.indianz.com; E-mail: indianz@indianz.com
Washington, DC office: (202) 630-8439 Fax 318-2182
Description: A Native American news, information, & entertainment web portal. Advertising accepted. *Mission*: To provide quality news, information, and entertainment from a Native American perspective. Launched 1999.

INDIGENOUS ENVIRONMENTAL NETWORK
INDIGENOUS AQUACULTURE NETWORK
P.O. Box 485 • Bemidji, MN 56619
(218) 751-4967 Fax 751-0561
Website: www.ienearth.org; E-mail: ienenergy@ienearth.org
Tom Goldtooth (Dine/Dakota), Executive Director
Dallas Goldtooth (Dakota/Dne'), Keep It in the Ground Organizer
E-mail: dallas@ienearth.org
Manuel Pino (Acoma Pueblo), Board member
Purpose: To maintain & further develop its information clearing-house, provide advocacy for environmental justice & health; to convene local, regional & national meetings on environmental justice issues & providing support, resources & referral to Indigenous communities & youth throughout North America and in recent years, globally. Established 1990.

INDIGENOUS PEOPLES COUNCIL ON BIOCOLONIALISM
850 Numana Dam Rd., P.O. Box 72 • Nixon, NV 89424
(775) 574-0248 Fax 574-0345
Website: www.ipcb.org; E-mail: ipcb@ipcb.org
Debra Harry (Northern Paiute), Executive Director
Le'a Malia Kanehe (Kanaka Maoli), Legal Analyst
Judy Gobert (Blackfeet, Nakota, Salish), Chairperson
Jonathan Marks, Vice Chairperson
Pemina Yellow Bird (Mandan Hidatsa/Arikara), Secretary/Treasurer
Mission: To assist indigenous peoples in the protection of their genetic resources, indigenous knowledge, cultural and human rights from the negative effects of biotechnology; provides educational & technical support to indigenous peoples in the protection of their biological resources, cultural integrity, knowledge & collective rights. *Activities*: Internships. *Publications*: Primers; Briefing Papers; Annual Reports. Established 2000.

INDIGENOUS RESEARCH CENTER
2103 Eton Ave. SE #4 • Albuquerque, NM 87106
Colleen Gorman, Executive Administrator
E-mail: ctgorman_artist@yahoo.com
Roger Cultee & Tracy Greer, Executive Council
E-mail: racultee@yahoo.com
Description: An independent group of artists & musicians. *Purpose*: To document & preserve visual language found encoded in "all" ancient arts of the world. *Activities*: Contemporary Fine Arts Gallery with the art of Harrison Begay; art & music of Colleen Gorman; the music & jewelry of Roger Cultee, and the art of Tracy Greer.

INDIGENOUS RESEARCH CENTER OF THE AMERICAS (IRCA)
Department of Native American Studies, University of California, Davis
2419 Hart Hall, One Shields Ave. • Davis, CA 95616
(530) 752-3237 Fax 752-7097; E-mail: indigenous@ucdavis.edu
Website: www.repositories.cdlib.org/irca
Purpose: Seeks to understand & express both the local & global dimensions of indigenous peoples in the American Hemisphere. Provides an open forum for indigenous scholars, indigenous communities, spiritual & political leaders & non-indigenous researchers concerned with the realities of indigenous peoples of the Americas. Sponsored by UC-Davis through the Native American Organized Research Program (NAORP). *Publications*: Paper series. Established 1994.

INDIGENOUS WELLNESS RESEARCH INSTITUTE
School of Social Work - University of Washington
Box 354900, 4101 15th Ave. NE • Seattle, WA 98105
(206) 616-8731 or 616-2658; Website: www.iwri.org
Karina L. Walters (Choctaw of Okla.), Director
E-mail: kw5@uw.edu
Tessa Evans-Campbell (Snohomish), Associate Director & Director, Center for Indigenous Child & Family Research
E-mail: tecamp@uw.edu
Myra Parker, JD (Mandan/Hidatsa), Associate Director – Community Engagement & Outreach Core
E-mail: myrap@uw.edu
Shana Ava, Administrative Director; E-mail: afshana@uw.edu
Bonnie Duran (Opelousas/Coushatta), Director, Center for Indigenous Health Research

Purpose: To support the inherent rights of Indigenous peoples to achieve full and complete health & wellness by collaborating in decolonizing research & knowledge building & sharing. *Goal*: To marshal community, tribal, academic, and government resources toward innovative, culture-centered interdisciplinary collaborative social & behavioral research & education. *Projects/Programs*: Young Native Women's Wellness Study; Alcohol Problems & Solutions; Supporting Native Mother & Their Families; Cross-Site Multicultural Community-Based Participatory Research; The Native Youth Enrichment Program; The Healthy Hearts Across Generations Project; The Indigenous HIV/AIDS Research Training Program.

INSTITUTE FOR AMERICAN INDIAN RESEARCH (IFAIR)
Native American Studies, MSC06 3740
1 University of New Mexico • Albuquerque, NM 87131
(505) 277-1822
Lloyd L. Lee (Dine'), Director; E-mail: triplel@unm.edu
Mission: To facilitate research that contributes to the decolonization, sovereignty, & self-determination of Indigenous peoples by providing initiatives that support research endeavors & by providing a forum for interdisciplinary conversation between & among Native & non-Native faculty & students committed to such issues. *Faculty members*: Jennifer Denetdale (Dine'), Beverly Singer (Santa Clara/Dine'), Luci Tapahonso (Dine'), Sherri Thomas (Taos), Mary Alice Tsosie (Dine'), Kamilla Venner (Athabascan), Steven Verney (Tsimishian), Kathleen Washburn. *Programs*: Colloquium Series Presentation; Annual Indigenous Book Festival; scholarships & research grants. Established 2004.

THE INSTITUTE FOR AMERICAN INDIAN STUDIES –
MUSEUM & RESEARCH CENTER
38 Curtis Rd., P.O. Box 1260 • Washington, CT 06793
(860) 868-0518 Fax 868-1649
Website: www.iaismuseum.org
Lisa Piastuch, Interim Executive Director, Director
E-mail: lpiastuch@iaismuseum.org
Lucianne Lavin, Research & Collections
E-mail: llavin@iaismuseum.org
Darlene Kascak, Education Coordinator
E-mail: dkascak@iaismuseum.org
Purpose: To discover, preserve, and interpret information about the lifeways of the first peoples of the Northeast Woodlands area of the U.S., and to enhance appreciation for their cultures & achievements. Facilities: Museum & Research Center; Gift Shop. *Activities*: Maintains an (outside) authentically constructed Algonkian Village settlement with three wigwams, a longhouse, a rock shelter, and a garden planted with corn, beans & squash, and walking trails with native plants. Conducts archaeological surveys & excavations; provides indoor exhibits; sponsors archaeological training sessions, teacher workshops, craft workshops, summer youth programs-educational programs to school groups. *Publication*: Artifacts, quarterly magazine; annual research report; bibliography & educational resource pamphlets. Annual conference, with symposium - in November, Lowell, MA. Established 1971.

INSTITUTE FOR PUEBLO INDIAN STUDIES (IPIS)
Indian Pueblo Cultural Center
2401 12th St. NW • Albuquerque, NM 87104
(866) 855-7902; (505) 843-7270; Website: www.indianpueblo.org
Michael Canfield (Laguna Pueblo), President
Dwayne Virgint, Vice President & COO
Travis Suazo (Laguna/Acoma/Taos Pueblos), Cultural & Community Engagement
Monique Fragua (Jemez Pueblo), Museum Director
Ron Shutiva (Acoma Pueblo), Board Chairperson
Chris L. Baca (Santa Clara Pueblo), Vice Chairperson
Mission: To plan & direct educational programming & research projects, as well as to provide an information center for use by Pueblo Indians, scholars, and others concerned with Pueblo Indian studies. Established 1976.

INSTITUTE FOR THE STUDY OF TRIBAL GAMING LAW & POLICY
Northern Plains Indian Law Center-University of North Dakota School of Law
215 Centennial Dr., Stop 9003 • Grand Forks, ND 58202
(701) 777-2104
Dean Kathryn R.L. Rand, Co-Director; E-mail: rand@law.und.edu
Dr. Steven Andrew Light, Co-Director; E-mail: steven_light@und.nodak.edu
Co-Directors Kathryn R.L. Rand (Law) & Steven Andrew Light (Political Science) founded the Institute for the Study of Tribal Gaming Law and Policy at the University of North Dakota in 2002 as the first university-affiliated institute in the U.S. dedicated to the study of Indian gaming. Rand & Light are internationally recognized experts on Indian gaming, having published over 30 journal articles, book chapters, essays, and three books: Indian Gaming Law: Cases and Materials (Carolina Academic Press, 2008), Indian Gaming Law and Policy (Carolina Academic Press, 2006), and Indian Gaming and Tribal Sovereignty: The Casino Compromise (University Press of Kansas, 2005).

ASSOCIATIONS & ORGANIZATIONS 97

They have twice testified on Indian gaming regulation before the U.S. Senate Committee on Indian Affairs in Washington, D.C., and were featured on C-SPAN's Book TV. They frequently present their research & perspectives on Indian gaming before diverse audiences, including professional & trade groups, tribal & non-tribal civic associations, academic conferences, and university endowed lectures. Both are members of the International Masters of Gaming Law, and Rand is on the Editorial Board of the Gaming Law Review. Rand and Light write a column, "Indian Gaming Today," that appears regularly in Casino Lawyer magazine; have written for Casino Enterprise Management and Indian Gaming magazines. They blog on Indian gaming and the legal, political, and public policy issues raised by the tribal gaming industry at their website, Indian Gaming Today, at indiangamingnow.com. *Activities*: The Institute provides legal and policy assistance and analysis to all interested individuals, governments, & organizations, & conducting scholarly & practical research in the area of tribal gaming. The Institute adopts a unique "team-based" interdisciplinary approach to legal & policy analysis of the complicated and highly technical issues related to Indian gaming, including regulation and agency authority, policy & socioeconomic impact analysis, tribal-state compacting, Class II vs. Class III gaming, tribal law and sovereignty, federal Indian law, labor relations, state referenda and voter initiatives, the federal acknowledgment process, land-into-trust applications, & "off-reservation" gaming. The Institute provides legal & policy assistance related to tribal gaming enterprises to all interested governments and organizations, assists tribes with gaming enterprises in pursuing reservation economic development and building strong tribal governments, and contributes to the scholarly and practical research and literature in the area of tribal gaming. The Institute's primary focus is on the particular issues faced by tribes in the Great Plains, including North Dakota, South Dakota, Nebraska, Iowa, Kansas, Wyoming, and Montana. The institute offers an interdisciplinary perspective on tribal gaming, incorporating law, political science, and public administration. *The Native American Law Project* - This project, offered some semesters, provides legal assistance to the Spirit Lake Nation of the Fort Totten Indian Reservation. Second and third year law students provide legal services under the supervision of a practicing attorney. The project has also served as the Tribe's Prosecutor for criminal matters.

INSTITUTE FOR TRIBAL ENVIRONMENTAL PROFESSIONALS (ITEP)
Northern Arizona University, P.O. Box 15004 • Flagstaff, AZ 86011
(866) 248-4576; (928) 523-9555 Fax 523-1266
Website: www7.nau.edu; E-mail: itep@nau.edu
Ann Marie Chischilly, Executive Director
  E-mail: ann-marie.chischilly@nau.edu
Mehrdad Khatibi, Director (523-0946); E-mail: mehrdad.khatibi@nau.edu
Description: Works to assist Indian tribes in the management of environmental resources through training & education programs. *Programs*: Student internships; scholarships. *Staff*: Todd Barnell, Program Coordinator; Lydia Scheer, Training Coordinator; Sarah Kelly, Resource Center Manager. *Publication*: Native Voices. Established 1992.

THE INSTITUTE FOR TRIBAL GOVERNMENT
Hatfield School of Government, Center for Public Service
Portland State University, 506 SW Mill St., Suite 570 • Portland, OR 97201
(503) 725-9000 Fax 725-8250; Website: www.pdx.edu/tribal-gov/
Don Sampson, Executive Director; E-mail: d.sampson@pdx.edu
Elizabeth Furse, Founder/Director; Peggy Harris, Program Coordinator
Michelle J. Singer (Navajo), Member, Policy Board;
  Communications Coordinator for the One Sky Center
Purpose: To serve elected tribal governments (560+) from across the nation and also to provide training to local, state & federal government agencies & others who are interested in learning more about tribal governments, legal foundations, & tribal governmental authorities & duties. *Instructors*: Elizabeth Furse; Michelle J. Singer (Dine'); Christopher Porter, Roy Sampsel (Choctaw/Wyandotte); Robert Miller, Esq. (Eastern Shawnee); Howard Arnett, Esq.; Don Wharton, Esq.; Robert Anderson (Bois Forte Band Ojibwe); Marcus D. Ingle; Jaime A. Pinkham (Nez Perce); Billy Frank, Jr. (Nisqually); Alan Parker, Esq. (Chippewa Cree); Kathryn Harrison (Grand Ronde Molalla); Russ Lehman; George McKenzie-Grieve; Brian McDonald (Champagne & Aishihik First Nations). *Activities*: Tribal Governance Trainings; Government Agency Trainings; Great Tribal Leaders of Modern Times Interview Project & Curriculum Project. Tribal Leadership Forum, P.O. Box 610 • North Plains, OR 97133 (503) 962-0650 (nonprofit organized & operated exclusively for charitable, scientific, literary, and educational purposes). Projects include, The Great Tribal Leaders of Modern Times Video & Curriculum projects.

INSTITUTE OF THE GREAT PLAINS
Museum of the Great Plains, 601 Ferris, Elmer Thomas Park
P.O. Box 68 • Lawton, OK 73502
(580) 581-3460 Fax 581-3458; Website: www.museumgreatplains.org
John Hernandez, Executive; E-mail: john.h@discovermgp.org
Bart McClenny, Deputy Director/Development Director
  E-mail: bart.m@discovermgp.org
Deborah Baroff, Senior Curator/Special Collections Curator
  E-mail: deb.b@discovermgp.org
Janice Bell, Board Chairperson; Paul Fisher, Secretary
Dr. Edward Chappabitty & Teresa Moses, Board Members
Membership: 825. *Purpose*: To further the study & understanding of the history, ecology, anthropology, archaeology, and sociology of the Great Plains of North America. *Activities*: Conducts research; maintains the Museum of the Great Plains, the Great Plains Archives, Bookstore & Library. *Publications*: Great Plains Journal, annual; irregular newsletter; books for sale. Established 1961.

INTERNATIONAL INDIAN DOG OWNERS & BREEDERS ASSOCIATION
Hermitage, TN 37076 (615) 874-1435; Website: www.iidoba.org
  Kim La Flamme (Blackfoot), President & Founder
  E-mail: laflamme@earthlink.net
  Pat Cummins, Vice President
Purpose: To stress the cultural value & importance of preservation for the "Common" or "Plains" Indian dog, and to promote this rare & primitive dog in a positive light to the general public. Established 2001.

INTERNATIONAL INDIAN TREATY COUNCIL (IITC)
Information Office: The Redstone Bldg.
2940 16th St. #305 • San Francisco, CA 94103
(415) 641-4482 Fax 641-1298
Website: www.iitc.org; E-mail: iitc@treatycouncil.org
Andrea Carmen (Yaqui), Executive Director
  Email: andrea@treatycouncil.org
Administration Office: 456 N. Alaska St. • Palmer, AK 99645
(907) 745-4482 Fax 745-4484
Francisco Cali (Guatemala), Board President
Hinewirangi Kohu (Maori Nation), Board Vice President
Ron Lameman (Cree), Board Treasurer
Board members: William A. Means (Oglala Lakota), Leonard Foster (Navajo), Faith Gemmill (Athabascan), Rodney Factor (Seminole of Oklahoma), Radley David (Pit River/Wintu), Lisa Bellanger (White Earth Anishnabe), Naniki Reyes (Taino), Pu'uhonoa Kanahele (Hawaii), Yamilka Hernandez (Kuna, Panama), Roberto Borrero, (Taino)
Description: "An organization of Indigenous Peoples from North, Central, South America, & the Pacific working for the sovereignty & self-determination of Indigenous peoples working for the recognition & protection of Indigenous rights, traditional cultures & sacred lands. In 1977, the IITC became the first organization of Indigenous Peoples to be recognized as a non-governmental organization (NGO) with consultative status to the United Nations Economic & Social Council." *Programs*: IITC's Bay Area Indian Youth Mentorship Program (Sherri Norris, Program Coordinator), initiated in 1996, provides high school & college youth with experiences in community organizing, advocacy & activism, building leadership & capacity & links between urban & rural Indian communities in California, nationally & internationally. In 2003, IITC initiated the Tribal Health and Mercury Education project in partnership with the Pit River Indian Nation to address the widespread yet largely unknown health & environmental crisis of the mercury contamination in San Francisco & Northern California. *Activities*: Makes regular presentations to the U.N. Commission on Human Rights. Maintains a research and documentation center in South Dakota and an Information Center in New York City. *Publication*: Treaty Council News, quarterly. Annual conference. Established 1974.

INTERNATIONAL INSTITUTE FOR INDIGENOUS RESOURCE MANAGEMENT
444 S. Emerson St. • Denver, CO 80209
(303) 733-0481 Fax 744-9808; Website: www.iiirm.org
Mervyn L. Tano, President; E-mail: mervtano@iiirm.org
Jeanne M. Rubin, General Counsel; E-mail: jeannerubin@iiirm.org
David Conrad, Board Chairperson; Jack Hibbert, Secretary-Treasurer
Description: Internationally-based legal scholars & researchers who work on cutting-edge projects designed to empower native peoples by examining the role law can play in establishing & enhancing indigenous people's control over and management of their lands & resources. *Activities*: Annual Indigenous Film & Art Festival. Established 1997.

INTERNATIONAL LEONARD PELTIER DEFENSE COMMITTEE (ILPDC)
Mailing address: P.O. Box 24 • Hillsboro, OR 97123
c/o Indigenous Rights Center LLC, 202 Harvard SE, Albuquerque, NM 87106
(505) 217-3612; Website: www.whoisleonardpeltier.info
  Leonard Peltier, Director; E-mail: contact@whoisleonardpeltier.info
Purpose: To obtain justice for Leonard Peltier & all political prisoners; equality under the law. *Activities*: Public education; lobbying; Prisoner art program; pilot program with Dr. Jeffrey Timmons (Harvard) on economic reform on Pine Ridge; Dr. Stuart Selkin (NY) on health care reform on Rosebud; year round food & clothing drive. *Contact*: Leonard Peltier #89637-132, USP Coleman I, U.S. Penitentiary, P.O. Box 1033, Coleman, FL 33521. *Publication*: Spirit of Crazy Horse, bimonthly newspaper.

INTERTRIBAL AGRICULTURE COUNCIL

100 North 27th St. Suite 500 • Billings, MT 59101
(406) 259-3525 Fax 256-9980
Website: www.indianaglink.com; E-mail: info@indianaglink.com
Richard Bowers, President; Ross R. Racine, Executive Director
Vicki Hebb, Special Projects; Nathan Notah, Program Manager
Purpose: To pursue & promote the conservation, development & use of Indian resources for the betterment of Indian people. *Programs*: Technical Assistance; Annual Indian Agriculture Symposium; American Indian Foods; Business Development Program; Farmer-to-Farmer Program. *Publications*: National Indian Agriculture Profile; Indian Borrowers Guide to Agriculture Lending Programs of the FmHA & BIA; Indian Guide to Farmer Programs of the Soil Conservation Service, USDA, and the Indian Guide on the use of the "Made by American Indians" trademark. Established 1987.

INTER-TRIBAL INDIAN CEREMONIAL ASSOCIATION

206 W. Coal Ave. • Gallup, NM 87301
(505) 863-3896 Fax 863-9168
Website: http://gallupceremonial.com/
E-mail: ceremonial@qwestoffice.net
Terry Frazier, Executive Director
Membership: 350. *Description*: Indian people, businessmen, dealers in Indian arts & crafts, and other individuals interested in the annual Inter-Tribal Indian Ceremonial. *Goals*: The preservation & promotion of American Indian culture, with an emphasis on the handmade arts & crafts. *Activities*: Annual Inter-Tribal Indian Ceremonial, a four day Indian exposition of dances, sports, crafts, rituals and a rodeo, held each August in Gallup, New Mexico; Summer Indian Dance Program; the Indian Country Guide Service; bestows awards; conducts specialized educational & children's services; maintains biographical archives; plans a Hall of Fame; publishes educational materials on Indian crafts for teachers; color slides of Indian ceremonials available. Closely associated with the Red Rock Museum, which houses the majority of Association's collections. *Scholarships*: Indian art scholarships to accredited colleges & universities beginning in 1995. *Publications*: Inter-Tribal America Magazine, quarterly newsletter; A Measure of Excellence, annual; "So You Want to Buy A Navajo Rug?" information pamphlet. Library. Annual meeting in Gallup, NM in August. Established 1922.

INTERTRIBAL MONITORING ASSOCIATION ON INDIAN TRUST FUNDS

(ITMA) 2309 Renard SE, Suite 212 • Albuquerque, NM 87106
(505) 247-1447 Fax 247-2013
Mary Zuni Chalan, Executive Director; Brian Gunn, Esq., Legal Counsel
Michael Finley (Confederated Tribes of Colville), Chairperson
Scott Russell (Crow), Vice Chairperson; Chief George Thurman, Secretary
Tamsey Dreadful Water Leake (Cherokee), Treasurer
Description: A national tribal consortium of 66 federally recognized tribes whose purpose & objectives is to ensure fair compensation to tribes for the historical trust funds mismanagement. *Publication*: Newsletter. Established 1990.

INTERTRIBAL TIMBER COUNCIL

1112 NE 21st Ave., Suite 4 • Portland, OR 97213
(503) 282-4296 Fax 282-1274
Website: www.itcnet.org; E-mail: itc1@teleport.com
Laura Alvidrez, Program Manager; Don Motanic, Technical Specialist
Philip Rigdon (Yakama), Board President
Venon Stearns, Jr. (Spokane), Vice President
Orvie Danzuka (Confederated Tribes of Warm Springs), Secretary
Timothy P. Miller (Grand Portage Ojibwe), Treasurer
Purpose: To promote sound, economic management of natural resources so as to sustain Indian forests & dependent economies in accordance with tribal goals and objectives for the benefit of Indian people. *Activities*: Annual National Indian Timber Symposium; annual scholarship awards for Native American & Native Alaskan students pursuing a higher education in Natural Resources. Established 1979.

LAKOTA LANGUAGE CONSORTIUM, INC.

2620 N. Walnut St. • Bloomington, IN 47404
(888) 525-6828; Fax (812) 961-0141
Website: www.lakhota.org; E-mail: help@lakhota.org
Website: www.languagepress.com; E-mail: sales@lakhota.org
Wilhelm K. Meya, Chairperson & Executive Director
E-mail: meya@lakhota.org
Jan F. Ullrich, Linguistic Director
Joy Laughter, Communications Associate
Regional Office: 125 W. Dakota Ave. • Pierre, SD 57501
(605) 945-4374 Fax 224-0069
Description: Consists of Native community leaders, linguists and volunteers. *Mission*: The preservation, revitalization, and promotion of the Lakota language "one of only a few Native American languages left that has a significant chance of survival." *Activities*: Lakota Summer Institute; Lakota Language Forum (Lakhotiya Owaakhiye Othi) - formed to preserve the Lakhota language by learning it and studying the language & discussing topics directly related to it; trains the teachers, produces language materials (audio/video), sponsors community & educational events, and directs other efforts to preserve the identity that the Lakotas have maintained through their language; Lakota Language Consortium Press, LLC Bookstore - publishes material on and for the Lakota language. *Publications*: Newsletter; New Lakota Dictionary, 2nd Ed.

D'ARCY McNICKLE CENTER FOR AMERICAN INDIAN & INDIGENOUS STUDIES

The Newberry Library, 60 West Walton St. • Chicago, IL 60610
(312) 255-3563/4 Fax 255-3696
Website: www.newberry.org/mcnickle-center
E-Mail: mcnickle@newberry.org
Patricia Marroquin Norby, Director (255-3569)
E-mail: norbyp@newberry.org
Description: A research & education center on Indian history. *Purpose*: To improve the quality of teaching & scholarship about American Indian history and culture through the use of the Newberry Library's prestigious collection of rare books, manuscripts, photographs, maps, and art. *Resources*: Website – Indians of the Midwest, Past & Present. *Programs*: Offers numerous fellowships, including the Power-Tanner Fellowship for PhD candidates and postdoctoral scholars of American Indian heritage, the Frances C. Allen Fellowships for women of Native American heritage, & Rockefeller Foundation fellowships for community-centered research projects; Newberry Consortium in American Indian Studies; Seminar Series in American Indian Studies; Spring Workshop in Research Methods; Graduate Student Conference; Summer Institute. *Publications*: "Meeting Ground," bimonthly newsletter; publications list available. The Newberry Library. Established 1972.

MIDWEST ALLIANCE OF SOVEREIGN TRIBES (MAST)

1011 Main St., P.O. Box 265 • Gresham, WI 54128
(715) 787-4494 Fax 787-4468
Website: www.m-a-s-t.org; E-mail: m.a.s.t@frontiernet.net
Scott R. Vele (Stockbriidge-Munsee), Executive Director
Aaron A. Payment (Sault Ste. Marie Ojibwe), Acting President & VP
Eugene Magnuson (Pokagon), Treasurer
Melanie Benjamin (Mille Lacs Ojibwe), Secretary
Description: Represents the 35 sovereign tribal nations of Minnesota, Wisconsin, Iowa, and Michigan; represents about 134,000 American Indian people. *Goals*: To "advance, protect, preserve & enhance the mutual interests, treaty rights, sovereignty, gaming, and cultural way of life. Annual Fall meeting. Established 1996.

MIGIZI COMMUNICATIONS, INC.

1516 East Lake St. #300 • Minneapolis, MN 55406
(612) 721-6631 Fax 721-3936
Website: www.migizi.org; E-mail: info@migizi.org
Elaine Salinas, President & CEO
Graham Hartley, Director of Programs
John Gwinn, Project Coordinator/Media Specialist
Syd Beane (Mdewakanton Dakota/Santee Sioux), Chairperson
Jina Downwind-Jubera (Red Lake), Vice Chairperson
Purpose: To engage in the planning, development, implementation & evaluation of facilities & programs in the fields of communications & educational & literary activities & youth services in the areas of health & recreation to enhance the capacity of the American Indian community to meet the needs of its people. *Mission*: To educate elementary, secondary & adult students using the tools of communications; and to commit resources to address problems in partnership with the American Indian community. *Goals*: To improve the success rates of our students; increase organizational effectiveness through partnerships; and address problems through a greater use of communications. *Programs*: First Person Productions - consists of multimedia production (film, video, radio) and a New Media Pathway Program to train American Indian youth to produce & distribute content via conventional and virtual media. Provides production training to about 50 Minneapolis Indian youth each year. Specializes in promotional videos, training & educational media, public service announcements, documentaries, radio program & podcasts. *Native Academy* - created in 1995 as a partner to schools with a primary focus on improving academic performance and to increase the number of American Indians moving into higher education, particularly in science or technology career fields. *Native Youth Futures* – a three-year project designed to create an urban Native youth entrepreneurship pathway that leads to economic self-sufficiency for individual youth. National Native Internet Communications (www.nnic.com) - provides professional website services & acts as a provider of affordable Internet services for tribes, businesses, individuals & community non-profit organizations. *Publication*: Communicator, organization newsletter; "Aozanzanya," student newsletter. Established 1977.

MISS INDIAN WORLD

Gathering of Nations, 3200 Coors NW #K235 • Albuquerque, NM 87120
 (505) 836-2810; Website: www.atii.com/gathering.of.nations
Description: An annual contest to select Miss Indian World to serve as a goodwill ambassador for a year. Participants must be at least one quarter Indian to qualify and have a good knowledge of tribal traditions. Takes place at annual Gathering of Nations powwow, 4th weekend of April, in Albuquerque.

MORNING STAR INSTITUTE

410 15th St. SE • Washington, DC 20003
 (202) 547-5531 Fax 546-6724
 Suzan Shown Harjo (Cheyenne/Muscogee), President
Purpose: To secure statutory protections for Native peoples' sacred sites & religious freedom. *Activities*: Conducts programs for environmental and youth concerns promoting Native images & voices in popular culture; provides small grants to support cultural work of others. *Publications*: Bulletin, periodic. Established 1984.

MOUNTAIN CHIEF INSTITUTE
A CENTER FOR TRIBAL EXCELLENCE, INC.

161 Sagebrusg Dr. • Corrales, NM 87048
 (505) 506-0949; Website: www.mountainchiefinstitute.org
 David Powless (Oneida), President; E-mail: dapowless@gmail.com
Mission: To benefit educational institutions and related activities, focusing specifically on adult, continuing education programs. *Activities*: Spirit of Hoops Basketball Camps. Training camps for Native American boys & girls 6-17 years of age. Dedicated to improving self-esteem and emphasizes team participation and a sense of importance & belonging.

JOSEPH A. MYERS CENTER FOR RESEARCH
ON NATIVE AMERICAN ISSUES

Institute for the Study of Societal Issues
UC, Berkeley, 2420 Bowditch St. #5670 • Berkeley, CA 94720
 (510) 643-7237 Fax 642-8674; E-mail: crnai@berkeley.edu
 Joseph A. Myers (Pomo), Co-Chairperson
 Martin Sanchez-Jankowski (Yaqui), Co-Chairperson
 Christine Trost, Academic Coordinator
Mission: To provide the people of Indian country with pragmatic research products that can be employed to improve the quality of life for Native Americans throughout the U.S. *Activities*: Seminars, conferences, publications, programs and other events. *Published work*: The Power & Promise of Culture in Economic Development: Drawing on Language for Healing, Nation Building, Sovereignty, and Development Practices in the Hoopa Nation, by Fellow Ricardo Huerta Nino.

NATIONAL ADVISORY COUNCIL ON INDIAN EDUCATION (NACIE)

U.S. Dept. of Education-Office of Indian Education
400 Maryland Ave., SW 5C152 • Washington, DC 20202
 (202) 260-7485 Fax 260-7779; E-mail: oese@ed.gov
 Deborah J. Cavett, Executive Director
 Appointed members: Joely Proudfit, Phyllis J. Anderson, Mandy Broaddus,
  Dahkota Kicking Bear Brown
Purpose: To assist the Secretary of Education in carrying out responsibilities under Section 441(a) of the Indian Education Act (Title IV of P.L. 92-318), through advising Congress, the Secretary of Education, the Under Secretary of Education, and the Assistant Secretary of Elementary & Secondary Education with regard to education programs benefiting Indian children & adults. *Activities*: Full Council/Subcommittee meetings in the field on or near Indian reservations to receive public testimony regarding Title IV monies. *Publications*: Newsletters and annual reports. Library. Established 1972.

NATIONAL ALLIANCE TO SAVE NATIVE LANGUAGES

1455 Pennsylvania Ave., NW • Washington, DC 20004
 (206) 420-4638 Fax (202) 659-1340
 Website: www.savenativelanguages.org
 E-mail: r_lakota@hotmail.com
 E-mail: gsmith@smithbrownyazzie.com
 Ryan Wilson (Oglala Lakota), President
Description: A coalition of stakeholders including tribes, schools & individuals, regional & national organizations. *Purpose*: To promote the revitalization of Native languages. Established 2006.

NATIONAL AMERICAN INDIAN COURT JUDGES ASSOCIATION
NATIONAL TRIBAL JUSTICE RESOURCE CENTER

1942 Broadway, Suite 215 • Boulder, CO 80302
 (303) 449-4112 Fax 449-4038
 Website: www.naicja.org; E-mail: info@naicja.org
 Hon. Richard Blake (Hupa-Yurok), Board President
 Hon. Kevin Briscoe (Mississippi Choctaw), First Vice President
 Hon. Lawrence Lujan (Ysleta Del Sur Pueblo), Second Vice President
 Hon. Susan Wells (Native Village of Eklutna), Secretary

 Hon. Winona Tanner (Salish & Kootenai), Treasurer
 Hon. Cheryl Fairbanks & Leona Colgove, At-Large Members
Membership: 360. Indian court judges. *Purpose*: To improve the American Indian court system throughout the U.S. by furthering knowledge & understanding of it, and maintaining its integrity in providing equal protection to all persons. *Resources*: Resource Center provides training & technical assistance to tribal justice systems through federally funded projects, referrals, and as a fee-for-service onsite. Offers periodic training sessions on criminal law & family law/child welfare; conducts research & continuing education programs; annual meeting. Library. *Publication*: Indian Courts Newsletter, quarterly. Publications for sale. Annual meeting. Established 1968.

NATIONAL AMERICAN INDIAN HOUSING COUNCIL (NAIHC)

900 2nd St., NE, Suite 107 • Washington, DC 20002
 (800) 284-9165; (202) 789-1754 Fax 789-1758
 Website: www.naihc.net; E-Mail: housing@naihc.net
 Pamela M. Silas (Menominee/Oneida)), Executive Director
  (202) 454-0934; E-mail: psilas@naihc.net
 Shawn Pensoneau (Kickapoo), Director of Governmental Affairs
  (202) 454-0928; E-mail: spensoneau@naihc.net
 Shane Begay (Navajo), Administrative Support
  (202) 454-0936; E-mail: sbegay@naihc.net
 Sami Jo Difuntorum (Kwekaeke Shasta)), Board Chairperson
  E-mail: samijod@ctsi.nsn.us
 Gary Cooper (Cherokee), Vice Chairperson
  E-mail: gary.cooper@hacn.org
Description: Nonprofit organization which promotes & supports American Indians, Alaska Natives & native Hawaiians in their self-determined goal to provide culturally relevant & quality affordable housing for native people. *Activities*: Provides technical assistance & training programs for Indian housing authorities; conducts research on Indian housing issues; holds annual convention & legislative conferences. *Facilities*: Maintains Indian Housing Resource Center. *Publications*: Native American Housing News, Quarterly newsletter, "Pathway News"; NAIHC Annual Report. Established 1974.

NATIONAL ASSOCIATION OF NATIVE AMERICAN STUDIES

P.O. Box 6670 • Scarborough, ME 04070
 (207) 839-8004 Fax 839-3776
 Website: www.naaas.org; E-mail: natlaffiliates@earthlink.net
 Lemuel Berry, Jr., Executive Director/Founder
Activities: Holds national conference each year; regional meeting. *Publication*: Journal of Intercultural Disciplines, semiannual. *Activities*: Annual conference in February. Established 1999.

NATIONAL ASSOCIATION OF TRIBAL COURT PERSONNEL

1920 Spring Creek Circle • Green Bay, WI 54311
 (920) 468-8197 Fax 468-8198
 Hon. Robert Miller, President
A voluntary association previously known as the National Association of Tribal Court Clerks.

NATIONAL CAUCUS OF NATIVE AMERICAN STATE LEGISLATORS

c/o National Conference of State Legislatures
7700 E. First Place • Denver, CO 80230
 (303) 364-7700 Fax 364-7800
444 N. Capitol St. NW #515 • Washington, DC 20001
 (202) 624-5400 Fax 737-1069
 Website: www.ncsl.org; E-mail: state-tribal-info@ncsl.org
 Senator John McCoy (WA), Chairperson &
  Energy, Natural Resources & Transportation
 Senator Anastasia Pittman (OK), Vice Chairperson & Education Chair
 Representative Carolyn Pease-Lopez (MT), Secretary
 Representative Kevin Killer (SD), Treasurer
 Sen. Benny Shendo, Jr. (NM) Economic Development Chair & Peace Keeper
 Representative Susan Allen (MN), Health & Human Services Chairperson
Description: The caucus is comprised of approximately 71 members from 19 states. *Mission*: To promote a better understanding of state-tribal issues among policymakers and the public at large. *Goals*: To provide a forum for discussion & increased communication among Native American Legislators; to increase awareness of the diverse Native American cultures in the U.S.; to act as an advisory body on issues affecting Native Americans. *Activities*: Annual Meetings. Library. Established 1992.

NATIONAL CENTER FOR AMERICAN INDIAN ENTERPRISE
DEVELOPMENT (NCAIED) (Headquarters)

953 E. Juanita Ave. • Mesa, AZ 85204
 (800) 462-2433; (480) 545-1298 Fax 545-4208
 Website: www.ncaied.org; E-mail: info@ncaied.org
 Gary "Litefoot" Davis (Cherokee), President & CEO
 Melanie Sue, Chief of Staff (999-2299)
 Dalton Walker, Media & Content Mgr., Native American Global Trade Center

Derrick Watchman (Navajo), Chairperson
Patricia Parker, Vice Chairperson
Kip Ritchie (Forest County Potawatomi), Treasurer
Urban Giff, Secretary

Description: Business consulting firm that provides management services and technical assistance; sponsors Management Institute -- training for Indian managers; workshops & seminars. *Purpose*: To promote business & economic development among American Indians and tribes, in cooperation with the U.S. Dept. of Commerce, Minority Business Development Agency. *Resources*: American Indian Procurement Technical Assistance Center; National Resource Council; Native American Global Trade Center; National Center Teaming Alliance, Operates 3 regional offices and a subsidiary: Southwest, Pacific, Northwest, & Eastern Office UIDA (subsidiary); & two programs: California/Nevada Tribal Technical Assistance Program (CA/NV TTAP), & Marketing & Procurement Services Program (MPSP). *Publication*: Reporter, quarterly voice of American Indian business; National American Indian Business Directory, annual. Annual Indian Progress in Business Conference; annual awards banquet & periodic Reservation Economic Summit. Established 1970.

NATIONAL CENTER FOR GREAT LAKES NATIVE AMERICAN CULTURE, INC. (NCGLNAC)
P.O. Box 1063 • Portland, IN 47371
(765) 427-9324; Website: www.ncglnac.org
Kay Neumayr, Chairperson (426-3022)
  E-mail: kay.neumayr@ncglnac.com
Linda L. Andrews (Miami/Cherokee), Vice Chairperson
  E-mail: linda.andrews@ncglnac.com
Sara Wagar (Piqua Shawnee), Secretary
Linda Susie Dunham, Treasurer

A non-profit membership organization. *Purpose*: To preserve & promote Great Lakes Native American art, history and tradition. Since 1987, NCGLNAC's leaders have worked with tribes, schools, corporations, individuals & other institutions throughout the Great Lakes Region to raise awareness as to the millenniums-long heritage of Great Lakes & Algonquian Tribes. *Activities*: Organizes Great Lakes Native American arts & crafts workshops, Native American history symposiums, Great Lakes Native American traditional powwows, art & history exhibits for museums & galleries, educational programs & presentations for elementary & secondary schools as well as institutions of higher learning, & cooperative Great Lakes Native American cultural projects with local, state & national government agencies. Also networks with Great Lakes Native American artists & craftspeople to promote & sell their crafts & artwork. Established 1987.

NATIONAL COALITION FOR THE ADVANCEMENT OF NATIVES IN HGHER EDUCATION
P.O. Box 416 • Yuma, AZ 85366
  E-mail: nativehigheredcoalition@gmail.com
Jack P. Soto, Project Coordinator

Description: Consists of Native & non-Native higher education student service practitioners and scholars who want to build a useful network to manage the relationship between higher education institutions and the needs of American Indian students.

NATIONAL CONFERENCE OF STATE LEGISLATURES
State-Tribal Relations Project, 7700 East First Place • Denver, CO 80230
(303) 385-1414 Fax 364-7800
Website: www.ncsl.org; E-mail: state-tribal-info@ncsl.org
Andrea Wilkins, Director

Washington office: 444 N. Capitol St., NW, Suite 515, Washington, DC 20001
Purpose: To promote a better understanding of state-tribal issues among policymakers and the public at large. The Project tracks a variety of policy issues affecting state-tribal relations including economic development, environmental protection, human services, taxation, jurisdiction and law enforcement and trust land issues.

NATIONAL CONGRESS OF AMERICAN INDIANS
Embassy of Tribal Nations, 1516 P St., NW • Washington, DC 20005
(202) 466-7767 Fax 466-7797
Website: www.ncai.org; E-mail: ncai@ncai.org
Jacqueline Johnson-Pata, Executive Director; E-mail: jpata@ncai.org
Robert Holden, Deputy Director; E-mail: rholden@ncai.org
Nicole Hallingstad, Director of Operations; E-mail: nhallingstad@ncai.org
Samuel Owl, Chief Financial Officer; Email: sowl@ncai.org
Virginia Davis, Senior Advisor to Executive Director; E-mail: vdavis@ncai.org
Carolyn Hornsbuckle (Mohawk), Senior Program Manager
Ian Record Director of Partnership for Tribal Governance
  E-mail: irecord@ncai.org
Jamie Gomez, Director of External Affairs; E-mail: jgomez@ncai.org
John Dossett, General Counsel; E-mail: jdossett@ncai.org
Amber D. Ebarb (Tlingit); Budget Policy Analyst; E-mail: aebarb@ncai.org
Brian Cladoosby (Swinomish), Board President

Michael O. Finley (Colville) 1st Vice President
Robert Shepherd (Sisseton Wahpeton Oyate), Secretary
Dennis Welsh (Colorado River Tribes), Treasurer

Membership: 2,600. Consists of individuals and more than 250 tribal governments representing over one million Native Americans. *Purpose*: To protect Native American traditional cultural & religious rights; to conserve & develop Native American natural & human resources; to serve legislative interests of Indian tribes; to improve the health, education, & economic conditions of Native-Americans. *Programs*: Indians Youth Commission; Community Development; Health & Human Services; Land & Natural Resources; Cultural Protection; Tribal-State Relations; Tribal Governance. *Facilities*: Policy Research Center - 1301 Connecticut Ave., NW #200, Washington, DC 20036. *Activities*: Through its committees, the NCAI involves Executive Council & delegates in formulating positions in a wide variety of issues; conducts research on Indian problems as service to Indian tribes; bestows congressional awards; administers NCAI fund for educational & charitable purposes; legal aid program; nuclear waste program; welfare reform program; maintains speakers bureau. Semiannual Conferences & Annual Convention. *Publications*: Sentinel, quarterly newsletter; bulletin, NCAI News; Tribal Government Textbook; annual conference report. Established 1944.

NATIONAL CONGRESS OF AMERICAN INDIANS POLICY RESEARCH CENTER
1301 Connecticut Ave., NW, Suite 200 • Washington, DC 20036
(202) 466-7767 Fax 466-7797
Website: www.ncai.org/prc; E-mail: research@ncai.org
Malia Villegas (ugpiaq/Alutiiq), Director; E-mail: mvillegas@ncai.org
Carolyn Hornbuckle (Mohawk), JD, Senior Program Manager
Sarah Cline Pytalski, Policy Research & Evaluation Manager
Amber D. Ebarb (Tlingit), Program Manager; E-mail: aebarb@ncai.org

Mission: to pioneer a national tribal research center that would serve as a think tank focused on issues facing tribal communities. Guided by a diverse and distinguished advisory council, the NCAI Policy Research Center works with our partners to provide the tools necessary to inform public policy debates with meaningful information. Our work is focused on shifting the discourse in Native policy from a problem-focused approach to truly proactive, future-thinking strategy development. Provide tribal leaders with the best available knowledge to make strategically proactive policy decisions in a framework of Native wisdom that positively impact the future of Native peoples.

NATIONAL COUNCIL OF URBAN INDIAN HEALTH (NCUIH)
924 Pennsylvania Ave. SE • Washington, DC 20003
(202) 544-0344 Fax 544-9394; Website: www.ncuih.org
Donna Keeler, President; Rudy Soto, Policy Analyst
Aren Sparck, Government Affairs Officer
Sherry Salway Black (Oglala Lakota), Member of Advisory Committee

Purpose: To support & develop quality accessible healthcare programs for all American Indian & Alaska Natives living in urban communities through advocacy, training, education, & leadership development. *Facilities*: Knowledge Resource Center (KRC) is the first online tool devoted to the storage & dissemination of Urban Indian-specific research documents.

NATIONAL INDIAN CARBON COALITION FUND (NICC)
Indian Land Tenure Foundation (Website: www.iltf.org)
151 East County Rd. B2 • Little Canada, MN 55117
(651) 766-8999 Fax 766-0012; Website: www.indiancarbon.org
Erick Giles (Muscogee Creek), Program Director
  E-mail: egiles@indiancarbon.org
62 Old Farm Rd. • South Portland, ME 04106

Description: NICC is a greenhouse gas management service providing project development resources & training for American Indian nations & landowner associations entering the carbon credit market. It was created from a partnership between Indian Land Tenure Foundation & Intertribal Agriculture Council. *Purpose*: To develop & maintain relationships among tribal leaders & Indian farmers, ranchers & foresters & other organizations & businesses that may assist with the development if carbon-credit projects.

NATIONAL INDIAN CASINO SAFETY ASSOCIATION (NICSA)
c/o Sycuan Resort & Casino, 5469 Casino Way • EL CAJON, CA 92019
(619) 445-6002
Eddie Ilko, Chairperson; E-mail: eilko@sycuan.com

Serves the health, safety, security and emergency preparedness needs of Indian Country. the Inter-Tribal Safety Group in Southern California is taking the necessary steps to evolve into a National Association to be known as the, National Indian Casino Safety Association (NICSA). The NICSA had its first board meeting on December 14th at Viejas Resort & Casino in San Diego. In addition the Tribal Gaming Protection Network (TGPN) has entered into a partnership with NICSA, and fully supports this group in the industry in Indian Country. Having a culture of safety begins in changing the mentality of how each of us view safety. It starts with our thoughts, feelings and ends in our actions to make a safe environment for the guests, staff, and tribe. If you are interested please email me atahofstetter@bluebirdcpas.com or call at 951.923.8144. Andrew Hofstetter. TGPN Chairman

NATIONAL INDIAN CHILD WELFARE ASSOCIATION (NICWA)
5100 SW Macadam Ave. #300 • Portland, OR 97201
(503) 222-4044 Fax 222-4007
Website: www.nicwa.org; E-mail: info@nicwa.org
Sarah Kastelic (Alutiiq)), Executive Director; E-mail: skastelic@nicwa.org
Nicole Adams (Colville), Communications Manager
  E-mail: nadams@nicwa.org
Kim Christensen (Ojibwe), Development Director
  E-mail: kchristensen@nicwa.org
Terry Cross (Seneca), Senior Advisor; E-mail: tcross@nicwa.org
Matthew Scott (Siletz), Director of Operations; E-mail: mscott@nicwa.org
Melissa Bob (Lummi), Director of Community Development
  for Children's Mental Health & Youth Engagement
Gil Vigil (Tesuque Pueblo), Board President
Rochelle Ettawageshik (Little Traverse Bay Band of Odawa), Vice President
W. Alex Wesaw (Pokagon Potawatomi), Secretary
Gary Peterson (Skokomish), Treasurer
Jefferson Keel & Ernie Stevens, Jr., Strategic Leadership Council Members
Purpose: To preserve & protect Indian children by promoting safety, health, and a positive sense of Indian heritage. The Association claims to be "the only Native American organization focused specifically on issues of child abuse & neglect, and tribal capacity to prevent & respond effectively to these problems." *Activities*: Maintains clearinghouse of more than 4,000 articles, books, periodicals on Indian child welfare, mental health, and social work issues. Annual "Protecting Our Children" National American Indian Conference on Child Abuse & Neglect. *Publications*: NICWA News, quarterly newsletter; Pathways Practice Digest, bimonthly newsletter; National Indian Child Welfare Institute Directory (biennial); Heritage & Helping; Positive Indian Parenting; Cross Culture Skills; and Honoring the Children. Established 1987.

NATIONAL INDIAN COUNCIL ON AGING
10501 Montgomery Blvd. NE #210 • Albuquerque, NM 87111
(505) 292-2001 Fax 292-1922; Website: www.nicoa.org
Randella Bluehouse (Navajo), Executive Director
Rebecca Morgan (Eastern Cherokee), NMAO-TAC Project Coordinator
Eddie Tullis (Poarch Band Creek), Eastern Region – Chairperson
James DeLa Cruz (Quinault), Northwest Region – Vice Chairperson
Martha Adele Mihesuah (Comanche), Southern Plains Region – Secretary
JoAnna Jones (Ho Chunk), Midwest Region - Treasurer
Membership: 300. *Goal*: To bring about improved comprehensive services to American Indian & Alaska Native elders. *Purpose*: To act as a focal point for the articulation of the needs of Indian elderly; to provide meaningful part-time employment experience in community services; and to enroll elders into the SSI entitlement program. *Activities*: disseminates information on Indian aging programs; provides technical assistance and training to tribal governments and organizations in the development of their programs; conducts research on needs of Indian elderly. *Publication*: Elder Voices, monthly newsletter. Biennial conference. Established 1976.

NATIONAL INDIAN EDUCATION ASSOCIATION (NIEA)
1514 P St., NW, Suite B • Washington, DC 20002
(877) 809-1659; (202) 544-7290 Fax 544-7293
Website: www.niea.org; E-mail: niea@niea.org
Ahniwake Rose (Cherokee), Executive Director
  E-mail: arose@niea.org
Diana Cournoyer (Oglala Sioux), Program Manager
  E-mail: dcournoyer@niea.org
Matt de Ferranti, Legislative Director
  E-mail: mdeferranti@niea.org
Leah Salgado (Pascua Yaqui), Membership Recruiting Manager
  E-mail: lsalgado@niea.org
Dimple Patel, Federal Policy Associate; E-mail: dpatel@niea.org
Patricia Whitefoot (Yakama), President
Yatibaey Evans (Ahtna), President-Elect
Ronalda Warito-Tome (Dine'/Navajo), Vice President
Jolene Bowman (Stockbridge Munsee Mohican), Secretary
Membership: 4,000. Advocates educational programs to improve the social & economic wellbeing of American Indians & Alaskan Native people. *Purpose*: To evaluate & improve the delivery of state and local educational services; and to intercede & establish liaison with state & federal agencies. *Resources*: Library. *Activities*: Conducts annual National Conference on American Indian Education in October; holds workshops in conjunction with the conference; assesses & coordinates existing technical assistance sources. *Scholarship*: John Rouillard Scholarship. *Publications*: Indian Education Newsletter, quarterly; Contemporary Issues of the American Indian; and guides for establishing Indian libraries. Store (www.cafepress.com/niea). Established 1969.

NATIONAL INDIAN GAMING ASSOCIATION (NIGA)
224 Second St., SE • Washington, DC 20003
(800) 286-6442; (202) 546-7711 Fax 546-1755
Website: www.indiangaming.org; E-mail: questions@indiangaming.org
Jason Giles, Executive Director
  E-mail: jgiles@indiangaming.org
Danielle Her Many Horses, Deputy Executive Director
  E-mail: dhermanyhorses@indiangaming.org
Veronica Watters, Legislative Coordinator
  E-mail: vwatters@indiangaming.org
Ernest L. Stevens, Jr. (Oneida), Chairperson
  E-mail: estevens@indiangaming.org
Description: Non-profit trade association comprised of 184 American Indian Nations & other non-voting associate members. Operates as a clearinghouse & educational, legislative & public policy resource for tribes, policymakers and the public on Indian gaming issues & tribal community development. *Purpose*: To advance the lives of Indian people - economically, socially & politically. *Activities*: Holds Indian Gaming Enterprise & Management Law Seminars; & Annual Convention & Trade Show. Professional training for tribal casino management, staff, and for tribal start up operations. *Publications*: NIGA News, monthly newsletter; books - NIGA Indian Gaming Resource Directory; General Requirements & Parameters for Vendor Licensing; National Indian Gaming Minimum Internal Control Standards for Indian Casinos; The Indian Gaming Handbook. Maintains Library and Resource Center. Established 1985.

NATIONAL INDIAN GAMING COMMISSION (NIGC)
90 K St., NE, Suite 200 • Washington, DC 20002
(202) 632-7003 Fax 632-7066
Website: www.nigc.gov; E-mail: contactus@nigc.gov
Jonodev Osceola Chaudhuri (Muscogee Creek), Acting Chairperson
Daniel Little, Associate Commissioner
Purpose: To regulate gaming activities on Indian lands for the purpose of shielding Indian tribes from organized crime and other corrupting influences; to ensure that Indian tribes are the primary beneficiaries of gaming revenues; and to ensure gaming is conducted fairly & honestly by both operators & players. *Seven regional offices*:
90 K St., NE, Suite 200 • Washington, DC 20002
  (202) 632-7003; Cindy Altimus, Region Director
620 SW Main St., Solomon Bldg., Suite 212, Portland, OR 97205
  (503) 326-5095; Mark Phillips, Region Director
801 I St., Suite 489, Sacramento, CA 95814
  (916) 414-2300; Eric Schalansky, Region Director
3636 N. Central Ave., Suite 880, Phoenix, AZ 85012
  (602) 640-2951; Lance Vallo, Region Director
224 S. Boulder, Rm. 301, Tulsa, OK 74103
  (918) 581-7924; Tim Harper, Region Director
380 Jackson St., Suite 420, St. Paul, MN 55101
  (651) 290- 4004; Linda Durbin, Region Director
215 Dean A. McGee Ave., Suite 218, Oklahoma City, OK 73102
  (405) 609-8626; Thomas L. Cunningham, Region Director

NATIONAL INDIAN HEAD START DIRECTORS ASSOCIATION
P.O. Box 6058 • Norman, OK 73070
(405) 360-2919 Fax 360-3069
Laura Waukechon-Factor (Upper Skagit)), President
  E-mail: lauraw@upperskagit.com
Purpose: To promote & support high quality, comprehensive early childhood development & education services for Native Americans in the U.S. & Canada. Seek to preserve Native identity through culturally appropriate & relevant family centered, child development & educational services, believing the Head Start model is the best fit for Native communities. Training conference. Publication: Annual report.

NATIONAL INDIAN HEALTH BOARD (NIHB)
910 Pennsylvania Ave., SE • Washington, DC 20003
(202) 507-4070 Fax 507-4071; Website: www.nihb.org
Stacy A. Bohlen (Sault Ste. Marie Chippewa), Executive Director
  E-mail: sbohlen@nihb.org
Carolyn Angus-Hornbuckle, JD (Mohawk), Director of Public Health Programs
  E-mail: chornbuckle@nihb.org
Kristen Bitusie Tribal Health Care Reform Outreach & Education
Robert Foley, Chief Program Officer
  E-mail: rfoley@nihb.org
Lester Secatero (Navajo)), Board Chair & Albuquerque Area Rep.
Vinton Hawley (Pyramid Lake Paiute), Board Vice Chair & Phoenix Area Rep.
Lisa Elgin (Pomo), Board Secretary & California Area Rep.
Sam Moose (Mille Lacs Ojibwe), Board Treasurer & Bemidji Area Rep.
Lincoln Bean (Tlingit), Board Member-at-Large & Alaska Area Rep.
Purpose: To elevate the health status of American Indians and Alaska Natives equal to that of the rest of the U.S. population; to secure maximum tribal & consumer participation in the delivery of health services to Indian people; and

to enhance & promote education of Indian health issues. *Facilities*: Tribal Health Reform Resource Center; Tribal Technical Advisory Group. *Activities*: Provides technical assistance to members & Indian organizations; bestows awards; & sponsors annual health conference. *Publications*: NIHB Health Reporter, newsletter; health conference report. Library. Annual conference. Established 1972.

NATIONAL INDIAN JUSTICE CENTER (NIJC)
5250 Aero Dr. • Santa Rosa, CA 95403
(800) 966-0662; (707) 579-5507 Fax 579-9019
Website: www.nijc.org; E-mail: tcoord@nijc.org
Joseph A. Myers (Pomo), Executive Director
Jerry Burroni, Education Consultant
Margaret Browne, Training Coordinator
Raquelle Myers (Pomo), Nicole Myers-Lim (Pomo), Staff Attorneys
Christy Garcia, Program Specialist
William Johnson (Umatilla), Board President
William T. Thorne, Jr. (Pomo), Board Vice President
Hon. John St. Clair (Shoshone) & Michael Petoskey (Ottawa), Chief Judges
Ted Quasula (Hualapai), Consultant; Doug Nash (Nez Perce), Attorney
Description: An Indian-owned & operated non-profit corporation. An independent national resource for Native communities & tribal government. *Goals*: To design & deliver legal education, research, and technical assistance programs which seek to improve the quality of life for Native communities and the administration of justice in Indian country. *Special projects*: Communities Empowering Native Youth; Native American Children Training Forum; Correctional Systems & Alternatives on Tribal Lands; Turning Points: A Comprehensive Tribal Court Alcohol & Substance Abuse Training Programs, et al. *Programs*: Training & technical assistance services; alcohol & substance abuse, alternative methods of dispute resolution, child abuse & neglect, domestic violence, Indian youth & family law, juvenile justice, & federal Indian law. *Activities*: Publishes training manuals; produces videos; sells hats & posters. Established 1983.

NATIONAL INDIAN PROGRAMS TRAINING CENTER
1011 Indian School Rd. NW Suite 254 • Albuquerque, NM 87104
(505) 563-5400 Fax 563-5419; Linda G. Romero, Director
Resources: Media Production Center; Internet-Based Training; Video Teleconferencing; Computer Labs.

NATIONAL INDIAN SPORTS ASSOCIATION
1093 South 500 West • Provo, UT 84601
Website: www.nationalindiansports.com
E-mail: indiansports@aol.com
Bobby Letterman (Cherokee), President & CEO
Website: www.nativeweb.org/resources/sports_athletics/

NATIONAL INDIAN TELECOMMUNICATIONS INSTITUTE
110 N. Guadalupe St., Suite 9 • Santa Fe, NM 87501
(505) 986-3872; Karen Buller, Founder & President
Description: Native-founded & run organization dedicated to using the power of electronic technologies to provide American Indian & Alaskan Native communities with extensive educational tools, equal opportunity and a strong voice in self-determination.

NATIONAL INDIAN YOUTH COUNCIL, INC.
318 Elm St., SE • Albuquerque, NM 87102
(505) 247-2251 Fax 247-4251
Norman Ration (Laguna-Navajo), Executive Director
E-mail: nration@niyc-alb.org
Cecilia Belone (Navajo), President; Kay McGowan, Vice President
Juanita Rodgers (Navajo), Secretary/Treasurer
Sophia Wilson, Albuquerque Field Office Manager
E-mail: swilson@niyc-alb.org
Board members: Viola Hatch (Arapaho), Norbert S. Hill, Jr. (Oneida)
Dr. Shirley Hill Witt (Mohawk), James Nez (Navajo)
Field offices: 653 West Broadway, Farmington, NM 87401
(505) 327-5341 Fax 327-4786; Angelita Joe, Field Manager
E-mail: ajoe@niyc-alb.org
407 South Cliff, Suite B, Gallup, NM 87301 (505) 863-6639 Fax 863-2167
Jacqueline Watson, Field Manager
E-mail: jwatson@niyc-alb.org
Membership: 45,000. *Purpose*: To provide young Indian people with a working knowledge of serving & understanding their tribal communities & to implement educational resources through research, training & planning on local, regional & national levels. *Programs*: Indian health, education, & employment; annual meeting. *Publication*: Americans Before Columbus, bimonthly tabloid; Indian Voter Survey Reports, periodic describing political attitudes of Native Americans living on reservations. Annual meeting in June. Established 1961.

NATIONAL INDIAN YOUTH LEADERSHIP PROJECT
2501 San Pedro NE, Suite 116 • Albuquerque, NM 87110
(505) 554-2289 Fax 554-2291
Gallup office: 305 Sunde St., P.O. Box 2140 • Gallup, NM 87305
(505) 722-9176 Fax 722-9794; Website: www.niylp.org
McClellan Hall (Cherokee), Founder & Executive Director
Elizabeth Wonson, International Director of Operations (879-1041)
Roger McKinney (Kickapoo), Chairperson
Purpose: To develop leadership in Native youth.

NATIONAL INSTITUTE FOR NATIVE LEADERSHIP IN HIGHER EDUCATION (NINLHE)
Office of the Provost & Executive VP for Academic Affairs
University of Northern Colorado, 501 20 St. • Greeley, CO 80639
(970) 351-2823 Fax 351-1880; Website: www.unco.edu/ninlhe
Augustine McCaffery (Comanche), Governing Council Chairperson
E-mail: amccaf@u.washington.edu
Governing Council Executive Board Members:
Michael Hanitchak (Choctaw/Chickasaw)
E-mail: mhanitchak@gmail.com
Steven Abbott, Council Executive Board Member
Geni D. Cowan (Choctaw) E-mail: gcowan@csus.edu
Liz Gilbert, E-mail: elizabeth.gilbert@unco.edu
Mission: To transform higher education in the United States & Canada in ways that improve the experiences & educational outcomes of Native students, which includes Native American, Alaska Native, Native Hawaiian, & Aboriginal peoples; works to enhance the professional skills and bolster resilience of higher education professionals, both Native & non-native, responsible for improving Native student recruitment, retention and graduation rates. By strengthening the capacity of these individuals, who are essential for Native student success, & promoting culturally appropriate practices NINLHE improves the educational training experience of Native students as well as the professional environment for staff and faculty across the United States and Canada. As a peer among other professional associations, NINLHE will use our collective expertise & influence to provide leadership to the national higher education community. *Activities*: Annual Summer Institute; Grant Awards.

NATIONAL NATIVE AMERICAN AIDS PREVENTION CENTER
1031 33rd St., Suite 270 • Denver, CO 80205
(720) 382-2244 Fax 382-2248
Website: www.nnaapc.org; E-mail: information@nnaapc.org
Alexander White Tail Feather (Kashia Pomo), Executive Director
E-mail: awhitetailfeather@nnaapc.org
D'Shane Barnett (Mandan/Arikara), Board Chairperson
Purpose: To stop the spread of HIV & related diseases among American Indians, Alaska Natives, and Native Hawaiians by improving their health status through empowerment & self determination. *Special programs*: Conduct outreach to Native organizations & communities; trains community-based HIV educators; & provides technical assistance in community organizing. *Activities*: Operates a national clearinghouse for Native-specific HIV/AIDS information; provides ongoing information services; & develops curricula for target populations. Division of Client Services, 205 West 8th St., Suite 103, Lawrence, KS 66044 (913) 865-4297 Fax 842-0145; National Indian AIDS Media Consortium (Native-owned newspapers, radio stations, and television programs), 1433 E. Franklin Ave., Suite 3A, Minneapolis, MN 55404 (612) 872-8860 Fax 872-8864; Ahalaya HIV Case Management Project, 1200 N. Walker, Suite 605, Oklahoma City, OK 73101 (405) 235-3701 Fax 235-1801. *Publications*: Seasons, quarterly magazine; Raven's Guide, resource guide; Poster series; Policy Guidelines; Speaker's directory; books & videos. Library. Established in 1987.

NATIONAL NATIVE AMERICAN BAR ASSOCIATION (NNABA)
P.O. Box 11145 • Tempe, AZ 85284
Website: www.nativeamericanbar.org
E-mail: info@nativeamericanbar.org
Ann Marie Downes, Executive Director
E-mail: executivedirector@nativeamericanbar.org
Diandra Benally (Yavapai), President
Thomasina Real Bird, JD, Treasurer
Board members: Gabriel S. Galanda, JD (Round Valley); David Blockorby, JD; Lauren van Schilfgaarde, JD; D. Michael McBride, III, JD; Meghan Topkok, JD; Robert Saunooke, JD. *Description*: Members include Native American attorneys, judges, law professors & law students. *Purpose*: To promote issues important to the Native American community & works to improve professional opportunities for Native American lawyers. *Projects*: Stop Academic Ethicist Fraud/"Box-Checking"; Include Indian Law on State Bar Exams; Include Federal Indian Law in Law School Curriculum – "Indian Law Modules"; Increase Natives & Tribal Court Judges in the Judiciary; The Tribal Partnership Program: Matching Pro Bono Law Firms with Tribes; Increase the Number of Native American Law Students. Established 1973.

NATIONAL NATIVE AMERICAN COOPERATIVE
NORTH AMERICAN INDIAN INFORMATION & TRADE CENTER

P.O. Box 27626 • Tucson, AZ 85726-7626
(520) 622-4900 Fax 622-3525; Website: www.usaindianinfo.com
Fred Synder, Director/Consultant; E-mail: fredusaindian@aol.com

Description: Lists about 2,800 artists from 410 different tribes. Includes Native American artists & craftsmen, cultural presenters, dance groups, & individuals interested in preserving American Indian crafts, culture, & traditional education. *Purpose*: To collect, organize, & disseminate current information on Native Americans of North America; to provide incentives to Native Americans to encourage the preservation of their culture. *Activities*: Publish books; maintains museum of major crafts from contemporary artists, such as basketry, beadwork & quillwork; Indian doll collection; sponsors three major events each year: Native American Month Social Powwow & Craft Market (Thanksgiving weekend, Tucson); Indian America Competition Powwow & Indian Craft Market (New Year's weekend, Tucson); American Indian Exposition (first 15 days in February, Tucson); also maintain a research library containing over 5,000 books & research papers. Provides educational programs; serves as a clearinghouse of information; offers assistance marketing American Indian crafts and locating material that is difficult to find; supplies referral information on public health, education, career counseling, scholarships & funding sources, marketing; sponsors crafts & cultural demonstrations; compiles statistics; operates speaker's bureau; maintains museum; annual meeting. *Published works*: Northwest Native American Business Directory; Indian Information Packets; Powwow on the Red Road, annual. Established 1969.

NATIONAL NATIVE AMERICAN LAW STUDENTS ASSOCIATION

(NNALSA) 1001 Marquette Ave., NW • Albuquerque, NM 87196
(505) 289-0810; Website: www.nationalnalsa.org
Meghan Sigvanna Topkok, President; E-mail: nnalsa.president@gmail.com
Taylor Burdick, Vice President; E-mail: nnalsa.vicepresident@gmail.com
University of Arizona College of Law, Class of 2015
Stacie Crawford, Secretary; E-mail: nnalsa.secretary@gmail.com
Jacob Metoxen, Treasurer; E-mail: nnalsa.treasurer@gmail.com
Alexandra Mojado, Secretary; E-mail: nnalsa.secretary@gmail.com

Membership: 165. American Indian & Native Alaskan law students. *Description*: Divided into eight chapters or regions. Each chapter or region has a student representative. *Purpose*: To promote the study of Federal Indian Law, Tribal Law & traditional forms of governance, and to support Native Americans in law school; to reach out to Native communities and encourage Native People to pursue legal education; to educate the legal community about Native issues; To promote unity, communication & cooperation among Indian law students. *Programs*: Financial aid, & summer employment opportunities; research projects & curriculum development in Indian law; maintains speakers bureau of students in the field of Indian law. *Publication*: Newsletter. Annual meeting. Established 1970.

NATIONAL NATIVE AMERICAN PURCHASING ASSOCIATION

P.O. Box 365 • Oneida, WI 54155
(920) 496-7409 Fax 496-2868
Website: www.nativeamericanpurchasing.org
Patrick Stensloff, President; E-mail: pstenslo@oneidanation.org
Ginger Johnson, First Director.
Annual Training Conference

NATIONAL NATIVE AMERICAN VETERANS ASSOCIATION

3903 County Road 382 • San Antonio, TX 78253
P.O. Box 891973 • Oklahoma City, OK 73189
(405) 692-6365 Fax 692-7353; Website: www.nnava.org
Thomas Berry (Choctaw of Okla.), Founder/Director
James Cates, National Chairperson; E-mail: jdsetac@yahoo.com
Blackhawk Fornelli , National Vice Chairperson & Nation Elder

Purpose: To provide Native American veterans representation & assistance in dealing with the Dept. of Veteran Affairs; to educate & assist Native American veterans. *Program*: Project Moccasin Fund - To send a new pair of moccasins to each Native American troop deployed. Established 2004.

NATIONAL NATIVE NEWS – NATIVE AMERICA CALLING

4401 Lomas Blvd. NE, Suite C • Albuquerque, NM 87110
(505) 999-2404 Fax 999-2401
Website: www.nativenews.net; E-mail: nnn@nativenews.net
Art Hughes, Executive Producer-National Programs (999-2444)
E-mail: ahughes@koahnic.org
Antonia Gonzales, Producer & Anchor; (702-8571)
E-mail: agonzales@nativenews.net
Nola Daves Moses, Distribution Director – Native Voice One (999-2403)
E-mail: nola@nv1.org

Description: A weekday, five-minute radio newscast. It's one of Koahnic Broadcast Corporation's four nationally syndicated radio programs produced in Albuquerque, NM. The show is heard on 52 stations in the U.S. & Canada by approximately 500,000 listeners each week. *Production Company*: Koahnic

Broadcast Corp., 3600 San Jeronimo, #475, Anchorage, AK 99508 (907) 793-3500. See Media section. *Purpose*: To provide Native & non-Native public radio listeners with news about Native issues. Covers the social, economic and cultural issues that affect every community, & helps radio listeners understand the interconnectedness between Native people & their non-Native neighbors. It is the only daily news and information program produced from a Native perspective that can be heard on public radio stations nationwide and in Canada; distributed by Public Radio International. Production began 1987.

NATIONAL RESOURCE CENTER FOR AMERICAN INDIAN,
ALASAKA NATIVE & NATIVE HAWAIIAN ELDERS

University of Alaska, Anchorage, College of Health & Social Welfare
3211 Providence Dr., Suite 205 • Anchorage, AK 99508
(907) 786-4329 Fax 786-4440; E-mail: afgpc1@uaa.alaska.edu
George P. Charles (*Kanaqiak*) (Yup'ik), Director

Purpose: To enhance knowledge about older Native Americans in order to increase and improve service delivery to this population. Each NRC must address one of four areas of primary concern as defined by the AoA: health issues, long term care including in-home care, Elder abuse, mental health, and other issues facing Native communities.

NATIONAL RESOURCE CENTER ON NATIVE AMERICAN AGING
(NRCNAA) NATIONAL INDIGENOUS ELDER JUSTICE INITIATIVE (NIEJI)

Center for Rural Health, The University of North Dakota
School of Medicine & Health Sciences, Rm. 4535
1301 N. Columbia Rd., MS 9037 • Grand Forks, ND 58202-9037
(800) 896-7628; (701) 777-3720 Fax 777-6779
Website: www.nrcnaa.org E-mail: info@nrcnaa.org
Paula Carter, Director (777-3720)
E-mail: paula.carter@med.und.edu
Jacque Gray, Associate Director, Indigenous Programs (777-3265)
E-mail: jacqueline.gray@med.und.edu
Brad Gibbens, Deputy Director (777-3720)
E-mail: brad.gibbens@med.und.edu
Collette Adamsen, Project Coordinator (777-0676)
E-mail: eric.souvannasacd@med.und.edu

Funded by the AoA. Provides support, advocacy & information for older Native Americans. *Mission*: To identify & increase awareness of evolving Native elder health & social issues; to empower Native people to develop community-based solutions; to provide legal information & references, geriatric leadership training, cultural awareness, & publications. *Publication*: Native Aging Visions

NATIONAL SOCIETY OF AMERICAN INDIAN ELDERLY (NSAIE)

P.O. Box 50070 • Phoenix, AZ 85076
(602) 424-0542; Victoria Collins, Executive Director
Dollie Chauvin (Hopi-Tewa), AmeriCorps VISTA Supervisor
Steve Wilson (Muscogee Creek), Chairperson
Delia Carlyle (Ak Chin), First Vice-Chairperson
Oneida Winship (Choctaw of Okla.), Secretary/Treasurer

Description: Works to assist all Indian elderly service programs, both on reservation and off, to improve quality of life for American Indian elders. *Project*: Tribal AmeriCorps VISTA Program - works with tribes & elder services in training, including project management, resource development, grant writing, & volunteer management. Established 1987.

NATIONAL TRIBAL CHILD SUPPORT ASSOCIATION (NTCSA)

P.O. Box 154 • Ada, OK 74820
(580) 436-7016
Jerry Sweet, President; E-mail: jsweet@otcse.com
Eddie Brakes (Tlingit-Haida), V.P.; E-mail: ebrakes@ccthita.org
Detra Kingfisher (Cherokee), Secretary
E-mail: detra-kingfisher@cherokee.org

Purpose: To provide resources for tribal efforts to serve Native American children through child support programs. *Activities*: Annual Conference & Expo. Established 2001.

NATIVE AMERICA BASKETBALL INVITATIONAL (NABI) FOUNDATION

Salt River Pima-Maricopa Community, P.O. Box 25606 • Phoenix, AZ 85002
(480) 446-7052 Fax 446-7053
Website: www.nabifoundation.org; E-mail: info@nabifoundation.org
GinaMarie Scarpa, Co-founder & CEO
Angelo Johnson (Apache/Hopi/Tohono O'odham), Program Coordinator
Ernie Stevens, Jr. (Oneida), Advisor
Bert Wells (Cherokee/Caddo), Board President
Derrick Watchman (Navajo) BoardVice President
Corrine Wilson (Paiute/Shoshone), Treasurer

Description: An all Native American national professional basketball team; called "Native America," was founded by Spider Ledesma, a Mission/Mexican Native, who played one season for the Los Angeles Clippers and then in Europe for many years. The team is to join the American Basketball Association." The 1st season began November 2004 and is located in

Albuquerque, NM. *Purpose*: To support Native American youth by implementing programs that encourage higher education, sports, health & wellness, and community building.

NATIVE AMERICA HUMANE SOCIETY (NAHS)
Website: www.nativeamericahumane.org
E-mail: info@nativeamericahumane.org
Diana Webster (White Earth Band of Ojibwe), {Founder, President & CEO)
David C. Yu, Chief Financial Officer:
Marilou Chanrasmi, Vice President, Community Healing Programs
Laura Cull, Vice President, Development
Henry Halpern (Cayuga), Operations Manager
Stan Moore, Fund-Raising Counsel
Dr. Tolani Francisco (Pueblo of Laguna), Director of Executive Committee
  for Veterinary Services & Public Health
Mission: To empower Native communities to become healthier, happier and safer by providing information, support & resources for animal care programs in Indian country.

NATIVE AMERICAN ALASKA NATIVE COALITION
FOR FEDERAL AVIATION EMPLOYEES
Website: www.naanfaa.org
Kathleen Simmons, National President
Edwin Doney, National 1st V.P.; E-mail: edoney@naanfaa.org
Sharon Padilla, Secretary (Alaska Region Representative)
  E-mail: spadilla@naanfaa.org
Cheri Brady,Chair for NAAN Scholarships; E-mail: cbrady@naanfaa.org

NATIVE AMERICAN ALLIANCE FOUNDATION
5820 4th St. NW • Albuquerque, NM 87107
  (800) 516-9340; (505) 345-9340 Fax 345-0171
Janna Gourd-Gallegos, Exec. Director; Chico Gallegos, Assoc. Director
Description: A Native-owned & operated not-for-profit organization that develops training programs & direct service protocols that improve tribal justice systems, reduce adult crime and juvenile delinquency, and increase tribal community wellbeing.

NATIVE AMERICAN ASSOCIATION OF GERMANY e.V.
Rodenbacher Str. 22 • 67661 Kaiserslautern, Germany
  0173-10 12 55 3 (inside Germany) 0049-6301-60 966 40 (outside)
  Website: www.naaog.de; E-mail: chairwoman@naaog.de
Carmen Kwasny, Chairperson; Glenda Yellowhorse (Navajo), Vice Chair
  E-mail: vice-chairwoman-g.yellowhorse@naaog.de
Ulrich Wick, Treasurer; E-mail: treasurer-u.wick@naaog.de
U.S. contact: P.O. Box 51 • Anadarko, OK 73005
Purposes: To provide a meeting point for Native Americans living in Europe, temporarily stationed by U.S. military in Europe, and for Native Americans visiting Europe. To assist Native American artists; cooperates with Native American organizations; hosts Native American guests; organizes sight-seeing tours; acts as an education information center for Europeans interested in Native American culture. Organizes meetings, arranges powwows, supports Native Americans throughout their activities during the federally recognized "National American Indian Heritage Month" during November.

NATIVE AMERICAN BANKCORPORATION CO. (NABNA)
Headquarters: 999 18th St., Suite 2460 • Denver, CO 80202
  (800) 368-8894; (303) 988-2727 Fax 963-5540
  Website: www.nabna.com; E-mail: info@nabna.com
Retail Branch: P.O. Box 730 • Browning, MT 59417
  (800) 307-9199; (406) 338-7000 Fax 338-7008
Loan Production Office: 613 Sundance Rd. • Box Elder, MT 59521
  (406) 395-4355 Fax 395-4356
Thomas D. Ogaard, President & CEO (Denver)
  E-mail: togaard@nabna.com
Joel Smith, Sr. VP & Chief Credit Officer
  E-mail: jsmith@nabna.com
Tracie Davis, VP, CFO, Secretary/Treasurer (Denver)
  E-mail: tdavis@nabna.com
Shannon Loeve, VP & Chief Lending Officer (Denver)
  E-mail: sloeve@nabna.com
Debbie Emhoolah, VP Human Resources & Community Relations Officer
  E-mail: demhoolah@nabna.com
Thomas D. Ogaard, Native American Bancorp. Board Chairperson
Lewis A. Anderson (Mille Lacs Ojibwe), Native American Bank Chairperson
David Burrell (Sac & Fox of Mississippi), Vice Chairperson
Description: Owned by a collection of 26 tribal nations, tribal enterprises & Alaskan Native corporations. *Purpose*: To assist Native American & Alaskan Native individuals, enterprises & governments to reach their goals by providing affordable & flexible banking & financial services.

NATIVE AMERICAN BUSINESS ALLIANCE (NABA)
1490 William Floyd Parkway, Suite 107 • Shirley, NY 11967
  (631) 924-1780; Website: www.nativebusiness.com
Description: Represents Native Americans to the private sector; facilitates business & cultural educational programs. *Activity*: Annual NABA National Business Conference. *Publication*: Newsletter.

NATIVE AMERICAN CANCER RESEARCH (NACR)
P.O. Box 27494 • Denver, CO 80227
3022 Nova Rd. • Pine, CO 80470-7830
  (800) 537-8295; (303) 838-9359
  (303) 975-2449/2461 Fax 975-2463
  Website: www.natamcancer.org
Linda Burhansstipanov (Cherokee), Founder/President/Grants Director
Rick Clark, Co-Founder & Vice President
Lisa D. Harjo (Choctaw), Executive Director/Project Supervisor
Purpose: To reduce Native American cancer incidence & mortality, and to increase survival from cancer among Native Americans. Office: *Programs*: Native American Cancer Educational Services (NACES); Native American Cancer Initiative (NACI) Implements cancer primary prevention, secondary prevention, risk reduction, screening, education, training, research, diagnosis, control, treatment, and support programs. *Meeting*: National Native American Cancer Survivors/Thrivers Conference & Workshop. *Publication*: Newsletter, 3x/year. Established 1993.

NATIVE AMERICAN CENTER OF EXCELLENCE CONSORTIUM
University of Oklahoma Health Sciences Center
Colleges of Dentistry & Medicine
P.O. Box 26901 • Oklahoma City, OK 73190
  (888) 684-7473; (405) 271-1976
  Website: www.ouhsc.edu/nace; E-mail: nace@ouhsc.edu
Jerry Tahsequah, Associate Director
Purpose: To recruit & retain Native Americans to medical and dental school; recruit Native American faculty in medicine & dentistry; stimulate research on Native American health issues. *Activities*: MCAT Preparation; enrichment programs; faculty development programs; tutoring programs; extensive recruitment. Library. Established 1993.

NATIVE CHILD ALLIANCE (NCA)
101 West Broadway • Muskogee, OK 74401
  (918) 683-5291 Fax 683-3397; Website: www.nativechildalliance.org
Geri Wisner Foley (Muscogee Creek), JD, Chief of Staff
Saunie Wilson (Oglala Lakota), Vice President
Patrick Anderson, JD (Tlingit/Aleut), Treasurer
Kathryn England-Aytes (Delaware/Cherokee), Secretary
Mission: To protect Native children & eliminate children's physical, sexual, psychological & spiritual abuse by awareness, training, building partnerships in respectful ways that honors tribal sovereignty, empowers communities, develops tribal readiness for Seven Generations. Established 1999.

NATIVE AMERICAN COMMUNITY BOARD (NACB) - THE NATIVE
AMERICAN WOMEN'S HEALTH EDUCATION RESOURCE CENTER
P.O. Box 572 • Lake Andes, SD 57356-0572
  (605) 487-7072 Fax 487-7964; Website: www.nativeshop.org
Charon Asetoyer (Comanche), Founding Director & CEO
  E-mail: Charon@charles-mix.com
Eiizabeth BlackBull, Administrative Director
Rolene Provist, Reproductive Justice Outreach Coordinator
Chaske' Rockboy, Dakota Culture Archivist
Cindy Knudsen, Shelter Director
Diane Merrick, Dakota Language Instructor & Family Facilitator
Description: A non-membership organization that supports the educational, social, & economic advancement of American Indians. Concerned with treaty & environmental issues involving Native Americans. *Purpose*: To protect the health & human rights of Indigenous Peoples pertinent to our communities through cultural preservation, education, coalition building, reproductive justice, environmental justice, & natural resource protection while working toward safe communities for women & children. *Programs*: College Internships; Dakota Language Immersion Program; *Activities*: Women Health Education Resource Center provides self-help programs & workshops on issues such as fetal alcohol syndrome, AIDS awareness, family planning, child & domestic abuse. Conducts adult education classes, employment services; scholarship program; conducts charitable programs; offers children's services; maintains speaker's bureau & placement service. *Publication*: Wicozanni-Wowapi, quarterly newsletter; also publishes brochures & pamphlets. Established 1984.

NATIVE AMERICAN COMMUNITY DEVELOPMENT CORP. (NACDC)
Headquarters: 2929 3rd Ave. N., Suite 300 • Billings, MT 59101
  (800) 307-9199; (406) 259-3804 Fax 259-4569; Website: www.nacdc.org
Leonard Smith (Assiniboine Sioux), Executive Director (294-7994)
  E-mail: lsmith@nadc-nabn.org

Mary Walks Over Ice, Assiniboine Gros Ventre/Turtle Mountain Ojibwe),
PTAC Program Manager; E-mail: mwalksoverice@nadc-nabn.org
Tom Jefferson (Crow), Accounts Manager E-mail: tomj@wtp.net
Loren Whte, Jr. (Arikiara/Hidatsa/Mandan), Organizational Planner
E-mail: lwhite@wtp.net
Tm Guardipee (Little Shell/Blackfeet), Project Director (259-3804)
E-mail: tguardipee@nadc-nabn.org
Gordon Jackson (Ojibwe/Potawatomi), Project Director (294-8061)
E-mail: gjackson@nadc-nabn.org
Darrell LaMere (Winnebago), Project Coordinator (294-8060)
E-mail: dlamere@nadc-nabn.org
Description: A non-profit affiliate of Native American Bancorporation. *Mission*:
To remove barriers which exist in Indian Country and which prohibit the flow of
capital & credit. Addresses critical needs in Indian communities related to
sustainable economic development. Works with communities that are investors
in the Native American Bank to meet the mission of effectively addressing
issues that inhibit the flow of financial capital to its owner Tribes & Native
Alaskan corporations. Established 2001.

NATIVE AMERICAN COMMUNITY DEVELOPMENT INSTITUTE (NACDI)
1414 East Franklin Ave. • Minneapolis, MN 55404
(612) 235-4976 Fax 392-0064
Website: www.nacdi.org; E-mail: info@nacdi.org; arts@nacdi.org
Robert Lilligren (White Earth Ojibwe), President & CEO (284-1091)
E-mail: rlilligren@nacdi.org
Cole St. Arnold (Jicarilla Apache/Ojibwe), Operations & Project Manager
E-mail: cstarnold@nacdi.org
Taylor Payer (Ojibwe), Gallery Associate; E-mail: tpayer@nacdi.org
Robert Lilligren, Chairpersonl Rev. Marlene Helgemo, Vice Chairperson
Dr. Patrick Rock, Treasurer
Board members:
Elaine Salinas, Sam Olbekson, Joe Hobot, Christine McDonald
Mission: To partner with American Indian communities to build & execute 21st
century community development strategies. *Projects*: American Indian Cultural
Corridor; All My Relations Gallery; planning & implementing a visitor gateway &
public arts market for the American Indian Cultural Corridor Website:
www.aiculturalcorridor.com at the Hiawatha LRT Franklin Light Rail Station
area. Arts/Culture; Land/Housing; Entertainment/Media; Health/Wellness.
Activities: Annual Golf Tournament. *Publication*: E-newsletter. Estab. 2007.

NATIVE AMERICAN COMPREHENSIVE PLAN (NACP)
1908 Grand Ave. • Nashville, TN 37212
(877) 899-2780; (615) 340-7295; Website: www.gbod.org
Rev. Anita Phillips, Executive Director
E-mail: aphillips@gbod.org (918) 686-8444
Mission: United Methodist entity that resources, strengthens, and advocates
for the local church in Native American communities. *Goals*: To develop and
support new and existing Native American churches & faith communities.
Published work: The Connection, biannual newsletter.

NATIVE AMERICAN CONGRESSIONAL INTERNSHIPS
The Morris K. Udall & Stewart L. Udall Foundation
130 S. Scott Ave. • Tucson, AZ 85701
(520) 901-8500 Fax 670-5530
Website: www.udall.gov; E-mail: info@udall.gov
Phil Lemanski, Executive Director (901-8560); E-mail: lemanski@udall.gov
Jane Curlin, Director, Education Programs (901-8565)
E-mail: curling@udall.gov
Stephanie Kavanaugh, Acting Director, DC Office of the Udall Foundation
(202) 540-1041; E-mail: kavanaugh@udall.gov
Destiny Khalil, Internship Program Manager (901-8561)
E-mail: khalil@udall.gov
Mike Lopez, Senior Program Manager, Native American & Alaska Native
Program (901-8542); E-mail: lopez@udall.gov
Description: A ten-week summer internship in Washington, DC, for Native
American & Alaska Native students. Funded by the Native Nations Institute for
Leadership, Management, and Policy, founded by the Udall Foundation and
the University of Arizona in 2001 as a self-determination, self-governance, and
development resources for Native nations. Foundation provides transportation,
housing, food & incidentals, and a stipend at the end of the program.

NATIVE AMERICAN CONSTITUTION & LAW DIGITIZATION PROJECT
University of Oklahoma - College of Law
300 W. Timberdell Rd. • Norman, OK 73072
(405) 325-4699; Website: http://thorpe.ou.edu; E-mail: mnicely@ou.edu
David Selden (NILL) & Marilyn Nicely (OU), Coordinators
Description: A cooperative effort by the University of Oklahoma Law Library
(OU) & The National Indian Law Library (NILL) of the Native American Rights
Fund, and Native American tribes providing access to the Constitutions, Tribal
Codes, and other legal documents. *Publication*: The Handbook of Federal
Indian Law. Established 1995.

NATIVE AMERICAN CONSULTING
2308 Mt. Vernon Ave., Suite 358 • Alexandria, VA 22301
(202) 642-4724 Fax (888) 312-7731 Or (703) 535-7567
Website: www.nativeamericanconsulting.com
E-mail: info@nativeamericanconsulting.com
Description: A Native American owned professional services company that
conducts seminars & on-site training on relevant issues impacting the Native
American community. Focus is on Indian law & policy.

NATIVE AMERICAN CONTRACTORS ASSOCIATION (NACA)
750 First St. NE, Suite 950 • Washington, DC 20002
(202) 758-2676 Fax 758-2699
Website: www.nativecontractors.org
E-mail: membership@nativecontractors.org
Michael G. Anderson, Executive Director
Chelsea Wilson (Cherokee), Legislative Director
Rachel Miranda (Aleut), Membership & Operations Manager
Julie Potter (Eastern Cherokee), Communications Manager
Kristina Woolston, Chairperson; Annette Hamilton, Vice Chairperson
Kimberly TeeHee, Secretary; Jon Panamaroff, Treasurer
Purpose: To establish, promote & defend policies, regulations and laws that
foster a fair level of participation by Tribes, Alaska Native corporations, &
Native Hawaiian organizations in the federal government marketplaces. Also
seeks to serve as a vehicle for information sharing & partnership opportunities
between & among its members.

NATIVE AMERICAN CULTURL CENTER
Abalone: The Online Cultural Center for NACC
Website: www.nativecc.com

NATIVE AMERICAN FATHERHOOD & FAMILIES ASSOCIATION (NAFFA)
1215 East Brown Rd. • Mesa, AZ 85203
(480) 833-5007 Fax 833-5009
Website: www.aznaffa.org; E-mail: info@aznaffa.org
Albert M. Pooley (Hopi/Navajo), President & Founder
E-mail: apooley@aznaffa.org
Amy Fa'atoafe (Navajo/Hopi), Program Director
E-mail: amyf@aznaffa.org
Elvira James (Navajo), Facilitator Coordinator
E-mail: elviraj@aznaffa.org
Mary Owen, Strategic Planning Coordinator, VISTA
E-mail: maryo@aznaffa.org
Mission: To teach fathers & mothers responsible leadership qualities to help
strengthen the institution of family & community. *Programs*: Fatherhood Is
Sacred & Motherhood Is Sacred - created to specifically meet the needs of
Native American fathers & mothers. *Materials*: Training Manuals, Evaluation
Methodologies, Program Workbooks. *Activities*: Annual conference.

NATIVE AMERICAN FINANCE OFFICERS ASSOCIATION
1101 30th St., NW Suite 500 • Washington, DC 20007
(202) 631-2003
Website: www.nafoa.org; E-mail: info@nafoa.org
Dante Desiderio (Sappony), Executive Director
E-mail: dante@nafoa.org
Cody Harjo (Navajo), Education Coordinator
(202) 407-2368; E-mail: cody@nafoa.org
Michelle Taunton, Events & Projects Manager (202) 853-0405
E-mail: michelle@nafoa.org
VaRene Martin, Director of Tribal Relations (619) 322-9285
E-mail: varene@nafoa.org
Christina Morbelli, Program Manager (602) 466-8697
E-mail: christina@nafoa.org
Cristina Danforth (Oneida of Wisconsin), President
VaRene Martin (Mvskoke (Creek), 1st Vice President
E-mail: varene@nafoa.org
Christina L. Jimerson (Seneca), 2nd V.P.
Dawson Her Many Horses (Oglala Lakota), Secretary
Kim Peone (Eastern Cherokee/Colville), Treasurer
Membership: Over 100 tribal governments & organizations, as well as, private
sector sponsors. *Purpose*: To provide a professional organization dedicated to
the improvement & quality of financial & business management of Native
American governments & businesses that will strengthen tribal governments
through sound financial management. *Activities*: Maintains a clearinghouse
network; runs a forum for information, training & technical assistance to Native
American organizations; provides legislative recommendations; develops &
maintains financial standards; develops & supports a scholarship training and
internship program for Native American students and tribal employees from the
financial & business areas; quarterly seminars; annual training conference.
Publication: Quarterly newsletter; New Financial Reporting Model for Tribal
Governments; Tribal Business Structure Handbook, 2009. Established 1982.

NATIVE AMERICAN FISH & WILDLIFE SOCIETY

1055 17th Ave., Suite 91 • Longmont, CO 80501
Public Information Office: 8515 Pearl St., Suite 203 • Thornton, CO 80229
(866) 890-7258; (303) 466-1725 Fax 466-5414
Website: www.nafws.org; E-Mail: webmaster@nafws.org
D. Fred Matt, Executive Director; E-mail: fmatt@nafws.org
Ronald D. Rodgers, Deputy Director; E-mail: rdr@nafws.org
Sasha Hoskie, Education Coordinator; E-mail: shoskie@nafws.org
Membership: 224 tribes. *Description*: Made up of Native professionals & technicians engaged in tribal natural resource management. *Purpose*: To facilitate & coordinate inter-tribal communications in regard to fish/wildlife issues; to promote the prudent use of Native natural resources; to educate Native youth toward professional management of tribal natural resources; and works to improve the welfare of tribal people. *Special program*: Summer Youth Practicum - to encourage Indian youth to pursue careers in the fish and wildlife fields. *Publication*: "Eagle's Nest", newsletter. Established 1983.

NATIVE AMERICAN FITNESS COUNCIL

P.O. Box K • Flagstaff, AZ 86002
(928) 774-3048 Fax 774-3049
Website: www.nativeamericanfitnesscouncil.com
E-mail: info@nativeamericanfitnesscouncil.com
Brian Laban (Hopi/Tewa), Director of Training & Instruction
Elfreida Barton (Navajo), Director of Group Fitness
John A. Blievernicht, Executive Director
Description: A division of the Institute for Sports, Health & Fitness. *Purpose*: To empower fitness leaders in Native American communities; to develop programs which teach people to train other Natives in proper exercise & healthy lifestyles. *Programs*: Instructor Certification; Youth Programs; Community Programs. Established 2004.

NATIVE AMERICAN GRANT SCHOOL ASSOCIATION (NAGSA)

P.O. Box 726 • Flagstaff, AZ 86002
(928) 299-1595 Fax 429-0515; Website: www.nagsa.net
Jeffrey Mike, Director (928) 255-7594; E-mail: jmike_fl@yahoo.com
Victoria Nez (Navajo), Board President; E-mail: vickienez@yahoo.com
Ardell Nachie (Navajo), Vice President; Veronica James (Navajo), Treasurer
Mission: To serve the needs of grant schools created for Indian Country by the Tribally Controlled Schools Act of 1988; to advocate for tribally controlled schools; to advance Native American educational programs; to empower local communities; to ensure quality education for Native American students.

NATIVE AMERICAN & INDIGENOUS STUDIES ASSOCIATION (NAISA)

Website: www.naisa.org
James Cox & Shannon Speed, Co-founders & Directors
  (The University of Texas at Austin)
Jace Weaver, Board President; E-mail: jweaver@uga.edu
Brenda J. Child (Red Lake Ojibwe), President-Elect
  E-mail: child011@umn.edu
Council: Susan Hill (Haudenosaunee), Renae Watchman (Dine'), Shannon Speed (Chickasaw); Jean Dennison (Osage). *Purpose*: A professional organization dedicated to supporting those who work inside & outside the academic world in the scholarly field of Native American, American Indian, First Nations, Aboriginal & Indigenous Studies. *Activities*: Annual meeting in June. *Publication*: Journal (published by the University of Minnesota Press). Established 2008.

NATIVE AMERICAN JOURNALISTS ASSOCIATION

University of Oklahoma, Gaylord College
395 W. Lindsey St. • Norman, OK 73019
(405) 325-1649 Fax 325-6945
Website: www.naja.com; E-mail: info@naja.com
Pamela Silas, Executive Director
Rebecca Landsberry, Membership & Communications Manager
  E-mail: rebeccalandsberry@naja.com
Mary Hudetz, Board President; E-mail: maryhudetz@naja.com
Jason Begay (Navajo), Vice President; Tristan Ahtone (Kiowa), Treasurer
Tetona Dunlap (Eastern Shoshone), Secretary
Board members: Mark Dreadfulwater (Chair of Education Committee); Dalton Walker (Ojibwe), Shannon Shaw-Duty (Osage), Eugene Tapahe (Navajo)
Purpose: To improve communications among Native people and between Native Americans & the general public; to serve & empower Native journalists through programs & actions designed to enrich journalism & promote Native cultures; to support & increase the involvement of Native Americans in the media. *Programs*: Provides educational & training for 500 plus Native communicators at its annual conference; recruits more Native Americans into the field of journalism through its summer high school workshops, college scholarships, career days & job referral service. Scholarships available for qualified American Indian journalist students. *Publication*: NAJA News, quarterly newsletter. Established 1984.

NATIVE AMERICAN LAW CENTER

Tribal Court Public Defense Clinic
University of Washington School of Law
William Gates Hall, Box 353020 • Seattle, WA 98195
(206) 685-3253; Website: www.law.washington.edu/indianlaw
Robert Anderson (Bois Forte Ojibwe), Director & Professor of Law
Ron Whitener (Nisqually), Center Executive Director & Clinic Director
William H. Rodgers, Jr., Professor of Environmental Law
Molly Cohan, Clinic Supervising Attorney/Lecturer
Purpose: To provide direct assistance to the tribes in Washington State and across the nation. The Clinic partners with the Tulalip, Squaxin Island, Port Gamble S'Klallam & Puyallup Tribes to serve as their public defender on these reservations. *Special Projects*: Indigenous Research Toolkits; Tribal Juvenile Justice Reform; Tribal Public Defense Clinic; Service & Training. *Resources*: Annual Indian Law Symposium, in September.

NATIVE AMERICAN LEGAL RESOURCE CENTER

Oklahoma City University - School of Law
2501 Blackwelder • Oklahoma City, OK 73106
(405) 208-5337; E-mail: lawquestions@okcu.edu
Dennis W. Arrow (Cheyenne-Arapaho), Associate Director
  E-mail: darrow@okcu.edu (208-5179)
C. Blue Clark, Intertribal Governmental & Cultural Advisor
  E-mail: bclark@okcu.edu (208-5847)
Mission: To provide capacity building services to tribal communities & creates opportunities for students, faculty, staff and the broader University community to utilize knowledge & resources to serve the needs of Indian Country in a culturally appropriate & efficient manner for a maximum positive impact. Also provides various services to the tribal governments in the State of Oklahoma, as well as trial governments across the U.S. *Native American Externship Program*: The Jodi G. Marquette American Indian Wills Clinic (888) 678-6836.

NATIVE AMERICAN LITERATURE SYMPOSIUM

Minnesota State University, Mankato
P.O. Box 541 • Mankato, MN 56002
(507) 389-5508 Fax 389-5362; Website: www.mnsu.edu/nativelit
Gwen N. Westerman, Director; E-mail: gwen.westerman@mnsu.edu
Virginia Carney, Tribal College Liaison
Description: An independent group of Indigenous scholars committed to making a place where Native voices can be heard. *Award*: The Beatrice Medicine Award for Scholarship in American Indian Studies (two awards given for outstanding essay & best book published in annual year.)

NATIVE AMERICAN MANAGEMENT & EDUCATIONAL SERVICES

230 Louisiana Blvd. • Albuquerque, NM 87108
(505) 265-8063
Purpose: To develop programs to help American Indian students.

NATIVE AMERICAN MANAGEMENT SERVICES, INC. (NAMS)

1800 Robert Fulton Dr. #100C • Reston, VA 20191
(571) 323-5635 Fax 323-2102
Website: www.namsinc.org; E-mail: mail@namsinc.org
Patricia Parker (Choctaw of Oklahoma), Founder/President & CEO
Tonya Parker (Choctaw of Oklahoma), Co-founder & Vice President
Description: Native American women-owned, small disadvantaged business that provides business consultation to the Native American business community, including, financial services, technical assistance, & program implementation & support. *Regional offices*: Oklahoma: TriTAC Program, P.O. Box 1221, Pawhuska, OK 74056 (918) 287-1650. North Dakota office. Established 1992.

NATIVE AMERICAN MEDIA (NAM)

907 Westwood Blvd.. #403 • Los Angeles, CA 90024
(310) 475-6845 Fax 475-9844
Website: www.nativeamericanmedia.org
E-mail: info@nativeamericanmedia.org
Mike Nathanson, Director of Government & Media Relations
Purpose: To benefit the Native American community in communications, employment, business enterprise development, cultural awareness, and social service referrals. *Goal*: To improve the socio-economic status of the Native American community, by way of creating strategic alliances with employers, and others who are committed to minority outreach & diversity initiatives. *Initiatives*: "Preserving Heritage & Traditions," & "Native American in the Workplace," a mentoring program. Also, a 25-minute documentary film entitled, "Native America – Yesterday & Today." Established 1974 in partnership with the American Indian Historical Society.

NATIVE AMERICAN MUSIC AWARDS & ASSOCIATION (NAMA)

511 Ave. of the Americas, Suite 371 • New York, NY 10011
(212) 228-8300 Fax (646) 688-6883
Website: www.nativeamericanmusicawards.com

Ellen Bello, Founder/President

Purpose: Dedicated to the archival and preservation of all Native American music & promotion of its artists; to directly assist Native American musicians & continue educating the general public; to create greater performance opportunities for award-winning & nominated artists. *Activities*: Annual Native American Blues Festival; Annual NAMA Awards. Established 1998.

NATIVE AMERICAN NEWS SERVICE

Native Americans Online; Website: www.native-americans-online.com
Purpose: To disseminate news online to Native Americans and other interested people.

NATIVE AMERICAN PREVENTION RESEARCH CENTER

University of Oklahoma Health Sciences Center
800 N.E. 15th St., Rm. 532 • Oklahoma City, OK 73104
(405) 271-6285; Website: www.ouhsc.edu/ouprc
E-mail: naprc@ouhsc.edu
Description: Works in partnership with American Indian tribes, communities & individuals to develop approaches to health promotion & disease prevention in Indian communities. *Program*: Tribal Health Planning & Education Program. Publications & presentations available.

NATIVE AMERICAN RECREATION & SPORT INSTITUTE (NARSI)

116 W. Osage • Greenfield, IN 46140
(317) 604-1649 Fax 462-4245; Website: www.charismapros.com/p/narsi.htm
Judith G. Shepherd, Founder/Instructor; E-mail: gramshep@yahoo.com
David Bray (Iroquois), Executive Director
Consultants: Billy Mills, Lakota Sioux), Sally Tuttle, (Oklahoma Choctaw).
Description: Offers youth recreation & sport directors & coaches training programs in America. The emphasis is on training adults to work with children ages 5-14 and the overall wellbeing of these youths. Established 1995.

NATIVE AMERICAN RESEARCH LABORATORIES (NARL)

Montana State University – Division of Biological Sciences
P.O. Box 173150 • Bozeman, MT 59717
(406) 994-7658 Fax 994-1975
Website: www.dbs.umt.edu/narl; E-mail: mus-epscor@montana.edu
Ray Callaway, Project Director; E-mail: ragan.callaway@umontana.edu
Todd Kipfer, Associate Director & Project Administrator
E-mail: tkipfer@montana.edu
Mission: To provide Native American undergraduates & graduate students with advanced hands-on research opportunities in the natural sciences & biomedical sciences in an interdisciplinary research setting guided by culturally relevant faculty role models/ mentors. NARL recognizes the importance of training Native scholars in an intertribally & interculturally diverse scientific setting. Montana EPSCoR is partnering with NARL to increase the number of Native American students participating in NARL opportunities.

NATIVE AMERICAN RESEARCH & TRAINING CENTER (NARTC)

The University of Arizona, Department of Family & Community Medicine
College of Medicine, 1642 E. Helen St. • Tucson, AZ 85719
(520) 621-5920 Fax 621-9802
Teshia G. Arambula Solomon (Choctaw/Mexican-American),
Associate Professor & Director; E-mail: solomont@email.arizona.edu
Francine C. Gachupin, Assistant Professor & Assistant Director
E-mail: fcgachupin@email.arizona.edu
Natalie Pool, Program Coordinator AIRCH
E-mail: nataliepool@email.arizona.edu
Purpose: To serve as a resource in health related research & training for Native American communities nationwide. *Mission*: To conduct health related research & training projects that will help improve the quality of life for Native Americans; to provide training & technical assistance and to conduct respectful research to benefit the health and well-being of Native people, families, and communities. Because of their commitment to the realization of self-determination, one of the primary objectives of the Center is to promote active participation and partnership with Native American communities in all NARTC research and training programs. Current projects include the AIRCH program, involvement in the National Children's Study, and the Native American Cancer Partnership. Established 1983.

NATIVE AMERICAN RIGHTS FUND

1506 Broadway • Boulder, CO 80302
(303) 447-8760 Fax 443-7776; Website: www.narf.org/about-us/
John E. Echohawk (Pawnee), Executive Director
David Selden, Library Director, Boulder
Moses K.N. Haia III (Hawaiian), Board Chairperson
Mark Macarro (Pechanga Luiseno), Vice Chairperson
Tex G. Hall (Three Affiliated Trbes), Board Treasurer
Larry Olinger (Agua Caiiente Cahuilla), Executive Committee Member
Offices: 1514 P St., NW, Washington, DC 20005 (202) 785-4166 Fax 822-0068; 745 W. 4th Ave. Suite 502, Anchorage, Alaska 99501 (907) 276-0680

Fax 276-2466. *Staff attorneys (partial)*: Boulder office – Sue Noe; Brett Lee Shelton (Oglala Lakota); Donald R. Wharton; Steven C. Moore; K. Jerome Gottschalk; David L. Gover (Pawnee/Choctaw); Melody McCoy (Cherokee); Heather Whiteman Runs Him (Crow); Matthew L. Campbell (Native Village of Gambell). *Washington office* – Richard A. Guest; Joel Williams (Cherokee). *Anchorage office* – Erin Dougherty Lynch; Matthew N. Newman; Heather R. Kendall-Miller (Athabascan); Natalie Landreth (Chickasaw)
Purpose: The protection of Indian rights; the preservation of tribal existence; the protection of tribal natural resources; the promotion of human rights; the accountability of governments to Native-Americans; and the development of Indian law. *Activities*: Serves as National Indian Law Support Center; maintains the National Indian Law Library. *Publications*: NARF Legal Review, quarterly; Indian Law Support Center Reporter, monthly; monthly newsletter; National Indian Law Library Catalogue, supplemented quarterly; indexes to Indian Claims Commission Decisions; annual report. Semiannual board of directors' meeting in May and November. Established 1970.

NATIVE AMERICAN SPORTS COUNCIL

1235 Lake Plaza Dr. #221 • Colorado Springs, CO 80906
(719) 632-5282; Website: www.nascsports.org
E-mail: information@nascsports.org
Purpose: To promote athletic excellence & community wellness within Native American communities through culturally appropriate youth-oriented sports programs that combine traditional Native American values with those of the modern Olympics. *Programs*: Athlete Development & Assistance; Sports & Wellness Leadership Development; Sports Partnerships; and the Sports Academic Training Institute which purpose is to assist educators, counselors & coaches to better prepare the student-athlete to select the appropriate institution of higher education, given his or her academic and sports goals.

NATIVE AMERICAN TECHNOLOGY & ART

P.O. Box 73 • Storrs, CT 06268
Website: www.nativetech.org
Tara Prindle, Director; E-mail: tprindle@nativetech.org
Description: An Internet resource for indigenous ethno-technology focusing on the arts of Eastern Woodland Indian Peoples, providing historical & contemporary background with instructional how-to's & references. *Categories*: Beadwork, Birds & Feathers, Clay & Pottery, Leather & Clothes, Metalwork, Plants & Trees, Porcupine Quills, Stonework & Tools, & Weaving & Cordage.

NATIVE AMERICAN TELECOM ENTERPRISE, LLC

Crow Creek, P.O. Box 2316 • Sioux Falls, SD 57101
(605) 477-7777; Website: www.nativeamericantelecom.com
Gene DeJordy, CEO; Tom Reiman, President
E-mail: tom@nativeamericantelecom.com
Description: A telecommunications service & economic development company that works with Native American tribes to establish tribally-owned telecommunications systems aimed at driving economic development on reservations.

NATIVE AMERICAN YOUTH MINISTRIES

ROCK Ministries, P.O. Box 12291 • Glendale, AZ 85318
(602) 564-1891 Fax 375-2002
Website: www.naym.org; E-mail: mail@naym.org
Gerald & Deanna Wright, Directors; E-mail: wright@naym.org
Mark & Nancy Smith, Work Team Ministries; E-mail: smith@naym.org
Mission: To minister to Native American people through means of evangelism, encouragement, and equipping. Committed to working with Christian Native American leaders, churches, and other ministries.

NATIVE AMERICANS IN PHILANTHROPY (NAP)

2801 21st Ave. S. #132D • Minneapolis, MN 55407
(612) 724-8798 ext. 2 Fax 879-0613
Website: www.nativephilanthropy.org; E-mail: info@nativephilanthropy.org
Sarah Eagle Heart, CEO/Executive Director (767-9810)
E-mail: seagleheart@nativephilanthropy.org
Jennifer Fairbanks, Communications Associates (767-9812)
E-mail: jfairbanks@nativephilanthropy.org
Ashley Wheeler, Executive Assistant (767-9814)
E-mail: awheeler@nativephilanthropy.org
Shirley Sneve (Sicangu Lakota), Board Chairperson
Dan Martin (Assiniboine Sioux), Board Vice-chairperson
Jo-Anne E. Stately (Ojibwe), Treasurer; Alesha Towns-Bain (Aleut), Secretary
Mission: Seeks to engage Native & non-Native peoples in understanding & advancing the role of philanthropy through practices that support Native traditional values. *Program*: Annual Conference, Native Philanthropy Institute (NPI). *Publication*: Monthly E-newsletter.

NATIVE ART NETWORK

7966 W. 17th Ave. • Lakewood, CO 80214
(877) 522-6843; Website: www.nativeart.net
Paul Kabotie (Hopi/Santa Clara Pueblo), Co-owner

Lesley Yellowtail Jackson Kabotie (Crow), Co-owner

Description: 100% Indian owned & operated. A website for Native American fine art. A non-profit Native American arts service organization founded as a national advocate for Native American art. *Goals*: To heighten awareness of indigenous aesthetics and modes of expression; to promote the vitality of contemporary Native American art through self determination in cultural expression; to create an informational network between Native American artists and arts; and provide training opportunities & economic development for Native American artists. *Purpose*: To promote & showcase Native artists in an ethical & culturally appropriate way while informing & educating about the art, tribes & culture of North American indigenous peoples. *Activities*: Traveling Exhibit Service; technical assistance & consulting services; sponsors annual workshops; hosts a national biennial conference for Native artists & administrators (Native Arts Network); and maintains resource files on Native artists & art organizations; Native Art Travel. *Website*: www.nativearttravel. com. Specializes in Native American art shows, powwows, and Native Conferences. *Publications*: Native Arts Update, quarterly newsletter; From Village, Clan and City (poetry & short stories); Directory of Native American Performing Artists; maintains a National Registry of Native American artists; periodic special reports (Survey of State Arts Agency Support of Native Arts Programs); exhibition catalogs. Established 1998.

NATIVE ARTS & CULTURES FOUNDATION (NACF)

400 E. Evergreen Blvd., Suite 102 • Vancouver, WA 98660
(360) 314-2421; Website: www.nativeartsandcultures.org
E-mail: info@nativeartsandcultures.org
T. Lulani Arquette (Hawaiian), President/CEO
Rupert Ayton, Vice President, Finance & Operations (334-7266)
  E-mail: Rupert@nativeartsandcultures.org
Francene J. Blythe (Dine'/Sisseton-Wahpeton/Eastern Cherokee),
  Program Director; (334-7271)
  E-mail: francene@nativeartsandcultures.org
Valerie Egan, Development Coordinator (334-7286)
  E-mail: Valerie@nativeartsandcultures.org
Elizabeth Madrigal, Project Manager (334-7260)
  E-mail: elizabeth@nativeartsandcultures.org
Gabriella Tagliacozzo, Executive Associate & Board Liaison (334-7259)
  E-mail: gabriella@nativeartsandcultures.org
Susan Jenkins (Choctaw), Board Chairperson
Sven Haakanson (Alutiiq), Board Vice Chairperson
David R. Hatch (Siletz), Board Secretary
Barron M. Tenny, Board Treasurer & Finance Committee Chair
Cheryl Andrews-Maltais (Wampanoag), Governance Committee Chair

Description: Supports American Indian, Alaska Native & Native Hawaiian communities; stimulates tribal and Native philanthropic investment in the field by distributing direct grants to artists & organizations, and leveraging resources through a broad range of philanthropic partnerships. Established 2007.

NATIVE ELDER RESEARCH CENTER (NERC)

Centers for American Indian & Alaska Native Health
University of Colorado, School of Public Health
Nighthorse Campbell Native Health Bldg.
13055 E. 17th St. MS F800 • Aurora, CO 80045
(303) 724-1444 Fax 724-1474
Spero M. Manson, Center Director & Distinguished Professor
  E-mail: spero.manson@ucdenver.edu
Lori Trullinger, Center Administrator
  E-mail: lori.trullinger@ucdenver.edu
Gequinn Mattox, Program Coordinator
  E-mail: gequinn.mattox@ucdenver.edu
Candace Fleming, Director of Training
  E-mail: Candace.fleming@ucdenver.edu

Purpose: To promote the health & well-being of American Indians & Alaska Natives, of all ages, by pursuing research, training, continuing education, technical assistance, and information dissemination with a bio-psychosocial framework that recognizes the unique cultural contexts of this special population. *Activities*: Programs, projects & publications; Research Networks.

NATIVE HEALTH & INSURANCE NETWORK

1027 S. Main St., Suite 318 • Joplin, MO 64801
Website: www.youtube.com/nhandic
Facebook Page. www.facebook.com/NHandIN.
Robert Weaver (Quapaw), Director
  E-mail: rweaver_78@yahoo.com

Description: An online-based healthcare information hub that's geared toward Native Americans. *Mission*: To provide Native Americans with a central location to find the very latest information in health care & insurance. Healthcare information is provided by Robert Weaver and RWI Benefits, through the Native Health & Insurance Network as a free service to Native Americans and their tribal leaders. Established 2012.

NATIVE LEARNING CENTER

Seminole Tribe of Florida, 6363 Taft St. • Hollywood, FL 33024
(954) 985-2315 Fax 989-3864
Website: www.nativelearningcenter.com
E-mail: nlcenter@semtribe.com
Georgette Palmer Smith (Kiowa), Executive Director
  E-mail: georgettesmith@semtribe.com
Kyle Doney (Seminole/Gros Ventre), Deputy Vice President
  E-mail: kyledoney@semtribe.com
Vincent Franco, Compliance & Resource Development Director
  E-mail: vincentfranco@semtribe.com
Marie Dufour-Bonville, Director of Training & Tech. Assistance
  E-mail: mariedufour@semtribe.com
Patti Kay Mitchell (Cherokee), Training & Development Specialist
  E-mail: pattimitchell@semtribe.com

Description: A program of the Seminole Tribe of Florida, and was established in partnership with the U.S. Department of Housing & Urban Development in 2008. Offers tuition-free courses & training to Native Americans & Indigenous people with an emphasis on the educational needs of Tribal members and their communities. *Mission*: To provide Native & Indigenous people with knowledge & skills which improve quality of life through housing-related educational programs. Focuses on celebrating culture & language, financial wellness, grant education, housing strategies, and tribal government.

NATIVE NATIONS EVENTS

38 E. Ridgewood Ave. #223 • Ridgewood, NJ 07450
(201) 857-5333 Fax 857-5332

Mission: To create & execute unique, timely and lively educational networking forums within the Native American marketplace. *Purpose*: To program events that provide information on and insight into topics that are of the utmost importance to tribes and their leadership. *Advisory Board*: Thomas E. Linton Morongo Band Mission); Chris Kelley (Viejas Kumeyaay); Paul Brody (Mohegan); Jamie Fullmer; Tuari Bigknife (Viejas Kumeyaay); Cynthia Iyall (Nisqually); Cheryle Kennedy (Confederated Grand Ronde); Linda Roe; Rochanne Hackett; Tom Wucherer; Bob Garcia (Confederated Coos, Umpqua, Suislaw).

THE NATIVE NATIONS INSTITUTE (NNI) FOR LEADERSHIP, MANAGEMENT & POLICY

The Udall Center for Studies in Public Policy
University of Arizona, 803 East First St. • Tucson, AZ 85719
(520) 626-0664 Fax 626-3664
Website: www.nni.arizona.edu; E-mail: nni@email.arizona.edu
Stephen Cornell, faculty Chair & Director, The Udall Center
Joan Timeche (Hopi), NNI Executive Director
Yadira Cabellero (Dine'), Research Program Coordinator
Miriam Jorgensen, NNI Research Director; Research Professor, Udall Center
  E-mail: mjorgens@u.arizona.edu
Rachel Starks, MA (Zuni/Dine'), Senior Research Coordinator
  E-mail: rstarks@u.arizona.edu
Stephanie Carroll Rainie (Ahtna Athabascan), Associate Director,
  Manager-Tribal Health Program & Assistant Research Professor
  E-mail: scrainie@u.arizona.edu

Description: NNI is an outgrowth of the research programs of the Harvard Project on American Indian Economic Development. *Purpose*: To assist in the building of capable Native nations that can effectively pursue & ultimately realize their own political, economic, & community development objectives. *Activities*: Professional training & development programs; policy analysis & accessible research; The International Advisory Council - comprised of 24 indigenous leaders from the U.S. & Canada. Established 2001.

NATIVE PEOPLE'S CIRCLE OF HOPE

9770 SW Ventura Ct. • Tigard, OR 97223
(503) 970-8004 Fax 245-2253
Celeste (Cece) Whitewolf (Umatilla), Director
Bill Ward (White Mountain Apache), Board Chairperson

Description: A coalition of Native cancer survivors & support groups focusing on the states of Oregon, Washington and Idaho. *Mission*: To help Native American cancer survivors, their family members & caregivers understand that they are not alone.

NATIVE PEOPLES LAW CAUCUS

American Association of Law Libraries
c/o Yale Law School Lillian Goldman Library
127 Wall St. • New Haven, CT 06511
(203) 432-6443; Website: www.aallnet.org/caucus/nplc/
Sherri Nicole Thomas, Chairperson; Cate Kellett, Librarian Contact
  E-mail: catherine.kellett@yale.edu

Description: A caucus committee of the American Association of Law Libraries. *Purpose*: To provide a forum in which Native law and other issues that impact Indigenous Peoples worldwide can be discussed, ideas shared, information exchanged, & education offered. *Special project*: Tribal Law Cooperative - to facilitate the collection of the laws of 566 tribes & Alaska Native villages in U.S.

NATIVE P.R.I.D.E.
P.O. Box 471 • Corrales, NM 87048
(505) 897-7968 Fax 792-2735; Website: www.nativeprideus.org
Clayton Small (Northern Cheyenne), CEO (321-2808)
Maha Charani Small, Vice President
 E-mail: maha@nativeprideus.org (321-3048)
Raymond Reyes (Hopi/Mexican), Program Evaluator
Marie Kirk (Isleta Pueblo) & Jeni Small (Northern Cheyenne),
 Special Advisors
Description: P.R.I.D.E. (Prevention, Research, Intervention, Development, Education). Offers culture-based programs that focus on prevention, wellness, and leadership development. Programs are designed to assist individuals, families, communities, and organizations utilize their strengths, culture, and humor to overcome challenges and live "The Good Road of Life," A curriculum funded by the Administration for Native Americans (ANA). *Programs*: The Good Road of Life – the curriculum for Native families designed to assist Native men, women, and their children to address unresolved conflicts in relationships, improve communication skills, and keep Native families together; Native HOPE (Helping Our People Endure) is a prevention program that wants to reverse the high suicide trend among Native youth. *Publication*: Native News Network. Established 2007.

NATIVE TALENT NETWORK
Division of Platinum Talent Agency
P.O. Box 1106 • Morrison, CO 80465
(720) 297-0414; E-mail: nativetalentnetwork@gmail.com
Stephanie Jerome, CEO
Description: Talent agency representing clients & talent across Native America.

NATIVE VOICE ONE
The Annenberg National Native Voice Studios
4401 Lomas Blvd NE, Suite C • Albuquerque, NM 87110
(907) 793-3536 (Anchorage); (907) 999-2401 (Albuquerque)
Website: www.nv1.org
Shyanne Beatty, Network Manager; E-mail: sbeatty@knba.org
Nola Daves Moses, Station Relations Rep.; E-mail: nola@nv1.org
Purpose: To educate, advocate, and celebrates Native American life & culture by providing a program service from a Native point of view. Enables Native people to stay connected. Many Native stations & independent radio producers contribute Native-oriented programs to NV1 for inclusion in the NV1 program service. NV1 broadcasts the Native voice through affiliate & other radio stations and via Internet radio on www.nv1.org

NATIVEWEB
Website: www.nativeweb.org; Peter d'Errico (Navajo), President
 Carmel Vivier, V.P. & Executive Director
Description: An international, nonprofit, educational organization dedicated to using telecommunications including computer technology and the Internet to disseminate information from and about indigenous nations, peoples, and organizations around the world. *Purpose*: To foster communication between native & non-native peoples; to conduct research involving indigenous peoples' usage of technology and the Internet; and to provide resources, mentoring, and services to facilitate indigenous peoples' use of this technology. *Project*: NativeWiki - website: nativewiki.org: A free, open-to-the-public; to allow users to contribute information about indigenous nations & peoples (past & present) of the world.

NATIVE WELLNESS INSTITUTE (NWI)
2830 SE Cleveland Dr. • Gresham, OR 97080
(503) 666-7669 Fax 669-8339
Website: www.nativewellness.com; E-mail: info@nativewellness.com
Jillene Joseph (Gros Ventre), Executive Director
 E-mail: jillene.joseph@frontier.com
Shannon Kissinger, Project Director (503) 457-6520
 E-mail: shannonkissinger@gmail.com
Mission: To promote the well being of Native people through programs & trainings which embrace the teachings & traditions of our ancestors. *Programs*: Healthy Relationships; Adult & Youth Leadership; Wellness in the Workplace; Technical Assistance & Program Development. *Activities*: Annual Native Youth Leadership Academy (NYLA) and Adults Working With Native Youth; Wellness Retreats, Conferences & Trainings. *Publication*: NWI News; PDF reports.

NATIVE WORKPLACE, INC.
6401 Academy Rd. NE, Suite 145 • Albuquerque, NM 87109
(512) 462-9056, 445-9751; Website: www.nativeworkplace.com
E-mail: info@nativeworkplace.com

Cristala Mussato-Allen, Executive Director
 E-mail: cristala@nativeworkplace.com
Goal: To educate the community on "Green Collar" careers in renewable energy, to develop an American Indian & Veteran workforce for renewable industries, and to provide that workforce with consistent follow-up support. *Mission*: Our mission is to create opportunity while honoring Native culture with results that improve the quality of life for Native families. NWP entered the hemp and cannabis industries as Tribal Liaisons to assist tribes & corporations in the development of Cannabis-Hemp education and commerce. Their team of qualified Native professionals provide community education, workforce development & general project planning. NWP launched their effort by hosting the first Tribal Hemp & Cannabis Summit at the Indian Pueblo Cultural Center in Albuquerque, NM April 2015. *Programs*: Education, "Green Collar Career Day"; Training – helping Tribal Colleges become accredited training providers. *Services*: Grant writing. Maintains links to tribal job listings and other Native job boards in order to provide a comprehensive assortment of opportunities nationwide. *Publication*: Tribal Energy Handbook; Wind Power for Native Americans (U.S. Dept. of Energy). Established 2002.

NATIVE WRITERS' CIRCLE OF THE AMERICAS
University of Oklahoma, Dept. of Native American Studies
216 Ellison Hall, 633 Elm Ave. • Norman, OK 73019
(405) 325-2312 Fax 325-0842
 E-mail: nas@ou.edu; Geary Hobson, Project Director
Purpose: To maintain a Native American writer's address database.

NATIVE YOUTH ALLIANCE
P.O. Box 980104 • Ypsilanti, MI 48198
(734) 323-0762; Website: www.nativeyouthalliance.blogspot.com
E-mail: nativeyouthalliance@gmail.com
Nathan Phillips, Executive Director
Purpose: To ensure that traditional Native American cultural & spiritual ways continue for the coming generations. To maintain ongoing programs that provide children & youth the opportunity to observe & participate in the ceremonies, gatherings & culture practiced by members of their families & Nations for generations. Established 1990.

NAVAJO CODE TALKERS
P.O. Box 8440 • HOUCK, AZ 86506
 Website: www.navajocodetalkers.org; Roy Hawthorne, Vice President
 Keith Little, Treasurer (P.O. Box 1001, Navajo, AZ 87328)
Description: An organization of Indian marines that was responsible for developing the now highly celebrated code. 420 Navajos operated a division of communications along the pacific front during World War II that incorporated more than 400 words, eventually making up the Code Talkers Dictionary. Members: Samuel Tso, Arthur Hubbard, Sr., Merril Sandoval, Alfred Peaches.

THE NDAKINNA EDUCATION CENTER
23 Middle Grove Rd. • Greenfield Center, NY 12833
(518) 583-9958 Fax 583-9741
 Website: www.ndakinnacenter.org; E-mail: info@ndakinnacenter.org
 Joseph Bruchac III (Abenaki), Executive Director & Storyteller
 James Bruchac (Abenaki), Founder & Program Director
 Jesse Bruchac (Abenaki), Treasurer
Description: A 70-acre native preserve with marked trails, Native American structures with exhibits, and a traditional garden. An affiliate of the Greenfield Review Literary Center. A learning environment for those who wish to learn more about the Northeast's Native American culture. The wilderness based programs emphasize observation skills, interactive learning activities, critical thinking, cooperative problem solving & teambuilding for all ages. *Activities*: School field trips; guided tours, book sales; lectures; teachers workshops; skills courses. Gift Shop/Bookstore. Established 1987.

NIHEWAN FOUNDATION FOR NATIVE AMERICAN EDUCATION
9595 Wilshire Blvd., Suite 1020 • Beverly Hills, CA 90212
(808) 822-3111; Website: www.nihewan.org
 Buffy Sainte-Marie, Founder
Purpose: To help Native American students participate in learning. Programs: Scholarships. In the 1980s, the foundation expanded services to include K-12 education in the U.S. & Canada via Curriculum Development and what would become the Cradleboard Teaching Project. In the 1990s, the foundation added a Teacher training program & Cradleboard 101 Teacher Training workshops; Curriculum Development & the Nihewan Youth Council on Race. Established 1969.

NKWUSM SALISH LANGUAGE INSTITUTE
72040 Bitterroot Jim Rd., P.O. Box 5 • Arlee, MT 59821
(406) 726-5050 Fax 726-5051; Website: www.salishworld.com
 Kassandra Murphy-Brazill (Salish), Principal
 E-mail: kmurphybrazill@salishworld.com

Chaney Bell (Salish), Curriculum Specialist/Lead Teacher
  E-mail: chaney_bell@hotmail.com
Michelle Matt (Salish), Secretary
Echo Brown (Salish), Elisabeth DeRoche (Salish), Francis Brown
  (Salish), Gene Beaverhead (Salish), Jackson Sundown Adams (Salish),
  Gene Beaverhead (Salish), Steve Arca (Salish), Salish Language Specialists
Purpose: To ensure the continuation of the language in the community by maintaining, enhancing & creating comprehensive Salish language education programs for youth & adults. The Salish Language Immersion School is the only Salish school in the world.

NORTH AMERICAN INDIAN ASSOCIATION (NAIA)
22720 Plymouth Rd. • Detroit, MI 48239
  (313) 535-2966 Fax 535-8060; Website: www.naiadetroit.org
Brian Moore, Executive Director; E-mail: bmoore@naiadetroit.org
Sarah Brant, Program Manager; E-mail: sbrant@naiadetroit.org
Linda Schuyler, Board President; E-mail: linda.schuyler@att.net
Rochelle Ballard, Secretary; E-mail: rochelleballard@charter.net
Janice Deer-Tifrea, Treasurer; E-mail: deerskin5@gmail.com
Membership: 300. At least one-quarter North American Indian blood. *Purpose*: To promote economic development & self-sufficiency for American Indian people through human services. *Activities*: Employment & educational services; senior center offers nutrition, social & educational services; Indian child welfare provides protective services for Indian children & families; annual Native American Heritage Festival; Arts & Crafts Gallery business. Operates Native American Gallery; speaker's bureau. Russ Wright Scholarship Fund -- assists students with the expense of educational supplies. *Publication*: Native Sun, monthly newsletter. Library. Annual meeting & powwow. Established 1940.

NORTH AMERICAN INDIGENOUS GAMES (NAIG)
Suite 411, 35-2855 Pembina Hwy. Winnipeg, MB, Canada R3T 2H5
  (800) 453-7239 Fax (204) 800-3184
  Website: www.naigcouncil.com; E-mail: info@naigcouncil.com
Norman Ettawacappo, Coordinator
Description: A celebration of Indigenous cultures from across the North American continent. The event, a combination of sport & culture, will feature performances by hosting competitions from a variety of sporting events. The 2014 Games will be held in Regina, Saskatchewan

NORTH AMERICA INDIGENOUS MINISTRIES (NAIM)
P.O. Box 220, Station A • Abbotsford, BC V2T 6Z6
P.O. Box 499 • Sumas, WA 98295
  (888) 942-5468; (604) 850-3052 Fax 504-0178
  Website: www.naim.ca; E-mail: office@naim.ca
Ron Hartwig, Executive Director
Scott Markloff, Communications Director
  E-mail: communications@naim.ca
Tim Higginbotham, Operations Director; E-mail: operations@naim.ca
Membership: 110. *Purpose*: To establish indigenous Native American fellowship gatherings in urban centers & on reservations. *Programs*: Eight week summer program for college students who live on reserve during the program; Wilderness Trails program, similar to Outward Bound; conducts economic, educational, social, and rehabilitation programs; offers alcohol treatment, sexual abuse & AIDS seminars, & cross-cultural communication seminars. *Publications*: Intercessor, bimonthly; NAIM News, semiannual newsletter. Library. Annual meeting. Established 1949.

NORTHERN PLAINS INDIAN LAW CENTER
INSTITUTE FOR THE STUDY OF TRIBAL GAMING LAW & POLICY
University of North Dakota School of Law
215 Centennial Dr. Stop 9003 • GRAND FORKS, ND 58202
  (701) 777-2104 Fax 777-2047; Website: www.law.und.edu/npilc/gaming/
Dr. Keith Richotte, Law Center Director
Steven Andrew Light & Kathryn R.L. Rand, Co-directors,
  Institute for the Study of Tribal Gaming Law & Policy
Purpose: To assist tribal governments in addressing legal issues affecting tribal lands & members; and to promote diversity within the legal profession by increasing recruitment & retention of American Indian law students. A clearinghouse for American Indian legal materials and provides a forum for discussing and resolving legal issues confronting Indian tribes, the states, and the federal government. Also, supports tribal advocacy training programs. *Resources*: Institute for the Study of Tribal Gaming Law & Policy. *Programs*: Indian law Certificate; Northern Plains Tribal Judicial Training Institute; Native Americans Into Law Program; Tribal Environmental Law Project.

NORTHERN PLAINS RESERVATION AID
2401 Eglin St. • Rapid City, SD 57703
  (800) 370-0872; (605) 399-9905 Fax 399-9908
  Website: www.npraprogram.org; E-mail: info@npraprogram.org
Brian J. Brown, President; Elora Antoine, Program Coordinator

Purpose: A member of the National Relief Charities, the Council was organized to help Native American people improve the quality of their lives by providing opportunities for them to bring about positive changes in their communities. *Programs*: A non-profit organization that develops self-help programs & emergency relief services for Native Americans on reservations in ND, SD, NE, MT and WY. These services include: emergency food distribution, clothing & shoe distributions, winterization of homes, fuel assistance programs, school supplies, holiday dinners, gifts & stockings for children at Christmas & Easter, baby baskets for new mothers and incentive programs for seniors, adult volunteers & children. *Publication*: Quarterly newsletter. Established 1988.

NORTHWEST INDIAN BAR ASSOCIATION (NIBA)
611 Main St., Suite B-1 • Edmonds, WA 98020
  (360) 651-3444; Website: www.nwiba.org
Sarah Roubidoux Lawson (Iowa of KS &NE), President
  E-mail: slawson@schwabe.com
Holly Sprague (Colville), Secretary
  E-mail: holly.sprague@muckleshoot.nsn.us
Lisa L. Atkinson (Cherokee/Osage), Treasurer
  E-mail: lisa_l_atkinson@msn.com
Dylan Hedden-Nicely (Cherokee), Lauren J. King (Muscogee Creek),
  Christna Parker (Ojibwe Cree), Members-at-Large
Description: Comprised of Native attorneys, judges and Indian law practitioners in Alaska, Idaho Oregon & Washington, and in spirit in British Columbia and the Yukon Territory. *Mission*: To improve the legal & political landscape for the Pacific Northwest Indian country; to represent & foster the education & welfare of Native American attorneys, paralegals & tribal court personnel in the Pacific Northwest; to provide role models & mentors in the legal profession for Indian people, particularly Native American youth and law students; to encourage & promote pro bono legal work and civic involvement that benefits Indian people on reservations and in urban areas throughout the Pacific Northwest. Contains a tribal referral list; scholar-ships; events and their locations. *Publications*: Indian Law Newsletter; articles.

NORTHWEST INDIAN FISHERIES COMMISSION
6730 Martin Way E., Olympia, WA 98506
  (360) 438-1180 Fax 754-8659
  Website: www.nwifc.org; E-mail: contact@nwifc.org
Billy Frank, Jr., Co-founder & Chairperson; E-mail: bfrank@nwifc.org
Mike Grayum, Executive Director; E-mail: grayum@nwifc.org
Terry Wright, Director of Administration; E-mail: twright@nwifc.org
Purpose: To support tribal fisheries management activities and to enable the 19 Treaty Indian Tribes in western Washington to speak with a unified voice; to help the tribes develop cooperative fisheries plans & help coordinate such programs as enhancement and habitat management.

NORTHWEST REGIONAL EDUCATIONAL LABORATORY
Indian Reading & Language Development Program
101 SW Main St., #500 • Portland, OR 97204
  (503) 275-9500 Fax 275-0660; Website: www.educationnorthwest.org
Phyllis Ault, Practice Expert
Purpose: To provide high-quality, third party evaluation services, conducting research & development for improving educational outcomes in rural and Native American communities, and carrying out planning & quality assurance activities for the organization.

OMOHUNDRO INSTITUTE OF EARLY AMERICAN HISTORY & CULTURE
The College of William & Mary, P.O. Box 8781 • Williamsburg, VA 23187
  (757) 221-1114 Fax 221-1047
  Karin Wulf, Director; E-mail: kawulf@wm.edu
Purpose: To encourage study and research in American history before 1820, especially but not exclusively, through book & periodical publications, conferences, etc. *Programs*: Do not deal exclusively with American Indian history, but has been significantly represented in its recent activities; book publishing in conjunction with UNC Press. *Award*: Two-Year Postdoctoral Fellowships, annually--research topics on American Indian history, 1500-1820 are eligible. *Publications*: The William & Mary Quarterly. Library. Established 1943.

ONABEN - NATIVE AMERICAN BUSINESS NETWORK
6441 SW Canyon Court, Suite 104 • Portland, OR 97221
  (503) 968-1500 Fax 968-1548; Website: www.onaben.org
5332 S. Memorial Dr., Suite 200 • Tulsa, OK 74145
  (918) 624-9176 Fax 968-1548
Veronica Hix (Cherokee), Executive Director; (918) 624-9176
  E-mail: veronica@onaben.org
Kristi Burns, Deputy Director; E-mail: Kristi@onaben.org
Selena Yokoyama (Hawaiian), Administrative Services Director
  E-mail: selena@onaben.org
April Lemly (Cherokee), Marketing/Brand Services Manager
  E-mal: april@onaben.org
Jack Lenox (Coquille), Chairperson; E-mail: jack1067@gmail.com

Robert Whitener (Squaxin Island), Vice Chairperson
Aurolynn Stwyer-Pinkham (Warm Springs), Secretary/Treasurer
E-mail: aurolynp@gmail.com

Description: Founded by a consortium of native nations in the Pacific Northwest. *Purpose*: To increase self-reliance by promoting the development of tribal citizen-owned small businesses & the diversification of reservation economies; to serve the Native community by providing Products, Services and Networking. Products include the Indianpreneurship, Journey & Growing curricula. Services include the provision of comprehensive organizational development, program advisory & 'train-the-trainer' services to Native business service centers, emerging & established Native community development financial institutions (CDFIs), tribal economic development organizations, tribal enterprises and other organizations that support micro-enterprise and small business development, asset-building & business lending activities. With networking, it convenes gatherings that: bridge tribes, tribal enterprises, tribal communities & entrepreneurs; build business relationships; inform good governmental policy; present & explore best practices in business and entrepreneurship development; and serve as a catalyst to generate capital for Indian Country. We achieve networking goals primarily through our annual "Trading at the River" conference; our Northwest Native Peer Group; & our Building Capacity & Networks cohort. *Publications*: "*Indianpreneurship*: A Native American Journey Into Business," a small business training curriculum for the Native American entrepreneur. $19.95. "Northwest Native American Business Directory," $25.

ORDER OF THE INDIAN WARS
P.O. Box 1650 • Johnstown, CO 80534
(970) 587-9530; Website: www.indianwars.com
Mike Koury, Chairperson

Membership: 750. Professionals & informal historians interested in the study of the frontier conflicts between the Indians and the white man, and among Indian tribes during the early settlement of the U.S. *Purpose*: Seeks to protect and preserve historic sites related to those wars. *Activities*: Annual conferences & tours. *Publications*: Communique, monthly. Established 1979.

THE ORDER OF THE INDIAN WARS OF THE U.S.
9002 Belvoir Woods Pkwy. #302 • Fort Belvoir, VA 22060
Website: www.oiwus.org; Hon. Richard Bender Abell, Commander

Purpose: To perpetuate the history of the services rendered by the American military forces during the various conflicts and wars within the territory of the U.S. Established 1896.

PANTHER LODGE MEDICINE SOCIETY
(formerly the Bear Tribe Medicine Society)
P.O. Box 2388 • Mountain View, AR 72560
(870) 368-7877; (251) 583-5984
Website: www.winddaughterwestwinds.com
E-mail: winddaughter@centurytel.net
Panther Wind Woman (Wind Daughter), Medicine Chief

Description: Wind Daughter is the adopted daughter of BearHeart, a Muskogee Creek elder. *Purpose*: To teach people respect for the earth as the giver and sustainer of life. It uses the Native American ways of viewing the earth to help people find their connection with the earth so that people will begin to think about the effects of their actions on the earth. *Activities*: Educational workshops, lectures, tours, survival camps, visitor programs; operates a bookstore/mail order business; offers a barter or trade system for people who want to take their programs but cannot afford them--they offer their skills in return for the programs. *Publications*: West Winds Newsletter, semiannual; The Path of Power; The Medicine Wheel Book; Buffalo Hearts; The Self-Reliance Book. Established 2006.

PARTNERSHIP WITH NATIVE AMERICANS
Formerly NATIONAL RELIEF CHARITIES
16415 Addison Rd., Suite 200 • Addison, TX 75001
(800) 416-8102; (503) 641-5786 Fax 641-0495
Website: www.nrcprograms.org; E-mail: info@nrcprograms.org
Robbi Rice Dietrich, President/CEO
Alyce Sadongei (Kiowa-Tohono O'odham), Chairperson
Christina Kazhe (Navajo- Mescalero Apache), Vice Chairperson
Ann Marie Woessner-Collins, Treasurer
Nikki Pitre (Coeur d'Alene), Secretary; Rafael Tapia VP, Programs
Amber Kinney, Sr. VP & Chief Financial Officer
Alan Silva, VP Administration; Rodney Trahan, VP Development
Mark Ford, Director-Major Gifts & Partnerships
Helen Oliff, Public Relation Manager (877) 281-0808
Rodney Trahan (Northern Cheyenne), VP Development
Board of Directors: Kevin Diepolz; Leonard J. Smith (Fort Peck Assiniboine
& Sioux); Tracey Zephier (Cheyenne River Sioux); Makenley Barton
(Cherokee); Ronetta (Roni) Keeter Briggs

Purpose/Goals: To help Native American people improve the quality of their lives by providing opportunities for them to bring about positive changes in their communities. *Activities/Programs*: A non-profit organization that develops self-help programs and emergency relief services for Native Americans across the country. National Relief Charities is the umbrella organization for American Indian Relief Council, Council of Indian Nations, American Indian Education Foundation, & Southwest Indian Relief Council. Services of member programs AIRC, CIN and SWIRC include: emergency food distributions, clothing & shoe distributions, winterization of homes, fuel assistance programs, school supplies, holiday dinners, gifts & stockings for children at Christmas & Easter, baby baskets for new mothers & incentive programs for seniors, adult volunteers & children. AIEF programs include: purchasing essential school supplies & curriculum materials, supporting student incentive programs, funding repair of structural deterioration in schools & awarding grants to American Indian students for tuition & living expenses. *Publication*: Quarterly newsletters are published for each program. Established 1995.

POWWOW COUNTRY
Meadowlark Communications, P.O. Box 7218 • Missoula, MT 59807
(888) 728-2180; (406) 728-2180 Fax 549-3090
Website: www.powwowcountry.com
E-mail: info@powwowcountry.com
Chris Roberts, President

Purpose: To promote ethnic & Native American arts, culture & dance. *Activities*: Provides scholarships & educational programs; distribute visual materials on Native American culture; sell photos, books & videos by catalog and on the web; annual Powwow & Cultural Rendezvous, 2nd week in August. *Publications*: Powwow Country, 1992; Powwow Country: People of the Circle (Meadowlark Communications, 1998); Powwow Wall Calendar, 1998-present. Established 1991.

RED NATION CELEBRATION (RNC)
RED NATION FILM FESTIVAL (RNFF)
9420 Reseda Blvd., PMB 352 • Northridge, CA 91324
(818) 665-5753; 854-6515
Website: www.rednationfilmfestival.com; E-mail: aihm@rednation.com
Joanelle Romero (Redhawk) (Apache/Cheyenne), Founder/President

Description: A non-profit American Indian organization established to premiere contemporary & traditional American Indian artists to the mainstream media & to the global communities; to encourage understanding of the cultural traditions & modern day issues of the Native Americans. *Activities*: Annual Red Nation Film Festival; Red Nation Media Channel (the first and only American Indian Internet Television Channel); e-Newsletter; Sponsorship Opportunities. *Affiliated companies*: Red Nation Records; Spirit World Productions, founded in 1991 by Joanelle Romero. Film produced: "American Holocaust - When It's All Over I'll Still Be Indian", Directed, Produced & Written by Joanelle Romero. Established 1995.

RED PONY HERITAGE LANGUAGE TEAM
Website: www.redpony.us; E-mail: rphlt@redpony.us
(505) 491-3401; Dupree ShadowWalker (Mescalero Apache), Founder

Purpose: The revitalization of Heritage Languages. Creates electronic dictionaries for academics working with languages that have lost their people. Creates language learning modules, electronic dictionaries, fonts, and spell-check facilities for Tribes endeavoring to revitalize their language.

SACRED CIRCLE
P.O. Box 21451 • Keizer, OR 97307
(971) 239-5697 Website: www.deafnative.com
Teresa Norris (Ojibwe), Executive Director
E-mail: executive.director@deafnative.com
Mark Azure (Chippewa-Cree), Culture Consultant
Damara Paris (Cherokee/Blackfoot), Grant Coordinator/Treasurer
E-mail: grantcoordinator.treasurer@deafnative.com
Tina Terrance (Mohawk), Liaison; E-mail: terrance1960@yahoo.com

Mission: To provide education, information & referral, and training about American Indians, Alaska Natives & First Nations Indians who are deaf, deaf-blind, hard of hearing and late-deafened, to tribal councils, family members & other interested parties in order to improve the social, educational, vocational, health & spiritual well-being of this population. *Activities*: Annual Gatherings; Spiritual Retreat; SC/Native Workshop; Powwow, Native Health Fair; Native Conference. *Publication*: Sacred Circle News; Charlie Galbraith's News (blog).

SEQUOYAH NATIONAL RESEARCH CENTER
AMERICAN NATIVE PRESS ARCHIVES
University of Arkansas at Little Rock, 500 University Plaza
2801 S. University Ave.• Little Rock, AR 72204
(501) 569-8336 Fax 371-7585
Website: www.ualr.edu/sequoyah; E-mail: Sequoyah@ualr.edu
Daniel F. Littlefield, Director
Erin Fehr, Archivist; E-mail: ehfehr@ualr.edu
Bob Sanderson, Associate Director; E-mail: resanderson@ualr.edu
J.W. Wiggins, Curator; E-mail: jwwiggins@ualr.edu

Description: Archives copies of works by American Indian, Alaska Native, and Canadian First Nations writers, bibliographies of other works, biographical information, & portfolios of works by cartoonists & photographers. *Purpose*: To promote & foster academic research concerning the American Native press, those involved in it, and American Native periodical literature as a whole; disseminate research results; refine methodologies. The Center is home to over 2400-piece Dr. J.W. Wiggins Native American Art Collection; Tribal Writers Digital Library; the Ronald Anderson Collection; works by the Choctaw artist; the Barry Lindley Collection of Inuit works; the Jody & Mike Wahig Collection, featuring works from the American Plains; and the J.T. Moncravie Osage Collection, featuring works by Osage artists. Annual Meeting. *Publication*: SNRC Newsletters. Established 1983.

SEVENTH GENERATION FUND FOR INDIGENOUS PEOPLES, INC.

425 I St., P.O. Box 4569 • Arcata, CA 95518
(707) 825-7640 Fax 825-7639; Website: www.7genfund.org
Dr. Henrietta Mann (Southern Cheyenne), Board Chairperson
Tupac Enrique Acosta, Board Vice Chairperson
Chris Peters (Karuk), President & CEO
Tia Oros Peters (Zuni), Executive Director; E-mail: tia@7genfund.org
Isaac Kinney, Operations Manager; Louis Gordon, Program Officer
Description: Provides seed grants and technical assistance in order to increase self-reliance in Indian communities & decrease government dependency. The fund's title is drawn from the Haudenosaunee (Six Nations) principle of considering the impact upon the seventh generation in the decision-making process. *Purpose/Goals*: To support & promote the spiritual, cultural, and physical well being of the Native family. To reclaim & live on aboriginal lands; protect tribal lands & natural resources; redevelop self-sufficient communities through food production, appropriate technologies, and alternative energy; restore traditional indigenous forms of political organization or to modify existing governments along traditional lines. *Programs*: Arts & Cultural Expression; Environmental Health & Justice; Human Rights; Intergenerational Leadership Initiative; Sustainable Communities; Women's Leadership. *Activities*: Reports on such subjects as Native American rights, Indian family life, and judicial issues and cases affecting American Indians. General Support Grants; Training & Technical Support; Workshops & Conferences; Sponsorships. Media Center, Native Pulse Radio; Video & Photo Gallery. Library. Publication: Annual report. Established 1977.

SOCIETY FOR ADVANCEMENT OF CHICANOS & NATIVE AMERICANS IN SCIENCE (SACNAS)

P.O. Box 8526 • Santa Cruz, CA 95061 (National Office)
1155 16th St., NW • Washington, DC 20036 (Science Policy)
(831) 459-0170 Fax 459-0194
Website: www.sacnas.org; E-Mail: info@sacnas.org
Antonia O. Franco, Executive Director; E-mail: Antonia@sacnas.org
Ernest D. Marquez, Director of American Indian Affairs & Policy
 Washington, DC office; E-mail: Ernest@sacnas.org
Jenny Kurzwell, Director of Communications & Marketing
 E-mail: jenny@sacnas.org
Membership: 2,000. Includes college professors, science professionals, & students. *Purpose*: To encourage Chicano/Latino & Native American students to pursue graduate education in order to obtain the advanced degrees necessary for research careers & science teaching professions. *Facilities*: SACNAS Mathematical Science Summer Institute, SACNAS Conference; Graduate School Application Workshops; Conversations With Scientists Roundtable Discussions; K-12 Curriculum; Classroom Science Kits; Faculty Advising Program; Scholarship Fund; Scientific Symposia; Community Service Awards. *Publication*: SACNAS News, quarterly newsletter. Established 1973.

SOCIETY OF AMERICAN INDIAN DENTISTS (SAID)

5320 W. Sahara Ave., Suite 4 • Las Vegas, NV 89146
(702) 744-7243; Website: http://thesaidonline.org
E-mail: saidentistry@gmail.com
Imelda Lemon, Executive Administrator
Darlene A. Sorrell (Navajo), DMD, President
Winifred Booker (Piscataway), DDS, Vice President
Dave L. Smith (Oneida), DDS, Treasurer & Past President
Lisa Frechette (Menominee/Brothertown), DDS, Secretary
George Blue Spruce, Jr. (Pueblo, Laguna/Ohkay-Owingeh), DDS
President Emeritus & Founder E-mail: bluespruceasgret@aol.com
Executive Board:
 Nancy Reifel, DDS, MPH (Rosebud Lakota); Jerry Snell, DDS (Cherokee); Sandra Wilson, DDS (Northern Cheyenne); Jessica Bremerman (Yakama), DDS; Felicia Frizzell (Mescalero), DDS; Maximillion Jensen (Navajo), DDS; Jeremy John (Paiute), DMD
Description: A national, non-profit organization comprised of oral health professionals & students. *Purpose*: To promote & improve the oral health of the American Indian/Alaskan Native community; to provide advocacy for the American Indian/Alaskan Native dental professionals across the U.S. Annual conference. Established 1990.

SOCIETY OF AMERICAN INDIAN GOVERNMENT EMPLOYEES (SAIGE)

P.O. Box 7715 • Washington, DC 20044
(202) 564-0375 Fax 564-7899; Website: www.saige.org
Susan Johnson (Three Affiliated Tribes/Anishinaabe), Chairperson
Fredericka Joseph (Kaw), Vice Chairperson
Lori Windle (Anishinaabe), Secretary
Karen D. Wilde (Muscogee (Creek)/Pawnee), Treasurer
Purpose: To promote recruitment, hiring, retention, development & advancement of American Indians & Alaska Natives in the government workforce; to educate Federal agencies in the history & obligations of the Federal Indian Trust responsibility and to assist them in its implementation; to provide a national forum for issues & topics affecting American Indian & Alaska Native government employees. *Programs*: Youth Track. *Publication*: Talking Leaf, newsletter

SOUTHWEST CENTER FOR LAW & POLICY

475 S. Stone Ave. • Tucson, AZ 85701
(520) 623-8192 Fax 623-8246
Website: www.swclap.org; E-mail: info@swclap.org
Hallie Bongar White, Executive Director
 E-mail: bongarwhite@swclap.org
Arlene O'Brien (Tohono O'odham), Program Manager
 E-mail: Obrien@swclap.org
Karen Velasquez (Navajo), Information & Resources Specialist
 E-mail: velasquez@swclap.org
Description: A non-profit organization providing free legal training on domestic violence, sexual assault, abuse of elders & persons with disabilities, etc. & technical assistance to tribal communities & to organizations & agencies serving Native people. *Resources*: Hosts the National Tribal Trial College providing free legal training for attorneys, judges, law enforcement, advocates & community members. Publications; numerous articles; presentations.

SOUTHWEST INDIAN RELIEF COUNCIL (SWIRC)

1310 E. Riverview Dr. • Phoenix, AZ 85034
(866) 228-0124 Fax (480) 281-0708
Website: www.swirc.org; E-mail: info@swirc.org
Katie Tree, Chairperson; Lisa Begay, Program Coordinator
Purpose: A program of the National Relief Charities to help Native American people improve the quality of their lives by providing opportunities for them to bring about positive changes in their communities. *Activities/Programs*: A non-profit organization that develops self-help programs and emergency relief services for Native Americans on reservations in the Southwest. These services include: emergency food distribution, clothing & shoe distributions, winterization of homes, school supplies, holiday dinners, gifts & stockings for children at Christmas & Easter, baby baskets for new mothers & incentive programs for seniors, adult volunteers & children. *Publication*: Quarterly newsletter. Established 2000.

SOUTHWESTERN ASSOCIATION FOR INDIAN ARTS (SWAIA)

P.O. Box 969 • Santa Fe, NM 87504-0969
(505) 983-5220 Fax 983-7647
Website: www.swaia.org; E-mail: info@swaia.org
Dallin Maybee, JD (Norhtern Arapaho/Seneca), Chief Operating Officer
 E-mail: dallin.m@swaia.org
John Jones, JD, Chief Development Officer; E-mail: jjones@swaia.org
Henry Brown Wolf III (Kewa/Lakota), Artist Services Manager
 E-mail: hbrownwolf@swaia.org
Tammie Touchine (Navajo), Volunteer & Membership Coordinator
 E-mail: ttouchine@swaia.org
Elizabth Pettus, Board Chairperson
Roger Fragua (Jemez Pueblo), Board Vice Chairperson
Dominique Toya (Jemez Pueblo), Board Secretary
Purpose: To develop, sponsor & promote the Santa Fe Indian Market and other events that encourage cultural preservation, intercultural understanding & economic opportunity for American Indians through excellence in the arts. *Activities*: Santa Fe Indian Market - over 600 booths and more than 1,200 Indian artists - the third weekend in August each year. Provides educational programs that benefit the Native American artist. SWAI Fellowships (both youth & adult); lifetime achievement awards in the arts. *Publication*: Indian Market Magazine. Established 1922.

SUNDANCE INSTITUTE – NATIVE FILM PROGRAM

5900 Wilshire Blvd. #800 • Los Angeles, CA 90036
(310) 360-1981 Fax 360-1969; Website: www.sundance.org
 E-mail: native_program@sundance.org
Utah Office: 1825 Three Kings Dr. • Park City, UT 84060
(435) 658-3456 Fax 658-3457
N. Bird Runningwater (Cheyenne/Mescalero Apache), Program Director
Dustin Owl Johnson (Saginaw Ojibwe), Manager
Program: The program scouts worldwide for Indigenous artists with projects that can be supported through the Institute's Feature Film Program,

Documentary Film Program, Theatre Program, the Creative Producing Fellowship & Summit, and the Sundance Film Festival. Native Lab Fellowship and Native Producing Fellowship. Four projects are selected annually for the Fellowship from a national competition. The Festival hosts the annual "Native Forum" – a hub for the international indigenous film community, and a program of panel discussions, filmmaking discussions, & networking events that provide opportunities for Indigenous filmmakers.

SURVIVAL OF AMERICAN INDIAN ASSOCIATIONS
7803-A Samurai Dr., SE • Olympia, WA 98503
(206) 459-2679; Hank Adams (Assiniboine Sioux), National Director
Membership: 500. *Activities*: Provides public education on Indian rights and tribal government reform action; supports independent Indian educational institutions; speakers bureau. *Publication*: The Renegade: A Strategy Journal of Indian Opinion, annual. Established 1964.

SYCUAN INSTITUTE ON TRIBAL GAMING
Robert Payne School of Hospitality & Tourism Management
San Diego State University, 5500 Campanile Dr. • San Diego, CA 92182
(619) 594-4964 Fax 594-4443
Katherine Spilde, Chairperson; E-mail: kspilde@mail.sdsu.edu
Mission: In partnership and cooperation with tribal governments, The Research Center for the Sycuan Institute on Tribal Gaming (SITG) is the arm of the Institute that is focused on producing and disseminating unbiased research on tribal government gaming issues. The Institute focuses on research, policy studies, and education related to the area of tribal gaming management. It is centered in the largest tribal gaming community in the world, and is geared to studying tribal gaming within the broader industry of hospitality & tourism management. The functions of the Institute include: the conduct of timely and innovative research in tribal gaming such as governance, community & regional impact, marketing, tribal gaming operations, trends, etc.; the collection of benchmarking data in order to develop "best practices" in tribal gaming; the creation of an annual summit on tribal gaming that addresses policy, regulatory issues, trends, social issues, etc.; the implementation of an annual community lecture or symposium on topics geared to informing & engaging the community about tribal issues & community conflicts; & educating students, professionals, tribal personnel and interested others for positions in the tribal gaming industry. The Institute will facilitate the involvement of faculty with expertise from a variety of disciplines such as hospitality, business, mathematics, computer science, ethnic studies, policy studies, legal studies, marketing, management, and public relations in the process of creating and disseminating new knowledge in the area of tribal gaming. The Institute is managed and operated by the interdisciplinary Hospitality and Tourism Management Program at SDSU and supported by an endowment from the Sycuan Tribal Council of the Kumeyaay Indians.

TEKAKWITHA CONFERENCE NATIONAL CENTER
2225 N. Bolton Ave. • Alexandria, LA 71301
(318) 483-3908 Fax 483-3909
Website: www.tekconf.org; E-mail: tekconf@gmail.com
Sister Kateri Mitchell (Mohawk), Executive Director
Rev. Maurice Henry Sands (Ojibway/Ottawa/potawatomi), Executive Director of Black & Indian Missions
Membership: 1,800. Catholic missionaries among American Indians; Eskimo and American Indian deacons & lay people involved in ministry. *Purpose*: To develop Catholic evangelization in the areas of Native American Ministry, catechesis, liturgy, family life, spirituality, and theology. It serves as the Voice, Presence, Identity of the American Indian and Eskimo Catholics by affirming our Faith under the protection of Blessed Kateri Tekakwitha, a Mohawk who lived from 1656 to 1680, and who is a candidate for Sainthood in the Roman Catholic Church. The Conference encourages development of Native American catechists for ministry among their own people. Provides a forum for the exchange of ideas among Catholic Native Americans, Eskimos, and missionaries. Encourages development of Native American ministry by Indian people. *Activities*: Sponsors an annual conference in various regions throughout the country; sponsors two summer institutes: Basic Directions in Native Ministry (9 days) & Native Ministry & Catechesis (5 days). *Publications*: Cross & Feathers, five times annual newsletter; Sacramental Series of eight booklets. Library. Annual conference. Established 1939.

THREE FEATHERS ASSOCIATES
P.O. Box 5508 • Norman, OK 73070
(405) 360-2919 Fax 360-3069; Website: www.threefeathersassoc.com
Antonia Dobrec, President; E-mail: toni@threefeathersassoc.com
Kathryn Helsel, Treasurer; E-mail: kathryn@threefeathersassoc.com
Purpose: To promote the health, education & welfare of American Indian & Alaska Native people. *Programs*: Head Start services; media production services to Native American tribes. 22 ears direct experience working with tribal governments who operate federal programs. *Publication*: Bimonthly newsletter. Gift shop.

THUNDERBIRD AMERICAN INDIAN DANCERS
204 West Central Ave. • Maywood, NJ
Website: www.thunderbirdamericanindiandancers.org
(201) 587-9633; E-mail: thunderbirddancers@gmail.com
Louis Mofsie, Founding Director; E-mail: louismofsie@gmail.com
Membership: 30. Indians & non-Indians who raise money for the Thunderbird Indian Scholarship Fund for Indian students. *Activities*: Annual Thunderbird Grand Mid-Summer Powwow (last weekend in July); offers cultural classes in crafts, singing, dancing, & language; sponsors Indian studies programs for Indian youth; monthly powwows in New York City--open to public. Established 1963.

TRAIL OF TEARS ASSOCIATION (TOTA)
412 N. Hwy. 100, Suite "B", P.O. Box 329 • Webber Falls, OK 74470
(918) 464-2258; Website: www.nationaltota.org
E-mail: roybarnesokie@gmail.com
Jack D. Baker (Cherokee), President; E-mail: jackdbaker@cox.net
Sue Folsom (Choctaw), Vice President
E-mail: suefolsom@choctawnation.com
Patsy Edgar (Cherokee), Secretary; Email: edgpj@aol.com
John McLarty (Cherokee), Treasurer; E-mail: jmclarty@nwarpc.org
Purpose: To promote awareness of the forced removal of the Cherokees, Choctaw, Seminole, Chickasaw, Muscogee Creek, et al.; to promote & engage in protection & preservation of Trail of Tears National Historic Trail resources; to perpetuate the management & development techniques that are consistent with the National Park Service's trail plan. Annual Conference & Symposium.

TRIBAL ALLIANCE OF SOVEREIGN INDIAN NATIONS
P.O. Box 3137 • Patton, CA 92369
(888) 958-2748 Fax 958-8088
Website: www.tasin.org; E-mail: info@tasin.org
Lynn Valbuena, Chairperson; Andrew Masiel, Sr., Vice Chairperson
Rosemary Morillo, Treasurer; Brian McDonald, Secretary
The Tribal Alliance of Sovereign Indian Nations (TASIN) is an intergovernmental association of federally recognized tribal governments throughout Southern California. We are the descendants of Native Americans who have called California home for thousands of years. We are tribal governments - building schools, roads, water systems, health centers, and providing other vital services to our citizens. We are partners with our neighboring cities and counties. We are part of California – both its past and its future. Our mission is to protect & promote the tribal sovereign government rights, the cultural identity and interests of federally recognized tribes located within the Federal Central Judicial District within the State of California.

TRIBAL BUSINESS OPPORTNITIES, INC.
1305 Rio Grande Blvd. NW • Albuquerque, NM 87104
(505) 256-4911 Fax 256-5177
Website: www.tribalbusinessopportunities.com
E-mail: cbs@tribalbusinessopportunities.com
Board of Directors: Nancy J. Appleby, Turk Cobell, Zackeree Sean Kelin, Sean McCabe, Vincent C. Murphy, L. Stephine Poston, Kelly A. Skalicky, Catherine Baker Stetson, W. Richard West. *Description*: A consortium of legal, business and financial professionals bringing together experience to provide one-stop business and financial solutions for Indian Country.

TRIBAL CONNECTIONS PROJECT (TCP)
National Network of Libraries of Medicine (NLM)
Pacific Northwest Region, University of Washington
P.O. Box 357155 • Seattle, WA 98195
(206) 543-8262 Fax 543-2469; Website: www.tribalconnections.org
Roy Sahali, TCP Project Manager, Co-editor
Frederick B. Wood, Project Officer
NLM Office of Health Information Programs Development
Description: A database of health information resources available on the Internet for Native Americans & Alaska Natives, created in association with the National Library of Medicine (NLM), National Institutes of Health, U.S. Dept. of Health & Human Services. *Resources*: e-Health info/Resources, Education & Training; Grants & Funding; Government Resources; Health News; Technology Resources. Established 1998.

TRIBAL EDUCATION DEPARTMENTS NATIONAL ASSEMBLY (TEDNA)
309 NW 13th St. • Oklahoma City, OK 73103
(405) 563-7912
Website: https://tedna.org; E-mail: info@tedna.org
Quinton Roman Nose (Cheyenne), Executive Director
Gloria Sly (Cherokee), Board President
Angeline Boulley (Sault Ste. Marie Chippewa), Vice President
Description: A membership organization for the education departments of American Indian & Alaska Native tribes, serving education departments in Indian Country. Established 2003.

TRIBAL GOVERNMENT INSTITUTE

111 N. Peters, Suite 450 • Norman, OK 73069
(405) 329-5542 Fax 329-5543
Website: www.tgiok.com; E-mail: tgi@coxinet.net
Mission: Serves as a procurement technical assistance center to facilitate the growth of Indian-owned business enterprises in the domestic & international U.S. Government marketplace, and to utilize a comprehensive database to provide business related information and contracting opportunities, with the goal of raising the social & economic status of Native American business. *Activities*: Annual conference.

TRIBAL INTERNET GAMING ALLIANCE (TIGA)

Lac du Flambeau Band of Lake Superior Chippewa Indians
P.O. Box 67 • Lac du Flambeau, WI 54538
Duane Capman, Interim Chairperson
Kevin Maulson, TIGA Organizer (715) 892-1089
P. Katzen, TIGA Legal Counsel (Kanji & Katzen, PLLC)
E-mail: pkatzen@kanjikatzen.com
TIGA Treaty Council Representatives:
Jerome "Brooks" BigJohn, Duane Chapman, Bill Guelcher
Description: An alliance of Indian tribes working collectively to bring Internet gaming to Indian country. Developed an intertribal treaty to serve as the TIGA charter. *Purpose*: To organize tribes across the country to both offer and regulate Internet & mobile phone gaming. Until laws change, TIGA will accept real-money wagers only from people who are physically present in the member tribes' jurisdictions, such as patrons at tribal casinos and visitors to other tribal lands. When customers are outside of tribal jurisdiction, the games will be fun-play and will offer casino promotions. Games will be those categorized as Class II under IGRA, such as slot-like bingo, traditional bingo, pull tabs and poker. Because the games are Class II, no tribal-state compacts will have to be amended. Using this strategy, TIGA tribes will jump ahead of the online competition and get extremely valuable experience with real-money wagering before other tribes and gaming operations. The idea for TIGA began among tribes in Wisconsin, Minnesota and Michigan. TIGA developments are now being followed by 28 tribes in 13 states.

TRIBAL LAW & POLICY INSTITUTE (TLPI)

8235 Santa Monica Blvd. #211 • West Hollywood, CA 90046
(323) 650-5467 Fax 650-8149
Website: www.tribal-institute.org; Website: www.tlpi.org
Jerry Gardner (Cherokee), Executive Director; E-mail: jerry@tlpi.org
Heather Valdez Freedman, Program Director; E-mail: heather@tlpi.org
Jessica Harjo (Apache), Operations Director; E-mail: jessica@tlpi.org
Lauren van Schilfgaarde (Cochiti Pueblo), Tribal Law Specialist
E-mail: lauren@tlpi.org
Kori Cordero (White Mountain Apache), Tribal Justice Specialist
E-mail: kori@tlpi.org

Chia Halpern Beetso (Spirit Lake Dakota), Tribal Court Specialist
E-mail: chia@tlpi.org
Maureen White Eagle (Ojibwe/Cree), Tribal Advocacy Legal Specialist
Kelly Stoner (Cherokee), Victim Advocacy Legal Specialist
Abby Abinanti (Yurok), Board President
David Raasch (Stockbridge-Munsee), Board Vice President
Margaret Oberly Kelley (Osage/Comanche), Secretary-Treasurer
Minnesota office: 1619 Dayton Ave. #305 • St. Paul, MN 55104
(651) 644-1125 Fax 644-1157
Bonnie Clairmont (Ho-Chunk), Victim Advocacy Specialist
E-mail: bonnie@tlpi.org
Montana office: National Resource Center for Tribes
501 N. Sanders St., Suite 2 • Helena, MT 59601 (406) 431-5941
Elizabeth Deserly (Kickapoo), Program Coordinator
E-mail: Elizabeth@nrc4tribes.org
Kathy Deserly (Kickapoo), Associate Director
E-mail: kathy@cbc4tribes.org
Description: An Indian-owned & operated non-profit corporation organized to design & develop education, research, training, & technical assistance programs which promote the enhancement of justice in Indian country, and the health & well-being & culture of Native people. Dedicated to providing free publication resources, comprehensive training, and technical assistance for Native nations and tribal justice systems in pursuit of our vision to empower Native communities to create and control their own institutions for the benefit of all community members, now, and for future generations. *Projects*: Tribal Law Clearing-house. Publications. Established 1996.

UNITED INDIAN MISSIONS (UIM) INTERNATIONAL

P.O. Box 6429 • Glendale, AZ 85312
(623) 847-9227 Fax 934-5996; Website: www.uim.org
Dan Fredericks, Executive Director
Jerry & Linda Yonnie, Southwest U.S. Field Director
(928) 688-3015; E-mail: swdir@uim.org

Warren & Carol Cheek, Senior Missionaries
Mark & Gina Morris, Native Church Ministry
Bemus & Floranda Uqualla, Supai Ministry
Ernie Geeting, Greater U.S. Director; E-mail: usdir@uim.org
John Cosby, Missionary Development Director
E-mail: mddir@uim.org
UIM Information & Communications Center
P.O. Box 336010 • Greeley, CO 80633 (970) 785-1176
UIM Canada P.O. Box 800 • Houston, BC V0J 1Z0 (250) 845-2538
Doug & Sherrie Anderson, Canadian Field Directors
Purpose: To establish Indigenous, biblically sound churches among Native American peoples of North America. *Publication*: UIM Magazine, brochures. Established in 1956.

UNITED NATIONAL INDIAN TRIBAL YOUTH, INC. (UNITY)

1 N. MacDonald Dr., Suite 212 • Mesa, AZ 85201
(480) 718-9793 Fax 773-6369; Website: www.unityinc.org
Mary Kim Titla (San Carlos Apache), Executive Director
E-mail: mk.titla@unityinc.org
Lynnann Yazzie (Navajo), Project Coordinator
E-mail: l.yazzie@unityinc.org
Loretta Tuell, JD (Nez Perce), Board Chairperson
Jan English (Creek), Treasurer/Secretary
Purpose: To empower American Indian & Alaska Native youth with the spiritual, mental, physical, and social qualities necessary to strengthen their lives & communities; to establish a National Leadership Training Center for American Indian/Alaska Native Youth through the development of a national UNITY council, annual national leadership development conferences, development of tribal, village, community youth councils, and motivational seminars. *Video*: A four-minute video describes some of UNITY's efforts to address important issues of concern to Native youth. *Publications*: UNITY News, quarterly newsletter. Established 1976.

UNITED SOUTH & EASTERN TRIBES, INC. (USET)

711 Stewarts Ferry Pike #100 • Nashville, TN 37214
(615) 872-7900 Fax 872-7417; Website: www.usetinc.org
DC Office: 400 N. Capitol St., NW, Suite 585, Washington, DC 20001
(202) 624-3550 Fax 393-5218
Kitcki Carroll, Executive Director (467-1540)
E-mail: kcarroll@usetinc.org
Wanda Janes, Deputy Director (467-1541)
E-mail: wjanes@usetinc.org
Brian Patterson (Oneida), President
E-mail: bpatterson@usetinc.org
Randy Noka (Narragansett), Vice President
Chief Kirk Francis (Penobscot), Treasurer
Dr. Lynn Malerba (Mohegan), Secretary
Description: A non-profit inter-tribal organization of 24 federally recognized tribes: The Eastern Band of Cherokee (NC), Mississippi Band of Choctaws (MS), Seminole Tribe (FL); Miccosukee Tribe (FL); Chitimacha (LA), Coushatta Tribe (LA); Tunica Biloxi Tribe (LA); Jena Band of Choctaw (LA); Seneca Nation (NY); St. Regis Band of Mohawks (NY); Cayuga Nation (NY); Oneida Nation (NY); Passamaquoddy Pleasant Point (ME); Passamaquoddy Indian Township (ME); Houlton Band of Maliseets (ME); Penobscot Nation (ME); Aroostook Band of Micmac (ME); Mohegan Tribe (CT); Mashantucket Pequot (CT); Poarch Band of Creek (AL); Narrangansett Indian Nation (RI); Wampanoag Tribe of Gay Head (Aquinnah) (MA); Alabama Coushatta Tribe (TX); Catawba Nation (SC). *Purpose*: Dedicated to enhancing the development of Indian Tribes; to improve the capabilities of Tribal governments; and assist the member tribes and their governments in dealing effectively with public policy issues; to provide a forum for the exchange of information and ideas among the 24 USET Tribes; and, it provides a vehicle which allows these tribes to jointly receive contracts and grants from federal and state agencies, as well private sector. *Activities*: 10 USET committees which deal with tribal justice, education, EMS & fire protection, health, housing, natural resources, social services, community and economic development, culture & heritage, and taxation. Provides four $500 scholarships each year to Indian students in the USET service area; administers a Health Information Office; and a Strategic Planning program; The Calumet Development Corp., a for-profit entity of USET, is involved in several financial ventures; the Annual Washington Impact Week in February. Annual Board meeting in December; Semiannual Board meeting in June. Established 1969.

UNITY: JOURNALISTS FOR DIVERSITY, INC

P.O. Box 511783 • Milwaukee, WI 53203
(414) 335-1478; Website: www.unityjournalists.org
E-Mail: info@unityjournalists.org
Eloiza Altoro, Executive Director
Russell Contreras, President & CEO
E-mail: Russell.contreras@gmail.com

Description: A Strategic alliance advocating news coverage about people of color, and challenging journalists at all levels to reflect the nation's diversity. UNITY represents more than 10,000 journalists of color and is comprised of four national organizations: Native American Journalists Association, Asian American Journalists Association, and the National Association of Hispanic Journalists. *Activities*: Develops programs and institutional relationships; annual conference.

VIOLA WHITE WATER FOUNDATION FOR INDIAN CULTURE & EDUCATION P.O. Box 126128 • Harrisburg, PA 17112
(717) 652-2040; Sandy Gutshall, President
Jimmy Little Turtle, Secretary/Treasurer
Description: Non-profit organization dedicated to helping Native Americans live & educate their children in the traditional ways. "Main goal now is Mohawk Valley settlement in Fonda, NY." *Activities*: Funding of Akwesasne Freedom School, & Mohawk Valley settlement in Fonda, NY. Grants are made to individuals, schools & colleges. *Publication*: Quarterly newsletter. Established 1977.

VISION MAKER MEDIA (VMV)
NATIVE AMERICAN PUBLIC TELECOMMUNICATIONS (NAPT)
1800 North 33 St. • Lincoln, NE 68583
(402) 472-3522 Fax 472-8675
Website: www.visionmakermedia.org; E-mail: visionmaker@unl.edu
Frank Blyth (Eastern Cherokee/Sisseton-Wahpetin Dakota)
Founding Executive Director/Native Emeritus
Shirley K. Sneve (Rosebud Sioux), Executive Director
E-Mail: shirley.sneve@unl.edu; (472-0208)
Georgiana Lee (Navajo), Assistant Director
E-mail: Georgiana.lee@unl.edu (472-0497)
Susan Hartmann, Director of Communications
E-mail: shartmann@netad.unl.edu (472-8607)
Boots Kennedye (Kiowa), Documentary Producer
E-mail: ckennedye@netad.unl.edu (472-0494)
Board of Directors:
Robin Butterfield (Winnebago/White Earth Ojibwe), Chairperson
Mark Trahant (Shoshone-Bannock), Vice Chair; Dan Schiedel, Secretary;
Randal P. Hansen, Treasurer
Purpose: To provide Native Americans & the general public access, via telecommunications, to content & related interactive experiences that educate, inform, enlighten & entertain the culture, history, achievements & concerns of the Native American people both on and off the reservations. *Objective*: To carry out this mission as self-sufficiently as possible, & minimize dependence on outside sources for funds. *Program*: American Indian Radio on Satellite (AIROS) streaming Native American programming over the Internet via a 24/7 live web-stream on concerns & issues of Native American communities, while inventorying Native American content radio programs for the public radio system. *Activities*: Public Television Program Fund; provides training opportunities; new programs are screened & cataloged on a continuous basis from all available sources; bestows awards; sponsors workshops. Developed the Native American Public Radio Satellite Network in conjunction with the Indigenous Communications Association. Vision Maker Video (VMV) is a service of NAPT whose mission is to support the creation, promotion and distribution of Native public media. Library of videotapes, films & radio programs. Established 1977.

THE WALKER RESEARCH GROUP
P.O. Box 4147 • Boulder, CO 80306
(303) 492-6719 Fax 492-7970
Website: www.walkerresearchgroup.com
Candace J. Arroyo de Walker, President
Deward E. Walker, Jr., Vice President
Research Associates: Sylvester (Bus) Lahren, PhD
James Hester, PhD; Roderick Sprague, PhD
Purpose: To provide a wide range of applied social science services to Native Americans and other clients with specialized needs. "We have become familiar with the provisions & requirements of the Federal Heritage Legislation. Specifically, we have extensive experience with the Archaeological Resource Protection Act (ARPA), the National Historic Preservation Act as amended, Native American Graves Protection & Repatriation Act (NAGPRA), American Indian Religious Freedom Act (AIRFA), & Executive Orders including endangered species, sacred sites, and tribal consultation."

WALKING SHIELD, INC.
22541 Aspan St., Suite E • Lake Forest, CA 92630
(949) 639-0472 Fax 639-0474
Website: www.walkingshield.org; E-mail: info@walkingshield.org
John Castillo (Fort Sill Apache), Executive Director
E-mail: jcastillo@walkingshield.org
Lynda Estrella (Pascua Yaqui/Mexican), Education Program Manager
E-mail: lestrella@walkingshield.org

Mission: To improve the quality of life for American Indian families by coordinating programs providing shelter, healthcare, community development support, educational assistance, and humanitarian aid. Working closely with tribal leaders, Walking Shield provides a variety of services to American Indian families. *Programs*: Medical & Dental Support; Infrastructure Support; Housing Relocation; Humanitarian Aid; Education; et al. *Activities*: Annual golf tournament. Established 1986.

WELLBRIETY TRAINING INSTITUTE
White Bison, Inc., 5585 Erindale Dr., #203 • Colorado Springs, CO 80904
(877) 871-1495; (719) 548-1000 Fax 548-9407
Website: www.whitebison.org; E-mail: info@whitebison.org
Don Coyhis (Mohican), President & Founder
J. Carlos Rivera (Pomo), Executive Director
Council of Elders: Ozzie Williamson (Blackfeet); Della Bad Wound
(Oglala Lakota); Dr. Henrietta Mann (Northern Cheyenne)
Description: An American Indian non-profit organization offering sobriety, recovery, addictions prevention & wellbriety learning resources to the Native American community, nationwide. *Mission*: To assist in bringing Native American communities into healing by establishing Wellbriety Treatment Centers throughout Indian country; speaker's Bureau, & Wellbriety resources, including books, DVDs, audiotapes; holds conferences, specialized community training events and the grassroots "Firestarters" circles of recovery groups across the country. *Publication*: Wellbriety Newsletter. *Published works*: Recovery From the Heart, A Journey Through the Twelve Steps - Audio, 1990 & Workbook, 1994; Meditations With Native American Elders, 1993; The Red Roads to Wellbriety; In the Native American Way, 2002. Meditations With Native American Elders: The Four Seasons, 2007. All published by Coyhis Publishing & Consulting, Inc. an online store & White Bison, Inc.
See bibliography section. Established 1988.

WESLEYAN NATIVE MINISTRIES
P.O. Box 50434 • Indianapolis, IN 46250
(888) 719-4094; Website: www.wesleyan.org/wnm
E-mail: wnm@wesleyan.org
Rev. Larry Salway, Director; E-mail: salwayl@wesleyan.org
Darwin & Ann Tsosie (Navajo), Native Pastors
Purpose: To empower Native leaders across North America to transform their communities through compassionate outreach, economic and community development, leadership development, and church resourcing & multiplication.

WINGS OF AMERICA
The Earth Circle Foundation, Inc.
901 W. San Mateo, Suite M • Santa Fe, NM 87505
(505) 982-6761 Fax 989-8995; Website: www.wingsofamerica.org
E-mail: takeflight@wingsofamerica.org
William E. Channing, Chairperson & Founder
Andrew Hixon, Co-Founder
Della Warrior (Otoe-Missouria), Vice Chairperson
Dustin Martin (Navajo), Program Director
E-mail: dustin@wingsofamerica.org
Description: An American Indian youth development program. *Purpose*: To enhance the quality of life of American Indian youth. In partnership with Native communities, Wings uses running as a catalyst to empower American Indian & Alaskan Native youth to take pride in themselves and their cultural identity, leading to increased self esteem, health & wellness, leadership & hope, balance and harmony. *Programs*: The American Indian Running Coaches' Clinic; Wings Leadership/Camp Facilitator Training; Wings Running & Fitness Camps (for children 6-14 years old); Partnership & Outreach; Wind Messenger Foot races. Established 1988.

WOMEN EMPOWERING WOMEN FOR INDIAN NATIONS (WEWIN)
P.O. Box 556 • Klamath, CA 95548
(320) 532-4709 Fax 532-5800; Website: www.wewin04.org
Susan Masten, Founder & Co-Director; E-mail: susanmasten04@gmail.com
Veronica Homer (Shaster/Mohave), Co-Director
Description: A non-profit national organization of Indian women power players, including Susan Masten (founder & co-director), Veronica Homer (co-director), Veronica Homer, Rachael Joseph (secretary), Melanie Banjamin, Geri Small, Pat Parker (founding member), Nora McDowell Antone, and Cecilia Fire Thunder. *Purpose*: To provide advocacy, training, education, & leadership development for American Indian women leaders. *Activities*: Annual conference with workshops in July. Established 2005.

WORDCRAFT CIRCLE OF NATIVE WRITERS & STORYTELLERS
200 Rio Grande SW, Apt. 214 • Albuquerque, NM 87104
(505) 842-8425; Website: www.wordcraftcircle.org
Lee Francis, IV (Laguna), National Director
Kim Roppolo, Acting President of the Board
Jay Goombi, Board Vice President; Rain Gomez, Secretary/Treasurer

Description: Volunteer organization of 200 active members and 320 inactive members. *Mission*: To support the works and words of Native and Indigenous people in order to strengthen the impact of their voices in asserting community sovereignty, individual self-determination, traditional and cultural values, and creative expression. *Activities*: Host/hold "Gatherings" throughout the U.S. Presents honors and awards annually to Native and non-Native individuals in a variety of areas: Writer of the Year in Poetry; Writer of the Year in Prose (fiction, non-fiction, autobiography, CD recording, newspaper writing/editing, etc.) These honors are "open to the world." Honors limited to Wordcraft Circle members only are Wordcrafter of the Year, Intern of the Year. We also present, "Honors for Storyteller of the Year" (traditional, contemporary, readings, presentations, lectures) & Publisher of the Year (national, regional, small press, tribal, university, and outside the U.S.), Literary Agent of the Year, Sovereign Indigenous Native Nation of the Year. *Publication*: On-line juried journal: "Native Realities" - available to the general public. Dues: Regular, $40; Elder/Student, $25. Established 1992.

NATIVE AMERICAN OWNED & OPERATED FINANCIAL INSTITUTIONS

BANKS

BANK2
909 S. Meridian Ave. • Oklahoma City, OK 73108
(405) 946-2265 Fax 946-2287; (877) 409-2265
 Website: www.bank2online.com
 Ross Hill (Chickasaw), President & CEO
Owned by the Chickasaw Nation. Opened 2002.

FIRST NATIONAL BANK & TRUST CO. (FNB)
130 E. MacArthur • Shawnee, OK 74804
 (405) 275-8830; Website: www.fnbsshawnee.net
 Larry Briggs, President & CEO/Trust Officer
 Randy Waters, Executive V.P. Chief Lending Officer
 Annette Stuckey, Executive V.P. Chief Financial Officer
The largest tribally owned national bank in the U.S. Serves central & western Oklahoma. FNB has branches at Citizen Potawatomi Nation Tribal Headquarters, Shawnee, Holdenville, two in Lawton, Granite & Mangum Oklahoma. Established 1989.

LUMBEE GUARANTY BANK
403 E. Third St., P.O. Box 908 • Pembroke, NC 28372
 (919) 521-9707; Website: www.lumbeeguarantybank.com
 E-mail: supportservices@lumbeeguarantybank.com
 Larry Ray Charles, President (1987-present)
 Arnold Locklear, Chairperson; Dr. Martin L. Brooks, Vice Chairperson
The first Indian-owned bank in the U.S. Established 1973.

NATIVE AMERICAN BANK, N.A. (Corporate Headquarters)
999 18th St., Suite 2460 • Denver, CO 80202
 (800) 368-8894 Fax (303) 988-2727 Fax 988-5533
 E-mail: info@nabna.com; Website: www.nabna.com
 www.facebook.com/nativeamericanbank
 Tom Ogaard, President & CEO (720) 963-5501
  E-mail: togaard@nabna.com
 Tracie Davis, Executive VP & CFO
 Shannon Loeve, Sr. VP & Chief Lending Officer (720) 963-5528
 Jamie Yancy, Sr. VP & Chief Technical Officer
Seeking lending opportunities for qualified borrowers including Alaska Native Corporations, Native American Tribes, Tribal authorities and Native-owned businesses in amounts ranging between $250,000 and $2,000,000.
Retail Branch: 125 N. Public Square, Browning, MT 59417 (406) 338-7000
Loan Production: 613 Sundance Rd., Box Elder, MT 59521 (406) 395-4355

THE PEOPLE'S BANK OF SENECA
1615 Cherokee Ave. • Seneca, MO 64865
 (417) 776-2111
Owned by the Eastern Shawnee Tribe of Oklahoma

CREDIT UNIONS

FIRST AMERICAN CREDIT UNION
1001 N. Pinal Ave. • Casa Grande, AZ 85222
 (800) 759-9442; (520) 836-8848 Fax 421-1706
Hwy. 264, Route 12 • Window Rock, AZ 86515
 (928) 871-4772 Fax 871-4393

1375 N. Hwy. 491, Mesa View Plaza • Gallup, NM 87301
 (505) 863-9381 Fax 863-9382
 Website: www.firstamerican.org; E-mail: sc@firstamerican.org
 JR McEvoy, Chairperson; Joseph Hardy, Vice Chairperson
Originally founded as Navajoland Credit Union. First American Credit Union is a small, community oriented, non-profit financial institution. Our members and employees are people like you who live and work in the Casa Grande, The Bonito, Sells, & Gallup regions of Southwest Arizona & New Mexico. Originally founded as Navajoland Credit Union, we still take pride in our Navajo roots. But we welcome members from all Native American tribes, as well as from all the different ethnicities that weave the colorful fabric of our beautiful, historical region. We actively participate in community service and treat our members like part of the family, because we're just like you. Our members and employees live & work in the Casa Grande, Window Rock, and Gallup regions of Southwest Arizona and New Mexico. Welcome are members from all Native American tribes in the region.

SISSETON-WAHPETON FEDERAL CREDIT UNION
P.O. Box 627 • Agency Village, SD 57262
 Website: www.sisseton-wahpetonfcu.com
 (605) 698-3462 Fax 698-3907
 Colleen Eastman (Sisseton-Wahpeton Sioux), CEO
Purpose: To provide consumer credit to members and employees of the Sisseton-Wahpeton Sioux Tribe.

RESERVATION-BASED LOAN FUNDS

INDIAN LAND CAPITAL COMPANY
151 County Road B2 • Little Canada, MN 55117
 (651) 444-5759 Fax 766-0012
 Rjay Brunkow (Turtle Mountain Ojibwe), CEO
 Cris Stainbrook (Oglala Lakota), Board Chairperson
 David Tovey (Umatilla), Secretary/Treasurer
 Jay Marcus, Board Member
 Chandra Hampson (Winnebago/Ojibwe), Board Member
Description: A certified Native American Community Development Financial Institution (CDFI) providing financing to Native nations for economic development and land acquisition. ILCC grew out of an identified need in Indian Country for financial mechanisms that offered full faith and credit lending options for tribal land purchases. Unlike traditional lending institutions, ILCC responds directly to the financial needs of Native nations. As a Native-run business, ILCC understands and supports tribal sovereignty and recognizes the importance of land to Indian people. *Purpose*: To strengthen Native Nations & expanding tribal sovereignty through land acquisition; to provide tribal governments with flexible financing to purchase lands. As an Indian-controlled Community Development Financial Institution CDFI, ILCC is uniquely positioned to provide loans that respond to the distinct needs of Indian nations.

LAKOTA FUNDS
P.O. Box 340 • Kyle, SD 57752
 (605) 455-2500 Fax 455-2585
 Website: www.lakotafunds.org
 Tawney Brunsch, Executive Director
  E-mail: tbrunsch@lakotafunds.org
 LaVonne Randall, Financial Manager
  E-mail: lrandall@lakotafunds.org
 Stefanie Atene, Procurement Specialist
  E-mail: sateen@lakotafunds.org
Description: The first certified Native community development financial institution on a reservation. *Purpose*: Formed to help build a private sector economy on the Pine Ridge Reservation by providing loans, technical assistance & business training; and arts & crafts marketing assistance tribal members. *Activities*: Loans for small business & microenterprises. *Publication*: The Lakota Funds' newsletter.

SICANGU ENTERPRISE CENTER
P.O. Box 205, 516 West 2nd St. • Mission, SD 57555
 (605) 856-2955; Phyllis Halligan, Enterprise Development Specialist
 Kathy Frederick, Mktg. & Development Specialist
Purpose: To promote & develop micro-enterprises (home-based businesses), affordable, culturally appropriate housing, community revitalization & cultural arts. *Activities*: Youth Enterprise Project. *Publications*: Poster & workbook series for youth that is based on culturally relevant economic knowledge. Established 1990.

REGIONAL, STATE & LOCAL ORGANIZATIONS
(Includes Urban Indian Centers)

This section is an alpha-geographical listing of state & regional agencies & organizations concerned mainly with Native-American affairs in their particular state and/or region of the U.S.

ALABAMA

ALABAMA STATE DEPT. OF EDUCATION - INDIAN EDUCATION
Gordon Persons Bldg. • 50 N. Ripley St. • MONTGOMERY, AL 36104
(334) 242-8199 Fax 242-0496; Website: www.alsde.edu
Darryl Washington, Coordinator
Purpose: To serve as the liaison for the State Dept. of Education with the Indian Affairs Section of the U.S. Dept. of Education, the Indian Education Technical Assistance Center, the Alabama Commission on Indian Affairs, and local Indian education coordinators.

ALABAMA INDIAN AFFAIRS COMMISSION (AIAC)
771 S. Lawrence St., Suite 106 • MONTGOMERY, AL 36130
(800) 436-8261; (334) 240-0998 Fax 240-3408
Website: www.aiac.state.al.us; E-mail: aiac@att.net
Eloise Josey, Executive Director
Richard Greybull, Commission Chairperson
Purpose: To serve as a liaison agency between Alabama's seven state-recognized tribes (one of which is federally recognized), Indian individuals and the various levels of government & private sector entities. Recognizing the unique cultural & sociological needs of Alabama's "invisible minority", the Legislature specifically charged AIAC to "deal fairly & effectively with Indian affairs; to bring local, state, federal resources into focus…for Indian citizens of the State of Alabama; to provide aid…assist Indian Communities…promote recognition of the right of Indians to pursue cultural and religious traditions…" Noting that charge for action, AIAC is placed in a liaison/advocacy role between the various departments of governments and the Indian people of our tribal communities. AIAC stands alone to represent the Indian people of Alabama who wish to stand together with their fellow citizens while maintaining their own cultural and ethnic heritage. *Activities*: Sponsors an annual statewide powwow to raise money for the Alabama Indian Children's Scholarship Fund. Also, speaking engagements, presentations, workshops & seminars for schools, churches, military, governmental agencies, etc. regarding Alabama Indians. *Publications*: Annual Report; newsletters. Established 1984.

INTER-TRIBAL COUNCIL OF ALABAMA
771 S. Lawrence St., Suite 100 • MONTGOMERY, AL 36104
(888) 400-3533; (334) 262-4105 Fax 262-4279
Website: www.itcala.org; E-mail: itcala@yahoo.com
Sharon Keith, Director; Teresa Williams, Information Specialist
Chief James Wright, Chairperson; Chief Stan Long, Vice Chairperson
Program: Workforce Investment Act (WIA) is a federally funded grant program through the U.S. Dept. of Labor, Education & Training Administration, Indian & Native American Programs. Established 1991.

ALASKA

The Alaska Native Claims Settlement Act of December 18, 1971, established regional village corporations and associations, both profit & non-profit. Listings are arranged alphabetically.

AHTNA NATIYE, INC.
110 W. 38th Ave., Suite 100B • ANCHORAGE, AK 99503
(907) 868-8250 Fax 868-8285
William Anderson, Jr., Chief Executive Officer; E-mail: wanderson@ahtna.net
Roy Jake Tansy, Jr., Executive Vice President; E-mail: rtansy@ahtna.net
Jana Turvey, Vice President of Legal Affairs; E-mail: jturvey@ahtna.net

ALASKA FEDERATION OF NATIVES
1577 C St. #300 • ANCHORAGE, AK 99501
(907) 274-3611 Fax 276-7989; Website: www.nativefederation.org
Julie E. Kitka, President; E-mail: afninfo@nativefederation.org
Maude Blair, Vice President; E-mail: mblair@nativefederation.org
Benjamin Mallott, Vice President; E-mail: bmallott@nativefederation.org
Nicole Borromeo, General Counsel; Email: nborromeo@nativefederation.org
Jeff Silverman, Director of Communications
 E-mail: jsilverman@nativefederation.org
Membership: 77,000. Alaskan Natives (Aleut, Eskimo, & Indian); regional profit & non-profit corporations. *Purpose*: To act as lobbyist & advocate on behalf of statewide Native community and to provide technical assistance to these groups. *Activities*: Inuit Circumpolar Conference - An international organization of Inuit (Eskimo) from Alaska, Canada & Greenland holding non-governmental

organizations status with the United Nations. The ICC is committed to upholding & advancing the cultural, economic, political, & civil rights of indigenous people across the Arctic Rim countries & worldwide. Native Insight Competition: www.nativeinsight.org. A writing competition (500-1600 words) crafted to tap the wisdom & ingenuity of our Native communities & encourage Native thinkers to go public with their perspectives on the current economic & political landscape. *Publications*: Monthly newsletter; annual report. Maintains biographical archives & library of government reports & economic material. Annual meeting in October. Established 1966.

ALASKA HISTORICAL SOCIETY
P.O. Box 100299 • ANCHORAGE, AK 99510
(907) 276-1596; Website: www.alaskahistoricalsociety.org
E-mail: members@alaskahistoricalsociety.org
Rebecca Poulson, President, Sitka
Jim Simard, Vice President, Juneau
Jo Antonson, Executive Director
Linda Thibodeau, Director, State of Alaska, Libraries, Archives & Museums
Awards program. *Publications*: Alaska History News; books & research guides. Annual conference.

ALASKA INTER-TRIBAL COUNCIL
445 E. 5th Ave. • ANCHORAGE, AK 99501
(800) 995-9334; (907) 563-9334 Fax 563-9337
Steve Sumida, Acting Executive Director; Mike Williams, Chairperson
Purpose: To advocate for tribal governments across Alaska. *Activities*: The Council promotes indigenous self-determination by providing technical assistance to tribal governments, facilitating inter-governmental & inter-agency communications & collaboration, offering public education regarding Alaska Native cultures & tribal governments, advocating tribal initiatives & self governance.

ALASKA LEGAL SERVICES CORPORATION
1016 W. Sixth St. #200 • ANCHORAGE, AK 99501
(907) 272-9431 Fax 279-7417
Website: www.alsc-law.org; E-mail: anchorage@alsc-law.org
Nikole Nelson, Executive Director; Michelle Peters, AdmiNistrative Director
Supervising Attorneys: Maggie Humm (Anchorage, Kenai, Palmer;
 Leigh Dickey (Barrow, Bethel, Dilllingham, Kotzebue, Nome);
 Melony Lockwood (Fairbanks; Holly Handler (Juneau & Ketchikan)
Purpose: To provide legal assistance to Alaskan Natives. *Offices*: Barrow; Bethel; Bristol Bay; Fairbanks; Juneau; Kenai; Ketchikan; Kotzebue; Nome; Palmer. Established 1967.

ALASKA NATIVE ARTS FOUNDATION (ANAF)
500 West 6th Ave. • ANCHORAGE, AL 99501
(907) 258-2623 Fax 258-2611; Website: www.alaskanativearts.org
E-mail: info@alaskanativearts.org
Perry Eaton, Board Chairperson
Trina Landlord, Executive Director
Maintains the Alaska Native Arts Gallery. Established 2002.

ALASKA NATIVE HEALTH BOARD
4000 Ambassador Dr. • ANCHORAGE, AK 99508
(907) 562-6006 Fax 563-2001; Website: www.anhb.org
Verne Boener, President/CEO; Alberta Unok, Deputy Director
Brandon Biddle, Policy Analyst; Melonee Long, Administrative Coordinator
Purpose: To promote the spiritual, physical, mental, social & cultural wellbeing & pride of Alaska Native people. ANHB is a 25-member board entity. Established 1968.

ALASKA NATIVE HERITAGE CENTER
8800 Heritage Center Dr. • ANCHORAGE, AK 99506
(800) 315-6608; (907) 330-8000 Fax 330-8030
Website: www.alaskanative.net; E-mail: info@alaskanative.net
Jeff Kinneeveauk, Board Chairperson
Annette Evans-Smith (Athabascan/Alutiiq/Yup'ik), President & CEO
 E-mail: aevanssmith@alaskanative.net
Steven Alvarez (Mescalero Apache/Yaqui/Athabascan), Director of Education
Elizabeth Walls (Yup'ik), Cultural & Educational Coordinator
Purpose: To provide educational & cultural programs to all Alaskans, including workshops, demonstrations, and guided tours of indoor exhibits and outdoor village sites. Established 1987.

ALASKA NATIVE SCIENCE COMMISSION
429 L St. • ANCHORAGE, AK 99501
(877) 478-2672 (Alaska only); (907) 258-2672 Fax 258-2652
Website: www.nativescience.org
Patricia Longley Cochran (Inupiat Eskimo), Executive Director
Larry Merculiieff, Deputy Director
Elaine Abraham, Chairperson; Orville Huntington, Vice Chairperson

Purpose: To bring together research and science in partnership with the Native community. It serves as a clearinghouse for proposed research, an information base for ongoing and past research, and an archive for significant research involving the Native community. *Special Project*: Alaska Traditional Knowledge & Native Foods Database; Website: www.nativeknowledge.org. *Publications*: Newsletters, Presentations, Reports. Established 1994.

ALASKA NATIVE TRIBAL HEALTH CONSORTIUM (ANTHC)
4000 Ambassador Dr. • ANCHORAGE, AK 99508
(907) 729-1900; Website: www.anthctoday.org
Andy Teuber, Chair & President; Lincoln Bean, Vice Chairperson
Charlene Noliner, Secetary; Mike Zacharof, Treasurer
A not-for-profit health organization that provides statewide services in specialty medical care; operates the 150-bed, Alaska Native Medical Center Hospital; leads construction of water, sanitation & health facilities around Alaska; offers community health & research services; and offers professional recruiting to partners across the state. A member of the Alaska Native Health Board. Established 1998.

ALASKA STATE COUNCIL ON THE ARTS
161 Klevin St., Suite 102 • ANCHORAGE, AK 99508
(888) 278-7424; (907) 269-6610 Fax 269-6601
Website: www.eed.state.ak.us/aksca; E-mail: aksca.info@alaska.gov
Shannon Daut, Executive Director
Andrea Noble, Visual & Literary Arts Program Director
 E-mail: andrea.noble-pelant@alaska.gov
L. Saunders McNeill, Community & Native Arts Program Director
 E-mail: saunders.mcneill@alaska.gov
Laura Forbes, Arts Education Program Director
 E-mail: laura.forbes@alaska.gov
Purpose: Provides grants to support Native Alaskan art & crafts. *Publications*: ASCA Newsletter (online). Book: Eskimo Dolls, edited by Suzi Jones; $12.

ALEUT CORPORATION
4000 Old Seward Hwy. #300 • ANCHORAGE, AK 99503
(800) 232-4882; (907) 576-4300 Fax 563-4328
Website: www.aleutcorp.com; E-mail: info@aleutcorp.com
Thomas Mack (Aleut), President; David Gillespie (Aleut), CEO
Tracy Timothy Woo, Chief Financial Officer
Dick Jacobsen (Aleut), Chairman
Sharon Guenther Lind (Aleut), Vice Chairperson
Jenifer Samuelson-Nelson (Aleut), Vice President
Tara Bourdukofsky (Aleut), Secretary/Treasurer
Description: Native for-profit regional corporation. *Purpose*: To promote economic, cultural, & social growth for its shareholders through its subsidiaries, partnerships and foundation. Established 1972.

THE ALEUT FOUNDATION
703 W. Tudor Rd., Suite 102 • ANCHORAGE, AK 99503
(800) 232-4882; (907) 646-1929 Fax 646-1949
Website: www.thealeutfoundation.org
E-mail: taf@thealeutfoundation.org
Cynthia H. Lind (Aleut), Executive Director
Kathy Griesbaum (Aleut), Chairperson
Purpose: To support the economic & social needs of the Aleut people. *Programs*: Scholarships; Job & Career Development; Cultural Preservation.

ALEUTIAN/PRIBILOF ISLANDS ASSOCIATION
1131 E. International Airport Rd. • ANCHORAGE, AK 99518
(800) 478-2742; (907) 276-2700; Fax 279-4351
Website: www.apiai.org; E-mail: apiai@apiai.org
Demitri Philemonof, President/CEO
Christopher Merculief, Vice Chair
Trina Deuber, Administrative Operations Manager
Fred Bauer, Chief Information Officer
Carolyn Crowder, Health Dept. Director
Millie McKeown, Cultural Heritage Director
Ken Selby, Community Services Director
Tara Bourdukofsky, Human Services Director
Tribe: Aleut. *Services*: Provides a variety of programs to the Aleut Region, including Healthcare, Cultural Heritage, Human Services, and Community Services. Affiliated with Alaska Area Indian Health Service. Tribally operated.

ARCTIC SLOPE REGIONAL CORPORATION
3900 C St., Suite 801 • ANCHORAGE, AK 99503
(800) 770-2772; (907) 339-6000 Fax 339-6028
Website: www.asrc.com
Rex A. Rock, Sr. (Inupiat), President & CEO;
Ty Hardt (Inupiat), Director of Communications (339-6888)
 E-mail: thardt@asrc.com
Administrative & subsidiary office. Corporate office is located in Barrow.

BRISTOL BAY NATIVE CORPORATION
111 W. 16th Ave. #400 • ANCHORAGE, AK 99501
(800) 426-3602; (907) 278-3602 Fax 276-3924
Website: www.bbnc.net; Greta L. Goto, Executive Director
Marie Paul, President; Katrina Johnson, Vice President
Regional Native Corporation.

CALISTA CORPORATION
301 Calista Ct., Suite A • ANCHORAGE, AK 99518
(800) 277-5516; (907) 279-5516 Fax 272-5060
Website: www.calistacorp.com; E-mail: calista@calistacorp.com
Andrew Guy (Yup'ik), President & CEO
Description: Native for-profit regional corporation. Established 1972.

CHENEGA CORPORATION
3000 C St., Suite 301 • ANCHORAGE, AK 99503
(907) 277-5706 Fax 277-5700
Website: www.chenega.com; E-mail: info@chenega.com
Kristina Woolston (Yup'ik), Vice President of Government Relations
Description: An Alaska Native Village Corporation. *Purpose*: To represent the interests of the Chenega people, an Alutiiq people of Prince William Sound area of South Central Alaska, by performing prime contracts & 100 principal sub-contracts for its shareholders. Established 1974.

CHUGACH ALASKA CORPORATION
3800 Centerpoint Dr. #601 • ANCHORAGE, AK 99503
(907) 563-8866 Fax 563-8402
Website: www.chugach-ak.com
Sheri D. Buretta (Aleut), Chairperson
 E-mail: sheri.buretta@chugach-ak.com
Matthew P. McDaniel, Vice Chairperson
Native for-profit regional corporation.

COOK INLET NATIVE ASSOCIATION
P.O. Box 93330 • ANCHORAGE, AK 99509
(907) 274-8638 Fax 279-8836
Website: www.ciri.com; E-mail: info@ciri.com
Sophie Minich, President & CEO; Barbara A. Donatelli, Sr. V.P.
Ethan Schutt, Sr. V.P. Land & Energy Development
Jason Moore, Corporate Communications Director
Thomas Huhndorf (Yup'ik) Chair; Douglas W. Fifer (Tlingit), Vice Chair
Native non-profit association of approximately 1,500 Alaskan Natives & American Indians dedicated to nurturing pride in the heritage & traditions of Alaska Natives, and preserving the customs, folklore, and art of the people. Operates a health clinic, Alaska Native Community Center. *Publication*: Trail Blazer, quarterly newsletter. Established 1966.

COOK INLET TRIBAL COUNCIL, INC.
3600 San Jeronimo Dr. • ANCHORAGE, AK 99508
(877) 985-5900; (907) 793-3600 Fax 793-3422
Website: www.citci.com; E-mail: info@citci.com
Gloria O'Neill (Yupik), President & CEO
Clare Swan, Board Chairperson
Tim Blum, Communications Officer (793-3443)
 E-mail: tblum@citci.org
Bill Tsurnos, Program Director (441-0181)
 E-mail: btsurnos@citci.org
Description: Native for-profit regional corporation representing Alaska Natives of south central Alaska. *Goal*: To assist Alaska Native people achieve self-sufficiency through higher education, training, and ultimately employment. *Activities*: Workshops; educational, employment & training, and human service programs; child & family services; youth opportunities. CITCI has been instrumental in the development of the Alaska Native Heritage Center, Inc., which is seeking to build an Alaska Native cultural & educational center in Anchorage; and Koahnic Broadcast Corp., parent organization for the nation's first Native-owned urban public radio station. *Affiliations*: Cook Inlet Tribal Council; Alaska's People, Inc.; Cook Inlet Housing Authority; The CIRI Foundation; south central Foundation. *Publications*: Biannual newsletter; annual report, brochures. Established 1983 by CIRI, Cook Inlet Region, Inc.

EASTERN ALEUTIAN TRIBES
3380 C St., Suite 100 • ANCHORAGE, AK 99503
(907) 277-1440 Fax 277-1446; Website: www.eatribes.org
Joe Bearskin (Mayor of Akutan), President
William Dushkin, Sr., Vice President
Rita Uttecht (V.P. of Agdaagux of King Cove), Secretary/Treasurer
Other Board members:
 Alvin Osterback, Jr.; Lila Johnson; Melanie Hoblet; John Foster
Provides medical, dental, and behavioral health services in federally qualified health centers in the communities of Adak, Akutan, Cold Bay, False Pass, King Cove, Nelson Lagoon, Sand Point, and Whittier. Established 1991.

KONIAG, INC.
4300 B St., Suite 407 • ANCHORAGE, AK 99503
 (907) 561-2668; Website: www.koniag.com
 Tom Panamaroff, Interim President
 Ron Unger, Board Chairperson; E-mail: runger@koniag.com
Native for-profit regional corp. Headquarters located in Kodiak. *Activities*:
Sponsors a variety of economic activities for the benefit of its constituency.

ARCTIC VILLAGE TRADITIONAL COUNCIL
P.O. Box 22059 • ARCTIC VILLAGE, AK 99722
 (907) 587-5320 Trimble Gilbert, Chief
 Website: www.tananachiefs.org/tribes
Tribe: Gwitch'in Athapascan. *Elected officials*: Sarah James, Rose Lee,
Louie John, Steve Lee, Jim Christian. Fairbanks Agency.

ALASKA LEGAL SERVICES CORPORATION
P.O. Box 351 • BARROW, AK 99723
 (907) 855-8998 Fax 852-6356
 E-mail: barrow@alsc-law.org

ARCTIC SLOPE NATIVE ASSOCIATION
P.O. Box 1232 • BARROW, AK 99723
 (907) 852-2762 Fax 852-2763
 Website: www.arcticslope.org; Marie Carroll, Contact
Native nonprofit association servicing the Arctic Slope Inupiat. *Activities*:
Crafting/Hobby; Community Clubs; family & kids' activities; School activities;
scientific/academic interests; sporting activities; tourist/cultural activities.

ARCTIC SLOPE REGIONAL CORPORATION
P.O. Box 129 • BARROW, AK 99723
 (907) 852-8633 Fax 852-5733; Website: www.asrc.com
 Rex A. Rock, Sr. (Inupiat), President & CEO
 Crawford Ahkivgak Patkotak (Inupiat), Chairperson
Native for-profit regional corporation representing the business interests of the
Arctic Slope Inupiat. Corporate headquarters in Barrow with administrative &
subsidiary offices located in Anchorage and throughout the world. *Purpose*: To
preserve the Inupiat culture and traditions.

NORTH SLOPE BOROUGH HEALTH CORP.
P.O. Box 69 • BARROW, AK 99723
 (907) 852-0366 Fax -852-0389; Doreen Leavitt, Director
 Website: www.co.north-slope.org
 E-mail: doreen.leavitt@north-slope.org
Health Clinic.

ASSOCIATION OF VILLAGE COUNCIL PRESIDENTS
P.O. Box 219 • BETHEL, AK 99559
 (800) 478-3521; (907) 543-7300 Fax 543-3596
 Website: www.avcp.org; Myron P. Naneng, Sr., President
 Michael Hoffman, Vice President
Purpose: To provide human development, social services, and other culturally
relevant programs for the people; to promote self-determination protection &
enhancement of our culture & traditions through a working partnership with
member villages of the Yukon-Kuskokwim Delta. *Activities*: Childcare Development services; economic development; education, employment & training;
family justice; housing improvement; social services; tribal operations; financial
aid-higher education scholarships; operates Yup'ik Cultural Center & Museum;
Head Start Program. Established 1964.

ALASKA LEGAL SERVICES CORPORATION
P.O. Box 248 • BETHEL, AK 99559
 (800) 478-2230; (907) 543-2237 Fax 543-5537
 E-mail: bethel@alsc-law.org

YUKON-KUSKOKWIM HEALTH CORPORATION
P.O. Box 528 • BETHEL, AK 99559
 (907) 543-6000 Fax 543-6006
 Website: www.ykhc.org; E-mail: info@ykhc.org
 Gene Peltola, President & CEO; Ray Alstrom, Chairperson

CHITINA NATIVE CORPORATION
P.O. Box 3 • CHITINA, AK 99566
 (907) 823-2223 Fax 823-2202
 Website: www.chitinanative.com
 E-mail: chitina_native@cvinternet.net
 Anne Thomas (Anchorage), President
Native nonprofit association. Maintains tribal & community health center.
Tsedi Na (Chitina) Foundation www.tsedinafounation@gmail.com)
Arleen Lenard, President; focusing on cultural preservation & education.
Established 1973.

COPPER RIVER NATIVE ASSOCIATION
Drawer H • COPPER CENTER, AK 99573
 (907) 822-5241 Fax 822-8801; Website: www.crnative.org
 Lorraine Jackson, Board President
 Deborah Jones, Tribal & Community Services Director, CEO
 Gary Hay, Special Projects Director
Native nonprofit association. Maintains health clinic.

ALASKA LEGAL SERVICES CORPORATION
P.O. Box 176 • DILLINGHAM, AK 99576
 (907) 842-1452 Fax 842-1430; E-mail: dillingham@alsc-law.org

BRISTOL BAY AREA HEALTH CORPORATION
P.O. Box 130 • DILLINGHAM, AK 99576
 (800) 478-5201; (907) 842-5201 Fax 842-9354
 Website: www.bbahc.org; Robert J. Clark, President & CEO
Health clinic affiliated with Bristol Bay Native Association.
Established 1973.

BRISTOL BAY NATIVE ASSOCIATION
P.O. Box 310 • DILLINGHAM, AK 99576
 (907) 842-5257 Fax 842-5932; Website: www.bbna.com
 Ralph Andersen, President & CEO; E-mail: randersen@bbna.com
 DeeDee Bennis, Chief Administrative Officer; E-mail: dbennis@bbna.com
Regional native non-profit association of 31 Tribes, providing a variety of
educational, social, economic & related services to the Native people of the
region. Head Start Program.

ALASKA LEGAL SERVICES CORPORATION
1648 Cushman, Suite 300 • FAIRBANKS, AK 99701
 (907) 452-5181 Fax 456-6359; E-mail: fairbanks@alsc-law.org

ALASKA NATIVE KNOWLEDGE NETWORK
University of Alaska, P.O. Box 756730 • FAIRBANKS, AK 99775
 (907) 474-1902 Fax 474-1957; Website: www.ankn.uaf.edu
Purpose: To serve as a resource for compiling & exchanging information
related to Alaska Native knowledge systems and ways of knowing; to assist
Native people, government agencies, educators and the general public in
gaining access to the knowledge base that Alaska Natives have acquired
through cumulative experience over millennia.

ALASKA NATIVE LANGUAGE CENTER
P.O. Box 757680 • FAIRBANKS, AK 99775
 (907) 474-7874 Fax 474-6586
 Website: www.uaf.edu/anlc; E-mail: uaf-aknativelang@alaska.edu
 Lawrence Kaplan, Professor & Director; E-mail: ldkaplan@alaska.edu
 Gary Holton, Director of the Alaska Native Language Archive
Purpose: To document the languages of Indians and Eskimos. *Staff*: Oscar
Alexie, Sophie Alexie, Anna Berg, Ronald H. Browr, Sr., Walkie Charles, Perry
Gilmore, Gary Holton, Alex Jaker, James Kari, Jeff Leer, Patrick E. Marlow,
John Ritter, Hishinlai "Kathy" Sikorski, Siri Tuttle, Steve Jacobson.

CULTURAL HERITAGE & EDUCATION INSTITUTE
P.O. Box 73030 • FAIRBANKS, AK 99707
 (907) 451-0923 Fax 451-0910; Website: www.ankn.uaf.edu/chei
 Robert Charlie, Executive Director
Description: A Native non-profit organization preserving Athabascan culture,
and promoting healthy lifestyle and choices. *Products*: Traditional Athabascan
arts & crafts.

DOYON LIMITED
1 Doyon Place, Suite 300 • FAIRBANKS, AK 99701
 (888) 478-4755; (907) 459-2000 Fax 459-2060
 Website: www.doyon.com; E-mail: info@doyon.com
 Aaron M. Schutt, President & CEO; Orie G. Williams, Chair
Anchorage Office: 11500 C St., Suite 250 • Anchorage, AK 99515
 (907) 563-5530 Fax 375-4205
Native for-profit regional corporation.

FAIRBANKS NATIVE ASSOCIATION
605 Hughes Ave., Suite 100 • FAIRBANKS, AK 99701
 (907) 452-1648 Fax 456-4148
 Website: www.fairbanksnative.org; E-mail: info@fairbanksnative.org
 Steve Ginnis, Executive Director; Audrey Jones (Athabascan), President
Purpose: To provide professional, quality human services to membership and
Fairbanks community; to preserve Native culture and improve the quality of life
for the community. *Programs*: Elders program; Public Assistance & Family
Counseling; Employment, Education (small scholarships), Treatment Center
for Alcohol and Drug Abuse; Substance Abuse Counselor Training; Head Start
Program. *Publication*: Quarterly newsletter. Library. Established 1960.

INDIGENOUS LEADERSHIP INSTITUTE
P.O. Box 83467 • FAIRBANKS, AK 99708
 (907) 374-5950; Website: www.indigenousleadership.org
Enei Begaye Peter (Dine'/Tohono O'odham), Executive Director
Board members: Shawna Larson, Cathy Tagnak Rexford, Evon Peter
Description: A non-profit leadership training & development organization based in Alaska & specializing in transformative culturally based programs that incorporate culture, history, healing, spirituality, visioning, and social change.
Program: Arctic Institute for Indigenous Leadership.

INSTITUTE OF ALASKA NATIVE ARTS
455 3rd Ave., P.O. Box 70769 • FAIRBANKS, AK 99707
(907) 456-7491 Fax 451-7268
 Ron Manook, President; Susheila Khera, Executive Director
 Katherine Hunt, Program Director
Purpose: "To foster the continuation of Alaska Native traditions into contemporary expressions of the highest quality." *Activities*: Programs & services to enhance the artistic, professional & economic status of Alaska Native artists & to heighten awareness of Alaska Native aesthetics & traditions through exhibitions, workshops, scholarships, publications & technical assistance. Operates Information Center consisting of an artists' registry of hard copy files & slides; photographic files; and resource library with over 600 titles and audio & videotapes. Offers scholarships for academic study. *Publications*: Journal of Alaska Native Arts, quarterly; exhibit catalogs & resource materials on Alaska Native arts. Library. Established 1976.

TANANA CHIEFS CONFERENCE, INC.
122 First Ave. #600 • FAIRBANKS, AK 99701
 (800) 478-6822 in AK; (800) 770-8251
 (907) 452-8251 Fax 459-3950; Website: www.tananachiefs.com
 Victor Joseph, President/Chairman
Description: Regional nonprofit corporation. Maintains a health clinic. Head Start Program.

COUNCIL OF ATHABASCAN TRIBAL GOVERNMENTS
P.O. Box 33 • FORT YUKON, AK 99740
 (800) 665-2981; (907) 662-2587 Fax 662-3333
 Website: www.catg.org; Rhonda Pitka (Beaver), Chairperson
 Nancy James (Gwich'yaa Zhee), Vice Chairperson
 Jackie Ballum (Birch Creek), Secretary
Provides health services, education opportunities & natural resource management to the member tribes. Established 1985.

MOUNT SANFORD TRIBAL CONSORTIUM
P.O. Box 357 • GAKONA, AK 99586
 (907) 822-5399 Fax 822-5810; Website: www.mstc.org
 Evelyn Beeter, President; George Drinkwater, Health Director
Description: Consortium of two federally recognized tribal councils of Chistochina & Mentasta Lake. *Programs*: Community Healthcare, Diabetes, Clinics, Educational, Eldercare & Childcare. Established 1992.

AHTNA HERITAGE FOUNDATION
P.O. Box 213 • GLENNALLEN, AK 99588
 (907) 822-5778 Fax 822-5338
 Website: www.ahtnaheritagefoundation.com
 Liana Charley-John (Naltsiine), Executive Director
 Dorothy Shinn (Tazlina), Chairperson
 Charlene Nollner (Gakona), Vice Chairperson
 Eileen Ewan (Gulkana), Secretary/Treasurer
A non-profit corporation focused on education. Provides opportunities for shareholders and others to learn about the Ahtna people through cultural programs and our cultural center – C'ek'aedi Hwnax, which means "Legacy House" in the Ahtna language. *Resources*: Children's Language Project; Heritage Dancers; Culture Camps. Established 1986.

AHTNA, INC.
P.O. Box 649 • GLENNALLEN, AK 99588
 (907) 822-3476 Fax 822-3495
 Website: www.ahnta-inc.com; Nicolas Jackson, Chair
 Michelle Anderson, President; E-mail: manderson@ahtna.net
 Kathryn Martin, Sr. V.P.; E-mail: kmartin@ahtna-inc.com
A Native for profit regional corporation. *Activities*: Construction, real estate; student loans & scholarships; & loans to shareholders for business ventures. *Publications*: Annual reports; Shareholder's Handbook; books. Library.

ASSOCIATION OF ALASKA HOUSING AUTHORITIES
Copper River Basin Regional Housing Authority
P.O. Box 89 • GLENNALLEN, AK 99588
 (907) 822-3633 Fax 822-3662; Website: www.aahaak.org
 Teri Nutter, President; Guy Adams, Vice President
 Olen Harris, Secretary-Treasurer

ALASKA LEGAL SERVICES CORPORATION
419 6th Street, Suite 322 • JUNEAU, AK 99801
 (907) 586-6425 Fax 586-2449; E-mail: juneau@alsc-law.org

ALASKA STATE INDIAN EDUCATION OFFICE
801 W. 10th St., Suite 200, P.O. Box 110500 • JUNEAU, AK 99801
 (907) 465-2888 Fax 465-2989; Website: www.eed.state.ak.us
 Patricia Adkisson, Coordinator

ALASKA STATE OFFICE OF THE GOVERNOR
Indian Affairs Commission
P.O. Box 110001 • JUNEAU, AK 99811
 (907) 465-3500 FAX 465-3532

CENTRAL COUNCIL OF THE TLINGIT & HAIDA INDIAN TRIBES OF AK
320 W. Willoughby Ave. #300 • JUNEAU, AK 99801
 (800) 344-1432; (907) 586-1432 Fax 586-8970; Website: www.ccthita.org
 Richard J. Peterson, President; Edward K. Thomas, President Emeritus
 Rob Sanderson, Jr., 1st VP; Will Micklin, 2nd VP
 Ralph Wolfe, 3rd VP; Jacqueline L. Pata, 4th VP
 Marvin L. Adams, 5th VP; Edward (Sam) K. Thomas, Jr., 6th VP
 Miciana Hutcherson, Emerging Leader
 Corrine M. Garza, Chief Operating Officer – Tribal Operations
Description: A tribal government representing more than 28,000 Tlingit & Haida Indians worldwide. Under jurisdiction of the Southeast Agency of the Bureau of Indian Affairs.

SEALASKA CORPORATION
One Sealaska Plaza #400 • JUNEAU, AK 99801
 (907) 586-1512 Fax 586-2304; Website: www.sealaska.com
 Albert Kookesh, Board Chair; Rosita Worl, Vice Chair
 Chris E. McNeil, Jr., President & CEO; Rick Harris, Executive V.P.
 Doug Morris, Vice President & Chief Financial Officer
 Jaeleen Araujo, Vice President & General Council
 Todd Antioquia, Director of Corporate Communications
Description: A regional Native for-profit corporation, established by Congress under the Alaska Native Claims Settlement Act of 1971. *Activities*: Sealaska Timber Corp.; Forest Products Co.; Sealaska Heritage Institute; Sealaska Heritage Foundation. *Publications*: Sealaska Shareholder, bimonthly tabloid newspaper, also avail-able on the Internet; annual reports; Sealaska Heritage Foundation publishes books & videos on cultural subjects. Seattle Office: 13810 SE Eastgate Way, Suite 420, Bellevue, WA 98005 (425) 283-0600 Fax 283-0650.

SEALASKA HERITAGE INSTITUTE
105 S. Seward St., Suite 201 • JUNEAU, AK 99801
 (907) 463-4844 Fax 586-9293; E-mail: heritage@sealaska.com
 Website: www.alaskanativeartists.com
 Rosita Worl (Tlingit), President; E-mail: rosita.worl@sealaska.com
 Lee Kadinger, Chief of Operations; E-mail: lee.kadinger@sealaska.com
 Jackie Kookesh, Education Director; E-mail: Jackie.kookesh@sealaska.com
 Chuck Smythe, History & Culture Director
  E-mail: chuck.smythe@sealaska.com
Description: To perpetuate and enhance the arts & culture of the Tlingit, Haida, & Tsimshian people of Southeast Alaska through programs in language & cultural studies, traditional celebrations, scholarship-heritage studies, tribal archives, & Naa Kahidi theatre. *Publication*: Naa Kaani, a quarterly newsletter. Established 1981.

SOUTHEAST ALASKA REGIONAL HEALTH CONSORTIUM (SEARHC)
3100 Channel Dr., Suite 300 • JUNEAU, AK 99801
 (907) 463-4000 Fax 463-4075; Website: www.searhc.org
 Charles Clement (Tsimshian/Athabascan), President & CEO
 Dan Neumeister, Chief Operating Officer
 Leatha Merculieff (Aleut), VP of Executive Administration
 Michael Douglas, JD, VP, Chief Legal Officer
 Noble E. Anderson, MD, Medical Director
 Kimberley Strong (Klukwan), Board Chairperson
 Frederick Olsen, Jr. (Kasaan), Vice Chairperson
Description: A non-profit tribal health consortium of 18 Native communities which serves the health interests of the Tlingit, Haida, Tsimishian, and other Native people of Southeast Alaska. Established 1975.

ALASKA LEGAL SERVICES CORPORATION
P.O Box 2463, 100 Trading Bay Dr. Unit 5 • KENAI, AK 99611
 (907) 395-0352 Fax 395-0938; E-mail: kenai@alsc-law.org

ALASKA LEGAL SERVICES CORPORATION
306 Main Street #218 • KETCHIKAN, AK 99901
 (907) 228-9313 Fax 228-1915; E-mail: ketchikan@alsc-law.org

KETCHIKAN INDIAN CORPORATION
2960 Tongass Ave. • KETCHIKAN, AK 99901
  (907) 225-5158; Website: www.kictribe.org
A nonprofit Indian-controlled corporation. Tribal health clinic.

KLAWOCK COOPERATIVE ASSOCIATION
310 Bayview Blvd., P.O. Box 430 • KLAWOCK, AK 99925
  (907) 755-2265 Fax 755-8800
  Archie W. Demmert, III, President; Patricia Smith-Cottle, Vice President
Offers support & services to the Klawock community, Prince of Wales Island
and the State.

AFOGNAK NATIVE CORPORATION & ALUTIIQ, LLC
300 Alimaq Dr. • KODIAK, AK 99615
  (907) 486-6014; (800) 770-6014
  Website: www.afognak.com
  Dusty Kaser, President & CEO
Established 1971.

KODIAK AREA NATIVE ASSOCIATION (KANA)
3449 E. Rezanof Dr. • KODIAK, AK 99615
  (800) 478-5721; (907) 486-9800 Fax 486-9898
  Website: www.kanaweb.org; Andy Teuber, President & CEO
  E-mail: andy.teuber@kodiakhealthcare.org
  Margie Bezona, Sr. VP of Administration
  E-mail: Margie.bezona@kodiakhealthcare.org
  Tammy Hansen, VP of Health Services
  E-mail: tammy.hansen@kodiakhealthcare.org
  Loretta Nelson (Afognak), Chairperson
  Alfred B. Cratty, Jr. (Old Harbor), Vice Chairperson
  Arnold Kewan (Port Lions), Secretary; Jill Boskofsky (Ouzinkie), Treasurer
Description: A native non-profit association promoting pride on the part of the
Natives of Alaska in their heritage & traditions; promotes the physical,
economic, & social wellbeing of the natives of Alaska. *Activities*: Over 40
programs administered under the Department of Health, Education & Family
Services; community & economic development; health center. *Facilities*:
Village Clinics: Akhiok, Karluk, Larsen Bay, Old Harbor, Ouzinkie, Port Lions.
Scholarships: Higher education & adult vocational training scholarships funded
by the Bureau of Indian Affairs; education & social work scholarships funded
by the Department of Health & Human Services; Skip Eaton Scholar-ship, an
independent local award. *Publication*: KANA Quarterly Newsletter. Library.

KONIAG, INC.
194 Alimaq Dr. • KODIAK, AK 99615
  (800) 658-3818; (907) 486-2530 Fax 486-3325
  Website: www.koniag.com; E-mail: news@koniag.com
  Elizabeth Perry, CEO; E-mail: eperry@koniag.com
  Tom Panamaroff (Alutiiq), President (561-2668)
  E-mail: tpanamaroff@koniag.com
  Jessica Graham, Executive VP & General Counsel
  E-mail: jgraham@koniag.com
  Ron Unger (Alutiiq), Board Chairperson
  E-mail: runger@koniag.com
Anchorage Office: 4300 B St., Suite 407 • Anchorage, AK 99503
  (907) 561-2668 Fax 562-5258
Native for-profit regional corporation. *Activities*: Sponsors a variety of economic
activities for the benefit of its constituency. *Publications*: Newsletters; annual
reports.

ALASKA LEGAL SERVICES CORPORATION
P.O. Box 526 • KOTZEBUE, AK 99752
  (907) 442-3500 Fax 442-4111
  E-mail: kotzebue@alsc-law.org

MANIILAQ CORPORATION
733 2ⁿᵈ Ave., P.O. Box 256 • KOTZEBUE, AK 99752
  (800) 478-3312; (907) 442-3321 Fax 442-2381
  Website: www.maniilaq.org
  Tim Schuerch, President/CEO; Charlie Nelson, Vice President,
   Tribal Government Services Administrator
  Tom Bolen, Capital Projects Director
  Paul Hansen, Health Services Administrator
  Kelli Shroyer, Public Communications Manager
  E-mail: media@maniilaq.org
Description: A native non-profit corporation serving 12 Alaskan Eskimo villages
ranging from 100 to 3,000 in population. *Purpose*: Committed to individual
responsibility for health & quality care through tribal self-governance. *Activities*:
Provide health, tribal & social services, vocational training in the Northwest
Arctic Borough region of Alaska. *Resources*: Health Center; scholarships.
Established 1966.

NANA REGIONAL CORPORATION
NANA DEVELOPMENT CORPORATION
P.O. Box 49 • KOTZEBUE, AK 99752
  (800) 478-3301; (907) 442-3301 Fax 442-4161
  Website: www.nana.com; E-mail: news@nana.com
  Wayne Westlake (Inupiat), President/CEO
  Linda Lee (Shungnak), Board Chairperson
  Donald G. Sheldon (Noorvik), Vice Chairperson
Description: A native for profit regional corporation. *Purpose*: To improve the
quality of life for its shareholders, the Inupiat of Northwest Alaska. Established
1971.

ALASKA LEGAL SERVICES CORPORATION
P.O. Box 1429 • NOME, AK 99762
  (907) 443-2230 Fax 443-2239; E-mail: nome@alsc-law.org

BERING STRAITS NATIVE CORPORATION
110 Front St., Suite 300, P.O. Box 1008 • NOME, AK 99762
  (907) 443-5252 Fax 443-2985
  Website: www.beringstraits.com; E-mail: info@beringstraits.com
  Gail R. Schubert, President & CEO; Richard Foster, Executive VP
  Krystal Nelson, COO; Jerald Brown, VP of Nome Operations
  Henry Ivanoff, Board Chairperson; Lee Ryan, Vice Chairperson
Anchorage Office: 4600 DeBarr Rd., Suite 200 • Anchorage, AK 99508
  (907) 563-3788 Fax 563-2742
Description: A Native non-profit regional corporation dedicated to enhancing
educational & cultural preservation opportunities for Bering Straits Native
Corporation shareholders, their descendants, and the people of the Bering
Straits region. *Activities*: Sponsors a variety of economic & human service
activities including an arts & crafts cooperative. *Publication*: Agluktuk
Newsletter. Established 1972.

KAWERAK, INC.
500 Seppala Dr., P.O. Box 948 • NOME, AK 99762
  (907) 443-5231 Fax 443-4452
  Website: www.kawerak.org; E-mail: contact@kawerak.org
  Loretta Bullard, President; Eileen Norbert, Vice President
Description: A Native non-profit association organized to promote the social &
economic welfare of residents in 20 villages in the Bering Straits Region;
provides services to three culturally distinct groups of Eskimo people (Inupiaq,
Yup'ik & Siberian Yupik). *Activities*: Eskimo Heritage Program; Education,
Employment & Training; Community services; Human & Family Services
Natural Resources. *Publication*: Kawerak Newsletter. Established 1973.

NORTON SOUND HEALTH CORPORATION
1000 Greg Kruschek Ave., P.O. Box 966 • NOME, AK 99762
  (888) 559-3311; (907) 443-3311 Fax 443-2113
  Website: www.nortonsoundhealth.org
Description: A health care organization formed to improve the mental &
physical health of the people of the region to the highest possible levels
through education, preventive programs & high quality health care; and assist
in creating a healthy & economically positive environment. *Publication*:
Newsletter. Medical Library. Established 1970.

SOUTHEAST ALASKA INDIAN CULTURAL CENTER, INC.
106 Metlakatla St., Suite C • SITKA, AK 99835
  (907) 747-8061 (office) 747-8122 (studio)
  (907) 747-8189 (Fax studio & office)
  Gail Johansen Peterson, Executive Director
Purpose: To display Native arts produced in the Center over the past 20 years,
including woodcarving, silverwork, costumes, and robes. *Activities*: Audiovisual
programs; provides demonstrations of traditional native arts such as woodcarving, costume design, & metalworking that are representative of the Tlingit
people and Southeast Alaska. Established in 1969.

ARIZONA

DINEH COOPERATIVES, INC.
P.O. Box 569 • CHINLE, AZ 86503
  (928) 674-3411; Website: www.dineh.org; E-mail: info@dineh.org
The Navaho Nation's Community Development Corporation. *Purpose*: To
establish profit-making businesses and creates jobs to improve the quality of
life in the Navajo Nation.

BLACK MESA WATER COALITION
P.O. Box 613 • FLAGSTAFF, AZ 86002
  (928) 213-5909 Fax 213-5905
  E-mail: blackmesawc@gmail.com
  Website: www.blackmesawatercoalition.org
  Jihan Gearon (Dine'), Executive Director

Roberto Nutlouis (Dine'), Restorative Economy Program Coordinator
Wahleah Johns (Dine'), Black Mesa Solar Project Manager
Tony Skrelunas (Dine'), Board Chairperson
Enei Begaye (Dine'), Board Vice Chairperson
Mission: To preserve & protect Mother Earth & the integrity of Indigenous Peoples' cultures, with the vision of building sustainable & healthy communities. Established 2001.

FLAGSTAFF MISSION TO THE NAVAJOS
6 W. Cherry Ave. • FLAGSTAFF, AZ 86001
(928) 774-2802 Fax 773-9465; Website: www.chief.org
Daniel Taggart, Director; Beth Taggart, Storehouse Coordinator
Purpose: To serve Navajos living in its area. Serves as headquarters for the Mission's seven Navajo churches on the Navajo Reservation.

KEYA EARTH CORPORATION
P.O. Box 2092 • FLAGSTAFF, AZ 86003
Website: www.keyaearth.com
Gordon Isaac, President; E-mail: g.isaac.az@gmail.com
Description: A sustainable development & training firm focused on meeting the needs of large & small cultural groups. *Training Areas*: Planning & Strategic Facilitation Seminar; Master Planned Communities & Development Seminar; Education & Training Seminars & Programs.

NATIVE AMERICANS FOR COMMUNITY ACTION (NACA)
2717 N. Steves Blvd., Suite 11 • FLAGSTAFF, AZ 86004
(928) 526-2968 Fax 526-0708; Website: www.nacainc.org
Dr. Curtis Randolph, Interim CEO & Clinical Director of Behavioral Health
Gerald Clark, Chief Financial Officer
Dr. L. George Hershey, DO, Medical Director/Physician
Cheryl Blie, Director of Community Development
Joshua Butler, Board President; Deeda Williams, Vice President
Purpose: A community-based organization to meet the needs of Native Americans residing off reservation in Flagstaff. *Programs*: Family health center; substance abuse & child/family counseling; training assistance, employment; adult education; social services; youth & elders programs; economic development. *Publication*: Online magazine. Established 1971.

INDIAN CHILDREN'S PROGRAM (ICP)
In Arizona: Northern Arizona University, Institute for Human Development
P.O. Box 5630 • FLAGSTAFF, AZ 86011
(928) 523-8026 Fax 523-4909; Website: www.icpservices.org
In New Mexico: University of New Mexico Center for Development & Disability, Albuquerque, NM 87131; (866) 427-8661; (505) 272-8998
Description: A consortium of three universities – Northern Arizona University, Utah State University, and University of New Mexico. The ICP staff, located in Flagstaff at NAU and Albuquerque at UNM, are teams of specialists including: speech-language pathologists, physical therapists, developmental specialists, and psychologists. The program serves children who reside in the Navajo or Hopi Nations or the Pueblos in New Mexico. *Purpose*: To perform diagnostic services for children with special needs; to assist in health & education problems for Native American children in Arizona, Utah & New Mexico. *Activities*: Provides assessments in occupational, physical therapy, speech & language, psychological & vocational, & training for parents & agencies. Library. Established 1991.

NAVAJO NATION HEALTH FOUNDATION
Sage Memorial Hospital, P.O. Box 457 • GANADO, AZ 86505
(928) 755-4500 Fax 755-4659; Website: www.sagememorial.com
E-mail: info@sagememorial.com; Richie Nez, President
Purpose: To provide health services to members of the Navajo Nation about 200,000 members.

THE HOPI FOUNDATION
P.O. Box 301 • KYKOTSMOVI, AZ 86039
(928) 734-2380 Fax 734-9520
Website: www.hopifoundation.org; E-mail: info@hopifoundation.org
Monica Nuvamsa (Hopi), Executive Director
Marissa Nuvvayestewa (Hopi), Capacity Building Director
Laurel Sekakuku (Hopi), Program Director
Tiffany Bahnimptewa (Hopi), Natwani Coalition Program Manager
Kevin Nash, Hopi Substance Abuse Prevention Center Program Manager
Beatrice Norton (Hopi), Board Chairperson
Mission: "Our basic mission is to 'help people help themselves,' by promoting self sufficiency, proactive community participation in our own destiny, self reliance & local self determination." *Programs & Projects*: Hopi Leadership Program; Hopi Language Program; Center for Prevention & Resolution of Violence; Hopi Substance Abuse Prevention Program; KUYI Hopi Radio; Natwani Coalition; Owl & Pantha Project; Three Mesas Productions. *Publications*: Newsletters & updates.

AHCCCS AMERICAN INDIAN HEALTH PROGRAM
801 E. Jefferson, MD 4100 • PHOENIX, AZ 85034
(602) 417-4610 Fax 256-6536; Website: www.azahcccs.gov/tribal/
Bonnie Talakte, Tribal Relations Liaison
E-mail: bonnie.talakte@azahcccs.gov
Purpose: To research & analyze federal and state laws which may impact health care services for Native Americans; to provide technical assistance and training to improve access to health services.

ARIZONA COMMISSION OF INDIAN AFFAIRS (ACIA)
Office of Tribal Relations
1700 W. Washington St. #430 • PHOENIX, AZ 85007
(602) 542-4426 Fax 542-4428
Website: www.indianaffairs.state.az.us;
E-mail: gotrinfo@az.gov; E-mail: iainfo@az.gov
Kristine (Fire Thunder) Thomas, Executive Director
E-mail: kfirethunder@az.gov
Nathan Pryor (Dine'-Navajo)), Chairperson
Derreck Wheeler (White Mountain Apache), Vice Chairperson
Purpose: To improve state/tribal relationships in Arizona; to identify state and/or Indian concerns, to research, analyze & evaluate information gathered & to disseminate that information. *Activities*: Commission's staff attends Indian-related meetings, confers with state, federal, local & tribal government officials. *Publication*: "Tribal State Resource Directory," directs Indians to the right organizations for their specific needs.

ARIZONA DEPARTMENT OF COMMERCE TRIBAL LIAISON
1700 W. Washington St., Rm. 220 • PHOENIX, AZ 85007
(520) 638-6582 Fax 628-6694; Rafael Tapia, Regional Manager

ARIZONA INDIAN GAMING ASSOCIATION (AIGA)
521 S. 48th St., Suite 107 • TEMPE, AZ 85281
(480) 284-4034 Fax 284-4082; Website: www.azindiangaming.org
E-mail: info@azindiangaming.org
Valerie Spicer, Executive Director; Judy Ferreira, Deputy Director
Valerie Sanchez, Industry Relations Specialist
Louis J. Manuel, Jr. (Ak-Chin), Board Chairperson
Paul Russell (Yavapai), Vice Chairperson
Jerome Kasey III (White Mountain Apache), Secretary
Verlon M. Jose (Tohono O'odham), Treasurer

ARIZONA STATE DEPARTMENT OF EDUCATION
Office of Indian Education, 1535 W. Jefferson • PHOENIX, AZ 85007
(602) 542-5235 Fax 542-3100; Website: www.azed.gov/indian-education
Nadine Groenig, Director of Indian Education
E-mail: nadine.groenig@azed.gov
Superintendent of Public Instruction Diane Douglas & the Arizona Department of Education are committed to providing the highest quality education to Arizona's 60,000 American Indian students in the Arizona public/charter school system. The ADE Indian Education office is in the Special Projects Division in the Arizona Department of Education. Our mission is to promote leadership, education & training to schools, agencies & governments that are responsible for the quality of education of Arizona's American Indian children. The Indian Education program administers federal grants, including the Johnson-O'Malley Program, to meet the educational and cultural needs of participating LEAs and implements A.R.S. 15-244, Indian Education Act. Outreach is provided to all of Arizona's local educational agencies on reservations & urban areas with high populations of American Indian students. Technical assistance is provided in collaboration with all units at ADE that interface with these LEAs. Conferences and training, as well as parental involvement activities, are also provided on-site and at ADE. The Director of Indian Education serves as a liaison between the tribal education departments and the ADE, works via partnerships with outside agencies to provide resources for Native American students, and facilitates the Superintendent's initiatives to benefit the academic achievement and cultural awareness of Arizona's indigenous youth.

ARIZONA STATE DEPT. OF HEALTH SEVICES
Native American Liaison, Office of the Director
150 N. 18th Ave., Suite 595 • PHOENIX, AZ 85007
(602) 364-1041 Fax 542-1062; Website: www.azdhs.gov
Michael Allison (Dine'), ADHS Native American Liaison
The purpose of the Native American Liaison position is to serve as an advocate, resource, & communication link between the Department & Arizona's Native American health care community comprised of twenty-one tribal health offices, three Urban Indian Health Programs, three Indian Health Service Area Offices, Inter Tribal Council of Arizona, Inc., and other agencies and entities providing direct or indirect public health services to Arizona's Native American communities. Additionally, the Native American Liaison serves as an internal resource to Department staff on Native American issues, and representing the Department on Native American boards & commissions.

ARIZONA STATE DEPARTMENT OF HOUSING
Tribal Outreach Division
1700 W. Washington St., Rm. 210 • PHOENIX, AZ 85007
(602) 771-1085 Fax 542-1062; Karia Lee Basta, Tribal Liaison
E-mail: karia.basta@azhousing.gov

BLUE STONE STRATEGY GROUP
2200 N. Central Ave. #203 • PHOENIX, AZ 85004
(602) 354-3654 Fax 354-3972
Website: www.bluestonestrategy.com
Jamie L. Fullmer (Yavapai-Apache), Chairperson/CEO
John Mooers, President; Gary Hayes, Senior Tribal Advisor
Alvin H. Warren, (Santa Clara Pueblo), Partner, Exec. Vice President
California Office: 18851 Bardeen Ave. #240, Irvine, CA 92612
(949) 476-8828 Fax 261-8828
Senior Strategists: Janeen Goodman, Anthony Farese, Kevin Fitzgibbons,
John O'Neill
Tribal Advisors: W. Ron Allen (Jamestown S'Klallam), Samuel N. Penney (Nez
Perce), Kim Secakuku (Hopi), Daniel J. Tucker (Sycuan Kumeyaay Diegueno)
Purpose: To promote economic development & sustainability of Tribal Nations.
Focuses on providing services to strengthen Tribes & Tribal leadership through
sound governance & strategic planning for economic growth & community
development; to provide business & strategy advisory services in "Indian
Country" to Tribal leadership, Tribal enterprises, and corporate entities working
with Tribes. The company's primary focus is on sound analysis and strategic
planning for protecting Tribal sovereignty, economic growth & stability.
Activities: Southwest Native American Economic Development Conference.
California Office: Irvine, CA.

INTER-TRIBAL COUNCIL OF ARIZONA, INC
2214 N. Central Ave. Suite 100 • PHOENIX, AZ 85004
(602) 258-4822 Fax 258-4825
Website: www.itcaonline.com; E-mail: info@itcaonline.com
Maria Dadgar, Executive Director
Thomas Beauty (Yavapai-Apache), Board President (928) 567-3649
Kasey Velasquez (White Mountain Apache), 1st Vice President
Herman Honanie (Hopi), 2nd Vice President
Terry Rambler (San Carlos Apache), Secretary/Treasurer
Purpose: To provide the 20 member tribes with the means for action on
matters which affect them collectively & individually, to promote tribal
sovereignty & to strengthen tribal governments. *Programs*: Operates more
than 20 projects providing on-going technical assistance & training to tribal
governments; health clinic, e.g. Community Development, Emergency
Preparedness & Response, Environmental Quality, Health, Human Services,
Epidemiology & Research, Senior Services, Nutrition. *Member tribes*: Ak Chin
Indian Community, Cocopah Tribe, Colorado River Indian Tribes, Fort
McDowell Yavapai Nation, Fort Mojave Tribe, Gila River Indian Community,
Havasupai Tribe, Hopi Tribe, Hualapai Tribe, Kaibab-Paiute Tribe, Pascua
Yaqui Tribe, Quechan Tribe, Salt River Pima-Maricopa Indian Community, San
Carlos Apache Tribe, San Juan Southern Paiute, Tohono O'odham Nation,
Tonto Apache Tribe, White Mountain Apache Tribe, Yavapai Apache Nation, &
Yavapai-Prescott Indian Tribe. *Publication*: Annual Report. Established 1952.

NATIVE AMEICAN BAR ASSOCIATION OF ARIZONA
P.O. Box 1732 • PHOENIX, AZ 85001
Website: www.naba-az.com; E-mail info@naba-az.com
Theresa Rosier (Fort McDowell Yavapai), President (2016-17)
Purpose: To promote the development of Indian attorneys while advancing &
improving the practice of Indian law in Arizona. *Activities*: Annual Seven
Generations Awards Dinner & Ceremony; Annual Golf Tournament;
educational scholarships to Native law students pursuing degrees at one of the
three law schools in Arizona.

NATIVE AMERICAN CONNECTIONS (NAC)
4520 N. Central Ave. #600 • PHOENIX, AZ 85012
(602) 254-3247 Fax 256-7356
Website: www.nativeconnections.org
Diana Yazzie Devine (Navajo-Dine'), President & CEO
E-mail: d.devine@nativeconnections.org
Roxann Gallagher (Western Shoshone), Chairperson
Fonda Walters (Dine'-Navajo), Vice Chairperson
Purpose: To improve the lives of individuals & families through Native
American culturally appropriate behavioral health, affordable housing, and
community development services. Provides behavioral health services,
affordable housing, & community-based economic development opportunities.
NAC serves all populations with a targeted mission to serve Native Americans
living both in the Phoenix urban areas and from tribal communities. Offers
innovative research-based behavioral health counseling & substance abuse
treatment that is integrated with native cultural & traditional healing practices.
Begun 1972.

PHOENIX INDIAN CENTER, INC.
4520 N. Central Ave., Suite 250 • PHOENIX, AZ 85012
(602) 264-6768 Fax 274-7486
Website: www.phxindcenter.org; E-mail: info@phxindcenter.org
Patricia Hibbeler (Salish & Kootenai), Chief Executive Officer
E-mail: phibbeler@phxindcenter.org
Anthony Kahn (Navajo-Dine'), Board President
Satellite Offices: Flagstaff (928) 526-2968; Tucson (520) 882-8777
Prescott Field Location: 1519 W. Gurley St., Suite 6, Prescott, AZ 86305 (928)
759-2875. *Purpose*: To promote health, the social & economic self-sufficiency
of the American Indian population in Maricopa County. *Programs*: Employment
& Training; Family & Children Services; Education. Established 1947.

STATE BAR OF ARIZONA - INDIAN LAW SECTION
4201 N. 24th St., Suite 100 • PHOENIX, AZ 85016
(602) 340-7215 Fax 271-4930; Website: www.azbar.org
Betty Flores, Section Administrator
Virjinya Ruth Adair Torrez, Indian Law Executive Council Chair 2017-18
(520) 383-3410); E-mail: virjinya.torrez@tonation-nsn.gov
Robert Hershey, Richard Palmer, Jr., James Tucker, Members at Large
The general purposes of the section shall be the promotion of the objects of
the State Bar of Arizona (State Bar) within the particular fields designated by
the name of the section. To that end, it shall be the purpose of the section: To
advance the understanding, study, adoption, application, interpretation, and
improvement of the federal laws, tribal laws and, to the extent applicable, state
laws, rules, & regulations which pertain to Indians, to Indian tribes, or to Indian
country, and to their administration and enforcement; to understand and
improve the relationships of these bodies of law and judicial and administrative
systems, and to encourage and support mutual respect for, and understanding
of, the cultures, values, customs, & heritages which underlie them.
Furthermore, the Section will encourage the education of the general public,
both Indian and non- Indian, with respect to the application of laws and legal
procedures of particular relevance to the Indian communities and governments
thereof.

FOUR RIVERS INDIAN LEGAL SERVICES
P.O. Box 68 • SACATON, AZ 85247
(520) 562-3369; Website: www.http://www.sazlegalaid.org
Anthony L. Young, JD, Executive Director; Shirley Molina, Board President
Southern Arizona Legal Aid, Inc. (SALA) is an organization dedicated to
providing high quality advocacy services to low-income clients. The Sacaton
office serves residents of the Gila River Indian Community in Pinal & Maricopa
Counties; Ak-Chin Indian Community in Pinal County; Native Americans living
off-reservation in Maricopa County; Cocopah Indian Community and Ft. Yuma
Indian Community in Yuma County; Salt River Pima-Maricopa Indian
Community & Ft. McDowell; Mohave-Apache Tribe in Maricopa County; and
Camp Verde Yavapai-Apache Indian Community in Yavapai County.

TOHONO O'ODHAM COMMUNITY ACTION (TOCA)
P.O. Box 1790 • SELLS, AZ 85634
(520) 383-4966 Fax 383-5286; Website: www.tocaonline.org
Terrol Dew Johnson & Tristan Reader (Tohono O'odham), Co-Directors
Programs: Tohono O'odham Basketweavers Organization (TOBO); Community Food System; Arts & Culture; Youth/Elder Outreach. *Publications*: TOCA
News. Magazines, blankets, traditional O'odham foods; videos; articles. Annual
celebration of basketry & Native foods festival. Established 1996.

TOHONO O'ODHAM KI:KI ASSOCIATION
P.O. Box 790 • SELLS, AZ 85634
(866) 248-5059; (520) 383-2202 or 383-2259
C. Pete Delgado (Tohono O'odham), Executive Director
E-mail: pdelgado@tokahousing.org
Mildred D. Manuel (Pima/Pascua Yaqui), Chairperson
Description: A tribally designed housing entity. *Purpose*: To provide housing
services to the Tohono O'odham Nation.

THE AMERICAN INDIAN CHRISTIAN MISSION (AICM)
American Indian Christian School
924 Mission Lane #1 • SHOW LOW, AZ 85901
(928) 537-5912 Fax 537-5620
Website: www.aicm.org; E-mail: contact@aicm.org
Leslie Solliday, Executive Director & Bible Teacher
E-mail: executivedirector@aicm.org
Mission: To equip & evangelize Native Americans for Christ. Ministers to
Navajo & Apache children from two of the largest Indian reservations in
Arizona. *Publication*: Smoke Signals, quarterly newsletter.

AMERICAN INDIAN CHAMBER OF COMMERCE OF ARIZONA
c/o Au'Authum Ki, Inc., 1301 E. University Dr. #104 • TEMPE, AZ 85281
(480) 497-1997 Fax 377-1143; Website: www.aiccaz.org
Loren Tapahe, President & CEO

Shon Quannie, Chairperson; Joy Whitneybell, Secretary
Purpose: To provide a format for American Indian entrepreneurs to promote their business, for corporations to connect with American Indian businesses, to act as a liaison on tribal economic development issues and to offer the best in resources, training & networking for American Indian business. Established 1995.

ARIZONA INDIAN GAMING ASSOCIATION
521 S 48th St., Suite 107 • TEMPE, AZ 85281
(480) 284-4034 Fax 284-4082
Website: www.azindiangaming.org
E-mail: info@azindiangaming.org
Valerie Spicer, Executive Director; Judy Ferreira, Deputy Director
Louis J. Manuel, Jr. (Ak-Chin), Chairperson
Paul Russell (Yavapai), Vice Chairperson

COOK NATIVE AMERICAN MINISTRIES FOUNDATION
1414 W. Broadway Rd., Suite 105 • TEMPE, AZ 85282
(480) 968-9354 Fax 968-9357
Website: www.cooknam.org; E-mail: info@cooknam.org
Susan Ware-Diaz, Executive Director
Board of Trustees: Michael Allison (Navajo); Sallie Cuaresma (Cherokee); Gary Long (Muscogee/Creek); Michelle Hale (Navajo/Laguna/Chippewa/Ottawa); Susan Ware Larson (Kiowa); Ronald Lundeen; Gary Metoxen (Oneida); Irvin R. Porter (Pima/Tohono O'odham/Nez Perce); Eveline Steele (Choctaw); Rosita Tipppeconnic (Dine'); Betty Weston (Creek). Charles H. Cook was the missionary & teacher to the Pima Indians beginning in 1870. The Cook Bible School was established in 1911. *Mission*: To educate, empower, and equip Native Americans for leadership in their churches & communities. *Activities*: Workshops, elder programs.

ARIZONA ARCHAEOLOGICAL & HISTORICAL SOCIETY
Arizona State Museum, P.O. Box 210026
University of Arizona • TUCSON, AZ 85721
(520) 621-4011; Jesse Ballenger, President
Purpose: To encourage scholarly pursuits in areas of history and anthropology of the southwestern U.S. & Northern Mexico; to encourage the preservation of archaeological & historical sites; to publish the results of archaeological, historical & ethnographic investigations; & to provide educational opportunities through lectures, field trips & other activities. Provides scholarship, research & travel grants. *Publication*: Kiva: The Journal of Southwestern Anthropology and History. Established 1916.

TUCSON INDIAN CENTER
American Indian Association of Tucson, Inc.
97 E. Congress St., #101, P.O. Box 2307 • TUCSON, AZ 85702
(520) 884-7131 Fax 884-0240
Website: www.ticenter.org; E-mail: jbernal@ticenter.org
Jacob Bernal (Chemehuevi), Executive Director
Phoebe Mills-Cager (Yup'ik), Wellness Director
Vicky Mullins, Social Service Director
Purpose: To provide services to the urban Indian population of Pima County. *Activities/programs*: Social Services; Health & Wellness; Employment & Training Services (vocational training); Job Fair; Housing Assistance for emergency shelter; also Counseling & Prevention activities to youth at risk for drug & gang involvement, crisis intervention; and referrals to other resources. Publication: Native Wellness Voice. Established 1963.

DINEBEINNA NAHILNA BE AGADITAHE
DNA-PEOPLE'S LEGAL SERVICES
P.O. Box 306 • WINDOW ROCK, AZ 86515
(928) 871-4151 Fax 871-5036
Website: www.dnalegalservices.org
Kathy Gallagher, Director; Chee Smith, Jr., President
Charles Doughty, Vice President; Peter Ives, Secretary/Treasurer
Purpose: To provide legal assistance to Navajos and other Indians in Arizona, New Mexico, and Utah.

NAVAJO AREA SCHOOL BOARD ASSOCIATION
P.O. Box 3719 • WINDOW ROCK, AZ 86515
(520) 871-5226 Fax 871-5148
Grace M. Boyne, Director; E-mail: gmboyne@yahoo.com
Publication: Monthly newsletter.

NAVAJO ARTS & CRAFTS ENTERPRISES (NACE)
P.O. Box 160 • WINDOW ROCK, AZ 86515
(866) 871-4095; (928) 871-4090; Website: www.gonavajo.com
Larry Tsosie, E-Commerce Marketing Specialist
Purpose: The rehabilitation & better utilization of the resources of the Navajo & Hopi Tribes & reservations as (they) relate to the members of the Navajo Tribe. *Stores located in*: Cameron; Chinle; Kayenta; Navajo National Monument;

Shiprock; Gallup. *Activities*: Maintains retail outlets; operates an e-commerce, mail order & wholesale business; crafts exhibit held at Heard Museum. Established 1941.

NAVAJO LUTHERAN MISSION
One Mission Lane, Hwy. 191, P.O. Box 354 • ROCK POINT, AZ 86545
(928) 659-4201 Fax 659-4255; Website: www.nelm.org
Kate Adelman (Navajo), Executive Director
Alice Natale (Navajo), Chairperson
Purpose: To meet the educational, health, social & spiritual needs of the Navajo people.

NAVAJO NATION BAR ASSOCIATION, INC.
Postal address: P.O. Box 690 • WINDOW ROCK, AZ 86515
Physical: 100 Mt. Taylor Rd. Hwy. 264 #116A, ST. Michaels, AZ 86511
(928) 871-2211 Fax 871-2229
Website: www.navajolaw.org
E-mail: nnba@navajolaw.org
Michael J. Barthlelemy (Navajo), President
Raymond Etcitty, Jr. (Navajo), Vice President
Membership: 400+. Professional association of attorneys licensed and in good standing in the surrounding states of Arizona, New Mexico, Utah & Colorado, and tribal court advocates authorized by the Navajo Nation Supreme Court & practicing law on the Navajo Nation. *Purpose*: To regulate the practice of law on the Navajo Nation.

NAVAJO NATION COUNCIL
P.O. Box 3390 • WINDOW ROCK, AZ 86515
(928) 871-7160 Fax 871-7255
Website: www.navajonationcouncil.org
Johnny Naize, Speaker
Council: LoRenzo Bates, Kee Allen Begay, Jr., Nelson BeGaye, Benjamin Bennett, Nathaniel Brown, Tom Chee, Amber Kanazbah Crotty, Seth Damon, Herman Daniels, Jr., Davis Filfred, Jonathan Hale, Lee Jack, Sr., Jonathan Perry, Leonard Pete, Walter Phelps, Alton Joe Shepherd, Tuchoney Slim, Jr., Raymond Smith, Jr., Otto Tso, Leonard Tsosie, Dwight Witherspoon, Edmund Zazzi.

ARKANSAS

AMERICAN INDIAN CENTER OF ARKANSAS
235 N. Greenwood • FORT SMITH, AR 72901
(501) 785-5149 Fax 785-3510; Virginia Henry, Contact
Affiliate of Little Rock center. See listing below.

AMERICAN INDIAN CENTER OF ARKANSAS
1100 N. University, Suite #143 • LITTLE ROCK, AR 72207-6344
(800) 441-4513; (501) 666-9032 Fax 666-5875
Website: www.arindianctr.org
Lois Bethards (Choctaw), Executive Director
E-mail: lbethards@arindianctr.org
Wanda McGuire (Chickasaw/Mississippi Choctaw), E&T Career Manager
Mike Killingsworth, Trail of Tears Association
Tamara-Lynn Walkingstick (Cherokee), Chairperson
Suzanne Hirrel (Cherokee), Vice Chairperson
Carl Robertson (Cherokee), Secretary/Treasurer
Purpose: To advance the social, cultural and economic wellbeing of Indian people residing in Arkansas through job training. *Programs*: Education; Indian Manpower Program offers employment assistance, training & counseling. *Publication*: "Lodge Tales," quarterly newsletter. Established 1977.

CALIFORNIA

NATIVE AMERICAN HEALTH CENTER
677 W. Ranger Ave. • ALAMEDA, CA 94501
(510) 814-8440

SOUTHERN CALIFORNIA AMERICAN INDIAN RESOURCE CENTER, INC.
239 E. Main St. • EL CAJON, CA 92020
(888) 217-2247; (619) 328-0676 Fax 328-0724
Website: www.scair.org; E-mail: scair@hotmail.com
Wanda Michaelis, Executive Director
Farnk Pancucci, Program Coordinator
Randy Edmonds, Senior Advisor
Angelica Salazar, Eligibility & Intake Specialist
William H. Johnson II, Board President
Purpose: To provide career, educational, cultural, mental health & community services to urban tribal Native Americans and their families throughout San Diego County. *Resource*: Gallery. *Publication*: Monthly newsletter.

RESOURCES FOR INDIAN STUDENT EDUCATION (RISE)
P.O. Box 1878 • ALTURAS, CA 96101
(530) 233-2226 Fax 233-4776
April Lea Go Forth, Director; Email: rise@citlink.net

CENTER FOR INDIAN COMMUNITY DEVELOPMENT (CICD)
The Library, Humboldt State University, One Harpst St. • ARCATA, CA 95521
(707) 826-3711 Fax 826-5258; E-mail: cicd@humboldt.edu
Zo Devine, Associate Director
Purpose: To help facilitate partnerships between American Indian community members, tribes, Indian organizations, governmental agencies representatives & University departments such as fisheries, teacher education, social work, nursing, history & economics. *Activities*: Works with tribes, organizations & Indian communities to develop educational, economic & social programs to help gain Tribal self-determination. Established 1966.

KERN INDIAN EDUCATION & COMMUNITY RESOURCE CENTER
1001 Tower Way, Suite 230 • BAKERSFIELD, CA 93309
(661) 328-6206 Fax 328-6235
Lana Decker, Director; E-mail: ldecker@ovcdc.com

AMERICAN INDIAN COUNSELORS & RECRUITERS ASSOCIATION
Website: www.aicra.org; *Goal*: To act as a system wide work group designed to provide informational outreach services to the American Indian communities throughout the state targeting students, families, counselors, & the community at large. The UC campuses & California State University systems are involved including: UC, Berkeley, Davis, Irvine, Los Angeles, Merced, Riverside, San Diego, San Francisco, Santa Barbara, Santa Cruz.

CALIFORNIA INDIAN ENVIRONMENTAL ALLIANCE
P.O. Box 2128 • BERKELEY, CA 94702
(510) 848-2043; Website: www.ciea-health.org
Sherri Norris (Osage), Executive Director
E-mail: sherri@cieaweb.org
Kaylena Bray (Haudenosaunee/Seneca), Health Program Coordinator
E-mail: kaylena@cieaweb.org
Lauren Hughes (Cherokee/Muscogee Creek), Program Coordinator
Purpose: To conduct presentations & training for tribal members, tribal leaders, healthcare providers, & local community-based groups. *Program*: Mining Toxins & Tribal Health Program (produces health brochures, a monthly e-mail newsletter & maintains a clearinghouse of information, contacts, organizations, agencies, & projects relating to mercury in the environment, in fish, in the human body & efforts to move towards advocacy and cleanup.)

CALIFORNIA INDIAN LEGAL SERVICES (CILS)
873 Main St., Suite 120 • BISHOP, CA 93514
(800) 736-3582; (760) 873-3581 Fax 873-7461
Website: www.calindian.org
Dorothy Alther (Oglala Sioux), Executive Director & Senior Staff Attorney
Patricia De La Cruz-Lynas, Director of Administration & Board Secretary
See Escondido (principal office) listing for description of services.
Counties served: Alpine, Inyo, Kern, Mono, and Tuolumne.

OWENS VALLEY INDIAN EDUCATION CENTER
390 N. Barlow Lane • BISHOP, CA 93514
(760) 873-5740 Fax 873-4143

PIT RIVER HEALTH SERVICES, INC.
P.O. Box 2720 • BURNEY, CA 96013
(800) 843-7447; (530) 335-5090, 335-3651, 335-5090

AMERICAN INDIAN EMPLOYMENT PROGRAM
2450 S. Bascom Ave. • CAMPBELL, CA 95008
(408) 369-3620; Carl Begay, Contact
Job training & employment.

FOUR WINDS OF INDIAN EDUCATION
2345 Fair St. • CHICO, CA 95926
(916) 895-4212 Fax 895-4310
Rachel McBride, Education Director
E-mail: Rachel.4winds@sbcglobal.net

ROUND VALLEY INDIAN TRIBES EDUCATION CENTER
P.O. Box 448 • COVELO, CA 95428
(707) 983-1062 Fax 983-1073; James Russ, Director

FOOTHILL INDIAN EDUCATION ALLIANCE
P.O. Box 1418 • EL DORADO, CA 95623
(530) 621-3096 Fax 621-3097; E-mail: foothill@innercite.com
James Marquez, Executive Director

CALIFORNIA INDIAN LEGAL SERVICES (CILS)
609 S. Escondido Blvd. • ESCONDIDO, CA 92025
(800) 743-8941; (760) 746-8941 Fax 746-1815
Website: www.calindian.org
Dorothy Alther (Oglala Sioux), Executive Director & Senior Staff Attorney
Mark Radoff, Senior Staff Attorney; Mark Vezzola, Directing Attorney
Patricia De La Cruz-Lynas, Director of Administration & Board Secretary
Rachel Joseph (Lone Pine Paiute-Shoshone), Board Chairperson
Mark Romero (Mesa Grande Mission), Board Vice Chairperson
Description: The first India-controlled law firm organized to provide specialized legal representation to Indians & Indian tribes. A statewide nonprofit corporation organized to provide free legal services to qualifying individuals and organizations on a wide range of topics involving Indian law & legal issues unique to Native American people. CILS provides low-cost legal services to California Indian tribes that do not qualify for free services. Represents more than sixteen California Indian tribes on a wide range of legal issues. This is the principal office that houses the program administration and also serves as a field office. Counties served by Escondido Office: Imperial, Los Angeles, Orange, Riverside, San Diego, San Bernardino, Santa Barbara, Ventura. Services are provided by each office in counties within its service area. Each office has 2-3 attorneys and paralegals on staff. Other offices located in Bishop, Eureka, & Sacramento, CA. Indian Law Library. Established 1967.

CALIFORNIA INDIAN LEGAL SERVICES
324 F St., Suite A • EUREKA, CA 95501
(800) 347-2402; (707) 443-8397 Fax 443-8913
Website: www.calindian.org
Dorothy Alther (Oglala Sioux), Executive Director, Senior Staff Attorney
Patricia De La Cruz-Lynas, Director of Administration & Board Secretary
See Escondido (principal office) listing for description of services. *Counties served*: Del Norte, Humboldt, Lassen, Modoc, Shasta, Siskiyou, and Trinity.

INDIAN ACTION COUNCIL OF NORTHWEST CALIFORNIA, INC.
2905 Hubbard Lane, Suite C • EUREKA, CA 95501
(707) 443-8401 Fax 443-9281
Coleen Bruno, Director; E-mail: indianaction@att.net

NORTHERN CALIFORNIA INDIAN DEVELOPMENT COUNCIL
241 F St. • EUREKA, CA 95501 (707) 445-8451 Fax 445-8479
Website: https://ncidc.org; E-mail: andrekaruk@ncidc.org
Irma Amaro, Executive Director; Andre Cramblit, Operations Director
Description: A social service agency providing education & employment services through the Job Training and Partnership Act. Services Humboldt & Trinity Counties. *Resources*: American Indian Art & Gift Shop.

YA-KA-AMA INDIAN EDUCATION & DEVELOPMENT, INC.
7465 Steve Olson Lane • FORESTVILLE, CA 95436
(707) 887-1541 Fax 887-1585
Sherry Steele (Pomo), Executive Director; E-mail: pomomata@hotmail.com
Hailey Ferroni, WIA Program Coordinator; E-mail: hailey.ferroni@gmail.com
Mario Hermosillo, Jr., Board Chair; E-mail: mariohermosillojr@gmail.com
Laila DeRouen, Board Vice Chairperson; E-mail: lailabear@comcast.net
Purpose: Provide programs for five-county Native American population to advance their educational, economic, social & cultural opportunities necessary to the attainment of sovereignty & self-determination. *Special programs*: Vocational training in horticulture, business & merchandising. Operates Native plant nursery and organic produce; Native Arts Gallery and Native crafts store; library. *Publication*: Quarterly newsletter. Established 1972.

SOUTHERN CALIFORNIA INDIAN CENTER
10175 Slater Ave. #150 • FOUNTAIN VALLEY, CA 92708
(714) 962-6673 Fax 962-6343; Website: www.indiancenter.org
Paula Starr (Cheyenne), Executive Director; E-mail: pstarr@indiancenter.org
Starr Robideau (Cheyenne/Ojibwe), Operations Officer & American Indian Families & Partners Program Director; E-mail: srobideau@indiancenter.org;
Phil Hale (Navajo-Dine'), Education Component Director
E-mail: phale@indiancenter.org
Michael Folsom (Choctaw), Board President
Tracy Stanhoff (Potawatomi), Board Vice President
H. Starr Robideau (Cheyenne/Ojibwe), Secretary
Tahna Begay (Navajo), Treasurer
Purpose: To promote social & economic self-sufficiency for the American Indian communities of Los Angeles, Orange & Riverside counties by establishing & maintaining educational, cultural, & economic programs. *Special programs*: Senior citizens center, tutoring, annual powwow and job fair. *Publication*: SCIC News, monthly newsletter. Library. Established 1968.

CALIFORNIA INDIAN STORYTELLING ASSOCIATION (CISA)
P.O. Box 267 • FREMONT, CA 94537
(510) 794-7253; Website: www.cistory.org; E-mail: cistory@cistory.org
Lauren Teixeria (Castanoan/Ohlone), Executive Director & Co-founder

Paul Kealoha Blake (Hawaiian), Videographer/Musician
E-mail: paul@cistory.org
Kat High (Hupa), Videographer & Storyteller
Ernest Siva (Serrano/Cahuilla), Board Chairperson & Co-founder
Georgiana Sanchez (Chumash), Board Member & Storyteller
Purpose: To provide a storytelling forum for the indigenous people of the Americas. *Special program*: Emerging Voices. *Activities*: Annual California Indian Storytelling Festival. *Media Gallery*: Videos – The Art & Practice of Native Fishing; Bridging the Pacific with Native Voices. CD – Stories from Native California.

APPLIED EARTHWORKS, INC.
1391 W. Shaw Ave. Suite C • FRESNO, CA 93711
(559) 229-1856 Fax 229-2019
Offices: 3292 E. Florida Ave., Suite A • Hemet, CA 92544 (951) 766-2000
133 N. San Gabriel Blvd., Suite 201 • Pasadena, CA 91107 (626) 578-0119
743 Pacific St., Suite A • San Luis Obispo, CA 93401 (805) 594-1590
515 E. Ocean Ave., Suite G • Lompoc, CA 93436 (805) 737-4119
1410 Harder Lane • Albany, OR 97321 (541) 926-5886
Website: www.appliedearthworks.com
E-mail: info@appliedearthworks.com
Mary Clark Baloian, President/Senior archaeologist
Clayton Lebow, VP/Principal Archaeologist (Hemet Office)
E-mail: sgoldberg@appliedearthworks.com
Vanessa A. Mirro, VP/Principal Archaeologist (San Luis Obispo Office)
E-mail: bprice@appliedearthworks.com
Michael J. Moratto, Principal Archaeologist (Pasadena Office)
E-mail: mmoratto@appliedearthworks.com
Description: A California corporation consisting of archaeologists, historians, anthropologists, geologists, paleontologists, and other specialists that perform contract-supported research in archaeology & allied sciences for many governmental & private agencies. Native American consultation; Navajo WPA architecture.

INDIAN HOUSING AUTHORITY OF CENTRAL CALIFORNIA
4702 N. Bendel • FRESNO, CA 93722
(559) 271-9004 Fax 271-0125

OSA CENTER FOR INDIAN EDUCATION
2224 N. Fine, Suite 103 • FRESNO, CA 93727
(559) 252-8659 Fax 252-3824; Michelle Lira, Director
Purpose: To create a better understanding of the history, culture, contributions of California Indians; to stimulate and promote research and study of the early American Indian; to support the preservation of California's Native cultural heritage; and to encourage Indian parents to become involved in improving their children's education.

SIERRA TRIBAL CONSORTIUM - TURTLE LODGE RECOVERY HOME
610 W. McKinley Ave. • FRESNO, CA 93728
(888) 56SOBER; (559) 445-2691 Fax 445-3125
Website: www.sierratribal.org

ROUNDHOUSE COUNCIL, INC.
P.O. Box 217 • GREENVILLE, CA 95947
(530) 284-6866 Fax 284-6741; Website: www.roundhousecouncil.com
Mary Joseph (Maidu), Executive Director
E-mail: mary@roundhousecouncil.com
Reina Rogers, Board Chairperson
Danny Manning, Board Vice Chairperson
Wanda Carpenter, Board Secretary/Treasurer
Purpose: To provide educational opportunities and other resources to create & promote community wellbeing and positive attitudes which enhance the quality of life for Maidu and other Native American cultures.

BLUE STONE STRATEGY GROUP
19900 MacArthur Blvd., Suite 658 • IRVINE, CA 92612
(949) 476-8828 Fax 261-8828; Website: www.bluestonestrategy.com
Jamie L. Fullmer (Yavapai-Apache), Chairperson
See Phoenix, AZ main office listing for details.

AMERICAN INDIAN CHAMBER OF COMMERCE OF CALIFORNIA
555 W. Fifth St., 31st Fl. • LOS ANGELES, CA 90013
(213) 440-3232; Website: www.aicccal.org
Tracy Stanhoff (Potawatomi/Choctaw), President (714) 898-6364
E-mail: tracy@adproweb.com
Project operated by the National Center for American Indian Enterprise Development in cooperation with the U.S. Department of Commerce, Minority Business Development Agency. Operates the California/Nevada Tribal Technical Assistance Program (CA/NV TTAP), providing management and technical assistance for Native Americans residing in California & Nevada. Available for all stages of business from start-up to expansion.

AMERICAN INDIAN FAMILIES PARTNERSHIPS
5809 N. Figueroa St. • LOS ANGELES, CA 90042
(323) 274-1070 Fax 972-1575
Website: www.indianfamilies.org
Barbara Arvi, Director
E-mail: barvi@indiancenter.org
Services: In-home Visitation; Family Advocacy; Emergency Food/Shelter; Parenting Education; Crisis Counseling. *Publication*: A.I.F.P. News

LOS ANGELES CITY/COUNTY NATIVE AMERICAN INDIAN COMMISSION
3175 West 6th St. • LOS ANGELES, CA 90020
(213) 351-5308 Fax 626-7034
Website: www.lanaic.org; E-mail: contact@lanaic.org
Ron Andrade (Luiseno), Executive Director
E-mail: randrade@css.lacounty.gov
Rudy Ortega, Jr., Chairperson
Chrissie Castro (Navajo), Vice Chairperson
Duane Champagne (Ojibwe), Secretary
Cheri Thomas (Quinault/Yurok), Treasurer
Purpose: To promote the general welfare, public interest, and well being of the Los Angeles Indian community, the largest urban Indian population in the U.S. Established 1976.

UNITED AMERICAN INDIAN INVOLVEMENT, INC.
1125 W. 6th St. #103 • LOS ANGELES, CA 90017
(213) 202-3970 Fax 202-3977
Website: www.uaii.org; E-mail: info@uaii.org
David L. Rambeau, Executive Director
Terry McAullife, Board President; Curt Livesay, Vice President
Purpose: To provide assistance to the American Indian population within the Los Angeles County area suffering from the disease of alcoholism & other drugs. *Programs*: Health Project; Robert Sundance Family Wellness Center; Strengthening American Indian Families Project (SAIF). Counseling; nutrition; personal hygiene; health; housing assistance; youth diversion programs, family activities; day sleep facilities; sober living; limited detox and other crisis assistance as needed. Established 1974.

THREE RIVERS INDIAN LODGE
Native Directions, Inc., 13505 Union Rd.
P.O. Box 1552 • MANTECA, CA 95336
(209) 858-2421 Fax 858-4692
Website: www.nativedirections.org
E-mail: mona3riverslodge@aol.com
Administers & extends alcoholism treatment services for the individual needing a point of new beginnings. Provides services for positive life changes, by healing, educating & empowering. Annual powwow. Established 1974.

WOODFORDS INDIAN EDUCATION CENTER
96B Washo Blvd. • MARKLEEVILLE, CA 96120
(530) 694-2964 Fax 694-2739
Amber Bell (Washoe), Director; E-mail: lamber.bill@washoetribe.us
Maxine Emm (Washoe), Tutor Coordinator

AMERICAN INDIAN CHILD RESOURCE CENTER
522 Grand Ave. • OAKLAND, CA 94610
(510) 208-1870 Fax 208-1886
Website: www.aicrc.org; E-mail: aicrc@aicrc.org
Mary Trimble Norris, Executive Director; E-mail: mary@aicrc.org
Corrina Gould (Ohlone), Title VII Coordinator; E-mail: corrina@aicrc.org
Manny Lieras (Dine'/Comanche/Mexican), After School Coordinator
E-mail: manny@aicrc.org
Mary Ann Greycloud (Sisseton Sioux), Founding Board Member
Sandra La Framboise (Turtle Mountain Ojibwe), Chairperson
Purpose: To preserve & promote the integrity & culture of American Indian youth & their families.

INTERTRIBAL FRIENDSHIP HOUSE
523 East 14th St. • OAKLAND, CA 94606
(510) 452-1235; Carol Wahpepah (Ojibway), Executive Director
Lorena Rivera (Confederated Tribes of Grand Ronde/Mohawk),
Youth Program Coordinator
Sophia Taula-Lieras (Umatilla), Board Chairperson
Iona Mad Plume (Blackfeet), Vice Chairperson
Purpose: To serve the needs of American Indian people relocated from reservations to the San Francisco Bay Area, and to promote and maintain the wellbeing of American Indian life in the modern & traditional way. *Programs*: Cultural; social services; senior program; community history project. Gift Shop. Artifacts exhibit, visual arts & writing, tapes (video & music), historical records. *Activities*: Trading Post; Gallery. *Publication*: Quarterly newsletter. Established 1955.

NATIVE AMERICAN HEALTH CENTER, INC.
3124 International Blvd. • OAKLAND, CA 94601
  (510) 535-4400 Fax 261-0646; Website: www.nativehealth.org
  Susan Jamerson, Director
Locations: 160 Capp St., San Francisco, CA 94110; 333 Valencia St., San Francisco, CA 94110; Oakland 7 Directions, 2950 International Blvd, Oakland, CA 94601; Richmond Native Wellness Center, 2566 Macdonald Ave., Richmond, CA 94501; 677 W. Ranger Ave., Alameda, CA 94501. *Purpose*: To provide health services for the Native American population in the Oakland-San Francisco Bay area.

NESHKINUKAT: CALIFORNIA NATIVE ARTISTS NETWORK
P.O. Box 20719 • OAKLAND, CA 94611
  (510) 368-6663 Fax (413) 653-7556
  E-mail: neshkinukat@gmail.com
Description: Network of American Indian, Alaska Natives and other Indigenous artists who live in California. Open to Native artists of all traditions & contemporary art forms. Semiannual meetings. Artist's directory.

CAHUILLA INTER-TRIBAL REPATRIATION COMMITTEE
Agua Caliente Band of Cahuilla Indians
5401 Dinah Shore Dr. • PALM SPRINGS, CA 92264
  (760) 699-6800 Fax 699-6924; Website: www.cahuillarepatriation.org
  Patricia Tuck Garcia (Cahuilla), Director of Tribal Historic Preservation
  E-mail: ptuck@aguacaliente-nsn.gov
Member tribes: Agua Caliente Band (Cahuilla) of Indians, Palm Springs, CA; Augustine Band (Cahuilla) of Mission Indians, Indio, CA; Cabazon Band of Cahuilla Indians, Indio, CA; Cahuilla Band of Indians, Anza, CA; Morongo Band (Cahuilla & Serrano) of Mission Indians, Banning, CA; San Manuel Band (Serrano) of Mission Indians, Highland, CA; Santa Rosa Band (Cahuilla) of Mission Indians, Anza, CA; Torres-Martinez Desert Cahuilla Indian, Thermal, CA.

RICHMOND NATIVE WELLNESS CENTER
2566 Macdonald Ave. • RICHMOND, CA 94804
  (510) 232-7020
Services: Health System Navigation; Mental Health Support; Drug & Alcohol Recovery Support; Elder Support; Youth Health & Fitness; Youth After-School Support; Traditional Crafts & Cultural Events. Affiliated with the Native American Health Center, Oakland, CA.

CALIFORNIA ATTORNEY GENERAL'S OFFICE
Office of Native American Affairs
P.O. Box 944255 • SACRAMENTO, CA 94244-2550
  (916) 322-1818; Olin Jones, Director

CALIFORNIA INDIAN HERITAGE CENTER (CIHC)
Department of Parks & Recreation
P.O. Box 942896 • SACRAMENTO, CA 94296
  (916) 653-6995 Fax 654-6374
  Website: www.parks.ca.gov; E-mail: cihc@parks.ca.gov
The (CIHC) will be a distinctive and honorable place where past, present and future experiences & achievements of California Indians are recognized, celebrated and shared. The CIHC Foundation, the Native American Heritage Commission, California State Parks and the community are working together to create the California Indian Heritage Center. The Center is a place where Indian people can come together to celebrate past and present traditions. It is a place for all people from around the world to learn about the history of California's Indian communities and Native American culture. The CIHC will replace the California State Indian Museum when it opens. The California Indian Heritage Center honors the diversity & history of California Indian people by preserving cultural & tribal traditions, nurturing contemporary expressions, & facilitating research & education, for California, and the nation.

CALIFORNIA INDIAN LEGAL SERVICES (CILS)
117 J St., Suite 300 • SACRAMENTO, CA 95814
  (800) 829-0284; (916) 978-0960 Fax 400-4891
  Website: www.calindian.org
  Dorothy Alther (Oglala Sioux), Executive Director
  & Senior Staff Attorney (Escondido)
  Patricia De La Cruz-Lynas, Director of Administration
  & Board Secretary (Sacramento)
Counties served: Alameda, Amador, Butte, Calaveras, Colusa, Contra Costa, El Dorado, Fresno, Glenn, Kings, Lake, Madera, Marin, Mariposa, Mendocino, Merced, Monterey, Napa, Nevada, Placer, Plumas, Sacramento, San Benito, San Francisco, San Joaquin, San Luis Obispo, San Mateo, Santa Clara, Santa Cruz, Sierra, Solano, Sonoma, Stanislaus, Sutter, Tehama, Tulare, Yolo, Yuba. See Escondido (principal office) listing for description of services.

CALIFORNIA INDIAN MANPOWER CONSORTIUM (CIMC)
738 N. Market Blvd. • SACRAMENTO, CA 95834
  (800) 640-2462; (916) 920-0285 Fax 641-6338
  Website: www.cimcinc.com
  Lorenda T. Sanchez, Executive Director
  Benjamin Charley, Jr., Chairperson
  E-mail: lorendas@cimcinc.com
Purpose: To offer training, employment, and other activities designed to meet the employment & training needs of the client population; to promote community self-help programs & provide direct services to assist eligible American Indian population. *Programs*: Workforce Development Program; Native Entrepreneurs Training Program (2001) - series of workshops held in different areas throughout California; California Native Entrepreneurs Opportunity Fund (CNEOF) (2007) - promotes financial independence & self-reliance for Native families, their connection to Native culture, and strengthen tribal governments. Established 1978.

CALIFORNIA INDIAN LAW ASSOCIATION (CILA)
  Website: www.calindianlaw.org
  Courtney Cole (Cherokee/Choctaw), President
  Christina Snider (Pomo), Vice President
  Will Haney (Seminole of Oklahoma), Treasurer
  Geneva E.B. Thompson (Cherokee), Secretary
  Cheyenne Sanders (Yurok), Associate General Counsel
  Adam Crepelle (United Houma), Anna Hohag (Bishop Paiute),
  John H. haney (Seminole of Oklahoma), Board members
  Loretta Miranda (Morongo Band of Mission Indians), Public Interest Indian
  Law Fellow
Publication: Quarterly newsletter.

CALIFORNIA NATIONS INDIAN GAMING ASSOCIATION
2150 River Plaza Dr., Suite120 • SACRAMENTO, CA 95833
  (916) 448-8706 Fax 448-8758; Website: www.cniga.com
  Lee Acebedo, Executive Director; E-mail: lee@cniga.com
  Susan A. Jensen, Director of Communications
  E-mail: susan@cniga.com
  Daniel J. Tucker (Sycuan Band of Kumeyaay Nation), Chairperson
  Allen Lawson (San Pasqual Band of Mission Indians), Vice Chairperson
  Steve Stallings (Rincon Band of Luiseno Indians), Treasurer
  Eric Ramos (Blue Lake Rancheria), Secretary
Description: A non-profit organization comprised of federally recognized tribal governments. *Purpose*: To protect Indian gaming on federally recognized Indian lands. Acts as planning & coordinating agency for legislative, policy, legal and communications efforts on behalf of its members & serves as an industry forum for Information & resources. *Publication*: Periodic newsletter. Established 1988.

CALIFORNIA RURAL INDIAN HEALTH BOARD, INC. (CRIHB)
4400 Auburn Blvd., 2nd Floor • SACRAMENTO, CA 95841
  (916) 929-9761 Fax 929-7246; Website: www.crihb.org
  Mark LeBeau, CEO
  Marilyn Pollard, COO; E-mail: ops@crihb.org
  Michelle Jean Hayward (Wintu), Board Chairperson
A network of tribal health programs which are controlled and sanctioned by Indian people and their tribal governments. CRIHB develops and delivers policies, plans, programs & services that elevate the health status & social conditions of Indian people in California. Established 1969.

CALIFORNIA STATE DEPARTMENT OF EDUCATION
American Indian Education Office
1430 N St. #6408 • SACRAMENTO, CA 95814
  (916) 319-0506 Fax 319-0139
  Website: www.cde.ca.gov/sp/ai/
  Judy Martinez, Program Consultant
  E-mail: jmartinez@cde.ca.gov
Purpose: To provide statewide coordination & technical assistance.
Publication: "The American Indian: Yesterday, Today & Tomorrow: A Handbook for Educators."

CALIFORNIA STATE DEPARTMENT OF JUSTICE
Office of Native American Affairs - California Attorney General's Office
P.O. Box 944255 • SACRAMENTO, CA 94244
  (916) 445-1970; (916) 322-1818
  Olin Jones, Director; E-mail: olin.jones@doj.ca.gov
Mission: Serves as liaison and addresses justice-related issues for California's Indian citizens who reside on reservations, Rancherias and in urban communities for the overall improvement of the quality of life for Indian people.
Purpose: To develop & maintain cooperative relationships between California's Indian tribes, tribal organizations, Indian citizens & the Department of Justice.

CALIFORNIA TRIBAL BUSINESS ALLIANCE
1530 J St. #410 • SACRAMENTO, CA 95814
(916) 346-4205 Fax 346-4283; Website: https://www.caltba.org
Chris Lindstrom, Executive Director (916) 601-1969
E-mail: chris@caltba.org
Valerie Martinez, Communications Director (909) 917-3368
E-mail: Valerie.martinez@vmacommunications.com
David Quintana, Political Director (916) 217-2616
E-mail: q@gqhlobby.com
Robert Smith (Luiseno), Board Chairperson
Leslie Lohse (Nomlaki), Vice Chairperson
Description: Composed of California Indian tribes operating gaming facilities under the terms of tribal-state compacts. *Purpose*: To safeguard & enhance the success of the business enterprise of our tribal government members; to address an array of public policy matters of importance to the diverse business interests of the founding tribes, including business, housing, transportation, agriculture and environmental issues. Established 2004.

CAPITOL AREA INDIAN RESOURCES, INC.
1010 Hurley Way, Suite 190 • SACRAMENTO, CA 95825
(916) 971-9190 Fax 971-9199
Website: www.cair.us; E-mail: cair@cair.us
Cindy La Marr, Executive Director
Purpose: To encourage the development of all aspects of education for the American Indian community, while affirming & preserving Native cultural & traditional values in today's society.

INDIAN DISPUTE RESOLUTION SERVICES
1325 Howe Ave. • SACRAMENTO, CA 95825
(916) 482-5800 Fax 482-5808; Website: www.idrsinc.org
Steven Haberfeld (802-0243); E-mail: steven@idrsinc.org
Mark Thompson (803-7550); E-mail: mark@idrsinc.org
Purpose: To assist American Indian communities build the foundations for effective self-government; to introduce a "collaborative problem-solving process" that brings people together & supports them to address & solve the challenges confronting their communities. *Activities*: Offers leadership training in cross-cultural communication, negotiation, mediation & Board management skills; provide direct services in facilitation, conflict resolution, strategic planning and resource mobilization.

INTERTRIBAL COUNCIL OF CALIFORNIA, INC. (ITTC)
ITTC Central Office: 3425 Arden Way • SACRAMENTO, CA 95825
(916) 973-9581 Fax 973-0117
Website: www.itccinc.org; E-mail: intertribal.ca@itccinc.org
Connie Reitman-Solas, Executive DirectorFresno Regional Service Center,
433 E. Keats Ave. #3, Fresno, CA 93710
(559) 224-7145 Fax 224-7215
Crescent City/Elk Valley Rancheria Satellite Office, 2332 Howland Hill Rd.,
Crescent City, CA 95531 (707) 465-1840 Fax 465-1570
E-mail: tdavis@itccinc.org
Santa Rosa Satellite Office; (707) 521-4555
E-mail: ysparks@itccinc.org
LaWanda Quinnell (Elk Valley Rancheria), President (707) 464-4680
Aaron Dixon (Susanville Indian Rancheria), Vice President
Steve Smith (Dry Creek Rancheria), Treasurer (707) 473-2159
E-mail: ssmith@drycreekrancheria.com
The Inter-Tribal Council of California, Inc., (ITCC) is a tribal association of over 50 tribes in California. Since 1968, ITCC has provided a broad array of services geared toward improving the capacity of tribal government to work progressively & productively with governmental entities, non-governmental organizations (NGOs) and non-profit organizations providing services for tribal communities. ITCC recognizes the importance of strengthening sovereignty and improving the health and wellbeing of our tribal communities by providing a broad array of training and technical assistance workshops and resources.

NATIVE AMERICAN CAUCUS
CALIFORNIA DEMOCRATIC PARTY (CDP)
1401 21st St., Suite 100 • SACRAMENTO, CA 95814
Website: www.nativeamericancaucus.org
Andrew Masiel, Sr. (Luiseno), Chairperson
Mary Ann Andreas (Cahuila), 1st Vice Chair
Joely Proudfitt (Luiseno), 2nd Vice Chair
Debra Broner, Treasurer; Corrina Garbani (Luiseno), Secretary
Carol Robb, Chair of San Bernardino Co.
Members-at-Large: Betty McMillion, Matt Franklin, Paula Treat, Jason Hodge
The caucus was formed with the focus on including the Native American communities of California in the furtherance of Democratic ideals, issues, and political participation. *Purpose*: To increase educational, economic, and social opportunities while preserving cultural heritage of state's minority populations.

OFFICE OF THE GOVERNOR, EDMUND G. BROWN, JR.
915 Capitol Mall, Suite 1173 • SACRAMENTO, CA 95814
(916) 445-2841 Fax 558-3160
Cynthia Gomez, Tribal Advisor to the Governor
Heather Hostler, Chief Deputy Tribal Advisor to the Governor
Works with state agencies & tribal governments to strengthen communication, collaboration and consultation. Covers all tribal issues in the state on behalf of the Governor with the exception of gaming. Active in areas of health, natural resources, fisheries, water, broadband, fee to trust and developing systems for tribes to navigate state government to work in better partnership.

SACRAMENTO NATIVE AMERICAN HEALTH CENTER
2020 J St. • SACRAMENTO, CA 95811
(916) 341-0575 Fax 341-0574
Britta Guerrero (San Carlos Apache), Chief Executive Officer
Lisa McKay (Pomo), Chief Fiscal Officer
Eric Enriquez (Pomo/Wailaki), Director of Operations
Kaleb Clark, Chief Information Officer
Alan Williams, MD, Medical Director; Magnus Yang, DDS, Dental Director
Ricardo (Richard) Torres (Wintu), Board Chairperson
Michelle Villegas-Frazier (Pomo), Vice Chairperson
Anno Nakai (Navajo/Saami), Treasurer
Curtis Notsinneh (Jicarilla Apache), Secretary
Mary Tarango (Miwok), Tribal Advisor

COUNCIL OF AMERICAN INDIAN ORGANIZATIONS
OF SAN DIEGO COUNTY
4265 Fairmount Ave. #140 • SAN DIEGO, CA 92105
(619) 281-5964 Ext. 104; O. Pierre Romero, Chairperson

INDIAN HUMAN RESOURCE CENTER
4265 Fairmount Ave. #140 • SAN DIEGO, CA 92105
(619) 281-5964 Fax 281-1466; Website: www.indianhrcenter.wix.com
Juan Castellanos, Executive Director; Joe Renteria, Chair (Cherokee)
Purpose: To serve Native Americans in San Diego County by providing job training. *Activities*: Developed San Diego's American Indian Culture Center & Museum (AICCM) (See listing in Museum's section). Annual American Indian Cultural Days Powwow, Balboa Park, in May. *Publication*: Monthly newsletter. Established 1979.

SAN DIEGO AMERICAN INDIAN HEALTH CENTER
2602 First Ave., Suite 105 • SAN DIEGO, CA 92103
(619) 234-2158; Website: www.sdaihc.com
Paula Brim (Choctaw), Board Chairperson
Dale Squires (Chickasaw), Board Vice-chairperson
Purpose: To provide health services to Native Americans living in the San Diego area. Established 1979.

AMERICAN INDIAN CONTEMPORARY ARTS
23 Grant Ave. • SAN FRANCISCO, CA 94108
(415) 989-7003. Art gallery & studio.
Andrew Jolivette (Opelousa/Athakapa-Ishak; Choctaw),
Interim Executive Director

AMERICAN INDIAN ENVIRONMENTAL OFFICE
USEPA Region 9, 75 Hawthorne St. • SAN FRANCISCO, CA 94105
(415) 947-3561 Fax 947-3562
Laura Ebbert, Manager; Email: ebbert.laura@epa.gov

AMERICAN INDIAN FILM INSTITUTE
2940 16th St., Suite 304 • SAN FRANCISCO, CA 94103
(415) 554-0525 Fax 554-0542
Website: www.aifisf.com; E-mail: aifi.hq@gmail.com
Michael Smith, President
Annual Film Festival. E-mail: aifi.filmfest@gmail.com
American Indian Motion Picture Awards Show.

BAY AREA AMERICAN INDIAN TWO-SPIRITS
77 Van Ness Ave., Suite 101-1043 • SAN FRANCISCO, CA 94102
(415) 865-5616 Fax 255-4883
Website: www.baaits.org; E-mail: admin@baaits.org
Board of Directors: J. Miko Thomas (Chickasaw), Derek Smith (Anishinaabe), Nazbah Tom (Navajo), Jim Eagle (Sisseton Wahpeton), Ruth Villasenor (Chiricahua Apache/Mexican). *Description*: A community-based volunteer organization offering culturally relevant activities for Gay, Lesbian, Bisexual, Transgender & Intersex Native Americans, their families and friends. Two-Spirit refers to the commonly shared notion among many Native American tribes that some individuals naturally possessed & manifested both a masculine & feminine spiritual qualities. American society commonly identifies Two-Spirit People as Gay, Lesbian, Bisexual or Transgender. Bay Area

American Indian Two-Spirits comes together to socialize, share and network in an alcohol and drug-free environment. BAAITS sees itself as an organization for Two-Spirit people to explore their rich heritage in a safe environment. To that end, BAAITS is committed to offering culturally relevant activities for LGBT individuals of Native American ancestry and their families & friends. *Activities*: Annual Powwow; Photo Gallery.

FRIENDSHIP HOUSE ASSOCIATION OF AMERICAN INDIANS, INC.
56 Julian Ave. • SAN FRANCISCO, CA 94103
(415) 865-0964 Fax 865-5428; Website: www.friendshiphousesf.org
E-mail: info@friendshiphousesf.org
Helen Devore Waukazoo (Navajo), Chief Executive Officer
Anthony Tam (Navajo), Chief Financial Officer
Margie Mejia (Pomo), Board President
Edward Madril (Pascua Yaqui), Board Vice President
Robert Tamaka Bailey (Choctaw of Oklahoma), Board Secretary
Purpose: To promote healing & wellness in the American Indian community by providing a continuum of substance abuse prevention, treatment, and recovery services that integrate traditional American Indian healing practices & evidence-based substance abuse treatment methods.

AHMIUM LEARNING CENTER, INC.
617 E. Main St., Suite B • SAN JACINTO, CA 92582
(800) 924-8744; (951) 654-2781 Fax 654-3089
Website: www.ahmium.org
Ernie C. Salgado, Jr., Director
E-mail: erniesalgado51@hotmail.com
Description: Project NAPAP (Native American Parental Assistance Program).
Purpose: To disseminate a model program to empower Native American parents to join the educational system, to assume leadership roles, and participate in local & state decision making processes, and facilitate reform & restructuring efforts of tribal organizations and the education system.

INDIAN HEALTH CENTER OF SANTA CLARA VALLEY
Main Clinic: 1333 Meridian Ave. • SAN JOSE, CA 95125
Administration: 1211 Meridian Ave. • SAN JOSE, CA 95125
(408) 445-3400 Fax 448-1727; Website: www.indianhealthcenter.org
Elizabeth Hunt, Chief Executive Officer
Aldon Wayne Scott, Director of Operations; E-mail: awscott@ihcscv.org
Craig Pasqua (Modoc-Pit River Paiute-Cherokee), Board President
Cheryl Marsden (Tlingit-Haida-Tsimpsian), Secretary
Pablo Diego Viramontes (Nha Nhu-Otomi), Treasurer
Purpose: To provide comprehensive and affordable health care to American Indians/Alaska Natives & their families. *Programs*: Alcohol & Substance Abuse

AMERICAN INDIAN ALLIANCE OF SANTA CLARA VALLEY
5038 Hyland Ave. • SAN JOSE, CA 95127
Website: www.americanindianalliance.org
E-mail: aia@americanindianalliance.org
Vernon Medicine Cloud, President & Executive Director
Sherry LeBeau), Vice President
Purpose: A coalition of organizations & individuals dedicated to preserving & perpetuating the heritage, values & traditions of American Indians; to develop & enrich the local American Indian community with projects focusing on community development, human services, information & referral services, cultural awareness & education, as well as improved communication within the American Indian community. *Activities*: Monthly community meetings; the Annual Gathering Retreat; Powwows. *Publications*: Indian Valley News (monthly); annual Bay Area American Indian Powwow Calendar. Established 1993.

AMERICAN INDIAN EDUCATION RESOURCE CENTER
749 Story Rd., Suite 300 • SAN JOSE, CA 95122
(408) 299-0590 Fax 299-0591
Rene Samayoa, Director

THE CALIFORNIA INDIAN CULTURE & SOVEREIGNTY CENTER (CICSC)
333 S. Twin Oaks Valley Rd. • SAN MARCOS, CA 92096
(760) 750-3535; Website: www.csusm.edu/cicsc/
Joely Proudfit (Luiseno), Center Director & Professor of American Indian Studies; E-mail: jproudfi@csusm.edu
Mission: To foster collaborative research & community service relationships between the faculty, staff, and students of CSU San Marcos & members of local tribal communities, for the purpose of developing & conducting research projects which support the maintenance of sovereignty & culture within those communities. The CICSC fosters collaborative research & community service relationships between the faculty, staff, and students of CSU San Marcos and members of Tribal communities, for the purpose of developing and conducting research projects that support the maintenance of sovereignty and culture within those communities. *Objectives*: to support political & economic development, education, health & wellness, media & film, language

preservation, & natural resource management; to reinforce collaborative research fostering indigenous research methods; to champion sovereignty and cultural preservation; to create and sustain communication between tribes and scholars

MARIN AMERICAN INDIAN ALLIANCE
P.O. Box 150565 • SAN RAFAEL, CA 94915
Website: www.marinamericanindianalliance.org
E-mail: marinindnuz@aol.com
Sky Road Webb (Miwok), Board President
Ben Benavides (Apache), Board Chairperson
Jim Goss (Cherokee), Board Vice President
Valerie Welte (Oneida), Secretary
Lea King (Cherokee/Choctaw), Treasurer
Salina (Sally) Sherlock (Muscogee Creek), Founder & Historian
Mission: To provide the American Indians living in Marin County the news of current happenings & programs of interest. Also, cultural & educational gatherings. *Activities*: Publishes a quarterly newsletter; annual Turtle Island Award to those who have made a major environmental contribution to the land known as Turtle Island to many American Indian tribes. Established 1973.

AMERICAN INDIAN HEALTH & SERVICES CORPORATION
4141 State St. • SANTA BARBARA, CA 93110
(805) 681-7356 Fax 681-7358; Website: www.aihscorp.org
Linda J. Murray (Pima), Board Chairperson
Scott Black, Executive Director; E-mail: sblack@aihscorp.org
Deonna Perez, Director of Operations
Angelina Speltz, Newsletter editor; E-mail: newsletter@aihscorp.org
Joe Quiroga, Community Outreach Specialist
Dr. Hollanda Leon, Medical Director (681-7144)
Mission: To promote & provide quality services to improve the health & wellbeing of American Indian/Alaska Natives and other community members. *Departments*: Medical, Dental, Human Services, Community Outreach. *Programs*: Diabetes Wellness Program; Clinic on Wheels; Health Education. *Publication*: Native Sun Newsletter, quarterly.

INDIAN HEALTH COUNCIL – SANTA YSABEL CLINIC
P.O. Box 10 • SANTA YSABEL, CA 92070
See Rincon Clinic, Valley Center listing

LOCAL INDIANS FOR EDUCATION (LIFE)
P.O. Box 729 • SHASTA LAKE, CA 96019
(530) 275-1513 Fax 275-6280; Rod Lindsay, Executive Director
E-mail: rod@localindiansforeducation.com

NATIVE AMERICAN INDIAN CENTER
Edison High School, 1425 S. Center • STOCKTON, CA 95206
(209) 933-7000 ext. 8069 Fax 953-4261
Dale Fleming, Sr. Program Specialist
Purpose: To meet culturally related academic needs.

LASSEN COUNTY AMERICAN INDIAN ORGANIZATION
930.5 Joaquin St., P.O. Box 1549, SUSANVILLE, CA 96130
(530) 257-2687 Fax 257-9071
Laura Medvin, President; Sandra Lowry, Director

SUSANVILLE INDIAN RANCHERIA EDUCATION CENTER
745 Joaquin St. • SUSANVILLE, CA 96130
(530) 252-1651 Fax 251-2030
Michelle Godman, Director; E-mail: mgodman@frontier.com

CALIFORNIA INDIAN LEGAL SERVICES
Box 488, 200 W. Henry St. • UKIAH, CA 95482
(707) 462-3825 Fax 462-4235; Website: www.caindian.org
Devon Lee Lomayesva, Executive Director
Summer Morales, Executive Assistant; Maureen Geary, Contact
See Oakland (main office) listing. Counties served: Butte, Colusa, Glenn, Lake, Mendocino, Napa, Nevada, Plumas, Sierra, Sonoma, Sutter, and Yuba.

ADVOCATES FOR INDIGENOUS CALIFORNIA LANGUAGE SURVIVAL
221 Idora Ave. • VALLEJO, CA 95491
(707) 486-6806 Fax (866) 644-7616; Website: www.aicls.org
Richard Bugbee (Payoomkawichum), Board Chairperson
Marina Drummer, Administrator
Board members: Kayla Carpenter (Hupa/Yurok/Karuk), Julian Lang (Karuk), Vincent Medina (Chochenyo-Ohlone), Deborah Morillo (Chumash), Stan Rodriguez (Kumeyaay), Nancy Richardson Steele (Karuk), Carly Tex (Mono), Matthew Vestuto (Barbareno/Ventunero Mission), Leanne Hinton (Linguistic Advisor). *Goals*: To support 20 master-apprentice teams in California, and spread the master-apprentice model in California & elsewhere; to develop advanced teacher-training program for advanced apprentices & other

California Indians involved in language teaching; to develop an outreach program to tribes nationally offering a package of services for language revitalization.

INDIAN HEALTH COUNCIL – RINCON CLINIC
50100 Golsh Rd. • VALLEY CENTER, CA 92082
(760) 749-1410 Fax 749-1564; Website: www.indianhealth.com
Romelle Majel-McCauley, Chief Executive Officer
Daniel J. Calac, MD, Chief Medical Officer
Purpose: To create awareness & educate local Native American reservations on HIV/AIDS prevention. *Activities*: B.E.A.R. Program - Be Educated & Responsible, youth-adult program on HIV/AIDS awareness, prevention & incorporating wellness & healthy lifestyles.

RINCON INDIAN EDUCATION CENTER
1 W. Tribal Rd., P.O. Box 1147 • VALLEY CENTER, CA 92082
(760) 749-1386 Fax 749-8838; Hun-wut Turner, Director
E-mail: rinconeducation@yahoo.com

SOUTHERN CALIFORNA TRIBAL CHAIRMEN'S ASSOCIATION (SCTCA)
P.O. Box 1470 • VALLEY CENTER, CA 92082
(760) 742-8600 Fax 742-8611; Website: www.sctca.net
A multi-service non-profit corporation established in 1972 for a consortium of 19 federally recognized Indian tribes in Southern California. The primary mission of SCTCA is to serve the health, welfare, safety, education, cultural, economic and employment needs of its tribal members and enrolled Indians in the San Diego County urban areas. A board of directors comprised of tribal chairpersons from each of its member Tribes governs SCTCA. SCTCA coordinates & administers numerous grant programs for its members and the southern California Indian community, including: Tribal Temporary Assistance to Needy Families (TANF), Law Enforcement, Food Commodities, Information Technology Services, Rincon Community Day Care, Adult Vocational Training, Career Development Center, Low Income Home Energy Assistance Program (LIHEAP), the Library Program, Child Care Development Services, Tribal Digital Village (TDV) and Resource Prevention Program.

CALIFORNIA NATIVE AMERICAN HERITAGE COMMISSION
1550 Harbor Blvd., Suite 100 • WEST SACRAMENTO, CA 95814
(916) 373-3710 Fax 373-5471
Website: www.nahc.ca.gov; E-mail: nahc@nahc.ca.gov
Cynthia Gomez (Yokut), Tribal Advisor/Executive Secretary
James Ramos (Serrano/Cahuilla), Chairman
Laura Miranda (Luiseno), Vice Chairperson
Julie Tumamait-Stenslie (Chumash), Secretary
(916) 653-6251 – Carol Gaubatz, Program Analyst
Commissioners: William Mungary (Paiute/White Mountain Apache), Reginald Pagaling (Santa Ynez Chumash), Leslie Lohse (Nomlaki), Marshall McKay (Wintun), Jill Sherman (Hoopa), *Description*: Composed of California tribal members. *Purpose*: For the preservation & protection of Native American human remains, associated grave goods & cultural resources. The Commission is responsible for implementing California's repatriation laws.

CALIFORNIA INDIAN BASKETWEAVERS ASSOCIATION
P.O. Box 1348 • WOODLAND, CA 95776
(530) 668-1332 Fax 668-1386
Website: www.ciba.org; E-mail: ciba@ciba.org
Linda Navarro (Cahuilla/Shasta), Executive Director
Carrie Garcia (Luiseno/Cahuilla), Board Chairperson
Diania Caudell (Luiseno), Treasurer
Leah Mata (Northern Chumash) Secretary
Deborah McConnell (Yurok/Quinault/Hoopa), NW California Field Director
Home offices: P.O. Box 426, Hoopa, CA 95546 (530) 625-4057
Publication: Newsletter.

COLORADO

COLORADO INDIAN BAR ASSOCIATION
c/o Native American Rights Fund, 1506 Broadway • BOULDER, CO 80302
(303) 447-8760
Padraic McCoy (Quechan), President
E-mail: pmccoy@tildenmccoy.com
Purpose: To promote the development of Indian law for the maximum benefit of Indian people; strives for justice and effective legal representation for all Indian people; provides networking & support to encourage Native Americans to pursue careers in law; & promotes the nomination of Native American for judicial appointments. Scholarships.' Established 1986.

COLORADO COMMISSION OF INDIAN AFFAIRS (CCIA)
130 State Capitol • DENVER, CO 80203
(303) 866-3027 Fax 866-5469

Website: www.colorado.gov/cs
Joseph Garcia, Lt. Gov. & Chairperson
Ernest House, Jr., Executive Director (866-5470)
E-mail: ernest.house@state.co.us
Purpose: To improve the government-to-government relationship and overall quality of life of the Indian people of Colorado (primarily the two Ute tribes located in southwest Colorado - Ute Mountain Ute & Southern Ute Tribes) while preserving their culture and traditions. *Publication*: Colorado Directory of American Indian Resources.

DENVER INDIAN CENTER, INC.
4407 Morrison Rd. • DENVER, CO 80219
(877) 8-INDIAN; (303) 936-2688 Fax 936-2699
Website: www.denverindiancenter.org
Colleen Brave Honomichl, Executive Director
Lisa Harjo, Circle of Learning Program Director
Purpose: To empower our youth, families & community through self-determination, cultural identity and education. *Programs*: Native Workforce Program; Native Youth Program; Native Elders Program; The Circle of Learning Program embodies a cultural approach to teaching in a preschool setting. Indian culture is interwoven into all classroom activities. Developed a multicultural preschool curriculum model called The Circle Never Ends.

ROCKY MOUNTAIN INDIAN CHAMBER OF COMMERCE
924 W. Colfax #104F, P.O. Box 40749 • DENVER, CO 80204
(303) 629-0102 Fax 595-8880
Website: www.rmicc.org; E-mail: rmicc@rmicc.org
Shadana Dickerson (Oglala Lakota), Executive Director
Dee St. Cyr (Winnebago of Nebraska), Board Chairperson
Colleen Brave (Oglala Lakota), Vice Chairperson
Board members: Andrea Lesher (Cherokee), Shebon Kelin (Caddo), Russell Stands Over Bull (Crow), Chris Hazlett (Caddo)
Purpose: To enhance Native businesses in their path to growth; to empower Native professionals & entrepreneurs in their path to success; to encourage Native students in their path to continued education; and to embrace Partners in their path to reach the Native Community.

WESTERN AMERICAN INDIAN CHAMBER OF COMMERCE
1900 Wazee St. #100 • DENVER, CO 80202
(303) 620-9292 Fax 664-5139
Bob Outland (Choctaw), Vice President
Board members: Ted Byrant (Choctaw/Cherokee), Ava Hamilton (Arapaho), John Goes in Center (Lakota), Debbie Hedin (Lakota)
Purpose: To assist American Indians in the pursuit of self-sufficiency through business success; to provide a forum for members to address legislative issues & government concerns that affect American Indian business; t establish a network of Native American tourism interests in the country to cooperatively develop, market and present Indian tourism attractions. This network includes Indian tribes, individuals, associations & businesses both on and off the reservation. Established 1989.

CONNECTICUT

CONNECTICUT INDIAN AFFAIRS COUNCIL
79 Elm St. • HARTFORD, CT 06106
(860) 424-3066 Fax 424-4058
Edward W. Sarabia (Tlingit), Coordinator (2007-present)
Purpose: To provide services & programs to the reservation communities; advises the DEP Commissioner about the general health, safety and well-being of people residing on reservations; and advises the Commissioner on care & management of reservation lands and buildings. Established 1973.

CONNECTICUT INDIAN COUNCIL - NEW LONDON OFFICE
165 State St., NEW LONDON, CT 06320
(860) 437-0013
Darrell Waldron, Executive Director (see Rhode island Indian Council)
E-mail: dwaldron@rhodeislandindiancouncil.org
Contessa Bigcrow-Jenkins, Career Counselor
E-mail: cbigcrow@rhodeislandindiancouncil.org
Kara Waldron-Murray, Job Developer; E-mail: karawaldron@live.com

CONNECTICUT INDIAN COUNCIL-NORTH STONINGTON OFFICE
25 Norwich-Westerly Rd.
P.O. Box 221 • NORTH STONINGTON, CT 06359
(860) 535-1277 Fax 535-1279
Darrell Waldron, Executive Director (see Rhode island Indian Council)
E-mail: dwaldron@rhodeislandindiancouncil.org
Brenda Geer (599-1413), WIA Career Counselor
E-mail: bgeer@rhodeislandindiancouncil.org
A Rhode Island Indian Council location.

DELAWARE

DELAWARE DIVISION OF HISTORICAL & CULTURAL AFFAIRS
21 The Green • DOVER, DE 19901
(302) 736-7400 Fax 739-5660
Valerie Kauffman, Historic-Site Interpreter

DELAWARE INDIAN COUNCIL/NANTICOKE INDIAN CENTER
27073 John J. Williams Hwy. • MILLSBORO, DE 19966
(302) 945-3400 Fax 947-9400; Website: www.nanticokeindians.org
E-mail: info@nanticokeindians.org
Larry Jackson, Executive Director
Natosha N. Carmine, Chief; Isaac Jackson, Assistant Chief
Marilyn Jackson, WIA Career Counselor

DISTRICT OF COLUMBIA

AMERICAN INDIAN SOCIETY OF WASHINGTON, DC
P.O. Box 6431 • FALLS CHURCH, VA 22040
(804) 448-3707; (202) 492-1963; Website: www.aisdc.org
Hope Butler (Piscataway-Conoy), President
E-mail: aisdcpresident@gmail.com
Terry Rose (Choctaw), 1st Vice President
Reggie Tupponce (Upper Mattaponi), 2nd Vice President
E-mail: ais2ndvp@gmail.com
Daniella Johnson-Little (Seminole of Oklahoma), Treasurer
E-mail: aistreasurer2016@gmail.com
Angel (Sundown) Washington (Muscogee) (Creek) of Oklahoma
E-mail: aisdcsecretary2016@gmail.com
See listing under Virginia.

INDIAN ARTS & CRAFTS BOARD - U.S. DEPARTMENT OF INTERIOR
1849 C St., NW, MS: 2528, MIB • WASHINGTON 20240
(888) 278-3253; (202) 208-3773 Fax 208-5196
E-mail: iacb@ios.doi.gov
Meredith Z. Stanton, Director
Harvey Pratt (Cheyenne Arapaho), Chairperson
Rose Fosdick (Nome Eskimo), Vice Chairperson
Purpose: To promote the development of Indian and Alaskan Native arts & handicrafts. *Activities*: Provides business & personal professional advice, information, & promotion to artists & craftsmen & their organizations; operates the Museum of the Plains Indian, Browning, MT; Sioux Indian Museum, Rapid City, SD; and Southern Plains Indian Museum, Anadarko, OK. *Publication*: Source Director: Indian, Eskimo, Aleut Owned & Operated Arts & Crafts Businesses. Established 1935.

FLORIDA

FLORIDA GOVERNOR'S COUNCIL ON INDIAN AFFAIRS, INC.
625 N. Adams St. • TALLAHASSEE, FL 32301
(800) 322-9186; (850) 488-0730 Fax 488-5875
Website: www.fgcia.org; E-mail: info@fgcia.org
Curtis Osceola, Executive Director
E-mail: cosceola@fgcia.org
Terrance Clark, Training Coordinator
E-mail: tclark@fgcia.org
Joe Quetone, Consultant (Director Emeritus)
E-mail: quetonej@fgcia.org
Purpose: To create an awareness and serve the legal, social, and economic needs of the Native American citizens in the state of Florida. *Programs*: Employment & Training; Youth; Educational resources. Established 1974.

GEORGIA

AMERICAN CHEROKEE CONFEDERACY
619 Pine Cone Rd. • ALBANY, GA 31705
(229) 787-5722 Fax 787-0073
Website: www.acconfederacy.org
E-mail: info@acconfederacy.org
Publication: American Cherokee Confederacy News

AMERICAN INDIAN ENVIRONMENTAL OFFICE
USEPA Region 4, Office of the Regional Administrator, 14th Floor
61 Forsyth St., SW • ATLANTA, GA 30303
(404) 562-8357 Fax 562-9961
A. Stanley Meiburg, Acting Regional Coordinator

GEORGIA COUNCIL ON AMERICAN INDIAN CONCERNS
c/o Historic Preservation Division, Georgia Dept. of Natural Resources
2610 Hwy. 155 SW • STOCKBRIDGE, GA 30281
(770) 389-7265 Fax (404) 651-5871
Website: www.georgiaindiancouncil.org
Nealie McCormick, Chairperson; Ralph Crews, Treasurer
Purpose: To preserve the cultural legacy of Georgia Indians; to protect their burial & archaeological sites and to enhance their lives and well being in the present. Established 1992.

GEORGIA CHEROKEE HERITAGE FOUNDATION
56 Creek Run Ct. • DAHLONEGA, GA 30533
(706) 864-6010; James Hawkins, Contact

HAWAII

COUNCIL FOR NATIVE HAWAIIAN ADVANCEMENT (CNHA)
2149 Lauwiliwili St. • KAPOLEI, HI 96707
(800) 709-2642; (808) 596-8155 Fax 596-8156
Website: www.hawaiiancouncil.org
E-mail: info@hawaiiancouncil.org
Michelle Kauhane, President & CEO
E-mail: michelle@hawaiiancouncil.org
Napali Woode, Sr. VP & CFO
E-mail: napali@hawaiiancouncil.org
Description: The council is a non-profit statewide & national network of more than 100 Native Hawaiian organizations. *Purpose*: Dedicated to supporting Native Hawaiian communities and the organizations that serve them; operates a public policy center on Native Hawaiian issues, conducts resource development & organizational capacity training, and owns & operates an information technology company in partnership with 11 Indian tribes & Alaska Native firms. *Subsidiaries*: Hawaiian Homestead Technology, Inc.; Native Hawaiian Policy Center; Native Hawaiian Economic Alliance www.nativealliance.com (808) 596-8155 x 23. Established 2001.

OFFICE OF HAWAIIAN AFFAIRS
560 N. Nimitz Hwy., Suite 200 • HONOLULU, HI 96817
(808) 594-1835 Fax 594-1865
Kamanaopono Crabbe, Chief Executive Officer
OHA is focused on strategic priorities for improving the conditions of Native Hawaiians its culture, economic self-sufficiency, education, governance & health. OHA's advocacy involves conducting research whose findings are used to guide decisions and empower communities to inspire positive results in these areas. OHA's advocacy also calls for developing and shaping public policies that have broad implications for the Hawaiian community. OHA's advocacy is reflected in its efforts to help ensure that laws are complied with at the local, state & federal levels. In addition, OHA's advocacy requires working with communities to share information and build public support for Hawaiian issues.

IDAHO

IDAHO COUNCIL ON INDIAN AFFAIRS
450 W. State St. • BOISE, ID 83720
(208) 334-2475 Fax 334-2125
Rep. Marc Gibbs, Chairperson
Silas Whitman (Nez Perce), Vice Chair
Staff: Ryan Bush & Charmi Arregui
Purpose: To monitor & review legislation & state policies that impact state/tribal relation issues; to advise the governor, legislature & state departments; to establish advisory committees; cooperate or facilitate contracting between tribes and others.

IDAHO STATE DEPARTMENT OF EDUCATION OFFICE OF INDIAN EDUCATION
P.O. Box 83720 • BOISE, ID 83720-0027
(208) 334-2873 Fax 334-2664
Pamela Parks, Director
E-mail: parks@sde.idaho.gov
Johanna Jones, Indian Education Coordinator
E-mail: jjones@sde.idaho.gov
Purpose: To meet the educational needs of all students of Indian heritage in the State of Idaho & to promote greater understanding among all students in regards to the diverse backgrounds & cultures of American people. Established 1996.

NORTHWEST INDIAN HOUSING ASSOCIATION
Nez Perce Tribal Housing Authority, P.O. Box 188 • LAPWAI, ID 83540
(360) 466-4081 Fax 466-7219; Website: www.nwiha.org
Laurie Ann Cloud, Chairperson (208) 843-2229
E-mail: lauriec@nezperce.org
Joseph Diehl, Interim Executive Director (206) 290-5498

ILLINOIS

AMERICAN INDIAN ASSOCIATION OF ILLINOIS
6554 N. Rockwell St. • CHICAGO, IL 60645
(773) 338-8320 Phone & Fax; E-mail: aiaillinois@aol.com
Website: www.chicago-american-indian-edu.org
Dr. Dorene Wiese, Chief Executive Officer
Departments: Medicine Shield College Program
E-mail: dpwiese@aol.com; Chicago American Indian Museum
E-mail: zekezuni@yahoo.com
American Indian Urban Institute, E-mail: dpwiese@aol.com
Native Scholars Tutoring, E-mail: melaniecloud@yahoo.com
Black Hawk Performance Co., E-mail: zekezuni@yahoo.com
Bear Claw Multimedia & Tribal Wood Film Festival
E-mail: dpwiese@aol.com

AMERICAN INDIAN CENTER OF CHICAGO
1630 W. Wilson • CHICAGO, IL 60640
(773) 275-5871 Fax 275-5874
Website: www.aic-chicago.org; E-mail: aic50@aic-chicago.org
Vincent Romero (Laguna Pueblo), Executive Director
Tevelee Gudino (Dakota/Apache), Program Coordinator
Roberta Powless, Senior Program Assistant
Emily Loerzel, Project Beacon Program Manager
David Bender, Education Coordinator/Organizer
Cyndee Fox-Starr (Omaha/Odawa), Senior Program Coordinator &
Special Events Coordinator; E-mail: cyndee@aic-chicago.org
Les Begay, Board President; Adam A. Fahey, Vice Chairperson
Purpose: To promote the President & communication among Indian people of all tribes living in metro Chicago; to foster the economic & educational advancement of Indian people; to sustain cultural & artistic pursuits; and, to perpetuate Indian cultural values. *Activities*: Annual Powwow.

AMERICAN INDIAN ENVIRONMENTAL OFFICE
USEPA Region 5, 77 W. Jackson Blvd. • CHICAGO, IL 60604
(312) 353-2306 Fax 353-9533
Darrel Harmon, Director; E-mail: harmon.darrel@epa.gov

AMERICAN INDIAN HEALTH SERVICE OF CHICAGO
4081 N. Broadway • CHICAGO, IL 60613
(773) 883-9100 Fax 883-0005
Kenneth R. Scott, Executive Director
Urban Indian Health Program of the Indian Health Service (IHS)

CHICAGO-CITYWIDE AMERICAN INDIAN EDUCATION COUNCIL
7019 N. Ashland Ave., Room 209 • CHICAGO, IL 60626
(773) 534-2735 Fax 334-5234

ST. AUGUSTINE'S CENTER
4512 N. Sheridan Rd. • CHICAGO, IL 60640
(773) 784-1050; Elmira McClure, Director

MIDWEST SOARRING FOUNDATION
P.O. Box 275 • LYONS, IL 60534
133 W. 13th St., Lockport, IL 60441 (Cultural Center)
(708) 257-4300; Website: www.midwestsoarring.org
Joseph Standing Bear Schranz (White Earth Ojibwe), President
Myles Goddard (Ojibwe), Vice President of Education
Janet Sevilla, Vice President of Operations
Jay Thompson, Secretary; Karren Thompson, Treasurer
Purpose: To work toward repatriation, protecting sacred sites, educating the public & promoting community building among all people regarding indigenous lifeways. *Activities*: Annual Harvest Powwow; Cultural Center located at 1 Hickory Lane, Westchester, IL 60154

INDIANA

AMERICAN INDIAN CENTER OF INDIANA (AICI)
2236 E. 10th St. • INDIANAPOLIS, IN 46201
(800) 745-5872; (317) 917-8000 Fax 808-2390
Website: www.americanindiancenter.org
Doug Poe (Cherokee), Executive Director
E-mail: dpoe@americanindiancenter.org
Mark Bush, WIA Case Manager
E-mail: mbush@americanindiancenter.org
Andrea Warren (Cherokee), Secretary
Teri Cardwell (Cherokee), Chair; Anita Ray (Shawnee/Cherokee), Vice Chair
Purpose: To provide comprehensive workforce development services to nearly 40,000 American Indians residing in Indiana.

INDIANA NATIVE AMERICAN INDIAN AFFAIRS COMMISSION
100 N. Senate Ave., Room N103 • INDIANAPOLIS, IN 46204
(317) 234-4887 Fax 232-7487
Website: www.in.gov/inaiac/; E-mail: info@inaiac.in.gov
Kerry Steiner, Executive Director
Sally Tuttle (Choctaw of Oklahoma), Commission Chairperson
Purpose: To bring the Native American communities together, help identify & provide opportunities to the Native American community, and enhance social, cultural, community & economic development in Indiana; to study problems common to Native American citizens of Indiana in the areas of employment, education, civil rights, health, housing, and the promotion of Native American awareness...and to make recommendations.

AMERICAN INDIAN CENTER OF INDIANA, INC.
406 N. Broadway • PERU, IN 46970
(800) 887-5872; (765) 473-3010 Fax 473-3018
James Cyr, Director

IOWA

IOWA DEPARTMENT OF HUMAN RIGHTS
IOWA COMMISSION ON NATIVE AMERICAN AFFAIRS
Lucas State Office Bldg. 2nd Floor
321 E. 12th St. • DES MOINES, IA 50319
(515) 242-6334; Jill Avery, Executive Director
E-mail: jill.avery@iowa.gov

SIOUX CITY AMERICAN INDIAN CENTER
610 13th St. • SIOUX CITY, IA 51105
(712) 255-8957

MESQUAKIE FRIENDS CENTER
P.O. Box 36 • TOLEDO, IA 52342
(641) 484-2329; E-mail: mesquakiefriends@yahoo.com
Victor & Brenda White, Contacts

KANSAS

AMERICAN INDIAN ENVIRONMENTAL OFFICE
USEPA Region 7, 901 N. 5th St. • KANSAS CITY, KS 66101
(913) 551-7381 Fax 551-7053
Wolfgang Brandner, Tribal Program Coordinator
E-mail: brandner.wolfgang@epa.gov

FOUR WINDS NATIVE CENTER
1423 Haskell Ave. • LAWRENCE, KS 66044
(785) 832-8111; E-mail: 4.winds.nc@gmail.com
Cameron Whitaker, Executive Director
Patty Battese, Board President
Purpose: To provide community services, such as: emergency food, utility & shelter assistance, housing, job board, craft workshops. Operates Tall Grass Giftshop & Share/Care garden. Personnel: Dan Spurgin & Nicole Jay. Library.

KANSAS NATIVE AMERICAN AFFAIRS OFFICE
900 SW Jackson St., Room 100 • TOPEKA, KS 66612
(785) 296-1904 Fax 296-1795
Website: www.knaa.ks.gov; E-mail: knaa@ks.gov
Chris Howell, Executive Director/Tribal Liaison
Tribes: Iowa Tribe of Kansas & Nebraska; Kickapoo Tribe of Kansas; Prairie Band Potawatomi Nation; Sac & Fox Nation of Missouri in Kansas & Nebraska; Kaw Nation. Established 2011.

AMERICAN INDIAN CHAMBER OF COMMERCE OF KANSAS
P.O. Box 750222 • TOPEKA, KS 66046
(785) 749-8434 Fax 832-6605

KANSAS STATE GAMING AGENCY (KSGA)
420 SE 6th, Suite 3000 • TOPEKA, KS 66607
(785) 368-6202 Fax 291-3798
Website: www.kansas.gov/ksga/
E-mail: ksga@ksgaming.org
Mark Dodd (Prairie Band Potawatomi), Executive Director
Purpose: To foster a spirit of cooperation with all tribal gaming entities; to promote & maintain the public' trust in Kansas tribal gaming operations. *Kansas Tribal Casinos*: Casino White Cloud; Iowa Tribe Gaming Commission; Golden Eagle Casino, Horton; Kickapoo Tribe Gaming Commission, Horton; Prairie Band Potawatomi Casino, Mayetta; Prairie Band Potawatomi Nation Gaming Commission, Mayetta; Sac & Fox Casino, Powhattan. Est. 1996.

MID-AMERICA ALL-INDIAN CENTER, INC.
650 N. Seneca • WICHITA, KS 67203
(316) 350-3340 Fax 262-4216
Website: www.theindiancenter.org
April Scott, Executive Director (350-3341)
 E-mail: ascott@wichita.gov
Crystal Flannery-Bachicha, Education Coordinator (350-3345)
 E-mail: cbachicha@wichita.gov
Sarah Adams, Museum Director; (350-3342)
 E-mail: sadams@wichita.gov
Purpose: To promote awareness of Native American culture in the community; to offer emergency social services for members of the Native American community & transients. *Programs*: Job Training Program Assistance. *Activities*: Valentines Powwow; American Indian Festival, July; Kiva. Museum & Library. Established 1969.

KENTUCKY

THE KENTUCKY CENTER FOR NATIVE AMERICAN ARTS & CULTURE
P.O. Box 30 • CARROLLTON, KY 41008-0030
Website: www.kcnaac.org; E-mail: info@kcnaac.org
Mike Presnell (Cherokee), Board President
Stephen LeBoueff (*Black Bear*) (Blackfeet), Board Vice President
Darlene Applegate, Board Secretary/Treasurer
Purpose: To honor & celebrate Native American heritage & contributions to the Commonwealth of Kentucky, the Ohio River Valley region, and other contiguous states; to provide education on Native American heritage & contributions to Kentucky; to promote research of Native American cultures & history within Kentucky; to promote further economic development in Kentucky through Native American tourism; to promote the development of Native American arts & culture in Kentucky. *Resources*: Permanent & traveling exhibits; library with a research archive; auditorium for lectures & theatre; art gallery; outdoor native plant gardens; nature trails. *Publication*: Newsletter.

KENTUCKY NATIVE AMERICAN HERITAGE COMMISSION
300 Washington St. • FRANKFORT, KY 40601
(502) 564-7005 ext. 125 Fax 564-5820
Tressa Brown, Coordinator; E-mail: tressa.brown@ky.gov
Purpose: To educate and communicate the rich diversity & heritage of Native American peoples in Kentucky; to advocate Native American participation in state agencies & boards; to encourage state agencies to develop & support Native American programs. Established 1996.

LOUISIANA

INTERTRIBAL COUNCIL OF LOUISIANA
8281 Goodwood Blvd. #1 • BATON ROUGE, LA 70806
(225) 924-1291; Kevin Billiot, Director
Purpose: To develop communications among the five member tribes: Jena Band of Choctaws; Chitimacha Tribe of Louisiana; Coushatta Tribe of Louisiana; United Houma Nation; and Tunica-Biloxi Tribe.

INTERTRIBAL COUNCIL OF LOUISIANA
991 Grand Caillou Rd. • HOUMA, LA 70363
(985) 851-5408
Purpose: To develop communications among the five member tribes: Jena Band of Choctaws; Chitimacha Tribe of Louisiana; Coushatta Tribe of Louisiana; United Houma Nation; and Tunica-Biloxi Tribe.

LOUISIANA GOVERNOR'S OFFICE OF INDIAN AFFAIRS
150 N. Third St. #713, P.O. Box 94004 • BATON ROUGE, LA 70804
(800) 863-0098; (225) 219-8715 Fax 219-7551
 E-mail: indian.affairs@la.gov
Mark Ford, Executive Director; E-mail: mark.ford@la.gov
Purpose: To assist Louisiana American Indians in receiving education, realizing self-determination, improving quality of life, and developing mutual relationship between the state & the tribes. Program: Scholarships.

MAINE

MAINE STATE DEPT. OF EDUCATION
OFFICE OF INDIAN EDUCATION
39A Union St. • CALAIS, ME 04619
(207) 454-2126; Website: www.mie.bie.edu
Nancy Mullins, Coordinator; E-mail: nancy.mullins@maine.gov

MAINE TRIBAL/STATE RELATIONS OFFICE
6 River Rd. • INDIAN HEAD, ME 04468
(207) 827-7776; Priscilla A. Attean, Contact

MAINE INDIAN BASKETMAKERS ALLIANCE (MIBA)
P.O. Box 325 • OLD TOWN, ME 04468
(207) 859-9722; Website: www.maineindianbaskets.org
Jennifer Sapiel Neptune (Penobscot), Project Manager
 E-mail: jennifermiba@aol.com
Molly Neptune Parker (Pasamaquoddy), Board President
Fred Tomah (Maliseet), Board Vice President
Goals: To preserve & document the tradition of basket-making among the four tribes of Maine: Maliseet, Micmac, Passamaquoddy and Penobscot tribes; to expand markets for baskets; to provide outreach, education & apprenticeships to younger members of the tribes to ensure continuation of the traditions. *Activities*: In 2002, MIBA opened its first retail store, the Wabanaki Arts Center, in Old Town, Maine, to provide an outlet for the four tribe's basketmakers; annual Native American Festival & Basketmaker's Market.

MAINE INDIAN TRIBAL-STATE COMMISSION (MITSC)
P.O. Box 241 • STILLWATER, ME 04489
(207) 944-8376; Website: www.mitsc.org
E-mail: mitsced@roadrunner.com
John Dieffenbacher-Krall, Executive Director
Description: An intergovernmental agency concerned with the relationship between the state, the Passamaquoddy Tribe & Penobscot Indian Nation. Library.

MARYLAND

BALTIMORE AMERICAN INDIAN CENTER
113 S. Broadway, P.O. Box 6171 • BALTIMORE, MD 21231
(410) 675-3535 Fax 675-6909; Website: www.baic.org
Linda Cox, Chairperson; Juan Boston, Vice Chairperson
Dennis Seymour, Secretary; Jovina Chavis, Treasurer
Helen Heckwolf, Office Administrator
Purpose: To help American Indians with their cultural, social, economic, housing & educational needs. *Programs*: Cultural Preservation & Education Program; Seniors Program; Vera Shank Learning Center; Health & Healing Services; American Indian Education. *Activities*: BAIC Scholarship Fund; Rev. James Dial Memorial Fund; housing; business development; job placement; community services; alcoholism; youth program; Brantley Blue Awards; annual powwow. *Publication*: Smoke Signals, newsletter.

NATIVE AMERICAN LIFELINES
106 W. Clay St. • BALTIMORE, MD 21201
(410) 837-2258 Fax 837-2692; Website: www.nativeamericanlifelines.org
Crystal Godwin, Acting Executive Director
Dr. Shelly Wiechelt, Clinical Director
Christina Allen, Substance Abuse Counselor
Roger L. Locklear (Lumbee), Board Chairperson
Diane Hodges (Lumbee), Treasurer
Urban Indian Health Program (UIHP): Substance Abuse Prevention & Education; Medical/Dental Health; Prevention Workshops; Prison Outreach; Cultural Class; Transportation.

MARYLAND COMMISSION ON INDIAN AFFAIRS
301 W. Preston St. #1500 • BALTIMORE, MD 21202
(800) 735-2258; (410) 767-7631 Fax 333-7542
Website: www.americanindian.maryland.gov
E. Keith Colston (Tuscarora/Lumbee), Administrative Director
 E-mail: keith.colston@maryland.gov
Thomas W. Windsor II (Piscataway), Chairperson
Ashley Minner (Lumbee), Vice Chairperson
Description: Consists of nine members appointed by the Governor for three-year terms. *Purpose*: To support, initiate, coordinate & implement educational, social & economic projects that affect the diverse Indian communities in Maryland; and to increase public awareness & appreciation of the contributions that Indians have made to life in Maryland. Established 1976.

AMERICAN INDIAN INTER-TRIBAL CULTURAL ORGANIZATION
P.O. Box 775 • ROCKVILLE, MD 20848
(301) 869-9381 Fax (703) 823-0609
Kathy Frick, President; E-mail: aiitco@aol.com
Purpose: A membership group of Native Americans & non-Indians interested and active in the preservation & extension of knowledge of Native American cultures. Activities: annual powwow in Frederick, Maryland. *Publication*: Rattle & Drum (newsletter).

MASSACHUSETTS

AMERICAN INDIAN ENVIRONMENTAL OFFICE
EPA – New England, Region 1
5 Post Office Square, Suite 100 • BOSTON, MA 02109

(617) 918-1123 (phone & fax)
Mike Stover, Indian Program Manager; E-mail: stover.michael@epa.gov

MASSACHUSETTS CENTER FOR NATIVE AMERICAN AWARENESS, INC.
P.O. Box 5885 • BOSTON, MA 02114
(617) 642-1683 Fax 884-4889
Website: www.mcnaa.org; E-mail: mcnaa@aol.com
Burne Stanley-Peters, Founder & President
Board members: Dawn Duncan, Claudia Fox Tree, Kim Orben, Anthony Silva
Description: Consists of tribes, Native American organizations, non-profit organizations & groups in the New England area. *Purpose*: To serve the cultural, spiritual, and social needs of the Native American peoples residing in Massachusetts; to promote & preserve the cultural & traditional ways of the Native Americans of the land. *Programs*: Chief Red Blanket Scholarship Program; Slow Turtle Youth Empowerment & Cultural Enrichment Program; Fuel Assistance Program. *Activities*: National Native American Heritage Day Powwow; Annual Fundraising Auction & Luncheon in October; adult lecture series (Spring & Fall); children's workshops (mid-Winter & Spring); monthly festivals, powwows & socials. *Publication*: TurtleTalk, quarterly newsletter. Established 1989.

MASSACHUSETTS COMMISSION ON INDIAN AFFAIRS
100 Cambridge St. #300 • BOSTON, MA 02114
(617) 573-1291 Fax 573-1460
John A. Peters, Jr., Executive Director
E-mail: john.peters@state.ma.us
Description: Consists of seven members of American Indian descent representing the major tribes of the Commonwealth of Massachusetts. *Purpose*: To assist Native American residents of Massachusetts with any problem common to them - social services, legal assistance, housing, employment, civil rights, treaty rights, etc. *Programs*: Re-internment Program; Scholarship Program. Established 1976.

MASSACHUSETTS INDIAN ASSOCIATION
245 Rockland Rd. • CARLISLE, MA 01741-1303
(508) 369-1235; Marjorie M. Findlay, Director
Purpose: To help Native Americans go to college. Scholarship Fund: Provides financial assistance to Native Americans who live in Massachusetts and are interested in pursuing postsecondary education. Stipends range up to $500 for undergraduates and $1,000 for graduate students

NORTH AMERICAN INDIAN CENTER OF BOSTON
105 S. Huntington Ave. • JAMAICA PLAIN, MA 02130
(617) 232-0343 Fax 232-3863
Website: www.naicob.org; E-mail: info@naicob.org
Joanne Dunn, Executive Director
E-mail: jdunn@naicob.org
Crystal Rizzo, Employment & Training Director
Raquel Halsey (Three Affiliated Tribes), Board President
Jamie Morrison (Cherokee), Vice President
Description: A multi-service social delivery system for the American Indian community of the Greater Boston area, and provides a mechanism for cultural activities. *Programs*: Employment & training; adult education; Head Start; Day Care; elderly; crafts; Indian Health Service; battered women; housing assistance; alcoholic treatment with halfway house; and speakers bureau. *Publication*: The Circle, monthly newsletter. Library. Established 1970.

UNITED AMERICAN INDIANS OF NEW ENGLAND
284 Amory St. • JAMAICA PLAIN, MA 02130
(617) 286-6574 (phone & fax)
Website: www.uaine.org; E-mail: info@uaine.org
Activities: Annual National Day of Morning (Thanksgiving Day)

GREATER LOWELL INDIAN CULTURAL ASSOCIATION (GLICA)
P.O. Box 1181 • LOWELL, MA 01853
(978) 551-2203; Website: www.glica.net
Tom 'Eagle Rising' Libby, Chief
E-mail: tandslibby@comcast.net
Rich 'Crow Dancing' Dube, Warchief (995-3712)
E-mail: phlebotomy53@yahoo.com
Sarah 'Morning Flower' Libby, Keeper of the Wampum (551-2201)
Dawn 'Quiet Rabbit Seeking' Libby, Keeper of the Word (270-0879)
E-mail: dawn.libby82@gmail.com
Description: A family orientated group of Native American Indians that come together to acknowledge & share their religion, culture, spirituality & traditions in accordance with the ways of their Ancestors. GLICA is composed of many different tribes of people from various Indian Nations. Our strength lies in our diversity and our ability to live in the present while holding on the past and looking forward to the future of our people.

NORTH AMERICAN INDIAN CENTER - TECUMSEH HOUSE
107 Fisher Ave. • ROXBURY, MA 02120
(617) 731-3366; John Szwyd, Director
E-mail: jszwyd1011@aol.com

MICHIGAN

SOUTHEASTERN MICHIGAN INDIANS, INC.
26641 Lawrence St. • CENTER LINE, MI 48015
(586) 756-1350 Fax 756-1352
Purpose: To provide services to Native American Indians of the metro tri-county areas including: job placement, employment & training activities, classroom training, referrals for other services, emergency food and clothing, and the preservation of Indian culture. *Activities*: Senior programs & special summer youth programs; powwows, cultural activities; museum display area; arts & crafts store "The Crafts of Many Tribes"; in the process of setting up a library. *Publication*: Talking Peace pipe, bimonthly newsletter. Established 1975.

AMERICAN INDIAN HEALTH & FAMILY SERVICES OF SOUTHEAST MICHIGAN
P.O. Box 810 • DEARBORN, MI 48121
(313) 846-3718 Fax 846-0150
Ashley Tuomi (Confederated Tribes of Grand Ronde), Executive Director
Chasity Dial (Lumbee), Director of Operations
Dr. Alice Kachman, MD, Medical Director/Provider
Glenn Wilson, Interim Behavioral Health Director
Nickole Fox (Cherokee/Blackfoot), Director of Health Education & Prevention
Keith Dayson (Little Traverse Bay Odawa), Cultural Services Coordinator
Martha Hinojosa (Walpole Island Ojibwe), Youth Program Coordinator
John Lemire, JD (Grand Portage Ojibwe), Board Chairperson
Description: A non-profit organization that provides services to Native Americans living in southeastern Michigan including health promotion/disease prevention programming, medical, dental, mental health, HIV & substance abuse counseling.

NORTH AMERICAN INDIAN ASSOCIATION OF DETROIT (NAIA)
22720 Plymouth Rd. • DETROIT, MI 48239
(313) 535-2966 Fax 535-8060; Website: www.naiadetroit.org
Brian Moore, Executive Director; E-mail: bmoore@naiadetroit.org
Sarah Brant, Program Manager; E-mail: sbrant@naiadetroit.org
Membership: 450. *Purpose*: To promote self-sufficiency for Native Americans through education assistance, employment training, & awareness of available human services; and to foster & preserve North American Indian culture & heritage. *Programs*: Job Training & Employment through U.S. Dept. of Labor - WIA-DINAP; GED (30 weeks) Native Literacy; Food & Friendship for Seniors; Youth Programs; Arts & Crafts Gallery business. *Publication*: Native Sun, bimonthly newsletter. Library. Annual meeting & powwow. Small resource library. Established 1940.

MICHIGAN INDIAN EDUCATION COUNCIL
P.O. Box 378 • HASLETT, MI 48840
(517) 373-6059; Website: www.miec.org
Dr. Martin Reinhardt (Ojibwe), President
E-mail: mreinhar@nmu.edu
June Mamagona-Fletcher (Odawa), Treasurer
E-mail: mamagona2003@gmail.com
Mission: To ensure the Anishinabe culture & traditions through educational collaboration, coordination, networking & strategic planning.

MICHIGAN DEPARTMENT OF HEALTH & HUMAN SERVICES NATVE AMERICAN AFFAIRS
333 S. Grand Ave., P.O. Box 30195 • LANSING, MI 48909
(517) 335-7782; Website: www.michigan.gov/mdhhs
E-mail: MDHHS-NAA-MIFPA@michigan.gov
Stacey Tadgerson (Sault Ste. Marie Ojibwe), Director
The Native American Affairs office provides a broad range of services to protect, preserve and strengthen Native American families both on and off tribal lands. They support an Indian population of approximately 130,000 with various services provided in partnership with Michigan's federally recognized tribes, the state historic tribes, Indian organizations, federal government and other community and state organizations.

NATIVE AMERICAN ARTS & CRAFTS COUNCIL
725 Ridgewood Ave. • LANSING, MI 48910
(517) 393-7236 (Phone & Fax); Website: www.lansingarts.org
Robin Menefee, Director; E-mail: robin_menefee@yahoo.com
Purpose: The preservation & promotion of the Woodland Indian Culture of Michigan through cultural programs that highlight the traditions of Woodland Indian arts & crafts. *Activity*: Riverbank Traditional Powwow.

NOKOMIS LEARNING CENTER
5153 Marsh Rd. • OKEMOS, MI 48864
(517) 349-5777 Fax 349-8560; Website: www.nokomis.org
E-mail: nokomislearningcenter@gmail.com
Brian Moore (Ojibwe), President
Kathy Yates, Secretary; Jim Sumbler, Treasureer
Purpose: A Native American Cultural Center dedicated to the preservation & presentation of the history, arts, and culture of the Anishnaabe people - the Ojibwe, Odawa, & Potawatomi nations. *Programs*: Sacred Cycles/Native Circles; Fur Trade Program; Native Dance & Powwow Traditions; Contemporary Issues; Dream Catcher Workshop; School-wide Assembly Programs; Speaker's Bureau. *Activities*: Tours/Groups. *Membership*: Annual, $10, Established 1988.

INTER-TRIBAL COUNCIL OF MICHIGAN, INC.
2956 Ashmun St. Suite A • SAULT STE. MARIE, MI 49783
(800) 562-4957; (906) 632-6896 Fax 632-1810
Website: www.itcmi.org; L. John Lufkins (Ojibwe), Executive Director
Levi Carrick, Sr. (Ojibwe), Board President' Warren Chris Swartz, VP
Purpose: Programs that will improve the economy, education & quality of life for Michigan Indians. *Departments*: Michigan Indian Child Welfare Agency; Child Family Assistance; Behavioral Health Services; Environmental Services; Health Education & Chronic Disease. *Programs*: Families First Program; Commodity Food Program; Head Start & Parent Child Center Programs; Low Income Energy Assistance; Single Parent Program; Behavioral Health Program; Michigan Native American Tobacco Coalition (MNATC). Established 1968.

MICHIGAN INDIAN LEGAL SERVICES, INC.
814 S. Garfield Ave. • TRAVERSE CITY, MI 49686
(800) 968-6877 Fax (231) 947-3956; Website: www.mils3.org
Tanya Marie Gibbs (Mattawan), Chair
Lansing office: 215 S. Washington Sq., Suite C,
Lansing, MI 48933 (888) 218-9254 Fax (517) 316-0654

MINNESOTA

THE GROTTO FOUNDATION
1315 Red Fox Rd., Suite 100 • ARDEN HILLS, MN 55112
(651) 209-8010 Fax 209-8014
Website: www.grottofoundation.org
E-mail: info@grottofoundation.org
Sonja Moore, Executive Director;
E-mail: smoore@grottofoundation.org
Programs: Native Language Revitalization Initiative (NLRI). *Mission*: To advance the restoration of Minnesota's indigenous language with a focus on the various dialects of the Ojibwe & Dakota. The Tiwahe Foundation (replaces the American Indian Family Empowerment Program) will continue to expand its capacity to support individuals & families striving for self-determination. Established 1964.

MINNESOTA INDIAN GAMING ASSOCIATION (MIGA)
P.O. Box 218 • BEMIDJI, MN 56601
(218) 751-0560 Fax 751-2541
Website: www.mnindiangamingassoc.com
E-mail: info@mnindiangamingassoc.com
John McCarthy, Executive Director
Stanley R. Crooks, Chairperson
Purpose: Serves as a forum for discussion of the many issues facing tribes as they work to preserve gaming and renew their economic, social and cultural resources. Established 1987.

MINNESOTA INDIAN BUSINESS ALLIANCE
2513 94th Ave. North • BROOKLYN PARK, MN 55444
(763) 424-6257 Fax (866) 768-5080
Website: www.mniba.org
Madonna & Melvin Yawakie (Turtle Mountain & Zuni), Contacts

ANISHINABE LEGAL SERVICES, INC.
P.O. Box 157, 411 First St. N.W. • CASS LAKE, MN 56633
(800) 422-1335; (218) 335-2223 Fax 335-7988
Website: www.alslegal.org; E-mail: info@alslegal.org
Chris Allery (Anishinabe), Executive Directors
Chari LaDuke (Red Lake Ojibwe), Administrative Director
Jerome Song (Anishinabe), Staff Attorney
Steve Campbell, Staff Attorney (White Earth Satelite Office
Joe Plumer, Board Chairperson; Victor Smith, Vice Chairperson
Purpose: To provide legal assistance to low-income persons living within the boundaries of the Leech Lake, Red Lake, and White Earth Reservations in northern Minnesota. Limited law library for staff attorneys.

MINNESOTA INDIAN EDUCATION ASSOCIATION
P.O. Box 1210 • CASS LAKE, MN 56633
(218) 465-2812 Fax 475-2531
Website: www.minnesotaindianeducation.org
E-mail: miea@minnesotaindianeducation.org
Board of Directors – 3-Year Members: Billie Jo Annette (White Earth Ojibwe), Secretary; Jody Steile (White Earth Ojibwe); Ricky White (Naotkamegwanning First Nation); Steven Briggs (Fond du Lac Ojibwe); Priscilla Smith (Leech Lake Ojibwe); Donna Norquay (Turtle Mountain Ojibwe). 2-Year Member: Bill Blackwell, Jr. (Grand Portage Lake Superior Ojibwe), Treasurer

MENDING THE SACRED HOOP (MSH) – TECHNICAL ASSISTANCE (TA) PROJECT
202 W. 2nd St. • DULUTH, MN 55802
(888) 305-1650; (218) 623-HOOP Fax 722-5775
Website: www.mshoop.org
Tina Olson (Yaqui), MSH Founder & Executive Director
Jeremy NeVilles-Sorrell (White Earth Ojibwe), Training & Resource Director
Patti Larsen (Anishinaabe), Sacred Hoop Tribal Coalition Coordinator
Holly Oden (Anishinaabe), TA Project Resource & Information Specialist
Alyxis Feltus (Grand Portage Ojibwe), Coalition Outreach Coordinator
Goal: To change the way systems & service people respond to Indian people; to restore safety & integrity to Native women by assisting Native sovereign nations in strengthening their response to domestic violence & sexual assault. *Projects*: Technical Assistance (TA) Project; Cultural Services Project; Sacred Hoop Tribal Coalition. *Programs*: Create tribal programs to address violence against Native women.

AMERICAN INDIAN OPPORTUNITIES INDUSTRIALIZATION CENTER (OIC)
1845 East Franklin Ave. • MINNEAPOLIS, MN 55404
(612) 341-3358 Fax 341-3766; Website: www.aioic.org
Joe Hobot (Hunk Papa Band of Lakota) President & CEO
E-mail: joeh@aioic.org
Purpose: To fuse education & training with Native culture and the world of employment. *Facilities*: Career Immersion High School (contract-alternative diploma program that operates as a component of the Minneapolis Public Schools & which offers educational & career opportunities); School of Business & Office Technology. *Programs*: In-an-da'-we - provides support for the specific needs of urban American Indian women of the Minneapolis/St. Paul area; Vocational Education; Job Placements/Employment. *Publication*: AIOIC Newsletter. Established 1979.

INDIAN HEALTH BOARD OF MINNEAPOLIS, INC.
1315 East 24th St. • MINNEAPOLIS, MN 55404
(612) 721-9800 Fax 721-7870; E-mail: prock@ihb-mpls.org
Patrick M. Rock, MD, CEO & Medical Director
Hattie Thorn-Black, DDS, Dental Director
Purpose: To plan, carry out, and audit health services provided for the area's Indian community.

MINNEAPOLIS AMERICAN INDIAN CENTER
1530 E. Franklin Ave. • MINNEAPOLIS, MN 55404
(612) 879-1700 Fac 879-1795; Website: www.maicnet.org
Mary LaGarde, Executive Director (879-1750)
E-mail: mlagarde@maicnet.org
Julie Green, Program Director (879-1765)
E-mail: jgreen@maicnet.org
Sam Olbekson, Board President; Mark Erickson, Vice President
Goals: To foster the social & economic development of the Indian community of Minneapolis. Provides a variety of social, educational, cultural & economic programs & services, including: Indian Child Welfare; Chemical Dependency Counseling & Prevention Education; Adult Basic Education; JTPA Employment & Training; Youth Intervention; Recreation; and Senior Citizens. Operates Two Rivers Gallery art museum, First People's Gallery, and Circle Cafe. *Publication*: The Circle, monthly newspaper. Established 1974.

MINNESOTA INDIAN WOMEN'S RESOURCE CENTER
2300 15th Ave. S. • MINNEAPOLIS, MN 55404
(612) 728-2000 Fax 728-2039; Website: www.miwrc.org
Patina Park, JD, Executive Director; E-mail: ppark@miwrc.org
Heather Reynolds, Mental Health Director
Jo Lightfeather, Library/Training Director; E-mail: jlightfeather@miwrc.org
Terri Yellowhammer, Board Chairperson; Patina Park, JD, Vice Chairperson
Purpose: To assist American Indian women so they can enjoy a better quality of life for themselves and their families, by providing charitable services to American Indian women and their children in the following areas: housing, chemical dependency treatment, family reunification/crisis intervention, children's day care. *Special programs*: Employment & Training. *Activities*: Staff training, community lectures & program technical assistance services; and parenting education training. Library. Established 1974.

UPPER MIDWEST AMERICAN INDIAN CENTER
1035 West Broadway • MINNEAPOLIS, MN 55411
 (612) 522-4436; Dennis Morrison, Executive Director

ANISHINABE LEGAL SERVICES, INC.
P.O. Box 57 • NAYTAHWAUSH, MN 56566
 (877) 800-7295; (218) 935-5345 Fax 935-5186
 Website: www.alslegal.org
White Earth Reservation office. See Cass Lake listing.

ANISHINABE LEGAL SERVICES, INC.
P.O. Box 291 • RED LAKE, MN 56671
 (866) 679-2281; (218) 679-2281 Fax 679-2392
 Website: www.alslegal.org
Red Lake Reservation office. See Cass Lake listing.

MINNESOTA DEPARTMENT OF EDUCATION
INDIAN EDUCATION PROGRAM
1500 Hwy. 36 W. • ROSEVILLE, MN 55113
 (651) 582-8300 Fax 582-8879
 Dennis W. Olson, Director of Indian Education
 E-mail: dennis.w.olson@state.mn.us

AMERICAN INDIAN FAMILY CENTER
579 Wells St. • ST. PAUL, MN 55130-4134
 (651) 793-3803; Kevin Martineau, Executive Director
 Brian Joyce, Director of Family Services
 Elona Street-Stewart, Chairperson

MINNESOTA AMERICAN INDIAN CHAMBER OF COMMERCE
2345 Rice St., Suite 200 • ST. PAUL, MN 55113
 (612) 877-2117 Fax (651) 444-5270
 Website: www.maicc.org; E-mail: info@maicc.org
Jon Otto, Board President; Anthony Goze, Vice Chairperson
Purpose: To promote, advocate & create economic prosperity on behalf of American Indian businesses, organizations, professionals, & tribal enterprises in a global market.

MINNESOTA INDIAN AFFAIRS COUNCIL
161 St. Anthony St., Suite 919 • ST. PAUL, MN 55155
 (651) 296-0041 Fax 296-0309
Bemidji Office: 113 2nd St. NW, Suite 110A • BEMIDJI, MN 56601
 (218) 755-3825 Fax 755-3739; Website: www.mn.gov/indianaffairs/
 Robert L. Larsen, Chairperson
 Dennis Olson, Jr. (Ojibwe), Executive Director
  E-mail: dennis.w.olson@state.mn.us
 Melanie Franks (Whata Mohawk), Executive Assistant & Education Liaison
  E-mail: melanie.franks@state.mn.us
 Jim L. Jones, Jr. (Leech Lake Ojibwe), Cultural Resource Director
  E-mail: jim.jones@state.mn.us
 Melissa Cerda, Cultural Resource Specialist
  E-mail: melissa.cerda@state.mn.us
 Shannon Geshick, Grants & Legislative Liaison
  E-mail: shannon.geshick@state.mn.us
Urban Indian Advisory Council: Karen Bedeau, (Bemidji Rep.); John Day, Chairperson (Duluth Rep.); Bill Carter & Valerie A. Larsen (Minneapolis Reps.); Jay Hunter & Bill Ziegler (St. Paul Reps)
Purpose: The official liaison between state & tribal governments and advisor to the state on urban Indian issues & concerns: health, education, welfare & other public support, housing economic development, protection of the environment, and protection of tribal rights. The council is governed by the elected tribal chair of the eleven reservations throughout the state, and two at large members from other states. The council has an Urban Indian Advisory Committee. Minnesota has an American Indian population of about 52,000.

MISSOURI

AMERICAN INDIAN COUNCIL
310 Armour Rd., Suite 205 • N. KANSAS CITY, MO 64116
 (800) 546-4898; (816) 471-4898 Fax 471-8543
 Christine Molle, Executive Director; E-mail: aicmolle@kc.rr.com
Program: Indian Employment & Training Program.

KANSAS CITY INDIAN CENTER
600 West 39th St. • KANSAS CITY, MO 64111
 (816) 421-7608 Fax 421-6493
 Website: www.kcindiancenter.org
 E-mail: information@kcindiancenter.org
 Gaylene Crouser (Hunkpapa/Oglala), Executive Director
 E-mail: gcrouser@kcindiancenter.org

 Patrick Pruitt (Chickasaw), Morningstar Program Director
 Anna Maria Windham (Stoney Tribe, Fort Peck), CSBG Program Director
 Alice Flanagan (Crow), Chairperson
 David Barnett (Muscogee Creek), Vice Chairperson
 George Boswell (Cherokee) Treasurer
 Teddy Tatum (Red Lake Ojibwe), Secretary
Description: Kansas City area's only multi-purpose social service agency for Native Americans. *Programs*: Morningstar Outreach Program; Food Pantry; Youth Services. *Activities*: Annual Culture Camp; Blue Buffalo Trading Post. Established 1971.

SOUTHWEST MISSOURI INDIAN CENTER
543 S. Scenic Ave. • SPRINGFIELD, MO 65802
 (417) 869-9550; Mike Fields, Executive Director
Purpose: Established to alleviate the problems of low-income Native American Indians in the urban setting; to provide understanding between Indian people & the white dominated community; to provide cultural presentations to assist in the learning process. *Activities*: Social services, counseling, emergency services, referral, alcohol & drug abuse prevention program. *Publication*: "Rising Sun" monthly newsletter.

MONTANA

INDIAN HEALTH BOARD OF BILLINGS, INC.
1127 Alderson Ave. #1 • BILLINGS, MT 59102
 (406) 245-7318 Fax 245-8872; Website: www.ihbbilling.org
 Marjorie Bear Don't Walk (Salish), Executive Director
  E-mail: mbdwalk@yahoo.com
 Robert Ironmaker (Assiniboine/Plains Cree), Health Site Manager
  E-mail: rironmaker@ihhbilling.org
 Dee Dee Smith, Substance Abuse Manager
 Dr. Arnold Devous, Clinical Director
Description: An urban Indian health program providing a walk-in clinic, outpatient substance abuse & mental health programs, health education, & community outreach services. Established 1977.

ROCKY MOUNTAIN TRIBAL LEADERS COUNCIL
711 Central Ave., Suite 220 • BILLINGS, MT 59102
 (406) 252-2550 Fax 254-6355; Website: www.mtwytlc.com
 William "Bill" Snell, Jr., Administrative Executive Director
 Mike Andreini, Rocky Mountain Tribal Epidemiology Center Director
 Karen Manzo, Good Health & Wellness in Indian Country, Project Director
 Tony Prairiebear, Tribal Prevention Initiative (TIPI), Cultural Coordinator
The council, represents the following tribes: Blackfeet; Chippewa Cree of Rocky Boy; Fort Belknap Indian Community; Fort Peck Assiniboine & Sioux; Northern Cheyenne; Crow; Little Shell Tribe of Montana; Confederated Salish & Kootenai Tribes; Eastern Shoshone Tribal Council; Northern Arapaho Tribal Council; Shoshone Bannock Tribes of Ft. Hall

THE PIEGAN INSTITUTE
P.O. Box 890 • BROWNING, MT 58417
 (406) 338-3518; Website: www.pieganinstitute.org
Purpose: To research, promote & preserve Native languages; to increase the number of Blackfeet language speakers; to increase the cultural knowledge base of community members; and to actively influence positive community-based change. *National Objective*: To promote support for Native language issues through advocacy & education and to provide a voice to the national & international dialogue on Native Language restoration. *Programs*: Cuts Wood School - to use the Blackfeet language as the tool of instruction within a local context. Offers full day programming for children age 5 to 12. Film: Transitions: Death of a Mother Tongue. *Publication*: "American Indian Millennium: Renewing Our Ways for Future Generations" by Darrell Robes Kipp. Established 1987.

NORTH AMERICAN INDIAN ALLIANCE (NAIA)
55 E. Galena • BUTTE, MT 59701
 (406) 782-0461 Fax 782-7435
 Website: www.tribalnations.mt.gov/urbanindian
 Eric Lapier, Chairperson; Patty Stiffarm, Vice Chairperson
Purpose: To work for improved health & welfare of all eligible Native Americans in the Butte area; to sponsor cultural activities. *Programs*: Medical, Dental, Health Education; Mental Health; Youth. *Publication*: Monthly newsletter.

MONTANA INDIAN BUSINESS ALLIANCE
P.O. Box 2222 • COLSTRIP, MT 59323
 Website: www.mibaonline.org; E-mail: info@mibaonline.org
 Johnel Barcus (Blackfeet), Executive Director
 Barbara Stiffarm (Blackfeet), Board Chairperson
Established 2006.

INDIAN FAMILY HEALTH CLINIC

1220 Central Ave. #2B • GREAT FALLS, MT 59401
 (406) 268-1510; Website: www.indianfamilyhealth.org
 E-mail: execdirector@indianfamilyhealth.org
 Ernestine Belcourt, Executive Director; Henry Devereaux, Board Chairperson
Purpose: To provide high-quality & comprehensive health care services to urban Indians in the Great Falls area.

MONTANA INDIAN EDUCATION ASSOCIATION

909 Durango Dr. • GREAT FALLS, MT 59404
 (406) 531-0261; Website: www.mtiea.org
 Thomas Brown, Chairperson; Melville Stops, Vice Chairperson
Activities: Sponsors an annual conference. *Publication*: The Buckskin Journal, bimonthly newsletter. Established 1979.

HELENA INDIAN ALLIANCE

501 Euclid Ave. • HELENA, MT 59601
 Administration: (406) 442-9244 Fax 449-5797
 Clinic: (406) 449-5796 Fax 449-5371
 Website: www.helenaindianalliance.com
 E-mail: director@helenaindianalliance.com
 Mike Jetty (Dakota Chippewa), Chairperson
 Dan Pocha (Chippewa Cree), Vice Chairperson
Purpose: To provide programs aimed toward the development of the Native American community in the areas of health, education, mental health, employment, training & housing. *Facilities*: Leo Pocha Memorial Clinic. *Programs*: Diabetes, Behavioral Health, Tobacco Prevention; Seniors. *Publication*: Newsletter.

MONTANA DEPARTMENT OF COMMERCE
Indian Country Economic Development Program (ICED)

301 S. Park Ave., P.O. Box 200505 • HELENA, MT 59601
 (406) 841-2775 Fax 841-2731
 Heather Sobrepena-George, Manager
 E-mail: hsobrepena@mt.gov
 Kathleen Fleury, Coordinator
Purpose: To provide grant funds to support tribal business development projects, work force training projects, entrepreneurial training, feasibility studies and other types of economic development projects. The Department works closely with the State Tribal Economic Development Commission (STEDC) in coordinating economic development efforts in Montana's Indian Country. *Programs*: Indian Equity Fund - a grant to assist a current Native American business or a new Native American business owner. Availably only to enrolled members of Montana's federally recognized tribes in Montana enrolled members of the Little Shell Chippewa Tribe.

MONTANA DEPARTMENT OF COMMERCE
STATE TRIBAL ECONOMIC DEVELOPMENT COMMISSION (STEDC)

301 S. Park Ave., P.O. Box 200505 • HELENA, MT 59620
 (406) 841-2821 Fax 841-2731; Website: www.tribal.mt.gov
 Heather Sobrepena-George, Program Manager (841-2775)
 Shawn Real Bird (Crow), Chairperson
 Joe Durglo (Salish & Kootenai), Vice Chairperson
Commission members: Rodney Miller (Fort Peck); Shawn Real Bird (Crow); Terry Pitts (Salish & Kotenai); Gerald Gray, Little Shell); Richard Sangrey (Rocky Boy); Delina Cuts The Rope (Fort Belknap); Cheryl Reevis (Blackfeet); Tracy Robinson (Northern Cheyenne).
Purpose: To work with Native Americans to expand economic development opportunities on each of the seven reservations in partnership with tribal governments & the federal government. *Programs*: Indianpreneurship - develop the capacity of Indian organizations on the Reservation to mentor and support Indian business owners through classroom training, workshops, counseling & lending.

MONTANA GOVERNOR'S OFFICE OF INDIAN AFFAIRS

State Capitol Bldg. Rm. 202, P.O. Box 200801 • HELENA, MT 59620
 (406) 444-3702 Fax 444-1350; (406) 444-3111 Fax 444-5529
 Website: www.tribalnations.mt.gov; E-mail: oia@mt.gov
 Website: www.indianlaw.mt.gov (Montana Indian Law Portal)
 Jason Smith, State Director of Indian Affairs
 Lesa Evers, Tribal Relations Manager
 E-mail: levers@mt.gov
Purpose: To provide a greater understanding between Montana's Indian population & local, state & federal government agencies; to seek ways & means of communicating their opinions & needs to agencies of responsibility & actively assist them in organizing their efforts; and to act as representative for organized bodies of Indians. *Programs*: Indian Country Economic Development (ICED) *Publications*: Newsletter; Tribal Relations Report 2010: The Art of Cooperation; Tribal Relations Handbook: A Guide for State Employees on Preserving the State-Tribal Relationship.

MONTANA OFFICE OF PUBLIC INSTRUCTION
MONTANA ADVISORY COUNCIL ON INDIAN EDUCATION (MACIE)

Division of Indian Education Specialist
1300 11th Ave., 106 State Capitol
P.O. Box 202501 • HELENA, MT 59620
 (406) 444-3694 Fax 444-3924
 Mandy Smoker Broaddus (Assiniboine/Sioux), Director
 E-mail: mbroaddus@mt.gov
 Henry Real Bird, Montana's Poet
 Jennifer Stadum & Justin Jam, Implementation
 Julie Mitchell, Curriculum Coordinator (444-0754)
Council members: Dr. Robin Bighorn (Assiniboine Sioux); Spike Bighorn; Norma Bixby (Northern Cheyenne); Russell Boham (Little Shell Tribe); Emma Core Harold Dusty Bull (Blackfeet); Jennifer Flat Lip (Crow); Callen Gilbert; Janice Hawley. *Purpose*: To provide technical assistance and materials in the area of Indian education. *Activities*: Training for teaching Indian children is provided for parents, school boards and teachers.

MISSOULA URBAN INDIAN HEALTH CENTER

Native American Services Agency
830 West Central • MISSOULA, MT 59801
 (406) 829-9515 Fax 829-9519
 LeeAnn Bruised Head, MPH, Executive Director
 Cherith Smith, PhD, PharmD, Diabetes (SDPI) Coordinator
 Patricia LaPlant, MSW, Wellness Specialist
 Wilena Old Person, Board Chairperson
 Meagan Rides At the Door, Co-Chairperson
Purpose: To provide for the general welfare of the Missoula Urban Indian community through provision of healthcare, chemical dependency treatment & social services. *Programs*: Youth Indian Cultural Enrichment; Health Intervention & Prevention; AIDS/STD Awareness; Mental Health; Chemical Dependence & Substance Abuse; Child Welfare Act. *Publication*: Buffalo Grass Newsletter. Established 1970.

KICKING HORSE JOB CORPS CENTER

33091 Molman Pass Trail • RONAN, MT 59864
 (406) 644-2217 Fax 644-2343; Charles Camel, Director
Description: The first American Indian job corps center operated by the Flathead Reservation and complements job training activities with information on the Native American cultural heritage.

NEBRASKA

AMERICAN INDIAN COUNCIL

128 S. Potash • ALLIANCE, NE 69301
 (308) 762-3242; Mark Monroe, Contact

INDIAN CENTER, INC.

1100 Military Rd. • LINCOLN, NE 68508
 (402) 474-5231 Fax 438-5236; Website: www.indiancenterinc.org
 Clyde Tyndall (Omaha), Executive Director; E-mail: ctyndall@icindn.org
 Cuba Dabney (Omaha), WIA Site Director; E-mail: cdabney@icindn.org
 Nettie Grant Sikyta (Omaha), Minority Health Initiative Program Director
 E-mail: ngrantsikyta@icindn.org
Programs: Youth Suicide Prevention, Website: www.iciysp.org; Commodity Supplemental Foods Program; Native American Culture Nights; workshops. *Activities*: Annual Celebration Powwow. *Publication*: Lincoln Indian Journal.

NEBRASKA COMMISSION ON INDIAN AFFAIRS (NCIA)

State Capitol Bldg., 6th Fl. East
P.O. Box 94981 • LINCOLN, NE 68509-4981
 (402) 471-3475 Fax 471-3392
 Website: www.indianaffairs.state.ne.us
 Judi M. Gaiashkibos (Ponca of Nebraska), Executive Director
 E-mail: judi.gaiashkibos@nebraska.gov
 Scott Shafer, Admin. Assistant II; Sarah Frink, Admin. Secretary
Description: Nebraska Government website consisting of 14 commissioners appointed by the Governor. *Purpose*: To enhance the cause of Indian rights and to develop solutions to problems common to all Nebraska Indians. Act as liaison among the four headquarter tribes of the Omaha, Ponca, Santee Sioux & Winnebago Tribes of Nebraska. *Publication*: Quarterly newsletter. Established 1971.

NEBRASKA STATE DEPARTMENT OF EDUCATION
MULTICULTURAL & NATIVE AMERICAN EDUCATION

P.O. Box 94987 • LINCOLN, NE 68509
 (402) 471-2960 Fax 471-8127
 Carol Remp, Program Coordinator

NEBRASKA URBAN INDIAN HEALTH COALITION, INC.
2331 Fairfield St. • LINCOLN, NE 68521
 (402) 434-7177 Fax 434-7180
Office: 2240 Landon Court • OMAHA, NE 68102
 (402) 346-0902 Fax 342-5290; Website: www.nuihc.com
Dr. Donna Polk, LMHP, Chief Executive Officer
 E-mail: dpolk-primm@nuihc.com
Karen Foxx, LADC, Director of Behavioral Health (346-0902 ext. 204)
 E-mail: kfoxx@nuihc.com
Nicole Tamayo-Bergman, Soaring Over Meth & Suicide Project Director
 E-mail: nicole@nuihc.com
Tracy Hartman-Bradley (Alutiiq/Aleut), Board President
James Bollinger (Omaha/Oglala Lakota), Treasurer
Renee Geller (Omaha), Secretary
Facility: Intertribal Treatment Center, 2301 S. 15th St., Omaha, NE 68108

NEBRASKA INDIAN INTER-TRIBAL DEVELOPMENT CORPORATION
Route 1, Box 66A • WINNEBAGO, NE 68071
 (402) 878-2242; Daryl La Pointe, Sr., Director
Purpose: To aid in the social & economic development of the Omaha, Winnebago & Santee Sioux Tribes of Nebraska. *Programs*: Job Training Partnership Act; Indian Food Distribution Program; Economic & Community Development Programs; et al. Founded 1969.

ST. AUGUSTINE INDIAN MISSION SCHOOL
P.O. Box GG • WINNEBAGO, NE 68071
 (402) 878-2291 Fax 878-2760; Website: www.staugustinemission.com
E-mail: newsstaugustine@archomaha.org
Don Blackbird, Jr., (Omaha), Principal
 E-mail: dnblackbird@archomaha.org
Dwight Howe (Omaha/Ponca), Omaha Language/Outreach
Fr. Dave Korth, Mission Director; E-mail: dmkorth@archomaha.org
Purpose: To prepare students for their higher education; learn respect for their faith, themselves, their family, their elders; take responsibility for their own learning; understand the importance of interacting with others in a cooperative manner to solve problems. *Facilities*: Museum; Library. *Publication*: Trumpet Call, newsletter.

NEVADA

NEVADA INDIAN COMMISSION
5366 Snyder Ave. • CARSON CITY, NV 89701
 (775) 687-8333 Fax 687-8330; Website: www.nic.nv.gov
Sherry L. Rupert (Paiute/Washoe), Executive Director
 E-mail: srupert@nic.nv.gov
Chris Gibbons, Program Officer
Richard Arnold, Chairperson; John Hansen, Vice Chairperson
Alvin Moyle, Native American Representative
Jill Greiner, General Public Representative
Purpose: To study matters affecting the social and economic welfare & well-being of American Indians residing in Nevada; to improve cooperation between agencies & Indian groups; to enhance a general understanding of Indian law; and to assist tribes in acquiring or reacquiring federal land, identifying and researching problems to find solutions. *Publications*: Stewart (Indian School) Visions, quarterly newsletter; Directory; Supplement to Guide to Nevada Indian-Owned Businesses; and Population Profile. Established 1965.

NEVADA STATE DEPARTMENT OF EDUCATION
INDIAN EDUCATION CONSULTANT
700 E. Fifth St. • CARSON CITY, NV 89701
 (775) 687-9143 Fax 687-9250
Fredina Drye-Romero (Kaibab Paiute), Consultant
 E-mail: fromero@doe.nv.gov
Annual American Indian & Alaskan Native Education Summit.
Publication: Semiannual newsletter.

NEVADA URBAN INDIANS
232 E. Winnie Lane • CARSON CITY, NV 89706
 (775) 883-4439 Fax 883-698
Website: www.nevadaurbanindians.org
Janet Reeves, Executive Director; E-mail: jreeves@nvui.org
See Reno listing.

LAS VEGAS INDIAN CENTER
2300 W. Bonanza Rd. • LAS VEGAS, NV 89106
 (702) 647-5842 Fax 647-2647
Debra Reed, Executive Director
Sheela Gade, Associate Director
Promotes the social & economic self-sufficiency of American Indians through the provision of education & employment. *Special programs*: Social services,

adult education, career education, employment & training assistance, cultural activities, alcoholics anonymous, energy assistance, & special interest workshops and seminars. Established 1972.

AMERICAN INDIAN CHAMBER OF COMMERCE OF NEVADA
1785 E. Sahara Ave. • LAS VEGAS, NV 89104
 (702) 693-6698 Fax 894-9474
Debra Sillik, President; E-mail: dsillik@embarqmail.com

NEVADA URBAN INDIANS
6512 S. McCarran Blvd., Suite A • RENO, NV 89509
 (888) 885-8447 (775) 788-7600 Fax 788-7611
Website: www.nevadaurbanindians.org
Janet Reeves, Executive Director; E-mail: jreeves@nvui.org
Warren Cartright, Intake & Program Specialist
Dan Olsen, Chairperson; Lavina Pancho, Secretary/Treasurer
Purpose: To provide quality health care to the area's urban Indian population by providing a variety of social and health services using a blend of traditional & modern medicine. *Activities*: Community health care, health promotion & disease prevention, alcohol & drug abuse prevention and treatment program, mental health services. *Publications*: Reno Talking Leaf, quarterly newsletter; brochures on available services. Established 1975.

INTER-TRIBAL COUNCIL OF NEVADA
680 Greenbrae Dr. #280 • SPARKS, NV 89431
 (775) 355-0600 Fax 355-0648; Website: www.itcn.org
Daryl Crawford, Executive Director; E-mail: dcrawford@itcn.org
Michael Tinsley, CCDF Director; E-mail: mtinsley@itcn.org
Christine Harjo, Native Workforce Program Coordinator
 E-mail: charjo@itcn.org
Vinton Hawley (Washoe), President; Bobby Sanchez, Vice President
Chad Malone, Secretary; David Decker, Treasurer
Description: A tribal organization serving its member reservations & colonies in Nevada. *Goal*: To serve as a large political body for the small Nevada tribes. *Programs*: Health; Education, Social Services; Economic Development, Employment; provides information on the 26 tribes & community organizations that serve Indian peoples living in Nevada & the Great Basin region.

NEVADA-CALIFORNIA INDIAN HOUSING ASSOCIATION
31 W. Loop Rd. • YERINGTON, NV 89447
 (775) 463-2225 Fax 463-2316; Website: www.nv-cal.org
Phil Bush (Confederated Tribes Chehalis), Executive Director & Chairperson
 E-mail: modoclasseniha@thegrid.net
Mervin Hess, Vice Chair; E-mail: Mervin.hess@bishoppaiute.org
Darlene Tooley, Treasurer; E-mail: ncihatrb@pacific.net
Lee Ann Brown (Me-Wuk), Secretary; E-mail: leeann@mewuk.com

NEW HAMPSHIRE

NEW ENGLAND ANTIQUITIES RESEARCH ASSOCIATION (NEARA)
305 Academy Rd. • PEMBROKE, NH 03275
 (603) 485-5655; Website: www.neara.org
Terry Deveau, President; E-mail: president@neara.org
Doug Schwartz, VP; E-mail: vicepresident@nweara.org
Purpose: To explore the origins of enigmatic stone structures throughout the Northeastern U.S.; to form a better understanding of our historic & prehistoric past. *Research activities*: Anthropology, archaeology; Native American studies of stone works and related structures in the northeastern U.S. Archaeology in Maine & New Hampshire. *Publications*: NEARA Journal, Semiannual; NEARA Transit Newsletter Semiannual. Library. Founded 1964.

NEW JERSEY

THE NEW JESEY INDIAN COUNCIL
189 Stag Hill Rd. • MAHWAH, NJ 07430
 (201) 529-1171 Fax 529-3212
Darrell Waldron, Executive Director (see Rhode island Indian Council)
 E-mail: dwaldron@rhodeislandindiancouncil.org
Tony Powell, WIA Career Counselor
 E-mail: tpowell@newyorkindiancouncil.org
A Rhode Island Indian Council location.

NEW JERSEY COMMISSION ON AMERICAN INDIAN AFFAIRS
P.O. Box 300 • TRENTON, NJ 08625
 (609) 633-9627 Fax 777-2939
Lewis J. Pierce, Jr. (Nanticoke Lenni-Lenape), Chairperson
Urie Ridgeway (Nanticoke Lenni-Lenape), Representative
JoAnne Hawkins (Powhatan Renape), Representative
Rowena Madden, Lt. Governor's Delegate

LENAPE LIFEWAYS, INC.

P.O. Box 239 • STANHOPE, NJ 07874
(973) 691-2316 (Phone/Fax); Website: www.lenapelifeways.org
E-mail: lenapelifeways.inc@gmail.com; John T. Kraft, Director
Purpose: To preserve and interpret the prehistory (focusing on New Jersey's first people, the Lenape) of New Jersey and the surrounding region. *Programs*: All programs are curriculum-based & contain a slide presentation, stories, objects & artifacts, 60-90 minutes in length. Lenape Lifeways Family & Village Life (Grades 1-8); The Lenape-Delaware Indian Heritage (general audiences). *Activities*: Workshops to teachers & educators; loans of artifacts & traveling exhibits on regional prehistory are available to libraries, museums and other institutions; Traveling Exhibit: New Jersey's First Peoples - The Lenape-Delaware Indian Heritage. Publications (see Bibliography).

NEW MEXICO

ALBUQUERQUE INDIAN CENTER

105 Texas SE • ALBUQUERQUE, NM 87108
(505) 268-1751 Fax 268-8955
Website: www.abqindiancenter.com
Mary Garcia, Executive Director
E-mail: mary.garcia@abqindiancenter.com
Gordon Yawakia, Prevention Coordinator
E-mail: Gordon.yawakia@abqindiancenter.com
David Joe & Kiutus Tecumseh, Board members
Mission: To empower the Albuquerque urban Native American community and others through the provisions of wrap around services designed to promote wellness, education, self-sufficiency and tradition. *Services*: Counseling & Support; Legal; Prevention Activities; Behavioral Health.

AMERICAN INDIAN CHAMBER OF COMMERCE OF NM

2401 12th St. NW, Suite5-S • ALBUQUERQUE, NM 87104
(505) 766-9546 Fax 766-9499
Website: www.aiccnm.com; E-mail: info@aiccnm.com
Joel V. Orono, PhD (Isleta Pueblo), Executive Director
Monica Jojola (isleta Pueblo), Board Chairperson
E-mail: monica@montech-inc.com
Gail Chehak (Klamath), Secretary

FIRST NATIONS COMMUNITY HEALTHSOURCE

5608 Zuni Rd. SE • ALBUQUERQUE, NM 87108
(505) 262-2481 Fax 262-0781; Website: www.fnch.org
Tassy Parker (Seneca) RN, Board President
Janet Pacheco-Morton, Treasurer; Joyce Hudson (Navajo), Secretary
Purpose: To serve the Native American population of Albuquerque with programs & services designed to elevate the standard of health, socio-economic standing, and educational level. *Programs*: Primary Care Clinic; WIC Nutrition; Alcohol & Substance Abuse; Community Health & Health Education; Emergency Assistance; Information and Referral. Established 1985.

NEW MEXICO INDIAN EDUCATION ADVISORY COUNCIL

P.O. Box 1667 • ALBUQUERQUE, NM 87107
Website: http://www.ped.state.nm.us/indian.ed/NMIEAC.html
Kevin Shendo (Southern Pueblos Rep.), Chairperson
E-mail: shendo@jemezpueblo.org
Lester Sandoval, Vice Chairperson
E-mail: drapachesandoval@yahoo.com
Clarice Cata-Montoya (Northern Pueblos Rep.), Secretary
E-mail: saniteacher@hotmail.com

INDIGENOUS NATIONS LIBRARY PROGRAM (INLP)

Zimmerman Library, 2nd Floor, Room 226, MSC05 3020
1 University of New Mexico • ALBUQUERQUE, NM 87131
(505) 277-7433 E-mail: inlp@unm.edu
Paulita Aguilar, Director; E-mail: paulita@unm.edu
Sarah Kostelecky, Librarian; E-mail: sarahrk@unm.edu
Mission: To provide library outreach & information services to the UNM community & New Mexico Native American/Indigenous communities. Established 2004,

NATIVE AMERICAN TRANING INSTITUTE OF NEW MEXICO

1208 San Pedro NE #126 • ALBUQUERQUE, NM 87110
(505) 204-1347 Fax 869-9441; Website: www.nmnati.org
Patrick Trujillo (Cochiti Pueblo), Board President & Executive Director
Ramus Suina (Cochiti) & David Lenti (Isleta Pueblo), Directors
Mission: To empower individuals, families, and the community to create a safe & healthy environment so children & families can achieve their highest potential. Provides culturally relevant training & curriculum packages for professionals working with Native American children & families. *Activities*:

Conducts workshops & conferences throughout the year. Annual Professional Development Training on Indigenous Prevention/Treatment Strategies on Substance Use & Other Drug Related Issues. Online library.

SOUTHWEST INDIAN FOUNDATION - GALLUP CULTURAL CENTER

201 E. Highway 66 • GALLUP, NM 87301
(505) 863-4131 Fax 722-3730; Website: www.southwestindian.com
Purpose: To provide an outlet for local Native American handicrafts, including jewelry, clothing, mugs, books and toys. *Publication*: Catalog

EIGHT NORTHERN INDIAN PUEBLOS COUNCIL

P.O. Box 969 • SAN JUAN PUEBLO, NM 87566
(505) 747-1593 Fax 747-1599; Rob Corabi, Director
Head Start Program

TEWA WOMEN UNITED

P.O. Box 397 • SANTA CRUZ, NM 87567
(505) 747-3259 Fax 747-4067
Website: www.tewawomenunited.org
E-mail: info@tewawomenunited.org
Corrine Sanchez, Executive Director
E-mail: corrine@tewawomenunited.org
Kena Chavez, V.O.I.C.E.S Program Manager
E-mail: kena@tewawomenunited.org
Office address: 912 Fairview Lane, Espanola, NM 87532
Description: A support group for Tewa women concerned with various issues including alcoholism, suicide, and domestic & sexual violence. *Programs*: Environmental Justice; Established 1989.

NEW MEXICO INDIAN AFFAIRS DEPARTMENT (IAD)

Wendell Chino Bldg., 2nd Floor
1220 S. St. Francis Dr. • SANTA FE, NM 87505
(505) 476-1600 Fax 476-1601; Website: www.iad.state.nm.us
Kelly Zunie, Cabinet Secretary
Suzette Shije, Deputy Cabinet Secretary
David Mann, General Counsel
Laura Vanoni, Infrastructure Manager
Nicole Macias, Public Relations Coordinator
E-mail: Nicole.macias@state.nm.us
Sharon Ciahchischilliage, Co-chair Representative
John Pinto (Navajo), Co-chair Senator
Lillian Brooks, Administrative Services Director
Joann Lapington, Chief Financial Officer
Ben Fletcher, Program Officer; Autumn Monteau, General Counsel
Purpose: To serve as a coordinating agency for intergovernmental programs concerning tribal governments & the state of New Mexico; to recruit & place qualified Indians in jobs with state agencies. Established 2003.

NEW MEXICO OFFICE OF INDIAN ELDER AFFAIRS

2550 Cerrillos Rd. • SANTA FE, NM 87501
(505) 476-1084; Raymond F. Espinoza, Director, Tribal Liaison

NEW MEXICO STATE LEGISLATURE
INDIAN & CULTURAL AFFAIRS DEPARTMENT

411 State Capitol • SANTA FE, NM 87501
(505) 986-4600; John Pinto, Chairperson

NEW MEXICO STATE PUBLIC EDUCATION DEPARTMENT

Santa Fe Indian Education Bureau- Division of Indian Education
Jerry Apodaca Education Bldg., 300 Don Gaspar • SANTA FE, NM 87501
(505) 827-6679 Fax 827-6668; Website: www.ped.state.nm.us
Nancy Martine-Alonzo, Assistant Secretary of Education
Penny Bird, Program Manager
Ann Zuni & Patrick Werito, Education Administrators
Purpose: Responsible for promoting quality education for Indian students in New Mexico; To assist schools in preparing curricula for Indian students; disseminates information, plans sessions with tribal entities, & develops workshops.

POEH CULTURAL CENTER

78 Cities of Gold Rd. • SANTA FE, NM 87506
(505) 455-3334 Fax 455-0174
Gov. George Rivera, Executive Director
Website: www.poehcenter.com; E-mail: info@poehcenter.org
Description: Owned and operated by the Pueblo of Pojoaque & established as the first tribally owned & operated mechanism for cultural preservation & revitalization within the Pueblo communities of the Northern Rio Grande Valley. Emphasizes arts & cultures of all Pueblo people with focus on the Tewa-speaking Pueblos of Nambe, Pojoaque, San Ildefonso, San Juan, Santa Clara & Tesuque; and the Tewa speaking Pueblos of Picuris & Taos. *Mission*: To

support the future of Pueblo people by teaching the arts, collecting great works of art and promoting public understanding of and respect for Pueblo history & culture. Established 1988.

SOUTHWESTERN ASSOCIATION FOR INDIAN ARTS, INC. (SWAIA)
P.O. Box 969 • SANTA FE, NM 87504-0969
(505) 983-5220 Fax 983-7647
Website: www.swaia.org; E-mail: info@swaia.org
Dallin Maybee, JD (Northern Arapaho/Seneca), Chief Operating Officer
  E-mail: dallin.m@swaia.org
John Jones, JD, Chief Development Officer; E-mail: jjones@swaia.org
Purpose: To promote economic wellbeing of Native American artists. Produces the Santa Fe Indian Market - over 600 booths and more than 1,200 Indian artists - the third weekend in August each year. Provides educational programs that benefit the Native American artist. Scholarship program. Established 1922.

NEW YORK

TONAWANDA INDIAN COMMUNITY HOUSE
P.O. Box 326, 372 Bloomingdale Rd. • AKRON, NY 14001
(716) 542-6546; Ramona Charles, Director

NATIVE AMERICAN INSTITUTE OF THE HUDSON RIVER VALLEY
P.O. Box 10758 • ALBANY, NY 12201
(518) 369-8116; Website: www.naihrv.org; E-mail: info@naihrv.org
Sherry White, Director; E-mail: sloudbear@gmail.com
Kevin Fuerst, Vice Director; Larry Thetford, Treasurer
Purpose: To promote awareness of the First Nations of America through research & educational activities with emphasis on the Northeastern Algonquian peoples. *Activity*: Mohican Powwow, second weekend in August. *Publication*: Newsletter.

NY STATE DEPARTMENT OF EDUCATION
NATIVE AMERICAN EDUCATION UNIT
Rm. 461 EBA, 89 Washington Ave. • ALBANY, NY 12234
(518) 474-0537 Fax 474-3666
Adrian Cooke, Coordinator

THE NEW YORK INDIAN COUNCIL
981 Morris Park Ave. • BRONX, NY 10462
(718) 684-3993 Fax 684-3994
A Rhode Island Indian Council location.

REDHAWK NATIVE AMERICAN ARTS COUNCIL
726 42nd St. • BROOKLYN, NY 11232
(718) 686-9297 Fax 686-0012
Website: https://redhawkcouncil.org
E-mail: native@redhawkcouncil.org
Description: A group of Native American performing artists who educate & delight audiences by interpreting & presenting social, traditional, and contemporary Native American dances. The council is located in Brooklyn, NY (headquarters); San Francisco, CA; & Honolulu, HI. *Programs*: Youth program teaches Native American dance, music, and craft to Native American youth; traveling exhibits. Established 1994.

NATIVE AMERICAN COMMUNITY SERVICES OF ERIE & NIAGARA
COUNTIES, INC. 1005 Grant St. • BUFFALO, NY 14207
(716) 874-4460 Fax 874-1874; Website: www.nacswny.org
Purpose: Offers education, job training, placement assistance, youth programs, childcare and family services.

NATIVE AMERICAN PEOPLE'S ALLIANCE
3435 Main St. • BUFFALO, NY 14214
(716) 836-1070; Jessica Brant, President
Description: A federation of Native Americans living in the Buffalo-Niagara Falls area.

NEW YORK STATE OFFICE OF NATIVE AMERICAN SERVICES
295 Main St., Rm. 545 • BUFFALO, NY 14203
(716) 847-3123 Fax 847-3812; Website: www.ocfs.state.ny.us/main/nas/
Gladys Carrion, Esq., Commissioner
Kim M. Thomas, Native American Affairs Specialist
Purpose: To provide social services to Native Americans; to maintain liaison with Native American Nations and other Native Americans organizations. Activities: provides consultative information & referral services; searches & reviews historical files to assist Native Americans to research their ancestry. *Special programs*: Provides special training programs to local departments; child welfare development services. *Publication*: A Proud Heritage - Native American Services in New York State.

LONG ISLAND INDIAN COUNCIL
186 W. Montauk Hwy. Unit D-2 • HAMPTON BAYS, NY 11946
(631) 594-5594 fax 594-5595
Darrell Waldron, Executive Director
  E-mail: dwaldron@rhodeislandindiancouncil.org
Darlene Troge, WIA Career Counselor
  E-mail: dtroge@longislandindiancouncil.org

NORTHEASTERN NATIVE AMERICAN ASSOCIATION, INC.
P.O. Box 230266 • HOLLIS, NY 11423
(718) 978-7057 Fax 978-7200
  William "Wassaja" Gibson, President; E-mail: rgibson230@aol.com
Purpose: To honor, respect and keep alive the traditions and spirituality of our Native American ancestors. To acquaint our members with the current needs of our people. *Activities*: Oppose the desecration and commercialization of the graves and sacred places of all natives. *Publication*: Smoke Signals, quarterly newsletter. Established 1990.

IROQUOIS STUDIES ASSOCIATION
28 Zevan Rd. • JOHNSON CITY, NY 13790
(607) 729-0016 Fax 770-9610
  Website: www.otsiningo.com; E-mail: isa1@otsiningo.com
Description: An educational, non-profit organization. *Purpose*: To provide educational & cultural programs about American Indians, especially the Six Nations of the Iroquois. *Publications*: Otsiningo Circle, a semiannual newsletter covering Indian exhibits & events within a 200 mile radius of Binghamton, NY; Iroquois Beadwork books. Established 1977.

AMERINDA, INC. (AMERICAN INDIAN ARTISTS)
288 E. 10th St. • NEW YORK, NY 10009
(212) 598-0968 Fax 598-0125; Website: www.amerinda.org
  E-mail: amerinda@amerinda.org; Diane Fraher Thornton, Director
Purpose: American Indian Artists works to empower Native Americans, break down barriers, and foster understanding & appreciation for Native culture. Through a variety of arts programs, productions & services to artists, AMERINDA supports Native artists who embody the traditional practices and values that define Indian culture. AMERINDA also promotes the indigenous perspective in the arts to a wide audience through mainstream art forms-- visual, performing, literacy & media arts. *Publication*: "Talking Stick," Native arts quarterly. Established in 1987.

AMERICAN INDIAN COMMUNITY HOUSE (AICH)
39 Eldridge St., 4th Fl. • NEW YORK, NY 10002
(212) 598-0100 Fax 598-4909; Website: www.aich.org
  Ben Goboe, Interim Executive Director
  E-mail: healthdirector@aich.org
  Steve Peace Smith (Eastern Cherokee), Outreach Coordinator
  Claudette Bryant (Shinnecock), Community Health Representative
  E-mail: cbryant@aich.org
  Robert Robertsr Behavioral Health Coordinator
  E-mail: rroberts@aich.org
Purpose: To improve & promote the well-being of the American Indian community; to increase the visibility of American Indian cultures in an urban setting in order to cultivate awareness, understanding and respect. *Programs*: Job training & placement; higher education assistance, outpatient alcohol & substance abuse counseling & related services; health department; health education & referrals; social service advocacy; HIV/AIDS Project. education & case management; legal services; art gallery; The Circle, theater & rehearsal space. *Activities*: Annual Powwow; Wings of America Camp. *Publications*: AICH Bulletin, quarterly newsletter; Elders' Morning Drum: Women's Wellness, Diabetes, & Youth Program Information, bimonthly newsletter; NALCHA News, HIV/AIDS project newsletter. Library. Gift Shop. Established 1969.

AMERICAN INDIAN ENVIRONMENTAL OFFICE (AIEO)
EPA Headquarters, Federal Triangle Campus, Washington, DC
(212) 637-3790 Fax 637-3772; E-mail: tribal.portal@epa.gov
  JoAnne K. Chase, Director; E-mail: chase.joann@epa.gov
  Karin Koslow, Deputy Director; E-mail: koslow.karin@epa.gov
Purpose: to protect human health and the environment of federally recognized Tribes by supporting implementation of federal environmental laws consistent with the federal trust responsibility, the government-to-government relationship, and EPA's 1984 Indian Policy.

NUYAGI KEETOOWAH SOCIETY
200 W. 70th St., Suite 6C • NEW YORK, NY 10023
(212) 724-2398 Fax 724-2952; E-mail: mcore@nyc.rr.com
Grand Council Officers:
  Kenneth Scales, Chairperson; Dean Hutchins, Assistant Chairman, Historian; Georgia Scales, Treasurer; Stephanie Weems, Scribe, Frank Schaefer, Elder; Ray Evans Harrell, Medicine Priest

Description: Non-for-profit traditional Cherokee religious organization and Cherokee scholar's community. *Purpose*: To serve the New York Cherokee community with a library, newsletter, and community ceremonials.

NATIVE AMERICAN CULTURAL CENTER, INC.
121 Fitzhugh St. N. • ROCHESTER, NY 14614
 (585) 442-1100; Martha Fahrer, Director
Description: Urban Indian center providing employment, education, health and human services to an 18-county service delivery area in upstate New York. Video library. *Publication*: Newsletter. Established 1976.

LAKOTA CHILDREN'S ENRICHMENT
P.O. Box 581 • SCARSDALE, NY 10583
  Website: www.lakotachildren.org; E-mail: info@lakotachildren.org
 Maggie Dunne, Founder & CEO; Cindy Dunne, Esq., COO & Director
 Timothy Chilson Dunne, Treasurer
Mission: We empower Lakota youth & amplify their voices by providing opportunities in the arts, education, sports, leadership and mentorship. Lakota Children's Enrichment's programs are tailored to meet specific needs of schools and community partners, and incorporate input from LCE's Youth Advisory Board. LCE also provides education about the history and obstacles facing American Indian reservations today.

NORTH AMERICAN INDIAN PROJECT CULTURAL CENTER
740 N. Salina St. • SYRACUSE, NY 13208
 (315) 475-6229; Theresa Steele, Director

NORTH CAROLINA

METROLINA NATIVE AMERICAN ASSOCIATION
Queens University-Dana Bl;dg. Rm. 003
P.O. Box 38468 • CHARLOTTE, NC 28278
 (704) 750-9609 Fax 949-7354
  Website: www.metrolinanativeamericans.com
  E-mail: mnaa@metrolinanativeamericans.com
 Toni Henderson, Executive Director
  E-mail: tonihenderson@gmail.com
 Jessie Jacobs (Coharie), Board Chairperson
  E-mail: jeaglenc@gmail.com
Description: The official state representative for American Indians in the Metrolina Area. *Purpose*: To promote cultural awareness & economic development; provide job training & placement; provide for the well being of Indian people. *Programs*: Scholarship Program; Cultural Classes; Michael Scott Mater Foundation, Travel Abroad Summer Program; Annual Powwow. *Publication*: Newsletter.

CHEROKEE BOYS CLUB, INC.
52 Boys Club Loop, P.O. Box 507 • CHEROKEE, NC 28719
 (828) 497-9101 Fax 497-5818
 Website: www.cherokeeboysclub.com
 Tommy Lambert, General Manager
The Club provides services & educational programs for Cherokee youth. The Center operates a The Children's Home, emergency shelter, three child care centers, a substance abuse & crime prevention program for adolescents, two food pantries & clothes closets, parenting programs, transportation & utility assistance and a number of other social services. *Publications*: Club newsletter; Center newsletter, "Cherokee Voice." Established 1965.

THE CHEROKEE CHILDREN''S HOME
P.O. Box 507 • CHEROKEE, NC 28719
 (828) 497-5009; Monica Lambert, Assistant
  E-mail: monilamb@nc-cherokee.com
 Cris Weatherford, Manager (497-5813)
  E-mail: crisweat@nc-cherokee.com
Goals: To aid the family and/or the Department of Social Services in meeting the well-being needs of the child. The capacity is 13 Eastern Cherokee children. *Purpose*: To provide a home for Cherokee children.

CHEROKEE HISTORICAL ASSOCIATION
P.O. Box 398 • CHEROKEE, NC 28719
 (866) 554-4557; (828) 497-2111 Fax 497-6987
 Website: www.cherokeehistorical.org
 E-mail: cherokeehistorical.info@gmail.com
 John Tissue (Eastern Cherokee), Executive Director
 Christopher McCoy (Eastern Cherokee), Operations Manager
 Laura Bythe (Eastern Cherokee), Village Director
  E-mail: laura@cherokeeadventure.com
 Philenia Walkingstick (Eastern Cherokee), Program Coordinator
  E-mail: philenia@cherokeeadventure.com

Purpose: To preserve and perpetuate history and culture of the Eastern Band of Cherokee Indians. *Exhibits*: Unto These Hills, an outdoor drama which portrays history of the Cherokee Indians from 1540 to their removal to Oklahoma in 1838 (Mid-June thru late August); the Oconaluftee Indian Village, a replica of a Cherokee community of the 1750 period (Mid-May thru late Oct). *Program*: Tsalagi Touring Program E-mail: tsalagi.touring.cha@gmail.com. *Publication*: Annual souvenir booklet, $4. Established 1948.

CHEROKEE PRESERVATION FOUNDATION
P.O. Box 504 • CHEROKEE, NC 28719
 (888) 886-8524; (828) 497-5550 Fax 497-8929
 Website: www.cpfdn.org; E-mail: info@cpfdn.org
 Bobby Raines (Eastern Cherokee), Senior Program Director
  E-mail: braines@cpfdn.org
 Deb Owle, Program Operations Manager
  E-mail: dowle@cherokeepreservation.org
 Sasha Watty, Program Associate
  E-mail: swatty@cherokeepreservation.org
Mission: To preserve Eastern Cherokee native culture, protect & enhance our natural environment, and create appropriate & diverse economic opportunities, in order to improve the quality of life for the Eastern Band of Cherokee Indians and our neighbors in western North Carolina. Library. *Publications*: Newsletter; Annual Community Report. Established 2002.

CHEROKEE ROOTS
P.O. Box 525 • CHEROKEE, NC 28719
 (828) 497-9709; Website: www.cherokeeroots.com
 Bob Blankenship (Eastern Cherokee), Director
Description: A research service for those desiring more detailed information about their ancestry. The fee for research is $100 per person. *Publications*: Cherokee Roots, Vol. 1: East, $15; Vol. II: West, $25; 1924 Baker Roll: Eastern Band of Cherokee Indians - North Carolina; 1898 Dawes Roll "PLUS"; Guion Miller Roll "PLUS" (Cherokee Roots, $40).

CHEROKEE WELCOME CENTER
498 Tsali Blvd., P.O. Box 460 • CHEROKEE, NC 28719
 (800) 497-9195 Fax (828) 497-3220; E-mail: travel@nc-cherokee.com

SEQUOYAHFUND
810 Acquoni Rd. • CHEROKEE, NC 28719
 (828) 554-6720 Fax 359-5007
 Website: www.sequoyahfund.org
 Russ Seagle (Eastern Cherokee), Executive Director (359-5003)
  E-mail: russseagle@sequoyahfund.org
 Hope Huskey (Eastern Cherokee), Director of Program Development
  E-mail: hopehuskey@sequoyahfund.org; (359-5005)
 Gloria Griffin (Eastern Cherokee), Director-Cherokee Enterprise Development
 Jerry Boone (Eastern Cherokee), Board President
Description: A Native American Community Development Financial Institution (CDFI). *Mission*: To provide training, technical assistance, and resources to support entrepreneurship, business start-up and expansion, and community development in the seven far western counties of North Carolina and on the Qualla Boundary. Qualifying individuals must be enrolled members of the Eastern band of Cherokee Indians living on the Qualla Boundary or in the seven far-western counties of North Carolina. Established 2001.

COASTAL CAROLINA INDIAN CENTER & ASSOCIATION
106 Heverly Dr. • EMERALD ISLE, NC 28594
 (252) 354-4187; Website: www.coastalcarolinaindians.com
  E-mail: indiancenter@gmail.com
 Teresa Morris, Founding Director; E-mail: teresamorrisnc@gmail.com

CUMBERLAND COUNTY ASSOCIATION FOR INDIAN PEOPLE
2173 Downing Rd. • FAYETTEVILLE, NC 28312
 (910) 483-8442 Fax 483-8742; Website:
http://ncadmin.nc.gov/citizens/american-indians/american-indian-organizations
 Gladys Hunt, Executive Director; E-mail: ccaip@netzero.net
 Roy Maynor, Chairperson
Purpose: To assist American Indians in Cumberland County with their social services and economic, educational, and cultural needs. It offers job training, educational classes, cultural festivals, and other activity programs.

GUILFORD NATIVE AMERICAN ASSOCIATION, INC.
1100 Revolution Mill Dr., Studio #6
P.O. Box 5623 • GREENSBORO, NC 27435
 (336) 273-8686 Fax 272-2925
 Rick Oxendine, Executive Director
 Frances Stewart Lowry, Chairperson
Programs: Financial assistance programs. *Activities*: Annual Powwow & Cultural Festival held each Fall. *Facilities*: Art Gallery & Gift Shop. *Publication*: Newsletter.

LUMBEE REGIONAL DEVELOPMENT ASSOCIATION
P.O. Box 68 • PEMBROKE, NC 28372
(910) 521-8602 Fax 521-8625; Website: www.lumbee.org
E-mail: lrda@lumbee.org; James A. Hardin, Executive Director
William Locklear, Director -Education & Employment Department
Woodrow Dial, Chairperson; Horace Hunt, Vice Chairperson
Purpose: To analyze & develop solutions for the health, education, economic, and general welfare of rural & urban Indians in its part of North Carolina. *Special programs*: Child services; Head Start, Fall powwow; day care & infant mortality; employment - WIA. *Community services*: Food bank & clothes drives; housing; Lumbee homecoming. *Publication*: Bimonthly The Lumbee News & Reporter. Established 1968.

AMERICAN INDIAN CHAMBER OF COMMERCE OF NORTH CAROLINA
8200 Brownleigh Dr. • RALEIGH, NC 27617
(919) 247-4946 Fax 510-9668; Website: www.aiccnc.org
Roy Roberts, President; Scott Roberts, Executive Director
Purpose: To promote the growth & success of existing and new American Indian-owned businesses in North Carolina to improve the economic wellbeing of all American Indian employed by them. *Services*: Training/Education Seminars; Counseling. *Publication*: Newsletter.

NORTH CAROLINA COMMISSION OF INDIAN AFFAIRS
116 West Jones St., 1317 Mail Service Center • RALEIGH, NC 27699
(919) 807-4440 Fax 807-4461; Website:
https://ncadmin.nc.gov/about-doa/divisions/commission-of-indian-affairs
Furnie Lambert (Lumbee), Chairperson
Gregory Richardson, Executive Director
  E-mail: greg.richardson@doa.nc.gov
Shirley Freeman, Vice Chairperson
Kimberly Hammonds, Director-Economic Development Program
  E-mail: kimberly.hammonds@doa.nc.gov
Mickey Locklear, Director, Educational Talent Search Program
  E-mail: mickey.locklear@doa.nc.gov
Elk Richardson, Director, Workforce Development Program
  E-mail: elk.richardson@doa.nc.gov
North Carolina American Indian Student Legislative Grant: Financial assistance to American Indians in North Carolina who are interested in postsecondary education in an approved North Carolina school. Up to $500 per year. Deadlines vary with each school. *Publications*: Annual report; "Indian Times" newsletter.

NORTH CAROLINA INDIAN ECONOMIC DEVELOPMENT INITIATIVE, INC.
4904 Professional Court, Suite 100
P.O. Box 58096 • RALEIGH, NC 27609
(919) 232-9414 Fax 232-9416
W.A. "Tony" Hayes, CEO
Kelsie Balance, NCDOT Project Coordinator
Purpose: To foster, enhance & promote economic development in North Carolina's urban & tribal Indian communities by providing assistance with business plan development, feasibility studies, market analysis, etc.; helps business owners with referrals to credit institutions that most closely meet their business needs.

STATE ADVISORY COUNCIL ON INDIAN EDUCATION
NORTH CAROLINA DEPARTMENT OF PUBLIC INSTRUCTION
DIVISION OF INDIAN EDUCATION
6367 Mail Service Center • RALEIGH, NC 27699
(919) 807-3408 Fax 807-3445
Benita B. Tipton, Indian Education Liaison
Purpose: To advise the State Board of Education on ways to meet more effectively the education needs of Indian students.

TRIANGLE NATIVE AMERICAN SOCIETY (TNAS)
P.O. Box 26841 • RALEIGH, NC 27611
(919) 996-9822 Fax 233-7478
Kerry D. Bird (Lumbee/Sisseton-Wahpeton Oyate), President
Danny Bell (Lumbee), Vice President
Gwen Locklear (Lumbee), Treasurer; Clarice Dial, Secretary
Activities: Powwow. Mark Ulmer Native American Scholarship: Financial assistance to Native Americans in North Carolina who are interested in continuing their college education. The stipend is $500/year. *Deadline*: April.

NORTH CAROLINA AMERICAN INDIAN HEALTH BOARD
Maya Angelou Center for Health Equity
Medical Center Blvd. • WINSTON-SALEM, NC 27157
(919) 773-1236; Website: www.ncaihb.org
Gregory Richardson (Haliwa-Saponi), Executive Director
Charlene Hunt (Lumbee), Program Coordinator
Dr. Ronny Bell (Lumbee), Board Chairperson
Purpose: To promote quality health care & healthy lifestyles within American Indian families & communities in North Carolina through research, education.

NORTH DAKOTA

NATIVE AMERICAN TRAINING INSTITUTE (NATI)
3333 E. Broadway Ave. #1210 • BISMARCK, ND 58501
(701) 255-6374 Fax 255-6394; Website: www.nativeinstitute.org
Sandra Bercier (Turtle Mountain Ojibwe), Interim Director
  E-mail: sandra@nativeinstitute.org
Ina Olson (Turtle Mountain Ojibwe), Board Chairperson
  (701) 477-5688; E-mail: inao@tmcwfs.net
Vern Lambert, Vice Chairperson (701) 230-1104
  E-mail: vern_lambert@littlehoop.edu
Purpose: To provide unique, culturally-relevant training & curriculum packages for professionals working with Native American children & families within the four North Dakota tribes: The Standing Rock Sioux, the Three Affiliated Tribes, the Spirit Lake Sioux, the Turtle Mountain Band of Chippewa and the Trenton Indian Service Area. *Programs*: Foster Parenting; Youth Relationship Building/ HIV/AIDS Awareness; Care Coordinator Training; Wraparound in Indian Country; Child Welfare. *Activities*: Conducts workshops & conferences throughout the year. Training Media: Foster Care Orientation CD-ROM for Youth, What You Should Know! Wraparound in Indian Country: A CD-ROM Guide to Wraparound Meetings. Training Curricula: Extending Our Families Through Unity: Native American Foster Parent Training; We Are All Related: Relationships in Perspective: A Guide for Native American Youth.

NORTH DAKOTA DEPARTMENT OF PUBLIC INSTRUCTION
Native American Education, 600 E. Boulevard Ave. • BISMARCK, ND 58505
(701) 328-1718 Fax 328-4770
Lucy K. Fredericks, Director of Indian Education
  E-mail: lkfredericks@nd.gov
Purpose: To increase the capacity of the state & school districts to more effectively develop & conduct educational programs for American Indian learners; to provide technical assistance in developing awareness & understanding of Indian learner needs. *Activities*: Maintains networking/liaison efforts in support of Indian education. Small library. *Publications*: Centennial Curriculum of North Dakota Native Americans; 1994 North Dakota Tribal Curriculum; Bibliography of Resource Materials for Educators. Research Library. Established 1952.

NORTH DAKOTA INDIAN AFFAIRS COMMISSION
600 E. Boulevard Ave., Judicial Wing, Rm. 117 • BISMARCK, ND 58505
(701) 328-2428 Fax 328-1537
Website: www.nd.gov/indianaffairs; E-mail: ndiac@nd.gov
Scott J. Davis (Standing Rock Lakota), Executive Director
  E-mail: sjdavis@nd.gov
Helen Hanley, Executive Assistant to the Commissioner
  E-mail: hhanley@nd.gov
Erin Shanley, Judicial Systems Administrator
  E-mail: eshanley@nd.gov
Brad Hawk, Indian Health Systems Administrator
  Email: bhawk@nd.gov
Purpose: A liaison/referral agency established to facilitate tribal/state relations. *Programs*: Indian Education; Indian Youth Alcohol & Other Drug Prevention Programs. *Publications*: Update, quarterly newsletter; Directory of Statewide Indian Programs. Established 1949.

NORTHSTAR COUNCIL
P.O. Box 13969 • GRAND FORKS, ND 58208
(701) 330-1126. Website: www.northstarcouncil.com
Amber Finley (Three Affiliated Tribes), Executive Director
Tammy NaDeau (Turtle Mountain Chippewa), Board President
Courtney Souvannasascd, Native American Programs Liaison
  E-mail: courtney.souvannasascd@gfschools.org
Mission: To strengthen and empower indigenous people through research, education, & community development. Our focus service population will be the Native American urban population of northeast North Dakota, though we plan to partner with myriad organizations and groups to inform our work, & help provide the programming, education, & assistance. Further, Northstar Council wishes to serve as a resource for our region and the state in terms of culture and diversity issues as it relates to Native Americans. *Vision*: To facilitate a vibrant, healthy community of understanding, tolerance, inclusion, & appreciation for the diversity that surrounds us. Northstar plays a huge role in the education of our Native American youth living in Grand Forks and the surrounding areas. We diligently support the Native American Parent Committee, the Grand Forks Public Schools Native American Liaison, and the Native American educational programs. Activities: Educational Presentations & Training Workshops; Language Workshops.

NORTH DAKOTA INDIAN EDUCATION ASSOCIATION
P.O. Box 211 • ST. MICHAEL, ND 58370
 (701) 766-1400 Fax 766-1457
 Ms. Debbie Poitra, Board President (Turtle Mountain Community School)
 Charles Morin, Treasurer
Description: A state association of Native American teachers & educators.
Activities: Holds an annual meeting.

OHIO

NORTH AMERICAN INDIAN CULTURAL CENTER
304 E. Anthony St. • CELINA, OH 45822
 (419) 586-6567 Fax 586-1570
Services: Employment, education & training; youth programs; health education; Food Initiative; School Supply Initiative; and family & child welfare advocacy program. Established 1974.

NATIVE AMERICAN INDIAN CENTER OF CENTRAL OHIO (N.A.I.C.C.O.)
P.O. Box 7705 • COLUMBUS, OH 43207
 (614) 443-6120 Fax 443-2651
 Website: https://naicco1975.org; E-mail: naicco@aol.com
 Fred Johnson, Board President; Maurice Hotain, VP
 Masami Smith, Executive Director
 Tyrone Smith II, Circles of Care Project Director
Purpose: To serve the social & cultural needs of the Native American Indian community of central Ohio. *Programs*: Employment referrals; health services; cultural programs; tutoring; drug & alcohol programs; food & clothing. *Activities*: Powwows (Memorial Day weekend & Labor Day weekend). *Publication*: Quarterly newsletter. Library. Established 1975.

NATIVE AMERICAN INDIAN & VETERANS CENTER, INC.
4060 Columbia Woods Rd. • NORTON, OH 44203
 (330) 596-2482; Website: www.naivc.org
 Jack (Little Eagle) Lyons, Founder
 E-mail: jlyons@naivc.org
Description: A human service agency made up of American Indians, veterans, & volunteers. *Activities*: Provides social services, cultural recreational activities, and health education to low-income children, families, American Indians, and veterans at risk in Ohio.

AMERICAN INDIAN EDUCATION CENTER
2303 Brookpark Rd. • PARMA, OH 44134
 (216) 351-4488 Fax 351-6637; E-mail: aiecinc@aol.com
 Robert Roche, Executive Director
 Catalin Baker, Board Chairperson; James Weese, Vice Chairperson
Activities: Housing Program; Health-diabetes testing; Youth Council; Annual powwow, speaker's bureau. *Publication*: Smoke Signals, quarterly newspaper.

FRIENDS OF THE SERPENT MOUND & THE OHIO BRUSH CREEK
c/o Bev McKenzie, 186 Horner Chapel Rd. • PEEBLES, OH 45660
 Website: www.serpentmound.org
 Delsey Wilson, Executive Director (937) 205-0094
 Jeffrey Wilson, Board President (734) 891-2689
 E-mail: jeff.wilson@roadrunner.com
 Teresa Mahan, VP & Education Chairperson
 E-mail: tkmahan@roadrunner.com
Purpose: To protect, preserve & promote Serpent Mound and other Native American sites, while facilitating education & experiences for visitors.

NORTH AMERICAN INDIAN CULTURAL CENTER
111 West Ave. • TALLMADGE, OH 44278
 (800) 724-1280; (330) 724-1280 Fax 724-9298
 Website: www.ohioindians.org
 Ms. V. Lana Samaniego, Director; E-mail: naicc2@aol.com

OKLAHOMA

THE CHICKASAW FOUNDATION
P.O. Box 1726 • ADA, OK 74821
 (580) 421-9030; Website: www.chickasawfoundation.org
 E-mail: chickasawfoundation@chickasaw.net
 Johnna R. Walker (Chickasaw), Chief Executive Officer
 Tracie Carter (Chickasaw), Executive Assistant
 Deanna Hartley-Kelso (Chickasaw), Chairperson
 Lisa John (Chickasaw), Vice Chairperson
 Matthew Chestnut (Chickasaw), Treasurer
 Bill Lance (Chickasaw), Secretary
Mission: To promote the general welfare & culture of the Chickasaw people by supporting educational, health, historical & community activities & program.
Scholarships: Provides educational assistance for students who demonstrate

excellence in academics, community service, dedication to Native America and a commitment to learning. *Publication*: Newsletter

SOUTHERN PLAINS INDIAN HOUSING ASSOCIATION
P.O. Box 788 • ADA, OK 74821
 (580) 421-8880 Fax 421-8879; Website: www.spiha.org
 Renee Sweet (Chickasaw), President; E-mail: renee.sweet@chickasaw.net
 Gary Cooper (Cherokee), Vice President; E-mail: gary.cooper@hacn.org
 Kelly Cook (Chickasaw), Secretary/Treasurer
 E-mail: kelly.cook@chickasaw.net
 Anita Lee, 1st Member-at-Large; Brad Campbell, 2nd Member-at-Large
 Tribes from: Kansas, Oklahoma, Texas & Louisiana are welcomed.

COURT OF INDIAN OFFENSES
P.O. Box 368 • ANADARKO, OK 73005
 (877) 787-4237; (405) 247-8508 Fax 247-7240
 Stormy Levias, Court Clerk; E-mail: stormy.levias@bia.gov
 Angela Anderson, Deputy Court Clerk; E-mail: angela.anderson@bia.gov
The first Court of Indian Offenses in the area that was to become the State of Oklahoma was originally established prior to statehood in the Indian Territory in 1886. The original Court of Indian Offenses was created to provide law enforcement for the Kiowa, Comanche, & Apache (KCA) reservation. Several prominent tribal leaders served as judges of the court including Quanah Parker (Comanche), Lone Wolf (Kiowa) and several others. An Indian police force provided the law enforcement for the KCA, Cheyenne-Arapaho, and other reservations. Thus, the Court of Indian Offenses pre-dates Oklahoma state courts by several decades. After the reservations in Oklahoma were opened by land runs to non-Indian homesteading, and federal Indian policy sought to weaken tribal governments and break up tribal land holdings, the courts over time lost their funding and consequently ceased to function. With the void in the enforcement of tribal law, the state began to assert its authority over the remaining tribal and allotted Indian lands even though no jurisdiction properly existed. In recent decades, the Indian tribes have regained the jurisdiction over these lands and have re-established tribal court systems. The State of Oklahoma once contended that tribal governments had no authority to operate their own justice systems, arguing that the Indian nations had no land remaining under their jurisdictions. Much confusion arose because many thought that tribes only asserted jurisdiction over "reservation" lands. Many people in Oklahoma incorrectly assumed that reservations were terminated at statehood. Recent court decisions have made it clear that tribes assert jurisdiction over all lands that are "Indian country", including reservations, dependent Indian communities, and Indian allotments. These Indian country lands from the basis of tribal jurisdiction today. Since few Indian tribes had operating judicial systems in place in the late 1970's. When tribal jurisdiction was re-affirmed, the Court of Indian Offenses for the Anadarko Area Tribes now the Southern Plains Region Tribes was created. Courts of Indian Offenses are established throughout the U.S. under the Code of Federal Regulations (CFR), providing the commonly used name — the "CFR" Court. Until such time as a particular Indian tribe establishes their own tribal court, the Court of Indian Offenses will act as a tribe's judicial system. The only difference between CFR Courts and Tribal Courts is the form of laws they enforce. When the court was re-established in western Oklahoma in 1979, there were four CFR Courts covering eighteen Indian nations. A number of tribes have since established their own systems of justice. Accordingly, the CFR Courts for these tribes have been deactivated. In 1991, a separate CFR Court system was established for Eastern Oklahoma Region Tribes covering eastern Oklahoma, which is headquartered in Muskogee, Oklahoma.

FOUR TRIBES CONSORTIUM OF OKLAHOMA
115 SW 2nd St. • ANADARKO, OK 73005
 (405) 247-2021 Fax 247-2582
 Jeff Foster, Executive Director; E-mail: jeff_foster_99@yahoo.com
Four Tribes: Caddo, Kiowa, Wichita, Chickasaw, *Purpose*: To assist skilled men & women with employment and training; to educate Native American people of their civil rights, and to assist in mediating discrimination toward the Native American. *Publication*: Program pamphlet. Established 1987.

OKLAHOMA INDIAN ARTS & CRAFTS COOPERATIVE
715 E. Central Blvd. • ANADARKO, OK 73005
 (888) 247-3486; (405) 247-3486; LaVerna Standing-Capes, Manager
Purpose: To promote the careers of contemporary Oklahoma Indian artists & craftsmen by providing a sales outlet for their works. *Products*: beadwork, feather work, jewelry, fashion accessories, leatherwork, dance costumes & accessories, dolls, musical instruments, as well as original paintings by Native American artists. Established 1955.

AMERICAN INDIAN CHAMBER OF COMMERCE OF OKLAHOMA
P.O. Box 141424 • BROKEN ARROW, OK 74014
 (800) 652-4226; (918) 624-9382 Fax 872-6382
 Website: www.aiccok.org
 Boyd Miller (Choctaw), President

Linda Kay Sacks (Cherokee), Vice President
Brian Hartley, Treasurer (in charge of Native American Services
 of Oklahoma State Bank)
Linda Andre (Little River Band Ottawa), Secretary

CHEROKEE NATION BUSINESSES
777 West Cherokee St. • CATOOSA, OK 74015
 (918) 384-7474; Website: www.cherokeenationbusinesses.com
 Harold "Sam" Ray Hart, Board Chairperson
 Jerry Holderby, Chair of Executive Committee
 Bob R. Berry, Chair of Real Estate Committee
 Tommye Sue Wright, Chair of Cultural Committee
The economic engine of the Cherokee Nation employing more than 9,000
people. CNB owns companies in the gaming, hospitality, information technology, healthcare, personnel services, distribution, manufacturing, telecom-
munications, environmental services, & security & defense industries.

KOWETA INDIAN HEALTH FACILITY
31870 East Highway 51 • COWETA, OK 74429
 (918) 279-3200 Fax 279-1105; Website: www.creekhealth.org
 Becky Whitlow, Administrator; Dr. Monica Kidwell, Clinical Director
 Dr. Brandi L. Johnson, OD, Optometry
The health center is 58,903 square feet and is currently staffed with 108
employees. There are 20 exam rooms in Primary Care and 16 operatories in
Dental. Services available include: Primary Care, Pediatrics, Contract Health
Services, Dental Care, Optometry, Audiology, Physical Therapy, Radiology,
CT, Mammography, Ultrasound, Laboratory, Diabetes Prevention & Education,
Pharmacy & Pharmacy Mail Order Service, Behavioral Health, WIC Program,
and Community Health Representative Service (CHR).

REI NATIVE AMERICAN BUSINESS CENTERS
Headquarters: 2912 Enterprise Blvd. • DURANT, OK 74701
 (800) 658-2823; (580) 924-5094 Fax 920-2745
Three Memorial Place, 7615 East 63rd Pl., Suite 201 • Tulsa, OK 74133
 (918) 994-4370 Fax 994-4394; Website: www.reinabc.org
 James Ray, Center Project Director; E-mail: jray@reiok.org
 Cassidy Gilmore, Resource Coordinator; E-mail: cgilmore@reiok.org
Purpose: To provide business advisory services and other critical resources to
ensure the continued success and growth of minority-owned businesses. To
build successful Native American-owned businesses. Offers special training on
business plan development, technical assistance, etc. Resources: Choctaw
Nation Career Development Center.

EUFAULA INDIAN HEALTH CENTER
800 Forest Ave. • EUFAULA, OK 74432
 (918) 689-2547 Fax 689-3643; Bert Robison, Administrator
The health center is 7,287 square feet and is currently staffed with 41
employees. There are seven exam rooms. Services available include: Primary
Care, General Clinic, Diabetic Clinic, Contract Health Services, Dental Care,
Radiology, Women's Health Clinic, Laboratory, Pharmacy & Pharmacy Mail
Order Service, Public Health, Diabetes Prevention Program & Contract Health
Service (CHS).

KICKAPOO FRIENDS CENTER
P.O. Box 570 • McLOUD, OK 74851
 (405) 964-2606; Website: www.kickapoofriendscenter.org
 Brad Wood & Christina Wood (Kickapoo) Wood, Co-Directors
Description: A ministry of he Evangelical Friends Church providing ministry to
Native Americans and others in the area. Purpose: To provide native students
educational support in the public schools.

INTER-TRIBAL COUNCIL OF NORTHEASTERN OKLAHOMA
114 S. Eight Tribes Trail • MIAMI, OK 74354
 (918) 542-3443; Website: www.ninetribes.org
Purpose: To serve nine tribes: Eastern Shawnee, Shawnee, Seneca-Cayuga,
Wyandotte, Quapaw, Ottawa, Peoria, Miami, and Modoc. Services: Adult,
Youth, Food Distribution, SAO, WIC Program. Gift Shop.

MURROW INDIAN CHILDREN'S HOME
2540 Murrow Circle • MUSKOGEE, OK 74403
 (918) 682-2586 Fax 682-1170
Website: www.murrowindianchildrenshome.org
 Betty Martin, Executive Director; E-mail: murrowhomedirector@gmail.com
 Dr. Sharon Woolwine, President; E-mail: sewoolwine@gmail.com
Provides a residential home program to needy children from tribes across OK.

OSCAR B. JACOBSON HOUSE NATIVE ART CENTER
609 Chautauqua Ave. • NORMAN, OK 73069
 (405) 366-1667; Website: https://www.jacobsonhouse.org
 E-mail: jacobsonhouse@gmail.com
 Kricket Rhoads-Connywerdy, Executive Director

Daniel J. Brackett, Chairperson; Kimberly Tiger, Vice Chairperson
Description: A non-profit educational foundation concerned with the
understanding & preservation of Native American arts & culture. Goals: To
showcase American Indian fine art & culture; to preserve the historic Jacobson
House; and to serve the public. Facility: The Native Art Center. Programs:
Fine art exhibits; cultural exhibits & programs; classes in beadwork, weaving,
Indian flute playing, singing. Established 1986.

AMERICAN INDIAN CULTURAL CENTER & MUSEUM
900 N. Broadway, Suite 200 • OKLAHOMA CITY, OK 73102
 (405) 239-5500; Website: www.theamericanindiancenter.org
 E-mail: info@theamericanindiancenter.org
 J. Blake Wade, Chief Executive Officer
 Ryan Barnett, Chief Finance Officer
 Shoshana Wasserman (Muscogee-Creek), Director of Communications
 & Cultural Tourism
 Governor Bill Anoatubby (Chickasaw), Board Chairperson
 Gregg Wadley (Choctaw), Vice Chairperson
 Ken Fergeson, Secretary-Treasurer
Purpose: The center is in the process of development and will be opened in
2017. It will be a place to celebrate collective histories & contemporary cultural
expressions. The Museum will be located at 659 American Indian Blvd. (405)
672-9477. Publication: Monthly newsletter.

OFFICE OF THE GOVERNOR OF OKLAHOMA
NATIVE AMERICAN LIAISON
2300 N. Lincoln Blvd., Room 212 • OKLAHOMA CITY, OK 73105
 (405) 521-2342 Fax 521-3353; Mary Fallin, Governor
 Jacque Secondine Hensley (Kaw), Native American Liaison
Governor Fallin states: "Oklahoma's tribes have a valuable and unique impact
on Oklahoma's economy & our culture. My administration has always worked
closely with Oklahoma's tribes and will continue to do so in the future. The
appointment of Jacque Secondine Hensley as Native American liaison (July,
2012-present) will further enhance the partnership and communication
between the governor's office and Oklahoma's tribes."

OKLAHOMA CITY INDIAN HEALTH CLINIC
4913 W. Reno Ave. • OKLAHOMA CITY, OK 73127
 (405) 948-4900 Fax 948-4932
 Website: www.okcic.com; E-mail: administration@okcic.com
 Robyn Sunday-Allen (Cherokee), Chief Executive Officer
 Lysa Ross, Chief Operating Officer
 E-mail: lysa.r@okcic.com
 David Toahty (Pawnee/Kiowa/Creek/Cherokee), Chief Development Officer
 E-mail: david.t@okcic.com
 Hazel Lonewolf (Kiowa), Chief Quality Officer; E-mail: hazel.l@okcic.com
 Daniel Molina, MD, Chief Medical Officer; E-mail: daniel.m@okcic.com
 Dr. Everett Rhoades (Kiowa), Board Chairperson
 Brian Gabbard (Chickasaw), Vice Chairperson
 Meredith Rivas Brockman (Comanche), Secretary
 David Thomas (Cherokee), Treasurer
Purpose: To provide outpatient primary medical care; general medical and
dental services; mental health & substance abuse treatment; health education;
seminars; prevention & outreach. Established 1974.

OKLAHOMA HISTORICAL SOCIETY
American Indian Culture & Preservation Office, Oklahoma History Center
800 Nazih Zuhdi Dr. • OKLAHOMA CITY, OK 73105
 (405) 521-2491 Fax 522-5402; Website: www.okhistory.org
 William D. Welge, Director; (405) 522-5206
 E-mail: mrarchives@okhistory.org
 Tara Damron, Deputy Director (405) 522-2298
 E-mail: tdamron@okhistory.org
 Dennis W. Zotigh (Kiowa/San Juan Pueblo/Santee Dakota),
 American Indian Research Historian
Purpose: The preservation microfilming of documents relating to the Indian
tribes of Oklahoma. American Indian Archives & American Indian Records. A
significant portion of the American Indian Archives are federal records of the
various Indian agencies established to administer reservation activities among
the tribes relocated to the territory during the nineteenth century. These
records span the period from the 1860s to 1933. Agencies and tribes included
in this group are: Cheyenne and Arapaho; Kiowa (Apache, Comanche, Kiowa,
Wichita, Waco, Tawkoni, Caddo, Kichai & Delaware); Pawnee (Pawnee,
Ponca, Nez Perce, Ottawa, Confederated Peoria, Quapaw, Seneca, Eastern
Shawnee & Wyandot); Sac & Fox-Shawnee (Ioway, Mexican Kickapoo, Citizen
Band Potawatomi, Sac, Fox, & Absentee Shawnee). Maintains the Oklahoma
Museum of History & Archives and Manuscripts Division which acts as a
repository of a large body of U.S. Government Indian records and papers of
missionaries to the tribes of Oklahoma. Publication: Chronicles of Oklahoma,
quarterly historical journal. Library and museum.

OKLAHOMA INDIAN BAR ASSOCIATION (OIBA)
P.O. Box 1062 • OKLAHOMA CITY, OK 73101
(405) 943-6457 Fax 917-7060; Website: www.oiba.net
Arvo Mikkanen (Kiowa/Comanche), President
J. Lisa Impson (Chickasaw), Vice President
Leslie Taylor (Delaware), Secretary; Josie Stanley (Cherokee), Treasurer
Purpose: To provide a forum for Indian law practitioners to communicate with one another, exchange ideas on the issues involving the tribal sovereignty of Indian nations within the state.

OKLAHOMA INDIAN LEGAL SERVICES, INC.
4200 Perimeter Center Dr. #222 • OKLAHOMA CITY, OK 73112
(800) 658-1497; (405) 943-6457 Fax 917-7060
Website: www.oilsonline.org; E-mail: oils@oilsonline.org
Colline Wahkinney-Keely (Comanche), Executive Director
C. Steven Hager, Director of Litigation
 E-mail: hager@oilsonline.org
Stephanie Hudson (Kiowa), Senior Staff Attorney
 E-mail: hudson@oilsonline.org
Michael Mitchelson, Board Chairperson
Purpose: To provide legal services to low income Native Americans by direct representation on status related issues of significance; legal training. *Activities*: Sponsors & provides speakers to conference addressing Indian Child Welfare, Indian Housing, Tribal Sovereignty, Natural Resources, and Individual Rights; also sponsors Indian Law Legal Intern Program. Maintains Indian Law library. *Publications*: Handbook on the Indian Child Welfare Act; brochures. Established 1982.

OKLAHOMA STATE DEPARTMENT OF EDUCATION
OFFICE OF INDIAN EDUCATION
Hodge Education Bldg., 2500 N. Lincoln Blvd. • OKLAHOMA CITY, OK 73105
(405) 522-1591 Fax 522-1519
Dwight Pickering, Director of American Indian Education Culture/Heritage
 E-mail: Dwight.pickering@sde.ok.gov
Desa Dawson, Director World Languages (521-3035)
 E-mail: desa.dawson@sde.ok.gov
Purpose: To provide educators with continued Access to culturally appropriate resource/information and in-service that reflects teaching strategies and learning styles which ensure full inclusion of the Native American child in a positive learning environment. The department is in the process of developing certification for instructors of Native American languages in Oklahoma public schools. There are approximately 130,000 Native students in the Oklahoma Public School Districts. Under Title VII funds.

OKMULGEE INDIAN HEALTH CENTER (OIHC)
1313 East 20th • OKMULGEE, OK 74447
(918) 591-5762 Fax 758-1944; Kara Lee, Administrator
With a square footage of over 15,500 and a staff of 64 full-time personnel, the OIHC offers the following services to its patients: Family Clinic, along with a Women's Health Clinic, with a total of 11 exam rooms, Urgent Care/Walk-In Clinic, Pediatric Clinic with four exams rooms, Dental Clinic, Radiology, Laboratory, Pharmacy, Diabetic Prevention Program, Contract Health Services, Public Health Services, and Smoking Cessation Classes.

SAPULPA INDIAN HEALTH CENTER
1125 East Cleveland • SAPULPA, OK 74066
(918) 224-9310 Fax 224-9314
Sid Daniels, Acting Administrator
The health center is 15,200 square feet and is currently staffed with 58 employees. There are 15 exam rooms in Primary Care and five operatories in Dental. Services available include: Primary Care, Dental Care, Optometry, Radiology, Laboratory, Contract Health Services, Public Health Programs, Smoking Cessation Classes, Diabetes Prevention & Education, Pharmacy & Pharmacy Mail Order Service, and WIC Program. Behavioral Health is not located within the Sapulpa Health Center – please contact Daley Tearl for information on Behavioral Health Services.

AMERICAN INDIAN RESOURCE CENTER
110 W. Choctaw St. • TAHLEQUAH, OK 74464
(918) 456-5581; Website: www.aircinc.org; E-mail: info@aircinc.org
Pamela E. Iron (Cherokee/Laguna Pueblo), Executive Director;
 & Executive Director of the Institute for Native Studies
Linda Baker (Cherokee), Guidance Specialist
Georgia Dick (Cherokee), Four Directions Director
Wyman Kirk (Cherokee), Cultural Specialist
Pam Moore, Institute for Native Justice Director
Dana Tiger (Creek/Cherokee), Board President
Margaret Raymond (Cherokee), Secretary/Treasurer
Purpose: To develop culturally appropriate resources to meet the needs of American Indian communities; to provide professional expertise to an on behalf of American Indian tribes, organizations, schools, & other interested agencies;

to prepare Native Americans for teaching careers by offering degrees at the master's & doctoral level. *Programs*: Educational Talent Search; Institute for Native Justice; Four Directions; Project NATIVE (Native Americans Teaming In Visual Empowerment).

CHEROKEE NATIONAL HISTORICAL SOCIETY
Cherokee Heritage Center, P.O. Box 515 • TAHLEQUAH, OK 74465
(888) 999-6007; (918) 456-6007
Website: www.cherokeeheritage.org
Carey Tilley, Executive Director
Gina K. Burnett, Outreach Coordinator (456-6007 ext. 6144)
 E-mail: gina-burnett@cherokee.org
Purpose: To preserve the history & traditions of the Cherokee Nation, & provide educational & social services to members of the Cherokee Indian tribe. *Activities*: Operates the Cherokee Heritage Center, which includes Cherokee National Museum & Cherokee National Archives. Maintains a "living" Indian Village; sponsors annual Trail of Tears Indian art show; conducts a lecture series on Cherokee history & culture. Maintains Cherokee Hall of Fame. Also maintains the Ho-Chee-Nee Trail of Tears Memorial Chapel. Publication: The Columns, quarterly newsletter; Trail of Tears Drama Program, annual. Color prints of Indian art available. Founded 1963.

INDIAN HEALTH CARE RESOURCE CENTER OF TULSA
550 S. Peoria Ave. • TULSA, OK 74120
(918) 588-1900 Fax 582-6405; Website: www.ihcrc.org
Carmelita Wamego Skeeter, Chief Executive Officer
Michael Scott, MD, Medical Director
J.R. Hurt, Chief Operating Officer
Jim Cameron (Cherokee), Board President
Purpose: To promote quality health care by providing culturally sensitive access to comprehensive medical care; to provide quality, comprehensive health care to Tulsa area Indian people in a culturally sensitive manner that promotes good health, well being and harmony. Comprehensive health care includes acute & preventive care, chronic disease management, health education outreach and therapeutic services.

NATIVE AMERICAN COALITION OF TULSA, INC.
1740 West 41st St. • TULSA, OK 74107
(918) 446-8432; Website: www.nacths.com
Jeanette Tankersley, Executive Director
E-mail: jtankersley@nacths.com
Purpose: To serve tribes and Native Americans in the Tulsa area.
Programs: Head Start school; clothing & food donations for families; referrals.

OKLAHOMA NATIVE AMERICAN BUSINESS ENTERPRISE CENTER
7615 E. 63rd Pl., Suite 201 • TULSA, OK 74133
(918) 994-4370 Fax 592-1217; Website: www.oknabec.com
Purpose: To provide technical assistance to federally recognized tribes & Native Americans who are interested in starting a business or enhancing their present business; provides human resource development training, resume development, and employment referrals.

OKLAHOMA STATE BANK – NATIVE AMERICAN LENDING PROGRAMS
P.O. Box 278 • VINITA, OK 74301
Website: www.okstatebank.com/native-american.html#
(9918) 256-5585 Fax 256-3817; Brian Hartley, Contact

OREGON

MOTHER EARTH'S CHILDREN
90633 Cape Arago Hwy • COOS BAY, OR 97420
(541) 888-4584; Website: www.scoregon.com/resource.htm
Indian Resource Speakers: Delores Caldwell (Apache), Don Ivy (Coquille),
 Carol Leaton (Cherokee), Esther Stutzman (Yonkalla/Kalapuya/Coos).
Purpose: To promote positive Indian education, economic and social benefits through the development of innovative programs. *Activities*: An American Indian Repertory Theater that presents traditional Indian stories in a visual manner; The Anne C. Thornton Memorial Fund Scholarship, annual awards of $750 to four American Indian/Alaskan Native students who live in Oregon.

NANITCH SAHALLIE TREATMENT PROGRAM
5119 River Rd., NE • KEIZER, OR 97303
(503) 390-5904 Fax 390-6973; Alan Meyers, Division Manager
Description: A youth residential treatment program; a 44 bed facility for the treatment of Native American chemical dependent adolescents between the ages of 12 & 18 who reside in the Portland Area of the Indian Health Service.

ORGANIZATION OF THE FORGOTTEN AMERICAN
4509 S. 6th St. • KLAMATH FALLS, OR 97603
(503) 882-4441; Leonard Norris, Director

Purpose: To enhance the future of the Native American population. *Activities*: Administers the Job Training Partnership Act program for 22 counties; Employment and training services for eligible Native Americans. Branch offices in Astoria, Coos Bay, Medford, Pendleton, Roseburg, and The Dalles, Oregon.

CROW'S SHADOW INSTITUTE OF THE ARTS
48004 St. Andrews Rd. • PENDLETON, OR97801
(541) 276-3954 Fax 276-3397; Website: www.crowsshadow.org
Kay Fenimore-Smith, Administrator; E-mail: fjanzen@crowsshadow.org
Frank Janzen, Master Printer; James Lavadour, Board President
Description: A non-profit art facility designed to bring technology, instruction and cultural exchange to artists on the Umatilla Indian Reservation in Eastern Oregon. *Purpose*: To provide educational, social & economic opportunities for Native Americans through artistic development. *Facilities*: Printmaking studio, computer graphics lab & photography darkroom; library & private studio space. Established 1992.

COLUMBIA RIVER INTER-TRIBAL FISH COMMISSION (CRITFC)
729 NE Oregon St. #200 • PORTLAND, OR 97232
(503) 238-0667 Fax 235-4228; Website: www.critfc.org
Paul Lumley (Yakama), Executive Director
Rob Lothrop, Policy Development/Litigation Support Manager
 Email: lotr@critfc.org; (731-1291)
Jon Matthews (Nez Perce), Finance & Operations Director
 E-mail: matj@critfc.org; (238-3560)
Purpose: To ensure a unified voice in the overall management of the fishery resources; to protect reserved treaty rights through exercise of inherent sovereign powers of the tribes: Yakama, Nez Perce, Umatilla & Warm Springs. *Publication*: Wana Chinook Tymoo (Columbia River Salmon Stories), quarterly magazine.

LEGAL AID SERVICE OF OREGON (LASO)
Native American Program (NAPOLS)
1827 NE 44th Ave., Suite 230 • PORTLAND, OR 97213
(503) 223-9483 Fax 294-1429
Purpose: To provide legal representation to Oregon's Indian community, specializing in the protection of Indian rights. Case load includes: economic development, protection of archaeological, sacred & burial sites, worship, Indian health services, Indian Child Welfare Act and protection of Tribal-Federal relationship, treaty rights, federal Indian law training tribal sovereignty. Established 1979.

NATIVE AMERICAN BUSINESS ALLIANCE
8435 SE 17th Ave. • PORTLAND, OR 97202
(503) 233-4841*Description*: Non-profit organization. *Purpose*: To promote economic development for all Indians through the formation of an alliance of profit-oriented Indian businesses. *Activities*: Conduct quarterly meetings in Oregon and Washington. *Publication*: Indian Business Review, quarterly.

NATIVE AMERICAN REHABILITATIONASSOCIATION (NARA)
OF THE NORTHWEST
NARA Administration Oyate Bldg.
1776 SW Madison • PORTLAND, OR 97205
(503) 224-1044; Website: https://www.naranorthwest.org/
E-mail: mail:info@naranorthwest.org
Sue Ziglinski (Klamath, Seminole /Lumbee) Board President
Jack Cranford (Chippewa), Board Vice President
Jacqueline Mercer, Chief Executive Officer
Michael Watkins, Chief Operations Officer
Amanda Wright, Special Projects Coordinator
Indian owned & operated. *Purpose*: To achieve the highest level of physical, mental and spiritual well being for American Indian & Alaska Native peoples. Provides culturally appropriate education, physical & mental health services & substance abuse treatment. *Facilities*: Operates an Indian Health Clinic, an Outpatient Treatment Center, a Residential Treatment Center, a Family Wellness & Resource Center. Totem Lodge (mental health resource location) (See listings below). Programs: Women's Wellness. *Publications*: Drumbeat, quarterly newsletter; Diabetes Newsletter; Tobacco Prevention & Education Program Newsletter. Established 1970.

NARA OYATE FAMILY SERVICES
1776 SW Madison • PORTLAND, OR 97205
(503) 224-1044 Fax 231-1654

NARA INDIAN HEALTH CLINIC
15 N. Morris • PORTLAND, OR 97227
(503) 230-9875 Fax 230-9877

NARA - OUTPATIENT TREATMENT CENTER
1631 SW Columbia • PORTLAND, OR 97201
(503) 231-2641 Fax 231-1654

NARA - RESIDENTIAL TREATMENT CENTER
17645 NW St. Helens Hwy. • PORTLAND, OR 97231
(503) 621-1069 Fax 621-0200

NARA - OYATE FAMILY SERVICES
1776 SW Madison • PORTLAND, OR 97205
(503) 224-1044 Fax 621-2235

NARA - TATE TOPO
1310 SW 17th Ave. • PORTLAND, OR 97201
(503) 231-2641 Fax 467-4077
Provides adult mental health treatment.

NARA - TOTEM LODGE
1438 SE Division • PORTLAND, OR 97202
(503) 548-0346 Fax 232-5959

NATIVE AMERICAN ART COUNCIL
Portland Art Museum, 1219 SW Park Ave. • PORTLAND, OR 97205
(503) 226-2811
Description: An educational group organized to support the Portland Art Museum's collection of Native American art. This council, led by the Curator of Native American Art, explores Native American cultures & traditional & contemporary arts through lectures and meetings with artists, collectors, & scholars. Members enjoy behind-the-scenes views of the collection, social events, & great travel opportunities. *Activities*: Sponsors educational programs: guest speakers, films, demonstration and field trips. Established 1985.

NATIVE AMERICAN YOUTH & FAMILY CENTER
5135 NE Columbia Blvd. • PORTLAND, OR 97218
(503) 288-8177 Fax 288-1260
Website: www. http://nayapdx.org
Paul Lumley, Executive Director
Eddie Sherman (Dine'-Omaha) Chairperson
Mary Kay Eagle Staff (Lakota/Northern Arapaho/Northern Cheyenne),
 Board Secretary & Government Specialist
Vega Tom, Director of Finance
 E-mail: vegat@nayapdx.org
Tawna Sanchez, Director of Family Services
 E-mail: tawnas@nayapdx.org
Rey Espana, Director of Community Development
 E-mail: reye@nayapdx.org
Oscar Arana, Director of Strategic Development & Communications
 E-mail: oscara@nayapdx.org
Programs: Educational services; cultural arts programming; Youth, Family & Community Services. *Activities*: Annual Celebration (November); annual Powwow (May). *Publication*: NAYA Family Center News, quarterly newsletter; e-Newsletter.

NORTHWEST PORTLAND AREA INDIAN HEALTH BOARD
2121 SW Broadway #300 • PORTLAND, OR 97201
(503) 228-4185 Fax 228-8182
Website: www.npaihb.org; E-mail: npaihb@npaihb.org
Joe Finkbonner (Lummi), Executive Director
 E-mail: jfinkbonner@npaihb.org
Jacqueline Left Hand Bull (Sicangu Lakota), Administrative Officer
 E-mail: jlefthandbull@npaihb.org
James Fry (Colville), Director of Information Services
 E-mail: jfry@npaihb.org
Jim Roberts (Hopi/Sioux), Policy Analyst
Andy Joseph (Colville), Board Chairperson
Description: A federally funded, non-profit advisory board that represents the 40 Federally recognized Tribes in Oregon, Washington, and Idaho on health related issues. The board is composed of delegates representing each tribe. *Purpose*: To serve as liaison between tribes and the Indian Health Service; to provide training for tribal reps & tribal staff on various health issues; to conduct research and evaluation projects; to serve as a regional center for statistics for Northwest Tribes. *Special programs*: Northwest Tribal Recruitment Project (recruit health professionals for the 40 different American Indian tribes located in Washington, Oregon, and Idaho).

ONABEN – OREGON NATIVE AMERICAN BUSINESS
& ENTREPRENEURIAL NETWORK
6441 SW Canyon Court, Suite 104 • PORTLAND, OR 97221
(503) 968-1500 Fax 968-1548; Website: www.onaben.org
Veronica Hix (Cherokee), Executive Director (918) 624-9176
Kristi K. Burns, Deputy Director (Portland office)
Selena Yokoyama, Media Contact; E-mail: selena@onaben.org
Heather Rademacher Taylor, Communications & Programs Specialist
Jack Lenox (Coquille), Board Chairperson; E-mail: jack1067@gmail.com
Tina Retasket (Siletz), Vice Chairperson; E-mail: retasket@hotmail.com

Aurolyn Stwyer-Pinkham (Warm Springs), Secretary/Treasurer
E-mail: aurolynp@gmail.com
Satellite Office: 53332 S. Memorial Dr., Suite 200, Tulsa, OK 74145
Oregon Native American Chamber of Commerce. A Native American business network presented by Cow Creek Band of Upqua Indians. Established 1991 by four Oregon Indian tribes.

OREGON AMERICAN INDIAN CHAMBER OF COMMERCE (ONAC)
P.O. Box 69563 • PORTLAND, OR 97239
(503) 894-4525; Website: www.onacc.org
E-mail: ep.sherman@onacc.org
Herb Fricke (Mandan, Hidatsa, Arikara), Board President
Mission: To promote & support the education, training & cultural understanding of Native Americans, ONAC members and ONAC partners through access to economic development programs, services & resources; to advance the educational & economic opportunities for Native Americans in Oregon & Southwest Washington; and to increase networking among Native American businesses, professionals, ONAC members & partners, thereby strengthening & growing economic opportunity for all communities in Oregon & Southwest Washington. Scholarships available. *Publication*: Monthly newsletter.

OREGON INDIAN EDUCATION ASSOCIATION
LEWIS & CLARK COLLEGE
Graduate School of Education/Counseling Center for Community Engagement
Indigenous Ways of Knowing Program (IWOK)
0615 S.W. Palatine Hill Rd., Rogers Hall 105MSC 93
PORTLAND, OR 97219
(503) 768-6155 Fax 768-6045
Se-ah-dom Edmo, IWOK Coordinator
E-mail: oiea.president@gmail.com
Tana Atchley, Vice President; E-mail: oiea.vicepresident@gmail.com
Valerie Switzler (Confederated Tribes Warm Springs), Historian
E-mail: brent.spencer@pendleton.k12.or.us
Purpose: To promote Indian education in schools and Indian communities, and to inform association members of state & federal laws affecting Indian education. *Activities*: Textbook review projects; to communicate concerns of Indian educators to the U.S. Office of Education; & administers AIDS Education and Prevention Program.

PORTLAND INDIAN LEADERS ROUNDTABLE
Website: www.portlandindianleadersroundtable.org

PORTLAND URBAN INDIAN CLINIC
15 N. Morris St. • PORTLAND, OR 97213
(503) 230-9875; Jacqueline Mercer, Director
Purpose: To provide health services to the Indian community in Portland.

RESEARCH & DEVELOPMENT PROGRAM FOR INDIAN EDUCATION
Northwest Regional Educational Laboratory
101 SW Main St. #500 • PORTLAND, OR 97204
(503) 275-9500 Fax 275-9489
Purpose: To provide in-service training on school improvement to schools serving Indian children in the Northwest. *Activities*: Annual, one week, "Institute of Excellence in American Indian Education. *Publications*: Effective Practices in Indian Education: Teacher Curriculum, Administrator Monographs, an Administrator's Guide; and Teachers Do Make A Difference: What Indian Graduates Say About Their School Experience.

WISDOM OF THE ELDERS
3203 SE 109th Ave. • PORTLAND, OR 97266
(503) 775-4014; Website: www.wisdomoftheelders.org
E-mail: nisa@wisdomoftheelders.org
Mission: Native American cultural sustainability, multimedia education and race reconciliation. We record, preserve and share oral history, cultural arts, and traditional ecological knowledge of exemplary indigenous elders, storytellers & scientists in collaboration with diverse cultural organizations and educational institutions. *Turtle Island Storytellers Network*: American Indian online speakers bureau that promotes 80 tribal storytellers, historians, and song carriers. This network was developed to provide speaking & consulting opportunities for tribal elders, oral historians, storytellers and song carriers from 13 states in the Northwest & Northern Plains states. *Northwest Indian Storytellers Association* (NISA): NISA was formed in 2005 to encourage, preserve & strengthen traditional storytelling among tribes and urban Indian communities in Oregon, Washington & Idaho. In the spirit of race reconciliation, NISA shares tribal cultural arts with the entire regional community at our annual storytelling festivals. *Wisdom of the Elders Radio Program*, our first series of eight one-hour radio programs from Native America, continue to air on native radio stations nationwide on Native Voice One via www.nv1.org. It also continues to be available online from our website. The radio series was produced in Portland, OR and the host is Arlie Neskahi.

OREGON LEGISLATIVE COMMISSION ON INDIAN SERVICES
900 Court St. NE, Rm. 167 • SALEM, OR 97301
(503) 986-1067 Fax 986-1071
Website: www.oregonlegislature.gov/cis
Karen M. Quigley, Executive Director
E-mail: karen.m.quigley@state.or.us
Purpose: To improve services to Indians in Oregon. *Activities*: To develop & sponsor programs to make needs of Oregon Indians known to the public & private agencies which serve them; to recommend new or improved methods of meeting these needs; and to compile & disseminate information about services for Indians in Oregon. *Publication*: Oregon Directory of American Indian Resources (Internet only). Established 1975.

OREGON DEPARTMENT OF EDUCATION-INDIAN EDUCATION OFFICE
255 Capitol St. NE • SALEM, OR 97310
(503) 378-3600 ext. 2712 Fax 378-5156
Steve Woodcock, Coordinator; E-mail: steve.woodcock@state.or.us
April Campbell, Education Program Specialist (947-5810)

TAHANA WHITECROW FOUNDATION
2350 Wallace Rd. NW • SALEM, OR 97304
(503) 585-0564 Fax 585-3302; Website: www.tahanawhitecrow.org
Melanie Smith, Director
Purpose: To promote & provide multi approaches to low income urban Indians and other special needs pops through education, direct services & advocacy. *Activities*: Outpatient substance abuse & mental health; Native AA/NA meetings, youth assistance, transitional housing for combat vets; dual diagnoses self-help, community referral and advocacy. *Publication*: "Circle of Reflections," (occasional) poetry anthology. Library. Established 1987.

PENNSYLVANIA

COUNCIL OF THREE RIVERS AMERICAN INDIAN CENTER, INC.
Singing Winds – Administrative Offices,
120 Charles St. • PITTSSBURGH, PA 15238
(412) 782-4457 Fax 767-4808; Website: www.cotraic.org
Russell Sims, Executive Director; E-mail: rsimms3671@msn.com
Head Start & Pre-K Central Office: 201 Rochelle St., Pittsburgh, PA 15210
(412) 488-2750 Fax 488-7527
Purpose: Addresses the needs and secures services for the Native-American community. *Programs*: Indian manpower employment & training; Native-American elders program; Native-American cultural programs; Native American family & child services; Native-American Adoption Resource Exchange, and Indian Adoption Awareness Project (national); Singing Winds Head Start; Rainbow Project--adoption agency for western Pennsylvania. Financial assistance for education & training is provided through the Job Training Partnership Act Program; annual Powwow in September. *Publication*: The Singing Winds Newsletter, monthly; Powwow Booklet, annual. Library.

ERIE COUNTY COALITION FOR INDIAN AFFAIRS, INC.
2324 East 26th St. • ERIE, PA 16510
Edward Livingston, Contact

NATIVE AMERICAN INDIAN COMMUNITY
570 Pine Furnace Rd. • KITTANNING, PA 16201
(724) 548-7335; Brandy Weeasayha Myers, Director
Purpose: To educate all people about American Indians. *Activities*: Support programs dealing with Native people; educational program for schools; and Prison Outreach (counseling for prison inmates). Twice a year family gathering, 3 days of Native activities. *Publications*: Spirit Walker Newsletter; educational material on Native people; cookbook.

RHODE ISLAND

RHODE ISLAND INDIAN COUNCIL
807 Broad St. • PROVIDENCE, RI 02907
(401) 781-1098 Fax 781-2394; Website: www.riindiancouncil.org
Darrell Waldron, Executive Director
E-mail: dwaldron@rhodeislandindiancouncil.org
Chester Bliss, Career Counselor
E-mail: chesterbliss@yahoo.com
Judith O-Neil, Career Counselor
E-mail: joneil@rhodeislandindiancouncil.org
Purpose: To promote the social, economic & cultural well-being of all tribal communities in Rhode Island, which includes over 5,600 Indians in Rhode Island & Connecticut, each representing more than fifty tribes. Programs: Education; Job Training & Placement; GED Program; Domestic Violence Prevention; Youth Cultural Program. *Facilities*: The Algonquin House, opened 1996. *Activities*: Annual Powwow in July. Established 1975.

SOUTH CAROLINA

SOUTH CAROLINA COMMISSION FOR MINORITY AFFAIRS
SOUTH CAROLINA NATIVE AMERICAN AFFAIRS
2221 Devine St., Suite 408 • COLUMBIA, SC 29205
 (803) 333-9621 Fax 333-9627
 Website: www.cma.sc.gov/native-americann-affairs/
 Thomas Smith, Executive Director
  E-mail: tsmith@cfma.sc.gov
 Marcy L. Hayden, Native American Affairs Coordinator (832-8165)
  E-mail: mhayden@cfma.sc.gov
Mission: To strengthen the relationship between South Carolina's Native American Indian communities & government; to serve as liaison between South Carolina's Native American population and the South Carolina State government as well as local & federal government agencies. *Publication*: Columbia Metropolitan: Tribes & Tradition. Established 2003.

AMERICAN INDIAN CHAMBER OF COMMERCE OF SOUTH CAROLINA
9377 Koester Rd. • LADSON, SC 29456
 (843) 224-4000 Fax 569-1564; Website: www.aiccsc.org
 Alan Linnemann, President & Chairperson
  E-mail: alan.linnemann@aiccsc.org
 Noah Leask, President – Ex Officio
  E-mail: noah.leask@aiccsc.org
 Teresa Gore, Founder & Initial President
  E-mail: Teresa.gore@aiccsc.org
Annual Business Expo, first week of April.

FOUR HOLES INDIAN ORGANIZATION
1125 Ridge Rd. • RIDGEVILLE, SC 29472
 (843) 871-2126

SOUTH DAKOTA

DAKOTA INDIAN FOUNDATION
209 N. Main St., Box 340 • CHAMBERLAIN, SD 57325
 (605) 734-5472 Fax 234-5858
 Website: www.dakotaindianfoundation.org
 John Beheler, Executive Director
Purpose: To preserve the individual dignity, pride, hope, and self-determination of all Dakota Sioux people. *Activities*: Grants, Scholarship. *Resources*: Ella C. Deloria research papers; Dakota Plains Gallery & Gift Store. Established 1971.

ST. JOSEPH'S LAKOTA DEVELOPMENT COUNCIL
St. Joseph's Indian School • CHAMBERLAIN, SD 57326
 (605) 734-6021
A non-profit organization that sells products (Kachina dolls, leatherwork, beadwork, quilts, etc.) thru mail order and wholesale-retail.k

CHEYENNE RIVER INDIAN OUTREACH
121 Landmark Ave., P.O. Box 969 • EAGLE BUTTE, SD 57625
 (605) 234-3244; Website: www.crioutreach.org
 Margaret Donovan, Executive Director
Purpose: To help families, children and teenagers who live on the reservation.

DAKOTA PLAINS LEGAL SERVICES, INC.
100 E. Frontier St. • EAGLE BUTTE, SD 57625
 (605) 964-2175 Fax 964-1215
A Native American legal assistance organization.

FOUR BANDS COMMUNITY FUND
101 S. Main St., P.O. Box 932 • EAGLE BUTTE, SD 57625
 (605) 964-3687 Fax 964-3689
 Website: www.fourbands.org; E-mail: info@fourbands.org
 Tanya Fiddler (Cheyenne Lakota), Executive Director
  E-mail: tfiddler@fourbands.org
 Lakota Mowrer, Assistant Director
  E-mail: lakota@fourbands.org
 Becky Maher, Business Communications Specialist
  E-mail: becky@fourbands.org
 Mark Shupick, Director of Business Development Services
  E-mail: mark@fourbands.org
Description: A non-profit community & economic development corporation created to assist entrepreneurs of the Cheyenne River Indian Reservation with training, business incubation, and access to capital. Resources: South Dakota Indian Business Alliance, annual business conference in April. *Programs*: Education; revolving loan fund; incubator; social enterprise program, "Made on the Rez."*Publications*: Business Directory; Reports & Media. Established 2000.

UNITED NATIVE AMERICAN HOUSING ASSOCIATION
Cheyenne River Housing Authority
P.O. Box 480 • EAGLE BUTTE, SD 57625
 (605) 964-4265 Fax 964-1070; Sharon Vogel, Vice Chairperson
A federation of Native American housing authorities serving a number of tribes in its area.

DAKOTA PLAINS LEGAL SERVICES, INC.
P.O. Box 20 • FORT THOMPSON, SD 57339
 (605) 245-2341 Fax 245-2393
A Native American legal assistance organization.

LAKOTA FUNDS
P.O. Box 340 • KYLE, SD 57752
 (605) 455-2500 Fax 455-2585; Website: www.lakotafunds.org
 Tawney Brunsch, Executive Director
  E-mail: tbrunsch@lakotafunds.org
 LaVonne Randall, Financial Manager
 Elsie Meeks (Oglala Lakota), President
 Red Dawn Foster, Vice Chairperson
 Warren Cross, Secretary; Michael Her Many Horses,
  Brian Kirk & Dona Leavens, Board members
Purpose: To build a private sector economy on the Pine Ridge Indian Reservation by providing loans and technical assistance to Oglala Sioux tribal members. *Activities*: Small business loans; microenterprise loans; technical assistance & business training; & arts & crafts marketing assistance. *Publication*: The Lakota Fund, newsletter. Established 1986.

PINE RIDGE AREA CHAMBER OF COMMERCE
P.O. Box 375 • KYLE, SD 57752
 (605) 455-2685 Fax 455-2785; E-mail: pracc@gwtc.net
 Website: www.pineridgechamber.com
 Ivan Sorbel (Oglala Lakota), Executive Director
 Kimberly Tilsen - *Brave Heart*, (Oglala Lakota), Board President
Purpose: To create, sustain & enhance Indian-owned businesses to improve the quality of life on the Pine Ridge Reservation.

NATIVE AMERICAN WOMEN'S HEALTH EDUCATION
RESOURCE CENTER
Native American Community Board
P.O. Box 572 • LAKE ANDES, SD 57356
 (605) 487-7072 Fax 487-7964; Website: www.nativeshop.org
 Charon Asetoyer (Comanche), Executive Director & CEO
  E-mail: charon@charles-mix.com
 Elizabeth BlackBull (Dakota), Administrator Director
 Katrina Cantrell (Shoshone), Board Chairperson
Purpose: To provide direct services to Native women & families in South Dakota. *Mission*: To protect the health & human rights of Indigenous Peoples pertinent to our communities through cultural preservation, education, coalition building, environmental justice, reproductive justice, natural resource protection, et al., while working toward safe communities for women & children. *Programs*: Dakota Language & Youth Immersion Program; Reproductive Health & Justice; Food Pantry; Women's Lodge & Domestic Violence Programs; Environmental Awareness. Established 1988.

OWE AKU, BRING BACK THE WAY
P.O. Box 325 • MANDERSON, SD 57756
 (605) 455-2155; E-mail: lakota1@gwtc.net
 Debra White Plume (Lakota/Northern Cheyenne), Director
 Alex White Plume (Lakota), President
 Percy White Plume (Lakota), V.P.
Purpose: To preserve & revitalize the Lakota Way of Life; to promote & protect treaty rights & human rights focusing on the young generations. *Program*: Lakota Media Project - Video training for young adults to learn how to plan & create a documentary.

DAKOTA PLAINS LEGAL SERVICES, INC.
160 2nd St. • MISSION, SD 57555
 (605) 856-4444 Fax 856-2075
A Native American legal assistance organization.

SOUTH DAKOTA DEPARTMENT OF EDUCATION
OFFICE OF INDIAN EDUCATION
800 Governors Dr. • PIERRE, SD 57501
 (605) 280-7964 Fax 773-6139; Website: www.doe.sd.gov/
 Mato Standing High (Ogala Lakota), Director of Indian Education
  E-mail: mato.standinghigh@state.sd.us
 Marta Neuman, Admin. Assistant; E-mail: marta.neuman@state.sd.us
Purpose: To assist the Secretary of Education, while working in conjunction with the Indian Education Advisory Council, to address the educational

challenges that face American Indian students in South Dakota. It works to identify innovative strategies that aim to close the achievement gap between Native and non-Native students; promote educational models that are culturally relevant and where possible, create partnerships between the public school sector, the Bureau of Indian Education and tribal schools.

SOUTH DAKOTA DEPARTMENT OF TRIBAL RELATIONS
302 E. Dakota • PIERRE, SD 57501
  (605) 773-3415 Fax 773-6592; Website: www.sdtribalrelations.com
  Steve Emery (Rosebud Lakota), Secretary of Tribal Relations
Mission: To recognize the nine sovereign tribes who share our geographical borders as distinct political entities, to support their self-governance efforts, and to work with their chosen leaders in a cooperative government-to-government relationship in order to improve their quality of life. *Tribes*: Cheyenne River Sioux, Crow Creek Sioux, Flandreau Santee Sioux, Lower Brule Sioux, Oglala Sioux, Rosebud Sioux, Sisseton Wahpeton Sioux, Standing Rock Sioux, Yankton Sioux. *Purpose*: To establish & maintain and effective communication link between the Governor and the Tribal Government in the state; to recommend qualified Native Americans to boards, commissions and positions within the state government; to serve as an advocate for the Native American population. Established 1949.

SOUTH DAKOTA STATE HISTORICAL SOCIETY
900 Governors Dr. • PIERRE, SD 57501-2217
  (605) 773-3458 Fax 773-6041
  Jay D. Vogt, Director & State Historic Preservation Officer
  E-mail: jay.vogt@state.sd.us
  Ted Spencer, Director of Historic Preservation
  E-mail: ted.spencer@state.sd.us
Purpose: To preserve & exhibit the tangible reminders of South Dakota's history & heritage. *Activities*: Archaeological research, state archives, education programs, historic preservation, publications, historical markers, microfilming, museums. *Publications*: "South Dakota History," quarterly journal; "History Notes," newsletter; "Hoofprints," news for local history groups. Museums. Library. Established 1901.

SOUTH DAKOTA URBAN INDIAN HEALTH, INC.
1714 Abbey Rd. • PIERRE, SD 57501
  (605) 224-8841 Fax 224-6852; Website: www.sduih.org
  Aaron Swan (Rosebud Sioux), Board President
  Donna LC Keeler (Eastern Shoshoni), Executive Director (Sioux Falls office)
  Bonnie Cromwell (Crow Creek Sioux), Health Information Manager

DAKOTA PLAINS LEGAL SERVICES, INC.
P.O. Box 1989 • PINE RIDGE, SD 57770
  (605) 867-1020 Fax 867-1092
A Native American legal assistance organization.

SOUTH DAKOTA INDIAN EDUCATION ASSOCIATION
P.O. Box 2019 • PINE RIDGE, SD 57770-2019
  (605) 867-5633; Chris Bordeaux, President
Activity: Sponsors annual conference in October.

ALLIANCE OF TRIBAL TOURISM ADVOCATES (ATTA)
522 Seventh St. Suite 210 • RAPID CITY, SD 57701
  (605) 791-1058; Website: www.attatribal.com
  Daphne Richards Cook (Oglala Sioux), Executive Director
  E-mail: daphne_57752@yahoo.com
  Randy Ross, Project Manager; E-mail: rross61@msn.com
  Robert Cournoyer, Chairperson
  Myrna Leader Charge, Vice Chairperson
Purpose: To provide protection and preserve South Dakota Sioux tribal nations' culture. *Activities*: Provides information on tribal tours & attractions, accommodations, Native arts & crafts, news & events.

AMERICAN INDIAN RELIEF COUNCIL
2401 Eglin St. • RAPID CITY, SD 57703
  (800) 370-0872; Website: www.airc.org; E-mail: info@airc.org
  Brian J. Brown, President
A program of the National Relief Charities.

BLACK HILLS CENTER FOR AMERICAN INDIAN HEALTH
701 St. Joseph St., Suite 204 • RAPID CITY, SD 57701
  (605) 348-6100 Fax 348-6990; Website: www.bhcaih.org
  Jeffrey A. Henderson (Cheyenne River Sioux), MD, MPH, Board President
  E-mail: jhenderson@bhcaih.org
  Patricia Nez Henderson (Navajo), MD, MPH, Board Vice President
  E-mail: pnhenderson@bhcaih.org
Mission: To enhance the physical, mental, spiritual, and cultural wellness of American Indian tribes, communities, and individuals.

DAKOTA PLAINS LEGAL SERVICES, INC.
P.O. Box 1500 • RAPID CITY, SD 57709
  (605) 342-7171 Fax 348-5874
A Native American legal assistance organization.

NATIVE AMERICAN HERITAGE ASSOCIATION
P.O. Box 512 • RAPID CITY, SD 57709
  (605) 341-9110 Fax 341-9113
  Website: www.naha-inc.org; E-mail: info@naha-inc.org;
  Administrative: 830-F John Marshall Hwy. Front Royal, VA 22630
  (540) 636-1020 Fax 636-1464
  Pamela J. Myers, President & Board Chairperson
  Erin Hibbs, Treasurer & Secretary
Description: A non-profit organization dedicated to helping Native Americans living on the tribal reservations in South Dakota. Established 1993.

SACRED CIRCLE - NATIONAL RESOURCE CENTER
TO END VIOLENCE AGAINST WOMEN
Cangleske, Inc., 777 Deadwood Ave. N. • RAPID CITY, SD 57702
  (877) 733-7623 Fax (605) 341-2472; E-mail: scircle@sacred-circle.com
Description: Located on the Oglala Lakota Pine Ridge Reservation, Cangleska, Inc. is a nationally recognized organization, providing domestic violence & sexual assault prevention/intervention services & facilitates the coordinated response to domestic violence & sexual assault. Sacred Circle aids tribes & tribal organizations to stop violence against Native women. It addresses violence against Native women in the context of the unique historical, jurisdictional, and cultural issues that American Indian/Alaska Native Nations face. It provides the focal point to establish a multi-faceted systemic response to facilitate non-violence in American Indian/Alaska Native communities, and to establish a domestic violence &and sexual assault agenda for American Indian/Alaska Native tribes and tribal agencies. It also provides access to culturally specific information, materials, and specialized training institutes. The primary audience of Sacred Circle includes more than 500 federally recognized American Indian/Alaska native nations in the United States. Its focus is directed toward professional providers serving these communities, including tribal law enforcement personnel (judges, prosecutors and court workers), probation officers, shelter advocates, and batterer intervention providers. Established 1998.

SOUTH DAKOTA URBAN INDIAN HEALTH, INC.
711 N. Lake Ave. • SIOUX FALLS, SD 57104
  (605) 339-0420 Fax 339-0038; Website: www.sduih.org
  Donna Keeler, Executive Director; Micki Schmidt, CMP), Clinic Manager

DAKOTA PLAINS LEGAL SERVICES, INC.
518 Second Ave. E. • SISSETON, SD 57262
  (605) 698-3971 Fax 698-4156
A Native American legal assistance organization.

TENNESSEE

CHATTANOOGA INDIGENOUS RESOURCE CENTER & LIBRARY
200 Compress St. • CHATTANOOGA, TN 37405
  (423) 756-4555 Fax 756-0800

CHATTANOOGA INTER-TRIBAL ASSOCIATION (CITA)
209 Morningside Dr. • CHATTANOOGA, TN 37401
  (423) 781-0197; Website: www.moccasinbend.net/cita;
Purpose: To preserve our Native American heritage & burial grounds out on Moccasin Bend, just west of downtown Chattanooga.

THE NATIVE CULTURAL CIRCLE OF CLARKSVILLE
P.O. Box 549 • CLARKSVILLE, TN 37140
  (931) 326-5836; David G. Baker, Director
Activities: Annual Clarksville, TN Area Intertribal Powwow. Established 1997.

SOUTHEASTERN NATIVE AMERICAN ALLIANCE INTERNATIONAL
2324 Georgetown Rd. NW #602 • CLEVELAND, TN 37311
  (423) 614-7821
  Website: www.senaa.org; E-mail: senaa@senaa.org
  Al Swilling (Cherokee), Founder
Description: Non-profit, Indigenous American cultural & advocacy organization. *Purpose*: To address specific Native American concerns and to foster harmony between Native Americans and other races through cultural education & good will. *Publication*: Online newsletter. Established 1995.

THE RED ROAD: AN AMERICAN INDIAN EDUCATIONAL EXPERIENCE
P.O. Box 1565 • FRANKLIN, TN 37065
  (615) 595-5706; Website: www.theredroad.org

Charles Robinson, Director; E-mail: charles@theredroad.org
Purpose: To educate students on the ways of First Nations people; to develop & cultivate current empowerment opportunities for Natives living on reservations or within Native communities. Established 1999.

INDIAN CREEK PRODUCTIONS, INC.
1291 Ashwood Dr. • JEFFERSON CITY, TN 37760
(865) 475-6844; Website: www.indiancreekproductions.com
Mark & Sherry Finchum, Directors
Description: A non-profit organization dedicated to American Indian education. "Because our heritage is Cherokee, we focus on the history & culture of the Cherokee people." *Activity*: Annual Powwow. Established 2002.

AMERICAN INDIAN ASSOCIATION OF MILLINGTON
P.O. Box 775 • MILLINGTON, TN 38083
(901) 377-0613; Hal "Two Hawks" Colston, Chairperson
Established 1988.

NATIVE AMERICAN INDIAN ASSOCIATION OF TENNESSEE
230 Spence Ln. • NASHVILLE, TN 37201
(615) 232-9179 Fax 232-9180
Website: www.naiatn.org; E-mail: naia@naiatn.org
H. Ray Emanuel (Lumbee), Executive Director
Cheryl Prevatte (Lumbee) Board President
Description: A private, non-profit service agency for Indians of Tennessee. *Goals*: To improve the quality of life for approximately 10,000 Native American residents in Tennessee by improving services in education & decrease illiteracy; by expanding job opportunities & promote better employment; by promoting Indian unity & organization; by improving services in daycare, housing, health, social services and nutrition for low income Indian people; and by increasing knowledge & awareness of Indian culture. *Programs*: Emergency Assistance, Scholarship, Case Management to the homeless, Job Search, Cultural Revitalization & Speaker Bureau. Project: The Circle of Life Cultural Center is being planned on a 10-acre site in Davidson County/Nashville. *Activities*: Annual Powwow in October. Library. *Publication*: Newsletter. Established 1983.

TEXAS

TEXAS INDIAN COMMISSION (HISTORICAL REFERENCE)
Office of Attorney General
P.O. Box 12548 • AUSTIN, TX 78711-2548
(512) 463-2100 Fax 476-2653
Website: www.tshaonline.org

URBAN INTER-TRIBAL CENTER OF TEXAS
1283 Record Crossing Rd. • DALLAS, TX 75235
(214) 941-1050 Fax 946-4738 (Community/Health Services)
(214) 941-6535 (Employment/Training Services)
Angela Young (Choctaw), Interim CEO
E-mail: angela.young@uitct.com
Carlton Roach, Chief Financial Officer
E-mail: carlton.roach@uitct.com
Dr. Jimmie Edmonson, Board Chairperson
Rob Cerno (Pueblo of Laguna), Treasurer
Tommy Conalis (Sac & Fox), Secretary
Other Board members: Jimmy Stephens *Sac & Fox);
V.K. Oxendine (Lumbee); Mark Allen (Muscogee Creek/Tonkawa)
Purpose: To provide health care & other social services to Indian families residing in the Dallas/Fort Worth area. *Programs*: Community services such as: emergency food assistance, transportation, crisis intervention services, information & referral; Indian child welfare; medical-dental clinic; WIC Program; nutrition education services; health education; screening. *Publication*: DIC Smoke Signals, monthly newsletter.

AMERICAN INDIAN CHAMBER OF COMERCE OF TEXAS
7457 Harwin, Suite 307 • HOUSTON, TX 77036
(713) 614-1272 Fax (832) 251-6312
Website: http://northtexaslead.org/2012/12/american-indian-chamber-of-commerce-of-texas-aicct/
Anthony Patricio, President; Bob Whistler, V.P.
Jacob Click, Secretary & Cultural Director
Dan Callahan, Treasurer
Programs: Trade Fair; Scholarship Fund.

FOUR WINDS INTERTRIBAL SOCIETY
P.O. Box 10035 • KILLEEN, TX 76547
(512) 557-1228; Website: www.txfourwinds.org
Aaron Pyle, Secretary

Purpose: To provide a means for Native Americans in the area to meet with other Native Americans; to provide non-Native Americans to learn about Native American cultures; to educate the local community about Native American cultures. Annual Powwow first weekend of September. Established in 1992.

UTAH

ADOPT-A-NATIVE ELDER PROGRAM
P.O. Box 3401 • PARK CITY, UT 84060
(435) 649-0535; Website: www.anelder.org; E-mail: mail@anelder.org
Warehouse: 328 W. Gregson Ave. Salt Lake City, UT 84115 (801) 474-0535
Activities: Annual Navajo Rug Show & Sale in November.

UTAH DIVISION OF INDIAN AFFAIRS
Native American Legislative Liaison Committee
300 S. Rio Grande St. • SALT LAKE CITY, UT 84101
(801) 245-7208 Fax 521-4727; Website: www.indian.utah.gov
Shirlee Silversmith, Executive Director; E-mail: ssilversmith@utah.gov
James Toledo, Program Manager; E-mail: jtoledo@utah.gov
Description: 11 members - seven from House & four from Senate. The Committee serves as liaison between Utah tribes and the Legislature. *Purpose*: To assist tribes and Native American organizations in Utah in solving problems, and serve as a liaison between the State and all tribes & Indian organizations. *Activities*: Scholarships; Annual Conference in April.

UTAH STATE OFFICE OF EDUCATION - TITLE VII INDIAN EDUCATION
250 East 500 S • SALT LAKE CITY, UT 84114
(801) 538-7838 Fax 538-7769
Dr. Chuck Foster, Director; E-mail: chuck.foster@schools.utah.gov

VERMONT

VERMONT COMMISSION ON NATIVE AMERICAN AFFAIRS
109 State St. • MONTPELIER, VT 05609
(802) 828-3211; Website: www.vcnaa.vermont.gov
Lucy Cannon-Neel, Chair; E-mail: beehive1_2000@yahoo.com
Jeffrey Benay, Vice Chair; E-mail: jeffbenay@fnwsu.org
Charlene McManis, Secretary; E-mail: crwillingmcmanis@aol.com
Giovanna Peebles, State Archaeologist (828-3050)
Purpose: To recognize the historic & cultural contributions of Native American to Vermont; to protect & strengthen their heritage, and to address their needs in state policy, programs, and actions.

ABENAKI SELF HELP ASSOCIATION
48 Merchants Row • SWANTON, VT 05488
(802) 868-6255; 868-6457
Mark Rollo, Board President
Angela Gowing, Vice President
Cheryl Fregeau, Secretary
Mission: To raise the economic, educational & social conditions of those Native Americans of Abenaki decent residing in Vermont and related areas; to foster & promote interest & concern for the Abenaki Indian heritage both within and without the Abenaki Nation.

VERMONTERS CONCERNED ON NATIVE AMERICAN AFFAIRS
1374 Old Silo Rd. • ST. JOHNSBURY, VT 05819
(802) 868-4033 Fax 868-4265; Website: www.vcnaa.com
Mark Mitchell, Chairperson

VIRGINIA

AMERICAN INDIAN CHAMBER OF COMMERCE OF WASHINGTON, DC
P.O. Box 3366 • ALEXANDRIA, VA 22302
(703) 671-5335; J.D. Colbert, Delegate

THE VIRGINIA INDIAN HERITAGE PROGRAM
Virginia Foundation for the Humanities
145 Ednam Dr., P.O. Box 400749 • CHARLOTTESVILLE, VA 22903
(434) 924-3296 Fax 296-4714
Website: www.virginiahumanities.org/virginia-indian-program
Rob Vaughan, President; E-mail: vfhinfo@virginia.edu
Kevin McFadden, COO (243-5520); E-mail: kmcfadden@virginia.edu

Description: Interprets Virginia Indian history & cultures, past & present. *Activities*: Research leading to online database of information accessible to teachers, students & the public; Summer Institutes, curriculum resources for teachers; grants to organizations-tribes, museums & other sites; conferences & other events focusing on teaching Virginia Indian history in K-12 & higher education; publications on Virginia Indian history & culture; Virginia Indian Heritage Trail and related projects.

AMERICAN INDIAN SOCIETY OF WASHINGTON, DC
P.O. Box 6431 • FALLS CHURCH, VA 22040
(202) 492-1963; Website: www.aisdc.org; E-mail: info@aisdc.org
Hope Butler (Piscataway-Conoy), President
  E-mail: aisdcpresident@gmail.com
Terry Rose (Choctaw), 1st Vice President
  E-mail: ais1stvp@gmail.com
Reggie Tupponce (Upper Mattaponi), 2nd Vice President
  E-mail: ais2ndvp@gmail.com
Daniella Johnson-Little (Seminole of Oklahoma), Treasurer
  E-mail: aistreasurer2016@gmail.com
Angel (Sundown) Washington (Muscogee (creek) of Oklahoma
  E-mail: aisdcsecretary2016@gmail.com
Mitchell Bush, Newsletter Editor; Marietta Van Pelt, AIS Scholarship Chair
Purpose: To promote & preserve Indian tradition; provide scholarship assistance for young Indian people. Special program: American Indian Inaugural Ball. *Publications*: Monthly newsletter; American Indian Society Cookbook, $6. Established 1966.

MATTAPONI-PAMUNKEY-MONACAN, INC.
5036 Indian Neck Rd. • INDIAN NECK, VA 23148
(804) 769-4767 Fax 769-0742; Website: www.mpmjobs.org
G. Anne Richardson, Executive Director
Jean A. Adams, Fiscal Office; Dana Beals, Job Developer/Counselor
Description: Native American employment & training program.
Activities: Job Training & Career Placement Services.

UNITED INDIANS OF VIRGINIA
12111 Indian Hill Lane • PROVIDENCE FORGE, VA 23140
(804) 966-2719; Jerry Fortune (Rappahannock), Chairperson
Purpose: To enhance communication between & amongst the member tribes. To improve the general welfare & cultural survival of Virginia's tribal population. *Board members*: Chief Marvin Bradby (Eastern Chickahominy); Fred Bright (Nansemond); Floyd Jefferson (Chickahominy); Robert Gray (Pamunkey); Ray Adams (Upper Mattaponi). *Programs*: Education Fund; Memorial Park Project

ARCHAEOLOGICAL SOCIETY OF VIRGINIA
P.O. Box 70395 • RICHMOND, VA 23255
(804) 829-2272; *Activities*: Traveling program on Native American prehistory.

VIRGINIA COUNCIL ON INDIANS
P.O. Box 1475 • RICHMOND, VA 23218
(804) 225-2084
Description: 13 members - eight from Virginia tribes officially recognized by the Commonwealth, two members at-large from Indian population in Virginia, one from House of Delegates, one from Senate, and one from Commonwealth at-large.

WASHINGTON

NORTHWEST INDIAN NEWS
Tulalip Tribes Communications Dept.
1151 Ellis • BELLINGHAM, WA 98225
(800) 488-5867 ext. 2962; (360) 392-2962 Fax 647-0824
Website: www.nwin.tv
Rick Valentine (Tulalip) (716-4193)
  E-mail: rvalentine@tulaliptribes-nsn.gov
Niki Cleary (Tulalip) (716-4202)
  Email: ncleary@tulaliptribes-nsn.gov
Purpose: To develop and improve communications among Indian people and between Indians & the non-Indian public by offering consultant services among members, workshops, & presenting job opportunities. Annual meeting and a news bureau. Publishes the "Sequoyah Sentinel," a monthly newsletter to keep members informed on the state of the art.

CAMAS CENTER FOR COMMUNITY WELLNESS
The Kalispel Tribe, 1821 N. LeClerc Rd. #5 • CUSICK, WA 99119
(800) 561-7714; (509) 447-7122 Fax 445-0272
Website: www.camasinstitute.com
Purpose: To foster an environment that encourages life-long learning by providing opportunities to tribal members, Native Americans & the community at large. Annual Powwow. Opened 2001.

INDIGENOUS TRIBES ASSOCIATION
1030 S. 317th St. • FEDERAL WAY, WA 98003
(206) 839-5635; Fred Tidewaters Raven, Contact

AMERICAN INDIAN ART FROM THE PACIFIC NORTHWEST
P.O. Box 101 • LUMMI ISLAND, WA 98262
(360) 738-0488; Website: www.ebuynativeart.com

Description: A non-profit arts program serving Native American fine artists & craftspeople in Washington, Oregon, Idaho & Southeastern Alaska. *Purpose*: To promote, educate & preserve Pacific Northwest Native American traditional & contemporary fine art, crafts & culture.

NORTHWEST INTERTRIBAL COURT SYSTEM (NICS)
20818 44th Ave. West • LYNNWOOD, WA 98036
(425) 774-5808 Fax 778-7704
Website: www.nics.ws; E-mail: nics@nics.ws
Dan Kamkoff, Executive Director; E-mail: dank@nics.ws
Purpose: To provide judicial and prosecutorial services to its member tribes. Programs: Tribal Courts; Code Writing; Informal Dispute Resolution; Tribal Appellate Courts. *Publication*: "Appellate Opinions," codes for member tribes.

GOVERNOR'S OFFICE OF INDIAN AFFAIRS
210 -11th Ave., SW #415, P.O. Box 40909 • OLYMPIA, WA 98504-0909
(360) 902-8826 Fax 902-8829
Website: www.goia.wa.gov; E-mail: info@goia.wa.gov
Craig A. Bill, Executive Director; (360) 902-8827
  E-mail: craig.bill@goia.wa.gov
Mystique Hurtado, Executive Assistant
  E-mail: mystique.hurtado@goia.wa.gov
Rebecca George, Communications & Outreach
  E-mail: rgeorge@goia.wa.gov
Purpose: To act as a liaison office between the State of WA & the 27 federally recognized tribes, the nine non-federally recognized tribes, and various Indian organizations; to educate; to work with Indian tribes; to establish a relationship involving tribal, local, state & federal governments; to improve communications & joint problem-solving efforts. Also seeks to enhance the government-to-government relationship between the state & tribes. *Programs*: Conducts "State-Tribal Relations Training," twice a month - this two-day class covers federal legislation/policy, tribal governments, cultural identity, spirituality, reservation economies. Research library. Established 1980.

NORTHWEST INDIAN FISHERIES COMMISSION
6730 Martin Way E. • OLYMPIA, WA 98506
(360) 438-1180 Fax 754-8659; Website: www.nwifc.org
Billy Frank, Jr., Chairperson (528-4320)
Justin Parker, Executive Director; E-mail: jparker@nwifc.org
Purpose: To assist the tribes in conducting orderly & biologically sound fisheries and to provide member tribes with a single, unified voice on fisheries management & conservation issues. *Publication*: Quarterly newsletter. Established 1974.

WASHINGTON STATE INDIAN EDUCATION ASSOCIATION
Indian Education Office, Old Capitol Bldg.
P.O. Box 47200 • OLYMPIA, WA 98504
(360) 725-6160 Fax 701-4169; Website: www.wsiea.org
Ms. Robin Butterfield, Director
  E-mail: robin.butterfield@k12.wa.us
Rose Mary Miller, Board Chairperson
Joan Banker, Ex-Officio
  E-mail: joan.banker@k12.wa.us
Purpose: To administer 20 Johnson O'Malley Indian education programs, funded by the Bureau of Indian Affairs. *Activities*: Provides technical assistance to schools, communities, organizations, etc. in matters pertaining to Indian education. *Activities*: Sponsors annual conference & publishes newsletter, Washington State Indian Education Update.

WESTERN WASHINGTON NATIVE AMERICAN EDUCATION CONSORTIUM
P.O. Box 8291 • PORT ORCHARD, WA 98366
(360) 443-3579; Website: www.wwnaec.com
Mary Wilbur, President; E-mail: mwilber@lwsd.org
Heather Dismuke, Vice Chairperson
  E-mail: hdismuke@cloverpark.k12.wa.us

AMERICAN INDIAN ENVIRONMENTAL OFFICE
USEPA Region 10, 1200 Sixth St., Suite 900 • SEATTLE, WA 98101
(206) 553-2970; Gina Bonifacino, Tribal Lead Region Coordinator
  E-mail: bonifacino.gina@epa.gov
Sally Thomas, Manager, Tribal Trust & Assistance Unit
  E-mail: thomas.sally@epa.gov

AMERICAN INDIAN HERITAGE SCHOOL & PROGRAM
1330 North 90th St. • SEATTLE, WA 98103
(206) 298-7895
Operates a secondary school program attuned to the needs of Indian students. It also conducts educational programs on Native American culture in schools in the Seattle area.

CHIEF SEATTLE CLUB
410 2nd Ave., Ext. S. • SEATTLE, WA 98104
(206) 292-6214 Fax 621-1026. Website: chiefseattleclub.org
Colleen Echo Hawk (Pawnee/Athabascan), Executive Director (965-1291)
  E-mail: colleen.echohaw@chiefseattleclub.org
Derrick Belgarde (Siletz/Chippewa-Cree), Deputy Director (965-1290)
  E-mail: derrick@chiefseattleclub.org
Colleen Chalmers (Lakota), Program Manager (292-6214)
  E-mail: colleen.chalmers@chiefseattleclub.org
Denise Stiffarm (Gros Ventre), Attorney, Board President
Mission: To create a welcoming place of support, acceptance & ceremony for Seattle's Native population.

NATIVE AMERICAN LAW CENTER
Tribal Court Public Defense Clinic
University of Washington School of Law
William Gates Hall, Box 353020 • SEATTLE, WA 98195
(206) 685-3253; E-mail: boba@uw.edu
Website: www.law.washington.edu/indianlaw
Robert Anderson (Bois Forte Ojibwe), Director
Ron Whitener (Nisqually), Center Executive Director & Clinic Director
Purpose: To provide direct assistance to the tribes in Washington State and across the nation. The Clinic partners with the Tulalip, Squaxin Island, Port Gamble S'Klallam & Puyallup Tribes to serve as their public defender on these reservations.

SEATTLE INDIAN HEALTH BOARD
611 12th Ave. South, Suite 200 (98144)
P.O. Box 3364 • SEATTLE, WA 98114
(206) 324-9360 ext. 1102 Fax 324-8910
Website: www.sihb.org; E-mail: info@sihb.org
Esther Lucero, Chief Executive Officer
Liz Henry, Director of Operations Director; E-mail: lizh@sihb.org
Purpose: To assist American Indians & Alaskan Natives, living in the greater Seattle/King County region of western Washington State, improve their physical, mental, spiritual, and social well being with respect for cultural traditions, and to advocate for the needs of all Indian people, especially the most vulnerable members of the community. *Activities*: Multi-service community health center for medical, dental, mental health, substance abuse, and community education services. *Resources*: Seattle Indian Services Commission. Established 1970.

UNITED INDIANS OF ALL TRIBES FOUNDATION
Daybreak Star Indian Cultural Center, 5011 Bernie Whitebear Way
Discovery Park, P.O. Box 99100 • SEATTLE, WA 98199
(206) 285-4425 Fax 282-3640
Website: www.unitedindians.com; E-mail: info@unitedindians.com
Joey Gray, Executive Director (829-2214)
  E-mail: jgray@unitedindians.org
Abe Johnny, Facilities Manager (829-2224)
Katie Hess, Ina Makah Program Manager (829-2239)
Lynette Jordan, Family Services Director (829-2206)
Jeff Smith (Makah), Chairperson
Claudia Kauffman (Nez Perce), Intergovernmental Affairs Liaison
  for Muckleshoot Indian Tribe
Purpose: To establish an urban base for more than 25,000 Native Americans in the Seattle area. *Description*: Based at the Daybreak Star Cultural Center located on 20 acres in Seattle's Discovery Park. Over 25 years ago United Indians founder Bernie Whitebear and other Native Americans invaded this site, which was originally Indian land, to build a center that would improve the spiritual, social, economic, educational & cultural conditions of Native Americans. *Activities*: Provides social & educational services, from early child development & family counseling to housing homeless youth & preparing meals for the elderly. *Programs*: Education - Head Start & Early Childhood Education & Assistance Program; Elders Services; Employment; Family & Youth; Culture & Heritage - Arts Program, Sacred Circle Art Gallery of American Indian Art; annual Seafair Indian Days PowWow.

URBAN INDIAN HEALTH INSTITUTE (UIHI)
P.O. Box 3364 • SEATTLE, WA 98114
(206) 812-3030 Fax 812-3044
Website: www.uihi.org; E-mail: info@uihi.org
Esther Lucero (Navajo/Latina), CEO
Abigail Echo-Hawk, Director; E-mail: abigaile@uihi.org
Description: A division of the Seattle Indian Health Board. *Purpose*: To support the health & wellbeing of urban Indian communities through information, scientific inquiry, and technology. *Projects*: Communicable Disease Project; Diabetes Data Collection; Health Equity for Urban American Indians & Alaska Natives; Viral Hepatitis Expansion & STI Prevention Projects; The WEAVING Project; PSA Project; Archived Projects. Library. Established 2000.

URBAN INDIAN LEGAL CLINIC – CHIEF SEATTLE CLUB
410 Second Ave. Ext. S. • SEATTLE, WA 98104
(206) 292-6214 ext. 1286
Colleen Echohawk, Executive Director
  E-mail: colleen@chiefseattleclub.org

AMERICAN INDIAN COMMUNITY CENTER
801 E. 2nd Ave. #10 • SPOKANE, WA 99202
(509) 535-0886
Purpose: To develop and operate social and economic development programs to aid Indian in Eastern Washington and North Idaho.

THE NATIVE PROJECT
1803 W. Maxwell Ave. • SPOKANE, WA 99201
(509) 325-5502 Fax 325-9839; (509) 483-7535 Fax 487-7155 (Health)
Website: www.nativeproject.org; E-mail: info@nativeproject.org
Purpose: To provide quality services which promote wellness & balance, staff, families & communities. *Services*: Medical, Youth, Behavioral health. Affiliated with the Indian Health Service. Established 1989.

AMERICAN INDIAN EVANGELISM ASSOCIATION
1105 S. McKinley Rd. • TOPPENISH, WA 98948-0231
(509) 865-4158 Fax 865-4193
Purpose: To spread the good news of the Gospel of Jesus Christ to the American Indian people in the state of Washington. Established 1946.

CAMAS LEARNING CENTER
109 First St. • CUSICK, WA 99119
(509) 447-7140 Fax 445-0702
Website: www.kalispeltribe.com/camas-learning-center/
Deana Shrader, Youth Activities Supervisor
Operated by the Camas Institute and the Kalispel Tribe.

WISCONSIN

WISCONSIN INDIAN EDUCATION ASSOCIATION
Menominee Indian Tribe, P.O. Box 910 • KESHENA, WI 54135
(800) 362-4476; (715) 799-5110 Fax 799-1364
Website: www.wiea.org
Ashley Maki (Lac du Flambeau Ojibwe), Director
  E-mail: amaki@ldftribe.com
Brian Jackson (Lac du Flambeau Ojibwe), Board President
  E-mail: brian.jackson@ldfschool.org
Barbara Blackder-Mackenzie (Ho-Chunk), Vice President
  E-mail: Barbara.mackenzie@ho-chunk.com
Christine Munson (Oneida), Secretary
  E-mail: munson@ntc.edu
Virginia Nuske (Menominee-Stockbridge-Munsee), Treasurer
  E-mail: nuskerv@gmail.com
Purpose: To promote educational opportunities for Indian people of Wisconsin. *Programs*: Educational scholarships, awards, and grants for Indian students residing in Wisconsin. *Activities*: Annual Conference. *Publication*: WI Indian Education Resource Directory. Established 1985.

GREAT LAKES INTER-TRIBAL COUNCIL
P.O. Box 9 • LAC DU FLAMBEAU, WI 54538
(800) 472-7207; (715) 588-3324 Fax 588-7900
Website: www.glitc.org; E-mail: glitc@glitc.org
Michael W. Allen, Executive Director
  E-mail: mallen@glitc.org
Elaine Valliere (Family Health); Deputy Director
  E-mail: eallen@glitc.org
Jeff Muse (Education, Human Services), Deputy Director
  E-mail: jmuse@glitc.org
Wilfrid Cleveland, Board President; Robert Blanchard, Chairperson
Purpose: To support member tribes in expanding self-determination efforts by providing services & assistance to Native Americans in Wisconsin, Minnesota & Michigan. *Special program*: Economics, Education, Health Children, Family, Elders & Emergency Preparedness Programs. Established 1961.

WISCONSIN STATE-TRIBAL RELATIONS INITIATIVE
Wisconsin Dept. of Administration-Division of Intergovernmental Relations
101 E. Wilson St., 9th Fl. • MADISON, WI 53702
(608) 267-1824 Fax 267-6917; Website: www.witribes.wi.gov
Brian Vigue, Administrator; brian.vigue@wisconsin.gov
Dawn Vick, Team Leader; E-mail: dawn.vick@wisconsin.gov
Purpose: To study issues related to American Indians and the American Indian tribes & bands in Wisconsin; to develop specific recommendations and legislative proposals relating to these issues. Includes six-12 legislative and six-11 tribal members.

WISCONISN DEPARTMENT OF PUBLIC INSTRUCTION
AMERICAN INDIAN STUDIES PROGRAM
125 S. Webster St., P.O. Box 7841 • MADISON, WI 53707
(800) 441-4563; (608) 266-3390
Website: http://amind.dpi.wi.gov
David O'Connor, American Indian Studies Consultant
E-mail: david.oconnor@dpi.wi.gov
Purpose: to assist with the implementation of the curricular requirements in the areas of American Indian history, culture, and tribal sovereignty. The program is also responsible for American Indian Language & Culture Education.
Activities: Conferences & workshops.

GREAT LAKES NATIVE DIABETES PROJECT
2318 W. Merrill St. • MILWAUKEE, WI 53204
Laura Bearskin, Project Coordinator

GERALD L. IGNACE INDIAN HEALTH CENTER, INC.
930 West Historic Mitchell St. • MILWAUKEE, WI 53204
(414) 383-9526 Fax 649-2711; Website: www.gliihc.net
Dr. Lyle A. Ignace (Menominee/Coeur D'Alene), Executive Director
E-mail: lignace@gliihc.net
Dr. Mustansir Majeed, Physician & Medical Director
Garrett Boyd (Menominee), Chairperson
Steven Ninham (Oneida), Vice Chairperson
Purpose: To improve the health, peace, & welfare of Milwaukee's urban Indian community.

UNITED INDIANS OF MILWAUKEE, INC.
1554 W. Bruce St. • MILWAUKEE, WI 53204
(414) 384-8070
Description: An advocacy & service organization for Indians in the Milwaukee area. *Purpose*: To develop educational programs, social events, recreational activities & culturally spiritual activities and hold powwows.

GREAT LAKES INDIAN FISH & WILDLIFE COMMISSION
72682 Maple St., P.O. Box 9 • ODANAH, WI 54861
(715) 682-6619 Fax 682-9294; Website: www.glifwc.org
James Zorn, Executive Administrator; E-mail: jzorn@glifwc.org
Gerald DePerry, Deputy Administrator; E-mail: gdeperry@glifwc.org
Jen Vanator, Great Lakes Program Coordinator
E-mail: jvanator@glifwc.net
Purpose: To assist the eleven-member Ojibwe tribes; to implement & protect their court-affirmed treaty rights; to hunt, fish & gather in treaty-ceded territories of northern Michigan, Wisconsin & Minnesota; to promote tribal self-government & ecosystem protection. *Publications*: Mazina'igan, free quarterly newspaper; booklet: Treaty Rights: Understanding & Impact; manuals, brochures, videos; books: Plants Used by the Great Lakes Ojibwa; Ojibwe Journeys; Treaties, Sandy Lake & the Waabanong Run; Where the River Is Wide. Established 1984.

WISCONSIN JUDICARE, INC.
401 5th St., 2nd Floor, P.O. Box 6100 • WAUSAU, WI 54402
(800) 472-1638 (715) 842-1681 Fax 848-1885
Website: www.judicare.org; E-mail: info@judicare.org
Kimberly Haas, Executive Director; E-mail: khaas@judicare.org
Howard Bichler, Indian Law Office Director
Beth Ann Richlen, Civil Unit Director/Staff Attorney
Judith M. Stern, Special Project Director/Staff Attorney
Matthew Sunshine Lemieux, Staff Attorney, Indian Law Office
Genie Hedlund & Kristin Holmes, Staff Attorneys
W. Noah Lentz, Staff Ho-Chunk Attorney
Purpose: To provide representation to low income Native Americans in civil matters involving Indian law issues; provides legal assistance to Indian tribes on a variety of tribal projects through contracts and agreements with individual tribes. Library.

AMERICAN INDIAN CHAMBER OF COMMERCE OF WISCONSIN (AICCW)
AMERICAN INDIAN CONSTRUCTION & TRADES ASSOCIATION (AICTA)
10809 W. Lincoln Ave. #201 • WEST ALLIS, WI 53227
(414) 604-2044 Fax 604-2070
Craig Anderson (Sisseton Wahpeton Sioux), President & Executive Director
E-mail: craiga@aiccw.org
Gary Mejchar, Program Manager; E-mail: gary@aiccw.org
Purpose: To promote economic development in Wisconsin Indian country through directed services. *Mission*: The association provides American Indian tradesmen a voice in Wisconsin's trades industry; to provide access to information about federal, state, and local government policies; lobbies on behalf of American Indians in Wisconsin. *Programs*: American Indian Business Capacity Project; First American Capital Corp. (FACC) - provides financial products & services to American Indian entrepreneurs; Scholarships & Internships; Selig Scholars Program (scholarships, $10,000 each). *Activities*: Annual Golf Tournament. *Publication*: Quarterly newsletter. Established 1991.

WYOMING

WYOMING DEPARTMENT OF EDUCATION
Indian Education Office
Hathaway Bldg. 2nd Floor • CHEYENNE, WY 82002-2060
(307) 777-7675 Fax 777-6234
Julie Magee, Standards & Accountability Division Administrator
(307) 777-8740; E-mail: Julie.magee@wyo.gov
Rob Black, Education Consultant (307) 777-3747
E-mail: rob.back1@wyo.gov
Program: Tribal Children's Triad: The Wyoming Tribal Children's Triad (Triad) is a joint education venture between Wyoming communities, schools, and government, created to address educational challenges faced by Native American students on & near the **Wind River Indian Reservation**. The Triad is composed of nearly thirty partner organizations. The group is community-focused and works on educational goals such as improving attendance and graduation rates for Native American students. *Conference*: Annual Native American Education Conference

WYOMING INDIAN AFFAIRS COUNCIL
Select Committee on Tribal Relations • CHEYENNE, WY 82002
(307) 777-6779 Fax 777-6964
Gary E. Maier, Commissioner
Purpose: To serve the needs of about 12,000 Native Americans, primarily Northern Arapaho & Eastern Shoshone (although over 40 other tribes are represented at Wind River.) To act as liaison between the tribes of Wyoming and the Wyoming state government.

BUFFALO BILL HISTORICAL CENTER
720 Sheridan Ave. • CODY, WY 82414
(307) 587-4771 Fax 587-5714
Purpose: The preservation & exhibition of Western Americana pertaining to Rocky Mountain & Northern Plains region. Activities: Operates the Buffalo Bill Museum, Whitney Gallery of Western Art, Cody Firearms Museum, Plains Indian Museum, Draper Museum of Natural History, and the McCracken Research Library. *Publication*: Points West, quarterly magazine. Library. Established 1917.

WIND RIVER LEGAL SERVICES, INC.
P.O. Box 247 • FORT WASHAKIE, WY 82514
(800) 442-6170; (307) 332-6626 Fax 332-5763

BUREAU OF INDIAN EDUCATION (BIE)

Indian children attend Federal, public, private and mission schools. There are approximately 250,000 Indian students, age 5 to 18 years inclusive, enrolled in these schools in the U.S. Education of Indian children residing in the states of CA, ID, MI, MN, NE, OR, TX, WA, & WI is the responsibility of each State.

Currently, the Bureau of Indian Education oversees a total of 183 elementary, secondary, residential & peripheral dormitories across 23 states. 126 schools are tribally controlled under P.L. 93-638 Indian Self Determination Contracts or P.L. 100-297 Tribally Controlled Grant School Act. 57 schools are operated by the BIE The BIE also oversees two post-secondary schools: Haskell Indian Nations University & Southwestern Indian Polytechnic Institute. Lists Bureau of Indian Education (BIE) agencies & area offices with education program administrators, superintendents, and chairpersons; with phone & fax numbers; & E-mail addresses.

OFFICE OF INDIAN EDUCATION PROGRAMS
Bureau of Indian Education (BIE)
1849 C St., NW MS-3609-MIB • WASHINGTON, DC 20240-0001
(202) 208-6123 Fax 208-3312; Website: www.bie.edu
Dr. James Martin, Acting Associate Deputy Director
 & Chief, Division of Planning & Research
Brian Drapeaux, Sr., Chief of Staff
Jacqueline Cheek, Special Assistants to Director (208-6983)
Lorenda Begay, Staff Assistant to Sr. Mgmt. (208-5962)
Dr. Joe Herrin, Financial Systems Specialist (208-7658)
Katherine Campbell, Education Program Specialist (208-3345)
 Higher Education for Post Secondary Education (405) 605-6001

BIE OFFICE OF THE DIRECTOR
Department of the Interior
Bureau of Indian Education (BIE)
1849 C St., NW, MS-3609-MIB
WASHINGTON, DC 20240-0001
(202) 208-6123 Fax 208-3312
Tony Dearman, Director; E-mail: tony.dearman@bie.edu
Juanita Mendoza, Chief of Staff (208-3559)
 E-mail: juanita.mendoza@bie.edu
Jacqueline Cheek, Special Assistants to Director (208-6983)
 E-mail: jacqueline.cheek@bie.edu
Clint Bowers, Program Analyst, Policy (208-3479)
 E-mail: clint.bowers@be.edu
Travis Clark, Management Program Analyst (208-3612)
 E-mail: travis.clark@bie.edu
Dr. Joe Herrin, Financial Systems Specialist (208-7658)
 E-mail: joe.herrin@bie.edu
Susan McCabe, NASIS Specialist (208-4397)
 E-mail: susan.mccabe@bie.edu
Darren Cruzan, Special Advisor (208-5787)
 E-mail: Darren.cruzan@bie.edu
Katherine Campbell, Program Analyst, Post-Secondary (Restin, VA)
 E-mail: katherine.campbell@bie.edu

SCHOOL OPERATIONS DIVISION
1849 C St., NW, MS-3609-MIB
Washington, DC 20240-0001
Fax (202) 208-3312
Bart Stevens, Deputy Bureau Director (208-7388)
 E-mail: bart.stevens@bie.edu
Angela Salazar, Supervisory Financial Analyst (208-3628)
 E-mail: angela.salazar@bie.edu
Leo Moomaw, Sef Determination Advisor (703) 390-6365
 E-mail: leo.moomaw@bie.edu

DIVISION OF PERFORMANCE & ACCOUNTABILITY
Bureau of Indian Education
1951 Constitution Ave., NW MS: 312A-SIB
Washington, DC 20245
Jeffrey Hamley, Associate Deputy Director (208-2352)
 E-mail: jeffrey.hamley@bie.edu
Donald Griffin, Education Program Specialist (208-0268)
 E-mail: donald.griffin@bie.edu

ALBUQUERQUE SERVICE CENTER

DEPUTY DIRECTOR SCHOOL OPERATIONS
1011 Indian School Rd. NW, Suite 332
ALBUQUERQUE, NM 87104
 (505) 563-5265 Fax 563-5345
Deborah Lee, Acting Secretary - School Operations
 E-mail: deborah.lee@bie.edu

ASSOCIATE DEPUTY DIRECTOR, BUREAU OPERATED SCHOOLS
1011 Indian School Rd. NW, Suite 332
ALBUQUERQUE, NM 87104
 (505) 563-5265 Fax 563-5345
Jimmy Hastings, Acting Associate Deputy Director West
 E-mail: jimmy.hastings@bie.edu
Gloria Yepa, Education Program Specialist (563-5264)
 E-mail: gloria.yepa@bie.edu
Laura Lowe, Education Specialist (563-5389)
 E-mail: laura.lowe@bie.edu
Casey Sovo, Education Program Administrator (563-3690)
 E-mail: casey.sovo@bie.edu
Fred Shunkamolah, Education Specialist (563-5263)
 E-mail: frederick.shunkamolah@bie.edu
Reanna Albert, Education Specialist (563-3565)
 E-mail: reanna.albert@bie.edu
Ethel Davis, Education Specialist (563-3699)
 E-mail: ethel.davis@bie.edu

ASSOCIATE DEPUTY DIRECTOR, NAVAJO
BIA Bldg. #3, Club Rd.
P.O. Box 1449 • WINDOW ROCK, AZ 86515
 (928) 871-5932 Fax 871-5945
Tamarah Pfeiffer, Associate Deputy Director Navajo (871-5961)
 E-mail: tamarah.pfeiffer@bie.edu
Rena Yazi, Education Program Administrator (Shiprock, NM)
 (505) 368-3403; E-mail: rena.yazzi@bie.edu
Zonnie Sombrero, Education Program Specialist (871-5972)

ASSOCIATE DEPUTY DIRECTOR
TRIBALLY CONTROLLED SCHOOLS
2001 Killebrew Dr. • BLOOMINGTON, MN 55425
 (952) 851-5427 Fax 851-5439
Rose Marie Davis, Associate Deputy Director (952) 851-5424
 E-mail: rosemarie.davis@bie.edu
Margaret Claymore, Education Specialist (851-5425)
 E-mail: margaret.claymore@bie.edu

BIE EDUCATION LINE OFFICES

ARIZONA NAVAJO CENTRAL (CHINLE)
Navajo Rt. 7, Bldg. 136-C, P.O. Box 6003 • CHINLE, AZ 86503
 (928) 674-5130 Fax 674-5134
Gloria Hale-Showalter, Line Officer
Zonnie Sombrero, Education Specialist
Responsible for the following schools: Black Mesa Community School, Chinle Boarding School, Cottonwood Day School; Jeehdeez'a Academy, Inc. (Low Mountain); Lukachukai Boarding School; Many Farms High School; Nazlini Boarding School; Pinon Dormitory; Rock Point Community School; Rough Rock Community School;

ARIZONA NAVAJO NORTH EDUCATION LINE OFFICE
(WESTERN NAVAJO) P.O. Box 746 • TUBA CITY, AZ 86045
 (928) 283-2218 Fax 283-2286
Lemuel Adson, Line Officer (283-2221)
Dr. Dolly Manson, Education Specialist
Serves the following schools: Chilchinbeto Community School; Tonalea (Red Lake) Day School; Dennehotso Boarding School; Kaibeto Boarding School; Kayenta Community School; Leupp Schools, Inc.; Naa Tsis' Aan Community School; Richfield Schools; Rocky Ridge Boarding School; Shonto Preparatory Schools; Residential Hall, Tuba City Boarding School; Greyhills High School; and Little Singer Community School.

ARIZONA NAVAJO SOUTH EDUCATION LINE OFFICE
(FORT DEFIANCE) BIA Bldg. 3, Rm. 102 (Club Rd.)
P.O. Box 707 • WINDOW ROCK, AZ 86515
 (928) 871-5936 Fax 871-5966
Jacqueline N. Wade, Line Officer; E-mail: jacqueline.wade@bie.edu
Cindy G. Joe & Emily Arviso, Education Specialists

Responsible for the following schools: Crystal Boarding School; Dilcon Boarding School; Greasewood Springs Community School; Hunters Point Boarding School; Kin Dah Lichi'I Olta' (Kinlichee); Pine Springs Day School; Seba Dalkai Boarding School; Tiisyaakin Residential Hall (Holbrook); Wide Ruins Community School; Winslow Residential Hall.

ARIZONA NORTH EDUCATION LINE OFFICE (HOPI)
Hwy. 264, Bldg. 6 • KEAMS CANYON, AZ 86034
(928) 738-2262/3/4 Fax 738-5139
David Talayumptewa, Acting Line Officer
E-mail: david.talayumptewa@bie.edu
Carrie Watahomigie, Education Specialist
Responsible for the following schools: First Mesa Elementary School; Hopi Jr./High School; Havasupai Elementary School; Hopi Day School; Hotevilla Bacavi Community School; Keams Canyon Elementary School; Moencopi Day School; Second Mesa Day School.

ARIZONA SOUTH EDUCATION LINE OFFICE (PHOENIX)
2901 N. Central Ave., Suite 970 • PHOENIX, AZ 85012
(520) 361-3510 Fax 361-3514
Jim Hastings, Line Officer; E-mail: jimmy.hastings@bie.edu
Luvette Russell, Education Specialist (PIAP)
Cheryl Johnson, Education Specialist (Reading)
Responsible for the following schools: Blackwater Community School; Casa Blanca Community School; Dishchii'bikoh Community School (Cibecue); Gila Crossing Day School; John F. Kennedy Day School; Salt River Elementary School; San Simon School; Santa Rosa Boarding School; Santa Rosa Ranch School; Theodore Roosevelt School; Tohono O'odham High School.

BILLINGS EDUCATION LINE OFFICE
316 North 26th St. Rm. 3051 • BILLINGS, MT 59101
(406) 247-7953 Fax 247-7965
Barbara Parisian, Line Officer
Loverty Erickson, Education Specialist (PIAP)
Responsible for the following schools: Blackfeet Dormitory; Northern Cheyenne Tribal School; Shoshone-Bannock School District No. 512; St. Stephens Indian School; Two Eagle River School.

CHEYENNE RIVER EDUCATION LINE OFFICE
P.O. Box 2020 • EAGLE BUTTE, SD 57625
(605) 964-8722 Fax 964-1155
Dr. Cherie Farlee, Line Officer
Jane Azure, Special Education Coordinator
Responsible for the following schools: Cheyenne-Eagle Butte School; Pierre Indian Learning Center; Takini School; Tiospaya Topa School;

CROW CREEK/LOWER BRULE EDUCATION LINE OFFICE
190 Oyate Circle • LOWER BRULE, SD 57548
(605) 473-5531 Fax 473-9217
Dr. Kathie Bowker, Line Officer; E-mail: kathie.bowker@bie.edu
Diana Charles, Administrative Specialist (473-5573)
Responsible for the following schools: Crow Creek Reservation High School; Crow Creek Sioux Tribal Elementary School; Enemy Swim Day School; Flandreau Indian School; Lower Brule Day School; Tiospa Zina Tribal School.

MINNEAPOLIS EDUCATION LINE OFFICE
2001 Killebrew Dr., Suite 122 • BLOOMINGTON, MN 55425
(952) 851-5421 Fax 851-5439
Everett Bad Wound, Line Officer
Charmaine Weston, Education Specialist
Responsible for the following schools: JKL Bahweting Anishnabe School; Bug-O-Nay-Ge Shig School; Circle of Life Survival School; Circle of Nations School (Wahpeton Indian Boarding School); Fond du Lac Ojibway School; Hannahville Indian School; Nay Ah Shing School; Lac Courte Oreilles Ojibwa School; Menominee Tribal School; Meskwaki Settlement School (Sac & Fox); Oneida Nation School; Menominee Tribal School; Hannahville Indian School; Flandreau Indian School; Sac & Fox Settlement School

NEW MEXICO NAVAJO CENTRAL EDUCATION LINE OFFICE (EASTERN NAVAJO)
222 Code Talkers Dr., P.O. Box 328 • CROWNPOINT, NM 87313
(505) 786-6151 Fax 786-6112
Charlotte Garcia, Line Officer
E-mail: charlotte.garcia@bie.edu
Eleanor Jones, Education Specialist
Responsible for the following schools: Dibe Yazhi Habitiin Olta' (Borega Pass); Dzilth-Na-O-Dith-Hle Community School; Hanaa'dli Community School/ Dormitory, Inc. (Huerfano); Lake Valley Navajo School; Mariano Lake Community School; Na'Neelzhiin Ji'Olta (Torreon Day School); Ojo Encino Day School; Pueblo Pintado Community School; T'iis Ts'ozi'Bi'Olta (Crownpoint Community School); Tse'ii'ahi' Community School (Standing Rock);

NEW MEXICO NAVAJO NORTH EDUCATION LINE OFFICE
Hwy. 491 South Nataani Nez Complex, Bldg. 1381
P.O. Box 3239 • SHIPROCK, NM 87420
(505) 368-3400 Fax 368-3409; Website: www.oiep.bia.edu
Dr. Rena Yazzie, Line Officer (368-3403)
E-mail: rena.yazzie@bie.edu
Delphine Shunkamolah, Education Program Specialist
Geraldine Herrod, Education Program Specialist
Responsible for the following schools: Aneth Community School; Beclabito Day School; Cove Day School; Nenahnezad Community School; Red Rock Day School; Sanostee Day School; T'iisNazbas (Teecnospos) Community School; Tohaali' (Toadlena) Community School. *Grant schools*: Aztec Dormitory; Navajo Prepatory School; Shiprock Alternative Schools.

NEW MEXICO NAVAJO SOUTH EDUCATION LINE OFFICE
301 West Hill Ave., Rm. 118 • GALLUP, NM 87301
(505) 863-8332 Fax 863-8363
John McIntosh, Acting Line Officer
E-mail: john.mcintosh@bie.edu
Shirley Cook, Administrative Specialist
Cheryl Quimayousie, Education Specialist (PIAP)
Responsible for the following schools: Alamo Navajo School; Baca/Dlo'ay Azhi Community School; Bread Springs Day School; Chi-Ch'Il-Tah/Jones Ranch Community School; C'ooshgai Community School (Chuska); To'haali' Community School (Toadlena); To'Hajiilee Day School (Canoncito); Wingate Elementary School; Wingate High School.

NEW MEXICO NORTH EDUCATION LINE OFFICE (NORTHERN PUEBLOS AGENCY)
661 Roadrunner Rd., SAN JUAN, NM 87556
P.O. Box 4230, Fairview Station • ESPANOLA, NM 87533
(505) 753-1465 Fax 753-1475
Dr. Benjamin Atencio, Line Officer; E-mail: benjamin.atencio@bie.edu
Kimberly Garcia, Administrative Specialist
Darlene Eckleberry, Program Specialist; Ethel Davis, Education Specialist
Responsible for the following schools: Jicarilla Dormitory; Ohkay Owingeh Community School (San Juan); San Ildefonso Day School; Santa Clara Day School; Santa Fe Indian School; Taos Day School; Te Tsu Geh Oweenge Day School (Tesuque).

NEW MEXICO SOUTH EDUCATION LINE OFFICE (SOUTHERN PUEBLOS AGENCY)
Pete V. Domenici Indian Affairs Bldg.
1000 Indian School Rd. NW • ALBUQUERQUE, NM 87104
(505) 563-3692 Fax 563-3078
Casey Sovo, Line Officer; E-mail: casey.sovo@bie.edu
Reanna Albert, Education Program Specialist
Responsible for the following schools: Sky City Community School; Isleta Elementary School; Jemez Day School; Laguna Elementary School; Laguna Middle School; San Felipe Pueblo Elementary School; Zia Day School; Pine Hill School; Mescalero Apache School

OKLAHOMA EDUCATION LINE OFFICE
200 NW 4th St. Suite 4049 • OKLAHOMA CITY, OK 73102
(405) 605-6051 Fax 605-6055/7
Joy Martin, Line Officer
Carolyn Edwards-Johnson, Administrative Specialist
William Nuttle, Education Specialist
Catherine Fatheree, Education Specialist
Responsible for the following schools: Chickasaw Children's Village; Eufaula Dormitory; Jones Academy; Kickapoo Nation School; Riverside Indian School; Sequoyah High School.

PINE RIDGE EDUCATION LINE OFFICE
101 Thorpe Circle, P.O. Box 333 • PINE RIDGE, SD 57770
(605) 867-1306 Fax 867-5610
Rose Marie Davis, Line Officer; E-mail: rosemarie.davis@bie.edu
Responsible for the following schools: American Horse School; Crazy Horse School; Little Wound School; Loneman Day School; Pine Ridge School; Porcupine Day School; Wounded Knee District School.

ROSEBUD EDUCATION LINE OFFICE
1001 Avenue D, P.O. Box 669 • MISSION, SD 57555
(605) 856-4478 Fax 856-4487
Kathie Bowker, Acting Line Officer; E-mail: Kathie.bowker@bie.edu
Responsible for the following schools: Marty Indian School; Sicangu Owayawa Oti (Rosebud Dorm); Sicangu Oyate Ho., Inc (St. Francis Indian School).

SACRAMENTO EDUCATION LINE OFFICE
2800 Cottage Way • SACRAMENTO, CA 95825
(916) 978-6058 Fax 978-6056

Jim Hastings, Line Officer; E-mail: jimmy.hastings@bie.edu
Gwendolyn Knight, Administrative Specialist
Responsible for the following schools: Duckwater Shoshone Elementary School; Noli School; Pyramid Lake High School; Sherman Indian High School.

SEATTLE EDUCATION LINE OFFICE
909 1st Ave., Suite 192 • PORTLAND, OR 97232
(206) 220-7975 Fax 220-7981
John Claymore, Line Officer; Wendall Joe, Administrative Specialist
Janie Bedwell & Verla LaPlante, Education Specialists
Responsible for the following schools: Chemawa Indian School; Chief Leschi (Puyallup) School System; Coeur D'Alene Tribal School; Lummi Tribal School System; Lummi High School; Muckleshoot Tribal School; Paschal Sherman Indian School; Quileute Tribal School; Wa He Lut Indian School; Yakama Nation Tribal School

SOUTHERN & EASTERN STATES EDUCATION LINE OFFICE
545 Marriott Dr. #700 • NASHVILLE, TN 37214
(615) 564-6630 Fax 564-6631
Walter Swan, Jr., Line Officer
Responsible for the following schools: Ahfachkee Indian School; Beatrice Rafferty School; Boque Chitto Elementary School; Cherokee Central Elementary School & High School; Chitimacha Day School; Choctaw Central Middle School & High School; Indian Island School; Conehatta Elementary School; Indian Township School; Indian Island School; Miccosukee Indian School; Pearl River Elementary School; Red Water Elementary School; Standing Pine Elementary School; Tucker Elementary School.

STANDING ROCK EDUCATION LINE OFFICE
Agency Ave., P.O. Box E • FORT YATES, ND 58538
(701) 854-3497 Fax 854-7280
Robert Parisien, Line Officer; E-mail: robert.parisien@bie.edu
Responsible for the following schools: Rock Creek Day School; Littel Eagle Day School; Sitting Bull Day School (Tatanka Wakanyeja Oti); Standing Rock Community School; Tate Topa Tribal School (Four Winds); Theodore Jamerson Elementary School.

TURTLE MOUNTAIN EDUCATION LINE OFFICE
School St. Bldg. 6, P.O. Box 30 • BELCOURT, ND 58316
(701) 477-3463 Fax 477-5944; Norma Tibbitts, Line Officer
Responsible for the following schools: Dunseith Day School; Mandaree Day School; Ojibwa Indian School; Turtle Mountain Elementary & Middle School; Turtle Mountain High School; Twin Buttes Day School; White Shield School

ALABAMA

REEDS CHAPEL ELEMENTARY & CALCEDEAVER SCHOOLS
Choctaw Indian Reservation
1080 W. Red Fox Rd. • MT. VERNON, AL 36560
(205) 829-5500 Fax 829-5580

ALASKA

ARLICAQ SCHOOL
Yupiit School District, P.O. Box 227 • AKIAK, AK 99552
(907) 765-7212/5; Larry Ctibor, Principal
Grades K-12. *Enrollment*: 76. *Instructors*: Debbie Jackson, Elizabeth Lake, Ida Jasper, Lena Williams. *Special programs*: Bilingual Bicultural Education Program (Abbey Augustine, Coordinator); Yupiit Reading Project; Cultural Heritage Program. Library. Under jurisdiction of Anchorage Education Office.

CHEFORNAK IRA CONTRACT SCHOOL
CHEFORNAK, AK 99561 (907) 867-8707
Jerry Twitchell, Principal; Peter Panruk, Chair
Grades K-8. Under jurisdiction of Anchorage Education Field Office.

CHEVAK IRA CONTRACT SCHOOL
CHEVAK, AK 99563 (907) 858-7713
Alex Tatem, Principal; Xiver Atcherian, Chair
Day School; Grades K-12. Under jurisdiction of Anchorage Education Office.

KASIGLUK DAY SCHOOL
KASIGLUK, AK 99609 (907) 477-6714
Karen A. Rhoades, Principal; Yeako Slim, Chair
Grades K-8. Under jurisdiction of Anchorage Education Field Office.

KIPNUK DAY SCHOOL
KIPNUK, AK 99614 (907) 896-5513
Leslie Smith, Principal/Teacher; Peter J. Paul, Chair
Grades K-8. Under jurisdiction of Anchorage Education Field Office.

NEWTOK DAY SCHOOL
NEWTOK, AK 99559 (907) 237-2328
Rodney Sehorn, Principal; Joseph Tommy, Chair
Day School; Grades 1-8. Under jurisdiction of Anchorage Education Office.

NUNAPITCHUK DAY SCHOOL
NUNAPITCHUK, AK 99641 (907) 527-5711
Karen K. Waters, Principal
Jimmy Hastings; E-mail: jimmy.hastings@bie.edu
Under jurisdiction of Anchorage Education Field Office.

MT. EDGECUMBE HIGH SCHOOL
1332 Seward • SITKA, AK 99835 (907) 966-2201
Bill Denkinger, Principal; Larrae Rocheleau, Supt.
Boarding School; Grades 9-12; Enrollment: 300.
Special courses: Pacific Rim Cultures; Alaska Native History.

TOKSOOK BAY DAY SCHOOL
TOKSOOK, AK 99637 (907) 543-2746
Wilma M. Moore, Principal; Joseph Henry, Chair
Grades 1-6. Under jurisdiction of Anchorage Education Field Office.

TULUKSAK IRA CONTRACT SCHOOL
TULUKSAK, AK 99679 (907) 695-6212
Howard Diamond, Principal; Andrew Alexie, Chair
Grades K-8. Under jurisdiction of Anchorage Education Field Office.

ARIZONA

SKYLINE TECHNICAL HIGH SCHOOL
15220 S. 50th St. #109 • AHWAUTUKEE, AZ 85044
(480) 763-8425 Fax 763-8427
Grades 9-12. Tribal Grant Contract School.

CASA BLANCA COMMUNITY SCHOOL
3455 W. Casa Blanca Rd. P.O. Box 10940 • BAPCHULE, AZ 85221
(520) 315-3489 Fax 315-3505; Website: www.cbcschools.com
Jacque Bradley, Principal & CEO
Grades K-4. Tribal Grant Contract School.

IRA H. HAYES MEMORIAL APPLIED LEARNING CENTER
P.O. Box 10899 • BAPCHULE, AZ 85221
(520) 315-5110 Fax 315-5115; Richard Stoner, Contact
Grades 9-12. Tribal Grant Contract School.

WIDE RUINS COMMUNITY SCHOOL
P.O. Box 309 • CHAMBERS, AZ 86502
(928) 652-3251 Fax 652-3252
Mary Rule, Principal; E-mail: elizabethrule500@hotmail.com
Grades K-6. Tribal Grant Contract School.
Under jurisdiction of Arizona Navajo South Office.

CHINLE UNIFIED SCHOOL DISTRICT #24
P.O. Box 587 • CHINLE, AZ 86503
(928) 674-9600; Quincy Natay, Supt.
Website: www.chinleusd.k12.az.us; E-mail: admin@chinleusd.k12.az.us
Located in the middle of the Navajo Reservation
Canyon De Chelly Elementary School; K-6; Virginia Tulley, Principal
Chinle Elementary School; K-6; Alan Bingham, Principal
Chinle Junior High & High School; Many Farms Public School;
Mesa View Elementary; Tsaile Public School; Dr. Stephen Sorden, Principal

COTTONWOOD DAY SCHOOL
Navajo Rt. 4, P.O. Box 6003 • CHINLE, AZ 86503
(928) 725-3256 Fax 725-3243
Ronald Thompson, Principal
Grades K-8. Under jurisdiction of Arizona Navajo Central Office.

LOW MOUNTAIN BOARDING SCHOOL
Navajo Route 65 • CHINLE, AZ 86503
(928) 725-3308 Fax 725-3306
Dan Hundley, Principal; Venora Jimmy, Chairperson
Grades K-4. Under jurisdiction of Chinle Agency.

ROUGH ROCK COMMUNITY SCHOOL
P.O. Box 5000-PTT • CHINLE, AZ 86503
Website: www.roughrock.k12.az.us
(928) 728-3705 Fax 728-3502; Dr. Marc Space, Supt.
Jeannie Lewis, Principal, CEO/K-8 Principal (728-3710 Fax 728-3502)
Sandi Beeman, High School Principal (728-3730 Fax 728-3560)

Grades K-12. Enrollment: 450. Tribal Grant Contract School. Under jurisdiction of Arizona Navajo Central Office.

DISHCHII'BIKOH COMMUNITY SCHOOL (CIBECUE)
P.O. Box 80068 • CIBECUE, AZ 85911
 (928) 332-2444 Fax 332-2341; Website: www.dishchiibikoh.org
 Juan Aragon, Superintendent; E-mail: juanaragon46@hotmail.com
 Glenn Haven, Middle & High School Principal
 Tyler Bangert, Elementary School Principal
Day School; Grades K-12; Enrollment: 350. *Special courses*: Bilingual (Apache). *Special programs*: American Indian Day Pageant, in Sept.; Arts & Crafts Fair/Powwow, in May; Indian Club (children learn and perform Native American dances & music). Library Media Center with about 7,500 resources. *Publication*: Biweekly newsletter. Under jurisdiction of Arizona South Office.

BLACKWATER COMMUNITY SCHOOL
AKIMEL O'OTHAM PEE POSH CHARTER SCHOOL
3652 E. Blackwater School Rd. • COOLIDGE, AZ 85128
 (520) 215-5859 Fax 215-5862; Jacquelyne Power, Contact
Grades K-2. Tribal Grant Contract School. Arizona South Office.

DENNEHOTSO BOARDING SCHOOL
P.O. Box 2570 • DENNEHOTSO, AZ 86535
 (928) 658-3201 Fax 658-3221
 James T. Brown, Principal; E-mail: james.tbrown@bie.edu
Grades K-8. Under jurisdiction of Arizona Navajo North Office.

KINLANI BORDERTOWN DORMITORY
901 N. Kinlani Rd. • FLAGSTAFF, AZ 86001
 (928) 774-5279 Fax 556-9683
 Deana Dugi, Executive Director; E-mail: ddugi.fbd@gmail.com
Dormitory School; Grades 9-12. Tribal Grant Contract School. Under jurisdiction of Arizona Navajo North Office.

THE STAR SCHOOL
145 Leupp Rd. • FLAGSTAFF, AZ 86004
 (602) 412-3533 or (928) 606-5326; Website: www.starschool.org
 Dr. Mark Sorensen, Principal; E-mail: mark@ttn.org
 Thomas Walker, Jr., School Board President
Grades K-8. *Enrollment*: 108. A Tribal Grant Contract Elementary School promotes self-reliance, alternative building methods, and energy sources such as solar power. Hosts workshops about sustainable living technology and the arts. Opened in 2001.

THEODORE ROOSEVELT BOARDING SCHOOL
P.O. Box 567 • FORT APACHE, AZ 85926
 (928) 338-4464 Fax 338-1009; Mike Brock, Administrator
Day School; Grades 6-8. Under jurisdiction of Arizona South Office.

HMAN 'SHAWA ELEMENTARY SCHOOL
P.O. Box 17779 • FOUNTAIN HILLS, AZ 85269
 (480) 816-7140 Fax 816-0479
Grades K-8. Tribal Grant Contract School.

GREASEWOOD SPRINGS COMMUNITY SCHOOL
HC 58 Box 60 • GANADO, AZ 86505
 (928) 654-3331 Phone & Fax; Website: www.gscs-inc.net
 Lucinda Godinez, Principal
Boarding School; Grades K-8. Tribal Grant Contract School.

KIN DAH LICHI'I OLTA SCHOOL (KINLICHEE)
P.O. Box 800 • GANADO, AZ 86505
 Website: www.kindahlichii.org
 (928) 755-3439 Fax 755-3448; Ora James, Principal
Boarding School; Grades K-6. *Enrollment*: 110. 95% of students are Navajo. Library. Tribal Grant Contract School. Under jurisdiction of Arizona Navajo South Office.

NAZLINI COMMUNITY SCHOOL
HC58 Box 35 • GANADO, AZ 86505
 (928) 755-6125 Fax 755-3729
 Jeannie Lewis, Principal; E-mail: jmlewis_86503@yahoo.com
Grades K-6. Tribal Grant Contract School. Under jurisdiction of Arizona Navajo Central Office.

TIISYAAKIN RESIDENTIAL HALL (HOLBROOK)
1100 W. Buffalo • HOLBROOK, AZ 86025
 (928) 524-6222 Fax 524-2231
 Ronald Arias, Executive Director; E-mail: Ronald.arias@bie.edu
Grades 9-12. Tribal Grant Contract School. Under jurisdiction of Arizona Navajo South Office.

HOTEVILLA BACAVI COMMUNITY SCHOOL
Hwy. 264, P.O. Box 48 • HOTEVILLA, AZ 86030
 (928) 734-2462 Fax 734-2225
Grades K-8. *Enrollment*: 125. *Special programs*: Bilingual computer program; special education. Community library. *Publication*: Tales in Hopi Language (published by students). Under jurisdiction of Arizona North Office.

PINE SPRINGS SCHOOL
1001 Pine Springs Rd. P.O. Box 4198 • HOUCK, AZ 86506
 (928) 871-4311 Fax 871-4341; Lou Ann M. Jones, Principal
Grades K-4. Enrollment: 65. Under jurisdiction of Arizona Navajo South Office.

KAIBETO BOARDING SCHOOL
P.O. Box 1420 • KAIBETO, AZ 86053
 (520) 673-3480 Fax 673-3489
 Phyllis Newell-Yazzie, Principal; E-mail: Phyllis.newellyazzie@bie.edu
Grades K-8. Under jurisdiction of Arizona Navajo North Office.

CHILCHINBETO COMMUNITY SCHOOL
P.O. Box 740 • KAYENTA, AZ 86033
 (928) 697-3802 Fax 697-3448; Eugene Charley, Principal
Day School; Grades K-8. Enrollment: 126. Tribal Grant Contract School. Under jurisdiction of Arizona Navajo North Office.

KAYENTA COMMUNITY SCHOOL
HC 163 Box 188 • KAYENTA, AZ 86033
 (928) 697-3439 Fax 697-3490; Velma Eisenberger, Principal
Boarding School; Grades K-8. Tribal Grant Contract School. Under jurisdiction of Arizona Navajo North Office.

KAYENTA UNIFIED SCHOOL DISTRICT
US Hwy. 163, Monument Valley Blvd.
P.O. Box 337 • KAYENTA, AZ 86033
 (928) 697-3251 Fax 697-2160; Website: www.kayenta.k12.az.us
 Dr. Bryce Anderson, Superintendent
 Christina Yazzie, Supt./Governing Board Secretary
Over 2,000 students from K-12 of the Navajo Nation of Northeastern Arizona.
Kayenta Elementary School; Stephen Myers, Principal
 (928) 697-2429 Fax 697-2382
Kayenta Middle School; Evangeline Tso, Interim Principal
 (928) 697-2303 Fax 697-2308
Monument Valley High School; Jack Gilmore, Principal
 (298) 697-2228 Fax 697-2195
Publication: Olta'Baa Hane' Newsletter

HOPI JR. - SR. SCHOOL
P.O. Box 337 • KEAMS CANYON, AZ 86034
 (928) 738-5111 Fax 738-5333
 Gregory T. Sackos, Supt.; Edgar Shupla, Board President
 Fernando Madrid, Junor High Principal
 Alban Naha, Federal Programs Director
Charter School; Grades 7-12. 750 students, with about 80% Hopi and 20% Navajo. *Special project*: Hopilavayi Project – a Hopi tribal project to encourage the growth and acquisition of Hopi language and culture. Under jurisdiction of Arizona North Office.

KEAMS CANYON ELEMENTARY SCHOOL
P.O. Box 397 • KEAMS CANYON, AZ 86034
 (928) 738-2385 Fax 738-5519; Rachel Maho, Principal
Boarding School; Grades K-6. Under jurisdiction of Arizona North Office.

HOPI DAY SCHOOL
P.O. Box 42 • KYKOTSMOVI, AZ 86039
 (928) 734-2468 Fax 734-2470 Website: www.hdshawks.org
 George Silas, Board President
Grades K-6. Tribal Grant Contract School.

ROCKY RIDGE BOARDING SCHOOL
P.O. Box 299 • KYKOTSMOVI, AZ 86039
 (928) 725-3650 Fax 725-3655; David Moore, Principal
Boarding School; Grades K-8. Under jurisdiction of Arizona Navajo North Office.

GILA CROSSING COMMUNITY SCHOOL
AKIMEL O'OTHAM PEE POSH CHARTER SCHOOL
4665 W. Pecos Rd. • LAVEEN, AZ 85339
 (520) 550-4834 Fax 550-4252; Website: www.gccs.bia.edu
 Jacquelyne Wauneka, Principal
Day School. Grades K-8. Tribal Grant Contract School. Under jurisdiction of Arizona South Office.

LUKACHUKAI COMMUNITY SCHOOL
Navajo Rt. 13, P.O. Box 230 • LUKACHUKAI, AZ 86507
  (928) 787-4418 Fax 787-2311
  Stanley Kedelty, Principal; E-mail: skedelty@yahoo.com
Boarding School; Grades K-8. Tribal Grant Contract School.
Under jurisdiction of Arizona Navajo Central Office.

MANY FARMS DAY SCHOOL (CHINLE BOARDING SCHOOL)
P.O. Box 70 • MANY FARMS, AZ 86538
  (928) 781-6221 Fax 781-6376
  Dr. Elvira Bitsoi Largie, Director; E-mail: e_largie@yahoo.com
Boarding School; Grades K-8. Enrollment: 425 students.
Tribal Grant Contract School. Under jurisdiction of Arizona
Navajo Central Office.

MANY FARMS HIGH SCHOOL
P.O. Box 307 • MANY FARMS, AZ 86538
  (928) 781-6226 Fax 781-6355; Brian P. Dillon, Principal
  Website: www.chinleusd.k12.az.us
Boarding School; Grades 9-12. Under jurisdiction
of Arizona Navajo Central Office.

AK CHIN EARLY CHILDHOOD DEVELOPMENT PROGRAM
42507 W. Peters & Nall Rd. • MARICOPA, AZ 85239
  (520) 568-1064 Fax 568-1003; Anita Avila, Contact
Tribal Grant Contract School.

AHA MACAV HIGH SCHOOL/PILLAR ACADEMY
P.O. Box 6095 • MOHAVE VALLEY, AZ 86446
  (928) 346-3930 (phone & fax)
  Nichole Garcia, Principal; E-mail: ndenson@ftmojave.com
Grades 9-12. Tribal Grant Contract School.

PHOENIX INDIAN SCHOOL
P.O. Box 10 • PHOENIX, AZ 85001
  (520) 241-2126; Fred Wilson, Principal
Boarding School; Grades 9-12.
Under jurisdiction of Phoenix Area Office.

BLACK MESA COMMUNITY SCHOOL
P.O. Box 97 • PINON, AZ 86510
  (928) 674-3632 Fax (775) 659-8187
  Website: www.blackmesaschool.org
  Marie Rose, Principal; E-mail: wiyaa_rose@hotmail.com
  Irene Begaye, Board President; Victoria Nez, Vice President
Day School. Grades K-8. Tribal Grant Contract School.
Under jurisdiction of Arizona Navajo Central.

JEEHDEEZ'A ACADEMY, INC. (LOW MOUNTAIN)
P.O. Box 1073 • PINON, AZ 86510
  (928) 725-3308 Fax 725-3306
  Kimberly Peralto-Gee, Director; E-mail: kp23@nau.edu
Grades K-5. Tribal Grant Contract School.
Under jurisdiction of Arizona Navajo Central Office.

PINON COMMUNITY SCHOOL
P.O. Box 159 • PINON, AZ 86510
  (928) 725-3234 Fax 725-3232
  Oscar Tso, Principal; E-mail: tsooscar@yahoo.com
Boarding School; Grades K-12. Tribal Grant Contract School.

PINON UNIFIED SCHOOL DISTRICT NO. 4
P.O. Box 839 • PINON, AZ 86510
  (928) 725-3450 Fax 725-2123; Website: www.pusdatsa.org
  Dr. Jasvir Sethi, Supt.; (928) 725-2100; Email: jsethi@pusdatsa.org
  Lori Chee, High School Principal (928) 725-2401
  Jim Matthies, Middle School Principal; (928) 725-2301
  E-mail: jmatthies@pusdatsa.org
  Linda King, Elementary School Principal; (928) 725-2201
  E-mail: lking@pusdatsa.org

FIRST MESA ELEMENTARY SCHOOL
390 Main St., P.O. Box 750 • POLACCA, AZ 86042
  (928) 737-2581 Fax 737-2323l Website: www.fmes.bie.edu
  Sahmie S. Wytewa, Principal
Day School; Grades K-6. Under jurisdiction of Arizona North Office.

COVE DAY SCHOOL
P.O. Box 2000 • RED VALLEY, AZ 86544
  (928) 653-4457 Fax 653-4415; Deborah Belone, Acting Principal
Grades K-6. Under jurisdiction of New Mexico Navajo North Office.

RED ROCK DAY SCHOOL
P.O. Drawer 2007 • RED VALLEY, AZ 86544
  (928) 653-4456 Fax 653-5711
  David Nez, Principal
Grades K-8. Under jurisdiction of New Mexico Navajo North Office.

ROCK POINT COMMUNITY SCHOOL
Tse Nitsaa Deez'ahi Dine Bi'olta
38201 W. Indian School Rd. P.O. Box 560 • ROCK POINT, AZ 86545
  (928) 659-4221 Fax 659-4235; Website: www.rpcs.bia.edu
  Berdina Tsosie, Executive Director
  Corrina Charley, Secondary Principal
Grades K-12. Enrollment: 450. Tribal Grant Contract School.

VECHIJ HIMDAG MASHCHAMAKUD
P.O. Box 220 • SACATON, AZ 85247
  (520) 562-3286 Fax 562-2028; Kent Power, Principal
Grades K-12. Tribal Grant Contract School.

HUNTERS POINT BOARDING SCHOOL
Rt. 12, South Lupton Rd., P.O. Box 99 • ST. MICHAELS, AZ 86511
  (928) 871-4439 Fax 871-4435; Website: www.hpbs-az.org
  Dr. Berdina Tsosie, Principal
Boarding School; Grades K-5. Under jurisdiction of Arizona
Navajo South Office.

SALT RIVER ELEMENTARY SCHOOL
11562 E. Highland Ave. • SCOTTSDALE, AZ 85256
  (480) 362-2400 Fax 362-2401; Erik Haarstad, Principal
Grades K-8. Tribal Grant Contract School.
Under jurisdiction of Arizona South Office.

SALT RIVER HIGH SCHOOL
4827 N. Country Club Dr. • SCOTTSDALE, AZ 85256
  (480) 362-2000 Fax 362-2090; Victoria Corlett, Principal
Grades 9-12. Tribal Grant Contract School.
Under jurisdiction of Arizona South Office.

SALT RIVER PIMA-MARICOPA INDIAN COMMUNITY SCHOOLS ACCELERATED LEARNING ACADEMY
4815 N. Center St. • SCOTTSDALE, AZ 85256
  (480) 362-2130 Fax 362-2159
  Mary Ann Wood, Administrator

SECOND MESA DAY SCHOOL
P.O. Box 98 • SECOND MESA, AZ 86043
  (928) 737-2571 Fax 737-2565
  Alma Sinquah-Ashley, Principal
Grades K-6. Tribal Grant Contract School.
Under jurisdiction of Arizona North Office.

SAN SIMON SCHOOL
HC 101, Box 8292 • SELLS, AZ 85634
  (520) 362-2231 Fax 362-2405; Website: www.sansimon.k12.az.us
  Frank Rogers, Principal; E-mail: frank.rogers@bie.edu
Grades K-8. Under jurisdiction of Arizona South Office.

SANTA ROSA BOARDING SCHOOL
HC 101, Box 8400 • SELLS, AZ 85634
  (520) 361-2276 Fax 361-2511
  Louis Barajas, Principal
Grades K-8. Under jurisdiction of Arizona South Office.

SANTA ROSA RANCH SCHOOL
HC 02, Box 7570 • SELLS, AZ 85634
  (520) 383-2359 Fax 383-3960
  Delbert Ortiz, Principal
Grades K-8. Under jurisdiction of Arizona South Office.

TOHONO O'ODHAM HIGH SCHOOL
HC 01, Box 8513 • SELLS, AZ 85634
  (520) 362-2400 Fax 362-2256
  Leon O'osahwe, Principal
Grades 9-12. Under jurisdiction of Arizona South Office.

SHONTO PREPATORY SCHOOL
P.O. Box 7900 • SHONTO, AZ 86054
  (928) 672-3500 Fax 672-3501
  Dr. Fannie Spain, Principal (K-8); Sharon Singer, Supt.
Boarding School; Grades K-8. Enrollment: 550 students. Tribal Grant
Contract School. Under jurisdiction of Arizona Navajo North Office.

HAVASUPAI ELEMENTARY SCHOOL
P.O. Box 40 • SUPAI, AZ 86435
 (928) 448-2901 Fax 448-2108
 Greg Mooring, Principal
Grades K-8. Tribal Grant Contract School.
Under jurisdiction of Arizona North Office.

T'IIS NAZBAS COMMUNITY SCHOOL (TEECNOSPOS)
P.O. Box 2002 • TEEC NOS POS, AZ 86514
 (928) 656-3252 Fax 656-3486
 George Waybenais, Principal
Boarding School; Grades K-8.
Under jurisdiction of New Mexico Navajo North Office.

STUDENT CHOICE HIGH SCHOOL
1833 N. Scottsdale Rd. • TEMPE, AZ 85281
 (480) 947-9511 Fax 947-9624; Peggy Lynam, Principal
Grades 9-12. Tribal Grant Contract School.

NAA TSIS'AAN COMMUNITY SCHOOL (NAVAJO MOUNTAIN)
P.O. Box 100101 • TONALEA, AZ 86044
 (928) 672-2335 Fax 672-2609; Timothy Clashin, Principal
Grades K-8. Tribal Grant Contract School.
Under jurisdiction of Arizona Navajo North Office.

TONALEA DAY SCHOOL (RED LAKE)
P.O. Box 39 • TONALEA, AZ 86044
 (928) 283-6325 Fax 283-5158; Charles Fike, Principal
Grades K-8. Under jurisdiction of Arizona Navajo North Office.

MOENCOPI DAY SCHOOL
P.O. Box 185 • TUBA CITY, AZ 86045
 (928) 283-5361 Fax 283-4662
 Donald Harvey, Chief School Administrator
Grades K-6. Under jurisdiction of Hopi Agency.
Under jurisdiction of Arizona North Office.

TUBA CITY BOARDING SCHOOL
306 Main St., P.O. Box 187 • TUBA CITY, AZ 86045
 (928) 283-2330 Fax 283-2362; Don Coffland, Principal
 Website: www.tcbs.bie.edu
Grades K-8. Under jurisdiction of Arizona Navajo North Office.

GREYHILLS ACADEMY HIGH SCHOOL
P.O. Box 160 • TUBA CITY, AZ 86045
 (928) 283-6271 Fax 283-6604
 Dr. Loren Hudson, Principal; E-mail: loren.hudson@bie.edu
 Richard Grey, Assistant Principal; E-mail: Richard.grey@bie.edu
Boarding School; Grades 9-12. *Enrollment*: 450. An Academy High School with a uniquely Native American thrust in education. In partnership with Northern Arizona University and University of Hawaii in developing a curriculum based on a Laboratory school approach. Library. Tribal Grant Contract School. Arizona Navajo North Office.

HA:SAN PREPARATORY & LEADERSHIP SCHOOL
1333 E. 10th St. • TUCSON, AZ 85719
 (520) 882-8826 Fax 882-8651
 Sylvia Hendricks & Mike Norris, Contacts
 E-mail: mnorris_99@yahoo.com
Grades 9-12. Tribal Grant Contract School.

VISION HIGH SCHOOL
5901 S. Calle Santa Cruz • TUCSON, AZ 85750
 (520) 444-0241 Fax 741-8123
 Wilma Soroosh, Principal; E-mail: wsoroosh@aol.com
Grades 9-12. Tribal Grant Contract School.

JOHN F. KENNEDY DAY SCHOOL
P.O. Box 130 • WHITE RIVER, AZ 85941
 (928) 338-4591 Fax 338-4592
 Dr. Rea Goklish, Principal
Grades K-8. Under jurisdiction of Arizona South Office.

DILCON COMMUNITY SCHOOL
HC 63 Box G • WINSLOW, AZ 86047
 (928) 657-3211 Fax 657-3213; Website: www.dilconeagles.com
 Dauri Furgerson, Principal
Grades K-8. Tribal Grant Contract School. Under jurisdiction of Arizona South Office

LEUPP SCHOOLS, INC.
HC 61 Box D • WINSLOW, AZ 86047
 (928) 686-6211/6270 Fax 686-6216
 Emma Yazzie, Principal; E-mail: eyazzie@leuppschools.org
 James Rollison, Administrator
 E-mail: james.rollison@leuppschools.org
Grades K-12. Enrollment: 375. *Special course*: Entrepreneurship. *Publication*: Today at Leupp. Library. Under jurisdiction of Arizona Navajo North Office.

LITTLE SINGER COMMUNITY SCHOOL
P.O. Box AQ • WINSLOW, AZ 86047
 (928) 686-3217 Fax 686-6150; Etta Shirley, Principal
Boarding School; Grades K-6. Under jurisdiction of Arizona Navajo North Office.

SEBA DALKAI BOARDING SCHOOL
HC 63, Box H • WINSLOW, AZ 86047
 (928) 657-3208 Fax 657-3224
 May Bigboy, Principal; E-mail: maye.bigboy@bie.edu
Grades K-9. *Enrollment*: 185. *Special programs*: Special Education, Gifted & Talented; Intensive Residential Guidance Program; and Substance Abuse. Bilingual Education. Under jurisdiction of Arizona Navajo South Office.

TOLANI LAKE ELEMENTARY ACADEMY
HC61, Box 300 • WINSLOW, AZ 86047
 (928) 686-6101 Fax 686-6102
 Jim Wack, Principal; E-mail: rom8jwack@yahoo.com
Grades K-8. Tribal Grant Contract School.

WINSLOW RESIDENTIAL HALL
600 N. Alfred Ave. • WINSLOW, AZ 86047
 (928) 289-2379 Fax 289-2821; Chris Gilmore, Principal
 Sal Hernandez, Administrator; Sophia Francis, Board President
Grades 7-12. Tribal Grant Contract School. Under jurisdiction of Arizona Navajo South Office.

CALIFORNIA

SHERMAN INDIAN HIGH SCHOOL
9010 Magnolia Ave. • RIVERSIDE, CA 92503
 (888) 584-4004; (951) 276-6325 Fax 276-6336
 Website: www.sihs.bie.edu
 Sister Mary Yarger, Principal; E-mail: mary.yarger@bie.edu
 Roland W. Doepner III, Resources; E-mail: roland.doepner@bie.edu
Grades 9-12. Under jurisdiction of Sacramento Education Office.

NOLI INDIAN SCHOOL
24330 Sboba Rd., P.O. Box 700 • SAN JACINTO, CA 92581
 (951) 654-5596 Fax 654-7198
 Donovan Post, Principal; E-mail: noli_indianschool@yahoo.com
Grades 6-12. Under jurisdiction of Sacramento Education Office.

FLORIDA

AHFACHKEE DAY SCHOOL
30290 Josie Billie Hwy PMB 1005 • CLEWISTON, FL 33440
 (863) 983-6348 Fax 983-6535; Website: www.seminolewarriors.net
 Grant Richardson, Principal; E-mail: grantrichardson@semtribe.com
Grades K-12. Under jurisdiction of Southern & Eastern States Education Office.

MICCOSUKEE INDIAN SCHOOL
US Hwy. 41, Mile Marker 70 • MIAMI, FL 33144
 (305) 894-2364 Fax 894-2365
 Manuel Varela, Principal; E-mail: manuelv@miccosukeetribe.com
Grades K-12. Library. Under jurisdiction of Southern & Eastern States Education Office.

IDAHO

COEUR D'ALENE TRIBAL SCHOOL
P.O. Box 338 • De SMET, ID 83824
 (208) 686-5808 Fax 686-5080; Eric Kendra, Superintendent
 Donavon Chase, Principal; E-mail: dchase@tribalschool.org
Grades K-8. Under jurisdiction of Seattle Education Office.

SHOSHONE-BANNOCK SCHOOL DISTRICT NO. 512
17400 Hi Line Rd., P.O. Box 790 • POCATELLO, ID 83202
 (208) 238-4300 Fax 238-2629; Dr. Phillip Shortman, Supt.
Grades K-8. Under jurisdiction of Billings Office.

ILLINOIS

O-WAI-YA-WA SCHOOL
5120 N. Winthrop • CHICAGO, IL 60660 (312) 534-2518
An elementary and secondary school for Native Americans.

IOWA

MESKWAKI SETTLEMENT SCHOOL (SAC & FOX)
1608 305th St. • TAMA, IA 52339
  (641) 484-4990 Fax 484-3264; Website: www.msswarriors.org
  Jill Herink, Administrator, Chairperson
  E-mail: jherink@msswarriors.org
  Paul Henely, Elementary School Principal
  Eric Butikofer, Middle-High School Principal (484-9000 Fax 484-9090)
Grades K-12. Under jurisdiction of Minneapolis Office.

KANSAS

HASKELL INDIAN NATIONS UNIVERSITY
155 Indian Ave. #1305 • LAWRENCE, KS 66046
  (913) 749-8404 Fax 749-8411
  Clyde Peacock, Acting President, President
Grades: Freshman & Sophomore years. Administered by the
Bureau of Indian Affairs. Under jurisdiction of the Horton Agency.

KICKAPOO NATION SCHOOL
400 First St., P.O. Box 106 • POWHATTAN, KS 66527
  (785) 474-3365 Fax 474-3498
  Dr. Neil Trottier, Superintendent; Cliff Dunlap, Principal
Grades K-12. *Special programs*: Gifted & talented program; special education;
bilingual program for teaching Kickapoo language to students. Under jurisdiction of Oklahoma Office.

LOUISIANA

CHITIMACHA DAY SCHOOL
3613 Chitimacha Trail• JEANETTE, LA 70523
  (337) 923-9960 Fax 923-7346; E-mail: schoolinfo@chitimacha.gov
  Tanya Rosemond, Principal
Grades Pre K-8. Under jurisdiction of Southern & Eastern States Office.

CHOCTAW-APACHE OF EBARB INDIAN SCHOOL
P.O. Box 858 • ZWOLLE, LA 71486
  (318) 645-2744
Grades: K-12. *Enrollment*: 285. Only officially recognized
"Indian School" in the state of Louisiana.

MAINE

INDIAN ISLAND SCHOOL
10 Wabanaki Way • OLD TOWN, ME 04468
  (207) 827-4285 Fax 827-3599; Website: www.iis.bie.edu
  Ron Jenkins, Superintendent; E-mail: ronald.jenkins@bie.edu
  Linda McLeod, Principal; E-Mail: linda.mcleod@bie.edu
Grades Pre K-8. *Enrollment*: 120. *Special courses*: Native American studies;
Penobscot Language. Under jurisdiction of Southern & Eastern States Office.

BEATRICE RAFFERTY ELEMENTARY SCHOOL
22 Bayview Dr., Pleasant Point Reservation
RR 1, Box 338 • PERRY, ME 04667
  (207) 853-6085 Fax 853-2483
  Ron Jenkins, Supt. of Schools for Maine Indian Education
  E-mail: ronald.jenkins@bie.edu
  Michael W. Chadwick, Principal; E-mail: m_wchadwick@yahoo.com
Grades K-8. Under jurisdiction of Southern & Eastern States Office.

INDIAN TOWNSHIP SCHOOL
13 School Dr., Peter Dana Point • PRINCETON, ME 04668
  (207) 796-2362 Fax 796-2726; Ron Jenkins, Superintendent
  Terry Lux, Principal
Grades Pre K-8; *Enrollment*: 100. *Special course*: Passamaquoddy
Language/Culture. Under jurisdiction of Southern & Eastern States Office.

MICHIGAN

JOSEPH K. LUMSDEN (JKL) BAHWETING ANISHNABE SCHOOL
1301 Marquette Ave. • SAULT STE. MARIE, MI 49783
  (906) 635-5055 Fax 635-3805; Website: www.jklschool.com

  Lynn Methner, Principal; E-mail: lmethner@jklschool.org
Grades K-8. *Enrollment*: 450. Under jurisdiction of Minneapolis Office.

HANNAHVILLE INDIAN SCHOOL
NAH TAH WAHSH (SOARING EAGLE)
N14911 Hannahville B1 Rd. • WILSON, MI 49896
  (906) 466-2952 Fax 466-2556; Website: www.hannahvilleschool.net
  Website: www.potawatomilanguage.org
  Tom Miller, Superintendent; E-mail: tom.miller@hannahvilleschool.net
  William Boda, Principal; E-mail: bill.boda@hannahvilleschool.net
Grades K-12. *Publication*: Straight Up Newz.
Under jurisdiction of Minneapolis Office.

GRAND TRAVERSE BAND TRIBAL SCHOOL (WAABNO GIMAAK)
2605 N. West Bay Shore Dr. • SUTTONS BAY, MI 49682
  (231) 271-7505 Fax 271-7510
  John Concannon, School Board Chairman
Grades K-8. Owned and operated by the Grand Traverse
Band of Ottawa & Chippewa Indians.

MINNESOTA

BUG-O-NAY-GE SHIG SCHOOL
115353 Silver Eagle Dr. • BENA, MN 56626
  (800) 265-5576; (218) 665-3000 Fax 335-3024
  Website: www.bugonaygeshig.org
  Amanda Norman, Principal; Mary Trapp, Principal
Grades K-12. Under jurisdiction of Minneapolis Office.

FOND DU LAC OJIBWE SCHOOL
105 University Rd. • CLOQUET, MN 55720
  (218) 878-7571 Fax 878-7573; Website: www.fdlrezk12.com
  Jennifer Johnson, Principal (878-7284); E-mail: jenniferjohnson@fdlrez.com
Grades: K-12. *Enrollment*: 270. *Special courses*: Gifted & Talented; Ojibwe
  Language, Culture & History. *Publications*: Newsletter; newspaper. Library.
Under jurisdiction of Minneapolis Office.

NAY-AH SHING SCHOOL
Mille Lacs Band of Ojibwe, 43651 Oodena Dr. • ONAMIA, MN 56359
  (320) 532-4695 Fax 532-4675; Website: www.nas.k12.mn.us/
  Noah Johnson, Principal (6-12); E-mail: njohnson@nas.k12.mn.us
  Silvia Norberg, Elementary Principal
Grades K-12. *Special courses*: Native American Studies; Cultural Crafts;
Reservation History Curriculum; Native Ojibwe Language Curriculum; basic
core curriculum. *Publications*: Mille Lacs Nay Ah Shing School Newsletter.
Under jurisdiction of Minneapolis Office.

MOUNDS PARK ALL-NATIONS MAGNET SCHOOL
1075 E. 3rd St. • ST. PAUL, MN 55106
  (612) 293-5938; Dr. Cornel Pewewardy, Principal
Grades K-8. *Enrollment*: 400. *Special program*: Circle Time. Library.

CIRCLE OF LIFE ACADEMY
P.O. Box 447 • WHITE EARTH, MN 56591
  (218) 983-4180 Fax 983-3767; Website: www.col.pvt.k12.mn.us
  Ricky White, Administrator
Grades K-12. Under jurisdiction of Minneapolis Office.

MISSISSIPPI

RED WATER ELEMENTARY SCHOOL
107 Braves Blvd. • CARTHAGE, MS 39051
  (601) 267-8500 Fax 267-5193; Website: www.rw.bia.edu
  Terri Rhea, Principal
Grades K-8. *Enrollment*: 125. Under jurisdiction of Southern &
Eastern States Office.

STANDING PINE ELEMENTARY SCHOOL
538 Hwy. 487 East • CATHAGE, MS 39051
  (601) 267-9225 Fax 267-9129
  Jason Roberson, Principal; E-mail: Jason.roberson@bie.edu
Grades K-6. *Enrollment*: 100. Under jurisdiction of Southern &
Eastern States Office.

CHOCTAW CENTRAL HIGH SCHOOL
150 Recreation Rd. • CHOCTAW, MS 39350
  (601) 663-7777 Fax 663-7778
  Fredrick Hickmon, Principal; E-mail: Fredrick.hickmon@bie.edu
Grades 9-12. *Enrollment*: 800. Under jurisdiction of Southern &
Eastern States Office.

CHOCTAW CENTRAL MIDDLE SCHOOL
152 Recreation Rd. • CHOCTAW, MS 39350
(601) 656-7777 Fax 656-1558
Jackie Harpole, Principal
Grades 7-8. *Enrollment*: 400. Under jurisdiction of Southern
& Eastern States Office.

CHOCTAW TRIBAL SCHOOLS
122 Division of Schools Dr. • CHOCTAW, MS 39350
(601) 650-7302 Fax 656-9454
Website: www.cts.bie.edu
Grades K-12. *Enrollment*: 2,000 students in eight schools. Consists of six
elementary schools, one middle school, and one high school. Operated as
a division of the Mississippi Band of Choctaw Indians. Students attending
must be 1/4 Native American.

PEARL RIVER ELEMENTARY SCHOOL
470 Industrial Rd. • CHOCTAW, MS 39350
(601) 656-9051 Fax 656-9054
Suzanne Hyatt, Principal
E-mail: Suzanne.hyatt@bie.edu
Grades K-6. *Enrollment*: 450. Under jurisdiction of Southern
& Eastern States Office.

TUCKER ELEMENTARY SCHOOL
126 E. Tucker Circle • PHILADELPHIA, MS 39350
(601) 656-8775 Fax 656-9341
Joe Wood, Principal
Grades K-8. *Enrollment*: 120. Under jurisdiction of Southern
& Eastern States Office.

CONEHATTA ELEMENTARY SCHOOL
851 Tushka Dr. • CONEHATTA, MS 39057
(601) 775-8254 Fax 775-9229
Website: www.cone.bie.edu
Sylvia Johnson, Principal
Grades K-8. *Enrollment*: 200. Opened 2001.
Under jurisdiction of Eastern Regional Office.

BOGUE CHITTO ELEMENTARY SCHOOL
13241 Hwy. 491 North • PHILADELPHIA, MS 39350
(601) 389-1000 Fax 389-1002
Larry Robinson, Principal; E-mail: larry.robinson@bie.edu
Grades K-8. *Enrollment*: 200. Under jurisdiction of Southern
& Eastern States Office.

MONTANA

ST. LABRE INDIAN SCHOOL
P.O. Box 406 • ASHLAND, MT 59004
(406) 784-2347; Website: www.stlabre.org
Curtis Yarlott, Executive Director; William D. Walker, Supt.
Grades K-12. Under jurisdiction of Billings Office.

ROCKY BOY TRIBAL HIGH SCHOOL
Box 620, Rocky Boy Route • BOX ELDER, MT 59521
(406) 395-4291 Fax 395-4829; Sandra Murie, Acting Supt.
Grades 9-12. Under jurisdiction of Billings Office.

BLACKFEET DORMITORY
P.O. Box 627 • BROWNING, MT 59417
(406) 338-7441 Fax 338-5725
Grades 1-12. Under jurisdiction of Billings Office.

NORTHERN CHEYENNE TRIBAL SCHOOL (BUSBY SCHOOL)
One Campus Dr., P.O. Box 150 • BUSBY, MT 59016
(406) 592-3646 Fax 592-3645
Frank No Runner, Superintendent
E-mail: frank.norunner@cheyennenation.com
Teresa McMakin, K-12 Principal
E-mail: Teresa.mcmakin@cheyennenation.com
Grades K-12. Under jurisdiction of Billings Office.

TWO EAGLE RIVER SCHOOL
P.O. Box 160 • PABLO, MT 59855
(406) 675-0292 Fax 675-0294
Website: www.twoeagleriver.com
Clarice King, Superintendent
Grades 7-12. *Program*: Culturally-relevant curriculum.
Under jurisdiction of Billings Office.

NEVADA

DUCKWATER SHOSHONE ELEMENTARY SCHOOL
511 Duckwater Falls, P.O. Box 140002 • DUCKWATER, NV 89314
(775) 863-0242 Fax 863-0301; Keith Honnaker, Principal
Grades K-8. Under jurisdiction of Sacramento Education Office.

PYRAMID LAKE HIGH SCHOOL
711 State St., P.O. Box 267 • NIXON, NV 89424
(775) 574-1016 Fax 574-1037
Steven Chapin, Principal; Teresa Wright, Native Studies/Art
Grades 7-12. *Enrollment*: 125. Under jurisdiction of Sacramento Ed. Office.

NEW MEXICO

SKY CITY COMMUNITY SCHOOL
44 Pinsbaari Rd., P.O. Box 349 • PUEBLO OF ACOMA, NM 87304
(505) 552-6671 Fax 552-6672; Yvonne Haven, Principal
Grades K-8. *Enrollment*: 275. *Special courses*: Gifted & Talented; Computer
Laboratory. Library. Under jurisdiction of New Mexico South Education Office.

SOUTHWESTERN INDIAN POLYTECHNIC INSTITUTE
9169 Coors Rd., NW • ALBUQUERQUE, NM 87120
(800) 586-7474; (505) 346-2348 Fax 248-2343
Dr. Sherry Allison, President
Grades: Freshman & Sophomore years.
Administered by the Bureau of Indian Education (BIE).

AZTEC DORMITORY SCHOOL
1600 Lydia Rippey Rd. • AZTEC, NM 87410
(505) 334-6565 Fax 334-8630
John C. Nolan, Home Living Specialist
Grades 9-12. Under jurisdiction of Eastern Navajo Agency.

DZILTH-NA-0-DITH-HLE COMMUNITY SCHOOL
P.O. Box 5003 • BLOOMFIELD, NM 87413
(505) 960-0356 Fax 960-0355
Kathryn Coleman, Acting Principal; E-mail: kecoleman2000@yahoo.com
Day School: K-8; Boarding School: Grades 1-12; Public School: 9-12. *Special
Programs*: Annual Powwow in March; Annual Traditional Song & Dance
Contest in November. Under jurisdiction of Eastern Navajo Agency.

HANAA'DLI COMMUNITY SCHOOL/DORMITORY (HUERFANO)
P.O. Box 639 • BLOOMFIELD, NM 87413
(505) 325-3411 Fax 327-3591; Dwane Robinson, Acting Principal
Dormitory School – Grades 1-12; K on day basis.
Under jurisdiction of New Mexico Navajo Education Office.

TO'HAJIILEE-HE (CANONCITO)
P.O. Box 3438 • CANONCITO, NM 87026
(505) 908-2174 Fax 836-2914; Jane E. Pitts, Principal
Boarding School; Grades K-12. Under jurisdiction
of New Mexico Navajo South Education Office.

DIBE YAZHI HABITIIN OLTA' (BORREGO PASS)
P.O. Box 679 • CROWNPOINT, NM 87313
(505) 786-5237 Fax 786-7078
Glenn Whiteeagle, Principal; E-mail: gw_gl@yahoo.com
Boarding School; Grades K-8. Under jurisdiction
of New Mexico Navajo Education Office.

LAKE VALLEY NAVAJO SCHOOL
P.O. Box 748 • CROWNPOINT, NM 87313
(505) 786-5392 Fax 786-5956; Geraldine Thomason, Principal
Boarding School; Grades K-8. Under jurisdiction
of New Mexico Navajo Education Office.

MARIANO LAKE COMMUNITY SCHOOL
P.O. Box 787 • CROWNPOINT, NM 87313
(505) 786-5265 Fax 786-5203
Delores P. Bitsilly, Principal; E-mail: delores.bitsilly@bie.edu
Boarding School; Grades K-6. Under jurisdiction
of New Mexico Navajo Education Office.

T'IISTS'OOZI BI'O'LTA (CROWNPOINT) COMMUNITY SCHOOL
P.O. Box 178 • CROWNPOINT, NM 87313
(505) 786-6159 Fax 786-6163
Virginia I. Jumbo, Principal; E-mail: Virginia.jumbo@bie.edu
Boarding School; Grades K-8. Under jurisdiction
of New Mexico Navajo Education Office.

TSE'II'AHI' (STANDING ROCK) COMMUNITY SCHOOL
P.O. Box 828 • CROWNPOINT, NM 87313
(505) 786-5389 Fax 786-5635
Rebecca Goddard-Vesely, Principal
Boarding School; Grades K-4. *Description*: Provides academic, cultural enrichment & tutoring services for American Indian children, including instruction in Navajo language & culture. Under jurisdiction of New Mexico Navajo Education Office.

NA'NEELZHIIN JI'OLTA' (TORREON DAY SCHOOL)
HCR 79, Box 9 • CUBA, NM 87013
(505) 731-2272 Fax 731-2252; Website: www.njo.bie.edu
Kenneth Toledo, Executive Director; E-mail: ktoledo_rock@yahoo.com
Sylvia Largo, Principal; E-mail: sjlargo1@yahoo.com
Boarding School; Grades K-8. Under jurisdiction
of New Mexico Navajo Education Office.

OJO ENCINO DAY SCHOOL
HCR 79, Box 7 • CUBA, NM 87013
(505) 731-2333 Fax 731-2361; Yolando Denny, Principal
Day School; Grades K-8. Under jurisdiction of New Mexico
Navajo Education Office.

PUEBLO PINTADO COMMUNITY SCHOOL
HCR 79, Box 80 • CUBA, NM 87013
(505) 655-3341 Fax 655-3342
Notah Benally, Principal
Boarding School; Grades K-8. Under jurisdiction of New Mexico
Navajo Education Office.

JICARILLA DORMITORY SCHOOL
600 Circle Dr., P.O. Box 1009 • DULCE, NM 87528
(505) 759-3101 Fax 759-3338
David Montoya, Home Living Supervisor
Grades 1-12. Under jurisdiction of New Mexico North Education Office.

SANTA CLARA DAY SCHOOL
625 Kee St. • ESPANOLA, NM 87532
(505) 753-4406 Fax 753-8866
Robin Rodar, Principal
Grades K-6. Under jurisdiction of New Mexico North Education Office.

NAVAJO PREPARATORY SCHOOL
1220 W. Apache • FARMINGTON, NM 87401
(505) 326-6571 Fax 326-2155
Website: www.cyberport.com/~navajoprep/
Betty O'jay, Director; Sam Sage, Chairperson
Boarding School; Grades 9-12. Program: College preparatory with emphasis on Navajo language and culture. Under jurisdiction of Shiprock Agency.

WINGATE ELEMENTARY SCHOOL
12 Painted Horse Trail, P.O. Box 1 • FORT WINGATE, NM 87316
(505) 488-6300 Fax 488-6312
Dianne T. Owens, Principal
Boarding School; Grades K-8. *Enrollment*: 400. Library.
Under jurisdiction of New Mexico Navajo South Education Office.

WINGATE HIGH SCHOOL
1737 Shush Dr., P.O. Box 2 • FORT WINGATE, NM 87316
(505) 488-6400 Fax 488-6444
Gloria Arviso, Principal; E-mail: Gloria.arviso@bie.edu
Boarding School; Grades 9-12. Under jurisdiction
of New Mexico Navajo South Education Office.

NENAHNEZAD COMMUNITY SCHOOL
P.O. Box 337 • FRUITLAND, NM 87416
(505) 598-6922 Fax 598-0970; Website: www.nenah.bie.edu
Delphna Shunkamolah, Principal
E-mail: delphina.shunkamolah@bie.edu
Boarding School; Grades K-6. *Enrollment*: 445. *Special courses*: Navajo Language and Culture; Writing Labs in Navajo and English. Instructor: Rosalyn Junes, Writing Lab. *Special program*: Navajo Language programs for all grades. Under jurisdiction of Shiprock Agency.

BREAD SPRINGS DAY SCHOOL
750 Bread Springs Rd., P.O. Box 1117 • GALLUP, NM 87305
(505) 778-5665 Fax 778-5692
Carl S. Granfors, Principal
Grades K-3. *Enrollment*: 154. Under jurisdiction
of New Mexico Navajo South Education Office.

ISLETA ELEMENTARY SCHOOL
1000 Moonlight Dr., P.O. Box 550 • ISLETA, NM 87022
(505) 869-2321 Fax 869-1625
Gweneth Torivio, Principal
Grades K-6. *Enrollment*: 300. *Publication*: Isleta
Eagle Pride, newspaper. Under jurisdiction of New Mexico South
Education Office.

JEMEZ DAY SCHOOL
243 Day School Rd., P.O. Box 139 • JEMEZ PUEBLO, NM 87024
(505) 834-7304 Fax 834-7081
Mariam Toya, Principal; E-mail: Mariam.toya@bie.edu
Grades K-6. Under jurisdiction of New Mexico South Education Office.

LAGUNA ELEMENTARY SCHOOL
P.O. Box 191 • LAGUNA PUEBLO, NM 87026
(505) 552-9200 Fax 552-7294
Dr. Anthony Fairbanks, Executive Director
E-mail: a.fairbanks@lagunaed.net
Yolanda Batrez, Principal; E-mail: y.batrez@lagunaed.net
Grades K-5. Under jurisdiction of New Mexico South Education Office.

LAGUNA MIDDLE SCHOOL
P.O. Box 268 • LAGUNA PUEBLO, NM 87026
(505) 552-9091 Fax 552-6466
Dr. Anthony Fairbanks, Executive Director
E-mail: a.fairbanks@lagunaed.net
David Jiron, Principal; E-mail: d.jiron@lagunaed.net
Grades 6-8. Under jurisdiction of New Mexico South
Education Office.

ALAMO NAVAJO COMMUNITY SCHOOL
P.O. Box 907 • MAGDALENA, NM 87825
(575) 854-2543 Fax 854-2545
Alfonzo Garcia, Supt.; Susan Comisky, Principal
E-mail: scormisky@ansbi.org
Grades K-12. Under jurisdiction of New Mexico Navajo
South Education Office.

MESCALERO APACHE SCHOOL
249 White Mountain Dr., P.O. Box 230 • MESCALERO, NM 88340
(575) 464-4431 Fax 464-4822; Website: www.maschiefs,org
Mary Ross, Middle/High School Principal
Berdine Largo, K-5 Principal; E-mail: blargo@mescaleroas.org
Maria Saenz, Superintendent
Grades K-12. *Enrollment*: 525. Under jurisdiction of New Mexico
Navajo South Education Office.

CRYSTAL BOARDING SCHOOL
Hwy. 134, Bkdg. 301 • NAVAJO, NM 87328
(505) 777-2385 Fax 777-2648
Alberto Castruita, Principal; E-mail: alberto.castruita@bie.edu
Grades K-6. Under jurisdiction of Arizona Navajo South Office.

TOHAALI' (TOADLENA) COMMUNITY SCHOOL
P.O. Box 9857 • NEWCOMB, NM 87455
(505) 789-3201 Fax 789-3202
Dr. Loretta Wheeler, Principal; E-mail: loretta1.wheeler@bie.edu
Grades K-8. Under jurisdiction of New Mexico Navajo South
Education Office.

OHKAY OWINGEH COMMUNITY SCHOOL
307 Community School Rd.
P.O. Box 1077 • OHKAY OWINGEH, NM 87566
(505) 852-2154 Fax 852-4305
Patricia Archuleta, Acting Principal
E-mail: archuletapatricia@yahoo.com
Grades K-8. Under jurisdiction of New Mexico North Education Office.

PINE HILL SCHOOLS
P.O. Box 220 • PINE HILL, NM 87357
(505) 775-3242 Fax 775-3241; Gilbert Sage, Principal
Boarding School; Grades K-12. Under jurisdiction
of New Mexico Navajo South Education Office.

BACA/DLO'AY AZHI COMMUNITY SCHOOL
P.O. Box 1809 • PREWITT, NM 87045
(505) 972-2769 Fax 972-2310
Timothy Nelson, Principal; E-mail: timothy.nelson@bie.edu
Boarding School; Grades K-4. Under jurisdiction
of New Mexico Navajo South Education Office.

SAN FELIPE PUEBLO ELEMENTARY SCHOOL
711 Main Pueblo Rd., P.O. Box 4343
SAN FELIPE PUEBLO, NM 87001
(505) 867-3364 Fax 867-6253
Cynthia Luna, Acting Principal
Grades K-7. Under jurisdiction of New Mexico. Navajo South
Education Office.

SANOSTEE DAY SCHOOL
P.O. Box 159 • SANOSTEE, NM 87461
(505) 723-2476 Fax 723-2425; Jeannie G. Haskie, Principal
Grades K-3. Under jurisdiction of New Mexico Navajo South
Education Office.

SAN ILDEFONSO DAY SCHOOL
36 Tunyo Po, Route 5, Box 308 • SANTA FE, NM 87506
(505) 455-2366 Fax 455-2155; Delores Guzman, Principal/Teacher
Grades K-6. Under jurisdiction of New Mexico North Education Office.

SANTA FE INDIAN SCHOOL
1501 Cerrillos Rd., P.O. Box 5340 • SANTA FE, NM 87502
(505) 989-6302 Fax 989-6319; Website: www.sfis.k12.nm.us
Everett Chavez, Superintendent; Felisa Guilbert, Principal
Boarding School; Grades 7-12. Under jurisdiction of New Mexico
North Education Office.

TE TSU GEH OWEENGE DAY SCHOOL (TESUQUE)
Route 42, Box 2 • SANTA FE, NM 87506
(505) 982-1516 Fax 982-2090; Marcy Pompei, Principal
Grades K-6. Under jurisdiction of New Mexico North Education Office.

BECLABITO DAY SCHOOL
P.O. Box 1200 • SHIPROCK, NM 87420
(928) 656-3555 Fax 656-3557; Tanya Amrine, Principal
Grades K-4. Under jurisdiction of New Mexico North Education Office.

ATSA' BIYA AZH COMMUNITY SCHOOL
P.O. Box 1809 • SHIPROCK, NM 87420
(505) 368-2100 Fax 368-5102; Freda Nells, Principal
Dr. Leo Johnson, Executive Director; E-mail: leo.johnson@bie.edu
Grades K-6. Under jurisdiction of New Mexico North Education Office.

SHIPROCK NORTHWEST HIGH SCHOOL
Pinon St. Bldg, 1416, P.O. Box 1809 • SHIPROCK, NM 87420
(505) 368-2100 Fax 368-2076
Dr. Leo Johnson, Executive Director; E-mail: leo.johnson@bie.edu
Emil Kaul, Principal
Grades 7-12. *Enrollment*: 175. Under jurisdiction
of New Mexico Navajo North Education Office.

SHIPROCK RESERVATION DORMITORY
Pinon St. Bldg. 1416, P.O. Box 1809 • SHIPROCK, NM 87420
(505) 368-2074 Fax 368-2076
Dr. Leo Johnson, Executive Director; E-mail: leo.johnson@bie.edu
Boarding School. Grades 9-12. Under jurisdiction
of New Mexico Navajo North Education Office.

TAOS PUEBLO DAY SCHOOL
200 Rotten Tree Rd., P.O. Box 1850 • TAOS, NM 87571
(575) 758-3652 Fax 758-1566; Website: www.laplaza.org/edu/tds
Patricia Kessler, Principal
Grades K-8. Under jurisdiction of New Mexico North Education Office.

CH'OOSHGAI COMMUNITY SCHOOL (CHUSKA)
P.O. Box 321 • TOHATCHI, NM 87325
(505) 733-2700 Fax 733-2703/2715; Website: www.ccsbroncos.bie.edu
Lester Hudson, Executive Director; Danny Eoker, Principal
Boarding School; Grades K-8. Under jurisdiction of New Mexico Navajo
South Education Office.

CHI-CH'IL-TAH/JONES RANCH COMMUNITY SCHOOL
831 Cousins Rd., P.O. Box 278 • VANDERWAGEN, NM 87326
(505) 778-5574 Fax 778-5575; Marlene Tsosie, Acting Principal
Day School; Grades K-8. Under jurisdiction of New Mexico
Navajo South Education Office.

T'SIYA (ZIA) DAY SCHOOL
1000 Borrego Canyon Rd. • ZIA PUEBLO, NM 87053
(505) 867-3553 Fax 867-5079; Robin Rodar, Principal
Grades K-7. Under jurisdiction of New Mexico South Education Office.

NEW YORK

ST. REGIS MOHAWK SCHOOL
Gowanda Central School District - Indian Education Program
385 Church St. • HOGANSBURG, NY 13655
(518) 358-2763; Irving Papineau, Principal

AHKWESAHSNE FREEDOM SCHOOL
Mohawk Nation via P.O. Box 290 • ROOSEVELTOWN, NY 13683
(518) 358-2073 Fax 358-2081; Elvera Sargent, Director
Grades Pre-K to 8. *Description*: A Mohawk Immersion school with Mohawk
taught in levels Pre-K to 6. Levels 7 & 8 are the English transition classes. All
instructors are fluent speakers of the Mohawk Language and come from the
community of Ahkwesahsne.

NORTH CAROLINA

CHEROKEE CENTRAL ELEMENTARY SCHOOL
200 Ravenswood Dr., P.O. Box 134 • CHEROKEE, NC 28719
(828) 554-5020 Fax 554-5035
Website: www.cherokeecentral.sharpschool.com
Scott Penland, Superintendent (554-5089)
E-mail: spenland@cherokeecentrall.gaggle.net
Paula Coker, Principal; E-mail: cokerp1@hotmail.com
Grades K-6. Under jurisdiction of Southern & Eastern States
Education Office.

CHEROKEE CENTRAL HIGH SCHOOL
130 Ravenswood Dr., P.O. Box 134 • CHEROKEE, NC 28719
(828) 554-5030 Fax 554-5033
Website: www.cherokeecentral.sharpschool.com
Scott Penland, Superintendent (554-5089)
E-mail: spenland@cherokeecentrall.gaggle.net
Debora Foerst, Principal; (828) 554-5028
E-mail: dfoerstl@cherokeecentral.gaggle.net
Grades 9-12. *Total Enrollment*: Grads K-12, @1,500.
Program: Cherokee Boys Club. Under jurisdiction of Southern
& Eastern States Education Office.

CHEROKEE CENTRAL MIDDLE SCHOOL
130 Ravensford Dr. • CHEROKEE, NC 28719
(828) 554-5026 Fax 554-5029
Website: www.cherokeecentral.sharpschool.com
Scott Penland, Superintendent (554-5089)
E-mail: spenland@cherokeecentrall.gaggle.net
Cance Carnes, Principal
E-mail: ccarnes@cherokeecentral.gaggle.net
Grades 7-9. Under jurisdiction of Southern & Eastern States
Education Office

NORTH DAKOTA

OJIBWA INDIAN SCHOOL
9620 42nd Ave. NE, P.O. Box 600 • BELCOURT, ND 58316
(701) 477-3108 Fax 477-6039; Website: www.ojibwa.k12.nd.us
Michael Blue, Principal
Grades K-8. *Enrollment*: 280. Under jurisdiction of Turtle Mountain
Education Office.

TURTLE MOUNTAIN ELEMENTARY & MIDDLE SCHOOLS
1330 Braves Rd., P.O. Box 440 • BELCOURT, ND 58316
(701) 477-6471 Fax 477-8006/3973
Website: www.belcourt.k12.nd.us
Dave Gourneau, Elementary School Principal
E-mail: david.gourneau@bie.edu
Louis L. Dauphinais, Middle School Principal
Grades K-8. Under jurisdiction of Turtle Mountain Education Office.

TURTLE MOUNTAIN HIGH SCHOOL
1330 Braves Rd., P.O. Box 440 • BELCOURT, ND 58316
(701) 477-6471 Fax 477-8821; Website: www.belcourt.k12.nd.us
Melvin Laducer, Principal
Grades 9-12. *Enrollment*: 405. *Special courses*: Vocational (building, welding,
health, distributive education); special education (speech & emotionally
disturbed.) Library. Under jurisdiction of Turtle Mountain Education Office.

THEODORE JAMERSON ELEMENTARY SCHOOL
United Tribes Technical College
3315 University Dr. • BISMARCK, ND 58504
(701) 255-3285 Ext. 305 Fax 766-4766

Francis Sam Azure, Principal; E-mail: sazure@uttc.edu
Grades K-8. *Enrollment*: 95. *Special courses*: Math/Reading; Special Education; Gifted & Talented. Media Center-Library. Under jurisdiction of Standing Rock Education Office.

DUNSEITH DAY SCHOOL
P.O. Box 759 • DUNSEITH, ND 58371
  (701) 263-4636 Fax 263-4200; Yvonne St. Claire, Principal
Grades K-8. Under jurisdiction of Turtle Mountain Education Office.

TATE TOPA TRIBAL SCHOOL
FOUR WINDS COMMUNITY SCHOOL
7268 Hwy. 57, P.O. Box 199 • FORT TOTTEN, ND 58335
  (701) 766-1400 Fax 766-1475; Website: www.fourwinds.k12.nd.us
Pat Walking Eagle, Supt. & Elementary Principal
  E-mail: patricia.walkingeagle@sendit.nodak.edu
Mark Mindt, Middle School Principal; Four Winds High School
Grades K-8. Under jurisdiction of Standing Rock Education Office.

STANDING ROCK COMMUNITY SCHOOL
9189 Hwy. 24, P.O. Box 377 • FORT YATES, ND 58538
  (701) 854-3865 Fax 854-3878 (K-6)
  (701) 854-3819 Fax 854-7467 (7-9)
  (701) 854-3461 Fax 854-3785 (10-12)
  Website: www.fort-yates.k12.nd.us
Virginia Long Feather, Elementary Principal
  E-mail: virginia.longfeather@k12.nd.us
Tomi Kay Phillips, Middle School Principal
  E-mail: tomi.phillips@k12.nd.us
Bernadette Dauenhauer,, High School Principal
  E-mail: b.dauenhauer@k12.nd.us
Grades K-12. *Enrollment*: 800. Under jurisdiction of Standing Rock Education Office.

TWIN BUTTES ELEMENTARY SCHOOL
7997 7th St. North • HALLIDAY, ND 58636
  (701) 938-4396 Fax 938-4397; Website: www.twinbuttes.k12.nd.us
Sandy Starr, Supt./Principal; E-mail: sandy.starr@k12.nd.us
Grades K-8. Under jurisdiction of Turtle Mountain Education Office.

MANDAREE DAY SCHOOL
P.O. Box 488 • MANDAREE, ND 58757
  (701) 759-3311 Fax 759-3112
  Website: www.mandaree.k12.nd.us
  Carolyn Bluestone, Superintendent
Grades K-12. Enrollment: 250. *Special courses*: Hidatsa Language; Tribal History & Government; Special Education, Cultural. *Special programs*: Indian Club and Rodeo Club; Alternative Education; Gifted & Talented Programs. Under jurisdiction of Turtle Mountain Education Office.

WHITE SHIELD SCHOOL
2 2nd Ave. W. • ROSEGLEN, ND 58775
  (701) 743-4350 Fax 743-4501; Website: www.white-shield.k12.nd.us
John Jankowski, Superintendent
  E-mail: john.jankowski.1@sendit.nodak.edu
Stacey Blacksmith, High School Principal
  E-mail: Stacey.blacksmith@sendit.nodak.edu
Bobbi Shegrud, Margaret Breuer Elementary Principal
  E-mail: bobbi.shegrud@sendit.nodak.edu
Grades K-12. Under jurisdiction of Turtle Mountain Education Office.

CIRCLE OF NATIONS SCHOOL
(WAHPETON INDIAN BOARDING SCHOOL)
832 N. 8th St. • WAHPETON, ND 58075
  (701) 642-3796 Fax 642-1984; Website: www.circleofnations.org
Leroy Chief, CEO
Cheryl Poitra, Principal; E-mail: cherylpoitra@circleofnations.org
Grades 5-8. *Enrollment*: 250. *Special programs*: Intense Residential Guidance Program. Library (small museum in library). Under jurisdiction of Minneapolis Education Office.

OKLAHOMA

RIVERSIDE INDIAN SCHOOL
101 Riverside Dr. • ANADARKO, OK 73005
  (888) 886-2029; (405) 247-6670 Fax 247-5529
Tony Dearman, Superintendent; E-mail: tony.dearman@bie.edu
Sharon Hunter, Elementary School Principal; E-mail: Sharon.hunter@bie.edu
Milton Noel, High School Principal
Grades 4-12. Under jurisdiction of Oklahoma Education Office.

CARTER SEMINARY
2400 Chickasaw Blvd. • ARDMORE, OK 73401
  (580) 223-8547 Fax 223-6325
  Rebecca Kingsbery, Administrator; Becky Durringtron, Chairperson
Dormitory School; Grades 1-12. Under jurisdiction of Oklahoma Education Office.

SCHOOL OF CHOCTAW LANGUAGE
P.O. Box 1210 • DURANT, OK 74702
  (800) 522-6170; (580) 924-8280
Jim Parrish, Director; E-mail: jparrish@choctawnation.com
Richard Adams, Assistant Director
  E-mail: radams@choctawnation.com
Language Instructors: Curtis Billy, Teri Bryan, Bernie Davis, Mike Davis, Lola John, Lillie Roberts, Betty Ward, Nicholas Charelston, Virginia Espinoza, Justin Fite, Kandace Folsom, Elsie Hicks, Caleb Taylor, Angie Williston *Mission*: To preserve & perpetuate the Choctaw language; to promote & enhance cultural awareness by teaching traditional customs & historical facts. Bookstore. Owned & operated by the Choctaw Nation.

EASTERN OKLAHOMA TRIBAL SCHOOLS
601 N. Kelly Ave., #105 • EDMOND, OK 73003
  (405) 330-9236 Fax 330-9261
  Website: www.eots.org; E-mail: info@eots.org

EUFAULA DORMITORY
716 Swadley Dr. • EUFAULA, OK 74432
  (918) 689-2522 Fax 689-2438; E-mail: eufauladormitorylrc@hotmail.com
  Greg Anderson, Superintendent; E-mail: Gregory.anderson@bie.edu
Boarding School. Grades 1-12. Under jurisdiction of Oklahoma Education Office.

JONES ACADEMY
HCR 74, Rt. 1 Box 102-5 • HARTSHORNE, OK 74547
  (918) 297-2518 Fax 297-2364
  Website: www.jonesacademy.org; E-mail: info@jonesacademy.org
  Brad Spears, Supt.; E-mail: brad.spears@bie.edu
Boarding School; Grades 1-12. Under jurisdiction of Oklahoma Education Office.

CHICKASAW CHILDREN'S VILLAGE
1185 Village Rd. • KINGSTON, OK 73439
  (580) 564-3060 Fax 564-3605
  Jay Keel, Administrator; E-mail: jay.keel@chickasaw.net
  Sallie Wallace, Director; E-mail: sallie.wallace@chickasaw.net
Boarding School. Grades 1-12. Under jurisdiction of Oklahoma Education Office.

SEQUOYAH HIGH SCHOOL
17091 S. Muskogee Ave., P.O. Box 520 • TAHLEQUAH, OK 74465
  (888) 467-4746; (918) 453-5400 Fax 458-6257
  Website: www.sequoyah.k12.ok.us; Leroy Qualls, Supt.,
  Jolyn Carey-Rose, Principal
Boarding School; Grades 9-12. Under jurisdiction of Oklahoma Education Office.

OREGON

CHEMAWA INDIAN SCHOOL
3700 Chemawa Rd., NE • SALEM, OR 97305
  (503) 399-5721 Fax 399-5870; Website: www.chemawa.bie.edu
  Lora Braucher, School Supervisor; Amanda Ward, Academic Principal
Grades 9-12. Under jurisdiction of Seattle Education Office.

SOUTH DAKOTA

TIOSPA ZINA TRIBAL SCHOOL
1 Tiospa Zina Rd., P.O. Box 719 • AGENCY VILLAGE, SD 57262
  (605) 698-3954 Fax 698-7766; Website: www.tzts.bia.edu
  Ted Hamilton, Superintendent; Erick Heath, High School Principal
  Mindy Deutsch, Elementary School Principal
Grades K-12. Under jurisdiction of Crow Creek/Lower Brule Office.

AMERICAN HORSE SCHOOL
101 Main St., P.O. Box 660 • ALLEN, SD 57714
  (605) 455-1209 Fax 455--1045
  Gloria Coats-Kitopoulos, Superintendent
  E-mail: Gloria.kitsopoulos@bie.edu
  Jodi Richards, Principal; E-mail: Jodi.richards@bie.edu
Grades K-8. Under jurisdiction of Pine Ridge Office.

ROCK CREEK DAY SCHOOL
1 Indian School Rd., P.O. Box 127 • BULLHEAD, SD 57621
(605) 823-4971 Fax 823-4350; Linda Lawrence, Principal
Grades K-8. Under jurisdiction of Standing Rock Education Office.

ST. JOSEPH'S INDIAN SCHOOL
P.O. Box 300, 1301 N. Main St. • CHAMBERLAIN SD 57325
(800) 341-2235
Website: www.stjo.org; E-mail: saintjosephs@stjo.org
Jim Kinyon, Board Chairperson; Doug Knust, Vice Chairperson
Mission: To educate Native American youth, by housing 200 needy Lakota children each year. Teaching the Lakota culture by learning the Lakota language, studying Native American culture & healing the broken family circle from which they come. Established 1927.

CHERRY CREEK ELEMENTARY SCHOOL
CHERRY CREEK, SD 57622
(605) 538-4238; Faye Longbrake, Principal
Grades K-6. Under jurisdiction of Cheyenne River Agency.

CHEYENNE-EAGLE BUTTE SCHOOL
2004 E St., P.O. Box 672 • EAGLE BUTTE, SD 57625
(605) 964-8777 Fax 964-8776
Dr. Nadine Eastman, Superintendent & Elementary School Principal
James Nelson, High School Principal
Jesse Mendoza, Middle School Principal
Boarding School; Grades K-12. *Enrollment*: 900.
Under jurisdiction of Cheyenne River Office.

FLANDREAU INDIAN SCHOOL
1132 N. Crescent St. • FLANDREAU, SD 57028
(605) 997-3773 Fax 997-2601
Everall Fox, Chief School Administrator
Sheryl Burkhart, Assistant Principal
Grades 9-12. Enrollment: 750. Under jurisdiction of Minneapolis Area Office.

CROW CREEK SIOUX TRIBAL SCHOOLS
101 Crow Creek Loop, P.O. Box 469 • STEPHAN, SD 57346
(605) 245-2373 Fax 245-2310; Website: www.crowcreek.k12.sd.us
Cody Russell, Superintendent; Amelia Black Bear, Principal
Grades K-5. *Enrollment*: 200. Under jurisdiction of Crow Creek/Lower Brule Office.

TIOSPAYE TOPA SCHOOL
P.O. Box 300 • HOWES, SD 57652
(605) 733-2290 Fax 733-2299; Website: www.tzts.us
Eric Heath, High School Principal
Daniel Zimansky, Middle School Principal
Mindy Crawford, Elementary Principal; E-mail: mcrawford@tzts.us
Grades K-12. Under jurisdiction of Cheyenne River Office.

TAKINI SCHOOL
HC 77, Box 537 • HOWES, SD 57748
(605) 538-4399 Fax 538-4315; Website: www.takini.k12.sd.us
Ted Rowland, Superintendent
Lil Manthei, High School Principal
Jim Wika, Elementary School Principal
Grades K-12. *Enrollment*: 250+. *Special courses*: Tribal Government, Lakota Drum and Singing Group. *Special programs*: Annual Powwow and Wacipi in Spring for fund raising and honoring people. Library. *Publications*: Biweekly newsletter; yearbook. Under jurisdiction of Cheyenne River Office.

LITTLE WOUND SCHOOL
100 Main St., P.O. Box 500 • KYLE, SD 57752
(605) 455-6150 Fax 455-2340
Charles Cuny, Superintendent
Sharel Ricketts, High School Principal
Linda Hunter, Middle School Principal
Theresa Mendoza, Elementary School Principal (Grades K-4)
Grades K-12. *Enrollment*: 500. Under jurisdiction of Pine Ridge Office.

SITTING BULL DAY SCHOOL (TATANKA WAKANYEJA OTI)
1 School St., P.O. Box 26 • LITTLE EAGLE, SD 57639
(605) 823-4235 Fax 823-2292; Website: www.sittingbull.k12.sd.us
Dave Archambault, Superintendent; E-mail: joebuckinghorse@gmail.cm
Joe White Mountain, Jr., Principal
Grades K-8. Enrollment: 100. Under jurisdiction of Standing Rock Office.

LOWER BRULE SCHOOL
600 Crazy Horse St., P.O. Box 245 • LOWER BRULE, SD 57548
(605) 473-0216 Fax 473-0217

Cody Russell, Superintendent
Karen Whitney, PhD, High School Principal
John Beheler, Elementary School Principal
Grades K-12. *Enrollment*: 250. Under jurisdiction of Crow Creek/Lower Brule Office.

WOUNDED KNEE DISTRICT SCHOOL
100 Main St., P.O. Box 350 • MANDERSON, SD 57756
(605) 455-6350 Fax 867-1219
Website: www.woundedkneeschool.org
Marnie White Wolf, Principal
Grades K-8. *Enrollment*: 225. Under jurisdiction of Pine Ridge Office.

MARTY INDIAN SCHOOL
100 S. Main, P.O. Box 187 • MARTY, SD 57361
(605) 384-2212 Fax 384-5933; Website: www.martyindian.kkk1k2.sd.us
Jolene Arrow, Supt. for Education; E-mail: jolene.arrow@k12.sd.us
Everdell Wright, High School Principal; Russell Gade, Middle School Principal
Gina Curran, Elementary School Principal
Grades K-12. Under jurisdiction of Rosebud Office.

SICANGU OWAYAWA OTI (ROSEBUD DORM)
1001 Ave. D, P.O. Box 69 • MISSION, SD 57555
(605) 856-4486 Fax 856-4490; Nancy Keller-Hernandez, Director
Dormitory School; Grades 1-12. *Enrollment*: 250. Under jurisdiction of Rosebud Office.

LONEMAN DAY SCHOOL
P.O. Box 50 • OGLALA, SD 57764
(605) 867-6875 Fax 867-5109
Deborah Bordeaux, Principal
Grades K-8. Under jurisdiction of Pine Ridge Office.

PIERRE INDIAN LEARNING CENTER
3001 E. Sully Ave. • PIERRE, SD 57501-4419
(605) 224-8661 Fax 224-8465; Website: www.pilc.k12.sd.us
Dr. Vernica Pietz, Superintendent/Principal
E-mail: veronica.pietz@k12.sd.us
Boarding School; Grades 1-8. *Enrollment*: 100. *Special courses*: Special education school for children with learning disabilities or emotional problems. Contract school serving 15 reservations in North & South Dakota, & Nebraska. Under jurisdiction of Cheyenne River Office.

PINE RIDGE SCHOOL
101 Thorpe Circle, P.O. Box 1202 • PINE RIDGE, SD 57770
(605) 867-5198 Fax 867-5482; Website: www.prs.bie.edu
K-8 school: (605) 867-5193 Fax 867-1404
Website: www.prs.bia.edu; Mona Miyasato, Acting Principal
Dora Gwin, Assistant Elementary Principal
Grades K-12. *Enrollment*: 1,000. Under jurisdiction of Pine Ridge Office.

RED CLOUD INDIAN SCHOOL
100 Mission Dr. • PINE RIDGE, SD 57770
(605) 867-5491; 867-5889; Website: www.redcloudschool.org
Fr. George Winzenburg, S.J., President
James Mattern, High School Principal
Jennifer Sierra, Elementary School Principal
Theodore L. Hamilton, Superintendent
Peter Strong, Heritage Center Director (867-8257)
Boarding School; Grades K-12. *Special program*: Montessori pre-school (ages 3 and up, including some first graders.) *Facilities*: The Heritage Center. *Activities*: Red Cloud Indian Art Show.

PORCUPINE DAY SCHOOL
100 School Dr., P.O. Box 180 • PORCUPINE, SD 57772
(605) 867-5588 Fax 867-5480; Website: www.porcupinequills.org
Marty Pourier, Principal
Grades K-8. Under jurisdiction of Pine Ridge Office.

SICANGU OYATE HO., INC. (ST. FRANCIS INDIAN SCHOOL)
350 Oak St., P.O. Box 379 • ST. FRANCIS, SD 57572-0379
(605) 747-2299 Fax 747-2379; Website: www.sfiskl2.org
Richard Bad Milk, Superintendent
Wendy Castaneda-Leal, Middle School Principal
Dani Walking Eagle, Elementary School Principal
Grades K-12. Tribally controlled serving the Rosebud Sioux Indian Reservation in south central South Dakota. Under jurisdiction of Rosebud Office.

CROW CREEK RESERVATION HIGH SCHOOL
101 Crow Creek Loop • STEPHAN, SD 57346
(605) 852-2455 Fax 852-2140

Silas Blaine, Superintendent
Brian Sieh, High School Principal
Steve Swartout, Middle School Principal
Grades 6-12. *Enrollment*: 225. *Special programs*: Special Education; Intensive Residential Counseling; Career Counseling; Substance Abuse Counseling. Under jurisdiction of Crow Creek/Lower Brule Office.

CRAZY HORSE SCHOOL
101 School Rd., P.O. Box 260 • WANBLEE, SD 57577
(605) 455-6800 Fax 462-6510; Website: www.crazyhorse.k12.sd.us
Dr. Patrick Jones, Superintendent
Lyle Iron Horn, High School Principal
Justina Setalla-One Horn, Middle & Elementary School Principal
Grades K-12. Under jurisdiction of Pine Ridge Office.

ENEMY SWIM DAY SCHOOL
13525 446th Ave. • WAUBAY, SD 57273
(605) 947-4605 Fax 947-4188; Website: www.usds.us
Dr. Sherri Johnson, Superintendent
Virginia Donley, Principal; E-mail: vdolney@esds.us
Grades K-8. Under jurisdiction of Crow Creek/Lower Brule Office.

UTAH

ANETH COMMUNITY SCHOOL
P.O. Box 600 • MONTEZUMA CREEK UT 84534
(801) 651-3271 Fax 651-3272; Website: www.aneth.org
Brenda Whitehorse, Principal
Boarding School; Grades K-6. Under jurisdiction of Shiprock Agency.

RICHFIELD RESIDENTIAL HALL
P.O. Box 638 • RICHFIELD, UT 84701
(435) 896-5101 Fax 896-6157; Website: www.richfielddorm.org
Cody Workman, Executive Director; E-mail: cworkman@richfielddorm.org
Dormitory School; Grades 9-12. Under jurisdiction of Arizona Navajo North Office.

WASHINGTON

MUCKLESHOOT TRIBAL SCHOOL
39015 172nd Ave. SE • AUBURN, WA 98002
(253) 931-6709 Fax 939-2922; Richard Torralba, K-12 Principal
Michael Aaron, Supt.; E-mail: c_maaron@yahoo.com
Grades K-12. *Enrollment*: 350. *Description of program*: Early childhood education, special education, counseling program, multimedia curriculum for tribal language and culture, using computers, video & books, crossing all curriculum areas. Head Start. Under jurisdiction of Seattle Office.

LUMMI NATION SCHOOL
2334 Lummi View Dr. • BELLINGHAM, WA 98226
(360) 758-4300 Fax 758-3160; Website: www.lumminationschool.org
Laverne Lane, Superintendent; Heather Leighton, Principal
Grades K-12. Under jurisdiction of Seattle Office.

QUILEUTE TRIBAL SCHOOL
40 Ocean Dr., P.O. Box 39 • LA PUSH, WA 98350
(360) 374-2061 Fax 374-5784, 9608
Franklin Hanson, Superintendent
Al Zantua, High School Principal
Grades K-12. Under jurisdiction of Seattle Office.

WE HE LUT INDIAN SCHOOL
11110 Conine Ave. SE • OLYMPIA, WA 98513
(360) 456-1311 Fax 456-1319
Harvey Whitford, Principal; E-mail: Harvey.whitford@bie.edu

PASCHAL SHERMAN INDIAN SCHOOL
169 North End Omak Lake Rd. • OMAK, WA 98841
(509) 422-7590 Fax 422-7538
Website: www.psischiefs.org; Marcy Horne, Acting Principal
Tami Hickle, Superintendent; E-mail: thickle@psischiefs.org
Grades K-9. Under jurisdiction of Seattle Office.

CHIEF LESCHI SCHOOL SYSTEM (PUYALLUP)
5625 52nd St. East • PUYALLUP, WA 98371
(253) 445-6000 Fax 445-2350/2; Website: www.leschischools.org
Raymond Lorton, Superintendent; Lucy Dafoe, Principal
Grades Pre K-12. *Enrollment*: 350+. Library. Under jurisdiction of Seattle Office.

AMERICAN INDIAN HERITAGE SCHOOL
9600 College Way N. • SEATTLE, WA 98103
(206) 298-7895; Robert Eaglestaff, Principal
Grades 6-12. *Enrollment*: 120. All academic classes are taught with an enrichment from the Indian culture. Cultural classes in art, sewing, singing, dancing, drama, & computers. *Instructors*: Mary Lee Colby, R. Marina Sabbas, Courage Benally, Turk Markishtum, Marc Strash, & Bonnie Harding. *Special courses*: Native American Literature, History & Government. *Special programs*: American Indian Heritage Pupil Services Program - enrollment of 1,436 - provides, on a referral basis district wide, Indian cultural enrichment & awareness activities in various subjects & levels; Culture Night every Wednesday; two major powwows. Library. *Publication*: Pathways, monthly newspaper.

YAKAMA NATION TRIBAL SCHOOL
P.O. Box 151 • TOPPENISH, WA 98948
(509) 865-5121 Fax 865-6092, 6994; Website: www.yakama.org
Frank Mesplie, Principal; Anita L. Swan, Superintendent
Grades K-12. *Special course*: Yakama Language. Course emphasis on Native American culture. *Special programs*: Special Education; Higher Education Programs; Tribal *Scholarship*: Financial assistance to Yakama tribal members who wish to pursue postsecondary education. $1,500/year for undergraduate students; $3,000/year for graduate students. *Deadline*: January, April, June & October. Under jurisdiction of Seattle Office.

WISCONSIN

LAC COURTE OREILLES OJIBWE SCHOOL
88475 N. Trepania Rd., Route 2, Box 2800 • HAYWARD, WI 54843
(715) 634-8924 Fax 634-6058; Website: www.lcoschools.bie.edu
Michael Leahy, School Director; E-mail michael.leahy@bie.edu
Jessica Hutchison, Principal; E-mailj: jessica.hutchison@bie.edu
Grades K-12. *Enrollment*: 270. Under jurisdiction of Minneapolis Office.

MENOMINEE INDIAN SCHOOL DISTRICT
P.O. Box 1330 • KESHENA, WI 54135
(715) 799-3824 Fax 756-4659; Website: www.misd.k12.wi.us
Wendell Waukau, Superintendent
Shannon Chapman, Principal/Administrator
Stephanie Feldner, Middle School Principal
Leslie Shawanokastic, High School Principal
Grades K-12. *Enrollment*: 1,000. Includes Keshena Primary School, Menominee Indian Middle & High Schools, & an Adult Learning Center. *Special courses*: Menominee Culture. Library. Under jurisdiction of Minneapolis Office.

ONEIDA NATION SCHOOL
P.O. Box 365 • ONEIDA, WI 54155
(920) 869-1676 Fax 869-1684
Website: www.schools.oneidanation.org
Sharon A. Mousseau, Superintendent
E-mail: smoussea@oneidanation.org
Robert Ganka, High School Principal
Yvette Teguero, Elementary School Principal
E-mail: ypeguero@oneidanation.org
Grades K-12. *Enrollment*: 115. Under jurisdiction of Minneapolis Office.

WYOMING

ST. STEPHENS INDIAN SCHOOL
128 Mission Rd., P.O. Box 345 • ST. STEPHENS, WY 82524
(307) 856-4147 Fax 856-3742
Louis Headley, Superintendent
Russell Budmayr, High School Principal
Marilyn Groesbeck, Elementary Principal
Grades Pre K-12. Boarding School. Under jurisdiction of Billings Office.

The mission of the Indian Education Programs is to meet the unique educational & culturally related academic needs of American Indians & Alaskan Natives so that they can have an equal opportunity to achieve to the same challenging standards as all students.

ALABAMA

Escambia County Middle School
Indian Education Program, P.O. Drawer 1236 • Atmore, AL 36504
(251) 368-9105 Fax 368-0674; David Nolin, Director
Grades K-8. *Description*: Provides tutoring services & cultural enrichment programs. *Instructors*: Hazel Rolin, Mary Boytte, Joyce Pilyaw.

Washington County Schools
Indian Education Program, P.O. Drawer L • Chatom, AL 36518

Lawrence County Schools
Indian Education Program, Oakville Indian Mounds Park & Museum
1219 County Rd. 187 • Danville, AL 35619
(256) 905-2494 Fax 905-2428; E-mail: Indian@lawrenceal.org
Rickey Butch Walker, Director; Dexter Rutherford, Supt.
Grades K-12. *Description*: Provides a cultural heritage & enrichment program; sponsors a local Indian museum & annual multicultural Indian event in May. *Instructors*: Kelly Dutton, Lisa Terry, Pamela Jones, Tanya Malcom, Shannon Reed, Melody Morgan, Gina McCarley, Sam Steadman, Lori Crumpton.

Coffee County School System
Indian Education Program, 400 Reddoch Hill Rd. • Elba, AL 36323
(334) 897-5016 Fax 897-6207; Laura June Brown, Director
Grades K-12. *Description*: Provides culturally related academic activities and computer instruction for Indian students enrolled in the Coffee County School System. *Instructors*: Vicki Chamblee, Pam Flowers, Bonnie Campbell.

DeKalb County Schools
Indian Education Program, 209 Grand Ave. S. • Fort Payne, AL 3596

Fort Payne City Schools
Indian Education Program, P.O. Box 1029 • Fort Payne, AL 35967

Madison County Schools
Indian Education Program, P.O. Box 226 • Huntsville, AL 35804
(256) 852-7073 Fax 852-6708
Becky Jones & Tammy Hillis, Cultural Heritage Teachers
E-mail: rjones@madison.k12.al.us; E-mail: thillis@madison.k12.al.us
Grades K-12. *Description*: Designed to meet the academic and cultural needs of Indian students; works with high school students to get scholarships, participation in academic camps, etc. *Instructor*: Linda Williams. *Special project*: Develop cultural software

Mobile County Schools
Indian Education Program, P.O. Box 1327 • Mobile, AL 36633

Monroe County Schools
Indian Education Program, P.O. Box 967 • Monroeville, AL 36461

Mobile County Schools
Indian Education Program, 20185 Richard Weaver Rd. • Mt. Vernon, AL 36560

Scottsboro City Schools
Indian Education Program, 906 S. Scott St. • Scottsboro, AL 35971

ALASKA

Anchorage School District
Indian Education Program
5530 E. Northern Lights Blvd. • Anchorage, AK 99504
(907) 742-4445 Fax 742-4585
Doreen Brown, Supervisor; E-mail: brown_doreen@asdk12.org
Lauren Shutt, Cultural Enrichment Specialist
Jennifer Romer, Title VII Project Manager

ARKANSAS

Cedarville School District
Indian Education Program, P.O. Box 97 • Cedarville, AR 72932

Fort Smith School District
Indian Education Program, P.O. Box 1948 • Fort Smith, AR 72902
(479) 783-1202 Fax 784-8132; Judy Bivens Story, Director
Grades K-12.

ARIZONA

Ajo Unified School District
Indian Education Program, P.O. Box 68 • Ajo, AZ 85321

Colorado River Unified School District
Indian Education Program, 2251 Highway 95 • Bullhead City, AZ 86442

Casa Grande Schools
Indian Education Program, 1460 N. Pinal Ave. • Casa Grande, AZ 85222

Chandler Unified School District
Indian Education Program, 500 W. Galveston St. • Chandler, AZ 85224
(480) 224-3728; Vicki Narducci, Liaison
E-mail: narducci.victoria@chandler.k12.az.us
Publication: Quarterly newsletter

Chinle Unified School District
Indian Education Program, P.O. Box 587 • Chinle, AZ 86503

Coolidge Unified School District
Indian Education Program • Coolidge, AZ 85228

Flagstaff Unified School District
Indian Education Program, 3285 E. Sparrow Ave. • Flagstaff, AZ 86004

Window Rock Unified School District
Indian Education Program, P.O. Box 559 • Fort Defiance, AZ 86504

Fort Thomas Unified School District
Indian Education Program, P.O. Box 28 • Fort Thomas, AZ 85536

Fountain Hills Unified School District
Indian Education Program, 14605 No. Del Cambre • Fountain Hills, AZ 85268

Fredonia-Moccasin Unified School District
Indian Education Program, P221 E. Hortt St. • Fredonia, AZ 86022
(928) 643-7333 Fax 643-7044
Joseph B. Wright, Supt.; E-mail: jbwright@fredonia.org

Ganado Unified School District
Indian Education Program, P.O. Box 1757 • Ganado, AZ 86505

Gila Bend Unified School District #24
Indian Education Program, P.O. Box V • Gila Bend, AZ 85337

Glendale Unified School District
Indian Education Program, 4508 W. Northern Ave. • Glendale, AZ 85302

Globe Unified School District
Indian Education Program, 501 Ash St. • Globe, AZ 85501

Grand Canyon Unified School District
Indian Education Program, P.O. Box 519 • Grand Canyon, AZ 86023

Holbrook Unified School District
Indian Education Program, P.O. Box 640 • Holbrook, AZ 86025

Kayenta Unified School District
Indian Education Program, P.O. Box 337 • Kayenta, AZ 86033

Cedar Unified School District #25
Indian Education Program, P.O. Box 367 • Keams Canyon, AZ 86034

Laveen Elementary School District
Indian Education Program, P.O. Box 29 • Laveen, AZ 85339

Marana Unified School District #6
Indian Education Program, 11279 W. Grier Rd. • Marana, AZ 85653

Maricopa Unified School District #20
Indian Education Program, 45012 W. Honeycutt Ave. • Maricopa, AZ 85239

McNary Elementary School District
Indian Education Program, P.O. Box 598 • McNary, AZ 85930

Mesa Unified School District
Native American Education Program, 1025 N. Country Club • Mesa, AZ 85201
(480) 472-0580; Website: www.mpsaz.org/naep
Mikaela Thinn, Coordinator

Mohave Valley Elementary School District
Indian Education Program, P.O. Box 5070 • Mohave Valley, AZ 86440

Page Unified School District
Indian Education Program, 500 S. Navajo, Box 1927 • Page, AZ 86040

Parker Unified School District
Indian Education Program, P.O. Box 1089 • Parker, AZ 85344

Peach Springs Elementary. USD
Indian Education Program, P.O. Box 360 • Peach Springs, AZ 86434

Alhambra Elementary School District #68
Indian Education Program, 4510 N. 37th Ave. • Phoenix, AZ 85019-3206
(602) 336-2944 Fax 336-2271; Mary Beyda, Coordinator
Grades K-8. *Description*: Provides tutoring services and promotes parental involvement through communications, parent workshops, meetings, fund-raisers, and family activities. 550 Native American students, representing more than 20 tribes, have been identified and attend schools in Alhambra District. Instructors: Shirley Maves, Lois Lindsay.

Balsz School District
Indian Education Program, 4309 E. Bellview • Phoenix, AZ 85008

Creighton School District #14
Indian Education Program, 2702 E. Flower St. • Phoenix, AZ 85016

Isaac School District
Indian Education Program, 3801 W. Roanoke • Phoenix, AZ 85009

Madison Elementary School Dist. #38
Indian Education Program, 5601 N. 16th St. • Phoenix, AZ 85016

Murphy Elementary School District
Indian Education Program, 2615 W. Buckeye Rd. • Phoenix, AZ 85009

Osborn School District #8
Indian Education Program, 1226 W. Osborn Rd. • Phoenix, AZ 85013

Paradise Valley Unified School District
Indian Education Program, 15002 North 32nd St. • Phoenix, AZ 85032

Phoenix Elementary School District #1
Indian Education Program, 1817 North 7th St. • Phoenix, AZ 85006

Phoenix Union High School District
Native American Education Program
4502 N. Central Ave. • Phoenix, AZ 85012
(602) 271-3514 Fax 271-3204; Ted Hibbeler, Director
Grades 9-12. *Description*: Program focuses on the wellness of our Native American students. Creates activities that will insure the academic success, career development, cultural awareness, environmental preservation & healthy lifestyles of our Native American students in the Phoenix Union High School District. *Advisors*: Deanna Talayumptewa, Sam Hogue & Bernice Begay

Scottsdale Unified School District #48
Indian Education Program, 3811 N. 44th St. • Phoenix, AZ 85018

Washington Elementary School District
Indian Education Program, 8610 N. 19th Ave. • Phoenix, AZ 85201

Pinon Unified School District #4
Indian Education Program, P.O. Box 839 • Pinon, AZ 86510

Prescott Unified School District
Indian Education Program, 146 S. Granite St. • Prescott, AZ 86303

Sacaton Public Schools #18
Indian Education Program, P.O. Box 98 • Sacaton, AZ 85247

San Carlos School District
Indian Education Program, P.O. Box 207 • San Carlos, AZ 85550

Sanders Unified School District
Indian Education Program, P.O. Box 250 • Sanders, AZ 86515

Indian Oasis Baboquivari USD #40
Indian Education Program, P.O. Box 248 • Sells, AZ 85634

Snowflake Unified School District
Indian Education Program • Snowflake, AZ 85937
Pearl Evans, Contact

Stanfield Elementary School District
Indian Education Program; P.O Box 578 • Stanfield, AZ 85272

Red Mesa Unified School District
Indian Education Program, HCR 6100, Box 40 • Teec Nos Pos, AZ 86514

Kyrene Elementary School Dist. #28
Indian Education Program, 8700 S. Kyrene Rd. • Tempe, AZ 85284

Tempe School District No. 3
Indian Education Program, 2020 Carson Dr. • Tempe, AZ 85282
(480) 730-7411; Ronald Stiffarm, Coordinator
E-mail: rstiffar@tempeschools.org

Tempe Union High School District
Indian Education Program, 500 W. Guadalupe Rd. • Tempe, AZ 85283
(480) 838-3200 x40068; Valerie Molina, Coordinator

Union Elementary School District
Indian Education Program, 3834 S. 91st Ave. • Tolleson, AZ 85353

Tolleson Union High School District
Indian Education Program, 9419 W. Van Buren • Tolleson, AZ 85353

Tuba City High School Board
Indian Education Program, Box 160 • Tuba City, AZ 86045

Amphitheater School District
Indian Education Program, 701 W. Wetmore • Tucson, AZ 85705

Santa Rosa Ranch School
Indian Education Program, HCO4 #7570 • Tucson, AZ 85735

Sunnyside Unified School District
Indian Education Program, 2238 E. Ginter Rd. • Tucson, AZ 85706
(520) 741-2500 ext. 573; Sandy Lucas Tevis, Director
Grades K-12. *Description*: Provides mentoring, tutoring, service learning, cultural awareness, counseling.

Tucson Unified School District
Indian Education Program, P.O. Box 40400 • Tucson, AZ 85717

Tuba City Unified School District
Indian Education Program, P.O. Box 67 • Tuba City, AZ 86045
Chee Benally, Contact

White Mountain Apache Tribe
Indian Education Program, P.O. Box 999 • Whiteriver, AZ 85941
(928) 338-6080 Fax 338-1183; Harrison DeClay, Coordinator

Whiteriver Unified School Dist. #20
Indian Education Program, P.O. Box 190 • Whiteriver, AZ 85941

Winslow Unified School District
Indian Education Program, P.O. Box 580 • Winslow, AZ 86047
(928) 288-8368 Fax 288-8295
Denise Estudillo, Title VII JOM Director

CALIFORNIA

Alpine Union School District
Indian Education Program, 1323 Administration Way • Alpine, CA 92001

Viejas Indian School
P.O. Box 1389 • Alpine, CA 91903
(619) 445-4938 Fax 445-8912; Robert Brown, Director

Modoc Joint Unified School District
Indian Education Program, 906 West 4th St. • Alturas, CA 96101

Anderson Union High School
Indian Education Program, 1471 Perry St. • Anderson, CA 96007

Cascade Union Elementary District
Indian Education Program, 1645 W. Mill St. • Anderson, CA 96007

Happy Valley Union School District
Indian Education Program, 7480 Palm Ave. • Anderson, CA 96007

Auberry Union Elem. School District
Indian Education Program, 33367 N. Auberry Rd. • Auberry, CA 93602

Golden Hills School District
Indian Education Program, 33367 N. Auberry • Auberry, CA 93602

Placer Union High School District
Indian Education Program, P.O. Box 5048 • Auburn, CA 95603

Banning Unified School District
Indian Education Program, 161 W. Williams • Banning, CA 92220

Barstow Unified School District
Indian Education Program, 551 S. Avenue H • Barstow, CA 92311

Big Pine Unified School District
Indian Education Program, 500 S. Main St. • Big Pine, CA 93513

Bishop Union High School District
Indian Education Program, 301 N. Fowler St. • Bishop, CA 93514

Bonsall Union School District
Indian Education Program, P.O. Box 3 • Bonsall, CA 92003

Mountain Empire USD Campo/Clover Flat Elementary Schools
31360 Hwy. 94 • Campo, CA 91906
 (619) 478-2735 Fax 478-2609
 Steve Gordon, Special Projects Coordinator
Grades PreK-5. Serves about 50 Native American students
from the Campo, Manzanita, and La Posta Reservations.

San Juan Unified School District
Indian Education Program, 3738 Walnut Ave. • Carmichael, CA 95608
 (916) 971-5206; Isabel Johnson, Contact
Grades K-12. Indian cultural curriculum.

Surprise Valley Joint USD
Indian Education Program, P.O. Box 28-F • Cedarville, CA 96104

Ceres Unified School District
Indian Education Program, P.O. Box 307 • Ceres, CA 95307

ABC Unified School District
Indian Education Program, 16700 Norwalk Blvd. • Cerritos, CA 90701

Butte County Office of Education - Four Winds Charter School
Indian Education Program, 2345 Fair St. • Chico, CA 95928
 (530) 879-7411 Fax 879-7414
 Terri Tozier, Principal; E-mail: ttozier@bcoe.org
 Betty Jo Smith, Executive Director

Konocti School District
Indian Education Program, P.O. Box 577 • Clearlake Oaks, CA 95422

Colfax Elementary School
Indian Education Program, 24825 Ben Taylor Rd. • Colfax, CA 95713
Grades K-8. *Description*: Provides tutoring services, cultural activities
and education of Indian customs and heritage.

Colusa County School Districts
Native American Education Program
345-5th St., Suite C • Colusa, CA 95932
 (530) 458-0305; Joan Saltzen, Director
Grades K-12. *Description*: Promotes cultural awareness activities, and parental
involvement; monitors Native American students grades and attendance; and
acts as a resource center for the general public. *Instructor*: Serena Morrow,
Resource Specialist.

Round Valley Elementary School
Indian Education Program, P.O. Box 276 • Covelo, CA 95428
 (707) 983-6175 ext. 202 Fax 983-6377; Joy Mubleck, Principal
Grades PreK-5. Serves Native American students from the tribes represented
from the Round Valley Reservation. Emphasis is put on reading, language &
storytelling.

Del Norte County Unified School District
Indian Education Program
301 W. Washington Blvd. • Crescent City, CA 95531
Butte County Office of Education
Indian Education Program, 5 A County Center Dr. • Croville, CA 95965

Jefferson School District
Indian Education Program, 101 Lincoln Way • Daly City, CA 94015

Capistrano Unified School District
Indian Education Program, 24242 La Cresta Dr. • Dana Point, CA 92629
 (949) 248-7037 Fax 248-5507; Lois Madson, Coordinator
 Website: www.capousd.K12.ca.us/indian_ed
Grades K-12. *Description*: Over 600 American Indian students are enrolled.
Provides tutoring services, cultural activities & education of Indian customs &
heritage. Lobo Lodge: a hands-on, multimedia exhibit about the American
Indian experience, with presentations for all grade levels. *Instructor*: Martyne
Van Hofwegen.

Escondido Union High School District
Indian Education Program, 240 S. Maple St. • Escondido, CA 92025

Eureka City Schools
Indian Education Program, 3200 Walford Ave. • Eureka, CA 95501
 (707) 441-2454 Fax 445-1956; Sandra Burton, Director
Grades K-12. *Description*: Provides tutoring services & cultural enrichment
programs.

Fallbrook Union High School
Indian Education Program, 2400 S. Stagecoach Lane • Fallbrook, CA 92028

Farmersville Elementary School District
Indian Education Program, 281 S. Farmersville Blvd. • Farmersville, CA 93223

Fontana Unified School District
Indian Education Program, 9453 Citrus Ave. • Fontana, CA 92335

Fortuna Union High School District
Indian Education Program, 379 12th St. • Fortuna, CA 95540

Fresno Unified School District
Indian Education Program-Title VII, 2348 Mariposa St. • Fresno, CA 93726
 (559) 457-3634 Fax 457-3641; Margarita Villareal, Program Manager
 Frolyn Ramirez, Program Director
Grades Pre-school to 12th grade. *Description*: To assist American Indian
students by referrals to appropriate assistance programs; cultural enrichment
classes; cultural awareness - classroom presentations; activities to meet the
culturally related academic needs of Native American children. Instructors:
Cecelia DeAnda (school/community liaison (559) 457-3949; E-mail:
cxdeand@fresno.k12.ca.us).

Southern Humboldt USD
Indian Education Program, P.O. Box 129 • Garberville, CA 95542

Garden Grove Unified School District
Indian Education Program, 10331 Stanford Ave. • Garden Grove, CA 92640

Siskiyou Union H.S. District
Indian Education Program, P.O. Box 437 • Happy Camp, CA 96039

Hemet Unified School District
Indian Education Program, 2350 W. Latham Ave. • Hemet, CA 92343

Klamath-Trinity Unified School District
Hoopa Valley Elementary River Schools, P.O. Box 1308 • Hoopa, CA 95546
 (530) 625-4223 Fax 625-4697; Jennifer George-Lane, Principal

Klamath-Trinity Joint Unified School District
Indian Education Resource Center, P.O. Box 1308 • Hoopa, CA 95546
 (530) 625-4412 Fax 625-4697; Website: www.humboldt.k12.ca.us
 Sarah Supahan, Program Director
Grades K-12. Description: Dedicated to producing Native American cultural
curriculum materials of the highest quality that address the state standards;
tutoring. *Instructors*: Sarah Supahan, Sherlee Preston, Irene Treesong,
Cinnamon Rogers, Billie Sanderson. *Publications*: Indians of Northwest
California - a 12-unit binder which can be integrated into language, literature,
social studies, science & math curriculum. Children's books in Hupa, Karuk,
Yurok & English. All material was locally written & illustrated. Videos produced:
The Theft of Fire; How Panther Got Tear Marks; Karuk Basketmakers-A Way
of Life; Why Coyote Has the Best Eyes; Tribal Law.

Huntington Beach Union School District
Indian Education Program; Michael Folsom (Choctaw), Director
10251 Yorktown Ave. • Huntington Beach, CA 92646

Lake County Office of Education
Indian Education Program, 1152 S. Main St. • Lakeport, CA 95453

Barona Indian Charter School
1095 Barona Rd. • Lakeside, CA 92040
  (619) 443-0948 Fax 443-7280
  Austin McKeever, Principal; E-mail: amckeever@mybics.org
Grades: K-8. Enrollment: 100. The school continues to serve the Native-American student population as well as students from the surrounding communities of Lakeside, El Cajon, Poway, San Diego Country Estates, Ramona, and Santee. Currently, twenty-four Native-American students are enrolled with an additional sixty-four students attending from the neighboring communities. Established 2002.

Lakeside Union School District
Indian Education Program, P.O. Box 578 • Lakeside, CA 92040

Laytonville Unified School District-Laytonville Elementary School
Indian Education Program, P.O. Box 868 • Laytonville, CA 95454
  (707) 466-6200 Fax 984-8066; Paul Jones Poulton, Coordinator
Grades PreK-4. Serves about 45 students from the Laytonville Rancheria.

Lemoore Union School District
Indian Education Program, 101 E. Bush St. • Lemoore, CA 93245

Livermore Valley Joint Union School District
Indian Education Program, 685 E. Jack London Blvd. • Livermore, CA 94550

Long Beach Unified School District
Indian Education Program, 1400 East 20th St. • Long Beach, CA 90806
  Carol Pratt, Program Administrator; (562) 997-8047
  E-mail: cpratt@lbschools.net
  Kathy Leonard, Program Supervisor; (562) 218-1244
  E-mail: kleonard@lbschools.net

Los Angeles Unified School District
Indian Education Program, P.O. Box 513307 • Los Angeles, CA 90051
  (213) 241-7066 Fax 241-8035
  John Orendorff, Coordinator; E-mail: john.orendorff@lausd.net
  Sandra Franks, Consultant; E-mail: Sandra.franks@lausd.net
Grades K-12. *Description*: Provides cultural & academic enrichment programs for American Indian & Native Alaskan students.

Lone Pine Unified School District
Indian Education Program, P.O. Box 159 • Lone Pine, CA 93545

Mariposa Co. Unified School District
Indian Education Program, P.O. Box 127 • Mariposa, CA 95338

Alpine County Unified School District
Diamond Valley Elementary School
Indian Education Program, 43 Hawkside Dr. • Markleeville, CA 96120
  (530) 694-2238 Fax 694-2379; Deirdre Wallace, Coordinator

Contra Costa Area U.S.D.
Title VII Indian Education Program, 4105 Pacheco Blvd. • Martinez, CA 94553
  (925) 313-0430

Marysville Joint Unified School District
Dobbins/Yuba-Feather Elementary Schools
Indian Education Program, 1919 B St. • Marysville, CA 95901
  (530) 749-6195 Fax 742-0573; James D. Graham, Coordinator
Grades 1-4. Serves more than 75 Native American children, mostly from the Blackfeet, Cherokee, Choctaw, Maidu, Miwok, and Mono nations. Focuses on the use of technology & cooperative learning.

McKinleyville High School
Indian Education Program, 1300 Murray Rd. • McKinleyville, CA 95521

Placer Hills Union School District
Indian Education Program, P.O. Box 68 • Meadow Vista, CA 95722

Milpitas/Berryessa/Oak Grove School Districts
Indian Education Program, 1331 E. Calaveras Blvd. • Milpitas, CA 95035
  (408) 945-2387; Nicholas V. Comella, Contact
Grades K-12. Programs: Provides referral services, tutorial services, cultural classes, student advocacy, and parent training.

Mountain Union School District
Indian Education Program, Box 368 • Montgomery Creek, CA 96065

Napa Valley Unified School District
Indian Education Program, 2425 Jefferson St. • Napa, CA 94558

Needles Unified School District
Indian Education Program, 1900 Erin Dr. • Needles, CA 92363

Newcastle Elementary School District
Indian Education Program, Valley View Dr. • Newscastle, CA 95658

Chawanakee Joint School District
North Fork Elementary School, P.O. Box 707 • North Fork, CA 93643
  (559) 877-2215 Fax 877-2377; Gary Hudson, Principal
Grades PreK-4. Services 70 students from the Mono Tribe.
Provides in-class assistance in reading, language, and mathematics.

Twin Ridges Elementary School District
Indian Education Program, P.O. Box 529 • North San Juan, CA 95960

Oakland Unified School District
Indian Education Program, 1025 Second Ave. • Oakland, CA 94606

Orange Unified School District
Indian Education Program, 370 North Glassell • Orange, CA 92666

Oroville Union High School District
Indian Education Program, 2211 Washington Ave. • Oroville, CA 95966

Vivian Banks Charter School
Pala Band of Mission Indians, P.O. Box 80 • Pala, CA 92059
  (760) 742-3300 Fax 742-3102; Barbara Rohrer, Principal
  Grades K-12.

Palermo Union Elementary School District
Indian Education Program, 7350 Bulldog Way • Palermo, CA 95968

Palm Springs Unified School District
Indian Education Program; Sandia Williams, Contact
980 E. Tahquitz Canyon Way • Palm Springs, CA 92262

Valley Center-Pauma USD - Pauma Elementary School
Indian Education Program, P.O. Box 409 • Pauma Valley, CA 92061
  (760) 742-3741 Fax 742-1214; Olivia Leschick, Coordinator

Penryn Elementary School District
Indian Education Program, P.O. Box 349 • Penryn, CA 95663

Pittsburg Unified School District
Indian Education Program, 2000 Railroad Ave. • Pittsburg, CA 94565

El Dorado County Office of Education
Indian Education Program, 6767 Green Valley Rd. • Placerville, CA 95667
  (530) 622-7130 Fax 621-2543

Porterville Public Schools
Indian Education Program, 589 W. Vine • Porterville, CA 93257

Plumas Unified School District
Indian Education Program • Portola, CA 96122

Ramona Unified School District
Indian Education Program, 415 8th St. • Ramona, CA 92065
  (619) 788-5010; Pauline Parker, Director
Grades K-12. Provides tutorial, career guidance, financial aid information, and cultural awareness programs.

Gateway Unified School District - Toyon Elementary School
4411 Mountain Lakes Blvd. • Redding, CA 96003
  (530) 245-7982 Fax 245-7990; Judy Welcome, Coordinator
Grades PreK-4. *Program*: Baskets program provides language arts & math support to about 50 Native American children, mostly from the Wintu and Pit River tribes. After school program; tutorial support; cultural activities.

Richmond Unified School District
Indian Education Program, P.O. Box 4014 • Richmond, CA 94802

Buena Vista Child Development Center
1412 20th St. • Sacramento, CA 95811
  (916) 446-1200; Website: www.buenavistacdc.com

Amber Liacuna-Benavente, Director
Preschool-K. Serves low-income Native American children ages 2 through kindergarten and is owned by the Buena Vista Rancheria of Me-Wuk Indians. *Publication*: Monthly newsletter.

Sacramento City USD
American Indian Education Program, Caroline Wenzel Elementary School
6870 Greenhaven Dr., Rm. 22 • Sacramento, CA 95831
 (916) 643-9364

San Bernardino City USD
Indian Education Program, 777 North F St. • San Bernardino, CA 92410

San Diego Unified School District
Indian Education Program, 6880 Mohawk St., Rm. 3 • San Diego, CA 92115

San Francisco Public Schools - Buena Vista/Horace Mann K-8
Indian Education Program, 3351 23rd St. • San Francisco, CA 94110
 (415) 379-7770

Alum Rock Union Elementary School District
Indian Education Program, 2930 Gay Ave. • San Jose, CA 95127

East Side Union High School District
Indian Education Program, 830 N. Capital Ave. • San Jose, CA 95133
 (408) 272-6445

Oak Grove Elementary School District
Indian Education Program, 6578 Santa Teresa Blvd. • San Jose, CA 95119

San Lorenzo Unified School District
Indian Education Program, 15510 Usher St. • San Lorenzo, CA 94580
 (510) 317-4709

San Marcos Jr. High School
Indian Education Program, 650 W. Mission Rd. • San Marcos, CA 92069

Santa Clara Unified School District
Indian Education Program, P.O. Box 397 • Santa Clara, CA 95052

Mark West Union School District
Indian Education Program, 5187 Old Redwood Hwy. • Santa Rosa, CA 95401

Roseland School District
Indian Education Program, 950 Sebastopol Rd. • Santa Rosa, CA 95407

Santa Rosa City Schools
Indian Education Program, 211 Ridgway Ave. • Santa Rosa, CA 95401

Sebastopol Union Schools
Indian Education Program, 7611 Huntley St. • Sebastopol, CA 95472

Sonora Union High School
Indian Education Program, 251 S. Baretta St. • Sonora, CA 95370

San Mateo Co. Office of Education
Indian Education Program, 227 Arroyo Dr. • S. San Francisco, CA 94080

Stockton Unified School District
Native American Indian Center, 1425 S. Center • Stockton, CA 95206
 (209) 953-4803; Dale Fleming, Director
Grades K-12. *Description*: Provides tutoring, counseling, and cultural heritage programs; Native American science program. *Instructors*: Terri Johnson, Alberta Snyder, Rosalinda Fleming, Caroline Wilson.

Fremont Union High School District
Indian Education Program, P.O. Box F • Sunnyvale, CA 94087

Lassen Union High School District
Indian Education Program, 1110 Main St. • Susanville, CA 96130

Susanville Elem. School District
Indian Education Program, 2005 4th St. • Susanville, CA 96130

Coachella Valley Unified School District
Indian Education Program, P.O. Box 847 • Thermal, CA 92274

Sierra Union School District - Sierra Elementary School
Indian Education Program, 27444 E. Tollhouse Rd. • Tollhouse, CA 93667
 (559) 855-2332 Fax 855-2016
 Brad Barcus, Principal; E-mail: bbarcus@sierra.k12.ca.us

Tracy Public Schools
Indian Education Program, 315 E. 11th St. • Tracy, CA 95376

Summerville Elementary School District
Indian Education Program, 18451 Carter St. • Tuolumne, CA 95379

Summerville Union High School
Indian Education Program, 17555 Tuolumne Rd. • Tuolumne, CA 95379

Ukiah Unified School District
Indian Education Program, 925 N. State St. • Ukiah, CA 95482

Vacaville Unified School District
Indian Education Program, 751 School St. • Vacaville, CA 95688

Ventura Unified School District
Indian Education Program, 255 W. Stanley Ave. #100 • Ventura, CA 93001
 (805) 641-5000; Dr. Michele Dean, Coordinator
 E-mail: Michele.dean@venturausd.org

Warner School District
Indian Education Program, P.O. Box 8 • Warner Springs, CA 92086

Trinity County Office of Education
Burnt Ranch/Hayfork Elementary Schools
Indian Education Program, P.O. Box 1256 • Weaverville, CA 96093
 (530) 623-2861 Fax 623-4489; E-mail: sallyald@tcoek12.org
 Sally Aldinger, Coordinator
Grades PreK-4. Serves about 45 Native American children from the Chimanko, Lassik, Tsnungwe, Wintu, and Wylacki tribes; provides reading, language arts and math. Includes tutorials and language instruction in Tsnungwe.

Washington Unified School District
Indian Education Program, 930 West Acres Rd., W. Sacramento, CA 95691
 (916) 371-9300 ext. 70; Sarah Taylor, Director
Grades 5-9. *Description*: Provides academic, cultural and advisory services for about 150 Indian students enrolled in the program. *Instructor*: Lori L. Rigney.

Westminster School District
Indian Education Program, 14121 Cedarwood Ave. • Westminster, CA 92683

San Pasqual Valley USD
Indian Education Program, Rte. 1, 676 Baseline Rd. • Winterhaven, CA 92283

Yreka Union School District
Indian Education Program, 405 Jackson St. • Yreka, CA 96097

COLORADO

Adams-Arapahoe School District
Indian Education Program, 15700 East 1st Ave. • Aurora, CO 80011
 (303) 340-0510 ext. 302; Dr. D Woods, Director; Joyce Vigil, Coordinator
Grades K-12. *Description*: Provides academic, cultural enrichment, counseling and tutoring services for American Indian children in the Aurora schools. *Instructors*: American Indian artists, elders and scholars.

MCREL
Indian Education Program, 2550 S. Parker Rd., Suite 500 • Aurora, CO 80014

Boulder Valley School District
Indian Education Program, P.O. Box 9011 • Boulder, CO 80301

Colorado Springs School District 11
Indian Education Program, 1115 N. El Paso St. • Colorado Springs, CO 80903
 (719) 520-2145; Lynda Espinoza-Idle, Title VII Administrator
 Raika Payvar, Middle School Title VII Liaison

Montezuma Cortez District RE-1
Indian Education Program, P.O. Drawer R • Cortez, CO 81321

Colorado Dept. of Education
Indian Education Program, 201 E. Colfax Ave. • Denver, CO 80203

Denver Public Schools
Indian Education Program, 1330 Fox St., 2nd Floor • Denver, CO 80204
 (720) 423-8171 Fax 423-8167
 Rose Marie McGuire (Sisseton-Wahpeton Oyate), Manager
 E-mail: rose_mcguire@dpsk12.org
 Kathryn Redhorse, Education Specialist
 E-mail: Kathryn_redhorse@dpsk12.org

Mapleton Public Schools
Indian Education Program, 501 E. 80th Ave. • Denver, CO 80229

Cherry Creek School District
Indian Education Program, 4700 S. Yosemite St. • Englewood, CO 80111

Jeffco Public Schools
Indian Education Program, 1829 Denver West Dr. • Golden, CO 80401
  (303) 982-0388; Thompson Williams, Program Coordinator
  E-mail: towillia@jeffco.k12.co.us

Ignacio United School District
Indian Education Program, P.O. Box 460 • Ignacio, CO 81137

St. Vrain Valley School District
Indian Education Program, 395 S. Pratt Pkwy. • Longmont, CO 80501

CONNECTICUT

Bridgeport Board of Education
Indian Education Program, 45 Lyon Ter., Rm. 318 • Bridgeport, CT 06604

FLORIDA

Hendry County School District
Indian Education Program, 475 E. Osceola St. • Clewiston, FL 33440

Broward County School District
Indian Education Program, 701 N. 31st Ave. • Ft. Lauderdale, FL 33311

Collier County Public Schools
Indian Education Program, 3710 Estey Ave. • Naples, FL 33942

Okeechobee County. School District
Brighton Reservation, 700 SW 2nd Ave. • Okeechobee, FL 34974

IDAHO

American Falls School District #381
Indian Education Program, 827 Fort Hall Ave. • American Falls, ID 83211

Blackfoot School District #55
Indian Education Program, 270 E. Bridge • Blackfoot, ID 83221

Idaho State Department of Education
Native American Education Program, 650 W. State St. • Boise, ID 83720
  (208) 332-8800 Fax 334-2228; Shirley Spencer, Contact

Boundary Co. School District #101
Indian Education Program, P.O. Box 899 • Bonners Ferry, ID 83805

Shoshone-Bannock Jr./Sr. High School
P.O. Box 790 • Fort Hall, ID 83203
  (208) 238-4300 Fax 238-2628; Website: www.shoban.com
  Jim Philips, Principal; E-mail: jphilips@shoban.com
Grades 7-12. State accredited Jr./Sr. high school. Instructors: Kris Hansen, Ed Galindo, Tim Norton, Ramon Murillo, Roseanne Abrahamson, Barbara Hakiel, Frank Pebeahsy, Anna Ridley, June Ward, Don Pine, Adele Stacey, Ben Bloom, William Burns, Danielle Gunn, Pam Davis, Amy Snow.

Kamiah School District #304
Indian Education Program, P.O. Box 877 • Kamiah, ID 83536

Lapwai School District #341
Indian Education Program, P.O. Box 247 • Lapwai, ID 83540

Lewiston Independent School District #1
Indian Education Program, 3317 12th St., T-12 South • Lewiston, ID 83501
  (208) 748-3000 Fax 748-3059; Website: www.lewiston.k12.id.us
  Dawn Leighton, Coordinator, Indian Education
Description: Cultural enrichment activities K-12, tutoring K-6, career awareness and higher educational counseling, 7-12.

W. Benawah School District #42
Indian Education Program, P.O. Box 130 • Plummer, ID 83851

Bannock Co. School District #25
Indian Education Program, P.O. Box 1390 • Pocatello, ID 83204

Worley School District #275
Indian Education Program, P.O. Box 98 • Worley, ID 83876

ILLINOIS

Stockton Elementary School
Chicago Public Schools - Native American Resource Center
Title VII Indian Education Program
4420 N. Beacon, Rm. 221 • Chicago, IL 60640
  (773) 534-2874 Fax 334-5234
  Website: www.chicagotitlevii.org
  Jolene Aleck, Program Manager; E-mail: jfaleck@cps.edu
  Ernest M. Whiteman III, Specialist
  Isaac Salgado, Teacher, Yates Elementary School
Grades PreK-6. Offers services to all Native American students within the Chicago Public Schools; and a Native American studies class at Audubon Elementary School. *CAIEC (Chicago American Indian Education Council*: Norma Robertson & Ian Stroud, Community Representatives. Newsletter.

INDIANA

South Bend Community Schools
Indian Education Program, 635 S. Main St. • South Bend, IN 46635

IOWA

Davenport Community School District
Federal Program Coordinator
1002 W. Kimberly Rd. • Davenport, IA 52806
  (319) 386-0404; Denise Jensen, Title V Liaison

Sioux City Community Schools
Indian Education Program, 1221 Pierce St. • Sioux City, IA 51105

South Tama County Community Schools
Indian Education Program, 1702 Harding St. • Tama, IA 52339

KANSAS

Arkansas City Schools - USD #470
Indian Education Program, 420 South 5th • Arkansas City, KS 67005
  (620) 441-2000 Fax 441-2009; Glenn Clarkson, Director
Grades K-12. Provides school-home liaison.

Coffeyville Public School
Indian Education Program, 7th & Ellis • Coffeyville, KS 67337

South Brown County, USD #430
Indian Education Program, 522 Central • Horton, KS 66439
  (785) 486-2611 Fax 486-2496; Dr. Steven J. Davies, Superintendent
Grades K-12. Instructor: Viki Stone. *Program*: Tutorial program.

Royal Valley U.S.D. #337
Indian Education Program, P.O. Box 155 • Mayetta, KS 66509
  (785) 966-2251 or 986-6251 Fax (785) 986-6479
  Anita Evans, Director
Grades K-12. *Description*: Provides tutoring services, cultural enrichment programs, and guidance counseling. *Instructors*: Anita Evans, Connie Peters

U.S.D. #321 Kaw Valley Special Services
P.O. Box 578 - 303 E. Hwy. 24 • Rossville, KS 66533
  (785) 584-6731 Fax 584-6720
  Dorothy Rockefeller, PhD, Director
Grades K-12. *Description*: Provides tutoring in academic areas, cultural enrichment with related activities, & developing a plan for employment or education after graduation. Approximately 30 identified Native Americans in the district enrollment.

Topeka Public Schools
Native American Indian Education Program
2751 SW E. Circle Dr. S • Topeka, KS 66606
  (785) 295-3953

Wichita Public School
Native American Indian Education Program
Joyce Focht Instructional Support Center, 412 S. Main • Wichita, KS 67202
  (316) 973-5192; Jeff Watkins, Director

LOUISIANA

Rapides Parish School District
Indian Education Program, P.O. Box 1230 • Alexandria, LA 71309

Jefferson Parish School District
Indian Education Program, 501 Manhattan Blvd. • Harvey, LA 70058

Terrebonne Parish School District
Indian Education Program, 301 Academy St. • Houma, LA 70360
  (985) 851-1553 Fax 868-6278
  Gerald Picou, Director; Kirby Verret, Coordinator
Grades: K-12. *Description*: Provides tutoring, & improve attendance,
academic achievement, and cultural knowledge of Indian students.

LaSalle Parish School District
Indian Education Program, P.O. Drawer 90 • Jena, LA 71342

Sabine Parish School District
Indian Education Program, P.O. Box 1079 • Many, LA 71449

Allen Parish School District
Indian Education Program, P.O. Drawer C • Oberlin, LA 70655

Terrebonne Parish School
Indian Education Program, 2247 Brady Rd. • Theriot, LA 70397

Lafourche Parish School Board
Indian Education Program, P.O. Box 879 • Thibodeaux, LA 70302

MAINE

Indian Township School
Maine Indian Education, P.O. Box 412 • Calais, ME 04619
  Linda Leotsakos, Principal; Brian Smith, Supt.

Maine School Admin. District 29
Indian Education Program, P.O. Box 190 • Houlton, ME 04730

MARYLAND

Baltimore City Schools - Hampstead Hill Middle School
Indian Education Program, 101 S. Ellwood Ave. • Baltimore, MD 21224

Baltimore City Public Schools
Indian Education Program, 200 E. North Ave. • Baltimore, MD 21202

Charles Co. Board of Education
Indian Education Program, Box D • LaPlata, MD 20646

P.G. Co. Public Schools - Oxon Hill Staff Development Center
Indian Education Program, 7711 Livingstone • Oxon Hill, MD 20745

Montgomery Co. Public Schools
American Indian Education Program, 4910 Macon Rd. • Rockville, MD 20852
  (301) 230-0659

P.G. Co. Public Schools
Indian Education Program
14201 School Lane, Sasser Bldg. • Upper Marlboro, MD 20772

MASSACHUSETTS

Boston Public Schools
Indian Education Program, 26 Court St. • Boston, MA 02108

Martha's Vineyard Schools
Indian Education Program, RR 1, Box 161B • Gayhead, MA 02535

Mashpee School District
Indian Education Program, 150 Old Barnstable Rd. • Mashpee, MA 02649

Martha's Vineyard Schools
Indian Education Program;
Regional HS, Edgartown Rd. • Oak Bluffs, MA 02557

MICHIGAN

Avondale School District
Indian Education Program, 2950 Waukegan • Auburn Hills, MI 48326

Bay City Public Schools
Indian Education's Turtle Shell Program
407 West Ohio • Bay City, MI 48706
  (989) 667-4015 Fax 667-4015
  Sandi Dezelah, Program Manager

Brighton Area Schools
Indian Education Program, 4740 Bauer Rd. • Brighton, MI 48116

Brighton Area Schools
Indian Education Program, 125 S. Church St. • Brighton, MI 48116

Brimley Area Schools
Indian Education Program, P.O. Box 156 • Brimley, MI 49715

Les Cheneaux Community Schools
Indian Education Program, P.O. Box 366 • Cedarville, MI 49719

Chippewa Valley Schools
Indian Education Program
19120 Cass Ave. • Clinton Township, MI 48038
  (586) 723-2031 Fax 723-2021; Maria Chisholm, Facilitator
  E-mail: mchisholm@cvs.k12.mi.us

Big Bay de Noc School
Indian Education Program, HC 01, Box 62• Cooks, MI 49817
  (906) 644-2773 ext. 120 Fax 644-2615
  Colleen Weinert, Coordinator
Grades K-12. *Description*: Provides tutoring services, cultural activities
and education of Native American customs and heritage.

Davison School District
Indian Education Program, 1250 N. Oak St. • Davison, MI 48423
  (810) 591-3531 ext. 300 Fax 591-0918; Linda DeCamp, Coordinator
Grades K-12. *Description*: Title VII Indian Education Program providing
academic & cultural classes to Native American students.

Detroit Public Schools
Indian Education Program, 5057 Woodward Ave. • Detroit, MI 48202

East Jordan Public Schools
Indian Education Program, P.O. Box 399 • East Jordan, MI 49727

Mason Consolidated School District
Indian Education Program, 2400 Lakeside Rd. • Erie, MI 48133

Escanaba Area Public Schools
Indian Education Program, 1500 Ludington St. • Escanaba, MI 49829
  (906) 786-7462 ext. 213; E-mail: indianed@eskymos.com
  Robin Menard, Coordinator
Grades K-12. *Instructors*: Robin Menard & Peggy Derwin.

Algonac Community Schools - FH Elementary School
Indian Education Program, A361 Broad Bridge • Fair Haven, MI 48023

Hazel Park Schools
Indian Education Program
1700 Shevlin, Edison School • Ferndale, MI 48220

Carman-Ainsworth/Westwood Heights
Native American Education Program
Carmen-Ainsworth Support Services Center
5089 Pilgrim Rd. • Flint, MI 48507
  (810) 768-4970; Jean Keen, Specialist

Beecher Community School District
Indian Education Program, 1020 W. Coldwater Rd. • Flint, MI 48505

Flint City School District
Indian Education Program, 2421 Corunna Rd. • Flint, MI 48503
  (810) 760-1562 Fax 760-1898; Veda D. Balla, Director

Fowlerville Community Schools
Indian Education Program, P.O. Box 769 • Fowlerville, MI 48836

Gladstone School District
Indian Education Program, 400 S. 10th St. • Gladstone, MI 49837

Grand Haven School District
Indian Education Program, 1415 Beech Tree St. • Grand Haven, MI, 49417

Grand Rapids Public Schools
Indian Education Program, 143 Bostwick, NE • Grand Rapids, MI 49503

Grand Rapids Public Schools
Indian Education Program, 615 Turner NW • Grand Rapids, MI 49504

Harbor Springs Schools
Indian Education Program, 327 E. Bluff Dr. • Harbor Springs, MI 49740

Bark River-Harris School District
Indian Education Program, P.O. Box 350 • Harris, MI 49845-0350
  (906) 466-9981 Fax 466-2925; Website: www.dsisd.k12.mi.us/barkriver
  Russell Pirlot, Director/Elem. Principal; Thomas Bartol, Superintendent
Grades K-12. *Description*: Provides tutoring services & cultural activities.
Instructor: Sherry DeBen, Paula Reynolds.

Hart Public Schools
Indian Education Program, 300 Johnson St. • Hart, MI 49420

Hazel Park City School District
Indian Education Program, 23136 Hughes • Hazel Park, MI 48030

Huron Valley Public Schools
Indian Education Program, 5061 Duck Lake Rd. • Highland, MI 48356

Howell Public Schools
Indian Education Program, 511 N. Highlander Way • Howell, MI 48843

Wilson School
Indian Education Program, 100 Helen St. • Inkster, MI 48141

Kalamazoo City Schools
Indian Education Program, 604 W. Vine St. • Kalamazoo, MI 49008

L'Anse Township Schools
Indian Education Program, 201 N. Fourth • L'Anse, MI 49946

Lansing School District
Native American Program, 500 E. Thomas Rd. • Lansing, MI 48906
  (517) 755-5970

Mackinac Island Schools
Indian Education Program; Dan Seeley, Contact
Box 340, Lake Shore Dr. • Mackinac Island, MI 49757

Manistique Area Schools
Indian Education Program, 100 N. Cedar St. • Manistique, MI 49854
  (906) 341-2195 ext. 142; Janet Krueger, Coordinator
Grades K-12. *Description*: Provides tutoring & cultural awareness program.

Marquette Public Schools
Indian Education Program, 1201 W. Fair Ave. • Marquette, MI 49855

Clintondale School District
Indian Education Program, 35300 Little Mack • Mt. Clemens, MI 48043

Mt. Morris Central Schools
Indian Education Program, 1000 Genesee St. • Mt. Morris, MI 48458
  (810) 591-5740; Stephanie Lee, Coordinator
Grades K-12. *Description*: Academic tutoring & cultural awareness. *Instructors*:
Mary Iverson, Sr. High; Linda DeGuise, Jr. High; Sherry Ross, Moore
Elementary; Melissa Iverson, Montague Elementary; Kimberly Galbreath,
Pinehurst Elementary; Tiffany Schultz, Central Elementary.

Mount Morris Consolidated Schools
Indian Education Program, 12356 Walter St. • Mt. Morris, MI 48458

Mount Pleasant Public Schools
Saginaw Chippewa Education Department
7070 E. Broadway • Mt. Pleasant, MI 48858
  Carla Sineway, Director
Grades K-12 & Community College. *Description*: Provides tutoring services,
cultural activities & education of Indian customs & heritage; Ojibway language;
community education.

Munising Public Schools
Indian Education Program, 411 Elm Ave. • Munising, MI 49862
  (906) 387-3861 Fax 387-5311; Kim Swanberg, Director
Grades K-12. *Programs*: Cultural instruction, tutoring, college preparation,
job training & placement. *Instructors*: Kim Swanberg & Marnie Kate Sanders.

Muskegon Hts. School District
Indian Education Program, 2603 Leahy St. • Muskegon, MI 49444

Muskegon Public Schools
Indian Education Program, 1580 Park St. • Muskegon, MI 49440

Anchor Bay School District
Indian Education Program, 33700 Hooker Rd. • New Baltimore, MI 48047

Tahquamenon Area Schools
Indian Education Program, 700 Newberry Ave. • Newberry, MI 49868

Northport Public Schools
Indian Education Program, P.O. Box 188 • Northport, MI 49670

Pellston Public Schools
Indian Education Program, 4644 Tower Rd. • Pellston, MI 49769

Petoskey/Charlevoix Public Schools
Indian Education Program, 1500 Hill St. • Petoskey, MI 49770
  (231) 348-2169 Fax 348-2214; Connie Marshall, Coordinator
  Website: www.petoskeyschools.org/indianeducation
Grades K-12. *Description*: Provides support services to Native American
students K-12. Our major emphasis is academic but we provide referrals to
appropriate agencies for social needs. *Instructors*: Connie Marshall, Diann
Gaylord, Evelyn Chareriat, and Julie Weaver. Tutors: Karen Dickinson & Karen
Rockafellow.

Pontiac City School District
Indian Education Program, 350 E. Wide Track Dr. • Pontiac, MI 48058

Port Huron Area School District
Indian Education Program, 1320 Washington St. • Port Huron, MI 48061
  (810) 989-2727 Fax 984-6624; Sharon L. Kota, Director
Grades K-12. *Description*: Provides academic, cultural enrichment and tutoring
services for American Indian children residing in the district. *Instructors*:
American Indian artists, elders and scholars.

Rapid River Schools/Tri-Township Campus
Indian Education Program, P.O. Box 68 • Rapid River, MI 49878
  (906) 474-6411 Fax 474-9883; E-mail: leskofski@rapidriver.k12.mi.us
  Marlene M. Lollie Eskofski, Coordinator of Indian Education
Grades K-12. *Description*: Tutorial with craft classes; field trips, fun family
activities; Native American presentations; fry bread/blanket dog sales;
sponsors dances; promotes Native American Summer Youth Camps.
Instructors: Lynn D. Hill and M. Lollie Eskofski.

Chippewa Hill Schools
Indian Education Program, 3226 Arthur Rd., Rt. 2 • Remus, MI 49340

Rudyard Public Schools
Indian Education Program, Second & Williams • Rudyard, MI 49780

Sault Ste. Marie Area Public Schools
Indian Education Program, 460 W. Spruce St. • Sault Ste. Marie, MI 49783
  (906) 635-6620 Fax 635-6642; Adel Easterday, Director
Grades K-12. *Description*: Provides tutoring services, cultural activities and
education of Indian customs & heritage. *Instructors*: Mary Kessinger, Patti
O'Shelski.

Lake Shore Schools
Indian Education Consortium, Rodgers Elementary School
21601 L'Anse Ave. • St. Claire Shores, MI 48081
  (586) 285-8930 Fax 285-8933
  Nathan Heier, Director; Angela Dworzecki, Student Services
  E-mail: nheier@lsps.org

St. Ignace Area Schools
Indian Education Program, 840 Portage Rd. • St. Ignace, MI 49781

Suttons Bay Public Schools
Indian Education Program, P.O. Box 367 • Suttons Bay, MI 49682

Swartz Creek Community Schools
Indian Education Program, 8354 Cappy Lane • Swartz Creek, MI 48473
  (810) 591-2312 ext. 252; Cheryl Spaniola, Director
Grades K-12. *Description*: Basic skills reinforcement with culture and Great
Lakes area Native language. Provides academic, cultural enrichment and
tutoring services for American Indian children residing in the district. *Instructor*:
Cheryl Spaniola.

Taylor School District
Indian Education Program, 11010 Janet • Taylor, MI 48180

Taylor School District
Indian Education Program, 9601 Westlake • Taylor, MI 48180

Traverse City Area Public Schools
Indian (Anishinaabe) Education
3962 Three Mile Rd. N. • Traverse City, MI 49686
 (231) 933-5852 Fax 933-5851; E-mail: info@tcaps.net
 Cathy Bingham-Olson, Coordinator; E-mail: binghamca@tcaps.net

Walled Lake Cons. Schools
Indian Education Program, 615 N. Pontiac Trail • Walled Lake, MI 48390

Warren Consolidated Schools
Indian Education Program, 29500 Cosgrove • Warren, MI 48089

Warren Consolidated Schools
Indian Education Program, 2460 Arden • Warren, MI 48092

Watersmeet Township School District
Indian Education Program, C Ave., Box 217 • Watersmeet, MI 49969

Wayne-Westland Community Schools
Indian Education Program, 1225 S. Wildwood • Westland, MI 48185

MINNESOTA

Bemidji ISD
Indian Education Program, Title VII, 201-15th St., NW • Bemidji, MN 56601

Bloomfield Municipal Schools
Indian Education Program, 325 N. Bergin Lane • Bloomfield, MN 87413

Bloomington Public Schools
Indian Education – ISD 271, 4571 West 102nd St. • Bloomington, MN 55437
 (952) 806-7954 Fax 806-7951
 Heidi Hecker, Coordinator; E-mail: hhecker@bloomington.k12.mn.us
 Lisa Benjamin, Support; E-mail: lbenjamin@bloomington.k12.mn.us

Browns Valley Public School
Indian Education Program, P.O. Box N • Browns Valley, MN 56219

Carlton ISD #93
Indian Education Program, P.O. Box 310 • Carlton, MN 55718

Chisholm ISD
Indian Education Program, 300 SW 3rd Ave. • Chisholm, MN 55719

Centennial School District
Indian Education Program, 4707 North Rd. • Circle Pines, MN 55014

Cloquet Public Schools ISD #94
Indian Education Program, 302 14th St. • Cloquet, MN 55720
 (218) 879-6721 Fax 879-6724; E-mail: tgraves@cloquet.k12.mn.us

Greenway Schools ISD #316/319
Coleraine/Mashwauk Office of Indian Education
P.O. Box 520 • Coleraine, MN 55722
 (218) 295-1287 ext. 26; Jean E. Tyz, Director
Grades K-12. Description: Provides academic, cultural enrichment and tutoring services for American Indian children residing in the district. Also, post secondary opportunities. Instructors: Jean E. Tyz, Laurie J. Eide.

Anoka-Hennepin ISD
Indian Education Program, 11299 Hanson Blvd. NW • Coon Rapids, MN 55433

Deer River ISD #317
Indian Education Program, P.O. Box 307 • Deer River, MN 56636

Detroit Lakes ISD #22
Indian Education Program, 702 Lake Ave. • Detroit Lakes, MN 56501

Duluth Public Schools ISD 709
Indian Education Program, 215 N. 1st Ave. E., Rm. 113a • Duluth, MN 55802
 (218) 336-8700 Fax 336-8773; Edye Howes, Coordinator
Grades: Pre-K-12. Description: Provides tutorial after-school programs, bicultural pre-school, post-secondary preparation program, parental costs, advocacy. Instructors: Phyllis Stott, pre-school teacher; Gayle Daniel, Elem.

Ely ISD #696
Indian Education Program, 600 E. Harvey St. • Ely, MN 55731
 (218) 365-6196; Dawn Gerzin, Director
Grades K-12. Description: Provides cultural activities and tutoring.

Eveleth ISD #697
Indian Education Program, 801 Jones St. • Eveleth, MN 55734

Forest Lake Area Schools
Indian Education Program, 6100 North 210th St. • Forest Lake, MN 55025
 (651) 982-8100; Mike Huerth (328-1403)
 Dawn Quigley (982-8781), Carolyn Carr Latady (982-8350)

Fosston ISD #601
Indian Education Program, 301 E. First St. • Fosston, MN 56592
 (218) 435-1909 Fax 435-6340; Dianne Sonstelie, Title IX Director

Frazee/Vergas Public Schools
Indian Education Program, P.O. Box 186 • Frazee, MN 56544

Cook Co. ISD #166
Indian Education Program, P.O. Box 1030 • Grand Marais, MN 55604

Grand Rapids ISD #318
Indian Education Program
820 N. Pokegama Ave. • Grand Rapids, MN 55744
 (218) 326-1409; Caroline Stangel, Coordinator
Grades K-12. Description: Provides academic, special education, language & cultural enrichment, career counseling, placement services, & tutoring services for American Indian children residing in the district. Also, post secondary opportunities. Instructors: Kay Kirt, Carol Solberg, Patty Jo Erven.

Granite Falls Public School
Indian Education Program, 450 Ninth Ave. • Granite Falls, MN 56241

Hibbing ISD #701
Indian Education Program, 8th Ave. E. & 21st St. • Hibbing, MN 55746

Hinckley/Finlayson Public Schools
P.O. Box 308 • Hinkley, MN 55037

Isle School District ISD #473
Indian Education Program, Box 25 • Isle, MN 56342

Kelliher School District #36
Indian Education Program, P.O. Box 259 • Kelliher, MN 56650

Mahnomen Public Schools
Indian Education Program, P.O. Box 319 • Mahnomen, MN 56557
 (218) 935-2211 Fax 935-5921; Mitch Drobnick, Title VII Teacher
 Phyllis Wark & Hailie Brunner, Title VII Tutors

Osseo Area Schools ISD 279
Indian Education Program, 11200 93rd Ave. N. • Maple Grove, MN 55369
 (763) 391-7000 Fax 391-7070; Jan Charwood, Chairperson

McGregor ISD #4
Indian Education Program, P.O. Box 160 • McGregor, MN 55760

Four Winds School
Indian Education Program, 2300 Chicago Ave. S. • Minneapolis, MN 55404

Minneapolis Public Schools
Indian Education Program, 1250 West Broadway • Minneapolis, MN 55411
 (612) 668-0610 Fax 668-0615
 E-mail: indianed@mpls.k12.mn.us
 Danielle Grant, Director (668-0611) Stephanie Volante, Office Manager
 Joe Kingbird, Coordinator, All Nations Program (668-4300)
Resources: Library; Anishinabe Academy. Programs: All Nations Program; Indigenous Language.

Robbinsdale ISD #281
Multicultural Coordinator, 4148 Winnetka Ave. N. • Minneapolis, MN 55427

South West High School
3419 W. 47th St. • Minneapolis, MN 55410

Moorhead Public School
1330 8th Ave. N. • Moorhead, MN 56560
 Mary Jo Schmid, Contact

Mt. Iron/Buhl High School
Indian Education Program, 5720 Mineral Ave. • Mt. Iron, MN 55768
 (218) 735-8216; Renee M. Koski, Director
Grades K-12. *Description*: Offers services to Native American children. These services include resources of books, films, literature, as well as counseling, and tutorial services; cultural activities and education of Indian customs and heritage. Instructor: Sue Arko.

Nett Lake ISD #707
13090 Westley Dr. • Nett Lake, MN 55772

Robinsdale Area Schools, c/o New Hope School
Indian Education Program, 8301 47th Ave. N. • New Hope, MN 55428
 (763) 504-8067; Kenneth O. Turner, Program Director (504-8026)
 E-mail: kenneth_turner@rdale.org
Brenda Peterson (504-8067), Staff; E-mail: Brenda_peterson@rdale.org
Russell Wilkie (504-8066), Staff; E-mail: Russell_wilkie@rdale.org
Tamara Goggleye (504-8087), Staff; E-mail: tamara_goggleye@rdale.org

Onamia ISD #480
Indian Education Program, 35465 - 125th Ave. • Onamia, MN 56359
 (320) 532-4174 ext. 208 Fax 532-4658; Donna J. Burr, Instructor
Grades K-12. *Description*: Facilitate leadership opportunities for Indian students; tutor; language and cultural instructions; conduct monthly parent advisory committee meetings.

Park Rapids ISD #309
Indian Education Dept., P.O. Box 591 • Park Rapids, MN 56470

Pine City Public School
Indian Education Program, 1400 S. 6th St. • Pine City, MN 55063

Pine Poit SD #25
Indian Education Program, P.O. Box 61 • Ponsford, MN 56575

Red Lake ISD #38
Indian Education Program, Red Lake Indian Reservation
P.O. Box 280 • Red Lake, MN 56671
 Chris Dunshee, High School Principal

Red Wing ISD #256
Indian Education Program444 6th St. • Red Wing, MN 55066

Morton Public School District #652
Indian Education Program
100 George Ramseth Dr. • Redwood Falls, MN 56283

Remer ISD #118
Indian Education Program, Rt. 1, Box A • Remer, MN 56672

Rochester ISD #535
Indian Education Program, 615 SW 7th St. • Rochester, MN 55902

Eagan Public Schools
3455 153rd St. W • Rosemount, MN 55068
 (651) 423-7700

St. Louis Co. School ISD #706
Indian Education Program, P.O. Box 128 • Saginaw, MN 55779

Virginia ISD #706
Indian Education Program, Tech Bldg./5th Ave. S. • St. Louis, MN 55792

Mounds View School Dist. #621
Indian Education Program, 2959 Hamline Ave. • St. Paul, MN 55113

St. Paul Public Schools
American Indian Education Program
65 E. Kellogg Blvd. • St. Paul, MN 55119
 (651) 293-5191 Fax 293-5193
 Kathy Denman-Wilke, Supervisor

Sandstone Public Schools
Indian Education Program, Court Ave. at 5th St. • Sandstone, MN 55072

Shakopee ISD #720
Indian Education Program, 505 S. Holmes St. • Shakopee, MN 55379

Stillwater ISD #834
Indian Education Program, 1875 S. Greeley St. • Stillwater, MN 55082

Thief River Falls ID #564
Indian Education Program, 808 S. Crocker • Thief River Falls, MN 56701

Tower ISD #708
Indian Education Program, P.O. Box 469 • Tower, MN 55790

Virginia Public Schools
411 South 5th Ave. • Virginia, MN 55792
 (218) 742-3949; Dorothy Oie, Director
 E-mail: djoie@virginia.k12.mn.us
 Michele Maki, Academic Advisor; Email: mmaki@vmps.org
 Sarah Strong, Academic Advisor; E-mail: sstrong@vmps.org

Walker-Hackensack-Akeley ISD #113
Indian Education Program, P.O. Box 4000 • Walker, MN 56484

Warroad Public Schools - ISD #690
Indian Education Dept., 510 Cedar Ave. • Warroad, MN 56763
 (218) 386-1820 Fax 386-1909; Shirley Flick, Coordinator
 E-mail: shirley_flick@warroad.k12.mn.us
Grades K-12. *Description*: Provides tutorial assistance, information and referral services, post-secondary financial aid information, home/school liaison services, cultural awareness, & traditional teaching. *Instructors*: Sue Johnston - Middle School; Tim Oshie - Elementary.

Waubun-Ogema ISD #435
Indian Education Program, P.O. Box 98 • Waubun, MN 56589

MISSOURI

Independence School District
Indian Education Program, 1231 S. Windsor • Independence, MO 64055

N. Kansas City School District
Indian Education Program, 2000 N.E. 46th St. • Kansas City, MO 64116

Neosho R-5 School District
Indian Education Program, 511 Neosho Blvd. • Neosho, MO 64850

Seneca R7 School District
Indian Education Program, P.O. Box 469 • Seneca, MO 64865

School District of Springfield
Indian Education Program, 940 N. Jefferson St. • Springfield, MO 65802

MISSISSIPPI

Newton Co. School District
Indian Education Program, P.O. Box 97 • Decatur, MS 39327

Louisville Municipal School District
Indian Education Program, 200 Ivy Ave. • Louisville, MS 39339

Jones Co. School District
Indian Education Program, P.O. Drawer E • Sandersville, MS 39477

MONTANA

Arlee Public Schools
Indian Education Program, P.O. Box 37 • Arlee, MT 59821

Billings Public Schools
Indian Education Program, 415 North 30th St. • Billings, MT 59102
 (406) 281-5071 Fax 281-6187; Dulce Whitford, Coordinator
 Jennifer Smith, Implementation

Eastern Montana College
Indian Education Program, 1500 North 30th St. • Billings, MT 59101

Box Elder Public Schools
Indian Education Program, P.O. Box 205 • Box Elder, MT 59521

Rocky Boy Elementary S.D. #87-J
Indian Education Program, P.O. Box 620 • Box Elder, MT 59521

Bozeman Public Schools
Indian Education Program, P.O. Box 520 • Bozeman, MT 59771
 (406) 522-6027 Fax 522-6091
 Robin Arnold, Director; E-mail: robin.arnold@bsd7.org

Brockton Public S.D. #55-55F
Indian Education Program, P.O. Box 198 • Brockton, MT 59213

Browning Elem./HS Dist. #9
Indian Education Program, P.O. Box 610 • Browning, MT 59417

Butte School District #1
Indian Education Program, 111 N. Montana St. • Butte, MT 59701
 (406) 533-2548 Fax 533-2539; Judy Jonart, Curriculum Specialist
E-mail: jonartjm@butte.k12.mt.us

Charlo School District #7
Indian Education Program, P.O. Box 5 • Charlo, MT 59824

Culbertson Public School 17J/C
Indian Education Program, P.O. Box 615 • Culbertson, MT 59218

Cut Bank Public Schools
Indian Education Program, Title VII
101 Third Ave. S.E. • Cut Bank, MT 59427
 (406) 873-4421 Fax 873-4691; Doug Freeman, Coordinator
Grades K-12. *Description*: Offers culture club opportunities for all students and Native American studies at both the middle school and the high school level. *Instructors*: Angela Orr, Mary Lou deRoulhac, Ray Maier, Laurine Running Crane, Carol Flammond.

Dixon Elementary School District #9
Indian Education Program, P.O. Box 10 • Dixon, MT 59831

Dodson Elem. School District 2A
Indian Education Program, P.O. Box 278 • Dodson, MT 59524

Frazer School District 2-2B
Indian Education Program, P.O. Box 488 • Frazer, MT 59225

Great Falls Public School District
Indian Education Program, 1100 4th St. So. • Great Falls, MT 59405
 (406) 268-7340 Fax 268-7384; Corri Smith, Director (268-6003)
Resources: Native American Resource Library (268-6668)

Harlem P.S. District #12
Indian Education Program, P.O. Box 339 • Harlem, MT 59526

Havre Public Schools
Indian Education Program, P.O. Box 7791 • Havre, MT 59501

Hays/Lodge Pole Schools
Indian Education Program, P.O. Box 110 • Hays, MT 59527

Hays/Lodge Pole Public S.D. #150
Indian Education Program, P.O. Box 880 • Hays, MT 59527

Heart Butte School District #1
Indian Education Program, P.O. Box 259 • Heart Butte, MT 59448

Helena Public Schools
Indian Education Program, 55 S. Rodney St. • Helena, MT 59601
 (406) 324-2005 Fax 324-2018; Jan Jamruszka-Wilson, Coordinator
E-mail: jjamruszka-wilson@helena.k12.mt.us

State Office of Public Instruction
Indian Education Program, 1300 11th Ave. • Helena, MT 59620
 (406) 444-3694 Fax 444-3924; Lynn Hinch, Acting Director (444-3482)
Julie Saylor, Curriculum Coordinator

Kalispel Public Schools
233 First Ave. East • Kalispel, MT 59901
 (406) 751-3434 Fax 751-3416; Dan Zorn, Curriculum Director
E-mail: zornd@sd5.k12.mt.us

Lame Deer School
Indian Education Program, P.O. Box 96 • Lame Deer, MT 59043

Northern Cheyenne Tribal Education Department
Indian Education Program, P.O. Box 307 • Lame Deer, MT 59043
 (406) 477-6602; Norma Bixby, Director; E-mail: norma@rangeweb.net

Lodge Grass School District 2 & 27
Indian Education Program, Drawer AF • Lodge Grass, MT 59050

Missoula County Public Schools
Indian Education Program, 215 S. 6th West • Missoula, MT 59801
 (406) 728-2400 Fax 542-4009; Karen Allen, Administrator
E-mail: kallen@mcps.k12.mt.us; Kathy Sharbono, Title VII Specialist

Polson School District #23
Indian Education Program, 111 4th Ave. E • Polson, MT 59860

Poplar Public Schools
Indian Education Program, P.O. Box 458 • Poplar, MT 59255

Pryor Public S.D. 2 & 3
Indian Education Program, P.O. Box 229 • Pryor, MT 59066

Ronan School District #30
Indian Education Program, P.O. Box R • Ronan, MT 59864

St. Ignatius School District #28
Indian Education Program, P.O. Box 400 • St. Ignatius, MT 59865

Valier High/Elem. School
Indian Education Program, P.O. Box 528 • Valier, MT 59486

Wolf Point Public S.D. #45-45A
Indian Education Program/Title IX, 220 4th Ave. S. • Wolf Point, MT 59201
 (406) 653-2361 Fax 653-1881; Lisa Horsmon, Special Projects Coordinator
Grades K-12. *Description*: Provides tutoring services, cultural activities & education of Indian customs and heritage.

Wyola School District #29
Indian Education Program, P.O. Box 66 • Wyola, MT 59089

NEBRASKA

Alliance Public Schools
Indian Education Program, 1604 Sweetwater • Alliance, NE 69301
 (308) 762-1580 Fax 762-8249; Lonnie Sherlock, Coordinator
Grades K-12. *Description*: Provides for a variety of educational needs in an attempt to improve the attendance and academic standings of Native American students. Includes tutoring services, cultural activities and financial aid.

Alliance Middle School
Indian Education Program, 1115 Laramie St. • Alliance, NE 69301

Chadron Public Schools
Indian Education Program, Brooks Hall, 245 E. 10th • Chadron, NE 69337

Lincoln Public Schools
Indian Education Program, P.O. Box 82889 • Lincoln, NE 68501
 (402) 436-1988; Dr. Deila Steiner, Director; E-mail: dsteiner@lps.org
Joshua Cramer, Supervisor (436-1994); E-mail: jcramer@lps.org
Kris Ross, Indian Education Advocate 436-1963
Valery Killscrow Copeland, Advocate (436-1940); E-mail: vcopela@lps.org
Publication: Quarterly newsletter

Ponca Tribe of Nebraska
Indian Education Program, 1701 E St. • Lincoln, NE 68508
 (402) 438-9222 Fax 438-9226

Macy Public School
Indian Education Program, P.O. Box 280 • Macy, NE 68039

Norfolk Public Schools
Indian Education Program, 512 Philip Ave. • Norfolk, NE 68701
 (402) 644-2509 Fax 644-2506; Jan Beauvais, Director

Omaha Public Schools
Native American Indian Education, 3215 Cuming St. • Omaha, NE 68131
 (402) 557-2459 Fax 557-2509; Tami Maldonado-Mancebo, Director
 E-mail: tami.maldonado-mancebo@ops.org

Rushville Public Schools
Indian Education Program, P.O. Box 590 • Rushville, NE 69360

Santee Public School
Indian Education Program, Route 2, Box 207 • Santee, NE 68760

Scottsbluff/Gering Public Schools
Indian Education Program, 2601 Broadway • Scottsbluff, NE 69361
 Ronald Sylvester, Contact

Winnebago Public School
Indian Education Program, P.O. Box KK • Winnebago, NE 68071
(402) 878-2224 Fax 878-2472; Dan Fehringer, Supt.
Charles Curnyn, Principal (7-12 grades)
Tiffany Heese, Principal (K-6 grades)

Walthill Public School
Indian Education Program, Little & Main St., Box 3C • Walthill, NE 68067

Gordon Public Schools
Indian Education Program, P.O. Box 530 • Gordon, NE 69343

NEVADA

Lander County School District
Indian Education Program, P.O. Box 1300 • Battle Mountain, NV 89820

Carson City School District
Indian Education Program, P.O. Box 603 • Carson City, NV 89702

Elko County School District
Indian Education Program, P.O. Box 1012 • Elko, NV 89801

Churchill County School District
Indian Education Program, 545 E. Richards St. • Fallon, NV 89406

Douglas County School District
Indian Education Program • Gardnerville, NV 89410

Mineral County School District
Indian Education Program, P.O. Box 1540 • Hawthorne, NV 89415

Washoe County School District
Title VII - Indian Education Program
P.O. Box 30425 • Reno, NV 89520-3425
(775) 850-8017 Fax 851-5649
Website: www.washoe.k12.nv.us/indianed
Sheryl Hicks, Director
Graduation Specialists: Anthony Abbie, Bernadette DeLucchi, Rebecca Morrison. Grades 7-12. *Description*: Provides supplemental services and/or programs to enhance the learning opportunities for our Native American/ Alaska Native students. These include our student liaisons, graduation advisement; dropout prevention activities; college, career & personal advisement; tutoring, cultural enrichment & supplemental credit fee waivers. *Student Liaisons*: Bernadette Harry & Rebecca Cook. Services offered include tutoring, cultural enrichment & summer school tuition fee waivers.

Humboldt County School District
Indian Education Program, 310 E. 4th St. • Winnemucca, NV 89445

Lyon County School District
Indian Education Program, 25 E. Goldfield Ave. • Yerington, NV 89447

NEW JERSEY

Fairfield Twp. Board of Education
Indian Education Program, RD #4, Ramah Rd., Box 337 • Bridgeton, NJ 08302

Mahwah Twp. Public Schools
Indian Education Program, Admin. Center, Ridge Rd. • Mahwah, NJ 07430

Ringwood Borough Schools
Indian Education Program, 121 Carletondale Rd. • Ringwood, NJ 07456
Carla M. Alexander-Juarez, Director

NEW MEXICO

Albuquerque Public Schools
Indian Education Program
6400 Uptown Blvd. NE, Suite 460 West • Albuquerque, NM 87110
(505) 884-6392 Fax 872-8849
Daisy Thompson, Director; E-mail: Thompson_dai@aps.edu
Jay M. Leonard, Instructional Manager; E-mail: leonard_jay@aps.edu

Aztec Municipal Schools
Indian Education Program, 1118 West Boulevard • Aztec, NM 87410
(505) 334-9505 Fax 334-5676; Marie Charles, Director
E-mail: fpcharma@aztec.k12.nm.us

Bernalillo Public Schools
Indian Education Program, 224 N. Camino del Pueblo • Bernalillo, NM 87004
(505) 867-7840 Fax 867-7839; Mateo Sanchez, Contact

Bloomfield Public Schools
Indian Education Program, 325 N. Bergin Ln. • Bloomfield, NM 87413
(505) 632-4309 Fax 632-4371

Cuba Independent Schools
Indian Education Program, P.O. Box 70 • Cuba, NM 87013
(505) 289-3211 Fax 289-3314; Lenore Mace, Chairperson

Jemez Mountain Public Schools
Indian Education Program, HCR 17 Box 350 • Cuba, NM 87013
(505) 568-4491 Fax 568-0088
Pam Ebell, Director; E-mail: pam_jms@yahoo.com

Dulce Independent Schools
Indian Education Program, P.O. Box 547 • Dulce, NM 87528
(505) 759-3225 Fax 759-3533

Espanola Public Schools
Indian Education Program, 714 Calle Don Diego • Espanola, NM 87532
(505) 753-4775 Fax 753-2321; Wilma Martinez, Director

Farmington Municipal Schools
Indian Education Program, P.O. Box 5850 • Farmington, NM 87499
(505) 599-8616 Fax 599-8812
Arlene Kirstine, Director; E-mail: akirstine@fms.k12.nm.us

Jemez Mountain School District 53
Indian Education Program, P.O. Box 121 • Gallina, NM 87017

Gallup-McKinley County Schools
Indian Education Program, P.O. Box 1318 • Gallup, NM 87301
(505) 722-7711 Fax 722-4566

Grants Cibola County Schools
Indian Education Program, P.O. Box 8 • Grants, NM 87020
(505) 285-2605 Fax 285-2628
Marilyn Cheromiah, Director; E-mail: mcheromiah@netscape.net

Jemez Valley Public Schools
Indian Education Program, 8501 Hwy. 4 • Jemez Pueblo, NM 87024
(505) 834-7391 ext. 251 Fax 834-7394
Sandra Henson, Director; E-mail: henson7766@yahoo.com

Los Lunas Public Schools
Indian Education Program, P.O. Drawer 1300 • Los Lunas, NM 87031
(505) 866-2440 ext. 255 Fax 866-2180
Jeanette Garcia, Director

Magdalena Municipal Schools
Indian Education Program, P.O. Box 24 • Magdalena, NM 87825
(505) 854-2241 ext. 20 • Fax 854-2531
Keri James, Director; E-mail: kjames@magdalena.k12.nm.us

Penasco Independent Schools
Indian Education Program, P.O. Box 520 • Penasco, NM 87553
(505) 587-2513 ext. 1209 Fax 587-2513

Rio Rancho Public Schools
Indian Education Program, 500 Laser Rd. NE • Rio Rancho, NM 87124
(505) 896-0667 ext. 114 Fax 896-0662
Jerry Reeder, Director

Ruidoso Municipal Schools
Indian Education Program, 200 Horton Cr. • Ruidoso, NM 88345
(505) 257-4051 Fax 257-4150

Pojoaque Valley Public Schools
Indian Education Program
P.O. Box 3468 Pojoaque Station • Santa Fe, NM 87501
(505) 455-3618 Fax 455-0076; Vera T. Ortiz, Director

Santa Fe Public Schools
Indian Education Program, 610 Alta Vista St. • Santa Fe, NM 87501
(505) 467-2644; Glenda Frye, Coordinator

Tesuque Day School
Indian Education Program, Route 11, Box 2 • Santa Fe, NM 87501

Central Consolidated Schools
Indian Education Program, P.O. Box 1199 • Shiprock, NM 87420
(505) 368-5177 Fax 368-5232

Taos Day School
Indian Education Program, P.O. Drawer X • Taos, NM 87571

Taos Municipal School District
Indian Education Program, 213 Paseo del Canon • Taos, NM 87571
(505) 758-5246 Fax 758-5298; Liz Moya Herrera Contact
Grades 10-12. *Program*: Only public school in New Mexico that has made Native American history as part of the core curriculum. Focus is on Taos Pueblo history, & contributions made by Native Americans in the development of this nation. Instructors: Marge Neddo, John Romero.

St. Bonaventure Indian Mission & School
P.O. Box 610 • Thoreau, NM 87323
(877) 989-4100; (505) 862-7847 Fax 862-7029
Website: www.stbonaventuremission.org
A Roman Catholic social service mission working with impoverished Navajos. It offers school programs, health, food and other aid.

Zuni Public Schools
Indian Education Program, P.O. Drawer A • Zuni, NM 87327
(505) 782-5511 Fax 782-5870; Jeanette M. Davis, Director

NEW YORK

Akron Central Schools
Indian Education Program, 47 Bloomingdale Ave. • Akron, NY 14001

Buffalo School District - School #19
Indian Education Program , 97 W. Delavan • Buffalo, NY 14213

Center Moriches USD
Indian Education Program, 511 Main St. • Center Moriches, NY 11934

North Syracuse School District
Indian Education Program, CNS High Norstar Dr., Rt. 3 • Cicero, NY 13039

E. Bloomfield Central School
Indian Education Program, Oakmount Ave. • East Bloomfield, NY 14443

Salmon River Central Schools
Indian Education Program
Akwesasne Mohawk Project • Fort Covington, NY 12937
William Perkins, Principal; Ann Marie FitzRandolph, Director

Rush-Henrietta Central School District
Indian Education Project, 2034 Lehigh Station Rd. • Henrietta, NY 14467
(716) 359-5047; Jeanette Miller, Director
Grades K-12. *Description*: Teaches culture, history, arts & crafts; provides field trips for children; brings in speakers; teaches traditional dancing, singing, modified Mohawk language; provides workshops for teachers, & presentations on Native American culture.

Gowanda Central School District
Indian Education Program, Prospect St. • Irving, NY 14070

New York City Public Schools
Indian Education Program, 234 W. 109th St., Rm. 507 • New York, NY 10025

Niagara Falls City Schools
Indian Education Program
P.O. Box 399, 561 Portage Rd. • Niagara Falls, NY 14302

Rochester City School District
Native American Resource Center
353 Congress Ave.-Portable • Rochester, NY 14619
(585) 324-2710 Fax 324-2712; Perry Ground, Director
Grades K-12. *Mission*: To provide instruction & information to native Americans students about their cultural heritage including history, stories, art & crafts; to support Native students in their regular academic classes and help prepare them for state standardized tests; to act as a resource for non-Native educators seeking complete, accurate & up-to-date information about Native people, especially the Haudenosaunee. Instructor: Perry Ground.

Salamanca City Schools
Indian Education Program, 50 Iroquois Dr. • Salamanca, NY 14779

Silver Creek Central School
Indian Education Program, Box 270, Dickinson St. • Silver Creek, NY 14136

Southampton Schools
Indian Education Program, P.O. Box 59 • Southampton, NY 11968

Syracuse City Schools
c/o Blodgett School-Indian Education Program
725 Harrison St. • Syracuse, NY 13210
(315) 435-4288 Fax 435-6553; Bonnie White, Director
Grades K-12. *Description*: Culturally-based, community-building activities; tutoring, student advocacy; peer leadership training. *Instructors*: Eva Cook, Russell Smith, Kathleen Thomas.

North Syracuse Central Schools
Native American Education Program
5355 W. Taft Rd. • No. Syracuse, NY 13212
(315) 452-3189 Fax 452-3055; Theresa E. Schneider, Coordinator
Grades K-12. *Description*: Provides tutoring, cultural activities and a Spring cultural event. Instructors: Diane Fini, LEA; Kim Ostrander, Gail Henderson.

NORTH CAROLINA

Swain County Schools
Indian Education Program; Sue Carpenter, Contact
Whittier School, P.O. Box U • Bryson City, NC 28713

Wake County Public School System
5625 Dillard Dr. #1500 • Cary, NC 27518
Teresa Cunningham-Brown, Contact; E-mail: tcunningham@wcpss.net

Charlotte-Mecklenburg Schools
Indian Education Program, Oakhurst Administrative Bldg.
4511 Monroe Rd. • Charlotte, NC 28205
Fax (980) 343-5322; Karin Dancy, CMS Director of Grants
E-mail: k.dancy@cms.k12.nc.us

Clinton City Schools
Indian Education Program, P.O. Box 646 • Clinton, NC 28328
(910) 592-3132 ext. 1106; Terrace Miller, Director

Cabarrus County Schools
Indian Education Program. Box 388, 505 Hwy. 495 • Concord, NC 28025

Cumberland County Schools
Indian Education Program, P.O. Box 2357 • Fayetteville, NC 28302
(910) 678-2462; Trudy Locklear, Director

Guilford County Schools
Indian Education Program, 712 N. Eugene St. • Greensboro, NC 27401
(336) 621-4044 ext. 5; Jean Conley, Indian Education Teacher
Annual Indian Education Project activities: **Public and Mini Powwow a Native American Career Fair, an annual Native American Student Recognition Day and the North Carolina Native American Youth Organization State Youth Conference**

Halifax County Schools
Indian Education Program, P.O. Box 468 • Halifax, NC 27839
(252) 583-3111; Tyus Few, Director

Richmond County Schools
Indian Education Program, P.O. Box 1259 • Hamlet, NC 28345
(910) 582-5860; Debbie Wrenn, Curriculum Director
Billie Allen, K-5 Specialist/Tutor; Tina Bass, 6-12 Specialist

Scotland County Schools
Indian Education Program, 233 E. Church St. • Laurinburg, NC 28352

Harnett County Schools
Indian Education Program, P.O. Box 1029 • Lillington, NC 27546

Public Schools of Robeson County
Indian Education Program, P.O. Box 847 • Pembroke, NC 28372
(910) 521-2054 Fax 521-0942
Rita Locklear, Director; E-mail: rita.locklear@robeson.k12.nc.us

Hoke County School System
Indian Education Program, P.O. Box 370 • Raeford, NC 28376

Graham County Schools
Indian Education Program, P.O. Box 605 • Robbinsville, NC 28771

Person County Schools
Indian Education Program, P.O. Drawer 1078 • Roxboro, NC 27573

Smokey Mountain High School
Indian Education Program, 505 E. Main St. • Sylva, NC 28779
  (828) 586-2311 Fax 586-5450; Nancy Sherrill, Coordinator
Grades 9-12. *Description*: Works directly with Indian students on attendance, academics, & special programs; parental involvement on health issues, rules & regulations, scholarships & special programs. *Social worker*: Vangie Stephens.

Warren County School District
Indian Education Program, P.O. Box 110 • Warrenton, NC 27589
  (252) 257-3184; Tony Cozart, Director

Columbus County Schools
Indian Education Program, P.O. Box 279 • Whiteville, NC 28472

Smokey Mountain Elementary School
Indian Education Program, Rte. 1, Box 242 • Whittier, NC 28789
  (828) 586-2334 Fax 586-5450; Clarence Hubbell, Director
Grades K-8. *Description*: Provides tutoring services, and cultural enrichment programs. *Instructors*: Rose Long & Barbara Gilbert.

Hertford Co. Board of Ed.
Indian Education Program, P.O. Box 158 • Winton, NC 27986

NORTH DAKOTA

Belcourt School District
Indian Education Program, P.O. Box 440 • Belcourt, ND 58316

Bismarck Public Schools
Indian Education Program, 806 N. Washington • Bismarck, ND 58501
  (701) 323-4050 Fax 323-4001
  Sue Kramer, Project Coordinator
  E-mail: sue_kramer@bismarckschools.org

Devils Lake Public School
Indian Education Program, 325 7th St. • Devils Lake, ND 58301

Dunseith Public School District
Indian Education Program, P.O. Box 789 • Dunseith, ND 58329

Fargo/West Fargo Public Schools
Indian Education Program415 4th St. N. • Fargo, ND 58102-4514
  (701) 446-3641

Fort Totten Public School
Indian Education Program, P.O. Box 239 • Fort Totten, ND 58335

Fort Yates Public School
Indian Education Program, P.O. Box 428 • Fort Yates, ND 58538

Garrison Public School District
Indian Education Program, P.O. Box 249 • Garrison, ND 58540

Grand Forks Public Schools
Indian Education Program, P.O. Box 6000 • Grand Forks, ND 58201

Lake Agassiz Elem. School
Indian Education Program, 605 Stanford Rd. • Grand Forks, ND 58203

Twin Buttes Public Schools
Indian Education Program, RR 1, Box 65 • Halliday, ND 58636

Hazen Public Schools
Indian Education Program • Hazen, ND 58545

Mandaree Public Schools
P.O. Box 488 • Mandaree, ND 58757
  (701) 759-3311 Fax 759-3493; Ed Lone Fight, Supt.
Grades K-12. *Enrollment*: 250. *Description*: *Special courses*: Hidatsa Language; Tribal History & Government; Special Education; Culture. *Special programs*: Indian Club; Rodeo Club; Alternative Education; Gifted & Talented.

New Town Public School District
Indian Education Program, P.O. Box 700 • New Town, ND 58767

Parshall School District
Indian Education Program, P.O. Box 158 • Parshall, ND 58770

Rolette Public School District
Indian Education Program, P.O. Box 97 • Rolette, ND 58366
  Merrill Krueger, Contact

Mt. Pleasant School District
Indian Education Program, RR 1, Box 93 • Rolla, ND 58367
  Norman Baumgarn

White Shield School District
Indian Education Program, HC 1, Box 45 • Roseglen, ND 58775

St. John School District
Indian Education Program, P.O. Box 200 • St. John, ND 58369

Selfridge School District
Indian Education Program, P.O. Box 45 • Selfridge, ND 58568

Sheyenne Public School
Indian Education Program, P.O. Box 67 • Sheyenne, ND 58374

Solen School District
Indian Education Program, P.O. Box 128 • Solen, ND 58570

Eight Mile School District
Indian Education Program, P.O. Box 239 • Trenton, ND 58853

Warwick Public School District
Indian Education Program, P.O. Box 7 • Warwick, ND 58381
  Rocklyn Cofer, Contact

Williston Public School
Indian Education Program, P.O. Box 1407 • Williston, ND 58801

Warwick Public School District
Indian Education Program, P.O. Box 7 • Warwick, ND 58381

OHIO

Columbus Public Schools
Indian Education Program, 873 Walcutt Ave. • Columbus, OH 43219

OKLAHOMA

Achille Public Schools
Indian Education Program, P.O. Box 820 • Achille, OK 74720

Vanoss Public School
Indian Education/Title V, Rt. 5, Box 119 • Ada, OK 74820

Ada City Schools, I.S.D. #19
Indian Education Program, P.O. Box 1359 • Ada, OK 74820

Byng School I-16
Indian Education Program, Rt. 3 • Ada, OK 74820

Latta Public Schools
Indian Education Program, 13925 County Rd. 1560 • Ada, OK 74820
  (580) 332-3980; Susan Russell, Coordinator

Pickett-Center School
Indian Education Program, P.O. Box 1363 • Ada, OK 74820

Adair Public Schools
Indian Education Program, P.O. Box 197 • Adair, OK 74330

Afton Public School
Indian Education Program, P.O. Box 100 • Afton, OK 74331

Agra Public School I-134
Indian Education Program, P.O. Box 279 • Agra, OK 74824

Albion Grade School
Indian Education Program, P.O. Box 189 • Albion, OK 74521

Alex Public Schools
Indian Education Program, P.O. Box 188 • Alex, OK 73002

Allen Public Schools
Indian Education Program, P.O. Box 430 • Allen, OK 74825
  (580) 857-2419 Fax 857-2636; Gayla Hudson, Director
Grades K-12. *Description*: Provides academic, cultural enrichment and tutoring services for American Indian children in residence. *Instructor*: Diane Nemecek.

Anadarko Public Schools
Indian Education Center, 1400 S. Mission • Anadarko, OK 73005
  (405) 247-2288 Fax 247-6501; Website: www.apswarriors.com/AIE
  David Sullivan, Program Director; Pat Kopepasah, Program Assistant

Antlers Public Schools
Indian Education Program, 219 N.E. A • Antlers, OK 74523

Boone/Apache Public Schools
Indian Education Program, 522 E. Floyd St. • Apache, OK 73006
  (580) 588-2122 Fax 588-2577

Ardmore City Schools
Indian Education Program, 800 M St. NE Room 104 • Ardmore, OK 73401
  (580) 221-3001 Fax 226-7652
  Kim Smith, Director (221-3001 ext. 141)
    E-mail: kimsmith@ardmore.k12.ok.us
  Tracy Benson, Secretary (221-3001 ext. 140)

Dickson Schools
Indian Education Program, 4762 State Hwy. 199 • Ardmore, OK 73401
  (580) 223-9557 Fax 490-9152
  Teresa Bolin, JOM Director; E-mail: tabolin@dickson.k12.ok.us

Plainview Public Schools
Indian Education Program, 1140 S. Plainview Rd. • Ardmore, OK 73401
  (580) 490-3184

Arkoma Public School
Indian Education Program, P.O. Box 349 • Arkoma, OK 74901

Tushka Public Schools
Indian Education Program, Rt. 4, Box T 2630 • Atoka, OK 74525

Atoka Public Schools
Indian Education Program, 200 S. Oregon • Atoka, OK 74525
  (580) 889-6611

Harmony Public School
Indian Education/Title VII, Rt. 2, Box 2215 • Atoka, OK 74525
  (580) 889-3687 Fax 889-4631

Barnsdale Public School District I-29
Indian Education Program, P.O. Box 629 • Barnsdale, OK 74002

Bartlesville Public School District I-30
Bartlesville Family Learning Center
Indian Education Operation Eagle Program
Johnson O'Malley Title VII, P.O. Box 1357 • Bartlesville, OK 74005
  (918) 337-1631 ext. 1631; Fax (918) 336-0281
Monica Britt, Program Manager; E-mail: brittma@bps-ok.org

Binger/Olney ISD #15
Indian Education Program, P.O. Box 280 • Binger, OK 73009
  (405) 656-2304 Fax 656-2267

Bixby Public Schools - Bixby High School
Indian Education Program, 601 S. Riverview • Bixby, OK 74008
  (918) 366-2353; Sandy Fannell, Coordinator
  E-mail: sfannell@bixbyps.org

Blackwell Public Schools I-45
Indian Education Program, 934 South First • Blackwell, OK 74631

Blanchard Public Schools
Indian Education Program, P.O. Box 2620 • Blanchard, OK 73010

Rock Creek I.S.D.
Indian Education Program, P.O. Box 208 • Bokchito, OK 74849

Bokoshe Public Schools I-26
Indian Education Program, P.O. Box 158 • Bokoshe, OK 74930

Boswell School I-1
Indian Education Program, P.O. Box 839 • Boswell, OK 74727

Bowlegs Public School
Indian Education Program, P.O. Box 88 • Bowlegs, OK 74830

Boynton Public School
Indian Education Program, P.O. Box 97 • Boynton, OK 74422

Braggs Public Schools
Indian Education Program, P.O. Box 59 • Braggs, OK 74423

Braman School
Indian Education Program, P.O. Box 130 • Braman, OK 74632

Bristow Schools
Indian Education/Title V, 134 West 9th • Bristow, OK 74010

Broken Arrow Public Schools
Indian Education Program, 210 N. Main • Broken Arrow, OK 74012
  (918) 259-7402; Valeri Radford, Title VII Indian Education Assistant
  Annual College Fair; college prep course available.

Broken Bow ISD #74
Indian Education Program, 108 W. Fifth St. • Broken Bow, OK 74728

Lukfata School District #9
Indian Education Program, P.O. Box 940 • Broken Bow, OK 74728

Cache Public School
Indian Education Program, P.O. Box 418 • Cache, OK 73527

Caddo Public School
Indian Education Program, P.O. Box 128 • Caddo, OK 74729

Calera Public School
Indian Education Program, P.O. Box 386 • Calera, OK 74730

Calumet School
Indian Education Program, P.O. Box 10 • Calumet, OK 73014

Calvin Public School ISD #48
Indian Education Program, P.O. Box 127 • Calvin, OK 74531

Cameron School Grades 1-12
Indian Education Program, P.O. Box 190 • Cameron, OK 74932

Canton/Longdale Public School I-105
Indian Education Program, P.O. Box 639 • Canton, OK 73724

Carnegie ISD 33
Indian Education Program, P.O. Box 159 • Carnegie, OK 73015

Catoosa ISD #2
Indian Education Program, 2000 S. Cherokee • Catoosa, OK 74015

Checotah ISD 19
Indian Education Program, 310 Southwest Second • Checotah, OK 74426

Chelsea Public Schools
Indian Education Program, 508 Vine • Chelsea, OK 74016
  (918) 789-2528 Fax 789-3271; Nicky Harris, Coordinator
Grades PK-12. *Description*: Provides tutoring & counseling services, cultural activities & education of Indian customs & heritage.

Choctaw/Nicoma Park P.S.
Indian Education Program, 12880 N.E. 10th • Choctaw, OK 73020

Tiawah School
Indian Education Program, Rt. 7, Box 257 • Claremore, OK 74017

Verdigris School I-8
Indian Education Program, 6101 S.W. Verdigris Rd. • Claremore, OK 74017

Claremore Public Schools
The Cherokee Nation Co-Partner (JOM) Program
310 N. Weenonah • Claremore, OK 74017
  (918) 341-5270 Fax 341-8447
  Pam Leuthen, Counselor
Grades 1-12. Provides tutorial program, and counseling for grades 9-12.

Justus-Tiawah School
Indian Education Program, 14902 E. School Rd. • Claremore, OK 74019-4434

Clayton Public School District I-10
Indian Education Program, P.O. Box 190 • Clayton, OK 74536

Clinton Public Schools
Indian Education Program, P.O. Box 729 • Clinton, OK 73601

Coalgate Public Schools I-1
Indian Education Program, P.O Box 1368 • Coalgate, OK 74538

Cottonwood School
Indian Education Program, P.O. Box 347 • Coalgate, OK 74538

Colbert Public Schools
Indian Education Program, P.O. Box 310 • Colbert, OK 74733
(580) 296-2624; Wanda Williams, Programs Director
E-mail: williamsw@colbert.k12.ok.us
Linda Carter, Program Coordinator; E-mail: carterl@colbert.k12.ok.us

Colcord Public Schools
Indian Education Program, P.O. Box 188 • Colcord, OK 74338

Mosseley Public School
Indian Education Program, Rt. 4, Box 88 • Colcord, OK 74338

Collinsville Public Schools
Indian Education Program, 310 S. 14th St. • Collinsville, OK 74021
(918) 371-5449 Fax 371-3286; E-mail: cvilleindianed@yahoo.com
Janice Fields, Director; E-mail: jjfields@collinsville.k12.ok.us
Cherokee Language Class.

Commerce Public School District I-18
Indian Education Program, 420 D St. • Commerce, OK 74339

Collinsville Public Schools
Indian Education Program, 1119 W. Broadway • Collinsville, OK 74021

Coweta Public School I-17
Indian Education Program, P.O. Box 550 • Coweta, OK 74429

Butner Schools
Indian Education Program, P.O. Box 157 • Cromwell, OK 74837

Crowder Public Schools
Indian Education Program, P.O. Box B • Crowder, OK 74430

Cushing Public Schools
Indian Education Program, P.O Drawer 1609 • Cushing, OK 74023

Custer Public School
Indian Education Program, P.O. Box 200 • Custer City, OK 73639

Davis Public School
Indian Education Program, 400 East Atlanta • Davis, OK 73030

Delaware Public School I-30
Indian Education Program • Delaware, OK 74027

Leach School District 14
Indian Education Program, P.O. Box 211 • Delaware, OK 74368

Depew School District
Indian Education Program, P.O. Box 257 • Depew, OK 74028

Gypsy School D-12
Indian Education Program, Rt. 1, Box 400 • Depew, OK 74028

Dewar Public Schools
Indian Education Program, P.O. Box 790 • Dewar, OK 74431

Dibble Public Schools I-002
Indian Education Program, P.O. Box 9 • Dibble, OK 73031

Olive Independent S.D. I-17
Indian Education Program, Rt. 1, Box 337 • Drumright, OK 74030

Durant Public Schools I-72
Indian Education Program, 118 North 7th • Durant, OK 74701
(580) 924-1330; Carla Cavender, Director; Brent Cavender, Ass't Director
Grades K-12. E-mail: carla.cavender@durantisd.org;
E-mail: brent.cavender@durantisd.org

Silo School
Indian Education Program, HC-62, Box 227 • Durant, OK 74701
(580) 924-7000 Fax 924-7045; Sue Hopkins, Director
Grades K-12. *Description*: Provides tutorial services, arts & crafts and music programs. *Instructors*: Thelma Andrew, Michael Payne, Dolores Whiye, Sue Hopkins.

Dustin Public Schools
Indian Education Program, P.O. Box 660 • Dustin, OK 74893

Edmond Public Schools
Indian Education Program, 215 N. Boulevard • Edmond, OK 73034
(405) 715-6106 Fax 340-2917; Sydna Yellowfish, Coordinator
E-mail: sydna.yellowfish@edmondschools.net
Grace Smith, Alice Bones & Lynn Danvers, Educators

Elgin Public Schools I-16
Indian Education Program, P.O. Box 369 • Elgin, OK 73583

Stony Point School #124
Indian Education Program, Rt. 1, Box 2200 • Elgin, OK 73538

Darlington School
Indian Education Program, Box 145-A Rt. 3 • El Reno, OK 73036

El Reno ISD #34
Indian Education Program, P.O. Box 580 • El Reno, OK 73036

Enid Public Schools
Indian Education Program, 2102 Beverly Dr. • Enid, OK 73703
(580) 242-7185 Fax 242-6177; Margie E. Marney, Director
Grades 1-12. *Description*: Provides tutoring services, cultural activities and education of Indian customs & heritage. *Instructors*: Marsha Booth, Veryl Mills, Mary Chaplin, Susan Meyer, Gary Dowers, Robin Hatfield, Cindy Humphrey, Chris Smith.

Eufaula Public Schools I-1
Indian Education Program, P.O. Box 609 • Eufaula, OK 74432

Woodland Public Schools
Indian Education Program, P.O. Box 487 • Fairfax, OK 74637

Fairland Public Schools I-31
Indian Education, P.O. Box 689 • Fairland, OK 74343

Fanshawe School District #39
Indian Education, P.O. Box 55 • Fanshawe, OK 74935

McLish Public Schools
Indian Education, I-22, Box 29 • Fittstown, OK 74842

Ft. Cobb/Broxton Public S.D. I-17
Indian Education, P.O. Box 130 • Ft. Cobb, OK 73038

Fort Gibson Public Schools
Indian Education, P.O. Box 280 • Fort Gibson, OK 74434

Fort Towson Schools
Indian Education Program, P.O. Box 39 • Fort Towson, OK 74735
(405) 873-2712; James Gibbs, Supt.
Grades K-12. *Description*: Home liaison/curriculum aide to improve knowledge of Indian history/culture & home/school communications.

Foyil Public Schools
Indian Education Program, P.O. Box 49 • Foyil, OK 74031

Fox Public Schools
Indian Education Program, P.O. Box 248 • Fox, OK 73435

Frederick Public Schools
Indian Education Program, P.O. Box 370 • Frederick, OK 73542

Gans Public School
Indian Education Program, P.O. Box 52 • Gans, OK 74936

Geary Public Schools I-080
Indian Education Program, 110 SW Embree • Geary, OK 73040
(405) 361-1539
Deborah Newport, Title VII Coordinator
E-mail: Deborah@empowerstudentservices.com

Glenpool Public Schools
Indian Education Program, P.O. Box 1149 • Glenpool, OK 74033
(918) 322-9500 ext. 560; Kristi Collington, Director
E-mail: kacollington@glenpool.k12.ok.us
Angela Jackson, Secretary; E-mail: adjackson@glenpool.k12.ok.us

Gore Public School
Indian Education Program, P.O. Box 580 • Gore, OK 74435

Gum Springs School D-69
Indian Education Program, Rt. 1, Box 129-T • Gore, OK 74435

Grandfield Public Schools
Indian Education Program, P.O. Box 639 • Grandfield, OK 73546

Grove Public Schools
Indian Education Program, P.O. Box 450789 • Grove, OK 74345
(918) 786-3003 ext. 1110; Mrs. John Ann Thompson, Director
E-mail: jathompson@ridgerunners.net

Guthrie Public School
Indian Education Program, 802 East Vilas • Guthrie, OK 73044

Haileyville Public Schools
Indian Education Program, P.O. Box 29 • Haileyville, OK 74546

Hammon Public School I-66
Indian Education Program, P.O. Box 279 • Hammon, OK 73650

Hanna Public Schools
Indian Education Program, P.O. Box "H" • Hanna, OK 74845

Harrah Public School District ISD-1007
Indian Education Program, 20670 Walker St. • Harrah, OK 73045
(405) 454-6244 Fax 454-6844
Vernon L. Pierce, Assistant Supt.
Grades K-12. *Description*: Provides tutorial services, classroom/activity supplies, and a Native American Heritage Program. *Instructors*: Connie Norris, Cecillia Ann Fujii, Frances Benson, Laura Roberts.

Hartshorne Public School Dist. I-1
Indian Education Program, 520 S. Fifth St. • Hartshorne, OK 74547

Healdton Public School
Indian Education Program, 432 West Texas • Healdton, OK 73438

Haskell ISD #2
Indian Education Program, P.O. Box 278 • Haskell, OK 74436

Haworth Public School
Indian Education Program, P.O. Box 99 • Haworth, OK 74740

Heavener Public School
Indian Education Program, P.O. Box 698 • Heavener, OK 74937

Wilson School I-7
Indian Education Program, Rt. 1, Box 274 • Henryetta, OK 74437

Henryetta Public Schools
Indian Education Program, 618 W. Main • Henryetta, OK 74437

Ryal School
Indian Education Program, Route 2 • Henryetta, OK 74437

Hodgen Public School
Indian Education Program, P.O. Box 69 • Hodgen, OK 74939

Holdenville Schools
Indian Education Program, 210 Grimes St. • Holdenville, OK 74848-4036

Hominy Public Schools
Indian Education Program, 200 S. Pettit Ave. • Hominy, OK 74035

Howe Public Schools
Indian Education Program, P.O. Box 259 • Howe, OK 74940

Hugo City Public Schools
Indian Education Program, 208 N. 2nd St. • Hugo, OK 74743

Norwood School
Indian Education Program, Rt. 1, Box 537 • Hulbert OK 74441

McCurtain Co. School District
Indian Education Program, Court Plaza Bldg. • Idabel, OK 74745

Indiahoma Public School
Indian Education Program, P.O. Box 8 • Indiahoma, OK 73552

Inola Public School
Indian Education Program, P.O. Box 1149 • Inola, OK 74036

Jay Public Schools ISD #1
Indian Education Program, P.O. Box C-1 • Jay, OK 74346

Jenks Public Schools
Indian Education Program, 205 East "B" St. • Jenks, OK 74037
(918) 299-4415 ext. 2769 Fax 299-9197
Linda Rodgers, Director
Grades K-12. *Description*: Provides academic enhancement and advancement through tutoring, evening and/or summer school programs. Cultural enrichment through community and school assemblies, classes, and activities.

Jennings Public School
Indian Education Program, Drawer 439 • Jennings, OK 74038

Jones Public Schools
Indian Education Program, 412 S.W. 3rd St. • Jones, OK 73049
(405) 399-9118 Fax 399-9212
Grades K-12. *Description*: Provides tutoring services, counseling & cultural activities; education of Indian customs and heritage.

Kansas Public School
Indian Education Program, P.O. Box 196 • Kansas, OK 74347

Kellyville Public Schools
Indian Education Program, P.O. Box 99 • Kellyville, OK 74039

Keota Public Schools
Indian Education Program, P.O. Box 160 • Keota, OK 74941

Ketchum Public Schools
Indian Education Program, P.O. Box 720 • Ketchum, OK 74349

Kingston Public School
Indian Education Program, P.O. Box 370 • Kingston, OK 73439

Kinta Public Schools
Indian Education Program, P.O. Box 219 • Kinta, OK 74552

Kiowa Public Schools
Indian Education Program, P.O. Box 6 • Kiowa, OK 74553

Konawa Public Schools
Indian Education Program, Rt. 1, Box 3 • Konawa, OK 74849

Lane School
Indian Education Program, P.O. Box 39 • Lane, OK 74555

Lawton Public Schools
Indian Education Program, 753 Fort Sill Blvd. • Lawton, OK 73502
(580) 357-6900 ext. 279 Fax 585-6473
Website: www.lawtonps.org/lps/index.asp
Barry Beauchamp, Supt.
Dr. Anquanita Kaigler, Executive Director
E-mail: akaigler@lawtonps.org
Grades Pre-K-12. *Instructors*: Six elementary tutors; 3 secondary liaisons; 3 secondary tutors. *Description*: A Federally funded program designed to meet the needs of Native American students. The goals & objectives are to enhance positive school performance, academic achievement, good attendance, and to promote cultural awareness. *Programs*: Elementary tutoring program, cultural enrichment program, & secondary education program.

Leflore School Board
Indian Education Program, P.O. Box 147 • Leflore, OK 74942

Lexington Public Schools
Indian Education Program, 801 E. Broadway • Lexington, OK 73051
(405) 527-3810 ext. 138 Fax 527-3814
E-mail: mdawley@lexington.k12.ok.us

Locust Grove Public S.D. #17
Indian Education Program, P.O. Box 399 • Locust Grove, OK 74352

Lone Grove School
Indian Education Program, P.O. Box 1330 • Lone Grove, OK 73443

Lookeba-Sickley Public Schools
Indian Education Program, P.O. Box 34 • Lookeba, OK 73053

Macomb Public Schools
Indian Education Program, P.O. Box 10 • Macomb, OK 74852

Madill ISD #2
Indian Education Program, 601 W. McArthur • Madill, OK 73446

Mannford Public Schools
Indian Education Program, P.O. Box 100 • Mannford, OK 74044

Marble City School District 35
Indian Education Program, P.O. Box 1 • Marble City, OK 74945

Marietta School District I-016
Indian Education Program, P.O. Box 289 • Marietta, OK 73448

Mason School District I-2
Indian Education Program, Rt. 1, Box 143B • Mason, OK 74859

Maud ISD #117
Indian Education Program, P.O. Box 130 • Maud, OK 74854

McAlester Public Schools
Indian Education Program, P.O. Box 1027 • McAlester, OK 74502

McLoud Public Schools
Indian Education Program, P.O. Box 40 • McLoud, OK 74851

Meeker Public School
Indian Education Program, P.O. Box 68 • Meeker, OK 74855

Sparks Schools
Indian Education Program, P.O. Box 68 • Meeker, OK 74855

Milburn Public School
Indian Education Program, P.O. Box 429 • Milburn, OK 73450
 (405) 443-5522 Fax 443-5303; Richard McKee, Supt.
 Debbie Speers, Instructor

Mill Creek Public Schools
Indian Education Program, P.O. Box 105 • Mill Creek, OK 74856

Moffett Elementary School
Indian Education Program, P.O. Box 180 • Moffett, OK 74946

Monroe Elementary School
Indian Education Program, P.O. Box 10 • Monroe, OK 74947

Moore Public Schools
Indian Education Program, 1500 SE 4th St. • Moore, OK 73160
 (405) 735-4272; Gail Steelman, Director
 E-mail: gailsteelman@moreschools.com
 Robin Cunningham, Elementary Indian Education

Morris Public Schools
Indian Education Program, P.O. Box 80 • Morris, OK 74445
 (918) 733-4219; Ronald Martin, Project Coordinator
 Sonya Rock, Education Coordinator
 E-mail: srock@morris.k12.ok.us
 Robby McMurtry, Art/Cultural Coordinator
 E-mail: ekakwasu2@yahoo.com

Liberty Public Schools I-14
Indian Education Program, Rt. 1, Box 354 • Mounds, OK 74047

Mounds Public Schools
Indian Education Program, P.O. Box 189 • Mounds, OK 74047
 (918) 827-6758 Fax 827-3704; Yvette Britt, Director
 Grades K-12. *Description*: Provides tutorial services, Indian cultural awareness programs, & career counseling to Indian students in Mounds Public Schools.

Mountain View/Gotebo Public School
Indian Education Program, P.O. Box B • Mountain View, OK 73062

Moyers Public School
Indian Education Program, P.O. Box 88 • Moyer, OK 74557

Belfonte School District 50
Indian Education Program, Rt. 3, Box 282 • Muldrow, OK 74948

Muldrow Public Schools
Indian Education Program, P.O. Box 660 • Muldrow, OK 74948

Hilldale Public Schools, I-29
Indian Education Program, 500 E. Smith Ferry Rd. • Muskogee, OK 74403
 (918) 683-0273; Mr. Randy Goodsell, Director
 E-mail: randy_goodsell@hilldale.k12.ok.us
 Tammy McIntosh, Elementary; Oren Sikes, Middle & High School
 Lisa Scott, Specialist/Tutor

Muskogee Public Schools
Indian Education Program, 202 W. Broadway • Muskogee, OK 74401
 David Walkingstick, Director

Mustang Public Schools
Indian Education Program • Mustang, OK 73064
 (405) 376-2461; Candice Ryczkkowski, Chairperson
 Linda Atchley, Teacher Rep; E-mail: atchleyl@mustangps.org
 Kris Green, Title VII Secondary Teacher

Nashoba Public Schools
Indian Education Program, P.O. Box 17 • Nashoba, OK 74558

Newcastle Public Schools I-1
Indian Education Program, 101 N. Main St. • Newcastle, OK 73065
 (405) 387-4304; Sharon Giles, Director
 Grades K-12. *Description*: Provides academic tutoring and cultural heritage programs. *Instructors*: Deana Sykes, Georgia Small, Julie Wickersham.

Noble Public School I-40
Indian Education Program, P.O. Box 499 • Noble, OK 73068

Norman Public Schools
Indian Education Program, 4100 N. Flood Ave. • Norman, OK 73069
 (405) 366-5809 Fax 573-3516
 Lucyann Harjo, Coordinator; E-mail: lharjo2@norman.k12.ok.us

Nowata Public School
Indian Education Program, 707 West Osage • Nowata, OK 74048

Oaks Mission Public Schools
Indian Education Program, P.O. Box 160 • Oaks, OK 74359

Okay Public School
Indian Education Program, P.O. Box 188 • Okay, OK 74446

Okemah Public Schools
Indian Education Program, Second & Date Sts. • Okemah, OK 74859

Oklahoma City Public Schools
Native American Student Services, 900 N. Klein • Oklahoma City, OK 73106
 (405) 587-0000; Sarah Bradford, Program Coordinator
 Dr. Star Yellowfish, Administrator (587-0359); E-mail: elyellowfish@okcps.org

Okmulgee Public Schools District I-1
Indian Education Program, P.O. Box 1346 • Okmulgee, OK 74447

Oktaha Public Schools
Indian Education Program, P.O. Box 9 • Oktaha, OK 74437

Oologah-Talala Public School
Indian Education Program, P.O. Box 189 • Oologah, OK 74053
 (918) 443-6074; Cindy Deitz, Coordinator

Owasso Public Schools
Indian Education Program, 202 E. Broadway • Owasso, OK 74055
 (918) 272-8340 Fax 272-8341
 Joe Don Waters, Title VII Coordinator
 E-mail: joedon.waters@owasso.k12.ok.us
 Owen Hawzipta, Academic Advisor
 E-mail: owen.hawzipta@owasso.k12.ok.us

Paden Schools
Indian Education Program, P.O. Box 370 • Paden, OK 74860

Panama Public Schools
Indian Education Program, P.O. Box 550 • Panama, OK 74951

Keys Elementary School
Indian Education Program, P.O. Box 151 • Park Hill, OK 74451
(918) 456-4501 Fax 456-7559; Calvin Klugh, Principal
Grades K-6. *Description*: Provides transitional bi-lingual education.
Instructors: Norma Fourkiller, Kelly Porter, Kathy Roark.

Pauls Valley School I-18
Indian Education Program, P.O. Box 780 • Pauls Valley, OK 73075

Whitebread School
Indian Education Program, Rt. 3, Box 214 • Pauls Valley, OK 73975

Pawhuska School District I-2
Indian Education Program, 1505 N. Lynn Ave. • Pawhuska, OK 74056

Pawnee Public Schools
Indian Education Program, P.O. Box 615 • Pawnee, OK 74059

Peggs School
Indian Education Program, P.O. Box 49 • Peggs, OK 74452

Pittsburg Public School
Indian Education Program, P.O. Box 200 • Pittsburg, OK 74560

Pocola Public Schools
Indian Education Program, P.O. Box 640 • Pocola, OK 74902

Ponca City Public Schools
Indian Education Program, 111 W. Grand Ave. • Ponca City, OK 74602
(580) 767-8000; Chris LittleCook, Title VII Director

Porter Consolidated District I-365
Indian Education Program, P.O. Box 120 • Porter, OK 74454

Porum Public Schools
Indian Education Program, P.O. Box 189 • Porum, OK 74455

Poteau Public Schools
Indian Education Program, 100 Mockingbird Lane • Poteau, OK 74953
Kim Standriidge, Coordinator

Prue Public Schools
Indian Education Program, P.O. Box 130 • Prue, OK 74060

Quapaw Public Schools
Indian Education Program, P.O. Box 130 • Prue, OK 74060

Osage Elementary
Indian Education Program, P.O. Box 579 • Pryor, OK 74362

Purcell Public School K-12
Indian Education Program, 919 N. Ninth St. • Purcell, OK 73080

Quinton Public S.D. I-17
Indian Education Program, P.O. Box 670 • Quinton, OK 74561

Rattan Public School
Indian Education Program, P.O. Box 44 • Rattan, OK 74562

Red Oak Public Schools
Indian Education, P.O. Box 310 • Red Oak, OK 74563
(918) 754-2647; Eva Coleman, Director
Grades K-12. *Description*: Provides academic tutoring and cultural heritage
programs; 90 students enrolled in program. *Instructor*: Eva Coleman.

Frontier Public Schools I-4
Indian Education Program, P.O. Box 130 • Red Rock, OK 73651

Ringling Public Schools
Indian Education Program, P.O. Box 1010 • Ringling, OK 73456

Ripley Public School Dist. I-3
Indian Education Program, P.O. Box 97 • Ripley, OK 74062

Liberty School
Indian Education Program, P.O. Box 70 • Roland, OK 74954-0070

Kenwood School
Indian Education Program, Rt. 1, Box 179 • Salina, OK 74365

Salina Public S.D. I-16
Indian Education Program, PO. Box 98 • Salina, OK 74365

Wickliffe Public School
Indian Education Program, Rt. 1, Box 130 • Salina, OK 74365

Brushy School District D-36
Indian Education Program, P.O. Box 507 • Sallisaw, OK 74955

Central Public Schools
Indian Education Program, Rt. 1, Box 36 • Sallisaw, OK 74955

Sallisaw Public School I-1
Indian Education Program, 604 E. Cherokee • Sallisaw, OK 74955

Anderson Elementary School
Indian Education Program, Rt. 5, Box 161 • Sand Springs, OK 74063

Sand Springs Public Schools
Indian Education Program, P.O. Box 970 • Sand Springs, OK 74063
(918) 245-1088; Jerre Brokaw, Coordinator
Grades K-12. *Description*: Provides tutoring, cultural programs,
and college/vocational information. Staff is of Indian descent.

Sapupla Public Schools
Indian Education Program, 3 S. Mission • Sapulpa, OK 74066
(918) 224-9322 Fax 224-0174; Raymond Rodgers, Director
Grades K-12. *Description*: Covers academic needs and cultural heritage.
High school offers Muscogee (Creek) & Cherokee language courses.
Instructors: Linda Harjo, Beatrice Harrell, Dorothea Bemo, Sherry Garrett,
Naomi Pickering, Wanda Weaver.

Lone Star School
Indian Education Program, P.O. Box 1170 • Sapulpa, OK 74067

Sasakwa I.S.D. I-10
Indian Education Program, P.O. Box 323 • Sasakwa, OK 74867

Savanna Public Schools
Indian Education Program, P.O. Box 266 • Savanna, OK 74565

Schulter Public Schools
Indian Education Program, P.O. Box 203 • Schulter, OK 74460

Seiling Public Schools
Indian Education Program, P.O. Box 780 • Seiling, OK 73668

Pleasant Grove S.D. I-5
Indian Education Program, Rt. 1, Box 247 • Seminole, OK 74868

Seminole I.S.D. #1
Indian Education Program, P.O. Box 1031 • Seminole, OK 74868

Strother Public School
Indian Education Program, Rt. 3, Box 265 • Seminole, OK 74868

Varnum School
Indian Education Program, Rt. 4, Box 148 • Seminole. OK 74868

Shady Point Elementary
Indian Education Program, P.O. Drawer C • Shady Point, OK 74956

Bethel Public School ISD #3
Indian Education Program, 36000 Clear Pond Dr. • Shawnee, OK 74801

North Rock Creek S.D. 10
Indian Education Program, 42400 Garretts Lake Rd. • Shawnee, OK 74801

Pleasant Grove School
Indian Education Program, 1927 E. Walnut • Shawnee, OK 74801

Shawnee Public School I-93
Indian Education Program, 326 N. Union St. • Shawnee, OK 74801

Skiatook Public Schools
Indian Education Program, 355 S. Osage • Skiatook, OK 74070
(918) 396-1792 Fax 396-1799
Enrollment: Osage Nation students. *Program*: Annual powwow.

Smithville Public School I-14
Indian Education Program, P.O. Box 8 • Smithville, OK 74957

Soper Public Schools
Indian Education Program, P.O. Box 149 • Soper, OK 74759

Spavinaw Schools
Indian Education Program, P.O. Box 108 • Spavinaw, OK 74336

Sperry Public Schools
Indian Education Program, P.O. Box 610 • Sperry, OK 74073

Spiro Schools
Indian Education Program, 600 W. Broadway • Spiro, OK 74959

Springer Public Schools
Indian Education Program, P.O Box 249 • Springer, OK 73458

Sterling Public Schools
Indian Education Program, P.O. Box 158 • Sterling, OK 73567

Stidham Public School D-16
Indian Education Program, General Delivery • Stidham, OK 74461

Stigler Public Schools
Indian Education Program, 302 N.W. E St. • Stigler, OK 74462

Stillwater Independent School
Indian Education Program, 314 S. Lewis • Stillwater, OK 74074

Bell Elementary School
Indian Education Program, P.O. Box 346 • Stilwell, OK 74960

Dahlonegah Elem. School District #29
Indian Education Program, Rt. 1, Box 351 • Stilwell, OK 74960

Greasy Public School
Indian Education Program, P.O. Box 467 • Stilwell, OK 74960

Maryetta Public School District 22
Indian Education Program, Rt. 4, Box 413 • Stilwell, OK 74960

Peavine S.D. #19
Indian Education Program, P.O. Box 389 • Stilwell, OK 74960

Rocky Mountain S.D. 24
Indian Education Program, Rt. 1, Box 665 • Stilwell, OK 74960

Stilwell Public Schools
Indian Education Program, 1801 W. Locust • Stilwell, OK 74960

Zion School
Indian Education Program, P.O. Box 347 • Stilwell, OK 74960

Stonewall Public Schools
Indian Education Program, Rt. 2, Box 1-A • Stonewall, OK 74871
 (580) 320-2324; Shayna Stone, Contact; E-mail: shaynastone@yahoo.com

Stratford Public S.D. I-2
Indian Education Program, 241 N. Oak St., Box 589 • Stratford, OK 74872

Stringtown ISD #7
Indian Education Program, P.O. Box 130 • Stringtown, OK 74569

Stroud Independent S.D. 54
Indian Education Program, 212 W. 7th, Box 410 • Stroud, OK 74079

Sulphur Public Schools
Indian Education Program, 1021 West 9th St. • Sulphur, OK 73086

Swink Elementary School
Indian Education Program, P.O. Box 73 • Swink, OK 74761

Briggs Elementary School
Indian Education Program, Rt. 3, Box 656 • Tahlequah, OK 74464
 (918) 456-4221 Fax 456-4049; Mrs. Jessie Craig, Director
Grades K-8. *Description*: Organizes cultural trips and programs;
sponsors Indian Club; teaches Cherokee language.

Grand View School
Indian Education Program, Rt. 4, Box 195 • Tahlequah, OK 74464

Lowrey School D-10
Indian Education Program, HC-11, Box 190-1 • Tahlequah, OK 74464

Tahlequah Public School District I-35
Indian Education Program, P.O. Box 517 • Tahlequah, OK 74465
 (918) 458-4162 Fax 458-4103; Steve Merrill, Director
 Sherri Kelley, JOM Title VII Coordinator; Katie Penland, Cultural Specialist
Grades K-12. *Description*: Provides tutoring services, cultural activities and
education of Indian customs & heritage, arts & crafts. Sponsors Indian
Heritage Club activities for middle school and high school; also a youth group
called Native Reflections in which students perform service-learning projects in
the community. *Instructor*: Mike Daniel

Sequoyah High School
Indian Education Program, P.O. Box 948 • Tahlequah, OK 74465

Buffalo Valley Public School I-3
Indian Education Program, Rt. 2, Box 3505 • Talihina, OK 74571

Talihina Public Schools
Indian Education Program, P.O. Box 38 • Talihina, OK 74571

Tecumseh Public Schools
Indian Education Program, 302 S. 9th • Tecumseh, OK 74873

Temple Public Schools
Indian Education Program, 206 School Rd. • Temple, OK 73568

Tishomingo School District
Indian Education Program, 1300 East Main • Tishomingo, OK 73460
 (580) 371-9190 Fax 371-3765; Rex Lokey, Title VII Director

Tuskahoma Public Schools
Indian Education Program, P.O. Box 97 • Tuskahoma, OK 74574

Tonkawa Public Schools
Indian Education Program, P.O Box 10 • Tonkawa, OK 74653

Berryhill Public School I-10
Indian Education Program, 3128 South 63 West Ave. • Tulsa, OK 74107

Tulsa Public Schools
Indian Education Program, 209 S. Lakewood Ave. • Tulsa, OK 74112
 (918) 833-8362 Fax 833-8370; Jean Froman, Coordinator
 Marsha Allen (Cherokee), Academic Resource Advisor
 Helen Brumley (Osage), Cultural Resource Advisor
 Pat Farrell (Cherokee), Brett Coon (Cherokee),
 Jimi Hornbuckle (Cherokee/Choctaw), Roger McLain (Cherokee)
 Lillian Williams (Skidi Pawnee/Chickasaw/Cherokee), *Resource Advisors*
Enrollment: 400 American Indian students representing 89 federally-
recognized tribes in the Tulsa district.

Union Public Schools
Indian Education Program, 8506 E. 61st St. • Tulsa, OK 74133
 (918) 357-4321; Jackie White, Director

Tupelo Public Schools
Indian Education Program, P.O. Box 310 • Tupelo, OK 74572

Valliant Public Schools
Indian Education Program, 604 E. Lucas St. • Valliant, OK 74764

Vian Public School I-2
Indian Education Program, P.O. Box 434 • Vian, OK 74962

Vinita Public Schools I-65
Indian Education Program, 114 S. Scraper St. • Vinita, OK 74301
 (918) 256-2402 Fax 256-4199

Wagoner Public School Dist. I-19
Indian Education Program, 204 Casaver • Wagoner, OK 74467

Walter Independent S.D. I-00
Indian Education Program, 418 S. Broadway • Walter, OK 73572

Wanette Public School
Indian Education Program, P.O. Box 161 • Wanette, OK 74878

Wapanucka Public Schools
Indian Education Program, P.O. Box 88 • Wapanucka, OK 73461

Warner Public Schools
Indian Education Program, Rt. 1, Box 1240 • Warner, OK 74469

Washington Public Schools
Indian Education Program, P.O. Box 98 • Washington, OK 73093

Watonga Public School Dist. I-42
Indian Education Program, P.O. Box 310 • Watonga, OK 73772

Watts Public School Dist. I-4
Indian Education Program, P.O. Box 10 • Watts, OK 74964

Skelly School District I
Indian Education Program, Rt. 1, Box 918 • Watts, OK 74964

Wayne Public Schools
Indian Education Program, P.O. Box 40 • Wayne, OK 73095

Weatherford Public Schools
Indian Education Program, 516 N. Broadway • Weatherford, OK 73096

Webbers Falls Public Schools
Indian Education Program, P.O. Box 300 • Webber Falls, OK 74470

Welch School District I-17
Indian Education Program, P.O. Box 189 • Welch, OK 74369

Weleetka Public Schools I-31
Indian Education Program, P.O. Box 278 • Weleetka, OK 74880

Graham Public School
Indian Education Program, Route 1 • Weleetka, OK 74880

Tenkiller Public Schools
Indian Education Program, Rt. 1, Box 750 • Welling, OK 74653

Westville Public Schools
Indian Education Program, P.O. Box 410 • Westville, OK 74965

Justice School District 54
Indian Education Program, Rt. 1, Box 246 • Wewoka, OK 74884

Wewoka Public Schools
Indian Education Program, P.O. Box 870 • Wewoka, OK 74884

New Lima ISD 6
Indian Education Program, Rt. 1, Box 96 • Wewoka, OK 74884

Whitefield Elementary Schools
Indian Education Program, P.O. Box 188 • Whitefield, OK 74472

Whitesboro Public Schools I-65
Indian Education Program, P.O. Box 150 • Whitesboro, OK 74577

Wilburton Public S.D. I-1
Indian Education Program, 1201 W. Blair St. • Wilburton, OK 74578

Wilson Public Schools
Indian Education Program, 1860 Hewitt Rd. • Wilson, OK 73463
(580) 668-2306 Fax 668-2170
Darlene Buzidragis, Director (668-3136)
E-mail: dbuzidragis@wilson.k12.ok.us

Wister Public School
Indian Education Program, P.O. Box 489 • Wister, OK 74966

Wright City Public Schools
Indian Education Program, P.O. Box 329 • Wright, OK 74766

Wyandotte P.S. Dist. I-1
Indian Education Program, P.O. Box 360 • Wyandotte, OK 74370

Joy Public School
Indian Education Program, Rt. 1, Box 57 • Wynnewood, OK 73098

Wynona Public School
Indian Education Program, P.O. Box 700 • Wynona, OK 74084
(918) 846-2467 Fax 846-2883; Richard Nissen, Instructor
Grades: 9-12. *Program*: Indian history.

Yukon Public Schools
Indian Education Program, 1777 S. Yukon Ave. • Yukon, OK 73099
(405) 350-2032 Fax 265-4585

Kim McCathern, Title VII Coordinator; E-mail: kim.mccathern@yukonps.com
Glenda Bowen, Tutor Coordinator; E-mail: Glenda.bowen@yukonps.com

OREGON

Bandon School District #54
Indian Education Project, 455 9th St. SW • Bandon, OR 97411
(541) 347-4416 Fax 347-1898; Darcy Grahek, Title VII Coordinator
E-mail: darcyg@bandon.k12.or.us

Brookings-Harbor School District 17C
Indian Education Program, 629 Easy St. • Brookings Harbor, OR 97415
(541) 469-7131 Fax 469-6599; Website: www.brookings.k12.or.us
Linda Timeus, Title VII Coordinator

Burns Paiute Reservation
Indian Education Program, HC-71, 100 PaSiGo St. • Burns, OR 97720

Harney Co. School District 3
Indian Education Program, 55 N. Court Ave. • Burns, OR 97720
(541) 573-6811 Fax 573-7557; Website: www.harneyesd.k12.or.us
Becky Shull, Contact; E-mail: shullb@harneyesd.k12.or.us

Klamath Tribes Education & Employment Department
P.O. Box 436 • Chiloquin, OR 97624
(541) 783-2219 ext. 168 Fax 783-2029; Brenda Frank, Contact

Columbia School District 5J
Indian Education Program, 19069 Beaver Falls Rd. • Clatskanie, OR 97016
(503) 728-3172; Guy Dines, Title VII Coordinator

Coos County School District
Indian Education Coordination Program
90633 Cape Arago Hwy. • Coos Bay, OR 97420
(541) 888-4584; Jim Thornton, Title VII Coordinator
E-mail: indianed@harborside.com

Coquille School District #8
Indian Education Program, 201 N. Gould St. • Coquille, OR 97423
(541) 396-2914 Fax 396-4543; Website: www.coquille.k12.or.us
Bethany Sherrill, Title VII Coordinator

London School
Indian Education Program, 73288 London Rd. • Cottage Grove, OR 97424

Eugene School District 4-J
The Natives Program, 2295 Four Oaks Grange Rd. • Eugene, OR 97402
(541) 790-5900 Fax 790-5905; Website: www.brainard@4j.lane.edu
Brenda Brainard, Title VII Director; E-mail: brainard@4j.lane.edu

Reynolds School District 7
Indian Education Program, 1204 NE 201st Ave. • Fairview, OR 97024
(503) 661-7200 Fax 667-6932; Robert Siegel, Title VII Director

Willamina School District 30J
Indian Education Program, P.O. Box 7 • Grand Ronde, OR 97347
(541) 879-5210 Fax 879-5249; Carrie Zimbrick, Program Coordinator

Northwest Regional ESD
Indian Education Program, 5825 NE Ray Cir. • Hillsboro, OR 97124
(503) 614-1442 Fax 614-1468; Ruth Jensen, Facilitator

Klamath County School District
Indian Education Program, 10501 Washburn Way • Klamath Falls, OR 97603
(541) 883-5000 Fax 885-3362; Doug Smith, Title VII Director

Klamath Falls City Schools
Indian Education Program, 1336 Avalon • Klamath Falls, OR 97624
(541) 883-4700 ext. 168 Fax 885-4273
Don MacLaughlin, Title VIII Supervisor

Jefferson Co. School District 509-J
Indian Education Program, 445 SE Buff St. • Madras, OR 97741
(541) 475-6192 Fax 475-6856; Steve Johnson, Director

South Umpqua School District
Indian Education Program, 558 Chadwick Ln. • Myrtle Creek, OR 97457
(503) 863-3118; Bill Burnett, Director
Grades K-12. *Description*: Provides academic, cultural enrichment and tutoring services for American Indian children residing in the district.

Myrtle Point School District #41
Indian Education Program, 212 Spruce St. • Myrtle Point, OR 97458
(541) 572-2811 ext. 226 Fax 572-5401; Cindy Leibelt, Contact

Lincoln Co. School District
Indian Education Program, P.O. Box 1110 • Newport, OR 97365

North Bend School District #13
Indian Education Program, 1913 Meade St. • North Bend, OR 97459
Judy Rocha, Coordinator; E-mail: jrocha@nbend.k12.or.us

Oregon City School District
Indian Education Program, P.O. Box 591 • Oregon City, OR 97045
Ruth Jensen, Contact

Confederated Tribes of the Umatilla Indian Reservation
Title VII Indian Education Program, P.O. Box 638 • Pendleton, OR 97801
(541) 276-3165 Fax 276-3095
Zenaida Lyles, Director of Education

Umatilla School District
Indian Education Program, 2001 SW Rye • Pendleton, OR 97801

Portland Public Schools - Jefferson High School
Indian Education Project, 5210 N. Kerby • Portland, OR 97217
(503) 916-6499 Fax 916-2728; E-mail: kkitchen@pps.net
Karen Kitchen (Osage), Student Support Specialist
Enrollment: 650 pre K – 12 American Indian/Alaska Native students.

Powers School District #31
Indian Education Program, P.O. Box 479 • Portland, OR 97466
Peggy Stallard, Director

Roseburg Public Schools
Indian Education Program, 1419 Valley View • Roseburg, OR 97470
(541) 440-8275 Fax 440-4201; Juliana Marez, Title VII Coordinator
E-mail: jmarez@roseburg.k12.or.us

Salem-Keizer School District 24J
Indian Education Program, P.O. Box 12024 • Salem, OR 97309
(503) 391-4120 Fax 391-4097; Shelby Olson-Rogers, Contact

Lincoln County School District 352
Indian Education Program
5825 James Frank Ave. NW • Siletz, OR 97380
(541) 444-2523; Fred Rider, Title VII Director

Springfield Public Schools
Indian Education Program, 525 Mill St. • Springfield, OR 97477
(541) 726-3211 Fax 726-9555; Laurie Brown-Godfrey, Director
Virgil Martin, Native American Youth Assistant
E-mail: virgil.martin@springfield.k12.or.us
Grades K-12. *Description*: Provides educational & cultural services
to students enrolled in the program.

Region Nine WASCO ESD
400 E Scenic Dr., Suite 207 • The Dallas, OR 97058
(541) 298-3132 Fax 298-2894; Doug Mahurin, Title VII Coordinator

Columbia School District 5-J
Indian Education Program • Westport, OR 97016

Willamina School District 30-J
Indian Education Program, 324 SE Adams • Willamina, OR 97396

RHODE ISLAND

Charijo School District
Indian Education Program, Switch Rd. • Wood River Junction, RI 02894

SOUTH DAKOTA

Aberdeen Public Schools - Aberdeen Central High School
Indian Education Program, 2200 S. Roosevelt St. • Aberdeen, SD 57401
(605) 725-8116; Doug Neuharth, Coordinator
E-mail: doug.neuharth@aberdeen.k12.sd.us
There are about 310 Indian students in the district, which amounts to 8.5% of
the student body. The high school has about 100 Indian students. At Aberdeen
Central High School, tutoring & cultural activities are available through the
Native American Student Association (NASA).

Shannon Co. School District
Indian Education Program, P.O. Box 109 • Batesland, SD 57716

Bonesteel-Fairfax School District
Indian Education Program, P.O. Box 410 • Bonesteel, SD 57317

Dupree School District
Indian Education Program, P.O. Box 10 • Dupree, SD 57623

Eagle Butte School District
Indian Education Program, P.O. Box 260 • Eagle Butte, SD 57625

Flandreau Public School
Indian Education Program, 600 1st Ave. West • Flandreau, SD 57028

Fort Thompson Elementary School
Indian Education Program, P.O. Box 139 • Fort Thompson, SD 57339

Swift Bird Day School
Indian Education Program, HCR #3, Box 121 • Gettysburg, SD 57442

Hot Springs Public Schools
Indian Education Program, 1609 University Ave. • Hot Springs, SD 57747
(605) 745-4145 Fax 745-4178; Ronald J. Bergen, Director
Grades K-12. *Description*: Provides tutoring services & career education.
Instructors: Barbara Blosser, Arlene Chavez.

Isabel School District 20-2
Indian Education Program, P.O. Box 267 • Isabel, SD 57633-0267

Andes Central School
Indian Education Program, P.O. Box 40 • Lake Andes, SD 57356

Bennett Co. School District
Indian Education Program, P.O. Box 580 • Martin, SD 57551

Marty Indian School
Indian Education Program, P.O. Box 187 • Marty, SD 57361

McIntosh School District
Indian Education Program, Box 80 • McIntosh, SD 57641

McLaughlin School District
Indian Education Program, P.O. Box 880 • McLaughlin, SD 57642

Todd County School District
Indian Education Program, P.O. Box 87 • Mission, SD 57555
(605) 856-4869 Fax 856-2449; Richard Bordeaux, Supt.
Dennis Gaspar, Director
Grades Pre-K-12. *Description*: Serves over 2,100 Native American students,
mostly enrolled members of the Rosebud Sioux Tribe. Provides academic,
cultural enrichment and tutoring services for American Indian children.

Mitchell School District
Native Am. H/S Coordinator, P.O. Box 7760 • Mitchell, SD 57301

Mobridge District Schools
Indian Education Program, 114 East 10th • Mobridge, SD 57601

Pierre School District
Indian Education Program, 302 E. Dakota • Pierre, SD 57501

Rapid City School District
Indian Education Program, 300 Sixth St. • Rapid City, SD 57701
(605) 394-4071 Fax 394-4085; Jr. Bettelyoun, Director
Grades K-12. *Description*: Provides instructional assistance, and supplemental
special educational & culturally related needs to Native American Indian
students.

Sioux Falls School District
Indian Education Program, 201 E. 38th St. • Sioux Falls, SD 57105
(605) 367-4282 Fax 367-4379; Celeste Uthe-Burow, Supervisor

Sisseton Public School District
Indian Education Program, 302 E. Maple St. • Sisseton, SD 57262

Timber Lake School District
Indian Education Program, P.O. Box 1000 • Timber Lake, SD 57656

Vermillion School District
Indian Education Program, 17 Prospect St. • Vermillion, SD 57069

Wagner Community Schools
Indian Education Program, P.O. Box 310 • Wagner, SD 57380

Smee School District
Indian Education Program, P.O. Box 8 • Wakpala, SD 57658

Waubay School District
Indian Education Program, RR 1, Box 11 • Waubay, SD 57273

White Horse School District
Indian Education Program, P.O. Box 7 • White Horse, SD 57661

White River School District
Indian Education Program, P.O. Box 273 • White River, SD 57579

Wilmot School District 54-7
Indian Education Program
P.O. Box 100, 800 Ordway St. • Wilmot, SD 57279
  (605) 938-4647 Fax 938-4185
Tim Graf, Director; E-mail: tim.graf@K12.sd.us
Grades PS-12. *Description*: Provides tutoring services and cultural enrichment programs. *Instructor*: Donna Hansen.

Winner School District
Indian Education Program, P.O. Box 231 • Winner, SD 57580

Yankton School District
Indian Education Program, 1900 Ferdig Ave. • Yankton, SD 57078

TEXAS

Austin Independent School District
American Indian Education Program
Baker Center, Rm. 205, 3908 Avenue B • Austin, TX 78751
  (512) 414-0159 Fax 414-2626; Diane Tigges, Coordinator
  E-mail: diane.tigges@austinisd.org

Dallas I.S.D.
American Indian Education Program
3434 S. RL Thornton Fwy., Rm. 124 • Dallas, TX 75224
  (214) 932-5300 Fax 932-5171
Tracy Palmer, Specialist; E-mail: tpalmer@dallasisd.org

Ysleta I.S.D.
Indian Education Program, 9600 Sims • El Paso, TX 79925

Fort Worth I.S.D.
Indian Education Program • Fort Worth, TX
  (817) 871-2343; Yolanda Glass, Director

Grand Prairie I.S.D.
Indian Education Program, 202 West College • Grand Prairie, TX 75050
  (972) 343-6188; Diane Stedman, Director

UTAH

Neola Elementary School
Indian Education Program, P.O. Box 446 • Duchesne, UT 84021

Davis Co. School District
Indian Education Program, 45 E. State St. • Farmington, UT 84025

SLC Division of Indian Affairs
Indian Education Program, 324 S. State St., #103 • Salt Lake City, UT 841
Wil Numkena, Contact

Granite School District - Multicultural Center
Indian Education Program, 2500 South State • Salt Lake City, UT 84115
  (385) 646-4205 Fax 646-4203
  E-mail: dlawrence@graniteschools.org

Salt Lake City School District
Indian Education Program, 440 East 100 South • Salt Lake City, UT 84111
  (801) 578-8472

Canyons School District
Indian Education Program, 9361 South 300 East • Sandy, UT 84070
  (801) 826-5000; Standing Tall Program

Nebo School District
Indian Education Program, 350 S. Main • Spanish Fork, UT 84660
  (801) 798-4480; Eileen Quintana, Coordinator
  E-mail: Eileen.quintana@nebo.edu

VERMONT

Abenaki Self Help Association, Inc.
Indian Education, 49 Church St. • Swanton, VT 05488
  (802) 868-4033; Jeff Benay, Coordinator; E-mail: jeffbenay@fnwsu.org

VIRGINIA

Charles City Co. Public Schools
Indian Education Program, 10910 Court House Rd. • Charles City, VA 22030
Melvin Robertson, Contact

King William Co. School Board
Indian Education Program, P.O. Box 185 • King William, VA 23086
Miles A. Reid, Contact

WASHINGTON

Aberdeen School District
Indian Education Program, 216 North G St. • Aberdeen, WA 98520

Arlington School District
Indian Education Program, 600 E. First St. • Arlington, WA 98223

Auburn School District
Indian Education Program, 300 4th St. NE • Auburn, WA 98092

Bainbridge Island School District
8489 Madison Ave. NE • Bainbridge Island, WA 98110
LeNora Trahant, Contact; E-mail: ltrahant@bainbridge.wednet.edu

Bellingham High School
Indian Education Program, 2020 Cornwall Ave. • Bellingham, WA 98225

Bellingham School District #501
Indian Education Program, P.O Box 878 • Bellingham, WA 98227

Central Kitsap School District
Indian Education Program, 2900 Austin Dr. • Bremerton, WA 98312
Kathy Payne, Contact; E-mail: kathleenp@cksd.wednet.edu

White River School District
Indian Education Program, P.O. Box 2050 • Buckley, WA 98321
Dorothy Apple, Contact; E-mail: dapple@whiteriver.wednet.edu

Puget Sound Educational Service District
Indian Education Program, 400 SW 152nd St. • Burien, WA 98166
  (253) 778-7963 Fax 896-0621 (Tacoma area)
  (425) 917-7963 (Seattle area); Website: www.psesd.org
  Jason LaFontaine, Program Manager; E-mail: jlafontaine@psesd.org
  Nadine Cornelious, Program Specialist; E-mail: ncornelious@psesd.org
Grades K-12. *Description*: Provides culturally integrated literacy support to K-12 American Indian students in six school districts. Services include direct instruction, advocacy, and family involvement to ensure students meet high academic state standards in reading. *Instructors*: Dorothy Apple, Shana Cooper, David Norman, Martha Sherman, Leonard Treanton, Teresa Washington, Candi Turning Robe, Amanda Rambayon, and Laurie Collins (reading specialist).

Grand Coulee Dam School District
Indian Education Program, Stevens and Grant • Coulee Dam, WA 99116

Cusick School District #59
Indian Education Program; C. Crickman, Contact
305 Monumental Way, Box 270 • Cusick, WA 99119

Darrington School District #330
Indian Education Program, P.O. Box 27 • Darrington, WA 98241

Mt. Baker School District
Indian Education Program, P.O. Box 45 • Deming, WA 98244
  (360) 383-2015 ext. 4511 Fax 383-2029; Juan Ortiz, Director
Grades: 7-12. *Description*: Services include tutoring, grade improvement; class in Native culture, leadership and self-esteem.

Elma School District
Indian Education Program, 30 Elma Monte Rd. • Elma, WA 98541

Federal Way School District
Indian Education Program
32020 1st Ave. S #109 • Federal Way, WA 98003
  Maxine Alex, Contact; E-mail: malex@fwps.org

Ferndale School District #502
Indian Education Program, P.O. Box 428 • Ferndale, WA 98248

Fife School District
Indian Education Program, 5802 20th St. E • Fife, WA 98424
  Rebecca Kreth, Director, Native American Early Learning Project
  E-mail: rkreth@psesd.org

Queets-Clearwater S.D. #20
Indian Education Program, 146000 Hwy. 101 • Forks, WA 98331

Quillayute Valley S.D. #402
Indian Education Program, P.O. Box 60 • Forks, WA 98331

Glenwood School District #401
Indian Education Program, P.O. Box 12 • Glenwood, WA 98619
  (509) 364-3438 Fax 364-3689; Chris Anderson, Director
Grades K-12. *Description*: Provides support for students to attend youth
conference; cultural activities and awareness education; and summer school,
athletic and academic camps. Instructor: Emma Jane LaVallie.

Granger School District #204
Indian Education Program, P.O. Box 400 • Granger, WA 98932

Central Valley S.D. #356
Indian Education Program, E. 19307 Cataldo • Greenacres, WA 99016

Hoquiam School District
Indian Education Program, 312 Simpson • Hoquiam, WA 98550

Columbia School District #206
Indian Education Program, P.O. Box 7 • Hunters, WA 99137

Ocean Beach School District #101
Indian Education Program, P.O. Box 860 • Ilwaco, WA 98624

Inchelium School District #70
Indian Education Program, P.O. Box 285 • Inchelium, WA 99138

WA State Indian Education
Indian Education Program, P.O. Box 259 • Indianola, WA 98342

Crescent School District #313
Indian Education Program, P.O. Box 2 • Joyce, WA 98343

Kelso School District #453
Indian Education Program, 410 Elm St. • Kelso, WA 98626

Kent School District
Indian Education Program, 12033 SE 256th St. • Kent, WA 98031

La Conner School District
Indian Education Program, P.O. Box D • La Conner, WA 98257

La Push School District
Indian Education Program, P.O. Box 33 • La Push, WA 98350

North Thurston School District
Indian Education Program, 305 College St., NE • Lacey, WA 98506

Longview School District #122
Indian Education Program, 1410 8th Ave. • Longview, WA 98632
  (360) 575-7437 Fax 575-7456; Judy Duff, Coordinator
  Ann Cavanaugh, Director
Grades K-12. *Instructors*: Raquel Johnston, Tina Thompson, Benita Revis,
Jodi Traub, Tanya Beltz. *Programs*: Provides culture classes and tutoring;
classroom & community presentations; newsletter and annual powwow.

Lyle School District #406
Indian Education Program, P.O. Box 368 • Lyle, WA 98635

Edmonds School District
Indian Education Program, 20420 68th Ave. W. • Lynnwood, WA 98036

(425) 431-7133 Fax 431-7006
Laura Wong-Whitebear, Program Coordinator

Marysville School District
Indian Education Program, 4220 80th NE • Marysville, WA 98270

Monroe Public Schools
Skykomish Valley Indian Education, 200 E. Freemont • Monroe, WA 98272
  (800) 282-7818 (Western Washinington)
  (360) 804-2554 Fax 804-2529
  Mars Miller, Coordinator; E-mail: millerm@monroe.wednet.edu
Description: Offers academic support & cultural activities for Native American
& Alaskan Native students, preschool through high school in the Monroe,
Snohomish & Sultan public schools. *Activities*: Annual Powwow Memorial Day.

Nespelem School District #014
Indian Education Program, P.O. Box 291 • Nespelem, WA 99155

Nooksack Valley School District
Indian Education Program, P.O. Box 307 • Nooksack, WA 98276

North Kitsap School District
Indian Education Program, 18360 Caldart NE • North Kitsap, WA 98370

Oakville School District #400
Indian Education Program, P.O. Box H • Oakville, WA 98568

Okanogan School District #105
Indian Education Program, P.O. Box 592 • Okanogan, WA 98840
  (509) 422-3770; Dorothy Hamner, Director
Grades K-12. *Description*: Serves the special & unique needs of
Native American students. J.O.M.

Olympia School District #111
Indian Education Program, 1113 E. Legion Way • Olympia, WA 98501

North Beach School District #64
Indian Education Program, P.O. Box 159 • Ocean Shores, WA 98569

Washington State Dept. of Public Instruction
Indian Education Office, • Olympia, WA 98504

Omak School District #19
Indian Education Program, P.O. Box 833 • Omak, WA 98841

Port Angeles School District #121
Indian Education Program, 216 E. Fourth St. • Port Angeles, WA 98362

South Kitsap School District
Indian Education Program, 1962 Hoover SE • Port Orchard, WA 98366

North Kitsap School District
Indian Education Program, 18360 Caldart NE • Poulsbo, WA 98371

Puyallup School District
Indian Education Program, 105 7th St., SW • Puyallup, WA 98371
  Michelle Marcoe, Contact; E-mail: marcoma@puyallup.k12.wa.us

Lake Washington School District
Indian Education Program, P.O. Box 97039 • Redmond, WA 98073

Renton School District
Indian Education Program, 435 Main Ave. S • Renton, WA 98056
  Earline Bala, Contact; E-mail: ebala@renton.wednet.edu

American Indian Heritage Program
Middle College High School - North Seattle Community College
9600 College Way North • Seattle, WA 98103
  (206) 527-3733; Robert Eaglestaff, Principal
  E-mail: nsccinfo@sccd.ctc.edu. Grades: 6-12.

Huchoosedah Indian Education Program
1330 N. 90th St. • Seattle, WA 98103
  Mike Tulee, Program Manager
Grades K-12. *Description*: Conducts various social service activities that are
designed to assist Native American students acclimate to the urban public
school system.

Highline Public School District
Indian Education Program, 614 SW 120th St. • Seattle, WA 98146
  Barbara Fernandes-Kemp, Contact; E-mail: fernanb@hsd401.org

Seattle Public Schools
Native American Education Program
John Stafford Center for Educational Excellence
2445 3rd Ave. S. • Seattle, WA 98124
(206) 252-0948; Gail T. Morris, Program Manager
E-mail: gtmorrisi@seattleschools.org
Janine Tillotson (Tlingit), Native Education Intervention Specialist
E-mail: jetillotson@seattleschools.org
Vicki Segundo, Lead Teacher; E-mail: vsegundo@seattleschools.org

Sedro-Woolley S.D. #101
Indian Education Program • Sedro-Woolley, WA 98284

Cape Flattery S.D. #401
Indian Education Program, P.O. Box 109 • Sekiu, WA, 98381

Hood Canal S.D. #404
Indian Education Program, N. 111 Hwy. 106 • Shelton, WA 98584

South Bend Schools
Indian Education Program, P.O. Box 437 • South Bend, WA 98586
(360) 875-5707; Gary C. Johnson, Director
Grades K-12. *Description*: Serves 70 students in Chinook Indian Country; students learn about Chinook culture; counseling & educational guidance.

Spokane Public School District
Indian Education Program, Ad Bldg. N. 200 Bernard St. • Spokane, WA 99201
Don Barlow, Contact

Mary Walker School District #207
Indian Education Program, P.O. Box 159 • Springdale, WA 99173

Clover Park School District #400
Indian Education Program
10903 Gravelly Lake Dr. SW • Tacoma, WA 98499

Tacoma School District #10
Indian Education Program
601 So. 8th St., P.O. Box 1357 • Tacoma, WA 98401
(253) 571-1846 Fax 571-2637; Website: www.tacoma.k12.wa.us
David Syth, Coordinator; E-mail: dsyth@tacoma.k12.wa.us
Martha Sherman, Indian Education Specialist
Grades: K-12. *Description*: Two goals - career development for grades 9-12 and student advisement for grades K-12. Works cooperatively with Special Education; Learning Assistant Program (LAP); Title One; English as a Second Language, general education, career services & counseling to meet the needs of Indian students.

Taholah School District #77
Indian Education Program, P.O. Box 249 • Taholah, WA 98587

Toppenish School District #202
Indian Education Program • Toppenish, WA 98948

Yakima School District
Indian Education Program, P.O. Box 151 • Toppenish, WA 98948

Vancouver School District #37
Indian Education Program • Vancouver, WA 98668

Wellpinit School District #49
Indian Education Program, P.O. Box 390 • Wellpinit, WA 99040

Wapato School District #207
Indian Education Program, P.O. Box 38 • Wapato, WA 98951

Mt. Adams School District #209
Indian Education Program, P.O. Box 578 • White Swan, WA 98952

Educational Service District #105
Indian Education Program, 33 S. Second Ave. • Yakima, WA 98902

Yelm School District
Indian Education Program, P.O. Box 476 • Yelm, WA 98597

WISCONSIN

Appleton Area School District
Indian Education Program, P.O. Box 2019 • Appleton, WI 54913

Houdini Elementary School
Indian Education Program, 2305 W. Capitol Rd. • Appleton, WI 54915

Ashland School District
Indian Education Program, 1900 Beaser Ave. • Ashland, WI 54806

Baraboo School District
Indian Education Program, 101 Second St. • Baraboo, WI 53913

Bayfield School District-Supt.
Indian Education Program, P.O. Box 5001 • Bayfield, WI 54814

Black River Falls School
Indian Education Program, 301 N. 4th St. • Black River Falls, WI 54615
(715) 284-4357 Fax 284-7064
Shelly Severson, Title VII Administrator
E-mail: shelly.severson@brf.org
Michelle Cloud, Title VII PAC Chair

Bowler Public Schools
Indian Education Program, P.O. Box 8 • Bowler, WI 54416
(715) 793-4101 Fax 793-1302; Donna Miller, Program Director
Grades Pre K-12. *Description*: Provides tutorial assistance, cultural activities & opportunities, and resources for both staff and students.

Crandon School District
Indian Education Program, P.O. Box 310 • Crandon, WI 54520

Cumberland School District
Indian Education Program, P.O. Box 67 • Cumberland, WI 54829

West De Pere School District
Indian Education Program, 1155 Westwood St. • De Pere, WI 54115

Eau Claire Area School District
Indian Education Program, 500 Main St. • Eau Claire, WI 54701
(715) 852-3106; Shannon Mason Young, Indian Education Coordinator
Grades K-12. Description: Designed to meet the special educational needs of American Indian children in the Eau Claire School District.

Milwaukee Indian Community School
10405 W. St. Martins Rd. • Franklin, WI 53132
(414) 525-6100; Website: www.ics.milw.org
Alan Caldwell, Principal; Margaret Bublitz, Chief Operating Officer
David J.W. Kklauser (Ho-Chunk), Chairperson
Board members: Diane Amour (Priairie Band Potawatomi), Anne Egan-Waukau (Menominee), Carmen Flores (Oneida), Jone Stromberg (Ojibwe/Red Cliff), Kim Novak (Oneida), Sommer Drake (Oneida). Privately owned & operated urban intertribal school. Grades: K-8. *Enrollment*: 280 students from eleven area tribes.

Freedom Area School District
Indian Education Program, P.O. Box 1008 • Freedom, WI 54131

Green Bay Area Public School District
Indian Education Program, P.O. Box 23387 • Green Bay, WI 54305

Howard-Suamico School District
Indian Education Program, 1935 Cardinal Lane • Green Bay, WI 54313
(920) 662-7886 Fax 662-7900
Brian Stevens, Director; E-mail: briastev@hssd.k12.wi.us
Grades K-12. *Program*: Title VII Indian education program provides classroom teachers activities that are culture based and relevant to those students who are affiliated with tribes here in Wisconsin. *Activities*: Workshops that address Chapter 31, preparing sovereign rights of American Indians. Families are strengthened via Native staff whose responsibility includes providing support to both students and parents. *Instructor*: Brian Stevens.

Hayward Community Schools
Indian Education Program, P.O. Box 860 • Hayward, WI 54843
(715) 634-2619 Fax 634-3560; William Trautt, District Administrator
Grades: K-12. *Program*: Teaches the Ojibwa language & culture.
Instructors: Donna Johnson, Darlene Stockinger.

Menominee Indian School District
Indian Education Program, P.O. Box 399 • Keshena, WI 54135

Madison Metro. School District
Indian Education Program, 545 W. Dayton St. • Madison, WI 53703
Kenneth White Horse, Contact

La Crosse School District
Indian Education Program, 807 East Ave. South • La Crosse, WI 54601

Lac du Flambeau Public School
510 Old Abe Rd. • Lac du Flambeau, WI 54538

Madison Metropolitan School District
Indian Education Program, 545 W. Dayton St. • Madison, WI 53703
  (608) 663-8456 Fax 442-3471
  Timothy Fish, Title VII Coordinator; E-mail: twfish@madison.k12.wi.us
  Rachel Byington (Choctaw), Resource Teacher
  E-mail: rbyington@madison.k12.wi.us

Milwaukee Public Schools
Indian Education Program, P.O. Drawer 10-K • Milwaukee, WI 53201

Lakeland Union High School
Indian Education Program, 8669 Old Hwy. 70 West • Minocqua, WI 54548

Nekoosa Public Schools
Indian Education Program, 310 1st St. • Nekoosa, WI 54457

Osseo-Fairchild School District-Supt.
Indian Education Program, P.O. Box 130 • Osseo, WI 54758

Pulaski Community School District
Hillcrest Elementary School, Indian Education Program
P.O. Box 36 • Pulaski, WI 54162 (920) 272-6900 Fax 822-6005
  Emily Johnson, Native American Tutor

Seymour Community School District
Indian Education Program, 10 Circle Dr. • Seymour, WI 54165

Shawano-Gresham School District
Indian Education Program, 210 S. Franklin • Shawano, WI 54166

Siren School District
Indian Education Program, P.O. Box 29 • Siren, WI 54872

Stevens Point Public School
Indian Education Program, 1900 Polk St. • Stevens Point, WI 54481

Superior School District
Indian Education Program, 3025 Tower Ave. • Superior, WI 54880

Tomah Area School District
Indian Education Program, 901 Lincoln Ave. • Tomah, WI 54660

Wabeno School District
Indian Education Program, 4343 Mill Lane • Wabeno, WI 54566
  Debra Tucker Kruger, Contact

Washburn School District
Indian Education Program, 305 W. 4th St. • Washburn, WI 54891

Wausau School District
Indian Education Program, 415 Seymour St. • Wausau, WI 54401

Webster School District
Indian Education Program, 26428 Lakeland Ave. • Webster, WI 54893

Winter Community Schools
Indian Education Program, P.O. Box 7 • Winter, WI 54896

Wisconsin Dells School District
Director of Curriculum, 300 Vine St. • Wisconsin Dells, WI 53965

Wisconsin Rapids Public Schools
Native American Coordinator, 510 Peach St. • Wisconsin Rapids, WI 54494

Wittenberg-Birnamwood School
Indian Education Program, P.O. Box 269 • Wittenberg, WI 54499

WYOMING

Arapahoe School - Fremont County School District #38
P.O. Box 9211 • Arapahoe, WY 82510
  (307) 856-9333; Marilyn Clausen, Contact
Grades K-18. 270 students. Located on the Wind River Indian Reservation

Ft. Washakie School District #21
Indian Education Program, Box 110, Ethete Rd. • Fort Washakie, WY 82512

Wyoming Indian Education Office
Indian Education Program • Fort Washakie, WY 82514

Fremont Co. School District #1
Indian Education Program, Baldwin Creek Rd. • Lander, WY 82520

Riverton High School/S.D.#25
Indian Education Program, 2001 West Sunset • Riverton, WY 82501
  (307) 856-9491 ext. 13 Fax 856-2333; June Shakespeare, Director
Grades K-12. *Description*: Provides academic, cultural enrichment and tutoring services for American Indian children residing in the district; also service referrals, Indian clubs.

This section, alpha-geographically arranged, lists departments & personnel of various institutions of higher learning that offer courses on the American Indian. Includes both Indian colleges & universities with Native Studies departments, departments of anthropology, & other departments offering related courses.

ALASKA

UNIVERSITY OF ALASKA, ANCHORAGE
Department of Alaska Native Studies & Diversity
3211 Providence Dr. • ANCHORAGE, AK 99508
  (907) 786-4358 Fax 786-0804; Website: www.uaa.alaska.edu
  Maria Williams, Associate Professor; Director of Alaska Native Studies
    (786-6136) E-mail: mdwilliams6@uaa.alaska.edu
  Jeane (T'aaw xlwaa) Breinig, Professor & Associate Dean, CAS,
    Interim Associate Vice Chancellor for Alaska Natives & Diversity
    (Office: ADM-221; E-mail: jmbreinig@uaa.alaska.edu
  Edgar Blatchford, Associate Professor of Journalism & Communications
    & Aaslka Native Studies (786-4188) E-mail: eblatchford@uaa.alaska.edu
  Beth Leonard, Associate Professor of Alaska Native Studies (786-6140)
    E-mail: brleonard@alaska.edu
  Libby Eufemio, Assistant Professor of Alutiiq Studies, odiak College
    (486-1276) E-mail: epeufemio@kodiak.alaska.edu
  Karla Booth, Alaska Native & Rural Outreach Program (ANROP) Coordinator
    (751-7452) E-mail: khbooth@alaska.edu
  Sabrina Walker, Administrative Generalist, Alaska Native Studies
    (786-6135) E-mail: ssmit308@alaska.edu
Description: UAA serves over 2000 Alaska Natives, American Indian, and Native Hawaiian/Pacific Islander students. Graduates over 250 AN/AI students each year in over 25 degree programs. Campuses are located in Anchorage, Mat-Su, Kenai, Kodiak and Prince William Sound, located on the traditional homelands of the Dena'ina and Ahtna Athabascan, Alutiiq/Sugpiaq, and Eyak peoples. Anchorage is sometimes affectionately called "Alaska's largest village" and has been identified as the city with the highest percentage of Alaska Natives and American Indians in the United States; UAA offers a variety of Alaska Native programs, services, and opportunities.

*ILISAGVIK COLLEGE
P.O. Box 749 • BARROW, AK 99723
  (800) 478-7337; (907) 852-3333 Fax 852-1821
  Website: www.ilisagvik.edu
  Dr. Pearl Kiyawn Nageak Brower (Inupiaq), President
Purpose: A two-year college primarily serving the residents of the North Slope Borough; provides quality post-secondary academic, vocational and technical education in a learning environment that perpetuates and strengthens Iñupiat culture, language, values and traditions. It is dedicated to serving its students and developing a well-educated and trained workforce who meet the human resource needs of North Slope employers and the state of Alaska. *Program*: Inupiaq studies. *Publication*: Ilisagvik News. Tuzzy Consortium Library. Established 1995.

UNIVERSITY OF ALASKA, FAIRBANKS - KUSKOKWIM CAMPUS
201 Akiak Dr., P.O. Box 368 • BETHEL, AK 99559
  (800) 478-5822; (907) 543-4500; Website: www.bethel.uaf.edu
  Mary Pete, Director (543-4502); E-mail: mpete@alaska.edu
  Reyne Athanas, HUD Yupiit Piciryarait Coordinator (543-4538)
    E-mail: mathanas@alaska.edu
  Martha Simon, Coordinator, Hooper Bay Learning Center
    (758-4004); E-mail: mpsimon@alaska.edu
  Cheri Boisvert, Librarian (543-4571) E-mail: clboisvert@alaska.edu
Resources: Kuskokwim Consortium Library (543-4516)
  E-mail: tquiner@alaska.edu

UNIVERSITY OF ALASKA, FAIRBANKS
Dept. of Alaska Native Studies & Rural Development
College of Rural & Community Development (CRCD)
3rd Floor Brooks Bldg., P.O. Box 756500 • FAIRBANKS, AK 99775
  (888) 574-6528; (907) 474-6325
  Website: www.uaf.edu/danrd; E-mail: fydanrd@uaf.edu
  Evon Peter, Vice Chancellor (474-5824) E-mail: espeter@alaska.edu
  Diane Benson, Assistant Professor; E-mail: debenson2@alaska.edu
  Cathy Brooks, Assistant Professor & Faculty Advisor-Festival of Native Arts
    (474-6325) E-mail: cabrooks2@alaska.edu
  Jennifer L.L. Carroll, Assistant Professor (474-5405)
    E-mail: jlcarroll@alaska.edu
  Patricia Sekaquaptewa, Assistant Professor (474-1539)
    E-mail: pssekaquaptewa@alaska.edu
  Charlene Stern, Assistant Professor (474-5293)
    E-mail: cbstern@alaska.edu

Judith Ramos, Assistant Professor (786-0802)
  E-mail: jramos2@alaska.edu
Jenny Bell-Jones, Emeritus Professor & Adjunct
  E-mail: jbjones@alaska.edu
Courses: Native Cultures of North America, and Alaska; Arctic & New World Prehistory; seminars on specialized aspects of Eskimo, Aleut, & Athapaskan groups. Regular instruction in Inupiaq, Yup'ik, & Athabaskan offered by the Alaska Native Language Center. Offers Rural Development degree programs. *Instructors*: *Programs*: Graduate & faculty research on Eskimo-Aleuts & North American Indians; teaching assistant-ships to graduate students. *Activities*: Festival of Native Arts. *Resources*: University of Alaska Museum; Alaska Native Language Center; Elmer E. Rasmuson Library. *Publications*: DANSRD Newsletter; Anthropological Papers of the University of Alaska.

UNIVERSITY OF ALASKA
Northwest Campus, P.O. Box 400 • NOME, AK 99762
  (800) 478-2202; (907) 443-2201 Fax 443-5602
  Website: www.nwc.info@alaska.edu; E-mail: nwc.info@alaska.edu
  James R. Johnsen, President
  Brandi Berg, Executive Officer (450-8010)
    E-mail: ua-bor@gmail.com
  Gloria O'Neill, Board Chairperson (793-3278)
    E-mail: goneill@citci.org
A rural site of the Rural College of the University of Alaska, Fairbanks providing post-secondary education to the Seward Peninsula region.

ARIZONA

DINE' COLLEGE – CHINLE CENTER
575 Main St., P.O. Box 1997 • CHINLE, AZ 86503
  (928) 674-3319/3320 Fax 674-8488
  Cathy L. Bahe, Director; E-mail: clbahe@dinecollege.edu
Chinle site student enrollment ranges from 100 – 200. Most courses are held in the evenings on weekends. A one-stop site and our college is fully committed to provide efficient and effective student services in advisement, registration, testing, orientation, ITV courses and we have computers available for students, and field trips. Many students are non-traditional students. Some of them are parents and/or have full time jobs during the day. Many of these students prefer to remain home, take college courses, save money, care for their elder parents and grandparents and take care of livestock. Chinle Agency serves 13 Chapters. 20-30 students graduate each spring semester.

INDIAN BIBLE COLLEGE
P.O. Box 30880 • FLAGSTAFF, AZ 86003
  (928) 774-3890 Fax 774-2655; Website: www.indianbible.org
  Dr. Jason Koppen, President; Helen Yazzi, Alumni Director
Special program: Native American United Club. *Facilities*: Native American Cultural Center. *Affiliated facilities*: Department participates in the Museum of Northern Arizona Joint Scholar in Residence Program; a cooperative program with the Navajo Nation Archeology Dept. & the Hopi Nation; and has cooperative agreements with Grand Canyon National Park, Glen Canyon National Recreation Area, and Wupatki National Monument; Native Americans for Community Action, Flagstaff. *Publications*: Anthropological Papers; Technical Report Series.

NORTHERN ARIZONA UNIVERSITY
College of Social & Behavioral Sciences
Applied Indigenous Studies Department
SBS West Bldg. 70, Suite 100
P.O. Box 15020 • FLAGSTAFF, AZ 86011
  (928) 523-6624 Fax 523-5560
  Website: www.nau.edu/sbs/ais; E-mail: ais@nau.edu
  Karen Jarratt-Snider (Mississippi Choctaw), Chairperson & Associate
    Professor (523-6219) E-mail: karen.jarratt-snider@nau.edu
  Manley A. Begay, Jr., Professor; E-mail: manley.begay-jr@nau.edu
  Chad Hamill, PhD (Spokan), Associate Professor (523-3849)
    E-mail: chad.hamill@nau.edu
  Lomayumtewa Ishii, Associate Professor
    E-mail: lomayumtewa.ishii@nau.edu
  Octaviana Trujillo, Professor; E-mail: octaviana.trujillo@nau.edu
  Michael Lerma (Dine') (523-3392) E-mail: Michael.lerma@nau.edu
  Christopher Jocks, Senior Lecturer; E-mail: Christopher.jocks@nau.edu
  Alisse Ali-Joseph & Darold H. Joseph, Lecturers
Description: The major combines contemporary tribal management skills with respect for indigenous culture, knowledge, values & beliefs. Combine class-room education & traditional tribal knowledge to work effectively within indigenous communities; historical development of tribal self-determination & its impact on indigenous peoples. *Program*: Ethnic Studies Program. *Degrees*: BA & BS in AIS; Minor in AIS; Minor in Indigenous Health Studies; Minor in Native American Studies. *Affiliated Faculty*: Jeffrey Berglund (English);

Michael Vasquez (Anthropology). Lorenzo Max, Elder (523-6624) Email: Lorenzo.max@nau.edu. *Special program*: Native American United Club. *Facilities*: Native American Cultural Center. *Affiliated facilities*: Cline Library; Department participates in the Museum of Northern Arizona Joint Scholar in Residence Program; a cooperative program with the Navajo Nation Archeology Dept. & the Hopi Nation; and has cooperative agreements with Grand Canyon National Park, Glen Canyon National Recreation Area, and Wupatki National Monument; Native Americans for Community Action, Flagstaff. *Publications*: Anthropological Papers; Technical Report Series. *Scholarship available*: The Audrey Tsosie Memorial Scholarship.

NORTHERN ARIZONA UNIVERSITY
NATIVE AMERICAN CULTURAL CENTER
318 W. McCreary, Bldg. 14, P.O. Box 4085 • FLAGSTAFF, AZ 86011
(928) 523-9557 Fax 523-1270
Website: www.nau.edu/na-cultural-center/welcome/
Ora Marek-Martinez, Executive Director
E-mail: ora.marek-martinez@nau.edu
Purpose: To enhance the visibility & standing of on-going programs, both academic & service oriented that relate to Native American tribes, their culture, issues & future prospects. *Publication*: Newsletter.

NORTHERN ARIZONA UNIVERSITY
NATIVE AMERICAN STUDENT SERVICES
Native American Cultural Center (Bldg. 14, Rm. 100)
P.O. Box 5653 • FLAGSTAFF, AZ 86011
(877) 523-8125; (928) 523-8086 Fax 523-8855
Website: www.nau.edu/nass; E-mail: nassnatives@nau.edu
Simon Chief (Navajo), Program Coordinator (523-8061)
E-mail: simon.chief@nau.edu
Sharon S. Doctor (Navajo), Interim Director (523-6960)
E-mail: sharon.doctor@nau.edu
Andrea Sequaptewa (Hopi), Interim Assistant Director (523-5512)
E-mail: andrea.sequaptewa@nau.edu
Diana Onco (Navajo), Program Coordinator (523-3147)
E-mail: diana.onco@nau.edu
Purpose: To provide support services to Native American & Alaskan Native students at NAU representing more than 50 tribal affiliations throughout the U.S. tribal scholarships available. *Publication*: Smoke Signals.

NORTHERN ARIZONA UNIVERSITY
Department of Anthropology
Ralph M. Bilby Research Center, P.O. Box 6013 • FLAGSTAFF, AZ 86011
(928) 523-3180 Fax 523-9135; E-mail: anthropology@nau.edu
Kelly Laurila, Senior Coordinator (480) 215-0065
Laurie Thom, Coordinator (523-1569)
An agency of the Navajo Nation government dedicated to providing cultural resource management services to its clients at a reasonable cost, while preserving & protecting the cultural heritage of the Navajo people. Located on the Northern Arizona University Campus in the Bilby Research Center.

SAGU AMERICAN INDIAN COLLEGE
10020 N. 15th Ave. • PHOENIX, AZ 85021
(602) 944-3335 ext. 231 Fax 943-8299
Website: www.aicag.edu; E-mail: info@sagu.edu
Dr. David J. Moore, President; Email: dmoore@sagu.edu
Dr. Joseph J. Saggio, Dean of the College; E-mail: jsaggio@sagu.edu
The only fully accredited Pentecostal College with a focus on Native Americans. *Mission*: To equip Native Americans for Christian Service within a Christian Community. Established 1957.

SCOTTSDALE COMMUNITY COLLEGE (SCC)
AMERICAN INDIAN STUDIES (AIS); AMERICAN INDIAN PROGRAM (AIP)
9000 E. Chaparral St. • SCOTTSDALE, AZ 85256
(480) 423-6531 Fax 423-6786
Website: www.scottsdalecc.edu/aip
Ana Cuddington (Gila River Pima), AIP Director
E-mail: ana.cuddington@sccmail.maricopa.edu
Winona Thirion (Navajo), AIP Advisor
E-mail: winona.thirion@sccmail.maricopa.edu
Jonette Lewis (Colorado River Indian Tribes, Administrative Assistant
Scottsdale Community College is located on the tribal lands of the Salt River Pima-Maricopa Indian Community. *Mission*: To address the changing & highly diverse educational needs of American Indian students & Indian communities; to assist American Indian students in achieving academic & personal success at SCC. Located on the Salt River Pima-Maricopa Indian Community in Scottsdale. *Faculty*: Tia Bruised Head (Confederated Tribes, Yakama, Dine), Counselor E-mail: tia.bruisedhead@sccmail.maricopa.edu; Jaakko Puisto; Manuel F. Pino (Acoma Pueblo), AIS Director E-mail: manny.pino@sccmail.maricopa.edu; Roger McKinney (Kickapoo), Art; Michael LittleCrow (Turtle Mountain Chippewa), Math.

*TOHONO O'ODHAM COMMUNITY COLLEGE
P.O. Box 3129 • SELLS, AZ 85634
(520) 383-8401 Fax 383-8403
Website: http://tocc.edu; E-mail: info@tocc.edu
Paul M. Robertson (Tohono O'odham), President
Juana Clare Jose (Tohono O'odham), VP of Education
Mario Montes-Helu (Tohono O'odham), Academic Chairperson
Netallia Tsosie (Tohono O'odham), Academic Advisor
Sylvia Hendricks (Tohono O'odham), VP Student Services
Robert Spencer, Director of Operations
Ronald Geronimo (Tohono O'odham), Tohono O'odham Studies Director
Gaye Bumsted Perry (Tohono O'odham), Curriculum Coordinator
Annabah Conn, Director of Institutional Research
Elaine M. Cubbins, College Librarian; E-mail: ecubbins@tocc.edu
Bernard Siquieros, Board Chair; Jonas R. Robles, Board Vice Chair
Elizabeth "Libby" Francisco, Board Secretary
Anthony M. Chana, Dr. Ofelia Zepeda, Board Members
Mission: To facilitate the preservation of Tohono O'odham culture & tradition by requiring all students in degree programs to study Tohono O'odham language & culture, and by starting a program in agriculture & natural resource management. *Full-time Faculty* (partial list): Edison Cassadore (San Carlos Apache), Writing; Ron Geronimo (Tohono O'odham), Language & Culture; Phillip L. Miguel (Tohono O'odham), Language & Culture; Delores Saraficio (Tohono O'odham), GED; Estella Melendez (Tohono O'odham), Painting. Tohono O'odham Community College Library

ARIZONA STATE UNIVERSITY
DEPARTMENT OF AMERICAN INDIAN STUDIES
College of Liberal Arts & Sciences, Discovery Hall, Room 356
250 E. Lemon St., P.O. Box 874603 • TEMPE, AZ 85287
(480) 965-3634 Fax 965-2216
Website: www.asu.edu; E-mail: ais@asu.edu
James Riding In (Pawnee), Interim Director & Associate Professor
E-mail: pawnee1@asu.edu (965-9360)
Myla Vicenti Carpio (Jicarilla Apache, Laguna Pueblo/Isleta Pueblo),
Graduate Studies Director & Associate Professor (727-7989)
E-mail: vicenti@asu.edu
Alicia Richardson, Program Manager
(480) 727-6442; E-mail: alicia.richardson@asu.edu
Jennica Fulwilder, Student Advisor (727-7056)
E-mail: jennica.fulwilder@asu.edu
Aaron Woods, Program Coordinator
(480) 727-8691; E-mail: awoods@asurite.asu.edu
Faculty: James Riding In (Pawnee) see above
Myla Vicenti Carpio (Jicarilla Apache/Laguna Pueblo/Isleta Pueblo) above
David Martinez (Gila River Pima), Associate Professor (727-9818)
E-mail: david.martinez.3@asu.edu
Leo Killsback (Northern Cheyenne), Assistant Professor (727-0061)
E-mail: leo.killsback@asu.edu
Michelle Hale (Navajo), Assistant Professor (965-3634
E-mail: michelle.hale@asu.edu
Tennille Marley (White Mountain Apache), Assistant Professor (965-8308)
Simon Ortiz (Acoma Pueblo), Regents Professor (965-7999)
E-mail: simon.ortiz@asu.edu
Eunice Romero-Little (Cochiti Pueblo), Associate Professor (965-313)
E-mail: m.eunice@asu.edu
Cheryl Louise Bennett (Navajo, Comanche), Assistant Professor (727-0521)
E-mail: cheryl.louise.bennett@asu.edu
Jolyana Begay (Navajo), Instructor; (965-3634)
E-mail: jolyana.begay@asu.edu
Emeritus Faculty:
John W. Tippeconnic (Comanche-Cherokee) (727-0060)
E-mail: john.tippeconnic@asu.edu
Eddie F. Brown (Pascua Yaqui-Tohono O'odham), Professor
AIS/School of Social Work) E-mail: efbrown@asu.edu
Carol Lujan (Dine'), Emeritus Associate Professor
E-mail: caol.lujan@asu.edu
Affiliated Faculty:
Bryan Brayboy, Professor of Social Transformation (965-5327)
E-mail: bryan.brayboy@asu.edu
Robert Clinton, Professor of Law (965-3501)
E-mail: robert.clinton@asu.edu
Donald Fixico, Professo SHPRS (727-9082)
E-mail: donald.fixico@asu.edu
Robert J. Miller, professor of Law (965-4085)
E-mail: Robert.j.miller@asu.edu
Laura Tohe, Professor of English (965-5553)
E-mail: l.tohe@asu.edu
Monica Tsethlikai, Assistant Professor (965-6978)
E-mail: monica.tsethlikai@asu.edu

Adjunct Faculty:
Victor Begay (Navajo-Dine'), Academic Community Liaison Director
  E-mail: vbegay@asu.edu
Laura Gonzales-Macias, Assistant Director AISSS (965-1711)
  E-mail: lauragm@asu.edu
Traci L. Morris, Director-American Indian Policy Institute (965-9005)
  E-mail: t.morris@asu.edu
Facilities: Heard Museum; Pueblo Grande Museum; A.A. Dahlberg Memorial Collection of 9,000 Pima Indian dental casts & genealogies.

ARIZONA STATE UNIVERSITY – THE CENTER FOR INDIAN EDUCATION
School of Social Transformation (SST), College of Liberal Arts & Sciences
Payne Hall, Suite 302, P.O. Box 876403 • TEMPE, AZ 85287-6403
  (480) 965-6292 Fax 965-8115; E-mail: ciehelp@asu.edu
Website: https://center-for-indian-education.asu.edu
Bryan Brayboy (Lumbee), Professor of SST Justice & Social Inquiry
  Co-Director & Journal Co-editor (965-5327)
  E-mail: bryan.brayboy@asu.edu
Colin Ben, Postdoctoral Research Fellow
  E-mail: colin.ben@asu.edu
K. Tsianina Lomawaima (Creek), Professor, Center for Indian Education; Professor, SST Justice & Social Inquiry; Professor, SST Social & Cultural Pedagogy; E-mail: k.tsianina.lomawaima@asu.edu
Jeremiah Chin, Grad Teaching Associate
  E-mail: jeremiah.chin@asu.edu
Deborah Chadwick, Research Professional (727-6405)
  E-mail: deborah.chadwick@asu.edu
June Whitaker, Program Manager; E-mail: june.whitaker@asu.edu
Lindsey Cook, Student Support Coordinator (965-1999)
  E-mail: Lindsey.cook@asu.edu
Teresa McCarty, Professor Emerita & Journal Co-Editor (965-6292)
  E-mail: teresa.mccarty@asu.edu
Eunice Romero-little, Associate Professor (965-6977)
  E-mail: m.eunice@asu.edu
Elizabeth Sumida Huaman, Assistant Professor-Justice & Social Inquiry
  (965-2410) E-mail: esumidah@asu.edu
Andrea Underwood, Business Operations Specialist (965-8923)
  E-mail: andrea.underwood@asu.edu
Publication: Journal of American Indian Education, ASU, P.O. Box 871311, Tempe, AZ 85287

ARIZONA STATE UNIVERSITY - INDIAN LEGAL PROGRAM
Sandra Day O'Connor College of Law
McAllister & Orange Sts., Box 877906 • TEMPE, AZ 85287
  (480) 727-0420 Fax 965-2427; Website: www.law.asu.edu/ilp
E-mail: indianlegalclinic@asu.edu
Kathleen Rosier (Comanche of Oklahoma), Executive Director & Faculty
  E-mail: pafergus@asu.edu.
Patty Ferguson-Bohnee (Pointe-au-Chien), Faculty Director
  (Director, Indian Legal Clinic) (727-8580); E-mail: pafergus@asu.edu
Darlene Lester, Program Coordinator (965-7715)
  E-mail: darlene.lester@asu.edu
Established in 1988 to provide legal education & generate scholarship in the areas of Indian law and to undertake public service to tribal governments. The program trains students to effectively engage the representation of Native peoples & seeks to promote an understanding of the differences between the legal systems of Indian Nations and those of the state & federal governments. **Indian Law Certificate**—awarded to students who finish 21 hours of relevant curriculum, write a substantial paper, and complete practical work in the Indian Legal Clinic. **Rosette LLP, American Indian Economic Development Program**—provides an innovative and challenging curriculum for students; hosts annual conferences for students, attorneys, tribal leaders, tribal citizens, policy makers, entrepreneurs, developers, and financial advisors that focus on tribal economic development; creates a community outreach component. National conferences and lectures—top scholars and attorneys are invited to present cutting-edge legal issues in Indian country. **Native Vote Election Protection Project**—allows students to share information about individual voting rights. **Tribal Court Trial Skills Program**—an intensive week of training for tribal court advocates. **Pipeline to Law Initiative**—invites students and attorneys to assist in community outreach, mentorship, and pre-law advising to help improve access to justice in tribal communities - Learn more about Pipeline to Law Initiative. The ILP is preeminent among national programs for providing unique opportunities and experiences to its students; placing graduates in the practice of law, partnering with American Indian Nations and other Native governments and organizations, contributing to Indian Country, and providing superior teaching and Indian legal scholarship.
Faculty: Robert Miler; Robert N. Clinton, JD (Foundation Professor of Law); Kevin Gover, JD; Paul Bender; Dr. Don Warne (Oglala Lakota); Kathleen Rosier (Comanche of Oklahoma); Doreen Nanibaa Hobson, Director-Indian Legal Clinic; Rebecca Tsosie (On Sabbatical Leave). John J. Ross - William C. Blakley Law Library.

ARIZONA STATE UNIVERSITY - AMERICAN INDIAN POLICY INSTITUTE
250 E. Lemon St., Discovery Hall #272, Box 872603 • TEMPE, AZ 85287
  (480) 965-1055 Fax 965-6404;
  Website: https://aipi.clas.asu.edu; E-mail: aipi@asu.edu
Traci L. Morris (Chickasaw), Director (965-9005)
  E-mail: t.morris@asu.edu
Eddie F. Brown (Pascua Yaqui/Tohono O'odham), Emeritus Executive
  Director (727-8690); E-mail: efbrown@asu.edu
Sasha Pachito (Luiseno), Manager, Tribal Economic Leadership Program
  E-mail: sasha.pachito@asu.edu
Brian Howard (Tohono O'odham), Research & Policy Analyst
  E-mail: brian.howard.1@asu.edu
Sharon Torres (Navajo), Program Coordinator (965-1306)
  E-mail: Sharon.torres@asu.edu
Mission: To transform American Indian policy analysis using a trans-disciplinary approach by collaborating with other departments & centers at Arizona State University (ASU) as well as with organizations outside of ASU on its projects & initiatives. *Programs/Projects*: Tribal Organizational Assessment Project; Tribal Planning Summits; Tribal Financial Manager Certificate Program; Certified Public Managers for Tribal Managers; American Indian Entrepreneurship for Sustainable Development Initiative; Tribes & Towns Initiative; Tribal Environmental Sustainability Initiative; Air & Water Quality; Internships. *Publications*: Reports & Publications available.

ARIZONA STATE UNIVERSITY
LABRIOLA NATIONAL AMERICAN INDIAN DATA CENTER
ASU Libraries - Hayden Library, 2nd Floor
Box 871006 • TEMPE, AZ 85287-1006
  (480) 965-6490 Fax 965-0776; E-mail: archives@mainex1.asu.edu
Joyce Martin, Curator/Associate Librarian (965-0298)
  E-mail: joyce.martin@asu.edu
Ed Oetting, American Indian Studies; E-mail: edding@asu.edu
Supports the American Indian Studies Program & provides a facility where students can research & study. The Data Center actively solicits collections of manuscripts, photographs, personal papers, books, & other resource materials dealing with the language, education, & culture of all North American tribal groups. Collection contains information on all North American tribes including Alaskan Natives. Provides access to the information through the use of computer databases, the Internet, & CD-ROM. *Publication*: Triannual newsletter.

COOK NATIVE AMERICAN MINISTRIES FOUNDATRION
1414 W. Broadway Rd., Suite 122 • TEMPE, AZ 85282
  (480) 968-9354 Fax 968-9357; Website: https://.cooknam.org
Timothy J. Hansell, Executive Director/CEO
Gary Metoxen (Navajo), Board Chair
Della Pena (Navajo), Executive Assistant
Programs: AA Programs: Christian Ministry, American Indian Studies, Liberal Studies. Residency Program offers foundational studies and an AA Degree in Pastoral Studies. Member of the Native American Theological Education Consortium in the U.S. Theological Library Cooperative of Arizona.

*DINE COLLEGE
1 Circle Dr., 3rd Floor, Ned Hatathlie Center
P.O. Box 126 • TSAILE, AZ 86556
  (877) 988-3463; (928) 724-6600 Fax 724-3327
  Website: www.dinecollege.edu; E-mail: info@dinecollege.edu
Dr. Charles "Monty" Roessel (Navajo-Dine'), President
  E-mail: cmroessel@dinecollege.edu
Valerie Tom (Navajo-Dine), Special Assistant to the President
  E-mail: valtom@dinecollege.edu
Dr. Elvira Bitsoi-Largie, VP Academic & Student Affairs
Ronald R. Belloli, VP of Administration & Finance
Curtis Ray Benally, VP of Institutional Advancement
Velveena Davis, Dean of Institutional Planning & Reporting
  E-mail: veldavis@dinecollege.edu; (928) 724-6846
Priscilla A. Leonard, Dean of Enrollment & Student Services
Abraham Bitok, Interim Dean of Academics
Fully accredited & chartered by the Navajo Nation Council. Enrolls an average of 1,800 students. *Programs*: Associate of Arts, Associate of Applied Science; Pre-professional programs; Certification programs. Navajo history, language & culture are integrated into the traditional academic subjects of all College curriculum to enhance students' respect for the Navajo heritage. Navajo & *Indian Studies Program*: Offers many courses in the broad area of Navajo studies; some are directly related to the Navajo, and others are related to Indians in general. *Center for Dine Studies Faculty*: Tsaile Campus – Martha Austin-Garrison, Faculty Chair; Wilson Aronilth, Jr., Avery Denny, Martha Jackson, Gene Vecenti; Shiprock Campus - Martha Austin-Garrison, Dr. Herbert Benally, Tony Goldtooth; Window Rock Campus – Don Denetdeal, Lorene Legah; Center for Dine Teacher Education: Geraldine Garrity (724-6835) 6th Floor, Ned Hatathli Center, P.O. Box C-15, Tsaile, AZ 86556 (928)

724-6699 Fax 724-6835. E-mail: cdte@dinecollege.edu. *Community Campus Faculty*: Edna Braxton & Lorene Legah. DC West Community Campus Staff: Chinle Campus: Cathy L. Bahe, Director; Crownpoint Eastern Campus: Patrick Sandoval, Director; Ganado Campus: Paul Willeto, Director/Academic Advisor; Kaytenta Office: Lawrence Issac, Jr., Coordinator; Shiprock Branch, Priscilla Weaver, Director; Tuba City Campus: Phyllis Begay, Director; Window Rock Campus: Patrick Sandoval, Director. *Programs*: Special Services Program for academically unprepared students; Learning Center provides tutorial services for students. Research Institutes: Dine Policy Institute, P.O. Box 96, Tsaile, AZ 86556 (928) 724-6945 Fax 724-6837. Robert Yazzie, Executive Director; Dine Environmental Institute; Uranium Education Program. *Scholarships*: For information, contact the Financial Aide Office, ext. 223/224. *Facility*: College Library houses the Moses Donner Indian Collection; Hatathli Gallery - products include jewelry, paintings, rugs, sand paintings & other art items. Libraries: Crownpoint (505) 786-7391; Shiprock (505) 368-3542; Tsaile (928) 724-6757.

DINE' COLLEGE – TUBA CITY CENTER
P.O. Box 1716 • TUBA CITY, AZ 86045
(928) 283-5113; Phyllis Begay, Director
E-mail: ptbegay@dinecollege.edu

THE UNIVERSITY OF ARIZONA - SCHOOL OF ANTHROPOLOGY
College of Social & Behavioral Sciences
Emil W. Haury Anthropology Bldg., Rm. 210
1009 E. South Campus Dr., Bldg. #30
P.O. Box 210030 • TUCSON, AZ 85721
(520) 621-2585 Fax 621-2088
Website: www.anthropology.arizona.edu; E-mail: anthro@email.arizona.edu
Diane E. Austin, PhD, School Director (621-6298)
E-mail: daustin@email.arizona.edu
Faculty: Paul R. Fish, PhD (Archaeology); Suzanne K. Fish, PhD (Archaeology); E. Charles Adams, PhD (director of Homolovi Research Program; Pueblo groups); Diane Austin, PhD (Native American Environmental Policy); Thomas R. McGuire, PhD (Native American economic development); Richard W. Stoffle, PhD (Native peoples of the Southwest); M. Nieves Zedeno, PhD (American Indian cultural resource preservation).

THE UNIVERSITY OF ARIZONA
AMERICAN INDIAN LANGUAGE DEVELOPMENT INSTITUTE (AILDI)
Dept. of Teaching, Learning & Sociocultural Studies - College of Education
Rm. 517, 1430 E. Second St., P.O. Box 210069 • TUCSON, AZ 85721
(520) 621-8294 Fax 621-8174; E-mail: coe-aildi@email.arizona.edu
Ofelia Zepeda (Tohono O'odham), Director
E-mail: ofelia@email.arizona.edu
Alyce Sadongei (Kiowa/Tohono O'odham), Project Coordinator
Mission: To mobilize efforts to document, revitalize & promote Indigenous languages through outreach, training, & collaborative partnerships with educators, schools & Indigenous communities, internationally. *Programs*: American Indian Professional Training Program in Speech-Language Pathology & Audiology; Summer Program. *Faculty*: Jennie DeGroat (Navajo); Stacey Oberly (Southern Ute); Lucille Watahomigie (Hualapai); Depree ShadowWalker (Mescalero Apache).

THE UNIVERSITY OF ARIZONA
DEPARTMENT OF AMERICAN INDIAN STUDIES
College of Social & Behavioral Sciences
Harvill 218 1103 East 2nd St., P.O. Box 210076 • TUCSON, AZ 85721
(520) 621-7108 Fax 621-7952
Website: www.ais.arizona.edu; E-mail: aisp@email.arizona.edu
Ofelia Zepeda, Department Head; E-mail: ofelia@email.arizona.edu
Amy Fatzinger, Assistant Professor & Director of Undergraduate Studies (621-8440)
John Carbajal, Senior Program Coordinator (626-8143)
Keith James, Professor, Director of Tribal Initiatives
E-mail: keithjames@email.arizona.edu
Ronald Trosper, Professor, GIDP Chair, Director of Graduate Studies (621-7108)
Anne Marie Jones, Administrative Associate
E-mail: amjones@email.arizona.edu
Ann Samuelson, Academic Advisor (626-6027)
E-mail: anns@email.arizona.edu
The University of Arizona was the first educational institution in the U.S. to offer a freestanding PhD program in American Indian Studies. The Inter-Tribal Graduate Interdisciplinary Program in American Indian Studies (AIS) provides graduate programs offering advanced study across/integrating American Indian Law and Policy, Literatures, Societies & Culture, and American Indian Education. Outreach & Service Opportunities: Red Ink, a biannual publication providing opportunities for students to work on a nationally distributed publication of poetry, short stories, creative non-fiction, original artwork, book and film reviews; The American Indian Language Development Institute

(AILDI); Tribal Law & Policy Program. *Faculty*: Raymond Austin (Tribal Law & Federal Indian Law); Barbara Babcock (Southwestern Indian Cultures); Manley Begay, (tribal economic development); Ian Record, PhD (Sr. Lecturer); Karletta Chief; Benedict Colombi, (Indigenous resource management); Stephen Cornell (American Indian policy; economic development); Amy Fatzinger, (American Indian literature, film); Larry Evers (American Indian literature); T.J. Ferguson (anthropology & archaeology); Mary Jo Tippeconnic Fox, (Comanche/ Cherokee), Research Professor/Social Scientist; Stephanie Fryberg; Francine C. Gachupin (Native health); Mascha N. Gemein (environment, American Indian literatures); Patrisia Gonnzales (Indigenous healing systems); Robert A. Hershey, JD (Indian law); Tom Holm (Creek/ Cherokee), Emeritus (Federal Indian policy & history); James Hopkins (Aboriginal law); Susan Lobo (contemporary issues); K. Tsianina Lomawaima (Creek), (history of American Indian education, ethno-history); Eileen Luna Firebaugh (Choctaw/Cherokee), JD (Tribal governments, Federal Indian policy); Roger L. Nichols; Stacey Oberly, (Southern Ute, Native language); Nancy J. Parezo, (ethnohistory, especially Navajo); Richard Stoffle; Ronald L. Trosper, Program Head; Kathleen Van Vlack; Franci Washburn (Lakota), (American Indian literature; fiction & poetry; creative writing, fiction); Mary Ann Willie (Navajo) (Navajo syntax, Athabaskan linguistics); Leisy Wyman (Indigenous education); Ofelia Zepeda (Tohono O'odham language). *Resources*: Archaeological Field School; Native American Research & Training Center (520) 621-5075; Native American Speech & Hearing Program (520) 621-1969; American Indian Graduate Center; Native American Student Affairs (520) 621-3835; Western Archaeological Center; Arizona State Museum. *Publications*: Red Ink, annual journal of Native American literature; Anthropological Papers of the University of Arizona.

THE UNIVERSITY OF ARIZONA - THE KNOWLEDGE RIVER PROGRAM
School of Information Resources & Library Science
1103 E. Second St. • TUCSON, AZ 85721
(520) 621-5220 Fax 621-3279; E-mail: kriver@email.arizona.edu
Gina Macaluso, Assistant Professor & Program Manager
E-mail: ginamacaluso@email.arizona.edu
Knowledge River Program: A Masters program which focuses on library & information issues from needs & perspectives of Hispanics & Native Americans.

THE UNIVERSITY OF ARIZONA
INDIGENOUS PEOPLES LAW & POLICY (IPLP) TRIBAL JUSTICE CLINIC
James E. Roger College of Law, P.O. Box 210176 • TUCSON, AZ 85721
(520) 626-6497; Website: www.law.arizona.edu/depts/iplp/
E-mail: law-iplp@email.arizona.edu
Robert A. Williams, Jr. (Lumbee), Program Founding Director & Faculty Chair
E-mail: williams@law.arizona.edu
Justin Boro, Assistant Program Director (626-9224)
E-mail: justinboro1986@email.arizona.edu
Andrea Bojorquez, Program Coordinator (626-6497)
E-mail: mabojorq@email.arizona.edu
James Diamond, Clinic Director & Law Professor of Practice (626-9762)
E-mail: jamesdiamond@email.arizona.edu
Torivio A. Fodder, Indigenous Governance Program Manager (626-0236)
E-mail: taf05@email.arizona.edu
Melissa L. Tatum, JD, Research Professor of Law (626-9762)
Robert A. Hershey, Clinical Professor of Law; Director of Clinical Education
(621-5677) E-mail: hershey@law.arizona.edu
James C. Hopkins. Associate Clinical Professor, Affiliated Professor of American Indian Studies (621-7669; E-mail: hopkinsj@email.arizona.edu
Seanna Howard, Externship Coordinator, professor of Practice
E-mail: showard@email.arizona.edu
Jide James-Eluyode, Senior Research Fellow
Alisha Morrison, Program Specialist
Purpose: To protect & promote Indigenous peoples' rights. The new clinic combines the legal work, applied research, and clinical placements of the former Indigenous Peoples Law Clinic and Tribal Courts Clinic together under one faculty supervisor, with a focus on assisting indigenous communities and non-governmental organizations on a variety of legal issues and initiatives designed to support the improvement of tribal justice systems across Arizona, the United States, and the world. *Faculty*; Indigenous Peoples Law & Policy (IPLP) Tribal Justice Clinic, The University of Arizona: Stephen Cornell, Joseph Kalt, Miriam Jorgensen, Daryle Rigney. *Publication*: IPLP News.

THE UNIVERSITY OF ARIZONA
NATIVE AMERICAN RESEARCH & TRAINING CENTER (NARTC)
1642 E. Helen St. • TUCSON, AZ 85719
(520) 621-5920 Fax 621-9802; Website: www.nartc.fcm.arizona.edu
Teshia G. Arambula Solomon, PhD, Director of NARTC
E-mail: solomont@email.arizona.edu
Francine Gachupin, Assistant Director of NARTC & Assistant Professor
E-mail: fcgachupin@email.arizona.edu
Nataiie Pool, Program Coordinator; E-mail: nataliepool@email.arizona.edu
Lyle Shorty & Rodney C. Haring, Research Assistants

The Native American Research and Training Center was established in 1983 by The University of Arizona Board of Regents to serve as a resource in health related research and training for Native American communities nationwide. The Center is housed in the Department of Family and Community Medicine at the College of Medicine. The mission of NARTC is to provide training and technical assistance and to conduct respectful research to benefit the health & wellbeing of Native people, families, and communities. Because of our commitment to the realization of self-determination, one of the primary objectives of the Center is to promote active participation and partnership with Native American communities in all NARTC research & training programs. *Affiliated Faculty:* Lori Arviso-Alvord, Carlos Gonzales, MD; Jennie Joe; Patrisia Gonzales; Nina Wampler; Janelle Palacios. *Project:* American Indian Disability Legislation: Toward the Development of a Process that Respects Sovereignty & Cultural Diversity. *Publications:* Monographs; videos. Established 1983.

THE UNIVERSITY OF ARIZONA
NATIVE AMERICAN STUDENT AFFAIRS (NASA) CENTER
1439 E. Helen St., Robert L. Nugent Bldg., Rm. 203
P.O. Box 210040 • TUCSON, AZ 85721
  (520) 621-3835 Fax 621-9880; Website: http://nasa.arizona.edu/
  Steven Martin, Program Director; E-mail: stevenm1@email.arizona.edu
  Dr. Ronald Trosper, Faculty Fellow; E-mail: rtrosper@email.arizona.edu
The office of Native American Student Affairs (NASA), originally named the Native American Resource Center, was established in 1989 through student and community advocacy. The Native American student population then was 434 (1.2%). Since the inception of the Center, the Native American student population gradually increased to 1,069 (2.7%) in the year 2009-2010. NASA continues to serve as one of four ethnic cultural centers reporting through the Dean of Students office. There are more than 75 Native American tribes represented on campus with a majority of students coming from Arizona tribes. The UA campus lies in close proximity to a richness of Native American cultures; 13 miles from the New Pascua Yaqui reservation; 6 miles from the Old Pascua Yaqui community; 10 miles from the San Xavier Reservation and 60 miles from the Tohono O'odham reservation in Sells, Arizona.

THE UNIVERSITY OF ARIZONA - NATIVE NATIONS INSTITUTE
FOR LEADERSHIP, MANAGEMENT, AND POLICY (NNI)
803 East First St. • TUCSON, AZ 85719
  (520) 626-0664 Fax 626-3664
  Website: www.nni.arizona.edu; E-mail: nni@email.arizona.edu
  Joan Timeche (Hopi), Executive Director; E-mail: timechej@u.arizona.edu
  Miriam Jorgensen, Research Director; E-mail: mjorgens@u.arizona.edu
  Charissa Delmar (Navajo) & John McMinn, Research Specialists
  E-mail: cdelmar@email.arizona.edu; E-mail: johnmcminn@u.arizona.edu
  Mary Elizabeth Jager (Citizen Potawatomi), Research Analyst
  E-mail: jager@email.arizona.edu
  Stephanie Carroll Rainie (Ahta Athabascan), Associate Director, Manager –
  Tribal Health Program & Assistant Research Professor, Udall Center for
  Studies in Public Policy; E-mail: scrainie@u.arizona.edu
  Ian Record, Manager, Educational Resources Program (626-9839)
  Danielle Hiraldo (Lumbee) (Outreach Specialist) & Rachel Starks
  (Zuni/Navajo), Senior Researchers
  Stephen Cornell, Faculty Chairperson
  Yadira Caballero (Dine'), Research Program Coordinator
  Veronica Hirsch (Chiricu\ahua Apache), Coordinator, Digital Resources
  Lindsay Riggs (Navajo), Tribal Services Program Coordinator
  Desi Rodriguez-Lonebear (Northern Cheyenne), Graduate Research Assoc.
  Ryan Seelau, JD, Manager, Indigenous Governance Programs
Indigenous Governance Database. Established 2001 by the Morris K. Udall & Stewart K. Udall Foundation The Institute provides customized executive education programs designed to equip tribal leaders with knowledge and tools for Native nation building. These sessions are based on the executive education programs widely available to corporate CEOs, military leaders, members of Congress and other officials. NNI has adapted this model to serve Native leaders wrestling with challenges unique to Indigenous community and economic development. For more than 20 years, researchers from the Harvard Project on American Indian Economic Development & more recently, NNI have worked to understand the conditions under which sustained economic development can be successful on American Indian reservations in the United States and among First Nations in Canada. The results indicate that five elements are particularly important in successful nation building: *Sovereignty.* Native nations that have been willing and able to assert self-governing power have significantly increased their chances of sustainable economic development. *Capable governing institutions.* The chances of sustainable development rise as Indigenous nations put in place effective, non-politicized dispute-resolution mechanisms & build capable bureaucracies. *Cultural match.* Institutions that build & innovate upon Indigenous conceptions of authority fare better than those whose form departs from such conceptions. *A strategic orientation.* Successful Native nations tend to approach development not as a quick fix for poverty but as a means of building a society

that works. *Leadership.* In successful Indian nations, there is typically a group of individuals who recognize the need for fundamental change in the way things are done and can bring the community along with them in building that future. NNI's executive education sessions explore the research findings of NNI and the Harvard Project, drawing on cases from throughout Native America and around the world.

THE UNIVERSITY OF ARIZONA
NATIVE PEOPLES TECHNICAL ASSISTANCE OFFICE
1145 N. Mountain Ave., Rountree Hall, Rm. 206
P.O. Box 210176 • TUCSON, AZ 85721
  (520) 626-9181 Fax 626-1819; Website: www.nptao.arizona.edu
  Claudia E. Nelson, Director; E-mail: cen@email.arizona.edu
Purpose: Provides a comprehensive program of university-based technical assistance, technology transfer & research, and educational opportunities for Native peoples across Arizona & nation; to administer economic & community development projects in indigenous communities throughout Arizona; to facilitate educational & research opportunities for Native peoples in a top-ranked Research One public university setting; administers a ten year applied research program providing research capacity building for tribal college faculty, staff, & students. *Programs:* Teesto Chapter, Navajo Nation Community/Commercial Land Use Planning; The Hopi Tribe EDA Mapping Project; I-MIG, the Tohono O'odham word meaning "kinship." a counseling service program; Navajo Nation & Hopi Tribe Tourism Enhancement project. Established 1992.

DINE' COLLEGE – WINDOW ROCK CENTER
P.O. Box 1924 • WINDOW ROCK, AZ 86515
  (505) 786-7391 Fax 786-5240; Website: www.dinecollege.edu
  Patrick Sandoval, Director; E-mail: psandoval@dinecollege.edu
The Window Rock Center is located in the Tribal Hill area of Window Rock, just behind the Navajo Nation Council Chambers. Window Rock Center is unique in its own way. Located amongst the NN Government, Diné College instills the need to improve governmental personnel and structure by providing degrees in Liberal Arts, Social & Behavioral Sciences, Business Administration, and cultural values in language, history, and philosophy. Reaching out to area high schools is instrumental to strengthening young minds, to achieve success beyond the 2-year level.

ARKANSAS

UNIVERSITY OF ARKANSAS
Archaeological Field School, Department of Anthropology
Old Main 330 • FAYETTEVILLE, AR 72701
  (479) 575-2508 Fax 575-6595
  Website: www.uark.edu; E-mail: anth@uark.edu
  Peter S. Ungar, Chairperson, Distinguished Professor
Instructors: Archaeology - Ann Early; Thomas J. Green; Marvin Kay; George Sabo III; Rex Weeks. Cultural Anthropology - Kirstin Erickson. *Scholarships:* Arkansas residency for tuition purposes to tribes that once lived in the State (Caddo, Cherokee, Choctaw, Creek, Kickapoo, Osage, Quapaw, Shawnee & Tunica). S.C. Dellinger Award for promising anthropology students; minority graduate fellowships. *Facility:* University of Arkansas Museum. *Publications:* Plains Anthropologist; Arctic Anthropology; publications of the Arkansas Archaeological Survey.

UNIVERSITY OF ARKANSAS SCHOOL OF LAW
Project: Indigenous Food & Agriculture Initiative
1045 W. Maple St., Robert A. Leflar Law Center
Waterman Hall • FAYETTEVILLE, AR 72701
  (479) 575-4699; Website: www.law.uark.edu/ifai
  Janie Simms Hipp (Chickasaw), Director; E-mail: jhipp@uark.edu
The Indigenous Food & Agriculture Initiative at the University of Arkansas School of Law will encompass multi-disciplinary research, service, & education opportunities. To create new academic & executive education programs in food & agriculture, including law, policy, & tribal governance; To directly support Indian country by providing strategic planning & technical assistance, including research & publications in the following subject areas: Tribal Governance Infrastructure to Enhance Business & Economic Development Opportunities; Financial Markets & Asset Management, including Banking, Risk Management, and Stewardship of Land & Natural Resources; Health & Nutrition Policy for Tribal Community Wellness; Intellectual Property Rights & Protection of Traditional Knowledge. *Summer Leadership Summit: Native Youth in Agriculture.* Fifty selected students will travel to Fayetteville to participate in a week-long education & leadership summit designed to provide comprehensive training in the legal & business complexities unique to Indian Country land & agriculture. Students will engage in classroom & leadership learning, participate in cultural activities and receive specialized legal & land use education appropriate only to Native farmers & ranchers. All food, lodging, and instructional materials will be provided. Competitive travel scholarships to

the University are available. *First Nations Knowledge Webinar Series*: A series of educational webinars created & hosted by First Nations Development Institute. The series aims to educate Native Americans who are involved in food-systems work & agriculture, plus those who lead or work for Native nonprofit organizations. Through the webinars, we hope to build knowledge & skills and, thus, Native American business and organizational capacity.

CALIFORNIA

HUMBOLDT STATE UNIVERSITY-LIBRARY
CENTER FOR INDIAN COMMUNITY DEVELOPMENT (CICD)
ARCATA, CA 95521
Website: www.humboldt.edu/cicd; E-mail: cicd@humboldt.edu
In 1966, Humboldt State University (HSU) established the Center for Indian Community Development (CICD) to provide services & outreach to American Indian communities in Indian Country on behalf of HSU. CICD closed in 2013. CICD was a center for collaboration for 47 years it had facilitated partnerships between American Indian community members, Tribes, Indian organizations, governmental agencies representatives & University departments such as fisheries, teacher education, social work, nursing, history & economics. CICD support enables HSU faculty and Tribal clients to embark on exciting projects for mutual benefit. Frequently, the goals and needs within Tribal communities are intertwined with State & federal agencies & services such as public school districts, NOAA, the department of Agriculture & Caltrans. Native & non-Native students have spearheaded CICD projects such as the Tribal Constitution booklet, Tribal archives, graphic arts & book publications. The many students served by CICD over the decades have gone on to leadership roles in education, law, public agencies & Tribal & State governments. *CICD's primary services included*: American Indian languages & material development; Ethnographic & linguistic research & coordination for linguistic & ethnographic projects; Grant writing & grants administration; Development of materials and resources such as books, audio & video resources, language curricula, & Tribal archives; Representation of American Indian communities' interests in public forums & assisting in negotiations between the Tribal governments and federal, state, and local governmental agencies; Planning, coordination, & production of conferences, workshops, seminars, educational courses, & meetings; Technical assistance; Providing a conduit for Humboldt State University resources including faculty, services, & materials to Tribes, American Indian communities & organizations; Presentations & training including grant writing, curriculum development, Native American history, federal Indian law, linguistics, & cultural traditions; Research & development for general services such as needs assessments, distance learning opportunities, program development, & support for American Indian activities & projects. *American Indian Languages & Literature Program*: The program first adapted an internationally acknowledged, easy-to-learn uniphonetic alphabet to write Indian languages precisely, and then schooled fluent local speakers in its use & dissemination. The program enabled four northwestern California tribes to salvage their venerable literatures; publish them in tribally compiled textbooks; document their (pre-) history; and, record & compile their traditional music. The program produced five internationally acclaimed documentary films explicating this complex cultural regenerative process; & organized these elements into curricula for use in preschool, elementary & secondary schools, and in college & university classrooms. A scholarly curriculum was created in an intertribal network of American Indian community development projects. Many of the final products are available online through Humboldt Digital Scholar.

HUMBOLDT STATE UNIVERSITY
DEPARTMENT OF NATIVE AMERICAN STUDIES
1 Harpst St. • ARCATA, CA 95521
(707) 826-4329 Fax 826-4320
Website: www.humboldt.edu/nasp; E-mail: nas@humboldt.edu
Marion Sherman (Oglala Lakota), Professor & Department Chair (826-3821)
  E-mail: ms31@humboldt.edu
Kenna Kay Hyatt, Administrative Support Coordinator (826-3225)
  E-mail: kenna.kay.hyatt@humboldt.edu
Program: Native American Studies. Offers a B.A. & minor
Faculty:
 Joseph Giovannetti (Tolowa), Professor (826-5572)
  E-mail: jmg2@humboldt.edu)
 Kayla Begay, Assistant Professor (826-4316)
  E-mail: kayla.begay@humboldt.edu
 Rain Marshall, Lecturer (Yankton Sioux/Choctaw) (826-4925)
  E-mail: rla1@humboldt.edu)
 Cutcha Risling Baldy, Assistant Professor (826-4322)
  E-mail: crislingbaldy@humboldt.edu
 Cynthia Boshell, Lecturer E-mail: cynthia.boshell@humboldt.edu
 Kerri Malloy, Lecturer E-mail: kjm1@humboldt.edu
 Sara Obenauer, Lecturer; E-mail: sara.obenauer@humboldt.edu

HUMBOLDT STATE UNIVERSITY
INDIAN NATURAL RESOURCE, SCIENCE & ENGINEERING PROGRAM
Walter Warren House #38, 1 Harpst St. • ARCATA, CA 95521
(707) 826-4998 Fax 826-4995; Website: www.humboldt.edu/inrsep
E-mail: inrsep@humboldt.edu
Laurie Richmond, Interim Director (826-5641)
 E-mail: laurie.richmond@humboldt.edu
Lonyx Landry, STM Advisor (826-5642)
 E-mail: lonyx.landry@humboldt.edu
Mission: The Program is seeking American Indian, Alaskan Native, Native Hawaiian students who are interested & dedicated to the ideals of serving Indigenous People through the sciences. The purpose of the Indian Natural Resource Science and Engineering Program (INRSEP) is to provide academic and research support to underrepresented, low income, and historically disadvantaged students in STEM disciplines with a specific focus on American Indian and Indigenous students. INRSEP serves students by connecting them to research opportunities, providing academic and career counseling, assisting with entrance into graduate programs, & fostering an inclusive and supportive learning community within the INRSEP house. INRSEP is grounded in a holistic approach to STEM that accommodates diverse approaches to the natural world & draws from the traditional knowledge of Indigenous peoples. Courses pertinent to Native American natural resources (e.g. Native American water law, tribal government, and tribal perspectives toward natural resources. "We aim to work as partners with local tribal communities to learn from their wisdom and contribute to their goals. Our mission is to diversify and decolonize STEM fields by empowering our students to become leaders who give back to their communities, society, and future generations while strengthening connections with their heritage and culture."

HUMBOLDT STATE UNIVERSITY
INDIAN TRIBAL & EDUCATIONAL PERSONNEL PROGRAM (ITEPP)
Native American Center for Academic Excellence
1 Harpst St., Brero House #93 • ARCATA, CA 95521
(707) 826-3672 Fax 826-3675; Website: www.humboldt.edu/itepp/
Adrienne Colegrove-Raymond, Coordinator & Director (826-5197)
 E-mail: abc1@humboldt.edu
Marlette Grant-Jackson (Hoopa), Resource Coordinator & Academic Advisor
 E-mail: mmj5@humboldt.edu
Paula Tripp-Allen, Academic Advisor (826-5196)
 E-mail: pdt1@humboldt.edu
Description: A support program (the oldest in the nation) that recruits & trains American Indians to become educators & ancillary education personnel. Offers courses & fieldwork. *Special program*: American Indian Education Minor & Professional Development Certificate. The Native American Center for Academic Excellence is a support program dedicated to serving Native American students attending Humboldt State University. The goal of the program is to facilitate academic success while promoting tribal cultural values, recognizing the unique legal and political status of federally recognized tribes & advancing tribal self-determination & prosperity. We strive to: (a) support college readiness & access; (b) expand educational excellence and opportunities for American Indian & Alaska Natives consistent with Executive Order 13592 of December 2, 2011; & (c) provide advising, mentoring and a community of cultural support. ELITE Scholars (Excelling and Living Independently through Education) is a support program committed to empowering current and former foster youth succeed in navigating the pipe-line in the pursuit of attaining a quality college education. The staff provides students with a broad array of support services to build a strong foundation for their educational success. *Facility*: ITEPP's Curriculum Resource Center houses a collection of books, videos, microfilm, & curricula materials all relating to Native American issues and topics. Library

UNIVERSITY OF CALIFORNIA
NATIVE AMERICAN STUDIES PROGRAM
College of Letters & Science – Department of Ethnic Studies
506 Barrows Hall, # 2570 • BERKELEY, CA 94720
(510) 643-0796 Fax 642-6456
Website: www.berkeley.edu; E-mail: ethnicst@berkeley.edu
Shari Huhndorf, Professor & Director-Chair
 E-mail: huhndorf@berkeley.edu
Perla Pinedo, Academic Personnel Coordinator (643-6421)
Latonya Minor, Graduate Advisor (642-6643)
 E-mail: msminor@berkeley.edu
Laura Jimenez-Olvera & Dewey St. Germaine, Undergraduate Advisors
Ethnic Studies Library (643-1234) E-mail: esl@library.berkeley.edu
Core Faculty: Tom Biolsi, Shari Huhndorf, Beth H. Piatote.
 Patricia Hilden, Professor Emerita (Native American Studies)
Lecturers: JoEllen Anderson, Enrique Lima
Description: The program considers broadly the relationship of indigeneity and settler colonialism, foregrounding the historical contexts & constraints through which indigenous individuals and polities have expressed and continue to express themselves. Indigenous epistemologies, histories, languages, cultural

texts and social practices are key arenas of analysis as we examine the unique experiences of Native Americans. Grounded in the study of history, culture, language, law and policy, the frameworks that enrich our research include comparative global indigenous studies, women and gender studies, queer studies, subaltern studies, immigrant and refugee histories, and transnational and diasporic studies.

UNIVERSITY OF CALIFORNIA
AMERICAN INDIAN GRADUATE PROGRAM (AIGP)
327 Sproul Hall #5900 • BERKELEY, CA 94720
(510) 642-3228 Fax 643-8909; E-mail: aigp@berkeley.edu
Carmen A. Foghorn, Program Director
Cindy Andallo, Program Manager
John J. Dougherty, Professor of Naïve American studies
Description: Provides outreach, recruitment & student services to counteract the barriers that prevent the full participation of American Indian & Alaska Native students in graduate education. *Activities*: Directs American Indian Graduate Program to promote learning & development in American Indian/Alaska Native graduate students by encouraging experiences which lead to intellectual growth, appreciation of aesthetic & cultural diversity & achievement of personal goals; Supports and guides campus efforts to conduct outreach, recruit, admit, and graduate American Indian and Alaska Native students; Plans & implements outreach programs with specifically targeted institutions; Advises prospective applicants on necessary academic preparation; Plans and implements high visibility students events, such as commencements, research conferences, lecture series, campus community building and services to local American Indian communities and agencies

CALIFORNIA STATE UNIVERSITY, CHICO
THE CENTER FOR MULTICULTURAL & GENDER STUDIES
Butt Hall 611, 400 West First St. • CHICO, CA 95929
(530) 898-5688 Fax 898-5986; E-mail: mcgs@csuchico.edu
Sara Cooper, Center Director (898-5158)
E-mail: scooper@csuchico.edu
Lisa E. Emmerich, American Indian Studies Coordinator (898-6338)
E-mail: lemmerich@csuchico.edu
Kathleen J. Williams, Administrative Support Coordinator
Degree: Minor in American Indian Studies

D-Q UNIVERSITY (DEGANAWIDA QUETZECOATL)
33250 County Road 31, P.O. Box 409 • DAVIS, CA 95617
(530) 758-0470; E-mail: dquniversity@gmail.com
Stan Rodriguez (Santa Ysabel Lipay), Chairperson
Willie Carillo (Tule River), Vice Chairperson
Joseh Saulgue (Ut Utu Gwaitu Paiute), Treasurer
Description: Was a two-year community college opened in 1971, was tribally owned & controlled, ended its full-time college schedule due to loss of accreditation, declining enrollment, and alleged financial mismanagement in 2005; however, students & instructors who remained on campus have continued to use the campus for classes, gatherings and ceremony. Library

UNIVERSITY OF CALIFORNIA
DEPARTMENT OF NATIVE AMERICAN STUDIES
College of Letters & Science
One Shields Ave., 2401 Hart Hall • DAVIS, CA 95616
(530) 752-3237 Fax 752-7097
Zoila S. Mendoza, Dept. Chairperson & Professor (754-9283)
Email: zmendoza@ucdavis.edu
Justin Spence, Director of Native American Language Center &
Assistant Professor; E-mail: jspence@ucdavis.edu
Liza Grandia, Associate Director of Native American Language Center &
Director of Indigenous Research Center of the Americas (752-0357)
E-mail: emgrandia@ucdavis.edu
Rena Horse, Student Affairs Officer (752-6656)
E-mail: rdhorse@ucdavis.edu
Beth Rose Middleton, Associate Professor & Graduate Student Advisor
(754-4802) E-mail: brmiddleton@ucdavis.edu
Steven J. Crum (Western Shoshone), Professor
E-mail: sjcrum@ucdavis.edu
Ines Hernandez-Avila (Nez Perce/Tejana), Professor (752-4394
E-mai: ighernandez@ucdavis.edu
Hulleah J. Tsinhnahjinnie (Seminole/Muscogee/Dine'), Professor
& Director, C. N. Gorman Museum (752-0568)
E-mail: tsinhnahjinnie@ucdavis.edu
Veronica Passalacqua, Curator, C.N. Gorman Museum (754-9497)
E-mail: vpassalacqua@ucdavis.edu
Stella C. Mancillas, Graduate & Undergraduate Program Coordinator
E-mail: scmancillas@ucdavis.edu
Description: Interdisciplinary in its approach, the department focuses upon the indigenous people of the Americas - the peoples, nations, and tribes who have lived in North, Central, & South America for thousands of years. Offers

undergraduate & graduate degrees in Native American Studies. *Goals*: to encourage linguistic research on American Indian languages, to foster the intergenerational transfer of language knowledge in Native American communities, and to develop a sustained and productive relationship between American Indian linguistic scholarship and the needs and aspirations of Native American people. The Center encourages the active participation of scholars and students, both native and non-native, in the task of language preservation and revitalization, while also providing the resources & support for the training of a new and engaged generation of linguists. *Emeritus Faculty*: George C. Longfish (Seneca/Tuscarora); Martha Macri (Cherokee), Director Emerita of Native American Language Center - E-mail: mjmacri@ucdavis.edu; Stefano Varese (Emeritus). *Projects*: J. P. Harrington Database Project; Quechua Language & Society; Glyph Dwellers; Shasta Language Project (website under construction); Cherokee Dictionary Project (proposals in preparation). *Services/Programs*: Native American Organized Research Program (NAORP) (Director, Dr. Stefano Varese); EOP Outreach Services; Indigenous Research Center of the Americas; Counseling; workshops, educational programs, lectures, conferences. *Financial Aid*: Various awards; mentorships & internships. *Facilities*: Native American Language Center; Indigenous Research Center of the Americas; The C.N. Gorman Museum & Art Gallery - maintains a permanent collection and shows works by Indian & Chicano artists as well as staff & students. *Publications*: American Words...Native Words Used in English; A Model of Grassroots Community Development: The DQU Native American Language Project; History of Tecumseh Center; Racism, Scholarship & Pluralism in Higher Education; Religious Freedom & the Protection of Native American Places of Worship; The Papago-Apache Treaty of 1853: Property Rights & Religious Liberties.

KUMEYAAY COMMUNITY COLLEGE
Sycuan Band of Kumeyaay Nation Reservation
910 Willow Glen Dr. • EL CAJON, CA 92019
(619) 445-6917 Fax 445-5176; E-mail: llring@sycuan-nsn.gov
Website: www.kumeyaaycommunitycollege.com
Board of Trustees: Jamie LaBrake (Sycuan); Mark Romero (Mesa Grande); Stan Rodriguez (Santa Ysabel); Ral Christman (Viejas); Michael Hunter (Jamul); Larry Banegas (Barona); Lorraine Orosco (San Pasqual); Paul Cuero (Campo); Serves the eight reservations of the Kumeyaay Diegueno Nation. *Instructors*: Stan Rodriguez (Santa Ysabel); Martha Rodriguez (Kummeyaay), Richard Bugbee (Luiseno); Jane Dumas (Elder Kumeyaay); Michelle Garcia (Kumeyaay). Archives. Newsletter.

CALIFORNIA STATE UNIVERSITY, EAST BAY
DEPARTMENT OF ETHNIC STUDIES
4094 Meiklejohn Hall, CSUEB • HAYWARD, CA 94542
(510) 885-3255 Fax 885-3930
Website: www.csueastbay.edu/ethnicstudies
E-mail: Danielle.lowen@csueastbay.edu
Enrique Salmon, Associate Professor & Chairperson
E-mail: Enrique.salmon@csueastbay.edu
Program: Native American Studies. *Instructor*: Enrique Salmon (Tarahumara). *Special Facility*: Clarence E. Smith Museum of Anthropology. *Mission*: To provide an academically rigorous program that substantively contributes to the University's public commitment to provide a multicultural learning experience. Our comparative and interdisciplinary program covers five core areas: African American Studies; American Indian Studies; Asian American Studies; Latino/a and Latin American Studies; and Gender/Sexualities in Communities of Color. In our courses, we teach students to analyze social relations of race, class, gender, and sexuality; develop nuanced understandings of social justice; and act as socially responsible global citizens.

UNIVERSITY OF CALIFORNIA, IRVINE
AMERICAN INDIAN RESOURCE PROGRAM
407 Social Science Tower • IRVINE, CA 92697-2505
(949) 824-6502 Fax 824-8219; Website: www.airp.uci.edu
Joe L. Graham, Director; Yolanda Leon, Program Coordinator (824-0291)
The American Indian Resource Program (AIRP) in the Center for Educational Partnerships (CFEP) at UC Irvine provides a flexible array of institutional support services for tribal students, parents, & communities as they progress on their journeys through the various higher education systems of California, with a primary emphasis on accessing & navigating the University of California system. *Mission*: To assist American Indian & Indigenous stakeholders by pursuing, developing, coordinating, & initiating opportunities and experiences which assist Native American students in their assumption of leading professional roles in their selected disciplines. Beyond the ability to apply UCI credentials any where in the world, a critical aspect of student preparation is the retention of the ability of Indigenous individuals to contribute to the effective use & management of tribal community resources in a manner deemed culturally appropriate by their affiliated tribal entity; to give workshops to any K-12 educational institution, students, associations, & community organizations regarding American Indian related issues; to advise & assist departments on campus to develop appropriate American Indian curriculum &

programs; & to provide assistance to staff in programming activities involving American Indian students. *Program*: American Indian Summer Academy (AISA) - A residential summer program where students work with professors, college students, and invited American Indian community members to develop interactive story projects that combine computer game technology with traditional American Indian culture.

CALIFORNIA STATE UNIVERSITY
DEPARTMENT OF AMERICAN INDIAN STUDIES
College of Liberal Arts, 1250 Bellflower Blvd. • LONG BEACH, CA 90840
(562) 985-4644/8703; Website: www.csulb.edu/cla/ais/
Craig Stone, AIS Program Director & Professor; E-mail: cstone@csulb.edu
Michelle Seales, Staff (985-5305); E-mail: m.seales@csulb.edu
Theresa Gregor, Assistant Professor (985-1306)
  E-mail: theresa.gregor@csulb.edu
Cindi Alvitre, Lecturer (985-5305) Email: calvitre@csulb.edu
Faculty: Kathy Leonard; Anna H. Nazarian-Peters; Rebecca Sanchez. *Affiliated Faculty*: Carol Zitzer-Comfort; Susana Salas; Moira West. *Part-Time Adjunct Faculty*: Daniele Bolelli, Larry Smith, Judge Deborah Sanchez, Kimberly Robertson & Harrelson Notah (985-5637); Emeritus Professors: Dr. Troy Johnson, Dr. Lester Brown, Dr. Mary Ann Jacobs & Richard Glazer Danay. *Degree*: Minor & certificate in American Indian Studies. *Activities*: Annual powwow. The American Indian Studies faculty generally have a sustained history of participation within the urban American Indian community of Southern California, with the canoe cultures of the coastal indigenous people of Southern California and in the subject areas of the courses that they teach. American Indian Studies faculty work closely with the American Indian Student Council, the CSULB NAGPRA Committee, the CSULB American Indian Science and Engineering Student Chapter and with the office of American Indian Student Services. CSULB has a ranking from fifth to fifteenth in the nation for graduating American Indian Students depending upon the particular year and the specific major.

UNIVERSITY OF CALIFORNIA, LOS ANGELES
AMERICAN INDIAN STUDIES CENTER
3220A Campbell Hall, Box 951548 • LOS ANGELES, CA 90095-1548
(310) 825-7315 Fax 206-7060
Website: www.aisc.ucla.edu; E-mail: aisc@ucla.edu
Shannon Speed (Chickasaw), Director & Associate Professor,
  Dept. of Gender Studies & Anthropology (206-9673)
  E-mail: sspeed@aisc.ucla.edu
Renee White Eyes, MSO (206-7506); E-mail: rwhiteeyes@aisc.ucla.edu
Jamie Chan, Operations & Media Support (206-4380)
  E-mail: jchan@aisc.ucla.edu
Pamela Grieman, Publication Manager (206-7514)
  E-mail: grieman@ucla.edu
Judy De Tar, Senior Editor (206-7514)
  E-mail: senior-ed@aisc.ucla.edu
Clementine Bordeaux, Academic Coordinator, American Indian Studies
  Interdepartmental Program (825-6541)
  E-mail: clembordeaux@amindian.ucla.edu
Mishuana Goeman, Faculty Advisory Committee Chair
Ken Wade, Librarian (206-7510) E-mail: kwade@aisc.ucla.edu
Description: Founded in 1969, the Center ranks among the top research centers of its kind in the country serving the educational & cultural needs of the American Indian community. *Activities*: Sponsors research & administers competitive grants; offers a minor, masters and a con-current law program; publishes books; encourages the development of new courses, addresses recruitment of American Indian students and faculty; offers a forum for scholarly exchange for American Indian students, the community and alumni; and sponsors an annual powwow in the Spring quarter. *Facilities*: The Museum of Cultural History; AISC reference library; publishes books, bibliographies, & monographs. *Publication*: "American Indian Culture & Research Journal."

UNIVERSITY OF CALIFORNIA, LOS ANGELES
AMERICAN INDIAN STUDIES INTERDEPARTMENTAL PROGRAM (IDP)
3220 Campbell Hall, Box 951548 • LOS ANGELES, CA 90095-1548
(310) 825-7315 Fax 206-7060
Website: www.ucla.edu; E-mail: aisc@ucla.edu
Benjamin Madley, Associate Professor & Interim Chairperson (825-4601)
  E-mail: madley@ucla.edu
Clementine Bordeaux, Academic Coordinator (825-6541)
  E-mail: clembordeaux@amindian.ucla.edu
Hanay Geiogamah (Kiowa/Delaware), Director, Project HOOP
  E-mail: hgeiog@ucla.edu
Mishuana Goeman (Tonawanda Seneca), Faculty Advisory Committee Chair
  E-mail: goeman@anthro.ucla.edu
Carole Goldberg, Director, Tribal Legal Development Clinic
  E-mail: goldberg@law.ucla.edu
Staff: Julia Coates, Research Analyst; Ken Wade, Librarian;
  Pamela Grieman, Publications Manager.

Description: IDP at UCLA is one of the most well-known & revered programs in American Indian Studies throughout Indian Country. The Center ranks among the top research centers of its kind serving the educational & cultural needs of the American Indian community. *Faculty*: Paul Krosokrity E-mail: paulvk@ucla.edu; Duane Champagne (Turtle Mountain Chippewa); Peter Nabokov, Nancy Reifel (Rosebud Sioux);, Angela Riley (Citizen Potawatomi). *Affiliated Faculty*: Linda Garro, Hanay Geiogamah, Mishuana Goeman, Carole Goldberg, Jessica Cattelino, Pamela Munro, *Faculty Advisory Committee*: Peter Nabokov, Randall Akee, Stephen Aron, Duane Champagne, Mishuana Goeman, Paul Kroskrity, Benjamin Madley, Stella Nair, Nancy Reifel, David Shorter, Angela Riley (Citizen Potawatomi). *Activities*: Sponsors research & administers competitive grants; offers a minor, masters and a concurrent law program; publishes books; encourages the development of new courses, addresses recruitment of American Indian students & faculty; offers a forum for scholarly exchange for American Indian students, the community & alumni; sponsors an annual Powwow in the Spring quarter. *Program*: Administers an Interdepartmental Master's Program in American Indian Studies. *Fellowships*: Postdoctoral Fellowships in American Indian Studies. *Facilities*: The Museum of Cultural History; Library. Publishes numerous books, bibliographies, monographs. *Publication*: "American Indian Culture & Research Journal (AIC&RJ)."

CALIFORNIA STATE UNIVERSITY
AMERICAN INDIAN STUDIES PROGRAM
College of Humanities; Jerome Richfield 219, CSU Northridge
18111 Nordhoff St. • NORTHRIDGE, CA 91330
(818) 677-3418 Fax 677-3605
Website: www.csun.edu/humanities/american-indian-studies/
Scott Andrews (Cherokee); Director
  E-mail: scott.andrews@csun.edu
Brian Burkhart (Cherokee), Director & Faculty member (677-5280)
  E-mail: brian.burkhart@csun.edu
Maria Castillo, Administrative Coordinator (677-2736)
  E-mail: maria.castillo@csun.edu
Karren Baird-Olson (Wyandot); Faculty member
  E-mail: karren.bairdolson@csun.edu
Kimberly Robertson (Muscogee Creek), Faculty member
  E-mail: kimberly.robertson@csun.edu
Program: An interdisciplinary minor in American Indian Studies offers courses in contemporary & historical cultures of First Nations. *Mission*: To promote an understanding of American Indian history, cultures, and tribal sovereignty with a focus on Southern California tribes, and other indigenous peoples in a global context. *Activities*: American Indian Student Association; CSUN Powwow on Thanksgiving weekend.

MILLS COLLEGE - ETHNIC STUDIES DEPARTMENT
Mills Hall 341, 5000 MacArthur Blvd. • OAKLAND, CA 94613
(510) 430-2080 Fax 430-2067
Website: www.mills.edu/academics/undergraduate/eths
E-mail: ethnic_study@mills.edu
Nikole Wilson-Ripsom, Administrator, Cross-Departmental
  E-mail: nwilsonripsom@mills.edu
Melinda Micco (Oklahoma Seminole), Associate Professor
  E-mail: melinda@mills.edu (430-3324)
Visiting Scholars:
  Leece Lee, Assistant Adjunct Professor; E-mail: lelee@mills.edu
  Darby Li Po Price, Visiting Assistant Professor; E-mail: dprice@mills.edu
Degrees: Major & Minor in Ethnic Studies. *Purpose*: To promote critical thinking and creative analysis through comparative study of the social, economic, cultural, & environmental concerns & contributions of American Indians & Alaska Natives, as well as other ethnic minorities. Examines racial dynamics as they intersect with gender, sexuality, class, and nation. *Courses*: American Indian History; American Indian Women in the U.S.; Celluloid Native: American Indians in Film. *Activities & Resources*: Native American Heritage Month; Powwow

UNIVERSITY OF CALIFORNIA, RIVERSIDE
CALIFORNIA CENTER FOR NATIVE NATIONS (CCNN)
College of Humanities, Arts & Social Sciences
900 University Ave. • RIVERSIDE, CA 92521
(951) 827-1799; Website: www.ccnn.ucr.edu
Michelle Raheja, Director; E-mail: michelle.raheja@ucr.edu
Emily M. Rankin, Senior Director, Development (827-4365)
  E-mail: Emily.rankin@ucr.edu
Purpose: To initiate, facilitate, and executes research by, and about, and with American Indian people with a strong focus on California Native nations. To preserve the history, culture, language, & sovereignty of California's first nations through research. Rupert Costo (Cahuilla) and Jeannette Henry Costo (Cherokee) helped found UC Riverside in the mid-20th century. In 1986, the Costos created the Costo Chair of American Indian Affairs at UCR, the first chair in the nation endowed directly by American Indians. Later, they

established the Costo Library of the American Indian and Costo Archives, a unique collection dedicated to understanding the history and role of self-determination policy in Indian Country. Inspired by the generosity and vision of Rupert and Jeannette Costo, the California Center for Native Nations (CCNN) represents UC Riverside's ongoing commitment to research & service benefiting California Indians. In building upon the academic strengths of the university & UCR's unique connections with regional tribal leaders, the center's core activities address a central question: "How can tribal governments in California maximize their sovereign rights in ways that are culturally appropriate, economically sustainable & politically interactive?" The center also serves tribes by connecting them with the expertise found within the University of California to solve research problems unique to Native nations. The center focuses on unique and innovative research that leads to new interpretations that will influence the course of American Indian Studies. *Activities*: Conferences, Events. *Publication*: An Impact Analysis of Tribal Government Gaming in California.

UNIVERSITY OF CALIFORNIA, RIVERSIDE
College of Humanities, Arts & Social Sciences
INTS 3111, 900 University Ave.
Dept. of Ethnic Studies • RIVERSIDE, CA 92521
(951) 827-4707 Fax 787-5299; Website: www.ethnicstudies.ucr.edu
Keith Harris, Chairperson & Associate Professor
  E-mail: keith.harris@ucr.edu
Andrea Smith, Director of Graduate Studies (827-5140)
  E-mail: andy.smith@ucr.edu
Crystal Meza, Graduate Student Affairs Officer (827-1584)
  E-mail: crystal.meza@ucr.edu
Robert C. Perez, Associate Professor (American Indian history) (827-1828)
  E-mail: perezr@ucr.edu
Program: Native American Studies. *Instructors*: Victoria Bomberry & Robert Perez. *Special programs*: MA & PhD in American Indian History; California Indians and the Southwest; Oral History; American Indians & Public History. *Facilities*: Sherman Indian School Museum. *Publications*: American Indian Nations, student magazine; Native American Studies: University of California, Riverside, by Clifford Trafzer, 1991; Dear Christopher, Letters by Contemporary Native Americans to Christopher Columbus, by Darryl Wilson and Barry Joyce, 1992.

SONOMA STATE UNIVERSITY
NATIVE AMERICAN STUDIES DEPARTMENT
Nichols Hall 214, 1801 East Cotati Ave. • ROHNERT PARK, CA 94928
(707) 664-2458; Website: www.sonoma.edu/nams
Mike Ezra, Coordinator (664-3293) E-mail: ezra@sonoma.edu
Linnea Mullins, Administrative Coordinator (664-2486)
  E-mail: linnea.mullins@sonoma.edu
Gregory Sarris, Professor, Endowed Chair (664-2486)
  E-mail: sarrisg@sonoma.edu
The Native American Studies program is designed to provide a minor with a multidisciplinary approach to Native Americans through ethnography, history, sociology, & the humanities. By approaching the multiplicity of Indian cultures from a variety of academic perspectives, a deeper understanding of native societies past & present will emerge. The program is designed to present a variety of American Indian experiences and issues within the wider context of human history and evolution. The program is especially interested in providing teachers, community service personnel, tribal administrators, & interested persons with useful skills in dealing with this unique community. Special emphasis will be placed on assisting educators with practical and theoretical approaches to Indian education. Students in Native American studies are encouraged to apply toward the NAMS minor selected courses from history, anthropology, art, CALS, AMCS, & Education. Students may develop a special major in Native American studies; those interested should review the guidelines for special majors and consult the program coordinator.

CALIFORNIA STATE UNIVERSITY
NATIVE AMERICAN STUDIES PROGRAM
Department of Ethnic Studies, 6000 Jay St. • SACRAMENTO, CA 95819
(916) 278-6363 Fax 278-5156; Website: www.csus.edu/nas
  Annette L. Reed, Director; E-mail: alreed@csus.edu
Purpose: To broaden the educational opportunities for American Indian students by recruiting, counseling, tutoring & coordinating financial aid. Curriculum development & enhancement remains central to our program. *Degree*: BA in Ethnic Studies: major or minor with concentration in Native American Studies. *Activities*: Rumsey California Native American Scholarship; Summer Rez Program for Native American High School Students.

SAN DIEGO STATE UNIVERSITY
DEPARTMENT OF AMERICAN INDIAN STUDIES
College of Arts & Letters Mail Code: 6036
5500 Campanile Dr. • SAN DIEGO, CA 92182
(619) 594-6991 Fax 594-2646

E-mail: americanindianstudies@mail.sdsu.edu
Faculty:
David Kamper, Associate Professor & Chairperson (594-8081)
  E-mail: dkamper@mail.sdsu.edu
Olivia Chilcote (Luiseno), Assistant Professor
  E-mail: ochilcote@mail.sdsu.edu
Margaret Field, Professor (594-2779)
  E-mail: mfield@mail.sdsu.edu
Peter Nelson (Coast Miwok), Assistant Professor
  E-mail: pnelson@mail.sdsu.edu
Lecturers:
Richard Carrico, Lecturer; E-mail: rbrujo@sbcglobal.net
Michael Connolly Miskwish (Campo Band Kumeyaay)
  E-mail: tipaay@aol.com
Caleigh Cornell; E-mail: ccornell@mail.sdsu.edu
Linda Locklear, E-mail: llocklear@mail.sdsu.edu'
Devon Lomayesva; E-mail: dlomayesva@mail.sdsu.edu
Ozzie Monge; E-mail: omonge@mail.sdsu.edu
Seth San Juan; E-mail: ssanjuan@mail.sdsu.edu
Program: Offers a BA major & minor in American Indian studies offering courses on a variety of subjects from Indian heritage to contemporary society, literature, music, & history. *Special programs*: Outreach Programs; American Indian Storytelling. *Student Organization*: Native American Student Alliance. *Resources*: Library: Golsh Collection - consists of rare documents and books. Sycuan Institute on Tribal Gaming at the Robert Payne School of Hospitality & Tourism Management. *Activities*: American Indian Youth Empowerment Conference; American Indian Culture Week each spring; annual SDSU Powwow. *Publications*: Publications in American Indian Studies; American Indian Identity, edited by C.E. Trafzer; Strangers in a Stolen Land, by Carrico; The Quechens; Gods Among Us, by Coates.

SAN FRANCISCO STATE UNIVERSITY
AMERICAN INDIAN STUDIES DEPARTMENT
College of Ethnic Studies, 1600 Holloway Ave.
SAN FRANCISCO, CA 94132
(415) 405-3928 Fax 405-0496
  Website: www.sfsu.edu/~ais; E-mail: aismain@sfsu.edu
Robert Keith Collins, Associate Professor & Department Chair
  (338-2013) E-mail: rkc@sfsu.edu
Andrew Jolivette (Opelousa/Atakapa-ishak), Professor (405-3928)
  E-mail: ajoli@sfsu.edu
Melissa Kaye Nelson (Turtle Mountain Chippewa) (338-6422)
  E-mail: mknelson@sfsu.edu
Joanne Barker (Lenni-Lenape), Associate Professor (338-7062)
  E-mail: jmbarker@sfsu.edu
John-Carlos Perea, Assistant Professor (338-1664)
  E-mail: johnc@sfsu.edu
Gabriela Segovia-McGathan, Coordinator
  E-mail: gsegovia@sfsu.edu
The department's educational mission & objectives has a special responsibility to Native peoples of California and the United States. California is the land on which the university & department rests; CSU is a public institution in the United States education system. Therefore, significant aspects of the program and curriculum are focused on Natives of California, US-Native politics, and North American Indian cultures with the aim of preparing students to work with Native groups and urban communities in California and the United States. The program also includes an international, comparative perspective & coalitional politics with Native peoples of U.S. occupied territories and more broadly within the Americas and the Pacific. *Degrees*: BA & Minor in Native American Studies. *Lecturers*: Amy Casseleman, Phil Klasky, Kathy Wallace, Eddie Madrill. *Programs*: American Indian Studies Review Journal; Annual Powwow. *Financial Aid*: Jacques Johnet Scholarship for American Indians. Library. *Facility*: The Adan E. Treganza Anthropology Museum.

CALIFORNIA POLYTECHNIC STATE UNIVERSITY
ETHNIC STUDIES DEPARTMENT-INDIGENOUS STUDIES
1 Grand Ave., Bldg. 38 Rm. 136 • SAN LUIS OBISPO, CA 93407
(805) 756-1707 Fax 756-6188; Website: https://ethnicstudies.calpoly.edu
  E-mail: ethnicstudies@calpoly.edu
Denise Isom, Professor & Department Chair (756-7388)
  E-mail: disom@calpoly.edu
Yolanda Tiscareno, Department Coordinator (756-1707)
  E-mail: ytiscare@calpoly.edu
Kathleen J. Martin, Associate Professor (756-2827)
  E-mail: kamartin@calpoly.edu
Jenell Navarro, Assistant Professor (756-6268)
  E-mail: jnavar18@calpoly.edu
Elvira Pulitano, Professeor (756-1409)
  E-mail: epulitan@calpoly.edu
Program offers a minor in Ethnic Studies with concentration in American Indian Studies. *Publication*: SIYO; A Journal of New Writers. Library.

CALIFORNIA STATE UNIVERSITY, SAN MARCOS
CALIFORNIA INDIAN CULTURE & SOVEREIGNTY CENTER
333 S. Twin Oaks Valley Rd. • SAN MARCOS, CA 92096
  (760) 750-3535; Website: www.csusm.edu/cicsc/
  Joely Proudfit (Luiseno), Center Director & Professor of American Indian
  Studies; E-mail: jproudfi@csusm.edu
Description: The center is the first of its kind in the state of California & focuses on serving the unique needs of American Indian students by conducting original research and preserving the cultural heritage and languages of tribal communities. *Mission*: To foster collaborative research & community service relationships between the faculty, staff, and students of CSU San Marcos & members of local tribal communities, for the purpose of developing & conducting research projects which support the maintenance of sovereignty & culture within those communities. *Affiliated Faculty*: Juana Majel Dixon; Daniel Calac, MD, Chief Medical Officer; Deborah Morton, Associate Professor. *Program*: Certificate; Native Studies minor. *Project*: The Luiseno Language Preservation Project. *Publications*: Red Book: Southern California American Indian Education Resources; On Indian Ground; The State of American Indian & Alaskan Native Education in Calif., annual report; newsletter. Estab. 2011.

PALOMAR COLLEGE - AMERICAN INDIAN STUDIES PROGRAM
American Studies Dept., 1140 W. Mission Rd. • SAN MARCOS, CA 92069
  (760) 744-1150 ext. 2425 Fax 761-3564
  Website: www.palomar.edu; E-mail: ais@palomar,edu
  Patricia Ann Dixon (Luiseno), Chairperson; E-mail: pdixon@palomar.edu
  Alan Lechusza Aquallo (Luisen0/Maidu) E-mail: aaquallo@palomar.edu
  Deborah W. Dozier & Seth San Juan (Yaqui), Professors
  Linda Rose Locklear (Catabwa/Lumbee), Professor Emerita
  Steven J. Crouthamel, Professor Emeritus
  Naida Garcia (Luiseno), American Indian Education Center Specialist
   E-mail: ngarcia@palomar.edu
Programs: Certification Program in American Indian Studies. *Faculty*: Steven Crouthamel (Emeritus), Alan Lechusza Aquallo (Luiseno/Maidu), Patricia Ann Dixon, Deborah W. Dozier, Linda Rose Locklear (Catabwa/Lumbee); Seth San Juan (Yaqui). *Adjunct Faculty*: Flora Howe (Shawnee), Richard Hosey (Choctaw), Juana Majel-Dixon (Luiseno), Diana Ortiz (Chinook), Henrietta Moore (Cherokee), Evangeiina Franco (Yaqui), Temet Aguilar (Luiseno/Diegueno). *Activities*: Native American Student Alliance (NASA) established 1969 by Indian students at Palomar to encourage Indian participation & organization in education, & promotes cultural activities; American Indian Science & Engineering Society (AISES). Financial aid.

SANTA BARBARA CITY COLLEGE
NATIVE AMERICAN STUDIES PROGRAM
American Ethnic Studies Department
721 Cliff Dr. • SANTA BARBARA, CA 93109
  (805) 965-0581; Website: www.sbcc.edu/americanethnicstudies
  Alice Perez, Dean Ethnic Studies Dept.; E-mail: scharper@sbcc.edu
  Thomas Carrasco, Professor & Chairperson
  Tina W. Foss, Native American Studies Instructor; E-mail: foss@sbcc.edu
Program: Degree of Associates of Arts (AA). In these studies students will critically examines the interlocking forces of race, gender, class, sexuality, and other forms of social differentiation that shape the histories and experiences of marginalized groups. Career choices for all four of these degrees include the areas of teaching, prelaw, law, community services, cultural arts, museums and local, state and federal governmental agencies.

STANFORD UNIVERSITY - NATIVE AMERICAN CULTURAL CENTER
NATIVE AMERICAN STUDIES PROGRAM
Dept. of Comparative Studies in Race & Ethnicity
Old Union Clubhouse Ground Floor
524 Lasuen Mall • STANFORD, CA 94305
  (650) 725-6944 Fax 725-6900
  C. Matthew Snipp (Choctaw/Cherokee), Director & Professor of Sociology
   E-mail: snipp@stanford.edu (725-0414) (Bldg. 120, Room 138)
  Jordan Gray, Student Services Coordinator (724-2088)
   E-mail: jlgray@stanford.edu
  Greg Graves (Delaware), Graduate Recruitment & Retention Coordinator
   E-mail: ggraves@stanford.edu
Program: The Undergraduate Program in Comparative Studies in Race & Ethnicity; Native American Studies major & minor. *Faculty*: JoEllen Anderson (Ojibwe); Teresa LaFromboise (Miami); Kenneth Fields; Stacey Jessiman de Nanteuil; Sharon Nelson-Barber; C. Matthew Snipp (Choctaw/Cherokee); Michael Wilcox (Yuma). *Description*: A division of Student Affairs, the American Indian & Alaska Native Program & its Native American Cultural Center which provides resources & nurturing environments for Stanford's Native community. AIANP/NACC is the site of events, a headquarters for student organizations, the publisher of "ComingVoice," and liaison between local & national Native American groups, including Native Hawaiians. *Facilities*: Stanford American Indian Organization (SAIO); Resource Center & Library. *Activities*: Annual Stanford Powwow.

COLORADO

UNIVERSITY OF COLORADO
CENTERS FOR AMERICAN INDIAN & ALASKA NATIVE HEALTH
Colorado School of Public Health; E-mail: colorado.sph@ucdenver.edu
Nighthorse Campbell Native Health Bldg.
13001 E. 17th Pl. MS B119 • AURORA, CO 80045
  (303) 724-1414 Fax 724-1474; Website: www.ucdenver.edu
  Spero M. Manson, PhD, Distinguished Professor & Center Director
   E-mail: spero.manson@ucdenver.edu; (303) 724-1444
  Doug Novins, MD, Associate Director
   E-mail: douglas.novins@ucdenver.edu
  Lori Trullinger, Center Administrator
   E-mail: lori.trullinger@ucdenver.edu
  Judith Albino, Professor & President Emeritus
   E-mail: judith.albino@ucdenver.edu
  CeCe Big Crow, Field Office Director
  Candace Fleming, PhD, Director of Training
  Kelly Moore, MD, Associate Professor
   E-mail: Kelly.moore@ucdenver.edu
  Tracy Zacher, Field Study Coordinator
   E-mail: tracy.zacher@ucdenver.edu
  Ursula Running Bear, Instructor
   E-mail: Ursula.runningbear@ucdenver.edu
  Nancy Whitesell, Associate Professor
   E-mail: nancy.whitesell@ucdenver.edu
  Alicia Mousseau, Instructor
   E-mail: Alicia.mousseau@ucdenver.edu
Center for Native Oral Health Research (CNOHR)
  Terry Batliner, Associate Director
   E-mail: terry.batliner@ucdenver.edu
American Indian Alaska Natives Head Start Research Center (AIANHSRC)
  (303) 724-1460
Native Elder Research Center (NERC)
Resource Center for Minority Aging Research
  Matt de Caussin, Program Coordinator (303) 724-7889 Fax 724-1474
Special Diabetes Program for Indians Competitive Grant Program
Coordinating Center (SDPI/CGPCC)
  Spero Manson, PhD, Director (303) 724-1444
  Patricia Licari, Associate Director (303) 724-0325
Native Children's Research Exchange (NCRE) (303) 724-1460
The mission for the Centers for American Indian and Alaska Native Health (CAIANH) is to promote the health & wellbeing of American Indians & Alaska Natives, of all ages, by pursuing research, training, continuing education, technical assistance, & information dissemination within a biopsy-chosocial framework that recognizes unique cultural contexts of this special population.

UNIVERSITY OF COLORADO - DEPARTMENT OF ETHNIC STUDIES
Campus Box 134, P.O. Box 173364 • DENVER, CO 80217
  (303) 315-7205 Fax 315-7206; Website: www.ethnicstudies.colorado.edu
  E-mail: ethnic_studies@ucdenver.edu
  Donna Langston Martinez, Professor & Chair (315-7209)
   E-mail: donna.martinez@ucdenver.edu
  Danika Medak-Saltzman (Turtle Mountain Chippewa), Assistant Professor,
   American Indian Studies; E-mail: danika.medak-saltzman@colorado.edu
  Clint Carroll, Assistant Professor; E-mail: clint.carroll@colorado.edu
  Angelica Lawson, Asst. Professor; E-mail: angelica.lawson@colorado.edu
  Jennifer Williams Bordeaux (Lakota), Program Assistant in Ethnic Studies
Research activities: Comparative race & ethnicity & specific ethnic groups, including Native Americans.

UNIVERSITY OF COLORADO - CENTER FOR THE STUDY
OF INDIGENOUS LANGUAGES OF THE WEST (CSILW)
Dept. of Linguistics, UCB 295 • BOULDER, CO 80309-0295
  (303) 492-8456 Fax 492-4416; Website: www.colorado.edu/csilw
  Cynthia Clark, Director; E-mail: cynthia.clark@colorado.edu
  David Rood, PhD (Siouan & Caddoan languages)
   E-mail: david.rood@colorado.edu
  Andrew Cowell, PhD (Algonquian & Miwok languages)
   E-mail: james.cowell@colorado.edu
  Allan Taylor, PhD (Algonquian & Siouan languages) (emeritus)
   E-mail: allan.taylor@colorado.edu
Affiliate Faculty: Hartwell Francis (Arapaho/Cherokee), Della Bad Wound (Lakota), Armik Mirzayan (Wichita/Lakota), Fin Thye (Arapaho/Gros Ventre). *Research activities*: Collects data & conducts research on Native American languages of the Great Plains & Southwest, specializing in Algonquian, Siouan, Caddoan & Arapahoan languages. Also includes the Arapaho Project, which offers instructional materials to aid in learning Arapahoan language. Research Library.

UNIVERSITY OF COLORADO SCHOOL OF LAW
AMERICAN INDIAN LAW PROGRAM
AMERICAN INDIAN LAW CLINIC CERTIFICATE PROGRAM
401 UCB - Wolf Law Bldg., 2450 Kittredge Loop Rd. • BOULDER, CO 80309
(303) 492-8047 Fax 492-4587; Website: www.colorado.edu/law
Carla Fredericks (Mandan Hidatsa Arikara), Program Director,
& Director of the American Indian Law Clinic
  E-mail: carla.fredericks@colorado.edu
Kristen Carpenter, Professor of Law & Associate Dean for Research
  (492-6526) E-mail: Kristen.carpenter@colorado.edu
Richard Collins, Sarah Krakoff, Charles Wilkinson, Faculty Professors
Description: The American Indian Law Program provides students with opportunities to acquire specialized knowledge of American Indian law, through curriculum, the American Indian Law Clinic, the Certificate Program, National Tribal Court Law Clerks Program, research on federal & tribal Indian law issues, externships, conferences & events, et al; provides students hands-on experience in the practice of federal and tribal Indian law while providing low-income persons with quality legal representation. Under the supervision of the Clinic's director, student attorneys are involved in a wide spectrum of Indian law work including representing tribes or Indian parents in Indian Child Welfare Act cases, assisting individuals with tribal enrollment, advocating for protection of Indian religious practices and sacred lands and addressing racial discrimination. Students have the opportunity to work directly with Indian tribes on tribal constitution & code development. *Resources*: Externships with NARF, Native American Rights Fund, the Tribal Program of the U.S. Environmental Protection Agent (EPA), the Intertribal Council on Utility Policy, and the Southern Ute Tribal Court; Indian law career opportunities; scholarships & fellowships; Native American Law Students Association (NALSA). Wise Law Library.

UNIVERSITY OF COLORADO
AMERICAN INDIAN STUDENT SERVICES (AISS)
Student Commons 2007C, 1200 Larimer St.
P.O. Box 173364 • DENVER, CO 80217
  (303) 315-1882; Website: www.ucdenver.edu
  Gracie RedShirt Tyon, Director; E-mail: grace.tyon@ucdenver.edu
  Glenn T. Morris, JD (Dept. of Political Science), Faculty Advisor,
  Native American Student Organization (NASO) (315-1762)
    E-mail: glenn.morris@ucdenver.edu
American Indian Student Services (AISS) welcomes students of all American Indian & Alaska Native heritages! AISS serves both students who are tribally enrolled and those who identify but are not enrolled in their tribes. AISS provides culturally responsive educational support: Resource Referral, Scholarship Information, Advocacy, Cultural Events & Student Clubs. CU Denver American Indian and Alaska Native students represent more than 100 different tribes. The Denver Indian Community is strong! Many families in Denver live far from tribal homelands yet retain tribal identities and cultures. Twenty percent speak Native languages. The Southern Ute and the Ute Mountain Ute Tribes, located in the Four Corners area are the two federally recognized tribes in Colorado.

METROPOLITAN STATE UNIVERSITY OF DENVER
AMERICAN INDIAN STUDIES PROGRAM
MSU Denver Department of Political Science
Campus Box 43, P.O. Box 173362 • DENVER, CO 80217
  (303) 556-3220 Fax 871-4877
Program: Minor in Native American Studies. Developed to be reflective of Indian perspectives and the Indian faculty presents an interdisciplinary approach to the variety of beliefs & practices within American Indian communities & focuses on the current vitality & continuous development of the Indian people. *Courses*: Courses leading to a Certificate of Advanced Study in American Indian History and Cultures, as well as a Master of Liberal Arts with a concentration in American Indian Studies. *Instructors*: Rick Williams; John Compton; George Tinker; Jeanne Whiteing, JD; Suzanne Benally; Jan Jacobs; Mark Guthrie; Richard Conn; James Jordan; Lisa Harjo. *Resources*: On campus lectures by visiting Indian writers & scholars presented as free events to the community; Native American Student Alliance on campus. Financial aid available. *Facility*: Penrose Library.

FORT LEWIS COLLEGE – CENTER OF SOUTHWEST STUDIES
1000 Rim Dr. • DURANGO, CO 81301
  (970) 247-7456 Fax 247-7422
  Shelby Tisdale, Director; E-mail: stisdale@fortlewis.edu
  Jeanne Brako, Curator of Collections (382-6980)
   E-mail: brako_j@fortlewis.edu
  Michael Long, Library & Archives Specialist (382-6951)
   E-mail: mdlong@fortlewis.edu
  Elizabeth Quinn, Collections Manager/Registrar (247-7333)
   E-mail: eequinn@fortlewis.edu

Lara Aase, Librarian, Delaney Library & Archives (247-7135)
   E-mail: laase@fortlewis.edu
Resources: Archives, Library, Museum.
Mission: The Center of Southwest Studies at Fort Lewis College connects individuals and communities with opportunities to explore, study, and experience the Southwest's dynamic heritage.

FORT LEWIS COLLEGE - NATIVE AMERICAN CENTER
Student Union Rm. 020, 1000 Rim Dr. • DURANGO, CO 81301
  (970) 247-7221 Fax 247-7686; Website: www.fortlewis.edu/nac/
  E-mail: nativeamericancenter@fortlewis.edu
  Yvonne Bilinski (Navajo-Dine'), Director; (247-7222)
   E-mail: bilinski_y@fortlewis.edu
  Gabrielle Allan (Dine'/Turtle Mountain), Program Coordinator (247-7225)
   E-mail: gallan@fortlewis.edu
  Joey Dell, Student Support Specialist
   E-mail: jedell@fortlewis.edu
Mission: To promote the academic success & personal development of all Native American students who attend Fort Lewis College. *Resources*: Tutoring; workshops; speaker series; concerts; Elder-in-Residence program; professional development; Southern Ute archaeological field school, cooperative training & education program conducted with the Navajo Nation Archaeology Department (NNAD).

FORT LEWIS COLLEGE - DEPARTMENT OF NATIVE AMERICAN
& INDIGENOUS STUDIES
Rm. 284, 1000 Rim Dr. • DURANGO, CO 81301
  (877) FLC-COLO; (970) 247-6102 Fax 247-7221
  Website: www.fortlewis.edu/nais
  Majel Boxer (Sisseton-Wahpeton Dakota), Associate Professor & Chair
   E-mail: boxer_m@fortlewis.edu
  Peter McCormick, Interim Chair (2016-17)
   E-mail: mccormick_p@fortlewis.edu
  Frances Kay Holmes (Muscogee), Assistant Professor (247-7227)
   E-mail: fkholmes@fortlewis.edu
  Kathleen S. Fine-Dare, Professor of Anthropology (247-7438)
   E-mail: fine_k@fortlewis.edu
  Delilah Orr (Dine'), Professor of English (247-7627)
  Richard M. Wheelock (Oneida of Wisc.), Associate Professor Emeritus
   E-mail: wheelock_r@fortlewis.edu
Description: Offers major & minor in an interdisciplinary, comparative, & ultimately transformative approach to the study of the historical, political, social, & on-going experiences of Native Americans, Alaska Natives & Indigenous people within the U.S. & in the global community. *Visiting Faculty*: Jonathan Byrn. *Resources*: Internships. *Academic Programs*: Minor in Native American Studies; Minor in Heritage Preservation; paid internship opportunities in Durango, CO for Native Americans. A research oriented center with collections of documents focused on regional topics including the American Indian. *Purpose*: To serve as a museum & research facility and an interdisciplinary Southwest curriculum. *Resources*: The Native American Center - an academic & social support center for Native American students enrolled at Fort Lewis College. *Scholarships*: Tuition waiver for Native-American students certified by their respective tribes. Library. *Publication*: Timelines, bi-annual newsletter. Library. Established 1964.

COLORADO STATE UNIVERSITY - ETHNIC STUDIES DEPARTMENT
NATIVE AMERICAN STUDENT SERVICES
357 Aylesworth Hall SE, CD 1790 • FORT COLLINS, CO 80523
  (303) 491-2418 Fax 491-2717
  Website: http://ethnicstudies.colostate.edu
  Irene Vernon, Professor & Chairperson
   E-mail: irene.vernon@colostate.edu
  Roe Bubar, JD, Associate Professor
   E-mail: roe.bubar@colostate.edu
  Thomas Michael Swensen, Assistant Professor (214 Willard O. Eddy Hall)
   E-mail: thomas.swensen@colostate.edu
Purpose: To provide support services for Native American students of Colorado State University; to educate the university & Fort Collins communities about Native American culture and history. *Degree*: Certificates in Native American Studies & Ethnic Studies. *Faculty*: Roe Bubar, JD, Irene Vernon. *Project*: CA7AE: HIV/AIDS Prevention Project - funded by the Center for Disease Control & Prevention to develop & deliver Capacity Building Assistance (CBA) to organizations serving ethnic minorities at risk for or living with HIV/AIDS; Pamela Jumper-Thurman, Director (491-0251). *Services*: Native American Student Services. *Programs*: Recruiting; orientation; skill development workshops; tutorial assistance; employment opportunity advisement; financial aid assistance; peer counseling; social & cultural activities. *Publication*: Ethnic Studies, Biannual newsletter.

CONNECTICUT

UNIVERSITY OF CONNECTICUT, AVERY POINT
NATIVE AMERICAN & INDIGENOUS STUDIES (NAIS)
1084 Shennecossett Rd. • GROTON, CT 06340
(860) 405-9000; Website: www.uconn.edu/native_american_studies
Kevin McBride, NAS Coordinator at Storrs
 E-mail: kevin.mcbride@uconn.edu
Theodore Van Alst, Professor of NAIS at Avery Point
Nancy Shoemaker, Professor of History
 E-mail: nancy.shoemaker@uconn.edu
Joseph Comprone, Professor of English
 E-mail: joseph.comprone@uconn.edu
Program: An interdisciplinary program offering a NAIS Minor & Individualized Major focusing on Native American social studies, history, art & literature, as well as courses that would directly serve the particular economic needs & concerns of Native communities in New England & surrounding areas. Resources available: Native American Culture Club meets weekly & sponsors an annual powwow on campus. Financial aid available.

YALE UNIVERSITY
DEPARTMENT OF AMERICAN STUDIES & HISTORY
P.O. Box 208236 • NEW HAVEN, CT 06520
(203) 432-1186; Kathryn Dudley, Chairperson
Faculty: Ned Blackhawk; E-mail: ned.blackhawk@yale.edu

YALE UNIVERSITY - THE HOWARD R. LAMAR CENTER
FOR THE STUDY OF FRONTIERS & BORDERS
53 Wall St., P.O. Box 208201 • NEW HAVEN, CT 06520
(203) 432-2328 Fax 432-6846
Tom Conroy, Contact (432-1345)
 E-mail: tom.conroy@yale.edu
Howard R. Lamar, Sterling Professor Emeritus of History
John Mack Faragher, Professor of History & Center Director
Jay Gitlin, Lecturer & Associate Director
 E-mail: jay.gitlin@yale.edu
Ned Blackhawk (Western Shoshone), Professor of History/American Studies
Alejandra Dubbcovsky-Joseph, Faculty
Purpose: Seeks to encourage the study of frontier history. The principal priority is the support of graduate study in the departments of History & American Studies at Yale. *Activities*: Provides grants for dissertation research on topics relating to the Center's scholarly interests, the study of the frontier experience, the American West, and Native American history; sponsors an annual postdoctoral scholarship; holds an annual symposium of scholars in September, the annual Betts Lecture in November; and presents conferences and lectures by distinguished scholars throughout the academic year.

YALE UNIVERSITY LAW SCHOOL - THE AVALON PROJECT
Lillian Goldman Law Library, 127 Wall St. • NEW HAVEN, CT 06511
(203) 432-4992; Website: www.law.yale.edu
 Eugene R. Fidell, Senior Research Scholar (American Indian Tribal Law)
An online resource for documents in Law, History & Diplomacy back to the 18th century & earlier...includes treaties between the U.S. & Native American tribes. Established 2001.

YALE UNIVERSITY
NATIVE AMERICAN CULTURAL CENTER (NACC)
26 High St. • NEW HAVEN, CT 06520
(203) 432-2900
Kelly Fayard (Poarch Band Creek), Center Director, Assistant Dean
 & Professor of Contemporary Native America
Alyce Laronal (Haida/Tsimpsian/Hawaiian, Assistant Director of Center
Ned Blackhawk (Western Shoshone), Professor of History
 & American Studies
Christopher J. Cutter, Clinician Researcher & Director Medical Research Unit
Ruth Phillips, Native North American Art
Margaret P. Moss (Hidatsa/Fort Peck Sioux), Associate Professor of Nursing
Purpose: To promote Native American culture & explores the issues that Native Americans face in today's world; to serve as a gathering place for Yale's Native American students; to expose the Native community, as well as the greater Yale community, to Native American culture by bringing programming to campus that includes events such as speakers, dinners, study breaks, and movie nights. *Faculty & Advisors*: Ned Blackhawk (Western Shoshone), Alyssa Mt. Pleasant (Tuscarora); Jay Gitlin (Associate Director of Lamar Center at Yale), Amanda Kotlyar (Mississippi Choctaw), Elizabeth Anne Reese (Nambe), Allison Tjemsland (Jamestown S'Klallam), Ruth G. Torres (Schaghticoke). *Resources*: Native American & Indigenous Studies Resources; Association of Native Americans at Yale. Established 1993.

DISTRICT OF COLUMBIA

AMERICAN UNIVERSITY
WASHINGTON INTERNSHIPS FOR NATIVE STUDENTS (WINS)
School of Professional & Extended Studies, Tenley-Constitution Hall, Rm. 100
4400 Massachusetts Ave. NW • WASHINGTON, DC 20016
(202) 895-4879 Fax 895-4882; E-mail: wins@american.edu
Carola Weil, Dean of School & Lecturer
Donelle Broskow, Director of Extennded Studies & Assistant Dean,
 Bridge Programs; (895-4968) E-mail: broskow@american.edu
Description: Offers students of sovereign American Indian, Alaska Native & Native Hawaiian nations the opportunity to build leadership skills while living, studying, and interning in Washington, D.C. American University has played host to more than 600 Native American, Alaska Native, and Native Hawaiian college students from June 4 to August 15. Designed to give the students a Washington-based education, experience, and training that they can use to help their tribal communities. The WINS Program consists of three phases. The first year - a ten week internship at the White House, U.S. Congress, Dept. of HH, or other government agency & studying government at American University; the second year - an inter-tribal work-study program; and the third phase - for Native American graduate students to work and study on a reservation while writing their graduate thesis. Established 1994.

GEORGE WASHINGTON UNIVERSITY
NATIVE AMERICAN POLITICAL LEADERSHIP PROGRAM
1922 F St., NW Suite 401 • WASHINGTON, DC 20052
(202) 994-3284 Fax 994-8471
 Website: www.naplp.gwu.edu; E-mail: naplp@gwu.edu
 Gregory Lebel, Director, Semester in Washington Politics
 E-mail: siwp@gwu.edu
Purpose: To give Native American undergraduates an educational opportunity in the nation's capital. Partnering with Semester In Washington Politics, NAPLP students take classes at GW, participate in hands-on internships & interact with political leaders & policymakers. Includes a series of seminars devoted to public policy issues affecting Native American communities.

FLORIDA

UNIVERSITY OF FLORIDA
AMERICAN INDIAN & INDIGENOUS STUDIES
College of Liberal Arts & Sciences
2014 Turlington Hall, P.O. Box 117300 • GAINESVILLE, FL 32611
(352) 392-0780 Fax 392-3584
 Robin Wright, Associate Professor of Religion
 E-mail: baniwa05@ufl.edu; (392-1625 ext. 230)
 Ken Sassaman, Department of Anthropology (392-2253)
 E-mail: sassaman@anthro.ufl.edu
Program: Minor.

GEORGIA

UNIVERSITY OF GEORGIA
INSTITUTE OF NATIVE AMERICAN STUDIES (INAS)
NATIVE AMERICAN STUDIES PROGRAM
Franklin College of Arts & Sciences
Peabody Hall 1625 • ATHENS, GA 30602
(706) 542-5356 Fax 542-6724
 Website: www.instituteofnativeamericanstudies.com
 Jace Weaver, Director & Professor of Native American Studies & Religion
 E-mail: jweaver@uga.edu
 Robert Hill, Professor Emeritus of Native American Studies
 E-mail: bobhill@uga.edu
 Claudio Saunt, Associate Director (History); E-mail: csaunt@uga.edu
 Ervan Garrison, Professor of Anthropology & Geology
 E-mail: egarriso@uga.edu
 R. Alfred Vick, Associate Professor (Environmental Design)
 E-mail: ravick@uga.edu
 Laura Adams Weaver, Instructor in English
 E-mail: laweaver@uga.edu
 Victor Thompson, Professor, Director of center for Archaeological Sciences
 E-mail vdthom@uga.edu
Description: Undergraduate & graduate certificates for any degree in any "traditional" discipline. Central to the mission of both Native American Studies as a discipline and to INAS is the study of the indigenous peoples of the Americas from the perspective of the indigenes themselves. Our logo reflects our mission. The yellow circle reflects not only the hoop of existence but the life-giving sun, revered by the Mississippians, their Muscogean descendants,

and the Yuchi here in Georgia (as well as numerous peoples throughout the Americas). Within the circle is the name of the institute in Cherokee, written in Sequoyah's syllabary, the only internally invented alphabet for a Native language. Because both "institute" & "studies" are abstractions, and "Native American" a foreign construct, the title is impossible to translate with total accuracy. Reflecting our mission, we opted for "We Are Speaking Here." It is our intent to have Native nations and peoples speaking here through INAS. At the core of INAS are its undergraduate & graduate certificate programs. These permit students to earn UGA degrees in "traditional" disciplines such as religion, English, law, anthropology, or history (or many others), while developing an expertise in Native American Studies and demonstrating it through a separate credential. *Resource*: Archaeology Field School.

VALDOSTA STATE UNIVERSITY
NATIVE AMERICAN STUDIES PROGRAM (MINOR)
1500 N. Patterson St. • VALDOSTA, GA 31698
 (229) 333-5494; Website: www.valdosta.edu/nas
 E-mail: nativeamericanstudies@valdosta.edu
 Fred E. Knowles, Jr., Chairperson; E-mail: feknowles@valdosta.edu
 Marvin Smith (333-5490); E-mail: mtsmith@valdosta.edu
 Dixie Haggard (333-5497); E-mail: drhaggard@valdosta.edu
 Lavonna Lovern (333-7376); E-mail: llovern@valdosta.edu
 Brad Finson (333-7406); E-mail: bafinson@valdosta.edu
A minor in Native American Studies at Valdosta State University provides students with an interdisciplinary approach that accelerates a greater understanding of native peoples over time and highlights their contributions to the global community. Our courses explore the prehistoric times before the impact of colonization and after the Western settlement, the native people located in the Southeast and Caribbean to the northern valleys of Canada, and artwork created by Native Americans. Addresses the global & regional problems of Native American tribes.

HAWAII

UNIVERSITY OF HAWAII
AMERICAN INDIAN, ALASKA NATIVE, & NATIVE HAWAIIAN PROGRAM
1890 East West Rd., Moore Hall 405
School of Public Health • HONOLULU, HI 96822
 (800) 927-3297 Fax (808) 956-6230; Rick Haverkate, MPH, Director
Special program: Educational Opportunities Program recruits Native Americans into the School as part IHS emphasis to increase numbers of Native Americans with Master's Degrees. *Instructors*: Gigliola Baruffi, MD, MPH; Kathryn L. Braun, MPH, DrPH; John Casken, RN, MPH, PhD; Alan R. Katz, MD, MPH; Walter K. Partick, MPH; and Barbara Z. Siegel, PhD.

UNIVERSITY OF HAWAII AT MANOA
DEPARTMENT OF ETHNIC STUDIES
2560 Campus Rd., George Hall, Rm. 301 • HONOLULU, HI 96822
 (808) 956-8086 Fax 956-9494
 Website: www.ethnicstudies.hawaii.edu
 Monisha DasGupta, Chairperson (956-2914)
 E-mail: eschair@hawaii.edu
 Roderick Labrador, Academic Advisor (956-6915)
 E-mail: Labrador@hawaii.edu
Ethnic Studies provides introductory & advanced courses on theories & practices of ethnicity, race, class, & gender. The program also offers courses on the history and experiences of specific groups, including African Americans & Native Americans. Among groups in Hawai'i, Chinese, Filipinos, Hawaiians, and Japanese are subjects of separate courses. There are also courses dealing with critical topics such as ethnic identity, land tenure, social movements, and labor history. Students may earn a BA or the Certificate of Ethnic Studies. Graduates have gone on to successful work in public service, social service, business, law, labor organization, education, and other fields that require sensitivity to people and their backgrounds.

IDAHO

BOISE STATE UNIVERSITY
Department of Anthropology
1910 University Dr. HWSC, Rm. 55 • BOISE, ID 83725
 (208) 426-3023 Fax 426-4329; Website: www.boisestate.edu
 John P. Ziker, Professor, Department Chairperson
 E-mail: jziker@boisestate.edu
 Mark Plew, Graduate Program Coordinator
 E-mail: mplew@boisestate.edu
 Kendall House, Adjunct Assistant Professor
 E-mail: khouse@boisestate.edu
Program: The department coordinates minor programs in American Indian Studies.

LEWIS-CLARK STATE COLLEGE
Native American/Minority Student Services
500 8th Ave. • LEWISTON, ID 83501
 (800) 933-5272; (208) 792-2812 Fax 792-2193
 Website: www.lcsc.edu
 Robert F. Sobotta, Director; E-mail: bsobotta@lcsc.edu
 Sam White Temple, Retention Specialist (792-2744)
 E-mail: tswhite-temple@lcsc.edu
 Victoria Mitchell, Club President
Mission: To assist students of color in meeting their educational goals.
Degree: Minor in Native American Studies & Nez Perce Language.
Lewis-Clark State College is located at Lewiston, Idaho, where two rivers (Clearwater & Snake), two cities (Lewiston & Clarkston), and two states (Idaho and Washington) come together. It is also where two peoples and two cultures came together in friendship and discovery – the Nez Perce Tribe and the Lewis & Clark Corps of Discovery. Founded in 1893, Lewis-Clark State is a public undergraduate college with a three-part mission of academic programs, professional-technical programs, and community programs. The Pi'amkinwaas - American Indian Center for Educational Excellence - promotes a positive learning environment that provides student support services & consideration to the unique cultural and community values of American Indian people. The center is respectful and inclusive of student representatives of all Nations. The goal of the Native American Club is to assist and promote all Native American students toward completion of a college education. Students participate in activities such as the promotion and planning of "Native American Awareness Week," fundraising projects, social & cultural activities reflecting Native American culture, encouraging higher education to local communities, and to provide student-to-student support. All students are welcome to be a part of the Native American Club.

NORTH IDAHO COLLEGE - AMERICAN INDIAN STUDIES PROGRAM
1000 E. Garden Ave. • COEUR D'ALENE, ID 83814
 (877) 404-4536; (208) 769-3300
 Website: www.nic.edu/programs
 Evalene Melting Tallow, Advisor; (208) 769-3365
Degrees: AA or AS in American Indian Studies. *Transfer Program*: Designed in collaboration with the Coeur d'Alene Tribe and examines the contemporary & ancient experiences and ways of life of the first peoples of North America from their perspective. The curriculum is designed to provide a study of American Indians from a holistic and humanistic viewpoint by focusing on their cultural, historical, and contemporary life. It is an interdisciplinary program drawing on the arts, humanities, social sciences, natural resources, science, and professional studies.

UNIVERSITY OF IDAHO - AMERICAN INDIAN STUDIES (AIS) PROGRAM
Department of Sociology & Anthropology
875 Perimeter Dr. MS 1110 • MOSCOW, ID 883844
 (208) 885-6751 Fax 885-2034
 Website: www.uidaho.edu/class/soc-anthro
 Philip Stevens (San Carlos Apache), Program Director & Assistant Professor
 E-mail: pstevens@uidaho.edu
 Brian Wolf, Department Chairperson & Associate Professor (885-6777)
 E-mail: bwolf@uidaho.edu
 Mark Warner, Professor & Associate Dean for Graduate Studies (885-5954)
 E-mail: mwarner@uidaho.edu
 Yolanda Bisbee, Executive Director of Tribal Relations;
 Interim Chef-Diversity Office; E-mail: ybisbee@uidaho.edu
Program: To provide & advance quality education for and about American Indians of Idaho, the region, and the nation. In fulfilling this mission, the Program is committed to meet the changing needs of Idaho's Indian tribes and all Idaho citizens through excellence in teaching, research, & service. In its academic program, the department provides concentrated study through an undergraduate minor and a Master of Arts degree in Interdisciplinary Studies with an American Indian Studies emphasis. *Faculty*: Yolanda Bisbee; Harold Crook (Nez Perce); Rodney Frey; Ed Galindo; Lee Sappington; Jan Johnson; Anne Marshall; Rebecca Tallent; Jan Johnson (American Indian literature); J.D. Wulfhorst; D;Lisa Penney Pinkahm, Affiliate Faculty, Tribal Teacher.

IDAHO STATE UNIVERSITY - AMERICAN INDIAN STUDIES PROGRAM
Department of Anthropology, College of Arts & Letters
921 S. 8th Ave., CB 8005 • POCATELLO, ID 83209
 (208) 236-2629 Fax 282-4944
 Website: www.isu.edu; E-mail: centchri@isu.edu
 Christopher Loether, Program Director; E-mail: loetchri@isu.edu
 Katherine Reedy-Maschner, Associate Professor & Dept. Chairperson
 E-mail: reedkath@isu.edu
 Drusilla Guld, Senior Lecturer, Native Language Instructor
 E-mail: gouldrus@isu.edu
 Ernest "Skip" Lohse, Curator of Anthropology, Idaho Museum
 of Natural History

Program: The department coordinates minor programs in American Indian Studies, Linguistics, & Latino Studies as well as hosting Shoshoni Language Program. *Faculty*: Christopher Loether, Director (Linguistics; Language; Indians of California); Katherine Reedy-Maschner (Aleut, Yupiit & Inupiat of Alaska); Drusilla Gould (Senior lecturer, Native Language Instructor); Ernest Lohse (Native American Material Culture).

ILLINOIS

SOUTHERN ILLINOIS UNIVERSITY
NATIVE AMERICAN STUDIES (NAS) PROGRAM
Department of Anthropology
Peck Hall, Rm. 3426, CB 1608 • EDWARDSVILLE, IL 62026
  (618) 650-5044 Fax 650-5050; Julie Holt, Coordinator
Faculty: Sandra Charlson & Gray Whaley *Program*: Minor in Native American Studies. The interdisciplinary minor in Native American Studies consists of courses from anthropology, art, history, & philosophy. Areas of faculty interest\expertise: Native cultures/material culture of the Great Lakes; Cherokee ethno-history; native North Pacific Coast songs, oral tradition, & philosophy; archaeology of native Illinois & the Midwest; native North American art.

UNIVERSITY OF ILLINOIS AT URBANA-CHAMPAIGN
NATIVE AMERICAN HOUSE-AMERICAN INDIAN STUDIES (AIS)
1204 W. Nevada St. MC-138 • URBANA, IL 61801
  (217) 265-9870 Fax 265-9880
  Website: www.ais.illinois.edu; E-mail: ais@illinois.edu
  Adrian Burgos, Jr., Interim Director & Professor
    E-mail: burgosjr@illinois.edu
  John McKinn (Gila River Mariicopa), Associate Director (265-9878)
    E-mail: mckinn@illinois.edu
  Dulce Talavera, Office Support Associate; (333-4752)
    E-mail: talavera@illinois.edu
American Indian Studies Program: Undergraduate minor with a graduate minor under consideration. *Affiliated Faculty*: Brenda Farrell (Anthropology & AIS); Frederick E. Hoxie, Emeritus (History); Robert Dale Parker (English & American Indian Studies); Jenny L. Davis (Chickasaw) (Linguistics). Matthew Sakiestewa Gilbert (History). *Postdoctoral Fellows (2015-17):* Silvia Soto, Briana Theobald, Korinta Maldonado

INDIANA

INDIANA UNIVERSITY
AMERICAN INDIAN STUDIES RESEARCH INSTITUTE
422 N. Indiana Ave. • BLOOMINGTON, IN47408
  (812) 855-4086 Fax 855-7529
  Website: www.indiana.edu/~aisri; E-mail: aisri@indiana.edu
  Laura L. Scheiber, Director & Associate Professor of Anthropology
  Raymnd J. DeMallie & Douglas R. Parks, Co-Directors
  Sally Anderson (Linguistics); Jon Bowman, Director (CDEL)
Faculty: Brian Gilley (Anthropology); Jason Baird Jackson, (Folklore & Anthropology & American Studies); Philip S. LeSourd, (Anthropology); Laura L. Scheiber, (Anthropology); Christina Snyder (History & American Studies); John A. Erickson, (Anthropological Linguistics). *Research Associates*: Carolyn Anderson, Francis Flavin, Gregory Fields, Kellie Jean Hogue, Thomas Kavanagh, Paul Kroeber. *Mission*: To serve as an interdisciplinary research center for projects focusing on the Native peoples of the Americas. Projects stress Plains Indian languages, cultures, & history, & include software development that enhances linguistic documentation, analysis, & publication, as well as innovative instructional media for teaching Native American languages.

INDIANA UNIVERSITY
NATIVE AMERICAN & INDIGENOUS STUDIES (NAIS)
Dept. of American Studies, Ballentine Hall 521
1020 E. Kirkwood Ave. • BLOOMINGTON, IN 47405
  (812) 855-7718 Fax 855-0001
  Website: www.Indiana.edu; E-mail: nais@indiana.edu
  Christina Snyder, Associate Professor of History
    E-mail: snyderch@indiana.edu
  Nicholas Belle, Director of First Nations, Educational & Cultural Center
    E-mail: nbelle@indiana.edu
  Sarah Dees, NAIS Editor; E-mail: sdees@indiana.edu
Native American studies minor in both undergraduate & PhD programs. *Committee on Native American & Indigenous Studies*: Jason Baird Jackson (associate professor of folklore); Raymond DeMallie (Plains Indian peoples); Douglas R. Parks (linguistics); Philip S. LeSourd (Native American languages); Lauren Morris MacLean (political science in American Indian/Alaska Native communities); Laura Scheiber (Native American ethno-history); Brian Gilley (Anthropology); Christina Snyder (Native North American history); Sonya

Atalay (Indigenous Archaeology, NAGPRA). *Special Resources & Facilities*: American Indian Studies Research Institute (focuses on Native North American cultures, languages & ethno-history); Center for the Documentation of Endangered Languages Sound Laboratory (CDEL); Mathers Museum of World Cultures; American Indian Students Association; Native American Resources at the Herman B. Wells Library; First Nations Educational & Cultural Center (FNECC). *Activities*: Powwow; Annual Meeting; Financial Aid available. *Publication*: NAIS News.

INDIANA UNIVERSITY-PURDUE UNIVERSITY
AMERICAN INDIAN PROGRAMS
NATIVE AMERICAN & INDIGENOUS STUDIES
IU School of Liberal Arts, 425 University Blvd.
Cavanaugh Hall 325, INDIANAPOLIS, IN 46202
  (317) 274-8356 Fax 274-1325
  Website: www.liberalarts.iupui.edu/aip/
  Charmayne 'Charli" Champion-Shaw (Southern Cheyenne), Director
    E-mail: cchampio@iupui.edu
Mission: Our goal is to educate & inform students about the Native experience that comes from the rich cultural heritage of the sovereign Indigenous peoples of the United States. Another goal is to create a department that collaborates with Native communities and engages students in nation building.
The Native American & Indigenous Studies Program introduces students to differences in the perspectives of Native American cultures on a wide variety of topics. Students gain an awareness of the diversity and multiple layers of humanistic knowledge within the framework of the North American human experience. Native American Studies undergraduate students have the option to support the student organization called the Native American Student Alliance (NASA) that provides and supports education awareness and program development on campus. Graduate students, staff and faculty work together to enhance educational, professional & cultural opportunities for members of the Indiana University-Purdue University Native American community through the Native American Faculty Staff Council (NAFSC). *Special program*: Certificate in Native American Studies. *Instructors*: Dawn Marsh (Native American & indigenous peoples history); Lawrence Kuznar (Navajo); Richard E. Sutter (Chair, Anthropology); Alan R. Sandstrom (Emeritus of Anthropology); Chad L. Thompson (Linguistics).

BALL STATE UNIVERSITY
NATIVE AMERICAN STUDIES MINOR PROGRAM
Dept. of Anthropology
Burkhardt Bldg. (BB), Rm. 315 • MUNCIE, IN 47306
  (765) 285-1575 Fax 285-2163
  Colleen Boyd, PhD, Director; E-mail: ceboyd@bsu.edu
Description: Native American Studies Minor. Focuses on major aspects of Native American life in North America, such as history, culture, values, literature and art. *Mission*: To increase awareness of the diversity of cultures native to our continent. *Instructors*: John Boyd; Paul Chandler, PhD; Olon Dotson (Cherokee Freedman); Amy Gregg; Sharon RedHawk Love (Eastern Cherokee/Blackfeet); Carolyn MacKay; Kenan Metger (Cherokee/Ho-Chunk); Elizabeth Nesbitt (Miami); Frank Trechsel (Native American languages). *Activities*: Native American Student Alliance; Financial Aid available. *Facilities*: American Indian Center of Indiana; Archaeology Laboratory.

VALPARAISO UNIVERSITY
AMERICAN INDIAN STUDIES PROGRAM
Dept. of Geography & Meteorology
Kallay-Christopher Hall 201 • VALPARAISO, IN 46383
  (219) 464-5139 Fax 464-5381
  Website: www.valpo.edu/geography-meteorology/american-indian-studies/
  Ronald Janke, Program Director; E-mail: ronald.janke@valpo.edu
Program: American Indian Studies Minor - Covers Indian issues & culture through the study of historical geography, anthropology, and contemporary problems of a wide range of tribal groups and the changing perceptions of Indians in our society & the current socio-economic challenges these groups face. *Special programs*: Field courses; Plains Indians.

IOWA

IOWA STATE UNIVERSITY
CENTER FOR INTERCULTURAL STUDIES
AMERICAN INDIAN STUDIES PROGRAM (AISP)
College of Liberal Arts & Science, 208 Carver Hall • AMES, IA 50011
  (515) 294-9730 Fax 294-5104
  Sebastian Braun, Director (294-7139)
    E-mail: sfbraun@iastate.edu
Providing a Minor in American Indian Studies, the AISP reflects Contemporary American Indian Studies to an enrollment of over 500 students. Provides in-state tuition to members of tribes with a historical connection to the state of Iowa, specifically the Iowa, Kickapoo, Menominee, Miami, Missouri, Ojibwe

(Chippewa), Omaha, Otoe, Ottawa (Adawa), Potawatomi, Sac & Fox (Sauk, Meskwaki), Sioux & Winnebago (HoCak). *Faculty*: Grant Arndt; Christina Gish Hill; Jim Coppoc, PhD. *Facilities*: United Native American Student Organization, and the ISU chapter of the Association of Indian Science & Engineering Society. *Activities*: American Indian Symposium held each Spring.

UNIVERSITY OF IOWA
AMERICAN INDIAN & NATIVE STUDIES PROGRAM
College of Liberal Arts & Sciences
210 Jefferson Bldg., 129 E. Washington St. • IOWA CITY, IA 52242
(319) 335-0320 Fax 335-0314
Laura Kastens, Administrative Services Coordinator
E-mail: laura-kastens@uiowa.edu
Michelene Pesantubbee (Choctaw of Oklahoma), Associate Professor
E-mail: michelene-pesantubbee@uiowa.edu
A number of courses from the departments of American Studies, Anthropology, Art History, English, History and Law are approved courses leading to a certificate or minor in the undergraduate program. Phillip Round (English); Tom Arne Midtrod (History); Jacki Thompson Rand (History); Margaret Beck; Linda Bolton (English); Erica Prussing (Anthropology); Stephen Warren (History). *Special programs*: American Indian Science & Engineering Society; annual powwow, student conference. Financial aid: Iowa First Nations offers resident tuition to members of tribes historically connected to Iowa.

UNIVERSITY OF IOWA - COLLEGE OF LAW
416 Boyd Law Bldg., 130 Byington Rd. • IOWA CITY, IA 52242
(319) 335-6850; Ann Lacquer Estin, Contact
E-mail: ann-estin@uiowa.edu
Offers one of the strongest Native American law programs in the country. *Activities*: The Native American Law Student Association & the University of Iowa College of Law have established the Iowa Indian Defense Network, a computer bulletin board dedicated to the exchange of information, views, assistance, and rights, to Indian policy, tribal government, tribal news, and other Indian affairs questions.

KANSAS

*HASKELL INDIAN NATIONS UNIVERSITY
DEPARTMENT OF AMERICAN INDIAN STUDIES
College of Indigenous & American Indian Studies
127 Parker Hall, 155 Indian Ave. #1305 • LAWRENCE, KS 66046
(785) 749-8404 Fax 832-6643; Website: www.haskell.edu
Venida S. Chenault (Prarie Band Potawatomi), President
E-mail: vchenault@haskell.edu
Tonia Salvini, V.P. of University Services
Lee Pahcoddy (Comanche), Director of Facilities Management
Joshua Arce, JD, (Prairie Band Potawatomi), Chief Information Officer
Brenda Racehorse, Chief Financial Officer
Daniel Wildcat, Department of American Indian Studies Director
Faculty:
Julia Good Fox (Pawnee) E-mail: jgoodfox@haskell.edu
Melissa Holder (Winnebago) E-mail: mholder@haskell.edu
Michael Stewart (Choctaw) E-mail: mstewart@haskell.edu
Michael Tosee (Comanche) E-mail: mtosee@haskell.edu
Daniel Wildcat (Yuchee Creek) E-mail: dwildcat@haskell.edu
Eric Anderson (Citizen band Potawatomi
E-mail: eanderson@haskell.edu
Theresa Milk (Cheyenne River Sioux) E-mail: tmilk@haskell.edu
Cody Marshall (Salt River Pima) E-mail: pmarshall@haskell.edu
Beverly Fprtner (Navajo), Director, Academic Support Center,
Tommaney Library (832-6659); E-mail: bfortner@haskell.edu
Carrie Cornelius (Oneida of Wisconsin), Librarian-Tommaney Library
E-mail: ccornelius@haskell.edu
Haskell offers three AA degrees & a BS in elementary education, which is accredited for teacher certification by the State of Kansas. The instructional division of the college is committed to fostering the intellectual & personal growth of each student and to enable students to pursue constructive and responsible personal & professional lives grounded in Native American cultural values and an ethical concern for life. The program consists of college preparatory instruction in language arts and mathematics. Specific courses explore the history, institutions, values and contemporary issues of American Indians/Alaska Natives. *Programs*: Natural and Social Sciences, Humanities, Health and Physical Education, Business, Teacher Education. Haskell also provides a program of study that addresses issues, research, and law currently affecting tribal governments nationwide. The Tribal Management Program offers a unique approach in the study of the evolution of tribal government into the complexities of the 21st century. Operated by the Bureau of Indian Affairs.

UNIVERSITY OF KANSAS
Department of Anthropology, 622 Fraser Hall
1415 Jayhawk Blvd. • LAWRENCE, KS 66045
(785) 864-4103 Fax 864-5224
Website: www.ku.edu/~kuanth; E-mail: kuanthro@ku.edu
Instructors:
Donald Stull (Emeritus-Sociocultural Anthropology); (864-22641)
E-mail: stull@ku.edu
Akira Y. Yamamoto (Emeritus-Linguistic Anthropology)
E-mail: akira@ku.edu
Special programs: Dr. Yamamoto works closely with the Hualapai; Dr. Stull works closely with the Kansas Kickapoo. Research, technical assistance & employment opportunities are available in the areas of applied linguistics, applied anthropology, planning & development, tribal studies, & curriculum development. *Scholarships*: Graduate fellowships & teaching & research assistantships. *Facility*: Museum of Anthropology.

UNIVERSITY OF KANSAS
INDIGENOUS STUDIES PROGRAM
College of Liberal Arts & Sciences
1410 Jayhawk Blvd., Lippincott, Rm. 6 • LAWRENCE, KS 66045
(785) 864-2660 Fax 864-0370
Website: www.indigenous.ku.edu; E-mail: indigenous@ku.edu
Stephanie Fitzgerald, Program Director; Associate Professor of English
(864-2586) E-mail: sfitzger@ku.edu
Lauren Chaney, Graduate Academic Advisor (864-2306)
E-mail: lkchaney@ku.edu
Brandy Ernzen, ISP Program Coordinator
E-mail: bernzen@ku.edu; (864-6408)
Michael Zogry, Associate Professor, Native American/First Nations Religions
(864-9444) E-mail: mzogry@ku.edu
Christine M. Daley, Director, Center for American Indian Community Health
E-mail: cdaley@kumc.edu; (913-588-2477)
Program: Master's degree program & graduate certificate. *Affiliate Faculty*: Joshua Miner, Assistant Professor of Native/Indigenous film & media); Norman Akers (Osage), Director of Art Graduate Studies; Jay T. Johnson; Andrew McKenzie (Native American languages); Sharon O'Brien (Political Science, GINSP Graduate Advisor); Lizette Peter (Cherokee language); Elizabeth A. Kronk Warner, JD, (law). The Indigenous Studies master's degree program provides students with in-depth knowledge of Indigenous peoples' complex and diverse cultures and histories, as well as their impacts on the global society. Our multidisciplinary program offers students the advantage of studying relevant issues from a wide range of academic perspectives. The expertise of our affiliate faculty members includes Native American history, including medical and legal aspects; indigenous literature; ethno-botany; Indigenous peoples' cultural survival and political activism; American Indian tribal governments; indigenous geographies & cartographic history; Native American religions; and much more. Empowered by the resources on campus and in our community, we strive to provide unique learning opportunities for our students that go beyond the classroom. The mission of the multidisciplinary Indigenous Studies Program is to educate students and promote scholarship about the complexity and diversity of Indigenous peoples' cultures and histories, and to provide students with the knowledge to understand and assess the U.S. tribes' unique relationships to the U.S. government. Indigenous Studies encourages appreciation of the contributions of Indigenous peoples to the global society, provides students with an understanding of the difficulties confronting tribal nations and offers foundational knowledge to assist them in finding innovative solutions to solve those problems.

UNIVITY OF KANSAS - SCHOOL OF LAW
TRIBAL LAW & GOVERNMENT CENTER
406 Green Hall • LAWRENCE, KS 66045
Elizabeth A. Kronk Warner, JD, Center Director
(785) 864-1139; E-mail: Elizabeth.kronk@ku.edu
Website: http://www.law.ku.edu/academics/triballaw/center/
The Center represents Indian nations & tribes and requires an understanding of the laws, history and policies that affect them. The complexity of "Indian law," and the lack of specific programs designed to educate graduates about the unique legal and cultural needs of Indian people, has created a situation in which lawyers representing Indian tribes place too great an emphasis on state law and federal law when dealing with Indian nations. As a result, these lawyers may unconsciously be contributing to the weakening of unique tribal legal and governance traditions by recommending the adoption of tribal laws and policies founded upon the Anglo-American legal and political traditions rather than the unique traditions of their tribal clients. Through its activities, the Tribal Law & Government Center at KU Law aims to equip students and legal professionals who will represent Indian nations with the skills necessary to appreciate & strengthen the unique nature of indigenous tribal legal systems.

OTTAWA UNIVERSITY
1001 S. Cedar St. • OTTAWA, KS 66067
 (800) 755-5200 Fax (785) 229-1008; Website: www.ottawa.edu
Description: in 1865, The Ottawa Indians donated 20,000 acres for a university to ensure the education of the Baptist missionary's children. In exchange, the Baptists agreed to build & operate the school with a purpose to provide free education to the Ottawa Indians. In 2008, Ottawa University expanded the agreement with the Ottawa Tribe, wherein tribal members may attend any of OU's eight campuses or OU Online, in either the undergraduate or graduate program, free of charge - including room, board & fees. Today, there are more than 7,000 students attending the University.

JOHNSON COUNTY COMMUNITY COLLEGE
CENTER FOR AMERICAN INDIAN STUDIES (CAIS)
12345 College Blvd., Box 36 • OVERLAND PARK, KS 66210
(913) 469-8500 ext. 4823 Fax 469-2585
Website: www.jccc.edu/academics/cais
Sean M. Daley, Professor & Center Director; E-mail: smdaley@jccc.edu
Faculty: Sean M. Daley; Madison Huber-Smith, Curriculum Development
 Coordinator; Thomas "Ed" Smith II, Research Project Coordinator
Affiliated Faculty: Tai Edwards (History); Bruce Hartman (Nerman Museum);
Madison Huber-Smith (Anthropology); Jim Leiker (History & Political
Science); William McFarlane (Anthropology); Holly Milkowart;
Allison Smith (Art History).
Serves as a resource & advocate for American Indian & Alaska Native individuals and communities. We also act as a resource for JCCC students, faculty, staff & community members who are trying to better their understanding of these cultures, societies & ways of life. They welcome organizations academic institutes, Indian Nations, Indian communities and individuals (both Native & non-Native) who share our mission to seek to affect positive change in Indian country. The AIHREA scholarship is available to college students of any age, gender, socio-economic status, physical ability, and so forth who are seeking skills, a degree and/or a career working to improve the physical, mental, emotional and/or spiritual well-being of American Indians and Alaska Natives. While preference will be given to Native students, anyone, regardless of ethnicity, is welcome to apply. The AIHREA scholarship can be used at any community college, tribal college, four-year college or university in the United States. Any academic major is eligible to apply. The scholarship money can be used for tuition, fees, books & required class materials. The AIHREA Student Summer Internship Program allows high school, undergraduate & graduate students the opportunity to work on various community–based research projects with American Indian communities in Kansas and throughout the Plains region. During this 8-week paid internship, interns work with faculty and staff from both CAIS and the Center for American Indian Community Health at the University of Kansas Medical Center on research projects centering on American Indian health & education. Affiliated with the American Indian Health Research & Education Alliance (Website: www.aihrea.com. *Design Team members*: Brandon Roche, Blake Nofzinger, Matt Martiny, and Keri Sartain.

PITTSBURG STATE UNIVERSITY - 21st CENTURY LIBRARY ALLIANCE
College of Education, 106 Hughes Hall
1701 S. Broadway • PITTSBURG, KS 66762
(620) 235-4499 Fax 235-4520
Dr. Howard Smith, Dean of College of Education
 E-mail: smith@pittstate.edu
Dr. Alice Sagehorn, Department Chair
 E-mail: asagehorn@pittstate.edu
Description: The program, which is titled the 21st Century Library Alliance, is a collaborative effort between PSU, the nine Native American Tribes, 16 school districts with Native American student populations greater than 10 percent, and the American Indian Center for Excellence (AICE) at Northeast Oklahoma A & M. *Goal*: To enhance the quantity & quality of American Indian & American Indians serving Library Media Specialists in order to meet the information needs of the American Indian population in Oklahoma, Kansas, and Missouri. The schools that joined in a collaborative agreement are: Afton ISD, Bluejacket ISD, Commerce ISD, Fairland ISD, Grove ISD, Jay ISD, Ketchum ISD, Miami ISD, Quapaw ISD, Turkey Ford ISD, Welch ISD, White Oak ISD, Wyandotte ISD, Seneca R-7, Fort Scott USD 234 and Pittsburg USD 250. "A primary focus of the grant is to provide 25 library media specialists with a specially designed curriculum that empowers Native American scholars," said Sue Stidham, a professor in PSU's Department of Teaching & Leadership, who will administer the grant. Stidham further stated that, "by modifying the current library media specialist program, the hope is to heighten cultural sensitivity and strengthen the focus on how to provide services to Native American children and adults. Also, to educate media specialists in the organization, management, and preservation of materials in 21st century Native American heritage institutions. This project will also provide a collaborative environment for these media specialists to work with Native American tribal members, who can encourage cultural change and ensure an unbiased climate & curricula in school libraries and classrooms. "The practicum is an important part of this program. In order

to learn more about the tribes, candidates will not only spend time in school media centers, but will also spend 30 hours in tribal libraries and museums," she said. "The candidates will learn the tribal culture first hand, establish networks, and in return bring the latest technology skills for preserving and locating current & past documents to the tribal libraries & museums." President Scott said he hopes the new library media specialist program is just the beginning of greater collaboration between the university, the nine, et al.

KENTUCKY

NORTHERN KENTUCKY UNIVERSITY
NATIVE AMERICAN STUDIES PROGRAM (NAS)
College of Arts & Sciences, Department of Anthropology
217C Landrum Academic Center • HIGHLAND HEIGHTS, KY 41099
 (859) 572-5258 Fax 572-6086; Website: www.nku.edu
 Sharlotte K. Neely, Director/Founder, NAS; E-mail: neelys@nku.edu
Program: BA & BS with a minor in Native American Studies. *Faculty*: T. Eric Bates (Blackfoot, religion); Britteny M. Howell (cultural anthropology, Alaska Natives); Sharlotte Neely (cultural anthropology); Michael D. Striker, ABD (archaeology, especially Coeur d'Alene); Kristin E. Appleby. *Resources*: Museum of Anthropology; Kentucky Native American Commission; Kentucky Center for Native American Art & Culture. Native American studies has as its focus the prehistory, history, contemporary situation, and way of life of Native Americans (American Indians). For more than 95 percent of the time humans have lived in the Americas, the only people here have been Native Americans. To understand the history and cultures of the Americas, one must start with Native Americans. Far from disappearing either physically or culturally, Native Americans today are increasing in numbers and represent hundreds of vibrant and unique ways of life. To learn about Native Americans is to explore yet another avenue of what it means to be human. The commonwealth of Kentucky is rich in Native American culture. NKU is located in the heart of the prehistoric Ohio Valley mound-builder cultures of Adena, Hopewell, and Fort Ancient, on lands claimed by both the historic Shawnee and Cherokee. The university is only about 50 miles from the soon-to-be-built Kentucky Center for Native American Arts and Culture and is recognized by the Kentucky Native American Heritage Commission. NKU's Native American studies program is the only such program in Kentucky. There are two Native American student organizations at NKU: First Nations Student Organization and Kiksuya. Native American studies minors are encouraged to participate in both. Each year NKU anthropology faculty present the Outstanding Student in Native American Studies Award. NKU provides students with opportunities to do Native American studies outside the classroom and develop résumé-worthy skills important in the job quest. Through Kiksuya, every spring NKU students can go to a reservation in the Dakotas. Every summer students also have the opportunity to participate in an archaeological dig at a prehistoric Native American village site in Northern Kentucky. Students also have opportunities to work on museum exhibits.

MAINE

UNIVERSITY OF MAINE - NATIVE AMERICAN STUDIES PROGRAM
Wabanaki Center, 5717 Corbett Hall, Room 208 • ORONO, ME 04469
 (207) 581-1417 Fax 581-4760; Website: www.naps.umaine.edu
 Darren Ranco, Associate Professor of Anthropology & Program Chairperson
 & Coordinator of Native American Research
 E-mail: darren.ranco@umit.maine.edu
 John Bear Mitchell, Lecturer & Center Outreach Coordinator
 E-mail: john.mitchell@umit.maine.edu
Description: An interdisciplinary academic program offering a minor in Native American studies. The presence of the Wabanaki Tribes within the State of Maine provides a tie to the history, language, and vital culture unique to Maine and is a major focus of the program. *Purpose*: To teach students through Native perspectives, to understand Native people, their traditions, and their rights to self-determination. *Faculty*: Maureen Smith (Oneida), Darren Ranco, John Mitchell (Wabanaki Studies); Lisa Neuman; Micah Pawling. *Resources*: Northeast Indian Research & Resource Library.

MARYLAND

COMMUNITY COLLEGE OF BALTIMORE CO. CATONSVILLE
College of the Humanities & Social Studies
800 S. Rolling Rd., A 303 • BALTIMORE, MD 21228
 (443) 840-5916 Fax 840-5321; E-mail: nast@ccbcmd.edu
 Dr. Stephanie A.L. Mowles, Program Director
 E-mail: smowles@ccbcmd.edu
Program: Native American Studies. *Degree*: A.A. in Humanities & Social Sciences. It is the first and only program of its kind in the state of Maryland. Scheduled to start in the Spring 2012 semester, the program comes on the heels of Governor Martin O'Malley's executive order formally recognizing the Native American Piscataway Conoy & the Piscataway Indian

Nation tribes as a distinct people. The educational objective of this new program is to develop a greater understanding of the roles of Native American people, nations and communities both historically and contemporarily in the United States. In addition to providing a broad foundation in Indigenous cultures and current events, the program's curriculum in Native American histories, religions, literatures, arts and politics aims to generate knowledge and respect for Indigenous nations as well as foster critical thinking and socially responsible research.

MASSACHUSETTS

FIVE COLLEGE NATIVE AMERICAN & INDIGENOUS STUDIES
97 Spring St. • AMHERST, MA 01004
 (413) 542-4000; 256-8316; Website: www.fivecolleges.edu/natam
 E-mail: fcacademics@fivecolleges.edu
 Kathleen Brown-Perez, Co-Chair, Honors College (UMass, Amherst)
  E-mail: brown-perez@honors.umass.edu
 Christine DeLucia, Co-Chair & Professor of History (Mount Holyoke College)
  E-mail: cdelucia@mtholyoke.edu
 Lisa Brooks, Advisor Lecturer (Amherst College)
  E-mail: lbrooks@amherst.edu
 Janna White, Academic Programs Coordinator
  E-mail: jwhite@fivecolleges.edu
 Donal Carbaugh, Professor of Communication (UMass, Amherst)
  E-mail: dcarbaugh@fivecolleges.edu
 Pamela Stone, Advisor & Professor of Anthropology (Hampshire College)
  E-mail: pksns@hampshire.edu
 Christen Mucher, Advisor & Professor of American Studies (Smith College)
  E-mail: cmucher@smith.edu
 Alice Nash, Advisor & Professor of History (UMass, Amherst)
  E-mail: anash@history.umass.edu
The Five College NAIS Certificate Program is available to students of and comprised of faculty members at Amherst College, Hampshire College, Mount Holyoke College, Smith College, & University of Massachusetts Amherst. The program emphasizes the many long histories of Native American Indians as well as their contemporary lives & situations. A holistic & comparative interdisciplinary approach underlies the Certificate Program's requirements, enabling students to become familiar with the diversity of indigenous lifeways, including cultural forms, institutions, political economies, & modes of self-expression. In addition to this broader perspective, the program places some emphasis on the Native peoples of the Northeast so that Five College students can become acquainted with the history, culture & presence of indigenous peoples in this region. *Facilities*: Zoowie Banteah Cultural House - Crystal Allen, Coordinator (e-mail: allen21c@mtholyoke.edu). Provides cultural space for students who identify as Native American or of Native American ancestry.

UNIVERSITY OF MASSACHUSETTS, AMHERST
CERTIFICATE PROGRAM IN NATIVE AMERICAN INDIAN STUDIES
Anthropology Department, 314 Machmer • AMHERST, MA 01003
 (413) 577-1607 Fax 545-9494; Website: www.umass.edu/nativestudies/
 E-mail: cpnais@anthro.umass.edu
 Paulette F. Steeves (Cree-Metis), Interim Director (577-3781)
  E-mail: psteeves@anthro.umass.edu
 Joyce W. Vincent (Cherokee/Blackfoot), CPNAIS Assistant Director & Director of Dr. Josephine White Eagle Cultural Center (545-4932)
  E-mail: dvincent@acad.umass.edu
Description: The program offers students a structured understanding of historical & contemporary issues affecting the Western Hemisphere's First Nations. Students will learn how these issues are embedded in the long histories of Native peoples and their most recent interactions with Europeans and Africans. Those completing the requirements for the Certificate will gain a more sensitive understanding of the unique cultures rooted in this hemisphere. Students will also develop a greater appreciation for the indigenous peoples of eastern North America The program will encourage on-campus roles for visitors from Native communities, supervise student outreach to Native communities & Native related institutions, & enhance the knowledge of students going on to post-baccalaureate education & service. The curriculum is drawn from UMass at Amherst course offerings supplemented by courses offered at the four colleges (Amherst, Hampshire, Mount Holyoke, & Smith). The Director & participating university faculty & staff will guide students in creating a coherent & culturally diversified undergraduate experience. *Advisors*: Robert Paynter (Anthropology); Jean S. Forward (Anthropology); Alice Nash (History) E-mail: anash@history.umass.edu; Kathleen Brown-Perez, MBA, JD (Five Colleges); Rae Gould (Repatriation Coordinator); Lisa Wexler (Pubic Health); Laura Furlan (English); Marta Carlson (Anthropology); Ron Wellbrn (English). *Resources*: Josephine White Eagle Cultural Center; Native American students Services Program. Financial aid: Native students from Massachusetts Nations, e.g. Nipmuc & Wampanoag may be eligible for a tuition waiver.

UNIVERSITY OF MASSACHUSETTS, BOSTON
INSTITUTE FOR NEW ENGLAND NATIVE AMERICAN STUDIES (INENAS)
100 Morrissey Blvd. • BOSTON, MA 02125
 (617) 287-5784 Fax 287-6857; Website: www.umb.edu/inenas
 J. Cedric Woods (Lumbee), Director; E-mail: cedric.woods@umb.edu
 Robyn Hannigan, Founding Dean, School for the Environment (287-4857)
  E-mail: thegreendean@umb.edu
 Sophia Natalia Cisneros (Coos, Lower Umpqua, Suislaw), Adjunct Professor
  (287-6132) E-mail: sophia.cisneros@umb.edu
Purpose: To connect Native New England with university research, innovation, and education. Currently, he is working on projects with tribes in the areas of tribal government capacity building, Indian education, economic development, & chronic disease prevention; to develop collaborative relationships, projects, and programs between Native American tribes of the New England region and all of the UMASS campuses so that tribes may participate in and benefit from university research, innovation, scholarship, & education. *Financial aid*: Massachusetts scholarships available for Native American students. *Resource*: Commonwealth of Massachusetts Commission on Indian Affairs. *Facilities*: Boston Library Consortium. Library in Native American Resource Center. Established 2009.

UNIVERSITY OF MASSACHUSETTS BOSTON
NATIVE AMERICAN & INDIGENOUS STUDIES PROGRAM
College of Liberal Arts
McCormack Hall, Fl. 04, Rm. 631 • BOSTON, MA 02125
 (617) 287-6819; Josh R. Reid, Program Director & Professor of History
Degree: Minor in Native American & Indigenous Studies. *Purpose*: Seeks to engage students with this expanding academic field; to coordinate a number of resources and exciting opportunities for students to learn more about local, national, and international issues concerning indigenous peoples. These will include guest lectures, film screenings, and other relevant events. *Faculty*: Judith Zeitlin (Anthropology); Lauren Sullivan (Senior Lecturer Anthropology); Tom Sieber, (Dept. Chair, Anthropology); Christopher Fung (Anthropology); Stephen Silliman (Anthropology); Colleen Jose E. Martinez-Reyes, (Anthropology); J. Cedric Woods (Director, Institute for New England Native American Studies); Patrick Barron (English); Amy Den Ouden (Women's & Gender Identity) et al.

HARVARD UNIVERSITY - NATIVE AMERICAN PROGRAM
14 Story St., 4th Floor • CAMBRIDGE, MA 02138
 (617) 495-4923 Fax 496-3312; E-mail: hunap@harvard.edu
 Shelly C. Lowe (Dine'-Navajo), Executive Director
  E-mail: shelly_lowe@harvard.edu
 Dennis Norman (Cheyenne), Faculty Chairperson
  E-mail: dennis_norman@harvard.edu
 Jason Packineau (Mandan/Hidatsa/Arikara), Community Coordinator
  E-mail: jason_packineau@harvard.edu
Purpose: To bring together Native American, Alaska Native, and Native Hawaiian students & interested individuals from the Harvard community for the purpose of advancing the well-being of indigenous peoples through self-determination, academic achievement, & community service. Native Americans are recruited to the University & provided with the community support & academic resources necessary to succeed at Harvard and beyond. An important goal of the program is to foster a sense of community among students from reservation, rural, & urban backgrounds with diverse academic & research interests. *Resources*: The Newberry Consortium in American Indian Studies offers an annual workshop for graduate students; supports student & faculty research; educational forums & conferences; works with Native communities throughout North America, including the North American Indian Center of Boston; hosts monthly potlucks for students and their families; & organizes the annual Harvard University Native American Program powwow. *Publication*: HUNAP Opportunities E-Newsletter. Established 1970.

HARVARD UNIVERSITY - HARVARD PROJECT
ON AMERICAN INDIAN ECONOMIC DEVELOPMENT (HPAIED)
John F. Kennedy School of Government
79 JFK St. • CAMBRIDGE, MA 02138
 (617) 495-1480 Fax 496-3900
 Website: www.hpaied.org; E-mail: hpaied@hks.harvard.edu
 Joseph P. Kalt, Co-director of HPAIED; Ford Foundation Professor of International Political Economy (Emeritus), Harvard Kennedy School
  E-mail: joe_kalt@harvard.edu
 Stephen Cornell, Co-director of HPAIED (520) 884-4393
  Chair, Udall Center for Studies in Public Policy, University of Arizona)
  E-mail: scornell@email.arizona.edu
 Diane Enos (Salt River Pima-Maricopa), Director, Family Advocacy Center of the Salt River Pime-Maricopa Indian Community
 Nicole Grenier, Programs Coordinator (617) 495-1480
  E-mail: nicole_grenier@harvard.edu
 Megan Minoka Hill (Oneida of WI), Director of Honoring Nation
  E-mail: megan_hill@harvard.edu; (617) 496-4229

Miriam R. Jorgensen, Research Director
E-mail: miriam_jorgensen@harvard.edu
Purpose: To understand & foster the conditions under which sustained, self-determined social & economic development is achieved among American Indian nations. A systematic, comparative study of social & economic development on American Indian reservations. *Program*: Honoring Nations - a national awards program that identifies, celebrates, & shares outstanding examples of tribal governance. Established in 1998, the awards program spotlights tribal government programs & initiatives that are especially effective in addressing critical concerns & challenges facing the more than 560 Indian nations and their citizens. *Affiliated Faculty*: Alyce Adams (Cherokee); Keith Allred; Gavin Clarkson (Choctaw/Cherokee); Research Fellows: Randall Akee (Native Hawaiian); Amber Annis (Cheyenne River Sioux); Misko Beaudrie (Anishinabe); Eliza Bemis; Catherine Curtis; Kenneth W. Grant II; Eric C. Henson (Chickasaw); Amy Besaw Medford (Brothertown); Ted Robertson; Jonathan B. Taylor; Laura Davidoff Taylor. April D. Youpee-Roll (Fort Peck Sioux), Fellow, HPAIED. *Activities*: Research, advisory services executive education and the administration of a tribal governance awards program.

MICHIGAN

UNIVERSITY OF MICHIGAN - NATIVE AMERICAN STUDIES PROGRAM
Department of American Culture-College of Literature, Science & the Arts
3700 Haven Hall • ANN ARBOR, MI 48109-1045
(734) 763-1460 Fax 764-6554
Website: www.umich.edu/; E-mail: ac.inq@umich.edu
Faculty:
Philip J. Deloria (Lakota), Professor (764-6305)
E-mail: pdeloria@umich.edu.
Gregory E. Dowd, Professor (936-6872); E-mal: dowdg@umich.edu
Joseph P. Gone (Gros Ventre), Professor (647-3958)
E-mail: jgone@umich.edu
Barbra Meek (Comanche), Associate Professor (936-3192)
E-mail: bameek@umich.edu
Tiya Miles, Professor (764-5513) E-mail: tiya@umich.edu
Alphonse Pitawanakwat (Anishinaabe), Lecturer (615-8896)
E-mail: apitawan@umich.edu
Gustavo Verdesio, Associate Professor (647-2645)
E-mail: verdesio@umich.edu
Michael Witgen (Ojibwe), Associate Professor (647-5419)
E-mail: mwitgen@umich.edu
Robin Beck, Associate Professor (764-1240; 4101 Museums
E-mail: rabeck@umich.edu
Scott Richard Lyons (Ojibwe), Associate Professor (on Sabbatical until 2018)
E-mail: mwitgen@umich.edu
Degree: BA Minor in Native American Studies. *Programs*: Comprehensive Studies Program; American Culture: Ojibwe Language & Literature.

KEWEENAW BAY OJIBWA COMMUNITY COLLEGE
111 Beartown Rd., P.O. Box 519 • BARAGA, MI 49908
(906) 353-4640 Fax 353-8107; Website: www.kbocc.edu
Debra J. Parrish (Ojibwe), President (524-8414)
E-mail: debra.parrish@kbocc.edu
Cherie Dakota, Vice President of Operation (524-8403)
E-mail: cdakota@kbocc.edu
Lynn Aho, Dean of Instruction (524-8313)
E-mail: laho@kbocc.edu
Denise Cadeau, Chair, Anishinaabe Studies (524-8309)
E-mail: dcadeau@kbocc.edu
Mission: To provide a post-secondary education rich in Ojibwa culture, tradition & beliefs, supporting life-long learning. *Adjunct Faculty*: Lynn Aho (Communications); Violet Friisvail Ayres (Anishinaabe Studies); JoAnne Racette (Native American Studies). *Facilities*: Niiwin Akeaa (Four Directions) Center; Ojibwa Community Library. Chartered 1975.

*BAY MILLS COMMUNITY COLLEGE
12214 W. Lakeshore Dr. • BRIMLEY, MI 49715
(906) 248-3354 Fax 248-3351; Website: www.bmcc.edu
Michael C. Parish, JD (Ojibwe), President
E-mail: mparish@bmcc.edu
Samantha S. Jackson Cameron (Ojibwe), VP of Academic Affairs
E-mail: scameron@bmcc.edu
Debra J. Wilson (Ojibwe), Dean of Student Services
E-mail: dwilson@bmcc.edu
Mike Willis (Ojibwe), Chair of Native American Studies Dept.
E-mail: mlwillis@bmcc.edu
Kathleen LeBlanc (Ojibwe), Cultural Services Director
E-mail: kleblanc@bmcc.edu
Christine Miller, General Studies Faculty & Advisor
E-mail: cmiller@bmcc.edu

Kathy Adair, Director of Development & Social Sciences Dept. Chair
E-mail: kadair@bmcc.edu
Kathy Tassier, Curriculum Specialist & Education Department Chair
E-mail: ktassier@bmcc.edu
Elaine Lehre, Director of Admissions; E-mail: elehre@bmcc.edu
Megan Clarke, Library Director; E-mail: mclarke@bmcc.edu
Stacey Walden (Ojibwe), Human Resources Director
Dwight Teeple (Ojibwa), Chairperson, Board of Regents
Description: A two-year college providing career-oriented degree programs promoting the preservation of the customs & beliefs of Native Americans. Offers extension classes on every reservation in Michigan & many neighboring communities. *Degree programs*: Associate of Arts in Great Lakes Native American studies - Ojibway language, tribal history & literature; Associate of Applied Science in computer information systems, office technology & tribal administration; & Certificate programs in general business, and retailing. *Faculty*: Duane Bedell (Computer Dept. Faculty & Chair); Nancy Berkompas; Richard Elder; Idilko Melis; Christine Miller; Jan Miller; Vicki Thomas; John White; Mike Willis. *Special program*: Inter-Active Television Program. *Facilities*: Learning Center; James Keene Cultural Heritage Center. Financial aid available. Library.

UNIVERSITY OF MICHIGAN - DEARBORN
NATIVE AMERICAN ETHNOBOTANY
2134 CASL Annex, 4901 Evergreen Rd. • DEARBORN, MI 48198
(313) 593-5000
Dan Moerrman, Contact; E-mail: dmoerman@umich.edu
Description: A database of plants used as foods, drugs, dyes, fibers, etc., by native peoples of North America.

MICHIGAN STATE UNIVERSITY
AMERICAN INDIAN & INDIGENOUS STUDIES PROGRAM
College of Arts & Letters
655 Auditorium Dr. #414 • EAST LANSING, MI 48824
(517) 432-2193 Fax 432-2363
Website: www.aisp.msu.edu; E-mail: aisp@msu.edu
Dylan AT Miner (Metis), Program Director & Associate Professor
Arts & Humanities; E-mail: dminer@msu.edu
LeAnne E. Silvey (Odawa), Program Director & Associate Professor of Human Development & Family Studies; E-mail: silveyle@msu.edu
Matthew L.M. Fletcher (Grand Traverse Ottawa & Chippewa), Professor of Law, Director of Indigenous Law & Policy Center
E-mail: matthew.fletcher@law.msu.edu
Estrella Torrez, Co-Director, Indigenous Youth Empowerment Program & Associate Professor, Residential College in the Arts & Humanities
E-mail: torrezjs@msu.edu
Degree granted: Specialization (interdisciplinary minor). *Special Program*: Udall Internships - Congressional Internship is a ten-week summer internship in Washington, DC for Native American & Alaska Native students. *Partial Faculty*: Matthew L.M. Fletcher (Grand Traverse Ottawa & Chippewa) (Law); Kathryn E. Fort (Law); Lynn Goldstein, Director Archaeology Program & Professor of Anthropology; Gordon Henry (White Earth Chippewa); Heather Howard (Anthropology); William Lovis Curator of Anthropology – MSU Museum; Dylan AT Miner (see above); Mindy Morgan (Anthropology); John Norder, Director, Native American Institute & Professor of Anthropology; Jodie O'Gorman, Professor & Chair – Anthropology; Malea Powell (Miami/Eastern Shawnee/ EuroAmerican, Professor & Chair – Writing, Rhetoric & American Cultures; Christopher A. Scales, Associate Professor Arts & Humanities; Winona Singel (Odawa) (Law); Susan Sleeper-Smith (History); Laura Smith (Art); Kyle Powys Whyte (Potawatomi) (Philosophy). *Resources*: Native American Institute (NAI); Nokomis Learning Center; North American Indigenous Student Organization (NAISO); Woodcraft Circle of Native Writers & Storytellers; North American Indigenous Faculty & Staff Association (NAIFSA); EAGLE (American Indian Faculty & Staff Association); AISES (American Indian Science & Engineering Society); MSU College of Law Indigenous Law & Policy Center.

MICHIGAN STATE UNIVERSITY
INDIGENOUS LAW & POLICY CENTER
Law College Bldg., 648 N. Shaw Ln. Rm. 405 • EAST LANSING, MI 48824
(517) 432-6939 Fax 432-6801
Website: www.law.msu.edu; E-mail: indigenous@law.msu.edu
Matthew L.M. Fletcher (Grand Traverse Odawa), Professor of Law & Center Director; E-mail: matthew.fletcher@law.msu.edu; (432-6909)
Wenona T. Singel (Little Traverse Odawa), Center Associate Director & Associate Professor of Law (432-6915)
E-mail: singel@law.msu.edu
Kathryn E. Fort, Adjunct Professor & Staff Attorney & Director of the Indian Child & Welfare Act Appellate Project (432-6992)
E-mail: fort@law.msu.edu
Description: Offers one of only a few indigenous law certificate programs in the nation. Our mission is to educate law students and train lawyers to work on

behalf of indigenous people & tribes throughout the country, whether for tribal governments, private law firms or non-profit organizations. *Special programs*: Spring Speakers Series, new books in Indian law; Annual Conference. *Resources*: Annual Indigenous Law Conference in November; Committee on Institutional Cooperation American Indian Studies Consortium; EAGLE American Indian Faculty & Staff Association. Turtle Talk blog. Website: www.turtletalk.wordpress.com.

MICHIGAN STATE UNIVERSITY - NATIVE AMERICAN INSTITUTE

Justin S. Morrill Hall of Agriculture
446 W. Circle Dr., Rm. 406 • EAST LANSING, MI 48824
(517) 353-6632 Fax 432-2351
Website: www.nai.msu.edu; E-mail: nai@msu.edu
John Norder (Turtle Mountain Band of Chippewa, Director
E-mail: norder@msu.edu
Christie M. Poitra, Academic Specialist-Outreach & Research
E-mail: poitrach@anr.msu.edu
Mission: To work with tribes, American Indian organizations & various Michigan State University units to enhance the sovereignty, cultural continuity & wellbeing of tribes, Indian communities & Indian people. *Faculty*. *Activities*: Provides training, technical assistance, research, and educational assistance to Native American tribes & organizations in Michigan; serves Michigan officials and lawmakers by offering periodic information on policy alternatives regarding Indian issues; promote & enhance the public's knowledge & awareness of Michigan Indian communities, initiatives, history, and culture. *Publication*: Native Literatures Generations – provides a global forum for original works of literature by writers from the indigenous nations of North America & Hawaii.

NORTHERN MICHIGAN UNIVERSITY
CENTER FOR NATIVE AMERICAN STUDIES

112 Whitman Hall, 1401 Presque Isle Ave. • MARQUETTE, MI 49855
(906) 227-1397 Fax 227-1396; E-mail: cnas@nmu.edu
Website: www.nmu.edu/nativeamericanstudies/node/67
April Lindala (Grand River Six Nations), Center Director
E-mail: alindala@nmu.edu
Tina Moses, Principal Secretary; E-mail: cmoses@nmu.edu
Martin Reinhardt (Anishinaabe Ojibway), Chair, Faculty Affairs Committee
E-mail: mreinhar@nmu.edu
Program: Minor in Native American Studies. *Faculty*: April Lindala, Shirley Brozzo (Anishinaabe); Grace Chaillier (Sicangu Lakota-Rosebud Sioux); Aimee Cree Dunn (Metis); Violet Friisvall-Ayres (Anishinaabe of Keweenaw Bay Indian Community); Jamie Kuehnl; Leora Lancaster; Tina Moses, Martin Reinhardt (Anishinaabe Ojibway); Jud Sojourn. *Activities*: CLANS (The Creative & Learning Art in Native Settings) Project – a weeklong program for tribal youth; workshops; annual powwow, Indigenous People's Resistance Day Event. *Facilities*: Native American Student Association; Native American Student Empowerment Initiative. *Publication*: Anishinaabe News

CENTRAL MICHIGAN UNIVERSITY

College of Humanities & Social & Behavioral Sciences
Cultural & Global Studies
Warriner Hall 102 • MOUNT PLEASANT, MI 48859
(989) 774-3160 Fax 774-7267
Tracy Brown (Anthropology), Advisor; E-mail: brown3t@cmich.edu
Ari Berk (English), Advisor; E-mail: berk1ad@cmich.edu
Program: American Indian Studies Certificate. This 16-18 credit hour certificate is designed for undergraduate students who desire to gain greater competency in their understanding of diverse American Indian histories and cultures. The certificate will also help students gain greater understanding and appreciation of current issues relevant to American Indian peoples and steps American Indians are taking to build and strengthen their communities.

*SAGINAW CHIPPEWA TRIBAL COLLEGE

2274 Enterprise Dr. • MT. PLEASANT, MI 48858
(989) 775-4123 Fax 775-4528
Website: www.sagchip.edu; E-mail: sctcinfo@sagchip.edu
Carla Sineway, President; E-mail: csineway@sagchip.org
Cheryl Hassen-Swarthout, Dean of Instruction
E-mail: chassen-swarthout@sagchip.org
Tracy Reed, Dean of Research; E-mail: treed@sagchip.edu
Nathaniel Lambertson, Dean of Students
E-mail: nlambertson@sagchip.org
Amanda Flaugher, Registrar/Admissions
E-mail: aflaugher@sagchip.org
Gena Qualls, Grants & Special Projects Coordinator
E-mail: gequalls@sagchip.org
Colleen M. Green, Chair, Board of Regents
E-mail: green.colleen@sagchip.edu
Faculty: George Roy (Ojibwa Language); E-mail: groy@sagchip.edu
Adam Haviland (Native American Studies); E-mail: ahaviland@sagchip.edu

Tribal Library.

LAKE SUPERIOR STATE UNIVERSITY - NATIVE AMERICAN CENTER

650 W. Easterday Ave. • SAULT STE. MARIE, MI 49783
(906) 635-6664; Stephanie Sabatine, Director; E-mail: ssabatine@lssu.edu
Mission: To service the needs of Native American students by providing programs & services that support & enhance their educational experience as they work toward their educational goals; dedicated to preserving & teaching about our local Native American culture, history & traditions.

MINNESOTA

BEMIDJI STATE UNIVERSITY - AMERICAN INDIAN RESOURCE CENTER

1500 Birchmont Dr. NE #21 • BEMIDJI, MN 56601
(800) 475-2001; (218) 755-2032 Fax 755-2138
Website: www.bemidjistate.edu/airc; E-mail: airc@bemidjistate.edu
William Blackwell, Jr., Director; E-mail: wblackwell@bemidjistate.edu
Erika Bailey-Johnson, Sustainability Coordinator (755-2560)
E-mail: ebaileyjohnson@bemidjistate.edu
John Gonzalez, Professor (755-2881); E-mail: jgonzalez@bemidjistate.edu
Mary Fairbanks, Associate Professor (755-2523)
E-mail: mfairbanks@bemidjistate.edu
Anton Treuer, Professor of Ojibwe Language
E-mail: atreuer@bemidjistate.edu
Colette "Tori" Dahlke, Retention Counselor (755-2094)
E-mail: cdahlke@bemidjistate.edu
Tessa Marie Reed, Assistant Professor of Indian Studies (755-3979)
E-mail: treed@bemidjistate.edu
Vivian Delgado, Assistant Professor of Languages & Ethnic Studies
(755-2528) E-mail: vdelgado@bemidjistate.edu
Molly Aitken-Julin, Internship & Employment Coordinator
E-mail: maitken@bemidjistate.edu
Program: American Indian Studies. *Description*: Situated in the center of three reservations: White Earth, Red Lake & Leech Lake. Its location offers easy access to reservation culture life. People from the reservations are used as teachers & demonstrators. Bemidji State University offers an interdivisional program with a major in Indian Studies that includes lectures in the Division of Behavioral Science & Humanities, and Fine Arts and various student & service projects. *Mission*: To provide Ojibwe and other Indian students with a viable academic area of study relevant to their cultural heritage & diversity; and to enable all students to develop a better understanding & appreciation of Indian history, language & culture. *Resources*: Department of Modern Languages offers a minor in Ojibwe Language. The Council of Indian Students' activities include: Indian Week (first week in May), powwows, Ojibwe Art Expo, Native American culture classes.

CENTRAL LAKES COLLEGE

Department of Anthropology & Department of Ojibwe
501 W. College Dr. • BRAINERD, MN 56401
(800) 933-0346 (218) 855-8037 Fax 855-8220
Website: www.clcmn.edu *Programs*: American Indian Studies Certificate & Ojibwe Studies Certificate. Focuses on the language, history & culture of the Ojibwe within the context of the American Indian experience.

*LEECH LAKE TRIBAL COLLEGE

6945 Littlewolf Rd., NW, P.O. Box 180 • CASS LAKE, MN 56633
(218) 335-4200 Fax 335-4282; Website: www.lltc.edu
Patricia Broker (Ojibwe), Interim President (335-4268)
E-mail: pat.broker@lltc.edu
Vikki Howard, Dean of Academics (335-4255)
E-mail: vikki.howard@lltc.edu
Bill Frederickson, Director of Operations (335-4234)
E-mail: bill.frederickson@lltc.edu
Elaine Fleming, Arts & Humanities Department Chair & Instructor (335-4259)
E-mail: Elaine.fleming@lltc.edu
Melanie Wilson, Director of Assessment & Institutional Research (335-4280)
E-mail: melanie.wilson@lltc.edu
Nyleta Belgarde, Ojibwe Language Coordinator (335-4249)
E-mail: nyleta.belgarde@lltc.edu
Hannah Buckland, Director of Library Services (335-4240)
E-mail: Hannah.buckland@lltc.edu
Priscilla Fairbanks, Distance Education Coordinator (335-4237)
E-mail: Priscilla.fairbanks@lltc.edu
Kim Dickson, Learning Center Director (335-4242)
E-mail: kim.dickson@lltc.edu
Board of Trustees: Arnold Dahl, Chair; Gary Charwood, Vice-Chair.
Mission: To provide quality higher education grounded in Anishinaabe values. *Faculty*: Larry Aitken (Ojibwe Instructor); Bob Jourdain (Couchiching First Nations, Ojibwe language instructor); Audrey Thayer (History); among others. Library. Bookstore.

*FOND DU LAC TRIBAL & COMMUNITY COLLEGE
2101 14th St. • CLOQUET, MN 55720
(218) 879-0804 Fax 879-0814; Website: www.fdltcc.edu
Larry Anderson (Anishinaabe), President; E-mail: larrya@fdltcc.edu
Don Carlson, Vice President of Academics (879-0878)
Anna Fellegy, Director of Research & Planning (879-0848)
E-mail: afellegy@fdltcc.edu
Keith Turner, Dean of Student Services (879-0805)
E-mail: kturner@fdltcc.edu
Tara Graves, Nandagikendan Academy Director 879-0701)
E-mail: tgraves@fdltcc.edu
Lucia Bonacci, Ojibwe Immersion Academy Director (879-0842)
E-mail: lucia.bonacci@fdltcc.edu
Nancy Broughton, Library Director (879-0837)
E-mail: sam@fdltcc.edu; library@fdltc.edu
Description: 2,800 students. Tribal/state co-governed 1994 land grant 2-year liberal arts college offering more than 30 associate & certificate degree programs, including Anishinaabe language & culture, human services, law enforcement, nursing, business & finance, computer science, & environmental studies. Indian Studies *Faculty*: Richard Gresczyk, Daniel Jones, Victor Makes Room For Them, *Resources*: FDLTCC is a designated Center of Excellence in partnership with U.S. Dept. of Agriculture - National Resources Conservation Service focusing on soil science & conservation in application with Geographic Information Systems (GIS). Ruth A. Myers Library/Ojibwe Archives, special collection of regional Native American publications.

COLLEGE OF ST. SCHOLASTICA
AMERICAN INDIAN STUDIES MINOR
School of Arts & Letters, Department of History & Politics
Tower Hall, 1200 Kenwood Ave. • DULUTH, MN 55811
(218) 723-6046 Fax 723-6790; Website: www.css.edu
Barbara King, American Indian Studies Program Chair (723-6170)
E-mail: bking@css.edu
Michael Sullivan, Ojibwe Studies Program Chair (625-4860)
E-mail: msullivan@css.edu
Within Global, Cultural and Language Studies, St. Scholastica offers Ojibwe language courses. These classes seek to teach students the Ojibwe language while they learn about various aspects of both modern & traditional Ojibwe culture. A significant amount of time & effort is spent learning about traditional Ojibwe subsistence activities, while also becoming aware of the more modern practices for subsistence harvests. Rather than the more traditional structural approach that focuses on grammar, these Ojibwe language courses are centered around developing communicative abilities & developing the competency to actually use the language in speech and writing. *Faculty*: Elyse Carter-Vosen (Ojibwe language & culture). *Resources*: Indigenous Students' Alliance. *Courses*: Ojibwe History & Philosophy, et al.

UNIVERSITY OF MINNESOTA, DULUTH
AMERICAN INDIAN LEARNING RESOURCE CENTER
315 Kirby Plaza, 1208 Kirby Dr. • DULUTH, MN 55812
(800) 232-1339; (218) 726-6379/6293 Fax 726-6370
Website: www.d.umn.edu/ailrc; E-mail: ailrc@d.umn.edu
Rick J. Smith, Director (726-6293) E-mail: rsmith1@d.umn.edu
Lea Carr, Assistant Director (726-6976); E-mail: mcarr@d.umn.edu
Cassidy Capriglione, Counseor/Advisor (726-6192)
E-mail: ccaprigl@d.umn.edu
Mission: To provide campus-wide student support services to American Indian students. *Goals*: To increase the recruitment and retention of American Indian & Alaska Native students, & the enhancement of their educational experience. *Resources*: Academic, personal & financial aid counseling; recruitment; tutorial services; culturally oriented library; computer access; also consulting services to tribal governments & organizations; coordinates forums, seminars, and speakers. *Facility*: The Mishoomis Collection Library.

UNIVERSITY OF MINNESOTA, DULUTH
DEPARTMENT OF AMERICAN INDIAN STUDIES (AIS)
College of Liberal Arts
110 Cina Hall, 1123 University Dr. • DULUTH, MN 55812
(218) 726-7332 Fax 726-6386
Website: www.d.umn.edu/~umdais/; E-mail: umdais@d.umn.edu
Jill Doerfler (White Earth Anishinaabeg), Associate Professor
& Department Head (726-7192) E-mail: doerflj@d.umn.edu
Tadd Johnson (Bois Forte Chippewa), Director of the Master of
Tribal Administration & Governance (726-6878)
E-mail: taddjohn@d.umn.edu
Tami Lawlor, Program Associate, Master of Tribal Administration
& Governance Program (726-7332) E-mail: umdmtag@d.umn.edu
Jodi Carlson Grebinowski, Reference & Government Documents Librarian
E-mail: jlcarlso@d.umn.edu; (726-7880)
American Indian Studies (AIS) is an interdisciplinary academic department offering coursework committed to broadening knowledge of the worldview,

histories, languages, literatures, cultures, arts and contemporary experiences of American Indian nations and peoples. As American Indian nations maintain a distinct political relationship with the federal government rooted in historical treaties, congressional laws, & executive orders, AIS promotes an awareness for and understanding of tribal sovereignty and self-determination. AIS strives to protect the integrity & identity of the indigenous population of North America and to create an intellectual learning environment conducive to critical and creative thought. *Program Description*: BA & Minor in American Indian Studies; Works to prepare American Indian students for careers in professional fields including teaching, medicine, social work, and business administration. *Programs*: American Indian Teacher Training Program; Master of Social Work program with a special focus on American Indian communities; Master of Tribal Administration & Governance Program (Graduate Program). *Faculty*: Joseph Bauerkemper, Jill Doerfler, Kimberly Greiner, Linda Grover, Tadd Johnson, Erik Redix, Rebecca Webster. *Resources*: American Indian Learning Resource Center; Center of American Indian & Minority Health; Center of Excellence for American Indian Medical Education.

UNIVERSITY OF MINNESOTA MEDICAL SCHOOL, DULUTH
CENTER FOR AMERICAN INDIAN & MINORITY HEALTH
Medical School, 182 SMed, 1035 University Dr. • DULUTH, MN 55812
(218) 726-7235 Fax 726-8948
Website: www.caimh.umn.edu; E-mail: caimh@d.umn.edu
Mary J. Owen, MD, Director; E-mail: mjowen@d.umn.edu
Anna Wirta Kosobuski Ed.D., Associate Director
E-mail: awirta1@d.umn.edu
Sheilagh Amundsen, Executive Administrative Specialist
E-mail: samundse@d.umn.edu
Elyse Lawrey & Melissa DeVerney, Community Program Assistants
Mission: To provide support for American Indian & other underrepresented minority students who are pursuing or possess an interest in health careers. *Programs*: Designed to boost interest & knowledge base concerning American Indian health; Native Americans into Medicine (NAM) program. The NAM program exists to the current day and Native American students continue to learn and grow through their participation in it. CAIMH and the UM Medical School continue their dedication to training Native American physicians and healthcare providers. Programs & outreach efforts have expanded to students of all levels of education, encouraging them to consider careers in medicine or health care. In addition to its NAM program, CAIMH was one of the three original Health Resources & Services Administration (HRSA) Native American Center of Excellence (COE) programs funded from 1991 to 2005. CAIMH currently offers opportunities for high school, undergraduate and medical students through its Health Careers Opportunity Programs project. The HCOP project includes a partnership with Bemidji State University to provide outreach & advisement for American Indian undergraduate students in northwestern Minnesota. CAIMH is home to the Indian Health Service Indians into Medicine (INMED), a project that provides funding and services for American Indian students from the Kindergarten to high school levels and partnerships with INMED area Native American communities. This project also partners CAIMH with Bemidji State University in providing summer experiences for high school students, including the BSU INMED program. A partnership with the Fond du Lac Band of Lake Superior Chippewa allows us to offer additional programming for high school students. For the past 40 years, CAIMH and the UM Medical School have encouraged and supported Native American students of all educational levels as they explore and pursue their health career goals. CAIMH recognizes importance of creating a learning environment where Native American students can maintain community and cultural ties and how this prepares them to provide high quality health care for Native American communities.

*WHITE EARTH TRIBAL & COMMUNITY COLLEGE
2250 College Rd., P.O. Box 478 • MAHNOMEN, MN 56557
(218) 935-0417 Fax 936-5814; Website: www.wetcc.org
Tracy Clark, Interim President
Sheila M. Michaels, Academic Dean/Faculty
E-mail: Sheila.michaels@wetcc.org
Melinda Rustad, Dean of Student Services
Steve Dahlberg, Director of Extension Services/Faculty
E-mail: sdahlberg@wetcc.org
Tammy Bellanger, Extension Coordinator
Rebecca Dallinger, Special Projects Extension Coordinator
E-mail: rebecca.dallinger@wetcc.org
Sue Bishop, ABE Coordinator; E-mail: sbishop@wetcc.org
Tammmi Jalowiec, Librarian; E-mail: tammi.jalowiec@wetcc.edu
Faculty: Steve Dahlberg (Saami); David DeGroat (Oneida); Sheila M. Michaels; Patty Heath-Gordon (English); Errol Geniusz (Ojibwe & Native American studies). *Programs*: Education; Environmental Science; Human Services; Humanities, Arts & Social Sciences; Native American Studies; Business. Trustees: Sue Heisler, Chair; Joy Annette, Secretary; Michael Fairbanks, Member; Joan LaVoy, Indian Education member.

SOUTHWEST MINNESOTA STATE UNIVERSITY
INDIGENOUS NATIONS & DAKOTA STUDIES (INDS)
Department of Social Sciences, SS 103
1501 State St. • MARSHALL, MN 56258
(507) 537-6224 Fax 537-6115
Website: www.smsu.edu/academics/programs/americanindiandakotastudies/
Donald Robertson, Director of International Student Services (537-6699)
E-mail: don.robertson@smsu.edu
Michele Sterner, Associate Director/Academic Specialist/Counselor
E-mail: michele.sterner@smsu.edu (537-7382)
Description: Offers a Minor in the program that promotes awareness of native cultures & peoples in the U.S. through an examination of the ways in which traditional Native cultures have persisted & adapted over time & how these cultures are expressed in present-day life & affairs. Focuses on the Dakota people of Minnesota specifically. The interdisciplinary & multi-disciplinary nature of INDS will be illustrated by analytical concepts, methodologies, & contributions from key fields & disciplines such as anthropology, history, literature, & art. In a society & world characterized by diversity & multiculturalism, INDS serves both native & non-native students by broadening their knowledge of traditional & modern native history & culture. Decolonization provides both the theoretical framework and pedagogy for Indigenous Nations and Dakota Studies. Resources: Oyate Club; Library.

AUGSBURG COLLEGE - AMERICAN INDIAN STUDIES DEPARTMENT
2211 Riverside Ave. S., Memorial Hall 215
CB 115 • MINNEAPOLIS, MN 55454
(612) 330-1661 Fax 330-1695; Website: www.augsburg.edu/ais
Eric L. Buffalohead, Associate Professor & Chairperson
E-mail: buffaloe@augsburg.edu
M. Elsie Marubbio, Associate Professor (330-1523)
E-mail: marrubio@augsburg.edu
Sophia Jacobson, Dale Weston & Vinoodh Kutty, Instructors
Jennifer Simon (Cheyenne River Lakota), Director American Indian Student Support Program, Campus Box 122; E-mail: simonj@augsburg.edu
(612) 330-1144 Fax 330-1695; Website: www.augsburg.edu/aissp
Description: The Program is connected to many community & tribal agencies. We interface with the Minneapolis American Indian Center, the Indian Health Board, the Minnesota Indian Women's Resource Center, the Division of Indian Work, as well as Indian support programs in other institutions of higher education throughout the State. Works closely with tribal education offices & departments of Indian education for Minneapolis, St. Paul & the State of Minnesota. *Faculty*: Eric Buffalohead; M. Elise Marubbio; James W. Rock, Dale A. Weston, John Champe (Rochester, MN campus), Vinodh Kutty, Steve Juenemann (Rochester, MN campus). Established 1978.

MINNESOTA COMMUNITY & TECHNICAL COLLEGE
AMERICAN INDIAN STUDIES PROGRAM
Dept. of Arts & Sciences, H.3301
1501 Hennepin Ave. • MINNEAPOLIS, MN 55403
Website:
http://www.minneapolis.edu/Educational-Programs/Liberal-Arts-General-Education/American-Indian-Studies
(800) 247-0911; (612) 200-5451 Fax 659-6825
Elaine Beaudreau-Patton, Counselor (659-6744)
E-mail: Elaine.beaudreau-patton@minneapolis.edu
Program: American Indian Studies Certificate, A.A. Degree.
Faculty: Patricia Amo, Chris Mato Nunpa, Kristen Talbert, Katherine Beane.

UNIVERSITY OF MINNESOTA
DEPARTMENT OF AMERICAN INDIAN STUDIES
College of Liberal Arts-American Studies
19 Scott Hall, 72 Pleasant St. SE • MINNEAPOLIS, MN 55455
(612) 624-1338 Fax 626-7904
Katherine Hayes, Chair & Associate Professor; (626-5330)
E-mail: kathayes@umn.edu
Edna Day (Mille Lacs Ojibwe), Associate Administrator
E-mail: desja003@umn.edu
John Reynolds, Dakota Language Program Associate
E-mail: reyn0173@umn.edu
Faculty:
Christine Taitano DeLisle, Assistant Professor (625-3821)
E-mail: cdelisle@umn.edu
Vicente Diaz, Associate Professor (625-2376)
E-mail: vmdiaz@umn.edu
Brendan Fairbanks, Assistant Professor (Ojibwe Language Program) (625-2973) E-mail: fair0061@umn.edu
Juliana Hu Pegues, Assistant Professor (624-8217)
E-mail: pegue002@umn.edu
David Wilkins, Professor (624-1634) E-mail: wilkinsd@umn.edu
John Nichols, Professor Emeritus; E-mail: jdn@umn.edu
Programs: Dakota & Ojibwe Language Programs.

Affiliate Faculty:
Jean O'Brien, Professor (6626-5330)
E-mail: obrie002@umn.edu
Bianet Castelllanos, Associate Professor (624-8031)
E-mail: mbc@umn.edu
David Chang, Professor of History (624-9045)
E-mail: dchang@umn.edu
Brenda Child (Red Earth Ojibwe), Professor of American Indian History (625-0895) E-mail: child011@umn.edu
Teaching Specialists: Sisokaduta Joe Bendrickson (Sisseton Wahpeton Oyate), Zoe Brown (Ojibway Language Program); Alex Ghebregzi, Cantemaza Neil McKay (Senior Teaching Specialist, Dakota Language Program), Carter Meland (Lecturer). *Courses*: Ojibwe & Dakota language, literature, philosophies, art, & history. Offers a commitment to the education of American Indian students. *Resources*: American Indian Learning Resource Center, American Indian Student Cultural Center, OMSSA Summer Institute, five American Indian student organizations. Established 1969.

UNIVERSITY OF MINNESOTA LAW SCHOOL
Mondale Hall, 229 19th Ave. South • MINNEAPOLIS, MN 55455
(612) 625-1000; Website: www.law.umn.edu
Joan Howland (612) 625-9036; Professor of American Indian Law
E-mail: howla001@umn.edu
Todd Matha (Ho-Chunk), (320) 412-6179, Adjunct Professor
E-mail: math0066@umn.edu

MOORHEAD STATE UNIVERSITY
AMERICAN MULTICULTURAL STUDIES DEPARTMENT
1104 7th Ave South, 279 MacLean Hall • MOORHEAD, MN 56560
(218) 477-2196 Fax 477-5983; Website: www.mnstate.edu/amcs/
Kim Park Nelson, Coordinator (477-4058)
E-mail: parknelson@mnstate.edu
Donna Brown (Turtle Mountain Chippewa), Chief Diversity Officer
Program: Minor in American Indian Studies. *Faculty*: Yolanda Arauza, Phyllis May-Machunda,Kim Park Nelson.

ST. CLOUD STATE UNIVERSITY – AMERICAN INDIAN CENTER
DEPARTMENT OF ETHNIC & WOMEN'S STUDIES DEPARTMENT
720 4th Ave. South • ST. CLOUD, MN 56301
(320) 308-5449 Fax 308-5451; Website: www.stcloudstate.edu/aic
Website: www.stcloudstate.edu/ethnicstudies
E-mail: aic@stcloudstate.edu
Jim Knutson-Kolodzne (Ottawa), Director-American Indian Center
E-mail: jkolodzne@stcloudstate.edu (320) 308-5447
Luke Tripp, Professor of American Indian Studies
E-mail: ltripp@stcloudstate.edu
Jeanne Lacourt, Professor of American Indian Studies
E-mail: jalacourt@stcloudstate.edu
Description: Undergraduate minor in American Indian Studies. The primary purpose of the St. Cloud State University American Indian Center is to respond to the self-defined educational needs & goals of the current American Indian student. To this end, the American Indian Center, utilizing resources, empowers indigenous people through quality educational programming. *Programs*: Minor in American Indian Studies; American Indian Mentor Program; ENGAGE Program. *Activities*: Annual Native Studies Summer Workshop for Educators; Additionally, the center's outreach activities promote awareness, better understanding, & sensitivity to American Indian Cultures. Sponsors summer workshops in Native Studies and Native Skywatchers for teachers; co-sponsors the annual "Power in Diversity Leadership Conference" the 20-year-old center is host for community social & educational programs including a speakers bureau and an annual powwow & sponsors an American Indian Speakers series that has included leaders such Craig Howe, Janice Lafloe & Sherry Sanchez-Tibbets. AIC organizes a service trip to Northern Cheyenne Reservation in Montana during spring break. Scholarships; Powwow. Library & Resource Center. *Publication*: Quarterly Newsletter.

MISSOURI

WASHINGTON UNIVERSITY
KATHRYN M. BUDER CENTER FOR AMERICAN INDIAN STUDIES
George Warren Brown School of Social Work
One Brookings Dr., CB 1196 • ST. LOUIS, MO 63130
(314) 935-4510 Fax 935-8464; E-mail: bcais@wustl.edu
Website: https://buder.wustl.edu/Pages/default.aspx
Molly Tovar (Comanche/Hispanic), Director; E-mail: mtovar@wustl.edu
Kellie Thompson (Seneca), Assistant Director
E-mail: kellie.thompson@wustl.edu
David Patterson (Cherokee), Director of Research
E-mail: dpatterson22@wustl.edu
Lynn Mitchell, Program Coordinator; E-mail: lmitchell24@wustl.edu

Lindsay Elliott, Administrative Assistant; E-mail: lindsay.elliott@wustl.edu
Description: Established to promote the higher education of Native Americans & prepare educational & social work practitioner leaders to serve American Indians. A scholarship is offered to Native American students intending to teach or practice social work with Indian people. *Resources*: American Indian Student Association. *Activities*: Witaya Lecture Series; American Indian Awareness Week & Powwow, early April. Established 1990.

WASHINGTON UNIVERSITY SCHOOL OF LAW
AMERICAN INDIAN LAW SUMMER PROGRAM
Anheuser-Busch Hall, One Brookings Dr. • ST. LOUIS, MO 763130
Website: https://law.wustl.edu/clinicaled/pages.aspx?id=6891
(314) 935-6400; Steven Gunn, Director
Description: Law students at the Washington University have the opportunity to work with select American Indian tribes to help them safeguard their rights & develop their legal institutions, infrastructure, and economies. Students who participate in the program will work for the legal departments of an Indian tribe, on location n the tribe's reservation.

MISSOURI STATE UNIVERSITY
NATIVE AMERICAN STUDIES PROGRAM
College of Humanities & Public Affairs, 07 Public Affairs Classroom Bldg.
901 S. National Ave. • SPRINGFIELD, MO 65897
(417) 836-5529 Fax 836-8472; Website: www.missouristate.edu/nas
Dr. Pam Sailors, Administrator; E-mail: pamelasailors@missouristate.edu
William C. Meadows, Professor & Program Coordinator
 E-mail: williammeadows@missouristate.edu
Degree: Native American Studies minor.

MONTANA

MONTANA STATE UNIVERSITY, BILLINGS
NATIVE AMERICAN STUDIES PROGRAM
Department of Social Sciences & Cultural Studies
College of Arts & Sciences, 802 Liberal Arts Bldg.
1500 University Dr. • BILLINGS, MT 59101
(406) 657-2311; Website: www.msubillings.edu/cas/nams
Joy Honea, Department Chairperson; E-mail: jhonea@msubillings.edu
Faculty:
Reno Charette (Crow) (657-2144), Director of American Indian Outreach
 E-mail: rcharette@msubillings.edu
C. Adrian Heidenreich (657-1674), Professor Emeritus
 E-mail: aheidenreich@msubillings.edu
The Native American Studies Minor Program has four primary goals: (1) to offer a comprehensive academic program in Native American Studies for both Native American and non-native students; (2) to provide increased awareness of and appreciation for the rich cultural heritage, knowledge, and contributions of Native Americans in the United States; (3) to contribute actively to increased multicultural awareness and appreciation at MSU Billings; and (4) to cooperate with other MSU Billings programs in providing a supportive environment for Native American students.

*STONE CHILD COMMUNITY COLLEGE
8294 Upper Box Elder Rd. • BOX ELDER, MT 59521
(406) 395-4875 Fax 395-4836; Website: www.stonechild.edu
Ted Whitford, Regents Chairperson; Jody Lamere, Vice Chairperson
Nathaniel St. Pierre (Chippewa Cree), President
 E-mail: nstpierre@stonechild.edu
Cory Sangrey (Chippewa Cree), Dean of Academics
 E-mail: csangrey@stonechild.edu
Gerard Vandeberg, Curriculum Developer
 E-mail: gvandeberg@stonechild.edu
Paulette Standing Rock, ANA Language Specialist
 E-mail: pstandingrock@stonechild.edu
Mary Ruth St. Pierre (Chippewa Cree), Extension Program Director
 E-mail: mstpierre@stonechild.edu
Peggy Aquino (Chippewa Cree), Native American Vocational Technical
 Program Coordinator; E-mail: paquino@stonechild.edu
Barbara Bacon (Crow), Assessment Coordinator
 E-mail: bbacon@stonechild.edu
Mary Lou Rosette (Chippewa Cree), Learning Center Manager
 E-mail: mrosette@stonechild.edu
Helen Windy Boy (Chippewa Cree), Dean of Student Services
 E-mail: hwindyboy@stonechild.edu
Wilma Windy Boy (Chippewa Cree), ANA Program Coordinator
 E-mail: wwindyboy@stonechild.edu
Joy Bridwell (Chippewa Cree), Librarian
 E-mail: jbridwell@stonechild.edu
Description: A tribally controlled two-year college of the Chippewa Cree Tribe. *Native American Studies*.

MONTANA STATE UNIVERSITY
DEPARTMENT OF NATIVE AMERICAN STUDIES
2-179 Wilson Hall, P.O. Box 172340 • BOZEMAN, MT 59717
(406) 994-3881 Fax 994-3343
Website: www.montana.edu/wwwnas/; E-mail: nas@montana.edu
Walter Fleming, Department Head/Professor (994-5260)
 E-mail: wfleming@montana.edu
Francesca Pine, Graduate Program Coordinator
 E-mail: Francesca.pine@montana.edu
Lisa J. Stevenson, Busines Operations Manager
 E-mail: lisa.stevenson1@montana.edu
Rita Sand, Academic Advisor; E-mail: rsand@montana.edu
Francine Spang-Willis, Student Success Services Program manager
 E-mail: Francine.spangwillis@montana.edu
Richard White, Student Success Services Director
 E-mail: Richard.white5@montana.edu
Faculty:
Matthew D. Herman, Associate Professor (994-3992)
 E-mail: mherman@montana.edu
Kristin Ruppel, Associate Professor (994-5261)
 E-mail: ktruppel@montana.edu
Gail Small, Assistant Professor (994-3823)
 E-mail: gail.small@montana.edu
Henrietta Mann (Cheyenne) Emeritus (994-3881)
Wayne J. Stein (Turtle Mountain Chippewa), Emeritus (994-3881)
 E-mail: wstein@montana.edu
Description: An Online Graduate Certificate, an Undergraduate Minor and a Masters of Art in Native American Studies, the programs offer a complete array of Native American Studies courses from introductory courses to upper division courses specializing in Indian law, art, literature, federal policy, & environmental issues. *Faculty*: Henrietta Mann (Emeritus); Adele Pittendrigh & William Yellowtail (Affiliate); Scott Zander & Rita Sand, Student Advisors. *Resources*: American Indian Council. *Programs*: Katz Endowed Chair in Native American Studies; Phyllis Berger Memorial Lecture Series. *Activities*: Annual Powwow; scholarships.

MONTANA STATE UNIVERSITY
AMERICAN INDIAN RESEARCH OPPORTUNITIES (AIRO)
312 Roberts Hall, Box 173925 • BOZEMAN, MT 59717
(406) 994-3881 Fax 994-6879
Website: www.montana.edu/empower/airo.html
Amy Stix, Director (994-5567); E-mail: amy.stix@coe.montana.edu
Anne Camper, Associate Dean, College of Engineering
 (994-2272); E-mail: anne_c@montana.edu
Jennifer Clark, Student Success Coordinator, College of Engineering
 (994-7836) E-mail: Jennifer.clark6@montana.edu
Description: A consortium of Montana's seven tribal colleges (Cankdeska Community College, Chief Dull Knife College, Fort Belknap College, Fort Peck Community College, Little Big Horn College, Salish Kootenai College; and Stone Child College) & Montana State University-Bozeman (MSU). *Faculty/Staff*: Kimberly McKeehan & Jennifer Woodcock, Administrative Associates. *Purpose*: To provide opportunities for American Indian students in career fields where they are significantly underrepresented. An advisory board consists of representatives from the seven tribal colleges & MSU. *Programs*: A Minority Apprenticeship Program (MAP), a Minority Biomedical Research Support Program (MBRS), & a Minority Access-to-Research Careers Program.

*BLACKFEET COMMUNITY COLLEGE
504 SE Boundary St., P.O. Box 819 • BROWNING, MT 59417
(800) 549-7457; (406) 338-5441 Fax 338-3272; Website: www.bfcc.edu
Dr. Billie Jo Kipp (Blackfeet), President; E-mail: drkipp@bfcc.edu
Mike LaFrommboise (Blackfeet), Blackfeet Language & Culture Chair
 E-mail: mikel@bfcc.edu
Marvin Weatherwax (Blackfeet), Blackfeet Language Instructor
Trustees: Theda New Breast (Blackfeet), Chairperson
 Susan Webber, Vice Chairperson
 Linda Babcock, Tammy Hall Regan & Reis Fisher
Partial list of faculty: Bonita Begay, Brenda Bird, Gail Bird Rattler, Billie Jo Iron Pipe, Dr. Cheri Kicking Woman, Woody Kipp, Jay Longtime Sleeping, Crystal Old Chief, Amy Running Fisher, Andrea Running Wolf, Rose Mary Spotted Bear, Bob Tailfeathers, Melissa Weatherwax,

*LITTLE BIG HORN COLLEGE
8645 S. Weaver Dr. • CROW AGENCY, MT 59022
(406) 638-3100 Fax 638-3169; Website: www.lbhc.edu
David Yarlott, Jr. (Crow), President (638-3107)
 E-mail: davidyarlott@lbhc.edu
David Small (Crow), Dean of Administration (638-3110)
 E-mail: smalld@lbhc.edu
Frederica Lefthand (Crow), Dean of Academics (638-3131)
 E-mail: lefthandfv@lbhc.edu

Te-Atta Old Bear (Crow), Dean of Student Affairs (638-3106)
E-mail: oldbear@lbhc.edu
Letha Gun Shows (Crow), Title III Director (638-3154)
E-mail: gunshowsl@lbhc.edu
Aldean Good Luck (Crow), Chief Financial Officer (638-3152)
E-mail: goodluckav@lbhc.edu
Tana Stewart, Health & Wellness Center Director (638-3660)
E-mail: stewartt@lbhc.edu
Jon Ille, Archivist (Crow) (638-3182) E-mail: illej@lbhc.edu
Tim Bernardis, Library Director (638-3113); E-mail: tim@lbhc.edu
Mission: To preserve, perpetuate, & protect Crow culture & language. *Faculty*: Dr. Tim McCleary (Liberal Arts); Raphaelle Real Bird (Crow Studies); Lanny Real Bird (Business); Sharon Peregoy (Crow Studies); Berthina Nomee (Math Coordinator); Sara Plaggemeyer (Science). *Adjunct Faculty*: Teri Lea McCormick, Vera He Does IT, Amber Cummins. *Programs*: Crow Studies; One Year Certificate: Crow Studies-Tribal Management; Chartered by the Crow Tribe in 1980.

*AANIIIH NAKODA COLLEGE (FORT BELKNAP COMMUNITY COLLEGE)
P.O. Box 159 • HARLEM, MT 59526-0159
(406) 353-2607 Fax 353-2898; Website: www.ancollege.edu
Carole Falcon-Chandler, President; E-mail: cfalcone@hotmail.com
Sean Chandler, American Indian Studies Director/Instructor
E-mail: schandler@ancollege.edu
Robert Bell, Program Director; E-mail: rbell@ancollege.edu
Scott Friskics, Sponsored Programs Director; E-mail: friskics@hotmail.com
Carmen Taylor, Dean of Academics; E-mail: ctaylor@ancollege.edu
Lynette K. Chandler, White Clay Language Immersion School Director
Clarena Brockie, Dean of Student Affairs; E-mail: cbrockie@ancollege.edu
Donna Miller, Director, Teacher Training Program
E-mail: dmiller@ancollege.edu
Eva English, Library Director; E-mail: eenglish@ancollege.edu
Tribally controlled community college providing quality post-secondary educational opportunities for Indian residents (Assiniboine & Gros Ventre Tribes) of the Fort Belknap communities. About 500 full-time & part-time students attend. *Programs*: American Indian Studies; Native American Career & Technical Education Program (NACTEP); Natural Resource Program; Vocational & Cooperative Education; Academic. *Services*: Assistance to tribal institutions, departments in staff preparation, planning research & evaluation services. Resources: KGVA 88.1 FM Radio Station - Gerald Stiffarm, Manager (353-4656). Library. Financial aid available. Established 1984.

MONTANA STATE UNIVERSITY – NORTHERN
NATIVE AMERICAN STUDIES PROGRAM
College of Education, Arts & Sciences, Cowan Hall 306E
300 13th St. West, P.O. Box 7751 • HAVRE, MT 59501
(800) 662-6132; (406) 265-3751
Wade Cruzado, President; James M. Limbaugh, Chancellor
Kristi Peterson, Director of Admissions
Ligia Arango, Coordinator, Learning Success Center
Degree: Minor in Native American Studies.

FLATHEAD VALLEY COMMUNITY COLLEGE
NATIVE AMERICAN/MULTICULTURAL AFFAIRS
777 Grandview Dr. • KALISPEL, MT 59901
(406) 756-3945 Fax 756-3815
Website: www.fvcc.edu; E-mail: info@fvcc.edu
Jane A. Karas, President; E-mail: jkaras@fvcc.edu
Michael Ober, Librarian; E-mail: mober@fvcc.edu
Courses: Gender: Native vs. Non-Native Perspectives; ART/NAS: Native Beadwork & Adornments; Diversity in America. *Programs*: Native Arts/Crafts; Mutlicultural Arts/Crafts for Children. Financial Aid: Native American Tuition Waiver - to Indian students with financial need, from any North American tribe and a resident of Montana, and holding a 2.0 or better GPA.

*CHIEF DULL KNIFE COLLEGE
P.O. Box 98 • LAME DEER, MT 59043
(406) 477-6215 Fax 477-6219; Website: www.cdkc.edu
Dr. Richard Littlebear (Norhern Cheyenne), President (1999-present)
& Interim Dean of Cultural Affairs
Tribally controlled and located on the Northern Cheyenne Indian Reservation in southeastern Montana. *Special program*: Native American Studies Program, Dr. Richard Littlebear, Coordinator. *Facilities*: Dr. John Woodenlegs Memorial Library. *Resources*: Financial aid available.

UNIVERSITY OF MONTANA
PAYNE FAMILY NATIVE AMERICAN CENTER
NATIVE AMERICAN STUDIES DEPARTMENT
32 Campus Dr. • MISSOULA, MT 59812
(406) 243-5831 Fax 243-6432; Website: www.cas.umt.edu/nas
S. Neyooxet Greymorning, Professor & Co-Chairperson

E-mail: neyooxet.greymorning@mso.umt.edu
Theodore Van Alst, Jr., Associate Professor & Co-Chairperson (243-5883)
E-mail: Theodore.vanalst@umontana.edu
Willie Brown, Department Administrator (243-5851)
E-mail: willie.brown@umontana.edu
Michelle Guzman, Advisr; E-mail: michelle.guzman@mso.umt.edu
Kathryn Shanley, Professor & Special Assistant to the
Provost for Native American & Indigenous Education
E-mail: shanleykw@mso.umt.edu
George Price, Lecturer (243-2302) E-mail: george.price@mso.umt.edu
Richmond Clow, Professor (243-2702) E-mail: clowrl@mso.umt.edu
Wade Davies, Professor (243-5835); E-mail: wade.davies@mso.umt.edu
Heather Cahoon, Adjunct Lecturer (243-58838
E-mail: heather.cahoon@mso.umt.edu
Description: The first facility in the nation built expressly to accommodate a Department of Native American Studies, an American Indian Student Services office, & other related campus programming. Undergraduate emphasis in archaeology, linguistics, ethnic & cultural diversified studies, & forensic anthropology; graduate program offering a M.A. in Cultural Heritage Studies & forensic anthropology. *Programs*: Native American Studies; Ethnological & archaeological field courses. *Facilities*: The Payne Family Native American Center; American Indian Student Services (AISS) (406) 243-6306 Fax 243-6199. *Special resources*: Extensive study collections of Northwest Plains ethnological & archaeological materials; Northern Plains Ethno-history Project; Linguistics Laboratory & Reading Room maintains a strong collection of material on Native American linguistics. *Activities*: American Indian Heritage Day. Financial Aid: Undergraduate - Several competitive scholarships open to majors; Graduate - Teaching Assistants. *Publications*: Biannual Newsletter; Occasional Papers in anthropological linguistics.

UNIVERSITY OF MONTANA SCHOOL OF LAW
MARGERY HUNTER BROWN INDIAN LAW CLINIC
Alexander Blewett III School of Law
32 Campus Dr. #6552 • MISSOULA, MT 59812
(406) 243-4311 Fax 243-2576
Website: https://www.umt.edu/law/academics/clinics/mhb.php
Maylinn Smith, Clinical Supervisor & Co-Director (243-5351)
E-mail: maylinn.smith@umontana.edu
Monte Mills, Assistant Professor & Clinic Co-Chairperson (243-2544)
E-mail: monte.mills@umontana.edu
Stacey Gordon, (Indian Law Research), Director of Jameson Law Library
(243-6808) E-mail: stacey.gordon@umontana.edu
Andrew King-Ries, Summer Indian Law Program
E-mail: Andrew.king-ries@umontana.edu
Description: American Indian Law Certificate. The Clinic's goal is to provide students with practical experience regarding Indian law issues. Indian Law Clinic projects commonly focus on issues & problems affecting tribal governments, justice systems and Indian people. Students frequently appear in Tribal & State courts addressing Indian issues or representing Indian people and occasionally have the opportunity to appear in federal court. Students will work on variety of projects promoting tribal sovereignty, cultural preservation, access to justice & economic development within Indian Country. *Program*: Summer Indian Law Program. Established 1980.

*SALISH KOOTENAI COLLEGE
NATIVE AMERICAN STUDIES DEPARTMENT
P.O. Box 70 • PABLO, MT 59855
(406) 675-4800 Fax 675-4801; Website: www.skc.edu
Robert R. DePoe (Salish-Kootenai), College President
E-mail: robert_depoe@skc.edu
Sandra Boham (Salish-Kootenai), College President
E-mail: Sandra_boham@skc.edu
Dan Durglo, Vice President of Student Affairs
Audrew Plouffe, Vice President of Business Affairs
Tracie McDonald, Dean of Students
Anita Bigspring, Administrative Secretary
Dean Nicholai, Department Head
Frank Finley (Salish-Kootenai), Coordinator, Cultural Arts
E-mail: frank_finley@skc.edu
Jeffrey Bendremer (Mohegan), Coordinator, Tribal Historic Preservation
Fred Noel, Library Director (275-4873) E-mail: fred_noel@skc.edu
Mission: To serve the postsecondary needs of the Flathead Reservation as well as other Native Americans; to provide instruction in a wide variety of Native American culture programs. *Programs*: Native American Studies. *Faculty*: Lori Lambert (Mi'kmaq/Abenaki); Russell Boham E-mail: russell_boham@skc.edu Wilford Kenmille E-mail: wilfred_kenmille@skc.edu; Salisha Old Bulll E-mail: salisha_oldbull@skc.edu; Linda Ferris E-mail: linda_ferris@skc.edu; Steve Arca E-mail: steve_arca@skc.edu. Chairperson. *Resources*: Center for Prevention & Wellness. *Special Project*: Native American Career & Technical Education Project (NACTEP) (406) 275-4976. *Resources*: D'Arcy McNickle Library – Fred Noel, Director. Established 1977.

*FORT PECK COMMUNITY COLLEGE
NATIVE AMERICAN STUDIES PROGRAM
605 Indian Ave., P.O. Box 398 • POPLAR, MT 59255
  (406) 768-6300 Fax 768-5552; Website: www.fpcc.edu
  Haven Gourneau, President; E-mail: hgourneau@fpcc.edu
  Thomas Brown, Chair, Board of Directors
  Leslie Gourneau, Vice Chair, Board of Directors
Faculty: Margaret Abbott (English) E-mail: mabbott@fpcc.edu
  Richard DeCelles (Education) E-mail: rdecelles@fpcc.edu
  Michael J. Turcotte (American Indian studies) (768-6342)
   E-mail: mturcotte@fpcc.edu
  Brandi Lynn Wilkinson (English) E-mail: bwilkinson@fpcc.edu
  Anita Scheetz, Librarian; E-mail: ascheetz@fpcc.edu
Tribally controlled community college that is a fully accredited offering a two-year associates degree. *Programs*: Native American Studies; General Studies; workshops. *Financial aid*: Pell Grant; scholarships. *Publication*: Cannon Blast News. Facilities: James E. Shanley Tribal Library.

NEBRASKA

UNIVERSITY OF NEBRASKA, LINCOLN
NATIVE AMERICAN STUDIES DEPARTMENT
College of Arts & Sciences, Institute of Ethnic Studies
303 Seaton Hall, P.O. Box 880685 • LINCOLN, NE 68588
  (402) 471-1663 Fax 472-0531
  Website: www.unl.edu; E-mail: ethnicstudies@unl.edu
  Joy Castro, Director of Ethnic Studies; E-mail: jcastro2@unl.edu
  James Garza, Associate Director; E-mail: jgarza2@unl.edu
  Thomas C. Gannon, Academic Advisor; E-mail: tgannon2@unl.edu
  Victoria Smith (Cherokee/Delaware), Faculty Advisor,
  University of Nebraska Inter-Tribal Exchange (UNITE)
Description: The Institute is an interdisciplinary & multidisciplinary unit with three programs: African American & African Studies (AAAS), Latino & Latin American Studies (LLAS), and Native American Studies (NAS). *Degrees*: B.A. major & minor; PhD & MA with emphasis in Native American Studies. *Faculty*: Donna Akers (Choctaw) (History); Mark Awakuni-Swetland (adopted Omaha) (Anthropology); Thomas C. Gannon (Cheyenne River Lakota) (English); Martha McCollough (Anthropolog); Victoria Smith (Cherokee/Delaware) (History); Cynthia Willis-Esqueda (Cherokee) (Psychology) (Director & Coordinator, 1997-2005). *Activities*: Sponsors & cosponsors various lectures that bring indigenous leaders, scholars, and artists to the campus. *Resources*: The Native American Public Broadcasting Consortium; The Lincoln Indian Center.

*NEBRASKA INDIAN COMMUNITY COLLEGE
P.O. Box 428 • MACY, NE 68039
  (402) 494-2311 Fax 837-4183; Website: www.thenicc.edu
  Michael Oltrogge (Omaha), President; E-mail: moltrogge@thenicc.edu
  Mary Johnson, Academic Dean; E-mail: mjohnson@thenicc.edu
  Dawne Price, Dean of Student Services; E-mail: dprice@thenicc.edu
  Carlton LeCount (Omaha), Native American Studies Professor;
  NAS Division Head; Fnancial Aid Administrator
   E-mail: clecount@thenicc.edu
  Misty Frazier, Dakota Language Professor
   E-mail: mfrazier@thenicc.edu
  Alison Saunsoci, Omaha Language Professor
   E-mail: arsaunsoci@thenicc.edu
  Wynema Morris (Omaha), Board member; Instructor -
  Native American Studies), E-mail: wmorris@thenicc.edu
  Justin Kocian, Chief Information Officer, Title II Director
   E-mail: jkocian@thenicc.edu
  Wanda Henke & Susan Tyndall, Librarians
   E-mail: whenke@thenicc.edu
  Dawne Price, Dean of Student Services; E-mail: dprice@thenicc.edu
Description: Began as the American Indian Satellite Community College. A co-educational liberal arts & vocational education institution chartered by the Omaha, Santee Sioux & Winnebago Tribes of Nebraska. *Program*: Native American Studies.

CREIGHTON UNIVERSITY
NATIVE AMERICAN STUDIES (NAS) PROGRAM
Department of Cultural & Social Studies
2500 California Plaza, Admin. 437 • OMAHA, NE 68178
  (402) 280-3587 Fax 280-2108
  Website: https://www.creighton.edu/program/native-american-studies-minor
  Tracy Leavelle, Director (280-2652); E-mail: tracy.leavelle@creighton.edu
The Native American studies minor introduces students to Native American history, culture, identity and a wide variety of contemporary social and political issues. You'll engage in a multidisciplinary program that will allow you to understand the long history of Native peoples and the complex sets of

interactions with immigrant peoples around them. *Faculty*: Dr. Michael Brown (Philosophy); Dr. Lydia Cooper (English); Dr. Barbara Dilly (Anthropology); Fr. Don Doll, SJ (Photographer/Journalism); Fr. Michael Flecky, SJ (Fine & Performing Arts); Taylor R.M. Keen (Omaha); Dr. Michael Kelly (Law); Dr. Jay Leighter (Communications); Dr. Tracy Leavelle (History); Dr. Victoria Roche (Pharmacy Sciences); Dr. Richard Witmer (Political Science).

UNIVERSITY OF NEBRASKA, OMAHA
NATIVE AMERICAN STUDIES PROGRAM
College of Arts & Sciences
6001 Dodge St., Hall 287C • OMAHA, NE 68182
  (402) 554-3376 Fax 554-2794; Website: www.unomaha.edu
  E-mail: nas@unomaha.edu
  Dr. Beth Ritter, Director (554-3376)
   E-mail: britter@mail.unomaha.edu
Degrees: Offers an interdisciplinary undergraduate & graduate minor. *Program*: Native American Studies. *Faculty*: Jessiline Anderson (Omaha); Kent Blansett (History); Timi Barone; Michael C. Carroll (Emeritus); Audrey DeFrank (Arapaho); Michele Desmarais (Canadian Metis/Dakota); Brady DeSanti (Lac Courte Oreilles Ojibwe); David Peterson; Jeanne Reames; Dennis J. Smith (Assiniboine/Fort Peck); Linda Parker (Comanche) (Emerita); Jeanne Reames (Peoria/Miami); Beth Ritter (Native American Studies); Barbara Robins; Mark Scherer (History). *Resources*: American Indian Student Council; annual Powwow. Established 1992.

*LITTLE PRIEST TRIBAL COLLEGE
601 E. College Dr., P.O. Box 270 • WINNEBAGO, NE 68071
  (402) 878-2380 Fax 878-2355; Website: www.littlepriest.edu
  Maunka Morgan, President (878-3354) E-mail: president@littlepriest.edu
  Betty Redleaf-Collet, Academic Dean (878-3316)
   E-mail: bredleaf@littlepriest.edu
  Sunshine Bear, Chairperson; William Bass, Vice Chairperson
  Mary Austin, Library Director (878-3335) E-mail: maustin@littlepriest.edu
Faculty: Jerry Bartels, CassieKitcheyan, Haesong Kwon, Al Martyn, Dr. Kweku Ocran, Jody Wingert, janyce Woodard. *Resources*: Virtual Museum; Library.
The Winnebago Tribe of Nebraska chartered Little Priest Tribal College (LPTC) in May 1996. Its major focus is to provide a two-year associate degree, and prepare students to transfer and successfully complete a major at a four-year institution. Another equally important part of the college's mission is to provide language and culture classes and training opportunities for upgrading job skills and improving employability. Little Priest Tribal College is named after Chief Little Priest, the last true war chief of the Winnebago Tribe.

NEW HAMPSHIRE

DARTMOUTH COLLEGE - NATIVE AMERICAN STUDIES PROGRAM
The Sherman House, 37 N. Main St. • HANOVER, NH 03755
  (603) 646-3530 Fax 646-0333; Website: www.dartmouth.edu/~nas
  E-mail: native.american.program@dartmouth.edu
  Melanie B. Taylor, NAS Chair & Associate Professor
   E-mail: Melanie.b.taylor@dartmouth.edu
  Sheila C. Laplante, Program Administrator
   E-mail: sheila.c.laplante@dartmouth.edu
  N. Bruce Dithu, JD (Houma of Louisiana), Samson Occom Professor
   E-mail: n.bruce.duthu@dartmouth.edu
  Colin Gordon Calloway, Professor of History
  Sergei A. Kan, Professor of Anthropology (646-2481)
   E-mail: sergei.a.kan@dartmouth.edu
  Nicholas James Reo (Ojibwe), Assistant Professor, Environmental Sciences
   E-mail: Nicholas.j.reo@dartmouth.edu
  Dale Turner, Associate Professor of Government
   E-mail: dale.a.turner@dartmouth.edu
  Vera B. Palmer, Senior Lecturer
   E-mail: vera.b.palmer@dartmouth.edu
  Estevan Rael-Galvez, Lecturer
   E-mail: estevan.rael-galvez@dartmouth.edu
  Lara M. Evans, Lecturer; Kristofer Ray (History), Visiting Faculty
Mission: To develop interdisciplinary teaching & research & increase understanding of the historical experiences, cultural traditions & innovations, and political status of Indian peoples in the U.S. & Canada. *Structure & Responsibilities*: The Native American Program provides Native American student support services; works with students, administrators, campus-wide faculty & programs to insure the success of Native American students through their four-year residency on campus; strives to provide spiritual, emotional, personal support, and tutorial help -- often times on an individual basis -- to insure the success of all Native students. NAP works to increase understanding of native issues both on campus & beyond. Student graduation rates have grown significantly since the inception of the Native American Program in 1972. During the first decade of the program's existence, the Native student graduation rate averaged 50%; since then the average has risen to 72%,

nearly ten times the average graduation rate for Native Americans attending college nationwide. Currently, 117 Native American students are enrolled. *Faculty*: Colin G. Calloway (Professor of History & Samson Occom (Professor of Native American Studies); N. Bruce Duthu, JD (Program Chair) (Houma of Louisiana) (American Indian Law & Policy); Dale A. Turner (Teme-Augama Anishnabai from northern Ontario), (Government, Tribal Sovereignty, Contemporary Issues); Melanie Bensen Taylor (U.S. Southern studies); Sergei Kan (Anthropology, Peoples & Cultures of Native North America); Deborah L. Nichols (Archaeology, Ancient Native Americans); Vera B. Palmer (Tuscarora, Native American Literature); Angela Parker; Nicholas Reo (Environmental Studies). *Affiliated College Officials*: Jim Larimore, Comanche (Dean of the College); Colleen Larimore, Comanche (Support Services in First Year Office); Michael Hanitchak (Choctaw); The Native American House (a residential house for 16 upper class Native American students, and a central meeting & cultural activities center for students); Lori Alvord Arviso, Navajo (Assistant Director of Admissions, Dartmouth Medical School, surgeon, Dartmouth-Hitchcock Medical Center). *Special programs*: Native American Program (see below); Angela K. Parker, Mandan-Hidatsa (Admissions Recruiter for Native American students); Horizons Program & Native American Fly-In (Native American high school seniors come to Dartmouth in a group for a visit, all travel expenses paid for by the College, submit application to admissions office); Charles Eastman Fellowship (annual residential fellowship for Native scholars writing PhD dissertations, $25,000 salary, office support, $2,500 expense account; Class of 1943 Tribal Research Fellowship, up to $8,000). *Activities*: Conferences & symposia addressing current issues in Indian country, historical perspectives, religious traditions, education, material culture, language, sovereignty; Internship program, seniors majoring in NAS go on term-long internships in Indian country or Washington, DC; Annual Dartmouth College Powwow (usually held the Saturday before Mother's Day each Spring); annual guests, lectures, Talking Circle, cultural events to promote understanding. *Affiliates*: Native American Council (NAC), meets four times each term; Native American Visiting Committee (NAVC) alumni review committee, annual meetings & report; Native Americans at Dartmouth (NAD), student organization, sharing affinity and student life; Native American House (affinity residence house for Native American students & non-Native students interested in sharing cultural life); NAAA (Native American Alumni Assn); alumni group at Dartmouth College with over 500 members. *Honors Program*: Students may become honors majors in NAS upon application & a GPA of 3.00 or higher. *Facilities*: Native American Studies Center includes a research library (over 5,000 books, many newspapers, periodicals, tribal publications, language research project archives); Baker Library, main college library has excellent & broad collections on American Indian ethnography, history & contemporary life, art, material culture; Hood Museum of Art (collections of American Indian art, artifacts, & cultural objects).

NEW MEXICO

*SOUTHWESTERN INDIAN POLYTECHNIC INSTITUTE (SIPI)
9169 Coors Rd., NW • ALBUQUERQUE, NM 87184
(800) 586-7474; (505) 346-2348 Fax 346-2343; Website: www.sipi.edu
Sherry Allison (Dine'), President (346-4087); E-mail: sherry.allison@bie.edu
Monte Monteith, VP College Operations; E-mail: monte.monteith@bie.edu
Valerie Montoya, VP Academic Programs (346-2351)
 E-mail: valerie.montoya@bie.edu
Lori Tapahonso, Education Project Specialist
Allen R. Gachupin, Director of Student Services (346-7728)
 E-mail: allen.gachupin@bie.edu
A National Indian community college & land grant Institution, administered by the Bureau of Indian Affairs, under the jurisdiction of Albuquerque Area Office. SIPI is dedicated to training American Indian adults for jobs in the technical-vocational fields. *Student Services*: Program offers special assistance & support services to students & staff in the understanding and treatment of alcohol & drug abuse. Sponsors health promotion education class, support groups, sweat lodge, peer counseling training, & substance abuse education classes. Library. *Awards, honors*: Awarded the 2011 Indian Education Renewable Energy Challenge by the Assistant Secretary-Indian Affairs, Larry Echo Hawk of the Department of the Interior; Wins the 2nd National Argonne Lab Energy Challenge. *Publication*: SIPI News; numerous pamphlets related to substance abuse. Established 1974.

UNIVERSITY OF NEW MEXICO
AMERICAN INDIAN GRADUATE CENTER (AIGC)
3701 San Mateo Blvd. NE #200 • ALBUQUERQUE, NM 87110
(800) 628-1920; (505) 881-4584 Fax 884-0427; Website: www.aigcs.org
Angelique Albert (Confederated Salish & Kootenai), Executive Director
 E-mail: angelique@aigcs.org
Joan Currier, COO; E-mail: joan@aigcs.org
Marveline Vallo Gabbard (Pueblo of Acoma), Program Associate
 for Scholarships & Programs; E-mail: marveline@aigcs.org
Josh Lucio (Zuni Pueblo), Program Associate

for Scholarships & Programs; E-mail: josh@aigcs.org
Christa Moya (Dine), Director of Financial Aid/Student Services
 E-mail: christa@aigcs.org
Erin Griego, Coordinator of Operations & Events Specialist
 E-mail: erin@aigcs.org
Michael Bates (Cherokee), Academic Advisor
 E-mail: michael@aigcs.org
Sara LaBarge (Menominee), Academic Advisor
 E-mail: sara@aigcs.org
Board members: Rose Graham (Navajo), President
 Joel M. Frank, Sr. (Florida Seminole), Vice President
 Steve Stallings (Rincon Luiseno) Secretary-Treasurer
Description: Provides fellowship grants to Indian graduate students. Assists about 400 students from 105 tribes at over 200 colleges throughout the U.S. In 2000, AIGC became the administrator for the Gates Millennium Scholar program for the American Indian & Alaska Native population. Scholarships are awarded annually to ethnically diverse individuals that have demonstrated excellence in academic, leadership roles, & community involvement. AIGC also teams with Wells Fargo & Accenture to award undergraduate & graduate scholarships. Established 1969.

UNIVERSITY OF NEW MEXICO SCHOOL OF LAW
AMERICAN INDIAN LAW CENTER (AILC)
LAW & INDIGENOUS PEOPLES PROGRAM
1117 Stanford Dr. NE, P.O. Box 4456 • ALBUQUERQUE, NM 87131
(505) 277-5462 Fax 277-1035
 Website: www.ailc-inc.org; E-mail: begay@ailc-inc.org
Helen B. Padilla, Esq. (Isleta Pueblo), Center Director
 E-mail: padilla@ailc-inc.org
Heidi Nesbitt, PLSI Director & AILC Assistant Director
 E-mail: nesbitt@ailc-inc.org
Kenneth "Kip" Bobroff, Indigenous Peoples Program Director (277-1266)
 Email: bobroff@law.unm.edu
Mitzi Vigil, Indian Law Program Administrator (277-0405)
 E-mail: vigil@law.unm.edu
Francine M. Jaramillo, Esq. (Isleta Pueblo), Staff Attorney
 E-mail: jaramillo@ailc-inc.org
Melanie P. Fritzsche, Esq. (Laguna Pueblo), Staff Attorney
 E-mail: fritzsche@ailc-inc.org
Anthony Lee, Esq., Staff Attorney; E-mail: lee@law.unm.edu
Stephanie M. Salazar, Esq. (Navajo), Associate Attorney
 E-mail: salazar@law.unm.edu
Valerie S. Begay (Dine'), SWITCA Court Clerk & Office Administrator
Indian Law Faculty:
 Barbara Creel, Professor of Law, Director, Southwest Indian Law Clinic
 E-mail: creel@law.unm.edu
 John LaVelle, Dickason Professor of Law & Director of the Indian Law
 Program (505) 277-0951; E-mail: lavelle@law.unm.edu
 Jeanette Wolfley, Assistant Professor of Law (505) 277-3010
 E-mail: wolfley@law.unm.edu
 Christine Zuni Cruz, Professor of Law, Associate Dean for the Indian Law
 Program (505) 277-1007; E-mail: zunicruz@law.unm.edu
 Gloria Valencia-Weber, Emeritus faculty
Description: The oldest existing Indian-managed and Indian-operated legal & public policy organization in the country serving to strengthen, promote, and honor self-sustaining American Indian & Alaska Native communities through education, training, & leadership. *Mission*: To examine policy issues important to tribal governments; to assist in strengthening tribal justice systems; to ensure proper legal education for Native Americans. *Programs*: Indian Law Certificate Program; Southwest Indian Law Clinic (SILC) (277-2146); Pre-Law Summer Institute (PLSI) two month program which prepares American Indian & Alaska Native individuals for the rigors of law school by essentially replicating the first semester of law school; Southwest Intertribal Court of Appeals (SWITCA) provides an appellate court forum for tribes located in New Mexico, Colorado, Arizona & West Texas. Also provides training, technical assistance, legal research, and support services to tribal courts, tribal judges & tribal court staff. Provides an Indian Law Certificate. *Resources*: Law Library; Native American Law Students Association (NALSA); Annual Tribal Leadership Conference. *Publication*: Tribal Law Journal. Established 1967.

UNIVERSITY OF NEW MEXICO
AMERICAN INDIAN STUDENT SERVICES
1119 Mesa Vista Hall MSC06 3800
1-University of New Mexico • ALBUQUERQUE, NM 87131
(505) 277-6343 Fax 277-0033; E-mail: aiss@unm.edu
 Website: http://aiss.unm.edu/pages/pro_staff.html
Pamela Agoyo (Dine'), Director & Special Assistant to the President
 for American Indian Affairs; E-mail: pagoyo@unm.edu
Daniel Begay (Dine'), Program Manager; E-mail: debegay24@unm.edu
Roderick Lansing (Dine'), Program Analyst; E-mail: rodian@unm.edu
Katrina Sweetland (Dine'), Program Coordinator; E-mail: katrina4@unm.edu

Ashley Tso (Dine'), Student Programs Specialist; E-mail: aftso@unm.edu
Andrew Yazzie (Dine'), Student Recruitment Specialist
 E-mail: andi08@unm.edu
Description: Provides cultural & academic programming for American Indian students attending the University of New Mexico. Also a liaison for Native students attending local high schools & schools located on or near trial reservations; tribal & community colleges; tribal governments; tribal higher education programs & organizations that directly impact the recruitment & retention of American Indian students at the University of New Mexico. Established 1980.

UNIVERSITY OF NEW MEXICO - DEPARTMENT OF ANTHROPOLOGY
MSC01-1040, Anthropology 1 • ALBUQUERQUE, NM 87131
 (505) 277-4524 Fax 277-0874; Website: www.unm.edu/~anthro/
Les Field, Chair; E-mail: lesfield@unm.edu
Jennifer George, Department Advisor (277-1534)
 E-mail: jgeorge2@unm.edu
David A. Phillips, Interim Director, Maxwell Museum of Anthropology
Lloyd L. Lee (Dine'), Director, Institute for American Indian Research
 E-mail: triplel@unm.edu
Instructors: Patricia L. Crown (Archaeology); E. James Dixon (Director, Maxwell Museum), Patricia L. Crown (Archaeology); Bruce B. Huckell (Archaeology); David A. Phillips, Jr. (Archaeology); Willow R. Powers, Beverly R. Singer (Ethnology); Wirt H. Wills (Archaeology); Erin Debenport (Ethnology); David Dinwoodie (Ethnology). *Facility*: Institute for American Indian Research; Alfonzo Ortiz Center for Intercultural Studies; Maxwell Museum of Anthropology. *Publication*: Journal of Anthropological Research. Library.

UNIVERSITY OF NEW MEXICO
ALFONSO ORTIZ CENTER FOR INTERCULTURAL STUDIES
Department of Anthropology MSC01-1040
1 University of New Mexico • ALBUQUERQUE, NM 87131
 (505) 277-3027; Website: www.ortizcenter.unm.edu
 E-mail: ortizcenter@gmail.com

UNIVERSITY OF NEW MEXICO - HEALTH SCIENCE CENTER
MSC07 4255, 1 University of New Mexico • ALBUQUEQUE, NM 87131
Institute for Indigenous Knowledge & Development (IIKD)
 (505) 925-4377; E-mail: iikd@salud.unm.edu
Tassy Parker (Seneca), PhD, RN, Director (925-0776)
 E-mail: taparker@salud.unm.edu
Nathania Tsosie, MCRP, Associate Director (925-4377)
 E-mail: nttsosie@unm.edu
Norman Cooeyate (Zuni), Supervisor for Cultural Engagement (925-4439)
 E-mail: ncooeyate@salud.unm.edu
Center for Native American Health (CNAH)
Dept. of Family & Community Medicine, MSC07 4246
1001 Medical Arts Ave. NE • Albuquerque, NM 87102
 (505) 272-4100 Fax 272-6019; E-mail: hsc-cnah@unm.edu
The Center is the University of New Mexico's established organization for developing students, faculty, staff & community learners as Native Health professionals by applying the principles of tribal sovereignty, core values and collaboration in the institutional missions of research, education & service for improving Native American health & wellbeing. *Goals*: Advance Native American student recruitment into health professions by providing student mentorship opportunities; address Native American student enrollment & retention efforts at the University of New Mexico Health Sciences Center (UNM HSC); be a resource center for Native American research data, health education, & technical support for tribal communities and UNM HSC; facilitate partnerships between the UNM HSC and New Mexico's 22 Native American tribes to address tribal health priority needs. *Annual Meeting*: Tribal Leaders' Public Health Symposium (late June)

UNIVERSITY OF NEW MEXICO
HEALTH SCIENCES LIBRARY & INFORMATICS CENTER
Native American Health Information Services MSC 09 5100
1 University of New Mexico • ALBUQUERQUE, NM 87131
 (505) 272-2311; E-mail: reflib@salud.unm.edu
Holly Shipp Buchanan, Executive Director (272-0634)
 E-mail: hbuchanan@salud.unm.edu
Patricia Bradley, Native & Distance Services Librarian (272-0664)
 E-mail: pbradley@salud.unm.edu
The Native American Health Information Services Program connects HSLIC to Native Americans in New Mexico. The program offers resources to health care providers serving Native Americans and to community members of the 22 Native nations in the state. The program also addresses the health information needs of the Native American community at the University of New Mexico. Native American Health Information Services are focused on health information delivery, health information training & collection development consultation. Native Health Database - contains citations & abstracts of health-related articles, reports, surveys and other documents pertaining to the health & health care of American Indians, Alaska Natives & Canadian First Nations.

UNIVERSITY OF NEW MEXICO
NATIVE AMERICAN STUDIES DEPARTMENT (NAS)
University College, 1 University of New Mexico
Mesa Vista Hall 3080 • ALBUQUERQUE, NM 87131
 (505) 277-3917 Fax 277-1818
 Website: http://nas.unm.edu/ E-mail: nasinfo@unm.edu
Gregory A. Cajete (Santa Clara Pueblo), NAS Director, Associate Professor
Tiffany Lee (Dine'/Lakota), NAS Associate Director, Associate Professor
Lloyd Lee (Dine'), Associate Professor of NAS
Robin Minthorn (Kiowa), Assistant Professor
Leola Tsinnajinnie (Dine' & Filipino), Assistant Professor
Wendy Greyeyes (Dine'), Assistant Professor
Catherine Montoya (Dine'), Student Programs Specialist
Delia Halona (Dine'), Administrative Assistant
Margaret Lumpmouth (Cheyenne Arapaho), Senior Academic Advisor
 E-mail: maggie78@unm.edu (277-2631)
Description: Develops & promotes regional studies of Native Americans, their concerns & their communities. *Faculty*: Maria Williams (Tlingit), Associate Professor of Music & NAS; Tiffany Lee (Dine'/Lakota), Associate Professor of NAS; Mary K. Bowannie (Zuni/Cochiti), Lecturer & Senior Managing Editor of "Dawn of Nations Today"; *Special programs*: American Indian Student Services (AISS) (505) 277-6343, E-mail: aiss@unm.edu; Native American Intervention & Retention Project; Information & Materials Resource Collection. *Activities*: Sponsors lecture series, specialized seminars & conferences; regular course offerings. Library. *Facilities*: Institute for Native American Development; Kiva Club (A social group that focuses on Native American cultures & heritage & retention among Native American students). *Special programs*: Counseling; career planning & placement; Anizhone Week in April that features Native American speakers, films, contemporary singers, and ends with an on-campus powwow. Established 1952. *Financial aid*: Various scholarships available. *Publications*: NAS Newsline, monthly newsletter; Dawn of Nations Today (online newsletter); Pathways Off the Rez, a student handbook.

DINE' COLLEGE - CROWNPOINT CENTER
P.O. Box 57 • CROWNPOINT, NM 87313
 (505) 786-7391 Fax 786-5240; Website: www.dinecollege.edu
 Patrick Sandoval, Director; E-mail: psandoval@dinecollege.edu
Being one of four regional sites, the Crownpoint Center serves Eastern Agency through higher education as well as support services to community needs. Our main academic focus is to provide an education that will allow students to transfer to other colleges and universities throughout New Mexico & Arizona, including Ft. Lewis College in Durango, Colorado. The Crownpoint Library provides community services such as Internet access & data gathering through library collection, & workshop trainings in computer usage. With Gallup, NM (55mi), Farmington, NM (82 mi), and Albuquerque, NM (125 mi) surrounding Crownpoint. Our institution serves as the gateway to historic Chaco Canyon (40 mi). Academically, our students choose to improve their educational needs by completing their studies in Liberal Arts, Social & Behavioral Sciences, and Business Administration as well as the general education requirements within New Mexico, all focused on a long term plan to achieve a bachelor & master degree. Diné College also works with NN Workforce in creating a successful GED program for the community with testing done through the Shiprock ABE Program. See Dine College listing under Tsaile, AZ

NAVAJO TECHNICAL UNIVERSITY
P.O. Box 849 • CROWNPOINT, NM 87313
 (505) 786-4100 Fax 786-5644; Website: www.navajotech.edu
Dr. Elmer Guy (Navajo/Dine'), President (786-4112)
 E-mail: eguy@navajotech.edu
Casmir I. Agbaraji, Dean of Undergraduate Studies (786-4113)
 E-mail: cagbaraji@navajotech.edu
April Chischilly (Navajo/Dne'), Title III Director (786-4103)
 E-mail: achischilly@navajotech.edu
Deloris Becenti, Dean of Student Services (786-4104)
 E-mail: dbecenti@navajotech.edu
Dr. Lawrence Isaac, Director of ABE/GED Program (786-4206)
 E-mail: lisaac@navajotech.edu
Dr. Wesley K. Thomas, Professor & Chair of School of Dine & Law Studies
 (786-4333) E-mail: wthomas@navajotech.edu
Dr. Paul Platero (Dine'-Navajo) Professor of Linguistics & Navajo
 Language/Dept. Chair for School of Dine' Studies & Law (786-4100)
 E-mail: pplatero@navajotech.edu
Lupita Chicag (Navajo/Dine'), Dine' History & Government (786-4137)
 E-mail: lchicag@navajotech.edu
Joseph Hibbard, JD (Dine'-Navajo), Associate Professor of Law Advocate
 (786-4137) E-mail: jhibbard@navajotech.edu

Clyde Henderson, Librarian (786-4300)
E-mail: chenderson@navajotech.edu
Frank Todacheeny, Teec Nos Pos Site Coordinator
E-mail: ftodacheeny@navajotech.edu
Crownpoint Campus Faculty: Dr. Michele Kiser (Professor of Linguistics & Dine' Language); Bonnie Yazzie (Instructor of Dine' Traditional Arts Instructor); Robert Yazzie, JD, Associate Professor of Law Advocates

NEW MEXICO STATE UNIVERSITY
NATIVE AMERICAN STUDIES PROGRAM
Box 30001, MSC 3AISC • LAS CRUCES, NM 88003
(575) 646-2725 Fax 646-3725; Website: www.nmsu.edu
Rani Alexander, Department Head & Professor (646-5809)
E-mail: raalexan@nmsu.edu
Donald Pepion, Program Advisor
E-mail: dpepion@nmsu.edu
Fumi Arakawa, University Museum Director & Assistant Professor
E-mail: farakawa@nmsu.edu
Program: Undergraduate Minor in American Indian Studies. Focuses on Native American cultures & societies, deals with contemporary & historical experiences of American Indians, & examines the contributions of Indigenous peoples to life in the U.S. & other American nations. *Faculty*: E. Scott Rushforth, (Linguistics, Native American ethnography); Donald D. Pepion (Ethnohistory of the Indigenous Blackfoot peoples in Canada, U.S.); William Walker (Southwestern archaeology, ritual prehistory); Fumi Arakawa (Prehistoric American Southwest); Kelly L. Jenks (Historical Archaeology); Beth O'Leary (Southwest archaeology); *Affiliated Faculty*: Judy Berryman (cultural resource management; archaeologist); Jennifer Robles (Museum studies); Warren DeBoer (Anthropology). *Special programs*: American Indian Program (Student Services); Cultural Resources Management Division--specializing in New Mexico; summer field school in archaeology (Mogollon), Southwest studies; Indian Resource Development (see below). *Facilities*: American Indian Student Center, 3015 Andrew Wall Pl. (575) 646-4207 Fax 646-5291; University Museum; laboratories for research.

NEW MEXICO STATE UNIVERSITY
INDIAN RESOURCE DEVELOPMENT PROGRAM
Box 30001, MSC 3IRD • LAS CRUCES, NM 88003
(575) 646-1347 Fax 646-7740
Jeanelle Chavez, Program Specialist (646-6155)
E-mail: chavezj@nmsu.edu
Purpose: To encourage American Indian students to attend the university of their choice and major in natural resource related fields. *Publications*: Indian Country Student News; Sources of Financial Aid Available to American Indian Students (booklet). Established 1977.

NEW MEXICO HIGHLANDS UNIVERSITY
AMERICAN INDIAN STUDIES PROGRAM
College of Arts & Sciences-Department of Social & Behavioral Sciences
Shields Science Bldg., Rm. 341 • LAS VEGAS, NM 87701
(505) 454-3196 Fax 454-3331; Website: www.nmhu.edu
Tom Ward, Department Chair; E-mail: tsward@nmhu.edu
Description: Provides an opportunity for Indians & non-Indians to study Indian cultures and their significant contributions to contemporary U.S. culture. It is a component of the Behavioral Sciences Department with concentration of study in sociology/anthropology; provided in combination with courses containing Indian content offered in other University departments. *Faculty*: Mario Gonzales (Anthropology), Orit Tamir (History). *Resources*: Native American Club; American Indians in Science & Engineering (AISES). Scholarships available - write to Financial Aid Services.

INSTITUTE OF AMERICAN INDIAN ARTS
83 Avan Nu Po Rd. • SANTA FE, NM 87503
(505) 424-2302 Fax 424-0050; Website: www.iaia.edu
Robert Martin (Cherokee), President; E-mail: rmartin@iaia.edu
Charlene Teters, Academic Dean (424-2354)
Bill Sayre, Director of Institutional Research (424-2364)
Valerie Nye, Library Director; E-mail: vnye@iaia.edu
Stephen Wall (Ojibwe), Indigenous Liberal Studies Department Chair
For the Indigenous Liberal Studies Program
Patsy Phillips, Director of IAIA Museum (428-5901)
Lawrence Mirabal, Chief Information Officer (424-2316)
Daniel Banks, Performing Arts Dept. Chairperson (424-5952)
Felipe Colon, Museum Studies Department Chairperson (424-2372)
Jeff Kahm, Studio Arts Department Chairperson (424-2369)
James Lujan, Cinematic Arts Department Chairperson (424-5716)
Evelina Lucero, Creative Writing Department Chairperson (424-5708)
Craig Tompkins, Cine & Studio Arts Department Chairperson (424-5717)
Porter Swentzell, Professor of Indigenous Liberal Studies (424-5795)
Leveo V. Sanchez Board of Trustee Chairperson (984-9803)
Sandra M. Turner, Vice Chairperson (575) 218-4885

Frank Marchi, Secretary/Treasurer (269-1404)
LouElla Marr-Montoya, Member-at-Large (425-7108)
Description: A federally chartered private institution. The only accredited fine arts college devoted solely to the study of American Indian & Alaska Native art. Offers learning opportunities in the arts & crafts to Native American youth (Indian, Eskimo & Aleut.) The College of Contemporary Native Arts. Emphasis is placed upon Indian traditions as the basis for creative expression in the fine arts. *Facilities*: Museum of Contemporary Native Arts; Center for Lifelong Education (CLE). *Activities*: Maintains the Center for Arts & Cultural Studies. Sponsors Indian arts-oriented Junior College offering Associate of Fine Arts degrees in various fields as well as seminars, & exhibition program, & traveling exhibits; maintains extensive library, museum, & biographical archives. *Publications*: Coyote on the Turtle's Back, annual; Faculty & Student Handbooks & School Catalog, annual; Spawning the Medicine River, annual. Library. Established 1962.

SCHOOL FOR ADVANCED RESEARCH (SAR)
INDIAN ARTS RESEARCH CENTER (IARC)
P.O. Box 2188 • SANTA FE, NM 87504
(505) 954-7205 Fax 954-7207
Website: www.sarweb.org; E-mail: iarc@sarsf.org
Michael F. Brown, President & CEO, SAR
E-mail: mfbrown@sarsf.org
Brian D. Vallo, (Pueblo Acoma), IARC Director (954-7271)
E-mail: vallo@sarsf.org
Lisa Hsu Berrera, IARC & Collections Manager
E-mail: barrera@sarsf.org
Jennifer Day, Registrar; Elysia Poon, Program Coordinator
Maria Spray, Scholar Programs Coordinator
E-mail: spray@sarsf.org
Flannery Davis, Communications Coordinator (954-7264)
E-mail: davis@sarsf.org
Laura Holt, Librarian (954-7234); E-mail: lholt@sarsf.org
Goal: To bridge the divide between creativity & scholarship by supporting initiatives & projects in Native studies, art history, and creative expression that illuminate the intersections of the social sciences, humanities, and arts. *Special resources*: Collection of 12,000+ objects of Southwestern American Indian art and anthropology; archaeology laboratory. *Native American Artist Fellowships*: The Eric & Barbara Dobkin, Ronald & Susan Dubin, and Rollin & Mary Ella King fellowships; lectures and exhibitions; annual Native American Internship. *Fellowships*: Katrin H. Lamon Resident Scholar & Artist Fellowships for Native Americans. Resources: Online Exhibitions; Lectures & Recordings; Classroom Resources. *Publications*: Books pertaining to the Southwest & Native American arts and culture. Catherine McElvain Library.

*DINE' COLLEGE – SHIPROCK BRANCH
P.O. Box 580 • SHIPROCK, NM 87420
(877) 988-3463; (928) 368-3522 Fax 368-3519
Website: www.dinecollege.edu/locatios/shiprock.phb
Priscilla Weaver, Director; E-mail: pweaver@dinecollege.edu
North Campus (Educational & Research Programs;
Navajo Nation Archaeological Department)
South Campus (Student Success Center;
Senator John Pinto Library, Samanthi Hewakapuge, Branch Librarian
E-mail: shewakapuge@dinecollege.edu.

NEW YORK

STATE UNIVERSITY OF NEW YORK, BUFFALO
DEPARTMENT OF TRANSNATIONAL STUDIES
Native American Studies Program
732 Clemens Hall • BUFFALO, NY 14260
(716) 645-2082 Fax 645-5976
Website: www.americanstudies.buffalo.edu
Donald A. Grinde, Jr. (Iroquois), Professor & Director of Graduate Studies
E-mail: dgrinde@buffalo.edu
Deborah Pierce-Tate, Assistant to the Chair
E-mail: dpierce@buffalo.edu
Theresa McCarthy (Onondaga-Six Nations), Associate Professor
Alyssa Mt. Pleasant (Haudenosaunee-Iroquois) Assistant Professor
Munroe Eagles, Professor & Director of Canadian Studies
Degrees: BA, MA & PhD in American Studies with a focus in Indigenous/Native American Studies; Graduate Certificate in Canadian Studies. *Programs*: Linguistics; American Studies. Examines the histories, cultures, and contemporary issues affecting the indigenous peoples of the Americas. *Fields of interest*: Native American Studies, Haudenosaunee/Iroquois history, Native American thought, U.S. Indian Policy since 1871, Environmental Studies & Native Americans, American Indian activism in the U.S. Native American Studies, esp. Haudenosaunee traditionalism & languages in contemporary contexts, Haudenosaunee citizenship/clans, Haudenosaunee

women, Historiography of anthropological research on the Iroquois, Iroquois factionalism, linguistic research methodologies, community-based/applied research initiatives; specialization in Haudenosaunee (or Iroquois) history during the 18th & 19th centuries. *Faculty*: Oren Lyons, Professor Emeritus. *Resources*: Haudensaunee-Native American Studies Research Workshop. *Special program*: Contemporary North American Indians & Eskimos; Northeast U.S. prehistory. Library.

ST. LAWRENCE UNIVESITY - NATIVE AMERICAN STUDIES PROGRAM
112 Piskor Hall, 23 Romoda Dr. • CANTON, NY 13617
(315) 229-5221 Fax 229-5803
Website: www.stlawu.edu/academics/programs/native-american-studies
Melissane Schrems, Program Coordinator & Professor of History
  E-mail: mschrems@stlawu.edu; (229-5221)
Martha Idalia Chew Sanchez, Associate Professor of Global Studies
  E-mail: mchew@stlawu.edu; (229-5659)
Randy Hill, Associate Professor of Performance & Communications Arts
  E-mail: rhill@stlawu.edu; (229-5178)
Carrie Johns, Professor & Chair of Environmental Studies
  E-mail: cjohns@stlawu.edu; (229-5840
Program: BA Minor in Native American Studies. *Faculty*: Celia Nyamweru, Aswini Pai, Brenda Papineau (Director of Community-Based Learning).

STATE UNIVERSITY OF NEW YORK, CORTLAND
NATIVE AMERICAN STUDIES PROGRAM
School of Arts & Sciences – Sociology-Anthropology Department
Old Main, Rm. 122, P.O. Box 2000 • CORTLAND, NY 13045
(607) 753-5784 Fax 753-5973
Ellis McDowell-Loudan & Dawn Van Hall, Co-coordinators
  E-mail: ellie.mcdowell-loudan@cortland.edu
Program: Native American Studies Minor. SUNY Cortland's Native American studies minor is interdisciplinary. It is designed to complement numerous academic majors. Students choosing the minor will study the history & culture of Native Americans from the perspective of several disciplines. *Faculty Interest*: Haudenosaunee (Iroquois), New York State Native American History, Eastern USA Native American & Canadian First Nations Archaeology, Ethnology, Ethnohistory; Maya Language & Ethnology. *Resources*: Multicultural publications & audio-visual collection; Native American Film Festival; Guest speakers - Native American musicians, artists, craftspeople, and storytellers.

STATE UNIVERSITY OF NEW YORK, FREDONIA
AMERICAN INDIAN STUDIES PROGRAM
Department of Interdisciplinary Studies
E304 Thompson Hall • FREDONIA, NY 14063
(716) 673-3274 Fax 673-3173
Website:
www.fredonia.edu/department/interdisciplinary/American_indian_studies.asp
  E-mail: americanindian.studies@fredonia.edu
Jennifer Hildebrand, Coordinator
  E-mail: Jennifer.hildebrand@fredonia.edu
Program: American Indian Studies Minor. Provides an interdisciplinary study of the anthropological, historical, cultural, educational & political developments that have formed present-day Native America. The program is designed for students with the desire to better understand American Indian and Alaskan Native cultures by studying pre-contact history via oral tradition, post-European contact via biography, and present day "Indian Country" through federal policies, films, and literature. American Indian ethnic identities and stereotypes, as formed by these media, will be studied to promote new ways of thinking about race and culture. The multi-disciplinary nature of the minor allows for participation from students of all backgrounds in developing a new view of American Indian cultures while helping to dispel the Pan-Indian stereotype endemic in the American education system.

COLGATE UNIVERSITY - NATIVE AMERICAN STUDIES DEPARTMENT
115 Alumni Hall • HAMILTON, NY 13346
(315) 228-7806 Fax 228-7121; Website: www.colgate.edu/nast
Carol Ann Lorenz, Director & Associate Professor of Native American
  Studies (228-7184) E-mail: clorenz@colgate.edu
Description: Interdisciplinary topical concentration in Amerindian Studies, embracing the fields of Native American religion, astronomy, art, and archaeology. *Faculty*: Anthony F. Aveni, Jordan Kerber, Edie MacPherson, Jenna Reinbold, Christopher Vecsey, Heather Roller, Sarah Wider. *Special programs*: Native American Study Program in Santa Fe, NM (NAST); Summer Research Fellowships; College Bound program for American Indian youths; The Iroquois Study Group; Summer Archaeology Program; Native American Arts & Culture Festival (annual, October). *Resources*: Native American Student Association (NASA); ALANA Cultural Center; Longyear Museum of Anthropology -- features large collections of local Oneida Iroquois & Mesoamerican archaeological materials.

CORNELL UNIVERSITY - AMERICAN INDIAN & INDIGENOUS STUDIES PROGRAM (AIP)
450 Caldwell Hall • ITHACA, NY 14853
(607) 255-6587 Fax 255-6246
Website: www.aip.cornell.edu; E-mail: aipoffice@cornell.edu
Jolene Rickard (Tuscarora), Associate Professor & Director (255-1755)
  E-mail: jkr33@cornell.edu
Ann Bianchi, Administrative Manager
  E-mail: amb5@cornell.edu
Kathy Halbig (Onondaga), Student Services Associate
  E-mail: klh37@cornell.edu
Ansley Jemison (Seneca), Akw:kon Residence Hall Director
  E-mail: amj78@cornell.edu
Natani Notah (Navajo-Done'), Communications Assistant
  E-mail: ngn7@cornell.edu
Description: The American Indian Program is a multidisciplinary, academic program which serves students with diverse interests & goals; student support providing academic, financial & personal counseling; & community outreach which connects University resources with problems & concerns of Native communities. *Faculty*: Eric Cheyfitz (Native American literature & Federal Indian law); Laura Donaldson (Cherokee) (American Indian literature & culture); Charles C. Geisler, Emeritus (Environmental); Frederic W. Gleach (History); Angela Gonzales (Hopi) (Sociology); Denise N. Green (First Nations); John S. Henderson (Archaeology); Kurt Jordan (Archaeology of Iroquois); Karim-Aly Kassam (Alaska, Canada, Arctic); Jane Mt. Pleasant (Tuscarora) (Horticulture); Sarah Murray (Language); Paul Nadasdy (Canada's Yukon Territory); Jon Parmenter (Iroquois); Troy Richardson (Saponi/Tuscarora) (Education). *Interests*: Fiction writing, pleasure flying, hunting & camping. *Published works*: In progress: "Seaworthy Injun."

STATE UNIVERSITY OF NEW YORK, OSWEGO
NATIVE AMERICAN STUDIES PROGRAM
Anthropology Department, 307A Mahar Hall • OSWEGO, NY 13126
(315) 341-3290; Website: www.oswego.edu
Kevin White, Department Chair & Program Director
  E-mail: kevin.white@oswego.edu
Program: BA Minor, Native American Studies. *Faculty*: Douglas J. Pippin, Stephen Saraydar, Kevin White

STATE UNIVERSITY OF NEW YORK, POTSDAM
NATIVE AMERICAN STUDIES PROGRAM
Department of Anthropology, 246 MacVicar Hall • POTSDAM, NY 13676
(315) 267-2047 Fax 267-3176
Website: www.potsdam.edu/academics/interdisciplinary/nativeamerican/
Susan Stebbins, Program Director; E-mail: stebbisa@potsdam.edu
Program: BA Minor in Native American Studies. A U.S. and global studies program that uses an interdisciplinary approach to learning about indigenous peoples of the Americas. *Special program*: Mohawk language. *Faculty*: Susan Stebbins. Financial aid available. *Resources*: The Center for Diversity.

SYRACUSE UNIVERSITY - NATIVE AMERICAN STUDIES PROGRAM
College of Arts & Sciences, 441 Hall of Languages • SYRACUSE, NY 13244
(315) 443-1414 Fax 443-8093; E-mail: srassocdeancas@syr.edu
Website:
http://asacademics.syr.edu/NativeAmerican/requirements_NativeAmer.html
Scott Manning Stevens (Mohawk), Associate Professor & Director of
  Native American Studies & Associate Professor of English (443-8785)
  E-mail: scsteven@syr.edu
Robin Kimmerer (Citizen Band Potawatomi), Director- Center for Native
  Peoples; E-mail: rkimmer@esf.edu; (470-6785)
Program: B.A. minor in Native American Studies. *Faculty*: Percy Abrams; Douglas Armstrong (Anthropology); Philip Arnold (Languages); Christopher DeCourse (Anthropology); Sara French (Art & Music); Carrie Garrow (Law); Robin Kimmerer (Director, Center for Native Peoples); Gregg Lambert (Humanities); Richard Loder (Sociology); Jack Manno (Environmental Studies); Maureen Schwartz (Anthropology); Sascha Scott (Art & Music).

SYRACUSE UNIVERSITY
CENTER FOR NATIVE PEOPLES & THE ENVIRONMENT
College of Environmental Science & Forestry (SUNY-ESF)
354 Ilick Hall, 1 Forestry Dr. • SYRACUSE, NY 13210
(315) 470-6644 Fax 470-6651; Website: www.esf.edu/nativepeoples/
Dr. Robin Kimmerer (Citizen Band Potawatomi), Director
  E-mail: rkimmer@esf.edu
Neil Patterson, Jr. (Tuscarora), Assistant Director (470-6870)
  E-mail: nvpatter@esf.edu
Description: Focus is on developing connections between traditional ecological knowledge (TEK) and western scientific approaches. *Goal*: To create programs which draw on the wisdom of both indigenous & scientific knowledge to address environmental protection & restoration. Includes efforts in education, research & public outreach. *Faculty*: Robin Kimmerer, Colin

Beier, Stewart Diemont, James Gibbs, Jack Manno, Sharon Moran. *Advisory Board*: Henry Lickers (Mohawk); David Arquette (Haudenosaunee); Jeanne Shenandoah (Onondaga); Wendy Gonyea (Onondaga); Richard Hill (Haudenosaunee); Irving Powless (Onondaga). *Resources*: Annual Native Earth Environment Youth Camp (in Ugust).

NORTH CAROLINA

UNIVERSITY OF NORTH CAROLINA, CHAPEL HILL
AMERICAN INDIAN CENTER (AIC)
113A Abernathy Hall, CB 3457 • CHAPEL HILL, NC 27599
(919) 962-4189 Fax 962-4024; E-mail: aic@unc.edu
Website: http://americanindiancenter.unc.edu/about/staff/
Amy Loclear Hertel, (Lumbee), AIC Director
  E-mail: amy_hertel@unc.edu
Christina S. Theodorou, NC Native Asset Coalition Project Manager
  (962-5528) E-mail: ctheo@email.unc.edu
The AIC is a university-wide public service Center designed to advance the University's mission of research, education, and service with three primary goals. *Leadership in American Indian Scholarship & Research*. By creating an environment in which quality research and scholarship related to American Indians is strengthened and nurtured, the University can become the premier university in the east for American Indian research and knowledge dissemination. *Engagement with & Service to Native Populations*. By serving as the University's front door to American Indian communities, The AIC will enable Carolina, as the University of the People, to truly serve the First People of North Carolina as well as the First people of the south and the east. *Enrichment of Campus Diversity and Dialogue*. By facilitating the inclusion of the American Indian peoples, with their unique and rich cultures, traditions, beliefs, & histories, the learning environment of the entire Carolina community will be enriched.

UNIVERSITY OF NORTH CAROLINA, CHAPEL HILL
AMERICAN INDIAN & INDIGENOUS STUDIES (AIIS) PROGRAM
Department of American Studies
308 Greenlaw Hall, CB 3520 • CHAPEL HILL, NC 27599
(919) 962-5481 Fax 962-3520; E-mail: aic@unc.edu
Website: www.americanindianstudies.unc.edu
Daniel M. Cobb, Program Coordinator & Professor of History
  E-mail: dcobb@unc.edu
Goals: Leadership in American Indian scholarship & research; engagement with and service to North Carolina's first people; enrichment of campus diversity & dialogue. *Programs*: Major in American Indian Studies; American Indian Leadership Seminar; Tribal Leadership Workshop Series; Community Outreach; Elder In Residence Program; monthly Carolina Seminar on American Indian Studies; Michael D. Green Lecture in American Indian Studies. *Faculty*: Daniel M. Cobb (American Indian Studies); Jean Dennison (Osage) (Anthropology); Kathleen Duval (History); Amy Locklear Hertel (Lumbee); Valerie Lambert (Choctaw) (Anthropology); Malinda Maynor Lowery (History); C. Margaret Scarry (Anthropology); Vin Steponaitis (Anthropology); Christopher Teuton (American Studies); Jenny Tone-Pah-Hote (Kiowa) (American Indian Studies); Theda Perdue (Emerita - History & American Studies). *Resources*: American Indian Center. *Activities*: Annual Carolina Indian Circle Powwow in March.

WESTERN CAROLINA UNIVERSITY - CHEROKEE CENTER
1594 Acquoni Rd. • CHEROKEE, NC 28719
(828) 497-7920; Facebook Page: https://www.facebook.com/wcucherokee
Sky Sampson, Center Director; E-mail: ssampson@email.wcu.edu
Elias Huskey, Administrative Support Associate
  E-mail: ehuskey@email.wcu.edu
Purpose: To serve tribal & non-tribal residents of Cherokee, NC (Qualla Boundary) the surrounding communities; to provide information on educational opportunities, degree requirements, & transfer procedures as well as guidance in setting future career goals for tribal & non-tribal residents of Cherokee, NC and the surrounding communities. Established 1980.

WESTERN CAROLINA UNIVERSITY - CHEROKEE STUDIES PROGRAM
College of Arts & Sciences, 101 McKee Bldg. • CULLOWHEE, NC 28723
(828) 227-7268 Fax 227-7061; Website:
Jane M. Eastman (Eastern Cherokee), Program Director (227-3841)
  E-mail: jeastman@wcu.edu
Hartwll Francis (Eastern Cherokee), Cherokee Language Program Director
  (227-2303) E-mail: hfrancis@email.wcu.edu
Thomas Belt (Eastern Cherokee), Cherokee Language Coordinator
  (227-2721) E-mail: tbelt@email.wcu.edu
Lisa J. Lefler (Eastern Cherokee), Cherokee Health Program Director
  (227-2164) E-mail: llefler@email.wcu.edu

Special program: Interdisciplinary Minor in Cherokee Studies; Cherokee Studies Graduate Certificate; MA in American History, Cherokee Studies Track. Goals include expanding course offerings, especially in the Cherokee language, developing an exchange program involving faculty & students, increasing the enrollment of Cherokee and other Native American students at Western, increasing the number of Cherokee Studies students, involving members of the Eastern Band of Cherokee Indians in every class within the Cherokee Studies program as instructors, co-instructors, or presenters, increasing awareness of the cultural landscape of our campus, increasing awareness of Cherokee history and culture within the university community, & promoting long-term partnerships with the Eastern Band to foster community development & revitalization. *Faculty*: Roseanne S. Belt (Cherokee), Jim Veteto, Brett Riggs (Sequoyah Distinguished Professor), David Cozzo, Jane Eastman; Philip Coyle. *Resources*: Archaeology Laboratory, Human Relations Area Files & collection of documents related to Cherokees available in library.

UNIVERSITY OF NORTH CAROLINA AT PEMBROKE
DEPARTMENT OF AMERICAN INDIAN STUDIES (AIS)
SOUTHEAST AMERICAN INDIAN STUDIES PROGRAM (SAIS)
MUSEUMM OF THE SOUTHEAST AMERICAN INDIAN
Old Main Rm. 204, P.O. Box 1510 • PEMBROKE, NC 28372
(910) 521-6266 Fax 522-5795; Website: www.uncp.edu/ais/
Website: www.uncp.edu/nativemuseum/
E-mail: ais@uncp.edu; sais@uncp.edu; nativemuseum@uncp.edu
Mary Ann Jacobs (Lumbee), AIS Chairperson & Associate Professor
  (775-4262) E-mail: mary.jacobs@uncp.edu
Alesia J. Cummings (Lumbee), Administrative Support Associate & Web Information Coordinator; E-mail: alesia.cummings@uncp.edu
Alfred Bryant, Jr. (Lumbee), SAIS Founding Director (775-4009)
  E-mail: alfred.bryant@uncp.edu
Lawrence T. Locklear (Lumbee), SAIS Program Coordinator (775-4579)
  E-mail: Lawrence.locklear@uncp.edu
Myia Reyes (Lumbee), SAIS Community Engagement Specialist
  (775-4663) E-mail: myia.reyes@uncp.edu
Nancy Strickland Fields, Museum Director/Curator
Mission: To educate the public about the prehistory, history, culture, art & contemporary issues of American Indians, with special emphasis on the Robeson County Native American community; to conduct scholarly research. *Program*: Offers a BA, a minor, and an academic concentration in Southeast American Indian Studies. *Resources*: NARC offers a collection of authentic American Indian artifacts, handicrafts, art, books, cassettes, record albums, & filmstrips about Native Americans, with emphasis on the Lumbee Indians of Robeson County. *Faculty*: Mary Ann Jacobs, Alesia J. Cummings (Lumbee), Jane Haladay; Jesse Peters (English & Theatre); Michael Spivey (Sociology & Criminal Justice); Jay Hansford C. Vest (Monacan); Linda E. Oxendine (Lumbee - Professor Emeritus). *Adjunct Instructors*: Danielle Hiraldo (Lumbee), Assistant Professor; Maria Warren, Esq., Lecturer. *Resources*: Museum of the Southeast American Indian (formerly, The Native American Resource Center); Native American Speakers Series; Southeast Indian Studies Conference.

UNIVERSITY OF NORTH CAROLINA-WILMINGTON
NATIVE AMERICAN STUDIES PROGRAM
College of Arts & Science - Department of English
601 S. College Rd. • WILMINGTON, NC 28403
(910) 962-3539; Website: www.uncw.edu/nas
Lee Schweninger, Coordinator; E-mail: schweningerl@uncw.edu
Program: Interdisciplinary Minor in Native American Studies (NAS). Focuses on the history, cultures, religions, arts, and literatures of American Indians of North & South America. Departments: English, History, Anthropology, & Philosophy & Religion. *Faculty*: Walter H. Conser (Philosophy & Religion); David L. LaVere (History); Patricia Lerch (Anthropology); Lee Schweninger (American Indian Literature).

NORTH DAKOTA

*TURTLE MOUNTAIN COMMUNITY COLLEGE
10145 BIA Rd 7, P.O. Box 340 • BELCOURT, ND 58316
(701) 477-7862 Fax 477-7892; Website: www.tm.edu
James Davis (Ojibwe), President (477-7865)
  E-mail: jdavis@tm.edu
Kellie Hall (Ojibwe), Vice President (477-7822)
  E-mail: kmhall@tm.edu
Terri Martin Pariisien, Academic Dean (477-7986)
  E-mail: tmartinparisien@tm.edu
Judy Belgarde (Ojibwe), Executive Assistant (477-7978)
  E-mail: jbelgarde@tm.edu
Dave Ripley (Ojibwe), Title III Director (477-7915)
  E-mail: dripley@tm.edu

Mark Hamley (Ojibwe), Anishinabe Director; (477-7834)
E-mail: mhamley@tm.edu
JT Shining Oneside, Native American Culture Coordinator
E-mail: jshiningoneside@tm.edu
Cathie Gladue (Ojibwe), Student Teaching Supervisor (477-7981)
E-mail: cgladue@tm.edu
Cecilia Myerion, Native American Language Institute (477-7837)
E-mail: cmyerion@tm.edu
Laisee Allery (Ojibwe), Library Director (477-7812)
E-mail: lallery@tm.edu
Board of Directors: Duane Poitra (Ojibwe), Board President
Carla Peltier, Board Vice Chairperson; Lana Decoteau, Joanne Decoteau,
Cynthis Allery, Members
Description: Functions as an autonomous Indian controlled college on the Turtle Mountain Band of Chippewa Indian Reservation focusing on general studies & vocational education programs. Seeks to establish an administration, faculty & student body involved in community affairs. *Special programs*: Legal Studies Department is an Indian Law Education Program developed to strengthen legal justice curricula at the tribal college level as well as increase the numbers of tribal members knowledgeable about Indian law; Vocational Education (Sheila Trottier, CTE Director); Indian Entrepreneurship Program. Financial aid available. *Resources*: Association of Native Americans Project (designed for Native Language Revitalization & Preservation); Anishinabe Learning, Cultural & Wellness Center; Project CHOICE (Choosing Health Opportunities for Indian career Enhancement). *Publications*: The Mitchif Dictionary (local Native language); Chippewa/Cree Language; The Cree Dictionary; Course Catalog & Bulletin. Library. Established 1972.

*UNITED TRIBES TECHNICAL COLLEGE (UTTC)
3315 University Dr. • BISMARCK, ND 58504
(701) 255-3285 Fax 530-0605; Website: www.uttc.edu
Leander Russ McDonald (Dakota/Arikara), President
Lisa Azure, Vice President of Academic Affairs
E-mail: lazure@uttc.edu
Dennis J. Neumann, Public Information Officer; E-mail: opi@uttc.edu
Charlene Weis, Librarian; E-mail: cweis@uttc.edu
Board of Directors:
Mark Fox (Three Affiliated Tribes), Chairperson
Dave Flute (Sisseton-Wahpeton Oyate), Chairperson
Dave Archambault II (Standing Rock Sioux), Chairperson
Myra Pearson (Spirit Lake), Chairperson
Richard McCloud (Turtle Mountain Chippewa), Chairperson
UTTC is committed to the needs of the American Indians in the cultural preservation of their heritage. The Four Winds Cultural Center works to cultivate, preserve, and transmit traditional skills and knowledge by teaching American Indian arts & crafts, music, dance, and history of Indian people. *Special programs*: Certificate Programs, & Associate of Applied Science Degrees. *Annual events*: Native American Lifesavers Conference "Implementing Effective Interventions for Injury Prevention in Indian Country," held in mid-July; The United Tribes Annual International Powwow held the first Thursday through Sunday after Labor Day; The United Tribes Indian Art Expo & Market is held in May. *Resources*: Library. *Publications*: United Tribes News; Arrow Graphics Printing Dept. publishes the 'Indian Recipe Book,' $5.00; 'Powwow Questions & Answers,' $3; the American Indian Curriculum Development Program offers a series of curriculum manuals set up for students that incorporate Native American folklore, customs, and themes, available K-12 and adult skills.

NORTH DAKOTA STATE UNIVERSITY
NATIVE AMERICAN PROFESSIONAL PROGRAMS (NAPP)
College of Pharmacy, Nursing, and Allied Sciences
NDSU Dept. 2650, P.O. Box 6050
Sundry Hall, Rm. 123 • FARGO, ND 58108
(701) 231-7601 Fax 231-7606; Website: www.ndsu.edu
Charles Peterson, Dean & Professor
Donald Warne, Chair & Professor of Public Health
Dr. Daniel Friesner, Associate Dean for Student Affairs
E-mail: daniel.friesner@ndsu.edu
Dana Davis, Director of Outreach & Community Engagement
E-mail: dana.davis@ndsu.edu
Purpose: To address the shortage of Native American pharmacists in the U.S.; to recruit & facilitate the entry of Native American students into the College of Pharmacy, Nursing & Allied Sciences and to provide them with the necessary counseling & retention services. *Degree*: Doctor of Pharmacy.

*CANKDESKA CIKANA COMMUNITY COLLEGE
214 1st Ave., P.O. Box 269 • FORT TOTTEN, ND 58335
(701) 766-4415/4055 Fax 766-4077
Website: www.littlehoop.edu; E-mail: info@littlehoop.edu
Cynthia Lindquist (Sisseton-Wahpeton Sioux(, President
E-mail: president@littlehoop.edu

Teresa Harding, Academic Dean
E-mail: teresa.harding@littlehoop.edu
Lane Azure (Turtle Mountain Ojibwe), VP Academic Affairs
Stuart Young, Dean of Administration
E-mail: stuart.young@littlehoop.edu
Vern Lambert, Instructior – Dakota Studies
E-mail: vern.lambert@littlehoop.edu
Lorraine Greybear, Language Instructor
E-mail: Lorraine.greybear@littlehoop.edu
Dixie Omen, Director of Student Success
E-mail: dixie.omen@littlehoop.edu
Roxanne Wells, Head Start Director
E-mail: roxanne.wells@littlehoop.edu
Melvine Reierson, Library Director (766-1353)
E-mail: melvine.reierson@littlehoop.edu
Board of Regents: Paul Yankton, Jr., Chair; Alberta Redfox (Woodlake), Vice Chair; Jeanette Herald (St. Michael), Member; Iris Cavanaugh (Crownhill), Member; Wicahpi Tawacinhehomni (Fort Totten), Member. Head Start Program.

*SITTING BULL COLLEGE
1341 92nd St. • FORT YATES, ND 58538
(701) 854-8014 Fax 854-3403; E-mail: info@sittingbull.edu
Dr. Laurel Vermillion (Hunkpapa-Lakota), President
E-mail: laurel.vermillion@sittingbull.edu
Dr. Koreen Ressler, Vice President of Academics (854-8001)
E-mail: koreen.ressler@sittingbull.edu
Mark Holman, Librarian (854-8024)
E-mail: mark.holman@sittingbull.edu
Jonathan Anderson, TBIC Director (854-8122 Fax 854-3489)
E-mail: jonathan.anderson@sittingbull.edu
Offers A.A., A.A.S. & A.S. (two year degrees). McLaughlin (SD) Campus (605) 823-4318; Mobridge (SD) Campus (605) 845-5762. *Faculty*: Suzanne Albers, English Instructor, Special Services Program): Michael Moore (Native American Instructor); Christopher Fried, Division of Education Director. *Special programs*: B.A. degree through Minot State University; Irrigation Farm Management Program; scholarships. *Resources*: Lakota/Dakota Language & Culture Resources; Tribal Business Information Center (TBIC); American Indian Business Leaders (AIBL); Community Radio & Sitting Bull Radio Podcasts; American Indian Higher Education Consortium; Federal Depository Library Program; *Publication*: Quarterly newsletter.

UNIVERSITY OF NORTH DAKOTA
AMERICAN INDIAN STUDENTS SERVICES
315 Princeton St., Stop 8274 • GRAND FORKS, ND 58202
(701) 777-4291 Fax 777-3292
Website: www.und.edu/dept/aiss
Dr. Linda Neuerburg, Director (777-2578)
E-mail: linda.neuerburg@email.und.edu
Keith Malaterre, Courtney Souvannasacd, Program Coordinators
Resources: Indian Studies Assn (ISA); Indians Into Engineering; Indians Into Medicine (INMED); Native American Law Student Assn (NALSA); Native Americans Into Criminal Justice Assn (NACJA); American Indian Business Leaders (AIBL); Native Media Center; National Resource Center on Native American Aging; American Indian Students Services; Recruitment/ Retention of American Indians Into Nursing (RAIN); American Indian Science & Engineering Society (AISES); Art Collections; Indian Studies Assn (student & alumni organization), Holly Annis, President.

UNIVERSITY OF NORTH DAKOTA
DEPARTMENT OF AMERICAN INDIAN STUDIES
College of Arts & Sciences, O'Kelly Hall 202,
221 Centennial Dr., Stop 7103 • GRAND FORKS, ND 58202
(701) 777-4650 Fax 777-4145
Website: www.arts-sciences.und.edu/american-indian-studies
Brad Rundquist, Professor & Interim Department Chair
E-mail: Bradley.rundquist@und.edu
Paula Cox, Administrative Secretary; E-mail: paula.cox@und.edu
Birgit Hans, Distinguished Professor of English (777-4649)
Email: birgit.hans@und.edu
Jaynie Parrish, Lecturer; E-mail: jaynie.parrish@und.edu
Alan Shackelford, Assistant Professor of History (777-6388)
E-mail: alan.shackelford@und.edu
Program: A Major & Minor in American Indian Studies leading to a B.A. degree in American Indian Studies. Native Americans Into Law Program. *Faculty*: Birgit Hans (American Indian Literature); Alan Shackelford (History); Joseph Morsette, JD (Instructor/Director of Native American Into Law program); Gregory Gagnon (Lake Superior Chippewa) (Emeritus, History); Kimberly Cowden (Communications). *Resources*: ND Art Collections; Native Media Center; Indian Studies Assn. Established 1977.

UNIVERSITY OF NORTH DAKOTA
INDIANS INTO MEDICINE (INMED) PROGRAM
School of Medicine & Health Science, 501 N. Columbia Rd., Rm. 2101
Stop 9037 • GRAND FORKS, ND 58202
(701) 777-3037 Fax 777-3277
Website http://www.med.und.edu/indians-into-medicine/
Eugene DeLorme, JD, INMED Director (777-3039)
 E-mail: eugene.delorme@med.und.edu
Kathleen Fredericks, College Coordinator/Advisor (777-3464)
 E-mail: kathleen.fredericks@med.und.edu
Ardith Marsette, Summer Institute Program Coordinator/Student Services
 (777-3279) E-mail: ardith.marsette@med.und.edu
Mission: Offers assistance to American Indian students who aspire to be health professionals to meet the needs of our tribal communities and who are preparing to study or are currently studying to become physicians, nurses & other health professionals. *Summer Programs*: Pathway Program; Summer Institute Program; MCAT Prep Program. *Publication*: Serpent, Staff & Drum, a quarterly newsletter.

UNIVERSITY OF NORTH DAKOTA
INPSYDE PROGRAMS SUMMER INSTITUTE
Psychology Department, Corwin-Larimore Hall
319 Harvard St., P.O. Box 8380 • GRAND FORKS, ND 58202
(701) 777-3451 Fax 777-3454; Website:
https://arts-sciences.und.edu/psychology/inpsyde/summerinstitute.cfm
E-mail: und.inpsyde@und.edu
Justin Douglas McDonald (Oglala Lakota), Director
 E-mail: Justin.mcdonald@email.und.edu
Royleen J. Ross (Pueblo of Laguna), GSA/Administrator
Harmony Bercier (Turtle Mountain Chippewa), GSA/Recruiter
Pam Bethke, Administrative Support
Recruiters: Kaylee Trottier (Turtle Mountain Chippewa), Angie Gillis (Three Affiliated Tribes), Guy Keener (Cheyenne River Sioux). The INPSYDE Program Summer Institute is a two-week enrichment program for Native American Junior & Senior High School Students, who are interested in pursuing a degree in psychology related disciplines. The Summer Institute is designed to help students develop strong academic foundations in psychology & science that are vital to success in college behavioral science & psychology courses. Interested applicants must complete the INPSYDE Program application & be accepted to participate. Applications must include two letters of recommendation, letter of interest, career statement, and letter of tribal affiliation and degree of Indian heritage.

UNIVERSITY OF NORTH DAKOTA
QUENTIN N. BURDICK INDIANS INTO NURSING (RAIN) PROGRAM
College of Nursing, Nursing Bldg. Rm. 314
430 Oxford St., Stop 9025 • GRAND FORKS, ND 58202
(701) 777-3224 Fax 777-4558
Website: https://www.nursing.und.edu/rain/; E-mail: rain@email.und.edu
Deb Wilson (Mandan/Hidatsa), Program Director (777-4519)
 E-mail: deb.wilson@und.edu
Barb Anderson, Program Coordinator (777-4323)
 E-mail: barb.anderson@email.und.edu
RAIN Program: The Recruitment/Retention of American Indians Into Nursing (RAIN) Project is a support program for American Indians pursuing their bachelors or master's degrees in nursing at the University of North Dakota. *Financial aid*: Scholarships are based on availability of funds. *Publication*: RAIN Notes, newsletter.

UNIVERSITY OF NORTH DAKOTA - SCHOOL OF LAW
NORTHERN PLAINS INDIAN LAW CENTER
215 Centennial Dr., Stop 9003 • GRAND FORKS, ND 58202
(701) 777-2104; B.J. Jones, Director – Tribal Judicial Institute
 James M. Grijalva, Director – Tribal Environmental Law Project
The School of Law, in consultation with area tribes and Indian leaders, has established the Northern Plains Indian Law Center. The Center's purposes are to assist tribal governments in addressing legal issues affecting tribal lands and members, and to promote diversity within the legal profession by increasing recruitment and retention of American Indian law students. The Center is a clearinghouse for American Indian legal materials and provides a forum for discussing and resolving legal issues confronting Indian tribes, the states, and the federal government. It will also support tribal advocacy training programs. *Programs*: Northern Plains Tribal Judicial Training Institute, Native American Law Project, Tribal Environmental Law Project, Institute for the Study of Tribal Gaming Law & Policy. Project Components of the Center: Tribal Judicial Institute & Tribal Environmental Law Project. This project provides legal & policy assistance to tribal governments developing environmental programs intended to protect the health and welfare of tribal citizens, tribal natural resources, and the quality of reservations and ceded lands. The project also researches legal issues of general relevance to the authority of tribal governments to implement and administer civil regulatory programs.

UNIVERSITY OF NORTH DAKOTA - SCHOOL OF LAW
INSTITUTE FOR THE STUDY OF TRIBAL GAMING LAW & POLICY
215 Centennial Dr., Stop 9003 • GRAND FORKS, ND 58202
(701) 777-2104
Dean Kathryn R.L. Rand, Co-Director; E-mail: rand@law.und.edu
Dr. Steven Andrew Light, Co-Director; E-mail: steven_light@und.nodak.edu
Co-Directors Kathryn R.L. Rand (Law) & Steven Andrew Light (Political Science) founded the Institute for the Study of Tribal Gaming Law and Policy at the University of North Dakota in 2002 as the first university-affiliated institute in the U.S. dedicated to the study of Indian gaming. Rand & Light are internationally recognized experts on Indian gaming, having published over 30 journal articles, book chapters, essays, and three books: Indian Gaming Law: Cases and Materials (Carolina Academic Press, 2008), Indian Gaming Law and Policy (Carolina Academic Press, 2006), and Indian Gaming and Tribal Sovereignty: The Casino Compromise (University Press of Kansas, 2005). They have twice testified on Indian gaming regulation before the U.S. Senate Committee on Indian Affairs in Washington, D.C., and were featured on C-SPAN's Book TV. They frequently present their research & perspectives on Indian gaming before diverse audiences, including professional & trade groups, tribal & non-tribal civic associations, academic conferences, and university endowed lectures. Both are members of the International Masters of Gaming Law, and Rand is on the Editorial Board of the Gaming Law Review. Rand and Light write a column, "Indian Gaming Today," that appears regularly in Casino Lawyer magazine; have written for Casino Enterprise Management and Indian Gaming magazines. They blog on Indian gaming and the legal, political, and public policy issues raised by the tribal gaming industry at their website, Indian Gaming Today, atindiangamingnow.com. *Activities*: The Institute provides legal and policy assistance and analysis to all interested individuals, governments, & organizations, & conducting scholarly & practical research in the area of tribal gaming. The Institute adopts a unique "team-based" interdisciplinary approach to legal & policy analysis of the complicated and highly technical issues related to Indian gaming, including regulation and agency authority, policy & socioeconomic impact analysis, tribal-state compacting, Class II vs. Class III gaming, tribal law and sovereignty, federal Indian law, labor relations, state referenda and voter initiatives, the federal acknowledgment process, land-into-trust applications, & "off-reservation" gaming. The Institute provides legal & policy assistance related to tribal gaming enterprises to all interested governments and organizations, assists tribes with gaming enterprises in pursuing reservation economic development and building strong tribal governments, and contributes to the scholarly and practical research and literature in the area of tribal gaming. The Institute's primary focus is on the particular issues faced by tribes in the Great Plains, including North Dakota, South Dakota, Nebraska, Iowa, Kansas, Wyoming, and Montana. The institute offers an interdisciplinary perspective on tribal gaming, incorporating law, political science, and public administration. *The Native American Law Project* - This project, offered some semesters, provides legal assistance to the Spirit Lake Nation of the Fort Totten Indian Reservation. Second and third year law students provide legal services under the supervision of a practicing attorney. The project has also served as the Tribe's Prosecutor for criminal matters.

MINOT STATE UNIVERSITY
NATIVE AMERICAN CULTURAL AWARENESS CENTER
NATIVE AMERICAN STUDIES PROGRAM
Department of History - Administration 355
500 University Ave. West • MINOT, ND 58707
(701) 858-3322 Fax 858-3132; Website: www.minotstateu.edu/nas
Joseph C. Jastrzembski, Professor & Program Coordinator
 E-mail: joseph.jastrzembski@minotstateu.edu
Wylie Hammond, Center Director & Advisor (858-3112)
Purpose: The Center provides counseling, advising, and assistance to people of color & international students in dealing with personal, social, financial, academic, career & transitional issues. The interdisciplinary Native American Studies curriculum offers a wide range of courses in Native American art, literature, history, anthropology, science, & contemporary social issues. In addition, the program fosters service-learning opportunities at Native American reservations & important historical & archaeological sites. Minot State University offers both a minor & concentration in Native American studies. The Native American Cultural Awareness Center, on the campus of MSU, sponsors an annual powwow & honor dance in April at the MSU Dome. *Program*: Offers both a minor & concentration in Native American studies. *Faculty*: Walter Piehl (Art), Joseph C. Jastrzembski (History), Nelrene Yellow Bird (Social Work), Harry Hoffman (Sociology), Ursula Schittko (Biology), Chad Heizel (Geoscience), Ron Fischer (English), Patricia Lomire (Sociology), Lee Ellis (Sociology). *Resources*: Native American Cultural Awareness Club; Library maintains historical & current information on the five tribes/reservations in North Dakota. *Financial aid*: All Native American student scholarships. Library maintains historical & current information on the five tribes/reservations in North Dakota. *Activities*: Spring Honor Dance & Powwow Celebration.

NUETA HIDATSA SAHNISH COLLEGE
Formerly: Fort Berthold Community College
220 8th Ave. N., P.O. Box 490 • NEW TOWN, ND 58763
(701) 627-4738 Fax 627-3609; Website: www.nhsc.edu
Robert Rainbow, Jr., Director of Native American Studies
  E-mail: rrainb@nhsc.edu
Twyla Baker-Demaray, President; E-mail: tbaker@nhsc.edu
Waylon Baker, Vice President of Academics; E-mail: wbaker@nhsc.edu
Constance Frankenberry, VP Student Services; E-mail: cfrank@nhsc.edu
Kerry Hartman, Academic Dean; E-mail: khartm@nhsc.edu
Amy Solis, Director of Learning & Library Services
  E-mail: asolis@nhsc.edu
Patrick Packineau, Board Chairperson; Cory Spotted Bear, Vice Chair
Description: Located near the scenic Lake Sakakawea area of Fort Berthold
Reservation. Tribally owned & controlled. The curriculum is founded in liberal
arts, which integrates successfully with most professional & paraprofessional
career pursuits. *Native American Studies Instructors*: Shannon Fox (Art);
Delvin Driver (Language & Culture Instructor); Robert Rainbow; Valerin Three
Irons; Bernadine Youngbird. Resources: Library. *Program*: Associate of Arts
Degree in Native American Studies.

OHIO

THE OHIO STATE UNIVERSITY
AMERICAN INDIAN STUDIES (AIS) PROGRAM
College of Arts & Sciences, 455 Hagerty Hall
1775 College Rd. • COLUMBUS, OH 43210
(614) 247-7988; E-mail: ais@osu.edu
Daniel Rivers, Program Director & Professor of History (292-8301)
Christine Ballengee-Morris, Professor & Program Director
  E-mail: morris.390@osu.edu
Lucy Murphy, Associate Professor of History (Newark)
Shannon Gonzales-Miller, Director, Scholars Program, Office of Diversity
  & Inclusion; E-mail: Gonzales-miller.1@osu.edu
Chadwick Allen (Chickasaw), Director of Diversity & Identity Studies
  Collective (DISCO)
Timothy San Pedro, Assistant Professor
Marti Chaatsmith (Comanche/Choctaw), Associate Director,
  Newark Earthworks Center; E-mail: chaatsmith.1@osu.edu
Description: American Indian Studies is an interdisciplinary field of study that
focuses on the histories, experiences, languages, arts, and cultures of peoples
indigenous to the lands that now comprise the United States of America. It
seeks to broaden students' understandings of the diversity and complexity of
American Indian identities, communities, and nations; to make connections
between Native peoples & cultures in the U.S. & Indigenous peoples & cultures
across the Americas & around the globe; to provide comparative &
intersectional approaches to issues of race, ethnicity, gender, sexuality, class,
and citizenship; and to encourage linking educational & research initiatives to
community and political concerns. Central Ohio is a traditional homeland of the
Shawnee Nation; Delaware, Wyandot, and other Indigenous nations also have
strong ties to these lands. One hundred years ago, in October 1911, the
Society of American Indians (SAI), the first American Indian activist association
organized and run by Native people themselves held its first meetings on the
campus of The Ohio State University. *Degree*: Interdisciplinary Undergraduate
Minor in American Indian Studies. *Faculty*: Matt Anderson; Christine
Ballengee-Morris, Mansel Blackford (Emeritus History); Katherine Borland
(Comparative Studies); William Dancey (Emeritus Anthropology); Lindsay
Jones (Comparative Studies); John Low (Comparative Studies, Newark
Campus); Kenneth Madsen (Geography, Newark Campus); Daniel Reff
(Comparative Studies); Daniel Rivers (History); Richard Shiels (Emeritus
History, Newark Campus); Patricia Stuhr (Emerita Professor; Wisconsin Native
Americans); Christine Warner (Education); Anna J. Willow (Environment,
Anthropology, Marion Campus); Annmarie Amy Zaharlick (Emerita
Anthropology), et al. *Resources*: The Multicultural Center; (AIS) has strong
connections to the Newark Earthworks Center (NEC) on the Ohio State-
Newark campus and to the student organizations the American Indian Council
(AIC) and the American Indian Students in Engineering & Sciences (AISES),
with whom we collaborate on various projects & programming; Office of
Diversity & Inclusion; Multicultural Center.

MIAMI UNIVERSITY - MYAAMIA CENTER PROJECT
200 Bonham House, 351 E. Spring St. • OXFORD, OH 45056
(513) 529-5648 Fax 529-9234; Website: www.myaamiaproject.org
  E-mail: myaamiaproject@muohio.edu
Daryl Baldwin (Miami), Center/Project Director
  E-mail: baldwidw@miamioh.edu
George Ironstrack (Miami), Program Director & Education & Outreach
  E-mail: ironstgm@miamioh.edu
Dr. David J. Costa (Miami), Program Director, Language Research Office
  E-mail: costad@miamioh.edu

Bobbe Burke, Coordinator of Miami Tribe Relations & Education Special
  Projects for the Miami Tribe
  E-mail: burkebi@miamioh.edu
Jonathan Fox (Miami), Program Director – Communications & Publications
  E-mail: foxjm5@miamioh.edu
Description: The project, created in 2001, is a tribal initiative located within an
academic environment to advance the Miami Tribe of Oklahoma's language &
cultural revitalization efforts. *Purpose*: To conduct in-depth research to assist
tribal educational initiatives aimed at the preservation of Miami language &
culture; and to expose undergraduate & graduate students at Miami University
to tribal efforts in language & cultural revitalization. *Faculty Affiliates*: Alysia
Fischer (Center for American & World Cultures & Anthropology); Jonathan
Levy; Susan Mosley-Howard (Professor Emeritus); Kate Rousmaniere;
Douglas Troy (Professor Emeritus) *Programs*: Workshops, camps, field trips &
lectures. Publications on Miami history, language & culture.

OKLAHOMA

EAST CENTRAL UNIVERSITY
HAYES NATIVE AMERICAN STUDIES CENTER
Department of History & Native American Studies
Horace Mann Bldg. 3rd Floor, 1100 E. 14th St. • ADA, OK 74820
(580) 332-8000 Fax 436-3329; Website:
https://www.ecok.edu/centers-and-programs/hayes-native-american-study-center
  Dr. Thomas W. Cowger (Chickasaw Nation Endowed Chair),
  Director of Native American Studies & History Chair;
  Advisor to the Native American Student Association
  E-mail: tcowger@ecok.edu
Deanna Hartley-Kelso, General Counsel & Administrator
  for the Legal Division of the Chickasaw Nation
Scott Barton, Dept. Chairperson (559-5563)
  E-mail: sbarton@ecok.edu
Dr. Duane Anderson, Provost & VP of Academic Affairs
Shawna Jackson (Chickasaw), Director of Native American Academic
  Services & Student Services (559-5671) E-mail: sjackson@ecok.edu
Program: B.A. & Minor in Native Studies. *Faculty*: Scott Barton (Chair/
Professor) (History); Christopher Bean (History); Bradley Clampitt (History);
Laura Clark (Adjunct); Tom Cowger Chickasaw Nation Endowed Chair)
(HIstory); John Dyson (History); Houston Mount (History); Lillie Roberts
(History); Greg Sutton (History). *Resources*: Native American Student
Services; Native American Student Association.

UNIVERSITY OF SCIENCE & ARTS OF OKLAHOMA
AMERICAN INDIAN STUDIES PROGRAM
Division of Social Sciences & Business
1727 W. Alabama • CHICKASHA, OK 73018
(405) 574-1289 Fax 521-1220
Thurman Lee Hester, Jr. (Choctaw), Program Director & Professor
  of American Indian Studies; E-mail: fachesterl@usao.edu
Program: Major & minor in American Indian Studies. The American Indian
studies program provides knowledge of the traditions and history of the first
Americans and an understanding of the unique relationship of the United
States government to the tribes & individual American Indians. Its curriculum
has shifted to accommodate changing contemporary requirements of
students. Greater emphasis has been placed on acquiring quantitative skills
and on study in financial management & intergovernmental relations. The goal
of the American Indian studies program is to develop a diverse student body
to include American Indians from the many tribes in Oklahoma and the nation.
In addition to traditional on-campus offerings, the program also offers
extension in-service & mid-career training. As an academic program,
American Indian Studies is designed to advance USAO's interdisciplinary,
liberal arts mission & further enrich the IDS experience. Students are advised
to select a second major that is especially suited for acquiring marketable
skills that complement an American Indian studies degree for entry into a
chosen career upon graduation. American Indian tribes collectively make up
one of the largest employers in Oklahoma and holding a degree or a minor in
American Indian studies can improve employability in related fields. *Faculty*:
Jay Goombi (Kiowa-Apache); Thurman Lee Hester, Jr. (Choctaw) (Director).
Resources: Meredith Indigenous Humanities Center. *Special program*:
Internships with regional tribes & organizations. Financial aid available. Nash
Library.

ROGERS STATE UNIVERSITY
NATIVE AMERICAN STUDIES PROGRAM
1701 W. Will Rogers Blvd. • CLAREMORE, OK 74017
(918) 343-7777
Heather Isaacs (343-7740); E-mail: hisaacs@rsu.edu
Program: A.A. Minor in Native American studies option. Goals: Seeks to
enhance the student's understanding of American Indian culture,

history, spirituality, language, art, & contemporary tribal issues. Through course work & extracurricular activities such as an annual, on-campus storytelling & traditional arts festival, craft workshops, & observation of intertribal dances, this option provides a solid foundation for student interested in Native American culture.

SOUTHEASTERN OKLAHOMA STATE UNIVERSITY
NATIVE AMERICAN CENTER FOR STUDENT SUCCESS
NATIVE AMERICAN INSTITUTE
1405 North 4th, PMB 2747 • DURANT, OK 74701-0609
(580) 745-3220 Fax 745-7474
Website: www.homepages.se.edu/native-american-center
Michael Sean Burrage (Choctaw), University President
  E-mail: sburrage@se.edu
Bruce King (Choctaw of Oklahoma), Director, Native American Institute
  E-mail: bking@se.edu
Joni Trosin (Chickasaw), Academic Coordinator
  E-mail: jtrosin@se.edu
Jennifer Kemp (Choctaw), Academic Advisor/Retention Specialist
  E-mail: jkemp@se.edu
Amy Grantt (Chickasaw), Chickasaw Nation Recruitment & Retention
  Center Advisor; E-mail: agantt@se.edu
Programs: Native American Studies Minor. Native American Excellence in Education; Chickasaw Summer Leadership Academy. Scholarships.
Publication: Native American Center News

*COMANCHE NATION COLLEGE
American Indian Studies Department
Department of Native Languages
1608 S.W. 9th St. • LAWTON, OK 73501
(580) 591-0203 Fax 591-0643; Website: www.cnc.cc.ok.us
Robbie Wahnee (Comanche), President
  E-mail: rwahnee@cnc.cc.ok.us
Sunny Hegwood (Comanche), Director of Academics
  E-mail: shegwood@cnc.cc.ok.us
Johnny Poolaw (Comanche), V.P. for Student & Academic Affairs
  Email: jpoolaw@cnc.cc.ok.us
Kim M. Smith, Librarian (699-7226)
Programs: American Indian Studies; Native Languages. The American Indian Studies Department seeks to expose Comanche Nation College students to pre-contact history, culture, philosophy, sovereignty, spirituality, arts, politics, etc. with an emphasis on Comanche. The Department approaches academia from an American Indian perspective. The goal is for students to gain an understanding of all aspects of Native Studies through a "Comanche centered" education. *Faculty*: Sunny Hegwood (American Indian Studies); Kurtis Koll (Science); Annette Arkeketa (Art); Kelly Berry (Sociology); Janet Powers (Nursing); John T. Poolaw (Math & Native Science), LaNeal Pewewardy (GED), Amber Neely (Linguistics). Dorna Riding In-Battese (English); Edith Stillsmoking (Math). Chartered in 2002 by the Comanche Nation.

BACONE COLLEGE - CENTER FOR AMERICAN INDIANS (CAI)
2299 Old Bacone Rd. • MUSKOGEE, OK 74403
(918) 781-7340 Fax 781-7416
Website: http://www.bacone.edu/center-for-american-indians/
Dr. Pete G. Coser (Muscogee Creek), Assistant VP
Patricia (Patti Jo) King (Cherokee), Interim Division Chair of American Indian Studies; Professor of American Indian Studies; & Director of CAI (360-6471)
  E-mail: kingp@bacone.edu
Corey Still, Adjunct Professor of American Indian Studies
Kindle Holderby, Director-Loraine Bacone Learning Work
  Community Program
Shawna Drywater-Terhune (Cherokee), Director - American Indian Students of Promise Program
Shari Kamp (Cherokee), Director - American Indian Culture Clubs Program
Roseanna Hayes Spinks (Wintun), Manager - KIVA & Ataloa Lodge Museum
John Timothy (Muscogee Creek), Cultural Interpreter –
  Ataloa Lodge Museum
Zach Bro (Cherokee), Native American Recruiter
Description: 117 year-old, one-room schoolhouse at Cherokee Baptist Mission in Tahlequah (Indian Territory), Oklahoma's oldest continuing center of higher education, and the only church-related (American Baptist Church) college in the country with an educational mission to American Indians. *Purpose*: To coordinate American Indian scholarships, cultural programs, and supports American Indian academic programs & degrees. The Center seeks to further preserve the American Indian collections at Bacone College & conduct research related to collections and American Indian education. Additionally, the Center receives institutional administrative support as Bacone College continues to meet its historic educational mission with American Indians. The Center supports the American Indian Studies Program & anticipates the development of an American Indian Museum Sciences Degree and a four-year degree in Art with an American Indian concentration. The Center will

publish the Indian University Journal, develop the Ataloa Lodge Museum, support the Native American Student Association and the American Indian Science and Engineering Society organizations, expand the Kiva (home of the Center for American Indians) & develop Alumni relations *Programs*: Offers Associate degrees in the arts & sciences, and various certificate programs. *Resources*: The Center for Tribal Languages; American Indian art collection; Ataloa Lodge; Betts Library E-mail: library@bacone.edu; Indian Choir. *Publication*: The Baconian, student newspaper.

BACONE COLLEGE – THE CENTER FOR TRIBAL LANGUAGES
2299 Old Bacone Rd. • MUSKOGEE, OK 74403
(918) 683-4581; Website: http://www.bacone.edu/center-for-tribal-languages/
Jacob Manatowa-Bailey (Sauk, Sac and Fox of Oklahoma), Director
Terrie Kinsie (781-7260) E-mail: kinseyt@bacone.edu
Program: Bachelor's of Arts in Tribal Languages. Features courses designed specifically for tribal languages.

UNIVERSITY OF OKLAHOMA - AMERICAN INDIAN INSTITUTE
University Outreach-College of Continuing Education
1639 Cross Center Dr. • NORMAN, OK 73019
(800) 522-0772; (405) 325-4127 Fax 325-7757
E-mail: aii@ou.edu
Norma Neely (Potawatomi), Executive Director
  E-mail: nneely@ou.edu (325-1782)
Chelsea Wesner (Choctaw), Program Specialist (308-2409)
Purpose: To promote Indian education and research, training and career development opportunities, the development of human & natural resources; the perpetuation of tribal/band cultures & traditions and their histories; and to facilitate the utilization of University of Oklahoma resources by Indian tribes, bands, organizations and groups. *Facilities*: American Indian Prevention Resource Center (AIPRC); Prevention Resource Library. *Programs*: Early Head Start (EHS); Native Fitness Training; Substance Abuse Prevention. *Activities*: Historical/cultural research design & methodology; cultural resource identification & development; substance abuse training for schools & communities; and cultural curriculum development for schools & tribal/band education departments. *2013 Conferences*: Native Women & Men's Wellness Conference; Native Diabetes Prevention Conference; Native Fitness Training; annual Early Childhood Intervention Conference; annual National American Indian Conference on Child Abuse & Neglect; annual National Conference on Gifted & Talented Education for Native People; annual National Native American, Alaska Native, First Nations Cultural Curriculum Development Workshop; arts & crafts cultural workshops & exchanges. *Publications*: Native Horizons, quarterly newsletter; Resource Center catalog. Conference Proceedings; Cultural lessons: cultural curriculum, gifted & talented, math & science, and drug & alcohol. Established 1951.

UNIVERSITY OF OKLAHOMA
NATIVE AMERICAN STUDIES PROGRAM
College of Arts & Sciences, Department of Anthropology
860 Van Vleet Oval, Room 235 • NORMAN, OK 73019
(405) 325-2312 Fax 325-0842
Website: http://nas.ou.edu/; E-mail: nas@ou.edu
Amanda Cobb-Greetham (Chickasaw), Coca-Cola Professor & Chair of Native American Studies; E-mail: acobb@ou.edu
Edgar Heap of Birds (Cheyenne) Professor of Native American Studies
  E-mail: eheapofbirds@ou.edu
Jerry Bread (Kiowa/Cherokee), Outreach Coordinator
  E-mail: jcbread@ou.edu
Description: Offers interdisciplinary BA & MA degree programs designed to provide an academic context that will broaden an understanding of cultural diversity by focusing on Native American cultures & issues. These interdisciplinary degree programs include courses offered by several departments, including anthropology, English, history, music, art history, communication, & geography; Native American Language Program offers instruction by Native speakers in Cherokee, Choctaw, Creek/Seminole, and Kiowa; The Internship Program provides opportunities for students to have the experience of working in a tribal community. Internships will be available with tribal governments, cultural organizations, schools, and federal agencies that serve Indian people. *Faculty*: Christopher Basaldu (Assistant Professor); Hachivi Edgar Heap of Birds (Professor); Shanna Heap of Birds (Cheyenne - Professor); Heather Shotton (Wichita/Kiowa/Cheyenne – Assistant Professor); Terri McKnight (Staff Assistant). *Financial aid*: Graduate Teaching Assistantships. *Resources*: American Indian Science & Math Society; AIMSS Summer Institute; Diversity Project in Geosciences Project; Native American Studies Internship Program. *Facilities*: Western History Collection; Oklahoma Museum of Natural History; within easy access to representatives of more than 60 Indian tribes; the presence of an active Salvage archaeology program for the State of Oklahoma; the resources of the Stovall Museum, and an extensive library collection on the American Indian offer special opportunities for the study of the archaeology, linguistics, ethno-history & ethnology of the American Indian.

UNIVERSITY OF OKLAHOMA COLLEGE OF LAW
CENTER FOR THE STUDY OF AMERICAN INDIAN LAW & POLICY
300 W. Timberdell Rd. • NORMAN, OK 73019
(405) 325-4699 Fax 325-6282
Website: www.law.ou.edu/native; E-mail: law@law.ou.edu
Lindsay Robertson, JD, Faculty Director & Chickasaw Nation Endowed Chair in Native American Law; E-mail: lrobertson@ou.edu
Talawagi Helton, JD, Associate Director & Professor of Law
  E-mail: thelton@ou.edu
Kathleen R. Guzman, JD, Professor of Law; E-mail: kguzman@ou.edu
Stephen H. Greetham, Adjunct Professor (Chief general Counsel to the Chickasaw Nation Division of Commerce and as the Nation's Special Counsel on water & natural resources)
Gary Pitchlynn, Adjunct Professor of Law
  E-mail: gspitchlynn@pitchlynnlaw.com
Michael C. Smith (Chickasaw), Adjunct Professor; E-mail: msmith@ou.edu
Program: Certificate Program in American Indian Law. Provides counsel to tribal, state and national policymakers, and a forum for the interdisciplinary discussion and resolution of problems facing Native communities. The Center offers various speaker programs throughout the year as well as the Native American Law Certificate and the Latin American Fellows Program. *Other Faculty*: Rennard Strickland (Senior Scholar in Residence). *Resources*: Native American Constitution & Law Digitization Project; American Indian Law Review; National Indian Law Library. Founded 1990.

OKLAHOMA CITY UNIVERSITY SCHOOL OF LAW
AMERICAN INDIAN LAW & SOVEREIGNTY CENTER
800 N. Harvey • OKLAHOMA CITY, OK 73102
(405) 208-5337
Casey Ross-Petherick (Cherokee), Director (208-5312)
  E-mail: crosspetherick@okcu.edu
Professor Ross was the clinical professor of the American Indian Wills Clinic from the program's inception in January 2009 through August 2015. She also taught the Native American Victims Rights Clinic in the Spring and Fall semesters of 2008. In addition to clinical courses, Professor Ross also teaches doctrinal courses, including Legal Analysis, Wills, Trusts and Estates, Tribal Law, American Indian Law, Advanced Indian Law and Indian Gaming Law. Professor *Other professional posts*: Deputy Director, Native American Legal Resource Center; Professor Ross serves on the board of directors for the Oklahoma Indian Legal Services, a nonprofit organization that provides legal services to low income American Indian citizens (Her scholarship focuses on American Indian land and property issues in Oklahoma).; serves as University General Counsel for Oklahoma City University. *Past professional posts*: Prior to joining the faculty at Oklahoma City University School of Law, Professor Ross served as the Senior Legislative Officer for the Cherokee Nation, in its Washington, D.C. Office. There, she engaged in legislative & policy advocacy for tribal priorities. *Published works*: Works in areas of Indian Child Welfare, Domestic Violence & Taxation in tribal communities. Professor Ross has served as conference faculty for several statewide and national conferences on American Indian legal issues, has lectured internationally on Indian law topics, and presents frequently at events related to her area of scholarship.

OKLAHOMA CITY UNIVERSITY SCHOOL OF LAW
NATIVE AMERICAN LEGAL RESOURCE CENTER
2501 N. Blackwelder • OKLAHOMA CITY, OK 73106
(866) 529-6281; (405) 208-5337
Kelly A. Stoner, Director (208-5188); E-mail: kstoner@okcu.edu
Casey Ross-Petherick (Cherokee), Deputy Director (208-5312
  E-mail: crosspetherick@okcu.edu
Lee Peoples, Director of the Chickasaw Nation Law Library & Professor of Law; E-mail: lpeoples@okcu.edu
Mission: To provide capacity building services to tribal communities & creates opportunities for students, faculty, staff to utilize knowledge & resources to serve the needs of Indian Country. *Clinic*: The Jodi G. Marquette American Indian Wills Clinic at Oklahoma City University School of Law is accepting clients for estate planning services. Through this clinic, law students working under the supervision of a licensed attorney provide wills drafting services to American Indians who own an interest in Indian land in Oklahoma. These services will be provided free of charge, thanks to a generous anonymous donation of $250,000 to further the work of Wills Services Project, which received its initial funding from the Oklahoma Bar Foundation. The clinic first began in January 2009 as part of the NALRC's Native American Externship Program – with $20,000 in seed funds provided by the Oklahoma Bar Foundation. The program offers practical experience for students who provide needed legal services while receiving instruction and training in client relations, as well as the complex area of American Indian estate planning. For more information on the clinic, or to apply for the services, contact the American Indian Law and Sovereignty Center at Oklahoma City University School of Law at 405.208.5017. For information on Indian land in Oklahoma, contact the Office of Special Trustee for American Indians Beneficiary Call Center at 888.678.6836. Chickasaw Nation Law Library

UNIVERSITY OF OKLAHOMA HEALTH SCIENCES CENTER
CENTER FOR AMERICAN INDIAN HEALTH RESEARCH (CAIHR)
AMERICAN INDIAN DIABETES PREVENTION CENTER (AIDPC)
College of Public Health, 801 N.E. 13th St. • OKLAHOMA CITY, OK 73104
(405) 271-7500 Fax 271-7501 (AIDPC)
(877) 805-6901; (405) 271-2232 Fax 271-3039
Website: www.ouhsc.edu; E-mail: coph@ouhsc.edu
Dolores Subia Bigfoot, Native American Programs Director
  (405) 271-8858; E-mail: dee-bigfoot@ouhsc.edu
Elisa T. Lee, Director, CAIHR (271-3090)
  E-mail: elisa-lee@ouhsc.edu
Janie Braden, Project Making Medicine Coordinator
  E-mail: Janie-braden@ouhsc.edu
Robin Fitzpatrick, Native American Outreach Coordinator
  (405) 271-8999 ext. 46896
Dr. J. Neil Henderson, AIDPC Director
  E-mail: neil-henderson@ouhsc.edu
Dr. L. Carson Henderson, AIDPC Project Coordinator
  E-mail: carson-henderson@ouhsc.edu
Dr. Jim Gunter, AIDPC Administrator Director
  E-mail: jim-gunter@ouhsc.edu
CAIHR is a multidisciplinary research organization and conducts health-related studies with American Indian groups. The focus of the research at CAIHR is to improve the health status of the American Indian population. CAIHR conducts epidemiological & clinical studies of health problems among these populations, with emphasis on diabetes and its many complications including heart disease, retinopathy, renal disease, leg vessel disease, and cerebral vascular disease. CAIHR also conducts studies focusing on health promotion & disease prevention. CAIHR has developed a productive relationship with American Indian tribes in Oklahoma including the Apache, Caddo, Comanche, Delaware, Fort Sill Apache, Kiowa, the Wichita & Affiliated tribes located in southwestern Oklahoma, the Cherokee Nation in northeastern Oklahoma, and other tribes across the nation. http://caihr.ouhsc.edu **AIDPC** has several research, education, and tribal outreach projects designed to reduce the unjust health disparity of diabetes and its multiple co-morbidities in American Indian Nations. Experts from the Colleges of Public Health, Nursing, and Medicine are brought together in an interdisciplinary intellectual, research, & practice environment to reach the goal of a diabetes-free native world. Many key leadership positions are held by American Indian researchers including the Principal Investigator who is Oklahoma Choctaw. The AIDPC reaches all Oklahoma Indian Nations via their partnership with the Oklahoma Area Inter-tribal Health Board as well intensive collaborations with the Chickasaw Nation and the Choctaw Nation of Oklahoma. The AIDPC is funded by the National Institute on Minority Health & Health Disparities, a vital part of the National Institutes of Health. http://aidpc.ouhsc.edu/ *Program*: Headlands Indian Health Careers. *Financial aid*: Grants to Native American students who are interested in preparing for careers as health professionals.

UNIVERSITY OF OKLAHOMA - NATIVE AMERICAN
CENTER OF EXCELLENCE CONSORTIUM
Health Sciences Center & College of Medicine & College of Dentistry
P.O. Box 26901 • OKLAHOMA CITY, OK 73190
(888) 684-7473; (405) 271-1976
Website: www.ouhsc.edu/nace; E-mail: nace@ouhsc.edu
Jerry Tahsequah, Associate Director
A federally-funded collaborative program whose ultimate goal is to increase the number of Native American physicians practicing medicine in the U.S. Jointly sponsored by the Center for Tribal Studies, Northeastern State University (Tahlequah, OK) & University of Oklahoma College of Medicine. Established in 1993 at the University of Oklahoma Health Sciences Center in the Colleges of Dentistry and Medicine, the Native American Center of Excellence Consortium has been made possible with funds provided by the U.S. Public Health Service. Designated as the only Native American Center among the 54 dental schools in the United States and only one of four located in a College of Medicine, the activities of this center are directed toward accomplishing the following goals: Increasing interest in dental and medical careers among Native American high school & college students. Better preparing Native American students pursuing careers in dentistry and medicine. Enrolling & graduating more Native American students at the OUHSC Colleges of Dentistry and Medicine. Increasing awareness among all OU dental and medical graduates and other practitioners in Oklahoma of the health needs of Native Americans. Encouraging Native Americans to pursue careers in higher education, resulting in increased appointments to faculty and administrative positions. Fostering research related to the health of Native Americans. Established 1993.

*COLLEGE OF THE MUSCOGEE NATION
2170 Raven Circle, P.O. Box 917 • OKMULGEE, OK 74447
(918) 549-2800 Fax 549-2880; Website: www.mvsktc.org
Robert Bible (Muscogee), President; E-mail: rbible@mcn-nsn.gov
Dr. James King, Regent's Director; E-mail: jking@mcn-nsn.gov

Monte Randall, Dean of Academic Affairs; E-mail: mrandall@mcn-nsn.gov
Krystal Wind, Dean of Student Affairs; E-mail: kwind@mcn-nsn.gov
Mackie Moore, Tribal Services Instructor; E-mail: mmoore@mcn-nsn.gov
Norma Marshall (Muscogee), Native American Studies Instructor
  E-mail: nmarshall@mcn-nsn.gov
Mission: To serve Muscogee citizens & other citizens with the history, government, & culture of the Muscogee people as its primary focus. *Faculty*: Norma Marshall (Muscogee Language Studies Instructor); Mekko Tyner (Instructor Curriculum Specialist); David Tayrien (Gaming Instructor); Dr. Jennifer McAlpin (Research Specialist); Karen Haught (Librarian); Chelsea Clark, Academic Resource Specialist); Ronnie Sands (Math Instructor); Kasey McKenzie (Police Science Instructor). Member of the American Indian Higher Education Consortium. Established 2004.

PAWNEE NATION COLLEGE
861 Little Dee Dr., P.O. Box 470 • PAWNEE, OK 74058
  (918) 762-3343 Fax 762-3303
  Website: www.pawneenationcollege.org
  Michael Burgess (Pawnee), President
    E-mail: mburgess@pawneenationcollege.org
  Dr. Benes, Faculty Chairperson
    E-mail: drbenes@pawneenationcollege.org
  Staci Burns (Pawnee), Director of Admissions; Project Director
    E-mail: sburns@pawneenationcollege.org
  James Cook & Dennis Haga, Full-Time faculty
    E-mail: jcook@pawneenationcollege.org
    E-mail: dhaga@pawneenationcollege.org
  George Elton Howell (Pawnee), Board Chairperson
Mission: To meet the cultural & educational needs of the Pawnee Nation, as well as other surrounding Indian Nations, and all others who have the desire & ability to learn. *Program*: American Indian Studies. *Faculty*: Michael Burgess (Pawnee); Sarah Bourland (Osage); Stephani Brisbin; Amanda L. Burke; Jim Dailey (Osage); Anita Fields (Osage); Pam Ferguson; Andrew Gray (Osage); Dennis Haga; Carol Herring; Pat Howell (Quechan); Tom Knife Chief (Pawnee); Cheryl Maye; Laura Melton (Pawnee); Ted Moore (Otoe-Missouria/Pawnee/Osage/Sac & Fox); Peter Pitchford (Chippewa); Warren Pratt, Jr. (Pawnee); Brad Sewell; Alicia Seyler (Choctaw).

SOUTHWESTERN OKLAHOMA STATE UNIVERSITY
AMERICAN INDIAN STUDIES PROGRAM
409 E. Mississippi • SAYRE, OK 73662
  (580) 928-5533 Fax 928-1140; E-mail: sayre@swosu.edu
  Website: www.swosu.edu/sayre/academics/amer-indian
  John Hayden, Chairperson & professor (774-7072)
Program: Associate in Science Degree in General Studies — American Indian Studies & Tribal Administration

OKLAHOMA STATE UNIVERSITY
AMERICAN INDIAN STUDIES PROGRAM
NATIVE AMERICAN STUDENT ASSOCIATION
101 Murray Hall • STILLWATER, OK 74078
  (405) 744-6027 Fax 744-5780; Website: www.okstate.edu/
  John M. Chaney, Program Director; E-mail: john.chaney@okstate.edu
  Lindsey Claire Smith (744-9474); E-mail: Lindsey.c.smith@okstate.edu
  Morgan TwoCrow, Association President; E-mail: twocrow@okstate.edu
  Alex Hardison, Vice President; E-mail: alex.hardison@mail.okstate.edu
  Staci Riddle, Historian; E-mail: staci.riddle@okstate.edu
  Robin Starr Williams, Advisor; E-mail: robin.starr.williams@okstate.edu
Program: Certificate Program; Native American Resiliency Through Education & Leadership Program. *Resources*: Native American Student Association (website: www.orgs.okstate.edu/nasa); Native American Faculty & Staff Association; Native Americans in Biological Sciences American Indians Into Psychology. *Core Faculty*: Christopher Pexa, Lindsey C. Smith, Elizabeth Payne, Brad Bays, Louise Siddons, Doug Miller. *Affiliated Faculty*: Cristina Gonzalez, Brian Frehner, Jean Van Delinder, Melissa Burkley, Mark Perry. *Activities*: Miss American Indian OSU Scholarship Pageant; Fall Powwow.

NORTHEASTERN STATE UNIVERSITY
CENTER FOR TRIBAL STUDIES
Bacone House, 320 Academy St.
600 N. Grand Ave. • TAHLEQUAH, OK 74464
  (918) 444-4350 Fax 458-2073; E-mail: tribalstudies@nsuok.edu
  Sara Barnett (Muscogee), Director; E-mail: barnetts@nsuok.edu
  Alisa Douglas (Seminole of Oklahoma), Coordinator for Student Programs
    E-mail: douglasa@nsuok.edu
  Marsey Harjo (Seminole), Administrative Assistant
    E-mail: harjo02@nsuok.edu
The Center for Tribal Studies offers a variety of services to enhance the academic experience of students in a supportive environment that values the traditions of American Indian cultural heritage. The Center facilitates program development, cultural enrichment, student support, & professional develop-

ment opportunities for the University community. The Center serves all students, but administers many programs that are specifically designed to increase the educational attainment of American Indian populations. By nurturing educational leadership, cultural enrichment, & professional development among students, leaders and scholars emerge, many of whom will serve in professions benefiting tribal governments & communities. *Activities*: Annual NSU Symposium & Powwow in April. Established 1990.

NORTHEASTERN STATE UNIVERSITY
DEPARTMENT OF CHEROKEE & INDIGENOUS STUDIES
Seminary Hall 313, 609 N. Grand Ave. • TAHLEQUAH, OK 74464
  (918) 444-3500 Fax 458-2390
  Website: https://academics.nsuok.edu/cherokeeindigenous/
  Benjamin R. Kracht, Department Chairperson; Professor of Anthropology
    E-mail: kracht@nsuok.edu (444-3698)
  Tiffani Dawn Hardbarger (Ord) (Cherokee) (444-3599), Instructor
    E-mail: ord@nsuok.edu
  Candessa Tehee (Cherokee), Assistant Professor of American Indian
    Studies; E-mail: teheec@nsuok.edu
  Farina King (Navajo-Dine'), Assistant Professor of History
  Brad Montgomery-Anderson, Associate Professor (Cherokee language)
    E-mail: montgomb@nsuok.edu
  Kimberly Ann Lee, Associate Professor (Languages & Literatures)
    E-mail: lee36@nsuok.edu
  Wyman Kirk, Adjunct Professor
  Diane Hammons, JD (Cherokee), Assistant Professor (Legal)
    E-mail: hammonsa@nsuok.edu
  Virginia Whitekiller (Cherokee), Professor of Social Work (444-3517)
    E-mail: longvs@nsuok.edu
Program: B.A. in American Indian Studies; Ethnic Studies Minor. *Resources*: Center for Tribal Studies, (see listing above); Sequoyah Institute. *Activities*: Annual (in April) Symposium on the American Indian.

UNIVERSITY OF TULSA COLLEGE OF LAW
NATIVE AMERICAN LAW CENTER (NALC)
College of Law, 3120 E. 4th Place • TULSA, OK 74104
  (918) 631-2401 Fax 631-3126; Website:
  Judith Royster, Director of Native American Law Certificate Program
  Law Center Co-Director; E-mail: judith-royster@utulsa.edu
  Vicki J. Limas, Center Co-Director & Associate Dean of Students
    E-mail: vicki-limas@utulsa.edu
  Faye Hadley, Native American Resources Law Librarian
Prepares students for legal work on critical issues that concern American Indians & Native Alaskans. Studies include course work, research & practical experience in externships and tribal entities. Students completing the program receive the J.D. degree, LL.M in American Indian & Indigenous Law & Certificate in Native American Law. *Resources*: The University of Tulsa College of Law is a leading research center for Native American law & history. The Native American Law Certificate Program is enhanced by Tulsa's proximity to major tribal headquarters, lying within the original borders of the Muscogee Creek Nation. The Mabee Legal Information Center (631-2459). *Activities*: Native American Law Student Association at the University of Tulsa College of Law is devoted to meeting the social, cultural & educational needs of its membership. *Resources*: Native American Law Students' Association; specialized library collection in Indian & indigenous law; Gilcrease Museum. Established 2000.

OREGON

SOUTHERN OREGON UNIVERSITY
NATIVE AMERICAN STUDIES PROGRAM
College of Arts & Sciences, Taylor Hall, Rm. 018b
1250 Siskiyou Blvd. • ASHLAND, OR 97520
  (541) 552-6751 Fax 552-6439
  Website: https://inside.sou.edu/natam/index.html
  Brook Colley (Eastern Cherokee), Program Chairperson & Assistant
    Professor of Native American Studies; E-mail: colleyb@sou.edu
  David West (Citizen Potawatomi), Director Emeritus
    E-mail: dwest@sou.edu
  Brent Florendo, Native Nations Liaison (552-8580);
    E-mail: florendb@sou.edu
  Wesley Leonard (Miami of Oklahoma), Associate Professor
    of Native American Studies & Linguistics (552-8256)
    E-mail: leonardw@sou.edu
Program: A Certificate in Native American Studies prepares students to work effectively in Indian country. *Mission*: To educate all students about the Native experience & the rich cultural heritage of the Indigenous peoples of Oregon & North America. *Resources*: Native American Student Union (NASU); Konaway Nika Tillicum (Native American Youth Academy); Southern Oregon Historical Society.

OREGON STATE UNIVERSITY
NATIVE AMERICAN COLLABORATIVE INSTITUITE (NACI)
210 Ballard Hall, 1500 SW Jefferson St. • CORVALLIS, OR 97331
(541) 737-3467 Fax 737-5660; Website:
Dr. Kurt Peters (Blackfeet/Powhatan), NACI Director (737-5668)
E-mail: kpeters@oregonstate.edu
Purpose: To serve Oregon Native Americans as well as all citizens; to facilitate collaboration between tribal business, economic, natural resource, cultural resource, and education programs & Oregon State University faculty & staff. *Program*: Native American Studies, with special emphasis & coordination to programs in cultural resources, applied anthropology, cooperative studies with American Indians, historical archaeology, and ethno-history; summer field school in Oregon. *Resources*: Native American Cultural Center; Native American Longhouse.

OREGON STATE UNIVERSITY
NATIVE AMERICAN STUDIES PROGRAM
College of Liberal Arts-School of Language, Culture & Society
Department of Ethnic Studies, 252 Waldo Hall • CORVALLIS, OR 97331
(541) 737-0709 Fax 737-5660
Leonora Rianda, Office Coordinator, Program Contact
E-mail: Leonora.rianda@oregonstate.edu
Allison Davis-White Eyes, Instructor, Diversity & Cultural Engagement (737-4383)
Natchee Barnd, Assistant Professor of Ethnic Studies (737-1113)
Faculty: Natchee Barnd, David Lewis. *Resources*: Native American Longhouse

UNIVESITY OF OREGON SCHOOL OF LAW
ENVIRONMENTAL & NATURAL RESOURCES LAW CENTER
William W. Knight Law Center, 1221 University of Oregon
1515 Agate St. • EUGENE, OR 97403
(541) 346-3088
Howard Arnett, Pro Tem Instructor, Adjunct Professor of American Indian Law
E-mail: hga@karnopp.com (Partner at Karnopp Peterson LLP)
Mary C. Wood, Philip H. Knigh,t Professor, Faculty Director (346-3842)
Founding Director-Environmental & Natural Resources Law Center
E-mail: mwood@uoregon.edu
Adell Amos, Professor of Law & Associate Dean for Academic Affairs
E-mail: aamos@uoregon.edu
Treaty Rights, Land Issues, and Tribal Law – Covers the history of Indian law and policy, key legal principles of tribal sovereignty, the federal/tribal trust relationship, treaty rights, and jurisdiction in Indian country. Among other courses in water and land rights, there are seminars in Contemporary Issues in American Indian Law, Tribal Courts and Tribal Law, and Comparative Indigenous Peoples Law. Oregon Law, a national leader in Indian Law scholarship and teaching, hosts a variety of events that bring together the best and brightest in the industry , including the Rennard Strickland Indian Law Lecture Series, Native Environmental Sovereignty Project and Oregon Law's chapter of the Native American Law Students Association (NALSA). John E. Jaqua Law Library.

EASTERN OREGON UNIVERSITY
NATIVE AMERICAN STUDIES PROGRAM
Rural & Native American Program (RNAP)
Hoke 319, One University Blvd. • LA GRANDE, OR 97850
(541) 962-3588 Fax 962-3924
Website https://www.eou.edu/rnap/
Bennie Moses-Mesubed, Center Director (962-3094)
E-mail: mccenter@eou.edu
Jackie Leno-Grant, Program Coordinator; E-mail: jgrant@eou.edu
Purpose: To assist in the development of student potential so that they may achieve educational & personal goals. Assists American Indian & Alaskan Native students in financial aid, academic & career, and personal guidance. *Program*: Offers a Minor in Native American Studies. *Resources*: American Indian Science & Engineering Society; Speel-Ya Indian Student Organization — a cultural & social support group on campus working to educate the campus & community of La Grande on traditional & contemporary Native American life. Resources: Native American Student & Community Center, 710 SW Jackson, Portland, OR 97201 (725-9697). *Activities*: Annual Spring Powwow & Friendship Feast, first weekend in May; Annual Indian Arts Festival & Powwow in November.

OREGON HEALTH & SCIENCE UNIVERSITY - ONE SKY CENTER
P.O. Box 903 • LAKE OSWEGO, OR 97034
(503) 494-3703 Fax 494-2907
Website: www.oneskycenter.org; E-mail: onesky@ohsu.edu
R. Dale Walker, MD (Cherokee), Director & Professor (418-1771)
Douglas A. Bigelow, Deputy Director & Associate Professor
Patricia Silk Walker (Cherokee), Instructor
Michelle J. Singer (Navajo-Dine'), Communications Coordinator

Description: One Sky Center is a National Resource Center for American Indian & Alaska Native Health, Education & Research. The Center was developed with the assistance of a National Advisory Council that represented tribal governments, educators, clinicians, the Indian Health Service, the Bureau of Indian Affairs, the Addiction Technology Transfer Centers, and the Centers for the Application of Prevention Technology as well as the Substance Abuse and Mental Health Services Administration. The Advisory Council met quarterly and contributed strategic thinking, tactical planning, & implementation of the Center programs. *Mission*: To improve prevention & treatment of mental health & substance abuse problems & services among Native people. *Goals*: To promote & nurture effective & culturally appropriate mental health & substance abuse prevention & treatment services for Native populations; to identify & disseminate prevention & treatment practices; to provide technical assistance, training & products.

BLUE MOUNTAIN COMMUNITY COLLEGE
Native American Center - Native American Club
2411 NW Carden, P.O. Box 100 • PENDLETON, OR 97801
(541) 278-5935; Annie Smith, Native American Liaison
E-mail: asmith@bluecc.edu
Website: www.bluecc.edu/support-services/student-life/native-american-club
Officers: Annette Sampson, President
April Sheoships, Vice President
Shannon Galloway, Treasurer; Toni Cordell, Secretary
Special program: Provides assistance for Native American students in securing financial aid, academic & social counseling and general assistance.

LEWIS & CLARK COLLEGE
Graduate School of Education/Counseling Center for Community Engagement
Indigenous Ways of Knowing Program (IWOK), Rogers Hall 105MSC 93
0615 S.W. Palatine Hill Rd., • PORTLAND, OR 97219
(503) 768-6040 Fax 768-6045; E-mail: cce@lclark.edu
Matsya Siosal, Director; Se-ah-dom Edmo, IWOK Coordinator
Cynthia Cosgrave, Contact; E-mail: Cosgrave@lclark.edu
Purpose: To work to protect tribal citizens & strengthen sovereignty.

LEWIS & CLARK LAW SCHOOL - INDIAN LAW PROGRAM
10015 S.W. Terwilliger Blvd. • PORTLAND, OR 97219
(503) 768-6740; Website: www.law.lclark.edu/programs/indian_law
Carma Corcoran, Indian Law Summer School Coordinator
E-mail: Corcoran@lclark.edu
Michael Blumm, Professor of Law & Jeffrey Bain Faculty Scholar (768-6824)
E-mail: blumm@lclark.edu
Description: Provides a solid academic platform for advancement in the practice of Indian law and its diverse specialties. The law school incorporates the best aspects of classroom-based learning with many opportunities for the development of practical legal skills. The law school's emphasis on environmental issues as well as business reflects the ongoing development issues that face many tribes across the country. Our comprehensive curriculum produces graduates prepared to successfully face the challenges at the forefront of Indian law practice. The **Indian Law Summer Program** is a ten-week, multifaceted, intensive program that includes advanced courses in Indian law. Courses offered include a basic federal Indian law course and more advanced courses. In recent years Indian jurisprudence, Contemporary Issues in Indian Law, and Federalism and Indian Law have been among the offerings. Taught by nationally recognized scholars and teachers in the field of Indian law, the summer program allows students from across the country to train in the complex issues comprising the field of Indian law. *Programs*: Indian Law Summer Program; Community Partners of the Indian Law Program; Indian Law Internship; Academic Enhancement Program. *Core Faculty*:, J.B. Kim; Stephen Dow Beckham; Patrice H. Kunesh. *Visiting Faculty*: Gerald Torres (Indian Law Summer Program); Robert Miller (Eastern Shawnee of Oklahoma); Frank Pommerscheim; Alexander Tallchief Skibine; *Scholarships*: Sande Schmidt Memorial Scholarship; Quinault Allottees: Nelson D. Terry Scholarship.

PORTLAND STATE UNIVERSITY – INDIGENOUS NATIONS STUDIES
1633 SW Park Ave. • PORTLAND, OR 97201
(503) 725-5920 Fax 725-3953; E-mail: inst@pdx.edu
Josh Powell, Program Coordinator (725-9098); E-mail: inst@pdx.edu
Winston Grady-Willis, Director, School of Gender, Race & Nations (725-9333); E-mail: sgrn@pdx.edu
Grace Dillon (Anishinaabe), Professor of Indigenous Nations Studies
E-mail: dillong@pdx.edu; (725-8144)
Judy Bluehorse Skelton (Nez Perce/Cherokee), Fixed Term Faculty/Senior Instructor (725-9066) E-mail: judyblue@pdx.edu
Rochelle Nielsen (Shoshone/Bannock), Adjunct Instructor
Monty Herron (Grand Ronde), Adjunct Instructor
Sara Siestreem (Coos), Adjunct Instructor
Program: Minor in Indigenous Nations Studies. *Affiliated faculty*: Cynthia-Lou Coleman (Osage), Professor, Department of Communications; Katy Barber, Associate Professor of History; Virginia Butler, Anthropology; Maria Depriest,

English; Tim Garrison, History; LeaAnn Holer (Chickasaw), Assistant Director, Child Welfare Education Program; Melissa Bennett (Umatilla/Nez Perce/Sac & Fox), Senior Program Coordinator. *Resources*: Environmental Education Through Native American Lenses.

PORTLAND STATE UNIVERSITY
INSTITUTE FOR TRIBAL GOVERNMENT-TRIBAL LEADERSHIP FORUM
Hatfield School of Government, Center for Public Service
P.O. Box 751 • PORTLAND, OR 97207
(503) 725-9000
Don Sampson (Umatilla), Director (541) 215-2753
E-mail: d.sampson@pdx.edu
Peggy Harris, Program Coordinator (215-2919) E-mail: pharris@pdx.edu
Dan Trifone, Program Coordinator (725-5114) E-mail: dtrifone@pdx.edu
Elizabeth Furse & Michelle Singer, Policy Board
Description: A non-profit corporation, organized & operated exclusively for charitable, scientific, literary & educational purposes. *Program*: Certificate in Tribal Relations. *Projects*: Tribal Governance Trainings; Government Agency Trainings; Great Tribal Leaders of Modern Times Interview Video & Curriculum Projects & educational training. *Tribal Leadership Forum Members*: Edward T. Begay (Navajo); John Echohawk (Pawnee); Robert Miller, Esq. (Eastern Shawnee); Billy Frank, Jr. (Nisqually); Alan Parker, Esq. (Chippewa Cree); Kathryn Harrison (Grand Ronde Molalla); Gay Kingman (Cheyenne River Sioux); Andrew Lee (Seneca); Antone Minthorn (Cayuse); Olney Patt, Jr. (Warm Springs); Samuel Penney (Nez Perce); Roy Hunter Sampel (Choctaw & Wyandotte); Don Sampson (Umatilla); Sue Shaffer (Cow Creek Umpqua); Stanley Speaks (Chickasaw); Ernest Stensgar (Coeur d'Alene); Eddie L. Tullis (Poarch Band Creek); Mike Williams (Yupiaq).

PORTLAND STATE UNIVERSITY
NATIVE AMERICAN STUDENT & COMMUNITY CENTER (NASCC)
Cultural Resource Centers
1825 SW Broadway, Suite 228A • PORTLAND, OR 97207
(503) 725-5351 Fax 725-9699; E-mail: cultures@pdx.edu
Alina Begay (Navajo-Dine'), NASCC Manager (725-9697)
Melissa Bennett (Umatilla/NezPerce/Sac & Fox), NASCC Senior Program Coordinator (725-9701) E-mail: melissb@pdx.edu
Purpose: To provide a "cultural home" where Native American, Alaskan Native & Pacific Islander students connect to other students, faculty, staff and community members. *Program*: Native American Student Services (NASS) is a gathering space to celebrate and empower student success through culturally relevant programming, academic support, and inter-generational community engagement to preserve and perpetuate inter-tribal connection for Native American/Alaskan Native/Pacific Islander students and our allies through tradition, ceremony, and storytelling. The NASCC is one of five Cultural Resource Centers at PSU and is a part of Diversity and Multicultural Student Services.

WILLAMETTE UNIVERSITY - AMERICAN ETHNIC STUDIES PROGRAM
College of Liberal Arts, 900 State St. • SALEM, OR 97301
(503) 370-6264 Fax 375-5398; E-mail: aes-info@willamette.edu
Rebecca J. Dobkins, Chairperson & Professor of Anthropology (370-6639)
E-mail: rdobkins@willamette.edu
Elizabeth Bahe, Program Director (370-6960)
E-mail: ebahe@willamette.edu
Description: An interdisciplinary program focusing on the comparative cultural heritage & experiences of various marginalized groups within the U.S. including American Indians & Alaska Natives. The program fosters critical perspective that seeks, as its purpose of inquiry, to explore how social structures and ideological discourses shape, influence, and constrain human activity. In particular, members of our program are committed to the discovery and exploration of how complex social relations of race, ethnicity, culture, and indigeneity, in conjunction with other social systems and structures, can give rise to unjust social relations, limit human endeavor, and normalize privilege and oppression. The primary focus of our program is on traditionally underrepresented communities in the social imaginary of the United States. *Project*: The Art of Ceremony: Regalia of Native Oregon. *Special Resources & Facilities*: Byrd & Polleski Collection of Native North American ethnographic & archaeological materials; Native American Gallery of the Ford Museum of Art.

PENNSYLVANIA

PENNSYLVANIA STATE UNIVERSITY
CENTER FOR THE STUDY OF LEADERSHIP IN AMERICAN INDIAN EDUCATION - AMERICAN INDIAN LEADERSHIP PROGRAM (AILP)
The Pennsylvania State University – Educational Leadership
200 Rackley Bldg. • UNIVERSITY PARK, PA 16802
(814) 865-1487 Fax 865-1480; Website: http://ed.psu.edu/eps/edldr/ailp
Ed Fuller, Program Coordinator, Educational Leadership
E-mail: ejf20@psu.edu

Dolores Pavliska, Program Staff Assistant; E-mail: dlp5189@psu.edu
Felicia Wilkins Turner (Lumbee), Research Associate
E-mail: rqc2@psu.edu (865-1487)
Nona Prestine, Emeritus Faculty, Educational Leadership
E-mail: nap11@psu.edu; (865-2233)
Purpose: To serve as a clearinghouse on American Indian/Alaska Native Education, research, policy, and practice. *Activities*: Train qualified leaders for service to Indian nations by providing graduate degrees in educational administration & certification credentials for principal & superintendent; Fellowships. *Programs*: Provides advanced degrees offered are MBA, Med, MS, DEd & PhD; American Indian Special Education Teacher Training Program. In association with American Indian Leadership Program (AILP), this program is designed to prepare highly trained professionals for careers in the field. AILP is the oldest on-going graduate program for Native Americans in the country. The training of qualified leaders for service to Indian nations is the central aim of the program. The program integrates a behavioral approach to special education in the areas of autism, mental retardation, severe emotional disorders, mild learning & behavioral disabilities, & early childhood disabilities. Issues in American Indian special and regular education are emphasized in seminars and coursework. Graduates receive a master's or a doctoral degree in special education. *Resources*: American Indian Seminar; Native American Indian Student Association; Research Projects; National Conferences; Field Trips. Financial aid available in the form of fellowships & graduate assistantships. Publications. Library. Program established 1970, Center established 2010.

THE PENN CULTURAL HERITAGE CENTER
NATIVE AMERICAN & INDIGENOUS STUDIES (NAIS)
University of Pennsylvania, Penn Museum
3260 South St., Room 416 • PHILADELPHIA, PA 19104
(215) 898-6989; Website http://nais.sas.upenn.edu/
Margaret M. Bruchac (Abenaki) NAIS Coordinator & Assistant Professor of Anthropology (2013-present); E-mail: mbruchac@sas.upenn.edu
Daniel K. Richter, Professor of History & Director of the McNeil Center for Early American Studies (898-9251) E-mail: drichter@history.upenn.edu
Lucy Fowler Williams, Associate Curator & Sabloff Keeper of Collections - Penn Museum (898-4048) E-mail: wfowler@sas.upenn.edu
Catherine Struve, JD, Professor of Law (898-7068)
E-mail: cstruve@law.upenn.edu
Faculty Advisors: Eugene Buckley, Associate Professor of Linguistics; Clark Erickson, Professor of Anthropology; Timothy B. Powell, Lecturer in Religious Studies; Megan Kassabaum, Assistant Professor of Anthropology; Nancy H. Hornberger, Professor of Education

SOUTH CAROLINA

UNIVERSITY OF SOUTH CAROLINA, LANCASTER
NATIVE AMERICAN STUDIES (NAS) CENTEER
119 S. Main St. • LANCASTER, SC 29721
(803) 313-7172; Website: http://usclancaster.sc.edu/nas
E-mail: usclnasp@mailbox.sc.edu
Dr. Stephen Criswell, Director; (313-7108)
E-mail: criswese@mailbox.sc.edu
Christopher Judge, Assistant Director; (313-7445)
E-mail: judgec@mailbox.sc.edu
Brent Burginn, Director of Archives (313-7063)
E-mail: wburgin@sc.edu
Brittany Taylor, Instructor of Art, Curator of Collections; Director of NAS Center Galleries (313-7173)
Claudia Heinemann-Priest, Instructor of English, Catawba, & Native American Literature (313-7470) E-mail: chpriest@sc.edu
Description: Comprehensive center for the study of South Carolina Native American peoples, their histories, and their cultures. Maintains a collection of Catawba Indian pottery in existence; study primary & secondary texts on Native Americans in the Southeast; educational classes & programs. *Facilities*: NAS Center Galleries. *Publication*: NAS Quarterly newsletter. Established 2012.

SOUTH DAKOTA

SOUTH DAKOTA STATE UNIVERSITY
AMERICAN INDIAN EDUCATION & CULTURAL CENTER (AIECC)
AMERICAN INDIAN STUDIES PROGRAM (AIS)
American Indian Student Center
823 Medary Ave., Box 550 • BROOKINGS, SD 57007
(605) 688-6416 Fax 688-5887
April Eastman, Director of American Indian Education & Cultural Center
Richard Meyers (Oglala Lakota), Tribal Relations Director (2012-present); AIS Program Coordinator; E-mail: Richard.meyers@sdstate.edu

Degree: Major & Minor in American Indian Studies. Since its founding in 2010, the American Indian Education & Cultural Center (AIECC) at South Dakota State University (SDSU) houses the American Indian Student Services (AISS) and American Indian Studies (AIS) programs, and remains as the nexus of cultural programming, services & advocacy that supports the recruitment, transition, retention, persistence & graduation of American Indian students. Together, AISS & AIS actively promotes access to higher education & community resources, seeks to increase cross-cultural engagement, encourages the appreciation of cultural and human differences, and advocates for the respectful inclusion of Indigenous knowledge. AIS will include the interdisciplinary, comparative, and ultimately transformative approach to the study of the historical, political, social, and on-going experiences of American Indians, Alaska Natives & Indigenous people within the United States and the global community. Students will gain an awareness of indigenous outlooks that ground the national and international field of AIS, knowledge of the foundations of Federal Indian policy, sovereignty, cultural revitalization and continuance, economic development, the arts; and, in the deployment of appropriate and relevant research with Native & Indigenous communities. Additionally, AIS will explore the historic & contemporary experiences of Indigenous peoples both within & beyond the United States through a critical examination of colonialism and the manner in which Indigenous people throughout the world have countered, resisted, and continue to struggle for justice. Scholarships available.

PRESENTATION COLLEGE - LAKOTA CAMPUS
P.O. Box 1070 • EAGLE BUTTE, SD 57625
(888) 329-5973; (605) 964-4071 Fax 964-1111
Website: www.presentation.edu; Julie S. Thorstensen, M.S., Director
Branch campus of Presentation College in Aberdeen, SD. *Degree programs*: Nursing, Social Work, Business, General Education; Secondary Education. Library. Bookstore.

*OGLALA LAKOTA COLLEGE –
LAKOTA STUDIES DEPARTMENT
3 Mile Creek Rd., P.O. Box 490 • KYLE, SD 57752
(605) 455-6000 Fax 455-2787/6070
Website: www.olc.edu; E-mail: archives@olc.edu
Karen Lone Hill, Lakota Studies Dept. Chair (455-6100)
 E-mail: kloneh@olc.edu
Thomas Shortbull, College President (455-6020)
Julie Johnson, V.P. for Business (455-6011)
Dawn (Tobacco-Two Crow) Frank, V.P. Instruction (455-6035)
Sandra WhiteShield, Graduate Studies Administrator Coordinator (455-6128)
Thedna Zimiga, Foundational Studies Department Chairperson (455-6097)
Wayne Weston, Coordinator of Student Affairs (455-6083)
Theodore Hamilton, General Education Director (455-6097)
Shannon Amiotte, Dean of Education (455-6012)
Ahmed AlAsfour, Business Department Chairperson (455-6081)
Kimberly HeCrow, Humanities Department Chairperson (455-6093)
Christy LoneElk, Nursing Secretary (867-5856)
Monique Apple, Social Woork Chairperson (209-5141)
Dave West, Jr., Cheyenne River Center Director (964-8013)
Georgia Rooks, Eagle Nest Center Director (462-6274)
Colleen Provist, East Wakpamni Center Director (288-1834)
Keeley Claussen, LaCreek Center Director (685-1117)
Cindy Iron Cloud, Pahin Sinte Center Director (867-5404)
Leslie Heathershaw, Pass Creek Center Director (455-2757)
Stephanie Sorbel, Pejuta Haka Center Director (455-2450)
Shirley Brewer, Pine Ridge Center Director (867-5891)
Elizabeth Gibbons, Wounded Knee District Director (867-5352)
Paulina FastWolf, Oglala GED Director (867-5780)
Valerie Charging Eagle, Lakota Woglaka Wounspe School Coordinator
Pejuta Haka Director (455-2450)
Michelle May, Library Director (455-6064)
Description: Offers four degrees and a Lakota Language Certificate. *Mission*: To provide educational opportunities which enhance Lakota life. These opportunities include community services, certificates, GED, associate, bachelor, & graduate degrees. *Programs*: Native American Studies Program; Native American Studies Graduate Program; Nursing Program (Pine Ridge, SD); Headstart. *Instructional Faculty*: Andrew Thompson (Graduate Studies instructor), Charles White Buffalo, Corey Yellow Boy, Marcell Bull Bear, Matthew Uses The Knife, Patrick Lee, JD, Verine White. *Resources*: Resource Center; Library & Archives. Established 1971.

*IHANKTONWAN (YANKTON SIOUX) COMMUNITY COLLEGE
9100 388th Ave., P.O. Box 295 • MARTY, SD 57361
(605) 384-3997 Fax 384-3994; Website: www.iccoyate.com
Tony Garcia (Yankton Sioux), Chief Executive Officer/Academic Dean
 E-mail: drgarcia@iccoyate.com
Ella Rae Stone, Board Chairperson; E-mail: estone@iccoyate.com
Bill Roller, Librarian; E-mail: broller@iccoyate.com

Owned & operated by the Yankton Sioux Tribe. Programs: BA & BS degrees; Vocational Technology Education AA degrees.

*SINTE GLESKA UNIVERSITY –
LAKOTA STUDIES DEPARTMENT
P.O. Box 105 • MISSION, SD 57555
(605) 856-8100 Fax 856-4135; Website: www.sintegleska.edu
Lionel R. Bordeaux, President
 E-mail: lbordeaux@sintegleska.edu
Phil Baird, Provost/COO
Leshia Poignee, CFO/VP of Finance
Cheryl Medearis, VP of Academic Affairs (856-8117)
 E-mail: cheryl.medearis@sintegleska.edu
Debra Bordeaux, VP of Student Services
Sherry Red Owl Neiss, VP of Community Education
Victor Douville, Dean of Lakota Studies, History & Culture Coordinator
 E-mail: victor.douville@sintegleska.edu
William Akard, CRM Director; Ione Quigley, CRM Dept. Chair
Albert White Hat, Sr., Lakota Language Program Director
 E-mail: albertwh@sintegleska.edu
Marcella Cash, Archivist/Director (856-8232)
 E-mail: heritagecenter@sintegleska.edu
Peter Gibbs, Lakota Winter Count & Tipi Projects Coordinator
Description: The only reservation-based tribal university in the U.S. Established to provide postsecondary education on the Rosebud Sioux Reservation. Offers over 30 certificates, associates or bachelors degree programs. The only Masters in Education for elementary teachers located on an Indian Reservation. *Faculty*: Francis Cutt, Lakota Language Instructor; Victor Douville, Lakota History & Culture; Sam High Crane, Lakota Language; Rain Marshall, CRM Instructor. *Program*: Lakota Studies/Creative Writing Program. *Special program*: A Health Careers Opportunity Program (Oyate Kin Zanipi Ktelo-Health for the People) designed to increase the number of American Indians entering health professions—health careers financial aid information is available directly from the Health Careers Program. *Financial Aid*: Available through the College's Financial Aid Office. *Special Facilities*: Lakota Archives & Historical Center; Sicangu Heritage Center Museum & Archives; SGU Buffalo Ranch. *Activities*: Northern Plains Indian Art Market in September; annual creative writing & storytelling festival; poetry reading series & residences, & performances & lectures by writers, scholars, and oral tradition masters; awards for creative writing (fiction & poetry.) *Publication*: Wanbli Ho Journal, by creative writing program. Library.

*SISSETON-WAHPETON COLLEGE
BIA Rd. 700, Agency Village Box 689 • SISSETON, SD 57262
(605) 698-3966 Fax 698-3132/724-0394; Website: www.swc.tc
 Harvey DuMarcee (Sisseton-Wahpeton Sioux), President & Faculty
 Joey Mason, Student Services Director; E-mail: jmason@swc.tc
Dakota Studies Instructors:
 Erin Griffin; E-mail: egriffin@swc.tc
 Darren Renville; E-mail: drenville@swc.tc
 Eric DuMarce, (Dakota Language Instructor)
 E-mail: edumarce@swc..tc
Description: A two-year tribal college offering Associate of Arts degrees. *Special programs*: Community education; Dakota Studies Department. *Mission*: To provide higher education, research, vocational & technical education and continuing education to the members of the Sisseton Wahpeton Oyate of the Lake Traverse Reservation and others within the historical lands of the Sisseton Wahpeton Oyate. SWC will preserve & extend Dakota culture, language, and history while contributing to economic development through the provision of human capital & other resources. *Scholarship*: $500 for graduating high school senior that attend SWCC. *Facilities*: Tribal Archives Development. *Publication*: Dakota Language Text (3 texts for learning the Dakota Language). Established 1974.

BLACK HILLS STATE UNIVERSITY
CENTER FOR AMERICAN INDIAN STUDIES (CAIS)
1200 University St., Unit 9083 • SPEARFISH, SD 57783
(800) ALL-BHSU; (605) 642-6111 Fax 642-6762
Website: www.bhsu.edu
Thomas Jackson, Jr., President (642-6111)
 E-mail: tom.jackson@bhsu.edu
Rod Custer, Provost & Vice President for Academic Affairs (642-6504)
Dr. Urla Marcus, Director of Center & American Indian Studies (642-6578)
 E-mail: urla.marcus@bhsu.edu
Rosie Sprague, CAIS Assistant Director
 E-mail: victoria.sprague@bhsu.edu
John Henry Glover (Salish), Professor of American Indian Studies
 E-mail: john.glover@bhsu.edu
Janet DeCory (Lakota/Cheyenne River Sioux), Professor of History & American Indian Studies - E-mail: jace.decory@bhsu.edu

Description: Enrollment: 4,500 students. *Purpose*: To promote awareness of American Indian cultures, value systems, and social problems among Indian people and as members of the larger society. *Program*: American Indian Studies. *Faculty*: Kanda Guthmiller, Schlarship Coordinator. *Resources*: E.Y. Berry Library-Learning Center. Founded 1883.

UNIVERSITY OF SOUTH DAKOTA
AMERICAN INDIAN JOURNALISM INSTITUTE (AIJI)

Freedom Forum Neuharth Center
555 Dakota St. • VERMILLION, SD 57069
 (605) 677-6315; Jack Marsh, Executive Director
 Mary Hudetz (Crow), Faculty member; E-mail: maryhudetz@naja.com
Purpose: To train Native American college students in journalism; to recruit, train, mentor and retain diverse journalists for media careers. AIJI, a joint program of the Freedom Forum and USD, is a premier journalism training, scholarship & internship program for aspiring journalists from diverse backgrounds. Throughout the 10-day institute, students attend classes, learn basic journalism practices, participate in educational field trips, report, write and produce multimedia projects. Established 2001.

UNIVERSITY OF SOUTH DAKOTA
INSTITUTE OF AMERICAN INDIAN STUDIES
DEPARTMENT OF NATIVE STUDIES

College of Arts & Sciences, Native American Cultural Center
Slagle Hall Rm. 102, 414 East Clark St. • VERMILLION, SD 57069
 (605) 677-6497 Fax 677-6651
 Website www.usd.edu/institute-of-american-indian-studies/
 E-mail: iais@usd.edu
 Kurt Hackemer, Professor & Coordinator (677-5571)
 E-mail: kurt.hackemer@usd.edu
 Jennifer Mace, Secretary; E-mail: Jennifer.mace@usd.edu
Description: Serves as the focal point for American Indian related projects, activities, and programs involving the University of South Dakota. *Goals*: To promote Native studies. *Resources*: Dept. of Native Studies; The South Dakota Oral History Center; The American Indian Research Project; maintains access to the archives by appointment of the South Dakota Oral History Center (5,500+ oral history interviews by Indian & non-Indian peoples); Tiospaye (tribal law study club); Native American Student Services. *Activities*: Organizes campus programs to promote education & awareness of American Indian culture, issues, and problems; assisting University efforts to recruit & retain American Indian students & faculty; encouraging increased levels of research on American Indian life; and strengthening relations with tribes, tribal colleges, and other appropriate American Indian organizations in the state & region. University sponsored graduate/research assistantship for school year. *Goals*: To promote Native studies. *Programs*: BA & minor in Native Studies; Lakota language courses. *Faculty*: Elise Boxer, E-mail: elise.boxer@usd.edu; David Posthumus, E-mail: david.posthumus@usd.edu. *Resources*: The Institute of American Indian Studies; The South Dakota Oral History Center; The American Indian Research Project; The Joseph Harper Cash Memorial Library; The Herman P. Chilson Collection; The W.H. Over Museum; maintains access to the archives by appointment of the South Dakota Oral History Center (5,500+ oral history interviews by Indian & non-Indian peoples); Tiospaye (tribal law study club); Native American Student Services. Library.

TEXAS

TEXAS A&M UNIVERSITY
CENTER FOR THE STUDY OF THE FIRST AMERICANS

Department of Anthropology, College of Liberal Arts
4352 TAMU • COLLEGE STATION, TX 77843
 (979) 845-4046 Fax 845-4070
 Website http://csfa.tamu.edu/; E-mail: csfa@tamu.edu
 Dr. Michael R. Waters, Center Director; E-mail: mwaters@tamu.edu
 Dr. Ted Goebel, Associate Director & Editor of PaleoAmerica
 E-mail: goebel@tamu.edu
 Kelly Graf, Assistant Professor; E-mail: kgraf@tamu.edu
 Jim Wiederhold, Center Research Associate
 Christel Cooper (Chickasaw), Center Office Manager
Mission: Explores the questions surrounding the peopling of the Americas. The Center pursues research, education, and public outreach.

UNIVERSITY OF THE INCARNATE WORD
NATIVE AMERICAN STUDIES PROGRAM

Department of Anthropology • SAN ANTONIO, TX 78209
 (210) 829-3855; Eloise Stoker, Chairperson
Description: Interdisciplinary program includes study of land and native plants & animals. *Instructors*: Gilberto Hinojosa (history); Sara Kerr (Biology); Christy Mackinnon (Biology); Hugh Robichaux (Anthropology); Matthias Schubnell (Native American Literature); and Eloise Stoker. Library.

UTAH

BRIGHAM YOUNG UNIVERSITY
NATIVE AMERICAN STUDIES (NAS) PROGRAM

Department of History, 2141 JFSB • PROVO, UT 84602
 (801) 422-5327 Fax 422-0275
 Jay H. Buckley, Program Coordinator; E-mail: jay_buckley@byu.edu
 Howard Rainer, Reservation Liaison; E-mail: howard_rainer@byu.edu
 LaVay Talk, Multicultural Advisor
 Janice Clemmer, Teacher Education; E-mail: Janice_clemmer@byu.edu
 NAS Minor. *Faculty*: Jay Buckley (History); Larry Echohawk (Law); Dirk Elzinga (Linguistics-Numic/Shoshone); Deryle Lonsdale (Linguistics-Salish); Susie Preston (Linguistics-Navajo); et al. *Resources*: Museum of Peoples & Cultures; archaeological laboratories; Gates Collection on Middle American Languages. Library.

UNIVERSITY OF UTAH - THE AMERICAN WEST CENTER

College of the Humanities
1901 E. South Campus Dr., Rm. 1023 • SALT LAKE CITY, UT 84112
 (801) 581-7611 Fax 581-7612; Website: www.awc.utah.edu
 Gregory E. Smoak, Faculty & Director (587-9575)
 E-mail: greg.smoak@utah.edu
 Floyd A. O'Neil, Director Emeritus
 Cassandra L. Clark, Assistant Director, Program Coordinator
 E-mail: Cassandra.clark@utah.edu
Description: Research unit of the University of Utah, affiliated with the College of Social & Behavioral Sciences. The center consults, researches, publishes, provides educational & curricular support to Indian tribes, school districts, other organizations, and the general public. *Faculty*: Matt Basso, Director (587-9575); E-mail: matt.basso@utah.edu & Gregory E. Smoak, Co-principal Investigators, Shoshone-Bannock Project; *Activities*: Works with tribes to develop historical & ethnographical documentation to support legal claims. It has assisted 15 tribes to develop tribal archives relevant to their land, water, and culture. e.g. Ute Mountain Ute Tribal Archive; The Rivers & Fisheries of the Shoshone-Bannock Peoples; The Tohono O'odham Tribal Archive. It provided 1,500 interviews of Native Americans to the Doris Duke Indian Oral History Project. The Utah American Indian Digital Archive is a joint venture between the American West Center and the Marriott Library with generous support and guidance from the Division of Indian Affairs of the State of Utah. The project compiles essential Utah tribal primary source documents digitized for an online, key-word searchable archive. In undertaking this state-of-the-art venture, Center staff has built on the extensive research done across the country by Floyd O'Neil & Greg Thompson in their combined years of service at the American West Center. The goal is to create an archive that will serve more than just researchers, offering the tribes themselves unprecedented ease of access to information about their past. Now Available! Utah American Indian Digital Archive & The Utah Indian Curriculum Project. *New Project*: The historical register nomination for the Stewart Indian School located just south of Carson City, Nevada. The boarding school opened in 1880 in an attempt to Americanize Native youth through education. For nearly a century, the Stewart Indian School followed national models for the forced assimilation of Native American children. Established 1964.

UNIVERSITY OF UTAH - AMERICAN INDIAN STUDIES PROGRAM
AMERICAN INDIAN RESOURCE CENTER

Department of Ethnic Studies, Bldg. 308
1635 Campus Center Dr. • SALT LAKE CITY, UT 84112
 (801) 581-7019 Fax 581-8437; E-mail: ethnic@utah.edu
 Website: www.diversity.utah.edu/airc
 Ed Munoz, Director of Ethnic Studies (581-5886)
 E-mail: ed.munoz@utah.edu
 Franci Taylor, Resource Center Director (581-7019)
 E-mail: franci.taylor@utah.edu
 E. Daniel Edwards, Director of American Indian Studies
 Elizabeth Archuleta, Academic Program Manager (581-5499)
 E-mail: Elizabeth.archuleta@utah.edu
Minor in Native American Studies.

VIRGINIA

VIRGINIA TECH UNIVERSITY
AMERICAN INDIAN STUDIES PROGRAM

Department of Sociology, 644 McBryde
225 Stanger St. • BLACKSBURG, VA 24061
 (540) 231-9596 Fax 231-3860
 Website: www.sociology.vt.edu/ains
 Brenda Husser, Associate Professor (231-6878)
 E-mail: bhusser@vt.edu
 Samuel R. Cook, Associate Professor & Director
 E-mail: sacook2@vt.edu

Program: BA Minor in American Indian Studies; Virginia Indian Heritage Program. *Faculty*: Samuel Cook; Nick Copeland; *Affiliated Faculty*: Charles Dye; Joe Eska (Sociolinguistics); John Galbraith; Karl Precoda; Dan Thorp.

GEORGE MASON UNIVERSITY
NATIVE AMERICAN & INDIGENOUS STUDIES PROGRAM
Office of Diversity, Inclusion and Multicultural Education
College of Humanities & Social Sciences
405C Robinson Hall A, MS 3E4 • FAIRFAX, VA 22030
  (703) 993-1160 Fax 993-1161
  Eric Gary Anderson, Director & Professor of Native American Studies
  E-mail: eandersond@gmu.edu
Program: An interdisciplinary field of study (minor) committed to understanding both the unity & diversity of present and past Native American tribes, cultures, and experiences. *Resources*: Native American & Indigenous Alliance (NAIA).

LONGWOOD UNIVERSITY – INSTITUTE OF ARCHAEOLOGY
DR. JAMES W. JORDAN ARCHEOLOGY FIELD SCHOOL
Dept. of Sociology, Anthropology, & Criminal Justice Studies
West Ruffner 202, 201 High St. • FARMVILLE, VA 23909
  (434) 395-2875 Fax 395-2200
  Website: www.longwood.edu/sacjs; E-mail: archaeology@longwood.edu
  Brian D. Bates, Institute Executive. Director & Senior Principal Investigator
  E-mail: batesbd@longwood.edu (395-2875)
  J. Craig Rose, Principal Investigator & Senior Archaeologist
  James William Jordan, Anthropologist & Social/Cultural Consultant
Special program: The Archaeology Field School, founded in 1980 by James . Jordan, is engaged in a long-term project at the site of a Late Woodland prehistoric village located at Staunton River Battlefield State Park in Clover, VA. Library holds the O'Brien Collection of over 5,000 prehistoric Virginia Indian artifacts.

WASHINGTON

*MUCKLESHOOT TRIBAL COLLEGE
39811 Auburn-Enumclaw Rd. SE • AUBURN, WA 98092
  (253) 876-3183/3311 Fax 876-2883
  Website: www.muckleshoottribalcollege.org
  Wilma Cabanas (Muckleshoot), Administrator (876-3163)
  E-mail: wilma.cabanas@muckleshoot.nsn.us
  Denise Bill, Program Manager (876-3345)
  E-mail: denise.bill@muckleshoot.nsn.us
  Michele Rodarte, Academic Affairs (876-3291)
Staff: Mitzi Judge, Morgan Sohappy, Renee Lozier-Rojas, Laurie Collins, Jeramie Smith, Dennis Kinerk, Donovan Sather, Cord Rose, Alicia Woods.

*NORTHWEST INDIAN COLLEGE
2522 Kwina Rd. • BELLINGHAM, WA 98226
  (360) 392-2772 Fax 738-0136;
  Website: www.nwic.edu; E-mail: info@nwic.edu
  Justin P. Guillory (Nez Perce), President (2012-present)
  Steve Pavlik, Coordinator-Native American Studies
  Susan Given-Seymour, Director of Outreach, Extension & Training
  (392-4248)
  Dave Oreiro, Native American Studies; E-mail: doreiro@nwic.edu
  Rita Asgeirsson (Yup'ik Eskimo), Faculty In Native Environmental Science
  (392-4275) E-mail: ritaa@nwic.edu
  Melanie Solomon, Public Information Officer (392-4236)
Description: A tribally controlled institution chartered by the Lummi Indian Business Council, headquartered on Lummi Indian Reservation in Washington State, 20 miles from the Canadian border, Northwest Indian College is the only accredited tribal college in the states of Washington, Oregon and Idaho. NWIC grew from the Lummi Indian School of Aquaculture (founded in 1973), a single-purpose institution developed to provide a supply of technicians for employment in Indian-owned & operated fish & shellfish hatcheries throughout the United States & Canada. *Purpose*: To provide postsecondary opportunities for Indian people. Includes academic & vocational education. *Locations*: Lummi (main campus), Muckleshoot, Nez Perce, Nisqually, Port Gamble S'Klallam, Swinomish, Tulalip. Northwest Indian College is part of the Muckleshoot community. The College offers a variety of educational programs to meet the academic, vocational, & cultural needs of the Muckleshoot people & community. The NWIC Muckleshoot Extended Campus brings those programs into the community. At NWIC, Muckleshoot, students are encouraged to develop themselves and discover ways to contribute to their communities and families. They learn ways to understand & support the goals of the Muckleshoot Indian Tribe, especially in the areas of self-governance, as well as social and economic wellbeing. *Activities*: Provides in-service training, planning, research, & evaluation services to tribal institutions & departments. *Programs*: Associates Degrees in Native Environmental Science, Native Oksale Education, et al; Bachelor's Degrees in Native Environmental Science,

Native Studies Leadership, Tribal Governance & Business Management; Tribal Museum Studies Program; Tribal Casino Management Program. *Resources*: Coast Salish Institute. Lummi Library (392-4218).

WESTERN WASHINGTON UNIVERSITY
AMERICAN CULTURAL STUDIES/NATIVE AMERICAN STUDIES
Fairhaven College of Interdisciplinary Studies
516 High St. AH315 • BELLINGHAM, WA 98225
  (360) 650-3620 Fax 650-7668; Website: www.wwu.edu/fairhaven/acs
  E-mail: fairhaven.college@wwu.edu
  Larry J. Estrada, Director of American Cultural Studies
  E-mail: larry.estrada@wwu.edu (650-7717)
  Tanis S'eiltin, Coordinator - American Indian Studies Minor
  E-mail: tanis.seiltin@wwu.edu (650-6564)
Program: Major in American Cultural Studies; Minor in American Indian Studies. *Faculty*: John Feodorov, Chris Friday, Raquel Montoya-Lewis, James Loucky, Dave Oreiro, John Purdy, Dan First Scout Rowe, Tanis S'eiltin. *Resources*: Center for Law, Diversity & Justice; Archaeological & Ethnohistory Field Schools. Archaeological laboratory; The Department of American Cultural Studies offers, "The Native American Experience."

EASTERN WASHINGTON UNIVERSITY
AMERICAN INDIAN STUDIES PROGRAM
EWU Longhouse MS-21EC • CHENEY, WA 99004
  (509) 359-2441 Fax 359-2846
  Website: www.ewu.edu/css/programs/american-indian-studies
  Deirdre A. Almeida, EdD, Program Director & Professor (359-6242)
  E-mail: dalmeida@ewu.edu
  Nicole DeVon, Counselor/Recruiter (359-6665)
  E-mail: ndevon@ewu.edu
  Kimberly Murphy-Richards, Faculty (359-6666)
  E-mail: krichards@ewu.edu
Purpose: To explore the past, present & future of American Indians through studies in their history, literature, research & culture; to promote communication between Native American Alumni, EWU Native American students & Eastern Washington University; to support Native American students, faculty & staff; to provide a resource pool for EWU Native American students. *Program*: BA Minor in American Indian Studies. *Faculty*: Deirdre Almeida, Elise Boxer, Nicole DeVon, Kathleen Warren. *Resources*: Internships; Native American Student Association; Native American Alumni Association. Established 1965.

EVERETT COMMUNITY COLLEGE
TRIBAL ENTERPRISE MANAGEMENT PROGRAM
2000 Tower St., Olympus 214 • EVERETT, WA 98201
  (425) 388-9100 Fax 388-9559
  Lynn Munoz, Program Director
  E-mail: lmunoz@everettcc.edu
Degree: A.A. in Technical Arts. The Tribal Enterprise Management program is a unique opportunity to progress through a series of short-term certificates relevant to workers in such tribal enterprises as hotel, restaurant & gaming services. The goal of the courses and program is to enable workers to build skills and knowledge that move them from entry level positions into mid-management and administration.

EDMONDS COMMUNITY COLLEGE
THE TULALIP COLLEGE CENTER
20000 68th Ave. W. • LYNWOOD, WA 98036
  (425) 640-1459; Jean Hernandez, College President
The Center provides construction training & life skills to Native Americans. A partnership between the Community College and the Tulalip Tribes, and the Department of Education. The 10-week course provides students instruction in the basics of the construction trade. In addition they are awarded a flagging certification, First AID/CPR, and an OSHA 10 Hour Safety Card. Upon completion of the course students are ready to safely enter the construction work environment.

THE EVERGREEN STATE COLLEGE
NATIVE AMERICAN & INDIGENOUS STUDIES (NAIS)
2700 Evergreen Pkwy. NW • OLYMPIA, WA 98505
  (360) 867-6286 Fax 867-6553
  Website www.evergreen.edu/studies/native-studies
  E-mail: nwindian@evergreen.edu
  Kristina Ackley, Director; E-mail: ackleyk@evergreen.edu
  Michelle Aguilar-Wells, Director - Reservation Based Community
  Determined Program
  Tina Kuckkahn, Director (867-5075) Longhouse Education &
  Cultural Center (867-5344)
  Gail Tremblay (Onondaga/Micmac) (867-6334),
  Zoltan Grossman, Frances V. Rains, *Faculty*

Facilities: Northwest Indian Applied Research Institute (867-6614); Longhouse Education & Cultural Center. *Programs*: Master of Public Administration in Tribal Governance; Native Pathways Program; Northwest Coast Native Literature & Printmaking; Speaking Truth inn 20th & 21st Century Indigenous Arts: Legacy, Defiance, and Agency; First Peoples'; Tribal Reservation Based Community Determined Program - provides students the opportunity to explore tribal issues closest to their heart and write a case study based on their findings. Students from the Tulalip, Quinault, Makah, Muckleshoot, Nisqually, Port Gamble S'Klallam & Skokomish Tribes are offered the upper degree program. As of this date, 200 students have graduated from the program. *Resources*: Evergreen Library.

WASHINGTON STATE UNIVERSITY
NATIVE AMERICAN STUDENT CENTER (NASC)
Department of Critical Culture, Gender, & Race Studies
Wilson-Short Hall 111, P.O. Box 641046 • PULLMAN, WA 99164
  (509) 335-8618 Fax 335-0103; E-mail: tribal.liaison@wsu.edu
Barbara Aston (Wyandotte), Director & Special Assistant
  to the Provost/Tribal Liaison (335-8618) E-mail: aston@wsu.edu
Karen Chase, Program Coordinator (335-0012)
  E-mail: Karen.chase@wsu.edu
Faith Price, NASC Assistant Director (335-5849)
  E-mail: faith.price@wsu.edu
Ken Lokensgard, Assistant Director, Plateau Center for Native American
  Research & Collaboration (335-1055) E-mail: kenneth.lokensgard.wsu.edu
Autumn Jones (Blackfeet), Native American Outreach Coordinator
  (335-6718) E-mail: native.outreach@wsu.edu
Kay Kay Weso, Native American Retention Specialist (335-8677)
  E-mail: kaykay.weso@wsu.edu
Aleks Sils, Graduate Assistant & Mentor Program Coordinator
Barbara Aston (Wyandotte), Assistant to the Provost/Tribal Liaison
  E-mail: aston@wsu.edu (335-8618)
Ken Lokensgardm Assistant Director, Plateau Center for Native American
  Research & Collaboration (335-1055)
  E-mail: kenneth.lokensgard@wsu.edu
Mary B. Collins, Museum Director (335-4314)
  E-mail: collinsm@wsu.edu
Jeanette Weaskus (Nez Perce), Clinical Faculty, American Indian Studies
  (335-0565) E-mail: weaskusj@wsu.edu
Richard King, Professor (335-5113); E-mail: crking@wsu.edu
Programs: BA's in comparative ethnic studies & women's studies, and an MA & PhD in American Studies; Archaeology & Ethnography of the Western U.S., with emphasis on American Indian, Pacific & Asian cultural, anthropology, linguistics & archaeology; Native American Recruitment & Retention program; Summer Native American Youth Programs. *Affiliated Professors & Instructors*: Robert R. McCoy (History), Robert E. Ackerman (Emeritus, Archaeology), Andrew Duff (Dept. Chair, Archaeology), Timothy A. Kohler (Archaeology), William D. Lipe (Emeritus, Archaeology), Peter J. Mehringer, Jr. (Emeritus, Archaeology), Lillian A. Ackerman (Ethnographer), William Willard (Emeritus, Cultural Anthropology.) *Resources*: Native American Student & Graduate Student Centers; Clearinghouse on Native Teaching & Learning; Dept. of Anthropology; Research laboratories; Museum of Anthropology; extensive research & reference collections in western U.S. archaeology, botany, and ethnographic basketry.

SEATTLE UNIVERSITY SCHOOL OF LAW
CENTER FOR INDIAN LAW & POLICY
Sullivan Hall 115, 901 12th Ave.
P.O. Box 222000 • SEATTLE, WA 98122
  (206) 398-4284 Fax 398-4310; E-mail: cilp@seattleu.edu
Brooke Pinkham (Nez Perce), Staff Director
  E-mail: pinkhamb@seattleu.edu
Gregory Silverman (Mohegan), Professor & Faculty Director
  E-mail: gmsilver@seattleu.edu
Erica L. Wolf, Senior Attorney; Adjunct Professor;
  Director of Graduate Programs; E-mail: wolfer@seattleu.edu
Guadalupe Ceballos, Staff Attorney; E-mail: ceballosl@seattleu.edu
Michael Mirande, Adjunct Professor, Senior Fellow
  E-mail: mmirande@nwlink.com
Program: Certificate Program in Indian Law. *Mission*: To provide an emphasis on Indian law in the curriculum, research, programs & projects at Seattle University School of Law; to provide unique learning opportunities to students; to develop new programs that will assist Indian tribes & their members deal with the variety of unique laws that apply to them; to make information about current legal issues available to Indian tribes & people. *Faculty*: Catherine O'Neill (Senior Fellow), Michael Mirande (Adjunct Professor & Senior Fellow). The Faculty Fellows for the Center for Indian Law and Policy support the Center's mission and provide valuable input, ideas and suggestions in pursuit of the Center's goals. The Center's faculty fellows are: Catherine A. O'Neill, Professor of Law; Robert S. Chang, Associate Dean for Research and Faculty Development and Professor of Law; Lisa Brodoff, Director, Ronald A.

Peterson Law Clinic and Associate Professor; Ben B. Kim, Professor. The Center for Indian Law & Policy is honored to include the following individuals as Advisory Committee members: Bree Blackhorse, Galanda Broadman; Alix Foster, Swinomish Indian Tribal Community; Lisa Koop, Tulalip Tribes; Sarah Lawson, Snoqualmie Tribe; and Phil Katzen, Kanji & Katzen. *Publications*: CILP News; American Indian Law Journal.

UNIVERSITY OF WASHINGTON
DEPARTMENT OF AMERICAN INDIAN STUDIES
Padelford Hall C-514 Box 354305 • SEATTLE, WA 98195-4305
  (206) 543-9082 Fax 616-3122; E-mail: native@uw.edu
Christopher B. Teuton, Professor & Chairperson (616-6953)
  E-mail: teuton@uw.edu
Marcia Feinstein-Tobey, Office Administrator; E-mail: maf@uw.edu
Elissa Washuta (Cowlitz), Academic Counselor; E-mail: elissaw@uw.edu
Daniel Hart, Co-Director, Native Voices Program (616-7752),
  Director, Canadian Studies Program; E-mail: dhart@uw.edu
Luana Ross (Confederated Salish & Kootenai), Co-Director of Native Voices
  & Adjunct Professor of American Indian Studies (616-9375)
Programs: B.A. major & minor in American Indian Studies; Native Voices Program (Indigenous documentary filmmaking); American Indian Science Technology Education Consortium. *Faculty*: Chadwick Allen; Megan Bang; Cynthia Pearson; Tony Lucero; Charlotte Cote (Makah); Deana Dartt-Newton (Coastal Chumash); Stephanie Fryberg; Alexandra "Sasha" Harmon; Maria Elena Garcia; Daniel Hart (co-director of Native Voices Program; director, Canadian Studies Program); Cheryl Metoyer (Professor Emeritus-Information School); Dian Million (Tanana Athabascan); Marvin Oliver (Quinault/Isleta Pueblo; Professor Emeritus); Scott Pinkham (Nez Perce); Jonathan Tomhave, Lecturer; Michael Tulee, Lecturer; Cynthia Updegrave, Lecturer). *Resources*: The Indigenous Wellness Research Institute; The Ethnic Cultural Center, offers instruction in North American Indian languages, is an integral part of the Department; specialized library collection on the American Indian; Thomas Burke Memorial Museum (extensive collections of Northwest Coast Indians and Eskimos artifacts.)

UNIVERSITY OF WASHINGTON
INDIGENOUS WELLNESS RESEARCH INSTITUTE
4101 15th Ave. NE, Box 354900 • SEATTLE, WA 98105
  (206) 616-2658; Website: www.iwri.org
Karina L. Walters (Choctaw of Oklahoma), IWRI Director (543-5647)
  E-mail: kw5@uw.edu
Tessa Evans-Campbell (Snohomish), IWRI Associate Director;
  Director of the Center for Indigenous Child & Family Research
  E-mail: tecamp@uw.edu
Bonnie Duran (Opelousas/Coushatta), Director, Center for
  Indigenous Health Research; E-mail: bonduran@uw.edu
Cynthia R. Pearson, Associate Director; Research Core
  E-mail: pearsonc@uw.edu
Jordan Lewis (Aleut), Director of the Qualitative Research Division &
  Assistant Professor; E-mail: jplewis@uw.edu
Shana Ava, IWRI Administrative Director
  E-mail: afshana@uw.edu
Myra Parker, JD, PhD (Mandan/Hidatsa), Associate Director,
  IWRI Community Engagement & Outreach Core; E-mail: myrap@uw.edu
Tetana Oguara (Colville), Staff Administrator; E-mail: tetanao@uw.edu
Polly Olsen (Yakama), Director of Community Relations
  & Development Core; E-mail: polly@uw.edu
Chris Charles (Cowichan/Nanaimo/Duwamish), IWRI Media & Technology
  Division Director; E-mail: cchar@uw.edu
Leo Egashira, Research Coordinator, Center for Indigenous Health
  Research & Research Coordinator for the Creating Campus
  Change Projects; E-mail: seattleo@uw.edu
Meg MacDonald, Project Director, Indigenous HIV/AIDS Research
  Training Program & Director/Research Coordinator, Research Training
  & Education Core; Program Coordinator of Indigenous Substance Abuse,
  Medicines, And Addictions Research Training Program (ISMART)
  E-mail: mmacdo@uw.edu
Kerrie Sumner Murphy (Cherokee), Director, Native Youth Enrichment
  Program; E-mail: ksmurph66@uw.edu
Purpose: To support the inherent right of indigenous peoples to achieve full & complete health & Wellness by collaborating in decolonizing research & knowledge building & sharing. *Research coordinators*: Michelle Tiedeman (Alutiiq), Kerrie Murphy (Cherokee) & Caitlin Donald (Osage/Ponca), *Projects*: Sacred Journey: Young Native Women's Wellness Study; Caring for Our Generations; The Native Youth Enrichment Program; The Growing Our Own Project; The Healthy Hearts Across Generations Project; The Indigenous HIV/AIDS Research training program. *Resources*: Center for Indigenous Health Research; Indigenous HIV/AIDS Research Training Program; Native Youth Enrichment Program; Center for Indigenous Child & Family Research. *Activities*: Annual Conference; Newsletter. Publications & Scholarships.

UNIVERSITY OF WASHINGTON SCHOOL OF LAW
NATIVE AMERICAN LAW CENTER
William H. Gates Hall, Box 353020 • SEATTLE, WA 98195
(206) 685-3253; Website: www.law.washington.edu/Indianlaw
Robert Anderson (Bois Forte Ojibwe), Professor & Law Center Director
(206) 685-2861; E-mail: boba@uw.edu
Ron Whitener, Center Executive Director & Director of the Tribal Court Public
Defense Clinic; (206) 543-4099; E-mail: ronw@uw.edu
Peggy Jarrett, Reference Law Librarian (543-1941)
E-mail: pjarrett@uw.edu
Mission: Promote the development of Indian law, and encourage Native Americans, and others with an interest in Indian law, to attend law school. Acts as a resource to Indian tribes, other governments & individuals in the Pacific Northwest, Alaska and across the country. *Faculty*: William Rodgers (environmental law); Molly Cohen (supervising attorney/law lecturer; Brenda Williams; Stacey Lara (director of Parent Advocacy Clinic); Thomas P. Schlosser (part-time lecturer); Cynthia Fester, Editor-Research Publications..

GONZAGA UNIVERSITY SCHOOL OF LAW - INDIAN LAW CLINIC
721 N. Cincinnati St., P.O. Box 3528 • SPOKANE, WA 99220
(509) 313-3723; Website:
www.law.gonzaga.edu/academics/law-clinic/students/indian-law/
Degrees: The Indian Law Program curriculum is diverse & targeted toward developing a concentration in the law applicable to American Indian tribes, American Indians & indigenous peoples of Alaska & Hawaii. The Indian Law Clinic has a contract with the Kalispel Tribe to provide civil and misdemeanor criminal services to Kalispel members. We represent tribal members in state court, federal court, and tribal court. The Indian Law Clinic also serves as public defender for people charged with crimes in Kalispel Tribal Court.

WASHINGTON STATE UNIVERSITY
Department of Speech & Hearing Sciences
Native American Program, P.O. Box 1495 • SPOKANE, WA 99210
(509) 358-6888; Ella Inglebret, Director; E-mail: einglebret@wsu.edu
Anna Brown, Undergraduate Program; Jason Trosine, Graduate Program
Washington State University is currently recruiting Native Americans to train as speech-language pathologists. There's need for speech-language pathologists to serve Native American communities. In response to this need the Department of Speech & Hearing Sciences at Washington State University offers a special training program. This program assists Native students in obtaining financial aid and provides educational support for Native students as they pursue training in the field of speech-language pathology. Graduates are prepared to work in educational or medical settings with individuals who have difficulty with their speech, language, or hearing. They value the contribution that Native American students can make to the field of speech-language pathology. Therefore, we provide students with opportunities to explore this profession as it relates to Native culture through course work, observations, clinical experience, & research in Native communities. In addition, we provide professional mentorship. Some scholarships are available for tribally-enrolled, Native American students. To receive further information, contact:

MEDICINE CREEK TRIBAL COLLEGE
2002 E. 28th St. Bldg. #18 • TACOMA, WA 98404
(253) 573-7950 Fax 573-7895
Description: Located on the Puyallup Indian Reservation in Tacoma, WA, the college is owned & operated by the Puyallup Tribe of Indians. The name of the college reflects the historic Medicine Creek Treaty that recognized many of the tribes of the South Puget Sound region & serves American Indians and Alaska Native peoples. *Mission*: To provide educational opportunities & training to tribal members & Native American people living in the south Puget Sound area. Established 1993.

WASHINGTON STATE UNIVERSITY VANCOUVER
ARTS & SCIENCES - HISTORY DEPARTMENT
NATIVE AMERICAN PROGRAMS
14204 NE Salmon Creek Ave. • VANCOUVER, WA 98686
(360) 546-9738
Steven M. Fountain, Program Coordinator & Clinical Assistant
Professor of History; E-mail: sfountain@wsu.edu

WEST VIRGINIA

WEST VIRGINIA UNIVERSITY
NATIVE AMERICAN STUDIES PROGRAM
207 Knapp Hall, P.O. Box 6284 • MORGANTOWN, WV 26506
(304) 293-4626 Fax 293-3041; Website: www.wvu.edu
E-mail: native_american_studies@mail.wvu.edu
Bonnie M. Brown, Program Coordinator
Program: BA Minor in Native American Studies. *Faculty*: Bonnie Brown (Journalism/Media), Leilani Browning (Native Hawaiian), Tyler Boulware

(History), Ellesa Clay High, Joe Candillo (Pascua Yaqui), Cari Carpenter (English), Jane Dailey (Nursing), Angela Grabuloff (Social Studies), Travis Henline (lecturer), Ellesa Clay High (Eastern Shawnee), Melanie Hockenberry (Child Development & Family Studies), Thomas Keopuhiwa (Native Hawaiian), Karen Manzo (American Indian Health), Carol A. Markstrom (Education), Daniel W. McNeil (Psychology), Connie Pan (MFA Candidate), Robert Pirner (Rosebud Lakota), Anna M. Schein (Librarian), Darla Spencer (Archaeologist). *Event Programs*: Elder-in-Residence Program, Sycamore Circle Lecture Series; West Virginia Native American Heritage Series; NAS Research Colloquim; Student Organization. *Resources*: Grave Creek Mound; Meadowcraft Rock Shelter

WISCONSIN

NORTHLAND COLLEGE - INDIGENOUS CULTURE CENTER (ICC)
NATIVE AMERICAN STUDIES DEPARTMENT
Mead 116, 1411 Ellis Ave. • ASHLAND, WI 54806
(800) 753-1840; (715) 682-1204
Website: https://www.northland.edu/; E-mail: admit@northland.edu
Katrina Werchouski (Red Cliff Lake Superior Ojibwe), Director of ICC
(682-1344) E-mail: kwechouski@northland.edu
Joe Rose (Ojibwe), Program Coordinator; E-mail: jrose@northland.edu
Program: Native American Studies. *Degrees*. BA Major & Minor in Native American Studies. *Faculty*: Joseph Damrell, James Pete, Joe Rose, Elizabeth Wabindato, Karissa White. *Courses*: Ojibwe Language; Native American History; Tribal Legal Studies; Native American Woodland Skills; Native American Arts & Culture; Native American Philosophy, Beliefs, and Values; Northern Plains Cultures. *Resources*: Spring powwow; scholarships available. NAICC established 2011.

UNIVERSITY OF WISCONSIN-EAU CLAIRE
AMERICAN INDIAN STUDIES PROGRAM
Hibbard Hall 150, Box 4004 • EAU CLAIRE, WI 54702
(715) 836-6045 Fax 836-4104; E-mail: ais@uwec.edu
Website: http://www.uwec.edu/academics/college-arts-sciences/departments-programs/american-indian-studies/
Debra Barker, Professor of English & Program Director
E-mail: barkerdk@uwec.edu
Odawa White, Retention Coordinator-Multicultural Affairs
E-mail: whiteol@uwec.edu
Margaret Hebbring, Director of Gear Up Program
Mission: To study the cultures, values, history, and contemporary life of the Indigenous Nations & peoples of North America. Administers both a major & minor in American Indian Studies. *Program*: BA Major & Minor in American Indian Studies. *Faculty Interest*: Wisconsin Indian history & culture. *Faculty*: Ari Anand (Geography & Anthropology); Robert Bell (Lecturer); Lori Jahnke (Academic Dept. Associate); John Mason (Professor, History & Graduate Studies Director); Larry Martin (Philosophy & Religion); Heather Ann Moody, (American Indian Studies Lecturer); Gretchen Peters (American Indian Studies Lecturer); James Oberly (History); Karen O'Day (Art & Design); Gretchen Peters (Music & Theatre Arts); Geoffrey Peterson (Political Science); Jill Smith (Sr. Lecturer, Geography & Anthropology). Daniel Strouthes (Geography & Anthropology). *Resources*: Native American Student Association. Established 1976.

UNIVERSITY OF WISCONSIN, GREEN BAY
DEPARTMENT OF FIRST NATIONS STUDIES
WH 420, 2420 Nicolet Dr. • GREEN BAY, WI 54311
(920) 465-2937; Website: http://www.uwgb.edu/fns/
Lisa M. Poupart (Lac du Flambeau Lake Superior Anishinaabe-Ojibwe)
Chairperson/Advisor; Associate Professor-Ojibwe language
E-mail: poupartl@uwgb.edu
Faculty: Clifford Abbott (Professor-Oneida language); Forrest Brooks (Oneida of Wisconsin, lecturer); J.P. Leary (Assistant Professor); Lisa Poupart (Associate Professor-Ojibwe language). *Program*: An interdisciplinary degree program (BA Major & Minor in First Nations Studies; MS in Applied Leadership for Teaching & Learning with emphasis on indigenous education) that reflects the holistic worldview of the indigenous people of Turtle Island (North America). *Purpose*: To study American Indian culture, philosophy, language, & social, economic, political status of indigenous people & their communities; to preserve & promote the identity of the indigenous people of North America, with an emphasis on the oral traditions of American Indian communities of the western Great Lakes. *Project*: Oneida Language Project. *Resources*: The Education Center for First Nations Studies; Internships.

*LAC COURTE OREILLES OJIBWA COMMUNITY COLLEGE (LCOOCC)
13466 W. Trepania Rd. • HAYWARD, WI 54843
(888) 526-6221; (715) 634-4790 Fax 634-5049
Website: www.lco.edu
Diane Vertin (Ojibwe), President; E-mail: dvertin@lco.edu

Barb Lundberg (Ojibwa), Vice President of Academic & Student Affairs
E-mail: blundberg@lco.edu
Geralynne Berg (Ojibwe), Academic Dean; E-mail: gberg@lco.edu
Dennis White (Ojibwe), Faculty/Cultural Coordinator
E-mail: dwhite@lco.edu
Michelle Haskins (Ojibwe), Faculty-Native American Studies
E-mail: mhaskins@lco.edu
Roxanne Martinson (Ojibwe), Learning Center Program Coordinator
E-mail: rmartinson@lco.edu
Faculty Senate Officers: Tom Antell (Native American Studies Chair), President; Thelma Nayquonabe (Humanities Chair), Vice President; Jason Sanders (Humanities), Secretary. *Mission*: To provide Anishinaabe communities with post-secondary & continuing education while advancing language, culture, and history of the Ojibwa. *Native American Studies Faculty*: Tom Antell, David Scott Bisonette,

*COLLEGE OF MENOMINEE NATION
N172 Hwy. 47/55, P.O. Box 1179 • KESHENA, WI 54135
(715) 799-4921 Fax 799-1308; Website: www.menominee.edu
Diana Morris, Interim President & Chief Academic Officer
E-mail: dmorris@menominee.edu
Melinda Cook, Executive Administrator
Shannon Chapman, Director, MITW-Tribal Higher Education
E-mail: schapman@menominee.edu
Maria Escalante, Library Director
S. Verna Fowler (Menominee), Founding President
E-mail: vfowler@menominee.edu
Green Bay/Oneida Campus:
2733 S. Ridge Rd., Green Bay, WI 54304
(920) 965-0070; Kathy Denor, Interim Vice President
Description: Offers Associate of Arts & Associate of Science degrees in College Academics, Natural Resources, Health & Nursing, Early Childhood Education, and Hospitality Industry & Gaming Management from the National Indian Gaming & Hospitality Institute at the College. Credits are transferable to University of Wisconsin colleges & technical colleges. *Programs*: Student Support Services Program (SSS). *Resources*: National Indian Gaming & Hospitality Institute; Center for Cultural Research; Vocational Rehabilitation for Native Americans Project; Menominee Media Center (MMC); Skills Builder Lab; Walking/Nature Trail.

UNIVERSITY OF WISCONSIN
AMERICAN INDIAN STUDIES (AIS) PROGRAM
1155 Observatory Dr., 315 Ingraham Hall • MADISON, WI 53706
(608) 263-5501 Fax 262-7137; Website: www.amindian.wisc.edu
E-mail: aisp@mailplus.wisc.edu
Roberta Hill (Oneida of Wisconsin), Professor of English & Director of AIS
(262-6211) E-mail: rhill@wisc.edu
Denise Wiyaka, Associate Director of AIS (263-0633)
E-mail: dmwiyaka@wisc.edu
Affiliated Staff:
Aaron Bird Bear (Education) (262-8427); E-mail: abirdbear@wisc.edu
Rebecca Comfort (Education) (263-4174); E-mail: rcomfort@wisc.edu
Jessie Conaway (Nelson Institute) (265-6712); E-mail: dconaway@wisc.edu
Description: Recruits Indian faculty & develop courses that deal in depth with American Indians. Assists & encourages Indian students to pursue advanced & professional degrees. Provides information & assistance to individuals & groups interested in American Indians. *Program*: Certificate in American Indian Studies. *Faculty*: Roberta Hill (Oneida) (English); Larry Nesper (Anthropology); Shannon Sparks (Human Development & Family Studies); Rand Valentine (Linguistics). *Affiliated Faculty*: Erik Brodt (School of Medicine & Public Health); Sarah Clayton (Anthropology); Ada E. Deer (Social Work, Emerita); John Hall (History); John Hitchcock; Tom Jones (Art); Stephen Kantrowitz (History); Patricia Loew (Bad River Ojibwe); Truman T. Lowe (Ho-Chunk); Monica Macaulay (Linguistics); Richard A. Monette (Turtle Mountain Chippewa) (Law); Sheila Reaves; Sissel Schroeder (Anthropology). *Resources*: American Indian Student & Cultural Center (AISCC); American Indian Student Academic Services; Brown Bag Lecture Series; Resource Center; AIS Library; Student Organization, "Wunk Sheek"; Indigenous Law Student Association; Council of American Indian Graduate & Professional Students; American Indian Science & Engineering Society. *Publication*: Newsletter.

UNIVERSITY OF WISCONSIN LAW SCHOOL
GREAT LAKES INDIAN LAW CENTER
975 Bascam Mall, Law Bldg. Rm. 6112 • MADISON, WI 53706
(608) 263-7409; Website: www.law.wisc.edu/glilc
Richard A. Monette (Turtle Mountain Chippewa), Director
E-mail: rmonette@wisc.edu
Taniquelle Thurner, Deputy Director; E-mail: taniquelle@gmail.com
Mission: To improve the practical legal skills of all students interested in Federal Indian Law while providing a legal resource for Native American

tribes; to provide an academic & educational atmosphere and opportunity for law students to study Federal, State, and tribal laws affecting Indian tribes and their members; to provide legal assistance on uniquely tribal legal matters; to encourage & assist Indian students in obtaining a legal education. *Programs/Projects*: Tribal Externships - The externship program is designed to give law students a unique opportunity to gain real world experience by working and sometimes living on a reservation; Indian Business Development Project - This project is a partnership with Wisconsin Department of Transportation and the AICC/AICTA to assist Indian businesses & economic development programs on & off reservations in building their capacity to become Disadvantage Business Entity (DBE) certified. *Resources*: The Indigenous Law Student Association (ILSA). *Publication*: Indians In the News Today. Established 1992.

UNIVERSITY OF WISCONSIN-MILWAUKEE
AMERICAN INDIAN STUDIES PROGRAM
College of Letters & Sciences, Holton Hall 365
P.O. Box 413, 2442 E. Hartford Ave. • MILWAUKEE, WI 53201
(414) 229-6251; E-mail: ais-info@uwm.edu
Cary Miller (Anishinaabe), Associate Professor & AIS Director (229-6251)
E-mail: carym@uwm.edu
Celeste Clark, Senior Advisor, American Indian Student Academic Services
E-mail: n1lumbee@uwm.edu (229-5880)
Description: An interdisciplinary academic program offering an American Indian Studies major, or an American Indian Studies certificate. A unique aspect of American Indian Studies at UWM is its connection with the Electa Quinney Institute, which has a strong focus on American Indian education-related initiatives. The Institute supports research, service, and learning opportunities for both American Indians and non-Indians interested in working with tribal communities. *Faculty*: David Beaulieu (Education); Kimberly Blaeser (English); Donald Green (Sociology); Cary Miller (History); Margaret Noodin (English); Bernard Perley (Anthropology); (Robert) Jason Sherman (Anthropology); Laura Villamil (Anthropology); Michael Wilson (English). *Resources*: American Indian Student Association; American Indian Art Festival; Wisconsin Woodland American Indian Summer Field Institute.

UNIVERSITY OF WISCONSIN-STEVENS POINT
NATIVE AMERICAN CENTER-NATIVE AMERICAN STUDIES PROGRAM
College of Letters & Science, Department of Sociology & Social Work
464 College of Professional Studies • STEVENS POINT, WI 54481
(715) 346-3576 Fax 346-3577
Andrew Gokee, Center Director; (346-4147); E-mail: agokee@uwsp.edu
Henry St. Maurice, Program Coordinator; E-mail: hstmauri@uwsp.edu
Andrew Topping, President-American Indians Reaching for Opportunities
BriAnne Goss, President-American Indian Science & Engineering Society
Program: Minor in Native American Studies, Associates Degree. *Mission*: To develop & support educational programs, projects, and initiatives to encourage the perpetuation of tribal languages & cultural traditions among Native American communities in Wisconsin; to promote fellowship among the American Indian community of central Wisconsin; to foster the formal and informal educational goals of American Indian people; to identify, transform, and utilize educational resources that address the needs of Wisconsin tribes in a manner commensurate with the cultural values of tribal communities; to advance public education concerning American Indians on the UWSP campus and in surrounding communities. *Resources*: The NAC has developed an extensive collection of educational materials pertaining to Native Americans. The materials address a variety of topics including: Contemporary Tribal Government; Federal Indian Policy and Law; Tribal Economic Development; Gaming; Traditional Culture; Education; Social Issues. The Native American Resource Room collection includes hundreds of books, manuals, articles, research papers, cassettes, and videotapes which are available to students, faculty, staff, and the general public at no charge. Native American Language Preservation; Weekend College Program for Native Americans. Established 1978.

UNIVERSITY OF WISCONSIN-SUPERIOR
FIRST NATIONS CENTER - FIRST NATIONS STUDIES PROGRAM
Human Behavior, Justice & Diversity Department
Swenson Hall 3117, Belknap & Catlin • SUPERIOR, WI 54880
(715) 394-8007
Website: https://www.uwsuper.edu/acaddept/hbjd/firstnations/index.cfm
Gary W. Johnson, Assistant Professor & Center Director
E-mail: gjohnson@uwsuper.edu
Bret Evered, Lecturer, First Nation Studies
E-mail: abeal@uwsuper.edu
Description: A curriculum, developed and presented by Native Americans, that provides an opportunity to learn about the Native American way of life, and to share cultures & bridge the communication gap among the people of Northern Wisconsin. *Program*: Minor in First Nations Studies. *Resources*: Circle of Native Nations.

WYOMING

*WIND RIVER TRIBAL COLLEGE
P.O. Box 1190 • FORT WASHAKIE, WY 82514
(866) 701-8385; (307) 335-8243 Fax 335-8148
Website: www.aihec.org
Marlin Spoonhunter (Arapaho), President
 E-mail: mspoonhunter@windrivertc.org
Mitchell Stone, Academic Consultant
 E-mail: mstone@windrivertc.org
Tillie M. Jenkins, Cultural Resource Specialist & Arapaho Instructor
 E-mail: tjenkins@windrivertc.org
Board of Regents: Andrea Clifford, Pamela Gambler, Sandra Iron Cloud, Alfred Redman, Vernon Hill, Gloria C'Bearing.

UNIVERSITY OF WYOMING - AMERICAN INDIAN STUDIES PROGRAM
College of Arts & Sciences, Ross Hall 108
1000 E. University Ave.• LARAMIE, WY 82071
(307) 766-6520 Fax 766-2473
Website: www.uwyo.edu/aist/; E-mail: aist@uwyo.edu
Caskey Russell, Program Director (766-6521)
 E-mail: ccaskey@uwyo.edu
Judith Antell, Director Emerita
 E-mail: antell@uwyo.edu (766-6521)
Description: Undergraduate major & minor; MA & PhD minor. Examines Native North American culture & social life from both historical & contemporary perspectives. *Faculty*: Judith Antell; Debra Donahue; William Gribb; Michael E. Harkin; Pamela Innes; Angela Jaime; Jeffrey D. Means; Caskey Russell; Colin Samson, Visiting Eminent Scholar. *Resources*: High Plains American Indian Research Institute; Provides support services to Native students. Outreach efforts; American Indian Alumni Association; Honoring of American Indian Graduates. *Events*: Fall Forum each November brings renowned American Indian scholars, writers, and artists to the campus; and American Indian Week in March. *The High Plains American Indian Research Institute* (HPAIRI) aims to promote positive & productive relationships between the University of Wyoming & regional American Indian communities. Assisting with research, education, & service, the HPAIRI intends to facilitate tribal access to University resources and, at the same time, to help UW researchers connect with tribal communities in a coordinated fashion. The HPAIRI will facilitate collaborative research among tribal communities, UW and visiting faculty, and UW undergraduate and graduate students. Its research agenda will be based on the needs and interests of Native communities in the region and those communities will be full partners in research endeavors. Additionally, the HPAIRI is working toward establishing a collection of informational materials that may assist both tribal and UW researchers with their projects. In 2011, a survey was submitted to University of Wyoming faculty and staff to learn about research and educational activities between UW participants and tribal partners. The results indicate that a variety of UW units do have relationships with tribal communities in the region and a significant number of those relationships involve science, technology, engineering, and/or math (STEM) activities. The survey results will assist with the continued development of the HPAIRI & with the implementation of its activities. *Publication*: The Ledger

AMERICAN INDIAN COLLEGE FUND MEMBER COLLEGES

Aaniiih Nakoda College (Fort Belknap Community College), Harlem, MT
Bay Mills Community College, Brimley, MI
Blackfeet Community College, Browning, MT
Cankdeska Cikana Community College, Fort Totten, ND
Chief Dull Knife College, Lame Deer, MT
College of Menominee Nation, Keshena, WI
College of the Muscogee Nation, Okmulgee, OK
Comanche Nation College, Lawton, OK
Crownpoint Institute of Technology, Crownpoint, NM
Dine College, Tsaile, AZ
Fond du Lac Tribal & Community College, Cloquet, MN
Fort Belknap Community College, Harlem, MT
Fort Berthold Community College, New Town, ND
Fort Peck Community College, Poplar, MT
Haskell Indian Nations University, Lawrence, KS
Ilisagvik College, Barrow, Alaska
Institute of American Indian Arts, Santa Fe, NM
Keweenaw Bay Ojibwa Community College, Baraga, MI
Lac Courte Oreilles Ojibwa Community College, Hayward, WI
Leech Lake Tribal College, Cass Lake, MN
Little Big Horn College, Crow Agency, MT
Little Priest Tribal College, Winnebago, NE
Muckleshoot Tribal College
Nebraska Indian Community College, Macy, NE
Northwest Indian College, Bellingham, WA
Oglala Lakota College, Kyle, SD
Red Crow Community College, Alberta, Canada
Saginaw Chippewa Tribal College, Mt. Pleasant, MI
Salish Kootenai College, Pablo, MT
Shanktonwan (Yankton Sioux) Community College
Sinte Gleska University, Rosebud, SD
Sisseton Wahpeton College, Sisseton, SD
Sitting Bull (Standing Rock) College, Fort Yates, ND
Southwest Indian Polytechnic Institute, Albuquerque, NM
Stone Child Community College, Box Elder, MT
Tohono O'odham Community College,
Turtle Mountain Community College, Belcourt, ND
United Tribes Technical College, Bismarck, ND
White Earth Tribal & Community College, Mahnomen, MN
Wind River Tribal College, Ethete, WY

CANADA

ALBERTA

ATHABASCA UNIVERSITY - CENTRE FOR WORLD INDIGENOUS KNOWLEDGE & RESEARCH
1 University Dr. • ATHABASCA, AB T9S 3A3
(780) 675-6100 Fax 675-6437
Website: www.athabascau.ca/indigenous
Priscilla Campeau, Centre Chair & Program Administrator
 E-mail: pcampeau@athabascau.ca
Tracy Lindberg (Cree/Metis), Director of Indigenous Education
Maria Campbell, Elder in Residence; E-mail: ivyl@athabasca.ca
Degrees: Undergraduate, graduate & certificate programs.
Courses: Cree; The Metis; Indigenous Issues; etc.

UNIVERSITY OF CALGARY
INTERNATIONAL INDIGENOUS STUDIES PROGRAM
Department of Sociology, 2500 University Dr., NW • CALGARY, AB T2N1N4
 (403) 220-5521; Website: www.arts.ucalgary.ca/indg
 James S. Frideres, Program Coordinator; E-mail: frideres@ucalgary.ca
Degree: BA in International Indigenous Studies. Focuses upon such aspects of Indigenous peoples' experience as arts, cultures, ecologies, economies, histories, identities, knowledge, languages, literatures, music, community & political dynamics. Aboriginal related research projects. *Resources*: Native Centre.

RED CROW COMMUNITY COLLEGE
P.O. Box 1258 • CARDSTON, AB T0K0K
 (403) 737-2400 Fax 737-2101; Website: www.redcrowcollege.com
 Marie Smallface Marule, President
 Roy Weasel Fat, VP Academic Programs
 Henry Big Throat, VP Student Services
Mission: To meet the cultural, educational, and training needs for Kainaiwa and beyond; to provide leadership through its programs & services to nurture self-realization based on Kainaissinni. *Resources*: University of Calgary Library; Virtual Library. *Publication*: Quarterly newsletter.

UNIVERSITY OF ALBERTA - DEPARTMENT OF NATIVE STUDIES
2-31 Pembina Hall • EDMONTON, AB T6G 2H8
 (780) 492-2991 Fax 492-0527; Website: www.nativestudies.ualberta.ca
 E-mail: nativestudies@ualberta.ca
 Chris Andersen, Dean of Professor (492-2991)
 E-mail: nsdean@ualberta.ca
 Nathalie Kermoal, Associate Dean Academic & Associate Professor
 E-mail: Nathalie.kermoal@ualberta.ca (492-7207)
 Jessica Kolopenuk, Curriculum Developer & Special Projects
 E-mail: Jessica.kolopenuk@ualberta.ca
 Kirsten Linndquist, Director of Aboriginal Governance Program
 E-mail: kirstenl@ualberta.ca; (492-8062)
 Nathalie Kermoal, Associate Dean Academic, Director of Rupertsland Centre
 for Metis Research; E-mail: kewray@ualberta.ca; (492-7218)
Faculty: Isabel Altamirano-Jimenez; Ellen Bielawski; Sarah Carter; James Dempsey; Brenda Parlee, (Canada Research Chair); Sean Robertson; Dorothy Thunder (Full-time Cree Instructor); Frank Tough; Matthew Wildcat (Instructor); Richard Price & Pat McCormack (Emeritus). Resources: Rupertsland Centre for Metis Research

UNIVERSITY OF LETHBRIDGE
DEPARTMENT OF NATIVE AMERICAN STUDIES
The Faculty of Arts & Sciences, A414 University Hall
4401 University Dr. • LETHBRIDGE, AB T1K 3M4
 (403) 329-2635 Fax 380-1855; E-mail: nas@uleth.ca
 Muriel Mellow, Acting Chairperson (329-2168)
 E-mail: Muriel.mellow@uleth.ca
 Henrie Beaulieu, Faculty (329-2488) E-mail: beaulieu@uleth.ca
 Monique Giroux, Research Chair (394-3969)
 E-mail: moniique.giroux@uleth.ca
 Elizabeth Ferguson, Native Student Advisor
 E-mail: Elizabeth.ferguson@uleth.ca
Degree: BA in Native American Studies. *Faculty*: Henrie Beaulieu, Leroy Little Bear (Emeritus), Donald Frantz (Emeritus-Blackfoot & Tiwa Grammar), Maura Hanrahan (Associate Professor). *Resources*: Native American Student Association. *Activities*: Native Awareness Week.

BRITISH COLUMBIA

SIMON FRASER UNIVERSITY
DEPARTMENT OF FIRST NATIONS STUDIES
8888 University Dr. • BURNABY, BC V5A 1S6
 (778) 782-4774; Website: www.sfu.ca/fns
 Eldon Yellowhorn, Associate Professor & Chair
 Marianne Ignace, Director, First Nations Language Centre
Faculty: Eldon Yellowhorn, Marianne Ignace, Annie Ross, Deanna Reder, Rudy Reimer/Yumks. *Resources*: First Nations Language Centre.

VANCOUVER ISLAND UNIVERSITY
DEPARTMENT OF FIRST NATIONS STUDIES
900 5th St. • NANAIMO, BC V8R 5S5
 (250) 740-6194; 753-3245
 Laurie Meijer Drees, Dept. Chair; E-mail: laurie.meijerdrees@viu.ca
Program: BA major & minor in First Nations Studies. *Faculty*: Laura Cranmer; laura.cranmer@viu.ca, Allyson Anderson, Lara Cranmer, Delores Louie (Resident Elder), Laurie Meijer Drees, Ray Peter, Keith Smith.

VANCOUVER ISLAND UNIVERSITY
OFFICE OF ABORIGINAL EDUCATION
900 5th St. • NANAIMO, BC V8R 5S5
 (250) 740-6542
 Sharon Hobenshield (Gitxsan First Nations), Director of Aboriginal Education
 E-mail: Sharon.hobenshield@viu.ca
 Sylvia Scow (Dene), Associate Director; E-mail: Sylvia.scow@viu.ca
 Pam Botterill, Aboriginal Outreach Coordinator; E-mail: pam.botterill@viu.ca
 Sheila Cooper, Aboriginal Projects Manager; E-mail: Sheila.cooper@viu.ca
Programs: Aboriginal University Bridging Program Certificate:
1-Year Certificate Program.

UNIVERSITY OF NORTHERN BRITISH COLUMBIA
FIRST NATIONS STUDIES PROGRAM
Department of First Nations Studies
3333 University Way • PRINCE GEORGE, BC V2N 4Z9
 (250) 960-5595 Fax 960-5545; Website: www.unbc.ca/firstnations/
 Gary Wilson, Department Chair (960-5514) E-mail: gary.wilson@unbc.ca
 Ross Hoffman, Associate Professor of Native Studies (960-5242)
 E-mail: hoffmanr@unbc.ca
 Antonia Mills, Acting Chair (960-6690) E-mail: millsa@unbc.ca
 Paul Michel, Director of First Nations Centre; E-mail: michelp@unbc.ca
 Amanda Hancock, Academic Advisor (960-5272) Email: hanca000@unbc.ca
Degrees: Certificate, BA & MA in First Nations Studies. *Faculty*: Ross Hoffman, Rheanna Robinson, Assistant Professor & Senior Advisor to the President; Judy Thompson, Assistant Professor; , Margo Greenwood (Cree), Agnes Pawlowska-Manville; Margaret Anderson, Professor Emeritus); Antonia Mills, Professor Emeritus. *Adjunct Faculty*: Alyce Johnson (Kluane First Nation), Deanna Nyce, Wendy Aasen, Paul Michel (Shuswap First Nations), Earl Henderson (Sioux, Cree, Metis); Travis Holyk; Tina Fraser, Gregory Lowan-Trudeau (Metis) *Instructor*: Leona Neilson (Cree Culture & Language); Nellie Prince (Nak'azdli Band). *Sessional Instructors*: Leona Neilson (Cree); Nellie Prince (Nak'Azdli Band). *Facilities*: First Nations Centre. *Special program*: Northern Advancement Program.

THE UNIVERSITY OF BRITISH COLUMBIA
FIRST NATIONS & INDIGENOUS STUDIES PROGRAM
1866 Main St., Buchanan E266 • VANCOUVER, BC V6T 1Z1
 (604) 822-2905;Website: www.fnsp.arts.ubc.ca
 Daniel Justice (Cherokee), Chairperson
 Linc Kesler, Director & Sr. Advisor to President on Aboriginal Affairs
 Tanya Bob, Program Advisor & Practicum Coordinator; Coordinator
 of Aboriginal Student Affairs; E-mail: Tanya.bob@ubc.ca
 Sheryl Lightfoot (Anishinaabe), Canada Research Chair in Global
 Indigenous Rights & Politics
Faculty: Glen Coulthard (Yellowknives Dene'); Dory Nason; Daniel Justice (Cherokee); David Gaertner; Sarah Hunt (Kwagiulth); Dory Nason; Johnny Mack (Law);

UNIVERSITY OF VICTORIA - INDIGENOUS STUDIES PROGRAM
Department of History, First Peoples House – Room 143
P.O. Box 3050 STN CSC • VICTORIA, BC V8W 3P5
 (250) 472-5185 Fax 472-5185; Website: www.web.uvic.ca/isminor
 Christine O'Bonsawin, Program Director & Professor of History (853-3807)
 E-mail: cobonsaw@uvic.ca
 Karen Erwin, Interdisciplinary Programs Assistant
 E-mail: idpassis@uvic.ca
Program: BA Minor in Indigenous Studies.

UNIVERSITY OF VICTORIA
INDIGENOUS GOVERNANCE PROGRAM
Faculty of Human & Social Development
3800 Finnerty Rd., HSD Bldg. Rm. A260
P.O. Box 1700 STN CSC • VICTORIA, BC V8W 2Y2
(250) 721-6438 Fax 472-4724
Website: www.web.uvic.ca/igov; E-mail: igov@uvic.ca
Jeff Corntassel (Cherokee), Director & Associate Professor (721-6440)
  E-mail: ctassel@uvic.ca
Taiaiake Alfred (Mohawk), Graduate Advisor & Professor (721-6439)
  E-mail: gta@uvic.ca
Melvin Peters, Academic Administrative Officer (251-8034)
  E-mail: petersm@uvic.ca
Charlotte Loppie, Professor of Public Health & Social Policy (472-5451)
  E-mail: loppie @uvic.ca
Program: MA in Indigenous Governance; PhD by Arrangement

MANITOBA

UNIVERSITY OF WINNIPEG
DEPARTMENT OF INDIGENOUS STUDIES
Richardson College for the Environment & Social Complex
599 Portage Ave. 3rd Floor • WINNIPEG, MB R3B 2E5
(204) 786-9397 Fax 943-4695; Website: www.uwinnipeg.ca
Jacqueline Romanow, Chair; E-mail: j.romanow@uwinnipeg.ca
Kevin Lamoreux, Associate Vice-President of Indigenous Affairs
  (786-9931) E-mail: k.lamoureux@uwinnipeg.ca
Julie Pelletier, Associate Professor; E-mail: ju.pelletier@uwinnipeg.ca
Programs: BA in Indigenous Studies; MA in Indigenous Governance; MDP Master's in Development Practice in Indigenous Development; CATEP (Community-Based Aboriginal Teacher Education Program); Indigenous History Courses (PDF) Indigenous Spiritual & Pastoral Care Diploma is a two-year post-secondary program. The department is grounded in the intellectual and cultural heritage of Indigenous peoples in Canada and around the globe. Supports the teaching of the Indigenous languages Ojibwe and Cree. *Faculty*: Gabriel Ricardo Nemoga Soto; Jacqueline Romanow (Graduate Coordinator); Lorena Sekwan Fontaine; Shailesh Shukla; Tobasonnakwut (Indigenous Governance); Ida Bear & Annie Boulanger (Indigenous Languages)

NEW BRUNSWICK

ST. THOMAS UNIVERSITY - NATIVE STUDIES PROGRAM
51 Dineen Dr. • FREDERICTON, NB E3B 5G3
(506) 460-0366 Fax 450-9615; Website: www.stu.ca
Roland Chrisjohn, Associate Professor & Chairperson
Graydon Nicholas, Endowwed Chair in Native Studies
Part-time Faculty: Andrea Bear Nicholas, Professor & Chair of Studies in Aboriginal Cultures of Atlantic Canada; Mark Landry, Lecturer. *Program*: BA in Native Studies.

NOVA SCOTIA

CAPE BRETON UNIVERSITY - MI'KMAQ COLLEGE INSTITUTE
DEPARTMENT OF INDIGENOUS STUDIES
1250 Grand Lake Rd., P.O. Box 5300 • SYDNEY, NS B1P 6L2
(902) 563-1871 Fax 563-1693; E-mail: unamaki@cbu.ca
Website: www.cbu.ca/unamaki
Stephen Augustine, Associate Vice President, Indigenous Affairs
  & Unama'ki College (563-1827)
  E-mail: stephen_augustine@cbu.ca
Stephanie Inglis, Department Chairperson
  E-mail: Stephanie_inglis@cbu.ca
Catherine Arseneau, Director, Cultural Resources (563-1326)
  E-mail: Catherine_arseneau@cbu.ca
Ann Denny, Aboriginal Services Coordinator
  E-mail: ann_denny@cbu.ca (563-1402)
Leanne Simmons, Aboriginal Program Director
  E-mail: Leanne_simmons@cbu.ca (563-1240)
Diane Chisholm, Mi'qmaq Resource Centre Coordinator
  E-mail: diane_chisholm@cbu.ca (563-1660)
Description: Unama'ki College (formerly Mi'kmaq College Institute) of Cape Breton University strives to meet the needs of Mi'kmaw and other First Nations students & contribute to educational goals set by Mi'kmaw communities. *Degrees*: BA.BACS major in Mi'kmaq Studies; Certificate in Mi'kmaq Cultural Heritage Preservation; MBA (CED) First Nations Option. Courses examine aspects of Mi'kmaq culture including language, governance, spirituality & contemporary social issues. *Resources*: Mi'kmaq Resource Centre.

ONTARIO

QUEEN'S UNIVERSITY
ABORIGINAL TEACHER EDUCATION PROGRAM
Faculty of Education, Duncan McArthur Hall
511 Union St. • KINGSTON, ON K7M 5R7
(613) 533-6218 Fax 533-6584; E-mail: atep@queensu.ca
Lindsay Morcom, Coordinator; E-mail: morcoml@queensu.ca
Provides an opportunity for candidates to specialize in Aboriginal education.
Facilities: Resource library.

UNIVERSITY OF WESTERN ONTARIO
FIRST NATIONS STUDIES PROGRAM
Social Science Centre, Rm. 3254 • LONDON, ON N6A 5C2
(519) 661-2111 Fax 661-2062; E-mail: frstntns@uwo.ca
Susan Hill (Mohawk), Professor & Program Director; E-mail: shill26@uwo.ca
Chantelle Richmond, Associate Professor of Geography
  E-mail: crichmo2@uwo.ca
Rick Fehr, Assistant Professor & Acting Director
  E-mail: rfehr@uwo.ca
Program: BA Major & Minor in First Nations Studies. *Part-time Faculty*: & *Lecturers*: Ted Baker, Sadie Buck, David Kanatawakhon-Maracle, Mario Wassaykeesic. Research *Interests*: Mohawk & Ojibway customs & language. Library.

McMASTER UNIVERSITY - INDIGENOUS STUDIES PROGRAM (ISP)
1280 Main St. West, Hamilton Hall 103/B • HAMILTON, ON L8S 4K1
(905) 525-9140 ext. 27426 Fax 540-8443
Website: www.indigenous.mcmaster.ca; E-mail: indgdir@mcmaster.ca
E-mail: indigenous.director@mcmaster.ca
Rick Monture (Mohawk), Academic Director & Faculty
  E-mail: monture@mcmaster.ca
Dawn Martin-Hill (Mohawk), Associate Professor of Anthropology
MacPherson Chair in Indigenous Studies
  E-mail: dawnm@mcmaster.ca
Vanessa Watts (Mohawk), Professor of Sociology
  E-mail: wattsv@mcmaster.ca
Tracy Bomberry, Events & Outreach
  E-mail: indigenous.manager@mcmaster.ca
Josh Dockstader, Indigenous Student Counselor
  E-mail: indigenous.counsellor@mcmaster.ca
James Knibb-Lamouche, Associate Director of Indigenous Student Services
  E-mail: thomam27@mcmaster.ca
Mission: To recruit and assist Indigenous students in obtaining a degree in their area of interest; to increase awareness of Indigenous culture and issues; to work collaboratively with Aboriginal communities. *Programs*: ISP offers a three-year Combined Bachelor of Arts Degree in Indigenous Studies and Another Subject. Students have their choice of combining Indigenous Studies with a subject area from either Humanities or Social Sciences. However, students in other disciplines may take Indigenous Studies as a Minor or as electives. Sessional Lecturers: Ima Johnson (Mohawk); Renee Thomas-Hill (Mohawk); Amber Skye (Mohawk); Ali Darnay (Anishinaabe); Monique Mojica; Bernice Downey.

TRENT UNIVERSITY - DEPARTMENT OF INDIGENOUS STUDIES
1600 Westbank Dr. • PETERBOROUGH, ON K9J 7B8
(705) 748-1011 Fax 748-1416
Website: www.trentu.ca/academic/nativestudies
E-mail: indigenousstudies@trentu.ca
Christine Welter, Academic Program Coordinator
  E-mail: cwelter@trentu.ca
David Newhouse, Chair of Indigenous Studies
  E-mail: dnewhouse@trentu.ca
Vernon Douglas (Biidaaban), Cultural Advisor
Skahendowaneh Swamp (Mohawk), Chair of Indigenous Knowledge
Roroniake:wen – Dan Longboat (Mohawk), Director of
  Indigenous Environmental Studies Program
Lynne Davis, Director PhD Program in Indigenous Studies
  E-mail: lydavis@trentu.ca
Don N. McCaskill, Director, Thailand Year Abroad Program
  E-mail: dmccaskill@trentu.ca
Description: The department explores indigenous knowledge, aboriginal history, indigenous environmental knowledge, aboriginal modernity and post colonial/indigenous theory, Anishinaabe language & culture, Haudenosaunee culture & tradition and indigenous performance. The faculty is engaged in community-based research; all serve as advisors to Aboriginal, provincial & federal governments & organizations. *Program*: BA in Foundations for Indigenous Learning; MA in Canadian Studies & Indigenous Studies; PhD in Indigenous Studies. *Faculty*: Lynn Davis, Mark Dockstator, Chris Furgal,

Rosalie Jones (Pembina Chippewa), Dan Longboat (Mohawk), Edna Manitowabi (Odawa/Ojibway), Don McCaskill (Director of Thailand Year Abroad Program), Neal G. McLeod (Cree), Marrie Mumford, David Newhouse (Onondaga), Paula Sherman (Algonquin), Skahendo-waneh Swamp (Mohawk-Akwesasne), Professor emeriti, Shirley Williams (Pheasant) & Marlene Brant-Castellano. *Part-time faculty*: Nicole Bell & Tasha Beeds. *Special programs*: Thailand Year Abroad Program; Indigenous Women's Symosium. *Resources*: First Peoples House of Learning, Gzowski College; Nozhem Theatre at Gzowski College; Native Association; Alderville First Nation. *Activities*: Annual Elders & Traditional Gathering. *Publication*: E-Bimisay, electronic newsletter.

BROCK UNIVERSITY - TECUMSEH CENTRE FOR ABORIGINAL RESEARCH & EDUCATION
Welch Hall, University Rd. W • ST. CATHERNES, ON L2S 3A1
    (905) 688-5550 Fax 984-4869; Website: www.nativeadult.ed.brocku.ca
    Lorenzo Cherubini, Centre Director
    E-mail: Lorenzo.cherubini@brocku.ca
Description: The only multidisciplinary research entity in Ontario that builds educational programming for Aboriginal community needs & requirements. *Faculty*: Lorenzo Cherubini, Renee E. Bedard, Janie Hodson, Srah McGean, Judith Knight, Sakoieta' Widrick, Jennifer Brant. *Degree*: Bachelor of Education in Aboriginal Adult Education. Centre established in 2004.

ALGOMA UNIVERSITY – OJIBWE LANGUAGE PROGRAM
1520 Queen St. East • SAULT STE. MARIE, ON P6A 2G4
    (705) 949-2301; Website: www.algomau.ca
    Howard Webkamigad, Program Director & Assistant Professor
    of the Ojibwe Language; E-mail: howard.webkamigad@algomau.ca
    Eddie Benton-Banai, Sessional Instructor
    E-mail: eddie.benton-benai@algomau.ca
Program: Anishinaabemowin (Ojibwe Language degree). 3 year B.A. Study of the Ojibwe language in the Great Lakes Region.

LAURENTIAN UNIVERSITY – SCHOOL OF NATIVE HUMAN SERVICES
935 Ramsey Lake Rd. • SUDBURY, ON P3E 2C6
    (705) 675-1151; (800) 461-4030
    Website: www.laurentian.ca/program/indigenous-studies
    Dr. Taima Moeke-Pickering, Director
    E-mail: tmoekepickering@laurentian.ca
    Susan Manitowabi (Anishinawbe-Kwe), Assistant Professor
    Email: smanitowabi@laurentian.ca
    Herb Nabigon (Ojibway), Professor; E-mail: hnabigon@laurentian.ca
    Cheryle Partridge (Ojibway/Pottawatomi), Assistant Professor
    E-mail: cpartridge@laurentian.ca
Program: Indigenous Relations Program. The curriculum incorporates both Native-specific & social work courses with Native Studies courses.

UNIVERSITY OF SUDBURY
DEPARTMENT OF INDIGENOUS STUDIES
935 Ramsey Lake Rd. • SUDBURY, ON P3E 2C6
    (705) 673-5661 ext. 225
    Website: www.usudbury.ca/index.php/en/programs/indigenous-studies
    Darrel Manitowabi, Department Chairperson
    E-mail: dmanitowabi@usudbury.ca
    Kevin FitzMaurice, Associate Professor
    E-mail: kfitzmaurice@usudbury.ca
    Brock Pitawanakwat (Anishinaabe), Assistant Professor
    E-mail: bpitawanakwat@usudbury.ca
    Mary Ann Corbiere (Ojibwe), Assistant Professor
    E-mail: mcorbiere@usudbury.ca
    Emily Faires (Cree), Assistant Professor
    E-mail: efaries@usudbury.ca Michael Hankard, Assistant Professor
    E-mail: mhankard@usudbury.ca
Program: BA in Native Studies – courses on Cree & Ojibwe tradition & culture, legal & political issues; Aboriginal Legal Education Certificate.

LAKEHEAD UNIVERSITY - DEPARTMENT OF INDIGENOUS LEARNING
955 Oliver Rd. • THUNDER BAY, ON P7B 5E1
    (807) 343-8187; Website: www.lakeheadu.ca
    Dennis McPherson, Chairperson & Associate Professor (343-8984)
    E-mail: dennis.mcPherson@lakeheadu.ca
Description: The study of Aboriginal history, culture and values and strives to increase awareness/appreciation of the life experience of Aboriginal Peoples. *Faculty*: Ruby Farrell; Kristin Burnett; Robert Robson. *Resources*: The Northern Studies Resource Center.

UNIVERSITY OF TORONTO - ABORIGINAL STUDIES PROGRAM
North Borden Bldg., 2nd Fl. 563 Spadina Ave. • TORONTO, ON M5S 2J7
    (416) 978-2233; Website: www.utoronto.ca
    E-mail: aboriginal.studies@utoronto.ca

Jennifer Murrin, Administrative Assistant
    E-mail: director.aboriginal@utoronto.ca
    Connor Pion, Coordinator of Indigenous Language Initiative
Description: Aboriginal Studies is an interdisciplinary undergraduate program dedicated to the study and research of Indigenous peoples in Canada and throughout the world. The program offers courses that engender a rigorous & respectful understanding of Indigenous peoples' languages, cultures, histories, politics, arts, intellectual traditions & research methodologies. *Program*: BA Major & Minor in Aboriginal Studies; Aboriginal languages (Ojibwe, Oneida, Inukitut). *Faculty*: David Burman, Jill Carter (Anishnabe), Alana Johns (Anishnabe), Lee Maracle (Sto:Loh), Rauna Kuokkanen (Sami), Deborah McGregor, Alex McKay (Anishnabe), Erica Neegan, Connor Pion, Cheryl Suzack (Batchewana First Nation), Victoria Freeman. *Resources*: First Nations House (978-8227).

QUEBEC

McGILL UNIVERSITY
DEPARTMENT OF INTEGRATED STUDIES IN EDUCATION
FIRST NATIONS & INUIT EDUCATION (FNIE)
3700 McTavish St. • MONTREAL, PQ H3A 1Y2
    (514) 398-6696 Fax 398-4679; Website: www.mcgill.ca
    Ralf St. Clair & Elizabeth Wood, Co-directors (398-4525)
    Donna-Lee Smith, FNIE Program Director
Description: Provides an opportunity for Algonquin, Cree, Inuit, Mi'qmaq, & Mohawk people to become qualified as teachers. *Degree*: Certificate in Education for First Nations & Inuit.

SASKATCHEWAN

FIRST NATIONS UNIVERSITY OF CANADA
DEPARTMENT OF INDIGENOUS STUDIES
1 First Nations Way • REGINA, SK S4S 7K2
    (306) 790-5950 Ext. 2300 Fax 790-5994; Website: www.fnuniv.ca
    Edward Dolittle, Dept. Head, Indigenous Science, Environment &
    Economic Development; E-mail: edoolittle@fnuniv.ca (790-5950 ext. 3260)
    Lesley McBain, Dept. Head, Indigenous Languages, Arts & Cultures (DILAC)
    Saskatoon Campus; E-mail: lam128@fnuniv.ca (931-1800 ext. 7509)
    Anthony de Padue, Dept. Head, Indigenous Education, Health & Social Work
    (765-3333 ext. 7507)
The First Nations University of Canada's holistic approach to post-secondary education begins with the Elders, whose presence, wisdom, and counsel are the mainstay not only for students but also for the University as a whole. Their knowledge of First Nations' tradition, culture, and spirituality creates a unique support service. Consultation with the Elders takes place in an atmosphere of trust and respect. This tradition helps restore an individual's self-confidence and peace of mind, which in turn helps the learning process. The Elders reinforce our respect for, and understanding of, the Creator's role in our lives. Each of the university's three campuses benefit from Elders from nearby communities. Each contributes to the First Nations' holistic & cultural approach to learning at First Nations University of Canada throughout the academic year. Our Elders Offices: **Northern Campus (Prince Albert)** 306-765-3333 Ext 7139; **Saskatoon Campus** 306-931-1800 Ext 5475; **Regina Campus (Main)** 306-790-5950 Ext 3129

UNIVERSITY OF SASKATCHEWAN
DEPARTMENT OF NATIVE STUDIES
142 Kirk Hall, 117 Science Place • SASKATOON, SK S7N 5C8
    (306) 966-6209 Fax 966-6242; Website: www.usask.ca/nativestudies/
    E-mail: native.studies@usask.ca
    Winona Wheeler, Department Head (966-6210)
    E-mail: winona.wheeler@usask.ca
Faculty: Bonita Beatty, Denise Fucks, Adam Gaudry, Robert Alexander Innes, Priscilla Settee, Winona Wheeler. *Resources*: Native American & Indigenous Studies Association.

YUKON

YUKON COLLEGE
Yukon Native Language Centre
Box 2799 • WHITEHORSE, YUKON Y1A 5K4
    (867) 668-8820 Fax 668-8825
    Website: www.yukoncollege.yk.ca/ynlc
    E-mail: jjohnson@yukoncollege.yk.ca
    Jo-Anne Johnson, Coordinator
Instructors: John Ritter, Andre Bourcier, Linda Harvey. *Special programs*: Literacy & training sessions for Native language teachers. Library - collection of books on linguistics, languages, ethnography, history (Alaska, Yukon, B.C., & Northwest Territories), folklore, education, and reference. Established 1988.

Since 1955, the U.S. Public Health Service (PHS), through its Indian Health Service (IHS), an agency of the Department of Health and Human Services, is responsible for providing federal health services to American Indians & Alaska Natives. The provision of health services to federally recognized Indians grew out of a special relationship between the federal government & Indian tribes. This government-to-government relation-ship has been given form & substance by numerous treaties, laws, Supreme Court decisions, and Executive Orders. The IHS is the principal federal health care provider & health advocate for Indian people. The IHS provides health services to approximately two million American Indians and Alaska Natives who belong to 566 federally recognized tribes in 35 states. The goal is to raise their health status to the highest possible level; to ensure the equity, availability & accessibility of a comprehensive high quality health care delivery system providing maximum involvement of American Indians & Alaska Natives in defining their health needs, setting priorities for their local areas, and managing & controlling their health program. The IHS budget for fiscal year 2013 was $4.4 billion. This section lists hospitals, medical & health centers under the jurisdiction of the IHS. Arranged alpha-geographically.

DHHS HOTLINE NUMBER: (800) 447-8477
Office of the Inspector General (OIG) Hotline
P.O. Box 23489 • Washington, DC 20007
 Fax (800) 223-8164

INDIAN HEALTH SERVICE (Headquarters)
IHS HOTLINE NUMBER (301) 443-0658
 Website: www.ihs.gov
The Reyes Bldg. (RB) 801 Thompson Ave., Suite 400, Rockville, MD 20852
Twinbrook Metro Plaza (TMP) 12300 Twinbrook Pkwy., Rockville, MD 20852
Office of the Director: RB, 440 (301) 443-1083 Fax 443-4794
RADM Chris Buchanan (Seminole of Oklahoma), Acting Director
Mary L. Smith (Cherokee), Principal Deputy Director (2016-present)
Christopher Mandregan, Jr. (Aleut), Acting Deputy Director
Geoffrey Roth (Standing Rock Sioux), Sr. Advisor to the Director
CAPT. Michael Toedt, MD, Acting Chief Medical Officer
CAPT. Nicole Lurie, MD, MSPH, Acting Deputy Director-Quality Health Care
RADM Kevin Meeks (Chickasaw), Deputy Director Field Operations
P. Benjamin Smith (Navajo), Deputy Director for Intergovernmental Affairs
RADM Kelly M. Taylor (Choctaw), Acting Chief of Staff
Elizabeth A. Fowler (Eastern Cherokee) Deputy Director for Mgmt. Operations
P. Benjamin Smith, Director, Office of Tribal Self-Governance
 RB, Suite 240 (301) 443-7821 Fax 443-1050
Alec Thundercloud, MD (Ho-Chunk), Director, Office Clinical & Preventive Svcs
Gary J. Hartz, P.E., Director of Office of Environmental Health & Engineering
Lisa Gyorda (Oglala Lakota), Director, Office of Human Resources
Robert McSwain (Mono), Director – Office of Management Services
Roselyn Tso, Acting Director of Direct Services & Contracting Tribes
 RB, 220 (301) 443-1104 Fax 443-4666
Michael Mahsetky, J.D., Director Congressional & Legislative Affairs
 RB, 400 (301) 443-7261 Fax 480-3192
Raho Ortiz (Navajo), Acting Director, Office of Urban Indian Health Programs
 RB, 200 (301) 443-4680 Fax 443-8446
Capt. Francis Frazier, Acting Director, Office of Public Health Support
 PKLN, 4A-37 (301) 443-8220 Fax 480-2161

IHS NATIONAL PROGRAMS
INFORMATION TECHNOLOGY SUPPORT CENTER
5300 Homestead Rd. NE • Albuquerque, NM 87110
(888) 830-7280; (505) 248-4371 Fax 248-4393
Epidemiology Program (505) 248-4132
Chronic Disease Section - Nathaniel Cobb, Director
Diabetes Program (505) 248-4182; Kelly Acton, Director

INDIAN HEALTH SERVICE AREA OFFICES
(Alphabetically Arranged)

ALASKA AREA INDIAN HEALTH SERVICE
4141 Ambassador Dr., Suite 300 • ANCHORAGE, AK 99508-5928
(907) 729-3686 Fax 729-3689; Website: www.alaska.ihs.gov
Christopher Mandregan, Jr., MPH (Aleut), Director
Evangelyn "Angel" Dotomain, Executive Officer (729-3677)
Denman Ondelacy, Director - Office of Environmental Health & Engineering
 (729-3501) E-mail: denman.ondelacy@ihs.gov
Lanie Fox, Director of the Office of Tribal Programs (729-3677)
 E-mail: lanie.fox@ihs.gov
Rick Mills, Iris Gray & Tamara Dietrich, Indian Self-Determination Act
 Specialists

State served: Alaska. Provides comprehensive health services to about 143,000 Alaska Natives (Eskimos, Aleuts, and Indians). There are 44 tribal health centers, 160 tribal community health aide clinics & five residential substance abuse treatment centers. The Alaska Native Medical Center in Anchorage is the statewide referral center & gatekeeper for specialty care. Has jurisdiction over the following Indian hospitals in Alaska: Anchorage; Barrow; Bethel (Yukon-Kuskokwim Delta); Bristol Bay Area (Dillingham); Kotzebue; Mt. Edgecumbe (Sitka); Norton Sound (Nome); & the following health centers: Metlakatla; Fairbanks; Juneau; and Ketchikan.

ALBUQUERQUE AREA INDIAN HEALTH SERVICE
4101 Indian School Rd., NE • ALBUQUERQUE, NM 87110
(505) 256-6800 Fax 256-6847
Leonard D. Thomas, MD, Director & Chief Medical Officer (6735)
 E-mail: leonard.thomas@ihs.gov
Sandra Winfrey, Executive Officer (6736)
 E-mail: sandra.winfrey@ihs.gov
Russell Pederson, Director - Office of Environmental Health & Engineering
 & Acting Director of Tribal Support Office   (6737)
 E-mail: russel.pederson@ihs.gov
Debra Grabowski, Director – Division of Environmental Health Services
 (6815) E-mail: debra.grabowski@ihs.gov
Joseph F. Lucero, Director – Division of Information Management Services
 (6700) E-mail: joseph.lucero@ihs.gov
States served: New Mexico & Colorado. Has jurisdiction over the following Indian hospitals: Acomita-Canoncita-Laguna (San Fidel); Albuquerque; Mescalero; Santa Fe; and Zuni (all in NM); and the following health centers: Alamo Navajo (Magdalena); Jicarilla (Dulce); New Sunrise (San Fidel); Santa Clara (Espanola); Taos; Ramah; Pine Hill; in CO: Southern Colorado Ute, Ignacio and Towaoc; in TX: Ysleta Del Sur (El Paso); and Southwestern Indian Polytechnic Institute Dental Center (Albuquerque).

BEMIDJI AREA INDIAN HEALTH SERVICE
522 Minnesota Ave., NW • BEMIDJI, MN 56601
(218) 444-0452; Fax 444-0457; Website: www.ihs.gov/bemidji
Keith Longie (Turntle Mountain Chippewa), Area Director
 E-mail: keith.longie@ihs.gov
Antonio Guimaraes, MD, Acting Chief Medical Officer (0491)
Richard Gerry, Jr., Executive Officer (0453)
Louis Erdrich, Director of Office of Environmental Health & Engineering
States served: Minnesota, Michigan & Wisconsin. Has jurisdiction over the following Indian hospitals: Cass Lake & Red Lake (in MN); and the following *Indian Health Centers*: Min-No-Aya-Win Clinic (Cloquet, MN); White Earth (MN); Nimkee Memorial Wellness Center (Mt. Pleasant, MI); Stockbridge-Munsee Health Center (Bowler, WI); Ho Chunk Nation Health Dept. (Black River Falls, WI); Lac Courte Oreilles (Hayward, WI); Menominee Tribal Clinic (Keshena, WI); Chippewa Health Center (Lac du Flambeau, WI); Oneida Community Health Center (Oneida, WI); White Earth, MN.

BILLINGS AREA INDIAN HEALTH SERVICE
2900 4th Ave. North, P.O. Box 36600 • BILLINGS, MT 59107
(406) 247-7248; Fax 247-7230; Website: www.ihs.gov/billings
Dorothy A. Dupree (Assiniboine & Sioux), Area Director (7248)
Bryce Redgrave, Executive Officer (7106)
Jonathan Gilbert, MD, Health Care Programs (7110)
Garland Stiffarm, Deputy Director & Tribal Programs (7077)
Douglas Moore, MD, Area Chief Medical Officer (7129)
Dina Hansen, Information Management (7160)
Andrew Delgado, Director of Field Operation (7106)
States served: Provides health services to more than 70,000 American Indian & Alaska Native people in the states of Montana & Wyoming. Has jurisdiction over the following Indian hospitals: Browning; Crow Agency; Harlem; and the following Indian health centers: Blackfeet; Crow; Lodge Grass; Verne E. Gibbs Health Center, Poplar; Chief Redstone Health Clinic, Wolf Point; Lame Deer Health Center; and the tribally operated programs at Arapahoe Health Center, Arapahoe, Wyoming, Fort Washakie Health Center, Fort Washakie, Wyoming; Flathead Tribal Health, St. Ignatius, Montana & Rocky Boy Tribal Health, Box Elder, Montana.

CALIFORNIA AREA INDIAN HEALTH SERVICE
John E. Moss Federal Bldg., 650 Capital Mall, Suite 7-100
SACRAMENTO, CA 95814
(916) 930-3981 Fax 930-3952; Website: www.caoihs.org
Beverly Miller, CPA, MHA, Area Director (Ext. 302)
 E-mail: beverly.miller@ihs.gov
Steve Riggio, DDS, Deputy Area Director; Office of Public Health
 (Ext. 322) E-mail: steve.riggio@ihs.gov
Charles Magruder, MD, Chief Medical Officer (Ext. 367)
 E-mail: charles.magruder@ihs.gov
David Sprenger, MD, Behavioral Health Consultant (Ext. 321)
 E-mail: david.sprenger@ihs.gov

Travis Coleman, Indian Self-Determination Program Manager
(Ext. 319) E-mail: travis.coleman@ihs.gov
Edwin J. Fluette, Associate Director, Office of Environmental Health
& Engineering; (Ext. 334) E-mail: edwin.fluette@ihs.gov
State served: California. Contracted & Subcontracted Programs served: American Indian Council of Central California (Bakersfield); American Indian Health & Services (Santa Barbara); Berry Creek/Mooretown Tribal Health Organization (Oroville); California Rural Indian Health Board (Sacramento); Chapa-De Indian Health Program (Auburn); Central Valley Indian Health Project (Clovis); Consolidated Tribal Health Project (Ukiah); Hoopa Health Association (Hoopa); Fresno Indian Health Association (Fresno); Greenville Rancheria Tribal Health Program (Greenville); Indian Health Center of Santa Clara Valley (San Jose); Indian Health Council (Pauma Valley); Lake County Tribal Health Consortium (Lakeport); Lassen Indian Health Program (Susanville) Modoc Indian Health Project (Alturas); Northern Valley Indian Health (Willows); Pit River Health Services (Burney); Redding Rancheria Indian Health Services; Riverside/San Bernardino County Indian Health (Banning); Round Valley Indian Health Program (Covelo); Sacramento Urban Indian Health Project (Sacramento); San Diego American Indian Health Center (San Diego); Santa Ynez Tribal Health Program (Santa Ynez); Sonoma County Indian Health Program (Santa Rosa); Southern Indian Health Council (Al Pine); Shingle Springs Rancheria Tribal Health Program (Shingle Springs); Sycuan Medical/Dental Center (El Cajon); Toiyabe Indian Health Project (Bishop); Tule River Indian Health Center (Porterville); Tuolumne Rural Indian Health Program (Tuolumne); United Indian Health Services (Arcata); Urban Indian Health Board (Oakland); Warner Mountain Indian Health Project (Fort Bidwell);

Field Offices

Sacramento District Office
650 Capitol Mall, Suite 7-100 • Sacramento, CA 95814
(916) 930-3960 Fax 930-3954
CDR J. David Mazorra, Ext. 345, District Engineer
E-mail: david.mazorra@ihs.gov

Clovis Field Office
613 Harvard Ave., #101 • Clovis, CA 93612
(559) 322-7488 Fax 322-7445
Alice Queirolo, Ext. 303, Environmental Engineer
E-mail: alice.queirolo@ihs.gov

Ukiah Field Office
1252 Airport Park Blvd. #B5 • Ukiah, CA 95482
(707) 462-5314 Fax 462-6907
Lt. Charles Thompson, Contact, Ext. 104
E-mail: charles.thompson@ihs.gov

Redding District Office
1900 Churn Creek Rd. #210 • Redding, CA 96002
(530) 246-5339 Fax 246-5210
CDR Mark Hench, Ext 304, District Engineer
E-mail: mark.hench@ihs.gov

Arcata Field Office
1125 16th St. #100 • Arcata, CA 95521
(707) 822-1688 Fax 822-1692
Barry Jarvis, Ext. 203, Environmental Engineer Consultant
E-mail: barry.jarvis@ihs.gov

Escondido District Office
1320 W. Valley Pkwy., #309 • Escondido, CA 92029
(760) 735-6880 Fax 735-6893
Sean Bush, District Engineer (735-6885)
E-mail: sean.bush@ihs.gov

GREAT PLAINS AREA INDIAN HEALTH SERVICE
115 4th Ave., SE • ABERDEEN, SD 57401
(605) 226-7582; Fax 226-7321
James Driving Hawk (Lakota), Acting Area Director (7582)
John Kittredge, MD, Acting Chief Medical Officer (7502)
States served: Works in conjunction with its 19 Service Units to provide health care to approximately 122,000 Indians on reservations located in North Dakota, South Dakota, Nebraska, & Iowa. Service units include nine hospitals, eight health centers, two school health stations, and several smaller health stations & satellite clinics. Also operates an active research effort through its Area Epidemiology Program. The Great Plains Area IHS also provides health services to approximately 6,000 Native Americans who are not counted in the user population of the Area. This population does not reside within any service unit; however, they meet the IHS eligibility criteria for health services provided at IHS or Tribally operated direct care facilities. The largest concentrations of the non-service unit eligible are found in Aberdeen and Sioux Falls, South

Dakota and Bismarck and Grand Forks, North Dakota. Tribal involvement is a major objective of the program, and several tribes have assumed management for their own health care programs through contractual arrangements with the IHS.

Tribal Projects Specialists: Dennis Renvilles (Bismarck) (701) 222-3540; Priscilla Lee (Pierre) (605) 224-8544 Roger Condon (Aberdeen) (605) 226-7584; and Pat Giroux Rapid City) (605) 348-1900. *States served*: North & South Dakota & Iowa. Has jurisdiction over the following Indian hospitals: Eagle Butte (SD); Winnebago (NE); Pine Ridge (SD); Rapid City (SD); Rosebud (SD); Sisseton (SD); Fort Yates (ND); Belcourt (ND); Wagner (SD); and the following health centers: Fort Berthold (New Town, ND); Fort Totten (ND); Carl T. Curtis Health Center (Macy, NE); Sac & Fox Tribe of the Mississippi in Iowa (Tama, IA); Fort Thompson (SD); Lower Brule (SD); Kyle (SD); Wanblee (SD); McLaughlin (SD); Trenton-Williston (ND); and Youth Regional Treatment Center (SD).

NASHVILLE AREA INDIAN HEALTH SERVICE
711 Stewarts Ferry Pike • NASHVILLE, TN 37214
Website: www.ihs.gov/facilitiesservices/areaoffices/nashville
(866) 447-6261; (615) 467-1505; Fax 467-1501
Martha A. Ketcher (Cherokee), Area Director (1500)
E-mail: martha.ketcher@ihs.gov
Capt. Mihael Toedt, MD, Division Director & Chief Medical Officer (1681)
Ashley Metcalf, Acting Division Director of Office of Tribal Activities
(495-1297) E-mail: lindsay.king@ihs.gov
States served: Eastern states. Has jurisdiction over Cherokee Indian Hospital (Cherokee, NC); and Choctaw Health Center (Philadelphia, MS).

Field Offices

Atmore Field Office
5811 Jack Springs Rd., Atmore, AL 36502
(251) 446-4519 Fax 446-4536; Joe Watson, Contact

Bangor Field Office
304 Hancock St., Suite 3H, Bangor, ME 04401
(207) 941-9921 Fax 941-0116; Phil Rapp, Contact

Manilus Field Office
122 E. Seneca St., Manilus, NY 13104
((315) 682-3167 Fax 682-3189
John Ouellette, Health Systems Administrator

Opelousas Field Office
2341 Larkspur Lane, Suite 2, Opelousas, LA 70570
(337) 948-4328 Fax 948-7053; Glen Thibodaux, Contact

Urban Indian Health Programs

American Indian Community House
134 W. 29th St., 4th Floor • New York, NY 10001
(212) 598-0100 Fax 598-4909

Native American LifeLines Foundation - Baltimore
106 West Clay St. • Baltimore, MD 21201
(410) 837-2258 Fax 837-2692
Crystal Godwin, Acting Executive Director

Native American LifeLines Foundation – Boston
2077 Centre St. • West Roxbury, MA 02132
(857) 203-9680 Fax 203-9653

Service Units

Catawba Service Unit
2893 Sturgis Rd. • Rock Hill, SC 29730
(803) 366-9090 Fax 366-9141

Lockport Service Unit
6507 Wheeler Rd. • Lockport, NY 14094
(716) 280-3850

Micmac Family Health Clinic
8 Northern Rd. • Presque Island, ME 04769
(800) 750-1972; (207) 764-7219 Fax 764-7768

Mashpee Wampanoag Health Service Unit
483 Great Neck Rd. South • Mashpee, MA 02649
(508) 477-6967 Fax 477-0156

Unity Healing Center
448 Sequoyah Trail Dr., P.O. Box C201, Cherokee, NC 28719
(800) 322-6166; (828) 497-3958 Fax 497-6826
Rebecca Lambert, Director

NAVAJO AREA INDIAN HEALTH SERVICE (NAIHS)
P.O. Box 9020 • WINDOW ROCK, AZ 86515
(928) 871-5894 Fax 871-5896; E-mail: marie.begay@ihs.gov
Douglas Gene Peter, MD, Acting Area Director (5811)
  E-mail: john.hubbard@ihs.gov
Pete Hoskie, Tribal Affairs (5811)
Douglas G. Peter, MD, Chief Medical Officer (5813)
Ron C. Wood, Executive Officer (5812)
Randall Morgan, Office of Indian Self Determination (1444)
Henry Dodge, Acting Director of Administrative Services (5866)
Brian Johnson, Acting Associate Director of Environmental Health (5852)
Taylor McKenzie, MD, Administrator, Navajo Nation Div. of Health (6350)
States served: Northeast Arizona, Northwest New Mexico, Southern Utah. Has jurisdiction over the following Indian hospitals: Chinle; Fort Defiance (AZ); Tuba City (AZ); Crownpoint (NM); Gallup (NM); Shiprock (NM); and the following Indian health centers: Chinle (AZ), Tsaile (AZ), Tohatchi (NM); Kayenta (AZ); Inscription House (Tonalea, AZ); Pinon Health Center (Pinon, AZ); Winslow; & Dzilth-Na-O-Dith-Hle (Bloomfield, NM).
The NAIHS delivers health services to a user population of over 244,000 American Indians in five Federal service units on and near the Navajo Nation. The Navajo Nation is one of the largest Indian reservations in the United States. The Navajo Nation consists of more than 25,000 contiguous square miles and three satellite communities, and extends into portions of the states of Arizona, New Mexico, and Utah. NAIHS primarily delivers health services to members of the Navajo Nation and the San Juan Southern Paiute Tribe, and also provides services to other Native Americans, including Zunis, Hopis, and other American Indian beneficiaries. The five (5) Federal Service Units (SUs) include Chinle, Crownpoint, Gallup, Kayenta, & Shiprock SUs. NAIHS provides inpatient, emergency, outpatient, public health, & other services at four hospitals: Chinle Comprehensive Health Care Facility, Crownpoint Health Care Facility, Gallup Indian Medical Center, and Northern Navajo Medical Center (Shiprock, NM). These inpatient facilities comprise a total of 222 hospital beds. The Kayenta Health Center in Kayenta, AZ will transition to begin operating as an Alternative Rural Hospital in late 2017 by offering ten short stay nursing beds and ambulatory surgery. Navajo Area also has seven full-time health centers providing outpatient, community health, preventive health, and other services. There are also five part-time health stations. In addition to the NAIHS, the Navajo health care system includes an urban health program in Flagstaff, Arizona, the Navajo Department of Health (NDOH), and five Tribal health care corporations. Native Americans for Community Action, Inc. (NACA), founded in 1971, is one of 34 Urban Indian health programs in the United States. NACA provides outpatient, behavioral health, health promotion, and other services to the population in and around Flagstaff, Arizona. The NDOH, created in 1977, ensures access to quality and culturally acceptable health care. The NDOH offers nutrition, aging, substance abuse, education, community health outreach, and other services to the Navajo population through regulation, direct service delivery, and coordination with federal, state, and local partners. NDOH has a master contract with NAIHS under the auspices of Public Law 93-638, the Indian Self Determination and Education Assistance Act.

OKLAHOMA AREA INDIAN HEALTH SERVICE
701 Market Dr. • OKLAHOMA CITY, OK 73114
(405) 951-3820 Fax 951-3780; Website: www.ihs.gov/oklahoma
RADM Kevin D. Meeks (Chickasaw), MPH, Area Director (3899)
John Farris, MD, Chief Medical Officer (3776)
Ronald Grinnell, Executive Officer (3995)
Frank Williams, Assistant Area Director of Field Operations
Dale Keel, Deputy Area Director (3768)
Max Tahsuda, Office of Tribal Self-Determination (3761)
This is the largest IHS service population in the U.S. extending health care to more than 40 Tribes & Tribal Organizations, and more than 285,000 American Indians. Maintains 7 Indian hospitals and 40 outpatient health centers located throughout Oklahoma, northeastern Kansas, & Eagle Pass, Texas. Additional services are provided through two urban programs located in Wichita, Kansas and Dallas, Texas. *States served*: Oklahoma, Kansas & portions of Texas. Has jurisdiction over the following Indian hospitals: Carl Albert (Ada, OK); Claremore; Creek Nation (Okemah); Clinton; Lawton; W.W. Hastings (Tahlequah); and the following Indian health centers in Oklahoma: Anadarko, Ardmore, Broken Bow, Carnegie, Durant, El Reno, Eufaula, Hugo, McLoud, Miami, Muskogee, Norman, Nowata, Okemah, Oklahoma City, Okmulgee, Pawnee, Pawhuska, Ponca City, Salina, Salisaw, Sam Hider Jay, Shawnee, Stilwell, Tahlequah, Talihina, Tishomingo, Tulsa, Watonga, Wewoka, White Eagle (Ponca City), Wyandotte; in Kansas: Lawrence, Horton, Holton, and Wichita; and in Texas: Dallas and Eagle Pass.

PHOENIX AREA INDIAN HEALTH SERVICE
Two Renaissance Square, 40 N. Central Ave., #600 • PHOENIX, AZ 85004
(602) 364-5039 Fax 364-5042
RADM Charles Ty Reidhead (Three Affiliated Tribes) Director (5039)
Vincent A. Berkley, DO, Chief Medical Officer (5047)
Gary P. Breshears, Executive Officer (5039)
Rose oversees the delivery of health care to Native American users in the tri-state area of Arizona, Nevada and Utah. We are the Phoenix Area Indian Health Service. We provide health care and community health services to approximately 140,000 American Indians/Alaska Natives in the tri-state area of Arizona, Nevada, and Utah. Through ten Service Units including two Youth Regional Treatment Centers and a network of heath care facilities, a health care partner to over forty tribes. Our Area Office is based in Phoenix, Arizona, with 197 administrative and technical staff. Service Units employ over 2,400 staff. Our system of care includes IHS- and tribally-operated health care facilities that serve tribal communities as well as three Urban Indian health programs. These services are comprehensive and range from primary care (inpatient and outpatient) to tertiary care and specialty services; largest health care facility is the Phoenix Indian Medical Center (PIMC), located near downtown Phoenix. This Joint Commission accredited 127-bed hospital employs nearly 1,200 people to provide a comprehensive range of specialty services to both urban and rural tribal members. In addition, PIMC professional staff travels throughout the states in the Phoenix Area region, providing direct services & consultation & guidance to other IHS hospitals and health centers.

Center for Native American Health
1215 N. Beaver St. #201 • Flagstaff, AZ 86001
(928) 214-3920 Fax 214-3924; James M. Galloway, MD, Director

ORYX Program
5300 Homestead Rd. • Albuquerque, NM 87110
(505) 248-4152 Fax 248-4393; Michael Gomez, Director

Southwest Native American Cardiology Program
P.O. Box 245037 • Tucson, AZ 85724
(520) 694-7000 Fax 694-6712; James M. Galloway, MD, Director

Phoenix/Tucson Area Adolescent
Has jurisdiction over the following Indian hospitals: Parker; Fort Yuma; Keams Canyon; Phoenix Indian Medical Center; San Carlos; Whiteriver; and Owyhee Tribal Hospital (in NV); and the following Indian Health Centers: in AZ: Peach Springs; Havasupai; Second Mesa; Cibicue; Scottsdale Salt River Clinic; in NV: Elko (NV); McDermitt (NV); Pyramid Lake (Nixon, NV); Washoe Tribal Health center, Yerington Health dept., Las Vegas Tribal Health Clinic, Schurz Indian health Center, Reno Tribal Health Station, Reno Spark Health Center, Fallon Clinic; and in UT: Fort Duchesne (Roosevelt, UT). Consists of one medical center, eight hospitals, four health centers, and two school health clinics. *States served*: Arizona, Nevada & Utah. *Tribes served*: (47 separate tribes-Papago, Apache, Pima, Maricopa, Hopi, Paiute, Navajo, Ute, Goshute, Shoshone, Washoe, Hualapai, Havasupai, Mojave, Cocopah, Quechan, and urban tribes in the metropolitan area.) Number of professionals on staff: 772. Number of beds: 424. Numbers served annually: In-patient, 15,000; Outpatient, 450,000. *Services*: All primary medical services are provided. *Programs*: Accredited residency programs in obstetrics, pediatrics, family practice, dental, general practice, and public health nursing; continuing education; research (sponsored by the National Institutes of Health) at several facilities; Health Education Program--comprised of 15 professional staff who provide a coordinated program of health education throughout the Phoenix area; Indian Health Service Training Committee; Scholarships: Participates in the National Health Service Corps and the Indian Health Care Improvement Scholarship Programs. Library.

PORTLAND AREA INDIAN HEALTH SERVICE
1414 NW Northrup St., Suite 800 • Portland, OR 97204
(503) 414-5555 Fax 414-5554
Dean Seyler (Warm Springs Spokane), Director
  E-mail: dean.seyler@ihs.gov
Cat. Miles Rudd, MD, Chief Medical Officer
Jonathan Hubbard, Director - Div. of Information Resources
J. Michael Wood, Self-Governance Coordinator
Roselyn Tso, Office of Tribal Operations
Richard R. Truitt, Director of Office of Environmental Health & Engineering
Population served: 160,000 Indian residents of 42 tribes located in Idaho, Oregon and Washington. There are 15 health centers, eight tribally operated & seven federally operated. 23 Health stations, 22 are tribally operated & one federally operated. Ten tribally operated preventive programs, and three tribally operated urban programs. *Has jurisdiction over*: Yellowhawk (Pende-ton, OR); Warm Springs (OR); Chemawa Indian Health Centers (Salem, OR); Klamath Service Unit (Chiloquin, OR); Colville (Nespelem, WA); Neah Bay (WA);

Northwest Washington (Bellingham, WA); Puget Sound (Seattle, WA); Taholah (WA); Wellpinit (WA); Yakima (Toppenish, WA); Fort Hall (ID); and Northern Idaho (Lapwai, ID).

Field Offices

Fort Hall Field Office
P.O. Box 717 • Fort Hall, ID 83203
  (208) 238-0502; Michael Blasy, Contact

Olympic District Office
4060 Wheaton Way, Bldg. B, Suite E • Bremerton, WA 98310
  (360) 792-1235; Matthew Rasmusson, Contact

Port Angeles Field Office
1601 E. Front St., Bldg. B, Suite C • Port Angeles, WA 98362
  (360) 452-1196; Craig Haugland, Contact

Seattle District Office
2201 Sixth Ave., Rm. 300 • Seattle, WA 98121
  (206) 615-2794; Steve Anderson, Contact

Spokane District Office
1919 East Francis • Spokane, WA 99207
  (509) 484-9341; Alex Dailey, Contact

Yakama Field Office
341 Fort Rd. • Toppenish, WA 98948
  (509) 865-6300; Quentin Allen, Contact

TUCSON AREA INDIAN HEALTH SERVICE
7900 South "J" Stock Rd. • Tucson, AZ 85746
  (520) 295-2405 Fax 295-2602
  Dixie Gaikowski (Sisseton-Wahpeton Oyate), Director (2405)
  Peter Ziegler, MD, Acting Chief Medical Officer (2406)
  Robert L. Price, Tribal Activities Officer (2403)
  Bernard DeAsis, Executive Officer (2406)
  Robert L. Price, Tribal Activities Officer (2403)
State served: Arizona. Has jurisdiction over: Sells Indian Hospital, Sells, AZ; Santa Rosa Indian Health Center, Sells, AZ; and San Xavier Indian Health Center, Tucson, AZ.

IHS SERVICE UNITS

ALASKA

AKIACHAK NATIVE COMMUNITY
P.O. Box 70 • AKIACHAK, AK 99551
  (907) 825-4626 Fax 825-4029; George Peter, Tribal Administrator
Affiliated with Alaska Area Indian Health Service. Tribally operated.

ALASKA NATIVE MEDICAL CENTER
4315 Diplomacy Dr. • ANCHORAGE, AK 99508
  (907) 279-1994; Fax 729-1984; Website: www.anmc.org
  Dee Hutchinson, Hospital Administrator
Number of Beds: 170. Affiliated with Alaska Area Indian Health Service.

ALASKA NATIVE TRIBAL HEALTH CONSORTIUM (ANTHC)
4000 Ambassador Dr. • ANCHORAGE, AK 99508
  (907) 729-1900; 563-2662; (855) 882-684; Website: www.anthc.org
  Don Kashevaroff, President

ALEUTIAN/PRIBILOF ISLANDS ASSOCIATION
1131 E. International Airport Rd. • ANCHORAGE, AK 99518
  (800) 478-2742; (907) 276-2700; Fax 279-4351
  Website: www.apiai.org; E-mail: apiai@apiai.org
  Carolyn Crowder, Health Dept. Director
Tribe: Aleut. *Services*: Provides a variety of health programs to the Aleut Region, Affiliated with Alaska Area Indian Health Service. Tribally operated.

ANCHORAGE NATIVE PRIMARY CARE CENTER
4320 Diplomacy Dr. • ANCHORAGE, AK 99508
  (907) 729-3253 Fax 729-3265
  Kimberly Thorp. Health System Administrator

CHITINA TRADITIONAL VILLAGE COUNCIL
3701 Eureka, #16A • ANCHORAGE, AK 99503
  (907) 563-6643 (phone & fax); Harry Billum, President
Affiliated with Alaska Area Indian Health Service. Tribally operated.

CHUGACHMIUT NATIVES INCORPORATED
1840 Bragaw St., Suite 110 • ANCHORAGE, AK 99508
  (800) 478-4155 (in Alaska); Fax (800) 793-2891
  (907) 562-4155 Fax 563-2891
  Website: www.chugachmiut.org; E-mail: info@chugachmiut.org
  Patrick M. Anderson (Tlingit), Executive Director
  Fran Norman, Chairperson; James Kvasnikoff, Vice Chairperson
Tribe served: Tlingit. Natives of the Chugach region of Alaska. Affiliated with Alaska Area Indian Health Service. Tribally operated. Established 1973.

COOK INLET TRIBAL COUNCIL
3600 San Jeronimo Dr. • ANCHORAGE, AK 99508
  (877) 985-5900; (907) 793-3600 Fax 265-5996
  Website: www.citci.com; Gloria O'Neil, President/CEO

EASTERN ALEUTIAN TRIBES
3380 C St. #100 • ANCHORAGE, AK 99503
  (907) 563-1440 Fax 563-1446; Website: www.eatribes.org
  Chris Devlin, Executive Director; Martha Cotton, MD, Medical Director
Purpose: To promote healthy communities. Affiliated with Alaska Area Indian Health Service. Tribally operated.

SOUTHCENTRAL FOUNDATION
4501 Diplomacy Dr. #200 • ANCHORAGE, AK 99508
  (800) 478-3343; (907) 729-4955; Fax 265-5000
  Website: www.southcentralfoundation.com
  Katherine Gottlieb, President/CEO; James Segura, Chairperson
  Ted Mala, MD, Executive Planner
Mission: To achieve wellness through health & related services. *Services*: Primary Medical; Dental; Optometric; Behavioral health. Affiliated with Alaska Area Indian Health Service. Tribally operated.

ATKA CLINIC
P.O. Box 47047 • ATKA, AK 99547
  (907) 839-2232 Fax 839-2239
  Rosanna Snigaroff, Tribal Administrator

UKPEAGVIK INUPIAT CORPORATION
P.O. Box 29 • BARROW, AK 99723
  (907) 852-9247 Fax 852-6110; Max E. Ahgeak, President
Affiliated with Alaska Area Indian Health Service. Tribally operated.

ARCTIC SLOPE NATIVE ASSOCIATION
SAMUEL SIMMONDS MEMORIAL HOSPITAL
P.O. Box 1232 (Association) (907) 852-2762
P.O. Box 29 • BARROW, AK 99723
  (907) 852-4611 Fax 852-2763; Website: www.arcticslope.org
  Eben Hopson, Jr., Executive Director
Provides culturally sensitive quality healthcare for communities of the Arctic Slope. *Tribe served*: Inupiat. *Number of Beds*: 14. Affiliated with Alaska Area Indian Health Service. Tribally operated. Established 1964.

NORTH SLOPE BOROUGH DEPT. OF HEALTH & SOCIAL SERVICES
P.O. Box 69 • BARROW, AK 99723
  (907) 852-0260; Fax 852-0268; Doreen Knodel, Health Director
Affiliated with Alaska Area Indian Health Service. Tribally operated.

YUKON-KUSKOKWIM HEALTH CORPORATION
P.O. Box 528 • BETHEL, AK 99559
  (907) 543-6020; Fax 543-6006; Website: www.ykhc.org
  Gene Peltola, President/CEO; Orie Williams, Executive VP
  Donald Kruse, MD, Medical Director
Affiliated with Alaska Area Indian Health Service. Tribally operated.

YUKON-KUSKOKWIM DELTA REGIONAL HOSPITAL
P.O. Box 287 • BETHEL, AK 99559
  (907) 543-6014; Fax 543-6366; Mary Aranuk, VP, Health Services
Number of Beds: 50. Affiliated with Alaska Area Indian Health Service.

CHICKALOON VILLAGE TRADITIONAL COUNCIL
Health & Social Services, P.O. Box 1105 • CHICKALOON, AK 99674
  (907) 745-0704 Fax 745-0708; Website: www.chickaloon.org
  E-mail: cvhealth@chickaloon.org
  Doug Wade, Council Chairperson
  Rick Harrison, Vice Chairperso;
  Jennifer Harrison, Executive Director
  Gary Harrison, Traditional Chief
Tribe served: Athabascan Nation. *Population served*: 5,000. *Services*: Health; Housing; Education; Environmental; Transportation. Affiliated with Alaska Area Indian Health Service. Tribally operated.

CHITINA TRADITIONAL INDIAN VILLAGE COUNCIL
Chitina Tribal & Community Health Center
P.O. Box 31 • CHITINA, AK 99566
(907) 823-2213 Fax 823-2257; Website: www.chitinanative.com
E-mail: chitinahealthcenter@yahoo.com
Ronald Mahle, President; Harry Billum, Vice President

NATIVE VILLAGE OF EKLUTNA
26339 Eklutna Village Rd. • CHUGIAK, AK 99576
(907) 688-6020 Fax 688-6021; Website: www.eklutna-nsn.gov
E-mail: president@eklutna-nsn.gov; Dorothy Cook, President
Violet Rice, Nurse Practitioner; E-mail: nve.health@eklutna-nsn.gov
Services: Health & Wellness; Social Services & Mental Health. Affiliated
with Alaska Area Indian Health Service. Tribally operated.

COPPER RIVER NATIVE ASSOCIATION
Health & Human Services Dept.
Drawer H • COPPER CENTER, AK 99573
(907) 822-5241; Fax 822-8801
Nat Hall, Health Director; Donna Hicks, Deputy Health Director
Tribe served: Ahtna. *Services*: Medical, Outpatient; Behavioral Health;
Substance Abuse; Health Education; Referral Services. Affiliated with Alaska
Area Indian Health Service. Tribally operated.

ILANKA COMMUNITY HEALTH CENTER
P.O. Box 2290 • CORDOVA, AK 99574
(907) 424-3622 Fax 424-3275; Website: www.nveyak.com
Penney Benson, Clinic Administrator
Lee Morrisette, MD, Medical Director
Dr. Ron Ray, Family Nurse Practitioner
Services: Primary health care outpatient clinic; alcohol/substance abuse.
Affiliated with Alaska Area Indian Health Services.

BRISTOL BAY AREA HEALTH CORPORATION
KANAKANAK HOSPITAL
6000 Kanakanak Rd., P.O. Box 130 • DILLINGHAM, AK 99576
(800) 478-5201; (907) 842-5201; Fax 842-9354
Website: www.bbahc.org; Robert J. Clark, President/CEO
Lorraine M. Jewett, Executive VP & COO
Area served: 34 villages in Southwest Alaska, Bristol Bay region. *Population
served*: 8,000. *Number of Beds*: 16. *Professionals on staff*: 360. *Primary
medical services*: Medical, dental, optometry, audiology, health, alcohol/drug
rehabilitation, obstetrical; emergency services. *Special programs*: Laboratory;
medical imaging; pharmacy; home health care; WIC; infant learning; medical
supplies; environmental health & safety; injury prevention; health education;
dietary counseling. Medical Library. Affiliated with Alaska Area Indian Health
Service. Tribally operated. Established 1973.

NATIVE VILLAGE OF DIOMEDE HEALTH CENTER
P.O. Box 7079 • DIOMEDE, AK 99762
(907) 686-2175 Fax 686-2203; Eric Iyapana, President
Affiliated with Alaska Area Native Health Service. Tribally operated.

CHIEF ANDREW ISAAC HEALTH CENTER
1408 19th Ave. • FAIRBANKS, AK 99701
(907) 452-8251; Fax 459-3811; Jim Kohler, Director
Website: www.caihc.yourmd.com
Affiliated with Alaska Area Native Health Service. Tribally operated.

FAIRBANKS NATIVE ASSOCIATION HEALTH CENTER
201 First Ave., #200 • FAIRBANKS, AK 99701
(907) 452-1648 Fax 456-4849; Shirley L. Lee, Executive Director
Website: www.fairbanksnative.org
Affiliated with Alaska Area Indian Health Service. Tribally operated.

TANANA CHIEFS CONFERENCE, INC. HEALTH CENTER
122 First Ave. #600 • Fairbanks, AK 99701
(907) 452-8251; Fax 459-3850; Steve Ginnis, President
Website: www.tananachiefs.org/health
Affiliated with Alaska Area Indian Health Service. Tribally operated.

YUKON FLATS COMMUNITY HEALTH CENTER
Council of Athabascan Tribal Governments
P.O. Box 309 • FORT YUKON, AK 99740
(907) 662-2460 Fax 662-2709; Website: www.catg.org
Craig Fleener, Chief Administrator
Affiliated with Alaska Area Native Health Service. Tribally operated.

MT. SANFORD TRIBAL CONSORTIUM HEALTH CENTER
P.O. Box 357 • GAKONA, AK 99586
(907) 822-5399 Fax 822-5810; Website: www.mstc.org/health.html

Agnes Denny, Project Coordinator; Shirley Bergey, Diabetes Coordinator
Nora David, Mariah Craig, Mentasta Clinic Health Aides
Danielle Boston, Chistochina Clinic Health Aide
Tribes served: Cheesh'na; Athabascan. *Clinics*: Mentasta Lake & Chistochina.
Affiliated with Alaska Area Indian Health Service. Tribally operated.

SELDOVIA VILLAGE TRIBE HEALTH CENTER
880 East End Rd. • HOMER, AK 99603
(907) 226-2228 Fax 226-2230; Website: www.svt.org
Beckie Noble, Executive Director; Dr. Margit Sheinmel, DO, Medical Director
Population served: 500. *Services*: Medical & Dental; *Facilities*: SVT Wellness
Center - Behavioral & Nutrition Health.; Naturopathy; Massage Therapy;
Acupuncture. *Satellite Clinics*: Seldovia (907) 435-3262; Anchor Point (907)
226-2238. Affiliated with Alaska Area Indian Health Service. Tribally operated.

HOONAH INDIAN CORP. HEALTH CENTER
P.O. Box 602 • HOONAH, AK 99829
(907) 945-3545 Fax 945-3703; Johanna Dybadahl, Tribal Administrator
Affiliated with Alaska Area Indian Health Service. Tribally operated.

SEARHC JUNEAU MEDICAL CENTER
3245 Hospital Dr. • JUNEAU, AK 99801
(907) 463-4060; Fax 463-4075; Kenneth Brewer, President/CEO
Serves 19 communities and villages in Southeast Alaska. Affiliated with
Alaska Area Native Health Service. Tribally operated.

KARLUK TRIBAL HEALTH CENTER
P.O. Box 22 • KARLUK, AK 99608
(907) 241-2218 Fax 241-2208; Alicia Lynn Reft, President
Affiliated with Alaska Area Indian Health Service. Tribally operated.

DENA'INA HEALTH CLINIC
Kenaitze Indian Tribe, P.O. Box 988 • KENAI, AK 99611
(907) 335-7300; Fax 335-7239; Website: www.kenaitze.org
E-mail: clinic@kenaitze.org; Dr. Tim Scheffel, Medical Director
Tribe served: Kenaitze. *Services*: Primary Medical Outpatient. *Programs*:
Pediatric, Diabetes Prevention, Internal Medicine, Cancer Screening, Diagno-
sis & Treatment, Nutrition, Smoking Cessation, Behavioral Health Counseling.
Affiliated with Alaska Area Indian Health Service. Tribally operated.

KIC TRIBAL HEALTH CLINIC
Ketchikan Indian Community
2960 Tongass Ave. 3rd Fl. • KETCHIKAN, AK 99901
(907) 225-5158 Fax 247-0429; Debbie Patton, General Manager
Robert Sasse, MD, Medical Director
Services: Medical & dental; behavioral health. *Population served*: 4,500.
Affiliated with Alaska Area Indian Health Service. Established 1997.

SEARHC HEALTH CENTER
201 Deermount St. • KETCHIKAN, AK 99901
(907) 225-4156; Fax 247-6174
David Garrison, Director; Carol Alley, MD, Clinical Director
Affiliated with Alaska Area Indian Health Service.

KANA HEALTH CENTER
Kodiak Area Native Association (KANA)
3449 E. Rezanof • KODIAK, AK 99615
(888) 258-9870; (907) 486-9870; Website: www.kanaweb.org
Margaret Roberts, Chairperson, E-mail: mroberts.nok@gmail.com
Services: Medical, Dental, Pharmacy. *Programs*: Infant Learning, Behavioral
Health, Nutrition, and Fitness Center. *Village Clinics*: Akhiok, Karluk, Larsen
Bay, Old Harbor, Ouzinkie, Port Lions. Affiliated with Alaska Area Indian Health
Service. Tribally operated.

MANIILAQ HEALTH CENTER
436 5th Ave., P.O. Box 43 • KOTZEBUE, AK 99752
(800) 431-3321; (907) 442-3311 Fax 442-7678
Website: www.maniilaq.org; Helen Bolan, President & CEO
Robert Ottone, Administrator
Services: Medical, Dental, Clinical & Nursing, including eleven village clinics.
Affiliated with Alaska Area Indian Health Service. Tribally operated.

ANNETTE ISLAND SERVICE UNIT
Metlakatla Indian Community, P.O. Box 439 • METLAKATLA, AK 99926
(907) 886-4741; Fax 886-6976; Website: www.aisu.org
Harris Atkinson, Mayor; Rachael Askren, Service Unit Director
Dr. Kellene Lenz, Medical Director
Tribe served: Metlakatla Indian Community. *Population served*: 22,000 out-
patient visits each year. *Professionals on Staff*: 90. *Primary Health Services*:
Emergency & Urgent Care; Ambulatory Care; Laboratory/Radiology; Phar-
macy; Dental; Physical Therapy; Public Health & Education; Community

Health, including mental health & substance abuse. *Facilities*: Lepquinum Wellness Center. Affiliated with Alaska Area Indian Health Service.

NINILCHIK COMMUNITY CLINIC
P.O. Box 39368 • NINILCHIK, AK 99639
(907) 567-3970; Fax 567-3902
Helena Bock, Program Director
Website: www.ninilchiktribe-nsn.gov/health.html
Janet Mullen, Tribal Health Director; Brie Leman, Health Club Director
Affiliated with Alaska Area Indian Health Service. Tribally operated.

NORTON SOUND HEALTH CORPORATION
306 West 5th Ave., P.O. Box 966 • NOME, AK 99762
(888) 559-3311; (907) 443-3311 Fax 443-3139
Emily Hughes, President/CEO; David Head, MD, Chief-of-Staff
Tribes served: 20 Federally recognized tribes in the Bering Straits Region. *Professionals on staff*: Six physicians; three PAs. *Services*: Inpatient, Outpatient, Emergency, Mental Health & Substance Abuse. *Facilities*: New hospital opening 2012. *Programs*: Staff Education; Community Health Education. Scholarships provided to Natives of region who are interested in pursuing health careers. Library. Affiliated with Alaska Indian Health Service. Tribally owned & operated.

ST. GEORGE TRADITIONAL COUNCIL
P.O. Box 940 • ST. GEORGE ISLAND, AK 99591
(907) 859-2205 Fax 859-2242
Georgia Kashevaroff, Tribal Administrator
Affiliated with Alaska Area Indian Health Service. Tribally operated.

SELDOVIA VILLAGE TRIBE HEALTH CLINIC
206 Main St. • SELDOVIA, AK 99663
(907) 435-3262 Fax 234-7865; Website: www.svthc.org
Donna Fenske, ANP, Nurse Practitioner

SEARHC MT. EDGECUMBE HOSPITAL
222 Tongass Dr. • SITKA, AK 99835
(907) 966-8310; Fax 966-8656; Website: www.searhc.org
Frank L. Sutton, VP Hospital Services; E-mail: frank.sutton@searhc.org
Number of Beds: 60. Serves 18 tribes in Southeast Alaska.
Affiliated with Alaska Area Indian Health Service. Tribally operated.

TANANA IRA NATIVE COUNCIL HEALTH CENTER
P.O. Box 93 • TANANA, AK 99777
(907) 366-7160 Fax 366-7195; Julia M. Roberts, Director
Affiliated with Alaska Area Indian Health Service. Tribally operated.

TYONEK NATIVE VILLAGE HEALTH CENTER
P.O. Box 82029 • TYONEK, AK 99682
(907) 583-2201 Fax 583-2442; Peter Merryman, President
Affiliated with Alaska Area Indian Health Service. Tribally operated.

VALDEZ NATIVE TRIBE HEALTH CENTER
P.O. Box 1108 • VALDEZ, AK 99686
(907) 835-4951 Fax 835-5589; Benna Hughey, President
Affiliated with Alaska Area Indian Health Service. Tribally operated.

YAKUTAT TLINGIT TRIBAL HEALTH CENTER
P.O. Box 418 • YAKUTAT, AK 99689
(907) 784-3932 Fax 784-3595; Bert Adams, Sr., President
Affiliated with Alaska Area Indian Health Service. Tribally operated.

ARIZONA

YAVAPAI APACHE HEALTH CLINIC
2400 W. Datsi St. • CAMP VERDE, AZ 86322
(928) 567-2168 Fax 567-8499; Zahid Zhiek, Clinic Manager
Affiliated with Phoenix Area Indian Health Service.

CHINLE COMPREHENSIVE HEALTH CARE FACILITY (CCHCF)
P.O. Box "PH" • CHINLE, AZ 86503
(928) 674-7001 Fax 674-7372; Ronald Tso, Director
Number of Beds: 60. The CCHCF is a 60 bed hospital which serves as the health care hub for the region. The medical staff includes Family Physicians, Internists, Pediatricians, General Surgeons, OB/GYN's, Anesthesiologists, and a Psychiatrist.In addition to routine outpatient and inpatient primary care, services available to our patients include: Adult Intensive Care, General Surgery (including laparoscopic surgery), routine and operative Obstetrics, and 24-Hour Emergency Room Services. Health care services are provided to approximately 37,000 active users. Strong Navajo cultural traditions exist within the community, offering an opportunity to learn the Navajo language, or to learn about traditional Navajo medicine. Affiliated with Navajo Area Indian Health Service.

CIBECUE INDIAN HEALTH CENTER
P.O. Box 37 • CIBECUE, AZ 85941
(928) 332-2560 Fax 338-2418
Marc Fleetwood, Acting CEO
David Yost, MD, Clinical Director
E-mail: charlenemhamilton@wr.2phx@ihs
Tribes served: White Mountain Apache, Fort Apache Agency. *Total population served*: 1,500. *Number of beds*: 2. *Primary medical services*: Ambulatory care. Library. Affiliated with Phoenix Area Indian Health Service.

FLAGSTAFF INDIAN FAMILY HEALTH CENTER
1500 E. Cedar Ave. #26 • FLAGSTAFF, AZ 86004
(928) 773-1245 Fax 773-9429; Website: www.nacainc.org
E-mail: info@nacainc.org; Robert W. Robin, PhD, CEO
Evelina Y. Maho, Health Promotion Program Coordinator
Carmelita Coochyumptewa, Danette Reed-Sanchez,
Francine Begay, Sherri Begay, Patient Services Coordinators
Purpose: To promote & improve the health of individuals, families and the Flagstaff community through prevention & comprehensive treatment of illnesses or conditions. *Services*: Medical, diabetes & general health education programs. Affiliated with Phoenix Area Indian Health Service. *Publication*: Native Health newsletter. Established 1991.

SACRED PEAKS HEALTH CENTER
3480 E. Rt. 66 • FLAGSTAFF, AZ 86004
(928) 863-7333
Tribe served: Navajo. *Services*: non-urgent primary health care; Internal Medicine, Family Medicine, Pediatrics & Gynecology; also, laboratory, pharmacy, radiology & physical therapy. Affiliated with Navajo Area Indian Health Service.

FORT DEFIANCE INDIAN HOSPITAL
P.O. Box 649 • FORT DEFIANCE, AZ 86504
(928) 729-8000 Fax 729-8019; Franklin Freeland, EdD, Director
Daniel Johnson, Administrative Officer; David Downing, MD, Clinical Director
Number of Beds: 56. *Staff*: 850. *Services*: OBGYN Ward; Inpatient Adolescent Psychiatric Care Unit; Ambulatory Care Center; 24-chair Dental clinic. Adjacent to the hospital is a 193-unit government housing area. Affiliated with Navajo Area Indian Health Service.

**FORT McDOWELL INDIAN COMMUNITY
WASSAJA MEMORIAL HEALTH CENTER**
P.O. Box 17779 • FOUNTAIN HILLS, AZ 85269
(480) 837-5074 Fax 837-1270; Demetra Bass, MD, Health Director
Affiliated with Phoenix Area Indian Health Service. Tribally operated.

KAYENTA HEALTH CENTER
P.O. Box 368 • KAYENTA, AZ 86033
(928) 697-4000 Fax 697-4145
Linda L. White, R.P., Director
Stellar Anonye-Achampong, MD, Clinical Director
The Kayenta Service Unit population of 20,000 is spread across a remote and sparsely populated area. Kayenta is in a traditional part of the reservation. Services are provided to 200 patients each day in continuity or walk-in clinics and in a 24 hour/day, 7 day/week emergency room. The clinic has on site lab, x-ray and pharmacy services. Current medical staff is made up of Family Practice, Pediatrics, Internal Medicine and Psychiatry specialties. Affiliated with Navajo Area Indian Health Service.

**KEAMS CANYON PHS INDIAN HOSPITAL
SECOND MESA INDIAN HEALTH CENTER**
P.O. Box 98 • KEAMS CANYON, AZ 86034
(520) 738-2211 (hospital); 738-2297 Fax 738-5442 (health center)
Taylor Satala, Director
Tribes served: Hopi, Kaibab-Paiute, Navajo. *Number of professionals on staff*: 71. *Number of Beds*: 24. *Numbers served annually*: Inpatient, 950; outpatient: 33,000. *Community health education programs*: Substance abuse, health education, et al. Affiliated with Phoenix Area Indian Health Service.

AK CHIN CLINIC
48203 W. Farrel Rd. • MARICOPA, AZ 85238
(520) 568-2221 Fax 568-4217; Dr. Steve Macko, Facility Director

**COLORADO RIVER SERVICE UNIT
PARKER PHS INDIAN HOSPITAL**
12033 Agency Rd. • PARKER, AZ 85344
(928) 669-2137 Fax 669-2571; Timothy Taylor, PhD, CEO

Tribes served: Mojave, Hopi, Navajo, Chemehuevi, Hualapai, Havasupai. *Number of Beds*: This 17-bed JCAHO-accredited hospital is staffed by six primary care physicians & one physician's assistant. Provides the Indian community with general medical care & pediatric services. Specialty outpatient services are provided on-site by IHS, by contract specialists or by off-site referrals. Numbering more than 5,200, the Indians who live here are comprised of the Colorado River Indians (an ethnic mix of Mojave, Hopi, Navajo, and Chemehuevi), Hualapai, Havasupai, Chemehuevi, and Fort Mojave tribes. The most well-known tribe is the Havasupai, whose approximately 500 members inhabit a remote village on the floor of the Grand Canyon. Once a farming society, the residents now rely on the mule train that brings down their food and modern-day necessities five days a week. Affiliated with Phoenix Area Indian Health Service.

PEACH SPRINGS INDIAN HEALTH CENTER
P.O. Box 190 • PEACH SPRINGS, AZ 86434
(928) 769-2204 Fax 769-2701; Rosemary Sullivan, Director
Tribes served: Hualapai, Havasupai. *Professionals on staff*: 6. *Services*: General outpatient medical care; dental. *Program*: Community Health Education. Affiliated with Phoenix Area Indian Health Service.

INDIAN ASSOCIATION OF COMMUNITY HEALTH CENTER
320 E. McDowell Rd. #320 • PHOENIX, AZ 85012
(602) 253-0090 Fax 252-3620; Terry McPeters, Executive Director

PHOENIX INDIAN MEDICAL CENTER
4212 North 16th St. • PHOENIX, AZ 85016
(602) 263-1200 Fax 263-1618
John Meeth, Acting CEO; David Civic, MD, Clinical Director
Tribes served: Navajo, Hopi, Apache, Hualapai, Pima, Papago, Mohave, Yavapai, Havasupai, Cocopah, Paiute, & Pascua-Yaqui. *Population served*: 70,000 American Indians. *Professionals on staff*: 70 physicians, 400 nurses. *Number of Beds*: 127. PIMC provides direct health care services to over 140,000 patients. The Tribes that comprise the Phoenix Service Unit are The Fort McDowell Yavapai Nation, the Salt River Pima-Maricopa Indian Community, and the San Lucy District of the Tohono O'odham Nation, the Tonto Apache Tribe, the Yavapai-Apache Indian Tribe, and the Yavapai-Prescott Indian Tribe. Tribal members who receive care at PIMC are often residents of the greater Phoenix area and hail from Tribes throughout the U.S. PIMC also provides specialty care to rural and remote reservation health care facilities in Arizona, Nevada, & Utah. The tribal identity of eligible beneficiaries receiving care at PIMC is representative of 67% of the 566 federally recognized Tribes. The top 5 Tribes represented by the PIMC patient population are the Navajo Nation of Arizona, New Mexico and Utah, the Salt River Pima-Maricopa Indian Tribe, the Pascua Yaqui Tribe, the Gila River Pima Maricopa Tribe, & the Tohono O'odham Nation. *Services*: Primary Care/Family Practice, Pediatrics, Dental, OB-GYN, Surgery, Emergency Medicine, Mental Health, Ophthal-mology, Pharmacy, Physical Therapy, Podiatry, Radiology. *Programs*: Staff Education, Training & Research; Community Health Education. Library. *Publication*: The IHS Primary Care Provider. Affiliated with Phoenix Area Indian Health Service.

PINON HEALTH CENTER
Navajo Route 4, P.O. Box 10 • PINON, AZ 86510
(928) 725-9500 Fax 725-9540
Shirley Lewis, Acting Director
Pinon Health Center is Associated with Chinle Service Unit - Indian Health Service in the Heart of the Navajo Reservation - Northern AZ. Pinon Health Center provides care to approximately 11,000 patients - the majority of which are Navajo and many are traditional Navajo who still speak the language. A collegial group of providers offer services in primary care, women's health, counseling, dental, dietary & community nutrition, health promotions, lab, x-ray, native medicine, optometry, pharmacy, physical therapy, speech therapy, podiatry & public health nursing. Affiliated with Navajo Area Indian Health Service.

HOPI HEALTH CARE CENTER
PHS INDIAN HEALTH SERVICES
P.O. Box 4000 • POLACCA, AZ 86042
(928) 737-6000 Fax 737-6001; Daryl Melvin, CEO
Darren Vicenti, Clinical Director
Tribes served: Hopi & Navajo. *Population served*: 7,000.
The emergency room operates 24-hours a day and Sexual Assault Nurse Examiners (SANE) responders are available at all times. Diabetes prevention treatment is provided both individually & in-group settings, i.e. kitchen creation/ eating healthy programs are available. A nutritionist works as part of this team to monitor, track, & create healthy living & lifestyle recommendations. Podiatry services are available on a scheduled basis through contract specialists. Physical therapy & well-child visits are conducted in an outpatient setting, by appointment. Public health nursing works with the Hopi Tribe Community Health Workers to monitor, follow-up, and provide individual and group health

interventions. Tribal Behavioral Health Services are also available 24-hours a day. Affiliated with Phoenix Area Indian Health Service. Tribally operated.

DESERT VISIONS YOUTH WELLNESS CENTER
REGIONAL TREATMENT CENTER
198 S. Skill Center Rd., P.O. Box 458 • SACATON, AZ 85247
(520) 562-3801 Fax 562-3415; Eden Johnson, MD, Clinical Director

SACATON SERVICE UNIT
HU HU KAM MEMORIAL INDIAN HOSPITAL
Gila River Health Care Corp., P.O. Box 38 • SACATON, AZ 85247
(520) 562-3321 Fax 528-1240; Loren Ellery, CEO
Noel Habbib, MD, Clinical Director
Tribes served: Pima, Maricopa, Tohono O'odham. Affiliated with Phoenix Area Indian Health Service. Tribally operated.

BYLAS HEALTH CENTER
P.O. Box 208 • SAN CARLOS, AZ 85550
(928) 475-2686 Fax 475-7377
Affiliated with Phoenix Area Indian Health Service.

SAN CARLOS PHS INDIAN HOSPITAL
P.O. Box 208 • SAN CARLOS, AZ 85550
(928) 475-2371 Fax 475-7370; Robert Harry, MD, CEO
Carol Frost Lee, MD, Clinical Director
Tribe served: San Carlos Apache. *Population served*: 13,000.
Number of Beds: 28. Affiliated with Phoenix Area Indian Health Service.

SALT RIVER HEALTH CENTER
10005 E. Osborn Rd. • SCOTTSDALE, AZ 85256
(480) 946-9066 Fax 946-9415; Steve Thompson, Facility Director
Clinical services provided: Dental, Pharmacy, Laboratory Services, Medical Records, Nursing, Women's Clinic, Pediatrics, Renal, Podiatry, Ophthalmology/Optometry, JVN, Nutrition. Affiliated with Phoenix Area Indian Health Service.

THE SAN SIMON HEALTH CENTER
HC01 Box 8150 • SELLS, AZ 85634
(520) 362-7007; Sally Aday, Director (383-7003)
Peter Ziegler, MD, Clinical Director (383-7211)
Donna Hobbs, Nurse Supervisor (383-7256)
The San Simon Health Center (formerly called Westside Health Center) is located in the western village of San Simon of the Tohono O'odham Nation (approximately 39 miles west of Sells, AZ, off State Route 86, mile marker 74). The San Simon Health Center provides outpatient primary care to Tohono O'odham members and other eligible American Indians. Affiliated with the Tucson Area Indian Health Service.

SANTA ROSA HEALTH CENTER
HC01, Box 8700 • SELLS, AZ 85634
(520) 361-2261 Fax 383-5572
Website: www.ihs.gov/tucson/healthcarefacilities/santarosa/
Angela Fallon, Director; Peter Ziegler, MD, Clinical Director
Donna Hobbs, Nurse Supervisor (383-7256)
The Center (SRHC) is located 30 miles northwest of Sells Hospital in Gu Achi District off of Arizona State Route 15. SRHC has the smallest staff of all Tucson Area IHS facilities. The SRHC completed a major addition in 2011. The Dental and Optometry Clinic was constructed in front of the existing clinic and added 2,376 square feet of space to provide additional healthcare services. The clinic now has five outpatient exam rooms, three dental chairs, and an optometry exam room. The Health Center provides outpatient primary care to Tohono O'odham members and other eligible American Indians. Affiliated with the Tucson Area Indian Health Service.

SELLS INDIAN HOSPITAL
P.O. Box 548 • SELLS, AZ 85634
(520) 383-7200 Fax 383-7216
Website: www.ihs.gov/tucson/healthcarefacilities/sellshospital/
Patti Whitethorne, CEO (38307251)
Dr. Peter Ziegler, Clinical Director (383-7211)
Donna Hobbs, Nurse Supervisor (383-7256)
Tribe served: Tohono O'odham. *Number of Beds*: 40. The Hospital is a 14-bed facility with The Joint Commission accreditation and is physically located off of Arizona State Route 86, 60 miles west of Tucson in the Sells District of the Tohono O'odham Nation. A professional staff of physicians, physician assistants, dentists, nurses, podiatrists, optometrists, and auxiliary technical support personnel administer both inpatient & ambulatory services. Specialties include internal medicine, pediatrics, and family practice. Emergency services are provided and critical-care patients are transferred to one of several Tucson or Phoenix area hospitals. Affiliated with Tucson Area Indian Health Service.

INSCRIPTION HOUSE HEALTH CENTER
P.O. Box 7397 • SHONTO, AZ 86054
(928) 672-3000 Fax 672-3062
Morland McCurtain, Director
James Thomas, MD, Clinical Director
Tribe served: Navajo. *Population served*: 7,000. The Inscription House Health Center is part of the Kayenta Service Unit in the Western most part of the Navajo Nation. Inpatient needs are met by referral to the Tuba City Indian Medical Center, which is 65 miles South of Inscription House, Arizona. The Inscription House facility provides 40 hour per week ambulatory care for approximately 7,000 nearby residents. The facility is closed after 5 p.m. on weekdays and is closed on weekends. Most staff live in housing provided by the Indian Health Service. Affiliated with Navajo Area Indian Health Service.

HAVASUPAI INDIAN HEALTH STATION
P.O. Box 129 • SUPAI, AZ 86435
(520) 448-2641 Fax 448-2312
Tribe served: Havasupai. Staff: 1. *Primary medical services*: Provides 7 days a week 24 hours a day outpatient medical services to 4,200 patients, annually, at isolated site at bottom of the Grand Canyon. *Special programs*: Prenatal education, diabetic education, substance abuse program, weight reduction/exercise programs. Affiliated with Phoenix Area Indian Health Service.

FOUR CORNERS REGIONALL HEALTH CENTER (FCRHC)
US Hwy. 160 & Navajo Route 35
HCR 6100 Box 30 • TEEC NOS POS, AZ 86514
(928) 656-5000 Fax 656-5181; Ann Vaughn, MD, Clinical Director (5491)
Kent Anderson, DDS, Dental Supervisor
Tribe served: Navajo. *Population served*: 7,000. FCRHC provides ambulatory care services including family medicine, internal medicine, mental health, physical therapy, optometry, dental, social services, pharmacy, x-ray, laboratory, public health nursing, diabetes education, health promotion/disease prevention. The Health Center serves approximately 7,000 Native Americans, of which the majority are members of the Navajo Nation. Strong Navajo cultural traditions exist within the community, offering an opportunity to learn the Navajo language, or to learn about traditional Navajo medicine. Affiliated with Navajo Area Indian Health Service.

TSAILE HEALTH CENTER
P.O. Box 467 • TSAILE, AZ 86556
(928) 724-3600 Fax 724-3005
Lillie M. Haskie (Navajo), Health Administrator
Beulah Allen (Navajo), MD, Medical Director
Tribe served: Navajo, mainly. *Population served*: 9,000+ registered clients. Number of *Staff*: 53. *Services*: Outpatient, Family Medicine, Ambulatory Care; including Prenatal & Geriatrics. *Program*: Community Health Education. The Health Center is adjacent to Dine' College, the first Indian Tribe-controlled college established in the United States. Routine outpatient services are provided to a broad range of patients including prenatal & geriatrics. Affiliated with Navajo Area Indian Health Service.

TUBA CITY REGIONAL HEALTH CARE CORP.
167 N. Main St., P.O. Box 600 • TUBA CITY, AZ 86045
(928) 283-2501 Fax 283-2516; Website: www.tchealth.org
Joseph Engelken, Service Unit Director
Scott Deasy, MD, Clinical Director
Number of beds: 73. *Services*: Inpatient/outpatient emergency, dental & ophthalmology, orthopedics, OB/GYN, oral surgery, eye surgery, urology. Affiliated with Navajo Area Indian Health Service.

SAN XAVIER HEALTH CENTER
7900 South J Stock Rd. • TUCSON, AZ 85746
(520) 295-2550 Fax 295-2609
Website: www.ihs.gov/tucson/healthcarefacilities/sanxavier/
Ronald Speakman, Acting Director & Nurse Supervisor
Peter Ziegler, MD, Clinical Director (383-7211)
Tribe served: Tohono O'odham. *Services*: Outpatient ambulatory & primary care. The Center (SXHC) is located in the San Xavier District of the Tohono O'odham reservation, off of Interstate 19, exit 92 (San Xavier Road). The San Xavier compound comprise of the SXHC and Tucson Area IHS administrative and environmental health and engineering offices. The Health Center is 10 miles south of downtown Tucson where it provides outpatient primary care to Tohono O'odham members and other eligible American Indians. Affiliated with Tucson Area IHS & Office of Health Programs Research & Development.

WHITERIVER INDIAN HOSPITAL
P.O. Box 860 • WHITERIVER, AZ 85941
(928) 338-4911 Fax 338-3522
Michelle Martinez, CEO; John Umhau, MD, Clinical Director
Kay Tsouhlarakis, Administrative Officer
Tribe served: White Mountain Apache. *Population served*: 17,000. Staff: 22 physicians, 79 nurses. *Number of Beds*: 44. The Whiteriver Indian Hospital is located at Whiteriver, AZ on the Fort Apache Indian Reservation. The hospital is located about three miles north of Whiteriver & serves approximately 17,000 tribal members & other Native American communities around the area. Residents to the northwest are served through the Cibecue Health Center, fifty miles from Whiteriver. The hospital is designated as a Baby Friendly Hospital, & is JCAHO-accredited & staffed by 22 physicians, podiatrist, five nurse practitioners, five dentists, two optometrists, & about 79 nursing staff members. The hospital is a 45-bed facility. They provide general medical, pediatrics, alcohol treatment, mental health, obstetric services & ambulatory surgery. Patients requiring inpatient surgical procedures & complex medical care are referred to Phoenix Indian Medical Center or contract-care hospitals. Ground and air transport are available. The Whiteriver Hospital is also the base for major research projects that include gastroenteritis and pneumococcal diseases. The Cibecue Health Center is approximately 50 miles northwest of Whiteriver, Arizona, this health center is staffed by two physicians and one dentist, and provides outpatient, urgent care, optometry and dental services to the communities of Cibecue and Carrizo. These services receive support from the White Mountain Apache Tribal Emergency Medical Services program. Affiliated with Phoenix Area Indian Health Service.

WINSLOW INDIAN HEALTH CARE CENTER
500 N. Indiana Ave., WINSLOW, AZ 86047
(928) 289-4646 Fax 289-3447; Website: www.wihcc.com
Sally Pete, Director; Frank Armao, MD, Clinical Director
Affiliated with Navajo Area Indian Health Service.

FORT YUMA HEALTH CENTER
P.O. Box 1368 • YUMA, AZ 85364
(760) 572-4100 Fax 572-4183
Jacqueline Curley, CEO; Rodnet Cuny, MD, Clinical Director
Tribes served: Quechen & Cocopah. *Number of Beds*: 17. Population served: The Cocopah and Quechan are the two distinct tribes that are served at Fort Yuma. The Quechan Reservation consists of 45,814 desert acres along the Colorado River in California's Imperial County, just outside Yuma. The Cocopah Reservation is comprised of 1,772 acres near Somerton, AZ, a small town southwest of Yuma. The Cocopah & Quechan tribal members live a contemporary lifestyle but many still practice traditional ways. The cultural experiences run deep here. Even the native language bears linguistic similarities to the ancient Aztecs. *Services*: Patient Centered Medical Home Services: Preventive care; Wellness care including healthy lifestyle management; Health risk appraisals; Acute illness; Chronic illness management; Dental Care; Behavioral Health Counseling; Pediatrics. Affiliated with Phoenix Area Indian Health Service.

CALIFORNIA

NATIVE AMERICAN HEALTH CENTER
1151 Harbor Bay Parkway #203 • ALAMEDA, CA 94501
(510) 747-3030 Fax 748-0116; Website: www.nativehealth.org
E-mail: patriciaw@nativehealth.org
Larry Swimmer (Cheyenne River Sioux), Chairperson
Cindi Adams (Chippewa), Vice Chairperson
Ronald Williams (Dakota Sioux), Secretary
Carmen Foghorn (Isleta Pueblo/Navajo), Treasurer
Rev. Robert Little Cloud (Northern Cheyenne), Director
Malinda Walker (Wyandotte), Director; Darby Price (Cherokee), Director
Services: Human Resources; Information Technology. Affiliated with California Area Indian Health Service. *Publication*: Native Health News.

SOUTHERN INDIAN HEALTH COUNCIL
4058 Willows Rd. • ALPINE, CA 91901
(619) 445-1188 Fax 445-4131
Website: www.sihc.org; Joseph E. Bulfer, Director
Reservations served: Barona, Campo, Ewiiaapaayp, Jamul, La Posta, Manzanita, Viejas. *Total population served*: 8,000. *Medical services*: Outpatient primary care. Family practice, internal medicine, pediatrics, podiatry & GYN clinic. *Programs*: Dental, community health, social services, mental health, and La Posta Substance Abuse Center. Affiliated with California Area Indian Health Service. Tribally operated.

MODOC INDIAN HEALTH PROJECT
1203 Oak St. • ALTURAS, CA 96101
(530) 233-4591 Fax 233-3055; Belinda Brown, Director
Affiliated with California Program Office. Tribally operated.

UNITED INDIAN HEALTH SERVICES
1600 Weeot Way • ARCATA, CA 95521
(707) 825-5000; Jerome J. Simone, Director

Tribes served: All American Indians with verification. Professionals on staff: 8. Population served: 20,000 patients served annually. *Primary Medical Services*: Complete family practice including obstetrics. Awards to local American Indians who are pursuing health careers. Medical & dental libraries. Affiliated with California Area Indian Health Service. Tribally operated.

CHAPA-DE INDIAN HEALTH PROGRAM
11670 Atwood Rd. • AUBURN, CA 95603
  (530) 887-2800 Fax 887-2819; Carol Ervin, Director
Affiliated with California Area Indian Health Service. Tribally operated.

BAKERSFIELD EDUCATION CENTER FOR NATIVE AMERICANS
1830 Truxton Ave., Suite 100 • BAKERSFIELD, CA 93301
  (661) 859-2940; Annie Langdeaux, Director
Affiliated with California Program Office. Tribally operated.

RIVERSIDE/SAN BERNADINO CO. INDIAN HEALTH
11555 1/2 Potrero Rd. • BANNING, CA 92220
  (909) 849-4761 Fax 849-5612; Lin Killam, Executive Director
Affiliated with California Area Indian Health Service. Tribally operated.

LOS ANGELES NATIVE AMERICAN CENTER
9500 E. Artesia Blvd. • BELLFLOWER, CA 90708
  (310) 920-7272 Fax 920-5677
  William Beckley, DHSc, MPH, President/CEO
Total population served: 80,000. Medical services: General health care; dental care; prenatal & perinatal care; immunizations; W.I.C. program. *Special programs*: Residential recovery program; family shelter program; provides a variety of culturally-based activities. Established 1996.

TOIYABE INDIAN HEALTH COUNCIL
52 Tu Su Lane • BISHOP, CA 93515
  (760) 873-8464 Fax 873-3935; Lawrence Jordan, Director
  Website: www.crihb.org/toiyave.htm
Affiliated with California Program Office. Tribally operated.

PIT RIVER HEALTH SERVICES
36977 Park Ave. • BURNEY, CA 96013
  (530) 335-5091 Fax 335-5241
  Website: www.crihb.org/pitriver.htm
  Janie Butterfield, Director; Frank Kearns, Health Administrator
Affiliated with California Program Office. Tribally operated.

CONSOLIDATED TRIBAL HEALTH PROJECT
P.O. Box 387 • CALPELLA, CA 95418
  (707) 485-5115 Fax 485-8660
  Website: www.cthp.org; George Provencher, Director
Affiliated with California Area Indian Health Service. Tribally operated.

CENTRAL VALLEY INDIAN HEALTH, INC.
20 N. Dewitt #8 • CLOVIS, CA 93612
  (559) 299-2578 Fax 299-0245; Charles Fowler, Executive Director
Purpose: To provide culturally sensitive medical & dental services to Indian people in the Central Valley. Includes Fresno, Madera, and Kings Counties. Affiliated with the California Area Indian Health Service.

COLUSA INDIAN COMMUNITY COUNCIL
3710 Hwy. 45, Suite A. • COLUSA, CA 995932
  (530) 458-5501 Fax 458-8660; Debbie Adamak, Director
Affiliated with California Program Office. Tribally operated.

ROUND VALLEY INDIAN HEALTH PROGRAM
P.O. Box 247 • COVELO, CA 95428
  (707) 983-6404 Fax 983-6184; James Russ, Executive Director
  Website: www.rvindianhealth.com; E-mail: jruss@rvindianhealth.com
Purpose: To provide medical, laboratory, and dental services to Indians and non-Indians in rural areas. Affiliated with California Area Indian Health Service. Tribally operated.

SYCUAN MEDICAL/DENTAL CENTER
5459-C Sucuan Rd. • EL CAJON, CA 92019
  (619) 445-0707 Fax 445-9764; Charlotte Quiroga, Director
  Website: www.sycuan.com/medical_dental_center
Affiliated with California Area Indian Health Service.

WARNER MOUNTAIN INDIAN HEALTH PROJECT
P.O. Box 126 • Fort Bidwell, CA 96112
  (530) 279-6194 Fax 279-2233; Website: www.crihb.org/warner.htm
  Joseph Abinanti, Health Administrator
Affiliated with California Area Indian Health Service.

QUARTZ VALLEY INDIAN HEALTH PROGRAM
P.O. Box 24 • FORT JONES, CA 96032
  (530) 468-5907 Fax 468-5908; Aaron Peters, Director
Affiliated with California Area Indian Health Service. Tribally operated.

FRESNO INDIAN HEALTH ASSOCIATION
4991 E. McKinley #118 • FRESNO, CA 93727
  (209) 255-0261 Fax 255-2149; Dr. Eric Don-Pedro, Executive Director
Tribes served: Urban Native Americans residing in metropolitan Fresno. *Total population served*: 6,000. *Medical services*: Outpatient primary care; mental health. *Programs*: Free TB & Flu vaccines. Affiliated with California Area Indian Health Service.

GREENVILLE RANCHERIA TRIBAL HEALTH
P.O. Box 279 • GREENVILLE, CA 95947
  (916) 284-6135 Fax 284-7135; Susanne Weston, Director
  Website: www.greenvillerancheria.com/grthp
Affiliated with California Area Indian Health Service.

KARUK TRIBAL HEALTH PROGRAM
P.O. Box 1016 • HAPPY CAMP, CA 96039
  (530) 493-1600 Fax 493-2275; Lessie Aubrey, Acting Director
  Website: www.crihb.org/karuk.htm
Affiliated with California Area Indian Health Service. Tribally operated.

HOOPA VALLEY TRIBAL HEALTH
P.O. Box 1288 • HOOPA, CA 95546
  (530) 625-4261 Fax 625-4047; Emmett Chase, MD, Director
Affiliated with California Area Indian Health Service. Tribally operated.

HOPLAND BAND OF POMO INDIAN HEALTH
3000 Shanel Rd. • HOPLAND, CA 95449
  (707) 744-1647 Fax 744-1506; Jan Coppiner, Health Administrator
Affiliated with California Program Office. Tribally operated.

INDIAN FREE CLINIC
7300 South Santa Fe Ave. • HUNTINGTON PARK, CA 90225

SCOTTS VALLEY POMO INDIAN HEALTH
301 Industrial Ave. • KELSEYVILLE, CA 95453
  (707) 263-4220 Fax 263-4345; Bennett Wright, Director
Affiliated with California Program Office. Tribally operated.

LAKE COUNTY TRIBAL HEALTH
925 Bevins Ct. • LAKEPORT, CA 95453
  (707) 263-8382 Fax 263-0329; Michael Icay, Director
Tribe served: Pomo. *Services*: Outpatient. Affiliated with California Area Indian Health Service. Tribally operated.

SANTA ROSA RANCHERIA HEALTH PROGRAM
P.O. Box 8 • LEMOORE, CA 93245
  (559) 924-1541 Fax 924-2197; Chuck Fowler, Director
Affiliated with California Area Indian Health Service. Tribally operated.

UNITED AMERICAN INDIAN INVOLVEMENT
1125 West 6th St., #400 • LOS ANGELES, CA 90017
  (213) 202-3970 Fax 202-3977; Dave Rambeau, Director
Affiliated with California Area Indian Health Service.

NATIVE AMERICAN HEALTH CENTER, INC.
3124 International Blvd. • OAKLAND, CA 94601
  (510) 434-5481 Fax 261-0646; Website: www.nativehealth.org
  Martin Waukazoo, Director
Services: Family & Child Guidance Clinic; Youth Services; Women, Infants & Children (WIC. Affiliated with California Area Indian Health Service.

NATIVE AMERICAN HEALTH CENTER, INC.
3124 International Blvd. • OAKLAND, CA 94601
  (510) 535-4400 Fax 261-6438; Cindi Adams, Chairperson
  Website: www.nativehealth.org
Services: Dental; Nutrition & Fitness; Medical.
Affiliated with California Area Indian Health Service.

FEATHER RIVER TRIBAL HEALTH
2145 Fifth Ave. • OROVILLE, CA 95965
  (530) 534-5394 Fax 534-3820; William Holman, Director
Affiliated with California Area Indian Health Service.

INDIAN HEALTH COUNCIL, INC.
P.O. Box 406 • PAUMA VALLEY, CA 92061
  (760) 749-1410 Fax 749-1564; Devin Parlikar, Director

Tribes served: Luiseno, Digueno, Cahuilla & Cupeno, Bands of California Mission Indians in San Diego County. *Professionals on staff*: 12. *Population served*: 7,500, annually. *Services*: Medical & dental outpatient care including social services, public health nursing, counseling, etc. Affiliated with California Program Office. Tribally operated.

TULE RIVER INDIAN HEALTH CENTER
P.O. Box 768 • PORTERVILLE, CA 93258
(559) 784-2316 Fax 781-6514; Loleta Garfield, Director
Affiliated with California Area Indian Health Service. Tribally operated.

GREENVILLE RANCHERIA TRIBAL HEALTH
P.O. Box 100 • RED BLUFF, CA 96080
(530) 528-9000 Fax 528-9002; Marshall Gouze, MD, Director
Affiliated with California Area Indian Health Service. Tribally operated.

REDDING RANCHERIA HEALTH CENTER
3184 Chum Creek Rd. • REDDING, CA 96002
(530) 224-2700 Fax 224-2738; Ron Sisson, Director
Affiliated with California Area Indian Health Service. Tribally operated.

CONSOLIDATED TRIBAL HEALTH PROJECT
6991 N. State St. • REDWOOD VALLEY, CA 95470
(707) 468-5115 Fax 468-5199; Website: www.cthp.org
Maria Anaya, MPH, Director; Michael Knight, Chairperson
Tribe served: Pomo Tribes - Coyote Valley, Hopland Band, Guidiville Reservation, Laytonville Cahto Tribe, Pinoleville Indian Community, Potter Valley Rancheria, Redwood Valley Rancheria, Sherwood Valley Rancheria. *Professionals on staff*: 30-35. *Services*: Outpatient; Family Practice-Perinatal Program; Dental. *Programs*: Staff Education, Training & Research; Community Health Education. Affiliated with California Area IHS. Tribally operated.

COYOTE VALLEY TRIBAL HEALTH
P.O. Box 39 • REDWOOD VALLEY, CA 95470
(707) 485-8723 Fax 485-1247; Sharon Ibarra, Director
Affiliated with California Area Indian Health Service. Tribally operated.

NATIVE AMERICAN HEALTH CENTER
260 23rd St. • RICHMOND, CA 94804
(510) 232-7020 Fax 232-7015; Website: www.nativehealth.org
Services: Family & Child Guidance Clinic. Affiliated with California Area Indian Health Service. Tribally operated.

CALIFORNIA RURAL INDIAN HEALTH BOARD
4400 Auburn Blvd., 2nd Fl. • SACRAMENTO, CA 95841
(916) 929-9761 Fax 929-7246
James Crouch, Director
Affiliated with California Area Indian Health Service.

SACRAMENTO URBAN INDIAN HEALTH PROJECT
2020 J St. • SACRAMENTO, CA 95814
(916) 441-0918 Fax 441-1261; Britta Guerrero, Director
Affiliated with California Area Indian health Service. Tribally operated.

SAN DIEGO AMERICAN INDIAN HEALTH CENTER
2602 First Ave., Suite 105 • SAN DIEGO, CA 92103
(619) 234-0572/2158/0648 Fax 234-0206
3812 Ray St. • SAN DIEGO, CA 92104
(619) 298-9090 Fax 298-0677; Website: www.sdaihc.org
Joe Bulfer, Executive Director
Purpose: To provide medical, dental & mental health services to Native Americans living in the San Diego area. Affiliated with California Area HIS.

**FRIENDSHIP HOUSE ASSOCIATION OF AMERICAN INDIANS, INC.
NATIVE AMERICAN HEALTH CLINIC**
333 Valencia St. #400 • SAN FRANCISCO, CA 94103
(415) 865-0964 Fax 865-5428; Helen Waukazoo, Director
Affiliated with California Area Indian Health Service.

NATIVE AMERICAN HEALTH CENTER
160 Capp St. • SAN FRANCISCO, CA 94110
(415) 621-1170 Fax 255-7527; Website: www.nativehealth.org
Mark Espinoza, Executive Director; John Pakula, MD, Clinical Director
Services: Family & Child Guidance Clinic; Medical; Pediatric; Dental; HIV Services; Nutrition & Fitness; Women, Infants & Children (WIC). Affiliated with California Area Indian Health Service. Tribally operated.

INDIAN HEALTH CENTER OF SANTA CLARA VALLEY
1333 Meridian Ave. • SAN JOSE, CA 95125
(408) 445-3400 Fax 269-9273
Website: www.indianhealthcenter.org

Matthew L. Kendall, MPH, Director
Tribes served: Many Indian tribes served. *Professionals on staff*: 10. *Population served*: 500-600 outpatients per month. *Primary medical services*: Medical, dental, counseling. *Programs*: General medicine; prenatal; diabetes; weight management; alcohol & drug abuse counseling; nutrition; mental health outreach & referral; AIDS/HIV testing & counseling; dental; and community health education programs. Library. Affiliated with California Program Office.

AMERICAN INDIAN HEALTH & FAMILY SERVICES
4141 State St., A-1 • SANTA BARBARA, CA 93110
(805) 681-7356 Fax 681-7358
Scott Black, Executive Director
Affiliated with California Area Indian Health Service. Tribally operated.

URBAN INDIAN HEALTH PROJECT
610 Del Monte Ave. • SANTA BARBARA, CA 93101
(805) 965-0718. Affiliated with California Area Indian Health Service

LYTTON RANCHERIA HEALTH PROGRAM
1300 N. Dutton Ave., Suite A • SANTA ROSA, CA 95401
(707) 575-5917 Fax 575-6974; Lisa Miller, Health Administrator
Affiliated with California Area Indian Health Service. Tribally operated.

SONOMA COUNTY INDIAN HEALTH
P.O. Box 7308 • SANTA ROSA, CA 95407
(707) 544-4056 Fax 526-1016
Michael Roth, Director
Affiliated with California Area Indian Health Service. Tribally operated.

SANTA YNEZ INDIAN HEALTH
P.O. Box 539 • SANTA YNEZ, CA 93460
(805) 686-7070 Fax 688-2060
Kathleen Rodriguez, Director
Affiliated with California Area Indian Health Service. Tribally operated.

SHINGLE SPRINGS TRIBAL HEALTH PROGRAM
P.O. Box 1340 • SHINGLE SPRINGS, CA 95682
(530) 672-8059 Fax 672-2111
Beth Ann Bodi, Health Administrator
Affiliated with California Program Office. Tribally operated.

LASSEN INDIAN HEALTH CENTER
745 Joaquin St. • SUSANVILLE, CA 96130
(530) 257-2542 Fax 257-5208
Danny Ukestine, Director
Affiliated with California Area Indian Health Service.

GUIDIVILLE INDIAN RANCHERIA HEALTH
P.O. Box 339 • TALMAGE, CA 95481
(707) 462-3682 Fax 462-0644
Walter Gray, III, Director
Affiliated with California Area Indian Health Service. Tribally operated.

UNITED INDIAN HEALTH SERVICES
P.O. Box 420 • TRINIDAD, CA 95570
(707) 677-3693 Fax 677-3170; Jerry Simone, Director
Affiliated with California Area Indian Health Service. Tribally operated.

M.A.C.T. HEALTH BOARD
18382 Tuolumne Rd. • TUOLUMNE, CA 95370
(209) 928-4277 Fax 928-1295
Nancy Ehlers, Director
Website: www.macthealthboard.com
Affiliated with California Area Indian Health Service. Tribally operated.

TUOLUMNE ME WUK INDIAN HEALTH CENTER
19590 Me Wuk St. • TUOLUMNE, CA 95379
(209) 928-4277 Fax 928-1295; Website: www.tmwihc.org
Lester Alford, Director
Affiliated with California Program Office. Tribally operated.

PINOLEVILLE BAND OF POMO INDIANS HEALTH PROJECT
367 N. State St., Suite 204 • UKIAH, CA 95482
(707) 463-1454 Fax 463-6601; Don Rich, Director
Affiliated with California Area Indian Health Service. Tribally operated.

SHERWOOD VALLEY BAND POMO INDIAN HEALTH
190 Sherwood Hill Dr. • WILLITS, CA 95490
(707) 459-9690 Fax 459-6936
Trina Fitzgerrl, Health Administrator
Affiliated with California Area Indian Health Service. Tribally operated.

NORTHERN VALLEY INDIAN HEALTH
207 N. Butte St. • WILLOWS, CA 95988
(530) 934-9293 Fax 534-2204; Website: www.nvih.org
Victor Sansalone, Director. California Area IHS. Tribally operated.

FORT YUMA HEALTH CENTER
One Indian Hill Rd. • WINTERHAVEN, CA 92283
(760) 572-4100 Fax 572-4183
Jacqueline Curley, CEO; Rodnet Cuny, MD, Clinical Director

COLORADO

DENVER INDIAN HEALTH & FAMILY SERVICES
1633 Filmore St., G11 • DENVER, CO 80206
(303) 781-4050 Fax 781-4333
Del Nutter, Executive Director
Website: www.dihfs.org; E-mail: info@dihfs.org
Provides medical outpatient services, dental services, diabetes care, management & prevention, mental health & substance abuse services to an estimated 25,000 Indian population, members of federally recognized tribes who reside in the Denver metro area.

NATIONAL INDIAN HEALTH BOARD
1900 Grant St. #1000 • DENVER, CO 80203
(303) 861-7878

SOUTHERN COLORADO UTE SERVICE UNIT
P.O. Box 778 • Ignacio, CO 81137
(970) 563-9443 Fax 563-9447
Vernon Frost, General Services Officer
Affiliated with Albuquerque Area Indian Health Service. Tribally operated

SOUTHERN COLORADO UTE HEALTH CENTER
P.O. Box 778 • Ignacio, CO 81137
(970) 563-9443
Thomas Duran, Health Center Director
Matthew Clark, MD, Clinical Director
Affiliated with Albuquerque Area Indian Health Service.

UTE MOUNTAIN UTE HEALTH CENTER
General Delivery • Towaoc, CO 81334
(970) 565-4441 Fax 565-4945; E. David Ward, Jr., Health Director
Trina Begay, DO, Clinical Director
Affiliated with Albuquerque Area Indian Health Service.

IDAHO

KOOTENAIR TRIBAL HEALTH CLINIC
P.O. Box T • BONNERS FERRY, ID 83805
(208) 267-5223; Gary Leva, Dirctor
Affiliated with Portland Area Indian Health Service.

FORT HALL SERVICE UNIT
NOT-TSOO GAH-NEE INDIAN HEALTH CENTER
P.O. Box 717 • FORT HALL, ID 83203
(208) 238-2400 Fax 238-5463
Shirley Alvarez, Chief Executive Officer (238-5493)
E-mail: salvarez@fth.portland.ihs.gov
Carol Irwin, Administrative Officer; Douglas Lyons, DO, Clinical Director
Tribes served: Shoshone-Bannock & Northwestern Band of Shoshone. *Population served*: 13,500 registered American Indian & Alaska Natives. The Not-Tsoo Gah-nee Indian Health Center serves the ambulatory health care needs of the Shoshone-Bannock Tribes & the Northwestern Band of Shoshoni. Members of other federally recognized Tribes and Alaska Natives also receive care at the facility. The Fort Hall Service Unit was jointly accredited with the Shoshone-Bannock Tribes Tribal Health and Human Services Department by the Accreditation Association for Ambulatory Health Care, Inc. since 2000. The Fort Hall Indian Health Service is the first and only Federal Service Unit to attain and maintain this notable recognition. The facility serves over 13,380 registered American Indian and Alaska Natives. There are approximately 37,294 ambulatory patient visits per year. The center is staffed with 50 employees including 4 Clinic Physicians, 1 Physician Assistant, 3 Registered Nurses, 2 Licensed Practical Nurse, 4 Pharmacists, 2 Dentists, 3 Dental Assistants, 1 Dental Hygienist, 1 Optometrist, 1 Radiology Technician. Two Medical Technologists and a Medical Technician complete the clinical staff. The Not-Tsoo Gah-Nee Indian Health Center encompasses 28,915 square feet offering ambulatory medical, optometry & dental care. The facility features in-house lab, x-ray, & pharmacy services. The Purchased & Referred Care, Diabetes & Community Health Nursing Program are located within the facility. Affiliated with Portland Area Indian Health Service.

NORTHERN IDAHO INDIAN HEALTH SERVICE UNIT
P.O. Drawer 367 • LAPWAI, ID 83540
(208) 843-2271 Fax 843-2102
Joseph Moquino, Unit Director
Tina Orton, Administrative Officer
Helen Wootton, MD, Clinical Director
Tribe served: Nez Perce. *Total population served*: 3,110. *Medical services*: Clinic - outpatient primary care; community health/preventive; mental health; health education. *Programs*: Diabetes; safety; holistic health; tribal environmental restoration waste management; tribal well-child care. Library. Affiliated with Portland Area Indian Health Service.

BENEWAH MEDICAL CENTER
P.O. Box 388 • PLUMMER, ID 83851
(208) 686-1931; Debra Hanks, Director
Affiliated with Portland Area Indian Health Service.

IOWA

SAC & FOX TRIBE OF THE MISSISSIPPI
IN IOWA INDIAN HEALTH CENTER
TAMA, IA 52339 (515) 484-4094
Affiliated with Aberdeen Area Indian Health Service.
Tribally operated.

KANSAS

PHS INDIAN HEALTH CENTER
100 West 6th St. • HOLTON, KS 66436
(785) 364-2177 Fax 364-3691
Richard Harris, MD, Service Unit Director
Tribes served: Kickapoo of Kansas, Potawatomi, Sac & Fox of Kansas & Nebraska, & Iowa Tribe. *Professionals on staff*: 8. *Services*: General outpatient medical care, with laboratory & pharmacy. Library. Affiliated with Oklahoma City Area Indian Health Service.

KICKAPOO TRIBE HEALTH CENTER
Rt. 1, Box 221C • HORTON, KS 66439
(785) 486-2154 fax 486-2158
Debbie Whitebird, Facility Director
Affiliated with Oklahoma City Area Indian Health Service. Tribally operated.

HASKELL INDIAN HEALTH CENTER
2415 Massachusetts St. • LAWRENCE, KS 66044
(785) 843-3750 Fax 843-8815
CDR Kelly Battese, CEO
E-mail: kelly.battese@ihs.gov(832-4824)
Chelsea Anglin, Administrative Officer
E-mail: chelsea.anglin@ihs.gov
Mark James, MD, Clinical Director; E-mail: mark.james@ihs.gov
Tribes served: Students attending Haskell Indian Junior College - representing over 135 different tribes; Indians residing in Northeast Kansas. *Professionals on staff*: 20. *Numbers served*: 34,000 outpatients served annually. Primary Medical Services: Family medicine, substance abuse, optometry, dental, behavioral health, disease prevention, laboratory, nutrition, contract care. *Programs*: Staff education; community health education. Library. Affiliated with Oklahoma City Area Indian Health Service. Opened 1978.

WHITE CLOUD HEALTH STATION
3349-B Thrasher Rd. • WHITE CLOUD, KS 66094
(785) 595-3450
CDR Kelly Battese, Facility Director (832-4824)
E-mail: kelly.battese@ihs.gov
Tribes served: Iowa Tribe of Kansas & Nebraska; Kickapoo Tribe of Kansas; Prairie Band Potawatomi Nation; Sac & Fox Nation of Missouri in Kansas & Nebraska. *Services*: The White Cloud Health Station recently moved into a new building with four treatment rooms. The facilities located on the Iowa Tribe in Kansas and Nebraska Reservation. It is located close to the Nebraska and Missouri state borders, near the town of White Cloud, KS. The clinic is located inside of a tribally owned service building and includes a triage area/lab, two treatment rooms, offices, and a pharmacy. The clinic is staffed full time by a Family nurse practitioner, nurse, diabetic nurse educator, pharmacist, health systems specialist, and medical support assistant. Services offered include general family medicine (pediatrics through geriatrics), acute care, and chronic disease management. The clinic contracts for routine services including specimen testing, x-ray, podiatry, dental care, eye care, & registered dietician consultation. The clinic is an appointment-based clinic offering outpatient, general & family practice medicine including laboratory testing. Affiliated with Oklahoma City Area Indian Health Service.

HUNTER HEALTH CLINIC
2318 E. Central • WICHITA, KS 67214
(316) 262-2415 Fax 262-0741
Suzette Schwartz, Executive Director
Affiliated with Oklahoma City Area Indian Health Service.

MAINE

MICMAC FAMILY HEALTH CLINIC
8 Northern Rd. • PRESQUE ISLAND, ME 04769
(800) 750-1972; (207) 764-7219 Fax 764-7768
Services offered include: Health Education; Preventative Health Exams; Chronic Disease Management; Acute Care; Confidential Testing & Counseling for HIV/AIDS & Sexually Transmitted Disease (STD); Tobacco Cessation; Alcohol & Substance Abuse Counseling; Lab Services; Immunizations; Pharmacy Supplies & Medications; Case Management; Referrals; 24-Hour Medical Instructions & Advice; Electrocardiogram (EKG)
Youth Services 58 Sunset Loop, Presque Isle, ME 04769
207-769-2114 Monday - Friday, 8:00 AM - 4:00 PM ET
The youth program focuses on bringing Micmac youth together & exposing them to many different experiences. These experiences help to bring out their strengths, function as a team & make group decisions. The program exposes young people to Micmac culture through tribal traditions and arts and crafts, teaches a healthy lifestyle through prevention awareness and provides outings such as powwows, camping, bowling and hiking.

MARYLAND

NATIVE AMERICAN LIFELINES
106 West Clay Ave. • BALTIMORE, MD 21201
(410) 837-2258 Fax 837-2692
Website: www.nativeamericanlifelines.org
Susan Roth, Executive Director; E-mail: susan.nal@verizon.net
Travis Locklear, Tobacco & Outreach Coordinator
E-mail: travis.nal@verizon.net
Shelly Wiechelt, Substance Abuse & Mental Health Therapist
E-mail: shelly.nal@verizon.net
Programs: Substance Abuse & Mental Health; Youth; Tobacco Prevention; Prison Outreach; HIV/AIDS & Hepatitis Prevention. *Publication*: Drum Beat. Established 2000.

MASSACHUSETTS

MASHPEE WAMPANOAG HEALTH SERVICE UNIT
483 Great Neck Rd. South • MASHPEE, MA 02649
(508) 477-6967 Fax 477-0156
The mission of Mashpee Wampanoag Service Unit is to provide quality, comprehensive health care to Native American members and their families in a culturally sensitive manner promoting good health, safe-lifestyles, wellbeing and harmony. The Mashpee Wampanoag Service Unit is committed to the elimination of health disparities. We strive to be progressive in the development & expansion of family-focused medicine and traditional practice. We promote physical, mental and emotional wellness that strengthens and empowers our native community, while honoring our Creator, Mother Earth, our Elders & our Children. Affiliated with Nashville Area Indian Health Service.

MICHIGAN

KEWEENAW BAY INDIAN COMMUNITY HEALTH CLINIC
102 Superior Ave. • BARAGA, MI 49908
(906) 353-8700 Ext. 25 Fax 353-8799
John Seppanen, Director
Geoffrey Coleman, MD, Clinical Director
Tribe served: Keweenaw Bay Indian Community.
Affiliated with Bemidji Area Office. Tribally operated.

BAY MILLS INDIAN COMMUNITY HEALTH CLINIC
12124 W. Lakeshore Dr. • BRIMLEY, MI 49715
(906) 248-5527 Fax 248-2508; Website: www.baymills.org
Laurel Keenan, Director; Vicki Newland, Clinical Director
Tribe served: Bay Mills Indian Community.
Affiliated with Bemidji Area Office. Tribally operated.

MIN-NO-AYA-WIN CLINIC
927 Trettel Lane • CLOQUET, MI 55720
(888) 888-6007; (218) 879-1227 Fax 879-8379
Phil Norrgard, Director
Tribe served: Fond du Lac Band of Lake Superior Ojibwe.
Affiliated with Bemidji Area Office. Tribally operated.

MATCH-E-BE-NASH-SHE-WISH POTTAWATOMI
Gun Lake Health Dept., P.O. Box 218 • DORR, MI 49323
(916) 681-0360 Fax 681-0380
Phyllis Davis, Health Director
Tribe served: Pottawatomi. Affiliated with Bemidji Area Office.
Tribally operated.

POKAGON BAND OF POTAWATOMI HEALTH SERVICES
57392 M51 So. • DOWAGIAC, MI 49047
(616) 782-4141 Fax 782-8797
Christine Daugherty, Health Director
Tribe served: Pokagon Band of Potawatomi.
Affiliated with Bemidji Area Office. Tribally operated.

LITTLE TRAVERSE BAND OF ODAWA HEALTH DEPARTMENT
7500 Odawa Cir. • HARBOR SPRINGS, MI 49740
(231) 242-1700 Fax 242-1660
Sharon Sierzputowski, Director
Tribe served: Little Traverse Bay Band of Odawa.
Affiliated with Bemidji Area Office. Tribally operated.

LITTLE RIVER BAND OF OTTAWA INDIANS' HEALTH DEPARTMENT
310 9th St. • MANISTEE, MI 49660-0314
(231) 723-8299 Fax 398-2968; Jessica Burger, Health Director
Tribe served: Little River band of Ottawa Indians.
Affiliated with Bemidji Area Office. Tribally operated.

NIMKEE MEMORIAL WELLNESS CENTER
2591 S. Leaton Rd. • MT. PLEASANT, MI 48858
(517) 775-4600 Fax 773-2028
Gail George, Health Director
Tribes served: Saginaw Chippewa Indians of Michigan, and other federally recognized tribes. *Professionals on staff*: 25. *Services*: Primary patient care; dental, nursing, psychological, substance abuse counseling, and health education & fitness. *Programs*: Staff Education, Training & Research; Community Health Education. Scholarships. Affiliated with Bemidji Area Office. Tribally operated.

GRAND TRAVERSE OTTAWA/CHIPPEWA HEALTH CLINIC
2300 N. Stallman Rd., Suite A • PESHAWBESTOWN, MI 49682
(231) 534-7200 Fax 534-7806
Soumit Pendharker, Director
Tribe served: Grand Traverse Ottawa/Chippewa Indians.
Affiliated with Bemidji Area Office. Tribally operated.

LITTLE TRAVERSE BAY BAND OF ODAWA HEALTH DEPARTMENT
7500 Odawa Circle • HARBOR SPRINGS, MI 49740
(231) 242-1700; Arlene Naganashe, Health Director
Tribe served: Little Traverse Bay Band of Odawa.
Affiliated with Bemidji Area Office. Tribally operated.

SAULT STE. MARIE HEALTH & HUMAN SERVICES CENTER
2684 Ashmun St. • SAULT STE. MARIE, MI 49783
(906) 632-5200 Fax 632-5276
Bonnie Culfa, RN, MSN, Health Director
Tribe served: Sault Ste. Marie Tribe of Chippewa Indians. *Total population served*: 15,500. *Medical services*: Family practice. *Programs*: Dental, lab, radiology, mental health & substance abuse counseling, HIV prevention & treatment; optical; podiatry; audiology; pharmacy; community health. Library. Affiliated with Bemidji Area Office. Tribally operated.

HURON POTAWATOMI BAND HEALTH CLINIC
2775 W. Dickman Rd., Suite K • SPRINGFIELD, MI 49052
(888) 662-2808; (616) 966-1101 Fax 966-1113
Mark Smit, Health Director
Tribe served: Huron Potawatomi Band of Indians.
Affiliated with Bemidji Area Office. Tribally operated.

LAC VIEUX DESERT BAND HEALTH DEPARTMENT
P.O. Box 249 • WATERSMEET, MI 49969
(906) 358-4587 Fax 358-4208
Terry Fox, Health Administrator
Tribe served: Lac Vieux Desert Band of Lake Superior Chippewa.
Affiliated with Bemidji Area Office. Tribally operated.

HANNAHVILLE INDIAN COMMUNITY HEALTH CLINIC
N14911 Hannahville B1 Rd. • WILSON, MI 49896
(906) 466-2782 Fax 466-7454; Susie Meshigaud, Director
Affiliated with Bemidji Area Office. Tribally operated.

MINNESOTA

LEECH LAKE BAND HEALTH CLINIC
6530 US 2 NW • CASS LAKE, MN 56633
(218) 335-4500 Fax 335-8219; Eli Hunt, Health Director
Tribe served: Leech Lake Band of Chippewa Indians.
Affiliated with Bemidji Area Office.

CASS LAKE PHS INDIAN HOSPITAL
425 7th St. NW • CASS LAKE, MN 56633
(218) 335-3200 Fax 335-3300
Robert Malone, MD, Chief Executive Officer
Number of Beds: 22. Affiliated with Bemidji Area Office.

MIN-NO-AYA-WIN HEALTH CLINIC
927 Trettel Lane • CLOQUET, MN 55720
(218) 879-1227; Phil Norrgard, Director
Harlen Whitling, R.N., Medical Coordinator
Charles Vergona, MD, Medical Staff
Tribe served: Fond du Lac Band of Chippewa. 17 professionals on staff. 3,700 outpatients and 400 inpatients annually. *Primary services*: Outpatient medical and dental services; public health nursing; social services Professional staff education, training and research programs. Community health education programs. Library. Affiliated with Bemidji Area Office. Tribally operated.

GRAND PORTAGE CHIPPEWA HEALTH CLINIC
P.O. Box 428 • GRAND PORTAGE, MN 55605
(218) 475-2235 Fax 475-2261; Grace Bushard, Health Director
Tribe served: Grand Portage Band of Chippewa Indians.
Affiliated with Bemidji Area Office. Tribally operated.

UPPER SIOUX COMMUNITY HEALTH CLINIC
P.O. Box 147 • GRANITE FALLS, MN 56241
(320) 564-2360 Fax 564-3264
Patricia Blue, Administrator
Tribes served: Upper Sioux Community - two counties, Yellow Medicine County & Chippewa County. Medical Services: Contract Health, Mental Health, Chemical Dependency; Indian Child Welfare; Community Health. Affiliated with Bemidji Area Office. Tribally operated.

INDIAN HEALTH BOARD OF MINNEAPOLIS
1315 East 24th St. • MINNEAPOLIS, MN 55404
(612) 721-9800; Website: www.ihb-mpls.org
E-mail: dlapointe@ihb-mpls.org
Patrick Rock, MD (Leech Lake Ojibwe), CEO
Anton Becker, Chairperson
Population served: Provides health needs of the American Indian community living in Minneapolis, about 7,000. *Services*: Medical, including primary, adult, OB/GYN & pediatric care with emphasis on family planning, diabetes care, & health, wellness & education; dental, emer-gency treatment, preventive care, & specialist referral; Counseling. Resource library.

LOWER SIOUX COMMUNITY HEALTH CLINIC
P.O. Box 308 • MORTON, MN 56270
(507) 697-6185 Fax 637-4380; Teri Schemmel, Health Director
Affiliated with Bemidji Area Office. Tribally operated.

BOIS FORT TRIBAL HEALTH CLINIC
13071 Nett Lake Rd. • NETT LAKE, MN 55771
(218) 757-3650 Fax 757-0234
Jeneal Goggleye, Health Director; Ray Hawk, Clinical Director
Tribe served: Bois Forte band of Chippewa Indians.
Affiliated with Bemidji Area Office. Tribally operated.

MILLE LACS BAND NE-IA-SHING HEALTH CLINIC
43500 Migizi Dr. • ONAMIA, MN 56359
(320) 532-4163 Fax 532-4354
Robin Carufel, Executive Director
Tribe served: Mille Lacs Band of Ojibwe. *Total population served*: 3,000. *Medical services*: Family Medicine; Internal Medicine; Medical Laboratory; Radiology; Pharmacy. *Special programs*: Dental & oral surgery; optometry & optical, audiology, home care, social nutrition, emergency assistance; Migizi elder services; public health; WIC; psychology; chemical dependency; social services. Believed to be the first clinic in the nation built with casino profits. Affiliated with Bemidji Area Office. Tribally operated.

SHAKOPEE MDEWAKANTON SIOUX HEALTH CLINIC
2320 Sioux Trail, NW • PRIOR LAKE, MN 55372
(952) 496-6150 Fax 233-4224; Melanie Dunlap, Health Director
Affiliated with Bemidji Area Office. Tribally operated.

RED LAKE COMPREHENSIVE HEALTH SERVICE
P.O. Box 249 • RED LAKE, MN 56671
(218) 679-3912 Fax 679-3990
Constance James, Health Director; John Robinson, Clinical Director
Tribe served: Red lake Band of Chippewa Indians.
Affiliated with Bemidji Area Office. Tribally operated.

RED LAKE PHS INDIAN HOSPITAL
Hwy. 1 • RED LAKE, MN 56671
(218) 679-3912 Fax 679-00181
Norine Smith, Chief Executive Officer
Number of Beds: 23. Affiliated with Bemidji Area Office.

PRAIRIE ISLAND COMMUNITY HEALTH CLINIC
1158 Island Blvd. • WELCH, MN 55089
(651) 385-4148 Fax 385-4110;Terri Buck, Health Director
Affiliated with Bemidji Area Office. Tribally operated.

WHITE EARTH HEALTH CENTER
P.O. Box 418 • WHITE EARTH, MN 56591
(218) 983-3285 Fax 983-3641; Alan Fogerty, Chief Executive Officer
Tribe served: White Earth Band of Chippewa Indians.
Affiliated with Bemidji Area Office. Tribally operated.

MISSISSIPPI

CHOCTAW HEALTH CENTER
Route 7, Box R-50 • PHILADELPHIA, MS 39350
(601) 656-2211; Marianna Hane, Director; Nolan Fulton, M.D., Chief of Staff
Hospital. *Number of Beds*: 40. Affiliated with Nashville Area Office.
Tribally operated.

MONTANA

ROCKY BOY CHIPPEWA/CREE HEALTH CENTER
P.O. Box 664 • BOX ELDER, MT 59521
(406) 395-4486; Fawn Tadios-Hawn, CEO
Tribes served: Chippewa/Cree; any enrolled member of a federally-recognized tribe. *Total population served*: 13,000. *Professionals on staff*: 20. *Services*: Primary patient care; emergency medical services; community health. *Programs*: HIV/AIDS Prevention Program; Tobacco Cessation. Affiliated with Billings Area Indian Health Service. Tribally operated.

BLACKFEET COMMUNITY HOSPITAL
P.O. Box 760 • BROWNING, MT 59417
(406) 338-6100 Fax 338-2959; Tim Davis, Acting Director
Dee Hutchison, Chief Executive Officer
Stacey Thomas, Acting Administrative Officer
Richard Odegaard, MD, Clinical Director (6202)
Number of Beds: 34. Affiliated with Billings Area Indian Health Service.

CROW/NORTHERN CHEYENNE HOSPITAL
P.O. Box 9 • CROW AGENCY, MT 59022
(406) 638-3500 Fax 638-3569; 638-3350 (Clinic)
Darren Crowe, CEO; Roberta Spotted Horse, Administrative Officer
Robert Byron, MD, Clinical Director
Tribes served: Crow & Northern Cheyenne. *Number of Beds*: 34.
Affiliated with Billings Area Indian Health Service.

FORT BELKNAP HOSPITAL
669 Agency Main St. • HARLEM, MT 59526
(406) 353-3100 Fax 353-3227; Steve Fox, Chief Executive Officer
Thomas Champagne, Administrative Officer
Tribe served: Gros Ventre & Assiniboine. *Number of Beds*: 18.
Affiliated with Billings Area Indian Health Service. Tribally operated.

EAGLE CHILD HEALTH STATION
P.O. Box 620 • HAYS, MT 59527
(406) 673-3777 Fax 673-3835
Tribes served: Gros Ventre & Assiniboine.

HEART BUTTE HEALTH STATION
P.O. Box 80 • HEART BUTTE, MT 59448
(406) 338-2151 Fax 338-5613

LAME DEER PHS INDIAN HEALTH CENTER
P.O. Box 70 • LAME DEER, MT 59043
(406) 477-4400 Fax 477-4427
Debbie Bends, Service Unit Director
Beverly Stiller, Administrative Officer
Affiliated with Billings Area Indian Health Service. Tribally operated.

LODGE GRASS PHS INDIAN HEALTH CENTER
P.O. Box AD • Lodge Grass, MT 59050
 (406) 639-2317 Fax 639-2976
 Dan Gun Shows, Administrative Officer
 Charles Lambiotte, MD, Medical Officer
Affiliated with Billings Area Indian Health Service.

VERNE E. GIBBS HEALTH CENTER
P.O. Box 67 • POPLAR, MT 59255
 (406) 768-3491 Fax 768-3603
 Julie Bemer, Director
 Edna Wetsit, Administrative Officer; Scott Merchant, Clinical Director
Tribes served: Assiniboine & Sioux. Affiliated with Billings Area HIS.

PRYOR HEALTH STATION
P.O. Box 9 • PRYOR, MT 59066
 (406) 259-8238 Fax 259-8290. *Tribe served*: Crow.

FLATHEAD PHS INDIAN HEALTH CENTER
P.O. Box 880, Mission Dr. • ST. IGNATIUS, MT 59865
 (406) 745-3525; Kevin Howlett, Director
 Yvonne Grenier, Administrator
Tribes served: Confederated Salish & Kootenai Tribes-Flathead Reservation. 10 professionals on staff. Outpatient clinics with main focus on Women's Clinics. *Special Program*: Narcotic Treatment Program, Sherry Saddler, Director. Community health education programs. Affiliated with Billings Area Indian Health Service. Tribally operated.

CHIEF REDSTONE HEALTH CLINIC
P.O. Box 729 • WOLF POINT, MT 59201
 (406) 653-1641 Fax 653-3728
 Edna Wetsit, Health Systems Specialist
Tribes served: Assiniboine & Sioux. Affiliated with Billings Area HIS.

NEBRASKA

CARL T. CURTIS HEALTH CENTER
MACY, NE 68039
 (402) 837-5381 Fax 837-5303
 Pat Medina, Health Director
Tribes served: Omaha & Winnebago or any other Native American on the reservation needing medical care. *Professionals on staff*: 2. *Services*: Ambulatory Care, Family Practice, OB/GYN, Well Child, WIC, & Community Health. *Programs*: Staff Education, Training & Research; Community Health Education. Library. Affiliated with Aberdeen Area IHS. Tribally operated.

NEBRASKA URBAN INDIAN HEALTH COALITION
2240 Landon Ct. • OMAHA, NE 68103
 (402) 434-7181; Website: www.nuihc.com
 Donna L. Polk-Primm, Executive Director
 Brett Robinson, MD, Medical Director
Facility: Intertribal Treatment Center, 2301 S. 15th St., Omaha, NE 68108.

WINNEBAGO PHS INDIAN HOSPITAL
P.O. Box H • WINNEBAGO, NE 68071
 (402) 878-2231 Fax 878-2535
 Sherrian Moore, Chief Executive Officer
 Ahmed Mohammed, MD, Clinical Director
Tribes served: Omaha & Winnebago. *Number of Beds*: 13. Supplies basic health care to members of the Winnebago & Omaha Tribes, and to a significant number of Indians living in the Sioux City area. The facility maintains a drug and alcohol dependency unit of 16 beds. The hospital provides Level Three emergency room services. The outpatient services include dental and specialty clinics. The University of Nebraska has an OB/GYN clinic in Winnebago, & Marion Health Center in Sioux City has a direct-link computerized EKG interpretation. The Winnebago Diabetes Project is one of two within the Great Plains Area Indian Health Service. Its two main objectives are to improve the quality of patient care and to reduce the number of diabetic complications. The Winnebago facility also shares some health services with the nearby Omaha Tribal Reservation. Affiliated with Aberdeen Area Indian Health Service.

NEVADA

ELKO SERVICE UNIT PHS INDIAN HEALTH CENTER
515 Shoshone Cir. • ELKO, NV 89801
 (888) 823-6000; (775) 738-2252 Fax 738-5859
 Jim Driving Hawk, CEO; Thomas Scott, MD, Clinical Director
Tribe served: Te-Moak Tribe of Western Shoshone. Clinic hours are 7 a.m. to 6 p.m. Monday through Thursday and 8 a.m. to 5 p.m. on Fridays. The

ambulatory clinic provides many people with essential health care. Staffed by 2 physicians, 2 physician assistants, 1 dentist, & 1 psychologist, this AAAHC accredited family practice clinic offers direct medical, dental, mental health and substance abuse services. The total number of staff consists of 39 employees. Visiting specialties include audiology, cardiology, hematology, psychiatry & rheumatology. We also offer tele-health services including dietary, cardiology, diabetic retinopathy screening, pain management, psychiatry & rheumatology. Contract health care services are also coordinated by referring to hospitals and clinics both locally & in nearby cities. On-site pharmacy services are available including an automated refill line. A 24/7 Nurse Advice Hotline is another resource available to our community. Tele-education opportunities are available for all staff members. Southern Bands Health Center has successfully incorporated the use of Electronic Health Records into our practice. We also provide services through our Battle Mountain Field Clinic twice monthly. In isolated communities, transportation and employment are often scarce. We must reach all the people to promote awareness of our programs. Our community health outreach services include public health nursing, mental health, and environmental health programs. *Tribal Health Facilities*: Duckwater, Ely and Goshute reservations also offer direct and contract health care services to their communities. Clinic days/hours and services vary by facility. Affiliated with Phoenix Area Indian Health Service. Tribally operated.

NEWE MEDICAL CLINIC
400 A Newe View • ELY, NV 89301
 (775) 239-2134 Fax 289-4728

FALLON TRIBAL HEALTH CENTER
1001 Rio Vista Dr. • FALLON, NV 89406
 (775) 423-3634 Fax 423-1453; Cindy Curley, Tribal Health Director
Affiliated with Phoenix Area Indian Health Service. Tribally operated.

WASHOE TRIBAL HEALTH CENTER
950 Hwy. 395 S. • GARDNERVILLE, NV 89410
 (702) 265-4215 Fax 265-3429; John Ketcher, Tribal Health Director
Affiliated with Phoenix Area Indian Health Service. Tribally operated.

LAS VEGAS PAIUTE TRIBAL CLINIC - MOAPA HEALTH CLINIC
6 Paiute Dr. • LAS VEGAS, NV 89106
 (702) 865-2700 Fax 865-282; Michael Watkins, Health Director
Affiliated with Phoenix Area Indian Health Service. Tribally operated.

McDERMITT TRIBAL HEALTH CENTER
P.O. Box 315 • MCDERMITT, NV 89421
 (775) 532-8522 Fax 532-8024
 Loren Ellery, Director, Nevada Area Operations
 Wendy Dexter, Diabetes/Wellness Program Director
Tribes served: Paiute/Shoshone. *Number of professionals on staff*: 6. General medical services provided. Affiliated with Phoenix Area IHS. Tribally operated.

PYRAMID LAKE HEALTH DEPARTMENT
P.O Box 227 • NIXON, NV 89424
 (775) 574-1018 Fax 574-1028; Leah Exendine, Tribal Health Director
Tribe served: Pyramid Lake Paiute. *Professionals on staff*: 4. *Services*: General outpatient medical care. *Program*: Community Health Education. Affiliated with Phoenix Area Indian Health Service. Tribally operated.

OWYHEE PHS INDIAN HOSPITAL
P.O. Box 130 • OWYHEE, NV 89832
 (775) 757-2415 Fax 757-2066
 Anthony Marshall, Acting CEO; David Levitt, MD, Clinical Director
Tribes served: Northeastern Nevada Tribes of Western Shoshone. *Population served*: 3,140. *Staff*: 57 professionals. *Number of Beds*: 15. Outpatient medical services. Community health education programs. Affiliated with Phoenix Area Indian Health Service.

NEVADA URBAN INDIANS
1190 Bible Way • RENO, NV 89502
 (775) 788-7600 Fax 788-7611
 Alicia Hanson, RN, Executive Director
Affiliated with Phoenix Area Indian Health Service.

RENO-SPARKS TRIBAL HEALTH STATION
34 Reservation Rd. • RENO, NV 89502
 (775) 329-5162 Fax 785-9160
 Richard Skelskey, Director
Affiliated with Phoenix Area Indian Health Service. Tribally operated.

SCHURZ SERVICE UNIT PHS INDIAN HEALTH CENTER
Drawer A • SCHURZ, NV 89427
 (775) 773-2345 Fax 773-2425

Stephen Fox, Jr., CEO; John Gray, MD, Clinical Director
Tribes served: Shoshone, Washoe, Paiute. *Population served*: 12,000.
Number of Beds: 14. Affiliated with Phoenix Area Indian Health Service.

WALKER RIVER PAIUTE TRIBAL HEALTH CENTER
P.O. Drawer "C" • SCHURZ, NV 89427
(775) 773-2005 Fax 773-2576
Kenneth Richardson, Tribal Health Director
Affiliated with Phoenix Area Indian Health Service.

YERINGTON HEALTH DEPARTMENT
171 Campbell Lane • YERINGTON, NV 89447
(775) 463-3335 Fax 463-3016
Darrell Holloway, Tribal Health Director
Affiliated with Phoenix Area Indian Health Service.

NEW MEXICO

ALBUQUERQUE IHS DENTAL CLINIC
P.O. Box 67830 • ALBUQUERQUE, NM 87193
(505) 346-2306 Fax 346-2311; Maureen Cordova, CEO
Affiliated with Albuquerque Area Indian Health Service.

ALBUQUERQUE PHS INDIAN HOSPITAL
801 Vassar Dr., NE • ALBUQUERQUE, NM 87106
(505) 248-4000 Fax 248-4088; Maria Rickert, Acting CEO
Charles North, MD, Clinical Director
Number of Beds: 54. Affiliated with Albuquerque Area IHS.

FIRST NATIONS COMMUNITY HEALTHSOURCE
5608 Zuni Rd. SE • ALBUQUERQUE, NM 87108
(505) 262-2481 Fax 262-0781; Website: www.fnch.org
Linda Son-Stone, Executive Director
Services: Family primary medical, dental, and behavioral health needs for American Indian/Alaska Native in the local Albuquerque area. Includes diabetes prevention, HIV/AIDS prevention & case management; substance abuse prevention, emergency assistance, and traditional healing. Affiliated with Albuquerque Area Indian Health Service. Established 1972.

SOUTHWESTERN INDIAN POLYTECHNIC INSTITUTE DENTAL CENTER
9169 Coors Rd. NW • P.O. Box 67830 • ALBUQUERQUE, NM 87193
(505) 897-5306 Fax 897-5311
Darlene Sorrell, DMD, Chief of Dental Program
Tribes served: Albuquerque Urban Indians, Zia, Sandia, Santa Ana, Alamo Navajo, Jemez, and Isleta. *Total population served*: 27,000. *Program*: Dental, Includes periodontics, orthodontics, prosthodontics; & pediatric dentistry. Research Library. Affiliated with Albuquerque Area Indian Health Service.

SANDIA HEALTH CLINIC
P.O. Box 6008 • BERNALILO, NM 87004
(505) 867-4487; Billie Schuler, Health Clinic Director
Affiliated with Albuquerque Area Indian Health Service.

SANTA ANA HEALTH CLINIC
P.O. Box 37 • BERNALILO, NM 87004
(505) 867-2497; Pedro Solis, Health Clinic Director,
Affiliated with Albuquerque Area Indian Health Service.

DZILTH-NA-O-DITH-HLE HEALTH CENTER
6 Road 7586 • BLOOMFIELD, NM 87413
(505) 632-1801 Fax 368-8009
Caitlin Hall, MD, FAAP, Acting Clinical Director (368-8101)
Ardith C. Aspaas, BSN, RN, Supervisory Clinical Nurse (368-8122)
Tribe served: 85% Navajo. Professionals on staff: 7. *Population served*: 20,000 people per year. The Health Center (DZHC) operates as part of the Shiprock Service Unit (SRSU), the primary referral center being Northern Navajo Medical Center (NNMC), located 70 miles northwest of Dzilth-Na-O-Dith-Hle Health Center. The health center provides ambulatory care to patients, primarily Navajo, living in the Eastern Area of the Navajo Nation. Constructed in 1984, the facility in 1999 expanded, currently serves approximately 20,000 patients. The health center is equipped with a two-bed urgent care room for the evaluation, treatment & stabilization of patient presenting with urgent/emergent conditions. The Center (DZHC) provision of primary care includes the following departments: Outpatient, urgent care, laboratory, radiology, pharmacy, optometry, dental, mental health, social services & public health nursing. The specialty services including internal medicine, women's health & obstetrics and diabetes education are available at scheduled times and staffed with providers from Northern Navajo Medical Center. The Administrative Services comprise of Facility Maintenance, Housekeeping, General Service, Security, Business

Office Services, Health Information Management & Administration Office. *Services*: Complete diagnostic medical treatment services are provided: medical outpatient clinic, dental service, counseling service, community health nursing service. Affiliated with Navajo Area HIS.

CHINLE COMPREHENSIVE HEALTH CARE FACILITY
P.O. Box "PH" • CHINLE, AZ 86503
(928) 674-7001 Fax 674-7372
The Chinle Comprehensive Health Care Facility (CCHCF) is based in Chinle, Arizona (Northeast Arizona near Canyon De Chelly National Monument). The CCHCF is a 60-bed hospital that serves as the health care hub for the region. The medical staff includes Family Physicians, Internists, Pediatricians, General Surgeons, OB/GYN's, Anesthesiologists, & a Psychiatrist. In addition to routine outpatient & inpatient primary care, services available to our patients include: Adult Intensive Care, General Surgery (including laparoscopic surgery), routine & operative Obstetrics, & 24-Hour Emergency Room Services. Health care services are provided to approximately 37,000 active users. Strong Navajo cultural traditions exist within the community, offering an opportunity to learn the Navajo language, or to learn about traditional Navajo medicine.

COCHITI HEALTH CLINIC
255 Cochiti St. • COCHITI, NM 87072
(505) 465-2587 Fax 465-3018
Affiliated with Albuquerque Area Indian Health Service.

CROWNPOINT HEALTH CARE FACILITY
P.O. Box 358 • CROWNPOINT, NM 87313
(505) 786-5291 Fax 786-6435
Website: www.ihs.gov/navajo/crownpoint/
Fanessa Comer, Service Unit Director
Harry Goldenberg, MD, Clinical Director
Reservation served: Eastern Agency of the Navajo Indian Reservation. *Total population served*: 20,000. *Number of Beds*: 32. The staff consists of primary care physicians, physician assistants, and nurse practitioners, at a 32 bed hospital. The daily inpatient load is nine; daily outpatient visits are 151; annual OB cases are 275; and annual ER cases number about 5,500. Affiliated with Navajo Area Indian Health Service.

JICARILLA PHS INDIAN HEALTH CENTER
12000 Stone Lake Rd., P.O. Box 187 • DULCE, NM 87528
(505) 759-3291 Fax 759-3532
James Sutton, Acting CEO
Nancy Kitson, MD, Clinical Director
Affiliated with Albuquerque Area Indian Health Service.

SANTA CLARA PHS INDIAN HEALTH CENTER
RR 5, Box 446 • ESPANOLA, NM 87532
(505) 753-9421 Fax 753-5039
Richanda Bears Ghost, Health Center Director
Affiliated with Albuquerque Area Indian Health Service.

GALLUP INDIAN MEDICAL CENTER
P.O. Box 1337 • GALLUP, NM 87305
(505) 722-1000 Fax 722-1397
Floyd Thompson, Service Unit Director
Bennie Yazzie, Administrative Officer
Gary Escudero, MD, Clinical Director
Population served: 23,000. *Number of Beds*: 99. *Services*: Internal Medicine, Cardiology, Anesthesia, OB/GYN, General Surgery, Orthopedics, Ophthalmology, Pediatrics, Psychiatry, Emergency Medicine, Pathology & Urology. Gallup Indian Medical Center (GIMC) is a 99-bed hospital in Gallup, New Mexico, on the border of the Navajo Reservation. The workload at Gallup is one of the largest in the Indian Health Service with 250,000 outpatient encounters and 5,800 inpatient admissions annually. GIMC has the largest staff of all Navajo Area IHS facilities. Affiliated with Navajo Area Indian Health Service.

ISLETA HEALTH CENTER
P.O. Box 580 • ISLETA, NM 87022
(505) 869-3200; David Antle, Health Clinic Director

JEMEZ HEALTH CLINIC
P.O. Box 256 • JEMEZ, NM 87024
(505) 834-7413; Ledora McDougal, Health Clinic Director

KAYENTA HEALTH CENTER
P.O. Box 368 • KAYENTA, AZ 86033
(928) 697-4000 Fax 697-4145; Website: www.ihs.gov/navajo/kayenta
Tribe served: Navajo. Affiliated with the Navajo Area IHS unit, one of eight. Tribally operated.

ALAMO NAVAJO HEALTH STATION
P.O. Box 907 • MAGDALENA, NM 87825
 (505) 854-2626 Fax 854-2545
Affiliated with Albuquerque Area Indian Health Service. Tribally operated.

MESCALERO PHS INDIAN HOSPITAL
P.O. Box 210 • MESCALERO, NM 88340
 (505) 464-4441 Fax 464-4422
 Dorilyn Simmons, CEO
Affiliated with Albuquerque Area Native Health Service. Tribally operated.

PINE HILL PHS INDIAN HEALTH CENTER
P.O. Box 310 • PINE HILL, NM 87357
 (505) 775-3271 Fax 775-3240
 Carolyn E. Finster, Director
Affiliated with Albuquerque Area Indian Health Service. Tribally operated.

ACOMA-CANONCITO-LAGUNA SERVICE UNIT
P.O. Box 130 • SAN FIDEL, NM 87049
 (505) 552-5300 Fax 552-5490
 William Thorne, Jr., CEO
 Barbara Felipe, Administrative Officer
 Dental Clinic (505) 552-5310
Affiliated with Albuquerque Area Indian Health Service.

SAN FELIPE HEALTH CLINIC
P.O. Box 4344 • SAN FELIPE, NM 87001
 (505) 867-2739 Fax 867-6527
Affiliated with Albuquerque Area Indian Health Service.

EW SUNRISE REGIONAL TREATMENT CENTER
P.O. Box 210 • SAN FIDEL, NM 87049
 (505) 552-5500 Fax 552-5530; Anthony Yepa, Program Director
Affiliated with Albuquerque Area Indian Health Service.

SANTA FE PHS INDIAN HOSPITAL
1700 Cerrillos Rd. • SANTA FE, NM 87501
 (505) 988-9821 Fax 983-6243; Robert Lyon, CEO
 Joseph L. Montoya, Administrative Officer
 Bret Smoker, MD, Clinical Director
Number of Beds: 55. Affiliated with Albuquerque Area Indian Health Service.

SANTO DOMINGO HEALTH CLINIC
P.O. Box 340 • SANTO DOMINGO, NM 87052
 (505) 465-2996 Fax 465-2505
Affiliated with the Albuquerque Area Indian Health Service.

SHIPROCK - NORTHERN NAVAJO MEDICAL CENTER
P.O. Box 160, Hwy. 491 North • SHIPROCK, NM 87420
 (505) 368-6001 Fax 368-6260
 George Baacke, MD, Director
 Gloria Redhorse-Charley, Human Resource Specialist (368-6095)
Tribe served: Mostly Navajo. *Population served*: 45,500. *Number of beds*: 55.
The Center is located in the Four Corners area of the United States where New Mexico, Arizona, Colorado and Utah meet. It's one of five facilities located within the Shiprock Service Unit. The Shiprock Service Unit is the largest service unit of the Navajo Nation. Approximately 80,837 Native Americans (mostly Navajo) are enrolled at Northern Navajo Medical Center. The inpatient load is 29 per day and the outpatient volume averages 600 per day. A variety of services are available including internal medicine, family practice, urgent & emergency care, pediatrics, general surgery, women's health, mental health, respiratory therapy, outpatient rehabilitation services, pharmacy, optometry, dental, public health nursing, social services, health promotion/ disease prevention, radiology, laboratory and benefits coordination. Northern Navajo Medical Center employs 827 full-time employees. The medical staff consists of 50 physicians and 20 mid-level providers. Northern Navajo Medical Staff work with a variety of other facilities both locally & nationally. Specialists are consulted both within the IHS system, as well as outside our system. We have strong relationships with private providers in the Four Corners region, as well as at University of New Mexico, and the Brigham and Women's Hospital in Boston, MA. Affiliated with the Navajo Area Indian Health Service.

TAOS/PICURIS HEALTH CENTER
P.O. Box 1956 • TAOS, NM 87571
 (505) 758-4224 Fax 758-1822
 Merlin Gilham, Director
 Gail W. Osborne, Administrator Officer
 Christopher Keane, Clinical Director
Affiliated with the Albuquerque Area Indian Health Service.

TOHATCHI HEALTH CARE CENTER
P.O. Box 142 • TOHATCHI, NM 87325
 (505) 733-8100 Fax 733-8239
 Valerie Leslie, Facility Director
Services: 40-hour per week ambulatory care for approximately 8,000 nearby residents. Inpatient needs are met by referral to the Gallup Indian Medical Center. The Center is one of the newest facilities operated by the Navajo Area Indian Health Service and is staffed by four physicians and specialty clinics are operated by consultant staff from the Gallup Indian Medical Center. In addition to pediatrics, internal medicine and family medicine, services provided include pharmacy, physical therapy, x-ray, laboratory, public health nursing, optometry, dental, & health education. Leading reasons for visits include those consistent with eight Navajo Area IHS facilities. Seasonal occurrences include episodes of care for Hantavirus, plague and other conditions endemic to the Region. Affiliated with Navajo Area Indian Health Service. Opened 1994.

ZIA HEALTH CLINIC
155 Capital Sq. • ZIA, NM 87053
 (505) 867-5258; Pedro Solis, Health Clinic Director,
Affiliated with Albuquerque Area Indian Health Service.

ZUNI PHS INDIAN HOSPITAL
P.O. Box 467 • ZUNI, NM 87327
 (505) 782-4431 Fax 782-7405; Jean Othole, CEO
 Clyde Yatsattie, Administrative Officer; David Kessler, MD, Clinical Director
Number of Beds: 45. Affiliated with Albuquerque Area Indian Health Service.

NEW YORK

LOCKPORT SERVICE UNIT
6507 Wheeler Rd. • LOCKPORT, NY 14094
 (716) 280-3850
Mission: To provide quality, comprehensive health care to Native American members and their families in a culturally sensitive manner promoting good health, safe-lifestyles, wellbeing & harmony. Affiliated with Nashville Area Indian Health Service.

NORTH CAROLINA

CHEROKEE PHS INDIAN HOSPITAL
CHEROKEE, NC 28719
 (828) 497-9163 Fax 497-5343
 Casey Cooper (Eastern Cherokee), CEO
 Arnold Wachacha, Administrative Officer
 Mary Anne Farrell, MD, Clinical Director
 Rob Myers, Director of Nursing
Number of Beds: 35. Affiliated with Nashville Area Indian Health Service.

CHEROKEE TECHNICAL SUPPORT CENTER
P.O. Box 429, Butler Bldg., Rt. 1 • CHEROKEE, NC 28719
 (828) 497-5030 Fax 497-5104
 Mary G. Wachacha, Health Education Coordinator
Affiliated with Nashville Area Indian Health Service.

UNITY HEALING CENTER
P.O. Box C-201, 441 N. Sequoyah Trail Dr. • CHEROKEE, NC 28719
 (828) 497-3958 Fax 497-6826; Rebecca HillaneLAmbert, Director
Unity Healing Center is a sixteen-bed coed facility. Services are provided in a home-like environment; a place of healing where the physical, mental, emotional and spiritual needs of each resident are addressed. The average length of stay is between 80-90 days depending upon the resident's needs. The treatment program incorporates the 12 Step Program of Recovery with the uniqueness of Native American culture. *Mission*: Unity is dedicated to breaking the cycle of addiction and restoring hope and wellness to Native American youth, their families and communities. Unity Healing Center will always be committed to helping Native American youth and their families gain freedom from addiction and other life-negating problems. We will guide our clients to healthy sustainable lifestyle transformations by addressing their physical, emotional, spiritual and cultural needs through the philosophy of the 12 step program, evidence based treatments and by providing a safe haven to engage in activities that will allow them to develop their individual strengths. Affiliated with Nashville Area Indian Health Service.

LUMBEE INDIAN HEALTH CARE CLINIC
304 N. Cedar St. • PEMBROKE, NC 28372
 (919) 521-7861; Fred Rogers, Founder & Executive Director
Mission: To provide primary health care to the American Indian population of Robeson & surrounding counties. Opened 2010.

NORTH DAKOTA

BELCOURT PHS INDIAN HOSPITAL
P.O. Box 160 • BELCOURT, ND 58316
　(701) 477-6111 Fax 477-8410; LaVerne Parker, Director
Todd Bercier, Administrative Officer
Penny Wilkie, MD, Clinical Director
Tribe served: Turtle Mountain Sioux. *Number of Beds*: 46.
Affiliated with Aberdeen Area Indian Health Service.

QUENTIN N. BURDICK MEMORIAL HEALTH CARE FACILITY
P.O. Box 160 • BELCOURT, ND 58316
　(701) 477-6111 Fax 477-8410
Serves population of approximately 13,100, has 27 beds and 11 physicians (Inpatient and Outpatient). In addition to inpatient care, the hospital provides general surgery, podiatry, ENT surgery, obstetrics, & CAT scan. The outpatient department offers basic service & specialty clinics with contracted specialists. The dental program has a full clinic at the hospital. The facility also includes a mental health department that consists of one full-time consulting clinical psychologist, one staff psychologist, a psychiatric nurse, and a psychiatrist.

SPIRIT LAKE HEALTH CENTER
P.O. Box 309 • Fort Totten, ND 58335
　(701) 766-1600 Fax 766-4295
Angeline Cloudman, Chief Executive Officer
Ramona Cannon Administrative Officer
Vernon D. Azure, MD, Clinical Director
Tribe served: Devils Lake Sioux Tribe. *Professionals on staff*: 11. *Services*: Family Practice. Staffed by three physician ambulatory care facility. Complex outpatient services or inpatient care are referred to a contract facility. Fort Totten operates a dental clinic and a diabetes program with comprehensive screening, education, and treatment. The center is also one of three in the Great Plains Area to receive a grant to study cardiovascular disease among Indians. *Programs*: Staff Education, Training & Research; Community Health Education. Medical Library. Affiliated with Aberdeen Area IHS.

FORT YATES PHS INDIAN HOSPITAL
P.O. Box J • FORT YATES, ND 58538
　(701) 854-3831 Fax 854-7399; Lisa Guardipe, Director
Carl Ducheneaux, Administrative Officer
Eduardo Lago, MD, Clinical Director
Number of Beds: 12. Staffed by three permanent physicians and two nurse practitioners. Comprehensive services include inpatient, outpatient, emergency, dental, behavioral health, optometry & a dialysis unit (8 stations). Dental care is provided in the main clinic at the hospital by two dental officers. An outpatient health center at McLaughlin has one permanent physician & two Registered Nurses. There are also health stations at Cannonball, Bullhead, and Wakpala. The health stations provide minimal outpatient care and are staffed by a physician's assistant, a public health nurse, and a community health representative. The health stations are visited at least once a week by a physician from the Fort Yates Hospital. Affiliated with Aberdeen Area Indian Health Service.

FORT BERTHOLD PHS INDIAN HEALTH CENTER
P.O. Box 400 • NEW TOWN, ND 58763
　(701) 627-4701 Fax 627-4318; Michelle Leach, Chief Executive Officer
Affiliated with Aberdeen Area Indian Health Service.

TRENTON-WILLISTON INDIAN SERVICE AREA
P.O. Box 210 • TRENTON, ND 58853
　(701) 774-0461 Fax 774-8003; Ron Falcon, Tribal Health Director
Bhanat K. Patel, MD, Medical Officer
Affiliated with Aberdeen Area Indian Health Service. Tribally operated.

OKLAHOMA

CARL ALBERT INDIAN HOSPITAL
1001 N. Country Club Dr. • ADA, OK 74820
　(580) 436-3980 Fax 421-4552
Bill Lance, Administrative Officer
Joanne Chinnici, D.O., Clinical Director
Professionals on staff: 4. *Number of Beds*: 53. *Services*: Offers general outpatient medical services; workshops and in-service training. Affiliated with Oklahoma City Area Indian Health Service. Tribally operated.

ANADARKO INDIAN HEALTH CENTER
201 Parker McKenzie Dr. • ANADARKO, OK 73005
　(405) 247-7900 Fax 247-4945
Terry Hunter, Director; E-mail: terry.hunter@ihs.gov

Anadarko is a community of approximately 6,560, located fifty miles from Oklahoma City, Oklahoma and forty miles from Lawton, Oklahoma. Anadarko boasts many restaurants, grocery stores, clothing stores, gasoline stations, florists, a movie theatre, a public library, numerous different faith churches, and excellent educational facilities for children. Anadarko has less congestion than an urban setting and is near recreational sites and a major airport located in Oklahoma City, Oklahoma. The climate is generally mild. The Center has a multidisciplinary outpatient department that provides a wide range of services including primary care, acute care, & management of chronic health conditions for our community, providing approximately 50 to 80 visits a day. In addition, we provide a weekly diabetes clinic that is supported by several ancillary departments, enabling a broad range of care to our diabetic population. There are several specialty clinics provided on a monthly basis including Rheumatology, Endocrinology, Mammography, Nursing, Podiatry, Wound Care, & Women's Health. We partner with our tribal Community Health Representatives and the Public Health Department to provide preventative services in our community and to the students at the Riverside Indian School. The Anadarko Indian Health Center opened in its current location in 1984. The Health Center is situated in a newly renovated 20,000 sq. ft. building. We utilize evolving concepts such as the Electronic Health Record. The Health Center offers in-house specialty clinics, as well as a referral system to specialists. Affiliated with Oklahoma City Area Indian Health Service.

ARDMORE CHICKASAW HEALTH CLINIC
2510 Chickasaw Blvd. • ARDMORE, OK 73401
　(580) 226-8181 Fax 226-4868; Amy Stinson, Clinic Coordinator
Tribe served: Chickasaw. *Professionals on staff*: 7. *Numbers served*: 5,400 annually. *Services*: Offers general outpatient medical services; workshops & in-service training. Library. Affiliated with Oklahoma City Area Indian Health Service. Tribally operated.

CHOCTAW NATION HEALTH CLINIC
205 E. 3rd St. • BROKEN BOW, OK 74728
　(580) 584-2740 Fax 584-2073; Jill Mayes, Director
Affiliated with Oklahoma City Area Indian Health Service. Tribally operated.

CARNEGIE INDIAN HEALTH CENTER
212 East 4th • CARNEGIE, OK 73105
　(580) 654-1100 Fax 654-2533; Terry Hunter, Director
The Center relocated from the Kiowa Tribal Complex to this newly constructed facility in 2011. The clinic provides outpatient medical care to patients of all ages with one full time family medicine provider. Pediatrics, Podiatry, Nursing, and Optometry specialty clinics are offered weekly. The Town of Carnegie is a vibrant community of 1,723 people located on the western edge of Caddo County, Oklahoma. Early settlement in the area straddled both sides of the Washita River with the early community being called Latham. As there was already a town by that name in the territory, the settlement changed its name to Carnegie, in honor of steel magnate and philanthropist Andrew Carnegie. Affiliated with Oklahoma City Area Indian Health Service.

CLAREMORE INDIAN HOSPITAL
101 S. Moore Ave. • CLAREMORE, OK 74017
　(918) 342-6200 Fax 342-6585; E-mail: health@cherokee.org
George Valliere, Chief Executive Officer
　E-mail: george.valliere@ihs.gov
LCDR Carl Murray, Administrative Officer
　E-mail: carl.murray@ihs.gov
Cathy Smith, Ambulatory Care Director
　E-mail: cathy.smith@ihs.gov
Number of Beds: 50. Description: A general medical & surgical facility, also offering optometry, dental, audiology, mental health, social services, nutrition & community health, and nursing services. Specialty clinics are also offered in OB-GYN, pediatrics, internal medicine & emergency medicine. *Total population served*: 80,000; 160,000 outpatient visits per year. The staff consists of 375 employees in various professional, paraprofessional & technical positions. Affiliated with Oklahoma City Area Indian Health Service. Operated by the Cherokee Indian Nation.

CLINTON INDIAN HEALTH CENTER
10321 N. 2274 Rd. • CLINTON, OK 73601
　(580) 331-3300
April Wazhaxi, Chief Executive Officer
　E-mail: april.wazhaxi@ihs.gov
CDR. Joseph Bryant, Administrative Officer
　E-mail: joseph.bryant@ihs.gov
Dr. Sarah Hartnett, Clinic Director
　E-mail: sarah.hartnett@ihs.gov
Provides quality health care services focusing on prevention, restoration & collaborative relationships that are valued & "exceeds the needs" of our patients, community and tribal partners.

CLINTON PHS INDIAN HOSPITAL
Route 1, Box 3060 • CLINTON, OK 73601
(580) 323-2884 Fax 323-2884 Ext. 211
Terri Schmidt, CEO; Dolly Garcia, MD, Clinical Director
Number of Beds: 14. Affiliated with Oklahoma City Area Indian Health Service.

CHICKASAW/DURANT HEALTH CENTER
1702 W. Elm • DURANT, OK 74701
(580) 920-2100 Fax 920-1191; Lynn Garner, MD, Facility Director
Affiliated with Oklahoma City Area Indian Health Service.

EL RENO HEALTH CENTER
1801 Parkview Dr. • EL RENO, OK 73036
(405) 234-8400 Fax 262-8099
April Wazhaxi, CEO (580) 331-3300)
E-mail: april.wazhaxi@ihs.gov
LCDR Andrea Jackson, Center Director (422-8400)
E-mail: andrea.jackson@ihs.gov
Dr. Sarah Hartnett, Clinical Director (580) 331-3300
E-mail: sarah.hartnett@ihs.gov
Service: The staff of three medical providers see about 26,000 primary care visits per year. Located in the Oklahoma City suburb of El Reno, the El Reno Indian Health Center provides the usual primary services to the Indian population of Canadian County and part of Oklahoma County. The staff of 3 medical providers sees about 26,000 primary care visits per year. Provide quality health care services focusing on prevention, restoration and collaborative relationships that are valued and "exceeds the needs" of our patients, community and tribal partners. Affiliated with Oklahoma City Area Indian Health Service.

EUFAULA INDIAN HEALTH CLINIC CREEK NATION OF OKLAHOMA
800 Forrest Ave. • EUFAULA, OK 74432
(918) 689-2547 Fax 689-3643; Bert Robison, Administrator
Tribes served: Mostly Creek, but all tribes within area. *Professionals on staff*: 21. *Services*: General outpatient medical care; dental, laboratory, counseling, nursing. *Program*: Community Health Education. Affiliated with Oklahoma City Area Indian Health Service. Tribally operated.

HUGO - CHOCTAW NATION INDIAN HEALTH CLINIC
P.O. Box 340 • HUGO, OK 74743
(580) 326-7561; Linda Miller, Director
Affiliated with Oklahoma City Area Indian Health Service. Tribally operated.

SAM HIDER JAY COMMUNITY CLINIC
1015 Washburn, P.O. Box 350 • JAY, OK 74346
(877) 293-4271; (918) 253-4271 Fax 434-5397
Ron Little, Director - E-mail: health@cherokee.org
Services: 25,000 outpatient visits per year. Provides outpatient medical services, public health nursing, laboratory, pharmacy, dental, WIC, radiology, mammography, community nutrition & contract care. Affiliated with Oklahoma City Area Indian Health Service. Operated by the Cherokee Nation.

LAWTON INDIAN HOSPITAL
1515 Lawrie Tatum Rd. • LAWTON, OK 73501
(580) 354-5000 Fax 354-5105
Travis Scott, CEO; (354-5100) E-mail: travis.scott@ihs.gov
John Bear, Administrative Officer (354-5103) E-mail: john.bear@ihs.gov
Bryan Beals, MD, Clinical Director (354-5157) E-mail: bryan.beals@ihs.gov
Lenora Littledeer, Chief Nurse Executive (354-5407)
E-mail: Lenora.littledear@ihs.gov
Tribes served: Caddo, Comanche, Delaware, Fort Sill Apache, Kiowa, Apache & Wichita. *Population served*: 25,000. Full-service hospital. *Number of Beds*: 26. *Staff*: 23 physicians, et al. The Hospital is modern facility with 26 beds and a staff over 30 full time credentialed providers. The facility offers inpatient care including general surgery, gynecology, internal medicine, pediatrics, as well as outpatient services in medicine, dentistry, nursing, pharmacy, radiology, laboratory, nursing, optometry, podiatry, and audiology to name a few. There is also a community health staff of nurses, educators, social workers, and environmental health specialists. The hospital provides over 800 admissions and 100,000 out patient per year. Improving Patient Care is a central theme. The Patient Centered Medical Home model is followed to provide care to over 23,000 active patients. Affiliated with Oklahoma City Area IHS.

CHOCTAW NATION INDIAN HEALTH CENTER
903 E. Monroe • MCALESTER, OK 74501
(918) 423-8440 Fax 423-6781; Karen Neal, Facility Director
Tribes served: All tribes in this area, predominantly Choctaw. *Total population served*: 15,000 annually. *Medical services*: Family practice; Dental Clinic. *Programs*: Diabetic & pre-natal classes; hypertension; well-child clinics; immunization program; home health care; service services; audiology; dietition. Affiliated with Oklahoma City Area Indian Health Service. Tribally operated.

KICKAPOO HEALTH CENTER
P.O. Box 1059 • McCLOUD, OK 74851
(405) 964-2081 Fax 964-2722
John Okemah, MD, Health Director
Affiliated with Oklahoma City Area Indian Health Service.

NORTHEASTERN TRIBAL HEALTH SYSTEM
P.O. Box 1498 • MIAMI, OK 74355
(918) 542-1655 Fax 540-1685; Sharon Dawes, Director
Tribes served: Seneca-Cayuga, Miami, Modoc, Ottawa, Quapaw, Peoria, Cherokee. *Professionals on staff*: 15; *Numbers served*: Outpatients, 35,000 annually. *Medical services*: Medical, pharmacy, dental, optometry, mental health, public health nursing & laboratory. *Community programs*: Educational activities in the schools & tribal communities. Small medical library.

MUSKOGEE INDIAN HEALTH CENTER
212 South 38th St. • MUSKOGEE, OK 74401
(918) 687-0102 Fax 687-0665; E-mail: health@cherokee.org
Rhonda Cockran, Facility Director
Services: 17,000 outpatient visits per year. Serves eligible members of both the Creek & Cherokee Nations. Offers outpatient medical services; WIC; laboratory; pharmacy; and behavioral health services. Affiliated with Oklahoma City Area Indian Health Service. Operated by the Cherokee Nation.

KAW NATION - KANZA HEALTH CLINIC
P.O. Box 474 • NEWKIRK, OK 74647
(580) 362-1039 Fax 362-2988; Karen McConnell, Health Director
Affiliated with Oklahoma City Area Indian Health Service. Tribally operated.

ABSENTEE SHAWNEE TRIBAL CLINIC
15702 E. Hwy. 9 • NORMAN, OK 73071
(405) 447-0300 Fax 447-2250; Gary Wabunsee, Clinical Director
Affiliated with Oklahoma City Area Indian Health Service.

NOWATA INDIAN HEALTH CLINIC
Cherokee Nation of Oklahoma, 202 E. Galor • NOWATA, OK 74048
(918) 273-0192; (877) 273-2147
Myron Taylor, Clinic Director; E-mail: health@cherokee.org
Services: 14,500 outpatient visits per year. Offers outpatient medical services; public health nursing, laboratory, pharmacy, WIC, community health representatives, and contract care. Affiliated with Oklahoma City Area Indian Health Service. Operated by the Cherokee Nation operated.

CREEK NATION COMMUNITY HOSPITAL
Creek Nation of Oklahoma, P.O. Box 228 • OKEMAH, OK 74859
(918) 623-1424 Fax 623-9016
JoAnne Skaggs, Health Service Administrator
Affiliated with Oklahoma City Area Indian Health Service. Tribally operated.

OKEMAH INDIAN HEALTH CENTER
309 N. 14th St. • OKEMAH, OK 74859
(918) 623-0555 Fax 623-9016
JoAnne Skaggs, Health Systems Administrator
Affiliated with Oklahoma City Area Indian Health Service. Tribally operated.

OKLAHOMA CITY INDIAN CLINIC
Central Oklahoma American Indian Health Council
4913 W. Reno Ave. • OKLAHOMA CITY, OK 73127
(405) 948-4900 Fax 948-4932; Terry Hunter, Executive Director
Purpose: To provide outpatient primary medical care, general medical and dental services, mental health & substance abuse treatment, health education; seminars, prevention and outreach. Established 1974.

CREEK NATION DENTAL CLINIC
700 N. Mission, Box 10 • OKMULGEE, OK 74447
(918) 756-2860; Doug White, Dental Officer. Tribally operated.

OKMULGEE HEALTH CENTER
1313 East 20th • OKMULGEE, OK 74447
(918) 758-1926 Fax 758-1944
Debra Isham, Health Administrator
Affiliated with Oklahoma City Area Indian Health Service.

WAH-ZHA-ZHI HEALTH CENTER
715 Grandview • PAWHUSKA, OK 74056
(918) 287-4491 Fax 287-4491
James F. Barnett, Facility Director
The Center is located on the Osage Nation Campus in Pawhuska, Oklahoma. This ambulatory care facility has three fulltime medical providers, and offers in-house laboratory and radiology services. Affiliated with Oklahoma City Area Indian Health Service.

PAWNEE INDIAN HEALTH CENTER
1201 Heritage Circle • PAWNEE, OK 74058
  (918) 762-2517; CDR Seneca Smith, CEO
  Capt. Pearl Dry, Administrative Officer; Robert Chesbro, MD, Clinical Director
Tribe served: Pawnee. *Number of patients served*: 38,000 out patient visits annually. *Staff*: 4 physicians, 1 Pediatrician, 1 Nurse Practitioner. The Center is a modern, 67,000 square ft. facility completed in 2004. Each year, the Center provides approximately 38,000 outpatient visits to its patients. The facility provides quality healthcare to patients through a multitude of primary care services & specialty services including cardiology, pediatrics, diabetic counseling, rheumatology, wound care, and women's health, and is equipped with on-site diagnostic services including mammography, ultrasound, CT, and general x-ray. The Office of Environmental Health and Engineering (OEH&E) Sanitation Facilities Construction (SFC) & Environmental Health (EH) Programs are located at Pawnee Indian Health Center. The SFC program works with Tribes and communities to assist in the provision of safe drinking water, wastewater disposal, & solid waste disposal for Tribal communities and Indian homes. The EH program works with Tribal programs that have direct interactions with the public (food establishments, childcare facilities, etc.,) to ensure that programs provide safe & reliable services to the tribal communities they serve. Affiliated with Oklahoma City Area Indian Health Service.

WHITE EAGLE PHS INDIAN HEALTH CENTER
P.O. Box 2071 • PONCA CITY, OK 74601
  (580) 765-2501 Fax 765-6348; Johanna Pokebro, Director
Affiliated with Oklahoma City Area Indian Health Service.

CHOCTAW NATION INDIAN HEALTH CLINIC
109 Kerr Ave. • POTEAU, OK 74953
  (918) 649-1100 Fax 649-1199
Affiliated with Oklahoma City Area Indian Health Service.

SALINA A-MO COMMUNITY CLINIC
900 N. Owen Walter Blvd., P.O. Box 936 • SALINA, OK 74365
  (877) 434-8500; (918) 434-2995; E-mail: health@cherokee.org
  Shawn Terry, Clinic Administrator; *Services*: 22,500 outpatient visits per year. Offers outpatient medical services; public health nursing, laboratory, pharmacy, WIC, community nutrition, optometry, and radiology. Affiliated with Oklahoma City Area IHS. Operated by the Cherokee Nation.

REDBIRD SMITH HEALTH CENTER
301 S. JT Stities Ave. • SALLISAW, OK 74955
  (918) 775-9159 Fax 775-4778; E-mail: health@cherokee.org
  Robert Park, Clinic Administrator
Services: 38,500 outpatient visits per year. Offers outpatient medical services; public health nursing, dental, optometry, laboratory, pharmacy, WIC, radiology, behavioral health, community nutrition, and contract care. Affiliated with Oklahoma City Area Indian Health Service. Operated by the Cherokee Nation.

SAPULPA HEALTH CENTER
Creek Nation of Oklahoma, 1125 E. Cleveland • SAPULPA, OK 74066
  (918) 224-9310; Judy Aaron, Director
Affiliated with Oklahoma City Area Indian Health Service. Tribally operated.

CITIZEN POTAWATOMI NATION HEALTH CLINIC
2307 S. Gordon Cooper Dr. • SHAWNEE, OK 74801
  (405) 273-5236 Fax 878-4835; Randy Hall, Facility Director
Affiliated with Oklahoma City Area Indian Health Service. Tribally operated.

SHAWNEE PHS INDIAN HEALTH CENTER
2001 S. Gordon Cooper Dr. • SHAWNEE, OK 74801
  (405) 275-4270 Fax 275-4270 Ext. 268
  James Cussen, Director; Ronald Fried, DO, Clinical Director
Serves patients from various tribes. *Professionals on staff*: 30. Numbers served: 45,000 outpatients, annually. *Primary service*: Family practice. *Programs*: Staff education & training; community health education. Scholarships available. Library. Affiliated with Oklahoma City Area HIS.

WILMA P. MANKILLER HEALTH CENTER
Rt. 2, Box 93 • STILWELL, OK 74960
  (918) 696-8800 Fax 696-8840; E-mail: health@cherokee.org
  Darrell O'Field, Facility Director
Services: 41,500 outpatient visits per year. Offers outpatient medical services; public health nursing, dental, optometry, laboratory, pharmacy, WIC, radiology, behavioral health, community nutrition, & contract care. Affiliated with Oklahoma City Area Indian Health Service. Operated by the Cherokee Nation.

BLACK HAWK HEALTH CENTER
Sac & Fox Nation of Oklahoma, Rt. 2, Box 247 • STROUD, OK 73079
  (918) 968-9531 Fax 968-4453; Karen Simmons, Director
Affiliated with Oklahoma City Area Indian Health Service. Tribally operated.

W.W. HASTINGS HOSPITAL
100 S. Bliss Ave. • TAHLEQUAH, OK 74464
  (918) 458-3100 Fax 458-3262; Edwin McLemore, CEO
  Keith Barrick, Administrative Officer; E-mail: health@cherokee.org
Number of Beds: 65. *Description*: A general medical and surgical facility, also offering optometry, dental, audiology, mental health, social services, nutrition and community health, and nursing services. Specialty clinics are also offered in OB-GYN, pediatrics, internal medicine and emergency medicine. *Total population served*: 80,000 eligible Indians; 150,000 outpatient visits per year. The staff consists of 300 employees in various professional, paraprofessional & technical positions. Affiliated with Oklahoma City Area Indian Health Service. Operated by the Cherokee Nation.

CHOCTAW NATION HEALTHCARE CENTER
DIABETES TREATMENT CENTER
1 Choctaw Way • TALIHINA, OK 74571
  (800) 349-7026; (918) 567-7000 Fax 567-2631
  Sharon Passmore, Facility Director; Reese Sherill, Administrator
  Tom Bonin, MD, Chief of Staff
Tribes served: Choctaw and all nationally recognized tribes. Professionals on staff: 77. *Number of Beds*: 37. *Numbers served*: 1,300 inpatients & 32,000 outpatients, annually. *Primary medical services*: Audiology; behavioral health; dental; diabetes treatment; dietition services; emergency room - OB/GYN - lab services; optometry; pediatrics; pharmacy; physical therapy; radiology; respiratory therapy; surgery. *Programs*: WIC Program; social services; contract health; substance abuse recovery; community health reps; public health nursing. Library. Affiliated with Oklahoma City Area IHS. Tribally operated.

TISHOMINGO CHICKASAW HEALTH CENTER
815 E. 6th St. • TISHOMINGO, OK 73460
  (580) 371-2392 Fax 371-9323; Norma Bratcher, Director
Tribe served: Chickasaw. Professionals on staff: 8. Numbers served: 8,000 annually. Library. Affiliated with Oklahoma City Area IHS. Tribally operated.

INDIAN HEALTH CARE RESOURCE CENTER OF TULSA
550 S. Peoria Ave. • TULSA, OK 74120
  (918) 382-1201 Fax 582-6405; Website: www.administration.ihcrc.org
  Carmelita Skeeter, Executive Director; E-mail: cskeeter@ihcrc.org
Tribes served: All. *Population served*: 26,000. *Medical services*: Pediatrician, OB/Gyn, Adult Acute and Chronic Medicine, Dental, Optometry, Mental Health & Substance Abuse Counseling-Adult & Children. *Special programs*: Diabetes, HIV/AID'S, WIC, REACH, Well baby classes, Outreach, Public Health Nursing, Transportation, Pharmacy. Library.

WATONGA INDIAN HEALTH CENTER
1305 S. Clarence Nash Blvd. • WATONGA, OK 73772
  (580) 623-4991 Fax 623-5490
  April Wazhaxi, CEO (580) 331-3300; E-mail: april.wazhaxi@ihs.gov
  LCDR Andrea Jackson, Facility Director; E-mail: andrea.jackson@ihs.gov
  Dr. Sarah Hartnett, Clinic Director; E-mail: sarah.hartnett@ihs.gov
Tribes served: Primarily Cheyenne & Arapaho; members of all local tribes. *Professionals on staff*: 10. *Numbers served annually*: 4,500; 4,000 outpatient visits each year. *Medical services*: General outpatient medical & dental services. *Community programs*: Weekly diabetic and prenatal clinics; head start dental prevention and nursing bottle caries prevention. Small medical library. Affiliated with Oklahoma City Area Indian Health Service.

WEWOKA INDIAN HEALTH CENTER
P.O. Box 1475 • WEWOKA, OK 74884
  (405) 257-6282 Fax 257-2696
  Farrel Smith, CEO (257-7326); E-mail: farrel.smith@ihs.gov
  Andy Wilson, Administrative Officer (257-7322) E-mail: andy.wilson@ihs.gov
  Ronald Fried, DO, Clinical Director (257-7355) E-mail: ronald.fried@ihs.gov
Tribe served: Wewoka. *Staff*: 5 professionals. *Services*: The Community Health Department operates several clinics as well as numerous outreach programs with a focus on education; Pharmacy Dept. The Health Center is a small rural Joint Commission accredited ambulatory health center. The center employs three physicians and two family nurse practitioners. The clinic renders outpatient services in general medicine, medical imaging (including onsite mammography), audiology, pharmacy, optometry, dentistry, asthma clinic, counseling for emotional problems, and nutrition counseling. They offer an evidenced based wound care clinic and have many advanced technologies available for our patients. In house services include ultrasound, orthopedics, nephrology, rheumatology, endocrinology, and psychiatry. The Community Health Department operates several clinics as well as numerous outreach programs with a focus on education. Staff includes a Health Educator, Program Assistant, DM Nurse Educator, Dietician, 2 Exercise Specialists, and 2 Public Health Nurses who work closely with the medical staff to offer a team approach to disease prevention, management and treatment. Affiliated with Oklahoma City Area Indian Health Service.

BEARSKIN HEALTH CENTER
P.O. Box 30 • WYANDOTTE, OK 74370
(918) 678-2297 Fax 678-2759; Dennis Fitzgerald, Facility Director
Affiliated with Oklahoma City Area Indian Health Service.

OREGON

BURNS-PAIUTE WADATIKA HEALTH CENTER
HC 71, 100 PaSiGo St. • BURNS, OR 97220
(541) 573-7312; Twila Teeman, Director
Affiliated with Portland Area Indian Health Service.

COQUILLE TRIBAL HEALTH CENTER
P.O. Box 3190 • COOS BAY, OR 97420
(541) 888-9494. Affiliated with Portland Area Indian Health Service.

GRAND RONDE HEALTH & WELLNESS CENTER
P.O. Box 38 • GRAND RONDE, OR 97347
(503) 879-5211; Michael Watkins, Director
Affiliated with Portland Area Indian Health Service.

KLAMATH TRIBAL HEALTH CENTER
3949 S. Sixth St. • KLAMATH FALLS, OR 97603
(541) 882-1487; Leroy Jackson, Director
Affiliated with Portland Area Indian Health Service.

YELLOWHAWK PHS INDIAN HEALTH CENTER
P.O. Box 160 • PENDLETON, OR 97801
(503) 278-3870; Doris W. Thompson, Director
Allan Jio, Pharm., Clinical Director
Services: Contract health, dental care, environmental health, health education, Lab/X-ray, mental health, outpatient clinic, pharmacy, public health nursing, and wellness programs. Affiliated with Portland Area Indian Health Service.

NATIVE AMERICAN REHABILITATION ASSOCIATION (NARA) OF THE NORTHWEST
Indian Health Clinic, 15 N. Morris • PORTLAND, OR 97227
(503) 230-9875 Fax 230-9877
Services: Provides a variety of healthcare services from family medicine including women's exams, diabetes classes & testing; mental health assessments, evaluations & counseling. Approaches healthcare in a holistic manner.

NATIVE AMERICAN REHABILITATION ASSOCIATION (NARA) OF THE NORTHWEST
Outpatient Treatment Center, 1631 SW Columbia • PORTLAND, OR 97201
(503) 231-2641 Fax 231-1654; Website: www.naranorthwest.org
Services: Provides a variety of treatment services, mental heath assessment, referrals for outpatient treatment, and adolescent treatment services.

COW CREEK TRIBAL CLINIC
2371 N. Stephens St. #200 • ROSEBURG, OR 97470
(541) 672-8533; Sharon Stanphill, Director
Affiliated with Portland Area Indian Health Service.

WESTERN OREGON SERVICE UNIT - CHEMAWA HEALTH CENTER
3750 Chemawa Rd., NE • SALEM, OR 97305
(503) 304-7600; In OR (800) 452-7823; James E. Edge, MPH, Director
Lorraine A. Hesketh, Administrative Officer
Mark J. Nurre, MD, Clinical Director
Tribes served: Confederated Tribes of Siletz; Confederated Tribes of Grand Ronde; Cow Creek Band of Umpqua Tribe; Confederated Tribes of Coos, Lower Umpqua, Siuslaw; Coquille Tribe. Also provides student health services for the Chemawa Indian School. *Number of professionals on staff*: 30. *Numbers served*: 18,200 registered patients. *Services provided*: Outpatient medical, dental, pharmacy, mental health, nutrition, public health nursing. Primary & well child care; prenatal & post delivery care; family planning; minor surgical & orthopedic care. Affiliated with Portland Area Indian Health Service.

CONFEDERATED TRIBES OF SILETZ COMMUNITY HEALTH CLINIC
P.O. Box 320 • SILETZ, OR 97380
(800) 648-0449 Fax (503) 444-1278
Provides comprehensive health care to federally recognized American Indians.

WARM SPRINGS HEALTH & WELLNESS CENTER
P.O. Box 1209 • WARM SPRINGS, OR 97761
(541) 553-1196 Fax 553-2454
Carol A. Prevost, MHSA, RN, Chief Executive Officer
E-mail: carol.prevost@ihs.gov
Roberta Queahpama, Administrative Officer
Thomas Manning, MD, Clinical Director

Services provided: Outpatient clinical; dental care; contract health; nutrition; and public health nursing. Mission: To provide an innovative, caring, & diverse healthcare system that is trusted & responsive to the needs of our community. The Center is a primary care clinic that is dedicated to providing quality healthcare to all eligible American Indians and Alaska Natives in the Warm Springs Service Unit Area. The Center provides a comprehensive system of healthcare services including treatment of a wide range of medical & dental conditions. The Center is a primary care clinic that offers medical, dental, optometry, pharmacy, laboratory, radiology & podiatry services. It is the goal of the Wellness Center to assist our patients in promoting and improving the health of the Warm Springs community to the highest possible level. Equally important is our staff's commitment to the prevention of illness and injury. Works closely with the Confederated Tribes of Warm Springs Health Programs to provide seamless care. They're involved in numerous health promotional programs that encourage our patients to be active participants in their own healthcare & issues within the healthcare field. Some examples include: Diabetes Walk, Women of Warm Springs (WOW), Kids Clinic Fun Day, health fairs & conducting health screenings in the community. We work closely with Confederated Tribes of Warm Springs Health programs to ensure effective & high quality healthcare that responsive to the needs of the Warm Springs community. Affiliated with Portland Area Indian Health Service.

SOUTH CAROLINA

CATAWBA SERVICE UNIT
2893 Sturgis Rd. • ROCK HILL, SC 29730
(803) 366-9090 Fax 366-9141
The Catawba Service Unit strives to raise the health status of American Indians/Alaskan Natives through Health Promotion/Disease Prevention, education, & treatment using holistic, culturally sensitive, patient-centered health care delivery systems that partner health care teams with patients and their family members in order to maximize resources while meeting organizational objectives & community health care needs in a healing environment that provides safe, timely, effective, efficient, and equitable care. The Catawba Service Unit excels in meeting the health care needs of the residents of its service area & among the Nashville Area health care providers in the delivery of transparent, accountable, inclusive, patient centered health care; exceeding patient expectations by providing highly valued health and wellness services, disease prevention and management and the enhancement of community stewardship. Under Nashville Area HIS.

SOUTH DAKOTA

EAGLE BUTTE PHS INDIAN HOSPITAL
P.O. Box 1012 • EAGLE BUTTE, SD 57625
(605) 964-7724 Fax 964-1169
Charles Fischer, CEO
Justin Keckler, Deputy CEO (964-0506)
Rodney Vizcarra, Clinic Director (964-0503)
Johanna Watt, Director of Nursing (964-0504)
Tribe served: Cheyenne River Sioux. *Professionals on staff*: 6. *Number of Beds*: 26. 680 inpatients and 3,600 outpatients, annually. *Primary services*: Acute medicine; OB/GYN' Pediatrics. Community Health Education Programs. Affiliated with Aberdeen Area Indian Health Service.

FORT THOMPSON INDIAN HEALTH CENTER
P.O. Box 200 • FORT THOMPSON, SD 57339
(605) 245-1540 Fax 245-2384
Sherry Lulf, Managed Care Nurse (245-1502)
Helen Thompson, Administrative Officer (245-1617)
Affiliated with Aberdeen Area Indian Health Service.

KYLE HEALTH CENTER
P.O. Box 540 • KYLE, SD 57752
(605) 455-2451 Fax 455-2808
Karol Parker, Administrative Officer; Steven Beliel, MD, Clinical Director
Located on the Pine Ridge Reservation; it's an ambulatory care center with outpatient services. The outpatient department is staffed with four physicians four nurses, pharmacist, optometrist, laboratory technician, & radiology technician. In addition, the Health Center offers dental services, with four operatories staffed by two dentists, mental health services, public health nurses, & environmental health care. Affiliated with Aberdeen Area Indian Health Service.

LOWER BRULE INDIAN HEALTH CENTER
601 Gall St. • LOWER BRULE, SD 57548
(605) 473-5526 Fax 473-0607; Georgia Amiotte, CEO
Clarenda Menzie, Administrative Officer
Affiliated with Aberdeen Area Indian Health Service.

McLAUGHLIN PHS INDIAN HEALTH CENTER
P.O. Box 879 • MCLAUGHLIN, SD 57642
(605) 823-4458 Fax 823-4181; Marie Claymore, Administrative Assistant
Tribes served: Standing Rock Sioux, Cheyenne River Sioux, Rosebud Sioux, Fort Totten Sioux, Fort Thompson Crow Creek Sioux, and Yankton Sioux. *Program*: Chief Gall Education Program: Dedicated to facilitating the development and maintenance of education and learning as an integral part of a healthy lifestyle for American Indian Youth. *Professionals on staff*: 8. 9,500 outpatients, annually. *Primary services*: Outpatient & dental services. Library. Affiliated with Aberdeen Area IHS.

GREAT PLAINS YOUTH REGIONAL TREATMENT CENTER
P.O. Box 68 • MOBRIDGE, SD 57401
(605) 845-7181 Fax 845-5072; Tom Eagle Staff, Director
LaVonne Booth, Administrative Officer; Amy Yellow, Clinical Director
Provides drug and alcohol treatment for adolescents ages 13 - 17 years of age who are enrolled as a member of a federally recognized American Indian tribe. Affiliated with Aberdeen Area Indian Health Service. Tribally operated.

PINE RIDGE HOSPITAL
P.O. Box 1201 • PINE RIDGE, SD 57770
(605) 867-5131 Fax 867-3271; Bill Pourier, Chief Executive Officer
Nichelle Keith, Administrative Officer; Rory Sumners, Clinical Director
Number of Beds: 45. Affiliated with Aberdeen Area Indian Health Service.
The 45 bed Pine Ridge Hospital, serving a Sioux Indian population of more than 17,000, is the largest in the Great Plains Area. A 16 physician staff sees medical, obstetrical, pediatric, and surgical patients. The facility located in Pine Ridge, South Dakota, includes full service general surgery, an obstetrical ward, and dental. Kyle and Wanblee Health Centers and three health stations (Allen, Manderson, and Porcupine) operate within the Pine Ridge Service Unit.

SIOUX SAN HOSPITAL
3200 Canyon Lake Dr. • RAPID CITY, SD 57702
(605) 355-2500 Fax 355-2504; Lorraine Jewett, Chief Executive Officer
Helen Thompson, Administrative Officer; Brenda Farris, DO, Clinical Director
Number of Beds: 39. Affiliated with Aberdeen Area Indian Health Service.

ROSEBUD PHS INDIAN HOSPITAL
P.O. Box 400 • ROSEBUD, SD 57570
(605) 747-2231 Fax 747-2216; Shelly Harris, Chief Executive Officer
Randy Jordan, Deputy SUD; Valerie Parker, MD, Clinical Director
Number of Beds: 35. Offers a full range of services, including dental, vision, and 24 hour ambulance services. The hospital and several field clinics are staffed by 11 physicians, nurse/midwives, and physician assistants. An optical department and dental care are also offered. The hospital is the primary source of health care for the Rosebud Sioux people, who reside across 20 communities, some of which lie outside the boundaries of the Reservation. Affiliated with Aberdeen Area Indian Health Service.

SISSETON INDIAN HOSPITAL
5 Chestnut St. E • SISSETON, SD 57262
(605) 698-7606 Fax 698-4270; Richard Huff, Chief Executive Officer
Gail Williams, Administrative Officer; Sandeep Patel, MD, Clinical Director
Number of Beds: 20. Affiliated with Aberdeen Area Indian Health Service.

WOODROW WILSON KEEBLE MEMORIAL HEALTH CARE CENTER
100 Lake Traverse Dr. • SISSETON, SD 57262 (605) 698-7606
On May 14, 2009 the Sisseton Wahpeton Oyate Health Care Center changed its name to the Woodrow Wilson Keeble Memorial Health Care Center to honor the memory of Master Sergeant Woodrow Wilson Keeble. Woodrow Keeble is a full-blooded member of the Sisseton Wahpeton Oyate and a veteran of both World War II and the Korean War. In March 2008 Woodrow Keeble was awarded the Medal of Honor for his actions in the Korean War. He is the first full-blooded Sioux to receive this honor.

WAGNER INDIAN HEALTH SERVICE - YANKTON SERVICE UNIT
111 Washington Ave. NW • WAGNER, SD 57380
(605) 384-3621 Fax 384-5229; Mike Horned Eagle, Chief Executive Officer
Rebecca Jandreau, Administrative Officer
Grisel Rodriguez, Clinical Director; Susan Knudsen, Director of Nursing
Tribes served: Yankton Sioux and Santee Sioux. Wagner IHS is located on the Yankton Sioux Reservation and provides services to patients from surrounding reservations and communities throughout South Dakota, Iowa, Minnesota and Nebraska. The clinic contains nine exam rooms, Lab, X-ray, Pharmacy, Dental, Lactation Consultant, Dietician Consultants, Maternal Child Health Program, Healthy Heart Program, Diabetes Program, Public Health Nursing, Behavioral Health Services, Fitness Program, Physical Therapy, and Optometry Services. Obstetric care is provided by contract with the Sacred Heart Hospital in Yankton. *Professionals on staff*: 30; *Number of Beds*: 26. *Medical services*: In-patient; medical & surgical. Library. Affiliated with Aberdeen Area Indian Health Service.

WANBLEE HEALTH CENTER
P.O. Box 290 • WANBLEE, SD 57577
(605) 462-6155 Fax 462-6551; Francis Red Willow, Director
Affiliated with Aberdeen Area IHS.

TEXAS

DALLAS INTER-TRIBAL COUNCIL HEALTH CENTER
209 E. Jefferson • DALLAS, TX 75203
(214) 941-1050 Fax 941-6537; Dr. Rodney T. Stapp, Executive Director
Affiliated with Oklahoma City Area Indian Health Service.

EAGLE PASS HEALTH CENTER
HCI, Box 9700 • EAGLE PASS, TX 78852
(830) 757-0322 Fax 757-9228; Maricella Mendoza, Health Director
Affiliated with Oklahoma City Area Indian Health Service.

YSLETA DEL SUR SERVICE UNIT
119 S. Old Pueblo Rd. P.O. Box 17579 • EL PASO, TX 79907
(915) 859-7913 Fax 859-2988; George Haddy, CEO
Affiliated with Albuquerque Area Service Unit.

ALABAMA-COUSHATTA TRIBE OF TEXAS HEALTH CENTER
Rt. 3 Box 640 • LIVINGSTON, TX 77351
(936) 563-2058 Fax 563-2731; Myra Sylestine, Health Director

UTAH

UINTAH & OURAY SERVICE UNIT
FORT DUCHESNE PHS INDIAN HEALTH CENTER
P.O. Box 160, 6822 E. 1000 S. • FORT DUCHESNE, UT 84026
(866) 879-9475; (435) 722-5122 Fax 722-9137
Lawrence Zubel, MD, Acting Chief Executive Officer
Dr. Dwight Humphreys, Clinical Director
Slade Flitton, Director of Nursing; Dr. Joe Myers, Chief Dental Officer
Tribes served: Northern Ute; Paiute Tribe of Utah; and Skull Valley Goshute. *Population served*: 4,250. *Professionals on staff*: 47. The ambulatory 40-hour facility is staffed by three physicians, two physician's assistant, & two dentists. We provide comprehensive public health services including general medical, surgical follow-up, pediatric, prenatal and postpartum care. Dental & optometry services are also available. Other clinical specialties are provided by visiting consultants and are scheduled periodically. Patients requiring more complex medical care are referred to the hospital or other contract facilities. After-hours and weekend needs are handled through the emergency rooms at Uintah Basin Medical Center in Roosevelt, Ashley Valley Medical Center in Vernal, and at the Urgent Care Centers in Roosevelt & Vernal. Provides community health education. Affiliated with Phoenix Area Indian Health Service. Fort Duchesne encompasses the small northwestern band of Shoshone Indians, the Paiute Indian Tribe of Utah and the Skull Valley Band of Goshute Indians as well as the Ute Tribes of the Uintah and Ouray Reservations. However, only the Ute Tribes of the reservations have direct access to the health center. We serve this community of about 4,250 people. The other tribes receive care through contract health services and other state-aided health care programs.

INDIAN WALK-IN CENTER
120 West 1300 South • SALT LAKE CITY, UT 84115
(801) 486-4877 Fax 486-9943; Dena Ned, MSW, Executive Director
Affiliated with Phoenix Area Indian Health Service.

WASHINGTON

LUMMI PHS INDIAN HEALTH CENTER
2592 Kwina Rd. • BELLINGHAM, WA 98226
(206) 676-8373; Marilyn M. Scott, Director
Affiliated with Portland Area Indian Health Service.

INCHELIUM CLINIC
P.O. Box 290 • INCHELIUM, WA 99138
(509) 722-3331; Philip Arnold, Director
Affiliated with Portland Area Indian Health Service.

SOPHIE TRETTEVICK INDIAN HEALTH CENTER
P.O. Box 410 • NEAH BAY, WA 98357
(360) 645-2233; Leslie Dye, Service Unit Director
Shirley M. Johnson, Administrative Officer; Tracy Lind, FNP, Clinical Director
Affiliated with Portland Area Indian Health Service.

COLVILLE INDIAN HEALTH CENTER
P.O. Box 71, Agency Campus • NESPELEM, WA 99155
(509) 634-2913; Colleen F. Cawston, MPA, CEO

Loren L. Lewis, MD, Clinical Director; *Services*: Comprehensive Medical, Nursing, Laboratory, Radiology, Dental, Optometry, Pharmacy, Patient & Referred Care & Health Admin. services are provided. The 40,000 square foot IHS clinic in Nespelem was completed in June 2007. It was a collaborative process with between Indian Health Services & Colville Tribes. It is planned in phase implementation. Phase one consisted of the medical, radiology, laboratory, pharmacy & optometry patient services. Additionally the Patient and Referred Care formerly (Contract Health Services) and Administration were included in phase one. Plans remain to expand the final area for the needed administrative area. Affiliated with Portland Area Indian Health Service.

CHEHALIS TRIBAL CLINIC
P.O. Box 536 • OAKVILLE, WA 98568
 (360) 273-5504; Richard Bellon, Acting Director
Affiliated with Portland Area Indian Health Service.

OMAK CLINIC
617 Benton St. • OMAK, WA 98841
 (509) 422-7416; *Services*: Comprehensive Medical, Nursing, Laboratory, Radiology, Dental, Optometry, Pharmacy, Patient & Referred Care & Health Administration services are provided.

PUGET SOUND PHS INDIAN HEALTH STATION
2201 Sixth Ave., Rm. 300 • SEATTLE, WA 98121
 (206) 615-2781; Ernest H. Kimball, Director
Affiliated with Portland Area Indian Health Service.

SEATTLE INDIAN HEALTH BOARD
606 - 12th Ave. South • SEATTLE, WA 98144-2008
 (206) 324-9360 ext. 1102 Fax 324-8910
 Ralph Forquera, Exec. Director; Rebecca Gonzales, Director of Operations
Population served: A multi--service community health center serving the Indian population of Greater Seattle/King County region. *Medical services*: Full-service outpatient primary medical clinic providing preventive, acute, and chronic care, dental, mental health, substance abuse & treatment, outreach and case management, & community education services. Affiliated with the Indian Health Service (IHS). Established 1970.

TAHOLAH INDIAN HEALTH CENTER
P.O. Box 219 • TAHOLAH, WA 98587
 (206) 276-4405; Dorothy L. DeLaCruz, Director
 Carl Schilling, Clinical Director. Affiliated with Portland Area IHS.

YAKAMA INDIAN HEALTH CENTER
401 Buster Rd. • TOPPENISH, WA 98948
 (509) 865-2102 Fax 865-2116; Don Kruse, MD, Director
 Frances M. Spencer, Admini. Officer; Daniel Hocson, MD, Clinical Director
Tribe served: Yakama. *Population served*: 12,500. *Services*: Ambulatory primary care; public health; dental; mental health; optometry & audiology; Internal medicine; women's health care; elder care clinic & pediatrics; Inpatient services at local private hospital facility; The White Swan Health Clinic (satellite). Affiliated with Portland Area Indian Health Service.

DAVID C. WYNECOOP MEMORIAL CLINIC
P.O. Box 357 • WELLPINIT, WA 99040
 (509) 258-4517 Fax 258-6757; April Flores, Service Unit Director
 Bill Wiles, Administrative Officer; Ellen Kemper, Clinical Director
Tribes served: Kalispel & Spokane. Located on the Spokane Indian Reservation in the northeast section of Washington State. Services: Medical & dental. Specialty clinics include Ear, Nose & Throat, Pediatric, Dental Hygiene, Women's Health, Podiatry, Orthopedics, Diabetes & oral Surgery. The DCWMC consists of one ambulatory care health center at Wellpinit, Washington. The DCWMC primarily serves the ambulatory needs of the Spokane and Kalispel Tribes. The DCWMC is staffed with 34 employees including 2 Physicians, 1 Family Nurse Practitioner, 4 Registered Nurses, 1 Dentist, 1 Medical Technologist, 2 Pharmacists, 1 X-ray Technician, 1 Public Health Nurse and other support staff. Services include medical and dental, and also we offer a number of specialty clinics. Our specialty clinics include Ear, Nose and Throat, Pediatric, Dental Hygiene, Women's Health, Podiatry, Orthopedics, Diabetes and Oral Sugery. In FY 2003 23,736 outpatient visits were made to the DCWMC. The total active patients served at the DCWMC is 2,316. Affiliated with Portland Area Indian Health Service.

WISCONSIN

RED CLIFF HEALTH SERVICES
P.O. Box 529 • BAYFIELD, WI 54814
 (715) 779-3707 Fax 779-3777; Patricia Deragon-Navarro, Director
Tribe served: Red Cliff Band of Chippewa Indians.
Affiliated with Bemidji Area Office. Tribally operated.

HO CHUNK NATION HEALTH DEPT.
P.O. Box 636 • BLACK RIVER FALLS, WI 54615
 (715) 284-7548/7830 Fax 284-9592; Elliot Blackdeer, Health Director
Tribe served: Ho-Chunk Nation. Affiliated with Bemidji Area Office. Tribally operated.

STOCKBRIDGE-MUNSEE BAND OF MOHICAN HEALTH & WELLNESS CENTER
P.O. Box 86 • BOWLER, WI 54416
 (715) 793-5031 Fax 793-4120
 Sheila Miller, Director; Richard Dalve, MD, Clinical Director
Tribe served: Stockbridge-Munsee Band of Mohican.
Affiliated with Bemidji Area Office. Tribally operated.

FOREST CO. POTAWATOMI COMMUNITY HEALTH/WELLNESS CENTER
P.O. Box 396 • CRANDON, WI 54520
 (715) 478-4300 Fax 478-4499; Dori Shewano, Health Administrator
Tribe served: Forest County Potawatomi.
Affiliated with Bemidji Area Office. Tribally operated.

SOKAOGAN CHIPPEWA INDIAN COMMUNITY CLINIC
3163 State Hwy. 55 • CRANDON, WI 54520
 (715) 478-5180 Fax 478-5904; Paulette Smith, Health Administrator
Tribe served: Sokaogan Chippewa Indians.
Affiliated with Bemidji Area Office. Tribally operated.

LAC COURTE OREILLES TRIBE COMMUNITY HEALTH CENTER
13380 W. Trepania Rd. • HAYWARD, WI 54843
 (715) 638-5102 Fax 634-6107; Don Smith, Health Administrator
Tribe served: Lac Courte Oreilles. Bemidji Area Office. Tribally operated.

MENOMINEE TRIBAL CLINIC
P.O. Box 970 • KESHENA, WI 54135
 (715) 799-5482 Fax 799-3099
 Jerry L. Waukau, Health Director; Kevin Culhane, MD, Clinical Director
Tribe served: Menominee. *Professionals on staff*: 80. Consists of four full-time physicians with staff privileges at the Shawano Community Hospital. *Services*: The Community Health Nursing Service consists of a staff of eight that provides a number of outreach services to the community; the Human Resource Center provides outpatient mental health services; Emergency Medical Services. *Programs*: Staff education, training and research; community health education; environmental health program. Library. Affiliated with Bemidji Area Office. Tribally operated.

BAD RIVER HEALTH SERVICES
P.O Box 250 • ODANAH, WI 54861
 (715) 682-7133 Fax 685-2601; Mary Bigboy, Health Director
Tribe served: Band River band of Lake Superior Chippewa.
Affiliated with Bemidji Area Office. Tribally operated.

ONEIDA COMMUNITY HEALTH CENTER
P.O. Box 365 • ONEIDA, WI 54155
 (920) 869-2711 Fax 869-1780; Bill Wild, Director
Tribe served: Oneida Tribe of Indians of Wisconsin.
Affiliated with Bemidji Area Office. Tribally operated.

ST. CROIX HEALTH SERVICES
4404 State Rd. 70 • WEBSTER, WI 54893
 (715) 349-8554 Fax 349-2559; John Seppanen, Director
Tribe served: St. Croix Chippewa Indians of Wisconsin.
Affiliated with Bemidji Area Office. Tribally operated.

WYOMING

ARAPAHO HEALTH CENTER
P.O. Box 1310 • ARAPAHO, WY 82510
 (307) 856-9281 Fax 856-1630
 Margaret Cooper, Clinical Coordinator
Tribe served: Northern Arapaho. Affiliated with Billings Area Indian Health Service.

FORT WASHAKIE HEALTH CENTER
P.O. Box 128 • FORT WASHAKIE, WY 82514
 (307) 332-7300 Fax 332-3949; Richard Brannan, Chief Executive Officer
 Michelle Antone, Administrative Officer; JoLynn Davis, RN, Clinical Director
Tribe served: Eastern Shoshone. Reservation served: Wind River Indian Reservation. *Tribe served*: Eastern Shoshone & Northern Arapaho. *Total population served*: 10,000. *Medical services*: Outpatient clinic. Library. Affiliated with Billings Area Indian Health Service.

An alpha-geographical listing of museums, monuments & parks maintaining permanent exhibits or collections related to the Native American. Where no annotation follows a listing, the museum failed to answer our questionnaire, but is known, from other sources, to display Indian artifacts.

NATIONAL MUSEUM OF THE AMERICAN INDIAN
SMITHSONIAN INSTITUTION
4th St. & Independence Ave., SW
P.O. Box 23473 • Washington, DC 20026-3473
 (202) 633-1000 Fax 633-6920
Website: www.nmai.si.edu; E-mail: nmaicollections@si.edu
Kevin Gover (Pawnee/Comanche), Director
Ann McMullen, Curator; Leonda Levchuffice of Public Affairs
 (202) 633-6613 E-mail: levchuk@si.edu
The museum is located on The National Mall in Washington, DC. It was opened September 21, 2004. It's a living memorial dedicated to the collection, preservation, study & exhibition of American Indian languages, literature, history, art and culture. The centerpiece of the new museum is the priceless collection of almost One million objects, once stored in the Museum of the American Indian, Heye Foundation in New York City, representing 10,000 years of history from more than 1,000 indigenous cultures. This collection, that includes a library, photo archives and other resource materials, has been transferred to this new National Museum in Washington, DC. Also, a Resource Center. All three resource centers will be digitally connected, and information will flow between all facilities. Visitors to NMAI on The National Mall will be able to access information and materials from either of the other NMAI Resource Center locations, and vice versa. The Mall Resource Center will contain 18 public access computers in the Interactive Learning Center, a work-study area, book stacks, workrooms and a classroom.

NATIONAL MUSEUM OF THE AMERICAN INDIAN
CULTURAL RESOURCES CENTER
4220 Silver Hill Rd. • Suitland, MD 20746
 Bruce Bernstein, Assistant Director of Cultural Resources
 Pat Nietfeld, Collections Manager (301) 238-1454
 Caleb Strickland, Director, Community Services Department
 Thomas Sweeney, Director of Public Affairs Ext. 6404
 Marti Kriepe De Montano, Director, Resource Dept. Ext. 6404
 Stephanie Makseyn-Kelley, Repatriation Office Ext. 6393 (301) 238-6624
One of three Resource Centers of the National Museum of the American Indian, providing storage facilities, & containing research, conservation and repatriation offices.

NATIONAL MUSEUM OF THE AMERICAN INDIAN
THE GEORGE GUSTAV HEYE CENTER
U.S. Custom House, One Bowling Green • New York, NY 10004
 (212) 514-3700 Fax 514-3800
 John Haworth, Director; Karen Savage, Assistant Director
 Gaetana DeGennaro, Resource Center Manager
One of three Resource Centers of the National Museum of the American Indian exhibiting artifacts of the North & South American Indians.

NATIVE AMERICAN HOLOCAUST MUSEUM
Website: www.nahm.org

ALABAMA

POARCH CREEK INDIAN HERITAGE CENTER
HCR 69A, Box 85B • ATMORE, AL 36502
 (205) 368-9136; Patricia L. Brewer, Executive Director
 Sandra L. Ridley, Curator
Museum under construction. Collections will pertain to Creek Indians of the Southeast. Library. Opened in 1990.

RUSSELL CAVE NATIONAL MONUMENT
3729 County Road 98 • BRIDGEPORT, AL 35740
 (256) 495-2672 Fax 495-9220; Website: www.nps.gov/ruca
 William Springer, Supt.; Larry N. Beane, Curator
 Stephen McGee, Park Ranger; E-mail: ruca_ranger_activities@nps.gov
Description: An excavated, 310-acre archaeological site that shows the life of the people Russell Cave sheltered for 8,000 years. From archaic man to Indians--Woodlands & Cherokee. Museum contains artifacts from the Archaic, Woodland, and Mississippian periods. Special program: Indian Day - April, includes demonstrations of prehistoric techniques, arts & crafts. Publication: Investigations in Russell Cave. Library. Opened 1961.

OAKVILLE INDIAN MOUNDS PARK & MUSEUM
1219 County Road 187 • DANVILLE, AL 35619
 (205) 905-2494 Fax 905-2428; E-mail: indian@lawrenceal.org

Rickey Butch Walker, Director
Description: The pre-Columbian Indian mound is one of the largest domiciliary Indian mounds in the Tennessee Valley. The museum contains Indian artifacts.

ALABAMA STATE ARCHIVES & HISTORY MUSEUM
624 Washington Ave. • MONTGOMERY, AL 36130
 (205) 242-4363
Description: Collections include artifacts that trace the culture of five American Indian tribes that lived in Alabama.

MOUNDVILLE ARCHAEOLOGICAL PARK & MUSEUM
The Jones Archaeological Museum, 634 Mound Park • MOUNDVILLE, AL 35474
 (205) 371-2234 Fax 371-4180; Website: www.moundville.ua.edu/museum/
 Bill Bomar, Director; Eugene Futato, Curator
Description: A park and museum located on the Black Warrior River, preserves 325 acres of what was once a large & powerful Southeastern Indian community of about 3,000 @ 1300 A.D. The site is internationally known for its 20 preserved mounds and the building of the wooden palisade that once defended the site. An Archaeological Museum holds one of the largest and most important collections of Native American artifacts & related materials for scientific research anywhere in the Southeast. Activities: Moundville Native American Festival featuring Southeastern Native American crafts, food, storytelling, musicians and dancers; other special programs with Native Americans from Choctaw, Creek, Cherokee, and Seminole tribes. Opened 1939.

FORT TOULOUSE-JACKSON PARK
2521 W. Ft. Toulouse Rd. • WETUMPKA, AL 36093
 (205) 567-3002 Ned Jenkins, Site Manager
Description: A 165-acre National Historic Landmark situated at the junction of the Coos and Tallapoosa Rivers where they form the Alabama River. Occupied by the mound builder Alabama Indians, who were part of the Creek Confederacy. Like the other mound builders in the area, these Indians were the first farmers-corn, beans and squash. When DeSoto passed through in 1540 this area was probably a part of the chiefdom of Talise.

ALASKA

AKUTAN ALEUT HERITAGE MUSEUM
P.O. Box 89 • AKUTAN, AK 99553
 (907) 689-2300 Fax 689-2301
 Jacob Stepetin, Director; Opened 1995.

SIMON PANEAK MEMORIAL MUSEUM
P.O. Box 21085, 341 Mekiana Rd. • ANAKTUVUK PASS 99721
 (907) 661-3413 Fax 661-3414; Vera Kalik Wood, Curator
Description: Local history & culture museum pertaining to the "Nunamiut" or inland Eskimos of Alaska's Central Brooks Range. Collections represent a combination of archaeological & ethnographic objects as well as extensive oral history, photographic & archival materials. Special Education Program: Work in conjunction with the North Slope Borough School District and the Borough's Inupiaq History, Language & Culture Commission to research & produce educational materials based on oral history research with Nunamiut elders about traditional tools, implements, practices & values. Library. Opened 1986.

ALASKA HERITAGE MUSEUM AT WELLS FARGO
301 W. Northern Lights Blvd. • ANCHORAGE, AK 99510
 (907) 265-2834 Fax 265-2860
 Artemis Bona-Dea, Curator; E-mail: bonadear@wellsfargo.com
Description: Interprets Alaska Native culture through exhibits supported by a reference library of more than 2,500 books on Alaska subjects. A collection of paintings by Alaska's major artists, featuring a fine arts collection of Sydney Laurence paintings.

ALASKA NATIVE HERITAGE CENTER
8800 Heritage Center Dr. • ANCHORAGE, AK 99503
 (907) 330-8000 Fax 330-8030; Jon Ross, Director; Scott Neel, Curator
Description: A statewide culture center dedicated to the perpetuation of Alaska Native culture, language, arts, and customs and will serve as a learning center, a gathering place, and a clearinghouse. Includes a theater and outside traditional village exhibits representing the five major cultural groups. Opened 1999.

ANCHORAGE MUSEUM AT RASMUSON CENTER
625 C St. • ANCHORAGE, AK 99501
 (907) 929-9200 Fax 929-9290; Website: www.anchoragemuseum.org
 E-mail: museum@anchoragemuseum.org; Patricia B. Wolf, Director
Description: Permanent exhibits on Alaskan art and artifacts of all periods. Eskimo, Aleut, Tlingit and Athapaskan crafts. 8,000 ethnographic pieces. Special programs: Annual Native Heritage Festival (March) which features 10-20 contemporary Alaskan Native craftsmen and artists; Summer Native dance series provided by Cook Inlet Tribal Council. Publications: An Introduction to the Native Art of Alaska; monthly newsletter. Library. Museum shop. Opened 1968.

ANVIK HISTORICAL SOCIETY & MUSEUM
P.O. Box 110 • ANVIK, AK 99558
 (907) 663-6360; Donna V. MacAlpine, Director
 E-mail: donnamac@cgrathalaska.net
Description: Collections include local Athabaskan artifacts from mid-19th century to the present, historic photographs & artifacts from the Anvik Mission Opened 1887.

INUPIAT HERITAGE CENTER - ILISAGVIK COLLEGE
5421 North Star St., P.O. Box 749 • BARROW, AK 99723
 (907) 852-4594 Fax 852-4224; Website: www.nps.gov/inup/
 Beverly Hugo, Director & ECHO Project Manager

YUPIIT PICIRYARAIT CULTURAL CENTER & MUSEUM
University of Alaska, Kuskokwim Campus Library
P.O. Box 219 • BETHEL, AK 99559
 (907) 543-1819 Fax 543-1885; Website: www.ypmuseum.org
 Vivian Korthius & Mary Woods, Contacts; E-mail: vkorthius@avcp.org
Description: Exhibits Yup'ik Eskimo artifacts of southwest Alaska, such as baskets, clothing, utensils, ceremonial regalia, masks, and other items of historical value. *Programs*: Elder Mentor Program; Community Educational Programming Outreach; Interactive Exhibitions & Seasonal Yup'ik Ceremonies & Festivals. Gift Shop. Opened 1994.

NAY'DINI'AA NA TRIBAL CULTURAL CENTER
P.O. Box 1105 • CHICKALOON, AK 99674
 (907) 745-0707 Fax 745-7154; Jennifer Dahle Harrison, Director
Description: Exhibits describing the Athabascan people of Chickaloon Village from the 1800's to the present. *Activities*: Assists Elders in teaching the tribe's traditions to children attending the first tribal school in Alaska, the Ya Ne Dah Ah School. Opened 2000.

CORDOVA HISTORICAL MUSEUM
622 First St., P.O. Box 391 • CORDOVA, AK 99574
 (907) 424-6665 Fax 424-6666
Website: www.cordovamuseum.org; E-mail: museum@cordovamuseum.org
 Cathy Sherman, Director; Judy Fulton, Collections Manager

ILANKA CULTURAL CENTER, MUSEUM & GIFT GALLERY
110 Nicholoff Way, P.O. Box 322 • CORDOVA, AK 99574
 (907) 424-7903 Fax 424-3018; Website: www.ilankacenter.org
 Larue Barnes, Director of Cultural Center
 Mary Babic, Native Arts Consortium Director
Description: Historical & contemporary exhibits of the Native peoples & cultures of the Copper River & Prince William Sound area.

SAMUEL K. FOX MUSEUM
306 D St., West, P.O. Box 273 • DILLINGHAM, AK 99576
 (907) 842-4831; Deb Burton, Chairperson
Description: Houses a large collection of Central Yup'ik Eskimo arts & crafts, and Siberian Yup'ik & Inupiak Eskimo artifacts. Also, a collection of art from the late Eskimo artist Sam Fox.

DILLINGHAM HERITAGE MUSEUM
DILLINGHAM, AK 99576 (907) 842-5601/5221
 Irma O'Brien, Coordinator; Norma Adkison, Chairwoman
Description: Alaskan Indian museum with southwest Yup'ik Eskimo arts & crafts, and Siberian Yup'ik and Inupiak Eskimo artifacts.

EAGLE HISTORICAL SOCIETY & MUSEUMS
P.O. Box 23 • EAGLE CITY, AK 99738
 (907) 547-2325; Jean Turner, Museum Director
 E-mail: ehsmus@aptalaska.net
Description: A collection of Han Indian exhibits. Archives & photograph collection. Gift shop. Admission: $7.

UNIVERSITY OF ALASKA MUSEUM OF THE NORTH
907 Yukon Dr., P.O. Box 756960 • FAIRBANKS, AK 99775
 (907) 474-7505 Fax 474-5469; Website: www.uaf.edu/museum/
 Aldona Jonaitis, PhD, Director; E-mail: museum@uaf.edu
 E-mail: ajonatis@alaska.edu
Description: Large collection of Alaskan arctic archaeology, Tlingit, Athapascan, Aleut, Alutiiq, Inupiat, Yupik, Siberian Yupik ethnology, contemporary artwork by Alaskan Natives. *Programs*: "Northern Inua" 50-minute summer program of Alaskan Native athletics and dance; "Gatherings North" winter celebration of Alaskan Native Culture. *Publications*: Museum Guide; "Reflections" annual newsletter. Opened 1922.

C'EK'AEDI HWNAX – 'LEGACY HOUSE'
The Ahtna Heritage Foundation Cultural Center
P.O. Box 213 • GLENNALLEN, AK 99573

 (907) 822-3535; E-mail: legacy@coppervalleyak.net
Katherine McConkey (Taltsiine), Director
 E-mail: ahtnaheritage.kathy@gmail.com
 Tana Finnesand, Curator Collections; E-mail: ahtnaheritage.tkfinn@gmail.com
Purpose: To collect, preserve, study, exhibit & stimulate appreciation for the cultural resources of the Ahtna people; to provide a central repository to house Ahtna cultural resources within the Ahtna region; to encourage opportunities for cultural education, and perpetuate & increase the vitality of Ahtna people, culture & language.

ALASKA INDIAN ARTS, INC.
24 Fort Seward Dr., P.O. Box 271 • HAINES, AK 99827
 (907) 766-2160; Carl W. Heinmiller, Executive Director
 Website: www.alaskaindianarts.com
Description: Indian Living Village Museum, collection of Tlingit Indian costumes & art; Totem carving, silkscreen & silver carving with Native artists; Chilkat Indian dancing. Small reference library.

JILKAAT KWAAN CULTURAL HERITAGE CENTER
HAINES, AK 99827 Website: http://jilkaatkwaanheritagecenter.org
Special collection: Klukwan Whale House Collection

SHELDON MUSEUM & CULTURAL CENTER
11 Main St., P.O. Box 269 • HAINES, AK 99827
 (907) 766-2366 Fax 766-2368; Website: www.sheldonmuseum.org
 Jerrie Clarke, Director; Blythe Carter, Operations Coordinator
 E-mail: curator@sheldonmuseum.org
Description: Historical & Tlingit art museum, depicting the Tlingit Indian culture & history of the Upper Lynn Canal (northern part of Southeast Alaska). Tlingit artifacts, including blankets, baskets, costumes, &\and implements. *Special programs*: Movies/slide shows; Haines Mission (Indian school/orphanage); travelling & special exhibits-often including native artists; school programs; Tlingit Awareness Week; Tlingit Language classes. *Publications*: A Personal Look at the Sheldon Museum; Haines: The First Century; The Tlingit Indian: Journey to the Tlingits; historical monographs about local history & Tlingit culture. Library. Opened 1925 (private), 1975 (public).

ALASKA STATE MUSEUM
395 Whittier St. • JUNEAU, AK 99801-1718
 (907) 465-2901 Fax 465-2976; Website: www.museums.state.ak.us
 Bruce Kato, Chief Curator (465-4866); E-mail: bruce_kato@eed.state.ak.us
 Steve Henrikson, Curator of Collections (465-4826)
Description: Maintains a collection of more than 10,000 objects relating to the Eskimo, Tlingit, Northwest Coast, Athabascan, Aleut, & Haida. Resource Library. Publications: Bulletin, Review, Concepts, Occasional exhibit catalogs; traveling exhibitions. Established 1900.

KENAI VISIOTRS & CULTURAL CENTER
11471 Kenai Spur Hwy. • KENAI, AK 99611
 (907) 283-1991 Fax 283-2230; E-mail: info@visitkenia.com
 Natasha Ala, Executive Director
Description: Features Athabaskan, Aleut & Russian cultural exhibits.

KENAITZE INDIAN TRIBE: TS'ITSANA CENTER/TRIBAL ARCHIVES
10 N. Willow, P.O. Box 988 • KENAI, AK 99611
 (907) 283-3633 Fax 283-4437
 Dana Verrengia, Tribal Archivist; E-mail: archives@kenaitze.org
Description: Archives for the Kenaitze Indian Tribe, over 600 items reflecting Kenaitze Dena'ina culture, tradition, and history. Extensive collection of Dena'ina language videos, tapes, and documentation.

KETCHIKAN INDIAN MUSEUM
P.O. Box 5454 • KETCHIKAN, AK 99901
 (800) 252-5158; (907) 228-4900

SOUTHEAST ALASKA DISCOVERY CENTER, USDA FOREST SERVICE
50 Main St. • KETCHIKAN, AK 99901
 (907) 228-6220 Fax 228-6234; Tim Fisher, Center Director
Description: Tsimshian, Haida & Tlingit totem poles; a Native fish camp scene.

TOTEM HERITAGE CENTER - TONGASS HISTORICAL MUSEUM
629 Dock St. • KETCHIKAN, AK 99901
 (907) 225-5900 Fax 225-5901
 Website: www.city.ketchikan.ak.us/departments/museums/totem.html
 E-mail: museum@city.ketchikan.ak.us
 Michael Naab, Director; Chris Hanson, Curator of Programs
 Richard H. Van Cleave, Curator of Collections
Description: City of Ketchikan's museum department & archives holdings include photographs on all Alaska villages with totem poles; index to all Alaska totem poles; vertical file on Northwest Coast Indian art & culture. Covers Tlingit, Haida & Tsimshian tribes - art, anthropology, totem poles. Displays the world's finest

collection of 19th century totem poles, retrieved from old village sites. *Programs*: Native Arts Studies Program offers an annual series of workshops, seminars, and classes in Tlingit, Haida, & Tsimshian arts and culture, with college credit available. The program is designed for all levels. Art and crafts slides available for use; lecture series on traditional Alaska Native arts & culture. Museum shop offers a selection of Alaska Native crafts, books, clothing & momentos. Library. *Publication*: Quarterly newsletter. Opened 1961.

ALUTIIQ MUSEUM & ARCHAEOLOGICAL REPOSITORY
215 Mission Rd., Suite 101 • KODIAK, AK 99615
(907) 486-7004 Fax 486-7048
Website: www.alutiiqmuseum.org; E-mail: alutiiq2@ptialaska.net;
Alisha S. Drabek, Executive Director; E-mail: Alisha@alutiiqmuseum.org
Frank Peterson, Director of Operations; Email: frank@alutiiqmuseum.org
Marya Halvorsen, Heritage Education Specialist
 E-mail: marya@alutiiqmuseum.org
Amy F. Steffian, Director of Research & Publication
 E-mail: amy@alutiiqmuseum.org
Patrick G. Saltonstall, Curator of Archaeology
 E-mail: Patrick@alutiiqmuseum.org
Description: An educational facility, research center, & repository. Exhibits archaeological, ethnographic & archival materials from Alutiiq sites dating between 100 and 7500 years ago. *Special programs*: Hosts annual traveling exhibit on Native American Alaskan culture; provides educational outreach programs; and conducts archaeological excavations. Library. Opened 1995.

BARANOV MUSEUM/ERSKINE HOUSE
Kodiak Historical Society, 101 Marine Way • KODIAK, AK 99615
(907) 486-5920 Fax 486-3166
 Ann Stone, President; Marian Johnson, Director; E-mail: baronov@ak.net
Description: The Kodiak Historical Society operates the Baranov Museum in the old Russian warehouse, the Erskine House, in downtown Kodiak. The collection consists of Aleut, Koniag, Russian & American objects from the area prehistoric to present. Research Center for Kodiak and the Aleutians with photos, rare books, papers and maps. *Publications*: Educational papers. Museum store.

KOTZEBUE MUSEUM, INC.
P.O. Box 46 • KOTZEBUE, AK 99752
 (907) 442-3401 Fax 442-3742; Gene Moore, Manager
Description: Contains Eskimo & Indian artifacts, arts & crafts, costumes.

NANA MUSEUM OF THE ARCTIC
P.O. Box 49 • KOTZEBUE, AK 99752
 (907) 442-3301 Fax 442-2866; Gia Hanna, Director
Description: Inupiat Museum of the Arctic houses land and sea mammal exhibits, arts & crafts, technical diorama & slide presentations. *Activities*: Eskimo dancers and a traditional Eskimo Blanket Toss. *Program*: Maintains a multimedia interpretive program explaining traditional Inupiat skills & culture. Opened 1976.

DUNCAN COTTAGE MUSEUM
P.O. Box 8, Tait St. • METLAKATLA, AK 99926
 (907) 886-8687 Fax 886-4436; LaVerne Welcome, Director/Curator
Description: Historic House, 1894--home of Father William Duncan, missionary teacher of the Tsimshian Indian people of Metlakatla.

ALFRED STARR NENANA CULTURAL CENTER
415 Riverfront, P.O. Box 70 • NENANA, AK 99760
 (907) 832-5520 Fax 832-5532; Carol Gallo, Contact
Description: The history & culture of Nenana area including Athabaskans, beadwork, land claims, naïve place names. Gift shop with Native made items.

BERINGIA MUSEUM OF CULTURE & SCIENCE
P.O. Box 948 • NOME, AK 99762
(907) 443-4340 Fax 443-4452
Description: Eskimo heritage archives covers the indigenous
cultures of the Bering Strait region.

CARRIE M. McLAIN MEMORIAL MUSEUM
223 Front St., P.O. Box 53 • NOME, AK 99762
 (907) 443-6630 Fax 443-7955; Laura Samuelson, Director
 Website: www.nomealaska.org; E-mail: museum@nomealaska.org
Description: Old Eskimo artifacts. Library.

CLAUSEN MEMORIAL MUSEUM
203 Fram St., Box 708 • PETERSBURG, AK 99833
 (907) 772-3598; Sue McCallum, Director
Description: Collections of material on Tlingit Indians, including canoes & tools.

SELDOVIA NATIVE ASSOCIATION
Fine Arts and Cultural Center Museum
P.O. Box 201 • SELDOVIA, AK 99663

SEWARD COMMUNITY LIBRARY & MUSEUM
Resurrection Bay Historical Society
336 3rd Ave. • SEWARD, AK 99664
 (907) 224-3902; Website: cityofseward.us.
 Lee Poleski, Library Director
 Patricia Linville, Director; E-mail: plinville@cityofseward.net
 Rachel James, Program Coordinator
 Amy Carney, Museum & Archives Collections Coordinator
Description: Contains almost 5,000 objects, photographs, and archives pertaining to the diverse history of Seward.

SHELDON JACKSON MUSEUM
104 College Dr. • SITKA, AK 99835
 (907) 747-8981 Fax 747-3004; Website: www.museums.state.ak.us
 Rosemary Carlton, Curator of Collections
 Website: www.educ.state.ak.us/lam/museum/home.html
Description: Museum is the oldest museum in the state of Alaska and is housed in the first concrete building erected in Alaska. Present collections are representative of the four major Native groups in Alaska. Features Alaskan Eskimo, Aleut, Athapascan, Tlingit, Haida & Tsimshian artifacts (period 1888-1930). *Special collections*: Argillite carvings; 400 Eskimo dance masks. *Programs*: Interpretation & education for groups; artist demonstrator program in summer. *Publications*: Tlingit Women's Root Basket; Tlingit Legends. Library/Archives. Museum Shop. Opened 1887.

SOUTHEAST ALASKA INDIAN CULTURAL CENTER
106 Metlakatla St. • SITKA, AK 99835
 (907) 747-8061 Fax 747-5938
 Kathie Wasserman, Director; E-mail: seaicc@ptialaska.net
Description: Displays Native arts produced in the Center over the past 30 years, including woodcarving, silverwork, costumes, and robes. *Activities*: Audiovisual programs & workshops; Provides demonstrations of traditional Tlingit art such as woodcarving, costume design, and metalworking that are representative of the Tlingit people and Southeast Alaska. Opened 1967.

SITKA HISTORICAL MUSEUM
330 Harbor Dr. • SITKA, AK 99835
 (907) 747-6455 Fax 747-6588
 Website: www.sitkahistory.org; E-mail: sitka.history@yahoo.com
 Robert Medinger, Director
Description: A collection of Tlingit, Russian and early American artifacts. Local hand-crafted items related to collections.

SITKA NATIONAL HISTORICAL PARK
103 Monastery St. • SITKA, AK 99835
 (907) 747-6281 Fax 747-5938; Mary Miller, Supt.
 Sue Thorsen, Curator; Ramona East, Park Museum Specialist
 E-mail: sue_thorsen@nps.gov
Description: A collection of more than 4,000 artifacts; Tlingit ethnographic items; Tlingit & Haida totem poles & Chilkat Robes; traditional Native arts such as woodcarving, costume design, and metalworking. *Publication*: Carved History: A Guide to the Totem Poles of Sitka National Historical Park. Library.

SKAGWAY MUSEUM & ARCHIVES
700 Spring St., P.O. Box 521 • SKAGWAY, AK 99840
 (907) 983-2420 Fax 983-3420
 Judy Munns, Director; E-mail: info@skagwaymuseum.org
Description: Artifacts, photographs & historical records of the past century from the Klondock Gold Rush of 1898 and an Alaska Native heritage collection of baskets, beadwork & carvings.

SOLDOTNA HISTORICAL SOCIETY & MUSEUM
461 Centennial Park Rd., P.O. Box 1986 • SOLDOTNA, AK 99669
 (907) 262-3832
Description: Homesteaders' village; Native artifacts; wildlife displays.

TATITLEK MUSEUM & CULTURAL CENTER
P.O. Box 171 • TATITLEK, AK 99677
 (907) 325-2311 Fax 325-2298

MUSEUM OF THE ALEUTIANS
314 Salmon Way, P.O. Box 648 • UNALASKA, AK 99685
 (907) 581-5150 Fax 581-6682
 Zoya Johnson, Director; E-mail: Aleutians@akwisp.com
Description: Exhibits on the cultural & artistic heritage of the Aleutian Island area. Focus is on Aleut/Unangan prehistory & ethnographic items.

MAXINE & JESSE WHITNEY MUSEUM
303 Lowe St., P.O. Box 97 • VALDEZ, AK99686
 (907) 834-1690 Fax 835-8933; E-mail: wgoldstein@pwscc.edu

Description: Maintains one of the world's largest collections of Native Alaskan art & artifacts. Includes Native Alaskan dolls, beadwork, baskets, masks, archaeological artifacts, and a large collection of ivory carvings & tools.

DOROTHY PAGE MUSEUM & OLD WASILLA TOWNSITE PARK
323 N. Main St. • WASILLA, AK 99654
(907) 373-9071 Fax 373-9072; Margaret Rogers, Museum Aide
E-mail: museum@wasilla.ak.us
Description: A collection of Alaska Native & natural history.

TRIBAL HOUSE OF THE BEAR
P.O. Box 868 • WRANGELL, AK 99929
(907) 874-3747; Nora Black-Rinehart, Director
Margaret Sturtevant, Curator
Description: Located on Shakes Island, this Indian Museum is housed in Tribal House with exhibits of costumes, Tlingit totem poles, ancient wood carving. *Publication*: Guide to Shakes Island. Opened 1938.

WRANGELL MUSEUM
P.O. Box 1050 • WRANGELL, AK 99929
(907) 874-3770 Fax 874-3785; Dennis Chapman, Director/Curator
Description: Displays Tlingit totem poles & artifacts; photo collection.
Publication: The History of Chief Shakes and His Clan; newsletter.

ARIZONA

MONTEZUMA CASTLE NATIONAL MONUMENT
P.O. Box 219 • CAMP VERDE, AZ 86322
(520) 567-3322; Glen E. Henderson, Supt.
Description: Prehistoric Pueblo Indian ruins. Museum: Indian artifacts obtained from the Monument excavations. Library.

YAVAPAI-APACHE VISITOR ACTIVITY CENTER
P.O. Box 219 • CAMP VERDE, AZ 86322
(520) 567-5276
Description: Exhibits depict historic & contemporary Indian lifestyles. *Programs*: A slide presentation of area's prehistoric Indian cultures and a film on the Yavapai-Apache tribe.

CANYON DE CHELLY NATIONAL MONUMENT
P.O. Box 588 • CHINLE, AZ 86503
(928) 674-5518 Fax 674-5507; Website: www.nps.gov
Anna Marie Fender, Supt.
Tara Travis, Historian/Curator; E-Mail: tara_travis@nps.gov
Description: One of the largest archaeological preserves in North America (A National Historic Landmark) with over 2,500 sites within the 83,00 acres. The area is still inhabited by members of the Navajo Nation. Exhibits concentrates on the occupational sequence of American Indians at Canyon de Chelly National Monument: Archaic, Basketmaker, Anasazi, Puebloan, and Navajo culture. Displays Anasazi and Navajo Indian artifacts from the area. *Programs*: Navajo Guides are available to provide tours for school and tour groups. *Publication*: Park brochure available. Library. Bookstore. Opened in 1931.

CASA GRANDE RUINS NATIONAL MONUMENT
1100 N. Ruins Dr. • COOLIDGE, AZ 85228
(520) 723-3172 Fax 723-7209; Sam R. Henderson, Supt.
Museum: Located on the Hohokam village site of 500-1450 A.D.; contains pre-Columbian Pueblo & Hohokam Indian artifacts; ethnological material of the Pima and Papago Indians--basketry & pottery. A National Historic Landmark. Library.

THE AMERIND MUSEUM
P.O. Box 400 • DRAGOON, AZ 85609
(520) 586-3666 Fax 586-4679; Dr. John A. Ware, Director
Website: www.amerind.org; E-mail: amerind@amerind.org
Eric Kaldahl, Chief Curator; E-mail: ekaldahl@amerind.org
Ron Bridgemon, Associate Curator of Public Programs
Tammy Stansberry, Museum Store Manager
Archaeology & Ethnology Museum: Maintains collections of North American and some Central and South American ethnological and archaeological materials; slides and photos; manuscripts; field notes. *Special programs*: Advanced seminars, visiting scholars. Museum shop. Art Gallery. Library. *Publications*: Archaeology & New World Studies Series. Opened 1937.

MUSEUM OF NORTHERN ARIZONA
3101 N. Fort Valley Rd. • FLAGSTAFF, AZ 86001
(928) 774-5211 Fax 779-1527; Michael J. Fox, President
David R. Wilcox, Curator
Description: Exhibits the arts and artifacts of the Indians of Northern Arizona, with specific reference to the Hopi and Navajo. Annual art show. Bookstore. *Publication*: Plateau, quarterly journal; bimonthly newsletter; Archaeological Research Papers; bulletins. Library.

WALNUT CANYON NATIONAL MONUMENT
Walnut Canyon Rd. • FLAGSTAFF, AZ 86004
(520) 526-3367; Sam Henderson, Supt.
Description: Located on the site of approximately 400 prehistoric Indian ruins of the Sinagua Indians dating back to 1100-1270 A.D. Displays artifacts excavated from the site. Library.

WUPATKI & SUNSET CRATER NATIONAL MONUMENT
HC 33, Box 444A • FLAGSTAFF, AZ 86001
(520) 527-7152 Fax 556-7154
Henry L. Jones, Supt.; Anna Fender, Chief Ranger
Description: Exhibits four sets of ruins: Lomaki, Nalakihu-Citadel, Wuwoki, and Wupatki. Displays artifacts excavated from the ruins. Library.

WHITE MOUNTAIN APACHE CULTURAL CENTER & MUSEUM
P.O. Box 507 • FORT APACHE, AZ 85926
(928) 338-4625 Fax 338-1716; Karl A. Hoerig, PHD, Director
Website: www.wmat.nsn.us
Description: Art, archives, and material culture of the White Mountain Apache Tribe and Fort Apache Historic Park. Programs: Arts & crafts demonstrations; guided tours, Fort Apache Heritage Reunion each May. Library. Originally opened 1969; new facility opened June 1997.

FORT McDOWELL MOHAVE-APACHE CULTURAL CENTER
Fort McDowell Indian Community, P.O. Box 1779 • FOUNTAIN HILLS, AZ 85269
(602) 837-5121 Fax 837-4896; Louis Hood, Director
Opened 1998.

HUBBELL TRADING POST NATIONAL HISTORIC SITE
P.O. Box 150 • GANADO, AZ 86505
(520) 755-3475; Charles D. Wyatt, Supt.; Shirley Harding, Curator
Description: The oldest continually operating Indian trading post (1878) maintains artifacts related to Lorenzo Hubbell - his historic 1902 home and furnishings are part of the collection. Extensive collections of Native American and Southwest art on display. *Special programs*: Navajo rug weaving and silversmithing demonstrations; tours; buying and selling Navajo, Hopi, Pueblo, Zuni and other tribal crafts. Library. Opened 1967.

GILA COUNTY HISTORICAL MUSEUM
Box 2891, 1330 N. Broad St. • GLOBE, AZ 85502
(520) 425-7385 Wilbur A. Haak, Director
Description: Maintains prehistoric Indian artifacts, Apache basket collection and photographs (1125-1400 A.D.) Library. Opened 1972.

TUSAYAN RUIN & MUSEUM
Grand Canyon National Park, P.O. Box 129 • GRAND CANYON, AZ 86023
(520) 638-2305; Robert S. Chandler, Supt.
Carolyn Richard, Curator
Description: Exhibits artifacts from the Tusayan prehistoric ruins; from Grand Canyon area Native American cultures...over 200,000 objects in six areas: archaeology, history, geology, ethnography, biology & paleontology. *Programs*: Guided tours. Library. A National Historic Landmark. Established 1919. Museum erected 1931.

MOHAVE MUSEUM OF HISTORY & ARTS
400 W. Beale St. • KINGMAN, AZ 86401
(520) 753-3195; Robert R. Yost, Director
Karin Goudy, Photographs; Mona Cochran, Library & Archives
Description: The Walapai Room: Houses a life size Indian wickieup and figures, Hopi kachinas; also Hualapai, Mohave basketry & pottery. Mohave Miniature: A miniature rendition of a typical Mohave Indian Village. *Publication*: The History of Mohave County to 1912; monthly newsletter, Mohave Epic. Research Library. Opened 1960.

AK CHIN INDIAN HIM-DAK MUSEUM/ARCHIVES
42507 W. Peters & Nall Rd. • MARICOPA, AZ 85239
(520) 568-9480 Fax 568-9557; Elaine F. Peters, Director
Description: Maintains 8,000 square feet of Ak-Chin artifacts - over 700 boxes of artifacts on exhibit and storage. Archives: Ak-Chin Tribal Records from early 1900's to present. *Special program*: Language programs. *Publication*: Tribal newsletter. Library. Opened in 1991.

COLORADO RIVER INDIAN TRIBES MUSEUM
Route 1, Box 23-B • PARKER, AZ 85344
(520) 669-1335 Fax 669-5675; Dr. Michael Tsosie, Executive Director
Description: Indian Museum displaying Mohave, Chemehuevi, Navajo and Hopi artifacts, including pottery, baskets, silver, wool rugs, fine arts, Kachinas, beadwork; also prehistoric Mogollon, Anasazi, Hohokam & Patayan collections. *Special collections/exhibits*: Chemehuevi Basket Collection; Mohave Pottery; historical information; Old Presbyterian Indian Church; Mohave & Chemehuevi Archives. Library. Opened 1966.

SAN CARLOS APACHE CULTURAL CENTER
P.O. Box 760 • PERIDOT, AZ 85542
  (928) 475-2894; Website: www.apacheculture.com
  Herb Stevens, Director
Description: A special exhibit, "Window on Apache Culture," describes the Apache's Spiritual beginnings & ceremonies such as the Changing Women. Educational programs and demonstrations are available for schools and other groups. Gift shop with fine crafted items, Cradle Boards ornamental; jewelry, paintings, carvings & sculptures, and books. Opened 1995.

THE HEARD MUSEUM OF NATIVE CULTURES & ART
2301 N. Central Ave. • PHOENIX, AZ 85004
  (602) 252-8840 Fax 252-9757; Website: www.heard.org
  Letitiia Chambers (Cherokee), Director
  Gloria Lomahaftewa, Assistant to Director - Native American Relations
  Michele Crank, Director of Public Affairs & Government Relations
  Mario Nick Klimiades, Library & Archives Director
Description: Living museum dedicated to Native art & cultures exhibiting works by American Indians. Paintings, prints, sculpture, and the finest in contemporary craft arts are regularly on exhibit, as well as an extensive exhibit of historic materials from the Southwest. Southwestern archaeological & ethnological collection of more than 32,000 works of traditional & contemporary Native arts & crafts. Includes artifacts from North American Indian tribes, as well as native cultures of South America, Asia & Africa. The Museum staff has developed social studies instructional materials. Special collections: Hopi Kachina dolls, and Navajo rugs & blankets. Special programs: Guided tours; lectures; workshops; annual Indian Fair & Market; Speakers Bureau; films; traveling exhibitions. Publication: EarthSong, Museum Journal; Museum membership newsletter; variety of catalogues accompanying exhibitions. Library & Archives. Opened 1929.

PUEBLO GRANDE MUSEUM & ARCHAELOGICAL PARK
4619 E. Washington St. • PHOENIX, AZ 85034
  (602) 495-0901 Fax 495-5645; Website: www.pueblogrande.com
  E-mail: pueblo.grande.museum.pks@phoenix.gov
  Roger W. Lidman, Administrator; Holly Young, Collections Curator
  Laura Andrew, Education & Programs; Research Librarian
Description: Archaeological site museum containing exhibits of prehistoric Hohokam cultural material, circa A.D. 500 to A.D. 1450. Ethnographic material from the Indians of the Greater Southwest. Special programs: Annual Indian market in early December; how-to workshops taught by Native-Americans. Publications: Pueblo Grande Museum Anthropology Papers; museum brochures & catalogs. Library. Opened 1929.

SMOKI MUSEUM, INC.
147 N. Arizona Ave., P.O. Box 10224 • PRESCOTT, AZ 86304
  (928) 445-1230 Fax 777-0573; Website: www.smokimuseum.org
  E-mail: director@smokimuseum.org; Cindy Gresser, Executive Director
Description: Indian Museum featuring archaeological & ethnological artifacts of Southwest & Plains Indians; Kate T. Cory paintings & photographs; Edward S. Curtis prints; artifacts of the Tuzigoot, King & Fitzmaurice ruins. Activities: Annual Southwest Indian Arts Festival held the 2nd weekend in May. Library. Trading Post. Opened 1935 & Incorporated 1991.

TONTO NATIONAL MONUMENT
HC 02 Box 4602 • ROOSEVELT, AZ 85545
  (520) 467-2241 Fax 467-2225; Brad Traver, Superintendent
Description: Prehistoric Salado Cliff Dwellings in Sonoran Desert setting. Museum: Collection of prehistoric Salado artifacts--pottery, cloth, tools, etc. Special programs: Upper Cliff Dwelling tours on weekends from November thru April. Library.

GILA RIVER INDIAN CENTER & MUSEUM
P.O. Box 457 • SACATON, AZ 85247
  (520) 963-3981 Fax 315-3968; Jon Long, Director
Description: Contains a park with reconstructed Indian villages that depict more than 2,000 years of Native American life in the Gila River Basin. The Hohokum, Papago, & Apache cultures are represented. A museum and craft center adjoin the park. Opened 1970.

HOO-HOOGAM KI MUSEUM
Salt River Pima-Maricopa Tribal Museum & Cultural Center
10005 E. Osborn Rd. • SCOTTSDALE, AZ 85256
  (480) 850-8191 Fax 850-8961; Doreen Duncan, Director
Description: Displays Pima baskets, Maricopa red clay pottery, and other tribal artifacts. Opened 1987.

HOPI CULTURAL CENTER MUSEUM
P.O. Box 7 • SECOND MESA, AZ 86043
  (520) 734-6650; Anna Siles, Director

Description: Dedicated to the maintenance and preservation of Hopi traditions and to the presentation of aspects of these traditions to our non-Hopi visitors.

COCOPAH MUSEUM
County Rd. 15 & G Ave. • SOMERTON, AZ 85350
  (520) 627-1992 Fax 627-2280; Lisa Wanstall, Director
Library. Opened 1994.

HAVASUPAI TRIBAL MUSEUM
P.O. Box 10 • SUPAI, AZ 86435
  (520) 448-2731 Ext. 520; Matthew Putesoy, Director. Opened 1971.

EASTERN ARIZONA COLLEGE MUSEUM OF ANTHROPOLOGY
626 Church St. • THATCHER, AZ 85552
  (520) 428-1133; Betty Graham Lee, Director
Description: Displays artifacts from Mogollon, Anasazi & Hohokam material culture; ethno-graphics in Apache, Navajo and Hopi. Library.

NAVAJO NATIONAL MONUMENT
HC 71 Box 3 • TONALEA , AZ 86044-9704
  (928) 672-2366; Russ Bodnar, Supt.
Description: Exhibits materials of the Kayenta, Anasazi & Navajo cultures. Located on the site of three prehistoric Cliff Villages. Library. Arts & crafts for sale.

THE NED A. HATATCHLI CENTER MUSEUM
Dine College, P.O. Box 37 • TSAILE, AZ 86556
  (928) 724-3311 Fax 724-3349; Harry Walters, Director. Opened 1976.

THE ARIZONA STATE MUSEUM
Box 210026, University of Arizona • TUCSON, AZ 85721-0026
  (520) 621-6281 Fax 626-6761; Website: www.statemuseum.arizona.edu
  Hartman H. Lomawaima, Director
Description: Collections include artifacts related to the cultural history of the Greater Southwest. Prehistoric materials include Hohokam & Mogollon decorated ceramic bowls, human figurines of clay and stone, carved shell jewelry, and turquoise beads. Also maintains extensive collections of objects from contemporary Indian cultures of Arizona & Mexico. Historic tools, clothing, and other utensils help Indian & non-Indian scholars understand past lifestyles. Programs: "Documentary Relations of the Southwest," archival research project focusing on the history of Spanish contact with Native peoples of the Greater Southwest; annual Southwest Indian Art Fair in late February. Publications: Paths of Life," a companion piece to a new permanent exhibit and presents the origins, histories & contemporary lives of Native people of the Southwest; Archaeological series reports distributed by University of Arizona Press. Library. Opened 1893.

MISSION SAN XAVIER DEL BAC
1950 W. San Xavier Rd. • TUCSON, AZ 85746
  (520) 294-2624; Father Michael Dallmeier, Rector
Description: Historic building and site of the Spanish-Colonial Indian Mission of 1783. Library.

COCHISE VISITOR CENTER & MUSEUM
c/o Willcox Chamber of Commerce
1500 N. Circle I Rd. • WILLCOX, AZ 85643
  (520) 384-2272; Description: Collections include Apache Indian artifacts.

NAVAJO NATION MUSEUM
P.O. Box 9000 • WINDOW ROCK, AZ 86515
  (520) 871-6673 Fax 871-7886; Russell P. Hartman, Director/Curator
Description: Exhibits approximately 4,500 objects relating to the history and culture of the Navajo Indians and the prehistory and natural history of the Four-Corners area. Photo archive of about 35,000 negatives and prints, mostly from 1930-1960, relating to the Navajos. Special programs: Art exhibits/sales; Navajo information service; school and group tours. Publications. Opened 1961.

QUECHAN TRIBAL MUSEUM
P.O. Box 1899 • YUMA, AZ 85366
  (760) 572-0661 Fax 572-2102; Pauline P. Jose, Director
Description: Houses the Spanish Era, the Military, and the Quechan history. Artifacts. Special activities: Celebrates the yearly Yuma Crossing day commemorating the first crossing of the Colorado River from Arizona side to California. Opened 1969.

ARKANSAS

UNIVERSITY OF ARKANSAS MUSEUM
202 N. Garland • FAYETTEVILLE, AR 72701
  (479) 575-3466 Fax 575-8766; Website: www.uark.edu/museum
  Mary Suter, Curator of Collections

Description: Native Arkansas archaeology collections; exhibits Mimbres pottery, Plains Indian artifacts, ethnographic artifacts, and South American artifacts. Established in 1873.

HOT SPRINGS NATIONAL PARK
P.O. Box 1860 • HOT SPRINGS, AR 71901
Description: Interpretive programs about the life of the Caddo Indians and their predecessors and explains the use of the thermal springs by the Indians. Museum: Exhibits Indian artifacts. Publications: Indians of Tonico; The Valley of the Vapors.

MUSEUM OF SCIENCE AND HISTORY
MacArthur Park • LITTLE ROCK, AR 72202
Description: Exhibits include material relating to Arkansas Mound Builders, American Plains Indians, and Southwestern Indians. Library.

KA-DO--HA INDIAN VILLAGE
P.O. Box 669 • MURFREESBORO, AR 71958
(870) 285-3736; Sam Johnson, Director
E-mail: caddotc@alltel.net; Website: www.caddotc.com
Description: Prehistoric Caddo Indian (Mound Builders) grounds with museum housing artifacts from the excavation of the site. Publications for sale. Library.

TOLTEC MOUNDS ARCHAEOLOGICAL STATE PARK
490 Toltec Mounds Rd. • SCOTT, AR 72142
(501) 961-9442 Fax 961-9221; Randall Watts, Supt.
E-mail: toltecmounds@arkansas.com
Robin Gabe, Susan Nichols, Park Interpreters
Description: Situated in the modern farmlands of the Arkansas River Valley, 16 miles southeast of North Little Rock, off US Hwy. 165, are the remains of a large group of ancient Indian earthworks known as Toltec Mounds. Maintains a museum displaying a collection of prehistoric artifacts of the Plum Bayou Indian culture. Designated a National Historic Landmark in 1978, Toltec contained 16 mounds a century ago. Today, several mounds and a remnant of the embankment are visible. Activities: Archaeological research & interpretive programs; tours; workshops. *Publication*: "Toltec Mounds & Plum Bayou Culture: Mound D Excavations," Surveyors of the Ancient Mississippi Valley. Opened 1975.

ARKANSAS STATE UNIVERSITY MUSEUM
P.O. Box 490 • STATE UNIVERSITY, AR 72467
(870) 972-2074 Fax 972-2793; Charlott A. Jones, PhD, Director
E-Mail: squalls@choctaw.astate.edu
Description: Displays Native American artifacts including Arkansas--Quapaw, Caddo, Osage, Cherokee, Choctaw & Chickasaw; Southwestern -- Navajo, Hopi, Pueblo & Apache; & an exhibit of Indian baskets & Indian dolls. Newsletter. Library.

CALIFORNIA

GOUDI'NI NATIVE AMERICAN ARTS GALLERY
Humboldt State University, BSS Bldg. Room 133
ARCATA, CA 95521 (707) 826-5253

MALKI MUSEUM
11795 Fields Rd., Morongo Indian Reservation
P.O. Box 578 • BANNING, CA 92220
(951) 849-7289 Fax 849-3549; Susan Phillips, Director
Website: www.malkimuseum.org; E-mail: malkimuseummail@gmail.com
Dr. Katherine Siva Saubel, President/Founder
Nathalie Colin, Conservator/Ethno-historian
Description: Adobe museum building housing Southern California Indian artifacts of the Cahuilla, Serrano, Luiseno, and other tribal groups; large collection of Indian basketry. *Programs*: College scholarship program for Southern California Indian students; research on California Indians; Annual Malki Museum fiesta on Sunday of Labor Day weekend. *Publications*: Journal of California & Great Basin Anthropology, twice annually; brochures on the Cahuilla, Serrano, Chemehuevi and Chumash; Malki Museum Press publishes books on the California Indians. Library. Museum store. Opened 1964.

PHOEBE HEARST MUSEUM OF ANTHROPOLOGY
103 Kroeber Hall, University of California • BERKELEY, CA 94720
(510) 642-3682 Fax 642-6271; Mari Lyn Salvador, Director
E-mail: pahmu@montu.berkeley.edu
Website: www.hearstmuseum.berkeley.edu
Victoria Bradshaw, Head of Collections
Natasha Johnson, North American Collections
Anthony Garcia, Repatriation Coordinator; Bradley Marshall, Tribal Liaison
Description: Research & study collections include California archaeological and ethnographical items, majority of which are basketry items representing practically every tribe in California; also Eskimo & Aleut material, and Plains Indian artifacts; large collections of baskets and carvings from Northwest Coast

tribes, especially Haida, Tlingit & Tsimshean. Also an extensive collection of recorded materials. *Special programs*: Monthly lectures, demonstrations, and panel discussions. Library. *Publication*: Tribal Relations, newsletter. Museum store.

OWENS VALLEY PAIUTE-SHOSHONE INDIAN CULTURAL CENTER MUSEUM
P.O. Box 1281 • BISHOP, CA 93514
(619) 873-4478; Dorothy Stewart & Pat Howard, Directors. Opened 1986.

C.N. GORMAN MUSEUM
1316 Hart Hall - NAS, University of California
One Shields Ave. • DAVIS, CA 95616
(530) 752-6567 Fax 752-7097; Website: www.gormanmuseum.ucdavis.edu
E-mail: cngorman@ucdavis.edu
Hulleah Tsinhnahjinnie, Director; Veronica Passalcqua, Curator
Description: Maintains a permanent collection of California basketry, Navajo weavings, and contemporary American Indian art, and shows works by Indian & Chicano artists as well as staff & students. *Special program*: Changing exhibitions program - 4 each year with specific focus on American Indian issues. *Publications*: Artist monographs for each exhibition with artist interviews.

CABOT'S OLD INDIAN PUEBLO MUSEUM CALIFORNIA INDIAN MONUMENT
67-616 E. Desert View Ave. • DESERT HOT SPRINGS, CA 92240
(619) 329-7610 Fax 329-1956; Colbert H. Eyraud, President & Chief Curator
Description: A four story Hopi Indian style Pueblo built by Cabot Yerxa as a tribute to the Indian cultures; Peter Toth sculpture--monument 43' high, 20 tons from a Sequoia redwood; Pueblo Art Gallery. Exhibits: Inuit collection; and Sioux collection from the Battle of the Little Big Horn; Chumash & Pueblo culture collections. *Special programs*: Slide & lecture presentations to schools & organizations; sculpting for the handicapped; single artist exhibitions; arts interview radio show. *Publication*: Musings From the Pueblo. Trading Post. Library. Opened 1968.

HOOPA TRIBAL MUSEUM
P.O. Box 1348 • HOOPA, CA 95546
(530) 625-4110 Fax 625-1693; David E. Hostler, Curator
Description: A living museum which maintains a collection of baskets from the Hupa, Yurok and Karuk tribes; also jewelry, artifacts, and Indian dance regalia with feathers used in the dances. *Special programs*: Ceremonial displays, cultural shows and village tours. Publications: Museum brochures; Hoopa history books and pamphlets. Opened 1974.

EASTERN CALIFORNIA MUSEUM
155 N. Grant St., Box 206 • INDEPENDENCE, CA 93526
(760) 878-0258; William H. Michael, Director; E-mail: ecmuseum@qnet.com
Description: Collections of Inyo County Paiute, Shoshone, Washoe & Yokut Indian artifacts, including basketry, beadwork and lithics. Publication: Quarterly newsletter; book - Mountains to Desert: Selected Inyo Readings. Library. Opened 1928.

CABAZON CULTURAL MUSEUM
Cabazon Band of Mission Indians, 84-245 Indio Springs Dr. • INDIO, CA 92203
(619) 342-2593 Fax 347-7880
John James, Tribal Chairperson; Judy Stapp, Cultural Programs Manager
Description: Collections of historical and local exhibits; memorial to the genocide of Indian people in North and South America. Future exhibits will depict economic development of local tribes. *Programs*: Two annual powwows, Thanksgiving weekend and the last weekend in March. *Publication*: "The Cabazon Circle" tribal newsletter. Opened 1993.

END OF THE TRAIL MUSEUM/TREES OF MYSTERY
15500 Hwy. 101 N. • KLAMATH, CA 95548
(707) 482-2251 Fax 482-2005; Website: www.treesofmystery.net
John Thompson, General Manager (Trees of Mystery); Marylee Smith, Curator
Description: Private museum permanently exhibiting the collection of Marylee Smith (over 2,000 objects.) Five rooms of continent-wide Indian baskets, clothing, tools, kachinas, Navajo rugs, Northwest Coast carvings, pottery, masks. *Special collection*: extensive collection of baby baskets and cradles from entire North American Continent; extensive collection of original Edward Curtis photographs. Research library. Opened 1983.

BARONA CULTURAL CENTER & MUSEUM
1095 Barona Rd. • LAKESIDE, CA 92040
(619) 443-7003 ext. 2 Fax 443-0173; Cheryl M. Hinton, Director/Curator
Website: www.baronamuseum.org; E-mail: chinton@barona.org
John George, Collections Manager; Richard Rodriguez, Education Coordinator
Description: Maintains artifacts of southern California Indian tribes focusing on 'Iipay/Kumayaay prehistory; pottery, baskets, bone, shell & historic artifacts; current Indian art. *Special programs*: Barona senior events; NMAI workshops;

Ancient Spirits Speak classes; Southern California Indian Seminar for Educators; Outreach programs. Library. *Publications*: Quarterly newsletter; museum publication series. Opened 2001.

ANTELOPE VALLEY INDIAN MUSEUM
15701 East Ave. M • LANCASTER, CA 93534
  (661) 942-0662; Website: www.avim.parks.ca.gov

THE LOMPOC MUSEUM
200 South H St. • LOMPOC, CA 93436
  (805) 736-3888 Fax 736-2840
Website: www.lompocmuseum.org
Lisa A. Renken, PhD, Director, Curator of Anthropology
Angie Pasquini, Administrative Assistant
Description: Holds a large collection of archaeological & ethnographic specimens, mostly from northern Santa Barbara County. Other areas include northern California & Oregon. *Special Collection*: Clarence Ruth Collection: Chumash & Western Alaskan Indian artifacts. *Publication*: Galleries, bi-monthly newsletter. Research Library. Opened 1969.

AUTRY NATIONAL CENTER-MUSEUM OF THE AMERICAN WEST
4700 Western Heritage Way • LOS ANGELES, CA 90027
  (213) 667-2000 Fax 660-5721; Alicia Gonzalez, Director
John L. Gray, Executive Director/CEO
Description: Art, artifact & research collections relating to trans-Mississippi Western history & culture. *Programs*: Educational (children's workshops); docent tours, lectures, symposia. Research Center. *Publication*: "Spur" membership newsletter. Opened 1988.

AUTRY NATIONAL CENTER
SOUTHWEST MUSEUM OF THE AMERICAN INDIAN
234 Museum Dr. • LOS ANGELES, CA 90065
  (323) 221-2164 Fax 224-8223
Dr. Kathleen Whitaker, Chief Curator
Dr. Duane H. King, Executive Director
E-mail: dking@annex.com
Website: www.southwestmuseum.org
E-mail: dking@autrynationalcenter.org
Description: Collections focus on Native peoples of the Americas, mostly North America west of the Mississippi, including 13,400 baskets, 11,000 ceramics, 2,000 textiles, 700 kachinas, 800 pieces of Southwest jewelry; archaeological items, pertaining to the American Indian, Eskimo, & Aleut from prehistoric, historic & modern times; 150,000 photographs; archival materials; paintings, & prints. Special collections: Plains, California, Southwest, and Northwest Indians. *Special program*: Intertribal Marketplace (over 120 artisans) first weekend in November; Mercado! (Mexican and Central American marketplace) each Spring. *Publications*: The Masterkey, quarterly journal; "Common Threads: Navajo & Pueblo Textiles in the Southwest Museum" & "Southwest Textiles: Weavings of the Navajo and Pueblo." Braun Research Library. Museum shop. Opened 1907.

MARIPOSA MUSEUM & HISTORY CENTER, INC.
P.O. Box 606 • MARIPOSA, CA 95338
  (209) 966-2924; Muriel Powers, Curator
Description: Located on the museum grounds is an Indian Village and its bark houses and sweat house, constructed by local Indians. *Publication*: Quarterly newsletter. Library.

ONTEREY STATE HISTORICAL PARK
20 Custom House Plaza • MONTEREY, CA 93940
  (408) 649-2836; Mary Wright, Director; Kris Quist, Curator
Description: Holman Exhibit of American Indian Artifacts. Primarily California and Western North America basketry and weavings.

SIERRA MONO MUSEUM
P.O. Box 275 • NORTH FORK, CA 93643
  (209) 877-2115; Anna Dandy, Director
Description: Maintains a collection of baskets and artwork by the Mono Indian People. Other tribes are also represented with their baskets and beadwork.

MARIN MIWOK MUSEUM
2200 Novato Blvd. @ Miwok Park • NOVATO, CA 94948
  (415) 897-4064 Fax 892-7804
Website: www.marinindian.com; E-mail: office@marinindian.com
Colleen Hicks, Executive Director; Bradley Marshall, Board President
Description: Collections oriented to Native-American cultures of western North America, with particular emphasis on Indian cultures of California, especially local Coast Miwok people of Marin & southern Sonoma Counties. The Kettenhofen Collection of Edward Curtis Photogravures. Includes archival materials from Alaska. *Special program*: Educational classes, lectures, and instruction. *Publication*: Surface Scatter, quarterly newsletter. Library. Opened 1973.

THE OAKLAND MUSEUM
1000 Oak St. • OAKLAND, CA 94607 (510) 834-2413
Description: Exhibits present native Californians in pre-contact times.

WILL ROGERS STATE HISTORIC PARK
1501 Will Rogers State Park Rd. • PACIFIC PALISADES, CA 90272
  (310) 454-8212 Fax 459-2031; Nancy Mendez, Museum Curator
Description: Ranch belonged to the American humorist, Will Rogers (of Cherokee Indian descent), containing original buildings and furnishings; Indian artifacts, rugs & blankets. *Publication*: Monthly newsletter. Library. Opened 1944.

CUPA CULTURAL CENTER
P.O. Box 445 • PALA, CA 92059
  (760) 742-1590 Fax 742-4543; Leroy Miranda, Director
Description: Located on the Pala Indian Reservation in San Diego County, the Cultural Center maintains a museum exhibiting Cupeno artifacts and historic pictures; also other Native American artifacts; historical information about the removal of Cupa Indians. *Special programs*: Teaching of traditional dancing, songs & Cupeno language; annual event, "Cupa Days" in remembrance of the removal of Cupenos from Warners Hot Springs in 1903, is held the first weekend in May.

MUSEUM OF MISSION SAN ANTONIO DE PALA
P.O. Box 70 • PALA, CA 92059 (619) 742-3317
Description: Historic Mission Building (Pala Indians.) Exhibits Indian artifacts--basketry, stone carvings, pottery & jewelry. *Activities*: Dance festivals.

AGUA CALIENTE CULTURAL MUSEUM
901 E. Tahquitz Canyon Way, Suite C-204 • PALM SPRINGS, CA 92262
  (760) 778-1079 Fax 322-7724/0350; Website: www.accmuseum.org
E-mail: mail@accmuseum.org
Michael Hammond, PhD, Executive Director
  E-mail: mhammond@accmuseum.org
Dawn Wellman, Curator/Director of Programs
  E-mail: dwellman@accmuseum.org
Jackie Bagnall, Office Manager
  E-mail: jbagnall@accmuseum.org
Ursula Cripps, Lead Museum Interpreter
Description: 50-acre museum complex adjacent to the Indian Canyons includes a 98,000 sq. ft. museum building which includes galleries & cultural facilities for artifacts & archives; Education Center with classrooms & meeting rooms; Research Library; and 150-seat Theatre. *Location*: 219 S. Palm Canyon Dr. at the Village Green Heritage Center in downtown Palm Springs. *Programs*: Graves Protection & Repatriation (www.cahuillarepatriation.org). *Activities*: Camelot Theaters (760) 325-6565 - Annual Palm Springs Native American Film Festival (www.nativefilmfest.org), part of the annual cultural weekend in March. Opened 1991.

PALM SPRINGS DESERT MUSEUM
101 Museum Dr. • PALM SPRINGS, CA 92262
  (760) 325-7168 Fax 327-5069; Dr. Janice Lyle, Director
  E-Mail: psmuseum@aol.com
Description: Western American & Native American Art - These galleries will include selections from the Museum's permanent collection of traditional & contemporary artworks depicting the American West. A combination of paintings, sculpture and Native American objects will show the diversity of Western American art over the past 100 years. Opened 1938.

CHAW SE REGIONAL MUSEUM
P.O. Box 1458 • PINE GROVE, CA 95665 (209) 296-7488
Located at 144881 Pine Grove Volcano Rd. Opened 1978.

SAN BERNARDINO COUNTY MUSEUM
2024 Orange Tree Lane • REDLANDS, CA 92374
  (714) 798-8570; Dr. Allan Griesemer, Director
  Carol Rector, Curator of Anthropology
Description: Displays various artifacts & lithic tools of Indian occupation of San Bernardino County; history and artifacts of local bands--Serrano, Cahuilla, Mojave, Chemehuevi, and others are being preserved. *Publication*: Bi-monthly newsletter; quarterly journal. Library. Opened 1956.

SHERMAN INDIAN MUSEUM
9010 Magnolia Ave. • RIVERSIDE, CA 92503
  (909) 275-6719 Fax 276-6332; Lorene Sisquoc, Director
Opened 1970.

CALIFORNIA STATE INDIAN MUSEUM
2618 K St. • SACRAMENTO, CA 95816
  (916) 324-0971 Fax 322-5231; Joann Helmich, Lead Ranger
Website: www.gov.state.parks

Description: Collections pertain to the cultures of the Indians of California. Pomo feather baskets; artifacts from Ishi; north coast redwood dugout. Emphasis is on lifestyle, spiritual & the continuing culture. *Special programs*: Summer programs for the 4th-6th grades; sell books pertaining to California Indians & Indian handcrafted items. Opened 1940.

ANTHROPOLOGY MUSEUM

University of San Diego, 5998 Alcala Park • SAN DIEGO, CA 92110
(619) 260-4525 Fax 260-2260
Description: David W. May Indian Artifacts Collection consists primarily of about 1,650 prehistoric and contemporary objects from the American Southwest.

AMERICAN INDIAN CULTURE CENTER & MUSEUM

Inspiration Point, Balboa Park, 2135 Park Blvd. • SAN DIEGO, CA 92101
(619) 281-5964 Fax 281-1466; Richard Bugbee, Associate Director
E-mail: hunwut@aol.com; aiccm@aol.com
Purpose: To interpret the history & culture of American Indian people from ancient times to the present in order to foster public appreciation & understanding, to enhance the preservation, perpetuation, and study of American Indian history & culture, to develop and provide educational resources locally & nationally, and to encourage American Indian participation. Description: Features an Inter-tribal exhibit hall, the San Diego County Indians exhibit (Kanap Kwahan) that will focus on the maritime traditions of the Indians of San Diego County; a RezTV station that will be connected to the Tribal Digital Village; advocated for Indigenous California Language workstations; an Art Studio/Gallery where talented Native artists can develop, exhibit, and sell their art work; the Performance Arts Center, a 100-seat community performance, audio-visual, lecture, and presentation space; a Gift Shop; and Research Library. Opened 2002.

AMERICAN INDIAN HISTORICAL SOCIETY

1451 Masonic Ave. • SAN FRANCISCO, CA 94117
Jeanette Henry Costo, Director
Description: Maintains a library & museum of Indian Arts. In the process of establishing the Rupert Costo Hall of American Indians at the University of California.

SANTA BARBARA MUSEUM OF NATURAL HISTORY

2559 Puesta del Sol • SANTA BARBARA, CA 93105
(805) 682-4711 Fax 569-3170; John R. Johnson, Curator
Description: 60,000 archaeological specimens from Santa Barbara Channel region of California and 2,500 ethnographic objects from western North America. Includes Chumash linguistic records, Cahuilla Basketry, rock art drawings. Library with special emphasis on the Chumash Indians.

JESSE PETER MUSEUM

1501 Mendocino Ave. • SANTA ROSA, CA 95401
(707) 527-4479 Fax 524-1861; Website: www.santarosa.edu/museum
E-mail: museum@santarosa.edu
Benjamin F. Benson, Director/Curator; Christine Vasquez, Exhibit Specialist
Description: Collections of traditional Native-American art, including California basketry, Southwest pottery & basketry; Navajo textiles & jewelry; Plains, Plateau and Great Lakes beadwork; Eskimo & Arctic stone carvings and regalia; Living wall - photographic essay of Native Americans of today from several cultures; Pomo Roundhouse and baskets. Special program: Self-guided tours for elementary, secondary and college classes. *Publications*: Hopitu -- A Collection of Kachina Dolls of the Hopi Indians; Straw Into Gold (North American Basketry) by Foley Benson. Small reference library. Opened 1932.

STANFORD UNIVERSITY MUSEUM OF ART

Lomita Dr. • STANFORD, CA 94305
(415) 725-0462; Thomas K. Seligman, Director; Ruth W. Franklin, Curator
Description: Collection of Native American works, especially basketry of the Yurok, Karuk, and Hupa tribes of California; and a group of Haida argilites. *Publication*: Museum Journal, biennial.

THE HAGGIN MUSEUM

1201 N. Pershing Ave. • STOCKTON, CA 95203
(209) 462-4116; Tod Ruhstaller, Director; Barry J. Ward, Archivist
Description: Fine art & regional history collections, including significant displays on Native Americans of the area. Library. Publications. Opened 1931.

LAVA BEDS NATIONAL MONUMENT

P.O. Box 867 • TULELAKE, CA 96134
(916) 667-2282; Gary Hathaway, Curator
Description: Site of the Modoc Indian War (November 1872 to June 1873.) Museum: Modoc Indian artifacts; Indian rock art & pictographs on walls of caves.

GRACE HUDSON MUSEUM

431 S. Main St. • UKIAH, CA 95482
(707) 467-2836 Fax 467-2835
Website: www.gracehudsonmuseum.org; E-mail: gracehudson@pacific.net
Sherrie Smith-Ferri, Director; Marvin A. Schenck, Curator
Description: Collections consist of more than 30,000 inter-related objects, with significant holdings of Pomo Indian artifacts (particularly basketry) ethnographic field notes, unpublished manuscripts, historic photographs & the world's largest collection of Grace Hudson paintings. Newsletter. Museum store. Opened 1986.

YOSEMITE MUSEUM

P.O. Box 577 • YOSEMITE NATIONAL PARK, CA 95389
(209) 372-0282; David M. Forgang, Curator
Craig D. Bates, Curator of Ethnography
Description: Collection of over 4,000 Sierra Miwok, Mono Lake Paiute and other ethnographic materials; over 20,000 archaeological specimens. A reconstructed Miwok/Paiute village & museum exhibits depicts the traditional culture of the Miwok and Paiute people of the Yosemite region, from pre-contact times through present day. *Special Programs*: Conducts walks & lectures, classes; demonstrations of native crafts. *Publications*: Various, including "Tradition and Innovation: A Basket History of the Indians of the Yosemite - Mono Lake Area." Library. Opened 1915.

SISKIYOU COUNTY MUSEUM

910 S. Main St. • YREKA, CA 96097
(916) 842-3836 Fax 842-3166
E-mail: hismus@inreach.com; Michael Hendryx, Director
Description: Contains displays on Indians of Siskiyou County--, Karuk, Shasta, and Modoc. Maintains an extensive basket collection of the Karuk and Shasta tribes. Special programs: School program for 3rd graders; interpretive programs; field trips. Library. Publications: The Siskiyou Pioneer, 1947-1999; occasional paper series; technical leaflets - "Walking the Medicine Path," and "Plants & the People - Ethnobotany of the Karuk Tribe. Opened 1950.

COLORADO

LUTHER E. BEAN MUSEUM

Adams State College, Richardson Hall • ALAMOSA, CO 81102
(719) 589-7121 Fax 589-7522; Rosalie Martinez, Curator
Description: Exhibits Pueblo Indian cultural artifacts, primarily pottery; Navajo weavings. Programs: Monthly art shows showcasing local (San Luis Valley) artists - ranging from paintings, pottery and bronze sculptures. Opened 1984.

SAND CREEK MASSACRE MONUMENT

Hwy. 96 • CHIVINGTON, CO 81031
Description: A monument to the over 500 Cheyenne Indians who were massacred in November 1864 by the U.S. Army led by Major John Chivington.

THE TAYLOR MUSEUM FOR SOUTHWESTERN STUDIES

Colorado Springs Fine Arts Center
30 West Dale St. • COLORADO SPRINGS, CO 80903
(719) 634-5581 Fax 634-0570
Cathy L. Wright, Curator & Director
Description: Collections of Native-American arts of the Southwest, Great Plains, Great Basin, and California, including: Navajo textiles & jewelry, Pueblo textiles, baskets and pottery, kachinas, and jewelry. *Special collection*: John Frederick Huckel Collection of Navajo sandpainting reproductions. *Special exhibition*: "Mountain--Family--Spirit: The Arts and Culture of the Ute Indians," the first national exhibition featuring the arts and rich traditions of the Nuche - the Ute people of Colorado and eastern Utah, also identified as the Eastern Ute. The exhibition and accompanying catalog provide an overview of Ute history, culture and art from the prehistoric period through the historic period to the present day. With 140 historical artifacts and over 40 contemporary works including many rare examples of art from major museum & private collections, as well as numerous photographs, the exhibition interprets daily and spiritual aspets of Ute life. *Publications*: Navajo Sandpainting: The Huckel Collection; Arroyo Hondo: The Folk Art of a New Mexican Village; Pottery of the Pueblos of New Mexico, 1700-1940. Library.

CROW CANYON CENTER FOR SOUTHWESTERN ARCHAEOLOGY

23390 County Rd. K • CORTEZ, CO 81321
(303) 565-8975; Ian Thompson, Director
Research activities: Archaeological investigation, including excavation & cataloging of artifacts. Specializes in Anasazi Indian culture, excavates sites in the Four Corners area of the southwest U.S. Research expeditions open to the public.

COLORADO HISTORY MUSEUM

Colorado Historical Society, 1300 Broadway • DENVER, CO 80203
(303) 866-3682 Fax 866-5739; James E. Hartmann, President
Description: Extensive ethnological and photographic collections of Plains and Southwest Indians; source materials on the Indian Wars; earliest known Cheyenne Dog Soldier ledgerbook. Publications: "The Colorado History Journal"; "Colorado Heritage" magazine. Library. Opened 1879.

DENVER ART MUSEUM
100 W. 14th Ave. Pkwy. • DENVER, CO 80204
   (720) 865-5000 Fax 865-5028; Website: www.denverartmuseum.org
   Nancy Blomberg, Dept. Head/Curator of Native Arts
   E-mail: nblomberg@denverartmuseum.org
   Roger C. Echo-Hawk, Repatriation Coordinator
Description: Encyclopedic collection of American Indian art from all tribes across the U.S. and Canada from prehistoric times to the present; also, an ethnographic collection of Indian women's costumes, Navajo and Pueblo pottery, Hopi kachina dolls, Blackfoot ceremonial equipment, and wood carvings of the Northwest Coast. Special programs: Lectures; programs for childrem; annual Powwow; and classes. Publications: Membership newsletter; exhibition & collection catalogues. Library. Opened 1893.

DENVER MUSEUM OF NATURAL HISTORY
2001 Colorado Blvd. • DENVER, CO 80205
   (303) 370-6388 Fax 370-6313
   Dr. Robert B. Pickering, Chair/Curator of Anthropology
   Joyce I. Herold, Curator of Ethnology; Ryntha Johnson, Collections Manager
Description: Hall of Prehistoric People of the Americas: Exhibits on early man, and collections of Paleo-Indian specimens. Emphasis includes North American Indian archaeological & ethnographic material. Basketry from around the world. *Special collection*: Crane Collection of American Indian Materials. *Publications*: Proceedings of DMNH (scientific publications); exhibit catalogs; symposia volumes; children's books on natural history subjects. Library. Opened 1900.

ANASAZI HERITAGE CENTER
27501 Hwy. 184 • DOLORES, CO 81323
   (970) 882-4811 Fax 882-7035; LouAnn Jacobson, Director
Description: Preserved sites of two late Anasazi communities. Museum exhibits of Northern San Juan prehistory; 2.5 million artifacts and archives. Includes Anasazi farming, food preparation, crafts, and trade. *Activities*: "Hands-on activities: weaving, microscopes, computers. Videos. Traveling exhibits. Library. Opened 1988.

HISTORICAL MUSEUM & INSTITUTE OF WESTERN COLORADO
4th and Ute • GRAND JUNCTION, CO 81501
   (303) 242-0971
Special collections: Ute Indian Collection and Teller Indian School Collection: Basketry, artifacts, manuscripts and photographs of the Ute Indians. Library.

SOUTHERN UTE INDIAN CULTURAL CENTER & MUSEUM
P.O. Box 737 • IGNACIO, CO 81137
   (970) 563-9583 Fax 563-4641; Lynn Brittner, Director
   Website: www.succm.org; E-mail: info@succm.org
Description: Located on the Southern Ute Indian Reservation, 1/4 mile north of Sky Ute Casino on Highway 172. Maintains photo and artifact collections pertaining to Ute and neighboring tribes, historical to contemporary. *Activities*: It sponsors art festivals, Native American dance recitals, hobby workshops, and lectures. Gift Shop. Opened 1972.

KOSHARE INDIAN MUSEUM
P.O. Box 580, 115 W. 18th St. • LA JUNTA, CO 81050
   (719) 384-4411 Fax 384-8836; Website: www.kosharehistory.org
   Joe Clay, Director of Programs
Description: Maintains a collection of Native American art & artifacts emphasizing the Plains and Pueblo tribes. Artists range from Taos founders (Denton, Phillips, Couse, Sharp and others) to notables such as Woody Crumbo, T.E. Mails, Joseph Imhof, Bettina Steinke, and Ernesto Zepeda. Pottery by the Martinez and Nampeyo families are featured, as is baskets, beadwork and quillwork. *Special programs*: Koshare Indian Dancers present a variety of Plains & Pueblo dances biannually. Winter Ceremonials are held in December; Summer shows are held June thru August. *Publication*: Koshare News. Library. Trading Post. Indian arts and crafts for sale.

MANITOU CLIFF DWELLINGS MUSEUM
U.S. Hwy 24, Box 272 • MANITOU, CO 80829
   (719) 685-5242; *Description*: Depicts the lives and architectural achievements of the Indians of the Southwest during the Great Pueblo Period, 1100-1300 A.D.

MESA VERDE NATIONAL PARK MUSEUM
MESA VERDE NATIONAL PARK, CO 81330
   (970) 529-4465; Website: www.visitmesaverde.com
   Donald C. Fiero, Chief of Interpretation
Description: A prehistoric Pueblo Indian community -- pithouses, cliff dwellings, etc. Museum preserves Anasazi archaeological remains dating from 500-1330 A.D. *Activities*: Annual Indian Arts & Culture Festival held on Memorial Day weekend. Library.

UTE INDIAN MUSEUM - OURAY MEMORIAL PARK
17253 Chipeta Dr. • MONTROSE, CO 81402

   (970) 249-3098 Fax 252-8741; C.J. Brafford, Director
   E-mail: cj.brafford@state.co.us
Description: Indian History Museum located on the site of Chief Ouray's 400 acre farm. Depicts the history of the Utes through use of dioramas and objects which the Utes made and used; photographs and maps; portraits of some Ute leaders. *Activities*: Exhibits artifacts; maintains botanical gardens of plants used by the Native American Culture; hanging exhibit gallery; lectures; and American Indian Heritage Day, a cultural fair in November. *Publication*: Colorado History News. Library. Opened 1956.

UTE MOUNTAIN TRIBAL PARK & MUSEUM
P.O. Box 109 • TOWAOC, CO 81334
   (970) 565-9653 Fax 564-5317; Veronica Cuthair, Director
   E-mail: utepark@fone.net
Description: Collection contains Anasazi artifacts and rare Ute photographs. Special program: Tours of the Tribal Park. Publication: The Other Mesa Verde, by Gene Atkins, about the Tribal Park. Opened 1972.

CONNECTICUT

CONNECTICUT HISTORICAL SOCIETY MUSEUM
1 Elizabeth St. • HARTFORD, CT 06105
   (860) 236-5621 Fax 236-2664
   Website: www.chs.org; E-mail: research_center@chs.org
   Kate Steinway, Executive Director; E-mail: kate_steinway@chs.org
   Diane Lee, Collections Manager; E-mail: diane_lee@chs.org
Description: Collections of more than 100,000 artifacts, including Native American baskets, tools, and lithic materials. Special collection: Bates Collection of Native American baskets, tools, and implements. Library. Publications: Notes & News, newsletter; Bulletin, quarterly scholarly journal; numerous books relating to Connecticut. Opened in 1825.

MUSEUM OF CONNECTICUT HISTORY
Connecticut State Library, 231 Capitol Ave. • HARTFORD, CT 06115
Special collection: George Mitchelson Collection: Contains pottery, tools, arrowheads, & other artifacts of Native-American culture of Connecticut. Library.

MASHANTUCKET PEQUOT MUSEUM & RESEARCH CENTER
110 Pequot Trail, P.O. Box 3180 • MASHANTUCKET, CT 06338-3180
   (800) 411-9671; (860) 396-6814 Fax 396-6914
   Website: www.pequotmuseum.org; E-mail: reference@mptn.org
   Theresa Bell, Executive Director; E-mail: tbell@mptn-nsn.gov
   Trudie Lamb-Richmond, Director of Public Programs
    E-mail: trichmond@mptn-nsn.gov
   Kevin McBride, Director of Research (396-6814)
    E-mail: kmcbride@mptn-nsn.gov
   Kathleen Knowles, Acting Tribal Historic Preservation Officer
    E-mail: kknowles@mptn-nsn.gov
   Steve Cook, Head Curator (396-6813); E-mail: scook@mptn-nsn.gov
   Meredith Vasta, Collections Manager (396-6806)
    E-mail: mvasta@mptn-nsn.gov
Description: A 308,000 square-foot building located on the Mashantucket Pequot Reservation. It is open to the general public, but it also serves people conducting scholarly research on American Indians, particularly natives of the Eastern Woodlands. There are three main exhibits: the era up to European contact; the era of increasing aggression by the English, leading up to the Pequot Massacre of 1637; and what life at Mashantucket has been like in the 350 years since. *Exhibits*: Dioramas of paleo or prehistoric era up to European contact; Clash of Cultures; The Mashantucket Pequots Today; photos, sculptures & craft work, diaries and other documents, and tribal voices are all used to personalize the museum. *Facilities*: Maintains a recreated Pequot village of 350 years ago; the Research Center contains a research library, research laboratories; and herbarium; photo/technical rooms. The museum houses a 300-seat auditorium; gift shop; and cafe-style restaurant with full banquet and varied meeting facilities.

EELS-STOW HOUSE
Milford Historical Society, 34 High St., Box 337 • MILFORD, CT 06460
   (203) 874-2664; Virginia Hoagland, President
Special collection: Claude C. Coffin Indian Collection: Indian relics and artifacts primarily from the Milford-Stratford area of southern Connecticut. Library.

MOHEGAN MUSEUM
Mohegan Church • UNCASVILLE, CT 06382
   (800) MOHEGAN ext. 6144
   E-mail: museum@moheganmail.com
   Melissa Tantaquidgeon, Tribal Historian
Description: Mohegan Chief Occum (Lemuel Fielding), who led the Tribe from 1903 to 1928. His regalia is displayed along with significant artifacts relating to the church, which for 172 years has stood as a symbol of the Mohegan Tribe's survival.

TANTAQUIDGEON INDIAN MUSEUM
Rte. 32, 1819 Norwich-New London Rd.
UNCASVILLE, CT 06382 (860) 848-9145
  Harold Tantaquidgeon, Manager
Description: Built in 1931 by the late John Tantaquidgeon and his son, Harold, direct descendants of Uncas, Chief of the once powerful Mohegan Nation. Gladys Tantaquidgeon who was owner & curator for more than 70 years is now deceased. *Goal*: To preserve and perpetuate the history and traditions of the Mohegan and other Indian tribes; to display objects of stone, bone, and wood made by Mohegan and other New England Indian artists & craftsmen, past and present. Opened 1931.

THE INSITUTE FOR AMERICAN INDIAN STUDIES
38 Curtis Rd., Box 1260 • WASHINGTON, CT 06793
  (860) 868-0518 Fax 868-1649; Website: www.iais.org
  Elizabeth McCormick, Executive Director
Purpose: To discover, preserve, and interpret information about the lifeways of the first peoples of the Northeast Woodlands area of the U.S., and to enhance appreciation for their cultures & achievements. Focus is on the Algonkian peoples who make up the Northeast's many native groups. *Collections*: Ethngraphic - 6,000 cultural items focusing on Eastern Woodlands Peoples; Archaeological – 300,000 artifacts; Education & Research Library - 2,000+ books, journals & periodicals. *Activities*: Conducts archaeological surveys & excavations; provides indoor & outdoor exhibits; sponsors archaeological training sessions, teacher workshops, craft workshops, summer youth programs-educational programs to school groups. *Publications*: Artifacts, quarterly magazine; annual research report; bibliography & educational resource pamphlets. Annual events: Maple Sugaring Festival in March; Primitive Skills Day in late Spring; Green Corn Festival in August; Archaeological Roundtable in Autumn; Veterans Day in November; Storytelling in November; Indian market in December. Annual conference, with symposium. Museum. Gift shop. Established 1971.

DELAWARE

NANTICOKE INDIAN MUSEUM
Rt. 13, Box 170A • MILLSBORO, DE 19966
  (302) 945-7022; Pat Harmon, Joan Ridolfi, Docent
Description: Collection contains Native American artifacts - clothing, baskets, pottery, etc. Special programs for school groups. Annual Nanticoke Powwow. Library. Opened 1984.

DISTRICT OF COLUMBIA

NATIONAL MUSEUM OF NATURAL HISTORY
Department of Anthropology/National Museum of Man
MRC 112, Smithsonian Institution • WASHINGTON, DC 20560
  (202) 357-4760; JoAllyn Archambault, Director-American Indian Program
  R.H. Ives Goddard, III, Curator-Linguistics
  William C. Sturtevant, Curator-Ethnology
Description: Established in 1986 to serve as an outreach program to Native American reservations & communities; to make the Smithsonian more accessible to Indian people; and to encourage collection, research, exhibitions, and public programming by and about Indian peoples. Collection includes about 62,000 ethnological objects representing historic Indian groups from all parts of North America, and 250,000 archaeological specimens; film and video materials of Native Americans are part of the museum's Human Studies Film Archives and include historic film from the early 20th century, as well as more recent ethnographic footage. In the Department of Anthropology are eight curators with research specialties in North American Indian/Inuit ethnology, archaeology, linguistics, and ethno-history. Supervised internships and research fellowships are available through the Native American Awards Program. *Special activities*: Provides outreach and training to Native tribes, communities and individuals; Repatriation Office. *Publication*: Handbook of North American Indians, William C. Sturtevant, General Editor. Library of over 75,000 volumes.

SMITHSONIAN INSTITUTION
American Indian Museums Studies Program
Center for Museum Studies MRC 427
Arts & Industries Bldg., Room 2235 • WASHINGTON, DC 20560
  (202) 357-3101; Karen Cooper, Curriculum Program Manager
Description: Provides information services, educational opportunities, and access to resources to Native Americans working in museums.

U.S. DEPT. OF THE INTERIOR MUSEUM
1849 C St., NW, MS 1221-MIB • WASHINGTON, DC 20240
  (202) 208-4743 Fax 208-6950
  Debra Berke, Director; E-mail: dberke@ios.gov
  John Sherrod, Project Mgr.
Description: Exhibits include dioramas, scientific specimens, and paintings. A collection of Native American pottery, baskets, carvings, beadwork and other artifacts such as kachinas and weavings. *Special program*: Interview with an Interior staff person who is an American Indian and grew up on or near a reservation. Opened 1938.

FLORIDA

AH-THA-THI-KI MUSEUM
Big Cypress Seminole Reservation
HC 61, Box 21-A • CLEWISTON, FL 33440
  (863) 902-1113 Fax 902-1117; Website: www.seminoletribe.com/museum
  E-mail: museum@semtribe.com; Billy L. Cypress, Executive Director
  Peggy Davis Osceola, Development Specialist
  Tom Gallaher, Development Coordinator
Description: Ethnographic & historic (Seminole specific) collections. *Special programs*: Historical Reinactment, 1st weekend in February; Seminole Arts School, in October; Native Arts Celebration, in November. Library. *Publications*: Museum News, quarterly newsletter. Opened 1997.

LOWE ART MUSEUM
University of Miami, 1301 Stanford Dr.
CORAL GABLES, FL 33124-6310
  (305) 284-3535 Fax 284-2024; Website: www.lowemuseum.org
Description: The Native American Collection consists of more than 3,000 objects: the Alfred I. Barton Native American Collection includes blankets, Pueblo pottery, Plains Indian baskets, kachina dolls, jewelry, costumes & ceramics, largely of Southwestern origin. the Samuel K. Lothrop Guatemalan Textile Collection; and one of the largest collections of the art of ancient Mexico, Mesoamerica, and the Andes; in the Southeast U.S. of ceramic, stone, bone, metal, wood, and textile examples. *Special programs*: Group tours, art classes; annual outdoor arts festival is held on the grounds of Lowe each January. Publications. Library.

ST. LUCIE COUNTY HISTORICAL MUSEUM
414 Seaway Dr. • FORT PIERCE, FL 33450
Description: Features Seminole Indian pictures, artifacts and records from the Brighton Seminole Indian Reservation. Indian-made handicrafts are sold.

INDIAN TEMPLE MOUND MUSEUM
P.O. Box 4009, 139 Miracle Strip Pkwy.
FT. WALTON BEACH, FL 32549
  (850) 833-9595; Anna Peele, Director
Description: Exhibits prehistoric Indian artifacts found within a 40-mile radius of the museum are displayed interpreting 10,000 years of Gulf Coast living. The Temple Mound, a National Historic Landmark, is the largest Mississippian Temple Mound on the Gulf Coast. *Special programs*: Educational programs; guided tours. Publications: Indians of the Florida Panhandle; Pottery of the Fort Walton Period; The Buck Burial Mound. Library. Museum Shop.

JACKSONVILLE CHILDREN'S MUSEUM
1025 Gulf Life Dr. • JACKSONVILLE, FL 32207
Description: Displays artifacts of the Florida Indians of the past & present, including the Seminole and Miccosukee tribes. Research library.

HISTORICAL MUSEUM OF SOUTHERN FLORIDA
101 W. Flagler St. • MIAMI, FL 33130
  (305) 375-1492; Randy Nimnicht, Executive Director
Description: A depository of maps, manuscripts, and published materials of Southern Florida and the Caribbean. Permanent & temporary exhibitions, 28,600 artifacts, including Seminole & Miccosukee objects. *Programs*: Folklife programs, research, off-site programs for all ages; annual Harvest Festival. Publications. Library. Opened 1940.

MICCOSUKEE INDIAN MUSEUM
P.O. Box 40021, Tamiami Sta. • MIAMI, FL 33144
  (305) 223-8388 Fax 223-1011; Steven Tiger, Director
Founded in 1983, the Miccosukee Indian Museum offers visitors a glimpse into the Tribe's unique way of life. Among the many fascinating exhibits are photographs of tribal members from past generations and elaborate native attire worn by men and women. This is also where the Tribe proudly displays the government documents that gave them their sovereignty in 1962. Museum guests will appreciate the colorful native paintings and handcrafted sculptures as well as the special area, which highlights the relationship between the Miccosukee and the Mississippi Band of Choctaw Indians. Visitors will also admire the works of local artist Stephen Tiger and vibrant Everglades plant and animal displays. At the Miccosukee Museum, people partake in the historic beauty of: Tribal artifacts, Unique Miccosukee clothing, Native paintings, special cooking utensils, and rarely seen photographs & informative film.

SAN LUIS ARCHAEOLOGICAL & HISTORIC SITE
2020 W. Mission Rd. • TALAHASSEE, FL 32399
  (904) 487-3711/3655; Bonnie G. McEwan, Director

Description: An active dig that was on the site of a 17th century Apalachee Indian village and a Spanish mission. Maintains trails with interpretive displays describing the excavations and history of the site. The 50-acre outdoor museum offers exhibits across the site, a visitor center and a history shop. Collection consists primarily of archaeological remains from the Apalachee and Spanish residents of the mission community. *Publications*: Apalachee: The Land Between the Rivers, by John Hann; and The Spanish Missions of La Florida, edited by Bonnie McEwan (University Press of Florida). Opened 1983.

SOUTHEAST ARCHAEOLOGICAL CENTER
P.O. Box 2416 • TALLAHASSEE, FL 32316
 (904) 222-1167; Richard D. Faust, Chief

TALLAHASSEE JUNIOR MUSEUM, INC.
3945 Museum Dr. • TALLAHASSEE, FL 32304
Special collection: Gundrum Collection: Displays reproductions of pre-Columbian Florida Indian pottery and weapons; Apalachee Indian Farm (Reconstructed.)
Publication: Apalachee Indian Farm Guide.

GEORGIA

KOLOMOKI MOUNDS STATE HISTORIC PARK
Route 1, Box 114 • BLAKELY, GA 31723
 (229) 724-2150 Fax 724-2152
 Eric T. Bentley, Park Manager; E-mail: kolomoki@alltel.net
 Website: www.geocities.com/kolomokistatepark
Description: Historic site--13th-century Indian burial mound and village--artifacts from the excavations are on display. About 1,300 acres located six mile north of Blakely off Hwy. 27. Museum - exhibits artifacts and interprets the seven Indian mounds and Indian culture. Museum is built on top of an Indian mound. Special program: Kolomoki Festival, 2nd Sat. in October. *Publication*: Report of the Excavations at Kolomoki. Opened 1938.

NEW ECHOTA HISTORIC SITE
1211 Chatsworth Hwy. N.E. • CALHOUN, GA 30701
 (706) 624-1321 Fax 624-1323; David Gomez, Director
Description: A Preservation Project -- 1825 Capitol town of the Cherokee Nation. Museum and several historical buildings housing archaeological materials used by the Cherokees in the early 1800's. Research: Cherokee genealogy; Trail of Tears. Library. Opened 1961.

ETOWAH INDIAN MOUNDS HISTORIC SITE
813 Indian Mounds Rd., S.W. • CARTERSVILLE, GA 30120
 (404) 387-3747; Libby Forehand Bell, Manager
Description: A National Historic Landmark. Large Indian site with seven mounds surrounded by a moat partially filled. Materials recovered from the excavations are on display. The Etowah Indians occupied the Valley between A.D. 700 & 1650. Several thousand Indians lived in this fortified town. Opened 1953.

INDIAN SPRINGS STATE PARK MUSEUM
678 Lake Clark Rd. • FLOVILLA, GA 30216
 (770) 504-2277 Fax 504-2178; Don Coleman, Park Manager
Description: Traces the history of Indian Springs including items that reflect stages of Indian civilizations, treaties signed, Chief McIntosh's Assassination, Resort Era, and Civilian Conservation Corps; and exhibits Creek Indian artifacts. Research: Creek Indians in Georgia. *Special programs*: Assorted Native American arts & crafts; *Primitive Skills*: hunting techniques, pottery, basket making, pictographic writing, etc. Opened in 1825.

OCMULGEE NATIONAL MONUMENT
1207 Emery Highway • MACON, GA 31201
 (912) 752-8257; Mark Corey, Supt.
 Sylvia Flowers, Cultural Resource Specialist
 Sam Lawson, Park Ranger/Interpretive Specialist
Description: Site of seven mounds constructed by a group of farming Indians one thousand years ago. Located on the eastern edge of Macon, GA, along U.S. 80. An estimated 2,000 people lived here at one time. *Archaeology Museum*: Collections explain the culture of the Indians who constructed the area mounds, and of five other Indian groups that have inhabited the area since. Publications. Creek Indian Trading Post. Library. A National Historic Landmark. Opened 1936.

CHIEFTAINS MUSEUM
501 Riverside Pkwy., P.O. Box 373 • ROME, GA 30162
 (706) 291-9494 Fax 291-2410; Website: www.chieftainsmuseum.org
 Claudia M. Oakes, Executive Director
Description: History museum housed in a 1794 log cabin, and an 1820 plantation house belonging to Cherokee leader Major Ridge. Contains items from archaic Indian occupation to the present. Artifacts reflect life style of a rapidly changing Indian society; story of removal to the west. Maintains rotating art and history exhibits, local history. *Special programs*: Lecture series; educational programs. *Publication*: Quarterly membership newsletter. Library. Opened 1970.

THE CHIEF JOHN ROSS HOUSE
P.O. Box 863 • ROSSVILLE, GA 30741
 (706) 861-3954; Frances Jackson, President
Description: Historic house of 1797 with displays of artifacts Cherokee alphabet.

TAMA MUSEUM
Tama Tribal Town, 107 Long Pine Dr. • WHIGHAM, GA 31797
 (912) 762-3165 Fax 762-3165

IDAHO

IDAHO STATE HISTORICAL MUSEUM
610 N. Julia Davis Dr. • BOISE, ID 83702
 (208) 334-2120; Website: www.idahohistory.net
 Linda Morton-Keithley, Administrator
Description: A collection of prehistoric & historic artifacts of the Shoshone, Nez Perce, Northern Paiute, with general Plains Indian material represented; a large collection of Northwest Coast and Alaskan material collected in the early 1900's. Publications: Idaho Yesterdays, quarterly magazine; newsletter. Library.

SHOSHONE-BANNOCK TRIBAL MUSEUM
P.O. Box 793 • FORT HALL, ID 83203
 (208) 237-9791; Rosemary DaVinney, Director
 Website: www.shoshonebannocktribes.com
Description: Views prehistoric and contemporary lifestyles of the Shoshone-Bannock Tribes. Several exhibits display artifacts, photographs & contemporary fine art of tribal members. Special programs: Hosts a Spring and Fall Art Show for local artists; special tours to view tribes buffalo herd and a monument marking the original Fort Hall site in the "Bottoms" area (an important fish and wildlife habitat on the Snake River) of the Reservation. Library. *Publication*: Sho-Ban News, weekly newspaper. Opened 1985.

SACAJAWEA CENTER
200 Main St. • SALMON, ID 83467
 (208) 756-1222/1188; Angie Hurley, Director
 Website: www.sacajaweacenter.org; E-mail: info@sacajaweacenter.org
Description: Interpretive exhibits focus on Sacajawea, her role in the Lewis & Clark Expedition, and the Agaidika Shoshone perspective and the Indians of the Columbia Basin Plateau (stone, bone tools, tool making, physical culture); photo-essay of culture & lifestyle. *Special programs*: School of Discovery presents skills & techniques of the Expedition; Salmon Outdoor School; Photo-essay and slide show of Lewis & Clark Expedition; Meriweather Theater & Outdoor Amphitheater provides summer interpretive programs related to area Indians and the Lewis & Clark Expedition. *Publications*: Pacific Northwest Resources (resource book for area teachers). Research Library. Gift shop. Open from mid April to mid September. Opened 1940.

NEZ PERCE NATIONAL HISTORICAL PARK & MUSEUM
P.O. Box 93, Hwy. 95 • SPALDING, ID 83551
 (208) 843-2261; Website: www.nps.gov/nepe
 Franklin C. Walker, Supt.; Susan J. Buchel, Curator
Description: 24 sites that illustrate the history & culture of the Nez Perce Indians, and historic events which affected them. Museum houses exhibits of Nez Perce ethnological material; 4,000 photos of Nez Perce Indians. *Research*: Nez Perce Indians. *Publications*: Sapat'gayn: 20th-Century Nez Perce Artists, 72 page book; Nez Perce Country - 220 page book. Library.

HERRETT CENTER FOR ARTS & SCIENCE
College of Southern Idaho
315 Falls Ave., P.O. Box 1238 • TWIN FALLS, ID 83303
 (208) 732-6655 Fax 736-4712; Website: www.csi.edu/herrett
 E-mail: herrett@csi.edu; James C. Woods, Director
Description: Maintains collections on American Indians, archaeology & ethnology.

IDAHO HERITAGE MUSEUM
2390 Hwy. 93 S. • TWIN FALLS, ID 83303
 (208) 655-4444; *Description*: Maintains collections of Indian artifacts.

ILLINOIS

SCHINGOETHE CENTER FOR NATIVE AMERICAN CULTURES
347 S. Gladstone, Dunham Hall, Aurora University • AURORA, IL 60506
 (630) 844-5402 Fax 844-8884; Dr. Michael Sawdey, Director
 E-Mail: msawdey@admin.aurora.edu
Description: Contemporary Native American art & ethnographic materials, including beadwork, pottery, clothing, textiles, basketry, some prehistoric stone tools. Special collections: Southwestern pottery & kachinas. *Special program*: Annual Native American Festival & Powwow in May. *Publication*: Spreading Wings, member newsletter. Library. Opened 1990.

FIELD MUSEUM OF NATURAL HISTORY
Roosevelt Rd. at Lake Shore Dr. • CHICAGO, IL 60605
(312) 922-9410; Dr. William Boyd, President
Dr. Bennett Bronson, Chairman-Anthropology
Description: Seven exhibit halls devoted to the American Indian. Collections cover prehistoric and living Indians and Eskimos from Alaska to Cape Horn. *Publications*: Field Museum Bulletin; catalogs, handbooks, leaflets. Library. Opened 1893.

CAHOKIA MOUNDS STATE HISTORIC SITE
INTERPRETIVE CENTER MUSEUM
30 Ramey St. • COLLINSVILLE, IL 62234
(618) 346-5160 Fax 346-5162; Dr. Mark Esarey, Site Manager
E-mail: cahokiamounds@ezl.com; Website: www.cahokiamounds.com
Description: Contains over 30 exhibits, including life size village diorama, 7 exhibit islands with graphics, artifacts, dioramas & videos which interpret the archaeology & the Mississippian culture and their accomplishments at Cahokia, the largest prehistoric site north of Mexico with over 100 mounds. Woodhenge reconstruction. *Special programs*: Orientation show; Rediscover Cahokia festival; storytelling; slide/tape presentations; guided tours; Native-American craft classes; lecture series. *Publications*: Cahokia: City of the Sun; Journey to Cahokia; Cahokian, newsletter. *Video*: "Cahokia Mounds: Ancient Metropolis". Museum shop. Library. A National Historic Landmark. Opened 1989.

MADISON COUNTY HISTORICAL MUSEUM
715 N. Main St. • EDWARDSVILLE, IL 62025
(618) 656-7562; Anna Symanski, Director
Special collection: John R. Sutter and Raymond P. Smith Collections--Contains more than 3,000 American Indian artifacts of local and south central Illinois, as well as some from Southwest tribes. Library. Publication: Museum newsletter.

SCHOOL OF NATIONS MUSEUM
Principia College • ELSAH, IL 62028
(618) 374-2131 ext. 5236; Dan Hanna, Director; E-mail: drh@prin.edu
Description: Maintains a collection of American Indian crafts--baskets, clothing, dolls, pottery, textiles, etc. Library.

MITCHELL MUSEUM OF THE AMERICAN INDIAN
2600 Central Park Ave. • EVANSTON, IL 60201
(847) 475-1030 Fax 475-0911; Website: www.mitchellmuseum.org
Janice B. Klein, Director; E-mail: jklein@kendall.edu
Description: 10,000 objects relating to the art, history & culture of the Native peoples of North America, from Paleo-Indian period through the present day. Special programs: Workshops, lectures, demonstrations, performances, kids craft mornings, book club. Library. Opened 1977.

DICKSON MOUNDS MUSEUM
LEWISTON, IL 61542 (309) 547-3721 Fax 547-3189
Judith A. Franke, Director
Description: Exhibits archaeological material from west central Illinois, Mississippian and Middle Woodland sites on grounds -- Paleo-Indian to Mississippian cultures.

HAUBERG INDIAN MUSEUM
Black Hawk State Park, 1510 46th Ave. • ROCK ISLAND, IL 61201
(309) 788-9536 Fax 788-9865
Website: www.blackhawkpark.org/hauberg.htm
Elizabeth A. Carvey, Director; Neil Rangen, Supt.
Description: Located on the site of the main villages of the Sauk and Fox Indian Nations. Contains artifacts on permanent display are of Sauk and Mesquakie origin; also other Eastern Woodland artifacts; includes many articles of Plains origin; large basket collection of the Northwest, West and Southwest; four dioramas depicting the daily life of the Sauk and Mesquakie about 1800. *Publication*: Two Nations, One Land: A Cultural Summation of the Sauk and Mesquakie in Illinois.

TRICKSTER GALLERY
190 S. Roselle Rd. • SCHAUMBURG, IL 60193
(847) 301-2090; Website: www.trickstergallery.com
E-mail: trickstergallery@aic-chicago.org
Description: Established to support the Arts Department of the American Indian Center of Chicago. The Gallery is the only Native American owned & operated arts institution in the State of Illinois and is dedicated to providing space for fist-voice arts. The Gallery features Native art (post 1960s) and augments exhibits with film screenings, featured speakers, panel discussions, school tours & educator workshops. A Native arts institution dedicated to meeting the needs of artists by providing a vehicle for artistic expression in all disciplines and at all levels by taking a role in the cultivation, exhibition, and dissemination of contemporary Indigenous American art. *Purpose*: To address the state of Native America today while sharing thoughts of terminology for the sake of projecting positive images beyond romantic iconography. Gift Shop. Established 2005.

ILLINOIS STATE MUSEUM
Corner of Spring & Edwards Sts. • SPRINGFIELD, IL 62706
(217) 785-0037 Fax 785-2857; Website: www.museum.state.il.us
E-Mail: anthro@museum.state.il.us; Dr. R. Bruce McMillan, Director
Description: Collections of Midwestern archaeology; prehistory & history; North American ethnographic materials especially western basketry, southwestern pottery & textiles. *Special programs*: Dickson Mounds Museum, Lewiston, IL skeletal collection; field trips, archaeology lecture series. *Publications*: Reports of Investigations; Scientific Papers; Research Series; Dickson Mounds Anthropological Studies; The Living Museum. Library. Opened 1877.

MUSEUM OF NATURAL HISTORY
University of Illinois • URBANA, IL 61801
Description: Maintains prehistoric and historic exhibits of Indians of North America, with emphasis on the prehistory of Illinois, the Navajo & Pueblo Indians, and the Eskimo of Greenland.

STARVED ROCK STATE PARK
P.O. Box 509 • UTICA, IL 61373
(815) 667-4726 Fax 667-5353; Jon Blume, Complex Supt.
Description: Located on the site of former Indian village of Illinois Indians, later occupied by Ottawa and Potawatomi Indians, 1673-1760.

INDIANA

INDIANA UNIVERSITY MUSEUM
Student Bldg. • BLOOMINGTON, IN 47401
Description: Exhibits approximately 100,000 archaeological & ethnological specimens on American Indians from many areas of the New World. *Special collection*: Wanamaker Collection of American Indian Photographs, taken by Joseph Dixon--includes about 15,000 items. Library.

MATHERS MUSEUM OF WORLD CULTURES
601 East Eighth St. • BLOOMINGTON, IN 47408-3812
(812) 855-6873 Fax 855-0205; Geoffrey W. Conrad, Director
Website: www.indiana.edu/~mathers; E-mail: mathers@indiana.edu
Description: Contains more than 24,000 ethnographic artifacts from all over the world, including over 3,000 from indigenous cultures of North, Central and South America. *Special collection*: Wanamaker Collection of American Indian Photographs - features over 7,500 images (primarily portraits) of American Indians taken between 1908 and 1922 under the direction of photographer, Dr. Joseph Dixon, including about 400 images of American Indians veterans of World War I. Opened 1963.

ANGEL MOUNDS STATE HISTORIC SITE
8215 Pollack Ave. • EVANSVILLE, IN 47715
(812) 853-3956; Rebecca Means Harris, Director
Kate Jones, Curator
Description: A 103-acre prehistoric Mississippian Indian archaeological site. Ten mounds, 1250-1450, inhabiting 1000 people; reconstructed structures: portion of a stockade house, and the temple. *Special programs*: Monthly lecture series on archaeology and nature; Native American Days Festival, annual in August. Publication: Smoke Signals, quarterly newsletter; Ancient Treasure of the Americas: A Pre-Columbian Exhibition, exhibit catalogue. Library. Opened 1939.

THE POTAWATOMI MUSEUM
P.O. Box 631 • FREMONT, IN 46737
Description: Exhibits over 5,000 material cultural items of prehistoric and historic periods. Library.

CHILDREN'S MUSEUM OF INDIANAPOLIS
3010 N. Meridian St. • INDIANAPOLIS, IN 46208
Description: Collections consist of over 2,000 objects representing the tribes of Woodlands, Southeast, Plains, Plateau, Southwest, Northwest Coast, California & Canadian Indians. *Publication*: Newsletter. Library.

EITELJORG MUSEUM OF AMERICAN INDIANS & WESTERN ART
500 W. Washington St. • INDIANAPOLIS, IN 46204
(317) 636-9378 Fax 264-1724; Website: www.eiteljorg.org
John Vanausdall, President & CEO
Tamara Winfrey Harris, Director of Communications & Marketing
E-mail: tharris@eiteljorg.com
James Nottage, Jennifer Complo McNutt, Ray Gonyea,
& Dr. Suzan Campbell, Curators
Description: The American Western collection spans the early 19th century to the present and includes paintings, drawings, graphics, and sculpture - works by members of the original Taos art colony, such as Joseph Henry Sharp, E.I. Couse, Ernest Blumenschein, and Victor Higgins, as well as Western American artists, including Albert Bierstadt, Frederic Remington, Charles Russell, and Georgia O'Keeffe; the Native American collection consists of art & artifacts from throughout North America, & includes pottery, basketry, woodcarvings, and

clothing. Facilities: The new Nina Mason Pulliam Education Center provides experiential programming in visual & performing arts studios & outdoor spaces. In its Stephen & Sharon Zimmerman Resource Center visitors have access to materials from the Watanabe Family Library, the museum's education collection, and the archive of print, film, video, and digitized resources created for past & continuing exhibitions. *Special programs*: Conducts research on Native American culture; lectures, film series, workshops, & craft demonstrations; special programs for school children; Annual Indian Market (June); Artists-in-Residence; Buckaroo Bash (October). Small library. *Publication*: Eiteljorg Museum quarterly newsletter; exhibition catalogues. Museum Shop. Opened 1989.

FULTON COUNTY HISTORICAL SOCIETY MUSEUM
37 E. 375 N. • ROCHESTER, IN 46975
   (574) 223-4436; E-mail: fchs@rtcol.com; Website: icss.net/~fchs
Indian Awareness Center. Potawatomi Trail of Death, Chief White Eagle & Ervin Stuntz Indian artifact collections. Historic Encampments at Trail of Courage Living History Festival: French & Indian War, Plains Indians, Woodland Indians - Miami & Potawatomi life ways; Chippewa Village - 3rd weekend of September. Reference library. Admission: Adults, $5; ages 6-12, $2.

NORTHERN INDIANA HISTORICAL SOCIETY MUSEUM
808 W. Washington St. • SOUTH BEND, IN 46601
Description: Exhibits on prehistoric Indians, the Mound Builders in Indiana; an historic Indian exhibit on the lifestyle of the Potawatomis & Miamis of northern Indiana. *Publication*: The Old Courthouse News, quarterly magazine.

SONOTABAC PREHISTORIC INDIAN MOUND & MUSEUM
P.O. Box 941 • VINCENNES, IN 47591
   (812) 885-4330/7679; John A. Ward, President
Description: Indian Museum and Historic Site located at the foot of the largest Ceremonial Mound in Indiana, containing exhibits covering 10,000 B.C. to the present. *Publication*: Monthly newsletter.

IOWA

UNIVERSITY OF NORTHERN IOWA MUSEUM
31st and Hudson Rd. • CEDAR FALLS, IA 50613
Description: Maintains a collection of approximately 8,000 Indian artifacts.

PUTNAM MUSEUM OF HISTORY & NATURAL SCIENCE
1717 W. 12th St. • DAVENPORT, IA 52804
   (563) 324-1054 Fax 324-6638; Christopher J. Reich, Director/CEO
   Website: www.putnam.org; E-mail: museum@putnam.org
Description: Maintains collections of prehistoric Indian artifacts from Mounds in central Mississippi River Valley; Southwestern basketry & pottery; and ethnological items from various tribes, primarily from the upper Great Lakes region and Plains. Special programs: Presents a variety of programs for schools and the general public based on its collections and exhibits. Library. Opened 1867.

STATE HISTORICAL SOCIETY OF IOWA MUSEUM
600 E. Locust • DES MOINES, IA 50319
   (515) 281-4221 Fax 242-6498; Website: www.iowahistory.org
   E-mail: jerome.thompson@dca.state.ia.us
   Jerome Thompson, Museum Bureau Chief
Description: Displays Indian beadwork; historic & prehistoric artifacts, photos, and relative written material. *Publications*: The Annals of Iowa, quarterly scholarly journal; Iowa Heritage Illustrated. Library. Opened 1892.

MISSISSIPPI RIVER MUSEUM
400 E. 3rd St., Box 266 • DUBUQUE, IA 52004
   (319) 557-9545; Jerome A. Enzler, Director
Description: History of the Mississippi River from prehistoric times to present. Collections include Indian-made circa 1860 dugout canoe, two birchbarks made in Chippewa tradition, several prehistoric stone artifacts from the Upper Mississippi, and historic trade material from Euro-American contact period - Winnebago, Mesquakie, Crow, and Cheyenne. The museum houses a small collection of baskets and pottery (Zuni & Navajo). *Publications*: Museum monographs. Library. Opened 1964.

EFFIGY MOUNDS NATIONAL MONUMENT
151 Hwy. 76 • HARPERS FERRY, IA 52146
   (563) 873-3491 Fax 873-3743; Phyllis Ewing, Supt.
   Website: www.nps.gov/efmo
   E-mail: efmo_superintendent@nps.gov
Description: A 2,500-acre park with visitor center, the collection contains archaeological and archival material from 500 BC to the present. Preserves 206 prehistoric Woodland Indian burial mounds with an archaeological museum exhibiting artifacts excavated from the mounds area. *Special programs*: Bird walks, moonlight hikes, American Indian Heritage celebration, Chautauquas, Hawk Watch. Library. Opened 1949.

SIOUX CITY PUBLIC MUSEUM
2901 Jackson St. • SIOUX CITY, IA 51104
Description: Exhibits artifacts of the Plains & Eastern Woodlands Indians. Library.

KANSAS

KAW INDIAN MISSION, ALLEGAWAHO HERITAGE MEMORIAL PARK
THE KANZA MONUMENT - KAW MISSION STATE HISTORIC SITE
500 N. Mission • COUNCIL GROVE, KS 66846
   (620) 767-5410; Website: www.kshs.org
   E-mail: kawmission@kshs.org; Ron Parks, Director
Description: Mission school opened by the Methodist Episcopal Church in 1851 for the Kaw (Kansa) Indians. An historic house & museum featuring Kaw Indian relics. *Special program*: Wah Shun Gah Days, summer.

SHAWNEE INDIAN MISSION
Kansas State Historic Site, 3403 W. 53rd • FAIRWAY, KS 66205
   (913) 262-0867; Website: www.kshs.org
   E-mail: shawneemission@kshs.org; Anita Faddis, Site Administrator
Description: A 12-acre site, re-creation of Indian Manual Labor School attended by Shawnee, Delaware & other Indian nations from 1839-1862. The Shawnee Mission served as an early territorial capitol, supply point on the Santa Fe & Oregon Trails and a camp for Union soldiers during the Civil War. *Special program*: Workshops; slide show of the history of the Mission.

FORT HAYS STATE HISTORIC SITE
Kansas State Historic Site, 1472 U.S. Hwy. 183 Alt. • HAYS, KS 67601
   (785) 625-6812; E-mail: thefort@kshs.org

NATIVE AMERICAN HERITAGE MUSEUM
1737 Elgin Rd. • HIGHLAND, KS 66035
   (785) 442-3304; Website: www.kshs.org; E-mail: nahm@kshs.org
   Mark A. Hunt, Director; Andrew Clements, Curator
Description: Once a Presbyterian Mission, a three story stone house serving as a mission to the Iowa, and Sac and Fox Indians, built in 1845 on the Oregon-California Trail to educate Iowa & Sac & Fox children. Includes collections of quillwork, baskets & other artwork of present-day descendants of Great Lakes Indians were forced to emigrate to Kansas in the 1800s, adapting their traditional woodlands cultures to the rolling prairies of Kansas. Interactive exhibits of Native Americans telling stories in their own words. Displays Iowa, and Sac and Fox Indian artifacts.

MUSEUM OF ANTHROPOLOGY
University of Kansas • LAWRENCE, KS 66045
   (913) 864-4245; Alfred E. Johnson, Ph.D., Director
   Anta Montet-White, Doct., Curator; Robert J. Smith, Ph.D., Curator
Description: Maintains a collection of over 100,000 prehistoric American Indian artifacts, mainly from the Midwestern U.S.; about 4,000 North American Indian ethnographic items from the Plains, Southwest, and Northwest Coast; and an extensive skeletal collection. Special collection: Contemporary American Indian art displayed in the Lawrence, Kansas Indian Art Show. *Publication*: Quarterly newsletter. Library. Opened 1979.

CORONADO-QUIVIRA MUSEUM
221 E Ave. South • LYONS, KS 67554
   (316) 257-3941; Clyde Ernst, Director/Curator
Description: Exhibits Coronado and Quivira Indian artifacts, and Papago Indian baskets, pre-1934.

RILEY COUNTY HISTORICAL SOCIETY & MUSEUM
2309 Claflin Rd. • MANHATTAN, KS 66502
   (913) 565-6490; D. Cheryl Collins, Director
Special collection: The Walter Collection--900+ Indian relics and artifacts of northeast Kansas and southwest Nebraska, especially arrowheads and stone tools. Publication: Newsletter. Library. Opened 1914.

LAST INDIAN RAID MUSEUM
258 S. Penn Ave. • OBERLIN, KS 67749
   (913) 475-2712; Fonda Farr, Director
Description: Historical museum located near the sites of the 1878 Last Indian Raid on Kansas soil with the Northern Cheyenne Indians. One room dedicated to the Native American artifacts and the story of the Last Indian Raid. Publication: Quarterly newsletter. Opened 1958.

OLD DEPOT MUSEUM
135 W. Tecumseh • OTTAWA, KS 66067
   (913) 242-1232; Deborah Barker, Director
Special collection: Indians of Franklin County, and Early Indian Clothing. Displays scrolls of membership in the Chippewa Tribe, and maps locating tribal

lands. Maintains archives that contain over 10,000 photographs, vertical files and original documents from city, county and various institutions. Opened 1963.

PAWNEE INDIAN VILLAGE MUSEUM
Kansas Historical Society, 480 Pawnee Trail • REPUBLIC, KS 66964
(785) 361-2255 Fax 272-8682; Website: www.kshs.org
E-mail: piv@kshs.org; Richard Gould, Director
Description: Archaeology museum located on the best preserved 1820s Pawnee earth lodge site on the Plains. The museum enclosed the excavated floor of one of the largest displays describe Pawnee life on the Great Plains. *Special program*: Lectures, video series, and living history programming; Pawnee Indian dancers and singers. Brochure. Library. Opened 1901.

THE SAC & FOX TRIBAL MUSEUM
Sac & Fox Nation of Missouri, Rt. 1, Box 60 • RESERVE, KS 66434
(913) 742-7471 Fax 742-3785
Opened 1996.

EL QUARTELEJO KIVA INDIAN MUSEUM
c/o News Chronicle Printing Co., Inc.
P.O. Box 218 • SCOTT CITY, KS 67871
Description: Displays Cheyenne and Pueblo artifacts, especially Taos; Indian War material.

KANSAS MUSEUM OF HISTORY
Kansas State Historical Society
6425 SW 6th St. • TOPEKA, KS 66615-1099
(785) 272-8681 Fax 272-8683
E-mail: information@kshs.org; Website: www.kshs.org
Mark A. Hunt, Director; Diane Good, Curator
Description: Collection features Indian relics--tools, utensils and clothing of Kansas Indian tribes. Library. Opened 1876.

MID-AMERICA ALL-INDIAN CENTER MUSEUM
650 N. Seneca • WICHITA, KS 67203
(316) 262-5221 Fax 262-4216
E-mail: icm@southwind.net; Deborah Roseke, Director
Description: Located on the site of old Indian Council grounds. Maintains collections of Native American art and artifacts. Research: Native-American life, art, & religion. Publication: Gallery Notes, quarterly newsletter. Library. Opened 1975.

KENTUCKY

MUSEUM OF ANTHROPOLOGY
Northern Kentucky University
200 Landrum Academic Center • HIGHLAND HEIGHTS, KY 41099
(606) 572-5259; James F. Hopgood, Director
Description: Collections focus on contemporary Native American arts of the Southeast and Southwest U.S. Library.

WILLIAM S. WEBB MUSEUM OF ANTHROPOLOGY
University of Kentucky, 211 Lafferty Hall • LEXINGTON, KY 40506-0024
(859) 257-8208 Fax 323-1968
Website: www.uky.edu/as/anthropology.museum/museum.htm
Dr. George M. Crothers, Director; E-Mail: gmcrot2@uky.edu
Description: Exhibits document 12,000 years of human history in Kentucky including Native American, African American, & European American archaeological material as well as cultural & biological anthropology. *Special program*: Tours for groups. Research library maintains archaeological reports & records of projects conducted in the state. Opened 1931.

SPEED ART MUSEUM
2035 S. Third St. • LOUISVILLE, KY 40208
(502) 634-2700 Fax 636-2899; Ruth Cloudman, Curator
Description: Maintains ethnological & archaeological exhibits illustrating Indian life of 19th and early 20th century Plains groups. *Special collection*: The Charles & Charlotte Price Gallery for Native American Art consists primarily of works from the Plains region. Objects from many tribes including Dakota or Sioux, the Cheyenne, the Arapaho, the Kiowa, and the Crow are represented. Frederick Weygold Collection--Work in flint, stone & bone from prehistoric Kentucky & southern Indiana. Publication: Quarterly Program Guide; J.B. Speed Art Museum Handbook. Library. Opened 1927.

WICKLIFFE MOUNDS STATE HISTORIC SITE
P.O. Box 155, 94 Green St. • WICKLIFFE, KY 42087
(270) 335-3681 Fax 335-5486; Carla Hildebrand, Park Manager
E-mail: wmounds@brtc.net; Website: www.parks.ky.gov
Description: Operated by Kentucky Department of Parks, the park is based on the archaeological site of the Mississippi period, dated ca. A.D. 1100-1350. The museum displays artifacts from the excavations of the Mound Builders. *Special programs*: Educational; special events. Opened 1932.

LOUISIANA

LOUISIANA ARTS & SCIENCE CENTER
100 S. River Rd. • BATON ROUGE, LA 70801
Description: Exhibits Eskimo soapstone carvings, artifacts and lithographs; North American Indian crafts, contemporary pottery and weaving.

LAFAYETTE NATURAL HISTORY MUSEUM
637 Girard Park Dr. • LAFAYETTE, LA 70503
Special collection: Contemporary Baskets of Chitimacha and Koasati Indians of Louisiana--Baskets & weaving of the Acadian culture and Louisiana Indian cultures. Publications. Library.

TUNICA-BILOXI REGIONAL INDIAN CENTER & MUSEUM
P.O. Box 331 • MARKSVILLE, LA 71351 (318) 253-8174 Fax 253-7711
Bill Day, Director; E-mail: bill_day@tunica.org
Opened 1989.

MAINE

ABBE MUSEUM
P.O. Box 286, 26 Mt. Desert St. • BAR HARBOR, ME 04609
(207) 288-3519 Fax 288-8979; E-mail: abbe@midmaine.com
Website: www.abbemuseum.org; Diane R. Kopec, Director
Rebecca Cole-Will, Curator
Description: Displays archaeological, ethnographic and contemporary art collections; Native-American prehistoric and ethnographic materials with emphasis on Maine & the Maritime provinces. Includes baskets, woodcarvings, and artifacts. Also, quillwork, and birchbark of Passamaquoddy Penobscot, Micmac and Malicite artists ca. 1800 - contemporary. *Special collection*: Mary C. Wheelwright Collections of ethnographic northeastern baskets of ash, birchbark and quill; archival photos & documents. Special programs: Workshops, demonstrations, & children's programs throughout the summer. School programs year around. Lecture series for specific exhibits. Publications: Bulletin series on Native American arts & crafts and archaeological research. Library. Open mid-May to mid-October. Opened 1923.

THE PEARY-MacMILLAN ARCTIC MUSEUM
Bowdoin College, 9500 College Sta. • BRUNSWICK, ME 04011
(207) 725-3416; Dr. Susan A. Kaplan, Director
Dr. Genevieve LeMoine, Curator
Description: An exhibition of Peary & MacMillan Arctic explorations -- Labrador, Baffin & Greenland Inuit and Indian cultures; photographic archives. Collections include historic artifacts, photographs and Inuit art, clothing and equipment. Special programs: Lecture series; tours. *Publication*: Occasional exhibit catalogs; posters. Library.

WILSON MUSEUM
P.O. Box 196 • CASTINE, ME 04421
(207) 326-8753; E.W. Doudiet, Director
Patricia L. Hutchins, Curator
Description: North American and some South American Indian stone artifacts, pottery and baskets, most obtained between 1880 and 1920. *Publications*: Triannual newsletter; pamphlets and book on local history. Open May 27th thru September 30th, 2-5 PM, except Monday. Established 1921.

NOWETAH'S AMERICAN INDIAN MUSEUM
2 Colegrove Rd. • NEW PORTLAND, ME 04961-3821
(207) 628-4981; Website: www.mainemuseums.org
Nowetah Wirick, Owner/Curator
Description: Displays American Indian art & crafts focusing on the Abenaki of Maine, including over 400 old Maine Indian baskets and bark containers. Special program: Educational programs, visits & classes available for schools & scout groups. Library. *Publications*: Illustrated booklets on past Indian life including, "The History of Indian Wampum," "Brain Tanning Hides," "How to Weave an Indian Rug," "The Abenaki Indian 1724 Massacre at Narrantsauak (Maine)," "Indian Legends, Recipes, & Names," "The Ancient Wisdom & Knowledge of the Abenaki Indians." Gift Store. Opened 1969.

PENOBSCOT NATION MUSEUM
12 Down St. • INDIAN ISLAND, ME 04468
(207) 827-4153; James E. Neptune, Director
Website: www.penobscotnation.org/museum/index.htm
E-mail: info@penobscotculture.com

WAPONAHKI MUSEUM & RESOURCE CENTER
Pleasant Point Passamaquoddy Tribe, P.O. Box 295 • PERRY, ME 04667
(207) 853-4001 Fax 853-6039; Joseph A. Nicholas, Director
Description: A collection of artifacts of the Passamaquoddy Indians. Opened 1987.

MARYLAND

PISCATAWAY INDIAN MUSEUM
16816 Country Ln. • WALDORF, MD 20616
(240) 432-7878; E-mail: info@piscatawayindians.org
Website: www.piscatawayindians.org/museum
Description: Serves as an educational institution to preserve the history of the Piscataway Tribe as well as the cultural & natural history of early American times. *Resources*: Piscataway Trading Post & Gift Shop. Opened 1993.

MASSACHUSETTS

ROBERT S. PEABODY MUSEUM OF ARCHAEOLOGY
Phillips Academy • ANDOVER, MA 01810
(978) 749-4490 Fax 749-4495
Malinda S. Blustain, Director
E-mail: rspeabody@andover.edu
Website: www.andover.edu/~rspeabody/
Description: One of the nation's major repositories of Native American archaeological collections, representing nearly every culture area in North America. Collections are especially strong in the Northeast, Southeast, Midwest, Southwest, Mexico, and the Arctic, in many areas from Paleo-Indian (11,500 years ago) to European contact. Material includes stone & bone tools, pottery, and carved shell & copper artifacts. Ethnographic collection, from the last 150 years, includes baskets, textiles, and other objects. *Special collections*: Kidder collection from Pecos Pueblo; pre-contact Southeastern ceramics; West Coast baskets (19th century); Tehuacan Valley collection; artifacts of the Northeast. *Special programs*: Outreach; hosts meetings, special classes, and visiting speakers. Research library - 5,000 volumes and a large collection of historical photographs. Publications. Opened 1901.

CHILDREN'S MUSEUM
Museum Wharf, 300 Congress St. • BOSTON, MA 02210
(617) 426-6500; Lou Casagrande, Director
Joan Lester, Native American Collection Consultant
Description: Collection includes Penobscot, Passamaquoddy, Iroquois, Chippewa, Wampanoag and Narragansett materials from both past & present traditions. Special exhibit: We're Still Here--American Indians in New England Long Ago and Today. Programs: Workshops/courses. Museum Shop. Library. Museum open daily 10 am - 5 pm.

PEABODY MUSEUM OF ARCHAEOLOGY & ETHNOLOGY
Harvard University, 11 Divinity Ave. • CAMBRIDGE, MA 02138
(617) 496-1027 Fax 495-7535; Website: www.peabody.harvard.edu
William L. Fash, Director
Description: Contains large collections of archaeological & ethnographic materials of global scope, but primarily North America and Central America. Also, substantial ethnographic & archaeological photo archives. *Special exhibits*: "Change & Continuity," considers how native peoples across the continent responded to the arrival of Europeans. "Encounters with the Americas," explores native cultures of Mesoamerica before and after Spanish contact. "Painted by a Distant Hand: Mimbres Pottery of the American Southwest" examines the development & artistry of the Peabody's extensive and rare collection of prehistoric painted pottery. "From Nation to Nation Examining Lewis and Clark's Indian Collection" illustrates the role of Native Americans in Lewis & Clark's journey and displays the only surviving Native American objects brought back by Lewis & Clark. *Publication*: "Symbols," newsletter; scientific papers and memoirs. Library. Opened 1866.

INDIAN HOUSE MEMORIAL
Box 121, Main St. • DEERFIELD, MA 01342
(413) 772-0845; John Abercrombie, President
Description: Collections include Native American artifacts, decorative arts, pottery, weaving, and looms.

LONGHOUSE MUSEUM
Hassanamisco Reservation • GRAFTON, MA 01519
Description: Memorial to the Eastern Native-American: Artifacts of the Nipmuc Tribe (central Massachusetts); beadwork, utensils, baskets, paintings & rugs. Publications. Library.

FRUITLANDS MUSEUMS
102 Prospect Hill Rd. • HARVARD, MA 01451
(978) 456-3924 Fax 456-8078
Michael Volmar, Curator
Description: Indian museum collection focus on New England and Plains ethnographic materials, Southwestern pottery and basketry, California & Northwest Coast baskets & Eastern Woodlands. Exhibits: Dioramas of local Indian scenes and specimens of historic Indian arts and industries. *Special programs*: Educational programs; tours for school groups. Library. Opened 1928.

WISTARIAHURST MUSEUM
238 Cabot St. • HOLYOKE, MA 01040
(413) 534-2216 Fax 534-2344; Sandra Christofordis, Director
Description: Maintains a collection of Native American art & artifacts, including Iroquois masks & rattles; pottery of the Southeast & Southwest; basketry of the Southwest, Plains & Northwest Coast; Iroquois & Plains Indian beadwork. Programs: Craft workshops for children. Library.

MASHPEE WAMPANOAG TRIBAL MUSEUM
P.O. Box 1048 • MASHPEE, MA 02649
(508) 477-0208 Fax 477-1218
Website: www.mashpeewampanoagtribe.com/museum.htm
Description: Mashpee Wampanoag art & artifacts.
Annual Mashpee Wampanoag Powwow in July.

PLIMOTH PLANTATION
Wampanoag Indian Program
P.O. Box 1620 • PLYMOUTH, MA 02360
(508) 746-1622 ext. 8385 Fax 645-6026; Website: www.plimoth.org
Nancy Brennan, Executive Director, Plimoth Plantation
Linda Coombs, Associate Director, Indian Program
E-mail: lcoombs@plimoth.org
Description: An outdoor living history museum which displays Native American artifacts from the colonial period, and recreates the life and times of a Wampanoag family which lived at Plymouth in the 1620's. Researches & depicts original 17th-century indigenous Wampanoag history & culture. *Activities*: "Strawberry Thanksgiving" special event 4th Saturday in June; staff demonstrations & discussions. *Publication*: "Almanack" membership newsletter. "Visible Images - Invisible People: Four Centuries of Wampanoag History" - conference series-proceedings. Library. Established 1947; Wampanoag Indian Program established 1972.

MICHIGAN

MUSEUM OF ANTHROPOLOGY
University of Michigan • ANN ARBOR, MI 48109-1079
(734) 764-0485 Fax 763-7783; Dr. Robert Whallon, Director
Description: Contains extensive holdings in North American archaeology & ethnography. Special collections: Hinsdale Collection--Great Lakes Basketry; Greenland Eskimo Collection; Seri & Tarahumara Indian Collection. *Publications*: Papers, memoirs, and technical reports. Library.

CRANBROOK INSTITUTE OF SCIENCE
1221 N. Woodward, P.O. Box 801
BLOOMFIELD HILLS, MI 48303-0801
(810) 645-3200 Fax 645-3034; Gretchen Young-Weiner, Director
Description: Exhibits cover all major culture areas of North America, especially Woodlands & Plains. *Activities*: School group program. Publications: Bimonthly newsletter & brochure; bulletin series; annual report. Selective government depository. Library. Opened 1930.

CULTURAL HERITAGE CENTER
Bay Mills Community College
12214 W. Lakeshore Dr. • BRIMLEY, MI 497715
(906) 248-5645 Fax 248-3351; Roger J. Pilon, Director. Opened 1989.

CHILDREN'S MUSEUM
Detroit Public Schools, 67 East Kirby • DETROIT, MI 48202
Special collection: American Indian Collection--basketry, costumes, crafts, dolls, textiles, musical instruments, tools and weapons for various cultural areas of American Indians. Reference Library.

DETROIT INSTITUTE OF THE ARTS
5200 Woodward Ave. • DETROIT, MI 48221
(313) 833-7900 Fax 883-3756; Dr. David Penney, Contact
Special collection: The Chandler-Pohrt Collection - 19th-century Native American objects from tribes of the North American woodlands, prairies, and plains. It is notable for being focused on the artistic quality of Indian material at a time when it was not considered art. Items include clothing, pipes, drums, shields, drawings, etc. *Publications*: Monthly DIA magazine; exhibition & permanent collection catalogues. Library. Opened 1885.

MUSEUM OF ANTHROPOLOGY
Wayne State University, 6001 Cass Ave. • DETROIT, MI 48202
(313) 577-2598/3056; Tamara Bray, PhD, Director
Description: A collection of American Indian artifacts. Research Library.

MICHIGAN STATE UNIVERSITY MUSEUM
Div. of Anthropology • EAST LANSING, MI 48824
(517) 355-2370 Fax 432-2846
William A. Lovis, Curator of Anthropology

Charles E. Cleland, PhD, Curator-Great Lakes Arch. & Ethnology
Special collection: Indians of the Great Lakes--Contains 30 displays relating to the history, technology, religion, and social organization of the Indians of the Great Lakes area.

PUBLIC MUSEUM OF GRAND RAPIDS
272 Pearl St. NW • GRAND RAPIDS, MI 49504
 (616) 456-3977 Fax 456-3873; E-Mail: info@grmuseum.org
 Dale Robertson, President & CEO
 Marilyn Merdzinski, Collections; Tom Bantle, Exhibits
Description: Exhibits Hopewell archaeological material and artifacts from the Historic Site--Norton Indian Mounds (Hopewell.) They manage the Norton Mounds site, the only National Historic Landmark in Michigan devoted solely to Native American culture *Special collection*: Maintains a large permanent exhibit on Native people of West Michigan, "Anishinabek: The People of This Place." Publication: Beads: Their Use by Upper Great Lakes Indians (1977); newsletter & magazine.

FORT DE BUADE MUSEUM, INC.
5123 W. St. Joseph Hwy. #104 • LANSING, MI 48917-4028
 (906) 643-8686; Donald E. Benson, Director
Description: Indian Museum located on the site of 1681, Fort de Buade, built by the French. Displays artifacts, beadwork, photos, lithos, and oils of Woodland Indians.

MICHIGAN HISTORICAL MUSEUM
Michigan History Div.-Dept. of State
505 N. Washington Ave. • LANSING, MI 48918
Description: Maintains Indian exhibits related to the history of Michigan and the old Northwest Territory.

MACKINAC ISLAND STATE PARK MUSEUM
P.O. Box 370 • MACKINAC ISLAND, MI 49757
 (906) 847-3328 Fax 847-3815
Description: Features Indian material from the upper Great Lakes; Chippewa Indian costumes. Publications. Library.

TEYSEN'S WOODLAND INDIAN MUSEUM
P.O. Box 399, 415 W. Huron Ave. • MACKINAW CITY, MI 49701
 (616) 436-7011; Kenneth Teysen, CEO
Description: Collections include Indian artifacts from the Great Lakes area, including tools, weapons, clothes, food, and trade items.

MANISTEE COUNTY HISTORICAL MUSEUM
425 River St. • MANISTEE, MI 49660 (616) 723-5531
Description: Collection of artifacts on local Native Americans.

MARQUETTE COUNTY HISTORICAL SOCIETY MUSEUM
213 N. Front St. • MARQUETTE, MI 49855
 (906) 226-3571 Frances Porter, Executive Director
Description: Displays Indian archaeological & historical material of the upper peninsula of Michigan, with main focus on the Chippewa. Dioramas depicting a Chippewa family group. Includes baskets, beadwork, medicine bags, calumets, moccasins, canoes. Publications: Indians of Gitche Gumee; Harlow's Wooden Man, quarterly magazine; books for sale. Library. Established 1918.

MENOMINEE COUNTY HISTORICAL MUSEUM
P.O. Box 151 • MENOMINEE, MI 49858 (906) 863-9000
Description: Collection of artifacts on local Native Americans.

CENTER FOR CULTURAL & NATURAL HISTORY
Bellows St., 102 Rowe Hall • MT. PLEASANT, MI 48859
 (517) 774-3829 Fax 774-3542
Description: Collection of artifacts on local Native Americans.

ZIIBIIWING CENTER OF ANISHINABE CULTURE & LIFEWAYS
6650 E. Broadway • MT. PLEASANT, MI 48858
 (800) 225-8172; (989) 775-4750 Fax 775-4770
Description: Maintains permanent, educational, sacred & ceremonial collections of the Saginaw Chippewa Indian Tribe (SCIT). *Exhibit*: "Diba Jimooyung: Telling Our Story" includes century old artifacts & contemporary objects; baskets, pottery, dolls, tools & weapons, beadwork and personal artifacts.

FORT ST. JOSEPH MUSEUM
508 East Main St. • NILES, MI 49120
 (269) 683-4702 Fax 684-3930; Website: www.ci.niles.mi.us
 Carol Bainbridge, Director
Special collections: Collection of Lakota Indian artifacts; 12 drawings by Sitting Bull; large pictograph tapestry by Rain-in-the-Face; Potawatomi and early Native American objects (projectile points, stone tools). Established 1932.

NOKOMIS LEARNING CENTER
5153 Marsh Rd. • OKEMOS, MI 48864
 (517) 349-5777 Fax 349-8560; Website: www.nokomis.org
 Ted Moore, President
Description: A Native American cultural learning center located near Lansing, MI, dedicated to the preservation and presentation of Anishinaabeg (Ojibwa, Odawa & Potawatomi) arts, culture and history. Opened 1988.

EYAAWING MUSEUM & CULTURAL CENTER
Grand Traverse Band of Ottawa & Chippewa Indians
2304 N. West Bayshore Dr. • PESHAWBESTOWN, MI 49682
 (231) 534-7764 Fax 534-7568; E-mail: museum@gtbindians.com
Mission: To preserve the history, language, and culture of the Grand Traverse Band. Odaawa Gamik - The Museum Store.

CROOKED TREE ARTS COUNCIL
461 E. Mitchell St. • PETOSKEY, MI 49770
 (616) 347-4337 Fax 347-3429; Sean Ley, Director
Description: Maintains a fine arts collection with emphasis on Indians of the Great Lakes area. *Research*: Art of Ojibway, Odawa, and Nishnawbe Indians.

FATHER MARQUETTE NATIONAL MEMORIAL & MUSEUM
Father Marquette State Park, 720 Church St. • ST. IGNACE, MI 49781
 (906) 643-8620
Description: Displays artifacts, including an Indian longhouse & canoe, and maintains exhibits of early French and Indian cultures.

MUSEUM OF OJIBWA CULTURE
500 N. State St. • ST. IGNACE, MI 49781
 (906) 643-9161 Fax 643-9380
 Website: www.stignace.com/attractions/ojibwa/
 Molly M. Perry, Director
Description: Displays artifacts & reproductions relating to Ojibwa culture. Portrays a vivid picture of Straits of Mackinac life over 300 years ago when Ojibwa, Huron, Odawa, and French lifestyles met at this protected bay. *Special programs*: Native American Art Festival, 3rd weekend in August; Powwow on Labor Day weekend; traditional arts & crafts workshops; educational programs, and archaeological digs. Opened 1987.

LUCKHARD'S MUSEUM-THE INDIAN MISSION
612 E. Bay St. • SEBEWAING, MI 48759 (517) 883-2539
Description: Using 17th century archaeological items, the museum interprets the Ojibwa who lived in the area prior to contact, and the Huron & Ojibwa refugees who came. The French fur trader and Jesuits and their impact on Native culture. Exhibits Indian artifacts & pioneer relics of the 19th-century, housed in original Indian mission of the Chippewa Indians (1845.) *Special program*: A video presentation on the Ojibwa family - the importance of every member, the interdependence. *Publications*: "The Story of Wafted Across," and "Southern Feather's Story," by Margaret Peacock, short stories about an Ojibwa family (fiction).

SEBEWAING INDIAN MUSEUM
612 E. Bay St. • SEBEWAING, MI 48759
 (517) 883-3730; Jim Bunke, CEO
Description: An 1849 mission home, with collections of Native American canoes, arrowheads, and headress.

THE DENNOS MUSEUM CENTER
Northwestern Michigan College
1701 E. Front St. • TRAVERSE CITY, MI 49686
 (231) 995-1055; Website: www.dennosmuseum.org
 E-mail: dmc@nmc.edu; Eugene Jenneman, Executive Director
 Diana Bolander, Curator of Education
Description: Collection of Native American artwork that includes Ottawa baskets, Alaskan Inuit dolls, and Hopi Kachina Dolls.

INDIAN DRUM LODGE MUSEUM
Mail: 2308 North U.S. 31, Camp Greilick
4754 Scout Camp Rd. • TRAVERSE CITY, MI 49684
 Martin A. Melkild, Curator
Description: Indian Museum housed in 1850, Chief Peter Ringnose's log cabin, maintaining ceremonial artifacts, clothing, and wood crafts. Museum store.

MINNESOTA

FOND DU LAC CULTURAL CENTER & MUSEUM
Fond du Lac Band of Lake Superior Chippewa Indians
1720 Big Lake Rd. • CLOQUET, MN 55720 (218) 878-7582
Description: Located on the Fond du Lac Indian Reservation, the center houses Ojibwe arts & crafts including: birch bark baskets, feather masks, rice baskets,

tall birch bark baskets, modern sculpture & wigwam model; also, other artifacts from the Native peoples that inhabited the lakes area of Minnesota for thousands of years. Open to the public, Monday-Friday.

GRAND PORTAGE NATIONAL MONUMENT
170 Mile Creek Rd., P.O. Box 426 • GRAND PORTAGE, MN 55605
(218) 475-0123 Fax 475-0174; Website: www.nps.gove/grpo

GRAND MOUND HISTORY CENTER
6749 Hwy. 11 • INTERNATIONAL FALLS, MN 56649
(218) 279-3332; Michael K. Budak, Director
Description: A prehistoric Native American mounds & habitation area exhibiting ceramics, lithics, and bone tools from the site. Programs: Monthly programs Jan.-Aug. on regional American Indian history and culture, archaeology, and natural environment. Publication: "Grand Mound". Library. Opened 1976.

TWO RIVERS GALLERY
Minneapolis American Indian Center
1530 E. Franklin Ave. • MINNEAPOLIS, MN 55404
(612) 879-1780 Fax 879-1795; Website: www.maicnet.org
J. Espinoa, Director; E-mail: jespinosa@maicnet.org
Description: More than 100 oil paintings by various American Indian artists. Ongoing visual arts exhibitions of both contemporary and more traditional art forms. Programs: School tours; special lectures. Publication: The Dragonfly, biannual newsletter.

THE ROURKE ART MUSEUM
521 Main Ave. • MOOREHEAD, MN 56560
(218) 236-8861; James O'Rourke, Director
Description: Permanent collections include both historic & contemporary Native American art as well as Inuit and Pre-Columbian art of Mexico. Temporary exhibitions of Native American art and Eskimo sculpture. Publications: Catalogs for special exhibitors. Museum Shop. Opened 1960.

LOWER SIOUX AGENCY HISTORIC SITE
32469 County Hwy. 2 • MORTON, MN 56270
(507) 697-6321; Mary C. Talbot, Acting Site Manager
Description: 260 acre site of beginning of U.S.-Dakota War of 1862. Site includes History Center and new exhibits and interactive activities telling the story of the Eastern Dakota people from white contact to just after the U.S.-Dakota war. Special programs: Focus on various aspects of Native and Euro-American history and culture, during the summer season. Also, new walking trails with interpretive signage. Publications: Minnesota Historical Society publications and others pertaining to Dakota and Plains Indians history; also books and sales items of Indian culture. Library. Museum Store. Opened 1972.

MILLE LACS INDIAN MUSEUM
Mille Lacs Indian Reservation • ONAMIA, MN 56359
(320) 532-3632 Fax 532-4625; Joyce Shingobe-Wedll, Director
Description: This trading post & museum portrays Ojibwa culture. Houses the Jeanette & Harry Ayer large collection of Ojibwa arts & crafts; exhibits include life-size dioramas showing typical scenes of Ojibwe life for each season; elders talk about the Anishinabeg's past, and demonstrations of traditional activities. Operated by the Minnesota Historical Society. Opened 1964.

PIPESTONE COUNTY MUSEUM
113 S. Hiawatha • PIPESTONE, MN 56164
(507) 825-2563
Website: www.pipestone.mn.us/museum/homepa~1.htm
Dave Rambow, Director; Joe Ager, Curator
Description: Contains artifacts from the Dakota and Ojibwa Tribes--Plains Indian saddle, ceremonial pipes. Library. Publication: Quarterly journal. Opened 1880.

PIPESTONE NATIONAL MONUMENT
UPPER MIDWEST INDIAN CULTURE CENTER
Pipestone National Monument, P.O. Box 727 • PIPESTONE, MN 56164
(888) 209-0418 Fax (507) 825-2903
Website: www.authenticpipestone.com
Maddie Redwing, Director (507) 825-5463
Vincent J. Halvorson, Supt. (507) 825-5464
Description: Original pipestone (catlinite, named for noted painter of Indians, George Catlin) quarry from which the Dakota Sioux fashioned their ceremonial pipes. Local History Museum exhibits Indian ceremonial pipes and pipestone objects; pipestone quarries. Special program: Cultural demonstration programs-April thru October,-pipe carving, beadwork, quillwork, etc. Publications: Pipes on the Plains, Pipestone: A History; and Circle Trail booklet. Library. Opened 1955.

MINNESOTA HISTORICAL SOCIETY MUSEUM
345 Kellogg Blvd. W. • ST. PAUL, MN 55102
(651) 259-3000/3100 Fax 296-1004; Website: www.mnhs.org
Nina M. Archabal, Director; Michael Fox, Deputy Director-Programs
Jennifer Jones, Head of Collections; E-mail: jennifer.jones@mnhs.org
Marcia Anderson, American Indian Collections
Travis Zimmerman, Program Coordinator, Indian Advisory Committee
Description: Exhibits depicting prehistoric & contemporary Indian life in Minnesota. Major collecting areas include Dakota & Ojibwa material; Jeanette & Harry Ayer donated their large collection of Ojibwa arts & crafts to the Society in 1959. The collection is currently housed at the Mille Lacs Indian Museum & Trading Post and are accessible through the Society's library catalog; photo collection. Maintains Grand Mound History Center. Publication: Minnesota History, quarterly magazine; Historic Sites Travel Guide brochure; publications from the Minnesota Historical Society Press. Library.

MINNESOTA MUSEUM OF ART
75 W. Fifth St. • ST. PAUL, MN 55102
(651) 292-4355; Katherine Van Tassell, Curator
Description: American art 1850 to the present. Small collection of Native American artifacts (half Southwestern, half Northwest Coast). Special programs: Occasional shows of Native American artists. Publications: Newsletter; occasional catalogs. Opened 1927.

SCIENCE MUSEUM OF MINNESOTA
120 W. Kellogg St. • ST. PAUL, MN 5102
(651) 221-9424 Fax 221-4525
E-mail: oshane@smm.org; Website: www.smm.org
Orrin C. Shane, III, Curator; Faith G. Bad Bear, Asst. Curator
Description: Large collection on the North American Indian. Library.

WALKER WILDLIFE & INDIAN ARTIFACTS MUSEUM
St. Hwy. 200, Box 336 • WALKER, MN 56484
(218) 547-1257; Renee Geving, Manager
Description: Collections include Ojibway & Chippewa Indian handicraft and artifacts from 1892-1962.

WINNEBAGO AREA MUSEUM
WINNEBAGO, MN 56098
(506) 893-3692; Marion Muir, President
Description: An archaeological museum exhibiting Oneonta (900-1500 A.D.) artifacts, Woodland (1000-8000 B.C.) artifacts; beadwork of the Chippewa and Sioux. Library.

MISSISSIPPI

WINTERVILLE INDIAN MOUNDS STATE PARK
Rt. 3, Box 600 • GREENVILLE, MS 38701
Description: Maintains museum with a collection of Indian artifacts, excavated from the Mounds area. Library.

COBB INSTITUTE OF ARCHAEOLOGY
Drawer AR • MISSISSIPPI STATE UNIVERSITY, MS 39762
(601) 325-3826; E.J. Vardaman, Director
Description: Exhibits Indian materials of Mississippi culture.
Publication: Indians of Mississippi. Library.

GRAND VILLAGE OF THE NATCHEZ INDIANS
400 Jefferson Davis Blvd. • NATCHEZ, MS 39120
(601) 446-6502 Fax 359-6905; James F. Barnett, Jr., Director
Description: A 128-acre National Historic Landmark site is the location of the ceremonial mound center for the Natchez tribe during the French colonization of the area (ca. 1682-1730.) Contains Indian and European artifacts gathered from the excavations & interpreted exhibits on the Natchez & Southeastern Indians. Special programs: Educational programs; slide lectures & guided tours. Library.

OLD SPANISH FORT AND MUSEUM
4602 Fort St. • PASCAGOULA, MS 39567
Description: Features Indian artifacts, tools and implements; and maps showing Indian settlements prior to 1700. Library.

CHOCTAW MUSEUM OF THE SOUTHERN INDIAN
Mississippi Band of Choctaw Indians
P.O. Box 6010 • PHILADELPHIA, MS 39350
(601) 650-1685 Fax 656-6696; Bob Ferguson, Director
Description: Houses many permanent exhibits and occasionally offers traveling exhibits. Promotes continuation of Choctaw crafts and culture. Opened 1981.

MISSOURI

MUSEUM OF ANTHROPOLOGY
University of Missouri, 104 Swallow Hall • COLUMBIA, MO 65211
(573) 882-3764 Fax 884-5450; Dr. Michael J. O'Brien, Director
Molly K. O'Donnell, Associate Curator

Description: Displays of Native American material, Missouri archaeology, & Missouri history. Maintains collections of ethnographic material from the around the world. *Special collection*: The Grayson Collection of archery and archery-related material; Museum Curation Center. *Special programs*: Tours; Outreach. Gift Shop. Opened 1939.

TOWOSAHGY STATE HISTORIC SITE
Big Oak Tree State Park, 13640 S. Hwy. 102 • EAST PRAIRIE, MO 63845
(573) 649-3149; Ruben Templeton, Park Supt.
Description: This 64-acre state historic site preserves the remains of a once-fortified Indian village, which was an important ceremonial center. Indians of the Mississippian Culture inhabited the site between 1000 A.D. and 1400 A.D. Archaeologists periodically excavate at the site. Collections are currently curated off-site and are not on public display. *Programs*: Interpretive shelter and trail focusing on stockaded, multi-Mound Mississippian Culture prehistoric civic-ceremonial center AD 100-1400. *Publications*: Site brochure; information guides being developed. Opened 1967.

MISSOURI STATE MUSEUM
State Capitol • JEFFERSON CITY, MO 65101
Description: Collections include Musquakie ceremonial material, pottery, Kema Cave artifacts, Indian burial mound material, archaic Indian artifacts.

OSAGE VILLAGE HISTORIC SITE
P.O. Box 176 • JEFFERSON CITY, MO 65102
(314) 751-8363 Fax 751-8656; Larry Grantham, Contact
Description: Houses collections of excavated materials and conducts research on Osage Indians.

KANSAS CITY MUSEUM
3218 Gladstone Blvd. • KANSAS CITY, MO 64123
(816) 483-8300; Christopher Leitch, Director
Rebecca Schroeder, Curator of Education
Description: The American Indian collections number about 2,500 pieces, most of which were collected by Col. Daniel Dyer and Ida Dyer during his tenure as Indian Agent at Fort Reno, Oklahoma in 1884-85, includes clothing & textiles, rocks & minerals, tools and technology, and archival documents. Also, other collections include artifacts from Southern & Central Plains, Eastern Woodlands, the Southwest and Northwest Coast Indian cultures. Two notable objects in the collection are the First Greenville Treaty Peace Medal and the Second Greenville Treaty Peace Pipe. The Peace Medal dates to 1795, when it was presented by a representative of George Washington to Chief White Swan of the Wea tribe. The Pipe is one of three presented to Wyandotte, Delaware & Shawnee Tribes by a representative of President James Madison at the Second Treaty of Greenville, Ohio in 1814. *Publication*: Quarterly newsletter. Reference Library. Opened 1939.

WILLIAM ROCKHILL NELSON GALLERY/ATKINS MUSEUM OF FINE ARTS
4525 Oak St. • KANSAS CITY, MO 64111
Description: Exhibits Native arts of the Americas, with emphasis on the Southwest, Mesoamerica, and South America. Publications. Library.

THE ST. LOUIS ART MUSEUM
One Fine Arts Dr., Forest Park • ST. LOUIS, MO 63110
(314) 721-0072; James Burke, Supt.
John W. Nunley & Jackie Lewis Harris, Curators
Description: Maintains a collection of artifacts, pottery, carvings, basketry and clothing of the Pueblo, Pueblo Mimbres, Plains, West Coast, and Mound Builder Indians. Bulletin. Library. Opened 1904.

MONTANA

CHEYENNE INDIAN MUSEUM
St. Labre Indian School, P.O. Box 216 • ASHLAND, MT 59003
(406) 784-2741 Fax 784-6161; Website: www.stlabre.org
Dewanda Little Coyote-Backbon, Director; Opened 1971.

CUSTER BATTLEFIELD MUSEUM
Elizabeth Custer Library & Museum of Frontier Women of the West
P.O. Box 200 • GARYOWEN, MT 59031
(406) 638-1876 Fax 638-2019; Website: www.custermuseum.org
E-mail: info@custermuseum.org; Christopher Kortlander, Founding Director
Special collection: The David F. Barry Collection - Indian & cavalry artifacts from the Battle of the Little Big Horn and military life & Plains Indians. Online store selling books, magazines, maps, movies & CDs, prints.

MUSEUM OF THE ROCKIES
Montana State University • BOZEMAN, MT 59717
(406) 994-2251; Arthur H. Wolf, Director
Leslie B. Davis, PhD, Curator; Christopher Hill, PhD, Associate Curator

Special collections: "Enduring Peoples" - 1,500-piece Ethnology Col-lection, primarily an exhibit collection, represents Native Americans of the Plains, Northern Rockies and Plateau culture areas; and The Prehistoric Archaeology Collection - 100,000 artifacts of stone, bone and antler.

MUSEUM OF THE PLAINS INDIAN
P.O. Box 410 • BROWNING, MT 59417
(406) 338-2230 Fax 338-7404; Website: www.doi.gov/iacb
Loretta F. Pepion, Curator
Description: Administered by the Indian Arts & Crafts Board. Presents historic arts created by the tribal peoples of the Northern Plains, including the Blackfeet, Crow, Northern Cheyenne, Sioux, Assiniboine, Arapaho, Shoshone, Nez Perce, Flathead, Chippewa, & Cree. Displays the varied traditional costumes of Northern Plains men, women and children in complete detail on life-size figures. *Special programs*: North American Indian Days - annual public event presented in the second week of July on the Blackfeet Tribal Fairgrounds, adjacent to the museum. A four-day program of Indian dancing, games & sports events, and parades; slide presentation, "Winds of Change"--about the evolution of Indian cultures on the Northern Plains, narrated by Vincent Price; series of one-person exhibitions; painted tipis on the grounds during summer; demonstrations of Native American arts & crafts techniques; tours. *Publications*: Illustrated catalogs and brochures. Opened 1941.

INDIAN CHIEF TWO MOONS HISTORICAL MONUMENT
BUSBY, MT 59016

LITTLE BIGHORN BATTLEFIELD NATIONAL MONUMENT
P.O. Box 39 • CROW AGENCY, MT 59022
(406) 638-2621 Fax 638-2623; Website: www.nps.gov/libi/
Neil C. Mangum, Supt.; Kitty Belle Deernose, Curator
Description: Historic site of the Battle of the Little Big Horn, June 25-26, 1876. Arapaho, Sioux, and Cheyenne Indians fought & defeated Lt. Col. George Armstrong Custer and his troops of the 7th U.S. Cavalry. Arikara and Crow Indians scouted for military. *Museum*: Educational & interpretive exhibits and a permanent museum collection of 24,000 objects, includes historical documents authored by or associated with George A. Custer, the Battle of the Little Big Horn, and other events and persons associated with the Indian Wars on the Northern Plains (1865-1891.) Military & ethnographic specimens relating to the conflict, including items associated with the Sioux, Crow, & Northern Cheyenne Tribes. Special programs: Talks on the Battle; 30 minute documentary film, "Last Stand at Little Bighorn" available on request to schools and organi-zations; tours. Publications available from Southwest Parks & Monuments Assn (SPMA). White Swan Memorial Library: 2,050 volumes. Opened 1952.

CROW TRIBE HISTORICAL & CULTURAL COMMISSION
P.O. Box 173 • CROW AGENCY, MT 59022
(406) 638-2328

H. EARLE CLACK MUSEUM
P.O. Box 1675 • HAVRE, MT 59501
(406) 265-9641; Duane Nabor, Director; Mrs. Louis Clack, Curator
Description: Exhibit includes historic artifacts from the Chippewa and Cree Indians, excavated from site area; dioramas.

MONTANA HISTORICAL SOCIETY MUSEUM
225 No. Roberts • HELENA, MT 59620
(406) 444-2394; Lawrence Sommer, Director; Susan R. Near, Curator
Description: Collection contains approximately 3,500 pieces of ethnographic artifacts primarily of tribes of the region, mostly Blackfeet & Sioux. The Photographic Archives contains over 2,000 photo prints & negatives that depict Indians, primarily of the Blackfeet, Sioux, Crow and Flathead. *Special collection*: Towe Ford Collection--Features the chronological story of Montana's frontier through dioramas and other displays. C.M. Russell Gallery of Western Art. *Publication*: Montana: The Magazine of Western History, quarterly. Library. Established 1865.

CENTRAL MONTANA MUSEUM
P.O. Box 818, 408 NE Main St. • LEWISTON, MT 59457
(406) 538-5436; Frank Machler, Curator
Description: A collection of Native American artifacts.

SQELIX / AQ SMAKNI·K CENTER MUSEUM
The Peoples Center - Confederated Salish & Kootenai Tribes
Flathead Indian Reservation, P.O. Box 278 • PABLO, MT 59855
(800) 883-5344; (406) 675-0160 Fax 675-0260
Website: www.peoplescenter.org; Vicki Munson, Director; Opened 1994.

FORT PECK TRIBAL MUSEUM
P.O. Box 115 • POPLAR, MT 59255
(406) 768-5155 Fax 768-5478; Curley Youpee, Director
Opened 1978.

CHIEF PLENTY COUPS STATE PARK & MUSEUM

P.O. Box 100 • PRYOR, MT 59066
  (406) 252-1289 Fax 252-6668; Website: www.plentycoups.org
  Rich Furber, Park Manager

Description: Memorial museum to Chief Plenty Coups - last chief of the Crow - includes personal collection of medicine bundles, clothing, weapons, pictures, documents; Crow Indian artifacts; ethnographic material of the Crow people; paintings, drawings; prehistoric artifacts. Special program: Crow Life ways programs (cultural demonstrations) on Saturdays during July and August; Chief Plenty Coups "Day of Honor." Research Library. Opened 1932.

FLATHEAD INDIAN MUSEUM

Flathead Indian Reservation, #1 Museum Lane • ST. IGNATIUS, MT 59865
  (406) 745-2951; Jeanine Allard, Director; Col. Doug Allard, Curator

Description: Indian artifacts from the Flathead Tribe and other Western tribes. *Special collection*: Flathead Photo Collection. Established in 1975.

BIG HOLE NATIONAL BATTLEFIELD

P.O. Box 237 • WISDOM, MT 59761
  (406) 689-3155 Fax 689-3151
  John James, Supt.; Bob Chenoweth, Curator

Description: A 655 acre battlefield which preserves the scene of a battle between Nez Perce Indians and the Seventh U.S. Infantry, fought on August 9 & 10, 1877. The Heritage Center is located in the historic old school building constructed in 1888 by Jesuit priests. *Museum*: Exhibits detailing Nez Perce culture and soldier life of the 1870's; Native American art, including paintings, graphics, and sculptures; artifacts from battle participants, including beadwork. Special programs: Audiovisual program; self-guiding trails; presentations by rangers. Library. Gift Shop. *Publications*; Information packets; brochure.

NEBRASKA

JOHN G. NEIHARDT FOUNDATION

P.O. Box 344 • BANCROFT, NE 68004
  (402) 648-3388; (888) 777-4667
  Website: www.neihardtcenter.org; E-mail: neihardt@gpcom.net

MUSEUM OF THE FUR TRADE

HC 74, Box 18, 6321 Hwy. 20 • CHADRON, NE 69337
  (308) 432-3843; Charles E. Hanson, Jr., Director
  Brenda Olsen, Curator

Description: Maintains a collection of material illustrating the cultures of North American Indians, and the influence of the fur trade on those cultures. Restored and outfitted 1833 Indian trading post and warehouse. Indian garden for crops obtained from Mandan, Dakota, Assiniboine, Arikara, Hidatsa & Omaha Indians. *Publication*: Quarterly magazine. Library. Opened 1955.

FORT ROBINSON MUSEUM

Nebraska State Historical Society, P.O. Box 304 • CRAWFORD, NE 69339
  (308) 665-2919 Fax 665-2917; Website: www.nebraskahistory.org
  E-mail: fortrob@bbc.net; Thomas R. Buecker, Curator

Description: Interpretive exhibits housed in 1905 Post Headquarters with displays of artifacts from Fort Robinson (1874 to 1948.) Crazy Horse, the great Oglala warrior, met his death there in 1877. Microfilm records of Red Cloud and Spotted Tail Indian Agencies. Guided tours.

HASTINGS MUSEUM

P.O. Box 1286 • HASTINGS, NE 68902
Description: A collection of Indian artifacts; Sioux Indian habitat group. Indian film. Publications.

FORT KEARNEY MUSEUM

311 South Central Ave. • KEARNEY, NE 68847
Description: Displays Indian art from the Rosebud Indian Reservation.

INDIAN CENTER, INC.

1100 Military Rd. • LINCOLN, NE 68508
  (402) 438-5231 Fax 438-5236; Jackie Jackson, Director
  E-mail: indianctr@navix.net

MUSEUM OF NEBRASKA HISTORY

Nebraska State Historical Society, P.O. Box 82554 • LINCOLN, NE 68501
  (402) 471-4754 Fax 471-3314; Ann Billesbach, Director
  Website: www.nebraskahistory.org

Description: A 5,000 square foot exhibit "The First Nebraskans," Plains Indian archaeology, and historic artifacts primarily from the 19th & 20th centuries. Period settings include a Pawnee earth-lodge, and a Winnebago Reservation house. *Publications*: Nebraska History, quarterly; Historical Newsletter; monographs on Nebraska history and anthropology; educational materials. Library/Archives. Museum Shop. Established 1878.

UNIVERSITY OF NEBRASKA STATE MUSEUM

Morrill Hall • LINCOLN, NE 68508
  (402) 472-5044 Fax 472-8949; Website: www.museum.unl.edu
  Priscilla Grew, Director; Thomas Myers, Curator

Description: Features more than 2,500 Native American ethnographic artifacts with emphasis on Plains & Southwest. Includes costumes & artifacts of Indians of Nebraska. *Special exhibit*: "Nomads of the Plains" Gallery. *Publication*: "Magic in Clay," and Birth and Rebirth of the Omaha." Established 1879.

HERITAGE HOUSE MUSEUM

107 Clinton • WEEPING WATER, NE 68463
  (402) 267-4765; Deborah Freeman, President

Description: Maintains a prehistoric Indian artifact collection with items that date back 20,000 years.

NEVADA

NEVADA STATE MUSEUM

600 N. Carson St. • CARSON CITY, NV 89701
  (775) 687-4810 Fax 687-4168; Website: www.nevadaculture.org
  James Barmore, Director; Eugene Hattori, Curator of Anthropology

Description: Maintains extensive archaeological collections from Nevada; Great Basin and California basketry and other ethnographic materials collections. *Special programs*: Under One Sky: Nevada's Native American Heritage - chronicles Native American history and prehistory in Nevada; Behind the Scenes tours, last Friday of the month; annual Native American art exhibition. Publications. Library. Established 1939.

NORTHEASTERN NEVADA MUSEUM

1515 Idaho St. • ELKO, NV 89801
  (702) 738-3418; Howard Hickson, Executive Director
  Shawn Hall, Assistant Director

Description: Contains ten local Shoshone Indian exhibits. Special programs: Talks on Native American culture & customs; continuous art exhibit featuring two different artists each month. *Publication*: Quarterly historical journal. Library. Opened 1969.

NEVADA STATE LOST CITY MUSEUM OF ARCHAEOLOGY

721 S. Moapa Valley Blvd., P.O. Box 753 • OVERTON, NV 89040
  (702) 397-2193; Kathryn Olson, Curator

Description: Collections include prehistoric, proto-historic, & historic Native American material culture, including: lithics, basketry, fiber arts, articles of adornment, historic photos, etc. Housed in Adobe facility constructed in 1935. Pueblo artifacts excavated from Pueblo Grande de Nevada, Lost City, Paiute Indian artifacts, and southwestern Indian crafts. *Special collection*: Photographs of 1920-30 Lost City Excavations and local history. Library.

PYRAMID LAKE MARINA MUSEUM

2500 Lake View Dr. • SUTCLIFFE, NV 89510
  (702) 476-1156; Marsha Livingston, Director. Opened 1995.

NEW HAMPSHIRE

MUSEUM OF NEW HAMPSHIRE HISTORY

6 Eagle Square • CONCORD, NH03301
  (603) 228-6688 Fax 228-6308
  Wesley G. Balla, Director of Collections; E-mail: wballa@nhhistory.org

MT. KEARSARGE INDIAN MUSEUM

18 Highland Rd., P.O. Box 142 • WARNER, NH 03278
  (603) 456-2600 Fax 456-3092; Website: www.indianmuseum.org
  E-mail: mkim@conknet.com
  Shawn Olson, Executive Director
  Carolyn Bullock, Deputy Director/Store Manager
  Edie Daigle, Education Manager

Description: Contains a collection of over 1,000 objects, including Native American basketry, pottery & weavings. *Programs*: Educational tours; the Cultural Center is dedicated to increasing public awareness of Native American traditions, philosophy & art through exhibitions & programs. *Facilities*: Education & Cultural Center. Programs: *Activities*: Annual Intertribal powwow in July. *Publication*: Quarterly newsletter. Research library. Dream Catcher Store, museum & online store.

NEW JERSEY

WOODRUFF MUSEUM OF INDIAN ARTIFACTS

Bridgeton Free Public Library
150 E. Commerce St. • BRIDGETON, NJ 08302
  (856) 451-2620; Gail S. Robinson, Director
  Website: www.bridgetonlibrary.org/museum.htm

Description: Located within the Bridgeton Public Library, the museum includes approximately 20,000 Indian artifacts collected within a 30-mile radius of the library. The library has a collection of 2,000 volumes on Cumberland County history, local genealogy, and Woodland Indians. Opened 1976.

CUMBERLAND COUNTY PREHISTORICAL MUSEUM
1461 Bridgeton Rd., P.O. Box 16 ¶ GREENWICH, NJ 08323
  (856) 455-4055
Description: Artifacts of the Indians who inhabited the lower Delaware Valley. The Lenape, known today as the Delaware. *Programs*: Educational Series. Publications are available to the public regarding the Indian's culture. *Publication*: Newsletter.

THE MONTCLAIR ART MUSEUM
3 S. Mountain Ave. • MONTCLAIR, NJ 07042
  (973) 746-5555 Fax 746-9118; Patterson Sims, Director
  Twig Johnson, Curator of Native American Art
  E-mail: tjohnson@montclairartmuseum.org
  Website: www.montclairartmuseum.org
Description: Exhibits feature over 4,000 objects representing all the major culture areas: Southwest, Northwest Coast, Plains, Woodland, California, Southeast Tribes & Arctic. Exhibits of Native American art & artifacts. *Special programs*: Monthly Native American programs; teacher training workshops. Includes costumes, jewelry, and archaeological & ethnological artifacts. *Publications*: Collection & exhibition catalogs. Library. Opened 1914.

MORRIS MUSEUM
6 Normandy Heights Rd. • MORRISTOWN, NJ 07960
  (973) 971-3700 Fax 538-1842; Website: www.morrismuseum.org
  Steven H. Miller, Executive Director; E-mail: info@morrismuseum.org
Description: Woodland Indians Gallery: Shows the development of Woodland culture from the Paleo-Indian through Archaic to Woodland and historic periods. North American Indian Gallery: Exhibits on the Northwest Coast, the Southwest, and the Plains Indians. Special programs: Educational programs for children & adults. *Publications*: Exhibition catalogs. Museum shop. Opened 1913.

THE NEWARK MUSEUM
49 Washington St. • NEWARK, NJ 07102
  (973) 596-6550; Mary Sue Sweeney Price, Director
  Christa Clarke, Curator of Africa, Americas & Pacific
Description: Maintains a permanent Native American Gallery with Indian art and artifacts representative of major culture areas of the U.S., and some from Canada. Includes pottery & textiles of the Southwest, extensive basket collection, bead & quillwork. Publications. Library. Opened 1909.

PRINCETON UNIVERSITY-MUSEUM OF NATURAL HISTORY
9 Eno Hall • PRINCETON, NJ 08544
  (609) 258-5807; Elizabeth G. Horn, Director
Description: Exhibits Northwest Coast Indian art; also, artifacts, mainly Tlingit, of Yukatat & Sitka areas, Alaska, period 1876-1886. Publications. Library.

POWHATAN RENAPE NATION INDIAN HERITAGE MUSEUM
P.O. Box 225 • RANCOCAS, NJ 08073
  (609) 261-4747 Fax 261-7313; Roy Crazy Horse, Director
Description: Located on the Rankokus Indian Reservation. Shows the Life of the Creation; an Ancestral Village; and exhibits crafts & artifacts of the Powhatan Renape Nation. Art Gallery; Gift shop. Opened 1992.

SETON HALL UNIVERSITY MUSEUM
College of Arts & Sciences, Fahy Hall
400 South Orange Ave. • SOUTH ORANGE, NJ 07079
  (973) 761-9543
Description: An archaeology & Indian museum featuring Eastern Woodlands Indian artifacts, with emphasis on New Jersey prehistory - Paleo-Indian to European contact. Includes petroglyphs, effigies, ceramics. *Publications*: Occasional publications concerning the Lenape/Delaware Indians, prehistoric archaeology; report of excavations, etc. Library. Established 1960.

LENAPE INDIAN VILLAGE AT THE HISTORIC VILLAGE OF WATERLOO
525 Waterloo Rd. • STANHOPE, NJ 07874
  (973) 347-0900 Fax 347-3573; Website: www.waterloovillage.org
  John T. Kraft, Curator; E-mail: info@waterloovillage.org
Description: Recreated late Woodland Lenape (Delaware) Village - longhouses, ceremonial areas, simulated archaeological site, bark wigwams, et al. Established 1985.

CIVIL WAR & NATIVE AMERICAN MUSEUM
2202 Kuser Rd. • TRENTON, NJ 08690
  (609) 585-8900

Description: Displays Civil War artifacts from the Mercer County area, and Lenape Indian artifacts, including rare Delaware Indian tools & relics. *Programs*: Educational tours for local schools. Gift shop.

NEW JERSEY STATE MUSEUM
205 W. State St., P.O. Box 530 • TRENTON, NJ 08625
  (609) 292-6300; 292-6464 (recorded)
  E-mail: karen.flinn@sos.state.nj.us
  Eric Pryor, Executive Director
  Nicholas Ciotola, Curator; Karen Flinn, Assistant Curator
Description: Maintains a collection of ethnographic artifacts of the Lenni Lenape; also, Plains Indian beadwork, & material from Southwest, Eskimo & Northeast Indians. Library.

NEW MEXICO

ACOMA (HAAK'U) MUSEUM
Sky City Cultural Center, Pueblo of Acoma
P.O. Box 310 • ACOMITA, NM 87034
  (800) 747-0181; (505) 469-1052 Fax 552-7204
  Website: www.skycity.com; Connie Garcia, General Manager
Description: 40,000 sq. ft. facility that preserves & showcases the art, culture & history that have shaped Acoma and its people for more than a thousand years; exhibits, photo archives & documents relating to the history of Acoma. *Special activities*: Annual Feast Day, Sept. 2nd; Christmas Celebration, Dec. 24-28; open to the public. Daily walking guided tours of "Sky City." Gift shop. Library. *Publication*: One Thousand Years of Clay, catalog. Library. Opened 1977.

M. TULAROSA BASIN HISTORICAL SOCIETY
1301 White Sands Blvd., P.O. Box 518
ALAMOGORDO, NM 88310
  (505) 437-4760; Terry Benson, Director
Description: Maintains a collection of Indian artifacts from the area. Opened 1978.

INDIAN PUEBLO CULTURAL CENTER
2401 12th St., NW • ALBUQUERQUE, NM 87104
  (800) 766-4405 (outside NM); (505) 843-7270 Fax 842-6959
  Website: www.indianpueblo.org; Ronald J. Solimon, President & CEO
Description: The Main Museum consists of prehistoric to contemporary arts & crafts. A vast collection that traces the development of the Pueblo culture. Pueblo House Children's Museum offers a unique "hands on" experience for children. *Special programs*: Arts & crafts demonstration program each weekend. Library/Archives. Gift Shop. Opened 1976.

MAXWELL MUSEUM OF ANTHROPOLOGY
University & Ash, NE • ALBUQUERQUE, NM 87131
  (505) 277-4404
  David A. Phillips, Interim Director; E-mail: dphillips@unm.edu
  Mary Beth hermans, Public Programs Coordinator
  Amy Grochowski, Curator of Education
Description: Exhibits relating to cultures around the world, with a special emphasis on the cultural heritage of the Southwest. Permanent exhibit: "People of the Southwest." Rotating exhibits periodically feature Native American items, including Navajo weaving, Mimbres & Pueblo pottery, Hopi Kachinas, North American Indian basketry. *Publications*: Seven Families in Pueblo Pottery; Anasazi Pottery, et al. Library. Navajo & Pueblo silver jewelry for sale.

AZTEC RUINS NATIONAL MONUMENT
AZTEC MUSEUM & PIONEER VILLAGE
84 Road 2900 • AZTEC, NM 87410
  (505) 334-6174/9829 Fax 334-6372
  Charles B. Cooper, Supt.; Deah Folk, Director; Dana Howlett, Curator
Description: Prehistoric Pueblo Indian ruin. Two (cultural) phase inhabitation, Chaco Canyon and Mesa Verde. Archaeology Museum: Anasazi artifacts gathered from excavations of area sites, and from sites in the Lower San Juan Basin. Library. Open June-August. A National Historic Landmark. Opened 1923.

CORONADO STATE MONUMENT
P.O. Box 95 • BERNALILLO, NM 87004
  (505) 867-5351; Nathan Stone, Manager
Description: Site of a partially reconstructed Pueblo Indian village ruin occupied circa 1300-1600. Includes a completely reconstructed underground ceremonial kiva, which was the first to be discovered bearing ceremonial murals. Exhibits material from the excavations and Pueblo Indian culture.

RED ROCK MUSEUM
Box 10 • CHURCH ROCK, NM 87311
  (505) 863-1337 Fax 863-1297; Website: www.ci.gallup.nm.us
  E-mail: rrsp@ci.gallup.nm.us; John R. Vidal, Curator

Description: Collections consists of ethnographic & archaeological objects of the four corners cultures; fine arts & crafts of southwest Native American cultures; & photographs & archives of the history of the Gallup area. Material of prehistoric Anasazi and Navajo, Hopi, Zuni, Rio Grande Pueblos, Apache and Plains Indians. Special collection: Zuni kachina dolls. Special programs: Monthly art shows & traveling exhibits; artist presentations. Library. Opened 1951.

DEMING LUNA MIMBRES MUSEUM
301 S. Silver St. • DEMING, NM 88030
  (505) 546-2382; Treva L. Mester, Coordinator
Description: Exhibits Mimbrano Indian artifacts, and pottery.

JICARILLA ARTS & CRAFTS & MUSEUM
P.O. Box 507 • DULCE, NM 87528
  (505) 759-4274; Brenda Julian, Director
Description: Collections of Jicarilla Apache baskets, paintings, pottery & beadwork. Opened 1965.

SAN JUAN COUNTY ARCHAEOLOGICAL RESEARCH CENTER
FARMINGTON, NM 87401
  (505) 632-2013 Fax 632-1707
  Larry L. Baker, Executive Director
Description: Contains exhibits of artifacts taken from the Anasazi-Salmon Ruin: 1.5 million prehistoric Pueblo artifacts, replicated domiciles & exhibits representing Navajo, Ute, Jicarilla & Hispanic cultures; slides of rock art; oral history tapes; maps. *Special programs*: Educational programs & guided tours to Chaco Canyon & remote Navajo pueblos. *Publications*: Division of Conservation Archaeology Report Series; Cultural Resource Management Reports; 4,000+ archaeological reports; & historical publications. Research library. Opened 1973.

WALATOWA VISITOR CENTER
P.O. Box 100 • JEMEZ PUEBLO, NM 87024
  (505) 834-7235 Fax 834-7331
  Christine Waquie, Director
Description: Maintains a replica ancestral field house; photo exhibit; nature walk. Offers visitor information and a gift shop featuring Jemez pottery and souvenirs. Activities: Three annual arts & crafts shows. Opened 1993.

BANDELIER NATIONAL MONUMENT
HCR 1 Box 1, Rte. 4, #15 • LOS ALAMOS, NM 87544
  (505) 672-3861; John D. Hunter, Supt.
Description: Approximately 29,000 acres of ruins of the Pueblo (Anasazi) culture, dating from about 1200-1600 A.D. Publications. Library. A National Historic Landmark.

MESCALERO APACHE CULTURAL CENTER MUSEUM
181 Chiricahua Plaza, P.O. Box 227 • MESCALERO, NM 88340
  (505) 671-4944 Fax 671-9191; Website: www.apacheculture.com
  Ellyn Big Rope, Director
Description: Collections provide insight to the history & culture of the Mescalero people. Opened 1972.

GADSEN MUSEUM
Barker Rd. and Hwy. 28, P.O. Box 147 • MESILLA, NM 88046
  (505) 526-6293; Mary Veitch Alexander, Curator/Owner
Description: Collections include Indian artifacts from the Southwest.

SALINAS NATIONAL MONUMENT
Route 1, Box 496 • MOUNTAINAIR, NM 87036
  (505) 847-2585; Thomas B. Carroll, Supt.
Description: Located on the site of prehistoric pithouses, 800 A.D.; prehistoric Indian ruins 1100-1670 A.D.; four Spanish Mission ruins, 1627-1672. An archaeology museum maintains a collection of artifacts from the ruins. Library.

CHACO CULTURE NATIONAL HISTORIC PARK
P.O. Box 220 • NAGEEZI, NM 87037-0220
  (505) 786-7014; C.T. Wilson, Supt.; Philip LoPiccolo, Curator
Description: A National Historic Landmark - 13 major prehistoric Anasazi sites, and over 400 smaller village sites. *Museum*: Features 26 exhibits on Anasazi and Navajo cultures. Special collections: Large archaeological collection of two million artifacts & samples; Associated Documentation mostly Chaco Project including: 2,000 maps, Field Notes and Archives, 35,000 photographs and negatives, and over 5,000 color slides. Library. *Publications*: 1,500 published and unpublished manuscripts housed in Albuquerque, NM.

PECOS NATIONAL HISTORICAL PARK
P.O. Drawer 418 • PECOS, NM 87552
  (505) 757-6414; Duane L. Alire Supt.; Judy Reed, Cultural Resources Manager
Description: Pecos preserves the ruins of the great Pecos Pueblo (1400-1838) and two associated Spanish colonial missions, 17th & 18th centuries; visitor center displays over 100 artifacts, historical timeline and ten-minute introductory film. *Special collection*: Kidder Collection - 15,000 artifacts excavated from Pecos Pueblo from 1915-1929. *Publication*: Pecos: Gateway to Pueblo & Plains: The Anthology. Library. Opened 1965.

PICURIS PUEBLO MUSEUM
P.O. Box 487 • PENASCO, NM 87553
  (505) 587-2957; Website: www.picurispueblo.net
  Sheila Miller, Director; Opened 1969.

BLACKWATER DRAW SITE & MUSEUM
Eastern New Mexico University, Station 3 • PORTALES, NM 88130
  (505) 562-2202 Fax 562-2291; Matthew J. Hillsman, Curator
Description: Maintains collection of Paleo-Indian archaeology & anthropology. Archaeological site "Clovis." *Programs*: Films, tours & lectures. *Publications*: ENMU Contributions in Anthropology. Opened 1969.

PALEO-INDIAN INSTITUTE
Eastern New Mexico University, P.O. Box 2154 • PORTALES, NM 88130
  Dr. George Agogino, Director
Description: Maintains exhibits illustrating the life of the paleo-archaic and modern Indian. Library.

EL MORRO NATIONAL MONUMENT
RAMAH, NM 87321 (505) 783-5132
  Douglas Eury, Supt.
Description: Archaeological site of Inscription Rock, prehistoric Pueblo ruins. Library.

STRADLING MUSEUM OF THE HORSE
P.O. Box 40 • RUIDOSO DOWNS, NM 88346-0040
  Anne C. Stradling, Director
Description: Equine and Indian Museum. Library.

INDIAN ARTS RESEARCH CENTER
School of American Research
P.O. Box 2188 • SANTA FE, NM 87504
  (505) 954-7205 Fax 954-7207; Website: www.sarweb.org
  E-mail: iarc@sarsf.org; Kathy Whitaker, PhD, Director
  Shannon Parker, Collections Manager
Description: Collection of 11,000+ objects of Southwestern American Indian art and anthropology; archaeology laboratory. Includes ceramics, textiles, jewelry, silverwork, paintings, basketry, katsinam, & miscellaneous objects (clothing, cradleboards, musical instruments, etc.) Native American Artist Fellowships: The Eric & Barbara Dobkin, Ronald & Susan Dubin, and Rollin & Mary Ella King fellowships; lectures & exhibitions; annual Native American Internship. *Fellowships*: Katrin H. Lamon Resident Scholar and Artist Fellowships for Native Americans. *Publications*: Books pertaining to the Southwest & Native American arts & culture. Library.

INSTITUTE OF AMERICAN INDIAN ARTS
MUSEUM OF CONTEMPORARY NATIVE ARTS
108 Cathedral Place • SANTA FE, NM 87501
  (505) 983-8900/1777 Fax 983-1222
  Website: www.iaia.edu/museum; E-mail: museum@iaia.edu
  Marguerite L. Wood, Manager
  Tatiana Lomahaftewa Slock, Associate Curator of Collections
Description: Maintains contemporary Native American Fine Art. The collection primarily documents the history of the Institute since its inception in 1962. *Special collection*: Student Honors Collection--Contains approximately 8,000 items--paintings, graphics, sculpture, ceramics, textiles, costumes, jewelry, and ethnological material of Native American students' work. Also, more than 1,000 items of non-student work done by Indian artists throughout the U.S. Museum staff: Thomas Atencio, Jary Earl, Maria Favela, Magdalene Ohnesorgen, Alison Ryan, Tatiana Slock. *Special programs*: Exhibits, tours, art festival, lectures, workshops; museum store. Publication: Spawning the Medicine River, quarterly. Native American Videotape Archives. Library. Opened 1972.

MORNING STAR GALLERY
513 Canyon Rd. • SANTA FE, NM 87501
  (505) 982-8187 Fax 984-2368; Website: www.morningstargallery.com
  E-mail: indian@morningstargallery.com
  Henry Monahan, Director
Description: Antique American Indian art.

MUSEUM OF INDIAN ARTS & CULTURE
Laboratory of Anthropology-Museum of New Mexico
708-710 Camino Lejo, P.O. Box 2087 • SANTA FE, NM 87504
  (505) 476-1269 Fax 476-1330; Website: www.miaclab.org
  Duane Anderson, Director; E-mail: danderson@miaclab.org
  Joyce Begay-Foss, Cultural Affairs Director (476-1272)
  E-mail: joyce.begay-foss@state.nm.us

Diane Bird, Archivist; Valerie Verzuh, Collections Manager
Chris Baca, Information Systems; John Torres, Curator of Archaeology
Description: Consists of over 15,000 ethnographic objects and more than 26,000 archaeological objects, with emphasis on artifacts from the prehistoric, ethnographic, & present-day Indian Southwest. Features permanent exhibitions of Southwestern Indian culture. *Publications*: Papers in Anthropology; Research Records; Lab Notes; & Archaeological Surveys. Library. Laboratory established 1930. Opened 1987.

MUSEUM OF NEW MEXICO - MUSEUM OF FINE ARTS
107 West Palace Ave., P.O. Box 2087 • SANTA FE, NM 87501
(505) 476- 5072 Fax 476-5076; Website: www.mnm.state.nm.us
Marsha Bol, Director; E-mail: mbol@mnm.state.nm.us
Special collection: Indian Arts Fund Collection--Contains pottery, jewelry, and costumes; art of the Southwest. Museum shop. Library.

MUSEUM OF NEW MEXICO
Palace of the Governors, 105 West Palace Ave.
P.O. Box 2087 • SANTA FE, NM 87501
(505) 476-5100 Fax 476-5104; Website: www.mnm.state.nm.us
Fran Levine, Director; E-mail: flevine@mnm.state.nm.us
Carolotta Boettcher, Portal Program Manager
E-mail: cboettcher@mnm.state.nm.us
Tomas Jaehn, Photo Archives Curator; E-mail: tjaehn@mnm.state.nm.us
Special programs: Museum of Fine Arts; Museum of Indian Arts & Culture; Native American Vendors Portal Program (505) 827-6474 Fax 827-6521 - Includes traditional crafts of the 22 recognized New Mexico tribes and pueblos, with more than 775 Native American artists and craftspeople displaying & selling their work beneath the portal, or front porch of the museum; History Library/Photo Archives (505) 476-5090; Museum of New Mexico Press (800) 622-8667

POEH CULTURAL CENTER & MUSEUM
78 Cities of Gold Rd. • SANTA FE, NM 87506
(505) 455-3334 Fax 455-0174
Website: www.poehcenter.com; E-mail: info@poehcenter.org
George Rivera, Center Executive Director; Melissa Talachy, Curator
Alma Garcia (Taos Pueblo), Poeh Arts Program Director
Description: Located on the Pojoaque Pueblo Reservation, the Poeh Museum exhibits the art & culture of the Pueblo peoples with an emphasis on the Tewa-speaking pueblos of Nambe, Pojoaque, San Ildefonso, San Juan, Santa Clara, and Tesuque. Opened 1988.

SAN ILDEFONSO PUEBLO MUSEUM
Route 5, Box 315-A • SANTA FE, NM 87501
(505) 455-2424 Fax 455-7351; Opened 1982.

WHEELWRIGHT MUSEUM OF THE AMERICAN INDIAN
P.O. Box 5153, 704 Camino Lejo • SANTA FE, NM 87502
(505) 982-4636 Fax 989-7386; Website: www.wheelwright.org
Jonathan Batkin, Director; Cheri Falkenstein-Doyle, Curator
Description: Collections of Southwest ethnology--Navajo textiles and silver; Navajo, Apache & Hopi basketry; Pueblo pottery; Navajo, Apache, Pueblo cradleboards; Navajo sandpainting reproductions. *Special programs*: Lecture series; textile and basket-weaving workshops; craft demonstrations; Indian arts & crafts and books for sale. *Publication*: Catalogs of exhibitions; bimonthly newsletter; annual magazine. Library.

WESTERN NEW MEXICO UNIVERSITY MUSEUM
1000 W. College Ave. • SILVER CITY, NM 88061
(505) 538-6386 Fax 538-6178
Website: www.wnmu.edu/univ/museum.htm
Dr. Cynthia Ann Bettison, Director & Archaeologist
Special collection: Eisele Collection of Southwest Pottery & Artifacts; the largest permanent display of Mimbres pottery & culture in the world; Casas Grandes pottery, mining displays, traveling exhibits. Publication: Newsletter. Opened 1974.

KIT CARSON HISTORIC MUSEUMS
P.O. Drawer CCC • TAOS, NM 87571
(505) 758-0505; 758-0062 (Archives) Fax 758-0330
Website: www.taosmuseums.org
Karen Young, Director; Skip Miller, Supt.
E-mail: skipper@laplaza.org
Description: Kit Carson's 21 room Spanish colonial fortified hacienda & museum - Historic Landmark. Displays artifacts of prehistoric Indian culture of Taos and the Southwest. Southwest Research Center of Northern New Mexico. *Publications*: Taos Lightnin' - Kit Carson Historic Museums newsletter.

THE HARWOOD MUSEUM OF ART
238 Ledoux St. • TAOS, NM 87571
(575) 758-9826 Fax 758-1475; Website: www.harwoodmuseum.org

E-mail: harwoodmuseum.com; Susan Longhenry, Director
Jina Brenneman, Curator
Description: Collection includes over 1,700 works of art and a photographic archive of 17,000 images spanning a period from the 19th century to the present. Gift shop.

MILLICENT ROGERS MUSEUM OF NORTHERN NEW MEXICO
P.O. Box A • TAOS, NM 87571
(575) 758-2462 Fax 758-5751
Website: www.millicentrogers.org; E-mail: mrm@newmex.com
Dr. Shelby Tisdale, Executive Director
Description: Permanent collections feature prehistoric to contemporary works in pottery, jewelry, textiles by Native American artists & designers of the Southwest and the Plains. *Educational programs*: Lectures, workshops, guided tours. Research library. *Publications*: Membership announcements, catalogues. Opened 1956.

TAOS ART MUSEUM
227 Paseo del Pueblo Norte • TAOS, NM 87571
(575) 758-2690; Website: www.taosartmuseum.org
Description: Collection of paintings by the masters of the Taos Society of Artists. Opened 1994.

A:SHIWI A:WAN MUSEUM & HERITAGE CENTER
P.O. Box 1009 • ZUNI, NM 87327
(505) 782-4403 Fax 782-4503; E-mail: aamhc_museum@yahoo.com
James Enote, Executive Director
Description: Prehistoric artifacts excavated in the early 1900's at an ancestral ruin site. Historic photographs & CDs. Jewelry, pottery, stone carvings, minimal textiles. *Special programs*: Summer science (archaeology) program & other youth/family oriented cultural learning programs throughout the year. Library. Opened 1992.

ZUNI CULTURAL RESOURCE ENTERPRISE
Pueblo of Zuni, P.O. Box 1149 • ZUNI, NM 87327
(505) 782-4814 Fax 782-2393; E-mail: zcre@nm.net
Jonathan Damp, Principal Investigator
Description: Archaeological site record files & comprehensive map file and air photo file of the Reservation and surrounding areas. Unpublished manuscripts on Zuni history and archaeology are maintained. Historic photographs. *Publications*: Report Series; Research Series. Library. Opened 1975.

NEW YORK

NEW YORK STATE MUSEUM
Cultural Education Center, Rm. 3122, Empire State Plaza • ALBANY, NY 12224
(518) 474-5813; Website: www.nysm.nysed.gov
Toni Benedict, Specialist in Indian Culture
Special collections: Morgan Collection--Mid 19th century Seneca ethnographic material; The Beauchamp Collection--Onondaga ethnographic material; The Parker Collection--Late 19th & 20th century Iroquois ethnological & general New York archaeological materials. *Activities*: Annual Algonquian Peoples Seminar in April. Publications. Library.

CAYUGA MUSEUM IROQUOIS CENTER
Rt. 38A Emerson Park, 203 Genesee St. • AUBURN, NY 13021
(315) 253-8051 Fax 253-9829; Website: www.cayuganet.org/cayugamuseum
E-mail: cayugamuseum@cayuganet.org; Eileen McHugh, Director
Description: A collection of Iroquois and Owasco Native American artifacts including baskets, pottery, a model longhouse, French missionary rings, crosses, etc. Ely Parker, Redjacket items, and John S. Clark maps. *Special programs*: Craft classes for children in beadwork, Iroquois food, games & myths. Crafts for sale. *Publication*: Quarterly museum newsletter. Library.

KATERI GALLERIES
National Shrine of North American Martyrs • AURIESVILLE, NY 12016
(518) 853-3033; Rec. Robert J. Boyle, S.J., Director
Rev. John M. Dovlan, S.J., Curator
Description: Located on the site of the martyrdom of Father Isaac Jogues, French Jesuit priest, & his companions who were killed by the Mohawk Indians in 1642. Also, the 1656 Birthplace of Kateri Tekakwitha. *Special collection*: Mohawk Indian Culture Collection--Indian artifacts & handicrafts; Indian longhouse dioramas. *Publication*: Pilgrim, quarterly magazine. Library.

TONAWANDA-SENECA MUSEUM
Tonawanda-Seneca Reservation • BASOM, NY 14013

THE BROOKLYN CHILDREN'S MUSEUM
145 Brooklyn Ave. • BROOKLYN, NY 11213
Description: Exhibits Plains Indian material; also, Southwestern, Eastern Woodlands and Northwest Indian artifacts. Library.

BUFFALO & ERIE COUNTY HISTORICAL SOCIETY MUSEUM
Humboldt Park • BUFFALO, NY 14211
Description: Maintains a collection of Niagara frontier Indian artifacts, including clothing, masks, and tools, mostly of Iroquois village life. Publications. Library.

CULTURAL CENTER OF THE TAINO NATION OF THE ANTILLES
58 Brightside Ave. • CENTRAL ISLIP, NY 11722
  (516) 348-0786 Fax 348-1981; Miguel Angel Macano Alvarez, Chair
Purpose: To promote the history and culture of the Taino peoples located on various islands in the Caribbean; and to reclaim, restore and preserve the Taino peoples' heritage and natural language. Programs: Educational & tutorial programs. Another center is also located in Santa Isabel, Puerto Rico

ROCKWELL MUSEUM OF WESTERN ART
111 Cedar St. • CORNING, NY 14830
  (607) 937-5386 Fax 974-4536; Website: www.rockwellmuseum.org
  E-mail: info@rockwellmuseum.org; Kristin Swain, Executive Director
Description: Houses a collection of American western and Native American art in the Eastern U.S. The collection contains masterworks by 19th & early 20th century painters & sculptors like Remington, Russell, Bierstadt, Sharp, Dallin, Moran, as well as recent works by Native American and emerging western artists like Butterfield, Quick-to-See Smith, Warhol, WalkingStick, and McHorse. *Special programs*: Tours on Native American art for all ages; hands-on collections; teacher training & outreach programs on the Iroquois. Library. Trading Post. Opened 1976.

MUSEUM OF THE HUDSON HIGHLANDS
The Boulevard, P.O. Box 181 • CORNWALL-ON-HUDSON, NY 12520
  (914) 534-7781; Charles I. Keene, Director
Special collection: Eastern Woodlands Indians--Exhibits more than 80 stone artifacts; 40 modern reproductions made by group of Iroquois. *Special program*: Native American educational aides for programs and presentations to school groups, kindergarten to fourth grades. An Indian Loan Kit comprised of Iroquois pack basket filled with artifacts and reproductions designed for teachers to use to complement the NYS fourth grade history curriculum. Library. Opened 1962.

TEKAKWITHA SHRINE NATIVE AMERICAN EXHIBIT
THE MOHAWK-CAUGHNAWAGA MUSEUM
Route 5, Box 627 • FONDA, NY 12068
  (518) 853-3646 Fax 853-3371
  Rev. Kevin Kenny, Director; E-Mail: kkenny@klink.net
Description: Religious Shrine & Historic Archaeological Site, 1666-1693. Located on the site of the 1666-1693 excavated Caughnawaga Indian Village; Mohawk Indian Castle: residence of Kateri Tekakwitha. Displays North, South and Central American Indian artifacts, with emphasis on the Iroquois of central New York State. Comprehensive collection of Native American artifacts, mostly Iroquois. *Publication*: Tekakwitha Nesletter, published three times annually. Library. Opened 1935.

LONGYEAR MUSEUM OF ANTHROPOLOGY
Colgate University • HAMILTON, NY 13346
  (315) 824-7543
Description: Features large collections of local Oneida Iroquois and Mesoamerican archaeological materials.

AKWESASNE MUSEUM - AKWESASNE CULTURAL CENTER
St. Regis Mohawk Nation, 321 State Rt. 37 • HOGANSBURG, NY 13655
  (518) 358-2461 Fax 358-2649; Website: www.akwesasneculture.org
  E-mail: akwmuse@northnet.org; Glory Cole, Director
Description: Museum interprets the continuing culture of the Akwesasne Mohawk people through exhibits, guided tours, gallery guides, & education kits. Traveling exhibit sponsored by NYSCA & IMLS available for bookings. The museum shop features Mohawk black ash & sweetgrass baskets, other native-made items & publications. *Special programs*: The museum is a partner in "Teaching American History Through Hotinonshonni Eyes" sponsored by the U.S. Department of Education. *Publication*: Sweetgrass Is Around Us-Basketmakers of Akwesasne; Library. Opened 1972.

IROQUOIS INDIAN MUSEUM
324 Caverns Rd., P.O. Box 7 • HOWES CAVE, NY 12092
  (518) 296-8949 Fax 296-8955; Website: www.iroquoismuseum.org
  E-mail: info@iroquoismuseum.org; Erynne Ansel, Director
  Stephanie Shuttes, Curator; Mike Tarbell, Museum Educator
Description: A 45-acre nature park with educational trails explaining the ethnobotany of Iroquois culture. Maintains an extensive collection of contemporary Iroquois fine art & craftwork for all six Iroquois nations; archaeological collections from the local area; photographic collections of contemporary Iroquois arts, ethnographic objects, events and people. *Special programs*: Children's museum - a restatement of the adult museum designed to break down stereotypes and to introduce children the Iroquois people of today; educational programs; two Annual Iroquois Indian Festivals (Memorial Day weekend, and Labor Day

weekend). *Publications*: Museum Notes, quarterly newsletter; Directory of Iroquois Artists & Crafts People; "Joe Jacobs, Iroquois Art," "Pete Jones: Iroquois Art," and Visual Voices of the Iroquois," and other recent exhibition catalogs. Library. Opened 1980.

STE. MARIE AMONG THE IROQUOIS
P.O. Box 146, Onondaga Lake Park • LIVERPOOL, NY 13088
  (315) 457-2990; Robert Geaci, Director; Valerie Bell, Curator
Description: A reconstructed 1656 French settlement among Onondaga Iroquois. Maintains archaeological material from area sites--Onondaga cultural material. *Special programs*: Living History Program--interpretation of Onondaga Indian culture; lectures. *Publication*: Onondaga Portrait of a Native People. Library.

AMERICAN INDIAN GALLERY & GIFT SHOP
American Indian Community House
11 Broadway, 2nd Fl. • NEW YORK, NY 10004
  (212) 598-0100 ext. 241 Fax 598-4909
  Website: www.aich.org/gallery/gal.htm
  Kathleen Ash-Milby, Curator; Monica Green, Gift Shop Manager
Description: Displays Native-American artwork. Established 1978.

AMERICAN MUSEUM OF NATURAL HISTORY
79th St. & C.P.W. • NEW YORK, NY 10024
  (212) 769-5375; Ian Tattersall, PhD, Chairman
  Stanley A. Freed, PhD, Curator
Special collections: Eskimo Exhibit, & Indians of the Northwest Coast--Artifacts of the Coast Salish, Nootka, Haida, Tsimpshean, Thompson, Bella Coola, Tlingit, and Kwakiutl; also, shamanistic regalia and ceremonial objects. *Publications*: Natural History; Curator; Bulletin; Anthropological Papers. Library/Reading Rm.

SMITHSONIAN NATIONAL MUSEUM OF THE AMERICAN INDIAN
GEORGE GUSTAV HEYE CENTER
1 Bowling Green • NEW YORK, NY 10004
  (212) 283-2420 Fax 491-9302
  Website: www.americanindian.si.edu; Dr. Duane King, Director
  Richard West, Director (Washington, DC office)
  Mary Jane, Curator of North American Ethnology
  Peter Scott Brill, Curator of Exhibits; Lee A. Callander, Registrar
  Carmen Sanchez, Public Affairs Specialist
  Judith A. Brundin, Head Educator
  Elizabeth Weatherford, Curator/Film & Video Center
  Barbara J. Christ, Manager, Museum Store
  Ellen Jamieson, Publications Manager
Description: Acknowledged to be one of the largest & finest assemblage of artifacts representing the Native cultures of North, Central & South America, the Museum (founded 1916) is a national treasury unsurpassed for its potential for education and research. Its areal and temporal scope is vast, ranging from Alaska to Chile and from the Paleo-Indian period to the present, encompassing societies as diverse as the 20th century hunting band societies of the Arctic & subarctic & the ancient agricultural civilizations of the Aztec & Inca. The artifacts in the collections range from precious ornaments to commonplace tools, from projectile points to abstract paintings by contemporary Indian artists. The Central & South American & the Caribbean collections include ancient ornaments of Mexican jade & turquoise, ancient gold, silver, basketry, fabrics, & pottery, stone, & shell sculptures from the Antilles. The North American collections include silver & turquoise jewelry, weavings, & pottery from the Southwest; painted wooden sculptures from the Northwest Coast; ancient carved shell artifacts from the Southeast; and carved ivory & stone from the Arctic. *Special programs*: Education Department offers guided tours, visiting Native American artists & artisans, and a lecture series; The Film & Video Center researches & exhibits film & video productions concerned with Inuit & Indian peoples of the Americas; The Indian Information Center makes available to the public a wide variety of information concerning the native peoples of the Americas; The Museum Store offers a wide variety of contemporary Indian crafts from many tribes, and books, slides, etc. *Publications*: Indian Notes; quarterly newsletter; Museum schedule of exhibits & public programs; exhibition catalogs, archaeological reports, ethnological studies, bibliographies & biographies published by the Museum for sale; Native American Film & Video Catalog. Photographic Archives: Contains approximately 70,000 photographs documenting Native American life in the Western Hemisphere. Slides & prints are available for purchase. Library.

SIX NATIONS INDIAN MUSEUM
1462 County Route 60 • ONCHIOTA, NY 12989
  (518) 891-2299; John Fadden, Director
  Website: www.thebeadsite.com/mus-f4.htm; E-mail: redmaple@northnet.org
Description: Located in the northeastern Adirondack Mountains. Dedicated to preserving the culture of the Iroquois Confederacy (Mohawks, Senecas, Onondagas, Oneidas, Cayugas & Tuscaroras), the Museum exhibits pre-Columbian, historic, as well as contemporary items of Iroquois culture--clothing, tools, crafts, baskets, and objects of art; a collection of charts, posters, and written material. Provides the viewing of 3,000+ artifacts with an emphasis on

the Six Nations of the Iroquois Confederacy. *Special programs*: Lectures on Native-American history & culture, story telling; gift shop carries Mohawk baskets, beadwork, soapstone carving, & acrylic paintings reflecting Six Nations Iroquois culture. Open July-August; open by appointment to groups June & September. Closed on Mondays. Admission. Opened 1954.

SHAKO:WI CULTURAL CENTER
Box 5, 5 Territory Rd. • ONEIDA, NY 13421
  (315) 829-8210 Fax 829-8253; Website: www.one-web.org/oneida/
  Brenda Hicks, Program Manager; E-mail: bhicks@oneida-nation.org
Description: Contains historic & contemporary exhibits. *Activities*: Tours, craft & dance workshops, lectures, language & literature classes. Opened 1993.

THE YAGER MUSEUM OF ART & CULTURE
Hartwick College • ONEONTA, NY 13820-9989
  (607) 431-4480; Website: www.harwick.edu/academics/museum
  Donna Anderson, Coordinator; Dr. David Anthony, Curator of Anthropology
  Gary Norman, Collections Manager
Description: A collection of upper Susquehanna Indian artifacts, and Southwest basketry and pottery. Library. Museum shop. Opened 1928.

ROCHESTER MUSEUM & SCIENCE CENTER
657 East Ave. • ROCHESTER, NY 14607
  (716) 271-4320 Fax 271-0492; Website: www.rmsc.org
  Kate Bennett, President
  Dr. George McIntosh, Director of Collections
  E-mail: george-mcintosh@rmsc.org
Description: Exhibits & collections of natural science, regional history, and anthropology. Exhibits & collections in archaeology, from 12,000 B.C. through the 19th century, and in ethnology, from the 18th through the 20th centuries, relating to non-Indians & to American Indians with emphasis on New York State Haudenosaunee people, especially Senecas. Special archaeological & ethnological collections: Lewis Henry Morgan mid-19th Century collection of Woodlands, Plains, & Southwestern Indian material; Indian Arts Project collection produced by Haudenosaunee arts & crafts workers in the 1930's and 40's. "At the Western Door," permanent exhibit detailing story of contact between Senecas, Europeans and Americans in western New York, A.D. 1550 to the present. *Publications*: Members' newsletter; Research Records series, & exhibit catalogs. Research library. Opened 1912.

SENECA-IROQUOIS NATIONAL MUSEUM
Allegany Indian Reservation, 814 Broad St. • SALAMANCA, NY 14779
  (716) 945-1760 x 3455 Fax 945-1760; Website: www.senecamuseum.org
  Jare R. Cardinal, Director; E-mail: jcardinal@sni.org
  Trish Scanlon, Curator; E-mail: trisha.scanlon@sni.org
Description: Devoted to the presentation of the prehistory, history, and contemporary heritage of the Seneca Nation of Indians, and, in a wider sense, the Iroquois culture. Collection includes an extensive array of prehistoric Iroquois artifacts, post-contact trade beads, material culture items, and contemporary Iroquois art, as well as photos and papers. Special programs: Special exhibits on a regular basis, which have included Iroquois basketry, Iroquois Veterans in Two Worlds, and the Death & Rebirth of Iroquois Pottery. Also limited off-site cultural presentations. *Publication*: 1981 Collections of the Seneca-Iroquois National Museum. Library. Museum shop. Opened 1977.

SHINNECOCK NATION CULTURAL CENTER & MUSEUM
Shinnecocok Indian Reservation
P.O. Box 5059 • SOUTHAMPTON, NY 11969-5059
  (631) 287-4923 Fax 287-7153; Website: www: shinnecock-museum.org
  E-mail: shinnecockmuseum@yahoo.com; David Bunn Martine, Director
Description: Collections span the six cultural phases of history from paleolithic to historic, consisting of baskets, arrowheads, painted murals, woodcarvings, photographs, whalebone, stuffer animals. Programs: Education, art festivals, oral history. *Activities*: Monthly cable show "Voices of Native America," Channel 25 cable vision. Archives - documents, books, photos. Opened 1994.

SOUTHOLD INDIAN MUSEUM
The Incorporated Long Island Chapter, New York State Archaeological Assn.
1080 Main Bayview Rd., P.O. Box 268 • SOUTHOLD, NY 11971
  (631) 965-5577 Fax 765-5577; Website: www.southoldindianmuseum.org
  E-mail: indianmuseum@optonline.net; Ellen Barcel, President
Description: Collections include artifacts of Long Island Indians including wood, stone & bone tools. Colorful murals list the subdivisions of Algonquins that inhabited Eastern Long Island and illustrate their mode of life. Also a large collection of Algonquin ceramic pottery, pots & bowls carved out of soapstone and a collection of projectile points (arrow heads). *Special programs*: Educational for students in grades K-5; Summer programs for students in grades 3-6. Activities: Guided tours of the Algonquin Flint Mines at Coxsackie, New York. *Publications*: Southold Indian Museum News (quarterly newsletter); teachers kits, informational leaflets, museum guide, and other educational materials. Library. Gift shop. Opened 1962.

GANONDAGAN STATE HISTORIC SITE
P.O. Box 239, 1488 State Rt. 444 • VICTOR, NY 14564
  (585) 924-5848 Fax 742-2353; Website: www.ganondagan.org
  G. Peter Jemison, Historic Site Manager
Description: Located at the late 17th century Seneca Indian settlement. Maintains collections of site related artifacts. Seneca artifacts & other Haudeno-saunee (Iroquois) artifacts. Also, contemporary Iroquois arts and crafts. *Special programs*: Lectures, workshops, demonstrations and festivals, i.e. Native American Dance & Music Festival, last weekend in July. Small reference library. *Publications*: Si Wong Geh, newsletter; Art from Ganondagan; War Against the Seneca by John Mohawk. Hours: 9-5 Tues.-Sun., mid-May to end of October. Opened 1987.

NORTH CAROLINA

RESEARCH LABORATORIES OF ARCHAEOLOGY
University of North Carolina
CB #3120 Alumni Bldg. • CHAPEL HILL, NC 27599
  (919) 962-6574; Vincas Steponaitis, Director
Description: Large collection of Southeastern archaeological materials, including over 5 million specimens, extensive photographic collection dating from the 1930s. *Publication*: "North Carolina Archaeology," published jointly with the North Carolina Archaeological Society. Library.

MUSEUM OF THE CHEROKEE INDIAN
P.O. Box 1599 • CHEROKEE, NC 28719
  (828) 497-3481 Fax 497-4985; Website: www.cherokeemuseum.org
  Ken Blankenship, Director; E-mail: kenblank@cherokeemuseum.org
  James "Bo" Taylor, Archivist; E-mail: botaylor@cherokeemuseum.org
  Barbara Duncan, Education; E-mail: bduncan@cherokeemuseum.org
  Sharon Littlejohn, Store Manager; E-mail: littlejohn@cherokeemuseum.org
Description: Exhibits Cherokee Indian artifacts, relics & documents. *Publication*: Journal of Cherokee Studies, semiannual. Library. Museum Store. Opened 1948.

FRISCO NATIVE AMERICAN MUSEUM & NATURAL HISTORY CENTER
P.O. Box 399 • FRISCO, NC 27936
  (252) 995-4440 Fax 995-4030
  Website: www.nativeamericanmuseum.org
  E-mail: admin@nativeamericanmuseum.org
  Joyce Bornfriend, Director of Education
  Thomas Garman, Media Coordinator
  Barbara Miller, Assistant Curator
Description: Houses Native American artifacts, art & culture. Located on The Hatteras Island in the vilage of Frisco, at the southern end of the Outer Banks of North Carolina. *Activities*: Annual Museum Day in September; maintains a Nature Trail; annual powwow. Summer programs. Gift shop. Opened 1987.

**THE SCHIELE MUSEUM OF NATURAL HISTORY & CENTER
FOR SOUTHEASTERN NATIVE AMERICAN STUDIES**
1500 E. Garrison Blvd. • GASTONIA, NC 28054
  (704) 866-6900 Fax 866-6041; Website: www.schielemuseum.org
  Ann Tippitt, President/Director; E-mail: annt@cityofgastonia.com
  Alan May, Curator of Archaeology; Tony Pasour, Head of Education
Description: Maintains extensive holdings of Native-American artifacts, clothing, utensils, rugs, pottery, jewelry, costumes, arts & crafts, etc. spanning known history; collections of 12 major cultural areas throughout the U.S. & Canada; specialized collections on Southeast Indians, especially pottery; also, lithic material from the Southeast with special sections relating to local areas of North Carolina. The Catawba Village: A replicated Southeastern Indian village, circa 1550, representing Catawba & Southeastern Indian architecture and lifestyles from the 16th through 19th centuries. *Special programs*: Catawba Village Study-Tour Program designed for grades 4 and up, where students explore the ways and means of aboriginal life; contract courses; workshops; The Southeastern Indian Culture Study Group; annual Native-American Fall Festival in September. Reference Library. Museum Store.

INDIAN MUSEUM OF THE CAROLINAS
607 Turnpike Rd. • LAURINBURG, NC 28352
  (910) 276-5880; Dr. Margaret Houston, Director
Description: Exhibits Indian archaeological material & modern Native American art & artifacts of North & South Carolina, and the Southeast U.S. Comparative displays show artifacts from other geographic areas. Special programs: Evening speakers program; guided tours. Library.

TOWN CREEK INDIAN MOUND STATE HISTORIC SITE
509 Town Creek Mound Rd. • MT. GILEAD, NC 27306
  (910) 439-6802 Fax 439-6441; Website: www.towncreek.ncmail.net
  E-Mail: towncreek@ncmail.net; Archie C. Smith, Jr., Site Manager
Description: A reconstructed 12th century Native American ceremonial center, based on archaeological data & early documents, includes town house on an earthen mound, priest house, mortuary, game pole, and stockade surrounding

the ceremonial area. Museum: Exhibits interpreting way of life of the Pee Dee culture at Town Creek. Includes artifacts discovered during excavation of the site. Special program: 18-minute video presentation on way of life of the Pee Dee culture at Town Creek; guided tours; Living history program, open-hearth cooking, Flint knapping, pottery, cordage, etc. *Activities*: Eastern Woodland Weekend in April; Native American Heritage Festival, last weekend in June, Native drum, singing, dance, food & craft vendors. Opened 1937.

MUSEUM OF THE SOUTHEAST AMERICAN INDIAN

University of North Carolina at Pembroke
P.O. Box 1510 • PEMBROKE, NC 28372
 (910) 521-6282; Website: www.uncp.edu/nativemuseum
 E-mail: nativemuseum@uncp.edu
 Nancy Strickland Fields, Director/Curator; E-mail: nancy.fields@uncp.edu
 Becky Goins, Associate Museum Curator; E-mail: becky.goins@uncp.edu
Description: The name of the Native American Resource Center has been changed to The Museum of the Southeast American Indian. As part of the Southeast American Indian Studies Program at UNC Pembroke, The Museum of the Southeast American Indian maximizes the capacity of the University to address the complex historical, cultural & contemporary issues facing American Indian communities in North Carolina & the American Southeast. The Museum's cross-disciplinary collaborations greatly enhance the University's programs of research, service, outreach & instruction. The Museum of the Southeast American Indian is a multi-faceted museum and resource for scholarly research and community outreach. The Museum contains exhibits of authentic Indian artifacts, arts & crafts from Indian communities all over the Americas, and especially from the American Southeast. Many items come from North Carolina Native communities, with special emphasis on Robeson County Indian people. Specific focus is placed on the largest North Carolina tribe, the Lumbee, but our outreach activities have extended into Virginia and South Carolina with plans for further outreach throughout the Southeast. *Mission*: to educate and serve the public about the prehistory, history, culture, art and contemporary issues of American Indians, with special emphasis on the Native American communities of Robeson County, of North Carolina and of the American Southeast; to conduct scholarly research; to collect and preserve the material culture of Native America; to encourage American Indian artists & crafts persons; and to cooperate on a wide range of research and service projects with other institutions and agencies concerned with American Indians. *Publications*: "Spirit!" quarterly newsletter; Along the Trail: A Reader About Native Americans; Robeson Trails Archaeological Survey. Library. Opened 1979.

MUSEUM OF ANTHROPOLOGY

Wake Forest University, Box 7267 • WINSTON-SALEM, NC 27109
 (919) 759-5282 Fax 759-5116; Website: www.wfu.edu/museum.html
 Dr. Mary Jane Berman, Director/Curator; E-Mail: berman@wfu.edu
Description: An anthropology museum exhibiting North & South American Indian cultures. *Special programs*: School tours and lectures, kindergarten to 8th grade; college classes, adult education; traveling exhibitions. Library. *Publication*: Newsletter; gallery guides. Opened 1963.

NORTH DAKOTA

TURTLE MOUNTAIN CHIPPEWA HERITAGE CENTER

Hwy. 5, P.O. Box 257 • BELCOURT, ND 58316
 (701) 477-6140; Website: www.chippewa.utma.com
 Denise Lajimodierre, CEO & Chair; Juanita Bennett, Director
Description: Maintains collections of Chippewa Indian artifacts and contemporary art. Opened 1981.

STATE HISTORICAL SOCIETY OF NORTH DAKOTA

North Dakota Heritage Center, Capitol Grounds • BISMARCK, ND 58505
 (701) 224-2666; James E. Sperry, Supt.
Description: Collections include ethnological, ethnographical, and prehistory materials of all types dating throughout the eras of known occupation of the northern Great Plains by human beings (circa 10,000 B.C. to present.) *Publications*: North Dakota History: Journal of the Northern Great Plains; Plains Talk, Newsletter. Archives & Library.

BUFFALO TRAILS MUSEUM

Box 22, Main St. • EPPING, ND 58801
 (701) 859-4082; John Hanson, President
Description: Depicts Indian culture native to the region (Upper Missouri area.) Exhibits Plains Indian artifacts; Diorama of Assiniboine Indian Village; Diorama of Fortified Hidatsa Village. *Publication*: Museum brochure. Library. Opened 1966.

NORTH DAKOTA MUSEUM OF ART

Box 7305, University Sta. • GRAND FORKS, ND 58202
 (701) 777-4195; Laurel J. Reuter, Director
Displays American Indian art.

MUSEUM OF THE BADLANDS

P.O. Box 198 • MEDORA, ND 58645
 (701) 623-4444
Description: Exhibits attire and crafts of North American Indian tribes.

FORT ABRAHAM LINCOLN STATE PARK

4480 Fort Lincoln Rd. • MANDAN, ND 58554
 (701) 667-6340 Fax 667-6349
 E-mail: falsp@state.nd.us; Website: www.state.nd.us/ndparks
 Dan Schelske, Director; Dale Carlson, Curator
Description: Museum houses artifacts from Great Plains tribes including the Mandan. There is also a reconstructed Mandan Indian Village within walking distance. *Special program*: Cultural Indian Celebration (Nu'Eta Corn & Buffalo Festival) held first weekend each August. Library. Established 1907.

THREE AFFILIATED TRIBES MUSEUM

P.O. Box 147 • NEW TOWN, ND 58763
 (701) 627-4477 Fax 627-3805; Website: www.mhanation.com
 E-Mail: tatmuseum@restel.net; Marilyn Hudson, Administrator
Description: History & cultural artifacts, including clothing, art & photos related to the Mandan, Hidatsa & Arikara people of the Fort Berthold Reservation in North Dakota from the early 1800's to the present time. *Programs*: Presentations at schools, meetings, symposiums, etc. Library. Opened 1964.

KNIFE RIVER INDIAN VILLAGES NATIONAL HISTORIC SITE

P.O. Box 9 • STANTON, ND 58571
 (701) 745-3300 Fax 745-3708; Website: www.nps.gov/knri
 Lisa Eckert, Supt.; E-mail: knri_info@nps.gov
Description: Established as a National Historic Site in 1974 to preserve remnants of the culture and agricultural lifeways of the Northern Plains Indians. Exhibits, an orientation film, and a full-sized earth lodge show the day-to-day life & customs of the Northern Plains Indians; includes Hidatsa/Mandan cultural artifacts. *Programs*: Weekend activities and special events may include demonstrations on gardening, hide tanning, tool making, clothing decorating, or Native American dancing; laboratory provides for continuing archaeological research. The Northern Plains Indian Culture Fest is in the 4h weekend of July. *Publication*: Brochure. Library. Opened 1974.

OHIO

MOUND CITY GROUP NATIONAL MONUMENT

16062 State Rt. 104 • CHILLICOTHE, OH 45601
 (614) 774-1125; William Gibson, Supt.; Robert Petersen, Park Ranger
Description: A 240-acre park preserving 23 burial mounds and two Hopewell earthen enclosures. Collections illustrate the wide spread Hopewell trade network between B.C. 200 & 500 A.D. Museum: Exhibits of Hopewell artifacts. Library. Opened 1923.

CINCINNATI ART MUSEUM

Eden Park • CINCINNATI, OH 45202
 (513) 721-5204 Fax 721-0129
 Barbara K. Gibbs, Director; Bill Mercer, Curator
Description: Displays archaeological & ethnographic objects. Archaeological -- principally Mound Builder, also Adena, Hopewell, Fort Ancient cultures from Ohio; stone, bone, metal, shell, and pottery from Tennessee and Arkansas; Casas Grandes pottery. Ethnographic collections primarily Northwest Coast, Plains and Pueblo pottery. Some prehistoric & historic Woodlands material in collection. Special collection: A permanent exhibition gallery for Native American art; periodic special temporary exhibitions programming (speakers and art demonstrations) related to Native American art. *Publication*: "Art of the First Americans" & "Singing the Clay: Pueblo Pottery of the Southwest Yesterday and Today" exhibition catalogs. Library. Opened 1881.

JOHNSON-HUMRICKHOUSE MUSEUM

300 N. Whitewoman St., Roscoe Village • COSHOCTON, OH 43812
 (740) 622-8710 Fax 622-8710 *51; Website: www.jhm.lib.oh.us
 E-mail: jhmuseum@clover.net
 Patti Malenke & Terry Reddick, Co-directors;
Description: Native American Gallery exhibits paleo to modern North American Indian & Inuit arts, crafts, basketry, beadwork, blankets & jewelry. Chronologically arranged prehistoric artifacts date back thousands of years and include projectile points, primitive tools & pottery made by Ohio's aboriginal people. *Special collection*: Indian-made baskets are displayed geographically, depicting various designs & styles from tribes coast to coast. Special programs: Educational programs. *Publication*: Quarterly newsletter; "American Indian Basketry," a catalog featuring baskets in the museum's collection. Reference library. Opened 1931.

RUTHERFORD B. HAYES PRESIDENTIAL CENTER

Spiegel Grove • FREMONT, OH 43420
 (800) 998-7737 Fax (419) 332-4952; Website: www.rbhayes.org

Dr. Murney Gerlach, Director; E-mail: mgerlach@rbhayes.org
Description: A collection of artifacts, largely of the Plains Indians, the Sioux, & some Pueblo; prehistoric Ohio Indian artifacts. *Publications*: The Statesman, newsletter. Library. Opened 1916.

FLINT RIDGE STATE MEMORIAL

The Ohio Historical Society, 7091 Brownsville Rd. SE • GLENFORD, OH 43739
(614) 787-2476; James Kingery, Site Manager
Andy Hite, Educational Specialist
Description: The museum is built around an original Hopewell Flint Quarry site and emphasizes the uses of flint by prehistoric Native Americans. Collections include art objects and other media representing achievements of the Adena & Hopewell cultures 1000 B.C. to 700 A.D. Special collection: Display objects made of flint; depict Native Americans quarrying & chipping the mineral. Programs are scheduled for the general public.

FORT ANCIENT MUSEUM

LEBANON, OH 45036 (513) 932-4421
Description: Located 7 miles southeast of Lebanon, 240 feet above the Little Miami River, the prehistoric Hopewell Indians (ca. 100 B.C. - A.D. 500) constructed earth and stone walls 4-23 feet high. Around A.D. 1200, groups of Fort Ancient Indians established themselves in villages. Exhibits models and life study groups of the Hopewell & Fort Ancient people who occupied the site. A National Historic Landmark.

SCHOENBRUNN VILLAGE STATE MEMORIAL

P.O. Box 129, East High Ave. • NEW PHILADELPHIA, OH 44663-0129
(216) 339-3636; Susan Goehring, Site Mgr.
Description: Founded by David Zeisberger in 1772 as a Moravian mission to the Delaware Indians. Restored to appear as it did over 200 years ago. Museum: Tells the story of the Christian Delawares and the Moravian missionaries at Schoenbrunn. Special program: Volunteer interpreters conduct daily life demonstrations in period costume. Publication: Schoenbrunn and the Moravian Missions in Ohio. Opened in 1923.

NEWARK EARTHWORKS STATE MEMORIAL
THE OHIO INDIAN ART MUSEUM

99 Cooper Ave. • NEWARK, OH 43055
(800) 589-8224; (740) 344-1919; Website: www.ohiohistory.org
Jim Kingery, Site Manager; E-Mail: jkingery@ohiohistory.org
Andy Hite, Education Specialist
Description: Prehistoric Indian Art Museum & Historic Site depicting The Great Circle Earthworks--ceremonial grounds of prehistoric Hopewell Indians, circa 1000 B.C. - 700 A.D. Exhibits art objects and other relics representing Adena & Hopewell cultures. The art museum is the nation's first museum devoted to prehistoric Native American art. It is centered around a prehistoric timeline. Exhibits follow this timeline from paleo to Fort Ancient peoples. Programs are scheduled for the general public.

INDIAN MUSEUM OF LAKE COUNTY

391 W. Washington • PAINESVILLE, OH 44077
(440) 352-1911; Ann L. Dewald, Director
Description: Houses pre-contact artifacts: crafts and art of Native North American cultures from 1800 to the present. Library. Opened 1980.

SERPENT MOUND MUSEUM

State Rt. 73, Box 234 • PEEBLES, OH 45660
(937) 587-2796; Website: www.ohiohistory.org
Keith A. Bengtson, Site Manager
Description: One of 63 sites maintained by the Ohio Historical Society. The museum has displays on the prehistoric cultures that occupied the area. *Special programs*: Archaeology Days Festival; 4th grade educational programs.

PIQUA HISTORICAL AREA STATE MEMORIAL
WOODLAND INDIAN MUSEUM

9845 N. Hardin Rd. • PIQUA, OH 45356-9707
(800) 752-2619; (937) 773-2522 Fax 773-4311
Andy Hite, Site Manager; E-mail: johnstonfarm@mail2.wesnet.com
Website: www.ohiohistory.org
Description: Restored 1829 home & outbuildings of federal Indian agent John Johnston. He was well respected by the Indians of Ohio and handled many of the important treaties of his era. The site has been recently renovated to include exhibits telling the story of the Woodland peoples of Ohio from the time of Euro-American contact to 1843. The impact of trade between these people is a major focus, as is the story of the Pickawillany village site, also a part of this 250-acre State Memorial. The story is told through objects of the time period, many from the site itself, and a life-size diorama featuring a trade scene between the Indians and an English trader. There are several interactive exhibits containing artifacts of Native American tools, art, canoes, costumes, etc. A collection of McKenney-Hall prints as well as Catlin prints are displayed. Museum shop. Opened 1972.

OKLAHOMA

CHICKASAW CULTURAL CENTER

520 E. Arlington St., P.O. Box 1548 • ADA, OK 74820
(405) 436-2603 Fax 436-7226
E-mail: cnation@chickasaw.com
Glenda A. Galvan, Director
Description: Preserves artifacts, pictures & items used by Chickasaws. *Activities*: Oral history videos, public speaking, demonstrations, storytelling, tours, traveling exhibits; Chickasaw language & genealogy research. Opened 1986.

DELAWARE TRIBAL MUSEUM

Delaware Cultural Preservation Office
P.O. Box 825 • ANADARKO, OK 73005
(580) 247-2448 Fax 247-9393
Website: www.delawarenation.com/nagpra.html
Tamara Francis, Director; Somier Harris, Office Coordinator
Jason Ross, Museum Assistant; Joan Subieta, Library Assistant

INDIAN CITY, USA, INC.

P.O. Box 695 • ANADARKO, OK 73005
(800) 433-5661; (580) 247-5661 Fax 247-2467
Website: www.indiancityusa.com; George F. Moran, Director
E-mail: info@indiancityusa.com
Description: Features reconstructed Plains Indian dwellings; also, Indian history museum located on site of 1887, Tonkawa Massacre. Exhibits Indian artifacts, including pottery, paintings, weapons, traditional clothing, dance costumes, and dolls. *Activities*: Guided tours through reconstructed Indian dwellings year 'round; traditional dance performances during summer months. Opened 1955.

NATIONAL HALL OF FAME FOR FAMOUS AMERICAN INDIANS

Hwy. 62, Box 808 • ANADARKO, OK 73005
(580) 247-3331 Fax 247-5571
Allie Reynolds, President; Paul T. Stonum, Executive V.P.
Description: An outdoor museum containing sculptured bronze portraits of famous American Indians in a landscaped area. Includes portraits of Will Rogers, Jim Thorpe, Pocahontas, Chief Joseph, Sacajawea, Chief Quanah Parker, Charles Curtis, Osceola, Sequoyah, Pontiac, Hiawatha, et al. *Special programs*: Annual dedication ceremonies in August, when an honoree is inducted; educational seminars regarding inductee's history and contribution to the American way of life.

SOUTHERN PLAINS INDIAN MUSEUM

715 E. Central Blvd., P.O. Box 749 • ANADARKO, OK 73005
(580) 247-6221 Fax 247-7593; Website: www.iacb.doi.gov
Rosemary Ellison, Curator
Description: Presents the richness and diversity of historic arts created by the tribal peoples of western Oklahoma, including the Kiowa, Comanche, Kiowa-Apache, Southern Cheyenne, Southern Arapaho, Wichita, Caddo, Delaware, and Fort Sill Apache. Exhibits the creative achievements of Native American artists & craftspeople of the U.S. Highlighting the exhibit is a display of the varied traditional costumes of Southern Plains men, women and children, presented in complete detail on life-size figures; four dioramas and a mural illustrating historic Indian cultural subjects, created by artist and sculptor, Allan Houser, a Fort Sill Apache and native Oklahoman. *Special programs*: Annual series of one-person exhibitions; demonstrations of Native American arts & crafts techniques; hosts events honoring Native-Americans; The American Indian Exposition, in August, features a week-long event of dance contests, arts & crafts; tours and Gallery discussions. *Publications*: Illustrated catalogs and brochures. Craft shop. Administered by the Indian Arts & Crafts Board. Opened 1947.

WICHITA & AFFILIATED TRIBES MUSEUM

P.O. Box 729 • ANADARKO, OK 73005
(580) 247-2425 Fax 247-2430
Description: General collection consists of very small displays depicting traditional homes, clothing, food, and/or household items; cultural artifacts of religious significance; pictures of tribal members and places of importance with explanations of mythology, religious occasions or ceremonials. Also traditional construction of dwellings with a display of a grass lodge diorama; and displays of various items found by archaeologists at several digging sites. *Publications*: Wichita Tribal Newsletter, quarterly; book - "The Wichita People," by W.W. Newcomb, Jr.; two pamphlets: "Wichita Memories" & "Southern Plains Lifeways," Apache & Wichita. Opened 1978.

APACHE HISTORICAL SOCIETY MUSEUM

101 W. Evans Ave. • APACHE, OK 73006
(580) 588-3392

FORT SILL APACHE TRIBAL MUSEUM

Rt. 2, Box 121 • APACHE, OK 73006
(580) 588-2298 Fax 588-3133; Ruey Barrow, Director

WOOLAROC MUSEUM
RR 3, Box 2100 • BARTLESVILLE, OK 74003
(918) 336-0307 Fax 336-0084; Website: www.woolaroc.org
Kenneth Meek, Interim Director
Description: Exhibits art and artifacts of the Plains & Southwest Indian tribes, as well as archaeological material from Oklahoma excavations & elsewhere. *Special program*: Docent-led tours. Publications. Library. Opened 1929.

CADDO HERITAGE MUSEUM
P.O. Box 487 • BINGER, OK 73009
(405) 656-2344 Fax 656-2892; Website: www.caddonation-nsn.gov
E-mail: museum@caddonation.org
Kim Penrod, Director; E-mail: kimpenrod@yahoo.com
E-mail: kpenrod@caddonation.org
Description: A collection of mostly Caddo pottery from archaeological sites in Louisiana, Texas, Arkansas & Oklahoma, as well as traditional dance regalia, artwork, photos, sound & video recordings. *Special programs*: Sponsors two exhibits each year, workshops, & various community outreach programs; annual dance. Library. Opened 2000.

MEMORIAL INDIAN MUSEUM
P.O. Box 483 • BROKEN BOW, OK 74728
(405) 584-6531; LaMarr Smith, Director
Description: A collection of prehistoric Indian artifacts, early beadwork; displays modern textiles and basketry. *Research*: Prehistoric Caddo Indians and their pottery. Library.

CADDO INDIAN TERRITORY MUSEUM & LIBRARY
108 Buffalo St. • CADDO, OK 74729 (580) 367-2787

KIOWA TRIBAL MUSEUM
P.O. Box 369 • CARNEGIE, OK 73015
(405) 654-2300 Fax 654-2188; Juanita Ahtone, Director
Exhibit: "The View From Rainy Mountain." The New Kiowa Murals by Parker Boyiddle, Mirac Creepingbear, & Sherman Chaddleson. Each artist produced three 6'x8' paintings depicting periods of Kiowa existence. Listening to their elders, they selected highlights from the creation stories, pre-history, and historic periods. A tenth mural, a collaborative painting represents Kiowa reality today and its journey into tomorrow.

WILL ROGERS MEMORIAL & BIRTHPLACE
P.O. Box 157 • CLAREMORE, OK 74018
(918) 341-0719; Website: www.willrogers.com
Joseph H. Carter, Director; Jim Williams, Ranch Manager
Description: Consists of eight main galleries displaying the personal effects and memorabilia belonging to Will Rogers. The family tomb adjoins the Memorial building. *Special collection*: The original manuscripts and papers belonging to Will Rogers. *Activity*: An annual Will Rogers Day celebration is held on November 4th to commemorate his birthday. Library.

CHEYENNE CULTURAL CENTER
RR 1 Box 3130 • CLINTON, OK 73601
(580) 323-6224; Lawrence H. Hart, Director

CHEYENNE & ARAPAHO TRIBES CULTURE & HERTAGE PROGRAM
700 N. Black Kettle Blvd., P.O. Box 38 • CONCHO, OK 73022
(800) 247-4612; (405) 422-7541 Fax 422-1184
Website: www.c-a-tribes.org; Goirdon Yellowman, Coordinator

FORT WASHITA HISTORIC SITE
Star rt. 213 • DURANT, OK 74701 (580) 924-6502
Description: Provided protection for the civilized Chickasaw & Choctaw Indians against the Plains Indians in the mid-1800's.

NO MAN'S LAND HISTORICAL MUSEUM
P.O. Box 278, Sewell St. • GOODWELL, OK 73939
(405) 349-2670 (phone & fax); Dr. Kenneth R. Turner, Director
Special collections: William E. Baker Archaeology Collection, W. Guy Clark Collection, & Duckett alabaster carvings. Contains artifacts of the Plains Indians collected by local residents of the Oklahoma Panhandle on their land to preserve the Indian cultures that preceded them on the land. Library. Opened 1932.

CHEROKEE COURTHOUSE
Rte. 2 Box 37-1 • GORE, OK 74435
(918) 489-5663; John Pruitt, Curator
Description: Displays & exhibits on the history of the Cherokee Indians.

MUSEUM OF THE RED RIVER
812 E. Lincoln Rd. • IDABEL, OK 74745
(580) 286-3616; Website: www.museumoftheredriver.org
Henry Moy, Director; E-mail: motrr@hotmail.com

Description: Collections include art & artifacts of historic, prehistoric & contemporary Native peoples of North & South America. Emphasis is on local Caddoan prehistory & early Oklahoma Choctaws. Regularly changing exhibits interpret other Native American arts & cultures. Library. *Publications*: Sherds, quarterly newsletter; leaflets supplement exhibits. Opened 1975.

KANZA MUSEUM
Drawer 50, 698 Grandview Dr. • KAW CITY, OK 74641
(405) 269-2552 Fax 269-2301; Website: www.southwind.net/kanza
James Pepper Henry, Director. Opened 1996.

COMANCHE NATIONAL MUSEUM & CULTURAL CENTER
701 NW Ferris Ave. • LAWTON, OK 73507
(580) 353-0404 Fax 492-3796; Website: www.comanchemuseum.com
E-mail: info@comanchemuseum.com; Phyllis Wahahrockah-Tasi, Director
Candy Morgan, Education & Public Programs Manager
Dr. Patsy Couts, Chairperson
Description: Tells the story of the Comanche people through interactive displays & historic artifacts. A place to preserve Comanche history, language & culture. *Programs*: Workshops, teaching programs & museum tours. Opened 2007.

MUSEUM OF THE GREAT PLAINS
601 NW Ferris Ave. • LAWTON, OK 73507
(580) 581-3460 Fax 581-3458; Website: www.museumgreatplains.org
E-mail: mgp@museumgreatplains.org; John Hernandez, Director
Deborah Baroff, Head Curator
Description: Maintains exhibits & artifacts representing the Plains Indian material culture from prehistoric times to the present. *Publications*: Great Plains Journal; newsletter; books for sale. Library.

ATALOA LODGE MUSEUM
Bacone College, 2299 Old Bacone Rd. • MUSKOGEE, OK 74403
(918) 683-4581 ext. 283 Fax 687-5913
Dr. Dennis Tanner, President; Thomas R. McKinney, Director
Description: Historic site. Displays Native American artifacts: rugs, beadwork, blankets, basketry, pottery and quillwork. *Special collections*: Large collection of San Ildenfonso pottery; items that were personal property of Native American chiefs; signed documents by President Abraham Lincoln & Chief John Ross of the Cherokee Nation. Library. *Publications*: Baconian and Smoke Signals, booklets; brochures on the museum. Opened 1967.

FIVE CIVILIZED TRIBES MUSEUM
1101 Honor Heights Dr. • MUSKOGEE, OK 74401
(918) 683-1701 Fax 683-3070; Website: www.fivetribes.org
E-mail: 5tribesdirector@sbcglobal.net
Lynn Hart Thornley, Director
Description: Exhibits art, artifacts, books, documents, and letters pertaining to the history & culture of the Cherokees, Choctaws, Creeks, Chickasaws, and Seminoles. Housed in the Indian Agency Building built in 1875. Depicts "Trail of Tears" travel and artifacts. Art Gallery of Traditional Indian Art, only by artists of Five Tribes heritage. Maintains an extensive art & sculpture collection, Jerome Tiger Originals; original carvings & sculptures of Willard Stone. *Special program*: Sponsors four competitive art shows annually - crafts, sculpture, paintings. *Publications*: Quarterly newsletter; Powwow Chow Cookbook; The Cherokees; The Muskogee Book; Limited edition artist signed art prints. Gift Shop. Library. Opened 1966.

THREE RIVERS MUSEUM
P.O. Box 1813 • MUSKOGEE, OK 74401
(918) 686-6624; Website: www.3riversmuseum.com
Linda Moore, Director

FRED JONES, JR. MUSEUM OF ART
University of Oklahoma, 410 W. Boyd St. • NORMAN, OK 73019
(580) 325-3272 Fax 325-7696; Website: www.ou.edu/fjjma
Eric M. Lee, Director/ Chief Curator
Description: Traditional & contemporary Native American art including painting, sculpture, ceramics, baskets & textiles. *Publications*: Exhibition catalogs. Library. Opened 1936.

OKLAHOMA MUSEUM OF NATURAL HISTORY
University of Oklahoma, 1335 Asp Ave. • NORMAN, OK 73019
(405) 325-4711; Dr. Michael A. Mares, Director
Description: Maintains a permanent exhibit on Oklahoma prehistory & historic Indian tribes; North American archaeological and ethnological specimens, depicting the development of Southern Plains, Southwest & Northwest Coast Indian cultures; also, material from the Spiro Mounds. *Special programs*: Educational; slide/tape programs: Wichita Memories, The Plains Apache, Native American Games, and Spiro Mounds. Publications: Newsletter; "Heritage at Risk"; Oklahoma Indian Artifacts. Opened 1899.

AMERICAN INDIAN CULTURAL CENTER & MUSEUM
900 N. Broadway, Suite 200 • OKLAHOMA CITY, OK 73102
(405) 239-5500; Website: www.theamericanindiancenter.org
Website: www.aiccm.com
Gena Timberman, Executive Director
Ryan Barnett, Director of Administration & Operations
Nancy Fields, Assistant to Outreach & Public Programs
Description: The center is in the process of development and will be opened in 2017. It will be a place to celebrate collective histories & contemporary cultural expressions. The Museum will be located at 659 American Indian Blvd. (405) 672-9477The collections will contain exhibitions & artifacts selected by members of the Oklahoma tribes from the national Smithsonian collection depicting the spirit & ethos of Native cultures. *Facilities*: Family Discovery Center; Film & Performance Venues; Gathering & Performance Forum; Orientation Theater; Oral History Theater. E-newsletter.

OKLAHOMA MUSEUM OF HISTORY
Oklahoma Historical Society
2100 N. Lincoln Blvd. • OKLAHOMA CITY, OK 73105
(405) 522-5248 Fax 522-5402
Website: www.ok-history.mus.ok.us
Dan Provo, Director
Jeff Moore, Ethnology Curator
Dennis W. Zotigh, American Indian Research Historian
Description: Maintains Indian & Regional History Museum exhibiting @ 3,000 prehistoric & 3,000 historic Indian artifacts; houses over a quarter of a million related photographs, 60,000 of which are of recent intertribal activities. Photos are from 1843 to the present, starting with the Cherokee Indian School. Collection includes 1,200 Indian music recordings and 600 oral interviews, 20% are on videotape & 600 recorded events including Indian conferences, powwows, meetings, dedications, etc. *Research*: OHS is one of several national locations serving as satellites of the National Archives and one of two Smithsonian Affiliates in the state of Oklahoma. The OHS Indian Archive includes more than 3.5 million documents and about 8,000 manuscripts, the majority of which are on microfilm. Included are the Indian Pioneer History Manuscripts from the 1937 Federal Writer's Project that includes over 400 subjects ranging from two-page documents to 100's of boxes. *Special programs*: The Oklahoma Museum is partnering with the National Museum of the American Indian (NMAI) to provide a database of original images of the NMAI collections relating to Oklahoma tribes. This database will be housed in the new Oklahoma Museum of History scheduled to open in November of 2005. The OHS has hired an American Indian to do specific tribal outreach for the new museum. His duties include meeting with Oklahoma's 39 tribal governments to collaborate appropriate content that will be included in the new museum. Included in this effort are interviews with Indian elders, ceremonial leaders and elected leaders. Currently, there are lectures and tours of the Indian Gallery available. A special traveling beading exhibit is also available. Library. Opened 1893.

RED EARTH INDIAN CENTER MUSEUM
2100 NE 52 St. • OKLAHOMA CITY, OK 73111
(405) 427-4228; Scott Tigert, Curator
Exhibits ethnographic items, late 1700s to present; paintings.

CREEK COUNCIL HOUSE MUSEUM
106 W. 6th • OKMULGEE, OK 74447
(918) 756-2324 Fax 756-3671
David Anderson, Director; Terry Bemis, President
Description: Displays arts & artifacts of the Muscogee (Creek) Nation. *Publications*: History & Legends of the Creek; Indians of Oklahoma; Creek Nation Capitol. Library. Red Stick Gallery Gift Shop has books on Muscogee history, culture and language. Opened 1923.

OSAGE NATION MUSEUM & LIBRARY
819 Grandview, P.O. Box 779 • PAWHUSKA, OK 74056
(918) 287-5441 Fax 287-1060
Website: www.osagetribe.com/museum
Kathryn Red Corn, Director
Description: Exhibits Osage artifacts, donations, books, clothing of the past; paintings, and pictures. *Special programs*: Culture classes - language (Osage); fingerweaving, ribbon work, beading on broadcloth, roach making; tribal history, Osage religion and family ties; workshops. Opened 1938.

PONCA CITY CULTURAL CENTER & MUSEUM
1000 E. Grand • PONCA CITY, OK 74601
(405) 767-0427; Kathy Adams, Director
Description: Collections feature clothing, utensils, photographs, weapons, art, musical instruments, and ceremonial materials of the tribes of the Ponca City area: the Osage, Kaw, Ponca, and Otoe; also, Hopi pottery & kachinas; relics from the early French-Indian trading post in Oklahoma; Northwest Coast material, and Quileute and other northern tribes' material. Library.

COO-Y-YAH COUNTY MUSEUM
P.O. Box 969 • PRYOR, OK 74362
(918) 825-2222
Description: Contains artifacts of Cherokee, Creek & Osage tribes.

SEQUOYAH'S HOME SITE
Rt. 1, Box 141 • SALLISAW, OK 74955
(918) 775-2413; Stephen Foster, Manager
Description: 1829 log cabin of Sequoyah, inventor of Cherokee Syllabary. Located 11 miles northeast of Sallisaw on State Hwy. 101. Includes personal furnishings and artifacts of the life of Sequoyah and western Cherokees. Special program: Computer printout of visitors name in Cherokee to help teach Cherokee language on site. Living history of early Cherokee life to large groups and schools. Library. Opened 1936.

CITIZEN POTAWATOMI NATION
CULTURAL HERITAGE CENTER MUSEUM
1601 S. Gordon Cooper • SHAWNEE, OK 74801
(405) 275-3121 Fax 275-0198; Website: www.potawatomi.org
Jon Boursaw, Executive Director; E-mail: jboursaw@potawatomi.org
Stacy Pero, Collections Manager; E-mail: spero@potawatomi.org
Grant Brittan, Tribal Heritage Project Manager
Description: Contains clothing and artifacts relevant to Citizen Potawatomi culture. *Activities*: Administers relevant culturally projects & programs on behalf of the Citizen Potawatomi Nation. Opened 1976.

SHAWNEE INDIAN MISSION
S. Gordon Cooper Dr. • SHAWNEE, OK 74801
Description: Located across from the Tecumseh Cemetery, this Society of Friends (Quakers) mission opened in 1871 and ministered to the local Indian tribes, mostly the Absentee Shawnee; for 53 years. Opened 1964.

DISTRICT CHOCTAW CHIEF'S HOUSE
P.O. Box 165 • SWINK, OK 74761
(405) 873-2301; Randle Swink, President; Gale Carter, Site Attendant
Description: An Historic 1832 Old Chief's House with furniture and furnishings of the 1800's. LeFlore family memorabilia - farm & ranch impliments. *Program*: Choctaw Trail of Tears tour. Opened 1994.

CHEROKEE NATIONAL MUSEUM (TSA-LA-GI)
Cherokee Heritage Center, P.O. Box 515 • TAHLEQUAH, OK 74464
(888) 999-6007; (918) 456-6007 Fax 456-6165
Website: www.cherokeeheritage.org
Carey Tilley, Executive Director; Michel Yantz, Museum Curator
Description: Located on the site of the original 1851 Cherokee Female Seminary and Ancient Village. The grounds contain a museum, Adams Corner (a typical Cherokee town in the 1800's), the Ancient Village (a typical Cherokee town in the 1600's), and an amphitheater for the outdoor "Trail of Tears: Nation" drama. Museum exhibits materials on Cherokee history, heritage & culture. *Activity*: The annual Trail of Tears Art Show is held in the Fall. Museum store. *Publication*: Columns Newsletter. Library.

CHICKASAW COUNCIL HOUSE MUSEUM
205 N. Fisher St. • TISHOMINGO, OK 73460
(580) 371-3351; Faye Orr, Director; Vickie Luster, Genealogist
Description: Indian museum exhibiting items pertaining to the history & culture--government, education, religious & social life--of the Chickasaw Indians. Emphasis is placed on the Chickasaw Governors, their families and administrations, from 1855 to the present day. Library. Opened 1971.

TONKAWA TRIBAL MUSEUM
RR 1 Box 436 • TONKAWA, OK 74653
(580) 628-5301 Fax 628-3378
Website: www.tonkawatribe.com/culture/museum.htm
Dawn Patterson, Director; Anna Beard & Cynthia Gould, Curators
Description: Tonkawa artifacts located in Tribal Housing Building. Opened 1970.

YELLOW BULL MUSEUM
Northern Oklahoma College, P.O. Box 310 • TONKAWA, OK 74653

PHILBROOK MUSEUM OF ART
2727 S. Rockford Rd., P.O. Box 52510 • TULSA, OK 74152
(800) 324-7941; (918) 749-7941 Fax 743-4230
Website: www.philbrook.org; E-mail: museumdirector@philbrook.org
Brian Ferriso, Executive Director
Special collections: Clark Field Collection--American Indian Basketry & Pueblo Pottery; Roberta Campbell Lawson Collection of American Indian Costumes & Artifacts; Philbrook Collection of American Indian Paintings; The Bright Roddy & Ellis Soper Collections of American Indian Artifacts; Artist Biographies. *Special programs*: Friends of Native American Art; Internships. *Publications*: Visions &

Voices: Native American Painting From the Philbrook Museum of Art (1996); Woven Worlds: Basketry From the Clark Field Collection (2001). Library. Opened 1939.

GILCREASE MUSEUM
1400 Gilcrease Museum Rd. • TULSA , OK74127
(918) 596-2700 Fax 596-2770; Website: www.gilcrease.utulsa.edu
Duane H. King, Executive Director & VP of Museum Affairs
Robert B. Pickering, Senior Curator
Eric Singleton, Assistant Curator of Anthropology
Lanette Coppage, Director of Education & Public Programs
Carole Klein, Associate Curator of Art
Randy Ramer, Director of Exhibitions & Publications
Description: The world's largest collection of art of the American West. The story of many cultures of North America is told through art, documents & artifacts from the pre-Columbian era through the 20th century. Exhibits artifacts relating to the culture of the Five Civilized Tribes. Internships: Charles Banks Wilson Internship for Native American Studies. Publications: Gilcrease Journal, Biannual; Catlin Catalogue. Library. Museum store.

CHOCTAW NATION MUSEUM
HC 64, Box 3270 • TUSKAHOMA, OK 74574
(918) 569-4465; Website: www.choctawnationculture.com/museum
Sue Folsom, Executive Director; E-mail: sfolsom@choctawnation.com
Regina Green, Director; E-mail: rgreen@choctawnation.com
Description: Located in the historic Choctaw Capitol Museum Building, built in 1884 and located at Tvshka Homma, Oklahoma; a three-story red brick & sandstone structure was completed in 1884 and houses the courtroom which seats three tribal judges appointed by the present Choctaw Chief. Exhibits: Trail of Tears; Choctaw History, Culture & Family Life Exhibits. Contains artifacts such as bone spoons, clay pots, and arrowheads; also items moved over the Trail of Tears are displayed; a spinning wheel & iron pots; vintage clothing, old documents & Choctaw pottery. Guided tours available. Gift Shop. Opened 1975.

SEMINOLE NATION MUSEUM
524 S. Wewoka Ave., P.O. Box 1532 • WEWOKA, OK 74884
(405) 257-5580 Fax 257-5580
Website: www.theseminolenationmuseum.org
E-mail: director@theseminolenationmuseum.org
Leta Smith, Administrator; Margaret Jane Norman, Curator
Description: Maintains exhibits & artifacts relating to the history of the Oklahoma Seminoles, the Freedmen, early pioneers and oil boom history of the area. Special exhibits: Dioramas depicting the Indian Stick Ball Game, The Seminole Whipping Tree, a life-size replica of the Florida Seminole home (Chickee), & exhibits depicting the Florida Seminoles, The Seminole Hunter Warrior, Law-Man (Lighthorseman), and Medicine Man. Special programs: Heritage Day - May 22; Sorghum Day - 4th Saturday of October; Annual Bazaar - Friday before Thanksgiving. Publication: Annual newsletter; Este Cate, a history of the Seminoles written by Museum Director, Tuskahoma B. Miller. Gift shop. Library. Opened 1974.

PLAINS INDIANS & PIONEERS MUSEUM
2009 Williams Ave. • WOODWARD, OK 73801
(580) 256-6136 Fax 256-2577; Louise B. James, Director
Description: Collection consists of archival materials, agricultural equipment, items from early settlers, and local Plains Indian items, including beadwork, tools & clothing. Special programs: Lectures. Library. Publication: "Below Devil's Gap", a history of Woodward County. Opened 1966.

JIM THORPE'S HOME
706 East Boston Ave. • YALE, OK 74085
(918) 387-2815; Website: www.jimthorpehistoricalhome.com

OREGON

HIGH DESERT MUSEUM
59800 S. Hwy. 97 • BEND, OR 97702
(541) 382-4754; Janeanne A. Upp, President
Description: The Henry J. Casey Hall of Plateau Indians - exhibit of Indian culture and art from before European settlement up to the present.

UNIVERSITY OF OREGON MUSEUM OF NATURAL HISTORY
1680 E. 15th Ave. • EUGENE, OR 97403
(541) 346-3024 Fax 346-5334
Website: www.natural-history.uoregon.edu
C. Melvin Aikens, Director; E-Mail: mnh@oregon.uoregon.edu
Description: Holdings include archaeological collections, primarily from Oregon and Alaska, and ethnographic collections from around the world. Programs: Occasional lectures and workshops on Native American topics. Small reference library. Publications: Field notes, quarterly newsletter; museum bulletin series. Opened 1936.

COLLIER STATE PARK LOGGING MUSEUM
P.O. Box 428 • KLAMATH FALLS, OR 97601
Description: Located on the Klamath Indian Reservation, the museum exhibits Indian stone utensils and unexcavated pit houses. Library.

FAVELL MUSEUM OF WESTERN ART & INDIAN ARTIFACTS
125 W. Main • KLAMATH FALLS, OR 97601
(541) 882-9996 Fax 850-0125; Website: www.favellmuseum.org
Gene H. Favell, Director
Description: Exhibits contemporary Western and wildlife art; 60,000 arrowheads; pictographs, baskets, pottery. Publication: The Favell Museum: A Treasury of Our Western Heritage. Opened 1972.

LINFIELD ANTHROPOLOGY MUSEUM
Linfield College • McMINNVILLE, OR 97128
(503) 472-4121. Special collection: John Dulin Native American Art Collection.

TAMASTSLIKT CULTURAL INSTITUTE
72789 Hwy. 331 • PENDLETON, OR 97801
(541) 966-9748 Fax 966-9927; Website: www.tomastslikt.com
Roberta Conner, Director; Malissa Minthorn-Winks, Archives Manager
Marjorie Waheneka, Temporary Exhibits Manager
Mike Cooper. Facility Manager; Susan Shoeships, Education Coordinator
Feather Huesties, Administrative Officer
Description: Exhibits which displays the history and culture of the Cayuse, Walla Walla, & Umatilla Tribes. Exhibits chronicle thousands of years on the Columbia Plateau before, during and after contact with Europeans. Research library. Museum store. Opened 1998.

OREGON HISTORY MUSEUM
1200 SW Park Ave. • PORTLAND, OR 97205
(503) 222-1741
Description: Extensive Native American collections include a large display of rare baskets; artifacts of village life, clothing, carvings and other art objects & historic photographs; also, a full-size totem pole.

PORTLAND ART MUSEUM
1219 SW Park Ave. • PORTLAND, OR 97205
(503) 226-2811 Ext. 231; Dan Monroe, President
Paul Faulstick, Curator-Native American Art
Special collections: Axel Rasmussen Collection of Northwest Indian Art--Contains approximately 500 objects--items of dress, tools and equipment used in hunting and fishing; also, Eskimo pieces; Pueblo Indian ceramic pieces & prehistoric stone sculpture from the Columbia River basin. Also, the Butler Collection-includes about 1,800 pieces dating from the 18th century to the 20th century from virtually every tribe and geographic region in the U.S. Publication: Art in the Life of the Northwest Coast Indian. Library.

SACAJAWEA CENTER
200 Main St. • SALMON, ID 83467
(208) 756-1188 Fax 756-4840; Website: www.sacajaweacenter.org

MUSEUM AT WARM SPRINGS
P.O. Box C • WARM SPRINGS, OR 97761
(541) 553-3331 Fax 553-3338
Website: www.warmsprings.com; Website: www.tmaws.org
Carol Leone, Executive Director
Evaline Patt, Archiving; E-mail: epatt@wstribes.org
Description: Created by the Confederated Tribes of Warm Springs. The museum contains more than 2,500 artifacts interpreting the culture & heritage of the Warm Springs, Wasco, and Paiute tribes in a 25,000 square foot building. In addition to its permanent exhibit, there are four shows a year in its changing exhibits gallery. Opened 1993.

PENNSYLVANIA

LENNI LENAPE HISTORICAL SOCIETY MUSEUM OF INDIAN CULTURE
2825 Fish Hatchery Rd. • ALLENTOWN, PA 18103
(610) 797-2121 Fax 797-2801; Website: www.museumofindianculture.org
E-mail: info@museumofindianculture.org
James Albany, President; Nome Alexander, Curator
Description: The heritage of the Lenni Lenape (Delaware Indians), the earliest known inhabitants of the Lehigh Valley. The museum exhibits inter-tribal artifacts and a traditional village and gardens. Special programs: Off-site American Indian Cultural Education Programs; pre-school, school, youth groups, special interest groups, as well as public workshops; Life Ways Demonstrations; Spring Corn Festival in May; Roasting Ears of Corn Ceremony, in August; & A Time of Thanks-giving, in October; slide/lectures, and arts & crafts workshops; speaker's bureau. Publications: The Time of the Autumn Moon; Native American Cookbook; Quarterly newsletter. Library. Gift Shop. Opened 1981.

THE POCONO INDIAN MUSEUM
Rt. 209, P.O. Box 1222 • BUSHKILL, PA 18324
  (570) 588-9338; E-mail: dream38@ptd.net
  Website: www.poconoindianmuseum.com
Description: Traces the history of the Delaware Indians through displays of ancient artifacts, weapons, & tools that form chronological commentary on life among the Indians for thousands of years. Library. Museum gift shop, also online. Open 7 days a week.

CUMBERLAND COUNTY HISTORICAL SOCIETY MUSEUM
21 North Pitt St., P.O. Box 626 • CARLISLE, PA 17013
  (714) 249-7610
Special collection: Carlisle Indian School (1879-1918) Collection -- Contains photographs, publications, and memorabilia. *Publications*: An Account of Illustrated Talks to Indian Chiefs, by Charles F. Himes; and The Indian Industrial School at Carlisle: Its Origin, Purpose, Progress and Difficulties, by Richard H. Pratt. *Programs*: Educational for county's school districts. Hamilton Library. *Publication*: Journal & newsletters.

BUSHY RUN BATTLEFIELD PARK
P.O. Box 468 • HARRISON CITY, PA 15636
Description: Located on the site of Chief Pontiac's rebellion of 1763. Museum: Contains copies of maps and letters relating to the Campaign of 1763, Pontiac's War; exhibits Indian artifacts.

HERSHEY MUSEUM
170 W. Hersheypark Dr. • HERSHEY, PA 17033
  (717) 534-3439; David L. Park, Jr., Director
  James D. McMahon, Jr., Curator
Description: The Hershey Museum began as the Hershey Indian Museum in 1933 and showcased the collection of Col. John Worth. He put together his extensive collection at the end of the 19th century. The museum has artifacts from the Eastern Woodland tribes, including archaeological objects from the Susquehannocks, as well as items representing Southwest, Plains, and Northwest Coast tribes. The museum also has an Eskimo collection.

THE AMERICAN INDIAN TRADING POST & EXHIBIT
United Indians of Delaware Valley
225 Chestnut St. • PHILADELPHIA, PA 19106
  (215) 574-0902 Fax 574-9024; Michelle Leonard, Director

CARNEGIE MUSEUM OF NATURAL HISTORY
4400 Forbes Ave. • PITTSBURGH, PA 15213
  (412) 665-2600 or 622-3131; Website: www.carnegiemnh.org
  Dr. Marsha C. Bol, Curator
Description: An American Indian Hall.

READING PUBLIC MUSEUM
500 Museum Rd. • READING, PA 19611
  (610) 371-5850; Website: www.readingpublicmuseum.org
  Ronald C. Roth, Director & CEO
Description: Exhibit includes examples of cultural materials, pottery, clothing, tools, toys, ceremonial objects of the following cultural areas: Woodland, Plains, Southwest Desert, California, Northwest Coast, and Inuit. *Special collections*: Study collection of southeastern Pennsylvania lithic objects, approximately 10,000 pieces; study collection of mound pottery; Speck Collection--Delaware material collected during Speck's research of Oklahoma & Canadian dwellings of Delaware peoples. *Special program*: A Museum-School Native-American Studies Project--Elementary education programs for local schools using exhibit areas and Museum classroom lessons. Publications. Library. Opened 1904.

EVERHART MUSEUM OF NATURAL HISTORY, SCIENCE & ART
1901 Mulberry St., Nay Aug Park • SCRANTON, PA 18510
  (570) 346-7186 Fax 346-0652; Website: www.everhart-museum.org
Description: Maintains American Indian Gallery with exhibits of American Indian art covering five major regions of the U.S. Library.

RHODE ISLAND

HAFFENREFFER MUSEUM OF ANTHROPOLOGY
Brown University, Mt. Hope Grant
300 Tower St. • BRISTOL, RI 02809
  (401) 253-8388 Fax 253-1198
  Website: www.brown.edu/facilities/haffenreffer
  E-mail: haffenreffermuseum@brown.edu
  Steven Lubar, Director; E-mail: steven_lubar@brown.edu
  Kevin P. Smith, Deputy Director & Chief Curator
    E-mail: kevin_p_smith@brown.edu
Description: Located on the lands significant to the Wampanoag peoples, the museum houses artifacts from the native peoples of the Americas and indigenous cultures from around the world. Collections of 15,000 ethnographic objects and 70,000 archaeological specimens. Extensive prehistoric Arctic collections. *Special programs*: Education programs for school children; lectures and seminars. *Publications*: Burris Hill: A 17th Century Wampanoag Burial Ground in Warren, RI; Hau, Kola! The Plains Indian Collection of the Haffenreffer Museum of Anthropology; Out of the North: The Subarctic Collection of the Haffenreffer Museum of Anthropology; Passionate Hobby: Rudolf Haffenreffer and the King Philip Museum; Gifts of Pride and Love: Kiowa and Comanche Cradles. Library. Opened 1956.

TOMAQUAG INDIAN MEMORIAL MUSEUM
Dovecrest Indian Cultural Center-Arcadia Village
390 Summit Rd. • EXETER, RI 02822
  (401) 491-9063 or 539-7213
  Website: www.tomaquagmuseum.com
  Loren M. Spears, Executive Director
Description: Archaeology, ethnology, and natural history exhibits related to southern New England Indian cultures; basketry of the Northeast. Facilities: Nuweetooun School. *Special programs*: Native American educational programs - dance, history, customs & culture, song & ceremony; storytelling; Thanksgiving program. *Publications*: Indians of Southern New England, by Princess Red Wing; Musical Expressions of Early Indians of Rhode Island; Indian Communications. Gift shop. Library. Opened 1954.

MUSEUM OF PRIMITIVE ART & CULTURE
1058 Kingstown Rd., P.O. Drawer A • PEACE DALE, RI 02883
  (401) 783-5711; Sarah Peabody Turnbaugh, Director
Description: An archaeological & ethnology museum exhibiting artifacts from around the world, with an emphasis on North America and especially the Northeast. *Special programs*: Community-oriented multicultural programming; evening lecture series; public education program; gift shop. *Publication*: "The Nineteenth-Century American Collector: A Rhode Island Perspective" (centennial catalog), 1992. Opened 1892.

RHODE ISLAND HISTORICAL SOCIETY MUSEUM
52 Power St. • PROVIDENCE, RI 02906
  (401) 331-8575; Nina Zannieri, Curator
Description: Maintains a collection of 11,000 objects & artifacts pertaining to Rhode Island history; displays Narragansett & Wampanoag Tribes' artifacts-- stone bowls, baskets, metal combs, jewelry, hair ornaments. *Publication*: Rhode Island History, journal. Library.

MUSEUM OF NATURAL HISTORY - ROGER WILLIAMS PARK
1000 Elmwood Ave. • PROVIDENCE, RI 02907
  (401) 785-9457 Ext. 221
  Website: www.providenceri.com/museum
  Elizabeth R.T. Fradin, Director; Marilyn Massaro, Curator
Description: Archaeological and ethnological collections from North America. *Special program*: An educational kit - Native Americans in the Northeast: An Archaeological Perspective. Exhibits feature Woodland Indian culture--model village; canoe; model Pueblo; Plains and Northwest Coast Indian artifacts; Eskimo material; American Indian plants; and maps. *Publication*: The Explorer Newsletter. Library. Opened 1896.

SOUTH CAROLINA

McKISSICK MUSEUM - UNIVERSITY OF SOUTH CAROLINA
College of Arts & Sciences • 816 Bull St. • COLUMBIA, SC 29208
  (803) 777-7251 Fax 777-2829; Website: www.cas.sc.edu/mcks
  Lynn Robertson, Executive Director; E-mail: robertso@mailbox.sc.edu
  Jill Koverman, Curator of Collections
Description: Exhibits more than 200 Catawba Indian pottery & baskets from the 19th & 20th centuries; Folk Art Resource Center with primary and secondary sources on South Carolina Indians.

FLORENCE MUSEUM
558 Spruce St. • FLORENCE, SC 29501
  (843) 662-3351; Website: www.florencemuseum.org
  E-mail: florencemuseum@me.com
  Andrew R. Stout, Director
Description: Collection includes Southwestern Pueblo pottery. *Special program*: Children's program available by appointment. Opened 1924.

CATAWBA CULTURAL CENTER
1536 Tom Steven Rd. • ROCK HILL, SC 29730
  (803) 328-2427 Fax 328-5791; E-mail: kcgw@ccppcrafts.com
  Beckee Garris, Director
Description: Houses departments of archaeology, language, archives, and exhibits and offers classes in Native arts on a weekly basis. The Center teaches Catawba history to the tri-county school district, area tour groups, and other local organizations. *Activities*: Powwow, The Yap Ye Iswa festival is held the Saturday after Thanksgiving. Opened 1989.

SOUTH DAKOTA

DACOTAH PRAIRIE MUSEUM
21 S. Main St., P.O. Box 395 • ABERDEEN, SD 57402
(605) 626-7117 Fax 626-4026
Website: www.dacotahprairiemuseum.com
Sue Gates, Director
Description: Exhibits Sioux (Lakota) artifacts--beadwork, quillwork, decorated ceremonial & functional leather items, tools, pictographs, and photographs. *Special program*: Lectures. Sales shop features contemporary Sioux handicrafts. Opened 1969.

SOUTH DAKOTA STATE AGRICULTURAL HERITAGE MUSEUM
SDSU Box 601 • BROOKINGS, SD 57007
(877) 227-0015; (605) 688-6226 Fax 688-6303
Website: www.agmuseum.com
E-mail: agmuseum@sdstate.edu
Special collection: Indian Agricultural Heritage Collection of South Dakota. Reference Library.

AKTA LAKOTA MUSEUM & CULTURAL CENTER
St. Joseph's Indian School, P.O. Box 89 • CHAMBERLAIN, SD 57325
(800) 798-3452; (605) 734-3455 Fax 734-3388
Website: www.aktalakota.org; E-mail: aktalakota@stjo.org
Jim O'Donnell, Director
Description: The Akta Lakota Museum is a tribute to the Sioux Nation striving to preserve & promote Sioux heritage & culture. Displays Native American art & artifacts; a collection of first class beadwork & quillwork. *Programs*: Visiting artists present lectures & shows; school tours; Native American history research. Library. Opened 1991.

CRAZY HORSE MEMORIAL & INDIAN MUSEUM OF NORTH AMERICA
12151 Avenue of the Chiefs • CRAZY HORSE, SD 57730
(605) 673-4681 Fax 673-2185; Website: www.crazyhorsememorial.org
E-mail: memorial@crazyhorse.org; Anne Ziolkowski, Director
Description: Maintains a collection of art and artifacts reflecting the diverse histories and cultures of the American Indian people. The Museum, designed to complement the story being told in stone on the mountain, speaks eloquently to present and future generations about American Indian life. *Special collections*: Sculpture, furniture and art work of Korczak Ziolkowski, creator of Crazy Horse Memorial. *Special programs*: Scholarship program for Native American students attending institutions of higher education in South Dakota; college classes offered on site in cooperation with Black Hills State University; Summer Lecture and Performance Series, and educational activities for students visiting the Indian Museum of North America. *Publications*: Books - Crazy Horse and Korczak; The Saga of Sitting Bull's Bones; 50th Anniversary of Crazy Horse Memorial; Indian Museum of North America; and Crazy Horse coloring books. Serial publication, Crazy Horse Progress, 3/yr. Library. Established 1948 and opened 1974.

HARVEY V. JOHNSON LAKOTA CULTURAL CENTER MUSEUM
Cheyenne River Sioux Reservation, P.O. Box 590 • EAGLE BUTTE, SD 57625
(605) 964-2542 Fax 964-4151; Website: www.sodak.net/~lakotaculture
James Picotte, Director
Description: Maintains a small exhibit of locally beaded artifacts dating back to the early 1800s, six large murals that decorate the rotunda, and photographs of the early years on the reservation. Gift shop. Opened 1973.

SICANGU HERITAGE CENTER MUSEUM & ARCHIVES
SINTE GLESKA UNIVERSITY
Antelope Lake Campus, P.O. Box 675 • MSSION, SD 57555
(605) 856-8211 Fax 856-5027
Website: http://www.sintegleska.edu/heritage-center.html
E-mail: heritagecenter@sintegleska.edu
Marcella Cash (Rosebud Lakota), Archivist/Director (856-8232)
Keli Herman, Museum Collections Manager (856-8211)
Purpose: To collect & preserve paper, objects & sites which document the history & culture of the Sicangu (Brule) people and to use the materials to educate tribal members & interested others. *Program*: The Lakota Archives & Historical Research Center (LAHRC). Collect, preserve, and make available to researchers, original materials e.g. papers, maps, oral histories, photos, and newspapers. Research library.

DAKOTA DISCOVERY MUSEUM
Dakota Wesleyan University
1300 E. University Dr. • MITCHELL, SD 57301
(605) 996-2122
Description: Collections of Indian artifacts includes beadwork, quillwork, clothing, dolls, etc. Tribes represented include the Sioux, Meti Chippewa-Ojibway, and Plains Cree. Four art galleries feature works by Oscar Howe, Leland Case, Charles Hargens, and other Indian artists of the Northern Plains.

MITCHELL PREHISTORIC INDIAN VILLAGE ARCAEOLOGICAL SITE
3200 Indian Village Rd. • MITCHELL, SD 57301
(605) 996-5473
Description: A 1,000-year old former Plains village. Facility: Museum houses a reconstructed life-sized lodge and many displays relating to village life.

OSCAR HOWE CULTURAL CENTER
119 W. 3rd • MITCHELL, SD 57301 (605) 996-4111
Description: A collection of twelve paintings by Oscar Howe of Native Americans in Wisconsin.

THE HERITAGE CENTER
Red Cloud Indian School
100 Mission Dr. • PINE RIDGE, SD 57770
(605) 867-5491 Fax 867-1291; Website: www.redcloudschool.org
Website: www.sinte.edu; Peter Strong, Director
Description: Maintains Indian Art Museum which is housed in 1888 Holy Rosary Mission, scene of Battle day after the Wounded Knee Massacre; maintains a collection of paintings by Native American artists from many different tribes; also, starquilt collection; Oglala Sioux beadwork and quillwork collection; and small pottery collection; graphics, Inuit prints, and Northwest Coast prints. *Special program*: Traveling shows; Red Cloud Indian Art Show held every summer. Publications: Standing Soldier: A Retrospective; Five Families: An Art Exhibition. Library. Opened 1982.

WHITE RIVER VISITOR CENTER
Rocky Fort RR • PORCUPINE, SD 57772
(605) 455-2878; (608) 698-7058; Fr. Norman Volk, Director
Description: Maintains Indian cultural exhibits and an audiovisual program.

SIOUX INDIAN MUSEUM
222 New York St., P.O. Box 1504 • RAPID CITY, SD 57701
(605) 394-2381 Fax 348-6182; Website: www.journeymuseum.org
E-mail: journey@journeymuseum.org
Description: Administered by the Indian Arts & Crafts Board of the U.S. Dept. of the Interior. Exhibits historic Sioux arts and other Native American arts & crafts of the U.S.; a permanent exhibit presents the rich diversity of historic Sioux arts and a special exhibition gallery is devoted to changing presentations promoting the creative works of outstandingly talented contemporary Native artists & craftsmen. *Special program*: One-person exhibition series with demonstrations of contemporary Native American arts & crafts techniques in a variety of media; tours. Brochures. Opened 1939.

BUECHEL MEMORIAL LAKOTA MUSEUM
St. Francis Mission, 350 S. Oak St.
P.O. Box 499 • ST. FRANCIS, SD 57572
(800) 808-8730; (605) 747-2361 Fax 747-5057
Website: www.sfmission.org; E-mail: sfmission@gwtc.net
Marie Kills In Sight, Museum Director; Fr. John Hatcher, SJ, Mission President
Description: Sioux Indian Museum exhibits ethnographic material (over 3,000 artifacts, and 2,100 photos) of the reservation period of the Rosebud and Pine Ridge Sioux. Church artifacts. *Special collections*: "Crying for a Vision" - photo exhibit; Rosebud Sioux quilts. *Publications*: A Grammar of Lakota; Everyday Lakota; Dictionary; Bible History in Lakota; Lakota Prayer Book; Lakota Names and Traditional Uses of Native Plants by Sigangu People; Crying for a Vision; A Rosebud Sioux Trilogy; Bettelyoun Manuscripts; Walker Papers; Buechel's Diary; and documents relating to Sioux culture. Museum store with Indian arts & crafts for sale. Resource Library. Opened 1947.

CENTER FOR WESTERN STUDIES
Augustana College, 2001 S. Summit Ave.
P.O. Box 727 • SIOUX FALLS, SD 57197
(800) 727-2844; (605) 274-4007 Fax 274-4999
Website: www.augie.edu/cws; E-mail: cws@augie.edu
Harry F. Thompson, Executive Director
Timothy M. Hoheisel, Director of Outreach & Communications
Description: An Historical Research & Archival Agency that maintains a collection of Native American (mostly Sioux) artwork & artifacts; Archive & Manuscript collections. *Research*: Native Americans. *Publications*: Sundancing at Rosebud & Pine Ridge; Yanktmai Sioux Water Colors; The Last Contrary; Tomahawk and Cross. Research Library. Book & Gift Shop.

SIOUXLAND HERITAGE MUSEUMS
200 W. 6th St. • SIOUX FALLS, SD 57104
(605) 367-4210 Fax 367-6004; Website: www.siouxlandmuseums.com
E-Mail: museum@minnehahacounty.org; Theresa Norman, Director
Special collections: The Pettigrew-Drady Collection: Objects & photographs related to the tribes of the Northern Plains. Chief emphasis is on Dakota (Sioux) Indian artifacts, circa 1870-1920, including: clothing, tools, pipes, weapons, tepee, Ghost Dance shirt; and a Photograph Collection covering 1870-1900. Library.

TEKAKWITHA FINE ARTS CENTER
401 S. 8th Ave. W., P.O. Box 208 • SISSETON, SD 57262
 (605) 698-7058 Fax 698-3801; Fr. Norman Volk, Director
Description: Maintains a collection of two dimensional art of the Lake Traverse Dakotah Sioux Reservation. *Activities*: Sponsors art festivals, concerts, workshops, and the annual Coteau Heritage Festival. Museum store.

BEAR BUTTE STATE PARK
Black Hills of South Dakota • STURGIS, SD 57785
 (605) 347-5240; Website: www.black-hills-south-dakota.com/bearbutte.htm
 E-mail: bearbutte@state.sd.us; William A. Gullet, Park Manager
Description: Located on a Native-American traditional religious site, 6 miles NE of Sturgis off SD Hwy. 79. *Museum*: Exhibits archaeological site materials; Native-American clothing & religious artifacts. *Research*: Native-American Indian religion, anthropology, archaeology & geography.

W.H. OVER MUSEUM
414 East Clark • VERMILLION, SD 57069-2390
 (605) 677-5228; Website: http://www.usd.edu/whom/
Displays Sioux artifacts from the late 19th century to the present. Lakota Family Tipi Exhibit. *Special collections*: Clark Memorial Collection of Lakota Artifacts; and Stanley J. Morrow Historical Photographs, 1869-1883. *Programs*: Tours, school loan kits. Library. Opened 1883.

WOUNDED KNEE MUSEUM
Located off Exit 110 on I-90 • WALL, SD
 (605) 279-2573; Website: www.woundedkneemuseum.org

DAKOTA TERRITORIAL MUSEUM
P.O. Box 1033 • YANKTON, SD 57078
Description: Exhibits Indian artifacts from the Dakota Territory, and the history of Yankton.

TENNESSEE

RED CLAY STATE HISTORICAL PARK
1140 Red Clay Park Rd., S.W. • CLEVELAND, TN 37311
 (423) 478-0339 Fax 614-7251; Website: www.tnstateparks.com
 Lois I. Osborne, Park Manager
Description: The 1832-1838 seat of the Cherokee Government, and site of 11 General Councils on national affairs. The visitor's center at Red Clay illuminates 19th century Cherokee life in the early republic and details the federal removal policy and the 1838 military removal of Cherokees from eastern Tennessee. *Collection*: Paleo, Archaic, Mississippian, Woodland, and historical period artifacts. Trail of Tears exhibit. *Research*: Cherokee Removal Story, 1832-1838. "The Cherokee Days," festival in August. Small Research Library of Cherokee history.

OLD STONE FORT ARCHAEOLOGICAL PARK
732 Stone Fort Dr., Rt. 7, Box 7400 • MANCHESTER, TN 37355
 (931) 723-5073; Ward Weems, Site Manager
Description: This 876-acre park offers The Old Stone Fort, a 2,000-year-old American Indian ceremonial site. It consists of mounds & walls that combine with cliffs & rivers to form an enclosure measuring 1-1/4 mile around. A museum exhibits Native American cultures. *Special programs*: Educational & entertaining programs. An exhibit hall complex includes exhibits relating to the history, archaeology, and legends surrounding the Old Stone Fort and its builders.

C.G. NASH MUSEUM - CHUCALISSA MUSEUM & ARCHAEOLOGICAL SITE
The University of Memphis, 1987 Indian Village Dr. • MEMPHIS, TN 38109
 (901) 785-3160 Fax 785-0519
 Website: www.chucalissa.org; E-mail: chucalissa@memphis.edu
 Robert Connolly, Director; E-mail: rcnnolly@memphis.edu
Description: Preserves the site of a 15th-century Mississippian-period village (in western Tennessee) partially reconstructed with life-size dioramas. The exhibit hall displays Southeast Indian culture, a collection of Indian artifacts from the site and adjacent areas. *Special programs*: group tours; demonstrations of hunting technologies; lecture series; Native American Days (end of October); Powwows; Changing exhibits; Choctaw Indian Heritage Festival; *Educational programs*: School visits, field trips, educational kits; demonstrations of art and traditional techniques; Tennessee Archaeology Awareness Week. *Publication*: Newsletter; Chucalissa Revisited; occasional papers. Library. Museum store. Opened 1955.

TENNESSEE STATE MUSEUM
James K. Polk Cultural Center
505 Deaderick St. • NASHVILLE, TN 37243
 (615) 741-2692 Fax 741-7231
 Website: www.tnmuseum.org; E-mail: museuminfo@tnmuseum.org
 Lois Riggins Ezzell, Executive Director
 Dan Pomeroy, Director of Collections

Description: A collection of over 10,000 artifacts of prehistoric & historic Indian cultures in Tennessee, including stone implements, ceremonial objects & ornaments, and pottery. *Publication*: "Art and Artisans of Prehistoric Middle Tennessee," by Stephen D. Cox. Library. Opened 1937.

PINSON MOUNDS STATE ARCHAEOLOGICAL AREA
460 Ozier Rd. • PINSON, TN 38366
 (731) 988-5614 Fax 424-3909; Mary L. Kwas, Area Supervisor
Description: A Middle Woodland Period ceremonial site with mounds and earthworks. *Collection*: Features a museum designed to replicate a Native American mound. It includes 4,500 square feet of exhibit space with historic & prehistoric material from throughout Tennessee & on-site fieldwork. *Special program*: Indian Culture Festival. Library.

SEQUOYAH BIRTHPLACE MUSEUM
576 Hwy. 360, P.O. Box 69 • VONORE, TN 37885
 (423) 884-6246 Fax 884-2102; Website: www.sequoyahmuseum.org
 E-mail: seqmus@tds.net; Robert Haynes, Director
Mission: A property of the Eastern Band of Cherokee Indians, the museum promotes the understanding & appreciation of the history & culture of the Cherokee Indians of Eastern Tennessee, particularly the life & contributions of Sequoyah (1776-1843) who gave his people an enduring gift, a writing system. *Publication*: Sequoyah Speaks.

TEXAS

CADDOAN MOUNDS STATE HISTORIC PARK
1649 State Hwy. 21 W • ALTO, TX 75925
 (936) 858-3218; Website: www.visitcaddomounds.com
 E-mail: caddo-mounds@thc.state.tx.us
 Jennifer L. Price-Toole, Site Manager
Description: An archaeological site of prehistoric Caddoan village & ceremonial center, with three earthen mounds occupied 750-1300 A.D. Collection: Dioramas and prehistoric artifacts of early Caddoan culture excavated at the site--ceramic vessels, stone tools, etc.; replicated Caddo house on site. *Activities*: School tours, teacher packet; outreach-off site presentations. *Publication*: Caddoan Mounds, Temples and Tombs of an Ancient People. Reference library. Opened 1979.

TEXAS MEMORIAL MUSEUM
University of Texas-College of Natural Sciences
2400 Trinity St. • AUSTIN, TX 78705
 (512) 471-1145 Fax 471-4794; Website: www.utexas.edu/tmm
 E-mail: mfischer@austin.utexas.edu; Margaret Fischer, Director
Description: Collections include artifacts from Native Americans throughout the U.S.; and a series of exhibits highlighting the major native North American cultural groups which includes: costumes & artifacts of Indians of the Plains, Woodlands, Southwest, Northwest Coast, & Eskimo populations. *Publications*: Newsletter; monographs; bulletin series. Library. Opened 1936.

PANHANDLE-PLAINS HISTORICAL MUSEUM
2503 4th Ave. • CANYON, TX 79015
 (806) 651-2244 Fax 651-2250; Website: www.panhandleplains.org
 Guy C. Vanderpool, Executive Director
Description: Hall of the Southern Plains: Exhibit of over 5,000 items from 70 groups, the majority from Southern Plains tribes--Comanche, Kiowa, Cheyenne, Arapaho, Apache & includes important collections of basketry, pottery, and beadwork; Nanvjo weavings; material on the Indian wars; trade goods. *Special programs*: Educational programs include Interpretive overviews and special-focus tours for students (grades K-12) & adults; Outreach programs - Native American Dance and Traditional Clothing; Life of the Southern Plains Indian. *Publication*: Panhandle Plains Historical Review, newsletter. Research Center houses archival material - more than 17,000 books (a 1,200 vol. art library) & more than 250,000 historical photographs. Museum Store. Opened 1933.

THE LIPAN APACHE MUSEUM & CULTURAL CENTER
The Lipan Apache Tribe of Texas
P.O. Box 8888 • CORPUS CHRISTI, TX 78426
 (361) 215-5121; Website: www.lipanapache.org/museum
 Jose G. Gonzalez, Curator

AMERICAN INDIAN HERITAGE CENTER OF TEXAS
Dallas Independent School District
1450 Preston Forest Sq. • DALLAS, TX 75201
 (972) 701-0074

YSLETA DEL SUR PUEBLO MUSEUM
Tigua Indian Reservation-Tigua Indian Cultural Center
305 Yaya Lane • EL PASO, TX 79907
 (915) 859-7700 Fax 859-8972; Nancy Torres, Manager

Description: Historic House, 1700-1850 Alderite/Candelaria House; on grounds of 1680 Ysleta and Sur Pueblos and Mission Church. Maintains a collection of art of the Pueblos. Publication: Tigua News. Gift shop.

ALABAMA-COUSHATTA INDIAN MUSEUM
571 State Park Rd. 56 • LIVINGSTON, TX 77351
(936) 563-1100 Fax 563-1341
E-mail: information@actribe.org
Tony Byars, Superintendent; Jo Ann Battise, Tribal Administrator
Description: Located on the Alabama-Coushatta Indian Reservation, the museum contains a dioramic historical display of tribes, and a Living Indian Village. Indian arts and crafts for sale.

AMERICAN INDIAN HORSE MUSEUM
American Indian Horse Registry
9028 State Park Rd. • LOCKHART, TX 78644
(512) 398-6642; Nanci Falley, President & Curator
Description: A collection of horse tack, art & books representing 19th century Southwest U.S. Library. Publication: American Indian Horse News. By appointment only. Library. Opened 1979.

CADDO INDIAN MUSEUM
701 Hardy St. • LONGVIEW, TX 75604
Mrs. James L. Jones, Director
Description: Collection includes approximately 30,000 artifacts pertaining to the prehistoric and historic Indian cultures who inhabited east Texas, primarily tribes of the Kad had acho, Hasinai, and Natchitoches confederacies of the Caddo Indians; extensive ceramic & stone pre-Columbian burial artifacts belonging to the prehistoric Indians of east Texas.

THE MUSEUM OF TEXAS TECH UNIVERSITY
3301 4th St., Box 43191 • LUBBOCK, TX 79409
(806) 742-2490 Fax 742-1136
E-mail: museum.texastech@ttu.edu
Description: Exhibits Yaqui, Comanche and other Indian artifacts. Publications. Research Library. Museum shop. Opened 1929.

SFASU ANTHROPOLOGY & ARCHAEOLOGY LABORATORY
Stephen F. Austin State University (SFASU)
Dept. of Social & Cultural Analysis
1936 North St. • NACOGDOCHES, TX 75962
(936) 468-3979/3980
Website: www.sfasu.edu/archaeologyllab
Jerry Williams, Chair; Leslie G. Cecil, Lab Director
Special collection: Caddo Indian Artifacts Collection--beads, pottery, arrow points, pipes, etc. from the site of new Lake Nacogdoches, as well as from various Indian sites across the County. Opened 1985.

CROCKETT COUNTY MUSEUM
404 11th St., Box 667 • OZONA, TX 76943
Special collection: Frank Mills Indian Collection--ornaments, jewelry, pottery, weapons, utensils, implements & ceremonial costumes. Cave exhibits. Library.

THE WITTE MUSEUM
3801 Broadway • SAN ANTONIO, TX 78209
(210) 357-1900 Fax 357-1882; Website: www.wittemuseum.org
E-mail: witte@wittemuseum.org; Marise McDermott, President/CEO
Amy Fulkerson, Collections Manager; Chuck Drew, Exhibits Manager
Description: Periodic displays of artifacts of the Plains Indian (Lakota, Kiowa, Comanche, Apache, Navajo), Great Basin (Paiute), California, Eastern Woodlands, Northwest Coast, and Alaskan Native Peoples including basketry, pottery, weavings & clothing; Casas Grandes pottery; permanent exhibit of archaic archaeological materials from the Lower Pecos area of Texas & Northern Mexico. Library. Museum store. Opened 1926.

SUNSET TRADING POST OLD WEST MUSEUM
Rt. 1, Box 365C • SUNSET, TX 76270
(817) 872-2027; Jack N. Glover, Owner/Curator
Description: Exhibits Indian artifacts. Publication: Sex Life of American Indians. Library.

UTAH

EDGE OF THE CEDARS STATE PARK
MUSEUM & HISTORICAL MONUMENT
660 West 400 North • BLANDING, UT 84511
(435) 678-2238 Fax 678-3348
Teri Paul, Museum/Park Manager
Debbie Westfall, Curator
Description: Located on the Anasazi Ruin dating from 700-1200 A.D., ancient dwellings of the Anasazi Indian culture. Maintains artifacts of prehistoric Anasazi

Indian Tribe; Anasazi pottery; also, Navajo, Ute and Paiute Indian artifacts. Special collection: Rock Art Exhibit. Indian arts & crafts for sale. Reference Library. Publication: Spirit Windows--Native American Rock Art of Southeastern Utah. Opened in 1978.

ANASAZI STATE PARK MUSEUM
P.O. Box 1329 • BOULDER, UT 84716
(435) 335-7308 Fax 335-7352
Mike Nelson, Park Manager
William R. Latady, Curator
Description: Located on a 1050-1200 A.D. excavated Anasazi village site. Museum: Maintains and exhibits a collection of artifacts representative of the Kayenta Anasazi culture; diorama of Anasazi village (Coombs site). Special programs: Primitive technology demonstrations; guided tours of ruins; 14 video presentations. Small library. Opened 1970.

UTE TRIBAL MUSEUM
P.O. Box 190, Highway 40 • FORT DUCHESNE, UT 84026
(435) 722- 4992; Clifford Duncan, Director
Description: Located on the site of U.S. Cavalry & Old Fort Duchesne. Maintains Indian produced artwork in various media artifacts. Research: Ute history archives; personal interviews with elderly to document verbal Indian history. Publication: A History of Northern Ute People. Library.

MUSEUM OF MOAB
118 E. Center St. • MOAB, UT 84532
(435) 259-7985; John Foster, Director
Displays baskets, pottery, arrowheads, clothing and other artifacts of ancestral Puebloan (Anasazi), Ute & Navajo cultures. Objects belonging to an Ancestral Puebloan village between A.D. 855 and 1020. Established 1958.

COLLEGE OF EASTERN UTAH PREHISTORIC MUSEUM
155 East Main St. • PRICE, UT 84501
(800) 817-9949; (435) 613-5754 Fax 613-5759
Website: www.ceu.edu; Ken Carpenter, Director
Don Burge, Curator; don.burge@ceu.edu
Description: Utah archaeological exhibits, including 9th century Indian material of the Fremont culture. Emphasis on Nine Mile Canyon cultural and rock art area, Anasazi artifacts, life-size Ute Indian diorama, Ute life-ways. Special collections: Pillings Figurines - set of 10 Fremont Indian clay figurines; two proto-historic painted hides and one Shoshone painted robe by Charlie Washakie. Special programs: Utah Prehistory and Heritage Week Celebration; lectures, children's programs; tours to archaeological sites. Publication: "Al's Archives" a quarterly newsletter. Library. Opened 1960.

MUSEUM OF PEOPLES & CULTURES - BRIGHAM YOUNG UNIVERSITY
105 Allen Hall, 700 North 100 East • PROVO, UT 84602
(801) 422-0020 Fax 422-0026; Website: www.mpc.byu.edu
E-mail: mpc@byu.edu; Paul Stavast, Director
Kari Nelson, Curator of Education
Description: An archaeology and ethnology museum exhibiting artifacts of prehistoric & historic native cultures. Collections: Changing exhibitions highlighting the Great Basin, Southwest, Mesoamerica, Polynesia. Special programs: Certificate in Museum Practices, graduate level program in conjunction with a masters degree in another discipline. Activities: Guided tours; teaching kits; scout patch program; training in museum practices & archaeological field techniques. Publications: Papers; technical series. Library. Opened 1946.

FREMONT INDIAN STATE PARK & MUSEUM
3820 W. Clear Creek Canyon Rd. • SEVIER, UT 84766
(435) 527-4631 Fax 527-4735; Bob Hanover, Park Manager
Description: Collections of artifacts, petroglyphs, & pictographs left behind by the Fremont Indians (A.D. 400-1300). Includes pottery, baskets & arrowheads. Museum store.

UTAH FIELD HOUSE OF NATURAL HISTORY STATE PARK MUSEUM
496 E. Main St. • VERNAL UT 84078
(801) 789-3799; Alden H. Hamblin, Supt.; Sue Ann Bilbey, Curator
Description: Ute Indian Hall: Exhibits Ute Indian artifacts. Library. Museum store. Opened 1948.

VERMONT

CHIMNEY POINT HISTORIC SITE
Junction of Rts. 125 & 17 • ADDISON, VT
(802) 759-2412; Website: www.historic vermont.org/#chimney
Description: The site is the State of Vermont's museum of Native American culture. Houses an interpretive exhibit called, "People of the New Dawn & the People of New France."

FAIRBANKS MUSEUM
1302 Main St. • ST. JOHNSBURY, VT 05819
  (802) 748-2372 Fax 748-1893; Website: www.fairbanksmuseum.com
Description: Overview of the Northern Forest and its environment & culture, including Abenaki culture.

ABENAKI TRIBAL MUSEUM & CULTURAL CENTER
100 Grand Ave. • SWANTON, VT 05488
  (802) 868-2559; Website: www.abenakination.org/museum.htm
  Frederick M. Wiseman, Director
Description: Western Abenaki material culture, 1600-2000 (no archaeological collections) specializing in tourist items of the 19th & early 20th centuries. *Special programs*: Extensive teaching of school groups K-12 & college; currently focusing on research & collections documenting cultural continuity for tribal petition for federal recognition. Opened 1998.

VIRGINIA

MONACAN ANCESTRAL MUSEUM
2009 Kenmore Rd. • AMHERST, VA 24521
  (434) 946-5391; Website: www.monacannation.com/museum
  Phyllis Hicks, Director; Opened 1999.

SOUTHWEST VIRGINIA MUSEUM HISTORICAL STATE PARK
P.O. Box 294 • BIG STONE GAP, VA 24219
  (276) 523-1322; Website: www.swvamuseum.org
  Janet H. Blevins, Park Manager
Description: Maintains artifacts representing the culture of the southern Appalachians, including artifacts of the Cherokee and Shawnee Nations. Developing a children's program on Native Americans. Library. Gift shop. Opened 1948.

HAMPTON UNIVERSITY MUSEUM
American Indian Educational Opportunities Program
11 Frissell Ave. • HAMPTON, VA 23669
  (757) 727-5308 Fax 727-5170; Website: www.museum.hamptonu.edu
  E-mail: museum@hamptonu.edu
  Vernon S. Courtney, Director
  Vanessa D. Thaxton-Ward, Curator of Collections
Description: Maintains a permanent gallery devoted to the school's historic American Indian education program. It also sponsors changing exhibitions of American Indian art and other programs.

SYMS-EATON MUSEUM & KECOUGHTAN INDIAN VILLAGE
418 W. Mercury Blvd. • HAMPTON, VA 23666
  (804) 727-6248; Charles E. Smith, Manager
Description: Historic Kecoughtan Indian Village; exhibits artifacts from Village area. Publication: Indian Recipe.

PAMUNKEY INDIAN MUSEUM
Pamunkey Indian Reservation
175 Lay Landing Rd. • KING WILLIAM, VA 23086
  (804) 843-4792; Warren Cook, Director
Description: A collection of Pamunkey Indian crafts & artifacts from the area. Videos available. Gift Shop. Opened 1979.

HISTORIC CRAB ORCHARD MUSEUM & PIONEER PARK
3663 Crab Orchard Rd. • TAZEWELL, VA 24651
  (276) 988-6755; Website: www.craborchardmuseum.com
  E-mail: info@craborchardmuseum.com
  Charlotte Whitted, Executive Director; Cortney Honaker, Curator
Description: Located on Big Crab Orchard Archaeological and Historic Site, exhibiting prehistoric Woodlands Indian artifacts. *Publication*: Quarterly newsletter. Library.

MATTAPONI INDIAN MUSEUM & TRADING POST
Mattaponi Indian Reservation , Rt. 2, Box 255 • WEST POINT, VA 23181
  (804) 769-2194; Minnie-Ha-Ha Gertrude Custalow, Director
Description: Tells the history of the people of Powhatan & Pocahontas and has artifacts dating back over 5,000 years. The museum is located on the Mattaponi reservation and is operated by the Custalow family. *Activities*: Develops specialized program presentations when requested.

JAMESTOWN SETTLEMENT
P.O. Box 1607 • WILLIAMSBURG, VA 23187
  (888) 593-4682; (757) 253-4838 Fax 253-5299; Website: www.historyisfun.org
  Joseph A. Gutierrez, Jr., Sr. Director of Museum Operations & Education
  Dr. Thomas E. Davidson, Sr. Curators
Description: Museum of Virginia history focusing on 17th century English colonization, and the Powhatan Indians. Exhibits prehistoric artifacts of the Virginia coastal plain. Also, other Indian artifacts and European and African items of the 17th century; recreated Powhatan Indian village. *Publication*: Jamestown-Yorktown Foundation Dispatch, periodical newsletter; Jamestown Settlement Guidebook. Library. Opened 1957.

WASHINGTON

LELOOSKA FAMILY MUSEUM
P.O. Box 526 • ARIEL, WA 98603
  (360) 225-9522 Fax 225-7416; Website: www.lelooska.org
  Darwin Goodey, Chairperson
Description: Collection of artifacts from many regions: the Northwest, Midwest, Northeast, Southwest & Arctic. Includes baskets, parfleches, cornhusk bags, dolls, spoons, cradles, moccasins, tomahawks, pipes, pipe bags, dresses, a 15-foot birch bark canoe.

WHATCOM MUSEUM OF HISTORY & ART
121 Prospect St. • BELLINGHAM, WA 98225
  (360) 778-8930
Description: First Nations - Northwest Coast & Inuit exhibitions - Contains Native American artifacts includes examples of the use of natural materials to enhance the quality of native life, including baskets, bent-wood boxes, masks, canoe, fishing gear, Salish & Chilat blankets, mats, hats, and other tools & accessories. Also, a video on contemporary Lummi basketweaver Anna Jefferson.

CHELAN COUNTY HISTORICAL MUSEUM & PIONEER VILLAGE
600 Cottage Ave., P.O. Box 22 • CASHMERE, WA 98815
  (509) 782-3230; Bill Rietveldt, Director
Description: Recreates the history of the Columbia River Indians before the arrival of the first pioneers and maintains an extensive collection of artifacts.

LEWIS COUNTY HISTORICAL MUSEUM
599 Northwest Front St. • CHEHALIS, WA 98532
  (206) 748-0831 Fax 740-5646; James Buckman, President
Description: Native American Diorama - collection of Chehalis Indian artifacts. Indian archive collection in library.

ALPOWAI INTERPRETIVE CENTER
13766 Hwy. 12 • CLARKSTON, WA 99403
  (509) 758-9580. *Description*: Home of Chief Timothy, a trusted friend of the early settlers in the area. Maintains an ethnology & Indian museum exhibiting Nez Perce Indian artifacts from 1880-1920; Nez Perce canoe. Exhibits include the story of Lewis & Clark's meeting with Nez Perce Indians. *Research*: Nez Perce Indians.

COLVILLE CONFEDERATED TRIBES MUSEUM
512 Mead Way, P.O. Box 233 • CHELAN, WA 99116
  (509) 633-0751 Fax 633-2320; Website: www.colvilletribes.com
  Cheryl Grunlose, Director; Andrew C. Joseph, Director/Curator
Description: Museum exhibits include an 1801 Thomas Jefferson Peace Medal, given to Nez Perce on the Snake River in 1805. There is an authentic Indian Village Sweatlodge and Tulle Mat Tipi, a fishing scene (12,000 - 100 years ago), and a cedar & bear grass basketmaking display and video. The collection includes arrowheads and spearpoints, pestles and other tools. Special collection: Tribal membership photos from 1855 to 1950. *Publication*: "Salish" Okanagan/Colville Indian language cassette tapes with dictionary ($24.95), by staff. Gift Shop. Opened 1990.

WANAPUM HERITAGE CENTER MUSEUM
15655 Wanapum Village Lane SW • BEVERLY, WA 99321
Mail: P.O. Box 878 • EPHRATA, WA 98823
  (509) 754-5088 Fax 754-5074; (800) 422-3199 (in WA State)
  Website: www.wanampum.org; E-mail: wanapum@grantpud.org
  Angela Buck, Director; E-mail: abuck@gcpud.org
  Angela Neller, Curator
Description: Includes a Living Culture Program that maintains artifacts of the way of life, language & traditional physical culture of the Wanapum. *Programs*: Language Program; Archaeology Days with demonstrations of making beadwork, hemp cordage and tools like arrowheads, and traditional fish nets; guest speakers; school visits. Opened 1962.

MAKAH CULTURAL & RESEARCH CENTER
P.O. Box 160 • NEAH BAY, WA 98357
  (360) 645-2711 Fax 645-2656; Website: www.makah.com
  E-mail: makahmuseum@centurytel.net
  Janine Bowechop, Director; Keely M. Parker, General Manager
Description: Exhibits include photographs, traditional clothing, basketry & carvings. Ethno-botanical Garden with native plants. *Programs*: Makah Language; Education; Historic Preservation; Guided tours. Archives & Library. Museum store. Opened 1979.

SWINOMISH COMMUNITY LIBRARY
LUSHOOTSEED LANGUAGE & CULTURE
Social Services Bldg., 17337 Reservation Rd. • LA CONNOR, WA 98257
  (360) 466-7356; Carmen Pastores-Joe, Librarian

SACAJAWEA INTERPRETIVE CENTER
Sacajawea State Park, 2503 Sacajawea Park Rd. • PASCO, WA 99301
  (509) 545-2361
Description: Interpretive exhibits focus on Sacajawea, her role in the Lewis & Clark Expedition, and the Indians of the Columbia Basin Plateau (stone, bone tools, tool making, physical culture); photo-essay of culture & lifestyle. *Publications*: Pacific Northwest Resources (resource book for area teachers). Research Library. Gift shop. Open from mid April-mid September. Opened 1940.

FORT OKANOGAN INTERPRETIVE CENTER
c/o Alta Lake State Park, HCR 88, Box 40 • PATEROS, WA 98846
  (509) 923-2400; Mike Nickerson, Supt.
  Steve Wang, Chief-Interpretive Services
Description: Exhibits fur trade items, and Indian and pioneer artifacts--basketry, weapons, etc. *Special program*: Verbal presentation of the history of the area.

THE BURKE MUSEUM OF NATURAL HISTORY & CULTURE
Box 353010, University of Washington • SEATTLE, WA 98195
  (206) 543-7907 Fax 685-3039; Website: www.burkemuseum.org
  E-Mail: theburke@u.washington.edu
  Dr. Julie Stein, Executive Director; Polly Olsen, Tribal Liaison
  Dr. Robin Wright, Curator-Native American Art
  Marvin Oliver, Adjunct Curator-Contemporary Native Art
  Deana Dartt-Newton, Curator-Native American Ethnology
Description: Exhibits the largest USA collection of Northwest Coast Native art west of the Mississippi; maintains ethnological & archaeological collections of the Pacific Rim and Islands. *Special programs*: Exhibits, workshops, lectures, family days. Library. Publications. Museum shop. Opened 1899.

SACRED CIRCLE GALLERY OF AMERICAN INDIAN ART
Discovery Park, P.O. Box 99100 • SEATTLE, WA 98101
  (206) 285-4425 Fax 285-3640; E-mail: info@unitedindians.com
  Merlee Markishtum, Director
Description: General meeting venue for Native American conferences & cultural studies activities. Has a gallery featuring the paintings, prints, textiles & sculpture of contemporary Canadian, U.S. and Indian artists. *Activities*: Presents contemporary Native artist exhibitions throughout the year.

SKOKOMISH TRIBAL CENTER & MUSEUM
80 N. Tribal Center • SHELTON, WA 98584
  (360) 426-4232 Fax 877-5943; Delbert Miller, Cultural Resources Director
Description: Collections of artifacts, woodcarvings, totems, baskets, historical photos & documents. Opened 1989.

SQUAXIN ISLAND TRIBE MUSEUM, LIBRARY & RESEARCH CENTER
150 SE K'Wuh-Deegs-Altxw • SHELTON, WA 98584
  (360) 432-3851/3840; Website: www.squaxinislandmuseum.org
  Charlene Krise, Museum Director; Mandy McCullough, Curator
  Liz Yeahquo, Librarian/Gift Shop Manager
Description: Features exhibits and rare artifacts, including art displays, baskets, wood carrvings, totems, original tools, hunting & fishing artifacts, historical photos & written texts and documents that tell the unique story of the people who lived & prospered along the shores of the inland Salish Sea for many centuries. Gift shop.

NORTHWEST MUSEUM OF ARTS & CULTURE
Cheney Cowles Center, Eastern Washington State Historical Society
2316 West 1st Ave. • SPOKANE, WA 99204
  (509) 456-3931 Fax 363-5303; Website: www.northwestmuseum.org
  E-mail: themac@northwestmuseum.org
  Ronald Rector, Executive Director
  Ginger Ewing, American Indian Education
  Tisa Matheson, Curator of American Indian Collections
Description: American Indian collections consist of more than 35,000 items representing all cultural groups of the Americas, with special emphasis on the Plateau tribes. In 1992, the Museum of Native American Cultures turned over its holdings to make the combined collections one of the largest and most extensive in the Northwest. *Major collections*: Plateau baskets, beadwork, cornhusk bags, regalia and other examples of material culture; Photograph collection of approximately 20,000 images; Manuscript Collection: Clifford Drury, Estelle Reel, Sr. Providencia. *Special programs*: Exhibits; Friendship Dance; Plateau Indian market. *Publications*: Exhibit catalogs, "Beadwork of the Native American;" "Patriotic Symbols," "The Chap C. Dunning Collection;" and "From Earth & Sky." Book - Cornhusk Bags of the Plateau Indian; Text/fiche of 170 cornhusk bags (both sides illustrated.) Exhibition poster on sale, Native American Collection. Research Library & Archives. Opened 1916.

STEILACOOM CULTURAL CENTER & MUSEUM
1515 Lafayette St., P.O. Box 88419 • STEILACOOM, WA 98388
  (253) 584-6308 Fax 584-0224
  Website: www.steilacoomtribe.com/culturalcenter.html
  Danny Marshall, President of Tribal Museum Assn.; Joan K. Ortez, Director
Description: Promotes cultural & educational exhibits to insure the preservation of the history & culture of the Steilacoom tribe. *Special exhibits*: Gallery I - changing gallery with a new exhibit on a Native American theme about every six months; Gallery II - a permanent exhibit on the history & contemporary lifestyles of the Steilacoom Tribe, beginning with first European contact in 1792; Gallery III - "Visions of the Past...Legacy to the Steilacoom Tribe" - prehistory of traditional homeland of Steilacoom Tribe. *Special programs*: Education programs - tours in education Coast Salish culture; lectures, conferences, & cultural demonstrations. Gift Shop. Library. Opened 1988.

SUQUAMISH MUSEUM & ARTS CENTER
15838 Sandy Hook NE • POULSBO, WA 98370
  (360) 394-8956 Fax 598-5495
  Website: www.suquamish.org/museum.aspx
  Leonard Forsman, Superintendent
  Marilyn Jones, Director; Charles Sigo, Curator
Description: The Museum is dedicated to preservation of Suquamish and other Puget Sound Indian culture and history. *Exhibit*: The Eyes of Chief Seattle - The history and culture of the Puget Sound Indians; Old Man House - The people and their way of life at D'Suq'Wub' and it tells the history of a 600 foot traditional longhouse located on what is now known as the Port Madison Indian Reservation, home to the Suquamish Indian Tribe of 750 members. *Publications*: Suquamish Museum Newsletter; "Eyes of Chief Seattle" Exhibit Catalogue. Library - Suquamish Tribal Archives. Opened 1983.

PUYALLUP TRIBAL MUSEUM
2002 E. 28th St. • TACOMA, WA 98404
  (253) 597-6200 Fax 593-0197; Mary Frank, Director. Opened 1981.

WASHINGTON STATE HISTORY MUSEUM
1911 Pacific Ave. • TACOMA, WA 98402
  (888) 238-4373; (253) 272-3500 Fax 272-9518
  Website: www.washingtonhistory.org
  David Nicandri, Director; Redmond Barnett, Head of Exhibits
  Lynette Miller, Head of Collections
Description: Exhibits & collections focus on the history of the people & forces that shaped the history of Washington State. Collection contains about 6,500 objects focusing on tribes of the Pacific Northwest, including basketry, tools, carvings, clothing, and personal artifacts. *Publications*: Columbia Magazine, quarterly journal of popular history. Opened 1891.

QUINAULT CULTURE MUSEUM
807 5th Ave. #1 • P.O. Box 189 • TAHOLAH, WA 98587
  (360) 276-8215 Fax 276-4191; Leilani Jones-Chubby, Manager
Description: Contains tribal artifacts, historical photos, documents & Quinault language material. Maintains a small reference library.

TOPPENISH MUSEUM
1 South Elm St. • TOPPENISH, WA 98945
  (509) 865-4510; Marian Ross, Chairperson; Tish Cooper, Director
Description: Historic Museum housed in 1923 first Agency Building for the Yakama Indian Nation. Exhibits artifacts and Indian baskets. Library.

YAKAMA INDIAN NATION
Higher Education Programs, Dept. of Human Services
P.O. Box 151 • TOPPENISH, WA 98948
  (800) 543-2802; (509) 865-5121 Fax 865-6994
  Helen B. Louise, Museum Director; Dan Brosz, Curator of Collections
  Kathryn Higdon, Curator of Exhibits; *Description*: Exhibits of Sioux items collected by Delorme W. Robinson prior to 1910 and the Mary C. Collins collection of Lakota items. Lakota game pieces collected by J. Walker, paintings by Oscar Howe. Life-size buffalo & tipi. Opened 1901.

YAKAMA NATION MUSEUM
Yakama Nation Cultural Center
P.O. Box 151 - Spiel-yi Loop • TOPPENISH, WA 98948
  (509) 865-2800 ext. 4752 Fax 865-5749
  Website: www.yakamamuseum.com; E-mail: sheryl@yakama.com
  Pamela K. Fabela, Program Manager/Curator
Description: Collection reflects traditional crafts of the Yakama people, including utility & ceremonial items; also, items from Southwest & Plains tribes, but mainly items important to Yakama (or Columbia Basin Plateau area) tribes & bands culture & history. Includes baskets, parfleches, beaded clothing, stones, pipes; Navajo blankets, kachinas, clothing & jewelry; several large oil paintings of Columbia Plateau family elders. Publications: Time Ball; Mother Nature Is Our Teacher. Library. Gift shop. Opened 1980.

HIBULB MUSEUM & LIBRARY
Tulalip Tribes - Hibulb Cultural Center
6410 - 23rd Ave. NE • TULALIP, WA 98271
(360) 716-2635; Hank Gobin, Director
Melissa Parr, Senior Curator; Lita Mowrer, Librarian
Description: To preserve the heritage & culture of the Tulalip Tribes (Snohomish, Snooqualmie, Skykomish, Skagit, Samish, and allied bands. Opened 2011.

WEST VIRGINIA

WEST VIRGINIA STATE GOVERNMENT ARCHIVES & HISTORY MUSEUM
Capitol Complex-Science & Cultural Center
Dept. of Archives & History • CHARLESTON, WV 25305
Charles Morris, III, Museum Director
E-mail: charles.W.Morris@wv.gov
Joseph N. Geiger, Jr., Director-Archives/History
E-mail: joe.n.geiger@wv.gov
Greg Carroll, Historian (Native American)

DELF NORONA MUSEUM
801 Jefferson Ave. • MOUNDSVILLE, WV 26041
(304) 843-4128 Fax 843-4131
Website: www.wvculture.org/sites/gravecreek.html
Description: Grave Creek Mound Archaeology Complex. One of the largest & famous burial mounds built by the Adena people. Artifacts & exhibits interpreting the lifestyle of the Adena people are displayed in the museum that is adjacent to the 2,000 year-old mound. *Facilities*: Theater & Fine Arts Gallery; gift shop. Opened 1978.

WISCONSIN

RED CLIFF TRIBAL MUSEUM
Arts & Crafts Cultural Center • BAYFIELD, WI 54814
(715) 779-5609/5805; Francis Montano, Director

LOGAN MUSEUM OF ANTHROPOLOGY
Beloit College, 700 College St. • BELOIT, WI 53511
(608) 363-2677; Website: www.beloit.edu/logan
William Green, Director
Description: Exhibits material (over 200,000 artifacts) of North American Indian ethnology (Great Lakes, Plains, & Southwest), Arikara-Mandan archaeology, Archaic and Woodland archaeology, and northern Wisconsin. *Special collection*: The Albert Green Heath Collection of Native American artifacts. *Program*: Field Schools. Museum Studies. Library. *Publications*: Newsletter; exhibit catalogs; occasional papers. Opened 1893.

ARVID E. MILLER LIBRARY/MUSEUM
N8510 Moh He Con Nuck Rd., P.O. Box 70 • BOWLER, WI 54416
(715) 793-4270 Fax 793-4836; Website: www.mohican-nsn.gov
E-mail: library.museum@mohican-nsn.gov
Nathalee Kristiansen, Manager; Leah Miller, Specialist
Description: The official depository for the public records of the Mohican Nation, Stockbridge-Munsee Band. Maintains a collection of cultural and historical artifacts from pre-contact to the Mission school eras. *Programs*: Basket Weaving. *Publication*: Library/Museum News. Gift Shop.

FOREST COUNTY POTAWATOMI COMMUNITY CULTURAL CENTER, LIBRARY & MUSEUM
5460 Everybody's Rd., P.O. Box 340 • CRANDON, WI 54520
(800) 960-5479; (715) 478-7474 Fax 478-7482
Website: www.potawatomimuseum.com; Mike Alloway, Sr., Director
Description: Contains a collection of historical & contemporary photographs; audio/video, books, treaties, manuscripts, language material, et al.

CHIPPEWA VALLEY MUSEUM
P.O. Box 1204 • EAU CLAIRE, WI 54702
(715) 834-7871 Fax 834-6624
Website: www.cvmuseum.com; E-mail: info@cvmuseum.com
Susan McLeod, Director
Description: Maintains a collection of artifacts & historical photographs of the Ojibwe & Winnebago Indians. Exhibit: "Paths of the People" - traces Ojibwe history. *Publications*: Guide to Archives & Manuscripts in the Chippewa Valley Museum; Paths of the People: The Ojibwe in the Chippewa Valley. Glenn Curtis Smoot Library & Archives. Opened 1964.

CHIEF OSHKOSH MUSEUM
7631 Egg Harbor Rd. • EGG HARBOR, WI 54209
(414) 868-3240; Jeanette L. Hutchins, Director/Curator
Description: Indian Museum exhibiting Indian artifacts, craftwork & possessions belonging to the late Chief Oshkosh, last Chief of the Menominees. Open May-October. Opened 1975.

MENOMINEE INDIAN TRIBE OF WISCONSIN ONLINE CULTURAL MUSEUM
P.O. Box 910, Keshena, WI 54135
(715) 799-5100 Fax 799-3373
Website: www.menominee-nsn.gov/culturalmuseum
Description: This online museum project is intended to give the public a view of Menominee history & culture by showing artifacts in the museums and that will hopefully be returned someday to the future Menominee Cultural Museum.

MENOMINEE LOGGING CAMP MUSEUM
Menominee Indian Tribe of Wisconsin Historic Preservation Dept.
P.O. Box 910 • KESHENA, WI 54135
(715) 599-5258 Fax 799-4524

GEORGE W. BROWN, JR. OJIBWE MUSEUM & CULTURAL CENTER
P.O. Box 804 • LAC DU FLAMBEAU, WI 54538
(715) 588-3333 Fax 588-9408
Website: www.ldfojibwe.com
Gregg Guthrie, Director
Description: Displays collections of artifacts from the Lac du Flambeau Chippewa Indian Reservation. Maintains a four seasons diorama and other exhibits including a 24-foot dugout canoe, smaller birchbark canoes, Ojibwe arts & crafts, traditional clothing, a French fur trading post. *Activities*: Year-round programs, classes, special events. Opened 1989.

LAC DU FLAMBEAU CHIPPEWA MUSEUM & CULTURE CENTER
603 Peace Pipe, P.O. Box 804 • LAC DU FLAMBEAU, WI 54538
(715) 588-3333

MUSEUM OF THE STATE HISTORICAL SOCIETY OF WISCONSIN
30 N. Carroll St. (exhibits) 816 State St. (collections) MADISON, WI 53703/6
(608) 264-6555; William C. Crowley, Director of Museum
Joan E. Freeman, Curator of Anthropology
Description: Historic Wisconsin & Plains Indian artifacts & prehistoric archaeological artifacts from Wisconsin. *Special collections*: H.P. Hamilton Collection--Contains old copper implements from Wisconsin. Ethnological collections are from all Wisconsin tribes, Plains Indians, Northwest Coast, and Eskimo. *Special programs*: Classroom lessons on Wisconsin Indian life; photograph, manuscript & tape collections. *Publications*: Magazine of History; six volumes on History of Wisconsin. Library. Opened 1846.

RAHR-WEST ART MUSEUM
610 North 8th St. • MANITOWOC, WI 54220
(414) 683-4501; Richard Quick, Director
Special collection: Exhibits stone, copper, and bead artifacts from a personal collection obtained in the Manitowoc County area. Library. Opened 1941.

THE HISTORIC INDIAN AGENCY HOUSE
3110 E. Hampshire St. • MILWAUKEE, WI 53911
(608) 742-6362

MILWAUKEE PUBLIC MUSEUM
800 W. Wells St. • MILWAUKEE, WI 53233
(414) 278-2700 Fax 278-6100; Website: www.mpm.edu
Michael Stafford, PhD, President/CEO
Alex W. Barker, PhD, Head, Anthropology Section
E-mail: barker@mpm.edu
Dawn Scher Thomae, Anthropology Collections Manager
Description: Maintains a collection of approximately 23,000 North American ethnographic Indian items representing more than 180 Native American groups and tribes, including Inuit; Also holds significant North American archaeological collections (some 47,000 objects or lots), with strengths in Midwestern prehistory. *Special collections*: James Howard collection of 20th-century powwow outfits and artifacts. Dioramas, including "A Tribute to Survival" and the Crow Bison Hunt; Indian photograph collection (ca. 10,000 prints and 10,000 negatives). Special programs: Study collections; tours of American Indian areas from schools and other groups. *Publications*: Lore, quarterly member magazine; North American Indian Lives; Building a Chippewa Indian Birchbark Canoe; Prehistoric Indians of Wisconsin, etc.; Wisconsin Indian Resource Pages (WIRP), at www.mpm.edu/wirp. Reference Library. Opened 1882.

ONEIDA NATION MUSEUM
P.O. Box 365 • ONEIDA, WI 54115
(920) 869-2768 Fax 869-2959
Website: www.museum.oneidanation.org
Rita Lara, Director; E-mail: rlara@oneidanation.org
Description: Exhibits artifacts & photographs about Iroquois/Oneida culture & history. Primarily ethnographic collection focusing on Oneida in Wisconsin. Artifacts include baskets, clothing, beadwork, and other cultural items. *Activities*: Annual cultural Festival in June; guided tours & outreach programs available by request. Small library. *Publication*: Post-contact newsletter. Opened 1979.

OSHKOSH PUBLIC MUSEUM
1331 Algoma Blvd. • OSHKOSH, WI 54901
 (920) 236-5799; Brad Larson, Director; Debra Daubert, Curator
Description: Maintains a collection of Wisconsin Indian archaeological & ethnographical artifacts. Menominee items. Library. Museum store.

WAUKESHA COUNTY HISTORICAL SOCIETY & MUSEUM
101 W. Main St. • WAUKESHA, WI 53186
 (262) 521-2859 Fax 521-2865; Susan K. Baker, Executive Director
Description: Collections focus on Waukesha County from Native American settlement to the present, exhibiting Native American artifacts from the area. Research Center Library contains historic documents, photographs, maps. *Publication*: Landmark, quarterly; book - "From Farmland to Freeways: A History of Waukesha County," includes a chapter on Americans Indians including some mound maps. Opened 1914.

WINNEBAGO INDIAN MUSEUM
WISCONSIN DELLS, WI 53965
 Roxanne Tallmadge Johnson, Manager; Bernadine Tallmadge, Curator
Description: An extensive collection of stone artifacts, clothing, methods of ornamentation (i.e., beadwork, quillwork, metal) as well as oil paintings. *Special programs*: On-site lectures describing current & traditional issues; festival. Opened 1953.

WYOMING

BRADFORD BRINTON MEMORIAL MUSEUM
P.O. Box 460, 239 Brinton Rd. • BIG HORN, WY 82833
 (307) 672-3173 Fax 672-3258; Kenneth L. Schuster, Director
 Website: www.bradfordbrintonmemorial.com
Description: Exhibits Native American objects of art - costumes, bead and quill work, tools, baskets, blankets, weapons, & interpretive materials; mostly Plains tribes, but some from Southwest and Northwest Coast. Library. Opened 1961.

THE NELSON MUSEUM OF THE WEST
1714 Carey Ave. • CHEYENNE, WY 82001
 (307) 635-7670; Website: www.nelsonmuseum.com
 E-mail: office@nelsonmuseum.com
 Robert L. Nelson, Founder; E-mail: nelsonwy@aol.com
Description: Dedicated to the preservation of the Cowboy & Native American objects as well as fine Western art. Rodeo & Native American objects comprise the largest part of the Museum's collection of more than 6,000 artifacts. Includes Plains Indian art exhibit, and Indian weaponry.

WYOMING STATE MUSEUM
2301 Central Ave. • CHEYENNE, WY 82002
 (307) 777-7025 Fax 777-5375
 Website: www.wyomuseum.state.wy.us
 Manny Vigil, Museum Supervisor
 Mandy Langfaid & Mariah Emmons, Curators of Collections
Description: Collection contains over 100,000 artifacts related to Wyoming's heritage. Strengths include textiles, firearms, household artifacts, military artifacts, and Native American artifacts from the Lakota, Arapaho, Crow, Shoshone, and Flathead tribes among others. Library. Museum store. Exhibition brochures & handouts. Opened 1895.

PLAINS INDIAN MUSEUM
Buffalo Bill Historical Center, 720 Sheridan Ave. • CODY, WY 82414
 (307) 578-4052 Fax 578-4076; Website: www.bbhc.org
 Bruce Eldredge, Executive Director
 Emma Hansen, Curator; Mary Robinson, Library Director
Description: Contains over 5,000 ethnographic items representing the Northern, Central, & Southern Plains people: Sioux, Cheyenne, Shoshone, Crow, Arapaho, Blackfeet, Gros Ventre. Exhibits provide an introduction to economic, religious and social lives of Plains Indians, and include a re-creation of an 1890 Sioux camp as well as a gallery of contemporary art. *Programs*: Annual Northern Plains powwow in June at the Robbie Powwow Grounds; the Plains Indian Art Seminar, a symposium relating to Plains cultures each Fall; and a variety of temporary exhibitions which explore elements of the Plains Indian culture. Buffalo Bill Museum. Whitney Gallery of Western Art. The McCracken Research Library. *Publications*: Catalogues of exhibitions; papers & proceedings from Plains Indian Seminar. Opened 1979.

SHOSHONE TRIBAL CULTURAL CENTER
P.O. Box 1008 • FORT WASHAKIE, WY 82514
 (307) 332-9106 Fax 332-3055; Joyce Posey, Director. Opened 1988.

UNIVERSITY OF WYOMING ANTHROPOLOGY MUSEUM
12th & Lewis Sts., Anthropology Bldg. • LARAMIE, WY 82070
 (307) 766-2208; E-mail: arrow@uwyo.edu; Dr. Charles Reher, Director
Description: Maintains a collection of American Indian artifacts. Opened 2008.

COLTER BAY INDIAN ART MUSEUM
Grand Teton National Park, P.O. Drawer 170 • MOOSE, WY 83012
 (307) 739-3591 Fax 739-3504
Description: Displays approximately 1,500 items of American Indian art (collected by David T. Vernon) from most culture areas and the Reservation Period, 1850-1920, with emphasis on the high plains. *Special programs*: Cultural films during the summer, museum tours, guest artists, and Native-American crafts demonstrations. Programs during summer months. Opened 1972.

RIVERTON MUSEUM
7th East & Park Ave. • RIVERTON, WY 82501
 (307) 856-2665; E-mail: lrnjost@yahoo.com
Description: Collections include Shoshone and Arapaho costumes and artifacts.

These alpha-geographically arranged listings, like those in the Museums section, include libraries with both large and small collections, pertaining, in whole or part, to the subject of the North American Indian.

ALABAMA

POARCH CREEK INDIAN HERITAGE CENTER LIBRARY
5811 Jack Springs Rd. • ATMORE, AL 36502
(205) 368-9136 Fax 368-4502; Sandra Ridley, Director
Description: Maintains a collection on Southeastern Creek Indians, specifically, and Five Civilized Tribes, generally.

ALASKA

ANCHORAGE MUSEUM LIBRARY & ARCHIVES
Atwood Alaska Resource Center, 625 C St. • ANCHORAGE, AK 99501
(907) 929-9235 Fax 929-9290
Website: www.anchoragemuseum.org/archives
E-mail: resourcecenter@anchoragemuseum.org
Teressa Williams, Librarian; Megan Peacock, Resource Center Manager
Description: Collection includes more than 1,000 volumes on the Tlingit, Haida, Northwest Coast, Athapaskan, Aleut & Eskimo cultures with an emphasis on material culture; 1890-1960 photographic collection. Interlibrary loans. Open to the public.

ARCTIC ENVIRONMENTAL INFORMATION & DATA CENTER
Alaska Resources Library & Information Service (ARLIS)
University of Alaska, Anchorage, Library Bldg., Suite 111
3211 Providence Dr. • ANCHORAGE, AK 99508
(907) 27-ARLIS; E-mail: reference@arlis.org
Research activities: Conducts field studies & provides assistance on resource management issues in Alaska, including Native land selection under the Alaska Native Claims Settlement Act. Maintains a collection of over 1,770 historic photos of Alaska from the early 1970s.

INSTITUTE OF SOCIAL & ECONOMIC RESEARCH
University of Alaska, Anchorage
3211 Providence Dr. • ANCHORAGE, AK 99508
(907) 786-7710 Fax 786-7739; Website: www.iser.uaa.alaska.edu
E-mail: ayiser@uaa.alaska.edu; Heather Hudson, Director
Research activities: Conducts Alaska Native studies, federal-state relations, economic development, natural resources management, social & economic impact studies, etc. *Publication*: Alaska Review of Social & Economic Conditions.

HANS VAN DER LAAN MEMORIAL BROOKS RANGE LIBRARY
Simon Paneak Memorial Museum
P.O. Box 21085, 341 Mekiana Rd. • ANAKTUVUK PASS, AK 99721
(907) 661-3413 Fax 661-3414; Grant Spearman, Curator
Description: 1,000 volumes concerning the natural and cultural history of the Arctic with special emphasis on the Brooks Range of Alaska. Opened 1986.

TUZZY CONSORTIUM LIBRARY
P.O. Box 2130 • BARROW, AK 99723
(800) 478-6916; (907) 852-4050 Fax 852-4059
Website: www.tuzzy.org; E-mail: tuzzy@tuzzy.org
Christie Burke, Director; E-mail: christie.burke@tuzzy.org
Erin Hollingsworth, Public Services Librarian
E-mail: erin.hollingsworth@tuzzy.org

ALASKA'S MOTION PICTURE FILM ARCHIVE CENTER
University of Alaska, P.O. Box 95203 • FAIRBANKS, AK 99701
(907) 479-7296; Reg Emmert, Director
Description: A repository of Alaskan archival film. Catalog of available films.

ALASKA NATIVE KNOWLEDGE NETWORK
University of Alaska, Fairbanks, P.O. Box 756730 • FAIRBANKS, AK 99775
(907) 474-1902 Fax 474-2477; Website: www.ankn.uaf.edu
Dr. Ray Barnhardt, Director
Research activities: Resource materials related to Alaska Native people and Alaska Native education. Publications. Opened 1995.

ALASKA NATIVE LANGUAGE CENTER
University of Alaska, Fairbanks
305 N. Tanana Lop, Rm. 423, Box 757680 • FAIRBANKS, AK 99775-7680
(907) 474-7874 Fax 474-6586; Website: www.uaf.edu/anlc
E-mail: fyanlp@uaf.edu; Dr. Lawrence Kaplan, Director
Sophie Alexie, Instructor of Yup'ik Eskimo

Ronald H. Brower, Sr., Instructor of Inupiaq
Walkie Charles, Instructor of Yup'ik Eskimo
Edna Ahgeak MacLean (Inupiaq linguist currently working
    on a reference dictionary of the Inupiaq language)
Hishinlai Sikorski (Gwich'in Athabascan), Instructor
Siri Tuttle, Ass't Professor of Athabascan languages
Description: Recognized as the major center in the U.S. for the study of Eskimo & Northern Athabascan languages. Archival collection of more than 10,000 items: books, journals, papers, and archival material; everything ever written in or about Alaska Native languages. Copies of all the documentation of the languages including the earliest word lists & field notes. *Special activities*: Publish books in & on Alaska Native languages. Open to public. Opened 1972.

INSTITUTE OF ALASKA NATIVE ARTS INFORMATION CENTER
P.O. Box 70769 • FAIRBANKS, AK 99707
(907) 456-7406; Susheila Khora, Executive Director
Description: A resource library with more than 600 titles, audio & video tapes, and magazines/periodicals. Also consists of an artist registry of hard copy files and slides, and photographic files.

ELMER E. RASMUSON LIBRARY
University of Alaska, 310 Tanana Dr. • FAIRBANKS, AK 99775
(907) 474-6691
Special collections: Skinner Collection--Contains material regarding Alaska and the Polar regions (Arctic & Antarctic); more than 4,000 volumes on the Athapaskan, Haida, Tlingit, Tsimshean, & Eskimo. University Archives & Manuscript Collections (Alaskana only) Consists of journals, records, historic photos, tape recordings (Alaska Native Stories); 4,000 historic photos of Alaska Natives.

AHTNA, INC. LIBRARY
P.O. Box 649 • GLENNALLEN, AK 99588
(907) 822-3476 Fax 822-3495
Website: www.ahtna-inc.com; Ken Johns, President
Description: Contains mostly publications dealing with land and resources in interior Alaska, with some on native culture (Athabascan.)

SHELDON MUSEUM & CULTURAL CENTER LIBRARY
Chilkat Valley Historical Society, P.O. Box 269 • HAINES, AK 99827
(907) 766-2366 Fax 766-2368; Website: www.sheldonmuseum.org
Jerrie Clarke, Director
Description: Material on Tlingit and other Indian art and culture; local history; Alaska history. Also, archives with unpublished local documents (diaries, city records, school records, etc.) Open to public. Opened 1975.

ALASKA STATE LIBRARY & HISTORICAL COLLECTIONS
333 Willoughby Ave., 8th Floor, P.O. Box 110571 • JUNEAU, AK 99811
(907) 465-2921 Fax 465-2665; Website: www.library.state.ak.us
Linda Thibodeau, Director
Jim Simard, Librarian; Anastasia Tarmann Lynch, Librarian

TONGASS HISTORICAL MUSEUM LIBRARY
629 Dock St. • KETCHIKAN, AK 99901
(907) 225-5600 Fax 225-5602
Description: Vast collection on Alaskana and books relating to Tlingit, Tsimshian and Haida culture & heritage & Northwest Coast Native art.

TOTEM HERITAGE CENTER LIBRARY
629 Dock St. • KETCHIKAN, AK 99901
(907) 225-5900 Fax 225-5602
Description: City of Ketchikan's museum department & archives holdings include photographs on all Alaska villages with totem poles; index to all Alaska totem poles; vertical file on Northwest Coast Indian art & culture. Covers Tlingit, Haida & Tsimshian tribes - art, anthropology, totem poles. *Programs*: Art and crafts slides available for use; lecture series on traditional Alaska Native arts & culture.

BARANOV MUSEUM LIBRARY
Kodiak Historical Society, 101 Marine Way • KODIAK, AK 99615
(907) 486-5920 Fax 486-3166; Website: www.baranov.us
E-mail: baranov@ak.net; Ann Stone, President; Marian Johnson, Director
Description: The Kodiak Historical Society operates the Baranov Museum in the old Russian warehouse, the Erskine House, in downtown Kodiak. Research Center with over 5,000 photos, 300 rare books covering Kodiak & the Aleutians with some emphasis on major Alaskan events. Also 30 educational albums from the archives covering Kodiak events.

KODIAK AREA NATIVE ASSOCIATION LIBRARY
3449 E. Rezanof Dr. • KODIAK, AK 99615
(907) 486-9800 Fax 486-9898
Museum/Cultural Center & Research Library in planning stages.

NADIA MULLAN ALUTIIQ HERITAGE LIBRARY
Native Village of Afognak, 323 Carolyn St. • KODIAK, AK 99615
 (907) 486-6357 Fax 486-6529; E-mail: tribe@afognak.org
Description: Maintains a collection of more than 1,000 items that deal with the Alutiiq culture, the Kodiak Archipelago, Alaska Native culture & Native American culture in general, and Alaskana in general.

NOME LIBRARY/KEGOAYAH KOZGA PUBLIC LIBRARY
Front St., Box 1168 • NOME, AK 99762
 (907) 443-5133; Dee J. McKenna, Librarian
Description: Collection contains about 15,000 books, 3,000 cassette tapes, 1,200 AV programs, photographs, and bilingual and oral history materials on Alaska, Eskimos, and Gold Rush artifacts.

SEWARD COMMUNITY LIBRARY
238 5th Ave., P.O. Box 2389 • SEWARD, AK 99664
 (907) 224-4082 Fax 224-3521
 Website: www.cityofseward.net/library
 Valerie Kingsland, Director (224-4008)
Description: Partners with Qutekcak Native Tribe. Maintains a collection of Native American resources: videos & reference works, legends & tales pertain-ing to Native American culture.

SITKA NATIONAL HISTORICAL PARK LIBRARY
103 Monastery St. • SITKA, AK 99835
 (907) 747-6281 Fax 747-5938; Carol Burkhart, Director
Description: Contains about 1,400 books; 150 tapes, 150 films & special papers on Tlingit Indians, Northwest Coast Indian arts & culture. Substantial research materials on Russian-American history. Research library. Opened 1966.

ARIZONA

CANYON DE CHELLY NATIONAL MONUMENT LIBRARY
P.O. Box 588 • CHINLE, AZ 86503
 (928) 674-5518 Fax 674-5507; Website: www.nps.gov/cach
 Tara Travis, Historian/Curator; E-Mail: tara_travis@nps.gov
Description: Collection consists of library materials pertinent to the research & management of the park's resources. Archival materials consist of maps, photographs, documents & reports on Canyon de Chelly National Monument. *Special programs*: Ranger Talks. Open to public by appointment. Opened 1931.

CIBECUE COMMUNITY LIBRARY
P.O. Box 80008 • CIBECUE, AZ 85911
 (928) 332-2621 Fax 332-2442; Website: www.navajoco.lib.az.us
 Reva DeClay, Director; E-mail: cbq@navajo.lib.az.us
A branch of Whiteriver Public Library.

CASA GRANDE RUINS NATIONAL MONUMENT LIBRARY
1100 N. Ruins Dr. • COOLIDGE, AZ 85228
 (520) 723-3172 Fax 723-7209; Website: www.nps.gov/cagr
Description: Contains a collection of 1,500 volumes on Hohokam archaeology and culture; Indians of area.

FULTON-HAYDEN MEMORIAL LIBRARY
The Amerind Foundation, 2100 N. Amerind Rd.
P.O. Box 400 • DRAGOON, AZ 85609
 (520) 586-3666 Fax 586-4679
 Website: www.amerind.org; E-mail: libros@amerind.org
 John A. Ware, Executive Director; Sally Newland, Librarian
Description: Reference materials focusing on archaeology, anthropology, ethnology, Greater American Southwest; ethnology, history & art; Parral Archives on microfilm; 28,000 books, 2,260 pamphlets & reprints, 550 manuscripts, 250 maps, 12,000 slides and photos, 150 journals & other serial subscriptions. Open to researchers & scholars with director's ok. Opened 1962.

CLINE LIBRARY
Northern Arizona University, P.O. Box 6022 • FLAGSTAFF, AZ 86011
 (928) 523-6802 Fax 523-3770; Website: www.library.nau.edu
 E-mail: library.officeofthedean@nau.edu; Karen J. Underhill, Archivist
Special Collections & Archives Department: Subjects include Navajo & Hopi Indians, & Southwestern U.S. *Special collections*: Alexander & Dorothea Leighton Collection; Apachean Language Collection, including Chiricahua dialects - 320 cassettes; A.F. Whiting, Leo Crane, Jo Mora, and Phillip Johnston, United Indian Traders, Milton Snow. Opened 1968.

HAROLD S. COLTON MEMORIAL LIBRARY
Museum of Northern Arizona
3101 N. Fort Valley Rd. • FLAGSTAFF, AZ 86001
 (928) 774-5211 ext. 256 Fax 779-1527
 Website: www.musnaz.org; E-mail: library@mna.mus.az.us
 Dr. Robert Breunig, Director

Description: Special collections on Hopi & Navajo Indians, and archaeology of the Southwestern U.S. Also contains a major repository of documentation on Native American art. Opened 1928.

THE WHITE MOUNTAIN APACHE CULTURAL CENTER MUSEUM/LIBRARY
P.O. Box 507 • FORT APACHE, AZ 85926
 (928) 338-4625 Fax 338-1716; Website: www.wmat.nsn.us
 Karl A. Hoerig, PHD, Director
Description: Non-circulating library of materials relevant to Apache culture & history, Fort Apache, and Fort Apache Indian Reservation. Opened 1997.

FORT McDOWELL YAVAPAI NATION LIBRARY
16708 N. Ft. McDowell Rd. • FORT McDOWELL, AZ 85264
 Mailing address: P.O. Box 17779 • FOUNTAIN HILLS, AZ 85269
 (480) 816-7848/50 Fax 816-7858
 Website: www.ftmcdowelltriballibrary.org
 Jacquelyn McCalvin, Director; E-mail: jmccalvin@ftmcdowell.org

KAIBAB PAIUTE PUBLIC LIBRARY
Pipe Springs Rd., HC 65, Box 2 • FREDONIA, AZ 86022
 (928) 643-6004 Fax 643-7260; Jeri Segundo, Director
 E-mail: jsegundo@kaibabpaiute-nsn.gov

HUBBELL TRADING POST LIBRARY
P.O. Box 150 • GANADO, AZ 86505
 (928) 755-3475 755-3405
Description: Contains materials relevant to Native American and Southwest history; Navajo culture, Indian arts & crafts, oral interviews, and trading posts and Indian traders; and NPS planning documents, standards and policies.

GILA COMMUNITY COLLEGE LIBRARY
8274 Six Shooter Canyon Rd. • GLOBE, AZ 85501
 (928) 425-8481; Website: www.gilacc.org/library.htm
 Norma Rios, Librarian; E-mail: norma.rios@eac.edu
 Kristen Becker, Library Director; E-mail: kristen.becker@eac.edu

KAYENTA COMMUNITY LIBRARY
P.O. Box 280 • KAYENTA, AZ 86033
 (928) 697-5563 Fax 697-5564; Trina Lipscomb, Director
A branch of Navajo Nation Library

HOPI PUBLIC LIBRARY
c/o Hopi Education Dept., P.O. Box 123 • KYKOTSMOVI, AZ 86039
 (928) 734-3503 Fax 734-3509
 Nelia Naha, Administrative Secretary
 E-mail: nnaha@hopi.nsn.us
 Noreen Sakiestewa, Education Director
 E-mail: nsakiestewa@hopi.nsn.us

AK CHIN (HIM-DAK) INDIAN COMMUNITY LIBRARY/EDUCATION CENTER
46521 W. Farrell Rd. • Maricopa, AZ 85239
 (520) 568-1676 Fax 568-4566
 Melanie Toledo, Director; E-mail: mtoledo@ak-chin.nsn.us
Description: Collection of Native American publications, videos & audios, oral histories; Archives of tribal records.

AVA ICH ASIIT TRIBAL LIBRARY
500 Merriman Ave. • NEEDLES, CA 92363
 Location: Fort Mojave Indian Tribe
 1605 Plantation Rd. • MOHAVE VALLEY, AZ 86440
 (928) 346-2665 Fax 346-2666; E-mail: library@ftmojave.com
 Candace Montijo, Director

COLORADO RIVER INDIAN TRIBES LIBRARY/ARCHIVES
Tribal Administration Center, 2nd & Mohave Rd.
Rt. 1, Box 23-B • PARKER, AZ 85344
 (928) 669-1332 Fax 669-8262; Website: www.critlibrary.com
 Amelia Flores, Library Director; Anna Scott, Assistant Director
Description: Holdings include 12,000 volumes in the general sections. Extensive collection of artifacts on Native Americans. Archives includes over 1,000 documents, videotape & oral history tapes, personal correspondence, and works of historians, ethnologists & anthropologists; also microfilm relating to the history & culture of the four tribes of the Colorado River Indian Reservation - the Mohave, Chemehuevi, Navajo & Hopi. Also includes a Photograph Collection. Interlibrary loans. Opened 1958.

EDWARD McELWAIN MEMORIAL LIBRARY
460 Hualapai Way, P.O. Box 179 • PEACH SPRINGS, AZ 86434
 (928) 769-2200/16 Fax 769-2250; E-mail: nyachyu@yahoo.com
 Cheryle Beecher, Director
 Lucille Watahomigie, Director of Education & Training

PEACH SPRINGS SCHOOL LIBRARY
403 Diamond Creek Rd., P.O. Box 360 • PEACH SPRINGS, AZ 86434
(928) 769-2202 Fax 769-2276; Website: www.psusd.k12.az.us
Stephanie McKie, Librarian

ARIZONA STATE LIBRARY, ARCHIVES & PUBLIC RECORDS
History & Archives Records, Carnegie Center
1101 W. Washington • PHOENIX, AZ 85007
(602) 926-3365 Fax 255-3314; Website: www.lib.az.us/archives
Don Langlois, Arizona History Librarian
Description: Contains over 105,000 volumes on Arizona & the Southwest, including material on Southwestern Indians. Open to the public.

PERKINS COIE BROWN & BAIN, P.A. LIBRARY
2901 N. Central Ave. #2000 • PHOENIX, AZ 85012
(602) 351-8000 Fax 648-7000; Website: www.perkinscoie.com
Catherine Horan, Resource Manager; E-mail: choran@perkinscoie.com
Description: A special collection on American Indian law.

DOROTHY CUMMINGS MEMORIAL LIBRARY
American Indian Bible College
10020 N. 15th Ave. • PHOENIX, AZ 85021
(602) 944-3335; John S. Rose, Director
Description: Maintains a special Native American collection of books, audiocassettes, and microfiche.

BILLIE JANE BAGULEY LIBRARY & ARCHIVES
Heard Museum, 2301 N. Central Ave. • PHOENIX, AZ 85004
(602) 252-8840 Fax 252-9757; Website: www.heard.org
Mario Nick Klimiades, Library & Archives Director
 E-mail: mario@heard.org
Description: Maintains a collection of approximately 30,000 volumes in the areas of Native American art & culture with an emphasis on the Greater Southwest, contemporary Native American fine arts, Native American writings, ethno-arts, anthropology & museum studies; 240 current periodical subscriptions-journals and newsletters; pamphlet file; archives of manuscripts, posters & library prints, photographs & negatives, & museum papers; sound recordings include audiocassettes & record albums of primarily native Southwestern music, taped lectures, and interviews; 500 films & videos; and thousands of slides. *Special program*: Native American Artists Resource Collection - includes files on about 22,000 traditional to contemporary artists working in all media. Artists, collectors, students, and art enthusiasts can contribute information to the collection. Open to the public for reference only - appointments are necessary for archives & videos and sound recordings. Opened 1929.

JOHN J. ROSS - WILLIAM C. BLAKLEY LAW LIBRARY
Arizona State University Mail Code 9620
111 E. Taylor St., Suite 348 • PHOENIX AZ 85004-4467
(480) 965-6144 Fax: 480-965-4283
Website: https://web.law.asu.edu
Beth DiFelice, Associate Director (965-4871) E-mail: beth.difelice@asu.edu
David Gay, Reference Lbrarian (965-4860) E-mail: William.gay@asu.edu
Description: Maintain a collection of primary authority and secondary source materials. Some collection emphases include Indian Law, English Legal History and a growing student Study Skills Collection.

MARICOPA COUNTY LAW LIBRARY
East Court Bldg., 2nd Floor, 101 W. Jefferson St. • PHOENIX, AZ 85003
(602) 262-3677; Elizabeth Kelley Schneider, Director
Description: A special collection on Native American law.

PHOENIX INDIAN MEDICAL CENTER HEALTH SCIENCES LIBRARY
4212 North 16th St. • PHOENIX, AZ 85016
(602) 263-1200 Fax 263-1669
Jean Crosier, Administrative Librarian
Description: Basic professional & medical collection with small Native American collection includes medical, cultural, fiction and non-fiction titles about and written by Native Americans; also focus is on Southwestern tribes (approx. 200 books and documents). Open to the public.

PHOENIX PUBLIC LIBRARY
1221 N. Central Ave. • PHOENIX, AZ 85004
(602) 262-4636; Website: www.phoenixpubliclibrary.org
Description: Arizona Room - Collections include subjects covering Southwestern Indians. Special collection: James Harvey McClintock Papers, 1864-1934.

PUEBLO GRANDE MUSEUM LIBRARY
4619 East Washington St. • PHOENIX, AZ 85034
(877) 706-4408; (602) 495-4901 Fax 495-5645
Website: www.pueblogrande.com
E-mail: pueblo.grande.museum.pks@phoenix.gov

Description: Collection is primarily on Southwest archaeology with volumes pertaining to the American Indian. Open to scholars on appointment basis only.

SHARLOT HALL MUSEUM ARCHIVES & LIBRARY
415 W. Gurley St. • PRESCOTT, AZ 86301
(928) 445-3122 Fax 776-9053; Website: www.sharlot.org/archives
Libby Coyner, Director
Description: History of Yavapai County & Central Mountain Region of Arizona. Collections include information on the area's archaeology & anthropology, and the history/prehistory of the Yavapai Indians. Special activities: Prescott Indian Arts Market each July. Opened 1928.

SMOKI MUSEUM LIBRARY
147 N. Arizona Ave., P.O. Box 10224 • PRESCOTT, AZ 86304
(928) 445-1230; Website: www.smokimuseum.org
John Tannous, Director; E-mail: info@smokimuseum.org
Description: All books are cataloged (Dewey) & entered on Yavapai Library Network. Periodicals are recorded in Prescott Union List, published annually. Free access by appointment. Opened 1935, Incorporated 1991.

YAVAPAI-PRESCOTT TRIBAL LIBRARY
530 E. Merritt • PRESCOTT, AZ 86301
(928) 777-9448 Fax 778-9445; Website: www.ypit.com
Barbara Royer, Director
Description: Maintains a collection (non-circulating) of approximately 5,000 volumes with special emphasis on the education, history & culture of the Yavapai Indians and Native Americans, with emphasis on Native Americans of the Southwest. *Special programs*: Public access computers for tribal & community members provided by Bill & Melinda Gates Foundation. Weekly story times provided for tribal pre-school and after school programs. Open to tribal & tribal community members.

IRA H. HAYES MEMORIAL LIBRARY
Gila River Indian Community
94 N. Church St., P.O. Box 97 • SACATON, AZ 85247
(520) 562-3225 Fax 562-3903; Ramona Tecumseh, Director

SAFFORD-THATCHER STAKES FAMILY HISTORY CENTER
Church of Jesus Christ of Latter-Day Saints
1803 S. 8th Ave. • SAFFORD, AZ 85546
(520) 428-3194; Lorin W. Moffett, Director
Description: A special collection on Indian tribes.
Genealogical Society Series; microfiche; films.

SAN CARLOS PUBLIC LIBRARY
P.O. Box 545 • SAN CARLOS, AZ 85550
(928) 475-2611 (phone & fax); Website: www.gila.lib.az.us
Emma Victor, Director; E-mail: emma_victor08@yahoo.com

SALT RIVER TRIBAL LIBRARY
Salt River Pima-Maricopa Indian Community
10005 Osborn Rd. • SCOTTSDALE, AZ 85256
(480) 362-2557 Fax 362-2556
Leigh A. Thomas, Director; E-mail: leigh.thomas@srpmic-ed.org
Description: Southwest/Native American Collection; the Sebastian Juan Memorial Collection contains books & periodicals on the Pima, Maricopa & other tribes in Arizona history & culture. *Programs*: Arts & Crafts & Reading. Opened 1978.

VENITO GARCIA LIBRARY & ARCHIVES
P.O. Box 837 • SELLS, AZ 85634
(520) 383-5756 Fax 383-2429; David Shaul, Librarian & Archivist

TOHONO O'ODHAM COMMUNITY COLLEGE LIBRARY
P.O. Box 3129 • SELLS, AZ 85634
(520) 383-0032 Fax 383-0029; Elaine Cubbins, Librarian

COCOPAH TRIBAL LIBRARY
14250 South Ave. I , County 15th & Ave. G • SOMERTON, AZ 85350
(928) 627-8026 Fax 627-2510
E-mail: cococvt@cocopah.com; Sandy L. Johnson, Director

HAVASUPAI VILLAGE LIBRARY
P.O. Box 40 • SUPAI, AZ 86435
(928) 448-2901 Fax 448-2551; Leo M. McCormick, Director

THE ARIZONA COLLECTION
University Libraries, Arizona State University
Charles Trumbull Hayden Library, Dept. of Archives & Special Collections
Box 871006, Mail Code: 1006 • TEMPE, AZ 85287
(480) 965-9277 Fax 965-0776; Website: www.asu.edu/lib/archives

Robert Spindler, Head Archives/Manuscript Librarian
   E-mail: rob.spindler@asu.edu
Patricia A. Etter, Archivist for Information Services
   E-Mail: patricia.etter@asu.edu
Description: A research repository containing over 30,000 titles in addition to primary source materials covering prehistoric Arizona to the present. There are ephemeral materials and 500,000 photographic prints & negatives. Contains information on prehistoric, historic, and current tribes in Arizona & New Mexico. *Special collections*: Manuscript material includes papers of Carlos Montezuma, the Odd Halseth Papers and the Thomas H. Dodge Collection. Open to public.

CENTER FOR INDIAN EDUCATION
Arizona State University, Mary Lou Fulton College of Education
Farmer Education Bldg., Rm. 402 • TEMPE, AZ 85287
   (480) 965-6292; Website: www.cde.asu.edu/cie/
   David Beaulieu, Director; Denis Viri, Associate Research Professional
   Harold G. Begay, University Liaison; Robin J. Notah, Research Specialist
Description: Covers all phases of American Indian education & related interdisciplinary issues. *Purpose*: To serve as a major research & resource clearinghouse in the field of Indian Education & related fields; and to provide various services to Indian communities & the ASU community of students, staff & faculty. *Program*: Native Teacher Preparation Programs - Rachel Carroll, Administrator & Gilbert Innis, Program Coordinator. *Publications*: Journal of American Indian Education; books: One Voice, Many Voices: Recreating Indigenous Language Communities, by T. McCarty & O. Zepeda, Editors; "To Remain an Indian" Lessons in Democracy from a Century of Native American Education, by K. Tsianina Lomawaima & T. McCarty; The Power of Native Teachers: Language & Culture in the Classroom, David Beaulieu & A. Figueira, Editors. Established 1959.

LABRIOLA NATIONAL AMERICAN INDIAN DATA CENTER
University Libraries, Arizona State University, Charles Trumbull Hayden Library
Dept. of Archives & Special Collections, Box 871006 • TEMPE, AZ 85287
   (480) 965-0270 Fax 965-0776
   Website: www.asu.edu/lib/archives/labriola.htm
   Joyce Martin, Director; E-mail: joyce.martin@asu.edu
   Patricia A. Etter, Professor Emerita (Labriola Center)
   E-mail: patricia.etter@asu.edu
Description: Serves as a national repository of research materials on North American Indians & First Nations people. It provides access to this information through the use of computer databases, the Internet, & CD-ROM. The collection is international in scope & brings together current & historic information on government, education, culture, religion and worldview, social life & customs, tribal history, and biography. The online, "American Indian Index" gives access to thousands of photographs, pamphlets, newsletters, & articles dealing with Native Americans. Contains 6,000 books, films, slides, cassette tapes, and video in addition to CD-ROM indexes. Holds numerous manuscript collections, including the papers of Peterson Zah, former President of the Navajo Nation, and Wayne T. Pratt, Assistant Chief of the Branch of Education, Bureau of Indian Affairs, Papers of Kevin Gover, Assistant Secretary of Indian Affairs in the Clinton Administration. Includes personal photographs & calendars; & photographs of Fr. Augustine Schwarz, OFM, 1916-1940. Open Monday-Friday from 11 a.m. to 5 p.m. and by appointment. Opened 1993.

MARY MILDRED McCARTHY LIBRARY
Cook College & Theological School
708 S. Lindon Lane • TEMPE, AZ 85281
   (480) 968-9354 Fax 968-9357; Mark Thomas, Librarian
Description: Houses 13,000 vols. The major areas emphasis in the collection includes religious & Native American Studies special collection of about 1,500 books on Native American history and culture. Interlibrary loans. Opened 1911.

MUSEUM AT PAPAGO PARK LIBRARY & ARCHIVES
Arizona Historical Society, 1300 N. College Ave. • TEMPE, AZ 85281
   (480) 929-0292
Description: The Phoenix History Project is comprised of photos, documents, & 500 oral history interviews collected in the mid-1970s. Photograph collections display a visual record of Phoenix and central Arizona from the late 19th century to the present.

NAVAJO NATIONAL MONUMENT LIBRARY
HC 71 Box 3 • TONALEA, AZ 86044
   (928) 672-2700 Fax 672-2703; Russ Bodnar, Supt.
Description: A collection of approximately 600 volumes on Southwest archaeology, history of Hopi & Navajo culture. Open to the public by appointment only.

DINE COLLEGE LIBRARIES - CHARLIE BENALLY LIBRARY
One Circle Dr. Rt. 12 • TSAILE, AZ 86556
   (928) 724-6757 Fax 724-6759
   Website: www.library.dinecollege.edu
   Rosita Klee, Director; E-mail: rklee@dinecollege.edu

Special collection: Collection of over 45,000 volumes and an extensive pamphlet file on more than 100 Indian-related topics. Central to the collection is the Moses Donner Indian Collection--An extensive collection of publications on American Indians.

ARIZONA HISTORICAL SOCIETY RESEARCH LIBRARY
949 East 2nd St. • TUCSON, AZ 85719
   (520) 628-5774 Fax 629-8966
   Website: www.ahs.state.az.us
   Deborah Shelton, Library Head
Description: Holdings include 50,000 books, 750,000 photographs, 5,000 maps, 1,000 manuscript collections, 1,000 oral histories, and periodicals & ephemera related to Arizona, the Southwest and northern Mexico, 1540 to the present. Special programs and exhibits. Opened 1884.

ARIZONA STATE MUSEUM LIBRARY
University of Arizona, Box 210026 • TUCSON, AZ 85721
   (520) 621-4695 Fax 621-2976; Website: www.statemuseum.arizona.edu
   Mary Graham, Librarian; E-mail: megraham@email.arizona.edu
   Christina Antipa, Assistant Librarian; E-mail: cantipa@email.arizona.edu
Description: A major U.S. repository of documentation on Native American art. Contains approximately 43,000 volumes of published materials as well as archives of unpublished documents, field notes, diaries, with emphasis on prehistory & ethnology of Greater Southwest and Northern Mexico, and cultures of Arizona & New Mexico; many of which are on the subject of Native Americans; extensive microfilm collection. Online catalog located at www.larc.asmua. arizona.edu. Interlibrary loans (limited). Open to the public.

DANIEL F. CRACCHIOLO LAW LIBRARY
University of Arizona, James E. Rogers College of Law
1201 E. Speedway Blvd., P.O. Box 210176 • TUCSON, AZ 85721
   (520) 621-5604 Fax 621-3138; Sean H. Crane, Reference Librarian
Description: Maintains a special collection on law relating to the American Indian. Subjects includes Federal laws, Indian constitutions, laws & codes, tribal court reports, U.S. Congressional hearings & reports, periodicals, treatises, and treaties. Interlibrary loans. Open to the public.

NATIVE AMERICAN RESEARCH & TRAINING CENTER
University of Arizona, 1642 E. Helen • TUCSON, AZ 85719
   (520) 621-5075 Fax 621-9802; Website: www.nartc.fcm.arizona.edu
   Jennie R. Joe, PhD, MPH, Director
Mission: To conduct health related research & training projects that will help improve the quality of life for Native Americans. *Research activities*: Health & rehabilitation of disabled & chronically ill Native Americans. Studies the impact of government policy on the delivery of health care. Serves as a national resource for all North American tribes & Alaska Natives. Opened 1983.

MISSION SAN XAVIER DEL BAC LIBRARY
1950 W. San Xavier Rd. • TUCSON, AZ 85746
   (520) 294-2624; Fr. Michael Dallmeier, Rector
Description: A collection of more than 5,000 volumes pertaining to Aztec & Native-American ethnography and anthropology.

DR. FERNANDO ESCALANTE COMMUNITY LIBRARY/RESOURCE CENTER
Pascua Yaqui Tribe Education Division
7441 S. Camino Cocoim, TUCSON, AZ 85746
   (520) 883-5181 Fax 883-5014; Website: www.pascuayaqui-nsn.gov
   Oscar Hernandez, Librarian
Description: Collection of books on the Yaqui people and other books to meet the educational, cultural and information needs of the Pascua Yaqui community.

SOUTHWEST FOLKLORE CENTER
University of Arizona • TUCSON, AZ 85706
   (520) 626-3392
Description: Contains four videotaped conversations: Navajo singer Andrew Natonabah, writers Leslie Marmon Silko, N. Scott Momaday, & Papago storyteller, Ted Rios. Available on two videotapes.

SAN XAVIER LEARNING CENTER LIBRARY
2018 W. San Xavier Rd. • TUCSON, AZ 85746
   (520) 807-8621 Fax 807-8689; Yvonne Corella, Director
   Gertrude Lopez, Coordinator; E-mail: glopez@waknet.org
A branch of Venito Garcia Library & Archives.

WHITERIVER PUBLIC LIBRARY
Whiteriver Apache Tribe, P.O. Box 370 • WHITERIVER, AZ 85941
   (928) 338-4884 Fax 338-4470; Lena M. Fall, Director

OFFICE OF THE NAVAJO NATION LIBRARY
Window Rock Public Library, P.O. Box 9040 • WINDOW ROCK, AZ 86515
   (928) 871-6376/6526 Fax 871-7304; Website: www.nnlib.org

Irving Nelson, Program Supervisor; E-mail: inelson979@yahoo.com
Linda Curtis, Senior Office Specialist; E-mail: lynda_rock@hotmail.com
Purpose: To plan, develop, and implement a library and information system that will serve the residents of the Navajo Nation. To be the primary source of information for all who are interested in the Navajo people, their land and culture. *Special collections*: General Reference Collection: 2,500 books & documents; Environmental Assessment Collection: 200 folders; Navajo Nation Government Documents Collection: 1,000 documents & publications; Navajo Times Today Collection: 120 boxes of hard copy and micro-film copies; Vertical File Collection: 930 folders of articles; *Correll Collection*: 30 filing cabinets of historical documents; Native American Music Collection: 350 cassettes; Oral History Collection: 200 cassettes; Native American Research Library Collection: 2,000 books. Subjects covered are Navajo Indians; Southwest archaeology, Indians of America, and Arizona history. Bookmobile services: 2 bookmobiles provide services to 90 communities across the reservation within Arizona, New Mexico and Utah. Audio Visual Services. Computer Software Service: *Special program*: Book Project - distribute free book materials, non-book materials, and equipment to eligible organizations and individuals. Established 2001.

YUMA LIBRARY & ARCHIVES
Arizona Historical Society, 248 S. Madison Ave. • YUMA, AZ 85364
(928) 782-1841
Description: One of four repositories of the Society. Contains 12,600 photos, 400 maps, hundreds of manuscripts, 578 oral histories, 800 books, 795 periodicals, 36 films/videos, & other materials that document the history of the lower Colorado River region from 1540 to the present. Collections are available to researchers by appointment only.

ARKANSAS

MUSEUM LIBRARY & ARCHIVES - ARKANSAS STATE UNIVERSITY
Dean B. Ellis Library, 100 Cooley Dr. • JONESBORO, AR 72467
(870) 972-2074 Fax 972-2793
Website: www.museum.astate.edu
Marti L. Allen, PhD, Director
Description: Contains over 1,200 books & reference material on Indian history & culture with focus on Southeast, Southwest and Plains groups related to Arkansas native tribal groups; ethnology & archaeology exhibits. Interlibrary loans via Dean B. Ellis Library. Open to the public.

AMERICAN NATIVE PRESS ARCHIVES
Sequoyah Research Center, 301A Ottenheimer Library
University of Arkansas at Little Rock
2801 S. University Ave.• LITTLE ROCK, AR 72204
(501) 569-8336 Fax 371-7585
Website: www.anpa.ualr.edu; E-mail: jwparins@ualr.edu
Description: Archives copies of works by American Indian, Alaska Native, and Canadian First Nations writers, bibliographies of other works, biographical information, and portfolios of works by cartoonists & photographers. *Purpose*: To promote & foster academic research concerning the American Native press, those involved in it, and American Native periodical literature as a whole; disseminate research results; refine methodologies. Annual Meeting. Opened 1983.

SOUTHWEST ARKANSAS REGIONAL ARCHIVES
P.O. Box 134 • WASHINGTON, AR 71862
(870) 983-2633 Fax 983-2636; Website: www.southweatarchives.com
E-mail: southwest.archives@arkansas.gov
Peggy S. Lloyd, Archival Manager
Description: Subjects cover the history of Southwest Arkansas, Caddo Indians. Opened 1978.

CALIFORNIA

CURRICULUM RESOURCE CENTER (CRC)
Indian Teacher & Educational Personnel Program
Humboldt State University, Brero House #93
1 Harpst St. • ARCATA, CA 95521
(707) 826-3672 Fax 826-3675; Website: www.humboldt.edu/itepp
Marlette Grant-Jackson, CRC Coordinator; Suzanne M. Burcell, Director
Description: Houses a collection of over 3,500 books, videos, audiocassettes, periodicals, CD-ROM's, posters, and 100+ microfilm rolls dating back to the 1850's. Curricula materials are all related to Native American issues and topics.

MALKI MUSEUM LIBRARY
Morongo Indian Reservation
11795 Fields Rd., P.O. Box 578 • BANNING, CA 92220
(951) 849-7289 Fax 849-3549; Website: www.malkimuseum.org
E-mail: malkimuseummail@gmail.com; Susan Phillips, Director
Description: Collection consists of 500 volumes on Southern California Indians.

BANCROFT LIBRARY & THE HEARST MUSEUM OF ANTHROPOLOGY LIBRARY
University of California, 103 Kroeber Hall • BERKELEY, CA 94720
(510) 642-3781 Fax 642-7589 (Bancroft)
(510) 642-3682 (Heart Museum Library)
Website: www.bancroft.berkeley.edu; E-mail: bancroft@library.berkeley.edu
Charles Faulhaber, Director
Description: Major U.S. repositories of documentation on Native American art.

ETHNIC STUDIES LIBRARY - UNIVERSITY OF CALIFORNIA, BERKELEY
Native American Studies - Library Collection
30 Stephens Hall, #2360 • BERKELEY, CA 94720
(510) 643-1234 Fax 643-8433
Website: www.eslibrary.berkeley.edu; E-mail: esl@library.berkeley.edu
Lillian Castillo-Speed, Head Librarian; E-mail: csl@library.berkeley.edu
Description: The collection is focused on Native Americans, First Nations peoples of Canada, and some representation of Native peoples in Central and South America in all topical areas. Estimated holdings: 15,000 monographs; 1,000 serial titles (200 current); 400 sound recordings in varied formats; 300 videotapes; 1,000 35mm slides; 1,000 photos. NAS Bibliographic Database - 30,000 records. *Special collections*: American Indian Correspondence: The Presbyterian Historical Society Collection of Missionary Letters, 1833-1893; Annual Reports of the Commissioner of Indian Affairs, 1849-1949; John Collier papers, 1922-1968; Survey of the Conditions of the Indians of the U.S., 1929-1944; Records of the Bureau of Indian Affairs; Indian Census, 1885-1941; Harvard University Peabody Museum papers and memoirs, 1896-1957; Indian Rights Association papers, 1864-1973; Papers of the Society of American Indians; Indian Claims Commission Reports; California Indian Library Collection (CILC); U.S. Congressional & Senate Reports; Dissertations on microfilm; 72 feet of vertical files and ephemera. *Special programs*: Readings by Native Authors and indigenous Story Telling. Opened 1969 to the public for reference use only. Interlibrary loan via main UC Berkeley campus library.

YOCHA DEHE LIBRARY
Yocha Dehe Wintun Nation, P.O. Box 18 • Brooks, CA 95606
(530) 796-3400 Fax 796-2143; Website: www.yochadehe-nn.gov
E-mail: info@yochadehe-nsn.gov
Collection: 8,000 books, magazines, and audio & videotapes.

SEQUOYAH LIBRARY
D-Q University, P.O. Box 409 • DAVIS, CA 95617
(530) 758-0470 ext. 1018 Fax 758-4891; Betty J. Mason, Director

THE UNIVERSITY LIBRARY
The University of California, Davis, 100 NW Quad • DAVIS, CA 95616
(530) 752-6561; Website: www.lib.ucdavis.edu
Collections: Steve Talbot Papers - Collection includes materials on Native American political activism in the San Francisco Bay area during the 1960's. David Risling Papers - Materials relating to Native American education, the Native American Rights Fund, and the California Indian Legal Services. Jack Forbes Papers - Native American serials from the 1970's & 1980's. Contains articles, reports, monographs, serials, microfilm & photos relating to Native American history, civil rights, ethnic studies and Native American education.

CABOT'S OLD INDIAN PUEBLO MUSEUM LIBRARY
67-616 East Desert View Ave. • DESERT HOT SPRINGS, CA 92240
(760) 329-7610 Fax 329-1956; Colbert H. Eyraud, Director
Description: Contains ten 4-drawer file cabinets of Desert Hot Springs newspapers; a collection of historical papers of city on microfilm, dated 1940-1980 at public library; City Government meetings, dated 1976-1990.

KUMEYAAY COMMUNITY COLLEGE ARCHIVES
Sycuan Band of Kumeyaay Nation
5478 Sycuan Rd. #10 • EL CAJON, CA 92019
(619) 445-6917 Fax 445-5176
Website: www.kumeyaaycommunitycollege.com/archives
Description: The primary repository of documents, books, diaries, field notes, and other culturally significant items serving the Kumeyaay/ Diegueno Nation.

FRESNO COUNTY FREE LIBRARY
2420 Mariposa St. • FRESNO, CA 93721
(559) 488-3195 Fax 488-1971; Website: www.fresnolibrary.org
Laurel Prysiazny, Librarian
Description: Covers American Indians of Fresno County, including Mono, Miwok, and Yokut tribes. *Special collection*: Ta-Kwa-Teu-Nee-Ya-Y...200 books.

AMERICAN INDIAN RESOURCE CENTER (AIRC)
Huntington Park Public Library
6518 Miles Ave. • HUNTINGTON PARK, CA 90255
(323) 583-2794 Fax 587-2061; Website: www.colapublib.org
E-mail: airc@library.lacounty.gov; Michael McLaughlin, Librarian

Description: Serves as an information referral center for & about American Indians. Maintains a collection of approximately 20,000 titles (Southwest, Plains, Woodlands); including books, magazines, scholarly journals, newspapers, theses, & dissertations. The collection covers the full spectrum of American Indian experience in the continental U.S. & Alaska - from pre-Columbian times to the present. Non-book items include films, photographs, audiocassettes, videocassettes, & compact discs. 130 periodical titles; 100 16mm films; 250 videocassettes; 500 audiocassettes; 300 records; current events clipping file (8 drawers, 350 subject headings). AIRC has a large microfilm collection that includes monographs, oral histories, federal government publications, tribal government publications, & tribal newspapers & newsletters. Federal Government publications useful in genealogical research including the entire 692 reel set of Indian Census Rolls, 702 microfilm reels & Records of the Indian Claims Commission, 6,128 microfiche; copies of the Code of Federal Regulations (CFR) 25 Indians, treaties, & other government reports. Tribal government publications include tribal codes, tribal bylaws, & other specialized publications. The Vertical Files (VF) consist of about 800 alphabetically arranged files by subject headings with unique significance to American Indians - notable individuals, organizations, Indian specific issues, and events - historic & contemporary. Also, maintains directories of the B.I.A. offices & tribal government offices throughout the U.S. & Alaska. Special programs: Information & referral services; outreach program; meeting room (free for Indian groups). Interlibrary loans. Open to the public. Affiliated with Los Angeles County Public Library. Opened 1979.

CABAZON TRIBAL REFERENCE LIBRARY
Cabazon Band of Mission Indians
84-245 Indio Springs Dr. • INDIO, CA 92203

LAKE COUNTY HISTORICAL SOCIETY LIBRARY
P.O. Box 1011 • LAKEPORT, CA 95453
(707) 279-4466; Jean Beeson, President
Description: Covers Pomo Indian history & culture. Includes photographs, manuscripts, oral history tapes, and genealogical data. Publications.

BARONA CULTURAL CENTER RESEARCH LIBRARY
1095 Barona Rd. • LAKESIDE, CA 92040
(619) 443-7003 ext. 219 Fax 443-0173; Website: www.baronamuseum.org
Katy Duperry, Librarian/Archivist; E-mail: kduperry@barona-nsn.gov
Description: Research primarily on Southern California Indians with a focus on Barona 'Ipay/Kumayaay. Opened 2001.

WIYOT TRIBAL LIBRARY
1000 Wiyot Dr. • LOLETA, CA 95551
(707) 733-5055 Fax 733-5601; Website: www.wiyot.com/library
Marilyn Wilson, Library Director
Mission: Serves as a bridge between the past and the future of the Wiyot Tribe.

LOMPOC MUSEUM LIBRARY
200 South H St. • LOMPOC, CA 93436
(805) 736-3888 Fax 736-2840; Website: www.lompocmuseum.org
Description: Contains over 1,000 volumes on Chumash Indians, Indians of southern California, and Lompoc history and archaeology.

AMERICAN INDIAN STUDIES CENTER & LIBRARY – UCLA
3214 Campbell Hall, Box 951548 • LOS ANGELES, CA 90095-1548
(310) 206-7510 Fax 206-7060
Website: www.aisc.ucla.edu/aisclibrary.htm
Ken Wade, Librarian; E-mail: kwade@ucla.edu
Description: Coordinates educational, research, and action-oriented programs designed to meet the needs of American Indian students at UCLA and the American Indian communities in general. *Activities*: Encourages the development of new courses; promotes hiring of Native American faculty; sponsors research on American Indians; publishes journals, books, monographs, and other media reflecting contemporary Indian research and issues. Library: Approximately 8,000 volumes comprise the Library's core collection, covering the subject of the Indians of North America, with a strong emphasis on California and the Southwest. The primary focus is on American Indian cultures in both historical and contemporary perspectives. Augmenting the circulating and reference collections are serials/periodicals, and a vertical file. Publication: American Indian Culture and Research Journal.

AUTRY LIBRARY - MUSEUM OF THE AMERICAN WEST
4700 Western Heritage Way • LOS ANGELES, CA 90027
(323) 667-2000 Fax 660-5721; Website: www.theautry.org
Alicia Gonzalez, Director
Description: Contains over 25,000 book and serial titles; 2,000 linear feet of non-book materials, including manuscripts, photographs, maps, sound recordings, music scores, films, etc. that document the history of the American West. *Special collections*: Fred Rosenstock collection, which contains more than 15,000 rare titles of Western Americana; the Foundation for American Indian Tribal History collection. Opened 1988.

BRAUN RESEARCH LIBRARY
Southwest Museum, Autry National Center
Institute for the Study of the American West
234 Museum Dr. • LOS ANGELES, CA 90065
(323) 221-2164 Fax 224-8223
Website: www.southwestmuseum.org
Kim Walters, Librarian
Description: Collection consists of 50,000 volumes of books & serials; includes 700 manuscript collections, 1,300 sound recordings, and over 147,000 photographs. The Photo Archive is strongest on Indians of the Southwest, with many pictures of Native Americans of Alaska, the Northwest Coast, California, and the Plains. *Special collections*: The Papers of Frederick Webb Hodge, Frank Hamilton Cushing, George Bird Grinnell, Charles F. Lummis, and George Wharton James. Special programs: Lecture series (quarterly). Opened 1907.

LOS ANGELES PUBLIC LIBRARY
History/Genealogy Department
630 W. Fifth St. • LOS ANGELES, CA 90071
(213) 228-7400 Fax 228-7419; Website: www.lapl.org
Description: Maintains a special collection on the American Indian; 8,000 volumes on the Indians of the Americas with an emphasis on the Southwestern U.S. Monographs, periodicals, pamphlet material, and specialized newsletters and newspapers are accessed through the general catalog and through the Indian File, a detailed computer based index. Interlibrary loans. Open to public.

UCLA LIBRARY - SPECIAL COLLECTIONS
405 Hilgard Ave. • LOS ANGELES, CA 90095
(310) 825-1201; Website: www.library.ucla.edu
Description: A major U.S. repository of documentation on Native American art.

FORT MOJAVE TRIBAL LIBRARY
500 Merriman Ave. • NEEDLES, CA 92363
(760) 629-4591 Fax 629-5767; Debbie Jackson, Contact

MARIN MUSEUM OF THE AMERICAN INDIAN LIBRARY
P.O. Box 864, 2200 Novato Blvd. • NOVATO, CA 94948
(415) 897-4064; Katharine J. Volz, Executive Director
Description: A reference library of approximately 1,000 books and periodicals oriented heavily to California Indians, especially Coast Miwok.

OAKLAND PUBLIC LIBRARY
American Indian Library Project - Dimond Branch Library
3565 Fruitvale Ave. • OAKLAND, CA 94602
(510) 482-7844 Fax 482-7824
Description: Collection contains 1,500+ volumes on Native American literature, culture, and history.

CALIFORNIA STATE ARCHIVES
1020 O St. • SACRAMENTO, CA 95814
(916) 653-7715 Fax 653-7363
Website: www.sos.ca.gov/archives

NATIONAL ARCHIVES & RECORDS ADMINISTRATION - PACIFIC REGION
1000 Commodore Dr. • SAN BRUNO, CA 94066
(650) 238-3501 Fax 238-3510
Website: www.nara.gov; Daniel Nealand, Director
David Piff, Archivist; E-mail: david.piff@nara.gov
Description: Archival records of the Federal agencies and U.S. Courts in Nevada (except Clark County), northern & central California, Hawaii, American Samoa & the Trust Territory of the Pacific Islands. Holdings include over 53,000 cubic feet of original records created by various Federal agency field offices from 1850 to 1970, a large collection of National Archives microfilm, and over 2,900 cubic feet of records of the Bureau of Indian Affairs in California & Nevada. Special programs: Genealogy & other historical records workshops; internships & volunteer programs. Opened 1969.

AMERICAN INDIAN STUDIES LIBRARY
Dept. of American Indian Studies
San Diego State University • SAN DIEGO, CA 92182
(619) 594-6991
Description: The Golsh Collection of rare documents and books.

PALOMAR COMMUNITY COLLEGE LIBRARY
1140 W. Mission Rd. • SAN MARCOS, CA 92069
(619) 744-1150; Judy J. Carter, Director
Description: A collection of 3,500 volumes pertaining to American Indian culture, history, arts and crafts, and social problems; Bureau of Ethnology Reports.

THE HUNTINGTON LIBRARY
1151 Oxford Rd. • SAN MARINO, CA 91108
(626) 405-2191 Fax 449-5720; Website: www.huntington.org

David S. Zeidberg, Director
Description: A major U.S. repository of documentation on Native American history, culture, and art. Includes scores of manuscript collections that documents political, military, religious or educational contacts between American Indians & Euro-Americans, particularly in the 19th & 20th centuries. Researchers interested in more details about the Huntington's manuscript holdings should consult the institution's website, online catalog & Guide to American Historical Manuscripts in the Huntington Library (San Marino, CA, 1979). Not open to the public. Established 1919.

MESA GRANDE RESERVATION LIBRARY
P.O. Box 270 • SANTA YSABEL, CA 92070
 (619) 782-3835; Small tribal library.

HELD-POAGE RESEARCH LIBRARY
603 West Perkins St. • UKIAH, CA 95482-4726
 (707) 462-6969; Lila J. Lee, Director
Description: Local history and ethnography collection of over 6,000 volumes; many on American Indians. *Special collections*: Estle Beard Collection-research material for Genocide & Vendetta: The Round Valley Wars of Northern California; the Edith Van Allen Collection for Indian Uses of native plants; California & western states anthropology and archaeology; and Photographic Negative Collection; artifacts, maps.

UNIVERSAL CITY STUDIOS RESEARCH DEPARTMENT LIBRARY
UNIVERSAL CITY, CA 91608
Special collection: 7,500 books dealing with Western Americana and the American Indian.

YOSEMITE MUSEUM LIBRARY
P.O. Box 577 • YOSEMITE NATIONAL PARK, CA 95389
 (209) 372-0282; Linda Eade, Librarian
Description: Contains approximately 20,000 volumes and a large archival and photographic collection relating to Yosemite & Central California Indian people.

COLORADO

CENTER FOR THE STUDY OF NATIVE LANGUAGES OF THE PLAINS & SOUTHWEST (CSILW) LIBRARY
University of Colorado, Dept. of Linguistics, UCB 295
BOULDER, CO 80309-00295
 (303) 492-8456 Fax 492-4416; Website: www.colorado.edu/csilw
 Barbara Fox, Director
Description: Collection of several hundred volumes of primary & secondary materials on Native American languages.

NATIONAL INDIAN LAW LIBRARY
Native American Rights Fund, 1522 Broadway • BOULDER, CO 80302
 (303) 447-8760 Fax 443-7776; Website: www.narf.org/nillindex.html
 David Selden, Director; E-mail: dselden@narf.org
Description: American Indian law and tribal law collection, including tribal codes, constitutions, intergovernmental agreements, legal pleadings from major Indian law cases, law review articles, handbooks, manuals and books related to Federal Indian law & tribal law; government documents. *Special program*: Indian Law current awareness bulletin service. Publications: Landmark Indian Law cases. Provides reference and research, assistance and document delivery for the public. Opened 1972.

COLORADO SPRINGS FINE ARTS CENTER LIBRARY
30 West Dale St. • COLORADO SPRINGS, CO 80903
 (719) 634-5581; Roderick Dew, Director
Description: A collection of approximately 9,000 volumes on Indians of the Southwest, Mexico and Guatemala, with emphasis on art, textiles and pottery. Contains a large collection of periodicals, some from the late 19th century. Open to the public.

COLORADO HISTORICAL SOCIETY, STEPHEN H. HART LIBRARY
1300 Broadway • DENVER, CO 80203
 (303) 866-2305 Fax 866-5739; Katherine Kane, Director
Description: Walker Collection (Sioux); W.H. Jackson Photos (Southwestern tribes); many other photos - emphasis on the Ute, Cheyenne, Arapaho, Navajo, Hopi, Zuni; extensive ethnological collections on Plains and Southwest Indians; Mesa Verde Plains & Mountain Indian materials; source materials on the history of the Indian wars; materials from the Rosebud Indian Agency, 1885-1890; and photograph collection. Open to the public.

FOURTH WORLD CENTER FOR THE STUDY OF INDIGENOUS LAW & POLITICS
University of Colorado at Denver
CB 190, P.O. Box 173364 • DENVER, CO 80217
 (303) 556-2850; Glenn T. Morris, Prof.

DENVER ART MUSEUM LIBRARY
100 West 14th Ave. Pkwy. • DENVER, CO 80204
 (720) 865-5000 Fax 865-5028; Nancy Simon, Director
Description: Holdings include more than 25,000 volumes; 50 journals; and a special collection on the American Indians.

CENTER FOR SOUTHWEST STUDIES
Fort Lewis College, 120 Miller Student Center
100 Rim Dr. • DURANGO, CO 81301
 (970) 247-7590 Fax 247-7686; Website: www.fortlewis.edu
 Duane Smith & Philip Duke, Directors; E-mail: duke_p@fortlewis.edu
Description: Includes significant historical & ethnographic collections pertaining to American Indians, including books, periodicals, microfilm, printed materials, archives, photographs, maps & artifacts. *Special programs*: Courses on archival management & oral history; train Indian students in the interpretation of cultural resources. Opened 1964.

REED LIBRARY - FORT LEWIS COLLEGE
1000 Rim Dr. • DURANGO, CO 81301-3999
 (970) 247-7662 Fax 247-7422
 Margaret C. Landrum, Director; Elaine Silversmith, Librarian
Description: Collection includes hundreds of volumes on the North American Indian, Fort Lewis College began as an Indian school in the late 1800's.

GRAND CANYON NATIONAL PARK LIBRARY
P.O. Box 129 • GRAND CANYON, CO 86023
 (928) 638-7768 Fax 638-7776; Website: www.library.nps.gov
 Susan Eubank, Librarian
Description: Maintains a collection of approximately 10,000 volumes. Material on the Grand Canyon, natural history, archaeology, etc. Interlibrary loans. Opened 1940.

MUSEUM OF WESTERN COLORADO ARCHIVES
248 S. 4th St. • GRAND JUNCTION, CO 81501
 (303) 242-0971; Judy Prosser-Armstrong, Archivist
Description: Covers the history of western Colorado; anthropology of southwestern Indians.

KOSHARE INDIAN MUSEUM RESEARCH LIBRARY
P.O. Box 580 • LA JUNTA, CO 81050
 (719) 384-4411 Fax 384-8836
 Joe Clay, Director of Programs; E-mail: kiva_clerk@ojc.edu
Description: Collection contains 2,000 volumes on Indian history, religion, legends, art, handicrafts, etc. Reference use only.

MESA VERDE RESEARCH LIBRARY
MESA VERDE NATIONAL PARK, CO 81330
 (970) 529-4465; Beverly J. Cunningham, Librarian
Description: Maintains more than 6,500 volumes on archaeology and ethnography, with many on the Indians of the Mesa Verde area, and North America. Interlibrary loans.

UTE MOUNTAIN TRIBAL LIBRARY
Education Center, 450 Sunset, P.O. Box CC • TOWAOC, CO 81334
 (970) 564-5348 Fax 564-5342

CONNECTICUT

CONNECTICUT HISTORICAL SOCIETY LIBRARY
1 Elizabeth St. • HARTFORD, CT 06105
 (203) 236-5621 Fax 236-2664; Website: www.chs.org
 E-mail: research_center@chs.org
 Jody Blankenship, Executive Director
 E-mail: jody_blankenship@chs.org
 Diana McCain, Head of Research Center
 E-mail: diana_mccain@chs.org
Description: Collection contains 70,000 volumes and two million manuscripts relating to Connecticut and New England history and genealogy.

CONNECTICUT STATE LIBRARY
231 Capitol Ave. • HARTFORD, CT 06115
 (866) 886-4478; (860) 757-6500 Fax 757-6503
 Website: www.cslib.org; Sharon Brettschneider, Director
Description: Maintains an American Indian collection emphasizing languages and history; its core deriving from the library of J. Hammond Trumball.

MASHANTUCKET PEQUOT RESEARCH LIBRARY
ARCHIVES & SPECIAL COLLECTIONS - CHILDREN'S RESEARCH LIBRARY
110 Pequot Trail, P.O. Box 3180 • MASHANTUCKET, CT 06338-3180
 (860) 396-6897 Fax 396-7005 (Reference)
 (860) 396-7001 (Archives) 396-6899 (Children's)

Website: www.pequotmuseum.org
E-mail: reference@mptn-nsn.gov; archive@mptn-nsn.gov;
   childrenslibrary@mptn-nsn.gov
Kevin McBride, PhD, Director, Research & Information Resources
E-mail: kmcbride@mptn-nsn.gov
Description: The Information Resources Dept. is comprised of a Research Library, a Children's Research Library, and an Archives & Special Collections Department. The Research Library's collection contains over 40,000 titles of current and historical works on the histories and cultures of indigenous peoples north of Mexico, including Canada, Alaska & Hawaii, with an emphasis on 20th century materials. Print formats include books, serials, maps, pamphlets and brochures. The collection includes visual & audio recordings & electronic media. The collection consists of 800+ titles including journals, magazines, newspapers, newsletters & auction catalogs supporting the Library's mission. It includes a large collection of tribal publications. Archives & Special Collections are comprised of two interconnected collecting areas. The Archives is a repository for the historical materials and non-current records of the Mashantucket Pequot Tribal Nation. It also holds the family papers of tribal members. The Special Collections contains a variety of materials that document the histories & cultures of Native America, including letters and other manuscripts, maps, pamphlets, ephemera, rare books, & photographs. The Children's Library introduces students to the Mashantucket Pequot Tribal Nation and other North American indigenous peoples through programs and through its collections. The Children's Library serves students through 8th grade, adults who work with children, and researchers of children's literature. The collection contains current & historical materials by and about Native Americans, and includes fiction and non-fiction books, serials, reference works, and multimedia. The Education Collection supports the educational aims of the museum and includes materials on educational theory and curriculum development relating to Native American studies. *Special programs*: Educational workshops, lectures and orientations. Opened 1998.

YALE UNIVERSITY LIBRARY
120 High St. • NEW HAVEN, CT 06520
   (203) 432-2798 Fax 432-7231; Website: www.library.yale.edu/
   Scott Bennett, PhD, Director
Description: A major U.S. repository of documentation on Native American art. Interlibrary loans.

EVA BUTLER LIBRARY - INDIAN & COLONIAL RESEARCH CENTER
P.O. Box 525 • OLD MYSTIC, CT 06372
   (860) 536-9771; Website: www.theicrc.org
   Joan Cohn, President/Director
Description: Subjects cover Native American genealogy, culture, history, and colonial history & local family genealogy. *Special programs*: School programs available for a fee; speaker at annual meeting in November each year. Open to the public. Opened 1965.

INSTITUTE FOR AMERICAN INDIAN STUDIES RESEARCH LIBRARY
38 Curtis Rd., Box 1260 • WASHINGTON, CT 06793
   (860) 868-0518 Fax 868-1649; Website: www.birdstone.org
   Elizabeth McCormick, Director; Dr. Lucianne Lavin, Director of Research
Purpose: The discovery, preservation, & interpretation of Native American cultures of the Northeastern Woodlands region of the U.S. *Activities*: Conducts surveys for prehistoric & historic evidence of human occupation; excavations of historic sites. *Research Library*: Collection of 2,000 volumes, periodicals, archival documents, and maps. For use by members, scholars & students with letters from professors. By appointment only.

DELAWARE

NANTICOKE INDIAN MUSEUM LIBRARY
27073 John J. Williams Hwy. • MILLSBORO, DE 19966
   (302) 945-7022; E-mail: info@nanticokeindians.org
   Pat Harmon, Joan Ridolfi, Docent
Description: A collection of about 500 books on the Nanticoke and other tribes.

DISTRICT OF COLUMBIA

AMERICAN HISTORICAL ASSOCIATION LIBRARY
400 A St., SE • WASHINGTON, DC 20003
   (202) 544-2422 Fax 544-8307; Website: www.historians.org
   E-mail: info@historians.org

DAR LIBRARY - NATIONAL SOCIETY
DAUGHTERS OF THE AMERICAN REVOLUTION
1776 D St., NW • WASHINGTON, DC 20006
   (202) 879-3229 Fax 879-3227; Website: www.dar.org
   E-mail: library@dar.org; Eric G. Grundset, Library Director
Description: Covers American Indian history, genealogy & culture. Opened 1896.

LIBRARY OF CONGRESS
101 Independence Ave., SE • WASHINGTON, DC 20540
   (202) 707-5522; Website: www.loc.gov
   James H. Billington, Librarian
GENERAL REFERENCE & BIBLIOGRAPHY DIVISION: A collection of more than 16,000 volumes covering virtually all subjects relating to North American tribes. Includes various bibliographies, catalogs, & guides to other collections containing material on Indians, such as Dictionary Catalog of the Edward E. Ayer Collection of Americana and American Indians, the Dictionary Catalog of the American Indian Collection, Huntington Free Library & Reading Room, New York, & the Biographical and Historical Index of American Indians and Persons Involved in Indian Affairs. *MICROFORM READING ROOM*: Contains much Indian-related material from a variety of print & non-print sources. For example: North American Indians: Photographs from National Anthropological Archives, Smithsonian Institution, compiled by Herman Viola--contains approximately 4,700 photographs on microfiche of Indians & Indian artifacts; individual & group portraits; Doctoral Dissertation Series. University Microfilms has published North American Indians: Dissertation Index, written between 1904-1976 at North American universities; Early State Records--The study of colonial relations with Indians; also includes public & private collections noted for Indian-related material, such as: The Connecticut Archives Indian Volumes, 1647-1820; The Henry O'Reilly Papers, 1744-1825--Relating to the Six Nations and Indians of the Old Northwest; Records of the Five Civilized Tribes, 1840-1905; The Penn Manuscripts, 1687-1801; & The Timothy Horsfield Papers, 1733-1771--The last two collections involving Indians in Pennsylvania and surrounding areas;
Pamphlets in American History--Microfiche collection of rare pamphlets includes many dealings with American Indians; British Manuscripts Project--contains abundant source material on Indians especially for the period of the French and Indian War. *MANUSCRIPT DIVISION*: The Papers of the President, military officers, agents in Indian affairs, and other public & private individuals who dealt with Indians at various periods, such as those of Thomas A. Jesup, Henry L. Dawes, Edward S. Godfrey, Henry Rowe Schoolcraft, Philip Sheridan, Samuel P. Heintzelman, and John M. Schofield. Important collections available on microfilm include the papers of the American Missionary Society, the American Indian Correspondence Collection, and the Moravian Archives, as well as the papers of Timothy Pickering, Henry Knox, and Lyman C. Draper. Contains transcripts and photocopies of collections in foreign archives and libraries, such as the Indian records in the Public Archives of Canada. *SERIAL & GOVERNMENT PUBLICATIONS DIVISION*: The Senate Confidential Executive Documents and Reports: Dating from the 17th Congress (1821) -- comprised of formerly confidential documents that relate primarily to treaties. Patrons who wish to use this material should write to the Chief of this Division of the Library of Congress, or phone (202) 707-5647. *PRINTS & PHOTOGRAPHS DIVISION*: Maintains holdings of nearly 4,000 prints, photographs, & engravings. The Edward S. Curtis Collection--Contains more than 1,600 photographs of Indians of the Plains, the Central Plateau, the Northwest Coast, the Southwest, & California; The Heyn-Matzen Collection--Contains approximately 550 photo-graphs, mostly of Sioux, Crow & other Plains tribes; The John Grabill Collection--Consists mainly of photographs of Western frontier life, but includes many of Indians; also more than 200 stereo views of Indians, & a miscellaneous collection of uncataloged & unsorted prints & photographs. Copies of the division's material not covered by copyright may be purchased from the Library's Photo-duplication Service. ARCHIVE OF FOLK CULTURE: Joseph C. Hickerson, Head. The Smithsonian-Densmore Collection -- Contains more than 3,500 cylinder recordings of songs of 35 tribal groups, compiled from 1907-1932; Peabody Museum Collection--Compiled in the 1890's by anthropologist Jesse Walter Fewkes, this collection contains more than 50 recordings reproducing the music & language of tribes like the Passamaquoddy, Hopi & Zuni; The Willard Rhodes Collection--Contains the music of 50 Indian tribes, recorded on disc & tape from 1940-1952, when Rhodes worked for the B.I.A. 20 long-playing records of selections from these & other collections are available for purchase. The Federal Cylinder Project- Judith A. Gray, Ethnomusicologist - began in 1979 to organize, catalog, duplicate for preservation, & disseminate wax cylinder recordings, most of which document the music & lore of American Indian cultures. Includes recordings of 15 Native American groups initially resident in the Northeastern & Southeastern woodlands-Passamaquoddy, Chippewa, Menominee, Seminole, & Winnebago recordings. Also contains recordings from the Great Basin/Plateau regions & 20 collections from the Pacific Northwest & Arctic areas. Maintains a file of bibliographies & related lists. For information & descriptive literature write the Archive, or phone (202) 707-5510. *MOTION PICTURE, BROAD-CASTING & RECORDED SOUND DIVISION*: Contains films of ceremonial dances & of everyday Indian life; maintains several filmographies & guides to titles of films about Indians. For information regarding viewing films & videotapes write Division.

NATIONAL ANTHROPOLOGICAL ARCHIVES
National Museum of Natural History - Smithsonian Institution
Museum Support Center, 4210 Silver Hill Rd. • SUITLAND, MD 20746
   (301) 238-2872 Fax 238-2883; Website: www.nmnh.si.edu/naa
   John P. Hormiak, Director

Description: The nation's only repository dedicated exclusively to preserving the ethnographic, archaeological & linguistic field notes, physical anthropological data, photographs, & recordings of American anthropologists & the records of anthropological organizations. It holds the records of the National Congress of American Indians & the National Tribal Chairman's Association, and includes the largest collection of Plains Indian ledger art. Fellowship: Native American Community Scholar Awards for research on Smithsonian collections.

NATIONAL ARCHIVES & RECORDS ADMINISTRATION (NARA)
8th & Pennsylvania Ave., NW • WASHINGTON, DC 20408
(866) 272-6272; (202) 501-5395 Fax 501-7170
Mailing address: 8601 Adelphi Rd. • COLLEGE PARK, MD 20740
(301) 837-0482 Fax 837-0483; Website: www.archives.gov
Cynthia G. Fox, Branch Chief
Description: The textual records of the Bureau of Indian Affairs (BIA) are in the custody of the Archives I Reference Branch, NARA, 8th & Penn Ave. NW, Washington, DC 20480. Motion pictures accessioned from the BIA are in the custody of the Motion Picture, Sound & Video Branch; Photographs showing activities of BIA are in custody of the Still Picture Branch; and Maps created by the BIA & accessioned by the National Archives are in the custody of the Cartographic & Architectural Branch of NARA all located at 8601 Adelphi Rd., College Park, MD 20740-6001 - (301) 713-7200 Fax 713-7205. Information about NARA holdings is available online. *Publications*: The NARA Archival Information Locator (NAIL) includes information about NARA holdings of the BIA, with some item lists; The "Guide to Federal Records in the National Archives of the U.S.;" "Information About the National Archives for Researchers," pamphlet.

NATIONAL GEOGRAPHIC SOCIETY LIBRARIES
1145 17th St., NW • Washington, DC 20036
(202) 857-7783 Fax 429-5731; Susan Fifer Canby, Director
Website: www.nationalgeographic.com
Description: Contains 50,000 books, 400 periodicals on discovery & exploration, geography & natural sciences. Interlibrary loans. Open to the public by appt.

NATURAL RESOURCES LIBRARY
U.S. Department of the Interior
1849 C St., NW • WASHINGTON, DC 20240
(202) 208-5815; Victoria Nozero, Project Director
Description: Holdings include all publications issued by the Bureau of Indian Affairs: Native American treaties, history, policy; and Native American education. Open to the public.

U.S. DEPARTMENT OF THE INTERIOR LIBRARY
1849 C St., NW, MS 5412-MIB • WASHINGTON, DC 20240
(202) 208-5815; John Sherrod, Project Manager
Description: Maintains a large collection of Indian reference material.

U.S. DEPARTMENT OF JUSTICE ENVIRONMENT LIBRARY
10th & Pennsylvania Ave., NW, Rm. 2333 • WASHINGTON, DC 20530
Lee Decker, Branch Librarian
Description: Serves the Environment & Natural Resources Division at the Dept. of Justice, including the Indian Resources section; holdings of 18,000 volumes, many of which on Indian claims & natural resources as related to Indian lands.

FLORIDA

WILLIE FRANK MEMORIAL LIBRARY
Big Cypress Reservation, HC 61 Box 46A • CLEWISTON, FL 33440
(863) 983-6724 Fax 983-3539; E-mail: libbc@semtribe.com
Gretchen DeBree, Site Manager
E-mail: gretchendebree@semtribe.com
Description: Collection includes books, manuscripts, periodicals, photographs on the history & culture of the Seminole Tribe of Florida. *Special programs*: Summer program for children; story hours. Opened 1976.

INDIAN TEMPLE MOUND MUSEUM LIBRARY
P.O. Box 4009, 139 Miraclestrip Pkwy SE
FORT WALTON BEACH, FL 32549
(850) 833-9595; Anna Peele, Museum Director
Description: Collection consists of 1,500 volumes on the archaeology of the site & related sites, and Indians of the region; slides & photographs. Open to the public. Opened 1970.

DOROTHY SCOTT OSCEOLA MEMORIAL LIBRARY
3100 N.W. 63rd Ave. • HOLLYWOOD, FL 33024
(954) 989-6840 Fax 233-9536; E-mail: libho@semtribe.com
David Blackard, Site Manager; E-mail: davidblackard@semtribe.com
Diane Diaz, Librarian
Description: Collection includes books, manuscripts, periodicals, photographs on the history & culture of the Seminole Tribe of Florida. *Special programs*: Summer program for children; story hours weekly. Opened 1981.

IMMOKALEE RESERVATION LIBRARY
303 Lena Frank Dr. #3 • IMMOKALEE, FL 33934
(239) 657-3400 Fax 657-9547; E-mail: libim@semtribe.com
Jaime Yzaguirre, Site Manager; E-mail: jaimeyzaguirre@semtribe.com
Description: Small collection includes books, manuscripts, and periodicals of the Seminole Tribe of Florida. *Special programs*: Summer library program; tutoring. Opened 1992.

FLORIDA HISTORICAL SOCIETY LIBRARY
1320 Highland Ave. • MELBOURNE, FL 32935
Description: Holdings are mainly of Seminole Indian material.

BILLY OSCEOLA MEMORIAL LIBRARY
Rt. 6 Box 668 • OKEECHOBEE, FL 34974
(863) 763-4236 Fax 763-0679; Norman H. Tribbett, Librarian/Director
Deborah Johns, Site Manager; E-mail: djohns@semtribe.com
Description: Contains books, manuscripts, periodicals, photographs, microfilm and rare books on the history and culture of the Seminole Indian Tribe of Florida. *Special programs*: Summer children's program; story hours. Opened 1976.

JOHN C. PACE LIBRARY
Special Collections/West Florida Archives - The University of West Florida
11000 University Pkwy. • PENSACOLA, FL 32514
(850) 474-2213 Fax 474-3338; Website: www.library.uwf.edu
E-mail: ddebolt@uwf.edu; Dean DeBolt, Librarian
Description: Collection of manuscripts, archival records, microfilms, & research materials dealing with history of West Florida which includes materials on the Creek Indians of the Southeast from earliest contact with white men, up to present-day organizations recognition as tribes. Opened1967.

TAMPA RESERVATION LIBRARY
5219 Orient Rd. #K • TAMPA, FL 33610
(813) 626-5765 Fax 626-5489

GEORGIA

NEW ECHOTA - CHEROKEE CAPITAL STATE HISTORIC SITE LIBRARY
1211 Chatsworth Hwy. N.E. • CALHOUN, GA 30701
(706) 624-1321 Fax 624-1324; Website: www.ga.stateparks.org
David Gomez, Director
Description: General Cherokee Indian history & culture; microfilm of the 1828-1834 Cherokee Phoenix (Indian's Advocate), 1832 Georgia Land Lottery survey information, Cherokee census & enrollment records & applications, Cherokee 1835 property evaluations, biographical & autobiographical information on early 19th century Georgia State, Cherokee & federal government officials involved in the Trail of Tears. Opened 1962.

OCMULGEE NATIONAL MONUMENT LIBRARY
1207 Emery Hwy. • MACON, GA 31201
(912) 742-0447
Description: A collection of 1,000+ volumes on anthropology, archaeology, & prehistoric & historic Indians of the area; history of the Southeast U.S.

CHIEFTAINS MUSEUM LIBRARY
501 Riverside Pkwy. • ROME, GA 30162
(404) 291-9494; Josephine Ransom, Director
Description: Holdings include books & magazines dealing with Cherokee history, local history; videocassettes. Hours: Tue-Fri 11-4PM; Sunday 2-5PM; $1/adults.

IDAHO

IDAHO STATE HISTORICAL SOCIETY LIBRARY & ARCHIVES
450 N. 4th St. • BOISE, ID 83702
(208) 334-3356 Fax 334-3198
Linda Morton-Keithley, Administrator
Description: Collections include more than 200 volumes of Lapwai Agency records of 1871-1883; diaries & private papers. The Alice Fletcher-Jane Gay Nez Perce Allotment Photograph Collection, 1882-1892; Idaho Superintendency & other Indian records (National Archives microfilm); Indian files in the territorial section of State Archives; Nez Perce & Shoshone literature. Interlibrary loans. Open to the public.

INDIAN HERITAGE COUNCIL LIBRARY
Oakwood Dr., P.O. Box 752 • McCALL • ID 83638
(423) 277-1103; Homer Hooban, Librarian
Description: Maintains a collection of Native American books, pamphlets and letters on Indian religion & history. Includes the Great American Indian Bible, The Scorched Earth, Indian Nation, The Native American Anthology of Poetry, and other books. *Special activities*: Publishes Indian books approved by the Board and that are deemed worthy. Open to the public by appointment. Established 1988.

PACIFIC NORTHWEST ANTHROPOLOGICAL ARCHIVES
Laboratory of Anthropology, University of Idaho • MOSCOW, ID 83844
  Roderick Sprague, Director
Description: Originals or copies of virtually all sources of material pertaining to Pacific Northwest ethnography, archaeology, physical anthropology, and anthropological linguistics. Also, personal papers of Don Crabtree, Alfred W. Bowers, & Frank C. Leonhardy. Also, the Don Crabtree Lithic Technology collection of publications, reprints, correspondence, & specimens. Holdings number about 5,000. Area most strongly covered is the Plateau, secondly the Northwest. Open to the public.

NEZ PERCE NATIONAL HISTORICAL PARK
RESEARCH CENTER ARCHIVES & LIBRARY
39063 U.S. Hwy. 95 • SPALDING, ID 83540
  (208) 843-2261 ext. 142 Fax 843-2124
  Website: www.nps.gov/nepe
  Robert Applegate, Archivist
Description: Collection consists of about 1,700 volumes on Nez Perce Indian history & culture, and culture & history of other Columbia Plateau & Pacific Northwest tribes. *Special collection*: 5,000 historical photographs. Open to the public by appointment. Opened 1965.

ILLINOIS

FIELD MUSEUM OF NATURAL HISTORY LIBRARY
Roosevelt Rd. at Lake Shore Dr. • CHICAGO, IL 60605
  (312) 922-9410
Description: A major U.S. repository of documentation on Native American art.

LIBRARY MEDIA PROJECT
1807 W. Sunnyside #1D • CHICAGO, IL 60640
  (800) 847-3671; (773) 275-0133 Fax 878-8404
  Website: www.librarymedia.org; E-mail: info@librarymedia.org
  Mary M. Kirby, Director
Description: A non-profit organization providing public librarians, Native American organizations, and tribal libraries with a listing of Native American videos suggested by a panel of Native Americans. Many of these works are independent films normally not seen on TV or in collections by major distributors. *Publications*: Video forum (1993), first issue includes Native American videos.

THE NEWBERRY LIBRARY
D'Arcy McNickle Center for American Indian History
60 W. Walton • CHICAGO, IL 60610
  (312) 255-3564 Fax 255-3696; Website: www.newberry.org
  E-Mail: mcnickle@newberry.org; Scott M. Stevens, Director
Goals: To encourage the use of the Newberry collections on American Indian history; improve the quality of what is written about American Indians, educate teachers about American Indian culture, history, and literature; assist American Indian tribal historians in their research; and provide a meeting ground where scholars, teachers, tribal historians, and others interested in American Indian studies can discuss their work with each other. *Description*: The Edward E. Ayer & Everett O. Graff collections contain 150,000+ volumes on American Indians, and includes manuscripts, art, maps, and photographs devoted to American Indian peoples from Indian-White contact to the middle of the 20th century. Also houses a curriculum library of its own that includes books, tribal newspapers, and reference works. *Activities*: Offers numerous fellowships, including the Power-Tanner Fellowship for PhD candidates & postdoctoral scholars of American Indian heritage, the Frances C. Allen Fellowships for women of Native American heritage, and Rockefeller Foundation fellowships for community-centered research projects; coordinates the Committee on Institutional Cooperation's American Indian Studies Consortium, and alliance of the Big Ten universities, plus the University of Chicago & University of Illinois at Chicago. *Publication*: "Meeting Ground," a national bimonthly newsletter. Opened 1887.

CAHOKIA MOUNDS STATE HISTORIC SITE LIBRARY
30 Ramey St. • COLLINSVILLE, IL 62234
  (618) 346-5160 Fax 346-5162
  Website: www.cahokiamounds.com
  E-mail: cahokia.mounds@sbcglobal.net
  Dr. Mark Esarey, Site Manager
Description: Contains books, periodicals, & papers that focus on the archaeology of Cahokia Mounds & surrounding region; the Mississippian culture; Illinois archaeology; general North American & Eastern U.S. archaeology; Native American cultures, crafts, and technology. Open to the public by appointment. Opened 1989.

THE STANLEY GOLDER LIBRARY
Mitchell Museum of the American Indian
2600 Central Park Ave. • EVANSTON, IL 60201
  (847) 475-1030 Fax 475-0911; Janice B. Klein, Director
  Website: www.mitchellmuseum.org

Description: Contains about 5,000 books & journals relating to Native American history and culture. Interlibrary loans. Opened 1977.

INDIANA

THE ARCHIVES OF TRADITIONAL MUSIC
Indiana University, Morrison Hall 117 • BLOOMINGTON, IN 47405
  (812) 855-4679; E-mail: atmusic@indiana.edu; Daniel Reed, Director
Description: A library of sound recordings of world music, including a significant number of recordings of Native American music & language, and other oral data made from the late 1890s to the present. *Special collection*: Edward S. Curtis Collection of American Indian Music. *Special program*: Outreach program that helps Native American communities obtain copies of recordings of their own music & enhances the existing documentation of these materials. *Publication*: Resound, quarterly. Opened 1954.

INDIANA UNIVERSITY MUSEUM LIBRARY
Student Bldg. 107 • BLOOMINGTON, IN 47401
Description: A collection of 2,000 volumes on the American Indian.

AMERICAN INDIAN STUDIES RESEARCH INSTITUTE
Indiana University, 422 N. Indiana Ave. • BLOOMINGTON, IN 47408
  (812) 855-4086 Fax 855-7529
  Website: www.indiana.edu/~aisri; E-mail: aisri@indiana.edu
  Douglas R. Parks & Raymond J. DeMallie, Co-directors

THE POTAWATOMI MUSEUM LIBRARY
P.O. Box 631 • FREMONT, IN 46737
Description: Holdings include 1,000 reference books on the American Indian.

WATANABE FAMILY LIBRARY
Eiteljorg Museum of American Indians & Western Art
500 W. Washington St. • INDIANAPOLIS, IN 46204
  (317) 636-9378 Fax 264-1724; Website: www.eiteljorg.org
  Dana Duffy, Librarian; E-mail: dduffy@eiteljorg.com
Description: Collections consist of more than 5,000 books, exhibition catalogs, videos, DVDs, & CDs on Native American ethnology, archaeology, art, & language; American Western art; also, periodicals; Bureau of American Ethnology annual reports; historical accounts of early contact; treaties; and literature. Tribal works emphasize Northwest Coast, Eskimo, Southwest, California, Great Plains, Eastern Woodlands, and works on Central & South American tribes. Collections are searchable through the Indianapolis-Marion County Public Library online catalog www.imcpl.org.

IOWA

STATE HISTORICAL SOCIETY OF IOWA LIBRARY
402 Iowa Ave. • IOWA CITY, IA 52240-1806
  (319) 335-3916 Fax 335-3935; Website: www.iowahistory.org
  Shaner Magalhaes, Director
Description: A collection of 150,000 books & bound periodicals, microforms, historical newspapers, census, journals, manuscripts, photographs, maps, oral history, and books relating to Iowa and upper Mississippi Valley including state history journals from all over U.S. *Special collections*: Includes Duren H. Ward, Joseph Svacina, Johnathan L. Buffalo, and Leander Clark (an Indian agent) relating to the Meskwaki (or Fox) Indians including documents, photos, etc.; documents from Indian Claims Commission court cases, theses, manuscripts, maps, paintings & drawings. Interactive CD-ROM of primary source materials, Meskwaki history, is available to patrons for a fee as are photo reproductions of selected photos. Opened 1857.

EFFIGY MOUNDS NATIONAL MONUMENT LIBRARY
151 Highway 76 • HARPERS FERRY, IA 52146
  (563) 873-3491 Fax 873-3743; Website: www.nps.gov/efmo
  Phyllis Ewing, Supt
Description: Books and periodicals relating to prehistoric Indians, archaeology, history of Iowa, Wisconsin, Mississippi River, natural resources, and specifically on the archaeology & ethnography of Effigy Mounds region. Opened 1949.

MORNINGSIDE COLLEGE LIBRARY
SIOUX CITY 51106
Description: Contains a special collection on the American Indian.

KANSAS

HASKELL INDIAN NATIONS LIBRARY
Tommaney Hall Library, 155 Indian Ave.
P.O. Box 5013 • LAWRENCE, KS 66046
  (785) 749-8470 Fax 749-8473
  Marilyn Russell, Director; E-mail: mrussell@haskell.edu

MENNONITE LIBRARY & ARCHIVES
Bethel College, 300 E. 27th • N. NEWTON, KS 67117
  (316) 284-5304 Fax 284-5843; Website: www.bethelks.edu/jthiesen
  John D. Thiesen, Archivist & Co-Director; E-mail: jthiesen@bethelks.edu
Special collection: Includes the H.R. Voth Manuscript & Photograph Collection on Hopi Indians; and Rodolphe Petter Manuscript Collection on Cheyenne Indians. Also includes microfilm, audiotapes, & maps. Interlibrary loans.

PAWNEE INDIAN VILLAGE - STATE HISTORIC SITE LIBRARY
480 Pawnee Trail • REPUBLIC, KS 66964
  (785) 361-2255; Website: www.kshs.org
  Richard Gould, Director; E-mail: piv@kshs.org
Description: A resource/research center with books, articles, photographs and materials; specializes on the Pawnee Nation. Open to the public. Opened 1968.

MID-AMERICA ALL INDIAN CENTER LIBRARY
650 N. Seneca • WICHITA, KS 67203
  (316) 350-3340; Website: www.theindiancenter.org
  April Scott, Executive Director; E-mail: ascott@wichita.gov
Description: Contains a collection of over 1,200 books on the American Indian. Open to the public.

KENTUCKY

SPEED ART MUSEUM LIBRARY
2035 S. Third St. • LOUISVILLE, KY 40208
  (502) 634-2700 Fax 636-2899; Website: www.speedmuseum.org
  E-mail: info@speedmuseum.org; Ruth Cloudman, Curator
Description: Collection includes over 14,300 books, 72 periodical subscriptions; artists pamphlet files: 54 drawers. *Special collection*: Frederick Weygold's books on American Indians. Open to the public by appointment.

LOUISIANA

GRINDSTONE BLUFF MUSEUM LIBRARY
501 Jenkins Rd. • SHREVEPORT, LA 71107
Description: Collection consists of approximately 3,600 volumes with emphasis on Caddo and other area Indians.

MAINE

ABBE MUSEUM LIBRARY
P.O. Box 286 • BAR HARBOR, ME 04609
  (207) 288-3519; Rebecca Cole-Will, Curator
Description: Includes over 5,000 volumes on Native Americans, archaeology, Maine prehistory and Maine Native peoples. Open to members & scholars by appointment only.

WAPONAHKI MUSEUM & RESOURCE CENTER
Pleasant Point Passamaquoddy Tribe
P.O. Box 343 • PERRY, ME 04667
  (207) 853-2600 Fax 853-6039

MARYLAND

ASSOCIATION ON AMERICAN INDIAN AFFAIRS, INC. LIBRARY
966 Hungerford Dr. • ROCKVILLE, MD 20850
  (240) 314-7155 Fax 314-7159; Jack Trope, Director
Description: Contains over 400 books relating to American Indians. Available to general public.

OFFICE OF MINORITY HEALTH RESOURCE CENTER
c/o AMTIS-HeiTech LLC
8400 Corporate Drive, Suite 500 • Landover, MD 20785
  Office (301) 251.1797 X3108 I *Direct* (301) 238.4403(
  Toll-Free (800) 444-6472 I *Fax* 301) 251-2160 I *TDD* (301) 251-1432
  Website: www.minorityhealth.hhs.gov/opac
  Faye Williams, MS I Knowledge Center Manager
The center opened in 1986 as a contract service of the federal office. Serves all minority populations, but have specific ongoing education and training programs, and a library collection that relates to American Indian health. The Knowledge Center library has an online catalog with over 55,000 records, 6,000 of which are directly related to American Indian health issues:
https://www.minorityhealth.hhs.gov/omh/browse.aspx?lvl=2&lvlid=15
Capacity Building division, provides training on disease prevention, and grant writing training for AI/NA communities:
https://www.minorityhealth.hhs.gov/omh/browse.aspx?lvl=2&lvlid=16
Maintain a statistical health profile which is frequently used by students & researchers:
https://www.minorityhealth.hhs.gov/omh/browse.aspx?lvl=3&lvlid=62

The federal office also supports an Advisory Committee related to Native American research: https://www.minorityhealth.hhs.gov/hrac/

MASSACHUSETTS

ROBERT S. PEABODY MUSEUM OF ARCHAEOLOGY LIBRARY
Phillips Academy • ANDOVER, MA 01810
  (978) 749-4490 Fax 749-4495; Malinda S. Blustain, Director
Description: 5,000 archaeological, anthropological & ethnological sources; rare book, journals; and historical photographs.

CHILDREN'S MUSEUM RESOURCE CENTER
300 Congress St. • BOSTON, MA 02210
  (617) 426-6500; Lou Casagrande, Director
  Joan Lester, Native American Collection Consultant
Description: Holdings include 10,000 cultural materials relating to the American Indian. Open Sept. - May: Tues, Thurs. & Saturday, 10 am - 5 pm; and June - August: Monday-Friday, 10 am - 5 pm.

TOZZER LIBRARY – HARVARD UNIVERSITY
21 Divinity Ave. • CAMBRIDGE, MA 02138
  (617) 495-2248; Lynne M. Schmelz-Keil, Librarian
Description: A major U.S. repository of documentation on Native American art. Collection consists of over 175,000 volumes relating to the major subfields of anthropology, including archaeology, biological anthropology; cultural anthropology, and linguistics; strong collection on Mayan archaeology and ethnology. *Publications*: Author & Title Catalogues of the Tozzer Library (microfiche); Bibliographic Guide to Anthropology & Archaeology, annual; Anthropological Literature: An Index to Periodical Articles & Essays, quarterly. Interlibrary loans. Open to public.

BOSTON INDIAN COUNCIL LIBRARY
105 S. Huntington • JAMAICA PLAIN, MA 02130
  (617) 232-0343
Description: Collection of materials related to Indian programs, history & culture.

PLIMOTH PLANTATION LIBRARY
P.O. Box 1620 • PLYMOUTH, MA 02362
  (508) 746-1622 ext. 8385 Fax 830-6026
  Carolyn Freeman Travers, Director; Website: www.plimoth.org
Description: In addition to Pilgrim related topics, there is a growing body of southern New England Native literature. Not opened to the public.

PHILLIPS LIBRARY
Peabody Essex Museum, East Indian Square • SALEM, MA 01970
  (508) 745-1876
Description: Collection contains 1,000 books, plus periodicals and pamphlets on the history & culture of North American Indians, with emphasis on the Northeastern section of the U.S. *Special collections*: Papers of Native American researchers Frank Speck & E. Tappan Adney. Interlibrary loans. Open to public.

CHAPIN LIBRARY OF RARE BOOKS
Williams College • WILLIAMSTOWN, MA 01267
  (413) 597-2462 Fax 597-2929
  Website: www.williams.edu/resources/chapin
  Robert L. Volz, Custodian; E-mail: chapin.library@williams.edu
Description: Collection of 15th to 20th-century books relating to Indians of North and South America. Open to the public. Opened 1923.

AMERICAN ANTIQUARIAN SOCIETY LIBRARY
185 Salisbury St. • WORCESTER, MA 01609 (617) 755-5221
Description: A collection of five million books, prints, maps, and periodicals on American history, archaeology, and life through 1876.

MICHIGAN

WILLIAM L. CLEMENTS LIBRARY - UNIVERSITY OF MICHIGAN
909 S. University St. • ANN ARBOR, MI 48104
  (734) 764-2347 Fax 647-0716; Website: www.clements.umich.edu
  Dr. John C. Dann, Director
Description: Collection consists of over 75,000 books & bound periodicals, 600,000 manuscript items & other materials relating to the Americas to 1930, including Indian relations, especially in the later 18th century. Open to the public. Established 1922.

KEWEENAW BAY COMMUNITY COLLEGE LIBRARY
111 Beartown Rd. • BARAGA, MI 49908
  (906) 353-4600; Website: www.kbocc.org
Description: Collection contains a large selection of books, periodicals and movies as well as fiction and non-fiction, children's books and audio books. Open to the public. Opened 2002.

BAY MILLS COMMUNITY COLLEGE & HERITAGE CENTER LIBRARY
12214 W. Lakeshore Dr. • BRIMLEY, MI 49715
(906) 248-8418 Fax 248-2432
Website: www.bmcc.org/libraries.htm
E-mail: library@bmcc.edu; Megan Parish, Director
E-mail: meganparish@bmcc.edu

BAY DE NOC COMMUNITY COLLEGE
Learning Resource Center, 2001 N. Lincoln Rd. • ESCANABA, MI 49829
(906) 786-5802 Fax 786-6912
C.J. Havill, Director; E-mail: havillc@baycollege.edu

BISHOP BARAGA ASSOCIATION ARCHIVES
347 Rock St. • MARQUETTE, MI 49855
(906) 227-9117 Fax 228-2469; Elizabeth Delene, Archivist
Description: Collection contains papers of Bishop Frederic Baraga, the first bishop of the Upper Peninsula of Michigan and missionary to the Indians (1830-1868). Includes Native American records from the early 1800's. Baraga published a dictionary of the Ojibway language in 1853 & several other Ojibway books for which they also have records. Records also include Office of Indian Affairs, Fur Company Papers and material pertaining to the Great Lakes region. Special activities: Bishop Baraga Days, annual; Mass in Crypt of Bishop Baraga, monthly *Publications*: The Baraga Bulletin (quarterly, membership is $10 per year); His Diary & Shephard of the Wilderness, which deal with Frederic Baraga's encounters with the Ojibway & Ottawa. Open to public by appointment for research only. Opened 1930.

SAGINAW CHIPPEWA TRIBAL LIBRARY
7070 E. Broadway • MT. PLEASANT, MI 48858
(989) 775- 4519
Website: www.sagchip.org/education/library/index/htm
Jami Cromley, Librarian

LAKE SUPERIOR STATE COLLEGE - MICHIGAN COLLECTION
SAULT STE. MARIE, MI 49783
Description: Collection of 1,000 volumes on the history of Michigan's Upper Peninsula, including Indians and local history.

GTB HERITAGE LIBRARY
Grand Traverse Band of Ottawa & Chippewa Indians
2605 NW Bay Shore Dr. • SUTTONS BAY, MI 49682
(231) 271-3538 Fax 271-4861
Description: Maintains many books, publications, periodicals, videos, and CD ROMs on Native American events, history, culture, etc.

MINNESOTA

LEECH LAKE TRIBAL COLLEGE LIBRARY & ARCHIVES
6945 Little Wolf Rd. NW, P.O. Box 180 • CASS LAKE, MN 56633
(218) 335-4240 Fax 335-4209; Website: www.lltc.edu/academics/library
Melissa Pond, Library Director

RUTH A. MYERS LIBRARY - FOND DU LAC TRIBAL & COMMUNITY COLLEGE LIBRARY
2101 14th St. • CLOQUET, MN 55720
(218) 879-0837 Fax 879-0814; Website: www.fdltcc.edu
Website: www.fdl.cc.mn.us/web/library; E-mail: library@fdltcc.edu
Nancy Broughton, Library Director
Description: Special collection of regional Native American publications.

BECKER COUNTY HISTORICAL SOCIETY LIBRARY
P.O. Box 622 • DETROIT LAKES, MN 56502
Dean Sather, Director
Description: Holdings include 1,500 volumes pertaining to the White Earth Indian Reservation, covering twelve townships of Becker County, Minnesota.

MINNEAPOLIS COLLEGE OF ART & DESIGN LEARNING RESOURCE CENTER
200 East 25th St. • MINNEAPOLIS, MN 55404
Special collection: The American Indian Book Collection.

MINNEAPOLIS ATHENAEUM
300 Nicollet Mall • MINNEAPOLIS, MN 55401
(612) 630-6351 Fax 630-6210
Website: www.mplib.org/athenaeum.asp
Edward R. Kukla, Director
Description: Holdings include approximately 500 volumes dealing with Indian affairs & activities on 18th & 19th century travel books. Specializing in the following tribes: Dakota (Sioux); Mandan; and Ojibwa (Chippewa). Open to the public. Opened 1859.

UPPER MIDWEST INDIAN CULTURE CENTER LIBRARY
Pipestone National Monument, P.O. Box 727 • PIPESTONE, MN 56164
(507) 825-5463; Maddie Redwing, Director
Description: Collection of 500 volumes on Indian history of the northern Plains. Opened 1955

RED LAKE NATION TRIBAL ARCHIVES & LIBRARY
P.O. Box 297 • RED LAKE, MN 56671
(218) 679-2324 Fax 679-3378; Website: www.rlnn.com/archives.html
Kathryn "Jodie" Beaulieu, Director
Purpose: To collect, preserve, and make available the history of the Red Lake Band of Chippewa Indians. Description: Exhibits are changed seasonally and oral history presentations are provided. Opened 1989.

MINNESOTA HISTORICAL SOCIETY RESEARCH CENTER
345 Kellogg Blvd. W. • ST. PAUL, MN 55102-1906
(651) 259-3240 Fax 296-9961
Website: www.mnhs.org/library; E-mail: reference@mnhs.org;
Robert Horton, Director
Jennifer Jones, Head of Collections; Kathryn Otto, Head of Reference
Description: A major U.S. repository of documentation on Native American art. Maintains a collection of material on the Ojibwe and Dakota tribes, plus a small amount on Winnebago; includes information on Indian education, state census schedules with listings of Indian people, and correspondence on Indian matters in the Governor's papers. Library catalogs the Jeanette & Harry Ayer collection of Ojibwa arts & crafts. Collections include books, photos, newspapers, periodicals, oral histories, sound & visual recordings, and artworks. Also, Dakota and Ojibwa dictionaries, histories of Native peoples in Minnesota, and material on the U.S.-Dakota conflicts of 1862. *Activities*: Mini-classes on genealogy resources, house history research, etc. Interlibrary loans. Open to the public.

MISSISSIPPI

THE GRAND VILLAGE OF THE NATCHEZ INDIANS--LIBRARY
400 Jefferson Davis Blvd. • NATCHEZ, MS 39120
(601) 446-6502; James F. Barnett, Jr., Director
Description: A collection of 300 volumes on archaeology & Southeastern Indians. Special programs: Seminars, workshops, and educational programs. Open to public for reference only.

NATCHEZ TRACE PARKWAY LIBRARY
2680 Natchez Trace Parkway • TUPELO, MS 38804
Description: Maintains a special collection of 200 items of papers and letters relating to Choctaw and Chickasaw Indians.

MISSOURI

SOUTHEAST MISSOURI STATE UNIVERSITY LIBRARY
CAPE GIRARDEAU, MO 63701
Description: Extensive collection on North American archaeology and American Indians.

KANSAS CITY MUSEUM LIBRARY
3218 Gladstone Blvd. • KANSAS CITY, MO 64123
(816) 483-8300; David Ucko, President
Description: Maintains a general reference library with about 4,000 volumes covering primarily local and regional history, Native American art and history, natural sciences, material culture, and museum-related publications.

NATIONAL ARCHIVES-CENTRAL PLAINS REGION
2312 East Bannister Rd. • KANSAS CITY, MO 64131
(816) 268-8000 Fax 268-8038; Website: www.archives.gov
Diana Duff, Director; E-mail: kansascity.archives@nara.gov
Description: Collection consists of Federal Indian records created on Indian reservations & schools in North & South Dakota, Minnesota, Kansas & Nebraska. The tribes included on these reservations include the Chippewa & the various tribes of the Sioux Confederation, as well as the Iowa, Kickapoo, Omaha, Potawatomi, Ponca, Sac & Fox, Winnebago & Munsee; also, records of the Bismarck, Flandreau, Haskell, Pierre, Pipestone, Rapid City, and Wahpeton Indian schools. Information contained are: censuses, tribal enrollment rosters, annuity payrolls, individual Indian bank account ledgers, land allotment rolls, employee payrolls & student case files; also extensive series of superintendent's (agent's) correspondence files. *Activities*: Monthly Indian study group. Open to the public, M-F 8 a.m. - 4 p.m.

UNIVERSITY OF MISSOURI-KANSAS CITY
Miller Nichols Library-Native American Studies
5100 Rockhill Rd. • KANSAS CITY, MO 64110
(816) 235-1534 Fax 333-5584; Website: www.umkc.edu/lib/

Special collection: Snyder Collection of Americana--25,000 volumes; historical and Indian-related works.

MISSOURI HISTORICAL SOCIETY LIBRARY
P.O. Box 11940 • ST. LOUIS, MO 63112-0040
  (314) 746-4500 Fax 746-4548; Website: www.mohistory.org
  Emily Jaycox, Librarian; E-mail: library@mohistory.org
Description: Holdings include more than 2,000 volumes on the American Indian. Strongest on the fur trade in the Trans-Mississippi West. Open to the public. Established 1866.

MONTANA

STONE CHILD COLLEGE LIBRARY
8294 Upper Box Elder Rd. • BOX ELDER, MT 59521
  (406) 395-4313 Fax 395-4836

CENTER FOR NATIVE AMERICAN STUDIESLIBRARY
University of Montana • BOZEMAN, MT 59717
  (406) 994-3881; Dr. Wayne J. Stein, Director
Research activities: American Indian studies, including research on Montana tribal histories and culture and Indian-white relations.

BLACKFEET COMMUNITY COLLEGE - MEDICINE SPRING LIBRARY
P.O. Box 819 • BROWNING, MT 59417
  (406) 338-5411 Fax 338-5454; Virginia "Ginny" Weeks, Director

LITTLE BIG HORN COLLEGE LIBRARY
P.O. Box 370 • CROW AGENCY, MT 59022
  (406) 638-3113 Fax 638-3170
  Tim Bernardis, Director; E-mail: tim@lbhc.edu

WHITE SWAN MEMORIAL LIBRARY
LITTLE BIGHORN BATTLEFIELD NATIONAL MONUMENT
P.O. Box 39 • CROW AGENCY, MT 59022
  (406) 638-2621 ext. 131 Fax 638-2623
  John Doerner, Historian/Librarian
Elizabeth & George Custer Collection – Contains correspondence with statesmen and military personnel of the period; 2,000 photographs, including military personnel, the Custer family; Native Americans (Crow, Sioux, Cheyenne).

MILES ROMNEY MEMORIAL LIBRARY
Bitter Root Valley Historical Society
205 Bedford Ave. • HAMILTON, MT 59840
  (406) 363-3338; Website: www.cybernet1.com/rcmuseum/
  Helen Ann Bibler, Director; E-mail: rcmuseum@cybernet1.com
Description: Subjects include Indian history, pioneer and the Lewis & Clark expedition. *Special programs*: Sunday Series Program; Bitter Root Days; MacIntosh Apple Day.

FORT BELKNAP COLLEGE LIBRARY
P.O. Box 159 • HARLEM, MT 59526
  (406) 353-2607 x 311 Fax 353-2898
  Eva English, Director; E-mail: evaenglish@yahoo.com

MONTANA HISTORICAL SOCIETY RESEARCH CENTER
225 N. Roberts, P.O. Box 201 • HELENA, MT 59620
  (406) 444-2681 Fax 444-5297
  Website: www.montanahistoricalsociety.org
  E-mail: mhslibrary@mt.gov; Charlene Porsild, Director
Description: Holdings include published works, state agency publications & records, manuscript collections, oral histories & photographs on Montana history, frontier life, Indians & Indian affairs, the Lewis & Clark Expedition, and other early expeditions & related subjects. Open to the public. Opened 1865.

DR. JOHN WOODENLEGS MEMORIAL LIBRARY
CHIEF DULL KNIFE COMMUNITY COLLEGE
P.O. Box 98, 1 College Dr. • LAME DEER, MT 59043
  (406) 477-8293 Fax 477-6575; Website: www.cdkc.edu/lib2
  Joan Hantz, Director; E-mail: jhantz@cdkc.edu
Description: Contains over 14,000 circulated items; Special Cheyenne Collection; more than 100 periodical titles and newspapers.

UNIVERSITY OF MONTANA - SCHOOL OF LAW LIBRARY
MISSOULA, MT 59801
Description: Maintains a special collection on Indian law; 120 treaties.

D'ARCY McNICKLE LIBRARY - SALISH KOOTENAI COLLEGE
P.O. Box 70 Hwy. 93 • PABLO, MT 59855
  (406) 275-4876 Fax 275-4812
  Fred Noel, Director; E-mail: fred_noel@skc.edu

FORT PECK TRIBAL LIBRARY
Box 398, 605 Indian • POPLAR, MT 59255
  (406) 768-6340 Fax 768-6301
  Anita Scheetz, Director; E-mail: ascheetz@fpcc.edu

BIG HOLE NATIONAL BATTLEFIELD RESEARCH LIBRARY
P.O. Box 237 • WISDOM, MT 59761
  (406) 689-3155 Fax 689-3151; Jon James, Supt.
Description: Collection contains over 400 volumes on Nez Perce history, culture; military history of the 1870s, Nez Perce War related materials, & frontier army.
Special program: Interpretive program guided walks of the historic site in summer. Open to the public by appointment for reference only.

NEBRASKA

CENTER FOR GREAT PLAINS STUDIES
UNIVERSITY OF NEBRASKA-LINCOLN
P.O. Box 880250 • LINCOLN, NE 68588-0250
  (402) 472-0599 Fax 472-0463; Website: www.unl.edu/plains
  Reece Summers, Director
Description: A collection of Western art and fiction with emphasis on American Indian art. Also, a large collection of reference books on Canada. A complete set of photos of American Indians by Edward S. Curtis from his, The North American Indian (1907-1930). Six art exhibitions displayed each year with accompanying opening talk. Opened 1980.

UNIVERSITY OF NEBRASKA STATE MUSEUM
Nebraska Hall • LINCOLN, NE 68588
  (402) 472-6365; Hugh H. Genoways, Director
Research activities: Studies include the culture & history of the Plains Apache.
Publication: Bulletin of the U. of Nebraska State Museum.

NATIVE AMERICAN PUBLIC TELECOMMUNICATIONS LIBRARY
1800 North 33rd St. • LINCOLN, NE 68583
  (402) 472-3522 Fax 472-8675
  Website: www.nativetelecom.org; E-mail: native@unl.edu
Description: A collection of videotapes & films include Native-American programs that have been screened & evaluated by the Consortium for technical quality and accuracy of portrayal and content. Topics include: history, culture, education, economic development, current events and the arts.

NEBRASKA STATE HISTORICAL SOCIETY LIBRARY/ARCHIVES
P.O. Box 82554, 1500 R St. • LINCOLN, NE 68501
  (402) 471-4751 Fax 471-8922; Website: www.nebraskahistory.org
  Andrea Faling, Archivist
Description: Holdings include more than 70,000 volumes on Nebraska history, Indians of the Great Plains, genealogy; 465 photographs in the John A. Anderson Photograph Collection of Brule Sioux. A collection of videotapes on several Nebraska tribes including storytelling, history, and elders' reminiscences by members of the Lakota, Brule Sioux, Santee Sioux, Omaha, Pawnee and Winnebago tribes.

NEBRASKA INDIAN COMMUNITY COLLEGE LIBRARY
Omaha Tribal Library, P.O. Box 428 Omaha Hill • MACY, NE 68039
  (402) 837-5078 Fax 837-4183
  Mary Johnson, Director; E-mail: mjohnson@thenicc.edu

NEBRASKA INDIAN COMMUNITY COLLEGE LIBRARY
Santee Campus, 425 Frazier Ave. N., Suite 1 • NIOBRARA, NE 68760
  (402) 857-2434 x 2577 Fax 837-4183
  Mary Johnson, Director; E-mail: mjohnson@thenicc.edu

LITTLE PRIEST TRIBAL COLLEGE LIBRARY
WINNEBAGO PUBLIC LIBRARY
601 E College Dr., P.O. Box 270 • WINNEBAGO, NE 68071
  (402) 878-3334 Fax 878-2319; Mary Austin, Director
Description: The first tribal college library to become a government depository library. Holdings include over 19,000 items, including 70 journal subscriptions, 13 newspaper subscriptions, audio books, 700 videotapes, and paperback books. The Native American collection contains over 2,700 items. Begun 1991.

NEVADA

NEWE LIBRARY - TE-MOAK BAND OF WESTERN SHOSHONE
37 Mountain View Dr. #C • BATTLE MOUNTAIN, NV 89820
  (775) 635-2004 Fax 635-8016

COLLEGE CAREER & VOCATIONAL RESOURCE LIBRARY
Nevada Urban Indians, 1190 Bible Way • RENO, NV 89502
  (775) 788-7600 Fax 788-7611; Belvin Hill, Director

Description: Provides information on all major colleges with Native American Studies Programs from across the nation. Includes brochures & applications, scholarships, grants and vocational schools.

NEW HAMPSHIRE

MT. KEARSARGE INDIAN MUSEUM LIBRARY
P.O. Box 142 • WARNER, NH 03278
(603) 456-2376 Fax 456-3092
Website: www.indianmuseum.org
Tricia Stott, Library Manager
Description: Maintains more than 1,600 volumes on American Indians.
Hours: Tuesday, Thursday & Saturday, 10 am - 2 pm or by appointment.

NEW JERSEY

LE BRUN LIBRARY - MONTCLAIR ART MUSEUM
3 South Mountain Ave. • MONTCLAIR, NJ 07042
(973) 746-5555; Website: www.montclairartmuseum.org
Jeff Guerrier, Librarian
Description: Maintains a collection of 40,000 items supporting the Museum; collections of American & Native American art. Includes 8,000 exhibition catalogues; several thousand slides; 7,000 bookplates; artist & subject files. Special programs: Friend's Committee, "Conversations with Authors." Friends of the Le Brun Library. Interlibrary loans. Open to the public by appointment: Wed.-Fri., 10-noon, 2:30-4:30. Opened 1914.

NEWARK MUSEUM LIBRARY
49 Washington St. • NEWARK, NJ 07102
(973) 596-6625 Fax 642-0459; William A. Peniston, Librarian
Description: Collection covers American Indian art, crafts, life, ethnology, etc. Interlibrary loans. Open to the public by appointment only. Opened 1926.

PRINCETON UNIVERSITY LIBRARIES
PRINCETON, NJ 08540 (609) 452-3180
Description: A major U.S. repository of documentation on Native American art.

SETON HALL UNIVERSITY MUSEUM LIBRARY
S. Orange Ave. • SOUTH ORANGE, NJ 07079
(201) 761-9543
Description: A collection of 1,000 volumes on prehistoric Indians of New Jersey.

NEW MEXICO

ACOMA PUEBLO LIBRARY & COMPUTER CENTER
Sky City Cultural Center, Pueblo of Acoma
P.O. Box 309 • ACOMITA, NM 87034
(800) 747-0181; (505) 552-6108 Fax 552-7204
Brian D. Vallo, Director
Description: Contains photographs and documents relating to the history of Acoma Pueblo. Opened in 1977.

AMERICAN INDIAN LAW CENTER LIBRARY
UNIVERSITY OF NEW MEXICO-SCHOOL OF LAW
P.O. Box 4456, Station A, 1117 Stanford N.E. • ALBUQUERQUE, NM 87196
(505) 277-5462
Description: Maintains a special collection on American Indian law.

CLARK FIELD ARCHIVE & LIBRARY
MAXWELL MUSEUM OF ANTHROPOLOGY
University of New Mexico, MSC01 1050 • ALBUQUERQUE, NM 87131
(505) 277-8675; Website: www.unm.edu/~maxwell/clark_field.htm
Alan M. Shalette, Director; E-mail: alshal@unm.edu
Description: Collection of 12,000 volumes & 200 journals on world anthropology & archaeology, with special emphasis on the American Southwest. Collections are cataloged online at www.libros.unm.edu. *Activities*: Annual Albuquerque Antiquarian Book Fair Fundraiser, 1st weekend in April.

NATIVE AMERICAN STUDIES - INFORMATION
& MATERIALS RESOURCE COLLECTION
U. of New Mexico, 1812 Las Lomas Dr. NE • ALBUQUERQUE, NM 87131
(505) 277-3917 Fax 277-1818
Alison Freese, PhD, Information Specialist
Description: A resource/research center with books, journals, Native newspapers, videos, and news clippings on Native issues, specializing in stereotyping, Native American economic development, Southwestern history, Native American literature, Native perspectives of American history, and a quincentennial archive. *Special programs*: Speakers series; computer networking with tribal offices, schools, & libraries. *Publication*: Monthly newsletter. Open to the public.

PUEBLO ARCHIVES & RESEARCH LIBRARY
Institute for Pueblo Indian Studies - Indian Pueblo Cultural Center
2401 12th St., NW • ALBUQUERQUE, NM 87104
(505) 843-7270 ext. 329 Fax 842-6959
Ted Sturm, Associate Director
Description: Collection consists of books and monographs; periodicals; newspapers; Newspaper Clipping File, Government documents; microfilmed documents; maps, photographs and postcards, slides; audio, visual tapes & recordings; special collections concerning Pueblo Indians. *Special programs*: Sponsors education programs; seminars and symposia; research projects dealing with Pueblo Indians and issues affecting them. Open to the public. Opened 1976.

SOUTHWEST INDIAN POLYTECHNIC INSTITUTE LIBRARY
P.O. Box 10146 • ALBUQUERQUE, NM 87184
(505) 346-2352 Fax 346-2381
Website: www.sipi.bia.edu/acadprog/imc
Valerie Montoya, Acting Librarian

AZTEC RUINS NATIONAL MONUMENT LIBRARY
84 Road 2900 • AZTEC, NM 87410
(505) 334-6174
Description: A collection of 300 volumes on the ethnography and archaeology of Southwestern Indians and prehistoric Pueblo Indians.

DINE COLLEGE LIBRARY
P.O. Box 57 • CROWNPOINT, NM 87313
(505) 786-7391 Fax 786-5240
Andrea Winship, Librarian
NAVAJO TECHNICAL COLLEGE
Lowerpoint Rd. State Hwy. 371 • CROWNPOINT, NM 87313-0849
(505) 786-4130 Fax 786-5644
Clyde Henderson, Librarian; E-mail: chenderson@navajotech.edu

SAN JUAN COUNTY ARCHAEOLOGICAL RESEARCH CENTER LIBRARY
FARMINGTON, NM 87401
(505) 632-2013 Fax 632-1707; Kurt Mantonya, Librarian
Description: Research library focusing upon archaeology and history of the Four Corners area, including archaeological reports, historical documents, slides of Navajo rock art; 4,000 books, 1,200 pamphlets, 35 oral history tapes, photographs & color slides, transcriptions, and maps; and an on-loan collection of Navajo material. Open to the public. Opened 1973.

GALLUP INDIAN MEDICAL CENTER LIBRARY
PHS -- Indian Health Service
P.O. Box 1337 • GALLUP, NM 87301
Description: Maintains a special collection on the Navajo Indians.

GALLUP PUBLIC LIBRARY
115 West Hill • GALLUP, NM 87301
Description: A collection of rare, out-of-print & contemporary titles on Southwestern tribes: Navajo, Hopi and Zuni.

ISLETA PUEBLO LIBRARY
P.O. Box 1290 • ISLETA, NM 87022
(505) 869-8119 Fax 869-7690

LAGUNA PUBLIC LIBRARY
P.O. Box 194 • LAGUNA, NM 87026
(505) 552-6280

BANDELIER NATIONAL MONUMENT LIBRARY
LOS ALAMOS, NM 87544 (505) 672-3861
Description: Contains a collection of 2,000 volumes on the archaeology of the area, and Pueblo Indians.

CHACO CULTURE NATIONAL HISTORICAL PARK LIBRARY
P.O. Box 220 • NAGEEZI, NM 87037-0220
(505) 786-5384
Description: Study library housing hundreds of volumes on prehistory & history of Chaco area, Southwestern archaeology, ethnology, including journals, photographs, and records of historic period.

NAVAJO NATION LIBRARY SYSTEM
Navajo Community Library • NAVAJO, NM 87328
See listing under Window Rock, AZ.

PALEO-INDIAN INSTITUTE LIBRARY
Eastern New Mexico University
Campus Box 2154 • PORTALES, NM 88130

EL MORRO NATIONAL MONUMENT LIBRARY
RAMAH, NM 87321
 (505) 783-5132
Description: A collection of 400 volumes on the archaeology of the prehistoric site and historic Pueblos.

FORT BURGWIN RESEARCH CENTER
SOUTHERN METHODIST UNIVERSITY
P.O. Box 300 • RANCHOS DE TAOS, NM 87557
 (505) 758-8322; Dr, William B. Stallcup, Jr. Research Director
Research activities: Includes field studies in prehistoric pithouses & Pueblo settlements. Performs archaeological site preservation technology.

STRADLING MUSEUM OF THE HORSE LIBRARY
RUIDOSO, NM 88345
Description: Maintains a collection of 1,000 volumes on Indian history; Indian rugs.

HISTORY LIBRARY/PHOTO ARCHIVES
PALACE OF THE GOVERNORS-MUSEUM OF NEW MEXICO
110 Washington Ave. • SANTA FE, NM 87501
 (505) 476-5090/5092 Fax 476-5104
 Website: www.mnm.state.nm.us
 Tomas Jaehn, Curator

INSTITUTE OF AMERICAN INDIAN ARTS LIBRARY
83 Avan Nu Po Rd. • SANTA FE, NM 87508
 (505) 424-5715 Fax 424-3131; Website: www.iaiancad.org
 Valerie Nye, Director; E-mail: reference@iaia.edu
 Grace Nuvayestewa & Jennifer James, Librarians
Description: Collection consists of more than 20,000 volumes on North American Indian art, history & culture; 800 videotapes, recording tribal & reservation history, tribal projects and activities, such as the reservation medical center or tribal government--30,000 Smithsonian photographs of Native American culture; more than 900 recordings of Native American music; 9,000 slides of art of all types and Native American art objects. Open to the public for research only. Opened 1962.

LABORATORY OF ANTHROPOLOGY LIBRARY
MUSEUM OF INDIAN ARTS & CULTURE-MUSEUM OF NEW MEXICO
P.O. Box 2087, 708 Camino Lejo • SANTA FE, NM 87504
 (505) 476-1263 Fax 476-1330; Website: www.miaclab.org
 Mara Yarbrough, Librarian
Description: A major U.S. repository of documentation on Native American art. Focuses on Native American cultures of the Southwest from prehistory to contemporary times. Southwest anthropology research library of more than 15,000 items with holdings in 1,000 journal titles; as well as the personal library of Sylvanus G. Morley with many rare Mesoamerican titles.

WHEELWRIGHT MUSEUM OF THE AMERICAN INDIAN
MARY CABOT WHEELWRIGHT RESEARCH LIBRARY
P.O. Box 5153, 704 Camino Lejo • SANTA FE, NM 87501
 (505) 982-4636; Steve Rogers, Curator
Description: Maintains about 10,000 volumes on the art, history, & religions of the Navajo & other tribes; archives contain 1,000 examples of Navajo ceremonial art, 3,000 Navajo ceremonial music recordings, 100 Navajo myth texts, 1,000 Navajo sand paintings on slides, and 100 music & prayer tapes. Open to the public by appointment.

DINE COLLEGE LIBRARY
P.O. Box 580, 1228 Yucca St. • SHIPROCK, NM 87420-0580
 (505) 368-3542 Fax 368-3539; Website: www.crystal.ncc.cc.nm.us
 Annie Lewis, Librarian
Description: Collection of books, periodicals, videotapes, pamphlets, and maps. Special collections: Native American Special collection, and the Caswell and Betty Silver Southwest Geoscience Collection. Interlibrary loans. Opened 1969.

GILA CLIFF DWELLINGS NATIONAL MONUMENT -
VISITOR CENTER LIBRARY
Route 11, Box 100 • SILVER CITY, NM 88061
Description: A collection of books on prehistoric Mogollon Indians, archaeology and natural history.

SOUTHWEST RESEARCH CENTER OF NORTHERN NEW MEXICO
P.O. Drawer CCC, 238 Ledoux St. • TAOS, NM 87571
 (505) 758-5440 Fax 758-0330; Nita Murphy, Librarian
Description: Combined Kit Carson Museum & Harwood Museum libraries. Contains a collection of 6,500 volumes on the prehistoric Indian culture of Taos and the Southwest from the Kit Carson Museum library and the Harwood collection with an emphasis on art. Open to the public. Opened 1999.

MILLICENT ROGERS MUSEUM OF NORTHERN NEW MEXICO LIBRARY
P.O. Box A • TAOS, NM 87571
 (505) 758-2462 Fax 758-5751; Dr. Shelby Tisdale, Executive Director
Description: Research library related to collections.

A:SHIWI A:WAN MUSEUM & HERITAGE CENTER LIBRARY
P.O. Box 1009 • ZUNI, NM 87327
 (505) 782-4403 Fax 782-4503
 E-mail: aamhc_museum@yahoo.com
 James Enote, Executive Director
Description: Collection of books on Zuni & other Southwestern Native American tribes.

ZUNI PUBLIC LIBRARY
27 E. Chavez Circle, P.O. Box 339 • ZUNI, NM 87327
 (505) 782-4575 Fax 782-2700
 Cordelia "Codi" Hooee, Librarian/Director; Joseph Dishta, Director
Description: Comprehensive holdings concerning Zuni prehistory, archaeology, history, & land use. 3,000 books, 300 bound periodical volumes, 3,250 reports, journals & other serials. Unpublished field notes, ethnographic interviews, papers & published works are on file. Opened 1978.

NEW YORK

TONAWANDA INDIAN COMMUNITY LIBRARY
P.O. Box 326, 372 Bloomingdale Rd. • AKRON, NY 14001-0326
 (716) 542-5618; Ramona Charles, Director

INSTITUTE FOR ARCHAEOLOGICAL STUDIES – SUNY AT ALBANY
Social Science, Rm. 263, 1400 Washington Ave. • ALBANY, NY 12222
 (518) 442-4700; Prof. Dean R. Snow, Director
Description: Northeastern archaeology, ethnology & linguistics. Supports research activities on Native Northeastern peoples, primarily Algonquian and Iroquois tribes. *Publication*: Man in the Northeast.

CAYUGA MUSEUM LIBRARY & ARCHIVES
203 Genesee St. • AUBURN, NY 13021
 (315) 253-8051 Fax 253-9829
Description: Includes manuscripts, books, & periodicals relating to the history of the Iroquois in central New York State.

NATIONAL KATERI CENTER LIBRARY
The National Shrine of N.A. Martyrs • AURIESVILLE, NY 12016
 (518) 853-3033; Rec. Robert J. Boyle, S.J., Director

BROOKLYN MUSEUM OF ART LIBRARY & ARCHIVES
200 Eastern Pkwy. • BROOKLYN, NY 11238
 (718) 501-6308 Fax 501-6125
 Website: www.brooklynmuseum.org
 E-mail: library@brooklynmuseum.org
 Dierdre Lawrence, Librarian & Coordinator of Research Services
 E-mail: deirdre.lawrence@brooklynmuseum.org
Description: A major U.S. repository of documentation on Native American art. Holds extensive research documents on Native North & South American art and culture. Has many published textual and visual resources which document objects, people and places. The Archives, in addition to institutional records, hold the Stewart Culin Archives that represents the documentation assembled by the Museum's First Curator of Ethnology (1903-1929).

BUFFALO & ERIE COUNTY HISTORICAL SOCIETY LIBRARY
5 Nottingham Court • BUFFALO, NY 14216
Description: Holdings include books & manuscripts related to the Seneca Indians and other Indians of the Niagara frontier.

THE MOHAWK-CAUGHNAWAGA MUSEUM LIBRARY
Route 5, Box 627, RD 1 • FONDA, NY 12068
 (518) 853-3646; Rev. Nicholas Weiss, Director
Description: A collection of 4,500 volumes on American Indians and American history.

AKWESASNE LIBRARY - AKWESASNE CULTURAL CENTER
ST. REGIS MOHAWK RESERVATION
321 State Rt. 37 • HOGANSBURG, NY 13655
 (518) 358-2240 Fax 358-2649
 Website: www.akwesasneculturalcenter.org/library
 Glory Cole, Director
Description: Public library with holdings of 27,000 volumes on most nations of the U.S. & Canada, with special collection on the North American Indian. Books in English, French, Mohawk & Seneca languages. Interlibrary loans. Open to the public.

IROQUOIS INDIAN MUSEUM LIBRARY
P.O. Box 7, Caverns Rd. • HOWES CAVE, NY 12092
(518) 296-8949; Website: www.iroquoismuseum.org
E-Mail: info@iroquoismuseum.org
Thomas M. Elliott, Director
Description: A collection of books, periodicals, pamphlets and files relating to the Iroquois.

THE SENECA NATION LIBRARY
The Cattaraugus Reservation Branch
3 Thomas Indian School Dr. • IRVING, NY 14081
(716) 532-9449 Fax 532-6115
Pamela Bowen, Library Director
Karen F. John, Branch Supervisor
Description: A collection of books & periodicals, with a special collection the history of the Iroquois Indians on microfilm; videotapes, books on tape, periodicals, large print books, and college & career catalogs. *Special programs*: Native American Art Show; speakers & displays; classes, exhibits & cultural presentations; Summer Reading program; Lupus Resource Center; Native American film programs. *Publication*: Seneca Nation Arts & Crafts Directory. Allegany Reservation Branch in Salamanca, NY. Interlibrary loans. Open to the public.

CORNELL UNIVERSITY LIBRARIES
257B Kroch Library • ITHACA, NY 14853
(607) 255-9480 Fax 255-6305
Website: www.library.cornell.edu/about/libhours.html
David Block, Curator of Native American & Latin American Collections
E-Mail: db10@cornell.edu
Description: Received the Huntington Free Library's Native American collection in June of 2005. The Collection, one of North America's premier aggregation of information on Native American studies, contains more than 40,000 volumes on the archaeology, art, ethnology, & history of the Native peoples of the Americas, as well as exceptional selections in Indian languages, codices, current Native American affairs, and Indian biography and related ephemera; maintains a large collection of Indian newspapers, manuscripts & field notes, and microform & audio-visual material. Interlibrary loans (photocopies only). Open to the public by appointment.

CHAUTAUQUA-CATTARAUGUS LIBRARY SYSTEM
106 West Fifth St. • JAMESTOWN, NY 14701
(716) 484-7135 Fax 483-6680; Website: www.cclslib.org
Catherine Way, Director
Tina Scott, Assistant Director; E-mail: tscott@cclslib.org

AMERICAN INDIAN COMMUNITY HOUSE LIBRARY
134 W. 29th St., 4th Floor • New York, NY 10001
(646) 357-6761 Fax (917) 591-5458
Description: Indian books, periodicals, newspapers & subject files.
Access by appointment to educators, students & community members.

AMERICAN MUSEUM OF NATURAL HISTORY
DEPARTMENT OF LIBRARY SERVICES
Central Park West at 79th St. • NEW YORK, NY 10024
(212) 769-5406; Nina J. Root, Dept. Chairperson
Description: A major U.S. repository of documentation on Native American art. Out of a collection of 410,000 volumes, approximately 50,000 volumes on the anthropology of North American Indian tribes (ethnology and archaeology - especially strong holdings on Northwest Coast cultures) along with accounts and descriptions of explorers; 125,000 photographs, primarily black-and-white of the early 20th century and some recent color photographs of artifacts. Maintains a special film collection with a limited number of films on Indians. Interlibrary loans. Open to the public.

THE NEW YORK PUBLIC LIBRARY
42nd St. & Fifth Ave. • NEW YORK, NY 10018
(212) 930-0826
Timothy Troy, Bibliographer of American Indian Material
Description: A major U.S. repository of documentation on Native American art. Maintains one of the largest collections of Indian bibliographical material in the world. Includes material from all cultural areas and time periods, from pre-Columbian eras to the present. The collections range through the disciplines of anthropology, archaeology, history, linguistics, and literature. Contains writings by Indians, runs of related periodicals & serials, pictures (photographs & engravings), works on Indian place names, and a collection of Indian captivity journals. Collects contemporary Native-American literature (in English or Indian languages.) The Library has materials in all written Indian languages from throughout the Western Hemisphere. Many items concerning the Indians of the Americas, particularly 16th & 17th century material in Spanish and English, are located in various special collections.

YAGER MUSEUM LIBRARY
Hartwick College • ONEONTA, NY 13820
(607) 432-4200; E-mail: reference@hartwick.edu
Description: A collection of over 1,000 volumes on North American Indian history and culture.

ROCHESTER MUSEUM & SCIENCE CENTER
Schuyler C. Towson Research Library
657 East Ave. • ROCHESTER, NY 14607
(585) 697-1947 Fax 271-0492 or 697-7608
Website: www.rmsc.org/museum/library
Leatrice M. Kemp, Librarian; E-mail: lea_kemp@rmsc.org
Description: Field & laboratory work in anthropology, natural science, and regional history (especially American Indians and Genesee Valley region during 16th-20th centuries). Library: Contains more than 30,000 books, 50,000 photographic slides, and numerous manuscripts & photographs on the history, technology and anthropology of the Genesee Valley region, with emphasis on archaeology & ethnography of New York Haudenosaunee (Iroquois) peoples, especially Seneca.

SENECA-IROQUOIS NATIONAL MUSEUM LIBRARY
Allegany Indian Reservation, 794-814 Broad St. • SALAMANCA , NY14779
(716) 945-1738; David George-Shongo, Archivists

THE SENECA NATION LIBRARY
The Allegany Reservation Branch, P.O. Box 231 • SALAMANCA, NY 14779
(716) 945-3157; Ethel E. Bray, Library Director
Dorsie Familo, Branch Supervisor
Description: A collection of books & periodicals, with a special collection on the history of the Iroquois Indians on microfilm; videotapes, and college & career catalogs. *Special programs*: Native American Art Show; speakers & displays; exhibits & cultural presentations; Native American film programs. *Publication*: Seneca Nation Arts & Crafts Director. Cattaraugus Reservation Branch in Irving, NY. Interlibrary loans.

NORTH CAROLINA

MUSEUM OF THE CHEROKEE INDIAN LIBRARY
P.O. Box 770-A, U.S. Hwy. 441 North • CHEROKEE, NC 28719
(704) 497-3481
Description: Collection contains more than 3,000 volumes on Cherokee Indian history and culture. Reference use only.

SCHIELE MUSEUM REFERENCE LIBRARY
Center for Southeastern Native American Studies
1500 East Garrison Blvd. • GASTONIA, NC 28054
(704) 866-6900 Fax 866-6041; Website: www.schielemuseum.org
Karl McKinnon, Assistant Director, Operations
Description: Contains a collection of more than 6,000 volumes serving the Reference Centers for the Library of Congress. 20 of holdings, including subject index files, graduate papers, monographs, as well as bound volumes, are on broad areas of Native-American topics representing all major Indian groups in U.S. and Canada with special emphasis on Indians of the Southeast. *Special collections*: Lilly Hobbs Schiele Collection; W.M. Modisette Collection; The Red Dawn Collection; & The McCuen Collection. Open to the public by appointment.

GUILFORD NATIVE AMERICAN ART GALLERY
GREENSBORO CULTURAL CENTER AT FESTIVAL PARK
200 N. Davie St., Box 6 • GREENSBORO, NC 27401

INDIAN MUSEUM OF THE CAROLINAS LIBRARY
607 Turnpike Rd. • LAURINBURG, NC 28352
(910) 276-5880; Dr. Margaret Houston, Director
Description: Maintains a collection of 500 volumes on Indian literature, archaeology, and history. Reference.

NATIVE AMERICAN LIBRARY
Lumbee Indian Education, Lumbee Regional Development Association
P.O. Box 637 • PEMBROKE, NC 28372

NATIVE AMERICAN RESOURCE CENTER & LIBRARY
PEMBROKE STATE UNIVERSITY
College Rd. • PEMBROKE, NC 28372
(919) 521-4214; Website: www.uncp.edu/museum
Dr. Robert C. Hersch, Librarian
Description: Research into Lumbee Indians, American Indian tribal histories & culture. Conducted in conjunction with tribal organizations. *Library*: A collection of 500 volumes with emphasis on Lumbee Indians of North Carolina; audio-visual material; archival documents. *Publications*: SPIRIT! (quarterly newsletter); Robeson Trails Archaeological Survey.

NORTH DAKOTA

TURTLE MOUNTAIN COMMUNITY COLLEGE LIBRARY
P.O. Box 340 • BELCOURT, ND 58316
 (701) 477-7862 Fax 477-7805; Website: www.turtle-mountain.cc.nd.us
 Don Ost, Library Director
Description: Has 27,500 cataloged items including three special collections: 5,400 Native American items (books, videos, audio-cassettes, software), 283 elementary education books, and 25 items in the Louise Erdrich collection.

ND STATE ARCHIVES & HISTORICAL RESEARCH LIBRARY
612 E. Boulevard Ave. • BISMARCK, ND 58505
 (701) 224-2668 Fax 328-2650; Website: www.state.nd.us/hist
 Gerald Newborg, Librarian
Description: Holdings include over 115,000 books & periodicals, 10,000 maps, more than 150,000 photographic images, over 1,600 historical manuscript collections & nearly 3,000 archival records series. Also, 1,400 titles of newspapers, over 1,200 recorded oral histories, & 3.5 million feet of film. Extensive genealogical resources & items on North Dakota history. Interlibrary loans of microfilm only. Opened 1905.

UNITED TRIBES TECHNICAL COLLEGE - UTTC LIBRARY
3315 University Dr. • BISMARCK, ND 58504
 (701) 255-3285 Fax 530-0625; Website: www.uttc.edu/library
 Charlene Weiss, Director; E-mail: cweiss@uttc.edu

CANDESKA CIKANA COMMUNITY COLLEGE
VALERIE MERRICK MEMORIAL LIBRARY
P.O. Box 479 • FORT TOTTEN, ND 58338
 (701) 766-1353 Fax 766-1307
 Website: www.littlehoop.edu/cccc/lib_res.html
 Antonette Halsey, VP Library Services

SITTING BULL COLLEGE LIBRARY
9299 Hwy. 24 • FORT YATES, ND 58538
 (701) 854-8008 Ext. 224 Fax 854-3403
 Website: www.sittingbull.edu/library; Mark Holman, Director

UNIVERSITY OF NORTH DAKOTA CENTER FOR RURAL HEALTH
501 Columbia Rd. • GRAND FORKS, ND 58203
 (701) 777-3848; Jack M. Geller, Ph.D., Director
Description: Research into rural health care delivery, including Native American health care. *Publication*: Focus on Rural Health.

GORDON B. OLSON LIBRARY - MINOT STATE UNIVERSITY
500 University Ave. W. • MINOT, ND 58707
 (701) 858-3200 Fax 858-3581
 Website: www.misu.nodak.edu/library/index1.htm
 Larry Greenwood, Director; E-mail: reference@minotstateu.edu
Description: Maintains a 1,500-volume collection focusing on Indians of the North Central U.S. & South Central Canada. Open to the public. Interlibrary loan.

FORT BERTHOLD COMMUNITY COLLEGE LIBRARY
P.O. Box 788 • NEW TOWN, ND 58763
 (701) 627-4738 Ext. 255 Fax 627-4677
 Website: www.fortbertholdcc.edu; Quincee D. Baker, Director
Description: A collection of 10,000 books, videos, and microfiche serving the Three *Affiliated Tribes*: Arikara, Hidatsa, & Mandan, and the Fort Berthold Community College. An Indian studies collection reflects the cultural interests of tribal residents. Emphasis recently has been placed on children's programming and services. Established 1985.

OHIO

MOUND CITY GROUP NATIONAL MONUMENT LIBRARY
16062 State Rte. 104 • CHILLICOTHE, OH 45601
 (614) 774-1125
Description: A collection of 1,500 volumes on Hopewell & Adena Indian culture, and other Indian culture of Ohio; archaeological research on Hopewell and Adena cultures is conducted at Monument.

RUTHERFORD B. HAYES PRESIDENTIAL CENTER LIBRARY
Spiegel Grove • FREMONT, OH 43420
 (800) 998-7737 Fax (419) 332-4952; Website: www.rbhayes.org
 Nan J. Card, Curator of Manuscripts; E-mail: ncard@rbhayes.org
Description: Contains a collection of 1,000 books and pamphlets on Plains tribes and Wyandot. Also microfilm sets of the record of the Michigan Supt. of Indian Affairs, 1814-1851; General George Crook Papers; correspondence of Rev. James B. Finley, minister to the Wyandot Indians; diary of John G. Bourke, ethnologist, 1872-1895; photos and stereo views of students at Carlisle Indian Industrial School; Western Expedition Photos, 1873; Ledger Art, 63 pictographs

by five artists, 3 identified Arapaho, Cheyenne and Sioux. Interlibrary loans. Open to the public in 1916.

OKLAHOMA

CHICKASAW NATION TRIBAL LIBRARY
530 East Arlington, P.O. Box 1548 • ADA, OK 74821
 (580) 436-2603 ext. 7301; Website: www.chickasaw.net/heritage

DELAWARE TRIBAL LIBRARY
Delaware Cultural Preservation Office
P.O. Box 825 • ANADARKO, OK 73005
 (405) 247-2448 Fax 247-9393
 Website: www.delawarenation.com/nagpra.html
 Tamara Francis, Director; Somier Harris, Office Coordinator
 Jason Ross, Museum Assistant; Joan Subieta, Library Assistant

WOOLAROC MUSEUM LIBRARY
RR 3, Box 2100 • BARTLESVILLE, OK 74003
 (918) 336-0307 Fax 336-0084; Website: www.woolaroc.org
 Kenneth Meek, Interim Director
Description: A collection of 1,000 volumes on American Indians and Oklahoma history.

CADDO NATION LIBRARY & RESOURCE CENTER
P.O. Box 487 • BINGER, OK 73009
 (405) 656-2344 Fax 656-2892
 Website: www.caddonation-nsn.gov/history/library.html
 Kim Penrod, Director
Description: Collection of 400 books & periodicals relating to Caddo history, language & culture, with additional material on tribes of Oklahoma & general American Indian topics.

MEMORIAL INDIAN MUSEUM LIBRARY
P.O. Box 483, Second & Allen Sts. • BROKEN BOW, OK 74728
 (405) 584-6531
Description: Maintains a collection of 3,000 volumes on American Indian history and culture.

KIOWA TRIBAL LIBRARY
P.O. Box 369 • CARNEGIE, OK 73015
 (405) 654-2300; Grace Bointy, Librarian
Description: Maintains a collection of books & documents on Kiowa Indian tribal history and culture.

NASH LIBRARY - UNIVERSITY OF SCIENCE & ARTS OF OKLAHOMA
17th & Grand • CHICKASHA, OK 73018
 (405) 574-1343 Fax 574-1220; Website: www.usao.edu/library
 Kelly Brown, Director; E-mail: kbrown@usao.edu
Description: Collection includes monographs on Native Americans, especially tribes located in Oklahoma & the Southwest. Some ephemera & manuscripts are also included. Open to the public. Opened 1908.

WILL ROGERS MEMORIAL LIBRARY
P.O. Box 157 • CLAREMORE, OK 74018
 (918) 341-0719; Patricia Lowe, Librarian
Description: Contains the original papers of Will Rogers; also, 2,500 volumes concerning Will Rogers and his times; 6,000 photos of Roger's family and others; and Will Rogers memoirs.

MUSEUM OF THE RED RIVER LIBRARY
812 E. Lincoln Rd. • IDABEL, OK 74745
 (405) 286-3616
Maintains a collection of approximately 2,500 books relating to American Indians, with emphasis on Choctaw Indians.

KAW NATION LIBRARY & LEARNING CENTER
803 Washungah Dr. • KAW CITY, OK 74641
 (580) 269-2738

COMANCHE NATION LIBRARY
1608 SW 9th St. • LAWTON, OK 73501
 (580) 591-0203; Website: www.cnc.cc.ok.us/library
 Kim M. Smith, Librarian

MUSEUM OF THE GREAT PLAINS RESEARCH LIBRARY
601 NW Ferris Ave. • LAWTON, OK 73507
 (580) 581-3460 Fax 581-3458; Deborah Anna Baroff, Librarian
Description: Collection consists of a special collection of over 26,000 volumes on Plains Indian history & prehistory; history of Great Plains; photography & agricultural emphasis. Open to the public by appointment only. Opened 1961.

MIAMI NATION LIBRARY & ARCHIVES
202 S. Eight Tribes Trail, P.O. Box 1326 • MIAMI, OK 74355
 (918) 542-4505 Fax 542-7260; Website: www.myaami.org
 Karen Alexander, Librarian
Description: A collection of 18,000 volumes serving all Native Americans of all tribes, emphasizing the Northeast Eight Tribes of Oklahoma. *Special programs*: Roots & Wings, CHARLIE Library Network; partnerships with Miami University, Oxford, Ohio. Affiliated with the Miami Tribe of Oklahoma. Open to the public. Opened 1987.

OTTAWA TRIBE OF OKLAHOMA ARCHIVES LIBRARY
 (918) 540-6162 Fax 542-3214; Website: www.ottawatribe.org
 Rhonda Dixon, Librarian
Description: Collection of books & archive material on the Ottawa Tribe of Okla.

BACONE COLLEGE LIBRARY
2299 Old Bacone Rd. • MUSKOGEE, OK 74403
 (918) 683-4581 ext. 263; Website: www.bacone.edu
 Frances A. Donelson, Librarian
Description: Maintains a rare book collection of over 10,000 books on Native American culture, including some of the original Dawes Commission papers. Open to the public.

OKLAHOMA ANTHROPOLOGICAL SOCIETY LIBRARY
1000 Horn St. • MUSKOGEE, OK 74403
 (405) 364-2279
Description: Holdings of more than 35,000 volumes; archives contain over three million documents of the Five Civilized Tribes; newspaper library.

AMERICAN INDIAN INSTITUTE LIBRARY
Prevention Resource Center
555 Constitution St., Suite 237 • NORMAN, OK 73072-7820
 (405) 325-1782/4127 Fax 325-7757; Jane Goble-Clark, Director
 Website: www.aii.ou.edu/resource-center-resource-library/
 Ann Barnes (Choctaw), Office Manager; E-mail: annbarnes@ou.edu
 Gail Ripley, Director of Early Head Start
Description: Resource library containing over 3,000 books, periodicals, and newspapers on art, economics, education, government, head start, health, history, language, social & human services, and substance abuse. Programs: Substance Abuse; Drug & Alcohol Rehabilitation; Tobacco Prevention; Suicide Prevention; Violence & Abuse; Maternal & Child Health. *Activities*: Conferences; Curriculum Guides & Videos.

UNIVERSITY OF OKLAHOMA LAW LIBRARY
300 Timberdell Rd. • NORMAN, OK 73019
 (405) 325-4311 Fax 325-6282; Darin K. Fox, Director
Description: Maintains a collection on American Indian law and law relating to Native Americans, including mineral rights, water issues, land titles, jurisdiction, and the like, with emphasis on Oklahoma tribes. *Programs*: Native American Constitution & Law Digitization Project. *Special collection*: Native Peoples Collection - 2,300 titles on indigenous peoples, mostly Native American. Interlibrary loans. Open to the public.

WESTERN HISTORY COLLECTION – DIVISION OF MANUSCRIPTS & LIBRARY - UNIVERSITY OF OKLAHOMA
630 Parrington Oval, Rm. 452 • NORMAN, OK 73019
 (405) 325-3641 Fax 325-6069
 Website: www-lib.ou.edu/depts/west/index.htm
 Donald L. DeWitt, Curator
Description: A major collection of Indian-related books, serials, photographs, manuscripts, and sound recordings. The collection includes 40,000 books and microforms; 200,000 historic photos; 275 manuscript collections; and 21 sound recording collections. *Publication*: "American Indian Resource Materials in the Western History Collections, University of Oklahoma, Norman" (University of Oklahoma Press, 1990). Opened 1927.

COOKSON INSTITUTE LIBRARY
623 Culbertson Dr., Suite A • OKLAHOMA CITY, OK 73105
Description: A collection of 1,000 volumes on American Indian thought with emphasis on Cherokee, Arawak, Maya, & Caddo Indians. Available to research scholars associated with the Institute.

OKLAHOMA CITY UNIVERSITY-SCHOOL OF LAW LIBRARY
2501 N. Blackwelder • Oklahoma City, OK 73106
 (405) 521-5062 Fax 521-5172; Website: www.okcu.edu/law/awlib
 Judy Morgan, Librarian
Description: An extension collection of Indian-law materials with special emphasis on Federal & Tribal Law (including tribal casework). Special attention is also given to historical materials and books about Plains tribes and tribes now residing in Oklahoma. Open to the public. Opened 1987.

OKLAHOMA HISTORICAL SOCIETY INDIAN ARCHIVES DIVISION
2100 N. Lincoln Blvd. • OKLAHOMA CITY, OK 73105
 (405) 522-5248 Fax 522-5402
 Jack Wettengel, Public Information Director
 Dennis W. Zotigh, American Indian Research Historian
Description: Holdings include thousands of books about Oklahoma's history and more than 6,000 books covering the subject areas of the Creek Nation, and Indian and pioneer history; 3.5 million documents and 8,000 manuscripts, the majority of them on microfilm, recordings, photographs, and newspapers of Indian Territory. many rare books are available for research.

RED EARTH MUSEUM
Red Earth, Inc., 6 Santa Fe Plaza • OKLAHOMA CITY, OK 73102
 (405) 427-5228 Fax 427-8079
 Website: www.redearth.org; E-mail: info@redearth.org
 Barbara Jobe, Executive Director
 Eric Oesch, Deputy Director/Director of Communications
 E-mail: eric@redearth.org; Erin Merryweather, Director of Programs
Description: Collection of 300 books & periodicals. *Activities*: Annual Red Earth Native American Cultural Festival in June. Opened 1978.

CREEK COUNCIL HOUSE MUSEUM RESEARCH LIBRARY
106 W. 6th • OKMULGEE, OK 74447
 (918) 756-2324 Fax 756-3671
 Debbie Martin, Director
Description: Contains a collection of over 500 volumes on Muscogee (Creek) culture and history; records of early day Creek Government; diaries & journals of past principal chiefs; also, Indian readers, dictionaries, documents & newspapers on Oklahoma and Indian history.

MUSCOGEE (CREEK) NATION LIBRARY
P.O. Box 580 • OKMULGEE, OK 74447
 (918) 732-7733 Fax 758-0649

OSAGE NATION MUSEUM & LIBRARY
819 Grandview, P.O. Box 779 • PAWHUSKA, OK 74056
 (918) 287-5441 Fax 287-1060
 Website: www.osagetribe.com/museum
 Kathryn Red Corn, Director
Description: Exhibits Osage artifacts, donations, books, clothing of the past; paintings, and pictures. Opened 1938.

IOWA TRIBE OF OKLAHOMA LIBRARY
3560 West 76th Rd., Rt. 1, Box 721 • PERKINS, OK 74059
 (405) 547-2402 ext. 213 Fax 547-1032
 Website: www.iowanation.org/government/library.html.
 E-mail: library@iowanation.org
 Sandy Tharp-Thee, Librarian; E-mail: stharp@iowanation.org
 Opened 1985.

QUAPAW TRIBAL LIBR
905 Whitebird St. • QUAPAW, OK 74363
 (918) 674-2454 Fax 542-4694; Website: www.quapawtribe.com
 P. Billings, Librarian; E-mail: pbillings@quapawtribe.com

CITIZEN POTAWATOMI CULTURAL HERITAGE CENTER ARCHIVES & LIBRARY
1601 S. Gordon Cooper • SHAWNEE, OK 74801
 (405) 275-3121 Fax 275-0198
 R. Blake Norton, Archivist/Librarian
Description: Houses all tribal archival material and other items of anthropological significance, the keys to the spiritual, historical and cultural aspects of the Citizen Potawatomi Nation and its people.

OKLAHOMA STATE UNIVERSITY LIBRARY
Curriculum Materials Laboratory • STILLWATER, OK 74074
Description: A children's collection of books on the Indians of North America.

SAC & FOX NATIONAL PUBLIC LIBRARY
Sac & Fox Nation of Oklahoma
Rt. 2, Box 246 • STROUD, OK 74079
 (918) 968-3526 Fax 968-4837; Kathy Platt, Director
 Website: www.sacandfoxnation-nsn.gov
Description: Maintains a 5,000-volume collection of general interest, including a large collection of books on Native Americans, especially Sac & Fox & Oklahoma tribes. Also available are public access computers & video/DVD collections. The archives contain Sac & Fox history, photographs, tribal newspapers, allotment rolls, government documents, oral histories & genealogies. *Special programs*: Photo & art exhibits; seminars on tribal archives; arts & crafts shop; book sales; Sac & Fox language classes. Opened 1985.

CHEROKEE HERITAGE CENTER LIBRARY
P.O. Box 515, TSA-LA-GI • TAHLEQUAH, OK 74464
  (888) 999-6007; (918) 456-6007; Website: www.cherokeeheritage.org
  Carey Tilley, Executive Director
Description: A collection of 2,500 volumes on Cherokee heritage,
including manuscripts and photographs.

JOHN VAUGHAN LIBRARY
Northeastern State University • TAHLEQUAH, OK 74464
  (918) 456-5511 ext. 3252 Fax 458-2197
  Delores T. Sumner, Special Collections Librarian
  E-mail: sumner@cherokee.nsuok.edu
Special collections: Approximately 12,600 books on Cherokee history; tribes of
Oklahoma; American Indian mythology & religion; Oklahoma history; Indian
Territory history; American Indian history, culture, social structures, and condi-
tions; local towns, counties, city histories; Tribal language materials (majority
Oklahoma tribes); Oklahoma tribal rolls; houses microfilm copies of important
regional historical newspapers of the late 1800's and early 1900's such as the
Cherokee Advocate, Indian Chieftain, and Tahlequah Arrow; U.S. Office of
Indian Affairs, and the Historical Information Relating to Military Posts and Other
Installations. Also with the Indian Affairs microfilms are records from the U.S.
Army and the U.S. Department of War (1800-1823). Contains microfilm of
American Indian & Oklahoma-related subjects; John Ross Letters; Indian Affairs
Miscellaneous Letters; Ballenger Miscellaneous Letters; Ballenger Manuscripts
Relating to Cherokee History; Andrew Nave Collections (Business Accounts and
Letters); Letters To and From Stand Watie. All bound volumes typed from the
originals. Originals are housed in Archives. *Special program*: Symposium on the
American Indian held annually at NSU. Open to the public.

CHICKASAW COUNCIL HOUSE LIBRARY
205 N. Fisher St. • TISHOMINGO, OK 73460
  (405) 371-3351; Faye Orr, Director
Description: Contains about 150 volumes on Chickasaw Indian history,
geography and genealogy.

H.A. & MARY K. CHAPMAN LIBRARY
Philbrook Museum of Art, 2727 S. Rockford Rd. • TULSA, OK 74114
  (918) 748-5306 Fax 748-5303
  Thomas E. Young, Librarian; E-mail: tyoung@philbrook.org
Description: Visual arts & art history reference library with one area of
specialization relates to Native American art. Also includes special collections,
including the Roberta Campbell Lawson Indian Library with about 1,000 volumes
on North America & Native American art & history. A major U.S. repository of
documentation on Native American art. A collection of approximately 2,000
volumes on Indian art & history. Reference only. Open to the public by
appointment.

**THOMAS GILCREASE INSTITUTE OF AMERICAN
HISTORY & ART LIBRARY**
1400 Gilcrease Museum Rd. • TULSA, OK 74127
  (918) 596-2700 Fax 596-2770
  Sarah Erwin, Curator of Archival Collections
Description: A major U.S. repository of documentation on Native American art.
Contains a collection of about 7,500 volumes relating to most American Indian
tribes with emphasis on the Five Civilized Tribes. Includes 40,000 manuscript
items, 10,000 imprints, and 10,000 photographs. *Special collections*: John Ross
Papers (Cherokee); Peter Pitchlynn Papers (Choctaw); John Drew Papers
(Cherokee); Cherokee Papers; Chickasaw Papers; Choctaw Papers; Creek
Papers; and Seminole Papers. Open to the public by appointment only.

THE McFARLIN LIBRARY - UNIVERSITY OF TULSA
800 S. Tucker Dr. • TULSA, OK 74104
  (918) 631-2496; https://utulsa.edu/mcfarlin-library/special-collections/
  Ann Blakely, Reference Librarian
Description: The repository for many unique primary documents and published
works pertinent to Native-Americans and governmental relations of the historic
period in eastern Oklahoma and adjacent areas. The Department of Special
Collections & University Archives hosts world-class collections of rare books,
manuscripts, photographs, artwork and other objects, including one of the five
largest collections in the world on the celebrated Irish writer James Joyce and
the life archive of Nobel Laureate Sir V.S. Naipaul. Other significant collections
include a wide variety of British, Irish and American modernist literature, a large
and varied collection of materials on World War I, Native American history and
culture and Tulsa Race Relations.

TULSA CITY-COUNTY LIBRARY
American Indian Resource Center (AIRC)
400 Civic Center • TULSA, OK 74103
  (918) 596-7977; Website: www.tulsalibrary.org
  E-mail: askus@tulsalibrary.org; Teresa Washington Runnels, Coordinator

Description: Contains over 4,000 books, and more than 2,000 recordings &
videos on the American Indian.

UNIVERSITY OF TULSA - COLLEGE OF LAW LIBRARY
Maybee Legal Information Center, 3120 E. 4th Pl. • TULSA, OK 74104
  (918) 631-2404 Fax 631-3556; Website: www.law.utulsa.edu
  Richard Ducey, Director; E-mail: richard-ducey@utulsa.edu
  Louise W. Lindsey, Associate Director
Description: A collection of 750 volumes on Indian law.

SEMINOLE NATION MUSEUM - LIBRARY
524 S. Wewoka, P.O. Box 1532 • WEWOKA, OK 74884
  (405) 257-5580; Leta Smith, Administrator
Description: Contains books & documents on the history of the Seminoles, the
history of Wewoka, & the history of oil in Oklahoma. *Special exhibit*: Cultural
Continuities in Seminole County, Oklahoma--provides detailed information on the
clans, bands, churches, and homes of the Seminoles; and the Dawes rolls for
reference into Seminole genealogy. Open to the public. Opened 1974.

OREGON

GRAND RONDE TRIBAL LIBRARY
9615 Grand Ronde Rd. • GRAND RONDE, OR 97347
  (800) 422-0232; (503) 879-5211 Fax 879-5964
  Website: www.grandronde.org
Description: Collection of more than 10,000 items with a significant Native
American section. Sponsors various programs and displays throughout the year.

COQUILLE INDIAN TRIBAL (CIT) LIBRARY
3050 Tremont Blvd. • NORTH BEND, OR 97459
  (541) 756-0904 Fax 756-0847
  Website: www.coquilletribe.org/coquille-indian-tribe-library.html
  Chris Tanner, Librarian; E-Mail: ctanner@coquilletribe.org
Description: A collection of about 2,500 books & 45 periodical subscriptions
focuses on Coquille culture & history, Southwest Oregon history, natural history
& topics of interest (health, education, etc.) from the perspective of Indian tribes
and Native Americans. Established 1993.

NATIONAL INDIAN CHILD WELFARE ASSOCIATION LIBRARY
5100 SW Macadam Ave. #300 • PORTLAND, OR 97239
  (503) 222-4044 ext. 138 Fax 222-4007
  Website: www.nicwa.org; E-mail: info@nicwa.org
  Lois C. Chilcott, Library Assistant
Description: A clearinghouse of over 3,000 articles, books, periodicals on Indian
child welfare, mental health, and social work issues.

THE REX ARRAGON LIBRARY
1219 SW Park Ave.• PORTLAND, OR 97205
  (503) 226-2811 Fax 226-4842; Website: www.pam.org
  Dan Lucas, Director; E-mail: library@pam.org
Description: Library of the Portland Art Museum & Pacific Northwest College of
Art. Consists of over 25,000 volumes on art & art history. Special collection:
American Indian art books, particularly Pacific Northwest Coast Indians.
Interlibrary loans. Open to the public.

PENNSYLVANIA

**LENNI LENAPE HISTORICAL SOCIETY
MUSEUM OF INDIAN CULTURE LIBRARY**
2825 Fish Hatchery Rd. • ALLENTOWN, PA 18103
  (610) 797-2121 Fax 797-2801; Website: www.lenape.org
  Carla J.S. Messinger, Executive Director
Description: A resource library which maintains 300+ video tapes, audiotapes,
CD ROMs; about 3,000 books concerning Lenni Lenape & other Native peoples.

HAMILTON LIBRARY
Cumberland County Historical Society, 21 N. Pitt St. • CARLISLE, PA 17013
  (717) 249-7610 Fax 258-9332; Website: www.historicalsociety.com
  Linda Witmer, Executive Director; E-mail: librarian@historicalsociety.com
Description: Maintains a special collection of publications, photographs, and
school-related memorabilia of the Carlisle Indian Industrial School. Tours
available of the site of the school at Carlisle Barracks. *Publication*: Carlisle
Indian Industrial School, by Linda Witmer.

**HARCOURT LIBRARY
AMERICAN INDIAN RESEARCH & RESOURCE INSTITUTE**
Gettysburg College • GETTYSBURG, PA 17325
  (717) 337-6265; Dr. Frank W. Porter, III, Director
Description: Harcourt Library maintains a special collection on Native Americans;
also the Herman Finkelstein Primitive Mask Collection. Opened 1983.

MAGILL LIBRARY – HAVERFORD COLLEGE
Associated Executive Committee of Friends on Indian Affairs
Quaker & Special Collections, 370 Lancaster Ave. • Haverford, PA 19041
(610) 896-1161 Fax 896-1102; E-mail: hc-special@haverford.edu
Website: www.haverford.edu/library/special/
Description: 2,400 items. Missionary project of the Religious Society of Friends (Quakers.) *Purpose*: To bear testimony to the Christian faith & teachings by word and deed; to persist in calling for integrity in all phases of the administration of Indian affairs; to encourage pride of all Indians in their heritage; to assist those with whom the ACFIA works to build a strong sense of community & personal responsibility. *Special collection*: The Quaker Collection. *Activities*: Runs an academy in Alabama among the Mowa-Choctaws; church meetings; runs youth/children programs in Oklahoma (Wyandotte, Seneca-Cayuga, Kickapoo & Osage) and in Iowa (Mesquakie); social welfare assistance at all centers; school in Alabama for 2004-05 year (only pre-K and Kindergarten class). *Publication*: Quaker Serials; journals & diaries. Established 1869.

AMERICAN PHILOSOPHICAL SOCIETY LIBRARY
105 South 5th St. • PHILADELPHIA, PA 19106
(215) 440-3400 Fax 440-34232; Website: www.amphilsoc.org
Patrick Spero, Librarian & Director; E-mail: librarian@amphilsoc.org
Timothy B. Powell, Director of the Center for Native American
& Indigenous Research (CNAIR); E-mail: tpowell@amphilsoc.org
Description: A major U.S. repository of documentation on Native American art. *Special collection*: American Indian linguistics; Franz Boas collection of 18th & 19th century Indian vocabularies. Appointment only. Opened 1743.

FREE LIBRARY OF PHILADELPHIA
Social Science & History Department, Logan Sq. * PHILADELPHIA, PA 19103
Special collection: The Wilberforce Eames Collection on American Indians.

HISTORICAL SOCIETY OF PENNSYLVANIA LIBRARY
1300 Locust St. • PHILADELPHIA, PA 19107
(215) 732-6200 Ext. 209 Fax 732-2680
E-mail: library@hsp.org; Website: www.hsp.org
Lee Arnold, Director of Library
Description: Maintains library & archives of the Indian Rights Association, Indians of North America Collection; Colonial & Early American History; Civil War; Family History, Local History, & Ethnic Studies. *Activities*: Publications; tours, workshops, lectures. Open to public, Opened 1824.

UNIVERSITY OF PENNSYLVANIA - MUSEUM LIBRARY
3260 South St. • PHILADELPHIA, PA 19104-6324
(215) 898-7840 Fax 573-2008; E-mail: muselib@pobox.upenn.edu
Website: library.upenn.edu/museum/museum.html
Description: A major U.S. repository of documentation on Native American art. The collection consists of 150,000 volumes on world archaeology, anthropology & ethnology. *Special collection*: Brinton Collection--Aboriginal American linguistics and ethnology. Interlibrary loans. Open to the public.

COUNCIL OF THREE RIVERS AMERICAN INDIAN CENTER LIBRARY
120 Charles St. • PITTSBURGH, PA 15238
(412) 782-4457 Fax 767-4808
Website: www.cotraic.org; E-mail: gnowinsky@cotraic.org
Description: Cultural library on Indian tribes, cultures, customs & traditions. Maintains the Indian Child Welfare Resource Library.

CENTER FOR THE STUDY OF LEADERSHIP IN AMERICAN INDIAN EDUCATION LIBRARY
College of Education, Penn State University
302A Rackley Bldg. • UNIVERSITY PARK, PA 16802
(814) 863-1626 Fax 865-1480; Website: www.ed.psu.edu/educ/eps/ailp
John W. Tippeconnic & Susan C. Faircloth, Co-Directors
Description: 1,000 volumes on American Indian education; clearinghouse on American Indian & Alaska Native education, research, policy & practice.

RHODE ISLAND

HAFFENREFFER MUSEUM OF ANTHROPOLOGY LIBRARY
Brown University, Mt. Hope Grant, 300 Tower St. • BRISTOL, RI 02809
(401) 253-8388 Fax 253-1198; Website: www.haffenreffermuseum.org
Kevin P. Smith, Deputy Director & Chief Curator
Description: Contains a collection of about 5,000 volumes on the archaeological heritage, ethnography, & contemporary cultures of the Americas. Archaeological & ethnographic collections (ca. 80,000) document the prehistoric & historic diversity of Native American cultures, through material culture, across the Americas. *Special programs*: Active programs of outreach & on-site K-12 education plus lectures & events for family & adult audiences.

TOMAQUAG INDIAN MEMORIAL MUSEUM LIBRARY
390B Summit Rd. • EXETER, RI 02822-1808 (401) 539-7795

CENTER FOR THE STUDY OF RACE & ETHNICITY IN AMERICA
Brown University, Box 1886 • PROVIDENCE, RI 02912
(401) 863-3080; Rhett S. Jones, Director

JOHN CARTER BROWN LIBRARY
Brown University, Box 1894 • PROVIDENCE, RI 02912
(401) 863-2725 Fax 863-3477; Norman Fiering, Librarian
Description: A collection of historical sources pertaining to the discovery, exploration, colonization, settlement, & development of the New World (those relating to Native American populations & development.) Includes native language materials published in colonial era. *Activities*: Exhibitions, lectures, conferences, publications for sale. Research fellowships awarded.

SOUTH CAROLINA

SOUTH CAROLINA ARCHIVES & HISTORY CENTER
8301 Parklane Rd. • COLUMBIA, SC 29223
(803) 896-6100 Fax 896-6167; Website: www.state.sc/scdah
Alexis J. Helsley, Director-Education
Special collections: Cherokee Indian Treaties, 1759-77; Journals of the Commissioners of Indian Trade, 1710-18; Documents Relating to Indian Affairs, 1750-65; Evidence of Leasehold and Taxes Paid, Catawba Indian Lands, 1791-1856; Supt. of the Catawba Nation Record Book of Plots and Leases, 1810-25, and Accounts of Rents, 1810-1831; Records of the Commissioner to Carry into Effect the Treaty of Nation Ford 1840: and Journal of a Journey to the Catawba Nation, 1727-28.

SOUTH DAKOTA

PRESENTATION COLLEGE LIBRARY
1500 N. Main St. • ABERDEEN, SD 57401
(605) 229-8546; Website: www.presentation.edu/library
E-mail: pclibrary@presentation.edu; Lea Briggs, Director

CRAZY HORSE MEMORIAL LIBRARY
Ave. of the Chiefs • CRAZY HORSE, SD 57730
(605) 673-4681 Fax 673-2185
Website: www.crazyhorsememorial.org
E-mail: memorial@crazyhorse.org; Ruth Ziolkowski, Director
Description: A research library with a collection of 22,000 plus volumes on American Indian art, culture & history. Emphasis on Native American literature. Opened 1974.

SI TANKA COLLEGE/HURON LIBRARY; ELLEN McINTIRE LIBRARY
749 Illinois Ave. SW • HURON, SD 57350
(605) 353-2050 Fax 353-2416; Website: www.sitanka.edu/library
Robert Behlke, Director

BADLANDS NATIONAL MONUMENT LIBRARY
P.O. Box 72 • INTERIOR, SD 57750
Description: Maintains a collection of 1,000 books and 500 bound periodicals on the Badlands and Indians of South Dakota.

OGLALA LAKOTA COLLEGE ACADEMIC/PUBLIC LIBRARY & ARCHIVES
3 Mile Creek Rd., P.O. Box 310 • KYLE, SD 57752
(605) 455-6069 Fax 455-6070; Website: www.library.olc.edu
E-mail: library@olc.edu; LaVera Rose, Director/Archivist (455-6064)
Sharon Running Hawk, Assistant Director (455-6067)
E-mail: srunninghawk@olc.edu
Agnes Gay, Assistant Archivist (455-6063; E-mail: agay@olc.edu
Theresa Bettelyoun, Library Outreach Coordinator
E-mail: tbettelyoun@olc.edu

THE OGLALA LAKOTA HISTORICAL CENTER LIBRARY
Oglala Lakota College, P.O. Box 490 • KYLE, SD 57752
(605) 455-2321 Fax 455-2787
Description: Holdings include tribal college & government records; personal papers of Dr. Valentine T. McGillycuddy; photographs & oral histories, and other historical material.

AMERICAN INDIAN CULTURE RESEARCH CENTER (AICRC)
Blue Cloud Abbey, P.O. Box 98 • MARVIN, SD 57251
(605) 398-9200 Fax 398-9201; Website: www.bluecloud.org
Colleen Cordell, Director
Description: A collection of more than 3,000 books on Native American history & culture. Purpose: To support Indian leaders, & educators in their ambitions for rebuilding the Indian community; aids in teaching the non-Indian public of the culture & philosophy of the Indian. *Programs*: Compiled oral history & photographic collection; conducts workshops & seminars; maintains speakers bureau. *Publication*: Blue Cloud Quarterly. Opened 1967.

SINTE GLESKA UNIVERSITY LIBRARY
101 Antelope Lake Circle, P.O. Box 105 • MISSION, SD 57555
 (605) 856-8195 Fax 856-2011; Website: www.sinte.edu/library
 La Donne Moosman, Director; E-mail: ladonne.moosman@sintegleska.edu

SOUTH DAKOTA STATE HISTORICAL SOCIETY ARCHIVES
900 Governors Dr. • PIERRE, SD 57501
 (605) 773-4233 Fax 773-6041; Website: www.sdhistory.org
 Marvene Riis, Librarian
Description: Contains books, manuscripts, government records, photos, & maps relating to Indian tribes & reservations in South Dakota & northern Great Plains region. Opened 1975.

THE HERITAGE CENTER LIBRARY
Red Cloud Heritage Center, 100 Mission Dr. • PINE RIDGE, SD 57770
 (605) 867-5491; Website: www.redcloudschool.org
Description: Collection of about 1,000 volumes on Lakota history & culture; Native American art.

LAKOTA ARCHIVES & HISTORICAL RESEARCH CENTER
Sinte Gleska University, P.O. Box 490 • ROSEBUD, SD 57570
 (605) 747-2263; Marcella Cash, Director
Description: Archival repository for the records of the Rosebud Sioux Tribe and Sinte Gleska College; Native American Periodicals & Oral History collections; & manuscript material related to the Rosebud Sioux Reservation, including records of the Episcopal Mission which date back to the 1870's. Open to the public.

THE CENTER FOR WESTERN STUDIES LIBRARY
Augustana College, Box 727 • SIOUX FALLS, SD 57197
 (605) 274-4007 Fax 274-4999
 Harry F. Thompson, Director of Research Collections
Description: The collections focus is on the Northern Plains history & cultures, including native (mostly Sioux) and immigrant peoples. A reference library of 30,000 volumes on the American West with emphasis on South Dakota and the Northern Plains plus 4,000 linear feet of archives and manuscripts. Includes the Papers of the Riggs family of missionaries to the Sioux. *Activities*: Annual Dakota Conference in the spring; annual art show; book publications on the Northern Plains with special emphasis on Sioux life and art. Interlibrary loans.

SISSETON WAHPETON COLLEGE LIBRARY
P.O. Box 689 • SISSETON, SD 57262
 (605) 698-3966 Ext. 702 Fax 698-3132
 Website: www/swcc.cc.sd.us.library.net
 Delight Robinson, Acting Librarian; E-mail: drobertson@swc.tc

BLACK HILLS STATE UNIVERSITY
E.Y. BERRY LIBRARY-LEARNING CENTER
1200 University • SPEARFISH, SD 57799
 (605) 642-6359 Fax 642-6298; Website: www.iis.bhsu.edu/lis
 E-mail: bhsulibrary@bhsu.edu; Scott Ahola, Director
 Roberta Sagi, Special Collections Librarian
Description: Subjects deal with Dakota Indians & North American Indians.

BUECHEL MEMORIAL LAKOTA MUSEUM ARCHIVES
350 S. Oak St., P.O. Box 499 • ST. FRANCIS, SD 57572
 (605) 747-2745 Fax 747-5057; Website: www.littlesioux.org
 Mike Marshall, Director
Description: Archives house photographs & documents of post-reservation era. Native American subjects, church subjects, diaries and documents related to Sicango (Rosebud Sioux) history. Opened 1954. Open to the public Memorial Day to Labor Day.

INSTITUTE OF AMERICAN INDIAN STUDIES LIBRARY
UNIVERSITY OF SOUTH DAKOTA
Dakota Hall, 414 E. Clark St. • VERMILLION, SD 57069
 (605) 677-5209; Dr. Herbert Hoover, Director
Description: American Indian Research Project: Maintains a collection of 1,500 oral interview tapes with emphasis on tribes of the northern plains; subject matter is widely varied; also a collection of about 1,000 books on ethnology & contemporary affairs of the northwest Plains Indians. Open to public by appt.

SOCIAL SCIENCE RESEARCH INSTITUTE
U. of South Dakota • VERMILLION, SD 57069
 (605) 677-5401; Prof. Thomas E. Allen, Jr., Director
Description: Research includes studies in medical & educational problems on American Indian reservations. Conducts anthropological studies. Contains recent studies on impact of Indian law and communities.

W.H. OVER MUSEUM LIBRARY
414 E. Clark St. • VERMILLION, SD 57069
 (605) 677-5228; Website: www.usd.edu/whom/

Description: Collection on local history, Indian history, and northern Plains ethnography and history. Open to the public for reference use only.

TENNESSEE

CHUCALISSA ARCHAEOLOGICAL MUSEUM--LIBRARY
1987 Indian Village Dr. • MEMPHIS, TN 38109
 (901) 785-3160; Gerald P. Smith, Director
 Mary L. Kwas, Curator of Education
Description: Contains a collection of 2,000 volumes on Indian history, culture and archaeology. Material available to public upon request.

TENNESSEE STATE LIBRARY & ARCHIVES
403 Seventh Ave. North • NASHVILLE, TN 37243-0312
 (615) 741-2764 Fax (615) 532-2472
 Dr. Edwin S. Gleaves, State Librarian & Archivist
 Website: www.state.tn.us/sos/statelib/tslahome.htm
Description: Reference works deal mainly with Tennessee history and items of material culture; Indian-related works deal with tribes of the Southeastern U.S., and are concerned mostly with genealogical research; photographic archives. *Special programs*: Conducts occasional workshops & seminars dealing with Indian genealogical research; exhibit of Indian materials constructed during the Year of the American Indian. *Publication*: Native American (Cherokee) Research at the Tennessee State Library & Archives. Interlibrary loans. Open to the public.

PINSON MOUNDS STATE ARCHAEOLOGICAL AREA LIBRARY
Rt. 1, Box 316, Ozier Rd. • PINSON, TN 38366
 (901) 988-5614
Description: 400 volumes on the archaeology of Pinson Mounds area.

TEXAS

TEXAS STATE LIBRARY & ARCHIVES
1201 Brazos • AUSTIN, TX 78711-2927
 (512) 463-5455; E-mail: info@tsl.state.tx.us
Archives & Manuscripts: Indian Relations in Texas; Texas Indian Commission: An Inventory of Records, 1957-1989; Texas Indian Commission, Profile & History, 20-page report.

PANHANDLE-PLAINS HISTORICAL MUSEUM--LIBRARY & ARCHIVES
P.O. Box 967, W.T. Sta. • CANYON, TX 79016
 (806) 656-2261 Fax 656-2250; Lisa Lambert, Librarian
Description: Contains a collection of about 400 titles on the Indians of the Southern Plains, such as Comanche, Apache, Kiowa, Navaho, Cheyenne, and Indians of Oklahoma; & archaeology of the Texas Panhandle. Also photographs of individual tribe members, maps, brochures, periodicals, etc. Open to public.

AMON CARTER MUSEUM PHOTOGRAPHY COLLECTION
3501 Camp Bowie Blvd. • FORT WORTH, TX 76107
 (817) 738-1933 Fax 738-4066
 John Rohrbach, Curator of Photographic Collections
 E-mail: john.rohrbach@cartermuseum.org
Description: E.A. Brininstool Collection: 3,500 items (2,680 prints, 550 negatives) - b/w images of natives 1868-1937, sometimes staged environments as well as natural landscapes; photographs of geographic locations, monuments, battlefields of the Plains & Indian wars. Helen M. Post Collection: 11,000 pieces (6,000 prints, 4,000 negatives) - B/W documentation from 1936-41 of Indian reservation life, primarily Sioux, Navajo & Crow on a personal and intimate level; Laura Gilpin *Collection*: 25,000 prints, 27,000 negatives & transparencies, b/w & color documentation of Navajo life, 1930s-70s.

ALABAMA-COUSHATTA TRIBE OF TEXAS TRIBAL LIBRARY
571 State Park Rd. 56 • LIVINGSTON, TX 77351
 (936) 563-1316 Fax 563-4397
 Delores Poncho, Librarian; E-mail: library@actribe.org
Description: Small one-room library containing Native American books & reference materials & assorted software for computers to serve K-12, service to Head Start program & special resource for continuing education. Includes a computer room with Internet access. Moderately supplied video library and a special Tony Hillerman collection.

AMERICAN INDIAN RESOURCE CENTER (AIRC)
SAN ANTONIO, TX 78217
 (210) 655-1300; E-mail: jonhook@wt.net
Dedicated to improving the lives of Native Americans living in South Texas.

INCARNATE WORD COLLEGE LIBRARY
4301 Broadway • SAN ANTONIO, TX 78209
 (210) 829-3855
Description: Contains titles in all areas of Native American studies. Native American art history particularly strong.

SUNSET TRADING POST OLD WEST MUSEUM--LIBRARY
Route 1 • SUNSET, TX 76270
(817) 872-2027
Description: A collection of 500 volumes on American Indians, and the frontier.

UTAH

**EDGE OF THE CEDARS STATE HISTORICAL MONUMENT
& MUSEUM LIBRARY**
660 West 400 North • BLANDING, UT 84511
(435) 678-2238; Michael M. Nelson, Museum/Park Manager
Description: Materials related directly to archaeology, and Native American cultures of the American Southwest, particularly the Four Corners area.

UTE TRIBAL MUSEUM LIBRARY
Ute Tribe, P.O. Box 190, Highway 40 • FORT DUCHESNE, UT 84026
(435) 722-4992 Fax 722-2374
Description: Maintains a collection of books on the Ute Indians;
American Indian history & culture; & early Western American history.

THE UNIVERSITY OF UTAH - AMERICAN WEST CENTER
1901 E. South Campus Dr., Rm. 1023 • SALT LAKE CITY, UT 84112
(801) 581-7611 Fax 581-7612
Dr. Daniel C. McCool, Director; E-mail: dan.mccool@poli-sci.utah.edu
Description: Research includes American Indian history & traditions; hunting, fishing, water rights, and voting rights.

UTAH STATE HISTORICAL SOCIETY LIBRARY
300 Rio Grande • SALT LAKE CITY, UT 84101
(801) 533-5755; Melvin T. Smith, Director
Description: A collection of books and periodicals on the history of Utah, Mormons, Indians, and the West.

VIRGINIA

GREENWOOD LIBRARY - LONGWOOD UNIVERSITY
Redford & Race Sts. • FARMVILLE, VA 23909
(434) 395-2633 Fax 395-2453; Website: www.longwood.edu
Wendell Barbour, Dean of Library; Patricia Howe, Librarian;
Special collection: O'Brien Collection-5,000+ prehistoric Virginia Indian artifacts.

HAMPTON UNIVERSITY LIBRARY
American Indian Educational Opportunities Program • HAMPTON, VA 23668
(757) 727-5981 Fax 727-5084; Dr. Paulette F. Molin, Director
Description: Maintains archival, photographic and art collections

WASHINGTON

**CENTER FOR PACIFIC NORTHWEST STUDIES
WESTERN WASHINGTON UNIVERSITY**
High St. • BELLINGHAM, WA 98225
(206) 676-3284/3125; Dr. James W. Scott
Purpose: To collect materials of every sort--manuscripts, business records, maps, photographs, tapes, etc.--of the people & activities of the Pacific Northwest, past & present. Publications: Publishes two series: Occasional Papers (21 to-date) & Informational Papers (5 to-date.) Archive-Library. Opened 1971.

LUMMI LIBRARY at NORTHWESTERN INDIAN COLLEGE
2520 Kwina Rd. • BELLINGHAM, WA 98226
(360) 392-4214 Ext. 214 Fax 733-3385
Website: www.nwic.edu/lummilibr; E-mail: library@nwic.edu
Vallerie McBeth, Director; E-mail: vmcbeth@nwic.edu

LEWIS COUNTY HISTORICAL LIBRARY
599 N.W. Front St. • CHEHALIS, WA 98532
(206) 748-0831
Description: Holdings of about 1,600 volumes in the Indian archive collection.

**LITTLE BOSTON LIBRARY
PORT GAMBLE BAND OF S'KLALLAM TRIBE**
31912 Little Boston Rd. NE • KINGSTON, WA 98346
(360) 297-2646 Fax 297-7097; Website: www.pgst.nsn.us
Suzanne Jones, Director. Tribal library open to the public.

MAKAH CULTURAL & RESEARCH CENTER
P.O. Box 160 • NEAH BAY, WA 98357 (206) 645-2711
Description: Studies Makah language, culture, & ethnohistory; comparative Wakashan linguistics and Nootkin studies. Publication: Portraits In Time.

CHIEF GEORGE MANUEL MEMORIAL LIBRARY
Center for World Indigenous Studies
PMB 214, 1001 Cooper Point Rd. SW, Suite 140 • Olympia, WA 98502
(360) 450-5183 Fax (253) 276-0084; Website: www.cwis.org/gml/
Dedicated to the memoray of Secwepemc (Chief George Manuel), 1921-89) and to the nations of the Fourth World. Contains over 100,000 full text documents/reports, and publications from American Indian nations and indigenous nations from around the globe.

WEUSSO: NISQUALLY TRIBAL LIBRARY
4814 She-Nah-Num Dr. SE • OLYMPIA, WA 98513
(360) 456-5221 Fax 438-8618
Faith Hagenhofer, Librarian; Website: www.trlib.org
Description: Maintains a collection of over 5,000 books, Native American periodicals, and 750+ videos. Emphasis is on Native American and children's materials. Serves the community's members, both tribal & nontribal. Programs: Vocational education computer training. Interlibrary loans. Opened 1987.

NORTH AMERICAN INDIAN MISSION (NAIM) MINISTRIES LIBRARY
P.O. Box 151 • POINT ROBERTS, WA 98281
(604) 946-1227 Fax 946-1465; Website: www.naim.ca
Ray Badgero, President;
Description: Collection contains 600 volumes including audio and video tapes.

AMERICAN INDIAN HERITAGE SCHOOL LIBRARY
1330 N. 90th St. • SEATTLE, WA 98103
(206) 298-7895
Description: Large Native American collection -both print and audio-video.

UNIVERSITY OF WASHINGTON LIBRARIES
Special Collections, Box 352900 • SEATTLE, WA 98195-2900
(206) 543-1929 Fax 543-1931; Carla Rickerson, Head
Website: www.lib.washington.edu/specialcoll/
E-mail: speccoll@u.washington.edu
Description: Holds materials of all types on Pacific Northwest American Indians, with the main focus on coastal tribes. Materials in collection include books, photographs, & manuscript collections. A main focus of the manuscript collections is languages, including recordings of native speakers; many of the American Indian manuscript collections were compiled by anthropologists working with the tribes. *Special collection*: A Photographic Record: Over 4,000 photographs plus a 17,000 entry index - microfiche (112 sheets); Viola E. Garfield Albums on Totem Art: 1,749 photographs - microfiche (60 sheets), $1.84 per fiche. Open to the public.

JAMESTOWN S'KLALLAM TRIBAL LIBRARY
1033 Old Blyn Hwy. • SEQUIM, WA 98382
(360) 681-4614 Fax 681-4643; Website: www.jamestowntribe.org
Patsy Adams, Librarian; E-mail: library@jamestowntribe.org
Description: Books, videos & archives; special collection of rare reference materials that tell the story of the S'Klallams and other native people of the Olympic Peninsula. Native American law.

SQUAXIN ISLAND TRIBE MUSEUM, LIBRARY & RESEARCH CENTER
150 SE K'WUH-DEEGS-ALTXW • SHELTON, WA 98584
(360) 432-3851; Website: www.squaxinislandmuseum.org
Liz Yeahquo, Librarian
Description: Features exhibits and rare artifacts, as well as books and documents that tell the unique story of the people who lived & prospered along the shores of the inland Salish Sea for many centuries.

EASTERN WASHINGTON HISTORICAL SOCIETY
Northwest Museum of Arts & Culture
2316 W. First Ave. • SPOKANE, WA 99204
(509) 363-5313 Fax 363-5303
Website: www.northwestmuseum.org
Rose Krause, Curator of Special Collections
E-mail: archives@northwestmuseum.org
Description: The American Indian portion of the collection contains approximately 8,000 books on the American Indian; manuscript collections, 20,000 photographs, ephemera; newspaper clippings; and oral history tapes. Open to the public Tues.-Thurs., 11 am - 5 pm. Opened 1916.

JESUIT OREGON PROVINCE ARCHIVES
Foley Library, Gonzaga University • SPOKANE, WA 99258
(509) 323-3814 Fax 324-5904
Website: www.gonzaga.edu/foley/jopa.html
David Kingma, Archivist
Special collections: Jesuit Missions Collections of the Pacific Northwest & Alaska--150 volumes of Jesuit missionaries among Indians of Northwest--Blackfeet, Coeur d'Alene, Yakamas, Cheyenne. Northwest Mission Papers; 500 boxes, 45,000 items--correspondence, diaries, photos, microfilm, relating to

Jesuit Missionary activity in Alaska, and the Northwest States, including the Athapaskans & Eskimos to the previous tribes mentioned. The Indian Language Collection -- 50,600 pages - manuscript dictionaries, grammars, catechisms, gospels, prayer books, sermons in the Indian languages of the Rocky Mountains, and the Eskimo languages of Alaska. Among the languages are: Assiniboine, Blackfoot, Crow, Chinook, Columbia, Colville, Gros Ventre, Inuit, Kalispel, Nez Perce, Okanagan, Sioux, Tlingit, and Yakima. Most are contained on microfilm-125 reels. Open to the public. Opened 1925.

STEILACOOM TRIBAL CULTURAL CENTER LIBRARY
1515 Lafayette St., P.O. Box 88419 • STEILACOOM, WA 98388
(206) 584-6308; Joan K. Ortez, Director
Description: Research material - books, articles, videotapes & other material... all on Native Americans.

SUQUAMISH MUSEUM LIBRARY
P.O. Box 498 • SUQUAMISH, WA 98392
(360) 598-3311 Fax 598-6295; Website: www.suquamish.nsn.us
Description: The Suquamish Tribal Archives has a large collection of written documents, oral history tapes & transcripts, historical photographs, maps, and historical & cultural texts, relating to the Suquamish & other Puget Sound tribes.

WASHINGTON STATE HISTORICAL SOCIETY SPECIAL COLLECTIONS
1911 Pacific Ave. • TACOMA, WA 98402
(253) 272-3500 Fax 597-9518; Website: www.washingtonhistory.org
Edward W. Nolan, Head of Special Collections
Description: A collection of books, pamphlets, manuscripts & photographs that include Pacific Northwest Indians in general and Washington tribes in particular. Complete set of Edward Curtis with folios; papers of Louis Mann (Indian activist), 1914-36; Judge George Boldt (Indian fishing rights decision); Records of Indian Shaker Church of WA; papers of George R. Chute (historian of Native North Pacific halibut fishery, 1925-50); R.B. Milroy papers (Indian agent in Washington Territory, 1880-90), fragmentary; Yakima Indian Agency Records, 1880-1900, fragmentary; photo collections include 600 negatives of Makah tribe taken by Morse; and a file of newspaper clippings. Open to the public by appointment.

SHOALWATER BAY TRIBAL COMMUNITY LIBRARY
P.O. Box 130 • TOKELAND, WA 98590
(360) 267-8190
Description: Collection contains extensive Native American works.

TOPPENISH MUSEUM LIBRARY
1 South Elm • TOPPENISH, WA 98945
(509) 865-4510
Description: Maintains a collection of 18,500 volumes including many on the Indians of the Northwest, & Native-American history & culture.

YAKAMA NATION LIBRARY
Yakama Nation Cultural Heritage Center
P.O. Box 151, 101 Speil-Yi-Loop • TOPPENISH, WA 98948
(509) 865-5121 Fax 865-6101; Vivian M. Adams, Administrator
Description: Special collections include the Nipo Strongheart, Bob Pace, Dr. Helen Schuster, & special reference books & videos. Regular collections are historical reference books, contemporary native-related books, periodicals, magazines, and tribal newspapers.

WISCONSIN

ARVID E. MILLER MEMORIAL LIBRARY-MUSEUM
Mohican Nation Stockbridge-Munsee Band
N8510 Moh He Con Nuck Rd. • BOWLER, WI 54416
(715) 793-4270 Fax 793-4836; Website: www.mohican-nsn.gov.com
E-mail: library.museum@mohican-nsn.gov
Nathalee Kristiansen, Manager, Library/Museum
Cindy Jungenberg, Librarian Specialist
Description: Holds the largest collection of material, rare books, missionary journals, maps, microfilm, historical papers on Mohican Indians; also called Stockbridge-Munsee; includes artifacts such as baskets made of splints and birch bark, arrow heads, projectile points, tobacco pipes, stone axes; fur trade era & missionary era. *Activities*: Winter Ceremony; annual powwow; Mohican History Conference. Publications for sale. Opened 1974.

FOREST COUNTY POTAWATOMI CULTURAL CENTER, LIBRARY & MUSEUM
P.O. Box 340 • CRANDON, WI 54520
(800) 960-5479; (715) 478-7474 Fax 478-5280
Website: www.potawatomimuseum.com
Mike Alloway, Sr., Director
Description: Contains a collection of historical & contemporary photographs; audio/video, books, treaties, manuscripts, language material & other memorabilia. 4,000 library books.

HOARD HISTORICAL MUSEUM LIBRARY
407 Merchant Ave. • FORT ATKINSON, WI 53538
Description: Maintains a special collection of rare books on the Black Hawk War, 1800-1840.

LAC COURTE ORIELLES OJIBWA COLLEGE COMMUNITY LIBRARY
13466 W. Trepania Rd. • HAYWARD, WI 54843
(715) 634-4790 Ext. 108 Fax 634-5049
Website: www.lco-college.edu/library
Caryl Pfaff, Director; E-mail: pfaff@lco.edu

COLLEGE OF MENOMINEE NATION LIBRARY
P.O. Box 1179 • KESHENA, WI 54135
(715) 799-5600 Ext. Fax 799-1336
Website: www.menominee.edu/library
E-mail: mescalante@menominee.edu
Maria Escalante, Director

MENOMINEE TRIBAL/COUNTY LIBRARY
W2760 Chief Little Wave R, P.O. Box 1090 • KESHENA, WI 54135
(715) 799-5212 Fax 799-6516
Website: www.menominee-nsn.gov
Michael Wilbur, Director

STATE HISTORICAL SOCIETY OF WISCONSIN LIBRARY/ARCHIVES
816 State St. • MADISON, WI 53706
(608) 264-6535 Fax 264-6404
Website: www.wisconsinhistory.org
Peter Gottlieb, Director
Description: A major U.S. repository of documentation on Native American history. *Special collection*: "Largest library in the nation devoted to North American history." Extensive holdings on North American Indians; Native American newspapers & periodicals; manuscripts & photographs. Interlibrary loans. Open to the public. Established 1846.

MARQUETTE UNIVERSITY LIBRARY
Special Archives • MILWAUKEE, WI 53201
(414) 288-6838 Fax 288-3755
Website: www.marquette.edu/library
Mark G. Thiel, Archivist
Description: Collections primarily document Native American socio-culture change, education, legal issues, & Catholic Church relationships, 1870-present in U.S. & Canada. Also includes special website (www.marquette.edu/library/neh/general/index.htm) on K-12 curricula about Native Americans, funded by the National Endowment for the Humanities. Interlibrary loans. Open to the public.

ONEIDA COMMUNITY LIBRARY
Cultural Heritage Dept., 201 Elm St., P.O. Box 365 • ONEIDA, WI 54155
(920) 869-6213 Fax 869-1299; Louis J. Williams, Director

WYOMING

WYOMING STATE ARCHIVES
2301 Central Ave., Barrett Bldg. • CHEYENNE, WY 82002
(307) 777-7826 Fax 777-7044; Roger Joyce, Director
Description: Collections contain the records of the State of Wyoming and political subdivisions. Non-government collections focus on the history of Wyoming & the American West. Includes periodicals, maps, photographs, oral history, military & census records; primary sources for Native American history, especially Wyoming tribes. Open to the public. Opened 1895.

McCRACKEN RESEARCH LIBRARY – BUFFALO BILL HISTORICAL CENTER
720 Sheridan Ave. • CODY, WY 82414
(307) 578-4059 Fax 527-6042; Website: www.bbhc.org
Nathan E. Bender, Housel Curator
Frances B. Clymer, Librarian
Description: Research collection focusing on the Great Plains and Northern Rockies culture & history, including much on Plains Indians specifically and Native American studies in general. Library collection has 25,000 volumes with 3,000 linear feet of archival collections. Photograph holdings are particularly strong for the Crow, Cheyenne and other Plains Indian peoples, with collections from photographers D.F. Barry, Thomas Marquis, W.A. Petzoldt, J.H. Sharp, L.A. Huffman, George Bird Grinnell and others; Bureau of American Ethnology Annual Reports, 1880's to 1940's. Interlibrary loans. Opened to the public.

ORGANIZATIONS

ABLEZA - A NATIVE AMERICAN ARTS & FILM INSTITUTE
1279 Mildred Ave. • San Jose, CA 95125
(408) 267-4609 Fax 267-9609
E-mail: ableza@ableza.org; Website: www.ableza.org

ABORIGINAL PEOPLES TELEVISION NETWORK
339 Portage Ave. • Winnipeg, MB R3B 2C3 • Canada
(204) 947-9331; Website: www.aptn.ca

AIROS NATIVE RADIO NETWORK
1800 N. 33rd St. • Lincoln, NE 68503
(402) 472-3287 Fax 472-8675
Website: www.airos.org; E-mail: airos@unl.edu

AMERICAN INDIAN FILM & VIDEO COMPETITION
Red Earth, Inc., 2100 NE 52nd St. • Oklahoma City, OK 73111
(918) 747-8276; Website: www.redearth.org

AMERICAN INDIAN FILM INSTITUTE
333 Valencia St., Suite 322 • San Francisco, CA 94103
(415) 554-0525 Fax 554-0542; Website: www.aifisf.com

AMERICAN INDIAN TV (AITV)
245 E. 19th St., Suite 11R • New York, NY 10003
(212) 982-2152; Website: www.americanindiantv.com
E-mail: info@americanindiantv.com

AMERIND ENTERTAINMENT
65 N. Allen Ave., Suite 105 • Pasadena, CA 91106
(818) 384-0344

BEAR TRIBE VIDEOS
P.O. Box 959 • Canandaigua, NY 14424
(716) 554-4906 (phone & fax). Distributes videos.

BROWN EYES PRODUCTIONS
933 E. 12th #3 • Anchorage, AK 99501
(907) 257-1110 Fax 257-1835

CHARIOT DISTRIBUTION
1274 Lambert Cir. • Lafayette, CO 80026 (800) 477-5128

CHEROKEE LANGUAGE & CULTURE
4158 E. 48th Pl. • Tulsa, OK 74135 (918) 749-3082

CHEROKEE TRIBAL TELECOMMUNICATIONS CO.
Cherokee, NC 28719 (704) 497-7380
Website: www.cherokee-corp.com

CORPORATION FOR PUBLIC BROADCASTING
901 E St., NW • Washington, DC 20004
(202) 879-9742 Fax 783-1019

DESCENDING EAGLE
2017 Mission St. #303 • San Francisco, CA 94110
(415) 750-9036

FIRST AMERICAN AWARDS
First Americans in the Arts, P.O. Box 17780 • Beverly Hills, CA 90209
(310) 278-3848 Fax (818) 772-9772

FIRST NATIONS FILM & VIDEO FESTIVAL
Institute for Native American Development
Truman College, 1145 W. Wilson Ave. • Chicago, IL 60640
(312) 907-4665 Fax 907-4464; Website: www.fnfvf.com

FIRST VOICES INDIGENOUS RADIO
WBAI NY 99.5 FM, 120 Wall St., 10th Floor • New York, NY 10005
(212) 209-2800; Website: www.first voicesindigenousradio.org
E-mail: tiokasin@gmail.com

FULL CIRCLE VIDEOS
1131 S. College Ave. • Tulsa, OK 74104
(800) 940-8849 Fax (918) 585-3911; E-mail: fullcir@aol.com

INDIGENOUS COMMUNICATIONS ASSOCIATION
P.O. Box 932 • Hoopa, CA 95546
(916) 625-5033 Fax 625-5231; E-mail: kroica@aol.com

NATIVE AMERICA CALLING
Koahnic Broadcast Corp. (KNBA 90.3 FM)
3600 San Jeronimo Dr., Suite 480 • Anchorage, AK 99508
(888) 278-5622; (907) 793-3500 Fax 793-3536
Website: knba.com; E-mail: feedback@knba.com
Website: www.nativeamericacalling.com; Website: www.nativecalling.org
Website: indiannet.indian.com/NAC/html; Jaclyn Sallee, President/CEO
P.O. Box 40164 • Albuquerque, NM 87196
(800) 99-NATIVE; (505) 277-8009 Fax 277-4286; E-mail: chato@unm.edu

NATIVE AMERICAN BROADCASTING
Website: www.jlc.net/~jcatlin/interworld/nab.htm

NATIVE AMERICAN HOLLYWOOD
Website: www.angelfire.com

NATIVE AMERICAN INDIANS IN FILM
65 N. Allen Ave., Suite 105 • Pasadena, CA 91106
(818) 578-0344 Fax 578-0344

NATIVE AMERICAN MEDIA ENTERPRISES
1750 N. Wilcox #223 • Los Angeles, CA 90028 (213) 463-8535

NATIVE AMERICAN PUBLIC TELECOMMUNICATIONS, INC.
P.O. Box 83111 • Lincoln, NE 68501
(800) 835-7087; (402) 472-3522 Fax 472-8675
Website: www.nativetelecom.org; E-mail: native@unl.edu
Frank Blythe, Founding Executive Director/Native Emeritus
E-mail fblyth1@yahoo.com,
Shirley Sneve (Sicangu Lakota), Executive Director
E-mail: shirley.sneve@unl.edu; (472-0208)
Georgiana Lee (Navajo), Assistant Director
E-mail: Georgiana.lee@unl.edu; (472-0497)
Brian Bull (Nez Perce), Board Chairperson
Laura Waterman Wittstock (Seneca), Vice Chairperson

NATIVE YOUTH MEDIA INSTITUTE
Native Media Center - UND School of Communication
P.O. Box 7169 • Grand Forks, ND 58202 (701) 777-2478

NATIVERADIO.COM
1212 Bath Ave., 1st Floor Suite 2 • Ashland, KY 41101
(606) 326-1917; Website: www.nativeradio.com

NORTHWEST INDIAN NEWS
1151 Ellis • BELLINGHAM, WA 98225
(800) 488-5867 ext. 2962; (360) 392-2962 Fax 647-0824
Website: www.nwin.tv; Website: www.kvos.com
E-mail: jbrowder@kvos.com; E-mail: litasheldon@yahoo.com

PATH OF THE SUN IMAGES
3020 Lowell Blvd. • Denver, CO 80211 (303) 477-8442

RED EAGLE PRODUCTIONS
1704 Elaine St. • Billings, MT 59105 (406) 254-2396

RED EARTH, INC.
2100 NE 52nd St. • Oklahoma City, OK 73111 (405) 427-5228

RED NATION MEDIA CHANNEL
9420 Reseda Blvd., PMB 352 • Northridge, CA 91324
(818) 904-9256; Website: www.rednation.com

SERENE FX HEDIN PRODUCTIONS
12089 W. Dakota Dr. • Lakewood, CO 80228-2935
(303) 980-8582

SHENANDOAH FILM PRODUCTIONS
538 G St. • Arcada, CA 95521 (707) 822-1030

SPIRIT WORLD PRODUCTIONS
9420 Reseda Blvd., PMB 352 • Northridge, CA 91324
(818) 904-9256; Website: www.rednation.com

SPOTTED EAGLE PRODUCTIONS
2524 Hennepin Ave. #6 • Minneapolis, MN 55405
(612) 377-4212 Fax 377-7020; E-mail: cseagle@maroon.tc.umn.edu

TWO RIVERS NATIVE FILM & VIDEO FESTIVAL
Native Arts Circle • 3121 Elliot Ave. • Minneapolis, MN 55407-1507
(612) 870-7173 Fax 870-0327. Usually held in mid-October.

UNITED NATIVE AMERICAN TELEVISION PROJECT
Website: www.jlc.net/~jcatlin/interworld/main1.ht

VISIONMAKER VIDEO
1800 N. 33rd St. • Lincoln, NE 68503
  (877) 868-2250; (402) 472-3522 Fax 472-8675
  Website: www.visionmaker.org; E-mail: visionmaker@unl.edu

VISION QUEST FILM & VIDEO PRODUCTIONS, INC.
7 Milburn Lane • Huntington, NY 11743 (516) 385-7459

WRITTEN HERITAGE VIDEOS
P.O. Box 1390 • Folsom, LA 70437
  (504) 796-5433 Fax 796-9236

A list of radio & television stations, programs, and projects throughout the U.S. arranged alpha-geographically.

AIROS (American Indian Radio on Satellite)
  (402) 472-3287; E-mail: airos@unl.edu; Website: www.airos.org

ALABAMA

WASG - 550 AM & WYDH - FM
Alabama Native American Broadcasting Co.
1210 S. Main St. • ATMORE, AL 36502
  (205) 368-2511 Fax 368-4227

ALASKA

BROWN EYES PRODUCTIONS 933 E. 12th #3 • ANCHORAGE, AK 99501
  (907) 257-1110 Fax 257-1835

INDIGENOUS BROADCAST CENTER
Alaska Public Radio Network, 810 E. 9th Ave. • ANCHORAGE, AK 99501
  (907) 263-7427 Fax 263-7450

KOAHNIC BROADCAST CORP. (KNBA 90.3 FM)
3600 San Jeronimo, Suite 475 • ANCHORAGE, AK 99508
  (907) 793-3500 Fax 793-3536
  Website: www.knba.org; E-mail: feedback@knba.org

ONE SKY INTERNATIONAL PRODUCTIONS, INC.
612 E. 14th, Suite A • ANCHORAGE, AK 99501
  (907) 563-7440 Fax 563-9309; Website: www.onesky.org
  E-mail: onesky@onesky.org; E-mail: dennisgreene@ak.net

ASRC COMMUNICATIONS, INC.
P.O. Box 129 • BARROW, AK 99723
  (907) 852-8633; Website: www.asrcc.com

KBRW - 680 AM Silakkuagvik Communications, Inc.
P.O. Box 109 • BARROW, AK 99723
  (907) 852-6811/6300 Fax 852-2274; Website: www.kbrw.org

KYUK - 640 AM/TV Bethel Broadcasting, Inc., Pouch 468
640 Radio St. • BETHEL, AK 99559 (907) 543-3131 Fax 543-3130
  Website: www.kyuk.org; E-mail: gm@kyuk.org

KCUK - 88.1 FM Kashunaniut School District • CHEVAK, AK 99563
  (907) 858-7014 Fax 858-7114; Peter Tuluk, Manager
Yupik Eskimo. Repeats KYUK. Noncommercial station.

KDLG - 670 AM P.O. Box 670 • DILLINGHAM, AK 99576
  (907) 842-5281 Fax 842-5645; Website: www.kdlg.org

KZPA - 900 AM P.O. Box 126 • FORT YUKON, AK 99740
  (907) 662-2587 Fax 662-2222
KBBI 890 AM
Kachemak Bay Broadcasting, 3913 Kachemak Way • HOMER, AK 99603
  (907) 235-7721 Fax 235-2357
  Website: www.kbbi.org; E-mail: cab@kbbi.org

KTOO – FM 360 Egan Dr. • JUNEAU, AK 99801
  (907) 586-1670 Fax 586-361; Website: www.ktoo.org

KDLL - 91.9 FM - KENIA, AK Website: www.kdllradio.org

KRBD - 105.3 FM 123 Stedman St. • KETCHIKAN, AK 99901
  (907) 225-9655; Website: www.krbd.org

KOTZ - 720 AM
Kotzebue Broadcasting, Inc., P.O. Box 78 • KOTZEBUE, AK 99752
  (907) 442-3434 Fax 442-2292
  Website: www.kotz.or; E-mail: kotzengr@eagle.ptialaska.net

KSKO 870 AM P.O. Box 195 • McGRATH, AK 99627
  (907) 524-3001 Fax 524-3436; Website: www.ksko.org

METLAKATLA INDIAN COMMUNITY CABLE TV
P.O. Box 8 • METLAKATLA, AK 99926

KSDP 830 AM SAND POINT, AK

KUHB - 91.9 FM Pribiloff School District • ST. PAUL, AK 99660
  (907) 546-2254 Fax 546-2327

KNSA - 930 AM P.O. Box 178 • UNALAKLEET, AK 99684
  (907) 624-3101 Fax 624-3130

ARIZONA

KUYI 88.1 FM HOPI RADIO P.O. Box 1500 • KEAMS CANYON, AZ 86034
  (928) 738-5530; Website: www.kuyi.net
  E-mail: info@kuyi.net; Monica Nuvamsa, General Manager
  Richard Alun Davis, Station Manager
  Macadio Namoki, Development & Marketing Coordinator

CHANNEL 3 P.O. Box 5968 • PHOENIX, AZ 85010

APACHE CABLEVISION 12 San Carlos Ave. • SAN CARLOS, AZ 85550
  (520) 475-2550

KNCC – FM Navajo Community College • TSAILE, AZ 85445 (602) 724-3311

KGHR - 91.3 FM
Navajo/Greyhills High School, P.O. Box 160 • TUBA CITY, AZ 86045
  (520) 283-6271 Fax 283-6604; Website: www.kghr.org

KPYT-LP 100.3 FM
Pascua Yaqui Tribe , 7474 S. Camino De Oeste, TUCSON, AZ 85746
  (520) 838-7111; E-mail: hector.youtsey@pascuayaqui-nsn.gov

KUAT – AM University of Arizona • TUCSON, AZ 85721

KNNB - 88.1 FM (Apache)
White Mountain Apache Tribe, P.O. Box 310 • WHITERIVER, AZ 85941
  (520) 338-5211 Fax 338-1744; Phoebe Nez, Manager

KTNN - 660 AM (Navajo) Native Broadcast Enterprise
P.O. Box 2569 • WINDOW ROCK, AZ 86515
  (866) 415-8189; (928) 871-3553 Fax 871-3479
  Website: www.ktnnonline.com; E-mail: sales@ktnnonline.com

NAVAJO NATION BROADCAST SERVICES & FILM OFFICE
P.O. Box 2310 • WINDOW ROCK, AZ 86515
  (520) 871-6656 Fax 7355

CALIFORNIA

KTQX 90.5 FM BAKERSFIELD, CA

AMERICAN INDIAN CABLE TV
9500 Artesia Blvd. • BELLFLOWER, CA 90706 (310) 920-7227 ext. 22

KPFA, KPFB, KFCF 94.1 FM BERKELEY, CA

KZFR - 90.1 FM CHICO, CA 95929
KIDE - 91.3 FM
Hoopa Tribal Broadcasting Co., P.O. Box 1220 • HOOPA, CA 95546
  (530) 625-4245 Fax 625-4594; E-mail: kide@hoopa-nsn.gov
  Website: www.hoopa-nsn.gov/departments/kide.htm

THE AMERICAN INDIAN HOUR
American Indian Liberation Crusade
4009 S. Halldale Ave. • LOS ANGELES, CA 90062
  (323) 299-1810; Website: www.indiancrusader.org

NATIVE AMERICAN MEDIA
1015 Gayle Ave., Suite 1024 • LOS ANGELES, CA 90024
  (310) 475-6845; Website: www.nativeamericanmedia.org
  E-mail: info@nativeamericanmedia.org

WORLD ONE RADIO KECG 97.1 FM
Program: Native Son Rising (510) 233-0611

KPFA - 94.1 FM International Indian Treaty Council
2390 Mission St., Suite 301 • SAN FRANCISCO, CA 94117-1836
(415) 566-0251 Fax 566-0442

KPOO - 89.5 FM P.O. Box 11008 • SAN FRANCISCO, CA 94101
(415) 346-5373
Program: Red Voices of Native Nations - Tuesday, 7 pm

KKUP RADIO 91.5 FM
1275 Franklin Mall, PMB 9150 • SANTA CLARA, CA 95050
(408) 260-2999 & (831) 255-2999
Website: www.kkup.com; E-mail: webmeister@kkup.org
Program: Indian Time, Tues. 8-10 pm
Program: Global Winds Native Roots
America's Edition-2nd Sunday of each month, 1-3 pm

COLORADO

KRZA - 88.7 FM 528 9th St. • ALAMOSA, CO 81101
(719) 589-9057 Fax 589-9258; Website: www.krza.org
Programs: National Native News, 11 a.m. weekdays;
AIROS, Sunday, 1-3 p.m.

KGNU - 88.5 FM Public Radio P.O. Box 885 • BOULDER, CO 80306
(303) 449-4885 Fax 447-9955
Website: kgnu.org/indianvoices; E-mail: halsey@bvsd.k12.co.us
Program: "Indian Voices" Sunday from 3-4pm

KSJD - 91.5 FM 33051 Hwy. 160 • MANCOS, CO 81328
(970) 564-0808 Fax 564-8450; Website: www.ksjd.org
Program: Native America Calling

KUVO 89.3 FM - ALTERNATIVE VOICES
Path of the Sun Images, P.O. Box 11443 • DENVER, CO 80211
(303) 480-9272 Fax 291-0757; Website: www.kuvo.org
E-mail: producer@alternativevoices; Z. Susanne Aikman, Host/Producer
Program: ALTERNATIVE VOICES on American Indian Radio on Satellite
network. Live every Sunday mornings from 7-8 a.m. on Denver's Public Radio,
KUVO.FM 89.3.

KSUT - 91.3 FM Southern Ute Tribe, P.O. Box 737 • IGNACIO, CO 81137
(303) 563-0255 Fax 563-0396; Website: www.ksut.org
Carlos Sena, Manager. *Program*: Native America Calling

LOUISIANA

KUHN 88.9 FM United Houma Nation, Inc.,
20986 Hwy. 1 • GOLDEN MEADOW, LA 70357

MICHIGAN

WCUP 105.7 FM (906) 353-9287 Fax 353-9200

MINNESOTA

FIRST AMERICAN TELEVISION, INC.
MINNEAPOLIS, MN 55408 (612) 825-9525
Weekly TV programs: "First Americans Journal," "Indian News Network,"
"Sovereignty On Our Own Terms," "Native American Forum."

FIRST PERSON RADIO KFAI Radio 90.3 FM, 106.7 AM
Migizi Communications, 3123 E. Lake St., # 200 • MINNEAPOLIS, MN 55406
(612) 387-4915 Fax 721-3936
Website: www.migizi.org; E-mail: lwmpls@visi.com

WUSA – TV 1113 W. Broadway • MINNEAPOLIS, MN 55411

RED LAKE CHIPPEWA TRIBE - NATIVE AMERICAN RADIO PROJECT
RED LAKE, MN 56671 (218) 679-3331

KTCA-TV Channel 2 172 E. 4th St. • ST. PAUL, MN 55101
(612) 646-4611. Native American TV Program

MISSISSIPPI

WHTV (CABLE TV) Mississippi Band of Choctaw Indians
P.O. Box 6010 • PHILADELPHIA, MS 39350 (601) 656-5251

MONTANA

KGVA - 88.1 FM Fort Belknap College, RR 1, Box 66 • Harlem, MT 59526
(866) 353-KGVA; (406) 353-4656 Fax 353-4808
Website: www.fbcc.edu/html/kgva

KHMT - Channel 4 445 S. 24th St. W., Suite 404 • BILLING, MT 59102
(406) 652-7366 Fax 652-6963

NATIVE VOICES PUBLIC TELEVISION
VCB Rm. 222, Montana State University • BOZEMAN, MT 59717
(406) 994-6218 Fax 994-6545; E-mail: hart@sesame.kusm.montana.edu
Website: www.kusm.montana.edu/nativevoices/

BLACKFEET MEDIA Blackfeet Tribe
P.O. Box 850 • BROWNING, MT 59417

KBFT – FM P.O. Box 819 • BROWNING, MT 59417

KFBB - TV Channel 5 P.O. Box 1139 • GREAT FALLS, MT 59401
(406) 453-4377. *Program*: Native-American TV Program
4th Sunday of each month at 11:30 am

1230 AM RADIO HARDIN, MT 59034

KOBL - TV
Dull Knife Memorial College, P.O. Box 98 • LAME DEER, MT 59043

KZIN - FM; KSEN 1150 AM 830 Oilfield Ave. • SHELBY, MT 59474
Wednesday & Friday at 9:10 am

NEBRASKA

KCSR - AM   CHADRON, NE 69337 (308) 432-5545

KZUM - 89.3 FM AIROS (American Indian Radio on Satellite)
University Television/NAPT, P.O. Box 83111 • LINCOLN, NE 68501
(800) 571-6885; (402) 472-9333 Fax 472-8675

OMAHA CABLE TV SERVICE
Omaha Indian Reservation, P.O. Box 368 • MACY, NE 68039

NEW MEXICO

KABR - 1500 AM P.O. Box 907 • MAGDALENA, NM 87825
(505) 854-2543; Trowen Hulett, Owner
Website: www.nv1.org/kabrstations.html
Special programs: "National Native News,"
"Native America Calling," "Rezervations with Dawn Karima"
P.O. Box 22114, Albuquerque, NM 87154

KNME - TV 1130 University Blvd., NE • ALBUQUERQUE, NM 87102
(505) 277-2121; Website: www.knme.org

KOAT – TV P.O. Box 25982 • ALBUQUERQUE, NM 87125
(505) 884-7777 Fax 884-6324; Website: www.koat.com

KUNM - 89.9 FM University of New Mexico Radio
Onate Hall • ALBUQUERQUE, NM 87102
(505) 277-4806; Website: www.kunm.org

CROWNPOINT CABLE TV CROWNPOINT, NM 87313 (505) 786-5541

KCIE - 90.5 FM Jicarilla Apache Tribe, P.O. Box 603 • DULCE, NM 87528
(505) 759-3681 Fax 759-9140; Website: www.kcie.org

KGLP - 91.7 FM 200 College Rd. • GALLUP, NM 87301
(505) 863-7626 Fax 863-7633
Website: www.kglp.org; E-mail: kglpradio@kglp.org

KABR - 1500 AM
Alamo Navajo School Board, P.O. Box 907 • MAGDALENA, NM 87825
(505) 854-2632 Fax 854-2641; Website: www.nv1.org/kabrstations.html

KTDB - 89.7 FM
Ramah Navajo School Board, P.O. Box 40 • PINEHILL, NM 87357
(505) 775-3215 Fax 775-3551; Website: www.nv1.org/ktdbstations.html

KSHI - 90.0 FM P.O. Box 339 • ZUNI, NM 87327
(505) 782-4811 Fax 782-2700

NEW YORK

WBAI - 99.5 FM 505 Eighth Ave. • NEW YORK, NY 10018
(212) 279-0707; Jim Buck, Host/Producer; Website: www.wbai.org
Program: Circle of Red Nations - Mondays at 9 pm.

CKON - 97.3 FM Akwesasne Communication Society
P.O. Box 140 • ROOSEVELTOWN, NY 13683
(518) 358-3426 Fax 358-9456; Website: www.cnwl.igs.net/~ckon/
E-mail: ckonfm@yahoo.com; Kallen M. Martin, General Manager
Mohawk Program: National Native News 12 noon, 4pm, 8pm daily.

WGWE – 105.9 FM
Seneca Nation, 90 Oh:yo' Way • SENECA NATION (via NY) 14779
(716) 945-8142; David Kimelberg (Seneca), Chief Executive Officer

CHANNEL 25 CABLE VISION Shinnecock Indian Tribe
Box 59, Rte. 27A, Montauk Hwy. • SOUTHAMPTON, NY 11968
(516) 283-1643. *Program*: Voices of Native America. Monthly .

NORTH CAROLINA

EASTERN BAND OF CHEROKEE
Indian Cable TV Service, P.O. Box 455 • CHEROKEE, NC 28719
Website: www.cherokee-nc.com/tv

WPSU – TV Pembroke State University • PEMBROKE, NC 28372
Website: www.wpsu.org

WYRU - 1160 AM P.O. Box 0711 • RED SPRINGS, NC 28377
(919) 843-5946 Fax 521-8694

NORTH DAKOTA

KEYA - 88.5 FM Turtle Mountain Chippewa Tribe
P.O. Box 190 • BELCOURT, ND 58316
(701) 477-5686 Fax 477-3252; Website: www.keya.utma.com

KABU - 90.7 FM FORT TOTTEN, ND

STANDING ROCK CABLE TV SERVICE
P.O. Box 470 • FORT YATES, ND 58538 (701) 854-3895

KAEN - 89.5 FM Standing Rock Sioux Radio Project
P.O. Box D • FORT YATES, ND 58538 (701) 854-7226

KMHA - 91.3 FM Fort Berthold Communications Enterprise
HCR 3, Box 1 • NEW TOWN, ND 58763
(701) 627-3333 Fax 627-4212;
Website: www.nv1.org/kmhastations.html

OKLAHOMA

KACO - 98.5 FM
Kiowa Tribal Radio Station, P.O. Box 361 • CARNEGIE, OK 73015
(405) 654-2300; Website: www.kiowaok.com/radio.htm

KGOU - 106.3 FM
Copeland Hall, Rm 300, University of Oklahoma • NORMAN, OK 73019
(405) 325-3388 Fax 325-7129; Website: www.kgou.org
Program: Indian Times," Biweekly, Sat. & Sun. 6 pm

KROU - 105.7 FM SPENCER/OKLAHOMA CITY, OK
Program: Indian Times," Biweekly, Sat. & Sun. 6 pm

KOTV – TV 302 S. Frankfort • TULSA, OK 74107

OREGON

KBOO – FM 20 SE 8th Ave. • PORTLAND, OR 97214
(503) 231-8032 Fax 231-7145; Website: www.kboo.fm/listen
Program: Indian World - Mondays from 8-9 pm

WISDOM OF THE ELDERS, INC.
3203 SE 109th Ave. • PORTLAND, OR 97266
Website: www.wisdomoftheelders.org
E-mail: rose@wisdomoftheelders.org
Wisdom of the Elders Program; Tribal Rhythms Program

CONFEDERATED TRIBES TELECOMMUNICATION PROJECT
P.O. Box 584 • WARM SPRINGS, OR 97761

KWSO - 91.9 FM Warm Springs Confederated Tribes
P.O. Box 489 • WARM SPRINGS, OR 97761
(503) 553-1968 Fax 553-3348
Website: www.kwso.org; E-mail: smatters@wstribes.org

SOUTH DAKOTA

YANKTON SIOUX TRIBE RADIO PROJECT
KONA, Inc. - Marty School, P.O. Box 222 • MARTY, SD 57361
(605) 384-5431

PINE RIDGE CABLE TV PINE RIDGE, SD 57770
(605) 867-1166; Website: www.prctv.com

KILI - 90.1 FM
Lakota Communications, P.O. Box 150 • PORCUPINE, SD 57772
(605) 867-5002 Fax 867-5634; Website: www.kiliradio.org

KINI - 96.1 FM P.O. Box 419 • ST. FRANCIS, SD 57572
(605) 747-2291 Fax 747-5057; Website: www.gwtc.net/~kinifm/

KSWS - 89.3 FM Sisseton-Wahpeton Sioux Tribe
Dakota Nation Broadcasting Corp., P.O. Box 142 • SISSETON, SD 57262
(605) 698-7972 Fax 698-7897

SOUTH DAKOTA PUBLIC BROADCASTING
South Dakota Public Radio Network
P.O. Box 5000 • VERMILLION, SD 57069
(605) 677-5861 Fax 677-5010
Programs: South Dakota Forum & Voices of the Plains

UTAH

AMERICAN INDIAN TV SERVICES HRCB, BYU • PROVO, UT 84602

KRCL COMMUNITY RADIO STATION 91 FM
208 West 800 South • SALT LAKE CITY, UT 84101
(801) 363-1818; Website: www.krcl.org
Indian programming on Sundays, 7-10 am.

WASHINGTON

TULALIP CABLEVISION MARYSVILLE, WA 98270 (360) 653-0235

OLYMPIC TV CABLE P.O. Box 88 • PORT ORCHARD, WA 98366

KSFC - 89.3 FM SPOKANE, WA

QUINAULT TRIBE RADIO PROJECT P.O. Box 332 • TAHOLAH, WA 98587
(206) 276-4353

KOTY - 1490 AM Yakama Nation Radio • TOPPENISH, WA
Website: www.1490koty.com

WISCONSIN

WOJB - 88.9 FM Lac Court Oreilles Ojibwe Broadcasting Corp.
Rt. 2, Box 2788 • HAYWARD, WI 54843
(715) 634-2100 Fax 634-3906; Website: www.wojb.org

WYOMING

KIEA – FM Wind River Indian Education Association
Wyoming Indian High School • ETHETE, WY 82520
(307) 332-2793

this section lists, alphabetically, those periodicals that deal directly or indirectly with the history, culture, & contemporary issues of the North American Indian and Eskimo.

ABSENTEE SHAWNEE NEWS
2025 S. Gordon Cooper • Shawnee, OK 74801
(405) 275-4030 Fax 275-5637; Website: www.astribe.com

ADAWE NEWS
Ottawa Tribe of Oklahoma, P.O. Box 110 • Miami, OK 74355
(918) 540-1536 Fax 542-3214; Website: www.ottawatribe.org/resources

AGUA COUNCIL NEWSLETTER
960 E. Tahquitz Wat, Suite 106 • Palm Springs, CA 92262

AH-WAH-KO-WA
Yavapai Prescott Indian Tribe, 530 E. Merritt • Prescott, AZ 86301
(520) 445-8790

AHTNA KANAS
Ahtna, Inc., P.O. Box 649 • Glennallen, AK 99588 (907) 822-3476
Bimonthly shareholder newsletter of Ahtna, the Copper River Native Assn.

AICH NEWSLETTER
American Indian Community House
134 W. 29th St., 4th Fl. • New York, NY 10001
(212) 598-0100 Fax 598-4909
Website: www.aich.org; Reports on activities of the organization, which serves the needs of Native Americans residing in the New York metropolitan area. News and reviews of interest to American Indians. 5x/yr. Donations requested. Begun 1969.

AISES EDUCATION NEWSLETTER
American Indian Science & Engineering Society, P.O. Box 9828, Albuquerque, NM 87119-9828 (505) 765-1052 Fax 765-5608. Quarterly.

AK-CHIN O'ODHAM RUNNER NEWS
Ak-Chin Indian Reservation, 16600 N. Maricopa Hwy.
Maricopa, AZ 85139 (520) 568-1375 Fax 568-1376
E-mail: runner@ak-chin.nsn.us Raychel Peters, Editor
Bi-monthly newspaper includes articles, photos, puzzles & recipes provided by Ak-Chin members. Articles deal with events that pertain to the people of Ak-Chin Indian community. Advertising accepted. No charge. Begun 1986.

AKIING (THE LAND)
Indian Country Communications, Inc., 8558N County Road K Hayward, WI 54843-2052 (715) 634-5226 Fax 634-3243; Advertising (715) 634-1429
E-mail: nficad@cheqnet.com; Website: www.indiancountrynews.com
Paul DeMain, Editor; Kimberlie Hall, Advertising
Monthly Great Lakes publication devoted to the Algonquian speaking communities of Wisconsin, Michigan & Minnesota. Includes Canadian First nations. Special features, local and regional news, health, letters, language. $22/year. Advertising. Begun 1996.

AKWESASNE NOTES
Mohawk Nation, P.O. Box 868 • Hogansburg, NY 13655
(518) 358-3326 Fax 358-3488
Website: www.slic.com/~mohawkna/mnnotes.htm
Teresa David, Publisher; Douglas M. George - Kanentiio, Editor
Covers news by and about indigenous people in the Americas: poetry, cultural essays, book reviews, current event lists, pow-wows, conferences, and letters. Bimonthly tabloid. 12,000 cir. $15/year. Complimentary copies, exchanges. Microfilm/fiche available. Begun 1968.

ALASKA FEDERATION OF NATIVES (AFN) NEWS
1577 C St. #100 • Anchorage, AK 99501
(905) 274-3611; Julia E. Kitka, Editor Monthly newsletter.

ALASKA GEOGRAPHIC
The Alaska Geographic Society, P.O. Box 93370
Anchorage, AK 99509-3370 (907) 562-0164 Fax 562-0479
Penny Rennick, Editor; Pattey Mancini, Contact; E-mail: akgeo@anc.ak.net
Deals with the culture, history or region of Alaska or northwestern Canada including extensive coverage of Alaska's native peoples. Quarterly magazine. 8,000 circulation. $49/year; prices of individual issues vary. Free catalog available. Begun 1968.

ALLIGATOR TIMES
Seminole Tribe, 6073 Stirling Rd. • Hollywood, FL 33024
Monthly Seminole news.

ALMANACK
Plimoth Plantation, Wampanoag Indian Program
P.O. Box 1620 • Plymouth, MA 02362
(508) 746-1622 Fax 830-6026
Nanepashemet, Editor. Membership newsletter.

THE AMBASSADOR
Americans for Indian Opportunity, 1001 Marquette Ave. NW
Albuquerque, NM 87102 (505) 842-8677 Fax 842-8658
Website: www.aio.org; E-mail: jmcgee@aio.org
Jasmine McGee & Anna Epperson, Editors
Quarterly newsletter highlighting AIO's award-winning initiative, the American Indian Ambassador's Program. Covers news of nearly 150 Native American leaders working to implement their Indigenous values in their day-to-day lives and their work, spanned across the globe. Tribal leaders, filmmakers, policy-makers, community organizers, business entrepreneurs, educators, scholars, & philanthropic representatives all read and are represented in this log of cutting edge leadership development. *Annual subscription*: Minimum donation of $35.

AMERICAN CHEROKEE CONFEDERACY NEWSLETTER
619 Pine Cone Rd. • Albany, GA 31705-6906 (229) 787-5722
Prin. Chief William "Rattlesnake" Jackson, Editor
Covers tribal events. Quarterly, 4-page newsletter. Advertising accepted. Began 1976.

AMERICAN INDIAN
Smithsonian National Museum of the American Indian
4th St. & Independence Ave., SW • Washington, DC 20024
(202) 633-6611 Fax 633-6920 Website: www.americanindian.si.edu
Thomas Sweeney, Editor; E-Mail: sweeneyt@si.edu
Quarterly magazine for members of the National Museum of the American Indian, and media. Reflects the historic & contemporary cultures of the Native peoples of the Americas by telling their stories in new & meaningful ways. Tells the story of the museum's exhibitions, public programs, community services, and collaborations with Native peoples through the first-person Native voice and through tribal perspectives. 85,000 circulation. *Subscription*: Basic, $20. $6 per issue at the museum. Begun 2000.

AMERICAN INDIAN & ALASKA NATIVE MENTAL HEALTH RESEARCH JOURNAL
American Indian & Alaska Native Programs
University of Colorado Health Sciences Center
Dept. of Psychiatry • Nighthorse Campbell Native Health Bldg.
P.O. Box 6508, MS: F800 • Aurora, CO 80045-0508
(303) 724-1414 Fax 724-1474; Spero M. Manson, PhD, Editor
Website: www.uchsc.edu/sm/ncaianmhr
Provides better understanding of current mental health issues and concerns of Native Americans and Alaska Natives. Began 1987.

AMERICAN INDIAN ART MAGAZINE
7314 E. Osborn Dr., Suite B • Scottsdale, AZ 85251
(480) 994-5445 Fax 945-9533; Website: www.aiamagazine.com
E-mail: aiamagazine@qwestoffice.net
Mary G. Hamilton, Publisher; Roanne P. Goldfein, Editor
Quarterly art journal devoted exclusively to the art forms of the American Indian. Art forms are presented by full-color photographs and articles written by leading scholars in the field. Also includes book and exhibition reviews, legal news, auction listings, and listings of major museum & gallery exhibitions. Sells a Calendar featuring 13 full-color reproductions of work by American Indian artists, $12.95, includes shipping. Circulation: 30,000 circulation. $6/copy. $20/year (4 issues), $30/year, Canada & foreign; $36 (8 issues); $56 Canada & foreign. Advertising. Began 1975.

AMERICAN INDIAN BASKETRY MAGAZINE
P.O. Box 66124 • Portland, OR 97266 (503) 233-8131
John M. Gogol, Ed. & Publisher
Quarterly. Contains articles, book reviews, and lists of new exhibits; sponsors research & communications in the study of American Indian basketry. 5,000 cir. $7/copy; $30/yr. Advertising. Began 1979.

AMERICAN INDIAN CULTURE & RESEARCH JOURNAL
U. of California, Los Angeles, American Indian Studies Center
3220 Campbell Hall, Box 951548 • Los Angeles, CA 90095-1548
(310) 206-7508 Fax 206-7060; Website: www.aisc.ucla.edu
Hanay Geiogamah, Editor; E-mail: editor@aisc.ucla.edu
An interdisciplinary research forum for scholars and innovators in the areas of historical and contemporary American Indian life and culture. Book reviews; essays, poems, and monographs. Quarterly. $25/individuals; $60/institutions; foreign, add $10. Advertising accepted. Began 1971.

AMERICAN INDIAN GRADUATE MAGAZINE
4520 Montgomery Blvd., NE, Suite 1-B • Albuquerque, NM 87109
(505) 881-4584; Website: www.aigcs.org
Susan Duran & Stephine Poston, Editors
Bi-annual (Spring & Fall) Magazine describes graduate opportunities for American Indians & Alaska Natives. No subscription price; it's usually circulated to students, Indian higher education programs and those who are interested in contributing to the organization. 1992.

AMERICAN INDIAN HORSE NEWS
American Indian Horse Registry, Route 3, Box 64 • Lockhart, TX 78644
(512) 398-6642 Nanci Falley, Editor. Quarterly breed publication of the AIHR.

AMERICAN INDIAN JOURNAL
Institute for the Development of Indian Law
2600 Summit Dr. • Edmond, OK 73034-5984
Lynn Kickingbird, Editor
Contains scholarly articles on American Indian history & law, as well as articles of current interest in Indian affairs. Book reviews. Quarterly. 350 cir. $13/copy; $50/year. Advertising. Began 1971.

AMERICAN INDIAN LAW NEWSLETTER
American Indian Law Center, U. of New Mexico-School of Law
1117 Stanford Dr., NE, P.O. Box 4456 • Albuquerque, NM 87196
(505) 277-5462; Website: www.law.unm.edu. Published irregularly.

AMERICAN INDIAN LAW REVIEW
University of Oklahoma Law Center, Andrew M. Coats Hall
300 Timberdell Rd. • Norman, OK 73019
(405) 325-2840 Fax 325-6282
Website: www.adams.law.ou.edu/ailr
Stephanie Moser Goins, Editor-in-Chief; Michael Waters, Editorial Advisor
This semiannual journal documents and analyzes legal, cultural, and historical issues of interest to Native American communities. Includes articles by legal professionals & scholars, notes written by students, and recent developments in the federal courts on American Indian issues. Book reviews. Advertising. Contest: The American Indian Law Writing Competition. $20/year. Back copies available from William S. Hein & Co. by calling toll-free (800) 828-7571.

AMERICAN INDIAN LAWYER TRAINING PROGRAM NEWSLETTER
American Indian Resource Institute, 319 MacArthur Blvd. • Oakland, CA 94610
(510) 834-9333 Fax 834-3836

AMERICAN INDIAN LIBRARIES NEWSLETTER
American Indian Library Association-School of Library and Information Studies
University of Oklahoma, 401 W. Brooks • Norman, OK 73019
(405) 325-3921 Fax 325-7648; Rhonda Taylor, Editor
Contains information of interest to those interested in library services to Native Americans in the U.S. and Canada. Includes news, items of interest, reviews, advertisements, and Association information. Quarterly newsletter. 1,500 Cir. $10 membership in Association for individuals, $5, students, $25, institutions. Send subscriptions to: Joan Howland, Law Library, University of Minnesota, 229 19th Ave. S., Minneapolis, MN 55455. Began 1976.

AMERICAN INDIAN NATIONS
California Center for Native Nations, University of California, Riverside
College of Humanities, Arts & Social Sciences • Riverside, CA 92521
(951) 827-1974; Website: www.americanindian.ucr.edu
Native American studies student magazine.

AMERICAN INDIAN NEWS SERVICE
National Museum of the American Indian
4th St. & Independence Ave. SW • Washington, DC 20560
Website: www.americanindiannews.org
Kara Briggs (Yakama/Snohomish), Editor
E-mail: editor@americanindiannews.org
c/o Red Hummingbird Media Corporation
8825 34th Ave. NE, Suite L-154 • Tulalip, WA 98271 (503) 577-0012

AMERICAN INDIAN QUARTERLY
Orders to: University of Nebraska Press
111 Lincoln Mall • Lincoln, NE 68588-0630
(800) 755-1105 Fax (800) 526-2617; (402) 472-3584 (outside U.S.)
Website: www.nebraskapress.unl.edu/journalinfo/1.html
Amanda J. Cobb-Greetham, Editor; E-mail: journals@unlnotes.unl.edu
An interdisciplinary journal of Native American studies including the history, anthropology, literature, and arts of Native North America. Book reviews. Peer-reviewed articles; reviews of films and exhibits. Published as two double issues per year. AIQ is a peer-reviewed academic journal. $30/year, individuals; $75/year, institutions; single issue, $24. Advertising accepted. Begun 1979.

AMERICAN INDIAN REHABILITATION RESEARCH & TRAINING CENTER
Institute for Human Development, Northern Arizona University
CU Box 5630 • Flagstaff, AZ 86011; Website: www.nav.edu/~ihd
(520) 523-4791 Fax 523-9127; Dr. Timothy Thomason, Editor
Quarterly newsletter covering the activities of the Center that aims to improve the lives of American Indians with disabilities. Articles on rehabilitation. No charge. Begun 1983.

AMERICAN INDIAN REPORT
The Falmouth Institute, Inc., 3702 Pender Dr. #300 • Fairfax, VA 22030
(800) 992-4489; (703) 352-2250 Fax 352-2323
Website: www.falmouthinst.com
Marguerite Carroll, Editor; E-mail: mcarroll@falmouthinst.com
A monthly magazine focusing on national issues, financial news, law, environmental news, education, health, news and issues affecting American Indians and Alaska natives. $29.95, annual subscription. A complimentary issue is available upon request. Begun 1985.

AMERICAN INDIAN RESOURCE CENTER NEWSLETTER
Los Angeles County Public Library
6518 Miles Ave. • Huntington Park, CA 90255

AMERICAN INDIAN SERVICES DIRECTORY
NAES College Press, 2838 W. Peterson • Chicago, IL 60659-3813
(312) 761-5000; Ronald Bowan, Editor; Florence Dunham, Publisher

AMERICAN INDIAN SOCIETY NEWSLETTER
American Indian Society of Washington, DC
22258 Cool Water Dr. • Ruther Glen, VA 22546
(804) 448-3707 Fax 448-2493; Website: www.aisdc.org
Mitchell Bush, Editor
Community newsletter that reports on Indian life in Washington, DC metro area. It features a calendar of coming events of interest to local Indians. Monthly. 650 cir. $17/year. Accepts material for review. Begun 1966.

AMERICAN INDIAN STUDIES NEWSLETTER
University of Minnesota, Dept. of American Indian Studies
102 Scott Hall, 72 Pleasant St. SE • Minneapolis, MN 55455

AMERICAN JOURNAL OF ARCHAEOLOGY
Archaeological Institute of America
675 Commonwealth Ave. • Boston, MA 02215
(617) 353-9361. Quarterly. Professional archaeological journal with book reviews on New World archaeology.

AMERICAN NATIVE PRESS
American Indian & Alaska Native Newspapers & Periodicals Resources
2801 S. University • Little Rock, AR 72204
(501) 569-3160; Dan Littlefield, Editor
Native American book reviews. Quarterly newsletter. Cir: 1,100. Began 1983.

AMERICAN WEST
Buffalo Bill Memorial Association
Buffalo Bill Historical Center, P.O. Box 1000 • Cody, WY 82414
(307) 587-4771; Published six times per year.

AMERICANS BEFORE COLUMBUS
National Indian Youth Council, 318 Elm St., SE • Albuquerque, NM 87102
(505) 247-2251 Fax 247-4251; Sherry Robinson
Covers tribal rights & values through education & litigation. Bimonthly newsletter. Free to members; $20/year to non-members.

AN-CHI-MO-WIN
Rocky Boys Reservation, Chippewa Cree Tribe • Box Elder, MT 59521

ANISHINAABE NEWS
Native American Studies Program, UW-College of Letters & Sciences
P.O. Box 413 • Milwaukee, WI 53201

ANISHINAABEG MOM-WEH NEWSLETTER
220 N. 30th St. • Escanaba, MI 49829 (906) 786-0556 Fax 786-8108

ANISHINAABEG TODAY
White Earth Reservation Tribe, P.O. Box 418 • White Earth, MN 56591
(218) 983-3285 Norma L. Felty, Editor; Website: www.whiteearth.com

THE APACHE SCOUT
Mescalero Apache Tribe, P.O. Box 227 • Mescalero, NM 88340
Website: www.ws.apache.org/scout/

ARCHAEOLOGICAL CONSERVANCY NEWSLETTER
415 Orchard Dr. • Santa Fe, NM 87501 (505) 982-3278

ARCHAEOLOGY MAGAZINE
36-36 33rd St. • Long Island City, NY 11106
 (718) 472-3050 Fax 472-3051; E-mail: editorial@archaeology.org
 Claudia Valentino, Editor-in-Chief; E-mail: cvalentino@archaeology.org
Provides consistent treatment of the archaeology of North and South American Indians; book reviews on the art and archaeology of the Americas. Bimonthly by the Archaeological Institute of America. Subscription, $20/year; $26, foreign; $3.95 each issue. Subscriptions: Box 50260, Boulder, CO 80321. Advertising.

ARIZONA TRIBAL DIRECTORY
Arizona Commission on Indian Affairs
1400 W. Washington St. #300 • Phoenix, AZ 85007
 (602) 542-3123 Fax 542-3223; Diane C. Dankerl, Editor
 Eleanor Descheeny-Joe, Executive Director
Indian tribes & associations, government agencies & other organizations concerned with Indian affairs in Arizona. Annual.

ARROW
Labre Indian School
P.O. Box 406 • Ashland, MT 59003 (406) 784-2347

ARROW NEWS
Mandaree Day School , P.O. Box 488 • Mandaree, ND 58757
 (701) 759-3311

ARTIFACTS
The Institute for American Indian Studies
38 Curtis Rd., P.O. Box 1260 • Washington Green, CT 06793
 (203) 868-0518 Alberto C. Meloni, Director. Quarterly membership magazine.

ARTWINDS
Institute of American Indian Arts, 83 Avan Nu Po Rd. • Santa Fe, NM 87508
 (800) 804-6422; (505) 424-2300 Fax 424-4500
 Website: www.iaiancad.org; Quarterly.

ASSOCIATION OF AMERICAN INDIAN PHYSICIANS -- NEWSLETTER
1235 Sovereign Row #C-7 • Oklahoma City, OK 73108
 (405) 946-7072; Website: www.aaip.org
 Margaret Knight, Executive Director; Quarterly.

ASSOCIATION OF CONTRACT TRIBAL SCHOOLS (ACTS) NEWSLETTER
c/o St. Francis Indian School, P.O. Box 379 • St. Francis, SD 57572
 (605) 747-2296; Monthly.

ATOKA INDIAN CITIZEN
P.O. Box 160 • Atoka, OK 74525

AU-AUTHM ACTION NEWS
Salt River Pima-Maricopa Indian Community
10005 E. Osborn • Scottsdale, AZ 85256
 (480) 850-8089 Fax 850-8064
 Website: www.srpmic-nsn.gov/community/auathm
 Dodie Manuel, Editor; E-mail: dodie.manuel@srpmic-nsn.gov
Monthly tribal newspaper. Adveritisng. $31 per year.

B

BAH-KHO-JE JOURNAL
Iowa Tribe of Oklahoma, Rt. 1, Box 721 • Perkins, OK 74059
 (405) 547-2402 Fax 547-5294; Website: www.iowanation.org/newsletter.html
 E-mail: newsletter@iowanation.org. Tribal newsletter published 6x per year.

BAY MILLS NEWS
Bay Mills Indian Community of Michigan
12140 W. Lakeshore Dr. • Brimley, MI 49715
 (906) 248-3241 Fax 248-3283/5492; Website: www.baymillsnews.com
 E-mail: newspaper@baymills.org; Shannon Jones, Editor
 Kalvin Perron, Associate Editor; E-mail: kalvin@bmic.net
Bi-weekly newspaper for the Bay Mills Indian Community and the Eastern Upper Peninsula. Subscription: $25/year; $20, seniors.

BERING STRAITS AGLUKTUK
Bering Straits Native Corporation, P.O. Box 1008 • Nome, AK 99762

BIG HORN COUNTY NEWS
Crow Reservation, P.O. Box 400 • Crow Agency, MT 59022
 (406) 638-2601 Fax 638-2380; Website: www.bighorncountynews.com

BILLINGS INDIAN NEWSLETTER
Billings American Indian Council
208 N. 29th St. #228 • Billings, MT 59101 (406) 248-3343

BISHINIK TRIBAL NEWSPAPER
Choctaw Nation of Oklahoma
16th & Locust, P.O. Box 1210 • Durant, OK 74702
 (800) 522-6170; Fax (580) 924-4148; Lisa Reed, Editor
 E-mail: bishinik@choctawnation.com; E-mail: lisareed@choctawnation.com
Monthly tribal newspaper.

BIZHII
Cibecue Community School, P.O. Box 80068 • Cibecue, AZ 85911
 (520) 332-2480. Student magazine. Published four times per year.

BLACKFEET TRIBAL NEWS
Blackfeet Media, P.O. Box 850 • Browning, MT 59417

BOIS FORTE NEWS
1101 Sibley Memorial Hwy. #507 • Lilydale, MN 55118
 (651) 260-2420 Fax 365-1349; Website: www.boisforte.com/news.htm
 Helen Wilkie, Editor; E-mail: helenwilkie@comcast.net
Monthly tribal newspaper distributed free to enrolled Band members over the age of 18. Also available by subscription: $10 per year. Past issues are available online in PDF format at no charge.

BOSTON INDIAN CENTER NEWSLETTER
105 S. Huntington Ave. • Jamaica Plain, MA 02130
 (617) 232-0343

BTIR TRIBAL NEWSLETTER
Burns Paiute Reservation, HC 71, 100 Pa Si Go St. • Burns, OR 97720

BUREAU OF CATHOLIC INDIAN MISSIONS NEWSLETTER
2021 H St., NW • Washington, DC 20006
 (202) 331-8542 Fax 331-8544
Covers news and concerns of the Bureau, especially those issues pertaining to the Catholic Church and the Indian community. Updates on legislation affecting the Indian community. 10x/yr. No charge. Begun 1977.

BUREAU OF INDIAN AFFAIRS RESEARCH BULLETIN
Indian Education Center, P.O. Box 26567 • Albuquerque, NM 87125

BUREAU OF INDIAN AFFAIRS TRIBAL NEWSLETTER
Phoenix Area Office, Box 10, 1 N. 1st St. • Phoenix, AZ 85001

C

THE CABAZON CIRCLE
Cabazon Band of Mission Indians, 84-245 Indio Springs Dr. • Indio, CA 92203
 (760) 342-2593 Fax 347-7880; Tribal newsletter.

CAHOKIAN (Newsletter)
Cahokia Mounds Museum Society, Publisher
30 Ramey St. • Collinsville, IL 62234
 (618) 344-7316; Chris Pallozola, Editor

CALIFORNIA INDIAN BASKETWEAVERS ASSOCIATION NEWSLETTER
16894 China Flats Rd. • Nevada City, CA 95959
 (916) 292-0141 E-mail: ciba@oro.net; Quarterly.

CALIFORNIA NATIONS INDIAN GAMING INTERNET NEWSLETTER
Website: www.pechanga.net

CAMP CRIER
Fort Belknap Agency, RR 1, Box 66 • Halem, MT 59526

CANKU OTA (MANY PATHS)
Website: www.cankuota.com; Vicki Lockard, Editor; Paul Barry, Webmaster
Online newsletter, e-zine for & about Native America, celebrates the traditions & cultures of Native Americans, Alaskan Natives, and First Nations People. Each biweekly issue contains articles about events & issues contributed by some premier writers & artists. Also stories, recipes, opportunities, school news, projects. Resource pages offer links to Native websites and other websites of interest to students, educators and the general public.

CAROLINA INDIAN VOICE
P.O. Box 1075, College Plaza • Pembroke, NC 28372
 (919) 521-2826 Connie Brayboy, Editor

Community newspaper to give Indians in North Carolina (and other minorities) a united voice to be heard from coast to coast. Weekly. $12/year in NC; $15/year, elsewhere. Advertising. Begun 1973.

CASINO CRIME DIGEST
The Falmouth Institute, 3702 Pender Dr., #300 • Fairfax, VA 22030
  (800) 992-4489; (703) 352-2250 Fax 352-2323; Linda Clark, Editor
  Website: www.falmouthinst.com; E-mail: lclark@falmouthinst.com
Monthly newsletter summarizing news relevant to the casino industry. Contains reports from casinos of the latest cheats, scams, security breaches and legal issues that impact casinos. $129/year.

CATCHING THE DREAM NEWSLETTER
8200 Mountain Rd. NE Suite 203 • Albuquerque, NM 87110
  (505) 262-2351; Dr. Dean Chavers, Editor
Triannual; includes updates on federal legislation & association activities. Price is membership dues. Advertising. Begun 1988.

CENTER FOR INDIAN EDUCATION NEWSLETTER
302 Farmer Education Bldg., Rm. 302
Arizona State University • Tempe, AZ 85287

CHAR-KOOSTA NEWS
Confederated Salish & Kootenai Tribes
P.O. Box 98 • Pablo, MT 59855 (406) 275-2830 Fax 275-2831
  Website: www.charkoosta.com; E-mail: charkoosta@cskt.org
  Kim Swaney, Editor/Publisher; Sam Sandoval, Assistant Editor
Weekly newspaper featuring news of interest to Native Americans focusing on members of the Confederated Salish & Kootenai Tribes of the Flathead Indian Reservation, MT & reservation residents. Book reviews. 4,000 circ. $18/year, local; $20/year, in state; $25/year, out-of-state; $45/year, foreign. Advertising. Begun 1957.

CHATICKS SI CHATICKS
Pawnee Nation of Oklahoma, P.O. Box 470 • Pawnee, OK 74058
  (918) 762-3621 Fax 762-6446; Website: www.pawneenation.org
  Dawna Hare, Editor; Quarterly tribal newspaper.

CHEHALIS TRIBAL NEWSLETTER
420 Howanut Rd. • Oakvilke, WA 98568
  (360) 273-5911 Fax 273-5914; Fred Shortman, Editor
Website: www.chehalistribe.org/docs/newsletters
E-mail: newsletter@chehalistribe.org

CHEMAWA AMERICAN
Chemawa Indian School, 5495 Chugach St., NE • Chemawa, OR 97303

CHEMAWA CHATTER
Indian Health Service, Chemawa Indian Health Center
3750 Chemawa Rd. NE • Salem, OR 97305 (503) 399-5931

CHEROKEE ADVOCATE
Cherokee Nation Communications Dept.
P.O. Box 948 • Tahlequah, OK 74465-0948
  (918) 456-0671 Fax 458-5580
  Website: www.cherokee.org
  Lynn Adair, News Bureau Manager & Editor; E-mail: lyadair@cherokee.org
Tribal newspaper contains information on programs, services, etc. regarding & tribal government of the Cherokee Nation. Book reviews. Monthly newspaper. 90,000 circ. $12.50/year in-state, and $15/year out. Advertising. Begun 1977.

THE CHEROKEE E-NEWSLETTER
Eastern Band of Cherokee Indians, P.O. Box 460 • Cherokee, NC 28719
  (800) 438-1601 Fax (828) 497-2505
  Website: www.cherokee-nc.com/newsletter

CHEROKEE OBSERVER
P.O. Box 487 • Blackwell, OK 74631-0487 (580) 363-5438
  Website: www.cherokeeobserver.org
  E-mail: cwyob@cherokeewoods.com
Cherokee Nation online, independent newspaper.

CHEROKEE ONE FEATHER
Eastern Band of Cherokee Indians
P.O. Box 501 • Cherokee, NC 28719-0501
  (828) 497-1751 Fax 497-1753
  Website: www.cherokeeonefeather.ypgs.net
  Richard Welch, Editor
Provides information on tribal policies and news. Book reviews. Weekly tabloid. 2,000 circ. $20/yr. Advertising. Began 1966.

CHEROKEE PHOENIX
Cherokee Nation of Oklahoma, P.O. Box 948 • Tahlequah, OK 74465
  (918) 453-5269 Fax 207-0049; Website: www.cherokeephoenix.org
  Mark Dreadfulwater, Multimedia Editor
  E-mail: mark-dreadfulwater@cherokee.org
  Will Chavez, Reporter (207-3961); E-mail: will-chavez@cherokee.org
Monthly tribal newsletter. *Subscription*: $12/year, $22/two years, $28/three years. Weekly digital newsletter.

CHEYENNE & ARAPAHO TRIBAL TRIBUNE
Cheyenne & Arapaho Tribes, 700 N. Black Kettle Blvd.
P.O. Box 38 • Concho, OK 73022
  (800) 247-4612; (405) 422-7608 Fax 422-1184
  Website: www.c-a-tribes.org/tribes.org
  Dana Attocknie, Editor; E-mail: dattocknie@c-a-tribes.org
Monthly tribal newsletter.

CHEYENNE RIVER AGENCY NEWS BULLETIN
Eagle Butte, SD 57625

CHICAGO'S NATIVE AMERICAN URBAN INDIAN RETREAT
1630 W. Wilson Ave. • Chicago, IL 60640
  (773) 275-5871; Vincent Romero, Interim Executive Director
Quarterly newsletter of the organization.

CHICKASAW TIMES
Chickasaw Nation Tribal Government
P.O. Box 1548 • Ada, OK 74821-1548
  (580) 332-2977 Fax 332-3949; Tom Bolitho, Editor/Publisher
  Website: www.chickasawtimes.net; E-mail: times.chickasaw@chickasaw.net
Monthly newspaper containing information on judicial news, legislative news and news of & for the Chickasaw people, including tribal operations, procedures, and services. Book reviews. 8,500 cir. Begun 1970.

CHOCTAW COMMUNITY NEWS
Mississippi Band of Choctaw Indians
Box 6010-Choctaw Branch • Philadelphia, MS 39350
  (601) 656-5251 Julie Kelsey, Editor
Monthly tribal newspaper containing articles; primarily concerned with local events that involve Mississippi Choctaws. Book reviews. 5,000 circulation. Limited advertising. Free subscription, donations accepted. Begun 1970.

CHOCTAW PRODUCTIONS & CABLE PROGRAMMING
Mississippi Band of Choctaw Indians (601) 656-5251
Rt. 7, Box 21 • Philadelphia, MS 39350-9807

THE CIRCLE
Boston Indian Council, 105 S. Huntington Ave. • Jamaica Plain, MA 02130
  (617) 232-0343; Helen Blue, Editor
Monthly newspaper containing information on urban Indians, particularly in the Boston area, as well as significant events involving Native peoples in New England & throughout the U.S. and Canada. Book reviews. 5,000 circ. $10/yr. Advertising. Begun 1976.

THE CIRCLE NEWS
The Circle Corp., P.O. Box 6026 • Minneapolis, MN 55406
  (612) 722-3686 Fax 722-3773; Website: www.thecirclenews.org
  E-mail: thecirclenews@gmail.com; Catherine Whipple, Managing Editor
Monthly tabloid size newspaper covering the news and events of the Native Americans in Minnesota. Includes reviews of books, movies, arts, etc. 15,000 circ. Subscription: $37/year; $70/two years. Advertising accepted. Begun 1979.

COCOPAH NEWSLETTER
P.O. Box G • Somerton, AZ 85350 (520) 627-2102

COEUR D'ALENE COUNCIL FIRES
Coeur D'Alene Tribe, P.O. Box 408 • Plummer, ID 83851
  (208) 686-0154 Fax 686-1182; Website: cdatribe-nsn.gov/cf
  E-mail: jfletcher@cdatribe-nsn.gov; Jennifer L. Fletcher, Editor
Tribal newspaper.

COKV TVLVME
Seminole Nation of Oklahoma, P.O. Box 1498 • Wewoka, OK 74884
  (405) 257-7283 Fax 257-7209; E-mail: news@seminolenation.com
  Jennifer Johnson, Editor
Official monthly newspaper of the Seminole Nation of Oklahoma.

COLORADO HISTORY NEWS
Ute Indian Museum, Ouray Memorial Park
P.O. Box 1736 • Montrose, CO 81402
  Glen Gross, Editor

THE COLUMNS
Cherokee National Historical Society, P.O. Box 515 • Tahlequah, OK 74465
 (918) 456-6007 Fax 456-6165; Tom Mooney, Editor; Quarterly newsletter.
 Website: www.powersource.com/powersource/heritage

COMANCHE NATION NEWS
Comanche Tribe of Oklahoma, P.O. Box 908 • Lawton, OK 73502
 Website: www.comanchenation.com; Jolene Schonchin, Editor
 E-mail: jolenes@comanchenation.com; Tribal newspaper.

THE COMMUNICATOR
Migizi Communications, Inc.
3123 E. Lake St., Suite 200 • Minneapolis, MN 55406
 (612) 721-6631 Fax 721-3936; Laura Wittstock, Director

COMMUNIQUE
Order of the Indian Wars (OIW)
P.O. Box 1650 • Johnstown, CO 80534 (970) 226-5549
 Website: www.indianwars.com; Monthly newsletter.

COMMUNITY BULLETIN
American Indian Community House
134 W. 29th St., 4th Fl. • New York, NY 10001
 (212) 598-0100 Fax 598-4909; Website: www.aich.org
 Carrese P. Gullo, Editors
Quarterly newsletter. Reports on activities of the organization, which serves the need of Native Americans residing in the New York metropolitan area. News and reviews of interest to Native Americans. Circulation: 12,000+. Price: Donations accepted.

CONFEDERATED INDIAN TRIBES
Washington State Penitentiary, P.O. Box 520 • Walla Walla, WA 99362

CONFEDERATED TRIBES OF COOS, LOWER UMPQUA & SIUSLAW INDIANS - TRIBAL NEWSLETTER
338 Wallace Ave. • Coos Bay, OR 97420 (503) 267-5454; Monthly.

CONFEDERATED UMATILLA JOURNAL
P.O. Box 638 • Pendleton, OR 97801
 (541) 966-2033/4/5 Fax 966-2043
 Website: www.umatilla.nsn.us/news
 E-mail: cuj@ctuir.com; Debra Croswell, Publisher
 Wil Phinney, Editor; Tara Burnside, Reporter
Monthly tribal newspaper.

COQUILLE INDIAN TRIBE "TRIBAL TIDBITS"
3050 Tremont Blvd. • North Bend, OR 97459
 (541) 756-0904 Fax 756-0847; Website: www.cooquilletribe.org
 E-Mail: cit@coquilletribe.org; Tribal monthly newsletter.

COUNCIL DRUM NEWS
Grand Valley American Indian Lodge
2512 Union Ave. NE • Grand Rapids, MI 49505
 (616) 361-5380. Monthly newsletter.

COUNCIL FIRES
Coeur D'Alene Tribal Council, Plummer, ID 83851

COUNCIL OF ENERGY RESOURCE TRIBES (CERT) REPORT
695 S. Colorado Blvd., Suite 10 • Denver, CO 80246
 (303) 282-7576 Fax 282-7584; A. David Lester, President

COUNCIL SIGNALS
Montana Department of Indian Affairs
1218 E. 6th Ave. • Helena, MT 59620

COYOTE ON THE TURTLE'S BACK
Institute of American Indian Arts, College of Santa Fe Campus
83 Avan Nu Po Rd. • Santa Fe, NM 87503 (505) 988-6463
Published annually.

CRAZY HORSE PROGRESS
Crazy Horse Memorial Foundation
Avenue of the Chiefs--The Black Hills • Crazy Horse, SD 57730
 (605) 673-4681; Website: www.crazyhorse.org/news/shtml
 Robb DeWall, Editor; Published 3x/year. No charge.

CREEK NATION NEWS
Creek Nation of Oklahoma, P.O. Box 580 • Okmulgee, OK 74447
 (918) 732-7637 Fax 758-0824;
 Website: www.muscogeenation-nsn.gov/communications/mnnarchives.htm

CRIT NEWSLETTER
Colorado River Indian Tribes, Rte. 1, Box 23-B • Parker, AZ 85344
 (480) 669-9211 Fax 669-5675; Quarterly tribal newsletter.

CROSS & FEATHERS
Tekakwitha Conference National Center
P.O. Box 6768 • Great Falls, MT 59406
 (406) 727-0147 Fax 452-9845; Website: www.tekconf.org
 E-mail: tekconf@att.net; Sister Kateri Mitchell, Executive Director
Staff: Wilson Boni, Billie Jo Moore, Terri Jarvey, and Christine Collins.
Description: Newsletter containing articles addressing religious, social, and legislative issues concerning Native American Catholics or people involved with the blessed Kateri Tekakwitha (a Mohawk who lived from 1656 to 1680, and who is now a Saint in the Roman Catholic Church.) Reports on workshops, conferences & meetings. $12, membership. Begun 1979.

CROWNDANCER
San Carlos Apache Tribe, P.O. Box 0 • San Carlos, AZ 85550

CRY OF THE CRANE
Miami Nation of Indians of Indiana, P.O. Box 41 • Peru, IN 46970
 (800) 253-3578; (765) 473-9631 Fax 472-4162
 Website: www.miamiindians.org; Quarterly tribal newsletter.

CULTURAL SURVIVAL QUARTERLY
Cultural Survival, Inc., 215 Prospect St. • Cambridge, MA 02139
 (617) 441-5400 Fax 441-5417; Website: www.cs.org
 E-mail: culturalsurvival@cs.org
 Tara Tidwell Cullen, Editor; E-mail: ttidwell@cs.org
World report on the input, voices and visions of indigenous peoples. Includes news, resources, and general-interest articles. Subscription: $45 per year, individuals; $60, institutions; $5/issue. Circulation: 20,000 copies. Begun 1972.

CURTIS (CARL T.) HEALTH CENTER NEWS
Omaha Indian Reservation, P.O. Box 368 • Macy, NE 68039

CUSTER BATTLEFIELD NATIONAL MONUMENT NEWSLETTER
P.O. Box 39 • Crow Agency, MT 59022
(406) 638-2622. Published quarterly.

D

DAKOTA JOURNAL
Lakota Media, Inc. (owned by Flandreau Santee Sioux Tribe)
P.O. Box 31, Flandreau, SD 57703 (605) 573-2684 Fax 573-2685
 Marty Two Bulls, Owner; Nestor Ramos, Editor
 E-mail: editor@dakotajournal.com
Published weekly. Covers nationwide & east river (SD) area, "Dakota" Sioux are primarily east river. Cir: 85,000. Subs.: $1/issue;

DAKOTA WOWAPIPHI
P.O. Box 157 • Marty, SD 57361

DARTMOUTH NATIVE ALUMNI NEWS
P.O. Box A-162 • Hanover, NH 03755

DAWN OF NATIONS TODAY
Native American Studies Department
University of New Mexico, Mesa Vista Hall 3080
MSC06 3740 • Albuquerque, NM 87131 (505) 277-9271
 E-mail: dawnofnationstoday@gmail.com
 Mary K. Bowannie (Zuni/Cochiti Pueblos), Sr. Managing Ed.

DAYBREAK STAR INDIAN READER
P.O. Box 99100 • Seattle, WA 98199
 (206) 285-4425 Fax 282-3640; Kathryn Onetta, Director
A 24-page, monthly (October through May) children's learning resource featuring culturally focused articles of interest to students in grades 4-6. Includes creative writing exercises, games & puzzles, legends, math & science activities, book and movie reviews. See publisher for multiple copy rates.

DELAWARE NEWSLETTER
P.O. Box 825 • Anadarko, OK 73005

DENVER NATIVE AMERICANS UNITED NEWSLETTER
4407 Morrison Rd. • Denver, CO 80219 (303) 937-0401

DESERT WIND
Lipan Apache Tribe of Texas, P.O. Box 261110 • Corpus Christi, TX 78426
 (361) 985-1381; Robert Soto, Editor; Tribal newsletter.

DINE BI KEYAH MAGAZINE
P.O. Box 580 • Window Rock, AZ 86515

DIRECTORY OF AMERICAN INDIAN BUSINESSES
National Center for American Indian Enterprise Development
953 E. Juanita Ave. • Mesa, AZ 85204
  (800) 462-2433; Fax (480) 545-4208; Ken Robbins, Editor

**DIRECTORY OF NATIVE AMERICANS IN
SPEECH-LANGUAGE PATHOLOGY & AUDIOLOGY**
American Indian Professional Training Program in Speech-Language
Pathology & Audiology - Dept. of Speech & Hearing Sciences
U. of Arizona • Tucson, AZ 85721 (520) 621-1969/1644
  Betty Nunnery, Program Coordinator

DISTANT DRUMS
Nevada Baptist Convention
150 South Hwy. 160, Suite C8 #173 • Pahrump, NV 89048
  (775) 340-5967; Robert D. Johnson, Native American Consultant
  E-mail: rdj89048@gmail.com; E-mail: rdj@bigfoot.com
A religious-oriented publication of the Nevada Baptist Convention.
Covers annual gathering of Nevada's Native American Christians.

THE DRAGONFLY
Two Rivers Gallery-Minneapolis American Indian Center
1530 E. Franklin Ave. • Minneapolis, MN 55404
  Sammy Watso & Mason Riddle, Directors
A cultural arts department newsletter.

DREAM CATCHER QUARTERLY
HUD Northwest Office of Native American Programs
909-1st Ave., Suite 300 • Seattle, WA 98104
  (206) 220-5273 E-mail: jan_engle@hud.gov
  Website: www.codetalk.fed.us/dremcach.html

DRUM BEAT
Native American Rehabilitation Association (NARA) of the Northwest
17645 NW St. Helens Hwy.• Portland, OR 97231
  Website: www.naranorthwest.org; E-mail: info@naranorthwest.org
  (503) 224-1044 Fax 621-0200; Quarterly newsletter.

THE DRUMBEAT
Confederated Tribes of Siletz-Salem Area Office
3789 River Rd. N. Suite D • Keizer, OR 97303
  (503) 390-9494; Monthly newsletter.

DSUQ' WUB' SIATSUB
Suquamish Tribe, P.O. Box 498 • Suquamish, WA 98392

DUCK VALLEY ROUNDUP
P.O. Box 219 • Owynee, NV 89832

DWOQ'WUB'STATSUB
Suquamish Tribe, P.O. Box 498 • Suquamish, WA 98392-0498

E

E'YANAPAHA
Devil's Lake Sioux Tribe, Public Information Office • Fort Totten, ND 58335

THE EAGLE
P.O. Box 2372 • Marysville, CA 95901 (916) 633-4038
Bimonthly. Published by the Cherokees of California.

EAGLE BUTTE NEWS
P.O. Box 210 • Eagle Butte, SD 57625

EAGLE FREE PRESS
Phoenix Indian Center, Inc.
333 W. Indian School Rd. • Phoenix, AZ 85013-3215
  (602) 256-2000

THE EAGLE WHISTLE
North American Indian Center of Boston
105 S. Huntington Ave. • Jamaica Plain, MA 02130
  (617) 232-0343 Fax 232-3863
Bi-monthly newsletter containing information relevant both to Native Americans
living in the New England area and throughout the U.S. and Canada. Powwow
listings.

EAGLE'S EYE
Brigham Young University
Multicultural Student Services, 1320 WSC • Provo, UT 84602
  Harold D. Nez, Editor; E-mail: eagleseye@byu.edu
  Website: www.byu.edu/stlife/campus-life/multi/eagle.html
Magazine published each semester for Native American and other mutlicultural
students at BYU. Book reviews. 3,500 circ. Free upon request. Begun 1967.

EAGLE'S NEST
Native American Fish & Wildlife Society
750 Burbank St. • Broomfield, CO 80020
  (303) 466-1725 Fax 466-5414; Ken Poynter, Executive Director
  E-Mail: nafws@usa.net; Newsletter.

EAGLE'S VOICE
Sinte Gleska College, Box 8 • Mission, SD 57555 (605) 856-2321
Contains literature on Native American experiences
on the High Plains. Text also in Lakota. Begun 1975.

EARTH WALK
Council for Native American Indian Progress
280 Broadway, #316 • New York, NY 10007
  (212) 732-0485; Newsletter.

EARTHSONG
The Heard Museum, 2301 N. Central Ave. • Phoenix, AZ 85004
  (602) 252-8840 Fax 252-9757; Rebecca Murray, Editor
  Website: www.heard.org
Newsletter targeted at Museum members. Content includes articles on
upcoming exhibitions and events, as well as behind-the-scenes features
on museum happenings. Published five times a year.

ECH-KA-NAV-CHA NEWSLETTER
Fort Mojave Indian Tribe, 500 Merriman Ave. • Needles, CA 92363
  (619) 326-4810

ECHO–TOWAOC COMMUNITY NEWSPAPER
Ute Mountain Ute Tribe • Towaoc, CO 81334 (970) 565-3751

EL PALACIO
Museum of New Mexico, Box 2087 • Santa Fe, NM 87504-2087
  (505) 827-6794; Karen Meadows, Editor
Articles on anthropology, archaeology, fine arts, folk arts, Southwest history
and geography. Book reivews. Triannual magazine. 3,000 circulation. $6/copy;
$18/year. Begun 1913.

ELDER VISIONS
National Indian Council on Aging
10501 Montgomery Blvd. NE #210 • Albuquerque, NM 87111-3846
  (505) 292-2001 Fax 292-1922; Larry Curley, Editor
  Website: www.nicoa.org/publications/elder-visions
Covers issues affecting Native American elders, including services and
related legislative issues. Published periodically. Begun 1977.

ELKO COMMUNITY NEWS
Nevada Intertribal Council, 806 Holman Way • Sparks, NV 89431
  (702) 355-0600

ETHNIC REPORTER
National Association for Ethnic Studies
Dept. of English, Arizona State University • Tempe, AZ 85287-0001
  (480) 965-3391 Fax 965-1093; Gretchen Bataille, Editor
Covers NAES activities. Semiannual newsletter. $35/year, individuals;
$45/year, institutions; $5/copy. Advertising.

**ETHNOARCHAEOLOGY: JOURNAL OF ARCHAEOLOGICAL,
ETHNOGRAPHIC, AND EXPERIMENTAL STUDIES**
Left Coast Press, Inc., 1630 N. Main St. #400 • Walnut Creek, CA 94596
  (925) 935-3380 (phone & fax); Website: www.lcoastpress.com
  E-mail: explore@lcoastpress.com
Focuses on ethno-archaeological & experimental approaches to
anthropological research. Semiannual, April & October. 256 pages
Subscription: $42 per year, individuals; $149, paper & $249, electronic for
institutions.

ETHNOHISTORY
American Society for Ethnohistory, Duke University Press • Durham, NC 27708
  (919) 688-5134 Fax (888) 651-0124; Website: www.duke.edu/web/dupress/
  Shepard Krech, III, Editor; Studies of native peoples in the Americas and
throughout the world. Quarterly journal. 1,200 cir. $34/year, institutions; $21,
individuals. Begun 1953.

EYAPAHA
American Indian Center Newsletter
4115 Connecticut • St. Louis, MO 63116 (314) 773-3316

EYAPIOAYE
Assiniboine & Sioux Tribes, P.O. Box 1027 • Poplar, MT 59255

F

FAIRBANKS NATIVE ASSOCIATION NEWSLETTER
201 First Ave. • Fairbanks, AK 99701 (907) 452-1648
 Monthly newsletter.

FAMILY SERVICES NEWSLETTER
Family Services Program, Toiyabe Indian Health Project
P.O. Box 1296 • Bishop, CA 93515
 (760) 873-6394 Fax 873-3935
Focuses on concerns of Indian families, such as drugs and alcohol, child
abuse & neglect, and women's concerns. Quarterly. No charge. Begun 1980.

FEATHER REVIEW
P.O. Box 149 • Mountain View, OK 73062 (405) 347-2875
 Deborah Ahtone, Editor/Publisher
Monthly statewide Indian & government agencies newspaper. $15/year.

FIRST NATIONS BUSINESS ALERT
First Nations Development Institute
The Stores Bldg., 11917 Main St. • Fredericksburg, VA 22408
 (540) 371-5615 Fax 371-3505; Website: www.firstnations.org
Quarterly newsletter providing business news about and of interest
to tribes. No charge to tribes; $12/year, others. Advertising.

FIVE CIVILIZED TRIBES MUSEUM NEWSLETTER
Agency Hill on Honor Heights, Muskogee, OK 74401 (918) 683-1701

FLAGSTAFF INDIAN CENTER NEWSLETTER
2717 N. Steves Blvd. #11 • Flagstaff, AZ 86004

FLANDREAU SANTEE SIOUX TRIBAL NEWSLETTER
P.O. Box 283 • Flandreau, SD 57028
 (800) 922-0016; (605) 997-3891 Fax 997-3878
 Website: www.fsst.org/newsltr.htm
 Carol Robertson, Editor; E-mail: carol.robertson@fsst.org
Published monthly. Covers tribal activities and related events.

FLANDREAU SPIRIT
Flandreau Indian High School • Flandreau, SD 57028

THE FLOWERING TREE NEWSLETTER
Good Medicine Band (Free Cherokees), HC 62 Box 378 • Old Joe, AR 72658
 (501) 499-8083; Quarterly.

FOCUS: INDIAN EDUCATION
Minnesota Dept. of Education, Capitol Square Bldg. • St. Paul, MN 55101

FOND DU LAC NEWS
105 University Dr. • Cloquet, MN 55720

FORT APACHE SCOUT
White Mountain Apache Tribe, P.O. Box 890 • Whiteriver, AZ 85941
 (928) 338-4813 Fax 338-1894; Kathy Antonio, Office Manager
Biweekly newspaper covering news of the tribe and its people. 2,800 cir.
$12/year to reservation residents; $16 in Arizona off-reservation; $22, outside
Arizona. Advertising. Begun 1962.

FORT BELKNAP NEWS
Fort Belknap Community, RR 1, Box 66 • Harlem, MT 59526
 (406) 353-8475 Fax 353-2797
 Website: www.fortbelknapnations-nsn.gov/fbnews.php
 E-mail: fortbelknapnews@netscape.net

FORT BERTHOLD COMMUNITY ENTERPRISE
P.O. Box 699 • New Town, ND 58763

FORT McDOWELL NEWSLETTER
Southwestern Marketing, P.O. Box 18244 • Fountain Hills, AZ 85269
 (480) 837-4282 Fax 837-7750; E-mail: swmarke@aol.com

FOUNDATION FOR INDIAN LEADERSHIP NEWSLETTER
P.O. Box 5335 • Santa Fe, NM 87502 (505) 988-6291

FOUR DIRECTIONS
3315 University Dr. • Bismarck, ND 58763 (701) 255-3285

THE FOUR DIRECTIONS: AMERICAN INDIAN LITERARY MAGAZINE
Snowbird Publishing Co., P.O. Box 729 • Tellico Plains, TN 37385
 (423) 253-3680; Joanna & William Meyer, Editors
Contains all-Native American authored poetry, short stories, essays & articles.
Reviews. Published irregularly. $6/issue. Begun 1992.

FOUR WINDS
Hundred Arrows Press, P.O. Box 156 • Austin, TX 78767
 (512) 472-8877/956-7048; Quarterly magazine focusing
on Native American art, literature and history. $22/year.

FOUR WINDS NEWSLETTER
Confederated Indian Tribes Washington State Penitentiary
P.O. Box 520 • Walla Walla, WA 99362

THE FREE CHEROKEE NEWSLETTER
Wild Potato Band of Free Cherokees of Mass.
P.O. Box 385 • Feeding Hill, MA 01030
 (413) 785-5912. Chief Rainbow Newmoon Shootingstar

G

GAH'NAVAH / YA TI' NEWSPAPER
Yavapai-Apache Nation, Office of Public Relations
2400 W. Datsi • Camp Verde, AZ 86322
 (928) 567-1071 Fax 567-1082; Website: www.yavapai-apache.org
 E-mail: editor@yan-tribe.org; Trapper Moore, Editor
 Kim Secakuku, Public Relations Liaison; E-mail: ksecakuku@yan-tribe.org
Monthly newspaper covering news, special events, and community information
for tribal members and the general public.

GALLERY NOTES
The Indian Museum, Mid-America All Indian Center
650 North Seneca • Wichita, KS 67203; Quarterly newsletter.

GAMYU
Hualapai Tribe, P.O. Box 179 • Peach Springs, AZ 86434 (520) 769-2216

GIIKENDAAM CHIWIIKWEGAMAG
Keweenah Bay Indian Community, 16429 Beartown Rd. • Baraga, MI 49908
 (906) 353-6623 Fax 353-7540; Website: www.kbic-nsn.gov/newsletter
Tribal newsletter.

GILA RIVER INDIAN NEWS
P.O. Box 459 • Sacaton, AZ 85247
 (520) 562-9715/6/7/8 Fax 562-9712
 Website: www.grin.nsn.us; E-mail: grin@gric.nsn.us
 Mihio Manus, Editor; E-mail: mihio.manus@gric.nsn.us
 Jeri Thomas, Office Manager; E-mail: jeri.thomas@gric.nsn.us
 Arthur Felder, Treasurer; John Giff, Secretary. Monthly tribal newspaper.

GILCREASE JOURNAL
Thomas Gilcrease Museum Association
1400 Gilcrease Museum Rd. • Tulsa, OK 74127-2100
 (918) 596-2700 Fax 596-2770; Carol Haralson, Editor
 E-mail: gilcreas@ionet.net; Website: www.gilcrease.org
Features stories concerning art, artifacts, & archival materials of the Gilcrease
Museum. Includes photographic & artistic reproductions from the collections.
The collections emphasize the Old West & the American Indian. Semiannual.
4,500 cir. $50/year membership; $18/copy; $35/year for libraries. Begun 1958.

GLACIER REPORTER
Blackfeet Reservation, P.O. Box 349 • Browning, MT 59417
 (406) 338-2090 Fax 338-2410; John McGill, Editor
 Website: www.goldentrianglenews.com/glacier_reporter
Weekly newspaper. Cir. 2,215.

GRAND TRAVESE BAND (GTB) NEWS
Grand Traverse Band of Ottawa & Chippewa Indians
2605 N. W. Bayshore Dr. • Peshawbestown, MI 49682
 (231) 271-7366 Fax 271-7724; Website: www.gtbindians.com
 Dave Spinniken, Editor; E-mail: dave.spinniken@gtbindians.com
Monthly tribal newsletter. Cir. 2,800. Free to member households
in the tribe's service area; available $24/year to non-members.

GREAT LAKES INDIAN ARTISTS ASSOCIATION NEWSLETTER
14360 Woodbury Rd. • Haslett, MI 48840

GREAT PLAINS JOURNAL
Institute of the Great Plains, Museum of the Great Plains
P.O. Box 68 • Lawton, OK 73502
Contains articles concerning the history, archaeology, ecology or
natural history of ten-state Great Plains region. Published annually.

GREAT PLAINS QUARTERLY
Center for Great Plains Studies, University of Nebraska-Lincoln
1155 Q St., Hewitt Place, Box 880245 • Lincoln, NE 68588-0245
 (402) 472-6058 Fax 472-0463; Dr. Charles A. Braithwaite, Editor
 E-Mail: gpq@unl.edu; Website: www.unl.edu/plains
This scholarly, interdisciplinary journal publishes refereed articles about the
Great Plains region of the U.S. & Canada in the following disciplines: anthropology, ethnology, folklore, fine arts, geography, history, literature, political
science, sociology, & rhetoric. Book reviews. Subscription: Individuals: U.S. -
$25/year, $48/2 years; Canada - $34/year; $60/2 years; Overseas - $38/year,
$72/2 years. Institutions: U.S. $50/year, $90/2 years; Canada - $60/year,
$110/2 years; Overseas - $75/year, $130/2 years. $8 (issue). Begun 1981.

GREAT PLAINS RESEARCH
Center for Great Plains Studies, Univesity of Nebraska-Lincoln
1155 Q St., Hewitt Place, Box 880245 • Lincoln, NE 68588-0245
 (402) 472-6058 Fax 472-0463; Dr. Robert F. Diffendal, Jr., Editor
 E-Mail: gpq@unl.edu; Website: www.unl.edu/plains
This biannual multidisicplinary journal publishes refereed scholarly papers in
the natural and social sciences on issues of regional concern. Book reviews.
Advertising. Subscription: U.S. - $25/year, $45/2 years; Canada - $30/year,
$50/2 years; Overseas - $35/year, $55/2 years/ Institutions: $60/year, $110/2
years. $15, single issue. Begun 1991.

H

HANNAHVILLE HAPPENINGS
Hannahville Indian Community
N-14911 Hannahville B-1 Rd. • Wilson, MI 49896
 (906) 466-2270 Fax 466-2933; Website: www.hannahville.net
Bi-weekly tribal newsletter.

HARVARD INDIAN NEWSLETTER
Harvard University Native American Program
Cambridge, MA 02138 (617) 495-4923
 Website: www.hunap.harvard.edu/news_events
 Carmen Lopez, Executive Director; E-mail: carmen.lopez@harvard.edu

HASKELL INDIAN JUNIOR COLLEGE
LEARNING RESOURCE CENTER NEWSLETTER
P.O. Box H1305 • Lawrence, KS 66044

HEART OF AMERICA INDIAN CENTER NEWSLETTER
1340 E. Admiral Blvd. • Kansas City, MO 64124; (816) 421-7608

HELLO CHOCTAW
P.O. Box 59 • Durant, OK 74701

HOCAK WORAK
Ho-Chunk Tribal Office Bldg.
W9814 Airport Rd., P.O. Box 667 • Black River Falls, WI 54615
 (800) 472-3089; (715) 284-2388 Fax 284-7852
 Website: www.ho-chunknation.com; E-mail: tracy.pecore@ho-chunk.com
 Tracy Pecore, Editor; Bimonthly tribal newsletter.

HOPI TUTUVENI
P.O. Box 123 • Kykotsmovi, AZ 86039
 (928) 734-2441 ext. 190 Fax 734-6648
 E-mail: tutuveni@hopi.nsn.us. Bimonthly. $20 for six months; $35 per year.

HOW NI KAN
Citizen Band Potawatomi Tribe
1901 S. Gordon Cooper • Shawnee, OK 74801
 (405) 275-3121; Patricia Sulcer, Editor
Monthly tribal newsletter. Subscription: $6/year.

I

ICE (INDIAN CINEMA ENTERTAINMENT)
American Indian Film Institute
333 Valencia St., Suite 322 • San Francisco, CA 94103
 (415) 554-0525 Fax 554-0542; Quarterly. $25 per year.

IKHANA
Office of Native American Ministries, The Episcopal Church Center
815 Second Ave. • New York, NY 10017 (800) 334-7626
 Warren Anderson, Contact
The newsletter of American Indian/Alaska Native Ministry of the Episcopal
Church. Focuses on American Indian affairs. Informs readers of programs and
projects of the Committee & other groups affiliated with the Episcopal Church.
Quarterly. Free. Begun 1979.

IN HARMONY
Institute for the Study of Natural Systems
P.O. Box 637 • Mill Valley, CA 94942 (415) 383-5064
Semiannual newsletter including articles on the preservation of
Native American sacred sites. 8,000 cir. $15/year. Begun 1987.

INDEPENDENT AMERICAN INDIAN REVIEW
1840 E. Warner Rd., Suite A105, PMB 268 • Tempe, AZ 85284
 (480) 839-8355 Fax 839-8223; Website: worldviewsintl.com
 E-mail: wvi@worldviewsintl.com; Mimi McBride, Senior Editor
Publishes articles written about contemporary diverse American Indian nations,
and reviews of books, CDs, tapes, and other multi-media written from
American Indian perspectives. Published 3x per year, Winter/Spring, Summer
& Fall. Begun 1993.

INDEX TO REPRODUCTIONS IN ART PERIODICALS
Data Arts, P.O. Box 30789 • Seattle, WA 98103-0789
Quarterly index to reproductions in in art periodicals for American Indian arts,
African arts, arts of Asia, and art in America. $44/year. Begun 1987.

INDIAN AFFAIRS
Association on American Indian Affairs
966 Hungerford Dr., Suite 12-B • Rockville, MD 20850
 (240) 314-7155 Fax 314-7159; Jack F. Trope, Executive Director
 E-mail: general.aaia@verizon.net; Website: www.indian-affairs.org
Covers current news about and of interest to American Indians and to those
interested in Indian affairs. Published 3x a year with occasional special issues.
45,000 cir. $25/year. Begun 1949.

INDIAN AFFAIRS NEWSLETTER
Office of Indian Affairs, 1951 Constitution Ave., NW • Washington, DC 20245

INDIAN ARIZONA TODAY
IDDA, 4560 N. 19th Ave. #200 • Phoenix, AZ 85015-4113

INDIAN ARTIFACT MAGAZINE
Indian Artifact Magazine, Inc., RD #1, Box 240 • Turbotville, PA 17772-9599
 (717) 437-3698; Gary L. Fogelman, Editor
Concentrates on American Indian pre-history: artifacts, tools, lifestyles,
customs, archaeology, tribes, etc. Book reviews included. Published quarterly.
Advertising accepted. $17/year. Sample, $5. Begun 1982.

IACA NEWSLETTER
Indian Arts & Crafts Association
4010 Carlisle NE, Suite C • Albuquerque, NM 87108
 (505) 265-9149 Fax 265-8251; Helen Skredergard, Editor
Contains information on markets, meetings, new members, applications, and
other news of interest to those in the industry; helps in the education of
consumers. Advertising accepted from members only. Published monthly for
IACA members and a limited press list. Begun 1974.

INDIAN AWARENESS CENTER NEWSLETTER
Fulton County Historical Society, 37 E 375 N • Rochester, IN 46975
 (574) 223-4436; Shirley Willard, Editor
Covers projects and activities of the Center which encourages the awareness,
appreciation, & preservation of Native American culture & traditions, especially
that of the Potawatomi and Miami Indians of northern Indiana. Had Potawatomi
Trail of Death" declared a Regional Historic Trail by the state legislatures of
Indiana, Illinois, Missouri & Kansas. Quarterly. $10/year. Begun 1984.

INDIAN BUSINESS & MANAGEMENT MAGAZINE
National Center for American Indian Enterprise Development
953 E. Juanita • Mesa, AZ 85204
 (800) 462-2433; Fax (480) 545-4208
Quarterly.

INDIAN BUSINESS REVIEW
Native American Business Alliance
8435 SE 17th Ave. • Portland, OR 97202 (503) 233-4841
Covers programs & projects of the Alliance and its efforts to promote economic
development for all Indians. Quarterly. $10/year; free to members.

INDIAN COMMUNICATIONS
Dovecrest Indian Cultural Center, 390 Summit Rd. • Exeter, RI 02822
Monthly newsletter.

INDIAN COUNTRY NEWS
Muscogee Creek Nation of Oklahoma, P.O. Box 580 • Okmulgee, OK 74447
(800) 482-1979; (918) 756-8700

INDIAN COUNTRY TODAY
Four Directions Media, Inc., Corporate & Editorial Headquarters:
3059 Seneca Turnpike • Canastota, NY 13032
(888) 327-1013; (315) 829-8355 Fax 829-8028
Website: www.indiancountry.com; E-mail: editor@indiancountry.com
  Editorial Fax (315) 829-8393
Ray Halbritter, President & CEO; Peter Golia, COO
Tim Johnson, Executive Editor; Duane Champagne, Senior Editor
Ken Polisse, Jr., Managing Editor
Washington DC Bureau:
  400 N. Capitol St., NW, Suite 585 • Washington, DC 20001
  (202) 783-0212 Fax 393-5218
Description: A weekly newspaper serving 21 Indian reservations in North &
South Dakota, Nebraska & Montana. Washington, DC bureau, it also covers
the U.S. Capitol from an Indian perspective. 25,000 cir. (largest independent
Indian-owned weekly). $48/year, local; $83/year, Canada & Mexico; $227/year,
Overseas. Advertising. Began 1981.

INDIAN COUNTRY TODAY
P.O. Box 2180 • Rapid City, SD 57709
(605) 341-0011 Fax 341-6940

INDIAN COURTS
National American Indian Court Judges
1000 Connecticut Ave., NW, Suite 1206 • Washington, DC 20036
(202) 296-0685. Quarterly newsletter.

INDIAN CRUSADER
American Indian Liberation Crusade, Inc.
4009 S. Halldale Ave. • Los Angeles, CA 90062
(323) 299-1810; Basil M. Gaynor, Editors
Reports on programs to aid Indian reservations. Quarterly.
No charge (tax deductible donations accepted.) Begun 1954.

INDIAN EDUCATION
National Indian Education Association
700 N. Fairfax, Suite 210 • Alexandria, VA 22314
(703) 838-2870 Fax 838-1620; John W. Cheek, Executive Director
Robin Butterfield, President

INDIAN EDUCATION NEWS
Coos County Indian Education Coordination Program
9140 Cape Arago Hwy. • Coos Bay, OR 97420 (503) 888-4584

INDIAN EDUCATION NEWSLETTER
United Sioux Tribes of South Dakota, P.O. Box 1193 • Pierre, SD 57501

INDIAN EDUCATION UPDATE
National Indian Training & Research Center
2121 S. Mill Ave. #216 • Tempe, AZ 85282
(480) 967-9484; Quarterly newsletter.

**INDIAN, ESKIMO, ALEUT OWNED & OPERATED
ARTS BUSINESS SOURCE DIRECTORY**
Indian Arts & Crafts Board, Rm. 4004, U.S. Dept. of the Interior
Washington, DC 20240 (202) 208-3773. Published annually.

INDIAN EXTENSION NEWS
New Mexico State University, Box 3AP • Las Cruces, NM 88003

INDIAN FORERUNNER
Eight Northern Pueblos, P.O. Box 927 • San Juan Pueblo, NM 87566

INDIAN GAMING MAGAZINE
ArrowPoint Media, Inc., 14205 SE 36th St., Suite 100 • Bellevue, WA 98006
(425) 519-3710 Fax 883-7209; Website: www.igmagazine.com
Steve Burke, Publisher (425) 885-6997; E-mail: steveigm@aol.com
Monthly magazine for the industry.

INDIAN HEALTH COMMUNICATOR
5600 Fishers lane, Rm. 6-35 • Rockville, MD 20857
THE INDIAN HISTORIAN
American Indian Historical Society

1451 Masonic Ave. • San Francisco, CA 94117
(415) 626-5235; Jeanette Henry, Editor
Back issues of magazines covers American Indian culture & history.

INDIAN HUMAN RESOURCE CENTER, INC. COMMUNITY NEWSLETTER
4040 30th St., Suite A • San Diego, CA 92104
(619) 281-5964 Fax 281-1466; E-mail: ihrc5@onp.wdsc.org
Monthly newsletter which serves the San Diego County American Indian
community. Subscriptions: $5/yr., $8/two yrs. Advertising. Begun 1987.

INDIAN LAW REPORTER
American Indian Lawyer Training Program
1-25 W. Vine St. • Stockton, CA 95203
(209) 460-0924 Fax 460-0934
Website: www.indian.awreporter.org; E-mail: dmailp@earthlink.net
Legal reporting service reporting current developments in Indian law. Monthly
journal. 650 cir. $396/year. *Publication*: Indian Tribes As Sovereign Govern-
ments. Begun 1973.

INDIAN LAW SUPPORT CENTER REPORTER
Native American Rights Fund, 1506 Broadway • Boulder, Colorado 80302
(303) 447-8760 Fax 443-7776
Monthly newsletter providing local legal services attorneys with information on
developments in the area of Indian law. Includes summaries of recent court
decisions in Indian country; Federal Register highlights, and new publications
and materials. $36/year.

THE INDIAN LEADER
Haskell Indian Nations University
155 Indian Ave. • Ross Hall, Rm. 122 • Lawrence, KS 66046
(785) 749-8477 Fax 749-8408
Theresa Milk, Editor; Glen Gary, Assoc. Editor
E-mail: idnldr@ross1.cc.haskell.edu
Bimonthly publication produced by the students of Haskell Indian Nations
University. $15/year.

INDIAN LIFE NEWSPAPER
Indian Life Ministries
Canada: P.O. Box 3765, RPO • Winnipeg, Manitoba R2W 3R6
U.S: Box 32, Pembina, ND 58271 (204) 661-9333 Fax 661-3982
James Uttley, Editor; E-mail: ilm.editor@indianlife.org
Website: www.indianlife.org
Bimonthly. Covers culturally relevant material to Native North Americans,
evangelistic outreach in content. $15/six issues; single copy, $3.00. 23,000
circ. Begun 1979.

INDIAN MARKET MAGAZINE
Southwestern Association for Indian Arts (SWAIA)
P.O. Box 969 • Santa Fe, NM 87504 (505) 983-5220 Fax 983-7647
E-mail: info@swaia.org; Website: www.swaia.org
Quarterly magazine on the Santa Fe Indian market and other events.

INDIAN NATION NEWS
American Indian Nations Ministries
P.O. Box 70 • Honobia, OK 74579 (918) 755-4570 Fax 755-4577

INDIAN NEWS NOTES
Public Information Office, Office of Indian Affairs
1849 C St., NW MS: 1340 MIB • Washington, DC 20240
(202) 208-3710 Fax 501-1516
Biweekly publication of the Bureau of Indian Affairs.

INDIAN NOTES
Museum of the American Indian - Smithsonian Institution
1 Bowling Green • New York 10004 (212) 283-2420 Fax 491-9302
Quarterly newsletter

THE INDIAN RELIC TRADER
P.O. Box 88 • Sunbury, OH 43074
Janie Jinks-Weidner, Editor
Features articles on prehistoric relics, current archaeological findings and
research; calendar of events and meetings; sources for books and supplies.
Advertising. Subscription: $8/year; sample copies available, $1.00 each.

INDIAN RECORD
Office of Indian Affairs, 1951 Constitution Ave., NW • Washington, DC 20245

INDIAN REPORT
Friends Committee on National Legislation
245 Second St., NE • Washington, DC 20002
(202) 547-6000 Fax 547-6019; E-mail: fcnl@fcnl.org

Website: www.fcnl.org; Aura Kanegis, Editor
Archive of articles focusing on issues & national legislation of interest to American Indians & Alaskan natives. Complimentary copies available upon request. Begun 1977. Ended 2013. Native American Legislative Updates (NALU) provides up-to-date information and action suggestions on legislation affecting Native Americans. Available by e-mail, fax, or via FCNL's web page. Hard copy versions available by mail.

INDIAN TIME
Akwesasne Notes, P.O. Box 868, Mohawk Nation
Hogansburg, NY 13655-0868 (518) 358-9535/9531
  Website: www.mohawknation.org
Promotes unity for all Mohawk groups through communicating information on the environment, health, women, youth & Iroquois history; Native American and Canadian news. An eight page weekly newspaper of the St. Regis Mohawk Reservation (New York-Quebec-Ontario.) Advertising. Subscription: $33/year, U.S.; $40/year, Canada. Sample copies, $1.00 each. Begun 1983.

INDIAN TRADER
Indian Trader, Inc., P.O. Box 1421 • Gallup, NM 87305
  (505) 722-6694; Martin Link, Publisher; William Donovan, Editor
  E-mail: trader@cia-g.com
Covers American Indian arts & crafts, cultures & history, contemporary Indian news items, and western Americana. Book reviews. Monthly newspaper. 4,000 cir. $2/copy; $20/year; Canada, $32/year. Advertising. Begun 1969.

INDIAN VOICES
618 E. Carson St., Suite 305 • Las Vegas, NV 89101 (702) 382-0808
  Rose Davis, Editor/Publisher; E-mail: rdavis4973@aol.com

INDIANZ.COM
Noble Savage Media & Ho-Chunk, Inc.
1000 Industrial Pkwy. • Winnebago, NE 68071 (800) 296-4170
  (402) 878-2400 Fax (402) 878-2771; (202) 318-2182
  E-mail: indianz@indianz.com
Provides news, information, and entertainment from a Native American perspective.

INDIGENOUS POLICY JOURNAL (IPJ)
Indigenous Studies Network; Website: www.indigenouspolicy.org
  Tad Connor, Principal Contact; E-mail: conner03@nmsu.edu
  Thomas Brasdefer, Support Contact; E-mail: tbrasd1@lsu.edu
Publishes articles, commentary, reviews, news, & announcements concerning Native American and international Indigenous affairs, issues, events, nations, groups and media.

INI-MI-KWA-ZOO-MIN
Minnesota Chippewa Tribe, P.O. Box 217 • Cass Lake, MN 56633
  Betty Blue, Editor

INTER-COM NEWSLETTER
Native American Educational Service
2838 W. Peterson Ave. • Chicago, IL 60659 (312) 761-5000
  Faith Smith, Editor; Monthly newsletter.

INTER-TRIBAL TIMBER COUNCIL NEWSLETTER
Intertribal Timber Council, 4370 NE Halsey St. • Portland, OR 97213

INTER-TRIBAL TIMES NEWSPAPER
Inter-Tribal Council, Inc., P.O. Box 1308 • Miami, OK 74355
  (918) 542-4486 Fax 540-2500; Liz Gaines, Editor
  Newakis Burkybile, Advertising
Involves at least seven Northeastern Oklahoma area tribal news-letters, each using a full page to announce their monthly news. Also included is a national, state, and local news that holds interest for local tribal members. Monthly. 10,000 circulation in northeastern Oklahoma, Arkansas, Missouri & Kansas. Advertising. Begun 1994.

INTERTRIBAL NATIVE NEWS
219 Manchester St. W. • Battle Creek, MI 49017
Website: www.mia.org/inn/; News and powwow list.

INTERTRIBAL NEWS
Native American Center
Fort Lewis College, College Hts. • Durango, CO 81137
  (303) 247-7221 Fax 247-7108; Rick Wheelock, Faculty Sponsor
Indian student tabloid-size newspaper. Published biweekly - Fall & Winter trimesters only. 1,000 cir (approx. 450 Indian students). No charge. Advertising accepted. Limited number of complimentary copies available. Begun 1981.

ISLETA EAGLE PRIDE
Isleta Elementary School, P.O. Box 312 • Isleta, NM 87022
  (505) 869-2321; School newspaper.

J

JAH-NOO
Hopland Band of Pomo Indians, 3000 Shanel Rd.
Hopland, CA 95449 (707) 744-1647 Fax 744-1506
  Website: www.hoplandrancheria.com
  E-mail: amaldonado@hoplandtribe.com

JICARILLA CHIEFTAIN
Jicarilla Apache Tribe, P.O. Box 507 • Dulce, NM 87528-0507
  (505) 759-3242 Ext. 224 Fax 759-3005
  Mary F. Polanco, Editor; Lori M. Vicenti, Co-Editor
Biweekly newsletter containing information of general importance to tribal members, as well as national and state news pertaining to other tribes and Indian affairs. Book reviews. 1,200 cir. $12/year, local; $24/year, foreign. Advertising. Begun 1960.

JOURNAL OF ALASKA NATIVE ARTS
Institute of Alaska Native Arts, P.O. Box 70769 • Fairbanks, AK 99707
  (907) 456-7491 Fax 451-7268; Susheila Khera, Editor
A 10-page quarterly journal containing interviews with Alaska Native artists; news of opportunities of interest to artists; and photographs, poetry & issues affecting Alaska Native artists. 1,400 circ. $25/year.

JOURNAL OF AMERICAN INDIAN EDUCATION
Center for Indian Education, Arizona State University, Box 871311
Tempe, AZ 85287-1311 (480) 965-6292 Fax 965-8115
  Bryan Brayboy, Co-editor; E-mail: bryan.brayboy@asu.edu
  Teresa McCarty, Co-editor; E-mail: teresa.mccarty@asu.edu
  Jeston Morris, Managing Editor; E-mail: jeston.morris@asu.edu
Publishes papers directly related to the education of North American Indians and Alaskan Natives. Emphasis is on research - basic and applied. Published three times per year (October, January, and May.) Submits five complimentary copies of the Journal to authors of accepted manuscripts. 700 cir. $16/year, U.S.; $18.50/year, Canada & foreign. Available microfilm from Xerox University Microfilms, 300 North Zeeb Rd., Ann Arbor, Michigan 48106. Begun 1961.

JOURNAL OF ARIZONA HISTORY
Arizona Historical Society, 949 E. Second St. • Tucson, AZ 85719
  (520) 628-5774 Fax 628-5695; Bruce J. Dinges, Editor
A quarterly history journal containing articles, critical essays, and book reviews on the history of Arizona and the Southwest, and northern Mexico when appropriate. Articles often include appraisals of American Indian life and lore, the Indian wars and Anglo-Indian relations. 2,400 circulation. Subscription: $40/year. Begun 1960.

JOURNAL OF CALIFORNIA & GREAT BASIN ANTHROPOLOGY
Dept. of Anthropology, University of California • Riverside, CA 92521
  (714) 787-7317; Philip J. Wilke, Editor
Publishes original manuscripts on ethnography, languages, arts, archaeology, and prehistory of their Native peoples of California, the Great Basin, & Baja California. Book reviews. Semiannual. $18/year. Advertising. Begun 1974. Back issues for $30 each may be obtained from Malki-Ballena Press, P.O. Box 578, Banning, California 92220 (951) 849-7289. www.malkimuseumstore.org.

JOURNAL OF CHEROKEE STUDIES
Museum of the Cherokee Indian
P.O. Box 770-A • Cherokee, NC 28719 (704) 497-3481
  Duane King, Editor; Published semiannually.

JOURNAL OF THE WEST
Box 1009, 1531 Yuma • Manhattan, KS 66502-4228
  (913) 539-1888; Robin Higham, Editor
Covers western history & culture containing articles, book reviews, pieces about the West. A Quarterly. Advertising accepted. $30/year, individuals; $40/year, institutions. Begun 1962.

K

KALIHWISAKS
Oneida Indian Nation of Wisconsin, P.O. Box 365 • Oneida, WI 54155
  (800) 236-2214; (920) 869-4340 Fax 869-4252
  Website: www.oneidanation.org; E-mail: dwalschi@oneidanation.org
  Dawn Walschinski, Managing Editor

KANZA NEWS
Kaw Nation, Drawer 50 • Kaw City, OK 74641
(580) 269-2552 ext. 236
Website: www.kawnation.com/kanza news.php
Jennie Baker, Editor; Quarterly tribal newsletter.

KARUK TRIBE OF CALIFORNIA NEWSMAGAZINE
P.O. Box 1016 • Happy Camp, CA 96039
(800) 505-2785; (530) 493-1600 Fax 493-5322
Website: www.karuk.us/newsletters
Sara Spence, Editor; Quarterly tribal newsmagazine.

KEE-YOKS
Swinomish Tribal Community
P.O. Box 388 • La Connor, WA 98257

KEETOOWAH CHEROKEE NEWS
United Keetoowah Band of Cherokee Indians
P.O. Box 746 • Tahlequah, OK 74465 (918) 456-6533 Fax 453-9345
Website: www.unitedkeetoowahband.org
E-mail: ukbnews@unitedkeetoowahband.org
Sam L. Still, Editor
Monthly newspaper. *Subscription*: $18 per year; $30 for two years.

KIOWA VOICES
Kiowa Tribe, P.O. Box 397 • Carnegie, OK 73015
(405) 347-2875; Deborah Ahtone, Editor
Monthly tribal newspaper. No charge to tribal members.

**KIVA: THE JOURNAL OF SOUTHWESTERN
ANTHROPOLOGY & HISTORY**
Arizona Archaeological & Historical Society
Arizona State Museum, University of Arizona
Tucson, AZ 85721 (520) 621-4011; Gayle Harrison Hartmann, Editor
Covers original research relating to the prehistoric & historic archaeology
& ethnology of the southwestern U.S. and northwestern Mexico. Quarterly.
1,100 cir. $25/year.

KLAH'CHE'MIN
Squaxin Tribal Center, SE 70 Squaxin Ln. • Shelton, WA 98584

KLALLAM NEWSLETTER
Port Gamble-Klallam Nation Tribal Council
P.O. Box 280 • Kingston, WA 98346

KLAMATH NEWS
Klamath Tribes of Oregon, P.O. Box 436 • Chiloquin, OR 97624
(541) 783-2219 Fax 783-2029; David Taylor, Editor. Monthly tribal newsletter

KO-BUN-DA
Potawatomi Indian Nation (Pokagon Band)
43237 Town Hall Rd. • Dowagiac, MI 49047
(616) 782-6323 Fax 782-9625

KOOTAH
P.O. Box 157 • Crow Agency, MT 59022

KUKADZE'ETA TOWNCRIER
Pueblo of Laguna, P.O. Box 685 • Laguna, NM 87026
(505) 552-6652 Fax 552-0605; Annette Nunez, Editor
Monthly community newspaper.

KUMTUX
Native American Network, 419 Occidental So. • Seattle, WA 98104
(206) 528-9585 Fax 625-9791; Helen Night Raven, Editor
Monthly calendar of events in Washington State's Indian country. $18/yr.

K'WEN 'INISH-HA (TRIBAL TIDBITS)
Coquille Indian Tribe, P.O. Box 783 • North Bend, OR 97459
(800) 622-5869; (541) 756-0904 Fax 756-0847
Website: www.coquilletribe.org; Monthly tribal newsletter.

L

LAC COURTE OREILLES JOURNAL
LCO Graphic Arts, Rt. 2 • Hayward, WI 54843 (715) 634-8934

LAGH'-WEGH A-MOO-E'SHA
Confederated Tribes of the Umatilla, P.O. Box 638 • Pendleton, OR 97801

LAKOTA COUNTRY TIMES
316 Main St. • Martin, SD 57551
(605) 685-1868 Fax 685-1870
Connie Louise Smith, Owner-Publisher; Vi Waln, Editor
Website: www.lakotacountrytimes.com
E-mail: connie@lakotacountrytimes.com
E-mail: editor@lakotacountrytimes.com
Weekly online/print legal newspaper for Pine Ridge/Rosebud Tribes.

THE LAKOTA FUNDS NEWSLETTER
P.O. Box 340 • Kyle, SD 57750 (605) 455-2500 Fax 455-2585
Tawney Brunsch, Exec. Director; E-mail: tbrunsch@lakotafunds.org
A fund formed to help build a private sector economy on the Reservation by
providing loans and technical assistance & business training; and arts & crafts
marketing assistance tribal members.

THE LAKOTA JOURNAL
Lakota Media, Inc. (owned by Flandreau Santee Sioux Tribe)
1321 Concourse Dr. • Rapid City, SD 57703
(605) 399-1999 Fax 399-1998; Website: www.lakotajournal.com
E-mail: editor@lakotajournal.com
Marty Two Bulls, Owner; Nestor Ramos, Editor
Published weekly. Covers nationwide and west river (SD) area,
as "Lakota" Sioux are mostly west river. Cir: 85,000. Subs: $1 per issue.

LAKOTA LANGUAGE NEWS
Lakota Language Consortium, 2620 N. Walnut St. • Bloomington, IN 47404
(888) 525-6828; (812) 340-3517 Fax 339-3135
Website: www.lakhota.org; E-mail: news@lakhota.org
Wilhelm K. Meya, Executive Director
Jan F. Ullrich, Lingustic Director
Karen Little Wounded, Educational Coordinator

LDF NEWS
Lac du Flambeau Band of Lake Superior Chippewa Indians
P.O. Box 67 • Lac du Flambeau, WI 54538
(715) 588-3303 Fax 588-7930; Website: www.ldfojibwe.com
Monthly tribal newsletter

LITTLE HOOP COMMUNITY COLLEGE BULLETIN
P.O. Box 269 • Fort Totten, ND 58335 (701) 766-4415 Fax 766-4077

LITTLE ROCKIES WEEKLY
Fort Belknap Reservation, P.O. Box 320 • Hays, MT 59527
(406) 673-3281

LODGE TALES
American Indian Center of Arkansas
1100 N. University, Suite 133 • Little Rock, AR 72207
(501) 666-9032 Fax 666-5875; Paul S. Austin, Director
Quarterly newsletter.

LUMBEE NEWS
Lumbee Tribe of North Carolina, P.O. Box 2709 • Pembroke, NC 28372
(919) 521-7861 Fax 521-8625

LUMMI INDIAN NEWS
2616 Kwina Rd. • Bellingham, WA 98226 (206) 734-8180
A bi-weekly community newsletter.

M

MAINE INDIAN NEWSLETTER
Maine Indian Affairs Commission
State Health Station No. 38 • Augusta, ME 04333

MAKAH NEWSLETTER
Makah Indian Tribal Council, P.O. Box 160 • Neah Bay, WA 98357
(360) 645-2201 Fax 645-2788; Website: www.makah.com
Monthly newsletter covering general news about Neah Bay's programs;
town news.

THE MAMMOTH TRUMPET
Center for the Study of the First Americans
Department of Anthropology, 4352 TAMU • Texas A&M University
College Station, TX 77843-4352 (979) 845-4046 845-4070
Website: www.centerfirstamericans.com; E-mail: csfu@tamu.edu
Quarterly journal. Articles about the First Americans include breaking news
on important discoveries & issues facing First Americans research.

MANASSEH-JOURNAL OF THE TRIBES
Eagle Communications, 29 Brimmer St. • Brewer, ME 04412
  Reginald Roberts, Jr., Publisher; Quarterly. $24/year.

MANATABA MESSENGER
Colorado River Indian Reservation
26600 Mohave Rd., Rt. 1, Box 23-B • Parker, AZ 85344
  (928) 669-9211 Fax 669-1216; Website: www.critonline.org
  E-mail: messenger@critonline.org

MANDAN, HIDATSA & ARIKARA TIMES
Three Affiliated Tribes, HC 3, Box 2, Administration Bldg.
New Town, ND 58763 (701) 627-4781 Fax 627-3626

MANIILAQ DIRECTORY
Maniilaq Association, P.O. Box 256 • Kotzebue AK 99752
  (800) 478-3312; (907) 442-3311 Fax 442-2381
  Website: www.maniilaq.org
  Barbara Janitscheck, Interim CEO/President
Annual directory of members.

MANUAL OF INDIAN GAMING LAW
The Falmouth Institute, Inc., 3702 Pender Dr., Suite 300 • Fairfax, VA 22030
  (800) 992-4489; (703) 352-2250 Fax 352-2323
  Web site: www.falmouthinst.com; James Casey, Esq., Editor
Addresses virtually every legal, regulatory, administrative & policy issue
affecting Indian gaming. Fully indexed & annotated. 2-volume set with 3
updates per year. $484; renewal, $329.

MARIN MUSEUM OF THE AMERICAN INDIAN – MUSEUM QUARTERLY
P.O. Box 864, 2200 Novato Blvd. • Novato, CA 94948 (415) 897-4064

MARYLAND AMERICAN INDIAN DIRECTORY
Maryland Commission on Indian Affairs
100 Community Place • Crownsville, MD 21032 (410) 514-7651

MASINAIGAN
Great Lakes Indian Fish & Wildlife Commission
P.O. Box 9 • Odanah, WI 54861 (715) 682-6619
Monthly newspaper.

THE MASTERKEY
Southwest Museum, P.O. Box 41558 • Los Angeles, CA 90041
  (323) 221-2164 Fax 224-8223; Steven Le Blanc, Editor
Devoted to the anthropology & archaeology of the Americas; contains articles,
book reviews, and a conservation column. Book reviews. Quarterly journal.
5,500 cir. $15/year. Begun 1927.

MAWIW-KILUN
Tribal Governors, Inc., Indian Township • Princeton, ME 04668
Contains community news, tribal activities, health & social service articles.
Published bimonthly.

A MEASURE OF EXCELLENCE
Inter-Tribal Indian Ceremonial Association
226 W. Coal Ave.• Gallup, NM 87301 (505) 863-3896
  Laurence D. Linford, Editor. A full-color annual publication focusing
on each year's top art award-winners
at the Ceremonial.

MEETING GROUND
D'Arcy McNickle Center for American Indian History
60 W. Walton St. • Chicago, IL 60610 (312) 255-3564
  Harvey Markowitz, Editor; E-Mail: mcnickle@newberry.org
A national biannual newsletter containing information on the Center's activities,
research, and teaching materials. 1,000 circ. Begun 1972.

MENOMINEE NATION NEWS
Menominee Indian Tribe of Wisconsin
P.O. Box 910 • Keshena, WI 54135 (715) 799-5167 Fax 799-5250
  Website: www.menominee.com/mnn/home.html
  E-mail: derdmann@mitw.org; Devin Erdmann, Editor
  Christopher Anderson, Reporter
Biweekly tribal newspaper. 1,400 cir. Advertising. Begun 1976.

MESKWAKI NATION TIMES
Sac & Fox Tribe of the Mississippi in Iowa
349 Meskwaki Rd. • Tama, IA 52339
  (641) 484-4678 Fax 484-5458
  Website: www.meskwaki.org/newsletter

MICCOSUKEE EVERGLADES NEWS
Miccosukee Tribe of Florida
Box 440021, Tamiami Station • Miami, FL 33144

MICHIGAN INDIAN QUARTERLY
Michigan Commission on Indian Affairs
741 N. Cedar St., Suite 102, P.O. Box 30026 • Lansing, MI 48909
  (517) 334-8632 Fax 335-1642. Quarterly newsletter.

MID-AMERICA ALL INDIAN CENTER NEWSLETTER
650 N. Seneca • Wichita, KS 67203 (316) 262-5221 Fax 262-4216
  John A. Ortiz, Executive Director; E-Mail: wichita@esc.ttrc.dolteta.gov

MILLE LACS PROGRESS
Goff & Howard, Inc., 255 E. Kellogg Blvd. #102 • St. Paul, MN 55101
  (651) 292-8062 Fax 292-8091
Bi-annual newspaper for Mille Lacs Band Ojibwe members & tribal government
employees reporting on the Band's successes.

THE MOCCASIN
San Carlos Apache Tribe, P.O. Box 1711 • San Carlos, AZ 85550
  (928) 475-2361 Fax 475-2567
Tribal newspaper featuring news about the San Carlos Apache people
and its tribal government.

MOCCASIN TELEGRAPH
9 E. Burnam Rd. • Columbia, MO 65203
  (573) 817-3301 Fax 817-3244; E-mail: wordcraft@sockets.net
  Lee Francis, III, PhD, Editor; Joseph Bruchac, III, Co-Editor
  D.L. "Don" Birchfield, Contributing Editor
A monthly news journal for Native writers and storytellers particularly members
of Wordcraft Circle of Native Writers and Storytellers. Includes original poetry,
fiction, and essays by Native writers. Also reports on writer's conferences and
workshops, and profiles of Native authors. $24/yr. $2 for sample copy.

MOHICAN NEWS
Stockbridge-Munsee Tribe
N 8480 Moheconnuck Rd., P.O. Box 70 • Bowler, WI 54416
  (715) 793-4389 Fax 793-1307; Jeff Vele, Editor
  E-mail: mohican-news@mohican.com. Biweekly tribal newspaper.

MOLE LAKE ENVIRONMENTAL NEWSLETTER
Sokaogon Chippewa Community, Rt. 1, Box 625 • Crandon, WI 54520
  (715) 478-7616 Fax 478-7618

MONTANA INTER-TRIBAL POLICY BOARD NEWSLETTER
P.O. Box 850 • Browning, MT 59417 (406) 652-3113
  Merle R. Lucas, Executive Director

MONTANA, THE MAGAZINE OF WESTERN HISTORY
Montana Historical Society, Roberts & Sixth Ave. • Helena, MT 59601
Deals with Western history, often touching upon the Indian's involvement.
Quarterly.

MUSEUM NOTES
Iroquois Indian Museum, P.O. Box 7, Caverns Rd. • Howes Cave, NY 12092
  (518) 296-8949
A newsletter reporting on the museum's activities; scholarly articles
on the Iroquois. Subscription: $10 per year.

THE MUSCOGEE NATION NEWS
The Muscogee (Creek) Nation, P.O. Box 580 • Okmulgee, OK 74447
  (918) 756-8700 Fax 758-0824
  Rebecca Landsberry, Editor; E-mail: rlandsberry@mcn-nsn.gov
Monthly tribal news tabloid of the Muscogee (Creek) Nation. No charge to tribal
members. 8,100 cir. $12/year to non-tribal members. Begun 1971.

MUSEUM OF THE GREAT PLAINS NEWSLETTER
P.O. Box 68 • Lawton, OK 73502 (405) 353-5675

MUSEUM OF INDIAN HERITAGE NEWSLETTER
500 W. Washington St. • Indianapolis, IN 46204
  (317) 293-4488. Quarterly.

N

NACIE NEWSLETTER
National Advisory Council on Indian Education
Switzer Bldg., 330 C St., SW #4072 • Washington, DC 20202
  (202) 205-8353 Fax 205-8897; Robert K. Chiago, Exec. Director

NAHGAHCHIWANONG DIBAHJIMOWINNAN
Fond du Lac Band of Lake Superior Chippewa
1720 Big Lake Rd. • Cloquet, MN 55720
  (218) 878-2682 Fax 879-4146; Website: www.fdlrez.com

NAICCO
Native American Indian Center of Central Ohio
P.O. Box 07705, 67 E. Innis Ave. • Columbus, OH 43207
  (614) 443-6120 Fax 443-2651; Carol Welsh, Executive Director
  E-mail: naicco@aol.com; Website: www.naicco.tripod.com
Bimonthly newsletter.

NAJA NEWS
Native American Journalists Association
University of Oklahoma Gaylord College
365 W. Lindsey St. • Norman, OK 73019
  (405) 325-9008 Fax 325-6945
  E-mail: info@naja.com; Website: www.naja.com
  Dan Lewerenz, President; E-mail: lewerenz@naja.com
Quarterly newsletter distributed to members of the association. The only
publication by, for and about Native American communicators. 2,000 circ.
Begun 1984.

NAPA NEWS
Native American Preservation Association of Georgia
P.O. Box 565 • Rome, GA 30162 (706) 295-0012
  E-mail: napanewsletter@cs.com
  Carlton & Brenda Yancey, Editors; Monthly newsletter.

NARF LEGAL REVIEW
Native American Rights Fund, 1506 Broadway • Boulder, CO 80302
  (303) 447-8760 Fax 443-7776; Ray Ramirez, Editor
E-mail: ramirezr@stripe.colorado.edu; Website: www.narf.org
A biannual newsletter covering NARF's involvement in Indian legal issues and
updates NARF's cases. Discusses current Indian law issues, legislation and
court decisions. Announcements of NARF's services and publications through
the National Indian Law Library. No charge. Donations accepted. Begun 1973.

NASHAUONK MITTARK
Mashpee Wampanoag Indian Tribal Council
89 Shellback Way #N • Mashpee, MA 02649
  (617) 477-1825; Quarterly.

NASP NEWS
Native American Student Program
University of California-233 Library South • Riverside, CA 92521
  (714) 787-3821

NATION NOTES
Penobscot Nation Newsletter
Community Bldg., 6 River Rd. • Indian Island • Old Town, ME 04468

**NATIONAL ADVISORY COUNCIL
ON INDIAN EDUCATION NEWSLETTER**
Switzer Bldg., 330 C St., SW, Rm. 4072
Washington, DC 20202-7556 (202) 205-8353 Fax 205-9446

**NATIONAL AMERICAN INDIAN CATTLEMAN'S
ASSOCIATION NEWSLETTER & YEARBOOK**
c/o Tim Foster, President, 1541 Foster Rd. • Toppenish, WA 98948
  (509) 854-1329; Monthly newsletter.

NATIONAL ASSOCIATION OF BLACKFEET INDIANS BULLETIN
P.O. Box 340 • Browning, MT 59417

**NATIONAL CENTER FOR AMERIAN INDIAN
ENTERPRISE DEVELOPMENT REPORTER & REVIEW**
953 E. Juanita Ave. • Mesa. AZ 85204
  (800) 462-2433; Fax (480) 545-4208
  Ken Robbins, President
The voice of American Indian business. Quarterly journals.

NATIONAL CONGRESS OF AMERICAN INDIANS NEWS
1301 Connecticut Ave., NW #200 • Washington, DC 20036
  (202) 466-7767 Fax 466-7797

NATIONAL INDIAN HEALTH BOARD (NIHB) HEALTH REPORTER
Office of Diversity, Campus Box AO49
4200 E. 9th Ave. • Denver, CO 80262 (303) 315-5598
  Linda Yardley, Contact; Bimonthly newsletter, No charge.

NATIONAL INDIAN SOCIAL WORKERS ASSOCIATION
P.O. Box 45 • Valentine, AZ 86437-0045
  Mary Kihega, Secretary/Treasurer
Quarterly newsletter containing a calendar of events, news of members,
research, and awards. Price is membership dues.

THE NATIONS NEWS
Nations Ministries, P.O. Box 70 • Honobia, OK 74549
  (918) 755-4570; Riley Donica, Editor; Quarterly newsletter.

NATIVE AMERICAN CONNECTIONS
Gloria J. Davis, Publisher
P.O. Box 579 • Winchester, CA 92596 (909) 926-2119
  Dayne E. Lopez & Robert Kendall, Editors
  E-mail: ponchefoo@com; Website: www.hispanictimescarees.com
A yearbook & directory, published annually in July for Native Americans
and businesses. $28 plus postage per year. Begun 1993.

NATIVE AMERICAN COUNCIL NEWS
204 Hagested Student Center
University of Wisconsin • River Falls, WI 54022

NATIVE AMERICAN CULTURAL CENTER NEWSLETTER
1344 University Ave. #230 • Rochester, NY 14607

NATIVE AMERICAN DIRECTORY
National Native American Co-op, P.O. Box 1000 • San Carlos, AZ 85550
  (520) 622-4900; Fred Synder, Editor
Provides information about American Indian events, organizations, & crafts.
Includes powwows & celebrations, Indian rodeos, conventions, arts & crafts
shows; also, Indian crafts guilds & cooperatives & Indian performing artists,
dancers and exhibitors. Published periodically.Quarterly newsletter.

NATIVE AMERICAN LAW DIGEST
The Falmouth Institute, Inc., 3702 Pender Dr., Suite 300 • Fairfax, VA 22030
  (800) 992-4489; (703) 352-2250 Fax 352-2323
  Website: www.falmouthinstitute.com
  E-mail: information@falmouthinstitute.com
  Gregory Smith, Esq., Editor
A monthly summary of all legal decisions significant to the Indian community.
This comprehensive law digest covers all issues affecting tribes and tribal
organizations. In addition to summarized cases, the digest publishes numerous
law review articles covering topics such as Indian gaming, Indian taxation,
sovereign immunity and tribal self-governance. $299 per year.

NATIVE AMERICAN POLICY NETWORK NEWSLETTER
Barry University, 11300 NE 2nd Ave. • Miami Shores, FL 33161
  (305) 899-3000 Fax 899-3279
An offset newsletter for 425 policy makers, political scientists and Native
American leaders, issued three times per year. Articles and news relevant to
Native American policy issues. Book reviews. 1,500 cir. $5/year. Begun 1980.

NATIVE AMERICAN PROGRAMS NEWSLETTER
University of North Dakota, P.O. Box 1874 • Grand Forks, ND 58202
  (701) 777-4291 Fax 777-3292

NATIVE AMERICAN REPORT
CD Publications (Business Publishers Co.)
222 Sedwick Rd. • Durham, NC 27713
  (855) 237-1396 Fax (800) 508-2592
  Website: www.cdpublications.com; E-mail: info@cdpublications.com
  Jim Rogers, Editorial Director
The Native American Report brings you the latest news from Congress, the
courts and federal agencies as well as updates from around the country on
developments that could affect your tribal interests. Our Washington DC
reporting staff is credentialed by Congress to cover events others often can't,
so you gain the benefit of our exclusive insights, comprehensive coverage, and
unbiased reporting on unfolding issues. Plus, you'll benefit from our thorough
coverage in our other areas such as health, education and social services and
programs affecting seniors, youth, children, and families. You'll find detailed
coverage and updates in such areas as: Bureau of Indian Affairs;
Federal/state/tribal taxation; HUD, BIA and EPA regulations; Trends in Native
American law; The impact of new legal rulings; Sovereignty/Jurisdiction;
Tribal/state gaming disputes. You'll also find out what's being done not only in
Washington but around the country with local efforts to improve access to
health, health promotion & disease management; increase educational
performance and opportunities at all levels; to address employment and job
training difficulties; and many more endeavors related to the development of
the Native American tribes & peoples. Published monthly. Price: $299 E-
subscription-yearly; $399 E-subscription plus print, yearly.

NATIVE AMERICAN SCHOLAR
Bureau of Indian Affairs, Higher Ed. Program
P.O. Box 26567 • Albuquerque, NM 87125 (505) 766-3170

NATIVE AMERICAN STUDIES
Edwin Mellon Press, 240 Portage Rd., Box 450 • Lewiston, NY 14092
(716) 754-8566 Fax 754-4335

NATIVE AMERICAN TIMES
P.O. Box 411 • Tahlequah, OK 74465
(918) 708-5838 Fax (888) 689-4873
Website: www.nativetimes.com; E-mail: lisa@nativetimes.com
Lisa Snell, Editor & Publisher; Sam Lewin, News Editor
Monthly national Indian newspaper. Circulation: 36,000. Subs: 13 issues, $16.25; 26 issues, $32.50; 52 issues, $65. Advertising.

NATIVE CULTURAL ORGANIZATIONS SURVEY
RESULTS & TECHNICAL ASSISTANCE NEEDS ASSESSMENT
ATLATL, INC. • P.O. Box 34090 • Phoenix, AZ 85067-4090
(602) 277-3711 Fax 277-3690
E-mail: atlatl@atlatl.org; Website: www.atlatl.org
A 70-page publication profiling Native-controlled organizations and the technical needs of Native artists and cultural workers. $30.

NATIVE DRUMS
LOST/League of Separated Tribes, P.O. Box 68 • Saltsburg, PA 15681
Pat Selinger, Editor

NATIVE HOOP MAGAZINE
Website: www.nativehoopsmagazine.com; James Morales, Publisher
Monthly online publication. *Goals*: To promote & support Native culture, traditions, and its people in a positive way.

NATIVE LIFE & TIMES
2003 S. Muskogee Ave., Suite 115 • Tahlequah, OK 74464
(918) 456-1876

THE NATIVE NEVADAN
Reno-Sparks Indian Colony, 98 Colony Rd. • Sparks, NV 89502-1288
(702) 359-9449; Becky Lemon, Editor
Covers all facets of Native American life, primarily in Nevada and California. Book reviews. Monthly newspaper. 2,200 cir. $15/year; $2/copy. Advertising. Begun 1964.

NATIVE NEWS
Indian Education - Title VII Program
2295 Four Oaks Grange Rd. • Eugene, OR 97405
(541) 687-3489 Fax 687-3892
Brenda Brainard, Editor; E-mail: brainard@4j.lane.edu
Monthly newsletter for families & Native American students enrolled in Eugene, Bethel, Fern Ridge, Creswell, Lowell, Junction City, Crow-Applegate-Lorane, South Lane & Pleasant Hill School Districts; and for Native American community members. Includes overview of student activities plus a monthly educational theme, complete with reading lists, visual material references, website information and a recipe page. Free upon request.

NATIVE NEWS & B.I.A. BULLETIN
Bureau of Indian Affairs, P.O. Box 3-8000 • Juneau, AK 99801

NATIVE PEOPLES MAGAZINE
5333 N. 7th St. #224 • Phoenix, AZ 85014
(602) 265-4855 Fax 265-3113; Website: www.nativepeoples.com
E-mail: editorial@nativepeoples.com
Subscriber customer service, P.O. Box 18449 • Anaheim, CA 92817
(800) 999-9718; Daniel Gibson, Editor
A full-color, bimonthly magazine portraying the history, arts and lifeways of Native peoples of the Americas. Includes book and audio/video reviews, Native American foods, collectors corner, guest essays, and in the news section on Native American role models. Affiliated with ten organizations including the National Museum of the American Indian/Smithsonian Institution. $4.95/copy; $17.95/year, 6 issues; $29/2-year, 12 issues, foreign. Advertising. Begun 1987.

NATIVE PLAYWRIGHTS' NEWSLETTER
P.O. Box 664 • Cocoa, FL 32923
Published three times per year. $15/year.

NATIVE PRESS RESEARCH JOURNAL
University of Arkansas, Little Rock
Stabler Hall 502, 2801 S. University • Little Rock, AR 72204
Daniel F. Littlefield, Jr., Editor' Back issues available.

NATIVE REFLECTIONS
Wesleyan Native American Ministries
P.O. Box 7038 • Rapid City, SD 57709 (605) 343-9054
E-mail: wnam2000@aol.com; Quarterly. $15.

THE NATIVE SCHOLAR
Catching the Dream, 8200 Mountain Rd. NE, Suite 203
Albuquerque, NM 87110 (505) 262-2351 Fax 262-0534
Website: www.catchingthedream.org; E-mail: nscholarsh@aol.com
Dean Chavers, Editor
Annual 48-page magazine published in October. Catching the Dream makes grants to Indian schools to help them improve. Contains feature stories about outstanding Indian graduates and how they are impacting Indian people. Advertising accepted. Circulation: 20,000.

NATIVE SELF-SUFFICIENCY
The Seventh Generation Fund
P.O. Box 4569 • Arcata, CA 95521
(707) 825-7640 Fax 825-7639

NATIVE SOUTH
University of Nebraska Press, P.O. Box 880484 • Lincoln, NE 68588
(800) 848-6224 Fax (800) 272-6817; (402) 472-3581 Fax (800) 526-2617
E-mail: customerservice@longleafservices.org; mpress@unl.edu
Website: www.nebraskapress.unl.edu
James T. Carson, Robbie Ethridge & Greg O'Brien, Editors
Focuses on the investigation of Southeastern Indian history with the goals of encouraging further study & exposing the influences of Indian people on the wider South. Book reviews. *Subscription*: $31/year, individuals; $52/year, institutions.

NATIVE SPIRIT NEWS
P.O. Box 293127 • Nashville, TN 37229 (615) 889-9636
Cherokee Mangus, Editor; E-mail: cherokee mangus@juno.com
The only Indian newspaper in Tennessee since the Cherokee Nation's "Cherokee Phoenix," 1828. Begun 2001.

NATIVE SUN
North American Indian Association of Detroit
22720 Plymouth Rd. • Detroit, MI 48239
(313) 535-2966 Fax 535-8060; Andrew Butterfly, Editor
Reports on news & activities of the center; and issues of importance to American Indians of Wayne Co., Michigan. Monthly newsletter. 200 cir. $1/copy; $8/year. Begun 1975.

THE NATIVE VOICE
2218 Jackson Blvd., Suite 7 • Rapid City, SD 57702
(800) 449-8176; (605) 718-9141 Fax 718-9143
Frank J. King, III, Publisher/Editor-in-Chief
Lise Balk King, Co-editor; E-Mail: info@native-voice.com
Website: www.native-voice.com; Biweekly. 50,000 Cir.

NATIVE VOICES
The Mail Order Catalog, P.O. Box 180 • Summertown, TN 38483
(800) 695-2241
Source for books on Native history, culture, crafts, etc. Also children's books and Native music and video. Semiannually. No charge

NATIVE WIND
P.O. Box 205 • Plummer, ID 83851
(800) 524-1588; (208) 686-1176 Fax 686-1817
Website: www.gospelcom.net/ibs/native-wind. Monthly. Christian.

NATIVE WRITERS INK
Institute of Alaska Native Arts
P.O. Box 80583, 524 Third Ave. • Fairbanks, AK 99708
(907) 456-7491/7406

NATIVE YOUTH MEDIA INSTITUTE
Native Media Center, UND School of Communications
P.O. Box 7169 • Grand Forks, ND 58202 (701) 777-2478

NATIVE YOUTH MAGAZINE.COM
Website: www.nativeamericanyouth.com
Marry Kim Titla, Publisher. A handful of Native youth contribute articles on a regular basis.

NATIVENET
43 Jackson Rd. • Somerville, MA 02145
Gary Trujillo, Contact (617) 776-0121. Computer online service.

NAVAHO-A MAGAZINE FOR THE DINEH
Maazo Publishing, P.O. Box 1245 • Window Rock, AZ 86515
 (520) 729-2233
Covers Navajo Indian culture. Quarterly. $12/year; $28/year, foreign.

NAVAJO AREA NEWSLETTER
Office of Indian Affairs, P.O. Box 1060 • Gallup, NM 87301
 (505) 863-8314 Fax 863-8324; Frank Hardwick, Editor
Contains information of interest to Navajo Area, B.I.A.'s employees on
education, personnel actions, Bureau policy, etc. Monthly. 4,000 cir. Free.

NAVAJO COMMUNITY COLLEGE NEWSLETTER
Publications Dept. • Tsaile, AZ 86556

NAVAJO EDUCATION NEWSLETTER
Navajo Area Office, Office of Indian Affairs • Window Rock, AZ 86515

NAVAJO-HOPI OBSERVER
2224 E. Cedar Ave., Suite 2 • Flagstaff, AZ 86001
 (877) 627-3787; (928) 226-9696 Fax 226-1115
 Website: www.navajohopiobserver.com; Website: www.nhonews.com
 Doug Wells, Publisher; Wells Mahkee, Jr. (Zuni), Managing Editor
 Lynda Duffy, Editor
Description: Weekly newspaper containing tribal news, human interest stories,
community events, sports, school & health related information for the Western
Navajo tribe and all of the Hopi reservation. Circulation: 13,500. *Subscription*:
$40/year in Coconimo County; $50/year, all other areas.

NAVAJO SOUTHWEST SCENE
P.O. Box 580 • Window Rock, AZ 86515 (505) 371-5392

THE NAVAJO TIMES
The Navajo Times Publishing Co., P.O. Box 310 • Window Rock, AZ 86515
 (928) 871-6641 Fax 871-6409; Website: www.navajotimes.com
 Tom Arviso, Jr., Publisher/CEO; (928) 871-7359
  E-mail: tarviso@navajotimes.com
 Duane Beyal, Editor (928) 871-6632; E-mail: duane@navajotimes.com
 Paul DeMain, Board Chairperson
Reporters: Jason Begay, Chee Brossy, Bill Donovan,
 Jan-Mikael Patterson, Marley Shabala
Mission: To inform the Navajo people of events, news & issues of importance
to them, whether from within the boundaries of the Navajo Nation or throughout
the U.S. Book reviews. 4,500 cir. $90/year. Advertising. Begun 1959.

NAVAJOLAND PUBLICATIONS
Navajo Tribal Museum • Window Rock, AZ 86515

NETT LAKE NEWS
Nett Lake, MN 55772

NETWORK NEWS
Devils Lake Sioux Tribe, P.O. Box 400 • Fort Totten, ND 58335
 (701) 766-4211 Fax 766-4618

NEW MEXICO HISTORICAL REVIEW
1013 Mesa Vista Hall • U. of New Mexico • Albuquerque, NM 87131
 (505) 277-5839 Fax 277-0992; Website: www.unm.edu/~nmhr
 E-mail: nmhr@unm.edu; Dr. Durwood Ball, Editor
Covers New Mexico & Southwest history, its people and their cultures.
Includes articles, book reviews, essays & notes, & history news notes dealing
with American Indian topics. Quarterly journal. $48/year, institutions; $28/year,
individuals; single copies, $10. Advertising accepted. Begun 1926.

NEW MEXICO INDIAN AFFAIRS SOURCE
LaVilla Revera Bldg., 224 E. Palace Ave. • Santa Fe, NM 87501

THE NEW PHOENIX
The Free Cherokees, P.O. Box 414 • Chaptico, MD 20653
 (301) 884-0143
Official newsletter of the Free Cherokees, an independent tribe dedicated to
the preservation of authentic Native American teachings. $16/year.

NEWS FROM INDIAN COUNTRY
Indian Country Communications, Inc.
8558N County Rd. K • Hayward, WI 54843-2052
 (715) 634-5226 Fax 634-3243; (715) 634-1429 (Advertising)
Web site: www.indiancountrynews.com; E-mail: nficad@cheqnet.com
 Paul DeMain, Managing Editor & CEO;
 Kimberlie Acosta, Advertising/Marketing/Anchor on NHU/Host of RezStyle
 Willard Gouge, Subscriptions/Pow wow Updates
Columnists: Mark Trahant (Shoshone Bannock); Doug George Kanentio

(Mohawk); Richard Wagamese (Ojibwe); D.J. Vanas (Odawa);
 Kristine Shotley (Ojibwe); Arigon Star (Kickapoo); Arne Vainio, MD (Ojibwe);
 Jim Northrup (Ojibwe).
Correspondents/Contributors: Winona Duke Ojbwe); Sandra Hale Schulman;
 Albert Bender (Cherokee); Stan Bindell; Terry Crawford Jansen (Winnebago
 (Nebraska HoChunk); Ranee Fajardo Anstine; Dawn Karima Pettigrew
 (Creek/Cherokee); Carol Craig (Yakama); Sandra Wilson; Danny Beaton
 (Mohawk)
Description: National compact size newspaper (biweekly) with circulation in
Canada & 21 other countries. Covers news & community events of the
American Indian, business activities, and cultural events. Special features on
treaty rights, legislation; year-round powwow locations, etc. Also available as
an electronic edition sent to your PC through www.indiancountrynews.com
home page. $35/year. Advertising. EEO/AA Job Search. Begun 1977.

NEWS FROM NATIVE CALIFORNIA
c/o Heyday Books, P.O. Box 9145 • Berkeley, CA 94709
 (510) 549-2802 Fax 549-1889; Website: www.heydaybooks.com/news
 E-mail: nnc@heydaybooks.com
 Malcolm Margolin, Publisher; Margaret Dubin, Managing Editor
Written for major figures and organizations in the California Indian community,
from individuals on reservations to government officials. Quarterly magazine.
3,500 circ. $25/year; $5.95 per single copy; $45/year, foreign. Begun 1987.

NEWS & NOTES
American Indian Ritual Object/Repatriation Foundation
463 E. 57th St. • New York, NY 10022 (212) 980-9441 Fax 421-2746
Published twice yearly.

NEWSLETTER FROM THE NATION OF WOBAN AKI
Abenaki Self Help Association, P.O. Box 276 • Swanton, VT 05488
 (802) 868-2559 Fax 868-5118

NEWSWINDS
Institute of American Indian Arts , 83 Avan Nu Po Rd. • Santa Fe, NM 87505
 (505) 424-2351; Website: www.iaia.edu; E-mail: jvillani@iaia.edu
 John Villani, Editor
Quarterly review of IAIA activities & ongoing projects. Free to donors & alumni.

NEZ PERCE TRIBAL NEWSPAPER
P.O. Box 305 • Lapwai, ID 85341

NI-MI-KWA-ZOO-MIN
Minnesota Chippewa Tribe, P.O. Box 217 • Cass Lake, MN 56633

NI YA YO
Mohegan Tribe, 5 Crow Hill Rd. • Uncasville, CT 06382
 (800) MOHEGAN; Fax (860) 862-6115; Website: www.mohegan.nsn.us
 Jonathan S. Hamilton, Editor; Nancy Trimble, Managing Editor
Mohegan Tribal newspaper.

NISHNAWBE NEWS
Organization of North American Indian Students
Northern Michigan University - Mike Wright, Editor
140 University Center • Marquette, MI 49855
Monthly magazine. 8,500 cir. $5/year. Begun 1971.

NMIEA NEWSLETTER
New Mexico Indian Education Association (NMIEA)
P.O. Box 16356 • Santa Fe, NM 87506 (505) 989-5569

NOOKSACK NEWSLETTER
P.O. Box 157 • Deming, WA 98244

NORTH AMERICAN INDIAN MUSEUMS ASSOCIATION NEWSLETTER
c/o Seneca Iroquois National Museum
Allegany Indian Reservation, P.O. Box 442 • Salamanca, NY 14779
 (716) 945-1738

NORTH AMERICAN NATIVE AUTHORS CATALOG
The Greenfield Review Press. P.O. Box 308 • Greenfield Center, NY 12833
 (518) 583-1440 Fax 583-9741
 Website: http://www.nativeauthors.com
 James Bruchac, Editor; E-mail: asban@aol.com
A catalog of publications by Native American authors, including more than 600
titles from over 90 different publishers; mostly books, but including current and
back issues of Native periodicals. Catalog, $2. Begun 1980.

NORTH AMERICAN POW-WOW MAGAZINE
JTH Industries, 8129 N. 35th Ave. #2-305 • Phoenix, AZ 85051
 Jessie Two Hawks, Editor/Publisher

NORTH DAKOTA HISTORY: JOURNAL OF THE NORTHERN PLAINS
State Historical Society of North Dakota
612 E. Boulevard Ave. • Bismarck, ND 58505
  (701) 328-2799 Fax 328-3710
  Website: www.state.nd.us/hist/
  Janet Daley, Editor/Historian; E-mail: jdaley@state.nd.us
A quarterly scholarly journal that focuses on the history & culture of the northern Great Plains. Each issue contains 2/3 articles that are refereed. 1,800 circ. $4/issue; $30/year for individuals. subscribers are members of the Historical Society of North Dakota Foundation.

NORTH DAKOTA QUARTERLY
University of North Dakota, P.O. Box 7209 • Grand Forks, ND 58202
  (701) 777-3322 Fax 777-2373
  Robert W. Lewis, Editor; E-mail: ndq@und.nodak.edu
Quarterly university journal in the humanities, arts, and social sciences, with a special interest in Native American writing & writing about it. $25/year; $8 per single issue. Begun 1910.

NORTHERN CHEYENNE NEWS
P.O. Box 401 • Lame Deer, MT 59043

NORTHERN PUEBLOS AGENCY NEWS DIGEST
P.O. Box C-22 • Santa Fe, NM 87501

NORTHLAND NATIVE AMERICAN NEWS
Northland College • Ashland, WI 54806

NORTHWEST ARCTIC NUNA
Maniilaq Association, P.O. Box 256 • Kotzebue, AK 99752
  (907) 442-3311
Monthly newsletter includes local news & program information. No charge.

NORTHWEST ETHNIC NEWS
Ethnic Heritage Council, 305 Harrison St. #326 • Seattle, WA 98109
  (206) 443-1410 Fax 443-1408
  Sarah Sarai, Editor
Monthly newspaper covering arts and issues relevant to ethnic communities of the Pacific Northwest. 13,000 cir. $12/year. Begun 1984.

NORTHWEST NATIVE BUSINESS TODAY (NWNBT)
P.O. Box 275 • Everett, WA 98206
  (206) 595-8227
  Website: www.nwnativebusinesstoday.com
  E-mail: nwnbt@nwnativebusinesstoday.com

NORTHWESTERN BAND OF SHOSHONE NEWS
P.O. Box 12926 • Ogden, UT 84412
  (435) 734-2286 Fax 478-5713
  Website: www.nwbshoshonenews.com
  E-mail: bryhardin@nwbshoshonenews.com
  Bryon Hardin, Editor-in-Chief

NPAIHB HEALTH NEWS & NOTES
Northwest Portland Area Indian Health Board
520 SW Harrison #440 • Portland, OR 97201
  (503) 228-4185; Quarterly.

NTEC ENVIRONMENTAL INSIGHTS
National Tribal Environmental Council (NTEC)
4520 Montgomery Blvd. NE, Suite 3 • Albuquerque, NM 87109
  (505) 242-2175 Fax 242-2654
  Website: www.ntec.org/insights.htm
  E-mail: mvelarde@ntec.org; Bimonthly newsletter.

NU QWAH NEUM
North Fork Rancheria, P.O. Box 929 • North Fork, CA 93643
  (559) 877-2461 Fax 877-2467; Quarterly tribal newsletter

NUGGUAM
Quinault Indian Nation, P.O. Box 189 • Taholah, WA 98587
  (888) 616-8211; (360) 276-8211 Fax 276-4191
  Website: www.quinault.org; Monthly tribal newspaper.

NUMA NEWS
Fallon Paiute Shoshone Tribe, 565 Rio Vista Rd. • Fallon, NV 89406
  (775) 423-6075 Fax 423-5202
  E-mail: numanews@fpst.org
  Len George, Editor; Tribal newsletter.

O

O-HE-YOY NOH
Seneca Nation of Indians, Plummer Bldg., Box 231 • Salamanca, NY 14779
  Eldena Halftown, Editor
Monthly newsletter devoted to the Seneca Nation of Indians.
500 cir. Begun 1970.

OCB TRACKER; CALIFORNIA'S NATIVE NEWS
OCB Trading Post, 657 E. Arrow Hwy. #M • Glendora, CA 91740
  Website: www.ocbtracker.com; E-mail: ltr@ocbtracker.com

THE ODAWA RED LETTER
Andrews Cultural Resources, 2120 Pennsylvania • Harbor Springs, MI 49740
  (231) 526-0869; Wesley L. Andrews, Editor
A newspaper by and for the Little Traverse Bay Bands of Odawa Indians

ODAWA TRAILS
Little Traverse Bay Band of Odawa Indians
7500 Odawa Cir. • Harbor Springs, MI 49740
  (231) 242-1400 Fax 242-1414; Tribal newsletter

OGLALA WICAHPI
Journalism Department, Oglala Lakota College
P.O. Box 490 • Kyle, SD 57752

OJIBWA NEWS
Keweenaw Bay Indian Community, Rt. 1 Box 45 • Baraga, MI 49908
  (906) 353-6623; Paul Peterson, Editor

OJIBWE INAAJIMOWIN
Mille Lacs Band of Ojibwe, 43408 Oodena Dr. • Onamia, MN 56359
  (320) 292-8062 Fax -292-8091
  Website: www.millelacsojibwe.org/newsletr.asp
  Kelly Sam, Editor; E-mail: kellys@goffhoward.com
Monthly newspaper for members & tribal government employees.

OJIBWE NEWS
Native American Press, 3501 Lakeside Dr. NE • Bemidji, MN 56601
  (218) 444-7800; Website: www.press-on.net; E-mail: presson@isd.net
Weekly newspaper both print and online covering the Ojibwe bands in north Minnesota including Red Lake, Leech Lake, White Earth, & Mille Lacs reservations, and the Dakota Shakopee-Mdewakanton and lower Sioux in central and southern Minnesota. Subscription: $58/year for print and $50/year online. Advertising.

OKLAHOMA ANTHROPOLOGICAL SOCIETY NEWSLETTER
OK Anthropological Society, Rt. 1 Box 62B • Cheyenne, OK 73628
  (918) 682-5091; Frieda Odell, Editor & Publisher
Information on statewide archaeological investigations & articles of Oklahoma history & prehistory. Book reviews. Monthly newsletter (September-May). 600 cir. *Subscription*: $12/year. Individuals; $17/year, institutions; $20/year, foreign. Begun 1952.

OKLAHOMANS FOR INDIAN OPPORTUNITY NEWSLETTER
555 Constitution • Norman, OK 73069

OLD NORTHWEST CORPORATION NEWSLETTER
Sonotabac Prehistoric Indian Mounds and Museum
P.O. Box 941 • Vincennes, IN 47591
  (812) 885-4330/7679; Published monthly.

ON EAGLE'S WINGS
P.O. Box 8264 • Cranston, RI 02920
Newsletter of Native New England.

ON THE WAY UP
American Indian Science & Engineering Society
P.O. Box 9828 • Albuquerque, NM 87119-9828
  (505) 765-1052 Fax 765-5608. Published three times per year.

ONEIDA NATION NEWSLETTER
Oneida Indian Nation, P.O. Box 1 • Vernon, NY 13476
  (315) 361-7711 Fax 361-7721; Ray Halbritter, Nation Representative
  E-mail: sbarbano@oneida-nation.org; Website: www.oneida-news.net
Provides tribal and reservation news.

OREGON DIRECTORY OF AMERICAN INDIAN RESOURCES
Commission on Indian Services, 167 State Capitol • Salem, OR 97310
  (503) 986-1067 Fax 986-1071

Gladine G. Ritter, Editor; E-mail: gladine.g.ritter@state.or.us
Web site: http://www.leg.state.or.us. Published biennially.

OREGON INDIAN EDUCATION NEWSLETTER
Oregon Indian Education Association, 2125 N. Flint • Portland, OR 97227
(503) 275-9600

OREGON INDIANS: CULTURE, HISTORY & CURRENT AFFAIRS
Oregon Historical Society Press, 1230 SW Park Ave. • Portland, OR 97205

OSAGE NATION NEWS
619 Kihekah • Pawhuska, OK 74056 (918) 287-5668 Fax 699-5282
  Website: www.osagenews.org; E-mail: osagenews@osgaetribe.org
  Shannon Shaw-Duty (Osage), Editor; E-mail: sshaw@osagetribe.org
  Benny Polacca (Hopi/Havasupai/Pima/Tohono O'odham),
  Staff Writer; E-mail: bpolacca@osagetribe.org
  Jacelle Ramon-Sauberan (Thono O'odham), Reporter
  E-mail: jrsauberan@osagetribe.org
  Chalene Toehay (Osage/Kiowa), Photographer, Assistant Editor
  E-mail: ctoehay@osagetribe.org
Awards, honors: Won first place for 2012 General Excellence from the Native American Journalists Association; first place for 2012 Personal Columns from the Oklahoma Press Association.

OSHKAABEWIS NATIVE JOURNAL
Indian Studies Program, Bemidji State U.
1500 Birchmont Dr. NE, Staford Hall, Box 19 • Bemidji, MN 56601

OTSININGO CIRCLE
Iroquois Studies Association Newsletter
28 Zevan Rd. • Johnson City, NY 13790
  (607) 729-0016 Fax 770-9610
  Website: www.otsiningo.com; E-Mail: isal@otsiningo.com

OURSELVES
Minnesota Chippewa Tribe, P.O. Box 217 • Cass Lake, MN 56633

OWENS VALLEY INDIAN EDUCATION CENTER NEWSLETTER
P.O. Box 1648 • Bishop, CA 93514

OYATE-ANISHNANABE NEWS
American Indian Student Cultural Center
104 Jones Hall, 27 Pleasant SE • Minneapolis, MN 55404

OYATE WO'WAPI
Tahana Whitecrow Foundation, P.O. Box 18181 • Salem, OR 97305
  (503) 585-0564. Quarterly.

P

PAN-AMERICAN INDIAN ASSOCIATION NEWS
8335 Sevigny Dr. • N. Fort Myers, FL 33917-1705
  (941) 731-7029 or 543-7727
  Cindy "Spirit Catcher" Barnard, Editor
Heritage revival for Native Americans and other tribal peoples. Help in genealogy; networking of groups & resources. Book reviews. Irregular. 16-page tabloid. 5,000 cir. $5/year; $10/year, foreign. Advertising. Begun 1984.

PANA PANA NEWSLETTER
National Indian Youth Council, 318 Elm, SE • Albuquerque, NM 87102
  (505) 247-2251 Fax 247-4251

PANHANDLE-PLAINS HISTORICAL REVIEW
Panhandle-Plains Historical Museum
P.O. Box 967, W.T. Station. 2401 Fourth Ave. • Canyon, TX 79016
  (806) 655-7194

PAPAGO BULLETIN
P.O. Box 364 • Sells, AZ 85634

PASCUA PUEBLO NEWS
4821 W. Calle Vicam • Tucson, AZ 85706

PATHWAY NEWS
National American Indian Housing Council
900 2nd St., NE #305 • Washington, DC 20002
  (202) 789-1754 Fax 789-1758; Quarterly newsletter

THE PAYSON ROUNDUP
Tonto Apache Tribe, P.O. Box 2520 • Payson, AZ 85547

(928) 474-5251 Fax 474-1893; E-mail: editor@payson.com
Tribal newspaper.

THE PEOPLE BEFORE COLUMBUS
Southwest Indian Student Coalition
1812 Los Lomas • Albuquerque, NM 87131
  (503) 277-6065; Annual journal.

THE PEOPLE'S VOICE
Kanienkehaka Territory, P.O. Box 216 • Hogansburg, NY 13655
  (518) 358-3022; Cindy Terrance, Editor
Weekly newspaper for the St. Regis Mohawk Reservation (both U.S. & Canadian portions); also serves Mohawk people in Kahnawake Quebec (near Montreal) & California. Begun 1987.

PEQUOT TIMES
Mashantucket Pequot Tribal Nation
P.O. Box 3130, 110 Pequot Trail • Mashantucket, CT 06338-3130
  (860) 396-6572 Fax 396-6570; Website: www.pequottimes.com
  E-mail: pequottimes@mptn.org; Anthony Kulla, Editor
Monthly tribal newspaper. Free; circ: 25,000. Begun 1992.

PHOENIX INDIAN CENTER NEWSLETTER
333 W. Indian School Rd. • Phoenix, AZ 85013 (602) 256-2000

THE PIIKANI SUN "OOKAMOOTAPI" (The Truth Shall Prevail)
Spirit Talk Press, P.O. Box 477, East Glacier
Blackfoot Nation, MT 59417 (406) 338-2882
  Website: www.blackfoot.org
  E-mail: longstandingbearchief@blackfoot.org
Published quarterly.

PILGRIM – KATERI NEWS & EVENTS
Shrine of Our Lady of Martyrs, 136 Shrine Rd. • Fultonville, NY 12016
  (518) 853-3033 Fax 853-3051; Beth Lynch, Editor
Newsletter for persons interested in the three martyrs venerated here: Sts. Isaac Joques, Rene Goupil, and John Lalande - and in the Shrine itself, and in Blessed Kateri Tekakwitha, the young Mohawk-Algonquin woman who was born here. She was canonized by the Roman Catholic Church on 10/21/2012.

PIMA-MARICOPA ECHO
Gila River Indian Community, P.O. Box 97 • Sacaton, AZ 85247

PLAINS ANTHROPOLOGIST
Plains Anthropological Society
c/o PRIAM, P.O. Box 1535 • Panhandle, TX 79068
  (806) 537-5040 Fax 537-3656
  Website: www.ou.edu/cas/archsur/plainsanth
  Susana R. Katz, PhD, Editor; E-mail: katzes-priam@msn.com
Quarterly peer review journal of the Plains Anthropological Society containing articles, short reports & book reviews pertaining to all aspects of anthropology in the Great Plains region of the U.S. & Canada. Book reviews. 900 cir. $45/year, individuals; $30/year, students; $55/year, institutions. Began 1954.

PLAINS TALK
State Historical Society of North Dakota
612 E. Boulevard Ave. • Bismarck, ND 58505
  (701) 328-2799 Fax 328-3710
  Janet Daley, Editor; E-Mail: jdaley@state.nd.us
  Website: www.state.nd.us/hist/
Quarterly newsletter about the activities of the State Historical Society of North Dakota. No charge to members.

POARCH CREEK NEWS
Poarch Band of Creek Indians, Route 3, Box 243-A • Atmore, AL 36502

POCAHONTAS TRAILS - QUARTERLY
Pocahontas Trails Genealogical Society
6015 Robin Hill Dr. • Lakeport, CA 95453
Focuses on the pursuit and study of the genealogy of Pocahontas and Powhatan. Membership dues. Begun 1983.

POINT HOPE NEWS
Point Hope Village • Point Hope, AK 99766

POKEGNEK YADJDANAWA
Pokagon Band of Potawatomi, P.O. Box 180 • Dowagiac, MI 49047
  (616) 782-8998 Fax 782-6882; Monthly tribal newsletter

PONCA CITY NEWS
Ponca Tribe • Ponca City, OK 74601

PORTLAND PUBLIC SCHOOLS
INDIAN EDUCATION ACT PROJECT NEWSLETTER
Portland Public Schools, 8020 N.E. Tillamook • Portland, OR 97213
(503) 280-6474

POTAWATOMI TRAVELING TIMES
P.O. Box 340 • Cranden, WI 54520
E-mail: times@fcpotawatomi.com
Winda Collins, Managing Editor; Bi-weekly tribal newspaper.

POTTERY SOUTHWEST
Albuquerque Archaeological Society
6207 Mossman Place NE • Albuquerque, NM 87110
(505) 881-1675; Carries news and queries on prehistoric pottery of the Indians of New Mexico, Arizona, Utah, Colorado, and parts of Texas and Mexico. Quarterly. $3/yr. Begun 1974.

POW WOW CALENDAR
Native American Cooperative, P.O. Box 27626 • Tucson, AZ 85726
(520) 622-4900
Quarterly schedule of events. Free with priority mail SASE.

POW WOW TRAIL NEWS
P.O. Box 1132 • Fairbanks, AK 99707

PUEBLO HORIZON
Indian Pueblo Cultural Center, 2401 12th St. NW • Albuquerque, NM 87102

PUEBLO COUNCIL NEWS
P.O. Box 3256 • Albuquerque, NM 87190

PUEBLO TIMES
Pueblo Times Publishing Co., 1860 Don Pasqual Rd. • Los Lunas, NM 87031
(505) 865-4508; George E. Gorospe, Owner/Publisher
Weekly (Wednesday) newspaper for the 19 Indian Pueblos of northern New Mexico. Distribution includes part of the Navajo Nation. Circ. 10,000. Begun 1985.

PUYALLUP TRIBAL NEWS
4412 6th Ave., Suite 4 • Tacoma, WA 98406
(253) 759-5773 Fax 759-5780
Website: www.puyalluptribalnews.net
E-mail: news@tacomaweekly.com
John Weymer, Publisher; Weekly newspaper.

PYRAMID LAKE INDIAN RESERVATION NEWSLETTER
P.O. Box 256 • Nixon, NV 89424

Q

QUALLA RESERVATION NEWS
Cherokee Agency • Cherokee, NC 28719

QUECHAN NEWS
Fort Yuma Indian Reservation, P.O. Box 1352 • Yuma, AZ 85364
(760) 572-0213 Fax 572-2102

QUIN-A-MONTH-A'
Stockbridge Historical Museum, Route 1, Box 300 • Bowler, WI 54416

QUINAULT NATURAL RESOURCES
Quinault Department of Natural Resources & Economic Development
P.O. Box 189 • Tahola, WA 98587. Jacqueline Storm, Contact

R

RAIN NOTES
Recruitment and Retention of American Indians in Nursing (RAIN)
UND College of Nursing, P.O. Box 9025 • Grand Forks, ND 58202
(701) 777-4519 Fax 777-4558; Published twice yearly.

THE RAVEN CHRONICLES
12346 Sand Point Way N.E. • Seattle, WA 98125
(206) 941-2955; Website: www.ravenchronicles.org
E-mail: editors@ravenchronicles.org
Phoebe Bosche (Seattle), Editor & Publisher
Philip H. Red Eagle (Tacoma), Editor & Publisher
Multi-cultural journal of the arts and literature, including Native American literature. $12/yr. $3 sample issue.

THE RAWHIDE PRESS
Spokane Indian Tribe, P.O. Box 100 • Wellpinit, WA 99040
(509) 458-6587; E-mail: rawhide@spokanetribe.com
Monica Peone, Editor; Monthly newspaper covering news regarding Indian affairs including historical features, biographies, etc. on Indian culture. Book reviews. 800 cir. $12/year. Advertising. Begun 1972.

RED CLIFF TRIBAL NEWS
88385 Pike Rd. • Bayfield, WI 54814
Red Cliff Reservation's monthly newspaper. $32 per year.

RED CLOUD COUNTRY
Red Cloud Indian School, Holy Rosary Mission, Pine Ridge, SD 57770
(605) 867-5491; Fr. Roger, S.V., Editor
Contains information about Red Cloud School. Sent to donors, friends and benefactors of the school. Quarterly newsletter. $10/year.

RED HILLS NEWSLETTER
Kaibab Tribal Council, Tribal Affairs Bldg. • Fredonia, AZ 86022

RED INK: A NATIVE AMERICAN STUDENT PUBLICATION
American Indian Studies , The Harvill Bldg, Room 218
P.O. Box 210076 • Tucson, AZ 85721
(520) 621-7108 Fax 621-7952; E-mail: redink@ccit.arizona.edu
Website: www.w3.arizona.edu/~aisp.redink.htm
Ian Record & Christina Castro, Editors; A semi-annual student-run publication (magazine) that solicits creative writing and artistic submissions from indigenous peoples of the Western Hemisphere, including: poetry, short stories, original artwork, book & film reviews. Red Ink also publishes scholarly articles dealing with contemporary indigenous issues. One-year individual subscription is $15; institutional subscriptions is $25. Begun 1990.

RED LAKE NATION NEWSPAPER - RED LAKE NET NEWS
P.O. Box 80 • Redby, MN 56670 (218) 679-5995
Website: www.rlnn.com; E-mail: news@rlnn.com
Michael Barrett, Editor; E-mail: mbarrett@rlnn.com
Newsletter for the Red Lake Band of Chippewa Indians.

RED VOICES
American Indian Training Institute, Inc.
4153 Northgate Blvd. • Sacramento, CA 95834
(916) 920-0731

REDSKIN MAGAZINE
P.O. Box 321 • Ohsweken, ON N0A 1M0
(877) 794-0804; (519) 518-2009
Website: redskinmargazine.ca; E-mail: info@redskinmagazine.ca
Jody Martin, Owner; Mathew Hill, Operator
Hilary Chambers, Associate Editor/Media Relations
The First Indigenous Adult Entertainment Magazine.

REDSMOKE INDIAN NEWS
Vietnam Era Veterans Inter-Tribal Association
805 Rosa • Shawnee, OK 74801 (405) 382-3128
Provides news of interest on American Indians who served in the Vietnam War. Quarterly.

THE RENEGADE: A STRATEGY JOURNAL OF INDIAN OPINION
Survival of American Indian Associations
7803-A Samurai Dr., SE • Olympia, WA 98503
(206) 459-2679. Published annually.

THE RENO TALKING LEAF
Nevada Urban Indians, Inc., 917 E. 6th St. • Reno, NV 89512
(702) 329-2573; Contains community events, activities, services & resources, and educational articles. Monthly newsletter.

REPORT TO INDIAN COUNTRY
Senate Committee on Indian Affairs
838 Hart Senate Office Bldg. • Washington, DC 20510
(202) 224-2251 Fax 228-2589

RESERVATION TIMES
Seneca Nation Education Department, 1500 Route 438 • Irving, NY 14081

REZNET NEWS
University of Montana, School of Journalism, Missoula, MT 59812
(406) 243-2191; Website: www.reznetnews.org
E-mail: dmcauliffe@reznetnews.org
Denny McAuliffe, Founder & Project Director

Steven Chin, Managing Editor; Online newspaper by Native American college students. Project of the University of Montana School of Journalism and the Robert C. Maynard Institute for Journalism Education. Winner of the Native American Journalists Association's 2003 Native Media Award for Best Internet News Site, each year, Reznet hires 20 Native American college students from as reporters/photographers to cover their tribal communities & colleges. Purpise: To produce more Native Americans entering professional journalism.

RIDGE NOTES
Chieftains Museum, P.O. Box 373 • Rome, GA 30162
 (706) 291-9494; Janine E. Joslin, Editor
Quarterly membership newsletter focusing on museum activities and historical articles on the region's history.

ROCKY BOY'S NEWS
Rocky Boy's Rte. • Box Elder, MT 59521

ROSEBUD SIOUX HERALD
P.O. Box 430 • Rosebud, SD 57570

ROUGH ROCK NEWS
Dine'Biolta'Daahani-Rough Rock Demonstration School
P.O. Box 217 • Chinle, AZ 86503
Provides a view of the life-style and attitudes of a desert community that is determined to control its own destiny. Published monthly of academic year.

S

SAC & FOX NEWS
Rt. 2, Box 246 • Stroud, OK 74079 (918) 968-3525 Fax 968-4837
 Website: www.talksauk.com; Boyd W. Cummings, Managing Editor

SACRED DIRECTIONS
P.O. Box 293688 • Lewisville, TX 75029 (214) 436-7727

SAIIC NEWSLETTER
South & Meso American Indian Information Center
P.O. Box 28703 • Oakland, CA 94604 (510) 834-4263 Fax 834-4264
Contains articles about issues of importance to indigenous people in Central and South America.

SAIL: STUDIES IN AMERICAN INDIAN LITERATURES
Association for the Study of American Indian Literatures
Michigan State University, 273 Bessey Hall
Dept. of American Thought & Language
East Lansing, MI 48824—1033 (517) 355-5256 Fax 353-5250
 Malea Powell, General Editor; E-mail: sail2@msu.edu
 Website: www.oncampus.richmond.edu/faculty/asail/sail-hp.html
Advertising & Subscription: University of Nebraska Press
Customer Service, Lincoln, NE 68588-0255
(800) 755-1105; (402) 472-3584 Robert M. Nelson, Contact
 E-mail: rnelson@richmond.edu; Website: www.nebraskapress.unl.edu
Quarterly scholarly journal that focuses exclusively on American Indian literatures, including written, spoken & visual texts created by Native peoples. Subscription rates: $28 (individuals) and $56 (institutions) per year. Outside the U.S. add $20; Canadian subscribers add 7% GST. Available online through Project MUSE. Back issues available. Begun 1977.

SAN CARLOS MOCCASIN
P.O. Box 0 • San Carlos, AZ 85550 (520) 475-2361

SANTA FE INDIAN MARKET MAGAZINE
Website: www.santafenewmexican.com

SATWIWA NEWS
Friends of Satwiwa, 4126 Potrero Rd. • Newbury Park, CA 91320
 (805) 499-2837 (phone & fax)

THE SAULT TRIBE NEWS
Sault Ste. Marie Tribe of Chippewa Indians
523 Ashmun St., Sault Ste. Marie, MI 49783
 (906) 635-6050 Fax 635-4969
 E-mail: saulttribenews@saulttribe.net; Monthly newspaper

SAY MAGAZINE
1522 Logan Ave. • Winnpeg, MB, Canada R3E 1S3
 Website: www.saymag.com; E-mail: info@saymag.com
 Kirk Say, Creator; Lifestyle magazine for Native people. Webstore.- University & College Guide for Native Students, $6.95; Aboriginal Tourism (Canada) Guide, $5. Established 2002.

SCHOHARIE MUSEUM OF THE IROQUOIS INDIAN-MUSEUM NOTES
P.O. Box 158 • Schoharie, NY 12157
 (518) 295-8553/234-2276
 Dr. John P. Ferguson, Editor
A newsletter reporting on the Museum's activities; scholarly articles on Iroquois. Subscription: $10/year. Complimentary copies upon request.

THE SCOUT
Fort Berthold Community College
P.O. Box 490 • New Town, ND 58763 (701) 627-3274 Fax 627-3609

SEALASKA SHAREHOLDER
Sealaska Corporation, One Sealaska Plaza, 400 • Juneau, AK 99801
 Ross Soboleff, Editor

SEASONS
The National Native American AIDS Prevention Center
 436 14th St., Suite 1020 • Oakland, CA 94609
 (510) 444-2051 Fax 444-1593; Ronald Rowell, MPH, Director
 Andrea Green Rush, Editor; A quarterly newsletter featuring articles by Native Americans with HIV & Native American health educators, and health care providers. 3,000 circulation. No charge.

SECCI NEWSLETTER
Southeastern Cherokee Confederacy
120 Will Hatcher Rd. • Albany, GA 31705
 White Wolf Crider & Elk Dreamer Crider, Editors
Monthly newsletter of the Southeastern Cherokee Confederacy.

SEMINOLE TRIBUNE
Seminole Tribe of Florida, 6300 Stirling Rd. • Hollywood, FL 33024
 (954) 967-3416 Fax 967-3482; Virginia Mitchell, Editor
 Website: www.seminoletribe.com/tribune; E-mail: tribune@semtribe.com
Biweekly newspaper providing news about the Seminole Tribe from five reservations in Florida; also, news about other tribes across the country. Book reviews. $30/year. 6,000 cir. Advertising. Begun 1973.

SENECA TRIBAL NEWSLETTER
Cattauragus Indian Reservation, 1490 Route 438 • Irving, NY 14081
 Debbie Hoag, Editor

SENTINEL
White Shield School, HC 1-Box 45 • Roseglen, ND 58775
 (701) 743-4350

THE SENTINEL
National Congress of American Indians
1301 Connecticut Ave., NW #200 • Washington, DC 20036
 (202) 466-7767 Fax 466-7797; Emily Segar, Editor
Focuses on national issues affecting Native Americans. Examines federal legislation and governmental policy developments that affect Indians. Book reviews. Monthly magazine. 3,000 cir. $25/year, individuals; $50/year, institutions. Advertising. Begun 1944.

SHAMAN'S DRUM
Cross-Cultural Shaman's Network
Box 270 • Williams, OR 97544 (541) 846-1313 Fax 846-1204
 Timothy White, Editor; Covers experiential international shamanism, native medicine ways & spirituality. Book reviews. Quarterly magazine. 14,000 cir.$6/copy; $18/year, individuals; $35/year, institutions; $24/year, foreign. Advertising. Begun 1985.

THE SHAWNEE NEWS-STAR
215 N. Bell • Shawnee, OK 74801
 (800) 332-2305; (405) 273-4200 Fax 273-4207
 Website: www.news-star.com; Website: www.onlineshawnee.com
 Michael Hengel, Publisher
 E-mail: michael.hengel@news-star.com
 Mike McCormick, Executive Editor
 E-mail: michael.mccormick@news-star.com
 Karen Green, Managing Ed.; E-mail: karen.green@news-star.com
Shawnee Nation news.

SHENANDOAH NEWSLETTER
736 W. Oklahoma St. • Appleton, WI 54914
 (414) 832-9525; Paul A. Skenandore (Scan doa), Publisher/Editor
21-page monthly newsletter which discusses the history & legal rights of the native peoples of Great Turtle Island. Reports news of treaty & discrimination disputes. 1,000 circulation. $1.75 each; $17.50/year, individuals; $22.50/year, institutions; $30/year, foreign. Begun 1973.

SHO-BAN NEWS
Shoshone Bannock Tribes, Fort Hall Indian Reservation
P.O. Box 900 • Fort Hall, ID 83203
(208) 478-3701/3888 Fax 478-3702
Website: www.shobannews.com; E-mail: shobnews@ida.net
Lori Edmo-Suppah, Editor
Roselynn Wahtomy, Assistant Editor; Carmencita Mejia, Reporter
Weekly tribal newspaper covering local, regional and national news of interest to American Indians. Advertising accepted. Subscription: $30/year, Shoshone-Bannock tribal members; $35/year, non-members; 75¢ each. Begun 1970.

SHO-PAI NEWS
Shoshone-Paiute Tribes of the Duck Valley Indian Reservation
P.O. Box 219 • Owyhee, NV 89832 (208) 759-3100 Fax 759-3928
Website: www.shopaitribes.org; E-mail: shopainews@shopai.org
Yvonne Powers, Editor; E-mail: powers.yvonne@shopai.org

SHOALWATER BAY NEWSLETTER
Shoalwater Bay Indian Tribe, P.O. Box 130 • Tokeland, WA 98590
(800) 633-5218; (360) 267-8202 Fax 267-6778
E-mail: lthomas@shoalwaterbay-nsn..gov
Leah Thomas, Publisher/Editor
Monthly tribal newsletter.

SHOOTING STAR
Eastern Shawnee Tribe of Oklahoma Tribal Newsletter
P.O. Box 350 • Seneca, MO 64865 (918) 666-2435 Fax 666-3325

SICANGU SUN TIMES
P.O. Box 750 • Rosebud, SD 57570 (605) 747-2058 Fax 747-2789
Website: www.sicangusun.tipod.com/sicangusun
E-mail: sicangusun@mail.com; PR Gregg-Bear, Editor
Biweekly tribal newspaper.

SILETZ NEWS
Confederated Tribes of Siletz , P.O. Box 549 • Siletz, OR 97380
(503) 444-2532 ext. 134; Website: www.ctsi.nsn.us/pio.html
Monthly tribal newspaper.

THE SINGING WINDS NEWSLETTER
Council of Three Rivers American Indian Center, Inc.
Rt. 2, Box 247-A • Dorseyville, PA 15238
(412) 782-4457 Fax 767-4808; Russell Simms, Editor
Monthly newsletter focusing on the activities of the Center.

SINTE GLESKA COLLEGE NEWS
Library-Media Center, Box 107, Rosebud Reservation • Mission, SD 57555

SIOUX JOURNAL
Cheyenne River Sioux Tribal Council
P.O. Box 590 • Eagle Butte, SD 57625

SIOUX MESSENGER
Yankton Sioux Tribe, Route 248 • Marty, SD 57361

SMOKE & FIRE NEWS
P.O. Box 166 • Grand Rapids, OH 43522
(419) 878-8564 Fax 878-3653
Donlyn Meyers & David Weir, Editors/Publishers
Monthly newspaper that covers all living history periods on a regular schedule supplying Living History Participants with event dates, articles, recipes, updates, information resources, cartoons, etc. $18 per year.

SMOKE SIGNALS
Bacone College, 2299 Old Bacone Rd. • Muskogee, OK 74403

SMOKE SIGNALS
Baltimore American Indian Center, 113 S. Broadway • Baltimore, MD 21231
(410) 675-3535; Archie Lynch, Editor
Contains news & events concerning the Native American community of the Baltimore metropolitan area. No charge; donations accepted.

SMOKE SIGNALS
Colorado River Indian Tribes, Route 1, Box 23-B • Parker, AZ 85344

SMOKE SIGNALS
Northeastern Native American Association, Inc.
P.O. Box 230266 • Hollis, NY 11423 (718) 978-7057 Fax 978-7200
E-Mail: rgibson230@aol.com; William "Wassaja" Gibson, President
Quarterly newsletter.

SMOKE SIGNALS
Confederated Tribes of the Grand Ronde Community
9615 Grand Ronde Rd. • Grand Ronde, OR 97347
(800) 422-0232; (503) 879-2254 Fax 879-2173
Dean Rhodes, Editor; E-mail: dean.rhodes@grandronde.org
Ron Karten, Staff Writer; E-mail: ron.karten@grandronde.org
Twice monthly tribal newspaper, 5,500 cir. Covers Grand Ronde tribal news, local & regional tribes. Award winner - Best Layout and Design for twice-monthly Native paper given by the Native American Journalists Association. No charge. Begun 1980.

SMOKE SIGNALS
Dallas Inter-Tribal Center, 209 E. Jefferson Blvd. • Dallas, TX 75203
(214) 941-1050 Fax 941-6537; Cindy McKnight, Editor
Covers the news and events of the Native American community in the Dallas area. Quarterly newsletter. 1,200 cir. (nationwide distribution). No charge.

SMOKI CEREMONIALS & SNAKE DANCE
Smoki People, P.O.Box 123 • Prescott, AZ 86302
(520) 778-5228; Published annually.

SNEE-NEE-CHUM
Nooksack Indian Tribe, P.O. Box 157 • Deming, WA 98925
(360) 592-0162; Website: www.nooksack-tribe.org/newsletters
Carmen Solomon, Executive Editor
E-mail: csolomon@nooksack-tribe.org

SOTA IYA YE YAPI
Sisseton Wahpeton Oyate Tribe of the Lake Traverse Reservation
P.O. Box 509 • Agency Village, SD 57262
(605) 938-4452 Fax 938-4676; Website: www.earthskyweb.com/sota.html
E-mail: earthskyweb@cs.com; C.D. Floro, Managing Editor
Weekly newspaper of the Sisseton-Wahpeton Dakota Tribe.

THE SOUNDER
Skokomish Tribal Nation, 80 N. Tribal Center Rd. • Skokomish, WA 98584
(360) 426-4232 ext. 253 Fax 877-5943; E-mail: sounder@skokomish.org
Mark Warren, Editor. Monthly tribal newspaper.

THE SOURCE
New Mexico Office of Indian Affairs
O1A, Villa Rivera Bldg., 224 E. Palace Ave. • Santa Fe, NM 87501
(505) 827-6440 Fax 827-7308
Provides information on intergovern-mental relations, commissioner activities, culture, arts, and educational issues of the American Indians. Triannual. Begun 1985.

SOUTH DAKOTA HISTORY
South Dakota State Historical Society
900 Governors Dr. • Pierre, SD 57501-2217
(605) 773-3458 Fax 773-6041; Website: www.sdhistory.org
Nancy Tystad Koupal, Editor
A quarterly scholarly, refereed journal designed for professional historians and lay readers interested in Western & Great Plains history. Book reviews. 1,600 circ. $35/year; $60, foreign. Begun 1972.

SOUTHERN CALIFORNIA INDIAN CENTER, INC. - NEWS
10175 Slater Ave. #150 • Fountain Valley, CA 92708
(714) 962-6673; Ms. Starr, Executive Director
Cathi Garfield, Editor
Monthly newsletter. Community articles, news on local powwow; promotes in-house programs. Complimentary copiesupon request. Begun 1985.

SOUTHERN CHEYENNE & ARAPAHO NATION NEWS
P.O. Box 91 • Concho, OK 73002

SOUTHERN PUEBLOS AGENCY BULLETIN
BIA, 1000 Indian School Rd., NW • Albuquerque, NM 87103

SOUTHERN UTE DRUM
P.O. Box 737 • Ignacio, CO 81137 (970) 563-0118

SOUTHOLD INDIAN MUSEUM NEWS
1080 Main Bayview Rd., P.O. Box 268 • Southold, NY 11971
(631) 965-5577; E-mail: indianmuseum@aol.com
Ellen Barcel, President; Quarterly newsletter.

SOUTHWEST MUSEUM NEWS
P.O. Box 41558 • Los Angeles, CA 90041
(213) 261-2164 ext. 233

SOUTHWESTERN ASSOCIATION FOR INDIAN AFFAIRS, INC.
INDIAN MARKET MAGAZINE
P.O. Box 969 • Santa Fe, NM 87504-0969
 (505) 983-5220 (505) 983-5220
Quarterly journal covering Indian arts, crafts & writing. 1,000 cir. $15/Year.
Begun 1964.

SOVEREIGN NATIONS
Tribal Self-Governance Demonstration Project
Alumni Indian Business Council, 2616 Kwina Rd. • Bellingham, WA 98226

SPEAKING LEAVES
American Indian Cultural Group, P.O. Box 2000 • Vacaville, CA 95688

SPEAKING OF OURSELVES - NI-MI-KWA-ZOO-MIN
Minnesota Chippewa Tribe, P.O. Box 217 • Cass Lake, MN 56633

THE SPIKE
P.O.Box 368 • Milltown, NJ 08850
 (908) 656-0074; Website: http://typn.com/thespike
Monthly newsletter on Native East Coast events.

SPILYAY TYMOO
Confederated Tribes of Warm Springs
P.O. Box 870 • Warm Springs, OR 97761
 (541) 553-1338 Fax 553-1552; Dave McMechan, Executive Director
 E-mail: dmcmechan@wstribes.org; Bi-weekly newsletter.

SPIRIT!
Native American Resource Center
Pembroke State University • Pembroke, NC 28372 (919) 521-4214
Contains news of projects and events of the Center.
Quarterly. No charge. Begun 1987.

SPIRIT OF CRAZY HORSE
Leonard Peltier Defense Committee
P.O. Box 583 • Lawrence, KS 66044
 (785) 842-5774 Fax 842-5796; Pat Benabe, Editor
 E-Mail: lpdc@idir.net
 Website: www.members.xoom.com/freepeltier/index.html.
Bimonthly newspaper dealing with the current campaign to free Leonard
Peltier, as well as Indigenous, environmental, social and political issues.
Statements from Leonard Peltier appear in each publication. $15/year; $22,
international; Free to prisoners.

SPIRIT TALK NEWS
Spirit Talk Press, The Blackfoot Nation
P.O. Box 477 • East Glacier, MT 59434
 (406) 338-2882; E-mail: longstandingbearchief@blackfoot.org
 Long Standing Bear Chief, Editor
Newsletter issued 6/year in celebration of Indian culture. Topics include:
Respect for the earth, the sacredness of the family, stories and legends,
profiles of significant people, Indian music and dance, Indian art and artisans,
history; books, movie and video reviews; cultural seminars; places to visit in
Indian Country; and events in Indian Country: celebrations, rodeos and fairs.
5,000 cir. $8.50 per year. Begun 1994.

SPIRIT WALKER
Native American Indian Community Newsletter
Rd. 2 Box 247A • Kittanning, PA 16201 (412) 548-7335

SPIRIT WIND
United Native American Educational Council
P.O. Box 17052 • Spartanburg, SC 29301 (803) 574-8633

SPRING CREEK PACKET
3925 Bissell Rd. • Springfield, IL 62707 (217) 525-2698
Lists powwows; other Native news items. Monthly. $15/year.

SQUOL - QUOL
Lummi Nation Tribal Office, 2616 Kwina Rd. • Bellingham, WA 98255
 (360) 384-1489

SRMT KAWENNI:IOS
St. Regis Mohawk Reservation, RR 1, Box 8A • Hogansburg, NY 13655
 (518) 358-2272 Fax 358-3203; Website: www.srmt-nsn.gov
 E-mail: public.information@srmt-nsn.gov
 David T. Straddon, Editor
Monthly tribal newsletter covering news of the St. Regis Mohawk community
and the Akwesasne Cultural Center. Circulation: 1,100 cir. Free. Began 1970.

STANDING ROCK SIOUX TRIBAL NEWSLETTER
P.O. Box D • Fort Yates, ND 58538

STILLY SMOKE SIGNALS
Stillaguamish Tribe of Indians Quarterly tribal newsletter.
P.O. Box 277 • Arlington, WA 98223
 (360) 652-7362 Fax 659-3113
 Website: www.stillaguamish.com; Isiah Coley, Director

STOCKBRIDGE MUNSEE TRIBAL NEWSLETTER
RR 1 • Bowler, WI 54416

STOWW INDIAN VOICE
P.O. Box 578 • Sumner, WA 98390

STUDIES IN AMERICAN INDIAN LITERATURES (SAIL)
Publisher: University of Nebraska Press
1111 Lincoln Mall • Lincoln, NE 68588-0630
 (800) 755-1105 or (402) 472-3584 Fax (800) 526-2617 or (402) 472-6214
 E-Mail: journals@unlnotes.unl.edu
 Website: www.nebraskapress.unl.edu/journalinfo/23.html
 Daniel Heath Justice & James H. Cox, Editors
Description: SAIL is a journal of the Association for the Study of American
Indian Literatures and the only journal in the U.S. focused exclusively on
American Indian literatures. It defines "literatures" broadly to include all written,
spoken, and visual texts created by Native peoples. SAIL is a per-reviewed
scholarly journal, published quarterly, and includes reviews, interviews,
bibliographies, scholarly and theoretical articles. $28/yr., individuals; $56/yr.,
institutions; $20, single issues. Orders/advertising inquiries should be directed
to the publisher. Submissions should be directed to the editor. Begun 1989.

SUNDEVIL ROUNDUP
Rough Rock Community High School, Star Rt. 1 • Rough Rock, AZ 85021

SUQUAMISH NEWS
Suquamish Tribe, P.O. Box 498 • Suquamish, WA 98392
 (360) 598-3311 Fax 598-3135; E-mail: ntvedt@suquamish.nsn.us
 Wayne George, Editor-in-Chief
 Monthly tribal newspaper.

SUSQUEHANNA VALLEY NATIVE AMERICAN EAGLE
P.O. Box 99 • Loganville, PA 17342-0099
 (717) 428-1440; Gerald Dietz, Editor
Bi-monthly newsletter for Native & non-Native people interested in current
events, powwows, festivals, and historic articles on Native people of the mid-
Atlantic region. $6/year.

SURFACE SCATTER
Marin Museum of the American Indian
P.O. Box 864, 2200 Novato Blvd. • Novato, CA 94947
 (415) 897-4064; Quarterly newsletter.

SWAIA INDIAN MARKET
Southwestern American Indian Arts
320 Galisteo, Suite 600 • Gallup, NM 87501

T

TALKING LEAVES
American Indianist Society, 15 Mattson Ave. • Worcester, MA 01606
 (508) 852-6271

TALKING PEACEPIPE
Southeast Michigan Indians, Inc., 26641 Lawrence St. • Centerline, MI 48015
 (810) 956-1350 Fax 756-1352; Website: www.semii.itgo.com
 E-mail: semii@mail.com. Monthly newsletter. Advertising. $3/year.

THE TALKING RAVEN
Quileute Indian Tribe, P.O. Box 279 • La Push, WA 98350
 (360) 374-6163 Fax 374-6311
 Website: www.quileutenation.org/community/newsletter
 E-mail: talkingraven@quileutenation.org
 Emily Foster, Editor; Monthly tribal newsletter.

TALKING STICK
American Indian Artists (AMERINDA), INC.
c/o AFSC, 15 Rutherford Pl. • New York, NY 10003
 (212) 598-0968 Fax 529-4603; Website: www.amerinda.org
 Diane Fraher Thornton, Artistic Director
 E-mail: amerinda@amerinda.org; Native arts quarterly.

TEKAKWITHA CONFERENCE NEWSLETTER
Tekakwitha Conference National Center
1800 9th Ave. S., Box 6759 • Great Falls, MT 59406-6759
  (406) 727-0147; Gilbert Hemauer. Quarterly. 15,000 cir. Begun 1979.

TEQUESTA
Historical Association of Southern Florida
101 West Flagler St. • Miami, FL 33130 (305) 375-1492
  Website: www.historical-museum.org
Paul S. George, PhD, Editor; E-Mail: hasf@ix.netcom.com
Annual scholarly journal focusing on southern Florida and the Caribbean.
3,500 cir. $35/annual dues. Begun 1941.

THEATA
Cross Cultural Communications Department
University of Alaska, Alaskan Native Program • Fairbanks, AK 99708
  (907) 474-7181; Pat Kwachka, Editor
Alaskan Native college students writing on traditional & contemporary topics.
Annual journal. 4,000 cir. $5/year. Begun 1973.

THUNDERCHILD NEWS
Thunderchild Treatment Center, 1000 Decca Rd. • Sheridan, WY 82801
  (307) 750-2255 Fax 750-2260
Published three times per year.

TI SWANNI ITST
Skokomish Indian Tribal Center, Rt. 5, Box 432 • Shelton, WA 98584

TLIN TSIM HAI
Ketchikan Indian Corporation, 429 Deermount • Ketchikan, AK 99901

TLINGIT/HAIDA TRIBAL NEWS
Tlingit/Haida Central Council, One Sealaska Plaza, Suite 300
Juneau, AK 99801 (312) 784-1050

TONI-WE-KEE-TOH
Peoria Tribe of Indians of Oklahoma (Quarterly newsletter)
P.O. Box 1527 • Miami, OK 74355 (918) 540-2535 Fax 540-2538
  Website: www. peoriatribe.com/uploads/peoria_news
  Mandie Ferguson, Editor; E-mail: mferguson@peoriatribe.com

TRAILBLAZER
Cook Inlet Native Association • Anchorage, Alaska 99503 (907) 278-4641

TRC NEWS
Tribal Research Center-NAES College
2838 W. Peterson Ave. • Chicago, IL 60659 (312) 761-5000
Reports on the activities of the center. Monthly newsletter. Begun 1987.

TREATY COUNCIL NEWS
International Indian Treaty Council
2390 Mission St., Suite 301 • San Francisco, CA 94110
  (415) 641-4482 Fax 641-1298
  Andrea Carmen, Executive Director
$10/year, individuals; $15/year, institutions.

TRENDS IN INDIAN HEALTH
Indian Health Service, 5600 Fisher's Ln. • Rockville, MD 20857
  (301) 443-1083; Annual publication.

TRIBAL ADVOCATE
Piliero Mazza & Pargament, PLCC
888 17th St., NW, Suite 1100 • Washington, DC 20006
  (202) 857-1000 Fax 857-0200; Website: www.pmplawfirm.com
  Pamela J. Mazza & Susan B. Brock, Eds.
  E-mail: pmazza@pmplawfirm.com
Subscription newsletter, published 10/year, devoted exclusively to legal &
business issues affecting tribes, Alaska Native corporations & businesses.
Also, conducts interviews. $159 per year.

TRIBAL COLLEGE JOURNAL
American Indian Higher Education Consortium
P.O. Box 720 • Mancos, CO 81328 (970) 533-9170 Fax 533-9145
  Website: www.tribalcollegejournal.org; E-mail: info@tribalcollegejournal.org
  Rachael Marchbanks, Publisher; E-mail: rachael@tribalcollegejournal.org
  Tina Deschenie, Editor; E-mail: editor@tribalcollegejournal.org
  Marvene Tom, Office Manager; Marjane Ambler, Freelance Writer
The quarterly journal of the Consortium, 37 tribal colleges & universities.
Focuses on post-secondary education of 30,000+ students from more than 250
tribal nations. $39/yr. Begun 1989.

TRIBAL DIRECTORY
Arizona Commission on Indian Affairs
1400 W. Washington St. #300 • Phoenix, AZ 85007
  (602) 542-3123 Fax 542-3223; Jack C. Jackson, Jr., Executive Director

TRIBAL LAW JOURNAL
University of New Mexico Law School
1117 Stanford, NE, Rm #1222 • Albuquerque, NM 87131
  Website: www.tlj.unm.edu; E-mail: tlj@law.unm.edu
  Christine Zuni-Cruz (Isleta Pueblo), Editor-in-Chief
Publication: Tribal Court Handbook

TRIBAL NEWSLETTER
Confederated Tribes of Coos, Lower Umpqua & Suislaw Indians
1245 Fulton Ave. • Coos Bay, OR 97420 (541) 888-9577 Fax 888-5388

TRIBAL OBSERVER
Saginaw Chippewa Indian Tribe
7070 E. Broadway • Mt. Pleasant, MI 48858
  (989) 953-4000 Fax (888) 613-3109. Biweekly tribal newspaper.

TRIBAL REPORT
Northern Cheyenne Nation, P.O. Box 128 • Lame Deer, MT 59043
  (406) 477-8077 Fax 477-6829; Leo Killsback, Editor
  Website: www.cheyennenation.com/tribalreport
  E-mail: nctribalreport@hotmail.com; Eugene D. Little Coyote, President

TRIBAL TRIBUNE
Colville Confederated Tribes, P.O. Box 150 • Nespelem, WA 99155
  (509) 634-8835 Fax 634-4617; Sheila Whitelaw, Editor
Monthly newspaper of the Confederated Tribes of the Colville Reservation.
4,500 cir. $15/year in Washington; $20/year outside Washington.

TRIBAL VISION
National Tribal Environmental Council
2221 Rio Grande NW • Albuquerque, NM 87104
  (505) 242-2175; Jerry Pardilla, Executive Director
  E-mail: ntec@ntec.org; Website: www.ntec.org
Quarterly newsletter focusing on the environmental concerns
of Native Americans.Begun in 1991.

TRIBE OF FIVE FEATHERS NEWS
P.O. Box W • Lompoc, CA 93436

TSISTSISTAS PRESS
P.O. Box 693 • Lame Deer, MT 59043

TU'KWA HONE' NEWSLETTER
Burns Paiute Tribe, HC-71, 100 PaSiGo' St. • Burns, OR 97720
  (503) 573-2088 Fax 573-2323
Weekly tribal newsletter.

TURTLE MOUNTAIN TIMES
Turtle Mountain Tribe , P.O. Box 1270 • Belcourt, ND 58316
  (701) 477-6451 Fax 477-6836
  Brenda Greenwood & Orie Richard, Co-editors.
Weekly tribal newspaper.

TURTLE PRESS
Nottawaseppi Huron Band of Potawatomi Indians
Pine Creek Indian Reservation, 2221 - 1.5 Mile Rd.
Fulton, MI 49052 (269) 729-5151 Fax 729-5920
  Website: www.nhbpi.com/newsletter/newsletter.html
  Kathy Mackety, Newsletter Editor; E-mail: kmackety@nhbpi.com

TURTLE TALK: LAW BLOG
The Leading Law Blog on American Indian Law & Policy
Website: www.turtletalk.wordpress.com

TURTLE TALK NEWSLETTER
Massachusetts Center for Native American Awareness
P.O. Box 5885 • Boston, MA 02114
  (617) 884-4227 Fax 884-4889
  Website: www.mcnaa.org; E-mail: mcnaa@aol.com
  Burne Stanley, Editor; Quarterly newsletter.

TURTLE TALK
Native American Prevention Services
615 Turner NW, Rm. 32-B • Grand Rapids, MI 49504
  (616) 458-4078

THE TURTLE TIMES
The Free Cherokees-Turtle Clan
3200 Lenox Rd. NE #A-107 • Atlanta, GA 30324
  (404) 381-0628; Satinka Browne, Editor

U

UMATILLA AGENCY NEWSLETTER
Office of Indian Affairs, P.O. Box 520 • Pendleton, OR 97801

UNITED INDIANS OF ALL TRIBES FOUNDATION—TA NEWSLETTER
United Indians of All Tribes, P.O. Box 99100 • Seattle, WA 98199

UNITED LENAPE NATION NEWSLETTER
P.O. Box 1198 • Fredonia, AZ 86022

UNITED LUMBEE NATION TIMES
United Lumbee Nation of N.C. and America
HC 78 Box 57 • Termo, CA 96132
  (530) 336-6701
Tribal newspaper containing articles and information concerning members of the Lumbee Nation of Indians. Published 3-4 times per year. 1,500 cir. $2 per copy. Complimentary copies available upon request. Advertising. Begun 1979.

UNITY NEWS
United National Indian Tribal Youth (UNITY)
P.O. Box 800 • Oklahoma City, OK 73101-0800
  (405) 424-3010; J.R. Cook, Executive Director
Sherry Kast, Communications Director
  E-Mail: unity@unityinc.org; Quarterly newspaper for Native American youth, youth advisors and coordinators, and others interested in American Indian and Alaskan Native youth. promotes the activities, training sessions & conferences of UNITY, & promotes the positive actions & leadership ability of outstanding Native youth ages 15-24. Advertising. Free.

UTE BULLETIN
Uintah & Ouray Tribe, P.O. Box 100 • Fort Duchesne, UT 84026
  (435) 722-8541; Website: www.utetribe.com-utebulletin
  E-mail: bulletin@utetribe.com; Mariah Cuch, Managing Editor
Monthly newspaper covering American Indian interests.
Book reviews. 1,500 cir. $25/year. Advertising. Begun 1974.

V

VALLEY ROUND UP
Shoshone-Paiute Business Council
P.O. Box 219 • Owyhee, Nevada 89832

THE VISION MAKER
Native American Public Telecommunications
1800 North 33rd St. • Lincoln, NE 68501
  (402) 472-3522 Fax 472-8675; Justin Grotelueschen, Editor
E-mail: native@unl.edu; Website: www.nativetelecom.org

VISIONS
Communications Publishing Group, Inc.
3100 Broadway, Suite 225 • Kansas City, MO 64111
  (816) 756-3039; Georgia Lee Clark, President & Editor
A resource guide for Native American students containing individual profiles, scholarships & financial aid information, calendar of events, etc. Semiannually in March and September. $1.50 each.

THE VOICE
Denver Indian Center, 4407 Morrison Rd. • Denver, CO 80219
  (303) 937-0401; Lisa Harjo, Editor; Monthly newsletter. $10/yr.

W

WAAYP 'ESTIK BARONA NEWS
Barona Band of Mission Indians Tribal Newsletter
1095 Barona Rd. • Lakeside, CA 92040 (619) 443-6612
  Laura White Cloud, Editor; E-mail: lwhitecloud@barona.org

WAHPETON HIGHLIGHTS
Wahpeton Indian School • Wahpeton, ND 58075

WALKER RIVER PAIUTE TRIBAL NEWS NOTES
Walker River Paiute Tribe, P.O. Box 220, Schurz, NV 89427
  (702) 773-2306 Fax 773-2585

WANA CHINOOK TYMOO
Columbia River Inter-Tribal Fish Commission
729 N.E. Oregon, #200 • Portland, OR 97232 (503) 238-0667
  Laura Berg, Editor; Carol Craig & Dan Kane, Staff
Columbia River salmon stories. Quarterly magazine. 6,000 cir.

WANBLI HO: A LITERARY ARTS JOURNAL
Lakota Studies/Creative Writing Program
Sinte Gleska College, P.O. Box 8 • Mission, SD 57555
  Victor Douville, Editor; Features short fiction, poetry, literary articles, oral tradition texts, and artwork. Focuses on contemporary and traditional Native-American literature and art. Published twice a year. Subscription: $7.50/year; $4.50 each issue.

WARM SPRINGS TRIBAL NEWSLETTER
P.O. Box C, Warm Springs, OR 97761 (541) 553-1161 Fax 553-1924

THE WARRIOR
American Indian Center, 1630 W. Wilson • Chicago, IL 60640
  (312) 275-5871/561-8183

WASHOE TRIBAL MONTHLY NEWSLETTER
Washoe Tribe, 919 Hwy 395 S. • Gardnerville, NV 89410
  (775) 265-8600 Fax 265-6240
  Careen Sibbring, Editor; E-mail: careen.sibbring@washoetribe.us

WELLPINIT INDEPENDENT WATCHDOG
P.O. Box 213 • Wellpinit, WA 99040 (509) 238-0667

WHIRLING RAINBOW - VOICE OF THE PEOPLE
Pan-American Indian Association Quarterly Newsletter
8335 Sevigny Dr. • N. Fort Myers, FL 33917-1705
  (941) 731-7029 or 543-7727 ; Cindy "Spirit Catcher" Barnard, Editor

WHISPERING WIND MAGAZINE
Written Heritage, P.O. Box 1390 • Folsom, LA 70437-1390
  (800) 301-8009; (985) 796-5433 Fax 796-9236
  E-mail: info@whisperingwind.com; Website: www.whisperingwind.com
  Jack B. Heriard, Managing Editor
Bimonthly magazine of American Indian crafts and material culture. Includes how-to craft articles, old photos, history, powwow dates and reports, and video and book reviews. 24,000 cir. Single copies, $5. $25 for 6 issues; $40 for12 issues. Advertising. Began 1967.

WHITE EARTH RESERVATION NEWS
P.O. Box 274 • White Earth, MN 56591

WHITE MOUNTAIN APACHE NEWSPAPER
P.O. Box 700 • White River, AZ 85941

THE WICAZO SA REVIEW
A Journal of Native American Studies
University of Minnesota Press c/o Chicago Distribution Center
11030 S. Langley Ave. • Chicago, IL 60628
  (800) 621-2736 Fax 621-8476; (773) 702-7000 Fax 702-7212
  Website: www.upress.umn.edu
  James Riding In, Editor (The Red Pencil Review)
Bi-annual. 600 cir. Individuals, $20/year, $15 back issues; Institutions, $50, back issues, $37.50 ea. Available online through Project MUSE and JSTOR. Begun 1985.

WICOZANNI WOWAPI
Native American Community Board, P.O. Box 572 • Lake Andres, SD 57356
  (605) 487-7072 Fax 487-7964; Charon Asetoyer, Editor
Newsletter of the Native American Community Board concerned with Native American issues. No charges; donations accepted. Quarterly.

WI GUABA
Havasupai Tribal Council, P.O. Box 10 • Supai, AZ 86435

WIIGEGABA
Havasupai Tribe, P.O. Box 8010 • Supai, AZ 86435
  (520) 448-2731; Tribal newspaper.

WILLIAM & MARY QUARTERLY
Institute of Early American History & Culture
P.O. Box 8781 • Williamsburg, VA 23187-8781
  (757) 221-1120 Fax 221-1047
  Philip Morgan, Editor; Ann Gross, Managing Editor
Scholarly journal articles on American Indians, in the period up to about 1820. 3,600 circ. $30/year, individuals; $50, institutions; $15, students.

WIN-AWENEN-NISITOTUNG
Sault Ste. Marie Tribe of Chippewa Indians
206 Greenough St., 2nd Floor • Sault Ste. Marie, MI 49783
 (906) 635-6398 Fax 635-7016
 E-mail: saulttribenews@saulttribe.net
 Jennifer Dale-Burton, Editor
Monthly tribal newspaper. Subscription: $18/year, U.S.; $25/year, Canada;
$36/year, other foreign countries. 15,000 circ. Advertising accepted.
Begun 1978.

WIND RIVER JOURNAL
Shoshone Tribe, P.O. Box 157 • Fort Washakie, Wyoming 82514

WIND RIVER RENDEZVOUS
St. Stephan's Mission Foundation, P.O. Box 278 • St. Stephan, WY 82524
 (307) 856-6797; Ron Mamot, Editor
Covers the history of Western USA, cultural contribution of the Native
American, and pastoral programs for the Arapaho & Shoshoni people at
St. Stephens Mission. Quarterly magazine. 41,000 cir. $10/year. Begun 1971.

WINDOW ROCK SCENE
P.O. Box 580 • Window Rock, AZ 86515 (505) 371-5392

WINDS OF CHANGE
A.I.S.E.S. Publishing, Inc., P.O. Box 9828 • Albuquerque, NM 87119
 (505) 765-1052 Fax 765-5608; Karen English, Editor (617) 872-3395
Provides positive program information and successful role models for Indian
students & professionals of all disciplines (not just science & engineering.)
Information about education & career opportunities, as well as tribal culture &
events. A new section highlights articles & information about environmental
concerns & issues of interest to Native Americans. Quarterly magazine. 50,000
cir. $24/year.

WINDSPEAKER ONLINE
Aboriginal Multi-Media Society
(Canada's National Aboriginal News Source)
 Website: www.ammsa.com/windspeaker/

WINNEBAGO INDIAN NEWS
P.O. Box 687 • Winnebago, NE 68071 (402) 878-3221
 Jerome LaPointe, Sr., Editor; Website: www.winnebagotribe.com
 E-mail: winnebagoindiannews@yahoo.com
Biweekly newspaper for the Winnebago Tribe of Nebraska.

WITECHI WI - HARD MOON
Lower Sioux Indian Community, P.O. Box 308 • Morton, MN 56270
 (507) 697-6185; Website: www.lowersioux.com/newspaper
Monthly tribal newspaper.

WOLF POINT HERALD NEWS
Fort Peck Reservation (Montana)
Website: www.wolfpoint.com/news.htm

WOLF SONGS
The Tiospaye, P.O. Box 200 • Wamblee, SD 57577 (605) 462-6544
Quarterly. 4 issues for $10.

WOODLAND VOICE
Mille Lacs Band of Ojibwe, 43408 Oodena Dr. • Onamia, MN 56359
 (320) 532-4181 ext. 7486 Fax 532-4209
A quarterly newsletter for the Mille Lacs Ojibwe community, employees of
Grand Casino Mille Lacs & Grand Casino Hinckley, the media, tribal
government employees, legislators, & state government officials.

WOTANGING IKCHE
Native American News; Website: www.nanews.org
 E-mail: gars@nanews.org; Gary Night Owl, Distributor
Weekly electronic Native American news.

WOTANIN WOWAPI
Fort Peck Assiniboine & Sioux Tribes
P.O. Box 1027 • Poplar, MT 59255
 (406) 768-5155 Ext. 2370; Bonnie Red Elk, Editor
Weekly newspaper of articles and photos of news pertinent to the Assiniboine
and Sioux people residing on the Fort Peck Reservation. Also contains
complete tribal government meetings; also a historical review of the tribes.
Complimentary copies available upon request. Advertising. Begun 1976.

Y

YA-KA-AMA INDIAN EDUCATION NEWSLETTER
6215 East Side Rd. • Forestville, CA 95436

YAKAMA NATION REVIEW
Yakama Indian Nation, P.O. Box 310 • Toppenish, WA 98948
 (509) 865-5121 Fax 865-2794; E-mail: ynreview@yakama.com
 Ronnie Washines, Managing Editor
Contains articles pertaining to and affecting Native Americans, human interests
involving Native American population, governmental action on national, state
and local levels relevant to the Yakama Tribal Government structure. Biweekly
newspaper. 5,500 cir. $26/year. Complimentary copies available upon request.
Advertising. Begun 1970.

YANKTON SIOUX MESSINGER
P.O. Box 248 • Marty, SD 57361

YAQUI TIMES
7474 S. Camino De Oeste, Tucson, AZ 85746
 (800) 883-5000; (520) 883-5010 Fax 883-5014
 Website: www.pascuayaqui-nsn.gov

**YELLOW MEDICINE REVIEW: A JOURNAL OF INDIGENOUS
LITERATURE, ART & THOUGHT**
c/o Judy Wilson, Dept. of English
Southwest Minnesota State University, 1501 State St. • Marshall, MN 56258
 Website: www.yellowmedicinereview.com
 E-mail: editor@yellowmedicinereview.com

YUGTARVIK REGIONAL MUSEUM NEWSLETTER
P.O. Box 338 • Bethel, AK 99559
Monthly.

Z

ZUNI CARRIER
Zuni Pueblo • Zuni, NM 87327

ZUNI TRIBAL NEWSLETTER
Box 339, Zuni Tribal Office
Zuni, NM 87327

ALABAMA

HA'NO:WA:
1865 Will Logan Rd. • Ozark, AL 36360
 (334) 379-2504; E-mail: stlanders51@yahoo.com
 Sonia Turley-Landers (Onondaga), Artist/Owner
Products: Pencil portraits, beadwork, cornhusk dolls, dance regalia.

ALASKA

ALASKA WATERCOLOR
3212 West 30th Ave. • Anchorage, AK 99517
 (907) 248-0454; Website: www.alaskakodiakwatercolor.com
 Helen Simeonoff (Sugpiaq), Artist/Owner
E-mail: helen.simeonoff@ak.net
Subject matter, such as Alaska Natives, historical masks.

ALASKAN ESKIMO ARTS
1731 Cedrus Circle • Anchorage, AK 99507
 (907) 929-7736 Fax 575-9180
 Bryon Amos (Cup'ig Eskimo), Artist/Owner
 E-mail: bryonlamos@gmail.com
Products: Traditional ivory masks; sculptures.

BERING SEA ARTWORK
1515 Valarian St. • Anchorage, AK 99508
 (907) 744-2877 Fax 891-0144
Website: www.beringseaartwork.com
 Jimmy & Donna Carlisle (King Island Inupiaq), Owners
 E-mail: jimmy@beringseaartwork.com
Retail, wholesale. *Products*: Traditional & modern masks; sculpture; jewelry.

GENUINE ALASKAN WHOLESALE
1731 Cedrus Ct. • Anchorage, AK 99507
 (907) 349-1610 or 350-0066
 Bryon Amos (Kup'iq Eskimo), Artist/Owner
 E-mail: bryonlamos@hotmail.com
Wholesale by appt. only. *Products*: Traditional ivory masks; sculptures.

KAUWERAK INUPIAT TRADITIONS
8149 East 4th Ave. • Anchorage, AK 99504
 (907) 333-8680; Willy Topkok Inupiat Eskimo), Artisan
Wholesale, mail order. *Products*: Walrus ivory pendants, mukluks; cloth
Eskimo windbreakers; Alaska Native dancer notecards & matted art.

"OOMINGMAK" - MUSK OX PRODUCERS' COOPERATIVE
604 H St. • Anchorage, AK 99501
 (907) 272-9225; Sigrun C. Robertson, Manager
 E-mail: oomingmak@qiviut.com; Website: www.qiviut.com
Mail order, limited retail. Yupik & Inupiat Alaska Native cooperative.
Products: Handknitted Qiviut (the underwool of the arctic musk oxen),
garments such as caps, scarves, tunics, and nachaqs. Brochure price list.

SMALL TREASURES
8851 Cordell Circle #5 • Anchorage, AK 99502
 (907) 248-9639; Patrick W. Lind, Owner/Manager
Retail, wholesale; special orders. *Products*: Aleut arts & crafts; paintings;
birchwood products.

TAHETA ARTS & CULTURAL GROUP
1042 E. 6th Ave. • Anchorage, AK 99501
 (907) 272-5829; Rick Lonsdale, Manager
Retail, mail order, wholesale; special orders. Eskimo, Indian & Aleut nonprofit
cooperative. *Products*: Ivory, stone, wood, & bone carvings; baskets; ivory
carvings; jewelry; masks; etchings, drawings & prints.

WHALE DREAMS STUDIO
P.O. Box 112492 • Anchorage, AK 99511
 (907) 344-6789; Jerry Laktonen, Owner/Manager
Retail, mail order. Commissions accepted. *Products*: Alutiiq (Sugpiaq)
masks and paddles. Brochure and price list, $5.

RAVEN DESIGNS
P.O. Box 312 • Angoon, AK 99820
 (907) 788-3318; Ray Peck (Tlingit), Artist/Owner
Mail, Telephone orders. *Products*: Northwest Coast totemic carvings in cedar.

YUGTARVIK REGIONAL MUSEUM SHOP
P.O. Box 388 • Bethel, AK 99559
 (907) 543-2098; Penni K. Abraham, Manager

Wholesale/mail order. *Products*: Baskets, clothing, dolls, jewelry, sculpture,
carvings.

YUP'IK GIFT SHOP
P.O. Box 219 • Bethel, AK 99559
 (907) 543-1819; Mary Romer, Manager
Mail order. Special orders accepted. Nonprofit organization. *Products*: Grass
baskets, mats, trays, plates; wooden & ivory masks & carvings; Native made
clothing; bead, quilll & ivory jewelry; dolls; headdresses; drawings.

GALLERY OF ALASKAN NATIVE ART
P.O. Box 670423 • Chugiak, AK 99567
 (907) 235-9060; Karen Rifredi (Nulato), Artist/Owner
Retail by appt. *Products*: Authentic hand-made Native art in beadwork,
moccasins, masks ornaments, native dolls, ivory & soapstone.

CULTURAL HERITAGE & EDUCATION INSTITUTE
P.O. Box 73030 • Fairbanks, AK 99707
 (907) 451-0923 Fax 451-0910; Website: www.ankn.uaf.edu/chei
 E-mail: chei2@mosquitonet.com; Robert Charlie, Executive Director
Retail. *Products*: Traditional Athabascan arts & crafts.

ARCTIC WAYS
Box 69 • Fort Yukon, AK 99740
 (800) 478-2667 (Alaska only); (907) 662- 2667
 Website: www.arcticways.com; E-Mail: info@arcticways.com
 Carrie Supik, Owner
Retail, wholesale. *Products*: Jewelry, hand beaded & moose skin,
carving & woodwork, sun catchers.

ST. LAWRENCE ISLAND ORIGINAL IVORY COOPERATIVE, LTD.
P.O. Box 189 • Gambell, AK 99742
 (907) 985-5112/5649 Fax 985-5927; Clement Ungott, Manager
Mail order. Eskimo Cooperative. *Products*: Eskimo walrus ivory carvings
of animal figurines; bracelets; cribbage boards; etchings.

ALLTRIBES INDIAN ART LLC
75 W. Baseline Rd., Suite 6 • Gilbert, AZ 85233
 (800) 417-0024; (480) 963-2284; Website: www.alltribes.com
 Richard Candy, Owner
Wholesale & retail to the public. *Products*: Indian turquoise & silver jewelry; art,
kachina dolls, Navajo rugs, pottery, tomahawks, peace pipes, baskets, & other
Native American artifacts. Jewelry workshop. Buy & sell antique & old pawn
Native American jewelry & art.

CHILKAT VALLEY ARTS
209 Willard St., P.O. Box 145 • Haines, AK 99827
 (907) 766-2990 Fax 766-3090; Website: www.chilkatvalleyarts.com
 E-mail: sue@chilkatvalleyarts.com; Susan Folletti (Tlingit), Owner/Manager
Retail. *Products*: Silver jewelry, totemic designs of the Northwest Coast Tlingit
Indians. Second shop: The Far North, Haines, AK.

THE FAR NORTH
111 2nd Ave., P.O. Box 145 • Haines, AK 99827
 (907) 766-3535 Fax 766-3090; Susan Folletti, Owner/Manager
Retail. *Products*: Fine Eskimo art - ivory & soapstone carvings, baleen and
grass baskets, jewelry.

NORTHWEST COAST TEXTILE ARTS
P.O. Box 693 • Haines, AK 99827
 (907) 767-5581 Fax 767-5582; E-mail: lanihotch@aptalaska.net
 Lani Hotch (Chilkat Indian Village), Artist/Owner
Retail by appt. *Products*: Northwest Coast style weaving, including Chilkat &
Ravenstail blankets, tunics, bags, & leggings. beaded bracelets and necklaces;
baskets made of cedar.

ALASKAN TREASURES dba IVORY & BEADS
4321 Bayview Ct. • Homer, AK 99603
 (907) 235-6761; Website: www.alaskantreasures
 E-mail: alaskantreasures@alaska.net
 Peter & Darlene Lind (Aleut/Alutiiq), Artist/Owners
Products: Traditional Aleut/Alutiiq style bentwood hunting visors, harpoons,
ivory & bead jewelry; bronze sculptures (limited editions).

INUA - THE SPIRIT OF ALASKA
P.O. Box 4243 • Homer, AK 99603 (Branch: Anchorage, AK)
 (907) 235-6644 Fax 235-2053; Website: www.inua.net
 E-mail: inua2@alaska.net; William & Catlin Lovett, Owners
Retail, wholesale. *Products*: Native crafts from Alaska - Baskets, beadwork,
clothing, dolls, art, dream catchers, jewelry, miniatures, sculpture, carvings,
repair & restoration. *Appraisals*: Baskets, art, sculpture. *Membership*: IACA.

CLARISSA HUDSON, LLC.
P.O. Box 21453 • Juneau, AK 99802
 (978) 903-8386; Website: www.clarissarizal.com
 Clarissa Hudson (Tlingit), Artist/Owner
  E-mail: clarissa@clarissarizal.com
Retail, wholesale. *Products*: Ceremonial regalia robes;
contemporary paintings.

AMOS WALLACE
P.O. Box 478 • Juneau, AK 99802
 (907) 586-9000; Amos Wallace, Owner
Wholesale, mail order. Tlingit crafts. *Products*: Jewelry.
Special orders on totem poles, masks and paddles.

DIANE DOUGLAS-WILLARD (Haida artist)
P.O. Box 7613 • Ketchikan, AK 99901
 (907) 225-6817 Fax 617-2436; E-mail: r_ravenalaska@hotmail.com
 Products: Haida basketry, Chilkat weaving, beadwork.

EAGLE SPIRIT GALLERY
310 Mission St. • Ketchikan, AK 99901
 (907) 225-6626; Website: www.eaglespiritgalleryalaska.com
 E-mail: akgifts@ktn.net; Susan & Michael Peters, Owners
Retail, wholesale. *Products*: Native crafts from Alaska. *Membership*: IACA.

INUCRAFT
P.O. Box 49 • Kotzebue, AK 99752
 (907) 442-2800
Retail, mail order. A division of NANA Development Corp. *Products*: Eskimo
dolls, masks, birch bark baskets, carvings, jewelry, parkas and mukluks.

NANA MUSEUM OF THE ARCTIC CRAFT SHOP
100 Shore Ave. • Kotzebue, AK 99752
 (907) 265-4157 Fax 265-4123; Sheri Gerhard, Contact
Retail, mail order by special request. *Products*: Baskets, clothing, dolls, art,
jewelry, sculpture, carvings.

PAUL T. BRENDIBLE
440 Hillcrest, Box 409 • Metlakatla, AK 99926
 (907) 886-5284; Paul Brendible (Tsimshian), Artist/Owner
  E-mail: paul.brendible@metlakatla.com
Products: Wood carvings of traditional Tsimshian totem poles;
feast bowls, spoons; masks.

ANUQSRAAQ ART
P.O. Box 842 • Nome, AK 99762
 MaryJane Litchard (Inupiaq), Artist/Owner
Wholesale, mail order. *Products*: Seal skin finger dolls; baleen etchings,
baskets; India ink drawings (prints) depicting artist's own Eskimo designs.

MARUSKIYA'S OF NOME
P.O. Box 895 • Nome, AK 99762
 (907) 443-2955 Fax 443-2467
 E-mail: james@nome.net; Marty & Patti James, Owners
Retail, wholesale. *Products*: Native crafts from Alaska

KODIAK ISLAND KREATIONS
P.O. Box 70 • Port Lions, AK 99550
 (907) 454-2208; E-mail: kikreations@starband.net
 Sara Squartsoff, Artist/Owner
Products: Craftwork from handpainted wooden boxes to beaded earrings
& jewelry.

SAVOONGA NATIVE STORE
P.O. Box 100 • Savoonga, AK 99769
 Paul Rookok, Sr., Manager
Mail order. *Products*: Eskimo ivory carvings, jewelry. Price list available.

ARTISTS ALASKA
P.O. Box 3326 • Seward, AK 99664
 (907) 491-1110; Website: www.artistsalaska.com
 E-mail: contact@pjewebdesign.com

INDIAN VILLAGE ARTISTS
235 Lincoln St. • Sitka, AK 99835
 (907) 747-5857; Boyd Bidrickson (Tlingit), Owner
Products: Sea otter pillows & blankets; seal polar bear
handcrafted items; drums, whale bone, woodcarvings.

RAVEN ART STUDIO
820 Charles St. • Sitka, AK 99835
 (907) 747-3641; Teri Rofkar (Tlingit), Owner/Manager
 Website: www.terirofkar.com; E-mail: teri@terirofkar.com
Retail, limited wholesale; special commissions. *Products*: Tlingit traditional
spruce root & cedar bark baskets, recently revived Tlingit Raven's Tail wool
weavings.

TAHETA NATIVE STORE
990 S. Check St., Suite D • Wasilla, AK 99654
 (907) 376-7666 (phone & fax); Website: www.alaskaivory.com
 Leonard Savage, Owner
Distributor/wholesaler. *Products*: Natural crafts: Native ivory carvings, baskets,
masks, soapstone, whalebone sculpture.

MARDINA DOLLS
P.O. Box 611 • Wrangell, AK 99929
 (907) 874-3854; Marleita Wallace, Owner/Manager
Wholesale, mail order. *Products*: Tlingit-Tsimsian art, clothing, dolls.

ARKANSAS

CHIEF JOSEPH, INC.
28 E. Center St. • Fayetteville, AR 72702
 (479) 695-1680 Fax 444-6957; Raymond L. Niblock, Owner
 Website: www.chiefjoseph.biz; E-mail: sales@chiefjoseph.biz

ARIZONA

THE NAVAJO SILVERSMITH
P.O. Box 394 • Alpine, AZ 85920
 (928) 339-1948; Website: www.navajosilversmith.com
 E-mail: silversmith@3pmc.com
 Dennison R. Tsosie (Navajo), Artisan/Owner
Products: Jewelry, artwork.

BONANZA TRADING
2025 S. Weaver Dr. • Apache Junction, AZ 85220
 (719) 486-3020; Clyde & Mary McVicar, Owners
Retail. *Products*: Art, baskets, beadwork, clothing, dolls, jewelry, kachinas,
pottery, rugs, sandpaintings, sculpture, carvings. *Membership*: IACA.

MOONSHADOW TRADING CO.
3700 S. Tomahawk Rd. #43, P.O. Box 1477 • Apache Junction, AZ 85220
 (480) 983-5087; Jack & Phyllis Falcetti, Owners; E-mail: PhilFal@aol.com
Membership: IACA.

JESSE T. HUMMINGBORD (Cherokee)
102 Silver St. • Bisbee, AZ 85603
 (520) 432-7305 Fax 432-4306; E-mail: jessehummingbird@cs.com
Retail, wholesale. Products: Original acrylic contemporary paintings
of Cherokee and other Native American themes. Brochure & price list.
Memberships: IACA, SWAI, Intertribal Indian Ceremonial.

JOHNSON GALLERY
28 Main St., P.O. Box 211 • Bisbee, AZ 85603
 (520) 432-2126; Les Johnson, Owner
 E-mail: johnsongallery@sigmathree.com
Membership: IACA.

NAVAJO ARTS & CRAFTS ENTERPRISE
P.O. Box 464 • Cameron, AZ 86020
 (520) 679-2244
Retail, wholesale. Tribal Enterprise. *Products*: Art, baskets, beadwork, clothing,
dolls, jewelry, kachinas, pottery, sand paintings, sculpture, carvings, craft
supplies, repairs & restoration. Branch shop.

THE BOULDERS
P.O. Box 2090 • Carefree, AZ 85377
 (602) 9009 Fax 488-4118
 Melissa Brasch, William Nassikas, Kenneth Humes
Retail. *Products*: Baskets, ornaments, drums, pipes, fetishes, jewelry,
kachinas, pottery, rugs. *Membership*: IACA.

DESERT EAGLE FINE ART
6268 E. Cave Creek Rd. Gallery #8 • Cave Creek, AZ 85331
 (480) 437-1313 Fax 654-3504; Website: deserteaglecreations.com
 E-mail: dianelcarter@earthlink.net
 Diane L. Carter & Wendy Wells Bailey, Owners
Membership: IACA.

MOUNTAIN STUDIO, INC.
P.O. Box 12 • Cave Creek, AZ 85327
 (480) 595-2443; Judith Durr-Kull (Choctaw) , Owner
 Website: www.judydurr.50megs.com; E-mail: jdurr@bnswest.net
Retail, wholesale. *Products*: Oil paintings.

D.Y. BEGAY; NAVAJO WEAVING STUDIO
P.O. Box 1770 • Chinle, AZ 86503
 (602) 538-5339; D.Y. Begay (Navajo), Owner
 Website: www.navajo-indian.com; E-mail: dybegay@cox.net
Retail, by appointment only. *Products*: Traditional and contemporary
Navajo weavings--rugs, blankets & tapestries. Special orders accepted.

NAVAJO ARTS & CRAFTS ENTERPRISE
P.O. Box 608 • Chinle, AZ 86503
 (520) 674-5338
Retail, wholesale. Tribal Enterprise. *Products*: Art, baskets, bead-work,
clothing, dolls, jewelry, kachinas, pottery, sand paintings, sculpture, carvings,
craft supplies, repairs & restoration. Branch shop.

SPOTTED ANTELOPE DESIGNS
P.O. Box 459 • Chinle, AZ 86503
 (928) 674-5231; Adam & Rita Teller, Artisans/Owners
 Website: www.antelopehouse.com
Retail. *Products*: Traditional and contemporary Navajo jewelry
from Canyon de Chelly.

THUNDERBIRD LODGE
Canyon de Chelly, P.O. Box 548 • Chinle, AZ 86503
 (602) 674-5841; Mary Jones, Contact
Retail. *Products*: All. *Membership*: IACA.

NATIVE AMERICAN VISIONS
P.O. Box 1394 • Cortaro, AZ 85652
 (520) 616-9020; Website: www.nativeamericanvisions.com
Retail. Products: Craft supplies; beads, beading supplies, clamshell
trade goods, hand painted feathers, hair pipes. Catalog, $4.

BLACK MESA TRADERS
2930 E. Matterhorn Dr. • Flagstaff, AZ 86004-2213
 (928) 526-8354 Fax 774-9079; Rita Alexander & Rodger Berg, Contacts
Wholesaler. *Products*: Art, baskets, beadwork, ornaments, clothing, dolls, artifacts, jewelry, kachinas, miniatures, sculpture, carvings; repairs & restoration.
Appraisals: Kachinas. Specializes in Kachinas. *Membership*: IACA. Catalog.

TURQUOISE HOGAN
4 N. Leroux St. • Flagstaff, AZ 86001
 (928) 774-0174; Mary Jane & Franklin Kahn, Owners
Retail, wholesale. Products: Silver & turquoise jewelry; Navajo rugs,
baskets, Hopi kachinas, pottery, paintings, beadwork.

COOCHSIWUKIOMA
1819 N. Turquoise Dr. • Flagstaff, AZ 86001
 (928) 779-5500; Lorraine Honnanie, Manager
 Delbridge Coochsiwukioma Honanie (Hopi), Artist
Products: Traditional Hopi cottonwood root sculptures;
relief sculptural wall hangings; paintings

MILT'S INDIAN ARTS
P.O. Box 22007 • Flagstaff, AZ 86002
 (602) 526-0442; Milton Forsman, Owner
Wholesale. *Products*: baskets, rugs, sand paintings, sculpture, carvings.

JAN MUSIAL'SNAVAJO ARTS & CRAFTS
P.O. Box 1836 • Flagstaff, AZ 86002
 (928) 774-2098; Jan Musial, Owner
Membership: IACA.

NOHWIKE BAGOA: HOUSE OF OUR FOOTPRINTS MUSEUM SHOP
P.O. Box 507, Fort Apache, AZ 85926
 (928) 338-4625
 Ann Skidmore (White Mountain Apache), Manager
Products: Apache baskets, cradleboards, beadwork, jewelry, fine art.

JUMBO'S
P.O. Box 791 • Fort Defiance, AZ 86505
 (928) 729-2326; Darrell Jumbo (Navajo), Owner
Products: Silver & turquoise jewelry

DEE'S EXQUISITE JEWELRY
P.O. Box 235 • Fredonia, AZ 86022

 (602) 643-7093; Melvin Martin & Dolores Savala
Retail. *Products*: Jewelry.

HUBBELL TRADING POST
P.O. Box 388 • Ganado, AZ 86505
 (928) 755-3254 Fax 755-3405; Website: www.nps.gov/hutr
Retail, wholesale. *Products*: Navajo textiles, pottery, kachinas.

ARIZONA TRADING POST
7153 N. 57th Dr. Unit 4 • Glendale, AZ 85301
 (623) 931-6474 Fax 931-6475; Website: www.aztradingpost.com
 E-mail: contact@aztradingpost.com; Richard Wallace, Sr., Owner
Membership: IACA.

MELJOY INDIAN TRADERS
165 Amarilla Dr. • Globe, AZ 85501
 (602) 425-0216; Melvin & Joyce Montgomery
Wholesale, retail. *Products*: Baskets, beadwork, clothing, dolls, miniatures.
Membership: IACA.

GRAND CANYON SQUIRE INN
Box 130, Hwy. 64/180 • Grand Canyon, AZ 86023
 (520) 638-2681; Raymond Curley, Manager
Retail. *Products*: Art, baskets, beadwork, drums, pipes, jewelry, pottery, rugs,
weavings, sand paintings, sculpture, carvings.

VERKAMP'S, INC.
P.O. Box 96 • Grand Canyon, AZ 86023
 (928) 638-2242 Fax 638-9355; Website: www.verkamps.com
 E-mail: dashle@verkamps.com; Susie Verkamp & Dan Ashley, Owners
Membership: IACA.

PRINGLE'S SOUTHWEST, LTD.
P.O. Box 503 • Green Valley, AZ 85614
 (520) 648-1388; Don & Phyllis Pringle
Retail. *Products*: Baskets, fetishes, jewelry, miniatures, pottery, rugs,
weavings.

DINE YASHI AMERICAN INDIAN ARTS
P.O. Box 151 • Hotevilla, AZ 86030
 Dan Yazzi, Jr. (Navajo), Owner
Products: Dine fine art. Dine folk art: carvings, sculptures, and tribal carvings
with wood.

CHEE'S INDIAN STORE, INC.
I-40 Allentown Rd., Exit 351, P.O. Box 66 • Houck, AZ 86506
 (520) 688-2603; Clara Chee & Harrison Lauber, Karen Chee & Paul Schell
Retail. *Products*: All. *Membership*: IACA.

THE GIFT SHOP OF JEROME
114 Jerome Ave., P.O. Box 396 • Jerome, AZ 86331
 (520) 634-5105; Anna Rae Adams
Wholesale, retail. *Products*: All. Membership: IACA..

NAVAJO ARTS & CRAFTS ENTERPRISE
Hwys. 160 & 163, Kayenta, AZ 86033
 (520) 697-8611
Retail, wholesale. Tribal Enterprise. *Products*: Art, baskets, beadwork, clothing,
dolls, jewelry, kachinas, pottery, sand paintings, sculpture, carvings, craft
supplies, repairs & restoration. Branch shop.

McGEE'S INDIAN ART
Hwy. 264, P.O. Box 607 • Keams Canyon, AZ 86034
 (928) 738-2295 Fax 738-5250; Ron McGee, Owner
 Website: www.hopiart.com; E-mail: ronmcgee@hopiart.com
Wholesale, retail. *Products*: Art, baskets, beadwork, clothing, dolls, jewelry,
kachinas, pottery, sand paintings, sculpture, carvings, craft supplies, repairs &
restoration. *Membership*: IACA.

MORNING STAR INDIAN JEWELRY
P.O. Box 987 • Kingman, AZ 86402
 (928) 753-6434; Sarah J. Ellis, Owner
Retail. *Products*: All.

EVELYN FREDERICKS SCULPTURE
Box 134 • Kykotsmovi, AZ 87039
 (928) 734-9377; Website: www.evelynfredericks.com
 E-mail: mail@evelynfredericks.com
Products: Native American stone & bronze sculpture

GENTLE RAIN DESIGNS
P.O. Box 35 • Kykotsmovi, AZ 86039
(928) 734-9535 Fax 734-9539; James Poley (Hopi), Owner/Manager
Products: Hopi overlay silver, kachinas, pottery, baskets, paintings, and other traditional Hopi arts.

SOCKYMA'S HOPICRAFTS
P.O. Box 96 • Kykotsmovi, AZ 86039
(928) 734-1050 or 734-6667
Michael & Theodora Sockyma (Hopi), Artists/Owners
Retail. *Products*: Specializes in Hopi overlay jewelry in silver & gold; Hopi kachinas, pottery, baskets, weavings, oil paintings. Brochure.

ALBERT LONG: TRADER/CRAFTSMAN
P.O. Box 40 • Lake Havasu City, AZ 86405
(928) 453-5925; Albert Long, Owner
Mail order. *Products*: Dolls, jewelry. Brochure available.

SILVER DAWN INDIAN ARTS
320 Catclaw Ln. • Lake Havasu City, AZ 86403
(928) 854-3047 Fax 854-2896; Website: www.silverdawnindianarts.com
E-mail: sdia@citlink.net; Kay Daw, David & Harold Todd, Owners
Membership: IACA.

PERCHARO JEWELRY
RR 2, Box 790 • Laveen, AZ 85339
(520) 237-4249; Nathaniel & Lisa Percharo, Owners
Retail & mail order. *Product*: Jewelry.

SARAH J. BEGAY (Navajo Artisan)
244 W. Indigo St. • Mesa, AZ 85201
(480) 835-8405; E-mail: vazdibe@msn.com
Products: Navajo rugs, jewelry, misc. arts & crafts.

HEARTLINE TRADING
911 N. Somerset Cir. • Mesa, AZ 85205
(602) 969-6232; Barbara Stechnij, Owner
Retail. *Products*: Beadwork, fetishes, heishi, jewelry, knives, pottery, rugs, craft supplies. *Membership*: IACA.

INDIAN JEWELRY USA
6101 E. Main St. • Mesa, AZ 85204-0090
(602) 985-5146; Jack & Ranelle Adam, Owners
Wholesale, retail. *Products*: Art, beadwork, music, books, dolls, drums, pipes, fetishes, heishi, jewelry, kachinas, knives, miniatures, pottery, sand paintings, sculpture; repair & restoration. Appraisals. *Membership*: IACA.

MARILOU SCHULTZ
844 E. 8th Pl. • Mesa, AZ 85203
(480) 834-3791 Fax 964-3566; Website: www.navajrugsart.com
E-mail: mrischultz@msn.com
Products: Navajo weavings, rugs, weaving tools, weaving wool, jewelry; workshops. lectures.

SKYSTONE CREATIONS
833 E. Broadway • Mesa, AZ 85204
(480) 964-1922 Fax 964-2859; Website: www.skystonecreations.com
E-mail: skystonecreations@worldnet.att.net
Victor & Elka Staple, Owners
Membership: IACA.

SOUTHWEST NATIVE AMERICAN PROMOTIONS
844 E. 8th St. • Mesa, AZ 85203
(480) 834-3791 Fax 964-3566; Website: www.swnap.org
E-mail: ehquannie@swnap.org
Emerson H. Quannie (Hopi), Owner/Manager
Products: Hopi jewelry in gold & silver. Workshops, lectures and classroom instruction on the art of Indian jewelry

WHITE EAGLE TRADING CO.
911 N. Somerset Cr. • Mesa, AZ 85205
(602) 969-6232; Mark & Barbara Stechnij, Owners
Wholesale, retail. *Products*: Baskets, fetishes, jewelry, kachinas, pottery, rugs, sand paintings.

HUDSON TRADING CO.
P.O Box 1254 • Oracle, AZ 85623
(602) 896-2901; Raymond & Velveeta Volante, Owners
Wholesale. *Products*: Baskets, beadwork, fetishes, jewelry, kachinas, miniatures, pottery, rugs. *Membership*: IACA.

EMERY OHMASATTE'S CREATIVE INSTINCTS
P.O. Box 1 • Overgaard, AZ 85933
(928) 535-4884; Emery Ohmasattes (Zuni), Artist/Owner
Products: Zuni crafts, contemporary jewelry.

BLAIR'S DINNEBITO TRADING POST
P.O. Box 2903 • Page, AZ 86040
(520) 645-3008; Elijah & James Blair, Owners
Wholesale, retail. *Products*: All. *Membership*: IACA.

WAHWEAP GIFT SHOP
P.O. Box 1597 • Page, AZ 86040
(520) 645-2433; Kathy M. Parsons, Manager
Retail. *Products*: All.

COLORADO RIVER INDIAN TRIBES LIBRARY/MUSEUM STORE
Rt. 1, Box 23-B • Parker, AZ 85344
(602) 669-9211 ext. 335 Fax 669-1246
Website: www.critlibrary.com
Betty L. Cornelius, Director/Manager
Retail. *Products*: Beadwork, Navajo rugs, kachina dolls, pottery, bows & arrows, cradleboards.

DRUMBEAT INDIAN ARTS
4143 N. 16th St. • Phoenix, AZ 85016
(800) 895-4859; (602) 266-4823 Fax 265-2402
Website: www.drumbeatindianarts.com; Bob Nuss, Owner
Retail, wholesale, mail order. *Products*: American Indian recordings (cassettes, CDs, over 2,000 titles; DVDs, videos, books, crafts supplies, craft items. Catalog available, $3.

HAVENS TRADING COMPANY
3524 E. Becker Ln. • Phoenix, AZ 85028
(602) 482-5113; William Havens, Owner
E-mail: havenstrading@cox.net. *Membership*: IACA.

HEARD MUSEUM STORE
22 E. Monte Vista • Phoenix, AZ 85004
(602) 252-8344 Fax 251-0237
Website: www.heard.org; E-mail: bmcgee@heard.org
Retail. *Products*: Art, baskets, beadwork, boxes, dolls, fetishes, heishi, jewelry, kachinas, miniatures, pottery, rugs, sand paintings, sculpture. *Membership*: IACA.

NAVAJOLAND IMAGES
13421 N. 43rd Ave. #2111• Phoenix, AZ 85029
(602) 439-3946; Website: www.imageofarizona.com
E-mail: info@dejolie.com; LeRoy DeJolie (Navajo), Owner
Products: Fine art photography, photo workshops.

HOPI CARVINGS & PAINTINGS
P.O. Box 34321 • Phoenix, AZ 85067
(602) 906-8954, 980-3370; Website: www.hopicarvingsandpaintings.com
Buddy Tubinaghtewa@hotmail.com
Products: Authentic Hopi Katsina dolls, Hopi designs painted on canvas, various Hopi designs

KALLEY KEAMS
P.O. Box 86448 • Phoenix, AZ 85080
(602) 412-7905; Kalley Keams, Owner
Wholesale. *Products*: Baskets, rugs, weavings.

NATIVE AMERICAN FASHIONS, INC.
P.O. Box 44802 • Phoenix, AZ 85064
(602) 956-7581; Website: www.margaretwood.net
E-mail: margaretwood44@aol.com
Margaret Wood (Navaj0/Seminole, Owner/Manager
Retail, wholesale, mail order. Products: Clothing, rugs, quilted wall hangings, sculpture, carvings. Special orders accepted.

NAVAJO SILVERCRAFT
P.O. Box 2725 • Phoenix, AZ 85002
(602) 253-1594; Jane Yikazbaa Popovich
Retail. *Product*: Jewelry.

PUEBLO SPIRIT, INC.
5060 N. 40tj St. #200 • Phoenix, AZ85018
(602) 956-9600 Fax 956-9700; Pam Del Luca, Owner
Membership: IACA.

ROCKING HORSE DESIGNS
2415 W. Glenrosa • Phoenix, AZ 85015
 (602) 265-1061; Lani Randall
Wholesale, retail. *Product*: Jewelry. *Appraisals*: Jewelry. *Membership*: IACA.

WATERBIRD STUDIO
3723 E. Tayler • Phoenix, AZ 85008
(602) 244-9161
Website: www.kevinhoracequannie.com
E-mail: kquannie@yahoo.com
Products: Contemporary Hopi paintings, Hopi Katsina sculptures, bronze sculptures & jewelry; workshops & lectures on contemporary Hopi art mediums, paintings & jewelry

BLACK ARROW INDIAN ART, INC.
130 W. Gurley St. #204 • Prescott, AZ 86301
 (800) 621-668; (928) 776-4092 Fax 708-9702
Don & Annette Coffey, Owners
Website: www.blackarrowindianart.com
E-mail: info@blackarrowindianart.com
Membership: IACA.

AL QOYAWAYMA HOPI CERAMIC ART
P.O. Box 12464 • Prescott, AZ 86304
 Fax (928) 443-9706; Website: www.alqpottery.com
E-mail: alqoy@cableone.net

GILA RIVER ARTS & CRAFTS CENTER
P.O. Box 457 • Sacaton, AZ 85247
 (480) 963-3981; Jon Long, Manager
Retail, some mail order. Tribe-owned corporation. *Products*: Southwest Indian jewelry, pottery, rugs, kachina dolls, beadwork, basketry.

BROWN'S TURQUOISE SHOP
2248 First Ave. • Safford, AZ 85546
 (602) 428-6433; Bernice Brown, Owner
Retail, wholesale. *Products*: Art, baskets, beadwork, clothing, dolls, jewelry, kachinas, pottery, sand paintings, sculpture, carvings, craft supplies, repairs & restoration. *Membership*: IACA.

PHILLIP TITLA STUDIO
P.O. Box 497 • San Carlos, AZ 85550
 (602) 475-2361; Phillip Titla, Owner
Retail, mail order. *Products*: Art, dolls, sculpture, carvings. Brochure.

AMERICAN-INDIAN-ART.COM
(480) 558-5345; Website: www.american-indian.art.com
Online. *Products*: Paintings; jewelry, pottery, rugs, wall hangings; peace pipes; tomahawks, bows, arrows & quivers spears, knives; ceremonial attire; dolls, kachinas; flutes.

D.Y. BEGAY'S TEXTILE STUDIO
6929 E. Jenan Dr. • Scottsdale, AZ 85254
 (480) 922-9232 Fax 951-2357; Website: www.navajo-indian.com
E-mail: dybegay@cox.net; D.Y. Begay, Owner/Manager
Wholesale. Special orders accepted. Products: Museum quality traditional and contemporary Navajo weavings by the artist and other Navajo weavers; custom tapestries, rugs, and blankets.

THE EASTERN COWBOYS
4235 N. 86th Pl. • Scottsdale, AZ 85251
 (480) 945-9804 (phone & fax); Jay & Edith Sadow, Owners
E-Mail: EasternCow@aol.com; Website: www.xylem.web.com/eastcow
Wholesale. *Products*: All. Catalog.

GODBERS JEWELRY, INC.
Box 831, 7542 E. Main • Scottsdale, AZ 85252
 (480) 949-1133; Allie Mae & Ken Godber, Owners
Wholesale. *Products*: Art, baskets, dye charts, fetishes, heishi, jewelry, kachinas, pottery, rugs, sand painting, sculpture. *Membership*: IACA.

GREY WOLF
7239 E. First Ave. • Scottsdale, AZ 85251
 (480) 423-0004; Anne & Sid Billings, Owners
Wholesale, retail. *Products*: All. *Membership*: IACA.

INCA TRADERS
13641 N. 49th St. • Scottsdale, AZ 85254
 (480) 432-3608; John & Nancy Miller, Owners
E-mail: incatraders1@msn.com. *Membership*: IACA.

LEONA KING GALLERY
7171 E. Main • Scottsdale, AZ 85251
 (480) 945-1209; Sam & Sue King, Owners
Wholesale, retail. *Products*: Art, baskets, beadwork, clothing, drums, pipes, fetishes, jewelry, kachinas, knives, miniatures, pottery, rugs, sculpture, carvings. Appraisals: Art, pottery, sculpture, carvings. *Membership*: IACA.

ALSTON & DEBORAH NEAL
7077 E. Main St. #7 • Scottsdale, AZ 85251
 (480) 945-5432; Website: www.oldterritorialshop.com
Retail, Wholesale. *Products*: Indian baskets, jewelry, pottery, Navajo rugs & blankets.

RAIN BIRD OF SCOTTSDALE
7136 E. Main St. • Scottsdale, AZ 85251
 (480) 425-7585 Fax 425-7621; Website: www.rainbirdtrading.com
E-mail: rainbirdmarket@cox.net; Ju-Leigh Sharp & Sheree Stauder, Owners
Membership: IACA.

RIVER TRADING POST
7140 E. 1st Ave. • Scottsdale, AZ 85251
 (866) 426-6901; (480) 444-0001; Website: www.rivertradingpost.com
Retail, wholesale. *Products*: Navajo weavings, Pueblo pottery, Hopi kachina dolls, Zuni fetishes, sculpture, baskets, jewelry, Plains Indian art, Six Nations art.

SAR-JO & ASSOCIATES, INC.
10482 E. Balancing Rock Rd. • Scottsdale, AZ 85262
 (480) 502-8021 Fax 502-8022
E-Mail: sarjoassoc@aol.com; Joseph B. Levine, CEO
Wholesale. Southwest arts & crafts. *Products*: Baskets, dolls, drums, pipes, heishi, jewelry, kachinas, miniatures, rugs; repairs & restoration. *Membership*: IACA.

SEWELL'S INDIAN ARTS
7087 5th Ave. • Scottsdale, AZ 85251
 (480) 945-0962 Fax 991-3018; Website: www.buyindianarts.com
E-mail: sewells@buyindianarts.com;
Sandy, Sadeem & Nadiya Daiza, Owners
Retail. *Products*: All. *Appraisals*: Jewelry, kachinas. *Membership*: IACA.

SILVER EAGLE
3637 N. Goldwater Blvd. • Scottsdale, AZ 85251
 (480) 945-6781 Fax 945-6782; Website" silvereagleinc.com
E-mail: sei@silvereagleinc.com; Mike Othman & Tammi Lewis, Owners
Membership: IACA.

SILVER QUEEN
3945 N. Brown Ave. • Scottsdale, AZ 85251
 (480) 949-2422; Waleed & Murad Sarrar, Owners
E-mail: silverqueenaz.msn.com. *Membership*: IACA.

SOUTHWEST EVENTS ETC.
3200 N. Hayden Rd., Suite 100 • Scottsdale, AZ 85251-6653
 (480) 947-6800 Fax 947-6888; Nancy & Michael Pavlik, Owners
Retail. *Products*: Art, baskets, boxes, ornaments, fetishes, heishi, jewelry, kachinas, knives, miniatures, pottery, rugs, sculpture. *Membership*: IACA.

TRADER GENE
P.O. Box 13413 • Scottsdale, AZ 85267
 (800) 258-3746; (480) 945-5826 Fax 443-0355; Gene Benner, Owner
Wholesale. *Products*: Dolls, fetishes, jewelry, kachinas, rugs, sand paintings, sculpture, craft supplies.

TURQUOISE HOGAN, INC.
P.O. Box 657 • Scottsdale, AZ 85252-0657
 (480) 949-5122 (Phone & Fax; Judith & Donald Barajas, Owners
Wholesale, retail. *Products*: Fetishes, jewelry; repairs & restoration. *Membership*: IACA.

ANCIENT PATHWAYS
P.O. Box 412 • Second Mesa, AZ 86043
 (928) 306-7849; Bertram Tsavadawa (Hopi), Artist/Owner
Retail. *Products*: Old style Katsina dolls, two-dimensional art work; petroglyph symbols.

DAWA'S HOPI ARTS & CRAFTS
P.O. Box 127 (Hopi Reservation) • Second Mesa, AZ 86043
 (520) 734-2430; Bernard Dawahoya, Owner
Retail, mail order. *Product*: Jewelry. Specializes in Hopi overlay silver jewelry.

HONANI CRAFTS-GALLERY
P.O. Box 221 • Second Mesa, AZ 86043
 (520) 737-2238; King Honani, Sr., Owner/Manager
Retail, wholesale, mail order. Special orders accepted. *Products*: Hopi overlay gold & silver jewelry, pottery, weavings, paintings, kachinas, baskets; Zuni, Navajo, Santo Domingo jewelry; Navajo rugs.

HOPI GALLERY
Hopi Cultural Center, P.O. Box 316 • Second Mesa, AZ 86043
 (520) 734-2238; Phil Sekaquaptewa, Owner
Retail, wholesale, mail order. *Products*: Art, baskets, jewelry, kachinas, pottery, rugs. Brochure, catalog.

HOPI ARTS & CRAFTS - SILVERCRAFT COOPERATIVE GUILD
P.O. Box 37 • Second Mesa, AZ 86043
 (520) 734-2463 Fax 734-6647; Milland S. Lomakema, Sr. (Hopi), Manager
Retail, wholesale, mail order. Special orders accepted. *Products*: Hopi overlay silver jewelry, basketry, pottery, Hopi kachina dolls, paintings and textiles. Brochure, catalog.

HOPI SILVER ARTS & CRAFTS
P.O. Box 726 • Second Mesa, AZ 86043
 (928) 734-6695 Fax 699-4693; Weaver & Alberta Selina
Membership: IACA.

ISKASOKPU ARTS & CRAFTS
P.O. Box 329 • Second Mesa, AZ 86043
 (928) 734-9353 Fax 737-9370; Iva Casuse (Hopi), Owner/Manager
Retail, wholesale. Products: Hopi arts & crafts including jewelry, pottery, katsina dolls, baskets & silver supplies.

LOMANVENTEMA SILVER & HOPI CRAFTS
P.O. Box 66 • Second Mesa, AZ 86043
 Gerald Honwytewa (Hopi), Owner/Manager
Products: Traditional & contemporary jewelry, katsina dolls & Hopi crafts.

SECAKUKU ENTERPRISES & SHOP
P.O. Box 67 • Second Mesa, AZ 86043
 (520) 734-2401; 737-2632; Dorothy & Ferrell Secakuku, Owners
Retail, wholesale. Products: Art, baskets, kachinas, pottery.

TSAKUESHOVI
Box 234, Second Mesa, AZ 86043
 (928) 734-2478; Janice Day (Hopi), Owner
Products: Traditional Hopi arts, crafts, and cultural items.

BLUE-EYED BEAR
299 N. Hwy. 89-A • Sedona, AZ 86336
 (800) 371-9650; (928) 282-1158 Fax 282-4761; Bud & Linda Johnson
 Website: www.blueeyedbear.com; E-mail: info@blueeyedbear.com
Retail. *Products*: Fetishes, jewelry, pottery, rugs, sand paintings, sculpture, carvings. 2nd location: 671 Hwy. 179. *Membership*: IACA.

CLEAR CREEK TRADING CO.
435 N. Hwy 89A • Sedona, AZ 86336
 (928) 204-5805 Fax 204-4406; Website: www.clearcreektrading.com
 E-mail: sstrading@quest.net; Ron Bowling, Owner. *Membership*: IACA.

GARLAND'S INDIAN JEWELRY
Indian Gardens Hwy. 89-A, P.O. Box 1848 • Sedona, AZ 86336
 (928) 282-6632; Susan A. Garland, Owner
 Website: www.garlandsjewelry.com; E-mail: info@garlandsjewelry.com
Wholesale, retail. *Products*: Baskets, heishi, jewelry, kachinas, knives, miniatures, pottery, sand paintings. *Appraisals*: Jewelry. *Membership*: IACA.

GARLAND'S NAVAJO RUGS
P.O. Box 851, 411 Hwy. 179 • Sedona, AZ 86336
 (928) 282-4070 Fax 282-1059; Website: www.garlandsrugs.com
 E-mail: info@garlandsrugs.com; Daniel J. Garland, Owner
Retail. *Products*: Baskets, kachinas, miniatures, rugs, sand paintings. *Appraisals*: Rugs. *Membership*: IACA.

HOEL'S INDIAN SHOP
9589 N. Hwy. 89A • Sedona, AZ 86336
 (928) 282-3925; Website: www.hoelindianshop.com
Retail, wholesale. *Products*: Baskets, jewelry, kachinas, pottery, rugs.

THE NAJA, INC.
P.O. Box 1289 • Sedona, AZ 86339
 (928) 282-4755 Fax 282-1670; Website: www.thenaja.ocm
 E-mail: naja@sedona.net; William & Kathy Lamparter, Owners

TURQUOISE TORTOISE GALLERY
Hozho Center, 431 Hwy. 179 • Sedona, AZ 86336
 (928) 282-2262; Peggy J. Lanning-Eisler, Owner
Wholesale, retail. *Products*: Art, baskets, beadwork, boxes, clothing, fetishes, heishi, jewelry, kachinas, miniatures, sand paintings. *Membership*: IACA.

WAY WEST
115 N. House Rock Rd. • Sedona, AZ 86351
 (928) 634-5105; Brian O'Heir, Owner
 Website: www.way-west.com; E-mail: oheir@sedona.net. *Membership*: IACA.

GORDON WHEELER'S TRADING POST & MUSEUM
P.O. Box 2937 • Sedona, AZ 86339
 (928) 282-4255 Fax 282-2027; E-mail: lwheller@sedona.net
 Lois & Lee Wheeler, Owners. *Membership*: IACA.

COCOPAH NATIVE ART WORKS
9760 W. Hava St. • Somerton, AZ 85350
 (928) 627-8684
Retail, mail Order. *Products*: hand-drawn Native American artwork; Native American paintings; and reproductions of photos & portraits

INDIAN PONY TRADING POST
P.O. Box 767 • Sonita, AZ 85637
 (520) 394-2264
Retail. *Products*: Art, baskets, beadwork, pottery, sand paintings, sculpture, carvings.

MANY HORSES TRADING CO.
3266 Hwy. 82, P.O. Box 886 • Sonita, AZ 85637
 (520) 455-5545 Fax 455-5810
 E-mail: ha.byron@theriver.com; Helen Byron, Owner. *Membership*: IACA.

THE TRADING POST
8817 Montana • Sun Lakes, AZ 85248
 (520) 895-6072; Tom & Marilyn DeYoung, Owners
Wholesale, retail. *Products*: Beadwork, fetishes, jewelry, kachinas, knives. Membership: IACA.

TEEC NOS POS ARTS/CRAFTS
P.O. Box Z • Teec Nos Pos, AZ 86514-0113
 (928) 656-3228; Bill & Kay Foutz, Owners
Wholesale, retail. *Products*: Baskets, beadwork, boxes, ornaments, dolls, jewelry, kachinas, pottery, rugs, sand paintings, sculpture, carvings. *Membership*: IACA. Catalog.

E-PUEBLO.COM
1711 E. Knox Rd. • Tempe, AZ 85284
 (480) 730-1768; Kent S. Crudup, Owner
 Website: www.e-pueblo.com; E-mail: ksc@e-pueblo.com. *Membership*: IACA.

WADDELL TRADING COMPANY
P.O. Box 24782 • Tempe, AZ 85284-4782
 (480) 755-8080 Fax 755-3559; E-mail: wadtradeco@aol.com
 Website: www.waddelltradingcompany.com
Gene, Lisa & Laura Waddell & Erik Van Itallie, Owners
Retail. Products: Art, jewelry. *Membership*: IACA.

ARLENE'S SOUTHWEST SILVER & GOLD & ARLENE'S GALLERY
404 Allen St. (Silver & Gold); 415 Allen St. (Gallery)
P.O. Box 340 • Tombstone, AZ 85638 (520) 457-3678 Fax 457-2488
 E-mail: arlenes@theriver.com; Arlene & Adam Klein, Owners
Wholesale, Retail.Products: All. *Membership*: IACA.

TRADITIONS & INNOVATIONS NAVAJO SANDPAINTING
P.O. Box 154 • Tonalea, AZ 86044
 (928) 283-8820; Junior Whiterock (Navajo), Owner
Products: Navajo handmade pottery and sandpainting.

HATATHLI GALLERY
Navajo Community College • Tsaile, AZ 86556
 (928) 724-6650 Fax 724-3349; Ms. Bert Dempsey, Manager
Wholesale, retail. *Products*: Jewelry, paintings, rugs, sand paintings, beadwork, art items. Brochure.

PATRICK SCOTT
P.O. Box 3018 • Tuba City, AZ 86045
 (928) 283-5629; E-Mail: pscott3@frontiernet.net
 Website: www.ceremonialart.biz
Retail, wholesale. *Products*: Specializes in peyote & powwow feather fans.

TUBA TRADING POST
Box 247, Main & Moenave Sts.• Tuba City, AZ 86045
  (520) 283-5441 Fax 283-4144; Mark & Janet Shipley
Wholesale, retail. *Products*: Art, baskets, boxes, clothing, dolls, drums, pipes, jewelry, kachinas, pottery, rugs, sand paintings, sculpture. *Membership*: IACA.

OLD PRESIDIO TRADERS
Box 4023, #27 Tubac Rd. • Tubac, AZ 85646
  (520) 398-9333; Lisa & Garry Hembree. Retail.

TURQUOISE TORTOISE GALLERY
Box 2321, La Pradera Mall, Hwy. 82 • Tubac, AZ 85646
  (520) 398-2041; Esther & Larry Fitzpatrick
Retail. *Products*: Art, baskets, beadwork, boxes, clothing, drums, pipes, flutes, fetishes, heishi, jewelry, kachinas, rugs, sandpaintings. *Membership*: IACA.

BAHTI INDIAN ARTS
4300 N. Campbell Ave. • Tucson, AZ 85701
  (520) 577-0290; Mark Tomas Bahti, Owner
Retail. *Products*: All. *Membership*: IACA.

BAILEY'S BUFFALO TRADING CO.
6131 N. Panorama Pl. • Tucson, AZ 85704
  (408) 997-6471; Skip & Lori Bailey. *Membership*: IACA.

BAIR'S INDIAN TRADING CO.
P.O. Box 17476 • Tucson, AZ 85731
  (888) 290-4508; (520) 290-4508; Website: bairsindiantradingco.com
E-mail: info@bairsindiantradingco.com; Paul Bair, Owner
Membership: IACA.

BLACK ARROW TRADERS
2400 N. Calle de Maurer • Tucson, AZ 85749-9582
  (520) 749-4119; Sophie & Jack Guth
Wholesale, retail. *Products*: Baskets, beadwork, dolls, fetishes, heishi, jewelry, kachinas, rugs, sand paintings. *Membership*: IACA.

CANYON COUNTRY ORIGINALS
6030 E. Fangio Pl. • Tucson, AZ 85750
  (520) 529-5545 Fax 577-1456; Website: canyonart.com
E-mail: cainfo@canyonart.com; Jay Tallant, Owner. *Membership*: IACA.

DESERT SON INDIAN ART
4759 E. Sunrise Dr. • Tucson, AZ 85718
  (520) 299-0818; Steve Osborne, Owner
E-Mail: elrey@azstarnet.com; Website: www.desertson.com
Retail. *Products*: Hopi kachinas; gold & silver jewlery; Navajo rugs, baskets, pottery and moccasins. *Membership*: IACA.

FOURTH MESA LTD.
1642 E. Entrada Tecera • Tucson, AZ 85718
  (520) 615-4551 Fax 615-4551; Website: www.fourthmesa.com
Joan Oesterle & Gary Schuessler, Owners; E-mail: joan@fourthmesa.com
Membership: IACA.

GUARDIAN RAINBOW
P.O. Box 32078 • Tucson, AZ 85751
  (520) 885-8369 Fax 722-5872
Keith & Doris Palmer, Owners
Wholesale, retail. *Products*: Baskets, fetishes, jewelry, kachinas, pottery, rugs. *Appraisals*: Jewelry, kachinas, pottey, rugs. Membership: IACA.

INDIGENA FINE ART PUBLISHING CO.
P.O. Box 13222 • Tucson, AZ 85732-3222
  (520) 721-1886 Fax 721-2105; David B. Waine, Owner
Wholesale. *Products*: Contemporary art & historical Native American folding cards, postcards, posters; signed limited editions. Catalog to retailers only.

K & G CO., INC.
63647 E. Edgeview Lane • Tucson, AZ 85737
  Gloria Snook
Retail. *Products*: Art, baskets, beadwork, clothing, dolls, jewelry, kachinas, pottery, sandpaintings, sculpture, carvings, craft supplies. *Membership*: IACA.

KITT PEAK NATIONAL VISITOR CENTER
950 N. Cherry Ave. • Tucson, AZ 85719
  (520) 318-8451; Richard Fedele, Manager
E-mail: rfedele@noao.edu
Membership: IACA.

LA ZIA
201 N. Court Ave. • Tucson, AZ 85701
  (520) 670-0099 Fax 622-4421
  E-mail: lazianm@aol.com
  Steve Lee & Robert Southard, Owners
Membership: IACA.

MORNING STAR TRADERS, INC.
2020 E. Speedway Blvd. • Tucson, AZ 85719
  (520) 881-2112 Fax 881-5694
  Website: www.morningstartraders.com
  E-mail: morningstar@theriver.com
  Richard (Rick) & Mary Beth Rosenthal, Owners
Retail. *Products*: Southwestern Indian jewelry, baskets, pottery, and old Navajo rugs. Specializing in old pawn jewelry, old baskets and rugs, collectors items. Hopi jewelry by Bernard Dawahoya, Wilson Jim and Julian Lovato. *Membership*: IACA.

NATIONAL NATIVE AMERICAN COOP
P.O. Box 27626 • Tucson, AZ 85726-7626
  (520) 622-4900 Fax 622-3525; Fred Synder, Owner
  Website: www.usaindianinfo.org
Retail, Wholesale, Mail Order. *Products*: Authentic American Indian crafts from 2,700 artists representing over 400 tribal nations.

NATIVE AMERICAN COLLECTIBLES
2241 S. Double O Pl. • Tucson, AZ 85713
  John & Ruth Gruber
Wholesale, retail. *Products*: Baskets, drums, pipes, fetishes, heishi, jewelry, kachinas, pottery, rugs. *Appraisals*: Rugs. *Membership*: IACA.

RESERVATION CREATIONS
P.O. Box 27626 • Tucson, AZ 85726
  (520) 622-4900; Carole J. Garcia (Tohono O'odham), Owner/Manager
Retail, wholesale, mail order. *Products*: Art, baskets, beadwork, boxes, clothing, dolls, pottery, rugs, sculpture.

SILVERBELL TRADING
7119 N. Oracle Rd. • Tucson, AZ 85704
  (520) 797-6852; Website: www.silverbelltrader.com
  E-mail: silverbelltrader@aol.com
Retail. *Products*: Historic & contemporary baskets, fetishes, pottery, textiles & painting.

SO WEST TERRITORIES
186 N. Meyer Ave. • Tucson, AZ 85701
  (800) 851-6153; (520) 623-1871
  Linda & Harry Sheraw; E-mail: harlin@azstarnet.com
Retail. *Products*: Native American and Southwest art. *Membership*: IACA.

URSHEL TAYLOR'S OWL EAR STUDIO
2901 W. Sahuaro Divide • Tucson, AZ 85742
  (800) 487-0180; (520) 297-4456 Fax 544-4382
  Urshel & Tony Taylor, Owners
Retail, mail order. *Products*: Clothing, jewelry. *Membership*: IACA. Brochure.

TOUCH OF TURQUOISE
10951 E. Linden • Tucson, AZ 85749
  (520) 722-2265; Barbara Yoder, Owner
  Website: www.touchofturquois.com; E-mail: barb@touchofturquois.com
Membership: IACA.

TOWAYALANE TRADING CO.
6590 E. Tanque Verde, Suite A • Tucson, AZ 85715
  (520) 886-3542; Joe & Jan Douthitt
Wholesale. *Products*: Art, baskets, beadwork, clothing, dolls, jewelry, kachinas, pottery, rugs, sand paintings, sculpture, carvings. *Membership*: IACA.

TREASURES & TRIFLES
3030 N. Willow Creek Dr. • Tucson, AZ 85712
  (520) 881-2124; James & Elsie Deer, Owner
Retail. *Products*: Art, baskets, fetishes, heishi, jewelry, miniatures, craft supplies; repair & restoration. *Appraisals*: Baskets, fetishes, heishi, jewelry, miniatures. *Membership*: IACA.

UWIGA DESIGNS
3420 E. Maxim Pl. • Tucson, AZ 85739
  (520) 825-2830
Retail, Wholesale. *Products*: Clothing. Native American designs. Catalog, $6.

VINCENT MEIER
P.O. Box 5862 • Tucson, AZ 85703
  (520) 325-3209; Vincent Meier, Owner
Wholesale. *Products*: Baskets, beadwork, dolls, fetishes, jewelry, kachinas, knives, pottery, sand paintings.

WENDY'S HALLMARK
3652 S. 16th Ave. • Tucson, AZ 85713
  (520) 624-4143 Fax 297-0976; E-mail: swprops@hotmail.com
  Reese & Judy Carpenter, Owner. *Membership*: IACA.

THUNDER EAGLE
221 W. Rt. 66 • William, AZ 86046
  (623) 551-3160 Fax 551-3160
  Irena Weiher & John Peasley, Owners. *Membership*: IACA.

BEAR CANYON GALLERIES
P.O. Box 5455 • Window Rock, AZ 86515
  (928) 879-1546; Eddie A. Kaibetoney (Navajo), Owner
  Website: www.bearcanyongalleries.com
Internet only. *Products*: Jewelry, paintings, rugs; wood & stone sculptures, baskets, beadwork.

BENALLY'S INDIAN ARTS
P.O. Box 780 • Window Rock, AZ 86515
  (928) 871-5727; Ronald F. Benally, Owner. Wholesale.

NAVAJO ARTS & CRAFTS ENTERPRISE
P.O. Box 160 • Window Rock, AZ 86515
  (928) 871-4095 Fax 871-3340; Website: www.gonavajo.com
  E-mail: customerservice@gonavajo.com
  Eliott Mott, Manager
Retail, wholesale. Tribal Enterprise. *Products*: Indian art, jewelry, woven wool rugs, wood carvings, dolls, pottery, other Native craft products. Branch shops: Cameron, AZ; Chinle, AZ; Kayenta, AZ; Gallup, NM; Grants, NM. *Membership*: IACA.

CALIFORNIA

HHS EXPORT TRADING CO.
2305 Roark Dr. • Alhambra, CA 91803
  (626) 281-7769 Fax 281-5543
  E-mail: hhsetc@worldnet.att.net
  Hermann & Maria Schmidt, Owners
Retail, wholesale, mail order. *Products*: Native American jewelry & artifacts; Western & Southwestern apparel, products & accessories. Bison meat & products. *Appraisal*: Art, artifacts, fetishes, heishi, jewelry, kachinas, knives, pottery, sculpture, carvings. *Membership*: IACA. Brochure & catalog. Branch shop: Germany (exporter to Europe & the Pacific Rim countries).

SANTA FE CRAFTS
P.O. Box 298 • Altadena, CA 91003-0298
  (800) 421-7661; (818) 398-1789 Fax 398-1575
  Website: www.santafecrafts.com; Barbara Goldeen, Owner
Wholesale. *Products*: Baskets, ornaments, dolls, artifacts, fetishes, heishi,, jewelry, kachinas, miniatures, pottery. *Membership*: IACA.

MODERN ARTIFACTS
P.O. Box 2650 • Aptos, CA 95001
  (888) 385-3155; (831) 475-9194 Fax 475-9203
  Website: www.modernartifactsonline.com
  E-mail: bill@modernartifactsonline.com
  William E. Steinke & Leslie A. Sunell, Owners
Branch shop: 312A Capitola Ave., Capitola, CA 95010. *Membership*: IACA.

BEAR MOUNTAIN TRADING CO.
P.O. Box 6503, 42626 Moonridge Rd. • Big Bear Lake, CA 92315
  (714) 585-9676 Fax 585-0310; Gerry & Patty Taylor
Retail. *Products*: Art, baskets, beadwork, clothing, dolls, jewelry, kachinas, pottery, sand paintings, sculpture, carvings. *Membership*: IACA.

EASTERN SIERRA TRADING CO.
P.O. Box 731 • Bridgeport, CA 93517
  (619) 932-7231; Joe & Mary Lent, Owners
Retail. *Products*: Baskets, beadwork, jewelry, pottery.

KNOTT'S BERRY FARM
8039 Beach Blvd. • Buena Park, CA 90620
  (714) 220-5270; Fred Wagner, Mechandise Div.
Retail. *Products*: All. *Membership*: IACA.

A GALLERY OF NATIONS
2021 Gayle Way • Carlsbad, CA 98002
  Website: www.agalleryofnations.com
  E-mail: info@agalleryofnations.com
Online store featuring Zuni fetishes, turquoise & silver jewelry, and pottery.

THE WOODEN INDIAN
3019 State St. • Carlsbad, CA 92008
  (619) 729-1596; LaVon & Pete Ritter, Owners
Retail. *Products*: All. Appraisals: Art, baskets, beadwork, fetishes, heishi, jewelry, kachinas, pottery, rugs, sand paintings. *Membership*: IACA.

BLACK EAGLE
P.O. Box 621 • Copperopolis, CA 95228
  (209) 785-5259
Wholesale. *Products*: Original Shoshone & Northern Plains style artifacts

SOUTHWESTERN INDIAN DEN
1201 First St. #104 • Coronado, CA 92118
  (619) 435-3561; Ervin Tsosie, Owner. Retail. *Products*: Jewelry.

RONALD CHEE STUDIO
2914 Ellesmere Ave. • Costa Mesa, CA 92626
  (714) 549-0148 or 334-9052; E-mail: ronaldcheestudio@sbcglobal.net
  Ronald Chee (Navajo), Artist/Owner
Products: Oil-based ink monotypes; acrylic paintings & limited edition prints, contemporary format dealing with interpretations of traditional Navajo myths & culture.

WHITE PELICAN/DKP ENTERPRISES
34475 Golden Lantern • Dana Point, CA 92629
  (949) 240-1991 Fax 240-1954; E-mail: whitepelican@sbcglobal.net
  Website: danapointharbor.com/whitepelican
  Diana, George & Chad Poulos, Owners
Wholesale, retail. *Products*: All. *Membership*: IACA.

DELUNA JEWELERS
521 Second St. • Davis, CA 95616
  (916) 753-3351; Richard Luna, Owner
Wholesale, retail, mail order. *Products*: Baskets, beadwork, jewelry, pottery, rugs, sculpture, carvings.

AMERICAN INDIAN STORE
1095 Magnolia • El Cajon, CA 92020
  (619) 583-5389; G. Roy Cook, Owner
Mail order. Products: Art, baskets, beadwork, kachinas, jewlery, clothing, pottery, rugs, sculpture, carvings, craft supplies. Catalog.

AMERICAN INDIAN ART GIFT SHOP (NCIDC)
241 F St. • Eureka, CA 95501
  (707) 445-8451 Fax 445-8479
  Terry Coltra, Manager
Retail, wholesale, mail order. *Products*: Art, baskets, beadwork, clothing, dolls, jewelry, kachinas, pottery, rugs, sand paintings, sculpture, carvings, craft supplies. *Membership*: IACA. Special orders accepted. Brochure & price list.

GENERATIONS BY LINDA VIT
P.O. Box 3317 • Eureka, CA 95502
  (707) 442-8800 Fax 445-0745; Website: www.indianwest.com
  E-mail: indianwest@yahoo.com; Linda C. Vit (Karuk), Owner
Wholesale, retail, mail order. *Products*: Jewelry, pottery.
Special orders accepted. Catalog and wholesale price list.

STARCRAFT JEWELRY
1550 Myrtle Ave. • Eureka, CA 95501
  (707) 444-3354; Farrel Starr (Quinault), Artist/Owner
  E-mail: farrell@northcoast.com. *Products*: Jewelry.

PACIFIC WESTERN TRADERS
305 Wool St. • Folsom, CA 95630
  (916) 985-3851 Fax 985-2635; Website: www.pacwesttraders.com
  E-mail: pwtfolsom@aol.com; Herbert & Courtney Puffer, Owners
Native American Indian gallery and resource center. Traditional and contemporary arts of California's native people. *Membership*: IACA.

THE TURQUOISE NUT
321 N. Verdugo Rd. • Glendale, CA 91206
  (818) 243-1001; Tom & Helen Snyder, Owners
Wholesale, retail. *Products*: All. *Membership*: IACA.

MAR-BILL INDIAN STORE
1620 San Vicente Dr. • Hemet, CA 92543
  (509) 996-2470; Mary Luther, Owner
Retail. *Products*: Baskets, beadwork, clothing, dolls, jewelry, kachinas, pottery, rugs, sand paintings, sculpture, carvings, craft supplies. *Membership*: IACA. *Branch*: Winthrop, WA.

GEORGE BLAKE'S STUDIO
P.O. Box 1304 • Hoopa, CA 95546
  (916) 625-4619; George N. Blake, Owner
Wholesale, Retail. Hupa-Yurok crafts. *Products*: Drums, flutes, pipes, pottery, sculpture, carvings. Large and miniature canoes.

TEEWORD DESIGNS
P.O. Box 1409 • Hoopa. CA 95546
  (707) 499-1922; Tony J. Sylvia, Artist/Owner
Products: Wearable art (Native design only); paintings.

BADGER PAW INDIANCRAFTS
134 Main St. • Jackson, CA 95642
  (209) 223-0102 Fax 223-5131; Website: www.badger-paw.com
  E-mail: admin@badger-paw.com; Dennis & Fredericka Altergott, Owners
Membership: IACA.

SIERRA MADRE TRADING CO.
2038 Palo Verde Ave., P.O. Box 92016 • Long Beach, CA 90815
  (562) 598-6615; Ed & Arthela Cummings, Owners
Website: www. sierramadretrading.com
E-mail: treasure@sierramadretrading.com. *Membership*: IACA.

AUTRY MUSEUM OF WESTERN HERITAGE STORE
4700 Western Heritage Way • Los Angeles, CA 90027
  (323) 667-2000 Fax 666-4863; E-mail: mstore@autry-museum.org
  Website: www.autry-museum.org; John L. Gray, Executive Director
Retail. *Products*: All. *Membership*: IACA.

ROCKY MOUNTAIN HOUSE
2574 S. Bundy Dr. • Los Angeles, CA 90064
  (310) 393-8912; Ron Daleo, Owner
Wholesale. *Products*: Baskets, beadwork, clothing, drums, pipes, fetishes, jewelry, miniatures, pottery, rugs, sand paintings. *Membership*: IACA.

TRIBAL ARTS
P.O. Box 19965 • Los Angeles, CA 90019
  (213) 292-6808 Fax 295-1045; Judy Cross
Wholesale, retail. *Products*: Heishi, jewelry. *Membership*: IACA.

THE INDIAN STORE
50 University Ave. • Los Gatos, CA 95031
  (408) 354-9988 Fax 354-0828; Website: www.theindianstore.com
  Janice L. Benjamin, Owner. Retail. *Products*: All. *Membership*: IACA.

FIEGE'S COLLECTIBLES
15236 Lassan St. • Mission Hills, CA 91345
  (818) 892-6826; Kathleen & Gary Fiege, Owners. Wholesale, retail.

WAKEDA TRADING POST
P.O. Box 2114 • Oakdale, CA 95361
  (209) 848-0711; Cliff C. Paulsen, President
  E-Mail: wakeda@hotmail.com; Website: www.wakeda.com
Retail, wholesale, mail order. *Products*: Native American craft supplies, beads, feathers, clothing, botanicals, books, videos, recordings.

INTERTRIBAL FRIENDSHIP HOUSE GIFT SHOP
523 E. 14th St. • Oakland, CA 94606
  (510) 452-1235; Susie Astor, Manager
Retail, wholesale. *Products*: Beadwork, clothing, silver jewelry, rugs, blankets.

OJAI INDIAN SHOP
318 E. Ojai Ave. • Ojai, CA 93023-2739
  (805) 646-2631; George & Wendy LaBraque
Retail. *Products*: All. *Appraisals*: Baskets, rugs.

THE SOUTHWEST
P.O. Box 32 • Ontario, CA 91762
  (714) 981-5711; Debbie Zugzda, Owner
Retail. *Products*: Baskets, beadwork, boxes, dolls, drums, pipes, flutes, Northwest Coast art, heishi, jewelry, kachinas, miniatures, pottery, rugs.

MATOSKA TRADING CO.
611 W. Chapman Ave. • Orange, CA 928868

  (714) 516-9940 Fax 516-9941 Fax (800) 249-9375
  Website: www.matoska.com; E-Mail: service@matoska.com
  Brent Schellhase, Owner
Retail, wholesale, mail order. *Products*: Art, beadwork, books, clothing, drums, pipes, rugs. Catalog, $3.

REDROCK ARTS
1295 Adobe Lane • Pacific Grove, CA 93950
  (408) 624-5149; Steve & Carol Bishop, Owners
Retail. Products: Art, baskets, fetishes, heishi, jewelry, pottery, rugs.

INDIAN VILLAGE, INC.
#43 Town & Country Village • Palo Alto, CA 94301-2326
  (415) 328-7090; Beth & Ron Hale, Owners
Retail. *Products*: All. *Membership*: IACA.

PALOMAR MOUNTAIN GENERAL STORE & TRADING CO.
P.O. Box 100, Jct. S6 & S7 • Palomar Mountain, CA 92060
  (619) 742-3496 Fax 742-4233; Brian Beck
Retail. *Products*: Baskets, beadwork, boxes, drums, flutes, pipes, Northwest Coast art, artifacts, fetishes, heishi, jewelry, kachinas, pottery, rugs, sculpture, carvings. *Membership*: IACA.

THE INDIAN SHOP
P.O. Box 614 • Pauma Valley, CA 92061
  (619) 749-0130; Leo & Monte Calec, Owners
Wholesale, retail. *Products*: Art, baskets, clothing, dolls, drums, pipes, flutes, jewelry, rugs.

NIZHONIE SOUTHWEST SPIRIT
5 Nob Hill Ter. • Petaluma, CA 94952
  (707) 763-9231; E-Mail: cgniz@cs.com
  Corina Gneri, Owner. *Membership*: IACA.

MESA TRADING CO.
608-G Main St. • Pleasanton, CA 94566
  (925) 426-9229 Fax 426-8577; Website: www.mesastore@pacbell.net
  Rennie & Phyllis Couper. *Membership*: IACA.

LINDA SANTIAGO PETERSON
621 N. Main • Porterville, CA 93257
  (559) 730-1359; E-Mail: wildindians@arrival.net
Retail, wholesale. *Products*: Contemporary California
Native American painting & sculpture. By appointment.

MOON DANCER
1706 S. Catalina Ave. • Redondo Beach, CA 90277
  (310) 316-7200 Fax 316-7721; E-mail: rhausvick@uno.com
  Paula Hausvick & Dee Gavin, Owners
Retail. *Products*: All. *Membership*: IACA.

KOKOPELLI INDIAN ARTS
4567 Pacific St., P.O. Box 1258 • Rocklin, CA 95677
  (916) 630-8849 Fax 630-7202; Website: kokopellirocks.com
  E-mail: kokopelli@starstream.net; Richard & Gloria Riley, Owners
Membership: IACA.

GALLERY OF THE AMERICAN WEST
121 "K" St. • Sacramento, CA 95814
  (916) 446-6662; Leon W. Hodge, Owner
Retail. *Products*: Art, baskets, beadwork, clothing, dolls, fetsihes, heishi, jewelry, kachinas, pottery, sand paintings, sculpture, carvings, craft supplies, repairs & restoration. *Appraisals*: Baskets, fetishes, heishi, jewelry, kachinas, pottery, rugs, sand paintings. Membership: IACA.

NATIVE AMERICAN DOLLS & CREATIONS
8542 German Dr. • Sacramento, CA 95828
  (916) 9112-1426; Website: www.nativeamericandolls.net
  Irene Jewel Wilson, (Yurok), Owner. *Products*: Native American dolls.

BAZAAR DEL MUNDO GALLERY
2754 Calhoun St. • San Diego, CA 92110
  (619) 296-3161 Fax 296-3113; Website: www.bazaardelmundo.com
  E-mail: customerservice@bazaardelmundo.com; Diane Powers, Owner
Retail. *Products*: Art, beadwork, fetishes, jewelry, kachinas, pottery, rugs, sandpaintings, sculpture, carvings. *Membership*: IACA.

ENBEE COLLECTIBLES
6435 Crystalaire Dr. • San Diego, CA 92120
  (619) 582-3185; Norman & Bernice Harris
Wholesale/retail. *Products*: Baskets, pottery, sculpture, carvings.

TRAILS WEST SILVER & LEATHER CO.
821 W. Harbor Dr. • San Diegio, CA 92101
  (619) 232-0553 Fax 232-3236; Betty McAdams, Sec./Treasurer
Retail. *Products*: Indian jewelry, implements, drums, kachinas, fetishes, pottery, leather goods. Appraisals: P. *Membership*: IACA.

SKY LOOM
502 S. Darwood • San Dimas, CA 91773
  (714) 599-3071; Bob & Deborah Anderson. Wholesale, retail.

AMERICAN INDIAN CONTEMPORARY ARTS GALLERY
23 Grant Ave., 6th Fl. • San Francisco, CA 94108
  (415) 989-7003 Fax 989-7025; Janeen Antoine, Director
Wholesale, retail, mail order. *Products*: Art, baskets, beadwork, jewelry, pottery, rugs, sculpture. Gift shop.

KACHINA
2801 Leavenworth #J-22 • San Francisco, CA 94133
  (415) 441-2636; Farideh Petri, Owner
Wholesale, retail. *Membership*: IACA. *Branch*: Tiburon, CA.

MAYFLOWER GIFT SHOP
2770 40th Ave. • San Francisco, CA 94116
  (415) 982-1890; Doug & Julie Shinn, Owners. Retail. *Products*: All.

SCRIPSIT
1592 Union St. #356 • San Francisco, CA 94123
  (415) 586-4202; Glenn Billy, Owner/Manager
Retail, wholesale, mail order. *Products*: Greeting cards with Indian words, each with an Indian design; calligraphy on paper. Custom orders for certificates, honorary awards. Special orders accepted.

LA QUINTA TRADING CO., LTD.
P.O. Box 427 • Santa Barbara, CA 93102
  (619) 568-4188 Fax 568-6955; Randy Gillet, Owner
Retail. *Products*: All. *Membership*: IACA.

DONNA GOLD
P.O. Box 55277 • Sherman Oaks, CA 91413
  (818) 789-2559 Fax 789-1510; Donna Gold, Owner
Wholesale, retail. *Products*: Art, baskets, beadwork, clothing, dolls, jewelry, kachinas, pottery, rugs, sand paintings, sculpture, carvings. Northwest Coast Indian masks, rattles, bowls, graphics. Mail order only - pictures available.

SHOSHONE DEVELOPMENT, INC.
P.O. Box 67 • Shoshone, CA 92384
  (760) 852-4224 Fax 852-4250; Susan Sorrells, Owner
Website: www.shoshonevillage.com
E-mail: sorrells@kay-not.com. *Membership*: IACA.

AMERICAN INDIAN ARTS & CRAFTS
2214 Stanfield Dr. • Stockton, CA 95209
  (209) 478-5719; Louise Marcigan, Owner; E-mail: marcigan@cs.com

INDIAN ART CENTER OF CALIFORNIA
12666 Ventura Blvd. • Studio City, CA 91604
  (818) 763-3430; Website: www.indianartcenter.net
The largest & oldest Native American store in the city of Los Angeles. Contains the work of hundreds of Native American artisans…Southwest Native American jewelry & artifacts.

KACHINA
41 Reed Ranch Rd. • Tiburon, CA 94920
  (415) 389-8524; Farideh Petri, Owner
Wholesale, retail. *Membership*: IACA. *Branch*: San Francisco, CA.

CHIEF GEORGE PIERRE TRADING POST
620 The Village (Redondo Beach), P.O. Box 3202 • Torrance, CA 90510
  (213) 372-1048; Chief George Piere, Owner
Wholesale, retail, mail order. *Products*: Beadwork, jewelry, kachinas, rugs.

AB-ORIGINALS
P.O. Drawer 850 • Trinidad, CA 95570
  (707) 677-3738; Joy & Lisa Sundberg & Elaine Clary, Owners
Wholesale, retail. *Products*: Jewelry. Fashionable accessories such as chokers, hairpieces, necklaces, earrings, beaded neckties, belts.

ADOBE ROAD, INC.
1000 Universal Center Dr., #157 • University City, CA 91608
  (818) 622-3623; Prudence J. Gallop, Owner
Wholesale, retail. *Products*: All. *Membership*: IACA.

K.R. MARTINDALE GALLERY
1154 Grant Ave. • Venice, CA 90291
  (310) 822-9145 Fax 822-9179
Website: www.americanindianartshow.com
  E-mail: kmartindale@earthlink.net; Kim Martindale, Owner
Retail, Wholesale. *Products*: Specializing in the art of the Americas from pre-classic to contemporary.

ZUNI PEOPLE
222A Main St. • Venice, CA 90291
  (310) 399-7792
Retail, wholesale, mail order. Zuni tribal enterprise. *Products*: Zuni turquoise, shell, coral, jet & silver jewelry; pottery; fetishes; contemporary art. Jewelry catalog, $5.

RED FLUTE TRADERS
9620 Las Cruces • Ventura, CA 93004
  (805) 647-6437; E-mail: fbeller@vcss.k12.ca.us; Floyd & Sue Beller
Wholesale, retail. *Products*: Baskets, beadwork, heishi, jewelry, kachinas, rugs. Membership: IACA.

KACHINA ART GALLERY
12301 Whittier Blvd., P.O. Box 4800 • Whittier, CA 90607
  (213) 941-5635; Lynn & Mercedes Stermolle
Retail. *Products*: Art, baskets, beadwork, clothing, dolls, jewelry, kachinas, pottery, rugs, sand paintings, sculpture, carvings. Membership: IACA.

THE ANSEL ADAMS GALLERY
P.O. Box 455, The Village Mall • Yosemite, CA 95389
  (209) 372-4413 Fax 372-4714; Michael & Jeanne Adams
Retail. *Products*: Art, baskets, beadwork, clothing, dolls, jewelry, kachinas, pottery, rugs, sand paintings, sculpture, carvings. Catalog.

YOSEMITE PARK & CURRY CO.
P.O. Box 578 • Yosemite, CA 95389
  Yosemite Lodge (209) 372-1438
  Ahwahnee Hotel (209) 372-1409
  Cassandra Martin, Manager (Yosemite Lodge)
  Georgine Gray, Manager (Ahwahnee Hotel)
Retail. *Products*: All. *Membership*: IACA.

BARKER'S INDIAN TRADING POST
P.O. Box 2732, 6495 Washington St. • Yountville, CA 94599-2732
  (707) 944-8012; Frank & Wilda Barker
Wholesale/retail. *Products*: Art, baskets, beadwork, jewelry, pottery, rugs, sand paintings, sculpture. *Membership*: IACA.

GEODES & GEMS
57602 29 Palm Hwy. • Yucca Valley, CA 92284
  (760) 365-9614 Fax 365-3074; Debbie Fry, Owner
E-mail: dfry@e-universe.com
Wholesale, retail. *Products*: All. *Membership*: IACA.

COLORADO

EAGLE PLUME'S
9853 Hwy. 7 • Allenspark, CO 80510
  (303) 747-2861 Fax 747-2868
Website: www.eagleplume.com; E-mail: strangeowl@aol.com
  Ann Strange Owl-Raben, Nico Strange Owl-Hunt, Dayton Raben, Owners
Retail. *Products*: Baskets, beadwork, jewelry, kachinas, pottery, sculpture, carvings. American Indian arts & crafts. *Membership*: IACA.

D BAR L ENTERPRISES
16525 W. 74th Pl. • Arvada, CO 80007
  (303) 422-6230; Linetta LaBrant, Owner
E-mail: dbarlent@aol.com
Membership: IACA.

FOUR WINDS TRADING CO.
6355 Joyce Dr. • Arvada, CO 80403
  (800) 456-5444; (720) 890-8000 Fax 890-8008
  Richard & Cat Carey, Owners
Wholesale, Retail. *Products*: Media - music, video, books, audio books, posters, maps. *Membership*: IACA.

UP IN SMOKE, INC.
732 Blue Bird Ln. • Bailey, CO 80421
  (303) 838-6025; Dorothy & Wilbur Brown, Owners
E-mail: wfbdbuis@aol.com. *Membership*: IACA.

SANTA FE AMBIANCE
1116 Pearle St. • Boulder, CO 80302
  (303) 444-7200; Deborah Smith-Klein & Melinda Theis, Owners
Retail. *Products*: Art, baskets, beadwork, clothing, dolls, jewelry, kachinas, pottery, rugs, sand paintings, sculpture, carvings. Membership: IACA.

A.M. INDIAN ARTS, INC.
12 E. Bijou St. • Colorado Springs, CO 80903
  (719) 471-3235; Samuel M. Eppley, Owner
Retail. *Products*: Art, baskets, beadwork, pottery, rugs, sand paintings, sculpture.

ARIZONA ROOM
8085 Edgerton • Colorado Springs, CO 80919
  (719) 592-9106; Linda & Carl Radunsky, Owners
Retail. *Products*: Art, baskets, fetishes, jewelry, kachinas, pottery, rugs, sculpture. *Membership*: IACA.

ART OF THE SW
5634 Tuckerman Dr. • Colorado Springs, CO 80918
  (719) 264-0827; Website: www.artofthesw.com
  E-mail: patricia@artofthesw.com

BROADMOOR DRUG CO.
P.O. Box 1439 • Colorado Springs, CO 80901
  (719) 577-5740; Ben B. Finch, Owner
Retail. Products: Baskets, fetishes, heishi, jewelry, pottery.

THE FLUTE PLAYER GALLERY
2511 W. Colorado Ave. • Colorado Springs, CO 80904
  (719) 632-7702; John & Linda Edwards, Owners
Retail, wholesale. *Products*: Ornaments, fetishes, heishi, jewelry, kachinas, knives, miniatures, pottery, rugs, sand paintings, sculpture. Appraisals: Jewelry, pottery, rugs. *Membership*: IACA.

HIDDEN INN
529 S. 31st St. • Colorado Springs, CO 80904
  (719) 632-2303; Al Dickey, Owner. Retail. Membership: IACA.

THE SQUASH BLOSSOM & COGSWELL GALLERY
2531 W. Colorado • Colorado Springs, CO 80904
  (719) 632-1899; John Cogswell & Chris Jones, Owners
Retail. *Products*: Art, baskets, beadwork, clothing, dolls, jewelry, kachinas, pottery, rugs, sand paintings, sculpture, carvings. *Appraisals*: All products. Gallery specializes in Pueblo pottery; Navajo weavings; Hopi kachinas; Kiowa sculptures; Navajo, Hopi and Pima/Papago baskets; Navajo, Hopi and Zuni jewelry; Zuni fetishes; Navajo sand paintings. *Membership*: IACA. Catalog.

TABLE ROCK TRADING CO.
3815 Wapiti Way • Colorado Springs, CO 80908
  (719) 495-2765; Jeff & Sherrie Oram-Smith, Owners
  E-mail: jorasmith@aol.com. *Membership*: IACA.

CLIFF DWELLER
1004 E. Main St., P.O. Box 9 • Cortez, CO 81321
  (303) 565-3424; J.D. Tipton, Jr., Owner
Retail. Products: All. *Membership*: IACA.

DON WOODARD'S INDIAN TRADING POST
27688 E. Hwy. 160 • Cortez, CO 81321-9366
  (303) 565-3986; Don Woodard, Owner
Retail. *Products*: All. Appraisals. *Membership*: IACA.

MESA VERDE POTTERY
P.O. Box 9 • Cortez, CO 81321
  (800) (303) 565-4492; Jay Tipton, Jr.
Wholesale, retail. *Products*: All. *Membership*: IACA. Catalog.

ZACCHARIAH ZYPP & CO.
317 Elk Ave., P.O. Box 423 • Crested Butte, CO 81224
  (970) 349-5913 Fax 349-1502; Noel Adam, Owner
  E-mail: zypp@crestedbutte.net. *Membership*: IACA.

TRIBAL DESIGNS
P.O. Box 341 • Crestone, CO 81131
  (719) 256-4455
Retail, Wholesale. *Products*: Custom made handbags made with deer/elk hide, silver conchos, wool, Zapotec weavings.

THE BLACK BEAR
8753 E. Monmouth Pl. • Denver, CO 80237

  (303) 779-1316; John & Mary Claire Walter, Owners
Retail. *Products*: Art, fetishes, heishi, jewelry, kachinas, miniatures, pottery, rugs, sand paintings. *Membership*: IACA.

BOUCHER TRADING CO.
8505 E. Temple Dr. #473 • Denver, CO 80237-2542
  (303) 770-7718; Robert G. Boucher
Wholesale/retail. *Product*: Jewelry. *Membership*: IACA.

D & H GIFTS
1281 Phillips Dr. • Denver, CO 80233-1259
  (303) 457-3606 Fax 457-9944; H. & Diane Yamamoto
Wholesale/retail. Products: Jewelry, sand paintings. *Membership*: IACA. Branch: 11480 N. Cherokee St., Denver.

DENVER ART MUSEUM SHOP
100 W. 14th Ave. Pkwy. • Denver, CO 80204
  (303) 640-2672; Mary Jane Butler. Retail. *Products*: Art. *Membership*: IACA.

DENVER MUSEUM OF NATURAL HISTORY SHOP
2001 Colorado Blvd., City Park • Denver, CO 80205
  (303) 370-6366 Fax 331-6492; Thielma Gamewell & Ron Veenstra
Retail. *Products*: All. *Membership*: IACA.

DREAM WEAVER JEWELRY, INC.
9605 E. Kansas Cir. #53 • Denver, CO 80231
  (303) 750-0144; Ron & Mary Howe, Owner
Website: www. medwyngoodall.com;
  E-mail: ronhowe1@earthlink.net. *Membership*: IACA.

FIGHTING BEAR ENTERPRISES
5430 Conley Way • Denver, CO 80222
  (303) 758-9177; Fighting Bear, Owner
Retail. *Products*: Arts & crafts and stained glass.

MILLER STOCKMAN WESTERN WEAR
P.O. Box 5127 • Denver, CO 80217-5127
  (800) 688-9888
Retail, wholesale. *Products*: Native American clothing.

MORNING FLOWER PRESS
P.O. Box 11443 • Denver, CO 80211
  (303) 477-8442; Susanne Aikman & John Chingman, Owners
Wholesale, retail, mail order. *Products*: Art, sculpture; repairs & restoration. Traditional and contemporary crafts. Repairs beadwork.

NATIVE AMERICAN COLLECTION, INC.
Denver, CO (303) 321-1071 Fax 321-1156
  Website: www.nativepots.com;
  Jill Giller, Owner; E-mail: jillspots@aol.com
Retail. *Products*: Hopi, Navajo, Pueblo pottery, sculpture & wall art, folk art, baskets, jewelry, books, fetishes.

NATIVE AMERICAN TRADING CO.
213 W. 13th Ave. • Denver, CO 80204
  (303) 534-0771; E-mail: natcweb@aol.com
  Website: www.nativeamericantradingco.com
Retail, wholesale. *Product*: Fine Southwest and Native American art. Antique weavings, pottery, baskets, jewelry, artifacts, photographs Edward S. Curtis in the Rocky Mountain region.

LYNDA TELLER PETE (Navajo)
2142 Irving St. • Denver, CO 80211
  (303) 561-1582; Website: www.navajorugs.nativearts.net
  E-mail: ltellerpete@yahoo.com. Products: Navajo textile & beadwork

SAGUARO SKY, LTD.
2221 Lafayette St. • Denver, CO 80205
  (303) 861-8168 Fax 399-7751
Patricia Manning, Owner. *Membership*: IACA.

SAND CREEK ARTS
5344 Altura St. • Denver, CO 80239
  (303) 371-7636; William W. Phillips
Wholesale, retail. *Product*: Art. *Membership*: IACA.

SHALAKO
3023 East 2nd Ave. • Denver, CO 80206
  (303) 295-2713; Angie Yava & Mike O'Neil
Retail. *Products*: Art, baskets, beadwork, clothing, dolls, jewelry, kachinas, pottery, rugs, sand paintings, sculpture, carvings. *Membership*: IACA.

THE SQUASH BLOSSOM
1428 Larimer Square • Denver, CO 80202
 (303) 572-7979; Mark Alexander, Owner
Retail. *Products*: All. *Membership*: IACA. Catalog.

WEST SOUTHWEST GALLERY
257 Fillmore St. • Denver, CO 80206
 (303) 321-4139 Fax 321-8499; Website: www.westsouthwest.com
 E-mail: dudleysmith@aol.com; Dudley Smith & Becky Haines, Owners
Membership: IACA.

GLEN COMFORT STORE
2380 Big Thompson Canyon • Drake, CO 80515
 (970) 586-3878; Harold M. Tregent, Owner
Retail. *Products*: Baskets, clothing, dolls, jewelry, kachinas, pottery, rugs,
sand paintings, sculpture, carvings. *Membership*: IACA.

APPALOOSA TRADING CO.
501 Main St. • Durango, CO 81301
 (907) 259-1994
Retail, Wholesale. *Products*: Handcrafted leather belts, buckles, sterling bolos,
badges, etc.

DIAMOND CIRCLE INDIAN GIFT SHOP
651 Main Ave. • Durango, CO 81301-5423
 Skip & Marsha Wells, Owners. Retail. *Products*: All.

DURANGO TRADING CO.
602 Eagle Pass • Durango, CO 81301
 Sharleen & L.D. Daugherty, Owners
Retail, wholesale. *Products*: Pottery, rugs. *Membership*: IACA.

HELL BENT LEATHER & SILVER
741 Main Ave. • Durango, CO 81301
 (303) 247-9088; Lovvis Downs & Charles Glass, Owners
Retail. *Products*: Beadwork, fetishes, heishi, jewelry, kachinas, knives, pottery,
rugs, craft supplies. *Membership*: IACA.

INDIANAUCTION.COM; INDIANVILLAGE.COM
P.O. Box 9105 • Durango, CO 81301
 (970) 375-2400; John & Dillon Hartman, Owners
Website: www.indianvillage.com
Buy, sell & trade historic items from the Western frontier, including jewelry,
pottery, rugs & blankets, beadwork, baskets.

RAIN DANCE GALLERY
945 Main St. • Durango, CO 81301
 (888) 375-2708; (970) 375-2708 Fax 375-2706
 E-mail: raindancegallery@yahoo.com
Lori & Bob Curtis, Owners. *Membership*: IACA.

SORREL SKY GALLERY
870 Main Ave. • Durango, CO 81301
 (866) 878-3555; Shanan Campbell Wells, Owner
 Website: www.sorrelsky.com; E-mail: info@sorrelsky.com
 Barbara Longfellow, General Manager
Retail, wholesale. *Products*: Fine art, jewelry, crafts. Works from Cheri Dori,
Zina, Ben Nighthorse Campbell, and Toby Pomeroy. Quarterly newsletter.

TOH-ATIN GALLERY
145 W. 9th St., P.O. Box 2329 • Durango, CO 81301
 (800) 525-0384; (303) 247-8277 Fax 259-5390
Website: www.toh-atin.com; E-mail: toh-atin@fone.net
Jackson & Antonia Clark, Owners
Retail, wholesale. *Products*: All. *Appraisals*: Stones. *Membership*: IACA.

RED MAN HALL
P.O. Box 608 • Empire, CO 80438
 (303) 569-3243; Francine & Richard Frajola, Owners
Retail. *Products*: Art, baskets, beadwork, fetishes, jewelry, kachinas, pottery,
sand paintings, sculpture, carvings. *Membership*: IACA.

GLASS WAREHOUSE
3483 S. Broadway • Englewood, CO 80113
 (303) 781-0026 Fax 761-8073; Connie & Euljio Sanchez, Owners
Membership: IACA.

FALL RIVER TRADING POST
1875 Fall River Rd. • Estes Park, CO 80517
 (505) 586-6573; Wendell & Ann Keller, Owners
Retail. *Products*: All. *Membership*: IACA.

GRANDPA'S
Box 861, 230 W. Elkhorn Ave. • Estes Park, CO 80517
 (800) 242-4218; (970) 586-3539; Bob & Betty Hockaday, Owners
Retail. *Products*: All. *Membership*: IACA.

ROCKY MOUNTAIN GATEWAY
3450 Fall River Rd. • Estes Park, CO 80517
 (970) 577-0043; H.W. Stewart, Owner
 Website: www.rockymountain gateway.com
Retail. *Products*: baskets, ornaments, dolls, artifacts, jewelry,
pottery, rugs; repairs & restoration. *Membership*: IACA.

ROCKY MOUNTAIN NATIONAL PARK-TRAIL RIDGE STORE
P.O. Box 2680 • Estes Park, CO 80517-2680
 (970) 586-9319 Fax 586-8590; Don Wallace, VP
 Website: www.foreverresorts.com
Retail. *Products*: All. Winter address: Forever Resorts,
P.O. Box 29041, Phoenix, AZ 85038-9041. *Membership*: IACA.

SERENDIPITY TRADING CO.
117 E. Elkhorn Ave., Box 3945 • Estes Park, CO 80517
 (970) 586-8410 Fax 586-0463; Website: www.serendipitytrading.com
 E-mail: seren117@aol.com; John & Karen Ericson, Owners
Retail, wholesale, mail order. *Products*: All. *Membership*: IACA.

SILVER ARROW
28159 Hwy. 74, P.O. Box 23519 • Evergreen, CO 80437
 (303) 670-0552 Fax 670-4921; Shirley Anderson, Owner
 E-mail: silverarrow1@comcast.com. *Membership*: IACA.

BENZAV TRADING CO.
P.O. Box 911, 1716 E. Lincoln Ave. • Fort Collins, CO 80522
 (303) 482-6397; Steven Pickelner
Wholesale. *Products*: Baskets, beadwork, clothing, artifacts,
heishi, jewelry, pottery, rugs. Appraisals.

SIOUX VILLA CURIO
114 6th St. • Glenwood Springs, CO 81601-2988
 (303) 945-6134; John Gilcrest
Retail. *Products*: Beadwork, heishi, jewelry. *Membership*: IACA.

BANWARTH ENTERPRISES
8 Zodiac St. • Golden, CO 80401
 (970) 279-4870; Kay Dawn Todd. Wholesale, retail. *Product*: Jewelry.

HARVEY INDIAN GALLERY
130 N. 6th St. • Grand Junction, CO 81502
 (970) 243-4093; Jim & Nancy Harvey, Owners
Retail. *Products*: All. *Membership*: IACA.

THUNDEROCK
128 N. 5th St. • Grand Junction, CO 81501
 (970) 242-4890; Max & Judith Barnstead
Retail. *Products*: All. *Membership*: IACA.

GRAND LAKE LODGE
P.O. Box 569 • Grand Lake, CO 80447
 (970) 627-3165 Fax 627-9495; Website: www.grandlakelodge.com
 Sue & Reed James, Owners. *Membership*: IACA.

THUNDERBIRD ART GALLERY
1309 E. 16 St. • Greeley, CO 80631
 (970) 352-4397; Larry L. Mueller, Owner
 Website: www.thunderbirdgallery.com
 E-mail: tbgart@info2000.net. *Membership*: IACA.

FRED HARVEY TRADING CO.
6312 S. Fiddlers Green Cir. #600N • Greenwood Village, CO 80111
 (303) 338-2670 Fax 338-9320; E-mail: mkenny@xanterra.com
 Meg Kenny, Owner. *Membership*: IACA.

EAGLE DANCER TRADING CO.
P.O. Box 547 • Grand Lake, CO 80447
 (303) 726-9209; 627-3394; Dick & Nina Stasser, Owners
Retail. *Products*: All. Branch: Winter Park, CO. *Membership*: IACA.

NIGHTHORSE JEWELRY, INC.
P.O. Box 639 • Ignacio, CO 81137
 (970) 563-4623; Ben Nighthorse Campbell (Northern Cheyenne), Owner
Mail order. *Product*: Contemporary gold and silver jewelry.
Special orders accepted.

SKY UTE INDIAN GALLERY
P.O. Box 550 • Ignacio, CO 81137
 (970) 563-4531; Elise Redd & John Cole
Retail. Tribal Enterprise. *Products*: Art, beadwork, jewelry, pottery, sand painting, sculpture; repairs & restoration.

SOUTHERN UTE MUSEUM STORE
P.O. Box 737 • Ignacio, CO 81137
 (970) 563-4649; Helen Hoskins (Southern Ute), Director
Retail. *Products*: Art, beadwork, clothing, jewelry, pottery, rugs. *Appraisals*: All. *Membership*: IACA.

WALTON'S
12550 W. Second Dr. • Lakewood, CO 80228
 (303) 988-5580; Roger Alan Walton, Owner
Wholesale, retail. *Products*: Christmas ornaments, kachinas, pottery, sculpture, carvings. *Membership*: IACA.

J. NICHOLAS DBS HAGAN ASSOCIATES
1268 Fox Hill Dr. • Longmont, CO 80501
 (303) 774-0138; H.J. & A.S. Hagan, Owners. *Membership*: IACA.

DEER TRACK TRADERS LTD.
P.O. Box 448 • Loveland, CO 80539-0448
 (719) 669-6750 Fax 667-84; Alpine & Sue Rodman, Owners
Wholesale. *Products*: Art, baskets, beadwork, books, clothing, dolls, jewelry, kachinas, pottery, rugs, sand paintings, sculpture, carvings. *Membership*: IACA. Catalog.

DENNY HASKEW
540 N. Grant Ave. • Loveland, CO 80537
 (970) 663-6375
Wholesale. *Products*: Monumental to maquette bronze, stone sculpture. Corporate, private, and public commissions accepted. By appointment.

WAPATI, LTD
1732 W. 37th St. • Loveland, CO 80538
 (970) 667-0685 Fax 667-9180
Tim, Judy & Carry Oeterson, Owners. *Membership*: IACA.

ANASAZI TRADING POST
344 Main St., P.O. Box 320 • Lyons, CO 80540
 (719) 823-5681; Susan & Daniel Martin, Owner
Retail. *Products*: All. *Membership*: IACA.

ARA MESA VERDE CO.
P.O. Box 277 • Mancos, CO 81328
 (970) 533-7731; Lynn W. Marshall, Owner
Website: www.visitmesaverde.com
E-mail: mitchell-lynn@aramark.com
Retail. *Products*: All. *Membership*: IACA.

GARDEN OF THE GODS
324 Beckers Lane • Manitou Springs, CO 80829
 (800) 847-4515; (719) 685-9045 Fax 685-9377
Website: www.co-trading-post.com; E-mail: tpmail@co-trading-post.com
Angela Guido & Linda Landes, Owners. *Membership*: IACA.

MANITOU JACK'S
742 Manitou Ave. • Manitou Springs, CO 80829
 (719) 685-5004; Kendra Homer & Dawn Carnel, Owners
Wholesale, retail. *Products*: Art, jewelry, pottery, sand painting, sculpture, craft supplies; repairs & restoration. Membership: IACA.

PENGUIN & FRIENDS
742 Manitou Ave. • Manitou Springs, CO 80829
 (719) 685-0700; Website: www.penguin-gifts.com
E-mail: polargifts@msn.com; Al Dickey, Owner. *Membership*: IACA.

NAVA SOUTHWEST
61336 Hwy. 90 • Montrose, CO 81401
 (970) 325-4850 Fax 249-0733
Douglas & Elizabeth Nava, Owners
Retail, wholesale, mail order. *Products*: Native American arts & crafts, jewelry, pottery, rugs, fetishes. *Summer address*: Box 37, Ouray 81427

WINTERCOUNT
P.O. Box 889 • New Castle, CO 81647
 (970) 984-3685; Tom & Diane Voight, Owners
Wholesale, retail. *Products*: Art, books, t-shirts & calendars. *Membership*: IACA. Catalog.

BUCKSKIN TRADING CO.
P.O. Box 1876 • Ouray, CO 81427
 (303) 325-4044; P. David & Jan Smith
Retail. *Products*: All. *Membership*: IACA.

NORTH MOON
P.O. Box 51 • Ouray, CO 81427
 (303) 325-4885; Sandra K. Boles
Retail. *Products*: Beadwork, Northwest Coast art, fetishes, jewelry. *Membership*: IACA. *Branch shop*: Telluride, CO.

CLARISSA HUDSON
446 Loma St., P.O. Box 2709 • Pagosa Springs, CO 81147
 (970) 264-2491; Clarissa Hudson, Owner
Website: www.clarissahudson.com; E-mail: clarissa@clarissahudson.com
Products: Clarissa makes hand woven Chilkat & Ravenstail robes & regallia. Also, paintings, collages, beaded sculptures, carvings, silkscreened limited edition prints. She conducts appreticeships and workshops.

CHAPPELL ENTERPRISES
25178 Omaha Ave. • Parker, CO 80138
 (303) 840-8851; Ellen B. Chappell, Owner
E-mail: chappell45@comcast.net. *Membership*: IACA.

ADOBE ACRES TRADING COMPANY
5805 County Road #320 • Rifle, CO 81650
 (970) 625-2209; Chris Pearson, Owner
E-mail: geopear@willowwisp.net. *Membership*: IACA.

THE COLLECTOR'S ROOM
P.O. Box 3226, Vail National Bank #302
108 S. Frontage Rd. West • Vail, CO 81657
 (303) 476-9019; Paul & Betty Numerof, Owners
Retail. *Products*: P. *Membership*: IACA.

SQUASH BLOSSOM, INC.
198 Gore Creek Dr. • Vail, CO 81657
 (303) 476-3129 Fax 476-8984; John Cogswell, Owner
Retail. *Products*: All. *Appraisals*: Art, drums, pipes, flutes, artifacts, fetishes, heishi, jewelry, kachinas, knives, miniatures, pottery, rugs, sandpainting. Catalog.

PARKER BOYIDDLE EDITIONS
334 Phantom Rd. • Westcliffe, CO 81252
 (719) 783-2590; Parker Boyiddle (Kiowa/Western Delaware), Owner
Website: www.parkerboyiddle.com; E-mail: parkerboyiddle@aol.com
Products: Stone sculpture in alabaster & marble; bronze, paintings, drawings, watercolor, jewelry design, furniture, steel sculptures.

ELK HORN ART GALLERY
P.O. Box 197 • Winter Park, CO 80482
 (800) 285-4676; (970) 726-9292 Fax 726-8292
Tom Coblentz, Owner; E-mail: elkhorn@rkymtnhi.com
Website: elkhorngallery.com
Retail, wholesale, mail order. *Products*: Works of art by Native American artists, Jo Anne Bird, Robert Red Bird, and Michael C. McCullough. Also published limited edition prints with dealerships available. *Membership*: IACA. Brochure & Catalog available.

CONNECTICUT

BRIGHT HAWK PRODUCTIONS
54 Fritz Rd. • Colebrook, CT 06021
 (860) 738-0815; Vicki Hurst (Choctaw of OK), Artist/Owner
Products: Walking staffs, carvings, medicine pouches, necklaces, wood art, beadwork.

SOUTHWEST INDIAN ARTS
98 The Laurels • Enfield, CT 06082
 (860) 749-7332; Bud August, Owner; E-mail: baugust1@aol.com
Website: www.southwestindianarts.com
Retail, wholesale, mail order. *Products*: Jewelry, pottery, baskets, fetishes, dolls, artifact reproductions, candles, kids items, dream catchers, medicine wheels, wampum jewelry. *Memberships*: IACA.

SUN DANCER EAST
608F Shennecossett Rd. • Groton, CT 06340
 (860) 448-0834; Bern Mayhew, Owner
Website: www.sundancereast.com
E-mail: bern@sundancereast.com. *Membership*: IACA.

SOUTHERN EXPOSURE
Olde Mystic Village • Mystic, CT 06355
  (860) 572-1007 Fax 572-1381
  Website: www.shopsouthernexposure.com
  E-mail: info@shopsouthernexposure.com
  Lu & Leslie Lupovich, Owners
Membership: IACA.

RALPH W. STURGIS
97 Raymond St. • New London, CT 06320
  (203) 442-8005; Ralph Sturgis (Mohegan), Artisan/Owner
Retail. *Products*: Sculpture, marble carvings. Special commissions.

YAH-TA-HEY GALLERY
279 Captains Walk • New London, CT 06320
  (203) 443-3204; Dorothy Noga
Retail. *Products*: Art, baskets, boxes, dolls, drums, flutes, pipes, fetishes, jewelry, kachinas, rugs, sand painting, sculpture. *Membership*: IACA.

WILD WEST WEAVER
54 Danbury Rd. #248 • Ridgefield, CT 06877
  (203) 431-5717; Leslie Smith Jackson, Owner
  E-mail: wwweaver1@aol.com. *Membership*: IACA.

TRIBAL WEAR BY SKINZ
27 Summit Rd. • Riverside, CT 06878
  (203) 637-7884
Retail, wholesale. *Products*: Native American clothing.

SPIRIT OF THE LIONESS
94 Brookmoor Rd. • West Hartford, CT 06107
  (860) 313-1198; Irene Scheibner, Owner
  Website: spiritofthelioness.com
  E-mail: info@spiritofthelioness.com. *Membership*: IACA.

DELAWARE

AMERICAN INDIAN ART GALLERY
5801 A Kennett Pike • Wilmington, DE 19807
  (302) 576-1888 Fax 576-1870
  Website: www.americanindianartgallery.com
  E-mail: info@americanindianartgallery.com
  Peter & Carroll Shannon, Owners. *Membership*: IACA.

CACTUS WREN GALLERY
406 Delaware St. • New Castle, DE 19720
  (302) 328-7595 Fax 328-7594; Website: www.cactuswrengallery.com
  E-mail: info@cactuswrengallery.com; Barbara M. Vellrath, Owner
Membership: IACA.

DISTRICT OF COLUMBIA

THE INDIAN CRAFT SHOP
U.S. Dept. of the Interior, 1849 C St., NW, Rm. 1023 • Washington, DC 20240
  (202) 208-4056 Fax 219-1135; Website: www.indiancraftshop.com
  E-Mail: indiancraftshop@guestservices.com
  Susan M. Pourian, Shop Director
Retail. *Products*: Jewelry, weavings, basketry, beadwork, pottery, kachinas, sand paintings, fetishes, Alaskan walrus ivory and crafts, books. More than 45 tribal areas represented. *Memberships*: IACA, SWAIA, WACA, NMAI, IAIA..

FLORIDA

SHARED VISIONS GALLERY
10355 Prestwick Rd. • Boynton Beach, FL 33436
  (407) 272-4495; Kathleen & Chad Ragland, Owners
Retail, wholesale. *Products*: Art, baskets, dolls, Northwest Coast art, fetishes, jewelry, kachinas, pottery, rugs, sand paintings, sculpture. *Membership*: IACA. *Branch shop*: 504 E. Atlantic Ave., Delray Beach, FL 33483.

TURTLE ISLAND TRADERS
P.O. Box 9563 • Bradenton, FL 34206
  (813) 747-5653; C.G. "Bud" Horton, Owner
Retail. *Products*: Books, artifacts, miniatures, sculpture, carvings.

SUNDANCER GALLERY
6 Florida Ave. • Cocoa Village, FL 32922
  (407) 631-0092; Joan & Jim McCarthy, Owners
Retail, wholesale. *Products*: Southwest & Native American art & craftwork, and turquoise jewelry. *Branch shop*: This N' That, Cocoa Village.

THUNDERBIRD SHOP
16754 Willow Creek Dr. • Delray Beach, FL 33484
  Louis & Sheila Brilliant, Owners. Retail. *Products*: All.

THE PLAINSMEN GALLERY
542 Douglas Ave. • Dunedin, FL 34698
  (813) 446-4396; Betty Brown & Maria Alcoz, Owners
Retail. *Products*: Art, baskets, fetishes, jewelry, kachinas, rugs.

ABORIGINALS: ART OF THE FIRST PERSON
15194 Harbour Dr. • Fort Myers, FL 33908
  (800) 305-0185; (239) 395-2200 Fax 482-7025
  Website: www.tribalworks.com; zunilink.com
  E-mail: sanibelart@comcast.net; Susanne & William Waites, Owner
Retail, wholesale. *Products*: Arctic & Native American Art, including baskets, beadwork, dolls, jewelry, kachinas, pottery, rugs, sand paintings, sculpture, carvings; Cochiti & San Felipe fetish carvings. Appraisals. *Memberships*: IACA, SWAIA, Lee Co. Alliance of Arts, Sanibel-Captiva Chamber of Commerce.

MASSACHUSETTS BAY TRADING CO.
2611 S. 16th St. • Ft. Pierce, FL 34982
  (407) 465-2230; Dean & Jacie Davis, Owners
Wholesale, retail. *Products*: Art, clothing, artifacts, fetishes, jewelry, pottery, rugs. *Membership*: IACA.

AMERICAN INDIAN IMAGEMAKERS
6321 N.W. 34th St. • Hollywood, FL 33024
  (954) 983-7708; Jo Motlow North, Owner
Retail, wholesale. By appointment. *Products*: Art, clothing, jewelry.

CHUPCO INDIAN ART GALLERY
3621 North State Rd. 7 • Hollywood, FL 33021
  (954) 893-9460 Fax 893-9198; Website: www.chupcogallery.com
Retail. *Products*: Specializing in handmade Native American art, jewelry, beadwork, Seminole patchwork items, clothing, accessories.

RADFORD BEAD CO.
11451 Old Kings Rd. • Jacksonsville, FL 32219
  (904) 765-4886; Robin Radford, Owner
Mail order. Cherokee craftspersons. *Products*: Beadwork, clothing, masks, drums, flutes, pipes, sculpture, carvings. Special orders. Catalog, $4.

MICCOSUKEE GIFT SHOP & CULTURAL CENTER
Box 440021, Tamiami Station • Miami, FL 33144
  (305) 223-8380; Jim Kay (Miccosukee), Manager
Retail, wholesale. Miccosukee Tribal Enterprise. *Products*: Baskets, beadwork, clothing & accessories, dolls, sculpture, carvings.

FOUR WINDS GALLERY
340 13th Ave. So. • Naples, FL 34102
  (239) 263-7555 Fax 263-6875; E-mail: fwgnaples@aol.com
  Tim & Susan Brick, Owners. *Membership*: IACA.

NIZHONI DREAM CATCHERS
5141 Brixton Ct. • Naples, FL 33942-4782
  (239) 643-2026; Patricia Sauselein & Ralph Stevens, Owners
Retail. *Products*: Art, baskets, beadwork, clothing, dolls, jewelry, kachinas, pottery, rugs, sand paintings, sculpture, carvings. *Membership*: IACA.

PRODIGY GALLERY
4320 Gulf Shore Blvd. N., Suite 206 • Naples, FL 33940
  (239) 263-5881 Fax 263-5882; Karen Weinert-Kim & Sam Miller, Owners
Retail. *Products*: All. *Membership*: IACA.

NASHOBA INDIGENOUS CRAFTS
9668 Third Ave. • Orlando, FL 32824
  (407) 812-7134; Richard Jopling (Chickasaw), Artisan/Owner
Products: Jewelry, beads, crafts collectibles, custom bags, beadwork

NIZHONI KEYAH, INC.
Orlando, FL (407) 293-4757 Fax 293-4935
  Website: www.nizhonikeyah.co; E-mail: info@nizhonikeyah.com
  R. Threehawk Atcitty (Dine/Navajo)
Products: Designer silver, bone & natural mineral jewelry & chokers, breastplates, drums & carvings.

JOLIMA INDIAN CRAFTS
1403 N. 57th Ave. • Pensacola, FL 32506
  (904) 455-0874; John & Marie Varnes, Owners
Retail, wholesale; retail by appointment only. *Products*: Baskets, beadwork, drums, pipes, flutes, jewelry. Special orders accepted.

GREEN'S RINGS & THINGS
4151 Hidden Valley Cir. • Punta Gorda, FL 33982
 (239) 695-3559; Jeri & Larry Green, Owners
Retail, wholesale. *Products*: Art, beadwork, clothing & accessories, jewelry, pottery, rugs, sand paintings.

NATIVE TRADITIONS GALLERY
51-C Cordova St. • St. Augustine, FL 32084
 (904) 808-7361; Joyce E. Campbell (Cherokee of OK), Owner
 E-mail: injunstreet@gbso.net
Products: American Indian antique & vintage jewelry, dolls, original oil & watercolor paintings, bronzes, regalia & leather crafts.

RED CLOUD INDIAN ARTS
208 Beach Dr. NE • St. Petersburg, FL 33701-3414
 (727) 821-5824 Fax 823-7709; Steve & Harriet Rambeaux, Owners
 Website: www.redcloudindianarts.com; E-mail: redcloud@ij.net
Retail. *Products*: All. *Membership*: IACA.

SAGE SPIRIT
363 Corey Ave. • St. Petersburg, FL 33706 (727-) 367-8083
Retail. *Products*: Jewelry, artwork, pottery, gifts crafted by various American Indian tribes. *Branch*: Sarasota, FL.

THE ZUNI CONNECTION
116 S. Palmeto Ave. • Sanford, FL 32771
 (407) 688-8823 Fax (866) 843-9864; Website: www.thezuniconnection.com
 E-mail: carol@thezuniconnection.com; Carol & James Avant, Owners
Membership: IACA.

INDIAN SUN, INC.
3831 Monica Pkwy. • Sarasota, FL 34235
 (941) 366-0023; Joyce Kasanoukwas Sundheim, Owner
Retail, wholesale. Penobscot-Mohawk craftspersons.
Products: Jewelry, rugs, sandpaintings.

SAGE SPIRIT
17 Fillmore Dr. • Sarasota, FL 34236
 (941) 388-2975
Retail. *Products*: Jewelry, artwork, pottery, gifts crafted by various American Indian tribes. *Branch*: St. Petersburg, FL.

SEMINOLE CULTURAL CENTER
5221 Orient Rd. • Tampa, FL 33610
 (813) 623-3549; Leslie Stevens, Manager
Retail, mail order. *Products*: Baskets, beadwork, clothing, sculpture.

GEORGIA

CHEROKEE CONNECTION
Georgia Square Mall, 3700 Atlanta Hwy. • Athens, GA 30606
 (706) 559-0068 Fax 559-0062; Billy & Sharon Lacey, Owners
 E-mail: cherokee0068@bellsouth.net . *Membership*: IACA.

NATIVE AMERICA GALLERY
195 E. Clayton St. • Athens, GA 30601
 (706) 543-8425; Jane M. Scott, Owner
Retail. Products: Fetishes, jewelry, moccasins, sandpaintings, books, music, t-shirts. Brochure available. *Membership*: IACA.

COYOTE TRADING CO.
419 Moreland Ave. NE • Atlanta, GA 30307
 (404) 221-1512; David Simpson, Owner
Retail. *Products*: Art, fetishes, heishi, jewelry, kachinas, pottery.
Membership: IACA.

NATIVE AMERICAN TRADERS
3463 Evans Ridge Dr. • Atlanta, GA 30341
 (770) 491-8100 FAX 496-9797; Website: www.nativeamericantraders.com
 E-mail: peyton@nativeamericantraders.com
 Peyton & Elaine Alexander, Owners. Membership: IACA.

OUT OF THE WOODS GALLERY
22-B Bennett St., NW • Atlanta, GA 30309
 (404) 351-0446; Deb Douglas. Retail. *Products*: All.

HEARTLINES AUTHENTIC NATIVE AMERICAN JEWELRY
2299 Shasta Way • Atlanta, GA 30345
 (877) 779-4881; (404) 633-7728
 E-mail: anabeth@mindspring.com
 Anabeth Balance, Owner. *Membership*: IACA.

SOUTHWEST INDIAN ARTISANS
P.O. Box 941759 • Atlanta, GA 31141
 (770) 840-8111; Martha J. Hueglin, Owner
Wholesale, retail. *Products*: Art, baskets, drums, flutes, pipes, fetishes, jewelry, kachinas, pottery, rugs, sculpture, carvings. *Membership*: IACA. Catalog.

RAY'S INDIAN ORIGINALS
90 Avondale Rd. • Avondale Estates, GA 30002
 (404) 299-2397/4999; Ray Belcher, Owner
Wholesale/retail. *Products*: art, baskets, kachina dolls, jewelry, pottery, rugs.

MASSACHUSETTS BAY TRADING CO.
723 "A" E Main St. • Blue Ridge, GA 30513
 (706) 258-2290; 864-0060; Dean & Jacie Davis, Owners. *Membership*: IACA.

OGLEWANAGI GALLERY
9459 Hwy. 5, Suite F-G • Douglasville, GA 30135
 (404) 872-4213; Tom Perkins & Vickie Dunken, Owners
Retail. *Products*: Jewelry, kachinas, pottery, rugs.

TEKAKWITHA
8047 S. Main St., P.O. Box 338 • Helen, GA 30545
 (706) 878-2938; Ruth & Patti Lammers, Owners
 E-mail: tek@alltell.net. Retail. *Products*: All. *Membership*: IACA.

AMERICAN INDIAN MARKET ROLLING THUNDER ENTERPRISES
34 Rolling Thunder Dr. • Jasper, GA 30143
 (770) 735-6275; Chipa Wolfe, Owner
 Website: www.rthunder.com; Website: www.americanindianmarket.com
 E-mail: chipa1@earthlink.net; E-mail: aim68@earthlink.net

ARTISAN'S ALLEY
1470 Double Bridges Rd. • Madison, GA 30650
 (706) 343-0048 Fax 342-2255; E-mail: gordo300@bellsouth.net
 Gordon Clark, Owner. *Membership*: IACA.

WILLIAM D. ENTERPRISES, INC.
300 Davis Rd. • Richmond Hill, GA 31324
 (912) 604-0323 Fax 727-4052; Douglas W. Ratledge, Owner
 Website: www.nativeamericantraditions.com
 E-mail: native.story@comcast.net. *Membership*: IACA.

STONE BEAR GALLERY
120 Strand Hill Rd. • Tyrone, GA 30290
 (404) 631-3424; M. Barry Bartlett
Retail. *Products*: Art, boxes, jewelry, pottery, sculpture, carvings.
Membership: IACA.

WESTERN HEART
372 Powderhorn • St. Mary's GA 31558
 (912) 882-8976
Retail, wholesale. Products: Native American clothing.

SEVEN ARROWS ART GALLERY
8582 Main St. • Woodstock, GA 30188
 (770) 591-7045 Fax 591-7786; Cheryl West, Owner
 E-mail: cawest@bellsouth.net. *Membership*: IACA.

HAWAII

THE SANTA FE COLLECTION
2088 Alaeoloa St. • Honolulu, HI 96821
 (808) 734-2661 Fax 739-0350
 Raymond & Louanna Suppa
 E-mail: lousup@woldnet.att.net
Retail. *Products*: Art, baskets, clothing, dolls, jewelry, kachinas, pottery, rugs, sand paintings, sculpture, carvings. *Membership*: IACA.

IDAHO

6 FEATHERS INDIAN ARTS & CRAFTS
P.O. Box 430 • Blackfoot, ID 83221
 Barbara J. Dixey (Dine), Owner
Products: Authentic handmade beadwork.

KAMIAKIN KRAFTS
P.O. Box 358 • Fort Hall, ID 83203
 (208) 785-2546; Atwice Goudy Osborne, Owner
Retail, mail order. By appointment only. *Products*: Bags, beadwork, clothing/moccasins. Price list available.

TRADING POST CLOTHES HORSE
P.O. Box 368 • Fort Hall, ID 83203
 (208) 237-8433 Fax 237-9343; Gayle Shappert, Manager
Retail, wholesale, mail order. Shoshone-Bannock Tribal Enterprise. *Products*: beaded and Native-tanned buckskin, moccasins, drums. Special orders accepted. Brochure and price list available.

THE DREAM CATCHER OF IDAHO
P.O. Box 6586 • Ketchum, ID 83340
 (208) 726-1305; Donald & Jean Hartwich, Owners
 Website: www.dreamcatchergallery.com
 E-mail: dreamcatchergallery@hotmail.com. *Membership*: IACA.

MARSH'S TRADING POST
1105 36th St., N. • Lewiston, ID 83501
 (208) 743-5778; Lorna Marsh (Nez Perce), Owner
Retail, wholesale. *Products*: Contemporary and antique Nez Perce cornhusk bags and beadwork; Klickitat baskets; silver, turquoise, and pink mussel shell jewelry; beads & beading supplies.

WHITE EAGLE'S NEZ PERCE INDIAN ARTS
P.O. Box 4 • Orofino, ID 83544
 (208) 476-7753; Larry & Pam White Eagle (Nez Perce), Artisans/Owners
Products: Nez Perce traditional crafts: beadwork, paintings, leather goods,

ILLINOIS

TRIBAL EXPRESSIONS
7 S. Dunton Ave. • Arlington Heights, IL 60005
 (847) 590-5390 Fax 590-8634; Rob & Jeri Brooke, Owners
 E-mail: rbrooke@tribalexpressions.com; Website: www.tribalexpressions.com
Retail. *Products*: American Indian jewelry, pottery, baskets, rugs, sculpture, paintings, and other fine art. Newsletter.

GALL SOUTHWEST SILVER JEWELRY CO.
9014 W. 31st St. • Brookfield, IL 60513
 (708) 387-0460; Geraldine M. Gall, Owner. Retail. *Products*: All.

RIVER TRADING POST
314 N. River St. • East Dundee, IL 60118
 (866) 426-6901; (847) 428-0345 Fax 836-8218
 Website: www.rivertradingpost.com
 E-mail: trader@rivertradingpost.com; Joseph P. Zeller, Owner
Retail, wholesale. *Products*: Navajo weavings, Pueblo pottery, Hopi kachina dolls, Zuni fetishes, sculpture, baskets, jewelry, Plains Indian art, Six Nations art. *Membership*: IACA.

SILVER LINING GALLERY
697 Chancellor Dr. • Edwardsville, IL 62025
 (618) 692-1000; Lorraine Levy & Alison Sale, Owners
Retail. *Products*: Art, baskets, beadwork, books, clothing, dolls, jewelry, kachinas, pottery, rugs, sand paintings, sculpture, carvings. *Membership*: IACA.

DANCING BEAR GALLERY
1922 Central St. • Evanston, IL 60201
 (847) 869-8080 Fax 869-6130; Christopher K. Radke, Owner
 E-mail: leekya66@aol.com. *Membership*: IACA.

MITCHELL MUSEUM OF THE AMERICAN INDIAN
2600 Central Park Ave. • Evanston, IL 60201
 (847) 475-1030 Fax 475-0911; Website: www.mitchellmuseum.org
 E-mail: mitchellmuseum@mindspring.com
 Paddy Scwartz & Janice Klein, Owners. *Membership*: IACA.

SOUTHWEST TRADING COMPANY
477 S 3rd St., Suite 118 • Geneva, IL 60134
 (630) 584-5707 Fax 232-2898; E-mail: southwest trading@yahoo.com
 Steven & Janet Fabiani, Owners. Retail. Products: All. *Membership*: IACA..

SKYSTONE TREASURES
715 Valley Rd. • Glencoe, IL 60022
 (708) 835-3355; Patricia Schwartz, Manager
Retail. *Products*: Art, beadwork, clothing, dolls, jewelry, kachinas, pottery. *Appraisals*: Jewelry. *Membership*: IACA.

INDIAN IMAGES & PARTICULARS OF THE PAST
203 Asbury Ave. • Greenville, IL 62246
 (618) 664-3384; Bill & Kathy Brewer, Owners
Retail. *Products*: Replicas & restoration of historic Plains Indian artifacts. Illustrated price list, $2.

OBELISK, LTD.
5130 Center Ave. • Lisle, IL 60532
 (708) 955-0010; Nancy C. Kelly, manager
Retail. *Products*: beadwork, boxes, cards, Eskimo & Inuit art, fetishes, jewelry, kachinas, pottery, rugs, sculpture/carvings.

INDIAN GIVING
1355 S. Lake St. • Mundelein, IL60060
 (847) 566-5691 Fax 566-5778; Roger J. Kratz, Owner
 E-mail: indiangiving@aol.com. *Membership*: IACA.

HIZHONI GALLERY
103 W. Jefferson Ave. • Naperville, IL 60540
 (630) 717-8080 Fax 717-8152; Janet Smith, Owner
 Website: www.hizhonigallery.com; E-mail: hizhonigallery@aol.com
Retail. *Products*: Jewelry. *Membership*: IACA.

TRADEWINDS TRIBAL ARTS & CRAFTS
P.O. Box 804 • Richton Park, IL 60471
 (708) 534-5726; Delores Young, Owner
 E-mail: delores-yung@sbcglobal.net. *Membership*: IACA.

BEAR PAW, INC.
217 Ferry St. • Rockton, IL 61072
 (815) 624-7427; Patricia Davies & Joe Skeen
Wholesale, retail. *Products*: baskets, beadwork, clothing, moccasins, headdresses, drums, pipes, tomahawks, Eskimo & Inuit art, artifacts, fetishes, kachinas, pottery, rugs/weavings/wall hangings.

DRIFTSTONE PUEBLO, INC.
702 W. Tower Rd. • St. Elmo, IL 62458
 (618) 829-3158 Fax 829-3159; E-Mail: driftstone@papdocs.com
Retail, wholesale. Products: Beads, jewelry, baskets, Egyptian crystals, zingers. Catalog. *Membership*: IACA.

FOUR FEATHERS
120 Mill St. • Utica, IL 61373
 (815) 667-4499; Judith Rigby
Retail. *Products*: Art, baskets, beadwork, clothing, dolls, jewelry, kachinas, pottery, rugs, sand paintings. *Membership*: IACA.

INDIANA

BRAD HAWIYEH-EHI
4399 E. Moores Pike • Bloomington, IN 47401
 (812) 335-1240; Bill Roberts, Owner
Retail, wholesale, mail order. Cherokee craftsperson. *Products*: Drums, pipes, flutes, sculpture, carvings. Special orders/commissions accepted. Catalog, $2.

SUSAN LOCKE CHARLESWORTH
8080 Margie Dr. • Brownsburg, IN 46112
 (317) 852-5304; E-mail: suzer48@aol.com
 Susan Locke Charlesworth (Choctaw), Artison/Owner
Products: Handwoven Native American baskets.

SINGING EAGLE
9909 Stoops Rd. • Dillsboro, IN 47018
 (812) 432-5656; E-mail: singingeagle@earthlink.net
 B.J. Hollenbach, Owner. *Membership*: IACA.

SKYSTONE N' SILVER
1350 S. Lake Park Ave. • Hobart, IN 46342
 (219) 942-9022 Fax 942-9558; Pam Phillips, Owner
 Website: www.skystone n'silver.com; E-mail: pamskystone@earthlink.net
Retail, mail order. *Products*: All. *Appraisals*: Art, artifacts, jewelry, kachinas, rugs. Brochure. Membership: IACA.

SOUTHWEST OUTPOST
5302 Madison Ave. • Indianapolis, IN 46227
 (317) 783-3854; I. Sandy Craven, Owner
Retail, mail order, some wholesale. *Products*: All. Catalog & price sheet.

WHITE RIVER TRADER
Eiteljorg Museum, 500 W. Washington St. • Indianapolis, IN 46204
 (800) 878-7978 Fax (317) 264-1732
Retail. *Products*: Jewelry, art, books, CDs, posters, clothing.

ONE EARTH GALLERY & GIFTS
1022 Main St. • Lafayette, IN 47901
 (317) 742-7564; David R. Kurtz
Retail. *Products*: All. Price list.

DAYS PAST
1215 W. Grant St. • Thorntown, IN 46071
(317) 436-7200; Dan Bunderle, Owner
Retail. *Products*: Artifacts, jewelry, kachinas, pottery, rugs,
sand paintings, sculpture, carvings. *Membership*: IACA.

AMERICAN TREASURES
115 N. Chauncey Ave. • West Lafayette, IN 47906
(317) 743-6153; David R. Kurtz, Owner
Retail. *Products*: All. Price list available.

KANSAS

AMERICAN INDIAN ART CENTER
206 S. Buckeye Ave. • Abilene, KS 67410
(913) 263-0090; Patt Murphy (Iowa/Sauk), Owner
Retail. *Products*: Traditional & contemporary fine arts & crafts,
specializing in Woodland and Prairie Indian items.

DAWNHAWK PRODUCTIONS
34420 Wabaunsee Rd. • Alma, KS 66401
Website: www.dawnhawk.org; E-mail: wakinyan1@mac.com
Arthur J. Short Bull (Lakota), Artist/Owner
Products: Original watercolor & acrylic paintings depicting
Lakota poetry & history.

EDDIE MORRISON - WOOD CARVINGS, SCULPTURE
2 S. Main, P.O. Box 248 • Caldwell, KS 67022
(316) 845-2259; Eddie Morrison (Cherokee), Artist/Owner
Mail order. *Products*: Wood carvings, bronze & stone sculptures

SEES-THE-EAGLE
111 W. Orange • Caney, KS 67333
(316) 879-2634; Bill DeWitt, Manager
E-mail: wdewitt@terraworld.net; Margaret Ann Bird (Osage), Owner
Mail order. Osage craftsperson. *Products*: Beadwork, artifacts, rugs. Osage,
Cherokee, Delaware, Plains, & Woodland Indians traditional clothing for men &
women. Restoration & reproductions of museum pieces. Special orders.

LAURIE HOUSEMAN-WHITEHAWK
RR#3, Box 155-B • Lawrence, KS 66044
(913) 842-1948; Laurie Houseman-Whitehawk (Winnebago), Owner
Retail, wholesale. *Products*: Original paintings in watercolor;
limited edition prints.

THE SANTA FE CONNECTION
P.O. Box 7466 • Overland Park, KS 66207
(913) 897-4107; William & Sue Park, Owners
Retail. *Products*: Art, baskets, beadwork, clothing, dolls, jewelry, kachinas,
pottery, rugs, sand paintings, sculpture, carvings. *Membership*: IACA.

DOLORES PURDY CORCORAN (Caddo)
7031 S.W. Queen's Ct. • Topeka, KS 66614
(785) 478-4801 or 224-1655; Website: www.dolorespurdycorcoran.com
Products: Original transparent watercolors, mixed media paintings, limited
edition prints, large gourd pots & masks of Woodland designs.

INDIAN MUSEUM GIFT SHOP
Mid-America All-Indian Center, 650 N. Seneca • Wichita, KS 67203
(316) 262-5221 ext. 41 Fax 262-4216; Brema Kennedy, Director
Retail. *Products*: Art, baskets, beadwork, dolls, jewelry, kachinas, pottery.

SANDBAR TRADING
922 E. Douglas • Wichita, KS 67202
(316) 691-1482; Richard & Julie Gottsponer
Website: www.sandbartrade.com; E-mail: julie@sandbartrade.com
Membership: IACA.

KENTUCKY

BUFFALO ARROW HEADS
6365 Bethel Ch. Rd. • Kevil, KY 42053
(502) 462-3210; Al Puckett, Owner
Mail order. *Products*: Traditional arrow heads & crafts.

MAANII'S ART
3191 S. 3rd St. #3 • Louisville, KY 40214
(502) 552-0374; Maanii Bladon (Odawa), Artist/Owner
E-mail: mbaldon@insightbb.com
Retail. *Products*: Stained glass specializing in contemporary Native design.

BLACK BEAR
1370 Dry Branch Rd. • Morehead, KY 40351
Website: www.blackbear-pottery.com
Stephen LaBoueff (Blackfeet), Artist/Owner
Retail. *Products*: Traditional pottery materials & techniques.

LOUISIANA

CHEROKEE VISIONS
(337) 214-4171; Website: www.cherokeevisions.com
Products: Native American artifacts, regalia, gifts & home decor

NORTH AMERICAN NATIVE ARTS & CRAFTS
P.O. Box 15112 • Baton Rouge, LA 70895
Shirley M. Motlow (Seminole), Owner
Mail order. *Products*: Seminole patchwork apparel; sweet grass baskets;
beadwork jewelry; traditional palmetto fiber dolls.

MELISSA DARDEN
P.O. Box 191 • Charenton, LA
(337) 380-6888; Melissa Darden (Chitimacha), Artisan
Retail. Products: Chitimacha single & double weave baskets.

BAYOU INDIAN ENTERPRISES
P.O. Box 668 • Elton, LA 70532
(318) 584-2653; Bertney Langley (Coushatta), Owner
Retail, wholesale, mail order. Coushatta craftsperson. products: Items from the
(Koasati) Coushatta & other Southwestern tribes, including handmade Indian
flutes, Koasati Indian baskets, artwork, beadwork, jewelry, wall hangings.

MAINE

PAM CUNNINGHAM
397 Old Country Rd. • Hampden, ME 04441
(207) 941-9373; Pam Cunningham, Owner
Retail, wholesale, mail order. By appointment only. Penobscot craftsperson.
Products: Penobscot brown ash and sweet grass fancy baskets.

THREE FEATHERS NATIVE BASKETS
P.O. Box 1238 • Houlton, ME 04730
(207) 532-0862; E-mail: rr-rc@mfx.net; Rosella Silliboy (Micmac), Owner
Retail, wholesale. Micmac craftsperson. *Products*: Traditional brown ash utility
and workbaskets made by Micmac tribal members.

HOME & AWAY
26 Maine St., P.O. Box 950 • Kennebunkport, ME 04046
(207) 967-2122; David & Anne Schultz, Owners
Website: www.homeandaway.biz; E-mail: david@homeandaway.biz
Retail, wholesale. *Products*: Arctic & Indian arts, including Penobscot corn
baskets, Inuit sculpture, Navajo sterling silver inlay jewelry. *Membership*: IACA.

PUEBLO POTTERY IN MAINE
10 Chase Mill Rd., P.O. Box 45 • Limington, ME 04049
(207) 637-2547 Fax 637-3630; Paul J. Luise, Owner
Website: www.pueblopotteryme.com
E-mail: paul@pueblopotteryme.com. *Membership*: IACA.

NOWETAH'S AMERICAN INDIAN STORE & MUSEUM
2 Colegrove Rd. • New Portland, ME 04961-3821
(207) 628-4981; Ms. Nowetah Wirick, Owner/curator
Retail, mail order. *Products*: Art, baskets, beadwork, clothing, dolls, jewelry,
kachinas, pottery, rugs, sandpaintings, sculpture, carvings. Catalogs.

MAINE INDIAN BASKETMAKERS ALLIANCE
P.O. Box 3253 • Old Town, ME 04468
(207) 827-0391; Website: www.maineindianbaskets.org
E-mail: miba@gwi.net
Products: Traditional brown ash & sweet-grass baskets made by members of
the Maliseet, Micmac, Passamaquoddy & Penobscot tribes. Write for info.

PENOBSCOT QUILLWORKS
P.O. Box 195 • Old Town, ME 04468
(207) 827-6117; Martin Neptune & Jennifer Sapiel, Owners
Wholesale/retail jewelry.

LONGACRE ENTERPRISES, INC.
P.O. Box 196 • Perry, ME 04667
(800) 642-5024; (207) 853-2762; Cliv Dore, Owner
Wholesale, mail order. *Products*: Passamaquoddy baskets, beadwork, boxes,
children's items, dolls, drums, pipes, miniatures. Repairs & restoration. Price
list available.

BASKET BANK
Aroostook Micmac Council, 7 Northern Rd. • Presque Isle, ME 04769
(207) 764-1972; Alice B. Worcester, Manager
Mail order; some wholesale/retail. *Product*: Baskets. Special orders. Brochure.

RUNNING WATER AUTHENTIC INDIAN CRAFTS
505 Post Rd. • Wells, ME 04090
(207) 646-1206
Barbara (Running Water) Beckwith (Penobscot), Artisan/Owner
Special orders, Mail order. *Products*: Beadwork; bone, quill & turquoise jewelry; pottery, kachinas, flutes, birch bark items, sand-paintings, moccasins, dream catchers, limited edition Indian porcelain dolls.

THE CENTER OF NATIVE ART
813 U.S. Route 1, P.O. Box 247 • Woolwich, ME 04579
(866) 862-8483; (207) 442-8399 Fax 442-0099
Website: www.nativeartsonline.com; Chuck & Gloria Hagen, Owners
E-Mail: nativearts@suscom-maine.net
Retail. *Products*: Art, baskets, beadwork, clothing, dolls, jewelry, kachinas, pottery, rugs, sand-paintings, sculpture, carvings. *Membership*: IACA. Catalog.

THE LITTLE BULL
Railroad Ave., P.O. Box 383 • York Beach, ME 03910
(207) 363-7108 Fax 363-4970; Ed Bullock (Wampanoag), Owner
Website: www.thelittlebull.com; E-mail: info@thelittlebull.com
Retail. *Products*: Fine art gallery; Native jewelry; pottery, baskets, flutes, pipes & drums, kachinas, sand paintings, artifacts.

MARYLAND

SPIRIT CATCHER
996 Headwater Rd. • Annapolis, MD 21403
(410) 263-1776; Russell & Ellen Jones, Owners
Retail. *Products*: Art, baskets, beadwork, clothing, dolls, jewelry, kachinas, pottery, rugs, sand-paintings, sculpture, carvings. *Membership*: IACA.

DIFFERENT
505 Vogts Lane • Baltimore, MD 21221
(410) 391-0163; Carol Sullivan & Littletree Hughes, Owners
Retail, wholesale, mail order. *Products*: Jewelry - custom design, original, and unique creations; contemporary and traditional styles.

MASSACHUSETTS

WHITE FEATHER DESIGN
19 St. Paul St. • Blackstone, MA 01504
(508) 883-8670; Marie White, Owner
Website: www.whitefeatherdesign.com
Retail. *Product*: Indian clothes. Catalog: $2.50.

DANCING SPIRITS
2456 Mass. Ave. #103 • Cambridge, MA 02140
(617) 868-7368; Sharon Basch. Retail. *Products*: All. *Membership*: IACA.

THE WANDERING BULL, INC.
P.O. Box 496 • Carver, MA 02330
(800) 430-2855; (508) 866-2700 Fax 430-2855
Website: www.wanderingbull.com
E-mail: custsvc@wanderingbull.com; Janyte Bullock, Owner
Mail order. *Products*: Native American arts & crafts supplies; clothing & patterns; jewelry, Native music & instruments, Regalia items, Minnetonka moccasins; books & videos; Native pipes, hawks & supplies.

SILVER STAR, WAMPANOAG CRAFTS
P.O. Box 402 • Middleboro, MA 02346
(617) 947-4159; Anita G. Nielsen, Owner
Mail order. *Products*: Baskets, beadwork, quillwork, moccasins, bags and leather pouches.

THE KHALSA COLLECTION
P.O. Box 604 • Millis, MA 02054-0604
(508) 376-2804 Fax 376-0845; Arjankaur Khalsa
Retail, wholesale. *Products*: Books, fetishes, heishi, jewelry, kachinas, knives.
Membership: IACA.

BLACK MESA WEAVERS
P.O. Box 95204 • Newton, MA 02495
(866) 424-8776; Website: www.migrations.com
E-mail: carol@blackmesaweavers.org
Wholesale. *Products*: Weavings, wool, handspun Churro yarns, mini-mill Churro yarn, jewelry, pottery, clothing, baskets, pipes & fire-starters.

NEW ENGLAND TRADERS
P.O. Box 877 • Palmer, MA 01069
(413) 596-3129; Bob & Linda Schultz, Owners
Retail. *Products*: Art, baskets, beadwork, clothing, dolls, jewelry, kachinas, pottery, rugs, sand-paintings. *Membership*: IACA.

THE AMERICAN INDIAN STORE
139 Water St. • Quincy, MA 02169-6535
(617) 328-1951; Arlene F. Roberts, Owner
Retail. *Products*: art, baskets, beadwork, jewelry, pottery.
Rugs, weavings/wall hangings, sculpture, carvings. Appraisals.

MOHAWK TRADING POST
874 Mohawk Trail, Rt. 2 • Shelburne, MA 01370
(413) 625-2412 Fax 625-8134; Laurene L. York, Owner
E-Mail: LYork@mohawk-trading-post.com
Website: www.mohawk-trading-post.com
Retail. *Products*: Art, baskets, beadwork, clothing, dolls, jewelry, kachinas, pottery, rugs, sandpaintings, sculpture, carvings. *Membership*: IACA.

THE CORNER CAPE
P.O. Box 853 • Wellfleet, MA 02667
(508) 349-9694/9539; Althea Robida, Owner
Retail. *Products*: Beadwork, fetishes, heishi, jewelry, kachinas, miniatures, pottery, sculpture, carvings. *Membership*: IACA.

JOSEPH JOHNS
7 Russell St. • W. Peabody, MA 02535
(617) 535-2426; Joseph Johns, Owner
Special orders only. *Products*: carvings wood, slate or bone, based on forms & motifs of the Mushkogean culture. Illustrative material available upon request.

MOHAWK TRADING POST
874 Mohawk Trail • Shelburne, MA 01370
(413) 625-2412 Fax 625-8134; Laurene L. York, Owner
Website: www.mohawk-trading-post.com
E-mail: lyork@mohawk-trading-post.com
Membership: IACA.

NATIVE TREASURES
21 E. Turnpike Rd. • Southborough, MA 01772
(508) 624-9600 Fax 624-9603; John Cygielnik, Owner
E-mail: johcy44@yahoo.com. *Membership*: IACA.

SILVER HAWK WAMPUM WORKS
672 Spring St. • Winchendon, MA 01475
(800) 310-6929; (978) 297-3830; Website: www.silverhawkgallery.com
Retail. *Products*: Authentic Native American handcrafts, with a special interest in Eastern Woodland art. Native American owned & operated. Brochure.

MICHIGAN

DREAMDANCER
6997 N. ConwayRd. • Alanson, MI 49706
(231) 838-9738; Warren D. Petoskey (Odawa), Artisan/Owner
Products: Walking sticks, spirit sticks, and prayer sticks

FUNMAKERS
P.O. Box 130364 • Ann Arbor, MI 48113
(734) 332-9165; Lisa Johnson (Ojibwe), Owner
Website: www.funmakers.4t.us
Products: Felted pins, small animals, magnets, cat toys,
Items made from natural fibers.

BLUE HERON DESIGNS
255 S. Old Woodward Ave. • Birmingham, MI 48009
(248) 594-8300 Fax 594-8303
Website: www.yourblueheron.com
E-mail: blueherondesigns@sbcglobal.net; Heather Lufkins Robinson, Owner
Products: Jewelry, paintings, sculpture, pottery, bronzes, interior design svcs.

BEAR TRACKS DBA BUNDY'S BUNGALOW
125 Irwin St. • Brooklyn, MI 49230
(517) 592-3439 Fax 592-8022; Caryn Howard, Owner
Retail. *Products*: Jewelry, paintings, Pendleton blankets, coats, crafts, Tshirts.

THE CRAFTS OF MANY TRIBES
South Eastern Michigan Indians, Inc.
26641 Lawrence St. • Center Line, MI 48015
(810) 956-1350 Fax 756-1352\
Retail. *Products*: Native American art and crafts.

MOON BEAR POTTERY
1048 Silver Rd. • Coldwater, MI 49036
 (517) 238-5833; Shirley Brauker (Ottawa), Artist/Owner
 Website: www.cbpu.com/moonbea; E-mail: moonbear@cbpu.com
Products: Hand-carved authentic Native American design pottery, bronze sculpture, stone carvings, oil/acrylic paintings, wall hangings.

NOC BAY TRADING CO.
P.O. Box 295 • Escanaba, MI 49829
 (800) 652-7192; (906) 789-0505; Website: www.nocbay.com
Mail order craft supplies & materials. Catalog, $3.

FLYING FEATHERS
5686 Heights-Ravenna Rd. • Fruitport, MI 49415-9970
 (800) 795-1604 Fax (231) 788-4717; Rick Hewitt, Owner
Retail. *Products*: Contemporary & traditional Native American supplies & crafts.

PENINSULA SHORES GALLERY
P.O. Box 23 • Gould City, MI 49838
 (906) 477-6303; Jim O'Neil (Ojibwe), Artist/Owner
 Website: www.peninsulashoresgallery.com
Products: Wildlife and nature photography and artwork.

INDIAN ARTS & CRAFTS STORE
Native American Arts & Crafts Council
P.O. Box 1049 • Grayling, MI 49738
 (517) 348-3190; Robin L. Menefee, Executive Director
Retail, mail order by request only. *Products*: Art, baskets, beadwork, boxes, leatherwork.

ANNA M. CRAMPTON
14360 Woodbury Rd. • Haslett, MI 48840
 (517) 339-8856
Retail (by appointment only). *Products*: baskets, beadwork.

NOPIMING ARTWORK
2684 E. Garfield Rd. • Hesperia, MI 49421
 (231) 742-0718 or 861-5610
 Joyce Robertson (Odawa), Artisan/Owner
Products: Beadwork, regalia, blankets, artwork.

SPIRIT KEEPERS
17505 Buckhorn Lake Rd. • Holly, MI 48442
 (248) 328-0500; Nikki Brueger, Owner. *Membership*: IACA.

MONADNOCK TRADING CO., INC.
309 E. Central Ave., P.O. Box 400 • Mackinaw City, MI 49701
 (616) 436-5131 Fax 436-5158; Lawrence Goldman, Owner
Retail. *Products*: Art, beadwork, boxes, jewelry, pottery, rugs, sand-paintings, sculpture. Membership: IACA. *Branch office*: P.O. Box 6465, Apache Junction, AZ 85278.

SOUTHWEST MIRAGE
36643 Suffolk • Mt. Clemens, MI 48043
 (313) 791-3384; Frank & Joann Spatafore
Retail. *Products*: dolls, drums/pipes, fetishes, heishi, jewelry, kachinas, pottery, sandpaintings.

ZIIBIWING CENTER GIFT STORES
6650 E. Broadway • Mt. Pleasant, MI 48858
 (989) 775-4750; Nathaniel Lambertson, Manager
 Website: www.nativedirect.org; Website: www.sagcip.org
Products: Bead & quill work, paintings, baskets, pottery, sculpture, jewelry, clothing, herbs, native foods, books, music.

ELI THOMAS
2795 S. Leaton Rd. • Mt. Prospect, MI 48858
 (517) 773-4299. Retail, wholesale. *Product*: Baskets.

CRAZY HORSE
1982 W. Grand River Ave. • Okemos, MI 48864
 (517) 381-8744 Fax 381-8745; Michelle Haun, Owner.
Membership: IACA.

INDIAN HILLS TRADING CO. & INDIAN ART GALLERY
1581 Harbor Rd. • Petoskey, MI 49770
 (616) 347-3789; Victor S. Kishigo, Owner
Retail, mail order (by special request). *Products*: baskets, beadwork, drums, quillwork, jewelry, pottery, Navajo rugs.

NATIVE WEST GALLERY – UNIQUE AMERICAN SOUTHWEST ART
863 W. Ann Arbor Trail • Plymouth, MI 48170
 (734) 455-8838 Fax 455-1651; Annette & Ken Horn, Owners
Retail. *Products*: Art, boxes, clothing, dolls, jewelry, kachinas, pottery, rugs, sandpaintings, sculpture, carvings. *Membership*: IACA.

BAWATING ART GALLERY
2186 Shunk Rd. • Sault Ste. Marie, MI 49783
 (906) 632-0530 ext. 53529 Fax 635-4959; Elisabeth Dietz, Manager
Retail. *Products*: Native artist's paintings, wood & soapstone carvings, dreamcatchers. Artwork, including beadwork on birchbark, and birchbark paintings.

BIG BEAR TRADING POST
1904 Ashmun St. • Sault Ste. Marie, MI 49783
 (906) 632-8336; Catherine Boling, Owner
Retail. *Products*: Native American crafts and supplies.

PRINCESS PINE ENTERPRISES
P.O. Box 159 • Sault Ste. Marie, MI 49783
 Princess Pine (Ojibwe), Owner; E-mail: itchmm@yahoo.com
Products: Beadwork, dreamcatchers, calendars & cookbooks, sweetgrass & birch bark items; paintings.

THOMAS N. THOMPSON (Ottawa/Ojibwe)
P.O. Box 475 • Whitehall, MI 49461
 (231) 894-2968; E-mail: thompsontucker@netscape.net
Products: Beadwork, sculpture, carvings.

MINNESOTA

MANITOK FOOD & GIFTS/KENOO FINE HANDCRAFTS
P.O. Box 97 • Callaway, MN 56521
 (800) 726-1863 Fax (218) 375-4765; Dave Reinke (Ojibwe), Manager
Products: Handmade jewelry, dolls, quilts, birch bark baskets, canoes; gift baskets filled with hand-harvested and handmade food products.

BINESHII
P.O. Box 1329 • Cass Lake, MN 56633
 (218) 335-2803 Fax 335-8461; Website: www.bineshiiwildrice.com
 E-mail: bineshii@direcway.com; Kathleen M. Lausche (Ojibwe), Owner
Products: Handmade Ojibwe creations & foods. Includes birch bark baskets, canoes, dance regalia, dream catchers, artwork, and beadwork.

SHINING CLOUD WOMAN CREATIONS
225 1st St., N.W. #202 • Cass Lake, MN 56633
 (218) 335-0014; Margaret J. "Peggy" LaRoque (Ojibwe), Owner
Products: Jewelry & wearable art: beads, crystals, gem stones, feathers, textiles, etc.

R. DESJARLAIT STUDIO/GALLERY
5901 Rhode Island Ave. N. • Crystal, MN 55428
 (612) 535-0091; R. DesJarlait (Red Lake Ojibwe), Artist/Owner
Products: Traditional art: murals, paintings, illustrations, graphics.

LAKE OF THE WOODS OJIBWE
1535 Willard Ave. • Detroit Lakes, MN 56501
 (218) 846-9911; Karen Floan, Owner
Retail, wholesale. By appt. Chippewa craftsperson. *Products*: Applique-style hand beadwork of northern Ojibwe designs; other woodsy, lodge-style interior home products.

IKWE MARKETING
Route 1 • Isage, MN 56570
 (218) 573-3411/3049; Margaret Smith & Winona LaDuke, Managers
Retail/mail order. *Products*: baskets, beadwork, quillwork, rugs & quilts.

CBR, INC. TOUCH THE EARTH
7630 Excelsior Blvd. • Minneapolis, MN 55426
 (612) 690-1050 Fax 690-0440; Carol Howe, Owner. Retail, wholesale.

GRANDFATHER'S SPIRIT
4219 Cedar Ave. So. • Minneapolis, MN 55407
 (877) 946-6345; (612) 724-2294 Fax 724-2294
 Website: www.grandfathersspirit.com
 E-mail: customerservice@grandfathersspirit.com
 Beth Johns, Owner. *Membership*: IACA.

SPIRIT OF RED HORSE
7630 Excelsior Blvd. • Minneapolis, MN 55426
 (651) 204-4220 Fax 204-4221; Carole Howe, Owner
 E-mail: chowe@xrb-incorporated.com. *Membership*: IACA.

WOODLAND INDIAN CRAFTS
1530 E. Franklin Ave. • Minneapolis, MN 55404
 (612) 874-7766; Elaine & Charles Stately, Owners
Retail, mail order. *Products*: Baskets, beadwork, clothing, leatherwork,
masks, moccasins, jewelry & silverwork, rugs, weavings.

KEEWADIN WILD RICE
9462 State Hwy. #27 • Onamia, MN 56339
 (320) 492-5686; Bill Schaaf (Mille LacsOjibwe), Owner
Website: www.keewadinwildrice.com
E-mail: info@keewadinwildrice.com. *Products*: Birch bark crafts.

MILLE LACS INDIAN MUSEUM & TRADING POST
43411 Oodena Dr. • Onamia, MN 56359
 (320) 532-3632; Terry Vidal, Owner
Website: mnhs.org/millelacs. *Membership*: IACA.

PIPESTONE INDIAN SHRINE ASSOCIATION
Pipestone National Monument, P.O. Box 727 • Pipestone, MN 56164
 (888) 209-0418; (507) 825-5463 Fax 825-2903
Website: www.authenticpipestone.com
E-mail: sales@authenticpipestone.com
 Maddie Redwing, Business Manager; Caroll Derby, Sales Manager
Retail, wholesale, mail order. *Products*: beadwork, drums, pipes, flutes,
jewelry, pottery. Carvings in pipestone (catlinite) including pipes and jewelry;
beaded pipe bags. Brochure.

PAINTED TIPI, LTD.
725 Snelling Ave. N. • St. Paul, MN 55104
 (612) 854-9193 Fax 645-5745
Retail. *Products*: All. Appraisals: Art, artifacts, beadwork, books, clothing, dolls,
jewelry, kachinas, pottery, rugs. Membership: IACA.

STORMCLOUD TRADING COMPANY
725 Snelling Ave. N. • St. Paul, MN 55104
 (612) 645-0343 Fax 645-5745
 Sandra Graves, Owner; Jim Priest, Manager
Retail, wholesale, mail order. *Products*: Art, beadwork, books, artifacts, boxes,
jewelry, kachinas, pottery, rugs. Appraisals. *Membership*: IACA.

SHAKOPEE TRADING POST & GALLERY
723 West 1st Ave. • Shakopee, MN 55379
 (800) 547-5787; (952) 496-2263; Website: www.shakopeetradingpost.com
E-mail: nativeamerican@shakopeetradingpost.com
 Marlon & Mary Jean Estenson, Owners
Retail, wholesale. Native American arts & crafts specialty shop. *Products*:
Sterling silver & turquoise handmade jewelry, quillwork, beaded items, books.

MISSISSIPPI

CHOCTAW MUSEUM OF THE SOUTHERN INDIAN GIFT SHOP
P.O. Box 6010 • Philadelphia, MS 39350
 (601) 650-1685; Bob Ferguson, Manager
Retail, mail order. Tribal enterprise. *Products*: Baskets, beadwork, clothing,
dolls, jewelry, pottery. Special orders accepted. Send S.A.S.E. for Price list.

GRAMMY MO'S, INC.
P.O. Box 7524 • Gulfport, MS 39506
 E-mail: mohegan1@msn.com
 Captain Dan G. Romano (Mohegan), Artisan/Owner
Products: Handcrafted baskets, with custom markings.

SOARING EAGLE INDIAN JEWELRY
906 Spring St. • Waynesboro, MS 39367
 (601) 735-1195; Carolyn Stagg-White
Retail. *Products*: Baskets, jewelry, pottery. *Membership*: IACA.

MISSOURI

SOUTHWEST REFLECTIONS
13735 Co. Rd. #6950 • Caulfield, MO 65626
 (907) 258-9988; Nancy & Weyman Perez, Owners
Retail. *Products*: Art, baskets, boxes, ornaments, clothing, drums, pipes,
artifacts, jewelry, kachinas, knives, miniatures, rugs, sand-paintings.
Membership: IACA.

TURNER ARTWORKS
14323 Spring Dr. • De Soto, MO 63020
 (314) 337-4105; Kevin Skypainter Turner, Owner
Retail, wholesale, mail order. *Products*: Art, jewelry. Brochure, catalog.

NATIVE AMERICAN TRADING COMPANY
123 N. Main St. • Hannibal, MO 63401
 (573) 248-3451 Fax 221-4054; Michael O'cheltree
Website: www.nativeamerican trading.com
E-mail: natamtrd@sbcglobal.net. *Membership*: IACA.

MAHOTA HANDWOVENS
67 Horseshoe Dr. • Joplin, MO 64804
 (417) 782-7036
 Margaret Roach Wheeler (Chickasaw-Choctaw), Artisan/Owner
Retail. By appt. only. Chickasaw-Choctaw craftsperson. *Products*: American
Indian clothing (adapted for contemporary wear) & accessories, rugs.

THE GREEN DOOR
103 W. Washington • Kirksville, MO 63501
 (660) 627-5711 Fax 627-5711; E-mail: thegreendoor@cableone.net
 Rosalie & Jerry Caldwell, Owners. *Membership*: IACA.

SOUTHWEST STAR FINE ARTS
11123 E. 85 Terrace • Raytown, MO 64138
 (800) 992-8939; Roy A. Beers
Wholesale/retail. *Products*: Fine art. Appraisals. *Membership*: IACA. Catalog.

SILVER FOX TRADING POST
5104 King Hill Ave. • St. Joseph, MO 64504
 (816) 238-7560
Retail, wholesale. *Products*: Indian crafted items & artifacts.

SILVER CITY TRADING POST
724 S. Main St. • St. Charles, MO 63301
 (636) 255-8885; Richard Sellers, Owner
E-mail: silver_city@sbcglobal.net. *Membership*: IACA.

MONTANA

STAMPEDE TRADING COMPANY
439 Grand Dr., Suite 105 • Bigfork, WY 59111
 (888) 271-9369; Website: www.stampedetradingco.com
E-mail: info@stampedetradingco.com
Products: Native American Art, clothing, jewelry, kachina dolls,
pottery, sandpaintings, Native American masks.

BISON SPECIALTIES
9230 Pryor Rd. • Billings, MT 59101
 (406) 259-6342; Marla Little Light (Crow), Artisan/Owner
E-mail: bison@mch.net
Products: Traditionally tanned hides, handmade moccasins,
Native American dolls, educational video booklet.

BUFFALO CHIPS INDIAN GALLERY
327 S. 24th St. West • Billings, MT 59102-5669
 (406) 656-8954; Thom Myers, Owner
Retail, wholesale. *Products*: All. *Appraisals*: Beadwork, clothing,
dolls, jewelry, rugs; repairs & restoration. Catalog.

FLAMING STAR GALLERY
821 N. 27th St. #120 • Billings, MT 59101
 (888) 800-1876; Sarah Chapman, Owner
Website: www.flamingstargallery.com
E-mail: info@gonativeamerica.com. *Membership*: IACA.

TOUCH OF SANTA FE, INC.
112 N. Broadway • Billings, MT 59101
 (406) 259-6294 Fax 248-6533; Stanley E. Hoggatt, Owner
Membership: IACA.

SQUARE BUTTE TRADING POST & NATIVE ARTS SHOP
Hwy. 87, P.O. Box 54 • Box Elder, MT 59521
 (406) 352-3301; Website: www.squarebuttetradingpost.com
All merchandise is authentic Native American made items by Chippewa-Cree
Tribal members. *Products*: Beadwork, dresses, earrings, paintings, crafts.

INDIAN UPRISING GALLERY, LLC.
25 S. Tracy Ave. • Bozeman, MT 59715
 (406) 586-5831 Fax 582-9848; Iris Model, Owner
Website: www.indianuprisinggallery.com
E-mail: indianuprisinggallery@msn.com. *Membership*: IACA.

SCHNEES BOOTS & SHOES
6597 Falcon Ln. • Bozeman, MT 59715
 (800) 922-1562

Retail, wholesale. *Products*: Arrow Moccasin Co. – contemporary hand-sewn heavy moccasins.

BLACKFEET CRAFTS ASSOCIATION
P.O. Box 51 • Browning, MT 59417
 Mary F. Hipp, Manager
Retail, mail order. Products: Beadwork, clothing, jewelry.

BLACKFEET TRADING POST
P.O. Box 626 • Browning, MT 59417
 (406) 338-2050; Nora Lukin, Owner
Retail, mail order. Products: Art, baskets, beadwork, clothing, pottery. Special order accepted.

LEONDA FAST BUFFALO HORSE
P.O. Box 373 • Browning, MT 59417
 (406) 338-3158; Website: www.nativeamericanartshow.com
 Leonda Fast Buffalo Horse (Blackfeet), Artisan/Owner
Products: Porcupine quillwork, stained glass.

LODGEPOLE GALLERY & TIPI VILLAGE
P.O. Box 1832 • Browning, MT 59417
 (406) 338-2787 Fax 338-2778
 E-mail: tipicamp@3rivers.net
 Website: www.blackfeetculturecamp.com
Darrell Norman (Blackfeet), Owner/Manager
Products: Fine art from Blackfeet artists; other Plains Indian artists with sculptures, paintings and traditional art forms.

NORTHERN PLAINS INDIAN CRAFTS ASSOCIATION
P.O. Box E • Browning, MT 59417
 (406) 338-5661; Jackie Parsons, Manager
Retail, mail order. Blackfeet crafts persons. *Products*: Baskets, beadwork, clothing, dolls, jewelry. rugs. Send S.A.S.E. for Price List

NATIVE AMERICAN ART SALES
51761 Hillside Rd. • Charlo, MT 59824
 (406) 644-3046 (Flathead Indian Reservation)
 Website: www.nativeamericanartsales.com
 E-mail: questions@nativeamericanartsales.com
 Dacia Whitworth (Confederated Salish Kootenai), Owner
Products: Beadwork, jewelry, clothing, carvings, hangings, art.

YELLOWSTONE TRADING POST
Box 1129, Hwy. 212 • Cooke City, MT 59020
 (406) 838-2265; Bernie & Phyllis Kiley, Owners
Retail. *Products*: Art, beadwork, clothing dolls, drums, pipes, fetishes, jewelry, kachinas, sand-paintings. *Membership*: IACA.

MILLER'S BACKRESTS & TIPI ACCESSORIES
HC 66 - Hwy. Rt. 43 • Divide, MT 59727
 (406) 832-3195; Andy & Kathy Miller, Owners
Retail. *Products*: Willow backrests, parfleche cases, rawhide & tipi accessories. Brochure.

JAY CONTWAY ART
434 McIver Rd. • Great Falls, MT 59404
 (406) 452-7647; Jay Contway, Owner
Wholesale, retail. *Products*: Art, jewelry, rugs, sculpture. *Membership*: IACA. Catalog.

KING KUKA GRAPHICS
907 Ave. "C", NW • Great Falls, MT 59404
 (406) 452-4449; King Kuka (Blackfeet), Artist/Owner
Retail, wholesale, mail order. By appt. *Products*: Art-original watercolor, alabaster & bronze sculptures, carvings. Send S.A.S.E. for price list.

KINNEY'S TENTS & TEPEES
1407 N. Custer Ave. • Hardin, MT 59034
 (888) 523-3422 or (406) 665-3422
 Website: www.forevermontana.com; E-Mail: kinneystepees@aol.com
Retail. *Product*: Authentic Crow, Cheyenne, Blackfoot, Lakota/Sioux style tepees.

FORT BELKNAP VENTURES, INC.
RR 1, Box 66 • Harlem, MT 59526
 (406) 353-2205 ext. 403; Frankie Johnson, Manager
Retail, wholesale, mail order. Fort Belknap Gros Ventres and Assiniboine tribal enterprise. *Products*: Art, beadwork, clothing, dolls, jewelry. Quantity orders accepted.

H. EARL & MARGARET TURNER CLACK MEMORIAL MUSEUM
P.O. Box 1484 • Havre, MT 59501
 (406) 265-9913; Elinor Clack, Owner
Retail. *Products*: Art, beadwork, dolls, artifacts. Appraisals: Beadwork.

HARLAW E. RACINE ART
P.O. Box 92 • Heart Butte, MT 59448
 (406) 338-7082; Harlaw E. Racine (Blackfeet), Artisan/Owner
Products: Wood & stone carvings of animals of Blackfeet culture; beadwork, dream catchers; teepee furnishings; willow pillows & willow mats.

NEENEY
P.O. Box 84 • Joplin, MT 59531
 (406) 292-3890; Robert Harvey Allen, Owner
Retail. *Products*: Beadwork, fetishes, jewelry.

GREAT PLAINS GALLERY
P.O. Box 126 - Apt. 28 • Lame Deer, MT 59043-0126
 (800) 249-2296; (406) 477-9418
 Donald Hollowbreast (Northern Cheyenne), Artist/Owner
Retail, wholesale. Northern Cheyenne artist. *Products*: Oil paintings, watercolors, pen & ink drawings. Commissions from color photo-graphs and special orders accepted.

NORTHERN CHEYENNE ARTS & CRAFTS ASSOCIATION
Northern Cheyenne Indian Reservation • Lame Deer, MT 59043
 Carol A. White Wolf, Manager
Retail, wholesale. *Products*: Beadwork, clothing, jewelry.

MONTANA FUR TRADING COMPANY
9560 Hwy. 2 East, P.O. Box 260176 • Martin City, MT 59926
 (406) 387-5816 Fax 387-5008; Don & Jill Demoret, Owners
 Website: www.montanafurtrading.com
 E-mail: montanafurtrading@centurytel.net. *Membership*: IACA.

COUP MARKS
Box 532 • Ronan, MT 59864
 (406) 246-3216; Lorrain Big Crane & Dwight Billedeaux, Managers
Retail. *Products*: All. Special orders accepted

FLATHEAD INDIAN MUSEUM TRADING POST & ART GALLERY
P.O. Box 464 • St. Ignatius, MT 59865
 (406) 745-2951; L. Doug Allard (Flathead), Owner
Retail, wholesale, mail order. *Products*: Art, beadwork, clothing, jewelry. Special orders accepted on beadwork and buckskin items.

FOUR WINDS INDIAN TRADING POST
P.O. Box 580 • St. Ignatius, MT 59865
 (406) 745-4336 Fax 745-3595; E-Mail: 4winds@bigsky.net
 Preston Miller, President
Retail, wholesale, mail order. *Products*: Indian crafts and frontier collectibles. Catalog

ALL SORTS, INC.
P.O. Box 975 • Wolf Point, MT 59201
 (406) 653-3011
Retail, wholesale. *Products*: Native American clothing.

HAMILTON STORES, INC.
P.O. Box 250, Yellowstone National Park
West Yellowstone, MT 59758
 (406) 646-7325 Fax 646-7323
 David Reynolds & Eleanor Hamilton Povah
Retail. Products: All. *Membership*: IACA.

NEBRASKA

DONALD D. RULEAUX (Oglala Sioux)
335 Mears St. • Chadron, NE 69337
Products: Oil, acrylic and watercolor paintings; silverpoint drawings.

THE TURQUOISE SHOP
509 E. 5th St. • North Platte, NE 69101
 (308) 532-7023; Betty J. Kind
Retail. *Products*: Fetishes, heishi, jewelry, pottery, sculpture, craft supplies.

NORTHERN PLAINS STUDIO
P.O. Box 86 • Seneca, NE 69161
 (308) 639-3227; Jackie Sevier (Northern Arapaho), Artist/Owner
 Website: www.northernplainsstudio.com
Products: Pastels, mixed media, embossed paper with gold leaf.

ALLNATIVE.COM
P.O. Box 741 • Winnebago, NE 68071
(402) 878-2400 Fax 878-2771; Website: www.allnative.com
E-mail: info@allnative.com. *Membership*: IACA.

NEVADA

RAVENS ROOST
100 Great Basin National Park • Baker, NV 89311
(775) 234-7221 Fax 234-7269; Jane Murray, Manager
E-mail: ravensroost@550access.com
Retail. *Products*: All. *Membership*: IACA.

STEWART INDIAN MUSEUM TRADING POST
5366 Snyder Ave. • Carson City, NV 89701
(702) 882-1808; Suzi Lisa (Apache), Manager
Retail. Apache craftsperson. *Products*: Baskets, beadwork, dolls, silver
& turquoise jewelry, pottery, kachinas, rugs. Special orders accepted.

UGLY OTTER TRADING POST
1346 Idaho St., PMB #200 • Elko, NV 89801
(775) 753-5396 Fax 753-4093; Website: www.uglyotter.com
E-mail: uglyottermail@aol.com. *Product*: Southwestern Indian jewelry

FORUNATE EAGLE'S ROUND HOUSE GALLERY
7133 Stillwater Rd. • Fallon, NY 89406
(775) 423-2220; Adam Fortunate Eagle Nordwall, Owner
Retail. *Products*: Art, beadwork, clothing, drums, pipes, jewelry, pottery,
sculpture.

VIVIAN SNYDER (Yurok)
7A Inglewood Dr. • Fernley, NV 89408
(775) 575-5028
Products: Yurok baskets, medallions, necklaces; bone beads.

AMERICAN HERITAGE INDIAN ARTS
850 S. Boulder Hwy. #292 • Henderson, NV 89015-7564
Cynthia Judd & D.L. Uher, Sr.
Wholesale/retail. *Products*: Clothing, drums, pipes, rugs.
Membership: IACA. Catalog.

CASA DECOR
3375 S. Decatur Blvd. #14 • Las Vegas, NV 89102
(702) 222-3699 Fax 222-0021
E-mail: casadecor95@msn.com
Ronald & Nancy Gustafson, Ralph Robarts, Owners. *Membership*: IACA.

L PORTAL SOUTHWEST
310 E. Fremont St. • Las Vegas, NM 89101
(702) 382-3740; John & Eunes Lonetti, Owners. *Membership*: IACA.

NATIVE AMERICAN ARTS
P.O. Box 85273 • Las Vegas, NV 89185
Craig Jackson (Tlingit), Artist/Owner. Products: Jewelry, baskets.

MALOTTE STUDIO
South Fork Reservation, Star Route • Lee, NV 89829
(775) 744-4305; Jack Malotte, Owner
By appt. only. *Products*: Original drawings, graphic design and illustrations.

MOAPA TRIBAL ENTERPRISES
Paiute Tribal Enterprise, P.O. Box 340 • Moapa, NV 89025-0340
(702) 865-2787 Fax 379-4012; Linda Donahue, Manager
Wholesale, retail. *Products*: All. *Membership*: IACA.

MAGGI HOUTEN
P.O. Box 265 • Nixon, NV 89424
(775) 476-0205; Margaret Houten, Owner
Mail order. *Products*: Baskets, beadwork.

MICHAEL & SON'S BLACK HILLS TRADING COMPANY
2002A Harvard Way • Reno, NV 89502
(775) 829-9933; David & Shannon Lorenz
Wholesale, retail. *Products*: Baskets, clothing, dolls, jewelry, kachinas, pottery,
sandpaintings, sculpture, carvings; repairs & restoration. *Membership*: IACA.

THE TEPEE
2500 E. 2nd St. #38 • Reno, NV 89595
(775) 322-5599; Irene Ryan (Washoe), Owner
Retail, mail order. *Products*: Navajo, Zuni, Hopi and
Santo Domingo jewelry; baskets, kachinas, pottery, rugs.

ARAGON NATIVE SCULPTURE
P.O. Box 64 • Schurz, NV 89427
(775) 773-2542; Arnold Aragon, Artist/Owner
Retail, wholesale. *Products*: Art, sculpture, carvings.
Special orders accepted.

WINTER MOON TRADING COMPANY
P.O. Box 189 • Schurz, NV 89427
(775) 773-2088; Elvin Willie (Paiute), Owner
Retail, mail order. *Products*: Original artwork, baskets, beadwork,
jewelry. Send S.A.S.E. for price list.

WESTERN INTERNATIONAL
395 Freeport Blvd. #2 • Sparks, NV 89431
(800) 634-6737; (775) 359-4400 Fax 359-4439
John & Shirley Fritz, Owners
Wholesale. *Products*: Books. *Membership*: IACA. Catalog.

INDIAN OUTPOST
Box 829, 20 South C St. • Virginia City, NV 89440
(775) 847-9025; Paul & Marilyn Slick, Owners
Wholesale, retail. *Products*: Art, baskets, beadwork, fetishes,
jewelry, kachinas, miniatures, pottery, sculpture.

THE INDIAN TRADING POST
Box 671, Virginia City Mall #7 • Virginia City, NV 89440
(775) 847-0242; Winson Hong, Owner
Wholesale, retail. *Products*: All. *Membership*: IACA.

NEW HAMPSHIRE

FOUR WINDS TRADING COMPANY
1 Rhodora Dr. • Amherst, NH 03031-2242
(603) 672-2729; Colleen & Leo Trudeau, Owners
Retail. *Products*: All. *Membership*: IACA.

AMERICAN INDIAN ARTS
P.O. Box 476 • Epsom, NH 03234
(603) 736-9946; Lynn & Gardner Gray, Owners. Retail.

KOKOPELLI, INC.
1030 Route 16, P.O. Box 70 • Ossipee, NH 03864
(603) 539-4700 Fax 539-6711; E-mail: koko@worldpath.net
Mary Kelly & Paul Dumont, Owners. *Membership*: IACA.

KACHINA JUGGLER
70 Meadow Rd. • Portsmouth, NH 03801-3124
(603) 436-0253; Kevin & Elisa Marconi-Davis
Retail. *Products*: All. Membership: IACA.

NEW JERSEY

BLUE ZAT GEMS INDIAN ROOM
130 Atlantic St. • Bridgeton, NJ 08302
(609) 451-8059; Russell & Doris Harris, Owners
Retail, wholesale. *Products*: Art, jewelry, rugs, sandpaintings, sculpture.

ARCHEOCRAFT
22 Rose Terrace • Chatham, NJ 07928
(201) 635-1447; Kenneth O'Brien. Retail. *Product*: Pottery.

GEORGETOWN POINTS GIFTS
186-B Georgetown Rd. • Columbus, NJ 08022
(609) 298-9249 Fax 298-1029; David & Linda Stout, Owners
E-mail: georgetownpointsgifts@comcast.net. *Membership*: IACA.

JEAN MUIZNIEKS
13 Channing Way • Cranbury, NJ 08512
(609) 799-0448/1793; Jean Muiznieks
Retail, wholesale. *Products*: Beadwork, fetishes, heishi, jewelry.

THE MORNING DANCER COLLECTION
130F The Orchard • Cranbury, NJ 08512-2421
(908) 548-8423; Holly Sandiford & Chip Greenberg
Retail, wholesale. *Products*: Baskets, jewelry, pottery.
Membership: IACA.

TURQUOISE LADY
10 Horace Court • Cranbury, NJ 08512
(609) 936-1044; Jayne Davis
Retail. *Products*: Jewelry. *Membership*: IACA.

TWO RIVERS TRADING POST
1164 Stuyvesant Ave. • Irvington, NJ 07111
  (973) 351-1210; Carl Watson Longbow, Principal Chief
  (Cherokee Nation of New Jersey)
Retail. *Products*: Authentic Native American Indian crafts,
artifacts and jewelry; Native American herbs and oils.

SOUTHWEST AMERICAN INDIAN JEWELRY
76 Still Well Rd. • Kendall Park, NJ 08824
  (609) 799-0448; Jean M. Muiznieks, Owner
Retail, wholesale. *Products*: Beadwork, fetishes, heishi,
jewelry. *Membership*: IACA.

JUMBO'S
8 Tulip Crescent 2-A • Little Falls, NJ 07424
  (973) 890-0847; Darrell Jumbo (Navajo), Owner
Products: Silver & turquoise jewelry

SEIDEN AMERICAN INDIAN DESIGNS
P.O. Box 99, 14 Ridgewood Dr. • Livingston, NJ 07039
  (201) 992-4788 Fax 994-2795; Matthew & Gella Seiden, Owners
Wholesale, retail. *Products*: Fetishes, jewelry, kachinas, miniatures, rugs.
Membership: IACA.

CROSSROADS
65 Main St. • Madison, NJ 07940
  (201) 514-1616; Jan Keyes, Owner
Retail. *Products*: Art, baskets, beadwork, books, clothing, dolls, jewelry,
kachinas, pottery, rugs, sandpaintings. All native-made crafts. *Membership*:
IACA. Catalog.

SPIDER WOMAN
141 Idolstone Lane • Matawan, NJ 07747
  (908) 583-0829; John & Shaharazad Kleindienst, Owners
Retail. *Products*: Beadwork, dolls, fetishes, heishi, jewelry, kachinas,
knives, pottery. Membership: IACA. Branch: Secaucus, NJ.

GREY OWL INDIAN CRAFTS
P.O. Box 1185 • Neptune, NJ 07754
  (800) 487-2376; (732) 775-9010 Fax 774-9330
  E-mail: greyowlinc@aol.com; Website: www.greyowlcrafts.com
  Jim Feldman, Owner; Wesley Cochrane, Manager
Retail, Wholesale, Mail order. *Products*: Native American Indian craft supplies:
beads, bone hair pipes, blankets, kachinas, leathers, feathers; books &
recordings. 4,000+ items. Catalog, $3; free to Native Americans.

LONE BEAR INDIAN CRAFT CO.
300 Main St. #3F • Orange, NJ 07050
  James Lone Bear Revey, Owner
Mail order. *Products*: Woodland Indian craftwork. Price list.

TURQUOIS INDIAN
137 E. State Rt. 4 • Paramus, NJ 07652-5004
  (201) 797-1060; Dennis & Ingred Taormina, Owners
Retail. *Products*: All. *Appraisals*: Jewelry. *Membership*: IACA.

SELDIN'S TRINKETS
2 W. Front St. • Red Bank, NJ 07701
  (732) 741-6990 Fax 741-5353; Jamey Seldin, Owner
  Website: www.seldintrinkets.com; E-mail: trinkets1@aol.com
Membership: IACA.

MOON LAKE INDIAN JEWELRY
175 Hayes Dr. • Saddle Brook, NJ 07662
  (201) 797-8367; Bernard Ahrens, Owner
Retail. Products: Jewelry, kachinas; repairs & restoration.

SPIDER WOMAN
700 Plaza Dr. • Secaucus, NJ 07794
  (201) 223-1313; John & Shaharazad Kleindienst, Owners
Retail. *Products*: Beadwork, dolls, fetishes, heishi, jewelry, kachinas, knives,
pottery. *Membership*: IACA. *Branch*: Matawan, NJ.

ADOBE EAST GALLERY
445 Springfield Ave. • Summit, NJ 07901
  (908) 273-8282 Fax 277-148; Ted & Phyllis Schwartz
Retail. *Products*: Art, jewelry, pottery, rugs, sculpture. *Membership*: IACA.

COYOTE JUNCTION
7 Glenview Rd. • Towaco, NJ 07082
  (201) 299-0506; Joseph & Susan Ascione, Owners

Retail, wholesale. *Products*: Ornaments, fetishes, heishi,
jewelry, kachinas, pottery, sand-paintings. *Membership*: IACA.

NEW MEXICO

LILLY'S GALLERY
P.O. Box 342 • Acoma Pueblo, NM 87034
  (505) 552-9501; Maria "Lilly" Salvador (Acoma Pueblo), Owner
  Wayne Salvador, Manager. Retail. *Products*: Traditional Acoma Pueblo
pottery & figurines. *Membership*: SWAIA.

SQUASH BLOSSOM
822 N. White Sands Blvd. • Alamogordo, NM 88310-7112
  (505) 437-8126; Cliff & Sue Hall, Owners
Retail. *Products*: Navaho, Zuni & Hopi jewelry; Hopi kachina dolls; Navaho
rugs & sand-paintings; Mescalero Apache sculpture, baskets & paintings.
Appraisals: Pottery. *Membership*: IACA.

WOVEN STITCH-INDIAN DESIGN NEEDLEWORK
1828 Corte Del Ranchero • Alamogordo, NM 88310
  (505) 437-2934; Mike Mosier, President. Retail, wholesale, mail order.
Products: Indian designs in crochet, needlepoint, latch hook kits and patterns.

AGAPE SOUTHWEST PUEBLO POTTERY
414 Romero Rd. NW • Albuquerque, NM 87104
  (505) 243-2366 Fax 243-3002; Richard Myers, Owner
  Website: www.agapesw.com; E-mail: info@agapesw.com
Product: Southwest Pueblo pottery.

AMERICAN HERITAGE INDIAN ARTS
14024 Wind Mountain Rd. NE • Albuquerque, NM 87112
  (505) 271-1981; Cynthia Judd, Owner. Wholesale/retail.
Products: Clothing, drums, pipes, rugs. *Membership*: IACA. Catalog.

AMERICAN WEST TRADING CO.
1208 San Pedro NE, Suite 117 • Albuquerque, NM 87110
  (505) 265-8549; Ken Kaemmerle, Contact
Wholesale. *Products*: Northwest Coast art, kachinas, pottery, rugs, sculpture.
Membership: IACA.

AMERINJECO TRADING CO.
P.O. Box 13345 • Albuquerque, NM 87192
  (800) 874-1976; (505) 293-4727 (phone & fax)
  Layne E. Fuller, Director
Wholesale. *Products*: Fetishes, heishi, jewelry, kachinas, knives, pottery, rugs,
sand-paintings, sculpture. *Membership*: IACA. Catalog available.

ANITRAS, INC.
1701 Central NW • Albuquerque, NM 87104
  (800) 824-4149; (505) 242-1060; Anita Becker & William Blythe
Wholesale. *Product*: Jewelry. Catalog available.

ARMADILLO TRADING COMPANY
201 Wellesley Dr., SE • Albuquerque, NM 87106
  (505) 266-7698; Chuck Hall, Owner
Wholesaler. *Product*: Pottery. *Membership*: IACA.

AVILA RETAIL DEVELOPMENT & MANAGEMENT
5001 Ellison NE • Albuquerque, NM 87109
  (505) 341-3753 Fax 341-2835
  Website: www.avilaretail.com
  E-mail: jmedina@avilaretail.com
  John & Kathlee Avila & Jennifer Medina, Owners. *Membership*: IACA.

BEAR PAW INDIAN ARTS & GALLERY
326 San Felipe, NW, Old Town • Albuquerque, NM 87104
  (505) 843-9337; Jim, Mary, Michael & Marian Trujillo (Taos-Acoma Pueblo),
  Artisan/Owners. Retail, wholesale. *Products*: Art, Navajo & Zuni jewelry,
Pueblo pottery, baskets, Navajo dolls, drums, cedar flutes, pipes, sandpaintings. Special orders accepted.

BIEN MUR INDIAN MARKETING CENTER
Sandia Pueblo Tribal Enterprise
100 Ben Mur Dr. NE, P.O. Box 91148 • Albuquerque, NM 87199
  (800) 365-5400; (505) 821-5400 Fax 821-7674
  Website: www.bienmur.com; E-mail: info@bienmur.com
  Ron Fernandez, Owner
Retail, wholesale, mail order. *Products*: Art, jewelry, pottery, clothing, kachinas,
rugs. Authentic Native American arts & crafts. Special orders accepted.
Membership: IACA. Brochure.

CARLISLE SILVER CO., INC.
P.O. Box 26627, 750 Rankin Rd., NE • Albuquerque, NM 87125
(505) 345-5304 Fax 345-5445; H. William Pollack, III
Retail, wholesale. *Products*: Art, fetishes, heishi, jewelry, kachinas, pottery, rugs, sandpaintings. Catalog available.

CHRISTIN WOLF, INC.
2425 Monroe NE #B • Albuquerque, NM 87110
206 1/2 San Felipe NW • Albuquerque, NM 87104
(505) 242-4222; Jerry McKenzie, Owner
Wholesale/retail. *Products*: Fetishes, heishi, jewelry, knives.

CHRISTOPHER'S ENTERPRISES
P.O. Box 25621 • Albuquerque, NM 87125-0621
(505) 294-4581 Fax 294-4585
Christopher & Deborah Cates, Owners
Wholesale. *Products*: Jewelry. *Membership*: IACA. Catalog available.

CIBOLA TRAIL TRADERS EAST
P.O. Box 3362 • Albuquerque, NM 87190-3362
(505) 869-2044; Garry & Sue Zens
Wholesale. *Products*: Fetishes, jewelry, pottery.
Membership: IACA. *Branch*: P.O. Box 1500, Peralta, NM 87042.

R.L. COX FUR & HIDE CO., INC.
Box 25321, 708 1st St., NW • Albuquerque, NM 87125
(505) 242-4980 Fax 242-6101; R.L. Cox, Owner
Wholesale. *Products*: Tanned furs & leather for chaps, moccasins, garments & crafts. *Membership*: IACA.

D'ANZE
P.O. Box 27206, 4908 4th St. NW
Albuquerque, NM 87125-7206
(505) 345-2587; Dee Ann Price
Wholesale. *Product*: Jewelry. *Membership*: IACA.

DISTINCTIVE INDIAN JEWELRY
1028 Stuart Rd., NW • Albuquerque, NM 87114
(505) 897-4152; Ted & Randy Brackett
Wholesale. *Products*: Fetishes, heishi, jewelry, kachinas, rugs.
Membership: IACA.

UPTON ETHELBAH (GREYSHOES)
(Santa Clara Pueblo/White Mountain Apache)
3639 Cameo Dr. SW • Albuquerque, NM 87105
(505) 797-2884; Website: www.greyshoes.com
E-mail: ethelbah1@aol.com
Products: Native American stone & bronze sculptures inspired by the traditions of the Santa Clara Pueblo and White Mountain Apache.

GERTRUDE ZACHARY, INC.
1613 Second NW • Albuquerque, NM 87102
(505) 243-3711; Gertrude Schmidt
Wholesale. *Products*: Jewelry, kachinas, pottery.

THE GOLDEN FLEECE
10025 Acoma SE • Albuquerque, NM 87123
(505) 294-1604; Raphael Seidel
Wholesale. *Product*: Jewelry. Appraisals.

GOWAN ARTS LTD.
303 Romero NW #114 • Albuquerque, NM 87104
(800) 350-6099; (505) 242-6831 Fax 344-9500
Deborah Gowan, Owner; E-mail: goweninc@aol.com.
Membership: IACA.

DOROTHY GRANDBOIS
P.O. Box 2672 • Corrales, NM 87048
(505) 898-3754. Retail. *Products*: Combines photographic & printmaking to create her Native art.

GRANDFATHER EAGLE
202-A San Felipe NW • Albuquerque, NM 87104
(505) 242-5376; Mark & Sally Ann Blythe
Wholesale, retail. *Products*: Art, clothing, dolls, jewelry, kachinas, pottery, rugs, sand-paintings, sculpture, carvings. *Membership*: IACA. Catalog.

GUS'S TRADING COMPANY
2026 Central SW • Albuquerque, NM 87104
(505) 843-6381. Wholesale.

HILL'S INDIAN JEWELRY
3004 2nd St., NW • Albuquerque, NM 87107
(800) 545-6500; (505) 345-4110 Fax 345-5208
Martha & Hershel Hill. Wholesale. Navajo handmade sterling silver jewelry.

HOPI GALLERY OF SANTA FE
2902 Trellis N.W • Albuquerque, NM 87107
(505) 344-7689; Bennard & Frances Dallasvuyanoma (Hopi)
E-mail: BD87107@aol.com. *Products*: Jewelry, paintigngs, pottery,

HOUSE OF THE SHALAKO
First Plaza Galeria #65 • Albuquerque, NM 87102
(505) 242-4579; Gary & Sue Zens, Owners
Website: www.houseofshalako.com; E-mail: hshalako@aol.com
Retail. *Products*: Baskets, beadwork, books, clothing, dolls, jewelry, kachinas, pottery, rugs, sand-paintings, sculpture, carvings.
Membership: IACA.

INDIAN PUEBLO CULTURAL CENTER, INC.
2401 12th St., NW • Albuquerque, NM 87104
(800) 766-4405; (505) 843-7270; Website: www.indianpueblo.org
E-mail: info@indianpueblo.org; Keith Lucero (Pueblo), Manager
Retail, wholesale, mail order. Nonprofit organization of 19 New Mexican Pueblos. *Products*: Baskets, drums, pipes, jewelry, pottery, rugs, sculpture, carvings. Catalog.

INDIGENOUS ART
820 Madeira Dr. SE • Albuquerque, NM 87108
(505) 688-5965 Fax 265-5602; Website: www.indigenous-art.com
E-mail: iaweb@swcp.com; Rebecca England, Owner. *Membership*: IACA.

JAMES ROGERS SILVERSMITHS
3137 San Mateo Blvd., NE • Albuquerque, NM 87110
(505) 889-9327 Fax 889-9329; James Rogers
Wholesale. *Product*: Jewelry. Catalog available.

JUDY CROSBY'S AMERICANA ARTS
2119 San Mateo Blvd. NE • Albuquerque, NM 87110
(505) 266-2324; Judy Crosby, Owner
Wholesale. *Products*: Fetishes, heishi, jewelry, kachinas, knives, miniatures, pottery, sandpainitings, sculpture, carvings. *Membership*: IACA.

KENNEDY INDIAN ARTS
P.O. Box 6526, 602 Montano NW • Albuquerque, NM 87197
(505) 344-7538; John & Georgiana Kennedy, Owner
Wholesale. *Products*: All. *Membership*: IACA.

KHALSA TRADING COMPANY
1423 Carlisle NE • Albuquerque, NM 87110
(505) 255-8278 Fax 255-3877; S.S. Gurubachan Khalsa & Kulbir Puri
Wholesale. *Product*: Jewelry.

L.G. KINGS TRADING COMPANY
900 Coors SW • Albuquerque, NM 87105
(505) 836-2824; Leonard G. King. Wholesale. *Membership*: IACA.

MILAINES SANTA FE SILVER
2013 Ridgecrest Dr. SE • Albuquerque, NM 87108
(505) 268-8073 Fax 255-0659; Wayne Desantis
Wholesale. *Products*: Art, fetishes, dream-catchers, jewelry, pottery, sculpture, carvings. *Membership*: IACA. Catalog.

NARRANJO'S WORLD OF AMERICAN INDIAN ART
1911 Lomas Blvd. NW • Albuquerque, NM 87104-1207
Stella Naranjo Thompson, Manager
Wholesale/retail/mail order. *Products*: baskets, beadwork, dolls, jewelry, leatherwork, pottery, rugs. Price list available.

NAVAJO GALLERY
323 Romero NW, Suite #1 • Albuquerque, NM 87104
(505) 843-7666; Barbara Griffith, Manager
Wholesale/retail/and some mail order: paintings, sculpture, lithographs, and drawings by R.C. Gorman.

NIZHONI SPIRIT HORSE
1319 82nd St. SW • Albuquerque, NM 87121
(505) 830-1508; John I. King (Navajo), Owner
Website: www.nizhonispirithorse.com
E-mail: nizhonispirithorse@msn.com
Products: Native American tradition style watercolor prints & paintings.

OLD TOWN TRADING POST
Box 7036, 208 San Felipe NW • Albuquerque, NM 87194-7036
 (505) 243-0859; Bruce Mollenkopf
Wholesale, retail. *Products*: All. *Membership*: IACA.

PALMS TRADING COMPANY
1504 Lomas Blvd. NW • Albuquerque, NM 87104
 (800) 748-1656; (505) 247-8504 Fax 243-4011
Website: www.palmstrading.com; E-mail: info@palmstrading.com
Guy Berger, Owner. *Membership*: IACA.

PENFIELD GALLERY OF INDIAN ARTS
2043 S. Plaza NW • Albuquerque, NM 87104
 (877) 242-9696; (505) 242-9696; Julia & Ruth Reidy, Owners
Website: www.penfieldgallery.com;
E-mail: info@penfieldgallery.com. *Membership*: IACA.

PERFUMES OF THE DESERT & TRADING POST
208 San Felipe NW, P.O. Box 7036 • Albuquerque, NM 87194
 (505) 243-0859; Dian Kaehele & Elizabeth Torres, Owners
Website: www.desertperfumes.com. *Membership*: IACA.

PUEBLO DIRECT
7704 Brianne Ave. NW • Albuquerque, NM 87114
 (505) 922-8578 Fax 922-9508; Website: www.pueblodirect.com
E-mail: sales@pueblodirect.com; David & Karen Hooks, Owners
Membership: IACA.

SANTA FE SILVER FOX
7000 Louisiana NE #1005 • Albuquerque, NM 87109
 Joan & Robert Fox
Wholesale, retail. *Products*: Dolls, fetishes, heishi, jewelry,
kachinas, pottery. *Membership*: IACA.

SHAFFER'S INDIAN ART
P.O. Box 21700 • Albuquerque, NM 87154
 (505) 293-2217/264-0549; Richard L. Shaffer
Wholesale. Products: Baskets, boxes, fetishes, jewelry, kachinas,
miniatures, pottery. *Membership*: IACA.

SILVER HILLS
332 Los Ranchos Rd NW • Albuquerque, NM 87107
 (505) 898-6266 Fax 898-6650; Rita Lovato, Owner
E-mail: ryokoi@flash.net. *Membership*: IACA.

SILVER NUGGET
416 Juan Tabo NE • Albuquerque, NM 87123
 (505) 293-6861 Fax 292-0367; Gary DePriest, Owner
Wholesale/retail. *Products*: Dolls, fetishes, jewelry, kachinas;
repairs & restoration. *Membership*: IACA. Catalog.

SILVER SUN
2042 S. Plaza NW, Historic Old Town • Albuquerque, NM 87104
 (800) 662-3220; (505) 246-9692 Fax 246-9719
 Deanna Olson & Kathy Sanchez, Owners
Wholesale/retail. *Products*: Children's items, clothing, drums, pipes, fetishes,
heishi, jewelry, miniatures. Branch: 2011 Central NW, Albuquerque, NM; and
Santa Fe, NM. *Membership*: IACA. Catalog.

SOUND OF AMERICA RECORDS (SOAR CORP.)
5200 Constitution Ave. NE • Albuquerque, NM 87110
 (505) 268-6110 Fax 268-0237; Tom Bee, President
 E-mail: soar@rt66.com
Retail, wholesale, mail order. *Products*: Contemporary and traditional
Native American music…cassette, compact disc, & video. Brochure.

TECOLOTTE TILES & GALLERY
400 San Felipe, NW • Albuquerque, NM 87104-1462
 (505) 243-3403 Fax 296-6865; Richard & Priscilla Jupp
Retail. *Products*: Art, boxes, ornaments, dolls, jewelry, pottery.
Membership: IACA. Catalog.

TRACEY LTD.
2100 Aztec Rd. NE #A • Albuquerque, NM 87107-4204
 (800) 458-2500; (505) 883-8868 Fax 883-8806
 Ray Tracey & Kristen Middleton. Wholesale. *Products*: Jewelry.
Branch: 2407 E. Boyd #8A, Gallup, NM. *Membership*: IACA. Catalog.

THE TREASURE TRADERS
6000 Lomas NE • Albuquerque, NM 87110
 (505) 268-4343; Arnie & Norma Jean Sidman

Retail. *Products*: art, beadwork, cards, clothing, dolls, drums/pipes, heishi,
jewelry, kachinas, knives, miniatures, pottery, sculpture, carvings.

UTILITY SHACK, INC.
11035 Central NE • Albuquerque, NM 87123
 (505) 292-0174; Linda & David Stout
Wholesale/retail. *Products*: All. Appraisals: baskets, jewelry, pottery, rugs.

WADE'S AMERICAN INDIAN TRADERS
627 Fairway NW • Albuquerque, NM 87107
 (505) 343-9100 Fax 343-9101; Clare Wade
Wholesale, retail. *Products*: All. *Membership*: IACA.

WINDMILL TRADING COMPANY
P.O. Box 91656 • Albuquerque, NM 87199
 (505) 797-4869; Susan M. Rodin, Owner
Website: www.windmilltrading.com
E-mail: susan@windmilltrading.com. *Membership*: IACA.

WRIGHT'S INDIAN ART
1100 San Mateo Blvd. NE • Albuquerque, NM 87110
 (866) 372-1042; (505) 266-0120 Fax 266-0101
Website: www.wrightsgallery.com; E-Mail: info@wrightsgallery.com
 Sam Chernoff, Owner; Wayne Bobrick, Director
Retail. *Products*: Indian jewelry, pottery, art. *Membership*: IACA.

YELLOWHORSE
4314 Silver SE • Albuquerque, NM 87108
 (505) 266-0600; Artie Yellowhorse
Wholesale. *Product*: Pottery. *Membership*: IACA.

THE ED YOUNGS, INC.
2323 Krogh Ct. NW • Albuquerque, NM 87104
 (505) 864-1242; Ed Young, President
Wholesale. *Products*: Beadwork, clothing, dolls, jewelry, kachinas, pottery,
rugs, sandpaintings, sculpture, carvings. *Membership*: IACA. Catalog.

ZACH-LOW, INC.
7500 2nd St. NW • Albuquerque, NM 87184
 (800) 821-7443; (505) 848-1623; Joe & Katy Lowry
Wholesale. *Products*: Baskets, beadwork, dolls, fetishes, jewelry,
kachinas, miniatures, pottery, rugs, sand-paintings. Catalog.

GERTRUDE ZACHARY JEWLERY
1501 Lomas Blvd. NW • Albuquerque, NM 87104
 (800) 682-5768; (505) 247-4442 Fax 247-9253
Website: www.gertrudezachary.com
E-mail: showroom@gertrudezachary.com
Gertrude Zachary, Owner. *Membership*: IACA.

TA-MA-YA CO-OP ASSOCIATION
Santa Ana Pueblo, Star Route Box 37 • Bernalillo, NM 87004
 (505) 867-3301; Clara Paquin, President
Wholesale/retail. *Products*: Pueblo pottery, embroidery, weaving & clothing.

SOUTHWEST SUNSET INTERIORS
702 W. Broadway • Bloomfield, NM 87413
 (505) 632-3805; Brad & Marcia Magee. Wholesale/retail.

THE INDIAN PONY ART GALLERY
56 Comanche Dr. • Carlsbad, NM 88220-9474
 (505) 887-0065 Fax 887-0065; Wanda D. Spencer, Owner
 Website: www.cavemen.net/indianpony; E-mail: ndnpony@cavemen.net
Retail. *Products*: Indian artifacts, baskets, beadwork, jewelry, paintings, prints,
posters, pottery, sculpture, textiles & books. *Membership*: IACA.

THE PLAINS COMPANY
P.O. Box 186, 1014 E. Ave. • Carrizozo, NM 88301
 (505) 648-2472 Fax 648-2983; Woody Schlegel
Retail. *Products*: Art, jewelry, pottery, rugs, sculpture, carvings.
Membership: IACA.

UNICORN GALLERY
P.O. Box 917 • Chama, NM 87520
 (505) 756-1036; Chuck Sanders, Owner. *Membership*: IACA.

CLINES CORNERS OPERATING COMPANY
1 Yacht Club Dr. • Clines Corners, NM 87070
 (505) 472-5488 Fax 472-5487; Doug Murphy
Retail. *Products*: Art, baskets, beadwork, clothing, dolls, jewelry, kachinas,
pottery, rugs, sand-paintings, sculpture, carvings. *Membership*: IACA.

THE BEAR TRACK
P.O. Box 15, 502 Burro Ave. • Cloudcraft, NM 88317
 (505) 682-3046; Nita & Donald Lane
Retail. *Products*: All. *Membership*: IACA.

BIG SKY TRADERS
P.O. Box 461 • Corrales, NM 87048
 (800) 827-1992; (505) 899-1990; Phil & Margene Gibbs
Wholesale. *Products*: Baskets, drums, pipes, dye charts, fetishes,
jewelry, sand-paintings, sculpture. *Membership*: IACA.

CONTEMPORARY NAVAJO/DINE JEWELER
P.O. Box 657 • Crownpoint, NM 87313
 (505) 786-5678 or 879-3030; E-mail: henry.ronnie@gmail.com
 Ronnie Henry (Navajo), Artisan/Owner
Products: Sterling silver & turquoise jewelry.

CROWNPOINT RUG WEAVERS' ASSOCIATION
P.O. Box 1630 • Crownpoint, NM 87313
 (505) 786-5302 or 786-7386
 Website: www.crownpointrugauction.com
 Ena B. Chavez (Navajo), Manager; Christina Ellsworth (Navajo), Co-Manager
Navajo rugs sold at auction held monthly.

THE SILVER EAGLE
P.O. Box 158 • Crownpoint, NM 87313
 (505) 786-5591 Fax 786-5593; Jim Clinton, Owner
Wholesale/retail. *Products*: Baskets, beadwork, dye charts, jewelry,
kachinas, pottery, rugs, sandpaintings. *Membership*: IACA.

APACHE MESA GALLERY & GIFTS
Box 233, Jicarilla Inn, Hwy. 64 • Dulce, NM 87528
 (505) 759-3663; Eileen Vigil, Manager
Retail, wholesale. *Products*: art, Jicarilla baskets, beadwork,
jewelry, pottery, rugs. Special orders accepted.

JICARILLA ARTS & CRAFTS & MUSEUM
P.O. Box 507 • Dulce, NM 87528
 (505) 759-3242 ext. 274; Brenda Julian (Jicarilla Apache), Director
Retail, mail order. Jicarilla Apache tribal enterprise. *Products*: Art,
baskets, beadwork. Send S.A.S.E. for price list and brochure.

EAGLE NEST TRADING COMPANY
P.O. Box 7 • Eagle Nest, NM
 (505) 377-3619; JoLetha Nall & Tom Hogan, Owners
E-mail: joletha@kitcrason.net. *Membership*: IACA.

APPLE BLOSSOM ACCENTS
P.O. Box 850 • Espanola, NM 87532
 (505) 927-1827 or 753-6446
 Rosemary "Apple Blossom" Lonewolf (Santa Clara Pueblo), Owner
Website: www.abaccents.nativeart.net; E-mail: abaccents@aol.com
Retail, wholesale, mail order. *Products*: Incised native clay fine art pottery;
Southwestern design tiles, murals, benches, fountains.

PASSAGES EXPRESST
P.O. Box 1184 • Espanola, NM 87532
 Char Pully, Owner. Retail, wholesale, mail order.
Products: dolls, porcupine quill and leatherwork.

SANTA CLARA PUEBLO POTTERY
18 S. Santa Clara • Espanola, NM 87532
 (505) 753-1809; E-mail: judytafoya@hotmail.com
 Judy & Lincoln Tafoya (Santa Clara Pueblo-Tewa), Artisans/Owner
Products: Santa Clara Pueblo Pottery.

SINGING WATER GALLERY
Rt. 1, Box 472-C • Espanola, NM 87532
 (505) 753-9663; Joe Baca, Owner
Retail, wholesale. *Products*: Art, clothing, pottery. *Appraisals*: Pottery.

TERESITA NARANJO
Santa Clara Pueblo, Rt. 1, Box 455 • Espanola, NM 87532
 (505) 753-9655. Retail, wholesale. *Product*: Santa Clara pottery.
Special orders accepted.

TONI ROLLER INDIAN POTTERY STUDIO & GALLERY
Santa Clara Pueblo, Box 171 • Espanola, NM 87532
 (505) 753-3003; Toni Roller (Santa Clara Pueblo), Artisan/Owner
Website: www.toniroller.com
Products: Traditional Santa Clara pottery.

ROBERT NARANJO GALLERY
P.O. Box 4599 • Fairview, NM 87532
 (505) 753-9239
 Robert G. Naranjo (Santa Clara Pueblo), Owner/Craftsman
Products: Traditional Santa Clara pottery.

ROXANNE SWENTZELL (Santa Clara Pueblo)
P.O. Box 4154 • Fairview, NM 87533
 Website: www.swentzell.com. *Products*: Ceramic & bronze sculpture.

ARROYO TRADING CO., INC.
42 W. Main St. • Farmington, NM 87401
 (505) 326-7427 Fax 327-3711; Vince & Helen Ferrari, Owners
 Website: www.arroyotrading.com; E-mail: laf@cyberport.com
Retail, wholesale. *Products*: Art, clothing, jewelry, pottery.
Author brochure, "Introduction to Sand Painting." Catalog.
Membership: IACA.

THE FIFTH GENERATION TRADING COMPANY
232 W. Broadway • Farmington, NM 87401
 (505) 326-3211 Fax 326-0097; Joe Tanner, Jr.
Wholesale. *Products*: Baskets, clothing, dolls, jewelry, kachinas, ornaments,
pottery, rugs, sand paintings, sculpture, carvings. *Membership*: IACA.

NAVAJO BEADWORKS
2111 W. Apache • Farmington, NM 87401
 (505) 326-7427; Loree Ferari, Owner
Retail, wholesale. *Product*: Navajo beadwork.

RUSSELL FOUTZ INDIAN ROOM
301 W. Main St. • Farmington, NM 87401
 (505) 325-9413; Russell Foutz, Owner
Wholesale. *Products*: Baskets, ornaments, dye charts, jewelry,
kachinas, rugs, sandpaintings, sculpture. Membership: IACA.

SHIPROCK TRADING POST
301 W. Main St. • Farmington, NM 87401
 (505) 324-0881 Fax 324-0882; Kent & Hillary Morrow
 Website: www.shiprocktradingpost.com
 E-mail: info@shiprocktradingpost.com
Wholesale & retail. *Products*: Navajo rugs, jewelry, pottery,
sandpainting, sculpture, fine art.

ARVISO'S ORIGINALS
P.O. Box 737 • Fort Wingate, NM 87316
 Dennis Arviso (Navajo), Artist/Owner
Product: Original paintings depicting the traditional Navajo way of life.

ASHCROFT TRADERS
695 County Rd. 6100 • Fruitland, NM 87416
 (505) 598-9159; W.L. & Lori Ashcroft, Owners
 E-mail: stevelori@outerbounds.net
Retail, wholesale. *Products*: Baskets, dye charts, jewelry, rugs,
sandpaintings. *Membership*: IACA. *Appraisals*: Rugs. Catalog.

AMERICAN INDIAN FASHIONS
NAVAJO SPIRIT SOUTHWESTERN WEAR
815 E. Coal Ave. • Gallup, NM 87301
 (800) 377-6837; (505) 722-6837; Website: www.navajospirit.com
 Website: www.navajoaccents.com; E-mail: fashions@navajospirit.com
 Virginia Yazzie Ballenger (Navajo), Owner; Carl H. Ballenger, Manager
Retail, wholesale. Navajo designer. *Products*: Contemporary western wear
& traditional Navajo clothing; masks.

ANASAZI TRADERS OF GALLUP
400 E. Hwy. 66 • Gallup, NM 87301
 (800) 777-6952; (505) 863-9294 Fax 863-2088; Tom Mortensen
Wholesale. *Products*: Art, clothing, dolls, jewelry, kachinas, pottery, rugs,
sandpaintings, sculpture, carvings. *Membership*: IACA. Catalog available.

ANDY'S TRADING COMPANY
612 W. Wilson • Gallup, NM 87301
 (505) 863-3762; Greg & Cambria Masci, Owners
Retail, wholesale. *Products*: Baskets, beadwork, jewelry, kachinas, rugs.

ATKINSON TRADING COMPANY
P.O. Box 566, 1300 S. 2nd • Gallup, NM 87305
 (800) 338-7380; (505) 722-4435 Fax 863-5624
 Joe Atkinson, Owner; Roger Morris, Manager
Retail, wholesale. *Products*: Drums, pipes, flutes, dye charts, fetishes,
jewelry, kachinas, knives, pottery, rugs. *Membership*: IACA.

CAROLYN BOBELU
731 Kevin Court • Gallup, NM 87301
 (505) 722-4939 Carolyn Bobelu, Owner
Retail, wholesale. Zuni-Navajo craftsperson. *Products*: Pottery. Special orders.

CHEROKEE SILVER
419 Julie Dr. • Gallup, NM 87301
(505) 863-4989; Jim Harlin (Cherokee), Artisan/Owner
Website: www.cherokeesilver.com
Products: Works with silver, gold & colored stone.

EAGLEWINGS
922 Ute Cr. • Gallup, NM 87301
(505) 726-8300 Fax 722-2379; E-mail: mataya@cnetco.com
Patrick & Patricia Mataya, Owners. *Membership*: IACA.

FELIX INDIAN JEWELRY
P.O. Box 195 • Gallup, NM 87301
(505) 722-5369; Felix Gomez, Owner
Wholesale. *Product*: Pottery. *Membership*: IACA.

FIRST AMERICAN TRADERS
198 Historic Rte. 66 • Gallup, NM 87301
(505) 722-6601 Fax 722-6300; Dominic Biava, Owner
Wholesale, retail. *Products*: Art, dolls, drums, pipes, dye charts, fetishes, heishi, jewelry, kachinas, pottery, rugs, sandpaintings, sculpture.
Membership: IACA. Catalog available.

GALANIS TRADING COMPANY
101 W. Hwy. 66 • Gallup, NM 87301
(505) 722-5464 Fax 863-4717; George Galanis, Owner
E-mail: galanist@cia-g.com. *Membership*: IACA.

GALLUP GALLERY
108 W. Coal Ave. • Gallup, NM 87301
Retail. *Products*: Native American art.

THE INDIAN DEN TRADING COMPANY
1111 Caesar Dr. • Gallup, NM 87301
(505) 722-4141 Edward Gomez, Owner
Retail, wholesale. *Membership*: IACA.

INDIAN HANDICRAFTS
Southwest Indian Foundation, P.O. Box 86 • Gallup, NM 87305
(505) 863-9568 Fax 863-2760; William McCarthy, Manager
Retail, wholesale, mail order. *Products*: Indian jewelry, clothing, mugs, books and toys. Catalog

INDIAN JEWELERS SUPPLY COMPANY
601 E. Coal Ave. • Gallup, NM 87305
(505) 722-4451 Fax 722-4172
E-Mail: orders@ijsinc.com; Website: www.ijsinc.com
Retail, wholesale, mail order. *Products*: Precious base metals, jewelry parts, semi-precious stones, tools. Catalog.

INDIAN VILLAGE, INC.
2209 W. Hwy. 66 • Gallup, NM 87301
(505) 722-5524 Fax 863-9093
Nathan Ramadoss, Owner; E-mail: nathan@cia-g.com
Retail, wholesale, mail order. *Products*: Dolls, fetishes, jewelry, kachinas, pottery, sand paintings, sculpture. *Membership*: IACA. Catalog.

KIVA GALLERY
200-202 W. Hwy. 66 • Gallup, NM 87301
Retail. *Products*: Native American art.

STEVE LUCAS (KOYEMSI)
301 Calle Pinon • Gallup, NM 87301
Retail, wholesale. *Products*: Traditional & contemporary Hopi pottery.

M&M TRADINGO CO.
1218 E. 66 Ave. • Gallup, NM 87301
(877) 862-1480; (505) 863-4995; Website: www.newmexicocarvings.com
E-mail: mm@newmexicocarvings.com
Eurell T. Malone, Owner. *Membership*: IACA.

JOHNNY MURPHY'S TRADING COMPANY
1206 E. 66th Ave. • Gallup, NM 87301
(505) 722-5088; John E. Murphy, Owner
Retail, wholesale. *Products*: Baskets, beadwork, fetishes, jewelry.
Membership: IACA.

NAVAJO ARTS & CRAFTS ENTERPRISE
1512 E. Hwy. 66 • Gallup, NM 87301
(800) 790-6223. Wholesale Division. Tribal Enterprise. *Products*: Art, baskets, beadwork, clothing, dolls, jewelry, kachinas, pottery, rugs, sandpaintings, sculpture, carvings. Branch shop.

THE NUGGET GALLERY
1302 S. 2nd St. • Gallup, NM 87301-5813
(505) 863-3615; Chet Jones, Owner
Retail, wholesale. Products: Baskets, books, dye charts, fetishes, jewelry, kachinas, miniatures, rugs, sculpture.

O.B.'s INDIAN AMERICA
3330 E. Hwy. 66 • Gallup, NM 87301
(505) 722-4431 Fax 722-6394; Bill & Harlene O'Neil, Owners
Wholesale. *Products*: All. *Membership*: IACA.

OUTLAW TRADERS
600 Belle Dr. • Gallup, NM 87301
(505) 722-670; Diane & Larry Jinks, Owners
Retail, wholesale. *Products*: Art, baskets, beadwork, clothing, dolls, jewelry, kachinas, knives, rugs, sculpture, carvings.

RAINBIRD PAWN & TRADING CO.
1724 S. Second St. • Gallup, NM 87301
(505) 722-3292; Website: www.rainbirdtrading.com
E-Mail: info@rainbirdtrading.com
Retail, wholesale. Products: Jewelry, pottery.

RED SHELL JEWELRY
P.O. Box 764 • Gallup, NM 87305
(505) 722-6963; John Hornbek, Owner
Retail, wholesale. *Products*: Baskets, jewelry, pottery, sculpture.
Appraisals. *Membership*: IACA.

SHAFFER'S INDIAN ART
P.O. Box 5300 • Gallup, NM 87301
(505) 722-2526; Richard L. Shaffer, Owner
Wholesale. *Products*: Art, baskets, boxes, children's items, dolls, fetishes, jewelry, kachinas, miniatures, pottery.

SHUSH YAZ TRADING CO.
1304 S. Lincoln • Gallup, NM 87301
(505) 722-0130 Fax 722-7646; Website: www.shushyaz.com
E-mail: sales@sushyaz.com; Don Tanner & Allen Born, Owners
Retail, wholesale. *Products*: Kachina dolls, pottery & baskets, genuine Indian antique & contemporary silver & gold jewelry, Navajo rugs. Old pawn Indian jewelry. *Membership*: IACA.

SUNBURST HANDCRAFTS, INC.
306 County Rd. #1 • Gallup, NM 87301
(505) 863-454; Lionel McKinney
Wholesale. *Products*: Jewelry.

TOBE TURPEN'S INDIAN TRADING CO.
1710 S. 2nd St. • Gallup, NM 87301-5895
(505) 722-3806; Tobe J. Turpen & Art Quintana
Retail, wholesale. *Products*: Art, baskets, beadwork, clothing, dolls, jewelry, kachinas, pottery, rugs, sand paintings, sculpture, carvings. *Membership*: IACA.

TRACEY-KNIFEWING, INC.
P.O. Box 443 • Gallup, NM 87305
(505) 863-3635 Fax 722-4218; Ray Tracey & Warren Lyons
Wholesale. *Product*: Jewelry. *Membership*: IACA. Catalog.

ANCIENT MESAS GIFTS SOUTHWESTERN
P.O. Box 220 • Grants, NM 87020
(505) 285-4335; Patricia McClure & Kraig Williams, Owners
Retail. *Products*: Art, baskets, beadwork, clothing, dolls, jewelry, kachinas, pottery, rugs. *Membership*: IACA.

LEGACY GALLERY & STUDIO
P.O. Box 418 • Isleta, NM 87022
(505) 869-3317; Spencer Moss & Michael Kirk, Owners
Wholesale. *Product*: Jewelry.

TELLER POTTERY
P.O. Box 135 • Isleta, NM 87022
(505) 869-3118; Stella Teller, Owner
Wholesale. *Product*: Pottery. *Membership*: IACA.

CAJERO SCULPTURES LTD.
P.O. Box 377 • Jemez Pueblo, NM 87024
 (505) 867-3773; Joe Cajero, Jr. (Jemez Pueblo) Artist/Owner
 Website: www.cajerosculpture.com
Products: Limited editions bronze sculptures and one-of-a-kind clay
sculptures that reflect Native American Pueblo culture & spirituality.

CAROL G. LUCERO-GACHUPIN
P.O. Box 210 • Jemez Pueblo, NM 87024
 (505) 834-7757; Carol Lucero-Gachupin (Jemez Pueblo), Owner
Retail, wholesale. *Products*: Art, Christmas ornaments, clothing, pottery,
sculpture.

CAROL VIGIL
P.O. Box 443 • Jemez Pueblo, NM 87024
 Retail, mail order. *Product*: Jemez pottery.

ASHCROFT TRADERS
P.O. Box 1005 • Kirtland, NM 87417
 (505) 598-9159; W.L. & Lori Ashcroft, Owners
Wholesale, retail. Products: Baskets, dye charts, jewelry, rugs,
sandpaintings. *Membership*: IACA. *Appraisals*: Rugs. Catalog.

MONSTERSLAYER, INC.
P.O. Box 550 • Kirtland, NM 87417
 (505) 598-5322 Fax 598-0974; Website: www.monsterslayer.com
 E-mail: sales@monsterslayer.com; John & Jacqueline Foutx, Owners
Membership: IACA.

55 SILVER & SUPPLY
P.O. Box 688 • Kirtland, NM 87417
 (505) 598-5322; John & Jacqueline Foutz, Owners
Wholesale, retail. *Products*: Baskets, jewelry, rugs. *Membership*: IACA.

LAGUNA PUEBLO MART, INC.
P.O. Box 63 • Laguna, NM 87026
 (505) 552-9585 Fax 552-7446; Arne & Ron Fernandez, Owners
Retail, wholesale. *Products*: Baskets, beadwork, kachinas, miniatures, pottery.

MARIE S. TEASYATWHO
P.O. Box 311 • LaPlata, NM 87418
 (505) 326-3769. Retail. *Products*: Traditional and contemporary Navajo
weaving and beadwork. Special commissions accepted.

NAVAJO ARTS & CRAFTS ENTERPRISE
Alamo Trading Post, P.O. Box 1505 • Magdalena, NM 87825
 (505) 854-2987. Retail, wholesale. Tribal Enterprise. *Products*: Art, baskets,
beadwork, clothing, dolls, jewelry, kachinas, pottery, rugs, sandpaintings,
sculpture, carvings. Branch shop.

THE SILVERSMITH, INC.
2350 Calle Principal, P.O. Box 531 • Mesilla, NM 88046
 (505) 523-5561 Fax 523-5561; Charles & Diane Rogers, Owners
 Website: www.mesilla.com; E-mail: billythekid@mesilla.com
Retail. *Products*: Art, clothing, fetishes, jewelry, kachinas,
miniatures, pottery, sand-paintings. *Membership*: IACA.

THE WILLIAM BONNEY GALLERY
P.O. Box 27, 3 Calle de Parian • Mesilla, NM 88046
 (505) 526-8275; Dan & Della McKinney, Owners
Retail. *Products*: Art, baskets, clothing, dolls, jewelry, kachinas, pottery,
rugs, sand paintings, sculpture, carvings. *Membership*: IACA

KACHINA COUNTRY USA
P.O. Box 2836 • Milan, NM 87021
 (505) 285-4473 Fax 285-6376; E-mail: kachina@7cities.net
 Roy & Shawnee Yates, Owners. *Membership*: IACA.

LA ZIA
P.O. Box 1098 • Mesilla, NM 88046
 (505) 523-2213; Steven Rose & Robert Southard, Owners
 E-mail: lazianm@aol.com. *Membership*: IACA.

NATIVE AMERICAN HEIRLOOMS BY PEARL TALACHY
318 County Rd. 119 So. • Nambe Pueblo, NM 87506
 (505) 455-3429; Pearl Talachy (Nambe Tewa), Artisan/Owner
Products: Pottery from native clay stone-polished & traditionally fired.

SKY HUNTER ARTS
P.O. Box 1068 • Paguate, NM 87040
 (505) 552-9655

Website: www.skyhunterarts.com; E-mail: skyhunterarts@yahoo.com
De Haven Solimon Chaffins (Laguna & Zuni Pueblo), Artisan/Owner
Products: Acrylic on canvas.

WINDMILL TRADING COMPANY
Box 1297, 788 Hwy. 22 • Pena Blanca, NM 87041-1297
 (505) 465-2416; Susan M. Rodin, Owner
Retail, wholesale. *Products*: Heishi, jewelry, rugs. *Membership*: IACA.

CHUCK LEWIS EDITIONS
P.O. Box 917 • Questa, NM 87556
 (505) 751-2158; Churck Lewis (Blackfeet), Owner
Wholesale. Blackfeet craftsperson. *Products*: Art.

SANDS TURQUOIS
P.O. Box 37 • Raton, NM 87740
 (505) 445-2737; Worth Wilkins, OwnerRetail.
Products: Clothing, drums, pipes, flutes, jewelry, pottery, sand paintings.

C&D GIFTS
P.O. Box 44743 • Rio Rancho, NM 87124
 (505) 994-2412; Douglas & Celia Thresher, Owners
 Website: www.southwestindianpottery.com
 E-mail: canddgifts@msn.com. *Products*: Pottery. *Membership*: IACA.

NATIVE VISIONS
4110 La Merced • Rio Rancho, NM 87124
 (505) 891-0624; Soia Burdette & Doug Gomez, Owners
Retail, wholesale. *Products*: Pottery, rugs.

TWO SQUAWS
1109 W. Second • Roswell, NM 88201
 (505) 623-1921; Pat Mitchell & Garry Zens, Owners
Retail. *Products*: Baskets, beadwork, clothing, dolls, jewelry, kachinas,
pottery, rugs, sand-paintings, sculpture, carvings. *Membership*: IACA.

JERRY INGRAM (Choctaw/Cherokee)
P.O. Box 328 • Rowe, NM 87562
 (505) 421-2611; E-mail: ingrambead@plateautel.net
Products: Beadwork, porcupine quillwork, headdresses, clothing, bags,
moccasins, accessories; original watercolor & acrylic paintings.

CARMEL LEWIS HASKAYA (Acoma Pueblo)
P.O. Box 35, San Fidel, NM 87049
Products: Traditional Acoma pottery made of native clays,
painted with mineral paints in original Acoma and Anasazi designs.

PUEBLO POTTERY
P.O. Box 366 • San Fidel, NM 87049
 (800) 933-5771; (505) 552-6748 (phone & fax)
 Arthur & Carol Cruz (Acoma Pueblo), Artisan/Owners
Wholesale, retail. *Products*: Art, baskets, beadwork, clothing, dolls, jewelry,
kachinas, pottery, rugs, sand paintings, sculpture, carvings. *Appraisals*:
Pottery. Shop located in Acomita, NM. Catalog.

BEGAY-FOSS DESIGNS
P.O. Box 1322 • San Juan Pueblo, NM 87566
 (505) 852-4882; Joyce Begay-Foss (Navajo), Artisan/Owner
 Website: www.begayfossdesigns.com
Products: Navajo custom order saddle blankets and textiles.

OKE OWEENGE ART & CRAFTS
P.O. Box 1095 • San Juan Pueblo, NM 87566
 (505) 852-2372; April Crane Star, Manager
Retail, mail order. San Juan Pueblo craftspersons cooperative. *Products*: Art,
baskets, beadwork, clothing, dolls, jewelry, kachinas, pottery, rugs, sandpaintings, sculpture, carvings. Special orders accepted. Brochure and price list.

SHADES OF THE SOUTHWEST
28 Derek Rd. • Sandia Park, NM87047
 (505) 281-8876 Fax 281-0213; George Toya, Owner
 E-mail: soswtoya@nmmia.com. *Membership*: IACA.

ANASAZI INDIAN ARTS
P.O. Box 319, 1347 Hwy. 76 • Santa Cruz, NM 87567-0319
 (505) 753-4730; Joe & Belle Becker, Owners
Wholesale. *Products*: Art, pottery, rugs. *Membership*: IACA.

ADOBE GALLERY
221 Canyon Rd. • Santa Fe, NM 87501
 (505) 955-0550 Fax 955-1580; Website: www.adobegallery.com

E-mail: info@adobegallery.com; Alexander E. Anthony, Jr., Contact
Retail, wholesale, mail order. *Products*: Specialists in contemporary & antique Southwest Indian pottery & fine art; books on SW Indian Pueblo arts & crafts.

AGUILAR INDIAN ARTS
Rt. 5, Box 318C • Santa Fe, NM 87501
  Alfred Aguilar, Owner. Retail, some wholesale. San Ildefonso Pueblo Tewa artist-craftsperson. *Products*: Art, pottery.

KERI ATAUMBI (Kiowa)
76 Camino Tocido, Santa Fe, NM 87507
  (505) 424-3207; E-mail: ataumbi@msn.com.
Products: Jewelry, paintings, and sculpture.

BOYD INDIAN JEWELRY
521 Airport Rd. #31 • Santa Fe, NM 87507
  Allen & Paula Boyd (Navajo), Artisans/Owners
Products: Custom sterling silver & turquoise jewelry, coral, mother of pearl, various shells.

BLUE RAIN GALLERY
130 Lincoln Ave. • Santa Fe, NM 87501
  (505) 954-9902; Website: www.blueraingallery.com
  E-mail: info@blueraingallery.com. Retail. *Products*: Native American art, kachinas & crafts, representing Pueblo artists.

CHARLES AZBELL GALLERY
66-70 E. San Francisco St. • Santa Fe, NM 87501
  (505) 988-1875. Retail. *Products*: Native American art and sculpture.

CASE TRADING POST - THE WHEELWRIGHT MUSEUM
704 Camino Lejo, P.O. Box 5153 • Santa Fe, NM 87502
  (505) 982-4636 Fax 989-7386; Robb, Lucas, Manager
  Website: www.casetradingpost; E-mail: casetradingpost@cs.com
Retail. A museum store that is a replica of a turn-of-the-century trading post. *Products*: Native American pottery, textiles, jewelry, kachinas, baskets, and folk art. Also prints, cards, posters, and educational items for children. Over 2,000 book titles on Native American subject matter. *Membership*: IACA.

JOAN CAWLEY GALLERY
133 W. San Francisco St. • Santa Fe, NM 87501
Retail. *Products*: Native American art.

CONTEMPORARY SOUTHWEST GALLERY
123 W. Palace Pl. • Santa Fe, NM 87501
Products: Native American art.

CRISTOF'S
420 Old Santa Fe Trail • Santa Fe, NM 87501
  (505) 988-9881 Fax 986-8652; Louis Trevathan, Jr. & Pam Nicosin, Owners
  Website: www.cristofs.com; E-mail: buzzart@cristofs.com
Retail. *Products*: Jewelry, rugs, sandpaintings, sculpture. Navajo weavings, and other Southwest art; Hopi kachinas; Navajo & Acoma pottery. Brochure; catalog on website. *Membership*: IACA.

DEWEY GALLERIES, LTD.
76 E. San Francisco St. • Santa Fe, NM 87501
Retail. *Products*: Native American art.

DISCOVER SANTA FE INDIAN ARTS & CRAFTS
P.O. Box 2847 • Santa Fe, NM 87504
Retail. *Products*: Native American art.

DENNIS ESQUIVEL (Ottawa-Ojibwe)
P.O. Box 28804 • Santa Fe, NM 87592
  (505) 438-2062; E-mail: myingan@yahoo.com
Products: Fine furniture and woodworking using hardwoods

FREE AIR FINE ART
P.O. Box 23285 • Santa Fe, NM 87502
  (505) 474-4480. Retail. *Products*: Native American art

EVELYN FREDERICKS SCULPTURE
41 Canada Village • Santa Fe, NM 87505
  (505) 982-9440; Evelyn Fredericks (Hopi), Artist/Owner
  E-mail: mail@evelynfredericks.com; Website: www.evelynfredericks.com
Retail: *Products*: Native American images in sculpture. By appointment.

HAND GRAPHICS GALLERY
418 Montezuma Ave. • Santa Fe, NM 87501
Retail. *Products*: Indian handcrafts.

HOGAN IN THE HILTON
100 Sandoval St. • Santa Fe, NM 87504-2131
  (505) 984-0932; Paula Hausvick, Owner
Retail. *Products*: Baskets, beadwork, clothing, dolls, jewelry, kachinas, pottery, rugs, sand-paintings, sculpture, carvings. *Membership*: IACA.

ALLAN HOUSER, INC.
P.O. Box 5217 • Santa Fe, NM 87502
  (505) 471-9667. Retail: *Products*: Sculpture garden, gallery, appraisals, resales. Representing the estate of Allan Houser.

INSTITUTE OF AMERICAN INDIAN ARTS MUSEUM SHOP
108 Cathedral Place, P.O. Box 20007 • Santa Fe, NM 87504
  (888) 922-4242; Fax (505) 988-6281
  Marguerite L. Hill, Manager; Website: www.iaiancad.org/store/
  E-mail: shop@iaia.edu. Retail. *Products*: Art, pottery, sculpture.

KESHI: THE ZUNI COLLECTION
227 Don Gaspar • Santa Fe, NM 87501
  (505) 989-8728; Website: www.keshi.com
Retail. *Products*: Fetishes, jewelry, pottery.

KIVA FINE ARTS
102 E. Water St. • Santa Fe, NM 87501
  (505) 820-7413 Fax 820-7414; Website: www.kivaindianart.com
  E-Mail: info@kivaindianart.com; Paula Rhae McDonald, Owner
Retail. *Products*: Native American art, sculpture, pottery, weaving & fine art glass.

BRUCE LAFOUNTAIN
Rt. 19 Box 111V • Santa Fe, NM 87501
  (505) 988-3703. Retail. Native American sculptor

EDITH LAMBERT GALLERY
707 Canyon Dr. • Santa Fe, NM 87501
Retail. *Products*: Native American art

LIGHTS THE PIPE, INC.
P.O. Box 31550 • Santa Fe, NM 87594
  (505) 474-4521; Victoria Adams (Cheyenne/Arapaho), Owner
Products: Jeweler working with precious metals and gemstones

JOEL C. McHORSE
P.O. Box 1711 • Santa Fe, NM 87504
  (505) 989-7716; Joel C. McHorse, Owner
  E-mail: McHorse@ix.netcom.com
Retail, wholesale. *Products*: Micaceous pottery, traditional or contemporary. Silver jewelry & silverwork, such as miniature picture frames with hand-stamped designs; various stone sculpture. Special commissions accepted.

TED MILLER CUSTOM KNIVES
P.O. Box 6328 • Santa Fe, NM 87502
  (505) 984-0338; Ted Miller, Owner
Retail, wholesale, some mail order. Price list available.

MORNING STAR GALLERY
513 Canyon Rd. • Santa Fe, NM 87501
  (505) 982-8187 Fax 984-2368; Joe Rivera, President
  E-Mail: indian@morningstargallery.com
  Website: www.morningstargallery.com
Retail, wholesale, mail order. *Products*: Antique American Indian art. Catalog.

NEW TRENDS GALLERY
225 Canyon Rd. • Santa Fe, NM 87501
  (505) 988-1199
Retail. *Products*: Native American art, sculpture, and crafts.

NOFCHISSEY-McHORSE
P.O. Box 8638 • Santa Fe, NM 87504
  (505) 989-7716; Website: www.artnewmexico.com/artist/cmchorse
  Christine C. McHorse (Navajo), Owner; E-mail: McHorse@ix.netcom.com
Retail, wholesale. *Products*: Taos style, Navajo handbuilt micaceous pottery, traditional or contemporary. Silverwork of sandcast animal pins, jewelry, miniature picture frames with hand-stamped designs.

OTTOWI TRADING CO., INC.
P.O. Box 9152 • Santa Fe, NM 87504
  (505) 982-6881; Anthony Whitman, Owner
Retail, wholesale. *Products*: Fetishes, heishi, jewelry, miniatures, pottery, rugs. *Appraisals*. *Membership*: IACA. Catalog.

PACKARDS
61 Old Santa Fe Trail/On the Plaza • Santa Fe, NM 87501
 (800) 648-7358; (505) 983-9241 Fax 984-8174
 Website: www.collectorsquide.com/packards
 Richard & Carolyn Canon, Owners
Retail, mail order. *Products*: Native American jewelry, pottery, weavings,
kachinas & giftware. *Membership*: IACA, SWAIA. Brochure.

PENA STUDIO GALLERY
235 Don Gaspar • Santa Fe, NM 87505
 (505) 820-1400
Retail. *Products*: Native American posters, T-shirts, and art.

PEYOTE BIRD TRADING
P.O. Box 99 • Santa Fe, NM 87504-0099
 (505) 983-2480 Fax 982-8094; Mark Alexander, Owner
Wholesale. *Products*: Fetishes, heishi, jewelry, pottery. Catalog.

POPOVI DA STUDIO OF INDIAN ART
San Ildefonso Pueblo • Santa Fe, NM 87501
 (505) 455-2456; Anita M. Da, Owner
Wholesale, retail. *Products*: Art, baskets, jewelry, Navajo rugs,
Pueblo pottery.

PORTAL PROGRAM OF THE PALACE OF THE GOVERNORS
P.O. Box 2087 • Santa Fe, NM 87504-2087
 (505) 827-6474 Fax 827-6521; Carlotta Boettcher, Coordinator
 E-mail: cboettcher@mnm.statenm.us
Retail. *Description*: Traditional crafts of 22 recognized NM tribes & pueblos.
Products: Beadwork, jewelry, stonework, carving, pottery, sand painting.

JOEL McHORSE (Navajo-Taos Pueblo)
P.O. Box 1711 • Santa Fe, NM 87504
 (505) 989-7716; E-mail: McHorse@ix.netcom.com
Retail, wholesale. Products: Pottery, silver jewelry & silverwork.

MEDICINE MAN GALLERY, INC.
200 Canyon Rd. • Santa Fe, NM 87501
 (866) 894-7451; (505) 820-7451; Mark Sublette, Owner
 E-mail: art@medicinemangallery.com
 Website: www.medicinemangallery.com
Retail, wholesale. *Products*: Maria Martinez pottery.

MORNING MOON STUDIO
15 Wilowa Lane • Santa Fe, NM 87505
 (505) 466-3968; E-mail: misacoman@msn.com
 Website: www.morningmoonstudio.com
 Beverly Jose Sacoman (Mescalero Apache), Artist/Owner
Products: Hand-cut, hand-pulled serigraphs; oil paintings, watercolor,
pastel; dolls, bags, clothing, quilts.

RIVER TRADING POST
610 B. Canyon Rd. • Santa Fe, NM 87501
 (866) 426-6901; (505) 982-2805; Website: www.rivertradingpost.com
Retail, wholesale. *Products*: Navajo weavings, Pueblo pottery, Hopi kachina
dolls, Zuni fetishes, sculpture, baskets, jewelry, Plains Indian art, Six Nations
art.

RODICH, INC.
903 W. Alameda #114 • Santa Fe, NM 87501
 (505) 984-1801; Bob & Jane Matthews
Retail. *Products*: Art, fetishes, jewelry, pottery, rugs,
Sand paintings, sculpture. *Membership*: IACA.

SCRIPSIT
3089 Plaza Blanca • Santa Fe, NM 87505
 (505) 471-1516 Glen Billy, Owner
Retail, wholesale, mail order. *Product*: Calligraphy on paper
and leather. Special orders accepted.

SHIPROCK SANTA FE
53 Old Santa Fe Trail, 2nd Fl. • Santa Fe, NM 87501
 (505) 982-8478 Fax 989-1795
 Website: www.shiprocksantafe.com
Wholesale, retail. *Products*: Navajo artifacts, baskets, fetishes, fine art, jewelry,
katsina carvings, pottery, sculptures, textiles; books, folk art, furniture.

SHUSH YAZ TRADING CO.
1048 Paseo de Peralta • Santa Fe, NM 87501
 (505) 438-9150; Don Tanner, Owner
Retail. *Products*: All. Branch shop: Gallup, NM

SILVER SUN
656 Canyon Rd. • Santa Fe, NM 87501
 (800) 562-2036; (505) 983-8743 Fax 983-0553
 Website: www.silversun-sf.com; E-mail: info@silversun-sf.com
 Deanna Olson & Cheryl Ingram, Owners
Retail, wholesale. *Products*: Art, children's items, fetishes, heishi, jewelry,
pottery, sand paintings. *Membership*: IACA. Catalog.

THE SPANISH & INDIAN TRADING CO.
924 Paseo de Peralta, Suite 1 • Santa Fe, NM 87501
 (505) 983-6106
Retail. *Products*: Historic American Indian artifacts and jewelry.

MARTHA STRUEVER - AMERCAN INDIAN ART
P.O. Box 2203 • Santa Fe, NM 87504
 Website: www.indianartdealer.com; E-mail: info@marthastruever.com
Products: Indian paintings, pottery, rugs, jewelry.

SUNBOY STUDIO
622-B Canyon Rd. • Santa Fe, NM 87501
 (505) 983-3042; Terry Sunboy Hunt (Laguna-Acoma), Owner
 Website: www.sunboyjewelry.com; E-mail: sunboy@earthlink.net
Retail, some wholesale. *Products*: Pueblo-life scenes Indian jewelry;
wood sculpture.

SUNSHINE STUDIO
3180 Vista Sandia • Santa Fe, NM 87506
 (800) 348-9273; (505) 984-3216 Fax 986-0765
 Website: www.sunshinestudio.com
 E-mail: sunshine@sunshinestudio.com
 Challis & Arch Thiessen, Owners
Retail. *Products*: Southwest American Indian art; ethnic & natural stone bead
jewelry. *Membership*: IACA.

TRADE ROOTS
411 Paseo de Peralta • Santa Fe, NM 87501
 (800) 477-6687; (505) 982-8168 Fax 982-8688
 Jeffrey Lewis, Owner
Retail, wholesale. *Products*: Fetishes, jewelry. *Membership*: IACA.

JOE WADE FINE ARTS
102 E. Water St. • Santa Fe, NM 87501
Retail. *Products*: Indian arts & crafts.

ROBERT LONE EAGLE WAYNEE STUDIO
P.O. Box 15313 • Santa Fe, NM 87506
 (505) 466-3456 Fax 466-1248; Website: ww.loneeaglestudios.com
 Robert Waynee (Ojibwe), Owner. Retail, wholesale. *Products*: Sculpture,
carvings. Special orders accepted.

NAVAJO SANDPAINTERS
P.O. Box 1849 • Sheepsprings, NM 87364
 (505) 732-4542; Berta Yazzi (Navajo), Owner
Products: Navajo sand paintings.

FOUTZ TRADING COMPANY
Hwy. 64, P.O. Box 1904 • Shiprock, NM 87420-1894
 (800) 383-0615; (505) 368-5790 Fax 368-4441
 Website: www.foutztrade.com
 E-mail: info@foutztrade.com
 Bill & Kay Foutz, Owners
Retail, wholesale. *Products*: Beadwork, clothing, dolls, jewelry, kachinas,
pottery, rugs, sand paintings, sculpture, carvings. *Membership*: IACA. Catalog.

SHIPROCK TRADING CO.
P.O. Box 906 • Shiprock, NM 87420
 (505) 368-4585 Fax 368-5583; Ed Foutz & Jed Foutz, Owners
Retail, wholesale. *Products*: Art, baskets, beadwork, clothing, dolls, jewelry,
kachinas, pottery, rugs, sandpaintings, sculpture, carvings. Appraisals.
Membership: IACA.

TSINNIE'S GALLERY
Box 537 • Shiprock, NM 87410
 (505) 368-5936 Fax 368-4240; Orville Z. Tsinnie (Navajo), Artisan/Owner
Retail. *Products*: Navajo-made jewelry; buckles, squash blossoms, bracelets,
earrings, rings, conchos.

MANY NATIONS
46 Burnham St. • Silver City, NM 88061
 (505) 538-2471 Fax 538-8561; Rosalie & Robert Baker, Owners
Retail, wholesale. *Products*: All. *Membership*: IACA. Catalog.

ALL ONE TRIBE DRUMS
P.O. Drawer N • Taos, NM 87571
  (505) 751-0019 Fax 751-0509
  Feeny Lipscomb, Charles Conley, Bruce Ross, Owners
Retail, wholesale. *Products*: Art, baskets, beadwork, clothing, dolls, jewelry, kachinas, pottery, rugs, sand paintings, sculpture, carvings. *Membership*: IACA. Catalog.

BLUE RAIN GALLERY
117 S. Taos Plaza • Taos, NM 87571
  (505) 751-0066; Website: www.blueraingallery.com
Retail. Products: Native American art, kachinas & crafts, representing Pueblo artists.

BROKEN ARROW INDIAN ARTS & CRAFTS
P.O. Box 1601 • Taos, NM 87571
  (505) 758-430; Joel & Jess Payne, Owners
Retail. *Products*: All. Membership: IACA.

CARL'S INDIAN TRADING POST & WHITE BUCKSKIN GALLERY
P.O. Box 813 • Taos, NM 87571
  (505) 758-2378; Mary Schlosser, Owner
Retail, wholesale. *Products*: Art, baskets, clothing, dolls, jewelry, kachinas, pottery, rugs, sandpaintings. Papago baskets, Hopi kachinas, Pueblo pottery, Navajo rugs and sand paintings.

LILLY'S GALLERY
P.O. Box 342 • Taos, NM 87571
  (505) 552-9501
Retail. Products: Handcrafted Acoma pottery and figurines.

MILLICENT ROGERS MUSEUM STORE
P.O. Box A • Taos, NM 87571
  (505) 758-4316 Fax 758-5751; Melody Gladin-Kehoe, Manager
Retail. Products: B,D,U,V. *Branch shop*: Millicent Rogers Plaza Store, Taos Plaza, NM.

NATIVE SCENTS
P.O. Box 5639 • Taos, NM 87571
  (800) 645-3471; Website: www.nativescents.com
Retail, Mail Order. *Products*: Fine incense, essential oils, herbal teas, bulk botanicals, resins, facial clay, sweetgrass, etc. Catalog.

NAVAJO GALLERY
P.O. Box 1756 • 210 Ledoux St. • Taos, NM 87571
  (505) 758-3250 Fax 758-7590
  R.C. Gorman, Owner; Virginia Dooley, Director
  E-mail: navajo@rcgormangallery.com
  Web site: www.rcgormangallery.com
Retail, wholesale, some mail order. *Products*: Complete work of Navajo artist, R.C. Gorman. Brochure & catalog available.

SILVER & SAND TRADING CO.
129 A N. Plaza • Taos, NM 87571
  (505) 758-9698; Harold & Wanda Allcorn, Owners
Retail, wholesale. *Products*: All. *Membership*: IACA.

SIX DIRECTIONS
P.O. Box 1042 • Taos, NM 87571
  (505) 758-5844; Neva & Otis Wilson, Owners
Retail, wholesale. *Products*: All. *Membership*: IACA.

TAOS DRUMS
P.O. Box 1916 • Taos, NM 87571
  (800) 424-3786; (505) 758-3796 Fax 758-9844
  Bruce & Pat Allen, Owners
Retail, wholesale. *Products*: Drums, flutes, pipes. *Membership*: IACA.

TAOS GLASS ARTS & EDUCATION
1021 Salazar Rd. • Taos, NM 87571
  (866) 353-7435; (505) 613-5848
  Website: www.tonyjojola-tga.com; E-mail: info@tonyjojola-tga.com
  Tony Jojola (Isleta Pueblo), Artisan/Owner
Products: Free-blown glass & cast sculptural work

TEHN-TSA INDIAN ARTS & CRAFTS
P.O. Box 471 • Taos, NM 87571
  (505) 758-0173; Victor Trujillo, Owner
Retail, wholesale. Products: Art, beadwork, clothing, heishi. Paintings by Victor Trujillo, pottery.

TONY REYNA INDIAN SHOP
P.O. Box 1892, Taos Pueblo • Taos, NM 87571
  (505) 758-3835; Tony Reyna, Owner; Philip Reyna, Manager
Retail. *Products*: Art, drums, pipes, jewelry, kachinas. Navajo, Hopi, and Zuni jewelry.

WESTERN HERITAGE GALLERY
P.O. Box 1042 • Taos, NM 87571
  (505) 758-4489; Neva & Otis Wilson, Owners
Retail. *Products*: Art, jewelry, kachinas, pottery, rugs, sand paintings, sculpture, carvings. *Membership*: IACA.

MILLICENT ROGERS MUSEUM STORE
115 E. McCarthy Plaza • Taos Plaza, NM 87571
  (505) 758-4316 Fax 758-5751; Melody Gladin-Kehoe, Manager
Retail. *Products*: Baskets, books, pottery, rugs.
Branch shop: Millicent Rogers Plaza Store, Taos Plaza, NM.

CONTINENTAL DIVIDE INDIAN HANDCRAFTS
P.O. Box 1059 • Thoreau, NM 87323
  (505) 862-7350; Willie Janish
Wholesale. *Product*: Jewelry. *Membership*: IACA..

SOUTHWEST INDIAN SILVERSMITHS
30 Steeplechase Dr. • Tijeras, NM 87059
  (505) 281-5276; Channah Pruter-Edwards, Owner
Wholesale. *Products*: Fetishes, heishi, jewelry, pottery.
Membership: IACA.

THE TEE PEE
P.O. Box 734 • Tucumcari, NM 88401
  (505) 461-3773; Mike & Betty Callens, Owners
Retail. *Products*: Art, boxes, clothing, jewelry, kachinas, pottery.
Membership: IACA.

JOE MILO'S TRADING CO.
P.O. Box 296 • Vanderwagen, NM 87326
  (505) 778-5531 Fax 778-5314; Joe Milosevich, Owner
Retail, wholesale. *Products*: All. *Membership*: IACA.

CIRCLE W PAWN & TRADING CO.
3316 Hwy. 64, P.O. Box 256 • Waterflow, NM 87421
  (505) 598-9179 Fax 327-4712; Charles Webb, Owner
Reatil, wholesale. *Products*: Baskets, beadwork, jewelry, rugs, sculpture.
Membership: IACA.

HOGBACK TRADING CO.
3221 Hwy. 64 • Waterflow, NM 87421
  (505) 598-5154/9243; Tom & Ann Wheeler, Owners
Retail, wholesale. *Products*: Art, baskets, clothing, dolls, jewelry, kachinas, pottery, rugs, sand paintings, sculpture, carvings. *Membership*: IACA.

BLACK ROCK TRADING CO.
P.O. Box 804 • Zuni, NM 87327
  (888) 842-2782; (505) 783-4819 (phone & fax)
  E-mail: rhartwig@cia-g.com; Ray Hartwig, Owner. *Membership*: IACA.

BLUE JAY'S POTTERY & GIFTS
P.O. Box 703 • Zuni, NM 87327
  (505) 782-2124; Angelina Medina & Calsue Murray
Wholesale/retail. Products: Art, clothing, jewelry, kachinas, miniatures, pottery, sculpture/carvings.

CAROLYN BOBELU
P.O. Box 443 • Zuni, NM 87327
  (505) 782-2282; Carolyn Bobelu (Zuni-Navajo), Owner
Retail, wholesale, mail order. *Product*: Jewelry. Special orders accepted.

ERIACHO ARTS & CRAFTS
P.O. Box 912 • Zuni, NM 87327
  (505) 782-2122 Fax 782-5076; Website: www.eriachoarts.com
  E-mail: zunitraveler@msn.com
  Tony & Ola Eriacho (Zuni Pueblo), Owner
Products: Zuni inlay jewelry in sterling silver, fetishes, pottery, paintings & beaded items. *Membership*: IACA.

J/S BELLSON JEWELRY
P.O. Box 397 • Zuni, NM 87327
  (505) 782-2448; Shirley L. Bellson (Zuni), Artisan/Owner
Retail, mail order. *Products*: Handmade silver women's jewelry

PUEBLO OF ZUNI ARTS & CRAFTS
1222 Hwy. 53, P.O. Box 425 • Zuni, NM 87327-0425
(866) 515-7675; (505) 782-5531 Fax 782-2136
Website: www.puebloofzuniarts.com
E-mail: sales@puebloofzuniarts.com; Garrett Banteah, Manager
Retail, wholesale, mail order. Zuni Tribal Enterprise. *Products*: Authentic Zuni art, jewelry, fetishes, carvings. Custom orders accepted. Catalog, $5. *Branch shops*: Venice, CA, and San Francisco, CA. *Membership*: IACA.

QUANDELACY FAMILY
P.O. Box 266 • Zuni, NM 87327
(505) 782-2797; Faye Quandelacy, Owner
Retail, wholesale. *Products*: Fetishes, jewelry, sculpture.

TURQUOISE VILLAGE
Hwy. 53, P.O. Box 429 • Zuni, NM 87327
(800) 748-2405; (505) 9782-5521 Fax 782-2846
Website: www.turquoisevillage.com; E-mail: ddozark@mn.rr.com
Greg Hofmann & Loretta Weahkee, Owners. *Membership*: IACA.

ZUNI CRAFTSMEN COOPERATIVE ASSOCIATION
P.O. Box 426, Zuni Pueblo • Zuni, NM 87327
(505) 782-4425/4521; Arvella Latone, Manager
Retail, wholesale, mail order. *Products*: Art, beadwork, fetishes, jewelry, pottery. Catalog.

ZUNI INDIAN JEWELRY
Drawer F • Zuni, NM 87327
(505) 782-2869; Carlton & Julie Jamon
Retail, wholesale. *Products*: Beadwork, fetishes, jewelry, rugs, sculpture. *Membership*: IACA.

NEW YORK

DANIEL C. HILL
P.O. Box 22 • Akron, NY 14001
(716) 542-3637; Daniel C. Hill (Cayuga), Owner
Retail, wholesale. *Products*: Traditional carved flutes, Iroquois silverwork, music recordings, and flute performances.

MOHAWK IMPRESSIONS
P.O. Box 20 • Akwesasne, NY 13655
(518) 358-2467 Fax 358-6241; Website: www.nofacedolls.com
E-mail: okwari@nofacedolls.com
Gail General & Pam Brown (Mohawk), Artisans/Owners
Products: Iroquois cornhusk dolls, beadwork with quills & feathers, sweetgrass and black ash splint baskets, rag dolls.

AMERICAN WEST BOUTIQUE
475 Main St., P.O. Box 58 • Armonk, NY 10504
(914) 234-9165 Fax 234-6991; Mark & Laura Faller, Owners
E-mail: amwestboot@aol.com
Retail. *Products*: Art, beadwork, clothing, dolls, jewelry, kachinas, pottery, rugs, sand paintings, sculpture, carvings. *Membership*: IACA.

TURQUOISE INDIAN
South Shore Mall, Captree Corners • Bay Shore, NY 11706
(516) 968-5353 Fax 277-1532; John & Jane Fuchs
Retail, wholesale. *Products*: All. *Membership*: IACA.

PAULINGSTON COMPANY
197 St. Mark's Ave., P.O. Box 320164 • Brooklyn, NY 11232
(888) 894-5643; (718) 230-7930 Fax (909) 498-8644
Website: www.zunidepot.com; E-mail: info@zunidepot.com
Franz G. Paul, Owner/ *Membership*: IACA.

MESA TRADERS
2725 County Route 26 • Climax, NY 12042
(518) 669-2912; Amy & Stuart Krause, Owners
Website: www.mesa-traders.com; E-mail: krause@mesa-traders.com
Membership: IACA.

KIVA TRADING COMPANY
117 Main St. • Cold Spring Harbor, NY 11724
(516) 367-2875 Fax 367-2834; Kristin Quinn, Manager
Website: www.kivatrading.com/
E-Mail: Kiva1@excite.com; Richard & Vivian Sutton, Owners
Retail, mail order. *Products*: American Indian handmade crafts, jewelry and fine arts, specializing in Navajo Hopi, Zuni & Pueblo Nations of New Mexico and Arizona. *Branch shop*: P.O. Box 658, Placitas, NM 87043. *Membership*: IACA. Brochure. Catalog online.

ROCKWELL MUSEUM OF WESTERN ART TRADING POST
111 Cedar St. • Corning, NY 14830
(607) 974-4830 Fax 974-4536; Cindy Weakland, Manager
Website: www.rockwellmuseum.org
E-mail: weaklandc@rocklandmuseum.org
Retail. *Products*: Native American arts & crafts from the Southwest. Art reproduction of the permanent collections; books & educational tapes. *Membership*: IACA. Catalog.

BLITZ ANTIQUE NATIVE AMERICAN ART, LTD.
P.O. Box 400 • Crompond, NY 10517
(914) 739-9683
Retail. *Products*: Specializing in Native American articles of childhood.

BLACK BEAR TRADING POST
Rt. 9, Box 47 • Esopus, NY 12429
(914) 384-6786; Roy Blackbear, Owner
Retail, wholesale. *Products*: Baskets, beadwork, clothing, jewelry, kachinas, sculpture, carvings.

SHELL & STONE TURQUOISE GALLERY
313 Towne Shoppes at Towne Center
Fayetteville, NY 13066 (315) 637-4550
Website: shellandstoneturquoise.com
E-mail: dewrod@wcny.rr.com; Frank & Rosemary Rodriguez, Owners
Retail. *Products*: All. Appraisals: Art, fetishes, jewelry, kachinas, miniatures, pottery, rugs. *Membership*: IACA.

IROQUOIS DOLL MAKERS
13853 Route 438 • Gowanda, NY 14070
(716) 532-3117; Website: www.senecahuskdolls.com
Antoinette Scott (Seneca), Owner/Manager
Products: Cornhusk dolls and cornhusk doll sculptures; leather & beadwork; sculptures are available in posters or prints.

IROQUOIS BONE CARVINGS
3560 Stony Point Rd. • Grand Island, NY 14072
(716) 773-4974; Stanley R. Hill, Owner
Retail, wholesale, mail order on craftwork only.
Products: Bone carvings, Iroquois dolls, sculpture. Brochure.

MOHAWK IMPRESSIONS
P.O. Box 20, Mohawk Nation • Hogansburg, NY 13655
(518) 358-2467; Gail General, Pam Brown, Charles Clench, Owners
Retail, wholesale, mail order. *Products*: Art, baskets, beadwork, dolls, fetishes, jewelry. Iroquois dolls. Special orders accepted. Brochure and price list; catalog, $3.

SWEETGRASS GIFTSHOP
Akwesasne Museum, RR#1 Box 14C, Rt. 37 • Hogansburg, NY 13655
(518) 358-2461 Fax 358-2649; Sue Herne (Mohawk), Manager
Website: www.akwesasneculture.org; E-mail: akwmuse@northnet.org
Retail, mail order. *Products*: Mohawk-made black ash splint and sweetgrass baskets, beadwork, bone jewelry; acrylic paintings of Iroquois culture by John Fadden. Special orders accepted. Send S.A.S.E. for price list.

SOUTHWEST COLLECTIONS
1 N. Main St. • Homer, NY 13077
(607) 749-2913; Sharon Livingston (Navajo), Owner
Website: www.southwestcollectionsstore.com
Products: Navajo necklaces, sterling silver jewelry, woodworking, art, soap products, pottery, blankets, rugs, flutes.

ADOBE ARTS
26 Gerard St. • Huntington, NY 11743
(516) 385-8410 Fax 423-7596; Website: www.adobeartes.com
E-mail: adobeartes@aol.com; Sandy Chapin & Mary Anne Pettit, Owners
Retail. *Products*: Traditional and contemporary Native American art, jewelry, pottery, kachinas, fetishes, baskets. *Membership*: IACA.

CAYUGA TRADING POST
P.O. Box 523 • Ithaca, NY 14850
(607) 257-3138; Roy Schreck, Owner
Retail, wholesale. *Products*: Baskets, beadwork, books, children's items, drums, pipes, jewelry, sculpture. *Membership*: IACA.

LITTLE FEATHER TRADING POST
P.O. Box 3165 • Jamaica, NY 11431
(718) 658-0576; Marion Nieves, Owner
Retail, wholesale, mail order. *Products*: beadwork jewelry & accessories, leatherwork.

SUNRISE SOUTHWEST
29 Katonah Ave. • Katonah, NY 10536
(914) 232-2652; Larry & Suzanne Ulrich, Owners
Membership: IACA.

POOSPATUCK SMOKE SHOP & TRADING POST
207 Poospatuck Lane • Mastic, NY 11950
(877) 234-6282; (888) 628-4821 Fax (631) 281-5859
Website: www.poospatucksmokeshop.com
E-mail: info@poospatucksmokeshop.com
Retail. Located on the Poospatuck Indian Reservation, home of the Unkechaug
Indian Nation. *Products*: Cigarettes & tobacco (tax free) products; moccasins;
pottery; clothing. Native Coffee TradersGift shop.

SACRED EARTH STUDIOS
197 Longfellow Dr. • Mastic Beach, NY 11951
(516) 399-4539; Jamie Reason, Owner
Retail, wholesale, mail order dealers only. *Products*: carvings, featherwork.

ADIRONDACK ARTWORKS
Rte. 3 Main St. • Natural Bridge, NY 13665
(315) 644-4645; Donn & Nicole Alfredson, Owners
Retail. *Products*: Art, baskets, beadwork, books, clothing, dolls, jewelry,
kachinas, pottery, rugs, sand paintings, sculpture, carvings. *Appraisals*.
Membership: IACA.

ONONDAGA INDIAN TRADING POST
Onondaga Indian Reservation • Nedrow, NY 13120
(315) 469-4359; Dewasenta, Owner
Retail, wholesale. *Products*: Iroquois baskets, beadwork, cornhusk dolls.

AMERICA HURRAH
766 Madison Ave. • New York, NY 10021
(212) 535-1930
Retail, wholesale. *Products*: Pictorial beadwork, Navajo weavings,
corn husk bags, and other Native American articles

AMERICAN INDIAN COMMUNITY HOUSE GALERY/MUSEUM
708 Broadway, 2nd Floor • New York, NY 10003
(212) 598-0100 Fax 598-4909; Monica Greene, Manager
Retail. *Products*: Baskets, books, clothing, jewelry, pottery.

MARCY BURNS: AMERICAN INDIAN ARTS
520 E. 72nd St. #2C • New York, NY 10021
(212) 439-9257 (phone & fax); Website: www.marcyburns.com
E-Mail: info@marcyburns.com. Retail, Wholesale.
Products: American Indian basketry, pottery, textiles & jewelry.

THE COMMON GROUND, INC.
19 Greenwich Ave. • New York, NY 10014
(212) 989-4178. Retail. *Products*: Antique & contemporary arts
of the North American Indian.

FIRST PEOPLES GALLERY
114 Spring St. • New York, NY 10012
(212) 343-0167; Victoria Torrez
Wholesale, retail. *Products*: Art, baskets, beadwork, clothing, dolls, jewelry,
kachinas, pottery, rugs, sandpaintings, sculpture, carvings. *Membership*: IACA.

J. CACCIOLA GALLERY
125 Wooster • New York, NY 10012
(212) 966-9177. Retail. *Products*: Contemporary artwork from a variety
of artists including Tony and Elizabeth Abeyta.

KOKOPELLI: SOUTHWESTERN JEWELRY
152 Prince St. • New York, NY 10012
(212) 925-4411 Fax 226-0700; Paul Dumont, Owner
E-mail: kokopelli@firstgate.net
Retail. *Products*: Contemporary & traditional Native American
jewelry and hand crafted fetishes. *Membership*: IACA.

SAKIA
100 LaSalle St., #17D • New York, NY 10027
(212) 866-2193; Eugene A. Cam, Owner. Retail, wholesale.

UNIQUE NATIVE CRAFTS
505 LaGuadia Pl., #19-D • New York, NY 10012
(212) 777-8394; Audrey Bernstein, Owner
E-mail: uniquenativecrafts@yahoo.com
Retail. *Products*: Native American jewelry/crafts from Alaska
to Chile since 1989. By appointment. *Membership*: IACA.

VENTURA INDIAN COLLECTION
175 E. 74th St. • New York, NY 10021
(212) 988-8050; Bebe Ventura & Stan Rosenfeld
Retail, wholesale. *Products*: Jewelry. *Membership*: IACA.

CHICHESTER, INC.
2045 Niagara Falls Blvd. #9 • Niagara Falls, NY 14304
(716) 298-1183 Fax 298-0313; Website: www.chichesterinc.com
Paul Crosby & Michelle Spencer, Owners
E-mail: chichgroup@aol.com. *Membership*: IACA.

NATIVE AMERICAN CENTER FOR THE LIVING ARTS, INC.
25 Rainbow Mall • Niagara Falls, NY 14303
(716) 284-2427; Wanda Chew, Manager
Retail, wholesale. *Products*: Art, baskets, beadwork, clothing,
dolls, jewelry, pottery, rugs.

SQUASH BLOSSOM
49 Burd St. • Nyack, NY 10960
(845) 353-0550.
Retail. *Products*: Authentic American Indian jewelry,
Hopi kachinas and Pueblo pottery.

MINERAL & NEEDLE CRAFT CREATIONS
P.O. Box 614 • Oceanside, NY 11572
(516) 536-2220; Thelma Kirsch, Owner
Retail, wholesale. *Products*: All. *Appraisals*: Art, baskets, beadwork, clothing,
dolls, jewelry, kachinas, pottery, rugs, sand paintings, sculpture, carvings.
Membership: IACA.

SIX NATIONS INDIAN MUSEUM SHOP
HCR 1, Box 10 • Onchiota, NY 12968
(518) 891-2299; John Fadden (Mohawk), Director
Retail. *Products*: Art, baskets, beadwork, jewelry, sculpture.
Mohawk baskets, acrylic paintings of Iroquois culture. Brochure.

FULL WOLF MOON
49 Wolden Rd. • Ossining, NY 10562
(914) 762-7083; Jude Westerfield
Retail. *Products*: Jewelry, sculpture. *Membership*: IACA.

TEARS OF THE MOON
82 Arthur Ct. • Port Chester, NY 10573
(914) 690-9050; Wendy Alexander, Owner
E-mail: totm444@aol.com. *Membership*: IACA.

CHRISJOHN FAMILY ARTS & CRAFTS
RD #2, Box 315 • Red Hook, NY 12571
(914) 758-8238; Richard Chrisjohn, Owner
Retail, wholesale, mail order. *Products*: Clothing, dolls,
drums, pipes, jewelry. Brochure.

ELLIE'S SOUTHWESTERN ARTS & CRAFTS
32 Sissen Dr. • Rochester, NY 14623
(585) 334-53; Eleanor J. Oliver (Navajo), Artist/Owner
Products: Handmade earrings, necklaces, hairpieces, Native American dolls,
leatherwork, moccasins, beadwork, handwoven rugs.

M & J ENTERPRISES
42 Eagle Ridge Cir. • Rochester, NY 14617
(716) 342-5225; Mary Catherine Hickey, Owner
Retail. *Products*: Jewelry, rugs, sculpture. *Membership*: IACA.

SHADES OF THE SOUTHWEST
26 Oakbend Lane• Rochester, NY 14617
(315) 637-4550; Bobbie Bennedetto, Owner. *Membership*: IACA.

SOUTHWEST STUDIO CONNECTION
P.O. Box 3013 • Sag Harbor, NY 11963
(516) 283-9649; Kerry Sharkey-Miller, Owner
Retail. *Products*: Art, ornaments, fetishes, heishi, jewelry, pottery, sculpture.
Membership: IACA.

TAINO-NATIVE AMERICAN CREATIONS
P.O. Box 96 • St. Regis Falls, NY 12980
(518) 856-0083 Fax 856-0111
David (Old Griz) Marrus, Owner
E-mail: oldgriz@westelcom.com
Retail. *Products*: Historical beadwork; Native American Reproductions
Caribbean crafts.

AMERICAN INDIAN CRAFTS
719 Broad St. • Salamanca, NY 14779
(716) 945-1225; Lane & Lance Hoag, Owners
Retail, wholesale, mail order. *Products*: Mohawk baskets,
Seneca beadwork, Navajo and Zuni jewelry, Ute pottery. Brochure.

SENECA-IROQUOIS NATIONAL MUSEUM GIFT SHOP
794-814 Broad St. • Salamanca, NY 14779
(716) 945-1760 ext. 3455; Website: www.senecamuseum.org
Eva Aidman, Gift Shop Manager; E-mail: eva.aidman@sni.org
Retail, mail order. Tribal nonprofit organization. Products: Iroquois beadwork;
splint, porcupine quill and sweetgrasss baskets, clothing, pottery, sculpture.
Brochure. Data sheets and book list.

TUSKEWE KRAFTS
2089 Upper Mountain Rd. • Sanborn, NY 14132
(716) 297-1821 Fax 297-0318
John Wesley Patterson, Jr., Owner
Retail, wholesale, mail order. *Products*: Field lacrosse & box lacrosse sticks.
Brochure/price list.

TROTO-BONO
P.O. Box 34 • Shrub Oak, NY 10588
(914) 528-6604. Retail. *Products*: Indian and Eskimo artifacts of North
America. By appointment.

THE MEXICAN SHACK
256 Route 100 • Somers, NY 10589
(914) 232-8739 Fax 232-7820; Website: themexicanshack.com
E-mail: mexicanshack@aol.com; Steven & Mary Delzio, Owners
Retail. *Products*: All. *Appraisals*: Jewelry. Repairs & restoration.
Membership: IACA.

SHINNECOCK TRADING POST LTD.
P.O. Box 1286 • Southampton, NY 11968
(631) 283-8047 Fax 287-2590; E-mail: sioltd@i-2000.com
Website: www.shinnecocktradingpost.com
Lance A. Gumbs, Manager. *Membership*: IACA.

NATIVE PEOPLES ARTS & CRFATSHOP
P.O. Box 851, 210 Fabius St. • Syracuse, NY 13201
(315) 476-7425 Carol Moses, Manager
Retail, mail order by special request. *Products*: Baskets,
clothing, dolls, lacrosse sticks, pottery, sculpture/carvings.

ONEIDA SKY
5218 Patrick Rd. • Verona, NY 13478
(315) 361-8035 Fax 361-8034; Michelle Ferrante, Manager
Website: www.turningstone.com
Products: Fine art & Native American collectibles including paintings,
sculptures, beadwork, and jewelry.

PETER B. JONES
P.O. Box 174 • Versailles, NY 14168
(716) 532-5993; Roberta & Peter Jones (Onondaga), Owners
Retail, wholesale. Cattaraugus Reservation-Onondaga artists & crafts persons
Products: Peter B. Jones - original works in clay; one-of-a-kind ceramic
sculptures; neo-traditional Iroquois pottery; contemporary stoneware &
whiteware pottery; drums, pipes, flutes, rugs. Robert Jones - beadwork.

TRADITIONS
7834 North Rd. • Victor, NY 14564
(716) 924-7826 Marty Gingras
Retail. *Products*: Historic American Indian artifacts.

THE VILLAGE POTTER
P.O. Box 220 • Walker Valley, NY 12588
(914) 361-4401 Lois & Charles Garrison
Retail, wholesale. *Membership*: IACA.
Branch: 172 Sullivan St., Wurtsboro, NY l2790.

M. ZACHARY GALLERIES, INC.
347 Maple St. • W. Hempstead, NY 11552
(516) 538-4659 Lorraine & Martin Schmidt, Owners
Retail. *Products*: Baskets, jewelry, kachinas, pottery, sculpture.

FORTUNOFF
1300 Old Country Rd. • Westbury, NY 11590
(516) 542-4105 Fax 542-4188; Helene & Alan Fortunoff, Owners
Retail. *Product*: Jewelry. Catalog.

NORTH CAROLINA

CROWN DRUGS
400 Commerce Place, Bermuda Quay • Advance, NC 27006
(919) 998-6800 Fax 998-6846
Conrad Stonestreet, Ray Gentry, Douglas Sprinkle, Owners
Retail, wholesale. *Membership*: IACA.

TERRI E. HATCHER (Choctaw)
2321 Carmel Rd. • Charlotte, NC 28226
E-mail: hatcherstudio@aol.com. *Product*: Paintings.

BIG MEAT POTTERY
Cherokee, NC 28719
(828) 497-9544. Retail. *Product*: Cherokee pottery.

EL CAMINO INDIAN GALLERY
P.O. Box 482 • Cherokee, NC 28719
(828) 497-3600; Nathan Robinson, Owner
Retail. Products: Baskets, beadwork, clothing, dolls, jewelry,
sand paintings, sculpture. Seminole crafts.

GREAT SMOKIES FINE ARTS GALLERY
NATIVE AMERICAN CRAFT SHOP
P.O. Box 2077 • Cherokee, NC 28719
(828) 497-5444; Janene & Todd Lancaster, Owners
E-mail: gsfinearts@smnet.net. *Membership*: IACA.

NATIVE COLLECTIONS MAIDEN CHEROKEE
P.O. Box 1467 • Cherokee, NC 28719
(828) 488-8367; Beth Cline, Owner
Website: www.nativecollections.com; E-mail: nativeamercn@aol.com
Retail, mail order. Products: Authentic hand-made crafts locally crafted
in Cherokee, NC

QUALLA ARTS & CRAFTS MUTUAL, INC.
645 Tsali Blvd., P.O. Box 310 • Cherokee, NC 28719
(828) 497-3103 Fax 497-4841; Vicki Ledford, Manager
E-mail: quallart@dnet.net
Retail. Eastern Cherokee Tribal Enterprise. *Products*: Baskets, beadwork,
dolls, drums, pipes, pottery, sculpture. Catalog, $2.

STANDINGDEER TRADE CO.
172 Sallie Ann Dr. • Cherokee, NC 28719
(828) 497-9251; Theresa A. Frasher (Eastern Cherokee), Owner
Website: www.standingdeer.com; E-mail: theresa@standingdeer.com
Retail, wholesale. *Products*: Cherokee baskets, beadwork, pottery.

WHITE BUFFALO
2617 Shady Grove Rd. • Durham, NC 27703-8644
(919) 846-2771 (Phone & Fax); Donald, Marty & Steve Koehler, Owners
Retail. *Products*: All. *Membership*: IACA. Branch: Raleigh, NC.

GUILFORD NATIVE AMERICAN ART GALLERY
200 N. Davie St., Box 6 • Greensboro, NC 27401
(336) 273-6605 Fax 273-1771
E-mail: gallery7@bellsouth.net; Website: www.guilfordnative.org
Retail. Traditiyional and contemporary Native American art;
jewelry, pottery, baskets, prints, flutes, music

HALIWA-SAPONI TRIBAL POTTERY AND ARTS
P.O. Box 99, Hwy. 561 • Hollister, NC 27844
(919) 586-4017; Linda Cooper-Mills, Executive Director
Retail, wholesale, mail order. *Products*: Beadwork, pottery,
rugs, sculpture. Special orders accepted. Price list.

WAYAH'STI INDIAN TRADITIONS
P.O. Box 130, Rt. 561 • Hollister, NC 27844
(919) 586-4519; Patricia & Arnold Richardson, Owners
Mail order. *Products*: Beadwork, clothing, drums, pipes, pottery, sculpture.
Special orders accepted. Price list.

THE MEDICINE BAG
14225 N.C. Highway #18 South • Laurel Springs, NC 28644
(910) 359-2798 Fax 359-8834; Liz Rodgers, Owner
Retail. Products: All-natural herbs, smudges, local honey, and crafts. Brochure.

HELEN SMOKER MARTIN ART
1663 Well Rd. • Marble, NC 28905
(888) 527-1777 Fax (256) 423-2614
Website: www.artistsites.org/helensmokermartin/

E-mail: helensmokeremartin@yahoo.com
Helen Smoker Martin (Eastern Cherokee), Artist/Owner
Products: Paintings; portraits, pen & ink, beadwork, porcupine quillwork; mural; crafts

TUSCARORA INDIAN HANDCRAFT SHOP
Rt. #4, Box 172 • Maxton, NC 28364
(919) 844-3352; Leon Locklear, Owner
Retail, mail order. *Products*: Clothing, jewelry.
Special orders accepted. Price list.

NEW BERN NET & CRAFT CO.
2703 Hwy. 70 East • New Bern, NC 28560
(919) 633-2226 Fax 633-5760; Louise & Johnnie Thompson
Retail. *Products*: Baskets, beadwork, clothing, dolls, jewelry, kachinas, pottery, rugs, sand paintings. *Membership*: IACA.

ROBERT D. WAYNEE, SR.
P.O. Box 5232 • New Bern, NC 28560
(919) 637-2546
Retail, wholesale. *Products*: Native American wood sculptures. Catalog.

WHITE BUFFALO
7909 Falls of Neuse • Raleigh, NC 27615
(919) 846-2771; Donald, Marty & Steve Koehler, Owners
Retail. *Products*: All. *Membership*: IACA. Branch: Durham, NC.

LUMBEE INDIAN ARTS & CRAFTS
Rt. 1, Box 310AA • Rowland, NC 28383
(919) 521-9494; Hope Sheppard & Jane Oxendine, Owners
Mail order. *Products*: Baskets, beadwork.

EARTHWORKS ENVIRONMENTAL GALLERY
110 N. Main St. • Waynesville, NC 28786
(704) 452-9500; Susan & Jerold Johnson, Owners
Retail, wholesale. *Products*: All. *Membership*: IACA.

NORTH DAKOTA

GREAT PLAINS NATIVE AMERICAN ARTS CO-OP
c/o NDIAA • 401 N. Main St. • Mandan, ND 58554-3164
(701) 221-5328; Carol Good Bear, Owner
Wholesale, retail. *Products*: Art, baskets, beadwork, clothing, dolls, jewelry, kachinas, pottery, rugs, sandpaintings, sculpture, carvings. Membership: IACA. Catalog.

RENEE J. MAYER (Mandan, Hidatsa, Arikara)
500 5th St. N. • New Town, ND 58763
(701) 627-4861; E-mail: reneem@mhanation.com
Products: Contemporary beadwork, leather items, embroidery, traditional clothing.

THREE AFFILIATED TRIBES MUSEUM, ARTS & CRAFTS
P.O. Box 147 • New Town, ND 58763
(701) 627-4477. Retail. *Products*: Art, beadwork, books, rugs.
Misc. items related to Three Tribes.

WOLF'S TRADING POST
P.O. Box 877 • New Town, ND 58763
(701) 627-3393; (800) 735-6957
James H. Wolf (Hidatsa), Owner
Products: Handmade American Indian crafts: beadwork, quilts, dance regalia, powwow supplies, blankets.

OHIO

GOOD GIRL JEWELRY AT WHITE'S MILL
2 White's Mill Dr. • Athens, OH 45701
(740) 592-1521; Meg & Michael Toomey, Owners. *Membership*: IACA.

DREAM CATCHERS
262 N. Roanoke • Austintown, OH 44515
(216) 793-7468; Kathleen & Shawne Bowman
Retail, wholesale. *Products*: Art, beadwork, clothing, dolls, jewelry, kachinas, pottery, rugs, sand paintings, sculpture, carvings. *Membership*: IACA.

COYOTE WOMAN GALLERY
P.O. Box 868, • Bryan, OH 43506
(419) 636-3300; Terri & John Freudenberger
Retail. *Products*: All. *Membership*: IACA. *Branch*: Harbor Springs, MI.

QUEMAHONING COLLECTION
8060 Oxford Lane • Chesterland, OH 44026
(216) 247-0430
Retail. *Products*: Art, baskets, beadwork, clothing, dolls, jewelry, kachinas, pottery, rugs, sand paintings, sculpture, carvings. *Membership*: IACA.

AMERICAN INDIAN ARTS & CRAFTS
3547 Raymar Dr. • Cincinnati, OH 45208
(513) 871-1858; Dan & Pat Stricker
Retail. *Products*: All. Branch: 3512 1/2 Erie Ave. *Membership*: IACA.

MICHELLE RED ELK
2924 Urwiler Ave. • Cincinnati, OH 45211
(513) 389-1919; Michelle Red Elk (Comanche/Kiowa), Artist
E-mail: nokoni@cinci.rr.com
Products: Beadwork-flat pieces suitable for framing, beaded amulets, pencil drawings

FIRST PEOPLE'S GALLERY
1481 Clifton Pl. • Lakewood, OH 44107
(216) 696-1942 Fax 226-4863; John P. Kunikis, Owner
E-mail: jkunikis@n2net.net. *Membership*: IACA.

CREATIVE OUTLET
226 W. Main St. • Loudonville, OH 44842
(419) 994-5092 Fax 994-4999; Victoria B. Reinhard, Owner
Website: www.creativeoutlet.net; E-mail: outlet@bright.net
Membership: IACA.

BUFFALO GALLERY
130 E. Main St. • Lebanon, OH 45036
(513) 932-0792; William V. Jordan, Owner
Retail, wholesale. *Products*: All. *Appraisals*. *Membership*: IACA.

TURQUOISE VILLAGE
128 Front St. • Marrietta, OH 45750
(877) 561-2800; (740) 374-2800
Website: www.turquoisespirit.co; E-mail: griener@citynet.com
Douglas & Barbara Griener, Owners. *Membership*: IACA.

DESERT SUN
101 E. Wayne St. • Maumee, OH 43537
(419) 893-9630; Thomas & Denise Lawson
Retail. *Products*: Art, baskets, beadwork, clothing, dolls, jewelry, kachinas, pottery, rugs, sand paintings, sculpture, carvings. *Membership*: IACA.

BELLE FLEUR
8173 Ballash Rd. • Medina, OH 44256
(330) 769-3393 Fax 769-4884. *Membership*: IACA.

SOUTHWEST EXPRESSIONS OF OHIO, INC.
25576 Mill St. • Olmsted Falls, OH 44138
(216) 235-1177 (phone & fax); Randi & John MacWilliams, Owners
Retail, wholesale. *Products*: Art, clothing, dolls, jewelry, kachinas, pottery, rugs, sandpaintings, sculpture, carvings. Native American arts & crafts & Southwest home decor. *Membership*: IACA. Brochure.

FIRST PEOPLES GALLERY
19885 Detroit Rd. #253 • Rocky River, OH 44116
(888) 291-8217; (216) 226-4863 (phone & fax)
Website: www.firstpeoplesgallery.com
E-mail: firstpeoples@sbcglobal.net
Retail, wholesale. *Product*: Inuit art.

EARTH SPIRIT-NATIVE AMERICAN ART GALLERY
5758 N. Main #1 • Sylvania, OH 43560
(419) 885-7012; Chris & Pam Clayworth, Owners
Retail. *Products*: Art, books, drums, pipes, flutes, artifacts, jewelry, kachinas, pottery, rugs, sandpaintings. *Membership*: IACA.

OKLAHOMA

BRUCE C. CAESAR
Box 1183, 112 Prairie Village • Anadarko, OK 73005
(405) 247-2303
Retail, wholesale. *Product*: Jewelry. Specializes in Native American church type ornaments. Special orders accepted.

CIRCLE TURTLE NATIVE SPECIALTIES
P.O. Box 986 • Anadarko, OK 73005
(405) 247-7059; Linda S. Poolaw, Owner

Retail, mail order. *Products*: Southern Plains arts & crafts made to order by local arts & crafts people of S.W. Oklahoma, i.e., Kiowa, Comanche, Apache, Fort Sill Apache, Wichita, Caddo and Delaware.

DIXON PALMER HEADDRESSES & TIPIS
Rt. 3, Box 189 • Anadarko, OK 73005
 (405) 247-3983; Dixon Palmer (Kiowa), Artisan/Owner
Retail. By appointment only. *Products*: Headdresses of imitation eagle feathers; painted or plain tipi covers. Special orders only. Send S.A.S.E. for price quotation.

LITTLE CHIEF ART
Rt. 3 Box 109A • Anadarko, OK 73005
 (405) 464-2564; Barthall Little Chief (Kiowa/Comanche), Artist/Owner
Products: Original sculpture in alabaster & bronze reproductions.

PAUL McDANIELS, JR. (Kiowa-Oglala Sioux) (artisan)
P.O. Box 1144, Anadarko, OK 73005.
Products: Kiowa/Southern Plains style beadwork.

OKLAHOMA INDIAN ARTS & CRAFTS COOPERATIVE
Southern Plains Indian Museum Shop
P.O. Box 966 • Anadarko, OK 73005
 (405) 247-3486; LaVerna Jane Capes, Manager
Retail, wholesale, mail order. *Products*: Art, clothing, dolls, jewelry. Send S.A.S.E. for price list.

TOEHAY-POTTERY
Route 3 • Anadarko, OK 73005
 (405) 247-5268; Thelma Toehay Chapman, Owner
Retail. *Products*: Beadwork, pottery, oil paintings, shawls.

JOYCE L. VINEYARD
330 1/2 W, Main • Anadarko, OK 73005
 (405) 247-9770
Retail. *Products*: Beadwork, clothing. Special orders & commissions accepted.

KIAMICHI LEATHER CRAFTS
P.O. Box 55 • Antlers, OK 74523
 (580) 271-1107; Ronald C. Willison (Choctaw), Owner
Products: Primitive Indian flutes; buffalo nickel jewelry

VISIONS OF EYAHOTANKA
RR 3, Box 7820 • Bartlesville, OK 74003
 (918) 336-4110; Website: www.jalbroart.com
Janice Albro (Sisseton-Wahpeton Dakota), Artist/Owner
 E-mail: janicealbro@netzero.net
Products: Paintings & bronze sculptures; giclee prints & postcards.

PAUL HACKER KNIVES & FLUTES
6513 N.W. 20th Dr. • Bethany, OK 73008
 (405) 787-8600 (phone & fax)
 Paul Hacker, Owner; & Susan Trube, Manager
Retail, wholesale, mail order. *Products*: Art, books, boxes, drums, pipes, knives. *Membership*: IACA. Brochure.

CADDO HERITAGE MUSEUM GIFT SHOP
P.O. Box 497 • Binger, OK 73005
 (405) 656-2344; Website: www.caddonation-nsn.gov
 Rhonda S. Fair & Charlene Wright (Caddo), Managers
Products: Pottery beadwork, jewelry, art

2 BEARS N-D-N CRAFTS
Route 1 • Blackwell, OK 74631
 Website: www.2bearsden.tripod.com
 E-mail: twobearsden@peoplepc.com; Jerry Riddle (Chickasaw), Owner
Products: Hand crafted cedar boxes; beadwork & leather artwork.

ZIA CONTEMPORARY POTTERY
P.O. Box 192 • Canton, OK 73724
 (580) 886-2443; Leanore Toribio (Zia Pueblo), Owner
Products: Handmade wheel-thrown pottery, Hand-painted Indian design kiln fired (Pueblo style).

BLUE TIPI CREATIONS
103 Red Rock Rd. • Clinton, OK 73601
 (580) 323-1939 Fax 323-2236; Arthur Perez (Kickapoo), Owner
 Website: www.bluetipi.com; E-mail: art@bluetipi.com
Products: Artifact reproductions like tomahawks, peace pipes, bows & arrows, shields, medicine wheels, dream catchers.

J. BALES STUDIO
P.O. Box 193 • Cookson, OK 74427
 (918) 457-4136; Jean E. Bales (Iowa), Owner
 Don Lacy (Cherokee), Manager
Retail, wholesale. By appointment only. *Products*: Art, pottery, sculpture. Special orders accepted.

LONG WALKER NATIVE AMERICAN CRAFTS
P.O. Box 45 • Copan, OK 74022
 (918) 532-4938; John W. Sumpter (Delaware), Owner
Products: hand drums, red cedar boxes; gourd dance regalia.

BAH-KHO-JE ART GALLERY
P.O. Box 221 • Coyle, OK 73027
 (405) 466-3101; Frank Murray, Manager
Retail. Iowa Tribe of Oklahoma enterprise. *Products*: Art, beadwork, clothing, jewelry, pottery, sculpture.

TOUCHING LEAVES INDIAN CRAFTS
927 Portland Ave. • Dewey, OK 74029
 (918) 534-2859; Louise Dean, Owner; Jim Clear-Sky, Manager
Mail order. Products: Beadwork, clothing, jewelry. Catalog, $1.

JUST DUCKEE ORIGINALS
1901 N. Midwest Blvd. • Edmond, OK 73034
 (405) 341-9051; Website: www.justduckeeoriginals.com
 E-mail: justduckeeoriginals@yahoo.com
 Donna Sockey Pitts (Choctaw), Artisan/Owner
Products: Traditional style Choctaw clothing.

LES BERRYHILL
1800 Bunting Ln. • Edmond, OK 73034
 (405) 733-7350 or 330-1951; Les Berryhill (Yuchi/Creek), Artist/Owner
Retail, wholesale. Yuchi/Creek craftsperson. *Products*: Beadwork, artifacts. Cultural artifact replicas.

PONCA DESIGNS
Rt. 1 Box 56 • Fairfax, OK 74637
 E-mail: wponca@juno.com; Kimberly Wendy Ponca (Osage), Artist/Owner
Products: Traditional Osage Indian clothing, blankets & design; fine arts & contemporary clothing; hand silk screen prints.

PAHDOPONY GALLERY
209 NW Mamosa Lane • Lawton, OK 73507
 (580) 591-0203; Juanita Pahdopony (Comanche), Artist/Owner
Products: Visual artist; cradlemaker. *Activities*: Storyteller, lecturer, educator, writer, poet.

BILL GLASS, JR., STUDIO
HC64, Box 1410 • Locust Grove, OK 74352
 (918) 479-8884. Retail, mail order. *Products*: Pottery, sculpture. Special orders accepted.

WAK BOK OLA INTANNAP
P.O. Box 23 • Maysville, OK 73057
 (405) 867-5330; Richard Duane Robinson, Owner
Retail, mail order. Choctaw artist. *Products*: Abstract American Indian painting, ceramics, prints, and drawings. American Indian art consulting.

AMERICAN INDIAN HANDICRAFTS
P.O. Box 533 • Meeker, OK 74855
 (405) 279-2896; Shalah Rowlen (Sac & Fox-Pawnee), Artisan/Owner
Retail, wholesale. *Products*: Beadwork, boxes, clothing. Brochure & price list.

ADAWA TRIBAL GIFT SHOP
Ottawa Tribal Center, P.O. Box 110 • Miami, OK 74355
 (918) 549-1536

ALAMOONI STUDIO
49900 E. 20 Road • Miami, OK 74354
 (918) 541-3131; Julie Olds (Maimi of OK), Artist/Owner
 Website: www.joldsart.com; E-mail: jolds@miamination.com
Products: Original paintings in oil, acrylic, watercolor, gouache; original drawings in graphite, pastel; pottery, jewelry, sculpture.

BUFFALO SUN
P.O. Box 1556 • Miami, OK 74355
 (918) 542-8870; Ardina Moore (Quapaw-Osage), Owner
Retail, wholesale, mail order. Quapaw-Osage craftsperson. *Products*: Traditional and contemporary Indian fashions and accessories, jewelry, leatherwork. Send S.A.S.E. for brochure.

DOUG MAYTUBBIE
200 E. Lockheed Dr. • Midwest City, OK 73110
  (405) 733-8534; Doug & Donna Maytubbie (Choctaw), Owners
Retail, wholesale. *Products*: Original drawings, paintings, graphics, sculpture.
Price list.

SAM KIDD ORIGIALS
Rt. 2, Box 66-4 • Muldrow, OK 74948
  (918) 427-3793; Sam Kid (Cherokee), Artist
Retail. *Products*: Original artwork depicting various tribes from Plains
to Woodlands; limited edition prints.

FIVE CIVILIZED TRIBES MUSEUM TRADING POST
1101 Honor Hts. Dr. • Muskogee, OK 74401
  (918) 683-1701 Fax 683-3070; Mindi Thompson, Manager
  Website: www.fivetribes.org; E-mail: 5tribesdirector@sbcglobal.net
Retail, wholesale, mail order. Products: Art, baskets, books, ornaments,
clothing, jewelry, pottery, sculpture. Brochure.

TIGER ART GALLERY
2110 E. Shawnee St. • Muskogee, OK 74403
  (918) 687-7006; Johnny & Peggy Tiger, Owners
Retail, wholesale, mail order. *Products*: Art, clothing, sculpture.
Send S.A.S.E. for brochure.

THE DANCING RABBIT
814 N. Jones • Norman, OK 73069
  (405) 360-0512; Patta LT Joest (Choctaw), Artisan/Owner
Retail, wholesale. By appointment only. *Products*: Beadwork, jewelry.
Special orders accepted.

MEMORY CIRCLE STUDIO, INC.
P.O. Box 732 • Norman, OK 73070
  (405) 360-0751; George Sullivan, Owner/Manager
  Website: www.dorothyart.com; Dorothy Sullivan, Cherokee Master Artist
Retail, wholesale, mail order. *Products*: Art. Original paintings, drawings;
limited edition prints; greeting cards & mini prints; specializes in art of
Cherokee history, culture & legends based on extensive research.
Membership: IACA. Catalog, $5.

STUDIO 35
1024 W. Apache • Norman, OK 73069
  (405) 596-3415; Gerald Couurnoyer (Oglala Sioux), Owner
  Website: www.geraldcournoyer.com; E-mail: studio3502@yahoo.com
Products: Acrylic paintings on custom handmade canvases.

BOONE GENERAL STORE
329 NE 3rd St. #204 • Oklahoma City, OK 73104
  (405) 474-0106; David Carnie, Lee Stroud, Owners. *Membership*: IACA.

CHOCTAW INDIAN TRADING POST, INC.
1500 N. Portland Ave. • Oklahoma City, OK 73107
  (405) 947-2490 Fax 512-0005; Angela A. Askew, Manager
Retail. *Products*: All. *Membership*: IACA

CONNIE SEABOURN STUDIO
P.O. Box 23795 • Oklahoma City, OK 73132
  (405) 728-3903. Mail order. *Products*: Art.

MAVIS V. DOERING
5918 NW 58th St. • Oklahoma City, OK 73122
  (405) 787-6082. Retail. *Product*: Baskets.

BISON BISON - THE BUFFALO STORE
129 E. Main • Pawhuska, OK 74056
  (918) 287-3510; Mary Jo Mercer (Osage), Owner
  Website: www.bisonbison.gpg.com; E-mail: cyberbison2002@yahoo.com
Products: American bison products; jewelry, gift baskets, and authentic
Osage arts & crafts.

INDIAN ART OKLAHOMA
4716 N. MacArthur • Oklahoma City, OK 73122
  (405) 495-1800; Website: www.indianartoklahoma.com
  Email: Valerie@indianartoklahoma.com
Products: Native American items made by Native Americans, from art &
sculpture to jewelry & clothes.

OKLAHOMA INDIAN ART GALLERY
2335 SW 44th St. • Oklahoma City, OK 73119
  (405) 685-6162
Products: Indian art created by Native Americans in the Oklahoma City region.

OKLAHOMA NATIVE ART & JEWELRY
1316 S. Agnew Ave. • Oklahoma City, OK 73108
  (405) 604-9800; Website: www.oknativeart.com

BAH-KHO-JE ART GALLERY
Rt. 1 Box 721 • Perkins, OK 74059
  (405) 547-2402; Christy Cordova (Iowa of OK), Owner
  Website: www.iowanation.org/enterprise/gallery.html
  E-mail: gallery@iowanation.org
Products: Original paintings, prints, framing, sculpture, beadwork,
Iowa ribbon work, jewelry, shawls, Navajo textiles, beading supplies.

MONKAPEME
P.O. Box 457 • Perkins, OK 74059
  (405) 547-2948
  Remonia O. Jacobsen (Iowa-Otoe-Missouria), Artisan/Owner
Retail, wholesale. *Product*: Clothing. Special orders only.

ADAMS STUDIOS
Rt. 3, Box 615A • Ponca City, OK 74604
  (405) 765-5086; Jack & Anna Adams, Owners
Retail. *Products*: Art, beadwork, jewelry, knives, pottery.
Special orders accepted. Brochure.

CHEROKEE ARTIST STUDIO-GALLERY
Rt. 1, Box 263 • Prague, OK 74864
  (405) 567-2856; Ron Mitchell (Cherokee), Owner
Retail, mail order. By appointment. *Products*: Art, Miniatures. Original gouache
paintings; limited-edition prints with handmade miniature cultural items.
Catalog.

RABBIT STUDIO GALLERY
P.O. Box 34 • Pryor, OK 74362
  (800) 613-3716; (918) 825-3788 or 825-3716
  Bill & Traci Rabbit (Cherokee), Artist/Owners
Retail, wholesale. *Products*: Original paintings, limited edition prints, baskets,
knives, pottery, sculpture. Catalog.

SNAKE CREEK WORKSHOP
Box 147, Hwy. 33 • Rose, OK 74364
  (918) 479-8867; Knokovtee Scott, Owner
Retail, mail order. *Product*: Jewelry. Mussel shell gorget necklaces.
Brochure & price list.

MISTER INDIAN'S COWBOY STORE
1000 S. Main • Sapulpa, OK 74066
  (918) 224-6511; Bob (Creek) & Jo (Cheyenne) Arrington, Managers
Retail, some mail order. *Products*: Art, beadwork, clothing, dolls, jewelry,
rugs, sculpture.

KELLY HANEY ART GALLERY
P.O. Box 72 • Seminole, OK 74818
  (405) 382-3369 Fax 382-3324; Enoch Kelly Haney, Artist/Owner
  Website: www.kellyhaney.com; E-mail: haney.studio@sbcgoblobal.net
Products: Original Indian paintings, sculpture, jewelry, baskets, pottery.

SEMINOLE DESIGNS
1202 E. Strothers Ave. • Seminole, OK 74868
  (405) 248-6573; Stuart Pierce (Seminole-Creek), Owner
  E-mail: piercefromak@netscape.net
Products: Seminole patchwork clothing.

KELLY HANEY ART GALLERY
P.O. Box 3817 • Shawnee, OK 74801
  (405) 275-2270; Enoch Kelly Haney, Artist/Owner
  Website: www.kellyhaney.com; E-mail: haney.studio@sbcgoblobal.net
Retail, mail order. Seminole-Creek artist. *Products*: Original Indian paintings,
sculpture, jewelry, baskets, pottery. S.A.S.E. for brochure.

SUPERNAW'S OKLAHOMA INDIAN SUPPLY
P.O. Box 216, 303 • Skiatook, OK 74070
  (918) 396-1713 Fax 396-1711; Website: www.supernaw.com
  Kugee Supernaw (Quapaw-Osage), Artisan/Owner
Retail, wholesale, mail order. *Products*: Beadwork, boxes, jewelry, pottery,
rugs. Catalog.

THE STILWELL COLLECTION
P.O. Box 1287 • Stilwell, OK 74960
  (918) 696-3607 Fax 696-3723; Debi Kilgore, Owner
Retail, wholesale. *Products*: Baskets, beadwork, jewelry, rugs.
Membership: IACA.

CHEROKEE NATION GIFT SHOPS
P.O. Box 1037 • Tahlequah, OK 74464
 (800) 256-2123; (918) 456-2793
 Website: www.cherokeegiftshop.com
 Linda Taylor (Cherokee), Manager
Retail, mail order. Tribal Enterprise. *Products*: Art, baskets, beadwork, clothing, dolls, pottery, rugs, sculpture. Special orders accepted. Branch shop: Salisaw, OK. Catalog.

CHEROKEE NATIONAL MUSEUM GIFT SHOP
P.O. Box 515, TSA-LA-GI • Tahlequah, OK 74464
 (918) 456-6007; Betty Jo Smith, Manager
Retail, mail order. *Products*: Art, baskets. Price list.

JOYCE JOHNSON
4735 E. Latimer Place • Tulsa, OK 74115
 (918) 835-3069. Mail order. *Products*: Baskets. Cherokee baskets. Brochure & price list.

J. BALES STUDIO
One Plaza Soufe • Tahlequah, OK 74464
 (405) 247-3993; Jean E. Bales, Owner
By appointment. *Products*: Art, pottery, sculpture. Special orders accepted.

LITTLECROW TRADING POST
119 E. Grand Ave., P.O. Box 237 • Tonkawa, OK 74653
 (580) 628-9907; James & Janet Littlecrow, Owners
 Website: www.littlecrowtradingpost.com
Wholesale, retail. *Products*: Specializes in custom & in-stock powwow regalia for tribes of the Woodlands, Plains & Southeastern U.S.

GEMSTONE ENTERPRISES/LeGRAND TREASURES
TREASURE LEGEND WHOLESALE
5103 S. Sheridan #115 • Tulsa, OK 74145
Branch shop: 7413 E. 19th, Tulsa, OK 74112
 (918) 269-6336; Vernis Maxwell, Owner
 Website: www.legendtreasurel.com; Website: www.treasurelegend.com
 E-mail: vernis@legendtreasure.com. *Membership*: IACA.

GILCREASE MUSEUM SHOP
1400 Gilcrease Museum Rd. • Tulsa, OK 74127
 (918) 596-2724/5 Fax 596-2727; Website: www.gilcrease.org
 E-mail: museumshop@gilcrease.org; Amanda Burns, Manager
Wholesale, retail. *Products*: All. *Membership*: IACA. Catalog.

LYON'S INDIAN STORE
401 E. 11th St. • Tulsa, OK 74120
 (918) 582-6372 Fax 582-545; Larry & Janie Lyon, Owners
Retail, mail order. Products: Beadwork, clothing, jewelry, rugs. *Membership*: IACA. Brochure; catalog for craft supplies only. Branch shop: Woodland Hills Mall, Tulsa, OK.

ZADOKA POTTERY
12515 E. 37th St. • Tulsa, OK 74146
 (918) 663-9455; David Thompson, Owner
Retail, wholesale, mail order. *Product*: Earthenware storage vessels, vases and bowls.

CHOCTAW NATION CAPITOL MUSEUM GIFT STORE
HC64 Box 3270 • Tuskahoma, OK 74574
 (918) 569-4465. *Products*: Beadwork, jewelry, blankets, fabric, hats, prints.

TUSHKA HOMMA TRADING COMPANY
P.O. Box 29, HC64 Box 3364 • Tuskahoma, OK 74574
 (918) 569-4980; Website: www.nancysoutherland-holmes.com
 E-mail: nancy@nancysoutherland-holmes.com
 Nancy Southerland-Holmes (Choctaw), Artisan/Owner
Products: Designs 100% cotton Native American fabrics for quilters, sewers, quilt shops, decorators; handmade quilts, one-of-a-kind quilted /leather Buffalo shoulder bags.

HERITAGE ART MARKETING
76090 S. 300 Road • Wagoner, OK 74467
 (918) 485-1616 Fax 485-2892
 Website: www.heritageartmarketing.com
 E-mail: info@heritageartmarketing.com
 Randy E. Wassom (Cherokee), Owner/Manager
Products: Art work by Talamadge Davis (historical Native American realism artist).

TURTLE WOMAN STUDIO
1106 SE 7th St. • Wagoner, OK 74467
 (918) 485-5878; "Nancy" Janet L. Smith, Owner
Retail. By appointment only. *Products*: Art.

WEWOKA TRADING POST
Seminole Nation Historical Society
524 S. Wewoka Ave., P.O. Box 1532 • Wewoka, OK 74884
 (405) 257-5580
Retail, mail order. Products: Art, beadwork, clothing, dolls, jewelry, rugs. Special orders accepted. Brochure & catalog.

3 FEATHERS TRADING POST
1320 Hwy. 2 South • Wilburton, OK 74578
 (918) 448-2443 or 465-0508; John Johynson White (Choctaw-Kiowa), Owner
Products: Woodcarvings, pipes, paintings, jewelry, beadwork

ITI-HEKIA CEDAR BOXES
P.O. Box 692 • Wynona, OK 74084
 (918) 846-2611 or 636-9619; Website: www.itihekiaco.com
 E-mail: cedarboxes@itihekiaco.com; Thomas Hekia (Choctaw), Artist/Owner
Products: Cedar feather boxes, jewelry boxes, bone chokers, necklaces, leather dance belts.

OREGON

RED BEAR CREATIONS
358 N. Lexington Ave. • Bandon, OR 97411
 (503) 347-9725; Red She Bear, Owner
Retail, wholesale. *Products*: Traditional star quilts & drum covers made to order. Brochure.

OARD'S
42456 Hwy. 20 East • Burns, OR 97720
 (800) 637-0252; (503) 493-2535 Fax 493-2534
 Mavis F. Oard, Owner; E-mail: oardsgallery@aol.com
Retail. *Products*: All. *Membership*: IACA.

SEVEN FEATHERS HOTEL CASINO RESORT GIFT GALLERY
146 Chief Minaleta Lane • Canyonville, OR 97417
 (541) 839-1111 Fax 839-1303; Sue Hyers, Manager. *Membership*: IACA.

ART OF THE VINEYARD, INC.
1430 Willamette, Suite 24 • Eugene, OR 97401
 William & Jacqueline Kaufman, Owners
Retail. *Products*: Art, baskets, books, Northwest Coast art, jewelry, rugs. *Membership*: IACA.

DAKOTA'S DESIGNS
P.O. Box 114 • Grand Ronde, OR 97347
 (503) 879-4240; E-mail: sangretta@yahoo.com
 Dakota Whitecloud (Confederated Tribes Grand Ronde), Owner/manager
Products: Handcrafted leatherwork; sterling silver jewelry.

THE ALEUT CONNECTION
19415 SW Sycamore • Lake Oswego, OR 97035
 (503) 639-2686; Vivian A. Ross (Aleut), Owner
Products: Cedar bark basketry, stained glass art of Alaska, the Pacific Northwest and the Pacific Rim.

AMERICAN SHADOWS
1800 SE Hwy. 101, Suite G • Lincoln City, OR 97367
 (503) 996-6887; Patricia L. Erickson
Retail. *Products*: Art, baskets, beadwork, clothing, dolls, jewelry, kachinas, pottery, rugs, sand paintings, sculpture, carvings. *Membership*: IACA.

CAYUSE GALLERY
151 SE First St. • Pendleton, OR 97801
 (541) 966-1191; E-mail: cayusegallery@oregontrail.net
 Marlene(Navajo) & Maynard (Cayuse) White Owl Lavador, Artisan/Owners
Products: Traditional & contemporary beadwork, clothing, jewelry.

CROW'S SHADOW INSTITUTE OF THE ARTS
48004 St. Andrew's Rd. • Pendleton, OR 97801
 (541) 276-3954 Fax 276-3397; Melissa Ponte, Director
 Website: www.crowsshadow.org; E-mail: crow@crowsshadow.org
Printmaking studio & gallery located on the Confederated Tribes of the Umatilla Indian Reservation. *Products*: Fine art lithography, woodcuts, linocuts, etchings. *Activities*: Workshops in traditional Native American Plateau arts & crafts & printmaking.

NADINE'S NATIVE DOLLS
Rt. 1, Box 270 • Pendleton, OR 97801
  (541) 276-2566; Nadine Van Mechelen (Yurok-Karok-Tolowa),
  Craftswoman/Owner
Retail, wholesale. By appointment only. *Product*: Dolls dressed in authentic
Indian costume for collectors. Special orders accepted.

TAMASTSLIKT CULTURAL INSTITUTE
72789 Hwy. 331 • Pendleton, OR 97801
  (541) 966-9748; Website: www.tamastslikt.org
  Robert L. Conner (Confederated Tribes of Umatilla), Director
Products: Plateau jewelry, beaded bags, quillwork, moccasins, breast plates,
shawls.

WIND SONG GALLERY
7 SE Court • Pendleton, OR 97801
  (541) 276-7993; Nadine Van Mechelen (Yurok-Karok-Tolowa), Owner
Retail, wholesale. *Products*: Art, dolls, jewelry. Dolls dressed in authentic
Indian costume for collectors. Special orders accepted.

A GALLERY OF NATIONS
454 Elm St. • Phoenix, OR 97535
  Website: www.agalleryofnations.com; E-mail: infoor@agalleryofnations.com
  Eleanor Lefthand Bianchi (Arapaho), Owner
Products: Online store featuring Zuni fetishes, turquoise & silver jewelry,
pottery.

THE BEAD GOES ON
8721 S.E. Foster Rd. • Portland, OR 97266
  (503) 788-9533; Kellie LaBonty, Owner
Retail/wholesale. *Products*: Native American artwork & craft supplies.
Special orders accepted.

BLAZE GALLERY
228 SW 1st • Portland, OR 97204
  (503) 224-8101; Randall Blaze (Oglala Sioux), Artist/Owner
  Judi Blaze, Manager
Retail, wholesale, mail order. Oglala Sioux artist. *Products*: Art, jewelry,
pottery, sculpture. Commissions & special orders accepted.

G/M GALLERIES
7824 SW Capitol Hwy. • Portland, OR 97219
  (503) 244-3640 ; Marie & George Woodcock, Owners. *Membership*: IACA.

METAL ARTS GROUP
P.O. Box 80727 • Portland, OR 97280
  (800) 325-6958 Fax (877) 244-1167
  Website: www.native-american-indian-silver-jewelry.com
  E-mail: info@metalartsgroup.com
Retail, wholesale. Products: Silver jewelry; rings, necklaces, earrings,
bracelets, belt buckles, knives. Catalog available.

QUINTANA'S GALLERIES
501 SW Broadway • Portland, OR 97205-3425
  (503) 223-1729 Fax 223-6030; Cecil & Rose Quintana, Owners
  E-mail: qgallery@teleport.com; Website: www.quintanagalleries.com
Retail, mail order. *Products*: Contemporary Native American Indian art.
Specializes in Northwest Coast Indian & Inuit art, masks, totems, bentwood
boxes, etc. Also, a large collection of Inuit soapstone carvings. Accepts artwork
on consignment.

7SEASSELECT.COM
46585 Good Pasture Rd. • Vida, OR 97488
  (541) 896-3192; Gail Vander Vorst, Owner
  Website: www.7seasselect.com; E-mail: gail@7seasselect.com
Membership: IACA.

PENNSYLVANIA

INDIAN POST
1645 Hausman Rd. • Allentown, PA 18104
  (215) 395-5530; Carolyn Foreback, Owner; Connie Foreback, Manager
Retail. *Products*: Art, baskets, books, clothing, drums, pipes, jewelry,
rugs, sand paintings, sculpture. *Membership*: IACA.

TURTLE ISLAND TREASURERS
Lenni Lenape Historical Society, Museum of Indian Culture
2825 Fish Hatchery Rd. • Allentown, PA 18103-9801
  (610) 797-2121 Fax 797-2801; Carla J.S. Messinger, Manager
  E-mail: lenape@comcat.com; Website: www.lenape.org
Retail. *Products*: Art, beadwork, books, books, clothing, dolls, jewelry

TURQUOISE 'N TREASURES
21 E. High St. • Elizabethtown, PA 17022
  (717) 367-1848; Nancy Barnitz, Owner
Retail. *Products*: Art, beadwork, clothing, dolls, jewelry,
kachinas, pottery, rugs, sand paintings. *Membership*: IACA.

EICHER INDIAN MUSEUM SHOP
Ephrata Community Park, P.O. Box 601 • Ephrata, PA 17522
  (717) 738-3084; Beverly Flaherty, Manager
Retail. *Products*: Art, baskets, beadwork, clothing, dolls, jewelry,
kachinas, pottery, rugs, sand paintings, sculpture, carvings.

SOUTHWEST SELECTIONS
The Art Works at Doneckers
100 N. State St., Gallery 112 • Ephrata, PA 17522
  (717) 738-9593; Jeanne Loomis, Owner
Retail. *Products*: Fetishes, heishi, jewelry, kachinas, pottery,
rugs, sand paintings. *Membership*: IACA.

FITCH'S TRADING POST
230 N. 3rd St. • Harrisburg, PA 17101
  (717) 233-6832
  Delores Fitch-Basehore; Richard & Deirdre Basehore, Owners
Retail, mail order. *Products*: Native American fine art representing 32 tribes in
North America & tribe in Central America. *Appraisals*: All. *Membership*: IACA.

BRANT MACKLEY GALLERY
1017 Mt. Alem Dr. • Hummelstown, PA 17036
  (717) 566-0780 Fax 554-2176; E-mail: brantmackley@verizon.net
Retail. *Products*: Antique American Indian artifacts: beadwork, pottery, totems,
masks, rattles, baskets, weapons, pipes, blankets & rugs.

WESTERN LEGENDS GALLERY
1311 Old Ford Rd. • Huntingdon Valley, PA 19006
  (215) 659-7530; Robert & Annette Griffith, Owners
Retail. *Products*: Art, beadwork, clothing, dolls, jewelry, kachinas, pottery, rugs,
sand paintings, sculpture, carvings. *Membership*: IACA.

ART LEGENDS
P.O. Box 373 • Lahaska, PA 18931
  (866) 875-2900; (215) 862-6844
  Website: www.art-legends.com; E-mail: info@art-legends.com
  Alan Stifelman & Rosemary McQuate, Owners. *Membership*: IACA.

SILVER CREEK GALLERY
17 W. Chestnut St. • Lancaster, PA 17603
  (717) 299-1983; 656-4692; Donna & Bob Pleis, Owners
  Website: www.silvercreekgallery.us
  E-mail: silvercreekgallery@msn.com. *Membership*: IACA.

THE GALLANT BEAR
740 W. Brubaker Valley Rd. • Lititz, PA 17543
  (717) 626-9620; June Smith, Owner
  E-mail: juneasmith@peoplepc.com. *Membership*: IACA.

THE TURQUOISE SHOPPE
26 E. Main St. • Lititz, PA 17543
  (717) 626-1616; Carol Stocker, Owner
Retail. *Products*: Baskets, beadwork, clothing, dolls, jewelry, kachinas, pottery,
rugs, sand paintings, sculpture, carvings. *Membership*: IACA.

WESTERN LEGENDS GALLERY
1640 Stockton Rd. • Meadowbrook, PA 19046
  (215) 517-4464; Robert & Annette Griffith, Owners. *Membership*: IACA.

SOUTHWEST VISIONS
36 W. Mechanic St. • New Hope, PA 18938
  (215) 862-0323 Fax 797-1934; Sandie & Nikki Anthony
Retail. *Products*: Art, baskets, beadwork, clothing, dolls, jewelry, kachinas,
pottery, rugs, sand paintings, sculpture, carvings. *Membership*: IACA. Catalog.

DANDELION
1618 Latimer St. • Philadelphia, PA 19103
  (215) 972-0999; Beth Fluke, Owner
Retail. *Products*: Art, beadwork, clothing, dolls, jewelry, kachinas, pottery, rugs,
sand paintings, sculpture, carvings. *Membership*: IACA. *Branch*: 1718 Sansom
St., Philadelphia, PA.

BEVERLEY CONRAD
RR 1, Box 159 • Selinsgrove, PA 17870
  (717) 374-2647; Beverley Conrad (St. Regis Mohawk), Owner

Retail, wholesale. St. Regis Mohawk craftsperson. *Products*: Original artwork, limited edition prints, beadwork, clothing, moccasins, fetishes. Reproduction & original Eastern Woodland Indian products. Portraits & commissions accepted; museum work & demonstrations.

SOUTHWEST IMAGES
1041 Hilltown Plaza, Rt. 113 • Souderton, PA 18964
(215) 721-9606; Marla & Bill Hammerschmidt, Owners
Retail. *Products*: Art, clothing, dolls, jewelry, kachinas, pottery, sand paintings, sculpture, carvings. *Membership*: IACA.

SHADY LAMP WORKSHOP
1800 Mearns Rd., Bldg. JJ • Warminster, PA 18974
(215) 672-2350 Fax 672-6401; Eileen & Jack Wilson, Owners
Retail, wholesale. *Products*: Art, baskets, children's items, ornaments, jewelry, rugs. *Membership*: IACA. *Branch shop*: Peddler's Village, Lahaska, PA 18931.

TOMAR SERVICES, INC.
P.O. Box 233 • Wexford, PA 15090
(412) 367-2310; Todd & Mary Grant, Owners
Retail, wholesale. *Products*: Art, baskets, beadwork, dolls, jewelry, kachinas, pottery, rugs, sand paintings, sculpture, carvings.

RHODE ISLAND

DOVE TRADING POST
390 Summit Rd., Arcadia Village • Exeter, RI 02822-1808
(401) 539-2786 or 539-7795
Eleanor F. Dove, Owner; Dawn Dove, Manager
Retail, wholesale. *Products*: Beadwork, clothing, jewelry, pottery.

NATIVE SONS
685 West Shore Rd. • Warwick, RI 02889
(401) 732-1754; Talldog Monroe (Narragansett), Artist/Owner
Website: www.native-sons.com
Retail, wholesale. *Products*: Handmade Native American jewelry & crafts, specializing in wampum.

SAGE SPIRIT, LLC.
5 Old Usqupaugh Rd. • West Kingston, RI 02892
(401) 783-1916; 782-8230; Lou Torres, Owner
Website: www.sagespirit.net

SOUTH CAROLINA

SARA AYERS
1182 Brookwood Cr. • W. Columbia, SC 29169
(803) 794-5436; Sara Ayers, Artisan/Owner
Mail order. *Product*: Pottery. Special orders accepted. Price list.

WESTERN VISIONS, INC.
Wolf Creek Gallery, 1315 Celebrity Circle • Myrtle Beach, SC 29577
(800) 664-0484; (803) 448-4780 Fax 448-4733
Grace C. Krueger, Frank Fezzie, Karen Mattscheck, Owners
E-mail: wesvis@sccoast.net
Retail. *Products*: Native American jewelry, art, sculpture, drums, reproduction artifacts, books, incense, music. *Branch shop*: 4728 C Hwy. 17 South, North Myrtle Beach, SC 29582 (800) 745-5691; (803) 272-2698 Fax 272-3798. *Membership*: IACA.

CATAWBA INDIAN TRADITIONS, POTTERY & BEADWORK
Catawba Indian Nation, 2253 Indian Trail • Rock Hill, SC 29730
(803) 366-3317; Monte "Hawk" Branham & Anna "Speakswell" Branham (Catawba), Artisans/Owners. Retail. Special orders accepted.
Products: Traditional Catawba pottery and loom beading.

CATAWBA POTTERY BY CINDY ALLEN
1815 Baskins Rd. • Rock Hill, SC 29730
(803) 324-5088; Cindy Allen (Catawba), Artisan/Owner
By appointment. *Products*: Traditional 19th century Catawba pottery.

CREATIONS FROM THE GOOD EARTH
Catawba Indian Nation, 2253 Indian Trail • Rock Hill, SC 29730
(803) 329-2707 or (704) 788-4258
M. Caroleen Sanders (Catawba), Artisan/Owner
Products: Catawba Indian ceremonial pottery with ancient Catawba designs & motifs, traditionally handbuilt & outdoors fired.

ISWA WHISPERING SAGE
Catawba Indian Nation, 2253 Indian Trail • Rock Hill, SC 29730
(803) 329-2707 or (704) 788-4258

Carolyn Sanders (Catawba), Artisan/Owner
Products: Pre-Columbian pottery using ancient techniques.

ROBBINS FAMILY POTTERY
1599 Hagler Dr. • Rock Hill, SC 29730
(803) 324-0204
Earl, Viola & Margaret Robbins (Catawba), Artisans/Owners
Products: Traditional Catawba pottery.

SOUTH DAKOTA

TETON PAINTED LODGES
P.O. Box 484 • Allen, SD 57714
(605) 454-3450 or 455-2452
Warren "Gus" Yellow Hair (Northern Cheyenne/Lakota),
and Lori Whirlwind Horse (Lakota), Owners
Products: Custom painted lodges (tipis) sweat lodge coverings; buffalo hide painting; buffalo products, Lakota style beadwork, traditional quillwork; 1800's re-enactments, song & dance presentations.

JOANNE BIRD
P.O. Box 487 • Brookings, SD 57006
(605) 693-3183 Fax 693-3189; Website: www.joannebird.com
JoAnne Bird (Lakota), Artist/Owner. Retail, wholesale, mail order.
Products: Original acrylic paintings, sculpture, prints.

ST. JOSEPH LAKOTA DEVELOPMENT COUNCIL
St. Joseph's Indian School • Chamberlain, SD 57326
(605) 734-6021 ext. 307; Cy Maus, Manager
Retail, wholesale, mail order. *Products*: Art, beadwork, clothing, dolls, jewelry, rugs. Special orders accepted for quilts. Brochure.

NOXCUSESNONE!
P.O. Box 42 • Flandreau, SD 57028
(605) 491-4598; Lynn Hart (Yankton Sioux), Owner
E-mail: noxcusesnone@hotmail.com. *Products*: Decals, stickers, custom designs for businesses, featuring American Indian designs/imagery.

FOREVER RESORTS-BADLANDS LODGE
1 Cedar St. • Interior, SD 57750
(605) 433-5460 Fax 533-5560
Rex Maughan & Don Wallace, Owners. *Membership*: IACA.

GALLERY OF INDIAN ARTS
Xanterra Parks Rushmore , P.O. Box 178 • Keystone, SD 57751
(605) 574-2515 Fax 574-2495; Mark Parker, Manager
Website: www.rushmoregifts.com; E-mail: mparker@xanterra.com
Retail. *Products*: Art, dolls, drums, pipes, jewelry, pottery, rugs, sandpaintings, sculpture. *Membership*: IACA.

THE INDIANS
141 Winter St., P.O. Box 162 • Keystone, SD 57751
(605) 341-7452 Fax 666-4864; Bruce & Kathy Uhrig, Owners
Website: www.theindianskeystone.com;
E-mail: info@theindianskeystone.com
Retail. *Products*: Art, baskets, beadwork, clothing, dolls, jewelry, kachinas, pottery, rugs, sand paintings, sculpture, carvings. *Membership*: IACA.

CHEYENNE CROSSING STORE
HC-37, Box 1220 • Lead, SD 57754
(605) 584-3510; Jim & Bonnie LeMar, Owners
Retail. *Products*: Art, beadwork, clothing, dolls, jewelry, kachinas, pottery, rugs. *Membership*: IACA.

OYATE KIN CULTURAL COOPERATIVE
c/o Wesley Hare, Jr. • Marty, SD 57361
Mail order. *Products*: Beadwork, boxes, clothing, rugs. Special orders.

LAKOTA ARTS & CRAFTS
P.O. Box 143 • Mission, SD 57555
(605) 747-5445; Mike Marshall (Rosebud Sioux), Owner
E-mail: dcanyon@gwtc.net
Products: Authentic handmade Lakota arts & crafts.

SOLDIER WOMAN ART & GIFT GALLERY
P.O. Box 906 • Mission, SD 57555
(605) 856-4548; Paul & Linda Szabo (Sicangu Lakota), Owners
E-mail: soldierwoman@gwtc.com. Retail, wholesale, mail order.
Sicangu Lakota craftspersons. *Products*: Sterling silver & buffalo horn jewelry; Star quilts, Pendleton blankets; pottery, beadwork, quillwork, paintings, prints,

moccasins, dance regalia; Northern Plains tribes artwork. Custom designs. Special orders accepted.

JACKSON ORIGINALS
P.O. Box 1049 • Mission, SD 57555
(605) 856-2541; Jackie Colomb, Owner. Retail, wholesale, mail order. By appointment only. *Product*: contemporary apparel. Price list.

CRAZY HORSE
P.O. Box 153 • Pringle, SD 57773
(603) 436-3629; Lynn & Gardner Gray. Retail. *Products*: All.

CONTEMPORARY LAKOTA FASHION
121 Patton St. • Rapid City, OK 57701
(605) 718-9565; Geraldine Sherman (Oglala Lakota), Artist/Owner
Retail, wholesale, mail order. Sioux craftsperson.
Products: Contemporary fashions.

DAKOTA DRUM COMPANY
603 Main St. • Rapid City, SD 57701
(605) 348-2421; Website: www.dakotadrum.com
Retail, wholesale. *Products*: Authentic Native American drums, hide paintings, beadwork, etc.

LAKOTA ANGELS
211 St. Andrew • Rapid City, SD 57701
(605) 721-8075 Fax 721-0753; Website: www.lakotaangels.com
E-mail: peacock@rapidnet.com
Wanda Blacksmith Peacock (Lower Brule Sioux), Artisan/Owner
Retail, wholesale. *Products*: Handmade Indian angels, cradle babies, dream catcher ornament hangers,

PRAIRIE EDGE TRADING CO. & GALLARIES
P.O. Box 8303 • Rapid City, SD 57709
(800) 541-2388; (605) 342-3086 Fax 341-6415
Ray Hillenbrand, President; E-mail: prairie@rapidnet.com
Website: www.prairieedge.com
Retail, wholesale, mail order. *Products*: Plains Indian art and artifacts; jewelry, pottery, beads, craft supplies, books, tapes, CDs, DVDs, videos. Catalog.

SIOUX POTTERY
1441 E. St. Joseph St. • Rapid City, SD 57701
(800) 574-4366; (605) 341-3657
Website: www.siouxpottery.com; E-mail: salesp@siouxpottery.com
Rob Hammerquist & Gene Hensey, Owners. *Membership*: IACA.

SIOUX TRADING POST
415 6th St. • Rapid City, SD 57701
(800) 456-3394 (mail order); (605) 348-4822 Fax 348-9624
Website: www.siouxtrading.com; E-mail: prairie@rapidnet.com
Ray Hillenbrand, Manager
Retail, wholesale, mail order. Products: Authentic Plains Indian craft supplies & beadwork, clothing, dolls, drums, pipes, artifacts & reproductions, jewelry, kachinas, rugs & weavings, sculpture, carvings, stones & shells. *Membership*: IACA. Brochure; catalog, $2. *Branch shops*: Mission, SD, and Santa Fe, NM.

WHISPERING THUNDER
2107 Oak Ave. • Rapid City, SD 57701
(605) 716-7552; Mitchel Zephier (Lower Brule Lakota), Artisan/Owner
Retail, wholesale, mail order. *Products*: Northern Plains Indian design silver jewelry; Lakota arts & crafts; contemporary & traditional music,

BRULE SIOUX ARTS & CRAFTS COOPERATIVE
P.O. Box 230 • St. Francis, SD 57572
(605) 747-2019. Retail, wholesale. *Products*: Art, beadwork, jewelry, books.

PRAIRIE STAR GALLERY
207 S. Phillips Ave. • Sioux Falls, SD 57104
(605) 338-9300; John & Linda Boyd, Owners
Website: www.prairiestar.com; E-mail: linda@prairiestar.com
Membership: IACA.

RED HORSE ARTS & CUSTOM FRAMES
42614 Colony Rd. • Tabor, SD 57063
(605) 463-2614; Art Cleveland Red Horse (Navajo), Owner
E-mail: redhorsearts@peoplepc.com
Products: Paintings, prints, jewelry, beadwork, rattles.

WALL DRUG STORE, INC.
510 Main St., P.O. Box 401 • Wall, SD 57790
(605) 279-2175 Fax 279-2699; Ted H. Hustead, Manager

Website: www.walldrug.com; E-mail: walldrug@gwtc.net
Retail. *Products*: Art, baskets, beadwork, books, clothing, dolls, jewelry, kachinas, pottery. Membership: IACA.

BAD NATION CREATION
P.O. Box 87 • White River, SD 57579
(605) 208-4708 or 208-3240; Jay Burnett (Rosebud/Sicangu Lakota), Owner
Products: Jewelry; buffalo skulls & shoulder blades; all products are inlaid with various stones.

TENNESSEE

MICKIE OVERTON - "NATIVE2ME"
P.O. Box 243 • Bon Aqua, TN 37025
(931) 670-6687; Mickie Overton(Osage/Chickasaw), Artisan
E-mail: mickieo@bellsouth.net
Products: Dance clothing, shawls; specializing in children & young adults.

EAGLE FEATHER
Old Town Hall Market Place
144 E. Main St. • Jonesborough, TN 37659
(423) 753-2095; Jane Blair, Owner
Retail, mail order. *Products*: Art, baskets, beadwork, books, clothing, dolls, jewelry, kachinas, pottery, rugs, sand paintings. *Membership*: IACA.

VENUS BRIGHTSTAR
P.O. Box 314 • Lyles, TN 37098
(615) 585-1090; Venus Brightstar, Owner
Website: www.venusbrightstar.com
Retail. Products: Fine jewelry creations.

TEXAS

NATIVE AMERICAN IMAGES, INC.
P.O. Box 156 • Austin, TX 78767
(512) 472-3049; Ted Pearsall, Owner
Wholesale. *Product*: Art. *Membership*: IACA.

AMERICAN INDIAN JEWELRY
P.O. Box 2527 • Bandera, TX 78003
(830) 460-4100 Fax 796-4000; Bo Miller, Owner
Website: www.americanindianjewelry.com
E-mail: bo@americanindianjewelry.com. *Membership*: IACA.

BONHAM GALLERY
P.O. Box 938 • Burleson, TX 76097
(800) 333-5287; (817) 335-3491
H.E. Eugene Bonham, M.D. Retail, wholesale. *Product*: Art.

AMERICAN WEST TRADING COMPANY
1701 Laura Ln. • College Station, TX 77840
(505) 265-8549; Ken Kaemmerle, Owner
Wholesale. *Products*: Northwest Coast art, kachinas, pottery, rugs, sculpture. *Membership*: IACA.

GIFTS OF THE SPIRIT
1717 Waldron Rd. • Corpus Christi, TX 78418
(361) 937-1990; E-mail: donnfrankie@giftsofthespirit.com
Donald "Little Boy" Greenwood (Cherokee), Artisan/Owner
Products: Dream catcher jewelry (fancy & traditional; leather-covered earrings & necklace sets; Indian fans, shawls; photography.

RANCE HOOD STUDIO
PO. Box 72 • Denison, TX 75021
(903) 463-6020; Rance Hood (Comanche), Artist/Owner
Website: www.rancehoodstudio.com
E-mail: rance@rancehoodstudio.com
Products: Original paintings, limited edition prints, serigraphs, posters & notecards.

NASELLER.COM
422 Softwood Dr. • Duncanville, TX 75137
(214) 789-1109; Sharon I. Emery, Owner
Website: naseller.com; E-mail: naseller@sharonemery.com
Membership: IACA.

THUR-SHAN ARTS & CRAFTS CENTER
305 Yaya Lane • El Paso, TX 79907
(915) 859-5287 Fax 860-8972; Albert Alvidrez (Tigua Pueblo), Manager
Retail. Tigua Indian tribal enterprise. *Products*: Pottery, jewelry, and arts & crafts of the Pueblo.

TIGUA INDIAN RESERVATION CULTURAL CENTER
Box 17579, 122 S. Old Pueblo Rd. • El Paso, TX 79917
  (915) 859-3916; Pat Gomez (Tigua Pueblo), Manager
Retail. Tribal enterprise. *Products*: Jewelry, pottery.

YSLETA DEL SUR PUEBLO CULTURAL CENTER
122 S. Old Pueblo • El Paso, TX 79907
  (915) 859-3916 Fax 859-2889; Vince Munoz, General Manager
Retail, wholesale. Tribal enterprise. *Products*: Art, jewelry, kachinas,
pottery, rugs.

GUILDHALL, INC.
2535 Weisenberger • Fort Worth, TX 76107
  (800) 356-6733; (817) 332-6733 Fax 332-8100
  John M. Thompson, III, Owner
Retail, wholesale. *Products*: Art, baskets, beadwork, boxes, clothing,
Northwest Coast art, sculpture. *Membership*: IACA.

NATIVE TREASURES
260 Ridgewood Rd. Ext. • Georgetown, TX 78628
  (512) 930-5854; Karen M. Bullard, Owner
Retail, mail order. *Products*: Native American art and artifacts.

PUEBLO CONNECTION
334 S. Main St. • Grapevine, TX 76051
  (817) 481-7724; Patrick & Beverly Fairchild, Owners
  Website: www.puebloconnection.com; E-mail: shop@puebloconnection.com
Retail. *Products*: All. *Appraisals*: Rugs. *Membership*: IACA.

DINETKAH SILVER GALLERY
351 Memorial City Mall • Houston, TX 77024-2512
  Sue O'Dell, Owner
Retail. *Products*: Art, baskets, beadwork, jewelry, kachinas, pottery,
rugs, sand paintings, sculpture, carvings.

DONALD GREENWOOD GIFTS OF THE SPIRIT
10414 Autumn Meadow Lane, Houston, TX 77064 (918) 866-2653
  Donald "Little Boy" Greenwood, Owner
Retail, mail order, will consider wholesale & special orders. Cherokee
craftsperson. *Products*: Art, clothing, jewelry. Brochure and price list, $2.50.
Membership: IACA.

INDIAN SUN
2444 Times Blvd. #110 • Houston, TX 77005
  (713) 523-4288 Fax 523-4570; Merritt L. Smith, Owner
Membership: IACA.

SILVER MOON TRADERS
1110 Bay Oaks Rd. • Houston, TX 77008
  (713) 529-0848; Rebecca Burt, Owner
  Website: www.silvermoontraders.com
  E-mail: silvertrader@earthlink.net. *Membership*: IACA.

TRADEWINDS COLLECTIBLES
12007 N. Fairhollow Ln. • Houston, TX 77043
  (713) 688-4211 Fax 684-4657; C.W. & Elizabeth Saville, Owners
Membership: IACA.

ZAPOTEC ART/SOUTHWEST SPIRIT
1728 Sunset Blvd. • Houston, TX 77005
  (713) 529-0890 Fax 529-0365
  Website: www.zapotecart.co; E-mail: zapotecart@aol.com
  Michael C. McBride & Winifred Patton, Owners
Retail, wholesale. *Products*: Drums, pipes, fetishes, jewelry, kachinas, pottery,
rugs. *Membership*: IACA. Catalog.

INDIAN CREEK JEWELRY
5920 Lalagray Lane • Hurst, TX 76148
  (817) 268-4921; Betty Beaver, Owner
Retail. *Products*: beadwork, fetishes, heishi, jewelry, pottery.

NATIVE INNOVATION
930 Hidden Canyon • Katy, TX 77450
  (281) 300-5494; Jeff M. Hoffman, Owner
  Website: www.nativeinnovation.com
  E-mail: jhoffman02@earthlink.net. *Membership*: IACA.

CROW'S NEST ART GALLERY
230 Jefferson • La Porte, TX 77571
  (281) 471-4371 Fax 471-2468; Fern Yung, Owner
  E-mail: flyung@aol.com. Retail. *Products*: All. *Membership*: IACA. Brochure.

TARBRADA
611 Camilla Lane • Lantana, TX 76226
  (940) 728-2998; Virginia & Marlin Boswell, Owners. *Membership*: IACA.

EAGLE DANCER GALLERY
159 Gulf Fwy. So. • League City, TX 77573
  (713) 332-6028 Fax 554-2475; Greg Reynolds, Owner
  Website: www.eagledancergallery.com
  E-mail: information@eagledancergallery.com
Retail. *Products*: Baskets, beadwork, clothing, dolls, jewelry,
pottery, rugs. *Membership*: IACA.

HARJO FLUTES
202 Gavy Ct. • Livingston, TX 77351
  (936) 327-4308; William Harjo (Creek), Owner
  E-mail: wgharjo@livingston.net
Products: Native American flutes made from cane, cedar, hardwood.

L. DAVID EVENING THUNDER CONTEMPORARY NATIVE AMERICAN ART
5926 Indian Springs • Livingston, TX 77351
  (936) 563-3200; L. David Eveningthunder (Shoshone), Artist/Owner
Retail, wholesale. By appointment only. *Products*: Original art by L. David
Evening Thunder; other crafts persons: baskets, beadwork, clothing.

ALBAMA-COUSHATTA GIFT SHOP
Alabama-Coushatta Indian Reservation
571 State Park Rd. 56, Route 3, Box 640 • Livingston, TX 77351
  (936) 563-4391; (800) 392-4794 (TX); Roland A. Poncho, Manager
Retail, mail order. Alabama-Coushatta Tribes of Texas tribal enterprise.
Products: Baskets, beadwork, clothing, jewelry, pottery.

TATANKA TRADITIONS
325 Private Rd. 6602 • Mineola, TX 75773
  (903) 569-5613
Retail. *Product*: Custom bustles made to specifications utilizing natural
feathers.

ANNESLEY STUDIO
P.O. Box 3 • Missouri City, TX 77459
  (713) 729-8960; Robert H. Annsley, Owner
Mail order, some wholesale & retail. *Products*: Bronze sculpture,
original graphics and drawings, original paintings.

TIGER'S TURQUOISE SHOP
3807 Meeks Dr. • Orange, TX 77630
  (409) 886-7906; Abe Tiger, Owner
Retail. *Products*: baskets, beadwork, jewelry, Navajo rugs, pottery.

THE VICTORIAN DREAMER & THE COWBOY
1511 Browning Rd. • Orange, TX 77630
  (409) 882-9339; Josephine & Robert Walter
Retail. *Products*: Art, baskets, clothing, dolls, jewelry, kachinas, pottery, rugs,
sand paintings. *Membership*: IACA.

CRAZY CROW TRADING POST
1801 N. Airport Rd., P.O. Box 847 • Pottsboro, TX 75076
  (800) 786-6210; (903) 786-2287 Fax 786-9059
  Web site: www.crazycrow.com; E-Mail: info@crazycrow.com
  J. Rex & Ginger Reddick (Comanche), Owners
 Retail, wholesale, mail order. Products: Indian craft supplies, beads, buckskin,
feathers, needles, thread, simulated and genuine sinew, hides, furs, blankets,
books, videos, CDs and cassettes. Special orders accepted. Catalog, $4.

WHITEWOLF PHOTOGRAPHY
P.O. Box 297 • Redwater, TX 75573
  Ron Whitewolf Morgan, Owner
Mail order. *Products*: Original photographs of Indian & western themes.
Brochure.

GALLERY OF THE SOUTHWEST
16402 Hidden View Dr. • San Antonio, TX 78232
  (210) 494-7807 Fax 494-5281; R.D. & Ann K. Carlyon, Owners
  Website: www.galleryofthesouthwest.com
Retail, wholesale. Products: All. Membership: IACA.

KIRFISH KREATIONS
P.O. Box 701052 • San Antonio, TX 78258
  (210) 481-1658; Website: www.kirfishkreations.com
Retail. *Products*: clothing, Native American & Southwest designs;
Native American music & dance videos.

RATTLESNAKE & STAR
209 N. Presa • San Antonio, TX 78205
 (512) 225-5977; Gustin Aldrete, Owner
Retail. *Products*: Baskets, beadwork, dolls, jewelry, pottery,
rugs, sculpture.

THE RESERVATION
8802 Broadway • San Antonio, TX 78217
 (210) 820-3916 Fax 820-0633; Matt & Helen Walence, Owners
Wholesale/retail. *Products*: All. *Appraisals*: Jewelry, pottery.
Membership: IACA. Catalog.

MARTHA BERRY
14295 County Road 252 • Tyler, TX 75709
 (903) 509-3617; Martha Berry (Cherokee), Artisan
 Website: www.berrybeadwork.com; E-mail: berybeadwork@hotmail.com
Products: Traditional Cherokee & Southeastern Woodlands beadwork
including bandolier bags, ceremonial sashes, moccasins, belts.

BOB & DOT NATION'S TWO NATIONS TRADING CO.
109 Shadowyck Ave., P.O. Box 2441 • Universal City, TX 78148
 (512) 658-1185; Bob & Dot Nation, Owners
Wholesale/retail. *Products*: All. Membership: IACA.

BRAZOS ART
P.O. Box 796, 1407 Woodland Hills • Whitehouse, TX 75791
 (903) 839-7573; Linda Busby, Owner
Wholesale, Retail. *Products*: Art, baskets, beadwork, clothing, dolls, jewelry,
kachinas, pottery, rugs, sculpture, carvings. *Membership*: IACA.

THE TURQUOISE LADY
2310 Brook St. • Wichita Falls, TX 76301-6124
 (817) 766-2626 (phone & fax); Edna Redding, Owner
Retail. *Products*: Art, beadwork, clothing, artifacts, jewelry, pottery.
Appraisals: Jewelry.

TWO WHITE HATS
3808-B Kemp #128 • Wichita Falls, TX 76308
 (940) 766-0555; Debbie M. Maloney, Owner
 Website: www.twowhitehats.com; E-mail: info@twowhitehats.com
Membership: IACA.

UTAH

COW CANYON TRADING POST
P.O. Box 88 • Bluff, UT 84512
 (801) 672-2208; Liza Doran, Owner
Retail, wholesale. *Products*: Baskets, beadwork, clothing, artifacts, jewelry,
miniatures, pottery, rugs, sculpture.

TWIN ROCKS TRADING POST
913 E. Navajo Twins Dr. , P.O. Box 230 • Bluff, UT 84512
 (435) 872-2341; Steven B. Simpson, Owner
 Website: www.twinrocks.com
Retail, wholesale. *Products*: Baskets, rugs, jewelry, folk art,
sand painting, fetishes, pottery, sculpture. *Membership*: IACA.

RUBY'S INN GENERAL STORE
U-63 Hwy. 63 • Bryce, UT 84764
 (801) 834-5341 Fax 834-5483; Fred Syrett, Manager
 Website: www.rubysinn.com; E-mail: store@rubysinn.com
Retail. *Products*: All. *Membership*: IACA.

CHEROKEE TRAILS TRADING POST
P.O. Box 136 • Millville, UT 84326
 (435) 232-6882; Bob (StrongBear) Bates, Owner
 Website: www.trailstradingpost.com

LEMA INDIAN TRADING CO.
60 N. Main & 860 S. Main, P.O. Box 474 • Moab, UT 84532
 (801) 259-5055/5942/5217; Anthony & Carolyn Lema
Retail, wholesale. *Products*: Art, baskets, beadwork, clothing, dolls, jewelry,
kachinas, pottery, rugs, sandpaintings, sculpture, carvings. *Membership*: IACA.

REYES MADALENA
1070 Wagner • Moab, UT 84532
 (801) 259-8419; Reyes Madalena (Jemez Pueblo), Artisan
Products: Authentic Pueblo Indian pottery, traditional & contemporary
forms and shapes; free-hand painted and traditionally finished.

EAGLE FEATHER TRADING POST - EAGLECRAFTS, INC.
168 W. 12th St. • Ogden, UT 84404
 (801) 393-3991 Fax 745-0903; E-Mail: eglcrafts@aol.com
 Website: www.eaglefeathertradingpost.com
Retail, wholesale, mail order. *Products*: Art & arts & crafts supplies;
books. Catalog, $4.

BRYCE CANYON TRADING POST
2938 E. Hwy. 12, P.O. Box 371 • Panguitch, UT 84759
 (435) 676-2688; Barbara Sheen & Gayle Collins, Owners
 E-mail: brycetp@color-country.net
Retail. *Products*: Navajo, Zuni, Hopi and Santo Domingo Pueblo pawn jewelry;
Navajo rugs, Pueblo pottery, Hopi kachinas, & Navajo sandpaintings.
Membership: IACA.

RED CANYON INDIAN STORE
3279 Hwy. 12, P.O. Box 717 • Panguitch, UT 84759
 (801) 676-2690; Arthur Tebbs, Owner; Website: www.redcanyon.net
Retail. *Products*: Baskets, beadwork, clothing, dolls, jewelry, kachinas, pottery,
rugs, sandpaintings, sculpture, carvings. *Membership*: IACA.

SOUTHWESTERN EXPRESSIONS
Box 1162, 333 Main St. Mall • Park City, UT 84060
 (801) 649-1612; Monty J. Coates, Owner
Retail. *Products*: Art, baskets, clothing, dolls, jewelry, kachinas, pottery,
rugs, sand paintings, sculpture, carvings. *Membership*: IACA.

AIR TERMINAL GIFTS, INC.
AMF Box 22031, 750 N. Airport Rd. • Salt Lake City, UT 84122
 (801) 575-2540 Fax 575-2541; Thomas F. Crismon, Manager
 Website: www.gotoatg.com; E-mail: tom@gotoatg.com
Retail. *Products*: All. *Appraisals*: Fetishes, heishi, jewelry. *Membership*: IACA.

ZION NATURAL HISTORY ASSOCIATION
Zion National Park • Springdale, UT 84767
Council Hall/Capitol Hill • Salt Lake City, UT 84116
 (801) 538-1398; Jamie Gentry, Director; Mary-Delle Gunn, Owner
Retail. *Products*: Dolls, fetishes, jewelry, pottery, rugs, sand paintings.
Membership: IACA.

PIONEER CENTER
391 N. Main St. • Springville, UT 84663
 (801) 489-6853; Norma L. Suth, Owner
Retail, wholesale. *Products*: Baskets, jewelry, pottery, rugs. Navajo rugs,
Pueblo pottery.

TRIBAL ARTS, LLC
291 Zion Park Blvd., P.O. Box 539 • Springdale, UT 84717
 (435) 772-3353; Dawnita Udall & Crystal Wilson, Owners
 Website: www.tribalartszion.com; E-mail: info@tribalartszion.com
Membership: IACA.

VERMONT

LONG AGO & FAR AWAY
Box 809, Rt. 7A North • Manchester Center, VT 05255
 (802) 362-3435; Grant & Betsy Turner, Owners
Retail. *Products*: All. Appraisals: Baskets, beadwork, books, Northwest Coast
art, jewelry, rugs. *Membership*: IACA

RED ROCK TRADING CO.
P.O. Box 130 • Post Mills, VT 05058
 Ted & Joan Dunham, Owners
Retail, wholesale. *Products*: All. *Appraisals*: Art, baskets, jewelry, pottery, rugs,
sculpture. *Membership*: IACA.

VIRGINIA

ANCIENT IMAGES TRADING CO.
5314 C BirdsView Ln. • Alexandria, VA 22312
 (703) 927-1456 Fax 534-0752; Patricia Sloemer, Owner
 E-mail: ancientimages@cox.net. *Membership*: IACA.

DOG SOLDIERS
P.O. Box 7084 • Alexandria, VA 22307
 Website: www.dogsoldiersfigures.com
Retail. *Products*: Action figures.

TURQUOISE EAGLE
2258 Huntington Ave., Suite S19 • Alexandria, VA 22303
 (703) 960-3875; Wesley Mathews, Manager

Wholesale, mail order. *Products*: Handmade Native American crafts and jewelry. *Appraisals*: Baskets, Northwest Coast art, jewelry, kachinas, pottery, rugs.

AMERIND GALLERY
1691 Roanoke Rd., P.O. Box 588 • Daleville, VA 24083
 (540) 992-1066; Linda, Annette & Joe Anderson, Owners
 E-mail: lindatamerind@aol.com
Retail. *Products*: Art, baskets, books, clothing, dolls, jewelry, kachinas, pottery, rugs, sand paintings, sculpture, carvings. *Membership*: IACA.

FIRST NATIONS ARTS
11917 Main St. • Fredericksburg, VA 22408
 (703) 371-5615 Fax 371-3505; Dennis Fox, Jr., Rebecca Adamson, Owners
Wholesale, retail. *Products*: All. *Membership*: IACA; SWAIA, NMAI.

BASKETS BY TRADITION
12622 Holkein Dr. • Herndon, VA 20171
 (703) 453-0489; Gerald C. Barnes, Sr. (Passamaquoddy), Artisan/Owner
Products: Traditional handmade brown ash & sweetgrass fancy baskets. Basketmaking demonstrations available.

PAMUNKEY POTTERY & CRAFTS TRADING POST
Rt. 1, Pamunkey Indian Reservation • King William, VA 23086
 (804) 843-2851; Mrs. James Bradby, Manager
Retail. Tribal Enterprise. *Products*: Beadwork, miniatures, pottery, rugs.

EAGLE SPIRIT
1038 E. Ocean View Ave. • Norfolk, VA 23503
 (804) 491-2964; Carol Quanty, Owner
Retail. *Products*: Art, beadwork, books, clothing, dolls, jewelry, kachinas, pottery, rugs, sandpaintings, sculpture, carvings. *Membership*: IACA.

VIA GAMBARO STUDIO, INC.
P.O. Box 1117 • Stafford, VA 22554
 (703) 659-0130; Retha Walden Gambaro, Owner
Retail. *Products*: Drums, pipes, flutes, rugs, sculpture. Special orders accepted.

CHEROKEE JEWELRY
8160 Boss St. • Vienna, VA 22182
 (703) 356-0744; Jimmie D. Warnell (Cherokee), Artisan/Owner
 Website: www.cherokeejewelry.com; E-mail: jwarnell@cherokeejewelry.com
Mail order. *Products*: Handmade sterling silver jewelry.

GEORGTOWN COTTON & CO.
2070 Chain Bridge Rd., Suite G-99 • Vienna, VA 22182
 (703) 790-0711 Fax 442-7543
 Maureen Donovan & Moses Robbins, Owners
Retail. *Products*: Beadwork, fetishes, heishi, jewelry, miniatures. *Membership*: IACA.

EAGLE DANCER
1505 Brookfield Cove • Virginia Beach, VA 23464
 (804) 490-0477; Jacqueline LaCrone, Owner
Retail. *Products*: All. *Membership*: IACA.

SKY MAN GALLERY
364 Ridge Circle • Waynesboro, VA 22980
 (540) 946-7357; E-mail: nccrone@ntelos.net
 Makowa Ko Naranjo (Santa Clara Pueblo), Artisan/Owner
Products: Traditional Santa Clara pottery; paintings & prints.

EASTERN WIND CRAFTS
Mattaponi Indian Reservation
Rt. 2, Box 233 • West Point, VA 23181
 (804) 769-0289; Lionel Custalow, Owner
Retail, wholesale, mail order. *Products*: Beadwork, drums, pipes, pottery.

RIVER OF HIGH BANKS POTTERY SHOP
Mattaponi Indian Reservation
35 Nee-A-Ya Lane • West Point, VA 23181
 (804) 769-9331; Christine Rippling Water Custalow, Owner
Retail, wholesale, mail order. *Products*: Hand made pottery, beads and leather items. Brochure.

SNYDER ART STUDIOS
P.O. Box 1565 • Woodbridge, VA 22193
 (703) 670-0074; Kim L. Snyder, Owner
Retail, mail order. *Products*: Art, clothing, rugs, sculpture. Special orders and commissions accepted.

WASHINGTON

MARCH POINT INDIAN ARTS
815 S. March Point Rd. • Anacortes, WA 98221
 (206) 293-5632; Marvi & Joan Wilbur, Owners
Retail, mail order. *Products*: Baskets, clothing, dolls, jewelry, pottery, rugs, sculpture.

POTLATCH GIFTS
Northwind Trading Co., P.O. Box 217 • Anacortes, WA 98221
 (206) 293-6404; Tim King, Manager
Retail, wholesale, mail order. *Products*: Art, baskets, clothing, jewelry, pottery, sculpture. Special orders accepted on wood carvings and clothing. Brochure & price list.

LELOOSKA FAMILY GALLERY
5618 Lewis River Rd. * Ariel, WA 98603
 (206) 225-9522/8828; Patty Fawn, Manager
Retail, some mail order. *Products*: Art, dolls, Northwest Coast art, jewelry, sculpture. All items primarily Northwest Coast.

BUFFALO RIVER - FINE ART PHOTOGRAPHY
P.O. Box 1498 • Auburn, WA 98071
 (360) 825-5752; Bob Charlo (Kalispel), Artist/Owner
 Website: bcharlofineart.com
Products: Photography; museum quality posters of American Indian dancers, dance regalia and landscapes.

LIVERMORE FINE ARTS & DESIGN
P.O. Box 2173 • Bellingham, WA 98227
 (360) 647-9137; Earl Livermore (Blackfeet), Artist/Owner
Mail order. *Products*: Original art work and limited edition prints.

SONG STICK
P.O. Box 490 • Chimacum, WA 98325
 (360) 732-4279; Troy De Roche, Owner
Retail, wholesale, mail order. By appointment only. Blackfeet craftsperson. *Products*: Traditional handcrafted Native American flutes and accessories; cassettes of original traditional flute music. Price list and pictures, $1.

M.J.R. ENTERPRISE
126 SW 301 * Federal Way, WA 98023
 (206) 941-7333; Ron E. English, Owner
Retail, wholesale. *Products*: Baskets, jewelry, kachinas, sand paintings.

FRAN & BILL JAMES, LUMMI INDIAN CRAFTSMEN
4339 Lummi Rd. • Ferndale, WA 98248
 (360) 384-5292/758-2522
Retail, some mail order. *Products*: Beadwork, Northwest Coast art, rugs. Special orders accepted.

INDIAN ISABELLE'S LUMMI WORKSHOP
4435 Haxton Way • Ferndale, WA 98248
 (360) 734-5216; Isabelle Warbus, Owner
Retail. *Products*: Baskets, clothing, jewelry. Special orders accepted.

WHALE DREAMS STUDIO
P.O. Box 392 • Granite Falls, WA 98252
 (360) 691-7772; Jerry Laktonen (Alutiiq/Kodiak), Owner
 Website: www.whaledreams.com; E-mail: puffin-man@webtv.net
Products: Alutiq (Alaska) ceremonial items (masks, paddles) and sculpture of wood. By appointment only.

SOUTHWEST INDIAN ART & JEWELRY
16114 70th Ave. NE • Kenmore, WA 98028
 (425) 488-6341; Maria & Andrew Balicki, Owners. *Membership*: IACA.

MAKAH CULTURAL & RESEARCH CENTER
P.O. Box 160 • Neah Bay, WA 98357
 (360) 645-2711 Fax 645-2656; Janine Bowechop (Makah), Manager
Retail. Makah tribal enterprise. *Products*: Baskets, beadwork, clothing, drums, pipes, Northwest Coast art. Brochure.

TONGEL ART STUDIO
P.O. Box 636 • Nespelem, WA 99155
 (509) 634-4515; Georgia Orr Tongel (Colville), Owner
 Website: www.tongelart.com; E-mail: tongelart@cuonlinenow.com
Products: Fine art oil paintings on canvas and limited edition signed prints.

TIN-NA-TIT KIN-NE-KI INDIAN ARTS & GIFTS
P.O. Box 1057, 993 Hwy. 20 East • Republic, WA 99166

(509) 775-3077; Ot-Ne-We & Jim Swayne, Owners
Retail. *Products*: Art, baskets, beadwork, clothing, dolls, jewelry, kachinas, pottery, sand paintings, sculpture, carvings. Brochure.

NATIVE AMERICAN CONCEPTS & REZ REGALIA
P.O. Box 31713 • Seattle, WA 98199
  (206) 778-6721; Patricia Anne Davis (Choctaw-Navajo), Owner
  Website: www.nativeamericanconcepts.com
Products: Ceremonial clothing, powwow & designer shawls.

SACRED CIRCLE GALLERY OF AMERICAN INDIAN ART
P.O. Box 99100 • Seattle, WA 98199
  (206) 285-4425; Steve Charles (Tlingit/Haida), Manager
Retail. *Products*: Art, baskets, clothing, knives, pottery, beadwork, sculpture. Commissions accepted.

SUQUAMISH MUSEUM
Hwy. 305, Port Madison Reservation, P.O. Box 498 • Suquamish, WA 98392
  (206) 598-3311; Leonard Forsman, Manager
Retail, mail order. *Products*: Baskets, dolls, artifacts, sculpture. Special orders accepted.

TREASURES INDIAN JEWELRY
P.O. Box 64237 • Tacoma, WA 98464
  (800) 327-0852; (206) 564-2366; Dave & Judy MacMillan, Owners
Retail, wholesale. *Products*: Art, beadwork, dolls, jewelry, kachinas, pottery, rugs, sandpaintings, sculpture, carvings.

WEAVING WITH SHARON
5006 Hyada Blvd. NE • Tacoma, WA 98422
  (253) 719-8083; Sharon Nelson, Owner/Manager
Products: Cedar baskets and other weaved items.

BEAD LADY/CHEROKEE RAINBOWS
315-B Roosevelt • Wenatchee, WA 98801
  Dorothea C. Orndorff, Owner. Mail order (special orders only).
By appointment only. *Products*: Beadwork, clothing. Beadwork repairs.

ROGER E. AMERMAN (Choctaw of OK)
109 N. 55th Ave. • Yakima, WA 98908
  E-mail: chains04@msn.com
Retail. *Products*: Beadwork and Choctaw cultural attire;

WEST VIRGINIA

PANTHER PRIMITIVES
P.O. Box 32 • Normantown, WV 25267
  (304) 462-7718. Retail. *Products*: Early American items, including tipis; kegs, craft items, clothing. 180-page catalog, $2.

WISCONSIN

BEAR TRAP TRADING POST
Rt. 2, Box 419C • Ashland, WI 54806
  (715) 682-2209. Retail. *Products*: Crafts & supplies.

BUFFALO ART CENTER
Box 51, Hwy. 13 • Bayfield, WI 54814
  (715) 779-5858; Mardella Soulier, Manager
Retail. *Products*: Art, beadwork, clothing, jewelry, pottery, sculpture.

LIL TP
1114 Woodward Ave. • Beloit, WI 53511
  (608) 365-1009; Jim & Katy King, Owners
Retail. Products: Beadwork, jewelry.

SANTA FE SHOP
W62 N580A Washington Ave. • Cedarburg, WI 53012
  (262) 376-1497 Fax 376-1729; Gary & Judit Lukitsch, Owners
  Website: www.santafeshop.com
  E-mail: info@santafeshop.com
Membership: IACA

AMERICAN INDIAN GIFT STORE
132 Main St., Box 73 • Hayward, WI 54843
  (715) 634-2655; Gerald B. Diamond, Owner
Retail. *Products*: Authentic American Indian made crafts. *Membership*: IACA

C & S LTD.
4303 75th St. • Kenosha, WI 53142-4265
  (414) 694-3960; Gayle Chiodo

Retail. *Products*: Art, baskets, beadwork, clothing, dolls, jewelry, kachinas, pottery, rugs, sandpaintings, sculpture, carvings. *Membership*: IACA.

WA-SWA-GON ARTS & CRAFTS
Box 477, Hwy. 47 • Lac du Flambeau, WI 54538
  (715) 588-7636; Elizabeth Vetterneck, Manager
Mail order. Products: Beadwork, boxes, clothing, rugs, sculpture.

TOUCH THE EARTH
220 Main St. • LaCrosse, WI 54601
  (608) 785-2980; Dinah & Ron Klemmedson, Owners
Retail. Products: hand-crafted silver jewelry & pottery; art, beads and supplies.

KATY'S AMERICAN INDIAN ARTS
1803 Monroe St. • Madison, WI 53711
  (608) 251-5451/0014 Fax 251-5472; Katy Schalles, Owner
Retail. *Products*: All. *Appraisals*: Baskets, fetishes, heishi, jewelry, kachinas, pottery, rugs, sandpaintings. *Membership*: IACA.

HOCAK WAZIJACI LANGUAGE & CULTURE PROGRAM
P.O. Box 390 • Mauston, WI 53948
  (608) 847-5694 Fax 847-7203; Kenneth Funmaker, Sr. (Hocak), Manager
Products: White ash baskets, beadwork, leatherwork, featherwork, paintings; items of Ho-Chunk arts & crafts

AMERICAN INDIAN ART
2311 E. North Ave. #10 • Milwaukee, WI 53202
  E-mail: sambrushel@hotmail.com; Sam Brushel (Mohican), Artist/Owner
Products: Handmade Indian artwork, hickory bow & arrow sets, silver & turquoise string work.

WHITE THUNDER WOLF TRADING CO.
320 E. Clybourn St. • Milwaukee, WI 53202
  (414) 278-7424 Fax 278-8244; White Thunder Wolf, Owner
Products: Art, jewelry, drums, music, books, beads & supplies, crafts, gifts.

SWEET GRASS DESIGNS
3960 S. Avon Dr. • New Berlin, WI 53151
  Carol Zokan-Cameron (White Earth Ojibwe), Owner/Craftsperson
Products: Metal (copper) traditional & contemporary, Native Images – mix medium (sculpture, dream catchers, soft sculpture.

JO'S LOG CABIN TRADING POST
Box 294, Hwy. 54 • Oneida, WI 54155
  (414) 869-2505
Retail. *Products*: Crafts, Leatherwork, silver turquoise jewelry.

ONEIDA NATION MUSEUM SHOP
P.O. Box 365 • Oneida, WI 54155
  (800) 236-2214; (920) 869-2768; Website: www.oneidanation.org
  E-mail: museum@oneidanation.org; Deborah Schuler (Oneida), Manager
Retail, wholesale. Tribal enterprise. *Products*: Baskets, beadwork, books, boxes, clothing, dolls, pottery. Special orders accepted on beadwork and quillwork. Brochure.

TURTLE CLAN TRADERS
1090 Sunlite Dr. • Oneida, WI 54155
  (414) 434-6777; Sue Skenandore, Owner
Retail, wholesale. *Products*: Beadwork, clothing, jewelry, rugs.

SHEILA S, SMITH
1795 Poplar Lane • Seymour, WI 54165
  (414) 833-7366. Retail. *Products*: Iroquois costumes and accessories. Special orders accepted.

WINNEBAGO PUBLIC INDIAN MUSEUM
P.O. Box 441 • Wisconsin Dells, WI 53965
  (608) 254-2268; Bernadine Tallmadge (Winnebago), Owner
  Roxanne Johnson (Winnebago), Manager
Retail, mail order. *Products*: Winnebago baskets, beadwork, moccasins, deerskin products; Navajo rugs and silverwork. Brochure and price list.

WYOMING

BUFFALO BILL HISTORICAL CENTER MUSEUM SHOP
720 Sheridan Ave., P.O. Box 2630 • Cody, WY 82414-2630
  (800) 533-3838; (307) 587-3243 Fax 587-8003
  Website: www.bbhcstore.com
  Dean W. Swift, Manager; E-mail: deans@bbhc.org
Retail, wholesale. *Products*: All. Catalog available.

LA RAY TURQUOISE CO.
P.O. Box 83 • Cody, WY 82414
 (307) 587-9564; Ray & Laura Vallie (Ojibwe), Artisan/Owners
Retail, wholesale, mail order. Products: Navajo, Zuni, Hopi, Santo Domingo and Ojibwa silver & beadwork, Navajo rugs; Cheyenne, Sioux & Mohawk crafts. Special and custom orders accepted.

TECUMSEH'S TRADING POST
140 W. Yellowstone Ave. • Cody, WY 82414
 (307) 587-5362; E-mail: emailus@tecumsehs.com
Website: www.tecumsehs.com
Retail, mail order, online. *Products*: American Indian, cowboy, and frontiersmen's deerskin clothing, moccasins, weapons, accessories.

STEWART'S TRAPLINE GALLERY
P.O. Box 823 • Dubois, WY 82513
 (307) 455-2800; Mark & Catherine Stewart, Owners. Retail, wholesale.

FORT WASHAKIE TRADING CO.
P.O. Box 428 • Fort Washakie, WY 82514
 (307) 332-3557; Jeri Greeves, Owner
Retail, wholesale, mail order. *Products*: Baskets, beadwork, clothing, dolls, jewelry, kachinas, pottery, rugs. Special orders accepted. Brochure.

SHOSHONE CERAMICS
P.O. Box 105 • Fort Washakie, WY 82514
 (307) 330-4848 or 335-7329
 E-mail: shoshoneceramics@hotmail.com
Margaret C. Maukaas (Shoshone), Owner
Products: Ceramic waterfalls, lamps, clocks; jewelry, beadwork, visual arts & clothing.

BOYER'S INDIAN ARTS & CRAFTS
P.O. Box 647 • Jackson, WY 83001
 (307) 733-3773 Fax 733-4262
 Website: www.boyersindianart.com; E-mail: boyers@boyesindianart.com
John, Bonnie & Lila Boyer, Owners
Retail. *Products*: Baskets, beadwork, books, clothing, dolls, jewelry, kachinas, pottery, rugs, sandpaintings, sculpture, carvings. *Membership*: IACA.

RAINDANCE TRADERS
Box 3262, 103 E. Broadway • Jackson, WY 83001-3262
 (307) 733-1081; Barbara & Terry Kennedy. Retail. *Products*: All.

TWO GREY HILLS INDIAN ARTS
110 E. Broadway, P.O. Box 1252 • Jackson, WY 83001
 (307) 733-2677; Gary Mattheis, Owner; Website: www.fineindianart.com
 E-mail: artinfo@fineindianart.com
Retail. *Products*: Baskets, dye charts, fetishes, heishi, jewelry, kachinas, pottery, rugs, sandpaintings. *Membership*: IACA.

RED NATIONS ART
P.O. Box 388 • Lander, WY 82520
 (307) 349-1817; Sonny Tuttle, Owner
Website: www.spirithides.com. Membership: IACA.

GRAND TETON LODGE CO.
P.O. Box 250 • Moran, WY 83013
 (307) 543-2831 Fax 543-2569; Website: www.gttc.com
 Patricia Green, Manager; E-mail: pgreen@gttc.com
Retail. *Products*: Art, fetishes, jewelry, miniatures, sandpaintings. *Membership*: IACA. *Winter address*: Forever Resorts, P.O. Box 29041, Phoenix, AZ.

SIGNAL MOUNTAIN LODGE
P.O. Box 50 • Moran, WY 83013
 (307) 543-2831 Fax 543-2569; Website: www.foreverresorts.com
 E-mail: info@signalmtnlodge.com; Don Wallace, Manager
Retail. *Products*: Art, fetishes, jewelry, miniatures, sandpaintings. *Membership*: IACA. *Winter address*: Forever Resorts, P.O. Box 29041, Phoenix, AZ.

FOUR WINDS INDIAN TRADING POST
P.O. Box 580 • St. Ignatius, MT 59865
 (406) 745-4336 Fax 745-3595; Preston E. Miller & Carolyn Corey, Owners
 E-mail: 4winds@bigsky.net. Retail. *Products*: American Indian artifacts; traditional craft supplies; genuine Indian beadwork: moccasins, strike-a-lites, amulets, knife cases, etc. Catalog: $3.

TW RECREATIONAL SERVICES, INC.
Yellowstone Park, WY 82190
 (307) 344-5354 Fax (406) 848-7048; Peter White
Retail. *Products*: All. *Membership*: IACA.

TRIBAL ENTERPRISES

BIEN MUR INDIAN MARKETING CENTER, Albuquerque, NM
(Sandia Pueblo Tribal Enterprise)

MOAPA TRIBAL ENTERPRISES, Moapa, NV
(Paiute Tribal Enterprises)

NAVAJO ARTS/CRAFTS ENTERPRISES, Window Rock, AZ
(Navajo Tribal Enterprise)

PUEBLO OF ZUNI ARTS & CRAFTS, Zuni, NM
(Zuni Pueblo Tribal Enterprise)

QUALLA ARTS & CRAFTS, Cherokee, NC
(Eastern Cherokee Tribal Enterprise)

SOUTHERN UTE MUSEUM & GIFT SHOP, Ignacio, CO
(Southern Ute Tribal Enterprise)

FOREIGN STORES - AUSTRALIA

AMERICAN INDIAN TRADING COMPANY
P.O. Box 367 • Manly, N.S.W. 2095
 011-02-938-52; Ann O'Bryan, Kerry O'Bryan, Suzy Rochester
Wholesale, retail. *Products*: Art, beadwork, clothing, dolls, jewelry, kachinas, rugs, sandpaintings, sculpture, carvings. *Membership*: IACA.

THE CORN MAIDEN
P.O. Box 45, Ormeau, 4208 Queensland
 011-61-07-210-0518; Kym Quinn, Owner
Wholesale, retail. *Products*: Art, beadwork, clothing, dolls, jewelry, kachinas, pottery, sandpaintings, sculpture, carvings. *Membership*: IACA. Branch: 66 Charlotte St., Brisbane 4000.

THE COWBOY FROM DOWN UNDER
Dolphin Arcade-Surfer's Paradise , Queensland 4217; 011-61-07-592-0525
Wholesale, retail. *Products*: Art, clothing, dolls, jewelry, kachinas, rugs, sandpaintings, sculpture, carvings. *Membership*: IACA.

THUNDER DOWN UNDER
P.O. Box 903, 85 Grafton St., Mareeba, Queensland 4880
 011-61-07-051-1040; Greg & Jana Whittaker, Owners
Wholesale, retail. *Products*: Art, beadwork, clothing, dolls, jewelry, kachinas, rugs, sandpaintings, sculpture, carvings. *Membership*: IACA.

TWO FEATHERS TURQUOISE GALLERY
1 The Crescent • Sassafras 3787, Victoria
 011-61-03-755-1072 (Phone & Fax); Jacqueline & Paul Johnson, Owners
Wholesale, retail. *Products*: All. *Membership*: IACA.

CANADA - ALBERTA

PEIGAN CRAFTS LTD.
P.O. Box 100 • Brocker, Alberta T0K 0
 (403) 965-3755 Fax 965-3790; Website: www.peigancrafts.com
 E-mail: peigancrafts@telus.net; Albertine Crow Shoe, Owner
Membership: IACA.

PRAIRIE ROSE CRAFTS LTD.
P.O. Box 444 • Standorff, Alberta T0L 1
 (403) 553-3755 Fax 737-3812; E-mail: BTallman@telusplanet.net
Bert & Rose Tallman, Owners. *Membership*: IACA.

BRITISH COLUMBIA

CANADIAN INDIAN ART, INC.
1408 Crown St. • N. Vancouver, BC V7J 1
 (604) 980-1267 Fax 980-7249; Maike Marnet, Owner
Website: www.canadianindianart.com
E-mail: info@canadianindianart.com. *Membership*: IACA.

KHOT-LA-CHA ART GALLERY & GIFT SHOP
270 Whonoak St. • N. Vancouver, BC V7P
 (604) 987-3339 Fax 988-1930; Website: www.khot-la-cha.com
 E-mail: khot-la-char-art@shaw.ca; Nancy Nightingale, Owner.
Membership: IACA.

SPIRIT WRESTLER GALLERY
47 Water St. • Vancouver, BC V6B 1A1
 (888) 669-8813; (604) 669-8813; Website: www.spiritwrestler.com
 E-mail: info@spiritwrestler.com; Diane Douglas-Willard (Haida), Owner
Retail. *Products*: Inuit, Northwest Coast & Maori art.

THE PATH GALLERY
122 - 4338 Main St. • Whistler, BC V0N 1B4
 (604) 932-7570; Website: www.pathgallery.com
Retail, wholesale. *Products*: monumental to miniature art of the Northwest
Coast, including totem poles, masks, rattles, drums & jewelry.

MANITOBA

ARCTIC CO-OPERATIVES LTD.
1741 Wellington Ave. • Winnipeg, MB R3H 0G1
 (204) 786-4481; Terry Thompson, Owner. Wholesale. *Membership*: IACA.

ONTARIO

NATIVE RENAISSANCE II ART GALLERY & GIFT SHOP
P.O. Box 61, Tyendinaga Mohawk Territory • Deseronto, ON K0K 1X0
 (800) 334-9509 (613) 396-3520 Fax 396-3034
 Website: www.nativerenaissance.com; Thomas B. Maracle (Mohawk), Owner
 Email: tbm@nativerenaissance.com. Retail, mail order. *Products*: Original
stone sculptures, spirit dolls, reproductions, Native music.

WOLFWALKER ENT.
30 Hatt St. • Dundas, ON L9H 2E8
 (416) 627-1400; Wolf & Myrna Prudek, Owners
Wholesale, retail. *Products*: Art, Northwest Coast art, fetishes, jewelry,
kachinas, pottery, sculpture. *Membership*: IACA.

EARTH TO SPIRIT
340 King St. East • Kingston, ON K7L 3B6
 (613) 536-5252 fax 536-5554; Website: www.earthtospirit.com
 E-mail: earth@kingston.net; Chris Van der Vyver, Owner

INDIANICA.COM
79 St. Paul St. E. • Montreal, PQ
 (514) 866-1267 Fax 866-8988; Website: www.indianica.com
 E-mail: george@indianica.com; George Kiorpelidis, Jr., Owner

ENGLAND

EARTH DESIGN
The Craft Center Broadwindsor • Dorset DT8 3 • England
44-01-308-868-911 Fax 44-01-308-868-121
 E-mail: clive@earthdesign.co.uk; Clive Pettitt & Lisa Parkman, owners

WAMPUM
50 Hollyshaw Lane • Whitkirk, Leeds LS15 7BD
011-44-113264-3075 Fax 011-44-113294-4651
 Website: www.wampum.co.uk; E-mail: wampum@btconnect.com
Margaret R. Carroll, Owner. *Membership*: IACA.

GERMANY

VONHAND DESIGN Frankfurter Str. 8 • 61118 Bad Vilbel
 011-49-61-018-7938; Oliver Will & Isolde Eberle, Owners
Wholesale, retail. *Products*: Art, beadwork, clothing, dolls, jewelry,
kachinas, pottery, rugs, sandpaintings. *Membership*: IACA.

ARIZONA-GALERIE GAST & MORTELL GMBH
Grosse Bockenheimer, Strasse 37 60313 Frankfurt/Main 1
Frankfurt • Germany 011-49-06-928-7379 Fax 928-3362
 Anja & Hildegard Gast, Owners
Retail. *Products*: Art, beadwork, clothing, dolls, jewelry, kachinas, pottery,
rugs, sandpaintings, sculpture, carvings. *Membership*: IACA.

NAVAJO SILVER
Schmiedstrasse 2, 3342 Gields • Germany
 011-49-05-339-541 Fax 339-740; Hans-Jurgen & Le-Thu Grimm, Owners
Wholesale, retail. *Products*: Art, beadwork, clothing, dolls, jewelry, kachinas,
sandpaintings, sculpture, carvings. *Membership*: IACA. *Branch Shop*:
Weenderstrasse 75, 3400 Gottingen.

TRADING POST
Wilstorfer Str. 72 • 21073 Hamburg • Germany
 011-49-40-765-9699 Fax 765-6879

Wholesale, retail. *Products*: Beadwork, clothing, dolls, jewelry, kachinas,
sandpaintings, sculpture, carvings. *Membership*: IACA.

CHEROKEE WIGWAM
Ringseestr 9, 85053 Ingolstadt-Sud • Germany
 0-11-49-0841-69541 Fax 0841-69907
 A. Weger, Liselotte Nichols, Owners
Wholesale/retail. *Products*: Jewelry, sand paintings. *Membership*: IACA.

RIO GRANDE ARTS & CRAFTS GMBH
Xantener Str. 42, Meerbusch-Strl"mp 40670
 02159-81891 ; Carl Shroeter, Owner
Retail, wholesale. Products: All Indian arts & crafts.
Brochure & catalog. Branch shops. *Membership*: IACA.

HHS EXPORT TRADING CO., WINZLAR
Westerfeld 18, 31547 Rehburg-Loccum
 05037-3513; Hermann & Maria Schmidt, Owners
Wholesale, retail, mail order. *Products*: Native American, Western and
Southwestern products. *Appraisal*: Art, jewelry, kachinas, pottery, sand-
paintings, sculpture, carvings. *Membership*: IACA. Brochure & catalog.

RED CLOUD INDIAN STORE
Rossbachstr. 16, 88212 Ravensburg
 011-47-7-511-3755 (phone & fax); Michael Gribulis & Katharina Meyer
Wholesale, retail. *Products*: Art, beadwork, clothing, dolls, jewelry, kachinas,
sandpaintings, sculpture, carvings. *Membership*: IACA.

AMERICAN ART GALLERY
Bahnhofstrasse 29, D-6632 Saarwellingen
 011-49-6-838-6791; Hubert & Marlene Masloh
Wholesale, retail. *Product*: Art. *Membership*: IACA.

JAPAN

GALLERY SEDONA
16-60 Kita 5-Chome, Higashikaigan, Chigasaki, Kanagawa-Pref. 253-0
 011-81-046-787-0811 Fax 046-788-0058; Website: www.sedona.co.jp
 E-mail: webmaster@sedona.cp.jp; Shigeo & Nori Niida, Owmers
Retail, some mail order. *Products*: Art, beadwork, clothing, dolls, jewelry,
kachinas, pottery, rugs, sandpaintings. *Membership*: IACA. Brochure.

DUKE TRADING CO. LTD
2-30-11 Kitazawa Setagaya-ku • Tokyo 155-0
 (03) 3466 8776 Fax (03) 3466-8776
 Website: www.duke.ne.jp; E-mail: nobu@duke.ne.jp
 N. Matsubara & Ando Jun, Owners. *Membership*: IACA.

INDIAN CRAFT CO., LTD.
5-5-10 Akasada • Minato, Tokyo 107
 011-81-03-586-3737; Ms. Ayako Umemoto & Sumie Matsuda
Wholesale. *Products*: Heishi, jewelry, pottery, rugs, sandpaintings.

NATIVE SPIRIT
5-46-5 Chuo, Nakano, Tokyo 164-0
 81-3-5340-6322; Dye Masaki, Owner
 Website: www.native-spirit-trd-pst.com
 E-mail: changlishkawakan@hotmail.com. *Membership*: IACA.

JIMMIE D. WARNELL
U.S. Embassy, Tokyo, Japan, Unit 45004
Box 201 • APO AT 96337-5004
 Jimmie D. Warnell, Owner
Retail, mail order. Cherokee craftsperson. *Products*: Silver products, jewelry.

NETHERLANDS

CLASSIC WESTERN HOUSE
Kalverstraat 154, 1012 XE Amsterdam
 011-31-020-622-3329; Henk & Ilona Stots
Retail. *Products*: Art, beadwork, clothing, dolls, jewelry,
kachinas, rugs. *Membership*: IACA.

SCOTLAND

NATIVE ARTS TRADING
"Finella" by Drumtochty by Auchenblae
Kincardinshire, AB30 Scotland 0 (1561) 320914
 Sharon & Barry Holton; Website: www.nativeartstrading.com
 E-mail: cochise@nativeartstrading.com. *Membership*: IACA

**The following law firms either specialize in
Indian law or maintain an Indian law section**

AKIN GUMP STRAUSS HAUER & FELD, LLP

Robert S. Strauss Bldg., 1333 New Hampshire Ave., NW
Washington, DC 20036
(202) 887-4466 Fax 887-4288
Website: www.akingump.com/en/experience/practices/american-indian/
E-mail: washdcinfo@akingump.com
Donald R. Pongrace, Partner, Head, American Indian Law & Policy Group
 E-mail: dpongrace@akingump.com
Allison C. Binney (Pomo), Partner (887-4326)
 E-mail: abinney@akingump.com
Michael G. Rossetti, Partner (887-4311)
 E-mail: mrossetti@akingump.com
Merrill C. Godfrey, Senior Counsel (887-4195)
 E-mail: mgodfrey@akingump.com

American Indian Law & Policy Group practice provides legal & strategic advice to American Indian tribal governments & other entities that share a commitment to tribal political empowerment, sovereignty & economic development. Includes Indian gaming, real estate & finance; energy & renewal; natural resources & land use, et al. Advised the Osage Tribe in the largest-ever settlement of a claim made by a tribe against the U.S. government in October 2011. Established 1971.

ALBIETZ & SAMUEL LAW FIRM

2001 N. St., Suite 200 • Sacramento, CA 95814
(916) 442-4241; Website: www.aslawcorp.com
Judy Kammins Albietz, Principle; E-mail: judy@aslawcorp.com
Arnold Samuel, Partner; E-mail: arnold@aslawcorp.com

Albietz & Samuel Law Firm offers legal services and mediation services -- with more than 35 years of experience in negotiations, mediation and transactions, policy-making and litigation. Judith Albietz is not only an experienced attorney but also a trained mediator. She is recognized for her persistence and energy in assisting parties in finding a solution to complex problems without incurring the costs of expensive litigation. Because of these qualities, as well as her attention to detail, individuals, families, businesses, governmental entities and Indian tribes turn to Albietz Law Firm when in need of professional legal counsel on complex issues as well as services for negotiation and mediation to resolve matters outside of court -- helping parties put together agreements to address their particular needs. Albietz Law Firm specializes in the following practice areas: Environmental, Water, and Natural Resources Law; Mediation - Alternative Dispute Resolution; Real Property and Land Use Law; Federal Indian Law and Tribal Law; General Business Law; Estates and Trusts: Estate Planning and Trust Formation; Management and Distribution of Assets

ANDERSON INDIAN LAW

418-B C St. NE • Washington, DC 20002
(202) 543-5000 Fax 543-7716
Website www.mjaindianlaw.com
 Email: info@mjaindianlaw.com
Michael J. Anderson, Owner

Anderson's major focus is its strong government affairs practice. We have developed a team of attorneys with vast experience in Federal Indian law and legislation, including prior service in the United States Department of the Interior. Offers counseling in Business Enterprises & Economic Development; Environmental Law; Financing; Gaming Development and Enterprises; General Counsel to Indian tribes, Tribal Organizations, and Indian-owned Enterprises; Land Acquisition; Litigation; Taxation; Tribal Code Development (including regulations, policy & procedure manuals, legislation & documents critical to the effective operation of tribal governments); & Tribal Sovereignty. Established 2011.

APPLEBY LAW PLLC

333 North Fairfax St., Suite 302 • Alexandria, VA 22314
(703) 837-0001 Fax 997-4868
Website: www.applebylawpllc.com; E-mail: info@applebylawpllc.com
Nancy J. Appleby, Partner; E-mail: nancy@applebylawpllc.com

Nancy Appleby is a nationally recognized expert in real estate and project development on tribal land. Her strength & reputation are the result of a number of factors, including 30 years experience and expertise in commercial real estate, lending, Indian law and the Indian Financing Act, and her strong relationships and credibility with tribal counsel and with counsel and staff at the Department of Interior. Nancy's practice includes real estate and commercial development, real property and mortgage law; leasing; construction and permanent lending for commercial & residential projects; banking & title insurance; regulatory and agency matters; government-guaranteed loan programs & commercial litigation, both inside & outside of Indian country. She represents creditors, real estate developers, energy development companies, large and small corporations, business owners and contractors.

ATER WYNNE LLP

Lovejoy Bldg., 1331 NW Lovejoy, Suite 900 • Portland, OR 97209
(503) 226-1191 Fax 226-0079; Website: www.aterwynne.com
Claudia Powers (Portland), Indian Law – Partner
(503) 226-8652; E-mail: ckp@aterwynne.com
L. David Connell, Indian Law – Partner; Chair of Business Department
(503) 226-8605; E-mail: ldc@aterwynne.com
John M. Schultz, Indian Law – Partner
(503) 226-8647; E-mail: jms@aterwynne.com

Provides legal services to Indian tribes & tribal enterprises throughout the U.S. Emphasizes various aspects of tribal economic development & governance. Maintains a broad understanding of Federal Indian law and an appreciation of doing business in Indian Country. For more than two decades Ater Wynne has been providing legal services to Indian tribes and tribal enterprises throughout the United States. Our work emphasizes various aspects of tribal economic development and governance, including project finance, land acquisition and leasing, energy development, casino/hotel projects, taxation, infrastructure development housing, & recreational and healthcare facilities. Their extensive experience has given us a broad understanding of federal Indian law and an appreciation of the unique aspects of doing business in Indian Country. Our expertise includes: Casino development; Economic development; Energy & transmission projects, including renewables; Environmental/water rights; Gaming regulation; State-tribal compacts; Treaty rights; Tribal governance Ater Wynne works with public and private partners in major joint ventures, assisting with financing, international trade, construction, regulatory and governmental affairs. We bring added value to our regional, national, and international clients through our industry knowledge, contacts, and Pacific Rim presence. A representative sampling of projects includes: Advising a Southwest tribe on taxation issues and IRS audit; Assisting several Northwest tribes in the planning, financing, construction and leasing of tribal casinos; Acting as project counsel for a Southwest tribe on all aspects of developing major fossil fuel and renewable electric power generation and transmission facilities; Advising a Northwest tribe on amendments to state gaming compacts and on formulation of vendor/consultant contracts; Advising West Coast tribes on fee-to-trust applications, gaming regulatory, environmental and water rights issues; Representing several Northwest tribes in litigation involving employment, sovereign immunity, construction contracts land use and fishing rights; Serving as member of National Indian Gaming Commission advisory committee on environmental, public health and safety issues affecting tribal casinos; Serving as lead counsel on the first major international container port facility and light rail/economic development projects in Washington & Oregon. Representative Clients: Diné Power Authority of the Navajo Nation; North Fork Rancheria of Mono Indians; Puyallup Tribe and Marine View Ventures; Scotts Valley Band of Pomo Indians; Stillaguamish Tribe of Indians; Oregon tribes and tribal economic development entities; Tyonek Native Corporation; National Renewable Energy Laboratory.

BEST & FLANAGAN LLP

225 S. Sixth St., 40th Fl. • Minneapolis, MN 55402
(612) 339-7121; Website: www.bestlaw.com
Lenor A. Scheffler (Lower Sioux Dakota), Chairperson
Thomas B. Heffelfinger, Partner (349-5657)
James C. Diracles, Attorney (349-5642)
 E-mail: jcdiracles@bestlaw.com

The attorneys at Best & Flanagan are dedicated to working with Native American tribes throughout the United States addressing their legal needs. We add insight to complex issues. Our Native American practice group couples the background of a tribal member, judge & tribal in-house counsel with extensive tribal & federal government matter experience to provide a unique and effective understanding of the special needs of the sovereign tribal nations. Tribal Government. Their attorneys have served as special or general counsel to tribal government departments and tribal enterprise, to elected tribal councils or elected tribal chairs and their administrations. The legal services in this area include advice, counsel, research, drafting & advocacy regarding finance, tax, business, economic development, issues, constitutional revision, ordinances, statutes & inter-governmental relations advocacy both locally & nationally. We have tribal in-house legal experience working directly with tribal governments in areas of government relations, constitution reform, law & regulations & tribal court advocacy. *Business & Finance:* The attorneys have extensive experience with sophisticated financing for tribal gaming, infrastructure, creating tribal business development entities, advising tribal clients on labor and employment matters, business structures, contract drafting & review as well as advising on all legal aspects of economic development. Additionally, their attorneys represent tribes in financing transactions & underwritten bonds on behalf of tribes or trustees that have acted as fiduciaries on tribal financing transactions. *Gaming*: They have represented tribal gaming commissions for over 15 years in areas including negotiating gaming compact amendments, representation at hearings involving licensing matters, advocating for tribal clients before the National Indian Gaming Commission and state regulatory authorities and providing daily gaming regulatory advice. *Tax*: Their attorneys often are on the cutting edge of obtaining favorable tax solutions for tribal clients including beneficiaries of tribal minors' trusts and for tribal members participating in tribal housing & other social benefit programs. We have experience representing individual tribal members, tribal government & tribal entities both at the state revenue department and IRS levels. Several of our attorneys have also served on the IRS Advisory Committee on Tax Exempt and Government Entities. We are well versed in all areas of federal Indian law, ordinance laws, compacts and agency advocacy.

BERKEY WILLIAMS LLP
2030 Addison St., Suite 410 • Berkeley, CA 94704
(510) 548-7070 Fax 302-2811
Website: www.berkeywilliams.com; E-mail: info@berkeywilliams.com
Curtis Berkey, Managing Partner; Scott Williams, Managing Partner
Rovianee Leigh (Cherokee); Alexandra Page; Amy Cordalis (Yurok),
Jenna Macauley (Tuscarora), Attorneys
Loretta L. Miranda (Morongo Band Mission Indians), Indian Law Fellow
Washington, DC office: 888 16th St., NW, Suite 800 • Washington, DC 20006
(202) 302-2811 Fax 330-5293
Provides comprehensive legal services to Indian tribes and tribal organizations in California, Nevada, Colorado, New Mexico, Utah, & New York. Represents only Native American interests by providing a full range of legal services, from advocacy before administrative & legislative bodies to litigation in federal, state & tribal courts.

BLEDSOE DOWNES, PC
4809 E. Thistle Landing Dr., Suite 100 • Phoenix, AZ 85044
(480) 346-4216; Website: www.bdrlaw.com
E-mail: admin@bdrlaw.com
Bradley G. Bledsoe Downes, Founding Member
The attorneys of Bledsoe Downes, PC are admitted to practice in state, federal and tribal courts and have appeared in several courts & before administrative agencies at all levels. We represent Indian tribes in all aspects of relations before federal, state, & local governments, agencies and courts. They offer a wide range of services to Indian tribes, their subordinate departments/ agencies/commercial enterprises, & to entities seeking to engage in business with Indian tribes. *Practice Areas*: Federal Indian Law; Indian gaming; financing, development & management; Contracts; Government; relations; Indian Child Welfare; Economic Development; Construction; Environmental; Employment & Labor; Civil litigation; Tribal regulation; and Tribal enrollment.

BLUEDOG PAULSON & SMALL PLLP
Southgate Office Plaza, Suite 500
5001 West 80th • Bloomington, MN 55437
(952) 893-1813 Fax 893-0650
E-mail: contact@bpslawfirm.com
Kurt V. BlueDog, Managing Partner
Greg S. Paulson, Partner; Andrew M. Small, Partner
Provides legal counsel to tribal governments & tribal institutions, specializing in all aspects of Native American law. Represents several tribal gaming operations, and served as general counsel to every aspect of tribal business, government & regulatory operations. *Associates*: Jessica Ryan & Todd Roen.

ROBERT C. BRAUCHLI, ATTORNEY AT LAW
P.O. Box 64607 • Tucson, AZ 85728
(520) 299-8300 Fax 299-8302; Website: www.rbrauchlilaw.com
Robert C. Brauchli, Founding Partner
Representation of Tribes in Federal, State, and Tribal Courts, including the United States District Court for District of Arizona, Ninth Circuit Court of Appeals, United States Claims Court, Federal Circuit Court of Appeals, and the United States Supreme Court. Litigation & legal representation on issues involving Tribal sovereignty, education, Tribal self-government, Federal/Tribal relations, Tribal court jurisdiction, Tribal hunting and fishing rights, forestry and land use, leases, Indian reserved water rights, Tribal/State taxation issues and tax immunity, mismanagement & breach of trust claims against the Federal Government. Drafted Tribal civil & criminal codes, ordinances, resolutions, advisor to Tribal Council and Tribal departments; prepared Tribal testimony before Congressional & State Legislative Committees, prepared intergovern-mental agreements; construction litigation, contract disputes, represented Tribal enterprises, e.g. saw mill, ski area, construction & materials company, agriculture, livestock, gravel operations, commercial center, gaming casino; negotiated realty leases and transactions, joint ventures, extensive familiarity with land use & leasing regulations, Indian Child Welfare Act, Indian Self Determination Act, Indian Tax Status Act, business agreements and tax exempt bond issues; represented Tribe in administrative appeals before IBIA and IBCA, employee termination & grievance rights, application of HUD regulations & housing projects, collection issues involving surety law & bonds; involved in application of Environmental Protection Act and Endangered Species Act to Tribes, Indian Gaming Regulatory Act and Indian Forest Resource Management Act application. Foregoing list is not exhaustive of experience but illustrative.

BRIEN LAW LLC
P.O. Box 435, 310 Washington • Oskaloosa, KS 66066
(785) 863-3500 Fax 548-0691; Website: www.brienlawllc.com
Russell A. Brien (Iowa of Kansas & Nebraska), Owner
E-mail: russ@brienlawllc.com
Indian law practice is broad-based, including Indian law/tribal governance; general business, bankruptcy, municipal, corporate, securities & real estate. Established 1993.

COLEMAN INDIAN LAW
4601 N. Fairfax Dr., Suite 1200 • Arlington, VA 22203
(703) 763-5483; Website: www.colemanindianlaw.com
E-mail: colemanindianlaw@gmail.com
Penny Coleman, Principal
Represents Tribal Nations' legislative, regulatory & litigation interests before Federal, State & Indian Nation agencies, Congress, universities & organizations. Work with tribal leaders, commissions, and tribal lawyers to improve procedures & revenues and provide advice to tribal program managers as they work to comply with Federal & Indian Nation law.

LISA KATHLEEN CONDON
13428 Maxella Ave., Suite 118 • Marina Del Rey, CA 90292
(310) 741-1584 Fax 496-0237
Practice Area: Native American Law

CROWE & DUNLEVY LLP
Indian Law & Gaming Practice Group
500 Kennedy Bldg., 321 S. Boston Ave. • Tulsa, OK 74103
(918) 592-9800 Fax 599-6317; Website: www.crowedunlevy.com
D. Michael McBride III, Chairperson (918) 592-9824
E-mail: michael.mcbride@crowedunlevy.com
Christina M. Vaughn, Vice Chairperson, Director – Indian Law & Gaming, Litigation & Trial & Energy, Environment & Natural Resources Practice Group
E-mail: christina.vaughn@crowedunlevy.com
Susan E. Huntsman, Director (918) 592-9866
E-mail: susan.huntsman@crowedunlevy.com
Walter R. Echo-Hawk, Jr. Of Counsel (918) 592-9874
E-mail: walter.echohawk@crowedunlevy.com
324 N. Robinson Ave., Suite 100 • Oklahoma City, O 73102
(405) 235-7700 Fax 239-6651
Jimmy K. Goodman, Director & Vice Chair (405) 235-7717
E-mail: jimmy.goodman@crowedunlevy.com
The Indian Law & Gaming Practice Group provides strategic legal advice from the broad collective experience of attorneys throughout our Firm. They represent not only Indian tribal governments and Alaskan native entities on matters relating to sovereignty, economic development & governmental objectives, but also tribal corporations & affiliated entities, and the non-tribal clients who work with them. They provide counsel regarding the complex matters of federal Indian law and the interrelationship with state and tribal laws. The Firm works closely with tribal leadership and tribal attorneys, as well as others doing business with tribes, to provide advice to form the foundation for well-reasoned policy and strategic decisions as well as the implementation of these strategies to meet our clients' objectives. We have significant experience providing legal advice and counsel in a broad range of areas impacted in whole or in part by Indian law, including: Tribal sovereignty & tribal jurisdiction, including governmental infrastructure and tribal courts; Gaming development, regulation & compacts; State compact issues, cooperative agreements, including cigarette and tobacco tax matters relating to sales in Indian country and matters of mutual governmental interest including law enforcement, prisons, roads and health care; Economic development & strategic planning issues; Corporate, resort, casino & hospitality management; Federal recognition of tribes, appropriations, contracts and federal advocacy; Code of laws and tribal regulations/policies & constitutional issues; Elections and political law; Health law, including the Indian Health Service and healthcare entities and providers who work with or contract with tribes; Trial and appellate litigation in tribal, federal and state courts; Administrative and regulatory representation before tribal gaming commissions, National Indian Gaming Commission, Bureau of Indian Affairs, Bureau of Land Management, state gaming agencies, the Civilian Board of Contract Appeals, and the Interior Board of Indian Appeals

CROWELL LAW OFFICE – TRIBAL ADVOCACY GROUP
1487 W. 89A, Suite 8 • Sedona, AZ 86336
(425) 802-5369; Website: www.crowelllawoffice.com
Scott D. Crowell, Esq., Founder & Owner; E-mail: scottcrowell@clotag.net
10 N. Post, Suite 445 • Spokane, WA 99201
(509) 209-6038; Fax 290-6953
Bruce Didesch, Of Counsel, (509) 209-6038; E-mail: bdidesch@att.net
Chris A. Rule (Chickasaw), Member; E-mail: crule@clotag.net
Steffani A. Cochran (Chickasaw), Member; E-mail: scochran@clotag.net

The firm represents tribal governments exclusively. Services range from serving as general legal counsel to tribal governments to special litigation counsel on specific matters of Indian law. The firm has been extensively involved in Indian gaming issues in several states and on national issues, including as lead attorneys in several lawsuits involving the interpretation & application of IGRA (Indian Gaming Regulatory Act and has also served as lead negotiator in numerous tribal-state compact negotiations in the areas of gaming & taxation.

CUDDY & MCCARTHY, LLP
P.O. Box 4160 • Santa Fe, NM 87502
7770 Jefferson St. NE Suite 102 • Albuquerque, NM 87109
 (505) 988-4476 Fax (888) 977-3814
 Cheryl Demmert Fairbanks (Tlingit-Tsimpshian), Partner
 Patricia Salazar (Navajo-Dine'), Partner
Indian Law Program - advises a number of tribal clients in New Mexico as well as in other states. Our expertise encompasses all aspects of Indian law including the interweave of tribal, federal and state law. We provide general and special legal services to tribes, tribal agencies, schools, judiciaries and most recently a tribal gaming commission. Our legal representation extends to administrative, legislative, and judicial proceedings in tribal, state and federal forums. Our attorneys assist clients in many areas of Indian law, including: Tribal – state – federal agreements; Development and evaluation of tribal courts, including Peacemaker courts and dispute resolution processes; Water Law; Employment Law & Tribal employment rights; Tribal housing – Native American Housing Assistance and Self-Determination Act (NAHASDA); Tribal state & federal corporations; Tribal gaming; Indian Child Welfare; Indian tourism; Indian education; Tribal controlled School Grant Act; Indian Self-Determination Act and tribal governance; P.L. 93-638; Indigenous and customary tribal law; Tribal code development: including civil, criminal & special areas such as children's, traffic, probate, domestic violence, and commercial codes or ordinances; Consultation on tribal, federal and state legislation; Indian Civil Rights Act. Partner Cheryl Demmert Fairbanks has extensive experience working in Indian education and tribal courts. This Firm has represented the Institute of American Indian Arts and the Santa Fe Indian School and many Indian clients including the Alabama-Coushatta Tribe of Texas, Cochiti Pueblo, Mississippi Band of Choctaw Indians, Nambe Pueblo, Pechanga Indian Tribe, Picuris Pueblo, Saginaw Tribe of Chippewa Indians, Sandia Pueblo, Santa Clara Pueblo Gaming Commission, Zuni Pueblo and Zia Pueblo. Ms. Fairbanks also served as Chief Justice for the Yavapai-Apache Tribe for ten (10) years. Currently, Ms. Fairbanks serves as a Justice for the Inter-Tribal Court of Appeals of Nevada and is a member of the National American Indian Court Judges Association. Partner Patricia Salazar Ives is licensed to practice before all courts and agencies of the Navajo Nation. Ms. Ives regularly provides day-to-day advice to employers located on and/or doing business on the Navajo Nation on all aspects of Navajo law and regularly appears on their behalf before the Office of Navajo Labor Relations, the Navajo Nation Labor Commission and the Navajo Supreme Court. Ms. Ives also represents insurance companies and their insured before all Navajo Nation tribunals. The Firm advises clients regarding a wide scope of tribal, federal and state law and jurisdiction and we are experienced in drafting constitutions, agreements, codes, and other legal documents to ensure the protection and exercise of tribal sovereignty.

DAVIS GRAHAM & STUBBS LLP
1550 17th St., Suite 500 • Denver, CO 80202
 (303) 892-9400 Fax 893-1379
 Website https://www.dgslaw.com; E-mail: info@dgslaw.com
 Radcliffe Dan IV, Partner (892-7486)
 Laura K. Granier, Partner (892-7369)
 E-mail: laura.granier@dgslaw.com
 Catherine A. Hance, Partner (892-7480)
 E-mail: catherine.hance@dgslaw.com
 John R. Jacus, Partner; E-mail: john.jacus@dgslaw.com
 Zach C. Miller, Partner; E-mail: zach.miller@dgslaw.com
 Mave A. Gasaway, Associate; E-mail: mave.gasaway@dgslaw.com
For a century, Davis Graham and Stubbs LLP has served clients in the Rocky Mountain West – this history has given us a wealth of experience in the field of Indian law. Today, our attorneys represent companies doing business with tribes in a wide range of matters, and companies with project development that have other tribal concerns. We have handled matters involving Indian lands and other Indian law issues throughout the U.S., including New Mexico (Navajo, Jicarilla), Arizona (Navajo, White Mountain Apache, San Carlos Apache), Oklahoma (Osage), Colorado (Southern Ute, Ute Mountain Ute), Utah (Northern Ute), Wyoming (Shoshone-Arapahoe), Montana (Blackfeet, Crow, Fort Peck), North Dakota (Ft. Berthold, Yankton Sioux), Virginia (Mattaponi), and Nevada (Western Shoshone, Paiute). Because many Native American religious beliefs have connections to certain land areas, both on and off Indian reservations, the sensitive issue of Native American sacred sites increasingly arises in regard to project development. This occurs throughout the range of development in the West, from extractive and renewable energy projects, to transmission, transportation, recreation an educational facilities and activities. DGS attorneys are skilled in helping clients navigate this often highly-charged issue, from negotiating with tribes & federal agencies on mitigation or project re-siting, to litigating claims that clients' projects or activities harm such sites. They assist clients throughout the due diligence and negotiation process, including complex tribal jurisdictional issues, agreements under the Indian Mineral Leasing Act and the Indian Mineral Development Act, the HEARTH Act and obtaining the necessary approvals from the Bureau of Indian Affairs (BIA).

DENTONS LLP
Native American Law & Policy Practice
1301 K St., NW • Washington, DC 20005
 (202) 408-6400 Fax 408-6399; Website: www.dentons.com
1221 Ave. of the Americas • New York, NY 10020
 (212) 768-6700 Fax 768-6800
525 Market St., 26th Floor • San Francisco, CA 94105
 (415) 582-5000 Fax 582-0300
 V. Heather Sibbison, Partner, Chairperson (Washington, DC)
 (408-6439; E-mail: heather.sibbison@dentons.com
 Suzanne R. Schaeffer, Counsel (Washington, DC) (408-7097)
 Alan R. Fedman, Counsel (408-3954)
 E-mail: alan.fedman@dentons.com
 George T. Skibine (Osage), Counsel (Washington, DC) (408-8665)
 E-mail: george.skibine@dentons.com
 Samuel Daughety, Counsel (408-6427)
 E-mail: Samuel.daughety@dentons.com
 Josh Pitre (Houma), Managing Director (408-3942)
 E-mail: josh.pitre@dentons.com
 Robert Odawi Porter (Seneca), Senior Advisor (408-6348)
 E-mail: robert.porter@dentons.com
 Matthew Adams, Partner (San Francisco, CA) (415) 882-0351
 E-mail: paula.yost@dentons.com
 Jessica L. Duggan (Houma), Managing Associate (415) 882-0369
 E-mail: jessica.duggan@dentons.com
 Samuel Kohn (Crow), Associate (415) 882-5031
 E-mail: samuel.kohn@dentons.com
 Paula M. Yost, Partner (510) 496-7445
 E-mail: paula.yost@dentons.com
Assists tribal governments & tribal businesses navigate the kinds of legal and policy issues which require a thorough understanding of the complicated intersection of tribal governments, the federal agencies, the federal courts, and the United States Congress. Our clients benefit from a deep-bench of lawyers and other professionals with key federal government experience, including former high ranking officials from the Department of the Interior (Office of the Secretary, Bureau of Indian Affairs & Office of the Solicitor), from the National Indian Gaming Commission (former acting Chairman, & former head of Enforcement), from the Department of Justice (Indian Resources Section, Environmental Enforcement), & from several key congressional offices. What makes the depth of this federal expertise unique, however, is the complimentary depth of our tribal government expertise, brought to the practice by a former elected leader and former in-house tribal counsel. *U.S. News – Best Lawyers* 2015 guide has named Dentons "Law Firm of the Year" in the area of Native American Law.

Aboriginal Law (Canada) Dentons Canada LLP
1 Place Ville Marie, 39th Floor, Montreal, Quebec, Canada H3B 4M7
 Ann Bigue, Partner (Montreal) (514) 878-8808
 E-mail: ann.bigue@dentons.com
 Rick A. Neufeld, Partner (Calgary) (403) 268-7023
Aboriginal Law team to navigate the complexities of Aboriginal rights as they relate to your business. The rights of Indian, Inuit & Métis peoples are protected under the Canadian Constitution & can impact both Canadian businesses & foreign companies that invest in Canada. Aboriginal rights, whether they have been defined by treaties or the courts, or otherwise exist in relation to activities, practices & traditions of Canada's Aboriginal Peoples, must be taken into account when doing business in Canada. Dentons' Aboriginal Law team has helped companies to successfully resolve Aboriginal rights issues related to their business. Leverage our experience negotiating mutually beneficial agreements with Aboriginal groups & benefit from strategic advice on a variety of issues relating to Aboriginal rights & treaty rights, including the impact of Aboriginal land claims on the development of your projects & investments, & the implications of governments' duty to consult & accommodate Aboriginal Peoples, as appropriate.

DICKINSON WRIGHT / MARISCAL WEEKS, PLLC
Indian Law Section, 1875 Eye St., NW • Washington, DC 20006
 (202) 457-0160 Fax 659-1559
 Website: http://www.dickinson-wright.com/
 Dennis J. Whittlesey, Managing Partner (202) 659-6928
 E-mail: dwhittlesey@dickinsonwright.com

Patrick Sullivan, Associate (659-6936)
E-mail: psullivan@dickinsonwright.com
1850 N. Central Ave. #1400 • Phoenix, AZ 85004
(602) 285-5038 Fax 285-5100
Glenn M. Feldman, Partner (602) 285-5138
E-mail: gfeldman@dickinsonwright.com
199 Bay St. #2200, Commerce Court West • Toronto, ON M5L 1G4
(416) 777-0101 Fax 865-1398
Cherie L. Brant (Mohawk), Partner (416) 646-3845
E-mail: cbrant@dickinsonwright.com

Represents clients on Indian law issues throughout the U.S. and Canada. Has extensive experience and knowledge of Indian law, tribal rights & other issues impacting Native American, First Nations' peoples and those doing business with them. In addition to representing a wide range of tribes and tribal business enterprises, including tribal casinos & casino regulatory agencies, we counsel local governments, private companies and other non-Indian clients in their business dealings on Indian reservations or with tribal peoples. They actively represent clients in economic development transactions, including gaming, as well as assist in resolving the complex issues that arise regarding tribal sovereignty and jurisdiction tax matters. Team lawyers also litigate these and other cases involving Indian law, tribal rights and land claims in federal, state and tribal courts. In terms of project development, our team works to assure that projects are fully compliant with applicable laws & regulations while ensuring their economic integrity. Our tribal clients frequently seek our assistance in resolving problems with federal, state & local government agencies, & we always strive to solve those problems quickly & economically. Among the Indian Law practice's areas of expertise are: Providing general representation to tribes, including securing status clarification for unrecognized tribes; developing and drafting tribal constitutions, tribal codes, bylaws and ordinances; & assisting with land claims; Organizing & advising tribal business entities, including telephone companies and economic development agencies; Assuring protection of tribal trust resources and the environment, including resolving matters related to claims and title; water rights and fishing; hunting & gathering rights; & cultural resource protection; Assisting with all phases of tribal gaming and development of other business structures; Negotiating and documenting tribal casino financing; Negotiating leases for commercial developments on Indian reservations, including power plants, shopping centers and golf courses.

DOERNER, SAUNDERS, DANIEL & ANDERSON LLP

Two West Second St., Suite 700 • Tulsa, OK 74103
(918) 582-1211 Fax 925-5258
Jon E. Brightmire, Partner (591-5258); E-mail: jbrightmire@dsda.com
Stuart D. Campbell, Partner (591-5242); E-mail: scampbell@dsda.com
105 N. Hudson Ave., Suite 1000 • Oklahoma City, OK 73102
(405) 319-3500 Fax 319-3509
Michael Minnis, Of Counsel; E-mail: mminnis@dsda.com
1800 N. Interstate Dr., Suite 211 • Norman, OK 73072
(405) 319-3501 Fax 319-3531
David McCullough, Partner; E-mail: dmccullough@dsda.com

Throughout Oklahoma & in states from California to Iowa & Missouri, Doerner represents tribal councils & business committees on governance & economic development issues related to their sovereign entity status. We have advised all the major Oklahoma tribes since the state's tribal governments began major reorganizations in the late 1970s, and today assist tribes of all sizes in structuring their bylaws and codes, resolving inter- & intra-tribal disputes & administering their court systems. As tribes continue to expand gaming & non-gaming business enterprises, Offers advice on structuring trust ownership arrangements, arranging bond and other financing, and dealing with the Bureau of Indian Affairs (BIA), National Indian Gaming Commission (NIGC) & relevant state agencies. They have set up tribal gaming ordinances, negotiated pre-opening agreements for casinos and handled everything from labor agreements to contracts & licenses with gaming companies & suppliers, understanding that the economic interests of each tribe, and each company doing business in Indian Country, Provides tribal governments representation that respects their sovereign status. In emerging issues such as payday lending, water rights and renewable energy generation, they help tribes, businesses and regulators balance legal & economic concerns. Increasingly, tribes are investing in their own economic development, and Doerner provides insights to structure trust arrangements & establish joint ventures that advance tribal interests. Our lawyers are diligent in protecting the interests of smaller tribes as well as major tribal entities; & having expanded our practice as tribal governments have evolved, we work as partners with tribal clients to respect traditional values while seizing new opportunities.

DORSEY & WHITNEY, LLP

50 S. Sixth St., Suite 1500 • Minneapolis, MN 55402-1498
(612) 340-2686 Fax 340-2644; Website https://www.dorsey.com/
Skip Durocher, Co-Chair, Indian Law Practice Group (612-340-7855)
E-mail: Durocher.skip@dorsey.com
Mary J. Streitz, Partner & Co-Chair, Indian & Gaming Practice Group

E-mail: streitz.mary@dorsey.com; (340-7813)
Jesse Sixkiller (Cherokee), Associate (492-6182)
E-mail: sixkiller.jesse@dorsey.com
Forrest Tahdooahnippah (Comanche), Associate (492-6876
E-mail: forrest@dorsey.com
Anchorage Office: 1031 W. 4th Ave. #600, Anchorage, AK 99501
(907) 276-4557
Richard M. Rosston, Partner (907) 257-7837 (Anchorage Office)
E-mail: rosston.dick@dorsey.com

Dorsey was the first American law 100 firms to develop a full-service Indian & Alaska Native practice. The Indian Law Practice Group/Indian & Gaming Dept. represents Indian & Alaska Native tribal governments, tribal business & entities doing business with tribes across the country in connection with financings of reservation intra-structure, economic development, regulatory, gaming, etc.

DRUMMOND WOODSUM

Indian Law Group, 84 Marginal Way, Suite 600, Portland, ME 04101
(207) 772-1941 ext. 557 Fax 772-3627; Website: www.dwmlaw.com
Robert L. Gips, Special Counsel Indian Affairs; E-mail: rgips@dwmlaw.com
Kaighn Smith, Jr., Litigation/Tribal Employment
E-mail: ksmith@dwmlaw.com
Gregory W. Sample, Indian Law Group Founder, Tribal Housing
E-mail: gsample@dwmlaw.com

A nationally recognized Indian law group providing services to Indian nations and their enterprises and to companies that do business with tribes across the country. Our Indian law practice brings legal, business, & transactional experience to its work with some of the country's most successful Indian nations and enterprises. Their Indian Law Group is part of a full service law firm. Four of our Indian law attorneys are recognized by their peers as among the Best Lawyers in America in Native American law, and others in the Group are similarly recognized in other practice areas important to tribal clients. We draw upon a wide range of expertise in custom interdisciplinary teams as needed to best serve our clients. For example, we combine our Indian lawyers with: business and commercial lawyers for gaming and other economic development work; trial & appellate practitioners for litigation in federal, tribal, or state courts; labor specialists for personnel and employment matters; school lawyers for education-related matters; & tax & affordable housing specialists to address tribal housing needs. *Representative clients include*: Mashantucket Pequot Tribal Nation, Foxwoods Resort Casino and Foxwoods Development Company (CT); Mohegan Tribe of Connecticut (CT); Seminole Tribe of Florida (FL); Pokagon Band of Potawatomi Indians and Four Winds Casino Resort (MI); Little River Band of Ottawa Indians and Little River Casino Resort (MI); Little Traverse Bay Band of Odawa Indians (MI); Grand Traverse Band of Ottawa and Chippewa Indians (MI); Port Gamble S'Klallam Tribe (WA); Suquamish Tribe (WA); Jamestown S'Klallam Tribe (WA); Squaxin Island Tribe (WA); Snoqualmie Casino (WA); Pueblo of Laguna Department of Education (NM); Paskenta Band of Nomlaki Indians (CA); Penobscot Nation & Penobscot Indian Nation Enterprises (ME); Passamaquoddy Tribe (ME); Turtle Mountain Chippewa Housing Authorities (ND); Tribal First; Amerind Risk. *Indian Nations Labor & Employment Group* - works with Indian nations to enhance their governance of labor relations within Indian lands. Provides legal services to Indian tribes, tribal businesses & businesses that work with & provide services to tribes throughout the country.

ECHO HAWK LAW OFFICE

730 E. Clark #4166, P.O. Box 4166 • Pocatello, ID 83205
(208) 705-9503; (206) 904-3878
Paul Echo Hawk (Pawnee), Attorney; E-mail: paulechohawk@gmail.com
Licensed to practice in state and federal courts in Idaho, Utah, & Washington. Also licensed to practice in the Ninth, Tenth, and DC Federal Circuit Courts as well as the United States Supreme Court. *Specialties*: Federal Indian Law, Civil Litigation, Environmental Law, Water Law, Contracts, Business Disputes, Criminal Law, Administrative Law, Real Estate, Family Law, Divorce & Custody Disputes, General Practice

ECHO HAWK & OLSEN, PLLC

505 Pershing Ave., P.O. Box 6119 • Pocatello, ID 83205
(208) 478-1624 Fax 478-1670
Mark A. EchoHawk (Pawnee), Founding Partner
E-mail: mark@echohawk.com
Eric L. Olsen, Partner; E-mail: elo@echohawk.com
Joseph T. Preston, Attorney; E-mail: joseph@echohawk.com

Provides legal services to Indian tribal governments & tribal business enterprises in a cost-effective, efficient, & timely manner. Legal areas include: Federal Indian law, civil litigation, insurance defense, business representation, injury law, criminal law, creditor's rights & contract matters. Echo Hawk & Olsen, PLLC has a tradition of principled and zealous advocacy. They focus on providing specialized legal services to Indian tribal governments and tribal business enterprises. They also provides general legal services in all matters, including: personal injury, litigation, appeals, lobbying, business formation, business transactions, criminal law, creditor's rights, contracts, and family law.

FAEGRE BAKER DANIELS LLP

2200 Wels Fargo Center, 90 S. Seventh St. • Minneapolis, MN 55402
(612) 766-7000 Fax 766-1600; Website: www.faegrebd.com
Kent E. Richey, Partner (612) 766-6910
 E-mail: kent.richey@faegrebd.com
Aaron J. Harkins, Partner (612) 766-7442
 E-mail: aaron.harkins@faegrebd.com
Michael K. Coddington, Partner (612) 766-7328
 E-mail: michael.coddington@faegrebd.com
Richard A. Duncan, Partner (612) 766-8612
 E-mail: richard.duncan@faegrebd.com

Serves the legal needs of Indian tribes and the businesses that interact with them. They have worked on tribal financings totaling more than $10 billion and involving more than 120 tribes in 21 states. Projects include casinos, hotels, convention centers, infrastructure, and other investments. Working with tribal borrowers, lenders, developers, credit enhancers and underwriters, they handle transactions involving an array of financing tools, including bank loans, credit facilities, taxable & tax-exempt bonds, and bond offerings. In addition to financing transactions, they also maintain an active, nationwide Indian law practice where they represent tribes, tribal agencies & businesses, & other entities on a wide variety of topics affecting Indian country, especially business & commercial matters. They represent clients on general federal-Indian law issues, land into trust, Indian land determinations, BIA leases & approvals, IGRA, gaming compliance & tribal gaming commission matters, environmental law & regulations, taxation, federal recognition, labor & employment matters, construction matters, energy projects, & pro bono matters including Indian Child Welfare Act appeals and cultural items repatriation. They regularly represent tribes in litigation matters before federal & state courts and other bodies & they have substantial experience drafting tribal codes, ordinances, resolutions, and constitutional amendments. Their attorneys have years of experience with the BIA and NIGC and with tribal-state compact & gaming ordinance matters, which enables us to efficiently guide our clients through complicated & challenging federal processes.

FENNEMORE CRAIG, P.C.

2394 E. Camelback Rd., Suite 600 • Phoenix, AZ 85016
(602) 916-5421 Fax 916-5621
Timothy J. Berg, Chairperson & Director of Indian Law
 E-mail: tberg@fclaw.com
Attorneys: Michelle De Blasi (916-5496); Sean T. Hood (916-5475);
 Patrick Irvine (916-5406); Todd S. Kartchner (916-5461)

Provides legal services to American Indian Tribes of the Southwest covering a wide range of practice areas related to business & development both on and off Indian lands. Representation of client interests in the area of Indian Law often draws upon the diverse and substantial specialized resources within the firm ranging from government relations to taxation. This includes drawing upon knowledge of the challenges of commercial transactions in Indian Country, which the firm's managing partner, Tim Berg, helped address through a new national model secured transactions law for America's tribes. Released in 2005, the Model Tribal Secured Transactions Act was drafted by a committee of the National Conference of Commissioners on Uniform State Laws, chaired by Mr. Berg. The model act provides a secured transactions law for American Indian tribes modeled after the Uniform Commercial Code Article 9, which is the basis for commercial transactions across the country and is designed to assist the country's tribes, tribal entities and members to secure financing for commercial ventures. Offices in Denver, Las Vegas, Nogales, Reno & Tucson.

FLOYD, PFLUEGER & RINGER, P.S.

Indian Law Practice, 200 West Thomas St., Suite 500 • Seattle, WA 98119
(206) 441-4455 Fax 441-8484; Website: www.floyd-ringer.com
Francis S. Floyd, President
 E-mail: ffloyd@floyd-ringer.com
Thomas Nedderman
 E-mail: tnedderman@floyd-ringer.com

Represents American Indian tribes in the Pacific Northwest. Their primary goal is to promote, protect & preserve tribal sovereignty, culture & customs, as well as tribal resources.

FORMAN & ASSOCIATES

4340 Redwood Hwy., Suite E352 • San Rafael, CA 94903
(415) 491-2310 Fax 491-2313; Website: www.gformanlaw.com
George Forman, Principal; E-mail: gforman@gformanlaw.com
Jay Shapiro, Attorney; E-mail: jshapiro@gformanlaw.com
Jeff Keohane, Associate; E-mail: jeff@gformanlaw.com
Margaret Crow Rosenfeld, Associate
 E-mail: margaret@jformanlaw.com
Description: Provides legal counsel to American Indian tribal governments, tribal government agencies and businesses, and non-profit entities primarily serving Indian communities and people.

FOSTER PEPPER LLP

Native American Practice. 1111 Third Ave., #3400 • Seattle, WA 98101
(206) 447-8931 Fax 749-2117; Website: www.foster.com
Tim Filer, Attorney; (206) 447-2904; E-mail: tim.filer@foster.com
Jim McNeill, Attorney, (509) 777-1602; E-mail: jim.mcneill@foster.com
Attorneys: Joseph Brogan, J. Scott Galloway, Marc Greenough
Foster Pepper has a long history of service to Native American & Alaska Native peoples and organizations. From public service legal programs to multi-million dollar finance and infrastructure projects, we work closely with Tribes & Alaska Native Corporations to facilitate their community development and economic growth. We offer services & guidance to our Native clients in a vast array of areas, including bond finance, real estate & construction, employment & labor, environmental and land use, business, health care, and intellectual property protection.

FREDERICKS, PEEBLES & MORGAN LLP

Website: www.ndnlaw.com
California Office: 1001 Second St. • Sacramento, CA 95814
(916) 441-2700 Fax 441-2067
Colorado Office: 1900 Plaza Dr. • Louisville, CO 80027
(303) 673-9600 Fax 673-9155
Washington, DC Office: 401 9th St., NW • Washington, DC 20004
(202) 450-4887 Fax 450-5106
Michigan Office: 2848 Setterbro Rd. • Peshawbestwn, MI 49682
(231) 631-8558
Nebraska Office: 3610 North 163rd Plaza • Omaha, NE 68116
(402) 333-4053 Fax 333-4761
South Dakota Office: 910 5th St., #104 • Rapid City, SD 57701
(605) 791-1515 Fax 791-1915
North Dakota Office: 3730 29th Ave. • Mandan, ND 58554
(303) 673-9600 Fax (701) 663-5103
Tom W. Fredericks (Mandan, Hidatsa, Arikara), Partner (Louisville, CO)
 E-mail: tfredericks@ndnlaw.com
Conly J. Schulte, Partner (Louisville, CO)
 E-mail: cschulte@ndnlaw.com
John M. Peebles, Partner (Sacramento)
Lance Morgan (Winnebago of NE), Partner (Winnebago, NE)
 E-mail: lmorgan@ndnlaw.com; (402) 878-4383
John Fredericks III (Mandan, Hidatsa, Arikara) (Mandan, ND)
 E-mail: jfredericks@ndnlaw.com
Steven J. Bloxham, Partner (Sacramento, CA)
 E-mail: sbloxham@ndnlaw.com
Michael A. Robinson, Partner (Sacramento, CA)
 E-mail: mrobinson@ndnlaw.com
Tracey Zephier (Cheyenne River Sioux), Partner (Rapid City, SD)
 E-mail: tzephier@ndnlaw.com
John F. Petoskey (Ottawa & Ojibwe), Partner (Peshawbestwn, MI)
 E-mail: jpetoskey@ndnlaw.com
Patty Marks, Partner (Washington, DC)
 E-mail: pmarks@ndnlaw.com
Frances C. Bassett (Cherokee), Partner (Louisville, CO)
 E-mail: fbassett@ndnlaw.com
Danelle J. Smith (Winnebago of NE), Partner (Winnebago, NE)
 E-mail: dsmith@ndnlaw.com; (402) 878-4383
Jeremy J. Patterson (Cheyenne River Sioux), Partner (Louisville, CO)
 E-mail: jpatterson@ndnlaw.com
Leonika R. Charging (Mandan, Hidatsa, Arikara) (Omaha)
 Email: lcharging@ndnlaw.com
Joanne H. Curry (Cherokee), Partner (Louisville, CO)
 E-mail: jcurry@ndnlaw.com
Sheila D. Corbine (Lac Courte Oreilles), Partner (Winnebago, NE)
 E-mail: scorbine@ndnlaw.com; (402) 878-4383
Nicole Ducheneaux (Cheyenne River Sioux/Salish-Kootenai), Partner
 E-mail: nducheneaux@ndnlaw.com; Omaha, NE) (402) 333-4053
Timothy J. Kincaid, Of Counsel, Painesville, CO (440) 352-1000
John Nyhan, Of Counsel, Sacramento, CA (916) 441-2700

Represents American Indian tribes and Native American organizations throughout the U.S. Legal services in the areas of business transactions, litigation & governmental affairs; natural resource development, environmental law; gaming; finance; tribal sovereignty; taxation. Also interacts with local & federal agencies, the U.S. Congress and other organizations to protect & enhance tribal economic rights and privileges. *Goals*: To promote, protect & preserve tribal sovereignty, cultures and resources.

GALANDA BROADMAN, PLLC

8606 35th Ave. NE, Suite L1 • Seattle, WA 98115
P.O. Box 15146 • Seattle, WA 98115
(206) 557-7509 Fax 299-7690
Website: www.galandabroadman.com
E-mail: info@galandabroadman.com

Gabriel S. Galanda, Partner (300-7801)
E-mail: gabe@galandabroadman.com
Anthony S. Broadman, Partner (321-2672)
E-mail: Anthony@galandabroadman.com
Ryan D. Dreveskracht, Associate (909-3842)
E-mail: ryan@galandabroadman.com
R. Joseph Sexton, Scott Wheat, Amber Penn-Roco, and
Bree R. Black Horse, Attorneys

Description: An American Indian-owned law firm dedicated to advancing tribal legal rights and Indian business interests. The firm, with offices in Seattle, Washington and Bend, Oregon, represents tribal governments, businesses & members in critical litigation, business & regulatory matters, especially in matters of Indian Treaty rights, tribal sovereignty & taxation. *Awards, honors*: 2013 U.S. News – Best Lawyers, "Best Law Firms," in the arena of Native American Law.

GALLAGHER & KENNEDY LLP
2575 E. Camelback Rd. • Phoenix, AZ 85016
(602) 530-8000 Fax 530-8500; Website: www.gknet.com
1239 Paseo de Peralta • Santa Fe, NM 87501
(505) 982-9523 Fax 983-8160
Native American Law Attorneys:
Christopher W. Thompson, Terence W. Thompson, Mark A. Fuller,
Donald Peder Johnsen, Brian Zavislak

The Native American Law team at Gallagher & Kennedy provides strategic legal advice to Native American tribes, tribal organizations & affiliated entities. By working with Arizona's Native American tribes & entities, the attorneys are aware of the unique history & culture specific to these Native American tribal communities. They work closely with Native American clients to integrate the specific customs of tribal authorities into the working relationship. Provides representation for tribal governments on sovereignty, economic development & governmental objectives. In addition, they represent tribal corporations & affiliated entities on a wide array of matters, from initial organizational structuring to complex transactions and litigation.

GARVEY SCHUBERT BARER
Second & Seneca Bldg., 1191 Second Ave., 18th Floor • Seattle, WA 98101
(206) 816-1355 Fax 464-0125; Website: www.gsblaw.com
Flour Mill Bldg., 1000 Potomac St. NW Suite 200, Washington, DC 20007
(202) 965-7880 Fax 965-1729

Provides legal services to Indian tribes focusing primarily on treaty rights and relations between tribes and the federal government. Areas covered are economic development projects, labor & employment law, communications & media, federal representation, gaming, land use & environmental issues, financing & litigation. Represents the Tulalip & Muckleshoot and other tribes in the South and Southwest. Offices in Anchorage, Washington, DC, New York City, Portland, and Beijing, China.

GOWLING WLG CANADA LLP
550 Burrard St., Suite 2300, Bentall 5, Vancouver, BC V6C 2B5 Canada
(604) 683-6498 Fax 683-3558
Website: www.gowlingwlg.com
Indigenous Law Group
Merle C. Alexander (Kitasoo Xai'xais First Nation), Partner & Group Leader
(604) 891-2271; E-mail: merle.alexander@gowlingwlg.com
Maxime Faille, Partner & Group Leader (604) 891-2733 Fax 443-6741
E-mail: maxime.faille@gowlingwlg.com
Group Partners: Brian J. Kearl (Calgary), Graham S. Ragan (Ottawa),
David K. Law (Ottawa), Jaime Lickers (Hamilton),
Matthew Sherrard (Montreal), Elizabeth Burton (Calgary)

Since the 1950s, Gowling WLG has been at the forefront of Indigenous law in Canada. They've worked alongside Canada's First Nations, Métis & Inuit peoples in landmark self-government agreements, resource development projects and Supreme Court cases. We've also acted for project proponents and governments at every level. This singular legacy enables us to provide you with sophisticated legal advice in every aspect of Indigenous law — delivering practical, cost-effective solutions that help you advance your vision & achieve your goals. Gowling WLG is home to one of the largest and most respected Indigenous law practices in Canada. The needs and aspirations of Indigenous communities continue to grow in scope & complexity. Accordingly, the practice of Indigenous law increasingly demands specialized expertise in a wide range of areas. As a full-service law firm, Gowling WLG is equipped to meet your diverse legal needs — from treaty rights and inherent rights, land claims, self-government, taxes and trusts to energy, mining, economic development & environmental matters. We've served as trusted legal counsel to Canada's Indigenous peoples for over 50 years, and we're proud to have these same communities reflected in our own team. We actively recruit lawyers of Indigenous ancestry and support numerous initiatives that promote their advancement in the legal profession.

LAW OFFICES OF BRUCE R. GREENE ASSOCIATES, LLC
1500 Tamarack Ave. • Boulder, CO 80304
(303) 284-8654 Fax 284-8578; Website: www.greenelawyer.com
Bruce R. Greene, Founding Partner; E-mail: bgreene@greenelawyer.com

Specializes in all aspects of Federal Indian law & the representation of Native American Indian tribes. Offers Indian tribes throughout the country seasoned federal court litigation experience at the district court & appellate levels, together with expertise in a variety of areas particularly affecting tribes, including all aspects of Indian gaming natural resources protection, assertion & protection of treaty rights, including hunting, fishing, trapping & gathering rights; tribal economic development; federal project licensing; tribal/state taxation issues; water rights protection & adjudication; and protection of human remains & funerary objects. Established 2009.

GREENBERG TRAURIG, LLP
American Indian Law Practice Group
1200 17th St., Suite 2400 • Denver, CO 80202
(303) 572-6500 Fax 572-6540; Website: www.gtlaw.com
Troy A. Eid, Co-chair (572-6521); E-mail: eidt@gtlaw.com
Jennifer Harvey Weddle, Co-chair (572-6565); E-mail: weddlej@gtlaw.com

Description: Provides multidisciplinary legal representation to Native American tribal governments & associated entities, as well as to private & public institutions that do business with Indian tribes or invest in Indian country. *Areas of Practice*: Tribal Sovereignty, Energy, Environmental & Natural Resources; Corporate Counsel & Gaming Law; Tax, Benefits & Employment Law, Tribal Law Enforcement, Public Safety & Judicial Systems.

GUNGOLL, JACKSON, BOX & DEVOLL, P.C.
101 Park Ave., Suite 1400 • Oklahoma City, OK 73102
(405) 272-4710 Fax 272-5141
323 W. Broadway • Enid, OK 73701
(580) 234-0436
Website: www.gungolljackson.com
Robert Donald Gifford II (Cherokee), Senior Attorney
E-mail: gifford@gungolljackson.com

Practice Areas: Native American Law; civil litigation, commercial transactions, insolvency and reorganization, real estate transactions, trusts and estates, oil and gas, environmental law, family law, employment law, criminal defense, municipal law, personal injury and appeals are among the areas encompassed by the firm's practice.

HOBBS, STRAUS, DEAN & WALKER LLP
2120 L St., NW, Suite 700 • Washington, DC 20037
(202) 822-8282 Fax 296-8834; Website: www.hsdwlaw.com
Charles A. Hobbs, Partner; E-mail: chobbs@hobbsstraus.com
Jerry C. Straus, Partner; E-mail: jstraus@hobbsstraus.com
S. Bobo Dean, Partner; E-mail: sdean@hobbsstraus.com
Jennifer P. Hughes, Partner; E-mail: jhughes@hobbsstraus.com
Eliott A. Milhollin, Partner; E-mail: emilhollin@hobbsstraus.com
Michael L. Roy, Partner; E-mail: mroy@hobbsstraus.com
Joseph H. Webster, Partner; E-mail: jwebster@hobbsstraus.com
Branch locations:
(Portland) 806 S.W. Broadway, Suite 700, Portland, OR 97205
(503) 242-1745 Fax 242-1072
Edmund Clay Goodman, Partner; E-mail: egoodman@hobbsstraus.com
Craig A. Jacobson, Partner; E-mail: cjacobson@hobbsstraus.com
Steve D. Osborne, Partner; E-mail: sosborne@hobbsstraus.com
Starla K. Roels, Partner; E-mail: sroels@hobbsstraus.com
Geoffrey D. Strommer, Partner; E-mail: gstrommer@hobbsstraus.com
Christopher T. Stearns (Navajo), Of Counsel
E-mail: cstearns@hobbsstraus.com
Lee Shannon (Salish), Of Counsel; E-mail: lshannon@hobbsstraus.com
(Oklahoma City) 101 Park Ave., Suite 700, Oklahoma City, OK 73102
(405) 602-9425 Fax 602-9426
William R. Norman, Jr., Partner; E-mail: wnorman@hobbsstraus.com
W. Gregory Guedel, Partner; E-mail: gguedel@hobbsstraus.com
Chris Z. Cantrell, Of Counsel; E-mail: ccantrell@hobbsstraus.com
Kirke Kingingbird, Of Counsel; E-mail: kkickingbird@hobbsstraus.com
L. Susan Work, Of Counsel; E-mail: swork@hobbsstraus.com
Michael D. McMahan, Associate; E-mail: mmcmahan@hobbsstraus.com
Randi Dawn Gardner Hardin, Associate; E-mail: rhardin@hobbsstraus.com
(Sacramento) 1903 21st St., 3rd Floor, Sacramento, CA 95811
(916) 442-9444 Fax 442-8344
Stephen V. Quesenberry, Partner; E-mail: squesenberry@hobbsstraus.com
Timothy C. Seward, Partner
Adam P. Bailey Choctaw OK), AssociateE-mail: abailey@hobbsstraus.com
(Anchorage) 135 Christensen Dr., Suite 3B, Anchorage, AK 99501
(202) 374-4901 Fax (503) 242-1072
Kristi Williams, Advisor E-mail: kwilliams@hobbsstraus.com

Description: Dedicated to providing high quality legal services, including advocacy before federal, state and local governments, agencies and courts, to Indian & Alaska Native tribes & tribal organizations throughout the U.S. D.C. home office opened in 1982. Current clients include tribes, tribal organizations, and individual Indians in all regions of the U.S., including Alaska. Also provide legal & legislative services to national Indian organizations such as the National Congress of American Indians and Americans for Indian Opportunity, as well as to national & regional; Indian organizations representing the education, housing, health, child welfare, and gaming interests of Indian tribes and Indian people. *Practice areas*: Tribal Affairs; Self-Determination & Self-Governance; Indian Housing; Gaming; Child Welfare; Education; Healthcare. *Staff: DC office*: Lael Echo-Hawk, Of Counsel; M. Frances Ayer, Of Counsel; Carol L. Barbero, Of Counsel; Karen J. Funk, Legislative Analyst; Akilah J. Kinnison, Associate; Katie E. Klass, Associate; Caroline P. Mayhew, Associate; Duke McCloud, Of Counsel; Moriah K. O'Brien, Legislative Analyst; Dean B. Suagee, Of Counsel. *Portland, OR office* Of Counsel: Chris Cantrell, Kirk Kickingbird, L. Susan Work. Sacramento office Partners: Stephen Quesenberry, Timothy Seward.

HOGEN ADAMS PLLC
1935 W. County Rd. B2, Suite 460 • St. Paul, MN 55113
(651) 842-9100 Fax 842-9101; Website: www.hogenadams.com
Vanya S. Hogen (Oglala Lakota), Founding Partner
E-mail: vhogenmoline@hogenadams.com
Andrew Adams III (Muscogee Creek), Founding Partner
E-mail: aadams@hogenadams.com
Shauna L. Coons (Ojibwe), Associate Attorney
Jessica Intermill, Attorney (842-9104), Founding Member
E-mail: jintermill@hogenadams.com
William Szotkowski, Attorney; E-mail: bszotkowski@hogenadams.com
Colette Routel, Attorney; (651) 290-6327
E-mail: colette.routel@mitchellhamline.edu
Peter Rademacher, Attorney; E-mail: prademacher@hogenadams.com
Philip N. Hogen (Oglala Sioux), Attorney (South Dakota office)
(605) 787-6901; E-mail: phogen@hogenadams.com
South Dakota Office: 11312 N. High Meadows Dr., Black Hawk, SD 57718
Specializes in legal issues in Indian Country means understanding that every day is different for Tribes and their partners. Just as tribal governance and commerce covers the waterfront of legal issues, so does our practice. We have successfully negotiated multi-million dollar deals, drafted a wide range of tribal laws – from day-care regulations to burial codes, and litigated cases about hunting rights, Indian gaming, and tribal laws. But our commitment to legal excellence in Indian Country runs throughout each of these areas. Click on this list to explore the issues that we resolve most frequently: Business & Commercial Transactions; Environment & Natural Resources; Governance; Gaming; Litigation; Taxation. Their attorneys have worked in-house with tribes and as outside counsel to draft, review, and revise all types of tribal laws, from resolutions and ordinances to constitutions and bylaws. They have managed all aspects of complex federal litigation from treaty research to selecting expert witnesses to assisting in the development and presentation of Tribe's treaty case. Our attorneys have also successfully guided Tribes through the settlement & mediation process as an alternative to continued litigation. They have particular expertise in litigation concerning jurisdiction to tax tribal assets, tribal activities, tribal income, & on-reservation businesses. *Activities*: Assisted tribes in drafting & administering judicial codes, probate codes, civil & criminal codes, juvenile codes, and a variety of other laws; Developed trust and other benefit programs for tribal minors & adults; assisted tribes in negotiating and administering self-determination contracts; Developed tribal employment policies & procedures; Assisted tribes in implementing business-licensing ordinances, natural-resource regulations, zoning & building codes, ordinances governing tribal-business-enterprise development, & tribal membership; Drafted comprehensive tribal codes to govern all aspects of on-reservation commercial activity & taxation; Drafted law-enforcement agreements between tribes and local law-enforcement authorities to empower tribal police to provide services throughout reservations; and revised existing tribal constitutions and assisted tribes through all stages of securing approvals necessary to hold a federal secretarial election. **Gaming**: The attorneys at Hogen Adams have comprehensive tribal-gaming experience. We have negotiated & successfully closed gaming-development deals across the country & outside of the United States. In the specific area of Indian Gaming, we have extensive experience with gaming contract and regulatory-compliance issues both as attorney appearing before, & sitting on, the National Indian Gaming Commission

HOLLAND & HART LLP
Indian Law Practice Group, 555 17th St. #3200 • Denver, CO 80202
(303) 295-8244 Fax 295-8261/8376
Website: www.hollandhart.com
Andrew C. Emrich, Partner (Cheyenne office) (307) 778-4219
E-mail: acemrich@hollandhart.com

Kelly A. Johnson, Partner (Washington, DC office) (202) 393-6500
E-mail: kajohnson@hollandhart.com
Thomas L. Sansonetti, Partner (Denver office) (303) 290-1061
E-mail: tlsansonetti@hollandhart.com
Mark F. Sheridan, partner (Santa Fe office) (505) 988-4421
E-mail: msheridan@hollandhart.com
Robert J. Sutphin, Jr., Partner (Santa Fe office) (505) 988-4421
E-mail: rsutphin@hollandhart.com
Peter C. Houtsma, Partner (Denver office) (303) 295-8259
E-mail: phoutsma@hollandhart.com
Branch locations:
Cheyenne, WY: 2515 Warren Ave., Suite 45, Cheyenne, WY 82001
Washington, DC: 975 F St., NW, Washington, DC 20004
Denver, CO: 555 Seventeenth St., Suite 3200, Denver, CO 80202
Santa Fe, NM: 110 N. Guadalupe, Suite 1, Santa Fe, NM 87504
Provides legal services to Indian tribes, organizations & individuals in the form of advice and representation in litigation, business, natural resources and environmental matters. Established 1999.

HOLLAND & KNIGHT
Indian Law Practice Group
2099 Pennsylvania Ave., NW, Suite 100 • Washington, DC 20006
(202) 955-3000 Fax 955-5564; Website: https://www.hklaw.com
Shenan R. Atcitty (Dine), Partner, Senior Counsel
(202) 457-7128 E-mail: shenan.atcitty@hklaw.com
Teresa Ridle; E-mail: teresa.ridle@hklaw.com
Anchorage Office: 601 West Fifth Ave., Suite 700, Anchorage, AK 99501
Walter Featherly; Executive Partner, Anchorage office (907) 263-6395
E-mail: walter.featherly@hklaw.com
Los Angeles Office: 400 S. Hope St., 8th Floor, Los Angeles, CA 90071
Jerome L. Levine, Partner (Los Angeles office)
(213) 896-2565; Email: jerome.levine@hklaw.com
Provides legal representation to Indian tribal governments before Congress & Federal Agencies on issues such as comprehensive Indian energy legislation; economic development & tax incentives in Indian country; tribal sovereignty protection; land into trust; Indian gaming; infrastructure development on Indian lands; Indian health, housing & education; and evaluating the Dept. of the Interior's proposal to reorganize the Bureau of Indian Affairs.

HOMER LAW
1730 Rhode Island Ave., NW Suite 501 • Washington, DC 20036
(202) 955-5601 Fax 955-5605; Website: www.homerlaw.com
Elizabeth Lohan Homer, Principal; E-mail: ehomer@homerlaw.com
William D. Bettenberg, Attorney; E-mail: bbettenberg@homerlaw.com
Areas of Practice: Indian Gaming; Business Development; Alaskan Natives; Tribal Sovereignty; Intergovernmental Relations.

HUGHES HUBBARD & REED LLP
350 S. Grand Ave. • Los Angeles, CA 90071
(213) 613-2808 Fax 613-2950
Theodore H. Latty, Partner; E-mail: latty@hugheshubbard.com
In conjunction with our Gaming practice, our Native American practice has represented Indian nations and enterprises, financial institutions and others in some of the largest & most complex transactions in Indian Country, including: *Chumash Casino & Resort Enterprise*. Santa Ynez Band of Mission Indians; *River Rock Entertainment Authority*. Dry Creek Rancheria Band of Pomo Indians; *Oneida Indian Nation of New York*. Turning Stone Casino Resort; Guidiville Band of Pomo Indians; *Real Estate Investor*. Investigation of Native American casino and resort opportunities and obstacles in Northern California; *Investment and Commercial Banks*. with respect to Indian nations in Arizona, California, New Mexico, New York & Oklahoma. Our attorneys frequently speak at industry conferences & trade shows concerning gaming developments, operations, finance and other related topics and have published numerous articles on Indian gaming and other legal matters.

THE JACOBSON LAW GROUP
JACOBSON, MAGNUSON, ANDERSON & HALLORAN, P.C.
335 Atrium Office Bldg., 1295 Bandana Blvd. • St. Paul, MN 55108
(651) 644-4710 Fax (651) 644-5904 (612) 349-6254
Website: www.thejacobsonlawgroup.com
John E. Jacobson, General Partner & Of Counsel
E-mail: jjacobson@thejacobsonlawgroup.com
Mary B. Magnuson, Partner
E-mail: mmagnuson@thejacobsonlawgroup.com
Mark A. Anderson (Boise Forte Chippewa), Partner
E-mail: manderson@thejacobsonlawgroup.com
Joseph F. Halloran, Partner
E-mail: jhalloran@thejacobsonlawgroup.com
Susan L. Allen (Rosebud Lakota), Attorney
E-mail: sallen@thejacobsonlawgroup.com

Shawn R. Frank (Seneca), Attorney
E-mail: sfrank@thejacobsonlawgroup.com
R. Reid Lebeau II (Cheyenne River Sioux), Attorney
E-mail: rlebeau@thejacobsonlawgroup.com
Michael L. Murphy, Attorney
E-mail: mmurphy@thejacobsonlawgroup.com
Sara K. Van Norman, Attorney
E-mail: svannorman@thejacobsonlawgroup.com
Phil Mahowald's, Attorney
E-mail: pmahowald@thejacobsonlawgroup.com

Jacobson, Magnuson, Anderson & Halloran, P.C. is one of the premier Indian-law firms in the United States. Located in Saint Paul, Minnesota, we enjoy a national reputation for excellence in providing legal services to Indian tribes and non-Indian commercial interests on Indian-law issues. Founded in 1983, Jacobson Law prides itself on its responsiveness to client needs, efficiency of service, and expansive expertise in Indian law. Our lawyers have extensive & diverse experience representing tribes, federal agencies, state & local governments, as well as private interests, and are committed to providing responsive, comprehensive, & cost effective services to their clients. Indian law is a specialized, complicated, & multi-jurisdictional practice that encompasses not only a legal component, but a cultural component as well. Our experience in Indian Country and our ability to weave together the legal & cultural aspects of our clients' needs enables us to excel in the practice of Indian law. Half of our shareholders are members of federally recognized Indian tribes, so we appreciate cultural and ethnic diversity among our clients and understand the need to work cooperatively to ensure that our services respond to a community's specific needs. Since 1983, our philosophy has remained quite simple: provide outstanding, yet affordable, legal services for Indian tribes and businesses, not just in Indian Country but throughout the United States. This philosophy inspires everything we do. Half of shareholders are members of federally recognized Indian tribes with Indian law as the centerpiece of the firm. General counsel to Indian tribes, tribal governments, & other tribal enterprises. Represents both Indian tribes & non-Indian commercial interests and governmental interests with respect to Indian law issues throughout the U.S. Established 1973.

JORDAN LAW OFFICES PLLC

1730 Rhode Island Ave. NW • Washington, DC 20036
(202) 223-0893; Website: www.dbjordanlaw.com
Derril B. Jordan, Founder & Owner (Mattaponi of Virginia)
Michael D. Sliger, Of Counsel

The firm is dedicated to the representation of Indian tribal governments and other Native American organizations, and prioritizes the advancement and protection of tribal sovereignty, and the promotion of tribal self-sufficiency and self-determination. *Practice Areas*: Tribal Sovereignty, Economic Development, Trust Land Acquisition, Tribal Gaming, Inter-governmental Relations.

K&L GATES LLP

Native American Law (North America)
925 Fourth Ave., Suite 2900 • Seattle, WA 98104
(206) 370-7655 Fax 370-6064; Website: www.klgates.com
Bart J. Freedman, Partner; E-mail: bart.freedman@klgates.com
618 W. Riverside Ave., Suite 300 • Spokane, WA 99201
(509) 624-2100 Fax 456-0146

K&L Gates Indian Law lawyers understand the issues this expansion has raised and have extensive experience handling a wide variety of matters involving tribes and their business partners in Alaska, the Pacific Northwest, Pennsylvania, California, Michigan, Oklahoma, & Washington, DC. Our lawyers and public policy professionals have advised public and private clients, local governmental agencies, and Indian tribes on how to address and resolve issues involving many areas of Indian law. K&L Gates attorneys have helped clients with disputes, treaty issues, complicated real estate transactions in Indian Country, and Indian property rights outside Indian Country for water rights and access to hunting and fishing sites. We have represented local and regional governments on treaty matters & major litigation, & have represented tribes and other parties on policy matters in Washington, D.C. Because our experience includes working with both public and private entities, in addition to Indian tribes, we collaborate with many other groups at K&L Gates, including public policy, real estate, healthcare, litigation, tax, banking, intellectual property, and labor and employment. This interaction has helped us offer a full contingent of services to tribes and to other clients on Indian law matters. Represents tribes & Alaska Native Corporations. Our clients include both tribal governments & member-owned businesses. The firm addresses corporate and business issues and the interplay with treaty rights; taxation matters; federal and state litigation; and government lobbying. K&L Gates has advised on law and procedures created by IGRA under which Native American tribes may conduct gaming activities on Indian lands. We have analyzed related issues including the conditions under which a state must permit a tribe to conduct Class III (i.e., casino-type) gaming operations; sovereign and tribal immunity under IGRA; methods under which a tribe can establish gaming rights if a state refuses to negotiate a gaming compact; enforcement of prohibitions against such gaming; and whether a tribe may enter into a gaming compact with a state outside IGRA's procedures. Gates counsels tribal & government entities on disputes involving Indian law and administrative decisions from the Bureau of Indian Affairs.

KANJI & KATZEN, PLLC

303 Detroit St., Suite 400 • Ann Arbor, MI 48104
(734) 769-5400 Fax 769-2701
401 2ⁿᵈ St. S., Suite 700 • Seattle, WA 98104
(206) 344-8100 Fax (866) 283-0178
1250 Connecticut Ave., NW, Suite 200 • Washington, DC 20036
(202) 261-6528 Fax 2261-6537
Website: www.kanjikatzen.com; E-mail: info@kanjikatzen.com
Riyaz Kanji, Founding Member (Ann Arbor)
Phil Katzen, Founding Member (Seattle)
E-mail: pkatzen@kanjikatzen.com
Attorneys: Cory Albright, David Giampetroni, John Sledd
Jane Steadman, Philip Tinker
Of Counsel: Robert Anderson, Lucy Braun, Wenona Singel
Description: The firm is dedicated entirely to advocacy on behalf of Indian tribes & peoples. The firm represents Indian nations & tribes across the country on a wide variety of issues, including sovereignty & governance, treaty fishing & hunting rights, Indian gaming, environmental protection, reservation boundaries, taxation & jurisdictional matters. Works closely with the National Congress of American Indians and the Native American Rights Fund in their efforts to improve tribal success before the Supreme Court through the Tribal Supreme Court Project.

KARNOPP PETERSON LLP

360 SW Bond St., Suite 400 • Bend, OR 97702
(541) 382-3011 Fax 388-5410; Website: https://karnopp.com
Howard Arnett, Partner; E-mail: hga@karnopp.com
Ellen Grover, Partner; Josh Newton, Partner; John Ogan, Partner
Indian Law. Since 1955, Karnopp Petersen has represented tribes, tribally owned business enterprises, individuals & business entities in Indian country. We have maintained a long-term general counsel relationship and have employed our knowledge and experience in special counsel, litigation and project specific relationships. Our collective experience in all aspects of Federal Indian Law, state law affecting tribal interests and tribal law lays the foundation for our attorneys to confidently advise clients in navigating the complex matters that can arise in Indian country, including: tribal sovereignty; protection of treaty and other tribal rights, both on and off the reservation; natural resource and trust asset protection; intergovernmental relations; energy & project development & implementation; timber & forest resource management; gaming and tourism; tribal economic and business development; joint ventures and strategic partnerships; the Indian Child Welfare Act; tribal, federal and state legislation; contracting and compacting under the Indian Self-Determination and Education Assistance Act; dispute resolution. Karnopp Petersen Indian Law Blog.

KARSHMER & ASSOCIATES

765 Market St., Suite 28F • San Francisco, CA 94103
(415) 615-0201 Fax 777-1145; Website: karshmerindianlaw.com
Barbara Karshmer, P.C. E-mail: Barbara@karshmerindianlaw.com
Firm works extensively in the areas of Tribal self-government preparing codes, ordinances, and policies for tribes; water law; health law; energy issues; employment law; P.L. 93-638 contracting & compacting; & economic development. Her clients have ranged from small California tribes, to tribes and tribal organizations in Alaska, to the Navajo Nation.

KELIN LAW FIRM, P.C.

1309 Rio Grande Blvd. NW • Albuquerque, NM 87104
(505) 507-9310
Zackeree Sean Kelin (Caddo), Founder/Attorney

KILPATRICK TOWNSEND & STOCKTON, LLP

1420 Fifth Ave., Suite 3700, Seattle, WA 98101
(206) 467-9600 Fax 516-3097 Fax 374-8224
Website: www.kilpatricktownsend.com
Claire Newman, Associate (Seattle office)
Rob Roy E. Smith, Partner (Seattle office) (206) 224-2868
607 14ᵗʰ St., NW, Suite 900 • Washington, DC 20005
(202) 508-5844 Fax 585-0007
Keith M. Harper (Cherokee); Partner (Native American Affairs)
Catherine F. Munson, Partner (DC office) (202) 824-1435
Wade T. Blackmon, Counsel (New York office)
April Day (Cherokee), Associate (DC office); (202) 508-5838
The Grace Bldg., 1114 Ave. of the Americas, New York, NY 10036
(212) 775-8775 Fax 202-4976
1100 Peachtree St. NE, Suite 2800 • Atlanta, GA 30309
(404) 815-6058 Fax 541-3104; John W. Alden, Partner

Mark H. Reeves, Associate (Augusta, GA & DC offices)
(706) 823-4206 of (202) 824-1436
Provides legal services, public policy advice & counsel to tribal governments, tribal organizations, & other entities, to strengthen the government-to-government relationship between tribes and the U.S. The firm is committed to preserving, promoting, & protecting tribal sovereignty & self-determination for Indian Nations.

LAW OFFICES OF BARRY KLOPFER, P.C.
224 W. Coal Ave. • Gallup, NM 87301
(505) 722-9331 Fax 722-9335
Navajo Nation Employment Law. On the Navajo Nation the timeline for initiating a grievance against an employer in a dispute may be less than 20 days in some cases, and up to a year in others. It all depends on the Navajo Nation personnel policy manual, the collective bargaining agreement, the Navajo case law that interprets the Navajo Preference in Employment Act (NPEA), and whether or not you're employed by the Navajo Nation. If you're employed by the Navajo Nation, you may be required to file a "step grievance" with the Navajo Department of Personnel Management in order to initiate a Navajo hearing with the Navajo Office of Hearings and Appeals, or OHA, for wrongful termination on the Navajo Nation, or for workplace harassment on the Navajo Nation. Anyone who is being harassed at the workplace or who was suspended, demoted, or terminated from employment or is a member of Navajo Nation personnel should immediately be in contact with a counselor who is licensed by the bar. There is a strict process that must be followed by any Navajo Nation employee who has a personnel grievance and wishes to have a Navajo hearing on the situation, which will be overseen by the Office of Hearings and Appeals.

LEGAL ADVOCATES FOR INDIAN COUNTRY LLP (LAIC)
P.O. Box 1434 • Owasso, OK 74055 (home office)
(918) 376-0630 Fax 376-0631; Website: www.laic-law.com
E-mail: kedwards@laic-law.com
Charles H. Tripp (Cherokee), Founding Partner
Marsha L. Harlan, Partner
Michalah Anderson, Associate Attorney
P.O. Box 87 • Miami, OK 74355 (918) 376-0630 Fax 376--0631
Troy LittleAxe, Founding Partner
LAIC is a law firm that specializes in services to Tribal Nations, Tribal Businesses, Tribal Agencies, and individual tribal member legal representation. Specific areas of practice include: Tribal Gaming Law, Housing, Governmental & Domestic Relations, Child Support Enforcement, Indian Child Welfare Act cases, Tribal Sovereignty, Jurisdiction & Court Systems, Development of Tribal Codes, Policies, Compliance, et al. Maintains offices in Owasso, Stillwater, Miami, Wagoner, Norman, and a Washington State office in Seattle.

LEWIS ROCA ROTHERGERBER CHRISTI LLP
Tribal Affairs & Gaming Practice Group
Tribal Lands & Natural Resources Group
201 E. Washington St., Suite 1200 • Phoenix, AZ 85004
(602) 262-5311 Fax 262-5747; Website: www.lrrc.com
Paul Michael Bielecki, Principal (602-262-5354)
E-mail: mbielecki@lrrc.com
Stephen M. Hart, Partner (602-262-5787); E-mail: shart@lrrc.com
Tribal Affairs & Gaming Group Leader
Carla A. Consoli, Partner (262-5347); Email: cconsoli@lrrc.com
Tribal Lands Natural Resources Group Leader
Peter A. Larson, Partner (602-262-5796); E-mail: plarson@lrrc.com
Sean McGuinness, Partner (775-321-3407)
E-mail: smcguinness@lrrc.com
Kerry K. Patterson (Seneca), Partner (602) 262-5717)
E-mail: kpatterson@lrrc.com
Provides legal & strategic advice to its Tribal Government & Tribal Enterprise clients in Arizona, California, Idaho, Oregon, Texas & Washington. Locations: Tucson, Albuquerque, Las Vegas, Reno & Mountain View, CA. Lewis Roca lawyers' in depth knowledge of the specialized federal and Tribal laws & our substantive experience in environmental, water, natural resources and mining law combine to effectively represent our Tribal & non-Tribal clients. When required, we call on the strong knowledge base of the lawyers in our real estate, commercial, finance, government relations, gaming & litigation groups to assist & advise our clients. Lewis Roca lawyers understand that succeeding in matters involving Tribal natural resources and land issues

LOCKRIDGE GRINDAL NAUEN, P.L.L.P.
Indian Law Practice Group
100 Washington Ave. South, Suite 2200 • Minneapolis, MN 55401
(612) 339-6900 Fax 339-0981; Website: www.locklaw.com
Harry E. Gallaher, Managing Partner; E-mail: hegallaher@locklaw.com
Theodore H. Grindal, Partner (596-4038) E-mail: htgrindal@locklaw.com
Christopher K. Sanndberg, Partner, E-mail: cksandberg@locklaw.com

Represents various tribal concerns at the local, state & federal levels on issues ranging from Indian gaming to obtaining federal monies to promoting economic development on various Indian reservations. Special expertise in a broad range of Indian law issues including tribal sovereignty, jurisdictional issues, treaty rights, and employment law. Branch office: 415 Second St. NE, Suite 210, Washington, DC 20002 (202) 544-9840 Fax 544-9850

McELROY, MEYER, WALKER & CONDON, P.C.
1007 Pearl St., Suite 220 • Boulder, CO 80302
(303) 442-2021 Fax 444-3490; Website: www.mmwclaw.com
Scott B. McElroy, Managing Partner; E-mail: smcelroy@mmwclaw.com
Elizabeth Meyer, Partner; E-mail: emeyer@mmwclaw.com
Alice E. Walker, President; E-mail: awalker@mmwclaw.com
M. Catherine Condon, Partner; E-mail: ccondon@mmwclaw.com
Gregg de Bie, Partner; E-mail: gdebie@mmwclaw.com
Jennifer H. Walker, Partner; E-mail: jwalker@mmwclaw.com
Offers Indian tribes expertise in Federal Indian law in a variety of areas particularly affecting tribes, including: water rights, Indian gaming, natural resources protection, assertion & protection of treaty rights, federal recognition, hunting & fishing, taxation issues, tribal telecommunications & economic development, & Indian child welfare. Founded 1977.

MESSINA & HANKIN LLP
24910 Las Brisas Rd., Suite 102 • Murrieta, CA 92562
(951) 894-7772 Fax 346-3334; Website: www.messinahankinlaw.com
John A. Messina, Jr., Partner; E-mail: jmessina@messinahankinlaw.com
1400 Quail St., Suite 200 • Newport Beach, CA 92660
(949) 383-4356; (951) 894-7772
Ted Hankin, Partner; E-mail: thankin@messinahankinlaw.com
Practice Area: Native American Law - The Messina & Hankin litigation attorneys are engaged in a full range of disputed matters in Los Angeles, Orange and Riverside County courts, as well as a variety of alternative dispute resolution forums. John Messina, head of the Firm's Temecula Valley Office, is a licensed real estate broker and was the head of a mortgage banking firm in the San Gabriel Valley before turning to law. Ted Hankin, an attorney and CPA, heads the Firm's Newport Beach Office and was formerly the Division Chair of the Estates, Probate and Trust Division of Alvarado Smith APC.

MILLER NASH GRAHAM & DUNN LLP
(206) 777-7427; Website: www.millernash.com
Christine M. Masse, Team Leader
E-mail: christine.masse@millernash.com
Attorneys (Partners): D. Gary Christensen, Paul L. Havel, James H. Jordan, Jr., Christine M. Masse, Clifton Molatore, Aubrey Seffernick, Susan Eberle Stahlfeld, Guy Towie, Frank Van Dusen; Briana Coyle Jnes (Associate)
Locations: Bend, Oregon; Portland, Oregon; Seattle, Washington; Vancouver, Washington; Long Beach, California.
Provides legal counsel & guidance to many Northwest tribes and their enterprises. We have the extensive experience and understanding to address the complex & sophisticated legal needs of tribal governments, organizations, and enterprises, while protecting each tribe's sovereign immunity, tribal culture, and tribal resources.

MODRALL SPERLING LAWYERS
Native American/Indian Law Practice Group
P.O. Box 1000 • Albuquerque, NM 87103
(505) 848-1800 Fax 848-9710
Santa Fe office: P.O. Box 9318 • Santa Fe, NM 87504 (505) 983-2020
Website: www.modrall.com; E-mail: contact@modrall.com
Lynn H. Slade, Co-Chair (848-1828); E-mail: lynn.slade@modrall.com
Brian K. Nichols, Co-Chair (848-1852); E-mail: brian.nichols@modrall.com
Walter Stern, President & Chair of Executive Committee (848-1837)
E-mail: walter.stern@modrall.com
Attorneys: Deana Bennett, Jennifer Bradfute, Duane Brown, Stan Harris, Sarah Stevenson
Lawyers maintain expertise & experience in the wide range of disciplines critical to economic development in Indian country. While their knowledge of core Indian law principles and recent developments is at the highest level, our team includes practitioners who bring specialized expertise applying those principles in finance, land & resource acquisition, employment law, environmental and cultural resource permitting and management, and related fields—in Indian country. In Indian country, every aspect of the law applicable to a project, agreement, or dispute may be different from what applies off-Reservation. Successful development or dispute resolution requires a counsel team with knowledge & experience cutting across the subject matter pertinent to the client. Their Native American law practice is national in scope. The firm has represented clients in matters involving more than 40 tribes in more than 20 states, and is one of a very few firms, nationally, which focuses its Native American law practice primarily on the representation of developers, financial sector participants, utilities, and other businesses and others doing business

with tribes or tribal entities, engaged in dispute resolution, or addressing policy issues in Indian country. Their Indian Law professionals have extensive experience representing clients in transactions, permitting, and litigation in "Indian country" throughout the U.S. They have represented businesses, including tribally owned entities, in complex development and financing transactions, such as energy & natural resource development, and concerning taxation, leasing or contracting, and environmental management & permitting. They have handled complex litigation concerning tribal contracts, leases, permits, and regulation & understand the pitfalls that may thwart conventional approaches to litigation in Indian country. They also have represented non-tribal governments in issues concerning state and tribal taxation and regulation. Their Indian Lands and Public Lands lawyers help steer clients through the complexities that may otherwise delay or derail projects. Our Indian law practice encompasses: Business contract negotiation and dispute resolution; Business planning and finance; Business leasing, contracting, and facility siting; Acquiring rights-of-way and access; Analysis of Indian country jurisdictional issues; Indian sovereign immunity issues; Dual taxation issues involving states & tribes or pueblos Environmental planning and compliance, including air quality, solid & hazardous waste management; management of natural resource development operations, including permitting & reclamation issues; Mineral Royalty compliance; Water rights; Employment law & tribal employment rights ordinances; National Environmental Policy Act issues; Cultural resource management compliance; Representation in tribal courts, including Navajo Nation courts. *Participation in Indian Law Organizations*: Our lawyers participate actively in state & national Indian law organizations, speak and write frequently on Indian law subjects, and have taught classes at the University of New Mexico School of law on related subjects. Our Indian law lawyers have been involved at all levels of the federal & state courts (including the U.S. Supreme Court) and also represent businesses in tribal courts. In addition to Modrall Sperling's *pro hac vice* representation in various tribal courts, Brian Nichols is a licensed member of the Navajo Nation Bar Assn.

RICK DANE MOORE & ASSOCIATES LAW FIRM, PLLC
30630 S. Western Ave. • Norman, OK 73070
 (405) 839-7266; Website: www.okmoorelawfirm.com
 E-mail: info@okmoorelawfirm.com
 Rick Dane Moore, Principal (405) 366-0373
Practice Area: Native American Law

NORDHAUS LAW FIRM, LLP
6705 Academy Rd. NE • Albuquerque, NM 87109
 (505) 243-4275 Fax 243-4464
421 W. Riverside Ave. • Spokane, WA 99204 (509) 747-2502
1401 K St. NW, Suite 801 • Washington, DC 20005
 (202) 530-1270 Fax 530-1920
 Website: www.nordhauslaw.com
 Tom Peckham (Albuquerque, NM), Managing Partner
 E-mail: tpeckham@nordhauslaw.com
 Deirdre A. Lujan (Santa Ana Pueblo) (Albuquerque), Managing Partner
 E-mail: dlujan@nordhauslaw.com
 Don Grove (Washington, DC), Managing Partner
 E-mail: dgrove@nordhauslaw.com
 Daniel I.S.J. Rey-Bear (Spokane), Partner
 E-mail: dreybear@nordhauslaw.com
 Alan R. Taradash (Albuquerque), Partner
 E-mail: ataradash@nordhauslaw.com
 Timothy McLaughlin, Associate
 E-mail: tmclaughlin@nordhauslaw.com
Partners: Jill E. Grant (Washington, DC); Susan G. Jordan (Santa Fe, NM); Cynthia A. Kiersnowski (Albuquerque, NM); Teresa Leger (Santa Fe, NM); Dierdre A. Lujan (Albuquerque, NM); Daniel I.S.J. Rey-Bear (Albuquerque, NM); Alan R. Taradash (Albuquerque, NM). Nordhaus is one of the oldest & largest law firms in the U.S. that is dedicated to the representation of American Indian tribes & organizations, serving as counsel to more than 30 Indian nations & tribal governments in NM, AZ, CA, MN, LA, WY, & elsewhere. Offers legal representation/guidance on all matters related to Indian affairs, including government issues, gaming, real estate, trusts, taxation, finance, commercial law & natural resources. At its core, the firm is a collection of talented and energetic individuals who share a common purpose--to seek justice for Indian tribes and their citizens and to promote, protect, & preserve tribal sovereignty, cultures, and resources. This mission has guided the firm ever since its founding in 1979. Since its inception, the firm has grown selectively, attracting the best people from a wide variety of backgrounds. The firm's size and diversity allow it to provide multifaceted legal services of the highest quality. As a result, the firm is fortunate to have formed long-term relationships and true friendships with our tribal clients--forged by its commitment to tribal sovereignty. Because of the firm's mission, members, and dedication to tribal sovereignty, the firm is uniquely positioned to accomplish the goals of its tribal clients. The firm is pleased and privileged to share in greater detail some of the specifics of our practice areas and expertise in federal Indian law.

NORTHERN COMPASS GROUP, LLC
310 K St., Suite 401 • Anchorage, AK 99501
 (907) 264-6621 Fax 264-6683
 Website: www.northerncompassgroup.com
 E-mail: info@northerncompassgroup.com
 Mark P. Begich, President & CEO (former Senator from Alaska)
 E-mail: markbegich@northerncompassgroup.com
 Schawna Thoma, Vice President
 E-mail: schawnathoma@northerncompassgroup.com
 Rachel Barinbaum, Vice President for Strategic Communications &
 Business Development; E-mail: Rachel@northerncompassgroup.com
 Clare Boersma, Executive Manager & Project Liaison
 E-mail: clare@northerncompassgroup.com
Northern Compass Group utilizes its professional networks across Indian Country to bring shareholders together and move projects and communities forward. With decades of experience not only fighting for but also winning key battles advocating for Tribes, Alaska Native Corporations, & Native nonprofits on issues like subsistence rights, Indian Law & policy, education, rural/village issues, and tribal rights, Northern Compass Group knows how to tackle tough bureaucratic issues and deliver results that will last.

ORRICK, HERRINGTON & SUTCLIFFE LLP
Indian Tribal Finance Practice
1120 NW Couch St., #200 • Portland, OR 97209
 (503) 943-4800 Fax 943-4801; Website: www.orrick.com
 Douglas E. Goe, Partner (943-4810); E-mail: dgoe@orrick.com
Serves as counsel to state and local governments and Native American tribes regionally and across the U.S. and to financial institutions & investment banks doing business with tribal government and enterprise. Orrick's Indian Tribal Finance Group has unmatched experience in financings by or on behalf of Native American tribes and enterprises. They represent Indian tribal governments and enterprises, Alaska native villages and native corporations and major financial institutions (including investment and commercial banking firms and credit enhancement providers), as well as others doing business in Indian country. Over the last 20 years, Orrick lawyers have served as counsel in dozens of successful tribal financings (both taxable and tax-exempt) for a wide range of projects. Orrick is also the nation's leading bond counsel firm, ranked number one for more than a decade. Their lawyers are known for innovation in the field, having served as bond counsel on the first publicly offered tribal governmental bonds and having developed borrowing programs for tribal entities that have no recourse or limited recourse to the tribe itself. Our lawyers have also served on advisory committees for the IRS's Tax Exempt/Government Entities division. The Indian Tribal Finance Group is nationwide and comprises lawyers from our Public Finance, Banking and Tax departments.

LAW OFFICES OF PATRICIA PAUL, PLLC
P.O. Box 910 • LaConner, WA 98257
 (888) 994-1999 Fax (360) 466-1694
 Patricia Paul, Owner; Website: www.patriciapauljd.com
Native American law firm offering global perspective to resolution of conflicts.

PERKINS COIE
Native American Law & Policy
700 Thirteenth St., NW • Washington, DC 20005
 (202) 654-6200 Fax 654-6211; Website: www.perkinscoie.com
 Donald Baur, Co-chair & Partner; E-mail: dbaur@perkinscoie.com
 (202) 654-6234 Fax 654-6211
 Jena A. MacLean, Partner; E-mail: jmaclean@perkinscoie.com
 (202) 434-1648 Fax 434-1690
 Guy R. Martin, Of Counsel (202) 654-6363; (907) 279-8561
 E-mail: gmartin@perkinscoie.com
2901 N. Central Ave. #2000 • Phoenix, AZ 85012
 (602) 351-8000 Fax 648-7000
 Paul F. Eckstein, Partner; (602) 351-8222
 E-mail: peckstein@perkinscoie.com
 Philip R. Higdon, Partner; (602) 351-8468
 E-mail: phigdon@perkinscole.com
1888 Century Park East, Suite 1700 • Los Angeles, CA 90067
 (310) 788-9900 Fax 788-3399
 Frank Grant (Yurok), Senior Counsel; E-mail: fgrant@perkinscoie.com
Environment, Energy & Resources matters, including federal Indian law, are a core in Perkins Coie practice. The Natural Resources/Indian Law subgroup has extensive experience advising clients facing administrative review processes & related litigation that apply to the management & development of Indian lands throughout the U.S. More than 40 attorneys maintain significant experience in federal Indian law, gaming & government relations; environ-mental & natural resource disputes, land acquisitions & land claims; sovereign immunity issues. Represents institutions, organizations, government agencies, Indian tribes, Alaska native entities & organizations, & individuals dealing with these issues.

PITCHLYNN & WILLIAMS, PLLC
P.O. Box 427 • Norman, OK 73070
(405) 360-9600 Fax 447-4219
1717 S. Cheyenne Ave. • Tulsa, OK 74119
(918) 582-9292 Fax (405) 447-4219
Gary Pitchlynn, Senior Partner
E-mail: gspitchlynn@pitchlynnlaw.com
Stephanie Moser Goins, Associate Attorney
Areas of Practice: Federal Indian Law, Corporate & Business Law, General Litigation. Gaming, tribal taxation, tribal economic development & jurisdictional disputes as it pertains to the laws governing tribal authority in various tribal courts, federal courts, Court of Indian Offenses & before the U.S. Department of the Interior Office of Hearings & Appeals.

POUST LAW
8732 Skyline Dr., Los Angeles, CA 90046
(323) 919-1800; Teri Poust (Poarch Band Creek), Owner
E-mail: teri.poust@poustlaw.com.
Provides counsel on a broad range of Indian issues, with a particular emphasis on gaming facility regulation & operation

PROCOPIO, CORY, HARGREAVES & SAVITCH LLP
525 B St., Suite 2200 • San Diego, CA 92101
(619) 515-3277 Fax 744-5477
Theodore J. Griswold, Attorney
E-mail: ted.griswold@procopio.com
Our Native American Law Practice Group is comprised of attorneys experienced in representing and counseling Tribal governments, Tribal corporations, Inter-Tribal organizations and Tribal-affiliated clients in a wide range of legal matters. We understand and are sensitive to the unique qualities of Native American Tribal Governments and their legal status, including principles of tribal sovereignty and immunity, self-governance and government contracts. We recognize the uniqueness of each tribal population and their culture, and match our services to your tribal needs. Within this legal and cultural framework, we offer Tribal Governments & businesses assistance with the following: Self-governance compacts & administration; Cultural resources & sacred site protection; Intergovernmental negotiations & agreements; Indian healthcare clinic contracts and operations; Real estate acquisition & development; Indian Country Leasing, licenses of use agreements; Financing and construction of hotel, gaming and governmental facilities; Reservation land use plans; Tribal natural resource protection & use; Creation & implementation of tribal regulatory programs; Endangered Species Act, Section 404 and Clean Water Act permitting for tribes; Fee-to-trust transfers; Cultural Resource Protection litigation; Reservation boundary defense; Tribal employment matters; Indian water rights & water district agreements; Tribal environmental impact reports; Tribal access and Indian Reservation roads; Tribal ordinance & policy development; Business, construction & program contracts; Hospitality. Programs: Native American Internship Program; Indigenous San Diego Mobile App, presented in association with the Southern California Tribal Chairmen's Association and Maatam Naka Shin.

RESCH POLSTER & BERGER LLP
1840 Century Park East, 17th Floor • Los Angeles, CA 90067
(310) 788-7546 Fax 788-6646; Website: www.rpblaw.com
Richard Friedman, Partner; E-mail: rfriedman@rpblaw.com
Jeff Rabin, Partner; E-mail: jrabin@rpblaw.com
Native American practice includes real estate development & gaming clientele, including but not limited to high-yield and tax-exempt financing as well as syndicated lending. Leading our practice, Richard Friedman has joined Resch Polster Berger to bring his expertise in representing tribes wishing to expand & acquire funding for new projects. Specializing in hotels, casinos and shopping centers, Mr. Friedman understands & has extensive experience in real estate matters involving Indian law.

ROSENFELT LAW, P.C.
1418 Aliso Dr., NE • Albuquerque, NM 87110
(505) 266-3441 Fax 266-8972
Website: www.rbblaw.com
Daniel M. Rosenfelt, Founder
Practice Area: Native American law. Since 1982, I've been practicing law in New Mexico. For 21 years, I worked with a private law firm with offices in Albuquerque and the Navajo Nation and served as managing director. I have been an Assistant Solicitor with the U.S. Department of Interior, and now I work as a sole practitioner. Over the past 30 years I've represented hundreds of individuals in personal injury, family law, and employment cases. I served as school board attorney, general counsel for Indian tribes and counsel for small businesses. I've handled many tort claims against the federal government in the New Mexico & Arizona federal courts. My current areas of interest include litigation in Navajo, federal and state courts and school law, especially charter schools.

ROSETTE & ASSOCIATES, PC
Phoenix Office: 565 W. Chandler Blvd. #212 • Chandler, AZ 85225
(480) 889-8990 Fax 889-8997; Website: www.rosettelaw.com
Sacramento Office: 193 Blue Ravine Rd. #255 • Folsom, CA 95630
(916) 353-1084 Fax 353-1085
Kalamazoo Office: 25344 Red Arrow Hwy, Suite B, Mattawan, MI 49071
(269) 283-5005 Fax 913-6443
Washington, DC Office: 1100 H St. NW, Suite 400, Washington, DC 20005
(202) 652-0579 Fax 525-5261
Robert A. Rosette (Chippewa-Cree) (Phoenix), Partner
E-mail: rarosette@rosettelaw.com
Saba Bazzazieh (Washington, DC), Partner
E-mail: sbazzazieh@rosettelaw.com
Karrie S. Wichtman (Saulte Ste. Marie Chippewa) (Michigan), Partner
E-mail: kwichtman@rosettelaw.com
Nicole St. Germain (Sacramento) Partner
E-mail: nsgermain@rosettelaw.com
Richard Verri (Phoenix) Associate; E-mail: rverri@rosettelaw.com
Brett Stavin (Mohawk) (Washington, DC) Associate
E-mail: bstavin@rosettelaw.com
Tanya Gibbs (Little Traverse Bay Odawa) (Michigan) Associate
E-mail: tgibbs@rosettelaw.com
Jonathon Sanchez (Phoenix) Associate; E-mail: jsanchez@rosettelaw.com
Dion Killsback (Northern Cheyenne) (Phoenix) Associate
E-mail: dkillsback@rosettelaw.com
Helen Burtis (Phoenix), Of Counsel; E-mail: hburtis@rosettelaw.com
Vanessa V. Minteer (Phoenix) Of Counsel; E-mail: vminteer@rosettelaw.com
Jay Weiner (Phoenix) Of Counsel; E-mail: jdw9697@yahoo.com
John Simermyer (Coharie Tuscarora) (Washington, DC) Legislative Analyst
E-mail: jsimermeyer@rosettelaw.com
Rosette, LLP is a leading Indian-owned national law firm representing tribal governments & entities with offices in Phoenix, Arizona, Sacramento, California and Washington, D.C., and Kalamazoo, Michigan. Robert Rosette, formerly the managing partner of a nationwide Indian law firm, formed Rosette, LLP in February 2005. Specializes in federal Indian law, complex litigation, government negotiations, financial transactions and representation of internal tribal government matters. They represent tribal councils, gaming commissions, tribal courts, housing & utility authorities, clinics, and election boards; aid in the administration of tribal programs and agencies; procure self-determination contracts for programs such as water projects, sanitation facilities construction, health services & transportation; work with tribal governments on constitutional development & reform, drafting tribal policies, ordinances, and regulations & developing tribal adjudicatory systems; draft tribal gaming ordinances, assist tribal regulatory agencies.

ROTHSTEIN, DONATELLI, HUGHES, DAHLESTROM, SCHOENBURG & BIENVENU LLP
Website: www.rothsteinlaw.com
1215 Paseo De Peralta, P.O. Box 8180 • Santa Fe, NM 87504
(505) 988-8004 Fax 982-0307
500 4th St. NW, Suite 400 • Albuquerque, NM 87102
(505) 243-1443 Fax 242-7845
80 E. Rio Salado Pkwy., Suite 710 • Tempe, AZ 85281
(480) 921-9296 Fax 921-9249
Richard W. Hughes, Partner (Santa Fe, NM office)
Eric N. Dahlstrom, Partner (Tempe office)
Denten D. Robinson, Partner (Tempe office)
Donna M. Connolly, Partner (Santa Fe, NM office)
April Erin Olson, Partner (Tempe office)
Jaclyn R. Johnson, Associate (Tempe office)
Marissa Merculleff, Of Counsel (Tempe office)
Reed Bienvenu, Associate (Santa Fe office)
Martina Gast, Associate (Tempe office)
Caroline Manierre, Associate (Santa Fe office)
Provides representation of Indian tribes in New Mexico, Arizona & Wisconsin. Recognized for their expertise in Indian gaming matters with broad experience of Indian law subjects, including land and water rights, natural resources, economic development, jurisdiction, federal-tribal relations, and others. Since 1988, the firm has played a major role in representation of Indian tribes in New Mexico, & since the early 1990s it has become a leader in tribal representation in AZ and WI. Partners Richard W. Hughes, Eric N. Dahlstrom and Denten D. Robinson are widely recognized for their expertise in Indian gaming matters, and they and many of the firm's associates and support staff have broad experience in virtually the full range of Indian law subjects, including land & water rights, natural resources, economic development, jurisdiction, federal-tribal relations, and others. The firm is currently involved in two general stream adjudications on behalf of tribal clients in New Mexico, numerous tribal land claim & trespass disputes, major negotiations for economic development projects, jurisdictional disputes & many other matters. It provides day-to-day advice to tribal governments on tribal governmental legal issues.

RUSING LOPEZ & LIZARDI, LLP
Gaming & Native American Law Practice Group
6363 N. Swan Rd., Suite 151 • Tucson, AZ 85718
(520) 792-4800; Website: www.rllaz.com
Dan Quigley, Partner; (520) 529-4287; E-mail: dquigley@rllaz.com
Due in large part to their successful gaming operations, many Native American tribes have become strong economic and political forces in their regions. We have extensive experience representing Native American tribes and their economic enterprises, in a wide range of transactions and in litigation. The head of our Gaming and Native American practice group has nearly twenty years' experience in all aspects of tribal gaming, including constructing and financing Indian gaming facilities, federal, state, and tribal gaming regulation, internal controls, software licensing, and contractual matters. Our lawyers have negotiated and litigated significant water rights matters, litigated land use matters, negotiated and litigated disputes over gaming compacts, and have been involved in tribal election matters. Although we generally represent Native American tribes or their enterprises, we also advise parties who do business with tribes or tribal enterprises.

SCHWABE, WILLIAMSON & WYATT
Indian Law Group, 1420 5th Ave., Suite 3400 • Seattle, WA 98101
(206) 622-1711 Fax 292-0460
Website: www.schwabe.com; E-mail: info@schwabe.com
Jamilia A. Johnson, Shareholder (206) 407-1555
 E-mail: jajohnson@schwabe.com
Connie Sue M. Martin, Shareholder (206) 407-1556
 E-mail: csmartin@schwabe.com
Sarah Roubidoux Lawson (Iowa of KS & NE), Of Counsel
(206) 407-1507; E-mail: slawson@schwabe.com
The Indian law group comprises a team of attorneys dedicated to serving & protecting the interests of tribal governments, Alaska Native villages & corporations, and related business entities. Our team members have extensive experience working with tribes on a wide range of economic development, financial workout, natural & cultural resource protection, environmental regulation & cleanup, & intellectual property matters. Our Indian law team's philosophy encourages moving beyond the traditional attorney-client relationship, to building collaborative partnerships with each of our tribal clients. We function as trusted advisors, determining cost-effective approaches to each legal issue, taking into account the tribal government's or tribal enterprise's broader goals & objectives. We understand the legal & jurisdictional complexities that are unique to Indian Country, and are committed to assisting tribes in economic development and diversification, environmental protection, protection of sovereignty, & preservation of natural & cultural resources. We identify emerging industries & opportunities for economic growth for tribes, particularly in the area of sustainability, including green building & renewable energy development. We strive to advance the interests of our tribal clients through negotiation & consensus, rather than conflict, where possible. However, when the need arises, our litigators are able to provide our clients a strategic advantage, having accumulated the depth of experience & insight necessary to understand the most effective & efficient ways to reach successful resolution.

SACKS TIERNEY, P.A.
Indian Law & Tribal Relations Practice Group
4250 N. Drinkwater Blvd. #4 • Scottsdale, AZ 85251
(480) 425-2600 Fax 970-4610; Website: www.sackstierney.com
Judith M. Dworkin (425-2615), Practice Group Head
 E-mail: judith.dworkin@sackstierney.com
Patty A. Ferguson-Bohnee (Pointe au Chien) (425-2637)
Roxann S. Gallagher (425-2673);
Roger S. Owers (425-2614); Bryan Gottfredson (425-2643)
Advises tribal governments & tribal corporations in complex legal matters, and we assist private sector businesses in creating appropriate, beneficial enterprises on tribal land; represents tribes, tribal corporations & tribal enterprises, as well as individual Native Americans, in all aspects of Indian law.

SHEPPARD MULLIN RICHTER & HAMPTON LLP
Tribal & Indian Law Section
333 S. Hope St., 43rd Floor • Los Angeles, CA 90071
(213) 620-1780 Fax 620-1398
Derek Havel & Whitney Jones Roy, Managing Partners
Julie Penney, Office Administrator
12275 El Camino Real, #200 • San Diego, CA 92130
Website: https://www.sheppardmullin.com
Richard Freeman, Partner (858) 720-8909
30 Rockefeller Plaza • New York, NY 10112
(212) 653-8700 Fax 653-8701
Paul Garrity, Managing Partner
Christine L. Swanick (212) 634-3051

The firm handles an array of Native American issues, including, but not limited to, sovereign immunity, tribal sovereignty, Indian water rights, the Indian Gaming & Regulatory Act, tribal Compacts, tribal contracts & leases, Indian Tax issues, Indian environmental regulatory & compliance issues & labor & employment issues on tribal lands. Their art law attorneys have experience in resolving issues relating to Native American tribal & cultural objects, and provide advice on the creation & ongoing function of cultural centers & museums. Mr. Freeman specializes in Native American issues, including but not limited to sovereign immunity, Tribal sovereignty, Indian water rights, the Indian Gaming and Regulatory Act, Tribal Compacts, Tribal contracts and leases, Indian Tax issues, Indian environmental regulatory & compliance issues & labor & employment issues on tribal lands. Ms. Swanick concentrates her practice in the area of commercial financing and other credit transactions, including commercial loans, letter of credit facilities, syndicated credit facilities and note and bond financings, especially in the area of tribal-related financing projects. Additionally, Ms. Swanick advises on restructuring of tribal debt. She also represents tribes & entities doing business with tribes in contractual, gaming, regulatory & economic development matters. Her work puts her in regular contact with federal decision-makers, including attorneys at the National Indian Gaming Commission.

SHORT CRESSMAN & BURGESS PLLC
999 Third Ave. Suite 3000 • Seattle, WA 98104
(206) 682-3333 Fax 340-8856
Website: www.scblaw.com; E-mail: info@scblaw.com
Richard A. Du Bey, Partner; (206) 470-3587
 E-mail: rdubey@scblaw.com
Brian Epley; (206) 223-8938; E-mail: bepley@scblaw.com
Jennifer Sanscrainte, (206) 223-2001
 E-mail: jsanscrainte@scblaw.com
Nicholas Thomas, (206) 829-2703; E-mail: nthomas@scblaw.com
For More than 30 years, our attorneys have relied upon their unparalleled experience to navigate – and where necessary, to pave the way – through the complicated terrain that lies at the crossroads of federal, tribal, and state laws and their associated regulations. By understanding the unique nature of Indian law, our attorneys meet the diverse needs & interests of Native American tribes, tribal business enterprises, & other tribal instrumentalities. This unique expertise is valuable not only for our tribal clients, but also for non-tribal clients who seek to conduct business in Indian Country. Represents Tribal governments in environmental & natural resource litigation. We have successfully represented tribes in federal district courts, the Ninth Circuit Court of Appeals, the U.S. Supreme Court, tribal courts, and administrative agencies. Provides a wide range of legal services to tribes and tribal members, including: Tribal sovereignty and governance; Jurisdiction and venue matters; Drafting tribal laws, ordinances, and resolutions; enforcement of tribal environmental laws; Legislative counseling & advocacy; tribal business regulatory compliance; real estate, land use, and fee-to-trust transactions; Construction projects on tribal lands; Government permits & approvals; Labor & employment issues; & Public & media relations; serves as Special Environmental Counsel to tribal governments on a broad array of environmental, natural resource, and cultural issues, including: Tribal environmental & natural resource program development; Tribal hunting, fishing & gathering rights, and reserved water rights; Cultural resource and sacred site protection; Natural resource damage claims and Tribal service loss matters; Treatment-as-state status under the *Clean Water Act* and *Clean Air Act;* Federal and Tribal Superfund cleanup actions; Tribal brownfield program development & enforcement redevelopment; Intergovernmental cooperative agreements and state-tribal compacts

SMITH SHELLENBERGER & SALAZAR LLC
14694 Orchard Pkwy. Suite A-210 • Westminster, CO 80023
(303) 255-3588 Fax 255-3677; Website: www.ssrs-law.com
Keith C. Smith, Partner; E-mail: kcs@ssslawyers.com
Lisa R. Shellenberger, Partner; E-mail: lrs@ssslawyers.com
Joseph A. Salazar, Partner; E-mail: jas@ssslawyers.com
Specializes in all areas of Tribal & Federal Indian law. Dedicated to providing legal counsel to tribal governments, departments, agencies, schools, colleges & economic enterprises. Protecting and upholding tribal sovereignty is a fundamental value. The attorneys at Smith, Shellenberger & Salazar, LLC are skilled negotiators & Indian law experts with longstanding ties to the tribal nations of Arizona, Colorado, Nebraska, New York, South Dakota, & Okla. We have a deep commitment to tribal sovereignty, tribal self-government and tribal self-determination. It is our firm policy that representing parties against Indian nations, even if ethically permitted, is a direct conflict without dedication and commitment to promoting tribal sovereignty, tribal self-determination, and tribal self-governance, and disloyal to our tribal clients. This dedication to tribal sovereignty, tribal self-determination, & tribal self-governance is a cornerstone value upon which the firm is built.

SMITH & SMITH ATTORNEYS
2500 McGee Dr., Suite 149, Norman, OK 73072
 (405) 447-2224; Michael Smith (Chickasaw), Attorney
Practices Indian law, et al.

SNELL & WILMER LLP
One Arizona Center, 400 E. Van Buren St., Suite 1900
Phoenix, AZ 85004-2202
 (602) 382-6000 Fax 382-6070; Website: https://www.swlaw.com/
Offices: Denver, Las Vegas, Los Angeles, Costa Mesa, CA, Reno,
Salt Lake City, Tucson, and Los Cabos, Mexico.
Partners:
 John F. Lomax, Jr. (602-382-6305) E-mail: jlomax@swlaw.com
 Richard Mallery (602-382-6232) E-mail: rmallery@swlaw.com
 Craig R. McPike (602-382-6538) E-mail: cmcpike@swlaw.com
 Mark D. Ohre (602-382-6394) E-mail: mohre@swlaw.com
 David A. Sprentall (602-382-6260) E-mail: dsprentall@swlaw.com
 Heidi McNeil Staudenmaier (602-382-6366)
  E-mail: hstaudenmaier@swlaw.com
 Rebecca Winterscheidt (602-382-66343)
  E-mail: bwinterscheidt@swlaw.com
 Geoff Gunnersonn (602) 382-6108; E-mail: ggunnerson@swlaw.com
 Marvin S. (Bucky) Swift, Jr. (602-382-6211)
  E-mail: mswift@swlaw.com
 Sean Sherlock (Costa Mesa, CA) (714-427-7036)
  E-mail: ssherlock@swlaw.com
 Denise Dragoo (Salt Lake City) (801-257-1998)
  E-mail: ddragoo@swlaw.com
Associates: Jim P. Allen (Tucson & Salt Lake City)
 Anthony J. Carucci (Orange County)
Snell & Wilmer attorneys have been significantly involved in legal issues
involving Native American tribes & land throughout the western United States
for over 75 years. The Native American tribes and businesses they work with
face issues involving sovereign immunity; natural resource and environmental
protections; financing & developing hotels, retail centers, casinos & other types
of infrastructure & utilities; and a wide range of state & federal regulatory
concerns. We have represented a variety of Native American tribes, tribal
organizations and Native American-owned enterprises. They have represented
casinos & gaming organizations, resorts & recreational businesses, development & management companies, financiers, gaming vendors & others doing
business on Indian lands. Our representation has involved both Native
American and non-Native American clients in their affairs & transactions, along
with Native American tribes throughout the country.

SONOSKY, CHAMBERS, SACHSE, ENDRESON & PERRY LLP
1425 K St., NW, Suite 600, Washington, DC 20005
 (202) 682-0240 Fax 682-0249; Website: www.sonosky.com
 Rosemary Schmidt, Administrator; E-mail: rschmidt@sonosky.com
Partners: (Washington, DC office)
 Reid Peyton Chambers; E-mail: rchambers@sonosky.com
 Harry R. Sachse (hsachse@sonosky.com)
 Douglas Endreson (dendreson@sonosky.com)
 Anne D. Noto (anoto@sonosky.com)
 Mary J. Pavel, Partner; E-mail: mpavel@sonosky.com
 William R. Perry (wperry@sonosky.com)
 Donald J. Simon (dsimon@sonosky.com)
 Jodi A. Gillette (Hunkpapa & Oglala Lakota), Policy Advisor
  E-mail: jgillette@sonosky.com
A national law firm devoted to representing Native American interests in a wide
range of endeavors including trial & appellate litigation, federal Indian law,
tribal law, Indian self-determination & self-governance claims, natural resource
law, public land law, water law, land regulation, hunting & fishing rights,
environmental law, toxic torts, jurisdictional conflicts, gaming law, government
contracting, hydroelectric development & business development.
Branch locations:
Alaska: 900 W. Fifth Ave., Suite 700, Anchorage, AK 99501
 (907) 258-6377 Fax 272-8332
 Partners: Lloyd B. Miller; E-mail: lloyd@sonosky.net
 Marissa K. Flannery (Tohono O'odham)
  E-mail: marissa@sonosky.net
 Associates: Roger W. DuBrock; E-mail: roger@sonosky.net
 Kay E. Massen Gouwens; E-mail: kay@sonosky.net
 Mark P. Begich, Policy Advisor & Alaska Native & Native American Affairs
  E-mail: markbegich@northerncompassgroup.com
 318 Fourth St., Juneau, AK 99801 (907) 586-5880 Fax 586-5883
 Myra M. Munson, Partner; E-mail: myra@sonoskyjuneau.com
 Richard D. Monkman; E-mail: dick@sonoskyjuneau.com
 Office Manager: Denise R. Meek
  E-mail: deedee@sonoskyjuneau.com
New Mexico: 500 Marquette Ave., NW, Suite 1310, Albuquerque, NM 87102
 (505) 247-0147 Fax 843-6912

 Gary F. Brownell, Partner
 Vanessa L. Ray-Hodge (Pueblo of Acoma), Partner
 David C. Mielke
 Suzanne G. Dressler, Office Manager
  E-mail: sdressler@abqsonosky.com
California: 600 West Broadway, Suite 700, San Diego, CA 92101
 (619) 267-1306 Fax 267-1388
 Colin Cloud Hampson Winnebago/Ojibwe), Partner
  E-mail: champson@sonosky.com
 James E. Glaze, Partner; E-mail: jglaze@sonosky.com
  Lael M. Hoff, Office Manager; E-mail: lael@sonosky.com

SPIRIT ROCK CONSULTING
9 Forrest St. • Alexandria, VA 22305
 (202) 255-3220 Fax (703) 535-7567
 Website: www.spiritrockconsulting.com
 Aurene Martin, President (Bad River Band Lake Superior Chippewa)
  E-mail: amartin@spiritrockinc.com
Represents Indian tribes on Federal law & policy issues, specializing in the
areas of tribal land acquisition, tribal gaming & general tribal government
issues.

SQUIRE PATTON BOGGS, LLP
2550 M St., NW • Washington, DC 20037
 (202) 457-6000 Fax 457-6315
 Website: www.squirepattonboggs.com
 Trevor J. Tullius (Chickasaw), Associate (Washington, DC office)
  (202) 457-5108; E-mail: trevor.tullius@squirepb.com
Provides legal services to American Indians, Alaska Natives, Native
Hawaiians, and their organizations. The firm also assists non-Indian entities
desiring to do business with tribes and Alaska Native & Hawaiian Native
Corporations.

STEPTOE & JOHNSON
Government Affairs & Public Policy, American Indian Affairs
1330 Connecticut Ave., NW, Washington, DC 20036
 (202) 429-6242 Fax 429-3902; Website: www.steptoe.com
 Thomas C. Collier, Practice Leader; E-mail: tcollier@steptoe.com
 Markham Cho Erickson, Partner (429-8032) E-mail: merickson@steptoe.com
201 E. Washington St., Suite 1600, Phoenix, AZ 85004
 (602) 257-5212 Fax 257-5299
 Paul K. Charlton, Partner (257-5205) E-mail: pcharlton@steptoe.com
 Timothy W. Overton, Partner (257-5214) E-mail: toverton@steptoe.com
Represents American Indian & related interests before Congress, federal
agencies, and tribal, state & federal courts, including the U.S. Supreme Court;
legal issues as tribes & developers work together to build casinos, power
plants, telecommunications projects, & other investment vehicles on American
Indian land. Whether the issue is state or federal taxation of tribal businesses,
tribal membership qualifications, the role of the Department of Interior in the
approval of tribal ordinances, tribal election oversight, land in trust for landed
and landless tribes, tribal recognition or Indian gaming, Steptoe delivers well-
rounded, culturally relevant, and effective representation and legal advice to its
Native American & non-tribal clients. Advocate programs & operational issues,
budgetary concerns, or tribal proposals for receipt of federal funds, we provide
representation of tribes before all federal agencies with Indian programs &
services. Their attorneys seek policy modifications, clarifications, or reversals
from policy makers at these agencies and advise them on tribe-specific issues
related to federal operations or personnel. They identify key congressional
sponsors for tribe-specific legislation & facilitate one-on-one meetings between
tribal representatives & key decision makers on relevant matters. Their
attorneys also represent clients before federal administration tribunals, such as
Indian Board of Appeals, to resolve outstanding tribal claims or disputes. They
track & monitor major legislative proposals that could affect Indian policy (with
special attention to how the proposal would affect our clients). When proposed
legislation is detrimental to their clients' interests, they develop strategies to
address it. Steptoe attorneys represent American Indian & related interests
before Congress, federal agencies, and tribal, state & federal courts, including
the US Supreme Court. Steptoe's team handles significant legal issues that
may arise as tribes & developers work together to build casinos, power plants,
telecommunications projects, & other investment vehicles on American Indian
land. Bound by the interplay of federal, state, and tribal law, reservations offer
unique opportunities & challenges for investors. Legal sophistication is critical
for companies that wish to collaborate with American Indian tribes on
development projects, as well as for tribes interested in working with
development partners. Their attorneys provide focused, aggressive & effective
representation. Their relationships with tribal & governmental officials give
them additional credibility before key decision makers. In addition, they are
practiced at drafting & introducing legislation, appearing at hearings,
requesting rulemaking or agency action, commenting on proposed agency
action, filing litigation, & conducting negotiations. Steptoe arranges legislative
meetings in Washington & prepares tribal officials for those discussions.

STETSON & JORDAN, P.C.
1305 Rio Grande Blvd. NW • Albuquerque, NM 87104
(505) 256-4911 Fax 256-5177
Website: www.stetsonlaw.com; E-mail: info@stetsonlaw.com
Catherine Baker Stetson, Managing Partner; Derril Jordan, Partner
Attorneys: Timothy Humphrey, Sr. (Blackfeet), Bob Gruenig, James Burson
Of Counsel Attorneys: W. Richard West (Southern Cheyenne), Of Counsel;
Charlene D. Jackson (Navajo); Zackeree Sean Kelin (Caddo)
Provides general legal services to tribes & tribal entities in many states, representing them in administrative, legislative, and judicial proceedings and in tribal, state, & federal forums. Specializes in lobbying & consultation on federal legislation, tribal commercial development & taxation, tribal environ-mental regulation, land-into-trust, Indian gaming, and Indian housing. Branch location: 1201 Pennsylvania Ave., NW, Washington, DC 20004 (202) 7661-4623 Fax 661-4624. Begun 1997.

STOEL RIVES, LLP – INDIAN & ALASKA NATIVE LAW
Seattle office: 600 University St. #3600, Seattle, WA 98101
(206) 386-7564 Fax 386-7500; Website: www.stoel.com
Diana R. Bob (Lummi), Of Counsel; E-mail: diana.bob@stoel.com
Sacramento office: 500 Capitol Mall, Suite 1600 • Sacramento, CA 95814
(916) 447-0700 Fax 447-4781
Timothy M. Taylor, Partner, (319-4754); E-mail: tmtaylor@stoel.com
Portland office: 900 SW Fifth Ave. #2600 • Portland, OR 97204
(503) 224-3380 Fax 220-2480
Anchorage office: 510 L St., Suite 500 • Anchorage, AK 99501
(907) 277-1900 Fax 277-1920
Tina M. Grovier (263-8424), Managing Partner
E-mail: tina.grovier@stoel.com
William H. Timme, Of Counsel; E-mail: bill.timme@stoel.com
Provides counsel to Indian tribes and Alaska Native Corporations on business transactions, energy & natural resources, environmental laws, water rights, litigation & mediation, tax issues, employment & labor.

TILDEN McCOY & DILWEG LLP
Boulder office: 2500 30th St., Suite 207 • Boulder, CO 80301
(303) 323-1922 Fax 416-8707; Website: www.tildenmccoy.com
Mark C. Tilden (Navajo), Partner
E-mail: mctilden@tildenmccoy.com
Padraic I. McCoy (Quechan/Cherokee), Partner
E-mail: pmccoy@tildenmccoy.com
Carrie C. Doyle, Associate; E-mail: ccdoyle@tildenmccoy.com
Abby Davis, Associate; E-mail: adavis@tildenmccoy.com
Brandy K.M. Toelupe (Hawaiian); E-mail: btoelupe@tildenmccoy.com
Denver Office: 600 17th St., Suite 2800, Denver, CO 80202 (303) 323-1922
Justin Pless, Of Counsel; E-mail: jpless@tildenmccoy.com
Los Angeles Office: 13310 Maxella Ave., Unit 10, Marina Del Rey, CA 90292
(310) 386-7071 Fax (213) 596-3863
Rory Dilweg (Oneida of Wisconsin), Partner
E-mail: rdilweg@tildenmccoy.com
Sioux City Office: 5006 Sergeant Rd. #263, Sioux City, IA 51106
(303) 323-1922 Fax 416-8707
Sarah I. Wheelock (Meskwaki), Of Counsel
E-mail: swheelock@tildenmccoy.com
Nationwide Indian law & tribal governance practice representing tribal governments & businesses, development partners, and others on a variety of Indian country matters, with an emphasis on Indian law & tribal governance, including federal acknowledgement & Indian Child Welfare Act; Indian lands, and gaming, development, and finance.

VAN NESS FELDMAN
1050 Thomas Jefferson St., NW 7th Floor • Washington, DC 20007
(202) 298-1800 Fax 338-2416; Website: www.vnf.com
Richard A. Agnew, Chair & Partner (298-1815); E-mail: raa@vnf.com
Daniel S. Press, Partner (298-1882); E-mail: dsp@vnf.com
Alan L. Mintz, Partner (298-1837); E-mail: alm@vnf.com
Andrew M. VanderJack, Associate; E-mail: amv@vnf.com
Millennium Tower, 719 Second Ave., Suite 150 • Seattle, WA 98104
(206) 623-9372 Fax 623-4986
Matthew A. Love, Partner (829-1809); E-mail: mal@vnf.com
Represents Indian tribes, Alaska Native Corporations & private sector companies doing business with tribes & ANCs for more than 30 years. Forges successful business relationships between energy companies & Indian tribes. Offers expertise in representing Indian tribes & Alaska Native groups on a wide range of issues, including: land conveyance & exchanges between Alaska Native Corporations (ANC) & the federal government; protection of subsistence hunting & fishing rights; advocacy on Native issues, such as health, education, & cultural preservation; consultation on business transactions & strategic planning; and securing federal appropriations or grants. Serves as Washington counsel to tribes & ANCs.

WAGENLANDER & HEISTERKAMP, LLC
1700 Broadway • Denver, CO 80290-1201
(303) 832-6511 Fax 830-2246
James F. Wagonlander, Partner; David Heisterkamp, Partner
Amber L. Hunter, Associate; Batsukh Enkhbat, Of Counsel;
Sylvia A. Curley, Of Counsel
A concentration on Indian law and has a cross-cultural practice, working in Colorado, Mongolia and on Indian reservations throughout the United States, representing private, public and non-profit clients.

WILLIAMS, KASTNER & GIBBS, PLLC
Two Union Square, 601 Union St. #4100 • Seattle, WA 98101
(206) 628-6600 Fax 628-6611
Website: www.williamskastner.com; E-mail: info@williamskastner.com
Indian Law & Gaming Practice: Provides Indian tribes with legal counsel for both business & litigation matters. The firm represents many tribes, both in Washington State and throughout the region, and acts as general counsel for the Blackfeet Nation Tribe, located in Montana. *Attorneys*:
Hunter M. Abell (233-2885); E-mail: habell@williamskastner.com
Kimberly D. Baker (628-6606; E-mail: kbaker@williamskastner.com
Daniel A. Brown (Yakama) (233-2949); E-mail: dbrown@williamskastner.com
Sarah Stephens Visbeek (233-2873); E-mail: svisbeek@williamskastner.com
Susan E. Lehr (233-2929); E-mail: slehr@williamskastner.com
James L. Robenalt (628-6646); E-mail: jrobenalt@williamskastner.com
Branch offices: 1301 A St., Suite 900, Tacoma, WA 98402 (253) 593-5620 Fax 593-5625; Pioneer Office Tower, 888 SW Fifth Ave., Suite 600, Portland, OR 97204 (503) 228-7967 Fax 222-7261.

WILLIAMS & WORKS, P.A.
565 W. Ella Dr. • Corrales, NM 87048
(505) 899-7994 Fax 899-7972
Susan M. Williams (Sisseton-Wahpeton Dakota), Partner
An Indian-owned/woman-owned law firm. As a lead lobbyist in several successful Indian legislative efforts, Ms. Williams has impacted amendments such as one to treat Indian tribes as states under the Safe Drinking Water Act, the Clean Water Act, and the Indian Tribal Government Tax Status Act. In April of 1989, she successfully argued the Big Horn case before the U.S. Supreme Court. She represents Indian tribes on their water rights and other matters.

WISEMAN LAW CORPORATION
431 I St., Suite 201 • Sacramento, CA 95814
(916) 668-7353; Joseph J. Wiseman, Principal
Practice Area: Native American Law

JESSE J. WORTEN, III ATTORNEY AT LAW
537 Leahy Ave. • Pawhuska, OK 74056
(918) 287-2500 Fax 287-2503
416 E. 5th St. • Bartlesville, OK 74005
(918) 336-8114 Fax 336-6441; *Practice Area*: Indian Law

ZELL & COX LAW PC
1210 Hundy Place • Alexandria, VA 22307
(703) 660-6697; Patricia M. Zell (Navajo/Arapaho), Partner
A law firm that specializes in laws affecting American Indians, Alaska Natives and Native Hawaiians.

ZUCKERMN SPAEDER, LLP
1800 M St., NW, Suite 1000 • Washington, DC 20036
(202) 778-1800 Fax 822-8106; Website: www.zuckerman.com
Michael R. Smith, Partner (778-1832); E-mail: msmith@zuckerman.com
Eleanor H. Smith, Partner (778-1838; E-mail: esmith@zuckerman.com
William W. Taylor, III, Partner (778-1810); E-mail: wtaylor@zuckerman.com
R. Miles Clark, Partner (778-1863); E-mail: mclark@zuckerman.com
Steven Herman, Associate (778-1883); E-mail: Sherman@zuckerman.com
David A. Reiser, Of Counsel (778-1854); E-mail: dreiser@zuckerman.com
Zuckerman Spaeder LLP has been involved for decades in representing the interests of Native American tribes in negotiations with state & local governments, in government-to-government relationships with federal agencies, and in litigation in state and federal courts. Involved in cutting-edge litigation involving tribal sovereignty, tribal freedom from state taxation and regulation, tribal gaming rights, and tribal land rights. We understand tribes' compelling need to protect their tribal sovereignty and to express it in ways that assure political & socioeconomic success & independence. They are able to develop negotiation & strategies to resolve disputes with tribal adversaries without litigation—where that is possible—and is able to pursue intensive, high-stakes litigation where other resolutions are not possible. They have experience in litigation at all levels in the state and federal courts, including in the U.S. Supreme Court. The firm is nationally ranked in the field of Native American Law by *U.S. News & World Report* in its "Best Law Firms" list, and individual members of the practice have been recognized in *The Best Lawyers in America* and *Super Lawyers* in the same category.

NATIONAL INDIAN GAMING ASSOCIATION
224 Second St., SE • Washington, DC 20003
(202) 546-7711 Fax 546-1755
Website: www.indiangaming.org
Ernie Stevens, Jr. (Oneida), Chairperson
Mark Van Norman, Executive Director
(920) 869-4413 Fax 869-4317
Gordon Adams, Jr. (Ojibwe), Vice Chairperson
Charlie Colombe (Rosebud Sioux), Treasurer
Carla J. Nicholas, Director of Public Relations
Description: Non-profit trade association comprised
start up operations. Publications: NIGA News, m11onthly newsletter; books -
NIGA Indian Gaming Resource Directory; General Requirements & Parameters
for Vendor Licensing; National Indian Gaming Minimum Internal Control
Standards for Indian Casinos; The Indian Gaming Handbook. Maintains Library
and Resource Center.

NATIONAL INDIAN GAMING COMMISSION
1441 L St., NW, Suite 9100 • Washington, DC 20005
(202) 632-7003 Fax 632-7066
Website: www.nigc.gov
Philip N. Hogan, Chairperson
Nelson W. Westrin, Vice Chairperson
Cloyce V. Choney, Commissioner
Purpose: To regulate gaming activities on Indian lands for the purpose of
shielding Indian tribes from organized crime and other corrupting influences; to
ensure that Indian tribes are the primary beneficiaries of gaming revenues; and
to ensure that gaming is conducted fairly and honestly by both operators and
players.

Six Regional Offices:

Washington D.C. Regional Office (AL, CT, FL, LA, MS, NY, NC)
1441 L St., NW, Suite 9100 • Washington, DC 20005
(202) 632-7003 Fax 632-7066
Cindy Altimus, Regional Director

Northwest Regional Office (AK, OR, WA, ID)
Solomon Bldg., Suite 212, 620 SW Main St. • Portland, OR 97205
(503) 326-5095 Fax 326-5092
Randy Sitton, Regional Director

California Region (CA, NV)
801 I St., Suite 489 • Sacramento, CA 95814
(916) 414-2300 Fax 414-2310
Eric Schalansky, Regional Director

Southwest Regional Office (AZ, CO, NM, Southern NV)
Security Title Plaza, Suite 880
3636 N. Central Ave. • Phoenix, AZ 85012
(602) 640-2951 Fax 640-2952
Ken Billingsley, Regional Director

South Central Region (KS, MO, OK, TX)
224 S. Boulder, Rm. 301 • Tulsa, OK 74103
(918) 581-7924 Fax 581-7933
Tim Harper, Regional Director

North Central Region (IA, MI, MN, MT, NE, ND, SD, WI, WY)
190 E. 5th St., Suite 170 • St. Paul, MN 55101
(651) 290- 4004 Fax 290-4006
John Peterson, Regional Director

NATIONAL INDIAN GAMING & HOSPITALITY INSTITUTE
College of the Menominee Nation
P.O. Box 1179 • Keshena, WI 54135
(715) 799-5600 Fax 799-1308
Dr. Verna Fowler, Contact
Purpose: To explore and address economic, social and cultural issues related
to the development of gaming enterprises on American Indian reservations; to
provide certificate & associate degree education programs designed to expand
the trained work-force with expertise in Indian gaming nationally; to establish a
central clearinghouse and library; and a new gaming product development
center.

ALABAMA

CREEK TRIBE CASINO & BINGO PALACE
Hwy. 21 South at Poarch Rd. • ATMORE, AL 36502
(800) 826-9121; (251) 368-8007
Website: www.creekbingo.com

ARIZONA

At least 14 Arizona tribes have signed gaming compacts with the state of
Arizona. 17 casinos are open or in the planning stage. The only legal casino
gaming in Arizona is conducted by Indian tribes.

GOLDEN HA:SAN CASINO
HCO 3 Box 10 • AJO, AZ 85321
(866) 332-9467; (520) 362-2746
Julie Real, General Manager
Operated by the Tohono O'odham Tribe. *Location*: On the way to Organ Pipe
National Park and Rocky Point, Mexico. *Facilities*: Slot machines.

CLIFF CASTLE CASINO
555 Middle Verde Rd., P.O. Box 56677 • CAMP VERDE, AZ 86322
(800) 381-7568; (928) 567-7900 Fax 567-7901
Website: www.cliffcastlecasino.net
E-mail: general@cliffcastlecasino.net
Owned by the Pascua Yaqui Tribe. *Location*: in Camp Verde. *Facility*: 10,000
sq. ft. 475 slots, video poker, poker tables. 82 hotel rooms.

LONE BUTTE CASINO
P.O. Box 6790 • CHANDLER, AZ 85246
(800) 946-4452; (520) 796-7777 Fax 796-7712
Website: www.wingilariver.com
Owned & operated by the Gila River Pima-Maricopa Indian Community.
Location: 25 miles southeast of Phoenix. *Facility*: 30,000 sq. ft. 300 slots; video
poker/blackjack/keno. Bingo. Open 24/7.

VEE QUIVA CASINO
P.O. Box 6790 • CHANDLER, AZ 85246
(800) 946-4452; (520) 796-7777
Website: www.wingilariver.com
Owned & operated by the Gila River Pima Maricopa Indian Community.
Location: Off I-10 West at the corner of 51 Ave and Komatke Lane. *Facility*:
69,000 sq. ft. 500 slots; ten poker tables; 6 blackjack tables; bingo; live keno.

WILD HORSE PASS CASINO
P.O. Box 6790 • CHANDLER, AZ 85246
(800) 946-4452; (520) 796-7777 Fax 796-7712
Website: wingilariver.com
Owned & operated by the Gila River Pima-Maricopa Indian Community.
Facility: 750 slots; 100 video poker, blackjack, keno, roulette. Bingo.

TWIN ARROWS NAVAJO CASINO RESORT
22181 Resort Blvd. • FLAGSTAFF, AZ 86004
(855) 946-8946 (928) 856-7200 Fax 856-7608.
Website: www.twinarrows.com
Owned by the Navajo Nation. *Facilities*: Slots, live kino, table games, poker
room, bingo; open 24/7

CROSSING CASINO
101 Aztec Rd. • FORT MOHAVE, AZ 86426
Owned & operated by the Fort Mojave Indian Tribe.

FORT McDOWELL CASINO
Fort McDowell Rd. & State Rd. 87
P.O. Box 11839 • FOUNTAIN HILLS, AZ 85269
(800) 843-3678; (602) 837-1427 Fax 837-0844
Website: www.fortmcdowellcasino.com
Betty Humphries, Contact
Owned by the Fort McDowell Yavapai Nation. *Location*: 20 miles east of
Phoenix. *Facility*: 120,000 sq. ft. 475 slots; video poker, blackjack, keno; 40
poker tables. Bingo. Open 24/7.

PIPE SPRINGS RESORT & CASINO
HC 65, Box 3 • FREDONIA, AZ 86022
(800) WIN-7477; (520) 643-7777 Fax 643-7260
Owned by the Kaibab-Paiute Indian Community. *Location*: 200 miles northwest
of Flagstaff, north of Grand Canyon National Park, 4 miles from Utah border on
Hwy. 89. *Facility*: 7,000 sq. ft. Slots, video poker, keno.

HARRAH'S AK-CHIN CASINO RESORT
15406 N. Maricopa Rd. • MARICOPA, AZ 85239
(800) 427-7247; (480) 802-5000 Fax 802-5050
Martin J. Antone, Sr., Contact; Website: www.harrahs.com
Owned by the Ak-Chin Indian Tribe. Operated by Harrah's. *Location*: 35 miles south of Phoenix, I-10 exit 162A. *Facility*: 72,000 sq. feet, with a gaming area of 29,500 sq. feet. 475 slots, 40 table games. Open 24/7.

HUALAPAI CASINO
Grand Canyon West, P.O. Box 761 • MEADVILLE, AZ 86444
(602) 699-4161
Owned by the Hualapai Indian Tribe. *Location*: 50 miles north of Kingman, Ariz. *Facility*: Slots, video poker/keno.

SPIRIT MOUNTAIN CASINO
8555 S. Hwy. 95, P.O. Box 6588 • MOJAVE VALLEY, AZ 86440
(928) 346-2000 Fax 346-2007
Website: www.spiritmountainmojave.casinocity.com
Owned by the Fort Mojave Indian Tribe. *Location*: South of Bullhead City, Arizona, off I-40 on Hwy. 95, 1 mile northeast of the Needles bridge. *Facilities*: 6,500 sq. ft. 200 slots; video poker, keno.

BLUE WATER RESORT & CASINO
11300 Resort Dr. • PARKER, AZ 85344
(888) 243-3360; (928) 669-7000 Fax 669-5910
Website: www.bluewaterfun.com
Owned by the Colorado River Indian Tribes. *Location*: In Parker, 160 miles west of Phoenix on the Colorado River. *Facility*: 20,000 sq. ft. 470 slots; 50 video blackjack games; live poker, keno, bingo. Conference Center & theatre.

MAZATZAL CASINO
Hwy. 87, P.O. Box 1820 • PAYSON, AZ 85547
(800) 777-7529; (928) 474-6044 Fax 474-4238
Website: www.777play.com; Owned by the Tonto Apache Tribe. *Location*: One-half mile south of Payson, 75 miles NE of Phoenix on Hwy. 87. *Facilities*: 35,000 sq. ft. 400 slots, video poker/keno; live poker & blackjack, keno.

HON-DAH CASINO
777 Hwy. 260 • PINETOP, AZ 85953
(800) 929-8744; (928) 369-0299 Fax 369-0382
Website: www.hon-dah.com; Brent Kurth, General Manager
Owned by the White Mountain Apache Tribe. *Location*: Located in the scenic White Mountains area of eastern Arizona, 190 miles northeast of Phoenix, 3 miles south of Pinetop at Hwys. 73 & 260. *Facilities*: 128-room hotel, RV Park, Convention Center; 4,200 sq. ft. casino with 600 slots, 54 video poker, eight video keno, 12-seat keno, eight video blackjack, blackjack tables; two poker tables. Opened 1993.

BUCKY'S YAVAPAI CASINO
1500 E. Hwy. 69 • PRESCOTT, AZ 86301
(800) 756-8744; (928) 778-7909; Website: www.buckyscasino.com
Owned by the Yavapai Prescott Indian Tribe. *Location*: 96 miles north of Phoenix, east of downtown Prescott Junction off Hwy. 69 & 89. *Facilities*: 300 slots; blackjack & roulette tables. Open 24/7. 161 room Prescott Resort Hotel.

APACHE GOLD CASINO RESORT
P.O. Box 1210 • SAN CARLOS, AZ 85550
(800) APACHE-8; (520) 425-7692 Fax 425-7696
Website: www.apachegoldcasinoresort.com
Owned by the San Carlos Apache Tribe. *Location*: 5 miles east of Globe and 110 miles east of Phoenix on Hwy. 70. *Facilities*: 12,000 sq. ft. 500 video and reel slots; video poker, keno, and blackjack; and table games. Convention Center and Best Western Hotel.

CASINO ARIZONA
524 North 92nd St. • SCOTTSDALE, AZ 85256
(480) 850-7777; Website: www.casinoarizona.com
Owned by the Salt River Pima-Maricopa Indian Community. *Facilities*: 900 slots, 47 poker tables, blackjack, keno.

TALKING STICK RESORT & CASINO
8900 E. Chaparrel Rd. • SCOTTSDALE, AZ 85256
(480) 550-7777; Website: www.talkingstickresort.com
Owned by the Salt River Pima-Maricopa Indian Community. *Facilities*: Golf club; spa; 240,000 sq. ft. 50 table games; poker; 800 slots, blackjack, keno.

DESERT DIAMOND CASINO I-19
P.O. Box 22230 • TUCSON, AZ 85734
(520) 393-2700; (866) 332-9467; Website: www.desertdiamond.com
E-mail: comments@desertdiamondcasino.com
Owned by the Tohono O'odham Nation

COCOPAH BINGO & CASINO
15136 S. Ave, Box G • SOMERTON, AZ 85350
(800) 23-SLOTS; (520) 726-8066 Fax 344-8010
Website: www.casinosun.com
Owned by the Cocopah Tribe. *Location*: 13 miles southwest of Yuma on Hwy. 95. *Facilities*: 32,000 sq. ft. 475 slots, video poker and keno; bingo. Open Sun-Thurs. 6 am - 2 am; Fri-Sat., 24 hours.

CASINO OF THE SUN
7406 Camino de Oeste Rd. • TUCSON, AZ 85746
(800) 344-9435; (520) 883-1700 Fax 883-0983
Owned by Pascua Yaqui Indian Tribe. Location: South of downtown Tucson. *Facilities*: 24,500 sq. ft. 400 slots, 15 poker tables, video keno and poker; keno; 15 poker & blackjack tables; bingo. Open 24 hours, 7 days.

DESERT DIAMOND CASINO
7350 S. Nogales Hwy. , P.O. Box 22230 • TUCSON, AZ 85734
(520) 294-7777; (866) DDCWINS
Website: www.desertdiamond.com; Bruce Phillips, Contact
Owned by the Tohono O'odham Nation. *Location*: South of Tucson. *Facilities*: 45,000 sq. feet. 2,600 slots, video poker, keno; keno, poker, blackjack, craps.

WHITE MOUNTAIN APACHE CASINO
P.O. Box 700 • WHITERIVER, AZ 85941
(520) 338-4346
Owned by the White Mountain Apache Tribe. *Location*: South of Show Low, AZ, on Hwy. 60. *Facilities*: 1,800 electronic gaming machines.

QUECHAN PARADISE CASINO ARIZONA
P.O. Box 2737 • YUMA, AZ 85366
(888) 777-4946; (760) 572-7777
Website: www.paradise-casinos.com
Owned by the Quechan Tribe. *Facilities*: 735 gaming machines for video keno, reel slots, video poker and 8 poker tables, live keno and blackjack tables. 5 bingo rooms.

CALIFORNIA

VIEJAS CASINO
5000 Willows Rd. • ALPINE, CA 91901
(800) 847-6537; (619) 445-5400 Fax 659-1954
Website: www.viejas.com
Owned by the Viejas Band of Kumeyaay Indians. *Location*: 30 miles east of San Diego off Interstate Hwy. 8 on the Viejas Indian Reservation. *Facilities*: 100,000 sq. ft. 25 gaming tables. Open 24/7.

DESERT ROSE CASINO
901 County Rd. 56 • ALTURAS, CA 96101
(530) 233-3141 Fax 233-3170
Website: www.500nations.com/casinos/cadesertrose.asp
Owned by the Pit River Tribe of Alturas Rancheria. *Location*: In Northern California, Modoc County, 170 miles north of Reno, Nevada on U.S. 395. Facility: 5,000 sq. ft; 88 slots; 2 tables; bingo.

CAHUILLA CREEK RESTAURANT & CASINO
52702 Hwy. 371 • ANZA, CA 92539
(909) 763-1200; Website: www.cahuilla.com
Owned by the Cahuilla Band of Mission Indians. *Location*: Minutes from Palm Springs, an hour from San Diego, and a half hour from Riverside. *Facilities*: 225 slots; video poker; multi-game machines and table games.

MONO WIND CASINO
37302 Rancheria Lane, P.O. Box 1060 • AUBERRY, CA 93602
(559) 855-4350 Fax 855-4351
Owned by the Mono Indians of the Big Sandy Rancheria. *Facilities*: 10,000 sq. ft. casino. 329 slots; 10 table games.

BARSTOW CASINO & RESORT
Los Coyotes Band of Cahuilla & Cupeno Indians
Tom West, BarWest Gaming (517) 372-4400; E-mail: toms@mrgmi.com
The approximately 23-acre parcel in Barstow that is the subject of the Los Coyote Band's fee-to-trust & two-part determination application is about 115 miles from the Los Coyotes reservation. The Los Coyotes trust parcel was selected with the City's direct input into the most appropriate gaming location for the City. The parcel is located within the incorporated boundaries of the City of Barstow, San Bernardino County, California, just east of Interstate 15.

PAIUTE PALACE CASINO
2742 N. Sierra • BISHOP, CA 93514
(888) 372-4883; (760) 873-4150

Owned by the Bishop Paiute Tribe. *Location*: In the Owens Valley, north of Bishop on U.S. Hwy. 395 off I-15 and I-80. *Facilities*: 300 video slots, 38 video poker machines, gaming tables.

BLUE LAKE CASINO
P.O. Box 1128 • BLUE LAKE, CA 95525
  (707) 668-5101; Website: www.bluelakecasino.com
Owned by the Blue Lake Rancheria.

CACHE CREEK CASINO RESORT
P.O. Box 65 • BROOKS, CA 95616
  (530) 796-3118 Fax 796-2112
  Website: www.cachecreek.com
  Paula Lorenzo, CEO & Tribal Chairwoman
  Randy Takemoto, COO & General Manager
Owned & operated by the Rumsey Band of Wintun Indians. *Location*: 14455 Hwy. 16 in Brooks. Facility: 415,000 sq. ft, 200-room luxury hotel and health spa; 8 restaurants, and a 20,000 sq. ft., 1,000-seat Event Center; 74,7200 sq. ft. of casino space featuring 2,300 slots and 131 table games. High stakes bingo is played in the Event Center. Open 24/7.

PIT RIVER CASINO
20265 Tamarack Ave. • BURNEY, CA 96013
  (888) 245-2992; (530) 335-2334; Mike Avelar, Manager
  Website: www.pitrivercasino.com; E-mail: info@pitrivercasino.com
Owned by the Pit River Tribe of California. *Facilities*: 8,600 sq. ft. casino. 130 slots, two blackjack tables. 75-seat Bingo. Opened 1996.

MORONGO CASINO
49750 Seminole Dr., P.O. Box 366 • CABAZON, CA 92230
  (800) 252-4499; (714) 849-3080; Website: www.casinomorongo.com
Owned by the Morongo Band of Cahuilla Indians. *Location*: I-10, between Banning and Palm Springs. *Facilities*: 100,000 sq. ft. 2,000 slots; 46 blackjack tables, 35 poker tables. Open 24/7.

COYOTE VALLEY SHODAKAI CASINO
P.O. Box 388 • CALPELLA, CA
  (707) 485-0700 Fax 485-0730

AUGUSTINE CASINO
84-001 Avenue 54 • COACHELLA, CA 92236
  (888) PLAY 2 WIN; (760) 391-9500 Fax 398-4447
  Website: www.augustinecasino.com
Owned by the Augustine Band of Cahuilla Indians. *Location*: East of PGA West on Avenue 54 at Van Buren.

SPOTLIGHT29 CASINO
46-200 Harrison St. • COACHELLA, CA 92236
  (866) 3SPOT29; (760) 775-5566 Fax 775-4637
  Website: www.spotlight29.com
Owned by the Twenty Nine Palms Band of Luiseno Mission Indians. Location: Interstate 10 at Dillon Rd. *Facility*: 74,000 sq. ft. 48 table games, poker room, bingo. Open 24/7.

CHUKCHANSI GOLD RESORT & CASINO
711 Lucky Lane • COARSEGOLD, CA 93614
  (866) 794-6946; (559) 692-5200 Fax 692-5328
  Website: www.chukchansigold.com
  Bruce A. King, General Manager
Owned & operated by the Picayune Rancheria of the Chukchansi Indians. *Location*: Off Hwy. 41 on the Chicayune Rancheria in Coarsegold, Calif. *Facility*: 120,000 sq. ft. 1800 slots, 24 tables, poker, bingo. Open 24/7.

COLUSA INDIAN BINGO & CASINO
3770 Hwy. 45, P.O. Box 1267 • COLUSA, CA 95932
  (800) 655-8946; (530) 458-8844 Fax 458-2018
  Website: www.colusacasino.com
Owned by the Cachil DeHe Band of Wintun Indians of the Colusa Indian Community. *Facility*: 300 slots, poker, keno; Bingo.

ROLLING HILLS CASINO
2655 Barham Ave. • CORNING, CA 96021
  (888) 331-6400; (530) 528-3500 Fax 528-2473
  Website: www.rollinghillscasino.com
Owned & operated by the Paskenta Band of Nomlaki Indians. *Facilities*: 770 slots; blackjack & poker.

HIDDEN OAKS CASINO
76600 Hwy. 12 • COVELO, CA 95428
  (707) 983-6126 Fax 983-6128; Website: www.rvit.org
Owned & operated by the Round Valley Indian Tribes.

ELK VALLEY CASINO
2500 Howland Hill Rd. • CRESCENT CITY, CA 95531
  (888) 574-2744; (707) 464-1020 Fax 464-5188
  Website: www.elkvalleycasino.com
Owned by the Yurok and Tolowa Nation of the Elk Valley Rancheria. *Facilities*: 280 slots; gaming tables. Bingo.

SYCUAN RESORT & CASINO
5469 Casino Way • EL CAJON, CA 92019
  (619) 445-6002 Fax 445-1394; Website: www.sycuancasino.com
Owned by the Sycuan Band of the Kumeyaay Nation. *Location*: 18 miles east of San Diego on Interstate Hwy. I-8. *Facility*: 70,000 sq. ft. 368 slots, 25 poker tables; 40 video blackjack, 36 video keno, bingo. Open 24/7.

PARADISE CASINO CALIFORNIA
450 Quechan Dr. • FORT YUMA, CA 92283
  (888) 777-4946; (760) 572-7777; Website: www.paradise-casinos.com
Owned by the Quechan Tribe. *Facilities*: 735 gaming machines for video keno, reel slots, video poker & 8 poker tables, live keno & blackjack tables. Bingo.

TABLE MOUNTAIN CASINO
8184 Table Mountain Rd., P.O. Box 445 • FRIANT, CA 93626
  (559) 822-7777; (800) 541-3637; Website: www.tmcasino.com
Owned by the Yokut Tribe of the Table Mountain Rancheria. *Facility*: 250,000 sq. ft. 2,000 slots; blackjack & poker tables; bingo.

RIVER ROCK CASINO
3250 Hwy. 128 • GEYSERVILLE, CA 95441
  (707) 857-2777; Website: www.river-rock-casino.com
Owned by the Dry Creek Rancheria Band of Pomo Indians.

HAVASU LANDING RESORT & CASINO
P.O. Box 1707 • HAVASU LAKE, CA 92363
  (800) 307-3610; Website: www.havasulanding.com
Owned by the Chemehuevi Tribe. *Location*: western shores of Lake Havasu.

SAN MANUEL INDIAN BINGO & CASINO
777 San Manuel Blvd. • HIGHLAND, CA 92346
  (800) 359-2464; (909) 864-5050 Fax 862-3405
  Website: www.sanmanuel.com
Owned by the San Manuel Band of Serrano Mission Indians. Location: 7 miles from downtown San Bernardino, off Hwy. 30 E. *Facility*: 2,000 slots, 45 poker tables; bingo. Open 24/7.

HOPLAND SHOKAWAH CASINO & BINGO
13101 Nakomis Rd. • HOPLAND, CA 95449
  (888) 745-5292; (707) 744-1395 Fax 744-1698
  Website: www.shokawah.com
Owned by the Shokawah Band of Pomo Indians of the Hopland Reservation. *Location*: 45 minutes north of Santa Rosa in Northern California. *Facilities*: 1,200 slots, 16 table games. Bingo.

LUCKY BEAR CASINO & BINGO
P.O. Box 1348 • HOOPA, CA 95546
  (530) 625-4211 Fax 625-4594
  Website: www.hoopa-nsn.gov/enterprises/casino
  Website: www.casinocity.com
Owned by the Hoopa Valley Tribe of the Hoopa Valley Indian Reservation.

WINNEDUMAH WINNS CASINO
Fort Independence Indian Reservation
P.O. Box 67 • Independence, CA 93526
  (760) 878-5160; Owned by the Fort Independence Paiute Tribe. Casino houses Class II gaming operation and is attached to the Fort Independence Travel Plaza that provides fuel, sundries and a kitchen grill.

FANTASY SPRINGS CASINO
84-245 Indio Springs Dr. • INDIO, CA 92203
  (800) 827-2964; (760) 342-5000 Fax 347-7880
  Website: www.fantasyspringsresort.com
  Dan Comiskey, Executive Director; Joe DeRosa, General Manager
Owned by the Cabazon Band of Mission Indians. *Location*: 24 miles east of Palm Springs on Hwy. I-10. *Facilities*: 265,000 sq. ft. 2,000 slots, 39 poker tables. 800 video games (poker, keno, blackjack). Bingo.

BUENA VISTA CASINO
Website: www.buenavistatribe.com/tribal_gaming.htm
Online casino owned & operated by the Buena Vista Rancheria of Me-Wuk Indians. *Location*: Casino being built near Ione, Calif. on 67.5 acres of tribal land within the boundaries of the tribe's original reservation. *Facilities*: Slots, progressive jackpots, table games; restaurants; childcare.

JACKSON RANCHERIA CASINO & HOTEL
12222 New York Ranch Rd. • JACKSON, CA 95642
  (800) 822-WINN; (209) 223-1677 Fax 223-88385
  Website: www.jacksoncasino.com/index.htm
Owned by the Jackson Rancheria Band of Me-wuk Indians. *Location*: Off Hwy 88 or Hwy. 49. Facility: 33 tables; poker room, slots, bingo. Open 24/7.

CHICKEN RANCH BINGO
16929 Chicken Ranch Rd. • JAMESTOWN, CA 95327
  (800) 75-BINGO; (209) 984-3000 Fax 984-4158
Owned by the Chicken Ranch Band of Me-wuk Indians.
Facility: 100,000 sq. ft. 100 slots; bingo.

GOLD BEAR CASINO
158 Klamath Beach Rd. • KLAMATH, CA 95548
  (707) 482-0680; 954-7512 Fax 482-1623
  Website: www.goldbearcasino.com; Andrew Forsht, Contact
Owned by the Coast Indian Community of the Resighini Rancheria.

KONOCTI VISTA CASINO RESORT & MARINA
2755 Mission Rancheria Rd. • LAKEPORT, CA 95453
  (800) 386-1950; (707) 262-1900
  Website: www.konocti-vista-casino.com
  E-mail: kvcplayers@kvcasino.com
Owned by the Pomo Indians of Big Valley & Scotts Valley Rancherias.

BARONA VALLEY RANCH RESORT & CASINO
1932 Wildcat Canyon Rd. • LAKESIDE, CA 92040
  (888) 7-BARONA; (619) 443-2300 Fax 443-2856
  Website: www.barona.com; E-mail: info@barona.com
Owned by the Barona Band of Mission Indians. *Location*: Located in the Barona Valley, 21 miles east of San Diego on Hwy. 67. *Facilities*: 115,000 Sq. feet. Bingo. 2,000 slots; 63 table games; 400-room hotel, golf course and event center. Open 24/7.

RED FOX CASINO
P.O. Box 1763 • LAYTONVILLE, CA 95454
  (888) 473-3369; (707) 984-6800 Fax 984-6500
  Corey James, General Manager
Owned by the Cahto Tribe of Laytonville Rancheria.
Facility: 3,600 sq. ft. 93 slots.

TACHI PALACE HOTEL & CASINO
172225 Jersey Ave., P.O. Box 308 • LEMOORE, CA 93245
  (866) 472-5223; (559) 924-7751 Fax 924-7526
  Website: www.tachipalace.com
Owned & operated by the Tachi Yokut of the Santa Rosa Rancheria.
Facilities: 2,000 gaming devices; table games & bingo. Open 24/7.

THUNDER VALLEY CASINO
1200 Athens Ave. • LINCOLN, CA 95648
  (916) 408-7777 Fax 408-8372
Owned by United Auburn Indian Community of Auburn Rancheria.

BEAR RIVER CASINO
11 Bear Paws Way • LOLETA, CA 95551
  (800) 761-2327; (707) 733-9644 Fax 733-9611
  Website: www.bearrivercasino.com
Owned & operated by the Bear River Band of the Rohnerville Rancheria.
Facility: Slots, table games; poker den.

TWIN PINE CASINO & HOTEL
P.O. Box 789 • MIDDLETOWN, CA 95461
  (800) 564-4872; (707) 987-2958; Website: www.twinpine.com
Owned by the Middletown Rancheria Band of Pomo Indians.

ROBINSON RANCHERIA RESORT & CASINO
1545 E. Hwy. 20 • P.O. Box 4017 • NICE, CA 95464
  (800) 809-3636; or (707) 262-4000
  (707) 275-9000 Fax 275-9100; Website: www.rrrc.com
Owned by the Robinson Rancheria Pomo Indians. Location: 30 miles east of Hwy. 101 between Nice and Upper Lake. *Facilities*: 37,500 sq. ft. 285 slots; video poker, keno; 12 table games, poker & blackjack; Bingo. Open 24/7.

FEATHER FALLS CASINO & LODGE
3 Alverda Dr. • OROVILLE, CA 95966
  (877) 652-4646; (530) 533-3885 Fax 533-5794
  Website: www.featherfallscasino.com
  Steve Wilson, Director
Owned by the Concow-Maidu Tribe of the Mooretown Rancheria.
Facilities: 1,000 slots, gaming tables, poker rooms.

GOLD COUNTRY CASINO
4020 Olive Hwy. • OROVILLE, CA 95966
  (530) 534-3859 Fax 534-9173
Owned by the Tyme Maidu Tribe of the Berry Creek Rancheria.

SPA RESORT & CASINO
401 E. Amado Rd. • PALM SPRINGS, CA 92262
  (800) 258-2946; (760) 883-1000; Website: sparesortcasino.com
Owned by the Agua Caliente Band of Mission Indians. *Location*: Downtown Palm Springs. *Facilities*: 40,000 sq. ft. casino. 900 slots; 30 gaming tables. Hotel & Mineral Springs Spa has 228 rooms.

CASINO PAUMA
777 Pauma Reservation Rd., P.O. Box 1067 • PAUMA VALLEY, CA 92061
  (877) 687-2862; (760) 742-2177 Fax 742-2438
Owned by the Pauma-Yuima Band of Mission Indians. *Facilities*: 2500 Slots, gaming tables, bingo; Resort hotel & Spa; Events & Conference Center.

RED HAWK CASINO
1 Red Hawk Blvd. • PLACERVILLE, CA 95567
  (530) 677-7000; Owned by the Shingle Springs Band of Me-Wuk Indians.

EAGLE MOUNTAIN CASINO
P.O. Box 1659 • PORTERVILLE, CA 93258
  (209) 788-6220 Fax 788-6223
Owned by the Yokut Indians of the Tule River Indian Tribe.

AGUA CALIENTE CASINO
32-250 Bob Hope Dr. • Rancho Mirage, CA 92270
  (760) 321-2000; Website: www.hotwatercasino.com
Owned by the Agua Caliente Band of Cahuilla Indians. *Location*: Intersection of Bob Hope Dr. and Ramon Rd. at I-10 in Rancho Mirage, minutes from downtown Palm Springs. *Facility*: 45,000 sq. ft. casino. 1,100+ reel slots, video poker and progressives; 10 poker tables and 32 gaming tables. Bingo.

WIN-RIVER CASINO BINGO
2100 Redding Rancheria Rd. • REDDING, CA 96001
  (800) 280-8946; (530) 243-3377 Fax 243-0337
  Website: www.winrivercasino.co; E-mail: putmefirst@win-river.com
Owned by the tribes of the Redding Rancheria.

RED EARTH CASINO
3089 Norm Niver Rd. • SALTON SEA BEACH, CA 92274
  (760) 395-1200 Fax 395-0408
Owned & operated by the Torres-Martinez Desert Cahuilla Indians.

SOBOBA-LEGENDS CASINO
23904 Soboba Rd. • SAN JACINTO, CA 92583
  (866) 4-SOBOBA; (909) 665-1000 Fax 665-1321
Owned by the Soboba Band of Luiseno Mission Indians. *Location*: Between Ramona Expressway and Interstate 10. *Facilities*: 75,000 sq. ft; 2,000 slots, 21 gaming tables, blackjack, poker; bingo. Open 24/7.

CASINO SAN PABLO OF LYTTON RANCHERIA
13255 San Pablo Ave. • SAN PABLO, CA 94806
  (510) 215-7888

CHUMASH CASINO & RESORT
3400 East Hwy. 246 • SANTA YNEZ, CA 93460
  (877) CHUMASH; (800) 728-9997; (805) 686-0855
  Website: www.chumashcasino.com
Owned by the Santa Ynez Band of Chumash Indians. *Location*: In Santa Barbara County on Hwy 101 to Solvang exit then 6 miles east to Resort. *Facilities*: 2,000 slots; blackjack tables, 14 poker tables; bingo. Hotel with 106 rooms. Open 24/7.

SANTA YSABEL RESORT & CASINO
25575 Hwy. 79, P.O. Box 600 • Santa Ysabel, CA 92070
  (760) 787-0909
Owned by the Santa Ysabel Band of Diegueno Mission Indians.

LUCKY 7 CASINO
350 N. Indian Rd. • SMITH RIVER, CA 95567
  (707) 487-9255 Fax 487-5077; Website: www.lucky7casino.com
Owned by the Tolowa Tribe of the Smith River Rancheria.

DIAMOND MOUNTAIN CASINO
900 Skyline Dr. • SUSANVILLE, CA 96130
  (530) 252-1100 Fax 252-1236
  Website: www.diamondmountaincasino.com
Owned by the Susanville Indian Rancheria.

PECHANGA RESORT & CASINO
45000 Pechanga Pkwy. , P.O. Box 9041 • TEMECULA, CA 92589
  (877) 711-2WIN; (888) 732-4264; (951) 693-1819 Fax 695-7410
  Website: www.pechanga.com; E-mail: info@pechanga.com
  Patrick Murphy & Robert Bledsoe, Contacts
Owned by the Pechanga Band of Luiseno Mission Indians. *Location*: Just off I-15 in the Temecula Valley about an hour from Los Angeles and San Diego. *Facilities*: 522 room luxury resort; 186,000 square ft. casino; 2,000 slots, 160 table games, 54-table poker room; 7 restaurants; 3 bars/lounges, 2 nightclubs; 1,200 seat performance theater. *Activities*: Fourth of July weekend powwow.

CHER-AE HEIGHTS CASINO
1 Cher-Ae Lane, P.O. Box 610 • TRINIDAD, CA 95570
  (800) 684-2464; (707) 677-3611
  Website: www.cheraeheightscasino.com
Owned by the Cher-Ae Heights Indian Community of The Trinidad Rancheria.

BLACK OAK CASINO
19400 Tuolumne Rd. North, P.O. Box 777 • TUOLUMNE, CA 95379
  (877) 747-8777; (209) 928-9300 Fax 928-9301
  Website: www.blackoakcasino.com
Owned by the Tuolumne Band of Me-Wuk Indians of the Tuolumne Rancheria. *Location*: 8 miles east of Sonora off Hwy. 108.

RUNNING CREEK CASINO
635 E. Hwy. 20 • UPPER LAKE, CA 95485
  (707) 275-9209; Website: www.runnngcreekcasino.com
Owned by the Habematolel Pomo of Upper Lake Rancheria. *Location*: Highway 20 corridor of Upper Lake, California, in the beautiful Clear Lake region. *Facilities*: 349 slots, 6 table games.

HARRAH'S RINCON CASINO & RESORT
P.O. Box 68 • VALLEY CENTER, CA 92082
  (760) 749-1051 Fax 749-8901; Website: www.harrahsrincon.com
Owned by the Rincon Band of Luiseno Mission Indians. *Facilities*: 1600 slots, 60 table games; poker room; bingo.

VALLEY VIEW CASINO
16300 Nyemii Pass Rd. • VALLEY CENTER, CA 92082
  (760) 291-5500 Fax 291-5615
  Website: www.vviewcasino.com; E-mail: bhoward@vviewcasino.com
Owned by the San Pasqual Band of Diegueno Indians.

SHERWOOD VALLEY POMO CASINO & BLACK BART CASINO
100 Kawi Place • WILLITS, CA 95490
  (707) 459-7330 Fax 459-7337; Website: www.blackbartcasino.com
Owned by the Pomo Indians of the Sherwood Valley Rancheria. *Location*: On U.S. Hwy 101, 140 miles north of San Francisco. *Facilities*: 185 slot;

QUECHAN CASINO RESORT
525 Algodones Rd. • WINTERHAVEN, CA 92283
Owned by the Quechan Indian Tribe of Arizona & California

COLORADO

SKY UTE LODGE & CASINO
P.O. Box 340 • IGNACIO, CO 81137
  (800) 876-7017; (888) 842-4150
  (970) 563-3000 Fax 563-9546; Website: www.skyutecasino.com
Owned by the Southern Ute Indian Tribe. *Location*: 25 miles south of Durango on Hwy. 172. *Facilities*: 24,000 sq. ft. 400 slots; table games. 36 room hotel and conference center. Open 24/7.

UTE MOUNTAIN CASINO, HOTEL & RESORT
3 Weeminuche Dr. • TOWAOC, CO 81334
  (800) 258-8007; (970) 565-8800 Fax 565-7276
  Website: www.utemountaincasino.com
Owned by the Ute Mountain Ute Indians. *Location*: 11 miles south of Cortez on Hwy. 160 & 666, 425 miles southwest of Denver. *Facilities*: 30,000 sq. ft. 373 slots; table games; bingo. Open 8 am - 4 am daily.

CONNECTICUT

FOXWOODS RESORT & CASINO
39 Norwich-Westerly Rd., P.O. Box 410 • LEDYARD, CT 06339
  (800) FOXWOODS ; (860) 312-3000
  Website: www.foxwoods.com; Michael F. Speller, President
Owned by the Mashantucket Pequot Tribe. *Location*: Southeastern Connecticut, northeast of New London, Connecticut, 8 miles west of I-95 off exit 92 on State Road 2. *Facilities*: 250,000 sq. ft. 6,500 slots; 237 table games; 400 video poker; 140 blackjack tables; 60 poker tables, 24 crap tables; 26 roulette tables; 4 mini-baccarat. 320-room hotel. 3,200 seat Bingo hall. Open 24/7.

MOHEGAN SUN CASINO
Mohegan Sun Blvd., P.O. Box 548 • UNCASVILLE, CT 06382
  (888) 226-7711; (860) 204-8000 Fax 204-7419
  Website: www.mohegansun.som
Owned by the Mohegan Indian Tribe. *Location*: 15 miles west of Ledyard and Foxwoods; One mile from the interchange of I-395 and CT Rt. 2. *Facilities*: 300,000 sq. ft. Indian hotel casino complex with 1,176 rooms & 175 suites. 6,300 slots, 300 video poker, 141 table games; 10,000-seat arena for sporting events and concerts. Open 24/7.

FLORIDA

SEMINOLE CASINO-BRIGHTON CREEK
West of Okeechobee, Hwy. 721 • OKEECHOBEE, FL
  (866) 2-CASINO; (954) 977-6700; Website: www.seminoletribe.com
Owned by the Seminole Tribe of Florida. *Facilities*: 240 machines, 10 poker tables; 500-seat bingo hall. Opened daily at 10 a.m. Tues.-Sunday.

SEMINOLE CASINO-COCONUT CREEK
5550 Northwest 40th St. • COCONUT CREEK, FL
  (866) 2-CASINO; (954) 977-6700; Website: www.seminoletribe.com
Owned by the Seminole Tribe of Florida.

SEMINOLE INDIAN CASINO-IMMOKALEE
506 1st St. • IMMOKALEE, FL 33934
  (800) 218-0007; (941) 658-1313 Fax 658-1515
  Website: www.seminoletribe.com
Owned by the Seminole Indian Tribe. *Location*: 25 miles southwest of Ft. Myers Airport. *Facilities*: 525 video gaming machines, 15 poker tables; 500-seat high stakes bingo. Open 24/7.

SEMINOLE HARD ROCK HOTEL & CASINO-HOLLYWOOD
4150 N. State Rd. 7 • HOLLYWOOD, FL 33021
  (800) 323-5452; (954) 961-3220
  Website: www.seminolehardrockhollywood.com
Owned by Seminole Tribe of Florida. *Location*: 5 miles southwest of Ft. Lauderdale. *Facilities*: 1,000 slots, video pull-tabs, low 33 poker tables; 800-seat high stakes bingo hall. Open 24/7.

MICCOSUKEE RESORT & GAMING
500 S.W. 177th Ave. • MIAMI, FL 33194
  (800) 741-4600; (877) 242-6464; (305) 925-2555
  Website: www.miccosukee.com
Owned by the Miccosukee Tribe of Florida. *Facilities*: 1,000 slots, Video pull tabs, 58 poker tables, 1,300-seat bingo hall. Open 24/7.

SEMINOLE HARD ROCK HOTEL & CASINO-TAMPA
5223 N. Orient Rd. • TAMPA, FL 33610
  (866) 502-PLAY (7529); (813) 627-7625
  Website: www.hardrockhotelcasinotampa.com
Owned by the Seminole Indian Tribe. *Facilities*: 90,000 sq. ft. 1,850 slots; video pull tabs, 32 poker tables. Open 24/7.

IDAHO

KOOTENAI RIVER INN & CASINO
Kootenai River Plaza, Hwy. 95
7169 Plaza St. • BONNERS FERRY, ID 83805
  (800) 346-5668 (208) 267-8511; Website: www.kootenairiverinn.com
Owned by the Kootenai Tribe of Idaho. *Location*: 27 miles from the Canadian border on U.S. Hwy. 95. *Facilities*: 400 slots. Bingo and video pull-tabs

BANNOCK PEAK CASINO; FORT HALL CASINO
P.O. Box 868 • FORT HALL, ID 83203
  (800) 497-4231; (208) 237-8778; Website: www.sho-ban.com
Owned & operated by the Shoshone Bannock Tribes of the Fort Hall Reservation. *Location*: Five miles north of Pocatello. *Facilities*: Slots, 800-seat bingo room.

IT'SE-YE-YE BINGO & CASINO
404 Main St. • KAMIAH, ID 83536
  (877) 678-7423; (208) 935-1019; Website: www.crcasino.com
Owned & operated by the Nez Perce Tribal Gaming Enterprise.

CLEARWATER RIVER CASINO
17500 Nez Perce Rd. • LEWISTON, ID 83501
  (877) NP-TRIBE; (208) 746-0723; Website: www.crcasino.com

Owned & operated by the Nez Perce Tribal Gaming Enterprise. *Facility*: 18,000 sq. ft. Slots, bingo, video lottery terminals. Open 24/7.

COEUR D'ALENE CASINO RESORT/HOTEL
P.O. Box 236 • WORLEY, ID 83876
(800) 523-2464; (208) 686-0248 Fax 686-1503
Website: www.cdacasino.com
Owned by the Coeur d'Alene Tribe. *Location*: Northern Idaho on U.S. Hwy. 95, 30 miles south of Coeur d'Alene and I-90. *Facility*: 41,700 sq. ft. casino; 1,400+ Video slots, video pull-tabs, tables; high stakes bingo. 11,000 sq. ft. convention & meeting center. Open 24 hours. *Activities*: Annual Tribe Encampment and Powwow in July in Post Falls, Idaho, the largest outdoor powwow in the Northwest.

IOWA

BLACKBIRD BEND CASINO
17214 210TH St., P.O. Box 89 • ONAWA, IA 51040
(844) 622-2121; (712) 423-9646 Fax 423-9694
Website: www.blackbirdbendcasinos.com
Owned by the Omaha Tribe of Nebraska. *Location*: 32 miles south of Sioux City, Iowa; or 60 miles north of Omaha Nebraska. *Facility*: 30,000 sq. ft. 450 slots; 25 table games. Bingo. Gift shop. Open 24 hours, weekends; 8 am - 2 am, weekdays.

WINNAVEGAS CASINO
1500 330th St. • SLOAN, IA 51055
(800) 468-9466; (712) 428-9466 Fax 428-4219
Website: www.winnavegas.biz
Owned by the Winnebago Tribe of Nebraska. *Location*: 20 miles south of Sioux City, 3 miles west of Hwy. I-29 exit 127. *Facility*: 45,000 sq. ft. 715 slots, video poker & keno; 25 tables. Open 24/7.

MESKWAKI BINGO CASINO HOTEL
1504 - 305th St. • TAMA, IA 52339
(800) 728-4263; (641) 484-2108; Website: www.meskwaki.com
Owned by the Sac & Fox Indian Tribe of Mississippi in Iowa. *Location*: 40 miles west of Cedar Rapids, Iowa. *Facility*: 400 rooms, 1400 slots & 35 table games; poker room. Open 24/7.

KANSAS

GOLDEN EAGLE CASINO
1121 Goldfinch Rd., Rte. 1, Box 149 • HORTON, KS 66439
(888) GO-4-LUCK; (785) 486-6601; Website: www.goldeneaglecasino.com
Owned by the Kickapoo Tribe. *Location*: 45 miles north of Topeka off U.S. Hwy. 75 on K20 5 miles west of Horton. *Facility*: Slots & video poker; table games; poker.

7TH STREET CASINO
803 N. 7th St. • KANSAS CITY, KS

HARRAH'S PRAIRIE BAND CASINO
16281 "Q" Rd. • MAYETTA, KS 66509
(785) 966-2255 Fax 966-7640; Website: www.harrahs.com
Owned by the Prairie Band Potawatomi Tribe. *Location*: Off Hwy. 75 west of Mayetta. *Facility*: 60,000 sq. feet. Slots & video poker; table games; bingo.

SAC & FOX CASINO
1322 US Hwy. 75, Rt. 1, Box 105A • POWHATTAN, KS 66527
(800) 990-2946; (785) 467-8000 Fax 467-5001
Website: www.sacandfoxcasino.com
Owned & operated by the Sac & Fox Nation of Missouri.
Facilities: Slots & table games.

CASINO WHITE CLOUD
Rt. 1 Box 58A • WHITE CLOUD, KS 66094
(785) 595-3258 Fax 595-6610
Website: www.casinowhitecloud.org; Leon Campbell, Chairperson
Iowa Tribe of Kansas & Nebraska. *Location*: Northeast corner of Kansas on the Missouri River near the Nebraska border. *Facility*: 470 Slots, table games; bingo.

LOUISIANA

CYPRESS BAYOU CASINO
832 Martin Luther King Rd.
P.O. Box 519 • CHARENTON, LA 70523
(800) 284-4386; (337) 923-7284; Website: www.cypressbayou.com

Owned by Chitimacha Indian Tribe. *Location*: 45 miles south of Lafayette, off US Hwy. 90, exit 83 east to Baldwin. *Facility*: 45,000 sq. ft. 500 slots, video poker and 36 table games.

COUSHATTA CASINO RESORT
777 Coushatta Dr. • KINDER, LA 70648
(800) 584-7263; (337) 738-1300 Fax 738-7340
Website: www.coushattacasinoresort.com
Owned by the Coushatta Tribe of Louisiana. *Location*: 25 miles north of I-10 on U.S. Hwy. 165, exit 44, five miles north of Kinder. *Facility*: 100,000 sq. ft. with 2,850 slots & 75 table games.

PARAGON CASINO RESORT
711 Paragon Pl. • MARKSVILLE, LA 71351
(318) 253-1946 (800) WIN-1-WIN; Website: www.paragoncasinoresort.com
Owned by the Tunica-Biloxi Tribe of Louisiana. *Location*: 35 miles northeast of Alexandria, Louisiana, on Hwy 1 in Marksville. *Facility*: 120,000 sq. ft. 2,100 slots & 80 table games; bingo. Hotel with 335-rooms.

MICHIGAN

OJIBWA CASINO RESORT
797 Michigan Ave. • BARAGA, MI 49944
(800) 323-8045; (906) 353-6333 Fax 353-7618/8786
Website: www.ojibwacasino.com
Owned by the Keweenaw Bay Indian Community of the L'Anse Reservation. *Location*: 5 miles north of Baraga in Upper Michigan on M-38. *Facility*: 17,000 sq. ft. 400 slots, 11 game tables; 450-seat bingo hall. 40-room hotel. Open 24 hours, 7 days a week.

FIREKEEPERS CASINO
Pine Creek Indian Reservation
11177 Michigan Ave. • BATTLE CREEK, MI 49014
(269) 660-5705 or 789-4805; Website: www.firekeeperscasino.com
E-mail: info@firekeeperscasino.com; R. Bruce McKee, General Manager
Owned & operated by Nottawaseppi Huron Band of Potawatomi Indians. *Location*: Exit 104 off I-94 in Battle Creek, Mich. Facility: 107,000 sq. ft. 2,680 slots, 90 table games, 20 poker tables, bingo room. Opened 2009.

GUN LAKE CASINO
U.S. 131 • BRADLEY, MI
Website: www.gunlakecasino.com
Owned by the Match-E-Be-Nash-She-Wish Band of Pottawatomi Indians. Location: On U.S. 131 halfway between Grand Rapids & Kalamazoo at exit 61. Opened 2011.

BAY MILLS RESORT & CASINO
11386 Lakeshore Dr., P.O. Box 249 • BRIMLEY, MI 49715
(888) 422-9645; (906) 248-3715; Website: www.4baymills.com
Owned by the Bay Mills Indian Community. *Location*: On the Lakeshore, along the bank of the St. Mary's River. *Facility*: 17,000 sq. ft with 1,000 slots, video poker and tables, Caribbean stud poker & keno; Bingo. 144-room hotel. Open 24/7.

KINGS CLUB CASINO
12140 Lakeshore Dr., Rt. 1, Box 313 • BRIMLEY, MI 49715
(800) 575-5493; (906) 248-3227 Fax 248-3283
Website: www.4baymills.com/html/kingsclub/
Owned by the Bay Mills Indian Community. *Location*: 17 miles west of Sault Ste. Marie. *Facility*: 5,000 sq. feet. 275 slots, 8 table games.

KEWADIN CASINO - CHRISTMAS
Rt. 2, Box 223 • CHRISTMAS, MI 49862
(800) 682-6040; (906) 466-2941 Fax 387-5477
Website: www.kewadinchristmas.com
Owned by the Sault Ste. Marie Ojibwe (Chippewa) Tribe. *Location*: 40 miles east of Marquette in the Upper Peninsula of Michigan on the shores of Lake Superior. *Facility*: 1,266 sq. ft. with 80 slots & 4 tables.

GREEKTOWN CASINO
555 E. Lafayette St. • DETROIT, MI 48226
(313) 223-2999
Owned by the Sault Ste. Marie Ojibwe (Chippewa) Tribe.

ISLAND RESORT & CASINO
W399 Hwy. 2 & 41, P.O. Box 351 • HARRIS, MI 49845
(906) 466-2941 Fax 466-2949
Website: www.islandresortcasino.com
Tom McChesney, General Manager

Owned & operated by the Hannahville Indian Community - Potawatomi Tribe. *Location*: W 399 Hwy. 2 & 41, 13 miles west of Escanaba, MI and Lake Michigan's western shore on US Hwy. 41. *Facility*: 55,000 sq. ft. 970+ slot machines, live & video poker, and 8 table games; 350-seat bingo room. 113-room hotel. Open 24/7.

KEWADIN CASINO - HESSEL
3 Mile Rd., P.O. Box 789 • HESSEL, MI 49745
 (800) KEWANDIN; (906) 484-2903 Fax 484-3248
 Website: www.kewadinhessel.com
Owned by Sault Ste. Marie Tribe of Ojibwe (Chippewa) Indians. *Location*: In Michigan's Upper Peninsula on Hwy 134, 14 miles east of Interstate Hwy. 75 on the shore of Lake Huron. *Facility*: 3,850 sq. feet. 120 slots, 4 tables.

LITTLE RIVER CASINO RESORT
2700 Orchard Hwy. , P.O. Box 417 • MANISTEE, MI 49660
 (888) 568-2244; (231) 723-1535 Fax 398-2593
 Website: www.littlerivercasino.com
Owned & operated by the Little River Band of Ottawa Indians at Manistee. *Facilities*: Hotel with 292 rooms; 1,350 slots, video poker and table games; Event Center. Open 24/7.

KEWADIN CASINO - MANISTIQUE
5630 W. Hwy. 2 • MANISTIQUE, MI 49854
 (800) KEWADIN; (906) 341-5510 Fax 341-2951
 Website: www.kewadinmanistique.com
 Al Kerridge, General Manager
Owned by the Sault Ste. Marie Tribe of Ojibwa (Chippewa) Indians. *Location*: In Michigan's Upper Peninsula on the northern shore of Lake Michigan on Hwy. 2 east of Escanaba. *Facility*: 1,266 sq. ft. 80 slots, 4 tables.

OJIBWA CASINO - MARQUETTE
105 Acre Trail • MARQUETTE, MI 49855
 (888) 560-9905; (906) 249-4200 Fax 249-4401
 Website: www.ojibwacasino.com
Owned & operated by the Keweenaw Bay Indian Community of the L'Anse Reservation. *Facilities*: 10,000 sq. ft. 300 slots, 10 tables. Bingo. Open 24/7.

SOARING EAGLE CASINO & BINGO HALL
6800 Soaring Eagle Blvd. • Mt. Pleasant, MI 48858
 (888) 7EAGLE7; (989) 775-5777 Fax 775-3040
 Website: www.soaringeaglecasino.com
Owned by the Saginaw Chippewa Tribe of Michigan. *Location*: 75 miles north of Lansing on Hwy. 20. *Facilities*: 210,000 sq. ft. casino with 4,700 slots, 80 table games; bingo. 3,260-seat showroom, 54,000 sq. ft. expo space and 26,000 sq. ft. of meeting space. 512-room hotel resort. Slots open 24/7.

ODAWA CASINO RESORT
1760 Lears Rd. • PETOSKEY, MI 49770
 (877) 442-6464; (231) 439-6100; Website: www.odawacasino.com
Owned & operated by the Little Traverse Bay Bands of Odawa Indians. *Facilities*: Hotel with 128 rooms; 1,500 slots and video poker machines; table games; poker room.

KEWADIN CASINO - ST. IGNACE
3039 Mackinaw Trail • ST. IGNACE, MI 49781
 (800) 539-2346; (906) 643-7071 Fax 643-8472
 Website: www.kewadinstignace.com
Owned by Sault Ste. Marie Ojibwa (Chippewa) Tribe. *Location*: Upper Peninsula at the north end of the Mackinac Bridge, across the Straits of Mackinaw from Mackinaw City. *Facilities*: 56,000 sq. ft. with 2,400 slots, video poker, keno &30 table games. Hotel with 320 rooms. Open 24/7.

KEWADIN CASINO - SAULTE STE. MARIE
2186 Skunk Rd. • SAULTE STE. MARIE, MI 49783
 (800) 539-2346; (906) 632-0530 Fax 635-9155
 Website: www.kewadinsault.com
Owned by the Sault Ste. Marie Ojibwa (Chippewa) Tribe. *Location*: Upper penninsula on the Canadian border and the International bridge to Ontario. *Facility*: 85,000 sq. ft. with 1,000 slots, video poker & keno & 37 table games; bingo. 52-room hotel. Open 24/7.

SAGANING EAGLES LANDING CASINO
2690 Worth Rd. • STANDISH, MI 48658
 (888) 7-EAGLE-7; Website: www.saganing-eagleslanding.com
Owned by the Saginaw Chippewa Indian Tribe of Michigan. *Location*: On Worth Rd. in Standish, Mich. *Facilities*: 32,000 sq. ft. 800 slots, table games.

LEELANAU SANDS CASINO & BINGO
2521 NW Bayshore Dr. • Sutton Bay, MI 49682
 (800) 922-2WIN; (231) 271-4104 Fax 271-4136

Website: www.casino2win.com
Owned by the Grand Traverse Band of Ottawa & Ojibwe (Chippewa) Indians. *Location*: Lower Peninsula on the coastline of Lake Michigan, 20 miles north of Traverse City minutes from Suttons Bay. *Facilities*: 75,000 sq. ft. with 850 slots, video poker, video keno & 40 table games. The Leelanau Sands Casino Lodge has 51 rooms.

LEELANAU SUPER GAMING PALACE
2649 NW Bayshore Dr. • Sutton Bay, MI 49682
 (800) 922-2WIN; (616) 271-6852 Fax 271-4208
Owned by the Grand Traverse Band of Ottawa & Ojibwe (Chippewa) Indians. *Location*: 4 miles north of Sutton Bay. *Facility*: 6,000 sq. feet. with 437 slots, video poker, video keno & 5 tables.

LAC VIEUX DESERT RESORT CASINO
N5384 US 45, P.O. Box 129 • WATERSMEET, MI 49969
 (800) 583-3599; (906) 358-4226 Fax 358-0288
 Website: www.lvdcasino.com
Owned by the Lac Vieux Desert Band of Lake Superior Chippewa Indians. *Location*: East of U.S. Hwy. 45, just east of Land O' Lakes, Wisconsin. *Facility*: 25,000 sq. ft. 678 slots, video poker & 15 table games. Bingo. Dancing Eagles Hotel with 132 rooms. Open 24/7.

TURTLE CREEK CASINO
7741 M-72 East • WILLIAMSBURG, MI
 (888) 777-UWIN; Website: www.casino2win.com
Owned by the Grand Traverse Band of Ottawa & Chippewa Indians. *Facilities*: 60,000 sq. ft. 1,200 slots, 30 table games, 24 blackjack tables. 83-room hotel.

MINNESOTA

There are 16 Indian gaming facilities operating in Minnesota.
The compact agreements are all based on the National Indian
Gaming Act of 1988. The tribes offer slots, blackjack, and bingo.

BLACK BEAR CASINO RESORT
1785 Hwy. 210 , P.O. Box 777 • CARLTON, MN 55718
 (888) 771-0777; (218) 878-2317 Fax 878-2414
 Website: www.blackbearcasinoresort.com
 E-mail: blackbearcasino@fdlrez.com
Owned by the Fond du Lac Band of Lake Superior Ojibway (Chippewa) Indians. *Location*: 20 mins south of Duluth at intersection of I-35 and Hwy. 210. *Facilities*: 60,000 sq. feet. 1,200 slots, video poker/blackjack/craps, 32 blackjack tables; bingo. 158-room hotel. Open 24/7.

THE PALACE BINGO & CASINO
6280 Upper Cass Frontage Rd. NW • CASS LAKE, MN 56633
 (800) 228-6676; (877) 9-PALACE; (218) 335-6787 Fax 335-6899
 Website: www.palacecasino.com
Owned & operated by the Leech Lake Band of Ojibwe. *Location*: 2.5 miles northwest of Cass Lake; 12 miles east of Bemidji on U.S. Hwy. 2. *Facilities*: 30,000 sq. ft. with 500 slots, video poke & keno, and 6 blackjack tables; 800 seat bingo hall. 80-room hotel. Open 24/7.

WHITE OAK CASINO
45830 U.S. Hwy. 2 • DEER RIVER, MN 56636
 (800) 653-2412; Website: whiteoakcasino.com
Owned & operated by the Leech Lake Band of Ojibwe.
Facilities: 204 slots, blackjack tables.

FOND-DE-LUTH CASINO
129 E. Superior St. • DULUTH, MN 55802
 (800) 873-0280; (218) 722-0280 Fax 722-7505
 Website: www.fondduluthcasino.com
Owned & operated by the Fond du Lac Band of Lake Superior Chippewa. *Location*: Downtown Duluth. *Facilities*: 20,000 sq. ft. 341 slots & 16 table games; bingo hall. Open 24 hours.

GRAND PORTAGE LODGE & CASINO
70 Grand Portage Dr., P.O. Box 233 • GRAND PORTAGE, MN 55605
 (800) 543-1384; (218) 475-2401 Fax 475-2309
 Website: www.grandportage.com
 E-mail: lodgemanager@grandportage.com
 Steven StandingCloud, Enterprise Administrator
 E-mail: scloud@grandportage.com
 Todd DeLack, Casino Manager; E-mail: tdelack@grandportage.com
Owned & operated by the Grand Portage Band of Lake Superior Chippewa. *Location*: On Lake Superior, 5 miles south of the Canadian border on Lake Superior. *Facility*: 15,300 sq. feet. 400 slots & 8 blackjack tables; bingo hall. 100-room hotel. Open 24/7.

PRAIRIE'S EDGE CASINO RESORT
Rt. 2, Box 96 • GRANITE FALLS, MN 56241
 (866) 293-2121; (320) 564-2121 Fax 564-2547
 Website: www.prairiesedgecasino.com
Owned & operated by the Upper Sioux Community. *Location*: On Hwy. 67 miles east of Granite Falls, 130 miles west of Minneapolis. Facility: 24,000 sq. feet. 600 slots, 8 blackjack tables. 89-room hotel. Open 24/7.

TREASURE ISLAND RESORT & CASINO
P.O. Box 75 • RED WING, MN 55066
 (800) 222-7077; (651) 388-6300; E-mail: info@ticasino.com
 Website: www.treasureislandcasino.com
Owned by the Prairie Island Indian Community of Minnesota Mdwekanton Dakota. *Facilities*: 2,500 slots; 44 blackjack tables; 550-seat bingo hall. 800-seat showroom/event center.

GRAND CASINO - HINCKLEY
777 Lady Luck Dr., RR 3 Box 15 • HINCKLEY, MN 55037
 (800) 472-6321; (320) 384-7777 Fax 449-7757
 Website: www.grandcasinosmn.com
Owned & operated by Mille Lacs Band of Ojibwe (Chippewa). *Location*: 76 miles east of Duluth, on Hwy. 48, 1 mile east of I-35. *Facilities*: 140,000 sq. ft.; 2,400 slots; 28 blackjack tables; 388 video poker machines; Events & Convention Center; 281 rooms at the Grand Hinckley Inn. Open 24/7.

SHOOTING STAR CASINO
777 Casino Rd., P.O. Box 418 • MAHNOMEN, MN 56557
 (800) 453-STAR; (218) 935-2711 Fax 935-2701
 Website: www.starcasino.com
Owned & operated by the White Earth Band of Ojibwe (Chippewa) Indians. *Location*: 35 miles north of Detroit Lakes, on U.S. Hwy. 59. *Facilities*: 50,000 sq. ft. 1,300 slots, 150 video poker games, and 32 blackjack tables. 350-room hotel and event center with 1,600-seat capacity. Open 24/7.

JACKPOT JUNCTION CASINO HOTEL
39375 County Road 24, P.O. Box 420 • MORTON, MN 65270
 (800) WIN-CASH; (507) 644-3000 Fax 644-2645
 Website: www.jackpotjunction.com
Owned & operated by the Lower Sioux Indian Community. *Location*: 6 miles east of Redwood Falls, on US Hwy. 71 in southwest Minnesota, 110 miles from Minneapolis/St. Paul. *Facilities*: 440,000 sq. feet. 1,250 slots, keno, 6 poker tables, and 19 blackjack tables; 375-seat bingo hall. 276-room on-site lodge. Open 24/7.

GRAND CASINO - MILLE LACS
777 Grand Ave. • ONAMIA, MN 56359
 (800) 626-5825; (320) 532-7777 Fax 449-5992
 Website: www.grandcasinosmn.com
Owned & operated by Mille Lacs Band of Ojibwe (Chippewa). *Location*: 90 miles north of Minneapolis, on US Hwy. 169, 8 miles south of Garrison. *Facilities*: 130,000 sq. ft. 1,500 slots, 333 video poker & 35 blackjack tables; 350-seat bingo hall. Events & Convention Center; 284-room hotel. Open 24/7.

LITTLE SIX CASINO
2450 Sioux Trail NW • PRIOR LAKE, MN 55372
 (952) 445-8000; Website: www.littlesixcasino.com
Owned & operated by the Shakopee Mdewakanton Sioux Community. *Location*: 25 miles southwest of Minneapolis off I- 35 on the Shakopee Mdewakanton Sioux Reservation. *Facility*: 75,000 sq. ft. 800 slots & 8 blackjack tables; 1,100 seat bingo hall. 600-room hotel. Open 24/7.

MYSTIC LAKE CASINO & HOTEL
2400 Mystic Lake Blvd. • PRIOR LAKE, MN 55372
 (800) 262-7799; (952) 445-9000 Fax 496-7280
 Website: www.mysticlake.com; Leonard Prescott, CEO
Owned & operated by the Shakopee Mdewakanton Sioux Community. *Location*: 25 miles southwest of Minneapolis off I- 35 on the Shakopee Mdewakanton Dakota Reservation. *Facilities*: 375,000 sq. ft. 4,200 slots & 100 blackjack tables; 1,100 seat bingo hall. 600-room hotel. Open 24 hours daily.

SEVEN CLANS CASINO - RED LAKE
P.O. Box 574 • RED LAKE, MN 56671
 (888) 679-2501; (218) 679-2111 Fax 679-2666
 Website: www.sevenclanscasino.com/redlake
Owned & operated by the Red Lake Band of Ojibway (Chippewa) Indians. *Location*: 25 miles north of Bemidji, on Hwy. 1 near Red Lake. *Facilities*: 20,000 sq. feet. 86 slots, 3 blackjack tables; bingo.

SEVEN CLANS CASINO - THIEF RIVER FALLS
20595 Center St. E. • THIEF RIVER FALLS, MN

 (800) 568-6649; (218) 681-4062 Fax 681-8370
 Website: www.sevenclanscasino.com/thiefriverfalls
Owned & operated by the Red Lake Band of Ojibway (Chippewa) Indians. *Location*: County Rd. 3 off Hwy. 59, 8 miles south of Thief River. *Facilities*: 11,800 sq. feet. 750 slots, 8 blackjack tables. 151-suite hotel with 40,000 sq. ft. indoor water park. Open 24 hours, Wed. - Sat.; 8:30 am - 1 am, Sun.-Tues.

FORTUNE BAY RESORT CASINO
1430 Bois Forte Rd. • TOWER, MN 55790
 (800) 992-7529; (218) 753-6400 Fax 753-6404
 Website: www.fortunebay.com; Andy Datko, Manager
Owned & operated by the Bois Forte Band of Ojibway (Chippewa) Indians. *Location*: 5 miles west of Tower, on US Hwy. 169, on Lake Vermilion, on the Bois Forte Reservation. *Facilities*: 116-room resort; 40,000 sq. ft. 700+ machines; poker & blackjack tables; bingo hall. Heritage Center. Open 24/7.

NORTHERN LIGHTS CASINO & HOTEL
6800 Y Frontage Rd. NW • WALKER, MN 56484
 (877) 544-4879; (218) 547-1027 Fax 335-3101
 E-mail: info@northernlightcasino.com; Larry Hanks, General Manager
Owned by the Leech Lake Band of Ojibwe Indians. *Location*: On the Leech Lake Reservation, 4 miles south of Walker at junction of Hwys. 200 & 371. *Facilities*: 14,000 sq. ft. 900 slots & 12 blackjack tables; poker room; 9,000 sq ft. events center opened in 2003. 105-room hotel; 34-site RV Park. Open 24/7.

SEVEN CLANS CASINO - WARROAD
1012 E. Lake St. • WARROAD, MN 56763
 (800) 815-8293; (218) 386-3381 Fax 386-2969
 Website: www.sevenclanscasino.com/warroad
Owned & operated by the Red Lake Band of Ojibway (Chippewa) Indians. *Location*: Off Hwy. 11 at Lake of the Woods, 7 miles south of the Canadian border. *Facilities*: 14,000 sq. feet. 500 slots, video poker, keno, & 10 blackjack tables. 42-room motel.

TREASURE ISLAND RESORT & CASINO
5734 Sturgeon Lake Rd., P.O. Box 75 • WELCH, MN 55066
 (800) 222-7077; (888) 867-STAY
 Website: www.treasureislandcasino.com
 E-mail: info@ticasino.com
 Ed Buck, Executive Director, Gaming Commission
 E-mail: ebuck@piic.org
Owned & operated by Prairie Island Mdewakanton Sioux Tribe. *Location*: 45 miles southeast of St. Paul, 4 Miles south of US Hwy. 61 between Red Wing and Hastings. *Facilities*: 100,000 sq. ft. 1,300 slots & 53 blackjack tables; bingo hall. Open 24 hours daily.

MISSISSIPPI

PEARL RIVER RESORT - SILVER STAR HOTEL & CASINO
GOLDEN MOON HOTEL & CASINO
P.O. Box 6048 • CHOCTAW, MS 39350
 (866) 44-PEARL; (601) 656-3400 Fax 656-1992
 Website: www.pearlriverresort.com
Owned & operated by the Mississippi Choctaw Indians. *Location*: 40 miles north of Meridian on Hwy. 16W. *Facilities*: 40,000 sq. feet. 4,000 slots, 100+ gaming tables. Bingo. 1,000+ hotel rooms. Golf course, water park. Open 24/7.

MONTANA

NORTHERN WINZ CASINO
11031 US Hwy. 87, P.O. Box 3028 • BOX ELDER, MT 59521
 (866) 910-WINZ; (406) 395-5420 Fax 395-5430
 Website: northernwinz.com; Jim Rider, General Manager
Owned by the Rocky Boy Indian Tribe. *Location*: On the Rocky Boy Indian Reservation. *Facilities*: 8,000 sq. ft. with video poker, video keno and bingo. *Publication*: Newsletter.

GLACIER PEAKS CASINO
209 N. Piegan St. • BROWNING, MT 59417
 (406) 338-5751; Website: www.indiancasinos.com
Owned by the Blackfeet Tribe and operated by Siyeh Development, Inc. *Facilities*: 160-seat bingo amd video bingo

APSAALOOKE NIGHTS CASINO
71 Heritage Rd., P.O. Box 609 • CROW AGENCY, MT 59022
 (406) 638-4440; Website: www.apsaalookenightscasino.com
Owned by the Crow Indian Tribe. *Location*: The junction of I-90 and Hwy. 212 at exit 510 in Crow Agency, MT. *Facility*: 200 slots, video poker, video keno, and 200-seat bingo hall.

BIG HORN CASINO
#1 Main St. Parkdale Ct. • FORT SMITH, MT 59035
(406) 666-2449
Owned by the Crow Indian Tribe. *Location*: 55 miles southeast of Billings, on the Big Horn River and US Hwy. 90. *Facility*: 100 slots, video poker, video keno, and 200-seat bingo hall.

CHARGING HORSE CASINO & BINGO
P.O. Box 1259 • LAME DEER, MT 59043
(406) 477-6677; Website: www.indiancasinos.com
Owned by the Northern Cheyenne Indian Tribe. *Location*: Hwy. 212 southeast of Billings. *Facility*: 100 video keno and poker machines, and 500-seat bingo.

GRAY WOLF PEAK CASINO
27050 US Hwy. 93 N. • MISSOULA, MT 59808
(406) 726-3778 Fax 726-3138; Website: www.graywolfpeak.com
Owned by Confederated Salish & Kootenai Tribes of the Flathead Reservation. *Facilities*: 80 slots; poker and keno tables.

KWATAQNUK RESORT & CASINO
303 U.S. Hwy. 93 East • POLSON, MT
(406) 883-3636; Website: www.kwataqnuk.com
Owned by Confederated Salish & Kootenai Tribes of the Flathead Reservation. *Facilities*: 46 poker and keno tables. 112-room hotel; 350-seat meeting hall.

NEBRASKA

IRON HORSE CASINO
1010 S. Main St. • EMERSON, NE
Website: www.winnebagocasinos.com
Owned & operated by the Winnebago Tribe of Nebraska. *Facilities*: 54 gaming machines.

OHIYA CASINO
52946 Hwy. 12 #2 • NIOBRARA, NE 68760
(402) 857-2302 Fax 857-2393
Website: www.ohiyacasino.com
Owned by the Santee Sioux Tribe of Nebraska

NATIVE STAR CASINO
Hwy. 77 • WINNEBAGO, NE 68071
Owned & operated by the Winnebago Tribe of Nebraska. *Facilities*: 30 gaming machines.

NEVADA

AVI RESORT & CASINO
10000 Aha Macav Pkwy. • LAUGHLIN, NV
(800) 430-0721; (702) 535-5555 Fax 535-5514
Website: www.avicasino.com; E-mail: info@avicasino.com
Owned & operated by the Fort Mojave Tribe. *Facilities*: 25,000 sq. ft. 800 slots, 20 tables, keno lounge, bingo. 455-room hotel & spa.

NEW MEXICO

SKY CITY CASINO
Pueblo of Acoma, P.O. Box 310 • ACOMA, NM 87034
(800) 747-0181; (505) 552-6017 Fax 552-9256
Website: www.skycitycasino.com
Owned by the Pueblo of Acoma. *Location*: 55 miles west of Albuquerque on I-40 exit 102. *Facilities*: 600 slots, video poker, video keno, poker tables. 134-room hotel. Open 24/7.

ISLETA CASINO & RESORT
Pueblo of Isleta, 11000 Broadway SE • ALBUQUERQUE, NM 87105
(800) 843-5156; (505) 724-3800; Website: www.isleta-casino.com
Owned by the Pueblo of Isleta. *Location*: Exit 215 south on I-15 in Albuquerque. *Facilities*: 100,000 sq. ft. 1,700 slots, 300 video poker, 48 blackjack tables, 24 poker tables. Golf course & showroom.

SANDIA CASINO
Pueblo of Sandia, 30 Rainbow Rd, NE • ALBUQUERQUE, NM 87184
(800) 526-9366; (505) 897-2173 Fax 897-1117
Website: www.sandiacasino.com
Owned by the Pueblo of Sandia. *Location*: On I-25 & Ramsey Rd. 8 miles north of downtown Albuquerque nestled between the base of the Sandia Mountains and the Rio Grande River. *Facility*: 140,000 sq. feet with 2,100 slots, video poker, 15 poker tables, 28 blackjack tables; keno, high stakes bingo. Outdoor amphitheater. Open 24/7.

SANTA ANA STAR CASINO
Pueblo of Santa Ana, 54 Jemez Dam Canyon • BERNALILLO, NM 87004
(505) 867-0000 Fax 867-1472; Website: www.santaanastar.com
Owned by Santa Ana Pueblo. *Location*: Off I-25, 17 miles north of Albuquerque. *Facility*: 20,000 sq. ft. VIdeo slots, video poker; live poker. Open 24/7.

DANCING EAGLE CASINO
P.O. Box 520 • CASA BLANCA, NM 87007
(877) 440-9969; (505) 552-7777
Owned by the Pueblo of Laguna and the Laguna Development Corp. *Location*: I-40 exit 108, 40 minutes west of Albuquerque and 20 minutes east of Grants. *Facilities*: 25,000 sq. ft. with 500 slots, table games.

APACHE NUGGET CASINO
P.O. Box 219 • CUBA, NM 87013
(505) 289-2486 Fax 289-2337
Owned by the Jicarilla Apache Nation. *Location*: On Hwy. 64, near the Colorado border, 150 miles northwest of Santa Fe. *Facilities*: Video slots, video poker, live poker, blackjack, roulette & craps. Best Western Jicarilla Inn nearby. Open 24/7.

WILD HORSE CASINO
P.O. Box 650 • DULCE, NM 87528
(505) 759-3663 Fax 759-3170
Owned by the Jicarilla Apache Nation.

CASINO APACHE TRAVEL CENTER
Carrizo Canyon Rd., P.O. Box 205 • MESCALERO, NM 88340
(877) 277-5677; Website: www.innofthemountaingods.com
Owned by the Mescalero Apache Tribe.

INN OF THE MOUNTAIN GODS RESORT & CASINO
287 Carrizo Canyon Rd.
P.O. Box 269 • MESCALERO, NM 88340
(800) 545-9011; (575) 464-7777
(575) 257-5241 Fax 257-6173
Website: www.innofthenountaingods.com
Owned by the Mescalero Apache Tribe. *Location*: On I- 70, 26 miles northeast of Alamogordo. *Facilities*: 200 video slots, video poker, video keno, live poker, blackjack tables. Open 24/7.

CASINO HOLLYWOOD
Pueblo of San Felipe, 25 Hagan Rd. • SAN FELIPE PUEBLO, NM 87001
(877) 529-2946; (505) 867-6700
Website: www.sanfelipecasino.com
E-mail: info@sanfelipecasino.com
Owned by the Pueblo of San Felipe. *Location*: Between Albuquerque and Santa Fe on I-25, exit 252. *Facilities*: 100,000 sq. ft. 700 slots, gaming tables; 1,250-seat celebrity showroom. Open 24/7.

OH KAY CASINO & RESORT
P.O. Box 1270 • SAN JUAN PUEBLO, NM 87566
(877) 829-2865; (505) 747-1668 Fax 852-4026
Website: www.ohkaycasinoresort.com
Owned by the Pueblo of Ohkay Owingeh. *Location*: 2 miles north of Espanola Hwy. 28 miles north of Santa Fe nestled between the Sangre de Cristo and Jemez Mountains. *Facilities*: 80,000 sq. ft. with 575 video slots & video poker; blackjack, poker, bingo. 101-room hotel. Open 24/7.

CAMEL ROCK GAMING
Pueblo of Tesuque, Rt. 11, Box 3A • SANTA FE, NM 87501
(800) 462-2635; (505) 984-8414 Fax 989-9234
Website: www.camelrockcasino.com
Owned by the Pueblo of Tesuque. *Location*: 10 miles north of Santa Fe. *Facilities*: 60,000 sq. feet. 600 gaming devices, video slots, video poker, live poker; bingo. Open 24/7.

CITIES OF GOLD CASINO
Pueblo of Pajoaque, Rt. 11, Box 21-B • SANTA FE, NM 87501
(800) 455-3363; (505) 455-3313 Fax 455-7188
Website: www.citiesofgold.com
Owned by Pueblo of Pojoaque. *Location*: Located just outside Santa Fe. *Facilities*: 60,000 sq. ft. with video slots, video poker, video keno, video blackjack, live poker, and bingo. Open 24 hours daily.

TAOS MOUNTAIN CASINO
Pueblo of Taos, P.O. Box 777 • TAOS, NM 87571
(505) 758-4460 Fax 751-0578; Website: www.taosmountaincasino.com
Owned by Taos Pueblo. *Location*: 70 miles north of Santa Fe. *Facilities*: Video slots and video poker only. Open 24/7.

NEW YORK

AKWESASNE MOHAWK CASINO
St. Regis Indian Reservation, Rt. 37
P.O. Box 670 • AKWESASNE, NY 13655
 (877) 992-2746; (518) 358-2222 Fax 358-3203
 Website: www.mohawkcasino.com
Owned and operated by the St. Regis Mohawk Indian Tribe. Location: in Massena, NY about 50 miles southwest of Montreal. *Facilities*: 50,000 sq. ft. 280 slots, 35 table games: dice, roulette and card games; Bingo Palace.

MOHAWK BINGO PALACE & CLASS II CASINO
202 State Route 37, P.O. Box 720 • AKWESASNE, NY 13655
 (866) 452-5768; (518) 358-2246 Fax 358-2249
 Website: www.mohawkpalace.com

SENECA ALLEGANY CASINO
725 Broad St. • SALAMANCA, NY 14779
 (716) 945-3200; Website: www.senecaalleganycasino.com

SENECA NIAGARA CASINO
310 Fourth St. • NIAGARA FALLS, NY 14303
 (877) 873-6322; (716) 299-1100
 Website: www.senecaniagaracasino.com
Owned & operated by the Seneca Nation. *Location*: Just blocks from the Niagara Falls. *Facilities*: 105,000 sq. ft. casino with 2,900 slots, 114 gaming tables. 426-seat showroom-style theater.

TURNING STONE RESORT & CASINO
5218 Patrick Rd., P.O. Box 126 • Verona, NY 13478
 (800) 771-7711; (315) 361-7711 Fax 361-7901
 Website: www.turning-stone.com
Owned by the Oneida Indian Nation. *Location*: Upstate New York, 35 miles east of Syracuse off Hwy. I-90. *Facilities*: 95,000 sq. ft. Table games; 1,600 seat bingo hall; spa & 5,000-seat, events center; 98-room hotel. Golf course.

NORTH CAROLINA

HARRAH'S CHEROKEE SMOKEY MOUNTAIN CASINO
777 Casino Dr. • CHEROKEE, NC 28719
 (828) 497-7777 Fax 497-5076; Website: www.cherokee-wnc.com
Owned by the Eastern Band of Cherokee Indians. *Location*: 35 miles southeast of Ashville, NC at the base of the Great Smoky Mountains. *Facilities*: 50,000 sq. ft. with 2,300 video slots, 800 multi-game machines. No table games. High stakes bingo. 1,500-seat Pavillion Theater

NORTH DAKOTA

SKY DANCER CASINO & RESORT
P.O. Box 1449, Hwy. 5 W • BELCOURT, ND 58316
 (866) BIG-WINS; (701) 477-3281; Website: www.skydancercasino.com
Owned by the Turtle Mountain Band of Chippewa Indians. *Location*: On Hwy. 281 & Hwy. 5 W, 8 miles west of Belcourt in north central North Dakota near the Canadian border. *Facilities*: 25,000 sq. ft. with 417 slots & 10 blackjack and 4 poker tables; bingo. 200-room hotel. Open 24/7.

PRAIRIE KNIGHTS CASINO & RESORT
1806 Hwy. 24 • FORT YATES, ND 58538
 (800) 425-8277; (701) 854-7777 Fax 854-7785
Owned & operated by the Standing Rock Sioux Tribe. *Location*: In south central North Dakota on the Standing Rock Reservation, south of Bismarck on the Missouri River, 44 miles south of Mandan. *Facilities*: 75,000 sq. feet. 600 slots, high-stakes blackjack & gaming tables, video poker & keno. Convention & meeting center and entertainment facility. Open 24/7.

4 BEARS CASINO & LODGE
P.O. Box 579 • NEW TOWN, ND 58763
 (800) 294-5454; (701) 627-4018 Fax 627-4012
 Website: www.4bearcasino.com
Owned by the Three Affiliated Tribes - Mandan, Hidatsa & Arikara. *Location*: 4 miles west of New Town on Hwy. 23 & Lake Sakakawea, part of the Missouri River. *Facilities*: 30,000 sq. feet. 500 reel slots, blackjack tables, roulette & poker tables; 1 crap table; bingo; 97-room lodge.

DAKOTA MAGIC CASINO & HOTEL
16849 102ND ST. SE • HANKINSON, ND 58370
 (800) 325-6825; (701) 634-3000; Website: www.dakotamagic.com
Owned & operated by the Sisseton-Wahpeton Oyate Tribe. *Location*: On I-29, Exit 1 on border of South Dakota. *Facilities*: 50,000 sq. ft. casino with 700 slots & table games; bingo. Hotel & convention center. Golf course. Open 24/7.

SPIRIT LAKE CASINO & RESORT
7889 Hwy. 57 • ST. MICHAEL, ND 58370
 (800) WIN-U-BET; (701) 766-4747 Fax 766-1507
 Website: www.spiritlakecasino.com
 E-mail: chalgren@spiritlakecasino.com
 Mary Ketterling, General Manager
Owned by the Spirit Lake Nation Sioux Tribe. *Location*: Six miles south of Devil's Lake on Hwy. 57. *Facilities*: 40,000 sq. ft. with 600+ slots, video poker, gaming tables, three restaurants; 124-room hotel; full service marina; entertainment complex.

OKLAHOMA

ADA GAMING CENTER
1500 N. Country Club Rd. • ADA, OK 74820
 (580) 436-3740; Website: www.thepokeratlas.com
Owned by the Chickasaw Nation of Oklahoma.

GOLD RIVER BINGO & CASINO
P.O. Box 806 • ANADARKO, OK 73005
 (866) 499-3054; (405) 247-6979
Owned by the Apache Tribe of Oklahoma. *Location*: 2 miles north of Anadarko on Hwy. 281. *Facilities*: 250 slots; gaming tables. 300-seat bingo hall.

CHOCTAW CASINO-BROKEN BOW
1790 S. Park Dr., P.O. Box 487 • BROKEN BOW, OK 74728
 (580) 584-5450 Fax 584-5427; Website: www.choctawcasinos.com
Owned by the Choctaw Tribe of Oklahoma.
Facilities: Slots, gaming tables; bingo hall.

FEATHER WARRIOR CASINO
301 NW Lake Rd. • CANTON, OK 73724
 (580) 886-2490 Fax 886-2495; Gloria Smith, General Manager
Owned by the Cheyenne & Arapaho Tribes of Oklahoma.

CHEROKEE BINGO & CASINO
I44 & 193rd St. • CASTOOSA, OK
 (800) 760-6700; Website: www.cherokeecasino.com
Owned by the Cherokee Tribe of Oklahoma.
Facilities: Slots, gaming tables; bingo hall.

LUCKY STAR CASINO
101 N. Indian Hospital Rd. • CLINTON, OK 73022
 (580) 323-6599 Fax 323-3822; Website: www.thepokeratlas.com
 Samuel Barnett, General Manager
Owned by the Cheyenne & Arapaho Tribes of Oklahoma. *Location*: Located just off I-40 in Clinton, the only western Oklahoma casino. *Facilities*: 15,000 sq. ft. casino with over 400 Vegas-style games.

LUCKY STAR CASINO
7777 N. Hwy. 81 • CONCHO, OK 73022
 (405) 262-7612 Fax 262-4429
 Website: www.thepokeratlas.com
 Chris Derenzo, General Manager
Owned by the Cheyenne & Arapaho Tribes of Oklahoma. *Location*: 20 miles northwest of Oklahoma City. *Facilities*: 40,000 sq. ft. casino with 1,000+ Vegas-style themed games, blackjack and poker; high-stakes bingo; blackjack tables.

COMANCHE RED RIVER CASINO
Rt. 1 42 K • DEVOL, OK 73531
 (866) 280-3261; (580) 299-3370 Fax 299-3422
 Website: www.comancheredrivercasino.com
 Warren Mason, General Manager
Owned by the Comanche Nation. *Facilities*: More than 1,000 gaming machines; poker tables. Open 24/7.

KIOWA CASINO
SH 36, E. 1980 Rd., P.O. Box 100 • DEVOL, OK 73531
 (866) 370-4077; (580) 299-3333
 Website: www.kiowacasino777.com
Owned by the Kiowa Tribe of Oklahoma.
Facility: 900 slots; 20 table games; bingo. Open 24 hours.

CHOCTAW CASINO RESORT HOTEL
4202 S. Hwy. 69/75, P.O. Box 1909 • DURANT, OK 74702
 (800) 788-2464; (580) 931-8340 Fax 920-0864
 Darla Emerson, Director; Website: www.choctawinn.com
Owned by the Choctaw Tribe of Oklahoma. *Facilities*: Slots, gaming tables; bingo hall.

COMANCHE SPUR CASINO
9047 US Hwy. 62 • RR1 Box 4200 • ELGIN, OK 773538
(580) 492-5502 Fax 492-4020; Website: www.comanchespur.com
Owned by the Comanche Nation. *Facilities*: 140 slot machines; smoke shop.

CHOCTAW CASINO - GRANT
Rt. 1 Box 17-1 • GRANT, OK 74738
(580) 326-8397 Fax 326-3245; Website: www.choctawcasinos.com
Owned by the Choctaw Tribe of Oklahoma. *Facilities*: Slots, gaming tables; bingo hall.

GRAND LAKE CASINO & RESORT
24701 South 655th Road • GROVE, OK 74344
(800) 426-4640; (918) 786-8528; Sandra Slaughter, Compliance Officer
Owned by the Seneca-Cayuga Tribe. *Facilities*: 100,000 sq. feet. 1,200 slots, 18 table games.

CHOCTAW CASINO - IDABEL
1425 SE Washington • IDABEL, OK 74702
(800) 634-2582; (580) 286-5710 Fax 286-7239
Website: www.choctawcasinos.com
Owned by the Choctaw Tribe of Oklahoma. *Facilities*: Slots, gaming tables; bingo hall.

COMANCHE NATION CASINO
402 SE I-44, P.O. Box 347 • LAWTON, OK 73502
(866) 354-2500; (580) 354-2000; Website: www.comanchenationcasino.com
Owned by the Comanche Nation. *Publication*: Newsletter. Open 24/7.

CHOCTAW CASINO - McALESTER
1638 S. George Nigh Expwy. • McALESTER, OK 74501
(877) 904-8444; (918) 423-8161 Fax 423-7938
Website: www.choctawcasinos.com
Owned by the Choctaw Tribe of Oklahoma.
Facilities: Slots, gaming tables; bingo hall.

BUFFALO RUN CASINO
P.O. Box 231 • MIAMI, OK 74354
(918) 542-7140 Fax 542-7160; Website: www.buffalorun.com
Owned & operated by the Peoria Tribe of Indians. *Facilities*: 70,000 sq. feet of slots and gaming tables.

HIGH WINDS CASINO
61475 East 100 Road • MIAMI, OK 74354
(918) 541-9463; Website: www.ottawatribe.org/casino.htm
Frank Haas, General Manager
Owned & operated by the Ottawa Tribe of Oklahoma.

QUAPAW CASINO
58100 E. 64th Rd. • MIAMI, OK 74354
(918) 540-9100; Website: www.quapawcasino.com
Owned by the Quapaw Tribe. *Location*: Located 4 miles south of Quapaw on US 69. *Facilities*: Slots, poker, blackjack.

FIRST COUNCIL CASINO
12875 North Hwy. 77 • NEWKIRK, OK 74647
(877) 725-2670; Website: www.myfirstwin.com/firstcouncil
Owned by the Otoe-Missouria Tribe. *Location*: Located north of Newkirk and two miles south of Arkansas City. *Facilities*: 900 slots; 8 table games; poker room. Open 24/7.

NATIVE LIGHTS CASINO
12375 North Hwy. 77 • NEWKIRK, OK 74647
(877) 468-3100; (580) 448-3100; Website: www.nativelightscasino.com
E-mail: info@nativelightscasino.com
Owned by the Tonkawa Tribe of Oklahoma. *Facilities*: 16,000 sq. feet. 600 slots, 6 blackjack tables; poker tables. Open 24 hours.

SOUTHWIND CASINO & BINGO
5640 LaCann Dr., P.O. Box 171 • NEWKIRK, OK 74647
(866) 529-2464; (580) 362-2578 Fax 362-2726
Website: www.kawnationcasino.com
Owned by the Kaw Nation. *Facilities*: 22,000 sq. feet. 450 slots, 10 table games, 600 bingo seats.

THUNDERBIRD WILD WILD WEST CASINO
15700 E. State Hwy. 9 • NORMAN, OK 73071
(800) 259-5825; (405) 360-9270
Owned by the Absentee Shawnee Tribe of Oklahoma. *Location*: A few miles south of Oklahoma City. *Facilities*: 800 touch screen video gaming machines; high-stake bingo.

GOLDSBY GAMING CENTER
1038W. Sycamore Rd. • NORMAN, OK 73072
(405) 329-7892 Fax 321-7892; Website: www.chickasaw.net
Owned by the Chickasaw Tribe. *Facilities*: 15,462 sq. feet. 182 video gaming machines; 300-seat bingo. Open daily 8 a.m. to 6 a.m.

CREEK NATION CASINO OKEMAH
110 S. Woody Guthrie • OKEMAH, OK 74859
(918) 623-0051 Fax 623-0330
Web: www.creeknationcasin.com/okemah/index.html
Owned by the Thlopthlocco Tribal Town. *Facilities*: 1,800 sq. feet. 132 gaming machines; 110 seat bingo.

CREEK NATION OKMULGEE BINGO
P.O. Box 790 • OKMULGEE, OK 74447
Website: www.creeknationcasino.com

TRADING POST CASINO
P.O. Box 470 • PAWNEE, OK 74058
(918) 762-3621 Fax 762-6446
Website: www.tradingpostcasino.com
Website: www.pawneenationcasino.com
Owned & operated by the Pawnee Nation of Oklahoma.
Facilities: 90 slots and table games. Open 24/7.

CIMARRON BINGO CASINO
821 W. Freeman Ave. • PERKINS, OK 74059
(800) 522-4700; (405) 547-5352; Website: www.cimarroncasino.com
E-mail: info@cimarroncasino.com

CHOCTAW CASINO - POCOLA
3400 Choctaw Rd. • POCOLA, OK 74901
(800) 590-5825; (918) 436-7761 Fax 436-7606
Website: www.choctawcasinos.com
Owned by the Choctaw Tribe of Oklahoma.
Facilities: Slots, gaming tables; bingo hall. Open 24/7.

TWO RIVERS CASINO
101 White Eagle Dr. • PONCA CITY, OK 74601
(580) 762-3901 Fax 762-7563
Owned by the Ponca Tribe of Indians of Oklahoma. *Facilities*: Electronic games, from poker to slots.

7 CLANS PARADISE CASINO
7500 Hwy. 177 • RED ROCK, OK 74651
(580) 723-4005; Website: www.okparadisecasino.com
Owned by the Otoe-Missouria Tribe. *Location*: Located 20 miles north of Stillwater, Okla. *Facilities*: Slots, gaming machines. *Activities*: Annual tribal powwow 3rd weekend in July. Open 24/7.

CHEROKEE BINGO & CASINO
P.O. Box 1000 • ROLAND, OK 74954
(800) 256-2338; Website: www.cherokeecasino.com
Owned by the Cherokee Tribe of Oklahoma.
Facilities: Slots, gaming tables; bingo hall.

FIRELAKE GRAND CASINO
777 Grand Casino Blvd. • SHAWNEE, OK 74804
(405) 96-GRAND; Website: www.firelakegrand.com
Owned by the Citizen Band Potawatomi Tribe. *Facilities*: 125,000 square feet of gaming space with 100 table games including blackjack, poker, craps; 1,800 slots; bingo hall. Open 24/7.

SAC & FOX NATION CASINO
42008 W. Tech Rd. • SHAWNEE, OK 74804
(405) 275-4700; Website: www.oksacandfoxcasino.com
Owned and operated by the Sac & Fox Nation of Oklahoma.
Facilities: 8,600 sq. feet. 460 gaming machines, poker, blackjack. Open 24/7.

CHEROKEE BINGO & CASINO
U.S. Hwy. 412 & OK Hwy. 59 • SILOAM SPRINGS, OK 74954
(800) 754-4111; Website: www.cherokeecasino.com
Owned by the Cherokee Tribe of Oklahoma.
Facilities: Slots, gaming tables; bingo hall.

CHOCTAW CASINO - STRINGTOWN
895 N. Hwy. 69, P.O. Box 250 • STRINGTOWN, OK 74569
(580) 346-7862 Fax 346-7875; Website: www.choctawcasinos.com
Owned by the Choctaw Tribe of Oklahoma. *Facilities*: Slots, gaming tables; bingo hall.

SULPHUR GAMING CENTER
West First & Muskogee • SULPHUR, OK 73086

UNITED KEETOOWAH CASINO
2450 S. Muskogee Ave. • TAHLEQUAH, OK 74465
 (918) 456-6131; Website: www.keetowahgaming.com

TOUSO ISHTO GAMING CENTER
P.O. Box 149 • THACKERVILLE, OK 73459

CREEK NATION TULSA BINGO
P.O. Box 700833 • TULSA, OK 74170

COMANCHE STAR CASINO
Rt. 3 Box 82A • WALTERS, OK 73572
 (580) 875-3208
Owned by the Comanche Nation. *Facilities*: 33,000 sq. feet
with 176 gaming machines. Smoke shop.

FEATHER WARRIOR CASINO
1407 S. Clarence Nas • WATONGA, OK 73772
 (580) 623-7333 Fax 623-7403; Gloria Smith, General Manager
Owned by the Cheyenne & Arapaho Tribes of Oklahoma.

BORDERTOWN BINGO & CASINO
129 West Oneida St., P.O. Box 350 • WEST SENECA, OK 74370
 (800) 957-2435; (918) 666-9401; Website: www.bordertownbingo.com
Owned & operated by the Eastern Shawnee Tribe of Oklahoma.

INDIGO SKY CASINO
70220 East Hwy. 60 • WYANDOTTE, OK 74370
 (888) 992-SKY1; Website: www.indigoskycasino.com
Owned & operated by the Eastern Shawnee Tribe of Oklahoma.
Facilities: Hotel & RV Park; table games, poker, video games; bingo.

WYANDOTTE NATION CASINO
100 Jackpot Place • WYANDOTTE, OK 74370
 (866) 447-4946; (918) 678-4946; Website: www.wyandottecasinos.com
Owned & operated by the Wyandotte Nation.

OREGON

THE OLD CAMP CASINO
2205 W. Monroe • BURNS, OR 97720
 (888) 343-7568; (541) 573-1500 Fax 573-3963
 Website: www.oldcampcasino.net; Pamela Sherburn, General Manager
Owned by the Burns Paiute Tribe.

SEVEN FEATHERS CASINO RESORT
146 Chief Miwaleta Ln. • CANYONVILLE, OR 97417
 (800) 548-8461; (541) 839-1111 Fax 839-4300
 Website: www.sevenfeathers.com; Peter Ingenito, General Manager
Owned by the Cow Creek Band of Umpqua Tribe of Indians of Oregon.
Location: In southern Oregon at exit 99 on I-5, north of Medford and south of
Eugene. *Facility*: 29,000 sq. ft. 1,000 slots, video poker, blackjack & poker
tables; video keno; bingo. 146-room hotel. 22,000 sq. ft. convention center.
Open 24/7.

KLA-MO-YA CASINO CORP.
3433 Hwy.97 North • CHILOQUIN, OR 97624
 (888) 552-6692; (541) 783-7529 Fax 783-7543
 Website: www.klamoyacasino.com
Owned by the Klamath Tribes of Oregon.

THREE RIVERS CASINO & HOTEL
5647 Highway 126 • FLORENCE, OR 97439
 (877) 374-8377 (541) 997-7529 Fax 997-4802
 Website: www.threeriverscasino.com
Owned & operated by the Confederated Tribes of Coos, Lower Umpqua
& Suislaw Indians.

SPIRIT MOUNTAIN CASINO & RESORT
27100 SW Salmon River Hwy.
P.O. Box 39 • GRANDE RONDE, OR 97347
 (800) 760-7977; (503) 879-2350 Fax 879-2486
 Website: www.spirit-mountain.com
Owned by the Confederated Tribes of the Grand Ronde Community. Location:
In northwest Oregon, on Hwy. 16, 60 miles southwest of Portland. Facility:
60,000 sq. feet. 800 slots, 85 video poker, 36 blackjack and poker tables,
keno; bingo. Open 24/7.

CHINOOK WINDS CASINO
1777 NW 40th St. • LINCOLN CITY, OR 97367
 (888) 244-6665; (541) 996-5825 Fax 996-5491
 Website: www.chinookwindscasino.com
Owned by the Confederated Tribes of Siletz Indians of Oregon. *Location*: On
the Pacific Ocean Hwy. 101, 80 miles southwest of Portland. *Facilities*: 1,350
slots, blackjack and poker tables, keno; bingo. 20,000 sq. ft. convention center.
Open 24/7.

THE MILL CASINO
3201 Tremont • NORTH BEND, OR 97429
 (800) 953-4800; (541) 756-8800 Fax 756-0431
 Website: www.themillcasino.com
 Calvin Mukumoto, Chairperson & CEO; Larry Close, General Manager
Owned by the Coquille Indian Tribe of Oregon. *Location*: On Pacific Coast
Hwy. 101 Oregon's southwest coast. *Facilities*: 250 video slots, blackjack &
poker tables, keno; 1,200-seat bingo hall. Open 24/7.

WILDHORSE RESORT & CASINO
72777 Hwy. 331• PENDLETON, OR 97801
 (800) 654-9453; (541) 278-2274 Fax 276-3873
 Website: www.wildhorseresort.com
 E-Mail: info@wildhorseresort.com
 Al Tory, General Manager; Gary E. George, COO
Owned by the Confederated Tribes of the Umatilla Indians of Oregon.
Location: In northeast Oregon, 5 miles east of Pendleton at exit 216 on I-84.
Facilities: 40,000 sq. ft. casino with 650 slots; poker, blackjack, craps, roulette
table games; 800 seat high stakes bingo; 100-room hotel; 20,000 sq. ft.
conference & entertainment center; RV Park & Museum. *Activities*: Annual
October hot air balloon festival; powwow over July 4th weekend.

KAH-NEE-TA HIGH DESERT RESORT & CASINO
P.O. Box 1240 • WARM SPRINGS, OR 97761
 (800) 554-4SUN; (541) 553-6123
 Website: www.kahneetaresort.com
 Willy Fuentes & Orthelia Patt, Commissioners
Owned by Confederated Tribes of Warm Springs Reservation of Oregon.
Location: 6823 Hwy. 8, in north central Oregon on US Hwy. 25, 95 miles
southeast of Portland. *Facilities*: 139-room hotel; 25,000 sq. ft. with 300 slot
machines, video poker & keno, blackjack & poker tables. 675-people theatre;
banquet rooms.

SOUTH DAKOTA

ROYAL RIVER CASINO & HOTEL
607 S. Veterans St., P.O. Box 326 • FLANDREAU, SD 57028
 (800) 833-8666; (605) 997-3746 Fax 997-9998
 Website: www.royalrivercasino.com; Sherry Kriescher, General Manager
Owned by the Flandreau Santee Sioux Tribe. *Location*: On the Santee Sioux
Reservation, 7 miles off I-29, Exit 114, 35 miles north of Sioux Falls. *Facilities*:
15,000 sq. feet. 240 slots, blackjack & poker tables. Bingo. Hotel. Open 24/7.

LODE STAR CASINO
P.O. Box 140 • FORT THOMPSON, SD 57339
 (605) 245-6000 Fax 245-2240; Website: www.lodestar.com
Owned by the Crow Creek Sioux Tribe. Location: 50 miles southeast of Pierre
on Hwy. 35 & 47. *Facilities*: 13,000 sq. ft. 244 slots, blackjack & poker tables.

GOLDEN BUFFALO CASINO & RESORT
321 Sitting Bull St., P.O. Box 204 • LOWER BRULE, SD 57548
 (605) 473-5577; Website: www.lbst.org/casino.htm
Owned & operated by the Lower Brule Sioux Tribe. *Location*: 45 miles
southeast of Pierre, on the Lower Brule Sioux Reservation. *Facility*: 9,000 sq.
ft. with 175 slots & 15 table games. 38-room motel.

ROSEBUD CASINO
P.O. Box 21 • MISSION, SD 57642
 (800) 786-7673; (605) 378-3800; Website: www.rosebudcasino.com
Owned by the Rosebud Sioux Tribe. Location: In south central SD, 18 miles
north of the Nebraska border, 22 miles south of Mission, SD on Hwy. 83.
Facility: 7,000 sq. ft. Slots, video poker, blackjack and poker tables. 60-room
hotel & event center featuring music, powwows and rodeos. Open 24/7.

GRAND RIVER CASINO
P.O. Box 639 • MOBRIDGE, SD 57601
 (800) 475-3321; (605) 845-7104 Fax 845-3090
 Website: www.grandrivercasino.com
Owned by the Standing Rock Sioux Tribe. *Location*: On the Missouri River in
north central SD. *Facility*: 20,000 sq. ft. 250 slots, video poker, blackjack &
poker tables.

PRAIRIE WIND CASINO
HC 49, Box 10 • PINE RIDGE, SD 57770
(800) 705-9463; (605) 867-6300
Website: www.216.245.184.23/prairiewind/
Owned by the Oglala Sioux Tribe. *Location*: Just north of the Nebraska border in southwest SD on Hwy. 18 between Oglala and Oelrichs. *Facility*: Slots, video poker, blackjack and poker tables.

DAKOTA CONNECTION CASINO
I-29 & Hwy. 10, Veterans Memorial Dr.
P.O. Box 569 • SISSETON, SD 57262
(800) 542-2876; (605) 698-4273 Fax 698-4271
Website: www.dakotaconnection.net
Owned & operated by the Sisseton-Wahpeton Oyate Sioux Tribe of South Dakota. *Location*: In northeastern SD, 3 miles west of I-29 on Hwy. 10. *Facility*: 20,000 sq. ft. 50 slots, video poker, blackjack & poker tables; bingo.

FORT RANDALL CASINO HOTEL
Highway 46 West • WAGNER, SD 57380
RR 1, Box 100 • LAKE ANDES, SD 57356
(800) 553-3003; (605) 487-7871 Fax 487-7354
Website: www.fortrandallcasino.com
Sam Weddel & Raymond Stone, Contacts
Owned & operated by the Yankton Sioux Tribe. *Location*: Hwy. 46, in East Pickstown, 50 miles west of Yankton on the Missouri River near the Nebraska border. *Facility*: 24,000 sq. ft. 250 slots, video poker, blackjack & poker tables; 150-seat bingo. 57-room hotel. Open 24/7.

DAKOTA SIOUX CASINO
16415 Sioux Conifer Rd. • WATERTOWN, SD 57201
(605) 882-2051; (800) 658-4717; Website: www.dakotasioux.com
Wiley Shepher, Contact
Owned by Sisseton-Wahpeton Oyate Sioux Tribe of South Dakota. *Location*: In northeast SD on I-29, 32 miles from the Minnesota border. *Facility*: 7,400 sq. ft. 250 slots, poker & blackjack tables. Open 24/7.

TEXAS

SPEAKING ROCK CASINO
122 S. Old Pueblo • EL PASO, TX 79907
(915) 860-7777
Owned by the Ysleta Del Sur Pueblo Tribe. *Location*: In west Texas on the Rio Grande River. *Facility*: Slots & tables; bingo. Open 24/7.

KICKAPOO LUCKY EAGLE CASINO
7777 Lucky Eagle Dr. • EAGLE PASS, TX 78852
(210) 758-1995; Website: www.kickapooluckyeaglecasino.com
Owned by the Kickapoo Tribe of Texas. *Location*: In south Texas on the Rio Grande River. *Facility*: Slots, tables, poker, bingo.

WASHINGTON

NORTHERN QUEST CASINO
100 N. Hayford Rd., P.O. Box 1300 • AIRWAY HEIGHTS, WA 99001
(888) 603-7051; (509) 242-7000; Website: www.northernquest.net
Owned by Kalispel Indian Community of the Kalispel Reservation. *Facilities*: 625 slots; 30 live table games; keno and poker room.

SWINOMISH NORTHERN LIGHTS CASINO
12885 Casino Dr., P.O. Box 628 • ANACORTES, WA 98221
(800) 293-9344; (360) 293-2691 Fax 273-1273
Website: www.swinomishcasino.com; Claudine Bruner, Contact
Owned by the Swinomish Tribal Community. *Location*: Off Hwy. 20, nine miles west of I-5 along Skagit Bay in northwest Washington. *Facilities*: 63,000 sq. ft. with blackjack, craps, roulette & poker tables.

ANGEL OF THE WINDS CASINO
3438 Stoluckguamish Lane • ARLINGTON, WA 98223
(877) EXIT 210; (360) 474-9740 Fax 474-9773
Website: www.angelofthewinds.com; Travis O'Neill, General Manager
Owned & operated by Stillaguamish Tribe of Indians. *Location*: Exit 210 on I-5

MUCKLESHOOT INDIAN CASINO
2402 Auburn Way South, P.O. Box 795 • AUBURN, WA 98002
(800) 804-4944; (206) 804-4444 Fax 939-7702
Website: www.muckleshootcasino.com
Owned & operated by the Muckleshoot Indian Tribe. *Location*: On Hwy. 164 in western Washington, between Seattle & Tacoma off I-5. *Facility*: 95,000 sq. ft. with 2,000 slots, 70 blackjack, craps, roulette and poker tables; bingo.

MUCKLESHOOT CASINO II
2600 Auburn Way South • AUBURN, WA 98002
(800) 804-4944; (206) 804-4444 Fax 939-7702
Website: www.muckleshootcasino.com

MUCKLESHOOT INDIAN BINGO
2117 Auburn Way South • AUBURN, WA 98002
(800) 804-4944; (206) 735-2404 Fax 735-0384
Website: www.muckleshootcasino.com

SILVER REEF HOTEL, CASINO & SPA
4876 Haxton Way at Slater Rd. • FERNDALE, WA 98248
(866) 383-0777; (360) 383-0777 Fax 758-7545
Website: www.silverreefcasino.com; E-mail: feedback@silverreefcasino.com
Owned by the Lummi Indian Tribe. *Location*: 10 miles off I-5 near Bellingham. *Facility*: 10,000 sq. ft. 41 blackjack, craps, roulette & poker tables. Open 24/7.

SKAGIT VALLEY CASINO & RESORT
5984 N. Dark Lane • BOW, WA 98232
(877) 275-2448; (360) 724-7777; Website: www.scasinoresort.com
Owned by the Upper Skagit Indian Tribe. *Location*: In northwest Washington, 16 miles south of Bellingham. *Facilities*: 64,000 sq. ft. 600 slots, 50 gaming tables; 800-seat bingo.

DOUBLE EAGLE CASINO
2539 Smith Rd. • CHEWELAH, WA 99109
(509) 935-4406; Website: www.washingtoncasinos.com
Owned by the Spokane Tribe. *Location*: 50 miles north of Spokane. *Facilities*: Slots, video poker, craps, roulette, poker, pull-tabs.

COULEE DAM CASINO
515 Birch St. • COULEE DAM, WA 99155
(800) 556-7492; (509) 633-0766; Website: www.couleecasino.com
Owned & operated by the Colville Tribal Enterprise Corporation. *Location*: In eastern Washington on the Columbia River west of Spokane. *Facility*: Slots, video poker, video keno, blackjack, pull-tabs.

TWO RIVERS CASINO
6828-B Hwy. 25 S. • DAVENPORT, WA
(800) 722-4031; (509) 722-4000 Fax 722-4015
Website: www.tworiverscasinoandresort.com
Owned by the Spokane Tribe. *Location*: Where the Columbia & Spokane River meet. *Facilities*: 400 reel slots; table games.

NOOKSACK RIVER CASINO
5048 Mount Baker Hwy., P.O. Box 157 • DEMING, WA 98244
(877) 935-9300; (360) 592-5472 Fax 592-5753
Website: www.nooksackcasino.com; E-mail: info@nooksackcasino.com
Owned by the Nooksack Indian Tribe. *Location*: 14 miles off I-5, east of Bellingham on Hwy. 542 near Deming. *Facility*: 25,000 sq. ft. 400 slots; 25 blackjack, craps, roulette and poker tables; bingo.

SILVER REEF CASINO
4876 Haxton Way • FERNDALE, WA 98248
(866) 383-0777; (360) 383-0777
Website: www.silverreefcasino.com
Owned by the Nooksack Indian Tribe. *Location*: On I-5 exit 260. *Facility*: 28,000 sq. ft. 550 slots, gaming tables.

EMERALD QUEEN CASINO AT FIFE
5700 Pacific Hwy. E. • FIFE, WA 98424
(888) 820-3555 Fax (253) 517-2346; Website: www.emeraldqueen.com
Owned by the Puyallup Tribe. *Facility*: 1,000 slots; blackjack, roulette, craps, poker, pull tabs.

THE POINT CASINO
7989 Salish Lane NE • KINGSTON, WA 98346
(866) 547-6468; (360) 297-0070 Fax 297-8929
Website: www.the-point-casino.com
E-mail: info@the-point-casino.com
Owned by the Port Gamble S'Klallam Tribe. *Location*: Located in the northern end of the Kitsap Peninsula in Kitsap County in Washington State. *Facility*: Slots, table games, bingo.

QUILEUTE CASINO
P.O. Box 279 • LA PUSH, WA 98350
(206) 374-6163; Website: www.washingtoncasinos.com
Owned by the Quileute Indian Tribe. *Location*: Off Hwy. 110 on the Pacific coast on the Olympic peninsula. *Facility*: 15,000 sq. ft. with blackjack, craps, roulette and poker tables; Bingo.

NORTHWOOD CASINO
P.O. Box 31 • LYNDEN, WA 98264
(360) 592-5176 Fax 592-2125; Website: www.northwood casino.com
Owned by the Nooksack Indian Tribe of Washington.

MILL BAY CASINO
455 E. Wapato Lake Rd. • MANSON, WA 98831
(800) 648-2946; (509) 826-8050; Website: www.millbaycasino.com
Owned & operated by the Colville Tribal Enterprise Corporation. *Location*: In north central Washington on Lake Chelan. *Facilities*: 9,000 sq. ft. 200 slots; blackjack, craps, roulette and poker tables.

QUIL CEDA CREEK NIGHTCLUB & CASINO
10200 Quil Cedar Blvd. • MARYSVILLE, WA 98271
(888) 272-1111; (360) 716-6000 Fax 651-3119
Website: www.tulalipcasino.com; Steve Griffis, General Manager
Owned & operated by the Tulalip Tribes. *Location*: 30 miles north of Seattle off I-5, 5 miles north of Everett, Wash. in Snohomish County. *Facilities*: 15,000 sq. ft. 2,000 slots; 50 blackjack, craps, roulette & poker tables. Bingo; night club.

TULALIP RESORT CASINO
10200 Quil Ceda Blvd. • TULALIP, WA 98271
(888) 272-1111; (360) 716-6000; Website: www.tulalipcasino.com
Owned & operated by the Tulalip Tribes. *Location*: 30 miles north of Seattle off I-5, 5 miles north of Everett, Wash. in Snohomish County. *Facilities*: 15,000 sq. ft. 2,000 slots; 50 blackjack, craps, roulette/poker tables. Bingo; Amphitheatre.

QUINAULT BEACH RESORT & CASINO
78 State Rt. 115, P.O. Box 1119 • OCEAN SHORES, WA 98587
(360) 374-6163 Fax 374-6311; Website: www.quinaultbeachresort.com
Owned & operated by the Quinault Indian Tribe. *Location*: On the Pacific Ocean in Clallam County. *Facilities*: 16,000 sq. ft. Slots; gaming tables; live keno, bingo. 150-room hotel with full spa.

RED WING CASINO
12819 Yelm Hwy. SE • OLYMPIA, WA 98513
(360) 456-5221 Fax 438-8618; Website: www.redwingcasino.net
Owned & operated by the Nisqually Indian Tribe. *Location*: Located in Thurston County. *Facilities*: Slots, table games, live keno, bingo

OKANOGAN BINGO-CASINO
41 Appleway Rd. • OKANOGAN, WA 98840
(800) 559-4643; (509) 422-4646; Website: www.okanoganbingocasino.com
Owned & operated by the Colville Tribal Enterprise Corporation. *Location*: In north central Washington northwest of Spokane. *Facilities*: Slots, video poker, tables, bingo.

LOWER ELWHA S'KLALLAM TRIBE CASINO
2851 Lower Elwha Rd. • PORT ANGELES, WA 98363
(360) 452-8471 Fax 452-3428
Owned by the Lower Elwha S'Kallam Tribe. *Location*: In Port Angeles across from Victoria, British Columbia, Canada. *Facilities*: 36,800 sq. ft. Blackjack, craps, roulette and poker tables; keno bingo.

LUCKY EAGLE CASINO & BINGO
12888 188th Road SW • ROCHESTER, WA 98579
(800) 720-1788; (360) 273-2000; Website: www.luckyeagle.com
Owned by the Confederated Tribes of the Chehalis Reservation in Washington. *Facilities*: 50,000 sq. ft. 350 slots, blackjack, craps, roulette, poker, keno, pulltabs, bingo.

HARRAH'S SKAGIT VALLEY CASINO
2284 Community Plaza • SEDRO WOOLLEY, WA 98284
(360) 856-5501 Fax 856-3175
Owned by the Upper Skagit Indian Tribe. *Location*: 70 miles north of Seattle, 30 miles southeast of Bellingham. *Facilities*: 30,000 sq. ft. Blackjack, craps, roulette and poker tables. 800-seat bingo, keno.

7 CEDARS CASINO
2070756 Hwy. 101 E. • SEQUIM, WA 98382
(800) 4-LUCKY-7; (360) 683-7777 Fax 683-4366
Website: www.7cedarscasino.com
Owned by the Jamestown S' Klallam Tribe. *Location*: On the Olympic Peninsula 17 miles east of Port Angeles, 5 miles east of Sequim. *Facilities*: 30,000 sq. ft. with 33 tables: blackjack, craps, roulette and poker; bingo, keno.

LITTLE CREEK CASINO & HOTEL
W. 91 Hwy. 108 • SHELTON, WA 98584
(800) 667-7711; (360) 427-7711 Fax 427-7868
Website: www.little-creek.com

Owned by the Squaxin Island Tribe. *Location*: Northwest of Olympia on Hwy. 108. *Facilities*: 100,000 sq. ft. Slots, gaming tables, bingo. 92-room hotel.

LUCKY DOG CASINO
19330 N. US Hwy. 101 • SKOKOMISH, WA 98584
(360) 877-5656; Website: www.theluckydogcasino.com
Stan Lien, Director of Operations
Owned by the Skokomish Tribal Nation. *Facilities*: Slots, table games. *Publication*: Newsletter.

SNOQUALMIE CASINO
37500 SE North Bend Way, P.O. Box 999 • SNOQUALMIE, WA 98065
(425) 888-1234 Fax 888-3278; Website: www.casinosnoqualmie.com
Owned by the Snoqualmie Indian Tribe. *Facilities*: 170,000 sq. feet. 1,600 slots, 69 table games, poker.

CLEARWATER CASINO & RESORT
15347 Suquamish Way, NE • SUQUAMISH, WA 98392
(800) 375-6073; (360) 598-8700
Website: www.clearwatercasino.com
E-mail: reservations@clearwatercasino.com
Owned by the Suquamish Tribe of the Port Madison Reservation. *Location*: Across from Puget Sound 15 miles west via the Bainbridge Ferry. *Facilities*: 500+ video slots, blackjack, craps, roulette, poker; 300-seat bingo, pulltabs.

EMERALD QUEEN CASINO
2102 Alexander Ave. • TACOMA, WA 98404
(888) 831-7655; (253) 594-7777
Website: www.emeraldqueen.com
Owned by the Puyallup Tribe. *Location*: On the Puget Sound.
Facilities: 1,500 slots, blackjack, roulette, craps, poker, pulltabs.

SHOALWATER BAY CASINO
4112 Hwy. 105, P.O. Box 560 • TOKELAND, WA98590
(866) 834-7312; (360) 267-2048 Fax 267-6778
Website: www.shoalwaterbaycasino.com
Owned & operated by the Shoalwater Bay Indian Tribe.

YAKAMA LEGENDS CASINO
580 Fort Rd. • TOPPENISH, WA 98948
(877) 726-6311; (509) 865-8800 ext. 217
Website: www.legendscasino.com
Owned and operated by the Yakama Nation. *Location*: On Yakama Reservation in Toppenish. *Facilities*: 675 slots, table games, 600-seat bingo hall. 80-site campground. Annual Rodeo & Powwow in August.

WISCONSIN

HO-CHUNK CASINO
S3214 A Hwy. 12 • BARABOO, WI 53913
(800) 746-2486; (608) 356-6210 Fax 355-4035
Website: www.ho-chunknation.com
Owned & operated by the Ho-Chunk Nation. *Location*: On Hwy. 12, south of Lake Delton, 40 miles north of Madison. *Facilities*: 85,000 sq. ft. 1,200 slots and video poker 48 poker & blackjack tables. Open 24/7.

ISLE VISTA CASINO
Hwy. 13 North, Rt. 3 Box 3365 • BAYFIELD, WI 54891
(800) 226-8478; (715) 779-3712 Fax 779-3715
Website: www.islevistacasino.net
Owned by the Red Cliff Band of Lake Superior Ojibway (Chippewa). *Location*: In northern Wisconsin on the shores of Lake Superior, 70 miles east of Duluth, Minn. *Facilities*: 15,000 sq. ft. with 175 slots, video poker, video keno, blackjack tables, pull-tabs, bingo.

MAJESTIC PINES CASINO
Hwy. 54, Rte. 5, Box 433-G • BLACK RIVER FALLS, WI 54615
(800) 657-4621; (715) 284-9098 Fax 284-9739
Website: www.mpcwin.com
Facilities: 14,000 sq. ft. 246 slots & video poker; video keno; Bingo.

MOHICAN NORTH STAR CASINO & BINGO
W12180A County Rd. A • BOWLER, WI 54416
(800) 952-0195; (715) 787-3110 Fax 787-3129
Website: www.mohicannorthstar.com
Louis Raywinkle, Contact
Owned by the Stockbridge-Munsee Mohican Indians. *Location*: 50 miles northwest of Green Bay, north of Hwy. 29. *Facility*: 16,000 sq. ft. with 1,000 slots, video poker and keno; 18 blackjack tables. High-stakes bingo. 53-site RV park. Konkapot Lodge. Open 24 hours Fri.-Sat. 10am-2am, Sun.-Thurs.

MOLE LAKE CASINO, BINGO & HOTEL
Rte. 1, Box 625 • CRANDON, WI 54520
(800) 236-9466; (715) 478-5565 Fax 478-5275; Website: www.molelake.com
Owned by the Sokoagan Ojibwe (Chippewa) Indian Tribe. *Location*: East of Rhineland, 7 miles south of Crandon on Hwy. 55. *Facilities*: 30,000 sq. ft. 450 slots & video poker, and 20 blackjack tables.

HOLE IN THE WALL CASINO
P.O. Box 98 • DANBURY, WI 54830
(800) BET-UWIN; (715) 656-3444 Fax 656-3434
Website: www.holeinthewallcasino.com
Owned by the St. Croix Ojibwe Indians. *Location*: On Hwys. 77 & 35, 45 miles south of Duluth, Minnesota. *Facility*: 65,000 sq. feet. 300 slots & video poker; keno, bingo, and 84 blackjack tables.

ONEIDA BINGO & CASINO
2100 Airport Dr., P.O. Box 365 • GREEN BAY, WI 54155
(800) 238-4263; (414) 494-4500 Fax 497-5803
Website: www.oneidabingoandcasino.net; Louise King, Contact
Owned by the Oneida Tribe of Indians of Wisconsin. *Location*: Near Green Bay airport on Hwy. 172 just off U.S. Hwy 43 & 41. *Facilities*: 65,000 sq. ft. 2,500 slots & video poker & keno; and 84 blackjack tables; off-track betting; high-stakes bingo. 300-room Radisson Inn. Open 24 hours, 7 days a week.

LAC COURTE OREILLES CASINO
13767 W County Rd. B, Rte. 5, Box 505 • HAYWARD, WI 54843
(800) 422-2175; (715) 634-5643 Fax 634-6111
Website: www.lcocasino.com
Owned by the Lac Courte Orielles Band of Lake Superior Ojibwe. *Location*: Northwest Wisconsin, 55 miles east of Duluth, Minnesota; on County Rd. E, 9 miles south of Hayward. *Facilities*: 60,000 sq. ft. 450 slots & video poker; video keno and 12 blackjack tables.

MENOMINEE CASINO-BINGO-HOTEL
Hwy. 47, Box 7060 • KESHENA, WI 54135
(800) 343-7778; (715) 799-3600 Fax 799-4051
Website: www.menomineecasinoresort.com
Owned by the Menominee Indian Tribe of Wisconsin. *Location*: 40 miles northwest of Green Bay on Hwy. 47. *Facilities*: 27,500 sq. feet. 850 slots & 12 blackjack tables. 400-seat bingo hall. Conference and meeting center. 100-room hotel.

LAKE OF THE TORCHES RESORT & CASINO
510 Old Abe Rd. • LAC DU FLAMBEAU, WI 54538
(800) 258-6724; (715) 588-7070; Website: www.lakeofthetorches.com
Owned by the Lac du Flambeau Band of Lake Superior Chippewa. *Location*: On Hwy. 47, 160 miles northwest of Green Bay. *Facilities*: 15,000 sq. ft. 800 slots; video poker & keno; 12 blackjack tables; high-stakes bingo hall. 101-room hotel. Open 24/7.

DeJOPE GAMING
4002 Evan Acres Rd. • MADISON, WI 53718
(888) 248-1777; (608) 223-9576 Fax 224-1110
Website: www.dejope.com; E-mail: dejopeinfo@ho-chunk.com
Joyce Warner, General Manager
Owned by the Ho-Chunk Nation. *Location*: One-half mile east of I-90 exit 142B. *Facilities*: 1,000+ slots; high stakes bingo.

POTAWATOMI BINGO & CASINO
1721 W. Canal St. • Milwaukee, WI 53233
(800) PAYSBIG; (414) 645-6888 Fax 645-6866
Website: www.paysbig.com
Owned by the Potawatomi Tribe of Wisconsin. *Location*: The western shore of Lake Michigan. *Facilities*: 200 slots, video poker & keno; 2,000-seat High Stakes Bingo.

RAINBOW CASINO
949 County G Rd., P.O. Box 460 • NEKOOSA, WI 54615
(800) 782-4560; (715) 886-4560 Fax 886-4551
Website: www.rbcwin.com
Owned & operated by the Ho-Chunk Nation. *Location*: In central Wisconsin on the Wisconsin River south of Stevens Point; 14 miles off Hwy. 13. Facility: 37,000 sq. ft. 600 slots; video poker & keno; 24 blackjack and poker tables.

BAD RIVER LODGE & CASINO
US Hwy. 2, P.O. Box 8 • ODANAH, WI 54861
(800) 777-7449; (715) 682-7121 Fax 682-7149
Website: www.badriver.com
Owned by the Bad River Band of Lake Superior Tribe of Ojibwe (Chippewa) Indians. Location: 10 miles east of Ashland on US Hwy. 2 near Lake Superior.

Facilities: 20,000 sq. ft. casino. 500 slots, video poker & keno; 6 blackjack & poker tables; bingo. 600-seat theater.

ST. CROIX CASINO & HOTEL
777 US Hwy. 8 W • Turtle Lake, WI 54889
(800) 846-8946; (715) 987-4777 Fax 986-2800
Website: www.stcroixcasino.com
Owned by the St. Croix Ojibwe (Chippewa) Indians of Wisconsin. *Location*: In northwest Wisconsin on US Hwy. 8, 25 miles east of the Minnesota border. *Facility*: 65,000 sq. feet. 1,200 slots, video poker & keno; 20 blackjack tables. 158-room hotel. Open 24/7.

NORTHERN LIGHTS BINGO & CASINO
Hwy. 32, P.O. Box 430 • WABENO, WI 54566
(800) 487-9522; (715) 473-2021 Fax 473-6104
Website: www.cartercasino.com
Owned by Forest County Potawatomi Indian Community. *Location*: In northeast Wisconsin, 65 miles north of Green Bay on Hwy. 32. *Facility*: 12,000 sq. ft. 420 slots & video poker, and 13 blackjack tables; bingo. 70-room lodge.

WYOMING

WIND RIVER CASINO
10369 Hwy. 789 • RIVERTON, WY 82501
P.O. Box 508 • FORT WASHAKIE, WY 82514
(307) 856-3964 Fax 857-2707; Website: www.windrivercasino.com
Owned & operated by Northern Arapaho Tribe of the Wind River Reservation. High-stakes bingo; Lotto machines.

CANADA

MANITOBA

ASENESKAK CASINO - OPASKWAYAK, THE PAS
P.O. Box 10250 • OPASKWAYAK, MB
(204) 627-2276; Website: www.bestlittlecasino.ca
Owned by a consortium of six First Nations of Cree. *Location*: 5 minutes north on Hwy. 10 from the town of The Pas, on Opaskwayak Cree Nation reserve. *Facilities*: 177 slots; 8 table games.

ONTARIO

GOLDEN EAGLE CHARITABLE CASINO & ENTERTAINMENT CENTRE
P.O. Box 2860 • KENORA, ON P9N 3X8
(800) 336-4202; (807) 548-1331 Fax 548-5831
Website: www.casinokenora.com
Owned by Wauzhushk Onigum First Nation. *Location*: On the north shore of Lake of the Woods in northwest Ontario on Canada Hwy. 17. *Facility*: 7,500 sq. ft. No slots. 27 blackjack/roulette/poker tables.

CASINO RAMA RESORT
P.O. Box 178 • ORILLA, ON L0K 1T0
(705) 329-3325 Fax 329-3329; Website: www.casinorama.com
Owned by the Rama Chippewas First Nation. *Location*: 90 miles north of Toronto on Canada Hwy. 12. *Facility*: 50,000 sq. ft. 1,800 slots, 36 blackjack, roulette and poker tables. Hotel.

SASKATCHEWAN

BEAR CLAW CASINO
P.O. Box 221 • KENOSEE LAKE, SK S0C 2S0
(306) 577-4577 Fax 577-4899; Website: www.siga.sk.ca/bearclaw
Owned by the White Bear Indian Community. *Location*: In southeast Saskatchewan on Hwy. 9, 137 miles southeast of Regina. *Facility*: 10,000 sq.ft. with blackjack tables, roulette, bingo.

GOLDEN EAGLE CASINO
11906 Railway St. • N. BATTLEFORD, SK S9A 3K7
(306) 446-3833 Fax 446-7170
First Nations casino. *Location*: 88 miles from Saskatoon. *Facility*: 128 slots and 12 tables.

NORTHERN LIGHTS CASINO
PRINCE ALBERT, SK S6V 7L7
(306) 764-4777 Fax 922-1000
Website: www.northernlightscasino.com
First Nations casino.

This section lists Indian-related films, videos, recordings, filmstrips, picture-sets, & maps. Films & videos are color/sound unless otherwise stated in the listing. Entries are arranged alphabetically by title. At the end of each entry there are code letters that correspond to the distributor and address listed at the end of the section.

FILMS & VIDEOS

ABENAKI: THE NATIVE PEOPLE OF MAINE
Jay Kent, Producer/Director/Writer; 1976. 60 mins, color. Video. NAPBC.

ACORNS: STAPLE FOOD OF CALIFORNIA INDIANS
Clyde B. Smith, Producer; A film on the staple food of the Pomo Indians. Includes scenes showing original primitive methods. 1962. Grades 7 & up. 28 mins, color. UC & PSU.

ACTS OF DEFIANCE
Documents the long dispute over sovereign rights between the Mohawk of Kanesatake & the Province of Quebec. 1992. 104 mins, color. IU.

ADAM: MINORITY YOUTH
Adam, an American Indian youth, speaks candidly about his cultural heritage and his place in today's society. 1971. Grades 4 & up. 10 mins, color. PHO.

ADVENTURE OF YOUNG BRAVE
Two kids go on the trail to solve the mystery of a fortune in buried gold receive help from the spirit of Horton Laughing Feather. 92 mins. 1997. VHS. ME.

AGAIN, A WHOLE PERSON I HAVE BECOME
Will Sampson, Narrator
Three American Indian tribal leaders describe the wisdom of their shared culture. Grades 7 and up. 19 mins. Video. SH. Rental, $21. SH, PSU.

AGE OF THE BUFFALO
An indictment of the mass slaughtering of buffalos & systematic subduing of the Indians. Uses live footage & rare paintings to tell its story. 1964. Grades 4-8. 14 mins. Rental: $14. UCT.

AIDS AND THE NATIVE AMERICAN FAMILY
Addresses people's needs for cultural and family support. Includes preventive AIDS information for all ages. 1989. 11 minutes. Video. Purchase: $50. UP.

SUZANNE AKIMNACHI MAKES A BURCH-BARK BERRY BASKET
David E. Young, Trudy Nicks & David Strom, Producers
A Beaver Indian from northern Alberta, Suzanne documents in detail the entire production process. 1989. 23 mins. Video. Purchase: $70; rental, $20. UADA.

AKWESASNE: ANOTHER POINT OF VIEW
A portrait of the Mohawk people as they confront two choices: survival or assimilation. Explores some of the social, political, and legal obstacles faced by traditional Mohawks in recent years in their struggle to retain traditional rights. 1981. 28 minutes. ICARUS.

THE ALASKA NATIVE CLAIMS SETTLEMENT ACT SERIES
Bob Walker, Director; Five educational programs, explores the terms & implications of this major legislation. Examines its history; how it has settled native land claims and established native corporations; and what its impact may be in the future. 1979. 16-30 minutes. Video. In Inupiaq or English. NATC.

ALASKA: SETTLING A NEW FRONTIER
National Geographic Society; Recounts the history of Alaska and views life in Eskimo villages. 1966. 22 mins, color. Grades 3 and up. 16mm. Rental, $17.50. PSU.

ALASKA: THE YUP'IK ESKIMOS
Susan Duncan, Executive Producer; Larry Lansburgh & Gail Evanari, Co-producers; Gail Evanari, Writer; Yup'ik culture and way of life, with commentary provided by people from four communities: Bethel, Eek, Chevak, and Tooksook Bay. Grades 7-12; suitable for adult audiences. A study guide in English or Yup'ik is available. 1985. 27 mins. Video. CHE (free loan).

THE ALASKAN ESKIMO
Sarah Elder & Len Kamerling, Producers; A series of four films produced jointly with village councils to ensure authentic Alaskan Eskimo material and point of view. Now available on video. DER.

DENNIS ALLEY WISDOM DANCERS VIDEO
Dennis Alley presents eight dances, including hoop, Northern traditional, shield and spear, eagle, and war dance. Introduction by Willie Nelson. 30 minutes, color. Video. Purchase: $19.95. CAN.

AMERICA'S GREAT INDIAN LEADERS
Stories of four heroic Native American leaders and their respective tribes. Crazy Horse, Chief Joseph, Geronimo, Quanah Parker. 1995. VHS. 65 mins. $49. CHAR. $29.95. ME.

AMERICA BEFORE COLUMBUS
National Geographic; 90 mins. DVD, 2010. $10.49. Amazon.com.

AMERICA'S GREATEST INDIAN NATIONS
History of all six great Indian Nations, dramatically filmed on location at their native tribal lands across America. The Iroquois, Seminole, Shawnee, Navajo, Cheyenne, and Lakota Sioux. Grades 7 to adult. VHS. 65 mins. $49. CHAR. $29.95. ME.

AMERICA'S INDIAN HERITAGE: REDISCOVERING COLUMBUS (OHIO)
Roger Kennedy, of the Smithsonian's National Museum of American History, focuses on Columbus, Ohio and the earthworks, moundbuilders of ancient North America. 56 minutes. Video. 1992. FH.

*AMERICA'S WESTWARD EXPANSION
Grades 5 and up. Teacher's guide, bibliography. 30 mins. Video. KU.

THE AMERICAN AS ARTIST: A PORTRAIT OF BOB PENN
SD ETV, Producer; Penn offers his insights into the essence of being an artist and a Native-American in the U.S. 1976. 29 mins. Video. NAPBC.

THE AMERICAN EXPERIENCE: GERONIMO & THE APACHE RESISTANCE
Neil Goodwin; Portrays the profound transformation of a once-proud Indian society faced with the loss of its land and traditions. 1988. Grades 9 and up. 58 minutes Video. Rental, $12. PSU.

THE AMERICAN EXPERIENCE: INDIANS, OUTLAWS, & ANGIE DEBO
Barbara Abrash & Martha Sandlin; Recounts the life of Angie Debo (1890-1988), a courageous maverick scholar whose work in behalf of Native American tribal sovereignty and land rights is considered the cornerstone of Indian history. Grades 9 and up. 58 mins 1988. Video. Rental, $12. PSU.

THE AMERICAN INDIAN
Center for Educational Telecommunications
Examines the history of the American Indian from the turn of the century to the present day. 28 minutes 1980. 3/4" VHS. DT.

THE AMERICAN INDIAN - AFTER THE WHITE MAN CAME
Examines the profound impact white expansion had upon the many tribes of Native-Americans. The formation of U.S. governmental policies as well as contemporary social issues are discussed. Narrated by Iron Eyes Cody. 1972. 27 mins. VHS. Rental: $16. UCT.

AMERICAN INDIAN ARTISTS: Parts I & II
Tony Schmitz & Don Cirillo, Directors; Part I: Six programs, profiling seven contemporary Native American artists: Grace Medicine Flower and Joseph Lonewolf, potters; Fritz Scholder, R.C. Gorman, & Helen Hardin, painters; Allen Houser, sculptor; & Charles Loloma, jeweler. 1976. Part II: 3 programs--Larry Golsh's artistry in gold & precious stones; James Quick-To-See Smith, painter; and Dan Namingha, artist, 1984. 30 mins each. Video. Two Parts. NAPBC.

THE AMERICAN INDIAN DANCE THEATRE – FINDING THE CIRCLE
Includes dances from many Indian tribes as performed on stage and at outdoor powwows on their U.S. and international tours. Includes hoop dance, eagle dance, Apache Crown dance, Zuni rainbow dance, powwow dances, plains snake & buffalo dance and others. 1990. 60 mins. Video. Purchase: $35. CAN.

THE AMERICAN INDIAN DANCE THEATRE #2: DANCES FOR THE NEW GENERATION
The company performs dances from the Makah, Kwakiutl, Seneca & Penobscot, and Plains Nations. 1996. 60 minutes. Video. $35. CAN & OY.

AMERICAN INDIAN HOMELANDS: MATTERS OF TRUTH, HONOR & DIGNITY
Barry ZeVan, Director; Documentary about what the U.S. Government has done to the Native Americans. Includes the Dawes Act and other atrocities. 60 mins. DVD, 2007. $99.49. Amazon.com.

AMERICAN INDIAN IN TRANSITION
A North American Indian mother, living on a reservation, describes her family & tribal problems-relating her past & her dreams for the future. 1976. 22 minutes. 16mm. Rental: $11. UCT.

THE AMERICAN INDIAN INFLUENCE ON THE U.S.
Albert Saparoff, Producer; Barry Sullivan, Narrator; Depicts how life in the U.S. today has been influenced by the American Indian. Discusses the Pueblo Indians and the Spanish, Chief Massasoit and the Pilgrims, Hiawatha, Sitting Bull, Custer, Buffalo Bill, President Jackson, Sequoyah, Will Rogers, Jim Thorpe and Buffy St. Marie. 1972. Grades 5 and up. 20 mins. UK & UMN.

AMERICAN INDIAN PROPHECIES I & II
Dr. A.Chuck Ross, Narrator; I - Discover how to prepare for the coming earth changes, how the Black Hills can be returned, and more; II - Dr. Ross discusses the prophecies presented in the first video. Video. $20 each. CAN.

AMERICAN INDIAN RHYTHMS
Documentary of Indian dancers from various tribes show authentic Indian dances. 1930. 10 minutes, bxw. EG.

THE AMERICAN INDIAN SPEAKS
Documentary lets the Indian speak about his people & heritage, about the white man & the future. Visits with the Muskogee, Cree, Sioux & Nisqually. 1973. Grades 7 and up. 23 mins, color. 16mm. Purchase: BF. Rental: IU, PSU, UCLA & UMN.

AMERICAN INDIAN SWEAT LODGE CEREMONY
Shows the entire ceremony. A little hut of the woods used as a sauna/steambath. Also shows the sacred pipe ceremony. With Bill Elwell. 1989. 90 minutes. VHS. ME.

THE AMERICAN INDIAN TODAY
This is a lesson which contains material on American Indians circa 1969. 30 minutes. 1969. 1/2" reel. NETV.

AMERICAN INDIANS AS SEEN BY D.H. LAWRENCE
His wife, Frieda, speaks intimately about his beliefs & thoughts. Aldous Huxley presents selections from Lawrence, which reveal his deep insights into the religious & ceremonial impulses of Indian culture as shown by various ritual dances. 1966. Grades 7 and up. 14 mins UCT.

AMERICAN INDIANS BEFORE EUROPEAN SETTLEMENT
David Baerreis, Ph.D.; Where they came from, how they lived, and unique aspects of their cultures as related to their environment are examined. 1959. 11 mins. Grades 7 to 12. PHO. Rental: UA & UCT.

AMERICAN INDIANS OF TODAY
Describes the achievements and problems of Indians. 1957. Grades 3 and up. 16 minutes, bxw. 16mm. Rental: PSU & UCT.

AMERICAN INDIANS: YESTERDAY & TODAY
Don Klugman; Shows that various Indian tribes have different histories and ways of life. A young Shoshone-Paiute man from the Owens Valley in CA, an elderly Northern Cheyenne man from Lame Deer, MT, and a young Seneca woman from NY State tell about their history and modern lifestyles of their tribes. 1982. 19 mins, color. Grades K-8. FF.

AMERICAN OUTRAGE
Beth Gage & George Gage, Directors; Two Western Shoshone sisters put up a heroic fight for their land rights and their human rights. 56 mins. DVD, 2009. Amazon.com, $20.49.

AMERINDIAN LEGACY
Explores the many important contributions first made by the Amerindians. 1992. Grades 4 and up. 29 mins, color. PHO.

AMIOTTE
Bruce Baird, KUSD-TV, Producer; Explores Sioux painter Arthur Amiotte's art & reasons for returning to his native culture & religion. 1976. 29 mins. NAPBC.

AMISK
Alanis Obomsawin, Director/Producer; The traditional lands of the Cree of Misstassini in northern Quebec are being threatened by a Hydro-Electric Power project. Shows a festival, with Cree music and dance, to raise money to fight against this project. 1977. 38 mins. 16mm. NFBC.

ANASAZI: THE ANCIENT ONES
Questions and answers to the ancestors of the Navajo. 29 mins ME.

THE ANASAZI: BUILDERS OF AMERICA'S FIRST CITIES
Explores their cliff cities in the American Southwest between 700 BC and 1600 AD. Through live action footage of their ruins, the Anasazi lifestyle takes form. VHS. 1996. 19 mins. Teacher's guide and seven blackline masters. $95. UL.

THE ANASAZI & CHACO CANYON
This program looks at the fascinating finds at Chaco Canyon, the home of the Anasazi, ancestors of the Navajo. Also, the possible explanation for the disappearance of the highly advanced Anasazi culture. 1993. 43 mins. FH.

ANCESTRAL VOICES
Joy Harjo & Mary Tall Mountain; Native American Poetry. 60 mins. PBS

ANCIENT INDIAN CULTURES OF NORTHERN ARIZONA
Explores the ruins and ancient cultures of the Sinagua and Anasazi of Montezuma Castle, Wupatki, Tuzigoot, Walnut Canyon and Sunset Crater. 27 minutes, color. Video, $29.95. VVP. CH.

ANCIENT PLACES
Focuses on the Native American cultures of the Southwest. 1981. 30 minutes, color. 16mm. KS.

ANCIENT SPIRIT. LIVING WORD - THE ORAL TRADITION
The presentations & opinions of the Native Americans featured in this program culminate in a portrait of oral tradition, how it works and where it leads. 1983. 58 mins, color. Video. NAPBC.

THE ANCIENTS OF NORTH AMERICA
A dry cave/rock shelter with human remains was discovered in southeastern Utah. The site, dated 5500 B.C., offers a unique opportunity to examine the culture & remains of a people more than 7000 years old. 28 minutes. Video. Purchase: $149; rental: $75. FH.

...AND THE MEEK SHALL INHERIT THE EARTH
Examines the American Indians of Menominee County, Wisconsin. 1972. 59 minutes, color. 16mm. Rental: $25.25. IU & UMN.

...AND WOMAN WOVE IT IN A BASKET
Bushra Azzouz & Marlene Farnum, Producers/directors
The spiritual & cultural importance of basketweaving to Oregon's Klickitat Indians is explored in this portrait of master craftswoman Nettie Kuneki. 1989. 70 mins, color. Video & 16mm. WMM.

ANGOON - 100 YEARS LATER
Laurence Goldin, Producer/director/writer; Provides the history and culture of the Tlingit Indians while telling of the 1882 destruction of Tlingit Indian village of Angoon, Alaska, by U.S. Naval forces. 1982. 30 mins. Video. NAPBC.

ANGOTEE: STORY OF AN ESKIMO BOY
Douglas Wilkinson, Director; Documentary account of Indian boy's life from infancy to maturity. 1953. 31 mins, color. Grades 6 & up. English/French. PSU.

ANNIE & THE OLD ONE
Miska Miles, Writer; A dramatized film for young people with non-professional Navajo actors, about the relationship between a ten-year-old girl and her grandmother (the Old One.) 1976. Grades 1-8. 15 mins. PHO. Rental: UA, UCT & IU.

ANNIE MAE--BRAVE HEARTED WOMAN
Lan Brookes Ritz, Writer/producer/director
A documentary portrait of Annie Mae Pictou Aquash, a young Native American woman and activist for human rights, found dead on the prairie in South Dakota in 1974, a year after the Wounded Knee uprising. Explores the events leading up to her death and investigates her unsolved murder. 1982. 80 minutes. 16mm. *Purchase*: $1,090. Rental: $150. BBP and NAPBC.

ANOTHER WIND IS MOVING: THE OFF-RESERVATION INDIAN BOARDING SCHOOL
A documentary film about how difficult it is for Native Americans to learn about their culture. 59 mins, color. 1986. Video. UC & STULL.

APACHE - GERONIMO ON THE WARPATH
Two videos containing many photos detailing the life and times of the great Indian warrior. 1993. 90 mins. VHS. $12.99. ME.

THE APACHE INDIAN
The life of Apache Indians on their reservation in the White Mountains of Wyoming; their ancient ceremonies, and contemporary education, work, and the role of the tribal council in determining the direction of tribal affairs. 1975 revised edition. 10 mins, color. Grades K-6. UA & IU.

APACHE MOUNTAIN SPIRITS

John H. Crouch, Producer; Bob Graham, Director; An explanation of the role of the "Gaan", the Mountain Spirits who are the source of sacred power for the Apache. 1985. 58 mins. DVD. In English and Apache with English subtitles. NAPBC.

APACHES (APACHEN)

Gottfried Kolditz, Director; First Run Feature; A young Apache warrior sets out to avenge the extermination of his tribe...on the eve of the Mexican-American War. 94 mins. DVD, 2006. $17.99. Amazon.com.

ARCHAEOLOGY: PURSUIT OF MAN'S PAST

15 minutes. 16mm. Rental. UA.

ARCHAEOLOGY: QUESTIONING THE PAST

Betty Goerke, Producer; Includes two sequences of digging, one at an ancient Indian site in northern California and the other at Sand Canyon, an Anasazi pueblo site near Mesa Verde National Park in Colorado. Designed for students in introductory archaeology classes. 1988. 25 mins. DVD. UC.

ARCHAEOLOGY SERIES

Three, 20-minute tapes explores various aspects of the archaeology of Yup'ik Eskimo sites throughout Southwest Alaska, including an examination of the Smithsonian Museum's huge collection of artifacts collected by Edward Nelson. 1983. 60 mins. Video. Purchase: $24.95. KYUK.

ARCTIC SPIRITS

Katherine Marielle & Peter Raymont, Producers; Peter Raymont, Director An investigation of the rise of evangelical Christianity in Inuit villages in the Canadian Arctic. Follows three Canadian evangelists on their crusades in Arctic Quebec and the Northwest Territories. Interview Inuit. 1983. 27 mins. DVD. IP.

ARROW TO THE SUN

Gerald McDermott

Acoma Pueblo in New Mexico classic tale of a boy's search for his father: the universal search for identity, purpose, and continuity. 1973. Grades K-8. 12 mins. 16mm & video. Purchase: Video, $79. FI. Rental: 16mm, UCT.

ARROWHEADS, BLADES & KNIVES

Explores the world of flint arrowheads, blades and kniuves found in the heart of America-from Oklahoma to the southwest. VHS. 30 mins. $19.95. VIP.

THE ART OF BEING INDIAN: FILMED ASPECTS
OF THE CULTURE OF THE SIOUX

SD-ETV, Producer; Presents an overview of the cultural heritage of the Sioux from their early days in the Northeast to the Dakotas. Illustrates with paintings and sketches by George Catlin, Seth Eastman, and Karl Bochner; photography by Edward S. Curtis, Stanley Morrow, and the St. Francis Mission; & contemporary paintings by Sioux artist Bob Penn. 1976. 30 mins. Video. NAPBC.

THE ART OF NAVAJO WEAVING

Explores the traditional art of Navajo weaving and its origins. Shows the Durango Collection. 56 mins. VHS, $29.95. CH.

AS LONG AS THE GRASS IS GREEN

A summer experience with the children of the Woodland Indians of North America. Non-narrative. 11 mins, color. 1973. VHS. AP.

AS LONG AS THE GRASS SHALL GROW

Lynn Brown, Writer/Producer; A series of eight programs designed for classroom use with pre-school age children. Combines elements of Seneca life to teach children to count to ten in Seneca, and at the same time helps build positive self-images. 1978. 15 minutes each. Video. The SN.

AT THE TIME OF WHALING

Leonard Kamerling & Sarah Elder; Depicts an Eskimo whale hunt at Gambell, Alaska, a Yup'ik-speaking community on St. Lawrence Island in Bering Sea. 1974. 38 mins. DER.

AUGUSTA

Anne Wheeler, Director; Portrait of Augusta Evans, an 88 year-old granddaughter of a Shuswap chief, who lives alone in a cabin in the caribou country of British Columbia, Canada. She discusses her past and present. 1978. 17 mins. PHO & NFBC.

A BALANCE OF CULTURES

Looks at differences in western medicine & traditional Native healing practices. 1995. 26 mins. VHS. CHAR.

THE BALLAD OF CROWFOOT

Willie Dunn, Director; Graphic history of the Canadian West created by a film crew of Canadian Indians who reflect on the traditions, attitudes, and problems of their people. 1970. 11 mins, bxw. Grades 4 and up. 16mm. Rental: PSU, UCT & IU.

BARROW, ALASKA "A TRUE STORY"

Narrated by Jana Har-charek; Represents the voice of the Inupiaq people from Barrow, Alaska, featuring: The Subsistence Way of Life - a Whaling Culture; local craftspeople creating traditional art work; how we provide communications, water and other services in the Arctic; traditional Eskimo dancing; and local wildlife. Video. 30 mins. SH.

BASIC CHEYENNE BEADWORK

Vicki Little Coyote; Learn bead selection and sizing, plus application and placement; learn how to develop patterns; and garment decorations used by the Southern Cheyenne. VHS. 42 mins. $19.95. VIP.

BASKETRY OF THE POMO

Clyde B. Smith, Producer; A series of three 1962, color films. Ten Pomo basketmaking techniques. 30 mins. Techniques: A more detailed film on Pomo basketry techniques, showing how the various weaves were executed. 33 mins. Forms and Ornamentation: Illustrates the great variety of shapes, sizes, & design elements of Pomo baskets. 21 mins. UC Rental only, IU.

BATTLE FOR THE KLAMATH

Steven Johnson, Director; Documentary examining the regional fight over water and fishing rights and the extinction of the salmon, during the Bush Administration. Tribal fishermen explain how their life is threatened. 54 mins. DVD, 2007. $19.99. Amazon.com.

BATTLES OF CHIEF PONTIAC

Felix E. Feist, Director

Lex Barker portrays the fearless Indian scout in this tale of pre-Revolutionary Indian Wars in the area where Detroit now stands. Lon Chaney is sypathetic Chief Pontiac. 72 mins. bxw. DVD. $7.98. Amazon.com.

BEAUTIFUL TREE--CHISHKALE

Clyde B. Smith, Producer; The Southwestern Pomo called the tan oak chishkale (the beautiful tree.) Cooking methods and processing techniques used in making acorn bread are demonstrated. 1965. 20 minutes. Purchase: 16mm, $410; video, $195. Rental, $50. UC & PSU. Rental only, IU.

BEADWORK: A PRIMER

The art and history of Native American beadwork is shown and taught in this instructional video by Suzanne Aikman, VHS with booklet. 1990. 30 mins. $39. CHAR.

BEAVER STEALS FIRE / FIRE ON THE LAND

Confederated Salish & Kootenai Tribe; 2 DVD educational set showcasing the Salish & Pend d'Orielle tribes of the Flathead Indian Reservation in Montana explaining the traditional & contemporary uses of fire by American Indians. Companion to the book, Beaver Steals Fire; second disc provides a reading in Salish & English of the book, interviews with elders, a primer on fire ecology, etc. U. of Nebraska Press, 2007. $19.95.

BEAVERTAIL SNOWSHOES

Depicts the construction of traditional beavertail snowshoes by the Eastern Cree Indians of Misyassini Lake, Quebec. VHS. 40 mins. $99. TR.

BEFORE THE WHITE MAN CAME

John E. Maple; A feature film made in the Big Horn Mountains of Montana and Wyoming in the early 1920's with the cooperation of the Crow. An all-Indian cast presents authentic rites and ceremonies. 50 mins, bxw. 16mm. UUT.

BE-TA-TA-KIN

A cliff-dwelling of the Indians who lived in Arizona at the time of the Crusades. Shows the canyons and mesas of these early Indians; their lives, agriculture, and industry. 11 mins, color. Grades 9 and up. Rental, $13.50. NYU and PSU.

THE BELL THAT RANG TO AN EMPTY SKY

William Farley; A film essay using animation techniques and suggestive cutting to make a comment on the relationship between the expansion of white society onto Indian territories and the increase of wealth in the Federal Treasury. Commentary by Russell Means. 1977. Five mins. 16mm. CANYON.

BETRAYAL AT LITTLE BIG HORN

A&E Production; New discoveries challenge the understanding of Custer's last stand. 50 mins. DVD, 2005. $24.95. ME.

BETWEEN TWO RIVERS
Tells the story of the Indians' continuing battle for identity. The tragedy of Thomas Whitehawk caught between the world of the white man and the Indian. 1970. 26 mins. 16mm. Rental: UCT & UMN.

BETWEEN TWO WORLDS
Peter Raymont; Producer; Barry Greenwald, Director; Reviews the tragedies and contradictions of Canada's colonization of the Inuit people; in particular, the effects upon the life of Joseph Idlout, one of the world's most famous Inuit. 1991. 58 mins. ICARUS.

BETWEEN TWO WORLDS
Gryphon Productions; Two part video which looks at four young single Native mothers and their struggle to find support. Focuses on different programs which are available. 1995. Part 1, 33 mins. Part 2, 30 mins. VHS. Set. $150. CHAR.

BEYOND THE SHADOWS
Documentary about the legacy of Native American boarding schools. 1995. 30 mins. VHS. $145. CHAR.

BEYOND TRADITION - CONTEMPORARY INDIAN ART & ITS EVOLUTION
Presents more than 300 examples of prehistoric, historic and contemporary American Indian art. Carvings, paintings, sculptures, baskets, rugs, jewelry and pottery. The evolution of Indian art is traced through the centuries. 1989. 45 minutes, color. Video. Purchase: $29.95. NP, CAN. Rental: $16. UMN.

BIG BEAR
The Government and settlers staking claim to the Cree ancestral lands and hunting grounds, the Cree are forced from the land and torn between loyalty to their leader, Chief Big Bear and the white man. With Gordon Tootoosis & Michael Grayyeyes. 1998. VHS & DVD, $39.99. ME.

BIG CITY TRAIL: THE URBAN INDIANS OF TEXAS
Focuses on the 20,000 American Indian living in the Dallas/Ft. Worth area. Discusses the challenges these people face as they adjust to urban life, while resisting its homogenization. 28 minutes. Teacher's guide. $35. UT-ITC.

BILL REID
Jack Long, Director; Haida carver and jewelry-maker, Bill Reid, speaks of his work and what his Haida heritage has meant for him as an artist. 1979. 28 mins. 16mm. NFBC.

THE BIRTH OF CALIFORNIA
A documentary of the prehistory & history of California in the early days of exploration. 1927. 22 minutes, bxw. EG.

THE BISON HUNTERS
The painter George Catlin describes his enchantment with the life of the Plains Indians. 13 mins. Video. Purchase: $69.95. FH.

BLACK CLOUD
Rick Schroder & Tim McGraw, Directors; New Line Home Video Production An inspirational story about a young Native American boxer who overcomes challenges as he fights his way to a spot on the U.S. Olympic team. 97 mins. DVD. Amazon.com, $5.98.

BLACK COAL, RED POWER
Shelly Grossman, Producer; Examines the effects coal strip-mining has had on the Navajo and Hopi reservations in Arizona. 1972. 41 mins. 16mm. Rental. IU & UA.

THE BLACK HAWK WAR: UTAH'S FORGOTTEN TRAGEDY
Phillip B. Gottfredson, Producer; Black Hawk Productions Explores the story of the Ute Indian people and their Chief Black Hawk and the Mormon invasion of the mid 1850s and their attempt to convert them to Mormonism. Video. BHP.

THE BLACK HILLS ARE NOT FOR SALE
Sandra Osawa, Producer; Taped at the 1980, International Survival Gathering in South Dakota, Sioux people tell why the Black Hills are not for sale. Provides historical background on the Laramie Treaty of 1868 that guaranteed the Sioux ownership of their lands. 1980. 28 mins. Video. UP.

THE BLACK HILLS: WHO OWNS THE LAND?
NETV, Producer; A two-part program examines the roots of this problem, presenting the facts and beliefs that have fueled over a century of debate. Part 1. The Treaty of 1868 - Focuses on the original treaties; Part 2. Black Hills Claim - Highlights the physical and legal battles waged to gain and regain the Black Hills of South Dakota. 30 mins each. Video. Purchase: $50 per program; $70 for series. NETV.

BLACK INDIANS: AN AMERICAN STORY
Steven Heape & Chip Richie, Producer/Director An introduction to the blending of Native Americans and African Americans. Narrated by James Earl Jones. 2000. VHS & DVD. 60 minutes. $24.95. MALKI.

BLUNDEN HARBOR
Shows a group of Pacific Northwest Kwakiutl Indians living in Blunden Harbor and sustaining themselves by the sea. Includes the Legend of Killer Whale, and dance ceremony. 1951. Grades 7 & up. 20 mins, bxw. Rental, $14. PSU.

FRANZ BOAS, 1852-1942
T.W. Timreck; A profile of Franz Boas, his work with Northwest American Indian tribes and his teaching of anthropology. 1980. 59 minutes, color. Purchase: Beta or VHS, $250; rental, $90/week. PBS. Educator's guide. DER. Rental: 16mm, $24. PSU. Video rental, $14.65. IU.

BOLDT DECISION: IMPACTS AND IMPLEMENTATION
A discussion of the court ruling by U.S. Judge George Boldt who ruled that treaty Indians in Washington are entitled to half the harvestable catch of salmon and steelhead. 1976. 60 minutes. UW.

BOWS & ARROWS
Jim Hamm
Describes the art of making bows & arrows. 59 mins. VHS, $26.95. CMM.

BOX OF TREASURES
Chuck Olin, Producer/director; In 1921 the Kwakiutl people of Alert Bay, British Columbia, Canada, held their last secret potlatch. Fifty years later, the masks, blankets, and copper heirlooms that had been confiscated by the Canadian government were returned. The Kwakiutl built a cultural center to house these treasures and named it U'Mista something of great value that has come back. 1980. 28 mins. DER (U.S.); CFDW (Canada).

BOY OF THE NAVAJOS
Depicts life among the Navajos as seen through the eyes of Tony, a present day Navajo Indian boy. Revised 1975 edition. Grades K-6. 11 minutes, color. Purchase: 16mm, $270; video, $59. PHO. Rental. UA, IU.

BOY OF THE SEMINOLES (INDIANS OF THE EVERGLADES)
Wendell W. Wright, PhD
A visit to the Seminole tribe in the Everglades of Florida. 1956. Grades K-6. 11 mins. PHO.

BRAVEHEART
Indian tries to make it in white man's world, falls in love with white woman, alienates his tribe. Finally returns to Indian ways. 1925. 68 minutes, bxw. EG.

THE BROKEN CORD WITH LOUISE ERDRICH & MICHAEL DORRIS
Two Native American authors share their insights into the traditions & conditions of Native America today. 30 minutes. Video. $39.95. PBS.

BROKEN JOURNEY
Gary Robinson, Producer
A documentary which looks at the disease of alcohol through the personal stories of Native American inmates, men & women who have been incarcerated because of alcohol-related problems. 1986. 30 mins, color. NAPBC.

BROKEN RAINBOW
Victoria Mudd (Director) & Maria Florio, Producers/writers/editors A feature length documentary narrated by Martin Sheen, this film is concerned with the relocation of traditional Navajo from their homes in Big Mountain, Arizona. It provides a sympathetic view of the Navajo perspective on the history of the lands in dispute. Won the Academy Award for best documentary in 1985. 70 mins. 16mm & video. DC.

BROKEN TREATY AT BATTLE MOUNTAIN
Joel Freedman, Director; narrated by Robert Redford Shows the dramatic story of the traditional Western Shoshone Indians of Nevada and their struggle to regain 24 million acres of land stolen from them by the U.S. Government. Also, a portrait of the traditional Indian way of life. 1974. 60 mins. 16mm & video. CIN. Rental. UN & UW.

BRYAN BEAVERS: A MOVING POTRAIT
A Maidu Indian of California talks about his past, Indian spirits, his ancestral history, and his life. 1969. 30 mins. Grades 9 and up. 16mm rental, $15.90. IU

BUCKEYES: FOOD OF CALIFORNIA INDIANS
Clyde B. Smith, Producer; Shows harvesting, stone boiling, and leaching of buckeyes (horse chestnuts) by Niseanan Indians, a centuries-old method of changing poisonous nuts into edible mush or soup. 1961. 13 mins. UC & PSU.

BUFFALO, BLOOD, SALMON & ROOTS
George Burdeau, Writer/Director; Filmed at the Flathead, Kalispel and Coeur d' Alene Reservations in western Montana, the Idaho panhandle and eastern Washington, this film shows the old tribal ways of gathering and preserving food. 1976. 28 mins. 16mm & video. NAPBC and PBS.

THE BUFFALO SOLDIERS
Documentary revealing the exploits and heroism of black soldiers who fought Indians and pacified a great deal of the American West after the Civil War. 1992. 47 mins. VHS, $24.99. ME.

BUILDING AN ALGONQUIN BIRCHBARK CANOE
Their techniques are demonstrated by presen t day inhabitants of Maniwaki, Quebec. VHS. 54 minutes. $99. TR.

BURY MY HEART AT WOUNDED KNEE
Warner Bros Production; HBO
Inspired by Dee Brown's book of the same title. 133 mins. DVD, 2007. $6.38. Amazon.com.

THE BUSINESS OF FANCY DANCING
written & directed by Sherman Alexie
A modern "life on the rez" drama based on a Sherman Alexie short story. With Evan Adam & Michelle St. John. 2002. VHS, 19.98, DVD, $24.98. ME.

4-BUTTE-1: A LESSON IN ARCHAEOLOGY
Clyde B. Smith and Tony Gorsline; Shows the excavations and analyzes the artifacts of a Maidu Indian village in California Sacramento Valley. 1968. 33 mins. Purchase: 16mm, $660; VHS, $195, Rental: $50. UC. Rental only: 16mm, $24.50; VHS, $24. PSU.

BY NO MEANS CONQUERED PEOPLE
Verity Lund and John Moore; Richard Erdoes, photography
Presents issues that the Longest Walk, 1978, was organized around. The Walk was made across the U.S. to demonstrate their concern about proposed legislation: eleven bills, one of which would abrogate all treaties between the U.S. and Indian tribes. Dick Gregory and Clyde Bellacourt were speakers at the gathering. 1979. 26 mins., bxw. VHS. HSS.

BY SPIRITS MOVED
Explores spiritual beliefs & rituals of the Inuit (Eskimo) & other tribal people, and compares the role of the shaman with leadership in Western culture. 20 minutes. VHS. $50. TOP.

BY THE WORK OF OUR HANDS
Designed to be used with the text of the same name. However, it can be used independently. Focuses on drum making, and both oak and cane basket making. Teacher's guide. 30 mins. Grades 3-8. Purchase: video, $85. Rental, $10/two weeks. CHP.

BY THIS SONG I WALK: NAVAJO SONG
Larry Evers with Andrew Natonabah; Natonabah sings as he travels through Canyon de Chelly where the Navajo believe the songs were originally created and he discusses the songs and their origin. In Navajo with English subtitles. 1978. 25 mins. Video. ATL.

CAHOKIA LEGACY
Cahokia Mounds and Cahokia Archaeology. 20 minutes. Video, $10. CMM.

CAHOKIA MOUNDS: ANCIENT METROPOLIS
Traces the origins, people, places & products of Mississippian culture. Story of ancient mounds just east of St. Louis. VHS. 60 mins. $19.95. CMM, VIP & ME.

CAHOKIA MOUNDS VIDEO LIBRARY
Cahokia: A Prehistoric Legacy, 17 mins; The Cahokia Arrow Point, 13 minutes; Woodhenge Dedication Lectures, 1985; In Search Of...Ancient Indian Astronomies, series, 84 mins; 1987 Cahokia Culture Lecture Series, 155 mins. 2 week rentals, $2 per tape. CMM.

THE CALIFORNIA MISSIONS
Philomen Long, Director/writer; Martin Sheen, Narrator
Documentary exploring the heritage of the California missions, emphasizing the clash pf cultures between the Spanish Franciscan missionaries and the native California Indians. 1990. 22 minutes. Purchase: 16mm, $450; video, $195; rental, $50. UC.

CALIFORNIA RIVIERA
Looks at the history, culture, archaeology, and oceanography of southern California. Includes an interview with the present members of the Juaneno Indian tribe. 50 minutes. 1989. VHS and Beta. NU.

CALUMET, PIPE OF PEACE
Discusses rituals surrounding the calumet or peace pipes. Describes Indian use of pipes and tobacco, and shows traditional Indian methods of fashioning, decorating and consecrating pipe bowl and stem. 1964. 23 minutes. Purchase: 16mm, $460; video, $195. Rental: $50. UC. Rental only: PSU.

CANADA: PORTRAIT OF A NATION
Covers the environmental problems, and the social & political gains being made by the country's native Indians & Inuits. Grades 4-8. 5 VHS cassettes. 16 minutes each. $49. each. SVE.

CANADA'S ORIGINAL PEOPLES: THEN AND NOW
TV Ontario, Producer; Contrasts life of native Canadians before arrival Europeans with contemporary native life in Canada. 1977. 20 mins. Video. Rental, $40. NAPBC.

CANYON de CHELLY & HUBBELL TRADING POST
Visits both national parks containing Anasazi cliff dwellings and Navajo craftsmen. 30 minutes. 1979. VHS & Beta. VVP.

CATLIN
Documents, through his paintings, the customs and drama of Native Americans. Scenes of daily life: tribal camps, buffalo hunts, war parties, feasts, and ritual ceremonies. 16mm. 6 minutes. Free rental. NGA.

CELEBRATION & THE PIPE IS THE ALTAR
Chris Spotted Eagle, Producer/director; Two companion pieces presents aspects of contemporary Native American culture for Indians living in the Minneapolis-St. Paul area. CELEBRATION (1979), filmed at the Honor the Earth Powwow held annually on the Lac Courte Oreilles Reservation in Wisconsin, depicts the strengths of Native American life: powwow dancing, feasting, Indian sports, giveaways, etc. In THE PIPE IS THE ALTAR (1980) spiritual leader Amos Owen, a Sioux Indian living on the Prairie Island Reservation near Red Wing, Minnesota, shares his daily prayer ritual using the ceremonial pipe. 26 mins. Video (VHS, Beta). IN, MAI.

CELEBRATION OF THE RAVEN
Ken Kuramoto; Bill Reid is the acknowledged master of contemporary art in the ancient native tradition of the Haida. Since 1959, he has created a series of large works of sculpture, culminating in his 1980 masterwork, The Raven and the First Men. Traces evolution of this celebrated work of art. 1981. 12 mins. VHS. CFDW.

A CENTURY OF SILENCE...PROBLEMS OF THE AMERICAN INDIAN
Correlates the current problems of the American Indian to the past 100 years of contact with the white culture. Also addresses issues of cultural conflict, assimilation, & activism within the Indian community. 28 minutes. 1978. VHS and Beta. AP.

CESAR'S BARK CANOE
Bernard Gosselin, Director; Cesar Newashish, a Cree Indian, peels the bark from a birch tree and with his pocket knife and axe, constructs a canoe. Subtitles in Cree, French and English. 1971. 58 minutes. Grades 7-adult. EDC.

THE CHACO LEGACY
Graham Chedd, Director; Explores the excavations of the first monumental stone ruins discovered in North America, the Pueblo Bonito community in Chaco Canyon, New Mexico. Teachers guide. 1980. Grades 9 and up. 59 minutes, color. Purchase: 16mm, $600. Rental, $60. DER. Purchase: Video, $59.95. PBS. Rental: 16mm, $24; video, $12. PSU and IU.

A CHANGE FOR CHANGE
Depicts a young Native man caught between the city streets, his culture and family as he decides to get an AIDS test. Includes lesson guide & quiz. 1990. Grades 8-12. 30 mins. VHS. $145. CHAR.

CHARLES KILLS ENEMY, MEDICINE MAN
This film shows Kills Enemy in a Sweat Lodge Ceremony and a Lowanpi Ceremony. 30 minutes. 16mm. Purchase: $300; rental: $30. AICRC.

CHARLEY SQUASH GOES TO TOWN
An animated, imaginative simplification of the acculturation-identity crisis of an Indian. 1969. Grades 6 and up. 5 minutes, color. 16mm. Rental: UA & UCT.

CHEROKEE
Philip Hobel, Executive Producer; Examines the modern Cherokee's efforts to preserve native traditions. Cherokees are shown performing ceremonies and activities of the past, and discusses their heritage and hopes for the future. 1975. 26 minutes. Purchase: 16mm, $400; video, $340. Rental, $55 each. CG.

THE CHEROKEE ARTISTS SERIES
Jerome Tiger: The Man & His Legacy. 35 mins.; Willard Stone: Against the Odds. 28 mins. Bill Rabbit: Master Artist. 28 mins.; Woodrow Haney: Flutemaker. 28 mins.; Charles Banks Wilson. 28 mins. SH.

CHEROKEE BASKETMAKER
Ella Mae Blackbear; The life of a traditional Cherokee basketmaker; from gathering and dyeing to selling baskets at a museum store. Includes history of everyday Cherokee life in northeastern Oklahoma. VHS. 24 mins. $19.95. VIP.

CHEROKEE GENERAL
The Cherokee Nation & the Civil War. 1998. 30 mins. VHS, $24.95. ME.

THE CHEROKEE NATION: THE STORY OF NEW ECHOTA
Recorded at the New Echota historical site in Gordon Co. Georgia, the one time capital of the Cherokee Nation where the constitution was written, and many other events included in this VHS. 15 minutes. $14.95. VIP.

CHEYENNE AUTUMN
Based on an actual incident, this film tells of the valiant efforts of the Cheyenne Indians to escape to their Wyoming homeland from their wretched Oklahoma lands. With Richard Widmark & James Stewart. 1964. 156 mins. ME.

CHIEF MOUNTAIN HOTSHOTS
Blackfeet firefighters identify with traditional warrior societies. 2001. ME.

*CHIEF SEATTLE TELLS HIS OWN STORY
An actor depicts the hisoric personality, explaining the time he lived in; the political, social, & ethical battles they fought, and the contributions he made. Grades 4-8. 20 minutes. VHS, $89. SVE.

CHIEFS
Documentary on a winning Arapahoe basketball team. 2002. ME

CHILDREN OF THE LONG-BEAKED BIRD
Peter Davis and Swedish TV; Portrait of Dominic Old Elk, a 12 year old Crow Indian, exploring his life and interests; a view of Native American life and history. Seeks to erase many stereotypes. 1976. 29 mins, color. Grades 3 and up. BULL. Rental: $40. NAPBC.

CHILDREN OF THE PLAINS INDIANS
A view of Indian life on the Great Plains before the arrival of white settlers, featuring scenes of tribal activities. 20 mins, bxw. 1962. Video. CRM. UCT.

CHILDREN OF WIND RIVER
Traces the history of Shsohone and Arapaho family life and shows how the introduction of boarding schools disrupted traditional child rearing. Uses interviews and images from the reservation. 1989. 30 mins VHS. $49. CHAR.

CHOCTAW HERITAGE VIDEO
William Brescia, Producer; By the Work of Our Hands - Documents tribal members expert in making crafts: split-oak baskets, cane baskets, and drums. 1983. 30 mins; More Than Just a Week of Fun - Shows events of the Choctaw Fair, held on the reservation every summer. 1984. 12 mins; and Choctaw Tribal Government - Explains the structure & functions of Mississippi Choctaw tribal government, and a view of life on the Choctaw reservation today. 1985. Grades 5 and up. 17 minutes. Video. CVP.

CHOCTAW STORY
Bob Ferguson; Highlights the achievements of the tribal administration of Chief Phillip Martin, since 1979. 1985. 28 mins. Video. CVP.

THE CIRCLE
Drama tells the story of a Native American youth who has turned to alcohol to escape his anger and painful childhood memories. Includes a traditional healing circle and innovative programs. 1992. Grades 7 and up. 30 mins. VHS & Guide. $95. CHAR.

CIRCLE OF LIFE, Parts 1 & 2
American Indian youth on teenage pregnancy. Stresses the importance of education, prenatal care, and family planning. Part 1, 43 mins; Part 2, 32 minutes. Video. Rental: $16. UMN.

CIRCLE OF LIFE: THE ALABAMA-COUSHATTAS
Documentary exploring the cultural identity of the Alabama-Coushattas. 24 mins. Teacher's guide. $35. UT-ITC.

CIRCLE OF SONG
Cliff Sijohn and George Burdeau; Presents the Indian concept of the Circle of Life on which important life events and the songs and dances associated with them are point. In two parts. 1976. 28 mins each, color. NAPBC & PBS.

CIRCLE OF THE SUN
Colin Low, Director; Documents the life and ceremonial customs of the Blood Indians of Alberta, Canada, and contrasts their present existence on the reservation. 1960. Grades 7 and up. 30 mins. NFBC. Rental: UA, IU & UMN.

CIRCLE OF WARRIORS
Features nine Native Americans living with HIV infections and AIDS, discussing various aspects of their lives. A discussion guide is provided with the video. 27 mins. VHS. Purchase: $185; rental, $45. SH & NNA.

A CIRCLE OF WOMEN
Modern women meet women elders of Native American tribes in an effort to link their cultures. 60 minutes. 1991. IVA.

CIRCLES
Native justice shows an alternative approach to justice in the Yukon, focusing on ways to heal an offender, a victim, and community. 1997. 58 mins. CHAR.

CIVILIZED TRIBES
Philip Hobel, Executive Producer; Life is reconstructed at the Seminole Reservation in Florida to simulate that of their Seminole ancestors. Also focuses on their present conditions. 26 minutes, color. 1972. Purchase: 16mm, $400; video, $340. Rental, $55 each. CG. 16mm rental only, IU.

CLASH OF CULTURES
Scott Nielsen and Dick Blofson; Four elders from the Lakota tribe, drawing on the oral tradition of Indian life in the late 19th-century, explain the cultural attitudes of the Indians and the clash of attitudes with white settlers. 28 minutes. 1978. 16mm & VHS. UMA & KS.

CLASH OF CULTURES ON THE GREAT PLAINS (1865-1890)
Describes the traditional relationship of the Lakota people to their environment & explore conflicts with outsiders who moved into the area during the 1860s & 1870s. Grades 9-12. Teacher's guide. 20 mins. VHS, $125. AIT.

CLOUDED LAND
Randy Croce, Producer; A sensitive examination of Native American land claims of the White Earth Reservation in Minnesota. 1987/1989. 58 minutes, color. Purchase: 3/4" $160; 1/2" VHS - $110. Rental: IN & UMN.

CLUES TO ANCIENT INDIAN LIFE
Discusses the kind of clues ancient indians left behind, and the importance of preserving these artifacts for study. 1962. 10 mins. Video. AIMS.

COLLIDING WORLDS
The lives of the Mono women, representing three generations, are intertwined to form the body of this film. Shows how traditional Mono ways have clashed & collided with modern technology. 1978. 30 minutes. 16mm. Rental: $37. UCLA.

COLOURS OF PRIDE
Henning Jacobson; Four Indian artists of Canada are interviewed in their home studios by Tom Hill, a Seneca from the Six Nations Reserve in Ontario. 1974. 24 minutes, color. 16mm. NFBC.

COLUMBUS CONTROVERSY:
CHALLENGING HOW HISTORY IS WRITTEN
Nick Kaufman, Director; Examines the Columbus controversy using footage from the classroom of Bill Bigelow, along with historians John Mohawk and William McNeil. 1991. 24 minutes, color. Video. Purchase: $89. SRA.

COLUMBUS DIDN'T DISCOVER US
Robbie Leppzer, Director; Wil Echevarria, Producer; Features interviews with indigenous activists, filmed at the Quincen-tennial gathering in 1990 in Ecuador of 300 native peoples of North, South/Central America. A moving testimony of the impact of the Columbus legacy on the lives of indigenous peoples resulting from the European invasion. 1992. 24 mins. TTP & OY.

COME FORTH LAUGHING: VOICES OF THE SUQUAMISH PEOPLE
Suquamish Tribal Cultural Center, Producer; Provides an account of the life of the Suquamish Indian Tribe living in the Puget Sound region of Washington State over the past one hundred years. 1983. 15 mins. 16mm and video. SUQ.

A COMMON DESTINY
Gayil Nalls, Producer/Director; John Steele, Producer; Comprised of two films: "Walk in Both Worlds" - Jewell Praying Wolf James, a Lummi tribesman speaks of his ancestors and presents the 1853 message of Chief Seattle. And, "The Hopi Prophecy" - Thomas Banyacya, now in his 80s, is a spokesman for Hopi high religious leaders, interprets the prophetic symbols of a sacred petroglyph in AZ for visitors from other tribes, and speaks about the damage that industry has caused on the reservation. 1990. 52 mins Video. MFV.

COMPLETING OUR CIRCLE

Looks at the traditions of the Plains and West Coast Indians, the Inuit, and the first Europeans & settlers in Western Canada. Presents their arts and crafts. 1978. 27 mins. Video. Purchase: CRM. Rental: 16mm, $23. UMN.

CONCERNS OF AMERICAN INDIAN WOMEN

Will George, Director
Interviews with Marie Sanchez, North Cheyenne judge, and Dr. Connie Uri, Choctaw-Cherokee physician and law student. 1977. 30 minutes. Video. MAI.

THE CONQUERED DREAM

Features sequences on Eskimo art and folklore, traditional hunting methods, health problems & education of today's Eskimo. 51 minutes. CEN.

CONQUISTA

Narrated by Richard Boone; A look at how the history of Old West was affected by the fateful meeting of the Plains Indian and the horse. 1974. 20 mins. Video. CFH. Rental: 16mm, $14. UCT.

CONSONANTS WITH COYOTE

Animated Navajo language film. Consonants with common sounds to both Navajo & English. 9 minutes. All grades. 16mm & video. SAN.

CONTRARY WARRIORS: A STORY OF THE CROW TRIBE

Connie Poten & Pamela Roberts, Producers; Peter Coyote, narrator
Award-winning documentary on the Crow people of southeastern MT, as told by members of the tribe, documents the life of 97-year-old Robert Yellowtail as a focus for the telling of Crow history. 1985. 60 mins. DC. Rental, UMN.

CONTRASTS

Portrays the Plains Indians warriors and the U.S. Cavalrymen that faced off against each other in the 1870's. Filmed at the actual site of the Reno retreat crossing at Battle of the Little Big Horn. 45 mins. Video. Purchase: $25. OAP.

A CONVERSATION WITH VINE DELORIA, JR.

Larry Evers, University of Arizona; The writer discusses the gulf between Indian and non-Indian culture and the schizophrenia of white expectations for the Indian. 1978. 29 mins. NR. Rental, video. $37.50. ATL.

1987 COOK INLET FRIENDSHIP POTLATCH

Highlights of Alaska Native traditional dances, music, Native Olympic games & other activities. 1988. 12 minutes, color. Video. $7. NDM.

CORN & THE ORIGINS OF SETTLED LIFE IN MESO-AMERICA

Jack Churchill, Director; Presents the work of three scholars, Michael Coe, Paul Mangelsdorf, and Richard MacNeish. 1964. 40 minutes. 16mm. EDC.

COWTIPPING: THE MILITANT INDIAN WAITER

Randy Redroad; A Cherokee cafe waiter faces customers and their ignorance about American Indians. 1992. VHS. 17 mins. TWN.

COYOTE TALES

Don Mose, Director; Kent Tibbitts, Producer; A series of five animated Navajo language and culture-based curriculum films in Navajo language. 5 legendary coyote stories: Coyote and Beaver, 4 mins; Coyote & Lizard, 7 mins; Coyote and Rabbit, 10 mins; Coyote & Skunk, 9 mins; Coyote & Toad, 8 mins. SAN.

COYOTE WAITS

Robert Redford & Rebecca Eaton, Producers
Based on a mystery novel by Tony Hillerman and set on a Navajo reservation. Wes Studi & Adam Beach. 97 mins 2003. DVD, $24.95; VHS, $19.95. ME.

CRAZY HORSE - THE LAST WARRIOR

A&E Home Video; Story of Crazy Horse, leader of Sioux. 1993. 50 mins. ME.

CRAZY HORSE

Turner Network Production; Story of Oglala Sioux leader. Dream sequences. With Michael Greyeyes, Irene Bedard, Wes Studi, et al. 93 mins. 1996. ME.

A CREE HEALER

Consists of interviews with the healer and shows segments where he prepares for the sweatlodge ceremony. The interview concerns the issues & controversies encountered by this native healer in openly discussing the subject. 22 mins. VHS. UADA.

CREE HUNTERS OF MISTASSINI

Tony Ianzelo and Boyce Richardson, Directors
The setting up of a winter camp by 16 Cree Indians. Indian life is observed in the bush. 1974. Grades 7 and up. 58 mins. 16mm & Video. Purchase: Video, $245; rental, $60; 16mm, $70. DER & NFBC. Rental: DEC, PSU, UCT & UMN.

CREE WAY

Tony Ianzelo & Boyce Richardson, Director
Provides a view of a successful bilingual education project which connects Cree children to their past and future. 1977. 28 mins. 16mm. NFBC.

CREEK NATION VIDEO

Gary Robinson, Producer/director; For the past decade The Muscogee Creek Nation Communications Center, located in Okmulgee, OK, has been producing videotapes to present accurate and contemporary views of the Creek Nation. 17 programs on culture, history, and current affairs have been produced. MCN.

CROOKED BEAK OF HEAVEN

David Attenborough, Writer/Narrator; A Haida chief bestows lavish gifts on his tribesmen and then smashes his most valuable possessions, a potlatch ceremony. Contrasted with footage made of the Kwakiutl by Edward S. Curtis in 1912. 1976. 52 mins, color. 16mm. Rental: TW, UCLA, UCT, UI & UMN.

CROW DOG

Mike Cuesta & David Baxter, Directors; Documentary portrait of Sioux medicine man, Leonard Crow Dog, the spiritual leader of 89 American Indian tribes and the spokesman for the traditionalists. 1979. 57 minutes, color. Purchase: 16mm, $795; video, $350. Rental, $95. CG. Rental only, $30. UT.

CROW DOG'S PARADISE

A look at a Sioux Indian enclave where the Crow Dog family preserves the spiritual and intellectual heritage of their traditional American Indian culture. 1979. Grades 9 and up. 28 mins. 16mm & video. Purchase: VHS, $89; 3/4", $119. CC. Rental: VHS, $16; 16mm, $21.75. UMN.

1994 & 1995 CROW FAIR AND POW WOW

Views the pow wow dancing and parades at the Crow Fair, Crow Agency, Montana. The celebration of Crow lifeways through their unique music & songs. Two 60 minute videos. CAN.

CROW/SHOSHONE SUNDANCE...A TRADITIONAL CEREMONY

Documents the traditional Crow Lifeways & philosophies through authentic & legendary Crow/Shoshone Sundance Ceremony. 1991. 56 mins. Video. UMN.

CRY OF THE YUROK

Details the Yuroks, California's largest Native American tribe, with the many problems that beset them as they try to survive. 58 mins. FH.

CULTURAL CHANGES

Pre-reservation life of the buffalo hunting Indians of the southern Plains told through the use of pictographic drawings by Kiowa & Cheyenne young men imprisoned in Ft. Marion, FL, 1875. 1970. 17 mins. 16mm. Rental: $13. UMN.

THE CUP'IK OF ALASKA--ESKIMOS: A CHANGING CULTURE

Despite many technological & material changes, their resources are the same as their ancestors, and they still depend on ancient knowledge that helps them adjust to their environment. 1992. Grades 4 and up. 32 mins. Purchase: 16mm, $615; video, $375. Rental: 16mm, $95. PHO.

CUSTER'S LAST FIGHT

Thomas Ince, Producer
The 1925 release of the 1912 Ince film, with two reels added to fill out the story. 45 mins. Video. Purchase: $25. OAP.

THE DAKOTA CONFLICT

Floyd Red Crow Westerman & Garrison Keillor, Narrators
Recounts the war (sometimes called "the Great Sioux Uprising") that began the 30-year struggle for the Great Plains, a struggle that continued at the Little Big Horn & ended at Wounded Knee. Uses diaries, old photographs, sketchbooks, newspaper archives, trail transcripts, and oral histories passed down through the generations. 1993. 60 mins, color. VHS. $20.95. ME. Rental: $16. UMN.

DAKOTA EXILE

The story of the Dakota people's brave struggle to survive in 1862 after being expelled from Minnesota and the U.S.'s largest mass execution that occurred then. Robbie Robertson narrates. 1995. 60 mins. VHS, $20.95. ME.

DANCE ME OUTSIDE

Bruce McDonald, Director
1995 slice of Native Canadian life on a northern Ontario reserve. 91 mins. DVD. Amazon.com. $15.99.

DANCE TO GIVE THANKS

Looks at the 184th annual He-De-Wa-Chi (Festival of Joy) of the Omaha Indian Tribe. Learn aboiut the history of the festival and see traditional dance by tribal members. 30 mins. VHS & 3/4" U-matic. NAPBC.

DANCES WITH WOLVES
Kevin Costner, Director & Producer; Saga of a disallusioned soldier and his capture and joining the Lakota Sioux tribe. With Graham Greene, Rodney Grant & Kevin Costner as the soldier. 236 min. 1990. Extended cut DVD, 2003, $25.80. ME.

DANCING FEATHERS
Paul Stephens; Producer/Writer; Eric Jordan, Director
In this "Spirit Bay" program, Tafia, a young Ojibway girl, is apprehensive about performng a jingle dance at an upcoming powwow in Toronto. 1983. Grades 3-8. 28 mins. 16mm & video. Purchase: $149. ALT.

DANCING IN MOCCASINS: KEEPING NATIVE AMERICAN TRADITIONS ALIVE
Examines the needs & problems of today's Native Americans, both those who live on the reservation & those who have chosen the mainstream. The conclusion focuses on celebration & survival as reflected in the continuing tradition of the Pow Wow. 49 mins. Video, Purchase: $149; rental: $75. FH.

A DANCING PEOPLE
Dancers & musicians from nine Yup'ik Eskimo villages gathered in the Yukon town of St. Mary's for 'Yupiit Yuraryariat.' Three days of dancing, gift-giving & contests. 1983. 30 mins. Video. $24.95. KYUK.

DANCING TO GIVE THANKS
NETV, Producer; JR Mathews, Host; Celebrates the traditions and family customs of the Omaha Indian Tribe. Filmed at the Omaha Tribal headquarters near Macy, Nebraska. Interprets dance themes & traditions. 1988. 30 mins. Video. Rental: $20. GPN. Purchase: $150; Rental: $40. NAPBC.

DAUGHTERS OF THE ANASAZI
John Anthony; The legendary Acoma potter, Lucy Lewis, and her daughters Emma & Delores demonstrate the traditional way of making fine pottery from grinding the clay to forming the coils & bowls, polishing, painting & firing. 1990. 28 mins. Video. Purchase: $24.95. FI. Rental: $16. UMN.

DAUGHTERS OF THE COUNTRY
Norma Bailey, Producer; Focuses on four women of Native American heritage who find themselves drawn into the world of the white man and then rejected by it. Includes: Part 1 - "Ikwe," an Indian girl who lives in a remote area of North America in 1770; Part 2 - "Mistress Madeleine," she is half Native American in 1850; Part 3 - "Places Not Our Own," about a family in pre-Depression era in North America; and Part 4 - "The Wake," about Joan in 1985, a single American Indian parent with two small children whose father deserted them. 1987. 57 minutes each. Purchase: 16mm, $775 each; VHS, $150 each. Rental: $80 each. NFBC.

ROBERT DAVIDSON
Michael Brodie & Bill Roxborough, Producers/directors
Features one of the best known of contemporary artists, Robert Davidson. He is shown making a deer skin drum, with the entire process well portrayed. Discusses his technique, the philosophy behind the art of the Haida, and his personal connection. 1981. 29 mins. In English or French. Video. MVS & VOI.

THE DAWN RIDERS: NATIVE AMERICAN ARTISTS
Robert and Dona DeWeese
Three prominent Indian painters, Woody Crumbo (Potawatomi), Blackbear Bosin (Kiowa-Comanche) and Dick West (Cheyenne), talk about their work and influences on their art. 1969. 27 mins. 16mm. LF.

DE GRAZIA
Ted De Grazia, well-known Arizona artist, discusses how his life among the Indians and Mexicans of the Southwest is reflected in his work. 1967. 29 mins. 16mm. Rental. UA.

DEAD MAN
Johnny Depp, a young vet who has a price on his head, travels through the Badlands with a philosophical Indian, Gary Farmer, as his guide, who teaches him to face the dangers that follow a "dead man." 120 mins. b&w. 1996. VHS, $16.99; DVD, $29.99. ME.

THE DEATH MARCH OF DE SOTO
Archaeologists chart the conquistador's trail across Florida's Gulf Coast to the Gulf of the Mississippi and uncover now-extinct Native American cultures, their people victims of brutality, disease, and neglect. 1993. 28 mins. Video. Purchase: $149; rental: $75. FH.

THE DEATH OF THE BISON
The stories of the Indian chiefs, of Crazy Horse and Sitting Bull and their great battles to the events at Wounded Knee in 1973 demonstrates that the conflicts of the past have yet to be resolved. 13 mins. Video. Purchase: $69.95. FH.

DESERT DANCE
Includes single voice chanting with Native American flute by Carlos Nakai, drums, rattles, wind & rain. Cassette, $12. CH.

DESERT PEOPLE (PAPAGO)
1949. 25 minutes. Rental. UA.

DESERT REGIONS: NOMADS & TRADERS
A look at the Navajo Indians of Monument Valley and Bedouins of Jordan. 1980. 15 mins. Video. PHO.

DETOUR
Deron Twohatchet; Two mismatched drifters, Jim and James are on a voyage discovering the contours of homo/hetero, red/white, personal/political in an experimental narrative feast. In a critiique of the exotized American Trickster figure. 28 mins. Color & B&W. Video. Purchase: $175; rental, $60. TWN.

DIABETES: LIFETIME SOLUTIONS
Documentary about the prevention, care and maintenance of diabetes in Native American communities. Looks at the history and present day factors contributing to the disease amongst Native North Americans. 1999. 30 mins. VHS. $148. CHAR.

DIABETES: NOTES FROM INDIAN COUNTRY
Lorelei DeCora, a Winnebago public health nurse visits the Winnebago Indian Reservation in Nebraska, the Rosebud Sioux Tribe and the Porcupine Lakota community in South Dakota to present community solutions to this health care crisis. 1999. 20 mins. VHS. $50. CHAR.

DIARY: NATIVE AMERICAN MINNESOTANS
Documents the personal stories of several Native Americans living in Minnesota. Describes the process of getting in touch with their roots & fitting into the white American culture. 1992. 35 mins. Video. Rental: $16. UMN.

A DIFFERENT DRUM
The story of a young Comanche boy who is torn between his family's desire for him to attend college and his own natural aptitude for auto mechanics. 1974. 21 mins. Rental. UK.

DINEH: THE PEOPLE
Jonathan Reinis & Stephen Hornick; Documentary focusing on impending relocation of several thousand Navajo from a joint-use land area surrounding the Hopi Reservation which is located in the midst of the Navajo Reservation. Portrays the cultural & economic conditions which the Navajo attempt to survive while striving to preserve traditional values. 1976. 77 mins. NAPBC.

DISCOVERING AMERICAN INDIAN MUSIC
Bernard Wilets; Songs and dances of tribes from various parts of the country performed in authentic costumes featuring Louis Ballard, Cherokee composer's percussion ensemble combining natural instruments of numerous tribes. 1971. Grades 4 and up. 24 mins. SH. Rental: IU, UMN, UCLA, UCT, UT & UK.

THE DISPOSSESSED
Sympathetic view of the Pit River Indians' struggle to regain lands in northern California taken from them in 1853 and now controlled by Pacific Gas & Electric Co. Shows the Indians' impoverished living conditions, and describes how PG&E dams have destroyed salmon runs on which they depend. Traces the legal history of the land dispute. 1970. 33 mins. 16mm. Rental: UCLA.

DISTANT VOICE...THUNDER WORDS
Discusses the role of oral tradition in modern Native American literature. Includes interviews with storytellers & experts. 1990. 60 mins. Video. NAPBC.

THE DIVIDED TRAIL: A NATIVE AMERICAN ODYSSEY
Jerry Aronson & Michael Goldman; Follows the lives of three Chippewa as they moved from various stages of activism and discontent into vocational alternatives. 1977. 30 mins. PHO. Rental: $19.65. IU; 16mm, $24.25. UMN

DO WE WANT US TO?
The story about the heritage of the Tlinget Indians. 1979. Grades 7 and up. 20 mins. Video. NAC. Rental: $10. UCT.

DOCTOR, LAWYER, INDIAN CHIEF
Carol Geddes, Director; Gail Valaskakis, Narrator; Focuses on five Native Indian women from Canada; each talks about her personal difficulties in getting to where she is today, and about her life experiences. Includes: Sophie Pierre, the chief of St. Mary's Band in B.C.; Lucille McLeod, job-counselor for native women; Margaret Joe, the first native women to have become a minister in the Yukon government; Corrine Hunt, of Kwakiutl Nation, operates the hydraulic equipment on a commercial fishing boat off the coast of B.C.; & Roberta Jamieson, Canada's first native Indian woman lawyer. 1987. 29 mins. NFBC.

DOE BOY
James Duval, a half Cherokee, accidentally kills a doe and is nicknamed "Doe Boy". His grandfather teaches him the difference between hunting & killing. With Gordon Tootossis. 87 mins. 2002. VHS, $9.98; DVD, $14.98. ME.

DREAM DANCES OF THE KASHIA POMO
Clyde B. Smith, Producer; Pomo women dance the Bole Maru nearly a century after it first evolved, blending the native Kaksu cult with the Maru or dream religion. Five dances are shown. Shaman expresses her religious beliefs in her own words. 1964. 30 mins. UC. Rental: IU & PSU.

DREAMKEEPER
Lions Gate; With Nathaniel Arcand & Gerald Auger. American Indian legend told on film. 180 mins. DVD. 2004. ME. $14.99. Also available at Amazon.com.

DREAMSPEAKER
An emotionally disturbed boy runs away from an institution and is adopted by an old Indian shaman. The Indian vision of life and death are reviewed. 1977. 75 mins. Grades 9 and up. Rental, $42. PSU.

THE DRUM
Alaska Native Human Resource Development Project
Shows a Native American ritual. Grades 4-12. 1987. 15 mins. VHS. NDM

THE DRUM IS THE HEART
Randy Croce, Producer; Narrated entirely by Indian participants, ranging from children to elders, this film focuses on the Blackfeet, Blackfoot, Blood and Peigan tribes that make up the Blackfoot Nation at their celebrations, speaking about their contemporary lives and traditional values. 1982. 29 mins. Video. IN.

THE DRUMMAKER
Presents an Ojibwa Indian, William Bineshi Baker, Sr., on the Lac Court Oreilles Reservation in northern Wisconsin, one of the last of his people to continue the art of drum-making. Step-by-step he constructs a dance drum, and expresses his beliefs about tradition. 1978. 37 mins., bxw. PSU.

THE DRUMMER
Thomas Vennum, Jr.; William Bineshi Baker, Jr., an Ojibwa, living on the Lac Courte Oreilles Reservation in northern Wisconsin constructs a drum step-by-step. 1978. 37 mins., bxw. 16mm. PSU.

DRUMS ALONG THE MOHAWK
John Ford, Director; Historical drama of lawless frontier & Indian attacks before the Revolutionary War. Setting is the backwoods of New York State. Stars Henry Fonda & Claudette Colbert, John Carradine, et al. 104 mins. DVD, 2005. $14.98. Amazon.com.

DRUMS OF THE AMERICAN INDIAN
Suitable for practicing traditional dance steps. Cassette, $12. CH.

THE DRUMS OF WINTER (UKSUUM CAUYAI)
Sarah Elder & Leonard Kamerling; Documentary exploring traditional dance, music and spiritual world of the Yup'ik Eskimo people of Emmonak, a remote village at mouth of the Yukon River on Bering Sea coast. 1988. 90 mins. DER.

THE EAGLE & THE CONDOR
KBYU-TV, Provo Utah, Producer; Examines the interaction between the Native American cultures of North and South America. Native American entertainers of BYU's Laminite Generation tour South America performing and discussing differences & similarities in cultures. 1975. 29 mins VHS. NAPBC.

THE EAGLE & THE MOON
Wango Weng, Director; Animated Haida story presenting elements of Haida culture such as the class and their totem poles. 1971. 10 mins. 16mm. WALL.

THE EAGLE & THE RAVEN
Profiles the story of Native American Tlingit teenagers who were sentenced by their tribal court for robbery and the program and healing process. Grades 6 and up. 1996. 80 mins. VHS. $49. CHAR.

EARL'S CANOE: A TRADITIONAL OJIBWE CRAFT
Tom Vennum, Charles Weber, with Earl Nyholm
The making of a birchbark canoe and its meaning to the Ojibwe people of Wisc. 1999. 27 mins. Purchase: $145; rental, $40. DER.

THE EARLY AMERICANS
Traces the rise of man from his arrival in North America as an ice age wanderer, to builder of complex societies more than 2,000 years before Columbus. 1976. 42 minutes Grades 9 and up. Video. Rental, $18. UA & PSU.

THE EARLY AMERICANS, 1776
Daniel Wilson Productions; Describes the lifestyles of Americans west of the Appalachians in 1776 in New Mexico, Hawaii, Alaka & the Spanish Mission of California. Grades 7 and up. 28 mins. Rental: $10. UCT.

EARLY MAN IN NORTH AMERICA
1972. 12 mins. VHS. FILMS.

EARTH CIRCLES
Emphasizes the traditional closeness with nature that is a fundamental aspect of Native American life.Images are from Woodlands Indian prints & photos of wildlife in natural habitat. Study guide included. 10 mins. VHS. $50. TOP.

THE EARTH IS OUR HOME
Elizabeth Patapoff, Producer/writer; Produced in cooperation with members of the Burns Paiute tribe in Oregon to preserve a record of their traditional way of life and skills. 1979. 29 mins. 16mm & video. MP

EARTHSCAPE
Artists on the Copper River Delta/Alaska. Documents watercolorists, photographers, and sculptors as they travel to Alaska's Copper River Delta to paint and sculpt. Video. 20 mins. SH.

EARTHSHAPERS
A look at the sacred mounds created by the Woodland Native people. Grades 7 & up. 14 mins. VHS. NAPBC. Rental: $10. UCT.

EASTER IN IGLOOLIK: PETER'S STORY
Paulle Clark, Producer; A photographed look at Inuit life in a modern Arctic community, Igloolik, in Canada's Northwest Territories. 1987. Grades 7 and up. 24 mins. BULL.

EDGE OF AMERICA
Chris Eyre, Director; Showtime Entertainment
Inspirational story about loyalty & courage. English professor at Three Nations Reservation in Utah decides to take on the challenge of coaching the high school girls' basketball team. 106 minutes. DVD. Amazon.com. $9.21.

EDUCATION OF LITTLE TREE
Story of 8-year old Little Tree who goes to live with his Cherokee grandparents during the depression. He learns his culture & way of life. With Graham Greene, James Cromwell, Joseph Ashton. 180 mins. VHS, $19.99. ME.

EDUCATIONAL VIDEO
Two videos in one. Time Journey - explores the prehistoric time period of North America; and, Indian Diversity - examines the life of modern Indian cultures, Choctaw, Ponca, Pueblo, and Peoria/Miami. Plus two Indian stories. Includes handbook. $14. CMM.

THE ELDERS SPEAK..."NOW I LISTEN
Elders from around the country speak out on the needs of Native American, Native Alaskan & Native Hawaiian elders. 20 mins. Video. SH.

ELEGANT VISIONS: NATIVE AMERICAN WOMEN'S CLOTHING
44 models representing 24 tribes show 70 different outfits, including: Woodland tunics and ribbon-work; a Navajo wedding dress; and a Tlingit blanket. VHS. 30 minutes. $19.95. VIP.

ELLA MAE BLACKBEAR: CHEROKEE BASKETMAKER
Scott & Sheila Swearingen, Producers/directors/eds; Fran Ringold, Narrator
Ella Mae Blackbear practices the ancient art of Cherokee basket-making as it has survived in Oklahoma after the Cherokees' removal to the Indian Territory in the late 1830's. 1982. 25 mins. VHS. WH.

EMERGENCE
Barbara Wilk, Producer/writer/animator
Tells the story of the events leading to the entrance of Dineh, the Navajo people; traditional chants heard in the film are versions of the origin myths sung as part of certain Navajo healing rituals. 1981. 14 mins. Color animation. 16mm, video. CC & PR.

EMERGENCE: GRASS ROOTS ACCOUNT OF INDIAN ACTIVISM
Walter Verbanie; Documents how the Potawatomi in Kansas lost lands through disadvanta-geous treaties & divisions in the tribe between members of the Mission and Prairie bands. 1977. 35 minutes. 16mm. MAI.

THE EMERGING ESKIMO
Deals with the impact of the white man upon the native Eskimos. 15 minutes. Grades 1-8. Rental. UK.

THE ENCHANTED ARTS: PABLITA VELARDE
Irene-Aimee Depke, Producer/director; Presents a portrait of Santa Clara Pueblo, Pablita Velarde, one of the first Indian women to pursue painting professionally. 1977. 28 mins. Video. DEPKE.

END OF THE TRAIL: THE AMERICAN PLAINS INDIANS
Surveys the westward movement in America during the last century and the tragic impact of that movement on the American Indians. 1967. Grades 6 and up. 53 minutes. b&w. 16mm. CRM. Rental: IU, UA, UCT & UMN.

ESKIMO ARTIST - KENOJUAK
John Geeney, Director
Inuit artist Kenojuak shows the sources of her inspiration and methods used to transfer her carvings to stone. 1964. 20 minutes. Grades 7 and up. Purchase: 16mm, $410; and video, $300. Rental, $50. NFBC. Rental, $17. UK and PSU.

ESKIMO CHILDREN
Portrays the activities of a typical Eskimo family living on Nunivak Island off the Alaskan coast. 1941. 11 mins., bxw. Grades 4 and up. In English & Spanish. 16mm. Rental only. IU, UA & UK.

ESKIMO: FIGHT FOR LIFE
Asen Balikci, Advisor and Narrator; Shows the careful division of tasks among the different members of a group of Netsilek Eskimos camped together during the winter seal hunting season. 1970. Grades 7 & up. 51 mins. EDC & UW.

ESKIMO HUNTERS
Presents the life of the Eskimos of Northwestern Alaska. 1949. 21 mins. bxw. 16mm. Rental only. IU & UK.

THE ESKIMO IN LIFE & LEGEND
Shows how the Inuit's way of life, his legends, and his art of stone carving are interrelated. 1960. 22 mins. Grades 7 & up. Rental. UA.

THE ESKIMO SEA HUNTERS
How Eskimo people live in regions where the weather is always cold. 1949. 20 minutes/bxw. Rental. UK.

ESKIMOS: A CHANGING CULTURE
Wayne Mitchell
Examines the lives of two generations of Inuit Eskimos who live on Nunivak Island in the Bering Sea off the coast of Alaska. 1971. 17 mins. Grades 4 and up. PHO. Rental only, IU & BYU.

THE ESKIMOS OF POND INLET
Hugh Brody
Studies the Inuits (Eskimos) of Pond Inlet, Baffin Island. 1977. 52 mins. Video. Purchase: FI. Rental: $19. PSU.

ESTE MVSKOKE/THE MUSCOGEE PEOPLE
Marty Fulk & Gene Hamilton, Associate producers; Tim Bigpond, Narrator
Beginning with the "origin of clans," this program provides an overview of the history, culture, and modern achievements of the Creek Nation. 1985. 24 mins. Video. MCN & ODE.

THE ETERNAL DRUM
Don Priest, Producer; Looks at the social & spiritual significance of the contemporary American Indian Powwow & explains the traditions & the altruistic foundations of the American Indian societies. Grades 6 and up. 25 minutes. VHS. $195. SH, NDM

EVERY DAY CHOICES: ALCOHOL & AN ALASKA TOWN
Sarah Elder, Producer/director/editor; Shows how insidious, destructive, and pervasive the problem of alcohol is in native communities in the north, Yup'ik Eskimo villages in the Bethel, Alaska area. The film addresses stereotyped ideas of Native American alcoholism. 1985. 93 minutes. 16mm & video. NH.

EVERYONE COUNTS
Looks at the problem of prescription drug misuse in one Native American community. Part 2 of a 2 part series. 2000. 24 mins. VHS. $75. Part 1, "Knowledge Is the Best Medicine." CHAR.

EVERYTHING HAS SPIRIT
Explored the historical roots of Native American religious persecution and examines contemporary issues including preservation of sacred sites, First Amendment protection and the use of peyote in the Native American Church. Adult. VHS. 30 mins. $69. CHAR.

EXCAVATION OF MOUND 7
Archaeology work in the field and in the lab to piece together the mysteries of the Pueblo Indians of New Mexico. 1973. 44 mins. VHS, U-matic. NAC.

THE EXILES
Kent Mackenzie, Producer; Classic depiction of one anguished but typical night in the lives of three young American Indians who have left the reservation and come to live in downtown Los Angeles. 1961. 72 minutes, bxw. 16mm & video. UC. Rental: UA, UCLA, UMN, UK, IU & PSU.

EXPEDITION ARIZONA: MISSIONS OF OLD ARIZONA
Reviews the buildings of San Xavier del Bac which is still used by the Papago people after 260 years, and the contributions of Father Kino to Indian culture. 1960. 27 minutes, bxw. Rental. UA.

EXPEDITION ARIZONA: SHARDS OF THE AGES
Shows three ancient cultures: the Hohokam of the desert, the Mogollon of the mountains, & the Anasazi of the plateau regions of Arizona. 1960. 27 minutes, bxw. Rental. UA.

EYANOPAPI: THE HEART OF SIOUX
Details the historical and religious significance of the South Dakota Black Hills to the Sioux Nation. Grades 9 and up. 30 mins. CC.

EYES OF THE SPIRIT
Corey Flintoff, Producer/writer; Alexie Isaac, Director; Ina Carpenter, Narrator
Documents the work of a group of dancers, the Bethel Native Dancers, and three master carvers, in preserving and teaching Yup'ik Eskimo traditions and reviving the use of masks in Native dancing. 1983. 30 mins. VHS. KYUK.

THE FACE OF WISDOM: STORIES OF ELDER WOMEN
Catherine Busch-Johnston, Producer/Director; Julie Harris, host
Series of 8 videos, including one entitled: "Nellie Red Owl," a Native American elder of the Sioux tribe of SD. Born only 16 years after her tribe's massacre at Wounded Knee, she lives with the conviction that her land & native traditions must never again be compromised. 1993. 30 mins. Video. PHO.

FACE TO FACE
Contains 5 extended interviews with Native Americans living with AIDS. Each discusses various aspects of their lives. A discussion guide is provided with the video. 58 minutes. VHS. SH.

FACES OF CULTURE: 22 - NEW ORLEANS' BLACK INDIANS: A CASE STUDY IN THE ARTS
Follows the Black Indian tribes of New Orleans, a blend of American Indians and blacks. 1983. 30 mins. Video. Rental, $14. PSU.

THE FAITHKEEPER
Betsy McCarthy, Producer/director; Relates the guiding philosophy of Native Americans to our own today. Bill Moyers is the guest of Oren Lyons, who talks about the past and future of Native American peoples. Lyons is chief of the Turtle Clan of Onondaga Nation & a prominent member of the environmental movement. 1992. 58 minutes. VHS. Purchase: $29.95. MFV.

FAMILY LIFE OF THE NAVAJO INDIANS
Fries, Kluckhohn & Woolf, Producers; Highlights some of the ways in which the Navajo child develops into adulthood. 1943. 31 mins. NYU & UT.

A FAMILY OF LABRADOR
Kent Martin, Director; A story of corporate development and changing ways of life for Indian, Inuit and people of mixed ancestry. 1978. 59 mins. VHS. NFBC.

FANCY DANCE
Full Circle Communications; Close up and slow motion sequences show champion dancers in exciting contests. 30 minutes. VHS. $19.95. WH.

THE FAST RUNNER
Love murder and revenge in the Arctic Circle centuries ago. An all Native cast speaking Inuit language. 2001. DVD, $26.99; VHS, $99.99. ME.

FAT CITY: OBESITY
Roger Bingham; Looks at obesity on the Pima Indian Reservation in Arizona. Grades 7 and up. 1990. 28 mins. VHS. $70. CHAR.

FEATHERS
Larry Littlebird, Writer; Frank Marrero (WGBH), Producer; Dramatizes personal and social problems encountered by teenagers over how far they, as Indians, should go in joining the mainstream of American life. Emphasizes the closeness of family and community life. 1980. 30 mins. Video. WGBH.

FEDERAL INDIAN LAW
Joel Freedman; Joan Kaehl, Writer; Traces the development of federal Indian law through treaties, statutes, and court decisions. By using real life examples, it illustrates the impact that federal Indian law can have on tribal economics and community lifestyles, and how law can be made to work for your tribe.

Narrated by Kirke Kickingbird, Kiowa attorney and founder of the Institute for the Development of Indian Law. 1980. 19 mins. 16mm. IDIL.

THE FEMININE: ANCIENT VISION, MODERN WISDOM
Wabun Wind; Discusses matriarchy, patriarchy, women's power, moon cycles and menstrual cycles, stereotyping of women, sexuality, relationships, and raising children. 65 mins. Video. Purchase: $29.95. BTP & CH.

THE FIGHTING CHEYENNE
Depicts the Cheyenne Indians' battles with white travelers on the trail. Relates the historic tale of Dull Knife and his Cheyenne band. 30 mins. 16mm. UT.

FINDING THE CIRCLE: AMERICN INDIANB DANCE THEATRE
Native American dancing with all its colors and sacred ritual. 56 mins. Video. Purchase: $36. CH.

FIRES OF SPRING
Henry T. Lewis, Ph.D., Writer/Producer; Shows how, among the Slavey and Beaver tribes of northern Alberta, Canada, fire was used to carefully maintain and improve selected habitats of plants, game & furbearing animals. 1980. 33 mins. Purchase: 16mm, $250 (Canadian); video, $125. BINS. Rental: 16mm, $17.50. PSU; $20.50, UMN.

THE FIRST AMERICAN MELTING POT
The gradual arrival of new Indian groups on the Plains and their clash with bison-hunting horse culture. 1981. 30 mins. Video. KS.

THE FIRST AMERICANS
Story of Raymond Tracey, a young Indian man trying to get back to his roots & determine who the American Indians are. Grades 3-8. Produced in 1989 by Children's Television International & American Indian Heritage Foundation. In six 15-minute programs. $29.95 each, $131.70/set. Teacher's Guide, $2. GPN.

THE FIRST AMERICANS
Studies the major Indian tribes of the U.S.- their customs, culture and the land that belonged to them. Students will explore the special characteristics of individual tribes. Grades 4-6. 1988. 60 minutes. Video. Purchase: $129.95. Available as filmstrips and cassettes. TA.

THE FIRST AMERICANS
In two parts. Part I: And Their Gods-- (20 mins.) The migration of people into the Americas and the eventual setting and differentiating of these people into tribes. 11 mins. Part II: Some Indians of the Southlands-- (32 mins.) Depicts customs & beliefs of certain Indians in the southern half of U.S.: Natchez, the Moundbuilders, the Hopi, Zuni and Navajo. Grades 4-9. 1969. Purchase:. IFF; UT - 16mm rental, $20. Rental only, 16mm. IU & UCT.

THE FIRST AMERICANS
Discusses the 30,000 years of cultural development of the American Indian. 1979. 30 minutes. CET.

THE FIRST AMERICANS-SOME INDIANS OF THE SOUTHLAND
The customs, beliefs and history that shaped the daily patterns of life in the early cultures of the Natchez, the "Moundbuilders," the Hopi, the Zuni, and the Navajo. 1976. 18 mins. Grades 7 and up. 16 mm. Rental, $14. IU.

FIRST NATION BLUE
Documentary narrated by Graham Greene uncovering the changing attitudes of police officers serving Native American communities. 1996. 48 mins. CHAR.

FIRST FRONTIER
Chronicles the long process of defeat and destruction of the Native American community beginning with the 1540 penetration into North America by DeSoto and his forces, then the French and British. Made with the cooperation of the Mississippi Band of Choctaw and the Poarch Band of Creek Indians. 58 minutes. Video. Purchase: $250. BE.

FIRST NATION BLUE
Documentary narrated by Graham Greene about police officers serving Native American communities. VHS. 47.5 minutes $150. CHAR.

THE FIRST NORTHWESTERNERS: THE ARCHAEOLOGY OF EARLY MAN
Louis and Ruth Kirk, Producers; Examines the first northwest environment of more than 10,000 years ago and the first humans known to have lived there. 1979. 29 mins. Purchase: 16mm, $425; beta, $225; VHS, $215. UW.

FIRST PEOPLES
Explains how ancient people came to North America and compares their lifestyles before Europeans arrived. Myths & legends included. Grades 4-8. 15 mins. VHS, $125. AIT.

FISH HAWK
Fish Hawk (Will Sampson), an aging Indian hunter in turn-of-the-century rural America, struggles to overcome the lure of the bottle & local towns people.1994. 95 mins. VHS. $14.99. ME.

A FISHING PEOPLE: THE TULALIP TRIBE
Heather Oakson; Tells the story of their history as a fishing people and provides an overview of the tribe's current involvement with fishing as an industry. 1980. 17 minutes. The TT.

500 NATIONS
Kevin Costner, Director; Warner Bros.; 8-part documentary exploring the history of the indigenous peoples of North & Central America from pre-Colombian times through the period of European contact & colonialization, to the end of the 19th century. 372 minutes. DVD. Amazon.com. $36.49.

FOLKLORE OF THE MUSCOGEE (CREEK) PEOPLE
Rex Daugherty, Executive producer; Gary Robinson, Writer
Host Dr. Ruth Arrington (Creek Nation) describes the nature of folklore within Creek culture, and explains the breakdown of folklore into three categories: legends, myths and fables. Grades 3-12. 1983. 29 minutes. VHS. Purchase: $150; Rental: $40. MCN & NAPBC.

FOLLOWING THE STAR
Story of Russian Orthodox Christmas as practiced by the Yup'ik Eskimos of the Kuskokwim River Delta. 1987. 30 mins. VHS. $24.95. KYUK.

FONSECA: IN SEARCH OF COYOTE
Mary Louise King & Fred Aronow, Producers; Noted Native American artist Harry Fonseca relates the development of his "Coyote" series of paintings and drawings; shows how Fonseca's anthropomorphic coyote grew out of traditional North American India art forms and legends surrounding the famous "trickster." 1983. 30 mins. UMN.

FOREST SPIRITS
NEWIST, Producer; A series of seven 30-minute programs on the Oneida & Menominee tribes of Wisconsin. 1: To Keep a Heritage Alive--Oneida children learn their native tongue, religious code and moral ethic. 2: The Learning Path--The educational system and the Native American. 3: Land Is Life--Documents Oneida's troubles over land. 4: Ancestors Of Those Yet Unborn--Menominee lifestyle. 5: Living With Tradition--Menominee traditions and reaffirmation of heritage. 6 & 7: Dreamers With Power--Part 1: Explores stereotypes & truths about Menominee Reservation life; and Part 2: Menominee's history. Grades 4+. 1975-76. Teachers' Guide, $1. NAPBC & GPN.

FOREVER IN TIME: THE ART OF EDWARD S. CURTIS
Robert W. Mull, Producer; Curtis (1868-1952), one of the world's foremost photographers, in photos and film, the culture and lifestyle of the American Indian. He recorded tribal chants, narratives of Indian life and vocabulary translations. This documentary chronicles Curtis's career, featuring interviews with surviving family members, blending his motion picture footage, sound recordings & photographic portraits, original music score. 1990. 50 mins. UMN.

FORGET THE FISH...CULTURAL ASPECTS OF NURSING CARE FOR NAVAJOS
Reality-based story about a new nurse, Ann Davis, and her experiences with a Navajo patient & his wife. Her encounter with a medicine man helps her learn how to work with Navajo medicine people within the hospital setting. 1984. 25 minutes Video. Rental: $18.50. UMN.

THE FORGOTTEN AMERICAN
A documentary filmed in the Southwest and in the urban Indian communities of Los Angeles & Chicago. Shows the impoverishment of the American Indian, loss of identity & self-respect. 1968. 25 mins. 16mm. Purchase/rental. MAI-CFV. Rental: PSU, UA, UCT & UCLA.

FORGOTTEN FRONTIER
KAET-TV Phoenix, Producer; Documents Spanish mission settlements of southern Arizona, and the conversion and teaching of skills to Indians. 1976. 30 mins. Video. Rental, $40/week. NAPBC.

FORT PHIL KEARNEY: HATED POST ON THE LITTLE PINEY
A tour of Fort Phil Kerney, Fetterman Hill and the Wagon Box Fight, where the Sioux under Red Cloud clashed with U.S. Army for control of northern Wyoming's Powder River Country & Bozeman Trail. 30 mins. Video. $30. OAP.

FORTY-SEVEN CENTS
Lee Callister & Wendy Carrel, Producers
Focuses on the land claims of the Pit River Indians in northern California and the processes by which Indians are unfairly treated. 1973. 25 mins. bxw. 16mm & video. Purchase: $95; rental: $50. UC. Rental: 16mm, $14.75. UMN.

FOSTER CHILD
Gil Cardinal, Director; At age 35, Gil Cardinal searches for his natural family and an understanding of the circumstances that led to his coming into foster care as an infant. This is a documentary about the process of that discovery and a renewed sense of his Metis culture. 1988. 43 mins. Purchase: 16mm, $650; video, $300. Rental: $70. NFBC.

THE FOUR CORNERS: A NATIONAL SACRIFICE AREA?
Christopher McLeod, Glenn Switkes & Randy Hayes, Producers/directors
The Four Corners area of Utah, Colorado, New Mexico, and Arizona is rich in the history for Native Americans and also rich in coal, oil shale, and uranium. This film raises questions about the "hidden costs" of energy development in the Southwest. Features interviews with region's inhabitants and leaders - Navajo uranium miners, tribal officers, governors, ranchers, energy company spokesmen, and federal government officials. 1983. Grades 9 and up. 58 mins. Purchase: 16mm, $850; Video, $450; Rental: $85. BULL.

FOUR CORNERS OF EARTH
Bureau of Florida Folklife & WFSU-TV
Explores the roles and culture of Seminole women whose traditional values keep pace with the forces of today's technology. 1985. 30 mins. Rental: $40/week. NAPBC.

FRENCH & INDIAN WARS
CreateSpace, Producer; 49 mins. DVD, 2008. $16.95. Amazon.com.

FROM THE ELDERS
Katrina Waters, Producer & Director; A series of films from the Alaska Native Heritage Film Project presenting the stories and thoughts of one of three highly regarded Alaska Native elders. Provides a window of understanding into the Eskimo experience. Joe Sun - Immaluuraq (Joe Sun in English) tells of the legendary Inupiaq prophet, Maniilaq, who was his great uncle. 19 mins. In Iirgu's Time - an elder from the Siberian Yup'ik Eskimo village of Hambell on St. Lawrence Island. The Reindeer Thief - Pelaasi, an elder from Gambell speaks Siberian Yup'ik & tells about Chukchi, the Reindeer People. 13 mins. 1988. DER.

FROM THE FIRST PEOPLE
Leonard Kamerling and Sarah Elder; Shows change and contemporary life in Shungnak, a village on the Kobuk River in northwestern Alaska. An old man shares his feelings about the changes he has seen. 1976. 45 mins. DER. PSU.

FROM HAND TO HAND: BETHEL NATIVE ARTIST PROFILES
Gretchen McManus, Producer/camera/editor; Martha Larson, Narrator
Collection of short profiles of Yup'ik Eskimo artists and their work. Features practitioners who discuss the place of their art in traditional Yup'ik culture. Storyknifing, Lucy Beaver, Skin Sewer, Nick Charles, Carver, and Uncle John, Carver. 1985. 45 minutes. In Yup'ik or English. VHS. $24.95. KYUK.

FULFILLING THE VISION "OYATE IGLUKININI"
Examines the struggle of the Sioux generation that came of age in the 70's and 80's to redefine the nation's identity. Addresses contemporary socioeconomic issues, spirituality & traditional wisdom. Depicts Lakota spirituality as expressed in the Vision Quest & Sun Dance. 30 mins. Color. Video. $35. CAN.

FULL CIRCLE
Maria Gargiulo & John de Graaf
Documentary which relates the success story of Native American tribes of Washington state by depicting the diverse lives of tribal elders, business leaders, traditional artists, environmental activists, salmon fisherman, and innovative teachers. 1990. 50 mins. Video. Purchase: $295; rental, $60. UC.

GAME OF STAVES
Clyde B. Smith, Producer
Pomo boys demonstrate the game of staves, a variation of the dice game using six staves and 12 counters, played by most of the Indian tribes of North America. Explains the individualized pyrographic ornamentation of the staves and counters. 1962. 10 mins. Purchase: 16mm, $220; video, $195. Rental: $45. UC. Rental only: PSU.

GANNAGARO
Alexandra J. Lewis-Lorentz, Producer
The Seneca, one of the five Iroquois nations of New York State, lived at Gannagaro, an ancient Seneca village located just outside of Victor, New York. It was destroyed by the French in July, 1687. This film pieces together life at this 17th century Seneca village. 1986. 30 mins. Video. Purchase: $150; Rental: $40. NAPBC.

GATHERING OF NATIONS
The largest indoor powwow in North America recorded at Albuquerque, NM in 2004. 60 mins. VHS, $27.95. ME.

12th ANNUAL 1995 GATHERING OF NATIONS POW WOW
One of the largest powwows in America, this video includes excerpts of the Miss Indian World Pageant. CAN.

GATHERING UP AGAIN: FIESTA IN SANTA FE
Jeanette DeBouzek, Director
Examines the Santa Fe Fiesta; documents preparation for the fiesta; shows the formation of ethnic identities, the ongoing impact of cultures of conquest on Native Americans in the region. 1992. Grades 7-12. Purchase: $275; rental: $75. CG.

GATECLIFF: AMERICAN INDIAN ROCK-SHELTER
Led by Dr. David Hurst Thomas, amateur archaeologists attempt to discover the identity of ancient inhabitants of this shallow rock-shelter in Monitor Valley, Nevada. Teacher's guide. 1974. 24 mins. NGS.

GERONIMO: AN AMERICAN LEGEND
Geronimo leads a small band of warriors in escape. With Wes Studi, Rodney Grant, Matt Damon, Robert Duvall, Gene Hackman, et al. 1994. 115 mins. ME.

GERONIMO & THE APACHE RESISTANCE
Neil Goodwin & Jacqueline Shearer, Directors
Dscendants of those Apaches who fought so long ago tell their story, explaining the mysteries of Apache power. The story of Geronimo and his people is told, and his battles and broken promises that provoked them are discussed. 1988. 60 mins. DVD, $12.99. ME.

GERONIMO: THE FINAL CAMPAIGN
Host Will Rogers, Jr. draws viewers into Geronimo's fascinating history. Grades 9 and up. 30 mins. CC. Rental: Video, $17.75. IU.

GERONIMO: THE LAST RENEGADE
A&E Home Video; Biography of Geronimo. 1996. 50 mins. VHS, $19.99. ME.

GERONIMO JONES
A young American Indian of Apache & Papago descent, living on a reservation with his mother and grandfather, explores the conflicts he faces, torn between pride in his heritage and his future in modern American society. 1970. 21 mins. 16mm & video. Purchase: $250; rental, $75. PHO. Rental: UCT & UMN.

THE GIFT OF THE SACRED DOG
Cecily Truett, Producer; Larry Lancit, Director; LeVar Burton, Series host; Michael Ansara, Narrator; The narrator reads the book Gift of the Sacred Dog, written and illustrated by Paul Goble. A documentary film sequence presents Dan Old Elk and his family who live at Crow Agency, Montana, and shows them preparing for and participating in the festivities of the annual Crow Indian Fair, including tipi raising and powwow dancing. 1983. 30 mins. GPN.

GIFT OF THE WHALES
A Native American boy discovers a naturalist studying whales off the coast of his small Alaskan village. Grade 1-5. 30 mins. VHS. $19.95. VC.

GIFTS OF SANTA FE
Marguerite J. Moritz, Producer; Tells the story of the Santa Fe Indian Market, the largest and most prestigious competition of Native Amerian artists in the world. 1988. 22 mins. Video. Purchase: $150; Rental: $40. NAPBC.

GILA - CLIFF DWELLINGS
Explores the story of the cliff dwellers, a people who lived centuries ago. VHS. 15 mins. $17.95. VIP.

GIRL OF THE NAVAJOS
Norman Nelson; A story about two Navajo girls who become friends. 1977. Grades K-6. 15 mins. PHO.

GIVEAWAY AT RING THUNDER
Jan Wahl, Producer/writer; Christine Lesiak, Writer/narrator/editor
Documents a giveaway held during the annual Ring Thunder powwow on the Rosebud Sioux Reservation in South Dakota. The Menard family is celebrating the giving of Indian names to three children. Opens with archival photographs of Lakota Sioux life and a reflection on traditional customs in earlier times. 1982. 15 minutes. Video. NETV.

GLOOSCAP
Indian legend of how humans and animals were created to live in peace and plenty, and how evil intervened. 26 minutes. Video, Purchase: $89.95. FH.

GLOOSKAP
Recounts the Canadian Indian legend of the creation, as told by Glooskap, Father of all Indian children. He shows them how to survive and how to live in peace with man & nature. 1971. 12 mins. Grades 4-9. PHO.

GONE WEST
In Two Parts: Part I - The Lewis & Clark Expedition; Part II - The gold rush begins a mass migration west. Both parts show the affect of white migrations on Indian nations. 1972. 26 mins. each. Rental. UK.

A GOOD DAY TO DIE
Old Army Press, Producer
Computer graphics combine with aerial photographs to show Custer Battlefield; scenes from the Indian village; re-created by re-enactors including Sioux & Cheyenne Indians. 60 minutes, color. Video. Purchase: $25. OAP.

GOOD MEDICINE
Chris Gaul, Writer/Producer
Documentary on Native American medicine, narrated by John Bolindo, Kiowa-Navajo who was at the time of the film the executive director of the National Indian Health Board. Emphasizes the holistic nature of Indian medicine. Settings include the Rosebud & Navajo Reservations. 1979. 59 mins. WQED.

THE GOOD MIND
Robert Stiles, Producer; Steve Charleston, Narrator
Explores the similarities between Christian and Native American beliefs and practices of traditional Native American tribes in the words and life styles of contemporary Indians. 1983. 30 mins. VHS, U-matic. NAPBC.

GRAND CANYON
Dr. Joseph Wood Krutch journeys on mule down the canyon to the Colorado River. The Havasupai Indian settlement at Bright Angel Creek is compared with outside world. 1966. 26 mins. Rental. UA.

THE GRAND CIRCLE
Richard Ray Whitman & Pierre Lobstein
Two brothers and a friend take a cross-country journey through Indian Territory Oklahoma & Georgia. 12 mins. 1995. TWN.

GRANDFATHER SKY
A look at contemporary Native American life, with Charlie Lone Wolf, a young Navajo/Lakota street fighter, fighting to protect his identity on the streets of Denver. Drama explored role of cultural identity and traditional ways. Grades 7 & up. 1993. 50 mins. VHS & Guide. $89. CHAR.

GREAT AMERICAN INDIAN HEROES
The personal stories of leaders and chiefs who won the trust of their people and inspired their tribes in war and peace. Includes Tecumseh, Osceaola, Black Hawk, Pontiac, Chief Joseph, Sitting Bull, Geronimo, & Joseph Brant. Grades 4-6. 1988. Video. available as filmstrips and cassettes. TA.

THE GREAT INDIAN WARS: 1540-1890
Centre Communications, Producer
5 Part DVD Documentary Series of the 350-year struggle between European and American Indians. Includes biographies, timelines, rare photos and maps. 2005. Amazon.com. $9.98.

THE GREAT MOVIE MASSACRE
Narrated by Wil Sampson
Explores the motion picture image of the Indian warrior. 1982. DVD. VT.

THE GREAT SPIRIT WITHIN THE HOLE
Chris Spotted Eagle, KTCA, Producer/director
A narrative around the words of Indian people in our nation's prisons. The movie demonstrates how freedom of Indian religious practice aids in rehabilitation. Narrated by Will Sampson, with original soundtrack by Buffy Sainte-Marie. 1983. 60 mins. UMN.

THE GREEN CORN FESTIVAL
Gary Robinson, Producer/director; Mike Bigler, Narrator
Describes and explains the Green Corn Festival ceremonial activities practiced today by the Creek Indians of OK. Opens with archival footage shot in the 1940's, underscoring longevity of the ceremonial. 1982. 20 mins. DVD. MCN.

JOHNNY GREYEYES
A story of a Native American woman struggling to maintain strength, love, and spirit. Since the shooting death of her father, Johnny has spent most of her life in prison. 2001. 76 mins. VHS, $39.95; DVD, $24.95. ME.

HAA SHAGOON
Joe Kawaky, Producer; Documents a day of Tlingit Indian ceremony held along the Chilkoot River, ancestral home of the Chilkoot Tlingit of Alaska. Ceremony consists of time-honored prayers, songs and dances. 1983. 29 mins. English & Tlingit with English subtitles. UC.

HAD YOU LIVED THEN: LIFE IN THE WOODLANDS BEFORE THE WHITE MAN CAME
Indians show how their ancestors lived before the white man came and how deer were important in the survival of the Indians.1976. 12 mins. VHS. AIMS.

HAIDA CARVER
Richard Gilbert, Director; Shows a young Haida Indian artist on the Pacific coast of Canada shaping miniature totems from argillite, a soft dark slate. 1964. Grades 9 and up. 12 mins. UA & UCLA.

HAIRCUTS HURT
Randy RedroadA Native American woman andher son encounter racism in a barbershop. 1992. 10 mins. Purhcase: $300, 16mm, $200, VHS; Rental: $45, 16mm & VHS. TWN.

HANDS OF MARIA
A pictorial study of Maria Martinez, an Indian potter, and of her work which has brought fame to her and to her pueblo. 1968. 17 mins. Rental. UA.

HAROLD OF ORANGE
Dianne Brennan, Producer; Richard Weise, Director; Gerald Vizenor, Writer
Confronts the issue of the interconnection between reservation communities and the powerful bureaucracies on which they often must rely, presenting both a group of young Indian "tricksters" and a well-intentioned, though woefully paternalistic, white institution. 1983. 32 mins. FIC.

HASKIE
Jack L. Crowder; The story of a young Navajo Indian boy, who wants to become a medicine man but instead attends a boarding school to meet the requirements of compulsory education. 1970. 25 mins. IU.

HAT CREEK
Amarcord Productions; Hat Creek, a small community near Lillooet, British Columbia, Canada faces major environmental changes because of strip-mining and a coal-fired generating plant. Shows the affect it has had on the largely Indian population. 1981. 28 mins. Video. CFDW.

HAUDENOSAUNEE: WAY OF THE LONGHOUSE
Robert Stiles & John Akin, Producers/directors; Oren Lyons, Narrators
Documents the traditional culture of the six nations of the Iroquois Confederacy, the League of Haudenosaunee. Also documents the resiliency of Iroquois culture in the face of pressures to assimilate. 1982. Grades 6-9. 13 mins. Purchase: 16mm, $245, video, $160; rental, 16mm, $35. ICARUS.

HE WO UN POH: RECOVERY IN NATIVE AMERICA
Beverly Singer; The filmmaker, a member of the Santa Clara Tewa Pueblo, introduces us to the experiences of seven Native Americans on the road to recovery from alcohol abuse. 54 mins. TWN.

HEALING THE HURTS
Phil Lucas, Producer; The people of Alkali Lake, Albert, Canada participate in a ceremonial healing process focused on healing the hurt and shame of residential schools across North America. 60 mins. FOUR.

A HEALING OF NATIONS
Documentary of cultural revival in Native American communities. Focuses on youth empowerment, the value of traditional ceremonies and teachings. 1993. Grades 7 and up. 49 mins. VHS. $155. CHAR.

HE WO UN POH: RECOVERY IN NATIVE AMERICA
A series of vivid portraits of Native Americans in recovery from alcohol abuse. 1994. 55 mins. VHS. $74. CHAR.

HEALTH CARE CRISIS AT ROSEBUD
South Dakota ETV, Producer; Explores and offers some possible solutions to a serious shortage of physicians on the Rosebud Sioux Reservation in South Dakota. 1973. 20 minutes. Color. VHS. Rental: $40/week. NAPBC.

HEART OF THE EARTH SURVIVAL SCHOOL & CIRCLE OF THE WINDS
Chris Spotted Eagle, Producer/director; Presents aspects of contemporary Native American culture for Indians living in the Minneapolis-St. Paul area. Heart of the Earth Survival School (1980) documents an alternative Native American school in Minneapolis; and Circle of the Winds (1979) documents a Native American student art exhibition. 32 minutes. VHS. IN.

HEART OF THE NORTH
Presents the ideas & traditions of five contemporary artists from the Woodlands & Plains in their own words & images. Issues important to Indian artists are discussed while the five are shown quarrying, carving, painting, and designing. Includes study guide. 24 minutes. VHS. $50. TOP.

THE HEART OF WETONA
Chief's daughter is wronged by white man. 1918. 69 mins. bxw. EG.

HER GIVEAWAY: A SPIRITUAL JOURNEY WITH AIDS
Mona Smith, Producer/director
A candid portrait of Carole Lafavor, member of the Ojibwe tribe, activist, mother, registered nurse & person with AIDS. 1988. 21 mins. UMN.

HERITAGE
Provides an overview of early Native American life, before Columbus. Introduces us to oral traditions of Indian people and through slides tells of the differences and similarities in Native art, music, and religion, before the time of Columbus. 28 minutes, color. Grades 9 and up. Video, Purchase: $55. UP.

HERITAGE IN CEDAR: NORTHWEST COAST: INDIAN WOODWORKING, PAST & PRESENT
Louis and Ruth Kirk; From Oregon to Alaska, tribesmen lived in houses built of cedar planks and traveled in canoes hollowed from cedar logs. Explores the Northwest Coast Indian legacy by going to abandoned villages and to living villages, to archaeological digs and museums. 1979. 29 mins. UW.

HERITAGE OF THE SEA: MAKAH INDIAN TREATY RIGHTS
Louis and Ruth Kirk; Examines fishing as the Makahs presently practice it, regard it, and view it historically. In two parts: Part I - Makah reminisces about the past and comments on the future of their tribal salmon management programs. Part II - Represents comments by Makah fisherman and elders. 29 mins. each. UW.

HERMAN RED ELK: A SIOUX INDIAN ARTIST
South Dakota ETV, Producer; Bill Hopkins, Project Director
Red Elk speaks of his lifelong interest in art and of the influences of his grandfather's teachings. Points out the role of skin painting in Plains Indian history. 1975. 29 mins. NAPBC.

HIDALGO
A Disney film portraying the ghost dance and Wounded Knee Massacre with Viggo Mortensen as Dakota Territory horseman and racer Frank T. Hopkins, who worked for the U.S. Cavalry as a dispatch rider. 2004. DVD & VHS. ME.

HIGH HORSE
Randy Redroad; A narrative on the concept of "home" for Native Americans. Dislocated Native People search for and sometimes find their figurative - and literal - homes. 1995. 40 mins. TWN.

HISATSINOM - THE ANCIENT ONES
The history of an Anasazi outpost, Kayenta. People & culture are discussed. A portrait of the Anasazi historical sites at the Navajo National Monument. Grades 7 and up. 24 minutes, color. Rental: $10. UCT.

HISTORY OF SOUTHERN CALIFORNIA
In two parts: Part I, From Prehistoric Times to the Founding of Los Angeles - major sequences include, prehistoric life, Indian economy, European explorations, and establishment of pueblos, missions and presidios; Part II, Rise and Fall of the Spanish and Mexican Influences. 1967. Grades 4-9. 17 minutes each. Rental. UA.

HOHOKAM: AT PEACE WITH THE LAND
Bill Land; The archaeologist Emil Haury discusses his excavations at the earliest Hohokam site, Snaketown, which dates from approximately 2,000 years ago, and their descendants, the Pima and Papago, who still live in the region near Phoenix, Arizona. 1976. 20 mins. UA.

HOLLOW WATER
National Film Board of Canada; Sexual abuse, violence, healing, and restorative justice in Hollow Water, an isolated Ojibway Cree village in Northern Manitoba. 1999. 44 mins. CHAR.

HOME OF THE BRAVE
Helena Solberg-Ladd, Producer/director; David Meyer, Writer
Documentary examines the contemporary plight of Indian peoples of North and South America, focusing on the impact of development on native people, the crisis of identity, and the prospects for political organization to protect Indian lives and land. Includes interviews with Indian leaders.1985. 53 mins. CG.

HONORABLE NATIONS
Chana Gazit & David Steward, Directors/writers
For 99 years the residents of Slamanca, a town in upstate New York, rented the land beneath their homes from the Seneca Nation for $1 a year under the terms of a lease agreement imposed by Congress. This documentary charts the conflicts that arose when the lease's impendent expiration pitted the town's citizenry against the Seneca Nation. 1991. 54 mins. FIL. Rental, UMN.

HONORED BY THE MOON
Provides examples of traditional roles & beliefs of Indian women & men. Covers homosexuality & homophobia in the Indian community. 1989. 15 minutes. Video. Rental: $16. UMN.

THE HONOUR OF ALL
Phil Lucas, Producer/director; Two part series that recreates the story of the Alkali Lake Indian Band's heroic struggle to overcome & conquer its widespread alcoholism. Narrated by Andy Chelsea, Chief of the Alkali Lake Indian Band of British Columbia, Canada. In 2 parts: Part 1: (56 mins) examines the problem; Part 2: (43 minutes) outlines the community development process. 1987. Video. Purchase: $150/series; $75/program. NAPBC & GPN.

THE HOPI
Museum of Northern Arizona, Producer
Scenes of family life, work and rituals as seen through the role of corn in Hopi daily life. Shows how communal values and survival skills that have kept their culture alive for centuries are passed on. 15 mins. CAN.

THE HOPI INDIAN
Observes Hopi men and women in daily routines and in special celebrations, such as the secret Hopi wedding ceremony. Revised 1975. 11 mins. Grades K-6. PHOENIX. Rental: 16mm, $16.50. UA, PSU & IU.

HOPI INDIAN ARTS & CRAFTS
1945 & 1975 Editions. Shows traditional skills as the Hopi work at weaving, basket-making, silversmithing and ceramics. Grades K-6. 11 minutes, color. Purchase: 16mm, $250; video, $175. Rental, $40. PHO, IU & UA.

THE HOPI INDIAN & THE NAVAJO INDIANS
Documentary. 1925. 10 minutes, bxw. EG.

HOPI KACHINAS
Shows an artisan in the complete process of carving, assembling & painting a doll; also, Hopi life and dance. 1960. 10 mins. 16mm. UA.

HOPI SNAKE DANCE
Preparation of dancers, handling of snakes, costumes and part of a dance. 1951. 10 minutes, bxw. 16mm. UW.

HOPI: SONGS OF THE FOURTH WORLD
Pat Ferrero, Producer/director; narrated by Ronnie Gilbert
The study of the Hopi that captures their deep spirituality and reveals their integration of art and daily life. Two parts: Part I - Story of emergence into 4th world; explanation of corn (color and directions) & planting; Hopi courtship and marriage ceremonies; Hopi kachinas. Part II - Hopi religion; interviews with Hopi painter and potter; women's roles; child-raising and traditional education; games, clowns and Hopi humor. A study guide/resource book. 1983. Grades 4 and up. 16mm, 58 mins. 30 minute version for high school audiences-video only. NDF. Rental. UN, UMN & UW.

THE HOPI WAY
Shelly Grossman; Mary Louise Grossman, Writer; The history of the Hopi is discussd by David Mongnongyi who shows pictographs made by Hopi ancestors, presenting a picture of Hopi traditional-ism & current threats to that way of life. 1972. Grades 4 & up. 23 mins. FILMS. Rental, $16.20. UA.

HOPIIT
Victor Masayesva, Jr., Producer/director/camera; Ross Macaya & Victor Masayesva, Sr., Narrators; Provides an impressionistic view of a year in the Hopi community, including ordinary scenes of Hopi life. 1982. 15 minutes. Purchase: VHS, $80; Rental: 3$30. IN & IS. Rental: ATL.

HOPIS--GUARDIANS OF THE LAND
Dennis Burns, Producer; Explores the traditional Hopi way of life and the threat of men's desecration of the land and life they have known. 1971. 10 minutes. Purchase: 16mm, $150; VHS, $89. FF. Rental: $13. FF & UMN.

HOW BEAVER STOLE FIRE
Caroline Leaf; A retelling, through animation, of a Northwest American Indian legend of how the Animal People all worked together to capture fire from the Sky People. 1972. Grades K-4. 12 mins. AIMS. Rental: UCT, BYU & UI.

HOW MAN ADAPTS TO HIS PHYSICAL ENVIRONMENT
The film uses as examples the Pueblo Indians, Navahos, and the early Caucasians. 1970. 20 minutes. Rental. UA & IU.

HOW PANTHER GOT TEAR MARKS
Presentation of a traditional Karuk story is told in both English & the Karuk language. Grades 4-6. 11 minutes. VHS. $59.95. CB.

HOW TO BEAD: NATIVE AMERICAN STYLE
Full Circle Communications
Learn how to create your own designs; includes instructions on how to make a loom. VHS. Vol. 1 - Loom; Vol. 2 - Lazystitch; Vol. 3 - Peyote Stitch; Vol. 4 - Medallions; Vol. 5 - Needle Applique. 30 mins each. CAN, VIP & WH.

HOW TO BUILD AN IGLOO
Douglas Wilkinson, Director; Two Inuit Eskimos give a step-by-step demonstration of Igloo construction. 1950. Grades K-8. 11 minutes, bxw. Purchase: 16mm, $275; VHS, $200. Rental: $40. NFBC.

HOW TO DANCE: NATIVE AMERICAN STYLE: BEGINNING STEPS
Full Circle Communications; Learn the parts of a war dance song and master the basic steps by dance instructors Mike Pasetopah & Nancy Fields; learn how to dance "on the song." Suitable for ages 5 and up. VHS. 30 mins. $19.95. CAN, VIP & WH.

HOW TO MAKE MOCCASINS: VOL. 1 - HARD SOLE
Full Circle Communications; Simple teaching methods show how to make a pattern, how to adapt for men & women; any size and how to adapt to high top moccasins. Moccasin maker Annabelle Medicine-chips (Cheyenne/Caddo) demonstrates. VHS. 30 mins. $19.95. WH.

HOW TO MAKE A NATIVE AMERICAN DANCE SHAWL
Full Circle Communications; Step-by-step from selecting materials, cutting cloth & tying fringe. Ribbonwork techniques are also demonstrated. VHS. 30 minutes. $19.95. WH.

HOW TO TRACE YOUR NATIVE AMERICAN HERITAGE
Chip Richie, Director; How to obtain a CDIB card, tribal membership, internet sites and a list of over 500 federally recognized tribes. DVD. 60 mins. 2003. $24.95. MALKI.

HOW THE WEST WAS WON...AND HONOR LOST
Ross Devenish, Producer; A re-enactment, using photographs, paintings and newspaper accounts, telling the story of the white man's treatment of American Indians in the westward push for land. Broken treaties, railroad building, decimation of the buffalo, and the massacre at Wounded Knee. 1970. 25 mins. 16mm. PSU & IU.

HOW THE WEST WAS LOST
Discovery Channel; Comprehensive video history and eyewitness account free of popular myth and Hollywood stereotypes. Traces four centuries of American history. In siix videos: Navajo: A Clash of Cultures; Cheyenne: The Only Good Indian Is a Dead Indian; Seminoles: The Unconquered; Nez Perce: "I Will Fight No More Forever"; Apache: Always the Enemy; Iroquois: "Divided We Fall." 2000. $19.95 each. T-L.

HOW THE WEST WAS LOST
Document Associates and BBC, Co-Producers
Highlights the prime of Plains Indian civilization and focuses upon the temporary Indian effort to maintain a sense of their own identity. 1972. 26 minutes Purchase: VHS, $95. Rental, $55 each. CG.

HOW THE WEST WAS LOST
Documentary of the epic struggle for the American West; witnesses the plight of five Native American Nations: the Navajo, Nez Perce, Apache, Cheyenne & Lakota. In 3 volumes: Vol. 1 - Navajo & Nez Perce; Vol. 2 - Apache & Cheyenne; & Vol. 3 - Lakota & Northern Cheyenne. 100 mins. each. Video. Rental: $10 each; $25/set. HO.

HUNGER IN AMERICA
CBS, Producer; A researched study of hunger and malnutrition in the U.S., showing views of Navajo Indians in Arizona, as well as other impoverished groups. 1968. Grades 7 and up. 58 mins. 16mm. Rental, $31. UT.

RICHARD HUNT CARVES A BEAR MASK
A Kwakiutl artist from British Columbia, carves a bear mask. Documents in detail the entire production process. 1988. 25 mins., b&w. Video. Purchase: $70; rental, $20. UADA.

HUICHOL INDIAN CEREMONIAL CYCLE:
RESCUING IMAGES AT THE EDGE OF OBLIVION
A documentary based on 1934 film by anthropologist, Robert Zingg. Interprets several aboriginal Huichol rituals. 1997. 44 mins. 120 page booklet. PSU.

HUICHOL SACRED PILGRIMAGE TO WIRIKUTA
Larain, Boyll; Documentary following the annual pilgrimage and peyote hunt of the Huichol Indians of western Mexico. Focuses on the sacred sites, the traditional Huichol shamans and elders. Includes songs and music. 1991. 29 mins. Video. Purchase: $195; rental, $50. UC.

HUNTERS & BOMBERS: THE INNU FIGHT BACK
The Innu, indigenous inhabitants of Labrador-Quebec in northeast Canada, are fighting back against the Dutch, German, and British air forces that use the region for supersonic low-level bomber training. 52 minutes, color. Video. Purchase: $149; rental: $75. FH.

HUPA INDIAN WHITE DEERSKIN DANCE
Portrays the 10-day deerskin ceremony still held by the Hupa Indians of northwestern California. 1958. Grades 4 & up. 11 mins. 16mm. Rental: UCLA.

HUTEETL: KOYUKON MEMORIAL POTLATCH
Curt Madison, Producer/director/editor; Catherine Attla/Eliza Jones, Narrators
A documentary of an Athapascan Indian potlatch in interior Alaska. 1983. 60 minutes. In English and Koyukon Athabascan with English subtitles. Video. Purchase: $150; Rental: $80. KYUK and NAPBC.

I AM DIFFERENT FROM MY BROTHER: DAKOTA NAME-GIVING
Tony Charles, Director; A real-life docudrama depicting the Name-Giving Ceremony of three young Flandreau Dakota Sioux Indian children. 1981. Grades 3-9. 20 mins. Video. Purchase: $150; Rental: $40/week. NAPBC.

I HEARD THE OWL CALL MY NAME
Roger Gimbel, Producer; A story about how an Anglican priest, who with a short time to live learns acceptance of death from the Indians. 1974. Grades 7 and up. 78 minutes. 16mm. Rental: Video, $20; 16mm, $50.50. UA & UMN.

I KNOW WHO I AM
Sandra Sunrising Osawa, ProducerFocuses on cultural values important to Indian tribes of the Pacific coast and was shot on the Makah, Puyallup & Nisqually reservations. 1979. 28 mins. Video. UP.

I WILL FIGHT NO MORE FOREVER
Richard T. Efron, Director; Stan Margulies, Producer; A dramatization of the struggle of the Nez Perce Indians and their leader Chief Joseph, who attempted to take his people to Canada to avoid being placed on a reservation. 1975. 106 mins. 16mm. FILMS & UA. Video, $29.95. CH. VHS. $19.99. ME.

I'D RATHER BE POWWOWING
George P. Horse Capture, Producer; Larry Littlebird, Director
Presents an unstereotyped portrait of a contemporary Indian, Al Chandler (a Gros Ventre from the Fort Berthold Indian Reservation in North Dakota) a senior technical representative for a large corporation and explores the values that are central to his identity. Chandler and his son travel to a powwow celebration at the Rocky Boys Reservation near Havre, Montana. 1983. 27 minutes. VHS. Purchase: $50. BB.

IHANBLA WAKTOGLAG WACIPI
Henry Smith; A dance showcasing Solaris, a modern dance theatre company, and Sioux Indian dancers drawn from the nine reservations of the Lakota Nation in South Dakota. 1981. 60 minutes. Video. SO.

I'ISAW: HOPI COYOTE STORIES
Larry Evers, University of Arizona; With Helen Sekaquaptewa. In Hopi with English subtitles. 1978. 18 mins. NR. Rental (with Nawatniwa: A Hopi Philosophical Statement) - two programs on one tape, $52.50. ATL.

I'M NOT AFRAID OF ME
A true story of a young American Indian mother and daughter and AIDS. 28 mins. SH.

THE IMAGE MAKER & THE INDIANS
George I. Quimby, Bill Holm and David Gerth; Shows how the famous pioneer cinematographer, Edward S. Curtis, made the first full-length documentary film of Native Americans among the Northwest Coast Indians of 1914. Edited and restored in 1973. 17 mins. UW.

IMAGES OF INDIANS
Robert Hagopian & Phil Lucas, Producers/Directors/Writers
A five-part series, narrated by Will Sampson, examines the stereotypes drawn by the movies and questions what the effect of the Hollywood image has been on the Indian's own self-image. (1) "The Great Movie Massacre - Indian's warrior image." (2) "Heathen Injuns and the Hollywood Gospel" - The distortion and misrepresentation of Indian religion and values in Hollywood movies. (3) "How Hollywood Wins the West" - Deals with the one-sided presentation of Indian history despite the frequent use of Indian culture in Hollywood films. (4) "The Movie Reel Indians" - The image of Indians as savage murderers is commented on by Dennis Banks & Vine Deloria. (5) "Warpaint and Wigs" - Examines how the movie, Nobel Savage and the Savage-Savage, has affected the Native American self-image. 1980. contains a curriculum guide, student resource pages, video, and other learning resources (map, books, posters). Grades 7 and up, 30 mins. each. Video. OY, FOUR, GPN & NAPBC.

IMAGINING INDIANS
Victor Masayesva, Jr.; Visits tribal communities in Arizona, Montana, New Mexico, South Dakota, Washington, and the Amazon. 1992. 60 mins. DER.

IMPRINT
Michael Linn, Director; Shayla Stonefeather, a Native American attorney prosecuting a Lakota teen in a controversial murder trial, returns to the reservation to say goodbye to her dying father. 84 mins. DVD. Amazon.com. $15.87.

IN THE BEST INTEREST OF THE CHILD
Will Sampson, Narrator
Documents the legal issues involved in Indian child welfare cases. Trys to educate the public to the Indian Child Welfare Act. 1981. Grades 9 and up. 15 minutes, color. Video. Purchase: $245; rental: $45. SH. Rental, $21. PSU.

IN THE HEART OF BIG MOUNTAIN
Captures an intimate portrait of the traumatic consequences of relocation on one Navajo family. Through Katherine Smith's eyes and words, as a Navajo matriarch, the viewer experiences life on one of the most remote and traditional places in Indian country - Big Mountain, Arizona. Grades 5 and up. 1988. 28 minutes. Video. Purchase: $30. OY.

IN THE LAND OF THE WAR CANOES: KWAKIUTL INDIAN LIFE ON THE NORTHWEST COAST
Edward S. Curtis; Edited and Restored by George Quimby and Bill Holm
A saga of Kwakiutl Indian life filmed in 1914 in Vancouver Island, British Columbia, Canada. 43 mins. UW. Rental. UA & PSU.

IN OUR OWN BACKYARDS: URANIUM MINING IN THE U.S.
Pamela Jones & Susanna Styron
Explores the impact of uranium mining on the environment in the Southwest, and on the health of workers and nearby residents. 1981. Grades 7 and up. 29 minutes, color. Purchase: 16mm, $515; Video, $100; Rental: $50. BULL.

IN SEARCH OF HISTORY - CAPTIVES
A&E - The History Channel
Portraits of captives taken by both sides include: "White Indian" John Tanner who returned to his roots after 30 years of "civilization," and a woman rescued during a forced exchange who escaped to return to her Native American husband. 50 mins. DVD. $2.45. Amazon.com.

IN SEARCH OF THE LOST WORLD
Traces the origins of the lost civilizations of the Americas; tells the story of Indian cultures: complex, urbane & ancient. 1972. 52 minutes, color. 16mm. Rental. UA & UCLA.

IN THE WHITE MAN'S IMAGE
Covers the policies, methods, and tragic long-term consequences of attempts to "civilize" Native Americans in the 1870s. 1992. 60 minutes. Video. Purchase: $59.95. NAPBC. Rental: $10. HO; $16. UMN.

INCIDENT AT OGLALA: THE LEONARD PELTIER STORY
Michael Apted, Director; Robert Redford, Producer; Documentary. 1992. ME.

INDIAN AMERICA
The story of the American Indian and his desperate struggle against extinction. Indian activists, tribal leaders, and poor sheep herders tell about themselves and their heritage. 1970. Grades 4-adult. 80 mins. UA & UMN.

INDIAN ARTIFACTS OF THE SOUTHWEST
Examines the arts and crafts of several Southwestern tribes, including: Zuni, Hopi and Navajo. Stresses the history and tradition that are apparent in the objects. 1972. 15 minutes. 16mm. Rental. IU.

INDIAN ARTISTS OF THE SOUTHWEST
Deals with the history of American Indian paintings and its rich heritage from petroglyphs to the modern artists. Shows techniques, symbolism and style. 1972. 15 minutes. Grades 4 and up. 16mm. Rental; $23. IU, PSU & UA.

INDIAN ARTS AT THE HEARD MUSEUM
KAET-TV Phoenix, Producer; Dick Peterson, Director
Explores six major areas of Native American Art: 1: Basketry - Naomi White, guest; 2: Painting - Larry Golsh & Pop Chalee, guests; 3: Pottery - Mabel Sunn, guest; 4: Textiles - Martha Began & Lillian Dineyazhe; 5: Jewelry - John E. Salaby; & 6: Katchinas. 1975. 30 mins each. NAPBC.

INDIAN BOY IN TODAY'S WORLD
Presents a picture of life on the Makah Reservation and shows how the way of life on the Reservation is changing as a result of interaction with the outside world--the conflict of Indian and non-Indian cultures. 1971. Grades 4 and up. 14 minutes. Rental. UA & IU.

INDIAN BOY OF THE SOUTHWEST
Toboya, a Hopi Indian boy, tells of his life and his home on a high mesa in the Southwestern desert of the U.S. 1983 revised edition. Grades 4-9. 19 minutes. PHO. Rental only: UA.

INDIAN CANOES ALONG THE WASHINGTON COAST
Louis and Ruth Kirk; This film demonstrates how and with what tools a canoe is carved; also, river and salt water races are shown. 1971. 18 mins. UW.

INDIAN CONVERSATION
Portrays two Indians, one raised in an urban environment, the other on a reservation. Both are college graduates and explore their identities as Indians. 1974. 13 minutes. 16mm. Rental. UK.

INDIAN COUNTRY?
Document Associates & BBC; Indian journalist, Richard LaCourse, discusses the revolution of attitudes within the younger American Indians creating a new mood of militancy. Interviews with Indian educators discussing the efforts to preserve the integrity of the Native American culture. 1972. 26 minutes. CG.

INDIAN CRAFTS: HOPI, NAVAJO, AND IROQUOIS
Nancy Creedman, Producer; Illustrates the wide range of arts practiced by the Indians: basket-weaving, pottery-making, kachina carving, weaving, jewelry-making, and mask carving by the Hopi, Navajo & Iroquois. 1980. 11 minutes. Grades 4-9. Purchase: 16mm, $255; video, $150. Rental, $35. PHO.

INDIAN DIALOGUE
David Hughes, Director
Indians of Canada discuss many problems that cause them concern. 1967. 28 mins. NFBC.

INDIAN FAMILY OF LONG AGO: BUFFALO HUNTERS OF THE PLAINS
Tells the story of the Sioux Indian buffalo hunters who roamed the great western plains of the U.S. more than 200 years ago. 1957. Grades 4-9. 15 minutes. 16mm. Rental: UA, UCT & UMN.

INDIAN FAMILY OF THE CALIFORNIA DESERT
A woman from the Cahuilla Indian Tribe from the desert of Palm Springs recalls her primitive life and illustrates her tribe's culture. 1967. 16 minutes. Grades 4-9. 16mm. UA.

INDIAN FOR A CHANGE
Uses portraits of five Indian men and women to show the life of the American Indian as it really is, as opposed to the romanticized stereotype commonly accepted. 1970. 28 mins. UCT.

INDIAN HIDE TANNING
Illustrates the methods used by the Eastern Cree Indians of Mistassini, Quebec in the tanning of moose and caribou hides. VHS. 38 minutes. $99. TR.

INDIAN HOUSE: THE FIRST AMERICAN HOME
Remnants of the dwellings of Indians in the Southwest represent the oldest homes in America. 1950. 11 minutes/bxw. 16mm. Rental. UA.

INDIAN HUNTER-GATHERERS OF THE DESERT: KILIWA
R.C. Michelsen, J. Albrecht & V.W. Kjonegaard
Focuses on subsistence activities of Baja California Indians. 1975. 14 mins. PSU.

INDIAN INFLUENCES IN THE U.S.
David A. Baerreis, Ph.D.; Presents many aspects of Indian heritage in the mainstream of American society today, in music, art and the foods we eat. 1964. Grades 4-9. 11 mins. 16mm. Rental. IU, UA & UK.

INDIAN LAND: THE NATIVE AMERICAN ECOLOGIST
Herbert McCoy, Jr., Director/Producer; American Indians discuss their traditional veneration for the Earth. 21 minutes; color/bxw. FILMS.

INDIAN LEGENDS: GLOOSCAP
Records a segment of the creation myth of the North American Micmac Indians. 1985. 26 minutes, color. Video. Rental, $29. PSU.

INDIAN LEGENDS OF CANADA
Daniel Bertolino, Director
Series of 15 films (13 parts) provides an authentic backdrop against which to study the first native peoples of Canada. The Winter Wife (Ojibwa); The Windigo (Montagnais); The Invisible Man, Megmuwesug and Magic Box

(MicMac); The Path of Souls (3 films, Ojibwa); Moowis, Where Area You Moowis (Algonguian), and The Return of the Child (Carrier); Mandamin, Or the Legend of Corn (Ojibwa); Pitchie the Robin and The Path Without End (Ojibwa); The Spirit of the Dead Chief (Chippewa); Glooscap (Abnaki).1981-1983. 26 minutes each. Available in Native languages with English or French narration. Purchase: 16mm, $675 each; and VHS, $450 each. Rental: $65 each; series, $8,450. ITFE, FH & THA.

INDIAN MAINSTREAM
Thomas Parsons; Emphasizes rediscovery of language and rituals which have been suppressed over the last three generations, and the need to pass on the Indian heritage to the young before it is forgotten. Sponsored by the Dept. of Labor to regenerate the Indian culture of the tribes in northern California, specifically the Hupa, Karok, Tocowa, and Yurok tribes. 1971. Grades 9 and up. 25 mins. SH. Rental, $18. SH, PSU.

INDIAN PAINT
Norman Foster, Director; The heroic efforts of a 15-year-old Indian boy, son of a tribal chief, to raise a "painted" colt. The portrayal of Indian life in the far West before the coming of the white man. 1965. 91 mins. Rental: UCT.

INDIAN POTTERY OF SAN ILDEFONSO
Rick Krepela; Documentary of renowned Pueblo artist Maria Martinez making hand fired black pottery using techniques redeveloped after they had fallen from use. Maria, in her mid-eighties at the time, works closely with her son Popovi Da at San Ildefonso Pueblo, NM. 1972. 27 minutes. NAC. Rental: UCT.

INDIAN RELOCATION: ELLIOT LAKE: A REPORT
Probes the Canadian government's experiment to move 20 Indian families from their rugged northern Ontario reserves to a new town. Questions the wisdom of the program. 1967. 30 minutes, bxw. 16mm. Rental: $28. UCLA.

INDIAN RIGHTS, INDIAN LAW
Joseph and Sandra Consentino, Directors; Film documentary focusing on the Native American Rights Fund, its staff and certain casework. 1978. 60 minutes. Grades 10-adult. 16mm. Rental, $24. IRA, FILMS, PSU.

INDIAN SELF-RULE: A PROBLEM OF HISTORY
Selma Thomas, Producer; Michael Cotsones, Director
The history of white-Indian relations from 19th century treaties through the present, as tribal leaders, historians, teachers, and other Indians gather at a 1983 conference organized to reevaluate the significance of the Indian Reorganization Act of 1934. The experience of the Flathead Nation of Montana, the Navajo Nation of the Southwest, and the Quinault people of the Olympic Peninsula, Washington, illustrates some of the ways Indians have dealt with shifting demands upon them. 1985. 58 mins. DER.

INDIAN SPEAKS
Reveals some of the general cultural deprivation of Indians in Canada & depicts aspects of life on a reserve. Describes the gradual disappearance of the Indian culture & the plight of individual Indians who wish to preserve it. 1967. Grades 7 and up. 41 mins. UMN.

INDIAN STEREOTYPES IN PICTURE BOOKS
This video & accompanying script is about stereotypic images as a process over time; and learning to recognize these images. 25 mins. Rental: $10. HO.

INDIAN SUMMER
A summer experience of Chippewa Indian children on a woodland reservation, their relationship to animals & environment. 1975. Grades K-4. 11 mins, UCT.

INDIAN TIME
Native Multi-media Productions, Inc.; Presents Shingoose, Buffy Sainte-Marie, Charlie Hill, Laura Vinson, Tom Jackson, Bill Brittain and special guest, Max Gail in a variety special of America's finest Native American entertainers. 1988. 48 mins. Purchase: $150; Rental: $80. NAPBC.

INDIAN TO INDIAN
Shows Indians who are part of the work force explaining their lives and work. Describes how, though part of the work force, they retain their tribal heritages. 1970. 26 mins. 16mm & Video. Purchase: 16mm, $275; video, $110. NAC.

INDIAN TREATY RIGHTS BY REV. WILLIAM WANTLAND
Rev. Wantland (Seminole), an attorney & Episcopal Bishop, gives a 30 minute summary on "What is Sovereignty." Video. Purchase: $20; rental: $10. HO.

INDIAN TRIBAL GOVERNMENT
Filmed at the Gila River Indian Reservation, this film shows how effective tribal governments operate and what tribal members should expect from their governments. 1980. 16 minutes. 16mm. IDIL.

INDIAN WARRIORS - THE UNTOLD STORY OF THE CIVIL WAR
The History Channel; Native Americans who fought in the Civil War. 50 mins. DVD. Amazon.com. $9.99.

THE INDIANS
The story of the conflict between the Indian and the white man in the Colorado Territory during the time when white traders, trappers and settlers moved into the Great Plains. 1969. 31 mins. Grades 4-12.. GA. Rental. UA.

INDIANS IN THE AMERICAS
Surveys (using panoramas, still photos, paintings) the development of the American Indian civilizations from the first nomadic hunter to the European explorers. Revised 1985 edition. 22 mins. Grades 4-12. Purchase: 16mm, $475; video, $285. Rental: 16mm, $55. PHO. Rental: 16mm, $25; video, $23.50. IU & PSU.

INDIANS, THE NAVAJOS
Examines the winds of change that have been sweeping across the lives of 140,000 Navajos on the largest Indian reservation in the world. 1975. 14 minutes, color. 16mm. Rental: $9. UCT.

INDIANS OF CALIFORNIA
Tells the story of a primitive people as they lived before the white man came to the Pacific Coast. Two parts: Part 1, Village Life - includes trading, house building, basket-making, use of a tule boat, the sweat house, songs & dances. 15 mins. Part 2, Food - includes bow and arrow making, a deer hunt, gathering & preparing acorns, a family meal, and the storyteller. 14 mins. 1955. Also, a LP record, California Indian Songs, $5. UA.

INDIANS OF EARLY AMERICA
Classifies all of the Indians of early America according to four general geographic regions, & represents each region by one dominant & characteristic tribe. 1957. Grades 4+. 22 minutes, bxw. In English & Spanish. 16mm. Rental: $13. IU, UA, PSU & UMN.

INDIANS OF THE EASTERN WOODLANDS:
THE LEGACY OF THE AMERICAN INDIANS
Camera One, Producer; hosted by Wes Studi; Examines the Effigy Mounds, ancient structures & the Woodland Indians; legends & cultures of the various tribes. Ancient America Series. 1994. 60 mins. $20. CAN, CMM, VIP & WKV.

INDIAN OF NORTH AMERICA
John K. White, Consultant; produced by SVE
A series of three, 20 minute VHS cassettes exploring the diverse cultures of Native Americans. Grades 4-6. Vol. 1: Indians of the Northeast/Southeast; Vol. 2: Indians of the Plains/Northwest Coast; Vol. 3: Indians of the Southwest/Far North. SVE, $89 each.

INDIANS OF NORTH AMERICA
Schlessinger Video Productions; Twenty, 30-minute programs portray the history & culture of particular Indian communities, with insights & commentary from historians & contemporary tribal members attacking myths & stereotypes that remain even today. Includes photographic images, sketchings, portraits, and maps. *Programs*: The Apache; The Aztec; The Cherokee (Southeast); The Cheyenne; The Comanche; The Iroquois; The Maya; The Navajo; The Seminole; The Yankton Sioux; The Chinook; The Creek; The Crow, The Huron; The Lenape; The Menominee; The Narragansett; The Potawatomi; The Pueblo; & A History of Native Americans. 1993-94. Grades 4+. Closed captioned for the hearing impaired. Purchase: $39 each; $699 per set. CHAR.

INDIANS OF THE NORTHWEST:
THE LEGACY OF THE AMERICAN INDIANS
Camera One, Producer; hosted by Wes Studi; The origin of the totem pole; examines legends & cultures of various tribes. Ancient America Series. 1994. 60 mins. $20. CAN & WKV.

INDIANS OF THE PLAINS: LIFE IN THE PAST
This film describes how the Plains Indians depended on the buffalo for almost all the necessities of life. Also, quillwork, beadwork and painting are presented. 11 mins. 16mm. Rental. UT & PSU.

INDIANS OF THE PLAINS: SUN DANCE CEREMONY
Pictures erection of the tepee or tent for lodging. Features the Sweat Lodge, Sun Dance Ceremony and Grass Dance. 1954. Grades 4 and up. 11 minutes, color. 16mm. Rental: $15. UMN, UT & PSU.

INDIANS OF THE SOUTHWEST: LEGACY OF THE AMERICAN INDIANS
Camera One, Producer; hosted by Wes Studi
From Anasazi to Hohokam to Navajo & Pueblo; examines the legends & cultures of the various tribes. Ancient America Series. 1994. VHS. 60 minutes. $20. CAN, VIP & WKV.

INDIANS OF THE SOUTHWEST
Focuses on the history and culture of the Indians of the Southwest; their descendants, the Pueblos, and other tribes that settled in the Southwest, including the Navajos, Hopi and Zuni. 16 minutes. Grades 4-9. 16mm. FILMS.

INDIANS OF THE UPPER MISSISSIPPI SERIES
This three-part program documents the success of two tribes of Native Americans, the Winnebago & Menominee. Interviews reveal how these tribes won their struggle to stay on their ancestral lands & retain their culture & heritage. 86 mins. VHS, $275. Parts: History, 28 mins, $99.95; Culture, 29 mins, $99.9; Politics, 29 mins, $99.95. CC.

INDIANS, OUTLAWS & ANGIE DEBO
95-year-old Angie Debo, an early 20th century scholar and pioneer, recalls her life as the daughter of 19th century Oklahoma homesteaders. Deb unearthed troubling documents regarding a criminal conspiracy by major political figures to rob the Five Civilized Indian Tribes of Oklahoma of their mineral-rich lands. 1988. 60 minutes. PBS. Rental: $10. HO; $16. UMN.

THE INDIANS WERE THERE FIRST
Shows the path of the ancestors of the first North American Indians across the land bridge from Asia; the various tribes and some of their characteristics; and in particular, the distribution of Iroquois at the end of the 16th-century and the nature of their social and political organization. 13 mins. Purchase, $69.95. FH.

INSTITUTE FOR THE DEVELOPMENT OF INDIAN LAW
A series of five seven minute films providing a review of vital areas of federal Indian law and their effect on tribal government. They include: A Question of Indian Sovereignty, Indian Treaties, Indians and the U.S. Government, Indian Jurisdiction, and The Federal-Indian Trust Relationship. Purchase: 16mm, $550/set. IDIL.

INTO THE CIRCLE: INTRODUCTION TO NATIVE AMERICAN POWWOWS
Full Circle Communications
Witness the powwow, dance styles; interviews with tribal elders, dancers, singers, plus historic photos of early powwow. VHS. 60 mins. VIP & WH.

INUIT KIDS
Paulle Clark, Producer/Director
Helps children get the feel of Arctic life by sharing moments in the lives of two 13-year-old Inuit boys who are friends. 1986. 15 minutes, color. Grades 2-8. Purchase: Video, $245; Rental: $30. BULL.

INUPIAT ESKIMO HEALING
Nellie Moore, Producer; Daniel Housberg, Director/camera/editor
Looks at the practice of medicine in northern Alaska today by following several traditional doctors and their patients in three Inupiat villages. 1985. 30 minutes. In English & Inupiaq with English subtitles. Video. NATC.

THE IRON LODGE
Documentary - Native American men behind bars. 2003. VHS, $24.95. ME.

IROQUOIS SOCIAL DANCE I & II
Nick Manning; Presents, in 2 parts, social dances of the Mohawk Indians, filmed on the Reserve at St. Regis, Canada. Part I, 15 minutes; Part II, 11 minutes. Teacher's guide. Video. Purchase: $49 (both). SH, RM

IS THERE AN AMERICAN STONEHENGE?
Mayer, Producer; Relates Dr. John Eddy's efforts to prove his theory of a Wyoming solar observatory built and used by ancient American Indians. Grades 4-adult. 1982. 30 mins, color. Rental: IU & UT.

ISHI IN TWO WORLDS
Richard Tomkins, Producer
The story of the Yahi Indians of California. Ishi, the last of the Yahi, was the last person in North America known to have lived a totally aboriginal existence. 1967. Grades 9 and up. 19 mins, color. Rental: UCLA, UT, PSU & UA.

ISHI, THE LAST YAHI
Linda Hunt, Narrator; The story of Ishi, the last wild Indian in North America. For more than 40 years, Ishi had lived in hiding with a tiny band of survivors in northern California. He suddenly appeared in 1911, and was the last Yahi Indian alive. Yahi stories & demonstrated the traditional of life he once knew. Using Alfred Kroeber's notes & recordings taken at the time, the film provides a look at indigenous life in America before the arrival of Europeans. 1994. VHS. 57 mins. $19.95. VIP & ME.

IT COULD HAVE BEEN PREVENTED
Substance abuse/boating...a deadly combination. Filmed primarily in Kotzebue, Alaska on the Noatak River with Native people. 17 mins. SH.

ITAM HAKIM, HOPIIT
Victor Masayesva, Jr., Producer/director/camera; Ross Macaya, one of the last members of the Hopi tribal storytelling clan, recounts his life story and various epochs in Hopi history. 1984. 60 mins. In Hopi or English. Purchase: IN

IT'S NOT JUST A TIME FOR FUN
Looks at the annual Choctaw Fair held every June on the Choctaw Reservation. Introduces all the activities of the Fair. All grades. 15 minutes. Purchase: VHS, $85; rental, $10 (two weeks). CHP.

IYAHKIMIX, BLACKFEET BEAVER BUNDLE CEREMONY
Sacred bundles are collections of artifacts & sacred natural objects belonging to clan ancestors and passed on to their descendants. The ritual consists of dancing with the chanting to the bundle's individual parts. Presents religion's ritual in its entirety. 58 mins. 16mm. UAB.

JAUNE QUICK-TO-SEE SMITH
Jack Peterson, Producer; Anthony Schmitz, Director; Joy Harjo, Writer; N. Scott Momaday, Narrator
An imaginative introduction to the work and thought of an outstanding contemporary Native American painter. It conveys Jaune's personal vision and its relation to her painting. 1983. 29 mins. 16mm & video. NAPBC.

JOE KILLS RIGHT--OGLALA SIOUX
Jon Alpert (DTC-TV)
Portrait of a young Sioux man living in New York City. Scenes of Joe living in one of New York City's worst neighborhoods. He loses his job, begins drinking and using drugs, then enters a treatment center. After, he returns to the reservation. Includes dialogue of educational and health services on the reservation. 1980. 25 minutes. VHS. DTC.

JOHN CAT
Based on the story by W.P. Kinsella. An encounter with an older Indian leads two younger ones to a painful awareness of racial prejudice. 26 minutes, color. Video. Purchase: $149. BE.

JOHN KIM BELL
Anthony Azzopardi, Producer; Tells the story of a talented and passionate young man who has broken through social barriers and stepped into the limelight. Bell is the first Native American pursuing a career as a symphonic conductor. Film tracks Bell's early interest and development in music. 1983. 36 1/2 minutes. Video. Purchase: $150; Rental: $40. NAPBC.

JOHNNY FROM FORT APACHE
Records the readjustments in lifestyle the Russells, an Indian family, experience when they move from the reservation to San Francisco. 1971. 15 minutes. Grades 4-adult. 16mm. Rental. UA and IU.

JOSHUA'S SOAPSTONE CARVING
Joshua Qumaluk, an Eskimo, helps his Uncle Levi hunt, fish and trap. He learns to carve soapstone sculptures to sell. 23 minutes. Grades 4 and up. Purchase: video, $290. Rental: $60. PHO.

JOURNEY HOME
Gryphon productions; Looks at the lives of three Native Americans living with AIDS/HIV and examines ways in which they are finding help and support. 1994. 39 mins. VHS. $145. CHAR.

JOURNEY TO THE SKY: HISTORY OF ALABAMA COUSHATTA INDIANS
Robert Cozens, & KUHT-TV, Executive Producers; Paul Yeager, Director/writer; Marcellus Bearheart Williams, & Robert Symonds, Narrators
Alabama Chief, Fulton Battise relates in his native dialect the fantasy tale of three youths traveling to the ends of the earth and beyond. Describes the struggle of a people to preserve their way of life. 1982. 53 mins. Rental: $80/week. NAPBC.

JUST DANCING
Eskimo dancing. 1987. 60 minutes. VHS. $24.95. KYUK.

KAINAI
Raoul Fox, Director
On the Blood Indian Reserve, near Cardston, Alberta, Canada, a pre-fab factory has been built to employ the residents. 27 minutes. 16mm. NFBC.

KAMIK
Elise Swerthone; Inuit, Ulayok Kavlok, a hunter & seamstress, makes seal skin boots called Kamik. 15 mins. NFBC.

KAMINURIAK: CARIBOU IN CRISIS
Inuit Broadcasting Corp. & Don Snowden, Producers

Focuses on the ecological and cultural practices in the North which has affected the Caribou herds in the Inuit regions of Northern Canada. 33 interviews, 4-20 mins. each, presenting both sides of the issue and contrasting approaches to wildlife management. 1982-3. In Inuktitut & English. IBC.

KANEHSATAKE: 270 YEARS OF RESISTANCE
Alanis Obomsawin, Producer
Documents the confrontation between Mohawks & Canadian government forces in Quebec in 1990, outside the town of Oka. Raises vital questions about basic social injustices, the role of politicians, police, the military, and the press. 120 minutes, color. Video. Purchase: $275; rental: $90. BULL.

KARUK BASKET MAKERS, A WAY OF LIFE
Shows women & girls engaged in learning the art of basketmaking from Karuk elders who still practice it. Types & uses of baskets are discussed. Grades 4-6. 22 minutes. VHS. $69.95. CB.

KASHIA MEN'S DANCES: SOUTHWESTERN POMO INDIANS
Clyde B. Smith, Producer; Preserves four authentic Pomo dances as performed in full costume on the Kashia Reservation on the northern California coast. 1963. 40 mins. Purchase: 16mm, $800; video, $195. Rental: $60. UC. Rental: IU, PSU & UCLA.

KECIA: WORDS TO LIVE BY
Gryphon Productions; 15 year-old Kecia speaks of her expereicns--how she contracted the HIV virus, and her pride in her Native American traditions. 1991. Grades 8 and up. 30 mins. $145. CHAR..

KEEP YOUR HEART STRONG: LIFE ALONG THE POWWOW TRAIL
Deb Wallwork, Director/Producer
Provides an inside view of contemporary Native American culture in its most accessible and popular form - the Powwow. 1986. 58 mins, color. DVD. Purchase: $150; Rental: $80. NAPBC. Rental: $16. UMN, CIE, REV.

KEEPER OF THE WESTERN DOOR
Eight short films made on the Cattaraugus & Allegany Reservations in western New York. Each program investigates Seneca life. The Music and Dance of the Senecas, 11 minutes; A Seneca Language Class, 11 mins; Preparing Seneca Food, 18 mins; The Seneca People--Past & Present, 13 mins; A Visit to the Basketmaker, 12 mins; A Visit to the Beader, 15 mins; A Visit to the Seneca Museum, 15 mins; A Visit With a Seneca Artist, 17 mins. 1980. Video. SN.

KEVIN ALEC
Beverly Shaffer, Director; Kevin, an 11 year-old Indian boy from the Fountain Indian Reserve in British Columbia, Canada, whose parents are dead, lives with his grandmother. He leaves, participates and builds pride in the value of tribal life. 1976. 16 mins. Grades 1-8. MG.

KLEENA
H. Leslie Smith, Director/camera; Dann Firehouse, Writer
A small group of Kwakiutl Indians, organized by Peter Knox, the grandson of a famed carver Mungo Martin, sets out from their community at Alert Bay to participate in a traditional fishing activity. Narration gives economic and social facts related to kleena, the oil extracted from the oil-rich eulachon fish, a feast food for potlatches. 1981. 20 minutes, color. 16mm & video. CFDW.

KNOWLEDGE IS THE BEST MEDICINE
Looks at the correct use of prescription drugs as it applies to life in Native American communities. Part 1 of a 2 part series. 2000. 15 mins. VHS. $55. Part 2, "Everyone Counts." CHAR.

KWA' NU' TE': MICMAC & MALISEET ARTISTS
Catherine Martin & Kimberlee McTaggart, Directors
Interviews with eight Native American artists at work talking about the power of creation. 1993. 42 mins. Purchase: VHS, $250. Rental: $70. NFBC.

THE KWAKIUTL OF BRITISH COLUMBIA
Franz Boas; Bill Holm, Editor
A documentary film made by noted anthropologist Dr. Franz Boas, in 1930 at Fort Rupert on Vancouver Island. Includes scenes depicting traditional Kwakiutl dances, crafts, games, oratory and actions of a shaman. 1950. 55 minutes. Silent/bxw. UW. Rental, $19. IU.

KYUK VIDEO
John A. McDonald, Executive producer
Located in Bethel, Alaska, KYUK-TV, begun in 1972, has produced works on the lifestyles and native culture of the Yukon-Kuskokwim Delta, both in English and Yup'ik. Documentaries on the Yup'ik Eskimo way of life and the people's viewpoints on contemporary events & continuation of their cultural traditions. Several productions include: Eyes of the Spirit; From Hand to Hand: Bethel

Native Artist Profiles; A Matter of Trust; They Never Asked Our Fathers; Yupiit Yuraryarait/A Dancing People; Just a Small Fishery; Old Dances, New Dancers; Parlez-Vois Yup'ik; People of Kashunuk. For a complete list of video programs contact KYUK.

LA CROSSE STICK MAKER
Jack Ofield, Director/Producer; Helen-Maria Erawan, Writer/Narrator
Onondaga craftsmen of the sovereign Onondaga Nation, located in New York State, demonstrate the ancient craft of steaming and binding wood to make lacrosse sticks. They discusses tools and techniques, play a game and reflect on their cultural heritage and lifestyle. 1974. Grades 5 and up. 9 minutes, color. Purchase: 16mm, $125; video, $50. Rental, $30 each. NPP & BGF.

THE LAKOTA: ONE NATION ON THE PLAINS
Fran Cantor; Narrated by N. Scott Momaday, this film opens by evoking traditional Lakota philosophy, and conveys history as it is understood in the Lakota tradition. 1976. 29 minutes, color. 16mm & video. UMA & KS.

LAKOTA QUILLWORK: ART & LEGEND
H. Jane Nauman, Producer/director/editor; A documentary on Lakota quillworking, demonstrated and explained, with a re-enactment scene as it might have appeared 150 years ago. Two quillworkers demonstrate sewn and wrapped quilling. 1985. 27 mins. In English & Lakota. SDF & WH.

LAKOTA WOMAN
The life of Lakota activist Mary Crowdog and how she took a stand at Wounded Knee in 1973. 1994. 113 mins. VHS, $199.99. ME.

LAMENT OF THE RESERVATION
Thames TV, Producer; Discusses the living conditions of the 600,000 Indians on barren reservations, pointing out high infant mortality and suicide rates. Grades 7 and up. 23 minutes, color. 16mm. Rental. UT & IU.

THE LAND IS OURS
Laurence A. Goldin, Producer/director/editor; An historical documentary that tells the story of the Tlingits and Haidas, coastal Indians of southeast Alaska. Takes us into the Native's mystical aboriginal opast with time lapse photography and special effects. 57 minutes. Video & 16mm. 1996. AF.

LAND OF THE EAGLE
BBC & WNET's Nature Series; George Page, host & narrator
An 8-part series presenting an account of European colonization of North America. Narratives from American Indians communicate the spiritual naturalism - harmony between man and nature that existed until the "White Man" arrived. 1991. 8/60 minute programs. Video. Individual programs, $39.95. $249.95 complete. A 32-page teacher guide free with series purchase. PBS.

THE LAST DAYS OF OKAK
Anne Budgell & Nigel Markham, Directors
Shows what happens to a community (the Inuit of Labrador) when a disaster (1918-19 flu epidemic) that overwhelms its people also largely destroys the values by which they lived. 1985. 24 minutes, color. Purchase: 16mm, $500; video, $225. Rental: $50. NFBC.

THE LAST MENOMINEE
Describes what is happening to the Menominee Indians of Menominee County, Wisconsin. 1966. Grades 10 and up. 30 minutes, bxw. 16mm. Purchase: $250; rental, $12.15. IU.

THE LAST MOOSESKIN BOAT
Raymond Yakeleya, Director
The Shoteah Dene of the Northwest Territories built moose-skin boats to carry their families and cargo downriver to trading posts. A member of the Dene constructs the last boat of this type to be housed in a museum in Yellowknife. 1982. 28 minutes Video. Purchase: $27. NFBC.

THE LAST OF THE CADDOES
Ken Harrison, Producer/director/writer/editor
Set in rural Texas in the 1930s, this film follows James Edward Hawkins through a summer of self-discovery. Jimmy, age 12, learns that he is part Indian and seeks to learn about his heritage. 1982. 29 minutes. Purchase: video, $315. Rental: $52.50. PHO.

LAST OF HIS TRIBE
HBO Home Video, Producer
In 1800 there were 300,000 Native Americans living in California; by 1900 only 20,000 remained. It was thought that none remained until 1911, when Ishi was captured. This is the story about Ishi (Graham Greene) the last of the Yahi Tribe of California and the secrets of his people. John Voight as Dr. Kroeber. 1992. 90 mins. DVD. $9.98. ME.

THE LAST OF THE MOHICANS
  Michael Mann, Director
James Fenimore Cooper's classic tale of romance in colonial America. With Daniel; Day Lewis, Russell Means, West Studi, Eric Schweig, et al. 1992. 117 mins. DVD, 2001. $22.30. ME.

LAST SALMON FEAST OF THE CELILO INDIANS
Produced prior to the Dalles Dam inundation of the last major salmon fishery of the Wy-am Pum, a branch of lower Deschute Indians, the Yakimas and the Warm Springs, and other central Oregon tribes. 1955. 18 mins, bxw. Purchase: 16mm, $150; rental, $10. OHS.

LAST STAND AT LITTLE BIGHORN
  Rocky Collins, Director; N. Scott Momaday, Narrator
Re-examines the Battle of the Little Bighorn from both the white & Native American perspectives. 1992. 60 mins. DVD, $17.99. ME.

THE LEARNING PATH
  Loretta Todd, Director; Native control of Native education in Canada, to preserve their languages and identities. Schools in Edmonton and nearby Saddle Lake Reserve. 1991. 57 mins. VHS. Purchase: $27. NFBC.

LEGACY
  Chief Roy Crazy Horse & Jeff Baker, Directors
Examines the perpetuation of the romantic myths surrounding Christopher Columbus' "Discovery of the New World" in 1492. 1993. 22 mins. VHS. Purchase: $195. Rental, $50. CG.

LEGACY; NATIVE AMERICAN PHOTOGRAVURES & MUSIC
Historical look at the photogravure work of Edward C. Curtis. 2003. DVD, $19.99. ME.

LEGACY OF GENERATIONS: POTTERY BY AMERICAN INDIAN WOMEN
  Narrated by performer, Buffy Sainte-Marie
Set against the landscape of the American Southwest, this film showcases the art of master potters. 30 minutes. $19.95. PMI.

LEGACY OF MOUND BUILDERS
Story of a lost civilization born in the heartland of America over 2,000 years ago. VHS. 17 mins. $14.95. VIP.

LEGEND OF THE BOY & THE EAGLE
The Hopi legend of Tutevina, the young Indian boy who is banished from his tribe for freeing the sacrificial bird. 21 mins. 16mm. WD.

THE LEGEND OF THE BUFFALO CLAN
A lesson for teaching traditions, proper behavior, cultural history, and spiritual beliefs. The Buffalo chief does an authentic healing ceremony, reviving the child. 1993. 29 mins. PHO.

LEGEND OF THE MAGIC KNIVES
A totem village in the Pacific Northwest provides the setting for this portrayal of an ancient Indian legend, recounted by means of figures on a totem pole and authentic Indian masks. 1970. 11 mins. Grades 4 and up. PSU & IU.

LEGENDS & LIFE OF THE INUIT
  Richard Robesco, Director; Animated film looks at life today in an Inuit community and presents five legends. 1978. 58 mins. NFBC.

LEGENDS OF THE INDIANS
These stories of various Native American tribes are re-enacted by Native Americans to remember who they are and what they believe. The Return of the Child (Algonquin); The Legend of the Corn (Ojibway); The Winter Wife (Chippewa); Moowis, Where Are You, Moowis? (Algonquin); The Path of the Souls (Ojibway); Glooscap, Creation Legend; The World Between & The Path of Life. 26 mins each. FH.

LEGENDS OF THE SIOUX
Filmed in South Dakota, this film relates many of the legends of the Sioux Indians. 27 mins. UK.

LENAPE: THE ORIGINAL PEOPLE
  Thomas Agnello, Producer/director/editor
  David Oestreicher, Research coordinator
Briefly sketches Delaware, or Lenape history; focuses on two elders living in Dewey, Oklahoma, who retain the language and knowledge of old customs and beliefs. Edward Thompson describes his participation in a Big House Ceremony in 1924; and Nora Thompson Dean, also know as Touching Leaves Woman. Scenes of the first reunion of Lenape held in 1983 are included. 1986. 22 minutes. Purchase: 16mm, $325; video, $95. Rental: $45. AG.

LETTER FROM AN APACHE
  Barbara Wilk, Producer/writer/animator; Fred Hellerman, Narrator
An animated film presenting experiences of a Yavapai Indian of the early 20th century. The narration is adapted from a letter written by Carlos Montezuma, M.D., known as Wassajah, to Frederick W. Hodge to provide autobiographical information for the 1907 Handbook of American Indians. 1983. Grades 4-9. 11 minutes. Purchase: 16mm, $240; VHS, $89; 3/4", $119. CC.

LEWIS & CLARK AT THE GREAT DIVIDE
  CBS News; hosted by Walter Cronkite
The expedition nearly ends prematurely in 1805 when a young Indian girl turns out to be a Shoshoni chief's sister. Grades 3-8. 22 mins. PHOENIX.

LEWIS & CLARK: JOURNEY OF THE CORPS OF DISCOVERY
  Ken Burns, Producer/Director; Film documentary of the expedition led by Meriweather Lewis & William Clark and the Corps of Discovery into the heart of America in the early 19th century, and the aid they received from Indians. 1997. 240 minutes. DVD, 2004. $29.99. ME. Amazon.com, $24.99.

LEWIS & CLARK: EXPLORERS OF THE NEW FRONTIER
  A&E Home Video; Documents Lewis & Clark expedition. 2000. 50 mins. ME.

LEWIS & CLARK: GREAT JOURNEY WEST
  National Geographic; Brings to life the scientific expedition of the Corps of Discovery. 2002. 45 mins. VHS & DVD, $19.99. ME.

A LIFETIME OF CARING
Looks at the issues facing many seniors in many Native communities, including different forms of elder abuse and neglect. and promotes ways of providing improved care-giver services. Grades 9 and up. 1995. 25 mins. VHS. $145. CHAR.

LIGHTING THE SEVENTH FIRE
  Salmon Run Productions
The spear-fishing treaty rights in Wisconsin and the Ojibway prophecy of the Seventh Fire, and profiles some of the people trying to bring back the tradition of spear fishing. Documents contemporary racism against Native peoples in the U.S. 1995. Grades 5 and up. 48 minutes. Video. $50. OY.

LIKE THE TREES
Rose, a Metis Indian from northern Alberta, leaves the city to find her roots among the Woodland Cree. 15 minutes. 16mm. NFBC.

A LITTLE WHILE MORE YET
  Jan Marie Martell; Stephen Charleson, from the Hesquiat Band of the West Coast of Vancouver Island, talks about the difficulties in making the transition from his native com-munity to a city environment. 1976. 15 mins. CFDW.

LITTLE WHITE SALMON INDIAN SETTLEMENT
  Harry Dawson, Director; Leo Alexander, Advisor/narrator
Cooks Landing, the site of one of the oldest Indian fishing villages in North America, is the subject of this documentary produced in cooperation with members of the Yakima Indian Tribe. 1972. Grades 9 and up. 30 minutes. 16mm. Rental: PSU & UCLA.

LIVE AND REMEMBER
  Henry Smith, Producer; Using some footage of Vision Dance, as well as new interviews and footage shot on Rosebud Reservation in South Dakota, this film examines the role and sacred nature of dance, music and oral tradition in Lakota culture and what it means to be Indian living in America today. 1986. Grades 9 and up. 29 mins. CAN & NAPBC. Rental: $21. UMN.

THE LIVING STONE
  John Freeney, Director; Contemporary Inuit Eskimos of Cape Dorset on Baffin Island continue an ageless tradition of creative craftsmanship carving stone into evocative portrayals of Inuit life. 1958. Grades 7 & up. 33 mins. NFBC. Rental. IU.

LIVING TRADITIONS: FIVE INDIAN WOMEN ARTISTS
  Denise Mayotte, Kathee Prokop, Fran Belvin, Producers/directors/editors; Sherry Wilson, Narrator; The relationship between traditional Indian values and the handiwork of five Indian women artists from Minnesota is examined. Shows the role of culture handed down from generation to generation. 1984. 27 mins. IN.

THE LONG WALK OF FRED YOUNG
  Michael Barnes; The story of a child, Fred Young, who only spoke the Ute and Navajo languages, went to a medicine man when he was sick. Today, he is Dr. Frederick Young, a nuclear physicist. 1979. 58 mins. WGBH. Rental: UMN.

THE LONGEST TRAIL

Alan Lomax, Producer; Alan Lomax & Forrestine Paulay, Editors
Exploration of the dance traditions of the American Indian showing more than 50 Native American dances. Focuses on Native America, showing patterns of movement linking dances of Indians and Inuit from the Arctic Circle to Tierra del Fuego into one tradition. Also seeks to demonstrate a connection between these cultures and indigenous cultures in Siberia. 1986. 58 minutes, color. Purchase: 16mm, $995; video, $295. Rental, $60. UC. Rental: $23. UMN.

THE LONGEST WALK: S.F. TO D.C. 1978

A documentary of the spiritual and political walk across the nation from Alcatraz Island to Washington, D.C. to protest anti-Indian legislation and inform local communities about eleven bills then currently before Congress. 60 minutes. Also available are three 20 minute videotapes which are supplemental reference information: John Trudell--Pueblo Rally Speech; A Look Behind Indian Legislation; and, Dennis Banks--AIM Leader in Exile. CLP.

THE LONGEST WAR

Diane Orr, Director; An interview with Dennis Banks, founder of the American Indian Movement (AIM). Shows scenes of the occupation of Wounded Knee and the burning of the Courthouse at Custer, South Dakota in 1973. Interviews with participants at Wounded Knee. 1974. 30 mins. BF.

THE LONGHOUSE PEOPLE

Tom Daly, Producer
The life and religion of the Iroquois today. Shows a rain dance, a healing ceremony, and a celebration of a new chief. 1951. Grades 9 and up. 24 mins. NFBC. Rental: IU & UCLA.

THE LOON'S NECKLACE

Crawley Films, Producer; A Spanish language film recreating a Salish legend which tells how the loon came to receive his distinguished neckband. Authentic ceremonial masks establish the characters of the story. 1949, restored, 1990. 11 mins. Grades 4 and up. 16mm & video. Rental, $14. PSU, UMN, UT & IU.

LORD OF THE SKY

Ludmila Zeman & Eugen Spaleny, Director
Based on the legends of the Native peoples of the Pacific Northwest, this animated film is an artistic unity of form & content. An environ-mental parable. 13 minsNFBC.

LOS INDIOS NAVAJOS

A Spanish language film that shows the Navajo people in their own environment. 1939. 11 minutes; bxw. Grades 4-8. UA.

LOST IN TIME

Bruce G. Kuerten & Maryanne Culpepper, Producers; Dennis King, Narrator
Observes the work of archaeologists in the Tennessee Valley. Traces the history of the early native peoples, describing American prehistory beginning with the migration of Paleolithic hunters into the New World over the Bering land bridge. Briefly discusses the changes of Indian culture leading to the complex settled lifestyles of the Indians who built the great mounds of the Black Warrior River Valley in Alabama. 1985. 60 mins. AT & BE. Edited version, 30 mins, $195. BE.

LOST NATION: THE IOWAY

Tammy & Kelly Rundle; Documentary of two Ioway leaders and their struggle to save their people from inevitable American conquest, and the Ioway's current fight to reclaim & maintain their unique histority & culture. 57 mins. DVD, $22.99. Poster available, $8. 2008. FWF.

LOUISE ERDRICH & MICHAEL DORRIS

Bill Moyers, Host
Native American husband & wife team who write novels together. Their writings & beliefs in family, community & lifestyle reflect their heritage. 1988. 27 mins. UMN.

LOVING REBEL

A documentary profile of Helen Hunt Jackson, one of the 19th-century's foremost advocates of Native American rights and one of its most celebrated writers. This video features readings from her writings as well as rare photographs & drawings of her world. 1987. Grades 7 and up. 27 minutes. Purchase: VHS & Guide, $69; CHAR.

LUCY COVINGTON: NATIVE AMERICAN INDIAN

Steve Heiser, Director
Filmed on the Colville Reservation in eastern Washington, Lucy Covington, chairperson of the Colville tribe & granddaughter of Chief Moses, gives an account of her part in the effort to prevent federal termination of the tribe. She talks about the Indian heritage and Indian identity, and how the land is central to these. 1978. Grades 7+. 15 mins. 16mm. Rental: Video, $12. PSU & UCT.

LUCY SWAN

An Indian woman born on the Rosebud Reservation at the turn of the century remembers the old ways but does not entirely discount the new. 16mm. Purchase: $300; rental: $30. AICRC.

LUMAAQ - AN ESKIMO LEGEND

Co Hoedeman, Director; Lumaaq tells the story of a legend widely believed by the Povungnituk Inuit. 1975. Grades 7 and up. 8 mins, NFBC.

MAGIC IN THE SKY

Peter Raymont, Director/Writer; An examination of the impact of Canadian (CBC) TV on Inuit Eskimos on the Arctic coast of Quebec, and their efforts to establish their own network. Mirrors the struggle of any culture to preserve its unique identity. 1981. Grades 7 and up. 57 mins. NFBC.

MAKE MY PEOPLE LIVE: THE CRISIS IN INDIAN HEALTH CARE

Linda Harrar, Producer/director/writer; Lee Grant, Narrator
Investigates the state of health care for Indians. Details Native American life in four vastly different regions & discusses legislative and other issues, providing an introduction not only to health concerns but also to contemporary life of Native Americans across the country. Sites visited range from impoverished Rosebud Sioux Reservation to the Tlingit villages of Alaska; and from the Navajo Nation to the Creek Nation of Oklahoma. 1984. 60 mins. UT.

MAKE PRAYERS TO THE RAVEN

Mark Badger, Producer/camera/editor; Barry Lopez, Narrator
Public television series introducing the lifeways and traditions of interior Alaska's Koyukon Indians. Focuses on their relationship to the land, and explores their spiritual beliefs. Includes the Koyukon communities of Alatna, Allakaket, Hughes, & Huslia - located below the Arctic Circle. Video. KUAC.

MAKIAWISUG: THE GIFT OF THE LITTLE PEOPLE

22 minute animated video ...Mohegan oral tradition. MT.

THE MAKING OF A PORKY ROACH WITH KRIS WOERPOL

Noc Bay Publishing; The Porky Roach, worn by male dancers, is the universal headdress worn today in the powwow arena. A complete guide to construction includes sorting deer and porky hair, making of a hand-woven base, tying on the hair and care of the finished roach. 30 mins. WH.

MAKOCE WAKAN: SACRED EARTH

Robby Romero, Director/writer; Focuses on Native American sacred sites & their importance to Native American culture. Personal & political insights on the importance of protecting Native American sacred sites: Ben Nighthorse Campbell (Cheyenne); Richard Moves Camp (Oglala Lakota); Audrey Shenandoah (Onondaga); Franklin Stanley (San Carlos Apache); Suzan Shown Harjo (CVheyenne/Hodulgee Muscogee); Ola Cassadore (San Carlos Apache); & Leon Shenandoah (Iroquois). 1993. 30 minutes. VH-1.

THE MAN & THE GIANT: AN ESKIMO LEGEND

Co Hoedeman, Director; An Inuit legend acted out by the Inuit people themselves. They use their traditional form of singing, katadjak, or throat singing. 1978. 8 mins. PHO & NFBC.

MAN OF LIGHTNING

Gary Moss, Producer; Based on two Cherokee Indian legends, this film is a drama of the long-vanished world of the Cherokee years before European contact. 1982. 29 mins. NAPBC.

MAN ON THE RIM: THE PEOPLING OF THE PACIFIC, 4 - FLAMING ARROWS

Over 20,000 years ago Siberian hunters crossed the Bering Strait land bridge into Alaska and poured into the American prairie. The Indian emerged in North America. 1988. 58 minutes, color. Video. Rental, $24. PSU.

MARIA! INDIAN POTTERY OF SAN ILDEFONSO

National Park Service; Indian pottery maker Maria Martinez demonstrates the traditional India ways of pottery making. 27 minutes. Video, $29.95. CH.

MARIA & JULIAN'S BLACK POTTERY

Arthur E. Baggs, Jr.
Shows famous potters Maria and Julian Martinez in the step-by-step process of creating the famed black-on-black pottery that revived at San Ildefonso Pueblo, New Mexico. 1938/1977. 11 minutes, color. 16mm/silent. Purchase, 16mm, $190; VHS, $105. Rental: 16mm, $14; VHS, $13. PSU.

MARIA OF THE PUEBLOS

The life of the famous Pueblo potter, Maria Martinez. Provides an understanding of the culture, philosophy, art and economic condition of the Pueblo Indians of San Ildefonso, New Mexico. 1971. Grades 4 and up. 15 mins. PHO. Rental: UCT.

MARK OF THE UNCAS
Documentary exploring the legacy of Mohegan's greatest chief, Uncas. 60 mins. Video. MT.

MARKS OF THE ANCESTORS: ANCIENT INDIAN ROCK ART OF ARIZONA
Echo Productions; Produced in cooperation with the Museum of Northern Arizona, this video explores six different rock art sites. 40 mins. $24.95. TC.

THE MARMES ARCHAEOLOGICAL DIG
Louis & Ruth Kirk, Producers
Presents the oldest fully documented discovery of early man in the Western Hemisphere. 1971. 18 mins. UW.

MASHPEE
Maureen McNamara & Mark Gunning, Producers/ directors/ writers
Illustrates the land claims of the Mashpee Wampanoags of Massachusetts since 1976. Provides the complex background of the controversy, with interviews of Mashpee leaders, real estate developers, historians, legal experts, & trial lawyers presenting their sides of the story. 1985. 50 mins. McN.

THE MASKS OF CULTURE
Gryphon Productions; Explains the importance the wooden mask in tribal ceremonies. Grades 8 and up. 25 minutes. VHS. $250. NDM.

A MATTER OF CHOICE
The Hopi Nation and their efforts to find a place In the modern world. 60 minutes, color. Video. Purchase: $60. PBS.

A MATTER OF PROMISES
Introduces students to members of Native American tribes who describe their struggles to maintain cultural identity & political sovereignty. 60 mins. PBS.

A MATTER OF TRUST
Bill Sharpsteen, Producer/writer/editor/host; Bryan Murray, Narrator
Focuses on the Alaska Native Claims Settlement Act passed by Congress in 1971 and the problems it has posed for Alaska's Indians and Inuit. 1983. 28 minutes. Video. KYUK.

MATTHEW ALIUK: ESKIMO IN TWO WORLDS
Bert Sulzman, Writer/Director; The relationship of an Eskimo boy assimilated into the city life of Anchorage. Tells the story of a proud people's struggle for cultural survival in a changing world. 1973. 18 mins. LCA.

MEDICINE FIDDLE
Documentary celebrates the fiddling & dancing traditions of Native & Metis families on both sides of the U.S. & Canadian border. Features Ojibwe, Menominee, Metis & Ottawa fiddlers & dancers. 1990. 81 mins. UC.

MEDICINE LINE
Ken Mitchell, Director
A brief acount of Chief Sitting Bull of the Lakota Sioux during his years in exile in Canada. 1987. 10 mins. NFBC.

THE MEDICINE WHEEL
Native American spirituality/healing. Visually moving segments highlight the Sweat Lodge and Pipe Ceremonies. Grades 7 and up. 1996. 24 mins.. CHAR.

MEDOONAK, THE STORMMAKER
Les Krizsan, Director; MicMac Indian legend. 1975. 13 mins. UA.

MEET THE SIOUX INDIAN
Shows the transient life of the Sioux Indians. 1949. Grades K-6. 11 mins. Rental: UCT.

MENOMINEE
This documentary examines the historical development of the many social and political problems faced by the Menominee Indians of northwestern Wisconsin. 1974. 59 mins. NAPBC.

MESA VERDE
The story of ancient America and the Pueblo builders. 1997. 60 mins. ME.

MESA VERDE
National Park Service; Mesa Verde's cliff dwellings interpreted. 23 mins. CH.

MESA VERDE: MYSTERY OF THE SILENT CITIES
Views (using extensive aerial photography) the ruined cities and multiply family cliff dwellings of the 13th-century Indians of the Mesa Verde. 1975. 14 mins, color. 16mm. Rental, $11.20. IU.

MESQUAKIE
Alan Weber and Michael Bartell
Looks at the Mesquakie Indian settlement at Tama, Iowa, where carious activities of the traditional days are shown through old photographs and present-day film footage. 1976. 10 mins. ISU.

MIGHTY WARRIORS
During the mass migration west, the white man encountered the Plains Indians. Familiar battles are depicted in the light of the true facts. 1964. Grades 4 and up. 30 mins, bxwIU. Rental only, $16. PSU.

MI'KMAQ
A series of five programs recreating, in dramatized form, the seasonal round of Micmac life in Nova Scotia, Canada, before European contact as it might have been experienced by a single, extended Micmac family. Performed by Native people in the Micmac language. Available in French and English. Teacher's guide. Grades 6-adult. Video. NS.

MILLENIUM: TRIBAL WISDOM & THE MODERN WORLD
Biniman Productions & Adrian Malone Productions
Filmed in 15 countries, this ten-hour series tells the stories of people in 11 tribal cultures across the globe in an attempt to discover different ways of thinking about life as the turn of the century approaches. Two of the cultures covered include the Mohawk, and the Navajo. #6 - Touching the Timeless (Navajo); and #9 - The Tightrope of Power ((Mohawk & Ojibwe-Cree). 1992. 60 mins each. PSU.

MIN-BIMAADIZIWIN: THE GOOD LIFE
Deb Wallwork, Director/Producer
A portrait of a community on the White Earth Reservation in Minnesota where the people's lives revolve around annual harvest of wild rice. DVD. CIE, REV.

MINORITIES IN AGRICULTURE: THE WINNEBAGO
Ralph A. Swain, Briar Cliff College
Highlights the economic development programs of the Winnebago Tribe of Nebraska. 1984. 29 mins. Video. Rental: $40/week. NAPBC.

MINORITY YOUTH: ADAM
The narration of a teenage American Indian's view of himself, his race, and his cultural heritage that is in danger of being lost. 1971. 10 mins, color. 16mm. Rental, $9. IU.

MISS INDIAN AMERICA
KBYU-TV, Provo, Utah; Covers the 20th annual Miss Indian America Pageant in 1973 at Sheridan, Wyoming. Contest represents 30 American Indian tribes from all over the U.S. 59 minutes, color. Video. Purchase: $150; Rental: $80/week. NAPBC.

THE MISSING
Ron Howard, Director
Lots of Apache spoken in this film. With Tommy Lee Jones & Cate Blanchett. 130 mins. 2003. DVD, 28.99; VHS, $70.99. ME.

MISSION LIFE: ALTA CALIFORNIA 1776
22 minutes. 16mm. Rental. UA.

MISSION OF FEAR
Fernand Dansereau, Director
The story of the Jesuit martyrs who lived with their Huron converts, Indians of Midland, Ontario. 79 mins, bxw. NFBC.

MISSION SAN XAVIER DEL BAC
33 minutes. 16mm. Rental. UA.

MISSIONS OF CALIFORNIA: NEW WAYS IN NEW WORLD
21 minutes. 16mm. Rental. UA.

MISSIONS OF THE SOUTHWEST
15 minutes. 16mm. Rental. UA.

MITAKUYE OYASIN - "WE ARE ALL RELATED"
Dr. A. Chuck Ross, Narrator; Dr. Ross, a Santee Dakota educator & spiritual guide provides an introduction to Sioux religion and philosophy as detailed in his book "We Are All Related." 60 minutes, color. Video. $22.50. CAN.

MOCCASIN FLATS
A young boy learns to come to terms with his Native American heritage, and learns to be proud of his background and finally claims his Native American name, Moccasin Flats. 26 minutes. Purchase, VHS, $149. CC.

MOCCASIN MAKING

Frank E. White; Step-by-step instructions for making a side-seam moccasin. List of necessary tools and equipment, pattern-making, leather selection, advanced sewing techniques. VHS. 55 mins. $19.95. WP.

MODOC

Peter Winograd; By the use of archival photos by Edward S. Curtis and news clippings, this film tells the story of the Modoc Indians of California and their struggle to remain on their own lands. 1979. 15 mins. bxw. EM.

MOHAWK BASKETMAKING: A CULTURAL PROFILE

Frank Semmens, Producer; Features a sensitive and personal look at the life & work of master basket-maker Mary Adams. 1980. 28 mins. PSU.

MOMADAY: VOICE OF THE WEST

Scott Momaday's prose uniquely reflects the Native American experience. Momaday gives viewers a rare glimpse into the human dilemma that led to his strong identification with the land. 30 minutes. Video. $40. PBS.

MONUMENT VALLEY: LAND OF THE NAVAJOS

Shows the life of the Navajo Indians in the four-corner area where Arizona, New Mexico, Colorado & Utah meet. 1959. 17 mins. Grades 6-adult. 16mm. UA.

THE MOON'S PRAYER

Stories of the Northwest tribes struggles to reverse the unsound environmental practices that have been inflicted upon their land. 60 mins. HO.

MORE LEGENDS OF THE INDIANS

These are authentic stories from various Indian tribes, told by Native Americans to remember who they are and what they believe. 8-part series: Windigo; The Pleiades; The Magic Box; Pitchie the Robin; The Spirit of the Dead Chief; The Path Without End; The Invisible Man; & Megmoowesoo. 26 minutes each. Purchase: $89.95 each; $685 for all 8 parts. FH.

MORE THAN BOWS & ARROWS: LEGACY OF THE AMERICAN INDIANS

Roy Williams, Director; N. Scott Momaday, narrator; Camera One, Producer Documents the contributions of Native Americans to the development of the U.S. & Canada. N. Scott Momaday is a prominent Kiowa Indian writer and educator. 1994. VHS. 58 mins, color. $19.95. ME, CAN, CMM, VIP & WKV; rental: VHS, $10. UMN, PSU & HO.

MOTHER CORN

KBYU-TV, Provo, Utah
Examines the historical significance of various types of corn among Native American cultures. 1977. 29 mins. NAPBC.

MOTHER OF MANY CHILDREN

Alanis Obomsawin, Director
Agatha Marie Goodine, 108 year-old member of the Hobbema tribe, contrasts her memories with the conflicts that most Indian and Inuit woman face today. 1977. 58 mins. Grades 9 and up. NFBC.

A MOTHER'S CHOICE

Examines the root causes of FAS/FAE (Fetal Alcohol Syndrome - Fetal Alcohol Effects) from the perspective of Native mothers. 1995. 28 mins. CHAR.

MOUNTAIN WOLF WOMAN: 1884-1960

Naomi Russell, Narrator
Tells the life story of an American Indian in her own words & narrated by her granddaughter. Based on the book by Nancy Oestreich Lurie. Includes an authentic Winnebago wedding song, baskets, beads, wigwams, & scenes from a powwow. 1990. 17 mins. MN.

MOVABLE FEAST

Presents Indian & Eskimo ways of hunting, gathering, preparing, and celebrating food, through images by Native artists from all over North America. Includes study guide. 30 minutes. Video. $50. TOP.

MUNGO MARTIN: A SLENDER THREAD/THE LEGACY

Barb Cramer/The U'Mista Cultural Society; From the time of his birth, Mungo Martin was exposed to cultural rituals and traditions of his people. At a young age he learned the basic skills of designing, carving & painting in Northwest Coast traditional style of the Kwakwakawakw. 1991. 17 mins. CFDW.

MUSIC & DANCE OF THE MOHAWK

Frank Semmens, Producer/director/camera/editor
Traces the origin, development and meaning behind Iroquois social songs; and the making of Iroquois musical instruments. 1983. 25 minutes. 16mm & video. AM & IM.

MUSIC & DANCE OF THE SENECAS

Covers various aspects of the Seneca Indian culture. Introduces a variety of musical instruments with explanations. of how each one was taken from nature. 1981. 20 minutes. VHS. Rental: $25. UCLA.

MY FATHER CALLS ME SON: RACISM & NATIVE AMERICANS

David Fanning, Executive Producer for KOCE-TV
Examines the problem of discrimination and some of the parallel pressures against Indian people to give up their uniqueness and become more like whites. 1975. 29 mins. Video. PBS.

MY HANDS ARE THE TOOLS OF MY SOUL: ART & POETRY OF THE AMERICAN INDIAN

Arthur Barron & Zina Voynoz
A survey of American Indian achievements in poetry, music, sculpture, philosophy and history. Dialogue in tribal language as well as English. 1975. 52 minutes, color. 16mm & video. FI & TF. Rental: 16mm, PSU & UCT.

THE MYSTERY OF THE ANASAZI

Russ Morash, Director; WGBH, Producer
A study of the ruins of the Anasazi, the builders, ancestors of the Navajo. 1973. 50 mins, color. 16mm & video. TW & ISU. 16mm rental, $31. PSU.

THE MYSTERY OF THE LOST RED PAINT PEOPLE: THE DISCOVERY OF A PREHISTORIC NORTH AMERICAN SEA CULTURE

T.W. Timreck & William Goetzmann, Producers
Follows U.S., Canadian, and European scientists from the barrens of Labrador - where archaeologists uncover an ancient stone burial mound - to sites in the U.S., France, England, Denmark and Norway where monumental standing stones testify to links among seafaring cultures across immense distances. 1987. Grades 9 and up. 57 minutes, color. Purchase: 16mm, $895; Video, $495; Rental: $90. BULL. Rental: 16mm, $39. PSU.

THE MYTHICAL TRIBE

History of the Sioux tribe from their victory at Little Big Horn to their defeat at Wounded Knee. 1981. 30 minutes, video. KS.

MYTHS AND THE MOUNDBUILDERS

Graham Chedd, WGBH, Producer
Archaeologists probe mysterious mounds in the Eastern U.S. uncovering clues about a lost Indian civilization. Educator's guide. 1981. Grades 9 and up. 58 minutes, color. 16MM & Video. Purchase: 16mm, $750; Video, $145. Rental: 16mm, $70; Video, $40. NDM, PBS, DER, CAN & CH. Rental only: $20. PSU & IU.

NANOOK OF THE NORTH

Robert Flaherty
A documentary studying the life of an Eskimo hunter and his constant struggle for survival against the menaces of nature. 1948. 65 minutes, 16mm/bxw/silent. Grades 4 and up. Original silent version, MMA. Purchase: 16mm, $26; video, $12.50. PSU. 1975 (51 minutes) restored version with musical score-rental, $22. PSU. 16mm rental, $20.25. IU.

NANOOK REVISITED

This program revisits the site of Flaherty's filming, and learns that he staged much of what he filmed, sired children to whose future he paid no heed, and is himself part of Inuit myth. 60 mins, color. Purchase: $149; rental: $75. FH.

NATIONS WITHIN A NATION

Department of Sociology, OK State U.
Examines the historical, legal and social backgrounds of the issue of the right of sovereignty-self-government. Examples of tribal government in operation are drawn from Taos Pueblo, the Mescalero Apache Tribe, the Muscogee (Creek) Nation and the Sac and Fox Tribe. 1986. 59 mins. Video. Purchase: $150; Rental: $80. NAPBC.

NATIVE AMERICA: VOICES FROM THE LAND

32 documentaries examine Native North American culture, past & present, and its attempts to halt assimilation and retain native cultural traditions. Uses historical & contemporary photographs, paintings, artwork, archive footage, reenactments & interviews. 588 mins. DVD, 2010. $9.98. Amazon.com.

NATIVE AMERICAN ARTS

Indian Arts and Crafts Board; The development of Native American arts in the U.S. Shows contemporary artists and craftsmen (Indian Eskimo and Aleut) are making unique and significant contributions to the cultural life of our nation. 1974. 20 mins. 16mm & video. UCT & NAC.

NATIVE AMERICAN FOLKTALES

Tales from four different Native American tribes: Seneca, Pacific Coast Miwok, Pawnee, Pueblo. Grades 4-8. 1997. 22 mins. VHS & Guide. $95. CHAR.

NATIVE AMERICAN HEALING IN THE 21ST CENTURY: ANCIENT REMEDIES NOW ENDORSED BY MODERN MEDICINE
(produced by Rich-Heape Films); VHS & DVD. 40 mins. $24.95. MALKI.

NATIVE AMERICAN HERBS
Discover the healing properties & preparation of herbs. 2000. $24.95. ME.

NATIVE AMERICAN HISTORY: Part 1 WILDERNESS; Part 2 CIVILIZATION
Lionheart Television; Part 1, The Wilderness: Examines historical & contemporary attitudes toward Native Americans and reveals the extent to which the European invasion altered life for all Native Americans. Part 2, Civilization: Examines the way U.S. Government handled Native Americans after the battle at Wounded Knee in 1890. Grades 9-12. 50 mins each. PHO.

NATIVE AMERICAN IMAGES
Carol Patton, Producer; Profiles the lives, philosophies & works of Paladine Royce (Ponca), Donald Van (Cherokee) and Steve Forbes, three artists living in Austin, Texas. Forbes is a non-Indian who has devoted himself to the portrayal of contemporary Native Americans. 1984. 29 mins. Video. NAPBC.

NATIVE AMERICAN INDIAN SACRED PURIFICATION SWEAT LODGE CEREMONY
42 minute version of "American Indian Sweat Lodge Ceremony." Video. AV.

NATIVE AMERICAN MASTER ARTISTS VIDEO SERIES
Cherokee Basketmaker: Ella Mac Blackbear. VHS. 24 mins. The Strength of Life: Knokovtee Scott, Creek Shellworker. VHS. 28 mins. Ribbons of the Osage: Art & Life of Georgeann Robinson. VHS. 28 mins. $17.95 each. WH.

NATIVE AMERICAN MEDICINE
Explores the link between homeopathic medicine & native ceremony. 2001. DVD or VHS, $19.95. ME.

NATIVE AMERICAN MEN'S & WOMEN'S DANCE STYLES
Full Circle Communications; An hour of dancing, highlighting the styles of champion dancers. 2 Vols. Vol. 1: Men's Straight Dance, Northern Traditional, Grass Dance, Fancy, Women's Southern Cloth, Buckskin, Jingle Dress, Fancy Shawl. Vol. 2: Hoop Dance, Gourd Dance, Rabbit Dance, Two-Step, Round Dance, Team dancing. VHS. 60 mins each. $19.95 each. VIP & WH.

NATIVE AMERICAN MYTHS
An animated film introduced by Native American narrator Ned Romero, who briefly explains the relevant background information for each of five authentic myths: Sky Woman, a Seneca myth; How Raven Gave Daylight to the World, Haida myth; The First Strawberry, Cherokee myth; The People Came Out of the Underworld, Hopi myth. 1976. 23 mins. Grades 4-12. PSU & UT.

THE NATIVE AMERICAN POWWOW
An introduction to the powwow and information guide on how to enjoy a powwow. Illustrates the variety of dances; history of the powwow, interviews with tribal elders. 1994. 58 mins. VHS, $29.95. AUDIO.

THE NATIVE AMERICAN SERIES
Consists of three films, helps young people understand the origin of the American Indians, and the effect the coming Europeans had on the Indians. Indian Origins - The First 50,000 Years; Indian Cultures - From 2000 B.C. to 1500 A.D.; and The Indian Experience - After 1500 A.D. 19 minutes each. Video. Purchase: $305 each. BE.

NATIVE AMERICAN TALES
Video 1: The Dancing Stars (Iroquois) & The Friendly Wolf (Plains Indians); Video 2: The Fire Bringer (Paiute) & How Saynday Brought the Buffalo to the Indians (Kiowa); Video 3: The Angry Moon (Tlingit); Video 4: Coyote & Cottontail and Coyote & the Beaver People (Navajo). Grades K-5. Teacher's guide. 15 mins each. $125 each. AIT.

A NATIVE AMERICAN'S VIEW: COLUMBUS & EUROPEAN SETTLEMENT
Native American storyteller, Helen Herrara Anderson, answers 9 questions about Columbus & European explorers commonly asked her by her students. Grades 4-7. 8 minutes VHS. 1992. $145. SH, NDM.

NATIVE AMERICAN WOMAN ARTISTS
A documentary, 2 vol. set explores southwestern art of pottery & textiles. 1998. 60 mins. VHS, $24.95. ME.

NATIVE AMERICANS
TBS Productions; History of Native American peoples as told by them. 8 hrs. Native Americans, P.O. Box 2203, S. Burlington, VT 05407.

NATIVE AMERICANS: THE HISTORY OF A PEOPLE
Ten posters. 17" x 22". Individual posters, $7.95; set, $44.95. KU.

NATIVE AMERICANS: MYTHS & REALITIES
Young Native men & women from various tribes are shown trying to change some of the stereotypes attributed to them throughout the years. Grades 6 and up. 1997. 16 mins. VHS. $95. CHAR.

NATIVE GRACE
A selection of prints of Native American peoples, landscapes, creatures and plants done by famous artists who recorded the earliest days of exploration in North America. 30 mins. $29.95. CH.

NATIVE INDIAN FOLKLORE
a 5-video compilation: Christmas at Moose Factory (James Bay); The Man, the Snake & Fox (Ojibway legend); Medoonak the Stormmaker (Micmac legend); Salmon People (West Coast Indians); Summer Legend (Micmac legend). 1986. 71 mins. Video. Purchase: $35. NFBC.

NATIVE LAND
How the history & legacy of these peoples have survived through their myths & art. 58 mins. 1999. VHS, $14.95. ME.

NATIVE LAND; NOMADS OF THE DAWN
Alvin H. Perlmutter, Producer; John Peaslee, Director
Jamake Highwater, Writer/host
Examines the history and culture of the Native Americans who discovered and civilized the North and South American continents. Focuses on the function of myths as the basis of cosmology of ancient (and contemporary) society. 1986. 58 minutes. Video. Purchase: $350; rental, $95. CG. Rental: $27.50. UMN.

NATURALLY NATIVE
Three enterprising Americn Indian women start a cosmetics line. With Irene Bedard & Valerie Red Horse. 1998. VHS, $29.95. ME.

NATWANIWA: A HOPI PHILOSOPHICAL STATEMENT
Larry Evers, U. of Arizona; With George Nasoftie, a ceremonial leader, talks of cultivation of the land--how every crop and action has significance for his future life. In Hopi with English subtitles. 27 mins. Video. $175. NR.

NAVAJO
KBYU, Provo, Utah; Teaching children the way and heritage of the Navajo people. 1979. 29 minutes. Video. Purchase: $150; Rental: $40/week. NAPBC.

NAVAJO
The Navajos of the Grand Canyon. 16 minutes. Grades 7-12. 16mm. FILMS.

THE NAVAJO
Museum of Northern Arizona, Producer
Navajos tell their story of survival in northern Arizona. A child learns to tend sheep, a mother teaches how to card, spin, dye and weave wool for rugs. A family sacrifices a sheep. Story is cast against their history and the vital role of women in religious, social and cultural life. 1990. 15 mins. CAN.

THE NAVAJO
A visit to the Navajo Reservation in northeastern Arizona to discover the values held by this indigenous community. Navajo medical practices, religious rituals & beliefs are compared to modern practices, with a discussion of the problems of reconciling traditional Navajo ways with modern technology. 1959. 58 minutes, bxw. Grades 9 and up. Rental. UA & IU.

THE NAVAJO
Fred J. Pain, Jr.
The history, customs, and life of the Navajo Indian Nation (15 million acres within the Southwestern part of the U.S.) are described in this film. 1972. 21 mins. IU.

NAVAJO CANYON COUNTRY
Depicts the way of life of the Navajos and provides some of the historical background of Indian life in Arizona and New Mexico. 1954. 13 minutes. 16mm. Rental. IU & PSU.

NAVAJO CHILDREN
Deals with the semiannual migration of a Navajo family to its summer home. 1938. 11 mins, bxw. 16mm. Rental. UK.

NAVAJO CODE TALKERS
Tom McCarthy
Documentary using interviews and archival footage to show the vital role a small group of Navajo Marines played in the South Pacific during World War II. Interviews with Peter McDonald, Navajo Chairman; Carl Gorman, artist & scholar; and R.C. Gorman, Taos artist. 1986. 28 mins, color. VHS, $24.95. ME, CAN, NAPBC, NMFV. Rental: $10. UMN.

NAVAJO COUNTRY
Shows the nomadic life of the Navajo Indian in northwestern Arizona. 1951. Grades 1-6. 10 mins, color. 16mm & video. Rental. UA & IU.

NAVAJO COYOTE TALES: LEGEND TO FILM
Animate in English and Navajo. Shows how coyote films were animated on computer. 1972. Grades 6 and up. 18 minutes. 16mm. Purchase: 16mm, $260. SAN. Rental: SAN & UCLA.

NAVAJO FILMS THEMSELVES SERIES
  Sol Worth & John Adair
Concerned with seeing how Navajo Indians, taught the technology of film-making might show a definite Navajo perspective in their films. Five films are descriptive of processes; two are concerned with man's relationship to nature. "A Navajo Weaver," by Susie Benally; "A Navajo Silversmith," by Johnny Nelson; "Old Antelope Lake," by Mike Anderson; "The Shallow Well Project," by Johnny Nelson; "Second Weaver," by Alta Kahn; and, "The Spirit of the Navajo," by Maxine & Mary Jane Tsosie. 1966. Grades 9 and up. 9-27 mins, bxw. Purchase: $420 (3 cassettes); $85/title. MMA.

NAVAJO GIRL
Life on an Indian reservation in northeast Arizona. Focuses on life of a ten year old girl and her family. 1973. 20 mins. Grades 3-12. Purchase: VHS, $99. GA.

THE NAVAJO INDIAN
Provides a picture of the changing life styles of the Navajos who live on an Arizona reservation. 1975 revised edition. 10 minutes. Grades K-6. Purchase: 16mm, $265; video, $59. PHO. Rental only, $16.50. PSU; $9. IU.

NAVAJO INDIANS
Portrays the Navajos in their native environment. 1939. 11 minutes. Grades 4-9. 16mm/bxw. Rental. UA, PSU, UK & IU.

NAVAJO LIFE
Shows the National Monument of Canyon de Chelly, describing the life of the Navajo Indians living in the canyon. 1961. 9 mins.. 16mm. Rental, $9.35. IU.

NAVAJO MEDICINE
  hosted by West Studi; Documentary profiles Navajo health care by telling the stories of Navajo health care workers as they travel to remote health linics and care for their people. 1993. 30 mins. VHS. $89. CHAR.

NAVAJO MOON
This documentary-type story, photographed on the Navajo reservation in New Mexico, provides an inside look at the lives of three Navajo children. 28 minutes, color. Purchase: $89.95. FH.

THE NAVAJO MOVES INTO THE ELECTRONIC AGE
Briefly describes the background of the Navajo before World War II. Then points out how the tribal council invested income from oil discoveries into projects to benefit the entire tribe. 19 minutes. 16mm. Rental. UK and UA.

NAVAJO NIGHT DANCES
  Walter P. Lewisohn, Producer
Deals with a Navajo family at the Nine Day Healing Chant, a feast, and the Arrow, Feather & Fire Dance rituals. 1957. 12 mins. 16mm. Rental: UK & UA.

NAVAJO - A PEOPLE BETWEEN TWO WORLDS
  Francis R. Line; Effects of modern culture upon the largest remaining Indian tribe on a reservation in Arizona. 1958. 18 minutes. 16mm. Rental, $14. PSU.

NAVAJO, RACE FOR PROSPERITY
  Document Associates & BBC
Offers a contemporary view of life on the Navajo reservation and focuses upon the development of industries on the reservation. 1972. 26 mins. CG.

NAVAJO ROUND DANCE
A group of Navajo high school students perform the traditional Navajo Round Dance. Navajo music soundtrack, no narration. 1971. 3 mins. UCLA.

NAVAJO RUG WEAVING
Shows how the Navajo Indians weave their famous rugs. Explains the different operations; Provides a close view of the weaving technique. 10 minutes, color, silent. 16mm. Rental: $21. UCLA.

NAVAJO: SHEPHERDS OF THE DESERT
Describes a day in the life of a typical Navajo family. 1970. Nine minutes. Grades 4 and up. 16mm. Rental. UA.

NAVAJO SILVERSMITH
Traces a Navajo artisan's creation of some small Yeibachai figures from the mining of the silver to the finished works. 21 minutes, bxw. Grades 9 and up. Rental: 16mm, $15. PSU.

NAVAJO SILVERSMITHING
Focuses on a Navajo craftsman, Tom Burnside, on an Arizona reservation, who has come to grips with modern technology while still maintaining the values of his own culture. 1961. Grades 7 and up. 11 mins. PSU, UCT & UA.

NAVAJO: A STUDY IN CULTURAL CONTRAST
Portrays the culture, social organization, and physical environment of the Navajo Indian. 1969. Grades 6 and up. 15 mins. PSU, UCT & IU.

NAVAJO: THE LAST RED INDIANS
  Michael BainesContains scenes of Navajo ceremonies including diagnosing illnesses by trance-like hand trembling and a sing or healing ceremony. The integration of traditional healing practices with those of white doctors is shown. 1972. 35 mins. TW & UA.

THE NAVAJO WAY
  Robert Northshield, Director; Survival as a tribe within American society is said to come from the involvement with tradition, the Navajo way. Reflects the spiritual life of the traditional community. 1975. 52 mins, color. 16mm. FILMS.

THE NAVAJOS & ANNIE WAUNEKA
Annie Wauneka, awarded the Freedom Medal by President Kennedy for her achievements in public health education among her fellow Navajo Indian, visits the homes of her people instructing them in simple health measures. 1965. 26 minutes. Grades 9-adult. 16mm. Rental. UA.

NAVAJOS OF THE 70's
Deals with the customs, history, economics, current problems and future prospects of the Navajo Indians. Grades 1-8. 15 minutes. 16mm. Rental: UK.

NAWATNIWA: A HOPI PHILOSOPHICAL STATEMENT
  George Nasoftie; Ceremonial leader from Shongopavi relates the Hopi ceremonial cycle to agriculture and the sacred teachings. 1978. 20 minutes. Video. With I'isaw: Hopi Coyote Stories - two programs on one tape. Rental, $52.50. ATL.

NEHI CHEII TOAD COUNTS HIS CORN
Math concept of place value taught using coyote and toad. Available in English and Navajo version. Animated. Ten minutes. Grades 2-8. 16mm & video. Rental, $10/week. SAN.

NESHNABEK: THE PEOPLE
  Gene Bernofsky; Donald Stull, Project Director
Based on footage of the Prairie Band Potawatomi of Kansas by amateur anthropologist Floyd Schultz between 1927-1941, this film was edited & supplied with a soundtrack based on recent interviews with elderly Potawatomi. Covers reservation life, culture and the people. 1979. 30 minutes, 16mm, bxw. STULL, UK & KS.

NETSILIK ESKIMO 1
  Gilles Blais, Director
A 2-part video: 1) The Eskimo: Fight for Life, 51 minutes - This ethnographic documentary studies the traditional forms of play, work and education of the Netsilik Inuit during their last migratory camp in the 1960s; and 2) The Netsilik Eskimo Today, 18 minutes - shows the actual life of an Eskimo family in the settlement of Pelly Bay inside the Arctic Circle. Purchase: $35. NFBC.

NETSILIK ESKIMO SERIES
  Quenten Brown, Ph.D., Director
Nine films in 21 half-hour parts. Titles include: "At The Autumn River Camp": Two Parts: Part 1, In late autumn, the Inuit travel through soft snow and build karmaks in the river valley. Fishing through ice. 26 mins. Part 2, The men build an igloo, make a sleigh; women work on parka; children play. 33 mins. "At The Caribou Crossing Place": Two Parts: Part 1, Early autumn; caribou hunting and skins. 30 mins. Part 2, Caribou Hunting. 29 mins. "At The Spring Sea Ice Camp": Three Parts: Part 1, Two Inuit families travel across the wide sea ice; build small igloos. 27 mins. Part 2, The men hunt seal through ice, then skin it. 27 minutes. Part 3, Hunting & Fishing; women sewing; breaking camp moving ashore to tents for summer. 27 mins. "At The Winter Sea Ice Camp": Four Parts: Part 1, Seal hunting; making camp for winter. 36 mins. Part 2, Women with furs; men hunting; children play; games. 36 minutes. Part 3, Community igloos; games; hunting and fishing. 30 mins. Part 4, Family activities; games and music. 35 mins. "Building A Kayak": Two Parts: Part 1, Summer, ice melts, time to build a kayak. 33 mins. Part 2, Building a Kayak. 33 mins. "Stalking

Seal On The Spring Ice": Two Parts. Part 1, Seal hunt and skinning; use of fur and meat. 25 mins. Part 2, Seal hunt. 34 mins. "The Eskimo: Fight For Life; "People of the Seal: Eskimo Summer/Winter"; "Yesterday, Today: The Netsilik Eskimo". 1969. Grades 7-adult. DER, CDA & UEVA. Rental: UCT, IU & PSU.

THE NEW CAPITALISTS: ECONOMICS IN INDIAN COUNTRY
Portrays developments on some 30 reservations from Alaska to Florida. Examines the quantum leap into the 20th century being made by Native Americans. Provides insight into Native American culture. Narrated by Eric Sevareid. Adult. 1984. 60 mins. Video. Free loan to Indian organizations and the business and investment community. Purchase: 3/4" - $75, 1/2" $55. OP.

THE NEW INDIANS
Shows a young Creek woman as she attends an intertribal conference; a Kwakiutl chief; a Navajo woman attorney; etc. 1977. 59 minutes. Purchase: 16mm, $595; video, $545. NGS.

THE NEW PEQUOT - A TRIBAL PORTRAIT
Connecticut Public Television, Producer; A documentary exploring the history and future of Connecticut's Mashantucket Pequot Indians. 1989. 60 mins. Video. Purchase: $150; Rental: $80. NAPBC.

NEZ PERCE - PORTRAIT OF A PEOPLE
Deals with the cultural heritage of the Nez Perce and shows how the Nez Perce National Historical Park has influenced and preserved that culture. 23 minutes. Rental: Video, $10. UCT.

NI'BTHASKA OF THE UMONHON - A SERIES
Chet Kincaid, Producer; A three-program series about a 13 year-old boy from the Omaha tribe as he goes through the first summer of his manhood. Program 1: Turning of the Child; Program 2: Becoming a Warrior; Program 3: The Buffalo Hunt. 1987. 30 minutes each. NAPBC.

NINOS NAVAJOS
Spanish language film. 11 minutes. 16mm/bxw. Rental. UA.

NINSTINTS: SHADOW KEEPERS OF THE PAST
Spreitz-Husband Productions; Ninstints' located on Anthony Island, is the site of the last stand of totem poles anywhere on the Northwest Coast still remaining in their original location. The Haida abandoned the village in the late 1800's after falling prey to the white man's diseases and the intrusion of his lifestyle into the wider Haida culture. A study guide is available with the film. 1983. 27 mins. VHS. Purchase or rental. CFDW.

NISHNAWBI-ASKI: THE PEOPLE & THE LAND
Phyllis Wilson, Director; Illustrates the different ways the Cree & Ojibway of the Nishnawbi-Aski region are reacting to change. 1977. 28 mins. NFBC.

NO ADDRESS
Alanis Obomsawin, Director/writer; Focuses on the young native people who are homeless in Montreal. Describes three organizations that are helping the homeless of Montreal: the Montreal Native Friendship Centre, Dernier Recours, and La Mission Colombe. 1988. 56 minutes, color. Purchase: 16mm, $775; VHS, $350. Rental: $80. NFBC.

NOMADIC INDIANS OF THE WEST: THE LEGACY OF THE AMERICAN INDIANS
Camera One, Producer; hosted by Wes Studi; The world of the Plains Indians; examines the legends & cultures of the various tribes. Ancient America Series. 1994. 60 mins. $20. CAN & WKV.

THE NORTH AMERICAN INDIAN
Narrated by Marlon Brando; In three parts: Part 1: Treaties Made, Treaties Broken--presents the conflict between the Nisqually and Washington State over fishing rights. 18 mins. Part 2: How the West Was Won, And Honor Lost--presents a chronology of Indian-white relations from the landing of Columbus to the defeat of Geronimo in 1866. 25 mins. Part 3: Lament of the Reservation--presents the living conditions of the Sioux Indians on Pine Ridge Reservation in the Badlands of South Dakota. Also looks at another reservation in Washington State where suicide is above the national average. 1970. 24 mins. Music by Buffy St. Marie. Grades 6 & up. UMN, IU & PSU.

NORTH AMERICAN INDIAN ARTS & CRAFTS SERIES
Geoff Voyce; Commissioned by the Canadian National Indian Arts & Crafts Corporation, these film shows individual artists in their local setting and their artistic processes examined. The following films are available in English, French and Indian languages. A collection of ethnographic documentaries on outstanding Native American artists & artisans. Each artist recounts the history of their people and their craft while they work. A Teacher's Guide contains 200+ pp. of craft activities, history, maps, glossaries, print & non-print bibliographies (free with purchase of two or more videos). The titles include: A Pair of Moccasins for Mary Thomas, 15 minutes, (Shuswap); A Corn Husk Doll by Deanna Skye, 11 minutes (Cayuga); A Malecite Fancy Basket, 12 minutes (Malecite-Canada); A Moon Mask by Freda Deising, 10 minutes (Haida); Beads & Leather of Manitoba, 18 minutes (Cree-Canada); A Willow Basket by Florine Hotomani, 11 minutes (Assiniboine-Canada); Tony Hunt, a Kwakiutl Artist, 10 minutes; Joe Jacobs - Stone Carver, 11 minutes (Cayuga); Porcupine Quill Work, 11 minutes (Odawa-Canada); A Micmac Scale Basket, 12 minutes (Micmac-Canada); A Ceremonial Pipe by Guy Siwi, 10 minutes (Abenaki); Robert Bellegard, a Prairie Artist, 12 minutes (Cree-Canada); Sara Smith, Mohawk Potter, 18 minutes (Mohawk); Birch Bark Biting by Angelique Mirasty, 6 minutes (Cree-Canada); Wooden Flowers of Nova Scotia by Matilda Paul, 14 minutes (Micmac-Canada); Iroquoian Pottery by Bill Parker, 18 minutes; A Silver Chalice by Jeff Gabriel, 10 minutes (Mohawk); Fort Albany Carver, Lawrence Mark, 14 minutes (Cree-Canada). 1977-1979. Purchase: VHS, $49 each; 16mm, $129 each. Rental: $40 each. AMP & ITFE.

NORTH AMERICAN INDIAN LEGENDS
Dramatizes several Indian legends with special effects photography to emphasize their mythical quality. 1973. 21 minutes. Grades 1-8. Purchase: 16mm, $435; Video, $275; Rental, $65. PHO. Rental. IU and UA.

NORTH AMERICAN INDIAN TODAY
Covers contemporary attitudes of Indians as well as their cultural past. 1977. 25 minutes. Purchase: 16mm, $395; video, $360. NGS.

NORTH AMERICAN INDIANS & EDWARD S. CURTIS
Teri C. McLuhan, Producer/director
Focuses on Edward S. Curtis (1868-1952), photographer, whose life work was concerned with preserving a record of North American Indians and Alaskan Eskimos. 1985. 30 minutes. Color. 16mm, 3/4" video. PHO.

NORTH OF 60: DESTINY UNCERTAIN
TV Ontario, Producer; Five 30 minute programs exploring areas of Canada's Northwest Territories, the Yukon and Alaska. Depicts the reality of life in the far north, and the future of this land and the culture of its original inhabitants. 1983. 28 1/2 minutes each. Color. See NAPBC for titles and prices.

NORTHERN GAMES
Traditional games of the Inuit. 1981. 25 minutes. Video. Purchase: $27. NFBC.

THE NORTHERN LIGHTS
Alan Booth, Director; Explores the phenomenon of the aura borealis and illustrates how the legends & tales of the indigenous people of the north have helped us to understand the lights. 1993. 48 mins. NFBC.

JIM NORTHRUP: WITH RESERVATIONS
Mike Hazard & Mike Rivard, Producers; A 30 min. documentary of Indian country; portrait of the Anishanaabe/Ojibwe/Chippewa by activist/writer, Jim Northrup (Fond du Lac Ojibwe-www.jimnorthrup.org). DVD. CIE

NORTHWEST ARCTIC VIDEO
Bob Walker, Director; The Northwest Arctic Television Center at Kotzebue, Alaska, produces programs about cultural, social, and political issues pertinent to the region, including documentaries of traditional skills, public affairs programs, and looks at specific aspects of cultural transition in Inupiat Eskimo culture; programs on Inuit studies are also available. Series include: The Alaska Native Claims Settlement Act Series; Inupiat Legends of the Northwest Arctic Series; Traditional Inupiat Eskimo Health Series; Traditional Inupiat Eskimo Technology Series. For a complete list of programs contact NATC.

NORTHWEST COAST INDIANS: A SEARCH FOR THE PAST
Louis and Ruth Kirk; Archaeologists and students reconstruct the Ozette Indian Village at Cape Alava, Washington, an abandoned seafaring hunter's village site. 1973. 26 mins. UW.

NORTHWEST INDIAN ART
Walter P. Lewisohn, Producer
Shows material collected from six different museums, including double-faced mechanical masks. 1966. Ten minutes. 16mm. Rental. UK.

NORTHWESTERN AMERICAN INDIAN WAR DANCE CONTEST
Covers an annual contest portraying The War Dance, The Feather Dance, The Fancy Dance, and The Hoop Dance. 1971. 12 mins. UW.

NOW & FOREVER
Shows scenes of Oregon Indians from 1915-1945. 80 mins. bxw. Rental. OHS.

NOW THAT THE BUFFALO'S GONE
Shows how Europeans, who came to America looking for freedom of speech and religion, forgot those freedoms when it came to the Indians. 1991. 20 minutes, color. Video. Purchase: $149; rental, $75. FH. Rental: 16mm, $13.40.

NOW THAT THE BUFFALO'S GONE
Ross Deveish, Director; Analyzes the history of massacres, broken promises, worthless treaties, and land-grabbing that the Indian nations as a whole have suffered. Narrated by Marlon Brando. 1969. 65 minutes. Grades 9 and up. Purchase: 16mm, $995; video, 225. Rental, $80/3 days. MG. Rental only: 16mm, $35.50; VHS, $23. PSU.Rental: 16mm, $20. UCLA.

NUHONIYEH: OUR STORY
Mary & Allen Code
Explores the history & current circumstances of the Sayisi Dene, "a people of the ecological & cultural borderlands between Tundra & forest in Canada. 1993. 55 minutes. VHS. Purchase: $245; rental: $60. DER.

OBSIDIAN POINT-MAKING
Clyde B. Smith, Producer
A Tolowa Indian demonstrates an ancient method of fashioning an arrow point from obsidian. Describes various tribes' folklore customs connected with obsidian-chipping and explains the significance, history, and uses of obsidian points. 1964. 13 minutes. Purchase: 16mm, $280; video, $195. Rental: 16mm, $45. UC. Video rental, $19.50. PSU.

OJIBWAY & CREE CULTURAL CENTRE VIDEO
Dennis Austin, Executive Producer
Since 1979, the Ojibway and Cree Cultural Centre in Timmins, Ontario, has produced over 25 videotapes which portray traditional craft techniques, tales, and profiles of elders. The programs reflect the heritage of Indians in eastern Canada. For a complete list of programs contact O&C.

OLD DANCES, NEW DANCERS
Documents the first annual Young People's Eskimo Dance Awareness Festival organized at Chevak, Alaska. 1984. 30 minutes. VHS. $24.95. KYUK.

OMAHA TRIBE - FILM SERIES
David Conger, Director
Documentary of Native American life on a reservation presented through portraits of several Omaha people of different ages. The Land, The People, and The Family. 1979. 30 minutes each. 16mm & video. Purchase: $50 each; $105/series. GPN, NETV.

ON THE PATH TO SELF-RELIANCE
Peter J. Barton Productions; Narrated by James Billie,
Chairman of the Seminole Tribe of Florida, an overview of tribal history & current tribal economic development. 1982. 45 minutes. NAPBC.

ON THE SPRING ICE
Walrus as well as whales are hunted by the Eskimos of Gambell on St. Lawrence Island. 45 minutes. DER.

1,000 YEARS OF MUSCOGEE (CREEK) ART
Gary Robinson, Producer
Traces the development of Creek Indian art forms from the prehistoric period of the mound-builders to the present. Examines over 175 examples of Creek art. 1982. 28 mins. Rental: NAPBC.

ONENHAKENRA: WHITE SEED
Frank Semmons, Producer/director/camera
Explores the development of Iroquois culture; focuses on corn and people's reflections on its use as a way of presenting the audience with a view of Mohawk traditions. Features local people of Akwesasne. 1984. 20 mins. AM.

THE ORIGIN OF THE CROWN DANCE: AN APACHE NARRATIVE & BA'TS'OOSEE: AN APACHE TRICKSTER CYCLE
Larry Evers, U. of Arizona; With Rudolph Kane.
In Apache with English subtitles. 40 minutes. ATL.

ORIGINS
Takes the viewer across the continent looking at the history, geography, language and circumstance, and the roles each had in naming the places we all know. Includes the legacy of Indian languages (26 of the United States have Indian names.) 1989. 30 minutes, color. Video. Purchase: $30. COP.

OSCAR HOWE: THE SIOUX PAINTER
KUSD-TV, Producer; Vincent Price adds his narrative to the personal commentary of Oscar Howe, focusing on his art, philosophy and cultural heritage, as he designs and paints the brilliant Sioux Eagle Dancer. 1973. 27 minutes. Grades 9-adult. 16mm & video. PHO. NAPBC.

THE OTHER SIDE OF THE LEDGER:
AN INDIAN VIEW OF THE HUDSON'S BAY COMPANY
Martin Defalco and Willie Dunn, Directors; Presents the view of spokesmen for Canadian Indian & Metis groups. With archival materials and contemporary examples, this film includes scenes from a conference in which Hudson's Bay Co. officials respond to Native people's objections. 1972. 42 mins. NFBC.

OUR LAND, OUR TRUTH
Maurice Bulbulian, Director
Ethnographic description of the Inuit of James Bay. 1983. 54 minutes. NFBC.

OUR LIVES IN OUR HANDS
Karen Carter & Harold Prins, Producers; Karen Carter, Director
Presents the story of the Micmac basketmakers of Aroostook County, Maine, focusing on Donald Sanipass, and members of his extended family.Touches on survival of their language and tribal lands. 1986. 49 minutes, color. DER.

OUR PROUD LAND
Written and narrated from the Navajo point of view, this film presents a number of sequences of modern day life of the Navajo Indians. 30 mins. 16mm. UK.

OUR SACRED LAND
Chris Spotted Eagle, Producer/director; Focuses on the continuing struggle of the Sioux to regain the Black Hills of South Dakota. Examines the reasons why many Sioux have refused to accept the $105 million recently awarded by the Federal Government for the lands confiscated. 1984. 28 mins. NAPBC & SE.

OUR SONGS WILL NEVER DIE
Yurok, Karuk & Tolowa cultural summer camps are established for the purpose of reconstructing early village dance sites. 35 minutes. Video. SH.

OUR SPIRITS DON'T SPEAK ENGLISH: INDIAN BOARDING SCHOOLS
Rick-Heape Films; Documentary of history of the U.S. Government policy. DVD. $24.95. MALKI.

OUR TOTEM IS THE RAVEN
Features Chief Dan George in a contemporary tale of a young Indian boy's initiation into manhood and his acceptance of his Indian heritage. 1972. 21 mins, color. PHO. Rental: $14. IU & UMN.

OUR YOUTH, OUR FUTURE
About a bicultural drug and alcohol treatment center in Shiprock, New Mexico that serves Native American youth. 2000. 35 mins. VHS. $100. CHAR.

OURS TO CARE FOR
Emphasizes the special importance of good nutrition during pregnancy for the contemporary Native American woman. 6 mins. SH.

THE OWL & THE LEMMING: AN ESKIMO LEGEND
Co. Hoedeman, Director; An example of the Inuit art and folklore. 1971. 6 mins. All ages. NFBC. IU.

THE OWL & THE RAVEN: AN ESKIMO LEGEND
Co Hoedeman, Director; An Inuit legend is retold using puppets of sealskin in traditional Inuit design and accompanied by a music track of Inuit songs. 1974. 7 mins. Grades 1-6. All ages. NFBC.

OWNERS OF THE WATER: CONFLICT & COLLABORATION OVER RIVERS
Laura R. Graham, Director; Documentary film. 2011. DER.

THE OWL WHO MARRIED A GOOSE: AN ESKIMO LEGEND
Caroline Leaf, Director; An example of commitment and love. 1974. 8 mins, b&w. All ages. 16mm & video. C M. Rental: $14. PSU.

PABLITA VELARDE
Irene-Aimee Depke, Producer; Santa Clara Indian artist Pablita Velarde reminisces about her childhood at the Pueblo, her struggling years in a medium traditionally closed to Indian women, her philosophy and her existence in the white man's world, away from the pueblo. She demonstrates her "earth painting" technique, which begins with her gathering the stones & minerals from New Mexico soil. Ends with a classroom of first-graders, Santa Clara legend, "Why the Coyote Bays at the Moon." 29 mins, color. Video. DEPKE.

PADDLE TO SEATTLE
Mark Mascarin, Producer/Director
Documents a cooperative project undertaken by the Quileute & Hoh peoples of La Push, Washington, namely to embark on a journey made many times by their ancestors - a six day, 170 mile "paddle to Seattle." 1990. Grades 9-12. 45 mins. Video. Purchase: $78. QTS.

PAGES ON THE PAST
A series of four films which tell the story of the peoples of the Pacific Northwest from the time of the Ice Age to the coming of Lewis and Clark. An Age of Ice: How the peoples of the Northwest adapted & endured; After the Flood: Floods

13,000 years ago signaling the end of the Ice Age; Landmarks In Time: The time of the eruption of Mt. Mazama about 7,000 years ago; and, History In the Making: Portrays the expansion of Native American civilization throughout the region up to the coming of Lewis & Clark. Study guide & maps. 30 mins each. Grades 9 & up. Purchase: 16mm, (An Age of Ice only) $450; video, $250 each ($900/series). Rental: $50/week. TBM.

PAHA SAPA: THE STRUGGLE FOR THE BLACK HILLS
Mel Lawrence, Director; Cis Wilson, Exec. Producer
Story of the Lakota Sioux' struggle to get their sacred lands back. Told by Lakota Sioux & Cheyenne storytellers. The speakers recount the legends, customs, & history of their people. Includes archival paintings, photos, early documentaries and newsreels. Nominated for an Emmy in 1993. 60 mins. Color. VHS. $34.95. MFV.

CYNTHIA ANN PARKER: BLUE EYED COMANCHE
Jillian Preet, Writer/ Editor/Narrator
Story about a settler child who was abducted by the Comanche Indians. Archival photos & paintings evoke the triumph & tragedy of the American frontier. 1987. Grades 4 and up. 12 mins, color. Video. Purchase: $49. FI.

THE PATH OF OUR ELDERS
Several Pomo elders portray a way of life that has been handed down throughout the generations. 1986. Grades 4 and up. 20 mins, color. Video. Purchase: $245; rental: $45. SH. Rental: $20.50. UMN.

PAUL KANE GOES WEST
Gerald Budner, Director
Artist Paul Kane traveled Canada in the mid-19th century depicting the Indians through his sketches & paintings. 1972. 14 mins. Grades 4-12. Video. NFBC.

PEACEFUL ONES
Shows life and customs of the Hopi in the painted desert, including cultivating the land, harvesting crops, weaving, kachinas, and snake dance. 1953. 12 mins. Grades 4-adult. 16mm. Rental. UT, PSU and UA.

THE PEOPLE (INDIAN)
An analysis of Indian literature. 1981. 30 mins, video. KS.

THE PEOPLE AT DIPPER
Richard Gilbert, Jack Olfield
Shows life among the Chippewayan Indians of a reserve in northern Saskatch-ewan. 1966. 18 mins. Video. NFBC.

PEOPLE OF THE BUFFALO
Austin Campbell; Dramatic contemporary paintings of life on the Western Plains, portray the unique relationship between the Indians and buffalo. 1968 revised edition. 14 minutes, color. Grades 5 and up. Rental. PSU, IU, and UA.

PEOPLE OF THE FIRST LIGHT
WGBY-TV Springfield, Mass.
7-29 minute films about Native Americans living in RI, MA and CT: The Narragansetts, Pequots, Wampanoags, Mohegans, Nipnucs and Paugausetts, descendents of the original Eastern Woodland Algonquin Indians. Indians In Southern New England (The Survivors); The Wampanoags of Gay Head (Community Spirit and Island Life); The Boston Indian Community (Change and Identity); The Narragansett (Tradition); Indians of Connecticut (The Importance of Land); The Indian Experience: Urban and Rural (Survival); The Mashpee Wampanoags (Tribal Identity.) 1979. Color. Video. GPN and NAPBC.

PEOPLE OF KASHUNUK
A family portrait through sight & sound of the Yup'ik Eskimo village of Chevak. 1983. 30 minutes. VHS. $24.95. KYUK.

PEOPLE OF THE MACON PLATEAU
Introduction to the Indian cultures of the Macon Plateau with emphasis on the Mississippian Indian culture. Grades 7 and up. 12 mins. UCT.

PEOPLE OF THE SEAL
Michael McKennirey and George Pearson, Producers
Part I: Eskimo Summer - Documents the summer activities of th Netsilik Inuit, which take place on the land. Part II: Eskimo Winter - Search for seal holes; building igloos; seal hunting. 1971. 52 mins each. Grades 7-adult. Video. EDC.

PEOPLE OF THE SUN: THE TIGUAS OF YSLETA
Documentary surveying the history of the Tigua Indians as they struggle to gain recognition as a tribe & walk the fine line between being Texans in El Paso & Pueblo Indians. Teacher's guide. 56 mins. $45. UT-ITC.

PEPPER'S POW POW
Salmon Run Productions; Documents the enduring musical and cultural legacy of Jim Pepper, a contemporary jazz musician who was an innovator in jazz-rock fusion as well as world music. 1995. Grades 5 and up. 57 mins. OY.

THE PEYOTE ROAD
Gary Rhine, Producer/Director
A feature length documentary exploring the history of the use of the cactus Peyote as a religious sacrament by North American Indigenous people. Interviews with experts Dr. Huston Smith, Dr. Milner Ball and NAC Roadman Reuben Snake. 1993. 60 mins, color. VHS. $29.95. ME. Rental, $45. KF.

PETROGLYPHS: IMAGES IN STONE
Marianne Kaplan; A documentary focusing on the petroglyphs of the Coastal Salish, Kwakiutl and West Coast People and uses the carvings to depict their rituals and myth. 1985. 10 mins. 16mm or video. Purchase or rental. CFDW.

PINE NUTS
Clyde B. Smith, Producer; Members of the Paviotso & Paiute tribes demonstrate how the pine nut, from the pinon tree, were harvested & prepared as food, using ancient techniques. 1961. 13 mins, color. PSU.

PLAINS INDIAN WAR BONNET: HISTORY & CONSTRUCTION
Full Circle Communications; Explores the tradition and significance of this honored symbol of Native America. Includes the history and development along with close-ups of bonnets from the Gilcrease Collection. Construction is shown step-by-step. 45 mins. VHS. $19.95. WH.

PLAINS MOCCASINS
Vicki Little Coyote
Step-by-step procedure to making moccasins worn by the Southern Cheyenne. She demonstrates simple techniques. VHS. 86 minutes. $19.95. VIP.

PLAY & CULTURAL CONTINUITY: Part 4, MONTANA INDIAN CHILDREN
On the Flathead Indian Reservation and surrounding countryside, the play of Indian children ranges from the universal domestic activities and monster play themes of those mirroring individualistic cultural elements, such as wrapping of babies, drumming, singing, hunting. 1975. 29 mins. 16mm rental, $17.50. PSU.

POCAHONTAS: AMBASSADOR OF THE NEW WORLD
A&E Home Video; Biography. 2005. 50 mins. DVD, $24.95. ME.

POINTY SIDE UP: AN EASY WAY TO SET UP YOUR TIPI
Step-by-step video. VHS. 60 mins. $17.95. WH.

POMO BASKETWEAVERS: A TRIBUTE TO THREE ELDERS
This three-part series provides an in-depth introduction to the culture, history, and basketweaving traditions of the Pomo. Part 1: The People, the Baskets - presents an overview of Pomo culture & features a portrait of basketweaver, Laura Somersal. Part 2: A History of Change, a Continuing Tradition - recounts the history of the Pomo & explores the changes in the art & traditions of Pomo basketweaving. biographical tribute to Elsie Allen, most revered of all Pomo basketweavers. Part 3: The People, the Plants, and the Rules - examines the close relationship of the Pomo to their environment & explores spiritual rules & responsibilities of the Pomo to the natural world. Features a portrait of Mabel McKay, a famed dream weaver & Indian doctor. 1994. 29 mins each. UC.

POMO SHAMAN
William Heick, Producer; A shortened version of the complete research documentary, "Sucking Doctor." The second and final night of a shamanistic curing ceremony among the Kashia group of Southwestern Pomo Indians. 1964. 20 mins, bxw. UC. PSU & IU.

PORTAGE
Reviews the history of Canadian fur trapping and shows the building of a birch bark canoe by Indian craftsmen. 1941. 22 mins. Grades 6 and up. 16mm. Rental, $12.75. IU.

PORTRAIT OF LUCY SWAN
Elderly Lucy Swan, Cheyenne River Sioux, reminisces about family and tribal history. Illustrates past/present living conditions on the reservation. Adult. 30 mins. 16mm. Rental, $15. NILB.

POSITIVELY NATIVE
Portrays stereotypes and how Indians really live through the eyes of two teens, a Native American boy and his friend Sam of Korean descent. Grades 4-7. 1992. 15 mins. VHS. $95. CHAR.

POTLATCH PEOPLE
Document Associates & BBC; Presents the Indians of the Pacific Northwest and the ceremonial potlatch feast. 1972. 26 mins. CG.

POTLATCH: A STRICT LAW BIDS US DANCE
Dennis Wheeler, Director
Features the outlawed Kwakiutl Potlatch ceremony. The confiscation of an enormous and valuable collection of dancing masks and costumes. Shows a Potlatch given by the Cranmer family. Narrated by Gloria Cranmer Webster. 1975. 53 minutes. CFDW.

POUNDMAKER'S LODGE: A HEALING PLACE
Alanis Obomsawin, Director
Drug and alcohol abuse and treatment in St. Albert, Alberta. 1987. 29 minutes. Video. Purchase: $27. NFBC.

POW-WOW!
Displays North American Indian dances at a gathering of more than 20 tribes. Chiricahua Apaches perform their ancient sacred Fire Dance; Comanches execute the Gourd Dance; the Intertribal Dance; and, the War Dance. Indians speak of their traditions, ceremonies and heritage. Grades 7-12. 1980. 16 mins. Purchase: 16mm, $375; video, $59. PHO. Rental: $16mm, $20. UMN.

POW WOW HIGHWAY
Jonathan Wacks, Director; A comedy/drama set on the Northern Cheyenne Reservation in Lame Deer, MT. A committed activist, Buddy Red Bow (A. Martinez) battles a suspicious land-grab. 88 mins. DVD. Amazon.com, $5.87.

POW WOW: A NATIVE AMERICAN GATHERING
Documentary of intertribal gathering...ceremonies and traditions. Grades 5 and up. 30 mins. $70. CHAR.

POWWOW AT DUCK LAKE
Bonnie Sherr Klein, Director
A discussion at Duck Lake, Saskatchewan, where Indian-Metis problems are openly and strongly presented before a gathering of Metis Indians and Whites. 1967. 14 minutes. Video. Purchase: $22. NFBC.

POWWOW TRAIL SERIES
11 episodes filmed over a 2-year period produced for Canada's CBC-TV network, an episode every 2-3 months. Episode 1: The Drum. 2004; Episode 2: The Songs. 2004; Episode 3: The Dance. 2004; Episode 4: The Grand Entry. 2005; Episode 5: Grass Dance & Men's Traditional. 2005; Episode 6: The fancy Dance. 2005; Episode 7: Powwow Rock. 2005; Episode 8: Women. 2005; Episode 9: The Grand Exhibition. 2005; Episode 10: The White Man's Indian. 2006; Episode 11: Powwow Fever. 2006. 60 mins. each. DVD only, $19.95 each. ME & WH.

POWER OF THE WORD WITH BILL MOYERS: 3 - ANCESTRAL VOICES
Features three poets with distinctive heritages that influence their work: Joy Harjo (Creek-Cherokee), Garrett Hongo (Japanese-American), Mary TallMountain (Native American born in Alaska.) 1989. 58 mins. PSU.

POWERLESS POLITICS
Sandy Johnson Osawa--KNBC-TV, Producer
Provides an overview of legal relationship between the U.S. and Indian tribes showing how shifts and emphasis in the government Indian policy have had far reaching effects on Indian life. 1975. 28 mins. Video. Purchase: $55. BYU-N.

PREHISTORIC MAN
Traces the development of the Indians in the American West. 1967. Grades 7 and up. 17 minutes, color. Rental. UA & UCT.

PRIDE, PURPOSE & PROMISE: PAIUTES OF THE SOUTHWEST
Mitchell Fox, Producer/writer
Interviews with tribal leaders & members of the Kaibab Reservation in Arizona, the Shivwits Reservation in Utah, and the Moapa Reservation in Nevada. Discusses Southern Paiute tribal self-determination, tribal lands, history, education & economic development, & present day Indian reservation life. 1984. 28 mins, color. VHS. Rental: $40. NAPBC.

THE PRIMAL MIND
Alvin H. Perlmutter, Producer; Jamake Highwater, Writer/host
Documentary that explores the basic differences between Native American and Western cultures, while examining two cultures' contrasting views of nature, time, space, art, archaeology, dance & language. 1984. 58 mins, color. VHS, $19.99. ME. Rental: 16mm, $100. CG. Rental: VHS, $39. SH, PSU.

PRINCESS OF THE POW-WOW
A documentary focusing on Ella Aquino, a Lummi Indian woman, who has devoted her life toward the advancement of Indian culture and concerns. Examines issues of battles over land and fishing rights on behalf of the Puget Sound Indians. 22 mins. Color. Video. Purchase: $50. GPN.

THE PROBABLE PASSING OF ELK CREEK
Rob Wilson, Director; Documentary focusing on the controversy between a little town, Elk Creek, and the Grindstone Indian Reservation over a government planned reservoir. 1983. 60 mins, color. Purchase: 16mm, $895; 3/4" and 1/2" video, $350. Rental, $95. CG. NAPBC (members only).

THE PSORIASIS RESEARCH PROJECT - A CREE HEALER
Documents the healer's treatment practices under controlled conditions in a western health clinic. It also shows treatment of the same patients in a more traditional sweatlodge ceremony. 1985. 35 minutes. VHS, $100. In A CREE HEALER, which serves as an introduction to the psoriasis video, Russell Willier talks about traditional native medicine and the controversies he has encountered in openly discussing this subject. 1985. 22 minutes. Video. VHS, $75. Combines on One Tape, VHS, $150. UADA.

PUEBLO BOY
Tells the story of a young Indian boy being instructed in the ancient and modern ways and traditions of his people, the Pueblos of the Southwest. 24 minutes. 16mm. Rental. UK.

PUEBLO INDIANS OF TAOS, NM
1927 documentary of of the lives, customs and characters of the Pueblos of the area and some of the whites who lived among them. 10 minutes, bxw. EG.

THE PUEBLO PEOPLES: FIRST CONTACT
George Burdeau, Director; co-produced with Larry Walsh; Conroy Chino, host
Describes the early encounter between this peaceful Indian tribe and the destructive Spanish explorer Coronado. Told through the images and legends of the Pueblo people. 1990. 30 mins. Purchase: PBS. Rental. PSU.

THE PUEBLO PRESENCE
Hugh and Suzanne Johnston, WNET-13
Examines the continuity of ancient Pueblo civilization into the present. Zuni historian Andrew Napetcha discusses the ancestry of Pueblo peoples. Art, religion, ceremonials, language, architecture, & daily activities and relationship to the natural world. 1981. 58 minutes. 16mm & Video. JO.

PUEBLO RENAISSANCE
Philip Hobel, Executive Producer; Provides an authentic view of the sacred traditions, ancient religious and agricultural ceremonies of the Pueblo people. 1972. 26 minutes, color. CG and IU.

THE PUEBLO EXPERIENCE: MAKING A NEW WORLD
Richard Marquand, Director/Producer
The story of a 17 year-old girl, Charity, in Puritan Massachusetts in 1640. Captured by the Indians then returned, Charity rebels against the Puritan doctrine and treatment of the Indians. 1975. 31 minutes. All ages. LCA.

QAGGIQ
Zacharias Kunuk, Producer/director; A dramatization of past Arctic life, directed by an Inuit videomaker & improvised by Igloolik community members, far-flung families arrive via dogsled for a joyful reunion. 1989. 58 minutes, color. Video. Purchase: $1,250. IIP.

QUEEN VICTORIA & THE INDIANS
Animated film adaptation is based on a true story by noted American artist George Catlin. In the late 1840's a small group of Ojibwes journeyed to London to dance at the opening of the Indian Gallery. Grades 4-9. 11 minutes. Purchase: 16mm, $240; VHS, $89. CC.

QUILLWORKING DVD
A 55 minute easy to understand instructional video on the ancient craft of Quill Working. Sharon discusses the history of quill working, where to get the proper supplies, and mistakes to avoid. CROW, $25.

THE RAINBOW OF STONE
When drought threatens the grazing lands of the Navajos, an old chief tells his grandson the tribal legend of a wonderful country beyond The Rainbow of Stone. 1949. 23 minutes. 16mm. Rental: UCT & UT.

RAMONA: A STORY OF PASSION & PROTEST
Helen Hunt Jackson's novel of 1884 crystalized opinion about whites' maltreatment of Indians. This film uses feature film clips to recap the plot & historical sources & sites. 28 minutes. Video. Purchase: $89.95. FH.

REAFFIRMATION & DISCOVERY" THE FIRST POW-WOW ON HAWAII
Story of two women whose lives & vision come together in the creation of the first powwow on the big island, Hawaii - of the connection made between Native Americans & Native Hawaiians, 29 minutes. Video. Purchase: $250; rental: $45. SH.

THE REAL PEOPLE SERIES
KSPS-TV Spokane, Washington
Nine, 30-minute programs on Indian tribes of Northwest. The Colville, the Flathead, the Couer d' Alene, the Kalispel, the Kootenai, the Nez Perce and the Spokane. Examines the lifestyles, culture and lore of these seven tribes. Teacher's guide. 1976. Color. Grades 5-adult. 16mm & video. Purchase: $450/series, $65/program. Rental: $17.50/program. GPN & NAPBC.

RED BLOOD
The mob and Jimmy White Cloud and his reservation in Arizona where he rediscovers his heritage. With David Mid Thunder & Lee White Star. 90 mins. 2003. DVD, $24.99; VHS, $49.99. ME.

THE RED DRESS
Michael Scott, Director; Tells the story of conflicting loyalties to the past, the demands of the present day, traditional values and family affections. 1978. 28 minutes. Grades 7-adult. NFBC.

THE RED ROAD TO SOBRIETY
Contemporary Native American Sobriety Movement Dream Catchers Sobriety Fund - Documents the movement throughout Indian communities of North America. 1995. 90 mins. VHS, $34.95. KF. The Red Road to Sobriety Video Talking Circle is the companion video featuring many respected Native therapists and healers. Eight 15-minute segments. To be used as a prevention and recovery tool by individuals, clinics, programs, schools, and youth groups. 1995. 120 minutes. VHS, $34.95. ME & KF.

RED ROAD - TOWARD THE TECHNO-TRIBAL
KBDI-TV, Producer
Documentary presenting & exploring contemporary views of Native American philosophy, spirituality & prophecy. 1984. 27 mins. NAPBC.

RED SUNDAY
John McIntyre, Narrator
The story of the Custer battle, told in artwork, photographs, modern re-enactment and aerial photography. 1975. 28 minutes. Purchase: Video, $25. OAP. Rental: 16mm, $15. IU.

REDISCOVERY: THE EAGLE'S GIFT
Peter Prince
On a remote island off the Northwest coast of British Columbia, native and non-native youth learn about the unique Haida culture. They explore ancient villages, caves, totem and burial grounds, as they learn the drum song, dances & drama of the "Haida Potlatch". 1984. 29 minutes. CFDW.

RELOCATION & THE NAVAJO-HOPI LAND DISPUTE
Victoria Mudd, Director/producer
In 1974, Congress passed the Navajo-Hopi Land Settlement Act, partitioning 1.8 million acres of disputed land i Arizona equally between the Navajo and Hopi Indian tribes. Examines the historical and political forces behind the land dispute, and documents the struggle of 9,000 displaced Navajos to retain their homes, their culture, and their dignity. 1981. 23 mins. 16mm rental, $20. PSU.

RETURN OF THE RAVEN - THE EDISON CHILOQUIN STORY
Barry Hood Films, Producer
In 1954, in a policy that became known as "Klamath Termination," the Klamath Tribe of Oregon joined over 100 tribes throughout the country in loss of federal recognition. This is the true story of Klamath Termination and Edison Chilquin's ten-year struggle to preserve traditional values. 1985. 47 mins. Video. NAPBC.

RETURN OF THE SACRED POLE
Michael Farrell, Producer/director/writer; narrated by Roger Welsch
Documentary charting the return of a treasured religious object to the Omaha people, the sacred pole (Washabagel) that forms the center of Omaha spiritual life. 1990. 28 mins. Video. Purchase: $39.95. GPN.

RETURN TO THE CIRCLE
Illustrates the philosophy of recovery that the American Indian Family Healing Center has successfully implemented for over 25 years, and is now practicing for the treatment of women and children. 12 mins. Video. Purchase: $90; rental, $25. SH.

RETURN TO SOVEREIGNTY: SELF-DETERMINATION & THE KANSAS KICKAPOO
Donald Stull, Producer/writer; David Kendall, Director/writer/editor; Bernard Hirsch, Writer/narrator; A documentary film about the Kickapoo Indians of Kansas and their struggle to regain control of their future. Explores Indian self-determination & Education Assistance Acts. 1987. 46 mins. Video. Purchase, $95; rental, $50. UC. KS.

1492 REVISITED
Provides an alternative, "indigenous" perspective on the quincentennial of Columbus' arrival. Features artwork from the touring national exhibition Counter-Colonialism as well as challenging commentary by artists & scholars. Also raises important questions about the nature of history and its construction. 1993. 28 mins. Video. Purchase: $225; rental: $50. UC.

REVIVAL
Michael Brodie & Bill Roxborough, Prod/directors; Doreen Jensen, Narrator
Presents four contemporary artists of the Northwest Coast: Reg Davidson and Dorothy Grant, both Haida; Nishga artist Norman Tait oversees the printing of a silkscreen design of the beaver; and Noreen Jensen, Gitskan carver. These artists look to the artists of old to interpret the design vocabulary of the Northwest Coast tradition. 1983. 29 mins. VHS. MBP and VOI.

REZ-ROBICS
Exercise videos for & by Indians. Two videotapes. Free to Indian communities. Send Self-addressed box or padded envelope & $5 for shipping. DR.

RIBBONS OF THE OSAGE: THE ART & LIFE OF GEORGEANN ROBINSON
Relates the history of the Osage and stresses the importance of maintaining the traditions. Teacher's guide. VHS. 28 mins. $19.95. VIP.

RICHARD'S TOTEM POLE
Richard Harris, 16, is a Gitskan Indians living in British Columbia, Canada, while helping his father a master totem pole carver, he begins to take an interest in his heritage. Through his carving he discovers his roots, culture and family traditions. 25 minutes. Grades 4-adult. PHO.

THE RIGHT TO BE MOHAWK
George Hornbein, Lorna Rasmussen & Anne Stanaway, Producers/Directors
Members of the Mohawk Nation at Akwesasne describe their efforts to maintain identity & sovereignty in an ever-changing society. 1989. Grades 9-12. 17 mins. 16mm & VHS. Purchase: $250. NDF.

RIO GRANDE: WHERE FOUR CULTURES MEET
Explores the cultural and economic interdependence and interaction of Mexican, Spanish, Indian, and Anglo-American peoples of the Rio Grande Valley. Grades 7 and up. 15 mins. 16mm. Rental, $15. UT.

RITA JOE: THE SONG SAYS IT ALL
About the life & work of the contemporary Micmac poet, Rita Joe. 1988. 27 mins. Video. NS.

RIVER PEOPLE
The Pima Indians reconstruct their old ways of life for this film. 1949. 25 mins. Grades 4-adult. Rental. UA.

RIVER PEOPLE: BEHIND THE CASE OF DAVID SOHAPPY
Michael Conford, Michele Zacchero; narrated by Ruby Dee
Focuses on the case of David Sohappy, a Yakima spiritual leader, who was sentenced to a five-year prison term for selling 317 salmon out of season. Claiming an ancestral right to fish along the Che Wana, the indigenous name for the Columbia River, Sohappy openly defied state & federal fishing laws and has become a symbol of resistance for Native peoples of the Northwest. 1990. 50 mins. Video. Purchase: $395. FIL.

ROAD TO INDEPENDENCE
Transportation & independence for elders. A story of how the need is being met by the Chickasaw Nation & Delaware Tribe of Oklahoma. 14 mins. Video. Purchase: $100; rental: $25. SH.

THE ROADS LESS TAKEN
OPBS/Dorothy Velasco, Producer; The travels & travails of the pioneers who journeyed west in the mid-1840's are documented, with the focus on the exploration of less traveled routes and the impact on the Native Americans along the way. 1993. Grades 7 and up. 26 mins. Purchase: VHS, $260. NDM

ROCK ART TREASURES OF ANCIENT AMERICA:
THE CALIFORNIA COLLECTION
Dave Caldwell, Producer/director; Scott Beach, Narrator
Focuses on three major types of rock art - carvings, paintings, and ground figures - at three sites in southern California. Also contemporary Indian storytellers from tribes near these sites. 1983. 25 mins. 16mm, VHS. DCP.

THE ROMANCE OF A VANISHING RACE
Rick Heape Film; Includes three historic motion pictures of Native Americans and their life-style in the early 1900's Features tribal chiefs. Program #1 - The Romance of the Vanishing Race, 1916. 29 mins.DVD. Program #2 - Rodman Wanamaker Expedition, 1913. 26 mins. Program #3 - Winter Farm Life on a Crow Reservation, 1921. 8 mins. $24.95. MALKI.

ROOTS TO CHERISH

Evaluates young Indian pupils. A concept film designed to identify & illustrates consequences of cultural differences upon school performance; ways to conduct a more appropriate evaluation; & suggestions for program modifications. 30 mins. Video. Purchase, $245; rental, $45. SH.

ROPE TO OUR ROOTS

Bo Boudart, Producer/director/writer; Presents the Inuit Circumpolar Conference, an international organization of Eskimos and Inuit from Alaska, Canada, and Greenland founded in 1977. Discusses the commonalities and differences in life styles & concerns of the delegates. 1981. 30 minutes. BO.

ROSEBUD TO DALLAS

Jed Riffe and Robert Rouse; Tells the story of five families who come to Dallas from the Rosebud Sioux Reservation in South Dakota to make a better life through vocational education and on the job training. 1977. 60 mins. THRC.

ROUND DANCE

A group of dancers perform a round dance. Three minutes. All grades. Purchase: 16mm, $110. Rental, $10/week. Also available in video. SAN.

THE RUNAWAY

NETV, Producer; 14 year-old Darlene Horse runs away from a difficult home situation. Social workers and a Native American alcoholism counselor help the family through appreciation of their culture and use of counseling groups. 1989. 29 mins. VHS. Purchase: $150; Rental: $40. NAPBC.

RUNNING ON THE EDGE OF THE RAINBOW: LAGUNA STORIES/POEMS

Larry Evers, University of Arizona; With Leslie Marmon; Silko--reflects on the nature of Laguna storytelling, its functions and the problems she has faced as an Indian poet. 28 mins. Purchase: VHS, $175. NR. Rental: VHS, $37.50. ATL.

SACAGAWEA: HEROINE OF THE LEWIS & CLARK JOURNEY

Rolf Forsberg, Director
Reenacts her journey in her own words. 80 min. 2004. DVD, $17.99. ME.

SACAJAWEA

Neil Affleck; A 16 year-old Shoshone girl joins the Lewis & Clark Expedition. Still photos and drawings offer scope to the land they travelled while animation brings to life Sacajawea and the adventures she shared. She is followed into her later years as a traveller, mediator between Indian and white man and speaker in the councils of her tribe. 1991. 18 mins. Grades 4-9. CHAR.

SACAJAWEA

A young Indian guide of Lewis & Clark Expedition to the Pacific Northwest. Sacajawea recounts the events prior to the sighting of the Pacific Ocean in 1805. 24 mins, color. Video. Purchase: $79. FH.

SACRED BUFFALO PEOPLE

Deb Wallwork, Director/Producer; Documentary exploring the traditional relationship between the Plains Indians and the American Bison. REV, CIE.

THE SACRED CIRCLE

Donald K. Spence, Producer/director; Adrian Hope, Narrator
In two parts: Part I: Invites the viewer through a bold series of symbolic imagery to participate in the mystical harmony of the Native world. Culminates in the ritual expression of the Sun Dance. The film combines animation, documentary photographs, paintings and on location realism, augmented by lyrical narrative. Part II: Recovery--moves from the frontal assault on Native culture by missionaries and others in the last century to a series of vignettes reflecting its contemporary face, while conveying the tragedy of cultural loss. 1980. 29 mins. each. VHS. UAL.

SACRED GROUND

The story of the North American Indian's relationship to the land. Their intimate involvement and reverence for places throughout the land that hold a special religious and traditional significance for their race. Provides a detailed look at the specific geographic places all over America that are and always were sacred to the American Indian. Original music by Dr. Louis Ballard, and narrated & hosted by Cliff Robertson. 50 mins. Video, $19.95. NV.

THE SACRED TREE

Curriculum package including text, four videos, six resource books, posters and other visual aids. Presents many of the universal concepts and teachings handed down through the ages in Native societies throughout North America concerning nature, purposes & possibilities of human existence. $450. FOUR.

ST. MARY'S POTLATCH

Three villages participated in this huge potlatch, celebrating the traditional Yup'ik Eskimo Messenger feast, at which young people are honored as they come of age. 1981. 30 minutes. VHS. $24.95. KYUK.

SANANGUAGAT: INUIT MASTERWORKS OF 1,000 YEARS

Derek May, Director; An exhibition of Inuit carvings from public and private collections. Views of daily life in the Iglootik settlement of the Northwest Territories. 1974. 25 mins. Grades 7 and up. Purchase: 16mm, $500; video, $300. Rental, $50. NFBC. Rental, $19.50. PSU.

THE SAND CREEK MASSACRE: SEVEN HOURS THAT CHANGED AMERICAN HISTORY

Donald L. Vaslcek, Director; Olympus Films, Producer
A documentary. 22 mins. DVD, 2007. $24.95.

SAVE OUR SOUNDS

Smithsonan Institution's recording of the chants of a Native American tribe. 50 mins. DVD, 2009. $24.95. SI.

SCHOOL IN THE BUSH

Dennis Sawyer, Producer; Tony Lanzelo, Photographer
Cree values & culture. Touches on the jarring dichotomies experienced by (Canadian) Native children in city schools. Uses excerpts from two documentaries, "Cree Hunters of the Mistassini," & "Our Land is Our Life." 1986. Grades 7-12. 15 mins. 16mm & video. Purchase: $200. NFBC.

THE SEA IS OUR LIFE

Bo Boudart; Inuit speak out about the effects of offshore drilling. Shows the growing political awareness and their efforts to organize. 1979. 16 mins. BO.

THE SEARCH FOR THE FIRST AMERICANS

This program follows the trail of America's first inhabitants. 1993. 60 mins. FH.

SEASONS OF THE NAVAJO

John Borden, Producer/camera; Will Lyman, Narrator
Documentary on the lifestyles & traditions of modern Navajo families in Canyon de Chelly, Arizona - sacred songs, ceremonies and oral traditions. Aspects of Navajo life rarely seen on film are shown. Also filmed is the kinaalda, the ritual for young women. 1984. 60 mins. In English & Navajo with English subtitles. VHS, $15.95. ME.

SEASONS OF THE SALISH: SACRED ENCOUNTERS

Father De Smet and the Indians of the Rocky Mountain West examines the collision of catholic and Native worlds in MT and Idaho. 1996. 30 mins. ME.

A SEAT AT THE TABLE: STRUGGLING FOR AMERICAN INDIAN RELIGIOUS FREEDOM

Gary Rhine, Director; Phil Cousineau, Writer
Covers the right of Native American people to have their sacred sites and practices honored and protected. 2004. 90 mins. DVD & VHS. KF.

SECRETS OF THE LITTLE BIGHORN

By retracing the pattern of bullets & cartridge cases across the battlefield, archaeologists have been able to generate a computer simulation of the final, fatal moments of the Battle of the Little Bighorn. The reconstruction shows a Native American triumph rather than Custer's defeat. 1993. 28 mins. Video.

SEDNA; THE MAKING OF A LEGEND

John Paskievich, Director
Follows a team of Inuit carvers and a white man from Vancouver as they craft the first monumental sized Inuit sculpture for a private corporation. 1992. 58 mins. VHS. Purchase: $27. NFBC.

SEEKING THE FIRST AMERICANS

Graham Chedd; Archaeologists from Texas and Arkansas search for clues to the identity of the first North Americans. 58 mins. Adult. Purchase: 16mm, $750; rental, $60. Educator's guide. DER & PBS. Rental, IU.

SEEKING THE SPIRIT: PLAINS INDIANS IN RUSSIA

Dr. Bea Medicine & Dr. Liucija Baskaiskas
Russians interested in Native American culture. 1999. 27 mins. Video. DER.

THE SENECAS

Ron Hagell; Through interviews & narration, this film views the contemporary Seneca Indian of New York State and their history. 1980. 29 mins. VHS. WXXI.

SEPARATE VISIONS

Peter Blystone & Nancy Tongue, Producers
Profiles four pioneering American Indian artists: Baje Whitethorne, a Navajo painter: Brenda Spencer, a Navajo weaver; John Fredericks, a Hopi kachina carver; and Nora Naranjo-Morse, a Santa Clara sculptor. 1989. 40 mins. UMN.

SEQUOYAH

The story of the Cherokee Indian who developed the first written American Indian language. 15 mins. 16mm. WD.

SERVING NATIVE AMERICAN PEOPLE
Guidelines for health care providers. Illustrates the spiritual needs unique to traditional Native People, the meaning of healing and the role of the extended family. 30 mins. VHS. Purchase: $125; rental, $45. SH.

THE SETTLERS
Allied Film Artists, Inc., Producer; Explores the reasons for and history and impact of America's westward expansion. Including the destruction of Native American cultures. 1978. 22 mins. PHO.

SEYEWAILO: THE FLOWER WORLD
Larry Evers, University of Arizona; Yaqui Deer Songs as they are sung and danced to at a fiesta, the pahko. Yaqui with English subtitles. 51 minutes. Purchase: VHS, $290. NR. Rental: VHS, $52.50. ATL.

THE SHADOW CATCHER: EDWARD S. CURTIS & THE NORTH AMERICAN INDIAN
T.C. McLuhan, Director/Producer; A film of Edward S. Curtis, photographer, anthropologist & filmmaker. Features marked Kwakiutl dancers, a Navajo Yebechai Ceremony, and Curtis' own initiation into the Hopi Snake Fraternity. Soundtrack features original Indian music and contemporary Comanche variations. 1975. 88 mins, color. Grades 9 and up. SH, PHO. Rental: IRA, PSU, IU, UCT, UK, UMN, UCLA & UA.

SHAMANISM
Serge King & Terry Eaton, Producers; Terry Eaton discusses Native American spiritual values & traditions. 57 minutes. VHS video. TPH.

SHEM PETE MEMORIAL POTLATCH
Highlights of potlatch held in Tyonek, Alaska on October 7, 1989. Remarks by Bonnie McCord, Emil McCord, Sr., Jim Kari, Jim Fall, et al. Features the Tyuonek Dancers, Northern Lights Intertribal Pow-wow Club, Paul Theodore of Knik & the Dena'ina Indian cloth ceremony. 1990. 45 mins. VHS. $15. NDM.

SHENANDOAH FILMS
Vern & Carole Korb, Producers; Carole Korb, Director; A Yurok-owned production company, focuses on improving the education, employment skills, and cultural pride of Indian children and youth. Among the productions are: "Again, A Whole Person I Have Become" - Narrated by Will Sampson, this film features a Wintu medicine woman, a Karok spiritual leader, and a Tolowa headman who speak of wisdom of the old ways. 1985, 20 minutes; "In the Best Interest of the Child: Indian Child Welfare Act" - Narrated by Will Sampson, this film depicts an Indian child's removal from his home, to be placed in a non-Indian foster home. 20 minutes; "Our Songs Will Never Die" - Narrated by Juni Donahue. Yurok, Karok, and Tolowa summer camps have been established in California, where young people work together with tribal elders. 1983, 35 mins; "The Path of Our Elders" -Narrated by Pat Tswelmaldin. Pomo elders show how traditions are passed on, demonstrating traditional song and dance and the preparation and weaving of basketry. 1986, 20 minutes, video only; and "Roots to Cherish" - Directed by Marilyn Miles & Don Mahler, narrated by Carl Degado. A concerned mother, a Maidu educator, a traditional Hupa teacher, & a guidance counselor speak of the consequences their cultural differences have for Indian students. 1983, 30 mins. complete list of titles contact SH.

SHINNECOCK: THE STORY OF A PEOPLE
Dana Rogers, Producer; Joseph E. Miller, Director/writer
The Indians of the East Coast region who were the first to come into contact with the white man, when the original settlers arrived from Europe. Consequently, these Indians were the first to lose much of their own culture. 1976. 20 minute. Purchase: 16mm, $375; video, $215; Rental: $35. PHO.

SHUNGNAK: A VILLAGE PROFILE
Daniel Housberg, Director; Focuses on a tiny Inupiat Eskimo community in northwest Alaska, 75 miles north of the Arctic Circle. Villagers discuss their subsistence practices, contrast between past & present. 1985. 30 mins. NATC.

18th ANNUAL SIFC POW WOW 1996
The Saskatchewan Indian Federated College indoor powwow is one od Canada's largest. 25 drum groups and 600 dancers performed during the powwow. CAN.

THE SILENT ENEMY
H.P. Carver; Chief Yellow Robe, a noted Sioux, who acts in the film, points out the usefulness of the film in preserving an authentic image of the old days. Documents a band of Ojibway in winter. 1930. 90 mins. DVD, 2009. FCE. Amazon.com, $7.98.

SINCE 1634: IN THE WAKE OF NICOLET
In 1634, French explorer Jean Nicolet explores Wisconsin and details the subsequent history of the Native American tribes that Nicolet found when he got there - the Menominee & Winnebago. 90 minutes. Video. $25. CAN.

SINEW-BACKED BOW & ITS ARROWS
Clyde B. Smith, Producer; Follows the construction of a sinew-backed bow, by a Yurok craftsman. demonstrates making of arrows. 1961. 24 mins. UC.

SINGERS OF TWO SONGS
A story of Indian artists as they live in two worlds: traditional & contemporary. 25 mins. Video Purchase: $245; rental: $45. SH.

SINUMWAK
Jim & Justine Bizzocchi; Follows the (Bella Coola) process from catching oolichan (fish) to feasting on the result, while the many uses of oolichan grease are discussed. 1979. 20 mins. CFDW.

THE SIOUX
The Sioux were a people of war. Forced onto the grasslands by woodland tribes in the east, they had to fight to survive. The Sioux war ethic was a noble assertion of individuality. 25 minutes. Color VHS. $99.95. AVP.

SIOUX LEGENDS
Charles & Jane Nauman; Recreates some of the legends closest to the philosophy and religion of the Sioux culture. Demonstrates Indian feeling of identification with the forces of nature. 1973. Grades 4 & up. 20 mins. AIMS. Rental: $24.95. WH.

SITTING BULL
Sidney Salkow, Director; Story of a cavalry officer played by Dale Robertson and Carrol Naish as Sitting Bull. Co-stars Iron Eyes Cody, et al. Culminates in Custer's defeat at Little Big Horn. 112 mins. DVD, 2008. $7.98. Amazon.com.

SITTING BULL: CHIEF OF THE LAKOTA NATION
A&E Production; Shows us how the Sioux changed their tactics and defeated Custer. 1993. 50 mins. DVD, $24.95. ME.

SITTING BULL: A PROFILE IN POWER
The tragic but heroic saga of Indian/U.S. relations in this interview with Sitting Bull, portrayed by August Schellenberg. 1977. 26 mins. Purchase: 16mm, $325; rental, $30. LCA. Rental: 16mm, $20. UMN.

THE SIX NATIONS
Nick Gosling, Director; The President of the Seneca Nation and the Mayor of the town of Salamanca discuss the various aspects of Indian and white coexistence. The Iroquois League consists of the Mohawk, Oneida, Onondaga, Seneca, Cayuga and Tuscarora India tribes. Grades 7 and up. 1976. 26 mins. Purchase: 16mm, $400; video, $295. Rental: $55. CG. Rental: $30. UT.

SKINS
Chris Eyre, Director; Drama about the painful legacy of Indian existence. With Graham Greene & Eric Schweig. 2003. 84 mins. DVD, $6.99. ME.

SKINWALKERS
Chris Eyre, Director; Robert Redford, Producer; Based on mystery novel by Tony Hillerman set on Navajo reservation. With Wes Studi & Adam Beach. 2002. 97 mins. DVD, $24.95; VHS, $19.95. ME.

SKOKOMISH INDIAN BASKETS: THEIR MATERIALS & TECHNIQUES
Documents the varied techniques of basket-making by the Skokomish Indians from the Puget Sound region in western Washington State. 1977. 28 minutes/bxw/silent. Super 8mm and video. Rental. UW.

SMOKE SIGNALS
Chris Eyre, Director; A comedy which depicts contemporary reservation life. With Adam Beach, Evan Adams & Irene Bedard. 1998. 89 mins. DVD. ME.

SNAKETOWN
This study of the Snaketown archaeological excavation in southern Arizona, explores the Hohokam Indian culture. 1969. 40 mins. UC.

SOMEDAY, I'LL BE AN ELDER
Narrated by Will Sampson; This film is about a pilot substance prevention program, "Project Renewal." A story featuring Karuk tribal members as they conduct a 3 week summer camp program which emphasizes the renewal of traditional ways & values. 25 mins. SH.

SOMEPLACE YOU DON'T WANT TO GO
Vivid scenes show hardcore drug & alcohol abuse. Designed to educate elementary & high school Indian youth to drug & alcohol abuse. 22 mins. SH.

SOMETIMES WE FEEL
William Maheras, Director; Brad Stanley, Writer/Producer
A young Indian tells of a life of sorrow, poverty, neglect, and isolation on an Arizona reservation. Ten minutes. 16mm. Rental. UA.

SOMEWHERE BETWEEN
Hy Perspectives Media Group; Looks at the history of Canadian government legislation affecting Indian women and their traditional role in Indian society. 1982. 50 minutes. 16mm & video. Purchase or rental. CFDW.

A SONG FOR DEAD WARRIORS
Examines the reasons for the Wounded Knee occupation in the Spring of 1973 by Oglala Sioux Indians. Features many of the personalities involved, including Russell Means, tribal chairman Dick Wilson, Chief Charley Red Cloud, and Medicine Man Frank Fools Crow. 1973. 25 mins. 16mm. Rental: UCLA & UNI.

SONGS IN MINTO LIFE
Curt Madison, Producer/director; A documentary that explores the creativity and tradition in the songs of Tanana Indians living near Minto Flats, Alaska. Shows activities during the four seasons, with elders singing both contemporary songs and traditional khukal'ch'leek songs. 1985. 30 minutes, color. In English & Tanana Athapascan. Video. KYUK, NAPBC.

SONGS OF MY HUNTER HEART: LAGUNA STORIES & POEMS
Harold Littlebird; Author sings traditional and popular Pueblo songs. Includes his song-poem Talking 49 which describes the singing which takes place around a drum after a powwow. 1978. 34 minutes in English & Keres. ATL.

SONGS OF MY HUNTER HEART: LAGUNA SONGS & POEMS
Larry Evers, University of Arizona
Harold Littlebird continues the oral tradition of his people by incorporating contemporary themes into his work which retains the Pueblo reverence for the Spoken word. 1978. 34 minutes. Purchase: Video, $220. NR.

THE SONS OF THE GREAT BEAR
First Run Features; Gold is discovered on the lands of the Dakota Indians. Ruthless white settlers attempts to drive the Indians away, eventually defeated and resettled. 93 mins. DVD, 2006. $19.95. Amazon.com.

SOUTHWEST CULTURAL VIDEO SERIES
Designed & developed to help the classroom teacher. Four videos: Storytelling in Clay & Language - Native American sculptor Dorothy Trujillo demonstrating how to make a clay storyteller doll. 26 minutes. Creating Portraits in Art & Language - Sam English, a Native American painter, is shown demonstrating the art of self-portraiture to 3rd & 4th graders. 17 minutes. Space in Dance & Poetry - Jerome Marcus, a Taos Pueblo Indian, demonstrates the grass dance for 5th & 6th graders, and Jennifer Predock-Linnell, a modern dancer, is shown demonstrating a variety of creative dance movements to these students. 26 minutes. Mask, Dance & Character - Rosalie Jones, artistic director of Daystar Dancers, demonstrates Native American dance steps & use of costumes, masks, and button blankets for theatrical production. 17 mins. VHS. Purchase: $49.95 each; $100 each with curriculum package. ALA.

SOUTHWEST INDIAN ARTISTS SERIES
Seven videos introduces various arts & crafts of the Southwest. Baskets (Papago & Hopi); Kachina Dolls (Hopi); Pottery (Pueblo & Navajo); Jewelry (Navajo, Hopi & Zuni); Navajo Rug Makers; Sandpaimting (Navajo); Pueblo Storytellers. VHS. 40 mins. each. $19.95 ea. set of seven, $99.95. WH.

SOUTHWEST INDIAN ARTS & CRAFTS
Shows techniques in Navajo rug-making; San Ildefonso and Acoma pottery; Hopi and Zuni jewelry and kachina dolls; and Pima and Papago basket-making. 1973. 14 minutes. Grades K-12. Purchase: 16mm, $320; video, $225; Rental, $40. PHO. Rental. IU and UK.

SOUTHWEST INDIAN OF EARLY AMERICA
Uses Indian actors, dioramas, and narration to help recreate what life might have been like about 600 years ago for the Hohokam and Anasazi Indians of northern Arizona and New Mexico. 1973. 14 minutes. Grades 4-8. Purchase: 16mm, $350; video, $245. PHO. Rental. IU and UK.

SOVEREIGNTY & THE U.S. CONSTITUTION
By Senator Daniel S. Inouye, Chairman of the Senate Select Committee on Indian Affairs. 20 minutes, color. Video. Purchase: $20; rental: $10. HO.

SPEECHES COLLECTION
A sample of heartfelt addresses from Sitting Bull. 1997. 35 mins. ME.

SPIRIT BAY SERIES
Eric Jordan & Paul Stephens, Producers/directors; Keith Leckie, Director
An entertainment series of 13 films which reflect some of the reality of reserve life and debunks stereotypes about Indians. Filmed on the Rocky Bay Reserve in Ontario, it depicts a remote northern Indian community through the

experiences of its children, and shows how its residents have adapted to white society while retaining ties to the land. 1982-86. Grades 4 and up. 28 mins. each. In English, French, or Ojibway. VHS. $149 each. ALT & BE (U.S.); ML (Canada).

SPIRIT IN THE EARTH
The legend of a Western Indian tribe, describing the phenomenon of Old Faithful in terms of the Plains' Indians concept of original sin. 22 minutes. Rental. UK.

THE SPIRIT OF CRAZY HORSE
Milo Yellow Hair, Narrator; Reveals the modern Sioux struggle to regain their heritage, and how places like Wounded Knee became sites for a fight that continues still. Presents the militant confrontations of the 1960's & 1970's, the explosive results of 100 years of confinement on Indian reservations. 1989. 58 minutes. Purchase: Video, $19.95. CAN. Purchase: Video, $25. AUDIO; $40. PBS. Rental: Video, $10. HO, UMN & PSU.

SPIRIT OF THE HUNT
Narrated by Will Sampson, this film features a spiritual search for the essential elements of what the Buffalo meant historically and in the present to people of the Chippewa, Cree and Dogrib tribes. Historical footage combined with a modern hunt, illustrates the central concept. 1982. Grades 9 & up. 29 minutes. Purchase: 16mm, $675. TC. Purchase: VHS, $160; 3/4", $190. CC. Rental: 16mm, $20.50. UMN.

THE SPIRIT OF THE MASK
Peter von Puttkamer, Director; Gryphon Productions
Documentary explores the spiritual & psychological powers of the masks of the Northwest Coast Native people. Features ceremonies as well as commentary by important Indian spiritual leaders, Relates the colonial history of the Northwest Coast Indians. 1992. 50 mins. UC.

SPIRIT OF THE WHITE MOUNTAINS
Documents the activities of the White Mountain Apaches, and how they support themselves by developing the natural resources of their reservation. 1959. 13 mins. Grades 4-9. 16mm. Rental. IU & UA.

SPIRIT RIDER
Michael Scott, Director; Raised in foster homes, 16-year-old Native American Jesse Threebears is reluctantly repatriated to the reservation of his birth. 1993. Grades 4 & up. 90 mins. 2005, DVD. $7.98. Amazon.com. FI.

SPIRIT OF THE WILD
A mystical grandfather transforms the life of a modern day boy through the legends of Seeks-to-Hunt-Great. Michael Horse tracks a mountain lion for many months, learns from it and eventually gains its trust. Based on Native American folklore & the Medicine Wheel Way, this video brings an awareness of the important relationship with our environment. 30 minutes. CAN.

THE SPIRIT WITHIN
Gil Cardinal & Wil Campbell, Directors; Story of how Native prisoners in four western Canadian correctional facilities have won the right to practice their traditional spirituality. 1990. 51 mins. Rental: $80. NFBC.

SPIRITS OF THE CANYON: ANCIENT ART OF THE PECOS INDIANS
Artist Amado Pena & archaeologists analyze the paintings & pictographs on walls of the majestic southwest Texas canyons that date from about 3000 BC until the arrival of the conquistadors in the 16th century. 1992. 30 mins. Video, Purchase: $149; rental: $75. FH.

SQUANTO: A WARRIOR'S TALE
A young Indian warrior is kidnapped by 17th century English traders and exhibited as a wild man back in England. He escapes and returns home. 1994. With Adma Beach, Eric Schweig, Alex Norton, Mandy Patinkin. 97 mins. ME.

STANDING ALONE
Colin Low, Director; 25 years ago, Pete Standing Alone was the subject of a film by Colin Low which stressed the conflicts facing a young man of the Blood tribe caught between Indian and the white ways. Now middle-aged, Standing Alone lives on the Blood Indian Reserve in Alberta and is active in family and tribal affairs. Also considers the economic and political pressures that affect Indian tribes. 1983. 58 mins. 16mm. Rental: $80. NFBC

STANDING BUFFALO
Joan Henson, Director; An account of rug-making cooperative organized by Sioux Indian women of the Standing Buffalo Reserve in the Qu'Appelle Valley of southern Saskatchewan. 1968. 23 minutes. Purchase: $27. NFBC.

STANDING STRONG AGAINST THE CANCER ENEMY
Old Man Coyote Productions
Promotes healthful traditional practices of Native Americans as effective cancer prevention and control practices. Grades 5 and up. 1993. 30 mins. VHS. $49. CHAR.

STAR LORE
Faith Hubley, Producer/director
An animated, original and visually dynamic rendering of six Native American sky myths. Stories chosen include: an Inuit tale, and a Pawnee tale. 1984. 8 1/2 mins. 16mm, VHS. PFV.

STARBLANKET
Donald Brittain, Director; Video about Noel Starblanket and his methods of learning the political process. Looks at his Canadian reserve and what life was like for his people. 1973. 27 mins. Purchase: $27. NFBC.

STARTING FIRE WITH GUNPOWDER
David Poisey & William Hansen, Directors; Chronicles the origins and achievement of the Inuit Broadcasting Corp. Explores how Inuit TV is a critical element in the creation of a modern Inuit nation in Canada's Arctic. 1991. 57 minutes. Video. Purchase: $27. NFBC.

STEVE CHARGING EAGLE
A film about an American Indian man from Red Scaffold, South Dakota. Quiet, proud, a man of responsibility, he performs in a War Dance competition. 30 mins. AICRC.

STICKS & STONES WILL BUILD A HOUSE
Traces the development of Indian architecture in the Southwestern U.S. 1970. 30 mins. Rental, $19. IU.

STONE AGE AMERICANS
Jules Powers & Daniel Wilson, Producers; Discovery Series, NBC
Introduces the vanished Indians of the Mesa Verde in Colorado. The film presents the history of these farmer Indians by examining the cliff dwellings and artifacts discovered in 1888. 21 minutes. 16mm. Rental. UA.

STOP RUINING AMERICA'S PAST
Covers the problem of the destruction of archaeological sites by urban and industrial expansion, as illustrated by the case histories of two prehistoric Indian communities in Illinois - Cahokia Mounds and Hopewell Mounds. 1968. 22 mins, bxw. 16mm. Rental: UA.

STORIES OF NORTH AMERICA. Part II
Includes Stories of Native American Peoples - Joe Bruchac tells "The Earth on Turtle's Back" & "The Race With the Buffalo." 30 mins. NGS.

THE STORY OF TUKTU SERIES
Lawrence Hyde, Director; A children's adventure series, starring Tuktu, an Inuit boy, 13 film adventures. 1966-1968. 14 mins. each. Grades 1-8. FILMS.

STORYTELLER
A documentary, focusing on an important Pueblo tradition, this video tells the story of the increasingly popular clay sculpture of Helen Cordero of Cochiti Pueblo, NM. Grades 7+. 23 mins. Purchase: VHS, $79; 3/4", $109. CC.

THE STRENGTH OF LIFE
Scott & Sheila Swearingen & Gary Robinson, Producers/directors/writers
Portrays Creek-Cherokee artist Knokovtee Scott reviving an ancient art form of producing jewelry made with engraved shells, its motifs based on the incised shell tradition of the moundbuilder cultures of the ancient Southeast. 1984. 26 mins. VHS. $19.95. VIP, WH, NAPBC.

SUCKING DOCTOR
William Heick, Producer; A documentary presenting the final night of a curing ceremony held by the Kashia group of Southwestern Pomo Indians. The Indian Sucking Doctor is a prophet of the Bole Maru religion, spiritual head of the Kashia community. 1964. 45 mins, bxw. UC. Rental: 16mm, PSU & UCLA.

THE SUMMER OF JOHNSON HOLIDAY - NAVAJO BOY
Johnson Holiday lives in Monument Valley. During the summer he herds the family sheep and goats; during the winter he attends the white man's school. 12 mins. Grades 1-8. Rental. UK.

SUMMER OF LOUCHEUX: PORTRAIT OF A NORTHERN INDIAN FAMILY
Graydon McCrae, Producer/director; Profiles the Andre family, a Loucheux or Kutchin, one of the northernmost Indian peoples, living in both Canada and Alaska. 1983. Grades 7 and up. 28 mins, color. 16mm & video. In English or Loucheux. TAM (Canada, sales only.) 16mm rental, $27.50. UMN & PSU.

SUN BEAR: ON POWER & EARTH CHANGES
"On Power" - Sun Bear, medicine teacher and founder of the Bear Tribe, teaches people the first steps toward finding their own path of power. "Earth Changes" - Sun Bear draws on his own visions and Native prophecies to help people understand and come into harmony with these times of change. 65 mins each. VHS & Beta. $29.95 each.

THE SUN DAGGER
Anna Sofaer, Producer/Writer; Albert Ihde, Director/Editor
Tells the story of Anna Sofaer, A Washington, DC artist who having climbed to the top of a high butte in Chaco Canyon, New Mexico, saw a dagger of light pierce an ancient spiral rock carving. After careful study, she found that the dagger marks solstices, equinoxes, and the 19-year lunar cycle. Narrated by Robert Redford, this film explores the Anasazi culture that produced this calendar and thrived over 1,000 years ago in the Chaco Canyon environment. 1982. Grades 7 and up. 60 & 30 mins. versions. BULL. Rental: 30 minute-16mm version, UCT, UT & PSU. NAPBC.

SUN, MOON & FEATHER
Bob Rosen & Jane Zipp, Producers/directors
Documentary about three Native American sisters growing up in Brooklyn during the 1930s & 1940s. Blends musical theater (song & dance reenactments of family & tribal stories) & personal memoir (scenes filmed in Brooklyn home). 1989. 30 mins. CG.

SUNFLOWER JOURNEYS
Explores the heritage of Kansas. Each 30-minute video contains three separate stories. Includes: Native Americans (#209-200 Series, 1989); Glaciated Region - Iowa Tribe Powwow (#303-300 Series, 1990); Natives & Newcomers - Medicine Lodge Peace Treaty & Indian Self Determination (#502-500 Series, 1992); Indian Art Market (#513-500 Series, 1992); Artifacts of Culture - Sacred Spaces (#607-600 Series, 1993); Native Americans (#704-700 Series, 1994); Three Dimensional Art (#705-700 Series, 1994). KS.

THE SUNRISE DANCE
Gianfranco Norelli; A documentary showing an ancient, sacred Apache ritual that has never before been filmed. The Sunrise Ceremony marks the passage from adolescence to adulthood for young Apache women. 28 mins. Color. Video. 1994. Purchase: $145; rental, $40. DER.

SURVIVING COLUMBUS
Chronicles the Pueblo Indians' 450 years of contact with Europeans and their long struggle to preserve their culture, land & religion. Includes stories of Pueblo elders, interviews with Pueblo scholars & leaders, historical accounts as told by the Pueblo Indians of New Mexico & Arizona. VHS. 1992. Grades 7 and up. 120 mins. Purchase: $100. PBS & NAPBC. Rental, $14. UMN & PSU.

SWEATING INDIAN STYLE: CONFLICTS OVER NATIVE AMERICAN RITUAL
Susan Smith; A documentary about a group of non-Native women's search for self in "other". The focus is on a spoeciific group of New Age women in Ojai, California who construct a new sweat lodge and perform their own ceremony. 57 mins. Color. Video. 1994. Purchase: $145; rental, $40. DER.

TAHTONKA: PLAINS INDIANS BUFFALO CULTURE
Charles and Jane Nauman, Producers
A re-enactment of the Plains Indian's culture from the pre-horse era to the time of the Wounded Knee massacre. 1966. 30 mins, color. Grades 4-adult. Purchase: 16mm, $495 and video, $70. Rental, $50. AIMS & NILB. Rental: $24.95, WH.

TAKING TRADITION TO TOMORROW
N. Scott Momaday, PhD, Narrator
A video presentation and study guide, featuring significant cultural and scientific contributions that American Indians have made to society. Grades 7-college level. 32-page study guide. 30 mins. Video. $69.95. AISES.

TALES OF THE TUNDRA
Traditional Yup'ik Eskimo storytellers explore the legends of Southwest Alaska. 1992. 30 mins. VHS. $24.95. KYUK.

TALES OF WESAKECHAK
Marla Dufour, Storytellers Production; A series of 13 fifteen-minute programs based on well known Canadian Cree legends. Wesakechak, the teacher of the first Indian people. 1984. Color. Rental: $300/series; $40 each. NAPBC.

TALES OF WONDER, I & II
Gregory Howard; Howard (Cherokee/Powhatan) tells traditional Native American stories for children. VHS & DVD. 60 mins each. $24.95. MALKI. CD Soundtrack available for $15.95. WH, ME & RICH.

TALKING HANDS
Demonstrates the sign language of the Plains Indians. Tells the story of the Battle of the Washita in sign language with background narration. 20 mins. UT.

THE TAOS PUEBLO
Paulle Clark, Producer/Director; Spend a day at the 1000-year-old pueblo in Taos, New Mexico to discover more about the traditions that the resident Indians are trying to preserve. See young children doing ceremonial dances; learn about building homes with adobe clay; bread-baking; and making pottery. Includes study guide. 1986. 9 mins. Grades 2-8. BULL.

TEACHING INDIANS TO BE WHITE
Reviews the issues surrounding schooling of Native American children, where native children find it nearly impossible to balance the white view they are taught with the language & values they learn at home. The Seminole in Florida resist being integrated, the Miccosukee decided not to fight, and the Cree took back their own schools. 1993. 28 mins, color. Video. Rental: $16. UMN.

TEARS OF THE RAVEN
Examines the dissolution of Alaskan indigenous culture, suicide & alcoholism among Alaska's Natives, & explores some of the things the Natives are doing to bring health and hope back to their communities. 1993. 30 mins. CHAR.

TECUMSEH, THE LAST WARRIOR
About Shawnee warrior, Tecumseh and his attempt to win back the West. With Jesse Borrego, Tantoo Cardinal. 1995. 94 mins. VHS, $79.99. ME.

TEN THOUSAND BEADS FOR NAVAJO SAM
Focuses on Sam Begay, a full-blooded Navajo, who has left the reservation to make a new alien, but secure, life for himself and his family in Chicago. 1971. 25 mins, color. 16mm. Rental. IU & UCLA.

TENACITY
Chris Eyre (Cheyenne/Arapaho) Productions; The story of two Indian boys who encounter rednecks on a reservation road. A short narrative filmed in the Onondaga Territory near Nedrow, New York. 1995. VHS. 10 mins. Color. Purchase: $175; rental: $50. TWN.

THAT ONE GOOD SPIRIT - AN INDIAN CHRISTMAS STORY
Larry Cesspooch, Writer/Director; A clay animated tale of a young Ute Indian boy. 1981. 16 mins. Color. Grades K-3. Video. Rental: $40/week. NAPBC.

THE THEFT OF FIRE
Title V Indian Education Program staff
Based on a traditional Yurok story retold by elder Jimmie James, this video version features a running translation in Yurok & English. Curriculum Unit: discusses the traditional use of fire as a land management tool by Native Americans. Illus. by Frank Tuttle (Pomo/Maidu). Grades 6-8. 14 mins. VHS. $59.95 (includes Curriculum Unit). CB.

THESE ARE MY PEOPLE
Michael Mitchell, Director
Two Mohawk spokesmen explain historical and other aspects of Longhouse religion, culture and government which are interwoven. 1969. 13 mins. Video. Purchase: $22. NFBC.

THEY NEVER ASKED OUR FATHERS
Corey Flintoff, Producer/writer; John A. McDonald, Director/editor;
John Active, Narrator; Through interviews and scenes of various aspects of Yup'ik life on Nunivak Island, 20 miles from the mainland of southwest Alaska, this video presents the situation of a native people whose daily affairs are dominated by the federal government located thousands of miles away. 1980. 60 minutes. In English and Yup'ik with English subtitles. VHS. $24.95. KYUK.

THEY PROMISED TO TAKE OUR LAND
Document Associates & BBC; Discusses the misunderstanding by the white man of the value of land to the Indian. 1976. 26 mins, color. Purchase:16mm, $400; video, $295. Rental, $55. CG. Rental, $30. UT.

THIEVES OF TIME
Gerald Richman; Describes the problems of pot hunters looting valuable archaeological sites in Arizona. 1995. 30 mins. VHS, $15.95. ME.

THIS SIDE OF THE RIVER
Monona Wali; Focuses on concerns of Onondaga Indians of New York State. Discusses social problems and political awareness. 1978. 30 mins; bxw. WALI.

THIS WAS THE TIME
Eugene Boyko and William Brind, Directors
A recreation of Haida Indian life in a village in the Queen Charlotte Islands. Portrays the potlatch and totems which existed. 16 mins. 16mm. NFBC.

THIS WORLD IS NOT OUR HOME
Introduction to the history, culture, and traditions of the Pomo people of northern California, as seen through the eyes of Elvina Brown, a tribal elder. 1993. 13 mins, color. Video. Purchase: $125; rental: $40. UC.

THOSE BORN AT MASSET: A HAIDA STONEMOVING AND FEAST
Covers the Haida ritual, the modern equivalent of the traditional memorial potlatch. 1976. 70 mins/bxw. 16mm and video. UW.

A THOUSAND ROADS
Chris Eyre (Cheyenne/Arapaho) Director; W. Richard West (Southern Cheyenne) & Peter Guber, Executive Producers; Scott Garen & Barry Clark, Producers; 40-minute film in celebration of Native peoples & communities. DVD. NMAI. $16.95

THREE WARRIORS
Keith Merrill, Director; Portrays the problems encountered by a 13 year-old on the Warm Springs Indian Reservation in Oregon, and his coming to terms with his heritage. 1977. 105 minutes, color. 35mm & 16mm. ZAENTZ.

THROUGH THIS DARKEST NIGHT
Susan Malins, Producer; Daniel Salazar, Director;
Vivian Locust & Richard Peters, Narrators/advisors
Presents Indian people's experiences during the early reservation period, including some drawn from period accounts. Three speakers: a man speaks of the upheaval experienced when the buffalo were finally gone; a woman describes how she used her strength and traditional skills to ensure that her family would survive; and a third speaker tells of being sent to boarding school and the isolation and humiliation of that experience. 1986. 12 mins, color. Video. ADL & DAM.

THUNDER IN THE DELLS
Lance Tallmadge, a Wisconsin Winnebago, presents the history of his tribe and their legal struggle to remain in the Wisconsin Dells area in the mid-19th Century. Shows the effects of over 120 years of tourism on the Winnebagos, and discusses the importance of their traditional songs and dances to their well-being and survival. Also the preparation and weaving of black ash wood baskets. 1989. Grades 7 and up. 28 mins, color. Video. $20. CAN.

THUNDERHEART
Sony Pictures Home Entertainment; An FBI agent is sent to solve a murder on a Sioux Indian reservation. He learns of his Native culture and soon believes the U.S. government framed an innocent man. 1992. With Val Kilmer, Graham Greene, Chief Ted Thin Elk, Sam Shepard. 119 mins. DVD, $9.99. ME.

TI EKIYE: FINDING THE WAY HOME
Native American Advocacy Project, SD
This educational and training video with facilitator's guide addresses mental illness in Native American communities and the providing of culturally sensitive services. 1994. 60 mins. VHS & Guide. $55. CHAR.

THE LISA TIGER STORY
Educational video of a 29-year old, Muscogee Creek/Cherokee from Oklahoma, who is HIV positive, offers strength and inspiration for Native American youth with HIV and a message of prevention and protection for others. 1993. 27 mins. VHS. $50. CHAR.

TIKINAGAN
Gil Cardinal; Account of the difficulties along the path to Native self-determination. Foster care and a child welfare agency in Northwestern Ontario, Canada. 1991. 57 mins, color. Video. $27. NFBC.

TIME IMMEMORIAL
Hugh Brody, Director; Native land claims in Canada today; Aboriginal rights in Canada. Takes place in Nass Valley where the Nishga'a people bear witness to their struggle and that of their ancestors. 1991. 57 mins, color. Video. Purchase: $27. NFBC.

TIME OF THE CREE
Bob Rodgers and Gail Singer; Records a salvage archaeological dig near Southern Indian Lake on the Churchill River in northern Manitoba, Canada. Shows a Cree family in the area living a traditional way of life. 1974. 26 mins. 16mm. RS.

A TIME TO BE BRAVE
Eric Jordan, Producer/editor; Paul Stephens, Director/writer
Filmed in Ontario, Canada, this film focuses on the Shibagabo family - living on their trapline in winter. Scenes of the family at home and of tracking and trapping establish a good sense of daily life. 1982. 28 mins, color. 16mm & video. BE.

TIWA TALES: LITTLE FILTH & THE TLACHEES
Chuck Banner, Maggie Banner & Joseph Concha, Producers/Directors
A grandfather relates an ancient story. Interwoven with claymation live-action & video effects, bring to life the tale. 1990. Grades 2-8. 17 mins, color. Video. Purchase: $31.95. MP.

TO EVERY NATION...FROM EVERY TRIBE
An Episcopal film about the history of mission work among Indians to the present day. 28 minutes, color. Video. Rental: $10. HO.

TO FIND OUR WAY/FIRST STEPS
Two programs on one tape dealing with domestic violence in Native American communities. 1992. 32 mins. VHS. $150. CHAR.

TOBACCO FABLE "DOLPHIN MEETS OL' COYOTE"
A children's story on the effects of smoking abd chewing. 14 minutes. Video. Purchase: $200; rental, $45. SH.

TOM SAVAGE: BOY OF EARLY VIRGINIA
Dramatizes the story of a boy given to the Indians. Depicts his new life, and his learning of their language, skills and tribal customs. 1958. Grades 4-9. 22 mins. Rental: UA.

TOMORROW'S YESTERDAY
KBYU-TV Provo, Utah, Producer
Shows how the Pueblo people adapt to the challenges of modern civilization while maintaining their identity and culture. 1971. 29 minutes. Video. Rental: $40/week. NAPBC.

TOTEM POLE
Clyde B. Smith, Producer; Illustrates the seven types of totem poles and relates each to a social system and mythology that laid great stress on kinship, rank, and ostentatious displays of wealth. The carving of a pole by Mungo Martin, a famous carver and chief of the Kwakiutl is shown. 1963. 27 minutes, color. PSU.

TOTEMS
Shows the enormous cedar totems, with their ritualistic & religious carvings, made by the Wes Coast Indians of British Columbia. 1944. 11 minutes, color. 16mm. Rental: $19. UCLA.

TRADITIONAL USE OF PEYOTE
Gary Rhine, Producer/Director
A Summary of the Native American Church Crisis. The U.S. Supreme Court "Smith Decision." 17 minutes, color. Video. KF. Rental: $10. HO.

TRAGEDY & TRIUMPH - THE CHEROKEE STORY
The history of the Eastern Band of Cherokee told through tradition and a glimpse of their lives today in Western North Carolina. 30 minutes. Video. $29.95. CH.

TRAIL OF BROKEN TREATIES
Document Associates & BBC, Producer; Examines the past and present injustices and focuses on the attempt of Indian leaders to improve the situation. 1972. 26 mins. CG.

TRAIL OF THE BUFFALO
Eight minutes. 16mm. Rental: UA.

THE TRAIL OF TEARS
Traces westward expansion and the damage created to Indian culture. 13 minutes, color. Purchase: $69.95. FH.

TRAIL OF TEARS
WETA-TV Washington, D.C.; Focuses on the forced removal of the Cherokees from their homelands and their exodus to the West, the Cherokee's struggle to maintain their identity and their heritage. 20 minutes. Grades 7-12. 16-page teacher's guide, $1.95. Purchase: 16mm, $300; video, $150. AIT.

THE TRAIL OF TEARS: CHEROKEE LEGACY
Presented by Wes Studi; narrated by James Earl Jones
55 mins. Color. DVD. $34.95. MALKI.

TRANSITIONS: DESTRUCTION OF MOTHER TONGUE
Darrell Kipp & Joe Fisher; This program explores the relationship between language, thought & culture, and the impact of language disappearance in Native American communities. 1991. 25 minutes. Video. Rental: $10. HO.

TRAVELING THE DISTANCE
The colors, sounds, sights & essence of the Pow Wow, featuring dancers ablaze in colorful regalia, representing spirits, animals and tribal affiliations.

Native Americans from across the U.S. & Canada tell in their own words what the powwow means to them. The days that follow on the Shinnecock Indian reservation grounds on Long Island, NY, are inspirational. 1997. Won the Best Feature Documentary Award from the Long Island Film Festival. Video. 52 mins. SH.

THE TREASURE: INDIAN HERITAGE
Two teenage Indian brothers, after their father is arrested for defending tribal fishing rights, begin to weigh the worth of their heritage against today's commercial considerations. 1970. 13 minutes. PHO.

A TREASURY OF CALIFORNIA INDIAN BASKETRY
Dr. Gregory Schaaf; Illustrates hundreds of baskets in their natural environments. 1990. CIAC.

TREATIES
Sandra Osawa, Writer/Producer; Julian Finkelstein, Director
Retraces Indian treaty history from Colonial times to the present. Discusses the treaty as a legal concept and historical reality. A speech made by Chief Seattle during a treaty session in 1855 is dramatized by host, Nez Perce actor, John Kauffman. 1975. 28 minutes. Video. Purchase: $55. UP and BYU-N.

TREATIES MADE--TREATIES BROKEN
Discusses the land grabbing, broken promises and treaties made by the white man with the Nisqually Indian tribe of Washington State. 1970. 18 minutes, color. 16mm. Rental. UT and IU.

TREATIES, TRUTH & TRUST
Presents 10 of the most commonly asked questions on treaty rights. The answers are given by Wisconsin tribal leaders & religious leaders from various communities. 14 minutes. Video. Purchase: $20; rental: $10. HO.

TREATY 8 COUNTRY
Anne Cubitt and Hugh Brody, Producers/directors
Documents subsistence hunting of the Beaver Indians of the Halfway River Band in northeast British Columbia, and records their views on the current situation over the abrogation of their treaty rights. 1982. 44 minutes. 16mm (sales and rentals). CFDW.

THE TREATY OF 1868
NETV, Producer; Examines the roots of the dispute over the Lakota Sioux claim to the Black Hills of South Dakota. A series, two 30-minute videos. Program 1: The Treaty of 1868; Program 2: The Black Hills Claim. 1987. Color. Rental: $65/series; $40 each. NAPBC.

THE TREE IS DEAD
Describes one of the last Indian reservations in the State of Minnesota, Red Lake, and the disintegration of their own culture. 1955. Grades 4 and up. 11 minutes, bxw. 16mm. Rental: $13. UMN.

THE TRIAL OF STANDING BEAR
NETV, Producer; Tells the story of one man's struggle of self-determination in th 1879 court case "Standing Bear vs. Crook. The dramatic portrayal of the courageous Ponca Chief Standing Bear explores the personal side of the story as the Poncas were forced from their home on the Niobrara River (now northern Nebraska) to inhospitable Territory that is now modern-day Okla. 1988. 120 minutes. Video. Purchase: $40. GPN & NAPBC.

TRIBAL LAW
Title V Indian Education Program staff; Demonstrates students resolving a problem using the classroom system, and gives background information on underlying cultural values, as well as practical discussion for using a dispute resolution system based on the traditional "settleup" compensation principals of the tribes of Northwest California. Grades 4-6. 15 mins. VHS. $59.95 (includes Curriculum Unit). CB.

THE TRIBE & THE PROFESSOR: OZETTE ARCHAEOLOGY
Louis & Ruth Kirk, Producers
Professor Richard Daugherty and his students from Washington State University returned to Ozette Indian Village to resume archaeological investigation begun in 1966. Results in the reconstruction of the Makah's past. Revised 1978 ed. 44 minutes. UW.

TRIBE OF THE TURQUOISE WATERS
Records the life of the Havasupai Indians in Arizona, and how their lives are shaped by their environment. Shows food preparation & the use of sweat lodges. 1952. Grades 6 and up. 13 minutes, color. 16mm. Rental: UA & UCLA.

TRUST FOR NATIVE AMERICAN CULTURES & CRAFTS VIDEO
Todd Crocker, Producer/narrator/editor;
Henri Vaillancourt, Director/writer/camera/editor

Documents aspects of the material culture of northern Native Americans in Eastern Canada. Programs include: Beavertail Snowshoes - the construction of traditional Cree Indian beavertail snowshoes, 1981, 40 minutes; Building an Algonquin Birchbark Canoe, 1984, 57 minutes; and Indian Hide Tanning - the Cree of northern Quebec show s moose and caribou hide tanning process, 1981, 35 minutes. 3VHS. In English and native languages. TR.

TUBUGHNA, THE BEACH PEOPLE
Emil McCord, Sr., Film Coordinator
Documentary about life in the Athabascan village of Tyonek, Alaska from 1964 to 1984. 1988. 57 mins. CIRI.

TUKTU STORIES
Lawrence Hyde, Writer/Editor; A series of 13 stories on Inuit culture. 1969. 14 minutes each. 16mm. Grades 3-9. See FILMS for titles and prices.

TULE TECHNOLOGY: NORTHERN PAIUTE USES OF MARSH RESOURCES IN WESTERN NEVADA
Thomas Vennum, Jr., Producer; Louella George, Narrator
A film about Northern Paiute Indian people who have lived near the Stillwater marshes of western Nevada for generation. Focuses on Wuzzie George and members of her family constructing a duck egg bag, cattail house, duck decoy, and tule boat. 1983. 42 minutes. PSU.

TUNUNEREMIUT: THE PEOPLE OF TUNUNAK
Portrays aspects of the lives of the people (Eskimos) of Tununak, a village on the southwestern coast of Alaska. 1973. 35 minutes. Purchase: 16mm, $550; video, $195. Rental: 16mm, $60; video, $40. DER.

TURTLE SHELLS
Gary Robinson, Producer; Christine Hanneha, a Muscogee Creek Indian of Oklahoma demonstrates an ancient method of fashioning turtle shell leg rattles. 1987. 26 minutes. Video. Purchase: $150; Rental: $40. NAPBC.

THE 21ST ANNUAL WORLD ESKIMO-INDIAN OLYMPICS
Skip Blumberg, Producer/Director
Portraits of two Inupiat Eskimo athletes preparing for Olympics speak of their Eskimo heritage. 1983. 27 mins. EIA.

TWO INDIANS - RED REFLECTIONS OF LIFE
Documentary study of two North American Indian high school students and their classmates. 1973. 26 minutes. 16mm. Rental. UK.

TWO SPIRITS: NATIVE AMERICAN LESBIANS & GAYS
T. Osa Hidalgo-Dela Riva; Royal Eagle Bear Productions
A documentary exploring one Native belief in human adrogyny. Compiles interviews with First People throughout the Americas. 28 minutes. Color. Video, Purchase: $225; rental, $75. TWN.

UMEALIT: THE WHALE HUNTERS
John Angier (WGBH)
The Inuit and the controversy of whale hunting for subsistence versus the international effort to save the whales. 1980. 58 minutes. video. WGBH.

UNDERSTANDING A.I.R.F.A.
Gary Rhine, Producer/Director
A summary of the 1993 Congressional Amendment to the American Indian Religious Freedom Act which concerns protection of the use of sacred sites, eagle feathers & Peyote, and guarantees prisoner's rights. Features testimony by Indian law professor Vine Deloria, Native American rights attorney Walter Echo-Hawk, and Senator Daniel Inouye, Chair of the Senate Select Committee on Indian Affairs. 15 mins. HO.

UNIVERSITY OF CALIFORNIA: AMERICAN INDIAN FILM SERIES
Samuel A. Barrett and Clyde Smith
Each of 12 films uses the memories and oral traditions of contemporary Indians as well as anthropological records to document their cultural skills. Tribes filmed include: Southwestern Pomo, Kwakiutl, Yurok, Paviotso, Washo, Tolowa, Nisenan, and Brule Sioux. See UC for titles & prices.

UNLEARNING INDIAN STEREOTYPES
VHS tape & discussion guide. A teaching unit for elementary teachers & children's librarians contains: a study of stereotyping in picture books; 10 classroom don'ts for teachers; guidelines for publishers, illustrators, & writers; role playing strategies; Native American perspectives on Columbus Day, Thanksgiving, & Washington's Birthday. Rental: $10. HO.

URBAN ELDER
Documentary of Vern Harper, an urban Indian elder talking about traditional Indian culture and modern urban life. VHS. 28 mins. $139 with Guide. CHAR.

URBAN FRONTIER
Seattle Indian Center, Producer; Narrated by Dr. John Fuller & Will Sampson, this film provides an insight into the historical problems that have confronted Indian culture, and that have set the stage for the difficulties of adaptation in today's fast-paced society. A story which is told by Indians themselves, and illustrates how Indians have banded together in cities to form urban Indian centers; how they are putting their traditional values to work to help solve their problems. Two versions, 26 minutes & 17 mins. Purchase: COP. Rental: 16mm (26 min.), $16. UMN.

URBAN INDIANS
The story of Joe Killsright, an Oglala Sioux Indian from Pine Ridge Reservation who comes to New York City for a job and the problems he encounters as a result. 20 minutes. Color. Video. Purchase: $175; Rental, $40. DTC.

UTE INDIAN TRIBE VIDEO
Larry Cesspooch, Producer/director
Since 1979, the Ute Indian Tribe, from the Uintah and Ouray Ute Reservation in Colorado, has been documenting Ute traditions and tribal concerns on video. Includes interviews, historical photographs, and other materials to illustrate this decisive period in Ute history. include: Ute Bear Dance Story - 1983, 15 minutes; NOOdtVweep/Ute Indian Land - 1986, 18 minutes. VHS. UTE.

THE VANISHING AMERICAN
Richard Dix; Indian pre-history is the prelude to the story of Reservation Indians who are cheated by the Indian Agent, even after the Indians go fight in WW I. 1926. Grades 7 & up. 110 mins, bxw. EG. Rental: $16. UMN.

1994 VIDEOBOOK
Beverly Singer; In this video diary, Singer, a documentarian, video artist and member of the Santa Clara Tewa Pueblo, has created an introspective examination of her life and her memories. 6 minutes. VHS. 1994. TWN.

VILLAGE OF NO RIVER
Barbara Lipton, Writer/Director/Producer; Yup'ik Eskimo film, 1935-1940 & 1979-1980, illustrating change and continuity in the culture. Discusses present problems and concerns. 1981. 58 minutes. 16mm/bxw. In English and Yup'ik with English subtitles. NM.

VILLAGES IN THE SKY
Shows life in the high mesa villages of the Hopi. Women are shown making baskets and pottery, and baking; also, dances. 1952. Grades 6 and up. 12 minutes, color. 16mm. Rental: UT, UA & UCLA.

A VIOLATION OF TRUST
Bill Jersey, Producer/director; Jim Belson, Producer/writer
Presents a conference, the American Indian International Tribunal, which indicts the U.S. government for its violation of trust relationship guaranteed by treaties. American Indian activists (Bob Gregory-Inupiat Eskimo; the late Philip Deere-Muscogee Creek; Oren Lyons-Onondaga; Janet McCloud-Tulalip-Duwamish; Dennis Banks-Ojibwa; and Matthew King-Oglala Sioux) forcefully articulate their aims and goals. 1982. 26 minutes. Video. CAT.

VISION DANCE
Henry Smith & Skip Sweeney, Directors
Showcases the talents of SOLARIS Dance Theatre & Lakota Sioux Indian Dancers drawn from nine reservations of the Lakota Nation in South Dakota. Lakota legends, myths and spirit qualities are juxtaposed with modern dance interpretations. 1982. 58 mins. Purchase: Video, $300; rental, $75. SOLARIS.

VISION QUEST
Dramatization of the spiritual experience required of 14 year old Western Indian boy before his acceptance as a man and a warrior. Shows phases of Indian life. 1961. 30 minutes, color. Grades 7 and up. 16mm rental, $19. PSU.

A VISIT TO WILD RICE COUNTRY
A visit with the Chippewa Indians shows that harvesting techniques have changed very little in a thousand years. 1975. Grades 1-6. 10 minutes, color. 16mm. Rebtal: $14.35. UMN.

VOICES FROM THE TALKING STICK
Narrated by Robert Davidson, John Yeltarzie & Woodrow Morrison
Story of the past, present and future told by the Haida people, maintaining the oral tradition of their culture, the narrators embark on a journey in four vignettes. Discusses how art, culture, the environment, and family are part of the Haida identity. Video, 20 mins. SH.

WALELA: LIVE IN CONCERT
Benefiting the Sovereign Nations Preservations Project, a non-profit provider of educational media benefiting Native Americans. With Rita Coolidge, Laura

Satterfield and Priscilla Coolidge. 60 mins. 2004. VHS, $24.95; DVD, $24.95. CD available, $24.95. MALKI.

WALKING IN A SACRED MANNER
Stephen Cross; Joseph Epes Brown, Consultant
Opens with photography by Edward S. Curtis and the words of many Native American orators, this film conveys the respect felt by Native Americans for the natural world. 1982. 23 minutes, color. Purchase: 16mm, $425; video, $340. Rental: UCT, UA & IU.

WALKING WITH GRANDFATHER
Phil Lucas, Producer/director
A series of six,15-minute programs; stories, drawing upon the rich oral traditions of North American Indian people of several tribes. Presents basic human values. Teacher's guide. 1988. Color. Video. Teacher's Guide, $12. Purchase: $325/series, $70/program. FOUR (Canada); GPN (U.S.)

WANAGI IS GONE
Bruce Baird
The uncovering of a massive ancient gravesite raises questions about the excavations of such sites and examines Indian traditional views as well as scientific significance. 1978. 30 minutes. 2 quad, 1 videotape, VHS. KUSD.

WANDERING SPIRIT SURVIVAL SCHOOL
Marvin Midwicki, Les Holdway, Christopher Wilson
Canadian children learn Indian legends, traditions, languages and crafts. 1978. 28 minutes. Video. Purchase: $27. NFBC.

WAR AGAINST THE INDIANS
CBC Production
Explores the impact of our native peoples through conversations, scenery, paintings, photos, drama, & music. 3 tapes, 60 mins. each. VHS, $25.99. ME.

THE WARPATH
Western expansion and the breaking of treaties which led to war between the setlers and Indians. 13 minutes, color. Video. Purchase: $69.95. FH.

WARRIOR CHIEFS IN A NEW AGE
Dean Curtis Bear Claw
As a young man in the late 1800's, Chiefs Plenty Coups & Medicine Crow had prophetic visions concerning the future of the Crow people. This protrait of the transitional leaders tells the story of how these visions helped lead the Crow Indian Nation into the 20th century. 28 minutes, color. Rental: $10. HO.

WARRIORS
Deb Wallwork, Producer
Honoring Native American veterans of the Vietnam War. 1986. 57 minutes, color. Video. Purchase: $56.95. NAPBC.

WARRIORS AT PEACE
Depicts the life of the Apache Indians in eastern Arizona with emphasis on their customs and traditions. 1953. 12 minutes, color. Grades 4 and up. Rental: UA, UCLA & UK.

WARRIORS SONG: POST TRAUMATIC STRESS DISORDER
Explores the legacy of post traumatic stress disorder from a Native American perspective as three therapists and one author share their personal stories. Focuses on healing challenges facing veterans of war. 1996. 60 mins. CHAR.

WASHOE
Veronika Pataky; Depicts the transition of the Washoe Tribe in Nevada from traditional customs to the 20th century. 1968. Grades 7 and up. 57 mins, bxw. 16mm. In Washoe with English narration. Rental: UW, UK, IU, UCLA & UMN.

THE WATER IS SO CLEAR THAT A BLIND MAN COULD SEE
New Mexico's Taos Indians believe that all life (plant and animal) is sacred and live without disturbing their environment. Lumber companies are trying to get permission from the Federal Government to lumber the Taos Indian area. 1970. 30 minutes, color. 16mm. Rental: PSU, UCT & IU.

THE WAY
Sandra Osawa (KNBC-TV); A sketch of Native American religion and its place in contemporary Indian life. Focuses on the Cherokee, Cheyenne & Ojibwa religious practices, and Indian spirituality. 1975. 28 mins. BYU-N.

A WAY OF LIFE
CBC Northern Services, Producer; The lifestyle of Henry Evaluarjuk, Inuit carver, who, with his family and two other families, chose to live on an uninhabited and secluded inlet on Baffin Island. 1983. 28 mins. NAPBC.

THE WAY WE LIVE
Four, 10-15 minute videotapes showing several aspects of traditional Yup'ik Eskimo culture. 1981. 60 mins. VHS. $24.95. KYUK.

WAY OF OUR FATHERS
Bradley Wright; Members of several northern California Indian tribes depict unique elements of a way of life as it flourished before the imposition of European culture. 33 minutes, color. Grades 9 and up. Video. Purchase: $95; rental: $50. UC. Rental: 16mm, $24.50. PSU.

THE WAY WEST: HOW THE WEST WAS LOST & WON, 1845-1893
Ric Burns, Director; PBS Production; Six-hour documentary chronicles the final decades of the American frontier from the Gold Rush to the Indian Wars at Wounded Knee. 360 mins. DVD. PBS, $71.49.

WE ARE ONE
Chet Kincaid, Producer; Eight, 20-minute programs about the life and culture of a Native American family in early 19th century Nebraska∧ Focuses on 13-year-old Ni'bthaska and his younger sister Mi'onbathin and on the daily rituals and rites of passage that make up their lives. 1986. NAPBC.

WE ARE A RIVER FLOWING
Nick Clark, Producer; An exploration of Northern Irish and Native American cultures. A 10 year-old girl from Belfast travels to the Pine Ridge Indian reservation as a part of a program for children of political turmoil. 1985. 28 mins. IN.

WE ARE STILL HERE
Leigh Podgorski, Writer, Director, Producer
Ron Mulvihill, Co-producer; Brian Wescott, Assoc. Producer
A documentary featuring Katherine Siva Saubel who inspired the telling of her people's history & culture, the Cahuilla Indian Tribe of Southern California. 57 mins. DVD. Under the Hill Productions (818) 881-5100. Website: underthehill productions.com. 2007. $25. MALKI.

WE ARE THESE PEOPLE
Featuring Will Sampson, this film is designed to foster an appreciation for the richness of Native American cultures & promote social support by reinforcing traditional values. 15 minutes. Video. Purchase: $245; rental: $45. SH. Rental: 16mm, $21. UMN.

WE BELONG TO THE LAND
Reaffirms the relationship between Indians & the land; and explores lifestyles in natural resource careers of forestry, game management, range management, & related fields. 30 minutes. Video. Purchase, $245; rental, $45. SH.

WE OF THE RIVER
Documentary chronicles the arrival and the emergence into the 20th century of the Yup'ik Eskimo people who have lived in this area for more than 12,000 years. 1985. 60 mins. VHS. $24.95. KYUK.

WE OWE IT TO OURSELVES & TO OUR CHILDREN
Video uses cartoon images and live action Native health educators to discuss the causes, symptoms, treatments, and prevention of HIV & STDs. 8 mins. VHS, $5. NNA.

WE PRAY WITH TOBACCO
Focuses on the traditional cultural & ceremonial uses of this herb. 1998. 60 mins. VHS. $24.95. ME.

WE REMEMBER
Raymond Yakeleya; The history of the Dene people as told by Yakeleya, a Slavey Indian, and some of the elders of the Slavey and Loucheau tribes of Canada - their past, present and thoughts for the future. 1979. In two parts. 1979. 30 mins. each. 16mm and video. Purchase or rental. CFMDC.

WE SHALL REMAIN
Chris Eyre & Sharon Grimberg, Directors
5 documentaries that establish Native history as an essential part of American history. Spans 300 years of U.S. history from the Native American perspective. 420 mins. DVD, 2009. $44.99. Amazon.com.

A WEAVE OF TIME
Susan Fanshel (Director), with John Adair & Deborah Gordon, Producers; Follows the lives of four generations of the Burnsides, a Navajo family from the Pine Springs community in Arizona on the Navajo reservation. In 1938 anthropologist John Adair filmed daily activities and artistic techniques; explores many aspects of Navajo life. 1986. 60 mins. b&w & color. 16mm, 3/4" (sales only) and 1/2" (sales & rentals). SH, DC.

WEAVERS OF THE WEST
Shows the Navajo's process of rug-making. 1954. 13 mins, color. Rental, IU.

WELCOME HOME: THE GRAND OPENING OF THE NATIONAL MUSEUM OF THE AMERICAN INDIAN Sept. 21, 2004. DVD. NMAI. $14.98.

WELCOME TO NAVAHO LAND
Paul Auguston; Navajo children's drawings are animated with the children telling the stories their work illustrates. Navajo songs. In two parts: Part I, 12 mins; Part 2, 20 mins. video. UMC.

WEMAWE-FETISH CARVING OF THE ZUNI PUEBLO
A documentary of ten exceptional carvers of the Zuni Pueblo and in their own words their view of what carving means to the artists. Video. 26 mins. SH.

THE WEST
Insignia Films & WETA; A 9-part series of American expansionism. Teaches middle school and high school students about Native American tribes, American pioneers & homesteaders, & steady expansion of the U.S. across the continent. Begins with the arrival of the first Europeans and extends into the 20th century. Includes audiotapes, curriculum package, a printed index. 1996. $295. PBS.

WESTWARD EXPANSION
Follows the chain of events leading to the Indian Removal Act, manifest destiny, the Civil War, and the Indian wars. 1969. 25 mins, color. Grades 6 and up. 16mm. Rental, $15.25. IU.

WHAT MORE CAN I DO?...A NURSE'S EXPERIENCE WITH A NAVAJO CANCER PATIENT Story of a community health nurse, who through persistence & sensitivity, learns to integrate her own values & perceptions with those of a Navajo cancer patient & his family. 1986. 27 minutes, color. 3/4" U-mat. Rental: $16. UMN.

WHEN THE WHITE MAN CAME
Describes life among the major tribes across the U.S. when the Europeans arrived in the late 15th Century. 13 minutes. Video. Purchase: $69.95. FH.

WHERE HAS THE WARRIOR GONE?
Explores the life of Ted Clay, a typical Navajo father living on a reservation in Utah. 13 mins. Grades 1-8. Rental. UK.

WHERE THE SPIRIT LIVES
Bruce Pittman, Director; music by Buffy St. Marie; The story of Amelia, a young Blackfoot Indian girl, and her plight to escape the horrors that white society has forced upon her. Set in 1937 amid the Canadian Rockies. Amelia was kidnapped from her reserve by the government and placed in an Indian Residential School. 1989. 97 mins. Purchase: $295. BE. Rental: $16. UMN.

WHITE MAN'S WAY
Christine Lesiak & NETV, Producer
Beginning in the late 1800s, an experiment that endeavored to transform the American Indian took place; the federal government built the U.S. Indian School in Genoa, Nebraska, a military-style school for Indian children from more than 20 tribes. Here they taught the white man's language, traditions, lifestyles and were forbidden to practice their own. 1986. 30 mins, color. Video. Purchase: $40. NAPBC & GPN. Rental: $16. UMN.

WHY COYOTE HAS THE BEST EYES
Discusses the importance of stories & storytelling within Indian culture. An elder of the Hupa tribe shares his knowledge of nature & heritage with Indian children on the Hoopa Reservation. Grades K-3. 10 minutes. $59.95. CB.

WHY DID GLORIA DIE?
NET, Producer; Depicts the tragic life of Gloria Curtis, a Chippewa woman who died of hepatitis at age 17. Deals with the adjustments one must make from reservation to urban life. 1973. 27 mins. IU & UMN.

WILD RICE: THE TAMING OF A GRAIN
Waterstone Films, Producer; Traces the history of wild rice, a Native North American food, and the first wild grain to be brought into cultivation in modern history. 1988. Grades 7 and up. 18 mins. Purchase: VHS, $250. SH, NDM.

WINTER ON AN INDIAN RESERVATION
A film about children on a forest reservation. 1973. Grades K-4. 11 mins, color. 16mm. Rental: $9. UCT.

RUSSELL & YVONNE WILLIER TAN A MOOSE HIDE
David E. Young, Trudy Nicks, Ruth McConnell, David Strom, Producers Russell & Yvonee are Woods Cree Indians from northern Alberta. Documents the entire production process. 1989. 30 mins. UADA.

WIND RIVER
Story about Washakie, Chief of the Shoshone. With Wes Studi & Russell Means. 1998. VHS, $16.99; DVD, $24.99. ME.

WINDTALKERS
About WWII Navajo codetalkers and their protection during the war. With Nicholas Cage, Adam Beach. 2002. 134 mins. DVD, $24.99. ME.

WINDS OF CHANGE: A MATTER OF CHOICE
Carol Cotter, Writer/producer; Examines the struggle of Native Americans to maintain individual identities & sovereign Indian nations within the U.S. Hopi tribal members provide insights into the personal side of acculturation & assimilation, focusing on the exodus of their youth to the cities. Original score by R. Carlos Nakai. Hosted by Hattie Kauffman & N. Scott Momaday. 1990. 58 minutes. Video. Purchase: PBS. Rental: $12. PSU; $16. UMN.

WINDS OF CHANGE: A MATTER OF PROMISES
PBS, Producer; Kiowa author, N. Scott Momaday explores the plight of the American Indian in today's society. A visit to the Onondaga of New York, the Navajo in Arizona, and the Lummi in Washington. 58 mins. PBS & CAN. Rental: $10. HO & PSU; $16. UMN.

WINDWALKER
Story of a dying Cheyenne Indian whose life spans three generations of Cheyenne life. 108 mins. VHS, $19.99. ME.

WINTER WOLF: LEARNING ABOUT NATIVE AMERICAN CULTURE
Follows a young Native American girl as she seeks to understand age-old conflicts between mankind & wolves. 30 minutes. Purchase: VHS, $49. GA.

WIPING THE TEARS OF SEVEN GENERATIONS
Gary Rhine, Producer/Director; Documentary that examines U.S. history through the Lakota Sioux perspective, with emphasis on The Wounded Knee Massacre and The Bigfoot Memorial Ride. In English & Lakota with English subtitles. 1992. Grades 4 and up. 57 mins. ME. KF & OY. HO & UMN.

WITH HEART & HAND
Oak Creek Films, Producer; Documentary on the history of Southwestern Native American art as seen through a selected group of contemporary practitioners & storytellers. 1993. Grades 7 and up. 30 mins. VHS, $25. ME.

WITHIN THE CIRCLE
Dance styles. Powwows. Blacklodge Singers. VHS. 60 mins. $19.95. WH.

WOMEN IN AMERICAN LIFE
Five videos depicting women's roles in American history. How westward expansion, immigration, the two world wars, and government legislation have affected the lives of Native Americans. 1990. KS.

WOMEN & MEN ARE GOOD DANCERS
Arlene Bowman; Cree language of an intertribal powwow song. 1994. VHS. Six minutes. Purchase: $125; rental, $50. TWN.

WOODEN BOX: MADE BY STEAMING & BENDING
Clyde B. Smith, Producer; Indians of the Northwest Pacific Coast developed woodworking; a specialty was steaming and bending of a single wooden slab to form a box. This film follows, carefully, every stage of making the Kwakiutl box. 1962. 33 mins. Purchase: 16mm, $660; video, $195. Rental: $50. UC.

WOODLAND INDIANS OF EARLY AMERICA
Roy A. Price, EdD; Authentic reconstructions and scenes in the eastern and Great Lakes regions provide settings for this study of Woodland Indian life (Chippewa) prior to European influence. Revised 1980 edition. 10 minutes. Grades K-6. IU, UMN & PSU.

WOODLAND TRADITIONS: THE ART OF THREE NATIVE AMERICANS
Features three Woodland Indian artists who tell in their own words how & why they create. Follows the artists step-by-step from the point of inspiration through the actual creation to the final work of art. 1984. 27 mins. UMN.

WOONSPE (EDUCATION AND THE SIOUX)
SD ETV; Explores the problems of Native American education. 1974. 28 mins. Video. Rental: $40. NAPBC.

WORDS & PLACE: NATIVE LITERATURE FROM AMERICAN SOUTHWEST
Denny Carr, Director; Larry Evers, Producer; Series of 8 videotapes (produced by the University of Arizona, in cooperation with KUAT (Tucson, 1976-77) traditional & modern Native American literature as told/written by individuals of various South-western tribes: Apache, Yaqui and Hopi people speak of their traditional philosophy, rituals & songs. Titles: "By This Song I Walk" (A Navajo Song); "Seyewailo: The Flower World" (Yaqui Deer Songs);

"The Origin of the Crown Dance" (An Apache Narrative) & "Ba'ts'oosee" (An Apache Trickster Cycle); "Iisaw" (Hopi Coyote Stories); "Natwaniwa" (A Hopi Philosophical Statement); "Running on the Edge of the Rainbow" (Laguna Stories & Poems); "Songs of My Hunter Heart" (Laguna Songs & Poems); "A Conversation With Vine Deloria, Jr." 18-51 mins. Video. Purchase: $150-$290 each, $1425/series. NR. Rentals: ATL.

WORLD OF AMERICAN INDIAN DANCE
Dan Jones & Randy Martin, Directors
Documentary highlights the many dance styles incorporated into the culture from various Native American tribes & nations. 60 mins. DVD, 2003. $18.73. Amazon.com.

A WORLD OF IDEAS WITH BILL MOYERS 1 & 2: LOUISE ERDRICH & MICHAEL DORRIS
Louise Erdrich and Michael Dorris, a Native American wife-husband team who write novels based on their heritage. 1. Discuss the values & difficulties of modern Native Americans, the concept of "ironic survival humor," and the Native American's ability to live on the land in harmony with nature. 29 mins., color. 2. Observe how alcoholism & despair have shattered the lives of many Native Americans. Grades 9 and up. Rental: video, $11 & $14. PSU & IU.

WOVEN BY THE GRANDMOTHERS: 19TH CENTURY NAVAJO TEXTILES
Narrated by performer Buffy Sainte-Marie
Captures the rhythms of Navajo life; explores the 19th century Navajo textiles collection of the Museum of the American Indian. 30 mins. DVD. $19.95. PMI.

YAQUI
Arizona artist Ted De Grazia narrates this filmic story of his paintings that depict the Yaqui Indian Ceremony. 1973. Grades 4 and up. 19 mins. DVD. 16mm. Rental: UA.

THE YAQUI CUR
D.W. Griffith, Director
A young Yaqui brave is converted to Christianity, and refuses to fight when his tribe is attacked by Zuni neighbors. He later redeems himself. 1913. 12 minutes, bxw. EG.

YESTERDAY'S CHILDREN
Skokomish youth interview two elders on the Skokomish Reservation on Hood Canal in western Washington State. The elders talk about their lives and changes they have experienced. Teacher's guide and lesson plans. 30 minutes, color. Grades 9 and up. Purchase: Video, $110. Rental, $25. DSP.

YESTERDAY, TODAY: THE NETSILIK ESKIMO
Gilles Blais
Traces the adaptation of the Netsilik from a migratory people to settlers in a government village. 1974. 58 mins. Grade 7+. EDC & UA. Video, $27. NFBC.

YOU ARE ON INDIAN LAND
Mort Ransen, Director
Report of a protest demonstration by Mohawk Indians of the St. Regis Reservation on the international Bridge between Canada and U.S. 1969. 36 mins., bxw. Purchase: Video, $27. NFBC.

YOU CHOOSE
Features Nathan Chasing His Horse. Designed to discourage youth from chewing or smoking tobacco. 20 mins. SH.

YOUR HUMBLE SERPENT: THE WISDOM OF REUBEN SNAKE
Written & directed by Gary Rhine
Portrait of the late American Indian political and spiritual leader, Reuben A. Snake, Jr., in which he speaks out on ecology, sacredness, intuitive thinking and the "Rebrowning of America." 1996. 60 mins. VHS. $29.95. ME & KF.

YUMA CROSSING
Docu-drama Quechan storyteller, Joe Homer, traces the history of the Yuma Crossing in southwestern Arizona from prehistorical times until the opening of the Ocean to Ocean Highway Bridge 1916. Grades 6 to adult. 28 mins. CHAR.

1987 YUP'IK DANCE FESTIVAL
Villages from the Yukon & Kuskokwim Delta sent dancers to Bethel to participate in one of the largest festivals in recent memory. 1988. 120 mins. DVD. $24.95. KYUK.

FILMSTRIPS & SLIDES

AKWESASNE RESERVATION SLIDE SHOW
A complete package of slide carousel, tape & script. Includes Iroquois legends, cornhusk dollmaking, Mohawk basketmaking, Iroquois Wampum & Cradleboards. 1984. 10 mins. Rental, $15. AM.

AMERICA'S 19th CENTURY WARS
Covers the Indian Wars. Includes teacher's guide. Grades 7-12. Six filmstrips/cassettes. $141. LL.

AMERICAN INDIAN FOLK LEGENDS
Myths and legends of the American Indian. The White Buffalo; The First Tom-Tom; First Winter, First Summer; The Four Thunders, two parts; How Fire Came to Earth. Six filmstrips; records or cassettes. $130. RH.

AMERICAN INDIAN LEGENDS
Four filmstrips: The Magic Food (Iroquois); The Basket Lady (Ute); When the People Lived in the Dark (Cherokee); Mountain Spirit Dance (Mescalero Apache). 4 cassettes, guide. $129. SVE.

AMERICAN INDIAN LEGENDS
Adventure stories showing many customs & rituals of American Indians. Aids vocabulary growth. Grades 3-5. Six filmstrips & cassettes, $119.00; six filmstrips (captioned), $55. RH.

AMERICAN INDIAN LIFE
Nine color filmstrips comparing and contrasting the ways of life of Indians in different sections of the U.S. Grades 1-6. CMC.

AMERICAN INDIAN NATURE LEGENDS
The wonders of nature and reverence for life are interwoven into these American Indian legends. Grades 3-6. 6 filmstrips, 6 cassettes. $132. TA.

AMERICAN INDIAN SONGS
A broad cross-section of American Indian folk songs from every region in the U.S. Filmstrip, cassette & book. $34.95. ALF.

THE AMERICAN INDIAN: A STUDY IN DEPTH
Dr. Ethel J. Alpenfeis traces the history & development of the American Indians over the past 400 centuries. Six color filmstrips & cassettes. PHM.

AMERICAN INDIANS AND HOW THEY REALLY LIVED
The heritage and history of American Indians are revealed. Indian crafts and customs are depicted. Includes Hopi and Navajo, Seminoles, Crow, Chinook, and the Iroquois tribes. Grades 3-7. 5 filmstrips. $50; $10, individual. TA.

AMERICAN INDIANS OF THE NORTH PACIFIC COAST
Their history, arts and crafts, myths and ceremonies. Grades 4-6. Six filmstrips/cassettes. $119. PHO.

AMERICAN INDIANS OF THE NORTHEAST
A study of the rise and fall of the Algonquin and Iroquois Indian empires, migrants from Asia to the Northeastern U.S. and southern Canada. Who they are, their history, religion, handicrafts. Grades 4-6. Six filmstrips/cassettes. $119. PHO.

AMERICAN INDIANS OF THE PLAINS
Presents the history, tribes, culture, arts & crafts, and religion of the Plains Indians. Grades 4-9. Six filmstrips/cassettes. $119. PHO.

AMERICAN INDIANS OF THE SOUTHEAST
A full-blooded Cherokee explains their life today. Reveals the life of the Southeastern Indian tribes from prehistoric times to the present. Grades 4-9. Six filmstrips/cassettes. $119. PHO.

AMERICAN INDIANS OF THE SOUTHWEST
A history-oriented presentation of the Pueblo tribes, examining their customs & languages. Grades 4-9. Six filmstrips/cassettes. $119. PHO.

AMERICAN MUSEUM OF NATURAL HISTORY— PHOTOGRAPHIC & FILM COLLECTION
Contains thousands of bxw photographs, color slides, and color transparencies of Native Americans; may be rented for reproduction, or purchased. For films, short footage segments may be available for reproduction upon payment of film/video duplication costs and use fees. AM.

ANCIENT ART OF THE AMERICAN WOODLAND INDIANS
David Penney (guest curator of the National Gallery) discusses ancient Woodland Indian artifacts and explains their cultural and aesthetic significance. Includes maps showing the Archaic, Woodland, and Mississippian period sites from which the artifacts came. 27 slides; audiocassette & text. 32 minutes. Free rental. NGA.

THE BATTLE OF THE LITTLE BIGHORN
A detailed study of the impact of Custer's defeat by the Sioux and Cheyenne. Grades 7-12. Filmstrip/cassette. $26. LL.

BATTLE OF THE LITTLE BIG HORN
A series of 78 slides or filmstrip depicting the Battle which took place in 1876. Includes a booklet, teacher's guide, cassette tape, map and poster. $36.60. SI.

CAHOKIA SLIDE PACKAGE
Seven sets of 5 slides each with a cassette tape and written text, illustrating the history of Indian culture at Cahokia, as well as the archaeological techniques used to explore and study the site. $2 per strip. CMM.

CLIMBING THE HILL
A specialized filmstrip developed for men and women who are interested in following the kind of leadership demonstrated by the old Dakota Holy Men. $15. AICRC.

CONTEMPORARY INDIAN & ESKIMO CRAFTS OF THE U.S.
74 full-color, 35mm slides with lecture text booklet illustrating the great variety of distinctive craft forms created by numerous contemporary Native American craftsmen. $50. TIPI.

CONTEMPORARY NATIVE AMERICAN MASKS
20 color slides. $30. ATL.

CONTEMPORARY SIOUX PAINTING
77 full-color & bxw, 35mm slides with lecture text booklet. Illustrates the historic development of expressive forms of painting created by Sioux artists during the past 200 years. $50. TIPI.

THE CORPS OF DISCOVERY: THE LEWIS & CLARK EXPEDITION
An exploration that had a significant impact on opening up Western America. Grades 7-12. Two filmstrips; cassette. $31. LL.

COSTUMES & MASKS OF THE SOUTHWEST TRIBES
Shows Navajo, Apache, Hopi & Pueblo ceremonial attire, including masks & costumes. 27 slides, no narration. 1977. $10. UCLA.

DAKOTA WAY & THE SACRAMENTS
Filmstrip, with cassette & guide. $10. AICRC.

THE DRUM IS THE HEART
Randy Croce, Producer; Focuses on the Blackfeet, Blackfoot, Blood and Peigan tribes that make up the Blackfoot Nation at their celebrations, speaking about their contemporary lives and traditional values. Filmstrip and slide set. Purchase and rental. BM.

THE EARTH KNOWERS: THE NATIVE AMERICANS SPEAK
Statements of Indian wise men who relied on religious and cultural experience to deal with technological and social reorganization. Guide. Grades 7-12. Filmstrip/cassette. $26. LL.

ESKIMOS OF ALASKA (ARCTIC LIFE)
Four color filmstrips providing a picture of the life of Eskimos in Alaska. Emphasis is placed on activities of children. Grades 4-8. CMC.

EVERYTHING NEW
Audiotape with slides tells the story of creation; traditional chants and songs include Eskimo, and North American Indian people. 1973. 19 mins. $10. UT.

EXPLORING & COLONIZING
In 4 parts. One filmstrip on the First Americans. 4 filmstrips, 4 cassettes, 28 skill sheets, guide. $89. SVE.

FAMOUS INDIAN CHIEFS
Examines eight famous Indian chiefs: Pontiac (Ottawa), Joseph Brant (Mohawk), Tecumseh (Shawnee), Black Hawk (Sauk), Osceola (Seminole), Chief Joseph (Nez Perce), Sitting Bull (Sioux), and Geronimo (Apache). Grades 4-6. Eight filmstrips; cassettes. $149. PHO.

THE FAR NORTH
Deals with the art & culture of the Alaskan Eskimo Aleuts and the Athapascan and Tlingit Indians, focusing on the art and ways of life. 1975. 48 color slides. Free rental. NGA.

THE FIRST AMERICANS
Six sound filmstrips which studies the major Indian tribes of the U.S. - their customs, culture and the land that belonged to them. Indians of the Northeast, Southwest, Great Lakes, Plains, Southeast, & Northwest. Grades 4-6. $132.00; $22 each. Available as a video. TA.

THE FIRST PEOPLE OF NORTH AMERICA: INDIANS AND INUIT
Presents an historical overview of the various native cultures existing in North America. The distinctive lifestyles of native peoples of differing geographic regions are examined with an emphasis on environmental factors. One filmstrip is devoted to the study of the Inuit of the Arctic. Six filmstrips; cassettes; one sound filmstrip guide with discussion questions; one script booklet. $160. UL.

FOLKTALES OF ETHNIC AMERICA
Includes The Brahman, The Tiger, and The Six Judges (Indian); and The Blind Boy & the Loon (Alaskan.) Grades 3-6. Six filmstrips or cassettes. $119. RH.

FRENCH & INDIAN WARS: ROAD TO THE AMERICAN REVOLUTION?
Reviews the outstanding developments which lead to independence, including the French and Indian War 1689-1762. Grades 7-12. Two filmstrips/cassettes. $31. LL.

GHOST DANCE TRAGEDY AT WOUNDED KNEE
66-slide program which brings the Wounded Knee incident of December of 1890 alive -- its historical and religious background, and the events of that infamous day when members of the Seventh Cavalry (Custer's old regiment) confronted the Sioux who had gathered at the Pine Ridge agency. Includes booklet, teacher's guide, cassette tape, and 2 maps. $36.60. SI.

GREAT AMERICAN INDIAN HEROES
Personal stories of leaders and chiefs who won the trust of their people and inspired their tribes in war and peace. 8 sound filmstrips: Tecumseh, Osceola, Black Hawk, Pontiac, Chief Joseph, Sitting Bull, Geronimo, and Joseph Brant. Grades 4-6. $176; $22. each. Available as a video. TA.

HOMES OF ANCIENT PEOPLE
A color filmstrip showing the ruins of ancient Indian homes at Mesa Verde, Canyon de Chelly, and Walnut Canyon. Grades 4-8. CMC.

HOW THE INDIANS DISCOVERED A NEW WORLD
Paleo-Indian transition from hunting to farming, trade and communications. Grades 6-12. Two filmstrips; cassettes. $33. RH.

HUNGER WALKS AMONG INDIANS
Indian Ministries Task Force on some of the work they have done to alleviate hunger problems of Native Americans. 85 slides; cassette. Rental, $5. NILB.

INDIAN AMERICANS: STORIES OF ACHIEVEMENT
Four filmstrip set which portrays, in illustrations and soundtracks, the contributions of four great Indian Americans: Hiawatha, Ely S. Parker, Washakie, and Pocahontas. Four records or cassettes; teacher's guide. WD.

INDIAN ART IN AMERICA: THE ARTS & CRAFTS OF THE NORTH AMERICAN INDIANS 51 slides. MAI.

INDIAN HERITAGE
Six color filmstrips that explore the life and culture of the American Indian. Includes: Americans Before Columbus, Indian Children, Indian Homes, Indian Celebrations, Indian Legends, Indians Who Showed the Way. Grades 2-6. $60; $10 each. TA.

AN INDIAN JESUS
Richard West, a Cheyenne Indian, is a Christian and an artist. Through his paintings, he helps us see Jesus through Native American eyes. 42 frames; color. Reading script and guide. Grades 3-12. $10. FP.

INDIAN LEADERS OF TOMORROW
American Indian Science & Engineering Society, Producer
For encouraging Native American youth to further their education & pursue professional careers. Slide/tape. Purchase: $150; rental: $40. SH.

INDIAN PAINTING
63 subjects (slide sets.) See MAI for ordering information.

INDIAN ROCK ART
Portrays one of the most ancient art forms in New Mexico, illustrating the timeless images of a mysterious art. 12 minute slide-tape program. Available for loan or purchase. MNM.

INDIAN SOVEREIGNTY--INDIAN TREATIES--INDIANS AND THE U.S. GOVERNMENT--INDIAN JURISDICTION FEDERAL INDIAN TRUST RELATIONSHIP
A series of five instructional programs of four filmstrips each, explaining the legal concepts and the history behind many of the present areas of controversy involving Indian tribes. Researched by the Institute for the Development of Indian Law, Inc. Includes response sheet master for practice quizzes; trainer's guide for each. Pre/Post tests, $6 per topic. $120 each; $480 per set. COOK.

INDIAN VALUES IN A NEW WORLD
Council Energy Resource Tribes, Producer; A teenage brother & sister are troubled by their uncertain future as high school graduation nears. Through their grandfather they meet various role models who apply traditional values in pursuing their post-secondary education. Slide/tape. Purchase: $150; rental: $40. SH.

INDIAN VILLAGE ARCHAEOLOGY
Documents the rediscovery of ancient Ozette by archaeologists. 1972. 88 color frames; teacher's guide and cassette. UW.

THE INDIAN WOMEN OF THE EARLY DAWN
Presents a philosophic view of the Indian woman. Video/slide show; 10-20 minutes. Purchase: $150; rental, $40. SH.

INDIANS OF HISTORIC TIMES
Slide sets on the following areas: Eskimo and Arctic (33 subjects); Northwest Coast (221 subjects); Woodlands and Northeast (118 subjects); Southeast (38 subjects); Plains and Plateau (446 subjects); Southwest (184 subjects); and, Far West (73 subjects). See MAI for ordering information.

INDIANS OF NORTH AMERICA
North America's native peoples from ancient to modern times. A series of five sound filmstrips: The First Americans; The Eastern Woodlands; The Plains; West of the Shining Mountains; and, Indians Today. 13-14 minutes each. Grades 5-12. $99.50. NGS.

INDIANS OF NORTH AMERICA
Six filmstrips: Indians of the Northeast, Southeast, Plains, Northwest Coast, Southwest, Far North. Grades 4-6. Includes 6 cassettes, guide. $179. SVE.

INDIANS: THE SOUTHWEST AND THE PLAINS INDIANS
The history of the American Indian people and how they live today. The Southwest Indians and The Sundance People. Two filmstrips, cassettes each, $48 each. Grades 6-8. RH.

INSIDE THE CIGAR STORE: IMAGES OF THE AMERICAN INDIAN
Focuses on the contradictory stereotypes of the American Indian which have been perpetuated by mass media and textbooks, and pleads for the replacement of the inaccurate images with the knowledge about contemporary American Indian people. Filmstrip & cassette. MRC.

IT IS WRITTEN IN THE HEARTS OF OUR PEOPLE
Views contemporary Indian youth and points out their guardianship of the land and customs passed down by the elders. Based around the words of Chief Seattle's 1853 speech. Video/slide show. 10-20 mins. SH.

LEGENDS OF THE MICMAC
The use of puppetry and mask-making in providing an instructive introduction to one of the earliest tribes to settle in North America. Grades 2-5. Four filmstrips, cassettes; teacher's guide. $95. RH.

THE LIFE OF THE AMERICAN INDIAN
Two sound filmstrips: The Eastern Woodlands and the Plains - explains how eastern tribes utilize their environment; and The Northwest Coast and the Southwest - Southwestern Indians farm arid lands and dance for rain, while Northwest Coast Indians fish and hold potlatches. 1977. 13-14 minutes each. Grades K-4. $50. NGS.

THE MAKE-BELIEVE INDIAN: NATIVE AMERICANS IN THE MOVIES
Gretchen Bataille and Charles L.P. Silet; Demonstrates the influence of early travel narratives, literature, the visual arts, and the wild west shows on the Native American image in the movies. Examples are drawn from silent films, serials, and contemporary feature films. 140 slides & carousel tray; audio-cassette; bibliography; script; suggestions. Purchase: $99; rental, $15/3 days. MRC.

THE MAN FROM DEER CREEK, THE STORY OF ISHI
A Yahi Indian in 1911, the last of his tribe, and the last to grow up without contact with American civilization. Grades 7-12. Two filmstrips, cassette. $41. LL.

THE MARMES MAN DIG
Louis and Ruth Kirk, Producer; An account of an archaeological discovery in eastern Washington State. The remains of early man in the Western Hemisphere. A graphic exposition of the techniques of archaeology. 1968. 61 color frames. $10. UW.

MICMAC: THE PEOPLE AND THEIR CULTURE
A kit of nine filmstrips provide an overview of Micmac culture--structures, transportation, hunting & fishing, recreation & domestic crafts. Grade 6. NOVA.

NAKED CLAY: 3,000 YEARS OF UNADORNED POTTERY OF THE AMERICAN INDIAN Features American Indian artistry in modelled ceramics. Includes a 72-page catalog. 90 slides. MAI.

NATIVE AMERICAN LITERATURE
Literature by and about the Native American: The writings of John Smith, Cotton Mather, William Byrd; the Noble Savage; Cooper's novels, Longfellow's "Hiawatha;" the characteristics of Indian literature; song, dance, myth & rituals; the Cherokee alphabet; Chief Joseph's oratory; the work of Momaday. Two 15-minute filmstrips. $49.95. FH.

NATIVE PEOPLES OF THE SOUTHWEST
The Heard Museum; A multi-media instructional materials program designed to develop concepts and skills by focusing on traditional and contemporary Native American cultures. Five levels of instructional units are: Level 2: Inde: The Western Apache, Apache family life; Level 3: Hopi: The Desert Farmers, Hopi communities; Level 4: Anasazi: The Ancient Villagers, archaeology and culture history of livin Pueblo Indians; Level 5: O'odham: Indians of the Sonoran Desert, cultural geography and human adaptations to the desert environment; Level 6: Dine: The Navajo, cultures change and evolve. Each program consists of color slides, audiocassettes, overhead transparencies, 30 student booklets and teacher's guide, and artifacts. $295 each. Complete set, $1472. CA.

NAVAJO CULTURAL FILMSTRIPS & SLIDES
Contains 23 filmstrips with cassettes ranging in time from five minutes to 20 minutes. All grades. See SAN for titles and prices.

NORTH AMERICAN ARCHAEOLOGICALSLIDE SET SERIES
Paleoindians of Northeastern U.S.: 64 slides, $120; Sloan Dalton Site: 68 slides, $122; Ohio Hopewell: 100 slides, $161; Mississippian Cultures: 85 slides, $151; The Southeastern Ceremonial Complex: 86 slides, $151; Early Caddoan Cultures: 78 slides, $140; Late Caddoan Cultures: 70 slides, $122; Spiro Mounds: 80 slides, $140; The Tunica Treasure: 79 slides, $140; Poverty Point: 63 slides, $120; The Art of the Taino: 59 slides, $110; Weeden Island Culture: 65 slides, $120; Fort Center: 54 slides, $102;The Gulf of Georgia: 80 slides, $140; Stone Sculpture of the Fraser River: 50 slides, $94; Ozette: 58 slides, $110; Hoko River Complex: 80 slides, $140; Mesa Verde: 86 slides, $152; Canyon de Chelly: 78 slides, $140; Chaco Canyon: 65 slides, $120; Native American Rock Art of the Colorado Plateau: 52 slides, $102. PR.

NORTHWEST COAST INDIAN TRADITIONS TODAY: A CONTEMPORARY LOOK AT REMNANTS OF A HERITAGE Louis and Ruth Kirk, Producers
Features dugout canoes hollowed from cedar logs, the netting and preparation of fish, baskets made from swamp and saltwater marsh grasses, etc. 1972. 90 color/sound frames. 15 minutes. Cassette/booklet. $25. UW.

OUR HEARTS BEAT AS ONE
Provides an historical view of tribes in Oregon. Two carousel slide trays; 160 slides. Grades 6-adult. Rental, $15. NILB.

OZETTE ARCHAEOLOGY
Louis and Ruth Kirk, Producers; Tells the story of the past and the present as it is being continually uncovered at the Ozette Archaeological Dig, Cape Alava, Washington State. Summarizes the resources available to the Makah Indians living on the Northwest Coast of the Olympic Peninsula. 1979. 153 color; sound frames. 21 minutes. Cassette - booklet. $25. UW.

THE PAINTINGS OF CHARLES BIRD KING
King painted many prominent Amerian Indians. 34 slides. $31. SI.

A POINT OF PARTNERSHIP
Depicts some of the work of the National Indian Lutheran Board. All ages. 12 minutes. Filmstrip/cassette. NILB.

PRE-COLUMBIAN ARCHAEOLOGICAL SITES – NORTH AMERICA
Includes the following sites: Betatakin, AZ (17 slides); Sand Island, UT (8 slides); Hovenweep, UT (33 slides); Mesa Verde, CO (47 slides); Aztec Ruins, NM (19 slides); Salmon Ruins, NM (6 slides); Chaco Canyon, NM (79 slides); El Morro, NM (4 slides); Canyon de Chelly, NM (35 slides); Bandelier, NM (29 slides); Pecos, NM (9 slides); Gran Quivira, NM (19 slides); Quari, NM (5 slides); Abo, NM (4 slides); Gila Cliff Dwellings, NM (23 slides); Tonto Ruins, AZ (14 slides); Casa Grande, AZ (9 slides); Tuzigoot, AZ (10 slides); Montezuma's Castle, AZ (6 slides); Walnut Canyon, AZX (2 slides); Wupatki, AZ (9 slides); Cahokia Mounds, IL (6 slides); Sonotobac Mound, IN (1 slide). $2.45 ea. in sets; $2.95 ea. ordering individually. HLM.

PRE-COLUMBIAN CULTURES
A series of slide sets. United States (231 subjects); Canada (three subjects). All archaeological specimens are of pottery. MAI.

PUEBLO INDIANS OF NEW MEXICO
Examines the history & culture of the Pueblo Indians. Includes images of the people, ancient and modern villages, crafts and ways of life many of which are drawn from the Museum of New Mexico's collection of historic photographs & rare old hand-tinted glass slides. 17-minute slide-tape program. Available for loan or purchase. MNM.

THE PURITAN EXPERIENCE: MAKING A NEW WORLD
Life in Massachusetts--the Higgin's family daughter, a captive of the Indians for a while, resents the Puritans' treatment of the Indians, and challenges strict Puritan authority. Grades 7-12. Two filmstrips, cassettes. $60. LL.

READ ALONG AMERICAN INDIAN LEGENDS
Stimulates reading interest with tales of Indian lore. Vocabulary-building captions. Program guide. Grades 2-5. Six filmstrips, cassettes. $119. RH.

THE SACRED PIPE
A filmstrip of the Sacred Pipe, the central instrument of the Dakota religion. Gives the proper understanding of the origin and use of the Pipe. $15. AICRC.

SANDSTONE COUNTRY: THE CANYONS & INDIANS OF SOUTHWEST
Louis and Ruth Kirk, Producers; Arizona & Utah apartment-dwelling Indians before Columbus, reveals the ancient cities and the geological history. Teacher's guide. 1970. 70 color frames. $10. UW.

SICA HOLLOW
An historical and religious filmstrip. One of the old story of the flood--localized on the Sisseton-Wahpeton Reservation. $15. AICRC.

THE SIOUX
Black Elk's words from a broken treaty. Study of the Sioux, past and present, are analyzed to show the Indian in confrontation with cultural crisis & identity loss. Includes a script. Grades 7-12. Filmstrip & cassette. $30. LL.

SIX NATIVE AMERICAN FAMILIES
The Life of a Mohawk Family; The Life of Sioux Family; The Life of a Seminole Family; The Life of a Navajo Family; The Life of a Pueblo Family; The Life of a Kwakiutl Family. Grades K-6. 6 filmstrips, 6 cassettes, guide. $149. SVE.

THE SOUTHWEST: EARLY INDIAN CULTURES: THE SPANISH HERITAGE: THE EARLY ANGLO PERIOD: THE MODERN SOUTHWEST
The influence of the desert environment on the culture and lifestyle of the Indians. 4 sound filmstrips, two cassettes. Script/guide. $90. UL.

SOUTHWEST INDIAN FAMILIES
A day in the lives of four real families from four different tribes: Navajo, Zuni, Apache & Hopi. Grades 1-3. Four filmstrips, four cassettes; four filmstrips/captioned. $40. PHO.

SUBMULOC SHOW/COLUMBUS WOHS
Represents the theme of turning back the history of the Columbian legacy. 36 color slides. $60. ATL.

SURVIVAL: HISTORY OF NORTHWEST INDIAN TREATY FISHING RIGHTS
A slide presentation produced by the Point No Point Treaty Council. Recounts the history of Indian fishing before the arrival of white people in the Northwest, and of treaties & legal decisions culminating in the 1974 Boldt Decision. Teacher's guide and student handouts and worksheets. 20 minutes. Grades 4-adult. Purchase: $195; rental, $30. DSP.

TALES OF THE PLAINS INDIANS
Gives insight into the religion, culture, and relationship to nature of the Blackfeet, Sioux, Pawnee & Cheyenne tribes. Grades 3-5. Six filmstrips, cassettes. $119. RH.

TEXAS INDIANS: THE ALABAMA-COUSHATTA INDIANS
Presents the early history and present customs of the Alabamas and the Coushattas who have lived together in the Piney Woods of east Texas. 1971. 8 minutes. Filmstrip, $20; Slide set, $40; THE INDIAN TEXANS - Tribes of the 20th century who live together in Texas. The Dallas Intertribal Council's annual ceremonials are highlighted in this program. 1971. 7 minutes. Filmstrip, $25; slide set, $45; THE TIGUA INDIANS: OUR OLDEST TEXANS - Discusses the early (1680) settlement of the Tigua Pueblo Indians of Ysleta, near present El Paso, Texas, & the progress they are making through the Texas Commission on Indian Affairs to become completely self-sufficient and financially independent. 1971. 8 minutes. Filmstrip, $20; slide set, $25. UT-ITC.

TRIBAL ARCHIVES
In two parts: Part 1: An Introduction - Discusses what an archives is, what you need to establish one, and how you will benefit from an archives program. Slide/tape program; 110 slides; 1983, 13 minutes. Part 2: Getting Started - A slide/tape program. Includes a booklet containing script, a bibliography, a glossary, and a list of resources. 1986.. SI-OMP.

TWO EAGLES LEGEND
This filmstrip is a morality story; a young man, betrayed by his friend, is saved by two young eagles. (In Dakota tradition, the Eagle is always a symbol of God's presence.) $15. AICRC.

UNLEARNING INDIAN STEREOTYPES
Works with myths and images from books and television. 15 minutes. Grades 3-6. Filmstrip, cassette. Rental, $5. NILB.

A VISIT TO THE FATHER
Authentic Navajo origin legend in four filmstrip episodes. Translated and illustrated by Navajo artist Auska Kee. All ages. $67.50 with cassettes. CEN.

VOICES FROM THE CRADLEBOARD
Slide presentation of traditional child rearing practices, such as the use of legends & the cradleboard, which emphasizes the importance of children in past and present Indian societies. 30 minutes. Grades 9-adult. Purchase, $185; rental, $30. DSP.

WHITE MAN AND INDIAN: THE FIRST CONTACTS
Depicts the first explorers and their halting, initial contacts with the Indians of Eastern America. Grades 7-12. Two filmstrips, cassettes. $31. LL.

WOLF GIRL
This filmstrip is a morality story. In non-Indian myth, the Wolf is always an evil animal. Indian people, however, have discovered the wolf to be a friend and a helpful animal. $15. AICRC.

WOMEN OF SWEETGRASS, CEDAR & SAGE: CONTEMPORARY ART BY NATIVE AMERICAN WOMEN
20 color slides. ATL.

RECORDINGS

AH-K' PAH-ZAH
Douglas Spotted Eagle & Dan James; Dan James on synthesizer and Douglas Spotted Eagle on Native American flute. 60 mins. Cassette, $9.98. CAN.

AKA GRAFITTI MAN
John Trudell (Santee); A unique blend of poetry & music by songwriter/poet John Trudell. Cassette, $10; CD, $17. OY & ICC.

ALASKAN ESKIMO SONGS AND STORIES
Lorraine D. Koranda; illustrated by Robert Mayokok
42 stories and songs on one LP. Sung in Eskimo and told in English. 1971. 50 page booklet. UW.

ALL ONE EARTH: SONGS FOR THE GENERATIONS
Performed by Michael J. Caduto
A new dimension to the lessons of the Keepers books12 songs; Ten original compositions. 47 minutes. 1993. Cassette, $9.95; CD, $14.95. FUL.

ALLUVIA
performed by Evren Ozan; Flute playing. CD, $18. 2007. MB.

AN AMERICAN INDIAN
Kiowa-Apache flute player Andrew Vasquez presents his contemporary vision of tradition by combining musical styles of yesterday and today. CD, $14.98; Cassette, $9.98. MCP.

AMERICAN INDIAN DANCES

Recordings of the following Indian dances: Rabbit Dance, Sun Dance and Omaha Dance (Sioux); Devil Dance (Apache); Eagle Dance (San Ildefonso); Harvest Dance and Rain Dance (Zuni); Squaw Dance (Navajo); War Dance and Dog Dance (Plains); Snake Dance and Pow-Wow Dance (Flathead). LP. $9.98. VIP & CAN.

AMERICAN INDIAN GOSPEL/CHRISTIAN MUSIC

American Indian Hymn Singers - Christian Hymns in Creek - Arbor Shade Singers -Vol. 1: What a Beautiful Day, Vol. 2: Nizhonie Christmas, Vol. 3: Let It Shine; The Chinle Galileans; Country Gospel Singers; Johnny Curtis - Vol. 1: Apache Country Gospel Songs, Vol. 2: Leavin' This Reservation, Vol. 3: Johnny Curtis - With Apache Gospel Sounds, Vol. 4: In Loving Memories, Vol. 5: Spirit of God, Vol. 6: In Loving Memories; Larry Emerson - Vol. 1: Larry Emerson and Skyward -10 gospel songs, Vol. 2: Now is the Tim; The Gospel Light Singers -Volume One - 12 songs, Vol. 2: Jesus Died for Me Long Ago, Vol. 3: To My Mansion in the Sky, Vol. 4: Life's Railway to Heaven, Vol. 5: I'm Bound for that City, Vol. 6: If That Isn't Love; Harvey Family: Vol. 1: The Curtis Harvey Family, Vol. 2: Let's Tell the World; Murphy Platero: Murphy Platero and the Morning Star Band-When Shall It Be; Smith Family: Smith Family Gospel Singers with The Thunders. Cassettes. $7.98 each. CAN.

AMERICAN INDIAN LANGUAGES

Western Languages: Apache Language Program (4 audio tapes, 137 pp workbook; CD available), $74.95; Cheyenne Language Program (2 audio tapes, 57 pp. workbook), $39.95; Shoshone Indian Words, $14.95; Learning Through Hopi Songs CD, $15.95; Western Delaware (3 audio tapes & 21 lesson workbook), $59.95; Leni Lenape CD-ROM, $15.95; Kiowa Language Sampler & legend CD, $15.95; Lakota Language Programs - Introductory Lakota (15 audio cassettes with 87 pp. workbook; also available in CD format), $224.95; Everyday Lakota (audio tape & dictionary), $29.95; Navajo Language Programs - Breakthrough Navajo (audio-cassette with 234 pp. workbook), $49.95; Speak Navajo (two audio cassettes with 167 pp. workbook), $49.95; Southeastern Languages: Caddo Language Program (Nusht'uhti?ti Hasinay, CDs. $34.95); Cherokee Phrase Cards (with syllabary pronunciation tape), $12.95; Introduction to Cherokee (2 tapes plus 50-page workbook & glossary), $35.95; Cherokee Dictionary - Durbin Feeling, $18.95; Choctaw Language Program - Choctaw Language Sampler (audiotape with booklet), $19.95; Introduction to Choctaw (two audio cassettes, $49.95, CD, $54.95 with 60 pp. workbook); The Lord's Prayer & 23rd Psalm - read in Choctaw by Charlie Jones (audiocassette with both printed in Choctaw), $9.95; Conversational Choctaw (CD, $15.95); Choctaw for Kids (6 audio cassettes with 120 pp. booklet, $59.95); Choctaw Legends (CD with booklet, $19.95); Choctaw Singing (audio cassette with booklet, $17.95; Introduction to Chickasaw (audio cassette with workbook), $54.95; Chickasaw Language Programs - Let's Talk Chickasaw - CD, $15.95; Chickasaw Language Sampler (audio tape with phrase booklet), $17.95; Chickasaw Talking Dictionary (CD-ROM with over 7,000 words), $34.95; Muskogee Creek Language Program: Introduction to Muscogee (Creek) Language (audio cassette, $49.95; CD, $54.95); Muskogee Creek Sampler Program (audiocassette, $17.95, CD & booklet, $19.95). VIP.

AMERICAN INDIAN LEGENDS

Recorded in both Indian & English. Cherokee: "The Rabbit & the Bear," & "Why the Hog's Tail is Flat" (Sam Hider, storyteller), $12.95; Choctaw: "Choctaw Creation Story," 'The Little People," & "Why the Rabbit's Tail is Short," (Charlie Jones - storyteller), $12.95; Kiowa: "The Little Eagle" (EvaLu Ware Russell, storyteller), $12.95. VIP

AMERICAN INDIAN MEDICINE

Rolling Thunder, a Medicine Man, describes the difficulties Indians have had in preserving their philosophy and culture, while being captives in the white man's society. 60 minutes. cassette. BSR.

AMERICAN INDIAN MUSIC FOR THE CLASSROOM

Dr. Louis Ballard sings 27 songs of 22 Indian tribes in the authentic style of the tribal musician. He analyzes the song content so that the listener acquires an understanding of both the musical and cultural meaning of Indian vocal music. 4 LPs or cassettes. Includes a study guide, 20 study photographs, a complete set of spirit masters, and a bibliography of books for students who wish to pursue a further study of Indian cultures. Grades 1-12. $75. CAN.

THE AMERICAN INDIAN ORAL HISTORY COLLECTION

Dr. Joseph H. Cash & Dr. Herbert Hoover, General Editors

In two volumes, the series contains 30 interviews on audiocassettes conducted by historians and anthropologists for students and scholars. The tapes offer a broad account of the experience of being an Indian, from recollections of 19th-century Indian-white relations and indigenous Indian culture to the experience of today's young Indians struggling to survive in White America without sacrificing their ethnic identity. Includes the following: Volume I - The Sundance (Crow); Medicine Men and Women I & II (Cheyenne River Sioux, Crow and Rosebud Sioux); The Buffalo Hunt I & II (Crow); Kinship, I, II & III

(Crow); Legends (Chippewa); The Drum Society (Mille Lacs Chippewa); Little Bighorn; The BIA (Oglala Sioux); The BIA (Rosebud Sioux); Indian Students (Oglala Sioux); Life in 1900 (Cheyenne River Sioux). Volume II - A. Traditional Ways of Life: Religion (Rosebud Sioux , Winnebago & Northern Cheyenne, 5 tapes); Traditional Foods (Cheyenne River Sioux); Traditional Social Customs (Sisseton & Yankton Sioux); Legends (Spokane). B. Indian Leaders and Uprisings: Crazy Horse and Struck-by-the-Ree (Sioux); The Minnesota Uprising of 1862, I&II (Sioux). C. Contemporary Indian Problems: The City Vs. The Reservation (Spokane, Winnebago, Sioux); Problems of the Reservation (Crow Creek Sioux); Problems of the Urban Indian (Yankton Sioux & Winnebago); India Schools (Oglala Sioux). 30 minutes each. $15 each; Either Volume (15 tapes), $190; $350 per set (30 tapes). NR.

AMERICAN INDIAN SONGS

Dawley/McLaughlin; A broad cross-section of American Indian folk songs from every region in the U.S. LP or cassette. $9.95; book, $4.95. ALF.

AMERICAN INDIAN STAR TALES: THE FEATHER MOON

Stories told by Lynn Moroney about the sky, the stars, and the planets. Music is composed & performed on a Plains Indian flute. Cassette, $10. CH.

AMERICAN INDIANS IN FACT AND SYMBOL

In two parts by Dr. Joseph Henderson: Part 1: The American Indian and the Jungian Orientation --Dr. Henderson offers an historical sketch of the white man's attitudes and actions toward American Indians. Part 2: The American Indian--A Sioux Shaman -- Dr. Henderson speaks of Black Elk, who at the age of nine had a vision that later evolved into the seven secret rites of the soul. Three hours, two tapes. BSR.

ANAPAO

Indian tales. Spoken and written by Jamake Highwater. Cassette. $10.98. FR.

ANCESTRAL VOICES

R. Carlos Nakai and William Eaton

Flute & guitar combo with songs. $11.50. CAN & CMM.

THE ANGRY INDIANS

Documentary on American Indian Conference at the University of Chicago in 1961, whose objectives were to get Indians from all parts of the U.S. together so that they could discuss their common problems and determine what they want from the U.S. Government and people. 26 minutes. Cassette. AUDIO.

ANIMAL STORIES (in English)

Stories collected from the Navajo, Cheyenne, Hopi, Kwakiutl, Tlingit, and Iroquois. Narrated by Gerald Hausman. 1 cassette (60 minutes), $10.95. AUDIO.

ANTHOLOGY OF NORTH AMERICAN INDIAN & ESKIMO MUSIC

A two-record set, compiled by Michael I. Asch, of the music of many of the tribes of North America, including: music of the Plains Indians; Indians of the Southwest; Northwest Coast Indians; Sub-Arctic; Arctic; Northeast Indians; and Southeast Indians. LPs. $19.96. FR.

APACHE INDIAN RECORDS & TAPES

Apache-Cassadore; Remembering Murphy Cassa, 2 Vols.; Songs of the Arizona Apache-San Carlos & White Mountain; Songs of the White Mountain Apache. Cassettes. $7.98 each. CAN.

THE ARCHIVE OF FOLK CULTURE-NATIVE AMERICAN RECORDINGS

Contains the following material: 1) The Jesse Walter Fewkes' 1890 cylinders of Passamaquoddy Indians--earliest field recordings made anywhere in the world; 2) More than 3,500 cylinders assembled between 1895 and 1940 by Francis Densmore and others for the Smithsonian Institution, Bureau of American Ethnology; 3) Several hundred discs and tapes 1940 to 1952 by Willard Rhodes for the Bureau of Indian Affairs; and 4) numerous other collections. The following recordings were edited by William N. Fenton ($8.95 each): Songs From the Iroquois Longhouse; Seneca Songs From Coldspring Longhouse. The following were recorded and edited by Frances Densmore ($8.95 each): Songs of the Chippewa; Songs of the Sioux; Songs of the Yuma, Cocopa, and Yaqui; Songs of the Pawnee and Northern Ute; Songs of the Papago; Songs of the Nootka & Quileute; Songs of the Menominee, Mandan and Hidatsa. The following songs were recorded and edited by Willard Rhodes ($8.95 each): Northwest (Puget Sound); Kiowa; Indian Songs of Today; Delaware, Cherokee, Choctaw and Creek; Great Basin: Paiute, Washo, Ute, Bannock, Shoshone; Plains: Comanche, Cheyenne, Kiowa, Caddo, Wichita, Pawnee; Sioux; Navajo; Apache; Pueblo: Taos, San Ildefonso, Zuni, Hopi; Omaha Indian Music: Historic Recordings from the Fletcher/LaFlesche Collection, $10.95. Copies of most of the Archive's recorded collections can be ordered from: The Archive of Folk Culture, Library of Congress, Washington, DC 20540. (202) 707-5510. Photocopies of folklore & ethno-musicology material whnot protected by copyright or other restrictions may not be ordered.

ARCHIVES OF TRADITIONAL MUSIC
Dorothy Sara Lee; Maintains extensive recorded material on the North American Indian. Indiana University, Morrison Hall, Bloomington, IN 47405 (812) 335-8632

AS LONG AS THE GRASS SHALL GROW
Peter LaFarge sings 13 of his own songs. A 12-page brochure includes words and transcriptions of songs. LP. $9.98. CAN.

AUTHENTIC INDIAN LEGENDS
Each program has an Indian-language version on one side and an English version on the other. The Little Eagle (Kiowa), Creation, Little People, and Rabbit's Short Tail (Choctaw); The Rabbit and the Bear, and Why the Hog's Tail Is Flat (Cherokee); Raccoon (Passama-quoddy). One cassette each (30 minutes). $11.95 each. AUDIO.

AUTHENTIC INDIAN MUSIC #1 & 2
Field recorded in North America in mid 1900s. 2 Cassettes. $9.95 each. VIP.

BASIC MEDICAL NAVAJO
An elementary course for physicians & nurses who treat Navajo speakers. Each section consists of dialogues, vocabulary, questions & instructions, grammatical explanations & notes. 1 cassette (60 minutes) and 141 pp. text, $39. AUDIO.

BEARHEART: VISION QUEST
Marcellus (Bearheart) Williams; Journey to the Seven Directions with Lakota medicine man Marcellus Williams. Cassette, $6. ZANGO.

BEAUTIFUL BEYOND: CHRISTIAN SONGS IN NATIVE LANGUAGES
Anthology of hymns & songs.NMAI Press & Smithsonian/Folkways. $15.

BEGINNING CHEROKEE
Ruth Bradley Holmes & Betty Sharp Smith
A set of two cassettes for learning the Cherokee language. 3 hours, 332-page text. $39. CAN, CH & AUDIO.

BEGINNING PASSAMAQUODDY
Provides basic phrases, structures and vocabulary needed to speak Passamaquoddy in everday situations. Includes one cassette for basic phrase work, encyclopedia-type reference text with 3 cassettes for a spoken presentation of the material of the program, and one cassette for mastering the vowel sounds. 3.5 hours, 50 pp. phrasebook & 112 pp. reference text, and vowel sounds booklet. $59.50. AUDIO.

BEGINNING TLINGIT
A sytematic & structural introduction to Tlingit grammar with phrases & conversations for everyday use. 2 cassettes (two hours) and 208 pp. spiral-bound text in album. $55. AUDIO.

BLACK HILLS DREAMER, JOURNEY TO THE SPIRIT WORLD
Buddy Red Bow (Lakota). CD. $16.98. OY.

BLACK LODGE SINGERS: KID'S POW-WOW SONGS
The Black Lodge Singers of White Swan, Washington are one of the leading powwow drums in North America. Cassette, $6; CD, $9.15. ZANGO.

BLACKFEET GRASS DANCE SONGS
11 grass dance songs sung by Allen White Grass, Pat Kennedy & Stanley Whiteman. Recorded at Browning, Montana, July 2, 1960. Cassette/LP, $10. VIP & AIS.

BLACKFEET RECORDS & TAPES
Blackfeet Powwow Songs; Carlson Singers; From the Land of the Blackfeet (LP); Hand Game Songs - Thomas Big Spring and Floyd Heavy Runner; Heart Butte Singers, 2 Vols.; Kicking Woman Singers, 5 Vols.; Little Corner Singers - Powwow Songs; Spotted Eagle Singers - Intertribal Powwow Songs; Two Medicine Lake Singers, 2 Vols.; Young Grey Horse Society, 2 Vols.; Black Lodge Singers - Powwow Songs, 6 Vols. Cassettes, $7.98 each. CAN.

BLACKSTONE SINGERS - POW-WOW SONGS
Live recordings by the Blackstone Singers (Cree from Saskatchewan, Canada) at the 1991 Ft. Duchesne (Utah) Powwow. 57 minutes. Cassette, $6. CAN.

THE BLESSING WAYS
Sharon Burch (Navajo) and A. Paul Ortega (Mescalero Apache) sing of Navajo culture, especially about women and their ways. Cassette, $10. FTW.

BLOODY KNIFE: CUSTER'S FAVORITE SCOUT
Ben Innis; edited by Richard E. Collin
Audio book tells the story of Bloody Knife. 2 Cassette, 245 pp. $14.98. MCP.

BOAT PEOPLE
R. Carlos Nakai; Musical satire that takes a pointed look at the 500 years since Columbus. Nakai on the cedar flute and trumpet. Accompanied by Larry Yanez on the guitar and bass. 38 minutes. Cassette/CD. CAN.

BOOTS & SADDLES
Book-on-cassette depicting Elizabeth (Libbie) Custer's experiences during her stay in the Dakotas with her husband General George Armstrong Custer. Edited from the original 1886 edition. 2 cassettes, $14.98. MCP.

BREAKTHROUGH NAVAJO
Self-study audiocassette/book programs developed by Alan Wilson to give instruction in the Navajo language and to provide a deeper understanding of the culture & lifestyle of the Navajo. An Introductory Course: 2 cassettes (3 hours) & 234 pp. text, $49; Speak Navajo: Internediate: 2 cassettes (2 hours) & 180 pp. text, $49. AUDIO.

BUDDY RED BOW
Two albums: "Black Hills Dreamer" - country western songs; and "Journey to the Spirit World". Cassettes, $10 each. CAN and FWT.

BUFFALO BIRD WOMAN - MY LIFE ON THE NOTHERN PLAINS (1840-1890)
Narrative by Buffalo Bird Woman tells how the Hidatsa lived on the Missouri River in western ND during the late 1800's. 2 cassettes, $14.98. MCP.

BUFFALO SPIRIT
Original compositions by Fernando Cellicion. Cassette. $4.50. GDA.

BURNING SKY: CREATION
From the Dine of northern Arizona. Aaron White on guitar and Kelvin Bizahaloni on Native American flute with Michael Bannister on percussion. 39 minutes. Cassette, $6. CAN.

CADDO TRIBAL DANCES
4 turkey dance songs, 4 duck dance songs, 4 green corn dance songs, 4 bell dance songs, 2 fish dance songs, and 2 stirrup dance songs sung by Mr. & Mrs. Houston Edmonds, Mr. & Mrs. Lewis Edmonds, and Lowell Edmonds. Recorded at Anadarko, Oklahoma, March 1955. $9.95. VIP.

CAHUILLA CREATION STORY
Malki Museum; Robert Levi as the voice of Mukat; Interview with Dr. Katherine Siva Saubel & Dr. Lowell J. Bean. CD. $18. MALKI.

CANADIAN INDIAN RECORDS & TAPES
Assiniboine Jr. - 10 powwow songs recorded in Manitoba, $9.98; Elk's Whistle - 13 powwow songs recorded in Saskatoon, Saskatchewan, $9.98; Dakota Hotain Singers, Vol. 1 - 14 songs from Sioux Valley, Manitoba, and Vol. 2 - songs of the Dakota, $9.98 each; Whitefish Bay Singers - powwow songs by a popular Ojibway drum from Whitefish Bay, Ontario, $9.98; Chiniki Lake Singers (from Morley, Alberta) 4 Vols., $7.98 each; Vic Thunderbird and the Thunderchild Singers; Old Agency Drummers-13 grass dance & chicken dance songs from the Blood Reserve, Standoff, Alberta, $7.98. Cassettes. CAN.

CANYON TRILOGY
Carlos Nakai with his Native American flute, journeys to the past, records in a canyon to simulate the ambience of the now abandoned cliff-dwelling villages. Cassette, $12. CAN & CH.

CARRY THE GIFT
R. Carlos Nakai & William Eaton; The harmonies of Nakai's flute with Eaton's guitar. 59 minutes. Cassette/CD. CAN.

CEREMONIAL SONGS & DANCES OF THE CHEROKEE
Kevin Lewis sings 50 songs accompanied by a gourd or drum. 2 vols. Cassette, $11 ea. CAN, CMM, MFP & CH.

CHANGES
Native American flute music by R. Carlos Nakai. 40 mins. Cassette/CD. CAN.

CHEROKEE CEREMONIAL SONGS
Two cassettes. $9.95 each. VIP.

CHEROKEE LANGUAGE WORKBOOK & INSTRUCTIONAL CASSETTE TAPE Prentice Robinson. Booklet, 30 pp. and one cassette, $25. CH.

CHEYENNE LEGENDS
Eugene Blackbear, Sr. CD, booklet. $15.95. VIP.

CHEROKEE LEGENDS I
Kathi Smith. 30 minute cassette. $9. CH.

CHEYENNE NATION
The music of Joseph Fire Crow...traditional flute and contemporary instrumentation promoting the unity of the Cheyenne people. CD, $14.98; Cassette, $9.98. MCP.

6 CHEYENNE WARRIOR SONGS; 7 CROW GRASS DANCE SONGS
$9.95. VIP.

CHICKASAW
Gregg Howard. Language course containing words, phrases, and sentences around the themes of everyday living. Also includes recipes of authentic dishes; legends & bibliography of information on the Chickasaw Nation. 1994. 2 cassettes & 95-page book. $39.95. AUDIO.

CHICKASAW SOCIAL SONGS & STOMP DANCES
Chickasaw Nation Dance Troupe. CD, $15.95; or audio cassette, $10.95. VIP.

CHICKEN SCRATCH - POPULAR DANCE MUSIC OF THE INDIANS OF SOUTHERN ARIZONA
Chicken Scratch is a couples' social dance passed down from generation to generation among the desert tribes of Southern Arizona. The music is primarily polkas and chotes played on guitars, accordions, saxophones, and drums, and is performed at church, fiestas, tribal celebrations, family affairs, and weekend social dances. A series of 42 LPs and cassettes based on the Scratch Dance. See CAN for titles.

CHIPPEWA-CREE CIRCLE DANCE
13 cirlce dance songs sung by Rocky Boy Singers, Paul Eagleman, Charles Gopher, Bill Baker, John Gilbert Meyers, and Windy Boy. Recorded at Crow Agency, Mont, Aug. 1966. Cassette/LP, $10, AIS.

CHIPPEWA-CREE GRASS DANCE
14 grass dance songs sung by Rocky Boy Singers, Paul Eagleman, Charles Gopher, Bill Baker, John Gilbert Meyers, and Windy Boy.Recorded at Crow Agency, Montana, August 1966. Cassette/LP, $10, AIS.

CHOCTAW SINGING
Charlie Jones, Singer; With lyric booklet in Choctaw. Cassette. $14.95. VIP.

COMANCHE CHURCH HYMNS
Traditional hymns in the Comanche language. Cassette. CAN & GDA.

COMANCHE FLUTE MUSIC
Flute songs and narration by Doc Tate Nevaquaya as he discusses the flute and songs. LP. $9.98. CAN.

COMING LIGHT: CHANTS TO HONOR THE MOTHER EARTH
19 original chants on a 45-minute cassette. $10. CH.

THE CONTEST IS ON
Trick dance songs. Vol. 1 - Chiefly Ponca and Pawnee; Vol. 2 - Part of the annual Osage War Dance, Ponca Powwow and Ponca Heluska. Cassettes. $7.98 each. CAN & GDA.

COVERSATIONAL LAKOTA
Set of 6 tapes, $60. Set of 6 books (16 pp. each), $30. CAN.

COYOTE LOVE MEDICINE
Jessica Reyes uses the Native American courting flute with ritual percussion instruments & synthesizers. Cassette, $12. CH.

CREATION CHANT
Eric Casillas
Compilation of original chants & captivating stylizations. With Native American drums & West African polyrhythms. Cassette, $6; CD, $9.15. ZANGO.

CROW GRASS & OWL DANCE SONGS
12 grass dance songs & 1 owl dance song sung by Lloyd Old Coyote, Frank Bakcbone, Sr., Robert Other Medicine, & Lindsey Bad Bear; 3 owl dance songs sung by Warren Bear Cloud & John Strong Enemy. Cassette/LP, $10. AIS.

CRY FROM THE EARTH
Music of the North American Indians. 33 songs from 24 different tribes. LP. $14.95. VIP & CAN.

CULTURAL PLURALISM & THE RECOVERY OF THE CLASSIC
Uses poetry of the American Indian and reservation treaties of the 19th century to reveal the wisdom & philosophy of Indian leaders. 1972. 59 minute cassette. NCTE.

CYCLES
Native American flute music by R. Carlos Nakai. The music from Our Voices, Our Land. 33 minutes. Cassette/CD. CAN.

DAKOTA LANGUAGE (SANTEE) BY AGNES ROSS
Beginning language and simple sentence material. CAN.

DAKOTA THEOLOGY
30 minutes, bxw. VHS. $5.00. AICRC.

DANCES WITH RABBITS
R. Carlos Nakai & Jackalope; Musical satire that takes a pointed look at the 500 years since Columbus. Nakai on the flute and trumpet, with Larry Yanez on the keyboards and guitar. 38 minutes. Cassette/CD. CAN.

DANCES WITH WOLVES
John Barry; Soundtrack of film. Cassette, $8; CD, $13.50. ZANGO.

DANCING DAKOTA
Songs & stories of North Dakota singer/songwriter, Chuck Suchy. Cassette, $10; CD, $15. MCP.

DAWN LAND
Joseph Bruchac's first novel on audiocassette. 180 minutes, 2 cassettes. $16.95. FUL.

THE DAWNING: CHANTS OF THE MEDICINE WHEEL
17 original chants on a 60-minute cassette. $10. CH.

DESERT DANCE
Carlos Nakai with his Native American flute, drums, voice, rattles, wind and rain in his ritual expression of nature's beauty. Cassette, $12. CH.

DISTANT SHORES
Gary Stroutsos brings classical, jazz and Native American techniques to the cedar flute. CD, 14.98; cassette, $9.98. MCP.

DREAM CATCHER
Flute music by Tokeya Inajin (Kevin Locke). Cassette, $10.60; CD, $16. MCP.

DREAM'S FOR YOU
Susan Aglukark (Inuit). Audiotape. $10. OY.

DREAMS FROM THE GRANDFATHER
Robert Tree Cody; Flutist and singer, Robert Tree Cody, draws on his Dakota-Maricopa heritage as well as Zuni, Lakota and Acoma peoples. 48 minutes. Cassette. CAN.

DRUMS OF THE AMERICAN INDIAN
One side of drum beat; and other side includes a collection of different drums and beats accompanied by shaker, rattle, deer toes or bells. 40 minutes. Cassette. $4.50. GDA.

EARTH SPIRIT
Carlos Nakai presents sounds of the Native American flute and introduces the mysterious & sacred sounds of the eagle bone whistle. 59 minutes. Cassette, $11.50. CAN & CMM.

EARTHLODGE
Mandan-Hidatsa storyteller and performer, Keith Bear, shares songs of his people recorded in an earth-lodge built on the Plains of the Dakotas. This enhanced CD contains a ten-minute video about Keith Bear, his life and culture. CD, $14.98; Cassette, $9.98. MCP.

EASTERN INDIANS TAPES
Iroquois Social Dance Songs, 3 Vols.; Beginning Cherokee-book & 2 tapes ($33.93); Songs & Dances of Eastern Indians From Medicine Spring (Cherokee) & Allegany (Seneca); Ceremonial Songs & Dances of the Cherokee. Cassettes, $10 each. CAN.

ECHOES OF THE NIGHT: NATIVE AMERICAN LEGENDS OF NIGHT SKY
Tsonakwa & Dean Evanson
Stories from Hopi, Ojibway, Algonkian and other tribal traditions of star knowledge. Cassette, $11; CD, $17. MFP.

ECHOES OF THE UPPER MISSOURI
Flute music by Keith Bear (debut). Cassette, $10; CD, $15. MCP.

THE ELDERS SPEAK
Dakotah & Ojibway stories of the land told by Mary Louise Defender Wilson (Gourd Woman) and Francis Cree (Eagle Heart). The enhanced CD contains

maps & photos of the landmark areas & folk arts described in their stories. CD, $14.98; Cassette, $9.98. MCP.

ELECTRIC WARRIOR
Russell Means; AIM activist brings us what he calls "rap-ajo." Spoken work backed with traditional & contemporary percussion. Cassette. $9.95; $14.95, CD. VIP.

EMERGENCE
Songs of the rainbow by Carlos Nakai (flute music). Cassette, $11.50. CAN & CMM.

ENGLISH & AMERICAN INDIAN STUDIES
Robert Lewis sets forth dos and donts for English teachers who plan to use Native American materials. 1972. 35 minutes. NCTE.

ESKIMO MUSIC OF ALASKA & THE HUDSON BAY
Record and notes by Laura Boulton. LP. $9.98. CAN.

ESKIMO SONGS FROM ALASKA
Twenty contemporary and ancient songs recorded by Miriam C. Stryker on St. Lawrence Island. Edited by Charles Hoffman. Includes an illustrated brochure. LP. $9.98. CAN.

EVERYDAY KIOWA PHRASES
Provides a brief introduction to some of the most common words & phrases used in Kiowa. 1 cassette, $12.95. AUDIO.

FEATHER, STONE & LIGHT
R. Carlos Nakai & William Eaton; Nakai and Eaton, the cedar flute and guitar, respectively, is joined by Will Clipman who adds ethnic percussion to the music. 71 minutes. CD. CAN.

FEATHERSTONE CASSETTES
Gordon Bird Sings Traditional/Contemporary American Indian Songs-12 songs from the Mandan, Hidatsa and Arikara Nations; Dakota Songs by Wahpe Kute-12 traditional/contemporary songs of the Dakota Nation; New Town Singers-Live at Dakota Dance Clan Celebration; Mandaree Singers-Live at New Town, N.D.; Old Scout Singers-Live at White Shield, N.D.; Wahpe Kute-Live at Dakota Dance Clan Celebration, Sisseton, S.D.; Eagle Whistles-Live at Mandaree, N.D.; Leroy Strong and Johnny Smith "The Buckaroos"; Little Earth Singers-Live in the Twin Cities (Minneapolis/St. Paul, MN); Ft. Yates Singers-Live at Ft. Yates, N.D.; Rock Creek Singers-Live at Ft. Yates, N.D.; Mandaree Singers-Live at Bismarck, N.D.-Vol. 2; Eagle Whistles-Live at Bismarck, N.D.-Vol. 2; Assiniboine Singers-Live at Dakota Tipi; Dakota Tipi Live-Minneapolis Buckaroos, Red Nation Singers and the Assiniboine Singers; Red Nation Singers-Live at Ft. Totten Days; Dakota Language (Santee) by Agnes Ross; The White Buffalo Calf Woman as Told by Martin High Bear; Lakota Wiikijo Olowan by Kevin Locke, 2 Vols.; All Nation Singers-Flandreau Indian School; Songs of the People by Georgia Wettlin-Larsen. Cassettes. $8.25 each. CAN.

FIRE CROW
Joseph Fire Crow; Flute and vocals. CD, $14.98; cassette, $9.98. MCP.

THE FIRST FLUTE
Internationally acclaimed traditional flute player, Kevin Locke, interprets centuries-old songs of the Lakota. CD, $14.98; Cassette, $9.98. MCP.

THE FLASH OF THE MIRROR
Flute music Tokeya Inajin (Kevin Locke). Cassette, $9.98; CD, $14.98. MCP.

THE FLOOD & OTHER LAKOTA STORIES
Kevin Locke
Locke performs traitional Native American flute music between stories he tells. All stories reveal the values and beliefs of the Lakota. 60 minutes. 1993. Cassette. $11. CHA.

FLUTE MUSIC
4 cassettes. Sacred Feelings by Doug Spotted Eagle; Riding the Wind by Ketcheshawno; Moon Spirits by Tsa'ne Dos'e; and Out of the Fire by Tom Minton. $9.95 each. VIP.

FLUTE/NEW AGE TAPES
Each flute artist has his own style influenced by his tribal heritage, personal experiences and feelings. N. Carlos Nakai, Gordon Bird, Fernando Cellicion, Robert Tree Cody, Herman Edwards, Daniel C. Hill, Kevin Locke, Frank Montano, Cornel Pewewardy, John Rainer, Jr., Rainmaker, Stan Snake, Douglas Spotted Eagle, Robert Two Hawks, and Tom Mauchahty-Ware. See CAN for tape titles.

THE FLUTE PLAYER
Traditional Dakota flute music by Bryan Akipa. Cassette, $9.98; CD, $14.98. MCP & MFP.

FLUTE PUEBLO
Traditional Zuni Pueblo flute music of Fernando Cellicion. 10 songs from Zuni, Laguna, Sioux & Acoma tribes. Cassette, $10. CMM.

FOOLS CROW, HOLY MAN
A retrospective of noted Ceremonial Chief & spiritual leader of the Oglala Sioux. Cassette, $10.60. MCP.

FORT OAKLAND RAMBLERS: OKLAHOMA INTERTRIBAL & CONTEST SONGS
Ponca Flag Song, 6 intertribal songs, 2 patriotic giveaway songs, 4 contest songs, & 1 Ponca veterans' song sung by a variety of singers. Recorded at White Eagle, Oklahoma, 1992. Cassette/LP, $10. IH.

THE GIFT OF THE GREAT SPIRIT
Tehanetorens
These lesson stories, including The Story of the Monster Bear, are told by Mohawk Elder Tehanetorens in his inimitable style. 1988. All grades. Cassette, $9.95. OY.

GREAT AMERICAN INDIAN SPEECHES
Narrated by Vine Deloria, Jr. and Arthur S. Junalaska. Includes speeches of Geronimo, Standing Bear, Cochise, Black Elk and others. Grades 7-12. Two cassettes. $19.95. LL.

HEALING & PEYOTE SONGS IN SIOUX & NAVAJO
Harmonized chanting without percussion by Verdell Primeaux (Oglala/Yankton Sioux & Ponca), Johnny Mike (Dine) and Robert Attson (Dine). 43 minutes. Cassette. CAN.

HEALING SONGS OF THE AMERICAN INDIANS
Healing songs of the Chippewa, Sioux, Yuman, Northern Ute, Papago, Makah and Menominee Indians. Text included. LP. $14.95. VIP & CAN.

HEART OF THE WORLD
Mary Youngblood with special guest Joanne Shenandoah. Double chamber flutes, guitar, percussion, & Joanne's voice. CD, $15.98; cassette, $9.98. SWR.

HEART SONGS OF BLACK HILLS WOMAN
Paula Horne (Dakota Sioux) speaks her prose of each song in English before she sings it in her Native tongue. Cassette, $11; CD, $16. MCP.

HEARTBEAT: VOICES OF 1ST NATIONS WOMEN
Cassette, $10; CD, $15. OY & VIP

THE HERON SMILED
Anishinaabe singer/songwriter Annie Humphrey's contemporary style of love songs and political anthems. John Trudell contributes poetry and vocals. CD, $14.98 & Cassette, $9.98. MCP.

AN HISTORICAL ALBUM OF BLACKFOOT INDIAN MUSIC
Includes Medicine Pipe songs, Sun Dance songs, Owl Dance songs, Gambling songs. Historical recordings dating back to the turn of the century. LP. $9.98. CAN.

HO HWO SJU LAKOTA SINGERS TRADITIONAL SONGS BY THE SIOUX
Includes the Sioux National Anthem, among other traditional songs of the Sioux. Cassette, $10. IH.

HONORABLE SKY
Peter Kater & R. Carlos Nakai. CD, $15.98; cassette, $9.98. SWR.

HOPI KATCINA SONGS
Includes six other songs by Hopi Chanters. 17 songs and dances recorded by Dr. Jesse Walter Fewkes in Arizona in 1924. Text included. LP. $9.98. CAN.

THE HORSES STILL CRY
Native American flute music by Native American flutemaker Paul Hacker. Cedar flutes provide courting songs with sounds of nature background. Cassette, $11 or CD, $16. PH.

HOW THE WEST WAS LOST
Peter Kater & R. Carlos Nakai. Vol. 1 - Original soundtrack from six-hour PBS/Discovery Channel mini-series of 1994; Vol. II - from sequel series on the Discovery Channel. Cassette, $11 each; CDs, $17 each. SWR.

HYMNS OF PRAISE: THE NATIVE AMERICAN CHURCH
Public radio program examining the Peyote religion & way of life. 30 minute audiocassette. $11. KF.

IMPROVISATIONS IN CONCERT
Peter Kater & R. Carlos Nakai
A collection of songs performed live. CD, $15.98; cassette, $9.98. SWR.

IN THE LONG TIME AGO
11 legendary Cherokee stories told by Rogers Clinch, Sr., a Cherokee elder. He explains modern relevance to ancient stories. Cassette, $10. FTW.

INDIAN CHIPMUNKS
Alvin Ahoy-boy and his Indian Chipmunk Singers from Yuk-a-Day, Canada, sing powwow songs. 2 Vols. Cassettes. $7.98 each. CAN & GDA.

INDIAN COUNTRY-WESTERN
Apache Spirit, 10 vols. ($8.50 each) Three guys and a girl from Whiteriver, Arizona singing a combination of their own original compositions & popular country-western standards; Cody Bearpaw, 2 Vols. ($7.98 each); Louis Becenti - Eddie's Club in Gallup, NM presents Louis Becenti singing 12 country-western standards ($7.98); El Coochise, 3 Vols. ($7.98 each) - Hopi, Apache, and Navajo musicians provide back up for the vocals of Hopi musician and singer El Coochise; The Fenders, 2 Vols. ($7.98 each) - Navajo country-western band; Bill Johnson & the Jamborees, 3 vols. (7.98 each) - A Navajo country-western band; Harold Mariano & the Variations, 3 Vols. ($7.98 each); Joe Montana and the Roadrunners, 3 vols. ($8.98 each) - Hualapai Indian group from Peach Springs, Arizona; Navajo Clan, 3 vols. ($7.98 each); Navajo Sundowners, 13 Vols. ($8.50 each) - A popular country-western group from Farmington, NM; Night Ryders - Composed of members of the Hopi and White Mountain Apache tribes. ($7.98); Jimi Poyer - Juke Box Music ($7.98); The Rockin' Rebels - Navajo group ($8.50); Sioux Savages - A Sioux-Navajo band from Tuba City, AZ ($7.98); The Thunders, 3 vols. ($7.98 each); Undecided Takers - Navajo country-western and rock group from Kayenta, AZ ($7.98 each); Wingate Valley Boys - Navajo band from Fort Wingate, NM ($7.98); Zuni Midnighters, 4 Vols. - country-western dance band from Zuni Pueblo, NM ($7.98 each); Isleta Poorboys - Just Play 'N Good, songs by Clarence Jojola of Isleta Pueblo, NM. ($8.50). Cassettes. CAN.

INDIAN HOUSE RECORDS & TAPES
Includes the following records & cassettes: Round Dance Songs of Taos Pueblo, 2 vols.; Taos Round Dance, 2 parts; Taos Pueblo Round Dance; Ditch-Cleaning & Picnic Songs of Picuris Pueblo; Turtle Dance Songs of San Juan Pueblo; Cloud Dance Songs of San Juan Pueblo; Zuni Fair-Live; Navajo Sway Songs; Night & Daylight Yeibichei; Navajo Skip Dance & Two Step Songs; Navajo Round Dance; Navajo Gift Songs & Round Dance; Navajo Corn Grindings and Shoe Game Songs; Klagetoh Maiden Singers; Navajo Songs About Love - The Klagetoh Swingers, Six volumes; The San Juan Singers - Navajo Skip Dance Songs; Turtle Mountain Singers - Navajo Social Dance Songs, 2 vols.; Navajo Skip Dance & Two-Step Songs - The Rock Point Singers, 2 vols.; Southern Maiden Singers - Navajo Skip Dance & Two-Step Songs; Navajo Peyote Ceremonial Songs, 4 vols.; War Dance Songs of the Ponca, 2 vols.; Ponca Peyote Songs, Three vols; Cheyenne Peyote Songs, 2 vols.; Comanche Peyote Songs, 2 vols.; Handgame of the Kiowa, Kiowa Apache, & Comanche, 2 vols.; Kiowa Gourd Dance, 2 vols.; Kiowa 49 - War Expedition Songs; Kiowa Church Songs, 2 vols.; War Dance Songs of the Kiowa--O-ho-mah Lodge Singers, 2 vols.; Flute Songs of the Kiowa & Comanche - Tom Mauchahty-Ware; Kiowa & Kiowa-Apache Peyote Songs; Songs of the Muskogee Creek, 2 parts; Stomp Dance - Muskogee, Seminole, Yuchi, 4 vols.; Blackfoot A-1 Club Singers, 2 vols.; Old Agency Singers of the Blood Reserve, 2 parts; The Badland Singers -Assiniboine-Sioux Grass Dance; Sounds of the Badland Singers; The Badland Singers - Live at Bismarck; The Badland Singers at Home; Kahomini Songs - The Badland Singers; The Badland Singers, Live at United Tribes, 2 vols.; Ashland Singers - North Cheyenne War Dance; Ho Hwo Sju Lakota Singers - Traditional Songs of the Sioux; Love Songs of the Lakota, performed on Flute by Kevin Locke; Ironwood Singers - Songs of the Sioux, Live at the 106th Rosebud Sioux Fair; Yankton Sioux Peyote Songs, 8 vols.; Songs of the Native American Church - Sung by Rev. Joseph M. Shields; Rocky Boy Singers: Grass Dance & Jingle Dress Songs, 2 Vols.; Rocky Boy Chippewa-Cree Grass Dance Songs; Red Earth Singers, Live at Bismarck, 2 vols.; Sounds of Indian America - Plains & Southwest; Pueblo Songs of the Southwest; Turtle Mountain Singers-Welcome to Navajo Land & Early This Morning I Heard My Horse Calling; Eagle Society-Blackfoot Grass Dance Songs, Siksika Nation; Red Earth Singers of Tama, Iowa - "Live". American Indian Soundchiefs: Blackfeet Grass Dance Songs; Crow Grass Dance & Owl Dance Songs; Ponca & Pawnee Warriors Dance Songs; Ponca Tribal Songs; Caddo Tribal Dances; Kiowa-Comanche Peyote Songs; Cassette or LP recordings available for most selections. $12 for each cassette or LP. See HI for further information.

INDIAN KILLER
Sherman Alexie. Sherman reads from his novel. 3 hours. 1996. $21.95. OY.

INDIAN MUSIC OF THE CANADIAN PLAINS
Recordings of the Blood, Cree, Blackfoot and Assiniboine Indians made on the reservation. Includes war songs, greeting songs, stick games, Dance songs, etc. LP. $9.98. CAN.

INDIAN MUSIC OF THE PACIFIC NORTHWEST COAST
A two-record set containing 27 songs and dances recorded by Dr. Ida Halpern, mostly from the Kwakiutl Tribe with Nootka and Tlingit songs and dances included. LP. $19.96. CAN.

INDIAN MUSIC OF THE SOUTHWEST
Includes Hopi, Zuni, Navajo, Taos, San Ildefonso, Santa Ana, Mohave, Papago, Pima and Apache music. Record and notes by Dr. Laura Boulton. LP. $9.98. CAN.

INDIAN ROCK MUSIC
Hamana (2 LPs-$7.98 each): Hamana, and Butchamana and the Big Bang Brothers Band; Many Hogans: American Clan; Mr. Indian and Time: Medicine Dream; Redbone (2 LPs-$7.98 each): Message from a Drum, and Beaded Dreams Through Turquoise Eyes; Sand Creek: Endless Flight ($7.98); Winterhawk (3 cassettes-$8.50 each): Electric Warriors, Dog Soldier, and Winterhawk; XIT (7 cassettes-$8.98 each): Plight of the Redman, Silent Warrior, Entrance, Backtrackin', Relocation, Drums Across the Atlantic, and Tom Bee-Color Me Red. CAN.

INDIAN THEME CONTEMPORARY
B.Y.U. Musical Production - Lamanite Generation, 1985, Go My Son, and From the Eagle's Bed; Vincent Craig, Vol. 1 - (Navajo performer), and The Navajo Code Talker Song (45 rpm record); A. Paul Ortega - Mescalero Apache: Two Worlds, Three Worlds, and Blessing Ways; Buddy Red Bow - Journey to the Spirit World; Floyd Westerman: Custer Died for Your Sins, and The Land is Your Mother; Francis Country: The Peyote Dream; Homeland - 10 songs by Bugs Moran; Burt Lambert and the Northern Express: Just Arriving (LP-$7.98); Billy Thunderkloud and the Chieftones: Off the Reservation (LP-$5.98), and What Time of Day. Cassettes. $8.98 each. CAN.

INDIAN WISDOM STORIES
Dramatized legends recorded & produced by American Indians with authentic Salish Indian language chants, drum songs, and sound effects. Told by Jay Silverheels, Mohawk Indian actor. Includes 2 cassettes; four-color filmstrips, a script for each story; a teacher's guide by Dr. Jerry Blanche (Choctaw Indian educator). Grades 4-6. CAN.

INSPIRIATIONS OF THE GREAT SPIRIT
Richard Bell. Lyric tales of the Tahue people. Cassette, $6; CD, $10. ZANGO.

INTERTRIBAL GROUPS & COLLECTIONS
Bala Sinem Choir, 2 Vols. (American Indian Songs for Choir & Walk in Beauty My Children); Crow Celebration-10 Great Drums at Crow Fair; Denver Indian Singers-Arikara & Sioux (LP); Great Plains Singers & Songs; Hopi Sunshield Singers-Northern Style Pow Wow Songs; Kyi-Yo Pow Wow-9 Northern Plains Drums; Omak Pow Wow 1980 (Washington)-6 Drums from the Northwest; Pow Wow Songs - Music of the Plains Indians ($9.98-LP); The Song of the Indian-8 Tribal Groups & Soloists; White Eagle Singers-Intertribal Pow Wow Songs and Love Songs, 5 Vols.; Santa Fe Pow Wow, 2 Vols; Songs of the Earth, Water, Fire and Sky; Pow Wow Songs-Music of the Plains Indians. Cassettes, $7.98-$9.98 each; also available on compact disc, $16.98 each. CAN.

INTRODUCTION TO CHOCTAW
Provides a brief introduction to some of the most common words and phrases used in Choctaw. The seections revolve around the themes of everyday living, The native speaker is Charles G. Jones, past president of the Choctaw Indian Council. 2 cassettes (2 hrs, 20 mins); 60 pp. looseleaf binder album. AUDIO.

INTRODUCTORY LAKOTA
All recordings are by native speakers; text contains 15 lessons, the last lesson being a comprehensive review. Exercises for written practice are included, using the English alphabet. 15 cassettes (12 hours), 102 pp. text, 9 pp final exam. Purchase: $175. AUDIO.

IROQUOIS SOCIAL DANCE SONGS
Traditional Iroquois social dance songs from the Six Nations Reserve in Ontario, Canada. Singers are: George Buck, Raymond Spragge, Jacob Thomas & Wm. Guy Spittal. 3 Vols. Cassettes. $7.98 each. CAN.

IROQUOIS STORIES
Joseph Bruchac. 1988. All Grades. Cassette, $9.95. OY.

ISLAND OF BOWS
Flute music by R. Carlos Nakai. Recorded in a Buddhist temple in Kyoto, Japan. 48 minutes. Cassette/CD. CAN.

JACKALOPE
R. Carlos Nakai. The Native American flute and trumpet by Larry Yanez. 50 mins. Cassette/CD. CAN.

JIM BOYD
Two albums: "Reservation Bound" - first solo album, & "Unity" - original songs deal with a variety of issues concerning Native Americans today. Cassette, $6 each; CD, $9.75 each. ZANGO.

JOHNNY DAMAS & ME
John Trudell (Santee). The music of John Trudell, with the Graffiti Band. Cassette, $10; CD, $12. ICC.

JOSEPH FLYING BYE
Songs & teachings in the lakota oral tradition by a respected elder, and pejuta wicasa (medicine man) from the Standing Rock Reservation. CR.

JOURNEYS
Native American flute music. R. Carlos Nakai performs on several wooden flutes. 54 minutes. Cassette, $11.50. CAN & CMM.

KEEPERS OF THE ANIMALS & KEEPERS OF THE EARTH
Told by Joseph Bruchac, featuring the complete, unabridged stories from "Keepers of the Animals" and Keepers of the Earth" Represents the art of traditional Native American storytelling, performing stories drawn from the native cultures of North America. 110 & 133 minutes, respectively (two tapes each). Cassette, $16.95 each. FUL.

KEEPERS OF THE DREAM
Flute music by Tokeya Inajin (Kevin Locke). Cassette, $10.60; CD, $16. MCP.

KEVIN LOCKE (TOKEYA INAJIN)
"Dream Catcher," "Flash of the Mirror," "Keepers of the Dream," "Love Songs of the Lakota," "Open Circle." Traditional songs of the Meskwaki Dakota, and Lakota People, Native flute, voice, and drum. Cassettes, $6 each; CD, $9.75 each. ZANGO.

KIOWA CIRCLE & TWO-STEP SONGS
12 round dance songs sung by Leonard Cozad, Jasper Sankadota, Oscar Tahlo & Laura Tahlo. Recorded in 1964. Cassette/LP, $10. AIS.

KIOWA & COMANCHE PEYOTE SONGS
13 songs sung by Nelson Big Bow. Recorded at Crow Agency, Montana, August 1966. Cassette/LP, $10. AIS.

KIOWA-COMANCHE PEYOTE SONGS
6 songs sung by Nelson Big Bow, 6 songs sung by Edgar Gouladdie, 4 songs sung by Harding Big Bow & 7 songs sung by Walter Ahhaity. Cassette/LP, $10. VIP & AIS.

KIOWA FLAG SONG
Oklahoma Round Dance, Kiowa War Mothers & Comanche "49". Cassette. $45. GDA.

KIOWA HYMNS
Traditional church hymns for solo voice in the Kiowa language sung by Ralph Kotay. 2 cassettes. $15.95. CAN. $9. GDA.

KIOWA & KIOWA-APACHE PEYOTE RITUAL SONGS
4 songs sung by Emmett Williams, 4 songs sung by Nathan Doyebi, 4 songs sung by Edgar Gouladdie, & 8 songs sung by Nelson Big Bow. Cassette/LP, $10, AIS.

KIOWA MYTHS & LEGENDS
Kiowa Jill Momaday brings these traditional Native American tales to life. Each is accompanied by authentic tribal music. 2 cassettes (180 minutes), $21. AUDIO.

KIOWA PEYOTE MEETING
Documents the vision-producing peyote ritual. Recorded with the Anadarko, Oklahoma tribes and consists of both words & syllables with emotional connotations. 3 LP record set. Edited by Harry E. Smith. $29.94. CAN.

KIOWA PEYOTE RITUAL SONGS
18 ritual songs sung by the following: James Aunguoe, Ernest Redbird, Allen Tsontokoy, Francis Tsontokoy, and Oscar Tahlo. Cassette/LP, $10. AIS.

KIOWA PEYOTE RITUAL SONGS
15 Kiowa songs sung by Edward Hunmmingbird. Recorded at Crow Agency, ontana, in August 1966. Casette/LP, $10. AIS.

KIOWA ROUND DANCE SONGS
16 round dance songs, 2 Comanche 49 songs, 2 Kiowa War Mother's songs and a Kiowa Flag Song. Cassette. $7.98. CAN.

KIOWA SONGS & DANCES
Dance and war songs of the Kiowa Indians. LP. $9.98. CAN.

KIOWA STORYTELLER
Stories in the age-old oral tradition told by master storyteller & Pulitzer-Prize winner, N. Scott Momaday (Kiowa). 1 cassette (60 minutes), $10.95. AUDIO.

KOKOPELLI DREAMS
Flute music by Fernando Cellicion. Cassette/CD, $4.50. GDA.

KOKOPELLI'S CAFE
Flute music by R. Carlos Nakai Quartet. Cassette/CD. CAN.

KWAKIUTL INDIAN MUSIC OF THE PACIFIC NORTHWEST
25 songs including Raven, Hagok, Hamatsa, Thunderbird, Potlatch, Whale and others. Two LP records. $19.96. CAN.

LAKOTA LANGUAGE AUDIO CDs
A Collection of Lakota Children's Songs, Vol. 1; Picture Book Companion Audio CD - Vol. 1; Speak Lakota series: Level 1 Audio CD; Level 2 Audio CD, Level 3 Audio CD. $14.95 each.

LAKOTA LOVE SONGS & STORIES
Flute music by Tokeya Inajin (Kevin Locke). Cassette, $10. MCP.

LAUGHTER: THE NAVAJO WAY
Humorous stories of the Navajo. Each story is presented in Navajo with a word-for-word translation, colloquial English equivalents, and an explanation of the story with cultural notes. 1 cassette (80 mins) & 143 pp. text, $39. AUDIO.

LEARN TO PLAY NATIVE AMERICAN FLUTE
Dave Powell. Instruction for playing the Native American wood flute. Includes instructions and demonstrations, and lessons for playing four tunes are also included. 32 minutes. Cassette. $9.95. CAN.

LEARNING THROUGH HOPI SONGS
Anita Poleahla & Ferrell Seckuku; CD, booklet. $15.95. VIP.

THE LEGACY OF REUBEN SNAKE: NATIVE AMERICAN ELDER
Public radio portrait of Mr. Snake's life and work. 30 minute audiocassette. $11. KF.

LEGENDS OF NORTH AMEICAN INDIANS
Music by Jackie Crow Hiendlmayr. Cassette, $10.50. CMM.

LENAPE LANGUAGE LESSONS
Introductory-level course of the language of the Lennape (Delaware Indians) consists of 4 lessons on 2 audio cassettes (71 minutes) and two 30 pp. texts. $29.50. AUDIO.

LET'S 49!
25 singers record 49 songs from Oklahoma. Cassette. CAN & GDA.

LET'S SPEAK MOHAWK
Beginning-level course in conversational Mohawk provides the pronunciation, grammar, structures, and vocabulary needed to communicate in everyday situations. 3 cassettes, and 102 pp. text. $39.95. AUDIO.

LETTER FROM THE END OF THE 20TH CENTURY
Joy Harjo & Poetic Justice. Six piece band with lyrics by Harjo. CD, $15.98; cassette, $9.98. SWR.

ROBER LEVI SINGS: DESERT CAHUILLA BRIDSONGS
Robert Levi; Traditional birdsongs. 5 Vol. set. $18 each; $90/set. CDs. MALKI

LIBRARY OF CONGRESS
LPs: Seneca Songs from the Coldspring Longhouse; Songs of the Yuma, Cocopa, Yaqui; Songs of the Pawnee & Northern Ute; Songs of the Papago; Songs of the Nootka & Quilieute; Songs of the Menominee, Mandan & Hidatsa.

Cassettes: Songs of the Kiowa; Indian Songs of Today; Songs of the Paiute, Washo, Ute, Bannock, Shoshone; Songs of the Comanche, Cheyenne, Kiowa, Caddo, Wichita, Pawnee; Songs of the Sioux; Songs of the Navajo; Songs of the Apache; Pueblo: Taos, San Ildefonso, Zuni, Hopi; Omaha Indian Music. Cassettes & LPs, $9.98 each. CAN.

LIFE BLOOD
Joanne Shenandoah with Peter Kater. Ancient Iroquois melodies...piano with synthesizer, shakuhachi, bass, guitar, and percussion. CD, $15.98; cassette, $9.98. SWR.

KEVIN LOCKE CASSETTE SERIES
Three of Kevin Locke's first recordings. 3 cassettes, $24.98. MCP.

LONG AGO TIME
Cassette, $10. CMM.

LOVE FLUTE
Audio companion to Paul Goble's book put to the music of Bryan Akipa's flute. Cassette, $11; CD, $16. MCP.

LOVING WAYS
Joanne Shenedoah (Oneida) and A. Paul Ortega (Mescalero Apache) sing songs which reflect Native American philosophy and culture. 41 minutes. Cassette, $8.98. CAN & FWT.

MAKE ME A HOLLOW REED
Flute music by Tokeya Inajin (Kevin Locke). Cassette, $10. MCP.

MATRIARCH: IROQUOIS WOMEN'S SONGS
Joanne Shenandoah. Recorded at ancient village sites on Iroquois land. SWR.

MESA MUSIC CONSORT
Ben Tavera King, Joe Trevino & Eric Casillas. Drum, flute and keyboards. Three albums: "Medicine Flutes," "Spirit Feathers," and "Spirits of the Wild." Cassette, $6 each; CD, $9.15 each. ZANGO.

MIDWEST INDIANS RECORDS & TAPES
Chippewa War Dance Songs; Chippewa Grass Dance Songs; The Kingbird Singers; Mesquakie Bear Singers with War Dance Songs; Songs of the Chippewa; White Earth Pow-Wow; Winnebago Songs; Ojibway Music from Minnesota ($9.98); Honor the Earth Pow Wow - Songs of the Great Lakes Indians (Cassette, $9.98; compact disc, $16.98). Cassettes, $7.98 each. CAN.

MIGRATION
Peter Kater & R. Carlos Nakai. Piano & flute. CD, $15.98; cassette, $9.98. SWR.

MIGRATIONS
Ia Tulip. First album by flutist Ia Tulip of Sedona, AZ. Cassette, $9.98. CAN.

MITAKUYE OYASIN: LAKOTA SUNDANCE SONGS
I6 songs with booklet of words in Lakota and English. 2 cassettes. $16. BOND.

MORNING STAR
Flute music by Tom Marchanty-Ware, featuring, "Crazy Horse Song." Cassette, $4.50. GDA.

MUSIC OF THE ALASKAN KUTCHIN INDIANS
Traditional Athabascan language songs including love, medicine, crow and other plus jigs, reels and square dances played on a violin. Recorded in 1972 in the Fort Yukon area of Alaska. LP. $9.98. CAN.

MUSIC OF THE ALGONKIANS
19 songs, most of them about hunting. Includes those of the Woodland Indians: Cree, Montagnais, Naskapi. LP. $9.98. CAN.

MUSIC OF THE AMERICAN INDIANS OF THE SOUTHWEST
Includes the Navajo, Zuni, Hopi, San Ildefonso, Taos, Apache, Yuma, Papago, Walapai and Havasupai tribal music. Recorded by Willard Rhodes in cooperation with the Bureau of Indian Affairs. Notes by Harry Tschopik, Jr. and Willard Rhodes. LP. $9.98. CAN.

MUSIC OF THE PAWNEE
Contains 45 Pawnee Indian songs sung by Mark Evarts and recorded in 1935 by Dr. Gene Weltfish. Reflects all aspects of Pawnee life. LP. $9.98. CAN.

MUSIC OF THE PLAINS APACHE
15 songs recorded and edited by Dr. John Beatty. Includes children's songs, lullabies, church songs, dance songs, hand game songs, and peyote songs. Notes and background of songs included. LP. $9.98. CAN.

MUSIC OF THE PUEBLOS, APACHE, AND NAVAJOS
Recorded by David P. MacAllester and Donald N. Brown. 12 LP. TM.

MUSIC OF THE SIOUX AND THE NAVAJO
Sioux recordings include, among others, Rabbit Dance, Sun Dance, love songs; Navajo recordings include: Squaw Dance, Night Chant, riding song, etc. Notes included. Recorded by Willard Rhodes in cooperation with the Bureau of Indian Affairs. LP. $14.95. VIP.

MYTH, MUSIC, AND DANCE OF THE AMERICAN INDIAN
De Cesare. An introduction to the Native American culture. The teacher's resource book provides pronunciations, tribe information, maps & instructions on making Indian instruments. Cassette & teacher's resource book, $19.95; student's songbook, $4.95; student's workbook, $3.95. ALF.

CARLOS R. NAKAI - NATIVE AMERICAN FLUTE MUSIC
Includes the following cassettes: Winter Dreams, Changes, Trilogy, Natives, Cycles, Journeys, Earth Spirit, Carry the Gift, Sundance, Desert Dance. $15 each tape. RC.

NATIVE AMERICAN CURRENTS
Joanne Shenandoah, R. Carlos Nakai & Peter Kater, Robert Mirabal, Joy Harjo & Poetic Justice. CD, $15.98; cassette, $9.98. SWR.

NATIVE AMERICAN FLUTE MUSIC
Kevin Locke: Lakota Wiikijo Olowan, 2 Vols. ($8.25 each); Tom Mauchahty-Ware: The Traditional & Contemporary Indian Flute of Tom Mauchahty-Ware ($7.98); Carlos Nakai: Changes - Native American Flute Music, Vol. 1, Cycles - Native American Flute Music, Vol. 2, and Journeys: Native American Flute Music, Vol. 3 ($8.98 each); Stan Snake: Dan of Love ($8.98). Cassettes. CAN.

NATIVE AMERICAN LANGUAGES
Self-study audiocassette/book programs celebrating the languages, lives, legends and music of the Navajo, Lakota, Kiowa, Cherokee, Choctaw, Lenape, and Passaquoddy Indians; and Hawaiian Natives. Separate programs include: Navajo - Breakthrough Navajo-2 cassettes (3 hours) and 234 pp. text, $49; Laughter: The Navajo Way (humorous stories of the Navajo-1 cassette (80 minutes), and 143 pp. text, $39; Basic Medical Navajo-1 cassette (1 hour), and 141 pp. text, $39. Lakota - Introductory Lakota-15 cassettes (12 hours), and 102 pp. text, $175. Kiowa-1 cassette, $12.95. Cherokee - Beginning Cherokee-2 cassettes (3 hours), and 332 pp. text, $39.00. Lenape - Lenape Language Lessons-2 cassettes (71 minutes), and 2-30 pp. text., $29.50. Passamaquoddy - Beginning Passama-quoddy-5 cassettes (3.5 hours), 50 pp. phrasebook, 112 pp. text and vowel sounds booklet, $59.50. Hawaiian - Let's Speak Hawaiian-8 cassettes (8.5 hours), and 430 pp. text, $95. AUDIO.

NATIVE AMERICAN LISTEN & COLOR LIBRARY
Library of educational coloring books with accompanying cassettes portrays the symbols, settings, dress, & tribal decorations of 95 Indian tribes grouped into six major division: Northeast, Northwest, Southwest, Plains, Southeast, California. Each tribe is described and illustrated. 1994. Six, 32-page booklets, six, 60-minute cassettes. $39.95. AUDIO.

NATIVE AMERICAN MUSIC
Authentic music of four Native American tribes. Songs of the Cherokee, Songs of the Lenape, Songs of the Navajo, Songs of the Sioux. $11.95 each. AUDIO.

NATIVE AMERICAN SOUNDTRACK
Robbie Ribertson & Red Road Ensemble. From TBS series "Native Americans." Cassette, $12; CD, $20. MFP.

NATIVE AMERICAN WISDOM
Kent Nerburn & Louise Mengelkoch, Editors
Features flute music by R. Carlos Nakai. Read by Kent Nerburn, Paula Bruce & Marc Allen. The unabridged reading of the book, and the Native American oral tradition. Speeches and writings of peoples from many tribes. 1993. Cassette, 83 minutes. $10.95. NWL & MFP.

THE NATIVE HEART
Gary Stroutsos
The wooden flute with piano and hand percussion...world jazz with American Indian influences. CD, $14.98; cassette, $9.98. MCP.

NATIVE TAPESTRY
Collaboration between R. Carlos Nakai & composer James DeMars. Traditional Native American flute music combined with African percussion, piano, cello, sax and chamber orchestra. 59 minutes. Cassette/CD. CAN.

NATIVES
Peter Kater and Carlos Nakai with an improvisational exploration and expression of the seven directions. CD, $15.98; cassette, $9.98. SWR.

NAVAJO
Alan Wilson. Self-study audio-cassette/book programs on Navajo language. Also provides a deeper understanding of the Navajo culture & lifestyle. Includes the following programs: Breakthrough Navajo: An Introductory Course, 2 cassettes (3 hrs.) & 234-page text, $49; Speak Navajo: Intermediate, 2 cassettes (2 hrs.) & 180-page text, $49; Laughter: The Navajo Way (Humorous Stories of the Navajo), 1 cassette (80 mins.) and 143-page text, $39; and Basic Medical Navajo, 1 cassette (60 mins.) and 141-page text, $39. AUDIO.

NAVAJO CREATION STORIES
Sacred Twins & Spider Woman (stories); accompanied by drums & song, Geri Keams, Streak-of-Black-Forest Navajo Clan, brings listener into the circle & beauty way. 1994. 1 cassette, 60 minutes. $11.95. AUDIO.

NAVAJO & ENGLISH CASSETTES
20 cassettes. Grades K-6. See SAN for titles and prices.

NAVAJO EXPERIENCE STORIES
24 cassettes and booklets. Grades 1-6. See SAN for titles and prices

NAVAJO INDIAN RECORDS & TAPES
Beclabito Valley Singers, Vol. 3&4; Bita Hochee Travelers, Vols. 1,3&4; Chinle Valley Boys, 4 Vols.; Chinle Valley Singers, 2 Vols.; Chinle Valley Traditional Song and Dance Festival, 2 Vols.; Cove Nava-Tune Singers; Dennehotso Swinging Wranglers, 3 Vols.; Dine' Ba'Aliil of Navajoland (Navajo Songs and Dances)(LP); Four Corners Singers (Teec Nos Pos, Navajo Two Step & Love Songs), 7 Vols.; Four Corners Yei-Be-Chai; Lupton Valley Singers ($8.98); Memories of Navajoland; Davis Mitchell, 3 Vols.; Nanaba Midge Sings Traditional Navajo Songs; Natay, Navajo Singer; Navajo - Songs of the Dine; Navajo Squaw Dance Songs; Rock Point Singers, Vols. 3&4; San Juan Singers; Toh-Den-Nas-Shai Singers; Traditional Navajo Songs; Tsi Yi-Tohi Singers (Woodspring), 2 Vols.; Yei-Be-Chai Songs; Sweethearts of Navajoland, 2 Vols.; D.J. Nez, 2 Vols.Chinle Swingin' Echoes, 2 Vols.; Lupton Valley Singers, Vol. 1; Navajo Nation Swingers; Whippoorwill Singers, Vol. 1; Navajo Songs from Canyon de Chelly; Southwestern Singers. Cassettes & Compact discs. $7.98-$9.98; compact discs available, $16.98 each. CAN.

NAVAJO NIGHTS
Gerald Hausman. Navajo healing stories. 50 minutes. Cassette, $11.95. AUDIO.

NAVAJO PLACE NAMES
Arranged in alphabetical order, non-Navajo name first, then the Navajo name followed by literal translation of the complete Navajo term. 1 cassette & 100-page text which includes pronunciation guide and entire text of place names. $16.95. AUDIO.

THE NEW KICKING WOMAN SINGERS, Vol. 5
Intertribal Powwow Songs recorded live at Many Farms, AZ Powwow. 1988. Cassette, $7.98. CAN.

NEW WORLD RECORDS
A series of recordings compiled by Charlotte Heth, an ethno-musicologist and member of the Cherokee tribe. Includes: Songs of Love, Luck, Animals and Music - music of the Yurok and Tolowa Indians of Northern California; Songs & Dances of the Eastern Indians from Medicine Spring and Allegany - ritual, ceremonial and social music from the Cherokee (Oklahoma) and Seneca (Iroquois-Salamanca, NY); Oku Shareh - turtle dance songs recorded at San Juan Pueblo, NM; Songs of Earth, Water, Fire and Sky - an anthology of nine tribes: San Juan Pueblo, Seneca; Northern Arapaho; North Plains; Creek, Yurok, Navajo, Cherokee, and Southern Plains; Powwow Songs - Music of the Plains Indians. Cassettes. CAN.

NIGHT RIDERS & SKY BEINGS
Tsonakwa's second tape contains magical tales of the unseen world of the spirit told with warmth & power. 42 minutes. Cassette, $9.95. TOP & CH.

NOOTKA - INDIAN MUSIC OF THE PACIFIC NORTHWEST COAST
Includes canoe paddling songs, medicine songs, various animal songs, potlatch songs. Two LP record set. $19.96. CAN.

NORTH AMERICAN INDIAN & ESKIMO MUSIC
$14.95. VIP

NORTHERN PLAINS RECORDS & TAPES
Arapaho War Dance Songs and Round Dances; Arikara Grass Songs - White Shield Singers (LP); Cree Pow-Wow Songs, 2 Vols. - By the Parker Singers from Rocky Boy's Reservation; Flathead Stick Game Songs; Hays Singers - Gros Ventre Songs; Hidatsa Songs - By the Little Shell Singers (LP); The Mandaree Singers - Contemporary Powwow Songs, 2 Vols.; Powwow Songs

from Rocky Boy, 2 Vols.; Social Songs of the Arapaho Sun Dance - By Wind River Singers; Stick Game Songs; War Dances of the Crow; Sage Point Singers; Music of the Nez Perce; Nez Perce Stories. Cassettes, $7.98-$9.98 each. CAN.

NORTHWEST INDIAN RECORDS & TAPES
Canyon Wellpinit Singers - Spokane WA; The Chemiwai Singers; Songs & Stories from Neah Bay Makah (LP); Songs of the Warm Springs Indian Reservation; Songs of a Yakima Encampment; Stick Game Songs by Joe Washington - Lummi; Treaty of 1855 - Intertribal Powwow Songs; Umatilla Tribal Songs; Yakama Nation Singers of Satus Longhouse. Cassettes, $7.98. CAN.

OBSIDIAN BUTTERFLY
Alice Gomez with Madalyn Blanchett & Marilyn Rife. Flutes with percussion. CD, $15.98; cassette, $9.98. SWR.

THE OFFERING
Mary Youngblood (Aleut & Seminole) plays the flute. CD, $15.98; Cassette, $9.98. SWR.

OJIBWAY MUSIC FROM MINNESOTA: A CENTURY OF SONG FOR VOICE & DRUM Booklet by Thomas Vennum, Jr. 15 songs; 15-page booklet on Ojibway music and powwows. Cassette & booklet, $9.95. CAN.

OJIBWE INTERMEDIATE VOCABULARY
Ojibwe Mekana. One, 60-minute tape & translation book. $21. ICC.

OJIBWE VOCABULARY FOR ADVANCED LEARNERS
Ojibwe Mekana. Two, 60-minute language tapes; Ojibwe/English booklet. $33. ICC.

OJIBWE VOCABULARY FOR BEGINNERS
Ojibwe Mekana. One, 60-minute language tape; Ojibwe/English work manual. $22. ICC.

OKLAHOMA POWWOW
18 specialty dance songs, including, "Eagle Dance." Cassette, $4.50. GDA.

ONCE IN A RED MOON
Joanne Shenandoah. Joanne opened Woodstock '94 with songs from this album. Songs deal with Native American issues. Includes hit song, "America", performed at the White House and on TNT. 42 minutes. Cassette. CAN.

OPEN CIRCLE
The flute by Kevin Locke. CD, $14.98; cassette, $9.98. MCP.

ORENDA
Joanne Shenandoah and Lawrence Laughling. Songs are primarily from the Iroquois tradition. CD, $15.98; cassette, $9.98. SWR.

OUT OF THE ASHES
Shelley Morningsong. CD, $16.95. SWR. 2011.

OUT OF THE FIRE
Tom Minton flute music. Cassette. $9.95. VIP.

PAPAGO-PIMA INDIAN RECORDS & TAPES
Papago Dance Songs (Chelkona & Keihina Dance Songs) (LP); Songs from the Pima; Traditional Papago Music; Traditional Pima Dance Songs. Cassettes. $7.98 each. CAN.

PASSAMAQUODDY BRIEF HISTORIES
One cassette (30 minutes) in Passamaquoddy & bilingual, with 20 pp. booklet. $11.95. AUDIO.

PETER LA FARGE--ON THE WARPATH
Includes 14 contemporary protest songs by Peter La Farge, accompanied by Nick Navarro, Indian drums. LP. $9.98. CAN.

PEYOTE CANYON
Paul Guy, and Teddy Allen (Navajos) sing peyote songs. Cassette, $10. FTW.

PEYOTE MUSIC
Peyote - A Collection; Chants of Native American Church, Vol. 2 (LP); Intertribal Peyote Chants-Bill Denny, 5 Vols.; Kiowa Peyote Songs; Lord's Prayer Songs-Alfred Armstrong; Navajo Wildcat Peak-Peyote Songs, 5 Vols.; Navajo Wildcat Peak-Youth; Peyote Healing Chants of Native American Church (LP); Peyote Prayer Songs, 2 Vols.; Peyote Songs, Vol. 2.; Billy Nez-Peyote Songs from Navajoland; Nez & Yazzie-Peyote Voices; Guy and Allen. Cassettes. $7.98-$9.98 each. CAN.

PLIGHT OF THE REDMAN
by XIT. Cassette, $9.95; CD, $14.95. VIP.

PONCA TRIBAL SONGS
Songs sung by Lamont Brown, Sylvester Warrior, Alberta Waters, & Henry Snake. Recorded in 1967. Cassette/LP, $10. AIS.

PONCA WARRIORS DANCE SONGS & PAWNEE WARRIORS DANCE SONGS
10 Ponca warrior dance songs by Sylvester Warrior, Albert Waters & Francis Eagle; Pawnee Flag Song & 12 warrior dance songs sung by Frank Murrie, Lamont Pratt, Phillip Jim & Mrs, Jacob Leader. Cassette/LP, $10. AIS.

POW WOW SONGS
American Powwow by the Cathedral Singers; Powwwow Highway Songs & Powwow People, both by Black Lodge Singers; and Powwow Season by the Indian Creek Singers. Cassettes & CDs. $9.95 each. VIP.

POW WOW SONGS FROM OKLAHOMA
32 War Dance Songs from the O-Ho-Mah Lodge, Cheyenne, Pawnee and Ponca tribes sung by Tom Ware, Millard Clark, et al. 2 Vols. Cassettes. $15.96. CAN & GDA.

POW WOW SONGS OF THE MENOMINEE
Summer Cloud Singers in honor of the life of "Nepenanakwat" Johnson Awonohopay. Cassette, $12. ICC.

POW WOW & SPECIALTY DANCE SONGS FROM OKLAHOMA
18 songs including Comanche Flag Song, round, gourd, war eagle, hoop, etc. dance songs. Kiowa and Comanche singers. Cassette, $10. CMM & CAN.

POWWOW SONGS
1 audiocassette (48 minutes), $10.95. AUDIO.

PUEBLO INDIAN TAPES
Hopi Butterfly; Hopi Social Dance Songs, 2 Vols.; Songs from Laguna; Pueblo Indian Songs from San Juan; Zuni - Ceremonial Songs; Grand Canyon Hopi Dancers, recorded 1958-15 minutes ($6.95). Cassettes, $7.98 each. CAN.

PULLING DOWN THE CLOUDS: CONTEMPORARY NATIVE WRITERS READ THEIR WORK
CD anthology. NMAI Press, $15.

RED TAIL CHASING HAWKS: BROTHER HAWK
Calvin Standing Bear & James Torres
Native American flute and keyboards. Cassett, $6.; CD, $9.15. CAN.

REFLECTIONS
Tsonakwa tells stories & reminisces about his early life. 11 short tales told in "intimate leisurely style. 53 minutes. Cassette, $9.95.

THE RENAISSANCE OF THE AMERICAN INDIAN
Describes the social barriers the American Indian has had to face; his experiences in various careers, and the anachronistic traditions of Indian culture that confuses his progress. 1968. Cassette. AUDIO.

RESERVATION BLUES: THE SOUND TRACK
Jim Boyd & Sherman Alexie
Sherman Alexie (Spokane/Coeur D'Alene writer, author of the novel Reservation Blues) and Jim Boyd (Colville Confederated Tribes) collaborate on this soundtrack. Cassette, $6; CD, $10. OY.

ROBERT TREE CODY: LULLABIES & TRADITIONAL SONGS
Native American flute music. Cassette, $12. CH.

ROCK POINT SINGERS, Vol. 4
Traditional love tunes. 14 skip and two-step dance songs. Cassette, CAN

ROUND DANCE SONGS WITH ENGLISH LYRICS
48 songs. By Tom Mauchahty-Ware & Millard Clark. 4 LPs. $7.98 each. CAN & GDA.

RUMBLE: A TRIBUTE TO NATIVE MUSIC ICONS
Derek Miller (Mohawk); American Indian musicians. CD. NMAI, $14.95.

SACRED FEELINGS
Douglas Spotted Eagle combines the nature sounds of the earth-mother with Native American flute. Cassette, $12. CH.

SALISH
Language course for beginners in the Salish language, spoken today principally in British Columbia. 30 lessons providing vocabulary, phrases, and sentences on subjects of everyday interest, such as work, weather, directions,

food & money. 1994. 2 cassettes & 88-page text which includes 22 pp. index. $29.95. AUDIO.

SAN XAVIER FIDDLE BAND
O'odham old time fiddle music. 12 polkas, chotes and mazurkas. Cassette, $7.98. CAN

SELF-DETERMINATION FOR AMERICAN INDIANS:
1) DEVELOPMENT OF THEIR LANDS; 2) CULTURES IN CONFLICT
Recorded and edited by Henry W. Hough: 1) Traces the history of reservations and discusses the present development of resources on Indian reservations. 2) Why Indians cling to their way of life although proud of their American citizenship. 1968. Cassettes, 25 minutes each. AUDIO.

SELU: SEEKING THE CORN MOTHR'S WISDOM
Awiakta
In this companion to her book of the same name, Awiakta leads all who will listen along a deer trail that spirals into the Great Smokey Mountains to the Corn Motehr herself--and to her wisdoms. 3 hours. 1995. $16.95. OY.

SEMINOLE INDIANS OF FLORIDA
Dr Frances Densmore on cylinders. Includes corn dance, Cypress Swamp hunting and buffalo dance songs; plus songs for treatment of the sick and songs concerning removal of Seminole to Oklahoma. LP. $9.98. CAN.

SENECA SOCIAL DANCE MUSIC
30 songs from Allegany Reservation, Cattaraugus Co., New York. Recorded by M.F. Reimer. LP. $9.98. CAN.

SENECA SONGS FROM COLDSPRING LONGHOUSE
Songs include the Drum Dance, Bear Society, Fish Dance, & others. Recorded and edited in 1941-1945 by Willard N. Fenton. 16-page brochure. LP. $8.98, LC and $9.98. CAN.

THE SEVENTH DIRECTION
Flute music by Tokeya Inajin (Kevin Locke). Cassette, $10. MCP.

SHENANDOAH
JoAnne Shenandoah; Country tunes with contemporary ballads about Native American life. 40 minutes. Cassette/CD. CAN.

SIGNALS FROM THE HEART
Collection of "49" and round dance love songs using traditional drumming and style. Performed by Common Man Singers of the Standing Rock Sioux Reservation in North Dakota. Cassette, $11; CD, $17. MCP & MFP.

SILENT WARRIOR
by XIT. Cassette, $9.95; CD, $14.95. VIP.

SIOUX RECORDS & TAPES
Celebration on an Indian Theme; Denver Dakota Singers -Pow Wow Songs; Fort Kipp Celebration; Fort Kipp '77 Live; Fort Kipp Sioux Singers; Grass Dance Songs from Devil's Lake - By the Lake Region Singers; Ironwood Singers; Montana Grass Songs - By the Fort Kipp Singers; Porcupine Singers, 6 Vols. - At Ring Thunder, Traditional Sioux Songs, Concert in Vermillion, At the University of South Dakota, Rabbit Songs; Rock Creek Singers - Hunkpapa Sioux; Sioux Favorites; Sioux Grass Songs and Round Dances; Sioux Songs From Devils Lake - By the Lone Buffalo Singers; Sioux Songs of War and Love; Sisseton-Wahpeton Songs (LP); and Songs of the Sioux. Rock Creek Singers; Sioux-Assiniboine Singers, 2 Vols.; Red Nation Singers; Taku Wakan: Lakota Sundance Songs; Taku Skanskan: Lakota Yuwipi Songs. Cassettes, $7.98-9.98 each. CAN.

A SKY OF DREAMS
Neoprimitive solos for flutes of the world. By Barry Stramp of the Coyote Oldman duo. Cassette, $10; compact disc, $15. FTW & CH.

SMOKESIGNS
Rick Eby; Flute & synthesizer music. Cassette. $12.95. VIP.

SONG CARRIER
Robert Mirabal. Flute. CD, $15.98; cassette, $9.98. SWR.

SONGS & DANCES OF THE FLATHEAD INDIANS
A complete musical culture of the Salish people. Illustrated notes included. LP. $9.98. CAN.

SONGS & DANCES OF THE GREAT LAKES INDIANS
Music of the Algonquins and Iroquois. Recorded in Iowa, Wisconsin, Michigan and New York State by Gertrude P. Kurath. Text included. LP. $9.98. CAN.

SONGS FROM THE IROQUOIS LONGHOUSE
Selections include: Creator's Songs; Midwinter Festival Chants; Medicine Men's Celebration (Onondaga.) Recorded and edited by William N. Fenton in cooperation with the Smithsonian Institution. 34-page brochure. LP. $8.95, LC and $9.98, CAN.

SONGS OF THE CHEROKEE
Ceremonial songs & dances (CD); songs & dances of the Cherokee of North Carolina & the Seneca (CD). $11.95 each. AUDIO.

SONGS OF EARTH, WATER, FIRE & SKY
Traditional dance songs recorded on location by Pueblo, Seneca, Arapaho, Plains, Creek, Yurok, Navajo & Cherokee tribes. Cassette, $12. CH.

SONGS OF THE NATIVE AMERICAN CHURCH
Peyote songs by Billy McClellan. 2 Vols. $9. GDA.

SONGS OF THE NAVAJO
Traditional Navajo songs (CD); traditional Sioux songs (cassette); Taku Wakan: Lakota Sundance Songs (CD). $11.95 each. AUDIO.

SONGS, POEMS AND LIES
Lorenzo Baca (Isleta Pueblo/Mescalero Apache) sings songs with traditional chants and original poetry. Cassette, $10. FTW.

SONGS & STORIES FROM NEAH BAY - MAKAH
Legends and little songs by a favorite Makah storyteller, Helen Peterson. CAN.

SOUND OF AMERICAN RECORDS (SOAR)
Specializes in contemporary & traditional Native music from throughout North America. Contains hundred of recordings on CD and cassette as well as videos and audio books on CD. SOAR.

SOUNDS OF INDIAN AMERICA -- PLAINS & SOUTHWEST RECORDED LIVE AT THE GALLUP CEREMONIALS
Includes the Buffalo Dance, Jemez Eagle Dance, Ute Bear Dance, San Juan Butterfly Dance, Zuni Rain Song Dance by the Olla Maidens, Navajo Feather Dance, Taos Belt Dance, Pawnee Ghost Dance, Zuni Doll Dance, Crow Sun Dance, Kiowa Attack Dance. CD, $12. IH.

SOUNDS OF INDIAN SUMMER: CONTEMPORARY NATIVE MUSIC FROM THE NATIONAL MUSEUM OF THE AMERICAN INDIAN
CD. 80 minutes. NMAI, $15.

SOUTHERN PLAINS-OKLAHOMA INDIANS RECORDS & TAPES
Brave Scout Singers-Northern Style Otoe, Missourian & Pawnee; Gourd Dance Songs of the Kiowa-Koomsa Tribal Singers; Kiowa Back Leggings Society Songs-Bill Kaulaity; Kiowa Gourd Dance Songs; Kiowa "49" & Round Dance Songs; Kiowa Scalp & Victory Dance Songs-Koomsa Tribal Singers; Ponca War Dances-Ponca India Singers; Pow Wow - Southern Style War Dances; Songs of the Caddo, 2 Vols. (LP). CD. $9.98 each. CAN.

SOUTHERN SCRATCH: WAILA OF THE TOHONO O'ODHAM
Popular dance music of the native peoples of southern Arizona. 53 minutes. Cassette. CAN.

SOUTHERN THUNDER: INTERTRIBAL SONGS OF OKLAHOMA
Osage Flag Song, 14 intertribal songs, 2 Pawnee veterans' songs, & 1 Pawnee war dance song sung by a few different singers. Recorded at Hominy, Oklahoma, 1992. CD, $10. IH.

SOUTHERN THUNDER: REACHIN' OUT
14 intertribal songs by a number of singers. Recorded at Hominy, Oklahoma, 1993. CD, $10. IH.

SPACE AGE INDIAN
Tiger Tiger; CD, $14.95. VIP.

SPIRIT HORSES
R. Carlos Nakai with traditional cedar flute and contemporary concerto for Native American flute and chamber orchestra. CD, $12. CAN & CH.

SPIRIT JOURNEY - CORNEL PEWEWARDY
Dr. Pewewardy (Comanche/Kiowa) demonstrates his talents of singer, flute player & keeper of the drum. Cassette, $11; CD, $17. MCP & MFP.

SPIRIT OF SONG
Original digital recording of the "Spirit of Song" singers from the spring of 1990. The voices of Sissy & Credric Goodhouse, Earl & Tom Bullhead, Dave Archambault, et al. on the Lakota culture. CD, $14.98; CD, $9.98. MCP.

SPIRITS OF THE PRESENT: THE LEGACY FROM NATIVE AMERICA
Focuses on Native American histories, cultures, and modern realities. Explores American Indian religious fredom, the sovereignty of Native nations, stereotyping of Native people by sports teams and other commercial entities, and Native American art. 1991. 5 audiocassettes. $29.95. PUSA (800) 253-6476.

STAR LORE
Lynn Moroney (Cherokee/Chickasaw), tells the star lore to be found in the myths of Native Americans. Authentic music by Native American flute player. The Feather Moon, 1 casette; The Star Husband, 1 casette. 1994. 45 minutes each. $10.95 each. AUDIO.

STARGAZER
Gerald Hausman; Navajo supernatural myths & divination stories. 60 minutes. CD, $11.95. AUDIO.

STORYTELLER
N. Scott Momaday; Stories in the Native American oral tradition shared by a storytelling master of the Kiowa origin. 60 minutes. CD, $9.95. AUDIO.

SUNRISE
Flute music by Tom Mauchanty-Ware, featuring, "Zuni Sunrise Song." CD. $4.50. GDA.

SYMBOLIC SHAMANISM: A STUDY OF NAVAJO MEDICINE MEN
Dr. Donald Sandner describes the healing process of medicine men and attempts to explain the sandpaintings, how they are made, how images are evoked for each patient, and how cures are performed. CD. BSR.

SYMBOLS OF HOPI
Jill McManus, a jazz musician, has created a jazz album by arranging two songs each by a pair of Hopi composers who work within their own dance music tradition, and added three originals in the spirit of Hopi and Pueblo music. Includes two Hopi ceremonial songs, "Corn Dance" and "Cloud Blessing." Louis Mofsie, director of the famed Thunderbird Dance Troup, opens Mark Lomayestewa's Corn Dance on the cottonwood drum. CJ.

TAOS TALES
Robert Mirabal. In song, chant & music, Mirabal tells stories of the land known as Taos using flute, cello, guitar and percussion. CD, $15.98; cassette, $9.98.

TEAR OF THE MOON
Coyote Old Man. Compositions on Native American flute & Incan Pan Pipes. CD, $12. CH.

THE THIRD CIRCLE - SONGS OF LAKOTA WOMEN
Traditional & contemporary Lakota women's songs sung by Sissy Goodhouse. CD, $14.98. MCP.

THUNDER CHORD
Coyote Oldman. Native American flutes and panpipes. CD, $12. CH.

THUNDERDRUMS
Scott Fitzgerald uses drums from both Native America and Africa for sounds of nature. CD, $16. FTW.

TIWAHE
Sissy Goodhouse, her family & friends sing traditional & contempor-ary Lakota songs celebrating the meaning of family. CD, $14.98. MCP.

TO THOSE WHO'VE GONE BEFORE US
Native flute music. Paul Hacker and son, Jason, a duet of Native American flute traditional & gospel. CD, $16. PH

TOUCH THE EARTH
A unique performance of words and music on the sacredness of land and life by twelve distinguished Native American actors, musicians, artists, writers and spiritual leaders, based on T.C. McLuhan's best-selling book, Touch the Earth. 60 mins. Audiocassette. $10.95. MFV.

TOUCH THE FIRE
Native American poetry by Bob Annesley. CD, $7.50. GDA.

TOUCH THE SWEET EARTH
Sharon Burch; Her songs focus on importance of the maternal relationship to the Dine. In Navajo with some English. 1996. 36 mins. CD, $9.15. CAN.

TRACKS WE LEAVE
16 impressionistic compositions featuring William Eaton, with R. Carlos Nakai, Rich Rodgers, Claudia Tulip, Arvel Bird & Udi Arouh. Notes on the instruments

and performers included. 55 minutes. Cassette, $8.98; compact disc, $14.98. CAN & CH.

THE TRADITIONAL & CONTEMPORARY INDIAN FLUTE
Flute music by Tom Mauchanty-Ware. CD. $4.50. GDA.

THE TRADITIONAL & CONTEMPORARY INDIAN FLUTE
Flute songs by Fernando Cellicion. Cassette, $4.50. GDA.

TRADITIONAL INDIAN FLUTE OF FERNANDO CELLICION
10 flute songs. CD, $7.50. GDA.

TRIBAL MUSIC INTERNATIONAL
Music from the Hopi; Music from San Juan Pueblo; Red Eagle Wing Powwow Songs; Flute and Prayer Songs; Music from the Alliance West Singers; and 65th Inter-Tribal Ceremonial-Gallup Ceremonial; Music from Zuni Pueblo. CD. $8.98 each. CAN.

TRIBAL SONGS
Ceremonial and social songs and dances of eight Native American Indian tribes: Tohono O'odham (Papago), Apache, Sioux, Navajo, Crow, Ute, Shawnee, and New Taos. 1 cassette. $12.95. AUDIO.

TURTLE ISLAND ALPHABET
Gerald Hausman's anthology of myths & stories that study the symbols & images central to the Native American culture. 1 cassette (90 minutes), $10.95. AUDIO.

TURTLE MOUNTAIN SINGERS: EARLY THIS MORNING I HEARD MY HORSE CALLING
10 Navajo social dance songs sung by John Comanche, Jimmie Castillo, Samuel Harrison, & Kee Trujillo, Recorded Taos, NM, 1990. Cassette, $10. IH.

TURTLE MOUNTAIN SINGERS: WELCOME TO NAVAJO LAND
10 Navajo social dance songs sung by John Comanche, Jimmie Castillo, Samuel Harrison, Ernest Chavez, Kee Trujillo, Johnny B. Dennison & Benson Trujillo. Recorded at Lybrook, New Mexico, 1990. Cassette/LP, $10. IH.

UNDER THE GREEN CORN MOON: NATIVE AMERICAN LULLABIES
Performers represent 14 different Indian Nations, and include Joanne Shenandoah & Robert Mirabal. CD, $15.98; Cassette, $9.98. SWR.

UNITED TRIBES INTERNATIONAL POWWOW
Powwow recording featuring some of the best drum groups in the nation singing their best songs. 2 CD set, $19.98; 2 cassette set, $12.98. MCP.

UP WHERE WE BELONG
Buffy Sainte-Marie (Cree) Cassette, $10. OY.

UTES
Includes six northern war dance songs, three bear dances, and three sun dance songs. Singers from Ignacio, Colorado, and from the White Mesa, Utah. Cassette. $7.98. CAN.

VASQUEZ
Andrew Vasquez's flute. CD, $14.98; Cassette, $9.98. MCP.

VETERANS SONGS
Lakota Thunder; Songs honoring warriors from past to present. Included are songs of Sitting Bull, the Battle of the Little Bighorn, World Wars, Korean and Vietnam Wars. CD, $14.98; CD, $9.98. MCP.

A VOICE FOR THE AMERICAN INDIAN
A program on Indian culture and history, and the current struggles for political rights and power. Produced by Pacifica, KPFA. 1971. 54 minutes. AUDIO.

WALELA: LIVE IN CONCERT
Benefiting the Sovereign Nations Preservations Project, a non-profit provider of educational media benefiting Native Americans. With Rita Coolidge, Laura Satterfield & Priscilla Coolidge. $24.95. CD. MALKI.

WALKING THE RED ROAD
Earl Bullhead, a Lakota of the Standing Rock Reservation in North Dakota, sings traditional Lakota songs recorded in a contemporary style. Cassette, $10.60; CD, $16. MCP.

WAR WHOOPS AND MEDICINE SONGS
33 songs collected at the Upper Dells of the Wisconsin River where more than 200 American Indians from five different tribes assembled for the annual Star Rock Indian Ceremonial. Includes an illustrated brochure. Edited by Charles Hoffman. CD. $9.98. CAN.

WARRIOR MAGICIAN
Robert Mirabal. Flute music. CD, $9.98. SWR.

WASHO PEYOTE SONGS: SONGS OF THE AMERICAN INDIAN NATIVE CHURCH
Recorded by Dr. Warren d'Azevedo. CD. $9.98. CAN.

WEAVINGS
R. Carlos Nakai; Nakai on the Native American flute & trumpet with Larry Yanez on synthesizer with percussion & guitar. 49 mins. Cassette/CD. CAN.

WESTERN CANADIAN INDIAN RECORDS & TAPES
A-1 Club Singers - Vol. 2; Blackfoot A-1 Singers; Blackfoot Oldtimers - Songs from the Past; Calgary Drummer; Chiniki Lake Drummers; Crowfoot Drummers - Blackfoot, Alberta; The Drums of Poundmaker - With the Tootoosis Family, 2 Vols. (LP); Fraser Valley Spotted Lake Inter-Tribal Singers; Little Pine Singers - Cree Powwow Songs; Pigeon Lake Singers - Cree Tribal Songs, 2 Vols.; Powwow Songs - Treaty 6 Ermine Skin Band; Sarcee Broken Knife Singers, 2 Vols.; Sarcee Oldtimers; Pezhin Wachipi (Grass Dance) (LP); Scalp Lock Singers; Sioux Powwow Songs; Songs from the Blood Reserve - Kaispai Singers; Songs from the Battleford Pow-Wow; Songs of the Sarcee (LP); Stony Pow-Wow Songs - Eden Valley Powwow Club; Two Nation Singers - Round Dance Songs; Little Boy Singers - Powwow Songs, 2 Vols.; Northern Cree Singers, Vols. 3 - Live at Fort Duchesne; Blackstone Singers, Vol. 1 - Contest Songs - Live at Fort Duchesne; Sioux Assiniboine - Dakota Kahomini Songs; The Red Bull Singers, 2 Vols.; Dakota Hotain Singers, 2 Vols.; Cathedral Lakes Singers, 2 Vols.; Whitefish Bay Singers, 2 Vols.; Plains Ojibway Singers, Vol. 1; Stoney Eagle. CD $9.98 each. CAN.

WHEN THE EARTH WAS LIKE NEW
Chesley Goseyun Wilson & Ruth Longcor Harnisch Wilson
Songs and stories of the Apache. WMP.

WHISPERING TREE: ANISHINAABE STORIES & SONGS
Traditional stories and contemporary situations about friendship, hope, joy and trust by Annie Humphrey, John Trudell, Pato Hoffman, Larry Long and author Anne Dunn and friends. CD, $14.98. MCP.

THE WHITE BUFFALO CALF WOMAN AS TOLD BY MARTIN HIGH BEAR
Cassette, $8.25. CAN.

WHITE EAGLE SINGERS, Vol. 5
11 intertribal pow wow songs recorded live at the Numaga
Indian Days in Reno-Sparks, Nevada. Cassette, $7.98. CAN.

WHITE FISH BAY SINGERS, Vol. 6
One of Canada's most popular traditional drum groups. Powwow singing. CD, $11. MFP.

WIND RIVER
Andrew Vasquez's flute with friends, Rodney Grant & Rita Coolidge. CD, $14.98; MCP.

WINDS OF HONOR
Gary Stroutsos; Joining Stroutsos are various artists including Epaminondas Trimis, Jovano Santos Neto, the Goodhouse family with traditional vocals, and Joseph Fire Crow on vocals and hand drum. CD, $14.98. MCP.

WINDS OF THE PAST, Vol. I & II
Flute music by Choctaw/Cherokee flutemaker Paul Hacker. Blend of traditional and contemporary. CD, $21. PH

WINTER DREAMS
Native American Christmas music. R. Carlos Nakai & William Eaton arranged these old traditional European Christmas songs. CD, $12. CAN & CH.

WITHOUT REZERVATION
Urban Native Americans rapping a politico-ethnic funk about the struggle of the red brother and red sister. Features Chris LaMarr, Kevin Nez and Cory Aranaydo. 42 minutes. CD. CAN.

WIYUTA: ASSINIBOINE STORYTELLING WITH SIGNS CD
CD, $100. UTP.

WOOD THAT SINGS: INDIAN FIDDLE MUSIC OF THE AMERICAS
Charlotte Heth (Cherokee), Executive Producer
Anthology of songs. CD. NMAI, $15.

WOODLAND WINDS - THE WOODLAND CONSORT
Fusion of Native & Western instruments, with Ojibway flute. CD, $16. MCP.

WOPILA - A GIVEAWAY: LAKOTA STORIES
Dovie Thompson
Features the traditional flute music of Kevin Locke within the prose of tha artist. Grades PS-4. Cassette, $10.60. MCP.

THE WORLD IN OUR EYES
Storyteller Reuben Silverbird's view of the essence of our country's most ancient heritage. Tells of the Great Spirit, Mother Earth, Father Sky, the circle, the rain, the eagle and other elements of the creation stories. Two cassettes, $18; CD, $29. MFP.

A YAQUI WAY OF KNOWLEDGE
The group Wild Strawberries in a series of tone poems inspired by Carlos Castaneda's best-selling book of the same title. Cassette, $10; compact disc, $16. FTW.

YAZZIE GIRL
Sharon Burch
Her songs focus on the importance of the maternal relationship to the Dine. In Navajo with some English. 36 minutes. CD, $9.15. CAN.

YOUNG EAGLE'S FLIGHT
Robert Tree Cody
Collection of solo Native American flute contains nine traditional (Lakota and Dakota) and five original songs. 46 minutes. CD. CAN.

ZANGO MUSIC DISTRIBUTION
Zango Music is a wholesale distribution company specializing in Native American music. Their Tribal Fires catalog is a comprehensive and useful guide for ordering tapes and compact discs. They carry over 800 titles of flute, traditional, contemporary and pow-wow music. Half of these titles are given detailed reviews with pictures of the album accompanying them. The catalog has advertising from many different independent and Native-owned labels; also include a best seller page to take the confusion out of ordering. Free demos are available on almost all selections. Wholesale. Catalog. ZANGO.

PRINTS & PHOTOGRAPHS
PICTURE SETS, POST CARDS, POSTERS
CALENDARS, CRAFT KITS, FLAGS

ALASKAMEUT '86
Exhibition poster features masks by John Kailukiak, Kathleen Carlo & James Schoppert. 24x18", full color. $8.50, postpaid. IANA.

ALL-NEW NATIVE AMERICAN BRACELETS
by Geri Dawn Weitzman
This kit includes 750 seed beads, embroidery floss, felt, and a 16-page full-color book wioth step-by-step instructions. $7.95. TA.

AMERICAN INDIAN CUT & USE STENCILS
Ed Sibbett, Jr.
64 pp. $6.95. DOV.

AMERICAN INDIAN PERSEPCTIVES ON THANKSGIVING
Teaching poster. SI.

AMERICAN INDIAN PORTRAIT POSTCARDS
Charles Bird King
24 postcards. 9 x 12" $4.95. DOV & WH.

ARTS FROM THE ARCTIC
Exhibition poster featuring the artwork of Alvin Amason. 18x22", full color. $12.50, postpaid. IANA.

ATHABASCAN OLD-TIME FIDDLING POSTER
Features musicians and dancers. 18x24", black and silver duotone. $7.50, postpaid. IANA.

THE BEAUTY OF NATIVE AMERICAN CHURCH-POSTER
By Haroldton Begaye. 21 x 17. $3.95. CAN.

BENDING TRADITION
Exhibition poster featuring bentwood art by traditional and contemporary artists. 24" x 18" full color. Institute of Alaska Native Arts, $8.50, postpaid. IANA.

BLACKFOOT INDIAN PORTRAITS
Winold Reiss
A portfolio of 6 self-matted full-color prints. 9x12. $3.95. DOV.

BOSTON CHILDREN'S MUSEUM BORROW A KIT
The Indians Who Met the Pilgrims: Presents the Wampanoag people of Massachusetts past and present; Hopi Culture: Describes a public kachina dance and its connection to contemporary Hopi culture. These two kits may be used as curriculum units, include cultural objects, oral history, texts and guides, A-V materials, and classroom activities; prepared with the participation of Native American people. Two other kits, The Navajo and Northwest Coast Indians, contain cultural objects and related labels for classroom exhibit. CMB.

CAHOKIA ARTIFACTS POSTER
Full color poster showing artifacts found at Cahokia Mounds site. 38" x 25". $10. CMM.

CAHOKIA MOUNDS MURAL
Entrance scene in new Interpretive Center - artists conception of ancient city. 20" x 37". $10. CMM.

CATLIN'S NORTH AMERICAN INDIAN PORTFOLIO
The 1845 American edition is supplemented with six additional prints from the original British edition. Each set contains 31 plates measuring 16x22". Strictly limited to 950 sets. 1989. $1,250. A.

CHEROKEE POEM
8.5" x 11 poster. $2.50. VIP.

CHEROKEE POSTER
Kevin Smith, artist
17" x 21". $7.95. VIP.

CHOCTAW T-SHIRT
Kevin Smith, artist. $13.95. VIP.

CLOVIS CULTURE
Poster. $15. CMM.

CONCRETE TIPI: THE NATIVE AMERICAN EXPERIENCE IN NEW YORK CITY
20 color & b&w postcards. 2006. NMAI, $8.95.

CRAFT SUPPLIES
Beads, needles, thread, metal items, shawl fringe, feathers, herbs, books. CAN.

CUSTER'S FIGHT
Poster. 29" x 21" full color; flat. $1.50. DOV.

EARLY PALEO INDIAN PERIOD
Poster. $15. CMM.

EARLY TEXAS INDIAN MURAL POSTERS
George Nelson
Series of posters, full-color photographs of the actual 24" x 10" murals on the Institute of Texan Cultures' Floor. "A Caddo Farming Community in East Texas"; "Desert Farmers of Southwest Texas: The Mogollon Culture"; An Apache Encampment in the Texas Hill Country." Each poster, 36" x 21". $10 each; $25 for all three. UT-ITC.

EDUCATIONAL AID KITS
Children's touchable exhibits contained in a large footlocker-type trunk. Artifacts are compiled from the Museum of New Mexico's collections and various other sources in Santa Fe. Includes: Anglo Pioneer Family; Apache Family; Navajo Family; Pueblo Indian Family; and Spanish Frontier Family. Grades 1-6. Available for loan in the State of New Mexico only. Free one month rental. MNM.

ENCHANTING NEW MEXICO CALENDAR: WILLIE MURPHY— HEADING HOME, PAINTINGS OF THE NAVAJO NATION 2009
Paintings of Navajo life & lands. UNM. $12.95.

GEORGE CATLIN'S NORTH AMERICAN INDIANS
Box of 20 5x7" notecards & envelopes. 4 different designs. $11.95. A.

GREAT NATIVE AMERICAN LEADERS
Posters include a short biography including: Black Hawk, Chief Joseph, Chief Seattle, Geronimo, Red Cloud, and Sitting Bull. 18" x 24". Individual poster, $7.95. Set, $26.95. KU.

HOOP DANCER PRINT
Milton Denny, artist; $2.50. VIP.

HOPI KACHINAS: A POSTCARD COLLECTION
Cliff Bahnimptewa, illustrator; 20 full-color postcards. Illus. $7.95. NP.

HOWARD ROCK & HIS LEGACY
Exhibition poster featuring The Dance of Kakirnok, a painting by the late Howard Rock. 16x20", full color. $7.50, postpaid. IANA.

IDENTITY BY DESIGN: TRADITION, CHANGE, AND CELEBRATION IN NATIVE WOMEN'S DRESSES NOTECARDS 2006. NMAI, $9.95.

INDIAN DWELLING & HOMES OF THE U.S. POSTER
Revised 1984. 29" x 23". $5.25. CMM.

INDIAN PHOTOGRAPHS FROM THE SMITHSONIAN
There are four sets of five prints each. Set 1) Selected portraits: Kicking Bear, Geronimo, Chief Joseph, Quanah Parker, and Wolf Robe; Set 2-4) Lifestyles, Northwestern Indians - Southwestern Indians - Plains Indians. 11 x 14. SI.

INDIAN POW-WOW CALENDAR
NACO.

THE INDIANS OF THE PLAINS
Contains 46, 11 x 14 photos explaining the Plains Indians culture, government, society & habits; and how they were discovered in 1805. $73.50. DPA.

INTERWOVEN EXPRESSIONS
Exhibition poster featuring 20 Alaska Native baskets representative of all of the Alaska Native cultures. 24x18", full color. $8.50, postpaid. IANA.

KIOWA EAGLE PRINT
Ruth Blaylock Jones, artist; $3. VIP.

LIBRARY OF CONGRESS PRINTS & PHOTOGRAPHS DIVISION
Recently completed the processing and cataloging of 3,500 images of American Indians photographed over an 85-year period ending in the 1940s. Also an extensive collection of Edward S. Curtis photographs, more than 1,600 photos. The images are now accessible to researchers in the division's reading room in the Library's Madison building in Washington, DC. LC.

CARL MOON PHOTOGRAPHS
see publisher MPC for details and prices.

MUSEUM OF THE AMERICAN INDIAN-PHOTOGRAPHIC ARCHIVES
Covers all areas & aspects of Native American life in the Western Hemisphere. Includes photographs by Curtis, Matteson and Jackson; Pepper, Wildschut and Verrill. 42,000 negatives, 28,000 bxw prints, and 5,000 color transparencies and slides; bxw prints, 5x7 or 8x10 format; 35mm color slides; and 4x5 color transparencies. A slide list is available for a modest fee. MAI.

MUSEUM OF NEW MEXICO PHOTOGRAPHIC PORTFOLIOS
Includes three Native American photographic portfolios: Pueblo Indians of New Mexico; Apache Indians of New Mexico; and, Navajo Indians of New Mexico. Each set contains 16 photographs illustrating important aspects of the subject group's life and history during the late 19th and early 20th centuries. Large bxw photographs printed on heavy glossy paper. Each portfolio also contains a brief history of the group plus a vocabulary list, bibliography, and descriptive captions for the photographs. $6.95 each. MNM.

NATIVE AMERICAN CARDS
Tarot card deck & book set by Laura Tuan & Massimo Rotundo. 33 cards. $12.95. ACA.

NATIVE AMERICAN CRAFT KITS
Dream Catchers, $7.95.; Kachinas, $7.95; Clay Pots, $7.95. All-New Native American Bracelets, $7.95; Sand Painting, $6.95. TA & CLD.

NATIVE AMERICAN CULTURE
Ten posters. 17" x 22" including: The Plains, The Plateur, The Southeast, The Southwest, The Northwest, The Northwest Coast, The Great Basin, California, The Arctic, The Subarctic. Individual posters, $7.95; set, $44.95.

NATIVE AMERICAN FLAG
3' x 5'. $25. NACO.

NATIVE AMERICAN IMAGES
Exhibit posters and limited edition prints by Donald Vann, and original stone lithographs by Steve Forbes. NAI.

NATIVE AMERICAN PRINTS
Fine art prints & canvasses. Native American themes. GW

NATIVE AMERICAN TRIBES
Poster shows the names & locations of over 100 Native American tribes. Laminated. 16 x 20. Knowledge Unlimited. $7.95.

NATIVE AMERICAN VISIONS CALENDAR
12 exquisite Sam English (Ojibwa artist) full-color prints; calendar with 10x14 print and appointment calendar below; and selected quotes from historic and present-day tribal leaders. Available in August for upcoming year. $10.95. FUL.

NATIVE AMERICANS: THE HISTORY OF A PEOPLE
Ten posters. 17" x 22". Individual posters, $7.95; set, $44.95. KU.

NAVAJO CURRICULUM MATERIALS - DRUGS AND ALCOHOL
"Drug & Alcohol Myths" - poster set, 11x17-3 colors - 12 posters drawn with Indian people depicting common myth about drug and alcohol use and abuse. $5.10 per set; $8.95 laminated; "Fetal Alcohol Syndrome" - poster set, 11x17-2 color - 8 posters stating facts about fetal alcohol syndrome and its effect on new born babies. $3.40 per set; $6.80 laminated. SAN.

NAVAJO DESIGN GIFTWRAP PAPER
Elaine Norman. 4 sheets, 9x12. $3.95. DOV.

NAVAJO GUIDES, CULTURAL MANUALS, & TEXTBOOKS
See SAN for titles and prices.

NAVAJO INDIAN CULTURAL CARD SETS & POSTERS
Contains 16 in all. All grades. See SAN for titles and prices.

NAVAJO INSTRUCTIONAL PROGRAMS, KITS & PACKETS
See SAN for titles and prices.

NAVAJO RUG STIK-WITHIT NOTECUBES
Self Stick. Full color. 600 sheets, 3.5 x 3". $12. NP.

NEW TRADITIONS
Exhibition poster features The Hunter, by the late Sam Fox of Dillingham, AK. 18x30", blue/black duotone. $7.50, postpaid. IANA.

NORTH AMERICAN INDIAN DESIGN GIFTWRAP PAPER
Gregory Mirow; 4 sheets. 9x12. $3.95. DOV.

NORTH AMERICAN INDIAN DESIGNS LASER-CUT PLASTIC STENCILS
Charlene Tarbox. 8 designs. $7.95. DOV.

OLD WOMAN PRINT
Milton Denny, artist. $3. VIP.

THE ONEIDAS AT THE BATTLE OF ORISKANY
18 x 29" print commemorating the Oneida Indian allies that fought on the patriot side during the Revolutionary War battle of August 6, 1777. $225, limited edition; 22 x 35" giclee edition, $750. HAP.

PAINTINGS OF AMERICAN WEST POSTCARDS
Eiteljorg Museum. 16 pp. $3.95. DOV.

PEYOTE PRAYER-POSTER
By Doug Standing Rock. 28 x 21". $3.95. CAN.

THE PLAINS INDIANS
Two sets of 18 different photographs, featuring the fully captioned art of Howard Terpning, renowned painter of Plains Indian history. $44 each; $78 for both. DPA.

POSTCARDS OF HISTORIC TAHLEQUAH
BxW postcards of the capital of the Cherokee Nation. 4 sets available. $6 for each set of 6 views, all 4 sets, 24 cards, $10. VIP.

POW WOW: PORTRAITS OF NATIVE AMERICANS
photos by Ben Marra; Includes a personal statement from each Native American dancer. 2005. $12.99.

POWWOW
photos by Chris Roberts
Captures the energy of powwow dancers. Annual calendar. $12.95. ME.

PUEBLO PEOPLE CALENDAR: A PHOTOGRAPHIC PORTFOLIO OF PUEBLO INDIANS Marcia Keegan. $12. CL.

SACRED PEYOTE WATER BIRD-POSTER
By Doug Standing Rock. 21 x 14". $3.95. CAN.

SEASON'S GREETINGS: NOTECARDS FROM THE SMITHSONIAN'S NATIONAL MUSEUM OF THE AMERICAN INDIAN
20 holiday cards, 2005. $14.95. NMAI.

SELECTED PORTRAITS OF PROMINENT NORTH AMERICAN INDIANS
8x10 glossy or matte prints. SI.

SHAPED BY WIND & WATER: POSTCARDS OF THE NATIONAL MUSEUM OF THE AMERICAN INDIAN
20 color postcards. 2005. $8.95. NMAI.

SIX INDIAN CRAFTS POSTCARDS
Eiteljorg Museum
Full-color postcards of items on display at the Eiteljorg Museum of American Indian and Western Art in Indianapolis, Indiana. 6 cards, $1. TC.

SOUTHWEST INDIAN CALENDAR
Marcia Keegan; Large-format color pictures of life among the Pueblo Indians of New Mexico. 12 1/2 x 10 1/4". $12. NAV.

SOUTHWEST INDIAN GIFTWRAP PAPER
Muncie Hendler. 2 sheets. 9x12" $1.75. DOV.

SOUTHWEST INDIAN STICKERS
Madeleine Orban-Szontagh; 24 full-color, pressure-sensitive, designs adapted from the Hopi, Navajo and Pueblo tribes. 8 pp. $1. TC.

STORY IN STONE
Artifacts poster. 24" x 36". $10. CMM.

SUN RIVER WAR PARTY
Poster. 33" x 21" full color...flat. $1.50. DOV.

TEACHING RESPECT FOR NATIVE PEOPLES
A brief list of how, and how not to, teach about Native peoples in the classroom. 18" x 24". $10. OY.

A TREASURED HERITAGE
Exhibition poster featuring 11 works by Alaska Native artists representative of Yup'ik and Inupiaq Eskimo, Tlingit, Haida, Tsimshian and Athabascan Indian cultures. 24x18", full color. $8.50, postpaid. IANA.

TRIBAL FLAGS
Sault Ste. Marie Tribe of Chippewa Indians, Attn: Sherrie Lucas, 531 Ashmun St., Sault Ste. Marie, MI 49783. (800) 793-0660. E-mail: slucas@saulttribe.net.

TRIBAL PROFILE POSTER SERIES
3 wall displays of federally recognized U.S. tribes and bands. Packaged in 5 mil. lamination, comered and graumetted. TDR.

TRUST FOR NATIVE AMERICAN CULTURES & CRAFTS
a 17" x 22.5" poster featuring many of the traditional skills (canoe, snowshoe making, hide tanning, the manufacture of skin clothing, etc.) Represented are the Montagnais, Cree, Algonquin, and Attikamek groups. Color on one side and black & white on the reverse. $8. TR.

WHEN EARTH BECOMES AN "IT"
A poem, about what will happen if Mother Earth continues not to be respected, was a gift to us from Cherokee/Appalachian poet Awiatka. 11" x 14". $10. OY.

WINTERCOUNT
American Indian greeting cards, music, art, prose & poetry. WIN.

WOVOKA POSTER
I6 1/2 x 23" poster of the Northern Paiute Ghost Dance Prophet. $5.00. YPT.

XIT RELOCATION POSTER
23 x 35". $1.95. CAN.

MAPS

AMERICAN INDIAN HISTORY MAP
Documents the last 500 years of American Indian history. 24 x 36" full color shaded relief map with matte finish, printed on two sides. Informational booklet. $3.50. ATL

AMERICAN INDIAN NATIONS
A composite graphic of contemporary Indian America. 24x36" full-color shaded relief map. Illustrates diminished land base as Indians were forced westward be encroaching settlers. Locations of 300+ federally recognized reservations. Reservations with gaming facilities are indicated. $13 postpaid. TE.

ATLAS OF THE NORTH AMERICAN INDIANS
Carl Waldman; Map & illus. by Molly Braun; 1989. $16.95. FOF.

COLOR MAP
Shows the distribution of Indian tribes in New York City and vicinity during the 17th century. $1.50. MAI.

CONOZCA SUS RAICES / KNOW YOUR ROOTS: A MAP OF THE INDIGENOUS PEOPLES OF MEXICO & CENTROAMERICA
Dolan H. Eargle, Jr., Editor
A full color, 18"x24" poster, bilingual - Spanish & English with color-coded legend of contemporary ethnic homelands grouped by ling-uistic families. Mexico to Panama. Biblio. Trees Company Press, $5.

DISTRIBUTION OF INDIAN TRIBES OF NORTH AMERICA
Map by Dr. A.L. Kroeber. 21x28" map of the time of first contact with white men. SM.

EARLY INDIAN TRIBES, CULTURE AREAS, & LINGUISTIC STOCK
William Sturtevant-U.S. Geological Survey; Multi-colored map, shows geographic extent of major an minor Indian tribes, their culture areas, and 18 linguistic stocks for Alaska and the 48 states. Biblio. $3.10. WE.

THE GABRIELINO INDIANS AT THE TIME OF THE PORTOLA EXPEDITION
Map by Allen M. Welts. 22x15 map showing locations of ancient Indian villages in southern California. SM.

HISTORICAL MAP, WARM SPRINGS INDIAN RESERVATION
Map by Ralph M. Shane and Ruby D. Leno, showing historical trails, sites and modern Kah-Nee-Ta. 15x18 color. OHS.

INDIAN COUNTRY MAP
George Russell; 24x36" map representing a geographic history of 500 years of the American Indian. Identifies military forts & dates of activity, major battles & dates, and today's Indian tribes, nations, lands & reservations. The margins contain texts that discuss various topics & time periods. Accompanied with a pamphlet, 1998. Rolled, $12; folded, $8. TE.

INDIAN GAMING MAP
18X24" The map shows the Interstate Highway system & the geographical location of each gaming facility listed alfabetically by state. The map roster Lists the name, address, & telephone number of all 223 Indian gaming facilities. Endorsed by Indian Gaming magazine. $12. TE.

INDIAN LAND AREAS--GENERAL
Official map of the Bureau of Indian Affairs. A multicolor map that indicates the location & size of Federal Indian reservations, Indian groups, etc. $10. NACO.

INDIAN RESERVATIONS MAP
Black and white map of the U.S. showing where the Indian tribes, reservations, and settlements are located. IRA.

INDIAN TRIBES & LANGUAGES OF OLD OREGON TERRITORY
22x33 color map. OHS.

INDIANS OF NORTH AMERICA
An archaeological and ethnological map. 32x37" with ethnological descriptive notes and illustrations. 1979. NGS.

MAP`N'FACTS: NATIVE PEOPLES OF NORTH AMERICA
Two full-color maps show--before Columbus--and today. 23x35. Two bxw maps on reverse set forth population and language groups. $4.50. FP.

MAP OF NORTH AMERICAN INDIANS
16 x 20 color map on durable enamel finished paper, $2.95; laminated, $4.95. CH.

NATIVE AMERICAN INDIAN TRIBES - MAP
Shows four geographical areas. 20" x 16". $3. CMM.

NATIVE LANGUAGES & LANGUAGE FAMILIES OF NORTH AMERICA
Ives Goddard, Editor; A map which shows the locations and distriubution of the known languages spoken by Native peoples across North America at the time of first contact. U. of Nebraska Press, $14.95, folded study map; $19.95, wall display map. UNP.

NATIVE TRIBES MAP
Alfred L. Kroeber. $14.95. 1967. UCP

NAVAJOLAND
A full-color illustrated map of the Southwestern U.S. where the Navajos live. Covers four states and 16 million acres. KC.

NORTHWEST INDIAN GUIDE AND MAP
Features Native attractions, arts and businesses.
Affiliated Tribes of Northwest Indians (ATNI), 1995. $2.

THREE MAPS OF INDIAN COUNTRY
Haskell Indian Junior College, Lawrence Kansas 66044. No charge.

MICROFILM & MICROFICHE

AKWESASNE NOTES
Vols. 1-9, 1969-1981. 168 fiches. $588. KM.

AMERICAN CIVIL LIBERTIES UNION ARCHIVES
Contains issues surrounding the rights of Native Americans and the ACLU's work with them are included throughout. The BIA and Indian Rights Association are also subjects. 293 rolls of 35mm microfilm, $115 per roll, $33,695. SR.

AMERICAN CULTURE SERIES I (ACSI), 1493-1806
Series I: A Compact Overview of American Books & Pamphlets - 1493-1806 - this collection includes accounts of Indians and Indian captives. Microfilm. UM.

THE AMERICAN INDIAN COLLECTION, 1647-1940
Printed matter, manuscripts, photographs, and typescripts, 1647-1940, relating to Native Americans. Also the Mohegan Indian case in Connecticut, 1740-1750. 1 roll of 35mm microfilm with guide, $115. SR.

AMERICAN INDIAN CORRESPONDENCE: PRESBYTERIAN HISTORICAL SOCIETY COLLECTION OF MISSIONARIES' LETTERS, 1833-1893
Letters describe 60 years of ministry to 39 tribes all over America - from the Seneca of New York to Arizona's Navajo. All aspects of Indian and missionary life are detailed. 35 rolls of 35mm microfilm and guide. $4,025. SR.

AMERICAN INDIAN PERIODICALS
From the State Historical Society of Wisconsin. Tribal news, political issues, humor, community services, scholarly research. Silver halide film; 12 reels (approximate) 35mm silver halide microfilm. $585. From the Princeton University Library on Microfiche. Part 1, 96 titles: 2,068 fiche and two reels 35mm film, $5,000; Part 2, 34 titles: 401 fiche and two reels 35mm film, $1,000. See NR for individual titles and prices.

AMERICAN THEOLOGICAL LIBRARY ASSOCIATION (ATLA)
Mainstream Protestant publications dealing with missions to native Americans: The Baptist Home Mission Monthly (from 1878-1909 - 7 rolls of 35mm microfilm, $805); The American Missionary (1857-1933 - 19 rolls of 35mm microfilm, $2,185); Missionary Monthly (1939-1958 - 4 rolls of 35mm microfilm, $460); Presbyterian Home Missionary (1872-1886 - 3 rolls of 35mm microfilm. $345. SR.

AMERINDIAN: AMERICAN INDIAN REVIEW
Vols. 1-23, 1952-1974. 23 fiches, $80.50. KM.

APPLICATIONS FOR ENROLLMENT & ALLOTMENT OF WASHINGTON
INDIANS, 1911-1919 Reproduces the bulk of records relating to Special Agent Charles Roblin's enrollment of those Native Americans in western Washington State. National Archives Record Group 75. 6 rolls of 35mm microfilm, $204. SR.

APPLICATIONS FOR ENROLLMENT OF THE COMMISSION TO THE FIVE
CIVILIZED TRIBES, 1898-1914 Reproduced the application forms filled out by persons seeking official enrollment in the Five Civilized Tribes (Cherokee, Chickasaw, Choctaw, Creek and Seminole). National Archives Record Group 75. 468 rolls of 35mm microfilm, $15,912. SR.

APPLICATIONS FROM THE BIA, MUSKOGEE AREA OFFICE, RELATING
TO ENROLLMENT IN FIVE CIVILIZED TRIBES UNDER THE ACT OF 1896
54 rolls of 35mm microfilm, $1,836. SR.; Reproduced the application forms filled out by persons seeking official enrollment in the four of the Five Civilized Tribes (Cherokee, Chickasaw, Choctaw and Creek). National Archives Record Group 75. 54 rolls of 35mm microfilm, $1,836. SR.

ARCTIC EXPEDITION DIARIES OF VILHJALMUR STEFANSSON,
1878-1925 An Account of Eskimo Life and Culture Preserved on Microfilm. A record of native Arctic culture and geography with detailed documentation of Eskimo life before it was altered by white cultural values. Chronicles three expeditions made by V. Stefansson between 1906 & 1918. Provides factual and insightful accounts of Eskimo hunting trips, religious beliefs, legends & family traditions. Includes translations of Eskimo words and phrases, extensive charts and maps; & sketches illustrating Eskimo clothes. 5 reels of 35mm microfilm. UM.

THE BEYNON MANUSCRIPT
The Literature, Myths and Traditions of the Tsimshian People - Represents the most extensive body of Tsimshian literature available for linguistic, anthropological and theological scholarship. Provides documentation on North American Indian myths and traditions. The Tsimshian people, native to the territory along the international border between Alaska and British Columbia, originated the totem pole and other art forms characteristic of the Pacific Northwest coastal region. William Beynon was a native speaker of the Tsimshian language. He recorded the history, ethnography and literature of his people. Includes narratives of clan histories and myths, and descriptions of traditional ceremonies, practices and beliefs. 4 reels of 35mm microfilm. UM.

BUREAU OF INDIAN AFFAIRS RECORDS CREATED
BY THE SANTA FE INDIAN SCHOOL, 1890-1918
National Archives Record Group 75. 38 rolls of 35mm microfilm, $1,292. SR.

CANADIAN DEPT. OF INDIAN AFFAIRS ANNUAL REPORTS, 1880-1936
Library of Congress microfilm. 10 rolls of 35mm, $420. SR.

CHEROKEE ALMANAC
1838-1860. Text in English and Cherokee. 1 reel, 35mm. $50. KM.

CLAIMS FOR GEORGIA MILITIA CAMPAIGNS AGAINST INDIANS
ON THE FRONTIER, 1792-1827
National Archives Record Group 217. 5 rolls of 35mm microfilm, $170. SR.

THE JOHN COLLIER PAPERS, 1922-1968
The Author of a Sweeping Federal Indian Reform Strategy - Assimilation was the U.S. Indian policy from the late 1880's through the 1920's, and provoked widespread animosity as it eroded tribal culture, religion, history, and freedom. Collier's accomplishments in effecting major Indian rights reforms as executive secretary of the American Indian Defense Association and later as Commissioner of Indian Affairs during FDR's administration marked a turning point in federal Indian policy. His Indian New Deal proposed tribal self-government, culture preservation, and religious freedom for native Americans. Includes correspondence, speeches, government documents, court records and news clippings that record Collier's private thoughts and public impact during those years. 59 reels of 35mm microfilm. UM.

CONSTITUTION & LAWS OF THE AMERICAN INDIAN
Includes a hardbound copy of A Bibliography of the Constitution and Laws of the American Indian, and a listing of titles filmed. 157 separate constitutions. 7 reels, 35mm. $360. Contact KM for a complete list of tribes & nations included.

CORRESPONDENCE OF THE OFFICE OF THE ADJUTANT GENERAL
(MAIN SERIES) Letters relate to Indian matters. See SR for titles and prices.

DUKE INDIAN ORAL HISTORY COLLECTION
Consists of the tape-recorded verbal testimonies of knowledgeable Indian people, members of most of the Indian tribes of Oklahoma, concerning their history, culture and philosophy of life. 310 fiches with Index on 8 reels. 35mm. $1,450. KM.

EASTERN CHEROKEE APPLICATIONS OF THE U.S. COURT OF CLAIMS, 1906-1909
National Archives Record Group 123. 348 rolls. of 35mm microfilm. $11,832. SR.

ENCYCLOPEDIA ARCTICA
16 volumes of articles on the Arctic Region written by leading specialists from around the world. Compiled by by noted explorer and scholar Vilhjalmur Stefansson. Features articles and information on: The Sciences, Trade, Biographies, and Maps, diagrams and charts. 27 reels of 35mm microfilm. UM.

ENROLLMENT CARDS OF THE FIVE CIVILIZED TRIBES, 1898-1914
Reproduced the enrollment cards prepared by the staff of the Commission to the Five Civilized Tribes between 1898 and 1914. National Archives Record Group 123. 93 rolls. of 35mm microfilm. $3,162. SR.

FBI FILE ON OSAGE INDIAN MURDERS
Several dozen Osage Indians were murdered in the 1920s and the FBI was brought in on the investigation. 3 rolls of 35mm microfilm with guide, $345. SR.

VIOLA E. GARFIELD ALBUMS ON TOTEM ART
Anthropologist Viola E. Garfield (1899-1983) amassed a collection of 26 volumes of photographs and information on the totem art of the Native Americans of the Pacific Northwest Coast from Seattle to southeastern Alaska. Microfiche-60 sheets, $60 per set. UWL.

GEORGE BIRD GRINNELL PAPERS
Contains letterbooks, correspondence, and subject files, including photographs and writings, which document the life & work of naturalist and conservationist George Bird Grinnell. 47 rolls of 35mm microfilm with guide. $5,405. SR.

HISTORY OF THE PACIFIC NORTHWEST & CANADIAN NORTHWEST
Microfilm collection which makes available a number of rare primary source materials on the early history of the two regions. 511 texts, from reports of expeditions to political pamphlets. 50 reels, $2,325. 20-page microfilm reel index and Table of Contents, $30. RP.

INDEX TO LETTERS RECEIVED BY THE COMMISSION TO THE FIVE CIVILIZED TRIBES, 1897-1913
National Archives Record Group 75. 23 rolls of 35mm microfilm, $782. SR.

INDIAN CENSUS ROLLS
Contains biographies of Native Americans compiled each year by agents or supts. in charge of Indian reservations spanning the years 1885-1940. National Archives Record Group 75. 692 rolls of 35mm microfilm, $23,528. SR.

INDIAN CULTURE & HISTORY
A new microform index to Wisconsin Native American periodicals, 1879-1981. Edited by James P. Danky. Six computer-output microfiche; 42:1 reduction ratio. 1984. $30. GP.

INDIAN HISTORIAN
American Indian Historical Society. New series: Vols. 1-12, 1967-1979. 48 fiches. $168. KM.

INDIAN PIONEER PAPERS: 1860-1935
Consists of interviews of elderly early day settlers in Oklahoma collected in the late 1930's. Consists of typescripts of 7105 interviews. A subject index is included. 1019 fiches. $3.057. KM.

INDIAN RIGHTS ASSOCIATION PAPERS, 1864-1973
Documents the struggle for American Indian civil liberties, and includes information on Indian affairs, and supported federal and state court cases in its efforts to secure basic rights for Native Americans. Includes correspondence, printed materials, Herbert Welsh Papers, 1877-1934, photographs, & Council on Indian Affairs Papers, 1943-1968. 136 reels of 35mm microfilm. UM.

INDIAN RIGHTS ASSOCIATION PAPERS, 1885-1901
26 rolls of 35mm microfilm, $2,990. SR.

INDIAN TRUTH
Indian Rights Association. Nos. 1-260, 1924-1984. 59 fiches. $177. KM.

INDIAN'S FRIEND
National Indian Association. Vols. 1-63, 1888-1951. 3 reels, 35mm. $150. KM.

INDIANS - U.S. GOVERNMENT PRINTING OFFICE PUBLICATIONS
1927-1970. 168 fiches. $588. Contact KM for complete list of titles.

INDIANS OF NORTH AMERICA
1760-1952. Includes works by James B. Finley, Hampton Institute, and Peter Williamson. 2 reels, 35mm. $100. KM.

IROQUOIS INDIANS: A DOCUMENTARY HISTORY
Provides 8,000 reproductions of records from the early 1600s to the 1840s compiled by the D'Arcy McNickle Center for the History of the American Indian at the Newberry Library. Focuses on the Mohawk, Oneida, Onondaga, Cayuga, Seneca and Tuscarora nations comprising the Iroquois Confederacy. Includes a guide with chronological calendar and index of names, places, and tribes cited. 35mm microfilm. 1984. RP.

THE SHELDON JACKSON COLLECTION, 1855-1909
Papers of the missionary and U.S. general agent of education, Sheldon Jackson. He organized pioneer Presbyterian churches in the West and Alaska. 41 rolls of 35mm microfilm with guide, $4,715. SR.

THE LAKE MOHONK CONFERENCE OF FRIENDS OF THE INDIAN
From 1883 to 1916 the center of the movement to reform federal Indian policy was the annual Lake Mohonk Conference, and its significance on Indian-white relations in the U.S. Details the opinions & programs of a distinguished group of American reformers. Microfiche (80 fiche), $200. Index volume, $25. NR.

LETTERS RECEIVED BY THE U.S. GEOLOGICAL SURVEY, 1879-1901
National Archives Record Group 57. Includes a survey and investigation of irrigation on Indian reservations and disputes over the western boundary of the Yakima Reservation and the Seminole border. 118 rolls of 35mm microfilm, $4,012. SR.

LETTERS SENT BY OFFICE OF INDIAN AFFAIRS, 1824-1881
Contains correspondence from sources concerning Indian lands, emigration, treaty negotiations, subsistence, conflicts, claims, education, etc. National Archives Record Group 75. 962 rolls of 35mm microfilm. SR.

LETTERS SENT TO THE OFFICE OF INDIAN AFFAIRS BY THE PINE RIDGE AGENCY, 1875-1914
National Archives Record Group 75. 52 rolls of 35mm microfilm, $1,768. SR.

MISCELLANEOUS LETTERS SENT BY THE AGENTS OF SUPERINTENDENTS AT THE PINE RIDGE INDIAN AGENCY, 1876-1914
National Archives Record Group 75. 76 rolls of 35mm microfilm, $2,584. SR.

NATIVE AMERICANS OF THE PACIFIC NORTHWEST: A PHOTOGRAPHIC RECORD
A comprehensive graphic documentation of Pacific Northwest and Alaska Native Americans. Over 4,000 images were selected resulting in a 17,000 entry catalog. Microfiche-112 sheets, $115 per set. UWL.

THE PACIFIC NORTHWEST TRIBES INDIAN LANGUAGE COLLECTION OF OREGON PROVINCE ARCHIVES OF SOCIETY OF JESUS, 1853-1960
Edited by Robert C. Carriker. Includes the materials amassed by the Oregon Province Archives on 12 different Indian languages: Assiniboine, Blackfoot/Piegan, Chelan, Coeur d'Alene, Columbia Moses, Colville, Crow, Gros Ventre, Kalispel, Kootenai, Nez Perce, and Yakima. 21 rolls. of 35mm microfilm with guide, $2,415. SR.

THE PACIFIC NORTHWEST TRIBES MISSIONS COLLECTION OF THE OREGON PROVINCE ARCHIVES OF THE SOCIETY OF JESUS, 1853-1960
Edited by Robert C. Carriker. Papers and records of the Jesuit missions and missionaries in Oregon, Washington, Idaho, and western Montana from 1853 to 1960. Provides much insight on the Northwest tribes. 34 rolls. of 35mm microfilm with guide, $3,910. SR.

THE PAGAENT OF AMERICA
A vital, authentic pictorial history of the U.S. Volume 1: Adventures in the Wilderness - covers the early navigators, settlers, and explorers as they fought Native Americans and each other for mastery of the New World; Volume 6: The Winning of Freedom - from the early struggles with the Indians through the War of 1812. Microfiche. Each volume begins with an essay or outline. UM.

THE PAPERS OF CARLOS MONTEZUMA, M.D.
Edited by John W. Larner, Jr. Montezuma (1867-1923) speeches and monthly newsletter, Wassaja, promoting the Indian cause. 9 rolls of 35mm microfilm with guide, $1,035. SR.

THE PAPERS OF PANTON, LESLIE & CO.
Ethnographic collection for the study of the American Indians of the Southwest. Documents trading activities with the Cherokee, Chickasaw, Choctaw, & Creek Nations, and is a key collection for the study of the origins & early development of the Seminole Indians. Includes a guide to listed documents. 35mm microfilm; approximately 10,000 documents on 26 reels. $2,400. RP.

THE PAPERS OF JOHN PEABODY HARRINGTON IN THE SMITHSONIAN INSTITUTION, 1907-1957
Consists of over 750,000 pages of his documents. Includes a detailed guidebook giving the contents of each reel. Individual reels, $75. See KM for titles and prices.

PAPERS OF THE SOCIETY OF AMERICAN INDIANS, 1906-1946
Edited by John W. Larner, Jr. 5,600 documents from 45 repositories country wide. 10 rolls of 35mm microfilm with guide, $1,150. SR.

PARRAL PAPERS
Spanish-American History of the Southwest and Mexico - spanning the years 1631-1821, this Spanish-written collection includes official records, directives, treaties, court transcripts, wills, letters, and other documents relating to the Spanish Colonial Era. Includes information on Indian uprisings, plus an account of the 1720 peace treaties with the Apaches and the Texans. 324 reels of 35mm microfilm. Includes index in English or Spanish. UM.

PRE-1900 CANADIANA
Primary resource materials that preserve & document printed materials from Canada's past. Covers Canadian culture, politics, ethnology, history, art, economics, literature, religion & sciences. 35mm microfilm. UM.

THE PROFESSIONAL CORRESPONDENCE OF FRANZ BOAS
Franz Boas (1858-1942) anthropologist. Covers over 50,000 items, dating from 1881 through 1942, including correspondence with Margaret Mead, Albert Einstein, Alexander Graham Bell, and Presidents, Taft, Wilson and Roosevelt. 44 rolls. of 35mm microfilm with guide, $5,060. SR.

RATIFIED INDIAN TREATIES, 1722-1869
National Archives Record Group 11. 16 rolls of 35mm microfilm, $544. SR.

RECORDS CREATED BY BIA FIELD AGENCIES HAVING JURISDICTION OVER THE PUEBLO INDIANS, 1874-1900
National Archives Record Group 75. 32 rolls of 35mm microfilm, $1,088. SR.

RECORDS OF THE ALASKA DIVISION OF THE BIA CONCERNING METLAKATLA, 1887-1933
National Archives Record Group 75. 14 rolls of 35mm microfilm, $476. SR.

RECORDS OF THE CREEK FACTORY OF THE OFFICE OF INDIAN TRADE OF THE BIA, 1795-1821
National Archives Record Group 75. 13 rolls of 35mm microfilm, $442. SR.

RECORDS OF FIELD JURISDICTIONS
National Archives Record Group 75. See SR for number of rolls of 35mm microfilm and prices.

RECORDS OF HEADQUARTERS, ARMY OF THE SOUTHWESTERN FRONTIER, & HEADQUARTERS, SECOND & SEVENTH MILITARY DEPTS., 1835-1853
National Archives Record Group 393. 8 rolls of 35mm microfilm, $272. SR.

RECORDS OF THE MORAVIAN MISSION AMONG THE INDIANS OF NORTH AMERICA Microfilm collection of the Indian missionary records at the archives of the Moravian Church in Bethlehem, PA, provides important information on the history and activities of the Moravian Church in North America. Includes a 111-page Guide and two-volume, 135,000 entry index. 35mm microfilm. 40 reel;s, $19.10; 2-volume Index, $400. RP.

RECORDS OF THE U.S. INDIAN CLAIMS COMMISSION
Includes 550,000 pages--6,140 silver halide microfiche, $12,000. Historical, anthropological and economic reports of the American Indian. The Decisions, Volumes 1-47 & Appeals, 355 fiche, $750; Expert Testimony, 400 volumes, 100,000 pages, 1,270 fiche, $2,500/Supplement 1: 48 titles on 125 fiche, $250;2: 97 titles on 209 fiche, $400. Transcripts of Oral Expert Testimony, 400 volumes, 100,000 pages, 1,398 fiche, $2,800/Supplement; 77 titles, 420 fiche, $850. The Briefs, 3,000 volumes, 125,000 pages, 1,536 fiche, $3,000. GAO Reports, 80 volumes, 25,000 pages, 300 fiche, $600/Supplement; 11 titles, 34 fiche, $75. Index to Decisions, $25. Index to Expert Testimony, $25. Legislative History of the Indian Claims Commission Act, 12 fiche, $35. Docket Books, 41 fiche, $80. Journal, 32 fiche, $60. NR.

REPORTS OF INSPECTION OF THE FIELD JURISDICTIONS OF THE OFFICE OF INDIAN AFFAIRS, 1873-1900
Contains the Indian inspector's records pertaining to the conditions of Indians. National Archives Record Group 48. 60 rolls of 35mm microfilm, $2,040. SR.

RECORDS OF MILITARY DIVISIONS, DEPARTMENTS & DISTRICTS
National Archives Record Group 393. Letters in this publication revolve around problems in Indian-white relations. Describes scouting activities and armed expeditions against. Apache, Ute, Navajo, Kiowa and Comanche Indians. see SR for titles and prices.

REPORT BOOKS OF THE OFFICE OF INDIAN AFFAIRS, 1838-1885
Contains correspondence sent by the Office of Indian Affairs to members of the president's cabinet, and copies of letters to the president, members of Congress, and other government officials. National Archives Record Group 75. 53 rolls of 35mm microfilm, $1,802. SR.

REPORT...INDEX TO THE ANNUAL REPORTS, 1894-1905
Annual reports of the Dawes Commission and its successors from 1893-1920, with an index for the years, 1894-1905. The Commission was appointed by the president to negotiate with the Five Civilized Tribes to divide tribal property, to procure the concession of remaining tribal lands, and to prepare tribal rolls of citizenship. 2 rolls of 35mm microfilm, $84. SR.

HENRY ROWE SCHOOLCRAFT PAPERS
Schoolcraft (1793-1864, was the foremost pioneer in Indian studies. Includes his work as an ethnologist, Indian agent, explorer, mineralogist, geologist, and writer. 69 rolls of 35mm microfilm with guide, $2,898. SR.

SELECTED NATIVE AMERICAN PERIODICALS
The Red Man - an illustrated magazine printed by Indians, 1909-1917. 2 rolls of 35mm microfilm, $84; The Native American - devoted to Indian education, 1900-1931. 8 rolls, $336; The Indian's Friend - organ of the Women's National Indian Association - 1888-1940 (changed to National Indian Association in 1902). 14 rolls, $588. SR.

SELECTED RECORDS OF THE BIA RELATING TO THE ENROLLMENT OF INDIANS ON THE FLATHEAD RESERVATION, 1903-1908
National Archives Record Group 75. 3 rolls of 35mm microfilm, $102. SR.

SELECTED WORKS BY AMERICAN INDIAN AUTHORS
12 titles, 1860-1939. 2 reels, 35mm. $100. Contact KM for complete listing of authors.

SMITHSONIAN INSTITUTION BUREAU OF AMERICAN ETHNOLOGY BULLETINS & ANNUAL REPORTS Includes primary sources of information on the culture and history of North and South American Indian Tribes. Includes material on the prehistory, language, society and culture of many extinct tribal groups. Focuses on the history f Indian tribes within the U.S., with substantive information on the Indian tribes of Alaska, Hawaii, Mexico, Central America, and Canada. 42 reels of 35mm microfilm. Comes with a guide to Microfilm Edition of Smithsonian Publications Relating to the North American Indian. UM.

SUPERINTENDENTS' ANNUAL NARRATIVE & STATISTICAL REPORTS FROM FIELD JURISDICTIONS OF THE B.I.A., 1907-1938
Documents the operations and accomplishments at the agencies under the BIA, schools, hospitals, and other field jurisdictions. National Archives Record Group 75. 174 rolls of 35mm microfilm, $5,916. SR.

SURVEY OF THE CONDITIONS OF THE INDIANS OF THE U.S.
In Feb 1928, the U.S. Senate directed its Committee on Indian Affairs to study conditions among Native Americans, the effects of laws passed by Congress, & the effects of the policies of the BIA on Native American health, improvement and welfare. 9 rolls of 35mm microfilm, $378. SR.

U.S. BOARD OF INDIAN COMMISSIONERS. ANNUAL REPORT OF BOARD OF INDIAN COMMISSIONERS TO THE SECRETARY OF THE INTERIOR
Reports 1-63, 1869-1932. 3 reels, 35mm. $150. KM.

U.S. BUREAU OF INDIAN AFFAIRS
17 titles, 1966-1970. 17 fiches, $59.50. Contact KM for complete list of titles.

WASAJA - THE INDIAN HISTORIAN. A NATIONAL NEWSMAGAZINE OF INDIAN AMERICA Vols. 1-19, 1973-1982. 82 fiches. $287. KM.

WESTERN AMERICANA
Includes federal and state documents, directories, guidebooks, state and regional histories, memoirs, reminiscences and travel accounts, and conventional and secondary histories of the West. Two sub-collections may be purchased separately: Indians, and Other Ethnic Influences. Microfiche. UM.

WESTERN AMERICANA: FRONTIER HISTORY OF THE TRANS-MISSISSIPPI WEST, 1550-1900
Includes a broad selection of printed sources relating to the discovery, exploration, settlement, & development of North America. Provides information on Indian/White relations including missions, trade, government relations, and Indian wars. A 2-volume guide & index accompanies each order. 35mm microfilm. 617 reels; 11 units of 56-57 reels each, $2,880 each. RP.

THE WILLIAM WIRT PAPERS
Edited by John B. Boles. William Wirt (1772-1834) author and historian, attorney general from 1817 to 1829. Involved in the Cherokee cases of 1831-32 and was devoted to Indian causes throughout his life. 24 rolls of 35mm microfilm with guide, $2,760. SR.

COMPUTER NETWORK

INDIAN NATION NETWORK (INN) ELECTRONIC BULLETIN BOARD (EBB)
Devoted entirely to issues affecting and relating to Indian country. Access INN with phone line, modem, computer, and communications software. Features such issues as religious freedom, environmental degradation on Indigenous lands, stereotypes, and treaty rights. INN equips users with tools necessary for meaningful advocacy and action by offering Congressional bills significant to Native Americans, hearing write-ups, Federal Register Notices relating to Indian country, listing of federally recognized tribes, telephone/addresses of Congressional Committees, events in Indian Country, and more. $25/year. HO.

CD-ROMs, SOFTWARE & DATABASES

THE AMERICAN INDIAN CD-ROM
A library of Indian resources: Federal treaties; American State papers (through 1826); artistic view of the images and scenes-over 700 engravings; Books by Black Hawk & Right Hand Thunder; accounts from original observers. Includes Henry R. Schoolcraft's Archives of Aboriginal Knowledge; League of the Iroquois; Wigwam Evening-Sioux Folk Tales Retold; extensive data on Chippewa, Cherokees, Sioux, & other tribes; linguistic coverage-large

vocabulary lists, including a detailed analysis of Algonquin by Schoolcraft. The artwork of George Catlin's Letters & Notes on Manners, Customs & Conditions of the North American Indians. For IBM compatible multimedia PCs. $75. TP.

THE AMERICAN INDIAN: A MULTIMEDIA ENCYCLOPEDIA
Version 2.0. Covers more than 150 tribes of native peoples of the U.S., Canada, and northern Mexico - focusing on the history, culture, words, images, legends, and leaders. Includes the complete texts of four titles: Atlas of the North American Indian; Who Was Who in Native American History; Encyclopedia of Native American Tribes; and Voices of the Winds. There are sound bites of authentic Indian songs, over 900 VGA photographs, over 1,000 biographies, 250 color illustrations, the full text of over 250 documents from the 18th and 19th centuries, mor than 100 legends from over 60 tribes, maps, time lines, and lsitings of tribal locations, historical societies, and museums. 1996. $150 for single user; $500 for lab pack (allows 5 users simulatneously). FOF.

BIBLIOGRAPHY OF NATIVE NORTH AMERICANS ON DISC - CD-ROM
Timothy O'Leary & M. Marlene Martin, Editors
The Human Relations Area File's Ethnographic Bibliography of North America. Semiannual. CD-ROM or Network. IBM compataible. $1,045 for annual subscription for CD; $1,306 for one person network. SP.

ETHNIC NEWSWATCH
A full text multicultural general reference database on CD-ROM. Contains more than 70 newspapers published by the ethnic and minority press in America. Contains about 90,000 fully ndexed articles from more than 100 newspapers and magazines. Includes Native American newspapers, i.e., News From Indian Country, Navajo TimesSho-Ban News, Seminole Tribune, Tundra Times, Cherokee Advocate, Lakota Times, et al. SII.

INVENTING THE SOUTHWEST: THE FRED HARVEY COMPANY & NATIVE AMERICAN ART Kathleen L. Howard & Diana F. Pardue
Based on the exhibit of the Heard Museum. 90 color & 50 bxw photos. Biblio. 168 pp. Paper. $17.95. CD-ROM, $29.95. NP.

THE NATIONAL TRIBAL DIRECTORY SOFTWARE
Standard Edition provides education & connectivity for the tribes themselves as well as for those entities that serve & assist them. Includes contact, membership, culture, profile & history information on 600 federally recognized and non-recognized U.S. tribes and bands in the U.S. and basic contact information for over 200 non-recognized tribes that are currently in the process of petitioning the U.S. Dept. of the Interior for "recognition" status. Business Edition database includes all of information & features of the "standard" edition, plus, contact information for all of the 645+ First Nations & bands of Canada & includes over 10,000 Native American Service & Enterprise contacts; also BIA and other Federal agency offices. Updates are provided by a web-based "live update" system downloaded from the TDR server. $499. TDR.

NORTH AMERICAN INDIANS - CD-ROM
A database of text and image on the history of Native Americans. Includes information on leadership, tribal heritage, religion, family life, and customs. IBM compatible. 1991. $69.95. QP.

WEBSITES

WWW.ABORIGINALCONNECTIONS.COM

WWW.LIB.LAW.WASHINGTON.EDU
Indian & tribal Law Research

WWW.INDIANVILLAGE.COM
(970) 247-3100 Fax 259-6020; E-mail: info@indianvillage.com
Website: www.indianvillage.com. Lists authentic Native American Indian stores, galleries, stores, events, news and gaming.

NATIVE AMERICAN INTERNET GUIDE
Listing of about 1,500 websites for Native groups, organizations, nations, businesses and individuals. 96 pages. $40. Available also on diskette. TP.

WWW.NATIVEVILLAGE.ORG
Native American Indian & Indigenous Books Available Online. Thanks to Glenn Welker from Indigenous People's Literature

A TIME OF VISIONS: INTERVIEWS WITH NATIVE AMERICAN ARTISTS WEBSITE: WWW.BRITESITES.COM/NATIVE_ARTIST_INTERVIEWS
Table of Contents: Rick Bartow, Sara Bates, Patricia Deadman, Joe Feddersen, Anita Fields, Harry Fonseca, Bob Haozous, Melanie Printup Hope, Bobby Martin, Gerald McMaster, George Morrison, Shelley Niro, Joanna Osburn-Bigfeather, Diego Romero, Mateo Romero, Bently Spang, Ernie Whiteman, Richard Ray Whitman, Alfred Young Man.

WWW.TRIBALJURISDICTION.COM
This website is a general guide regarding which sovereign has jurisdiction to prosecute crimes which occur in Indian country: federal, tribal or state court.

AMERICAN INDIAN HISTORY ONLINE - FACTS ON FILE, INC.
Online Database offers fast access to more than 15,000 years of culture & history through topic entries, biographies, images, maps & charts, legends, primary sources, timeline entries, and a monthly editor's selection. Available on the website: www.factsonfile.com; or e-mail onlinesales@factsonfile.com (800) 322-8755 Fax (800) 678-3633. For free trial, www.factsonfile.com/trial (FOF)

COMPUTER GRAPHICS

NATIVE AMERICAN CLIP ART COLLECTIONS
Art Bernstein; For IBM PC & Macintosh: The Santa Fe Collection - Pueblo Indians and Spanishfluence, $179; Plains Collections - Indians of the Great Plains, $149; Northwest Collections - tribes of the Northwest to Alaska. 500 EPS images, 125 EPS borders. RT.

GAMES

POW WOW! THE GAME
Sarah Seeney Sullivan
A Native American board game featuring Native American concepts and designs that will challenge and entertain family members ages 8 and up. Includes Native American trivia cards. $19.95. LE.

GIFT ITEMS

HOPI KACHINAS
Edwin Earle and Edward A. Kennard
Second edition. Illus. 50 pp. National Museum of the American Indian, 1971. $12.50. Portfolioof 28 color plates from book, $3.50.

HOPI KACHINAS: A POSTCARD COLLECTION
Cliff Bahnimptewa, illustrator
20 full-color postcards. Illus. Northland Publishing, $7.95.

NAVAJO RUG STIK-WITHIT NOTECUBES
Self Stick; Full color. 600 sheets, 3.5 x 3". Northland Publishing, $12.

TRAVELING EXHIBITS

AKWESASNE TRAVELLING EXHIBITS
Teionkwahontasen Basketmakers of Akwesasne: Ten panel, color and bxw photo display detailing the history of basketry. Tsinikaiatotenne Ne Akwesasne - A Portrait of Akwesasne: Ten panel bxw historical photo display of Akwesasne family, religion, sports and lifestyles of the Mohawk of Akwesasne. Our Strength Our Spirit: Art exhibit by contemporary artists of Akwesasne. Catalog available. Cost negotiable. AM.

THE BUFFALO TOUR
The Institute for the Study of Natural Systems, P.O. Box 637 • Mill Valley, CA 94942 (415) 383-5064; James A. Swan, Project Director; Pete Sears, Musical Director; To support bison restoration on Indian reservations, a musical concert tour program is being produced by a coalition of Indian leaders, entertainers and ecologists. The tour will begin in 1992 and hold a series of concerts around the U.S. that will culminate in the first annual Buffalo Festival, which will be held in late July of 1993, in the LaCrosse, Wisconsin, area in cooperation with the first Inter-national Bison Conference. Each concert will include Indian and non-Indian artists, as well as educational materials and programs, Indian arts & crafts sales, & a chance for local community involvement.

CAHOKIA TRAVELING DISPLAYS
A large free-standing exhibit on Cahokia with texts, photos & artifacts. Depicts the phases of Illinois prehistory. A booklet, Illinois Archaeology, is included. Two weeks, no charge. Must be picked up by the borrower. CMM.

MUSEUM OF NEW MEXICO TRAVELING EXHIBITS
Maintains the following traveling exhibits: Art of the Rainmakers: Prehistoric Indian Art & Architecture; Crystal to Burnt Water: Navajo Regional Style Textiles; People of the Sun: Photographs by Buddy Mays; The Portrait: Historic Photographs of New Mexicans; Sacred Paths: Aspects of the Native American & Hispanic Religious Experience in the Southwest; Traditions in Transition: Contemporary Basket Weaving of the Southwestern Indians; and, Turquoise and Tobacco: Trade Systems in the Southwest. The exhibits include historical and contemporary artifacts, drawings, prints, photographs, and paintings that have been assembled for exhibition in museums, libraries, community and art

centers, and any other public space with controlled access. Pieces in the exhibitions are framed and matted with descriptive or interpretive labels printed directly on the mats & faced with plexi-glass. In addition, each exhibition contains a title and statement panel. The exhibitions are offered free of charge and are transported in sturdy, custom-built crates. MNM.

TEXAS INDIANS WHO LIVED IN HOUSES
Students can learn to cook Indian bread, make an adobe brick, or plant a garden. The trunk contains artifact reproductions, filmstrips, activity cards, audiocassettes, and books. Grades 3-8. Rental fee: $100 (30 days) UT-ITC.

FESTIVALS OF NATIVE AMERICAN FILM & VIDEO

AMERICAN INDIAN FILM FESTIVAL & VIDEO EXHIBITION
333 Valencia St., Suite 322 • San Francisco, CA 94103
 (415) 554-0525; Michael Smith, Contact
This festival (November) is the oldest international film exhibition dedicated to the presentation of Native Americans in cinema. It is competitive & features seven categories: documentary feature; documentary short, feature, docudrama, live short subject, animated short subject & industrial. Estab. 1975.

AMERICAN INDIAN FILM & VIDEO COMPETITION
2101 N. Lincoln, Jim Thorpe Bldg., Rm. 640 • Oklahoma City, OK 73105
(405) 521-2931; Patrick Whelan, Contact
All entries are publicly presented at the Red Earth Festival in Oklahoma City. Finalists in each category are screened & awards presented at the University of Tulsa during the conference. Established 1992.

DREAMSPEAKERS: THE FIRST PEOPLES WORLD FILM CELEBRATION
9914 76th Ave. • Edmonton, Alberta • Canada T6E 1K7
(403) 439-3456 Fax 439-2066; Russell Mulvey, Contact
Held in September, this noncompetitive event includes around 60 hours of public screenings. Also a Professional Development Symposium component each year.

NATIVE AMERICAN FILM & VIDEO FESTIVAL
Film & Video Center, George Gustav Heye Center
National Museum of the American Indian
Smithsonian Institution • 1 Bowling Green • New York, NY 10004
 (212) 283-2420; Millie Seubert & Elizabeth Weatherford, Contacts
A noncompetitive showcase of film, video & audio productions with a focus on works by independent & tribal community leaders. Each festival screens about 40 documentaries, short features & animations, introduced by their producers & members of the native communities represented. Established 1979.

TWO RIVERS NATIVE FILM & VIDEO FESTIVAL
Native Arts Circle • 1433 E. Franklin, Minneapolis, MN 55404 (612) 870-7173
 Juanita Espinoza, Contact
Presents a prize known as the "New Visionary" Award. Established in 1991.

TRIBAL FILM/VIDEO PRODUCERS

CHICKASAW NATION
c/o Cultural Center, P.O. Box 1548 • Ada, OK 74820
 (405) 436-2603 Fax 436-4287; Glenda Galvan, Contact
More than 200 oral histories have been recorded (a portion of these exist on audio only). Established 1986.

CHOCTAW VIDEO PRODUCTION (CVP)
P.O. Box 6010 • Philadelphia, MS 39350
 (601) 656-5251 Fax 656-6696; Bob Ferguson, Contact
In addition to 3/4" documentary & instructional videos on Choctaw history & culture, this production unit also does contract work for other tribes, including the Creek of Alabama, the Seneca of New York, and the Tunica-Biloxi of Louisiana. CVP also maintains a 24-hour TV station. Established 1983.

OJIBWAY & CREE CULTURAL CENTER
152 3rd Ave. • Timmins, Ontario • Canada P4N 1C6
 (705) 267-7911 Fax 267-4988; Esther Wesley, Contact
Produces documentaries on tribal practices, crafts & oral histories of elders, which are ideal for general audiences & classroom use. Maintains a catalog of about 20 titles with an average running time of 20 minutes. Established 1978.

CREEK NATION VIDEO
c/o Muskogee Creek Nation Communication Center
P.O. Box 580 • Okmulgee, OK 74447 (918) 758-8700 Fax 758-0824
Produces documentaries containing various archival material & video shot in the last 20 years on the history of the Creek people. The collection is divided into a four-volume video history; each volume contains 5-7 titles.

SUQUAMISH MUSEUM
c/o Suquamish Tribal Cultural Center, P.O. Box 498 • Suquamish, WA 98392
 (206) 598-3311 Fax 598-4666; Marilyn Jones or Alan Preston, Contacts
The Suquamish do not currently maintain an active video production unit, but the museum does hold several self-produced educational titles including "Come Forth Laughing," which features oral histories of Suquamish elders, and "Waterborne," which illustrates the processes involved in making canoes. Titles run under 30 minutes each.

TULALIP TRIBE
6700 Totem Beach Rd. • Marysville, WA 98271(206) 653-0255; Lita Sheldon
Video production within the tribe is divided nto two categories: industrial (public relations) video & documentation of oral histories. The public relations tapes are brief introductions to Tulalip culture: "My Indian People" (1991, 7 mins.); & "Tulalip Tribe: Administration for Native Americans" (1990, 10 mins). Also oral history shorts. Established 1989.

UTE INDIAN TRIBE
c/o Audio-Visual Dept., P.O. Box 190 • Fort Duchesne, UT 84026
 (801) 722-3736 Fax 722-4023; Larry Cesspooch, Contact
Approximately half of the 250 videotapes produced functions as legal documentation of meetings & agreements with local, staff and federal officials. The remainder serves as educational preservation of Ute history & culture practices. Much of this work is intended for audience, ages 5-13. Includes many oral histories as well as a variety of tribal ceremonies. Working on a low-power television station. Established 1979.

AUDIO-VISUAL AIDS DISTRIBUTORS

(A) Abbeville Press, 488 Madison Ave., New York, NY 10022 (800) 278-2665

(ACA) The Astrology Center of America, 207 Victory Lane, Bel Air, MD 21014 (800) 475-2272; (410) 638-7761 Fax 638-5154 Website: www.astroamerica.com

(ADL) Anti-Defamation League of B'nai Brith, 823 United Nations Plaza, New York, NY 10017 (212) 490-2525

(AF) Aurora Films, P.O. Box 022955, Juneau, AK 99802-0164 (907) 586-6696

(AG) Agnello Films, 31 Maple St., Ridgefield, NJ 07660 (201) 933-6698

(AICRC) American Indian Culture Research Center, Blue Cloud Abbey, P.O. Box 98, Marvin, SD 57251 (605) 432-5528

(AIMS) AIMS Media, 9710 DeSoto Ave., Chatsworth, CA 91311 (800) 367-2467; in CA/AK/HI (818) 785-4111 Fax (818) 376-6405

(AIS) American Indian Soundchiefs, Box 472, Taos, NM 87571 (505) 776-2953

(AISES) American Indian Science & Engineering Society, Video Department, 1630 30th St., Suite 301, Boulder, CO 80303 (303) 492-8658 Fax 492-7090

(AIT) Agency for Instructional Technology, Box A, Bloomington, IN 47402 (800) 457-4509

(ALA) A.L. Atkins, Special Projects, 223 Onate Hall, University of New Mexico, Albuquerque, NM 87131 (505) 277-5204

(ALF) Alfred Publishing , P.O. Box 10003, Van Nuys, CA 91410 (818) 891-5999 Fax 891-2369

(ALT) The Altschul Group, 1560 Sherman Ave., Suite 100, Evanston, IL 60201 (800) 323-5448; Fax (708) 328-6706

(AM) Akwesasne Museum, RR 1 Box 14C, Hogansburg, NY 13655 (518) 358-2240

(AMNH) American Museum of Natural History, Dept. of Library Services, Central Park West at 79th St., New York, NY 10024 (212) 873-1300 ext. 346/347

(AMP) Arthur Mokin Productions, P.O. Box 71, Issaquah, WA 98027

(AP) Atlantis Productions, 1252 La Granada Dr., Thousand Oaks, CA 91360 (805) 495-2790

(AT) Auburn Television, Auburn University, Auburn, AL 36849 (205) 826-4110

(ATL) ATLATL, P.O. Box 34090, Phoenix, AZ 85067 (602) 277-3711 Fax 277-3690

(ATNI) Affiliated Tribes of Northwest Indians, 222 N.W. Davis, Suite 403, Portland, OR 97209 (503) 241-0070 Fax 241-0072

(AUDIO) Audio-Forum, Jeffrey Norton Publishers, 96 Broad St., Guilford, CT 06437 (800) 243-1234; Fax (203) 453-9774

(AV) Artistic Video, 87 Tyler Ave., Sound Beach, NY 11789 (516) 744-0449 Fax 744-5993

(AVP) Ambrose Video Publishing, 28 W. 44th St., Suite 2100, New York, NY 10036 (800) 526-4663; Fax (212) 768-9282; Website: www.ambrosevideo.com

(BB) Buffalo Bill Historical Center, Education Dept., Box 1000, Cody, WY 82414 (307) 587-4771 Fax 587-5714

(BBP) Brown Bird Productions, 1971 N. Curson Ave., Hollywood, CA 90068 (213) 851-8928

(BE) Beacon Films, 1560 Sherman Ave., Suite 100, Evanston, IL 60201 (800) 323-5448; Fax (708) 328-6706

(BF) Britannica Films, 310 S. Michigan Ave., Chicago, IL 60604 (312) 347-7958 Fax 347-7966

(BGF) Bowling Green Films; Dist. by Jack Ofield Productions, P.O. Box 12792, San Diego, CA 92112 (619) 462-8266

(BHP) Black Hawk Productions, LLC, P.O. Box 63, Blachly, OR 97412 (801) 473-6697. Website: www.blackhawkproductions.com E-mail: moreinfo@blackhawkproductions.com

(BINS) Boreal Institute for Northern Studies, University of Alberta, CW-401 Biological Sciences Bldg., Edmonton, AB, Can. T6G 2E9 (403) 432-4409

(BM) Blackfeet Media, P.O. Box 850, Browning, MT 59417 (406) 338-7179 ext. 268

(BMP) Bishop Museum Press, P.O. Box 19000A, Honolulu, HI 96817 (808) 848-4134

(BO) Bo Boudart Films, 1032 Marker Ave., Palo Alto, CA 94301 (415) 856-2004

(BOND) Jim Bond, I.T., 35113 Brewster Rd., Lebanon, OR 97355 (503) 258-3645

(BTP) Bear Tribe Publishing, 3750A Airport Blvd. #223, Mobile, AL 36608

(BYU) Brigham Young University, Educational Media Center, 101 Fletcher Bldg., Provo, UT 84602 (801) 378-2713

(BYU-N) Brigham Young University--Native American Series, Multi-Cultural Education Dept., 115 BRMB, Provo, UT 84602

(BULL) Bullfrog Films, P.O. Box 149, Oley, PA 19547 (800) 543-3764; Fax (610) 370-1978

(CA) Cloud Associates, P.O. Box 39016, Phoenix, AZ 85069 (800) 888-7820; (602) 866-7820

(CAN) Canyon Records & Indian Arts, 4143 N. 16th St., Phoenix, AZ 85016 (602) 266-4823

(CANYON) Canyon Cinema, 2325 3rd St., Suite 338, San Francisco, CA 94107 (415) 626-2255

(CAT) Catticus Corporation, 2600 10th St., Berkeley, CA 94710 (510) 548-0854

(CB) Cook's Books, P.O. Box 650, Hoopa, CA 95546 (916) 625-4222

(CC) Centre Communications, 1800 30th St., Suite 207, Boulder, CO 80301 (800) 886-1166; (303) 444-1166

(CDA) Curriculum Development Associates, 1211 Connecticut Ave., NW, Suite 414, Washington, DC 20036 (202) 293-1760

(CEN) Centron Productions, 416 Rock Fence Place, Lawrence, KS 66049

(CET) Center for Educational Telecommunications, 9596 Walnut St., Dallas, TX 75243 (214) 952-0303

(CFDW) Canadian Filmmakers Distribution West, 1131 Howe St., Suite 100, Vancouver, BC, Canada V6Z 2L7 (604) 684-3014

(CFH) Center for Humanities, Communication Park, Box 1000, Mt. Kisco, NY 10549 (800) 431-1242; (914) 666-4100

(CG) The Cinema Guild, 1697 Broadway #506, New York, NY 10019 (800) 723-5522; Fax (212) 246-5525 E-Mail: thecinemag@aol.com; Website: www.cinemaguild.com/cinemaguild

(CH) Cherokee Publications, P.O. Box 256, Cherokee, NC 28719 (704) 488-2988

(CHA) Caedmon: Harper-Audio Div. of HarperCollins, 10 E. 53 St., New York, NY 10022 (212) 207-7000

(CHAR) Chariot Distribution, 1274 Lambert Cir., Lafayette, CO 80026 (866) 243-6414; (303) 666-4558 Fax 666-5808 Website: www.chariotdist.com. E-mail: info@chariotdist.com.

(CHE) Chevron USA, Community Affairs, 575 Market St., San Francisco, CA 94105 (415) 894-5193; Study Guide: Chevron USA, 742 Bancroft Way, Berkeley, CA 94710

(CIAC) Center for Indigenous Arts & Cultures, P.O. Box 8627, Santa Fe, NM 87504 (505) 473-5375 Fax 424-1025 E-mail: indians@nets.com Website: www.indianartbooks.com

(CIE) Center for Indian Education, 255 E. Kellogg #503, St. Paul, MN 55101 (651) 227-2240. Website: www.thecie.org

(CIMA) CIMA, 52 E. 1st St., New York, NY 10003 (212) 673-1666

(CIN) Cinnamin Productions, 19 Wild Rose Rd., Westport, CT 06880 (203) 221-0613 (phone & fax)

(CIRI) The CIRI Foundation, P.O. Box 93330, Anchorage, AK 99509 (907) 274-8638

(CJ) Concord Jazz, Inc., Box 845, Willow Pass Rd., Concord, CA 94522 (415) 682-6770

(CL) Clear Light Publishers, 823 Don Diego • Santa Fe, NM 87501 (800) 253-2747; Fax (505) 989-9519 E-mail: ordercl@aol.com Website: www.clearlightbooks.com

(CMB) The Children's Museum, Boston, Museum Wharf, 300 Congress St., Boston, MA 02210 (617) 426-6500

(CMM) Cahokia Mounds Museum Society, Video Rental, P.O. Box 382, Collinsville, IL 62234 (618) 344-9221

(COOK) Cook School, 708 S. Lindon Lane, Tempe, AZ 85281

(COP) Camera One Productions, 8523 15th Ave., NE, Seattle, WA 98115 (800) 726-3456; Fax (206) 523-3668

(CR) Center Records, 7809 Southtown Center #382, Minneapolis, MN 55431. Website: www.centerrecords.com

(CRM) CRM/McGraw Hill Films, 2233 Faraday Ave., Carlsbad, CA 92008 (619) 431-9800

(CROW) Crazy Crow Trading Post, 1801 N. Airport Rd., Pottsboro, TX 75076 (800) 786-6210. Website: www.crazycrow.com

(CT) Coast Telecourses, 11460 Warner Ave., Fountain Valley, CA 92708 (714) 241-6109

(CVP) Choctaw Video Productions, Choctaw Tribe, P.O. Box 6010, Philadelphia, MS 39350 (601) 656-5251

(DAR) Denver Art Museum, Education Dept., 100 W. 14th Ave. Parkway, Denver, CO 80204 (303) 575-2312

(DC) Direct Cinema Limited, P.O. Box 10003, Santa Monica, CA 90410 (800) 525-0000; Fax (310) 396-3233

(DCP) Dave Caldwell Productions, 26934 Halifax Pl., Hayward, CA 94542 (415) 538-4286

(DEPKE) Irene-Aimee Depke, 5627 N. Neva Ave., Chicago, IL 60631 (312) 774-2589

(DER) Documentary Educational Resources, 101 Morse St., Watertown, MA 02472 (800) 569-6621; Fax (617) 926-9519 E-mail: docued@der.org. Web site: www.der.org/docued

(DOV) Dover Publications, 31 E. 2nd St., Mineola, NY 11501 (800) 223-3130; Fax (516) 742-5049.

(DP) Dana Productions, 6249 Babcock Ave., N. Hollywood, CA 91606 (213) 877-9246

(DR) Dreamcatchers, Inc., 23852 PCH #766, Malibu, CA 90265 Website: www.dreamcatchers.org

(DPA) Documentary Photo Aids, P.O. Box 952137, Lake Mary, FL 32795 (800) 255-0763; Fax (904) 383-5679

(DSP) Daybreak Star Press Film & Video, United Indians of All Tribes Foundation, Daybreak Star Cultural Educational Center, Discovery Park, P.O. Box 99253, Seattle, WA 98199 (206) 285-4425

(DT) Dallas Telecourses, 9596 Walnut St., Mesquite, TX 75243 (214) 952-0303 Fax 952-0329

(DTC) DTC-TV Downtown Community Television, 87 Lafayette St., New York, NY 10013 (212) 966-4510

(EDC) Education Development Center, 55 Chapel St., Newton, MA 02158 (800) 225-4276; in MA (617) 969-7100

(EG) Em Gee Film Library, 6924 Canby, #103, Reseda, CA 91335 (818) 881-8110 Fax 981-5506

(FF) FilmFair Comunications, Gregg Ohara Films, P.O. Box 2187, Beverly Hills, CA 90213

(FH) Films for the Humanities, P.O. Box 2053, Princeton, NJ 08543 (800) 257-5126; (609) 275-1400 Fax 275-3767

(FI) Films Incorporated Video, 5547 N. Ravenswood Ave., Chicago, IL 60640 (800) 343-4312; Fax (312) 878-0416

(FIC) Film in the Cities, 2388 University Ave., St. Paul, MN 55114 (612) 646-6104 Fax 646-3879

(FIL) Filmakers Library, 124 E. 40th St., New York, NY 10016 (212) 808-4980 Fax 808-4983

(FILMS) Films, Inc., 5547 N. Ravenswood Ave., Chicago, IL 60640 (800) 323-4222

(FL) Flower Films, 10341 San Pablo Ave., El Cerrito, CA 94530 (415) 525-0942

(FM) Facets Multimedia, 1517 W. Fullerton Ave., Chicago, IL 60614 (312) 281-9075

(FOF) Facts on File, 132 West 31st St., New York, NY 10001 (800) 322-8755 Fax (800) 678-3633 or (917) 339-0325 Website: www.factsonfile.com

(FOUR) Four Worlds Development Project, Faculty of Education, The University of Lethbridge, 4401 University Dr., Lethbridge, AB, Canada T1K 3M4 (403) 329-2065 Fax 329-3081

(FP) Friendship Press Distribution Office, P.O. Box 37844, Cincinnati, OH 45237 (513) 761-2100

(FU) Fulton Films, 64 Orchard Hill Rd., Newton, CT 06070 (203) 426-2580

(FUL) Fulcrum Publishing, 350 Indiana St., Suite 350, Golden, CO 80401 (800) 992-2908 Fax (303) 279-7111 E-mail: info@fulcrum-books.com; Website: www.fulcrum-books.com

(FWF) Fourth Wall Films, P.O. Box 702, Moline, IL 61265 E-mail: iowayfilm@aol.com; Website: www.iowaymovie.com

(FWT) Four Winds Trading Co., P.O. Box 1887, Boulder, CO 80306 (800) 456-5444; (303) 499-4484

(GA) Guidance Associates, P.O. Box 1000, Mt. Kisco, NY 10549 (800) 431-1242; Fax (914) 666-5319

(GAUL) Chris Gaul, 1919 Old Turkey Point Rd., Baltimore, MD 21211 (301) 686-7273

(GDA) Gray Deer Arts, P.O. Box 2341, Edmond, OK 73083 (405) 340-6323

(GP) Greenwood Press, 88 Post Rd. West, Box 5007, Westport, CT 06881

(GPN) Great Plains National, P.O. Box 80669, Lincoln, NE 68501 (800) 228-4630; or (402) 472-2007 Fax (402) 472-1785

(GW) Greenwich Workshop, 151 Main St., Seymour, CT 06483 (800) 243-4246; Fax (203) 881-9575. Website: www.greenwichworkshop.com; E-mail: info@greenwichworkshop.com

(HAP) Historical Art Prints, P.O. Box 660, Southbury, CT 06488 (203) 262-6680 Fax 262-6979 Website: www.historicalartprints.com.

(HLM) H.L. Murvin, 500 Vernon St., Oakland, CA 94610

(HO) HONOR, Inc., 6435 Wiesner Rd., Omro, WI 54963 (414) 582-7142

(HSS) Henry Street Settlement, 265 Henry St., New York, NY 10002 (212) 766-9200

(IANA) Institute of Alaska Native Arts, P.O. Box 70769, Fairbanks, AK 99707 (907) 456-7491

(IBC) Inuit Broadcasting Corp., 251 Laurier Ave., West, Suite 703, Ottawa, ON, Canada K1P 5J6 (613) 235-1892

(ICARUS) Icarus-First Run Films, 153 Waverly Place, 6th Floor, New York, NY 10014 (800) 876-1710; Fax (212) 989-7649

(IDIL) Institute for the Development of Indian Law, 1104 Glyndon St., SE, Vienna, VA 22180 (703) 938-7822

(IF) Image Film, 37 Burkhard Place, Rochester, New York, NY 14620 (716) 473-8070

(IFF) International Film Foundation, 155 W. 72nd St., Rm. 306, New York, NY 10023 (212) 580-1111

(IH) Indian House, P.O. Box 472, Taos, NM 87571 (800) 545-8152; in NM (505) 776-2953

(IIP) Igloolik Isuma Productions, P.O. Box 223, Igloolik, NWT, Canada X0A 0L0 (819) 934-8809 Fax 934-8782

(IM) Image Film, 132 Hampshire Dr., Rochester, NY 14618 (716) 473-8070

(IN) Intermedia Arts Minnesota, 2822 Lyndale Ave. S., Minneapolis, MN 55408 (612) 627-4444

(IP) Investigative Productions, 48 Major St., Toronto, ON, Canada M5S 2L1 (416) 968-7818

(IRA) Indian Rights Association, Film Rental Program, c/o Janney Montgomery, 1601 Market St., Philadelphia, PA 19103 (215) 665-4523

(IS) IS Productions, P.O. Box 747, Hotevilla, AZ 86030

(ISU) Iowa State University, Media Resources Center, 121 Pearson Hall, Ames IA 50010 (515) 294-1540

(ITFE) International Tele-Film Enterprises, 47 Densley Ave., Toronto, ON, Canada M6M 5A8 (416) 241-4483

(IU) Indiana University, Instructional Support Services, Bloomington, IN 47405 (800) 552-8620; Fax (812) 855-8404

(IVA) Island Visual Arts, 8920 Sunset Blvd., 2nd Floor, Los Angeles, CA 90069 (213) 288-5382 Fax 276-5476

(JO) Hugh & Suzanne Johnston, 16 Valley Rd., Princeton, NJ 08540 (609) 924-7505

(KC) KC Publications, Box 14883, Las Vegas, NV 89114 (703) 731-3123

(KF) Kifaru Productions, 23852 PCH #766, Malibu, CA 90265 (800) 400-8433; (310) 457-1617 Fax 457-2688. E-mail: kifaru@aol.com; Web site: www.kifaru.com

(KM) Kraus Microform, Route 100, Millwood, NY 10546 (800) 223-8323; Fax (914) 762-1195

(KS) Kansas State Historical Society, 6425 S.W. Sixth St., Topeka, KS 66615 (800) 766-3777

(KU) Knowledge Unlimited, P.O. Box 52 • Madison, WI 53701 (800) 356-2303; (608) 836-6660; Fax (800) 618-1570; (608) 831-1570 Website: www.thekustore.com

(KUAC) KUAC-TV, University of Alaska, Fairbanks, AK 99775 (907) 474-7492

(KUHT) KUHT-TV, 4513 Cullen Blvd., Houston, TX 77004 (713) 749-7371

(KUSD) KUSD-TV, 414 E. Clark St., Vermillion, SD 57069 (605) 677-5861

(KUTV) KUTV, Promotion Dept., P.O. Box 30901, Salt Lake City, UT 84301 (801) 973-3375

(KYUK) KYUK Video Productions, Pouch 468, Bethel, AK 99559 (907) 543-3131

(LC) Library of Congress, Motion Picture, Broadcasting & Recorded Sound Division; and Prints & Photographs Division, Washington, DC 20540 (202) 707-8572 Fax 707-2371

(LCA) Learning Corporation of America; Distributed by PHO

(LE) Lenapehoking Enterprises, P.O. Box 310, Cheswold, DE 19936 (800) 897-4263

(LL) Listening Library, P.O. Box L, Old Greenwich, CT 06870 (800) 243-4504

(LLC) Lakota Language Consortium, 2620 N. Walnut St., Suite 1280, Bloomington, IN 47404 (888) 525-6828 Fax (812) 961-0141.

(LV) Library Video Co., P.O. Box 1110, Bala Cynwyd, PA 19004 (800) 843-3620; Fax (610) 667-3425

(MAI) National Museum of the American Indian, Film & Video Archives & Photographic Archives, The George Gustav Heye Center-Smithsonian Institution, Alexander Hamilton U.S. Customs House, One Bowling Green, New York, NY 10004 (212) 283-2420

(MALKI) Malki-Ballena Press, P.O. Box 578 • Banning, CA 92220 (951) 849-7289 Fax 849-3549 Website: www.malkimuseumstore.org

(MAN) Robert Manning, 53 Hamilton Ave., Staten Island, NY 10301

(MB) Margaret Brandon, 140 Ridgeway Rd., Woodside, CA 94062 (415) 369-0139

(MBP) Michael Brodie Productions, 590 Transit Rd., Victoria, BC, Canada V8S 4Z5 (604) 598-2308

(McN) Maureen McNamara, 12 Vincent St., Cambridge, MA 02140 (617) 661-0402

(MC) Meadowlark Communications, P.O. Box 7218, Missoula, MT 59807 (888) 728-2180; (406) 728-2180 Fax 549-3090 E-mail: info@powwowcountry.com Website: www.powwowcountry.com

(**MCN**) Muscogee Creek Nation Community Center, P.O. Box 580, Okmulgee, OK 74447 (918) 756-8700

(**MCP**) Makoche Recordings, P.O. Box 2756, Bismarck, ND 58502 (800) 637-6863; Fax (701) 255-8287. Website: www.makoche.com

(**ME**) Meadowlark Media, P.O. Box 7218, Missoula, MT 79807 (888) 728-2180 Fax (406) 549-3090. E-mail: info@powwowcountry.com Website: www.powwowcountry.com.

(**MFP**) Morning Flower Press, P.O. Box 114433, Denver, CO 80211 (303) 477-8442

(**MFV**) Mystic Fire Video, 524 Broadway, Suite 604, New York, NY 10012 (800) 292-9001; (212) 941-0999 Fax 941-1443

(**MG**) The Media Guild, 11562 Sorrento Valley Rd., Suite J, San Diego, CA 92121 (619) 755-9191

(**ML**) Magic Lantern Communications, Ltd., 775 Pacific Rd., Unit #38, Oakville, ON, Canada L6L 6M4 (416) 827-1155 in Canada (800) 263-1717

(**MMA**) Museum of Modern Art, 11 West 53rd St., New York, NY 10019 (212) 956-4204

(**MNM**) Museum of New Mexico, Programs & Education A-V Specialist, Santa Fe, NM 87503 (505) 827-2070

(**MP**) Mixtech Productions, P.O. Box 1100-304, Taos, NM 87571 (505) 758-9052

(**MPC**) Maurose Puiblishing Co., P.O. Box 2153, Moscow, PA 18444 (800) 391-0011 Fax (570) 842-4716; E-mail: maurose1@aol.com Website: www.carlmoon.com

(**MRC**) Media Resources Center, 121 Pearson Hall, Iowa State University, Ames, IA 50011 (515) 294-1540

(**MT**) The Mohegan Tribe, c/o Little People Publications, c/o The Mohegan Tribe, 67 Sandy Desert Rd., Uncasville, CT 06382 (860) 204-6107 Fax (704) 848-6115

(**NACO**) Native American Co-op, P.O. Box 27626, Tucson, AZ 85726 (520) 622-4900

(**NAI**) Native American Images, P.O. Box 746, Austin, TX 78767 (800) 531-5008; (512) 472-7701

(**NAPBC**) Native American Public Broadcasting Consortium, P.O. Box 83111, Lincoln, NE 68501 (402) 472-3522

(**NATC**) Northwest Arctic Television Center, P.O. Box 51, Kotzebue, AK 99752 (907) 442-3472

(**NAV**) Native Voices, P.O. Box 180, Summertown, TN 38483 (800) 695-2241 Fax (931) 964-2291. E-mail: catalog@usit.net

(**NCTE**) National Council of Teachers of English, 1111 Kenyon Rd., Urbana, IL 61801

(**NDF**) New Day Films, 121 W. 27th St., Suite 902, New York, NY 10001 (212) 645-8210 Fax 645-8652

(**NDM**) New Dimension Media, 85803 Lorane Hwy., Eugene, OR 97405 (800) 288-4456

(**NETCHE**) NETCHE is now NETV

(**NETV**) Nebraska Educational Television, P.O. Box 83111, Lincoln, NE 68501 (800) 228-4630; in HI & NE (402) 472-2007

(**NFBC**) National Film Board of Canada, 22D Hollywood Ave., Hohokus, NJ 07423 (800) 542-2164; Fax (201) 652-1973

(**NGA**) National Gallery of Art, Extension Services, Washington, DC 20565

(**NGS**) National Geographic Society, Educational Services, P.O. Box 98018, Washington, DC 20090 (800) 368-2728; Fax (301) 921-1575

(**NH**) Northern Heritage Films (For information on distribution and new productions contact MAI)

(**NM**) The Newark Museum, 49 Washington St., Newark, NJ 07101 (201) 733-6600

(**NMAI**) National Museum of the American Indian, 4th St. & Independence Ave. SW • Washington, DC 20580 (800) 242-6624

(**NMFV**) New Mexico Film & Video, Box 272, Tesuque, NM 87574 (505) 983-3094

(**NNA**) National Native American AIDS Prevention Center, 3515 Grand Ave., Suite 100, Oakland, CA 94610 (510) 444-2051 Fax 444-1593.

(**NOVA**) Nova Scotia Department of Education, Education Media Services, 6955 Bayers Rd., Halifax, NS, Canada B3L 4S4 (902) 453-2810

(**NP**) Northland Publishing, P.O. Box 1389, Flagstaff, AZ 86002 (800) 346-3257 Fax (800) 257-9082

(**NPP**) New Pacific Productions, P.O. Box 12792, San Diego, CA 92112 (619) 462-8266

(**NR**) Norman Ross Publishing, 330 W. 58th St., New York, NY 10019 (800) 648-8850; Fax (212) 765-2393

(**NU**) New & Unique Videos, 2336 Summac Dr., San Diego, CA 92105 (619) 282-6126 Fax 283-8264

(**NV**) New Visions, P.O. Box 599, Aspen, CO 81612 (303) 925-2640 Fax 925-9369

(**NWL**) New World Library, 58 Paul Dr., San Rafael, CA 94903 (800) 972-6657; Fax (415) 472-2100

(**NYU**) New York U. Film Library, 26 Washington Pl., New York, NY 10003

(**O&C**) Ojibway & Cree Cultural Center, 84 Elm South,

Timmons, ON, Canada P4N 1W6 (705) 267-7911

(**OAP**) Old Army Press, P.O. Box 2243, Fort Collins, CO 80522 (800) 627-0079

(**ODE**) Oklahoma Dept. of Education, Media Resources, Oliver Hodge Bldg., Oklahoma City, OK 73105

(**OHS**) Oregon Historical Society, Education Dept., 1230 S.W. Park Ave., Portland, OR 97205 (503) 222-1741 ext. 36

(**OP**) Odyssey Productions, 2800 NW Thurman St., Portland, OR 97210 (503) 223-3480

(**OY**) Oyate, 2702 Mathews St., Berkeley, CA 94720 (510) 848-6700 Fax 848-4815

(**PBS**) PBS Video, 1320 Braddock Place, Alexandria, VA 22314 (800) 344-3337; Fax (703) 739-5269

(**PFV**) Pyramid Film & Video, Box 1048, Santa Monica, CA 90406 (800) 421-2304

(**PH**) Paul Hacker Knives & Flutes, 6513 N.W. 20th Dr., Bethany, OK 73008 (405) 787-8600 (phone & fax)

(**PHO**) Phoenix/BFA Films, 2349 Chaffee Dr., St. Louis, MO 63146 (800) 221-1274; Fax (314) 569-2834

(**PIE**) Pacific International Enterprises, 1133 S. Riverside, Suite 1, Medford, OR 97501 (503) 779-0990

(**PMI**) Public Media, Inc., Home Vision Arts, 4411 N. Ravenswood Ave., Chicago, IL 60640 (800) 826-3456; Fax (773) 878-0416

(**PR**) Pictures of Record, 119 Kettle Creek Rd., Weston, CT 06883 (203) 227-3387 Fax 222-9673

(**PSU**) The Pennsylvania State University, Audio-Visual Services, Special Services Bldg., 1127 Fox Hill Rd., University Park, PA 16803 (800) 826-0132; In PA, HI & AK (814) 865-6314

(**PUSA**) Penguin USA, Academic Marketing Dept., 375 Hudson St., New York, NY 10014 (800) 253-6476

(**QP**) Quanta Press, 1313 Fifth St. SE, Minneapolis, MN 55414

(**QTS**) Quileute Tribal School, Old Coast Guard Rd., P.O. Box 39, La Push, WA 98350 (206) 374-6163 Fax 374-6311

(**RC**) Reservation Creations, P.O. Box 27626, Tucson, AZ 85726 (602) 622-4900

(**REV**) Red Eye Video, 255 E. Kellogg #502, St. Paul, MN 55101 (651) 224-5708; Website: www.redeyevideo.org

(**RH**) Random House--School Division, Dept. 9020, 400 Hahn Rd., Westminster, MD 21157 (800) 638-6460; in MD (800) 492-0782; in AK & HI (301) 876-2286

(**RICH**) Rich-Heape Films, Inc., 5952 Royal Lane, Suite 254, Dallas, TX 75230 (888) 600-2922; (214) 696-6916 Fax 696-6306 E-mail: orders@richheape.com; Website: www.rich-heape.com

(**RITZ**) Lan Brook Ritz, Brown Bird Productions, 1971 N. Curson Ave., Hollywood, CA 90046 (213) 851-8928

(**RM**) Robert N. Manning, 53 Hamilton Ave., Staten Island, NY 10301 (718) 981-0120

(**RP**) Research Publications, 12 Lunar Dr./Drawer AB, Woodbridge, CT 06525 (800) 732-2477; in CT call collect; in AK & HI (203) 397-2600; Fax (203) 397-3893

(**RS**) Distributed by Gail Singer Films, 82 Willcocks St., Toronto, ON, Canada M5S 1C8 (416) 923-4245

(**RT**) RT Computer Graphics, 602 San Juan de Rio, Rio Rancho, NM 87124 (800) 891-1600; (505) 891-1600 Fax 891-1350

(**SAN**) San Juan School District Media Center, Curriculum Division, 28 West 200 North (15-7), Blanding, UT 84511 (801) 678-2281

(**SDF**) Sun Dog Films, Box 232, Custer, SD 57730 (605) 673-4065,

(**SE**) Spotted Eagle Productions, 2524 Hennepin Ave. So. Minneapolis, MN 55405 (612) 377-4212

(**SH**) Shenandoah Film Productions, 538 G St., Arcata, CA 95521 (707) 822-1030 Fax 822-5334 Website: www.northcoast.com/~vern

(**SHSW**) State Historical Society of Wisconsin, 816 State St., Madison, WI 53706

(**SI**) Smithsonian Institution, Services Branch, National Anthropological Archives, Washington, DC 20560 (202) 357-4560

(**SI-OMB**) Smithsonian Institution, Office of Museum Programs, A-V Loan Program, Washington, DC 20560 (202) 357-3101

(**SII**) Softline Information, Inc., 20 Summer St., Stamford, CT 06901 (800) 524-7922; Fax (203) 975-8347

(**SM**) Southwest Museum, Highland Park, Los Angeles, CA 90042 (323) 221-2164 Fax 224-8223; E-mail: dking@annex.com Web site: www.southwestmuseum.org

(**SN**) Seneca Nation of Indians, P.O. Box 442, Salamanca, NY 14779 (716) 945-1738

(**SO**) Solaris, 264 West 19th St., New York, NY 10011 (212) 741-0778

(**SOAR**) Sound of America Records (SOAR), P.O. Box 8606, Albuquerque, NM 87198 (505) 268-6110 Fax 268-0237 E-mail: soar@rt66.com; Web site: www.soundofamerica.com

(**SP**) SilverPlatter, 100 River Ridge Dr., Norwood, MA 02062 (800) 343-0064

(SR) Scholarly Resources, 104 Greenhill Ave., Wilmington, DE 19805 (800) 772-8937; (302) 654-7713 Fax 654-3871 E-mail: sales@scholarly.com; Web site: www.scholarly.com

(SRA) Science Research Associates, P.O. Box 543, Blacklick, OH 43004 (800) 843-8855

(STULL) Donald D. Stull, 2900 Westdale Rd., Lawrence, KS 66044 (913) 842-8055

(SUPT) Superintendent of Documents, Government Printing Office, Washington, DC 20402

(SUQ) Suquamish Museum, P.O. Box 498, Suquamish, WA 98392 (206) 598-3311

(SVE) Society for Visual Education, N. Northwest Hwy., Chicago, IL 60631 (800) 829-1900 Fax (800) 624-1678

(SW) Strong Wind Records, P.O. Box 47, Massena, NY 13662 (315) 769-8727. Website: www.strongwindrecords.com

(SWR) Silver Wave Records, Inc., P.O. Box 7943, Boulder, CO 80306 (800) 745-9283 (303) 443-5617 Fax 443-0877 E-mail: info@silverwave.com Website: www.silverwave.com

(TA) Troll Associates, Instructional Materials, 100 Corporate Dr., Mahwah, NJ 07430 (800) 526-5289; Fax (201) 529-9347

(TAM) Tamarack Films, 11032-76 St., Edmonton, AB, Canada T5B 2C6 (403) 477-7958

(TC) Treasure Chest, P.O. Box 5250, Tucson, AZ 85703 (800) 969-9558

(TE) Russell Publications, 9027 N. Cobre Dr. • Phoenix, AZ 85028-5317 (800) 835-7220 Fax (602) 493-4691 Website: www.indiandata.com

(TL) Time-Life Video, 1450 East Parham Rd., Richmond, VA 23280

(TM) Taylor Museum, Colorado Springs Fine Arts Center, 30 West Dale, Colorado Springs, CO 80903

(TBM) Thomas Burke Memorial, Washington State Museum, DB-10, University of Washington, Seattle, WA 98195 (206) 543-5884

(TDR) Tribal Data Resources, 2576 Hartnell Ave., Suite 5, Redding, CA 96002 (530) 222-2964 Fax 222-8413 E-mail: tdr@tdronline.com; Web site: www.tdronline.com

(THA) Thomas Howe Associates Ltd., 1100 Homer St., Vancouver, BC, Canada V6B 2X8 (604) 687-4215

(THRC) Texas Human Resources Center, University of Texas, Arlington, Library, P.O. Box 19497, Arlington, TX 76019 (817) 273-2767

(TIPI) Tipi Shop, P.O. Box 1542, Rapid City, SD 57709

(TOP) The Origins Program, 4632 Vincent Ave. S., Minneapolis, MN 55410

(TP) Todd Publications, 3500 NE 6 Dr., Boca Raton, FL 33431 (561) 910-0440; Email: toddpub@aol.cm

(TPH) Theosophical Publishing House, 306 W. Geneva Rd., Wheaton, IL 60189 (800) 654-9430; in IL (312) 665-0123

(TR) The Trust for Native American Cultures & Crafts, P.O. Box 142, Greenville, NH 03048 (603) 878-2944

(TT) Tulalip Tribe, 3901 Totem Beach Rd., Marysville, WA 98270 (206) 653-0220

(TTP) Turning Tide Productions, P.O. Box 864, Wendell, MA 01379 (508) 544-8313

(TW) Time-Warner Video, P.O. Box 4367, Huntington Station, NY 11750 (800) 854-7200

(TWN) Third World Newsreel, 545 8th Ave. 10th Fl., New York, NY 10018 (212) 947-9277 Fax 594-6417 E-mail: twn@twn.org

(UA) University of Arizona, Media Services-Film Library, Tucson, AZ 85706 (602) 626-3282

(UAB) University of Alberta, Motion Picture Division, Edmonton, AB, Canada (403) 432-3302

(UADA) University of Alberta, Dept. of Anthropology, 13-15 HM Tory Bldg., Edmonton, ON T6G 2H4 Canada (403) 432-3879

(UAL) University of Alberta, Audio Visual Services, L2-6A Humanities Bldg., Edmonton, AB, Canada T6G 2E1 (403) 432-4962

(UC) University of California, Extension Media Center, 2000 Center St., Berkeley, CA 94704 (510) 642-0460 Fax 643-9271

(UCLA) University of California, Los Angeles, Instructional Media Library, Powell Library-46, Los Angeles, CA 90024 (310) 825-0755

(UCP) University of California Press, orders to: California/Princeton Fulfillment Services, 1445 Lower Ferry Rd., Ewing, NJ 08618 (800) 777 4726 Fax (800) 999-1958 Website: www.ucpress.edu

(UCT) University of Connecticut, Film Library, U-1, Storrs, CT 06268 (203) 486-2530

(UI) University of Illinois Film Center, 506 S. Wright St. #378, Urbana, IL 61801 (800) 367-3456; in IL (800) 252-1357

(UK) University of Kansas, A-V Center, 645 New Hampshire St., Lawrence, KS 66044 (913) 864-3352

(UL) United Learning, 6633 W. Howard St., P.O. Box 48718, Niles, IL 60714 (800) 424-0362

(UM) University Microfilms International, 300 North Zeeb Rd., Ann Arbor, MI 48106 (800) 521-0600; (313) 761-4700 ext. 789

(UMA) University of Mid-America (See GPN)

(UMC) Utah Media Center, 20 South West Temple, Salt Lake City, UT 84101

(UMN) University of Minnesota, Film & Video, 1313 Fifth St. SE, Suite 108, Minneapolis, MN 55414 (800) 847-8251; in MN (612) 373-3810

(UN) University of Nevada Film Library, Getchell Library, Reno, NV 89557 (702) 784-6037

(UNM) University of New Mexico Press, 721 Spirit Dr., SE, Albuquerque, NM 87106 (800) 249-7737 Fax (800) 622-8667 (505) 277-4810 E-mail:unmpress@unm.edu Website: www.unmpress.com

(UNP) University of Nebraska Press, P.O. Box 880484, Lincoln, NE 68588 (402) 472-3581 (800) 755-1105; Fax (800) 526-2617 E-mail: pressmail@unl.edu; Web site: www.nebraskapress.unl.edu

(UP) Upstream Productions, 420 1st Ave. W., Seattle, WA 98119 (206) 281-9177 Fax 284-6963

(UT) University of Texas, Film Library, Education Annex G-5, 20th at San Jacinto, Austin, TX 78713-7448 (512) 471-3572

(UTE) Ute Indian Tribe Audio-Visual, P.O. Box 129, Fort Duchesne, UT 84026 (801) 722-5141

(UTFL) The University of Texas Film Library, Drawer W, Austin, TX 78711 (512) 471-3573

(UT-ITC) The University of Texas, Institute of Texan Cultures at San Antonio, P.O. Box 1226, San Antonio, TX 78294-1226 (800) 776-7651; (210) 558-2235 Fax 558-2205

(UTP) University of Texas Press, P.O. Box 7819, Austin, TX 78713 (800) 252-3206 Fax (800) 687-6046 (512) 471-7233 Fax 320-0668 Website: www.utexas.edu/utpress

(UUT) University of Utah, Instructional Media Center, 207 Milton Bennion Hall, Salt Lake City, UT 84112 (801) 581-3170

(UW) University of Washington, Instructional Media Services, 23 Kane Hall, DG-10, Seattle, WA 98195 (206) 543-9909

(UWL) University of Washington Libraries, Special Collection Division--Microforms, Suzzallo Library, FM-25, Seattle, WA 98195

(VC) The Video Catalog, P.O. Box 64428, St. Paul, MN 55164 (800) 733-2232

(VH) VH-1, 1515 Broadway, New York, NY 10036 (212) 258-7800

(VIP) VIP Publishing, P.O. Box 833216, Richardson, TX 75083 (800) 776-0842

(VOI) Video Out International, 1160 Hamilton St., Vancouver, B.C., Canada V6B 2S2 (604) 688-4336

(VT) Video Tech, 19346 3rd Ave. NW, Seattle, WA 98177 (206) 546-5401

(VVP) Victorian Video Productions, P.O. Box 1540, Colfax, CA 95713 (800) 848-0284; (916) 346-6184

(WALI) Monona Wali, 886 S. Bronson Ave., Los Angeles, CA 90005 (213) 650-7341

(WALL) Alfred Wallace, 420 Riverside Dr., New York, NY 10025 (212) 865-8817

(WD) Walt Disney Educational Media Co., 500 South Buena Vista, Burbank, CA 91521

(WE) World Eagle, Inc., 64 Washburn Ave., Wellesley, MA 02181

(WGBH) WGBH Distribution Office, 125 Western Ave., Boston, MA 02134 (617) 492-2777

(WH) Written Heritage, P.O. Box 1390, Folsom, LA 70437 (800) 301-8009 Fax (985) 796-9236; E-mail: info@writtenheritage.com Website: www.writtenheritage.com

(WIN) Wintercount, P.O. Box 889, New Castle, CO 81647 (800) 473-8709; (970) 984-3685 Fax 984-3266. Website: www.wintercount.com. E-mail: info@wintercount.com

(WKV) Wood Knapp Video, 5900 Wilshire Blvd., Los Angeles, CA 90036 (800) 521-2666; Fax (213) 930-2742

(WMM) Women Make Movies, 462 Broadway, 5th Floor, New York, NY 10013 (212) 925-0606 Fax 925-2052

(WNET) WNET-13 Video Distribution, 356 W. 58th St., New York, NY 10019 (212) 560-3045

(WP) White Publishing, P.O. Box 342, Arlee, MT (406) 726-3627

(WQED) WQED-TV, Distribution Department, 4802 Fifth Ave., Pittsburgh, PA 15213 (412) 622-1356

(WXXI) WXXI-TV, 280 State St., P.O. Box 21, Rochester, NY 14601 (716) 325-7500

(YPT) Yerington Paiute Tribe Publications, 171 Campbell Lane, Yerington, NV 89447

(ZAENTZ) The Saul Zaentz Productions Co., 2600 Tenth St., Berkeley, CA 94710 (800) 227-0602

(ZANGO) Zango Music Distribution, P.O. Box 403, Cottage Grove, OR 97424 (800) 688-0187 (541) 942-1385 Fax 942-1564 (Wholesale only) Website: www.zangomusic.com

(ZC) Zia Cine, P.O. Box 493, Santa Fe, NM 87504 (505) 983-4127

A listing of Canadian Nations and Bands, with land areas of at least 1,000 acres. Many bands have more than one reserve in each province. Arranged by Reserve & Province.

ALBERTA

ALEXANDER FIRST NATION (KIPOHTAKAW)
P.O. Box 3419 • Morinville, AB T8R 1S3
(780) 939-5887 Fax 939-6166; Kurt Burnstick, Chief
Website: www.alexanderfn.com; E-mail: info@alexanderfn.com
Publication: The Kipooohtakaw Voice

ALEXIS NAKOTA SIOUX NATION
P.O. Box 7 • Glenevis, AB T0E 0X0
(780) 967-2225 Fax 967-5484; Clayton Tony Alexis, Chief
Website: www.alexisnakotasioux.com
Location: 72 kilometers west of Edmonton, Alberta.
Attractions: Eagle River Casino & Travel Plaza.

ATHABASCA CHIPEWYAN FIRST NATION
Box 366 • Fort Chipewyan, AB T0E 0X0 (888) 420-7011
(780) 697-3730 Fax 697-3500; Website: www.acfn.com
Allan Adam, Chief (2003-preent); E-mail: aadam@acfn.com

BEAVER FIRST NATION
P.O. Box 270 • High Level, AB T0H 1Z0
(780) 927-3544 Fax 927-4064; Website: www.beaverfirstnation.com
Trevor Mercredi, Chief

BEAVER LAKE CREE NATION
P.O. Box 960 • Lac LaBiche, AB T0A 2C0
(877) 610-3110; (780) 623-4549 Fax 623-4523
Germaine Anderson, Chief; Website: www.beaverlakecreenation.ca

BIGSTONE CREE NATION
P.O. Box 960 • Wabasca, AB T0G 2K0
(800) 268-6783; (403) 891-3836 Fax 891-3942
Website: www.bigstone.ca; E-mail: webmaster@bigstone.ca
Gordon T. Auger, Chief; Myles Auger, Executive Director

CHIPEWYAN PRAIRIE FIRST NATION
General Delivery • Chard, AB T0P 1G0
(780) 559-2259 Fax 559-2213; Walter Janvier, Chief

COLD LAKE FIRST NATIONS BAND
P.O. Box 1769 • Cold Lake, AB T9M 1P4
(780) 594-7183 Fax 594-3577; Bernice Martial, Chief
Website: www.clfns.com

DENE THA' TRIBE BAND
P.O. Box 120 • Chateh, AB T0H 0S0
(877) 336-3842; (780) 321-3842 Fax 321-3886
Website: www.denetha.ca; E-mail: info@denetha.ca
General Delivery • Meander River, AB T0H 2P0
(877) 5535-2260; (780) 535-2260 Fax 535-2261
P.O Box 958 • Bushe River, AB T0H 1Z0
(888) 926-6368; (780) 926-2422 Fax 926-2475

DRIFTPILE CREE NATION
General Delivery • Driftpile, AB T0G 0V0
(780) 355-3868 Fax 355-3650; Website: www.driftpilecreenation.com
Dean M. Giroux, Chief; Rodney Chalifoux, Administrator
Members: 1,500. Rea: 15,000 acres. Annual powwow in August.

DUNCAN'S FIRST NATION
Box 148 • Brownvale, AB T0H 0L0
(780) 597-3777 Fax 597-3920; E-mail: info@duncansfirstnation.ca
Donald Testawich, Chief & Council; E-mail: dt.chief@duncansfirstnation.ca
Shaun Green, CEO; E-mail: admin.cea@duncannsfirstnation.ca

ENOCH CREE NATION #440
P.O. Box 29 • Enoch, AB T7X 3Y3
(780) 470-4505 Fax 470-3380; Ronald Marin, Chief
Population: 2,100. *Facilities*: River Cree Resort & Casino

ERMINESKIN CREE NATION
P.O. Box 219 • Maskwacis, AB T0C 1N0
(780) 585-3741 Fax 585-3774; Website: www.ermineskin.ca
Randy Ermineskin, Chief; Bruce Littlechild, Tribal Administrator

FORT McKAY FIRST NATION
P.O. Box 5360 • Fort McMurray, AB T9H 3G4
(780) 828-4220 Fax 828-4393; Jim Boucher, Chief

FORT McMURRAY #468 FIRST NATION
P.O. Box 6130, Clearwater Sta. • Fort McMurray, AB T9H 4W1
(780) 334-2293 Fax 334-2457

FROG LAKE FIRST NATION
General Delivery • Frog Lake, AB T0A 1M0
(780) 943-3737 Fax 943-3966; Website: www.froglake.ca
Clifford Stanley, Chief; E-mail: cliffordstanley@froglake.ca

HEART LAKE FIRST NATION
P.O. Box 447 • Lac La Biche, AB T0A 2C0
(780) 623-2130 Fax 623-3505; Eugene Monias, Chief

HORSE LAKE FIRST NATION
P.O. Box 303 • Hythe, AB T0H 2C0
(780) 356-2248 Fax 356-3666; Dale Robert Horseman, Chief
As of 2014, the total population of the band was 1,053 people, of whom 466 (44%) lived on reserve or on Crown land and the rest living off reserve. The band has two reserves, Clear Hills and Horse Lakes with 3,100 acres.[2

KAINAIWA/BLOOD FIRST NATION
P.O. Box 60 • Standoff, AB T0L 1Y0
(780) 737-3753 Fax 737-2336; Website: www.bloodtribe.org
Chief Weasel Head; E-mail: cweaselhead@treaty7.org
Alva Weasel Moccasin, Chief & Council Executive Secretary
Population: 10,000. Area: 550 square miles.

KAPAWE'NO FIRST NATION
P.O. Box 10 • Gouard, AB T0G1C0
(800) 751-3800; (780) 751-3800 Fax 751-3864
Website: www.kapaweno.ca; E-mail: admin@kapaweno.ca
Frank T. Halcrow, Chief (1970-present)
Peter Chalifoux & Sydney Halcrow, Councillors

KEHEWIN CREE NATION
Box 220 • KEHEWIN, AB T0A !C0
(780) 826-3333 Fax 826-2355; Ernest Gadwa, Chief
Website: www.kehewincreenation.ca

LITTLE RED RIVER CREE FIRST NATION
P.O. Box 30 • John D'Or Prairie, AB T0H 1Z0
(780) 759-3912 Fax 759- 3780; Gus Loonskin, Chief
Website: www.lrrcn.ab.ca

LOON RIVER FIRST NATION
P.O. Box 189 • Red Earth Creek, AB T0G 1X0
(780) 649-3883 Fax 649-3873; Website: www.loonriver.net
Arthur Noskey, Chief

LOUIS BULL TRIBE
P.O. Box 130 • Maskwacis, AB T0C 1N0
(888) 281-7907; (780) 585-3978 Fax 585-3799
Rusty Threefingers, Chief
E-mail: laureenc@louisbulltribe.ca

LUBICON LAKE FIRST NATION
P.O. Box 6731 • Peace River, AB T8S 1S5
(780) 629-3945 Fax 629-3939; Bernard Ominayak, Chief
Website: www.lubiconlakenation.ca

MIKISEW CREE FIRST NATION
P.O. Box 90 • Fort Chipewyan, AB T0P 1B0
(800) 668-1634; (780) 697-3740 Fax 697-3826
Website: www.mikisewcree.ca; E-mail: ceo@mikisewcree.ca
Steve Courtoreille, Chief

MONTANA FIRST NATION
P.O. Box 70 • Hobbema, AB T0C 1N0
(866) 585-3744; (780) 585-3744 Fax 585-3264
Website: www.montanaband.net; Bradley Rabbit, Chief

O'CHIESE FIRST NATION
P.O. Box 1570 • Rocky Mountain House, AB T4T 1B2
(888) 256-3884; (403) 989-3943 Fax 989-3795
Website: www.ochiese.ca; Darren Whitford, Chief
Ian Arcand, Executive Officer; E-mail: ocfnianarcand@gmail.com

PAUL FIRST NATION
P.O. Box 89 • Duffield, AB T0E 0N0
(780) 892-2691 Fax 892-3402
Website: www.paulband.ca; Casey Bird, Chief

PIIKANI NATION
P.O. Box 70 • Brocket, AB T0K 0H0
(403) 965-3940 Fax 965-2030; Website: www.piikanination.com
Stanley Grier, Chief; E-mail: Stanley.g@piikanination.com

SADDLE LAKE CREE NATION
P.O. Box 100 • Saddle Lake, AB T0A 3T0
(780) 726-3829 Fax 726-3788; Website: www.saddlelake.ca
Leonard Jackson, Chief
Sheila Redcrow, Administrator; E-mail: sredcrow@saddlelake.ca

SAMSON CREE NATION
P.O. Box 159 • Maskwacis, AB T0C 1N0
(800) 661-2579; (780) 585-3793 Fax 585-2700
Website: www.samsoncree.com; Kurt Buffalo, Chief

SAWRIDGE FIRST NATION
P.O. Box 326 • Slave Lake, AB T0G 2A0
(780) 849-4331 Fax 849-3446
Website: www.sawridgefirstnation.com
E-mail: sawridge@sawridgefirstnation.com
Walter Patrick Twinn, Chief

SIKSIKA NATION
P.O. Box 1100 • Siksika, AB T0J 3W0
(800) 551-5724; (403) 734-5100 Fax 734-5110
Website: www.sikksikanation.com
E-mail: frontdesk@siksikanation.com
Vincent Yellow Old Woman, Chief

STONEY NAKODA FIRST NATION
P.O. Box 40 • Morley, AB T0L 1N0
(403) 881-3770 Fax 881-2676; Website: www.stoneynation.com
Ken Christensen, Tribal Administrator
Facilities: Stoney Nakoda Resort & Casino

STURGEON LAKE CREE NATION
P.O. Box 757 • Valleyview, AB T0H 3N0
(780) 524-3307 Fax 524-2711; Richard Kappo, Chief
Website: www.sturgeonlake.ca

SUCKER CREEK FIRST NATION
P.O. Box 65 • Enilda, AB T0G 0W0
(780) 523-4425/6/7 Fax 523-3111
Website: www.scfn.biz; James Badger, Chief
Location: About 22 kilometers east of High Prairie, Alberta.
Population: 2,100. *Area*: 6,000 hectares of reserve land.

SUNCHILD CREE FIRST NATION
P.O. Box 747 • Rocky Mountain House, AB T0M 1T0
(403) 989-3740 Fax 989-2533; Harry Goodrunning, Chief

SWAN RIVER FIRST NATION
P.O. Box 270 • Kinuso, AB T0G 1K0
(780) 775-3536 Fax 775-3796; Ryan Davis, Chief
Website: www.swanriverfirstnation.org

TALLCREE FIRST NATION
P.O. Box 100 • Fort Vermillion, AB T0H 1N0
(780) 927-3727 Fax 927-4375; Website: www.tallcreefirstnation.ca
Rupert Meneen, Chief
Location: Northern Alberta, near Fort Vermillion. 7 Reserves make up Tallcree that covers 23,195 total acres. *Population*: 1,044, with most (547) living away from the Reserves, while 493 live on-reserve.

TSUT'INA K'OSA NATION (SARCEE)
9911 Chula Blvd. #200 • Tsuu T'ina Nation, AB T2W 6H6
(403) 281-4455 Fax 251-5871; Roy Albert Whitney, Chief
Website: wwwtsutinanation.ca

WHITEFISH LAKE FIRST NATION #128
P.O. Box 271 • Goodfish Lake, AB T0A 1R0
(780) 636-7000 Fax 636-7006; Website: www.wfl128.ca
Brian Favel, Chief; E-mail: brian.favel@wfl128.ca
Dale Steinhauer, Administrator

WHITEFISH LAKE FIRST NATION #459
General Delivery • Atikameg, AB T0G 0C0
(780) 767-3914 Fax 767-3814; Eddie Tallman, Chief

WOODLAND CREE FIRST NATION
General Delivery • Cadotte Lake, AB T0H 0N0
(800) 465-8029; (780) 629-3803 Fax 629-3898
Isaac Laboucan-Avirom, Chief; Website: www.woodlandcree.net

METIS NON-STATUS

BUFFALO LAKE METIS SETTLEMENT
Box 16 • Castan, AB T0A 0R0
(780) 689-2170 Fax 689-2024; Website: www.buffalolakems.ca
Horace Paternaude, Chair; Harold Blyan, Vice Chair

EAST PRAIRIE METIS SELLEMENT
P.O. Box 1289 • High Prairie, AB T0G 1E0
(780) 523-2594 Fax 523-2777
Total population: 900. *Enrolled population*: 375. *Area*: 129 square miles.

ELIZABETH METIS SETTLEMENTS
P.O. Box 420 • Cold Lake, AB T9M 1P1
(780) 594-5026 Fax 594-5452; Website: www.elizabethms.ca
Richard Blyan, Administrator; E-mail: richardblyan@gmail.com

Area: Situated along the Alberta/Saskatchewan border. *Population*: 800.

FISHING LAKE METIS SETTLEMENT
General Delivery • Sputinow, AB T0A 3G0
(780) 943-2202 Fax 943-2575; Website: www.fishinglakems.ca
E-mail: administrator@fishinglakems.ca
Linda Isbister, Chair; E-mail: linda.isbister@fishinglakems.ca

FORT McKAY METIS #122
General Delivery • Fort McKay, AB T0P 1C0
(780) 828-4086 Fax 828-4111

GIFT LAKE METIS SETTLEMENTS
P.O. Box 60 • Gift Lake, AB T0G 1B0
(780) 767-3894 Fax 767-3888

KIKINO METIS SETTLEMENTS
General Delivery • Gift Lake, AB T0G 1B0
(780) 623-7868 Fax 623-7080

METIS NATION OF ALBERTA (Headquarters)
#100 11738 Kingsway Ave. • Edmonton, AB T5G 0X5
(780) 455-2200 Fax 452-8946 (800) 252-7553 in AB only
Website: www.albertametis.com
Audrey Poitras, President; Joe Pimlott, Vice President
The Métis Nation of Alberta governance structure is divided into six regional areas. Each designated region has a regional council consisting of a President and Vice-President and representation of Métis locals from within the region. *Communities*: Buffalo Lake, East Prairie, Elizabeth, Fishing Lake, Gift Lake, Kikino, Paddle Prairie, Peavine.

METIS SETTLEMENTS GENERAL COUNCIL
3rd Floor, 10525 - 170 St. • Edmonton, AB T5S 1K9
(780) 822-4096 Fax 489-9558; Website: www.msgc.ca
Randy Hardy, President; Stan Delorme, V.P.
E-mail: reception@msgc.ca

PADDLE PRAIRIE METIS SETTLEMENT
Box 58 • Paddle Prairie, AB T0H 2W0
(780) 981-2227 Fax 981-3737
Alden Armstrong, Chair; Bob Ghostkeeper, Vice Chair
Population: 1,464.

PEAVINE METIS SETTLEMENTS
Bag #4 • High Prairie, AB T0G 1E0
(780) 523-2557 Fax 523-2626; Website: www.peavinemetis.com
Ken Noskey, Chair; Sherry Cunningham, Vice Chair
Population: 995.

BRITISH COLUMBIA

ADAMS LAKE INDIAN BAND
P.O. Box 588 • Chase, BC V0E 1M0

(250) 679-8841 679-8813
Website: www.adamslakeband.org; E-mail: receptionist@alib.ca
Robin Billy, Chief; Albert Quinn, Band Manager

AHOUSAHT FIRST NATION
General Delivery • Ahousaht, BC V0R 1A0
(800) 991-1433; (250) 670-9531 Fax 670-9696
Website: www.www.ahousaht.ca; E-mail: info@ahousaht.ca
Greg Louie, Chief Councillor
Description: The largest of the Nuu-chah-nulth nations with more than 2000 members. About 1/3 of Ahousaht members live within Ahousaht traditional territories while the remainder live in other rural and urban areas.

AITCHELITZ FIRST NATION
8150 Aitken Rd. • Sardis, BC V2R 1A9
(604) 792-2404 Fax 858-7692; Johnny George, Chief

ALEXANDRIA FIRST NATION
c/o Tsilhoqot'in National Government
51D S. Fourth Ave. • Williams Lake, BC V2J 1J6
(250) 993-4324 Fax 398-5798; Bernie Elkins Mack, Chief
Thomas Billyboy & Howard Johnny, Councillors

ASHCROFT FIRST NATION
P.O. Box 440 • Ashcroft, BC V0K 1A0
(250) 453-9154 Fax 453-9156; Mae Boomer, Chief

BEECHER BAY FIRST NATION
4901-B East Sooke Rd. • Sooke, BC V9Z 1B6
(250) 478-3535 Fax 478-3585; Russ Chips, Chief
Website: www.beecherbaybc.com; E-mail: bb.fn@telus.net

BLUEBERRY RIVER FIRST NATION
P.O. Box 3009 • Buick Creek, BC V0C 2R0
(250) 630-2584 Fax 630-2588; Ryan Day, Chief
Website: www.bonaparteindianband.com
Martin Gerstmar, Director of Operations

BONAPARTE INDIAN BAND
P.O. Box 669 • Cache Creek, BC V0K 1H0
(877) 457-4944; (250) 457-9624 Fax 457-9550
Website: www.bonaparteindanband.com; Nels Terry Porter, Chief

BOOTHROYD FIRST NATION
P.O. Box 295 • Boston Bar, BC V0K 1C0
(604) 867-9211 Fax 867-9747; Richard Campbell, Chief

BOSTON BAR FIRST NATION
S.S. #1 • Boston Bar, BC V0K 1C0
(604) 867-8844 Fax 867-9317; Website: www.bostonbarfistnation.com
Delores O'Donoaghey, Chief

BRIDGE RIVER FIRST NATION
P.O. Box 190 • Lillooet, BC V0K 1V0
(250) 256-7423 Fax 256-7999; Susan James, Chief

BURNS LAKE FIRST NATION
P.O. Box 9000 • Burns Lake, BC V0J 1E0
(250) 692-7717 Fax 692-4214; Website: www.burnslakeband.ca
Dan George, Chief

CAMPBELL RIVER BAND
1650 Old Spit Rd.. • Campbell River, BC V9W 5W8
(877) 286-6949; (250) 286-6949 Fax 287-8838
Website: www.crband.ca; E-mail: reception@crband.ca
Robert Pollard, Chief

CANIM LAKE BAND
Box 1030 • 100 Mile House, BC V0K 2E0
(250) 397-2227 Fax 397-2769; Website: www.canimlakeband.com
Michael Archie, Chief

CANOE CREEK FIRST NATION
General Delivery • Dog Creek, BC V0L 1J0
(888) 220-4220; (250) 440-5645 Fax 440-5679
Website: www.canoecreekband.ca; E-mail: general@canoecreekband.ca
Patrick Harry, Chief; Marilyn Camille, Band Administrator

CARRIER SEKANI TRIBAL COUNCIL
1460 Sixth Ave., Suite 200 • Prince George, B.C. V2L 3N2
(800) 280-8722; (250) 562-6279 Fax 562-8206

Website: www.carriersekani.ca; Terry Teegee, Tribal Chief
Represents members from seven First Nations (5,000 member) who belong to the CSTC association, which includes: Burns Lake, Takla Lake, Tl'azt'en, Nak'azdli, Nadleh Whut'en, Saik'uz, & Wet'suwet'en Nations.

CAYOOSE CREEK FIRST NATION
P.O. Box 484 • Lillooet, BC V0K 1V0
(250) 256-4136 Fax 256-4030;Website: www.cayoosecreek.ca
Michelle Edwards, Chief

CHAWATHIL FIRST NATION
4-60814 Lougheed Hwy 7 • Hope, BC V0X 1L3
(604) 869-9994 Fax 869-761
Website: www.chawathil.org; E-mail: reception@chawathil.org
Rhoda Peters, Chief; Norman Florence, Vice Chief

CHEAM FIRST NATION
52130 Old Yale Rd. • Rosedale, BC V0X 1X0
(604) 794-7924 Fax 794-7456; Website: www.cheam.ca
Sidney Douglas, Chief

CHEHALIS INDIAN BAND
4690 Salish Way • Agassiz, BC V0M 1A1
(604) 796-2116 Fax 796-3946; Virginia Peters, Chief

CHEMAINUS FIRST NATION
RR 1 • Ladysmith, BC V0R 2E0
(250) 245-7155 Fax 245-3012; Robert Daniels, Chief

CHESLATTA CARRIER NATION
P.O. Box 909 • Burns Lake, BC V0J 1E0
(250) 694-3334 Fax 694-3632; Marvin Charlie, Chief

COLDWATER INDIAN BAND
P.O. Box 4600 • Merritt, BC V0K 2B0
(250) 378-6174 Fax 378-5351; Website: www.coldwaterband.ca
Lee Spahan, Chief

COLUMBIA LAKE FIRST NATION
P.O. Box 130 • Windermere, BC V0B 2L0
(250) 342-6301 Fax 342-9693; Joseph Nicholas, Chief

COMOX FIRST NATION
3320 Comox Rd. • Courtenay, BC V9N 3P8
(250) 339-7122 Fax 339-7053; Website: www.comoxband.ca
Robert Everson, Chief Councillor

COOK'S FERRY FIRST NATION
P.O. Box 130 • Spences Bridge, BC V0K 2L0
(250) 458-2224 Fax 458-2312; David Walkem, Chief

COWICHAN TRIBES
5760 Allenby • Duncan, BC V9L 5J1
(250) 748-3196 Fax 748-1233; Website: www.cowichantribes.com
William Seymour, Chief

DA'NAXDA'XW/AWAETLATLA NATION
Formerly TANAKTEUK FIRST NATION
P.O. Box 330 • Alert Bay, BC V0N 1A0
(250) 974-2179 Fax 974-2109; William McKenzie, Chief

DEASE RIVER FIRST NATION
P.O. Box 79 • Good Hope Lake, BC V0C 2Z0
(250) 239-3000 Fax 239-3003; Ruby Johnny, Chief; George Miller, Chair

DITIDAHT FIRST NATION
P.O. Box 340 • Port Alberni, BC V9Y 7M8
(250) 745-3366 Fax 745-3332; Website: www.ditidaht.ca
Robert Joseph, Chief
Shelly Edgar, Administrator; E-mail: sedgar@ditidaht.ca

DOIG RIVER FIRST NATION
P.O. Box 56 • Rose Prairie, BC V0C 2H0
(250) 827-3776 Fax 827-3778; Gerry Attachie, Chief
Population: 300

DOUGLAS FIRST NATION
P.O. Box 606 • Mount Currie, BC V0N 2K0
(604) 894-0020 Fax 894-0019; Website: www.xaxtsa.ca
Don Harris, Chief; E-mail: don.harris@xaxtsa.ca

EHATTESAHT FIRST NATION
P.O. Box 59 • Zeballos, BC V0P 2A0
(250) 761-4155 Fax 761-4156; Website: www.ehattesaht.com
Rose-Ann Michael, Chief

ESKETEMC FIRST NATION
Box 157 • Alkali Lake, BC V2G 2V5
(250) 440-5611 Fax 440-5614; Website: www.esketemc.ca
Charlene Belleau, Chief; E-mail: erobbins@esketemc.ca
Patricia Chelsea, Managing Director

ESQUIMALT FIRST NATION
1189 Kosapsum Crescent • Victoria, BC V9A 7K7
(250) 381-7861 Fax 384-9309; Website: www.esquimaltnation.ca
Andrew Benedict Thomas, Chief; E-mail: chiefthomas@esquimaltnation.ca
Janice Rose, Administrator; E-mail: Janice@esquimaltnation.ca

FORT NELSON FIRST NATION
RR 1, Mile 295 Alaska Hwy. • Fort Nelson, BC V0C 1R0
(888) 543-3636; (250) 774-7257 Fax 774-7260;
Website: www.fortnelsonfirstnation.org; Liz Logan, Chief

GINGOLX FIRST NATION
1304 Broad St. • Kincolith, BC V0V 1B0
(800) 736-5511; (250) 326-4212 Fax 326-4208
Website: www.gingolx.ca; Les Clayton, Chief Administrative Officer

GITANMAAX FIRST NATION
P.O. Box 440 • Hazelton, BC V0J 1Y0
(800) 663-4590; (250) 842-5297 Fax 842-6364
Website: www.gitanmaax.com; E-mail: info@gitanmaax.com
Margery McRae, Chief; Dianne Shanoss, Executive Director
E-mail: d.shanoss@gitanmaax.com

GITANYOW FIRST NATION (KITWANCOOL)
P.O. Box 340 • Kitwanga, BC V0J 2A0
(250) 849-5222 Fax 849-5787; Website: www.band.gitanyow.com
Tony Morgan, Chief Councillor; Edward Derrick, Deputy Chief/Operations

GITLAKDAMIX FIRST NATION
P.O. Box 233 • New Aiyansh, BC V0J 1A0
(250) 633-2215 Fax 633-2271; Herbert Morven, Chief

GITSEGUKLA FIRST NATION
36 Cascade Ave., RR #1 • South Hazelton, BC V0J 2R0
(250) 849-5490 Fax 849-5492; Donald Ryan, Chief

GITWANGAK FIRST NATION
P.O. Box 400 • Kitwanga, BC V0J 2A0
(250) 849-5591 Fax 849-5353; Glenford Williams, Chief

GITXAALA NATION
P.O. Box 149 • Kitkatla, BC V0V 1C0
(250) 848-2214 Fax 848-2238; Website: www.gitxaalanation.com
Merle Bolton, Chief; E-mail: contact@gitxaalanation.com

GITWINKSIHLKW FIRST NATION
P.O. Box 1 • Gitwinksihlkw, BC V0J 3T0
(250) 633-2294 Fax 633-2539; Harry Nyce, Chief

GLEN VOWELL FIRST NATION
RR#1, Comp 43, Site J • Hazelton, BC V0J 1Y0
(877) 653-8833; (250) 842-5241 Fax 842-5601
Website: www.sik-e-dakh.com; Tony Sampare, Chief
Mary Lou Malott, Band Administrator

GWA'SALA-'NAKWAXDA'ZW FIRST NATION
P.O. Box 998 • Port Hardy, BC V0N 2P0
(250) 949-8343 Fax 949-7402; Paddy Walkus, Chief

HAGWILGET FIRST NATION
P.O. Box 460 • New Hazelton, BC V0J 2J0
(250) 842-6258 Fax 842-6924; Website: www.hagwilget.com
Jack Sebastian, Chief

HAISLA NATION
P.O. Box 1101 • Kitamaat, BC V0T 2B0
(250) 639-9382 Fax 632-5311; Website: www.haisla.ca
Ellis Ross, Chief Councilor

HALALT FIRST NATION
7973 Chemainus Rd. • Chemainus, BC V0R 1K5
(250) 246-4736 Fax 246-2330; Website: www.halalt.org
James Thomas, Chief; Caroline Gladstone, Band Manager

HALFWAY RIVER GROUP
P.O. Box 59 • Wonowon, BC V0C 2N0
(250) 882-4107 Fax 785-2021
Website: www.halfwayrivergroup.ca
E-mail: info@halfwayrivergroup.ca; Gerry Hunter, Chief

HARTLEY BAY GITGA'AT NATION
445 Yayimisaxaa Way • Hartley Bay, BC V0V 1A0
(250) 841-2500 Fax 841-2541; Website: www.gitgaat.net
Arnold Clifton, Chief; E-mail: hbvc@gitgaat.net
Ellen Torng, CEO; E-mail: ellentorng@gitgaat.net

HEILTSUK FIRST NATION
P.O. Box 880 • BELLA BELLA, BC V0T 1Z0
(250) 957-2381 Fax 957-2544
Website: www.heiltsuknation.ca
E-mail: HTC-reception@heiltsuknation.ca

HESQUIAHT FIRST NATION
P.O. Box 2000 • Tofino, BC V0R 2Z0
(250) 670-1101 Fax 670-1102; Richard Lucas, Sr., Chief

HIGH BAR FIRST NATION
P.O. Box 458 • Clinton, BC V0K 1K0
(250) 459-2117; Rosemarie Haller, Chief

HOMALCO FIRST NATION
1218 Butte Crescent • Campbell River, BC V9H 1G5
(250) 923-4979 Fax 923-4987; Richard Harry, Chief

HUPACASATH FIRST NATION
5500 Ahahswinis Dr., Box 211 • Port Alberni, BC V9Y 7M7
(250) 724-4041 Fax 724-1232; Website: www.hupacasath.ca
Steven Tatoosch, Chief Councillr; E-mail: steve@hupacasath.ca
Rick Hewson, CEO/CFO; E-mail: rick@hupacasath.ca

HUU-AY-AHT FIRST NATION
P.O. Box 70 • Anacia, BC V0R 1B0
(250) 728-3414 Fax 728-1222
Website: www.huuayaht.org; E-mail: reception@huuayaht.org
Karen Haugen, Acting Executive Director
E-mail: karen.h@huuayaht.org

ISKUT FIRST NATION
P.O. Box 30 • Iskut, BC V0J 1K0
(250) 234-3331 Fax 234-3200; Website: www.iskut.org
Narie Quock, Chief; E-mail: mariequock@iskut.org

KAMLOOPS FIRST NATION
200-330 Chief Alex Thomas Way • Kamloops, BC V2H 1H1
(250) 828-9700 Fax 372-8833; Website: www.tkemlups.ca
Shane Gottfriedson, Chief

KANAKA BAR FIRST NATION
P.O. Box 210 • Lytton, BC V0K 1Z0
(250) 455-2279 Fax 455-2772; James Frank, Chief

KATZIE FIRST NATION
10946 Katzie Rd. • Pitt Meadows, BC V3Y 2G6
.(604) 465-8961 Fax 465-5949; Website: www.katzie.ca
Email: katzie.treaty@shawcable.com; Ed Pierre, Chief

KINCOLITH BAND COUNCIL
1304 Broad St. • Kincolith, BC V0V 1B0
(250) 326-4212 Fax 326-4208; Stuart Doolan, Chief

KISPIOX FIRST NATION
1336 Kispiox Valley Rd. • Kispiox, BC V0J 1Y4
(877) 842-5911; (250) 842-5248 Fax 842-5604
Website: www.kispioxband.com; E-mail: reception@kispioxband.ca
Julia Corbett, Finance Manager

KITASOO FIRST NATION
General Delivery • Klemtu, BC V0T 1L0
(250) 839-1255 Fax 839-1256; Percy Star, Chief

KITSELAS FIRST NATION
2225 Gitaus Rd. • Terrace, BC V8G 0A9
  (250) 635-5084 Fax 635-5333; Website: www.kitselas.com
  Joe Bevan, Chief Councillor; E-mail: chiefbevan@kitselas.com

KITSUMKALUM INDIAN BAND
P.O. Box 544 • Terrace, BC V8G 4B5
  (888) 635-1718; (250) 635-6177 Fax 635-4622
  Website: www.kitsumkalum..bc.ca; Steve Roberts, Band Manager

KLAHOOSE FIRST NATION
P.O. Box 9, Squirrel Cove • Manson's Landing, BC V0P 1K0
  (250) 935-6536 Fax 935-6997; John Elliott, Chief

KLUSKUS (LHOOSK'UZ DENE) NATION
P.O. Box 4639 • Quesnel, BC V2J 3J8
  (250) 992-3290 Fax 992-3291; Roger Jimmie, Chief

KWA-WA-AINEUK FIRST NATION
P.O. Box 344 • Port McNeill, BC V0N 2R0
  (250) 949-8732; Charlie Williams, Chief

KWAKIUTL FIRST NATION
P.O. Box 1440 • Port Hardy, BC V0N 2P0
  (250) 949-6012 Fax 949-6066; Alfred Hunt, Chief

KWANTLEN FIRST NATION
P.O. Box 108 • Fort Langley, BC V1M 2R4
  (604) 888-2488 Fax 888-2442; Alfred J. Gabriel, Chief
  Website: www.kwantlenfn.ca

KWIKWETLEM FIRST NATION
2-65 Colony Farm Rd. • Coquitlam, BC V3C 5X9
  (604) 540-0680 Fax 525-0772; Website: www.kwikwetlem.com
  Ron Geisbrecht, Chief Councillor; Ed Hall & Fred Hulbert, Councillors

KWIAKAH FIRST NATION
P.O. Box 437 STN A • Campbell River, BC V9W 5B6
  (250) 923-1556; Website: www.kwiakah.com
  Steven G. Dick, Chief; Frank Voelker, Band Manager
  E-mail: frankvoelker@kwiakah.com

KWIKWASUT'INUXW HAXWA'MIS FIRST NATION
Box 10 • Alert Bay, BC V0N 1A0
  (250) 974-3001 Fax 974-3036; Website: www.khfn.com
  Robert Chamberlin, Chief Councillor; E-mail: bobc@khfn.com
  Herb Chamberlin & Sandy Toby Johnson, Councillors

KYUQUOT/CHEKLESATH FIRST NATION
General Delivery • Kyuquot, BC V0P 1J0
  (250) 332-5259 Fax 332-5210; Website: www.kyuquot.ca
  Therese Smith, Chief

LAKALZAP FIRST NATION
General Delivery • Greenville, BC V0J 1X0
  (250) 621-3212 Fax 621-3320; Henry Moore, Chief

LAKE BABINE NATION
P.O. Box 879 • Burns Lake, BC V0J 1E0
  (250) 692-7555 Fax 692-7559; Website: www.lakebabine.com
  Wilfred Adam, Chief; Bessie West, Deputy Chief

LAKE COWICHAN FIRST NATION
P.O. Box 159 • Lake Cowichan, BC V0R 2G0
  (250) 749-3301 Fax 749-4286; Website: www.lakecowichanfn.ca
  Cyril Livingstone, Chief; Aaron Hamilton, Operations Manager

LAX-KW-ALAAMS FIRST NATION
206 Shashaak St. • Port Simpson, BC V0V 1H0
  (877) 725-3293; (250) 625-3474 Fax 625-3246
  Website: www.laxkwalaams.ca
  Garry Reece, Mayor; Helen Johnson, Deputy Mayor
  Linda Simon, Administrator; E-mail: linda_admin@laxband.com

LEQ'A:MEL FIRST NATION
43101 Leq':mel Way • Deroche, BC V0M 1G0
  (604) 826-7976 Fax 826-0362
  Website: www.leqamel.ca; E-mail: reception@leqamel.ca
  Alice Thompson, Chief Councillor; E-mail: maexe@live.ca

LHEIDI T'ENNEH FIRST NATION
1041 Whenum Rd. • Prince George, BC V2K 5X8
  (877) 963-8451; (250) 963-8451 Fax 963-6954
  Website: www.lheidli.ca; Dominic Frederick, Chief
  Jason Morgan, Executive Director; E-mail: info@lheidli.ca

LITTLE SHUSWAP LAKE INDIAN BAND
1886 Little Shuswap Lake Rd. • Chase, BC V0E 1M2
  (250) 679-3203 Fax 679-3220
  Website: www.lslib.com; E-mail: reception@lslib.com
  Oliver Arnouse, Chief; E-mail: oarnouse@lslib.com

LOWER KOOTENAY BAND
830 Simon Rd. • Creston, BC V0B 1G2
  (250) 428-4428 Fax 428-7686; Jason Louie, Chief
  Website: www.lowerkootenay.com
  Keith L. Clement, Director of Operations
  Lisa Three Feathers, Administrator

LOWER NICOLA FIRST NATION
181 Nawishaskin Lane • Merritt, BC V1K 0A7
  (250) 378-5157 Fax 378-6188; Aaron Sam, Chief
  Website: www.lnib.ca; E-mail: reception@lnib.net
  Helder Ponte, Executive Director; E-mail: helder@lnib.net

LOWER SIMILKAMEEN INDIAN BAND
P.O. Box 100 • Keremeos, BC V0X 1N0
  (250) 499-5528 Fax 499-5538
  Website: www.lsib.net; E-mail: reception@lsib.net
  Keith Crow, Chief; E-mail: chief@lsib.net
  Beverley Asmann, Band Manager; E-mail: bandmanager@lsib.net
  Publication: LSIB Moccasin (monthly).

LYACKSON FIRST NATION
7973A Chemanus Rd. • Chemainus, BC V0R 1K5
  (888) 592-5766; (250) 245-5019 Fax 246-5049
  Website: www.lyackson.bc.ca; E-mail: reception@lyackson.bc.ca
  Richard Thomas, Chief; E-mail: chiefthomas@lyackson.bc.ca
  Patricia McKinnon, Director of Operations
   E-mail: patricia.mckinnon@lyackson.bc.ca
  E-mail: chris.thompson@lyackson.bc.ca

LYTTON FIRST NATION
951 Main St., P.O. Box 20 • Lytton, BC V0K 1Z0
  (250) 455-2304 Fax 455-2291; Janet Webster, Chief
  Website: www.lyttonfirstnations.ca

MALAHAT FIRST NATION
110 Thunder Rd. • Mill Bay, BC V0R 2P4
  (250) 743-3231 Fax 743-3251; Website: www.malahatnation.ca

MAMALILIKULLA-QWE'QWA'SOT'EM BAND
1400 Weiwakum Rd. • Campbell River, BC V9W 5W8
  (250) 287-2955 Fax 287-4655; Robert Sewid, Chief

MATSQUI FIRST NATION
P.O. Box 10 • Matsqui, BC V4X 3R2
  (604) 826-6145 Fax 826-7009; Alice McKay, Chief

McLEOD LAKE FIRST NATION
61 Sekani Dr. • McLeod Lake, B.C. V0J 2G0
  (250) 750-4415 Fax 750-4420
  Website: www.mlib..ca; E-mail: info@mlib.ca
  Derek Orr, Chief

METLAKATLA FIRST NATION
P.O. Box 459 • Prince Rupert, BC V8J 3R2
  (250) 628-3234 Fax 628-9205; Website: www.metlakatla.ca
  Harold Leighton, Chief; Gordon Tomlinson, Executive Director
  E-mail: executive.director@metlakatla.ca

MORICETOWN FIRST NATION
RR 1, Site 15, Box 1 • Moricetown, BC V0J 2N0
  (800) 881-1218; (250) 847-2133 Fax 847-9291
  Website: www.moricetown.ca; info@moricetown.ca
  Duane Mitchell, Chief; E-mail: duane.mitchell@moricetown.ca

LIL'WAT NATION
P.O. Box 602 • Mount Currie, BC V0N 2K0
  (604) 894-6115 Fax 894-6841
  Website: www.lilwat.ca; E-mail: info@lilwat.ca

Lucinda Phillips, Chief; E-mail: lucinda.phillips@lilwat.ca
Curt Walker, Administrator; E-mail: curt.walker@lilwat.ca

MOWACHAHT FIRST NATION
P.O. Box 459 • Gold River, BC V0P 1G0
   (250) 283-2015 Fax 283-2335; Website: www.yuquot.ca
Council of Chiefs: Lawrence Andrews, Michael Maquinna,
Danny Savey, Ben Jack, Patrick James, Norman George
   Michael McGee, Administrator; E-mail: admin@yuquot.ca

MUSQUEAM INDIAN BAND
6735 Salish Dr. • Vancouver, BC V6N 4C4
   (604) 263-3261 Fax 263-4212
   Website: www.musqueam.bc.ca
   Wayne Sparrow, Chief; Doug Raines, Band Manager
   E-mail: bandmanager@musqueam.bc.ca

N'QUATQUA INDIAN BAND
P.O. Box 88 • D'Arcy, BC V0N 1L0
   (604) 452-3221 Fax 452-3295
   Website: www.nquatqua.ca
   Arthur Ralph Thevarge, Chief

NADLEH WHUTEN FIRST NATION
P.O. Box 36 • Fort Fraser, BC V0J 1N0
   (250) 690-7211 Fax 690-7316
   Website: www.nadleh.ca; Martin Louie, Chief

NAK'AZDLI FIRST NATION
P.O. Box 1329 • Fort St. James, BC V0J 1P0
   (250) 996-7171 Fax 996-8010
   Website: www.nakazdli.wordpress.com
   Fred Sam, Chief
   Nicholette Prince, COO; E-mail: coo@nakadli.ca

NAMGIS FIRST NATION
P.O. Box 210 • Alert Bay, BC V0N 1A0
   (250) 974-5556 Fax 974-5900; Website: www.namgis.bc.ca
   Debra Hanuse, Chief

NANOOSE FIRST NATION
209 Mallard Way • Lantzville, BC V0R 2H0
   (250) 390-3661 Fax 390-3365
   Website: www.nanoose.org; David Bob, Chief

NESKONLITH INDIAN BAND
P.O. Box 608 • Chase, BC V0E 1M0
   (250) 679-3295 Fax 679-5306
   Madene Joyce Manuel, Chief

NEW WESTMINSTER INDIAN BAND - QAYQAYT FIRST NATION
105 - 3680 Rae Ave. • Vancouver, BC V5R 2P5
   (604) 451-0531 (Phone & Fax); Rhonda Larrabee, Chief

NICOMEN INDIAN BAND
Box 670 • Lytton, BC V0K 1Z0
   (250) 455-2514 Fax 455-2517; Donna Gallinger, Chief

NOOAITCH FIRST NATION
18 Shackelly • Merritt, BC V0K 2B0
   (250) 378-6141 Fax 378-3699; Joyce Sam, Chief

NUCHATLAHT FIRST NATION
P.O. Box 40 • Zeballos, BC V0P 2A0
   (250) 332-5908 Fax 332-5907; Walter Michael, Chief
   Mason Decharme, Band Manager
   E-mail: administrator@nuchatlaht.com

NUXALK NATION
P.O. Box 65 • Bella Coola, BC V0T 1C0
   (604) 799-5613 Fax 799-5426
   Website: www.nuxalk.net; Edward Moody, Chief

OKANAGAN INDIAN BAND
12420 Westside Rd. • Vernon, BC V1H 2A4
   (866) 542-4328; (250) 542-4328 Fax 542-4990
   Website: www.okib.ca; Byron Louie, Chief
   Ken McGregor, Executive Director
   E-mail: ken.mcgregor@okanagan.org

OLD MASSETT VILLAGE COUNCIL
P.O. Box 189 • Old Massett, BC V0T 1M0
   (250) 626-3337 Fax 626-5440; Website: www.massetbc.com
   Ken Rea, Chief Councillor; E-mail: omvcrec@mhtc.ca
Description: A band government of the Haida people located at Old Massett,
British Columbia.

OREGON JACK CREEK FIRST NATION
P.O. Box 940 • Ashcroft, BC V0K 1A0
   (250) 453-9098 Fax 453-9097; Robert S. Pasco, Chief

OSOYOOS FIRST NATION
1155 SanPokChin Blvd. • Oliver, BC V0H 1T8
   (888) 498-3444; (250) 498-3444 Fax 498-4809
   Clarence Louie, CEO

OWEEKENO/WUIKINUXV FIRST NATION
P.O. Box 3500 • Port Hardy, BC V0N 2P0
   (250) 949-8625 Fax 949-7105; Rose Hackett, Chief

PACHEENAHT FIRST NATION
350 Kalaid St., Box 170 GD • Port Renfrew, BC V0S 1K0
   (250) 647-5521 Fax 647-5561; Arliss Daniels, Chief
   Website: www.pacheedahtfirstnation.com
   E-mail: info@pacheedahtfirstnation.com

PAUQUACHIN FIRST NATION
8960 W. Saanich Rd. • Sidney, BC V8L 5W4
   (250) 656-0191 Fax 656-6134; Edwin Mitchell, Chief

PENELAKUT TRIBE
P.O. Box 360 • Chemainus, BC V0R 1K0
   (250) 246-2321 Fax 246-2725; Website: www.penelakut.ca
   Earl Wilbur Jack, Chief

PENTICTON INDIAN BAND
RR 2, Site 80, Comp. 19 • Penticton, BC V2A 6J7
   (877) 493-0048; (250) 493-0048 Fax 493-2882
   Jonathan Kruger, Chief (250) 809-5109); E-mail: chief@pib.ca
   Greg Gabriel, Band Administrator; E-mail: ggabriel@pib.ca

PETERS FIRST NATION
16870 Peters Rd., RR 2 • Hope, BC V0X 1L2
   (604) 819-0297 Fax 794-7885; Norma Webb, Chief

POPKUM INDIAN BAND
P.O. Box 2 RR1 , BC V2R 4G5 • Rosedale, BC V0X 1X0
   (604) 794-7924 Fax 798-4790; James Murphy, Chief

PROPHET RIVER FIRST NATION
P.O. Box 3250 • Fort Nelson, BC V0C 1R0
   (250) 773-6555 Fax 773-6556; Lynette Tsakoza, Chief

QUALICUM FIRST NATION
5850 River Rd. • Qualicum Beach, BC V9K 1Z5
   (250) 757-9337 Fax 240-3354; (Gordon) Michael Recalma
   Website: www.qualicumfirstnation.com

QUATSINO FIRST NATION
P305 Quatishe Rd. • Coal Harbour, BC V0N 1K0
   (250) 949-6245 Fax 949-6249; Tom Nelson, Chief
   Website: www.quatsinofn.com; E-mail: qbc.general@quatsinofn.ca

LHTAKO DENE (RED BLUFF) NATION
1515 Arbutus Rd., P.O. Box 4693 • Quesnel, BC V2J 3J9
   (250) 747-2900 Fax 747-1341; Terry Boucher, Chief

SAIK'UZ FIRST NATION
135 Joseph St. • Vanderhoof, BC V0J 3A1
   (250) 567-9293 Fax 567-2998; Stanley Thomas, Chief

SAMAHQUAM FIRST NATION
P.O. Box 610 • Mount Curie, BC V0N 2K0
   (604) 894-3355 Fax 894-6188
   Website: www.inshuckch.com; Brenda Lester, Chief

SAULTEAU FIRST NATION
P.O. Box 1020 • Chetwynd, BC V0C 1J0
   (250) 788-3955 Fax 788-9158
   Website: www.salteau.com; Nathan Parenteau, Chief

SCOWLITZ FIRST NATION
P.O. Box 76 • Lake Errock, BC V0M 1N0
(604) 826-5813 Fax 826-6222; Colin Martin Pennier, Chief

SEABIRD ISLAND FIRST NATION
P.O. Box 650 • Agassiz, BC V0M 1A0
(604) 796-2177 Fax 796-3729
Clem Seymour, Chief; Daryl McNeil, Band CEO

SEMIAHMOO FIRST NATION
16049 Beach Rd. • Surrey, BC V3S 9R6
(604) 536-3101 Fax 536-6116; Willard Cook, Chief

SETON LAKE FIRST NATION
Site 3, Box 76 • Shalalth, BC V0N 3C0
(250) 259-8227 Fax 259-8384; Larry Casper, Chief

SHACKAN INDIAN BAND
P.O. Box 1360 • Merritt, BC V1K 1B8
(250) 378-5410 Fax 378-5219; Percy Anthony Joe, Chief

SHISHALH NATION
P.O. Box 740 • Sechelt, BC V0N 3A0
(604) 885-2273 Fax 885-3490
Website: www.shishalh.com; E-mail: hello@shishahl.com
Brian Jones, Administrative Services Division Manager
E-mail: bjones@shishelltnation.net
Nadine Hoehne, Chief Administrative Officer
E-mail: nroehne@secheltnation.net

SHUSWAP NATION
Suite 304-355, Yellowhead Hwy. • Kamloops, BC V2H 1H1
(250) 828-9789 Fax 374-6331; Wayne M. Christian, Chief
Website: www.shuswapnation.org

SHXW'OWHAMEL FIRST NATION
58700-A St. Elmo RD • Hope, BC V0X 1L2
(604) 869-2627 Fax 869-9903; Website: www.shxwowhamel.ca
Jesse James, Band Administrator; E-mail: secretary@shxwowhamel.ca

SIMPCW FIRST NATION - NORTH THOMPSON FIRST NATION
P.O. Box 220 • Barriere, BC V0E 1E0
(250) 672-9995 Fax 672-5858; Rita Matthew, Chief
Website: www.simpcw.com
Kerri Jo Fortier, Administrator; E-mail: kerrijo.fortier@simpcw.com

SISKA INDIAN BAND
P.O. Box 519 • Lytton, BC V0K 1Z0
(250) 455-2219 Fax 455-2539; Fred Sampson, Chief

SKAWAHLOOK FIRST NATION
58611-A Lougheen Hwy. • Agassiz, BC V0M 1A2
(604) 796-9129 Fax 796-9289
Maureen Chapman, Chief; E-mail: maureen@skawahlook.com
Debra Schneider, Councillor & Lands Manager
E-mail: debra@skawahlook.com

SKEETCHESTN FIRST NATION
P.O. Box 178 • Savona, BC V0K 2J0
(250) 373-2493 Fax 373-2494; Ronald Eric Ignace, Chief

SKIDEGATE FIRST NATION
P.O. Box 1301 • Haidi Gwaii, BC V0T 1S1
(250) 559-4496 Fax 559-8247; Website: www.skidegate.ca
Billy Yovanovich, Spokesperson; E-mail: haida@skidegate.ca

SKOOKUMCHUCK (In-SHUCK-ch) Nation
P.O. Box 190 • Pemberton, BC V0M 2L0
(604) 894-5262 Fax 894-6188; Paul Williams, Chief

SKOWKALE FIRST NATION
P.O. Box 2159 • Sardis, BC V2R 1A7
(604) 792-0730 Fax 792-1153; Robert Hall, Chief

SKUPPAH INDIAN BAND
P.O. Box 548 • Lytton, BC V0K 1Z0
(250) 455-2279 Fax 455-2772; Douglas McIntyre, Chief

SKWAH FIRST NATION
P.O. Box 178 • Chilliwack, BC V2P 6H7
(604) 792-9204 Fax 792-1093; Robert Combes, Chief

SKWAY (SHXWHA:Y) VILLAGE
P.O. Box 364 • Chilliwack, BC V2R 5M5
(604) 792-9316 Fax 792-9317; Tina Sam, Chief

SLIAMMON FIRST NATION
6686 Sliammon Rd. • Powell River, BC V8A 0B8
(604) 483-9646 Fax 483-9769; Clint William, Chief
Website: www.sliammonfirstnation.com

SNUNEYMUXW FIRST NATION
668 Centre St. • Nanaimo, BC V9R 4Z4
(250) 740-2300 Fax 753-3492; John Wesley, Chief
Website: www.snuneymuxw.ca; E-mail: johnw@snuneymuxw.ca
Activities: National Aboriginal Day. *Publication*: Newsletter.

SODA CREEK INDIAN BAND – XATSULL FIRST NATION
3405 Mountain House Rd. • Williams Lake, BC V2G 5L5
(844) 989-2323; (250) 989-2323 Fax 989-2300
Sheri Sellars, Chief; E-mail: reception@xatsull.com

SONGHEES FIRST NATION
1100 Admirals Rd. • Victoria, BC V9A 2P6
(250) 386-1043 Fax 386-4161; Ron Sam, Chief
Website: www.songheesnation.com

SOOWAHLIE INDIAN BAND
4172 Swoowahie Rd. • Cultus Lake, BC V2R 4Y2
(604) 858-4631 Fax 824-6751
Website: www.soowahlie.ca
Brenda Wallace, Chief

SPALLUMCHEEN (SPLATSIN) INDIAN BAND
Box 460 • Enderby, BC V0E 1V0
(250) 838-6496 Fax 838-2131; Website: www.splatsin.ca
Wayne M. Christian, Chief; E-mail: wayne_christian@splatsin.ca
Sue Brookes, Administrator; E-mail: sue.brookes@splatsin.ca
Darrell Jones, Education Director; Email: darrell_jones@splatsin.ca

SPUZZUM INDIAN BAND
Site 3, C-11, RR 1 • Yale, BC V0K 2S0
(604) 863-2395 Fax 863-2218; James Hobart, Chief

SQUAMISH FIRST NATION
P.O. Box 86131 • N. Vancouver, BC V7L 4J5
(604) 980-4553 Fax 980-4523; Website: www.squamish.net
Paul Wick, Administrator; E-mail: communications@squamish.net;
Ian Campbell, Chief

SQUIALA FIRST NATION
8528 Ashwell Rd. • Chilliwack, BC V2P 7Z9
(604) 792-8300 Fax 792-4522
Website: www.squiala.com; David Jimmie, Chief

ST. MARY'S INDIAN BAND
7470 Mission Rd. • Cranbrook, BC V1C 7E5
(250) 426-5717 Fax 426-8935; Jim Whitehead, Chief

STELLAT'EN FIRST NATION
P.O. Box 760 • Fraser Lake, BC V0J 1S0
(250) 699-8747 Fax 699-6430; Website: www.stellaten.ca
Archie Patrick, Chief; E-mail: chiefpatrick@stellatenfirstnation.ca
Sandra Nahornoff, Band Manager

SUMAS FIRST NATION
2788 Sumas Mountain Rd., RR 4 • Abbotsford, BC V3G 2J2
(604) 852-4041 Fax 852-4048; Website: www.sumasfirstnation.com
Dalton Silver, Chief; E-mail: Dalton.silver@sumasfirstnation.com

TAHLTAN CENTRAL GOVERNMENT
Box 69 • Tatl'ah (Dease Lake), BC V0C 1L0
(855) TAHLTAN; (250) 771-3274 Fax 771-3020
Website: www.tahltan.org; Chad Norman Day, President
Heather Hawkins, V.P.; E-mail: vicepresident@tahltan.org

TAKLA LAKE FIRST NATION
Unit 11 - 1839 1ˢᵗ Ave. • Prince George, BC V2L 2Y8
(250) 564-9321 Fax 564-9521; Website: www.taklafn.ca
John French, Chief; E-mail: chief@taklafn.ca

TAKU RIVER TLINGIT FIRST NATION
P.O. Box 132 • Atlin, BC V0W 1A0

(250) 651-7900 Fax 651-7909
Website: www.trtfn.com; Louise Gordon, Spokesperson
E-mail: govern.spokesperson@gov.trtfn.com

T'IT'Q'ET (LILLOOET) NATION
P.O. Box 615 • Lillooet, BC V0K 1V0
(250) 256-4118 Fax 256-4544; Website: www.titqet.org
Kevin Whitney, Chief Councillor; Shelly Leech, Tribal Chief
Wendy Phair, Administrator; E-mail: wendyp@titqet.org

TLA-O-QUI-AHT FIRST NATIONS
P.O. Box 18 • Tofino, BC V0R 2Z0
(250) 725-3350 Fax 725-3352; Website: www.tla-o-qui-aht.org
Francis Frank, Chief Councillor; E-mail: ffrank01@shaw.ca
Ted Adnitt, CEO, Chief; E-mail: ceo@tla-o-qui-aht.org

TLATLASIKWALA FIRST NATION
P.O. Box 339 • Port Hardy, BC V0N 2P0
(250) 974-2000 Fax 974-2010; Thomas Wallace, Chief
Website: www.tlatlasikwala.com; E-mail: info@tlatlasikwala.com

TL'AZT'EN NATION FIRST NATION
P.O. Box 670 • Fort St. James, BC V0J 1P0
(250) 648-3212 Fax 648-3250; Website: www.tlaztennation.ca
Justa Monk, Chief; E-mail: justa.monk@tlazten.bc.ca

TL'ETINQOX-T'IN GOVERNMENT OFFICE
P.O. Box 168 • Alexis Creek, BC V0L 1A0
(888) 224-3322; 250) 394-4212 Fax 394-4275
Website: www.tletinqox.ca; Joe Alphonse, Chief

TLOWITSIS NATION
1345 Butte Crescent • Campbell River, BC V9H 1G6
(250) 923-7815 Fax 923-7816; John Smith, Chief

TOBACCO PLAINS INDIAN BAND
3603 93 Hwy., P.O. Box 76 • Grasmere, BC V0B 1R0
(250) 887-3461 Fax 887-3424; Mary Mahseelah, Chief

TOOSEY FIRST NATION
P.O. Box 80 • Riske Creek, BC V0L 1T0
(250) 659-5655 Fax 659-5601; Francis Laceese, Chief

TOQUAHT FIRST NATION
P.O. Box 759 • Ucluelet, BC V0R 3A0
(250) 726-4230 Fax 726-4403
Website: www.toquaht.ca; Burt Mack, Chief

TSARTLIP FIRST NATION
#1 Boat Ramp Rd. • Brentwood Bay, BC V8M 1N9
(250) 652-3988 Fax 652-3788
Website: www.tsartlip.com; E-mail: admin@tsartlip.com
Don Tom, Chief; Karen Harry, Administrator

TSAWOUT FIRST NATION
P.O. Box 121 • Saanichton, BC V8M 2E4
(250) 652-9101 Fax 652-9114; Harvey Underwood, Chief

TSAWWASSEN FIRST NATION
1926 Tsawwassen Dr. • Delta, BC V4M 4G2
(604) 943-2112 Fax 943-9226; Website: www.tsawwassenfirstnation.com
Brice Williams, Chief; E-mail: bwilliams@tsawwassenfirstnation.com

TSAY KEH DENE BAND
1877 Queensway • Prince George, BC V2L 1L9
(250) 562-8882 Fax 562-8899
Website: www.tsaykeh..com; Dennis Izony, Chief

TSESHAHT FIRST NATION
P.O. Box 1218 • Port Alberni, BC V9Y 7M1
(250) 724-1225 Fax 724-4385; Website: www.tseshhaht.com
Hugh Braker, Chief Councillor; E-mail: hbraker@tseshaht.com
Wendy Gallic, Executive Director; E-mail: wgallic@tseshaht.com

TSEYCUM FIRST NATION
1210 Totem Lane • North Saanich, BC V8L 5S4
(877) 656-0858; (250) 656-0868 Fax 656-0868
Website: www.tseycum.ca; Vern Jacks, Chief

TSI DELDEL (ALEXIS CREEK) FIRST NATION
P.O. Box 69 • Chilanko Forks, BC V0L 1H0

(250) 481-3335 Fax 481-1197; Website: www.tsideldel.org
Percy Guichon, Chief

TS'KW'AYLAXW (PAVILION) FIRST NATION
P.O. Box 2200 • Lillooet, BC V0K 1V0
(250) 256-4204 Fax 256-4058; Francis Alec, Chief
Website: www.tskwaylaxw.com

TSLEIL-WAUTUTH (BURRARD) FIRST NATION
3082 Ghum-lye Dr. • N. Vancouver, BC V7H 1B3
(604) 929-3455 Fax 929-4714; Leonard George, Chief

T'SOU-KE FIRST ANTION
2154 Lazzar Rd., Box 307 • Sooke, BC V9Z 1G1
(250) 642-3957 Fax 642-7808; Website: www.tsoukenation.com
Gordon Planes, Chief; E-mail: gordonplanes@icloud.com
Michelle Thut, Administrator; E-mail: administrator@tsoukenation.com

TZEACHTEN FIRST NATION
45855 Promontory Rd. • Chilliwack, BC V2R 0H3
(866) 494-3888; (604) 858-3888 Fax 858-3382;
Website: www.tzeachten.ca; Glenda Campbell, Chief

UCHUCKLESAHT FIRST NATION
P.O. Box 1118 • Port Alberni, BC V9Y 7L9
(877) 677-1131; (250) 724-1832 Fax 724-1806
Website: www.uchucklesaht.ca
Charlie Cootes, Chief Councillor
E-mail: Charlie.cootes@uchucklesaht.ca
Scott Coulson, Chief Administrative Officer
E-mail: scott.coulson@uchucklesaht.ca

UCLUELET FIRST NATION
P.O. Box 699 • Ucluelet, BC V0R 3A0
(877) 726-7342; (250) 726-7342 Fax 726-7552
Website: www.ufn.ca; Les Doiron, President

ULKATCHO FIRST NATION
P.O. Box 3430 • Anahim Lake, BC V0L 1C0
(250) 742-3260 Fax 742-3411; Zach Parker, Chief

UNION BAR FIRST NATION
P.O. Box 788 • Hope, BC V0X 1L0
(604) 869-9930 Fax 869-9934; Andre Alex, Chief
Website: www.unonbarfirstnations.com

UPPER NICOLA FIRST NATION
P.O. Box 3700 • Merritt, BC V0K 2B0
(250) 350-3342 Fax 350-3311; Harvey McLeod, Chief

UPPER SIMILKAMEEN INDIAN BAND
P.O. Box 220 • Hedley, BC V0X 1K0
(250) 292-8733 Fax 292-8753; Charlotte Mitchell, Chief

WE WAI KAI NATION
P.O. Box 220 • Quathiaski Cove, BC V0P 1N0
(877) 915-5533; (250) 285-3316 Fax 285-2400
Ralph Dick, Sr., Chief; Website: www.wewaikai.com
Brian Kelly, Band Administrator
E-mail: briank@wewaikai.com

WEST MOBERLY LAKE FIRST NATION
P.O. Box 90 • Moberly Lake, BC V0X 1X0
(250) 788-3663 Fax 788-9792
Website: www.treaty8.bc.ca Roland Wilson, Chief

WESTBANK FIRST NATION
301 - 515 Highway 97 South • Kelowna, BC V1Z 3J2
(250) 769-4999 Fax 769-4377
Website: www.wfn.ca; Robert Louie, Chief

WET'SUWET'EN (NEE-TAHI-BUHN) INDIAN BAND
RR 2, Site 7, Comp. 28 • Burns Lake, BC V0J 1E0
(250) 694-3494 Fax 694-3492; Website: www.wetsuweten.com
Pius Jack, Chief; Debbie L. Pierre, Administrator
Allen Cummings, Governance Director

WHISPERING PINES-CLINTON FIRST NATION
615 Whispering Pines Dr. • Kamloops, BC V2B 8S4
(250) 579-5772 Fax 579-8367; Michael LeBourdais, Chief

WILLIAMS LAKE INDIAN BAND
3672 Indian Dr. • Williams Lake, BC V2G 5K9
(250) 296-3507 Fax 296-4750; Website: www.williamslakeband.ca
Marg Shelley, Band Administrator
Lisa Camille, Band Administrator

XAXLI'P (Formerly FOUNTAIN BAND)
P.O. Box 1330 • Lillooet, BC V0K 1V0
(888) 321-2711; (250) 256-4800 Fax 256-7892
Website: www.xaxlip.ca; Darrell Bob, Sr., Chief

YAKWEAKWIOOSE FIRST NATION
7176 Chilliwack River Rd., RR 2 • Sardis, BC V2R 1B1
(604) 858-1785 Fax 858-1775; Frank Malloway, Chief

YALE FIRST NATION
P.O. Box 1869 • Hope, BC V0X 1L0
(604) 863-2443 Fax 863-2467; Ken Hansen, Chief

YEKOOCHE FIRST NATION
1890 - 3rd Ave. • Prince George, BC V2M 1G4
(250) 562-0592 Fax 562-0530; Website: www.yekooche.com
Allen Joseph, Chief

YUNESIT'IN GOVERNMENT (FORMERLY STONE INDIAN BAND)
P.O. Box 158 • Hanceville, BC V0L 1K0
(250) 394-4295 Fax 394-4407; Russell Ross, Chief

METIS NON-STATUS

THE METIS NATION OF BRITISH COLUMBIA (MNBC)
30691 Simpson Rd. • Abbotsford, BC V2t 6C7
(800) 940-1150; (604) 557-5851 Fax 557-2024; Website: www.mnbc.ca
Bruce Dumont, President; E-mail: bdumont@mnbc.ca
The Métis Provincial Council of British Columbia was first incorporated under the Society's Act on October 23, 1996. In 2003 the Métis leadership ratified the Métis Nation British Columbia (MNBC) Constitution thereby establishing a new Métis Nation governance structure.

LABRADOR/NEWFOUNDLAND

BENOITS COVE BAND COUNCIL
General Delivery • John's Beach, NF A0L 1A0
(709) 789-3404; Bernard White, Councilor; E-mail: bwhite@qalipu.ca

FLAT BAY BAND COUNCIL
P.O. Box 4, Site 5 • St. George, NF A0N 1Z0
(709) 647-3445; Ben Bennett, Councilor; E-mail: bbennett@qalipu.ca

QALIPU MI'KMAQ FIRST NATION BAND - GLENWOOD OFFICE
45 Spruce Ave. • Glenwood, NF A0H 2K0
(709) 679-2338 Fax 679-2344
Francis Skeard, Councilor; E-mail: fskeard@qalipu.ca

**QALIPU MI'KMAQ FIRST NATION BAND
GRANDFALLS-WINDSOR OFFICE**
4a Bayley St., Suite 800 • Grandfalls-Windsor, NF A2A 2T5
(709) 489-6770 Fax 489-8417

INNU NATION
P.O. Box 119 • SHESHATSUI, NF A0P 1M0
(709) 497-8398 Fax 497-8397; Website: www.innu.ca
Anastasia Qupee, Grand Chief; E-mail: aqupee@innu.ca

MIAWPUKEK FIRST NATION (MICMACS)
P.O. Box 10, Baie d'Espoir • Conne River, NF A0H 1J0
(709) 882-2146 Fax 882-2292; Shayne McDonald, Chief

MUSHUAU INNU FIRST NATION
P.O. Box 107 • Davis Inlet, Labrador, NF A0P 1A0
(709) 478-8827 Fax 478-8936; Prote Poker, Chief

PORT-AUX-PORT EAST BAND COUNCIL
General Delivery • Port-Aux-Port East, NF A0N 1T0
(709) 648-2713; Litty McDonald, Councilor

QALIPU MI'KMAQ FIRST NATION BAND (Head Office)
3 Church St. • Corner Brook, NL A2H 2Z4
(709) 634-0996 Fax 639-3997; Website: www.qalipu.ca
Brenden Sheppard, Chief; E-mail: bsheppard@qalipu.ca

SHESHATSHUI INNU BAND COUNCIL
P.O. Box 160 • Northwest River, Labrador NF A0P 1M0
(709) 497-8522 Fax 497-8757; Daniel Ashini, Chief

QALIPU MI'KMAQ FIRST NATION BAND - ST. GEORGE'S OFFICE
P.O. Box 460 • St. Georges, NF A0N 1Z0
(709) 647-3016 Fax 647-3068
Karen White, Councilor; E-mail: kwhite@qalipu.ca

STEPHENVILLE CROSSING BAND COUNCIL
P.O. Box 149 • Stephensville Crossing, NF A0N 1C0
(709) 646-5305; Gerald White, Councilor

INUIT

HAPPY VALLEY INUIT COMMUNITY
P.O. Box 40 Sta C • Happy Valley, NF A0P 1E0
(709) 896-8582 Fax 896-5834

HOPEDALE INUIT COMMUNITY
P.O. Box 103 • Hopedale, NF A0P 1G0
(709) 933-3777 Fax 933-3746

LABRADOR INUIT ASSOCIATION
General Delivery • Rigolet, NF A0P 1P0
(709) 947-3383 Fax 947-3371

MAKKOVIK INUIT COMMUNITY
P.O. Box 132 • Makkovik, NF A0P 1J0
(709) 923-2365 Fax 923-2366

TOWN COUNCIL OF NAIN
P.O. Box 50 • Nain, NF A0P 1L0
(709) 922-2941 Fax 922-2295

POSTVILLE INUIT COMMUNITY
P.O. Box 74 • Postville, NF A0P 1N0
(709) 479-9880 Fax 479-9891

**NUNATUKAVUT COMMUNITY COUNCIL
LABRADOR METIS NATION**
P.O. Box 460 Sta. B • Happy Valley-Goose Bay, NL A0P 1C0
(709) 896-0592 Fax 896-0594; Website: www.nunatukavut.ca
Todd Russell, President; E-mail: trussell@nunatukavut.ca
Dorothy Earle, CEO; E-mail: dearle@nunatukavut.ca
The southern Inuit people of Labrador

MANITOBA

BARREN LANDS CREE NATION
General Delivery • Brochet, MB R0B 0B0
(204) 323-2300 Fax 323-2275; Michael Sewap, Chief

BERENS RIVER FIRST NATION
Berens River P.O. • Berens River, MB R0B 0A0
(204) 382-2161 Fax 382-2297
Website: www.berensriver.ca; Jackie Everett, Chief

BIRDTAIL SIOUX FIRST NATION
P.O. Box 22 • Beulah, MB R0M 0B0
(204) 568-4540 Fax 568-4770; Nelson Bunn, Chief
Website: www.birdtailsioux.ca

BLACK RIVER FIRST NATION
General Delivery • O'Hanly, MB R0E 1K0
(204) 367-4411 Fax 367-2000; Frank Abraham, Chief
Website: www.black-river.ca; E-mail: admin@black-river.ca
Population: 980.

BLOODVEIN FIRST NATION
General Delivery • Bloodvein, MB R0C 0J0
(204) 395-2148 Fax 395-2099; Roland Hamilton, Chief

BROKENHEAD OJIBWAY NATION
P.O. Box 180 • Scanterbury, MB R0E 1W0
(204) 766-2494 Fax 766-2306; Jim Bear, Chief
Website: www.brokenheadojibwaynation.net

BUFFALO POINT FIRST NATION
P.O. Box 1037 • Buffalo Point, MB R0A 2W0

(204) 437-2133 Fax 437-2368; John Thunder, Chief
Website: www.buffalopoint-firstnation.ca

BUNIBONIBEE (OXFORD HOUSE FIRST NATION)
P.O. Box 235 • Oxford House, MB R0B 1C0
(204) 538-2156 Irvin Sinclair, Chief

CANUPAWAKPA DAKOTA FIRST NATION
P.O. Box 146 • Pipestone, MB R0M 1T0
(204) 854-2959 Fax 854-2525; Franklin Brown, Chief
Website: www.canupawakpa.com

CHEMAWAWIN CREE FIRST NATION
P.O. Box 9 • Easterville, MB R0C 0V0
(204) 329-2161 Fax 329-2017; Clarence Easter, Chief
Website: www.chemawawin.ca

CROSS LAKE BAND OF INDIANS
P.O. Box 10 • Cross Lake, MB R0B 0J0
(204) 676-2218 Fax 676-3155; Catherine Merrick, Chief
Website: www.crosslakeband.ca. Cultural/Education Centre

DAKOTA TIPI (OJIBWAY) FIRST NATION
2020 Dakota Dr. • Portage La Prairie, MB R1N 3X6
(204) 857-4381 Fax 857-9855; David L. Pashe, Chief

DAUPHIN RIVER OJIBWAY FIRST NATION
P.O. Box 58 • Gypsumville, MB R0C 1J0
(204) 659-5370 Fax 659-4458; John Stagg, Chief

EBB & FLOW OJBWAY FIRST NATION
General Delivery • Ebb & Flow, MB R0L 0R0
(204) 448-2134 Fax 448-2305; Nelson Houle, Chief

FISHER RIVER FIRST NATION
P.O. Box 367 • Koostatak, MB R0C 1S0
(204) 645-2171 Fax 645-2653; David Crate, Chief
Website: www.fisherriver.com

FOX LAKE CREE NATION
P.O. Box 369 • GILLIAM, MB R0B 0L0
(866) 498-2746; (204) 486-2463 Fax 486-2503
Website: www.foxlakecreenation.com; Robert Wavey, Chief

GAMBLER FIRST NATION
P.O. Box 293 • Binscarth, MB R0J 0G0
(204) 532-2464 FAX 532-2495; David LeDoux, Chief
Website: www.gamblerfirstnation.ca
Population: 255.

GARDEN HILL FIRST NATION
P.O. Box 261 • Island Lake, MB R0B 0T0
(204) 456-2085 Fax 456-9315; Website: www.ghfn.ca
Arnold Flett, Chief. Population: 2,775.

GOD'S LAKE FIRST NATION
P.O. Box 258 • God's Lake Narrows, MB R0B 0M0
(204) 335-2130 Fax 335-2400
Website: www.ktc.ca; Gilbert G. Andrews, Chief
Population: 1,200.

HOLLOW WATER FIRST NATION
P.O. Box 2561 • Wanipigow, MB R0E 2E0
(204) 363-7278 Fax 363-7418; Ian Bushie, Chief
Website: www.hollowwater.ca
Population: 1,525. Area: 4,000 acres.

INTERLAKE RESERVES TRIBAL COUNCIL
General Delivery • Fairford, MB R0C 0X0
(204) 659-4465 Fax 659-2147
Website: www.irtc.ca; E-mail: info@irtc.ca
Anita Wilson, Executive Director

KEESEEKOOWENIN OJIBWAY NATION
P.O. Box 100 • Elphinstone, MB R0J 0N0
(204) 625-2004 Fax 625-2042; James Plewak Chief

KINOONJEOSHTEGON (JACKHEAD) FIRST NATION
P.O. Box 359 • Elphinstone, MB R0J 0N0
(204) 394-2255 Fax 394-2305; David Traverse, Chief
LAKE MANITOBA FIRST NATION

P.O. Box 69 • Lake Manitoba, MB R0C 3K0
(204) 768-3492 Fax 768-3036; Cornell McLean, Chief
LAKE ST. MARTIN FIRST NATION
P.O. Box 69 • Gypsumville, MB R0C 1J0
(204) 659-4539 Fax 659-2034; Adrian Sinclair, Chief

LITTLE GRAND RAPIDS FIRST NATION
P.O. Box 129 • Little Grand Rapids, MB R0B 0V0
(204) 397-2264 Fax 397-2340; Martin Owens, Chief

LITTLE SASKATCHEWAN (OJIBWAY) FIRST NATION
Box 98 • St. Martin, MB R0C 1J0
(204) 659-4584 Fax 659-2071; Hector Shorting, Chief

LONG PLAIN FIRST NATION
P.O. Box 430 • Portage La Prairie, MB R1N 3B7
(204) 252-3066 Fax 252-2588; Dennis Meeches, Chief
Website: www.longplainfirstnation.ca

MANTO SIPI CREE NATION (GOD'S RIVER)
P.O. Box 97 • God's River, MB R0B 0N0
(204) 335-2011 Fax 366-2282
Michael Yellowback, Chief; Website: www.mantosipi.com
Population: 650. Area: 700 acres.

MARCEL COLOMB FIRST NATION (BLACK STURGEON)
Box 1150 • Lynn Lake, MB R0B 0W0
(204) 356-2439 Fax 356-2330; Andrew Colomb, Chief
Erkki Pohjolainen, Chief Administrative Officer

MATHIAS COLOMB FIRST NATION
P.O. Box 135 • Pukatawagan, MB R0B 1G0
(204) 553-2090 Fax 553-2419; Arlen Dumas, Chief

MISIPAWISTIK CREE NATION (GRAND RAPIDS)
P.O. Box 500 • Grand Rapids, MB R0C 1E0
(204) 639-2219 Fax 639-2503; Harold Turner, Councillor
Website: www.misipawistikcreenation.net. Population: 720.

MOSAKAHIKEN CREE NATION
Moose Lake, MB R0B 0Y0
(204) 678-2113 Fax 678-2292; Jim Tobacco, Chief

NISICHAWAYASHIHK CREE NATION (NELSON HOUSE)
General Delivery • Nelson House, MB R0B 1A0
(204) 484-2332 Fax 484-2392; Marcel Moody, Chief

NORTHLANDS DENESULINE FIRST NATION (LAC BROCHET)
General Delivery • Lac Brochet, MB R0B 2E0
(204) 337-2270 Fax 337-2055; Leo Dettanikkeaze, Chief

NORWAY HOUSE CREE NATION
P.O. Box 250 • Norway House, MB R0B 1B0
(204) 359-6721 Fax 359-4186
Ron Evans, Chief; Website: www.nhcn.ca

O-CHI-CHAK-KO-SIPI FIRST NATION (CRANE RIVER)
General Delivery • Crane River, MB R0B 0J0
(204) 732-2490 Fax 732-2596; Eugene Eastman, Chief

OPASKWAYAK CREE NATION
P.O. Box 10880 • Opaskwayak, MB R0B 2J0
(204) 627-7100 Fax 623-3819; Michael Constant, Chief
Website: www.opaskwayak.ca

O-PIPON-NA-PIWIN CREE NATION (SOUTH INDIAN LAKE)
Box 13 • South Indian Lake, MB R0B 1N0
(204) 374-2271 Fax 374-2350; Chris Baker, Chief

PAUINGASSI FIRST NATION
P.O. Box 60 • Pauingassi, MB R0B 2G0
(204) 397-2371 Fax 397-2145; Michael Owen, Chief

PEGUIS FIRST NATION
Box 10 • Peguis, MB R0C 3J0
(204) 645-2359 Fax 645-2360; Glenn Hudson, Chief

PINAYMOOTANG FIRST NATION (FAIRFORD)
General Delivery • Fairford, MB R0C 0X0
(204) 659-5705 Fax 659-2068; Garnet Woodhouse, Chief

PINE CREEK ANISHINABE NATION
P.O. Box 70 • Camperville, MB R0L 0J0
(204) 524-2478 Fax 524-2801; Charlie Boucher, Chief

POPLAR RIVER FIRST NATION
General Delivery • Negginan, MB R0B 0Z0
(204) 244-2267 Fax 244-2690; Clifford Bruce, Chief

RED SUCKER LAKE FIRST NATION
Red Sucker Lake, MB R0B 1H0
(204) 469-5042 Fax 469-5966; Greg Harper, Chief

ROLLING RIVER ANISHINABE NATION
P.O. Box 145 • Erickson, MB R0J 0P0
(204) 636-2211 Fax 636-7823; Morris Swan Shannacappo, Chief

ROSEAU RIVER ANISHINABE FIRST NATION
P.O. Box 30 • Ginew, MB R0A 2R0
(204) 427-2312 Fax 427-2584; Ken Henry, Jr., Chief

SAGKEENG FIRST NATION
P.O. Box 3 • Fort Alexander, MB R0E 0P0
(204) 367-2287 Fax 367-4315; Derrick Henderson, Chief

SANDY BAY (OJIBWAY) FIRST NATION
P.O. Box 109 • Marius, MB R0H 0T0
(204) 843-2603 Fax 843-2706; Lance Roulette, Chief

SAPOTAWEYAK CREE NATION (SHOAL RIVER)
General Delivery • Pelican Rapids, MB R0L 1L0
(204) 587-2012 Fax 587-2072; Nelson Genaille, Chief

SAYISI DENE FIRST NATION (TADOULE LAKE)
General Delivery • Tadoule Lake, MB R0B 2C0
(204) 684-2069 Fax 684-2069; Ernie Bussidor, Chief

SHAMATTAWA FIRST NATION
P.O. Box 102 • Shamattawa, MB R0B 1K0
(204) 565-2340 Fax 565-2720; William Miles, Chief

SIOUX VALLEY DAKOTA FIRST NATION
P.O. Box 38 • Griswold, MB R0M 0S0
(204) 855-2671 Fax 855-2436; Robert J. Bone, Chief

SKOWNAN FIRST NATION (WATERHEN)
P.O. Box 106 • Skownan, MB R0L 1Y0
(204) 628-3373 Fax 628-3289; Cameron Catcheway, Chief

ST. THERESA POINT CREE NATION
St. Theresa Point, MB R0B 1J0
(204) 462-2106 Fax 462-2646; David McDougall, Chief

SWAN LAKE OJIBWAY NATION
P.O. Box 368 • Swan Lake, MB R0G 2S0
(204) 836-2101 Fax 836-2255; Francine Meeches, Chief
Website: www.swanlakefirstnation.ca

TATASKWEYAK CRE NATION (SPLIT LAKE)
General Delivery • Split Lake, MB R0B 1P0
(204) 342-2045 Fax 342-2270; Michael D. Garson, Chief

TOOTINAOOWAZIIBEENG TREATY RESERVE (VALLEY RIVER)
General Delivery • Shortdale, MB R0L 1W0
(204) 546-3334 Fax 546-3090; Barry McKay, Chief

WAR LAKE CREE NATION
General Delivery • Ilford, MB R0B 0S0
(204) 288-4315 Fax 288-4371; Betsy Kennedy, Chief

WASAGAMACK FIRST NATION
P.O. Box 1 • Wasagamack, MB R0B 1Z0
(204) 457-2339 Fax 457-2255; Alex McDougall, Chief

WAYWAYSEECAPPO FIRST NATION
P.O. Box 9 • Rossburn, MB R0J 1V0
(204) 859-2879 Fax 859-2403; Melville Wabash, Chief

WUSKWI SIPIHK FIRST NATION (INDIAN BIRCH)
P.O. Box 220 • Birch River, MB R0L 0E0
(204) 236-4201 Fax 236-4786; Albina Brass, Chief

YORK FACTORY FIRST NATION
York Landing, MB R0B 2B0
(204) 341-2180 Fax 341-2322; Ted Bland, Chief

METIS NON-STATUS

MANITOBA METIS FEDERATION, INC.
300-150 Henry Ave. • Winnipeg, MB R3B 0J7
(204) 586-8474 Fax 947-1816
Website: www.mmf.mb.ca; E-mail: info@mmf.mb.ca
David Chartrand, President; Alfred Anderson, V.P.

NEW BRUNSWICK

BOUCTOUCHE (TJIPOGTOTJG) MICMAC FIRST NATION
RR 2 Kent Co. • Buctouche, NB E0A 1G0
(506) 743-6493 Fax 743-8731; William Sanipass, Chief

BURNT CHURCH (ESGENOOPETITJ) FIRST NATION
RR 2 • Lagaceville, NB E0C 1K0
(506) 776-1200 Fax 776-1215; Wilbur Dedam, Chief

EEL GROUND (NATOAGANEG) FIRST NATION
47 Church Rd. • Eel Ground, NB E1V 4B9
(506) 627-4600 Fax 627-4602; Roger J. Augustine, Chief

EEL RIVER (UGPI'GANJIG) FIRST NATION
P.O. Box 1660 • Dalhousie, NB E0K 1B0
(506) 684-3360 Fax 684-5849; Thomas Everett Martin, Chief

ELSIPOGTOG FIRST NATION (formerly BIG COVE)
R.R. #1, 373 Big Cove Rd. • Elsipogtog First Nation, NB E4W 2S3
(506) 523-8200 Fax 523-8230; Arren James Sock, Chief

FORT FOLLY (AMLAMGOG) FIRST NATIONS
P.O. Box 1007 • Dorchester, NB E4K 3V5
(506) 379-3400 Fax 379-3408; Joe Knockwood, Chief
Website: www.fortfolly.nb.ca; E-mail: fortfolly@rogers.com

INDIAN ISLAND (L'NUI MENIKUK) FIRST NATION
61 Island Dr. • Indian Island, NB E4W 1S9
(506) 523-4875 Fax 523-8110; Ken Barlow, Chief
Website: www.indianisland.ca
Peter Levi, Band Administrator; E-mail: admin@iifn.ca

KINGSCLEAR (PILICK) INDIAN BAND
Comp. 19, RR 6, Site 6 • Fredericton, NB E3B 4X7
(506) 363-3028/9 Fax 363-4324; Stephen Sacobie, Chief

MADAWASKA MALISEET FIRST NATION
RR 2 • St. Basile, NB E0L 1H0
(506) 739-9765 Fax 735-0024

OROMOCTO (WOLAMUKTUK) FIRST NATION
P.O. Box 417 • Oromocto, NB E2V 2J2
(506) 357-2083 Fax 357-2628; Rupert J. Sacobie, Chief
Cultural Education Program, Bob Atwin, Director

PABINEAU (OINPEGITJOIG) FIRST NATION
RR 5, Box 385 • Bathurst, NB E2A 3Y8
(506) 548-9211 Fax 548-9849; Benjamin Peter Paul, Chief

RED BANK (METEPENNAGIAG) FIRST NATION
P.O. Box 293 • Red Bank, NB E9E 2P2
(506) 836-6111 Fax 836-7593; Noah Augustine, Chief
Website: www.metepenagiag.com

ST. MARY'S FIRST NATION
35 Dedham St. • Fredericton, NB E3A 2V7
(506) 472-9511 Fax 452-2763; Candice Paul, Chief
Population: 1,822.

TOBIQUE (NEQOTKUK) FIRST NATION
19 Band Office Lane, Tobique First Nation, NB E7H 1C6
(506) 273-5400 Fax 273-303; Stewart Paul, Chief

WOODSTOCK (MALISEET) FIRST NATION
3 Wulastook Ct. • Woodstock, NB E7M 4K6
(506) 328-3303 Fax 328-2420; Tim Paul, Chief
Website: www.woodstockfirstnation.com

NORTHWEST TERRITORY

BEHDZI AHDA' FIRST NATION
P.O. Box 53 • Colville Lake, NT X0E 1L0
(867) 709-2200 Fax 709-2202; Wilbert Kochon, Chief

DECHI LAO'TI DENE COUNCIL
P.O. Box 69 • Wekweti, NT X0E 1W0
(867) 713-2010 Fax 713-2030; Joseph Judas, Chief

DEH GAH GOT'IE DENE COUNCIL
General Delivery • Fort Providence, NT X0E 0L0
(867) 699-3402 Fax 699-3401; Joachim Bonnetrouge, Chief

DELINE BAND
P.O. Box 158 • Deline, NT X0E 0G0
(867) 589-3151 Fax 589-4208

DENE NATION
5125 – 50th St., P.O. Box 2338 • Yellowknife, NT X1A 2P7
(866) 511-4081; (867) 873-4081 Fax 920-2254
Website: www.denenation.ca
Edward Sangris, Chief (Dettah Council)
E-mail: esangris@ykdene.com
Ernest Betsina, Chief (Ndilo Council)
E-mail: ebetsina@ykdene.com

DENINU K'UE FIRST NATION
P.O. Box 1899 • Fort Resolution, NWT X0E 0M0
(867) 394-4335 Fax 394-5122; Bernadette Unka, Chief

DOGRIB RAE BAND
P.O. Box 8 • Rae Edzo, NT X0E 0Y0
(867) 392-6581 Fax 392-6150; Edward Erasmus, Chief

EHDIITAT GWICH'IN COUNCIL
P.O. Box 118 • Inuvik, NT X0E 0A0
(867) 978-2340 Fax 978-2937; Cece McCauley, Chief

FORD FITZGERALD FIRST NATION
P.O. Box 1470 • Fort Smith, NT X0E 0P0
(867) 872-3345; Henry Beaver, Chief

FORT GOOD HOPE FIRST NATION
General Delivery • Fort Good Hope, NT X0E 0H0
(867) 598-2231 Fax 598-2024; Everett Kakfwi, Chief

ACHO DENE KOE (FORT LIARD)
General Delivery • Fort Liard, NT X0G 0A0
(867) 770-4141 Fax 770-4144; Harry Deneron, Chief

FORT NORMAN BAND
General Delivery • Fort Norman, NT X0E 0K0
(867) 588-3341 Fax 588-3613; David Etchinelle, Chief

GAMETI FIRST NATION
P.O. Box 1 • Red Lakes, NT X0E 1R0
(867) 997-3441 Fax 997-3411

GWICHA GWICH'IN COUNCIL
P.O. Box 58 • Tsiigehtchic, NT X0E 0B0
(867) 953-3011 Fax 953-3018; Website: www.gwichin.nt.ca
Carolyn Lennie, President; E-mail: ggcpresident@northwestel.net

HAY RIVER DENE RESERVE No. 1
P.O. Box 1638 • Hay River, NT X0E 0R0
(867) 874-6701 Fax 874-3229; Pat Martel, Chief

INUVIK NATIVE BAND
P.O. Box 2570 • Inuvik, NT X0E 0T0
(867) 777-3344 Fax 777-3090

JEAN MARIE RIVER DENE NATION
General Delivery • Jean Marie River, NT X0E 0N0
(867) 695-9801 Fax 809-2002

KA'A'GEE TU FIRST NATION
P.O. Box 4428 • Hay River, NT X0E 1G3
(867) 825-2000 Fax 825-2002; Lloyd Chicot, Chief

LIIDLI KUE FIRST NATION
P.O. Box 469 • Fort Simpson, NT X0E 0N0
(867) 695-3131 Fax 695-3132; Jim Antoine, Chief

LUTSEL K'E DENE INDIAN BAND
General Delivery • Lutsel K'e, NT X0E 1A0
(867) 370-3551; Antoine Michel, Chief

NAHANNI BUTTE NATION
General Delivery • Nahanni Butte, NT X0E 0N0
(867) 602-2900 Fax 602-2910

NIHTAT GWICH'IN COUNCIL
P.O. Box 2570 • Inuvik, NT X0E 0T0
(867) 777-6650 Fax 777-6651

PEHDZEH K'I FIRST NATION
General Delivery • Wrigley, NT X0E 1R0
(867) 581-3321 Fax 581-3229
Alma Ekenale, Chief

SALT RIVER FIRST NATION
P.O. Box 960 • Fort Smith, NT X0E 0P0
(867) 872-2986 Fax 872-3550

SHAMAHQUAM FIRST NATION
General Delivery • Trout Lake, N.W.T. X0E 1E0
(867) 695-9800 Fax 695-2038; Edward Jumbo, Chief

TETLIT GWICH'IN COUNCIL
P.O. Box 30 • Fort McPherson, NT X0E 0J0
(867) 952-2330 Fax 952-2212; James Ross, Chief

WEST POINT FIRST NATION
#1-47031 Mackenzie Hwy. • Hay River, NT X0E 0R9
(867) 874-6677 Fax 874-6677

WHA'TI FIRST NATION
P.O. Box 92 • Wha'Ti, NT X0E 1P0
(867) 573-3012 Fax 573-3075; Isidore Zoe, Chief

INUIT

AKLAVIK INDIAN BAND
P.O. Box 118 • Akklavik, NT X0E0A0
(403) 978-2029 Fax 978-2937

ARCTIC BAY HAMLET
General Delivery • Arctic Bay, NT X0A 0A0
(867) 439-9917 Fax 439-8767

ARVIAT HAMLET
General Delivery • Arviat, NT X0C 0E0
(867) 857-2841 Fax 857-2519

BAKER LAKE HAMLET
P.O. Box 149 • Baker Lake, NT X0C 0A0
(867) 793-2874 Fax 793-2509

HAMLET OF BROUGHTON ISLAND
General Delivery • Broughton Island, NT X0A 0B0
(867) 927-8832 Fax 927-8120

CAMBRIDGE BAY HAMLET
P.O. Box 16 • Cambridge Bay, NT X0E 0C0
(867) 983-2337 Fax 983-2193

CAPE DORSET HAMLET
General Delivery • Cape Dorset, NT X0A 0C0
(867) 897-8943 Fax 897-8030

CHESTERFIELD INLET HAMLET
General Delivery • Chesterfield Inlet, NT X0C 0B0
(867) 898-9951 Fax 898-9108

CLYDE RIVER HAMLET
General Delivery • Clyde River, NT X0A 0E0
(867) 924-6220 Fax 924-6293

COPPERMINE HAMLET
P.O. Box 271 • Coppermine, NT X0E 0E0
(867) 982-4471 Fax 982-3060

CORAL HARBOUR HAMLET
General Delivery • Coral Harbour, NT X0C 0C0
(867) 925-8867 Fax 925-8233

HAMLET OF GJOA HAVEN
General Delivery • Gjoa Haven, NT X0E 1J0
(867) 360-7141 Fax 360-6309

HAMLET OF HALL BEACH
General Delivery • Hall Beach, NT X0A 0K0
(867) 928-8829 Fax 928-8945

HAMLET OF FORT FRANKLIN (DELINE)
Mayor Gina Dolphus • Deline, NT X0E 0G0
(867) 589-4800 FAX 589-4106; Raymond Taniton, Chief

HAMLET OF HOLMAN
General Delivery • Holman, NT X0E 0S0
(867) 396-3511 Fax 396-3256

HAMLET OF IGLOOLIK
General Delivery • Igloolik, NT X0A 0T0
(867) 934-8700 Fax 934-8757

LAKE HARBOUR HAMLET
General Delivery • Lake Harbour, NT X0A 0N0
(867) 939-2247 Fax 939-2045

MUNICIPAL OF SANIKILUAQ
General Delivery • Sanikiluaq, NT X0A 0W0
(867) 266-8874 Fax 266-8903

HAMLET OF PANGNIRTUNG
P.O. Box 253 • Pangnirtung, NT X0A 0R0
(867) 473-8953 Fax 473-8832

HAMLET OF PAULATUK
General Delivery • Paulatuk, NT X0E 1N0
(867) 580-3531 Fax 580-3703

HAMLET OF POND INLET
General Delivery • Pond Inlet, NT X0A 0S0
(867) 899-8934 Fax 899-8940

HAMLET OF RANKIN INLET
General Delivery • Rankin Inlet, NT X0C 0G0
(867) 645-2953 Fax 645-2146

HAMLET OF REPULSE BAY
Repulse Bay, NT X0C 0H0
(867) 462-9952 Fax 462-4144

HAMLET OF RESOLUTE BAY
General Delivery • Resolute Bay, NT X0A 0V0
(867) 252-3616 Fax 252-3749

HAMLET OF SACHS HARBOUR
General Delivery • Sachs Harbour, NT X0E 0Z0
(867) 690-4351 Fax 690-4802

HAMLET OF TALOYOAK
General Delivery • Taloyoak, NT X0E 1B0
(867) 561-6341 Fax 561-5057

HAMLET OF TUKTOYAKTUT
P.O. Box 120 • Tuktoyaktut, NT X0E 1C0
(867) 977-2286 Fax 977-2110

HAMLET OF WHALE COVE
General Delivery • Whale Cove, NT X0C 0J0
(867) 896-9961 Fax 896-9109

KUGAARUK OF PELLY BAY
General Delivery • Pelly Bay, NT X0E 1K0
(867) 769-6281 Fax 769-6069

METIS NON-STATUS

HAY RIVER METIS ASSOCIATION
St. 1 - 8 Gagnier St. • Hay River, NT X0E 1G1
(867) 896-9961 Fax 874-6888

NOVA SCOTIA

ACADIA FIRST NATION (Main Office)
10526 Hwy. #3 • Yarmouth, NS B5A 5J7
(902) 742-0257 Fax 742-8854; Deborah Robinson, Chief
Website: www.acadiafirstnation.ca; E-mail: frontdesk@acadiaband.com
Mi'kmaq. *Population*: 1,046. Encompasses five reserves - Yarmouth, Ponhook, Medway, Wildcat & Gold River.

AFTON FIRST NATION
RR 1 • Afton, NS B0H 1A0
(902) 386-2881 Fax 386-2043; Noel Francis, Chief

ANNAPOLIS VALLEY FIRST NATION
P.O. Box 8964 Gooowlane • Cambridge, NS B0P 1G0
(902) 538-7149 Fax 538-7734; Janette Peterson, Chief
Website: www.kinu.ns.ca. Mi'kmaq. *Population*: 233.

BEAR RIVER FIRST NATION
P.O. Box 210 • Bear River, NS B0S 1B0
(902) 467-3802 Fax 467-4143; Frank S. Meuse, Jr., Chief
Website: www.bearriverculturalcentre.com
Mi'kmaq. *Population*: 278.

CHAPEL ISLAND FIRST NATION
P.O. Box 538 • St. Peters, NS B0E 3B0
(902) 535-3317 Fax 535-3004; George W. Johnson, Chief

ESKASONI FIRST NATION
RR 2, East Bay • Cape Breton, NS B0A 1H0
(902) 379-2800 Fax 379-2172; Leonard Paul, Chief
Mi'kmaq

HORTON FIRST NATION
P.O. Box 449 • Hantsport, NS B0P 1P0
(902) 684-9788 Fax 684-9890; Joseph B. Peters, Chief

MEMBERTOU FIRST NATION
111 Membertou St. • Sydney, NS B1S 2M9
(902) 564-6466 Fax 539-6645; Terrance Paul, Chief
Website: www.membertou.ca. Mi'kmaq. *Population*: 1,131

MILLBROOK BAND
P.O. Box 634 • Truro, NS B2N 5E5
(800) 793-3112; (902) 897-9199 Fax 893-4785
Website: www.millbrookfirstnation.net
Bob Gloade, Chief; E-mail: bgloade@msn.com
Alex Cope, Band Administrator; E-mail: alexcope@eastlink.ca
Mi'kmaq. *Population*: 1,345. *Attraction*: The Glooscap Heritage Centre.

PAQTNKEK MI'KMAW NATION
19 RR 1 • Afton, NS B0H 1A0
(902) 386-2781 Fax 386-2043; Paul Prosper, Chief
Mi'kmaq. *Population*: 540.

PICTOU LANDING FIRST NATION
6537 Pictou Landinf Rd. • Trenton, NS B0K 1X0
(902) 752-4912 Fax 755-4715; Andrea Paul, Chief
Mi'kmaq. *Population*: 565.

POTLOTEK FIRST NATION
P.O. Box 538 • Chapel Island, NS B0E 3B0
(902) 535-3317 Fax 535-3004; Wilbert Marshall, Chief
Mi'kmaq. *Population*: 600.

SIPEKNE'KATIK FIRST NATION
522 Church St. • Indian Brook, NS B0N 1W0
(902) 758-2049 Fax 758-2606; Rufus Copage, Chief
Mi'kmaq. *Population*: 2,205.

WAGMATCOOK FIRST NATION
P.O. Box 237 • Baddeck, NS B0E 1B0
(902) 295-2598 Fax 295-3398; Norman Bernard, Chief
Mi'kmaq. *Population*: 665.

WHYCOCOMAGH FIRST NATION
P.O. Box 149 • Whycocomagh, N.S. B0E 3M0
(902) 756-2337 Fax 756-2393; Rod Googoo, Chief
Mi'kmaq. *Population*: 850.

ONTARIO

AAMJIWNAANG FIRST NATION
978 Tashmoo Ave. • Sarnia, ON N7T 7H5
(519) 336-8410 Fax 336-0382; Chris Plain, Chief
Website: www.aamjiwnaang.ca
Chippewa.

ALDERVILLE FIRST NATION
11696 2nd Line Rd., P.O. Box 46 • Roseneath, ON K0K 2X0
(905) 352-2011 Fax 352-3242; James Marsden, Chief (352-3000)
Website: www.aldervillefirstnation.ca; E-mail: jbmarsden@alderville.ca

ALGONQUINS OF PIKWAKANGAN FIRST NATION
1657A Misomis Inamo • Pikwakanagan, ON K0J 1X0
(613) 625-2800 Fax 625-2332; Kirby Whiteduck, Chief

ANIMBIIGOO ZAAGI'IGAN ANISHINAABEK (LAKE NIPIGON OJIBWAY)
P.O. Box 120 • Beardmore, ON P0T 1G0
(807) 875-2785 Fax 875-2786
Theresa Nelson, Chief; E-mail: tnelson@aza.ca

ANISHINAABEG OF NAONGASHIING (BIG ISLAND)
P.O. Box 535 • Morson, ON P0W 1J0
(807) 488-5602 Fax 488-5942
Patrick Big George, Chief; E-mail: chiefpatbg@naongashiing.ca

AROLAND FIRST NATION
P.O. Box 10 • Aroland, ON P0T 1B0
(807) 329-5970 Fax 329-5750
E-mail: arolandfirstnation@yahoo.ca
Sonny Gagnon, Chief

ATIKAMEKSHENG ANISHNAWBEK (WHITEFISH LAKE)
25 Reserve Rd. • Naughton, ON P0M 2M0
(800) 661-2730; (705) 692-3651 Fax 692-5010
Website: www.atikamekshenganishnawbek.ca
Edward (Steven) Miller, Chief & Council
Location: 19 km west of Greater City of Sudbury. *Area*: 43,747 acres, with 18 lakes in its boundaries. *Population*: 1150 members.

ATTAWAPISKAT FIRST NATION
P.O. Box 248 • Attawapiskat, ON P0L 1A0
(705) 997-2166 Fax 997-2116; Theresa Spence, Chief
Website: www.attawapiskat.org

AUNDECK OMNI KANING FIRST NATION
R.R. #1, Box 21, 13 Hill St. • Little Current, ON P0P 1K0
(705) 368-2228 Fax 368-3563; Website: www.aokfn.com
Patsy Corbiere, Chief; E-mail: corbierep@aokfn.com

BEARSKIN LAKE FIRST NATION
P.O. Box 25 • Bearskin Lake, ON P0V 1E0
(807) 363-2518 Fax 363-1066
Rosemary McKay, Chief; E-mail: rosemary_2008@live.ca

BEAUSOLEIL FIRST NATION
Cedar Point P.O. • Christian Island, ON L0K 1C0
(705) 247-2051 Fax 247-2239
Roland Monague, Chief; E-mail: bfnchief@chimnissing.ca

BEAVERHOUSE FIRST NATION
P.O. Box 1022 • Kirkland Lake, ON P2N 3L1
(705) 567-2022 Fax 567-1143
Marcia Brown Martel, Chief; E-mail: marciasbrown@hotmail.com

BIG GRASSY FIRST NATION
P.O. Box 414 • Morson, ON P0W 1J0
(807) 488-5614 Fax 488-5533
Carl Tuesday, Chief; E-mail: zigtuesday@hotmail.com

BIINJITIWAABIK ZAAGING ANISHINAABEK (ROCKY BAY)
501 Spirit Bay Rd. • MacDiarmid, ON P0T 2B0
(807) 885-3401 Fax 885-1218; Website: www.rockybayfn.ca
Bart Hardy, Chief; E-mail: chiefandcouncil@rockybayfn.ca

BINGWI NEYAASHI ANISHINAABEK (SAND POINT)
146 Court St. South • Thunder Bay, ON P7B 2X6
(807) 623-2724 Fax 623-2764; LauraAirns, Chief

BKEJWANONG TERRITORY - OJIBWAYS OF WALPOLE ISLAND
R.R. #3 • Wallaceburg, ON N8A 1R0
(519) 627-1481 Fax 627-0440; Website: www.wifn.org
Daniel Miskokomon, Chief; E-mail: drskoke@wifn.org

BRUNSWICK HOUSE FIRST NATION
P.O. Box 1178 • Chapleau, ON P0M 1K0
(705) 864-0174 Fax 864-1652
Kevin Tangie Chief; E-mail: bhfn.reception@hotmail.com

CALDWELL FIRST NATION
P.O. Box 388 • Leamington, ON N0P 1A0
(800) 206-7522; (519) 322-1766 Fax 322-1533
Larry Johnson, Chief; E-mail: cfnchief@live.com

CAT LAKE FIRST NATION
P.O. Box 81 • Cat Lake, ON P0V 1J0
(807) 347-2100 Fax 347-2116; Russell Wesley, Chief
E-mail: catlakefirstnation@knet.ca

CHAPLEAU CREE FIRST NATION
828 Fox Lake Rd., P.O. Box 400 • Chapleau, ON P0M 1K0
(705) 864-0784 Fax 864-1760
Doreen Cachagee, Chief; E-mail: chief@chapleaucree.ca

CHAPLEAU OJIBWE FIRST NATION
P.O. Box 279 • Chapleau, ON P0M 1K0
(705) 864-2910 Fax 864-2911; Website: www.chapleauojibwe.ca
Anita Stephens, Chief; E-mail: chief@chapleauojibwe.ca

CHIPPEWAS OF GEORGINA ISLAND
R.R. #2, N13 • Sutton West, ON L0E 1R0
(705) 437-1337 Fax 437-4597; Donna Big Canoe, Chief

CHIPPEWAS OF KETTLE POINT & STONY POINT FIRST NATION
6247 Indian Lane • Kettle & Stony Point FN, ON N0N 1J0
(519) 786-2125 Fax 786-2108; Website: www.kettlepoint.org
Thomas S. Bressette, Chief; E-mail: Thomas.bressette@kettlepoint.org

CHIPPEWAS OF RAMA FIRST NATION
5884 Rama Rd., Suite 200 • Rama, ON L0K 1T0
(705) 325-3611 Fax 325-0879; Website: www.ramafirstnation.ca
Rodney Noganosh, Chief; rodneyn@ramafirstnation.ca

CHIPPEWAS OF NAWASH FIRST NATION (CAPE CROKER)
R.R. #5 • Wiarton, ON N0H 2T0
(519) 534-1689 Fax 534-2130; Gregory Nadjiwon, Chief
E-mail: reception.admin@nawash.ca

CHIPPEWAS OF SAUGEEN FIRST NATION
R.R. #1, 6493 Hwy. 21 • Southampton, ON N0H 2L0
(800) 680-0744; (519) 797-2781 Fax 797-2978
Website: www.saugeenfirstnation.ca; E-mail: sfn@saugeenfirstnation.ca
Vernon Roote, Chief; Allen Delear, Band Administrator

CHIPPEWAS OF THE THAMES FIRST NATION
R.R. #1, 320 Chippewa Rd. • Muncey, ON N0L 1Y0
(519) 289-5555 Fax 289-2230
Website: www.cottfn.com; Leslee White-eye, Chief
Maintains Library & Resource Centre.

CONSTANCE LAKE FIRST NATION
P.O. Box 4000 • Calstock, ON P0L 1B0
(705) 463-4511 Fax 463-2222; Website: www.clfn.on.ca
Rick Allen, Chief; E-mail: chief@clfn.on.ca
Monica John-George, Executive Director

COUCHICHING FIRST NATION
R.R. #2, RMB 2027 • Fort Frances, ON P9A 3M3
(807) 274-3228 Fax 274-6458
Sara Mainville, Chief; E-mail: cfnchief@vianet.ca

CURVE LAKE FIRST NATION
22 Winookeeda Rd. • Curve Lake, ON K0L 1R0
(705) 657-8045 Fax 657-8708
Phyllis Williams, Chief; E-mail: chief@curvelakefn.ca

DEER LAKE FIRST NATION
P.O. Box 39 • Deer Lake, ON P0V 1N0
(807) 775-2141 Fax 775-2220
Roydale Meekis, Chief; E-mail: roydalemeekis@knet.ca

DELAWARE NATION (MORAVIAN OF THE THAMES)
R.R. #3 • Thamesville, ON N0P 2K0
(519) 692-3936 Fax 692-5522
Greg Peters, Chief; E-mail: gcpeters@explornet.ca

DOKIS FIRST NATION
940 Main St., P.O. Box 62 • Via Monetville, ON P0M 2K0
(705) 763-2200 Fax 763-2087; Website: www.dokisfirstnation.com
E-mail: info@dokisfirstnation.com
Denise Restoule, Chief; E-mail: denise.r@dokisfirstnation.com

EABAMETOONG FIRST NATION
P.O. Box 298 • Fort Hope, ON P0T 1L0
(807) 242-7221 Fax 242-1440; Elizabeth Atlookan, Chief
E-mail: elizabeth.atlookan@eabametoongfn.ca

EAGLE LAKE FIRST NATION
P.O. Box 1001 • Migisi Sahgaigan, ON P0V 3H0
(807) 755-5526 Fax 755-5696
Arnold Gardner, Chief; E-mail: chief@migisi.ca

FLYING POST FIRST NATION
P.O. Box 1027 • Nipigon, ON P0T 2J0
(807) 887-3071 Fax 887-1138
Murray Ray, Chief; E-mail: flypost@shawbiz.ca

FORT ALBANY FIRST NATION
P.O. Box 1 • Fort Albany, ON P0L 1H0
(705) 278-1044 Fax 278-1193
Andrew Solomon, Chief; Email: chief@fafnmail.com

FORT SEVERN FIRST NATION
P.O. Box 149 • Fort Severn, ON P0V 1W0
(807) 478-2572 Fax 478-1103
Joe Crow, Deputy Chief; E-mail: joecrow@knet.ca

FORT WILLIAM FIRST NATION
90 Anemka Dr. #200 • Thunder Bay, ON P7J 1L3
(807) 623-9543 Fax 623-5190; Website: www.fwfn.com
Peter Collins, Chief; E-mail: petercollins@fwfn.com
Ojibway.

GINOOGAMING FIRST NATION
P.O. Box 89 • Long Lac, ON P0T 2A0
(807) 876-2242 Fax 876-2495; Celia Echum, Chief
E-mail: celia.echum@ginoogamingfn.ca

GRASSY NARROWS FIRST NATION
General Delivery• Grassy Narrows, ON P0X 1B0
(807) 925-2201 Fax 925-2649; Roger Fobister, Sr., Chief
E-mail: chiefrogerfobistersr@gmail.com

HENVEY INLET FIRST NATION
295 Pickerel River Rd. • Pickerel, ON P0G 1J0
(705) 857-2331 Fax 857-3021; Wayne McQuabble, Chief
E-mail: waynemcquabble@henveyinlet.com

HIAWATHA FIRST NATION
123 Paudash St., R.R. #2 • Keene, ON K0L 2G0
(705) 295-4421 Fax 295-4424; Greg Cowie, Chief
E-mail: chiefcowie@hiawathafn.ca

HORNEPAYNE FIRST NATION
P.O. Box 1553 • Homepayne, ON P0M 1Z0
(807) 868-2040 Fax 868-2050; Dave Taylor, Chief

ISKATEWIZAAGEGAN No. 39 INDEPENDENT FIRST NATION
P.O. Box 1 Kejeck P.O. • Shoal Lake, ON P0X 1E0
(807) 733-2560 Fax 733-3106; E-mail: iskatewizaagegan@iifn39.ca
Fawn Wapioke, Chief; E-mail: fawnwapioke@iifn39.ca

KASABONIKA LAKE FIRST NATION
P.O. Box 124 • Kasabonika, ON P0V 1Y0
(807) 535-2547 Fax 535-1152; Eno Anderson, Chief

KASHECHEWAN FIRST NATION
P.O. Box 240 • Kashechewan, ON P0L 1S0
(705) 275-4440 Fax 275-1023; Derek Stephen, Chief

KEEWAYWIN FIRST NATION
202 Band Office Rd., P.O. Box 90 • Keewaywin, ON P0V 3G0
(807) 771-1210 Fax 771-1053; Chris Kakegamic, Chief

KIASHKE ZAAGING ANISHINAABEK (GULL BAY)
General Delivery • Gull Bay, ON P0T 1P0
(807) 982-0006 Fax 982-0009; E-mail: kzagullbay@gmail.com
Wilfred King, Chief; E-mail: wnking@shaw.ca

KINGFISHER LAKE FIRST NATION
P.O. Box 57 • Kingfisher Lake, ON P0V 1Z0
(807) 532-2067 Fax 532-2063
James Mamawka, Chief; E-mail: jamesm@kingfisherlake.ca

KITCHENUHWAYKOOSIB FIRST NATION
P.O. Box 329 • Big Trout Lake, ON P0V 1G0
(807) 537-2263 Fax 537-2574; James Cutfeet, Chief
E-mail: james.cutfeet.ki209@gmail.com

KOOCHECHING FIRST NATION
P.O. Box 32 • Sandy Lake, ON P0V 1V0
(807) 774-1576 Fax 737-3133
William Harper, Chief; E-mail: williamharper@gmail.com

LAC DES MILLES LACS FIRST NATION
1100 Memorial Ave. • Thunder Bay, ON P7B 4A3
(807) 622-9835 Fax 622-9866; Judy White Cloud, Chief
E-mail: ldmlfb@tbaytel.net

LAC LA CROIX FIRST NATION
P.O. Box 640 • Fort Frances, ON P9A 3M9
(807) 485-2431 Fax 485-2583
Norman Jordan, Chief; E-mail: norman.j@llcfn.ca

LAC SEUL FIRST NATION
P.O. Box 100 • Hudson, ON P0V 1X0
(807) 582-3211 Fax 582-3493
Clifford Bull, Chief; E-mail: cbull@lsfn.ca

LONG LAKE #58 FIRST NATION
P.O. Box 609 • Long Lac, ON P0T 2A0
(807) 876-2292 Fax 876-2757; Website: www.longlake58fn.ca
Allen Towegishig, Chief; E-mail: allen.towegishig@longlake58fn.ca

MAGNETAWAN FIRST NATION
P.O. Box 15, RR 1 • Britt, ON P0G 1A0
(705) 383-2477 Fax 383-2566
William Diabo, Chief; E-mail: chief@magfn.com

MARTEN FALLS FIRST NATION
General Delivery • Ogoki Post • Nakina, ON P0T 2L0
(807) 349-2509 Fax 349-2511; Bruce Achneepineskum, Chief
E-mail: bruce.achneepineskum@gmail.com

MATACHEWAN FIRST NATION
P.O. Box 160 • Matachewan, ON P0K 1M0
(705) 565-2230 Fax 565-2585
Alex Batisse, Chief; E-mail: chief@mfnrez.ca

MATTAGAMI FIRST NATION
P.O. Box 99 • Gogama, ON P0M 1W0
(705) 894-2072 Fax 894-2887
Walter Naveau, Chief; walternaveau@mattagami.com

MacDOWELL LAKE FIRST NATION
P.O. Box 321 • Red Lake, ON P0V 2M0
(807) 735-1381 Fax 735-1383; Ellen Vontane Keno, Chief
E-mail: lornadansereau@knet.ca

M'CHIGEENG (WEST BAY) FIRST NATION
P.O. Box 2 • M'Chigeeng, ON P0P 1G0
(705) 377-5362 Fax 377-4980
Joe Hare, Chief; E-mail: joehare39@gmail.com

MICHIPICOTEN FIRST NATION
Box 1, Site 8, R.R. #1 • Wawa, ON P0S 1K0
(705) 856-1993 Fax 856-1642
Joe Buckell, Chief; E-mail: jbuckell@michipicoten.com

MISHKEEGOGAMANG FIRST NATION
General Delivery • New Osnaburgh, ON P0V 2H0
(807) 928-2148 Fax 928-2077; Connie Gray-McKay, Chief
E-mail: conniegraymckay@knet.ca

MISSANABIE CREE FIRST NATION
1748, Hwy 17E, Bell's Point • Garden River, ON P6A 6Z1
(705) 254-2702 Fax 254-3292; Jason Gauthier, Chief
E-mail: jgauthier@misssanabiecree.com

MISSISSAUGA #8 FIRST NATION
P.O. Box 1299 • Blind River, ON P0R 1B0
(705) 356-1621 Fax 356-1740; Reginald Niganobe, Chief
E-mail: reg@mississaugi.com

MISSISSAUGAS OF NEW CREDIT FIRST NATION
2789 Mississauga Rd., R.R. #6 • Hagersville, ON N0A 1H0
(905) 768-1133 Fax 768-1225; Bryan LaForme, Chief
E-mail: bryanlaforme@newcreditfirstnation.com

MISSISSAUGAS OF SCUGOG NATION
22521 Island Rd. • Port Perry, ON L9L 1B6
(905) 985-3337 Fax 985-8828; Kelly LaRocca, Chief
E-mail: klarocca@mississaugafirstnation.com

MITAANJIGAMING (STANJIKOMING) FIRST NATION
P.O. Box 609 • Fort Frances, ON P9A 3M9
(807) 274-2188 Fax 274-4774; Janice Henderson, Chief
E-mail: mfnchief@mitaanjigaming.ca

MOCREBEC COUNCIL OF THE CREE NATION
P.O. Box 4 • Moose Factory, ON P0L 1W0
(705) 658-4769 Fax 658-4487; Allan Jolly, Chief
E-mail: allan.jolly@mocreebec.com

MOHAWKS OF AKWESASNE FIRST NATION
P.O. Box 579 • Cornwall, ON K6H 5T3
(613) 575-2348 Fax 575-2884; Abram Benedict, Grand Chief
E-mail: abram.benedict@akwesasne.ca

MOHAWKS OF THE BAY OF QUINTE
R.R. #1, 13 Old York Rd. • Deseronto, ON K0K 1X0
(613) 396-3424 Fax 396-3627; R. Donald Maracle, Chief
E-mail: rdonm@mbq-tmt.org

MOOSE CREE FIRST NATION
P.O. Box 190 • Moose Factory, ON P0L 1W0
(705) 658-4619 Fax 658-4734; Norm Hardisty, Jr., Chief
E-mail: norm.hardisty@moosecree.com

MOOSE DEER POINT FIRST NATION
P.O. Box 119 • Mactier, ON P0C 1H0
(705) 375-5209 Fax 375-0532; Barron King, Chief
E-mail: chief@moosedeerpoint.com

MUNSEE-DELAWARE NATION FIRST NATION
R.R. #1 • Muncey, ON N0L 1Y0
(519) 289-5396 Fax 289-5156; Roger Thomas, Chief
E-mail: chief.thomas@munsee-delaware.org

MUSKRAT DAM FIRST NATION
P.O. Box 140 • Muskrat Dam, ON P0V 3B0
(807) 471-2573 Fax 471-2540; Gordon W. Beardy, Chief
Email: gordonwbeardy@knet.ca

NAICATCHEWENIN FIRST NATION
P.O. Box 15, RR 1 • Devlin, ON P0W 1C0
(807) 486-3407 Fax 486-3704; Wayne Smith, Chief
E-mail: wayne.smith@bellnet.ca

NAMAYGOOSISAGAGUN FIRST NATION
684 City Rd., Unit 16 • Thunder Bay, ON P7J 1K3
(807) 6626-1780 Fax 626-8126; Helen Paavola, Chief
E-mail: chiefnfn@tbaytel.net

NAOTKAMEGWANNING FIRST NATION (WHITEFISH BAY)
Pawitik Post Office • Pawitik, ON P0X 1L0
(807) 226-5411 Fax 226-5389; Howard Kabestra
E-mail: h.kabestra2013@gmail.com

NESKANTAGA FIRST NATION (LANSDOWNE HOUSE)
P.O. Box 105 • Lansdowne House, ON P0T 1Z0
(807) 479-2570 Fax 479-2505; Wayne Moonias, Chief
E-mail: wayne.moonias@neskantaga.com

NIBINAMIK FIRST NATION
General Delivery • Summer Beaver, ON P0T 3B0
(807) 593-2131 Fax 593-2270; Johnny Yellowhead, Chief
E-mail: johnnyyellowhead52@gmail.com; E-mail: nibinammikfn@hotmail.com

NIGIGOONSIMINIKAANING FIRST NATION
P.O. Box 68 • Fort Francis, ON P9A 3M5
(807) 481-2536 Fax 481-2511; William Windigo, Chief
E-mail: chiefwindigo@nigig.ca

NIPISSING FIRST NATION
36 Semo Rd., R.R. #1 • Garden Village, ON P2B 3K2
(705) 753-2050 Fax 753-0207
Scott McLeod, Chief; E-mail: scottm@nnfn.ca
Tribe in residence: Ojibway. *In residence*: 1,971. *Area*: 52,000 acres.
Activities: Annual Powwow, feast, elders gathering. Library.

NISHNABWE-ASKI NATION
100 Back St. Unit 200 • Thunder Bay, ON P7J 1L2
(807) 623-8228 Fax 623-7730; Website: www.nan.on.ca
Alvin Fiddler, Grand Chief; E-mail: nbarkman@nan.on.ca

NORTH CARIBOU LAKE FIRST NATION
General Deiivery • Weagamow Lake, ON P0V 2Y0
(807) 469-5191 Fax 469-1315; Dinah Kanate, Chief
E-mail: dinahkanate@northcaribou.ca

NORTH SPIRIT LAKE FIRST NATION
General Delivery • North Spirit Lake, ON P0V 2G0
(807) 776-0021 Fax 776-0026; Caroline Kesic, Chief
E-mail: carolinekeesic@knet.ca

NORTHWEST ANGLE #33 FIRST NATION
P.O. Box 1490 • Kenora, ON P9N 3X7
(807) 226-2858 Fax 226-2860; Darlene Ross Sandy, Chief
E-mail: northwestangle33@bellnet.ca

NORTHWEST ANGLE #37 FIRST NATION
P.O. Box 267 • Sioux Narrows, ON P0X 1N0
(807) 226-5353 Fax 226-1164
Jim Major, Chief; E-mail: chief@nwa37.ca

OBASHKAANDAGAANG (WASHAGAMIS BAY) INDIAN BAND
P.O. Box 625 • Keewatin, ON P0X 1C0
(807) 543-2532 Fax 543-2964; Alfred Sinclair, Chief
E-mail: chartrand_brenda@hotmail.com

OCHIICHAGWE'BABIGO'INING FIRST NATION (DALLAS)
R.R. #1, Dalles Rd. • Kenora, ON P9N 2E7
(807) 548-5876 Fax 548-2337; Lorraine Cobiness
E-mail: chief@ochichag.ca

OJIBWAYS OF BATCHEWANA FIRST NATION
236 Frontenac St. • Sault Ste. Marie, ON P6A 5K9
(705) 759-0914 Fax 759-9171; Dean Sayers, Chief
E-mail: chiefdeansayers@batchewana.ca

OJIBWAYS OF GARDEN RIVER
7 Shingwauk St. • Garden River, ON 96A 6Z8
(705) 946-6300 Fax 945-1415; Lyle Sayers, Chief
E-mail: sayersl@gardenriver.org

OJIBWAYS OF ONIGAMING (SABASKONG)
P.O. Box 160 • Nestor Falls, ON P0X 1K0
(807) 484-2162 Fax 484-2737; Katherine Kishiqueb, Chief
E-mail: kathy.kishiqueb@onigaming.ca

OJIBWAYS OF PIC RIVER (HERON BAY)
P.O. Box 193 • Heron Bay, ON P0T 1R0
(807) 229-1749 Fax 229-1944; Duncan Michano, Jr., Chief
E-mail: Duncan.michano@picriver.com

ONEIDA NATION OF THE THAMES
2212 Elm Ave. • Southwold, ON N0L 2G0
(519) 652-3244 Fax 652-2930; Sheri Doxtator, Chief
E-mail: sheri.doxtator@oneida.on.ca

PAYS PLAT FIRST NATION
P10 Central Place • Pays Plat, ON P0T 3C0
(807) 824-2541 Fax 824-2206; Xavier Thompson, Chief
E-mail: ppchief@tbaytel.net

PIC MOBERT FIRST NATION
P.O. Box 717 • Mobert, ON P0M 2J0
(807) 822-2134 Fax 822-2850; Joshana Desmoulin, Chief
E-mail: chief Johanna@picmobert.ca

PIKANGIKUM FIRST NATION
P.O. Box 823 • Pikangikum, ON P0V 1L0
(807) 773-5578 Fax 773-5536; Paddy Peters, Chief

POPLAR HILL FIRST NATION
P.O. Box 1 • Poplar Hill, ON P0V 3E0
(807) 772-8838 Fax 772-8876; Alice Suggashie, Chief

RAINY RIVER FIRST NATION
P.O. Box 450 • Emo, ON P0W 1E0
(807) 482-2479 Fax 482-2603; Jim Leonard, Chief
E-mail: j.leonard@bellnet.ca

RED ROCK INDIAN BAND (LAKE HELEN)
P.O. Box 1030 • Nipigon, ON P0T 2J0
(807) 887-2510 Fax 887-3446; Pierre Pelletier, Chief
E-mail: rribchief@shaw.ca

SACHIGO LAKE FIRST NATION
P.O. Box 51 • Sachigo Lake, ON P0V 2P0
(807) 595-2577 Fax 595-1119; Titus Tait, Chief
E-mail: virginiabeardy@knet.ca

SAGAMOK ANISHNAWBEK FIRST NATION
P.O. Box 610 • Massey, ON P0P 1P0
(705) 865-2421 Fax 865-3307; Paul Eshkakogan, Chief
E-mail: eshkakogan_paul@sagamok.ca

SANDY LAKE (CHIPPEWAS) FIRST NATION
P.O. Box 12 • Sandy Lake, ON P0V 1V0
(807) 774-3421 Fax 774-1040
Bart Meekis, Chief; E-mail: bartmeekis@knet.ca

SAUGEEN FIRST NATION (SAVANT LAKE)
General Delivery • Savant Lake, ON P0V 2S0
(807) 928-2824 Fax 928-2710; Edward Machimity, Chief

SEINE RIVER FIRST NATION
P.O. Box 124 • Mine Centre, ON P0W 1H0
(807) 599-2224 Fax 599-2865
Earl Klyne, Chief; E-mail: earllklyne695@msn.com

SERPENT RIVER FIRST NATION
48 Indian Rd. • Cutler, ON P0P 1B0
(705) 844-2418 Fax 844-2757; Elaine Johnston, Interim Chief
E-mail: ejohnston.srfn@ontera.net

SHAWANAGA FIRST NATION
R.R. #1 • Nobel, ON P0G 1G0
(705) 366-2526 Fax 366-2740; Wayne Pamajewon, Chief
E-mail: sfnchief137@gmail.com

SHEGUIANDAH FIRST NATION
P.O. Box 101 • Sheguiandah, ON P0P 1W0
(705) 368-2781 Fax 368-3697; Georgina Thompson, Interim Chief
E-mail: georgina.thompson@sheguiandahfn.ca

SHESHEGWANING FIRST NATION
P.O. Box 1 • Sheshegwaning, ON P0P 1X0
(705) 283-3292 Fax 283-3481; Joseph Endanawas, Chief
E-mail: joe@sheshegwaning.org

SHOAL LAKE No. 40 FIRST NATION
P.O. Box 6 • Kejick, ON P0X 1E0
(807) 733-2315 Fax 733-3115; Erin Redsky, Chief
E-mail: erinredsky@hotmail.com

SIX NATIONS OF THE GRAND RIVER TERRITORY
P.O. Box 5000 • Ohsweken, ON N0A 1M0
(519) 445-2201 Fax 445-4208
Ava Hill, Chief; E-mail: avahill@sixnations.ca

Canada's most populous Aboriginal community.

SLAT FALLS FIRST NATION
48 Lakeview Dr. • Slate Falls, ON P0V 3C0
(807) 737-5700 Fax (888) 431-5617
Lorraine Crane, Chief; E-mail: lorrainecrane@knet.ca

TAYKWA TAGAMOU (NEW POST)
R.R. #2, P.O. Box 3310 • Cochrane, ON P0L 1C0
(705) 272-5766 Fax 272-5785; Dwight Sutherland, Chief
E-mail: dwight_sutherland@hotmail.com

TEMAGAMI FIRST NATION
Lake Temagamii, ON P0H 1C0
(705) 237-8943 Fax 237-8959; Arnold Paul, Chief
E-mail: chief@temagamifirstnation.ca

THESSALON FIRST NATION
40 Sugarbush Rd., R.R. #2 • Thessalon, ON P0R 1L0
(705) 842-2323 Fax 842-2332; Alfred Bisaillon, Chief
E-mail: chiefalfredbisallion@vianet.ca

WABAUSKANG FIRST NATION
P.O. Box 339 • Ear Falls, ON P0V 1T0
(807) 529-3174 Fax 529-3007; Martine Petiquan, Chief
E-mail: wabauskangchief@hotmail.com

WABIGOON LAKE OJIBWAY FIRST NATION
Site 115, R.R. #1, Box 300 • Dryden, ON P0K 1N0
(807) 938-6684 Fax 938-1166; Paul Watts, Chief
E-mail: chief-council@wlon.ca

WAHGOSHIG FIRST NATION (ABITIBI #70)
R.R. #3 • Matheson, ON P0K 1N0
(705) 273-2055 FAX 273-2900; David Babin, Chief
E-mail: wahgosh@ntl.sympatico.ca

WAHNAPITAE FIRST NATION
P259 Taighwenini Trail Rd. • Capreol, ON P0M 1H0
(705) 858-0610 Fax 858-5570; Ted Roque, Chief
E-mail: ted.roque@wahnapitaefn.com

WAHTA MOHAWKS (GIBSON)
P.O. Box 260 • Bala, ON P0C 1A0
(705) 762-2354 Fax 762-2376; Phillip Franks
E-mail: Philip.frank@wahtamohawkscouncil.ca

WAPEKEKA INDIAN BAND
P.O. Box 2 • Angling Lake, ON P0V 1B0
(807) 537-2315 Fax 537-2336; Brennan Sainnawap, Chief
E-mail: brennnnans@wapekeka.ca

WASAUKSING FIRST NATION (PARRY ISLAND)
P.O. Box 253 • Parry Sound, ON P2A 2X4
(705) 746-2531 Fax 746-5984; Warren Tabobondung, Chief
E-mail: chief@wasauksing.ca

WAUZHUSHIK ONIGUM FIRST NATION (RAT PORTAGE)
P.O. Box 1850 • Kenora, ON P9N 3X8
(807) 548-5663 Fax 548-4877; Chris Skead, Chief
E-mail: cskead@wonation.ca

WAWAKAPEWIN FIRST NATION
P.O. Box 449 • Sioux Lookout, ON P8T 1A8
(807) 442-2567 Fax 442-1162; Anne-Marie Beardy, Chief
E-mail: annemarieb@wawakapewin.ca

WEBEQUIE FIRST NATION
P.O. Box 268 • Webequie, ON P0T 3A0
(807) 353-6531 Fax 353-1218; Cornelius Wabasse, Chief
E-mail: corneliusw@webequie.ca

WEENUSK FIRST NATION
P.O. Box 1 • Peawanuck, ON P0L 2H0
(705) 473-2554 Fax 473-2503; Edmund Hunter, Chief
E-mail: edmundhunter@hotmail.com

WHITEFISH RIVER FIRST NATION
P.O. Box A, 46 Bay of Islands Rd. • Birch Island, ON P0P 1A0
(705) 285-4335 Fax 285-4532; Shining Turtle, Chief
Email: chief@whitefishriver.ca

WHITESAND FIRST NATION
P.O. Box 68 • Armstrong, ON P0T 1A0
(807) 583-2177 Fax 583-2170; Allan Gustafson, Chief
E-mail: allan_gus2006@yahoo.com

WHITEWATER LAKE FIRST NATION
307 Euclid Ave., Suite 414 • Thunder Bay, ON P7E 6G6
(807) 622-8713 Fax 577-5438; Arlene Slipperjack, Chief
E-mail: Arlene.wwater@tbaytel.net

WIKWEMIKONG UNCEDED INDIAN RESERVE
P.O. Box 112 • Wikwemikong, ON P0P 2J0
(800) 880-1406; (705) 859-3122 Fax 859-3851
Duke Peltier, Chief; E-mail: dukepeltier@wiky.net

WUNNUMIN LAKE FIRST NATION
P.O. Box 105 • Wunnumin Lake, ON P0V 2Z0
(807) 442-2559 Fax 442-2627; Rod Winnepetonga, Chief
E-mail: rodw@wunnumin.ca

ZHIIBAAHAASING (COCKBURN ISLAND) FIRST NATION
General Delivery • Silverwater, ON P0P 1Y0
(705) 283-3963 Fax 283-3964; Irene Sagon-Kells, Chief
Email: zhiiband@maitoulin.net

METIS NON-STATUS

METIS NATION OF ONTARIO
141 Holland Ave. • Ottawa, ON K1Y 0Y2
(800) 263-4889; (613) 798-1488 Fax 722-4225
Website: www.metistraing.org

METIS NATIONAL COUNCIL
350 Sparks St. #309 • Ottawa, ON K1P 7S9
(613) 232-3216 Fax 232-4262
Website: www.sae.ca/mbc

PRINCE EDWARD ISLAND

ABEGWEIT FIRST NATION (MI'KMAQ)
P.O. Box 36 • Mount Stewart/Scotchfort, PEI C0A 1T0
(902) 675-3842 Fax 892-3420; Brian Francis, Chief
Website: www.abegweitfirstnations.com
E-mail: bfrancis@mcpei.ca

LENNOX ISLAND FIRST NATION
P.O. Box 134 • Lennox Island, PEI C0B 1P0
(902) 831-2779 Fax 831-3153; Website: www.lennoxisland.com
Matilda Ramjattan, Chief; E-mail: matilda.ramjattan@lennoxisland.com

QUEBEC

ABENAKI BAND COUNCIL OF WOLINAK
10120, rue Kolipaio • Wolinak, PQ G0X 1B0
(819) 294-6696 Fax 294-6697; Denis Landry, Chief
Website: www.cawolinak.com; E-mail: secretaire@cawolinak.com

ABITIBIWINNI BAND COUNCIL (Algonquian)
45, rue Migwan • Pikogan, PQ J9T 3A3
(819) 732-6591 Fax 732-1569; Bruno Kistabish, Chief
Website: www.pikogan.com; E-mail: administration@pikogan.com
Algonquian.

BARRIERE LAKE BAND COUNCIL (Algonquian)
Kitiganik • Lac-Rapide (Québec) J0W 2C0
(819) 435-2181 Fax 435-2191; Casey Ratt, Chief
E-mail: rattcasey@gmail.com

CREE NATION OF CHISASIBI
1, Riverside Dr., P.O. Box 150 • Chisasibi, P.Q. J0M 1E0
(819) 855-2878 Fax 855-2875; Davey Bobbish, Chief
E-mail: ednakanatewa@chisasibi.ca

EASTMAIN BAND COUNCIL (Cree)
76, rue Nouchimi, P.O. Box 90 • Eastmain, PQ J0M 1W0
(819) 977-0211 Fax 977-0281; Ted Moses, Chief
E-mail: chief@eastmain-nation.ca

ESSIPIT MONTAGNAIS BAND COUNCIL
27, rue de la Reserve, P.O. Box 820 • Essipit, PQ G0T 1K0
(418) 233-2509 Fax 233-2888; Martin Dufour, Chief
E-mail: communaute@essipit.com

EAGLE VILLAGE KIPAWA BAND (Algonquian)
P.O. Box 756 • Eagle Village, PQ J0Z 3R0
(819) 627-3455 Fax 627-9428; Lance Haymond, Chief
E-mail: lanceh@evfn.ca

GESGAPEGIAG MICMAC BAND COUNCIL
Maria Indian Reserve, P.O. Box 1280 • Maria, PQ G0C 1Y0
(418) 759-3441 Fax 759-5856; Roderick Larocque, Jr., Chief
E-mail: micmacfinance@gesgepegiag.ca

GESPEG BAND COUNCIL (Micmac)
P.O. Box 69 • Gaspe, PQ G4X 6V2
(418) 368-6005 Fax 368-1272; Manon Jeannotte, Chief
E-mail: Micmac@globetrotter.net

HURON-WENDAT NATION COUNCIL
255, Place Chef Michel Laveau • Wendake, PQ G0A 4V0
(418) 843-3767 Fax 842-1108; Konrad Sioui, Chief
Max (Magella) Gros-Louis, Grand Chief; E-mail: administration@cnhw.qc.ca
Elected chiefs: Roger Picard, Reine Laine, Rene Duchesneau,
Arold Bastien, Michel Picard, Raymond Gros Louis. *Tribe served*: Huron -
Wendat. *In residence*: 850. *Total acreage*: 300. School and museum.

INNU TAKUAIKAN UASHAT MAK MANI-UTENAM COUNCIL
P.O. Box 8000 • Sept-Iles, PQ G4R 4L9
(418) 962-0327 Fax 968-0937; Mike McKenzie, Chief
E-mail: mathilda.fontaine@itum.qc.ca

KAHNAWAKE MOHAWK COUNCIL
P.O. Box 720 • Kahnawake, PQ J0L 1B0
(450) 632-7500 Fax 638-5958; E-mail: communications@mck.ca
Joseph Tokwiroh Norton, Grand Chief
Grand Chief & 10 council chiefs. *Council Chiefs*: Mike Bush, Martin Leborgne,
Peggy Mayo, Johnny Montour, Peter Paul, Marvin Zacharie, John Dee
Delormier, Warren Lahache, Kenneth McComber, Rhonda Kirby. *Tribe served*:
Mohawk of the Six Nations Iroquois Confederacy. *In residence*: 5,500. *Total
acreage*: 12,500. *Boundaries*: Triangular i shape, bounded on north by St.
Lawrence River with survey boundaries east & west. *Special programs*: Social
services; alcohol & drug abuse prevention; heath services program; social
assistance; economic & financial services; community development; human
resource development. *Publication*: Mohawk Nation News. Mohawk Council.

KANESATAKE MOHAWK COUNCIL
681 Ste. Philomene • Kanesatake, PQ J0N 1E0
(514) 479-8373 Fax 479-8249; Serge Otsi Simon, Grand Chief
E-mail: mckfinance@netc.net

KITIGAN ZIBI ANISHINABEG BAND COUNCIL (Algonquian)
P.O. Box 309 • Kitigan Zibi, PQ J9E 3C9
(819) 449-5170 Fax 449-5673; Jean-Guy Whiteduck, Chief
E-mail: scommanda@kza.qc.ca

LA ROMAINE MONTAGNAIS COUNCIL
90, rue du Large • La Romaine, PQ G0G 1M0
(418) 229-2917 Fax 229-2921; Alain Lalo, Chief
E-mail: dg.conseil@unamenshipu.qc.ca

LAC ST-JEAN MONTAGNAIS COUNCIL
1671, rue Quiatchouan • Mashteuiatsh, PQ G0W 2H0
(418) 275-2473 Fax 275-6212; Gilbert Dominique, Chief
E-mail: cdm@mashteuiatsh.ca

LAC-SIMON BAND COUNCIL (Algonquian)
1026, Cicip Blvd. • Lac Simon, PQ J0Y 3M0
(819) 736-4501 Fax 736-7311; Salmee McKenzie, Chief
Website: www.lacsimon.ca; E-mail: receptionconseil@lacsimon.ca

LISTUGUI MI'GMAQ FIRST NATION
P.O. Box 298, 17 Riverside West • Listujug, PQ G0C 2R0
(418) 788-2136 Fax 788-2058; Scott Martin, Chief
E-mail: sisaac33@hotmail.com

LONGUE-POINTE BAND COUNCIL (Algonquian)
P.O. Box 1 • Winneway River, PQ J0Z 2J0
(819) 722-2441 Fax 722-2579; Derek Mathias, Chief
E-mail: longpointfirstnationlb@sympatico.ca

MANAWAN ATIKAMEKW COUNCIL (Attikameks)
135, rue Kicik • Manawan, PQ J0K 1M0
(819) 971-8813 Fax 971-8848; Jean-Roch Ottawa, Chief
E-mail: conseil@manawan.com

MINGAN BAND COUNCIL (Innus Montagnais)
35, rue Manitou • Mingan, PQ G0G 1V0
(418) 949-2234 Fax 949-2085; Jean-Charles Pietacho, Chief
E-mail: chef.conseil@ekuanitshit.ca

MISTISSINI BAND COUNCIL (Cree)
187, rue Main • Mistissini , PQ G0W 1C0
(418) 923-3461 Fax 923-3115; Richard Shecapio, Chief
E-mail: administration@nation.mistissini.qc.ca

MALECITE DE VIGER FIRST NATION COUNCIL
217, Rue de la Greve • Cacouna, PQ G0L 1G0
(418) 860-2393 Fax 867-3418; Anne Archambault, Grand Chief
E-mail: info@malecites.ca

NASKAPI NATION OF KAWAWACHIKAMACH
1009 Naskapi Rd. • Kawawachikamach, PQ G0G 2Z0
(418) 585-2686 Fax 585-3130; Noah Swappie, Chief
E-mail: kawawa@naskapi.ca

NATASHQUAN MONTAGNAIS
78, rue Mashkush • Natashquan, PQ G0G 2E0
(418) 726-3529 Fax 726-3017; Rodrigue Wapistan, Chief
E-mail: sec.admin.conseil@nutashkuan.ca

NEMASKA BAND COUNCIL (Cree)
1, Lakeshore St. • Lac Champion • Nemaska, PQ J0Y 3B0
(819) 673-2512 Fax 673-2542; Thomas Jolly, Chief
E-mail: nation@nemaska.ca

OBEDJIWAN BAND COUNCIL (Attikameks)
22, rue Amiskw • Obedjiwan, PQ G0W 3B0
(819) 974-8837 Fax 974-8828; Christian Awashish, Chief
E-mail: cawashish@opticiwan.ca

ODANAK BAND COUNCIL (Abenaki)
102, rue Sibosis • Odanak, PQ J0G 1H0
(514) 568-2810 Fax 568-3553; Richard O'Bomsawin, Chief
Website: www.caodanak.com; E-mail: kgill@caodanak.com

OUJE-BOUGOUMOU CREE COUNCIL
207, rue Opemiska • Ouje-Bougoumou, PQ G0W 3C0
(418) 745-3911 Fax 745-3168
Reggie Neposh, Chief; E-mail: chief@ouje.ca

PAKUASHIPI MONTAGNAIS COUNCIL
P.O. Box 178 • Pakuashipi, PQ G0G 2R0
(418) 947-2253 Fax 947-2622; Denis Mestenapeo, Chief
E-mail: reception@pakuashipu.net

PESSAMIT INNUS COUNCIL
4, Metsheteu • Pessamit, PQ G0H 1B0
(418) 567-8488 Fax 567-2868; Rene Simn, Chief
E-mail: bureau.politique@pessamit.ca

SCHEFFERVILLE MONTAGNAIS COUNCIL
P.O. Box 1390 • Schefferville, PQ G0G 2T0
(418) 585-2601 Fax 585-3856; Real McKenzie, Chief
E-mail: realmck@hotmail.com

TEMISKAMING FIRST NATION (Algonquian)
24, Algonquin Ave. • Notre-Dame-Du-Nord, PQ J0Z 3B0
(819) 723-2370 Fax 723-2799; Terence McBride, Chief
Website: www.parolink.net; E-mail: tfncouncil@parolink.net

WASKAGANISH BAND COUNCIL (Cree)
P.O. Box 60 • Waskaganish, PQ J0M 1R0
(819) 895-8650 Fax 895-8901; Gordon Blackned, Chief
Email: tanya.trapper@waskaganish.ca

WASWANIPI BAND COUNCIL (Cree)
P.O. Box 8 • Waswanipi River, PQ J0Y 3C0
(819) 753-2587 Fax 753-2555; Marcel Happyjack, Chief
E-mail: info@waswanipi.com

NATION OF WEMINDJI (Cree)
21, Hilltop Dr., P.O. Box 60 • WEMINDJI, PQ J0M 1L0
(819) 978-0264 Fax 978-0258; Dennis Georgekish, Chief
E-mail: tgull@creenet.com

WEMOTACI BAND COUNCIL (Attikameks)
36, rue Kenosi, C.P. 221 • Wemotaci, PQ G0X 3R0
(819) 666-2237 Fax 666-2209; Francois Neashit, Chief
E-mail: sg.caw@wemotaci.com

CREE NATION OF WHAPMAGOOSTUI
P.O. Box 390 • Hudson Bay, PQ J0M 1G0
(819) 929-3384 Fax 929-3203; Stanley George, Chief
E-mail: pkawapit@whapmagoostuifn.ca

WOLF LAKE BAND COUNCIL (Algonquian)
P.O. Box 998 • Temiscamingue, PQ J0Z 3R0
(819) 627-3628 627-1109; Harold St. Denis, Chief
Website: www.wolflake.com; E-mail: wlfn@wolflake.com

INUIT

VILLAGE OF AKULIVIK
P.O. Box 50 • Akulivik, PQ J0M 1V0
(819) 496-2073 Fax 496-2200; Adamie Alayco, Mayor
E-mail: adaalamayor@nvakulivik.ca

VILLAGE OF AUPALUK
P.O. Box 6 • Aupaluk, PQ J0m 1X0
(819) 491-7070 Fax 491-7035
David Angutinguak, Chief; E-mail: mayor@nvaupaluk.ca

VILLAGE OF INUKJUAK
P.O. Box 234 • Inukjuak, PQ J0m 1M0
(819) 254-8845 Fax 254-8779; Siasi Smiler Irqumia, Mayor
E-mail: pinukpukmator@nvinukjuak.ca

VILLAGE OF IVUJIVIK
P.O. Box 20 • Ivujivik, PQ J0m 1H0
(819) 922-9940 Fax 922-3045; Peter Iyaituk, Mayor
E-mail: mayorivu@nvivujivik.ca

VILLAGE OF KANGIQSUJJUAQ
P.O. Box 60 • Kangiqsujjuaq, PQ J0m 1K0
(819) 338-3342 Fax 338-3237

VILLAGE OF KANGIQSUALUJJUAQ
Kangiqualujjuaq, PQ J0m 1N0
(819) 337-5271 Fax 337-5200; Aquuyaq Qisiiq, Mayor
E-mail: mayor@nvkangiqsujuaq.ca

VILLAGE OF KANGIRSUK
P.O. Box 90 • Kangirsuk, PQ J0M 1A0
(819) 935-4388 Fax 935-4287; Mary Nassak Annahatak, Mayor
E-mail: mayor@cnvkangisurk.ca

NORTHERN VILLAGE OF KUUJJUAQ
P.O. Box 210 • Kuujjuaq, PQ J0M 1C0
(819) 964-2943 Fax 964-2980; Tunu Napartuk, Mayor
E-mail: tnapartuk@kuujjuaq.ca

NORTHERN VILLAGE OF KUUJJURAPIK
P.O. Box 360 • Kuujjuarapik, PQ J0m 1G0
(819) 929-3360 Fax 929-3453; Lucassie Inukpuk, Mayor
E-mail: linukpuk@nvkuujjuarapik.ca

NORTHERN VILLAGE OF PUVIRNITUQ
P.O. Box 150 • Puvirnituk, PQ J0M 1P0
(819) 988-2828 Fax 988-2751; Aisara Kenuajuak, Mayor
E-mail: akenuajuak@nvpuvirnituq.ca

NORTHERN VILLAGE OF QUAQTAQ
P.O. Box 107 • Quaqtaq, PQ J0M 1J0
(819) 492-9912 Fax 492-9935; Eva Deer, Mayor
E-mail: mayor@nvquaqtaq.ca

NORTHERN VILLAGE OF SALLUIT
P.O. Box 240 • Salluit, PQ J0M 1S0
(819) 255-8953 Fax 255-8802; Paulusie Saviadjuk, Mayor
E-mail: mayor@nvsalluit.ca

NORTHERN VILLAGE OF TASIUJAQ
Case Postale 54 • Tasiujaq, PQ J0M 1T0
 (819) 633-9924 Fax 633-5026; Peter Angnatuk, Mayor
E-mail: panqnatuk@nvtasiujaq.ca

NORTHERN VILLAGE OF UMIUJAQ
P.O. Box 108 • Umiujaq, PQ J0M 1Y0
 (819) 331-7000 Fax 331-7057; Jobie Crown, Mayor
E-mail: mayor@nvumiujaq.ca

SASKATCHEWAN

AHTAHKAKOOP BAND OF THE CREE NATION
P.O. Box 220 • Shell Lake, SK S0J 2G0
 (306) 468-2326 Fax 468-2344; Barry Ahenakew, Chief
Member of the Battleford Agency Tribal Chiefs.

ASIMAKANISEEKAN ASKIY RESERVE
100 103A Packham Ave. • Saskatoon, SK S7N 4K4
 (306) 374-8118 Fax 374-7377

BEARDY'S & OKAMASIS FIRST NATION
P.O. Box 340 • Duck Lake, SK S0K 1J0
 (306) 467-4523 Fax 467-4404; Richard J.H. Gamble, Chief

BIG RIVER FIRST NATION
P.O. Box 519 • Debden, SK S0J 0S0
 (306) 724-4700 Fax 724-2161; Bruce Morin, Chief
Member of the Agency Chiefs Tribal Council.

BIRCH NARROWS DENE NATION
General Delivery • Tumor Lake, SK S0M 3E0
 (306) 894-2030 Fax 894-2060; Jean Campbell, Chief
Member of the Meadow Lake Tribal Council.

BLACK LAKE DENESULINE NATION
Box 27 • Black Lake, SK S0J 0H0
 (306) 284-2044 Fax 284-2101; Rick Robillard, Chief
Member of the Prince Albert Grand Council.

BUFFALO RIVER FIRST NATION
General Delivery • Dillon, SK S0M 0H0
 (306) 282-2033 Fax 282-2102; Gordon Billette, Chief
Member of the Meadow Lake Tribal Council.

CANOE LAKE CREE NATION
General Delivery • Canoe Narrows, SK S0M 0K0
 (306) 829-2150 Fax 829-2101; Frank Iron, Chief
Member of the Meadow Lake Tribal Council.

CARRY THE KETTLE FIRST NATION
P.O. Box 57 • Sintaluta, SK S0G 4N0
 (306) 727-2135 Fax 727-2149; James L. O'Watch, Chief
Member of the File Hills Qu'Appelle Tribal Council.

CLEARWATER RIVER DENE NATION
P.O. Box 389 • La Loche, SK S0M 1G0
 (306) 822-2021 Fax 822-2212; Frank Piche, Chief

COTE FIRST NATION
P.O. Box 1659 • Kamsack, SK S0A 1S0
 (306) 542-2694 Fax 542-3735; Norman Whitehawk, Chief
Member of the Yorkton Tribal Council.

COWESSESS FIRST NATION
P.O. Box 100 • Cowessess, SK S0G 5L0
 (306) 696-2520 Fax 696-276; Lionel Sparvier, Chief

CUMBERLAND HOUSE CREE NATION
P.O. Box 220 • Cumberland House, SK S0E 0S0
 (306) 888-2226 Fax 888-2084; Website: www.chcn.ca
Lorne Stewart, Chief Councillor
Member of the Prince Albert Grand Council.

DAY STAR FIRST NATION
P.O. Box 277 • Punnichy, SK S0A 3C0
 (306) 835-2834 Fax 835-2724; Cameron Kinequon, Chief
Member of the Touchwood Agency Tribal Council.

ENGLISH RIVER FIRST NATION
General Delivery • Patuanak, SK S0M 2H0
 (306) 396-2055 Fax 396-2155; Louis George, Jr., Chief
Member of the Meadow Lake Tribal Council.

FISHING LAKE FIRST NATION
P.O. Box 508 • Wadena, SK S0A 4J0
 (306) 338-3838 Fax 338-3635; Allan Paquachan, Chief

FLYING DUST FIRST NATION
8001 Flying Dust Reserve • Meadow Lake, SK S0M 1V0
 (306) 236-4437 Fax 236-3373; Richard Gladue, Chief
Member of the Meadow Lake Tribal Council.

FOND DU LAC DENESULINE NATION
Box 211• Fond du Lac, SK S0J 0W0
 (306) 686-2102 Fax 686-2040; Earl Lidguerre, Chief
Member of the Prince Albert Grand Council.

GEORGE GORDON FIRST NATION
P.O. Box 248 • Punnichy, SK S0A 3C0
 (306) 835-2232 Fax 835-2036; Wayne Morris, Chief
Member of the Touchwood Agency Tribal Council.

HATCHET LAKE DENESULINE NATION
General Delivery • Wollaston Lake, SK S0J 3C0
 (306) 633-2003 Fax 633-2040; Bartholomew J. Tsannie, Chief
Member of the Prince Albert Grand Council.

ISLAND LAKE FIRST NATION
P.O. Box 460 • Loon Lake, SK S0M 1L0
 (306) 837-2188 Fax 837-2266; Ernest Crookedneck, Chief
Member of the Meadow Lake Tribal Council.

JAMES SMITH CREE NATION
P.O. Box 1059 • Melfort, SK S0E 1A0
 (306) 864-3636 Fax 864-3336; Justin Burns, Chief
Member of the Prince Albert Grand Council.

JOSEPH BIGHEAD FIRST NATION
P.O. Box 309 • Pierceland, SK S0M 2K0
 (306) 839-2277 Fax 839-2323; Ernest Sundown, Chief

KAHKEWISTAHAW FIRST NATION
P.O. Box 609 • Broadview, SK S0G 0K0
 (306) 696-3291 Fax 696-3201; Louis Taypotat, Chief
Member of the Yorkton Tribal Council.

KAWACATOOSE FIRST NATION
P.O. Box 640 • Raymore, SK S0A 3J0
 (306) 835-2125 Fax 835-2178; Richard Poorman, Chief
Member of the Touchwood Agency Tribal Council.

KEESEEKOOSE FIRST NATION
P.O. Box 1120 • Kamsack, SK S0A 1S0
 (306) 542-2516 Fax 542-2586; Phillip Quewezance, Chief
Member of the Yorkton Tribal Council.

KEY FIRST NATION
P.O. Box 70 • Norquay, SK S0A 2V0
 (306) 594-2020 Fax 594-2545; Isabel O'Soup, Chief
Member of the Yorkton Tribal Council.

KINISTIN SAULTEAUX NATION
P.O. Box 2590 • Tisdale, SK S0E 1T0
 (866) 272-8188; (306) 878-8188 Fax 873-5235
 Website: www.kinistin.sk.ca; E-mail: info@kinistin.sk.ca
 Greg Scott, Chief. Member of the Saskatoon Tribal Council.
Population: 920.

LAC LA RONGE INDIAN BAND
P.O. Box 480 • La Ronge, SK S0J 1L0
 (425) 425-2183 Fax 425-2590; Tammy Cook-Searson, Chief
A progressive Woodland Cree First Nation located in the majestic boreal forest in north-central Saskatchewan. LLRIB is a multi-community Band and is the largest First Nation in the province. The central office is located on the Kitsaki reserve adjacent to the Town of La Ronge. Member of the Prince Albert Grand Council.

LITTLE BLACK BEAR FIRST NATION
P.O. Box 40 • Goodeve, SK S0A 1C0
 (306) 334-2269 Fax 334-2721; Clarence A. Bellegarde, Chief
Member of the File Hills Qu'Appelle Tribal Council.

LITTLE PINE FIRST NATION
P.O. Box 70 • Paynton, SK S0M 2J0
 (306) 398-4942 Fax 398-2377; Johnson Kakum, Chief
Member of the Battlefords Tribal Council.

LUCKY MAN CREE NATION
225-103B Packham Ave. • Saskatoon, SK S7N 2T7
 (306) 374-2828 Fax 934-2853; Andrew King, Chief
Member of the Battlefords Tribal Council.

MAKWA SAHGAIEHCAN FIRST NATION
P.O. Box 340 • Loon Lake, SK S0M 1L0
 (306) 837-2102 Fax 837-4448; Gerald Kisyeinwakup, Chief
Member of the Meadow Lake Tribal Council.

MISTAWASIS INDIAN BAND
P.O. Box 250 • Leask, SK S0J 1M0
 (306) 466-4800 Fax 466-2299
 Website: www.mistawasis.ca; E-mail: contact@mistawasis.ca
 Daryl Watson, Chief. Member of Saskatoon Tribal Council.
Population: 2,375.

MONTREAL LAKE CREE NATION
P.O. Box 210 • Montreal Lake, SK S0J 1Y0
 (306) 663-5349 Fax 663-5320; Edward Henderson, Chief

MOOSOMIN FIRST NATION
P.O. Box 98 • Cochin, SK S0M 0L0
 (306) 398-2206 Fax 398-2098; Gerald SwiftWolfe, Chief

MOSQUITO GRIZZLY BEAR'S HEAD FIRST NATION
P.O. Box 177 • Cando, SK S0K 0V0
 (306) 937-7707 Fax 937-7747; Jenny Spyglas, Chief
Member of the Battlefords Tribal Council.

MUSCOWPETUNG FIRST NATION
P.O. Box 1310 • Fort Qu'Appelle, SK S0G 1S0
 (306) 723-4747 Fax 723-4710; Paul Poitras, Chief
Member of the File Hills Qu'Appelle Tribal Council.

MUSKEG LAKE CREE NATION
P.O. Box 248 • Marcelin, SK S0J 1R0
 (306) 466-4959 Fax 466-4951; Website: www.muskeglake.com
 Gilbert Ledoux, Chief; Murray Browne, Director of Operations
Population: 1,900; 370 live on the reserve. Area: 35,123 acres.

MUSKODAY FIRST NATION
P.O. Box 99 • Muskoday, SK S0J 0G0
 (306) 764-1282 Fax 764-7272; Austin Bear, Chief
Population: 1,600.

MUSKOWEKWAN FIRST NATION
P.O. Box 249 • Lestock, SK S0J 3H0
 (306) 764-1282 Fax 764-7272; Austin Bear, Chief
Member of the Touchwood Agency Tribal Council.

NEKANEET FIRST NATION
P.O. Box 548 • Maple Creek, SK S0N 1N0
 (306) 662-3660 Fax 662-4160; Gordon Oakes, Chief
Member of the File Hills Qu'Appelle Tribal Council.

OCEAN MAN FIRST NATION
P.O. Box 157 • Stoughton, SK S0G 4T0
 (306) 457-2697 Fax 457-2933; Connie Big Eagle, Chief
Member of the Yorkton Tribal Council.

OCHAPOWACE FIRST NATION
P.O. Box 550 • Whitewood, SK S0J 5C0
 (306) 696-3160 Fax 696-3146; Denton George, Chief

OKANESE FIRST NATION
P.O. Box 759 • Balcarres, SK S0G 0C0
 (306) 334-2532 Fax 334-2545; Marie Ann Daywalker, Chief
Member of the File Hills Qu'Appelle Tribal Council.

ONE ARROW FIRST NATION
P.O. Box 147 • Bellevue, SK S0K 3Y0
 (306) 423-5900 Fax 423-5904
 Kirk Matchap, Chief; Mark Arcand, Vice Chief
Member of the Saskatoon Tribal Council. Population: 1,500.

ONION LAKE CREE NATION
P.O. Box 100 • Onion Lake, SK S0M 2E0
 (306) 847-2200 Fax 847-2226; Website: www.onionlake..ca
 Wallace Fox, Chief; E-mail: wallace.fox@onionlake.ca
 Henry Lewis, Treat Governance Director
 E-mail: henry.lewis@onionlake.ca

PASQUA FIRST NATION
P.O. Box 968 • Fort Qu'Appelle, SK S0G 1S0
 (306) 332-5697 Fax 332-5199; Lindsay Cyr, Chief
Member of the File Hills Qu'Appelle Tribal Council.

PEEPEEKISIS FIRST NATION
P.O. Box 518 • Balcarres, SK S0G 0C0
 (306) 334-2573 Fax 334-2280; Enoch Poitras, Chief
Member of the File Hills Qu'Appelle Tribal Council.

PELICAN LAKE FIRST NATION
P.O. Box 399 • Leoville, SK S0J 1N0
 (306) 984-2313 Fax 984-2029; Dennis Lewis, Chief
Member of the Agency Chiefs Tribal Council.

PETER BALLANTYNE CREE NATION
General Delivery • Pelican Narrows, SK S0P 0E0
 (306) 953-4400 Fax 953-4420; Peter A. Beatty, Chief
Member of the Prince Albert Grand Council.

PHEASANT RUMP NAKOTA NATION
P.O. Box 238 • Kisbey, SK S0C 1L0
 (306) 462-2002 Fax 462-2003; Kelvin J. McArthur, Chief

PIAPOT FIRST NATION
General Delivery • Zehner, SK S0G 5K0
 (306) 781-4848 Fax 781-4853; Art Kaiswatum, Chief
Member of the File Hills Qu'Appelle Tribal Council.

POUNDMAKER (CREE) FIRST NATION
P.O. Box 220 • Paynton, SK S0M 2J0
 (306) 398-4971 Fax 398-2522; Teddy Antoine, Chief
Member of the Battlefords Tribal Council.

RED EARTH CREE FIRST NATION
P.O. Box 109 • Red Earth, SK S0E 1K0
 (306) 768-3640 Fax 768-3440; Ian McKay, Chief
Member of the Prince Albert Grand Council.

RED PHEASANT FIRST NATION
P.O. Box 70 • Cando, SK S0K 0V0
 (306) 937-7717 Fax 937-7727; Mike Baptiste, Chief
Member of the Battleford Agency Tribal Chiefs.

SAKIMAY FIRST NATION
P.O. Box 339 • Grenfell, SK S0G 2B0
 (306) 697-2831 Fax 697-3565; Lindsey Kaye, Chief
Member of the Yorkton Tribal Council.

SAULTEAUX FIRST NATION
P.O. Box 159 • Cochin, SK S0M 0L0
 (306) 386-2424 Fax 386-2444; Gabriel Gopher, Chief
Member of the Battleford Agency Tribal Chiefs.

SHOAL LAKE CREE NATION
P.O. Box 51 • Pakwa Lake, SK S0E 1G0
 (306) 768-3551 Fax 768-3486; Carlton Bear, Chief
Member of the Prince Albert Grand Council.

STANDING BUFFALO DAKOTA NATION
P.O. Box 128 • Fort Qu'Appelle, SK S0G 1S0
 (306) 332-4685 Fax 332-595; Mel Isnana, Chief
Member of the File Hills Qu'Appelle Tribal Council.

STAR BLANKET (CREE) FIRST NATION
P.O. Box 456 • Belcarres, SK S0G 0C0
 (306) 334-2206 Fax 334-2606; Irvin Starr, Chief
Member of the File Hills Qu'Appelle Tribal Council.

STURGEON LAKE FIRST NATION
P.O. Box 5, Site 12, RR #1 • Shellbrook, SK S0J 2E0
(306) 764-1872 Fax 764-1877; Website: www.slfn.ca
Henry Felix, Chief; Donna Kingfisher, Administrator
Member of the Prince Albert Grand Council.

SWEETGRASS FIRST NATION
Box 147 • Gallivan, SK S0M 0X0
(306) 937-2990 Fax 937-701; Edward Standinghorn, Chief
Member of the Battleford Agency Tribal Chiefs.

THUNDERCHILD FIRST NATION
P.O. Box 600 • Turtleford, SK S0M 2Y0
(306) 845-3424 Fax 845-3230; Charles Paddy, Sr., Chief

WAHPETON DAKOTA FIRST NATION
P.O. Box 128 • Prince Albert, SK S6V 3B0
(306) 764-6649 Fax 764-6637; Leo Omani, Chief
Member of the Prince Albert Grand Council.

WATERHEN FIRST NATION
P.O. Box 9 • Waterhen Lake, SK S0M 3B0
(306) 236-6717 Fax 236-4866; Robert Fiddler, Chief
Member of the Meadow Lake Tribal Council.

WHITE BEAR FIRST NATION
P.O. Box 700 • Carlyle, SK S0C 0R0
(306) 577-4553 Fax 577-210; Bernard Shepherd, Chief

WHITECAP DAKOTA FIRST NATION
P.O. Box 82 Chief Whitecap Trail • Whitecap, SK S7K 2L2
(306) 477-0908 Fax 374-5899; Darcy Bear, Chief
Website: www.whitecapdakota.com; *Population*: 525.

WITCHEKAN LAKE FIRST NATION
P.O. Box 879 • Spiritwood, SK S0J 2M0
(306) 883-2787 Fax 883-2008; Ken Thomas, Chief
Member of the Agency Chiefs Tribal Council.

WOOD MOUNTAIN FIRST NATION
P.O. Box 104 • Wood Mountain, SK S0H 4L0
(306) 266-4422 Fax 266-2023; William Goodtrack, Chief
Member of the File Hills Qu'Appelle Tribal Council.

YELLOW QUILL (NUTT LAKE) FIRST NATION
P.O. Box 40 • Yellow Quill, SK S0A 3A0
(306) 322-2281 Fax 322-2304; John Machisknic, Chief
Population: 2,600.

YOUNG CHIPPEWAYAN FIRST NATION
P.O. Box 220 • Shell Lake, SK S0J 2G0
(306) 468-2326 Fax 468-2344; Barry L. Ahenakew, Chief
Member of the Battleford Agency Tribal Chiefs.

METIS NON-STATUS

METIS NATION OF SASKATCHEWAN
2nd Floor, 219 Robin Crescent • Saskatoon, SK S7L 6M8
(306) 343-8285 Fax 343-0171

YUKON

CARCROSS/TAGISH FIRST NATIONS
P.O. Box 130 • Carcross, YU Y0B 1B0
(867) 821-4251 Fax 821-4802
Website: www.ctfn.ca; Danny Cresswell, Chief
Shawn O'Dell, Executive Director; E-mail: shawn.odell@ctfn.ca

CHAMPAGNE & AISHIHIK FIRST NATIONS
P.O. Box 5310 • Haines Junction, YU Y0B 1L0
(867) 634-4208 Fax 634-2108; Website: www.cafn.ca;
Steve Smith, Chief; E-mail: ssmith@cafn.ca
Rose Kushniruk, Deputy Chief; E-mail: rkushniruk@cafn.ca
Ranj Pillai, Executive Director; E-mail: rpillai@cafn.ca

FIRST NATION OF NA-CHO NY'A'K DUN
P.O. Box 220 • Mayo, YU Y0B1M0
(867) 996-2265 Fax 996-2267
Website: www.nndfn.com; E-mail: main@nndfn.com
Simon Mervyn, Chief; E-mail: chief@nndfn.com
Millie Olsen, Deputy Chief; Greg Colburne, Executive Director

KLUANE FIRST NATION
P.O. Box 20 • Burwash Landing, YU Y1A 1V0
(867) 841-4274 Fax 841-5900; Website: www.kfn.ca
Mathieya Alatini, Chief; Monique Martin, Deputy Chief

KWANLIN DUN FIRST NATION
35 McIntyre • Whitehorse, YU Y1A 5A5
(867) 667-6465 Fax 668-5057; Ann Smith, Chief

LIARD RIVER FIRST NATION
P.O. Box 328 • Watson Lake, YU T0A 1C0
(867) 536-2131 Fax 536-2332; Dixon Lutz, Chief

LIARD RIVER INDIAN RESERVE #3
P.O. Box 489 • Watson Lake, YU T0A 1C0
(867) 779-3161 Fax 779-3371; George Miller, Deputy Chief

LITTLE SALMON/CARMACKS FIRST NATION
P.O. Box 135 • Carmacks, YU Y0B 1C0
(867) 863-5576 Fax 863-5710
Website: www.lscfn.ca; E-mail: info@lscfn.ca
Eric Fairclough, Chief; Leta Blackjack, Deputy Chief
Skeeter Wright, Executive Director

SELKIRK FIRST NATION
Box 40 • Pelly Crossing, YU Y0B 1P0
(403) 537-3331 Fax 537-3902; Website: www.selkirkfn.ca
Albert Drapeau, Executive Director; E-mail: staubv@selkirkfn.com
Kevin McGinty, Chief; Lori Sims, Deputy Chief

TA'AN KWACH'AN COUNCIL
117 Industrial Rd. • Whitehorse, YU Y1A 2T8
(867) 668-3613 Fax 667-4295
Website: www.taan.ca; E-mail: info@taan.ca
Kristina Kane, Chief; E-mail: kkane@taan.ca
Michelle Telep, Deputy Chief; E-mail: mtelep@taan.ca

TESLIN TLINGIT COUNCIL
Box 133 • Teslin, YU Y0A 1B0
(867) 390-2532 Fax 390-2204
Website: www.ttc-teslin.com; Email: admin@ttc-teslin.com
Carl Sidney, Chief; E-mail: carl.sidney@ttc-teslin.com

TR'ON DEK HWECH'IN FIRST NATION
P.O. Box 599 • Dawson City, YU Y0B 1G0
(877) 993-3400; (403) 993-7100 Fax 993-5753
Website: www.trondek.ca
Roberta Joseph, Chief; Simon Nagano, Deputy Chief
Jackie Olson, Executive Director; Amanda Taylor, Administration Manager
Andrea Moses, Council Administrator

VUNTUT GWITCHIN TRIBAL COUNCIL
General Delivery • Old Crow, YU Y0B 1N0
(403) 966-3261 Fax 966-3800; Roger Kaye, Chief

WHITE RIVER FIRST NATION INDIAN BAND
General Delivery • Beaver Creek, YU Y0B 1A0
(403) 862-7802 Fax 862-7806; Billy Blair, Chief

NATIONAL ASSOCIATIONS/ORGANIZATIONS

ABORIGINAL AMBASSADORS IN THE NATURAL SCIENCES & ENGINEERING (AANSE)
350 Albert St. • Ottawa, ON K1A 1H5
(613) 944-5803 Fax 947-3847; Website: www.nserc-crsng.gc.ca
E-mail: ambassadors@nserc-crsng.gc.ca

ABORIGINAL FINANCIAL OFFICERS ASSOCIATION OF CANADA (AFOA)
1066 Somerset St. West, Suite 301 • Ottawa, ON K1Y 4T3
(866) 722-2362; (613) 722-5543 Fax 722-3467
Website: www.afoa.ca; E-mail: info@afoa.ca
Rodney Nelson, Chair (422-1295)
 E-mail: nelson@globalgovernancegroup.com
Chris Sicotte, Vice Chair; E-mail: chris.sicotte@affinitycu.ca

ABORIGINAL HUMAN RESOURCE COUNCIL (AHRC)
708 - 2nd Ave. North • Saskatoon, SK S7K 2E1
(866) 711-5091; (306) 956-5360 Fax 956-5361
 Website: www.aboriginalhr.ca; E-mail: contact.us@aboriginalhr.ca
Kelly J. Lendsay, President & CEO; E-mail: klendsay@aboriginalhr.ca
Paula Sawyer, partner Coordinator (956-5395)
 E-mail: psawyer@aboriginalhr.ca

THE ABORIGINAL MULTI-MEDIA SOCIETY (AMMSA)
13245 - 146 St • Edmonton, AB T5L 4S8
(780) 455-2700 Fax 455-7639
Website: www.ammsa.com; E-mail: market@ammsa.com
Bert Crowfoot, CEO, Publisher & Founder
Paul Macedo, Director of Publishing Operations
Jennie Cardinal, Board President; Rose Marie Willier, Board V.P.
An aboriginal communications society dedicated to serving the needs of Aboriginal people throughout Canada. Presently publishes or operates the following divisions: Windspeaker Canada's National Aboriginal News Source); Alberta Sweetgrass (Alberta's Aboriginal Publication); Saskatchewan Sage (Saskatchewan Aboriginal Publication); Raven's Eye British Columbia's & Yukon's Aboriginal Publication); Ontario Birchbark (Ontario's Aboriginal Publication); CFWE-FM (The Native Perspective)

ABORIGINAL NURSES ASSOCIATION OF CANADA (ANAC)
16 Concourse Gate, Unit 600 • Ottawa, ON K2E 7S8
(866) 724-3049; (613) 724-4677 Fax 724-4718
 Website: www.anac.on.ca; E-mail: info@anac.on.ca
Brenda Thomas, Executive Director
Lisa Bourque-Bearskin, RN, MN PhD, President
Ada Roberts, RN, NP, V.P.

ASSEMBLY OF FIRST NATIONS (AFN)
NATIONAL INDIAN BROTHERHOOD
55 Metcalfe St., Suite 1600 • Ottawa, ON K1R 6L5
(866) 869-6789; (613) 241-6789 Fax 241-5808
Website: www.afn.ca; Perry Bellegarde, National Chief
Head Office: Territory of Akwesasne, Hamilton's Island, Summers-town, ON K0C 2E0 (613) 241-6789 Fax 241-5806. *Ontario Regional Chiefs*: 22 College St., 2nd Floor, Toronto, ON M5G 1K2 (416) 972-0212 Fax 972-0217. Harry Allen, Northern Region (403) 667-7631; Gordon Peters, Ontario Region (416) 972-0212; Konrad Sioui, Quebec & Labrador Region (418) 842-5020; Leonard Tomah, Atlantic Region (506) 328-3304; Ken Young, Manitoba Region (204) 956-0610; Bill Wilson, British Columbia Region (604) 339-6605; Roland Crowe, Saskatchewan Region (306) 721-2822. There are about 650 First Nations groups across Canada. *Purpose*: To represent the views & interests of Canada's First Nations in discussions with other levels of government on the issues: education, housing, economic development, health, and forestry; to inform other Canadians about the opportunities & issues relating to First Nation's self-government. *Activities*: The AFN Resource Centre; Educational scholarships; Awards in honour of "Heroes of Our Time". *Publications*: AFN Bulletin, $18/year. Library. Established 1969.

CANADIAN ABORIGINAL AIDS NETWORK
6520 Salish Dr. • Vancouver, BC V6N 2C7
(604) 266-7616 Fax 266-7612; Website: www.caan.ca
Ken Clement, CEO; Merv Thomas, Programs Manager
Halifax Office - Research & Policy Unit:
113-154 Willowdale Dr., Dartmouth, NS B2V 2W4
(902) 433-0900 Fax 433-3041

CANADIAN ALLIANCE IN SOLIDARITY WITH THE NATIVE PEOPLES
Box 574, Station "P" • Toronto, ON M5S 2T1
(416) 972-1573 Fax 972-6232; Sharon O'Sullivan, Coordinator

Membership: 1,250. Native and non-native people working together to bring a better understanding to non-native people. *Purpose*: To bring awareness issues to the public as identified by native people. *Committees*: Aboriginal Rights, Child Welfare Native, Focus on the Canadian Constitution, Justice, Native Rights, & Prisons. *Publications*: Phoenix, quarterly journal; Resource/ Reading List; Indian Giver: A Legacy of North American Native Peoples; Native Rights in Canada, Third Edition. Maintains small resource center. Annual meeting. Established 1960.

CANADIAN COUNCIL FOR ABORIGINAL BUSINESS
204A St. George St., Coach House • Toronto, ON M5R 2N5
(416) 961-8663 Fax 961-3995

THE CENTRE FOR FIRST NATIONS GOVERNANCE
610 – 100 Park Royal • West Vancouver, BC V7T 1A2
(866) 922-2052;(604) 922-2052 Fax 922-2057
Website: www.fngovernance.org; E-mal: services@fngovernance.org

Ottawa office: 204 – 150 Isabella St. • Ottawa, ON K1S 1V7
 Satsan (Herb George) (Wet'suwet'en), President
 Chris Robertson, Action Chief Operating Officer
 Brian Smith (Mi'kmaq), Director of Operations
 Len Hartley, Director of Public Education & Communications
Description: A non-profit organization that supports First Nations as they develop effective, independent governance. *Purpose*: To support First Nations by providing relevant & innovative knowledge and development of governance, services, products and events. Publications.

CENTRE FOR INDIGENOUS ENVIRONMENTAL RESOURCES
P.O. Box 26092 • Winnipeg, MB R3G 3R3
(204) 956-0660 Fax (866) 288-3919
 Merrell-Ann Phare, Executive Director
 Website: www.cier.mb.ca; E-mail: earth@yourcier.org
Purpose: To establish & implement environmental capacity-building initiatives for First Nations; to initiate, promote & increase First Nations' input in the deliberations & resolutions of all environmental issues; to develop & enhance the links between all First Nations in Canada & indigenous peoples world wide. Library.

CENTRE FOR INDIGENOUS PEOPLES' NUTRITION & ENVIRONMENT
McGill University - Macdonald Campus, CINE Bldg.
21111 Lakeshore Rd. • Sainte-Anne-deBellevue, PQ H9X 3V9
(514) 398-7757 Fax 398-1020; Website: www.mcgill.ca/cine
Purpose: To address concerns about the integrity of their traditional food systems, nutrition & environmental issues.

CENTRE FOR WORLD INDIGENOUS KNOWLEDGE & RESEARCH
Athabasca University, Edmonton Learning Centre, Peace Hills Trust Tower
1200, 10011 – 109 Street • Edmonton, AB T5J 3S8
(877) 593-2454 Fax: (780) 421-3298
E-mail: info@learning-communities.ca
Lois Shaw, Senior Liaison Officer
Dr. Lisa Carter, Director; Pricilla Campeau, Co-Director

CONGRESS OF ABORIGINAL PEOPLES
867 St. Laurent Blvd. • Ottawa, ON K1K 3B1
(888) 997-9927; (613) 747-6022 Fax 747-8834
Website: www.abo-peoples.org; E-mail: reception@abo-peoples.org
Betty Ann Lavallee, National Chief; Ron Swain, National Vice-Chief
Jim Devoe, CEO; E-mail: j.devoe@abo-peoples.org

FIRST NATIONS DEVELOPMENT INSTITUTE
2432 Main St., 2nd Fl. • Longmont, CO 80501
(303) 774-7836 Fax 774-7841
 Website: www.firstnations.org; E-mail: info@firstnations.org
Virginia Field Office: 2217 Princess Anne St., Suite 111-1,
Fredericksburg, VA 22401 (540) 371-5615

FIRST NATIONS HEALTH MANAGEMENT INSTITUTE
c/o Mohawk Council of Akwesasne
Box 579 • Cornwall, ON K6H 5R7
(613) 575-2341 Fax 575-1311

FIRST NATIONS NATIONAL GAMING COUNCIL
Suite 50, 666 Burrard St. • Vancouver, BC V6C 3H3
(800) 267-3216; (604) 687-3216 Fax 683-2780
Ferguson Gifford, Director

FIRST NATIONS SUMMIT
#208-1999 Marine Dr. • N. Vancouver, BC V7P 3J3
(604) 990-9939 Fax 990-9949

FIRST NATIONS TRIBAL JUSTICE INSTITUTE
P.O. Box 3730 • Mission, BC V2V 4L2
(250) 826-3691 Fax 826-9296

FIRST NATIONS WELLNESS SOCIETY
International Plaza Towers, 1959 Marine Dr. #365
N. Vancouver, BC V7P 3G1(604) 986-7424 Fax 984-0124

GRAND COUNCIL OF THE CREES (OF QUEBEC)
24 Bayswater Ave. • Ottawa, ON K1Y 2E4
(613) 761-1655 Fax 761-1388

GRAND COUNCIL OF TREATY No. 3 ASSN. OF OJIBWAY CHIEFS
Box 1720 • Kenora, ON P9N 3X7
(807) 548-4214 Fax 548-5041

INDIAN & NORTHERN AFFAIRS CANADA
Terrasses de la Chaudiere, 10 Wellington, North Tower, Hull, Quebec
Postal address: Ottawa, ON K1A 0H4
(800) 567-9604 Fax (866) 817-3977; (819) 953-1160 Fax 934-6103
Website: www.ainc-ainc.gc.ca
Chuck Strahl, Minister; Michael Wernick, Deputy Minister

INDIGENOUS BAR ASSOCIATION
P.O. Box 218, #708 - 438 Seymour St.
Vancouver, BC V6B 6H4 (604) 951-8807 Fax 951-8806
Website: www.indigenousbar.ca; E-mail: glangan@indigenousbar.ca
Germaine Langan, Contact

INDIGENOUS LAW PROGRAMS
4th Floor law Centre, U. of Alberta • Edmonton, AB T6G 2H5
(780) 492-7749 Fax 492-4924

INTERNATIONAL NETWORK OF INDIGENOUS PEOPLES ASSOCIATION
54 Lockearnest St. • Hamilton, ON L8R 1W (905) 523-7356

INTERNATIONAL SOCIETY OF HUMAN IDEAS ON ULTIMATE REALITY & MEANING
St. Regis College, 15 St. Mary St. • Toronto, ON M4Y 2R5
(416) 922-2476; Tibor Horvath, General Editor
Purpose: Interdisciplinary research on human effort to find meaning in our world; specifically how 63 North American and 72 South American Indian linguistic families with their 474 and 505 members respectively expressed the meaning of their lives & their concepts of ultimate reality & meaning. *Activities*: Biennial meetings and publications of essays in journal; scholars-experts in any of 979 American Indian groups listed in the Outline of the Research are welcome to submit essays following the guidelines of the Institute. *Publication*: Ultimate Reality & Meaning, newsletter. Library. Established 1970.

INTERTRIBAL CHRISTIAN COMMUNICATIONS
P.O. Box 3765, Sta. B • Winnipeg, MB R2W 3R6
(204) 661-9333; George McPeek, Director
Purpose: To assist the Indian church in its broadest sense to speak to the social, cultural & spiritual concerns of its own native people. *Activities/programs*: Seminars dealing with grief resolution. *Publications*: Indian Life Magazine; The Grieving Indian; Christian education curricula for Native youth.

INUIT ART FOUNDATION
2081 Merivale Rd. • Nepean, ON K2G 1G9
(800) 830-3293; (613) 224-8189 Fax 224-2907

INUIT BROADCASTING CORPORATION (IBC)
Box 700 • Iqaluit, NT X0A 0H0
(867) 979-6231 Fax 979-5853

INUIT CIRCUMPOLAR CONFERENCE
544-170 Laurier Ave. West • Ottawa, ON K1P 5V5
(613) 563-2642 Fax 565-3089; Mary Simon, President

INUIT TAPIRISAT OF CANADA
510-170 Laurier Ave. West • Ottawa, ON K1P 5V5
(613) 238-8181 Fax 234-1991; Rosemarie Kuptana, President
Purpose: National voice of Inuit in Canada. *Activities*: Lobby for Inuit rights, self-government, economic development, environment, & cultural preservation & development. *Publication*: Inuktitut Magazine. Library. Established 1971.

METIS NATIONAL COUNCIL
350 Spark St. #309 • Ottawa, ON K1P 7S9
(613) 232-3216 Fax 232-4262; E-mail: mnc@storm.ca

METIS NATIONAL COUNCIL OF WOMEN
#500 - 1 Nicholas St. • Ottawa, Ontario K1N 7B7
(613) 241-6028 Fax 241-6031

NATIONAL ABORIGINAL ACHIEVEMENT FOUNDATION
P.O. Box 759 • Ohsweken, ON N0A 1M0
(866) 433-3159; (416) 926-0775 Fax 926-7554
Website: www.learning-communities.ca
Roberta L. Jamieson, President & CEO

NATIONAL ABORIGINAL BUSINESS ASSOCIATION
c/o Neegan Enterprises, Inc.
Box 5566 • Fort McMurray, AB T9H 3G5
(780) 791-0654 Fax 791-0671

NATIONAL ABORIGINAL COMMUNICATIONS SOCIETY
47 Clarence St., Suite 430 • Ottawa, ON K2P 1M3
(613) 230-6244 Fax 230-6227

NATIONAL ABORIGINAL FORESTRY ASSOCIATION
875 Bank St. • Ottawa, ON K1S 3W4
(613) 233-5563 Fax 233-4329; E-mail: nafa@web.net
Website: www.omnimage.ca/clients/nafa/n

NATIONAL ABORIGINAL VETERAN ASSOCIATION
32 Moore Pl. • Saskatoon, SK S7L 3Z8
(306) 384-0565 Fax 382-6587

NATIONAL ASSN. OF CULTURAL EDUCATION CENTRES
191 Prominade du Portage #500 • Hull, PQ J8X 2K6
(819) 772-2331 Fax 772-1826

NATIONAL ASSOCIATION OF FRIENDSHIP CENTRES
275 MacLaren St. • Ottawa, ON K2P 0L9
(613) 563-4844 Fax 594-3428
Jerome Berthelette, Executive Director
Purpose: To act in the capacity of social advocate for Canadian Native Peoples in an urban setting by qualifying or lobbying for special projects funding in the areas of Native self-sufficiency, alcohol, drug & solvent abuse counseling, court work representation, etc. *Activities*: Handles core support to new & satellite centres, as well as training support, capital constructions, and renovations of existing centres. *Publication*: Monthly newsletter. Library.

NATIONAL INDIAN ARTS & CRAFTS CORP.
Les Artisans Indiens du Quebec, 540 Max Gros-Louis
Village des Hurons • Wendake, PQ G0A 4V0 (418) 845-2150
Wellington Staats, President
A national native-owned non-profit development organization. *Purpose*: To develop Indian arts & crafts industry; the promotion and development of viable native arts & crafts enterprises & industries. *Activities/programs*: Maintains a business referral & information service (BRS) answering inquiries from producers, distributors & other interested parties; sponsors exhibitions. *Publication*: Canadian Indian Artscraft, a national quarterly trade magazine. Library - maintains a collection of resource material including artists profiles, reference books & trade magazines; a series of video tapes entitled "NIACC Indian Arts & Crafts Film Series' available for viewing through a separate distribution company, titles available upon request. Established 1975.

NATIONAL INDIAN FINANCIAL CORPORATION
P.O. Box 2377 • Prince Albert, SK S6V 6Z1
(306) 763-4712 Fax 763-3255
#217-103B Packham Ave. • Saskatoon, SK S7N 4K4
(800) 667-4712; (306) 955-4712 Fax 477-4554

NATIONAL INDIAN & INUIT COMMUNITY HEALTH REPRESENTATIVES ORGANIZATION
P.O. Box 1019 • Kahnawake, PQ J0L 1B0
(514) 632-0892 Fax 632-2111

NATIONAL INUIT YOUTH COUNCIL
#510-170 Laurier Ave. West • Ottawa, ON K1P 5V5
(613) 238-8181 Fax 234-1991

NATIONAL NATIVE ALCOHOL & DRUG ABUSE PROGRAM
20 3rd St. E. • Portage La Prairie, MB R1N 1N4
(204) 857-6178

NATIONAL NATIVE ASSOCIATION OF TREATMENT DIRECTORS
8989 MacLeod Trail S.W. #410 • Calgary, AB T2H 0M2
(403) 253-6232 Fax 252-9210; Betty Bastien, Executive Director

NATIVE AMATEUR SPORTS ASSOCIATION
836 Lorne Ave. • Brandon, MB R7A 0T8
(204) 725-4686

NATIVE INVESTMENT & TRADE ASSOCIATION (NITA)
6520 Salish Dr. • Vancouver, BC V6N 2C7 1J9
(800) 337-7743; (604) 275-6670 Fax 275-0307
Website: www.native-invest-trade.com
Calvin Helin, President & CEO
  E-mail: ch@native-invest-trade.com
Vernita Helin, Manager, Western Canada
  E-mail: vh@native-invest-trade.com
Purpose: To promote economic self-reliance & strengthen Aboriginal participation in the mainstream economy; to promote the health and well-being of First Nations citizens by creating wealth through commercial enterprise. *Activities*: Trade shows; business con-ferences. Established 1989.

NATIVE LANGUAGE INSTITUTE
Lakehead University, Faculty of Education
955 Oliver Rd. • Thunder Bay • ON P7B 5E1
(807) 343-8198 Fax 346-7746

NATIVE LAW STUDENTS ASSOCIATION
U. of British Columbia-Faculty of Law
1822 East Mall • Vancouver, BC V6T 1Z1
(604) 822-3151 Fax 822-8108

NATIVE LAW CENTRE
University of Saskatchewan
150 Diefenbaker Centre • Saskatoon, SK S7K 3S9
(306) 966-6189; Don Purich, Director
  Website: www.library2.usask.ca/native
Purpose: To provide a head start program for people of native ancestry who wish to enter law school; to research problems related to native legal rights, e.g. land claims; to provide a resource to lawyers and researchers working in the area of native law; and, to back up the courses in native law taught in the College of Law, University of Saskatchewan. *Activities*: Summer program of legal study for native people; research. *Prizes*: Harvey Bell Memorial Prize, $1,000 for a student graduating from law school; Native Law Students Association Writing Competition, $200 book prize; book prize to student in summer program, $150. *Publication*: Canadian Native Law Reporter, quarterly journal; books for sale. Canadian Native Law Cases. Library.

NATIVE MENTAL HEALTH ASSOCIATION OF CANADA
Box 242 • Chilliwack, BC V2P 6J1
(604) 793-1983 Fax 793-4557
Clare Clifton Brant, Chairperson
Purpose: To provide mental health care services to Native peoples of Canada. *Activities*: Workshops; training programs; and information and referral services.

NATIVE PHYSICIANS ASSOCIATION OF CANADA
Box 8427, Sta. "D" • Ottawa, ON K1G 3H8
(613) 445-1676 Fax 445-1678

NATIVE SPORTS DEVELOPMENT PROGRAM
Box 1240 Sta. "M" • Calgary, AB T2P 2L2
(403) 818-6085 Fax 261-5676
Website: wwwaboriginalnet.com/sports

NATIVE WOMEN IN THE ARTS
101-141 Bathurst St. • Toronto, ON M5V 2R2
(416) 392-6800 Fax 392-6920

NATIVE WOMEN'S ASSOCIATION OF CANADA
P.O. Box 185 • Ohsweken, ON N0A 1M0
9 Mellrose Ave. • Ottawa, ON K1Y 1T8
(800) 461-4043; (613) 722-3033 Fax 722-7687
Gail Stacey-Moore, Speaker
Goals: To enhance, promote and foster the social, economic, cultural and political wellbeing of First Nations and Metis women with First Nations and Canadian societies. Awards granted. Established 1974.

NATIVE THEATRE SCHOOL
INDIGENOUS THEATRE CELEBRATION
Association for Native Development in the Performing & Visual Arts
27 Carlton St. # 208 • Toronto, ON M5B 1L2
(416) 977-2512

REGIONAL ASSOCIATIONS
ALBERTA

ATHABASCA NATIVE FRIENDSHIP CENTRE SOCIETY
4919 - 53 St. • ATHABASCA, AB T9S 1L1
  (780) 675-3086; E-mail: anfcs@telusplanet.net

BONNYVILLE CANADIAN NATIVE FRIENDSHIP CENTRE
Box 5399, 4711-50 Ave. • BONNYVILLE, AB TN9 2G5
  (780) 826-3374; Website: www.bcnfc.ca

ABORIGINAL FRIENDSHIP CENTRE OF CALGARY
342 - 14 St. • CALGARY, AB T2N 1Z7
(403) 270-7379

ABORIGINAL OPPORTUNITIES COMMITTEE
Calgary Chamber of Commerce
517 Centre St. S. • CALGARY, AB T2G 3C4
(403) 750-0400 Fax 266-3413

ASSEMBLY OF FIRST NATIONS OF ALBERTA
c/o Grand Council of Treaty No. 7
Suite 310, 6940 Fisher Rd. SE • CALGARY, AB T2H 0W3
(403) 927-3727 Fax 927-4375

CALGARY ABORIGINAL AWARENESS SOCIETY
Suite 360, 1207 11th Ave. SW • CALGARY, AB T3C 0M5
(403) 296-2227 Fax 296-2226

CALGARY ABORIGINAL URBAN AFFAIRS COMMITTEE
c/o City of Calgary, Box 2100, Sta. "M"
CALGARY, AB T2P 2M5 (403) 268-5188 Fax 268-5696

CALGARY NATIVE FRIENDSHIP SOCIETY
140 - 2nd Ave. SW • CALGARY, AB T2P 0B9
(403) 777-2263 Fax 265-9275
Laverna McMaster, Executive Director

CALGARY URBAN INDIAN YOUTH
1139 Riverdale Ave. S.W. • CALGARY, AB T2S 0Y9
(403) 243-1876

INDIGENOUS PEOPLES RESOURCE ASSOCIATION
221-1011 17th Ave., SW • CALGARY, AB T2T 0A8
(403) 228-9683

NATIVE COUNSELING SERVICES OF ALBERTA
#640, 615 MacLeod Trail, SE • CALGARY, AB T0K 0H0
(403) 237-7850 Fax 237-7857

PLAINS INDIAN CULTURAL SURVIVAL SCHOOL
1723 33 St. S.W. • CALGARY, AB T3C 1P4
(403) 246-5378

TREATY No. 7 MANAGEMENT CORPORATION
101 – 12111 40th St. SE • CALGARY, AB T2Z 4E6
(403) 281-9779 Fax 281-9783; Website: www.treaty7.org
Charles Weaselhead, Chief; Anne Many Heads, CEO
E-mail: amanyheads@treaty7.org

TSUT'INA K'OSA
Sarcee Cultural Program, Box 135
3700 Anderson Rd., SW • CALGARY, AB T2W 3C4
(403) 238-2677; Fax 251-5871; Jeanette Starlight, Director

ABORIGINAL AFFAIRS/ALBERTA
Rm. 1301, 10155-102nd St. • EDMONTON, AB T5J 4L4
(780) 427-2008 Fax 427-4019

ABORIGINAL MULTI-MEDIA SOCIETY OF ALBERTA (AMMSA)
15001, 112 Ave. • EDMONTON, AB T5M 2V6
(780) 455-2700 Fax 455-7639
Fred Didzena, President; Bert Crowfoot, General Manager
Newspaper: Windspeaker - Gary Gee, Editor

ALBERTA HERITAGE ABORIGINAL SOCIETY
12728 66th St. • EDMONTON, AB T5C 0A3
(780) 475-1699 Fax 472-1873

ALBERTA INDIAN ARTS & CRAFTS SOCIETY
501, 10105-109th St. • EDMONTON, AB T5J 1M8
  (780) 426-2048; Leonie Willier, President

ALBERTA NATIVE NEWS
330 - 10036 Jasper Ave. • EDMONTON, AB T5N 2W2
  (780) 421-7966 Fax 424-3951

ALBERTA NATIVE FRIENDSHIP CENTRE ASSOCIATION
10336- 121 St. #104 • EDMONTON, AB T5N 1K8
  (780) 423-3138 Fax 425-6277; Fred Campiou, President
  Website: www.anfca.com

ALBERTA NATIVE RIGHTS FOR NATIVE WOMEN
14211 - 130th Ave. • EDMONTON, AB T5L 4K8
  (780) 453-2808 or 454-8462

CANADIAN NATIVE FRIENDSHIP CENTRE
11205-101 ST. • EDMONTON, AB T5G 2A4
  (780) 479-1999 Fax 479-0043

CONFEDERACY OF TREATY No. 6 FIRST NATIONS
Suite 204 – 10310 0 176th St. • EDMONTON, AB T5S 1L3
  (780) 944-0334 Fax 944-0346; Website: www.treaty6.ca
Marvin Yellowbird, Grand Chief

**COUNCIL FOR THE ADVANCEMENT OF NATIVE
DEVELOPMENT OFFICERS**
Suite 240-10036 Jasper Ave., EDMONTON, AB T5J 2W2
  (800) 463-9300; (780) 990-0303 Fax 429-7487
  Website: www.incentre.net/cando

FIRST NATIONS COUNSELLING CENTRE
201-10010 106 St. • EDMONTON, AB T5J 2L8
  (780) 944-0172 Fax 944-0176

FIRST NATIONS RESOURCE COUNCIL
11748 Kingsway Ave. #101 • EDMONTON, AB T5G 0X5
  (780) 453-6114 Fax 453-6150

METIS NATION OF ALBERTA
#100-11738 Kingsway Ave • EDMONTON, AB T5G 04R
  (800) 252-7553; (780) 455-2200 Fax 452-8948

NATIVE COUNCIL OF CANADA
10426-124th St., NW • EDMONTON, AB T5N 1R6
  (780) 917-1203 Fax 488-2741; Doris Ronnenberg, President

NATIVE COUNSELLING SERVICES OF ALBERTA-EDMONTON
#800, Highfield Pl., 10010-106th St. • EDMONTON, AB T5J 3L8
  (780) 423-2141 Fax 424-0187

TREATY No. 8 FIRST NATIONS OF ALBERTA
18178 – 102 Ave. • EDMONTON, AB T5S 1S7
  (780) 444-9366 ext. 250 Fax 484-1465; Website: www.treaty8.ca
Tanya Kappo, Interim Grand Chief
Joseph Jobin, Chief Operating Officer

TRIBAL CHIEFS VENTURES, INC.
17628 103 Ave. NW • EDMONTON, AB T5S 1J9
  (780) 481-3363 Fax 483-1404; Website: www.tcvi.ca
Dave Scott, Executive Director
Deb Lawrence, Financial Controller; E-mail: dlawrence@tcvi.ca

INDIAN ASSOCIATION OF ALBERTA
P.O. Box 159 • HOBBEMA, AB T0C 1N0
  (800) 661-2579; (780) 585-3793; Fax 585-4700
  Roy Louis, President
Purpose: To advance the social and economic welfare of the Treaty Indians of Alberta; to promote programs designed to serve the educational and cultural interests of the Native people's it represents; to work in conjunction with other Indian bands and/or chiefs and councils to work with Federal, Provincial and Local Governments for the benefit of the Treaty Indians of Alberta. Established 1944.

ABORIGINAL RADIO & TELEVISION SOCIETY
Box 2250 • LAC LA BICHE, AB T0A 2C0
  (780) 447-2393 Fax 454-2820

INDIAN NEWS MEDIA
Box 120 • STANDOFF, AB T0L 1Y0

  (780) 653-3301; Gerri Manyfingers, Executive Director
Marie Smallface Marule, President
Blackfoot Radio Network; Bull Horn Video
Newspaper: Kainai News-Mary Weasel Fat, Editor

BRITISH COLUMBIA

U'MISTA CULTURAL CENTRE
Box 253 • ALERT BAY, BC V0N 1A0
  (250) 974-5403 Fax 974-5499
Wendy Jakobsen, Administrator

BELLA COOLA-NUXALK EDUCATION AUTHORITY
P.O. Box 778 • BELLA COOLA, BC V0T 1C0
  (250) 799-5453/5911; Stewart Clellamin, Coordinator

SAANICH NATIVE HERITAGE SOCIETY
Saanich Cultural Education Centre
Box 28 • BRENTWOOD BAY, BC V8M 1R3
  (250) 652-5980 Fax 652-5957; Philip Paul, Director

TANSI FRIENDSHIP CENTRE
P.O. Box 418 • CHETWYND, BC V0C 1J0
  (250) 788-2996 Fax 788-2353
Bev Davies, Executive Director

NAWICAN FRIENDSHIP CENTRE
1320 - 102 Ave. • DAWSON CREEK, BC V1G 2C6
  (250) 782-5202 Fax 782-8411; Keith Hall, Executive Director

FORT NELSON-LIARD NATIVE FRIENDSHIP SOCIETY
P.O. Box 1266 • FORT NELSON, BC V0C 1R0
  (250) 774-2993 Fax 774-2998; Don Potkins, Executive Director

FORT ST. JOHN FRIENDSHIP SOCIETY
10208 - 95th Ave. • FORT ST. JOHN, BC V1J 1J2
  (250) 785-8566 Fax 785-1507
Shirley Churchill, Executive Director

B.C. NATIVE WOMEN'S SOCIETY
Box 392 • KEREMMEOS, BC V2L 5B8
  (250) 562-9106 fax 562-0360; Janet Gottfriedson, President

INTERIOR INDIAN FREINDSHIP CENTRE
125 Palm St. • KAMLOOPS, BC V1J 8J7
  (250) 376-1296 Fax 376-2275
Ruth Williams, Executive Director

SECWEPEMC CULTURAL EDUCATION SOCIETY
345 Yellowhead Hwy. • KAMLOOPS, BC V2H 1H1
  (250) 828-9779 Fax 372-1127
Muriel Sasakamoose, Executive Director

CENTRAL OKANAGAN FRIENDSHIP SOCIETY
442 Leon Ave. • KELOWNA, BC V1Y 6J3
  (250) 763-4905 Fax 861-551
Tillie Goffic, Executive Director

LILLOOET FRIENDSHIP CENTRE
P.O. Box 1270 • LILLOOET, BC V0K 1V0
  (250) 256-4146 Fax 256-7928
Susan James, Executive Director

ED JONES CULTURAL/EDUCATION CENTRE
Box 189 • MASSET, BC V0T 1M0
  (250) 626-3337 Fax 626-5440; John Enrico, Director

CONAYT FRIENDSHIP CENTRE
P.O. Box 1989 • MERRITT, BC V1K 1B8
  (250) 378-5107 Fax 378-6676
Ross Albert, Executive Director

NATIVE WOMEN'S ASSN. OF CANADA - WEST REGION
Box 213 • MERRITT, BC V0K 2V0
  (250) 378-5969 Sharon McIvor, Director

MISSION INDIAN FRIENDSHIP CENTRE
33150 A First Ave. • MISSION, BC V2V 1G4
  (250) 826-1281 Fax 826-4056
Christina Cook, Executive Director

TILLICUM HAUS SOCIETY
927 Haliburton St. • NANAIMO, BC V9R 6N4
(250) 753-8291 Fax 753-6560
Grace Nielson, Executive Director

ABORIGINAL COUNCIL OF B.C.
Box 52038 • N. VANCOUVER, BC V7J 3T2
(604) 987-6225 Fax 987-6683

NATIVE ARTS & CRAFTS
445 W. 3rd St. • N. VANCOUVER, BC V7M 1G9
(604) 986-7321 Fax 990-9403

NATIVE BROTHERHOOD OF B.C.
415B W. Esplanade • N. VANCOUVER, BC V7M 1A6
(604) 987-9115 Fax 987-4419

PORT ALBERNI FRIENDSHIP CENTRE
3555 4th Ave., Box 23 • PORT ALBERNI, BC V9Y 4H3
(888) 723-7232; (250) 723-8281 Fax 723-1877
Wally Samuel, Executive Director

UNITED NATIVE NATIONS
5060 Argyle St. #144 • PORT ALBERNI, BC V9Y 2A7
(250) 723-8131 Fax 723-8132; Ron George, President

B.C. WOMEN OF THE METIS NATION
409 - 3rd Ave. • PRINCE GEORGE, BC V2L 3C1
(250) 564-9794 Fax 564-9793

PRINCE GEORGE NATIVE FRIENDSHIP CENTRE
1600-3rd Ave. • PRINCE GEORGE, BC V2L 3G6
(250) 564-3568 Fax 563-0924; Dan George, Executive Director

FIRST NATIONS WOMEN'S GROUP
Box 921 • PRINCE RUPERT, BC V8J 4B7
(250) 624-3200

FRIENDSHIP HOUSE ASSOCIATION OF PRINCE RUPERT
P.O. Box 512 • PRINCE RUPERT, BC V8J 3R5
(250) 627-1717 Fax 627-7533
Fred Anderson, Executive Director

QUESNEL TILLICUM SOCIETY FRIENDSHIP CENTRE
319 N. Fraser Dr. • QUESNEL, BC V2J 1Y9
(250) 992-8347 Fax 992-5708
Doug Sanderson, Executive Director

B.C. ASSN. OF INDIAN FRIENDSHIP CENTRES
#3-2475 Mt. Newton X Rd. • SAANICHTON, BC V8M 2B7
(250) 652-0210 Fax 652-3102; Marie Anderson, President
Florence Wylie, Coordinator

FIRST NATIONS TRAINING & CONSULTING SERVICES
P.O. Box 69 • SAANICHTON, BC V8M 2C3
(250) 652-7097 Fax 652-7039

FIRST PEOPLE'S CULTURAL FOUNDATION
7-2475 Mt. Newton X Rd. • SAANICHTON, BC V8M 2B7
(250) 652-2426 Fax 652-3431

COQUALEETZA CULTURAL EDUCATION CENTRE
P.O. Box 2370 • SARDIS, BC V2R 1A7
(604) 858-7196 Fax 858-8488; Shirley D. Leon, Manager

DZEL K'ANT FRIENDSHIP CENTRE
P.O. Box 2920 • SMITHERS, BC V0J 2N0
(250) 847-8959 Fax 847- 8974

KERMODE FRIENDSHIP SOCIETY
3313 Kalum St. • TERRACE, BC V8G 2N7
(250) 635-4906 Fax 635-3013; Sadie Parnell, Executive Director

ASSOCIATION FOR FIRST NATIONS WOMEN
#204-96 E. Broadway • VANCOUVER, BC V5T 4N9
(604) 873-1833 Fax 872-1845

ALLIED INDIAN METIS SOCIETY
2716 Clark Dr. • VANCOUVER, BC V5N 3H6
(604) 874-9610 Fax 876-3858
Marge White, Executive Director

B.C. ABORIGINAL DIRECTORY
#410-890 W. Pender St. • VANCOUVER, BC V6C 1J9
(800) 337-7743; (604) 684-0880 Fax (888) 684-0881

B.C. ABORIGIAL PEOPLES' FISHERIES COMMISSION
Box 52038 • N. VANCOUVER, BC V7J 3Y2
(604) 987-6225 Fax 987-6683; Ken Malloway, Chairperson

FIRST NATIONS CONGRESS OF B.C.
403-990 Homer St. • VANCOUVER, BC V6B 2W6
(604) 682-8516 Fax 682-8057; Bill Wilson, Vice-Chief

FIRST NATIONS FOCUS PROGRAM
403-318 Homer St. • VANCOUVER, BC V6B 2V2
(604) 681-6536 Fax 681-2117
E-mail: ala47738@bc.sympatico.ca

FIRST NATIONS HEALTH CAREERS
First Nations House of Learning
U.B.C., 1985 West Mall • VANCOUVER, BC V6T 1Z2
(604) 822-2115 Fax 822-8944

INDIAN ARTS & CRAFTS SOCIETY OF B.C.
540 Burrard St. #505 • VANCOUVER, BC V6C 2K1
(604) 682-8988; Noel C. Derriksan, President

INDIAN HOMEMAKERS ASSOCIATION OF BRITISH COLUMBIA
102 - 423 W. Broadway • VANCOUVER, BC V5Y 1R4
(604) 876-4929

NATIVE BROTHERHOOD OF B.C.
#200 - 1755 E. Hastings • VANCOUVER, BC V5L 1T1
(604) 255-3137 Fax 251-7107; Robert Clifton, President

NATIVE COMMUNICATIONS SOCIETY OF B.C.
1161 W. Georgia St. • VANCOUVER, BC V6E 3H4
(604) 684-7375 Fax 684-5375
Emma Williams, President; Tim Isaac, Managing Editor
Publication: Kahtou, newspaper.

NATIVE EDUCATION CENTRE
Urban Native Education Society
285 E. 5th Ave. • VANCOUVER, BC V5T 1H2
(604) 873-3761 Fax 873-9152

TILLICUM NATIVE CENTRE
2422 Main St. • VANCOUVER, BC V5T 3E2
(604) 873-3767 (phone & fax)

UNITED NATIVE NATIONS SELF-GOVERNBMENT
736 Granville St., 8th Fl • VANCOUVER, BC V6Z 1G3
(800) 555-9756; (604) 688-1821 Fax 688-1823

UNION OF B.C. INDIAN CHIEFS
500 - 342 Water St., 4th Fl. • VANCOUVER, BC V6B 1B6
(604) 684-0231 Fax 684-5726; Website: www.fns.bc.ca
Stewart Phillip, Grand Chief; E-mail: don@ubcic.bc.ca

VANCOUVER INDIAN CENTRE SOCIETY
1607 E. Hastings St. • VANCOUVER, BC V5L 1S7
(604) 251-4844 Fax 251-1986; Art Paul, Executive Director

B.C. ASSEMBLY OF FIRST NATIONS
Suite 507 – 100 Park Royal South • W. VANCOUVER, BC V7T 1A2
(604) 922-7733 Fax 922-7433; Website: www.bcafn.ca
Shane Gottfriedson, Regional Chief
E-mail: shane.gottfriedson@bcafn.ca
Elaine Alec, Director of Operations

ALLIED INDIAN & METIS SOCIETY
R.R. #7, Comp. 24, Site 11 • VERNON, BC V1T 7Z3
(250) 549-7413 Dave Parker, Executive Director

UNITED NATIVE FRIENDSHIP CENTRE
2902 - 29th Ave. • VERNON, BC V1T 1S7
(250) 542-1247 Fax 542-3707; Bertha Phelan, Executive Director

B.C. INDIAN LANGUAGE PROJECT
171 Bushby St. • VICTORIA, BC V8S 1B5
(250) 384-4544 Fax 384-2502

MINISTRY OF ABORIGINAL RELATIONS & RECONCILIATIONS
2957 Jutland Rd., P.O. Box 9100 • VICTORIA, BC V8W 9B1
(250) 387-6121; (604) 660-2421
(800) 663-7867; (800) 880-1022 (Toll-free Treaty & Information)
E-mail: abrinfo@gov.bc.ca; Website: www.gov.bc/arr/cont/
Tom Christensen (250) 953-4844 Fax 953-4856
Media Queries: (250) 356-0330

VICTORIA NATIVE FRIENDSHIP CENTRE
220 Bay St. • VICTORIA, BC V8W 3K5
(250) 384-3211 Fax 384-1586
Edmond Constantineau, Executive Director

HEILTSUK CULTURAL EDUCATION CENTRE
Box 880 • WAGLISLA, BC V0T 1Z0
(250) 957-2381/2626 Fax 957-2544
Jennifer Carpenter, Program Manager

FIRST NATIONS SUMMIT OF B.C.
Suite 1200 – 100 Park Royal South • WEST VANCOUVER, BC V7T 1A2
(866) 990-9939; (604) 926-9903 Fax 926-9923; Website: www.fns.bc.ca
Ed John, Grand Chief; E-mail: cbraker@fns.bc.ca

INDUSTRY COUNCIL FOR ABORIGINAL BUSINESS
Suite 600 - 100 Park Royal • WEST VANCOUVER, BC V7T 1A2
(604) 929-7379; Brenda Ireland, Executive Director
Website: www.icab.ca; E-mail: info@icab.ca
Keith Henry, President

CARIBOO FRIENDSHIP SOCIETY
99 3rd Ave. S. • WILLIAMS LAKE, BC V2G 1J1
(250) 398-6831 Fax 398-6115; Gail Madrigga, Executive Director

MANITOBA

BRANDON FRIENDSHIP CENTRE
303 - 9th St. • BRANDON, MB R7A 4A8
(204) 727-1407 Fax 726-0902
Louise Phaneuf-Miron, Executive Director

DAUPHIN FRIENDSHIP CENTRE
210 First Ave. NE • DAUPHIN, MB R7A 1A7
(204) 638-5707 • 638-4799; Stan Guiboche, Executive Director

WEST REGION TRIBAL COUNCIL
Indian Cultural Education Program
21-4th Ave., NW • DAUPHIN, MB R7N 1H9
(204) 638-8225 Fax 638-8062; Wally Swain, Program Head

FLIN FLON INDIAN & METIS FRIENDSHIP CENTRE
Box 188 • FLIN FLON, MB R8A 1M7
(204) 687-3900 Fax 687-5328
Marcie Johnson, Executive Director

LYNN LAKE FRIENDSHIP CENTRE
Box 460 • LYNN LAKE, MB R0B 0W0
(204) 356-2445 Fax 356-8223
Vicki Stoneman, Executive Director

PORTAGE FRIENDSHIP CENTRE
Box 1118 • PORTAGE LA PRAIRIE, MB R1N 3C5
(204) 239-6333 Fax 239-6534
Richard Chaske, Executive Director

KA-WAWIYAK FRIENDSHIP CENTRE
Box 74 • POWERVIEW, MB R0E 1P0
(204) 367-2892; Rhonda Houston, Executive Director

NATIVE WOMEN'S ASSOCIATION OF MANITOBA
P.O. Box 177 • RIVERTON, MB R0C 2R0
(204) 373-2396/378-2460

RIVERTON & DISTRICT FRIENDSHIP CENTRE
P.O. Box 359 • RIVERTON, MB R0C 2R0
(204) 378-2927 Fax 378-5705
Marlane Monkman, Executive Director

INDIAN COUNCIL OF FIRST NATIONS OF MANITOBA, INC.
Box 13, Group 10, R.R. #2 • SAINT ANNE, MB R0A 1R0
(204) 422-5193 Fax 422-8860; Andrew Kirkness, Grand Chief

BROKENHEAD CULTURAL CENTRE
SCANTERBURY, MB R0E 1W0
(204) 766-2494 Fax 766-2270; Harvey Olson, Director

INDIAN & METIS FRIENDSHIP CENTRE
347 Phyllis St. • SELKIRK, MB R1A 2J5
(204) 482-5896 Elsie Bear, Executive Director

SELKIRK FRIENDSHIP CENTRE
425 Eveline St. • SELKIRK, MB R1A 2J5
(204) 482-7525 Fax 785-8124; Jim Sinclair, Executive Director

SWAN RIVER INDIAN & METIS FRIENDSHIP CENTRE
Box 1448 • SWAN RIVER, MB R0L 1Z0
(204) 734-9301 Fax 734-3090
Elbert Chartrand, Executive Director

INDIAN COUNCIL OF FIRST NATIONS OF MANITOBA, INC.
P.O. Box 2857 • THE PAS, MB R9A 1M6
(204) 623-7227 Fax 623-4041

MANITOBA METIS WOMEN'S ALLIANCE
Box 1503 • THE PAS, MB R9A 1L4
(204) 623-7881

THE PAS FRIENDSHIP CENTRE
Box 2638 • THE PAS, MB R9A 1M3
(204) 623-6459 Fax 623-4268
Judy Elaschuk, Executive Director

MA-MOW-WE-TAK FRIENDSHIP CENTRE, INC.
122 Hemlock Crescent • THOMPSON, MB R8N 0R6
(204) 778-7337 Fax 677-3195; Larry Soldier, Executive Director
Cathy V. Menard, Program Coordinator
A social service organization existing to administer and implement programs to meet the needs of native people either migrating to or living in urban areas. *Special programs*: Counseling & referral service; social & recreational programs; cultural awareness & community development. *Native Resource Library*: Consisting of audio/visual & reading material. *Publication*: Interagency Quarterly Newsletter. Established 1976.

MANITOBA KEEWATINOWI OKIMAKANAK
200 – 701 Thompson Dr. • THOMPSON, MB R8N 2A3
(204) 677-1600 Fax 778-7655; Website: www.mkonorth.com
David Harper, Grand Chief

ABORIGINAL CONFERENCES
17 – 2595 Main St. • WINNIPEG, MB 2RV 4W3
(866) 225-9067 Fax (877) 825-7564
Website: www.aboriginalconferences.ca

ABORIGINAL COUNCIL OF WINNIPEG
181 Higgins Ave. • WINNIPEG, MB R3B 3G1
(204) 989-6380 Fax 942-5795

THE ABORIGINAL WOMEN OF MANITOBA
78 Grey Friars • WINNIPEG, MB R3T 3J5
(204) 269-0033; Pauline Busch, President

ASSEMBLY OF MANITOBA CHIEFS
200-275 Portage Ave. • WINNIPEG, MB R3B 2B3
(888) 324-5483; (204) 956-0610 Fax 956-2109
Website: www.manitobachiefs.com; E-mail: info@manitobachiefs.com
Derek Nepinak, Grand Chief
E-mail: gcnepinak@manitobachiefs.com

FIRST NATIONS CONFEDERACY
333 Garry St., 2nd Fl. • WINNIPEG, MB R3B 2G7
(204) 944-8245; Chief Ken Courchene, Chairperson

INDIAN & METIS FRIENDSHIP CENTRE
45 Robertson St. • WINNIPEG, MB R2W 5H5
(204) 586-8441 Fax 582-8261; Stirling Ranville, Executive Director

INDIAN CRAFTS & ARTS MANITOBA, INC.
348 Hargrave St. • WINNIPEG, MB R3B 2J9
(204) 944-1469; Pat Bruderer, President

INDIGENOUS WOMEN'S COLLECTIVE OF MANITOBA, INC.
120-388 Donald St. • WINNIPEG, MB R2B 2J4
(204) 944-8709/10 Fax 949-1336; Winnie Greisbretch, President

MANITOBA ABORIGINAL RESOURCE ASSOCIATION
286 Smith St., 5th Fl. • WINNIPEG, MB R3C 1K4
(204) 947-1647 Fax 942-3687

MANITOBA ASSOCIATION OF FRIENDSHIP CENTRES
P.O. Box 716 • WINNIPEG, MB R3C 2K3
(204) 942-6299 Fax 942-6308; David Chartrand, President

MANITOBA FIRST NATIONS REPATRIATION PROGRAM
#704, 167 Lombard Ave. • WINNIPEG, MB R3B 0B3
(800) 665-5762; (204) 957-0037 Fax 944-1015

MANITOBA INDIAN CULTURAL EDUCATION CENTRE
119 Sutherland Ave. • WINNIPEG, MB R2W 3C9
(204) 942-0228 Fax 947-6564; Dennis Daniels, Executive Director

MANITOBA METIS FEDERATION
300-150 Henry Ave. • WINNIPEG, MB R3B 0J7
(204) 586-8474 Fax 947-1816
Website: www.mmf.mb.ca; David Chartrand (Meeqwetch), President
Published works: The Struggle for Recognition: Canadian Justice and the
Metis Nation; The Canadian Michif Language Dictionary. Distributed by
Pemmican Publications

THE METIS CULTURE & HERITAGE RESOURCE CENTRE, INC.
506-63 Albert St. • WINNIPEG, MB R3B 1G4
(204) 956-7767 Fax 956-7765; Jeanette Goertzen, President
Website: www.metisresourcecentre.mb.ca
Lorraine Freeman, Founder
Published works: Michif Conversational Lessons for Beginners (book & two
audio CDs, $45); The Dances of the Metis - Li Dawns di Michif, $21.95 (VHS),
$24.95 (DVD). Distributed by Pemmican Publications.

SOUTHERN CHIEFS ORGANIZATION
105 – 1555 St. James St. • WINNIPEG, MB R3H 1B5
(866) 876-9701; (204) 946-1869 Fax 946-1871
Website: www.scoinc.mmb.ca; Terrance Nelson, Grand Chief
E-mail: grandchiefnelson@scoinc.mb.ca

WINNIPEG COUNCIL OF FIRST NATIONS
201 - 286 Smith St. • WINNIPEG, MB R2C 1K4
(204) 946-0804 Fax 946-0075

WINNIPEG NATIVE ALLIANCE
510 King St. • WINNIPEG, MB R2W 5L2
(204) 582-4127 Fax 586-1698

NEW BRUNSWICK

**THE ASSEMBLY OF FIRST NATIONS'
CHIEFS IN NEW BRUNSWICK**
P.O. Box 296, Station A • FREDERICTON, NB E3B 4Y9
(506) 455-1881 Fax 455-1893; Website: www.chiefsnb.ca

ASSEMBLY OF FIRST NATIONS COUNCIL OF ELDERS
R.R. #9 • FREDERICTON, NB E3B 4X9
(506) 457-2129 Fax 451-9386; Wallace Labillois, Chairperson

FREDERICTON NATIVE FRIENDSHIP CENTRE
361 King St. • FREDERICTON, NB E3B 1C8
(506) 459-5283 Fax 459-1756

NEW BRUNSWICK ABORIGINAL PEOPLES COUNCIL
320 St. Mary's St. • FREDERICTON, NB E3A 2S5
(506) 458-8422/3 Fax 450-3749; Phil Fraser, President
Raymond Gould, Vice President

NEW BRUNSWICK INDIAN ARTS & CRAFTS ASSOCIATION
212 Queen St. #402 • FREDERICTON, NB E3V 1A7
(506) 459-7312; David Paul, President

NEW BRUNSWICK NATIVE INDIAN WOMEN'S COUNCIL
65 Brunswick St. • FREDERICTON, NB E3A 2V5
(506) 458-1114 Fax 451-9386; Carol Wortman, President

UNION OF NEW BRUNSWICK INDIANS
370 Wilsey Rd. Comp. 43 • FREDERICTON, NB E3B 5N6
(506) 458-9444 Fax 458-2850; Website: www.unbi.org
Darrell Paul, Executive Director; E-mail: darrell@unbi.org

ASSEMBLY OF FIRST NATIONS/NEW BRUNSWICK/P.E.I.
5 Sunrise Ct. • WOODSTOCK, NB E7M 4K4
(506) 324-8184 Fax 328-4589; Leonard Tomah, Vice-Chief

NEWFOUNDLAND

FEDERATION OF NEWFOUNDLAND INDIANS
Box 956 • CORNER BROOK, NF A2H 6J3 1Z0
(709) 634-0996 Fax 634-0997; Gerard Webb, President

LABRADOR INUIT DEVELOPMENT CORP.
P.O. Box 1000, Sta. B • GOOSE BAY, NF A0P 1E0
(709) 896-8505 Fax 896-5834

LABRADOR METIS ASSOCIATION
Box 2164, Sta. B • GOOSE BAY, NF A0P 1E0
(709) 896-0592 Fax 896-0594; Reg Michelin, President
Ruby Durno, Vice-President

LABRADOR INUIT ASSOCIATION
Box 909, Sta. B • HAPPY VALLEY, NF A0P 1E0
(709) 896-8582 Fax 896-2610

LABRADOR NATIVE FRIENDSHIP CENTRE
P.O. Box 767, Station "B"
HAPPY VALLEY/GOOSE BAY, NF A0P 1E0
(709) 896-8302 Fax 896-8731; Renne Simms, Executive Director

LABRADOR NATIVE WOMEN'S ASSOCIATION
Box 542, Station "B" • HAPPY VALLEY, NF A0P 1M0
(709) 896-9420 Fax 896-0736; Annette Blake, President

LABRADOR INUIT ASSOCIATION
P.O. Box 70 • NAIN, NF A0P 1L0
(709) 922-2942; Fax 922-293; Joe Dicker, President

OKALAKATIGET SOCIETY
P.O. Box 160 • NAIN, NF A0P 1L0
(709) 922-2955 Fax 922-2293; Fran Williams, President

TORNGUSOK CULTURAL INSTITUTE
P.O. Box 40 • NAIN, NF A0P 1L0
(709) 922-2158 Fax 922-2863; Gary Baikie, Director

LABRADOR INUIT ASSOCIATION
95 Lemarchant Rd. #302 • ST. JOHN'S, NF A1C 2H1
(709) 754-2587 Fax 754-2364

ST. JOHN'S NATIVE FRIENDSHIP CENTRE
61 Cashen Ave. • ST. JOHN'S, NF A1E 3B4
(709) 726-5902 Fax 726-3557
Myrtle Blandford, Executive Director

NASKAPI-MONTAGNAIS INUIT ASSOCIATION
Box 119 • SHESHATSHIU, NF A0P 1N0
(709) 497-9800 Greg Penashue, President

NORTHWEST TERRITORY

INUIT CULTURAL INSTITUTE
Bag 2000 • ARVIAT, NT X0E 0E0
(867) 857-2803 Fax 857-2740; Roy Goose, Executive Director

KITIKMEOT INUIT ASSOCIATION
P.O. Box 88 • CAMBRIDGE BAY, NT X0E 0C0
(867) 983-2458 Fax 983-2158; John Maksagak, President

ZHAHTI KOE FRIENDSHIP CENTRE
General Delivery • FORT PROVIDENCE, NT X0E 0L0
(867) 699-3801 Fax 699-4355; Esther Lazore, Executive Director

DEH CHO SOCIETY FRIENDSHIP CENTRE
Box 470 • FORT SIMPSON, NT X0E 0N0
(867) 695-2577 Fax 695-2141
Bertha Norwegian, Executive Director

UNCLE GABE'S FRIENDSHIP CENTRE
Box 957 • FORT SMITH, NT X0E 0P0
(867) 872-3004 Fax 872-5313; Roger Rawlyk, Executive Director

BAFFIN REGION INUIT ASSOCIATION
P.O. Box 219 • FROBISHER BAY, NT X0A 0H0
(867) 979-5391

SOARING EAGLE FRIENDSHIP CENTRE
Box 396 • HAY RIVER, NT X0E 0R0
(867) 874-6581 Fax 874-3362; Abby Crook, Executive Director

COMMITTEE FOR ABORIGINAL PEOPLE'S ENTITLEMENT (COPE)
Box 2000 • INUVIK, NT X0E 0T0 (867) 979-3510
Inuit Association.

N.W.T. COUNCIL OF FRIENDSHIP CENTRES
INGAMO HALL FRIENDSHIP CENTRE
Box 1293 • INUVIK, NT X0E 0P0
(867) 979-2166 Fax 979-2837; Shirley Kisoun, Executive Director

BAFFIN REGIONAL INUIT ASSOCIATION
Box 219 • IQALUIT, NT X0A 0H0
(867) 979-5391 Fax 979-4325

KAKIVAK ASSOCIATION
Box 1419 • IQALUIT, NT X0A 0H0
(867) 979-0911 Fax 979-3707

BAFFIN REGIONAL INUIT ASSOCIATION
Box 219 • PROBISHER BAY, NT X0L 0G0
(867) 979-5391 Fax 979-4325; Louis Tapardjuk, President

RAE EDZO FRIENDSHIP CENTRE
Box 85 • RAE-EDZO, NT X0E 0Y0
(867) 392-6000 Fax 392-6093
Bertha Rabesca, Executive Director

INUIT BROADCASTING CORP.
Box 178 • RANKLIN INLET, NT X0C 0G0
(867) 645-2678 Fax 645-2937

KEEWATIN INUIT ASSOCIATION
Box 340 • RANKLIN INLET, NT X0C 0G0
(867) 645-2800 Fax 645-2885; Jack Anawak, President

SAPPUJJIJIT FRIENDSHIP CENTRE
Box 429 • RANKLIN INLET, NT X0C 0G0
(867) 645-2488 Fax 645-2538; Cecilia Papak, Executive Director

ASSEMBLY OF FIRST NATIONS
Dene Nation, 4701 Franklin Ave., Northway Bldg.
P.O. Box 2338 • YELLOWKNIFE, NT X1A 2P7
(867) 873-3310 Fax 920-2254

DENE CULTURAL INSTITUTE
Box 207 • YELLOWKNIFE, NT X1A 2N2
(867) 873-6617 Fax 873-3867; Joanne Barnaby, Executive Director

DENEDEH NATIONAL OFFICE – DENE NATION
5125 – 50th St., 1st Fl., P.O. Box 2338 • YELLOWKNIFE, NT X1A 2P7
(867) 873-4081 Fax 920-2254; Website: wwwdenenation.com
Bill Erasmus, National Chief; E-mail: berasmus@afn.ca

METIS ASSOCIATION OF THE N.W.T.
P.O. Box 1375 • YELLOWKNIFE, NT X1A 2P1
(867) 873-3505; Gary Bohnet, President

NATIVE COMMUNICATION SOCIETY OF WESTERN N.W.T.
Box 1919 • YELLOWKNIFE, NT X1A 2P4
(867) 920-2277 Fax 920-4205

NATIVE WOMEN'S ASSOCIATION OF N.W.T.
P.O. Box 2321 • YELLOWKNIFE, NT X1A 2P7
(867) 873-5509 Fax 873-3152
Helen Hudson-MacDonald, President

NUNASI CORPORATION
5022 49th St. #260 • YELLOWKNIFE, NT X1A 3R7
(867) 920-4587 Fax 920-4592

PRINCE OF WALES NORTHERN HERITAGE CENTRE
4750 48th St., P.O. Box 1320 • YELLOWKNIFE, NT X1A 2L9
(867) 873-7551 Fax 873-0205

Website: www.ppwnhc.ca; E-mail: pwnhc@gov.nt.ca
Sarah Carr-Locke, Director; E-mail: sarah_carr-locke@gov.nt.ca

TREE OF PEACE FRIENDSHIP CENTRE
Box 2667 • YELLOWKNIFE, NT X1A 2P9
(867) 873-2864 Fax 873-5185; Tom Eagle, President

N.W.T. METIS-DENE DEVELOPMENT FUND
4908 50th St., P.O. Box 1805 • YELLOWKNIFE, NT X1A 2P4
(888) 554-6333; (867) 873-9341 Fax 873-3492
Website: www.nwtmddf.com; Email: admin@nwtmddf.com
David Patrick, General Manager
Thomas Jarvis, Business Services
Jake Heron, Chair; Greg Nyuli, Secretary/Treasurer

N.W.T. NATIVE ARTS & CRAFTS SOCIETY
P.O. Box 2765 • YELLOWKNIFE, NT X1A 2R1
(867) 920-2854; Sonny McDonald, President

YELLOWKNIVES DENE BAND CORP.
P.O. Box 1287 • YELLOWKNIFE, NT X1A 2N2
(867) 873-6680 Fax 873-5969

NOVA SCOTIA

**ATLANTIC POLICY CONGRESS OF FIRST NATIONS
CHIEFS SECRETARIAT**
153 Willowdale Dr. • DARTMOUTH, NS B2V0A5
(877) 667-4007; (902) 435-8021 Fax 435-8027
Website: www.apcfnc.ca
John G. Paul, Executive Director; E-mail: john.paul@apcfnc.ca

MICMAC NATIVE FRIENDSHIP CENTRE
2158 Gottingen St. • HALIFAX, NS B3K 3B4
(902) 420-1576 Fax 423-6130; Gordon V. King, Executive Director
Purpose: To provide Native Indians with an education & occupational training in computer technology & office automation. A licensed trade school granting a certificate to all students who graduate. Library.

ASSEMBLY OF FIRST NATIONS/NS & NF
P.O. Box 327 • SHUBENACADIE, NS B0N 2H0
(902) 758-2142 Fax 758-1759

UNION OF NOVA SCOTIA INDIANS
Box 400 • SHUBENACADIE, NS B0N 2H0
(902) 758-2346

MICMAC ASSOCIATION OF CULTURAL STUDIES
Box 961 • SYDNEY, NS B1P 6J4
(902) 539-8037 Fax 539-6645
Peter Christmas, Executive Director

NATIVE COMMUNICATIONS SOCIETY OF NOVA SCOTIA
Box 344 • SYDNEY, NS B1P 6H2
(902) 539-0045 Fax 564-0430

NATIVE COUNCIL OF NOVA SCOTIA
75 Dodd St. • SYDNEY, NS B1P 1T7
(902) 567-1240 Fax 564-1123; Dwight Dorey, President

UNION OF NOVA SCOTIA INDIANS
201 Churchill Dr. #304 • MEMBERTOU, N.S. B1S 0H1
(902) 539-4107 Fax 539-6645; Website: www.unsi.ns.ca
Joe B. Marshall, Executive Director; E-mail: exd@unsi.ns.ca

CONFEDERACY OF MAINLAND MICMACS
P.O. Box 1590 • TRURO, NS B2N 5V3
(902) 895-6385 Fax 893-1520; Website: www.cmmns.com
Don Julien, Executive Director; E-mail: don@cmmns.com

NOVA SCOTIA MICMAC ARTS & CRAFTS SOCIETY
Box 978 • TRURO, NS B2N 5G7
(902) 892-7128

NOVA SCOTIA NATIVE WOMEN'S ASSOCIATION
P.O. Box 805 • TRURO, NS B2N 5E8
(902) 893-7402 Fax 897-7162; Clara Gloade, President

ONTARIO

ATIKOKAN NATIVE FRIENDSHIP CENTRE
P.O. Box 1510 • ATIKOKAN, ON P0T 1C0
 (807) 597-1213 Fax 597-1473
 Roberta McMahon, Executive Director
Purpose: To help create a better quality of life for urban Natives. Special programs: Youth programs; craft teachings, powwow's; traditional teachings; fundraising activities. Established 1983.

BARRIE NATIVE FRIENDSHIP CENTRE
175 Bayfield St. • BARRIE, ON L4M 3B4
 (705) 721-7689 Fax 721-4316; Ken Geroux, Director

UNITED INDIAN COUNCILS
7 Pinsent Ct. • BARRIE, ON L4N 6E5
 (705) 739-8422 Fax 739-8423

PINE TREE CENTRE OF BRANT
25 King St. • BRANTFORD, ON N3T 3C4
 (519) 752-5132 Fax 752-5612; Nancy Hill, President

WOODLAND INDIAN CULTURAL EDUCATION CENTRE
P.O. Box 1506 • BRANTFORD, ON N3T 5V6
 (519) 759-2650 Fax 759-8912; Joanna Bedard, Executive Director

ININEW FRIENDSHIP CENTRE
P.O. Box 1499 • COCHRANE, ON P0L 1C0
 (705) 272-4497 Fax 272-3597; Howard Restoule, Executive Director

AKWESASNE COMMUNICATIONS SOCIETY
Box 1496 • CORNWALL, ON K6H 5V5 (613) 938-1113

DRYDEN NATIVE FRIENDSHIP CENTRE
53 Arthur St. • DRYDEN, ON P8N 1J7
 (807) 223-4180 Fax 223-7136
 Irene St. Goddard, Executive Director

FORT ERIE INDIAN FRIENDSHIP CENTRE
796 Buffalo Rd. • FORT ERIE, ON L2A 5H2
 (905) 871-8931 Fax 871-9655
 Wayne Hill, Executive Director

UNITED NATIVE FRIENDSHIP CENTRE
P.O. Box 752 • FORT FRANCIS, ON P9A 3N1
 (807) 274-3207 Fax 274-4110
 Frank Bruyere, Executive Director

THUNDERBIRD FRIENDSHIP CENTRE
P.O. Box 430 • GERALDTON, ON P0T 1M0
 (807) 854-1060 Fax 854-0861
 Terry Dowhank, Executive Director

SIX NATIONS ARTS COUNCIL
RR 2 • HAGERSVILLE, ON N0A 1H0
 (905) 768-4965

SIX NATIONS ARTS & CRAFTS ASSN.
RR 6 • HAGERSVILLE, ON N0A 1H0 (905) 445-2451

HAMILTON REGIONAL INDIAN CENTRE
712 Main St. E. • HAMILTON, ON L8M 1K8
 (905) 548-9593 Fax 545-4077
 Cathy Staats, Executive Director

KAPUSKASING INDIAN FRIENDSHIP CENTRE
P.O. Box 26 • KAPUSKASING, ON P5N 1A8
 (705) 337-1935 Fax 335-6789
 Dorothy Wynne, Executive Director

GRAND COUNCIL TREATY No. 3
Box 1720 • KENORA, ON P7N 3X7
 (800) 665-3384; (807) 548-4215 Fax 548-5054
 Website: www.gct3.net
 Warren White, Grand Chief; E-mail: grand.chief@treaty3.ca

LAKE OF THE WOODS OJIBWAY CULTURAL CENTRE
Box 159 • KENORA, ON P9N 3X3
 (807) 548-5744 Fax 548-1591
 Joseph Tom, Director

NE'CHEE FRIENDSHIP CENTRE
P.O. Box 241 • KENORA, ON P9N 3X3
 (807) 468-5440 Fax 468-5340; Joe Seymour, Executive Director

KATAROKWI FRIENDSHIP CENTRE
28 Bath Rd., 2nd Fl. • KINGSTON, ON K7L 1H4
 (613) 548-1500 Fax 548-1847

ASSEMBLY OF FIRST NATIONS-ONTARIO
536 Queens Ave. • LONDON, ON N6B 1Y8
 (519) 660-6171 Fax 439-0467

ASSOCIATION OF IROQUOIS & ALLIED INDIANS
387 Princess Ave. • LONDON, ON N6B 2A7
 (519) 434-2761 Fax 675-1053; Website: www.aiai.on.ca
 Gord Peters, Grand Chief; E-mail: dstonefish@aiai.on.ca

N'AMERIND FRIENDSHIP CENTRE
260 Colborne St. • LONDON, ON N6B 2S6
 (519) 672-0131 Fax 672-0717
 Rossalyn McCoy-Mestes, Executive Director

GEORGIAN BAY NATIVE FRIENDSHIP CENTRE
175 Yonge St. • MIDLAND, ON L4R 2A7
 (705) 526-5589 Fax 526-7662
 Fred Jackson, Executive Director

MOOSONEE NATIVE FRIENDSHIP CENTRE
P.O. Box 478 • MOOSONEE, ON P0L 1Y0
 (705) 336-2808 Fax 336-2929; Bill Morrison, Executive Director

NIAGARA REGIONAL NATIVE CENTRE
RR #4, Queenston & Taylor Rd.
NIAGARA-ON-THE-LAKE, ON L0S 1J0
 (905) 688-6484 Fax 688-4033; Vince Hill, Executive Director

NORTH BAY INDIAN FRIENDSHIP CENTRE
980 Cassells St. • NORTH BAY, ON P1B 4A6
 (705) 472-2811 Fax 472-5251; Bill Butler, Executive Director

UNION OF ONTARIO INDIANS
Anishinabek Nation, P.O. Box 711 • NORTH BAY, ON P1B 8J8
 (877) 702-5200; (705) 497-9127 Fax 497-9135
 Pat Madahbee, Grand Council Chief; E-mail: gcc@anishinabek.ca

METIS NATION OF ONTARIO
141 Holland Ave. • OTTAWA, ON K1Y0Y2
 (800) 263-4889; (613) 798-1488 Fax 722-4225
 E-mail: tonyb@metisnation.con.ca; Website: www.metistraing.org

NATIVE BUSINESS INSTITUTE OF CANADA
2055 Carling Ave. #101 • OTTAWA, ON K2A 1G6
 (613) 761-9734 Fax 725-9031

ODAWA NATIVE FRIENDSHIP CENTRE
12 Stirling Ave. • OTTAWA, ON K1Y 1P8
 (613) 722-3811 Fax 722-4667; Jim Eagle, Executive Director
 E-mail: trinan@odawa.on.ca; Website: www.odawa.on.ca

PARRY SOUND FRIENDSHIP CENTRE
13 Bowes St. • PARRY SOUND, ON 92A 2K7
 (705) 746-5970 Fax 746-2612
 Vera Pawis-Tabobondung, Executive Director

PETERBOROUGH NATIVE FRIENDSHIP CENTRE
65 Brock St. • PETERBOROUGH, ON K9H 3L8
 (705) 876-8195 Fax 876-8806

RED LAKE INDIAN FRIENDSHIP CENTRE
Box 244 • RED LAKE, ON P0V 2M0
 (807) 727-2847 Fax 727-3253; Donna Prest, Executive Director

METIS NATION OF ONTARIO
244-143-A Great Northern Blvd.
SAULT STE. MARIE, ON P6B 4X9
 (705) 256-6146 Fax 256-6936

ONTARIO METIS ABORIGINAL ASSOCIATION
452 Albert St. E. • SAULT STE. MARIE, ON P6A 2J8
 (800) 461-5112; (705) 946-5900 Fax 946-1161
 Olaff Bjornaa, President

SAULT STE. MARIE INDIAN FRIENDSHIP CENTRE
122 East St. • SAULT STE. MARIE, ON P6A 3C6
(705) 256-5634 Fax 942-3227; Mary Desmoulin, Executive Director

NISHNAWBE-GAMIK FRIENDSHIP CENTRE
P.O. Box 1299 • SIOUX LOOKOUT, ON P8T 1B8
(807) 737-1903 Fax 737-1805
Laura Wynn, Executive Director

WAWATAY NATIVE COMMUNICATIONS SOCIETY
P.O. Box 1180 • SIOUX LOOKOUT, ON P0V 2T0
(807) 737-2951 Fax 737-3224

ASSOCIATION OF IROQUOIS & ALLIED INDIANS
Oneida Reserve, RR 2 • Southwold, ON N0L 2G0
(519) 652-3251 Fax 652-9287
Harry Dixtator, President

N'SWAKAMOK NATIVE FRIENDSHIP CENTRE
110 Elm St. W. • SUDBURY, ON P3C 1T5
(705) 674-2128 Fax 671-3539; Marie Meawasige, Executive Director
Purpose: To help Native people help themselves. Established 1972.

NATIVE ARTS & CRAFTS
McIntyre Centre, 1886 Memorial Ave.
THUNDER BAY, ON P7B 5K5 (807) 622-5731

ONTARIO NATIVE WOMEN'S ASSOCIATION
977 Alloy Dr. #7 • THUNDER BAY, ON P7B 5Z8
(800) 667-0816; (807) 623-3442 Fax 623-1104
Carol Nobigan, President

THUNDER BAY FRIENDSHIP CENTRE
401 N. Cumberland St. • THUNDER BAY, ON P7A 4P7
(807) 345-5840 Fax 344-8945; Ann Cox, Executive Director

OJIBWAY & CREE CULTURAL CENTRE
#304-210 Spruce St. S. • TIMMINS, ON P4N 2C7
(705) 267-7911 Fax 267-4988; Esther Wesley, Director
Purpose: To encourage & support Native People's involvement in the development of self-determination of the Nishnawbe-Aski Nation; to involve and provide opportunities for people; to support and maintain the use of Native languages; to produce & circulate educational printed & audio-visual material; to promote & encourage the establishment of a library and information services in the community. *Activities/programs*: Native Language program; Ojibway Cree Resource Center; Ojibway Cree media productions; Indian education programs. Grand Council Treaty #9 - Signed between the crown, the Provincial Government and the Cree-Ojibway of what is now known as Northern Ontario in 1905-06. This was one of a number of treaties made across Canada, following the Royal Proclamation of 1763. The area under Treat #9 covers about 210,000 square miles. There are over 40 Indian communities scattered throughout the area. 30 of these are accessible by air only. The Indian People of the Treat #9 area are known as the Nishnawbe-Aski. *Publications*: Catalogue of Materials for Sale. Library. Established 1976.

TIMMINS NATIVE FRIENDSHIP CENTRE
316 Spruce St. • TIMMINS, ON P4N 2M9
(705) 268-6262 Fax 268-6266
Christine Cummings, Executive Director

ABORIGINAL URBAN ALLIANCE OF ONTARIO
Box 46035, 444 Yonge St. • TORONTO, ON M5B 2L8
(416) 516-8836

CHIEFS OF ONTARIO
111 Peter St. • TORONTO, ON M5V 2H1
(416) 597-1266 Fax 597-8365
Website: www.chiefs-of-ontario.org
Isadore Day, ON Regional Chief; E-mail: iday@afn.ca

COUNCIL FIRE NATIVE CULTURAL CENTRE
252 Parliament St. • TORONTO, ON M5A 3A4
(416) 360-4350 Fax 360-5978

NATIVE CANADIAN CENTRE OF TORONTO
16 Spadina Rd. • TORONTO, ON M5R 2S7
(416) 964-9087 Fax 964-2111
Gayle Mason, Executive Director
Publication: Native Canadian.

NATIVE CHILD & FAMILY SERVICES OF METRO TORONTO
101-22 College St. • TORONTO, ON M5G 1K2
(416) 969-8510 Fax 969-9251

ONTARIO FEDERATION OF INDIAN FRIENDSHIP CENTRES
290 Shute St. • TORONTO, ON M5A 1W7
(416) 956-7575 Fax 956-7577
Vera Pawis Tabobondung, President
Sylvia Maracle, Executive Director
Assists and supports the 18 Indian Centres under its membership in Ontario. Promotes development of new centres, and provides programs and services to its member centres. Publications. Library.

UNION OF ONTARIO INDIANS
27 Queen St. East, 2nd Floor • TORONTO, ON M5C 1R2
(416) 693-1305 Fax 693-1620; Joe Miskokomon, President
K. Gayle Mason, Executive Director
Represents 40 Indian bands & their 35,000 members. A political organization offering technical and support services to member bands. Library.

OJIBWE CULTURAL FOUNDATION
P.O. Box 278, West Bay Indian Reserve • WEST BAY, ON P0P 1G0
(705) 377-4902 Fax 377-5460; Mary Lou Fox, Director

THE ONTARIO ARCHAEOLOGICAL SOCIETY
126 Willowdale Ave. • WILLOWDALE, ON M2N 4Y2
(416) 730-0797; Christine L. Caroppo, Director
Purpose: To preserve, promote, investigate record & publish an archaeological record of the Province of Ontario. *Activities/programs*: Excavations; workshops; annual Symposium; tours and trips; public lectures; volunteer program "Passport to the Past." *Publications*: Ontario Archaeology, refereed journal; Monographs in Ontario Archaeology; special publications. Established 1950.

CAN AM INDIAN FRIENDSHIP CENTRE
1684 Ellrose Ave. • WINDSOR, ON N8Y 3X7
(519) 258-8954 Fax 258-3795; Terry Doxtator, Executive Director

PRINCE EDWARD ISLAND

ABORIGINAL WOMEN'S ASSOCIATION OF P.E.I., INC.
P.O. Box 145 • LENNOX ISLAND, PE C0B 1P0
(902) 831-3059 Fax 831-3181; Madlene Sark, President
E-mail: madlene.sark@lennoxisland.com

LENNOX ISLAND CULTURAL EDUCATIONAL CENTRE
Box 134 • LENNOX ISLAND, PE C0B 1B0
(902) 831-2779 Fax 831-3153; Charles Sark, Director

NATIVE COUNCIL OF PRINCE EDWARD ISLAND
6 F.J. McAulay Ct. • CHARLOTTETOWN, PE C1A 1L2
(902) 626-2882 Fax 367-3779; Website: www.ncpei.com
Jamie Thomas, President

MI'KMAQ CONFEDERACY OF PEI
200 Read Dr. • SUMMERSIDE, PE C1N 5N7
(877) 884-0808; (902) 436-5101 Fax 436-5655
Website: www.mcpei.com; Don MacKenzie, Executive Director

QUEBEC

ASSEMBLY OF FIRST NATIONS OF QUEBEC & LABRADOR
250, Place Chef Michel Laveau, bureau 201 • Wendake (PQ) G0A 4V0
(418) 842-5020 Fax 842-2660; Website: www.apnql-afnql.com
Jane Gray, Chief of Operations; Diane McGregor, Coordinator
E-mail: apnql@apnql-afnql.com

CREE INDIAN CENTRE
95 rue Jaculet • CHIBOUGAMAU, PQ G8P 2G1
(418) 748-7667 Fax 748-6954; Judy Parceaud, Executive Director

JAMES BAY CREE CULTURAL EDUCATION CENTRE
Box 291 • CHISASIBI, PQ J0M 1M0
(819) 855-2473 Jane Pachano, Director

**NATIVE ALLIANCE OF QUEBEC & LAURENTIAN
ALLIANCE OF METIS & NON-STATUS INDIANS**
21 Brodeur Ave. • HULL, PQ J8Y 2P6
(819) 770-7763 Fax 770-6070; Rheal Boudrias, President

AVATAQ CULTURAL INSTITUTE, INC.
General Delivery • INUKJUAK, PQ J0M 1M0
 (866) 897(819) 254-8919 Fax 254-8148
 Johnny Epoo, President; Website: www.avataq.qc.ca
 E-mail: avataq@avataq.qc.ca
360 – 4150 Ste-Catherine O. • WESTMOUNT, PQ H3Z 2Y5
 (800) 361-5029; (514) 989-9031 Fax 989-8789
 E-mail: avataq-inukjuak@avataq.qc.ca
Purpose: To preserve and promote Nunavik (Northern Quebec) Inuit language & culture. *Activities/programs*: Building a community museum; language program; traditional medicine project; place name project; genealogy project; photo exhibits; retrieval of anthropological material; transcribe & translate recorded information. Documentation Center comprises historical photographs collection, interview with elders, and library and archives.

KANIEN'KEHAKA RAOTITIONHKWA CULTURAL CENTRE
Kahnawake Indian Band, P.O. Box 969
KAHNAWAKE MOHAWK TERRITORY, PQ J0L 1B0
 (450) 638-0880 Fax 638-0920; Jessica Hill, Coordinator
 Alexis Shakleton, Librarian

QUEBEC NATIVE WOMEN'S ASSOCIATION
P.O. Box 44 • KAHNAWAKE, PQ J0L 1B0 (514) 632-7452

KANESATAKE CULTURAL CENTRE
681 "C" Ste. Philomene • KANESATAKE, PQ J0N 1E0
 (514) 479-1783 Fax 479-8249; Chief George Martin, Contact

KATIVIK REGIONAL DEVELOPMENT COUNCIL
P.O. Box 239 • KUUJJUAQ, PQ J0M 1C0
 (819) 964-2035 Fax 964-2611

CENTRE D'AMITIE AUTOCCHTONE DE LA TUQUE
C.P. 335, 544 St. Antoine • LA TUQUE, PQ G9X 3P3
 (819) 523-6121 Fax 523-8637
 Rosanne Petiquay, Executive Director

CENTRE D'AMITIE AUTOCCHTONE DE QUEBEC
234, rue St-Louis • LORETTEVILLE, PQ G2B 1L4
 (418) 843-5818 Fax 843-8960
 Jocelyn Gros-Louis, Executive Director

JAMES BAY CREE COMMUNICATION SOCIETY
75 Riverside St. • MISTASSINI LAKE, PQ G0W 1C0
 (418) 923-3191 Fax 923-2088

CENTRE FOR NATIVE EDUCATION
1455 de Maissonneuve West • MONTREAL, PQ H3G 1M8
 (514) 838-7326 Fax 848-3599

NATIVE FRIENDSHIP CENTRE OF MONTREAL
2001 Boulevard St. Laurant • MONTREAL, PQ H2X 2T3
 (514) 499-1854 Fax 499-9436; Ida Williams, Executive Director

QUEBEC NATIVE WOMEN'S ASSOCIATION
460 Ste. Catherine W., #503 • MONTREAL, PQ H3A 1A7
 (800) 363-0322; (514) 954-9991 Fax 954-1899
 Michele Rouleau, President

GRAND COUNCIL OF THE CREES
2 Lakeshore Rd. • NEMASKA, CHAMPION LAKE, PQ J0Y 3B0
 (819) 673-2600 Fax 673-2606; Website: www.gcc.ca
 Matthew Coon-Come, Grand Chief; E-mail: mcc@gcc.ca

RESTIGOUCHE ECONOMIC DEVEL0PMENT COMMISSION
Box 298, 17 Riverside W. • RESTIGOUCHE, PQ G0C 2R0
 (418) 788-2136 Ext. 56 Fax 788-2058; Romey Labillois, Director

CENTRE FOR INDIGENOUS SOVEREIGNTY
Mohawks of Akwesasne, McDonald Rd. • ST. REGIS, PQ H0M 1A0
 (613) 575-1731 Fax 575-1443

CENTRE D'AMITIE AUTOCHTONE
910, 10e Ave., C.P. 1769 • SENNETERRE, PQ J0Y 2M0
 (819) 737-2324 Fax 737-8311; Louis Bordeleau, Executive Director

INNU FRIENDSHIP CENTRE
100 Laure Blvd., Suite 100 • SEPT-les, PQ G4R 1Y1
 (418) 968-2026

ALGONQUIN COUNCIL OF WESTERN QUEBEC
351 Central Ave. • VAL D'OR, PQ J2P 1P6
 (819) 770-7763 Fax 770-6070; Roger Brindamour, Director

CENTRE D'AMITIE AUTOCHTONE
1272, 7th St. • VAL D'OR, PQ J9P 3W4
 (819) 825-6857 Fax 825-7515; Diane Decoste, Executive Director

ASSEMBLY OF FIRST NATIONS/QUEBEC
430 Koska • WENDAKE, PQ G0A 1B6
 (418) 842-5020 Fax 842-2660

INSTITUT EDUCATIF ET CULTUREL ATTIKAMEK-MONTAGNAIS
7-40, rue Francois Gros-Louis • WENDAKE, PQ G0A 4V0
 (418) 843-0258 Fax 843-7313; Johanne Robertson, Director

LES ARTISANS INDIENS DU QUEBEC
540 Max Gros-Louis St., Village des Hurons
WENDAKE, PQ G0A 4V0 (418) 845-2150
 Therese Sioui, President

NATIVE CONSULTING SERVICES
50 boul. Maurice Bastien #100
Village des Hurons • WENDAKE, PQ G0A 4V0
 (418) 847-0322 Fax 843-7339

REGROUPMENT DES CENTRES D'AMITIE AUTOCHTONE DU QUEBEC
30 rue de l'ours, Village des Hurons • WENDAKE, PQ G0A 4V0
 (418) 842-6354 Fax 842-9795; Ida Williams, President

SECRETARIAT OF FIRST NATIONS OF QUEBEC & LABRADOR
430 Koska, Village des Hurons • WENDAKE, PQ G0A 4V0
 (418) 842-5020 Fax 842-2660; Konrad Sioui, Vice-Chief

SASKATCHEWAN

NATIVE COUNCIL OF SASKATCHEWAN
P.O. Box 132 • GREEN LAKE, SK S0M 1B0
 (306) 888-2125 Fax 288-4622; Harvey Young, President

FILE HILLS QU'APPELLE TRIBAL COUNCIL
Rm. 222 – 740 Sioux Ave., Box 985 • FORT QU'APPELLE, SK S0G 1S0
 (306) 332-8200 Fax 332-1811; Website: www.fhqtc.com
Serves 11 first nations: Carry the Kettle; Little Black Bear's Band; Nekaneet; Okanese; Pasqua; Peepeekisis; Piapot; Standing Buffalo; Star Blanket; Wood Mountain; Muscowpetung

QU'APPELLE VALLEY FRIENDSHIP CENTRE
P.O. Box 240 • FORT QU'APPELLE, SK S0G 1S0
 (306) 332-5616 Fax 332-5091; J. Peter Dubois, Executive Director
Purpose: To identify and cater to the social, cultural, and recreational needs of the Indian and Metis people of Fort Qu'Appelle and District; to enhance community participation by the people of Indian descent; and to promote better understanding and relations between Native and non-Native citizens. Programs: Youth Alternative Measures; Identification Program (fingerprinting children); Drug & Alcohol Counseling; Literacy, et al. *Publication*: Qu'Appelle Valley Quill, quarterly newsletter.

KIKINAHK FRIENDSHIP CENTRE, INC.
Box 254 • LA RONGE, SK S0J 1S0
 (306) 425-2051 Fax 425-3359; Norm Bouvier, Executive Director

NORTHWEST FRIENDSHIP CENTRE
P.O. Box 1780 • MEADOW LAKE, SK S0M 1V0
 (306) 236-3766 Fax 236-5451; Gladys Joseph, Executive Director

MOOSE JAW NATIVE FRIENDSHIP CENTRE
42 High St. E. • MOOSE JAW, SK S6H 0B8
 (306) 693-6966 Fax 692-3509; Ed Pelletier, Executive Director

BATTLEFORDS AGENCY TRIBAL CHIEFS, INC.
971 – 104th St. • NORTH BATTLEFORD, SK S9A 4B2
 (306) 446-1400 Fax 446-130; Website: www.batc.ca
 Neil Sasakamoose, Executive Director
 E-mail: neil.sasakamoose@batc.ca
 Alison (Ali) Tatar, Director of Governance
 E-mail: ali.tatar@batc.ca
Chiefs: Larry Ahenakew, Stewart Baptiste, Leo Moccasin, Lori Whitecalf, Ben Weenie, Brad Swiftwolfe

BATTLEFORDS INDIAN & METIS FRIENDSHIP CENTRE
12002 Railway Ave. E. • NORTH BATTLEFORD, SK S9A 3W3
  (306) 445-8216 Fax 445-6863; Daryl Larose, Executive Director

ABORIGINAL WOMEN'S COUNCIL OF SASKATCHEWAN
#101-118, 12th St. E. • PRINCE ALBERT, SK S6V 1B6
  (306) 763-6005 Fax 922-6034; Lil Sanderson, Contact

PRINCE ALBERT GRAND COUNCIL
Chief Joseph Custer Rsv #201
2300 9th Ave. West, P.O. Box 2350 • PRINCE ALBERT, SK S6V 6Z1
  (306) 953-7200 Fax 764-6272; Website: www.pagc.sk.ca
  Johnny Walker, Corporate Executive Officer (Peter Ballantyne Cree Nation)
  Ron Michel, Grand Chief (Peter Ballantyne Cree Nation)
  Brian Hardlotte, Vice Chief (Lac La Ronge Indian Band)
  Joseph Tsannie, Vice Chief (Hatchet Lake Denesuline First Nation)
First Nation Members: Black Lake; Cumberland House; Fond du Lac; Hatchet Lake; James Smith Cree; Lac La Ronge Indian Band; Montreal Lake Cree; Peter Ballantyne Cree; Red Earth Cree; Shoal Lake Cree; Sturgeon Lake; Wahpeton Dakota.

INDIAN & METIS FRIENDSHIP CENTRE
1409 1st Ave. • PRINCE ALBERT S6V 2B2
  (306) 764-3431 Fax 763-3205; Eugene Arcand, Executive Director

NATIVE INDIAN FINANCIAL CORPORATION
P.O.Box 2377 • PRINCE ALBERT, SK S6V 6Z1
  (306) 763-4712 Fax 763-3255

FEDERATION OF SASKATCHEWAN INDIAN NATIONS
1692 Albert St. • REGINA, SK S4P 2S6
  (306) 721-2822 Fax 721-2707; Alphonse Bird, Chief

FIRST NATIONS EMPLOYMENT CENTRE
3639 Sherwood Dr. • REGINA, SK S4R 4A7
  (306) 924-1606 Fax 949-0526

INDIAN & METIS FRIENDSHIP CENTRE
303 McGee Crescent • REGINA, SK S4R 6K8
  (306) 543-2745; Walter Schoenthal, Executive Director

REGINA FRIENDSHIP CENTRE
1440 Scarth St. • REGINA, SK S4R 2E9
  (306) 525-5459 Fax 525-3005
  Sharon Ironstar, President; Dona Racette, Executive Director

SASKATCHEWAN INDIAN ARTS & CRAFTS CORPORATION
2431-8th Ave. • REGINA, SK S4R 5J7
  (306) 352-1501 Dorothy Thomas, President

SASKATCHEWAN INDIAN HOUSING COMMISSION
109 Hodsman Rd. • REGINA, SK S4N 5W5
  (800) 721-2707; (306) 721-2822 Fax 775-2994

FEDERATION OF SASKATCHEWAN INDIAN NATIONS
Asimakaniseekan Askiy Reserve
#100 - 103A Packham Ave. • SASKATOON, SK S7N 4K4
  (306) 665-1215 Fax 244-4413; Website: www.fsin.com
  Kimberly Jonathan, Interim Chief
  E-mail: Kimberly.jonathan@fsin.com
  Bobby Cameron, E. Dutch Lerat, & Heather Bear, Vice Chiefs
Represents 74 First Nations in Saskatchewan. The goals and objectives of the FSIN are: The protection of Treaties & Treaty Rights; The fostering of progress in economic, educational & social endeavors of First Nation people; Co-operation with civil and religious authorities; et al.

INDIGENOUS GAMING REGULATORS, INC.
400-203 Packham Ave. • SASKATOON S7N 4K5
  (306) 477-5700 Fax 477-5704; Website: www.iga.ca

NATIONAL INDIAN FINANCIAL CORPORATION
#217, 103B Packham Ave. • SASKATOON, SK S7N 4K4
  (800) 667-4712; (306) 955-4712 Fax 477-4554

SASKATCHEWAN ARCHAEOLOGICAL SOCIETY
#5 - 816 1st Ave. N. • SASKATOON S7K 1Y3
  (306) 664-4124 Fax 665-1928; Tim Jones, Executive Director
Purpose: To actively promote and encourage the study, preservation and proper use of the archaeological resources of Saskatchewan. *Activities*: Educational programs; field school; seminars; field trips; Certification program;

operates the Regional Archaeology Volunteers Program. Member Funding Grants (four grants for members to complete special projects.) *Publication*: Tracking Ancient Hunters: Prehistoric Archaeology in Saskatchewan; Avonlea, Yesterday and Today, Annotated Bibliography of Saskatchewan Archaeology and Prehistory; Bimonthly newsletter; annual Journal. Founded 1963.

SASKATCHEWAN INDIAN CULTURAL CENTRE
305 - 2555 Grasswood Rd. East • SASKATOON, SK S7K 0K1
  (306) 244-1146 Fax 665-6520; Linda Pelly-Landrie, President
  Website: www.sicc.sk.ca; E-mail: info@sicc.sk.ca

SASKATCHEWAN INDIAN GAMING AUTHORITY
250 - 103 C Packham Ave. • SASKATOON, SK S7N 4K4
  (306) 477-7777; Zane Hansen, President
  Website: www.siga.sk.ca

SASKATCHEWAN NATIVE COMMUNICATIONS SOCIETY
104-219 Robin Cres. • SASKATOON, SK S7N 6M8
  (306) 244-7441 Fax 343-0171

SASKATOON INDIAN & METIS FRIENDSHIP CENTRE
168 Wall St. • SASKATOON, SK S7K 1N4
  (306) 244-0174 Fax 664-2536; Maurice J. Blondeau, Director

SASKATOON NATIVE THEATRE
919 Broadway Ave. • SASKATOON, SK S7N 1B8
  (306) 244-7779

SASKATOON TRIBAL COUNCIL
#200 – 335 Packham Ave. • SASKATOON, SK S7N 4S1
  (306) 956-6100 Fax 244-7273; Website: www.sktc.sk.ca
Felix Thomas, Chief; Mark Arcand, Vice Chief
Member Nations: Kinistin Saulteaux; Mistawasis; Muskeg Lake Cree; Muskoday; Ome Arrow; Whitecap Dakota; Yellow Quill.

AGENCY CHIEFS TRIBAL COUNCIL
100 Railway Ave. W. • SPIRITWOOD, SK S0J 2M0
  (306) 883-3880; Website: www.agencychiefs.com
  Bob Gerow, CEO
  Glenn Johnstone, Director of Operations
   E-mail: glenn.johnstone@agencychiefs.com
Bands: Witchekan Lake First Nation; Pelican Lake First Nation;
And Big River First Nation.

ABORIGINAL FRIENDSHIP CENTRES OF SASKATCHEWAN
c/o Yorktown Friendship Centre
139 Dominion Ave. • YORKTON, SK S3N 1P7
  (306) 782-2822 Fax 782-6662; Ivan Cote, Executive Director

YORKTON TRIBAL COUNCIL
21 Bradbrooke Dr. North • YORKTON, SK S3N 3R1
  (306) 782-3644 Fax 786-6264
  Gilbert Panipekeesick, Tribal Chief
First Nation Members: Cote; Keeseekoose; Key; Ocean Man; Sakimay; Kahkewistahaw.

YUKON

COUNCIL OF YUKON FIRST NATIONS
2166 – 2nd Ave. • WHITEHORSE, YUKON Y1A 4P1
  (867) 393-9200 Fax 668-6577; Website: www.cyfn.net
  Ruth Massie, Grand Chief; Michelle Kolla, Executive Director
Yukon First Nations: Carcross/Tagish; Champagne & Aishihik; Nacho Nyak Dun; Kluane; Little Salmon Carmacks; Selkirk; Ta'am Kwach'an; Teslin Tlingit Council; Tr'ondek Hwech'in; Ehdiitat Gwich'in; Gwichya Gwich'in Council; Nihtat Gwich'in Council; Tetlit Gwich'in Council.

SKOOKUM JIM FRIENDSHIP CENTRE
3159 - 3rd Ave. • WHITEHORSE, YU Y1A 1G1
  (403) 668-4465 Fax 668-4725
  Ruby Van Bibban, Executive Director

YE SA TO COMMUNICATIONS SOCIETY
22 Nisutlin Dr. • WHITEHORSE, YU Y1A 3S5
  (403) 667-2775 Fax 667-6923

YUKON INDIAN ARTS & CRAFTS CO-OPERATIVE LIMITED
4230-4th Ave. • WHITEHORSE, YU Y1A 1K1
  (403) 668-5955 Fax 668-6466; Stan Peters, President

YUKON INDIAN DEVELOPMENT CORP.
409 Black St. • WHITEHORSE, YU Y1A 2N2
(403) 668-3908 Fax 668-3127

YUKON INDIAN CULTURAL EDUCATION SOCIETY
11 Nisultin Dr. • WHITEHORSE, YU Y1A 3S5
(403) 667-4616 Fax 668-6577; Pat Martin, Coordinator

YUKON INDIAN WOMEN'S ASSOCIATION
11 Nisutlin Dr. • WHITEHORSE Y1A 3S4
(403) 667-6162 Fax 668-7539; Nina Bolton, President`

MUSEUMS & CULTURAL CENTRES

ALBERTA

LUXTON MUSEUM
Box 850 • BANFF, AB T0L 0C0
(403) 762-2388 Fax 760-2803
Western Canadian Indian museum.

OLDMAN RIVER CULTURAL CENTER
P.O. Box 70 • BROCKET, AB T0K 0H0
(403) 965-3939 Fax 965-2087; Reggie Crow Shoe, Director

TSUU T'INA MUSEUM & ARCHIVES
Box 135 • CALGARY, AB T2W 3C4
(403) 238-2677 Fax 251-0980; Jenette Starlight, Director
Purpose: Dedicated to the preservation of Tsuu T'ina
culture and history.

PROVINCIAL MUSEUM OF ALBERTA
Archaeology & Ethnology Section
12845 - 102 Ave. • EDMONTON, AB T5N 0M6
(780) 453-9147 Fax 454-6629
John W. Ives, Manager, Archaeology & Ethnology
E-mail: jives@mcd.gov.ab.ca
Susan J. Berry, Curator-Ethnology
Description: Collections focus on the material culture & lifeways of indigenous peoples of Alberta (Beaver, Slavey, Chipewyan, Northern and Plains Cree, Blackfoot, Blood, Peigan, Sarsi, Assiniboine, Kutenai, Sauteaux, Metis) and other groups relevant to the histories of indigenous peoples in Alberta (e.g. Iroquois.) Contains approxi-mately 12,000 items, strong in both functional and religious Plains materials; tipis and moccasins are extensive; Inuit clothing and other items from the Canadian Arctic. *Special programs*: Research & collecting projects--Native lifeways & material cultures in Alberta, focusing on 20th century items. *Publications*: Storyteller, monthly; books for sale. Library.

MASKWACHEES CULTURAL COLLEGE
P.O. Box 360 • HOBBEMA, AB T0C 1N0
(403) 585-3925 Fax 585-2080; Steve Skikum, Director

NAKODA LODGE/CULTURAL INSTITUTE
P.O. Box 149 • MORLEY, AB T0L 1N0
(403) 881-3949 Fax 881-3901; Dave Drews, Director

SIKSIKA NATION MUSEUM
Old Sun Community College
P.O. Box 1250 • SIKSIKA NATION, AB T0J 3W0
(403) 734-3862

NINASTAKO CULTURAL CENTER
P.O. Box 232 • STANDOFF, AB T0L 1Y0
(403) 737-3774 Fax 737-3786; Gloria Wells, Director

BRITISH COLUMBIA

U'MISTA CULTURAL CENTRE
P.O. Box 253 • ALERT BAY, BC V0N 1A0
(604) 974-5403 Fax 974-5499; Linda Manz, Director
Description: Houses one of the finest collections of carved masks depicting the Potlatch Ceremony of the Kwak'wala-speaking peoples. Exhibits of contemporary arts and crafts, including artifacts, audio & video, photographs, library and archival resources. Opened in 1980.

ATLIN MUSEUM
Fourth & Trainor Sts. • ATLIN, BC
Exhibits Tlingit Indian artifacts.

SAANICH NATIVE HERITAGE SOCIETY
P.O. Box 28 • BRENTWOOD BAY, BC V0F 1A0
(250) 652-5980 Fax 652-5957; Adelynne Claxton, Director

CAMPBELL RIVER MUSEUM
Box 101 • CAMPBELL RIVER, BC
Indian museum displaying Northwest Coast material.

COQUALEETZA EDUCATION TRAINING CENTRE
7201 Vedder Rd. Bldg. #1 • CHILLIWACK, BC V2R 4G5
(604) 858-3366 Fax 824-5226; Shirley Leon, Director

COWICHAN NATIVE VILLAGE/NATIVE HERITAGE
200 Cowichan Way • DUNCAN, BC V9L 4T8
(250) 746-8119 Fax 746-4143; John Parker, Director

'KSAN MUSEUM
P.O. Box 326 • HAZELTON, BC V0J 1Y0
(250) 842-5544 Fax 842-6533; Eve Hope, Director & Curator
Description: Museum is part of a reconstructed Indian village. Maintains a collection of Northwest Coast Indian artifacts, specifically Gitksan. *Special program*: Kitanmax School of Northwest Coast Indian Art - a 2-year program in woodcarving, design, tool making, serigraph. *Publications*: Weget Wanders On - prints and legends; Gathering What the Great Nature Provided; Robes of Dover. Opened 1959.

KAMLOOPS MUSEUM & ARCHIVES
207 Seymour St. • KAMLOOPS, BC V2C 2E7
(250) 828-3576 Ken Favrholdt, Director & Curator
Description: General history collection related to the natural and human history of the Kamloops district including artifacts & exhibits related to Native Indians of area. *Special collection*: Extensive archives including files on interior Salish Indians and local Shuswap Indians. Exhibits Indian artifacts, mostly Shuswap Indians, with some material relevant to other tribes of the Interior Salish. *Publication*: The Dispossessed (Salish Indians); local history publications. Archives and library. Opened 1937.

SECWEPMEMC MUSEUM & NATIVE HERITAGE PARK
355 Yellowhead Hwy. • KAMLOOPS, BC V2H 1H1
(250) 828-9801 Fax 372-1127; Ken Favrholdt, Director; Linda Jules, Curator
Description: Portrays the history and culture of the Secwepmemc (Shuswap) Nation of south-central British Columbia from prehistoric to contemporary times. Includes archives, gift shop, and a 12-acre heritage park including a 2,000 year-old village site. Contains canoes, a tule mat lodge, archaeological material, baskets, church and religious artifacts, photos, beadwork, trade items, leatherwork. Programs: Educational; Language; Trades training; Communications; workshops & conferences. *Publication*: Secwepmemc News, monthly newspaper. Library.

OKANAGAN INDIAN EDUCATIONAL RESOURCES SOCIETY
257 Brunswick St. • PENTICTON, BC V2A 5P9
(250) 493-7181 Fax 493-5302; Jeanette Armstrong, Director
E-mail: jarmstrg@web.net

MUSEUM OF NORTHERN BRITISH COLUMBIA
P.O. Box 669 • PRINCE RUPERT, BC V8J 3S1
(250) 624-3207 Elaine Moore, Curator/Director
Description: A collection of ethnographic artifacts representing Tsimshian native people (coast, Gitksan and Nisgha) and Haida and Tlingit to a lesser extent; Northwest Coast Indian artifacts, and other cultural remains relating to regional history. *Publication*: The Curator's Log, quarterly newsletter; book, Arts of the Salmon People; Totem Poles of Prince Rupert", illustrated guide; Guide to the Collection. Library.

KWAGIULTH MUSEUM & CULTURAL CENTRE
P.O. Box 8 • QUATHIASKI, BC V0P 1N0
(604) 285-3733 Fax 285-2400; Estelle Inman, Executive Director

ED JONES HAIDA MUSEUM
Second Beach Skidgate • QUEEN CHARLOTTE CITY, BC V0T 1S0
(250) 559-4643

UNIVERSITY OF BRITISH COLUMBIA MUSEUM OF ANTHROPOLOGY
6393 N.W. Marine Dr. • VANCOUVER, BC V6T 1W5
(250) 228-5087
Description: Major research and study collections include Northwest Coast archaeology & ethnology, & ethnological specimens from other North American Indian cultures. *Publications*: Anthropology at the Academy, newsletter; The Elkus Collection of Southwestern Indian Art; Hopi Kachina: Spirit of Life. Library.

THE VANCOUVER MUSEUM
1100 Chestnut • VANCOUVER, BC V6J 3J9
  (250) 736-4431 Dr. David Hemphill, Director
  Lynn Maranda, Curator of Anthropology
Special collections: Lipsett Native Indian collection; Ryan Collection of Haida argillite carvings. Publication: Muse News. Library.

HEILSTUK CULTURAL EDUCATION CENTRE
P.O. Box 880 • WAGLISLA, BC V0T 1Z0
  (604) 957-2626 Fax 957-2780; Jennifer Carpenter, Director

OKANAGAN NATION ALLIANCE (ONA)
101 – 3535 Old Okanagan Hwy. • WESTBANK, BC V4T 3L7
  (866) 662-9609; (250) 707-0095 Fax 707-0166
  Website: www.syilx.org; E-mail: admin@syilx.org
  Pauline Terbasket, Executive Director
  E-mail: director@syilx.org
  Stewart Phillip, Grand Chief, ONA Chair
  E-mail: president@ubcic.bc.ca
The Okanagan Nation Alliance (ONA) was formed in 1981 as the inaugural First Nations government in the Okanagan which represents the 8 member communities including; Okanagan Indian Band, Upper Nicola Band, Westbank First Nation, Penticton Indian Band, Osoyoos Indian Band and Lower and Upper Similkameen Indian Bands and the Colville Confederated Tribes on areas of common concern. Each community is represented through the Chiefs Executive Council (CEC) by their Chief or Chairman. The Okanagan Nation territory includes an area that extends over approximately 69,000 kilometers. The northern area of this territory scratches the area of mica Creek, just north of modern-day Revelstoke, BC, the eastern boundary between Kaslo and Kootenay Lakes. The southern boundary extends to the vicinity of Wilbur, Washington and the western border extends into the Nicola Valley.

MANITOBA

ESKIMO MUSEUM
James St. • CHURCHILL, MB R0B 0E0

CROSS LAKE CULTURAL/EDUCATION CENTRE
Cross Lake Indian Reserve • CROSS LAKE, MB R0B 0J0
  (204) 676-2268/2218

NORWAY HOUSE CULTURAL EDUCATION CENTRE
Norway House Cree Nation
P.O. Box 250 • NORWAY HOUSE, MB R0B 1B0
  (204) 359-6296 Fax 359-6262; Myra Saunders, R&D Coordinator

CULTURAL CENTER
Fort Alexander Band, P.O. Box 1610 • PINE FALLS, MB R0E 1M0
  (204) 367-8740

SAGKEENG CULTURAL EDUCATION CENTRE
Box 749 • PINE FALLS, MB R0E 1M0
  (204) 367-2612; Art Boubard, Director

MANITOBA INDIAN CULTURAL EDUCATION CENTRE
119 Sutherland Ave. • WINNIPEG, MB R2W 3C9
  (204) 942-0228 Fax 947-6564; Ron Missyabit, Director
Description: Maintains a collection of artifacts of native peoples of Manitoba. Library of books, films, tape/slides, and audio-visual presentations, artifacts, educational kits. *Publications*: Manitoba Elders, $6; Lifestyles of Manitoba Indians, $2 coloring book.

MANITOBA MUSEUM OF MAN & NATURE
190 Rupert Ave. • WINNIPEG, MB

NORTHWEST TERRITORIES

INUMMARIT COMMITTEE - SOD HOUSE MUSEUM
c/o Hamlet of Arctic Bay, General Delivery
ARCTIC BAY, NT X0A 0A0
  Dorothee Komangapik, Director

INUIT SILATTUQSARVINGAT
Inuit Cultural Institute • ESKIMO POINT, NT X0C 0E0
  (819) 857-2803 Luke Suluk, Director

DENE MUSEUM/ARCHIVES
c/o General Delivery • FORT GOOD HOPE, NT X0E 0U0

AUGMARLIK INTERPRETIVE CENTRE
P.O. Box 225 • PANGNIRTUNG, NT X0A 0R0
  (819) 473-8737 Fax 473-8685; Sheila Garpik, Director

SIPALASEEQUTT MUSEUM SOCIETY
PANGNIRTUNG, NT X0A 0R0; Koaguk Akulujuk, Director

DENE CULTURAL INSTITUTE
P.O. Box 207 • YELLOWKNIFE, NT X1A 2N2
  (403) 873-6617; Joanne Burnaby, Executive Director

NOVA SCOTIA

NOVA SCOTIA MUSEUM
1747 Summer St. • HALIFAX, NS B3H 3A6
  (902) 429-4610; Candace Stevenson, Director
Description: Contains an extensive collection and exhibit of Micmac material culture--stone tools, basketry, birch bark objects, quill boxes, and bone implements. *Publications*: Micmac Quillwork; Elitekey; Red Earth; Withe Baskets, Traps and Brooms. Library.

ONTARIO

WOODLAND CULTURAL CENTRE
P.O. Box 1506, 184 Mohawk St. • BRANTFORD, ON N3T 5V6
  (519) 759-2653 Fax 759-2445; Tom Hill, Director

JOSEPH BRANT MUSEUM
1240 North Shore Blvd. • BURLINGTON, ON
Description: A collection of Joseph Brant (Iroquois) memorabilia; general material on the Iroquois culture. Library.

NORTH AMERICAN INDIAN TRAVELLING COLLEGE
RR #3 • CORNWALL ISLAND, ON K6H 5R7
Mail: P.O. Box 273, Hogansburg, NY 13655
  (613) 932-9452 Fax 932-0092; Barbara Barnes, Director

GOLDEN LAKE ALGONQUIN MUSEUM
P.O. Box 28 • GOLDEN LAKE, ON K0J 1X0

LAKE OF THE WOODS OJIBWAY CULTURAL CENTRE
P.O. Box 159 • KENORA, ON P9N 3X3
  (807) 548-5744 Fax 548-1591; Donald Kavanaugh, Director
  E-mail: ojibwaycc@voyageur.ca

THE McMICHAEL CANADIAN ART COLLECTION
10365 Islington Ave. • KLEINBERG, ON L0J 1C0
  (416) 893-1121; Jean Blodgett, Curator of Native Indian and Inuit Art
Description: Collection includes contemporary Canadian Woodland and Plains paintings, drawings and sculpture; some Northwest Coast Indian material culture. *Special program*: School program and resource package entitled: "Contemporary Expressions: Indian Art." Publications: Quarterly newsletter; exhibition catalogs. Library.

MUSEUM OF INDIAN ARCHAEOLOGY
University of Western Ontario, Lawson-Jury Bldg.
LONDON, ON N6G 3M6 (519) 473-1360
  William D. Finlayson, Ph.D., Executive Director
  Debra Bodner, Curator
Description: Large (over one-half million specimens) archaeological collections from throughout southern Ontario; small ethnographic collection from Ontario, Canadian Plains, and the Arctic. Lawson Prehistoric Indian Village: An open-air facility featuring excavation, reconstruction and interpretation of a prehistoric Neutral village. *Programs*: Exhibition Gallery; study and layout space; tours and lectures; Research Associate Program; Archaeological Contracting and Consulting Services; archaeological field schools and courses. *Publications*: Newsletter; Bulletin; Research Reports. Library.

OJIBWA CULTURAL FOUNDATION
Excelsior Post Office, West Bay • MANITOULIN ISLAND, ON T0P 1G0
  (705) 377-4902/4899

CHIEFSWOOD MUSEUM
P.O. Box 5000 • OHSWEKEN, ON N0A 1M0
  (519) 752-5005 Fax 752-9578; Paula Whitlow, Director

NATIONAL MUSEUM OF MAN - NATIONAL MUSEUMS OF CANADA
OTTAWA, ON K1A 0M8 (819) 994-6113 (Archaeological Survey of Canada)
  (613) 996-4540 (Canadian Ethnological Service)
  Ian G. Dyck, Ph.D., Chief-Archaeology; A. McFadyen Clark, Chief Ethnologist

Archaeological Collection: Contains 2,500,000+ specimens from Canada & Alaska; collections from the Eastern Woodlands (Ontario eastward to the Atlantic Provinces) and the Eskimo (Arctic) areas; the Arctic Coast, Northwest Coast, Plateau, western Boreal forest, and Plains. *Ethnological Collection*: Approximately 50,000 artifacts, 90 of which are Canadian Indian and Inuit material (including modern works of Indian and Inuit art) with emphasis on Inuit and Pacific Coast Indian traditional material culture. *Programs*: Responsible for the survey & rescue of Canada's prehistoric sites; to record the languages & cultures of Canadian Indians, Inuit & Metis. Publications. Library.

LAURENTIAN UNIVERSITY MUSEUM & ARTS CENTRE
John St. • SUDBURY, ON P3E 2C6
  (705) 674-3271 Pamela Krueger, Director/Curator
Description: Collection areas relate to contemporary native and Inuit artists of Canada, and native and Indian artists of Northern Ontario; over 800 works by 600+ Canadian artists, historical & contemporary; over 25 exhibitions are presented each year. *Special programs*: Talks & tours; lectures; art courses; film series. *Publications*: Communique, published every six weeks; exhibition catalogues. Library.

OJIBWAY & CREE CULTURAL CENTRE
210 Spruce St. S., Suite 304 • TIMMINS, ON P4N 2M7
  (705) 267-7911 Fax 267-4988; Bertha Metat, Director
  E-mail: ojcc@onlink.net
Description: Exhibits materials describing the history of the Cree, Oji-Cree, and Ojibway of the Treaty #9 area of Northern Ontario. The Center has over 200 photographs both archival and contemporary, and 182 objects that include traditional dress, games, tools, and contemporary craftwork. Opened in 1975.

ROYAL ONTARIO MUSEUM
100 Queens Park • TORONTO, ON M5S 2C6
  (416) 586-5724 Fax 586-5863; Mima Kapches, Chairperson
Ethnology: Collections of material for the following geographical areas and tribes: Arctic--Eastern Canadian Eskimo, Netsilik Eskimo, Copper Eskimo, Western Canadian Eskimo; Northwest Coast--Kwakiutl, Tsimshian, Haida, Gitskan, Bella Bella; Northeast Coast--Iroquois, Cree Ojibwa, Montagnais-Naskapi; Plains--Blackfoot, Cree and Saulteaux, Canadian Plains. *Archaeology*: Provincial collections of Ontario archaeological material; and material from the rest of Canada; material from the U.S., including the Southwest and Mississippi Valley cultures. *Publications*: Archaeological Newsletter; Rotunda, quarterly magazine; Monographs and Papers; Round Lake Ojibwa (monograph); contemporary native arts catalogs; Native People of Canada (7 booklets); books for sale. Library.

QUEBEC

CANADIAN MUSEUM OF CIVILIZATION
100 Laurier St., P.O. Box 3100 Station B
GATINEAU, PQ J8X 4H2 (819) 776-8430
  Website: www.civilization.ca; Andrea Laforet, Director
  Morgan Baillargeon, Curator-Plains Indian Ethnology
  Gerald McMaster, Curator-Contemporary Indian Art
Description: Concerned with the national representation of artwork, artifacts & documentation relative to archaeology, ethnology, physical anthropology, folk culture and history. Library & Archives.

AVATAQ CULTURAL INSTITUTE, INC.
P.O. Box 230 • INUKJUAK, PQ J0M 1M0
  (819) 254-8919 Fax 254-8148

KANIEN'KEAKA RAOTITIONKWA CULTURAL CENTRE
P.O. Box 969 • KAHNAWAKE, PQ J0L 1B0
  (514) 638-0880 Fax 638-0920; Kana Pakta, Director
Description: To promote, preserve, & maintain the culture of the Kanien'kehaka and the Iroquois. Maintains a library, cultural exhibit, & photographic archives. Annual Proud Nation Powwow in July.

KANEHSATAKE CULTURAL CENTRE
681 Ste. Philomene • KANEHSATAKE, PQ J0N 1E0
  (514) 479-1783 Fax 479-8249; Steven L. Bonspille, Director

LISTUGUJ ARTS & CULTURAL CENTRE
2 Riverside West • LISTUGUJ, PQ G0C 2R0
  (418) 788-9088 Fax 788-5980; Olitha Isaac, Director

KITIGAN ZIBI CULTURAL EDUCATION DISPLAYS CENTRE
41 Kikinamage Mikan • MANIWAKI, PQ J9E 3B1
  (819) 449-1798 Gilbert Whiteduck, Director

MUSEE AMERINDIEN DE MASHTEWIATSH
1787 rue Amishk • MASHTEWIATSH, PQ G0W 2H0
  (418) 275-4842 Fax 275-7494; Florent Begin, Director

MUSEE DES ABENAKIS
108 Waban-aki St. • ODANAK, PQ J0G 1H0
  (514) 568-2600 Fax 568-5959; Nichole O'Bomsawin, Director
  E-mail: abenakis@enternet.com

AMERINDIAN MUSEUM
406 Amisk • POINTE-BLEUE, PQ G0W 2H0
  Carmen Gill Casavante, Director

INSTITUT EDUCATIF ET CULTUREL ATTIKAMEK-MONTAGNOMIS
40 rue Francois Gros-Louis, No. 7 • VILLAGE DES HURONS, PQ G0A 4V0
  (418) 968-4424 Fax 968-1841; Luc Anbre, Director

SASKATCHEWAN

BATTLEFORD NATIONAL HISTORIC PARK MUSEUM
P.O. Box 70 • BATTLEFORD, SK

PRAIRIE PIONEER MUSEUM
P.O. Box 273 • CARIK, SK

MOOSE JAW ART MUSEUM
Crescent Park • MOOSE JAW, SK

SASKATCHEWAN INDIAN CULTURAL CENTRE
P.O. Box 3085 • SASKATOON, SK S7K 0S2
  (306) 244-1146 Fax 665-6520; Linda Pelly-Landrie, Director

THE SASKATOON GALLERY & CONSERVATORY MUSEUM
Mendel Art Gallery, 950 Spadina Crescent E. • SASKATOON, SK

VIGFUSSON MUSEUM
University of Saskatchewan, Room 69, Arts Bldg. • SASKATOON, SK

LIBRARIES & ARCHIVES

ALBERTA

UNIVERSITY OF CALGARY LIBRARY
Arctic Institute of North America Collection
2500 University Dr. N.W. • CALGARY, AB T2N1N4
  (403) 220-5650 Fax 282-6837; Website: www.ucalgary.ca/library
  Eric Tull, Librarian; E-mail: tull@ucalgary.ca
Description: Covers Northern Studies of all disciplines.

HISTORICAL RESOURCES LIBRARY
Provincial Archives of Alberta, 12845 102 Ave. • EDMONTON, AB T5N 0M6
  (403) 427-1750 Fax 454-6629; Margaret E. Bhatnagar, Librarian
Description: A collection of 20,000 volumes on local history (Alberta), western Canadian history, archaeology & ethnology. *Publications*: Bibliography & Literature Guide. Interlibrary loans. Open to public.

UNIVERSITY OF ALBERTA - COLLEGE OF ST. JEAN LIBRARY
8406 91st St. • EDMONTON, AB T6C 4G9
Description: Maintains a collection of 50,000 volumes, many of which are on the anthropology and ethnology of North American Indians.

PETER BULL MEMORIAL LIBRARY
Maskwachees Cultural College, Box 360 • HOBBEMA, AB T0C 1N0
  (403) 585-3925 Fax 585-2080; Linacre Griffiths, Librarian
Description: Collection focuses on Cree, Alberta Natives, Canadian & North American Indigenous Peoples.

BRITISH COLUMBIA

UNIVERSITY COLLEGE OF THE FRASER VALLEY LIBRARY
33844 King Rd. • ABBOTSFORD, BC V2S 7M8
  (604) 504-7441 Fax 853-0796; Website: www.ucfv.bc.ca/library
  Patti Wilson, Coordinator
Description: Collection consists of about 1,500 monographs on Canada's First Nations, with a strong focus on British Columbia.

U'MISTA CULTURAL CENTER LIBRARY & ARCHIVES
P.O. Box 253 • ALERT BAY, BC V0N 1A0
  (250) 974-5403 Fax 974-5499

E-mail: umista@north.island.net
Description: Collection of over 2,000 volumes, audio recordings & microfiche on Indians of North America, Kwakwaka'Wakw (formerly Kwakiutl). Arts & Crafts of British Columbia.

MALASPINA UNIVERSITY LIBRARY
222 Cowichan Way • DUNCAN, BC V9L 6P4
(250) 746-3517 Fax 746-3531; Linda Leger, Librarian
E-mail: leger@mala.bc.ca
Description: Collection comprises all aspects of First Nations culture, religion, social issues, education, ethnography, etc. Subjects include B.C. Nations issues, Metis, & Indians of North America

LILLOOET PUBLIC LIBRARY
930 Main St., Box 939 • LILLOOET, BC V0K 1V0
(250) 256-7944 Fax 256-7928
Description: First Nations Interest Collection - 300 titles.

NISGA'A LANGUAGE & CULTURE CENTRE ARCHIVES
Box 100 • New Aiyansh, BC V0J 1A0
(250) 633-2234 Fax 633-2697; Fran Johnson, Library Technician

UNION OF B.C. INDIAN CHIEFS RESOURCE CENTRE
342 Water St., 4th Floor • VANCOUVER, BC V6B 1B6
(604) 602-9555 Fax 684-5726; Wendy Ancell, Librarian
Website: www.ubcic.bc.ca
Description: Collection focuses on Canada's First Nations with an emphasis on both historical & contemporary issues.

UNIVERSITY OF BRITISH COLUMBIA LIBRARY
Humanities & Social Sciences Division
1956 East Mall • VANCOUVER, BC V6T 1W3
(604) 228-2725 Fax 228-6465
Description: Maintains a strong academic collection, specializing in the Indians of the Northwest Pacific Coast (especially British Columbia) but also Canadian aboriginal peoples in general. Interlibrary loans. Open to public.

UBC LAW LIBRARY
1822 East Mall • VANCOUVER, BC V6T 1Z1
(604) 822-9379 Fax 822-6864; Website: www.law.library.ubc.ca
E-mail: law.library@ubc.ca
Elim Wong, Reference Librarian; E-mail: elim.wong@ubc.ca

XWI7XWA LIBRARY
First Nations House of Learning
1985 West Mall, University of British Columbia
VANCOUVER, BC V6T 1Z2 (604) 822-2385 Fax 822-3893
Website: www.library.ubc.ca/xwi7xwa
E-mail: doyle@interchange.ubc.ca; Ann Doyle, Librarian
Description: Collection provides curriculum & research support for UBC First Nations programs: the Native Indian Teacher Education Program, First Nations Law Program, Ts"kel Graduate Program, et al. Covers First Nations in BC.

MANITOBA

ESKIMO MUSEUM LIBRARY
242 La Verendrye St. • CHURCHILL, MB R0B 0E0
(204) 675-2541
Description: A collection of ethnographic material on the Eskimos.

CENTER FOR INDIGENOUS ENVIRONMENTAL RESOURCES
245 McDermot Ave., 3rd Floor • WINNIPEG, MB R3B 0S6
(204) 956-0660 Fax 956-1895; Larry Laliberte, Director
Website: www.cier.mb.ca
Description: Collection consists of First Nation environmental material, core western environmental texts & material that integrates traditional ecological knowledge with western scientific theory. Books in English, Cree & Ojibwa languages.

DEPARTMENT OF CULTURAL AFFAIRS & HISTORICAL RESOURCES PROVINCIAL ARCHIVES
200 Vaughan St. • WINNIPEG, MB R3C 0V8
Focus Program: A collection of master tapes & duplicates made with Indian people in Manitoba.

UNIVERSITY OF MANITOBA LIBRARIES
Elizabeth Dafoe Library • WINNIPEG, MB R3T 2N2
(204) 474-6846 Fax 474-7577; Website: www.ccu.umanitoba.ca
Description: Collection covers all aspects of Aboriginal culture & history with an emphasis on Woodland peoples of Eastern North America.

NEWFOUNDLAND

MEMORIAL UNIVERSITY OF NEWFOUNDLAND
Centre for Newfoundland Studies
Elizabeth Ave. • ST. JOHNS, NF A1B 3Y1
(709) 737-7476 Fax 737-3188; Anne Hart, Librarian
Description: Holdings include materials on Beothuk, Naskapi-Montagnais, Micmac, Dorset, Innu, Maritime Archaic, & Inuit peoples. Also an archives, holding a small collection of manuscript material on some of these peoples.

NORTHWEST TERRITORIES

AURORA COLLEGE-THEBACHA CAMPUS LIBRARY
Bag Service #2 • FORT SMITH, NT X0E 0P0
(867) 872-7544 Fax 872-4511; Alexandra Hook, Librarian
E-mail: ahook@auroracollege.nt.ca
Description: Collection of books on Native Studies & Northern Studies, focusing on Native Canadian related material. English, Cree & Chipewyan languages.

NORTHWEST TERRITORIES LIBARY SERVICES
Rm. 207 & 209 Wright Centre, 62 Woodland Dr. • HAY RIVER, NT X0E 1G1
(867) 874-6531 FAX 874-3321
Brian Dawson, Head of Tech. Services
E-mail: brian_dawson@gov.nt.ca
Description: Coordinates the operation of 19 public libraries through-out the NWT. Included in the collection is a "Northern" collection as well as items in the following languages: Inuktitut, Cree, Gwich'in, North Slavey, South Slavey, Chipewyan & Dogrib.

NOVA SCOTIA

DALHOUSIE UNIVERSITY MARITIME SCHOOL OF SOCIAL WORK LIBRARY
6420 Coburg Rd. • HALIFAX, NS B3H 3J5
Special collection: Native Peoples Collection- books and journals on Indians, Eskimos and Metis.

NOVA SCOTIA MUSEUM LIBRARY
1747 Summer St. • HALIFAX, NS B3H 3A6
Description: Contains a collection of books on Micmac material culture and ethnography.

MI'KMAQ RESOURCE CENTRE
c/o University College of Cape Breton
P.O. Box 5300 • SYDNEY, NS B1P 2L6
(902) 563-1660 Fax 562-8899; Patrick Johnson, Director
Description: Collection consists of material related to Mi'kmaq history, culture & language including basketmaking, costume & adornment, cultural assimilation, dances, dwellings, education, folklore, games, governmental relations, legal status/laws, legends.

ONTARIO

WOODLAND CULTURAL CENTRE LIBRARY & RESEARCH CENTRE
P.O. Box 1506 • BRANTFORD, ON N3T 5V1
(519) 759-2650 Fax 759-8912; Winnie Jacobs, Library Technician
Description: Collection includes contemporary books & current issues, First Nation's newspapers, magazines and journals, and an extensive collection on the Royal Commission Report on Aboriginal Peoples. Literature materials promoting the history, culture, heritage of First nations peoples, particularly of the Eastern Woodland areas.

KANHIOTE - TYENDINAGA TERRITORY PUBLIC LIBRARY
Tyendinaga Mohawk Territory
1644 York Rd. • DESERONTO, ON K0K 1X0
(613) 967-6264 Fax 396-3627; Karen Lewis, Librarian

NEW CREDIT PUBLIC LIBRARY
Mississaugas of the Credit First Nation
R.R. #6 • HAGERSVILLE, ON N0A 1H0
(905) 768-5686 Fax 768-1225; Mike Brant, Librarian
Description: Collection of material on the Anishnabeg community and material relating to other cultural groups.

INDIAN & NORTHERN AFFAIRS CANADA
INAC Departmental Library
Rm. 1400, 10 Wellington St. • GATINEAU, PQ K1A 0H4
(819) 997-0811 Fax 953-5491; Julia Finn, Librarian
Website: www.ainc-inac.gc.ca; E-mail: reference@ainc-inac.gc.ca

Description: Collections contain a total of more than 50,000 titles (70,000 volumes). The main focus is Canada's Aboriginal peoples and the Canadian North. The Library is an excellent source of information on the department's history and the evolution of its relations with Canada's Aboriginal peoples and the Canadian North. Other subjects covered include Canadian history, the environment, political science, economic development, public administration, and information technology. Includes a collection of Canadian Aboriginal and northern magazines, about 2,000 rare books, and a microfilm copy of the department's historic files on Indian affairs. *Special programs*: The Library's catalogue is available for searching on the internet at http://virtua.ainc-inac.gc.ca. Established 1966.

CHIPPEWAS OF THE THAMES LIBRARY & RESOURCE CENTER
RR #1 • Muncey, ON N0L 1Y0
 (519) 289-5555 Fax 289-2230; Delores Sturgeon, Librarian
Description: Native North American & Mexican collection dealing particularly with Ojibway history, language, political science, local history including Council books from the beginning of Department Governance. Collection consists mainly of Ojibway, and some Potawatomi materials; language tapes of Ojibwa, and some native newsletters.

ASSEMBLY OF FIRST NATIONS RESOURCE CENTRE
AFN Library, One Nicholas St. #1002 • OTTAWA, ON K1N 7B7
 (613) 241-6789 Fax 241-5808; Kelly Whiteduck, Coordinator
 E-mail: kwhiteduck@afn.ca
Description: Maintains a collection of 10,000 volumes on treaty and aboriginal rights, with special collections on education, alcohol and drug abuse, lands revenue & Trust Review, etc.; books and mono-graphs (unpublished reports); 100 Native-American periodicals; and law cases. A reference library - Monday-Friday, 9 AM - 5 PM.

INUIT TAPIRISAT OF CANADA LIBRARY
510 - 170 Laurier Ave. West • OTTAWA, ON K1P 5V5
 (613) 238-8181 Fax 234-1991; Paani Lecompte, Librarian
 Website: www.tapirisat.ca; E-mail: itc@tapirisat.ca

NATIONAL MUSEUMS OF CANADA LIBRARY
360 Lisgar St. • OTTAWA, ON K1A 0M8
Description: Maintains a collection of 35,000 volumes on anthropology, including many on the Indians and native peoples of Canada. Museocinematography: Ethnographic Film Programs.

LAURENTIAN UNIVERSITY MUSEUM & ARTS CENTRE LIBRARY
Laurentian University, Dept. of Cultural Affairs
SUDBURY, ON P3E 2C6 (705) 675-1151 Fax 674-3065
 Pamela Krueger, Librarian
Description: A collection of books covering all areas of art with special sections on native and Inuit peoples. Open to the public.

UNIVERSITY OF SUDBURY LIBRARY
Ramsey Lake Rd. • SUDBURY, ON P3E 2C6
 (705) 673-5661 Ext. 208 Fax 673-4912
 Website: www.usudbury.com
 Olga Beaulieu, Library Director
Description: Collection covers Indians of North America specializing in Indians in Canada, tribes & cultures.

OJIBWAY & CREE CULTURAL CENTRE LIBRARY
150 Brousseau Ave., Unit B • TIMMINS, ON P4N 5Y4
 (705) 267-7911 FAX 267-4988; Website: www.occc.ca
 Dianne Riopel, Executive Director; E-mail: driopel@occc.ca
 Kathy Perreault, Coordinator; E-mail: kperreault@occc.ca
 Angela Shisheesh, Native language Coordinator
 E-mail: ashisheesh@occc.ca
Description: Collection focuses on the Aboriginal people of the Nishnawbe Aski Nation & North America. Books in English, Cree & Ojibwa.

FIRST NATIONS HOUSE LIBRARY
University of Toronto, 563 Spadina Ave., 3rd Fl. • TORONTO, ON M5S 1A1
 (416) 978-8227 Fax 978-1893; Ece Soydarn, Librarian

ROYAL ONTARIO MUSEUM LIBRARY
100 Queen's Park • TORONTO, ON M5S 2C6
Description: A collection of 50,000 volumes, and 20 journals of anthropological interest; many books on the Indians & native peoples of Canada.

QUEBEC

CANADIAN MUSEUM OF CIVILIZATION LIBRARY & ARCHIVES
P.O. Box 3100 Station B, 100 Laurier St.
GATINEAU, PQ J8X 4H2 (819) 776-7173 Fax 776-7152
 E-mail: library@civilization.ca; M. Boudreau, Reference Librarian
Description: Collections include books on life & cultures of First Nations of Canada (Indians, Metis & Inuit).

KANIEN'KEHAKA RAOTITIONHKWA LIBRARY
P.O. Box 969 • KAHNAWAKE MOHAWK TERRITORY, PQ J0L 1B0
 (450) 638-0880 Fax 638-0920; Kara Dawne Zemel, Librarian
 Website: www.korkahnawake.org; E-mail: kor@korkahnawake.org
Description: Collection's main focus on the Iroquois more specifically the Mohawk. Houses 5,000+ books & articles. The library includes audio & video-tapes, microfiche, map reproductions, & other relevant documents.

SASKATCHEWAN

GABRIEL DUMONT INSTITUTE LIBRARY
48 - 12th St. East • PRINCE ALBERT, SK S6V 1B2
 (306) 922-6466 Fax 763-4834; Sharon Wood, Librarian
Description: Collection of books on Metis culture & history; teacher education. Books in English, Cree & Chipewyan languages.

SASKATCHEWAN INDIAN FEDERATED COLLEGE LIBRARY
University of Regina, 218 College West • REGINA, SK S4S 0A2
 (306) 779-6269; Website: www.sfic.edu
Description: A specialized collection of materials of over 50,000 items that include monographs, periodicals, newspapers, microfilm, audiovisual materials & kits. Covers Indigenous Peoples of North, South & Central America, of Indian, Inuit, and Metis ancestry.

NATIVE LAW CENTRE LIBRARY
University of Saskatchewan
101 Diefenbaker Place • SASKATOON, SK S7N 5B8
 (306) 966-6197 Fax 966-6207
 Website: www.library.usask.ca/dbs/natlaw.html
 Linda Fritz, Darlene Fichter, Library Coordinators
 E-mail: native_project@library.usask.ca
Description: A collection of 6,000 books, journals and legal decisions in all areas of Native law including self-government, constitutional developments, membership rights, child welfare and international law. A major retrospective cataloguing project has recently been completed, making historical documents from various native organizations & older published works accessible. Archival collection of materials from the Mackenzie Valley Pipeline Inquiry; and a complete collection of Native Law Cases.

SASKATCHEWAN INDIAN CULTURAL CENTRE LIBRARY
120 - 33rd St. East • SASKATOON, SK S7K 0S2
 (306) 244-1146 Fax 665-6520; Donna Ahenakew, Director
 E-mail: info@sicc.sk.ca
Description: Books, videos, films, microfilm, and vertical file material on First Nations of Saskatchewan: culture, history & language.

YUKON

YUKON COLLEGE LIBRARY
500 College Dr. • WHITEHORSE, YUKON Y1A 5K4
 (867) 668-8870 Fax 668-8808; Rob Sutherland, Librarian
 Website: www.yukoncollege.yk.ca/library
Description: Collection covers the subjects of the Yukon & Northern Canada's First Nations.

YUKON NATIVE LANGUAGE CENTRE
Yukon College, Box 2799 • WHITEHORSE, YUKON Y1A 5K4
 (867) 668-8820 Fax 668-8825; Website: www.yukoncollege.yk.ca/ynlc
 E-mail: jjohnson@yukoncollege.yk.ca; Jo-Anne Johnson, Coordinator
Description: Maintains a collection of books on linguistics, languages, ethnography, history (Alaska, Yukon, B.C., & Northwest Territories), folklore, education, and reference books. *Special programs*: Training sessions for Native Language teachers & literacy sessions with linguists, fluent speakers & Native language teachers. Not open to the public. Established 1988.

PERIODICALS & MAGAZINES

ABORIGINAL VOICES MAGAZINE
116 Spadina Ave. #201 • Toronto, ON M5V 2K6
(416) 703-4577 Fax 703-7996

ACHIMOWEN
Box 90 • Fort Chipewyan, AB T0P 1B0
(780) 697-3740 Fax 697-3826

AFN BULLETIN
Assembly of First Nations, One Nicholas St. #1002 • Ottawa, ON K1N 7B7
(613) 241-6789 Fax 241-5808. Bi-monthly newsletter. $18.00/year.

AKWESASNE NOTES
Mohawk Nation, Box 30 • St. Regis, PQ H0M 1A0
(613) 575-9531 Fax 575-2935

ALBERTA NATIVE NEWS
530-10036 Jasper Ave. • Edmonton, AB T5J 2W2
(403) 421-7966 Fax 424-3951

ALBERTA SWEETGRASS
The Aboriginal Multi-Media Society (AMMSA)
13245 - 146 St. • Edmonton, AB T5L 4S8
(780) 455-2700 Fax 455-7639; Shari Narine, Editor
Website: www.ammsa.com/sweetgrass/
E-mail: sweetgrass@ammsa.com. Alberta's aboriginal newspaper.

ANISHINABE NEWS
Nipissing First Nation, Box 711 • North Bay, ON P1B 8J8
(705) 497-9127 Fax 497-9135

ANTHROPOLOGICAL JOURNAL OF CANADA
Anthropological Association of Canada
1575 Forlan Dr. • Ottawa, ON K2C 0R8

ARTSCRAFT
The National Indian Arts and Crafts Corporation
1 Nicholas St. # 1106 • Ottawa, ON K1N 7B6 - Canada
(613) 232-2436 Claudette Fortin, Editor
A quarterly publication that includes feature articles on Indian arts and crafts; regional profiles and artist's profiles; & book reviews. Subscription, $16 per year. Begun 1989.

ASSOCIATION FOR NATIVE DEVELOPMENT IN THE PERFORMING & VISUAL ARTS NEWSLETTER
27 Carlton St. #208 • Toronto, ON M5B 1L2

AWA'K'WIS NEWSPAPER
Box 2490 • Port Hardy, BC V0N 1P0
(604) 949-9433 Fax 949-9677

BATCHEWANA FIRST NATION NEWSLETTER
236 Frontenac St. • Sault Ste. Marie, ON P6A 5K9
(705) 759-0914 Fax 759-9171; Darlene Syrette, Editor

BLOOD TRIBE NEWS (TSINIKSSINI)
Box 410 • Standoff, AB T0L 1Y0 (403) 737-2121 Fax 737-2336
Tsinnikssini: Tribal administration newsmagazine.

BROTHER OF TIME
Native Brotherhood of Millhaven, P.O. Box 280 • Bath, ON K0H 1G0

CANADIAN ETHNIC STUDIES
Research Centre for Canadian Ethnic Studies
University of Calgary, 2500 University Dr., N.W
Calgary, AB T2N 1N4 (403) 220-7257 Fax 282-8606
J.S. Frideres, Editor
Book reviews. Triannual journal. 1,250 cir. $30/year; institutions, $36/year.

CANADIAN INDIAN ARTCRAFTS
National Indian Arts & Crafts Corporation
One Nicholas St. #1106 • Ottawa, ON K1N 7B6
Published quarterly.

CANADIAN JOURNAL OF NATIVE EDUCATION
University of Alberta, 5-109 Education N. Bldg.
Edmonton, AB T6G 2G5 (403) 492- 2769 Fax 492-0762
Carl Urion, Editor

Semiannual. Covers the education of native peoples in North America with special focus on Canada. Includes Inuit, Metis and Indian people. Book reviews. 750 cir. $8/copy; $15/year. Advertising.

CANADIAN JOURNAL OF NATIVE STUDIES
Dept. of Native Studies, Brandon University
Brandon, MB R7A 6A9 Samuel W. Corrigan, Editor
An international refereed periodical published twice annually. It is the official publication of the Canadian Indian/Native Studies Association.

CANADIAN NATIVE LAW REPORTER
Native Law Centre, University of Saskatchewan
Rm. 141, Diefenbaker Centre • Saskatoon, SK S7N 0W0
(306) 966-6189; Zandra MacEachern, Editor
Contributing editors: Donald Purich, Phil Lancaster, Norman K. Zlotkin, and Nancy Ayers.
A specialized law report series, providing full, comprehensive coverage of native law judgments in Canada. *Research features*: subject index, statutes judicially considered; year-end cumulative indexes; articles & case comments. Advertising. Published quarterly (March, June, September & December.) *Subscription*: $50/year (Canadian). $45/year; 1979-1983, $30/year. Back issues available.

CENTRAL OKANAGON FRIENDSHIP SOCIETY NEWSLETTER
442 Leon Ave. • Kelowna, BC V1Y 6J3
(604) 861-4905 Fax 861-5514

CHIPPEWA TRIBUNE
978 Tashmoo Ave. • Sarnia, ON N7T 7H5
(519) 336-8410 Fax 336-0382

CLICKS & BITS COMMUNICATIONS, INC.
1902b - 11th St. S.E. • Calgary, AB T2G 3G2
(403) 265-5361 Fax 234-7061

COUNCIL FIRES
Box 2049 • Blind River, ON P0R 1B0
(705) 356-1691 Fax 356-1090

CREE AJEMON
James Bay Cree Communications Society
MISTASSINI, PQ G0W 1C0 (418) 923-319

DAKOTA TIMES
Box 151 • Griswold, MB R0M 0S0
(204) 855-2250

DAN SHA NEWS
Ye Sa to Communications Society
22 Nisutlin Dr. • Whitehorse YT Y1A 3S5
(403) 667-2775 Fax 668-6577
Joanne MacDonald, Publisher; Eric Huggard, Editor
Monthly newspaper covering Yukon Indian issues and community events. 2,700 cir. $12/year, individuals; $25/year, institutions. Advertising. Begun 1973.

DANNZHA
Ye Sa To Communications Society
22 Nisutlin Dr. • Whitehorse, Yukon Y1A 3S5
(403) 667-7636/2775

THE EAGLE'S VOICE
Box 2250 • Lac La Biche, AB T0A 2C0
(403) 453-6100 Fax 453-6259

EASTERN DOOR
Box 326 • Kahnawake, PQ J0L 1B0
(514) 635-3050 Fax 635-8479

ENOCH ECHO
Enoch Tribal Administration, Box 2, Site 2, RR 1 • Winterburn, AB T0E 2N0
(403) 470-4505

ESKIMO
P.O. Box 10 • Churchill, MB R0B E0E
(204) 675-2252 Guy Mary-Rousselier, Editor
Semiannual magazine on missionary history in the central and eastern Canadian Arctic and Inuit traditions. Published in French.

ESQUIMALT NEWS
542C Fraser St. • Victoria, BC V9A 6H7
(604) 381-5664 Fax 361-9283

ETHNIC DIRECTORY OF CANADA
Western Publishers, Box 30193, Sta. B • Calgary, AB
  (403) 289-3301; Vladimir Markotic, Editor
Published once every few years. Complimentary copies available.

ETUDES/INUIT/STUDIES
Inuksiutit Katimajiit Association
Dept. of Anthropology, Laval University • Quebec, P.Q. G1K 7P4
  (418) 656-2353 Fax 656-3023; Francois Therien, Editor
Semiannual journal devoted to the study of Inuit societies of Siberia,
Greenland, and Canada, either traditional or contemporary, in the perspective
of social sciences & humanities: archaeology, linguistics, symbolism, demog-
raphy, ethno-history and law. Contains articles in French and English on the
Inuit culture, language and history. Book reviews. 750 cir. $12/copy; $27/year,
individuals; $43/year, institutions. Back issues available. Advertising.

THE FIRST PERSPECTIVE
209 - 65 Dewdney Ave. • Winnipeg, MB R3B 0E1
  (204) 988-9400 Fax 988-9407

FIRST NATIONS COMMUNICATIONS, INC.
#2 - 875 Bank St. • Ottawa, ON K1S 3W4
  (800) 387-2532; (613) 231-3858 Fax 231-6613

FIRST NATIONS DRUM
2104 West 13th Ave. • Vancouver, BC V6K 2S1
  (604) 669-5539 (phone & fax)

FIRST NATIONS FREE PRESS
110 Athabasca Pl., 80 Chippewa Rd.
Sherwood Park, AB T8A 3Y1
  (403) 449-1803 Fax 449-1807

FIRST NATIONS LAW
c/o Ferguson Gifford, Barristers & Solicitors
666 Burard St., #500 • Vancouver, BC V6C 3H3
  (800) 267-3216; (604) 687-3216 Fax 683-2780

FIRST NATIONS MAGAZINE
CKND-TV, 603 St. Mary's Rd. • Winnipeg, MB R2M 4A5
  (204) 233-3304 Fax 233-5615

FIRST NATIONS STUDENTS VOICE
University of Manitoba
Box 02, University Centre • Winnipeg, MB R3T 2N2
  (204) 582-1522 Fax 989-2017

FIRST PEOPLES BUSINESS MAGAZINE
204-1111 Monroe Ave. • Winnipeg, MB R2K 3Z5

THE FIRST PERSPECTIVE
Brokenhead Ojibway Nation
General Delivery • Scanterbury, MB R0E 1W0
  (204) 766-2686

FOUR WORLDS EXCHANGE
Box 143 • Pincher Creek, AB T0K 1W0
  (403) 627-4411; Michael Bopp, Editor

FRIENDSHIP CENTRE NEWS
16 Spadina Rd. • Toronto, ON M5R 2S7
  (416) 964-9087

**GATHERINGS: THE EN'OWKIN JOURNAL OF FIRST
NORTH AMERICAN PEOPLES**
Theytus Books Ltd., P.O. Box 20040 • Penticton, BC V2A 8K3
Published annually by the En'owkin Centre of the International School of
Writing, a Native writer's school in Canada, affiliated with the University of
Victoria. Contents are poetry and fiction. 300 pages.

HA-SHILTH-SA
Box 1383 • Port Alberni, BC V9Y 7M2
  (604) 724-5757 Fax 723-0463

HOLMAN ESKIMO PRINTS
Canadian Arctic Producers Limited
P.O. Box 4132. Postal Station E • Ottawa, ON K1S 5S2

INDIAN & INUIT GRADUATE REGISTER
Canada Department of Indian Affairs and Northern Affairs
10 Wellington, • Ottawa, ON K1A 0H4

INDIAN FREE PRESS N'AMERIND
London's Indian Friendship Centre, 613 Wellington St. • London, ON

INDIAN LIFE MAGAZINE
P.O. Box 3765 Sta. B • Winnipeg, MB R2W 3R6

INDIAN LIFE MINISTRY
Intertribal Christian Communications
Box 3765 Sta. B • Winnipeg, MB R2W 3R6
  (204) 661-9333 Fax 661-3982; George McPeek, Director
  Jim Uttley, Editor & Publisher
Bimonthly. Contains feature news, first-person articles, photo features, family-
life material and legends. Focus is primarily on dealing with problems & issues
within contemporary North American Indian society.   150,000 cir. $1.50/copy;
$7/year. Advertising.

INDIAN MAGAZINE NEWSLETTER
Canadian Broadcasting Company, Publishers
Box 500, Station A • Toronto 116, ON

INDIAN NEWS
Canada Department of Indian Affairs and Northern Development
10 Wellington • Ottawa, ON K1A 0H4

INDIAN RECORD
480 Aulneau St. • Winnipeg, MB R2H 2V2
  (204) 233-6430; Rev. G. Laviolette, OMI, Editor
Contains articles on the Canadian Indians from coast to coast. Published
four /year. Advertising. Subscription: $4/year, $7/two years, $10/three years.

INDIAN TIME
Mohawk Nation, Box 189 • St. Regis, PQ H0M 1A0
  (518) 358-9531; (613) 575-2063 Fax 575-2935

THE INDIAN VOICE
Canadian Indian Voice Society, 429 East 6th St. N. • Vancouver, BC V7L 1P8
  (604) 876-0944 Donna Doss, Editor
Quarterly newsletter covering areas affecting the native Indian.
2,800 cir. $1/copy; $7/year. Advertising. Begun 1969.

INDIAN WORLD MAGAZINE
Union of British Columbia Indian Chiefs
440 W. Hastings, 3rd Fl. • Vancouver, BC V6B 1L1
  (604) 684-0231

INDIANS OF QUEBEC
c/o Coalition of Nations. P.O. Box 810
Caughnawaga, PQ J0L 1B0 (514) 632-7321

THE INDIGENOUS TIMES
#250 - 103C Packham Ave. • Saskatoon, SK S7N 4K4
  (306) 975-3969 Fax 975-3759

INUKTITUT
Inuit Tapirisat of Canada, 170 Laurier W. • Ottawa, ON K1P 5V5
  (613) 238-8181 Fax 234-1991; John Bennett & Alootook Ipellie, Editors
Quarterly magazine promoting the exchange of cultural information among
Inuit groups in Canada and to inform non-Inuit about Inuit life. 10,000 cir.
$7/copy. Advertising. Begun 1959.

INUVIALUIT
Committee for Original People's Entitlement
P.O. Box 200 • Inuvik, NT X0E 0T0

JOURNAL OF INDIGENOUS STUDIES
Gabriel Dumont Institute of Native Studies & Applied Research
121 Broadway Ave. E. • Regina, SK S4N 0Z6
  (306) 522-5691 Fax 565-0809; Catherine I. Littlejohn, Editor
Semiannual. 200 cir. Individuals, $10/copy; $20/year;
Institutions, $15/copy; $30/year. Begun 1989.

KAHTOU COMMUNICATIONS, INC.
Native Communications Society of BC
203-540 Burrard St. • Vancouver, BC V6C 2K1
  (604) 684-7375 Fax 684-5375; Tim Isaac, Managing Editor
Biweekly newspaper. $15/year.

KAHTOU NEWS: THE VOICE OF BC FIRST NATIONS
K'Watamus Publications, P.O. Box 192 • Sechelt, BC V0N 3A0
  (604) 885-7391 Fax 885-7397

KAINAI NEWS
Indian News Media, P.O. Box 120 • Standoff, AB T0L 1Y0
  (403) 653-3301 Fax 653-3437; Mary Weasel Fat, Editor
A weekly newspaper that covers issues of interest to status, non-status and Metis people of southern Alberta. Extensive coverage of the Treaty 7 tribes located in southern Alberta. The tribes are Blackfoot, Blood, Peigan, Carcee and Stoney. Coverage is extended to the urban cities of Calgary and Lethbridge. Advertising accepted. Complimentary copies are available upon request. Maintains a Calgary Bureau locate at Calgary Friendship Centre. $20/year; 50¢ per copy. Begun 1968.

KATERI
P.O. Box 70 • Kahnawake, PQ J0L 1B0
  (514) 525-3611 Rev. Henri Bechard, S.J., Editor
"Its aim is to promote the canonization of Blessed Kateri Tekakwitha; articles on life of the Beata, nes concerning the native peoples of North America, with special emphasis on her own people, the account of favors due to her intercession." Published quarterly. Subscription: $3/year. No advertising. Complimentary copies available upon request. Begun 1949.

KINATUINAMOT ILENGAJUK
Okalakatiget Society, Box 160 • Nain, Labrador, NF A0P 1E0
  (709) 922-2955 Fax 922-2293; Ken Todd, Editor
Newsletter.

THE LABRADORIAN
Box 39, Station "B" • Goose Bay, NF A0P 1E0
  (709) 896-3341 Fax 896-8781

LE CHEWITAN
Cree Indian Centre, 95 rue Jaculet • Chibougamau, PQ G8P 2G1
  (418) 788-2136 Fax 748-6954

LE METIS
410 McGregor St. • Winnipeg, MB R2W 4X5
  (204) 589-4327 Fax 586-6462

LISTUGUJ WI'GATIGN COMMUNITY NEWSLETTER
17 Riverside West • Listuguj, PQ H2V 4S0
  (514) 788-2136 Fax 788-2058

MACKENZIE TIMES
Box 499 • Fort Simpson, NT X0E 0N0
  (403) 695-3330 Fax 695-2922

MAL-I-MIC NEWS
320 St. Mary's St. • Fredericton, NB E3A 2S4
  (506) 458-8422 Fax 450-3749

MANITOBA ASSN. OF NATIVE LANGUAGES NEWSLETTER
119 Sutherland Ave. • Winnipeg, MB R2W 3C9
  (204) 943-3707 Fax 947-6564

MANITOBA INDIAN EDUCATION ASSOCIATION NEWSLETTER
305 - 352 Donald Ave. • Winnipeg, MB R3B 2H8
  (204) 947-0421 Fax 942-3067

MASENAYEGUN NEWSPAPER
45 Robinson St. • Winnipeg, MB R2W 5H5
  (204) 586-8441 Fax 582-8261

MAWIO'MI JOURNAL
240 - 10036 Jasper Ave. • Edmonton, AB T5J 2W2
  (800) 463-9300; (403) 990-0303 Fax 429-7487

MESSENGER
William Head Institute, Indian Education Club, Box 10 • Metochosin, BC
  M. Walkus, Editor; Quarterly newsletter. $1/year. Begun 1970.

METIS ONTARIO NEWSLETTER
193 Holland Ave. • Ottawa, ON K1Y 0Y3
  (800) 263-4889; (613) 798-1488 Fax 722-4225

MICMAC NEWS
Nova Scotia Native Communications Society
Box 344 • Sydney, NS B1P 6H2
  (902) 539-0045 Fax 564-0430; Roy Gould, Publisher; Brian Douglas, Editor
Bimonthly newspaper containing local provincial & national issues on Canadian Indians. $7.00 per year.

MICMAC-MALISEET NEWS
Confederacy of Mainland Micmacs, Box 1590 • Truro, NS B2N 5V3
  (902) 895-6385 Fax 893-1520

THE MIDDEN
Archaeological Society of British Columbia
Box 520, Sta. A • Vancouver, BC V6C 2N3
  Kathryn Bernick, Editor
Contains articles, book reviews, news items related to British Columbia archaeology--prehistoric and historic periods. Published five times per year. Subscription: $10/year; $12/year, overseas.

MIRAMICHI NEWS
Miramichi Indian Agency, P.O. Box 509 • Chatham, NB

MOOSE TALK
Box 125 • Moosonee, ON P0L 1Y0 (705) 336-2510

MOSAIK
696 Buckingham Rd. • Winnipeg, MB R3R 1C2
  (204) 888-8245; Ted Alcuitas, Editor & Publisher
Monthly tabloid of news and views on multicultural events and issues that impact on the multicultural community, Book reviews. 3,500 cir. $35/year; $45/year foreign. Advertising. Begun 1983.

MUSEUM OF INDIAN ARCHAEOLOGY NEWSLETTER
University of Western Ontario, Lawson-Jury Bldg. • London, ON N6G 3M6
  (519) 473-1360; Debra Bodner, Editor

THE NATION
Box 151 • Chisasibi, PQ J0M 1E0 (head office)
Box 48036 • Montreal, PQ H2V 4S0
  (514) 278-9914 (phone & fax)

NATIVE CANADIAN
Native Canadian Centre of Toronto, 16 Spadina Rd. • Toronto, ON M5R 2S7
  (416) 964-9087 Fax 964-2111

NATIVE HEROES
#3, 10032 - 29A Ave. • Edmonton, AB T6N 6H4
  (403) 448-3715Fax 448-3964

NATIVE ISSUES
Native Peoples Support Group of Newfoundland and Labrador
Box 582, Sta. C • St. John's, NF A1C 5K8

NATIVE ISSUES MONTHLY
816 E. 10th Ave. • Vancouver, BC V5T 2B1
  (604) 873-1408 Fax 873-1920

NATIVE JOURNAL
P.O. Box 49039 • Edmonton, AB T5L 4R8
  (403) 448-9693 Fax 448- 9694

NATIVE NETWORK NEWS
13140 St. Albert Trail • Edmonton, AB T5L 4H4
  (403) 454-7076 Fax 452-3468

NATIVE NEWS NETWORK
Social Science Center, 3rd Floor, Rm. 3254
London, ON N6A 5C2

NATIVE PERSPECTIVE
Box 2550 • LacLa Biche, AB T0A 2C0
  (403) 623-3333

NATIVE PRESS
Native Communications Society of the Western N.W.T.
P.O. Box 1919, Aquarius Bldg. • Yellowknife, NT X1A 2P4
  (403) 873-2661 Fax 920-4205; Lee Selleck, Editor
Weekly newspaper serving 26 communities in the Western Northwest Territories. Book reviews. 5,600 cir. $1/copy; $25/year. Advertising. Begun 1971.

NATIVE SCENE MAGAZINE
202-115 Bannatyne Ave. • Winnipeg, MB R3B 0R3
  (204) 943-6475 Fax 942-1380

THE NATIVE SISTERHOOD
P.O. Box 515 • Kingston, ON K7L 4W7

NATIVE SPORTS NEWS
205-15517 Stony Plain Rd. • Edmonton, AB T3P 3Z1
(403) 486-7766

NATIVE STUDIES REVIEW
University of Saskatchewan, Native Studies Dept.
104 McLean Hall • Saskatoon, SK S7N 0W0
(306) 966-6208 Fax 966-6242; Semiannual journal.

THE NATIVE VOICE
200 - 1755 E. Hastings St. • Vancouver, BC V5L 1T1
(604) 255-4696 Fax 251-7107

NATIVE WOMEN IN THE ARTS JOURNAL
#101 - 141 Bathurst St. • Toronto, ON M5V 2R2
(416) 392-6800 Fax 392-6920

NATIVE WOMEN NEWSPAPER
10032-29A Ave. • Edmonton, AB T6N 1A8
(403) 448-3715; Monthly.

NATIVE YOUTH NEWS
90 Sioux Rd. • Sherwood Park, AB T8A 3X5
(403) 449-1803 Fax 449-1807

NATIVEBEAT
Box 1260 • Forest, ON N0N 1J0
(519) 786-2142 (phone & fax)

NATOTAWIN NEWS
c/o The Pas First Nation, Box 197 • The Pas, MB R9A 1K4
(204) 623-5483 Fax 623-5263

NDOODEMAK (MY FRIENDS/RELATIVES)
Manitoba Association for Native Languages
119 Sutherland Ave. • Winnipeg, MB R2W 3C9
(204) 943-3707 Fax 943-9312

NEECHEE CULTURE MAGAZINE
273 Selkirk Ave. • Winnipeg, MB R2W 2L5
(204) 586-3667 Fax 586-5165

NEIGHBOURHOOD PROFILE
Box 2868 • Winnipeg, MB R3C 4B4
(204) 256-2699 Fax 254-5302

NEW BREED MAGAZINE
#204 - 845 Broad St. • Regina, SK S4R 8G9
(306) 569-9995 Fax 569-3533

NEWS & VIEWS
Canada Department of Indian Affairs and Northern Development
10 Wellington • Ottawa, ON K1A 0H4

NICOLA INDIAN
Nicola Valley Indian Administration, P.O. Box 188 • Merritt, BC V0K 2B0
(604) 378-6441/4235

NORTHERN REPORTER
Box 310, Sta. "B" • Goose Bay, NF A0P 1E0
(709) 896-2595

THE NORTHERN STAR
Box 2212 • Yellowknife, NT X1A 2P6
(403) 873-2719 Fax 920-7719

NUNATSIAQ NEWS
Box 8 • Iqaluit, NT X0A 0H0
(819) 979-5357 Fax 979-4763

OMUSHKEGOW ARROW
Box 370 • Moose Factory, ON P0L 1W0
(705) 658-4222 Fax 658-4250

ONTARIO ARCHAEOLOGY
The Ontario Archaeological Society
126 Willowdale Ave. • Willowdale, ON M2N 4Y2
(416) 730-0797; Charles Garrad, Administrator
A learned refereed journal dedicated to the archaeoogy & prehistory of Ontario and the Northeast. Back issues are available for sale. Included in membership.

ONTARIO BIRCHBARK
Aboriginal Multi-Media Society of Alberta
13245 - 146 St • Edmonton, AB T5L 4S8
(780) 455-2700 Fax 455-7639; E-mail: market@ammsa.com
Website: www.ammsa.com/birchbark
Monthly publication serving the Aboriginal peoples of Ontario.

ONTARIO INDIAN
Union of Ontario Indians, 27 Queen St. E., 2nd Fl. • Toronto, ON M5C 2M6
(416) 366-3527 Dennis Martel, Editor. Published monthly. $10 per year.

ONTARIO NATIVE EXPERIENCE
Ontario Federation of Friendship Centres
234 Eglington Ave., E. #203 • Toronto, ON M4P 1K5

ONTARIO NATIVE WOMEN'S ASSOCIATION NEWSLETTER
115 N. May St. • Thunder Bay, ON P7C 3N8
(807) 623-3442 Fax 623-1104

PAPERS OF THE ALGONQUIAN CONFERENCE
Carleton University, Dept. of Linguistics • Ottawa, ON K1S 5B6
(613) 788-2809; William Cowan, Editor
Publishes papers given at annual Algonquian Conference. 300 cir. $25/copy.

PEACE HILLS COUNTRY NEWSPAPER
Box 509 • Hobbema, AB T0C 1N0
(403) 474-6283 Fax 477-1699

PENTICTON INDIAN BAND NEWSLETTER
RR 2, Site 50, Comp. 8 • Penticton, BC V2A 6J7
(604) 493-0048 Fax 493-2882

THE PHOENIX
Canadian Alliance in Solidarity With the Native Peoples
Box 574, Station "P" • Toronto, ON M5S 2T1
(416) 972-1573 Fax 972-6232
Quarterly magazine. Current issues seen from a Native perspective; also poetry and book reviews. $20/year.

PRAIRIE FORUM
Canadian Plains Research Center
University of Regina • Regina, SK S4S 0A2
(306) 585-4795 Fax 586-9862; Alvin Finkel, Editor
Semiannual journal of research relating to the Canadian Plains.
Book reviews. 400 cir. $13/copy; $20/year, individuals; $25/year, institutions.
Advertising.

RAVEN'S EYE
Aboriginal Multi-Media Society of Alberta
13245 - 146 St • Edmonton, AB T5L 4S8
(780) 455-2700 Fax 455-7639; E-mail: market@ammsa.com
Website: www.ammsa.com/ravenseye
Monthly publication serving the Aboriginal people of British Columbia and the Yukon.

RECHERCHES AMERINDIENNES AU QUEBEC
Societe de Recherches Amerindiennes au Quebec
6742 rue St. Denis • Montreal, PQ H2S 2S2
(514) 277-6178 Carole Levesque, Editor
Quarterly journal on the Native peoples of Quebec with an anthropological perspective. Text mainly in French. Book reviews. 1,500 cir. $8/copy. $24/year, individuals; $30/year, institutions. Advertising.

REDSKIN MAGAZINE
P.O. Box 321 • Ohsweken, ON N0A 1M0
(877) 794-0804; (519) 518-2009
Jody Martin, Owner; Mathew Hill, Operator
Website: redskinmargazine.ca
Hilary Chambers, Associate Editor/Media Relations
The First Indigenous Adult Entertainment Magzine.

RENCONTRE
Secretariat aux Affaires Autochtones
875 Grande Allee est. • Quebec, PQ G1R 4Y8
(418) 643-3166 Ann Picard, Publisher
Quarterly government publication for Quebec's Amerindian and Inuit peoples.

THE RUNNER: NATIVE MAGAZINE FOR COMMUNICATIVE ARTS
c/o ANDPVA, 39 Spadina Rd., 2nd Fl. • Toronto, ON M5R 2S9
(416) 972-0871 Fax 972-0892; Gary Farmer, Editor/Publisher

Promotes the talents, products & services of established & upcoming Native individuals and groups in the arts and communication fields. Includes news for Native writers, actors, filmmakers & radio & television people. Quarterly. $20/yr., individuals; $24/yr., institutions.

THE SACRED FIRE
2-Spirited People of the First Nation
202-476 Parliament St. • Toronto, ON M4X 1P2
(416) 961-4725 Fax 944-8381

SASKATCHEWAN ARCHAEOLOGICAL SOCIETY NEWSLETTER
Saskatchewan Archaeological Society
816 1st Ave. North #5 • Saskatoon, SK S7K 1Y3
(306) 664-4124 Jim Finnigan, Editor
A bi-monthly publication. No advertising. Included in membership.

SASKATCHEWAN ARCHAEOLOGY
Saskatchewan Archaeological Society
816 1st Ave. North #5 • Saskatoon, SK S7K 1Y3
(306) 664-4124 Terry Gibson, Editor
An annual publication. Included with membership. Begun 1980.

SASKATCHEWAN INDIAN
c/o ABCOM Publishers, 215 - 103B Packham Ave. • Saskatoon, SK S7N 4K4
(306) 242-2372 Fax 664-8851
Alex Greyeyes, Publisher; Doug Cuthand, Editor
Monthly magazine providing communication among Saskatchewan's almost 50,000 Treaty Indians through information news, stories and editorial opinion. Book reviews. 8,500 cir. $15/year; $3/copy. Advertising.

SASKATCHEWAN INDIAN FEDERATED COLLEGE JOURNAL
College W. Bldg., 127 • Regina, SK S4S 0A2
(306) 584-8333 Joel Demay, Editor
Semiannual. $15/year, individuals; $25/year, institutions.

SASKATCHEWAN SAGE
Aboriginal Multi-Media Society of Alberta
13245 - 146 St • Edmonton, AB T5L 4S8
(780) 455-2700 Fax 455-7639
Website: www.ammsa.com/saskatchewansage
E-mail: market@ammsa.com; Christine Fiddler, Editor
Monthly publication serving the Aboriginal peoples of Saskatchewan. Circulation: 8,000. Advertising. Subscription: C$30 per year.

THE SCOUT
Indian-Metis Friendship Centre/Brandon Friendship Centre
836 Lorne Ave. • Brandon, MB R7A 0TB

SECWEPEMC NEWS
Secwepemc Cultural Education Society
345 Yellowhead Hwy. • Kamloops, BC V2H 1H1
(604) 828-9784 Fax 372-1127
Newspaper of the Shuswap Nation containing current political, social and economic issues & events affecting their lives and promoting the preservation of Shuswap history, language & culture. Published six times per year.

STO:LO NATION NEWS
Box 370 • Sardis, BC V2R 1A7
(604) 858-9431 Fax 858-8488

STRAIT ARROW
#16 - 1630 Crescent View Dr. • Nanaimo, BC V9S 2N5 (604) 754-5155

SWEETGRASS GROWS ALL AROUND HER
Native Woman in the Arts, 401 Richmond St. #363 • Toronto, ON M5V1X3
(416) 598-4078 Fax 340-8458. Annual.

TANSAI JOURNAL
207- 13638 Grosvenor Rd. • Surrey, BC V3R 5C9
(604) 581-2522 Fax 582-4820

TAQRALIK
Northern Quebec Inuit Association, P.O. Box 179 • Fort Chimo, PQ J0M 1C0

TAWOW MAGAZINE
First Nations Communications
#2, 875 Bank St. • Ottawa, ON K1A 3W4
(800) 387-8357; (613) 231-3858 Fax 231-6613

TEKAWENNAKE NEWSPAPER
Tekawennake Publications, Box 130 • Ohsweken, ON N0A 1M0
(519) 445-2238 Fax 445-2434; Roberta Green, Editor
Weekly tabloid. Advertising.

TEKAWENNAKE SIX NATIONS NEW CREDIT REPORTER
Woodland Indian Cultural Education Center
184 Mohawk St., Box 1506 • Brantford, ON N3T 5V6
(519) 753-5531; Roberta Green, Editor & Publisher
Weekly native newspaper for and about native peoples.
Book reviews. 1,550 cir. $30/year; $1/copy. Advertising.

TORONTO NATIVE TIMES
16 Spadina Rd. • Toronto, ON M5R 2S8 (416) 964-9087

TREATY No. 3 COUNCIL FIRE
37 Main St. S. • Kenora, ON P9N 1S8

TRENT NATIVE NEWS
Dept. of Native Studies, Trent University • Petersborough, ON K9J 7B7

TRIBAL INDIAN NEWS N'AMERIND
London's Indian Friendship Centre, 613 Wellington St. • London, ON

TUSAAYAKSAT (Newspaper)
Inuvialuit Communications Society
Box 1704, McKenzie Rd., Semmler Bldg. • Inuvik, NT X0E 0T0
(403) 979-2067; 977-2202; Vincent Teddy, Editor & President

TYENDINAGA TERRITORY NEWSLETTER
c/o Mohawk Band Office, RR 1 • Deseronto, ON K0K 1X0
(613) 396-3424 Fax 396-3627

UNITY
Association of Iroquois and Allie Indians
R.R. 2 • Southwold, ON N0L 2G0; Shelly Bressette, Editor
Quarterly newsletter covering news and issues of importance to the Indian peoples.

WA-WA-TAY CREE COMMUNICATIONS NETWORK
Fort Albany, ON P0L 1H0 (705) 278-1147

WAWATAY NATIVE NEWS
Wawatay Communications Society
Box 1180, 16-5th Ave. • Sioux Lookout, ON P0V 2T0
(807) 737-2951 Fax 737-322; Megan Williams, Editor
Bilingual, semi-monthly newspaper that carries all types of news for & about Nishnawbe-Aski Nation. Advertising. Circulation 10,000. Subscription: $11/year (individuals) in Canada; $12, U.S., and $16, foreign.

THE WESTERN CANADIAN ANTHROPOLOGIST
University of Saskatchewan, Dept. of Anthropology/Archaeology
Saskatoon, SK S7N 0W0 (306) 966-4175 Satya Sharma, Editor
Annual journal containing material of interest to anthropologists.
Book reviews. 400 cir. $10/copy.

WESTERN NATIVE NEWS
530-10036 Jasper Ave. • Edmonton, AB T5J 2W2
(403) 421-7966 Fax 424-3951
office: 201-1593 W. 3rd St. • Vancouver, BC V6J 1J8
(604) 736-3015

WHISPERING PINES
Northern Association of Community Councils
504-63 Albert St. • Winnipeg, MB R3B 1G4
(204) 947-2227 Fax 947-9446

WINDSPEAKER
Aboriginal Multi-Media Society of Alberta
13245 - 146 St • Edmonton, AB T5L 4S8
(780) 455-2700 Fax 455-7639; Debora Steel, Editor
Website: www.ammsa.com/windspeaker
E-mail: edwind@ammsa.com
Canada's National Aboriginal monthly newspaper. Special edition, "Guide to Indian Country," in June. Includes Alberta's Sweetgrass, Ontario Birchbark, Saskatchewan Sage, and Raven's Eye as special sections. 25,000 cir. $60/year; $40, foreign. Advertising.

WINNIPEG INDIAN TIMES
Indian and Metis Friendship Centre, 73 Princess St. • Winnipeg 3, MB

COLLEGES & UNIVERSITIES

ALBERTA

ATHABASCA UNIVERSITY - CENTRE FOR WORLD INDIGENOUS KNOWLEDGE & RESEARCH
1 University Dr. • ATHABASCA, AB T9S 3A3
(780) 675-6100 Fax 675-6437
Website: www.athabascau.ca/indigenous
Priscilla Campeau, Centre Chair & Program Administrator
  E-mail: pcampeau@athabascau.ca
  Tracy Lindberg (Cree/Metis), Director of Indigenous Education
  Maria Campbell, Elder in Residence
Degrees: Undergraduate, graduate & certificate programs.
Courses: Cree; The Metis; Indigenous Issues; etc.

RED CROW COMMUNITY COLLEGE
P.O. Box 1258 Cardston • CALGARY, AB T0K0K
(403) 737-2400 Fax 737-2101; Website: www.redcrowcollege.com
Marie Smallface Marule, President
Resources: University of Calgary Library; Virtual Library.
Publication: Quarterly newsletter.

UNIVERSITY OF CALGARY
INTERNATIONAL INDIGENOUS STUDIES PROGRAM
Department of Sociology, 2500 University Dr., NW • CALGARY, AB T2N1N4
(403) 220-5521; Website: www.arts.ucalgary.ca/indg
  James S. Frideres, Program Coordinator; E-mail: frideres@ucalgary.ca
Degree: BA in International Indigenous Studies. Focuses upon such aspects of Indigenous peoples' experience as arts, cultures, ecologies, economies, histories, identities, knowledge, languages, literatures, music, community & political dynamics. Aboriginal related research projects. *Resources*: Native Centre.

RED CROW COMMUNITY COLLEGE
P.O. Box 1258 • CARDSTON, AB T0K0K
(403) 737-2400 Fax 737-2101; Website: www.redcrowcollege.com
Marie Smallface Marule, President
Roy Weasel Fat, VP Academic Programs
Henry Big Throat, VP Student Services
Mission: To meet the cultural, educational, and training needs for Kainaiwa and beyond; to provide leadership through its programs & services to nurture self-realization based on Kainaissinni. *Resources*: University of Calgary Library; Virtual Library. *Publication*: Quarterly newsletter.

UNIVERSITY OF ALBERTA - DEPARTMENT OF NATIVE STUDIES
2-31 Pembina Hall • EDMONTON, AB T6G 2H8
(780) 492-2991 Fax 492-0527
Website: www.nativestudies.ualberta.ca
E-mail: nativestudies@ualberta.ca
Brendan Hokowhitu, Dean; E-mail: nsdean@ualberta.ca
Nathalie Kermoal, Associate Dean Academic & Associate Professor
  E-mail: Nathalie.kermoal@ualberta.ca (492-7207)
Chris Andersen, Associate Dean of Research & Associate Professor
  E-mail: chris.andersen@ualberta.ca; (492-4814)
Shalene Jobin Vandervelde, Director of Aboriginal Governance Program
  E-mail: shalene.jobin@ualberta.ca; (492-8062)
Kristine Wray, Rupertsland Centre Administrator
  E-mail: kewray@ualberta.ca; (492-7218)
Faculty: Isabel Altamirano-Jimenez; Ellen Bielawski; Sarah Carter; James Dempsey; Brenda Parlee, (Canada Research Chair); Sean Robertson; Dorothy Thunder (Full-time Cree Instructor); Frank Tough; Richard Price & Pat McCormack (Emeritus). Resources: Rupertsland Centre for Metis Research

UNIVERSITY OF ALBERTA
Faculty of Medicine, 2J2.11 W.C. MacKenzie Sciences Centre
EDMONTON, AB 6G 2R7 (780) 492-6350 Fax 492-7303
Anne-Marie Hodes, Coordinator
Program: Native Health Care Career Program

UNIVERSITY OF ALBERTA
Faculty of Law, 4th Floor, Law Centre • EDMONTON T, AB 6G 2H5
(780) 492-7749 Fax 492-4924
Programs: Indigenous Law Program.

GRANT MacEWAN COMMUNITY COLLEGE
City Centre Campus 5-174, 10700 104th Ave. • EDMONTON, AB T5J 4S2
(780) 497-5646 Fax 497-5630
Program: Native Communications Program.
OLD SUN COMMUNITY COLLEGE

P.O. Box 339 • GLEICHEN, AB T0J 1N0
(780) 734-3862; 264-9658
Blackfoot Cultural Centre - Gerald Sitting Eagle, Coordinator

MASKWACHEES CULTURAL COLLEGE
P.O. Box 360 • HOBBEMA, AB T0C 1N0
(403) 585-3925 Fax 585-2080; Dr. Fred Carnew, Director

UNIVERSITY OF LETHBRIDGE
DEPARTMENT OF NATIVE AMERICAN STUDIES
The Faculty of Arts & Sciences, A414 University Hall
4401 University Dr. • LETHBRIDGE, AB T1K 3M4
(403) 329-2635 Fax 380-1855
  Website: www.uleth.ca/artsci/native-american-studies
  T. Hamett, Acting Chairperson (329-2636)
  Elizabeth Ferguson, Native Student Advisor
  E-mail: Elizabeth.ferguson@uleth.ca
Degree: BA in Native American Studies. *Faculty*: Henrie Beaulieu, Yale Belanger, Leroy Little Bear (Emeritus), Donald Frantz (Emeritus-Blackfoot & Tiwa Grammar), Tanya Harnett, Linda Many Guns, Louis Soop, Jaime Warn, Dn McIntyre. *Resources*: Native American Student Association. *Activities*: Native Awareness Week.

UNIVERSITY OF LETHBRIDGE
School of Management-Indian, Inuit & Metis Peoples
4401 University Dr. • LETHBRIDGE, AB T1K 3M4
(403) 329-2114 Fax 329-2038

BLUE QUILLS FIRST NATIONS COLLEGE
Box 189 • SADDLE LAKE, AB T0A 3T0
(403) 645-4455 Fax 645-5215

BRITISH COLUMBIA

SIMON FRASER UNIVERSITY
DEPARTMENT OF FIRST NATIONS STUDIES
8888 University Dr. • BURNABY, BC V5A 1S6
(778) 782-4774; Website: www.sfu.ca/fns
  Eldon Yellowhorn, Associate Professor & Chair
  Marianne Ignace, Director, First Nations Language Centre
Faculty: Eldon Yellowhorn, Marianne Ignace, Annie Ross, Deanna Reder, Rudy Reimer/Yumks. *Resources*: First Nations Language Centre.

SIMON FRASER UNIVERSITY
Native Indian Teachers Education Program-UBC
345 Yellowhead Hwy. • KAMLOOPS, BC V2H 1H1
(250) 828-9817 Fax 828-9780; Chief Ron Ignace, Co-chair
  Muriel Sasakamoose, Executive Director
Currently in its first year of offering a university program for Native Indian students with focus on social science research and Native studies.

VANCOUVER ISLAND UNIVERSITY
DEPARTMENT OF FIRST NATIONS STUDIES
900 5th St. • NANAIMO, BC V8R 5S5
(250) 740-6194; 753-3245; Website: www.viu.ca/firstnations
Keith Smith, Dept. Chair; History Faculty; E-mail: keith.smith@viu.ca
Program: BA major & minor in First Nations Studies. *Faculty*: Laura Cranmer; laura.cranmer@viu.ca, Allyson Anderson, Lara Cranmer, Delores Louie (Resident Elder), Melody Martin, Maxine Matilpi, Dan McDonald, Laurie Meijer Drees, Ray Peter, Keith Smith, John Swift.

VANCOUVER ISLAND UNIVERSITY
OFFICE OF ABORIGINAL EDUCATION
900 5th St. • NANAIMO, BC V8R 5S5
(250) 740-6542; Website: www.viu.ca/aboriginal
  Sharon Hobenshield (Gitxsan First Nations), Director of Aboriginal Education
  E-mail: Sharon.hobenshield@viu.ca
  Sylvia Scow (Dene), Associate Director; E-mail: Sylvia.scow@viu.ca
  Pam Botterill, Aboriginal Outreach Coordinator; E-mail: pam.botterill@viu.ca
  Sheila Cooper, Aboriginal Projects Manager; E-mail: Sheila.cooper@viu.ca
Programs: Aboriginal University Bridging Program Certificate:
1-Year Certificate Program.

UNIVERSITY OF NORTHERN BRITISH COLUMBIA
FIRST NATIONS STUDIES PROGRAM
Department of First Nations Studies
3333 University Way • PRINCE GEORGE, BC V2N 4Z9
(250) 960-5595 Fax 960-5545; Website: www.unbc.ca/firstnations/
  Ross Hoffman, Program Chair (960-5242) E-mail: hoffmanr@unbc.ca
  Antonia Mills, Acting Chair (960-6690) E-mail: millsa@unbc.ca

Paul Michel, Director of First Nations Centre; E-mail: michelp@unbc.ca
Amanda Hancock, Academic Advisor (960-5272) Email: hanca000@unbc.ca
Degrees: Certificate, BA & MA in First Nations Studies. *Faculty*: Ross Hoffman, Antonia Mills, Margo Greenwood (Cree), Frye Jean Graveline (Metis Cree). *Adjunct Faculty*: Alyce Johnson (Kluane First Nation), Deanna Nyce, Wendy Aasen, Paul Michel (Shuswap First Nations), Earl Henderson (Sioux, Cree, Metis), Tina Fraser, Gregory Lowan-Trudeau (Metis) *Instructor*: Leona Neilson (Cree Culture & Language); Nellie Prince (Nak'azdli Band). *Sessional Instructors*: Leona Neilson (Cree); Nellie Prince (Nak'Azdli Band). *Facilities*: First Nations Centre. *Special program*: Northern Advancement Program.

UNIVERSITY OF BRITISH COLUMBIA
Dept. of Anthropology, 6303 N.W. Marine Dr. • VANCOUVER, BC V6T 1Z1
(604) 822-2878 Fax 822-6161
Instructors: David F. Aberle, PhD, Harry B. Hawthorn, PhD (Indians of Canada); J.E. Michael Kew, PhD (Indians of Canada), Bruce G. Miller, PhD (Indian-white relations); William Robin Ridington, PhD (Native American cosmology); Ruth Phillips, PhD (director of Museum of Anthropology; Iroquoian & Anishnaabe art & culture); James V. Powell, PhD (linguistics). *Special program*: Summer Field School in Archaeology. *Special facilities*: Research laboratories in archaeology, ethnomethodology, sociolinguistics, ethnography; Museum of Anthropology.

THE UNIVERSITY OF BRITISH COLUMBIA
FIRST NATIONS STUDIES PROGRAM
1866 Main St., Buchanan E266 • VANCOUVER, BC V6T 1Z1
(604) 822-2905;Website: www.fnsp.arts.ubc.ca
Daniel Heath Justice (Cherokee), Chairperson
Linc Kesler, Director & Sr. Advisor to President on Aboriginal Affairs
Tanya Bob, Program Advisor & Practicum Coordinator; Coordinator
 of Aboriginal Student Affairs; E-mail: Tanya.bob@ubc.ca
Faculty: Glen Coulthard (Yellowknives Dene'); Daniel Justice (Cherokee); Linc Kesler; Sheryl Lightfoot; Dory Nason; Johnny Mack (Law)

UNIVERSITY OF BRITISH COLUMBIA
Museum of Anthropology, 6393 N.W. Marine Dr. • VANCOUVER V6T 1W5
(604) 228-5087; Moya Waters, Administrative Officer
Michael M. Ames, Ph.D., Director/Professor
Special programs: Anthropology & archaeology of Northwest Coast of British Columbia, indigenous arts, material culture, ceramics, and development of innovative teaching programs in museology and the arts. *Financial aid*: The Lois McConkey Memorial Fellowship for Native Indian Work-Study Program - a fellowship for secondary school and university students of North American Indian descent. Research results published occasionally in professional journals & books; also publishes notes, catalogues, & museum profiles.

UNIVERSITY OF BRITISH COLUMBIA
First Nations Health Careers
1985 West Mall • VANCOUVER, BC V6T 1Z2
(604) 822-2115 Fax 822-8944

UNIVERSITY OF BRITISH COLUMBIA
Native Indian Teachers Education Program
1985 West Mall • VANCOUVER, BC V6T 1Z2
(604) 822-5240 Fax 822-8944
345 Yellowhead Hwy. • KAMLOOPS, BC V2H 1H1
(604) 828-9817 Fax 828-9780

UNIVERSITY OF BRITISH COLUMBIA
First Nation Legal Studies Program
1822 East Mall • VANCOUVER, BC V6T 1Z1
(604) 822-5559 Fax 822-8108

UNIVERSITY OF BRITISH COLUMBIA
Synala Honours Program, 1985 West Mall
VANCOUVER, BC V6T 1Z2 (604) 822-9697

UNIVERSITY OF BRITISH COLUMBIA
TS'KEL Program (MEd, MA, EdP, PhD)
Faculty of Education • VANCOUVER, BC V6T 1Z4
(604) 822-5857 Fax 822-6501

VANCOUVER SCHOOL OF THEOLOGY
Native Ministries Program, 6000 Iona Dr. • VANCOUVER, BC V6T 1L4
(604) 228-9031 Fax 228-0189

UNIVERSITY OF VICTORIA
Dept. of Anthropology, P.O. Box 3050 • VICTORIA V8W 3P5
(250) 721-7046 Fax 721-6215

Instructors: Michael Asch, PhD, Kathleen A. Berthiaume, PhD, Leland H. Donald, PhD, Eric A. Roth, PhD, Andrea N. Walsh, MA. *Special facilities*: Provincial Archives & Museum; archaeological, ethnological & linguistic (especially in Coast Salish languages through the Linguistics Department) field training; Pacific Studies; and Interdisciplinary Studies Program.

UNIVERSITY OF VICTORIA - INDIGENOUS STUDIES PROGRAM
Department of History, First Peoples House – Room 143
P.O. Box 3050 STN CSC • VICTORIA, BC V8W 3P5
(250) 472-5185 Fax 472-5185; Website: www.web.uvic.ca/isminor
Christine O'Bonsawin, Program Director (853-3996)
 E-mail: cobonsaw@uvic.ca
Karen Erwin, Interdisciplinary Programs Assistant
 E-mail: idpassis@uvic.ca
Program: BA Minor in Indigenous Studies.

UNIVERSITY OF VICTORIA INDIGENOUS GOVERNANCE PROGRAM
Faculty of Human & Social Development
3800 Finnerty Rd., HSD Bldg. Rm. A260
P.O. Box 1700 STN CSC • VICTORIA, BC V8W 2Y2
(250) 721-6438 Fax 472-4724
Website: www.web.uvic.ca/igov; E-mail: igov@uvic.ca
James Tully, Founding member of program
Taiaiake Alfred (Mohawk), Professor & Program Director
Angela Polifroni, Program Manager; Mick Scrow, Program Assistant
Jeff Corntassel (Cherokee), Associate Prof. & Graduate Advisor
Wazlyatawin (Dakota), Associate Professor & Research Chair
Heidi Kiiwetinepinesiik Stark (Ojbwe), Assistant Professor
Program: MA in Indigenous Governance; PhD by Arrangement

UNIVERSITY OF VICTORIA
Administration of Aboriginal Governments Program
School of Public Administration, P.O. Box 1700 • VICTORIA, BC V8W 2Y2
(250) 721-8089 Fax 721-8849

UNIVERSITY OF VICTORIA
First Nations Tax Administrators' Institute
School of Public Administration, P.O. Box 1700 • VICTORIA, BC V8W 2Y2
(250) 721-8083 Fax 472-4163

MANITOBA

UNIVERSITY OF BRANDON
Department of Native Studies, Aboriginal Heritage Committee
270 18th St. • BRANDON, MB R7A 6A9 (204) 727-7349

UNIVERSITY OF BRANDON
Northern Teachers Education Program
Rm. 13, Education Bldg., 270 18th St. • BRANDON, MB R7A 6A9
(204) 727-9669 Fax 727-0942

INTER-UNIVERSITIES NORTH
494 Princeton Dr. • THOMPSON, MB R8N 0A4
(800) 442-0462; (204) 677-6740 Fax 677-6589

UNIVERSITY OF MANITOBA
Aboriginal Focus Programs
188 Continuing Education • WINNIPEG, MB R3T 2N2
(800) 432-1960 ext. 740; (204) 474-6720 Fax 474-7660

UNIVERSITY OF MANITOBA
Continuing Education Division/Native Focus
Rm. 188, Continuing Education Complex • WINNIPEG, MB R3T 2N2
(204) 474-9921 Fax 474-7661

UNIVERSITY OF MANITOBA
Dept. of Anthropology • WINNIPEG, MB R3T 2N2
(204) 474-9361
Instructors: Louis Allaire, PhD, David H. Pentland, PhD, Linguistics, Kevin Russell, PhD, Joan B. Townsend, PhD, H. C. Wolfart, PhD (Linguistics), (Linguistics), Jillian E. Oakes, PhD (Native Studies); John D. Nichols, PhD (Native Studies), William W. Koolage, PhD (Cultural Anthropology); Gregory Monks, PhD (Archaeology); Dwight A. Rokala, PhD (Physcial Anthropology); & David H. Stymeist, PhD (Social Anthropology). *Special programs*: Population biology & medical anthropology of North American Indians; indigenous languages of Canada, especially Siouan & Algonquian (Cree Language Project.) *Special facilities*: Anthropology Laboratories; The Provincial Archives.

UNIVERSITY OF WINNIPEG - DEPARTMENT OF INDIGENOUS STUDIES
Richardson College for the Environment & Social Complex
599 Portage Ave. 3rd Floor • WINNIPEG, MB R3B 2E5
  (204) 786-9397 Fax 943-4695; Website: www.uwinnipeg.ca
  Jacqueline Romanow, Chair; E-mail: j.romanow@uwinnipeg.ca
  Julie Pelletier, Associate Professor; E-mail: ju.pelletier@uwinnipeg.ca
Programs: BA in Indigenous Studies; MA in Indigenous Governance; MDP Master's in Development Practice in Indigenous Development; CATEP (Community-Based Aboriginal Teacher Education Program); Indigenous History Courses (PDF) Indigenous Spiritual & Pastoral Care Diploma is a two-year post-secondary program. *Faculty*: Gabriel Ricardo Nemoga Soto; Jacqueline Romanow (Graduate Coordinator); Lorena Sekwan Fontaine; Shailesh Shukla; Tobasonnakwut (Indigenous Governance); Ida Bear & Annie Boulanger (Indigenous Languages).

UNIVERSITY OF WINNIPEG
Department of Anthropology, 515 Portage Ave. • WINNIPEG R3B 2E9
  (204) 786-9382
Instructors: Gary R. Granzberg, PhD, George Fulford, PhD, Peter Dawson, PhD. *Special program*: Archaeological Field School. *Special facilities*: Algonkian ethnological collections; Hudson's Bay Company Archives Research Centre; ethnology, archaeology, and physical anthropology laboratories.

NEW BRUNSWICK

ST. THOMAS UNIVERSITY - NATIVE STUDIES PROGRAM
51 Dineen Dr. • FREDERICTON, NB E3B 5G3
  (506) 460-0366 Fax 450-9615; Website: www.stu.ca
  Roland Chrisjohn, Program Director
Part-time Faculty: Andrea Bear Nicholas, Professor & Chair of Studies in Aboriginal Cultures of Atlantic Canada; Mark Landry, Lecturer. *Program*: BA in Native Studies.

UNIVERSITY OF NEW BRUNSWICK
Dept. of Anthropology • FREDERICTON E3B 5A3
  (506) 453-4975 Fax 453-3569
Instructors: William G. Dalton, PhD, Vincent O. Erickson, PhD, Peter R. Lovell, PhD, and Gail R. Pool, PhD. *Special resources*: Local fieldwork opportunities (Maliseet-Micmac Indian communities); archaeology-anthropology laboratory. Archives. Library.

UNIVERSITY OF NEW BRUNSWICK
Micmac-Maliseet Institute, Bag Service 45333 • FREDERICTON E3B 5A3
  (506) 453-4840 Fax 453-3569

NEWFOUNDLAND

MEMORIAL UNIVERSITY OF NEWFOUNDLAND
Dept. of Anthropology • ST. JOHN'S A1C 5S7
  (709) 737-8870
Instructors: Gordon Inglis, PhD, John C. Kennedy, PhD, Thomas F. Nemec, PhD, Adrian Tanner, PhD, & James A. Tuck, PhD. *Special foci*: Field research programs--Arctic, Subarctic, & circumpolar (especially Lapps, Algonquin, Inuit and white settlers); northern North Atlantic (Newfoundland, Labrador, Baffin, Iceland.) Special facility: Killam Arctic Library.

NOVA SCOTIA

CAPE BRETON UNIVERSITY - MI'KMAQ COLLEGE INSTITUTE
DEPARTMENT OF INDIGENOUS STUDIES
1250 Grand Lake Rd., P.O. Box 5300 • SYDNEY, NS B1P 6L2
  (902) 563-1871 Fax 563-1693; E-mail: unamaki@cbu.ca
  Website: www.cbu.ca/unamaki
  Stephen Augustine, Dean of Unama'ki College & Aboriginal Learning
    E-mail: Stephen_augustine@cbu.ca (563-1827)
  Stephanie Inglis, Department Chairperson
    E-mail: Stephanie_inglis@cbu.ca
  Ann Denny, Aboriginal Services Coordinator
    E-mail: ann_denny@cbu.ca (563-1402)
  Leanne Simmons, Aboriginal Program Director
    E-mail: Leanne_simmons@cbu.ca (563-1240)
  Diane Chisholm, Mi'qmaq Resource Centre Coordinator
    E-mail: diane_chisholm@cbu.ca (563-1660)
Description: Unama'ki College (formerly Mi'kmaq College Institute) of Cape Breton University strives to meet the needs of Mi'kmaw and other First Nations students & contribute to educational goals set by Mi'kmaw communities. *Degrees*: BA.BACS major in Mi'kmaq Studies; Certificate in Mi'kmaq Cultural Heritage Preservation; MBA (CED) First Nations Option. Courses

examine aspects of Mi'kmaq culture including language, governance, spirituality & contemporary social issues. *Resources*: Mi'kmaq Resource Centre.

ONTARIO

NORTH AMERICAN INDIAN TRAVELLING COLLEGE
R.R. #3 • CORNWALL ISLAND, ON K6H 5R7
  (613) 932-9452 Fax 932-0092
  Website: www.tuscaroras.com/nnatc/
  Barbara Barnes, President

McMASTER UNIVERSITY - INDIGENOUS STUDIES PROGRAM (ISP)
1280 Main St. West, Hamilton Hall 103/B • HAMILTON, ON L8S 4K1
  (905) 525-9140 ext. 27426 Fax 540-8443
  Website: www.indigenous.mcmaster.ca
  E-mail: indgdir@mcmaster.ca
  Rick Monture, Academic Director
    E-mail: indigenous.director@mcmaster.ca
  Tracy Bomberry, Program Administrator
    E-mail: indigenous.manager@mcmaster.ca
  Josh Dockstader, Indigenous Student Counselor
    E-mail: indigenous.counsellor@mcmaster.ca
  Michelle Thomas, Indigenous Student Recruiter
    E-mail: thomam27@mcmaster.ca
Mission: To recruit and assist Indigenous students in obtaining a degree in their area of interest; to increase awareness of Indigenous culture and issues; to work collaboratively with Aboriginal communities. *Programs*: ISP offers a three-year Combined Bachelor of Arts Degree in Indigenous Studies and Another Subject. Students have their choice of combining Indigenous Studies with a subject area from either Humanities or Social Sciences. However, students in other disciplines may take Indigenous Studies as a Minor or as electives. *Faculty*: Rick Monture (Mohawk); Vanessa Watts (Mohawk); Dawn Martin-Hill (Mohawk). Sessional Lecturers: Ima Johnson (Mohawk); Renee Thomas-Hill (Mohawk); Amber Skye (Mohawk); Ali Darnay (Anishinaabe); Monique Mojica; Bernice Downey.

QUEEN'S UNIVERSITY
ABORIGINAL TEACHER EDUCATION PROGRAM
Faculty of Education, Duncan McArthur Hall
511 Union St. • KINGSTON, ON K7M 5R7
  (613) 533-6218 Fax 533-6584
  Website: www.queensi.ca; E-mail: atep@queensu.ca
  Lindsay Morcom, Coordinator; E-mail: morcoml@queensu.ca
Provides an opportunity for candidates to specialize in Aboriginal education.
Facilities: Resource library.

UNIVERSITY OF WESTERN ONTARIO
Faculty of Education • LONDON, ON N6G 1G7
  (519) 661-3430 Fax 661-2157
Program: Native Language Teaching. *Instructors*: Chet Creider, PhD, Margaret Seguin, PhD (Director-Center for Research and Teaching of Candian Native Languages), Michael W. Spence, PhD, and Lisa Valentine, PhD. *Special facilities*: Center for Research & Teaching of Canadian Native Languages, administered within the Department, offers research funds & facilities for faculty & students working on Canadian Native languages; publishes a monograph series on interpretations of texts and occasional papers, and offers training in linguistics for Canadian Native persons. Recent research and publication have had a particular emphasis on Mohawk. Library. London Museum of Archaeology.

UNIVERSITY OF WESTERN ONTARIO
Journalism Program for Native People
Middlesex College • LONDON, ON N6A 5B7
  (519) 661-3380 Fax 661-3292

UNIVERSITY OF WESTERN ONTARIO
FIRST NATIONS STUDIES PROGRAM
Social Science Centre, Rm. 3254 • LONDON, ON N6A 5C2
  (519) 661-2111 Fax 661-2062; E-mail: frstntns@uwo.ca
  Website: www.anthropology.uwo.ca/firstnations
  Susan Hill (Mohawk), Professor & Program Director; E-mail: shill26@uwo.ca
  Rick Fehr, Assistant Professor & Acting Director; E-mail: rfehr@uwo.ca
  Mahillah Rafek, Program Coordinator; E-mail: mrafek@uwo.ca
Program: BA Major & Minor in First Nations Studies. *Faculty*: Susan Hill, Regna Darnell, Chantelle Richmond, Rick Fehr, Bob Antone. *Lecturers*: Ted Baker, Sadie Buck, Karen Hunter, David Kanatawakhon-Maracle, Eli Baxter, Dan Smoke, Mary-Lou Smoke. Research *Interests*: Mohawk & Ojibway customs & language. Library.

UNIVERSITY OF NIPISSING
100 College Dr. • NORTH BAY, ON P1B 8L7
(705) 474-3450 Ext. 4239 Fax 474-1947
Program: Native Teacher Certification Program

YORK UNIVERSITY
Faculty of Environmental Studies - Native/Canadian Relations Dept.
4700 Keele St. • NORTH YORK, ON M3J 1P3
(416) 736-5252 Fax 736-5679; Peter Homenuck, Director
Program: "Native/Canadian Relations (masters level program) focuses on multi-faceted, unique, bicultural relationships, between, on the one hand, the Native community & its organizations and, on the other, the broader Canadian society and its institutions, together with the issues that result from the relationships. An important component of Native/Canadian Relations is research conducted on the expressed need of Bands, Native communities, Native organizations, and government departments."

CARLETON UNIVERSITY
Centre for Aboriginal Education, Research & Culture
Rm. 2207 Dunton, 1125 Colonel By Drive
OTTAWA, ON K1B 5B6; (613) 520-4494 Fax 520-2512

TRENT UNIVERSITY - DEPARTMENT OF INDIGENOUS STUDIES
1600 Westbank Dr. • PETERBOROUGH, ON K9J 7B8
(705) 748-1011 Fax 748-1416
Website: www.trentu.ca/academic/nativestudies
E-mail: indigenousstudies@trentu.ca
Christine Welter, Academic Program Coordinator
 E-mail: cwelter@trentu.ca
David Newhouse, Chair of Indigenous Studies
 E-mail: dnewhouse@trentu.ca
Vernon Douglas (Biidaaban), Cultural Advisor
Skahendowaneh Swamp (Mohawk), Chair of Indigenous Knowledge
Roroniake:wen – Dan Longboat (Mohawk), Director of
 Indigenous Environmental Studies Program
Lynne Davis, Director PhD Program in Indigenous Studies
 E-mail: lydavis@trentu.ca
Don N. McCaskill, Director, Thailand Year Abroad Program
 E-mail: dmccaskill@trentu.ca
Description: The department explores indigenous knowledge, aboriginal history, indigenous environmental knowledge, aboriginal modernity & post colonial/indigenous theory, Anishnaabe language & culture, Haudenosaunee culture & tradition and indigenous performance. The faculty is engaged in community-based research; all serve as advisors to Aboriginal, provincial & federal governments & organizations. *Program*: BA in Foundations for Indigenous Learning; MA in Canadian Studies & Indigenous Studies; PhD in Indigenous Studies. *Faculty*: Lynn Davis, Mark Dockstator, Chris Furgal, Rosalie Jones (Pembina Chippewa), Dan Longboat (Mohawk), Edna Manitowabi (Odawa/Ojibway), Don McCaskill (Director of Thailand Year Abroad Program), Neal G. McLeod (Cree), Marrie Mumford, David Newhouse (Onondaga), Paula Sherman (Algonquin), Skahendo-waneh Swamp (Mohawk-Akwesasne), Professor emeriti, Shirley Williams (Pheasant) & Marlene Brant-Castellano. *Part-time faculty*: Nicole Bell & Tasha Beeds. *Special programs*: Thailand Year Abroad Program; Indigenous Women's Symosium. *Resources*: First Peoples House of Learning, Gzowski College; Nozhem Theatre at Gzowski College; Native Association; Alderville First Nation. *Activities*: Annual Elders & Traditional Gathering. *Publication*: E-Bimisay, electronic newsletter.

BROCK UNIVERSITY - TECUMSEH CENTRE FOR ABORIGINAL RESEARCH & EDUCATION
Welch Hall, University Rd. W • ST. CATHERNES, ON L2S 3A1
(905) 688-5550 Fax 984-4869; Website: www.nativeadult.ed.brocku.ca
Lorenzo Cherubini, Centre Director
 E-mail: Lorenzo.cherubini@brocku.ca
Description: The only multidisciplinary research entity in Ontario that builds educational programming for Aboriginal community needs & requirements. *Faculty*: Lorenzo Cherubini, Renee E. Bedard, Janie Hodson, Srah McGean, Judith Knight, Sakoieta' Widrick, Jennifer Brant. *Degree*: Bachelor of Education in Aboriginal Adult Education. Centre established in 2004.

ALGOMA UNIVERSITY – OJIBWE LANGUAGE PROGRAM
1520 Queen St. East • SAULT STE. MARIE, ON P6A 2G4
(705) 949-2301; Website: www.algomau.ca
Howard Webkamigad, Program Director & Assistant Professor
 of the Ojibwe Language; E-mail: howard.webkamigad@algomau.ca
Eddie Benton-Banai, Sessional Instructor
 E-mail: eddie.benton-benai@algomau.ca
Program: Anishinaabemowin (Ojibwe Language degree). 3 year B.A. Study of the Ojibwe language in the Great Lakes Region.

LAURENTIAN UNIVERSITY – SCHOOL OF NATIVE HUMAN SERVICES
935 Ramsey Lake Rd. • SUDBURY, ON P3E 2C6
(705) 675-1151; (800) 461-4030
Website: www.laurentian.ca/program/indigenous-studies
Dr. Taima Moeke-Pickering, Director
 E-mail: tmoekepickering@laurentian.ca
Susan Manitowabi (Anishinawbe-Kwe), Assistant Professor
 Email: smanitowabi@laurentian.ca
Herb Nabigon (Ojibway), Professor; E-mail: hnabigon@laurentian.ca
Cheryle Partridge (Ojibway/Pottawatomi), Assistant Professor
 E-mail: cpartridge@laurentian.ca
Program: Indigenous Relations Program. The curriculum incorporates both Native-specific & social work courses with Native Studies courses.

UNIVERSITY OF SUDBURY
DEPARTMENT OF INDIGENOUS STUDIES
935 Ramsey Lake Rd. • SUDBURY, ON P3E 2C6
(705) 673-5661 ext. 225
Website: www.usudbury.ca/index.php/en/programs/indigenous-studies
Darrel Manitowabi, Department Chairperson
 E-mail: dmanitowabi@usudbury.ca
Kevin FitzMaurice, Associate Professor
 E-mail: kfitzmaurice@usudbury.ca
Brock Pitawanakwat (Anishinaabe), Assistant Professor
 E-mail: bpitawanakwat@usudbury.ca
Mary Ann Corbiere (Ojibwe), Assistant Professor
 E-mail: mcorbiere@usudbury.ca
Emily Faires (Cree), Assistant Professor
 E-mail: efaries@usudbury.ca Michael Hankard, Assistant Professor
 E-mail: mhankard@usudbury.ca
Program: BA in Native Studies – courses on Cree & Ojibwe tradition & culture, legal & political issues; Aboriginal Legal Education Certificate.

LAKEHEAD UNIVERSITY
Dept. of Anthropology • THUNDER BAY, ON P7B 5E1
(807) 343-8632; *Special programs*: Native Studies; Boreal Studies.
Instructors: Paul Driben, PhD, and Joe D. Stewart, PhD (Chair).

LAKEHEAD UNIVERSITY
School of Engineering • THUNDER BAY, ON P7B 5E1
(807) 343-8399 Fax 343-8013; E-mail: nape@lakeheadu.ca
Program: Native Access Program for Engineering

LAKEHEAD UNIVERSITY
Faculty of Education, Native Language Intsitute
955 Oliver Rd. • THUNDER BAY, ON P7B 5E1
(807) 343-8003 Fax 346-7746
Program: Native Language Instructors Program & Native Teacher Education Program

LAKEHEAD UNIVERSITY
School of Nursing • THUNDER BAY, ON P7B 5E1
(807) 343-8446 Fax 343-8246; *Program*: Native Nurses Entry Program

LAKEHEAD UNIVERSITY - DEPARTMENT OF INDIGENOUS LEARNING
955 Oliver Rd. • THUNDER BAY, ON P7B 5E1
(807) 343-8187; Website: www.lakeheadu.ca
Dennis McPherson, Chairperson & Associate Professor (343-8984)
 E-mail: dennis.mcPherson@lakeheadu.ca
Description: The study of Aboriginal history, culture and values and strives to increase awareness/appreciation of the life experience of Aboriginal Peoples. *Faculty*: Ruby Farrell; Kristin Burnett; Robert Robson. *Resources*: The Northern Studies Resource Center.

UNIVERSITY OF TORONTO - ABORIGINAL STUDIES PROGRAM
North Borden Bldg., 2nd Fl. 563 Spadina Ave. • TORONTO, ON M5S 2J7
(416) 978-2233; Website: www.utoronto.ca
E-mail: aboriginal.studies@utoronto.ca
Alana Johns (Anishnabe), Director (978-2234) & Professor of Linguistics
 E-mail: director.aboriginal@utoronto.ca
Connor Pion, Coordinator of Indigenous Language Initiative
Description: Aboriginal Studies is an interdisciplinary undergraduate program dedicated to the study and research of Indigenous peoples in Canada and throughout the world. The program offers courses that engender a rigorous & respectful understanding of Indigenous peoples' languages, cultures, histories, politics, arts, intellectual traditions & research methodologies. *Program*: BA Major & Minor in Aboriginal Studies; Aboriginal languages (Ojibwe, Oneida, Inukitut). *Faculty*: David Burman, Jill Carter (Anishnabe), Alana Johns, Lee Maracle (Sto:Loh), Rauna Kuokkanen (Sami), Deborah McGregor, Alex McKay (Anishnabe), Erica Neegan, Connor Pion, Cheryl Suzack (Batchewana First Nation), Victoria Freeman. *Resources*: First Nations House (978-8227).

UNIVERSITY OF TORONTO
Aboriginal Health Professions Program
First Nations House, 563 Spadina Ave., 3rd Fl.
TORONTO, ON M5S 1A8 (416) 978-8227 Fax 978-1893

UNIVERSITY OF TORONTO
Dept. of Anthropology, Sidney Smith Hall
TORONTO, ON M5S 3G3 (416) 978-5416
Instructors: Gary Coupland, PhD, Ivan Kalmer, PhD, Martha A. Latta, PhD, Richard B. Lee, PhD, Krystyna Siesiechowicz, PhD, and Rosamund Vanderburgh, PhD, Mima Kapches, PhD, Alexander Von Gernet, PhD. *Special program*: Northern Yukon Research Project; excavations at historic and prehistoric Huron villages and older sites in Ontario; research among Canadian Indians, rural and urban.

UNIVERSITY OF WATERLOO
Dept. of Anthropology • WATERLOO N2L 3G1
 (519) 885-1211 ext. 2520
Courses: Prehistoric man in America/Great Lakes area - A survey; Inuit and Eskimo cultures; the contemporary Canadian Indian scene; comparative policies on native minorities; early man in the new world. *Instructors*: Thomas Abler, PhD, & Sally Weaver, PhD. *Award*: Graham Goddard Anthropology Medal--silver medal awarded annually to a 3rd and 4th year anthropology major or honors student who has demonstrated an interest in native peoples of North America.

QUEBEC

McGILL UNIVERSITY
Dept. of Anthropology, 855 Sherbrooke St. W.
MONTREAL H3A 2T7 (514) 398-4300 Fax 398-7476
Special programs: Canadian Studies Program; Northern Studies Minor; a group of Iroquoian archaeologists forms a core of an intimate group in archaeology. *Instructors*: Carmen Lambert, PhD, Toby Morantz, PhD, and Colin Scott, PhD, George Wenzel, PhD.

McGILL UNIVERSITY
Faculty of Education, 3700 McTavish St. • MONTREAL, PQ H3A 1Y2
 (514) 398-4533 Fax 398-4679
Program: Native and Northern Education.

McGILL UNIVERSITY
DEPARTMENT OF INTEGRATED STUDIES IN EDUCATION
FIRST NATIONS & INUIT EDUCATION (FNIE)
3700 McTavish St. • MONTREAL, PQ H3A 1Y2
 (514) 398-6696 Fax 398-4679; Website: www.mcgill.ca
 Ralf St. Clair & Elizabeth Wood, Co-directors (398-4525)
 Donna-Lee Smith, FNIE Program Director
Description: Provides an opportunity for Algonquin, Cree, Inuit, Mi'qmaq, and Mohawk people to become qualified as teachers. *Degree*: Certificate in Education for First Nations & Inuit.

UNIVERSITY OF MONTREAL
Department of Anthropology, CP 6128, Succursale 'A'
MONTREAL H3C 3J7 (514) 343-6560
Instructors: Franklin Auger (Doct. en Anth), Asen Balikci, PhD, Pierre Beaucage, PhD, Claude Chapdelaine, PhD, Norman Clermont, PhD, Louise I. Paradis, PhD, Remi Savard (Doct. en Ethnol.), Gilles Lefebvre, Ph.D. (Linguistics), and Marcel Rioux, M.A. (Sociology). *Special programs*: Northeast archaeology; Summer Field Programs (Inuit & Canadian Indian areas-ethnology.)

UNIVERSITE LAVAL
Department of Anthropologie, Cite Universitaire • STE-FOY G1K 7P4
 (418) 656-5867
Courses: ethnologie des Amerindiens; ethnologie des Inuit; dossiers autochtones contemporaries. *Instructors*: Paul Charest, Gerry McNulty, Bernard Saladin d'Anglure, Francois Trudel, PhD, Louis-Jacques Dorais, Pierre Miranda, and Yvan Simonis. *Special programs*: North American Indian; Canadian Inuit. *Special facility*: Centre d'etudes nordiques. *Publications*: Etudes Inuit Studies; Anthropologie et Societes.

SASKATCHEWAN

GABRIEL DUMONT INSTITUTE
48 12th St. E • PRINCE ALBERT, SK S6V 1B2
 (306) 764-1797 Fax 764-3995
Program: Saskatchewan Urban Native Teacher Education program (SUNTEP)

FIRST NATIONS UNIVERSITY OF CANADA
DEPARTMENT OF INDIGENOUS STUDIES
1 First Nations Way • REGINA, SK S4S 7K2
 (306) 790-5950 Ext. 2300 Fax 790-5994; Website: www.fnuniv.ca
 Edward Dolittle, Dept. Head, Indigenous Science, Environment & Economic Development; E-mail: edoolittle@fnuniv.ca (790-5950 ext. 3260)
 Lesley McBain, Dept. Head, Indigenous Languages, Arts & Cultures (DILAC) Saskatoon Campus; E-mail: lmcbain@fnuniv.ca (931-1800 ext. 7509)
 Anthony de Padue, Dept. Head, Indigenous Education, Health & Social Work Prince Albert Campus (765-3333 ext. 7507)
The First Nations University of Canada's holistic approach to post-secondary education begins with the Elders, whose presence, wisdom, and counsel are the mainstay not only for students but also for the University as a whole. Their knowledge of First Nations' tradition, culture, and spirituality creates a unique support service. Consultation with the Elders takes place in an atmosphere of trust and respect. This tradition helps restore an individual's self-confidence and peace of mind, which in turn helps the learning process. The Elders reinforce our respect for, and understanding of, the Creator's role in our lives. Each of the university's three campuses benefit from Elders from nearby communities. Each contribute to the First Nations' holistic & cultural approach to learning at First Nations University of Canada throughout the academic year. Our Elders Offices: **Northern Campus (Prince Albert)** 306-765-3333 Ext 7139; **Saskatoon Campus** 306-931-1800 Ext 5475; **Regina Campus (Main)** 306-790-5950 Ext 3129

SASKATCHEWAN INDIAN FEDERATED COLLEGE
University of Regina, 218 College West • REGINA, SK S4S 0A2
 (306) 584-8333 Fax 584-8334; Website: www.sfic.edu
 Dr. Oliver Brass, President; Prof. Paul J. Dudgeon, V.P. Academic
Programs: Undergraduate & graduate degree programs within an environment of Indian cultural affirmation. Elders are available to provide counseling and advice based on traditional Indian values. *Personnel*: Gloria Mehlmann, Director, R&D; Richard Laye, Director, Public Relations; Rolando Ramirez, Director, Centre for International Indigenous Studies & Development; Blair Stonechild, Dean; Brian Opikokew, Dean of Students; Robert Anderson, Registrar; Phyllis Lerat, Librarian. Department Heads: Bob Boyer, Indian Fine Arts; Edgar Epp, School of Social Work; Dr. Brent Galloway, Indian Languages, Literature & Linguistics; Dr. Pam Janz, Indian Education; David Reed Miller, PhD, Indian Studies. *Publication*: Saskatchewan Indian Federated College Journal, Bi-annual.

UNIVERSITY OF REGINA
Dept. of Anthropology • REGINA, SK S4S 0A2
 (306) 584-4189 Richard K. Pope, Head
Instructors: George W. Arthur, PhD, Head; J.J. McHugh, PhD, Richard K. Pope, and C.R. Watrall, PhD, David Reed Miller, PhD, Patrick Douard, PhD. Special facilities: Canadian Plains Research Centre; Saskatchewan Archives; Saskatchewan Indian Federated College. Publications.

SASKATCHEWAN INDIAN CULTURAL COLLEGE
University of Saskatchewan Campus
SASKATOON, SK S7K 3S9 (306) 244-1146

UNIVERSITY OF SASKATCHEWAN
College of Education. McLean Hall
#7-106 Wiggins Rd. • SASKATOON, SK S7N 5E6
 (306) 975-7095 Fax 975-1108
Program: Indian Teachers Education Program

UNIVERSITY OF SASKATCHEWAN
College of Nursing • Health Science Bldg.
107 Wiggins Rd. • SASKATOON, SK S7N 5E5
 (800) 463-3345; (306) 966-6224 Fax 966-6703
Programs: National Native Access Program to Nursing; Indian Health Careers Program

UNIVERSITY OF SASKATCHEWAN
Dept. of Anthropology & Archaeology
SASKATOON, SK S7K 5B1 (306) 966-4181 Fax 966-5640
 David Meyer, PhD, Head
Special Program: Native Studies & Ethnicity. Instructors: Alexander M. Ervin, PhD, Mary C. Marino, PhD, Ernest G. Walker, PhD, Robert G. Williamson, PhD, Urve Linnamae, PhD (part-time), and James B. Waldram, PhD (Native Studies Dept.). Special programs: Emphasis is given to research in the Prairie Provinces of western Canada, Arctic, Subarctic and Northwest Territories of Canada; summer fieldwork in archaeology & ethnology in Saskatchewan and/or NWT. Special facilities: Indian & Northern Curriculum Resources Centre, College of Education, with a specialized collection in North American Indian & cross-cultural education; Saskatchewan Provincial Archives; Reference Library.

UNIVERSITY OF SASKATCHEWAN
Native Law Centre, 101 Diefenbaker Centre
SASKATOON, SK S7N 5B8 (306) 966-6189 Fax 966-6207
 E-mail: hendrsny@duke.usak.ca
 Donald J. Purich, JD, Director
Established in 1973 to promote the development of the law and the legal system in ways that would better accommodate the advancement of native communities in Canadian society. One of the Centre's best-known activities is its annual pre-law orientation and screening program for native students, the Program of Legal Studies for Native People. *Instructors*: Linda Fritz, JD, Norman K. Zlotkin, JD, Donald J. Purich, JD, Fergus J. O'Connor, JD, and Zandra MacEachern, JD. *Special programs*: Research - aboriginal land rights; rights of indigenous peoples in international law; Indians & taxation and other areas. Summer program. *Publications*: The Canadian Native Law Reporter, quarterly journal, which provides full text reporting of current native law cases; Canadian Native Law Cases, 9 volumes. Library.

UNIVERSITY OF SASKATCHEWAN
DEPARTMENT OF NATIVE STUDIES
142 Kirk Hall, 117 Science Place • SASKATOON, SK S7N 5C8
(306) 966-6209 Fax 966-6242
Website: www.usask.ca/nativestudies/
E-mail: native.studies@usask.ca
Winona Wheeler, Department Head (966-6210)
 E-mail: winona.wheeler@usask.ca
Faculty: Bonita Beatty, Denise Fucks, Adam Gaudry, Robert Alexander Innes, Priscilla Settee, Winona Wheeler. *Resources*: Native American & Indigenous Studies Association.

YUKON

YUKON COLLEGE
Yukon Native Language Centre, Box 2799 • WHITEHORSE, YUKON Y1A 5K4
(867) 668-8820 Fax 668-8825
Website: www.yukoncollege.yk.ca/ynlc
E-mail: jjohnson@yukoncollege.yk.ca

 Jo-Anne Johnson, Coordinator
Instructors: John Ritter, Andre Bourcier, Linda Harvey. *Special programs*: Literacy & training sessions for Native language teachers. Library - collection of books on linguistics, languages, ethnography, history (Alaska, Yukon, B.C., & Northwest Territories), folklore, education, and reference. Established 1988.

MEDIA – RADIO & TV

ALBERTA

CKUA - AM/FM
Native Voice of Alberta. On the Air 4:30 PM, Sunday, in the following cities: Edmonton, Grand Prairie, Medicine Hat, Lethbridge, Red Deer, & Peace River.

'YR' RADIO
Native Voice of Alberta. On the Air 9:30 AM, Sunday, in the following cities: Hinton, Whitecourt, Edson, Jasper, Grand Cache.

CFAC – FM CALGARY, AB
Treaty No. 7 Radio Program; News Information Program.
On the Air 10:30 to 10:45 AM, Sunday.

CFWE RADIO (NATIVE PERSPECTIVE)
Aboriginal Multi Media Society of Alberta
15001 112th Ave. • EDMONTON, AB T5M 2V6
 (800) 661-5469; (780) 455-2700 Fax 455-7639
 Fred Didzena, President; Bert Crowfoot, Gen. Mgr.
 Thomas Droege, Host/Producer
 Gary Gee, Editor (Windspeaker-newspaper)

GREAT NORTH PRODUCTIONS
300-10359 82nd Ave. • EDMONTON, AB T6E 1Z9
 (780) 439-1260 Fax 431-0197

GREAT PLAINS PRODUCTIONS
202-10138 81st Ave. • EDMONTON, AB T2E 1X1
 (780) 439-4600 Fax 432-7354

CJOK - FM
FORT McMURRAY, AB
Native Voice of Alberta. On the Air 7:30 PM, Sunday.

SIKSIKA COMMUNICATIONS/FM 90
P.O. Box 1490 • GLEICHEN, AB T0J 1N0
(780) 734-5248 Fax 734-2355

CREE TV Box 539 • HOBBEMA, AB T0C 1N0
(780) 585-2021 Fax 585-2393

CFWE - 89.9 FM (CATCH THE SPIRIT)
Aboriginal Multi Media Society of Alberta
P.O. Box 2250 • LAC LA BICHE, AB T0A 2C0
 (780) 623-3333 Fax 623-2811; Ray Fox, Host, Station Manager
Program: Native Perspective. Aboriginal programming - news magazine format Cree/English 50/50 split. Broadcast 6-9 AM, Monday-Friday, via satellite. Alberta's only aboriginal radio station, rebroadcasts in 29 Native communities in Northern Alberta as well as across Canada and the U.S.

CILA - FM (RED ROCK RADIO)
LETHBRIDGE, AB
Native Rock Program. On the Air 1:00 to 2:00 PM, Sunday.

CJOC - FM LETHBRIDGE, AB
Native-American Radio Program catering to tribes of southern Alberta.
On the Air 11:30 AM to 12:00 PM, Sunday.

CKMR - 88.1 FM MORLEY, AB

CIOK – FM ST. PAUL, AB
Native Voice of Alberta. On the Air 8:00 PM, Sunday.

COKI - 103.1 FM
Siksika Communications, P.O. Box 1490 • SIKSIKA, AB T0J 3W0
(403) 734-5248

INDIAN NEWS MEDIA
Box 120 • STANDOFF, AB T0L 1Y0 (780) 653-3301
 Marrie Smallface Marule, President
 Gerri Manyfingers, Executive Director
 Mary Weasel Fat, Editor (Kainai News)
Blackfoot Radio Network; Bull Horn Audio Video; Newspaper.

CKTA – FM TABOR, AB
Native-American Elders Program.
On the Air 10:30 to 11:00 AM, Sunday.

BRITISH COLUMBIA

NUXALK COMMUNICATIONS SOCIETY
Box 368 • BELLA COOLA, BC V0T 1C0
(250) 799-5418

NNB-BC RADIO
Northern Native Broadcasting, Box 1090 • TERRACE, BC V8G 4V1
 (250) 638-8137 Fax 638-8027; Ray Jones, General Manager

THE NATIVE CANADIAN MEDIA CORPS.
600-444 Robson St. • VANCOUVER, BC V6B 2B5
 (604) 688-3877

CITR - NATIVE RADIO STATION
233-6138 Sub Blvd. • VANCOUVER, BC V6T 1Z1
 (604) 822-3017 Fax 822-9364

THE NATIVE VOICE
200-1755 E. Hastings St. • VANCOUVER, BC V5L 1T1
 (604) 255-3137

NATIVE VOICE BROADCAST SYSTEM
533 Yates St. • VICTORIA, BC V8W 1K7
 (604) 383-3211 Fax (384-1586. Radio & TV broadcasting.

MANITOBA

CFNC NATIVE BROADCASTING
Box 129 • CROSS LAKE, MB R0B 0J0
 (204) 676-231 Fax 676-2911

PIMICKAMAK MULTICHANNEL TV
Box 118 • CROSS LAKE, MB R0B 0J0
 (204) 676-2146 Fax 676-2540

PINESIW PRODUCTIONS, INC.
CROSS LAKE, MB R0B 0J0 (204) 676-2146 Fax 676-2540

POPLAR RIVER RADIO STATION
NEGGINAN, MB R0B 0Z0 (204) 244-2123 Fax 244-2690

CJNC (RADIO) NORWAY HOUSE
Norway House Communications, Inc.
Box 311 • NORWAY HOUSE, MB R0B 1B0
(204) 359-6775 Fax 359-6191

NATIVE MEDIA NETWORK
Box 848 • PORTAGE LA PRAIRIE, MB R1N 3C3
(204) 239-1920

NATIVE COMMUNICATIONS, INC.
76 Severn Cres. • THOMPSON, MB R8N 1M6
(204) 778-8343 Fax 778-6559; E-mail: nci@nor.comb.mb
Ron Nadeau, Chairperson & CEO; Henry Wilson, Director of Broadcasting

BLIND TREK
9-819 Grant Ave. • WINNIPEG, MB R3M 1Y1
(204) 287-2311. 30 minute live phone in show, Ch. 11

CHIKAK COMMUNICATIONS
316 St. Mary's Rd. • WINNIPEG, MB R2H 1J8
(204) 237-1170 Fax 233-5562

CKND TV
603 St. Mary's Rd. • WINNIPEG, MB R2M 3L8
(204) 233-3304 Fax 233-5615

FIRST CITIZEN TV TALK SHOW
517 Craig St. • WINNIPEG, MB R3G 3C2 (204) 774-8432

NATIVE COMMUNICATIONS, INC.
Unit C-130, 1666 St. James St. • WINNIPEG, MB
(204) 774-5939 Fax 774-5939

NATIVE MEDIA NETWORK
204-424 Logan Ave. • WINNIPEG, MB R3A 0R4
(204) 943-6475 Fax 942-1380

NATIVE MULTIMEDIA PRODUCTIONS - CKND TV
6 Elm Park Blvd.• WINNIPEG, MB R2M 0V9
(204) 231-1524 Fax 233-5615

OUR NATIVE LAND TV
CBC Radio, Box 160 • WINNIPEG, MB

THETA PRODUCTIONS, INC.
205-698 Corydon Ave. • WINNIPEG, MB R3M 0X9
(204) 284-0398

URBAN EAGLES
204 - 825 Sherbrook St. • WINNIPEG, MB R3A 1M5
(204) 772-6967 FAX 786-0860

WOODSMOKE & SWEETGRASS
CKY TV, Polo Park • WINNIPEG, MB R3G 0L7
(204) 775-0371 Fax 783-4841

NEW BRUNSWICK

C.F.N.T. - 104.5 FM
Maliseet Nation at Tobique Radio
P.O. Box 695 • PERTH ANDOVER, NB E0J 1V0
(506) 273-4307 Fax 273-9697

NEWFOUNDLAND

ATJIQANGITUT &LABRADORIMUIT
Box 160 • NAIN, NF A0P 1L0
(709) 922-2955 Fax 922-2293. Radio & TV, respectively.

OKALAKATIGET SOCIETY
P.O. Box 160 • NAIN, NF A0P 1L0
(709) 922-2896 Fax 922-2293; Robert Lyall, President
Ken Todd, Executive Director
Radio, TV. Publication: Kinatuinamot Ilengajuk (newsletter).

NORTHWEST TERRITORIES

CKQN-FM RADIO
BAKER LAKE, NT X0C 0A0 (867) 793-2962

SUDLIQVALUK RADIO SOCIETY
CORAL HARBOUR, NT X0C 0C0 (867) 925-9940

ARCIAQPALUK RADIO SOCIETY
ESKIMO POINT, NT X0C 0E0 (867) 857-2810

HALL BEACH RADIO SOCIETY
HALL BEACH, NT X0A 0K0 (867) 928-8852

INUVIALUIT COMMUNICATIONS SOCIETY
P.O. Box 1704 • INUVIK, NT X0E 1C0
(867) 979-2067 Fax 979-2744; Vincent Teddy, President

CFFB RADIO STATION
Canadian Broadcasting Corp. • IQALIUT, NT X0A 0H0
(867) 979-6100

IBC-TV - INUIT BROADCASTING CORP.
P.O. Box 700 • IQALIUT, NT X0A 0H0
(867) 979-6231 Fax 979-5853
Jobi Weetaluktuk, Executive Producer
Lynda Gunn, Regional Manager

TELEVISION NORTHERN CANADA (TVNC)
Box 1630 • IQALIUT, NT X0A 0H0
(867) 979-1707 Fax 979-1708

ALLANIQ RADIO SOCIETY
PANGNIRTUNG, NT X0A 0R0 (867) 473-8903

CBC KIVALLIQ
RANKIN INLET, NT X0C 0G0 (867) 645-2885

INUIT BROADCASTING CORP.
P.O. Box 178 • RANKIN INLET, NT X0C 0G0
(867) 645-2678 Fax 645-2937
Radio & television programs.

CBC NORTH
Northern Services Program
Box 160 • YELLOWKNIFE, NT X1A 2N2
(867) 920-5465 Fax 920-5440

CKLB RADIO
Native Communications Society of the Western NWT
Box 1919 • YELLOWKNIFE, NT X1A 2P4
(867) 920-2277 Fax 920-4205

CKNM-FM
Native Communications Society of the Western NWT
Box 1919 • YELLOWKNIFE, NT X1A 2P4
(867) 873-2661 Fax 920-4205
Percy Kinney, Radio Manager; Lee Selleck, Editor
Publication: Native Press (newspaper)

NCS-TV LTD.
Native Communications Society of the Western NWT
Box 1919 • YELLOWKNIFE, NT X1A 2P4
(867) 920-2277 Fax 920-4205

TELEVISION NORTHERN CANADA (TVNC)
5120-49th St., Box 3 • YELLOWKNIFE, NT X1A 1P8
(867) 669-7299 Fax 669-7930
E-mail: tvncda@arcticdata.nt.ca; Website: www.tvnc.ca

NOVA SCOTIA

NATIVE COMMUNICATIONS SOCIETY OF NOVA SCOTIA
P.O. Box 344 • SYDNEY, NS B1P 6H2
(902) 539-0045 Roy A. Gould, Exec. Director

NATIVE COMMUNICATIONS SOCIETY OF NOVA SCOTIA
P.O. Box 1005 • TRURO, NS B2N 5G7
(902) 895-6217 Brian Douglas, Editor
Publication: Micmac News.

ONTARIO

BEARSKIN LAKE RADIO STATION
BEARSKIN LAKE, ON P0V 1E0 (807) 363-2578

CKON - FM 97.3
Box 1496 • CORNWALL, ON K6A 5B7
(613) 575-2100 Fax 575-2935

"SMOKE SIGNALS" RADIO PROGRAM
Unit 61 - 1290 Sandford St. • LONDON, ON N5V 3X9
(519) 659-4682 Fax 453-3676

CHMO - AM
James Bay Broadcasting Corp.
P.O. Box 400 • MOOSONEE, ON P0L 1Y0
(705) 336-2301 Fax 336-3153

FIRST NATIONS, INC. CABLE TV & COMMUNICATIONS
Box 905 • OHSWEKEN, ON N0A 1M0
(519) 445-2981 Fax 445-4084

CHFN 100.3 FM
RR#5 • OHSWEKEN, ON N0H 2T0
(519) 534-1003 Fax 524-2130

CKRZ 100.3 FM
Box 189 • OHSWEKEN, ON N0A 1M0
(519) 445-4140 Fax 445-0177; E-mail: ckrz@worldchat.com

INUIT BROADCASTING CORP. (IBC)
703-251 Laurier Ave. • OTTAWA, ON K1P 5J6
(613) 235-1892 Fax 230-8824; E-mail: ibcicsl@sonetis.com
Doug Saunders, President; Debbie Brisebois, Executive Director

TV NORTHERN CANADA (TVNC)
1412 - 130 Albert St. • OTTAWA, ON K1P 5g4
(613) 567-1550 Fax 567-1834; Website: www.tvnc.ca

CKWE 105.9 FM
General Delivery • SHANNONVILLE, ON K0K 3A0
(613) 967-0463 (Phone & Fax)

WAWATAY COMMUNICATIONS SOCIETY
Box 1180, 15 - 5th Ave. • SIOUX LOOKOUT, ON P0V 2T0
(807) 737-2951 Fax 737-3224
Lawrence Martin, Executive Director
Megan Williams, Editor - WaWaTay (newspaper)
MOOSE FACTORY, ON P0L 1W0 (705) 658-4556
Vern Cheechoo, Sr. Producer (Radio & TV)

CIUT - 89.5 FM
91 St. George St. • TORONTO, ON M5S 2E8
(416) 595-0909 Fax 595-5604

CFRZ 91.5 FM
RR#3 • WALLACEBURG, ON N8A 4K9
(519) 627-6272 Fax 627-6074

WIKY TV5 VIDEO PRODUCTIONS
P.O. Box 112 • WIKWEMIKONG, ON P0P 2J0
(705) 869-3200 Fax 859-3851

FIRST PEOPLES FREE RADIO
334 Askin Ave. • WINDSOR, ON N9B 2X2
(519) 254-8596

MOCCASIN TELEGRAPH NATIVE RADIO PROGRAM
38 Burwick Ave. • WOODBRIDGE, ON L4L 1J7
(905) 856-5962 Fax 975-0466

QUEBEC

CHISASIBI TELECOMMUNICATIONS ASSOCIATION
Chisasibi First Nation • CHISASIBI, PQ J0M 1E0 (819) 855-2527

TAQRAMIUT NIPINGAT, INC.
Administrative Centre, 185 Dorval Ave. #501 • DORVAL, PQ H9S 5J9
(514) 631-1394 Fax 631-6258

CKRK-103.7 MOHAWK RADIO STATION
Box 1050 • KAHNAWAKE, PQ J0L 1B0
(450) 638-1313 Fax 638-4009

CKHQ KANESATAKE RADIO
P.O. Box 747 • KANASATAKE, PQ J0N 1E0
(514) 479-8321

QAJJALIK FM STATION
KANGIQSUALUJJUAQ, PQ J0M 1A0
(819) 935-4258

FM STATION OFFICE
KUUJJUAQ, PQ J0M 1C0
(819) 964-2921

TAQRAMIUT NIPINGAT, INC.
Television Production Centre, Box 360 • KUUJJUAQ, PQ J0M 1C0
(819) 964-2565 Fax 964-2252

CHME-FM 94.9
c/o Montagnais de les Escoumins
20 rue de la Reserve, Box 820 • LES ESCOUMINS, PQ G0T 1K0
(418) 233-2700 Fax 233-3326

CHRQ FM RADIO STATION
Riverside East • LISTUGUJ, PQ G0C 2R0
(418) 788-2449 Fax 788-2653

CKWE RADIO
Bande de la riviere Deserte, C.P. 10, rue Bitobi • MANIWAKI, PQ J9E 3B3
(819) 449-5097

JAMES BAY CREE COMMUNICATIONS SOCIETY
75 Riverside St. • MISTASSINI LAKE, PQ G0W 1C0
(418) 923-3191 Fax 923-2088

JAMES BAY CREE COMMUNICATIONS SOCIETY
1, Place Ville Marie, Suite 3434 • MONTREAL, PQ H3B 3N9
(514) 861-5837 Fax 861-0760; Soloman Awashish, Radio Director
Diane Reid, Director General
Publication: Cree Ajemon.

SANS RESERVE COMMUNICATIONS AUTOCHTONES
3575, boul. Saint-Laurent • MONTREAL, PQ H2X 2T7
(514) 843-6098

MONT NATASHQUAN RADIO
NATASHQUAN, PQ G0G 2E0 (418) 726-3327

NEMASKA RADIO STATION
NEMASKA, PQ J0Y 3B0
(819) 673-2046 Fax 673-2542

CREE COMMUNITY RADIO STATION
POSTE-DE-LA-BALEINE, PQ J0M 1G0
(819) 929-3397

CKPV FM RADIO
QUAQTAQ, PQ J0M 1J0 (819) 492-9946

TAQRAMIUT NIPINGAT, INC.
Television & Radio Production Centre
Box 120 • SALLUIT, PQ J0M 1S0
(819) 255-8822 (radio) Fax 255-8891
(819) 255-8901 (television); George Kakayuk, President

RADIO KUESHAPETSHEKEN/CKU 104.5 FM
1089, rue Dquen, C.P. 8000 • SEPT-LIES, PQ G4R 4L9
(418) 927-2440 Fax 927-2800

TEWEGAN COMMUNICATIONS SOCIETY
351 Central Ave. • VAL D'OR, PQ J9P 1P6
(819) 825-5192 Fax 631-6528
Noe Mitchell, Executive Director

WASWANIPI COMMUNICATIONS SOCIETY
20 Popular St. • WASWANIPI, PQ J0Y 3C0
(819) 753-2557 Fax 753-2555

WEMIDJI RADIO STATION
Reserve Indienne Wemidji
WEMIDJI, PQ J0M 1L0 (819) 978-0264 ext. 245

RADIO COMMUNAUTAIRE
545, Chef Thomas Martin, Village des Hurons
WENDAKE, PQ G0A 4V0 (418) 843-3937

SOCAM - AM RADIO
Societe de Communications Atikamekw Montagnais
85 Boul. Chef Maurice Bastien
C.P. 329, Village des Hurons • WENDAKE, PQ G0A 4V0
  (418) 843-3873 Fax 845-4198
  Bernard Hervieau, Producer; Diane Savard, General Manager

SASKATCHEWAN

CILX RADIO - BELANGER'S COMMUNICATIONS
P.O. Box 208 • ILE-ALA-CROSSE, SK S0M 1C0
  (306) 833-2173 Fax 833-2310

MISSINIPI BROADCASTING CORP.
Box 1529 • LA RONGE, SK S0J 1L0
  (306) 425-4003 Fax 425-3755
  Robert Merasty, Executive Director
  Rick Laliberte & William Dumais, Directors
Radio: Missinipi Atchimowin

RAM REBROADCASTING, INC.
Box 3075 • PRINCE ALBERT, SK S6V 3M4
  (306) 763-0396

SASKATCHEWAN NATIVE COMMUNICATIONS CORP.
2526 Eleventh Ave. • REGINA, SK S4P 0K5
  (306) 653-2253; Gary Laplante, Chairperson
  Ona Fiddler-Bertelg, Editor/Manager
Publication: New Breed

CJUS – FM
SASKATOON, SK
Native Voice of Alberta. On the Air 4:30 PM, Sunday.

GEMINI PRODUCTIONS, INC.
Box 7773 • SASKATOON, SK S7K 4R5
  (306) 665-8575 Fax 665-0008

MOCCASIN TELEGRAPH
c/o Saskatchewan Indian, 1630 Idylwyld Dr. • SASKATOON, SK S7K 3S9

QUEST
c/o Saskatchewan Indian Institute of Technologies
Moose Woods Reserve, RR 5, GB 139 • SASKATOON, SK S7K 3J8
  (306) 244-4444 Fax 244-1391

SASKATCHEWAN NATIVE COMMUNICATIONS SOCIETY
104, 219 Robin Cres. • SASKATOON, SK S7L 6M8
  (306) 244-7441 Fax 343-0171

O & O BROADCASTING, INC.
Thunderchild Reserve • TURTLEFORD, SK S0M 2Y0
  (306) 845-3170

YUKON

CHON-FM
Northern Native Broadcasting of Yukon
4228-A 4th Ave. • WHITEHORSE, YU Y1A 1K1
  (867) 688-2420 Fax 668-6612
  Ken Kane, Chairperson; Marion Telep, Radio Director
Radio broadcasting.

KEYAH PRODUCTIONS
4228-A 4th Ave. • WHITEHORSE, YU Y1A 1K1
  (867) 668-2420 Fax 668-6612; E-mail: nnby@yknet.yk.ca
Radio & TV productions.

YE SA TO COMMUNICATIONS SOCIETY
Council of Yukon Indians, 22 Nisutlin Dr. • WHITEHORSE, YU Y1A 3S5
  (867) 668-5477 Fax 667-6923; Elizabeth Jackson, President
Publication: Dan Sha (newspaper).

This section is an alphabetical listing of more than 7,500+ in-print books and 2,500 used books (available on Amazon.com, Alibris.com and Abebooks.com) available relating to Indians of North America. In each listing, the reader will find, where sufficient material has been provided, the title, author or editor, number of pages, whether illustrated, indexed, etc., name of publisher, year of publication & price. The address of the publishers are contained in the Publisher's Index. An asterisk (*) indicates it is primarily for juvenile audiences.

*ABC'S THE AMERICAN INDIAN WAY
Children learn the alphabet while learning about American Indians.
Grades K-2. Illus. Paper. Sierra Oaks, $7.95.

*ABC'S OF OUR SPIRITUAL CONNECTION
Kim Soo Goodtrack; First Nations people's common ethics and cultural values that identify them in their everday lives. Grades 3-8. Illus. 56 pp. Paper. Theytus, 1994. $9.95.

A.D. 1250: ANCIENT PEOPLES OF THE SOUTHWEST
Lawrence W. Cheek; Focuses on the cultures of the Anasazi, Sinagua, Mogollon, Hohokam, and Salado. Illus. 200 full-color photos and drawings. 176 pp. University of Arizona Press & Treasure Chest, 1994. $49.95.

THE A TO Z OF EARLY NORTH AMERICA
Cameron B. Wesson; Illus. 312 pp. Paper. Scarecrow Press, 2009. $45.

THE A TO Z OF THE INUIT
Pamela R. Stern; Illus. 248 pp. Paper. Scarecrow Press, 2009. $38.

THE A TO Z OF NATIVE AMERICAN MOVEMENTS
Todd Leahy & Raymond Wilson; Reference on topics dealing with key movements, organizations, leadeship strategies, and major issues. 248 pp. Paper. Scarecrow Press, 2009. $45.

A TO Z OF NATIVE AMERICAN WOMEN
Liz Sonneborn
Illus. 249 pp. Facts on File, 1998. $45; 215 pp. Paper. U. of Nebraska Press, 2000. $12.95.

*THE ABENAKI
Colin G. Calloway; Grades 5 and up. Illus. 104 pp. Chelsea House, 1988. $17.95.

*THE ABENAKI
Elaine Landau; Grades 5-8. Illus. 64 pp. Franklin Watts, 1996. $22; paper, $6.95.

*ABENAKI CAPTIVE
M.L. Dubois; Grades 4-7. 144 pp. Lerner, 1994. $16.95.

ABENAKI WARRIOR, THE LIFE & TIMES OF CHIEF ESCUMBUIT: BIG ISLAND POND, 1665-1727 FRENCH HERO! BRITISH MONSTER! INDIAN PATRIOT
Alfred E. Kayworth; Adolph Case, Editor; Illus. 260 pp. Amazon.com, 1998. $21.95.

THE ABNAKIS & THEIR HISTORY
Eugene Vetromile; Reprint. Illus. Paper. Amazon.com, 1999. $15.95.

ABORIGINAL BEST PRACTICES
Mark Cauchi; Amazon.com, 1997.

ABORIGINAL ECONOMIC DEVELOPMENT FORUM: A COMPREHENSIVE LEGAL, FINANCING & TAX UPDATE
Insight Information Staff, Ed.; Illus. 255 pp. Insight Press, 2001.

ABORIGINAL HEALTH IN CANADA: HISTORICAL, CULTURAL, & EPIDEMIOLOGICAL PERSPECTIVES Ann Herring, James B. Waldram, T. Kue Young
352 pp. University of Toronto Press, 2006. $79; paper, $35.95.

ABORIGINAL INDIAN BASKETRY: STUDIES IN TEXTILE ART WITHOUT MACHINERY
Otis Tufton Mason; Reprint of 1904 edition. Illus. 688 pp. The Rio Grande Press, $40.

ABORIGINAL LAW HANDBOOK
Shin Imai; 2nd Edition. Illus. 430 pp. Paper. Carswell, 1999. $37.50.

ABORIGINAL MONUMENTS OF THE STATE OF NEW YORK
E.B. Squier; Reprint of 1849 edition. Illus. 200 pp. Sourcebook, $18.95.

ABORIGINAL ONTARIO: HISTORICAL PERSPECTIVES ON THE FIRST NATIONS
Edward S. Rogers & Donald B. Smith, Eds.; 14 contributing authors review the historical experience of the First Nations of Ontario. 448 pp. University of Toronto Press, 1994. $25.

ABORIGINAL PEOPLE & COLONIZERS OF WESTERN CANADA TO 1900
Sarah Carter; History of Canada's aboriginal peoples after European contact. 152 pp. University of Toronto Press, 1999. $45; paper, $14.95.

ABORIGINAL PEOPLE & OTHER CANADIANS: SHAPING NEW RELATIONSHIPS
Martin Thornton & Roy Todd, Eds.; University of Toronto Press, 2001. $22.95.

ABORIGINAL PEOPLE & POLITICS: THE INDIAN LAND QUESTION IN BRITISH COLUMBIA, 1849-1989
Paul Tennant; 320 pp. University of British Columbia Press, 1990.

ABORIGINAL PEOPLES & GOVERNMENT RESPONSIBILITY: EXPLORING FEDERAL & PROVINCIAL ROLES
David C. Hawkes, Ed.; 370 pp. Paper. McGilll-Queen's University Press.

ABORIGINAL PEOPLES: TOWARD SELF-GOVERNMENT
Marie leger, Ed.; 250 pp. Consortium Book Sales, 1995. $39; paper, $20.

THE ABORIGINAL PIPES OF WISCONSIN
West; Reprint of 1905 article. 130 pp. Paper. Hothem House. $12.50.

ABORIGINAL PLANT USE IN CANADA'S NORTHWEST BOREAL FOREST
Robin J. Marles, et al; Describes the traditional Aboriginal uses of over 200 plants from Canada's boreal forest. Illus. 256 pp. UBC Press, 1999. $75.

ABORIGINAL SLAVERY ON THE NORTHWEST COAST OF NORTH AMERICA
Leland Donald; Illus. 379 pp. University of California Press, 1997. $50.

ABORIGINAL SOCIETY IN SOUTHERN CALIFORNIA
William D. Strong, Ralph Beals & Lowell J. Bean
Reprint of 1929 ed. Ethnographic material. 358 pp. Paper. Malki-Ballena Press, 1987. $30.

ABORIGINAL SUBSISTENCE TECHNOLOGY ON THE SOUTHEASTERN COASTAL PLAIN DURING THE LATE PREHISTORIC PERIOD
Lewis H. Larson; Illus. Maps. Biblio. 260 pp. University Press of Florida, 1980. $29.95.

ABORIGINAL TITLE & INDIGENOUS PEOPLES: CANADA, AUSTRALIA & NEW ZEALAND Louis A. Knafla & Haijo Westra, Editors; Cases of litigation for Aboriginal title. 272 pp. University of Washington Press, 2011. $85; paper, $35.95.

ABORIGINAL TITLE: THE MODERN JURISPRUDENCE OF TRIBAL LAND RIGHTS
P.G. McHugh; Oxford University Press, 2011. $145.

ABORIGINAL & TREATY RIGHTS IN CANADA
Michael Asch, Ed.; 288 pp. University of Washington Press, 1997. $65.

ABOVE THE LINE: NEW POEMS
Joseph Bruchac; Abenaki Indian writer. Paper. U. of New Mexico Press, 2007. $11.95.

*ABSALOKA
Council for Indian Education, 1971. 75¢.

ABSARAKA: HOME OF THE CROWS
Margaret I. Carrington; Illus. 285 pp. U. of Nebraska Press, 1983. $22.50; paper, $6.95.

ABSENTEE INDIANS & OTHER POEMS
Kimberly Blaeser; Illus. 131 pp. Paper. Michigan State University Press**, 2002. $24.95**

*THE ABSOLUTELY TRUE DIARY OF A PART-TIME INDIAN
Sherman Alexie; illus. by Ellen Forney; Novel. A Spokane Indian teenager attends an all-white high school. For young adults. Paper. Little Brown Publishers, 2007.

ACAOOHKIWINA & ACIMOWINA: TRADITIONAL NARRATIVES OF THE ROCK CREE INDIANS Robert A. Brightman; 228 pp. Paper. University of Chicago Press, 1994. $19.95.

ACCESS FIRST NATIONS
Directory of American Indian artists & craftspeople listing businesses that carry arts & crafts. $32.95. Order: Access First Nations, 69 Kelley Rd., Falmouth, VA 22405 (703) 371-5615.

AN ACCOUNT OF THE ANTIQUITIES OF THE INDIANS: CHRONICLES OF THE NEW WORLD ENCOUNTER Fray Ramon Pane; Jose Juan Arrom, Editor
Illus. 128 pp. Duke University Press, 2000. $39.95.

AN ACCOUNT OF THE HISTIRY, MANNERS & CUSTOMS OF THE INDIAN NATIONS WHO ONCE INHABITED PENNSYLVANIA & THE NEIGHBORING STATES 1819
John Gottlieb & Enerstus Heckewelder
Reprint. Illus. Paper. Kessinger Publishing, 2005. $24.50.

AN ACCOUNT OF THE ORIGIN & EARLY PROSECUTION OF THE INDIAN WAR IN OREGON Charles S. Drew; Reprint. Paper. 1973. Available from Amazon.com, $18.

ACCULTURATION IN SEVEN INDIAN TRIBES
Ralph Linton; 1963 Reprint. 526 pp. Amazon.com., $15.

ACOMA: THE PEOPLE OF WHITE ROCK
H.L. James; Revised 1970 edition. Presents Acoma, the "sky city" of New Mexico. Illus. 96 pp. Paper. Rio Grande Press, $14.95.

ACOMA & LAGUNA POTTERY
Rick Dillingham; with Melinda Elliott; Traces the development of pottery making at the two pueblos. Illus. Maps. Biblio. 256 pp. Paper. School for Advanced Research, 1992. $24.95.

ACOMA: PUEBLO IN THE SKY
Ward Alan Minge
Revised edition. Illus. 296 pp. Paper. University of New Mexico Press, 2002. $27.95.

ACROSS ARCTIC AMERICA, NARRATIVE OF THE FIFTH THULE EXPEDITION
Knud Rasmussen; Reprint of 1927 edition. Greenwood, $35.

ACROSS A GREAT DIVIDE: CONTINUITY & CHANGE IN NATIVE NORTH AMERICAN SOCIETIES, 1400-1900 Laura L. Scheiber & Mark D. Mitchell
Empirical archaeological research helps replace long-standing models of indigenous culture change rooted in colonialist narratives. 342 pp. U. of Arizona Press, 2010. $59.95.

ACROSS THE SHAMAN'S RIVER: JOHN MUIR, THE TLINGIT STRONGHOLD, AND THE OPENING OF THE NORTH
Daniel Henry; 256 pp. Paper. University of Alaska Press, 2017. $32.95.

*ACROSS THE TUNDRA
 Marjorie Vandervelde; Tale of two Eskimo boys hunting alone. Grades 4-9. 40 pp.
Council for Indian Education, 1972. $9.95; paper. $3.95.

*ACROSS THE WIDE RIVER
 William Hewitt; Historical novel based on true story of an American Indian boy and his
response to his father's death on the Korean War. 104 pp. University of New Mexico Press,

ACTS OF REBELLION: THE WARD CHURCHILL READER
 Ward Churchill; Illus. 480 pp.Paper. Routledge, 2002. $90.

ADA, OKLA., QUEEN CITY OF THE CHICKASAW NATION: A PICTORIAL HISTORY
 Marvin Kroeker & Guy Logsdon; Donning Co. Publishers, 1998.

**ADAMS: THE MANUFACTURING OF FLAKED STONE TOOLS
AT A PALEOINDIAN SITE IN WESTERN KENTUCKY**
 Thomas N. Sanders; Illus. 165 pp. Paper. Alibris.com, 1990. $15.95.

THE ADENA PEOPLE
 William S. Webb & Charles E. Snow
The prehistory of the Ohio Valley, largely concerned with the burial customs &
earth mounds. Reprint of 1945 edition. Paper. Amazon.com, $31.

THE EUGENE B. ADKINS COLLECTION: SELECTED WORKS
 foreword by David L. Boren; preface by Randall Suffolk
Reproductions of significant works from the Adkins Collection of Native American &
Southwestern art. Illus. 304 pp. University of Oklahoma Press, 2011. $60; paper, $29.95.

ADMINISTRATION IN NAVAJO RESERVATION SCHOOLS
 Bob Roessel; A guide for school administrators on the Navajo Reservation.
Paper. Rough Rock School Press, 2004. $20.

**ADOBE WALLS: THE HISTORY & ARCHAEOLOGY OF THE
1874 TRADING POST**
 Lindsay Baker & Billy Harrison
Illus. 430 pp. Paper. Texas A&M University Press, 1986. $29.50.

*ADOPTED BY INDIANS: A TRUE STORY
 Thomas Jefferson Mayfield; Malcolm Margolin, Editor
Gives younger readers a close-up view of traditional California Indians life and
early California. Grades 4 and up. Illus. 192 pp. Paper. Heyday Books, $10.95.

ADVENTURES IN CREATING EARRINGS
 Laura Reid; Ste-by-step instructions. Illus. 106 pp. Paper. Written Heritage, $9.95.

ADVENTURES IN PHYSICS & PUEBLO POTTERY
 Francis Harlow & Dwight Lanmon; Illus. 204 pp. Museum of New Mexico Press, 2016.
$34.95.

ADVENTURES IN STONE ARTIFACTS
 Livoti & Kiesa; A family guide to hunting and collecting Indian artifacts.
Illus. 254 pp. Paper. Hothem House, 1997. $15.95.

ADVENTURES ON THE WESTERN FRONTIER
 Maj. Gen. John Gibbon
A record of the lives of the Indians, soldiers and white settlers; Indian warfare;
Sioux Campaign of 1876.Illus. 288 pp. Amazon.com & Alibris.com, 1994. $24.95.

**ADVENTURES WITH A SAINT: KATERI TEKAKWITHA,
"LILY OF THE MOHAWKS"**
 Marlene McCauley; R. Allan McCauley, Ed.
Illus. 208 pp.Paper. Grace House Publishing, 1992. $8.

**ADVOCATES FOR THE OPPRESSED: HISPANOS, INDIANS,
GENIZAROS AND THEIR LAND IN NEW MEXICO**
 Malcolm Ebright; Illus. 448 pp. Paper. University of New Mexico Press, $34.95.

AFL TO ARROWHEAD: FOUR DECADES OF CHIEFS HISTORY & TRIVIA
 Mark Stallard; Illus. 222 pp. Paper. Addax Publishing Group, 2002.$9.95.

**AFRICAN AMERICANS & NATIVE AMERICANS IN THE
CHEROKEE & CREEK NATIONS, 1830S TO 1920S**
 Katja May; Revised edition. Illus. 312 pp. Amazon.com, 1996. $100.

AFRICAN CHEROKEES IN INDIAN TERRITORY: FROM CHATTEL TO CITIZENS
 Celia E. Naylor; Charts the experiences of enslaved & free African Cherokees from the
Trail of Tears to Oklahoma's entry into the Union in 1907. Illus. Maps. 376 pp. University of
North Carolina Press, 2008. $55; paper, $22.50.

AFRICAN CREEKS: ESTELVSTE & THE CREEK NATION
 Gary Zellar; University of Oklahoma Press, 2007.

AFRICANS & CREEKS: FROM THE COLONIAL PERIOD TO THE CIVIL WAR
 Daniel F. Littlefield, Jr.; Illus. Greenwood Publishing, 1979. $35.

**AFRICANS & INDIANS: AN AFROCENTRIC ANALYSIS OF RELATIONS
BETWEEN AFRICANS & AMERICAN IDNIANS IN COLONIAL VIRGINIA**
 Barbara A. Faggins; 112 pp. Routledge, 2001. $70.

**AFRICANS & NATIVE AMERICANS: THE LANGUAGE OF RACE & THE EVOLUTION
OF RED-BLACK PEOPLES** Jack D. Forbes; Explores key issues relating to the evolution
of racial terminology & European colonialists' perceptions of color. Illus. 352 pp. Paper.
University of Illinois Press, 1993. $25.

AFRICANS & SEMINOLES: FROM REMOVAL TO EMANCIPATION
 Daniel F. Littlefield, Jr.; Documents the interrelationship of two racial cultures in
antebellum Florida & Oklahoma. Reprint of 1977 edition. Illus. 296 pp. Paper. University
Press of Mississippi, 2001. $22.

AFTER & BEFORE THE LIGHTNING
 Simon J. Ortiz; Prose & verse poems of winter in South Dakota on the Rosebud Sioux
Reservation. 127 pp. Paper. University of Arizona Press, 1994. $17.95.

**AFTER COLUMBUS: THE SMITHSONIAN CHRONICLE OF THE NORTH AMERICAN
INDIANS** Herman J. Viola; The facts & implications of Indian & white interaction in
America. Illus. 288 pp. Paper. Smithsonian Institution Press, 1991. $24.95.

AFTER CUSTER: LOSS & TRANSFORMATION IN SIOUX COUNTRY
 Paul L. Hedren; Examines the war's effects on the culture, environment, and geography of
the norhern Great Plains, their Native inhabitants, and the Anglo-American invaders. Illus.
Maps. University of Oklahoma Press, 2011. $24.95.

**AFTER THE FIRST FULL MOON IN APRIL: A SOURCEBOOK OF HERBAL MEDICINE
FROM A CALIFORNIA INDIAN ELDER** Josephine Peters, with Beverly Ortiz
Instructs on personal & tribal history & illustrates the uses & doses of over 160 plants. Illus.
272 pp. University of Arizona Press, 2008. $75.

**AFTER KING PHILIP'S WAR: PRESENCE & PERSISTENCE IN INDIAN
NEW ENGLAND** Colin G. Calloway, Ed. & Intro.
Illus. 278 pp. Paper. University Press of New England, 1997. $27.95.

AFTER LEWIS & CLARK: THE FORCES OF CHANGE, 1806-1871
 Gary Allen Hood; Collection of paintings, drawings and prints from the Gilcrease Museum
in Tulsa, Okla. Illus. 96 pp. Paper. University of Oklahoma Press, 2008. $24.95.

AFTER REMOVAL: THE CHOCTAW IN MISSISSIPPI
 Samuel Wells & Roseanna Tubby, Editors
Illus. 168 pp. Spiral binding. University Press of Mississippi, 2004. $25.

**AFTER THE TRAIL OF TEARS: THE CHEROKEES' STRUGGLE FOR
SOVEREIGNTY, 1839-1880** William G. McLoughlin
450 pp. University of North Carolina Press, 1994. $49.95; paper, $19.95.

AFTER WOUNDED KNEE
 Jerry Green; 184 pp. Michigan State University Press, 1996. $39.95. e Book, $31.95.

AGAINST BORDERS: PROMOTING BOOKS FOR A MULTICULTURAL WORLD
 Hazel Rochman; Illus. 288 pp. Paper. ALA Books, 1993. $16.95.

AGAINST CULTURE: DEVELOPMENT, POLITICS, & RELIGION IN INDIAN ALASKA
 Kirk Dombrowski; Tlingit & Haida life in Southeast Alaska today. Illus. Map. 247 PP.
University of Nebraska Press, 2001. $60; paper, $19.95.

*AGALIHA': INDIAN SELF-ESTEEM CURRICULUM ACTIVITY BOOK
 Indian Developed Curriculum & Publishing Corp.
Encourages Indian students to feel pride in their heritage. Grades 1-8. 62 pp.
Daybreak Star Press, $12.95.

**AGAYUL? OUR WAY OF MAKING PRAYER: KEGGINAQUT, KANGIIT-ILU/YUP'IK
MASKS & THE STORIES THEY TELL**
 Ann Fienup-Riordan; Illus. 272 pp. Paper. University of Washington Press, 1996. $14.95.

**AGENTS OF REPRESSION: THE FBI's SECRET WARS AGAINST THE
LACK PANTHER PARTY & THE AMERICAN INDIAN MOVEMENT**
 Ward Churchill & Jim Vander Wall
2nd Ed. 538 pp. Amazon.com, 2002. $40; paper, $22.

AGRICULTURAL ORIGINS & DEVELOPMENT IN THE MIDCONTINENT
 William Green, Editor; University of Iowa, Publications Dept., 1993. $15.

AH MO: INDIAN LEGENDS FROM THE NORTHWEST
 Arthur Griffin, Ed.; Illus. 64 pp. Paper. Hancock House, 1990. $7.95.

AHTNA ATHABASKAN DICTIONARY
 James Kari, Ed.; Contains 6,000 Ahtna language entries. 700 pp.
Alaska Native Language Center, 1990. $50; paper, $25.

AIDS REGIONAL DIRECTORY: RESOURCES IN INDIAN COUNTRY
 Laurie McLemore, MD, Director
Association of Native American Medical Students, 1994, 2nd Ed. $23, postpaid.

AIRLIFT TO WOUNDED KNEE
 Bill Zimmerman; Illus. 348 pp. Amazon.com, 1976. $14.95.

AKWE:KON LITERARY ISSUE
Anthology of new fiction and poetry from 14 Native American authors. Akwe:kon Press, $8.

AKWESASNE HISTORICAL POSTCARDS; PEACEMAKER & HIAWATHA POSTERS
Akwesasne Museum, 50/postcard; 75/poster.

ALAAWICH (OUR LANGUAGE)
 Lucy Arvidson & Anne Galloway; Tubatulabal language spoken by the Indian people
whose ancestral home is in the Kern River Valley near the southern end of the Sierra
Nevada Mountains. Illus. 32 pp. Paper. Malki Museum Press, 1978. $5.

THE ALABAMA-COUSHATTA INDIANS
 Jonathan Hook; Illus. 208 pp. Texas A&M University Press, 1997. $29.95.

ALASKA AT 50: THE PAST, PRESENT, AND NEXT FIFTY YEARS OF ALASKA STATEHOOD G.W. Kimura, Editor; Essays include topics of culture, art, law, economy, people, etc. Photos. 264 pp. Paper. University of Alaska Press, 2009. $24.95.

ALASKA DAYS WITH JOHN MUIR
Samuel Hall Young; Illus. 240 pp. Paper. Gibbs Smith, 1991. $9.95

ALASKA ESKIMO FOOTWEAR
Jill Oakes; Illus. 176 pp. University of Chicago Press, $54.95; paper, $29.95.

THE ALASKA ESKIMOS: A SELECTED ANNOTATED BIBLIOGRAPHY
Arthur Hippler & John Wood; Paper. University of Alaska, 1977. $15.

ALASKA 1899: ESSAYS FROM THE HARRIMAN EXPEDITION
George Bird Grinnell; Records Grinnell's observations of native Alaskans. Illus. 136 pp. Paper. University of Washington Press, 1994. $14.95.

ALASKA: A HISTORY
Claus M. Naske & Herman E. Slotnick; A comprehensive history. Examines the region's geography & Native peoples who inhabit it. Illus. 15 maps. 520 pp. University of Oklahoma Press, 2011. $39.95.

ALASKA: A HISTORY OF THE 49TH STATE
Claus M. Naska & Herman Slotnick
2nd edition. Photos. Maps. 368 pp. Paper. University of Oklahoma Press, $18.95.

ALASKA HISTORY SERIES
Richard Pierce, Ed/Pub;J ohn Sabella & Associates.

*ALASKA IN THE DAYS THAT WERE BEFORE
Tanya Hardgrove; A Native elder tells stories from his life. Grades 3-10. 31 pp. Council for Indian Education, 1985. $8.95; paper, $2.95.

ALASKA NATIVE ALLOTMENT SUBDIVISION ACT
U.S. Senate Committee on Indian Affairs; 108th Congress, 1st Session 85 pp. U.S. GPO, 2003.

ALASKA NATIVE ARTS & CRAFTS
Alaska Geographic; In-depth review of the art and artifacts of Alaska's Native people. 210 pp. Alaska Natural History Association & The Alaska Geographic Society, $19.95.

THE ALASKA NATIVE CLAIMS SETTLEMENT ACT, 1991, & TRIBAL GOVERNMENT
Thomas A. Morehouse
Illus. 29 pp. University of Alaska, Institute of Social and Economic Research, 1988. $2.

ALASKA NATIVE LAND RIGHTS: HEARING BEFORE THE COMMITTEE ON ENERGY & NATURAL RESOURCES, U.S. SENATE, 105TH CONGRESS
USGPO Staff; 64 pp. U.S. GPO, 1998.

ALASKA NATIVE LANGUAGE CENTER PUBLICATIONS
Contains numerous titles covering the Inupiaq Eskimo, Central Yup'ik Eskimo, Alutiiq (Sugpiaq) Eskimo, Aleut, Siberian Yup'ik EskimoAhtna Athabaskan, Tanaina Athabaskan, Ingalik (Deg Hit'an) Athabaskan, Holikachuk Athabaskan, Upper Kuskokwim, Koyukon Athabaskan, Han Athabaskan, Lower Tanana Athabaskan, Tanacross Athabaskan, Upper Tanana Athabaskan, Kutchin (Gwich'in) Athabaskan, Eyak, Tlingit, and Haida. Also research papers, maps, and other sources of materials. Alaska Native Language Center.

ALASKA NATIVE LANGUAGES: PAST, PRESENT & FUTURE
Michael E. Krauss; Illus. 110 pp. Paper. Alaska Native Language Center, 1980. $6.

ALASKA NATIVE PARENTS IN ANCHORAGE: PERSECTIVES ON CHILDREARING
Julie E. Sproutt; 96 pp. Amazon.com & Alibris.com, 1992. $53.50.

ALASKA NATIVE POLICY IN THE 20TH CENTURY
Ramona E. Skinner; 140 pp. Garland, 1997. $65.

ALASKA NATIVE POLITICAL LEADERSHIP & HIGHER EDUCATION: ONE UNIVERSITY, TWO UNIVERSES
Michael L. Jennings; 224 pp. AltaMira Press, 2004. $96; paper, $38..

ALASKA NATIVE WAYS: WHAT THE ELDERS HAVE TAUGHT US
Martha Bristow & Roy Corral; Illus. 144 pp. Amazon.com, 2002. $39.95.

ALASKA NATIVES & AMERICAN LAWS
David S. Case & Anne D. Shinkwin
Reprint. 1st Ed. 586 pp. Paper. University of Alaska Press, 1997. $25.

ALASKA NATIVES & AMERICAN LAWS
David S. Case & David A. Voluck; 2nd Ed. A review & analysis of legal principles applicable to Alaska Natives in several substantive areas. 566 pp. University of Alaska Press, 2002. $60; paper, $29.95.

ALASKA NATIVES: A GUIDE TO CURRENT REFERENCE SOURCES IN THE RASMUSON LIBRARY
Mark C. Goniwiecha; 78 pp. Paper. University of Alaska, Rasmuson Library. $10.

ALASKA: REFLECTIONS ON LAND & SPIRIT
Robert Hedin & Gary Holthaus
22 selections by John Muir, John McPhee, Barry Lopez, et al...stories of the land & Eskimos who inhabit Alaska. Photos. 322 pp. Paper. U. of Arizona Press, 1989. $19.95.

ALASKA'S DAUGHTER: AN ESKIMO MEMOIR OF THE EARLY TWENTIETH CENTURY Elizabeth Bernhardt Pinson
Paper. Utah State University Press, 2006. $26.95, E-book, $15.50.

ALASKA'S NATIVE PEOPLE
Lael Morgan, Ed.; Illus. 304 pp. Paper. Alaska Northwest & The Alaska Geographic Society, 1979. Album style, $24.95.

ALASKA'S SOUTHERN PANHANDLE
Alaska Geographic; Explores the southern tip of southeastern Alaska including the Tlingit, Haida & Tsimshian Native groups. 96 pp. Paper. Alaska Geographic Society, 1997. $19.95.

ALASKA'S TOTEM POLES
Pat Kramer; Illus. 96 pp. Amazon.com, 2004. $16.95.

ALASKAMEUT '86
Exhibition catalog featuring interviews with & the artwork of 14 maskmakers representative of Aleut, Yup'ik, Inupiaq, Tlingit and Athabascan cultures. Illus. 48 pp. Paper. Institute of Alaska Native Arts, 1986. $10.50, postpaid.

ALASKAN ESKIMO LIFE IN THE 1890S: AS SKETCHED BY NATIVE ARTISTS
George Phebus, Jr.; Illus. Map. 168 pp. Paper. University of Alaska Press, 1995. $18.95.

*ALASKAN IGLOO TALES
Keithahn; illus. by Ahgupuk; Grades 3 and up. Paper. Graphic Arts Center, $12.95.

ALASKAN NATIVE FOOD PRACTICES, CUSTOMS & HOLIDAYS
Karen Halderson; Paper. Amazon.com, 1991. $10.

ALBERNI PREHISTORY
Alan D. McMillan & Denis St. Claire; Archaeological & ethnographic Investigations on Western Vancouver Island. Illus. 221 pp. Paper. Theytus, 1982. $9.95.

ALCATRAZ: INDIAN LAND FOREVER
Troy R. Johnson, Ed.; 144 pp. UCLA, American Indian Studies Center, 1994. $25.

ALCATRAZ! ALCATRAZ: THE INDIAN OCCUPATION OF 1969-71
Adam Fortunate Eagle
A personal account written by one of the organizers. 160 pp. Paper. Heyday Books, $9.95.

ALCOHOL PROBLEMS IN NATIVE AMERICA: THE UNTOLD STORY OF RESISTANCE & RECOVERY - "THE TRUTH ABOUT THE LIE."
Don L. Coyhis & William L. White; Paper. Coyhis Publishing/White Bison, Inc. 2007. $15.

ALEUT DICTIONARY
Knut Bergsland, Compiler; Documents the recorded vocabulary of the Aleut language; 1,600 Aleut place names on 33 maps; 600+ Aleut men's names; English index with 14,000 Aleut words & suffixes. 739 pp. Paper. Alaska Native Language Center, 1994. $37.50.

ALEUT TALES & NARRATIVES
Waldemar Jochelson; Knut Bergsland & Moses Dirks, Eds.; Aleut folklore in Aleut with English translations. 87 stories. Illus. 715 pp. Alaska Native Language Center, 1990. $25.

AN ALEUTIAN ETHNOGRAPHY
Lucien Turner; Ray Hudson, Editor
The study of Aleut communities & Aleutian cultures in three Aleut communities in the 19th century. Illus. 175 pp. University of Chicago Press, 2008. $45; paper, $26.95.

ALEUTS: SURVIVORS OF THE BERING LAND BRIDGE
William S. Laughlin; Illus. 166 pp. Paper. Amazon.com, 1981. $39.99.

SHERMAN ALEXIE: A COLLECTION OF CRITICAL ESSAYS
Jeff Berglund & Jan Roush; 344 pp. Paper. University of Utah Press, $24.95; eBook, $20.

*ALGIC RESEARCHES: NORTH AMERICAN INDIAN FOLKTALES & LEGENDS, VOL. 1 Henry Schoolcraft
Reprint of 1923 edition. Grades 4-8. Illus. 248 pp. Paper. Amazon.com, 2009. $14.

*ALGONKIAN: LIFESTYLE OF THE NEW ENGLAND INDIANS
Bob Eaton; Grades PS-4. Illus. Paper. Amazon.com, 1998. $11.95.

*ALGONQUIAN
Rita & Mary D'Apice; Grades 5-8. Illus. 32 pp. Amazon.com, 1990. $9.95.

ALGONQUIN APPRENTICE: DISCOVERING THE HISTORY & LEGEND OF THE BIRCHBARK CANOE David Gidmark; Illus. 224 pp. Paper. Stackpole Press, 1995. $16.

THE ALGONQUIN BIRCHBARK CANOE
David Gidmark; British book contains the history of canoes & tips on making & maintaining a birch bark canoe. Illus. 64 pp. Paper. Amazon.com, 1997. $14.

ALGONQUIN LEGENDS OF NEW ENGLAND
Charles G. Leland; Study of myths & folklore of the Micmac, Passamaquoddy & Penobscot tribes. Illus. 416 pp. Paper. Dover, $12.95.

*THE ALGONQUIAN OF NEW YORK
David M. Ostreicher; The Library of Native Americans. Ages 9 and up. Illus. 64 pp. Rosen Publishing, 2003. $29.95.

ALGONQUIN: THE PARK & ITS PEOPLE
Liz Lundell; Illus. 210 pp. Paper. Amazon.com, 2000. $24.95.

THE ALGONQUIAN PEOPLES OF LONG ISLAND FROM EARLIEST TIMES TO 1700
John A. Strong; Illus. 368 pp. Heart of the Lakes Publishing, 1997. $40.

ALGONQUIAN SPIRIT: CONTEMPORARY TRANSLATIONS OF THE ALGONQUIAN LITERATURES OF NORTH AMERICA
Brian Swann; Illus. 532 pp. Paper. University of Nebraska Press, 2005. $34.95.

*THE ALGONQUIANS
Patricia R. Quiri; Grades 4-6. Illus. 64 pp. Franklin Watts, 1992. $22.

THE ALGONQUIANS OF THE EAST COAST
Time-Life Series Editors
Illus. The Lenape and other coastal Algonquian people. Amazon.com, $19.95.

*ALL ABOUT ARROWHEADS & SPEAR POINTS
Howard E. Smith, Jr.; Grades 4-7. Illus. 80 pp. Amazon.com. 1989. $14.95.

ALL INDIANS DO NOT LIVE IN TEEPEES (OR CASINOS)
Catherine C. Robbins; Explores contemporary Native life. Illus. Map. 408 pp.
University of Nebraska Press, 2011. $26.95.

ALL MY RELATIONS: AN ANTHOLOGY OF CONTEMPORARY
CANADIAN NATIVE FICTION
Thomas King, Ed.; 220 pp. Paper. University of Oklahoma Press, 1992. $15.95.

ALL MY RELATIONS: A GUIDE TO LAKOTA KINSHIP
William K. Powers & Marla N. Powers; Guide to Lakota terms needed to address
& describe their relatives. Illus. Glossary. 52 pp. Paper. Lakota Books, $22.95.

ALL MY RELATIONS - MITAKUYE OYASIN: THE SIOUX, THE PUEBLO
& THE SPIRIT WORLD Jean Prugh; Deborah Susswein, Editor
Illus. 120 pp. Paper. Amazon.com, 1006. $5.95.

ALL MY RELATIONS: A NATIVE'S THOUGHTS, POEMS & PRAYERS
Victoria A. Summers; Reprint. 2nd Ed. Illus. 88 pp. Paper. Amazon.com, 1992. $6.95.

ALL MY RELATIVES: COMMUNITY IN CONTEMPORARY ETHNIC AMERICAN
LITERATURES Bonnie TuSmith; Includes the works of N. Scott Momaday,
Leslie Marmon Silko, et al. 232 pp. Paper. University of Michigan Press, 1993. $28.95.

ALL MY SINS ARE RELATIVES
W.S. Penn; Investigation of mixed-race identity. Illus. 268 pp.
Paper. U. of Nebraska Press, 1995. $25.

ALL-NEW NATIVE AMERICAN BRACELETS
Geri D. Weitzman; Paper. Amazon.com, 1997. $7.95.

ALL OUR RELATIONS: NATIVE STRUGGLES FOR LAND & LIFE
Winona LaDuke; Illus. 242 pp. Amazon.com, 1999. $40; paper, $16.

ALL ROADS ARE GOOD: NATIVE VOICES ON LIFE & CULTURE
Foreword by W. Richard West, Jr. & Preface by Clara Sue Kidwell
23 accomplished figures from diverse indigenous cultures throughout the Americas selects
objects of cultural, spiritual, artistic, or personal significance from the National Museum of
the American Indian's collection & reflects on their cultuiral heritage. Illus. 224 pp. Paper.
NMAI Press, 1994. $34.95.

ALL THAT GLITTERS: THE EMERGENCE OF NATIVE AMERICAN
MICAGCOUS ART POTTERY IN NORTHERN NEW MEXICO
Duane Anderson; Illus. 199 pp. Paper. School of American Research, 1999. $27.50.

ALL THAT REMAINS: A WEST VIRGINIA ARCHAEOLOGIST'S DISCOVERIES
THE ANTIQUITIES OF WISCONSIN, AS SURVEYED & DESCRIBED
I.A. Lapham; Details Wisconsin's mounds and mound groups. Reprint of 1855 ed. with
new introduction and foreword. Drawings. Maps. 184 pp. U. of Wisconsin Press, 2007.
$24.95.

ALL THAT REMAINS: A WEST VIRGINIA ARCHAEOLOGISTS DISCOVERIES
Robert Pyle; Betty L. Wiley, Ed.; Illus. Paper. Amazon.com, 1991.

ALL THAT REMAINS: VARIETIES OF INDIGENOUS EXPRESSION
Arnold Krupat; Essays on literary criticism in the 21st century. 248 pp. Paper.
University of Nebraska Press, 2009. $25.

ALLAPATTAH
Patrick D. Smith
Seminole Indian (FL) story. Fiction. Illus. 202 pp. Paper. Pineapple Press, 1987. $10.95.

ALLEGANY SENECAS & KINZUA DAM: FORCED RELOCATION
THROUGH TWO GENERATIONS
Joy A. Bilharz; Illus. Maps. 204 pp. Paper. University of Nebraska Press, 1998. $24.95.

THE ALLEN SITE: A PALEOINDIAN CAMP IN SOUTHWESTERN NEBRASKA
Doiuglas Bamforth, Editor; Illus. 304 pp. University of New Mexico Press, $60.

ALLIANCES: RE/ENVISIONING INDIGENOUS-NON-INDIGENOUS RELATIONSHIPS
Lynne Davis, Editor; University of Toronto Press, 2010. $80; paper, $35.

THE ALLOTMENT PLOT: ALICE E. FLETCHER & E. JANE GAY,
AND NEZ PERCE SURVIVANCE
Nicole Tonkovich; Illus. Maps. 440 pp. University of Nebraska Press, 2012. $65.

ALMANAC OF THE DEAD
Leslie Marmon Silko; Fiction. 792 pp. Paper. Penguin USA, $13.

ALONE IN THE WILDERNESS
Hap Gilliland; Fiction. Nature. Illus. 160 pp. Paper. Naturegraph Publishers, $14.95.

ALONG NAVAJO TRAILS: RECOLLECTIONS OF A TRADER, 1898-1948
Will Evans, Susan E. Woods & Robert S. McPherson
Illus. 270 pp. Paper. Utah State University Press, 2007. $28.95. E-book, $15.

ALPINE CENTINELS: A CHRONICLE OF THE SHEEP ESTER INDIANS
Tony Taylor; Illus. 52 pp. Paper. Brushhog Books, 2001. $9.95.

ALSO CALLED SACAJAWEA: CHIEF WOMAN'S STOLEN IDENTITY
Thomas H. Johnson with Helen S. Johnson; Conversations with Native peoples about the
true identity of Sacajawea. Illus. 124 pp. Paper. Waveland Press, 2008. $14.95.

ALTERNATIVE LEADERSHIP STRATEGIES IN THE PREHISPANIC SOUTHWEST
Barbara J. Mills; Illus. 300 pp. University of Arizona Press, 2000.$45.

ALTERNATIVES
Drew Hayden Taylor; 144 pp. University of Toronto Press, 2004. $13.95.

ALTERNATIVES TO SOCIAL ASSISTANCE IN INDIAN COMMUNITIES
Frank Cassidy & Shirley B. Seward; 120 pp. Paper. Amazon.com, 1993. $17.

ALWAYS A PEOPLE: ORAL HISTORIES OF CONTEMPORARY WOODLAND INDIANS
Rita Kohn & W. Lynwood Montell; oil portraits by Evelyn J. Ritter
Illus. 320 pp. Paper. Amazon.com & Alibris.com, 1997. $24.95.

ALWAYS GETTING READY, UPTERRLAINARLUTA: YUP'IK ESKIMO
SUBSISTENCE IN SOUTHWEST ALASKA
James H. Barker; Illus. 144 pp. Paper. University of Washington Press, 1993. $35.

AMAZING DEATH OF CALF SHIRT & OTHER BLACKFOOT STORIES: THREE
HUNDRED YEARS OF BLACKFOOT HISTORY Raymond J. DeMallie & Alfonso Ortiz
Maps. 250 pp. Paper. University of Oklahoma Press, 1996. $13.95.

AMBIGUOUS IROQUOIS EMPIRE: THE COVENANT CHAIN CONFEDERATION
OF INDIAN TRIBES WITH ENGLISH COLONIES
Francis Jennings; Reprint. Illus. 464 pp. Paper. W.W. Norton & Co., $17.95.

AMBIGUOUS JUSTICE: NATIVE AMERICANS & THE LAW IN
SOUTHERN CALIIFORNIA, 1848-1890 Vanessa Ann Gunther
191 pp. Paper. Michigan State University Press, 2006. $29.95; eBook, $23.95.

AMBIVALENT IDENTITIES: PROCESSES OF MARGINALIZATION & EXCLUSION
Paula A. Wagoner; Vicoria Cuffel, Ed.; 125 pp. Paper. Amazon.com, 1994. $4.50.

AMERICA A.D. 1000: THE LAND & THE LEGENDS
Ronald K. Fisher; Illus. 200 pp. Amazon.com, 1999. $16.

AMERICA THE BEAUTIFUL: LAST POEMS
Paula Allen; Paper. University of New Mexico Press, $12.95.

AMERICA BEFORE THE EUROPEAN INVASIONS
Alice B. Kehoe; Illus. 270 pp. Paper. Amazon.com, 2002. $23.

AMERICA FIRSTHAND & PUEBLO
Robert D. Marcus & Weber; 5th Ed. Paper. Bedford/St. Martin's, 2001. $38.70.

AMERICA IN 1492: THE WORLD OF THE INDIAN PEOPLES BEFORE THE ARRIVAL
OF COLUMBUS Alvin M. Josephy, Jr., Editor; 496 pp. Paper. Amazon.com, 1993. $20.

AMERICA IS INDIAN COUNTY: THE BEST OF INDIAN COUNTRY TODAY
Tim Johnson & Jose Barreiro; Compilation of selected editorials, essays and illustrations
from the periodical, "Indian County Today" published between the years 2000 and 2004.
Illus. 352 pp. Paper. Fulcrum Publishing, 2005. $16.95.

AMERICA - LAND OF THE RISING SUN
Don Smithana; Illus. 256 pp. Paper. Anasazi Publishing, 1990. $9.95.

AMERICA ON PAPER: THE FIRST HUNDRED YEARS
Lynn Glaser; Revised & enlarged ed. Illus. 288 pp. Associated Antiquaries, 1989. $32.50.

AMERICA STREET: A MULTICULTURAL ANTHOLOGY OF STORIES
Anne Mazer, Ed.; Paper. Amazon.com, 1993. $7.95.

AMERICA'S ANCIENT TREASURES
Folsom & Folsom; Guide to Canadian and U.S. archaeological sites. Photos.
4th Edition. 459 pp. Paper. Hothem House, 1993. $15.95.

AMERICA'S BLACK & TRIBAL COLLEGES: THE COMPREHENSIVE GUIDE TO
HISTORICALLY & PREDOMINANTLY BLACK & AMERICAN INDIAN COLLEGES
& UNIVERISITIES
J. Wilson Bowman; 3rd ed. Illus. 328 pp. Paper. RJ Enterprises, 1998. $21.95.

AMERICA'S FASCINATING INDIAN HERITAGE
Readers Digest Editors; Synthesis of North American Indian heritage. Illus.
Photos. 416 pp. Amazon.com & Cherokee Publications, 1978. $30.

AMERICA'S FIRST FIRST WORLD WAR: THE FRENCH & INDIAN WAR, 1754-1763
Timothy Todish; Monte Smith, Ed.
Illus. 120 pp. Paper. Eagles View Publishing, 1987. $10.95.

AMERICA'S FIRST WARRIORS: NATIVE AMERICANS & IRAQ
Steven Clevenger, photos & text; Images & interviews with Pueblo, Apache,
Navajo, Osage, and other Native men & women. Photos. 128 pp. Museum of
New Mexico Press, 2010. $39.95.

AMERICA'S HUNDRED YEARS' WAR: U.S. EXPANSION TO THE
GULF COAST & THE FATE OF THE SEMINOLE, 1763-1858
William S. Belko, Editor; Essays on topics ranging from internmational diplomacy
to Seminole military strategy. 280 pp. Paper. University of Florida Press, 2011.

AMERICA'S INDIAN STATUES
Marion Gridley; Paper. Brown Book Co., 1966. $3.95.

AMERICA'S INDIANS: UNIT STUDY OUTLINE
Donna R. Fisher; 11 pp. Paper. Amazon.com, 1993. $2.95.

AMERICA'S SECOND TONGUE: AMERICAN INDIAN EDUCATION & THE OWNERSHIP OF ENGLISH, 1860-1900
Ruth Spack; Examines the implementation of English-language instruction and its effects on Native students. Illus. 231 pp. University of Nebraska Press, 2002. $45.

AMERICAN, AFRICAN, AND OLD EUROPEAN MYTHOLOGIES
compiled by Yves Bonnefoy; trans. by Wendy DonigerA section covers myths of Native Americans, from the Inuit to Mesoamericans about topics of the cosmos, fire, creation. Illus. 296 pp. Paper. University of Chicago Press, 1991. $27.50.

*AMERICAN ARTIST.VOL. 1: NATIVE AMERICANS
Shanon Fitzpatrick
Grades 4-8. Illus. 36 pp. Paper. Creative Teaching Press, 1994. Student edition, $11.98.

AMERICAN BEGINNINGS: EXPLORATION, CULTURE, & CARTOGRAPHY N THE LAND OF NORUMBEGA Emerson W. Baker, et al, Eds.
Illus. 396 pp. University of Nebraska Press, 1995. $60.

AMERICAN BEGINNINGS: THE PREHISTORY & PALEONTOLOGY OF BERINGIA
Frederick H. West, Editor
Illus. Photos. Maps. 576 pp. University of Chicago Press, 1996. $100; paper, $42.50.

*AMERICAN BISON
Ruth Berman; Grades 2-5. Photos. Lerner, 1992. $16.95.

THE AMERICAN BUFFALO IN TRANSITION
John Rorabacher; Amazon.com Press, $6.50.

AMERICAN CARNAGE: WOUNDED KNEE, 1890
Jerome A. Greene; Illus. 648 pp. University of Oklahoma Press, 2014. $34.95.

AMERICAN COLONIAL HISTORY: CLASHING CULTURES & FAITH
Thomas S. Kidd; Illus. 344 pp. Paper. Yale University Press, 2016. $20.

THE AMERICAN DISCOVERY OF EUROPE
Jack D. Forbes; Investigates the voyages of America's Native peoples to the European continent before Columbus' 1492 arrival in the New World," revealing surprising Native American involvements in maritime trade and exploration. Illus. Maps. 272 pp. University of Illinois Press, 2008. $35.95; paper, $28.

THE AMERICAN EAGLE
Tom & Pat Leeson, photographers; Photos of the eagle with text exploring the historic symbolism, the Native American traditions & myths & the legends of the bald eagle. Illus. 88 color photos. 128 pp. Beyond Words Publishing, $39.95; paper, $24.95.

AMERICAN ENCOUNTERS
Howard Morrison; Illus. 80 pp. Paper. Amazon.com, 1992.

AMERICAN ENCOUNTERS: NATIVES & NEWCOMERS FROM EUROPEAN CONTACT TO INDIAN REMOVAL, 1500-1850 Peter C. Mancall & James H. Merrell, Editors
2nd Ed. Illus. 752 pp. Paper. Routledge, 2006. $40.46.

AMERICAN FRONTIERS: CULTURAL ENCOUNTERS & CONTINENTAL CONQUEST
Gregory H. Nobles; Illus. 304 pp. Amazon.com, 1997. $24; paper, $13.

AMERICAN GENOCIDE: THE U.S. AND THE CALIFORNIA INDIAN CATASTROPHE, 1846-1873 Benjamin Madley; Illus. 712 pp. Paper. Yale University Press, 2017. $22.

AMERICAN GYPSEY: SIX NATIVE AMERICAN PLAYS
Diane Glancy; Collection of six plays invoking the myths & realities of modern Native American life. Illus. 224 pp. University of Oklahoma Press, 2002. $34.95.

AMERICAN INDIAN
Lee F. Harkins, Editor; Reprint. Liveright, 1970. Slipcased, $99.99.

THE AMERICAN INDIAN
Clark Wissler; Reprint. Illus. Photos. Maps. 466 pp. High-Lonesome Books, $30.

AMERICAN INDIAN ACTIVISM: ALCATRAZ TO THE LONGEST WALK
edited by Troy Johnson, Joane Nagel & Duane Champagne; 368 pp. University of Illinois Press, 1997. $36.95; paper, $19.95. Also available from Amazon.com, $20

THE AMERICAN INDIAN & ALASKA NATIVE HIGHER EDUCATION FUNDING GUIDE
Gregory W. Frazier; 100 pp. Arrowstar, 1990. $21.90.

AMERICAN INDIAN & ALASKA NATIVE NEWSPAPERS & PERIODICALS, 1826-1924/1925-1970 Daniel Littlefield, Jr. & James Parins; 2 vols. 482 pp. 577 pp. Greenwood Publishing, 1984/86. $85 each.

AMERICAN INDIAN & ALASKA NATIVE TRADERS DIRECTORY
Gregory Frazier; 140 pp. Arrowstar, 1990. $21.45.

AMERICAN INDIAN/ALASKA NATIVE TRIBAL & VILLAGE HIV-1 POLICY GUIDELINES
48 pp. National Native American AIDS Prevention Center, 1991.

AMERICAN INDIAN & ALASKAN NATIVES IN POSTSECONDARY EDUCATION
Michael D. Parvel; Illus. 426 pp. Paper. U.S. Government Printing Office, 1998. $33.

THE AMERICAN INDIAN: THE AMERICAN FLAG
Richard A. Pohrt; Illus. 152 pp. Flint Institute of Arts, $12.50; paper, $9.

AMERICAN INDIAN ARCHERY
Reginald & Gladys Laubin
Reprint. Illus. 190 pp. University of Oklahoma Press, 2002. $24.95; paper. $19.95.

AMERICAN INDIAN ARCHIVAL MATERIAL: A GUIDE TO HOLDINGS IN THE SOUTHEAST R. Chepesiuk & A. Shankman, Editors
325 pp. Greenwood Publishing, 1982. $69.50.

AMERICAN INDIAN AREAS & ALASKA NATIVE VILLAGES, 1980
38 pp. Supt. of Documents, 1984. $2.75.

AMERICAN INDIAN ART, 1920-1972
Paper. Peabody Museum, 1973. $2.

AMERICAN INDIAN ART: THE COLLECTING EXPERIENCE
Beverly Gordon, with Melanie Herzog; Includes pottery, weavings, basketry, beadwork and carvings. Photos. 72 pp. Paper. University of Wisconsin Press, 1988. $19.95.

AMERICAN INDIAN ARTIFACTS: HOW TO IDENTIFY, EVALUATE & CARE FOR YOUR COLLECTION Ellen Woods; 232 pp. paper. Amazon.com, 1997. $18.95.

AMERICAN INDIAN ARTS & CRAFTS SOURCE BOOK
Anthony J. Cusmano, Editor; Paper. Media Publications, 1987. $6.95.

AMERICAN INDIAN ART SERIES
Gregory Schaaf; Vol. 1: Hopi-Tewa Pottery. 500 Artist Biographies. 199 pages, 500 illustrations in color and black & white, hardback. (sold out, except a few copies of the Collectors Edition bound in buffalo, gold embossments, slip case, limited to 200 copies, signed and numbered - $250; Vol. 2: Pueblo Indian Textiles. 750 Artist Biographies," 296 pages, 600 illustrations in color and black & white. Featuring Tewa potters from Santa Clara, San Ildefonso, San Juan, Tesuque, Nambe and Pojoaque. $55 hardback, Collectors Edition- $250. Vol. 3: American Indian Textiles: 2,000 Artist Biographies. 320 pages, 700 illustrations in color and black & white. Featuring over a 1,000 textiles created during the past 200 years by Navajo rug weavers, Hopi, Zuni, Rio Grande Pueblo, Apache, Cherokee, Osage, Comanche, Northwest Coast and other Native American textile artists, including 500 photographs of weavers holding their rugs & twenty years of auction records. $69.95 hardback, postpaid; Collectors Edition $250.

AMERICAN INDIAN AS PARTICIPANT IN THE CIVIL WAR
Annie H. Abel; Reprint. 403 pp. Amazon.com, $98

THE AMERICAN INDIAN AS SLAVEHOLDER & SUCCESSIONIST
Annie Heloise Abel; intro. by Theda Perdue & Michael D. Green
Reprint of 1919 edition. Illus. Map. 394 pp. Paper. U. of Nebraska Press, 1992. $25.

AMERICAN INDIAN AUTOBIOGRAPHY
H. David Brumble III; Historical study of Native American narratives and their methodology. Illus. 304 pp. Paper. University of Nebraska Press, 2008. $18.95

AMERICAN INDIAN BALLERINAS
Lili Cockerille Livingston; Biography of four 20th century American Indan ballerinas: Maria Tallchief, Rosella Hightower, Marjorie Tallchief, and Yvonne Chouteau. Photos. Biblio. 352 pp. University of Oklahoma Press, 1997. $24.95.

AMERICAN INDIAN BASKETRY
Otis Tufton Mason; Reprint. Illus. 800 pp. Paper. Hothem House & Dover, 1988. $17.95.

AMERICAN INDIAN BASKETS: 1,200 ARTIST BIOGRAPHIES
Gregory Schaaf; Richard M. Howard, Editor
Illus. 450 pp. Center for Indigenous Arts & Cultures (CIAC) Press, 2004. $50.

AMERICAN INDIAN BEADWORK
Ben W. Hunt & J.F Buck Burshears; Illus. 64 pp. Paper. Crazy Crow, 1995. $15.95.

THE AMERICAN INDIAN: BRONZE SCULPTURE BY GRIFFIN
Hampton Chiles; Illus. Paper. Hampton Chiles, 1221 Cloncurry Rd., Norfolk, VA 23505 (757) 423-5466. 1997. $35.

THE AMERICAN INDIAN CD-ROM
Guild Press; Includes original 1850s encyclopedia on American Indians, edited by Henry Schoocraft, over 4200 pages of first hand accounts, history, essays, & more; collection of authentic myths; Federal Treaties; American State Papers through 1826; Notebooks of George Catlin; guides to National Archives; lives of famous Indian chiefs. Illus. 10,000 pp. of text. Guild Press, 1999. $75.

AMERICAN INDIAN CEREMONIES: A PRACTICAL WORKBOOK & STUDY GUIDE TO THE MEDICINE PATH Hawk Medicine & Grey Cat
Reprint. Illus. 144 pp. Inner Light, $15.

AMERICAN INDIAN CHILDREN AT SCHOOL, 1850-1930
Michael C. Coleman; Study revealing white society's program of civilizing Indian schoolchildren. 230 pp. Amazon.com, 1993. $39.50.

*THE AMERICAN INDIAN COLORING BOOK
Tom B. Underwood; Reprint. Grades 1-4. 28 pp. Paper. Cherokee Publications, $4.95.

AMERICAN INDIAN CONSTITUTIONAL REFORM & THE REBUILDING OF NATIVE NATIONS Eric D. Lemont, Editor; Writings of tribal reform leaders, academics, & legal practitioners. 360 pp. Paper. University of Texas Press, 2006. $21.95.

AMERICAN INDIAN COOKING: RECIPES FROM THE SOUTHWEST
Carolyn Niethammer; Features 150 recipes & detailed illustrations of dozens of edible wild plants & their history; mail order sources. Illus. Map. 191 pp. Paper. University of Nebraska Press, 1998. $17.95.

AMERICAN INDIAN COOKING & HERB LORE
J. Ed Sharpe & Thomas Underwood; Contains dozens of recipes. Illus. 32 pp. Paper. Written Heritage, VIP Publishing & Cherokee Publications, $5.

AMERICAN INDIAN COUNTED CROSS-STITCH
Frankye Jones; Contains 28 cross-stitch patterns from designs of various American Indian tribes. Illus. 95 pp. Written Heritage, $16.95.

THE AMERICAN INDIAN CRAFT BOOK
Marz Minor and Nono Minor; Illus. 416 pp. Paper. U. of Nebraska Press, 1978. $15.

AMERICAN INDIAN & CRIME, 1992-2002
U.S. Dept. of Justice; American Indian crime report summarizing data on American Indians in the criminal justice system. Amazon.com.

AMERICAN INDIAN CULTURAL HEROES & TEACHING TALES: EVENINGS WITH CHASING DEER Kurt Kaltreider; Paper. Amazon.com, 2004. $13.95.

AMERICAN INDIAN CULTURE
Carole A. Barrett & Harvey Markowitz; Illus. 1,200 pp. Paper. Salem Press, 2004. $63.

AMERICAN INDIAN CULTURE & RESEARCH JOURNAL: VOL. 40, NO. I
Paper. UCLA, American Indian Studies Center Publications, 2017. $15.

AMERICAN INDIAN DESIGN & DECORATION
Leroy H. Appleton; Reprint. Illus. 280 pp. Paper. Dover & Written Heritage, $10.95.

AMERICAN INDIAN DIRECTORY
Various Indian Peoples Publishing Co.; A national listing of over 540 federally recognized American Indian nations & tribes. Paper. Malki-Ballena Press & VIP Publishing, $12.95.

AMERICAN INDIAN ECOLOGY
Donald J. Hughes; Revised 2nd Ed.. Illus. 190 pp. Texas Western Press, 1995. $20.

AMERICAN INDIAN ECONOMIC DEVELOPMENT
Sam Stanley, Editor; Illus. Maps. 609 pp. Amazon.com, 1978. $87.70.

AMERICAN INDIAN EDUCATION: A HISTORY
Jon Reyhner & Jeanne Eder; Comprehensive history of American Indian education from colonial times to present. Two editions. Illus. Map. 384 & 408 pp. Paper. University of Oklahoma Press, 2006 & 2017 repectively. $24.95 each.

THE AMERICAN INDIAN & THE END OF THE CONFEDERACY, 1863-1866
Annie Heloise Abel; intro. by Theda Perdue & Michael D. Green Reprint of 1919 edition. Illus. Map. 419 pp. Paper. University of Nebraska Press, $12.95.

AMERICAN INDIAN ENCYCLOPEDIA, CD-ROM
3 reference books on CD-ROM; text, pictures, sound. Facts-on-File, $295.

AMERICAN INDIAN ENERGY RESOURCES & DEVELOPMENT
Roxanne D. Ortiz, Ed.; Includes Transnational Energy Corporations & American Indian Development, by Richard Nafziger, and The Role of Policy in American Indian Mineral Development, by Lorraine Turner Ruffing. 80 pp. Paper. University of New Mexico, Native American Studies, 1980. $5.

AMERICAN INDIAN ENGLISH
William L. Leap; Documents & examines the diversity of English in American Indian speech communities. 352 pp. Paper. University of Utah Press, 1993. $37.50; paper, $20.

AMERICAN INDIAN ENVIRONMENTAL ETHICS: AN OJIBWA CASE STUDY
J. Baird Callicott & Michael P. Nelson; 176 pp. Paper. Prentice Hall PTR, 2003. $18.

AMERICAN INDIAN ENVIRONMENTS: ECOLOGICAL ISSUES IN NATIVE AMERICAN HISTORY C. Vecsy & R.W. Venables, Editors
Reprint of 1980 edition. Illus. 236 pp. Paper. Syracuse University Press, $16.95.

AMERICAN INDIAN ETHNIC RENEWAL: RED POWER & THE RESURGENCE OF IDENTITY & CULTURE Joane Nagel; Paper. Oxford University Press, 1997. $59.

***THE AMERICAN INDIAN EXPERIENCE**
(American Historic Places series); Explores Native American cultures through the study of existing historical sites. Illus. 160 pp. Grades 5-12. Facts on File, 1997. $18.95.

***THE AMERICAN INDIAN EXPERIENCE**
Liz Sonneborn; Grades 6-8. Lerner Publications, 2011. $37.99.

AMERICAN INDIAN FACTS OF LIFE: A PROFILE OF TODAY'S TRIBES & RESERVATIONS George Russell; Contemporary American Indian demographics with regard to populations, tribes & reservations. Includes maps, reservation rosters, graphics, tables, and reference sources. 80 pp. Paper. Amazon.com, $10.

AMERICAN INDIAN FAMILY SUPPORT SYSTEMS & IMPLICATIONS FOR THE REHABILITATION PROCESS: THE EASTERN BAND OF CHEROKEE INDIANS & THE MISSISSIPPI BAND OF CHOCTAW INDIANS: CHEROKEE TRANSLATION OF SUMMARY; EXECUTIVE SUMMARY & FINAL REPORT C.A. Marshall & L.K. Cerveny Translation of Summary, 200 pp. $3; Executive Summary, 16 pp. $4; Final Report, 8 pp. $13.75. Amazon.com, 1994.

AMERICAN INDIANS: FOLK TALES & LEGENDS
Keith Cunningham, Ed.; 400 pp. Paper. Advanced Global Distribution, 2001. $6.95.

***AMERICAN INDIAN FOODS**
Jay Miller; Grades 4 and up. 48 pp. Children's Press, 1996. $21; paper, $6.95.

***AMERICAN INDIAN GAMES**
Jay Miller; Grades 4 and up. 48 pp. Children's Press, 1996. $21; paper, $6.95.

AMERICAN INDIAN GENESIS: THE STORY OF CREATION
Percy Bullchild; Reprint. Illus. 200 pp. Amazon.com, $22.95.

AMERICAN INDIAN GHOST DANCE, 1870 & 1890: AN ANNOTATED BIBLIOGRAPHY
Shelley Anne Osterreich; 110 entries. 296 pp. Greenwood, 1991. $80.95.

AMERICAN INDIAN GRANDMOTHERS: TRADITIONS & TRANSITIONS
Marjorie M. Schweitzer, Editor
Essays. Illus. 248 pp. Paper. University of New Mexico Press, 1999. $35.

***AMERICAN INDIAN HABITATS**
Evelyn Wolfson; Grades 2-5. 155 pp. Paper. Amazon.com, 1978.

AMERICAN INDIAN HEALING ARTS: HERBS, RITUALS & REMEDIES
Barrie Kavasch & Karen Baar; 352 pp. Amazon.com, 1999. $17.95.

AMERICAN INDIAN HIGHER EDUCATIONAL EXPERIENCES: CULTURAL VISIONS & PERSONAL JOURNEYS
Terry Huffman; 228 pp. Paper. Peter Lang Publishing, 2008. $34.95.

AMERICAN INDIAN HISTORY
Carole A. Barrett, Ed.; Illus. 820 pp. 2 Vols. Salem Press, 2002. $104.

AMERICAN INDIAN HISTORY: CONQUEST OF A CONTINENT, 1492-1783
Robert W. Venables; Illus. 307 pp. Paper. Amazon.com, 2003. $16.95.

AMERICAN INDIAN HISTORY DAY BY DAY: A REFERENCE GUIDE TO EVENTS
Roger M. Carpenter; A chronology providing an overview of 500 years of Native American history. Bibliography. 429 pp. Greenwood Press, 2012. $89.

AMERICAN INDIAN HISTORY ON TRIAL: HISTORICAL EXPERTISE IN TRIBAL LITIGATION E. Rochard Hart
Illus. 240 pp. Paper. University of Utah Press, 2017. $29; eBoo, $23.

AMERICAN INDIAN HOLOCAUST & SURVIVAL: A POPULATION HISTORY SINCE 1492 Russell Thornton; Illus. Maps. 292 pp. Paper. U. of Oklahoma Press, 2002. $24.95.

AMERICAN INDIAN IDENTITY: TODAY'S CHANGING PERSPECTIVES
Clifford E. Trafzer; Seven American Indians provide essays. 51 pp. Paper. Amazon.com, 1986. $10.95.

THE AMERICAN INDIAN IN ALABAMA & THE SOUTHEAST
John F. Phillips; Illus. 213 pp. Amazon.com, 1986. $10.95; paper, $8.95.

***THE AMERICAN INDIAN IN AMERICA, Vol. II**
Jayne Clark Jones; Grades 5 and up. Illus. 96 pp. Paper. Lerner, $5.95.

THE AMERICAN INDIAN IN THE CIVIL WAR, 1862-1865
Annie Heloise Abel; intro. by Theda Perdue & Michael D. Green Reprint. Illus. Map. 403 pp. Paper. University of Nebraska Press, 1992. $29.95.

AMERICAN INDIAN IN ENGLISH LITERATURE OF THE 18TH CENTURY
Benjamin H. Bissell; Reprint. Illus. 225 pp. Gordon Press, $59.95.

THE AMERICAN INDIAN IN FILM
Michael Hilger; Illus. 206 pp. Scarecrow Press, 1986. $21.

THE AMERICAN INDIAN IN GRADUATE STUDIES: A BIBLIOGRAPHY OF THESES & DISSERTATIONS Frederick J. Dockstader; Two vols. Paper. National Museum of the American Indian, 1973. $10 each; $18 per set.

THE AMERICAN INDIAN IN NORTH CAROLINA
Douglas L. Rights; Illus. 298 pp. Paper. Amazon.com, $14.95.

THE AMERICAN INDIAN IN SHORT FICTION: AN ANNOTATED BIBLIOGRAPHY
Peter G. Beidler and Marion F. Egge; 215 pp. Scarecrow Press, 1979. $18.50.

THE AMERICAN INDIAN IN WESTERN LEGAL THOUGHT: THE DISCOURSE OF CONQUEST
Robert A. Williams, Jr.; 368 pp. Paper. Oxford University Press, 1992. $59.95.

THE AMERICAN INDIAN IN THE WHITE MAN'S PRISONS: A STORY OF GENOCIDE
Art Solomon, et al; Illus. 447 pp. Paper. Amazon.com, 1993. $25.

AMERICAN INDIAN INDEX: A DIRECTORY OF INDIAN COUNTRY
Gregory W. Frazier; Contains listings for American Indian and Alaska Native groups. 325 pp. Amazon.com, 1985. $21.45.

THE AMERICAN INDIAN: THE INDIGENOUS PEOPLE OF NORTH AMERICA
C. Taylor; Illus. 416 pp. Running Press, 2002. Text, $19.98.

THE AMERICAN INDIAN INTEGRATION OF BASEBALL
Jeff Powers-Beck; Illus. 269 pp. Paper. University of Nebraska Press, 2004. $19.95.

AMERICAN INDIAN INTELLECTUALS OF THE 19TH & EARLY 20TH CENTURIES
Margot Liberty; Biographical sketches of major American Indian intellectuals.
288 pp. Paper. University of Oklahoma Press, 2003. $19.95.

AMERICAN INDIAN INVENTIONS
Peter F. Ceaton; Jerry R. Elliott, Ed.; Illus. 192 pp. paper. Sterling House, 2002. $14.95.

AMERICAN INDIAN ISSUES IN HIGHER EDUCATION
206 pp. UCLA, American Indian Studies Center, 1981. $14.

AMERICAN INDIAN JEWELRY I: 1,200 ARTIST BIOGRAPHIES
Gregory Schaaf; Richard M. Howard, Ed.
Illus. 345 pp. Center for Indigenous Arts & Cultures (CIAC) Press, 2004. $65.

AMERICAN INDIAN LACROSSE, LITTLE BROTHER OF WAR
Thomas Vennum, Jr.; An account of the Native American game, and its functions in Indian life. Illus. 376 pp. Paper. Smithsonian Institution Press, 1994. $16.95.

AMERICAN INDIAN: LANGUAGE & LITERATURE
Jack W. Marken; Paper. Amazon.com, 1978.

AMERICAN INDIAN LANGUAGE: THE HISTORICAL LINGUISTICS OF NATIVE \AMERICA Lyle Campbell; Illus. 530 pp. Oxford University Press, 1997. $85.

AMERICAN INDIAN LANGUAGE SERIES
Mayan Linguistics, 267 pp., $5.00; Hualapai Reference Grammar, 575 pp., $17.50; and Chem'ivillu' (Let's Speak Cahuilla), 316 pp., $17.50. UCLA, American Indian Studies Center.

AMERICAN INDIAN LANGUAGES, Vol. 5
William Bright, Editor; 585 pp. Amazon.com, 1989. $99.

AMERICAN INDIAN LANGUAGES: CULTURAL & SOCIAL CONTEXTS
Shirley Silver & Wick R. Miller; 433 pp. Paper. University of Arizona Press, 1997. $39.95.

AMERICAN INDIAN LAW: CASES & MATERIALS
Robert N. Clinton, Neil Jessup Newton, Monroe Edwin Price
Illus. 1,375 pp. Michie Co., 1991.

AMERICAN INDIAN LAW: NATIVE NATIONS & THE FEDERAL SYSTEM
Robert N. Clinton, et al; Revised 4th ed. 1,500 pp. LexisNexis Publishing, 2005. $95.
Selected Federal Indian Law Provisions, 2005. $30

THE AMERICAN INDIAN LAW DESKBOOK
Conference of Western Attorney General Staff
4th Ed. Supplement, 160 pp. Paper. 2011. $21.95. 3rd Edition. 670 pp. 2004. $95.
2nd Ed. supplement, 80 pp. Paper 1999. $19.95. University Press of Colorado.

AMERICAN INDIAN LAW IN A NUTSHELL
William C. Canby, Jr.; 3rd edition, 463 pp. Paper. West Publishing, 1996. $29.95.

THE AMERICAN INDIAN LAW SERIES
A series of seven pamphlets: Indian Sovereignty; Indian Treaties; Indians and the U.S. Government; Indian Jurisdiction; The Federal Indian Trust Relationship; Indian Water Rights; and Introduction to Oil and Gas. Institute for the Development of Indian Law.

AMERICAN INDIAN LEADERS: STUDIES IN DIVERSITY
R. David Edmunds, Ed; Illus. Maps. 257 pp. Paper. U. of Nebraska Press, 1980. $17.95.

AMERICAN INDIAN LEGAL MATERIALS: A UNION LIST
Laura N. Gasaway, et al; Lists important works of Indian law, history, and policy. 200 pp. E.M. Coleman, 1979. $49.50.

AMERICAN INDIAN LEGAL STUDIES TEACHER'S MANUAL & TEXT
Institute for the Development of Indian Law. $20 each.

AMERICAN INDIAN LIFE
Elsie C. Parsons, Ed.; Reprint. Illus. 425 pp. Paper. University of Nebraska Press, $32.

AMERICAN INDIAN LIFE SKILLS DEVELOPMENT CURRICULUM
Teresa D.LaFromboise
Illus. 522 pp. Paper. Workbook edition. University of Wisconsin Press, 1995. $22.95.

AMERICAN INDIAN LINGUISTICS & ETHNOGRAPHY IN HONOR OF LAURENCE C. THOMPSON
Anthony Mattina & Timothy Montler; 497 pp. U. of Montana, 1993. $25; paper, $15.

AMERICAN INDIAN LINGUISTICS & LITERATURE
William Bright; 159 pp. Amazon.com, 1984. $41.25.

AMERICAN INDIAN LITERARY NATIONALISM
Jace Weaver, Craig Womack, Robert Warrior; Essays on Native American literature & criticism. 296 pp. Paper. U. of New Mexico Press, $27.95.

AMERICAN INDIAN LITERATURE: AN ANTHOLOGY
Alan R. Velie; Revised 1991 ed.. Illus. 374 pp. U. of Oklahoma Press, 2001. $32.95.

AMERICAN INDIAN LITERATURE, ENVIRONMENTAL JUSTICE, & ECOCRITICISM: THE MIDDLE PLACE
Joni Adamson; Discussions of such writers as Simon Ortiz, Louis Erdrich, Joy Harjo, and Leslie Marmon Silko. 214 pp. Paper. University of Arizona, 2001. $21.95.

AMERICAN INDIAN LITERATURE & THE SOUTHWEST: CONTEXTS & DISPOSITIONS
Eric Gary Anderson; Illus. Paper. University of Texas Press, 1999. $30.

AMERICAN INDIAN LITERATURES: AN INTRODUCTION, BIBLIOGRAPHIC REVIEW, & SELECTED BIBLIOGRAPHY LaVonne Brown Ruoff; Includes journals, films & videos, & Indian authors & their works. Also provides and index and chronology of notable American Indian events. 200 pp. Paper. Modern Language Association, 1990. $45; paper, $19.50.

*AMERICAN INDIAN LIVES (SERIES)
Profiles individuals from various fields of endeavor who have enriched, and continue to enrich, both the cultures of their tribes & American culture in general, from precolonial days to the present. Scholars, Writers, & Professionals, by Claire Wilson & Jonathan Bolton, 1994. 160 pp.; Spiritual Leaders, by Paul Robert Walker, 1994. 160 pp.; Political Leaders & Peacemakers, by Victoria Sherrow, 1994. 160 pp.; Artists & Craftspeople, by Arlene Hirschflder, 1994. 160 pp.; Performers, by Liz Sonneborn, 1995. 128 pp.; Athletes, by Nathan Aaseng, 1995. 144 pp.; Reformers & Activists, by Nancy J. Neilen, 1997. 144 pp.; Healers, by Deanne Durrett, 1997. 144 pp. Illus. Grades 6 and up. Facts on File. $25 each; $175 per set.

AMERICAN INDIAN MAFIA: AN FBI AGENT'S TRUE STORY ABOUT WOUNDED KNEE, LEONARD PELTIER, AND THE AMERICAN INDIAN MOVEMENT (AIM)
Joseph H. Trimbach & John M. Trimbach, Co-authors
Paper. Amazon.com. 2007. $24.95.

AMERICAN INDIAN MARRIAGE RECORD DIRECTORY FOR ASHLAND CO., WISC.
Michael D. Munnell; 279 pp. Paper. Chippewa Heritage Publications, 1993. $21.

THE AMERICAN INDIAN & THE MEDIA
Mark Anthony Rolo; Essays that explain many of the struggles facing Native people. Amazon.com, $15.

AMERICAN INDIAN MEDICINE
Rolling Thunder; Amazon.com, 1972. $10.

AMERICAN INDIAN MEDICINE
Virgil J. Vogel; The contribution of the American Indian to pharmacology & medicine. Reprint of of 1977 edition. Illus. 622 pp. Paper. University of Oklahoma Press. $29.95.

AMERICAN INDIAN MEDICINE WAYS: SPIRITUAL POWER, PROPHETS, AND HEALING Clifford Trafzer, Editor
Illus. 312 pp. University of Arizona Press, 2017. $$70; paper, $35. eBook available.

THE AMERICAN INDIAN MIND IN A LINEAR WORLD: AMERICAN INDIAN STUDIES & TRADITIONAL KNOWLEDGE Donald Lee Fixico
Illus. 224 pp. paper. Routledge & Amazon.com, 2003. $160; paper, $41.95; eBook, $29.37.

THE AMERICAN INDIAN: A MULTIMEDIA ENCYCLOPEDIA - CD-ROM
Incorporates four Facts on File publications: Atlas of the North American Indian; Native American Legends; Indians & Non-Indians from Early Contacts through 1900; and Encyclopedia of Native American Tribes. Also over 1,000 reproductions of images and maps from NARA publications and documents. Facts on File, 1993. $295.

AMERICAN INDIAN MTDNA, Y CHROMOSOME GENETIC DATA, & THE PEOPLING OF NORTH AMERICA Peter N. Jones; The Baur Institute Press, 2004. $21.95.

*AMERICAN INDIAN MUSIC & MUSICAL INSTRUMENTS
George S. Fichter; Grades 5-10. David McKay, 1978. $8.95.

AMERICAN INDIAN MYTHOLOGY
Alice Marriott & Carol K. Rachlin; Illus. 210 pp. Paper. Amazon.com, 1972. $3.95.

*AMERICAN INDIAN MYTHOLOGY
Evelyn Wolfson; Grades 2-5. 150 pp. Paper. Amazon.com, 2001.

AMERICAN INDIAN MYTHS & LEGENDS
Richard Erdoes & Alfonso Ortiz; 160 tales from 80 tribal groups from across North America. Illus. 528 pp. 1997. Amazon.com, $15.

AMERICAN INDIAN NATIONS FROM TERMINATION TO RESTORATION, 1953-2006
Roberta Ulrich; Overview of all terminations and restorations of Native American tribes from 1953 to 2006. 310 pp. Paper. University of Nebraska Press, 2013. $30.

AMERICAN INDIAN NATIONS: YESTERDAY, TODAY AND TOMORROW
George Horse Capture; Editor; Discusses tribal nationalism and educational initiatives and challenges; environmental issues, voting rights and the Native media. 334 pp. AltaMira Press, 2007. $88; paper, $36; eBook, $34.99

AMERICAN INDIAN NEEDLEPOINT DESIGNS
Roslyn Epstein; Illus. 38 pp. Paper. Dover & Written Heritage, $4.50.

AMERICAN INDIAN NONFICTION: AN ANTHOLOGY OF WRITINGS: 1760s-1930s
Bernd C. Peyers; University of Oklahoma Press, 2007.

THE AMERICAN INDIAN: NORTH, SOUTH & CENTRAL AMERICA
A Hyatt Verrill; Reprint. 508 pp. Paper. Amazon.com, 1927. $35.95.

THE AMERICAN INDIAN OCCUPATION OF ALCATRAZ ISLAND: RED POWER & SELF-DETERMINATION Troy R. Johnson; foreword by Donald L. Fixico
Photos. 304 pp. Paper. University of Nebraska Press, 2008. $18.95.

THE AMERICAN INDIAN ORAL HISTORY MANUAL: MAKING MANY VOICES HEARD
Charles Trimble, Barbara W. Sommer, Mary Kay Quinlan
160 pp. University of Arizona Press, 2008. $65; paper, $22.95.

AMERICAN INDIAN PERFORMING ARTS: CRITICAL DIRECTIONS
Hanay Geiogamah & Jaye T. Darby
293 pp. UCLA, American Indian Studies center, 2010. $60; paper, $25.

AMERICAN INDIAN PAINTERS: A BIOGRAPHICAL DIRECTORY
Jeanne Snodgrass; National Museum of the American Indian, 1968.

AMERICAN INDIAN PAINTING & SCULPTURE
Patricia Janis Broder; Survey of work by this century's leading Native American artists.
74 full-color illustrations, including 4 gatefolds. 168 pp. Abbeville Press, $45.

THE AMERICAN INDIAN PARFLECHE: A TRADITION OF THE ABSTRACT PAINTING
Gaylord Torrence; Illustrate with over 100 examples of parfleches in full color.
Written Heritage, $39.95.

THE AMERICAN INDIAN: PAST & PRESENT
Roger Nichols, Editor
Anthology. 6th ed. 448 pp. Paper. University of Oklahoma Press, 2008. $39.95.

AMERICAN INDIAN PERSISTENCE & RESURGENCE
Karl Kroeber, Ed.; 352 pp. Duke University Press, 1994. $59.95; paper, $21.95.

THE AMERICAN INDIAN: PERSPECTIVES FOR THE STUDY OF SOCIAL CHANGE
Fred Eggan; 185 pp. Cambridge University Press, 1981. $37.50.

AMERICAN INDIAN POETRY: AN ANTHOLOGY OF SONGS & CHANTS
George W. Cronyn; 336 pp. Paper. Amazon.com, 1991. $10.

AMERICAN INDIAN POLICY
Theodore W. Taylor; Illus. 230 pp. Lomond, 1983. $23.50. Microfilm, $12.95.

**AMERICAN INDIAN POLICY & AMERICAN REFORM: CASE STUDIES
OF THE CAMPAIGN TO ASSIMILATE THE AMERICAN INDIANS**
Christine Bolt; 228 pp. Paper. Amazon.com, 1987. $34.95.

AMERICAN INDIAN POLICY & CULTURAL VALUES: CONFLICT & ACCOMMODATION
Jennie R. Joe, Editor; 169 pp. Paper. UCLA, American Indian Studies Center, 1987. $10.

**AMERICAN INDIAN POLICY IN THE FORMATIVE YEARS: THE INDIAN TRADE
& INTERCOURSE ACTS, 1790-1834**
Francis P. Prucha; 310 pp. Paper. University of Nebraska Press, 1970. $5.95.

AMERICAN INDIAN POLICY IN THE JACKSONIAN ERA
Ronald N. Satz; Illus. Maps. 368 pp. Paper. University of Oklahoma Press, 2001. $19.95

AMERICAN INDIAN POLICY IN THE 20TH CENTURY
Vine Deloria, Jr., Ed.; 272 pp. Paper. University of Oklahoma Press, 1992. $19.95.

AMERICAN INDIAN POLICY: SELF-GOVERNANCE & ECONOMIC DEVELOPMENT
Lyman H. Legter & Fremont J. Lyden, Eds.; 240 pp. Greenwood, 1993. $91.95.

AMERICAN INDIAN POLITICS & THE AMERICAN POLITICAL SYSTEM
David E. Wilkins; Illus. 385 pp. Rowman & Littlefield, 2001. $90; paper, $34.95.

AMERICAN INDIAN POPULATION RECOVERY IN THE 20TH CENTURY
Nancy Shoemaker; Reprint. Illus. 176 pp. Paper. U. of New Mexico Press, 2000. $17.95.

AMERICAN INDIAN PORTRAIT POSTCARDS
Charles Bird King; Color prints; paintings on postcard format. Smoke & Fire Co., $4.95.

AMERICAN INDIAN POTTERY
Sharon Wirt; Studies pottery styles of the early natives and their significance.
Illus. 32 pp. Paper. Hancock House, 1984. $3.95.

AMERICAN INDIAN POTTERY: AN IDENTIFICATION & VALUE GUIDE
John W. Barry; 2nd Ed. Illus. 214 pp. Amazon.com, 1984. $29.95.

AMERICAN INDIAN PRAYERS & POETRY
J. Edward Sharpe, Editor; Illus. 32 pp. Paper. Cherokee Publications, 1985. $3.

THE AMERICAN INDIAN AND THE PROBLEM OF HISTORY
Calvin Martin; Paper. Oxford University Press, 1987. $77.

AMERICAN INDIAN PROPHECIES: CONVERSATIONS WITH CHASING DEER
Kurt Kaltreider; 220 pp. Paper. Amazon.com, 2003. $12.95.

**AMERICAN INDIAN PROPHETS: RELIGIOUS LEADERS & REVITALIZATION
MOVEMENTS** Clifford E. Trafzer; 138 pp. Paper. Sierra Oaks, 1986. $11.95.

AMERICAN INDIAN QUOTATIONS
Howard J. Langer; Illus. 288 pp. Greenwood, 1996. $68.95.

THE AMERICAN INDIAN READER SERIES
Jeannette Henry, Ed.; Five volumes covering separate subject areas: Anthropology, 174
pp.; Education, 300 pp.; Literature, 248 pp.; History, 149 pp.; and Current Affairs, 248 pp.
Paper. The Indian Historian, 1972-75. $4.50 each.

AMERICAN INDIAN REFERENCE BOOKS FOR CHILDREN & YOUNG ADULTS
Barbara Kuipers; An annotated bibliography of 200 entries for grades 3-12.
190 pp. Amazon.com, 1991. $25. Available on diskette.

**AMERICAN INDIAN RELIGIOUS FREEDOM ACT: A LEGISLATIVE HISTORY
OF PUBLIC LAW NO. 95-341**
William H. Manz, Editor; 4 Vol. set. William S. Hein & Co., 2012. $395.

AMERICAN INDIAN RELIGIOUS TRADITIONS: AN ENCYCLOPEDIA
Suzanne Crawford & Dennis F. Kelley; Three Volumes. 1,200 pp. ABC-CLIO, 2004. $285.

AMERICAN INDIAN RESOURCE MANUAL FOR PUBLIC LIBRARIES
Illus. 200 pp. paper. Amazon.com, 1994. $45.

AMERICAN INDIAN RESOURCE MATERIALS IN WESTERN HISTORY COLLECTION
Donald DeWitt; Illus. 290 pp. University of Oklahoma Press, 1990. $39.95.

AMERICAN INDIAN RHETORICS OF SURVIVANCE: WORD MEDICINE, WORD MAGIC
Ernest Stromberg, Editor; Essays on awareness of rhetoric understood from a Native
American perspective. Illus. Paper. University of Pittsburgh Press, 2006. $19.95.

AMERICAN INDIAN SCULPTURE
Paul S. Wingert; Reprint. Amazon.com, $22.50.

THE AMERICAN INDIAN: SECRETS OF CRYSTAL HEALING
Luc Bourgault; The teachings of the Apache & Cherokee tribes. Illus. 128 pp. Paper.
www.amazon.com, Barnes & Noble; www.bn.com, $8.50.

AMERICAN INDIAN SET
Multicultural Art Print Set. Vol. II. Amazon.com, 2002. $40.

**AMERICAN INDIAN SOCIETIES: STRATEGIES & CONDITIONS OF POLITICAL
& CULTURAL SURVIVAL** Duane Champagne, Ed.
2nd revised edition. 160 pp. Cultural Survival, 1989. $19.95; paper, $10.

AMERICAN INDIAN SONGS
Dawley & McLaughlin; American Indian folk songs from every region of the U.S.
40 pp. Paper. Amazon.com. $5.50. LP, $9.95; filmstrip/cassette/book, $34.95.

AMERICAN INDIAN SPORTS HERITAGE
Joseph B. Oxendine; Traditional Indian games and explores the apex of Indian sports
during the early 20th century and the decline since. Illus. 334 pp. Paper. U. of Nebraska
Press, 1995. $35.

**AMERICAN INDIAN SOVEREIGNTY & THE U.S. SUPREME COURT:
THE MASKING OF JUSTICE** David E. Wilkins
Tables. 421 pp. Paper. University of Texas Press, 1997. $35.

**AMERICAN INDIAN STEREOTYPES IN THE WORLD OF CHILDREN: A READER
& BIBLIOGRAPHY** Arlene B. Hirschfelder, Paulette Molin, Yvonne Wakim
2nd Ed. 384 pp. Paper. Scarecrow Press, 1999. $44.55.

*AMERICAN INDIAN STORIES
A 12 book series on the lives & achievements of great Native Americans: Carlos
Montezuma, Geronimo, Hole-in-the-Day, Ishi, Jim Thorpe, John Ross, Maria Tallchief,
Osceola, Plenty Coups, Sarah Winnemucca, Sitting Bull, & Wilma Mankiller. Grades 4-5.
Illus. Raintree, 1993. $19.95 each.

AMERICAN INDIAN STORIES, LEGENDS & WRITINGS
Zitkala-Sa (Red Bird); Cathy Davidson & Ada Norris, Eds.
Presents the pain and difficulty of growing up Indian in a white man's world.
Reprint. 320 pp. Paper. University of Nebraska Press, 2003. $12.95.

AMERICAN INDIAN STUDIES: A BIBLIOGRAPHIC GUIDE
Philip M. White; 165 pp. Amazon.com, 1995. $37.

**AMERICAN INDIAN STUDIES: AN INTERDISCIPLINARY APPROACH
TO CONTEMPORARY ISSUES** Diane Morrison, Ed.
2nd Ed. 456 pp. Paper. Peter Lang Publishing, Amazon.com & Alibris.com, 1997. $29.95.

**AMERICAN INDIAN TASK FORCE REPORT ON THE YEAR 2000: HEALTH
PROMOTION OBJECTIVES & RECOMMENDATIONS FOR CALIFORNIA**
41 pp. Paper. Amazon.com, $30.

AMERICAN INDIAN TEXTILES: 2,000 ARTIST BIOGRAPHIES
Gregory Schaaf; Richard M. Howard, Editor
Illus. 400 pp. Center for Indigenous Arts & Cultures (CIAC) Press, 2001. $60.

AMERICAN INDIAN THEATER IN PERFORMANCE: A READER
Hanay Geiogamah & Jaye T. Darby, Eds.
Presents the views of leading scholars, playwrights, directors, & educators in
contemporary Native theater. 414 pp. Paper. Amazon.com, 2000. $20.

AMERICAN INDIAN THEMES IN YOUNG ADULT LITERATURE
Paulette F. Molin; Analyzes American Indian characters & themes in young adult literatre.
Illus. 208 pp. Scarecrow Press, 2005. $46.20.

AMERICAN INDIAN THOUGHT
Anne Waters, Ed.; Illus. 400 pp. Amazon.com, 2003. $64.95; paper, $29.95.

AMERICAN INDIAN TOMAHAWKS
Peterson; Reprint. Illus. 142 pp. Hothem House. $49.95.

*AMERICAN INDIAN TOOLS & ORNAMENTS
Evelyn Wolfson; Grades 2-5. 160 pp. Paper. David McKay & Co., 1981.

AMERICAN INDIAN TRADITIONS & CEREMONIES
Karen Berman; Illus. 128 pp. Amazon.com, 1998. $45.

**AMERICAN INDIAN TREATIES: A GUIDE TO RATIFIED & UNRATIFIED COLONIAL,
U.S., STATE, FOREIGN, AND INTERTRIBAL TREATIES & AGREEMENTS, 1607-1911**
David H. DeJong; Illus. 272 pp. Paper. University of Utah Press, $40; eBook, $32.

AMERICAN INDIAN TREATIES: THE HISTORY OF A POLITICAL ANOMALY
Francis P. Prucha; Illus. 562 pp. Paper. University of California Press, 1994. $31.95.

THE AMERICAN INDIAN TREATY SERIES
Compiles treaties and agreements made between the U.S. Government and Indian Tribes. Nine volumes. Separate books for treaties and agreements of the Sioux Nation, the Pacific Northwest, the Northern Plains, eastern Oklahoma, the Southwest (western Oklahoma), the Five Civilized Tribes, the Chippewa, and the Great Lakes region. 102-278 pp each. Institute for the Development of Indian Law, 1973-1975.

AMERICAN INDIAN TRIBAL GOVERNMENTS
Sharon O'Brien; Examines the impact of federal policies on Indian tribes. Illus. Maps. Biblio. 368 pp. Paper. University of Oklahoma Press, 1989. $26.95.

*AMERICAN INDIAN TRIBES
The first book "Indians," is an overview of the Indian Tribes; tribes covered: Choctaw, Apache, Cherokee, Chippewa, Eskimo, Hopi, Navajo, Seminole, Sioux, Cheyenne, Shoshone, Nez Perce, Anasazi, Cayuga, Crow, Mandans, Mohawk, Oneida, Onandaga, Pawnee, Seneca, Tlingit, Tuscarora. Grades 2-3. Illus. Photos. 48 pp. each. Paper. Childrens Press, $.95 each; $125/set of 27 books.

*AMERICAN INDIAN TRICKSTER TALES
Richard Erdoes & Alfonso Ortiz, Eds. Grades 4-8. Reprint. Illus. 300 pp. Amazon.com, 2002. $25.

THE AMERICAN INDIAN & THE U.S.: A DOCUMENTARY HISTORY
Wilcomb E. Washburn, Ed. Four volumes. Greenwood Press, 1973. $195 per set; $50 each.

*AMERICAN INDIAN UTENSILS: HOW TO MAKE BASKETS, POTTERY & WOODENWARE WITH NATURAL MATERIALS
Evelyn Wolfson; Grades 2-8. Illus. 165 pp. Paper. Amazon.com. 1979. $8.95.

AMERICAN INDIAN WARRIOR CHIEFS: TECUMSEH, CRAZY HORSE, CHIEF JOSEPH, GERONIMO Jason Hook; Illus. 210 pp. Sterling Publishing, $24.95; paper, $14.95.

AMERICAN INDIAN WARS
Philip Katcher; Paper. Amazon.com, 1989. $10.95.

AMERICAN INDIAN WARS
Howard Hughes; 94 pp. Paper. Amazon.com, 2001. $6.99.

THE AMERICAN INDIAN WARS
John Tebbel & Keith Jennison; Illus. 310 pp. Paper. Sterling Publishing, 2001. $19.95.

THE AMERICAN INDIAN WARS, 1860-1890
Philip R.N. Katcher; Illus. 48 pp. Paper. MBI Distribution, 1992. $14.95.

AMERICAN INDIAN WATER RIGHTS & THE LIMITS OF LAW
Lloyd Burton; Illus. Maps. 192 pp. Paper. University Press of Kansas, 1991. $19.95.

AMERICAN INDIAN & WHITE CHILDREN: A SOCIOPSYCHOLOGICAL INVESTIGATION R.J. Havighurst & B.L. Neugarten
Reprint of 1969 edition. University of Chicago Press, $17.

AMERICAN INDIAN WOMEN: A GUIDE TO RESEARCH
Gretchen M. Bataille & Kathleen M. Sands; Contains over 1,500 annotated citations to resources & materials pertaining to American Indian women. 423 pp. Garland, 1991. $57.

AMERICAN INDIAN WOMEN OF PROUD NATIONS: ESSAYS ON HISTORY, LANGUAGE, AND EDUCATION Cherry Beasley, Mary Ann Jacobs & Ulrike Wiethaus
Vol. 2 in series, Critical Indigenous & American Indian Studies. 184 pp. Peter Lang Publishing, 2016. $78.95.

AMERICAN INDIAN WOMEN: TELLING THEIR LIVES
Gretchen M. Bataille & Kathleen Mullen Sands
211 pp. Paper. University of Nebraska Press, 1987. $16.95.

AMERICAN INDIAN WOMEN'S CALENDAR
12 beautiful women representing 18 different tribes. 10x13" Annual. Elan Marketing, 3404 S. McClintock, #905, Tempe, AZ 85282 (602) 892-3033. $12 postpaid.

THE AMERICAN INDIAN: YESTERDAY, TODAY & TOMORROW
Calif. Dept. of Education Staff
Illus. 88 pp. Paper. Amazon.com, 1991. $8.75.

AMERICAN INDIANS
Fandex Editors; Illus. Algonquinn Books of Chapel Hill, 2004.

*AMERICAN INDIANS
Grades Preschool-12. Amazon.com, $2.85.

AMERICAN INDIANS
Describes the Federal Government's economic policy affecting Indian tribes and Alaska natives. 45 pp. Paper. Supt. of Documents, 1984. $2.50.

*AMERICAN INDIANS
Bearl Brooks; Grades 4-6. 24 pp. ESP, 1977. Workbook, $5.

*AMERICAN INDIANS
J. Philip Di Franco Grades 5 and up. 120 pp. Paper. Chelsea House, 1995. $9.95.

*THE AMERICAN INDIANS
Roland W. Force; Grades 7-12. Illus. 112 pp. Chelsea House, 1990. $17.95.

AMERICAN INDIANS
William T. Hagan; Revised by Daniel M. Cobb; 4th edition. A history of the relationship between the white man and the Indian. Illus. 20 halftones. 256 pp. Paper. University of Chicago Press, 2012. $26. eBook, $10-26

AMERICAN INDIANS
Nancy Shoemaker, Ed.; Illus. 290 pp. Amazon.com, 2000. $66.95; paper, $31.95.

*THE AMERICAN INDIANS
Time-Life Book Editors; A series of books which reveals the customs & cultures, myth, magic & folklore of the American Indian. The titles in the series are: The First Americans, The Spirit World, European Challenge, People of the Desert, The Way of the Warrior, The Buffalo Hunter, Realm of the Iroquois, The Mighty Chieftains, Keeper of the Totem, Cycles of Life, The War of the Plains, Tribes of the Southern Woodlands, The Indians of California, People of the Ice & Snow, People of the Lakes, Tribes of the Atlantic Coast, The War of the West II, Plains Indians II, The Way of Beauty, Indians of the Western Range, &Villagers and Cliff Dwellers. Grades 4 and up. Illus. 176 pp. each. Paper. Time-Life Books, $14.95 each.

THE AMERICAN INDIANS
Edward H. Spicer; 176 pp. Paper. Harvard University Press, 1982. $6.95.

AMERICAN INDIANS
Herman J. Viola; Random House, 1997. $25.

AMERICAN INDIANS, AMERICAN JUSTICE
Vine Deloria, Jr. & Clifford M. Lytle; Reprint of classic indictment of mistreatment of Indian peoples. Illus. 280 pp. Paper. University of Texas Press, 1983. $23.95.

AMERICAN INDIANS, AMERICAN PRESIDENTS
Clifford Trafzer (Wyandot); Illus. 272 pp. NMAI Press, 2009; Amazon.com,. $29.99.

AMERICAN INDIANS: ANSWERS TO TODAY'S QUESTIONS
Jack Utter; 2nd edition. Illus. Photos. Maps. 495 pp. Paper. University of Oklahoma Press, 2001. $26.95.

AMERICAN INDIANS AT RISK
Jeffrey Ian Ross; Provides a current & comprehensive analysis & potential solutions of contemporary problems facing American Indians & Alaskan Natives. Two Volumes. 788 pp. Greenwood Press, 2013. $189.

AMERICAN INDIANS & CHRISTIAN MISSIONS: STUDIES IN CULTURAL CONFLICT
Henry W. Bowden; 256 pp. Paper. University of Chicago Press, 1981. $27.50.

AMERICAN INDIANS: A CULTURAL GEOGRAPHY
Thomas E. Ross, et al, Ed.; 2nd edition. Illus. 300 pp. Amazon.com, 1995. $39.95.

AMERICAN INDIANS & THE FIGHT FOR EQUAL VOTING RIGHTS
Laughlin McDonald; In-depth study of Indian voting rights, describing past and present-day discrimination against Indians, including land seizures, destruction of bison herds, attempts to eradicate Native language & culture, efforts to remove and in some cases exterminate tribes. Illus. Tables. 360 pp. Paper. University of Oklahoma Press, 2010. $26.95.

AMERICAN INDIANS: THE FIRST NATION: NATIVE NORTH AMERICAN LIFE, MYTH & ART Larry J. Zimmerman; Illus. 144 pp. Paper. Amazon.com, 2003. $22.99.

AMERICAN INDIANS: THE FIRST OF THIS LAND
C. Matthew Snipp; 450 pp. Paper. Russell Sage, 1989. $49.95.

AMERICAN INDIANS FROM 11TH DECENNIAL CENSUS REPORT OF THE U.S., 1890
Reprint editions of six census volumes. Dozens of color and b&w reproductions of maps, 25 water-color paintings of Indians, Indian Villages and Eskimos & 365 b&w photos & drawings. Amazon.com, $1,350.

*THE AMERICAN INDIANS IN AMERICA: VOLUME II: THE LATE 18TH CENTURY TO THE PRESENT Jayne Clark Jones
Grades 5 and up. 72 pp. Lerner Publications, 1991. $11.95; paper, $5.95.

AMERICAN INDIANS IN AMERICAN HISTORY, 1870-2001: A COMPANION READER
Sterling Evans, Ed.; 264 pp. Paper. Greenwood Publishing, 2002. $24.95.

AMERICAN INDIANS IN BRITISH ART, 1700-1840
Stephanie Pratt; Illus. 240 pp. Paper. University of Oklahoma Press, 2007. $21.95.

AMERICAN INDIANS IN COLORADO
Donald J. Hughes; Illus. Paper. Pruett, 1987. $8.95.

AMERICAN INDIANS & THE LAW
Lawrence Rosen; Reprint of 1976 edition. 230 pp. Amazon.com, $24.95.

AMERICAN INDIANS IN THE LOWER MISSISSIPPI VALLEY: SOCIAL & ECONOMIC HISTORIES Daniel H. Usner, Jr.
Illus. Maps. 225 pp. University of Nebraska Press, 1998. $55; paper, $29.95.

AMERICAN INDIANS IN THE MARKETPLACE: PERSISTENCE & INNOVATION AMONG THE MENOMINEES & METLAKATLAS, 1870-1920
Brian C. Hosmer; Photos. Maps. 312 pp. U. Press of Kansas, 1999. $35; paper, $19.95.

AMERICAN INDIANS, THE IRISH, & GOVERNMENT SCHOOLING: A COMPARATIVE STUDY Michael C. Coleman
Photos. Maps. 382 pp. University of Nebraska Press, 2007. $49.95; paper, $29.95.

AMERICAN INDIAN'S KITCHEN-TABLE STORIES: CONTEMPORARY CONVERSATIONS WITH CHEROKEE, SIOUX, HOPI, OSAGE, NAVAJO, ZUNI, & MEMBERS OF THE OTHER NATIONS
Keith Cunningham; 296 pp. Paper. Amazon.com, 1992. $16.95.

AMERICAN INDIANS & THE MASS MEDIA
Meta G. Carstarphen & John Sanchez, Editors
Illus.312 pp. Paper. University of Oklahoma Press, $24.95.

AMERICAN INDIANS IN A MODERN WORLD
Donald L. Fixico; Textbook. 286 pp. Paper. AltaMira Press, 2008. $33.

AMERICAN INDIANS & NATIONAL FORESTS
Theodore Catton; Illus. 384 pp. Paper. U. of Arizona Press, 2017. $26.95; eBook, $26.95

AMERICAN INDIANS IN SILENT FILM: MOTION PICTURES IN THE LIBRARY OF CONGRESS compiled by Karen C. Lund; Library of Congress, 1995.

AMERICAN INDIANS IN U.S. HISTORY: Second Edition
Roger L. Nichols; The history of tribes throughout the U.S. Two editions.
Illus. 216 pp. Paper. University of Oklahoma Press, 2004 & 2014

AMERICAN INDIANS AND THE RHETORIC OF REMOVAL AND ALLOTMENT
Jason Edward Black; Amazon.com, 2015. $65; paper, $30.

AMERICAN INDIANS IN WORLD WAR I: AT WAR & AT HOME
Thomas A. Britten; Illus. 264 pp. Paper. University of New Mexico Press, 1999. $30.

AMERICAN INDIANS & NATIONAL PARKS
Robert H. Keller & Michael F. Turek; Examines Federal policy & park/Indian relations.
Illus. 319 pp. Paper. University of Arizona Press, 1998. $24.95.

AMERICAN INDIANS OF THE SOUTHEAST
Michael G. Johnson; Southeastern history and material culture; clothes & weapons. Color photos. Illus. 48 pp. Paper. Wennawoods Publishing, Written Heritage & Smoke & Fire Co., $15.95.

AMERICAN INDIANS OF THE SOUTHWEST
Bertha P. Dutton; foreword by Alfred E. Dittert, Jr.; Revised edition. Illus. 4 maps.
Photos. 320 pp. Paper. University of New Mexico Press, 1983. $24.95.

AMERICAN INDIANS ON FILM & VIDEO: DOCUMENTARIES IN THE LIBRARY OF CONGRESS Compiled by Jennifer Brathode; Library of Congress, 1992.

AMERICAN INDIANS: A SELECT CATALOG OF NATIONAL ARCHIVES MICROFILM PUBLICATIONS Revised 1984 ed. 91 pp. Paper. National Archives, 1998. $3.50.

AMERICAN INDIANS & STATE LAW: SOVEREIGNTY, RACE, & CITIZENSHIP, 1790-1880 Deborah A. Rosen
Illus. 360 pp. University of Nebraska Press, 2007. $55; paper, $29.95.

AMERICAN INDIANS: STEREOTYPES & REALITIES
Devon A. Mihesuah; Reprint. Illus. 152 pp. Amazon.com, 1998. $14.95.

AMERICAN INDIANS & THE STUDY OF U.S. HISTORY
Ned Blackhawk; Paper. Oxford University Press, 2012. $7.

AMERICAN INDIANS, TIME & THE LAW: NATIVE SOCIETIES IN A MODERN CONSTITUTIONAL DEMOCRACY Charles F. Wilkinson
Examines Indian law from pre-Columbian times to the present.
227 pp. Paper. Yale University Press, 1987. $25. Ebook available.

AMERICAN INDIANS TODAY: ANSWERS TO YOUR QUESTIONS
Bureau of Indian Affairs; Pamphlet providing an overview of the role of federal government and its relationship to Native Americans. Includes general statistics, map, and bibliography. 36 pp. Paper. U.S. Government Printing Office, 1991.

*AMERICAN INDIANS TODAY: ISSUES & CONFLICTS
Judith Harlan; Grades 7 and up. Illus. 128 pp. Franklin Watts, 1987. $12.90.

AMERICAN INDIANS & U.S. POLITICS: A COMPANION READER
John M. Meyer, Ed.; 216 pp. Paper. Greenwood Publishing, 2002. $22.95.

AMERICAN INDIANS & WORLD WAR II: TOWARD A NEW ERA IN INDIAN AFFAIRS
Alison R. Bernstein; Illus. 264 pp. Paper. University of Oklahoma Press, 1999. $19.95.

AMERICAN INDIANS & THE URBAN EXPERIENCE
Susan Lobo & Kurt Peters, Eds.; Illus. 320 pp. AltaMira Press, 2000. $72; paper, $27.95.

AMERICAN LAZARUS: RELIGION & THE RISE OF AFRICAN-AMERICAN & NATIVE AMERICAN LITERATURES
Joanna Brooks; Oxford University Press, 2003. $115; paper, $44.95.

THE AMERICAN MILITARY FRONTIERS: THE U.S. ARMY IN THE WEST, 1783-1900
Robert Wooster; Illus. Maps. 379 pp. University of New Mexico Press, 2009. $39.95.

AMERICAN MULTICULTURAL STUDIES: DIVERSITY OF RACE, ETHNICITY, GENDER & SEXUALITY Sherry O. Pinder; Paper. CQ Press, 2012. $57.

AMERICAN NATIONS: ENCOUNTERS IN INDIAN COUNTRY, 1850 TO THE PRESENT
Frederick Hoxie, James Merrell et al, Eds; 400 pp. Paper. Amazon.com, 2001. $39.95.

AMERICAN NATIVE HISTORY BRIEF STUDY
Brenda M. Eagles; 5th Ed. 2 Vols. 375 pp. W.W. Norton & Co., 2000. $37.

AMERICAN PENTIMENTO: THE INVENTION OF INDIANS & THE PURSUIT OF RICHES Patricia Seed; Illus. 344 pp. University of Minnesota Press, 2001. $35.

AMERICAN PROTESTANTISM & U.S. INDIAN POLICY, 1869-1882
Robert H. Keller, Jr.; Illus. 400 pp. University of Nebraska Press, 1983. $32.50.

*THE AMERICAN PUEBLO INDIAN ACTIVITY BOOK
Walter C. Yoder, PhD; Grades 3 and up. 40 pages of activities. 48 pp. Paper.
Sunstone Press, $7.95.

AMERICAN PURITANISM & THE DEFENSE OF MOURNING: RELIGION, GRIEF, & ETHNOLOGY IN MARY WHITE ROWLANDSON'S CAPTIVITY NARRATIVE
Mitchell Breitwieser; 224 pp. University of Wisconsin Press, 1990. $40.00; paper, $15.50.

THE AMERICAN REVOLUTION IN INDIAN COUNTRY: CRISIS & DIVERSITY IN NATIVE AMERICAN COMMUNITIES
Colin G. Calloway; Illus. 353 pp. Paper. Cambridge University Press, 1995. $21.

*THE AMERICAN REVOLUTIONARIES: A HISTORY IN THEIR OWN WORDS
Milton Meltzer; Grades 7 and up. Illus. 256 pp. HarperCollins, 1987. $13.89.

AMERICAN TRAVELER - A GUIDE TO THE ANASAZI & OTHER ANCIENT SOUTHWEST INDIANS Eleanor H. Ayer; Travel book. Explores the Anasazi's lives, culture and dwellings. Illus. 48 pp. Paper. Primer Publishers, $6.95.

AMERICAN TRAVELER - INDIANS OF ARIZONA: A GUIDE TO ARIZONA'S HERITAGE
Eleanor H. Ayer; Travel book. Illus. 50 pp. Paper. Primer Publishers, $6.95.

AN AMERICAN URPHILOSOPHIE: AN AMERICAN PHILOSOPHY – BP (BEFORE PRAGMATISM) Robert Bunge; 218 pp. University Presses of America, 1984. $27.25.

THE AMERICAN WEST
Dee Brown; An account of the demise of the Native Americans of the Plains.
Illus. 304 pp. Scribners, 1994. $25.

THE AMERICAN WEST IN THE 20TH CENTURY: A BIBLIOGRAPHY
Richad W. Etulain & co-editors; Compiled over 8,000 entries focusing on the West after 1900. 464 pp. University of Oklahoma Press, 1994. $67.50.

THE AMERICAN WEST: PEOPLE, PLACES, AND IDEAS
Suzan Campbell; Views the collection of western & Native American art of The Rockwell Museum of Western Art. Illus. 160 pp. Western Edge Press, 2010. $24.95.

AMERICAN WOODLAND INDIANS
Michael Johnson & Richard Hook; History of the Eastern Woodland Indians.
Illus. Biblio. 48 pp. Paper. Wennawoods Publishing, 1990. $15.95.

AMERICANIZING OF THE AMERICAN INDIANS: WRITINGS BY THE FRIENDS OF THE INDIAN, 1880-1900
Francis P. Prucha, Ed.; 368 pp. Paper. University of Nebraska Press, $6.95.

AMERICANS RECAPTURED: PROGRESSIVE ERA MEMORY OF FRONTIER CAPTIVITY Moly K. Varley; 240 pp. U. of Oklahoma Press, 2014. $34.95; paper, $24.95.

AMERINDIAN REBIRTH: REINCARNATION BELIEF AMONG NORTH AMERICAN INDIANS & INUIT
Antonia Mills & Richard Slobodin, Eds.; Illus. 760 pp. University of Toronto Press, 1994.

AMERINDIANS & THEIR PALEO-ENVIRONMENTS IN NORTHEASTERN NORTH AMERICA, VOL. 288 Walter Newman & Bert Salwen
New York Academy of Science, 1977. $37.

AMIDST A STORM OF BULLETS: THE DIARY OF LT. HENRY PRINCE IN FLORIDA, 1836-1842 Frank Laumer, Ed.; 166 pp. University of Tampa Press, 1998. $29.95.

AMONG THE APACHES
Frederick Schwatka; Facsimile of 1887 articles. Collected observations of several visits to the Apache Indian agencies. Tells of life as it was. Illus. 32 pp. Paper. Amazon.com & Alibris.com, 1974. $4.

AMONG THE CHIGLIT ESKIMOS
E. Petitot; 202 pp. Paper. CCI, 1981. $10.

*AMONG THE PLAINS INDIANS
Lorenz Engel; Based upon the journals of the German explorer Maximilian, as well as upon the records of George Catlin during the early 1830's. Grades 5-12. Illus. 112 pp. Lerner, 1970. $9.95.

AMONG THE SIOUX OF DAKOTA: EIGHTEEN MONTHS EXPERIENCE AS AN INDIAN AGENT, 1869-70 D.C. Poole
Reprint. Illus. Photos. Map. 241 pp. Paper. Minnesota Historical Society, 1988. $8.95.

AMONG TURTLE HUNTERS & BASKET MAKERS: ADVENTURES WITH THE SERI INDIANS David Burckhalter; Illus. 160 pp. Paper. Treasure Chest Books, 2004. $16.95.

ANASAZI
Pike; Paper. Random House, $17.

*THE ANASAZI
Grades K-4. Illus. 48 pp. Childrens Press, $11.45.

ANASAZI AMERICA: SEVENTEEN CENTURIES ON THE ROAD FROM CENTER PLACE David E. Stuart; Illus. 264 pp. Paper. U. of New Mexico Press, 2002. $19.95.

*ANASAZI, THE ANCIENT VILLAGERS
Susan Shaffer; Grade 4. Illus. with 30 student booklets & teacher's manual; transparencies, slides & audiocassette. Heard Museum, 1987. $295.

ANASAZI ARCHITECTURE & AMERICAN DESIGN
Baker H. Morrow & V.B. Price, Editors
Illus. 220 pp. Paper. University of New Mexico Press, 1999. $21.95.

*ANASAZI COLORING BOOK: THE STORY OF THE ANCIENT ONES
Sandra Stemmler; Grades 4 and up. Illus. 28 pp. Paper. Amazon.com, $3.95.

ANASAZI HARVEST
R. Leland Waldrip; 333 pp. Paper. Amazon.com, 1998. $9.95.

*ANASAZI LEGENDS, SONGS OF THE WIND DANCER
Lou Cuevas; Grades 4 and up. Illus. 208 pp. Paper. Naturegraph, 1999. $12.95.

ANASAZI OF MESA VERDE & THE FOUR CORNERS
William M. Ferguson; Paper. University Press of Colorado, 1996. $34.95.

ANASAZI PAINTED POTTERY IN THE FIELD MUSEUM
Paul S. Martin; Limited edition. Illus. 284 pp. Martino Publisahing, $185.

ANASAZI PLACES: THE PHOTOGRAPHIC VISION OF WILLIAM CURRENT
Jeffrey Cook, text; Illus. 101 bxw photos. 152 pp. University of Texas Press, 1992. $45.

ANASAZI POTTERY
Robert H. Lister & Florence C. Lister; Illustrates ten centuries of prehistoric southwestern pottery. Illus. 100 pp. Paper. University of New Mexico Press & Amazon.com, $21.95.

ANASAZI: PREHISTORIC PEOPLES OF THE FOUR CORNERS
Museum of Northern Arizona.

ANASAZI REGIONAL ORGANIZATION AND THE CHACO SYSTEM
Edited by David E. Doyel; Illus. 208 pp. Paper. Amazon.com & Alibris.com, 2002. $29.95.

ANASAZI RUINS OF THE SOUTHWEST IN COLOR
William M. Ferguson & Arthur H. Rohn; Illus. Color photos. 310 pp. Paper. Amazon.com, 1987. $19.97.

*AN ANASAZI WELCOME
Kay Matthews; illus. by Barbara Belknap
Grades Preschool-3. Illus. 40 pp. Paper. Amazon.com, $6.95.

*ANCESTOR'S FOOTSTEPS
T. Moore; Two stories of young men who prove themselves. Grades 6 to 9. Illus. 40 pp. Council for Indian Education, 1978. $9.95; paper, $3.95.

THE ANCESTORS: NATIVE AMERICAN ARTISANS OF THE AMERICAS
Anna C. Roosevelt & James G.E. Smith, Eds.
Illus. 197 pp. Paper. National Museum of the American Indian, 1979. $17.50.

THE ANCESTORS' PATH: A NATIVE AMERICAN ORACLE FOR SEEKING GUIDANCE FROM NATURE & SPIRIT HELPERS
John Lavinder; Illus. 240 pp. Paper. Inner Ocean Publishing, 2003. $29.95.

ANCESTRAL HOPI MIGRATIONS
Patrick D. Lyons; 142 pp. Paper. University of Arizona Press, 2003. $16.95.

ANCESTRAL MOUNDS: VITALITY & VOLATILITY OF NATIVE AMERICA
Jay Miler; Illus. 218 pp. University of Nebraska Press, 2015. $55.

ANCESTRAL VOICE: CONVERSATIONS WITH N. SCOTT MOMADAY
Charles L. Woodard, Ed.; He explores his individual & Kiowa tribal identity, his philosophies on language & literature, and his painting theories & practices. Illus. 230 pp. Center for Western Studies, $21.50; paper, $9.95. Paper. U. of Nebraska Press, $9.95.

ANCIENT AMERICA
Marian Wood; Facts on File, 1990. $17.95.

ANCIENT AMERICAN INSCRIPTIONS: PLOWMARKS OR HISTORY?
William R. McGlone; Illus. 415 pp. Paper. Early Sites Research Society, 1993. $19.95.

THE ANCIENT AMERICANS: A REFERENCE GUIDE TO THE ART, CULTURE & HISTORY OF PRE-COLUMBIAN NORTH & SOUTH AMERICA, TWO VOLS.
Juan Schobinger, Ed., tr. by Carys Evans-Coraales
Illus. 288 pp. M.E. Sharpe, Inc., 200. $159.50.

ANCIENT ANCESTORS OF THE SOUTHWEST
Gregory Schaaf; Graphic Ats Center Publishing Co., 1996.

ANCIENT ARCHITECTURE OF THE SOUTHWEST
William N. Morgan; Explores concurrent Mogollon, Hohokam & Anasazi architecture. Illus. 339 pp. University of Texas Press, 1994. $60.

ANCIENT ART OF THE AMERICAN WOODLAND INDIAN
David S. Brose; Illus. 240 pp. Detroit Institute of Arts, 1985. $29.95.

THE ANCIENT AMERICAS: THE MAKING OF THE PAST
Earl H. Swanson, et al; Illus. 160 pp. Amazon.com, 1989. $24.95; paper, 16.95.

ANCIENT ART OF OHIO
Lar Hothem; Reviews most of the artifact types in all of Ohio's prehistoric periods. Illus. 272 pp. Hothem House, 1994. $45, postpaid.

ANCIENT BURIAL PRACTICES IN THE AMERICAN SOUTHWEST: ARCHAEOLOGY, PHYSICAL ANTHROPOLOGY, & NATIVE AMERICAN PERSPECTIVES
Edited by Douglas R. Mitchell & Judy L. Brunson-Hadley
Illus. Maps. 280 pp. Paper. University of New Mexico Press, 2001. $29.95.

ANCIENT CHIEFDOMS OF THE TOMBIGBEE
John H. Blitz; 256 pp. Paper. University of Alabama Press, 1993. $24.95.

THE ANCIENT CHILD
N. Scott Momaday; Novel which juxtaposes Indian lore and wild west legend. 336 pp. Paper. Amazon.com, $13.50.

ANCIENT DRUMS, OTHER MOCCASINS: NATIVE NORTH AMERICAN CULTURAL ADAPTATION Harriet J. Kupferer; Illus. 352 pp. Prentice-Hall, 1988. $34.67.

ANCIENT EARTHEN ENCLOSURES OF THE EASTERN WOODLANDS
Robert C. Mainfort & Lynne P. Sullivan
Illus. 288 pp. Paper. University Press of Florida, 1998. $29.95.

ANCIENT ECHOES: NATIVE AMERICAN WORDS OF WISDOM
Patricia Martin; 64 pp. Amazon.com, 1994. $6.50.

ANCIENT ENCOUNTERS: KENNEWICK MAN & THE FIRST AMERICA
James C. Chatters; Illus. 304 pp. Paper. Simon & Schuster, 2002. $15.

ANCIENT INDIAN POTTERY OF THE MISSISSIPPI RIVER VALLEY
Hathcock; 2nd Edition. Illus. 236 pp. Hothem House, 1988. $48, postpaid.

*ANCIENT INDIANS: THE FIRST AMERICANS
Roy Gallant; Grades 5-11. 128 pp. Amazon.com, 1989. $15.95.

ANCIENT LIFE IN THE AMERICAN SOUTHWEST
Edgar Lee Hewett; Reprint. Illus. 392 pp. High-Lonesome Books & Biblo-Moser, $30.

ANCIENT MIAMIANS: THE TEQUESTA OF SOUTH FLORIDA
William E. McGoun; foreword by Jerald T. Milanich; Covers the archaeological sites (10,000 years from 8,000 B.C. to 1761 A.D.) of the Native Americans the Spanish called Tequesta and their ancestors, Ancient Miamians. Illus. Maps. 128 pp. University Press of Florida, 2002. $24.95.

ANCIENT MODOCS OF CALIFORNIA & OREGON
Carrol Howe; Reprint. Illus. 264 pp. Paper. Binford & Mort, $12.95.

ANCIENT MONUMENTS OF THE MISSISSIPPI VALLEY
Squier & Davis; Covers earthworks in Ohio and Mississippi valleys. Diagrams & maps. 316 pp. Hothem House, 1998. $63, postpaid.

THE ANCIENT MOUNDS OF POVERTY POINT: PLACE OF RINGS
Jon L. Gibson; foreword by Jerald T. Milanich; The setting, meaning, and history of the ruins of a large prehistoric Indian settlement, the 3,500 year-old site in northeastern Louisiana.Illus. Maps. 292 pp. University Press of Florida, 2001. $59.95; paper, $24.95.

ANCIENT NATIVE AMERICANS OF THE WYOMING VALLEY: 10,000 YEARS OF PREHISTORY John B. Orlandini; 190 pp. Paper. Amazon.com, 1996. $15.95.

AN ANCIENT NEW JERSEY INDIAN JARGON, VOL. 5
J.D. Prince & G. Thomas; Reprint. 50 pp. Amazon.com, 1997. $28.

ANCIENT NORTH AMERICA: THE ARCHAEOLOGY OF A CONTINENT
Brian M. Fagan; Revised ed. Paper. Amazon.cm, 1995. $31.95.

ANCIENT OBJECTS & SACRED REALMS: INTERPRETATIONS OF MISSISSIPPIAN ICONOGRAPHY F. Kent Reilly, III & James F. Garber, Editors; Ten essays by leading experts in the field. Photos. Drawings. 312 pp. Paper. U. of Texas Press, 2007. $30.

ANCIENT PEOPLE OF THE ARCTIC
Robert McGhee; Univesity of Washington Press, 1996. $35.95.

ANCIENT PEOPLES OF THE AMERICAN SOUTHWEST
Stephen Plog; Illus. 224 pp. Paper. Amazon.com, 1998. $22.50.

ANCIENT PEOPLES OF THE GREAT BASIN & COLORADO PLATEAU
Steven R. Simms; 288 pp. University of Arizona Press, 2008. $65; paper, $26.95.

ANCIENT ROAD NETWORKS & SETTLEMENT HIERARCHIES IN THE NEW WORLD
Charles Trombold; 300 pp. Cambridge University Press, 1991.

ANCIENT RUINS OF THE SOUTHWEST: AN ARCHAEOLOGICAL GUIDE
David Grant Noble
90 bxw photos. 18 maps & diagrams. 232 pp. Paper. Amazon.com & Alibris.com, $15.95.

ANCIENT SOCIETY
Lewis H. Morgan; The primitive institutions of the Indians. Reprint. 608 pp. Paper. University of Arizona Press, $19.95.

ANCIENT SPIRIT WISDOM: AN ELDER'S GUIDEBOOK TO NATIVE SPIRITUALITY & BEYOND IlgaAnne "Spider Spirit Woman" Bunjer
Illus. Amazon.com, 2011. $35; paper, $17.95. Kindle ed., $9.99.

ANCIENT TREASURES: A GUIDE TO ARCHAEOLOGICAL SITES & MUSEUMS IN THE U.S. & CANADA Franklin Folsom & Mary Elting; 3rd Ed. U. of New Mexico Press, 1983.

ANCIENT TRIBES OF THE KLAMATH COUNTRY
Carol B. Howe; Illus. Paper. Binford-Metropolitan, 1968. $9.95.

ANCIENT VISIONS: PETROGLYPHS & PICTOGRAPHS OF THE WIND RIVER & BIGHORN COUNTRY, WYOMING & MONTANA
Julie E. Francis & Lawrence L. Loendorf; University of Utah Press. $35.

ANCIENT VOICES, CURRENT AFFAIRS: LEGEND OF THE RAINBOW WARRIORS
Steven McFadden; Explores the myth of the rainbow warriors through the teachings of indigenous peoples of the Americas, Australia, and Tibet. Illus. 176 pp. Paper. Inner Traditions International, $9.95.

ANCIENT WALLS: INDIAN RUINS OF THE SOUTHWEST
Chuck Place & Susan Lamb; 100 color photos. 112 pp. Fulcrum Publishing & Amazon.com, 1991. $34.95; paper, $19.95.

ANCIENT WASHINGTON: INDIAN CULTURES OF THE POTOMAC VALLEY, VOL. 6
Robert Humphrey & Mary Chambers; Amazon.com, $5.

AND EAGLES SWEEP ACROSS THE SKY: INDIAN TEXTILES OF THE NORTH AMERICAN WEST Dena S. Katzenberg; Illus. Baltimore Museum, 1977. $6.98.

*AND IT IS STILL THAT WAY: LEGENDS TOLD BY ARIZONA INDIAN CHILDREN
Byrd Baylor; Grades K-6. Demco, 1976. $13.05.

AND THE LAST WILL BE FIRST
Murray Angus; 170 pp. Paper. University of Toronto Press, 1991. $9.95.

ANDELE, THE MEXICAN-KIOWA CAPTIVE: A STORY OF REAL LIFE AMONG THE INDIANS J.J. Methvin; Illus. 133 pp. Paper. University of New Mexico Press, 1996. $30.

ANETSO, THE CHEROKEE BALL GAME: AT THE CENTER OF CEREMONY & IDENTITY Michael J. Zogry; Eastern Band of Cherokee Nation and the game of Lacrosse (Anetso). Illus. 318 pp. University of North Carolina Press, 2010. $49.95.

ANGEL SITE: AN ARCHAEOLOGICAL, HISTORICAL, AND ETHNOLOGICAL STUDY
Glenn A. Black; Excavations of Angel Mounds community in southwestern Indiana. 2 Vols. Illus. 620 pp. Indiana Historical Society & Hothem House, 1967. $80.

THE ANGUISH OF SNAILS: NATIVE AMERICAN FOLKLORE IN THE WEST
Barre Toelken; Examines Native American visual arts, dance, oral tradition (story & song), humor, and patterns of thinking and discovery. 270 pp. Utah State University Press, 2002. $39.95; paper, $22.95. E-book, $18.50.

THE ANIMALS CAME DANCING: NATIVE AMERICAN SACRED ECOLOGY & ANIMAL KINSHIP Howard L. Harrod; 170 pp. Paper. University of Arizona Press, 2000. $19.95.

ANISHINABE: SIX STUDIES OF MODERN CHIPPEWA
J. Anthony Paredes, Ed.; Illus. 447 pp. University Press of Florida, 1980. $41.95.

ANISHINAUBAE THESAURUS
Basil H. Jonston; 205 pp. Paper. Michigan State University Press, 2007. $39.95; eBook, $31.95

*ANNA'S ATHABASKAN SUMMER
Arnold Griese; Illus. by Charles Ragins; Grades PS-2. Illus. Boyds Mills Press, 1995. $14.95.

ANNALS OF SHAWNEE METHODIST MISSION & INDIAN MANUAL LABOR SCHOOL
Martha B. Caldwell
Reprint of 1939 edition. Illus. 120 pp. Paper. Kansas State Historical Society, $3.

ANNALS OF THE SUSQUEHANNOCKS & OTHER INDIAN TRIBES OF PENNSYLVANIA, 1500-1763
H. Frank Eshelman; 416 pp. Paper. Wennawoods Publishing, 2000. $29.95.

AN ANNOTATED BIBLIOGRAPHY OF AMERICAN INDIAN & ESKIMO AUTOBIOGRAPHIES H. David Brumble, III; 182 pp. U. of Nebraska Press, 1981. $16.50.

AN ANNOTATED BIBLIOGRAPHY OF AMERICAN INDIAN PAINTING
Doris O. Dawdy; 50 pp. Paper. National Museum of the American Indian, 1968. $2.50.

ANNOTATED BIBLIOGRAPHY OF FEDERAL & TRIBAL LAW: PRINT & INTERNET SOURCES Marilyn K. Nicely, Editor; University of Oklahoma Law Library, 2010.

ANOMPILBASHSHA' ASILHHA' HOLISSO: CHICKASAW PRAYER BOOK
Chickasaw Language Committee; with Joshua Hinson, John Dyson, and Pamela Munro 200 pp. The Chickasaw Press. Distributed by the University of Oklahoma Press, $36.

ANOOSHI LINGIT AANI KA / RUSSIANS IN TLINGIT AMERICA: THE BATTLES OF SITKA, 1802 & 1804 Nora Marks Dauenhauer, Richard Dauenhauer, Lydia T. Black Illus. Maps. 560 pp. University of Washington Press, 2008. $35.

ANOTHER AMERICA: NATIVE AMERICAN MAPS & THE HISTORY OF OUR LAND
Mark Warhus; Reprint. Illus. 240 pp. Amazon.com, 1997. $30; paper, $20.

*ANPAO: AN AMERICAN INDIAN ODYSSEY
Jamake Highwater; Grades 5-9. HarperCollins, 1977. $13.50; paper, $3.95.

ANSWERED PRAYERS: MIRACLES & MILAGROS ALONG THE BORDER
Eileen Oktavec; Explains the use of the tiny metal tokens depicting objects for which miracles are sought. Illus. 256 pp. University of Arizona Press, 1995. $36; paper, $17.95.

ANSWERING CHIEF SEATTLE
Albert Furtwangler; 208 pp. University of Washington Press, 1997. $27.50.

ANTHROPOLOGICAL PAPERS OF UNIVERSITY OF ALASKA
Linda Ellanna, Series Ed.; See Dept. of Anthropology, University of Alaska, Fairbanks, AK 99775 (907) 474-7288 for a complete listing with prices.

ANTHROPOLOGICAL STUDIES ON THE QUICHUA & MACHIGANGA INDIANS
Harry B. Ferris; Reprint of 1921 edition. Paper. Elliots Books.

ANTHROPOLOGISTS & INDIANS IN THE NEW SOUTH
Rachel A. Bonney & J. Anthony Paredes, Eds.; Essays that look at the changing relationships between anthropologists and Indians at the turn of the millennium. Illus. 328 pp. Paper. University of Alabama Press, 2001. $34.95. e-Book available.

ANTHROPOLOGY & THE AMERICAN INDIAN
Report of a symposium held in 1970 by the American Anthropological Association on the issues raised by Vine Deloria's book, "Custer Died for Your Sins." 125 pp. Paper. Amazon.com, 1973. $2.50.

ANTHROPOLOGY ON THE GREAT PLAINS
W. Raymond Wood and Margot Liberty, Editors
Illus. 310 pp. University of Nebraska Press, 1980. $27.95.

ANTHROPOLOGY OF THE NORTH PACIFIC RIM
William Fitzhugh & Valerie Chaussonnet, Editors; Investigates the anthropology, history, and art of the North pacific rim. Illus. 368 pp. Smithsonian Institution Press, 1993. $55.

ANTI-INDIANISM IN MODERN AMERICA: A VOICE FROM TATEKEYA'S EARTH
Elizabeth Cook-Lynn; Illus. 240 pp. Paper. University of Illinois Press, 2002. $26.

ANTIQUE NATIVE AMERICAN BASKETRY OF WESTERN NORTH AMERICA: A COMPREHENSIVE GUIDE TO IDENTIFICATION
John Kania & Alan Blaugrund; photos by Anthony Richardson
Illus. 312 pp. University of New Mexico Press, 2016. $95.

ANTIQUITIES OF THE MESA VERDE NATIONAL PARK
Jesse W. Fewkes; Reprint. 99 pp. www.gutenberg.org. Free.

ANTIQUITIES OF THE SOUTHERN INDIANS, PARTICULARLY OF THE GEORGIA TRIBES Charles C. Jones ; Frank Schnell, Editor & Intro.
Paper. University of Alabama Press, 1999. $44.95; eBook, $44.95.

ANTS & ORIOLES: SHOWING THE ART OF PIMA POETRY
Donald Bahr, Lloyd Paul & Vincent Joseph; Illus. University of Utah Press, $29.95.

ANY OTHER COUNTRY EXCEPT MY OWN
Hadley A. Thomas; The evolution of the Dine from prehistory to the present. The story of the Navajo. Illus. 270 pp. paper. Cross Cultural Publications, 1994. $19.95.

ANZA'S 1779 COMANCHE CAMPAIGN
Ron Kessler; 2nd Ed. 98 pp. Adobe Village Press, 2001. $12.95.

APACHE
Will L. Comfort; 274 pp. Paper. University of Nebraska Press, 1985. $7.95.

*APACHE
Barbara McCall; Grades 5-8. Illus. 32 pp. Amazon.com, 1990. $9.95.

·THE APACHE
Joseph Jastrzembski; Paul Rosier, Set Editor
Grades 6-12. Illus. 130 pp. Chelsea House, 2011. $35.

*THE APACHE
Patricia McKissack; Grades K-4. Illus. 48 pp. Childrens Press, $11.45.

*THE APACHE
Michael Melody; Grades 5 and up. Illus. 104 pp. Paper. Chelsea House, 1988. $9.95.

APACHE AGENT: THE STORY OF JOHN P. CLUM
W. Clum; Illus. 300 pp. Gordon Press, 1977. $59.95 (library binding.)

APACHE AUTUMN
Robert Skimin; Novel deals with the struggle of the Apaches to maintain their way of life against insurmountable odds. 427 pp. St. Martins Press, 1993. $22.95.

AN APACHE CAMPAIGN IN THE SIERRA MADRE
John G. Bourke; Illus. 150 pp. Paper. University of Nebraska Press, 1987. $4.95.

*APACHE CHILDREN & ELDERS TALK TOGETHER
Barrie E. Kavasch; Grades 4 and up. Rosen Group, 1998. $18.

APACHE DAYS & AFTER
Thomas Cruse; E. Cunningham, Ed.
Illus. 364 pp. U. of Nebraska Press, $27.95; paper, $9.95.

THE APACHE DIARIES: A FATHER-SON JOURNEY
Grenville Goodwin & Neil Goodwin; Illus. Maps. 304 pp. Paper. University of Nebraska Press, 2000. $35; paper, $16.95.

APACHE GOLD & YAQUI SILVER
J. Frank Dobie; Legend & lore. Explores the mysterious and alluring sagas of lost mines and adventure. Illus. 380 pp. Paper. University of Texas Press, $15.95.

APACHE INDIAN BASKETS
Clara Lee Tanner; Illus. 204 pp. University of Arizona Press, 1982. $45.

THE APACHE INDIANS
Frank C. Lockwood
Illus. Maps. 388 pp. Paper. University of Nebraska Press, 1987. $18.95.

*APACHE LEGENDS: SONGS OF THE WIND DANCER
Lou Cuevas; Grades 4 and up. Illus. 128 pp. Paper. Naturegraph, $8.95.

AN APACHE LIFE-WAY: THE ECONOMIC, SOCIAL, & RELIGIOUS INSTITUTIONS OF THE CHIRICAHUA INDIANS Morris E. Opler; intro. bu Charles R. Kraut
Reprint of 1941 edition. Based on the author's two years of field work. Illus. Maps. 530 pp. Paper. U. of Nebraska Press, 1996. $29.95.

APACHE: THE LONG RIDE HOME
Grant Gall; Story of a Mexican boy captured by Apaches and adopted into the tribe. 112 pp. Paper. Sunstone Press, 1998. $9.95.

APACHE MEDICINE-MEN
John G. Bourke; Intensive studies of 19th century American Indian life. Reprint. Photos. Illus. 176 pp. Paper. Dover, $8.95.

APACHE MOTHERS & DAUGHTERS: FOUR GENERATIONS OF A FAMILY
Ruth McDonald Boyer & Narcissus Duffy Gayton
Family history of four generations of Chiricahua Apache women from 1848 to the present. Illus. Maps. 416 pp. Paper. University of Oklahoma Press, 1993. $19.95.

APACHE, NAVAHO & SPANIARD
Jack D. Forbes; Apache & Navaho response to Spanish advance in the 17th century into northern Mexico and the Southwest U.S. 2nd Edition. Illus. Maps. Biblio. 328 pp. Paper. University of Oklahoma Press, 1994. $15.95.

APACHE NIGHTMARE: THE BATTLE OF CIBECUE CREEK
Charles Collins; Illus. Maps. University of Oklahoma Press, 1998. $27.95.

APACHE ODYSSEY: A JOURNEY BETWEEN TWO WORLDS
Morris E. Opler; intro. by Philip Greenfield; In 1933, Opler recorded the life story of a Mescalero Apache he called Chris. Illus. Maps. 302 pp. Paper. U. of Nebraska Press, 2002. $18.95.

APACHE RESERVATION: INDIGENOUS PEOPLES & THE AMERICAN STATE
Richard J. Perry; Discusses reservation issues and the historical development of the reservation system. Illus. Maps. 276 pp. University of Texas Press, 1993. $25.

APACHE: SACRED PATH TO WOMANHOOD
John Annerino; The right of passage for Apache young women. Illus. 118 pp. Paper. Amazon.com, 1998. $29.95.

APACHE SHADOWS
Albert R. Booky; Story of two Mescalero Apache brothers and the settlement of the West. 159 pp. Paper. Sunstone Press, 1998. $10.95.

APACHE VOICES: THEIR STORIES OF SURVIVAL AS TOLD TO EVE BALL
Sherry Robinson; Illus. 288 pp. Paper. University of New Mexico Press, $19.95.

APACHE WARS: AN ILLUSTRATED BATTLE HISTORY
E. Lisle Reedstrom; Illus. 256 pp. Sterling, 1990. $24.95.

APACHE WOMEN WARRIORS
Kimberly M. Buchanan; Illus. 62 pp. Paper. Texas Western Press, 1986. $12.50.

APACHEAN CULTURE HISTORY & ETHNOLOGY
Keith H. Basso & Morris E. Opler, Ed.
Reprint of 1971 edition. Illus. 176 pp. Paper. University of Arizona Press, $26.95.

APACHES AT WAR & PEACE: THE JANOS PRESIDIO, 1750-1858
William B. Griffen; Illus. 313 pp. Paper. University of New Mexico Press, 1998. $18.95.

THE APACHES: A CRITICAL BIBLIOGRAPHY
Michael Melody; 96 pp. Paper. Indiana University, 1977. $6.95.

APACHES DE NAVAJO: 17TH CENTURY NAVAJOS IN THE CHAMA VALLEY OF NEW MEXICO Curtis F. Schaafsma; Illus. 330 pp. University of Utah Press. $55.

THE APACHES: EAGLES OF THE SOUTHWEST
Donald Worcester; Illus. Maps. 407 pp. Paper. University of Oklahoma, 1979. $24.95.

APACHES: A HISTORY & CULTURE PORTRAIT
James L. Haley; Illus. 455 pp. Maps. Paper. University of Oklahoma Press, 1997. $24.95.

*THE APACHES & NAVAJOS
Craig & Katherine Doherty
Grades 3 and up. Illus. 64 pp. Paper. Franklin Watts, 1991. $4.95.

THE APALACHEE INDIANS & MISSION SAN LUIS
John H. Hann & Bonnie McEwan; Paints a picture of the Apalachee Indians of northwest Florida and their Spanish conquerors. Illus. 120 color reproductions. Maps. 208 pp. University Press of Florida & Amazon.com, 1998. $59.95; paper, $19.95.

APALACHEE: THE LAND BETWEEN THE RIVERS
John H. Hann
Illus. Biblio. 464 pp. University Press of Florida & Amazn.com, 1988. $39.95.

APAUK: CALLER OF BUFFALO
James W. Schultz; Reprint. Illus. 227 pp. Time-Life, 1993. $21.99.

APPLIED ANTHROPOLOGY IN CANADA: UNDERSTANDING ABORIGINAL ISSUES
Edward J. Hedican; 320 pp. Paper. University of Toronto Press, 2008.

APOCALYPSE OF CHIOKOYHIKOY: CHIEF OF THE IROQUOIS
Robert Griffin & Donald A. Grinde, Jr., Eds.; A dramatic Iroquois prophecy accompanied by a literary and historical commentary. 274 pp. Published by Les Presses de L'niversite Laval in Quebec, 1997. Available from Amazon.com, $27.

APOLOGIES TO THE IROQUOIS
Edmund Wilson; Illus. 356 pp. Paper. Syracuse University Press, $17.95.

APOSTATE ENGLISHMAN: GREY OWL THE WRITER & THE MYTHS
Albert Braz; 224 pp. Paper. Michigan State University Press, 2015. $31.95.

APPALACHIAN INDIAN FRONTIER: THE EDMOND ATKIN REPORT & PLAN OF 1755
Edmond Atkin; Wilbur R. Jacobs, Ed.
Reprint. Illus. 107 pp. Paper. Wennawoods Publishing, $14.95.

APPALACHIAN MOUNTAIN ANIYUNWIYA
A bibliographic research source which documents and discusses original tribal identities, traditions, culture, social and political configuration of the aboriginal people of the Appalachian mountain region and Piedmont of the eastern U.S. David Michael Wolfe.

APPALACHIAN MOUNTAIN CHEROKEE
David Michael Wolfe; Booklet specifically to Cherokee people of the present day Appalachian Mountain region encompassing the mountainous regions of West Virginia, Kentucky, Ohio and Pennsylvania. 24 pp. David. M. Wolfe.

APPLETON'S AMERICAN INDIAN DESIGNS
LeRoy H. Appleton
Illus. 80 pp. Paper. Dover Publications, 2003. $19.95, includes CD-ROM

APPLIQUE PATTERNS FROM NATIVE AMERICAN BEADWORK DESIGNS
Dr. Joyce Mori; Floral applique patterns in full size patterns and instructions. Illus. 96 pp. Paper. Collector Books, 1994. $14.95.

APPROACHES TO TEACHING MOMADAY'S THE WAY TO RAINEY MOUNTAIN
Kenneth M. Roemer, Editor
175 pp. Modern Language Association, 1988. $32; paper, $17.50.

APPROACHING FOOTSTEPS: PUGET SOUND INDIANS – BAINBRIDGE ISLAND SAWMILLS Velma H. Basworth; 113 pp. Paper. Panpress, 1998. $19.95.

*THE ARAPAHO
Loretta Fowler; Grades 5 and up. Illus. Chelsea House, 1989. $17.95.

THE ARAPAHO
Alfred L. Kroeber; Reprint. Discusses Arapaho culture; dance & design, Indian symbolism. Illus. 480 pp. University of Nebraska Press, 1983. $10.95.

ARAPAHO DIALECTS
A.L. Kroeber; Reprint oif 1916 edition. 67 pp. Paper. Coyote Press, $7.81.

THE ARAPAHO INDIANS: A RESEARCH GUIDE & BIBLIOGRAPHY
Zdenek Salzmann, Compiler; Greenwood, 1988. $35.

ARAPAHO JOURNEYS: PHOTOGRAPHS & STORIES FROM THE WIND RIVER RESERVATION Sara Wiles; Three decades of contemporary Northern Arapaho life in images & essays. Illus. Map. 256 pp. University of Oklahoma Press, 2011. $34.95.

THE ARAPAHO LANGUAGE
Andrew Cowell & Alonzo Moss, Sr.
544 pp. University Press of Colorado, $70; eBook, 55.

ARAPAHOE POLITICS, 1851-1978: SYMBOLS IN CRISES OF AUTHORITY
Loretta Fowler; Illus. Maps. 375 pp. Paper. University of Nebraska Press, 1982. $14.

ARAPAHO STORIES, SONGS, AND PRAYERS: A BILINGUAL ANTHOLOGY
Andrew Cowell, Alonzo Moss, William C'Hair
Illus. 584 pp. Paper. University of Oklahoma Press, 2014. $29.95.

ARAPAHO WOMEN'S QUILLWORK: MOTION, LIFE & CREATIVITY
Jeffrey D. Anderson; Illus. 256 pp. Paper. University of Oklahoma Press, $21.95.

THE ARAPAHOES, OUR PEOPLE
Virginia C. Trenholm; Illus. Map. Paper. University of Oklahoma Press, 1986. $21.95.

ARARAPIKVA: TRADITIONAL KARUK INDIAN LITERATURE FROM NORTHWESTERN CALIFORNIA translated & introduced by Julian Lang
Bilingual text. 122 pp. Heyday Books, 1994. $10.95.

THE ARBITRARY INDIAN: THE INDIAN ARTS & CRAFTS ACT OF 1990
Gail K. Sheffield; An in-depth analysis of the act, revealing its historical, legal, and social implications & exposing its fundamental flaws. 232 pp. University of Oklahoma Press, 1997. $27.50.

ARBORETUM AMERICA: A PHILOSOPHY OF THE FOREST
Diana Beresford-Kroeger; Reveals the history of trees in Native American culture, including their medicinal uses. Illus. 214 pp. Paper. U. of Michigan Press, 2003. $29.

ARCHAEOASTRONOMY IN THE NEW WORLD: AMERICAN PRIMITIVE ASTRONOMY
A.F. Aveni, Editor; 230 pp. Cambridge University Press, 1982. $39.50.

AN ARCHAEOLOGICAL HISTORY OF THE HOCKING VALLEY (OH)
James Murphy; The prehistory of Hocking Valley over six major time periods: Paleo-Indian, Archaic, Early, Middle & Late Woodland,and late Prehistoric. Illus. 419 pp. Amazon.com & Alibris.com, 1989. $19.95.

ARCHAEOLOGICAL INVESTIGATIONS IN THE UPPER SUSQUEHANNA VALLEY, NEW YORK STATE (VOLUME 1) Robert E. Funk
Illus. 400 pp. Amazon.com, 1994. $66.95.

THE ARCHAEOLOGICAL INVESTIGATIONS OF FORT KNOX II, FORT KNOX CO., INDIANA, 1803-1813 Marlesa Gray
Illus. 312 pp. Paper. Indiana Historical Society, 1988. $32.

ARCHAEOLOGICAL PERSPECTIVES ON THE BATTLE OF LITTLE BIGHORN: THE FINAL REPORT
Douglas D. Scott; Illus. 328 pp. Paper. University of Oklahoma Press, 2000. $24.95.

ARCHAEOLOGICAL STUDIES OF GENDER IN THE SOUTHEASTERN U.S.
Jane M. Eastman & Christopher B. Rodning; Illus. 220 pp. U. Press of Florida, 2001. $55.

AN ARCHAEOLOGICAL STUDY OF THE MISSISSIPPI CHOCTAW INDIANS
John H. Blitz
Illus. 120 pp. Paper. Mississippi Department of Archives and History, 1985. $7.50.

ARCHAEOLOGIES OF PLACEMAKING: MONUMENTS, MEMORIES, & ENGAGEMENT IN NATIVE NORTH AMERICA Patricia E. Rubertone
Examines modern historic preservation & commemoration projects. Illus. 288 pp. University of Arizona Press, 2008. $79.

ARCHAEOLOGIES OF THE PUEBLO REVOLT: IDENTITY, MEANING & RENEWAL IN THE PUEBLO WORLD Robert W. Preucel, Editor
Illus. 256 pp. Paper. University of New Mexico Press, 2002. $45..

ARCHAEOLOGY AS ANTHROPOLOGY: A CASE STUDY
William Longacre; Focuses on organizational and behavioral aspects of societies which emerged approximately 1500 B.C. through 1350 AD. 57 pp. Paper. University of Arizona Press, 1970. $5.95.

ARCHAEOLOGY & CERAMICS AT THE MARKSVILLE SITE
Alan Toth; Illus. Paper. University of Michigan, Museum of Anthropology, 1975. $2.

ARCHAEOLOGY & ETHNOHISTORY OF OMAHA INDIANS: THE BIG VILLAGE SITE
John M. O'Shea & John Ludwickson; Illus. 380 pp. U. of Nebraska Press, 1992. $55.

ARCHAEOLOGY, HISTORY, & CUSTER'S LAST BATTLE: THE LITTLE BIGHORN REEXAMINED Richard A. Fox, Jr.; Illus. Maps. 416 pp. Paper. University of Oklahoma Press, 1997. $24.95. Video-VHS, $29.95; & PAL, $29.95.

THE ARCHAEOLOGY & HISTORY OF THE NATIVE GEORGIA TRIBES
Max E. White; Spanning 12,000 years of Georgia's indigenous peoples. Illus. 160 pp. University Press of Florida, 2002. $65; paper, $24.95..

THE ARCHAEOLOGY & HISTORY OF PUEBLO SAN MARCOS: CHANGE & STABILITY Ann Ramenoofsky & Kari Schleher
Illus. 400 pp. University of New Mexico Press, 2017. $95.

ARCHAEOLOGY IN VERMONT
John C. Huden, Editor; Illus. Paper. Charles E. Tuttle, 1970. $6.50.

ARCHAEOLOGY IN WASHINGTON
Ruth Kirk & Richard D. Daugherty150 color Illus. 168 pp. University of Washington Press, 2007. $40; paper, $26.95.

ARCHAEOLOGY OF ABORIGINAL CULTURE CHANGE IN THE INTERIOR SOUTHEAST: DEPOPULATION DURING THE EARLY HISTORIC PERIOD
Marvin T. Smith; Illus. Biblio. 198 pp. U. Press of Florida, 1987. $55; paper, $24.95.

THE ARCHAEOLOGY OF ANCIENT ARIZONA
Jefferson Reid & Stephanie Whittlesey
Overview of prehistoric peoples: Hohokam, Patayan, Mogollon, Anasazi, Sinagua, and Salado. Illus. 310 pp. Paper. University of Arizona Press, 1997. $17.95.

THE ARCHAEOLOGY OF THE APPALACHIAN HIGHLANDS
Lynne P. Sullivan & Susan C. Prezzano, Editors
Illus. Maps. Amazon.com & Alibris.com, 2001. $55.

ARCHAEOLOGY OF BANDELIER NATIONAL MONUMENT: VILLAGE FORMATION ON THE PAJARITO PLATEAU, NEW MEXICO
Edited by Timothy Alan Kohler; Essays summarize the results of new excavation and survey research in Bandelier. Illus. Maps. 288 pp. University of New Mexico, 2004. $65.

THE ARCHAEOLOGY OF CA-MNO-2122: A STUDY OF PRE-CONTACT & POST-CONTACT LIFEWAYS AMONG THE MONO BASIN PAIUTE
Brooke S. Arkush; Illus. Paper. University of California Press, 1995. $55.

THE ARCHAEOLOGY OF THE CADDO
Timothy Perttula & Chester Walker, Editors
Illus. 536 pp. Paper. University of Nebraska Press, 2012. $60.

THE ARCHAEOLOGY OF CAPE NOME, ALASKA
John Bockstoce; Illus. 133 pp. Paper. University of Pennsylvania Museum, $25.

ARCHAEOLOGY OF THE FLORIDA GULF COAST
Gordon Willey; Reprint. Illus. 696 pp. University Press of Florida, $29.95.

ARCHAEOLOGY OF THE FROBISHER VOYAGES
William Fitzhugh & Jacqueline S. Olin, Editors; An account of the Frobisher voyage into the Canadian Arctic, 1576-1578. Illus. Maps. 368 pp. Smithsonian Institution Press, 1993. $45.

ARCHAEOLOGY OF THE LOWER MUSKOGEE CREEK INDIANS, 1715-1836
Howard Thomas Foster
University of Alabama Press, 2007. $54.95; paper, $34.95; eBook, $34.95.

ARCHAEOLOGY OF THE LOWER OHIO RIVER VALLEY
Jon Muller; Paper. Amazon.com, 1986. $47.50.

ARCHAEOLOGY OF THE MIDDLE GREEN RIVER REGION, KENTUCKY
William H. Marquardt & Patty Jo Watson; A new interpretation of data gathered over a 30-year period about the Native American people who lived along the middle Green River from about 4500 to 2000 B.C. Illus. Maps. 680 pp. Amazon.com, 2005. $65.

ARCHAEOLOGY OF MISSISSIPPI
Calvin S. Brown; Reprint 1926 ed. Illus. 230 pp. Amazon.com, 1993. $42; paper, $19.95.

THE ARCHAEOLOGY OF NAVAJO ORIGINS
Ronald H. Towner, Editor; Illus. Maps. University of Utah Press. $45.

THE ARCHAEOLOGY OF NEW ENGLAND
Dean R. Snow; This is the first book-length attempts to synthesize New England prehistory since Willoughby's 1935 Antiquities of the New England Indians. Illus. 379 pp. 1980. Amazon.com, $39.90.

THE ARCHAEOLOGY OF NEW YORK STATE
William A. Ritchie; 2nd revised edition. Illus. 400 pp. Paper. Amazon.com, 1994. $25.

*THE ARCHAEOLOGY OF NORTH AMERICA
Dean R. Snow; Grades 7-12. Illus. 128 pp. Chelsea House, 1989. $17.95.

ARCHAEOLOGY OF THE LOWER OHIO RIVER VALLEY
Jon Muller; Paper. Amazon.com, 1986. $ 47.50.

THE ARCHAEOLOGY OF NATIVE-LIVED COLONIALISM: CHALLENGING HISTORY IN THE GREAT LAKES
Neal Ferris; Historical archaeology. 240 pp. University of Arizona Press, 2008. $50.

ARCHAEOLOGY OF PRECOLUMBIAN FLORIDA
Jerald T. Milanich; Illus. Maps. Biblio. 456 pp. University Press of Florida, 1994. $24.95.

ARCHAEOLOGY OF PREHISTORIC NATIVE AMERICA: AN ENCYCLOPEDIA
Guy Gibbon, Editor; Survey of the early cultures of North America. Illus. Photos. 36 maps. 2 vols. 1,025 pp. Amazon.com, 1998. $205.

AN ARCHAEOLOGY OF THE SOUL: NORTH AMERICAN INDIAN BELIEF & RITUAL
Robert L. Hall; Illus. 336 pp. Paper. University of Illinois Press, 1997. $24.95.

ARCHAEOLOGY OF THE SOUTHWEST
Linda Cordell; Paper. Amazon.com, 1997. $45.

ARCHAEOLOGY OF SUMMER ISLAND: CHANGING SETTLEMENT SYSTEMS IN NORTHERN LAKE MICHIGAN David S. Brose
Illus. 273 pp. Paper. University of Michigan, Museum of Anthropology, 1970. $15.

THE ARCHAEOLOGY OF THREE SPRINGS VALLEY: A STUDY IN FUNCTIONAL CULTURAL HISTORY Brian D. Dillon & Matthew A. Boxt, Editors
Illus. 200 pp. Paper. University of California, Los Angeles, 1989. $19.

ARCHAIC OF THE FAR NORTHEAST
David Sanger & M.A.P. Renouf; Integrated view of Native American & Canadian First Nations cultures from 6000 B.C to 1000 B.C. from Maine to Newfoundland-Labrador & Quebec. Illus. Maps. Tables. 486 pp. University Iowa Press, 2006. $32.50.

ARCHAIC TRANSITIONS IN OHIO & KENTUCKY PREHISTORY
Olaf H. Prufer, et al, Editors; Illus. 359 pp. Paper. Amazon.com, 2002. $38.

ARCHITECTURE OF ACOMA PUEBLO: THE 1934 HISTORIC AMERICAN BUILDINGS SURVEY PROJECT Peter Nabokov; Illus. 144 pp. Paper. Amazon.com, $15.95.

ARCHITECTURE OF THE ANCIENT ONES
photos by Val Brinkerhoff; 80 pp. Illus. Paper. Amazon.com, 2000. $19.95.

THE ARCHITECTURE OF GRASSHOPPER PUEBLO
Charles R. Riggs; Reconstructs the Pueblo and everyday life of the community. Illus. University of Utah Press. $40.

THE ARCHITECTURE OF SOCIAL INTEGRATION IN PREHISTORIC PUEBLOS
William Lipe & Michelle Hegmon, Editors
Illus. 175 pp. Paper. Amazon.com & Alibris, 1990. $21.95.

THE ARCHIVE OF PLACE: UNEARTHING THE PASTS OF THE CHILCOTIN PLATEAU
William J. Turkel; Illus. 336 pp. Paper. University of Washington Press, 2008. $36.95.

ARCHIVES OF CALIFORNIA PREHISTORY
A series of 41 vols. on the archaeology of California. See Coyote Press for titles and prices.

ARCTIC ART: ESKIMO IVORY
James G. Smith; Examples of Eskimo art from the Museum's collection. The text discusses the people of the Arctic. 127 pp. Paper. National Museum of the American Indian, $19.95.

ARCTIC ARTIST
C. Stuart Houston, Editor; The journal and paintings of George Back, midshipman with Sir John Franklin, 1819-1822, Arctic explorer. Covers various native peoples. Illus. 392 pp. McGill-Queen's University Press, $45.

ARCTIC DREAMS
Alootook Ipellie; Inuit mythology. Illus. 200 pp. Paper. Theytus, 1993. $16.95.

ARCTIC HANDBOOK OF NORTH AMERICAN INDIANS, Vol. 5
David Damas & William C. Sturtevant, Editors; Illus. 862 pp. Smithsonian, 1985. $29.00.

*ARCTIC HUNTER
Diane Hoyt-Goldsmith; An Inupiat experiences ancient & modern cultures. Grades 4-6. Illus. 32 pp. Holiday House, 1992. $15.95; paper, $6.95.

ARCTIC JOURNEYS ANCIENT MEMORIES: SCULPTURE BY ABRAHAM ANGHIK RUBEN The Arctic Studies Center; Illus. 88 pp. Paper. NMAI Press, 2012. $24.95.

ARCTIC LIFE: CHALLENGE TO SURVIVE
M. Jacobs & J. Richardson, Eds; Illus. 208 pp. Paper. Carnegie Museum, 1982. $17.50.

*ARCTIC MEMORIES
Normee Ekoomiak
Bilingual - English/Inuit. Grades 3 and up. Illus. 32 pp. Amazon.com, 1988. $15.95.

·THE ARCTIC PEOPLES
Craig & Katherine Doherty; Grades 5-8. Illus. 152 pp. Chelsea House, 2008. $35.

ARCTIC SCHOOLTEACHER: KULUKAK, ALASKA, 1931-1933
Abbie Morgan Madenwald; Story of Abbie Morgan's experiences teaching Eskimo children in the Alaskan village of Kulukak in 1931. Reprint. Illus. Maps. 196 pp. U. of Oklahoma Press, $24.95; paper, $13.95.

THE ARCTIC SKY: INUIT ASTRONOMY, STAR LORE, & LEGEND
John MacDonald; Interviews with Inuit elders & historical records of arctic explorers. Illus. 348 pp. Paper. University of Toronto Press, 1998. $29.95.

ARCTIC TRANSFORMATIONS: THE JEWELRY OF DENISE & SAMUEL WALLACE
Lois Sherr Dubin; Illus. 239 pp. NMAI Press, 2005. $60.

ARCTIC VILLAGE: A 1930s PORTRAIT OF WISEMAN, ALASKA
Robert Marshall; Illus. Maps. 400 pp. University of Alaska Press, 1991. $28; paper, $20.

ARE YOU IN THERE GRANDPAR? BEGINNING BLACK INDIAN GENEALOGY: A LOOK AT THOSE OTHER COUSINS Gloria L. Smith
45 pp. Paper. Trailstones Heritage Adventures, 1994. $7.

ARGUING WITH TRADITION: THE LANGUAGE OF LAW IN HOPI TRIBAL COURT
Justin B. Richland; Explores language & inteeraction within a contemporary Native Amerian legal system. Illus. Maps. 176 pp. University of Chicago P{ress, $40; paper, $16.

ARIKARA NARRATIVE OF THE CAMPAIGN AGAINST THE HOSTILE DAKOTAS: JUNE 1876 Orin G. Libby, Editor; Illus. Paper. Amazon.com, 2005. $22.

ARIKARA NARRATIVE OF CUSTER'S CAMPAIGN & THE BATTLE OF THE LITTLE BIGHORN Orin G. Libby, Editor
Illus. Map. 240 pp. Paper. University of Oklahoma Press, 1998. $9.95.

THE ARIKARA WAR: THE FIRST PLAINS INDIAN WAR, 1823
William R. Nestor; 264 pp. Amazon.com, 2001. $18.

ARISTOCRATIC ENCOUNTERS: EUROPEAN TRAVELERS & NORTH AMERICAN INDIANS Harry Liebersohn; Illus. 192 pp. Paper. Cambridge University Press, 1998. $22.

ARIZONA: A HISTORY
Thomas E. Sheridan; 434 pp. Paper. University of Arizona Press, 1995. $22.

ARIZONA TRAVELER: INDIANS OF ARIZONA
Eleanor H. Ayer; Illus. 48 pp. Paper. Amazon.com, 1999. $4.95.

*ARKANSAS INDIANS: LEARNING & ACTIVITY BOOK
Berna Love; Paper. Amazon.com, 1996. $4.95

ARMS, INDIANS & THE MISMANAGEMENT OF NEW MEXICO
D. Vigil; David Weber, Ed. & Translator; Texas Western, $10.00; paper, $5.

THE ARMY & NAVY JOURNAL ON THE BATTLE OF THE LITTLE BIGHORN & RELATED MATTERS, 1876-1881 James S. Hutchins, Ed. & Intro.
Illus. 260 pp. Amazon.com, 2003. $75.

AROUND THE SACRED FIRE: NATIVE RELIGIOUS ACTIVISM INTHE RED POWER ERA James Treat; A narrative map of the Indian Ecumenical Conference. Illus. Map. 384 pp. Paper. University of Illinois Press, 2007. $31.

AROUND THE SHORES OF LAKE SUPERIOR: A GUIDE TO HISTORIC SITES
Margaret Beattie Bogue; Second Ed. Includes information and sites of the Ojibwe people. Illus. Maps. 352 pp. University of Arizona Press, 2007. $60; paper, $29.95.

AROUND THE WORLD IN FOLKTALE & MYTH: AMERICAN INDIAN
Lu Keatley; H.E. & L.K. Fraumann, Editors
96 pp. Paper. Amazon.com, 1989. $99.87.

ARROW CREEK STORIES
Faye Hathaway; Reprint. 32 pp. Council for Indian Education, 1994. $4.95.

ARROWHEADS & PROJECTILE POINTS
Lar Hothem; 2nd Edition. Illus. Photos. 224 pp. Paper. Hothem House, 1983. $7.95.

ARROWHEADS & SPEAR POINTS OF THE PREHISTORIC SOUTHEAST: A GUIDE TO UNDERSTANDING CULTURAL ARTIFACTS Linda Crawford Culberson
Illus. 118 pp. Paper. University Press of Mississippi, 1993. $22.

ARROWHEADS & STONE ARTIFACTS: A PRACTICAL GUIDE FOR THE SURFACE COLLECTOR & AMATEUR ARCHAEOLOGIST C.G. Yeager
A handbook for identifying various stone artifacts. The Arrowheads Video shows where to look and what to look for. VHS or Beta, 30 minutes. Illus. 247 pp. Paper. Amazon.com & Hothem House (book only), 2nd Ed. 2000. $16.95.

THE ARROYO HONDO ARCHAEOLOGICAL SERIES
Douglas W. Schwartz, General Editor
5 volumes. Illus. Biblio. Paper. School of American Research, 1990. $10-15.

ART & ENVIRONMENT IN NATIVE AMERICA
M.E. King and I.R. Traylor, Jr. Editors; Illus. 169 pp. Paper. Texas Tech Press, 1974. $8.

ART & ESKIMO POWER: THE LIFE & TIMES OF ALASKAN HOWARD ROCK
Lael Morgan; Illus. 260 pp. Paper. Amazon.com, 1988. $24.95; paper, $16.95.

ART AS PERFORMANCE, STORY AS CRITICISM: REFLECTIONS ON NATIVE LITERARY AESTHETICS Craig S. Womack; Focuses on Native American literature.
376 pp. University of Oklahoma Press, 2009. $16.95; paper, $14.95.

ART FROM FORT MARION: THE SILBERMAN COLLECTION
Joyce M. Szabo; Cheyenne & Kiowa prisoners of war at Fort Marion, Florida.
208 pp. University of Oklahoma Press, 2007. $49.95; paper, $24.95.

ART FOR AN UNDIVIDED EARTH; THE AMERICAN INDIAN MOVEMENT GENERATION Jessica L. Horton
Art history Illus. 312 pp. Duke University Press, $94.95; paper, $26.95.

ART IN THE LIFE OF THE NORTHWEST COAST INDIANS
Describes the Rasmussen Collection of Northwest Coast Indian art. Published by the Portland Art Museum, 1219 SW Park Ave., Portland, OR 97205 (503) 226-2811.

ART IN MOTION: NATIVE AMERICAN EXPLORATIONS OF TIME, PLACE & THOUGHT
John P. Lukavic & Laura Caruso, Editors
Illus. 108 pp. Paper. Univdersity of Oklahoma Press, $25.

ART IN OUR LIVES: NATIVE WOMEN ARTISTS IN DIALOGUE
Cynthia Chavez Lamar & Sherry Farrell Racette, with Lara Evans
Discussion and essays from a group of Native women artists who speak franklyn about the roles, responsibilities, and commitments in their lives while balancing this existnce with their art practice. Illus. 152 pp.

ART OF THE AMERICAN INDIAN
Levin, et al: Vandervelde, Editor; Paper. Council for Indian Education, 1973. $1.95.

THE ART OF AMERICAN INDIAN COOKING
Yeffe Kimball & Jean Anderson
Recipes divided into culktural areas. 224 pp. Paper. Amazon.com,, $12.95.

ART OF THE AMERICAN INDIAN FRONTIER: THE CHANDLER-POHRT COLLECTION David Penney, Editor
Illustrates the many objects in the collection. Includes memoirs, essay, and text. Illus. Photos. 368 pp. Paper. University of Washington Press, 1992. $39.95.

ART OF THE AMERICAN INDIAN FRONTIER: A PORTFOLIO
David W. Penney & Detroit Institute of Arts
Introduction to the art and culture of Native Americans in a portfolio format.
24 pp. booklet and 24 full-color plates. W.W. Norton & Co., $18.95.

THE ART OF AMERICANIZTION AT THE CARLISLE INDIAN SCHOOL
Hayes Peter Mauro; Illus. 256 pp. University of New Mexico Press, $45.

ART OF THE ANCESTORS: ANTIQUE NORTH AMERICAN INDIAN ART
George Everett Shaw, et al; Shows how American Indian art was effected by their environment and how their art objects embodied their spiritual devotion. 180 pp. 100 color photos. University of New Mexico Press, 2006. $65.

ART OF THE CHEROKEE: PREHISTORY TO THE PRESENT
Susan C. Power; Paper. University of Georgia Press & Cherokee Publications, $26.95.

ART OF CLAY: TIMELESS POTTERY OF THE SOUTHWEST
Lee M. Cohen; Works of 20 southwestern potters, including Maria Martinez, Nampeyo, Popovi Da, Margaret Tafoya, and Al Qoyawayma. Illus. 96 color photos. 139 pp. Amazon.com $39.95.

*ART OF THE FAR NORTH: INUIT SCULPTURE, DRAWING & PRINTMAKING
Carol Finley; Grades 5-8. Color photos. Maps. Biblio. 60 pp. Lerner, 1998. $17.95.

ART OF THE HOPI: CONTEMPORARY JOURNEYS ON ANCIENT PATHWAYS
Lois Jacka; photos by Jerry Jacka; 158 color photos. 146 pp. Amazon.com, 1998. $21.95.

THE ART OF THE INDIAN BASKET IN NORTH AMERICA
Carol Fallon; Illus. 56 pp. Paper. Amazon.com, 1975. $2.50.

THE ART OF NATIVE AMERICAN BASKETRY: A LIVING LEGACY
Frank W. Porter, III, Editor; Illus. Greenwood Publishing, 1990. $99.95.

ART OF THE NATIVE AMERICAN FLUTE
R. Carlos Nakai & James DeMars; With additional material by David P. McAllester & Ken Light. A summation of R. Carlos Nakai's years as an educator, performer and student of the Native American flute. Includes 16 transcriptions of songs fro Nakai's recordings, plus two DeMars compositions. Illus. 132 pp. Paper. Mel Bay Publications, 1997. $19.95.

ART OF NATIVE NORTH AMERICA
Nigel Cawthorne; Illus. 96 pp. 6 vol. set. Amazon.com, 1997. $22.

THE ART OF NEW MEXICO
Joseph Traugott; Explores New Mexico art from the 1880s to the present. Illus. 288 pp. Museum of New Mexico Press, 2010. $55.

ART OF THE NORTH AMERICAN INDIANS: THE THAW COLLECTION
Gilbert T. Vincent, Sherry Brydon & Ralph T. Coe, Editors 770 Illus. 550 pp. University of Washington Press, 1999. $85.

ART OF THE NORTHWEST COAST
Aldona Jonaitis; Illus. Maps. 344 pp. Paper. U. of Washington Press, 2006. $26.95.

ART OF THE NORTHWEST COAST INDIANS
Robert Bruce Inverarity
2nd edition. Illus. 258 pp. Paper. University of California Press, 1967. $29.95.

ART OF THE OSAGE
Garrick Bailey & Daniel C. Swan; Two centuries of Osage art, tracing the material culture, social organizations, cosmology, aesthetics, and rituals of the Osage. Illus. 232 pp. University of Washington Press, 2004. $40. Paper. Amazon.com, $20.

ART OF THE RED EARTH PEOPLE: THE MESQUAKIE OF IOWA
Gaylord Torrence & Robert Hobbs
Illus. 144 pp. University of Washington Press, 1989. $50; paper, $24.95.

THE ART OF THE SHAMAN: ROCK ART OF CALIFORNIA
David S. Whitley; Illus. Maps. University of Utah Press. $45.

THE ART OF SIMULATING EAGLE FEATHERS
Bob Gutierrez; How to create realistic imitation golden & bald eagle feather. Illus. Color photos. 32 pp. Paper. Written Heritage, $9.95.

THE ART OF HOWARD TERPNING
Elmer Kelton; Illus. 160 pp. Teacher Ed. Amazon.com, 2003. $60.

ART OF THE TOTEM
Marius Barbeau; Explains the historic origins & the significance of totem art among northwest tribes. Illus. 64 pp. Paper. Hancock House, 1984. $6.95.

THE ART OF TRADITION: SACRED MUSIC, DANCE & MYTH OF MICHIGAN'S ANISHINAABE, 1946-1955 Gertrude Kurath, Jane Ettawageshikand Fred Ettawwageshik; Michael McNally, Editor; 576 pp. Michigan State University Press, 2009., $79.95.

ART OF A VANISHED RACE: THE MIMBRES CLASSIC BLACK-ON-WHITE
Victor Giamattei & Nanci Reichert; Mimbres art of the 10th century Southwest. Illus. 2nd Ed. 100 pp. Paper. High-Lonsome Books, 1990. $11.95.

ART OF THE WARRIORS: ROCK ART OF THE AMERICAN PLAINS
James D. Keyser; Illus. 128 pp. University of Utah Press, 2004. $20.

ART QUANTUM: THE EITELJORG FELLOWSHIP FOR NATIVE AMERICAN FINE ART, 2009 James H. Nottage, Editor; Illus. 96 pp. Paper. U. of Washington Press, 2010. $26.95.

THE ART & STYLE OF WESTERN INDIAN BASKETRY
Hancock House, $7.95.

ARTIFACTS OF THE NORTHWEST COAST INDIANS
Hilary Stewart; Illus. 172 pp. Paper. Amazon.com, $12.95.

AN ARTIST'S PORTFOLIO: THE CALIFORNIA SKETCHES OF HENRY B. BROWN, 1851-1852
Thomas Blackburn; 37 drawings that depict landscape and Native Americans going about their daily lives. 96 pp. Malki-Ballena Press, 2007. $30.

ARTISTIC TASTES: FAVORITE RECIPES OF NATIVE AMERICAN ARTISTS
Barbara Harjo; Illus. 140 pp. Kiva Publishing, 1998. $12.95.

ARTISTRY IN NATIVE AMERICAN MYTHS
Karl Kroeber; Analyzes stories and forms of oral storytelling. 292 pp. University of Nebraska Press, 1998. $70; paper, $30.

THE ARTISTS BEHIND THE WORK
Suzi Jones, Editor; Features the life history & craft of four Alaska Native artists: Nicholas Charles, a Yup'ik Eskimo; Frances Demientieff, an Athabaskan bead worker & skin sewer; Lena Sours, an Inupiat skin sewer; and Jennie Thlunaut, a Chilkat Tlingit basket & blanket maker. Illus. Maps. Photos. Paper. Amazon.com, 1986. $17.50.

ARTISTS IN CLAY
Ervin G. Bublitz; Illus. 68 pp. Paper. Ervin G. Bublitz, 2000. $20.

ARTS & CRAFTS OF THE CHEROKEE
Rodney Leftwich
Illus. 146 photos. 160 pp. Paper. Written Heritage & Cherokee Publications, $11.95.

ARTS & CRAFTS OF THE NATIVE AMERICAN TRIBES
Michael Johnson & Bill Yenne; Illus. 256 pp. Firefly Books, 2011. $49.95.

ARTS FROM THE ARCTIC
Jan Steinbright & Caroline Atuk-Derrick, Eds.
An exhibition catalog documenting the Arts from the Arctic exhibition. Illus. 80 pp. Institute of Alaska Native Arts, 1993. $22.50, postpaid.

THE ARTS IN SOUTH DAKOTA: A SELECTIVE, ANNOTATED BIBLIOGRAPHY
Ron MacIntyre, Rebecca Bell, Arthur Amiotte, et al
A companion volume to An Illustrated History of the Arts in South Dakota. A section on Dakota/Lakota arts. Illus. 282 pp. Center for Western Studies, $12.50.

ARTS OF DIPLOMACY: LEWIS & CLARK'S INDIAN COLLECTION
Hillel S. Burger; Illus. 360 pp. Paper. University of Washington Press, 2003. $40.

ARTS OF THE INDIAN AMERICAS: NORTH, CENTRAL & SOUTH: LEAVES FROM THE SACRED TREE Jamake Highwater; Illus. 320 pp. Paper. HarperCollins, 1985. $22.50.

THE ARTS OF THE NORTH AMERICAN INDIAN: NATIVE TRADITIONS IN EVOLUTION
Edwin L. Wade, Editor; Illus. 324 pp. Paper. Amazon.com, Alibris.com, 1986. $35.

AS DAYS GO BY: OUR HISTORY, OUR LAND, OUR PEOPLE – THE CAYUSE, UMATILLA, AND WALLA WALLA
Edited by Jennifer Karson; Illus. Maps. 320 pp. Paper. U. of Washington Press, $23.95.

AS IF THE LAND OWNED US: THE ETHNOHISTORY OF THE WHITE MESA UTES
Robert S. McPherson; Ethnohistory of the Southern Utes. Illus. Maps. 448 pp. Paper. University of Utah Press, 2011. $29.95.

AS LONG AS THE GRASS SHALL GROW & RIVERS FLOW: A HISTORY OF NATIVE AMERICANS Clifford E. Trafzer; Amazon.com, 2000.

AS LONG AS THE RIVER SHALL RUN: AN ETHNOHISTORY OF PYRAMID LAKE INDIAN RESERVATION Martha C. Knack & Omar C. Stewart
Reprint of 2nd edition.Illus. 490 pp. Paper. University of Nevada Press, $19.95.

AS LONG AS THE RIVERS RUN: HYDROELECTRIC DEVELOPMENT & NATIVE COMMUNITIES IN WESTERN CANADA
James B. Waldram; Paper. University of Toronto Press, 1993. $19.95.

AS LONG AS THE WATERS FLOW: NATIVE AMERICANS IN THE SOUTH & EAST
Frye Gaillard; photos by Carolyn DeMeritt; Illus. Amazon.com, 2000. $21.95.

AS MY GRANDFATHER TOLD IT: TRADITIONAL STORIES FROM THE KOYUKUK / SITSY YUGH NOHOLNIK TS'IN
Catherine Attla; University of Alaska Press, $12.

AS WE ARE NOW: MIXEDBLOOD ESSAYS ON RACE & IDENTITY
W.S. Penn; Illus. 282 pp. Paper. University of California Press, 1998. $23.95.

THE ASCENT OF CHIEFS: CAHOKIA & MISSISSIPPIAN POLITICS IN NATIVE NORTH AMERICA Timothy R. Pauketat
Analysis of the origins of Cahokia. 256 pp. Paper. U. of Alabama Press, 1994. $34.95.

ASHES & SPARKS
R. Dell Davis; Illus. 185 pp. J. Franklin Publishers, 1989. Includes audiotape. $24.95.

AN ASIAN ANTHROPOLOGIST IN THE SOUTH: FIELD EXPERIENCES WITH BLACKS, INDIANS & WHITES Choong S. Kim; U. of Tennessee Press, 1977. $17.95; paper, $8.95.

ASSESSMENT OF AMERICAN INDIANS
T.C. Thomason; 18 pp. Paper. Northern Arizona U., 1995. Text, $2.

ASSESSMENT OF A MODEL FOR DETERMINING COMMUNITY-BASED NEEDS OF AMERICAN INDIANS WITH DISABILITIES THROUGH CONSUMER INVOLVEMENT IN COMMUNITY PLANNING & CHANGE C.A. Marshall, et al; Amazon.com, 1990.

ASSIMILATION'S AGENT: MY LIFE AS A SUPERINTENDENT IN THE INDIAN BOARDING SCHOOL SYSTEM Edwin L. Chalcraft; Cary C. Collins, Ed. Illus. 368 pp. Paper. University of Nebraska Press, 2004. $29.95.

AN ASSUMPTION OF SOVEREIGNTY: SOCIAL & POLITICAL TRANSFORMATION AMONG THE FLORIDA SEMINOLES
Harry A. Kersey, Jr.; Illus. 290 pp. Paper. University of Nebraska Press, 1996. $24.95.

ASPECTS OF UPPER GREAT LAKES ANTHROPOLOGY: PAPERS IN HONOR OF LLOYD A. WILFORD
Elden Johnson, Editor; Illus. 190 pp. Paper. Minnesota Historical Society, 1974. $9.50.

THE ASSAULT ON INDIAN TRIBALISM: THE GENERAL ALLOTMENT LAW (DAWES ACT) OF 1887 Wilcomb E. Washburn; 88 pp. Paper. Amazon.com, 1975. $7.50.

AN ASSUMPTION OF SOVERIGNTY: SOCIAL & POLITICAL TRANSFORMATION AMONG THE FLORIDA SEMINOLES, 1953-1979
Harry A. Kersey, Jr.; 278 pp. Paper. University of Nebraska Press, 2007. $24.95.

ASYLUM IN THE GRASSLANDS
Diane Glancy (Cherokee); Poetry. 106 pp. Paper. U. of Arizona Press, 2007. $15.95.

AT THE BODERS OF EMPIRES: THE TOHONO O'ODHAM, GENDER, AND ASSIMILATION, 1880-1934 Andrae M. Marak; Laura Teunnerman
Illus. 232 pp. Paper. University of Arizona Press, $29.95.

AT THE CROSSROADS: INDIANS & EMPIRES ON A MID-ATLANTIC FRONTIER, 1700-1763
Jane T. Merritt; Illus. 305 pp. U. of North Carolina Press, 2003. $39.95; paper, $19.95.

AT THE CROSSROADS: MICHILIMACKINAC DURING THE AMERICAN REVOLUTION
David Armour & Keith Widder; The Western Great Lakes region during the Revolutionary War. Illus. Maps. 280 pp. Wennawoods Publishing, $18.95.

AT THE DESERT'S GREEN EDGE: AN ETHNOBOTANY OF THE GILA RIVER PIMA
Amadeo M. Rea; Discusses the Piman people, environment, language, and botanical knowledge of 240 plants. Illus. 430 pp. University of Arizona Press, 1997. $65.

AT HOME ON THE EARTH: BECOMING NATIVE TO OUR PLACE: A MULTICULTURAL ANTHOLOGY David L. Barnhill, Editor; 327 pp. Paper. U. of California Press, 1999. $50.

AT HOME WITH THE BELLA COOLA INDIANS: T.F. McILWRAITH'S FIELD LETTERS, 1922-24 edited by John Barker & Douglas Cole
Illus. Map. 224 pp. Paper. University of Washington Press, 2002. $24.95.

*AT THE MOUTH OF THE LUCKIEST RIVER
Arnold Griese; Illus. by Glo Coalson
Grades 1-4. Illus. Boyds Mills Press, 1996 reissue. $7.95.

AT THE RISK OF BEING HEARD: IDENTITY, INDIGENOUS RIGHTS, AND POSTCOLONIAL STATES Bartholomew Dean & Jerome M. Levi, Editors
Case studies analyzing indigenous rights & the challenges confronting indigenous peoples in the 21st century. Photos. Maps. Paper. University of Michigan Press, 2003. $36.95.

AT STANDING ROCK & WOUNDED KNEE: THE JOURNALS & PAPERS OF FATHER FRANCIS M. CRAFT, 1888-1890
Thomas W. Foley; Illus. 288 pp. University of Oklahoma Press, 2009. $34.95.

*ATARIBA & NIGUAYONA
adapted by Harriet Rohmer & Jesus Guerrero; illus. by Consuelo Mendez
Taino tales. Grades 1-6. Illus. Amazon.com, $13.95.

ATHABASKAN LANGUAGE STUDIES: ESSAYS IN HONOR OF ROBERT W. YOUNG
Eloise Jelinek, Sally Midgett, Keren Rice, Leslie Saxon, Editors
16 original essays on Athabaskan language and Navajo language & culture.
506 pp. 4 maps. University of New Mexico Press, $55.

THE ATHABASKAN LANGUAGES: PERSPECTIVE ON A NATIVE AMERICAN LANGUAGE FAMILY Theodore Fernald & Paul Platero, Editors
352 pp. Oxford University Press, 2000. $165.

ATHAPASKAN LINGUISTICS
Eung-Do Cook, Editor
Current perspectives on a language family. 645 pp. Amazon.com, 1989. $125.

ATHABASCAN OLD-TIME FIDDLING COMMEMORATIVE BOOKLET
Festival booklet featuring musicians, dancers and history. Illus. 20 pp.
Institute of Alaska Native Arts, 1992. $8.50, postpaid.

ATHABASKAN STORIES FROM ANVIK COLLECTED BY JOHN W. CHAPMAN
James Kari, retranscriber; 16 stories. 186 pp. Alaska Native Language Center, 1981. $12.

ATHAPASKAN VERB THEME CATEGORIES: AHTNA
James Kari; 230 pp. Paper. Alaska Native Language Center, 1979. $10.

THE ATHABASKANS: PEOPLE OF THE BOREAL FOREST
Richard K. Nelson; Focuses on the Athabaskans' implements, translated tales & poems, and describes their significance. Illus. Maps. 68 pp. Paper. University of Alaska Museum, 1983. $9.95.

ATKA, AN ETHNOHISTORY OF THE WESTERN ALEUTIANS
Lydia T. Black; Illus. 219 pp. Limestone, 1984. $26.

ATLAS OF AMERICAN INDIAN AFFAIRS
Francis P. Prucha; Graphically presents the history of Native Americans in 109, full-page, black & white maps. Illus. Biblio. 190 pp. U. of Nebraska Press, 1990. $47.50.

ATLAS OF GREAT LAKES INDIAN HISTORY
Helen Hornbeck Tanner, Editor
Illus. Maps. 544 pp. Paper. University of Oklahoma Press, 1987. $49.95.

ATLAS OF INDIAN NATIONS
Anton Treuer; Illus.320 pp. National Geographic Society, 2014. $40.

ATLAS OF INDIANS OF NORTH AMERICA
Gilbert Legay; Grades 8 and up. Illus. 96 pp. Amazon.com, 1995. $16.95.

*ATLAS OF THE NORTH AMERICAN INDIAN
Carl Waldman; map & illus. by Molly Braun
Revision of the 1985 title provides a series of overviews on Native American history, culture, and locations of Native Americans in North & Central America. Grades 9 and up. 4 Vols. Illus. 110 Maps. Glossary. Bibliography. 464 pp. Facts on File, 2009. $85.

ATTITUDES OF COLONIAL POWERS TOWARD THE AMERICAN INDIAN
Howard Peckham & Charles Gibson, Editors; Paper. U. of Utah Press, 1969. $9.95.

THE ATTRACTION OF PEYOTE: AN INQUIRY INTO THE BASIC CONDITIONS FOR THE DIFFUSION OF THE PEYOTE RELIGION IN NORTH AMERICA
Ake Hultkrantz; 232 pp. Paper. Amazon.com, 1997. $54.50.

AUBE NA BING: A PICTORIAL HISTORY OF MICHIGAN INDIANS
M.T. Bussey, wit Legends by Simon Otto
Documentary. Illus. Photos. Michigan Indian Press, $15.95.

*AUNT MARY, TELL ME A STORY
as told by Mary Chiltoskey; 28 Cherokee legends & tales.
Grades 3 and up. Illus. 82 pp. Paper. Cherokee Publications, $4.95.

AUTHENTIC ALASKA: VOICES OF ITS NATIVE WRITERS
Susan B. Andrews & John Creed; Collection of essays and stories.
Illus. Map. 180 pp. Paper. University of Nebraska Press, 1998. $16.95.

AUTHENTIC AMERICAN INDIAN BEADWORK & HOW TO USE IT
Pamela Stanley-Millner; Illus. 48 pp. Paper. Smoke & Fire Co., $4.95.

AUTHENTIC INDIAN DESIGNS
Maria Naylor; 2,500 illustrations from reports of the Bureau of American Ethnology. Reprint of 1975 edition. Illus. 219 pp. Paper. Hothem House, Written Heritage, $15.95.

*AUTHENTIC NORTH AMERICAN INDIAN CLOTHING FOR SPECIAL TIMES SERIES
Little Bears Go Visiting Series. Preschool -3. Arctic Circle; California; Columbia River Plateau; Columbia River Plateau Yakima; Great Basin; Oregon; Pacific Northwest Coast; Plains; Southeast; Southwest; and Woodlands. See Amazon.com.

*AUTHENTIC NORTH AMERICAN INDIAN INDIAN CRADLEBOARDS
Baby Bears Go Visiting Series. Columbia River Plateau & California; Great Basin, Southeast and Southwest; Pacific Northwest Coast, Woodlands & Arctic Circle; and Plains. Amazon.com.

AUTOBIOGRAPHY OF RED CLOUD: WAR LEADER OF THE OGLALAS
R. Eli Paul; Illus. 240 pp. Paper. Montana Historical Society Press, 1999. $15.95.

THE AUTOBIOGRAPHY OF A WINNEBAGO INDIAN
Paul Radin; Reprint of 1920 edition. 91 pp. Paper. Dover, $4.95.

AUTOBIOGRAPHY OF A YAQUI POET
Refugio Savala; Kathleen M. Sands, Editor
Yaqui culture. 228 pp. Paper. University of Arizona Press, 1980. $22.95.

AVENGING THE PEOPLE: ANDREW JACKSON, THE RULE OF LAW, AND THE AMERICAN NATION J.M. Opal; Oxford University Press, 2017. $29.95.

AWAY FROM HOME: AMERICAN INDIAN BOARDING SCHOOL EXPERIENCES, 1879-2000 Margaret Archuleta, K. Tsianina Lomawaima & Brenda Child, Eds.
Illus. Photos. 144 pp. Paper. Heard Museum, 2000. Also available
from the Museum of New Mexico Press, $29.95.

NANCY AZARA: SACRED DWELLINGS: THE WORK OF NANCY AZARA
Flavia Bando & Arlene Raven
Illus. 32 pp. Paper. Tweed Museum of Art, University of Minnesota, Duluth, 1994. $10.

B

B STREET: GRAND COULEE DAM'S WORKING STIFFS & PRETTY LADIES
Lawney Reyes; The history & culture of Native Americans whose way of life was irrevocably altered by the dam. Illus. 144 pp. University of Washington Press, 2008.

*BABY RATTLESNAKE
told by Te Ata; adapted Lynn Moroney; Grades K-6. Illus. Childrens Press, $13.95.

BACAVI: A HOPI VILLAGE
Peter Whitely; 144 pp. Paper. Northlan, 1988. $14.95.

THE BACKBONE OF HISTORY
Richard H. Steckel & Jerome C. Rose, Eds.
Illus. 650 pp. Cambridge University Press, 2002. $75.

BACKGROUND OF TREATY-MAKING IN WESTERN WASHINGTON
Barbara Lane; 32 pp. Institute for the Development of Indian Law, $15.

BACONE INDIAN UNIVERSITY
Howard Meredith & John Williams
A history of the nation's oldest continuing Indian institution of higher learning from 1880 to 1980. Illus. 163 pp. Indian University Press, 1980. $14, postpaid.

BACK TO THE BLANKET: RECOVERED RHETORICS & LITERACIES IN AMERICAN INDIAN STUDIES
Kimberly G. Wieser; Illus. 264 pp. University of Oklahoma Press, 2017. $39.95.

BACKWARD: AN ESSAY ON INDIANS, TIME & PHOTOGRAPHY
Will Baker; Illus. 420 pp. North Atlantic, 1983. $24.95; paper, $12.95.

BAD FRUITS OF THE CIVILIZED TREE: ALCOHOL & THE SOVEREIGNTY OF THE CHEROKEE NATION Izumi Ishii; 278 pp. University of Nebraska Press, 2008. $45.

BAD GIRL & THE MAN WHO FOLLOWED THE SUN: AN ATHABASKAN INDIAN LEGEND FROM ALASKA Velma Wallis; Illus. 224 pp. Paper. Amazon.com, 1997. $12.95.

BAD MEDICINE & GOOD: TALES OF THE KIOWAS
Wilbur S. Nye; Illus. Maps. 320 pp. Paper. University of Oklahoma Press, 1997. $24.95.

BAD MEN & BAD TOWNS
Wayne C. Lee; Chronicles the violent events in Nebraska from 1823-1925, including Indian conflicts. Illus. paper. The Caxton Press, 1994. $14.95.

BADGER & COYOTE WERE NEIGHBORS: MELVILLE JACOBS ON NORTHWEST INDIAN MYTHS & TALES William R. Seaburg & Pamela T. Amoss, Eds.
Illus. 310 pp. Paper. Oregon State University Press, 2000. $22.95.

***A BAG OF BONES: LEGENDS OF THE WINTU INDIANS
OF NORTHERN CALIFORNIA**
Marcelle Masson; Grades 4 and up. Illus. Illus. 130 pp. Paper. Naturegraph, 1966. $8.95.

BAGS OF FRIENDSHIP: BANDOLIER BAGS OF THE GREAT LAKES INDIANS
Richard Pohrt, Jr. & David Penney; Illus. 32 pp. Paper. Amazon.com, 1996. $20.

BALEEN BASKETRY OF THE NORTH ALASKAN ESKIMO
Molly Lee; Illus. 96 pp. Paper. University of Washington Press, 1998. 19.95

BANDELIER NATIONAL MONUMENT
Patricia Barey; History of Bandelier canyons & mesas of the Pajarito Plateau
in northern New Mexico. Color photos. 48 pp. Paper. Amazon.com, $7.95.

*DENNIS BANKS: NATIVE AMERICAN ACTIVIST
Karyn Cheatham; Grades 6 and up. Illus. 112 pp. Amazon.com, 1997. $19.95.

THE BANNOCK OF IDAHO
Brigham D. Madsen; Study of the Bannock Tribe of southern Idaho, exploring broken
U.S. Government agreements. Illus. 390 pp. Paper. University of Idaho Press, $15.95.

MARIUS BARBEAU'S PHOTOGRAPHIC COLLECTION: THE NASS RIVER
Linda Riley, Editor; 294 photos. Map. Paper. U. of Washington Press, 1988. $19.95.

BARK CANOES: THE ART & OBSESSION OF TAPPAN ADNEY
John Jennings; Illus. 152 pp. Amazon.com, 2004. $35.

THE BARK CANOES & SKIN BOATS OF NORTH AMERICA
Edwin Adney & Howard Chapelle
Reprint of 1964 second edition. Illus. 242 pp. Paper. Smithsonian Institution Press, $29.95.

**BARTERING WITH THE BONES OF THEIR DEAD: THE COLVILLE CONFEDERATED
TRIBES & TERMINATION**
Laurie Arnold; Illus. Maps. 208 pp. Paper. University of Washington Press, 2015. $25.

WILLIAM BARTRAM ON THE SOUTHEASTERN INDIANS
edited by Gregory A. Waselkov & Kathryn E. Holland Braund
Illus. Maps. 343 pp. Paper. University of Nebraska Press, 1995. $25.

BASHFUL NO LONGER: AN ALASKAN ESKIMO ETHNOHISTORY, 1778-1988
W.H. Oswalt; Illus. Maps. 270 pp. University of Oklahoma Press, 1990. $24.95.

BASIC CALL TO CONSCIOUSNESS
Edited by Akwesasne Notes; foreword by Chief Oren Lyons; intro. by John Mohawk; new
material by Jose Barreiro; Revised edition featuring leaders of the Six Nations Iroquois
discuss the importance of honoring the sacred Web of Life and describe the spiritual roots
of the traditional lifestyle. Illus. Photos. 160 pp. Paper. The Book Publishing Co., $11.95.

BASIC GUIDE TO INDIAN COMMUNITY ADVOCACY
Institute for the Development of Indian Law, $7.50.

BASIC MEDICAL NAVAJO
Alan Wilson; 141 pp. Paper. Jeffrey Norton Publishers, 1992. Unabridged ed.,
$39.95, includes audiocassette. Paper. $18.95.

BASIN-PLATEAU ABORIGINAL SOCIOPOLITICAL GROUPS
Julian H. Steward; Ethnographic study of the Western Shoshoni and some of their
Northern Paiute, Ute, & Southern Paiute neighbors. Paper. U. of Utah Press, $19.95.

**BASKET TALES OF THE GRANDMOTHERS: AMERICAN INDIAN BASKETS IN MYTH
& LEGEND** William & Sarah Turnbaugh; Illus. 210 pp. Paper. Amazon.com, 1999. $29.95.

**BASKET WEAVERS FOR THE CALIFORNIA CURIO TRADE: ELIZABETH & LOUISE
HICKOX** Marvin Cohodas; Illus. 362 pp. University of Arizona Press, 1997. $45.

THE BASKET WOMAN
Mary H. Austin; Reprint. 222 pp. Classic Books, 1998. $88.

BASKETMAKER CAVES IN PRAYER ROCK DISTRICT, NORTHEASTERN ARIZONA
Elizabeth A. Morris; 158 pp. Paper. University of Arizona Press, 1980. $13.95.

BASKETRY
F.J. Christopher; Covers selection of material, patterns and weaving procedures
are explained and illustrated. 130 pp. Paper. Cherokee Publications, $2.95.

BASKETRY & CORDAGE FROM HESQUIAT HARBOUR
Kathryn Bernick; Illus. 160 pp. paper. UBC Press, 1998. $14.95.

BASKETRY OF THE INDIANS OF CALIFORNIA
Christopher L. Moser; 3 vols. Northern ($30), Southern ($45) & Central ($30). 300+ pp.
each. Paper. Riverside Museum Press, 1986, 1989 & 1993. 3 Vol. set, $130.

BASKETRY OF THE PAPAGO & PIMA INDIANS
Mary Lois Kissell; Reprint of 1916 edition. Illus. 158 pp. Rio Grande Press, $15.

BASKETRY OF THE SAN CARLOS APACHE INDIANS
Helen H. Roberts; Reprint of 1929 edition. Illus. 105 pp. Paper. Rio Grande Press, $10.

BASKETRY PLANTS USED BY WESTERN AMERICAN INDIANS
Justin Farmer; Specifics ae given for 57 Western American tribes. Illus.
Photos. 244 pp. Paper. Naturegraph Publishers, $19.95.

BATTLE AT SAND CREEK: THE MILITARY PERSPECTIVE
Gregory F. Michno; Amazon.com, 2004. $45.

BATTLE CANYON
Robert Hilgardner; Illus. 110 pp. Paper. Mid-America Publishing House, 1986. $8.95.

**BATTLE FOR THE BIA: G.E.E. LINDQUIST & THE MISSIONARY CRUSADE
AGAINST JOHN COLLIER** David W. Dailey; 216 pp. Paper. U. of Arizona Press, 2004.
$29.95.

BATTLE GROUNDS: THE CANADIAN MILITARY & ABORIGINAL LANDS
P. Whitney Lackenbauer; Canadian Government-First Nation Aboriginal interaction.
384 pp. Paper. University of Washington Press, 2006. $29.95.

THE BATTLE OF BEECHER ISLAND & THE INDIAN WAR OF 1867-1869
John J. Monnett; Illus. 248 pp. Paper. University Press of Colorado, 1993. $24.95.

BATTLE OF THE LOXAHATCHEE RIVER: THE SEMINOLE WAR
John B. Wolf; Illus. 32 pp. Paper. Florida Classics, 1996. $2.95.

BATTLE OF THE LITTLE BIGHORN
Mari Sandoz; Illus. Maps. 191 pp. Paper. Amazon.com, 1978. $7.95.

BATTLE OF THE ROSEBUD: PRELUDE TO THE LITTLE BIGHORN
Neil C. Mangum; Illus. 200 pp. Amazon.com, 1987. $35.

BATTLE ROCK, THE HERO'S STORY
Bert & Margie Webber, Editors; A true account-Oregon Coast Indian attack.
Illus. Maps. Biblio. 75 pp. Paper. Webb Research Group, $8.95.

**BATTLEFIELD & CLASSROOM: FOUR DECADES WITH THE AMERICAN INDIAN,
1867-1904** Richard H. Pratt; Robert Utley, Editor; foreword by David W. Adams
Pratt's meoirs about the carlisle Indian school which he founded in the late 1800s.
Originally published in 1964. Illus. Maps. 416 pp. Paper. U. of Oklahoma Press,
2004. $24.95.

***BATTLEFIELDS & BURIAL GROUNDS: THE INDIAN STRUGGLE TO PROTECT
ANCESTRAL GRAVES IN THE U.S.** Roger C. Echohawk & Walter R. Echohawk
Examines the historical & cultural roots behind the double standard perpetuated by
American society. Grades 7+. Illus. Photos. 80 pp. Lerner, 1993. $22.60; paper, $9.95.

BATTLES & LEADERS: THE INDIAN WARS EAST OF THE MISSISSIPPI
Michael A. Hughes; Illus. 210 pp. Paper. Amazon.com, 1999. $11.95.

BATTLES OF THE RED RIVER WAR
J. Brett Cruse. Texas A&M University Press, $40.

**BATTLES & SKIRMISHES OF THE GREAT SIOUX WAR, 1876-1877:
THE MILITARY VIEW** Jerome A. Greene, Editor
Illus. Maps. 256 pp. Paper. University of Oklahoma Press, 1993. $14.95.

**BAWAAJIMO: A DIALECT OF DREAMMS IN ANISHINAABE
LANGUAGE & LITERATURE** Margaret Noodin
234 pp. Paper. Michigan State University Press, 2014. $$29.95; eBook, $23.95.

BAY MILLS INDIAN COMMUNITY LAND CLAIMS SETTLEMENT ACT
U.S. Senate Committee Indian Affairs; 107th Congress, Second Session. USGPO. 2003.

**BAYONETS IN THE WILDERNESS: ANTHONY WAYNE'S LEGION IN THE
OLD NORTHWEST** Alan D. Gaff; How the U.S. Army conquered the first American
frontier, the 1790s Indian confederacy of the Ohio River Valley. Illus. Maps. 416 pp.
University of Oklahoma Press, 2004. $39.95.

BAYOU SALADO
Virginia M. Simmons; Illus. 280 pp. Paper. Century One, 1982. $8.95.

BE BRAVE, TAH-HY!: THE JOURNEY OF CHIEF JOSEPH'S DAUGHTER
Jack R. Williams; illus. by o Proferes
Illus. 136 pp. Paper. WSU Press, 2012. $29.95.

**BE DAZZLED! MASTERWORKS OF JEWELRY & BEADWORK
FROM THE HEARD MUSEUM** Gail Bird; Illus. 80 pp. The Heard Museum, 2001.

BE OF GOOD MIND: ESSAYS ON THE COAST SALISH
Bruce Granville Miller, Editor; Illus. Photos. Maps. University of Washington Press
& Amazon.com, 2008. $94; paper, $37.95.

BEAD ON AN ANTHILL: A LAKOTA CHILDHOOD
Delphine Red Shirt; 146 pp. Paper. University of Nebraska Press. 1997. $13.95.

*THE BEADED MOCCASINS
Lynda Durant; Grades 5-8. 185 pp. Amzon.com, 1998. $15.

BEADING IN THE NATIVE AMERICAN TRADITION
David K. Dean; Learn beadwork techniques passed down from generations of Native
Americans in this complete history opf native beadwork. Illus. 160 pp. Paper. Amazon.com
2002. $24.95. Written Heritage, $19.95.

**BEADS & BEADWORK OF THE AMERICAN INDIAN: A STUDY BASED ON
SPECIMENS IN THE MUSEUM OF THE AMERICAN INDIAN, HEYE FOUNDATION**
William C. Orchard
2nd revised edition. Illus. 168 pp. Paper. Eagle's View Publishing, 2000. $16.95.

BEADS TO BUCKSKINS
Peggy Sue Henry; Annual from 1989. Illus. 96 pp. each. Paper. Beads to Buckskins,
Vol. 1-9, $10.95 each; Vol. 10 and up, $12.95 each.

A BEADWORK COMPANION
Jean Heinbuch; Step-by-step, illustrated projects designed to teach Native American beadwork. Illus. 112 pp. Paper. Eagle's View Publishing,1992. $12.95.

BEADWORK TECHNIQUES OF THE NATIVE AMERICAN
Scott Sutton; Instruction & explanation of loom beadwork, groud stitch, applique & moccasin making. Illus. 323 full color photos. 96 pp. Paper. Written Heritage, $19.95.

BEADWORKING WITH TODAY'S MATERIALS
Loren & Donna Woerpel; Illus. Photos. Paper. Written Heritage, $6.95.

BEAR CHIEF'S WAR SHIRT
James W. Schultz and Wilbur Betts; Illus. 240 pp. Paper. Mountain Press, 1984. $8.95.

BEAR HEART: THE HEIRSHIP CHRONICLES
Gerald Vizenor; Sentiments of Manifest Destiny. 260 pp. U. of Minnesota Press, 1990. $24.95; paper, $12.95.

BEAR ISLAND: THE WAR AT SUGAR POINT
Gerald Vizenor
Recounts the "last Indian war" in verse. 112 pp. U. of Minnesota Press, 2006. $19.95.

THE BEAR KNIFE: AND OTHER AMERICAN INDIAN TALES
Ruth-Ing Heinze; Illus. 176 pp. Paper. Amazon.com, 1994. $19.95.

THE BEAR RIVER MASSACRE
Newell Hart; Illus. 300 pp. Cache Valley, 1982. $35.

THE BEAR RIVER MASSACRE & THE MAKING OF HISTORY
Kass Fleisher; Illus. 352 pp. SUNY Press, 2004. $71.50; paper, $23.95.

THE BEAR SHAMAN TRADITION OF SOUTHERN CALIFORNIA INDIANS
Cheryl Hinton; Amazon.com, 2002.

*THE BEAR THAT TURNED WHITE; & OTHER NATIVE TALES
Maurine Grammer, retold by
Stories with messages intended to teach young people about various aspects of Native American culture or tradition. Grades 4-10. Illus. 108 pp. Amazon.com, $11.95.

THE BEAR TRIBE'S SELF-RELIANCE BOOK
Sun Bear, Wabun & Nimimosha; Contains Native American philosophy, legends and prophecy. Illus. 202 pp. Paper. Prentice Hall Press, 1989. $8.95.

THE BEARER OF THIS LETTER: LANGUAGE IDEOLOGIES, LITERACY PRACTICES, AND THE FORT BELKNAP INDIAN COMMUNITY
Mindy J. Morgan; Maps. 328 pp. University of Nebraska Press, 2009. $50.

JOHN BEARGREASE: LEGEND OF MINNESOTA'S NORTH SHORE
Daniel Lancaster; Native American history in Minn. Paper. Holy Cow! Press, 2008. $14.95.

THE BEAUTIFUL & THE DANGEROUS: ENCOUNTERS WITH THE ZUNI INDIANS
Barbara Tedlock; Illus. 352 pp. Paper. University of New Mexico Press, $27.95.

*BEAUTY BESIDE ME, STORIES OF MY GRANDMOTHER'S SKIRTS
Seraphine G. Yazzie; illus. by Baje Whitethorne, Sr.; narration by Elsie E. Carr
Grades K-5. Illus. Amazon.com, 2008. with CD watercolor. $21.95.

BEAUTY FROM THE EARTH: PUEBLO INDIAN POTTERY FROM THE UNIVERSITY MUSEUM OF ARCHAEOLOGY & ANTHROPOLOGY
J.J. Brody & Rebecca Allen; Illus. 85 pp. University Museum Publications, 1990. $19.95.

BEAUTY, HONOR & TRADITION: THE LEGACY OF PLAINS INDIAN SHIRTS
Joseph D. Horse Capture & George P. Horse Capture
Illus. 160 pp. Paper. University of Minnesota Press, 2001. $34.95.

THE BEAUTY OF HOPI JEWELRY
Theda Bassman; 2nd Ed. reprint.Illus. 64 pp. Kiva Publishing, $14.95.

THE BEAUTY OF THE PRIMITIVE: SHAMANISM & WESTERN IMAGINATION
Andrei A. Znamenski; Oxford University Press, 2007. $54.

BEAVER STEALS FIRE / FIRE ON THE LAND
Confed. Salish & Kootenai Tribe; 2 DVD educational set. showcasing the Salish & Pend d'Oreille tribes of the Flathead Indian Reservation in Montana explaining the traditional & contemporary uses of fire by American Indians. Companion to the book, Beaver Steals Fire; second disc provides a reading in Salish & English of the book, interviews with elders, a primer on fire ecology, etc. University of Nebraska Press, 2007. $19.95.

BEAVER STEALS FIRE: A SALISH COYOTE STORY
Confed. Salish & Kootenai Tribe; illus. by Sam Sandoval
Grades 3 and up. Illus. 64 pp. Paper. University of Nebraska Press, 2008. $12.95.

JIM BECKWOURTH: BLACK MOUNTAIN MAN & WAR CHIEF OF THE CROWS
Elinor Wilson; Reprint 1972 ed. Illus. maps. Biblio. 248 pp. U. of Oklahoma Press, $14.95.

BECOMING BRAVE: THE PATH TO NATIVE AMERICAN MANHOOD
Laine Thom, Editor; Illus. 120 pp. Paper. Amazon.com, 1992. $18.95.

BECOMING BROTHERTOWN: NATIVE AMERICAN ETHNOGENESIS & ENDURANCE IN THE MODERN WORLD
Craig N. Cipolla; Histories of New England covering the 18th century to the present. Combines historical archaeology, gravestone studies, and discourse analysis to tell the story of the Brothertown Indians. Illus. 240 pp. The University of Arizona Press, 2013. $50.

BECOMING INDIAN: THE STRUGGLE OVER CHEROKEE IDENTITY IN THE 21ST CENTURY Circe Sturm; Examines Cherokee Identity politics & the phenomenon of racial shifting, people who have changed their racial self-odentification from non-Indian to Indian on the U.S. census. Illus. 280 pp. Paper. School for Advanced Research, 2011. $27.95.

BECOMING & REMAINING A PEOPLE: NATIVE AMERICAN RELIGIONS ON THE NORTHERN PLAINS Howard L. Harrod; Religious developments of the Mandans & the Hidatsas. 149 pp. Paper. University of Arizona Press, 1995. $19.95.

BECOMING TSIMSHIAN: THE SOCIAL LIFE OF NAMES
Christopher F. Roth; Examines the way in which names link members of a lineage to the past for the Tsimshian people of coastal British Columbia. Illus. Map. 296 pp. University of Washington Press, 2008. $60; paper, $26.95.

BECOMING TWO-SPIRIT: GAY IDENTITY & SOCIAL ACCEPTANCE IN INDIAN COUNTRY Brian Joseph Gilley; 218 pp. Paper. U. of Nebraska Press, 2006. $16.95.

BEDBUGS' NIGHT DANCE & OTHER HOPI TALES OF SEXUAL ENCOUNTER
Ekkehart Malotki; Illus. 390 pp. Paper. University of Nebraska Press, 1995. $16.95.

JOHN BEESON'S PLEA FOR THE INDIANS, HIS LONE CRY IN THE WILDERNESS FOR INDIAN RIGHTS: OREGON'S FIRST CIVIL RIGHTS ADVOCATE
John Beeson; Illus. 176 pp. Paper. Webb Research Group Publishers, 1994. $12.95.

BEFORE & AFTER THE HORIZON: ANISHINAABE ARTISTS OF THE GREAT LAKES
David W. Penney & Gerald McMaster (Plans Cree); Illus. 128 pp. Paper. NMAI Press, 2013. $24.95.

BEFORE & AFTER JAMESTOWN: VIRGINIA'S POWHATANS & THEIR PREDECESSORS Helen C. Rountree & E. Randolph Turner; Surveys 1,000 years of Powhatan history. Illus. 272 pp. U. Press of Florida, 2002. $39.95; paper, $24.95.

BEFORE CALIFORNIA: AN ARCHAEOLOGIST LOOKS AT OUR EARLIEST INHABITANTS Brian M. Fagan; Illus. 416 pp. Paper. AltaMira Press, 2004. $30.

*BEFORE CANADA: FIRST NATIONS & FIRST CONTACTS: PREHISTORY - 1523: HOW CANADA BECAME CANADA
Sheila Nelson; Grades 6-9. Illus. 87 pp. Paper. Mason Crest Publishers, 2006. $19.95.

*BEFORE COLUMBUS
Muriel Batherman; Daily life of earliest inhabitants, based on archaeological findings. Focus on Pueblos. Grades 5-9. Illus. Paper. Amazon.com 1990. $4.95.

*BEFORE COLUMBUS: THE AMERICAS OF 1491
Charles C. Mann; Grades 5-9. Illus. 117 pp. Paper. Atheneum Books, 2009. $12.95.

BEFORE THE COUNTRY: NATIVE RENAISSANCE, CANADIAN MYTHOLOGY
Stephanie McKenzie; University of Toronto Press, 2010. $64; paper, $29.95.

BEFORE THE GREAT SPIRIT: THE MANY FACES OF SIOUX SPIRITUALITY
Julian Rice; Illus. 175 pp. University of New Mexico Press, $45; paper, $22.50.

BEFORE THE HORSE: INDIAN MYTHS & LEGENDS
H. Lee Mason; Illus. 72 pp. Arc Press, 1999. $37.50.

BEFORE THE LONG KNIVES CAME
Millie House; Illus. 94 pp. Amazon.com, 1987.

BEFORE MAN IN MICHIGAN
R. Ray Baker; Reprint. Paper. George Wahr Publishing, $12.50.

BEFORE SANTA FE
Jason S. Shapiro; foreword by Frances Levine; Examines Santa Fe's pre-Hispanic past over 12,000 years, from earliest Paleoindians, Puebloi occupation, up to Spanish Entrada. Illus. Maps. Museum of New Mexico Press, 2010. $39.95.

*BEFORE THE STORM: AMERICAN INDIANS BEFORE COLUMBUS
Allison Lassieur; Grades 6-12. Illus. Maps. 160 pp. Facts on File, 1998. $25.

BEFORE THE WILDERNESS: ENVIRONMENTAL MANAGEMENT BY NATIVE CALIFORNIANS Tom Blackburn & Kat Anderson; Includes the full text of Patterns of Indian Burning. Reprint. Illus. 476 pp. Paper. Malki-Ballena Press, 1993. $32.50.

BEGINNING BLACK INDIAN HISTORY & GENEALOGY - THE CHEROKEES
Gloria L. Smith; 56 pp. Paper. Trailstones Heritage Adventures, 1995. $12.50.

BEGINNING BLACK INDIAN HISTORY & GENEALOGY - THE SEMINOLES
Gloria L. Smith; Revised ed. 76 pp. Paper. Trailstones Heritage Adventures, 1994. $14.

BEGINNING CHEROKEE
Ruth Bradley Holmes & Betty Sharp Smith; A Cherokee language grammar. 2nd edition. Illus. 346 pp. paper. U. of Oklahoma Press, 1977. $32.95. Set of two cassettes, $25.

BEGINNING CREEK: MVSKOKE EMPONVKV
Pamela Innes, Linda Alexander, Bertha Tilkens
Basic intriduction to the language and culture of the Muskogee (Creek) & Seminole Indians. Illus. Tables. 256 pp. Paper. University of Oklahoma Press, 2004. $32.95.

BEGINNING & END OF RAPE: CONFRONTING SEXUAL VIOLENCE IN NATIVE AMERICA Sarah Deer; University of Minnesota Press, 2015. $80.50; paper, $22.95.

BEGINNING WASHO
William H. Jacobsen, Jr.; Amazon.com, 1996.

BEGINNINGS – A MEDITATION ON COAST SALISH LIFEWAYS
Patrick J. Twohy; Paper. Amazon.com, 2003. $12.98.

BEHIND THE FRONTIER: INDIANS IN 18TH CENTURY EASTERN MASSACHUSETTS
Daniel R. Mandell; Illus. Maps. 257 pp. Paper. U. of Nebraska Press, 1996. $19.95.

BEHIND THE TRAIL OF BROKEN TREATIES: AN INDIAN DECLARATION OF INDEPENDENCE Vine Deloria, Jr.; Historical review of Indian political recognition and land title with respect to other nations. 310 pp. Paper. U. of Texas Press, 1985. $25.

BEING & BECOMING INDIAN: BIOGRAPHICAL STUDIES OF NORTH AMERICAN FRONTIERS James A. Clifton, Editor; Reprint. 337 pp. Paper. Waveland Press, 1993. $22.95.

BEING COMANCHE: A SOCIAL HISTORY OF AN AMERICAN INDIAN COMMUNITY
Morris W. Foster; Won the 1992 Erminie Wheeler-Voegelin Prize of the American Society of Ethnohistory. 230 pp. Illus. Paper. University of Arizona Press, 1991. $19.95.

BEING COWLITZ: HOW ONE TRIBE RENEWED & SUSTAINED ITS IDENTITY
Christine Dupres; Illus. 176 pp. University of Washington Press, 2015. $50.

BEING DAKOTA: TALES & TRADITIONS OF THE SISSETON & WAHPETON
Amos Oneroad & Alanson Skinner
Illus. 225 pp. Minnesota Historical Society Press, 2003. $29.95.

BEING IN BEING: THE COLLECTED WORKS OF SKAAY OF THE QQUUNA QIIGHAWAAY Robert Bringhurst, Editor & trans.
Haida myth. Illus. Map. 397 pp. University of Nebraska Press, 2002. $37.95.

BEING LAKOTA: IDENTITY & TRADITION ON PINE RIDGE RESERVATION
Larissa Petrillo with Melda & Lupe Trejo
Illus. Maps. 176 pp. University of Nebraska Press, 2007. $35.

BEING & PLACE AMONG THE TLINGIT
Thomas E. Thornton; Culture, Place & Nature. Illus. Maps. 280 pp. Paper. U. of Washington Press, 2007. $24.95.

BEING & VIBRATION
Joseph Rael & Mary E. Marlow; A Native American visionary shares information on the rise of human consciousness. Illus. 225 pp. Paper. Council Oak Books, 1993. $15.

BEING INDIAN IS: THE HUMOR OF REUBEN SNAKE
Reuben Snake
Humorous sayings from Reuben. Illus. 64 pp. Paper. Native Voices, 2007. $9.95.

BELIEF & WORSHIP IN NATIVE NORTH AMERICA
Ake Hultkrantz; Christopher Vecsey, Editor; 358 pp. Syracuse U. Press, 1981. $30.

BELIEFS & HOLY PLACES: A SPIRITUAL GEOGRAPHY OF THE PIMERIA ALTA
James S. Griffith; The Tohono O'odham, their places and traditions are covered. 218 pp. Paper. University of Arizona Press, 1992. $19.95.

BELLA BELLA: A SEASON OF HEILTSUK ART
Martha Black; Illus. 224 pp. Paper. University of Washington Press, 1997. $40.

THE BELLA COOLA INDIANS
T.F. McIlwraith; 2nd Edition. 2,750 pp. 2 vols. Paper. University of Toronto Press, 1992.

THE BELLA COOLA VALLEY: HARLAN I. SMITH'S FIELDWORK PHOTOGRAPHS, 1920-1924
Leslie H. Tepper; Illus. 256 pp. Paper. University of Washington Press, 1991. $24.95.

*BELLE HIGHWALKING: THE NARRATIVE OF A NORTHERN CHEYENNE WOMAN
Katheryne Weist, Editor
Grades 5-12. 66 pp. Council for Indian Education, 1979. $9.95; paper, $3.95.

BELOVED CHILD: A DAKOTA WAY OF LIFE
Diane Wilson; Illus. 224 pp. Paper. Minnesota Historical Society Press, 2017. $17.95.

BENDING TRADITION
Exhibiton catalog featuring traditional & contemporary bentwood containers, Aleut headgear and sculptures. Illus. 48 pp. Institute of Alaska Native Arts, 1990. $12.50, postpaid.

BENEATH THESE RED CLIFFS: AN ETHNOHISTORY OF THE UTAH PAIUTES
Ronald L Holt; foreword by Lora Tom; Recounts the survival of a people against all odds. Illus. 214 pp. Paper. Utah State University Press, 2005. $23.95.

THE BENTEEN-GOLDIN LETTERS ON CUSTER & HIS LAST BATTLE
John M. Carroll; Illus. Paper. Amazon.com, 1985. $18.95.

*THE BENTWOOD BOX
Nan McNutt; Grades 3-8. Illus. 35 pp. Paper. N. McNutt Associates, 1989. $9.95.

O.E. BERNINGHAUS - TAOS, N.M., MASTER PAINTER OF AMERICAN INDIANS AND FRONTIER WEST Gordon E. Sanders
Illus. 152 pp. Taos Heritage Press, 1985. $40.

BEST OF THE BEST - INDIAN ARTIFACTS OF THE DEEP SOUTH
Prehistoric artifacts of the Southeast including chipped points and blades, stone artifacts and pottery. Color photos. 220 pp. Hothem House, 1998. $60; paper, $24.95.

BETRAYING THE OMAHA NATION, 1870-1916
Judith A. Boughter; Illus. 304 pp. University of Oklahoma Press, 1998. $27.95.

A BETTER KIND OF HATCHET: LAW, TRADE, DIPLOMACY IN CHEROKEE NATION
John P. Reid; 262 pp. Penn State University Press, 1975. $27.50.

BETWEEN CONTACTS & COLONIES: ARCHAEOLOGICAL PERSPECTIVES ON THE PROTOHISTORIC SOUTHEAST Cameron B. Wesson & Mark A. Rees, Editor
Illus. 344 pp. University of Alabama Press, $57.50; paper, $29.95.

*BETWEEN EARTH & SKY - LEGENDS OF NATIVE AMERICAN SACRED PLACES
Joseph Bruchac; illus. by Thomas Locker; A young boy learns that everything living and inanimate has its place, should be considered sacred, and given respect. Grades 3-6. Meadowlark Communications, $16; paper, $7.

BETWEEN INDIAN & WHITE WORLDS: THE CULTURAL BROKER
Margaret Connell Szasz; 14 portraits of cultural brokers between the Indians & non-Indians. Illus. Maps. Biblio. 450 pp. Paper. University of Oklahoma Press, 1994. $19.95.

BETWEEN JUSTICE & CERTAINTY: TREATY MAKING IN BRITISH COLUMBIA
Andrew Woolford; 248 pp. University of Washington Press, 2005. $105; paper, $37.95.

BETWEEN TWO CULTURES: KIOWA ART FROM FORT MARION
Moira F. Harris; with Rodney C. Loehr; Reproduction of the drawings by Wo-Haw completed during his imprisonment. Illus. 148 pp. Amazon.com, 1989. $39.95.

BETWEEN WORLDS: INTERPRETERS, GUIDES, & SURVIVORS
Frances Karttunen; Tells the story of 16 men & women who served as interpreters & guides to explorers, soldiers, missionaries, and conquerors. Includes the stories of Sacajawea, Sarah Winnemucca, Charles Eastman, & Ishi. Rutgers U. Press, 1994. $24.95.

BEYOND BEAR'S PAW: THE NEZ PERCE INDIANS IN CANADA
Jerome A. Greene; Illus. Map. 264 pp. University of Oklahoma Press, 2010. $24.95.

BEYOND BOUNDS: CROSS-CULTURAL ESSAYS ON ANGLO, AMERICANN INDIAN & CHICANO LITERATURE Robert Franklin Gish
170 pp. Paper. University of New Mexico Press, 1996. $24.95.

BEYOND CLOTH & CORDAGE: ARCHAEOLOGICAL TEXTILE RESEARCH IN THE AMERICAS Penelope B. Drooker & Laurie D. Webster, Eds.
Illus. 340 pp. University of Utah Press, 2000. $60.

BEYOND CONQUEST: NATIVE PEOPLES & THE STRUGGLE FOR HISTORY IN NEW ENGLAND Amy Den Ouden; University of Nebraska Press, 2005.

BEYOND THE COVENANT CHAIN: THE IROQUOIS & THEIR NEIGHBORS IN INDIAN NORTH AMERICA, 1600-1800 Daniel Richter & James Merrell, Editors
Illus. 232 pp. Paper. Pennsylvania State University Press, 2003. $19.95.

BEYOND THE FOUR CORNERS OF THE WORLD: NAVAJO WOMAN'S JOURNEY
Emily Benedek; Illus. 376 pp. Paper. University of Oklahoma Press, 1998. $14.95.

BEYOND THE COVENANT CHAIN: THE IROQUOIS & THEIR NEIGHBORS IN INDIAN NORTH AMERICA, 1600-1800 Daniel K. Richter
232 pp. Paper. Pennsylvania State University Press, 2003. $19.95.

BEYOND THE FRONTIER: EXPLORING THE INDIAN COUNTRY
Stan Hoag; Reprint. Illus. Maps. 352 pp. University of Oklahoma Press, $17.95.

BEYOND THE HUNDRETH MERIDIAN: JOHN WESLEY POWELL & THE SECOND OPENING OF THE WEST
Wallace Stegner; Exploration of the Colorado River, the Grand Canyon, and homeland of Indian tribes of the American Southwest. Illus. 464 pp. Paper. Penguin USA, $12.

BEYOND THE LODGE OF THE SUN: INNER MYSTERIES OF THE NATIVE AMERICAN WAY Chokecherry Gall Eagle; 272 pp. Paper. Amazon.com, 2003.

BEYOND PONTIAC'S SHADOW: MICHILLIMACKINAC & THE ANGLO-INDIAN WARS OF 1763
Keith R. Widder; 360 pp. Michigan State University Press, 2013. $49.95; eBook, $29.95.

BEYOND THE REACH OF TIME & CHANGE: NATIVE AMERICAN REFLECTIONS ON THE FRANK A. RINEHART PHOTOGRAPH COLLECTION
Frank A. Rinehart; Simon J. Ortiz, Editor
172 pp. University of Arizona Press, 2005. $50; paper, $24.95.

BEYOND RED POWER: AMERICAN INDIAN POLITICS & ACTIVISM SINCE 1900
Daniel M. Cobb & Loretta Fowler, Editors; Essays on the American Indians use of institutions & political rhetoric for their own ends since 1900. Illus. Tables. 368 pp. School for Advanced Research, 2007. $24.95.

BEYOND THE RESERVATION: INDIANS, SETTLERS, & THE LAW IN WASHINGTON TERRITORY, 1853-1889
Brad Asher; Maps. Biblio. 288 pp. University of Oklahoma Press, 1999. $34.95.

BEYOND THE RIVER & THE BAY: THE CANADIAN NORTHWEST IN 1811
Eric Ross; Illus. Paper. University of Toronto Press, 1970. $9.95.

BEYOND SUBSISTENCE: PLAINS ARCHAEOLOGY & THE POSTPROCESSUAL CRITIQUE Philip Duke & Michael Wilson; 320 pp. Paper. U. of Alabama Press, 1995. $35.

BEYOND TRADITION: CONTEMPORARY INDIAN ART & ITS EVOLUTION
Lois Jacka; photos pby Jerry Jacka
203 color photos. 216 pp. Northland, 1988. $40; paper, $20.

BEYOND THE VILLAGE: A COLONIAL PARKWAY GUIDE TO THE LOCAL INDIANS USE OF NATURAL RESOURCES Helen Rountree; Paper. Amazon.com, 1999. $3.95.

BEYOND THE VISION: ESSAYS ON AMERICAN INDIAN CULTURE
William K. Powers; Illus. 200 pp. University of Oklahoma Press, 1987. $37.95.

BEYOND WHITE ETHNICITY: DEVELOPING A SOCIOLOGICAL UNDERSTANDING OF NATIVE AMERICAN IDENTITY RECLAMATION Kathleen J. Fitzgerald
Monograph; Lexington Books, c/o Rowman & Littlefield, 2006. $90; paper, $34.99.

A BIBLIOGRAPHICAL GUIDE TO THE HISTORY OF INDIAN-WHITE RELATIONS IN THE U.S. Francis P. Prucha; Lists and discusses more than 9,000 items including materials in the National Archives. Paper. University of Chicago Press, 1977. $12.

BIBLIOGRAPHY: NATIVE AMERICAN ARTS & CRAFTS OF THE U.S.
A selection of books & pamphlets chosen and annotated for their pertinence to the field of contemporary Native American arts & crafts of the U.S. 8 pp. Indian Arts & Crafts Board.

A BIBLIOGRAPHY OF THE ATHAPASKAN LANGUAGES
Richard T. Parr; Paper. National Museum of Canada, $3.95.

BIBLIOGRAPHY OF THE BLACKFOOT
Hugh Dempsey & Lindsey Moir; Illus. 255 pp. Paper. Scarecrow Press, 2003. $41.25.

BIBLIOGRAPHY OF THE CATAWBA
Thomas J. Blumer; 575 pp. Scarecrow Press, 1987. $65.

BIBLIOGRAPHY OF THE CHICKASAW
Anne Kelley Hoyt; 230 pp. Scarecrow Press, 1987. $52.75.

BIBLIOGRAPHY OF THE CONSTITUTION & LAWS OF THE AMERICAN INDIANS
Lester Hargrett; Facs. ed. Illus. William S. Hein & Lawbook Exchange, Ltd., 2003. $95.

A BIBLIOGRAPHY OF CONTEMPORARY NORTH AMERICAN INDIANS: SELECTED & PARTIALLY ANNOTATED WITH STUDY GUIDES
William H. Hodge; intro. by Paul Prucha; 320 pp. Interland Publishing, 1976. $27.50.

BIBLIOGRAPHY OF THE ENGLISH COLONIAL TREATIES WITH THE AMERICAN INDIANS, INCLUDING A SYNOPSIS OF EACH TREATY Henry F. De Puy
Reprint. Illus. 110 pp. Lawbook Exchange, & Martino Publishing, 2001. $50.

BIBLIOGRAPHY OF THE INDIANS OF SAN DIEGO COUNTY: THE KUMEYAAY, DIEGUENO, LUISENO, AND CUPENO Phillip M. White & Stephen D. Fitt
Illus. 288 pp. Scarecrow Press, 1997. $77.

BIBLIOGRAPHY OF LANGUAGE ARTS MATERIALS FOR NATIVE NORTH AMERICANS, 1975-1976: WITH SUPPLEMENTAL ENTRIES FROM 1965-1974
G. Edward Evans, Karin Abbey & Dennis Reed
A list of language art materials for 1975-76 and earlier years to supplement the 1977 Bibliography. 120 pp. Paper. UCLA, American Indian Studies Center, 1977. $5.

BIBLIOGRAPHY OF LANGUAGE ARTS MATERIALS FOR NATIVE NORTH AMERICANS, BILINGUAL, ENGLISH AS A SECOND LANGUAGE & NATIVE LANGUAGE MATERIALS, 1965-1974 G. Edward Evans, Karin Abbey & Dennis Reed
A compilation of Native language and bilingual education sources. 283 pp. Paper. UCLA, American Indian Studies Center, 1977. $5.

BIBLIOGRAPHY OF LANGUAGES OF NATIVE CALIFORNIA: INCLUDING CLOSELY RELATED LANGUAGES OF ADJACENT AREAS
William Bright; 234 pp. Scarecrow Press, 1982. $47.30.

BIBLIOGRAPHY OF NATIVE AMERICAN BIBLIOGRAPHIES
Phillip M. White; 240 pp. Greenwood Publishing, 2004. $89.95.

BIBLIOGRAPHY OF NATIVE NORTH AMERICANS ON DISC - CD-ROM
Timothy O'Leary & M. Marlene Martin, Eds; The Human Relations Area File's Ethnographic Bibliography of North America. Semiannual. CD-ROM or Network. IBM compataible. Amazon.com, $1,045 for annual subscription for CD; $1,306 for one person.

BIBLIOGRAPHY OF NORTH AMERICAN INDIAN MENTAL HEALTH
Dianne Kelso and Carolyn Attneave, Editors
Illus. 404 pp. Greenwood Publishing, 1981. $46.95.

BIBLIOGRAPHY OF THE OSAGE
Terry P. Wilson; 172 pp. Scarecrow Press, 1985. $41.80.

BIBLIOGRAPHY OF THE SIOUX
Jack W. Marken & Herbert T. Hoover; 388 pp. Scarecrow Press, 1980. $47.30.

*THE BIG AMERICAN SOUTHWEST ACTIVITY BOOK
Walter C. Yoder, PhD; The Southwest multicultural environment. Grades 3 and up. Illus. 64 pp. Paper. Sunstone Press, $8.95.

BIG BEAR: THE END OF FREEDOM
Hugh A. Dempsey; Illus. 227 pp. Paper. University of Nebraska Press, 1985. $8.95.

BIG BOOK OF INDIAN BEADWORK DESIGNS
Kay D. Bennett; Illus. 80 pp. Dover Publications, 1999. $6.95.

BIG CYPRESS: A CHANGING SEMINOLE COMMUNITY
M. Garbarino; Spindler, Editors; 131 pp. Paper. Waveland, 1972. $8.50.

THE BIG MISSIONARY: A STORY OF ONE MAN'S COMPASSION FOR THE NAVAJO
Jack Drake; Patricia B. Young, Ed.; Paper. Amazon.com, 1997 $ 7.95.

BIG SISTER, LITTLE SISTER: AMERICAN INDIAN WOMEN'S STORIES
Jocelyn Riley; 114 pp. Paper. Amazon.com, 1995. $45. with VHS.

BIG SYCAMORE STANDS ALONE: THE WESTERN APACHES, ARAVAIPAI, AND THE STRUGGLE FOR PLACE Ian W. Record; Examines the evolving relationship between Western Apaches and the corner of Arizona and Aravaipai Canyon. 384 pp. University of Oklahoma Press, 2009. $29.95; paper, $19.95.

BIGHORSE THE WARRIOR
Tiana Bighorse; Noel Bennett, Editor; Stories of the sufferings of the Navajo people. 115 pp. Paper. The University of Arizona Press, 1990. $16.95.

*BILL RED COYOTE IS A NUT
Hap Gilliland; Grades 1-8. 32 pp. Paper. Council for Indian Education, 1981. $3.95.

*BILLY BLACKFEET IN THE ROCKIES: A STORY FROM HISTORY
Marc Simmons; illus. by Ronald Kil; Grades 5-6. Story of a boy of mixed ancestry who, during a hunting trip to the Montana mountains, discovers something about himself and his Indian heritage. Illus. 56 pp. Map. University of New Mexico Press, $19.95.

THE BINGO PALACE
Louise Erdrich; A novel of gaming & competetion dancing & traditional Anishinabe culture. HarperCollins, 1994.

BIOARCHAEOLOGY OF VIRGINIA BURIAL MOUNDS
Debra L. Gold
Illus. Maps. 176 pp. U. of Alabama Press, 2004. $65; paper, $34.95. E-Book available.

A BIOBIBLIOGRAPHY OF NATIVE AMERICAN WRITERS, 1772-1925: A SUPPLEMENT
Daniel F. Littlefield, Jr. & James W. Parsons; 350 pp. Scarecrow Press, 1985. $66.

BIODIVERSITY & NATIVE AMERICA
Paul E. Minnis; Illus. 310 pp. Paper. University of Oklahoma Press, 2002. $14.95.

BIOGRAPHICAL DICTIONARY OF AMERICAN INDIAN HISTORY TO 1900
Carl Waldman; Revised ed. Illus. 464 pp. Facts on File, 2001. $71.50; paper, $24.95.

BIOGRAPHICAL DICTIONARY OF INDIANS OF THE AMERICAS
Contains nearly 2,000 detailed biographies of significant Indians past & present, and over 900 portraits. 2nd ed. 2 vols. 882 pp. American Indian Publishers, 1998. $385 per set.

THE BIOGRAPHICAL DIRECTORY OF NATIVE AMERICAN PAINTERS
Patrick D. Lester, Editor; 700 pp. University of Oklahoma Press, 1995. $49.95.

BIOGRAPHICAL & HISTORICAL INDEX OF AMERICAN INDIANS & PERSONS INVOLVED IN INDIAN AFFAIRS U.S. Dept. of the Interior
Biographical material on Native Americans who were involved in any way with the U.S. government up to 1965. G.K. Hall, 1966.

BIOGRAPHICAL PORTRAITS OF 108 NATIVE AMERICANS: BASED ON HISTORY OF THE INDIAN TRIBES OF NORTH AMERICA
Marc Newman & Thomas L. McKenney; Illus. U.S. Games Systems, 1999. $12.

BIOGRAPHY & HISTORY OF THE INDIANS OF NORTH AMERICA
Samuel Adams Drake; Illus. 628 pp. Paper. Amazon.com, 1995. $38.50.

THE BIRCH: BRIGHT TREE OF LIFE & LEGEND
John L. Peyton; Illus. 74 pp. Paper. McDonald & Woodward Publishing, 1994, $9.95.

BIRCHBARK CANOE: LIVING AMONG THE ALGONQUIN
David Gidmark; Reprint. Illus. 202 pp. Paper. Amazon.com, 2003. $20.

BIRCHBARK CANOES OF THE FUR TRADE
Kent; Examination of watercraft of the North American fur trade era. Sketches, photos. 2 Vols. 670 pp. Paper. Hothem House, 1997. $50 per set.

*THE BIRCHBARK HOUSE
Louise Erdrich; The story of an Ojibwe family. Grades 4 and up. HarperCollins, 2003. Available on audio CD.

BIRD GIRL & THE MAN WHO FOLLOWED THE SUN: AN ATHABASKAN INDIAN LEGEND FROM ALASKA Velma Wallis; Illus. 224 pp. Amazon.com, 1996. $12.95.

BIRD WOMAN: SACAGAWEA'S OWN STORY
recorded by James Willard Schultz; Illus. 143 pp. Paper. Amazon.com, $11.95.

BIRDS, BEADS & BELLS: REMOTE SENSING OF A PAWNEE SACRED BUNDLE
Diane Good; Illus. 25 pp. Kansas State Historical Society, 1989. $7.95.

BIRDS OF ALGONQUIN LEGEND
Robert E. Nichols, Jr.; illus. by Linda Hoffman Kimball
Illus. 168 pp. University of Michigan Press, 1996. $44.95.

THE BIRTH OF AMERICA
R.F. Locke; Amazon.com, $1.75.

BISON CULTURAL TRADITIONS OF THE NORTHERN PLAINS
Lauren M. McKeever; A report on the bison cultural presentationnn June 17, 1993 at Ethete, Wyoming on the Wind River Indian Reservation. Booklet. The InterTribal Bison Cooperative, 1993.

BISON & PEOPLE OF THE NORTH AMERICAN GREAT PLAINS
Geoff Cunfer & Bill Walser, Editors; Texas A&M University Press, $60.

BITTER FEAST: AMERINDIANS & EUROPEANS IN NORTHEASTERN NORTH AMERICA, 1600-1664
Denys Delage; Illus. 415 pp. Paper. University of Washington Press, 1993. $35.95.

BITTER WATER: DINE ORAL HISTORIES OF THE NAVAJO-HOPI LAND DISPUTE
Malcolm D. Benally, Editor & Translator; Narratives of four Dine women who have resisted removal. 136 pp. Paper. University of Arizona Press, 2011. $19.95.

BITTERNESS ROAD: THE MOJAVE, 1604-1860
Lorraine Sherer; Sylvia Vane & Lowell Bean, Editors
126 pp. Paper. Ballena Press, 1995. $13.95.

BITTERROOT CROSSING: LEWIS & CLARK ACROSS THE LOLO TRAIL
Gene & Mollie Eastman; Illus. Maps. 80 pp. Paper. University of Idaho Press, 2007. $12.

BITTERSWEET
Mary Summer Rain; Illus. 260 pp. Paper. Hampton Roads Publishing, 1995. $12.95.

BLACK, BROWN & RED: THE MOVEMENT FOR FREEDOM AMONG BLACK, CHICANO, LATINO & INDIAN
John Alan, Editor; Illus. 78 pp. Paper. News & Letters, $9.95.

BLACK ELK & FLAMING RAINBOW: PERSONAL MEMORIES OF THE LAKOTA HOLY MAN & JOHN NEIHARDT Hilda Neihardt
Illus. Map. 158 pp. Paper. University of Nebraska Press, 1995. $15.95.

BLACK ELK: HOLY MAN OF THE OGLALA
Michael F. Steltenkamp; Portrays the Sioux spiritual leader as a victim of Western subjugation. Illus. 240 pp. Maps. U. of Oklahoma Press, 1993. $22.95; paper, $11.95.

BLACK ELK LIVES: CONVERSATIONS WITH THE BLACK ELK FAMILY
Esther Black Elk DeSersa, Olivia Black Elk Pouier, et al.
Description of the lives of the grandchildren and great grandchildren of the Lakota holy man. Illus. 176 pp. University of Nebraska Press, 2000. $25; paper, $12.95.

*BLACK ELK: A MAN WITH VISION
Carol Greene; Grades K-3. Illus. 50 pp. Childrens Press, 1990. $11.95.

THE BLACK ELK READER
Clyde Holler, Editor; Illus. 370 pp. Paper. Syracuse University Press, $24.95.

NICHOLAS BLACK ELK: MEDICINE MAN, MISSIONARY, MYSTIC
Michael F. Steltenkamp; Interpretive biography of Black Elk, an Oglala Sioux religious elder. 296 pp. University of Oklahoma Press, 2010. $24.95.

BLACK ELK'S RELIGION: THE SUN DANCE & LAKOTA CATHOLICISM
Clyde Holler; 282 pp. Syracuse University Press, 1998. $39.95; paper, $16.95.

BLACK ELK: THE SACRED WAYS OF A LAKOTA
Wallace Black Elk & William Lyon
225 pp. Paper. HarperCollins & VIP Publishing, 1992. $9.95.

BLACK ELK SPEAKS
Nicholas Black Elk, as told through John G. Neihardt; Story of Lakota visionary & healer Nicholas Black Elk (1863-1950) and his people. This special edition features three prefaces by Neihardt, a map, a reset text, a listing of Lakota words newley translated. 22nd Ed. Illus. Photos. 320 pp. Paper. University of Nebraska Press, 2004. $14.95.

BLACK ELK'S WORLD (Website)
Full text of Black Elk Speaks; history & culture of the Lakotas; Native biographies and memoirs. www.blackelkspeaks.uni.edu; University of Nebraska Press.

BLACK EYES ALL OF THE TIME: INTIMATE VIOLENCE, ABORIGINAL WOMEN, AND THE JUSTICE SYSTEM Anne McGillivray & Brenda Comaskey; Based on the 1995 Winnipeg, Canada, study between the authors and 26 aboriginal women. 208 pp. University of Toronto Press, 1999. $55; paper, $18.95.

BLACK HAWK: AN AUTOBIOGRAPHY
Donald Jackson, Editor
Reprint of 1955 edition. Maps. 177 pp. Paper. University of Illinois Press, 1964. $16.95.

*BLACK HAWK & JIM THORP
Greison Bloom & Hap Gilliland; Biographies of two Sauk heros. Grades 5-12. 71 pp. Paper. Council for Indian Education. $4.95.

THE BLACK HAWK WAR, 1831-1832
Ellen M. Whitney, Editor; Two vols. Amazon.com.

THE BLACK HAWK WAR, INCLUDING A REVIEW OF BLACK HAWK'S LIFE
Frank E. Stevens; A detailed history of the war, with data on many participants. Illus. 323 pp. Paper. Amazon.com, $22.

THE BLACK HAWK WAR OF 1832
Patrick J. Jung; 288 pp. Paper. University of Oklahoma Press, 2010. $19.95.

THE BLACK HAWK WAR, WHY?
Lloyd H. Efflandt; Illus. 40 pp. Paper. Amazon.com, 1987. $1.95.

BLACK HAWK'S AUTOBIOGRAPHY
Roger L. Nichols, Editor; Iowa State University Press, 1999.

BLACK HILLS: SACRED HILLS
Tom Charging Eagle & Ron Zeilinger; Illus. 60 pp. Paper. VIP Publishing. 1987. $6.95.

BLACK HILLS/WHITE JUSTICE: THE SIOUX NATION VERSUS THE U.S., 1775 TO THE PRESENT Edward Lazarus; Case study in the history of Indian/white relations in North America. Illus. Maps. 500 pp. Paper. U. of Nebraska Press, 1999. $22.

BLACK HOLES & TEPEE RINGS ON COSMIC MYSTERIES & SPIRITUAL MYTHOLOGY Robert M. Watkins; Illus. 272 pp. Paper. Amazon.com, 1994. $12.

BLACK INDIAN GENEALOGY RESEARCH
Angela Walton-Raji; 180 pp. Paper. Amazon.com, 1993. $18.50.

BLACK INDIAN SLAVE NARRATIVES
Patrick Minges, Ed.; 200 pp. Paper. John F. Blair & Amazon.com, 2004. $14.95.

BLACK INDIANS: BIBLIOGRAPHY OF MATERIALS ON RELATIONSHIPS BETWEEN AMERICAN INDIANS & AFRICAN AMERICANS
Lisa Bier; 265 pp. Greenwood Publishing, 2004. $54.95.

BLACK KETTLE: THE CHEYENNE CHIEF WHO SOUGHT PEACE BUT FOUND WAR
Thom Hatch; 320 pp. John Wiley & Sons, 2004. $27.95.

BLACK, RED & DEADLY: BLACK & INDIAN GUNFIGHTERS OF THE INDIAN TERRITORIES Art Burton; Illus. 288 pp. Amazon.com, 1992. $9.95.

BLACK ROBE FOR THE YANKTON SIOUX: FR. SYLVESTER EISENMAN, O.S.B. (1891-1948) Mary E. Carson; Illus. 295 pp. Paper. Tipi Press, 1989. $11.95.

BLACK SAND: PREHISTORY IN NORTHERN ARIZONA
Harold S. Colton; Reprint of 1960 edition. Illus. 132 pp. Greenwood, $35.

THE BLACK SEMINOLES: HISTORY OF A FREEDOM-SEEKING PEOPLE
Kenneth W. Porter, Editor; History of Chief John Horse and his followers. Illus. Maps. 352 pp. Paper. University Press of Florida, 1996. $19.95.

THE BLACK SEMINOLES: THE LITTLE-KNOWN STORY OF THE FIRST SEMINOLES
Belinda Noah; Paper. Belinda Noah Productions, 1995. $9.95.

BLACK SHEEP, WHITE CROW AND OTHER WINDMILL TALES: STORIES FROM NAVAJO COUNTRY
Jim Kristofic; Illus. 120 pp. Paper. University of New Mexico Press, 2017. $19.95.

BLACK SILK HANDKERCHIEF: A HOM-ASTUBBY MYSTERY
D.L. Birchfield; Novel. 368 pp. University of Oklahoma Press, 2006. $26.95.

BLACK SUN OF THE MIWOK
Jack Burrows; Illus. 170 pp. Paper. University of New Mexico Press, 2000. $19.95.

BLACK, WHITE, AND INDIAN: RACE AND THE UNMAKING OF AN AMERICAN FAMILY Claudio Saunt; paper. Oxford University Press, 2006. $30.95.

BLACKBIRD'S SONG: ANDREW J. BLACKBIRD & THE ODAWA PEOPLE
Theodore J. Karamanski; 322 pp. Michigan State U. Press, 2012. $39.95; eBook, $31.95.

BLACKCOATS AMONG THE DELAWARE: DAVID ZEISBERGER ON THE OHIO FRONTIER Earl P. Olmstead; Illus. 300 pp. Paper. Kent State U. Press, 1991. $17.95.

·THE BLACKFEET
T. Jensen Lacey; Paul Rosier, Series Editor
Grades 6-12. Illus. 122 pp. Chelsea House, 2011. $35.

THE BLACKFEET: ARTISTS OF THE NORTHERN PLAINS: THE SCRIVER COLLECTION OF BLACKFEET INDIAN ARTIFACTS & RELATED OBJECTS, 1894-1990 Bob Scriver
406 color plates. 320 pp. Lowell Press & Written Heritage, 1992. $60.

BLACKFEET & BUFFALO: MEMORIES OF LIFE AMONG THE INDIANS
James W. Schultz; Keith Seele, Editor; Reprint of 1962 edition. Illus. Maps. Biblio. Paper. University of Oklahoma Press, 2002. $21.95.

BLACKFEET CRAFTS
John C. Ewers; Reprint of 1945 edition. Illus. 68 pp. Paper. R. Schneider, Publishers, Written heritage, $6.95.

BLACKFEET INDIAN STORIES
George Bird Grinnell; Reprinted from 1913 ed. With original N.C. Wyeth painting, Spring, on front cover. Illus. 224 pp. Paper. Amazon.com & Riverbend Publishing, $14.95.

THE BLACKFEET: RAIDERS ON THE NORTHWESTERN PLAINS
John C. Ewers; Reprint of 1958 edition. Illus. Maps. 377 pp. Paper. University of Oklahoma Press, 2000. $24.95.

BLACKFEET TALES FROM APIKUNI'S WORLD
James Willard Schultz; Tales of author's experiences with the Blackfeet. Illus. 320 pp. University of Oklahoma Press, 2002. $24.95.

BLACKFEET TALES OF GLACIER NATIONAL PARK
James Willard Schultz; 240 pp. Paper. Riverbend Publishing, $19.95.

*BLACKFOOT CHILDREN & ELDERS TALK TOGETHER
Barrie E. Kavasch; Grades 4 and up. Rosen Group, 1998. $18.

THE BLACKFOOT CONFEDERACY, 1880-1920: A COMPARATIVE STUDY OF CANADA & U.S. INDIAN POLICY
Hana Samek; Illus. 248 pp. Paper. U. of New Mexico Press, 1987. $30.

BLACKFOOT CRAFTWORKER'S BOOK
Adolf & Beverly Hungry Wolf; A collection of photos of traditional clothing, accessories, utensils, cradleboards, etc. Illus. 80 pp. Paper. The Book Publishing Co., $11.95.

BLACKFOOT GRAMMAR
Donald G. Frantz; 2nd Ed. 224 pp. University of Toronto Press, 2009. $70; paper, $32.95.

BLACKFOOT INDIAN PORTRAITS
Winold Reiss; Illus. Paper. Dover, 1992. $3.95.

BLACKFOOT LODGE TALES: THE STORY OF A PRAIRIE PEOPLE
George B. Grinnell
Reprint of 1892 edition. 322 pp. Paper. University of Nebraska Press, 2003. $14.95.

**THE BLACKFOOT MOONSHINE REBELLION OF 1881: THE INDIAN WAR
THAT NEVER WAS** Ron Carter; 112 pp. Amazon.com & Mountain Press, 1997. $12.95

BLACKFOOT MUSICAL THOUGHT: COMPARATIVE PERSPECTIVES
Bruno Nettl; 214 pp. Kent State University, 1989. $21.

BLACKFOOT PHYSICS: A JOURNEY INTO THE NATIVE AMERICAN UNIVERSE
F. David Peat; Amazon.com, 2002. $16.95.

**BLACKFOOT REDEMPTION: A BLOOD INDIAN'S STORY OF MURDER,
CONFINEMENT, AND IMPERFECT JUSTICE**
William E. Farr; 344 pp. University of Oklahoma Press, $24.95; paper, $21.95.

BLACKFOOT SPIRITUALITY, TRADITIONS, VALUES & BELIEFS (NI-KSO-KO-WA)
Long Standing Bear Chief; An E-book that explains the ancient past and puts the
teachings into a modern context. Amazon.com. $9.95.

BLACKFOOT WAR ART: PICTOGRAPHS OF THE RESERVATION PERIOD, 1880-2000
L. James Dempsey; Illus. 488 pp. University of Oklahoma Press, 2007. $45.

BLACKS, INDIANS & WOMEN IN AMERICA'S WAR OF INDEPENDENCE
Dudley C. Gould; 64 pp. Paper. Amazon.com, 2006. $9.95.

BLANKET WEAVING IN THE SOUTHWEST
Joe Ben Wheat; edited by Ann Lane Hedlund; Describes the evolution of southwestern
textiles-Pueblo, Navajo & Spanish American blankets. Illus. 444 pp. University of Arizona
Press, 2003. $75.

BLANKETS & MOCCASINS: PLENTY COUPS & HIS PEOPLE, THE CROWS
G. Wagner & W. Allen
Illus. 304 pp. University of Nebraska Press, 1987. $24.95; paper, $8.95.

BLEED INTO ME: A BOOK OF STORIES
Stephen Graham Jones; 152 pp. Paper. University of Nebraska Press, 2012. $16.95.

BLESSED ASSURANCE: AT HOME WITH THE BOMB IN AMARILLO TEXAS
A.G. Mojtabai; Illus. 259 pp. Paper. University of New Mexico Press, 1988. $10.95.

BLESSING FOR A LONG TIME: THE SACRED POLE OF THE OMAHA TRIBE
Robin Ridington & Dennis Hastings
Illus. 260 pp. Paper. University of Nebraska Press, 1997. $18.

BLESSINGWAY
Leland C. Wyman; The central rite of Navajo religion. Presents Navajo origin myths
and ritual poetry. Illus. 688 pp. University of Arizona Press, 1970. $50.

THE BLIND MAN AND THE LOOM: THE STPRY OF A TALE
Craig Mishler; Illus. Maps. 288 pp. University of Nebraska Press, 2013. $50.

BLONDE INDIAN: AN ALASKA NATIVE MEMOIR
Ernestine Hayes; Traces the author's life growing up in the Tlingit community.
200 pp. Paper. University of Arizona Press, 2006. $16.95

BLOOD AT SAND CREEK: THE MASSACRE REVISITED
Bob Scott; Illus. Biblio. 256 pp. Paper. The Caxton Press, 1994. $8.95.

BLOOD BROTHER
Elliott Arnold; 454 pp. Paper. University of Nebraska Press, 1979. $26.95.

**BLOOD MATTERS: THE FIVE CIVILIZED TRIBES & THE SEARCH FOR UNITY IN THE
EARLY 20TH CENTURY** Erik March Zissu; Illus. 176 pp. Amazon.com, 2001. $75.

BLOOD MONSTER: THE NEZ PERCE COYOTE CYCLE
Deward E. Walker, Jr.; 240 pp. Mountain Press. $32.50.

BLOOD OF OUR EARTH: POETIC HISTORY OF THE AMERICAN INDIAN
Dan C. Jones, Poet & Rance Hood, Artist
Poems grounded in American Indian history, mythology & religion focusing on American
Indian life on the Great Plains. Illus. 80 pp. Paper. University of New Mexico Press, $19.95.

**BLOOD ON THE BORERS: THE JOURNALS OF DON DIEGO DE VARGAS,
NEW MEXICO, 1694-1697**
John L. Kessell, et al, Eds.; Illus. 1,250 pp. University of New Mexico Press, 1997. $150.

**BLOOD POLITICS: RACE, CULTURE, & IDENTITY IN THE CHEROKEE NATION
OF OKLAHOMA** Circe Sturm
Illus. 267 pp. Paper. University of California Press, 2002. $28.95. E-Book available.

THE BLOOD RUNS LIKE A RIVER THROUGH MY DREAMS: A MEMOIR
Nasdijj; 224 pp. Teacher edition. Amazon.com, 2000. $23.

BLOOD STRUGGLE: THE RISE OF MODERN INDIAN NATIONS
Charles F. Wilkinson; Illus. 384 pp. W.W. Norton & Co., 2005. $19.95.

BLOOD & VOICE: NAVAJO WOMEN CEREMONIAL PRACTITIONERS
Maureen Trudelle Schwarz; Explores Navajo women's role in age-old ceremonies.
186 pp. University of Arizona Press, 2003. $50; paper, $24.95.

BLOOD WILL TELL: NATIVE AMERICANS & ASSIMILATION POLICY
Katherine Ellinghaus; Illus. 234 pp. University of Nebraska Press, 2017. $40.

BLOODLINES: ODYSSEY OF A NATIVE DAUGHTER
Janet Campbell Hale; Autobiographically-based book of essays traces the life
experiences of the author and her family, members of the Coeur d'Alene tribe. Reprint of
1993 edition. 187 pp. Paper. University of Arizona Press. $17.95.

**THE BLOODSTAINED FIELD: A HISTORY OF THE SUGARLOAF MASSACRE,
SEPT. 11, 1780** Rogan H. Moore; Illus. 112 pp. Paper.Amazon.com, 2001. $14.50.

BLOODY KNIFE: CUSTER'S FAVORITE SCOUT
Ben Innis; Richard E. Collin, Ed.
Illus. 320 pp. Paper. Amazon.com, 2002. $45; paper, $21.95.

THE BLOSSOMING: DRAMATIC ACCOUNTS IN THE LIVES OF NATIVE AMERICANS
Dale & Margene Shumway, Editors; 296 pp. Paper. Amazon.com, 2002. $12.95.

THE BLUE GOD: AN EPIC OF MESA VERDE
An epic poem based on the legends of the Zuni Indians who inhabited parts
of Colorado 7 centuries ago. 256 pp. High-Lonesome Books, $35.

THE BLUE, THE GRAY, & THE RED: INDIAN CAMPAIGNS OF THE CIVIL WAR
Thorn Hatch; Illus. 288 pp. Amazon.com, 2003. $29.95.

BLUE HORSES RUSH IN: POEMS & STORIES
Luci Tapahonso
A Navajo woman's life. 120 pp. Paper. University of Arizona Press, 1997. $13.95.

***BLUE JACKET: WAR CHIEF OF THE SHAWNEES**
Allen W. Eckert; Grades 7-adult. 177 pp. Paper. Amazon.com, 1983. $5.95.

BLUE JACKET: WARRIOR OF THE SHAWNEES
John Sugden; Illus. Maps. 400 pp. U. of Nebraska Press, 2000. $35; paper, $19.95.

BLUE SKY, NIGHT THUNDER: THE UTES OF COLORADO
Jess McCreede; 416 pp. Affiliated Writers of America, $19.95.

**BLUE STAR: THE STORY OF CORABELLE FELLOWS, TEACHER AT DAKOTA
MISSIONS, 1884-1888** Kunigunde Duncan; A church-sponsored teacher among the Sioux
& Cheyenne in the Dakota Territory in the 1880s. Illus. 216 pp. Photos. Map. Paper.
Minnesota Historical Society Press, 1990. $8.95.

***BLUE THUNDER**
Richard Throssel
Grades 5-12. 32 pp. Paper. Council for Indian Education, 1976. $8.95; paper, $2.95.

BLUE WATER CREEK & THE FIRST SIOUX WAR, 1854-1856
R. Eli Paul; Illus 256 pp. University of Oklahoma Press, 2007. $34.95.

BO'JOU, NEEJEE!: PROFILES OF CANADIAN INDIAN ART
Ted J. Brasser; Source of ethnographic information on central Indian artifacts. Illus.
204 pp. Paper. Amazon.com & U. of Chicago Press, 1976. $19.95.

**BOARDING SCHOOL BLUES: REVISITNG AMERICAN INDIAN EDUCATIONAL
EXPERIENCES** Clifford E. Treafzer, Jean A. Keller & Lorene Sisquoe, Editors
Illus. 274 pp. University of Nebraska Press, 2006. $45; paper, $20.

BOARDING SCHOOL SEASONS: AMERICAN INDIAN FAMILIES, 1900-1940
Brenda J. Child; Illus. 154 pp. Paper. University of Nebraska Press, 1998. $14.95.

***BOAT RIDE WITH LILLIAN TWO BLOSSOM**
Patricia Polacco; A story explores the magic of myth. Illus. 32 pp. Philomel, 1989. $14.95.

**FRANZ BOAS AS PUBLIC INTELLECTUAL, VOL. 1: THEORY, ETHNOGRAPHY,
ACTIVISM** Regna Darnell, Michelle Hamilton, Robert Hancock, Joshua Smith, Editors
480 pp. Universirty of Nebraska Press, 2015. $75.

FRANZ BOAS: THE EARLY YEARS, 1858-1906
Douglas Cole; Illus. Bibliog. 484 pp. University of Washington Pres, 1999. $50.

KARL BODMER'S NORTH AMERICAN PRINTS
Karl Bodmer; Brandon K. Ruud, Ed.; Illus. 400 pp. Paper. U. of Nebraska Press, $150.

KARL BODMER'S STUDIO ART: THE NEWBERRY LIBRARY BODMER COLLECTION
W. Raymond Wood, et al; Illus. 276 pp. Paper. University of Illinois Press, 2002. $20.95.

BONE DANCE: NEW & SELECTED POEMS, 1965-1993
Wendy Rose; Poetry. 108 pp. Paper. University of Arizona Press, 1994. $13.95.

BONE GAME
Louis Owens; A novel (murder mystery) by Louis Owens, of Choctaw-Cherokee-Irish
descent. 256 pp. Paper. University of Oklahoma Press, 1994. $14.95.

**BONES, BOATS, & BISON: ARCHAEOLOGY & THE FIRST COLONIZATION
OF NORTH AMERICA** E. James Dixon
Illus. Maps. 320 pp. Paper. University of New Mexico Press, 1999. $29.95.

BONES: DISCOVERING THE FIRST AMERICANS
Elaine Dewar; Illus. 640 pp. Paper. Amazon.com, 2004. $16.

THE BOOK OF THE AMERICAN INDIAN
Hamlin Garland; Keith Newlin, Editor; 342 pp. Paper. Amazon.com, 2002. $17.95.

BOOK OF AUTHENTIC INDIAN LIFE CRAFTS
Oscar E. Norbeck; Revised edition. Illus. 260 pp. Galloway, 1974. $10.95.

THE BOOK OF CEREMONIES: A NATIVE WAY OF HONORING & LIVING THE SACRED   Gabriel Horn; Illus. 256 pp. New World Library & Amazon.com, 2000. $20.

BOOK OF THE ESKIMOS
Peter Freuchen; Paper. Fawcett, 1981. $2.95.

BOOK OF THE FOURTH WORLD: READING THE NATIVE AMERICAS THROUGH THEIR LITERATURE   Gordon Brotherstein
Illus. 494 pp. paper. Cambridge U. Press, 1995. $24.95.

BOOK OF THE HOPI
Frank Waters; Reveals the Hopi view of life, kept secret for generations.
Illus. 384 pp. Paper. Penguin USA, 1977. $10.95.

THE BOOK OF INDIAN CRAFTS & INDIAN LORE
Julian H. Salomon; A general discussion of the Indians of the U.S. Reprint.
Illus. Biblio. Index. 418 pp. Paper. Amazon.com, $12.50.

THE BOOK OF MAZAKUTE: A LIFE STORY OF A SIOUX FAMILY
Gilbert Frazier; Illus. 400 pp. Sky & Sage Books, 1996. $25.

THE BOOK OF THE NAVAJO
Raymond Friday Locke; Navajo history and legends. The Navajo's own history taken from the authentic Navajo "Singer" folktales & extensive historical and anthropological research. 5th Ed. Illus. 512 pp. Paper. Amazon.com, $6.95.

THE BOOK OF ONE TREE
Annette R. Schober; Fiction. Story of of the struggle many Native Americans have today as they cope with urban life. 64 pp. Amazon.com, $9.95.

THE BOOK OF WOODCRAFT & INDIAN LORE
Ernest T. Seton; Reprint. Illus. 590 pp. Amazon.com, 2001. $127.50.

A BOOKMAN'S GUIDE TO THE INDIANS OF THE AMERICAS
Richard A. Hand; A compilation of over 10,000 catalogue entries with prices and annotations. 764 pp. Scarecrow Press, 1989. $80.

BOOKS & ISLANDS IN OJIBWE COUNTRY
Louise Erdrich; Symmie Newhouse, Ed.; Illus. 192 pp. Amazon.com, 2003. $20.

BOOKS ON AMERICAN INDIANS & ESKIMOS
Mary J. Lass-Woodfin; American Library Association, 1977. Text edition, $25.

BOOKS ON THE INDIAN WARS
Michael A. Hughes; Illus. 192 pp. Paper. Amazon.com, 2000. $12.95.

BOOKS WITHOUT BIAS: THROUGH INDIAN YES
Beverly Slapin & Doris Seale, Editors; Illus. 2nd Edition. 470 pp. Oyate, $25.

"BOOTS & SADDLES": OR, LIFE IN DAKOTA WITH GENERAL CUSTER
Elizabeth B. Custer; Reprint of the 1961 edition. Illus. Maps. 306 pp. Paper. University of Oklahoma Press, $19.95.

BORDER CITIZENS: THE MAKING OF INDIANS, MEXICANS, AND ANGLOS IN ARIZONA   Eric V. Meeks; Illus. Maps. 342 pp. Paper. U. of Texas Press, 2007. $30.

BORDER SETTLERS OF NORTHWESTERN VIRGINIA 1768-1795
Lucullus Virgil McWhorter; Biographical info about the Virginia/Ohio Valley frontier. Originally published in 1915. Illus. Maps. 520 pp. Paper. Wennawoods Publishing, $17.95.

BORDER TOWNS OF THE NAVAJO NATION
Aaron Yava; Second edition. Illus. 80 pp. Paper. Holmgangers, 1975. $4.

BORDER WARS OF TEXAS
James T. DeShields; Illus. 350 pp. Amazon.com, 1993. $29.95.

BORDERLANDER: THE LIFE OF JAMES KIRKER, 1793-1852
Ralph Adam Smith
Indian fighter. Illus. Maps. Biblio. 416 pp. University of Oklahoma Press, 1999. $32.95.

BORN A CHIEF: THE NINETEENTH CENTURY HOPI BOYHOOD OF EDMUND NEQUATEWA, AS TOLD TO ALFRED F. WHITING
edited by P. David Seaman; 193 pp. Paper. University of Arizona Press, 1993. $19.95.

BORN CREE: THE LIFE OF PETE HAWLEY, OF SITTING HORSE DRUM
Lee Micklin; Illus. Paper. Seattle Indian Services Commission, 1998. $17.95.

BORN IN THE BLOOD: ON NATIVE AMERICAN TRANSLATION
Brian Swann, Editor; Essays on should the translation of Native literature be don and who should do it. Illus. Maps. Tables. 488 pp. Paper. University of Nebraska Press, 2011. $45.

BORN OF CLAY: CERAMICS FROM THE NATIONAL MUSEUM OF THE AMERICAN INDIAN   Bruce Bernstein, Ann McMullen, Ramiro Matos & Felipe Solis
Illus. 96 pp. Paper. NMAI Press, 2005. $19.95.

BORN OF FIRE
Charles S. King; Biography of Margaret Tafoya (1904-2001), one of great masters of Pueblo ceramics. Photos. Illus. Museum of New Mexico Press, 2010. $45.

BOSQUE REDONDO: A STUDY OF CULTURAL STRESS AT THE NAVAJO RESERVATION   Lynn R. Bailey; Illus. 275 pp. Westernlore, $8.50.

BOTH SIDES OF THE BILLPEN: NAVAJO TRADE & POSTS
Robert S. McPherson; Illus. 376 pp. University of Oklahoma Press, 2017. $34.95.

HENRY BOUCHA - STAR OF THE NORTH
Mary Halverson Schofield; Biography about a Native American Olympic & NHL hockey player. Photos. Paper. Amazon.com, $14.95.

ELIAS CORNELIUS BOUDINOT: A LIFE ON THE CHEROKEE BORDER
James W. Parins; Illus. 262 pp. University of Nebraska Press, 2006. $60; paper, $24.95.

BOUND FOR SANTA FE: THE ROAD TO NEW MEXICO & THE AMERICAN CONQUEST, 1806-1848   Stephen G. Hyslop
Illus. 515 pp. U. of Oklahoma Press, 2002. $34.95.

BOUND TO HAVE BLOOD: FRONTIER NEWSPAPERS & THE PLAINS INDIAN WARS
Hugh J. Reilly; Shows how newspaper reporting influenced attitudes about the conflict between the U.S. and Native Americans. Illus. 192 pp. Paper. University of Nebraska Press, 2011. $15.95.

BOUNDARIES BETWEEN: THE SOUTHERN PAIUTES, 1775-1995
Martha C. Knack; The history of the Southern Paiutes. Illus. Maps. 471 pp.
University of Nebraska Press, 2001. $55.

BOUNDARIES & PASSAGES: RULE & RITUAL IN YUP'IK ESKIMO ORAL TRADITION
Ann Fienup-Riordan; Traditional Yup'ik rules and rituals. Illus. Maps. Biblio. 390 pp. Paper. University of Oklahoma Press, 1994. $19.95.

BOUNDLESS FAITH: EARLY AMERICAN WOMEN'S CAPTIVITY NARRATIVES
Henry L. Carrigan, Ed.; 224 pp. Amazon.com, 2003. $16.95.

BOUNTY & BENEVOLENCE: A HISTORY OF SASKATCHEWAN TREATIES
Ray & Miller; Illus. 312 pp. Paper. McGill-Queens University Press, 2002.

BOWS, ARROWS & QUIVERS OF THE AMERICAN FRONTIER
John Baldwin; Describes hundreds of bows, arrows, quivers, and bow cases. 40 photos. 96 pp. Writen Heritage, 1999. $69.95.

BOWS & ARROWS OF THE NATIVE AMERICANS
Jim Hamm; Illus. 160 pp. Paper. Amazon.com, 1989. $14.95.

*THE BOY WHO DREAMED OF AN ACORN
Leigh Casler; illus. by Shonto Begay; Based on a Native American rite known as the Spirit Quest. Grades PS-3. Illus. 32 pp. Putnam, 1994. $15.95.

*THE BOY WHO LIVED WITH THE SEALS
Rafe Nartin; illus by David Shannon; A Chinook Indian tale about loss & redemption. Grades PS-3. Illus. 32 pp. Putnam, 1993. $14.95.

*THE BOY WHO MADE DRAGONFLY: A ZUNI MYTH
Tony Hilleman
Grades 4 and up. Illus. 21 drawings. 87 pp. Paper. University of New Mexico Press. $13.95

BRACKETT'S BATTALION: MINNESOTA CAVALRY IN THE CIVIL WAR & DAKOTA WAR   Kurt D. Bergemann; 214 pp. Minnesota Historical Society Press, 2004. $15.95.

BRAID OF FEATHERS: AMERICAN INDIAN LAW & CONTEMPORARY TRIBAL LIFE
Frank Pommershein; Paper. 280 pp. Paper. University of California Press, 1997. $24.95.

BRAIDED LIVES: AM ANTHOLOGY OF MULTICULTURAL WRITING
Minnesota Humanities Commission, compiler; Illus. Paper. Amazon.com, 1992.

BRAIDING HISTORIES
Susan D. Dion; Aboriginal experience through education. 208 pp.
University of Washington Press, 2009. $94; paper, $37.95.

THE BRAINERD JOURNAL: A MISSION TO THE CHEROKEES, 1817-1823
Joyce B. Phillips & Paul Gary Phillips, Editors
Illus. Maps. 586 pp. University of Nebraska Press, 1998. $70.

JOSEPH BRANT, 1743-1807: A MAN OF TWO WORLDS
Isabel Thompson Kelsay; Illus. Map. 792 pp. Paper. Syracuse U. Press, 1996. $22.50.

MOLLY BRANT: A LEGACY OF HER OWN
Lois M. Huey & Bonnie Pulis; Paper. Smoke & Fire Co., $12.

BRAVE ARE MY PEOPLE: INDIAN HEROES NOT FORGOTTEN
Frank Waters; Biographies and history of Pontiac, Sequoyah, Geronimo, Sitting Bull, Chief Joseph, & Chief Seattle. Reprint. Illus. 207 pp. Paper. Ohio U. Press, 1994. $14.95.

*BRAVE BEAR & THE GHOSTS: A SIOUX LEGEND
Grades 1-5. Illus. Paper. Amazon.com, 1992. $4.95.

BRAVE EAGLE'S ACCOUNT OF THE FETTERMAN FIGHT
Paul Goble, Writer & Illus. 64 pp. Paper. University of Nebraksa Press, 1992. $9.95.

BRAVE WINDS: NATIVE AMERICAN EXPERIENCES
C.S. Corbett Curtis; 134 pp. Paper. Potpourri Publications, 1996. $9.95.

*BRAVE WOLF AND THE THUNDERBIRD
Joe Medicine Crow (Crow); illus. by Linda R. Martin (Navajo)
Tale. Grades 3 and up. Illus. 32 pp. NMAI Press & Abbeville Press, 1998. $14.95.

BREAD & FREEDOM
Ted Zuern; 160 pp. Paper. Tipi Press, 1991. $11.95.

BREAKING GROUND: THE LOWER ELWHA KLALLAM TRIBE & THE UNEARTHING OF TSE-WHIT-ZEN VILLAGE Lynda V. Mapes
Illus. Maps. 288 pp. Paper. U. of Washington Press, 2009. $29.95.

BREAKING THE IRON BONDS: INDIAN CONTROL OF ENERGY DEVELOPMENT
Marjane Ambler; Tribal resource management. 352 pp. Illus. Maps. Paper.
University Press of Kansas, 2000. $19.95.

BREAKING NEW GROUND FOR AMERICAN INDIAN & ALASKA NATIVE YOUTH AT RISK: PROGRAM SUMMARIES Illus. 102 pp. Paper. Amazon.com, 1995. $35.

BREATH OF THE INVISIBLE
John Redtail Freesoul; Illus. 226 pp. Paper. Amazon.com & Alibris.com, 1986. $8.95.

BREATHTRACKS
Jeannette C. Armstrong
Poetry by an Okanagan author/artist. Illus. 112 pp. Theytus, 1991. $9.95.

*A BREEZE SWEPT THROUGH: POETRY
Luci Tapahonso (Navajo); Poetry expresses Navajo life; some text in Navajo.
Illus. 55 pp. Oyate & University of New Mexico Press, $7.95.

THE BRIDGE OF THE GODS: A ROMANCE OF INDIAN OREGON
Frederic Homer Balch; intro. By Stephen Harris; Illus. Paper. WSU Press, 2017. $19.95.

BRIEF HISTORY OF KING PHILIP'S WAR
George M. Bodge; 45 pp. Amazon.com, 2004. $26.

BRIEF HISTORY OF THE QUAPAW TRIBE OF INDIANS
Vern F. Thompson; 44 pp. Paper. Mostly Books Publishing, 1994. $7.95.

A BRIEF HISTORY OF THE SENECA-CAYUGA TRIBE
Roberta Whitye Smith & Ruby White Sequichie
Illus. 176 pp. Paper. Amazon.com, 2000.

A BRIEF & TRUE REPORT OF THE NEW FOUND LAND IN VIRGINIA
Thomas Harriot; Reprint of 1588 edition. Illus. 106 pp. Paper. Dover, $8.95.

BRIEFCASE WARRIORS: STORIES FOR THE STAGE
E. Donald Two-Rivers; Six plays presenting contemporary American Indian urban life.
298 pp. University of Oklahoma Press, $16.95.

THE BRIGHT EDGE: A GUIDE TO THE NATIONAL PARKS OF THE COLORADO PLATEAU Stephen Trimble; Illus. 76 pp. Paper. Museum of Northern Arizona, 1979. $5.95.

BRING IN BEING: THE COLLECTED WORKS OF SKAAY OF THE QQUUNA QIIGHAWAAY Edited and trans. by Robert Bringhurst
Haida myths. Illus. Map. 397 pp. University of Nebraska Press, 2002. $37.95.

BRINGING HOME ANIMALS: RELIGIOUS IDEOLOGY & MODE OF PRODUCTION OF THE MISTASSINI CREE HUNTERS
Adrian Tanner; Bedford/St. Martin's Press, 1979. $27.50.

BRINGING INDIANS TO THE BOOK
Albert Furtwangler; Missionaries & explorers to the Northwest.
Illus. Map. 232 pp. Paper. University of Washington Press, 2005. $22.50.

THE BRINGING OF WONDER: TRADE & THE INDIANS OF THE SOUTHEAST, 1700-1783 Michael P. Morris; 176 pp. Greenwood Publishing, 1999. $55.

BRINGING THEM UNDER SUBJECTION: CALIFORNIA'S TEJON INDIAN RESERVATION & BEYOND, 1852-1864
George Harwood Phillips; Illus. Maps. 384 pp. U. of Nebraska Press, 2004. $59.95.

THE BRITISH MUSEUM ENCYCLOPEDIA OF NATIVE NORTH AMERICA
Rayna Green & Melanie Fernandez
Illus. 224 pp. Amazon.com & Alibris.com, 1999. $44.95; paper, $ 29.95.

THE BROKEN CIRCLE
Rodney Barker; A true story of murder and magic in Indian country.
367 pp. 1992. Amazon.com, $24.50.

THE BROKEN CORD
Michael Dorris; Story about an Indian family's ordeal with "Fetal Alcohol Syndrome."
300 pp. Paper. Harper Perennial, Amazon.com, $11.

A BROKEN FLUTE: THE NATIVE EXPERIENCE IN BOOKS FOR CHILDREN
Doris Seale & Beverly Slapin, Editors; A compilation of work by Native parents, children, educators, poets & writers. Textbook. 476 pp. Paper. AltaMira Press, 2006. $47.

*BROKEN ICE
Hap Gilliland
Grades 1-8. 35 pp. Paper. Council for Indian Education, 1972. $8.95; paper, $2.95.

BROKEN LANDSCAPE: INDIANS, INDIAN TRIBES, AND THE CONSTITUTION
Frank Pommersheim; Oxford University Press, 2009. $125.

BROKEN PATTERN - SUNLIGHT & SHADOWS OF HOPI HISTORY
Vada Carlson
The intrusion of the Spanish; life of the Hopi. Illus. 208 pp. Paper. Naturegraph, $8.95.

THE BROKEN RING: THE DESTRUCTION OF THE CALIFORNIA INDIANS
Van H. Sarner; Illus. Westernlore, 1982. $13.95.

BROKEN TREATIES: U.S. & CANADIAN RELATIONS WITH THE LAKOTAS & THE PLAINS CREE, 1868-1885
Jill St. Germain; Photo. Maps. 484 pp. University of Nebraska Press, 2009. $60.

BROTHER AGAINST BROTHER: AMERICA'S NEW WAR OVER LAND RIGHTS
Diana White Horse Capp; 240 pp. Paper. Amazon.com, 2002. $15.

*BROTHER EAGLE, SISTER SKY
Susan Jeffers; Grades 4 and up. Text based on the famous Chief Seattle speech of the mid-1950's. Illus. 26 pp. Amazon.com, $15.

BROTHERHOOD TO NATIONHOOD: GEORGE MANUEL & THE MAKING OF THE MODERN INDIAN MOVEMENT Peter McFarlane
Biography of George Manuel a prominent leader of Canada's modern Indian movemewnt.
Paper. University of Toronto Press, $15.95.

BROTHERS OF LIGHT, BROTHERS OF BLOOD: THE PENITENTS OF SOUTHWEST
Marta Weigle; Illus. 320 pp. Paper. Amazon.com, 1988. $12.95.

THE BROTHERS OF THE PINE
Tim Simmons; 350 pp. Paper. Blue Star Productions, 1995. $15.95.

THE BROTHERTOWN NATION OF INDIANS: LAND OWNERSHIP & NATIONALISM IN EARLY AMERICA, 1740-1840
Brad D.E. Jarvis; Examines the origins & experiences of a unique Christian (Brothertown Natives) community from a variety of New England tribes. Illus. Maps. Tables. 344 pp. University of Nebraska Press, 2010. $45.

DEE BROWN'S FOLKTALES OF THE NATIVE AMERICAN INDIAN: RETOLD FOR OUR TIMES Dee Brown; Reprint. Illus. 176 pp. Paper. Amazon.com, 1993. $12.

BRULE: THE SIOUX PEOPLE OF THE ROSEBUD
Paul Dyck; Reprint. Illus. Center for Western Studies, $50.

BRUSHED BY CEDAR, LIVING BY THE RIVER: COAST SALISH FIGURES OF POWER
Crisca Bierwert; 314 pp. University of Arizona Press & Amazon.com, 1999. $40.

BRYANT: A CREEK INDIAN NATION TOWNSITE
Mickey J. Martin; Illus. 343 pp. Fowble Press, 1998. $64.

BUCKSKIN & BEADS: NATIVE AMERICAN FOLK DOLLS
Florence Theriault; Illus. 50 pp. Gold Horse Publishing, 1998. $19.

BUCKSKIN & BUFFALO: THE ARTISTRY OF THE PLAINS INDIANS
Colin F. Taylor; Reprint. Illus. 128 pp. Amazon.com, 2000. $25.

BUCKSKIN HOLLOW REFLECTIONS
Maggie Culver Fry; Book of peotry by the author who was a former Oklahoma poet laureate. 95 pp. Amazon.com. $4.50.

BUFFALO, INC.: AMERICAN INDIANS & ECONOMIC DEVELOPMENT
Sebastian Felix Braun; Illus. University of Oklahoma Press, 2008. $26.95; paper, $16.95.

BUFFALO BILL & SITTING BULL: INVENTING THE WILD WEST
Bobby Bridger; Focuses on Buffalo Bill's life-long relationship with Plains Indians.
502 pp. University of Texas Press, 2002. $34.95.

BUFFALO BIRD WOMAN'S GARDEN: AGRICULTURE OF THE HIDATSA INDIANS
Buffalo Bird Woman as told to Gilbert Wilson
Reprint of 1917 ed. Illus. 129 pp. Paper. Minnesota Historical Society Press, 1987. $8.95.

BUFFALO COUNTRY: AMERICA'S NATIONAL BISON RANGE
Photos by Donald M. Jones; 72 pp. Paper. Riverbend Publishing, 2015. $14.95.

BUFFALO COUNTRY: A NORTHERN PLAINS NARRATIVE
Edward Raventon; Illus. 272 pp. Johnson Books, 2003. $20.

BUFFALO HEARTS
Sun Bear; An account of Native American history, culture, and religion from a Native viewpoint. Illus. 128 pp. Paper. Amazon.com, 1976. $5.95.

BUFFALO HUMP & THE PENATEKA COMANCHES
Jodyce & Thomas Schilz; Illus. 78 pp. Texas Western Press, 1989. $12; paper, $7.50.

*BUFFALO HUNT
Russell Freedman
The Plains Indians and the buffalo. Grades 4-6. Illus. 52 pp. Holiday House, 1988. $18.95.

THE BUFFALO HUNTERS
Charles M. Robinson, III; Illus. 192 pp. Amazon.com, 1995. $29.95; paper, $19.95.

THE BUFFALO HUNTERS: THE STORY OF THE HIDE MEN
Mari Sandoz; intro. by Michael Punke
The destruction of the great herds. 384 pp. Paper. U. of Nebraska Press, 2008. $16.95.

BUFFALO, INC.: AMERICAN INDIANS & ECONOMIC DEVELOPMENT
Sebastian Felix Braun; Bison ranching on the Cheyenne River Sioux Reservation.
280 pp. Paper. University of Oklahoma Press, 2010. $24.95.

*BUFFALO & INDIANS ON THE GREAT PLAINS
Noel Grisham & Betsy Warren; Grades K-4. Illus. Eakin, 1985. $8.95.

*THE BUFFALO JUMP
Peter Roop; illus. by Bill Farnsworth
Native American tale. Ages 6-8. Illus. 32 pp. Northland, $14.95.

BUFFALO NATION: AMERICAN INDIAN EFFORTS TO RESTORE THE BISON
Ken Zontek; Photos. Maps. Paper. University of Nebraska Press, 2007. $19.95.

THE BUFFALO SOLDIER TRAGEDY OF 1877
Paul Carlson; Illus. Texas A&M University Press, $24.95.

BUFFALO SOLDIERS, BRAVES, & THE BRASS: THE STORY OF FORT ROBINSON, NEBRASKA Frank N. Schubert; Illus. 250 pp. White Mane Publishing, 1993. $27.95.

BUFFALO SOLDIERS IN THE OLD SOUTHWEST
Ron Swartley; History of the all-black units serving on the western frontier during the Indian War period. Illus. 64 pp. Paper. Frontier Image Press, 2006. $7.95.

THE BUFFALO: THE STORY OF AMERICAN BISON & THEIR HUNTERS FROM PREHISTORIC TIMES TO THE PRESENT
Francis Haines; Illus. Biblio. Paper. University of Oklahoma Press, 1995. $14.95.

BUFFALO TIGER: A LIFE IN THE EVERGLADES
Buffalo Tiger & Harry A. Kersey, Jr.
Observations of Buffalo Tiger, the first tribal chairperson of the Miccosukees. Photos. Map. 208 pp. University of Nebraska Press, 2002. $16.95.

THE BUFFALO WAR: THE HISTORY OF THE RED RIVER INDIAN UPRISING OF 1874-1875 James L. Haley; Illus. 312 pp. Paper. Amazon.com, $17.95.

BUFFALO WOMAN COMES SINGING
Brooke Medicine Eagle; The Spirit Song of the Rainbow Medicine Woman. Illus. 512 pp. Paper. Amazon.com, $14.95.

*BUILDING A BRIDGE
Lisa Shook Begaye; Illus. by Libba Tracy
Picture book. Ages 5-8. Illus. 32 pp. Paper. Northland, $7.95.

BUILDING A CHIPPEWA INDIAN BIRCHBARK CANOE
Robert E. Ritzenhaler; 2nd revised ed. 42 pp. Amazon.com, 1984. $4.

BUILDING A NATION: CHICKASAW MUSEUMS & THE CONSTRUCTION OF HISTORY & HERITAGE Joshua M. Gorman
Illus. Maps. 224 pp. University of Alabama Press, 2011. $37.50. E-Book available.

BUILDING NATIVE AMERICAN NATIONS: THE LIVES & WORK OF MODERN TRIBAL LEADERS Manley Begay, Jr.; 240 pp. AltaMira Press, 2003. $70.

BUILDING ONE FIRE: ART & WORLD VIEW IN CHEROKEE LIFE
Chadwick Smith, Rennard Strickland, Benny Smith
Art/Photography. Illus. 224 pp. University of Oklahma Press, 2010. $24.95

BULL CREEK
Jesse D. Jennings and Dorothy Sammons-Lohse; Paper. U. of Utah Press, 1982. $15.

BULL TROUT'S GIFT: CONFEDERATED SALISH & KOOTENAI TRIBES
Sashay Camel, Illus. 70 pp. University of Nebraska Press, 2011. $21.95.

BULLYING THE MOQUI
Charles F. Lummis; edited by Robert Easton & Mackenzie Brown
Reprints articles that Lummis published in "Out West" in 1903. Text is a story of the attempts to forcibly "civilize" the Hopi Indians of Arizona. Illus. 132 pp. Amazon.com, $30.

BULWARK OF THE REPUBLIC: THE AMERICAN MILITIA IN ANTEBELLUM WEST
Mary Ellen Rowe; 250 pp. Greenwood, 2003. $69.95.

THE BURDEN OF HISTORY: COLONIALISM & THE FRONTIER MYTH IN A RURAL COMMUNITY Elizabeth Furniss; Ethnographic case study; Aboriginal land claims and place of Aboriginal people in Canadian society. 288 pp. UBC Press, 1999. $75.

BUREAU OF INDIAN AFFAIRS
Donald L. Fixico; 229 pp. Greenwood Press, 2012. $58.

THE BURIAL GROUND
Pauline Holdstock; 98 pp. Paper. New Star Books, 1991.

BURIAL MOUNDS OF THE RED RIVER HEADWATERS
Lloyd A. Wilford; Illus. 36 pp. Paper. Minnesota Historical Society, 1970. $2.

BURIED INDIANS: DIGGING UP THE PAST IN A MIDWESTERN TOWN
Laurie Hovell McMillin; American culture clash and a dramati narrative of on perceptions of what the "platform mounds" mean. Photos. Drawings. Map. 264 pp. University of Wisconsin Press, 2006. $60; paper, $24.95.

BURIED ROOTS & INDESTRUCTIBLE SEEDS: THE SURVIVAL OF AMERICAN INDIAN LIFE IN STORY, HISTORY & SPIRIT Mark A. Linquist & Martin Zanger
Illus. 160 pp. Paper. University of Wisconsin Press, 1995. $17.95.

NATALIE CURTIS BURLIN: LIFE IN NATIVE & AFRICAN AMERICAN MUSIC
Michelle Wick Patterson; Examines the life, work & legacy of Curtis circa 1900. Illus. 448 pp. University of Nebraska Press, 2010. $45.

A BURST OF BRILLIANCE: GERMANTOWN, PA & NAVAJO WEAVING
Dilys P. Winegrad, et al.
Illus. 72 pp. Paper. University of Pennsylvania Press, 1995. $19.95.

BURY MY HEART AT WOUNDED KNEE: AN INDIAN HISTORY OF THE AMERICAN WEST Dee Brown; 30th Anniversary edition.
Illus. 512 pp. Paper. Amazon.com., 1991. $16. Library edition, Amazon.com, $49.95.

BUSINESS DEVELOPMENT ON INDIAN LANDS: CONGRESSIONAL HEARING
Ben Nighthorse Campbell, Ed.; Reprint. 78 pp. Paper. Amazon.com, 2001. $25.

THE BUSINESS OF FANCYDANCING
Sherman Alexie; Stories and poems. 84 pp. Amazon.com, $18.00; paper, $10.

*BUTTERFLY DANCE
written & illus. by Gerald Dawavendewa (Hopi/Cherokee)
Grades 3 to 8. Illus. 32 pp. NMAI Press & Abbeville Press, , 2001. $14.95.

BUTTERFLY LOST
David Cole; A Hopi's story. 373 pp. Paper. HarperCollins, 1999. $5.99.

BUYING AMERICA FROM THE INDIANS: JOHNSON V MCINTOSH & THE HISTORY OF NATIVE LAND RIGHTS Blake A. Watson; 254 pp. University of Olahoma Press, $45.

BY CANOE & MOCCASIN. SOME NATIVE PLACE NAMES OF THE GREAT LAKES
Basil Johnston; Illus. Amazon.com, $10.95.

BY CHEYENNE CAMPFIRES
George B. Grinnell; A collection of war stories, mystery stories, tales of creation. Illus. 319 pp. Paper. University of Nebraska Press, 1971. $26.95.

BY NATIVE HANDS: WOVEN TREASURES FROM THE LAUREN ROGERS MUSEUM OF ART Stephen W. Cook, et al.; The history & context of Native American basketry with examples from Choctaw, Shoshone, Salish, Ojibwa, et al. Illus. 240 pp. University of Washington Press, 2005. $60; paper, $29.95.

BY THE POWER OF THE DREAMS: SONGS, PRAYERS & SACRED SHIELDS OF THE PLAINS INDIANS Maureen E. Mansell; Illus. 96 pp. Amazon.com, 1994. $16.95.

BY THE PROPHET OF THE EARTH: ETHNOBOTANY OF THE PIMA
L.S.M. Curtin; Reprint of 1949 edition. Illus. 156 pp. Paper. U. of Arizona Press. $10.95.

C

THE CADDO CHIEFDOMS: CADDO ECONOMICS & POLITICS 700-1835
David La Vere; Map. 199 pp. University of Nebraska Press, 1998. $50.

THE CADDO INDIANS: TRIBES AT THE CONVERGENCE OF EMPIRES, 1542-1854
E. Todd Smith; Maps. 240 pp. Texas A&M University Press, 1997. $18.95.

CADDO INDIANS: WHERE WE COME FROM
Cecile Elkins Carter; Illus. Maps. 432 pp. Paper. U. of Oklahoma Press, 1995. $14.95.

CADDO NATION: ARCHAEOLOGICAL & ETHNOHISTORIC PERSPECTIVES
Timothy K. Perttula; Illus. Maps. Tables. 352 pp. Paper. U. of Texas Press, 1992. $35.

CADDO VERB MORPHOLOGY
Lynette R. Melnar; Illus. 2214 pp. Paper. University of Nebraska Press, 2004. $24.95.

CADDOAN, IROQUOIAN & SIOUIAN LANGUAGES
Wallace L. Chafe; 98 pp. Paper. Amazon.com, 1976. $20.

CADDOS, THE WICHITAS, & THE U.S., 1846-1901
E. Todd Smith; History of reservation life among the tribes.
Maps. 198 pp. Texas A&M University Press, 1998. $29.95.

CAHOKIA: ANCIENT AMERICA'S GREAT CITY ON THE MISSISSIPPI
Timothy R. Pauketat; Reveals the story of the city and its people as uncovered by American archaeologists. 3rd Ed. 525 pp. Viking Press, 2009.

CAHOKIA & THE ARCHAEOLOGY OF POWER
Thomas E. Emerson; Paper. University of Alabama Press, 1997. $29.95.

CAHOKIA CHIEFDOM: THE ARCHAEOLOGY OF A MISSISSIPPIAN SOCIETY
George R. Milner; Illus. Maps. 240 pp. Paper. University of Florida Press, 2006. $24.95.

CAHOKIA: CITY OF THE SUN
Mink, Iseminger, Corley; About Cahokia Mounds. Illus. Full color.
76 pp. Paper. Amazon.com, 1992. $9.95.

CAHOKIA: DOMINATION & IDEOLOGY IN THE MISSISSIPPIAN WORLD
Timothy R. Pauketat & Thomas E. Emerson, Editors
Essays. Illus. 360 pp. University of Nebraska Press, 1997. $60; paper, $25.

CAHOKIA, THE GREAT NATIVE AMERICAN METROPOLIS
Biloine Young & Melvin Fowler; Illus. 366 pp. Paper. U. of Illinois Press, 1999. $29.95.

CAHOKIA: MIRROR OF THE COSMOS
Sally A. Chappell; Illus. 250 pp. University of Chicago Press, 2001. $45; paper, $25.

THE CAHOKIA MOUNDS
Warren King Moorehead; John Kelly, Editor
Paper. University of Alabama Press, 2000. $39.95; eBook, $39.95.

CAHOKIA: A WORLD RENEWAL CULT HETERARCHY
A. Martin Byers; Confronts conventional interpretations of the hierarchical socio-political organization of prehistoric Cahokia, and its rise in the 12th century. Illus. Maps. 616 pp. University Press of Florida, 2006. $69.95; paper, $34.95.

*THE CAHUILLA
Lowell Bean & Lisa Bourgeault
Grades 5 and up. Illus. 112 pp. Chelsea House, 1989. $17.95.

*THE CAHUILLA
Craig & Katherine Doherty; Grades 4-8. 32 pp. Amazon.com, 1994. $22.60.

CAHUILLA DICTIONARY
Hansjakob Seiler & Kojiro Hioki
Reprint of 1976 ed. Illus. Paper. Malki-Ballena Press, 2006. $40.

CAHUILLA GRAMMAR
Hansjakob Seiler & Kojiro Hioki; Paper. Malki-Ballena Press, 1977. $12.

THE CAHUILLA INDIANS OF SOUTHERN CALIFORNIA
Lowell J. Bean & Harry W. Lawton; Reprint of 1965 ed.
Morongo Indian Reservation. Illus. Paper. Malki-Ballena Press, 1997. $5.

THE CAHUILLA LANDSCAPE: THE SANTA ROSA & SAN JACINTO MOUNTAINS
Lowell J. Bean, Sylvia Brakke Vane & Jackson Young
Illus. 116 pp. Ballena Press, 1991. $19.95; paper, $14.95.

CALENDAR HISTORY OF THE KIOWA INDIANS
James Mooney
Reprint of 1895 17th Annual Report of the BIA. Illus. 460 pp. Paper. Smithsonian, $24.95.

CALIFORNIA
Robert F. Heizer, Editor; Illus. 800 pp. Smithsonian, $25.

CALIFORNIA ARCHAEOLOGY
Michael J. Moratto; Paper. Amazon.com, 1984. $45.

CALIFORNIA INDIAN BASKET POSTCARDS: 3. KITANEMUK (SOUTH-CENTRAL CALIFORNIA; 4. POMO (NORTH-CENTRAL CALIFORNIA Coyote Press, 1980. $.40.

CALIFORNIA INDIAN BASKETS: SAN DIEGO TO SANTA BARBARA & BEYOND TO THE SAN JOAQUIN VALLEY, MOUNTAINS & DESERTS
Ralph Shanks; Lisa Woo Shanks, Editor
Illus. 168 pp. University of Washington Press & Malki-Ballena Press, 2010. $39.95.

CALIFORNIA INDIAN COUNTRY: THE LAND & THE PEOPLE
Dolan H. Eargle, Jr., Editor; A pictorial guide to contemporary Native American peoples and places of California. 1st ed. Maps. 180 pp. Paper. Trees Company Press, 1992. $10.

CALIFORNIA INDIAN CRADLE BASKETS & CHILDBIRTH TRADITIONS
Brian Bibby; With an essay by Craig D. Bates. Illus. Photos. 146 pp.
Amazon.com, 2007. $24.50.

CALIFORNIA INDIAN FOLKLORE
Chris Brewer & Frank F. Latta; 210 pp. Paper. Bear State Books, 1999. $19.95.

CALIFORNIA INDIAN LANGUAGES
Victor Golla; Outlines the basic structural features opf more than two dozen language types. Illus. 400 pp. University of California Press, 2011. $90. E-book available.

CALIFORNIA INDIAN SHAMANISM
Lowell J. Bean & Sylvia Vane, Editors.
Illus. 274 pp. Paper. Malki-Ballena Press, 1992. $28.50.

CALIFORNIA INDIAN WATERCRAFT
Richard Cunningham; A summary of all known forms of primitive water transport of the Indians of California up to mid-19th century. Illus.128 pp. Amazon.com. $12.95.

CALIFORNIA INDIAN NIGHTS ENTERTAINMENT
E. Gifford and G. Block, Compilers
Reprint of 1930 edition. Illus. 325 pp. Paper. University of Nebraska Press, $9.95.

*CALIFORNIA INDIANS
C.L. Keyworth; Grades 5-8. Illus. 95 pp. Facts on File, 1990. $18.95.

*CALIFORNIA INDIANS: AN EDUCATIONAL COLORING BOOK
Linda Spizzirri & staff, Editors; Grades 1-8. Illus. 32 pp. Paper.
Spizzirri Publishing, 1981. Read & Coloring Book, $1.95; Cassette/book, $6.95.

CALIFORNIA INDIANS: PRIMARY RESOURCES
Sylvia Brakke Vane & Lowell J. Bean. A guide to manuscripts, artifacts, documents, serials, music, and illustrations. Illus. 366 pp. Paper. Malki-Ballena Press, 1990. $22.

THE CALIFORNIA INDIANS: A SOURCE BOOK
Robert F. Heizer & M.A. Whipple, Editors
2nd revised & enlarged edition. 619 pp. Paper. U. of California Press, 1972. $39.95.

CALIFORNIA INDIANS & THEIR ENVIRONMENT: AN INTRODUCTION
Kent G. Lightfoot & Otis Parrish
Illus. Maps. 512 pp. University of California Press, 2009. $50; paper, $26.95.

CALIFORNIA JOE: NOTED SCOUT & INDIAN FIGHTER
Joe E. Milner & Earle R. Forrest
Illus. 400 pp. University of Nebraska Press, 1987. $28.95; paper, $9.95.

*CALIFORNIA MISSIONS
Seven volume series examines California's early history. Organizaed regionally into siix volumes and a book on projects and layouts. An account of the establishment of the missions and their impact on existing cultures. Titles include: Projects and Layouts by

Libby Nelson; Missions of the Central Coast by June Behrens; Missions of the Inland Valleys by Pauline Brower; Missions of the Los Angeles Area by Dianne MacMillan; Missions of the Monterey Bay Area by Emily Abbink; Missions of the San Francisco Bay Area by Tekla White; Missions of the Southern Coast by Nancy Lemke. Grades 4-7. Illus. Photos. Maps. 80 pp. each. Lerner, 1996. $17.95 each; paper, $9.95 each.

THE CALIFORNIA MISSIONS SOURCE BOOK
David J. McLaughlin; Ruben Mendoza, contributing Editor; Detailed fact sheets about each of the 21 California missions. 78 color photos, 55 line drawings, 14 paintings, 14 architectural drawings, 19 maps. 68 pp. University of New Mexico Press, 2010. Spiral bound with flaps, $24.95

*THE CALIFORNIA NATIVE AMERICAN TRIBES
Mary Null Boule; A series of 26 individual books on each tribe of California. Pre-European tribal life of each tribe. Grades 2-6. Illus. Paper. Amazon.com, 1991. Boxed set, $108.

CALIFORNIA PLACE NAMES: THEIR ORIGIN & ETYMOLOGY OF CURRENT GEOGRAPHICAL NAMES Erwin G. Gudde; 380 pp. U. of California Press, 1998. $45

1500 CALIFORNIA PLACE NAMES: THEIR ORIGIN & MEANING
William Bright; Map. 172 pp. University of California Press, 1998. $12.95.

CALIFORNIA POWWOWS
Karen Doris Wright; Powwow dates and locations in the state of California.
Annual. 90 pp. California Powwow. $10.

*CALIFORNIA TRIBES
Ed Castillo; Grades 4-6. Two vols. Amazon.com, 1996. $3.95 each.

CALIFORNIA'S CHUMASH INDIANS
Santa Barbara Museum of Natural History
Extracted from The Chumash Peoples. Illus. 72 pp. Paper. Amazon.com. $5.95.

CALIFORNIA'S GABRIELINO INDIANS
Bernice Johnston; Illus. 198 pp. Southwest Museum, 1962. $12.50.

*CALIFORNIA'S INDIANS & THE GOLD RUSH
Clifford E. Trafzer; Grades 4-7. Illus. 60 pp. Paper. Sierra Oaks, 1990. $10.95.

CALIFORNIAN INDIAN NIGHTS
Edward W. Gifford & Gwendoline H. Block
Illus. 323 pp. Paper. University of Nebraska Press, 1990. $29.95.

CALL OF THE GREAT SPIRIT: THE SHAMANIC LIFE & TEACHINGS OF MEDICINE GRIZZLY BEAR Bobby Lake-Thom; A traditional Native American healer from the Karuk tribe sgares his personal story of reconnection to the Great Spirit in contemporary America. 256 pp. Paper. Inner traditions, 2001. $15.

CALL TO JUSTICE: THE LIFE OF A FEDERAL TRIAL JUDGE
Warren K. Urbom; Photos. 384 pp. Universit of Nebraska Press, 2012. $36.95.

CALUMET & FLEUR-DE-LYS; ARCHAEOLOGY OF INDIAN & FRENCH CONTACT IN THE MIDCONTINENT John Walthal & Thomas Emerson, Editors
Illus. 320 pp. Smithsonian Institution Press, 1992. $45.

THE CALUSA: LINGUISTIC & CULTURAL ORIGINS & RELATIONSHIPS
Julian Granberry; Defines the Calusa language, formerly spoken in southwestern coastal Florida, and traces its connetions to the Tunica language of northeast Louisiana. 104 pp. University of Alabama Press, 2011. $30. E-Book available.

THE CALUSA & THEIR LEGACY: SOUTH FLORIDA PEOPLE & THEIR ENVIRONMENTS Darcie A. MacMahon & William H. Marquardt; The history of the Calusa Indians who controlled all of south Florida when Europeans first arrived in the New World. Also, takes a look at the arts & culture of contemporary south Florida Indian people - the Seminole & Miccosukee. Illus. Maps. 240 pp. University Press of Florida, 2004. $39.95.

CALL FOR CHANGE: THE MEDICINE WAY OF AMERICAN INDIANN HISTORY, ETHOS, AND REALITY
Donald Fixico; Illus. 264 pp. University of Nebraska Press, 2013. $50.

A CALL FOR REFORM: THE SOUTHERN CALIFORNIA INDIAN WRITINGS OF HELEN HUNT JACKSON Henlen Hunt Jackson; Valerie Sherer Mathes & Phil Brigandi, Editors
Illus. 232 pp. University of Oklahoma Press, 2015. $29.95.

CAMBRIDGE HISTORY OF THE NATIVE PEOPLES OF THE AMERICAS
Stuart Schwartz & frank Salomon, Editors; Illus. 1,500 pp.
Cambridge University Press, 1998. $150.

CAMP BEALE'S SPRINGS & THE HUALAPAI INDIANS
Dennis G. Casebier; Illus. 240 pp. Tales Mojave Rd., 1980. $18.50.

CAMP, CUSTER & THE LITTLE BIGHORN: A COLLECTION OF WALTER MASON CAMP'S RESEARCH PAPERS ON GENERAL GEORGE A. CUSTER'S LAST FIGHT
Richard G. Hardorff; Illus. 136 pp. Amazon.com, 1997. $50.

CAMPAIGNING WITH CUSTER & THE 19TH KANSAS VOLUNTEER CAVALRY ON THE WASHITA CAMPAIGN, 1868-69
David L. Spotts; Illus. 215 pp. University of Nebraska Press, 1988. $19.95; paper, $6.95.

CAMPAIGNING WITH KING: CHARLES KING, CHRONICLER OF THE OLD ARMY
Don Russell; Paul Hedrin, Editor; Illus. 215 pp. University of Nebraska Press, 1991. $25.

CAMPAIGNS IN THE WEST, 1856-1861: THE JOURNAL & LETTERS
John Van Deusen Du Bois; Amazon.com, 2003. $48.

BEN NIGHTHORSE CAMPBELL: AN AMERICAN WARRIOR
Herman J. Viola; Biography of the Native American, U.S. Congressman
from Colorado. Illus. 368 pp. Johnson Books, 2002. $20.

THE CAMPO INDIAN LANDFILL WAR:
THE FIGHT FOR GOLD IN CALIFORNIA'S GARBAGE
Dan McGovern; Illus. 352 pp. Paper. University of Oklahoma Press, 1995. $24.95.

CAN YOU FEEL THE MOUNTAINS TREMBLE? A HEALING THE LAND HANDBOOK
Suugiina; Stephanie Klein, Ed.; 232 pp. Paper. Amazon.com, 2005. $10.

*CANADA: THE LANDS, PEOPLE, & CULTURES SERIES
Bobbie Kalman, Editor; 4 vols. Canada: The Land; Canada: The People; Canada: The
Culture; and Canada Celebrates Multiculturalism. Grades 3-9. Ilus. 32 pp. each. Crabtree,
1993. $20.60 each.

CANADA'S FIRST NATIONS: A HISTORY OF FOUNDING PEOPLES FROM
EARLIEST TIMES Olive P. Dickason; 3rd Ed. Illus. Maps. 576 pp. Paper.
University of Oklahoma Press, 2001. $37.50.

CANADA'S INDIANS: CONTEMPORARY CONFLICTS
J. Frideres; Paper. Prentice-Hall, 1974. $12.95.

*CANADA'S MODERN-DAY FIRST NATIONS: NUNAVUT & EVOLVING
RELATIONSHIPS Ellyn Sanna & William Hunter
Grades 5-10. Illus. 87 pp. Paper. Mason Crest Publishers, 2005. $14.95.

THE CANADIAN FUR TRADE IN THE INDUSTRIAL AGE
Arthur J. Ray; 285 pp. Paper. University of Toronto Press, 1990. $

CANADIAN INDIAN POLICY: A CRITICAL BIBLIOGRAPHY
Robert J. Surtees; Illus. 120 pp. Paper. Amazon.com & Alibris.com, 1982. $4.95.

CANADIAN INDIAN POLICY & DEVELOPMENT PLANNING THEORY
Alain Cunningham; Amazon.com,1998. $50.

THE CANADIAN IROQUOIS & THE SEVEN YEARS' WAR
D. Peter MacLeod; Looks at the social and economic impact of the war on both men and
women in Canadian Iroquois communities. Illus. 300 pp. U. of Toronto Press, 1996. $30.

THE CANADIAN MICHIF LANGUAGE DICTIONARY (METIS)
Manitoba Metis Federation; Introduction to the Michif language.
Includes dictionary & workbook. Paper. Pemmican, $5.95.

CANADIAN NATIVE LAW CASES
Brian Slattery and Linda Charlton
Nine volumes. Vol. 1, 1763-1869, 478 pp, 1980, $50; Vol. 2, 1870-1890, 634 pp., 1981,
$65; Vol. 3, 1891-1910, 663 pp., 1985, $65; Vol. 4 (1911-1930), $65; Vol. 5 (1931-1959),
$70; Vol. 8 (1974-1975), $77; Vol. 9 (1976-1978) $77. Vols. 6 & 7 are OP. Native Law
Centre Publications.

CANADIAN PREHISTORY SERIES
Each book includes time charts, graphs, maps, photos and drawings which picture the life
of native peoples of Canada before the arrival of Jacques Cartier. The titles are: Canadian
Arctic Prehistory, by Robert McGhee, the prehistoric ancestors of the Inuit. 136 pp., $8.50;
The Dig, by George MacDonald and Richard Inglis, the story of the Coast Tsimshian
people. 102 pp., $7.50; Maritime Provinces Prehistory, by James A. Tuck, the story of the
Micmacs nd Malecites. 112 pp., $12.95; Newfoundland and Labrador Prehistory, by James
A. Tuck. 135 pp. $5.50; Six Chapters of Canada's Prehistory, by J.V. Wright. 118 pp.
$5.50; Quebec Prehistory, by J.V. Wright. 128 pp. $5.50; Ontario Prehistory, by J.V.
Wright. 132 pp. Paper. $5.50. Paper. National Museums of Canada.

THE CANADIAN SIOUX
James H. Howard; 210 pp. University of Nebraska Press, 1984. $18.95.

T.C. CANNON: HE STOOD IN THE SUN
Joan Frederick in cooperation with Walter Cannon; Words & works of a contemporary
Native American artist. 70 color & 15 bxw photos. 45 sketches. 224 pp. Northland, $40.

A CANNNONEER IN NAVAJO COUNTRY: JOURNAL OF PRIVATE
JOSIAH M. RICE, 1851 Richard H. Dillon, Editor; Illus. Old West, 1970. $17.50.

THE CANOE: AN ILLUSTRATED HISTORY
Jim Poling, Sr.; Illus. 144 pp. Amazon.com, 2000. $29.95.

CANOE ROCKS: ALASKA'S TLINGIT & THE EURAMERICAN FRONTIER, 1800-1912
Ted C. Hinkley; 450 pp. Amazon.com, 1995. $86.50.

CANOEING WITH THE CREE
Eric Sevareid; Reprint 1935 ed. Illus. 206 pp. Paper. Minnesota Historical Society, $6.95.

CANTE OHITIKA WIN (BRAVE-HEARTED WOMEN): IMAGES OF LAKOTA
WOMEN FROM THE PINE RIDGE RESERVATION, SOUTH DAKOTA
Caroline Reyer; With the writings of Beatrice Medicine & Debra Lynn White Plume; photos
by Thomas Gleason & Tom Casey. Illus. 90 pp. Paper. Amazon.com; Alibris, $8.99.

CANVAS OF CLAY: SEVEN CENTURIES OF HOPI CERAMIC ART
Edwin L. Wade & Allan Cooke; Paper. University of New Mexico Press, $39.95.

CANYON DE CHELLY: ITS PEOPLE & ROCK ART
Campbell Grant; 290 pp. Paper. University of Arizona Press, 1978. $19.95.

CANYON DE CHELLY: THE STORY BEHIND THE SCENERY
Charles Supplee, et al; Photos. Maps. 48 pp. Paper. KC Publications, $6.95.

THE CAPE ALITAK PETROGLYPHS
Woody Knebel; Illus. 128 pp. Donning Co. Publishers, 2003.

CAPE DORSET SCULPTURE
Derek Norton & Nigel Reading; Contemporary Inuit stone scultpure.
Illus. Map. 144 pp. University of Washington Press, 2004. $27.95.

CAPTAIN JACK, MODOC RENEGADE
Doris P. Payne; Illus. Paper. Binford & Mort, 1979. $9.95.

CAPTIVE ARIZONA: INDIAN CAPTIVES & CAPTIVE INDIANS IN ARIZONA
TERRITORY, 1850-1912 Victoria Smith; Narrative history of the practice of taking captives
in early Arizona. Photos. Map. 304 pp. University of Nebraska Press, 2009. $40.

CAPTIVE & COUSINS: SLAVERY, KINSHIP & COMMUNITY IN THE
SOUTHWEST BORDERLANDS
James F. Brooks; Illus. 432 pp. U. of North Carolina Press, 2002. $55; paper, $22.50.

CAPTIVE HISTORIES: ENGLISH, FRENCH, AND NATIVE NARRATIVES
OF THE 1704 DEERFIELD RAID Evan Haefeli & Kevin Sweeney
Illus. Maps. 320 pp. University of Massachusetts Press, 2006. $80; paper, $22.95.

THE CAPTIVITY OF MARY SCHWANDT
Mary Schwandt; Reprint. 1975. Available from Amazon.com, $5.95.

CAPTIVITY OF THE OATMAN GIRLS: AMONG THE APACHES & MOJAVE INDIANS
Royal B. Stratton
Reprint of 1857 edition. Illus. 240 pp. Paper. Dover Publications, $9.95.

CAPTIVITY & SENTIMENT: CULTURAL EXCHANGE IN AMERICAN LITERATURE,
1682-1861 Michelle Burnham; Illus.223 pp. Paper. Dartmouth College Press.
Distributed by University Press of New England, 1997. $22.95.

CAPTORS & CAPTIVES: THE 1704 FRENCH & INDIAN RAID ON DEEREFIELD
Evan Haefeli & Kevin Sweeney; Illus. 408 pp. U. of Massachusetts Press, 2003. $37.50.

CAPTURED BY THE INDIANS: 15 FIRSTHAND ACCOUNTS, 1750-1870
Frederick Drimmer, Editor; Reprint of 1985 ed. 384 pp. Paper. Dover Publications. $9.95.

CAPTURED BY THE INDIANS: REMINISCENCES OF PIONEER LIFE IN MINNESOTA
Minnie Buce Carrigan; 40 pp. New Library Pr.Net, 2003. $88.

CAPTURED BY THE INDIANS: SELDOM TOLD CAPTIVITY STORIES
OF HORATIO JONES & THE BENJAMIN GILBERT FAMILY
Ron Wenning, Editor; Reprint. Illus. 304 pp. Wennawoods Publishing, $19.95.

CAPTURED HERITAGE: THE SCRAMBLE FOR NORTHWEST COAST ARTIFACTS
Douglas Cole; Paper. University of Oklahoma Press, 1998. $16.95.

CAPTURED IN THE MIDDLE: TRADITION & EXPERIENCE IN CONTEMPORARY
NATIVE AMERICAN WRITING
Sidner Larson; 180 pp. Paper. University of Washington Press, 1999. $21.95.

CAPTURING EDUCATION: ENVISIONING & BUILDING THE FIRST TRIBAL
COLLEGES Paul Boyer; Illus. 128 pp. Paper. University of Nebraska Press, 2015. $12.95.

CARBINE & LANCE: THE STORY OF OLD FORT SILL
Wilbur S. Nye; Reprint of the 1969 Centennial edition. Illus. Maps.
426 pp. Paper. University of Oklahoma Press, 1997. $24.95.

CARING FOR AMERICAN INDIAN OBJECTS: A PRACTICAL & CULTURAL GUIDE
Sherelyn Ogden, Editor; Illus. 272 pp. Paper. Minnesota Historical Society, 2004. $39.95.

CARRY FORTH THE STORIES: AN ETHNOGRAPHER'S JOURNEY
INTO NATIVE ORAL TRADITION
Rodney Frey; foreword by Leonard Bends; Ilus. Paper. WSU Press, 2017. $29.95.

KIT CARSON & HIS THREE WIVES: A FAMILY HISTORY
Marc Simmons; His biography finds his first wife was an Arapaho and his second wife
was Cheyenne. He adopted several Indian children and was an Indian agent for many
years. Illus. 224 pp. University of New Mexico Press, $24.95.

KIT CARSON: INDIAN FIGHTER OR INDIAN KILLER?
R.C. Gordon-McCutchan, Ed.; 120 pp. University Press of Colorado, 1996. $24.95.

KIT CARSON & THE INDIANS
Thomas W. Dunlay; Biography. Illus. 537 pp. University of Nebraska Press, 2000. $50.

STOKES CARSON: TWENTIETH-CENTURY TRADING ON NAVAJO RESERVATION
Willow Roberts; 246 pp. University of New Mexico Press, 1987. $24.95; paper, $13.95.

CARTIER'S HOCHELAGA & THE DAWSON SITE
James Pendergast & Bruce Trigger; Illus. 470 pp. U. of Toronto Press, 1972. $34.95.

CARTOGRAPHIC ENCOUNTERS: PERSPECTIVES ON NATIVE AMERICAN
MAPMAKING & MAP USE
G. Malcolm Lewis, Editor; 51 figures. 318 pp. University of Chicago Press, 1998. $75.

CARTOGRAPHIES OF DESIRE: CAPTIVITY, RACE, AND SEX IN THE SHAPING
OF AN AMERICAN NATION Rebecca Blevins Faery
Illus. Biblio. 288 pp. Paper. University of Oklahoma Press, 1999. $18.95.

CARVED HISTORY: A GUIDE TO THE TOTEM POLES OF SITKA NATIONAL
HISTORICAL PARK Alaska Natural History Association.

CARVING THE NATIVE AMERICAN FACE
Terry Kramer; Offers the wood carver a method for creating realistic Native American faces in wood. 250 color photos. 64 pp. Paper. Schiffer Books. $12.95.

CARVING TRADITIONS OF NORTHWEST CALIFORNIA
Ira Jacknis & Isabel T. Kelly; Reprinted with The Carver's Art of the Indians of Northwestern California by Isabel T. Kelly. Illus. Photos. 91 pp. Paper. University of Washington Press 1995. $18.

CARVINGS & COMMERCE: MODEL TOTEM POLES, 1880-2010
Michael D. Hall & Pat Glascock; Illus. 224 pp. U. of Washington Press, 2011. $60.

THE CASAS GRANDES WORLD
edited by Curtis Schaafsma & Carroll Riley; The history & meaning of the great site, covering Chihuahua, Sonora, NM, TX & AZ. Illus. Maps. U. of Utah Press. $60.

CASE & AGREEMENT IN INUIT
Reineke Bok-Bennema; 308 pp. Amazon.com, 1991. $75.

THE CASE OF THE SENECA INDIANS IN THE STATE OF NEW YORK
Reprint of 1980 Edition. 366 pp. E.M. Coleman. $32.50.

A CASE STUDY OF A NORTHERN CALIFORNIA INDIAN TRIBE: CULTURAL CHANGE TO 1860 Robert M. Peterson; R & E Research Associates, 1977. $11.95.

CASH, COLOR & COLONIALISM: THE POLITICS OF TRIBAL ACKNOWLEDGEMENT
Renee Ann Cramer; An analysis of the federal acknowledgement process for American Indians. Illus. 224 pp. University of Oklahoma Press, $24.95; paper, $19.95.

CASINO & MUSEUM: REPRESENTING MASHANTUCKET PEQUOT IDENTITY
John J. Bodinger de Uriarte; Contemporary Native American studies...economics & culture combine. 256 pp. University of Arizona Press, 2007. $50.

CARLOS CASTANEDA, ACADEMIC OPPORTUNISM, & THE PSYCHEDELIC SIXTIES
Jay Courtney Fikes; Illustrates the chronic ignorance about Native American religions. 275 pp. Amazon.com, 1992. $24.95; paper, $14.95.

CATALOGUE OF THE LIBRARY BELONGING TO MR. THOMAS W. FIELD
Thomas W. Field; Martino Publishing, 2004.

CATALOGUE RAISONNE OF THE ALASKA COMMERCIAL COMPANY COLLECTION: PHOEBE APPERSON HEARST MUSEUM OF ANTHROPOLOGY
Nelson H.H. Graburn, Molly Lee, & Jean-Loup Rousselot
Documents more than 2,200 Native Alaskan (Eskimo, Aleut, Northwest Coast, and Athapaskan) objects. Illus. 582 pp. Paper. University of California Press, 1996. $45.

CATAWBA INDIAN POTTERY: THE SURVIVAL OF A FOLK TRADITION
Thomas John Blumer; Illus. 353 pp. paper. U. of Alabama Press, 2004. $34.95.

CATAWBA NATION
Charles Hudson, Jr.; 152 pp. Paper. University of Georgia Press, 1970. $8.50.

*THE CATAWBAS
James H. Merrell; Grades 7-12. Illus. 112 pp. Chelsea House, 1989. $17.95.

CATCH THE WHISPER OF THE WIND
David Villasenor; Jean Villasenor, Illustrator; Compilation of 70 quotations from U.S. & Canadian tribes, with an accompanying cassette of songs in original tribal languages. Illus. 2nd revised edition. 128 pp. Paper. Horizon, 1995. $11.95.

CATCH THE WHISPER OF THE WIND: INSPIRATIONAL STORIES & PROVERBS FROM NATIVE AMERICA Cheewa James
Illus. 250 pp. Paper. Health Communications, 1995. $11.95.

CATHECHISM & GUIDE: NAVAHO-ENGLISH
Berard Haile; Reprint of 1937 edition. Paper. Amazon.com, $3.

CATHLAMET ON THE COLUMBIA
Thomas N. Strong; New edition. Illus. 178 pp. Binford & Mort, 1981. $12.95.

THE CATHOLIC CALUMET: COLONIAL CONVERSIONS IN FRENCH & INDIAN NORTH AMERICA Tracy Neal Leavelle; Examines interactions between Jesuits & Algonquian-speaking peoples of the upper Great Lakes & Illinois country, including the Illinois & Ottawas, in 17th & 18th centuries. Illus. 256 pp. U. of Pennsylvania Press, 2011. $39.95.

GEORGE CATLIN
Joseph R. Millichap; Illus. Paper. Boise State University, 1977. $2.95.

THE GEORGE CATLIN BOOK OF AMERICAN INDIANS
Hassrick; Reproductions of Catlin's famous paintings. 48 color & 121 bxw illustrations. 203 pp. Hothem House, 1988. $35 postpaid.

CATLIN'S LAMENT: INDIANS, MANIFEST DESTINY, AND THE ETHICS OF NATURE
John Hausdoerffer, Editor; Illus. 208 pp. University Press of Kansas, 1995. $39.95.

CATLIN'S NORTH AMERICAN INDIAN PORTFOLIO
George Catlin; Reprint. Illus. Abbeville Press, 1989. $1,250.

CATLIN'S NORTH AMERICAN INDIAN PORTFOLIO: A REPRODUCTION
George Catlin; Reprint of 1845 edition. AbeBooks.com Press, $200.

GEORGE CATLIN'S SOUVENIRS OF THE NORTH AMERICAN INDIANS: A FACSIMILE OF THE ORIGINAL ALBUM
George Catlin & William H. Truettner; Illus. 100 pp. Gilcease Museum, 2003.

CATLINITE PIPES
Lars Hothem; Basic booklet on Catlinite pipestone and the smoking instruments made from it. 38 photos of Plains and related pipes. 48 pp. Paper. Hothem House, 1998. $8.95.

CAVALIER IN BUCKSKIN: GEORGE ARMSTRONG CUSTER & THE WESTERN MILITARY FRONTIER
Robert M. Utley; Illus. Maps. 250 pp. Paper. U. of Oklahoma Press, 1991. $14.95.

CAW PAWA LAAKNI / THEY ARE NOT FORGOTTEN
Sahaptian Place Names Atlas of the Cayuse, Umatilla, and Walla Walla
Jennifer Karson, John Chess, Roberta Conner, Editors
Photos. Maps. 270 pp. Paper. University of Washington Press, 2011. $29.95.

*THE CAYUGA
Grades K-4. Illus. 48 pp. Childrens Press, $11.45.

THE CAYUSE INDIANS, THE ART OF MICHAEL G. BOOTH
Michael G. Booth; Illus. 130 pp. Paper. Art Wise Publications, 1995. $25.

THE CAYUSE INDIANS: IMPERIAL TRIBESMEN OF THE OLD OREGON
Robert Ruby & John Brown; Illus. 456 pp. University of Oklahoma Press, 1989. $29.95.

CEDAR: TREE OF LIFE TO THE NORTHWEST COAST INDIANS
Hilary Stewart; foreword by Bill Reid; The giant cedar tree was vital to the way of life, art, and culture of the early First Nations' people of the Northwest Coast. Illus. Map. 192 pp. Paper. University of Washington Press, 1984. $29.5.

CEDAR SMOKE ON ABALONE MOUNTAIN
Norla Chee; Poetry. 49 pp. Paper. Amazon.com, 2001. $12.

CELEBRATE NATVE AMERICA! AN AZTEC BOOK OF DAYS
Richard Balthazar; Explains the complex Aztec count of days. Illus. 80 pp. Paper. Amazon.com, $18.95.

*CELEBRATING THE POWWOW
Bobbie Kalman; Grades 2 to 5. Illus. 32 pp. Paper. Crabtree, 1997. $5.95.

A CELEBRATION OF BEING
Susanne Page; Illus. 175 pp. Paper. Northland Press, $24.95.

CELEBRATION: TLINGIT, HAIDA, TSIMSHIAN DANCING ON THE LAND
Rosita Worl; Essays by Marla Williams & Robert Davidson. Annual dance/culture festival held by Sealaska Heritage Institute of Southeast Alaska. 267 Illus. 178 color. 152 pp. University of Washington Press, 2008. $40.

CELILO TALES: WASCO MYTHS, LEGENDS, TALES OF MAGIC & THE MARVELOUS
Donald M. Hines; Illus. 266 pp. Amazon.com. $21.95.

CELLULOID INDIANS: NATIVE AMERICANS & FILM
Jacquelyn Kilpatrick, Editor; Overview of Native American representation in film over the past century. Illus. 261 pp. Paper. University of Nebraska Press, 1999. $23.

CENSUS OF THE BLACKFEET, MONTANA, 1897-1898
Jeff Bowen; Transcription of microfilm copies of a census of the Piegan Indians of Montana taken by George B. McLaughlin & Thomas P. Fuller, U.S. Indian Agents. 156 pp. Indexed. paper. Genealogical Publishing, 2004. $16.95.

CENSUS OF THE COMANCHE
Southwest Oklahoma Genealogical Society

CENTENNIAL CAMPAIGN: THE SIOUX WAR OF 1876
John S. Gray; Illus. Maps. 396 pp. Paper. University of Oklahoma Press, 1988. $18.95.

CENTER OF THE WORLD: NATIVE AMERICAN SPIRITUALITY
Rita Robinson & Don Rutledge; 136 pp. Paper. Career Press, 1992. $12.95.

CENTER PLACES & CHEROKEE TOWNS: ARCHAEOLOGICAL PERSPECTIVES ON NATIVE AMERICAN ARCHITECTURE & LANDSCAPE IN SOUTHERN APPALACHIANS
Christopher B. Rodning; Illus. University of Alabama Press, 2015. $59.95; eBook, $59.95.

CENTERING ANISHINAABEG STUDIES: UNDERSTANDING THE WORLD THROUGH STORIES Jill Doerfler, et al
446 pp. Paper. Michigan State University Press, 2013. $29.95; eBook, $23.95.

THE CENTRAL ESKIMO
Franz Boas; A record of Eskimo life in the 1880s. Reprint of 1884 edition. Illus. 280 pp. Paper. University of Nebraska Press, $9.95.

CENTURIES OF DECLINE DURING THE HOHOKAM CLASSIC PERIOD AT PUEBLO GRANDE edited by David R. Abbott
Illus. 265 pp. University of Arizona Press, 2003. $47.50.

A CENTURY OF COAST SALISH HISTORY: MEDIA COMPANION TO THE BOOK "RIGHTS REMEMBERED"
Pauline Hillaire & Gregory Fields; Paper. Amazon.com, $39.95.

A CENTURY OF DISHONOR: THE CLASSIC EXPOSE OF THE PLIGHT OF THE NATIVE AMERICANS
Helen Hunt Jackson; Reprint. Illus. 350 pp. Paper. Dover Publications, 2003. $11.95.

A CENTURY OF DISHONOR: A SKETCH OF THE U.S. GOVERNMENT'S DEALING WITH SOME OF THE INDIAN TRIBES Helen Hunt Jackson
Reprint of 1888 edition. 552 pp. Paper. University of Oklahoma Press & Cherokee Publications, 1995. $19.95.

CERAMIC PRODUCTION IN THE AMERICAN SOUTHWEST
Barbara J. Mills & Patricia L. Crown, Editors; 376 pp. U. of Arizona Press, 1995. $46.

CEREMONIES OF THE PAWNEE
James R. Murie; Douglas R. Parks, Editor
Reprint of 1981 edition. Illus. 500 pp. Paper. University of Nebraska Press, $19.95.

CEREMONY
Leslie Marmon Silko; A novel which captures the search for the identity
of the American Indian. 262 pp. Paper. Penguin USA, $8.

*CEREMONY IN THE CIRCLE OF LIFE
White Deer Autumn (Gabriel Horn); A tale of how Little Turtle is visited by the Star Spirit
and taught the mysteries of life through love & understanding pf Mother Earth & her four
seasons. Grades 1-5. Illus. 32 pp. Levite of Apache, $14.95. Paper. Amazon.com, $8.95.

**CEV'ARMIUT QANEMCIIT QULIRAIT-LLU: ESKIMO NARRATIVES & TALES
FROM CHEVAK, ALASKA** Anthony C. Woodbury, Editor
5 Chevak Yup'ik elders tell of traditional life, shamans, and history of the people of Chevak.
Illus. 88 pp. Paper. University of Alaska Press, 1989. $9.

CHACO ANASAZI: SOCIOPOLITICAL EVOLUTION IN PREHISTORIC SOUTHWEST
Lynne Sebastian; Illus.195 pp. Cambridge University Press, 1992. $64.95; paper, $20.95.

CHACO CANYON: ARCHAEOLOGY & ARCHAEOLOGISTS
Robert & Florence Lister; Illus. 298 pp. Paper. University of New Mexico Press, $24.95.

CHACO CANYON: A CENTER & ITS WORLD
Photos by Mary Peck; Essays by Stephen Lekson, Simon Ortiz, & John Stein
Archaeological ruins of Chaco Canyon; essays explore Chaco's unique role in the Anasazi
world. Illus. Maps. 80 pp. Paper. Museum of New Mexico Press, 2000. $24.95.

CHACO: A CULTURAL LEGACY
Michele Strutin; Color photos. 64 pp. Paper. Amazon.com, $9.95.

CHACO CULTURE NATIONAL HISTORICAL PARK
David Peterson; Childrens Press, 1999. $21.50.

THE CHACO HANDBOOK: AN ENCYCLOPEDIC GUIDE
R. Gwinn Vivian & Bruce Hilpert; Related sites, place-names & architectural features.
Illus. University of Utah Press. $55; paper, $17.95.

**CHACO & HOHOKAM: PREHISTORIC REGIONAL SYSTEMS IN THE
AMERICAN SOUTHWEST** Patricia Crown & W. James Judge
Illus. 380 pp. School of American Research, 1991. $35; paper, $15.95.

**THE CHACO MERIDIAN: CENTERS OF POLITICAL POWER IN THE ANCIENT
SOUTHWEST** Stephen H. Lekson; Illus. 256 pp. Paper. AltaMira Press, 1998. $23.95.

**CHACO REVISITED: NEW RESEARCH ON THE PREHISTORY OF CHACO CANYON,
NEW MEXICO** Carrie C. Heitman & Stephen Plog, Editors
Illus. 392 pp. University of Arizona Press, 2015. $65. E-Book available.

THE CHACOAN PREHISTORY OF THE SAN JUAN BASIN
R. Gwinn Vivian; 525 pp. Amazon.com, 1990. $85.

CHAHTA ANUMPA: A GRAMMAR OF THE CHOCTAW LANGUAGE (CD-ROM)
Marcia Haag & Loretta Fowler; CD-ROM. University of Oklahoma Press, 2001. $29.95.

**CHAIN HER BY ONE FOOT: THE SUBJUGATION OF NATIVE WOMEN IN 17TH
CENTURY NEW FRANCE** Karen L. Anderson; 250 pp. Paper. Amazon.com, 1993.

CHAIN OF FRIENDSHIP: NORTH AMERICAN INDIAN TRADE SILVER
Carter; Study of historic silver objects made for and treasured by the Indians.
Photos. Canadian edition. 256 pp. Paper. Hothem House, 1988. $23.95.

**CHAINBREAKER: THE REVOLUTIONARY WAR MEMOIRS OF GOVERNOR
BLACKSNAKE** Chainbreaker; Benjamin Williams & Thomas Abler, Editors
Illus. Maps. 310 pp. University of Nebraska Press, 1989. $35.

CHAIR OF TEARS
Gerald Vizenor; Novel. 152 pp. Paper. University of Nebraska Press, 2012. $16.95.

CHAIRS
Albert White Eagle; Mary Cadney, Editor; Illus. 150 pp. Amazon.com, 2003. $59.

CHALLENGE: THE SOUTH DAKOTA STORY
Robert Karolevitz; Illus. 325 pp. Amazon.com, $19.95; paper, $14.95.

**CHALLENGES TO ASSESSING & IMPROVING TELECOMMUNICATIONS
FOR NATIVE AMERICANS ON TRIBAL LANDS** GAO report
U.S. Government Accountability Office & Amazon.com.

**CHALLENGING TRADITIONS: CONTEMPORARY FIRST NATIONS ART OF THE
NORTHWEST COAST** Ian M. Thom; Examines the careers, working methods, and
philosophy of forty active Native American artists. Illus. 176 pp. University of Washington
Press, 2009. $65.

CHAMPIONS OF THE CHEROKEES: EVAN & JOHN B. JONES
William G. McLoughlin; 492 pp. Amazon.com, 1989. $35.

CHANCERS: A NOVEL
Gerald Vizenor; Centered on the issue of repatriation of Native American skeletal
remains. 168 pp. Paper. University of Oklahoma Press, 2001. $9.95.

CHANGING CULTURE OF AN INDIAN TRIBE
Margaret Mead; Reprint. Amazon.com, $5.50.

**CHANGING THE FACES OF MATHEMATICS: PERSPECTIVES ON INDIGENOUS
PEOPLE OF NORTH AMERICA** Judith E. Hankes & Gerald R. Fast; Walter Secada, Ed.
Illus. 283 pp. Paper. Amazon.com, 2002. $25.95.

**CHANGING HANDS: ART WITHOUT RESERVATION: CONTEMPORARY AMERICAN
INDIAN ART FROM THE SOUTHWEST** David NcFadden & Ellen N. Taubman
Illus. 224 pp. Dist. by Client Distribution Services, 2002. $59.95.

CHANGING MILITARY PATTERNS OF THE GREAT PLAINS INDIANS
Frank R. Secoy; Historical study of tribal change, conflicts and movements.
Maps. 120 pp. Paper. University of Nebraska Press, $15.

**THE CHANGING NATURE OF RACIAL & ETHNIC CONFLICT IN U.S. HISTORY:
1492 TO THE PRESENT** Leslie V. Tischauser
254 pp. Paper. Amazon.com, 2002. $52.50.

**CHANGING NUMBERS, CHANGING NEEDS: AMERICAN INDIAN DEMOGRAPHY
& PUBLIC HEALTH**
National Research Council; Illus. 328 pp. Paper. Amazon.com, 1996. $49.

CHANGING ONES: THIRD & FOURTH GENDERS IN NATIVE NORTH AMERICA
Will Roscoe; Illus. 334 pp. Palgrave Macmillan, 1998. $24.95.

**THE CHANGING PRESENTATION OF THE AMERICAN INDIAN: MUSEUMS & NATIVE
CULTURES** W. Richard West, et al; Six prominent museum professionals examine the
ways in which Indians and their cultures have been represented by museums in North
America. Illus. 120 pp. NMAI Press & U. of Washington Press, 1999. $25; paper, $18.95.

THE CHANGING WAYS OF THE SOUTHWESTERN INDIANS
Albert H. Schroeder; Reprint of the 1973 edition. Paper. Rio Grande Press.

CHANGING WOMAN: THE LIFE & ART OF HELEN HARDIN
Jay Scott; Native American art. Color & 10 bxw photos. 176 pp. Paper. Northland, $19.95.

THE CHANT OF LIFE: LITURGICAL INCULTURATION & THE PEOPLE OF THE LAND
Mark L. MacDonald, Ed.; Illus. 250 pp. Paper. Amazon.com, 2003. $18.95.

*CHANT OF THE RED MAN
Hap Gilliland; A fable for Americans. Grades 7-adult. Illus. 84 pp. Paper.
Council for Indian Education, 1976. $10.95; paper, $4.95.

CHANTS & PRAYERS: A NATIVE AMERICAN CIRCLE OF BEAUTY
Stan Padilla; Illus. 112 pp. Paper. The Book Publishing Co., 1996. $9.95.

KENNETH MILTON CHAPMAN: A LIFE DEDICATED TO INDIAN ARTS & ARTISTS
Janet Chapman & Karen Barrie; Illus. 384 pp. University of New Mexico, $34.95.

*CHARLES EASTMAN: PHYSICIAN, REFORMER, & NATIVE AMERICAN LEADER
Grades 4 and up. Illus. 128 pp. Childrens Press, $13.95.

*CHARLIE YOUNG BEAR
Katherine Van Ahnen & Joan Azure Young Bear
Grades K-3. 48 pp. Paper. Roberts Rinehart, 1994. $4.95.

*THE CHARM OF THE BEAR CLAW NECKLACE
Margaret Zehmer Searcy; 2 Stone Age Indian siblings living in what is now the
Southeastern U.S. Grades 3-8. Illus. 80 pp. Amazon.com, $13.95; paper, $6.95.

CHASING APACHES & YAQUIS ALONG THE U.S. - MEXICAN BORDER, 1876-1911
Shelley B. Hatfield; 202 pp. University of New Mexico Press, 1998. $35.

**CHASING RAINBOWS: COLLECTING AMERICAN INDIAN TRADE & CAMP
BLANKETS** Barry Friedman; Illus. 304 pp. Amazon.com, 2003. $50.

**CHASING SHADOWS: APACHES & YAQUIS ALONG THE U.S.-MEXICO BORDER,
1876-1911** Shelley Bowen Hatfield
Illus. Maps. 216 pp. Paper. University. of New Mexico Press, 1999. $35.

CHEHALIS RIVER TREATY COUNCIL & THE TREATY OF OLYMPIA
Robert & Barbara Lane; 75 pp. Institute for the Development of Indian Law, $15.

CHEMEHUEVI INDIANS OF SOUTHERN CALIFORNIA
Ronald & Peggy Miller
Reprint 1973 Brochure. Illus. Paper. Malki-Ballena Press, 1979. $5.

CHEMEHUEVI SONG: THE RESILIENCE OF A SOUTHERN PAIUTE TRIBE
Clifford E. Trafzer; Illus. Maps. 328 pp. University of Washingtpon Press, 2015. $45.

CHEM'IVULLU: LET'S SPEAK CAHUILLA
316 pp. Paper. UCLA, American Indian Studies Center, 1982. $17.50.

·THE CHEROKEE
Robert Conley; Paul Rosier, Series Editor
Grades 6-12. Illus. 112 pp. Chelsea House, 2011. $35.

*THE CHEROKEE
Emilie U. Lepthien; Grades K-4. Illus. 48 pp. Childrens Press, $11.45.

*THE CHEROKEE
Barbara McCall; Grades 5-8. Illus. 35 pp. Amazon.com, 1989. $9.95.

*THE CHEROKEE
Theda Perdue; Grades 7-12. Paper. Illus. 112 pp. Amazon.com, 1988. $9.95.

*CHEROKEE ABC COLORING BOOK
Daniel Pennington; Words in English & Cherokee characters with phoentic pronunciations. Grades K-3. Paper. VIP Publishing & Cherokee Publications, $5.

CHEROKEE ADAIRS
Mary Adair & Family members
A historical and genealogical book. 1,000+ pp. Illus. Adair Reunion Assoc., 2003. $66.

CHEROKEE AMERICANS: EASTERN BAND OF CHEROKEES IN THE 20TH CENTURY
John R. Finger; Illus. Maps. 250 pp. Paper. University of Nebraska Press & Cherokee Publications, 1991. $19.95

CHEROKEE ANIMAL STORIES
George F. Shear; Reprint. 80 pp. Paper. Amazon.com. $7.95.

CHEROKEE ARCHAEOLOGY: A STUDY OF THE APPALACHIAN SUMMIT
Bennie C. Keel; Reprint of 1975 ed. Illus. 290 pp. Paper. U. of Tennessee Press, $26.

CHEROKEE ASTROLOGY: ANIMAL MEDICINE IN THE STARS
Raven Hail; New edition of the Cherokee Sacred Calendar
Illus. 176 pp. Paper. Inner Traditions, 2008. $15.

CHEROKEE BIBLIOGRAPHY
Oukah; 145 pp. Paper. Triskelion Press, 1994. $25.

CHEROKEE BY BLOOD: RECORDS OF EASTERN CHEROKEE ANCESTRY IN THE CHEROKEE CROWN OF TANNASSY
William O. Steel; Sir Alexander Cuming's effort to charm the Cherokees into loyalty to England before the Revolutionary War. 162 pp. Cherokee Publications, $7.95.

CHEROKEE BY BLOOD: RECORDS OF EASTERN CHEROKEE ANCESTRY IN THE U.S. COURT OF CLAIMS, 1906-1910; Jerry W. Jordan; Series presents detailed abstracts of those applications including numerous verbatim transcriptions of affidavits by the applicants. 8 vols. Paper. Amazon.com, 1988-1992. $25 each.

THE CHEROKEE CASES: THE CONFRONTATION OF LAW & POLITICS
Jill Norgren; Paper. McGraw-Hill, 1995. $14.

THE CHEROKEE CASES: TWO LANDMARK FEDERAL DECISIONS IN THE FIGHT FOR SOVEREIGNTY Jill Norgren; foreword by Kermit L. Hall & Melvin I. Urofsky
Explores two landmark U.S. Supreme Court cases of the early 1830s.
Maps. 224 pp. Paper. University of Oklahoma Press, 2004. $21.95.

CHEROKEE CAVALIERS: FORTY YEARS OF CHEROKEE HISTORY AS TOLD IN THE CORRESPONDENCE OF THE RIDGE-WATIE-BOUDINOT FAMILY
Edward E. Dale & Gaston Litton
Reprint of 1939 edition. Illus. Map. 320 pp. Paper. University of Oklahoma Press, $15.95.

CHEROKEE CHRONICLES: FROM FIRST CONTACT TO THE TRAIL OF TEARS
Joel Koenig; Illus. 335 pp. Town & Country Publishing, 2003. $29.95.

*CHEROKEE CLOTHING & ACTIVITY BOOK
Sandy & Jesse T. Hummingbird; Illustrates traditional clothing of the Cherokee people. Grades 3-7. Illus. 24 pp. Paper. Book Publishing Co., $4.95.

CHEROKEE CONNECTIONS
Myra V. Gormley
Reprint of 1995 edition. Illus. Maps. 64 pp. Paper. Genealogical Publishing, 2006. $9.95.

CHEROKEE COOKLORE
Contains many Cherokee recipes; chart of herbs; Cherokee food preparation and a menu from a Cherokee Indian Feast. Reprint of 1949 edition. Illus. 72 pp. Paper. VIP Publishing & Cherokee Publications, $5.

CHEROKEE DANCE: CEREMONIAL DANCES & COSTUMES
Donald Sizemore; How-to-do book. Color illus. 176 pp. Paper. Book Publishing Co., Amazon.cm & Written Heritage, $24.95.

CHEROKEE DANCE & DRAMA
Frank G. Speck & Leonard Broom; Reprint. Illus. 112 pp. U. of Oklahoma Press, $9.95

CHEROKEE DIASPORA: AN INDIGENOUS HISTORY OF MIGRATION, RESETTLEMENT, AND IDENTITY
Gregory D. Smithers; Illus. 368 pp. Yale University Press, 2015. $40.

CHEROKEE DICTIONARY
Durbin Feeling; Paper. VIP Publishing, $22.95.

CHEROKEE DRAGON: A NOVEL
Robert J. Conley; 304 pp. University of Oklahoma Press, $19.95; paper, $5.95.

CHEROKEE EDITOR: THE WRITINGS OF ELIAS BOUDINOT
Theda Perdue
245 pp. Paper. University of Georgia Press & Cherokee Publications, 1996. $24.95.

A CHEROKEE ENCYCLOPEDIA
Robert J. Conley; A reference guide to people, places & things connected to the United Keetowah Band of Cherokees, the Cherokee Nation and the Eastern Band of Cherokees. Illus. 290 pp. University of New Mexico Press & Cherokee Publications, $24.95.

CHEROKEE-ENGLISH INTERLINER, FIRST EPISTLE OF JOHN OF THE NEW TESTAMENT Ralph E. Dawson, III and Shirley Dawson
25 pp. Indian University Press of Oklahoma, 1982. Spiral binding, $5.

THE CHEROKEE EXCAVATIONS: HOLOCENE ECOLOGY & HUMAN ADAPTATIONS IN NORTHEASTERN IOWA
Duane C. Anderson and Holmes Semken, Editors; Amazon.com, 1980. $54.50.

A CHEROKEE FEAST OF DAYS, 2 VOLS.
Joyce Sequichie Hifler; Philosophy & history of the Cherokee and other tribes.
2 Vols. 400 pp. each. Paper. Council Oak Books, 1997. $10.95 each.

CHEROKEE FOLK ZOOLOGY: ANIMAL WORLD OF A NATIVE AMERICAN PEOPLE
Arlene Fradkin; Reprint. 583 pp. Amazon.com, $10.

THE CHEROKEE FREEDMEN: FROM EMANCIPATION TO AMERICAN CITIZENSHIP
Daniel F. Littlefield, Jr.; Greenwood Press, 1978. $35.

THE CHEROKEE FRONTIER: CONFLICT & SURVIVAL, 1740-1762
David H. Corkran; Illus. Maps. 328 pp. Paper. U. of Oklahoma Press, 2016. $19.95.

THE CHEROKEE FULL CIRCLE: A PRACTICAL GUIDE TO CEREMONIES & TRADITIONS J.T. Garrett & Michael T. Garrett
Illus. 200 pp. Paper. Inner Traditions, 2002. $14.

*CHEROKEE FUN & LEARN BOOK
J. Ed Sharpe; Grades 4-6. 20 pp. Cherokee Publications, 1970. $4.95.

THE CHEROKEE GHOST DANCE
William G. McLoughlin; 525 pp. Mercer University Press, 1984. $34.95.

CHEROKEE GLOSSARY
Over 900 words with pronunciation guide. VIP Publishing. $9.95.

THE CHEROKEE HERBAL: NATIVE PLANT MEDICINE FROM THE FOUR DIRECTIONS J.T. Garrett; Illus. 240 pp. Paper. Inner Traditions, 2003. $15.

CHEROKEE HERITAGE
Duane King, Editor; The official guidebook to the Museum of the Cherokee Indian. Photos. 130 pp. Paper. Cherokee Publications, $4.

THE CHEROKEE INDIAN NATION: A TROUBLED HISTORY
Duane H. King; Reprint of 1979 ed. Illus. 256 pp. Amazon.com & Alibris.com & Cherokee Publications, $24.95.

THE CHEROKEE KID: WILL ROGERS, TRIBAL IDENTITY, AND THE MAKING OF AN AMERICAN ICON
Amy M. Ware; Illus. 328 pp. University Press of Kansas, 2015. $39.95.

CHEROKEE LANGUAGE WORKBOOK & INSTRUCTIONAL CASSETTE TAPE
Prentice Robinson; 30 pp. & cassette. Cherokee Publications, $25.

*CHEROKEE LEGENDS & THE TRAIL OF TEARS
Tom B. Underwood; Grades 4-12. Illus. 32 pp. Book Publishing Co., VIP Publishing & Cherokee Publications, 1956. $4.95.

*CHEROKEE LITTLE PEOPLE: THE SECRETS OF THE YUNWI TSUNSDI
Lynn Lossiah; Depicts the little people, elf-like beings of Cherokee life & culture. Grades 4 and up. Illus. 152 pp. Paper. Book Publishing Co. & Amazon.com, $23.95.

CHEROKEE MEDICINE, COLONIAL GERMS: AN INDIGENOUS NATION'S FIGHT AGAINST SMALLPOX. 1518-1824
Paul Kelton; Illus. 296 pp. University of Oklahoma Press, 2015. $29.95.

CHEROKEE MEDICINE MAN: THE LIFE & WORK OF A MODERN-DAY HEALER
Robert J. Conley; John Little Bear, his medicine during the Trail of Tears.
Illus. 160 pp. University of Oklahoma Press, $19.95.

CHEROKEE MESSENGER
Althea Bass; Illus. Map. 354 pp. Paper. University of Oklahoma Press, 1996. $17.95.

CHEROKEE NATION CODE ANNOTATED
Reviewed by Joan S. Howland; New ed. Recodification of the Cherokee Nation statutes. Contains tribal legislation passed through 1992. Two vols. West Publishing, 1993. $55.

*CHEROKEE NATION VS. GEORGIA: NATIVE AMERICAN RIGHTS
Victoria Sherrow; Grades 6 and up. 128 pp. Amazon.com, 1997.

THE CHEROKEE NATION: A HISTORY
Robert J. Conley; Tribal lore and tribal law; Cherokee origin myths & legends; thir forced migrations and Cherokee life today. Illus. 4 maps. 280 pp. Paper. University of New Mexico Press & Cherokee Publications, $24.95.

THE CHEROKEE NATION IN THE CIVIL WAR
Clarissa Confer; 200 pp. Paper. University of Oklahoma Press & Cherokee Publications, 2007. $24.95.

CHEROKEE NATIONAL TREASURES IN THEIR OWN WORDS
Shawna Morton-Cain, Pamela Jumper Thurman
Illus. 248 pp. University of Oklahoma Press, 2017. $29.95.

CHEROKEE NEW TESTAMENT
American Bible Society; Cherokee language. 408 pp. Paper. Cherokee Pubns, $3.95.

CHEROKEE NEWSPAPERS, 1828-1906: TRIBAL VOICE OF A PEOPLE IN TRANSITION Cullen Joe Holland; 578 pp. University of Oklahoma Press, 2014. $45.

THE CHEROKEE NIGHT & OTHER PLAYS
Lynn Riggs; Plays by the only active American Indian dramatist during first half of the 20th century. 368 pp. Paper. U. of Oklahoma Press, 2003. $14.95; leather edition, $39.95.

THE CHEROKEE PEOPLE: THE STORY OF THE CHEROKEES FROM EARLIEST ORIGINS TO CONTEMPORARY TIMES
Thomas E. Mails; Illus. 368 pp. Paper. Avalon Publishing, 1992. $29.95.

THE CHEROKEE PERSPECTIVE
L. French & J. Hornbuckle, Editors
The Cherokee today. Photos. 244 pp. Paper. Cherokee Publications, $7.95.

CHEROKEE PLANTERS IN GEORGIA, 1832-1838
Don L. Shadburn; Historical essays on eleven counties in the Cherokee Nation of Georgia. Illus. 422 pp. Paper. Cottonpatch, 2005. Limited 5th printing, $55.

CHEROKEE PLANTS
Hamel & Chiltoskey; Resource dictionary for over 400 plants and their uses by the Cherokee in food, medicine & religion. Illus. 72 pp. Paper. Book Publishing Co., VIP Publishing & Cherokee Publications, $4.95.

CHEROKEE PREHISTORY: THE PASGAH PHASE IN THE APPALACHIAN SUMMIT REGION Roy S. Dickens, Jr.
Reprint of 1976 ed. Illus. 260 pp. Paper. Amazon.com. $22.50.

CHEROKEE PROUD: A GUIDE TO TRACING & HONORING YOUR CHEROKEE ANCESTORS
Tony Mack McClure; 2nd Ed. 336 pp. Amazon.com, 1999. $29.95; paper, $22.95.

CHEROKEE PSALMS, A COLLECTION OF HYMNS
J. Ed Sharpe; tr by Daniel Scott; Illus. 32 pp. Paper. Cherokee Publications, 1991. $4.

CHEROKEE REFERENCE GRAMMAR
Brad Montgomery-Anderson
Illus. 536 pp. University of Oklahoma Press, 2015. $45; paper, $29.95.

THE CHEROKEE REMOVAL
Theda Perdue; 2nd Ed. 210 pp. Paper. Bedford/St. Martin's, 2004. $10.50.

CHEROKEE REMOVAL: BEFORE & AFTER
William L. Anderson, Editor
Maps. 176 pp. Paper. University of Georgia Press, 1991. $12.95.

CHEROKEE REMOVAL: THE WILLIAM PENN ESSAYS & OTHER WRITINGS BY JEREMIAH EVARTS Francis P. Prucha, Editor
320 pp. Amazon.com & Alibris.com, 1981. $28.95.

CHEROKEE RENASCENCE, 1794-1833
William G. McLaughlin; 472 pp. Amazon.com, 1987. $29.50.

CHEROKEE ROOTS
Bob Blankenship; Trace your Cherokee ancestry. Includes over 15,000 name entries from 1835 to 1924. Two vols. Vol. 1, Eastern Cherokee Rolls (164 pp.), $12; and Vol. 2, Western Cherokee Rolls (306 pp.), $18. Paper. 1992. Both vols. $25. Also the 1898 Dawes Roll "Plus", 275 pp. 1994. Paper, $25; & 1909 Gujon Miller Roll "Plus", 62,769 names & related information. 225 pp. 1994. Paper, $30. Cherokee Roots, VIP Publishing & Amazon.com.

THE CHEROKEE SACRED CALENDAR: A HANDBOOK OF THE ANCIENT NATIVE AMERICAN TRADITION Raven Hail; 152 pp. Paper. Inner Traditions, 2000. $12.95.

CHEROKEE SISTER: THE COLLECTED WRITINGS OF CATHERINE BROWN, 1818-1823 Theresa Strouth Gaul, Ed.; Illus. 352 pp. Paper. U. of Nebraska Press, 2014. $40.

CHEROKEE SONG BOOK
Agnes Cowen; A collection of favorite songs & hymns written in the Cherokee language. 112 pp. Paper. Cherokee Publications, $5.95.

THE CHEROKEE STRIP LIVE STOCK ASSOCIATION: FEDERAL REGULATION & THE CATTLEMAN'S LAST FRONTIER
William W. Savage, Jr.; Documents the role of federal governmental agencies in dealing with both white ranchers & Indian entrepreneurs. Illus. Map. 152 pp. Paper. University of Oklahoma Press, $14.95.

CHEROKEE STORIES OF THE PAST
Roy Cantrell; 80 pp. Paper. John F. Blair, 2010. $8.95.

*CHEROKEE SUMMER
Diane Hoyt-Goldsmith; A proud Cherokee girl lives in two worlds. Grades 4-6. Illus. 32 pp. Holiday House, 1993. $15.95.

THE CHEROKEE SYLLABARY: WRITING THE PEOPLE'S PERSEVERANCE
Ellen Cushman; Study traces the creation, dissemination, and evolution of Sequoyah's syllabary from script to print to digital forms. Illus. Tables. 256 pp. University of Oklahoma Press, 2011. $34.95; paper, $19.95.

CHEROKEE THOUGHTS: HONEST & UNCENSORED
Robert J. Conley; 26 essays on what it means to be Cherokee. 196 pp. Paper. University of Oklahoma Press & Cherokee Publications, $19.95.

CHEROKEE TRAGEDY: THE RIDGE FAMILY & THE DECIMATION OF A PEOPLE
Thurman Wilkins; Reprint of the 1970 revised second edition. Illus. Maps. 432 pp. Paper. University of Oklahoma Press, $24.95.

CHEROKEE VOICES: ACCOUNTS OF CHEROKEE LIFE BEFORE 1900
Vicki Rozema; Cherokee life, customs and historical events during the 18th century and first half of the 19th century. 128 pp. Paper. John F. Blair, , 2002. $12.95.

CHEROKEE WOMEN: GENDER & CULTURE CHANGE, 1700-1835
Theda Perdue; Examines the roles and responsibilities of Cherokee women during the 18th & 19th centuries. 254 pp. Paper. University of Nebraska Press & Cherokee Publication, 1998. $17.95.

CHEROKEE WOMEN IN CRISIS: TRAIL OF TEARS, CIVIL WAR, & ALLOTMENT, 1838-1907 Carolyn Ross Johnston
Illus. 272 pp. Paper. University of Alabama Press, 2003. $29.95. E-Book available.

CHEROKEE WORDS
Mary Ulmer Chitoskey; A simplified, illustrated Cherokee/English dictionary. 72 pp. Paper. Cherokee Publications, $3.50.

THE CHEROKEES
Grace Steele Woodward; Reprint of 1963 edition. Illus. Maps. 376 pp. Paper. University of Oklahoma Press & Wennawoods Publishing, $24.95.

*THE CHEROKEES
Elaine Landau; Grades 5-8. Illus. 64 pp. Paper. Franklin Watts, 1992. $6.95.

THE CHEROKEES & THEIR CHIEFS: IN THE WAKE OF EMPIRE
Stan Hoig; 352 pp. Paper. University of Arkansas Press, $24.95

THE CHEROKEES & CHRISTIANITY, 1794-1870: ESSAYS ON ACCULTURATION & CULTURAL PERSISTENCE William G. McLoughlin; edited by Walter H. Comser, Jr. Examines how the process of religious acculturation worked within the Cherokee Nation during the 19th century. 368 pp. University of Georgia Press, 1994. $45.

CHEROKEES AT THE CROSSROADS
John Gulik; With a new chapter by Sharlotte N. Williams. The cultural patterns of Eastern Cherokees during 1956-58. 222 pp. Institute for Research in Social Science, 1973. $7.

CHEROKEES, AN ILLUSTRATED HISTORY
Billy M. Jones & Odie B. Faulk; Overview of the Cherokee people, 1735 to 1984. Illus. 166 pp. Amazon.com & Alibris.com, 1984. $25.

CHEROKEES & MISSIONARIES, 1789-1839
William G. McLoughlin; 376 pp. Yale University Press, 1984. $37.50; Paper. University of Oklahoma Press, 1995. $18.95.

THE CHEROKEES OF THE SMOKEY MOUNTAINS
Horace Kephart; Photos. Map. 48 pp. Paper. Cherokee Publications, $4.95.

THE CHEROKEES, PAST & PRESENT
J. Edward Sharpe; An authentic guide to the Cherokee People...their history, language, food, dwellings, clothing, arts & crafts, religion, etc. Illus. 32 pp. Book Publishing Co., VIP Publishing & Cherokee Publications, 1970. $6.

THE CHEROKEES: A POPULATION HISTORY
Russell Thornton; Illus. Maps. 240 pp. Paper. University of Nebraska Press & Cherokee Publications, 1990. $18.95.

CHEVATO: THE STORY OF THE APACHE WARRIOR WHO CAPTURED HERMAN LEHMANN William Chebahtah & Nancy McGowen Minor
Photos. Maps. 292 pp. Paper. University of Nebraska Press, 2007. $24.95.

CHEW'S VOCABULARY OF TUSCARORA
William Chew & Gilbert Rockwell; Vol. 28. 60 pp. Amazon.com, 2002. $30.

THE CHEYENNE
George A. Dorsey; Reprint of 1971 edition. Paper. Rio Grande Press.

*CHEYENNE
Sally Lodge; Grades 5-8. Illus. 35 pp. Amazon.com, $9.95.

*THE CHEYENNE
Dennis B. Fradin; Grades K-4. Illus. 48 pp. Childrens Press, 1988. $11.45.

THE CHEYENNE
John H. Moore; Illus. 320 pp. Paper. Amazon.com, 1996. $70.95; paper, $26.95.

*THE CHEYENNE
Stanley Hoig; Grades 7-12. Illus. 112 pp. Paper. Amazon.com, 1989. $9.95.

·THE CHEYENNE
Samuel Crompton; Grades 6-12. Illus. 136 pp. Chelsea House, 2011. $35.

*CHEYENNE AGAIN
Eve Bunting; illus. by Irving Toddy; Grades 4 and up. Illus. 32 pp. Amazon.com, $14.95.

CHEYENNE & ARAPAHO MUSIC
Frances Densmore; Reprint of 1936 edition. 111 pp. Southwest Museum, $5.

THE CHEYENNE & ARAPAHO ORDEAL: RESERVATION & AGENCY LIFE IN THE INDIAN TERRITORY, 1875-1907 Donald J. Berthrong
Illus. Maps. Biblio. 418 pp. Paper. University of Oklahoma Press, 1976. $18.95.

CHEYENNE AUTUMN
Mari Sandoz; intro. by Alan Boye; The story of the Northern Cheyennes, who fled the reservation in 1878 to return to their ancestral hunting grounds. 2nd Ed. Illus. Map. 284 pp. Paper. University of Nebraska Press, 2005. $17.95.

CHEYENNE DOG SOLDIERS: A LEDGERBOOK HISTORY OF COUPS & COMBAT
Jean Afton, et al; Illus. 434 pp. Paper. University Press of Colorado, 1997. $39.95.

*CHEYENNE FIRE FIGHTERS: MODERN INDIANS FIGHTING FOREST FIRES
Henry Tall Bull & Tom Weist; Grades 4-12. Paper. Council for Indian Education, 1973. $1.95.

CHEYENNE FRONTIER DAYS, THE FIRST 100 YEARS: A PICTORIAL HISTORY
Illus. Amazon.com, 1996. $45.99.

THE CHEYENNE IN PLAINS INDIAN TRADE RELATIONS, 1795-1840
Joseph Jablow; Illus. 100 pp. Paper. University of Nebraska Press, 1994. $16.95.

THE CHEYENNE INDIANS: VOL. 1 - HISTORY & SOCIETY; VOL. 2, WAR – CEREMONIES & RELIGION
George Bird Grinnell; Reprint of 1923 edition. Two vols: Vol. 1, 406 pp.; Vol. 2, 478 pp. Illus. Map. Paper. University of Nebraska Press, Vol. 1, $27.95; Vol. 2, $27.95.

*CHEYENNE LEGENDS OF CREATION
Henry Tall Bull and Tom Weist
Grades 4-9. Paper. Council for Indian Education, 1972. $1.95.

CHEYENNE MEMORIES
John & Margot Liberty Stands in Timber
2nd Edition. Illus. 384 pp. Paper. Yale University Press,1998. $34.

CHEYENNE MEMORIES OF THE CUSTER FIGHT: A SOURCE BOOK
Richard G. Hardorff; Illus. Maps. 189 pp. Paper. U. of Nebraska Press, 1998. $13.95.

THE CHEYENNE NATION: A SOCIAL & DEMOGRAPHIC HISTORY
John H. Moore; Illus. 390 pp. University of Nebraska Press, 1987. $32.50.

*CHEYENNE SHORT STORIES
Grades 3-8. 32 pp. Council for Indian Education, 1977. $8.95; apper, $2.95.

CHEYENNE VOICE: THE COMPLETE JOHN STANDS IN TIMBER INTERVIEWS
John Stands In Timber & Margot Lberty; 504 pp. University of Oklahoma Press, $36.95.

*CHEYENNE WARRIORS
Henry Tall Bull and Tom Weist
Grades 2-12. 32 pp. Paper. Council for Indian Education, 1976. $8.95; paper, $2.95..

THE CHEYENNE WAY: CONFLICT & CASE LAW IN PRIMITIVE JURISPRUDENCE
Karl Llewellen and E. Adamson Hoebel
Reprint of 1941 edition. Illus. 375 pp. University of Oklahoma Press, $37.95; paper, $19.95.

CHEYENNES AT DARK WATER CREEK: THE LAST FIGHT OF THE RED RIVER WAR
William Y. Chalfant; Cheyenne life on the southern Plains. Illus. 232 pp. University of Oklahoma Press, 1997. $29.95.

CHEYENNES & HORSE SOLDIERS: THE 1857 EXPEDITION & THE BATTLE OF SOLOMON'S FORK William Chalfant; Illus,. by Roy Grinnell
Illus. 12 maps. 416 pp. Paper. University of Oklahoma Press, 2002. $19.95.

THE CHEYENNES: INDIANS OF THE GREAT PLAINS
E. Adamson Hoebel; A portrait of the Cheyenne Indians. 2nd edition. 125 pp. Paper. Amazon.com, 1978. $41.99.

THE CHEYENNES, MA HEO O'S PEOPLE: A CRITICAL BIOGRAPHY
Peter J. Powell; Illus. 160 pp. Paper. Amazon.com & Alibris.com, 1980. $4.95.

THE CHEYENNES OF MONTANA
Thomas Marquis; Tom Weist, Editor; Reference Publications, 1978. $19.95.

*THE CHEYENNES: PEOPLE OF THE PLAINS
Nancy Bonvillain; Grades 4-6. Illus. 64 pp. Amazon.com, 1996. $21.90.

THE CHICAGO AMERICAN INDIAN COMMUNITY, 1893-1988: AN ANNOTATED BIBLIOGRAPHY & GUIDE TO SOURCES IN CHICAGO
David Beck; Illus. 296 pp. Paper. Amazon.com, 1989. $39.95.

*THE CHICHI HOOHOO BOGEYMAN
Virginia Driving Hawk Sneve; illus. Nadema Agard
Grades 3-5. Illus. 64 pp. Paper. University of Nebraska Press, 2008. $9.95.

*THE CHICKASAW
Duane Hale; Grades 5 and up. Illus. Chelsea House, 1989. $17.95.

*THE CHICKASAW
Craig & Katherine Doherty; Grades 4-8. 32 pp. Amazon.com, 1994. $22.60.

CHICKASAW: AN ANALYTICAL DICTIONARY
Pamela Munro & Catherine Willmond; The first scholarly dictionary of the Chickasaw language. Biblio. 540 pp. Paper. University of Oklahoma Press, 1999. $21.95.

CHICKASAW GLOSSARY
Albert S. Gatchet; Reprint of 1889 edition. VIP Publishing, $15.95.

CHICKASAW LIVES, 4 Volumes
Richard Green; Volume 1: Explorations in Tribal History; Volume 2: Profiles & Oral Histories; Volume 3: Sketches of Past & Present; Volume 4: Tribal Mosaic. Illus. @200 pp. each. Published by Chickasaw Press. Distributed by the University of Oklahoma Press, 2007, 2009, 2011, 2013. Vols. 1 & 2, $24. each; Vol. 3, $20; Vol. 4, $24.

CHICKASAW RENAISSANCE
Phillip Carroll Morgan; 240 pp. University of Oklahoma Press, 2009. $34.95.

CHICKASAW SOCIETY & RELIGION
John R. Swanton; Map. 106 pp. Paper. University of Nebraska Press, 2006. $24.95.

CHICKASAW: UNCONQUERED & UNCONQUERABLE
Jeannie Barbour, Dr. Amanda Cobb-Greetham & Linda Hogan
128 pp. University of Oklahoma Press, 2007. $34.95.

THE CHICKASAWS
Arrell M. Gibson; Reprint of the 1971 edition. Illus. Maps. 339 pp. Paper. University of Oklahoma Press, $24.95.

CHIEF BENDER'S BURDEN: THE SILENT STRUGGLE OF A BASEBALL STAR
Tom Swift; Biography of Charles Albert Bender, from the White Earth Reservation (Ojibwe) to the Carlisle Indian School to professional baseball stardom. 15 photos. 346 pp. University of Nebraska Press, 2008. $24.95.

CHIEF BOWLES & THE TEXAS CHEROKEES
Mary Whatley Clark; Illus. 190 pp. Paper. University of Oklahoma Press, $19.95.

CHIEF - CHAMPION OF THE EVERGLADES: A BIOGRAPHY OF SEMINOLE CHIEF JAMES BILLIE Barbara Oeffner; Illus. 256 pp. Cape Cod Writers, 1995. $24.95.

CHIEF CORNPLANTER (GY-ANT-WA-KIA) OF THE SENECAS
Joseph A. Francello; 277 pp. Amazon.com, 1998. $39.95.

CHIEF DANIEL BREAD & THE ONEIDA NATION OF INDIANS OF WISCONSIN
Laurence Hauptman & L. Gordon McLester
Illus. 225 pp. University of Oklahoma Pres, 2002. $29.95.

*CHIEF HAWAH'S BOOK OF NATIVE AMERICANN INDIANS
Chris Brown; Grades 7 and up. Fiction. Paper. Consortium Book Sales, 2006. $14.99

CHIEF JOSEPH
Matthew Grant & Dan Zadra; Creative Education, 1987. $16.45.

CHIEF JOSEPH COUNTRY: LAND OF THE NEZ PERCE
Bill Gulick
Reprint of 1981 ed. Illus. 27 maps. Biblio. 316 pp. The Caxton Press, $39.95.

CHIEF JOSEPH & THE FLIGHT OF THE NEZ PERCE: THE UNTOLD STORY OF AN AMERICAN TRAGEDY Kent Nerburn; Amazon.com, 2005.

CHIEF JOSEPH: GUARDIAN OF THE NEZ PERCE
Jason Hook; Illus. 52 pp. Sterling, 1989. $12.95.

*CHIEF JOSEPH & THE NEZ PERCES
Robert A. Scott; Grades 6 and up. Illus. 144 pp. Facts on File, 1993. $25.

*CHIEF JOSEPH OF THE NEZ PERCE INDIANS: CHAMPION OF LIBERTY
Grades 4 and up. Illus. 130 pp. Childrens Press, $13.95.

CHIEF JOSEPH & THE NEZ PERCES: A PHOTOGRAPHIC HISTORY
Bill & Jan Moeller; Photos. 96 pp. Paper. Mountain Press. $15.

CHIEF JOSEPH, YELLOW WOLF & THE CREATION OF NEZ PERCE HISTORY IN THE PACIFIC NORTHWEST Robert R. McCoy; Illus. 272 pp. Amazon.com, 2004. $80.

CHIEF JOSEPH'S ALLIES: THE PALOUSE INDIANS & THE NEZ PERCE WAR OF 1877
Richard D. Scheuerman; Illus. Paper. Sierra Oaks, 1987. $10.95.

*CHIEF JOSEPH'S OWN STORY AS TOLD BY CHIEF JOSEPH IN 1879
Joseph Young; Foreword by Donald McRae; Autobiography. Grades 4 and up. 38 pp. Paper. Available from Amazon.com, $1.98.

CHIEF JOSEPH'S PEOPLE & THEIR WAR
Alvin M. Josephy, Jr.; Reprint. Illus. Paper. Amazon.com, 2002. $1.95.

CHIEF JUNALUSKA OF THE CHEROKEE INDIAN NATION
John F. Phillips; Biography. Illus. 90 pp. Amazon.com, 1988. $9.00; paper, $6.

CHIEF LEFT HAND: SOUTHERN ARAPAHO
Margaret Coel; Biography. Illus. Maps. 338 pp. Paper. University of Oklahoma Press, 1981. $19.95.

CHIEF LOCO: APACHE PEACEMAKER
Bud Shapard; Illus. Maps. 376 pp. University of Oklahoma Press, 2010. $24.95.

CHIEF LOGAN: AN ANTHOLOGY
Franklin Sawvel, Ron Wenning, et al; Includes Logan the Mingo by Sawvel, Tah-Ga-Jute: or Logan & Capt. Michael Cresap by Brantz & Chief Logan: Friend, Foe or Fiction by Wenning. Illus. Maps. Wennawoods Publishing, 2007. $19.95.

CHIEF MARIN: LEADER, REBEL, & LEGEND
Betty Goerke; Marin County, California, is named after this Coast Miwok chief. Paper. Heyday Books. $21.95.

CHIEF OF THE SEA & SKY: HAIDA HERITAGE SITES OF THE QUEEN CHARLOTTE ISLANDS George MacDonald; Illus. 96 pp. Paper. U. of Washington Press, 1989. $21.95.

*CHIEF PLENTY COUPS: LIFE OF THE CROW INDIAN CHIEF
Flora Hatheway; Grades 4-12. 36 pp. Council for Indian Education, 1971. $8.95; paper, $2.95.

CHIEF POCATELLO
Brigham D. Madsen; Reprint of 1986 edition. Illus. 142 pp. Paper. University of Idaho Press. $15.95.

*CHIEF SARAH: SARAH WINNEMUCCA'S FIGHT FOR INDIAN RIGHTS
Dorothy N. Morrison; Grades 4 and up. Illus. 195 pp. Paper. Amazon.com, 1990. $5.95.

*CHIEF STEPHEN'S PARKY
Ann Chandonnet; Hap Gilliland, Editor; Historical fiction looks at 1898 Alaska and a year in the life of Athapascan Chief Stephen's wife, Olga. Grades 4 and up. Illus. 72 pp. Paper. Council for Indian Education & Roberts Rinehart, 1993 ed. $7.95.

CHIEF WASHAKIE
Mae Urbanek; Illus. 150 pp. Amazon.com, $5.

CHIEFDOMS & CHEIFTAINCY IN THE AMERICAS
Elsa M. Redmond, Editor; Essays about native American chiefs and their rise to power, focusing on the leadership of chieftains. Illus. 416 pp. University Press of Florida, 1998. $65.

CHIEFLY FEASTS: THE ENDURING KWAKIUTL POTLATCH
Aldona Jonaitis; Portait of Kwakiutl culture. Illus. 300 pp. University of Washington Press, 1991. $60.

CHIEFS & CHALLENGERS: INDIAN RESISTANCE & COOPERATION IN SOUTHERN CALIFORNIA, 1769-1906 George Harwood Phillips
Illus. Maps. 384 pp. Paper. University of Oklahoma Press, 2014. $26.95

CHIEFS & CHANGE IN THE OREGON COUNTRY: INDIAN RELATIONS AT FORT NEZ PERCES, 1818-1855
Theodore Stern; Illus. 448 pp. Oregon State University Press, 1996. $39.95.

CHIEFS & CHIEF TRADERS: INDIAN RELATIONS AT FORT NEZ PERCES, 1818-1855
Theodore Stern; Illus. In Two Vols. Vol. 1 - Early interactions and the trade network, 288 pp. 1993; Vol. 2 - Changes the Indians underwent, 1996. Oregon State University Press. Vol. 1, $35.95; Vol. 2, $39.95.

THE CHIEFS HOLE-IN-THE-DAY OF THE MISSISSIPPI CHIPPEWA
Mark Diedrich; Legends recounting the lives of four generations of Chippewa leaders. Photos. Map. Biblio. 58 pp. Paper. Coyote Books, $14.95.

CHIEFS & WARRIORS: NATIVE NATIONS
Christopher Cardozo; Robert Janjigan, Ed.; Illus. 96 pp. Callaway Editions, 1996. $13.95.

CHIHULY BASKETS
Linda Norden & Murray Morgan; Diana Johnson, Editors
Illus. 150 pp. Paper. Portland Press, 1997. $25.

CHIHULY'S PENDLETONS
Chihuly; University of Arizona Press, $65.

*CHII-LA-PE & THE WHITE BUFFALO
John Nicholson; Adventures of a young Crow Indian boy. Grades 2-10. 44 pp. Paper. Council for Indian Education. $4.95.

CHIKASHA STORIES: VOLUMES 1, SHARED SPIRIT; VOL. 2, SHARED VOICES; VOL.3, SHARED WISDOM Glenda Galvan; illus. by Jeannie Barbour; Chickasaw stories from the tribe's oral tradition. Illus. 96 pp. each. The Chickasaw Press. Distributed by the U. of Oklahoma Press, 2011. $36, $36, $30, respectively.

A CHILD'S ALASKA
Claire Rudolf Murphy; Photos by Charles W. Mason. Children's photo-essay. Grades K-4. Illus. Photos. 48 pp. Graphic Arts Center, $14.95.

CHILD OF THE FIGHTING TENTH: ON FRONTIER WITH THE BUFFALO SOLDIERS
Forrestine Cooper Hooker, Steve Wilson
The drama of western settlement and the Indian wars as seen through the eyes of a young girl. Illus. 296 pp. Paper. University of Oklahoma Press, 2011. $19.95.

CHILDHOOD & FOLKLORE: A PSYCHOANALYTIC STUDY OF APACHE PERSONALITY L. Bryce Boyer; Illus. Paper. Psychohistory Press, 1979. $10.95.

CHILDHOOD & YOUTH IN JICARILLA APACHE SOCIETY
Morris E. Opler; Reprint of 1946 edition. Illus. 180 pp. Paper. Southwest Museum, $5.

CHILDREN IN THE PREHISTORIC PUEBLOAN SOUTHWEST
edited by Kathryn A. Kamp; Ethnographic evidence of children. Illus. Map. University of Utah Press. $35.

*CHILDREN INDIAN CAPTIVES
Roy D. Holt; Grades 4-7. Eakin Publications, 1980. $6.95.

THE CHILDREN OF AATAENTSIC: A HISTORY OF THE HURON PEOPLE TO 1660
Bruce G. Trigger; An analysis of the internal dynamism of Huron culture. Reprint of 1976 edition. Illus. University of Toronto Press, $80; paper, $29.95.

CHILDREN OF THE CIRCLE
Adolf & Star Hungry Wolf; A photographic history of Native American children from 1870s to 1920s. Includes over 20 tribes from American West. 90 photos. 160 pp. Paper. Center for Western Studies, Written Heritage, The Book Publishing Co., $9.95.

*CHILDREN OF CLAY: A FAMILY OF PUEBLO POTTERS
Rina Swentzell; Grades 4-6. Paper. Lerner Publications, 1992. $8.95.

CHILDREN OF COTTONWOOD: PIETY & CEREMONIALISM IN HOPI INDIAN PUPPETRY Armin Geertz & Michael Lomatuway'ma
Illus. 412 pp. University of Nebraska Press, 1987. $24.95; paper, $14.95.

CHILDREN OF THE DRAGONFLY: NATIVE AMERICAN VOICES ON CHILD CUSTODY & EDUCATION Robert Bensen, Editor; Documents Native Americans' struggle for cultural survival in the face of placement of their children in residential schools and in foster or adoptive homes. 280 pp. Paper. University of Arizona Press, 2001. $19.95.

*CHILDREN OF THE EARTH & SKY: FIVE STORIES ABOUT NATIVE AMERICAN CHILDREN Stephen Krensky
Grades PS-3. 40 pp. Demco, 1991. $10.15. Paper. Amazon.com, $4.99.

CHILDREN OF THE FIRST PEOPLE: A PHOTOGRAPHIC ESSAY
Dorothy Haegart; Illus. 127 pp. Paper. Left Bank, 1984. $18.95.

CHILDREN OF THE FUR TRADE: FORGOTTEN METIS OF THE PACIFIC NORTHWEST
John C. Jackson; 342 pp. Paper. Oregon State University Press, 2007. $21.95.

CHILDREN OF GRACE: THE NEZ PERCE WAR OF 1877
Bruce Hampton; Illus. Maps. 407 pp. Paper. University of Nebraska Press, 2002. $19.95.

*CHILDREN OF THE MORNING LIGHT: WAMPANOAG TALES AS TOLD BY MANITONQUAT Story Medicine; Grades 1 and up. Illus. 80 pp. Macmillan, 1994. $16.95.

CHILDREN OF SACRED GROUND: AMERICA'S LAST INDIAN WAR
Catherine Feher-Elston; Illus. 256 pp. Northland, 1988. $19.95.

CHILDREN OF THE SALT RIVER
Mary R. Miller; Paper. Resource Center for Language Semiotic, 1977. $11.

*CHILDREN OF THE TLINGIT
Frank J. Staub; Grades 4-7. Illus. Color photos. 48 pp. Lerner, 1999. $19.95.

*CHILDREN'S ATLAS OF NATIVE AMERICANS
Provides an in-depth view of Native American cultures; origins, cliff dwellers and mound builders, and the great civilizations of Central & South America, e.g. Mayans, Aztecs, and Incas. Grades 3-7. Illus. Maps. 80 pp. Amazon.com, $14.95.

CHILIES TO CHOCOLATE: FOOD THE AMERICAS GAVE THE WORLD
Nelson Foster & Linda Cordell, Editors; The foods Native Americans enjoyed before the arrival of the Europeans. 191 pp. Paper. University of Arizona Press, 1992. $14.95.

THE CHILKAT DANCING BLANKET
Cheryl Samuel; Reprint. Illus. 234 pp. Paper. U. of Oklahoma Press, 1990. $14.95.

CHILLS & FEVER: HEALTH & DISEASE IN THE EARLY HISTORY OF ALASKA
Robert Fortuine; Illus. 395 pp. University of Alaska Press, 1989. $29.95.

CHIMARIKO GRAMMAR: AREAL & TYPOLOGICAL PERSPECTIVE
Carmen Jany; Describes the Native language, Chimariko, spoken in Trinity County, California, and examines language contact in Northern California. 262 pp. Paper. University of California Press, 2009. $34.95. E-book available.

CHINIGCHINICH
Fr. Geronimo Boscana; Text based on Father Bocana's (Spanish Catholic priest) notes on mission life & local Indian culture. The title is named after native god, Chinigchinich. Reprint of 1978 ed. Malki-Ballena Press, 2005. $65.

CHINIGCHINIX, AN INDIGENOUS CALIFORNIA INDIAN RELIGION
James R. Moriarty; Illus. Maps. 70 pp. Southwest Museum, 1969. $12.50.

CHINLE TO TAOS
R.C. Gorman; Exhibition catalog-retrospective of R.C. Gorman at the Millicent Rogers Museum in June 1988. Illus. 64 pp. Navajo Gallery, $20.

*CHINOOK
Jessie Marsh; Grades K-6. 32 pp. Paper. Council for Indian Education, 1976. $2.95.

CHINOOK: A HISTORY & DICTIONARY
Edward Thomas; Second edition. 184 pp. Binford & Mort, $12.95.

THE CHINOOK INDIANS: TRADERS OF THE LOWER COLUMBIA RIVER
Robert H. Ruby & John A. Brown
Illus. Maps. 374 pp. Paper. University of Oklahoma Press, 1988. $19.95.

*THE CHINOOK - NORTHWEST
Clifford L. Trafzer; Grades 7-12. Illus. 112 pp. Chelsea House, 1990. $17.95.

CHINOOKAN PEOPLES OF THE LOWER COLUMBIA
Robert T. Boyd, Kenneth M. Ames & Tony Jonson, Editors
Illus. 448 pp. Illus. Maps. Paper. University of Washington Press, 2015. $30.

CHIPETA: QUEEN OF THE UTES
Cynthia S. Becker & P. David Smith; The story of Chipeta, the wife of Chief Ouray. Illus. Maps. 278 pp. Paper. Western Reflections Publishing, 2003. $18.95.

*THE CHIPPEWA
Alice Osinski; Grades K-4. Illus. 48 pp. Childrens Press, 1987. $13.27; paper, $3.95.

CHIPPEWA & DAKOTA INDIANS
Subject catalog of books, pamphlets, periodical articles and manuscripts in the Minnesota Historical Society. 131 pp. Paper. Minnesota Historical Society, 1970. $7.50.

CHIPPEWA & THEIR NEIGHBORS: A STUDY IN ETHNOHISTORY
Harold Hickerson; G. and L. Spindler, Editors
Reprint of the 1970 edition. 151 pp. Paper. Waveland Press, $9.50.

CHIPPEWA CHILD LIFE & ITS CULTURAL BACKGROUND
M. Inez Hilger; Reprint. Illus. Photos. Biblio. 204 pp. Amazon.com. Paper. Minnesota Historical Society, $10.95.

*CHIPPEWA CUSTOMS
Frances Densmore; Authoritative source for tribal history, customs, legends, traditions, art, music, economy & leisure activity of the Chippewa (Ojibway) Indians of the U.S. & Canada. Reprint. Illus. Biblio. 204 pp. 1995. Paper. Amazon.com. Library ed., $49.

CHIPPEWA FAMILIES: A SOCIAL STUDY OF WHITE EARTH RESERVATION, 1938
M. Inez Hilger; Illus. 204 pp. Paper. Minnesota Historical Society, 1998. $12.95.

THE CHIPPEWA LANDSCAPE OF LOUISE ERDRICH
Allan Chavkin, Ed.; 175 pp. Paper. University of Alabama Press, 1999. $16.95.

CHIPPEWA TREATY RIGHTS: THE RESERVED RIGHTS OF WISCONSIN'S CHIPPEWA INDIANS IN HISTORICAL PERSPECTIVE Ronald N. Satz
History of the Chippewa's treaty rights in Wisconsin. Illus. Maps. 272 pp. Paper. U. of Wisconsin Press, 1997. $24.95.

1826 CHIPPEWA TREATY WITH THE U.S. GOVERNMENT
Robert Keller; 45 pp. Institute for the Development of Indian Law, $10.

THE CHIPPEWAS OF LAKE SUPERIOR
Edmund J. Danziger, Jr.
Illus. Maps. 264 pp. Paper. University of Oklahoma Press, 1979. $16.95.

*THE CHIPEWYAN
James G. Smith; Grades 5 and up. Illus. Chelsea House, 1989. $17.95.

CHIRICAHUA APACHE ENDURING POWER: NAICHE'S PUBERTY CEREMONY PAINTINGS Trudy Griffin-Pierce; Reveals the conflicting meanings of power held by the federal government and the Chiricahua Apaches throughout history of interaction. Illus. 240 pp. U. of Alabama Press, 2006. $75; paper, $32.95. E-Book available.

THE CHIRICAHUA APACHE, 1846-1876: FROM WAR TO RESERVATION
D.C. Cole; Illus. 225 pp. University of New Mexico Press, 1988. $32.50.

THE CHIRICAHUA APACHE PRISONERS OF WAR: FORT SILL, 1894-1914
John A. Turcheneske, Jr.; Illus. 232 pp. University Press of Colorado, 1997. $32.50.

CHIRICAHUA APACHE WOMEN & CHILDREN: SAFEKEEPERS OF THE HERITAGE
H. Henrietta Stockel; Illus. 115 pp. Texas A&M University Press, 2000. $24.95.

CHIRICAHUA & JANOS: COMMUNITIES OF VIOLENCE IN THE SOUTHWESTERN BORDERLANDS, 1680-1880
Lance R. Blyth; Maps. 296 pp. University of Nebraska Press, 2012. $60; paper, $30.

JESSE CHISHOLM: AMBASSADOR OF THE PLAINS
Stan Hoig; Biography of a trailblazer, friend of Indian chiefs, linguist of Indian languages, scout, and lisiason between Indian tribes, the U.S. government and Republic of Texas. Illus. 240 pp. Paper. University of Oklahoma Press, $19.95.

JESSE CHISHOLM: TEXAS TRAIL BLAZER & PEACEMAKER
Ralph B. Cushman; Illus. 288 pp. Amazon.com, 1992. $12.95.

*THE CHOCTAW
E. Lepthien; Grades K-4. Illus. 48 pp. Childrens Press, 1987. $11.45.

*THE CHOCTAW
Jesse O. McKee; Grades 5 and up. Illus. Amazon.com, 1989. $17.95.

*THE CHOCTAW
John Bowes; Paul Rosier, Series Editor
Grades 6-12. Illus. 133 pp. Chelsea House, 2010. $35.

THE CHOCTAW ACADEMY: OFFICIAL CORRESPONDENCE, 1825-1841
Grenville & Neil Goodwin; Illus. 304 pp. University of Nebraska Press, 2000. $35.

*A CHOCTAW ANTHOLOGY, I & II
Papers written by Choctaw high school and college prep students on Choctaw history, culture & events. Grades 7-12. Choctaw Heritage Press, I--$2.75; II--$7.00. $8.50/set.

CHOCTAW-APACHE FOODWAYS
Robert Caldwell, Jr.; paper. Texas A&M University Press, $22.

THE CHOCTAW BEFORE REMOVAL
Carolyn K. Reeves, Editor; Illus. Paper. University Press of Mississippi, 1985. $25.

CHOCTAW & CHICKASAW EARLY CENSUS RECORDS
Betty C. Wiltshire; 180 pp. Paper. Amazon.com, 1997. $27.

CHOCTAW CRIME & PUNISHMENT, 1884-1907
Devon Abbott Mihesuah
Illus. Map. 352 pp. The Choctaw Store & University of Oklahoma Press, $35.

CHOCTAW GENESIS, 1500-1700
Patricia Galloway;; Illus. Maps. 413 pp. Paper. University of Nebraska Press, 1995. $30.

CHOCTAW HYMNS
252 pp. The Choctaw Store, $15.

CHOCTAW LANGUAGE AWARENESS TEACHERS MANUAL
Developed in cooperation with Choctaw Nation. 112 pp. manual and 6 audio tapes. Grades K-3. VIP Publishing. $59.95.

CHOCTAW LANGUAGE & CULTURE: CHAHTA ANUMPA
Marcia Haag & Henry Willis; foreword by Grayson Noley
Illus. 400 pp. Paper. University of Oklahoma Press, 2001. $26.95

CHOCTAW LANGUAGE DICTIONARY
The Choctaw Store, $25.

THE CHOCTAW LAWS
Reprint . Amazon.com & Alibris.com, $11.

CHOCTAW LEGENDS WITH TEACHER'S GUIDE
With audio tape. VIP Publishing. $9.95.

CHOCTAW MUSIC
Frances Densmore; Reprint. Illus. 110 pp. Amazon.com, 1990. $29; paper, $15.

CHOCTAW MUSIC & DANCE
James H. Howard & Victoria Lindsay Levine
Discusses all aspects of Choctaw dances and songs.Illus. 30 musical transcriptions, 144 pp. Paper. University of Oklahoma Press, 1989. $13.95.

CHOCTAW NATION DICTIONARY
The Choctaw Store, $44.95

CHOCTAW NATION: A STORY OF AMERICAN INDIAN RESURGENCE
Valerie Lambert; 368 pp. University of Nebraska Press, 2007. $45.

THE CHOCTAW OF OKLAHOMA
James C. Milligan; History of the Choctaw in Oklahoma. The Choctaw Store, 2003. $25.

CHOCTAW PROPHECY: A LEGACY OF THE FUTURE
Tom Mould; Illus. 352 pp. Paper. University of Alabama Press, 2003. $39.95.

A CHOCTAW REFERENCE GRAMMAR
George Aaron Broadwell; Illus. 378 pp. University of Nebraska Press, 2007. $70.

THE CHOCTAW REVOLUTION: LESSONS FOR FEDERAL INDIAN POLICY
Peter J. Ferrara; Illus. American for Tax Reform Foundation, 1998.

CHOCTAW TALES
Tom Mould; Stories are a gathering of oral traditions from the Mississippi Band of Choctaw Indians from the 1700s to today. Illus. 256 pp. Paper. U. Press of Mississippi, 2008. $25.

CHOCTAW VERB AGREEMENT & UNIVERSAL GRAMMAR
William D. Davies; Kluwer Academic, 1986. $48; paper, $19.50.

CHOCTAW WOMEN IN A CHAOTIC WORLD: THE CLASH OF CULTURES IN THE COLONIAL SOUTHEAST Michelene E. Pesantubbee
An ethnohistory. Illus. 220 pp. Map. Paper. U. of New Mexico Press, $24.95.

CHOCTAWS AT THE CROSSROADS: THE POLITICAL ECONOMY OF CLASS & CULTURE IN THE OKLAHOMA TIMBER REGION
Sandra Faiman-Silva; Illus. Maps. 285 pp. Paper. U. of Nebraska Press, 1997. $24.

THE CHOCTAWS IN OKLAHOMA: FROM TRIBE TO NATION, 1855-1970
Clara Sue Kidwell; 334 pp. Paper. University of Oklahoma Press, 2009. $19.95.

CHOCTAWS & MISSIONARIES IN MISSISSIPPI, 1818-1918
Clara Sue Kidwell; Explores how the Choctaws changed and adapted to U.S. policy of assimilation in their efforts to preserve their independence. Illus. 288 pp. Maps. Paper. University of Oklahoma Press, 1995. $14.95.

THE CHOCTAWS IN A REVOLUTIONARY AGE, 1750-1830
Greg O'Brien; Story of the Choctaws through the lives of Taboca and Franchimastabe, two leaders. Map. 160 pp. University of Nebraska Press, 2002. $45.

CHOOSING LIFE: SPECIAL REPORT ON SUICIDE AMONG ABORIGINAL PEOPLE
Royal Commission on Aboriginal People; Illus. 135 pp. Paper. Amazon.com, $24.95.

CHOTEAU CREEK: A SIOUX REMINISCENCE
Joseph Iron Eye Dudley; Growing up on the Yankton Sioux Reservation in South Dakota. 1993 Christopher Award Winner. Illus. 180 pp. Paper. U. of Nebraska Press, 1992. $15.95.

CHRISTIAN HARVEST
Bill B. DeGeer; 104 pp. Carlton Press, 1988. $8.95.

CHRISTIAN INDIANS & INDIAN NATIONALISM, 1855-1950: AN INTERPRETATION IN HISTORICAL & THEOLOGICAL PERSPECTIVES George Thomas
271 pp. Peter Lang, 1979. $41.

CHRISTIANITY & NATIVE TRADITIONS: INDIGENIZATION & SYNCRETISM
CHRONICLES OF AMERICAN INDIAN PROTEST Antonio R. Gualtieri
The actual views of Arctic missionaries of various denominations.
200 pp. Cross Cultural Publications, $19.95.

CHRONICLES OF BORDER WARFARE
Alexander Scott Withers; History of the settlement by the whites of Northwestern Virginia and Indian Wars of the State. Illus. Maps. 447 pp. Paper. Wennawoods Publishing, $16.95.

CHRONICLES OF BORDER WARFARE: HISTORY OF THE SETTLEMENTS BY WHITES OF NORTHWESTERN VIRGINIA Alexander S. Withers; Reprint. 7th revised ed. 468 pp. Paper. Amazon.com, 1997. $14.95.

CHRONOLOGY OF THE AMERICAN INDIAN
Examination of Indian history. Revised edition. Illus. 300 pp. American Indian Publishers, 1994. $85.

CHRONOLOGY OF AMERICAN INDIAN HISTORY
Liz Sonneborn; Updated edition. Illus. Photos. Map. Bibliography.
480 pp. Facts on File, Inc., 2007. $71.50.

CHRONOLOGY OF THE INDIAN WAR BATTLES & OTHER IMPORTANT EVENTS IN THE BOZEMAN TRAIL: POWDER RIVER COUNTRY FOR THE FRONTIER PERIOD - 1840 THROUGH 1900 Gil Bollinger; Illus. 25 pp. Paper. Gatchell Museum Association, 2000. 4.95.

CHRONOLOGY OF NATIVE NORTH AMERICAN HISTORY FROM PRE-COLUMBIAN TIMES TO THE PRESENT edited by Duane Champagne; Details important people, places, and events in the history of Native peoples. 574 pp. Amazon.com, 1994. $70.

TO THE CHUKCHI PENINSULA & TO THE TLINGIT INDIANS 1881/1882: JOURNALS & LETTERS BY AUREL & ARTHUR KRAUSE translated by Margot Krause McCaffrey; The expedition that brought knowledge of southern Alaska and its people, the Tlingit. Illus. Maps. 230 pp. Paper. University of Alaska Press, 1993. $17.50.

*THE CHUMASH
Robert O. Gibson; Grades 5 and up. Illus. 105 pp. Paper. Chelsea House, 1989. $9.95.

THE CHUMASH & COSTANOAN LANGUAGES
A.L. Kroeber; Reprint oif 1910 edition. 35 pp. Paper. Coyote Press, $4.06.

CHUMASH ETHNOBOTANY: PLANT KNOWLEDGE AMONG THE CHUMASH PEOPLE OF SOUTHERN CALIFORNIA Jan Timbrook, illus. by Chris Chapman; Features 1,500 species of plants; their traditional foods, medicine, etc. Paper. Heyday Books. $27.95.

CHUMASH HEALING
Phillip L. Walker & Travis Hudson; Medical & healing practices of a California Indian tribe--the Chumash of the Santa Barbara area. Reprint of 1993 ed. Illus. 161 pp. Paper. Malki-Ballena Press, 2004. $25.

*CHUMASH INDIAN GAMES
Travis Hudson & Jan Timbrook;
Reprint. Grades 2-6. Illus. 20 pp. Paper. Santa Barbara Museum, $4.95.

THE CHUMASH INDIANS OF SOUTHERN CALIFORNIA
Eugene Anderson, Jr.; Reprint of 1973 ed. Illus. Brochure. Malki-Ballena Press, 1989. $2.

THE CHUMASH PEOPLE
Santa Barbara Museum of Natural History
Revised reprint. Illus. 96 pp. Amazon.com. $12.95.

CHUMASH: A PICTURE OF THEIR WORLD
Bruce W. Miller, III; Illus. 144 pp. Paper. Amazon.com, 1988. $8.95.

THE CHUMASH & THEIR PREDECESSORS: AN ANNOTATED BIBLIOGRAPHY
Marie S. Holmes & John Johnson; 240 pp. paper. Santa Barbara Museum, 1998. $32.50.

THE CHUMASH WORLD AT EUROEAN CONTACT: POWER TRADE & FEASTING AMONG COMPLEX HUNTER GATHERERS Lynn H. Gamble
Illus. 376 pp. University of California Press, 2008. $55; paper, $29.95. E-book available..

CHURCH PHILANTHROPY FOR NATIVE AMERICANS & OTHER MINORITIES
Phyllis A. Meiners, Editor; Profiles over 50 grant programs & more than 25 loan programs from church & religious institutions for Native American, Hispanic, and other minority groups. each listing includes contact persons, special interests, sample grants, application deadlines & procedures, etc. CRC Publishing, 1994. $118.95.

CHURCHMEN & THE WESTERN INDIANS, 1820-1920
Clyde Milner, II, and Floyd O'Neil
Illus. Maps. 264 pp. University of Oklahoma Press, 1985. $28.95.

THE CIBECUE APACHE
Keith H. Basso; 106 pp. Paper. Waveland Press, 1970. $15.50.

THE CIRCLE IS SACRED: A MEDICINE BOOK FOR WOMEN
Scout Cloud Lee; Guide to women's ceremonies. Includes aboriginal medicine woman, Alinta, Cherokee Princess Moon Feathers, Spider Red-Gold, & Seneca elder, Grandmother Kitty. 137 bxw photos. 256 pp. Paper. Amazon.com, $17.95.

CIRCLE OF FIRE: THE INDIAN WAR OF 1865
John D. McDermott; Illus. 304 pp. Amazon.com, 2003. $26.95.

CIRCLE OF GOODS: WOMEN, WORK & WELFARE IN A RESERVATION COMMUNITY
Teresa Berman; Illus. 160 pp. State University of New York Press, $65.50; paper, $21.95.

A CIRCLE OF NATIONS: VOICES & VISIONS OF AMERICA INDIANS
John Gattuso; Reflection of the lives of contemporary American Indians through the eyes of well known Indian writers & photographers including Paula Gunn Allen, Leslie Marmon Silko, Joy Harjo, Simon Ortiz, White Deer of Autumn, David Neel, Monty Roessel & Ken Blackbird. Illus. 128 pp. Beyond Words Publishing, $39.95. Available in two-tape audiocassette, $15.95.

A CIRCLE OF POWER
William Higbie; Story of a Plains Indian boy seeking manhood. Illus. 90 pp.
Eagle's View, 1991. $13.95; paper, $7.95.

*THE CIRCLE OF THANKS: NATIVE AMERICAN POEMS & SONGS OF THANKSGIVING Joseph Bruchac; Illus. by Murv Jacob; Thanksgiving prayers of 14 Native American cultures. Grades PreK-3. Illus. 32 pp. Amazon.com, 1997. $11.21.

*CIRCLE OF WONDER: A NATIVE AMERICAN CHRISTMAS STORY
N. Scott Momaday, writer & illustrator; Illus. 18 color photos. 44 pp. University of New Mexico Press, 2001. Book, $19.95; audio tape, $5.95; book & tape package, $24.95.

CIRCLE & SQUARE TRACTS OF THE NOTTOWAY INDIANS
Martha Briggs & April Pittman; Illus. 13 pp. Paper. Dory Press, 1996. $5.25.

THE CIRCLE WITHOUT END: A SOURCEBOOK OF AMERICAN INDIAN ETHICS
Gerald & Francis Lombardi; Illus. 212 pp. Paper. Naturegraph, 1980. $8.95.

CIRCLES, CONSCIOUSNESS & CULTURE
James A. Mischke
Native American religious activities. Paper. Amazon.com, 1984. $2.50.

CIRCLES OF POWER
Ronald McCoy; Devoted to shields. Illus. 32 pp. Paper. Amazon.com., $6.

CIRCLES OF THE WORLD: TRADITIONAL ART OF THE PLAINS INDIANS
Richard Conn; Illus. 152 pp. Paper. Amazon.com, 1982. $14.95.

CITIZENS PLUS: ABORIGINAL PEOPLES & THE CANADIAN STATE
Alan C. Cairns; 208 pp. University of Washington Press, 2001. $43.95; paper, $35.95.

CITY INDIAN: NATIVE AMERICAN ACTIVISM IN CHICAGO, 1893-1934
Rosalyn Lapuer & David Beck; Illus. 288 pp. University of Nebraska Press, 2015. $40.

CLAIMING BREATH
Diane Glancy; Focuses on contemporary life of American Indians. 1993 American Book Award Winner. 119 pp. Paper. University of Nebraska Press, 1992. $12.

CLAIMING TRIBAL IDENTITY: THE FIVE TRIBES AND THE POLITICS OF FEDERAL ACKNOWLEDGEMENT Mark E. Miller; foreword by Chadwick Corntassel Smith
Illus. 480 pp. Paper. University of Oklahoma Press, $29.95.

CLAIMING TURTLE MOUNTAIN'S CONSTITUTION: THE HISTORY, LEGACY, AND FUTURE OF A TRIBAL NATION'S FOUNDING DOCUMENTS
Keith Richotte, Jr.; Illus. 304 pp. Paper. University of North Carolina Press, 2017. $95; paper, $32.95; eBook, $19.99.

CLAIMS FOR DEPREDATIONS BY SIOUX INDIANS
38th Congress, 1st Session; Reprint. 1974. Available from AbeBooks, $15.

*CLAMBAKE, A WAMPANOAG TRADITION
Russell M. Peters ; Grades 3-6. Illus. 48 pp. Lerner, 1992. $14.95.

*CLAMSHELL BOY: A MAKAH LEGEND
Terri Cohlene; Grades 1-5. Illus. Paper. Amazon.com, 1992. $4.95.

A CLAN MOTHER'S CALL: RECONSTRUCTING HAUDENOSAUNEE CULTURAL MEMORY Jeanette Rodriguez; ; Kevin J. Whte, Editor
120 pp. State University of New York Press, 2017. $75.

WILLIAM CLARK: JEFFERSONIAN MAN ON THE FRONTIER
Jerome O. Steffen
Reprint of 1977 edition. Illus. University of Oklahoma Press, $16.95; paper, $7.95.

A CLASH OF CULTURES ON THE WARPATH OF NATIONS: THE COLONIAL WARS IN THE HUDSON-CHAMPLAIN VALLEY
Theodore G. Corbett; Illus. 342 pp. Paper. Purple Mountain Press, 2002. $19.50.

CLASSIC HOPI & ZUNI KACHINA FIGURES
Barton Wright; photos by Andrea Portago
Photos of classic-era (1880s-1940s) Hopi & Zuni carved dolls from pprivate & public collections. Illus. 186 pp. Museum of New Mexico Press, 2008. $55.

CLASSIFICATION & DEVELOPMENT OF NORTH AMERICAN INDIAN CULTURES: A STATISTICAL ANALYSIS OF THE DRIVER-MASSEY SAMPLE
Harold E. Driver and James L. Coffin; Illus. Paper. Amazon.com, 1975. $15.

CLASSROOM ACTIVITIES ON WISCONSIN INDIAN TREATIES & TRIBAL SOVEREIGNTY Ronald N. Satz; 500 pp. Paper. Wisconsin Dept. of Public Instruction, 1995. $54.

CLAY, COPPER & TURQUOISE: THE MUSEUM COLLECTION OF CHACO CULTURE NATIONAL HISTORICAL PARKCHACO CULTURE NATIONAL HISTORICAL PARK STAFF, ET AL Western National Parks Association, 2004.

THE CLAY WE ARE MADE OF: HAUDENOSAUNEE LAND TENURE ON THE GRAND RIVER Susan M. Hill; 320 pp. Michigan State U. Press, 2014. $$62.95; Paper, $31.95

CLEARING A PATH: THEORETICAL APPROACHES TO THE PAST IN NATIVE AMERICAN STUDIES Nancy Shoemaker, Editor
225 pp. Paper. Amazon.com, 2001. $23.95.

THE CLIFF DWELLERS OF THE MESA VERDE, SOUTHWSTERN COLORADO
G. Nordenskiold; translated by D. Lloyd Morgan
Reprint of 1979 edition. Paper. Rio Grande Press, $27.50.

JOHN D. CLIFFORD'S INDIAN ANTIQUITIES: RELATED MATERIAL BY C.S. RAFINESQUE Charles Boewe, Editor; Clifford's letters, along with manuscript surveys and maps by Rafinesque. Illus. Amazon.com, 2000. $30.

CLOTHED-IN-FUR & OTHER TALES: AN INTRODUCTION TO OJIBWA WORLD VIEW
Thomas W. Overholt and J. Biard Callicott
198 pp. University Presses of America, 1982. $32.25; paper, $14.25.

*CLOUDWALKER: CONTEMPORARY NATIVE AMERICAN STORIES
Joel Monture; illus. by Carson Waterman
Grades 3 and up. Illus. 64 pp. Fulcrum Publishing, $15.95.

CLOVIS BLADE TECHNOLOGY: A COMPARATIVE STUDY OF THE KEVEN DAVIS CACHE, TEXAS Michael B. Collins & Marvin Kay; Illus. Tables. 250 pp. Paper. University of Texas Press, 1999. $29.95.

CLOWNS OF THE HOPI: TRADITION KEEPERS & DELIGHT MAKERS
Barton Wright; photos by Jerry Jacka; Looks at Hopi clowns, their purposes & historical backgrounds. Illus. 30 color photos. 148 pp. Amazon.com, $14.95.

*CLUES FROM THE PAST: A RESOURCE BOOK ON ARCHAEOLOGY
Pam Wheat & Brenda Whorton, Editors
Grades 3 and up. Illus. 200 pp. Paper. Hendrick-Long, 1990. $17.95.

COACH TOMMY THOMPSON & THE BOYS OF SEQUOYAH
Patti Dickinson; Cherokee athlete & football coach. 256 pp.
Paper. University of Oklahoma Press, 2010. $19.95.

COACOOCHEE'S BONES: A SEMINOLE SAGA
Susan A. Miller; Photos. Maps. 232 pp. University Press of Kansas, 2003. $34.95.

COAST SALISH: THEIR ART & CULTURE
Reg Ashwell; Illus. 88 pp. Paper. Amazon.com, 2006. $14.95.

COAST SALISH: THEIR ART, CULTURE & LEGENDS
Reg Ashwell; Illus. 88 pp. Paper. Amazon.com, 1978. $4.95.

THE COAST SALISH OF BRITISH COLUMBIA
Homer Barnett; Reprint of 1955 edition. Illus. 320 pp. Greenwood, $25.

COAST SALISH ESSAYS
Wayne Suttles; Paper. Amazon.con, 1987. $18.95.

*THE COAST SALISH PEOPLE
Frank W. Porter; Grades 5 and up. Illus. Chelsea House & Amazon.com, 1989. $17.95.

COAST SALISH SPIRIT DANCING: THE SURVIVAL OF AN ANCESTRAL RELIGION
Pamela Amoss; Amazon.com, 1978. $51.50.

COAST SALISH TOTEM POLES: MEDIA COMPANION AT "A TOTEM POLE HISTORY"
Pauline Hillaire & Gregory Fields; Paper. Amazon.com, $20.

COASTAL ENCOUNTERS: THE TRANSFORMATION OF THE GULF SOUTH IN THE 18TH CENTURY Richmond E. Brown, Editor
Illus. Maps. 328 pp. Paper. University of Nebraska Press, 2008. $24.95.

COASTAL INDIANS: READY-TO-USE ACTIVITIES & MATERIALS
Dana Newmann; Illus. 200 pp. Paper. Amazon.com, 1996. Teacher edition, $24.95.

COCHISE: CHIRICAHUA APACHE CHIEF
Edwin R. Sweeney; Biography of Cochise, the most resourceful & most feared Apache chief. Illus. Maps. Biblio. 502 pp. Paper. University of Oklahoma Press, 1991. $24.95.

THE COCHISE CULTURAL SEQUENCE IN SOUTHEASTERN ARIZONA
E.B. Sayles, et al; 192 pp. Paper. University of Arizona Press, 1983. $15.95.

COCHISE: FIRSTHAND ACCOUNTS OF THE CHIRICAHUA APACHE CHIEF
Edwin R. Sweeney; Illus. 320 pp. Paper. University of Oklahoma Press, 2014. $26.95.

COCHITI: A NEW MEXICO PUEBLO, PAST & PRESENT
Charles H. Lange; Illus. 650 pp. Paper. University of New Mexico Press, 1990. $22.50.

*COCHULA'S JOURNEY
Virginia Pounds Brown; The effect of the Spanish entrada upon Southeastern Indian culture as told through a young Indian woman taken captive by Spanish explorer DeSoto in 1539. Grades 6-8. 160 pp. Amazon.com, 1996. $18.

COCOPA ETHNOGRAPHY
William H. Kelly; A study of the Cocopa Tribe of the Colorado River Delta during the late 1880s. 150 pp. Paper. University of Arizona Press, 1977. $24.95.

CODE OF FEDERAL REGULATIONS, TITLE 25: INDIANS
U.S. Dept. of the InteriorPresents regulations relating to Native Americans administered by the U.S. Dept. of Interior in the areas of human services, education, tribal government, finance, land & water, energy & minerals, fish & wildlife, housing, heritage preservation, Indian arts & crafts, gaming, and relocation. 1,157 pp. Bernan Publciations, 2002. $60.

RALPH T. COE & THE COLLECTING OF AMERICAN INDIAN ART
Ralph T. Coe; J.C. King, et al tr.; Illus. 328 pp. Paper. Amazon.com, 2003.

THE COEUR D'ALENE INDIAN RESERVATION
Glen Adams; Government documents between government and the Coeur d'Alene tribe describing the sale of about 185,000 acres of tribal land in 1898. Reprint. 92 pp. Paper. Amazon.com. $29.95.

THE COEUR D'ALENE INDIAN RESERVATION: OUR FRIENDS THE COEUR D'ALENE INDIANS Lawrence Palladino
Two booklets in one binding. Facsimile of 1967 ed. 50 pp. Amazon.com, 2000. $7.95.

COEUR D'ALENE, OKANOGAN & FLATHEAD INDIANS
James Teit & Franz Boas; From the 45th annual report of the Bureau of American Ethnology, 1927-28. 382 pp. Amazon.com, $25.95; paper, $17.95.

COGEWEA, THE HALF-BLOOD
Mouning Dove; A depiction of the great Montana cattle range. 302 pp.
Paper. University of Nebraska Press, 1981. $16.95.

FELIX S. COHEN'S HANDBOOK OF FEDERAL INDIAN LAW
Felix S. Cohen; Facsimile of 1942 edition. 950 pp. University of New Mexico Press, $25.

THE COLD & HUNGER DANCE
Diane Glancy; The process and problems of language for modern Native authors.
Illus. 114 pp. Paper. University of Nebraska Press, 1998. $17.95.

COLD RIVER SPIRITS: STORY OF AN ATHABASCAN-IRISH FAMILY IN TWENTIETH CENTURY ALASKA Jan Harper-Haines
Illus. 225 pp. Amazon.com, 2000. $16.95.

MICHAEL COLEMAN
Illus. Paper. University of Nebraska Press, 1979. $12.95.

COLLABORATING AT THE TROWEL'S EDGE: TEACHING & LEARNING IN INDIGENOUS ARCHAEOLOGY Stephen W. Silliman; Covers the current state of collaborative indigenous archaeology in North America. 288 pp. University of Arizona Press, 2008. $65; paper, $35.

THE COLLECTED WORKS OF BENJAMIN HAWKINS
Benjamin Hawkins; intro. by Howard T. Foster; In 1795, Hawkins, a former U.S. senator & advisor to George Washington, was appointed U.S. Indian agent & supt. of all tribes south of the Ohio River. He lived among the Creek Indians from 1796-1816. His journals detail the ethnohistory of the Choctaw, Cherokee, Chickasaw, and, especially, the Creek Indians and the natural history of their territory. Illus. 664 pp. The University of Alabama Preee, 2003. $75; paper, $39.95. E-Book, 31.95.

THE COLLECTED WORKS OF EDWARD SAPIR
William Bright & Philip Sapir, Editors; Vol. V: American Indian Languages, 584 pp., 1990; Vol. VI: American Indian Languages, 559 pp. 1991; Vol. VII: Wishram Texts & Ethnography, 518 pp. 1990; Vol. X: Southern Paiute & Ute Linguistics & Ethnography, 932 pp. 1993; Northwest California Linguistics, XIV, 950 pp. 2000. $274. Amazon.com.

THE COLLECTED WRITINGS OF SAMSON OCCUM, MOHEGAN
Samson Occum; Oxford University Press, 2006. $65.

COLLECTING INDIAN KNIVES: IDENTIFICATION & VALUES
Lar Hothem, Ed.; 2nd revised ed. Illus. 176 pp. Paper. Amazon.com, 2000. $19.95.

COLLECTING NATIVE AMERICA, 1870-1960
Shepard Krech, III & Barbara A. Hail
Photos. 298 pp. Smithsonian Institution Press, 1999. $45.

COLLECTING NORTH AMERICAN INDIAN KNIVES
Lar Hothem; Illus. 300 pp. Paper. Hothem House, 1986. $14.95.

COLLECTING THE NAVAJO CHILD'S BLANKET
Joshua Baer; Illus. 60 pp. Paper. Amazon.com, 1986. $21.

THE COLLECTING PASSIONS OF DENNIS & JANIS LYON
Diana F. Pardue; The Heard Museum, 2004.

COLLECTING THE PRE-COLUMBIAN PAST: A SYMPOSIUM AT DUMBARTON OAKS
Elizabeth H. Boone, Editor; Illus. 368 pp. paper. Amazon.com, 1990. $40.

COLLECTING THE WEAVER'S ART: THE WILLIAM CLAFLIN COLLECTION OF SOUTHWESTERN TEXTILES Laurie D. Webster
Paper. Peabody Museum of Archaeology & Ethnology, 2003. $19.95.

COLLECTING THE WEST: C.R. SMITH COLLECTION OF WESTERN AMERICAN ART
Richard H. Saunders; Illus. 224 pp. University of Texas Press, 1988. $35.

COLLECTIONS OF SOUTHWESTERN POTTERY
Allan Hayes & John Blom; Candlestickls to Canteens, Frogs to Figurines. Anasazi to Zuni. 52 color photos. Paper. Northland Press, $9.95.

COLLECTOR'S GUIDE TO INDIAN PIPES: IDENTIFICATION & VALUES
Lar Hothem; Study of American Indian pipes of all major classes. 1,000 photos, 700 in color. 300 pp. Paper. Collector Books, 1998. $29.95.

COLLECTIVE WILLETO: THE VISIONARY CARVINGS OF A NAVAJO ARTIST
Essays by Shonto Begay, Walter Hopps, Lee Kogan, and Greg Lachapelle; photos by Bruce Hucko. Illus. 120 pp. Museum of New Mexico Press, 2000. $45; paper, $29.95.

JOHN COLLIER'S CRUSADE FOR INDIAN REFORM, 1920-1954
Kenneth R. Philp; Commissioner of Indian Affairs under FDR, Collier rejected the idea of Americanizing Indians in favor of preserving their traditions. 304 pp. Paper. University of Arizona Press, 1977. $8.95.

COLLOQUIAL NAVAJO: A DICTIONARY
Robert W. Young & William Morgan; A practical guide to colloquial terms and idiomatic expressions of the Navajo language. 461 pp. Paper. Amazon.com, 1994. $16.95.

COLONIAL AMERICAN TROOPS, 1610-1774
Rene Chartrand; Illus. 48 pp. Paper. MBI Distribution Services, 2002. $14.95.

COLONIAL DISCOURSES, COLLECTIVE MEMORIES, & THE EXHIBITION OF NATIVE AMERICAN CULTURES & HISTORIES IN THE CONTEMPORARY U.S.
C. Richard King; 250 pp. Amazon.com, 1998. $50.

COLONIAL ENCOUNTERS IN A NATIVE AMERICAN LANDSCAPE:
THE SPANISH & DUTCH IN NORTH AMERICA
Nan A. Rothschild; Illus. 272 pp. Smithsonian Institution Press, 2003. $39.95.

COLONIAL ENTANGLEMENT: CONSTITUTING A TWENTY-FIRST-CENTURY OSAGE NATION Jean Dennison (Osage); Looks at the debates about blood, culture, minerls, and sovereignty during the 2004-06 Osage reform process.

COLONIAL GENOCIDE IN INDIGENOUS NORTH AMERICA
Alexander Laban Hinton, Andrew Wollford, Jeff Benvenuto
Essays on genocide and colonial expansion. Illus. 360 pp. Duke University Press, 2014. $99.95; paper, $27.95.

COLONIAL INITMACIES: INDIAN MARRIAGE IN EARLY NEW ENGLAND
Ann Marie Plane; Reprint. Illus. 272 pp. Cornell U. Press, 2000. $39.95; paper, $ 17.95.

COLONIAL WRITING & THE NEW WORLD, 1583-1671: ALLEGORIES OF DESIRE
Thomas J. Scanlan; Illus. 152 pp. Cambridge University Press, 1999. $80.

COLONIZED THROUGH ART: AMERICAN INDIAN SCHOOLS & ART EDUCATION, 1889-1915 Marinella Lentis; Illus. 450 pp. University of Nebraska Press, 2017. $65.

COLONIZING BODIES: ABORIGINAL HEALTH & HEALING IN BRITISH COLUMBIA, 1900-1950 Mary-Ellen Kelm; Looks at the impact of government policy on the health of native people. 272 pp. Paper. University of Washington Press, 1999. $35.95.

COLOR-LINE TO BORDERLANDS: THE MATRIX OF AMERICAN ETHNIC STUDIES
Johnella E. Butler, Editor; Essays on the historical development of Ethnic Studies. 326 pp. Paper. University of Washington Press, 2001. $25.

THE COLOR OF THE LAND: RACE, NATION, & THE POLITICS OF LAND OWNERSHIP IN OKLAHOMA, 1832-1929 David Chang; Histories of Creek Indians, African Americans, and whites in Oklahoma. Illus. Maps. 312 pp. University of North Carolina Press, 2010. $59.95; paper, $22.95.

MANGAS COLORADAS: CHIEF OF THE CHIRICAHUA APACHES
Edwin R. Sweeney; Illus. Maps. 610 pp. Paper. U. of Oklahoma Press, 2011. $32.95

THE COLORADO PLATEAU: THE LAND & THE INDIANS
K.C. Compton, Editor; photos by Tom Till & Stephen Trimble
An overview of the geology and the indigenous cultures of the Colorado Plateau region of Colorado, Utah, Arizona and New Mexico--the Four Corner states.. Pueblo, Ute, Navajo, Jicarilla Apache, and Paiute cultures. photographs Pennington collection of Durango, Colorado. Illus. 88 pp. Amazon.com, 1999. $14.95.

*A COLORING BOOK OF AMERICAN INDIANS
Grades K-3. Paper. Bellerophon, $3.95.

*A COLORING BOOK OF HIDATSA INDIAN STORIES
Roberta Krim & Thomas Thompson
Grades K-3. 32 pp. Paper. Minnesota Historical Society Press, $3.50.

*COLORS OF THE NAVAJO
Emily Abbink; Introduces children to the history, traditions, and daily life of the Navajo. Grades 1-4. Illus. Map. Paper. Lerner, 1998. $5.95.

THE COLOUR OF RESISTANCE: A CONTEMPORARY COLLECTION
OF WRITING BY ABORIGINAL WOMEN Connie Fife
A collection of writing by 45 Native women from throughout North America,some of the strongest voices in Native literature. Paper. Amazon.com, 1993.

THE COLUMBIA GUIDE TO AMERICAN INDIANS OF THE GREAT PLAINS
Loretta Fowler; Illus. 305 pp. Columbia University Press, 2003. $90; paper, $32; e-Book, $31.99

THE COLUMBIA GUIDE TO AMERICAN INDIANS OF THE NORTHEAST
Kathleen Bragdon; Illus. 352 pp. Columbia University Press, 2002. $90; paper, $32; e-Book, $31.99

THE COLUMBIA GUIDE TO AMERICAN INDIANS OF THE SOUTHEAST
Theda Perdue; Illus. 320 pp. Columbia University Press, 2001. $90; paper, $32; e-Book, $31.99

THE COLUMBIA GUIDE TO AMERICAN INDIANS OF THE SOUTHWEST
Trudy Griffin-Pierce; Illus. 320 pp. Columbia University Press, 2010. $90; paper, $32; e-Book, $31.99

COLUMBIA RIVER BASKETRY: GIFT OF THE ANCESTORS, GIFT OF THE EARTH
Mary Dodds Schlick; The material culture of the Columbia River region. Includes traditional designs and techniques of construction. Color photos. Illus. 240 pp. Biblio. Paper. University of Washington Press, $35.

COLUMBUS & BEYOND: VIEWS FROM NATIVE AMERICANS
A look at Columbus by prominent Native writers including Paula Gunn Allen, Lee Francis III, Linda Hogan, Simon Ortiz, et al. Western National Parks Association, $7.95.

COLUMBUS DAY
Jimmie Durham; Poems, prose, drawings & speeches. 110 pp.
Paper. U. of New Mexico Press, $8.95.

*COLUMBUS DAY
Vicki Liestman; illus. by Rick Hanson; Grades K-3. Deals with the mistreatment of the Indians by Columbus & the Spaniards. Illus. 50 pp. Lerner, 1991. $15.95; paper, $5.95

COLUMBUS: HIS ENTERPRISE: EXPLODING THE MYTH
Hans Koning; Depicts Columbus for who he was and describes the consequences of his actions on the Native people and the environment. Amazon.com, 1991. $8.95.

COLUMBUS & LAS CASAS: THE CONQUEST & CHRISTIANIZATION OF AMERICA, 1492-1566 David M. Traboulay; Illus. 468 pp. Paper. U. Press of America, 1994. $47.

COLUMBUS & THE NEW WORLD: MEDICAL IMPLICATIONS
Guy A. Settipane, et al; Illus. 150 pp. Amazon.com, 1995. $49.50.

COLUMBUS, SHAKESPEARE & THE INTERPRETATION OF THE NEW WORLD
Jonathan Hart; 248 pp. Palgrave Macmillan, 2003. $65.

COLUMNS OF VENGEANCE: SOLDIERS, SIOUX, AND THE PUNITIVE EXPEDITIONS, 1863-1864 Paul N. Beck; 328 pp. U. of Oklahoma Press, 2010. $34.95; paper, $19.95.

*THE COMANCHE
Willard Rollings; Grades 7-12. Illus. 112 pp. Chelsea House, 1989. $17.95; paper, $9.95.

*THE COMANCHE
T. Jensen Lacey; Paul Rosier, Series Editor
Grades 6-12. 136 pp. Chelsea House, 2010. $35.

COMANCHE CENSUS
Southwest Oklahoma Genealogical Society

COMANCHE CODE TALKERS OF WORLD WAR II
William C. Meadows; Interviews with surviving members. Photos. Tables. 320 pp. Paper. University of Texas Press, 2003. $30.

COMANCHE DICTIONARY
Comanche Language & Cultural Preservation Committee

COMANCHE DICTIONARY & GRAMMAR
Lile Robinson & James Armagost; Paper. Amazon.com, 1990.

THE COMANCHE EMPIRE
Pekka Hamamainen; Illus. Maps. 512 pp. Paper. Yale University Press, 2009. $26.

COMANCHE ETHNOLOGY: FIELD NOTES OF E. ADAMSON HOEBEL, WALDO R. WEDEL, ET AL compiled & edited by Thomas W. Kavanagh
Archive of traditional cultural information on Comanches. Photos, figures. 571 pp. University of Nebraska Press, 2008. $55.

COMANCHE LESSONS
Comanche Language & Cultural Preservation Committee

COMANCHE MOON: A PICTURE NARRATIVE ABOUT CYNTHIA ANN PARKER, HER TWENTY-FIVE YEAR CAPTIVITY AMONG THE COMANCHE INDIANS-AND HER SON QUANAH PARKER, THE LAST CHIEF OF THE COMANCHES
Jack Jackson; 129 pp. Paper. Texas A&M University Press, 1979. $5.95.

COMANCHE POLITICAL HISTORY: ETHNOHISTORICAL PERSPECTIVE 1706-1875
Thomas W. Kavanagh; Illus. Maps. 586 pp. U. of Nebraska Press, 1996. $47; paper, $20.

COMANCHE SOCIETY
Gerald Betty; Illus. Paper. Texas A&M University Press, $22.95.

COMANCHE SONGS
Comanche Language & Cultural Preservation Committee

COMANCHE TALKING DICTIONARY
Comanche national Museum; Website> www.comanchemuseum.com/dictionary

COMANCHE TREATIES DURING THE CIVIL WAR
R.J. DeMallie; 30 pp. Institute for the Development of Indian Law, $10.

COMANCHE TREATIES: HISTORICAL BACKGROUND
R.J. DeMallie; 20 pp. Institute for the Development of Indian Law, $7.50.

COMANCHE TREATIES OF 1835 WITH THE U.S.
R.J. DeMallie; 20 pp. Institute for the Development of Indian Law, $7.

COMANCHE TREATIES OF 1846 WITH THE U.S.
R.J. DeMallie; 16 pp. Institute for the Development of Indian Law, $6.50.

COMANCHE TREATIES OF 1850, 1851, 1853 WITH THE U.S.
R.J. DeMallie; 60 pp. Institute for the Development of Indian Law, $12.50.

COMANCHE TREATIES WITH THE REPUBLIC OF TEXAS
R.J. DeMallie; 20 pp. Institute for the Development of Indian Law, $7.50.

COMANCHE VOCABULARY: TRILINGUAL EDITION
Manuel Garcia Rejon, Compiler; Daniel J. Gelo, translator & editor
106 pp. Paper. University of Texas Press, 1995. $19.95.

*COMANCHE WARBONNET
Troxey Kemper; Fiction. About famous Comanche chief Quanah Parker.
Paper. Amazon.com, $12.50.

THE COMANCHERO FRONTIER: A HISTORY OF NEW MEXICAN-PLAINS INDIAN RELATIONS   Charles L. Kenner; History of the Comancheros, or Mexicans who traded with the Comanche Indians in the early Southwest. Illus. Maps. Biblio. 270 pp. Paper. University of Oklahoma Press, 1994. $15.95.

COMANCHES & GERMANS ON THE TEXAS FRONTIER: THE ETHNOLOGY OF HEINRICH BERGHAUS
Daniel Gelo & Christopher Wiickham; Texas A&M University Press, 2017. $35.

THE COMANCHES: A HISTORY, 1706-1875
Thomas W. Kavanaugh; In-depth historical study of Comanche social and political groups. Illus. 588 pp. Paper. University of Nebraska Press, 1999. $20.

COMANCHES IN THE NEW WEST, 1895-1908: HISTORIC PHOTOGRAPHS
Stanley Noyes, et al; Photos. 127 pp. University of Texas Press, 1999. $24.95.

THE COMANCHES: LORDS OF THE SOUTH PLAINS
Ernest Wallace and E. Adamson Hoebel
Reprint of 1952 edition. Illus. Map. 400 pp. University of Oklahoma Press, $24.95.

COMANCHES & MENNONITES ON THE OKLAHOMA PLAINS
Marvin E. Kroeber; Illus. 196 pp. Paper. Kindred Productions, 1997. $18.95.

COMB RIDGE AND ITS PEOPLE: THE ETHNOHISTORY OF A ROCK
Robert S. McPherson
Southeastern Utah. Illus. Paper. Utah State University Press, 2010. $31.95

COMBING THE SNAKES FROM HIS HAIR
James T. Stevens; Iroquois story of healing; poetry. 143 pp. Paper. Michigan State University Press, 2002. $23.95.

"COME, BLACKROBE": DE SMET & THE INDIAN TRAGEDY
John J. Killoren, S.J.; Evaluation of DeSmet, known as "Blackrobe," an evangelist among the Coeur d'Alenes, the Flatheads, the Kalispels, the Blackfeet, and the Kutenais. Illus. Maps. Biblio. 448 pp. Paper. University of Oklahoma Press, 1994. $18.95.

*COME TO OUR SALMON FEAST
Martha F. McKeown; Grades 4-9. Illus. 80 pp. Binford & Mort, 1959. $7.95.

COMEUPPANCE AT KICKING HORSE CASINO & OTHER STORIES
Charles Brashear; 200 pp. Paper. UCLA, American Indian Studies Center, 2000. $15. Also available from Amazon.com, Albris.com.

COMING BACK SLOW: THE IMPORTANCE OF PRESERVING SALISH INDIAN CULTURE & LANGUAGE   Agnes Vanderburg; Views of leading Salish elders on the preserving of Salish Indina culture. 16 pp. paper. SKC Press.

COMING DOWN FROM ABOVE: PROPHECY, RESISTANCE, AND RENEWAL IN NATIVE AMERICAN RELIGIONS
Lee Irwin; Comprehensive survey of prphetic movements in Native North America. 528 pp. University of Oklahoma Press, 2010. $75.00.

COMING FULL CIRCLE: SPIRITUALITY & WELLNESS AMONG NATIVE COMMNITIES IN THE PACIFIC NORTHWEST
Suzanne Crawford O'Brien; Illus. 480 pp. University of Nebraska Press, 2013. $90.

*THE COMING OF COYOTE
Donald J. Boon
Grades 4 and up. Illus. 64 pp. Paper. Amazon.com, 1994. $9.95.

THE COMING OF THE SPIRIT OF PESTILENCE: INTRODUCED INFECTIOUS DISEASES & POPULATION DECLINE AMONG NORTHWEST COAST INDIANS, 1774-1874 Robert Boyd; Illus. Maps. 428 pp. University of Washington Press, 1999. $60.

COMING TO LIGHT: CONTEMPORARY TRANSLATIONS OF THE NATIVE LITERATURES OF NORTH AMERICA edited by Brian Swann
Native American narratives and poetry. 525 pp. U. of Nebraska Press, $60; paper, $24.50.

COMING TO STAY: A COLUMBIA RIVER JOURNEY
Mary Dodds Schlick; The relationship between a non-Indian family and their Indian neighbors on the Colville, Warm Springs & Yakama Reservations. Illus. Map. 208 pp. Paper. University of Washington Press, 2007. $22.50.

COMMAND OF THE WATERS: IRON TRIANGLES, FEDERAL WATER DEVELOPMENT, & INDIAN WATER Daniel McCool
Reprint 1987 ed. Illus. 321 pp. Paper. University of Arizona Press, 1994. $19.95.

COMMANDERS & CHIEFS: A BRIEF HISTORY OF FORT MCDOWELL, AZ, 1865-1890, IT'S OFFICERS & MEN & THE INDIANS THEY WERE ORDERED TO SUBDUE
Elaine Waterstrat; Illus. 116 pp. Paper. Munt McDowell Press, 1993. $6.95.

COMMERCE BY A FROZEN SEA: NATIVE AMERICANS & THE EUROPEAN FUR TRADE   Ann Carlos & Frank Lewis; A cross-cultural study of a century of contact between North America native peoples & Europeans. 260 pp. U. of Pennsylvania Press, 2010.

THE COMMISSIONERS OF INDIAN AFFAIRS, 1824-1977
Robert Kvasnicka & Herman Viola; Discusses the leaders of the Bureau of Indian Affairs. Illus. University of Nebraska Press, 1977.

COMMON & CONTESTED GROUND: A HUMAN & ENVIRONMENTAL HISTORY OF THE NORTHWESTERN PLAINS Theodore Binnema
History of northwestern plains between A.D. 200 and 1806. Illus. Maps. 288 pp. University of Oklahoma Press, 2001. $29.95.

THE COMMON POT: THE RECOVERY OF NATIVE SPACE IN THE NORTHEAST
Lisa Brooks; Significance of writing to colonial-eraNative American reisistance. Illus. Maps. 352 pp. University of Minnesota Press, 2008. $67.50; paper, $22.50.

COMMON THREADS: PUEBLO & NAVAJO TEXTILES IN THE SOUTHWEST MUSEUM
Kathleen Whitaker; 64 pp. Paper. Southwest Museum, 1998.

COMMONERS, TRIBUTE, & CHIEFS: THE DEVELOPMENT OF ALGONQUIAN CULTURE IN THE POTOMAC VALLEY Stephen R. Potter; Archaeological and documentary information on the Indianpeoples who lived in the Potomac Valley from A.D. 200 to 1650. 280 pp. Amazon.com, 1993. $29.95.

COMMUNICATION & DEVELOPMENT: A STUDY OF TWO INDIAN VILLAGES
Y.V. Rao; Reprint of 1966 edition. Paper. Books on Deamnd, $38.

COMMUNITY-BASED RESEARCH: A HANDBOOK FOR NATIVE AMERICANS
Susan Guyette; 358 pp. Paper. UCLA, American Indian Studies Center, $15.

A COMPANION TO AMERICAN INDIAN HISTORY
Neal Salisbury & Philip J. Deloria, Eds.; Illus. 515 pp. Amazon.com, 2001. $131.95.

A COMPANION TO THE ANTHROPOLOGY OF AMERICAN INDIANS
Thomas Biolsi, Editor; 27 original contributions on the anthropological knowledge of Indian people. 592 pp. Amazon.com, 2005. $169.95; paper, $49.95.

COMPARATIVE CHUKOTKO-KAMCHATKAN DICTIONARY
Michael Fortescue; Maps. 496 pp. Amazon.com, 2005. $235.20.

COMPARATIVE HOKAN-COAHUILTECAN STUDIES
Margaret Langdon; Illus. 114 pp. Paper. Amazon.com, 1974. $58.50.

COMPARATIVE INDIGENEITIES OF THE AMERICAS: TOWARD A HEMISPHERIC APPROACH M. Bianet Castellanos, et al; Paper. University of Arizona Press, $37.95.

COMPARATIVE STUDIES IN AMERINDIAN LANGUAGES
Esther Matteson, et al; 251 pp. Paper. Amazon.com, 1972. $55.75.

A COMPARATIVE STUDY OF LAKE IROQUOIAN ACCENT
Karin Michelson; Kluwer Academic, 1988. $89.

COMPASS OF THE HEART: EMBODYING MEDICINE WHEEL TEACHINGS
Loren Cruden; Offers insight & suggestions based on the author's lifetime of work with Native American & other earth-oriented traditions. Illus. 224 pp. Inner Traditions, 1996. $14.95.

THE COMPLEAT STOMP DANCER
James H. Howard
Performed in Eastern Oklahoma. Illus. 23 pp. Paper. Lakota Books, 1995. $9.95.

COMPETING VOICES FROM NATIVE AMERICA: FIGHTING WORDS
D.J. Ball & Joy Porter; Illus. Map. 328 pp. Greenwood Publishing, 2009. $65.

THE COMPLETE BOOK OF NATURAL SHAMANISM
Robert J. Titus; Amazon.com, $11.45 postpaid.

THE COMPLETE BOOK OF SEMINOLE PATCHWORK
Beverly Rush & Lassie Wittman
From Traditional Methods to Contemporary Uses. Illus. 128 pp. Paper. Dover, $9.95.

COMPLETE DELAWARE ROLL 1898
Dorothy Mauldin & Jeff Bowen; 100 pp. NativeStudy.com, 2001.

COMPLETE GUIDE TO TRADITIONAL NATIVE AMERICAN BEADWORK
Joel Monture; A definitive study of authentic tools, materials, techniques & styles. Illus. John Wiley & Sons, $14.

THE COMPLETE HOW-TO BOOK OF INDIAN CRAFT
W. Ben Hunt; 68 projects. Illus. 186 pp. Written Heritage, 1973. $13.95.

THE COMPLETE IDIOT'S GUIDE TO NATIVE AMERICAN HISTORY
Walter C. Fleming; Illus. 366 pp. Paper. Amazon.com, 2003. $18.95.

COMPLETE NATIVE AMERICAN RESOURCE LIBRARY: READY-TO-USE ACTIVITIES & MATERIALS
Dana Newmann; 4 vols. Coastal Indians; Desert Indians; Plains Indians, and Woodland Indians. Illus. 200 pp. ea.; Paper. Amazon.com. 1996. $25 ea.

THE COMPLETE SEYMOUR: COLVILLE STORYTELLER
Peter Seymour; compiled & edited by Anthony Mattina
Illus. 816 pp. University of Nebraska Press, 2015. $55. E-Book available.

COMPLETING THE CIRCLE
Virginia Driving Hawk Sneve; Stories of Native American women.
Illus. 120 pp. University of Nebraska Press, 1995. $25; paper, $8.95.

CONCERNING THE LEAGUE: THE IROQUOIS LEAGUE TRADITION AS DICTATED IN ONONDAGA BY JOHN ARTHUR GIBSON
Hanni Woodbury, Editor; Paper. Syracuse University Press, 1993. $80.

A CONCISE DICTIONARY OF MINNESOTA OJIBWE
John D. Nichols & Earl Nyholm
An expanded, revised edition. 320 pp. Paper. University of Minesota Press, 1994. $16.95.

A CONCISE DICTIONARY OF INDIAN TRIBES OF NORTH AMERICA
Barbara Leitch et al; Keith Irvine, Editor
Revised 2nd edition. Reference Publications, 1995. $75.

CONCISE ENCYCLOPEDIA OF THE AMERICAN INDIAN
Bruce Grant; Over 800 entries covering legends, lore, weapons and wars, beliefs, tools, information on each tribe. Illus. 352 pp. Cherokee Publications, 1989. $7.99.

THE CONCISE LAKHOTA DICTIONARY: ENGLISH TO LAKHOTA
Cheyenne River Sioux Tribal Members
Features over 4,000 entries of words from the Lakhota dialect of the ancient Sioux language. 70 pp. Paper. Todd Publications, 2000. $35.

A CONCISE NUXALK-ENGLISH DICTIONARY
H.F. Nater; Illus. 184 pp. Paper. University of Chicago Press, 1993. $15.95.

THE CONFEDERATE CHEROKEE: JOHN DREW'S REGIMENT OF MOUNTED RIFLES
W. Craig Gaines; Updated edition. Illus. 192 pp. Paper. The LSU Press, 2017. $24.95.

CONFEDERATE COLONEL & CHEROKEE CHIEF: THE LIFE OF WILLIAM HOLLAND THOMAS E. Stanley Godbold, Jr. & Mattie U. Russell; A white man from western North Carolina, he was adopted by a small Cherokee Indian band and later became its chief. Paper. Amaazon.com & University of Tennessee Press, 2007. $19.95.

THE CONFLICT BETWEEN THE CALIFORNIA INDIAN & WHITE CIVILIZATION
Sherburne F. Cook; Reprint. 4 vols. in one. Amazon.com, $14.50; paper, $10.50.

CONFLICT & SCHISM IN NEZ PERCE ACCULTURATION
Deward Walker; Illus. 171 pp. Paper. University of Idaho Press, 1968. $10.95.

THE CONFLICT OF EUROPEAN & EASTERN ALGONKIAN CULTURES, 1504-1700: A STUDY IN CANADIAN CIVILIZATION
Alfred Bailey; Second edition. Paper. University of Toronto Press, 1969. $9.95.

CONFLICTING VISIONS IN ALASKA EDUCATION
Richard Dauenhauer; The education of Natives in Alaska. Published by Tlingit Readers, Inc. 48 pp. Paper. University of Alaska Press, 1997. $6.50.

CONFOUNDING THE COLOR LINE: THE INDIAN-BLACK EXPERIENCE IN NORTH AMERICA
James F. Brooks, Editor; Illus. Map. U. of Nebraska Press, 2002. $70; paper, $29.95.

CONFRONTING RACE: WOMEN & INDIANS ON THE FRONTIER, 1815-1915
Glenda Riley; Paper. University of New Mexico Press, $21.95.

CONNECTICUT'S INDIGENOUS PEOPLES: WHAT ARCHAEOLOGY, HISTORY, & ORAL TRADITIONS TEACH US ABOUT THEIIR COMMUNITIES AND CULTURES
Lucianne Lavin; Rosemary Volpe, Editor
Illus. 528 pp. Paper. Yale University Press, 2015. $25.

CONNECTICUT UNSCATHED: VICTORY IN GREAT NARRAGANSETT WAR, 1675-1676 Jason W. Warren
The King Philip's War. Illus. Maps. 240 pp. University of Oklahoma Press, 2014. $29.95.

CONNOTATIONS
Maurice Kenny; Poetry. Native American Studies. Paper. White Pine Press, 2008. $15.

CONOZCA SUS RAICES / KNOW YOUR ROOTS: A MAP OF THE INDIGENOUS PEOPLES OF MEXICO & CENTROAMERICA Dolan H. Eargle, Jr., Editor
A full color, 18"x24" poster, bilingual - Spanish & English with color-coded legend of contemporary ethnic homelands grouped by linguistic families. Mexico to Panama. Biblio. Trees Company Press, $5.

CONQUEST BY LAW: HOW THE DISCOVERY OF AMERICA DISPOSSESSED INDIGENOUS PEOPLES OF THEIR LANDS Lindsay G. Robertson
Illus. 272 pp. Oxford University Press, 2007. $30.95; eBook available.

CONQUEST & CATASTROPHE: CHANGING RIO GRANDE PUEBLO SETTLEMENT PATTERNS IN THE 16TH & 17TH CENTURIES
Elinore M. Barrett; Illus. 192 pp. University of New Mexico Press, 2004. $39.95.

THE CONQUEST OF THE KARANKAWAS & THE TONKAWAS, 1821-1859
Kelly F. Himmel; Explores how geopolitical factors, economic factors & cultural differences as a major cause of the groups' destructions. 224 pp. Texas A&M U. Press, 1999. $32.95.

THE CONQUEST OF PARADISE: CHRISTOPHER COLUMBUS & THE COLUMBIAN LEGACY Kirkpatrick Sale; Re-examination of colonialism & its wake of ecological destruction. 464 pp. Paper. Penguin USA, 1993. $12.95.

THE CONQUEST OF TEXAS: ETHNIC CLEANSING IN THE PROMISED LAND, 1820-1875 Gary Clayton Anderson; Illus. 544 pp. University of Oklahoma Press, $29.95.

CONQUEST: SEXUAL VIOLENCE & AMERICAN INDIAN GENOCIDE
Andrea Smith; Winona LaDuke, contributor
Native women. 264 pp. Paper. Duke University Press, 2015. $23.95.

CONQUESTS & HISTORICAL IDENTITIES IN CALIFORNIA, 1769-1936
Lisbeth Haas; Illus. 284 pp. University of California Press, 1995. $40.

CONSERVATION & INDIAN RIGHTS
David W. Felder; 48 pp. Paper. Wellington Press, 1996. $8.95.

CONSERVATISM AMONG THE IROQUOIS AT THE SIX NATIONS RESERVE
Annemarie Shimony; Ethnography. Includes the practices of the Longhouse religion, the events of the Iroquoian life cycle, the use of folk medicine, witchcraft, and rituals of death & burial. 348 pp. Paper. Syracuse University Press, 1994. $19.95.

CONQUERING HORSE
Frederick Manfred; 370 pp. Paper. University of Nebraska Press, 1983. $8.95.

CONQUEST & CATASTROPHE: CHANGING RIO GRANDE PUEBLO SETTLEMENT
Elinore M. Barrett; Maps. 192 pp. Paper. University of New Mexico Press, 2001. $30.

CONQUEST OF APACHERIA
Dan Thrapp; Illus. 406 pp. Maps. University of Oklahoma Press, 1967. $19.95.

CONQUEST OF THE KARANKAWAS & THE TONKAWAS, 1821-1859
Kelly F. Himmel; 224 pp. Texas A&M University Press, 1999. $32.95.

CONQUISTADOR IN CHAINS: CABEZA DE VACA & THE INDIANS OF THE AMERICAS
David A. Howard; Illus. 240 pp. Paper. University of Alabama Press, 1997. $29.95.

CONSERVATISM AMONG THE IROQUOIS AT THE SIX NATIONS RESERVE
Annemarie Shimony; Reprint. 344 pp. Paper. Syracuse University Press, $19.95.

CONSOLIDATED NATIVE LAW STATUTES, REGULATIONS & TREATIES
600 pp. Paper. Carswell, 1999. $34.50.

CONSPIRACY OF INTERESTS: IROQUOIS DISPOSSESSION & THE RISE OF NEW YORK STATE Laurence M. Hauptman
Photos. Maps. Biblio. 272 pp. Syracuse U. Press, 1999. $34.95.

THE CONSTITUTION & LAWS OF THE CHOCTAW NATION
Reprint. 3 vols. Amazon.com & Alibris.com, $12.

CONSTITUTION, LAWS & TREATIES OF THE CHICKASAWS
Reprint. Amazon.com & Alibris.com, $17.

THE CONSTITUTION OF THE FIVE NATIONS – THE IROQUOIS BOOK OF THE GREAT LAW Arthur C. Parker; Paper. Amazon.com, $5.95.

CONSTITUTIONALISM & NATIVE AMERICANS, 1903-1968
John R. Wunder, Editor; Reprint. Illus. 408. Garland, $77.

THE CONSTITUTIONS & LAWS OF THE AMERICAN INDIAN TRIBES
This program presents the complete collection of the written constitutions and laws of the American Indian tribes to 1906 when tribal governments in Indian territory were abolished. The constitutions for the following tribes are included: The Chickasaw, Osage, Cherokee, Choctaw, Muskogee, Creek, and Sac & Fox. Two series. 53 vols. See Amazon.com & Alibris.com for titles, descriptions and prices.

CONSTRUCTING CULTURES THEN & NOW: CELEBRATING FRANZ BOAS & THE JESUP NORTH PACIFIC EXPEDITION Laurel Kendall & I.I. Krupnik, Eds.
Illus. 365 pp. Paper. Arctic Studies Center, National Museum of Natural History, 2003.

CONSTRUCTING FLORIDIANS: NATIVES & EUROPEANS IN THE COLONIAL FLORIDAS, 1513-1783 Daniel S. Murphree
Illus. 200 pp. Paper. University Press of Florida, 2017. $19.95.

CONSTRUCTING LIVES AT MISSION SAN FRANCISCO: NATIVE CALIFORNIANS & HISPANIC COLONISTS, 1776-1821 Quincy Newell; Examines the complexity of cultural contact between Franciscans & the Native populations at Mission San Francisco. Illus. 3 maps. 277 pp. University of New Mexico Press, $39.95; paper, $30.

CONSULTING WITH TRIBES FOR OFF-RESERVATION PROJECTS
Dean B. Suagee; American Bar Association, 2010. $19.95.

CONSUMER'S GUIDE TO SOUTHWESTERN INDIAN ARTS & CRAFTS
Mark T. Bahti; Guide to determining the quality & authenticity of rugs, blankets, jewelry, and pottery. Includes buying tips, and a list of hallmarks of well known silversmiths. Illus. 32 pp. Paper. Treasure Chest, $3.

THE CONSUMER'S RIGHTS UNDER WARRANTIES
Institute for Development of Indian Law, $3.50.

CONTACT & CONFLICT: INDIAN-EUROPEAN RELATIONS IN BRITISH COLUMBIA, 1774-1890 Robin Fisher
2nd Ed. Illus. 282 pp. Paper. University of Washington Press, 1992. $35.95.

CONTACT POINTS: AMERICAN FRONTIERS FROM THE MOHAWK VALLEY TO THE MISSISSIPPI, 1750-1830 Andrew R. Cayton & Fredricka J. Teute, Eds.
Illus. 410 pp. University of North Carolina Press, 1998. $55; paper, $19.95.

CONTACT ZONES: ABORIGINAL & SETTLER WOMEN IN CANADA'S COLONIAL PAST Edited by Katie Pickles & Myra Rutherdale
256 pp. Paper. University of Washington Press, 2005. $37.95.

CONTEMPORARY AMERICAN INDIAN LITERATURES & THE ORAL TRADITION
Susan Berry Brill de Ramirez; 272 pp. Paper. University of Arizona Press, 1999. $21.95.

CONTEMPORARY AMERICAN INDIAN WRITING: UNSETTLING LITERATURE
Dee Horne; 218 pp. Peter Lang & Amazon.com, 1999. $29.95.

CONTEMPORARY ARCHAEOLOGY: A GUIDE TO THEORY & CONTRIBUTIONS
Mark P. Leone, Editor; Illus. 476 pp. Paper. Amazon.com, 1972. $17.95.

CONTEMPORARY ART ON THE NORTHWEST COAST: SALISH, NUU-CHAH-NULTH, MAKAH Karen Norris; Amazon.com, $45.50.

CONTEMPORARY ARTISTS & CRAFTSMEN OF THE CHEROKEE INDIANS
Illus. 145 pp. Amazon.com & Cherokee Publications, 1990. $9.95.

CONTEMPORARY COAST SALISH ART
Rebecca Blanchard & Nancy Davenport
Illus. 112 pp. Paper. University of Washington Press & Amazon.com, 2005. $13.95.

THE CONTEMPORARY COAST SALISH: ESSAYS
Bruce Grandville Miller & Darby Stapp; Illus. Paper. Amazon.com, $19.95.

CONTEMPORARY FEDERAL POLICY TOWARD AMERICAN INDIANS
Emma R. Gross; 165 pp. Greenwood Publishing, 1989. $39.95.

CONTEMPORARY GREAT LAKES POW WOW REGALIA
Marsha MacDowell, Editor
Essays. 71 pp. Paper. Michigan State University Press, 1997. $24.95.

CONTEMPORARY INDIAN ART FROM THE CHESTER & DAVID HERWITZ FAMILY COLLECTION Thomas W. Sokolowski; Illus. 88 pp. Paper. Amazon.com, 1985. $15.

CONTEMPORARY INDIAN SCULLPTURE: AN ALGEBRA OF FIGURATION
Josef James, Editor; Illus. 144 pp. Oxford University Press, 1999. $49.95.

CONTEMPORARY NATIVE AMERICAN ARCHITECTURE: CULTURAL REGENERATION & CREATIVITY Carol Krinsky
Reprint. Illus. 277 pp. Paper. Amazon.com, 1999. $20.

CONTEMPORARY NATIVE AMERICAN AUTHORS: A BIOGRAPHICAL DICTIONARY
Kay Juricek & Kelly J. Morgan; 320 pp. Fulcrum Publishing, $95.

CONTEMPORARY NATIVE AMERICAN CULTURAL ISSUES
Duane Champagne, Ed.; 328 pp. AltaMira Press, 1999. $72; paper, $26.95.

CONTEMPORARY NATIVE AMERICAN LITERATURE
Rebecca Tillett; Paper. Oxford University Press, 2007. $38.95.

CONTEMPORARY NATIVE AMERICAN POLITICAL ISSUES
Troy Johnson, Editor; 328 pp. Alta Mira Press, 1998. $72; paper, $26.95.

CONTEMPORARY NAVAJO AFFAIRS
Norman Eck; 243 pp. Rough Rock School Press, 1982. $15.

CONTEMPORARY NAVAJO WEAVING; THOUGHTS THAT COUNT
Ann Lane Hedlund; Discusses what it means to be a Navajo weaver, including history of the rugs, their designing and making, buying & collecting, and the future of weaving. Illus. 32 pp. Paper. Museum of Northern Arizona, $6.95.

CONTEMPORARY SOUTHERN PLAINS INDIAN METALWORK
Explores an important tradition of distinctive jewelry and ornamentation created of nickel-silver by modern tribal craftsmen of the Southern Plains region. Illus. Map. 80 pp. Catalog. Amazon.com & Abebooks.com, $8, postpaid.

CONTEMPORARY SOUTHERN PLAINS INDIAN PAINTING
A survey of contemporary painting by Indian artists of tribally diverse Southern Plains region. Illus. Map. 80 pp. Catalog. Amazon.com, 1972. $7, postpaid.

CONTENT & STYLE OF AN ORAL LITERATURE: CLACKAMAS CHINOOK MYTHS & TALES Melville Jacobs; 285 pp. University of Chicago Press, 1959. $17.50.

CONTEST FOR EMPIRE, 1500-1775
Essays by George Waller, James Brown, John Tepaske, George Rawlyk, Jack Sosin, and Thomas Clark. 95 pp. paper. Indiana Historical Society, 1975. $2.75.

CONTESTED ARCTIC: INDIGENOUS PEOPLES, INDUSTRIAL STATES, AND THE CIRCUMPOLAR ENVIRONMENT Eric Alden Smith & Joan McCarter, Editors
176 pp. Paper. University of Washington Press, 1997. $20.

CONTESTED GROUND: COMPARATIVE FRONTIERS ON THE NORTHERN & SOUTHERN EDGES OF THE SPANISH EMPIRE Donna J. Guy & Thomas Sheridan, Eds
Indian-White relations. 275 pp. Paper. University of Arizona Press, 1998. $25.95.

THE CONTESTED PLAINS: INDIANS, GOLDSEEKERS, & THE RUSH TO COLORADO
Elliott West; Photos. 422 pp. Paper. University Press of Kansas, 2000. $18.95.

CONTESTED TERRITORY: WHITES, NATIVE AMERICANS & AFRICAN AMERICANS IN OKLAHOMA Murray R. Wickett
Illus. 260 pp. Louisiana State University Press, $59.95; paper, $26.95.

CONTESTING CONSTRUCTED INDIAN-NESS: THE INTERSECTION OF FRONTIER, MASCULINITY, & WHITENESS IN NATIVE AMERICAN MASCOT REPRESENTATIONS
Michael Taylor; Monograph. 154 pp. Lexington Books, c/o Rowman & Littlefield, 2013. $63; paper, $34.99. eBook, $34.95.

CONTESTING KNOWLEDGE: MUSEUMS & INDIGENOUS PERSPECTIVES
Edited by Susan Sleeper-Smith; Essays on the importance and effects of Indigenous perspectives for museums around the world. Examines the National Museum of the American Indian, Oneida Nation Museum, Zuni Nation Museum, et al. Photos. Maps. 374 pp. Paper. University of Nebraska Press, 2009. $35.

CONTINUUM ENCYCLOPEDIA OF NATIVE ART
Hope B. Werness; Illus. 500 pp. Continuum International Publishing, 2000. $50.

CONTOURS OF A PEOPLE: METIS FAMILY, MOBILITY, AND HISTORY
Nicole St-Onge, Carolyn Podruchny, Brenda McDougal, Editors
Illus. 520 pp. Paper. University of Oklahoma Press, $24.95.

CONTRACTS & YOU
Institute for Development of Indian Law, $3.50.

CONTRARY NEIGHBORS: SOUTHERN PLAINS & REMOVED INDIANS IN INDIAN TERRITORY
David La Vere; Illus. Map. 304 pp. U. of Oklahoma Press, 2000. $29.95; paper, $21.95.

CONTRIBUTIONS TO ANTHROPOLOGY: SELECTED PAPERS OF A. IRVING HALLOWELL A. Irving Hallowell; University of Chicago Press, 1976. $40.

CONTRIBUTIONS TO THE ARCHAEOLOGY & ETHNOHISTORY OF GREATER MESOAMERICA William J. Folan, Editor; 368 pp. Amazon.com, 1985. $28.95.

CONTRIBUTIONS TO THE ETHNOGRAPHY OF THE KUTCHIN
Cornelius Osgood; Reprint of 1936 edition. 190 pp. Paper. Amazon.com, $15.

CONTRIBUTIONS TO OJIBWE STUDIES: ESSAYS, 1934-1972
A. Irving Hallowell; Jennifer S.H. Brown & Susan E. Gray, Editors
Ojibwe essays. Photos. Maps. Tables. 648 pp. Paper. U. of Nebraska Press, 2010. $50.

CONTRIBUTIONS TO THE STUDY OF THE DORSET PALEO-ESKIMOS
Patricia D. Sutherland, Editor
Illus. Maps. 180 pp. Paper. University of Washigton Press, 2005. $29.95.

CONVERGING CULTURES: ART & IDENTITY IN SPANISH AMERICA
Diana Fane; The Brooklyn Museum, 1996.

CONVERGING STREAMS: ART OF THE HISPANIC & NATIVE AMERICAN SOUTHWEST FROM PRECONQUEST TIMES TO THE 20TH CENTURY
William Wroth & Robin Farwell Gavin, Editors
Illus. photos. 256 pp. Museum of New Mexico Press, 2010. $55; paper, $39.95.

A CONVERSATIONAL DICTIONARY OF KODIAK ALUTIIQ
Jeff Leer, Editor; 119 pp. Paper. Alaska Native Language Center, $4.

CONVERSATIONS: THE EITEJORG CONTEMPORARY ART FELOWSHIP 2015
Ashley Holland & Jennifer C. McNutt, Editors
136 pp. Paper. University of Oklahoma Press, 2015. $30.

CONVERSATIONS WITH THE HIGH PRIEST OF COOSA
Edited by Charles M. Hudson; University of North Carolina Press, 2003.

CONVERSATIONS WITH LOUISE ERDRICH & MICHAEL DORRIS
Allan Chavkin & Nancy Feyl Chavkin, Editors
224 pp. Amazon.com, 1994. $39.50; paper, $15.95.

CONVERSATIONS WITH LESLIE MARMON SILKO
Ellen L. Arnold, Ed.; 200 pp. Amazon.com, 2000. $45; paper, $18.

CONVERTING CALIFORNIA INDIANS & FRANCISCANS IN THE MISSIONS
James A. Sandos; Illus. 272 pp. Paper. Yale University Press, 2004. $28.

CONVERTING THE WEST: A BIOGRAPHY OF NARCISSA WHITMAN
Julie Roy Jefffrey; Pioneer missionary to the Cayuse Indians of Oregon Territory. Illus. Maps. 238 pp. Paper. University of Oklahoma Press, $12.95.

COOKING WITH SPIRIT; NORTH AMERICAN INDIAN FOOD & FACT
Lisa Railsback & Darcy Williamson; Cookbook, healing guide & folklore anthology. Illus. 111 pp. Paper. Cherokee Publications & Amazon.com., $12.95.

COOSA: THE RISE & FALL OF A SOUTHEASTERN MISSISSIPPIAN CHIEFDOM
Marvin T. Smith; Illus. 150 pp. University Press of Florida, 2000. $49.95.

COPING WITH THE FINAL TRAGEDY: DYING & GRIEVING IN CROSS CULTURAL PERSPECTIVE
David & Dorothy Counts, Editors; 285 pp. Baywood , 1992. $34.95; paper, $24.95.

COPPER ARTIFACTS IN LATE EASTERN WOODLAND PREHISTORY
Goodman; Illus. 104 pp. Hothem House, 1984. $17.75 postpaid.

COPPER BELL TRADE PATTERNS IN THE PREHISPANIC U.S. SOUTHWEST & NORTHWEST MEXICO
Victoria D. Vargas; 106 pp. Paper. Amazon.com, 1995. $14.95.

COPPER PALADIN: THE MODOC TRAGEDY
Walter H. Palmberg; Looks at some of the leading figures in one of the most costly Indian wars. 194 pp. Amazon.com, 1982. $12.

THE COPPERS OF THE NORTHWEST COAST INDIANS: THEIR ORIGIN, DEVELOPMENT, & POSSIBLE ANTECEDENTS
Carol F. Jopling; Illus. Paper. Amazon.com, 1987. $25.

CORN AMONG THE INDIANS OF THE UPPER MISSOURI
George F. Will and George E. Hyde; intro. by Douglas R. Parks
Originally published in 1964. Illus. 323 pp. Paper. U. of Nebraska Press, 2002. $17.95.

CORN RECIPES FROM THE INDIANS
Frances G.W. Altney; Illus. 32 pp. Paper. Smoke & Fire Co., $5.

CORNHUSK BAGS OF THE PLATEAU INDIANS
Cheney Cowles Memorial Museum; Microfiche. Illus. 335 photos.
4 color fiches. 34 pp. University of Chicago Press, 1976. $62.50.

CORPORATE & FOUNDATION FUNDRAISING MANUAL FOR NATIVE AMERICANS
A step-by-step guide to securing private sector grants, outlining basic fundraising and research procedures. Helps Native American planners diversify their funding base with private sector dollars. 3rd Ed. 288 pp. Paper. CRC Publishing, 1996. $129.95.

THE CORPORATION & THE INDIAN: TRIBAL SOVEREIGNTY & INDUSTRIAL CIVILIZATION IN INDIAN TERRITORY, 1865-1907
H. Craig Minor; Illus. Map. 236 pp. Paper. University of Oklahoma Press, 1976. $14.95.

THE COSTANOAN/OHLONE INDIANS OF THE SAN FRANCISCO & MONTEREY BAY AREA: A RESEARCH GUIDE
Lauren S. Teixeira; Illus. 130 pp. Malki-Ballena Press, 1997. $25; paper, $17.95.

COSTUMES OF THE PLAINS INDIANS & STRUCTURAL BASIS TO THE DECORATION OF COSTUMES AMONG THE IN PLAINS INDIANS
Clark Wissler; Reprint. Illus. color photos. 64 pp. Paper. Written Heritage, $19.95.

THE COTTONPATCH CHRONICLES: REFLECTIONS ON CHEROKEE HISTORY, PEOPLE, PLACES, AND THE EVENTS IN FORSYTH COUNTY, GEORGIA
Don L. Shadburn; Illus. 570 pp. Cottonpatch Press, 2003. $39.99.

*COULD IT BE OLD HIARI
Marjorie Vandervelde; Grades 5-9. 30 pp. Paper. Council for Indian Ed., 1975. $2.95.

COUNCIL FIRES ON THE UPPER OHIO
Randolph C. Downs; Illus. 384 pp. Paper. University of Pittsburgh Press, 1969. $22.95.

COUNCIL OF THE RAINMAKERS ADDRESS BOOK
David Dawangyumptewa, artist; 24 paintings of Hopi artist David Dawanyumptewa's paintings. 110 pp. Amazon.com, 1993. $12.95.

COUNSELING AMERICAN INDIANS
Laurence A. French; 216 pp. Paper. Amazon.com, 1997. $55.

THE COUNSELING SPEECHES OF JIM KA-NIPITEHTEW
Freda Ahenakew & H.C. Wolfart, Edited & tr. by
A highly respected orator speaks of his concern for young people and the proper performance of rituals. Paper. University of Toronto Press, 1998. $24.95.

COUNT ZINZINDORF & THE INDIANS 1742
William Reichel, Editor; First hand account of the Indians of the Philadelphia, PA area in 1742. Illus. Maps. Wennawoods Publishing, 2007. $49.95.

*COUNTING COUP: BECOMING A CROW CHIEF ON THE RESERVATION & BEYOND
Joseph Medicine Crow; Herman Viola; Autobiography of Dr. Joseph Medicine Crow (Absarokee). Grades 5-9. Paper. Amazon.com, 2006.

A COUNTRY BETWEEN: THE UPPER OHIO VALLEY & ITS PEOPLES, 1724-1774
Michael N. McConnell; History of Indians in Upper Ohio Valley. Illus. Maps. 359 pp. University of Nebraska Press, 1992. $55; paper, $20.

*COURAGEOUS SPIRITS: ABORIGINAL HEROES OF OUR CHILDREN
Joann Archibald; editorial by Richard Wagamese
Grades 4 and up. Illus. 76 pp. Paper. Theytus, 1993. $9.95; teachers guide, $5.95.

THE COVENANT CHAIN: INDIAN CEREMONIAL & TRADE SILVER
Jaye Frederickson and Sandra Gibb
Reprint of 1980 edition. Illus. 168 pp. Paper. University of Washington Press, $19.95.

COWBOYS & CAVE DWELLERS: BASKETMAKER ARCHAEOLOGY IN UTAH'S GRAND GULCH Fred M. Blackburn & Ray A. Williamson
Illus. 196 pp. Paper. School of American Research Press, 1997. $27.95.

COWBOYS, INDIANS & THE BIG PICTURE
Heather Fryer, et al, Editors; Illus. 117 pp. Paper. Dist. for McMullen Museum of Art, Boston College. University of Chicago Press, 2003. $30.

THE COYOTE: DEFIANT SONGDOG OF THE WEST
Francois Leydet; Revised 1988 ed. Illus. 224 pp. Paper. U. of Oklahoma Press, $11.95.

*COYOTE & THE FISH
Lorna Garrod; A Mimbre Indian trickster story tells how the first rainbow trout got its colors. Grades 3-7. Illus. 36 pp. Filter Prss, 1993. $4.

*COYOTE & THE GRASSHOPPERS: A POMO LEGEND
Terri Cohlene; Grades 4-8. Illus. 48 pp. Paper. Amazon.com, 1992. $4.95.

COYOTE HEALING: MIRACLES IN NATIVE MEDICINE
Lewis Mehl-Madrona; Illus. 288 pp. Paper. Inner Traditions, 2003. $16.

*COYOTE IN LOVE WITH A STAR
Marty Kreipe de Montano (Prairie Band Potawatomi); illus. by Tom Coffin
Grades 3 to 8. Illus. 32 pp. NMAI Press & Abbeville Press, 1998. $14.95.

*COYOTE & KOOTENAI
Louie Gingras and Jo Rainboldt
Grades 2-6. Paper. Council for Indian Education, 1977. $1.95.

*COYOTE & LITTLE TURTLE
as told by Hershel Talashoema; edited & translated by Emory Sekaquaptewa & Barbara Pepper; A traditional Hopi tale. Grade 1-4. Illus. 95 pp. 1995. Paper. Amazon.com. $9.95.

COYOTE MEDICINE: LESSONS FROM NATIVE AMERICAN HEALING
Lewis Mehl-Madrona; Simon & Schuster, 1997. $23.50.

*COYOTE & NATIVE AMERICAN FOLK TALES
Joe Hayes; illus. by Lucy Jelinek; 10 tales about the origins of Native American myth & spirituality. Grades 4 and up. 80 pp. Paper. Amazon.com, $11.95.

*COYOTE PLACES THE STARS
Harriet Peck Taylor
Wasco Indian legend. Grades K-4. Illus. 32 pp. Paper. Amazon.com, 1997.

A COYOTE READER
William Bright; Illus. 200 pp. Paper. University of California Press, 1993. $21.95.

*COYOTE & THE SKY: HOW THE SUN, MOON & STARS BEGAN
Emmett Garcia; Victoria Pringle
Illus.. Grades 4 to 8. Santa Ana Pueblo creation legend. University of New Mexico Press, $18.95.

*COYOTE STEALS THE BLANKET: A UTE TALE
Janet Stevens; Grades K-3. Illus. 32 pp. Holiday House, 1993. $15.95; paper, $5.95.

*COYOTE STEALS FIRE: A SHOSHONE TALE
Northwestern Band of the Shoshone Nation; Tamara Zollinger, Illus.
Grades 2-4. Illus. 32 pp. Shoshone tale about the arrival of fire in the northern Wasatch region. With audio CD voice of Helen Timbimboo telling the story in Shoshone & singing two traditional songs. Utah State University Press, 2005. Ebook, $15.50.

*COYOTE STORIES
Mourning Dove (Humishuma); edited by Heister Dean Guie
Reprint of 1933 edition. Grades 4 and up. Illus. 246 pp. U. of Nebraska Press, 1990. $12.95.

*COYOTE STORIES FOR CHILDREN: TALES FROM NATIVE AMERICA
Susan Strauss; illus by Gary Lund; Coyote tales with true-life anecdotes about coyotes & Native wisdom. Grades 1-6. Illus. 50 pp. Beyond Words Publishing, $10.95; paper, $6.95.

*COYOTE STORIES OF THE MONTANA SALISH INDIANS
Salish Culture Committee; Three traditional Salish coyote stories reocrded by Salish elders and illustrated by Indian artists. Grade 4. 64 pp. Paper. SKC Press, $7.50.

*COYOTE TALES
Evelyn Dahl Reed; Collection of tales from the Indian Pueblos. Grades 4 and up. 64 pp. Paper. Sunstone Press, $8.95.

*COYOTE: A TRICKSTER TALE FROM THE AMERICAN SOUTHWEST
Gerald McDermott
Grades Pre-3. Illus. 32 pp. Meadowlark Communications, 1994. $14.95; paper, $6.

COYOTE WARRIOR: ONE MAN, THREE TRIBES & THE TRIAL THAT FORGED A NATION Paul VanDevelder
Tells the story of the three tribes that saved Lewis & Clark's Corps of Discovery from starvation and their long battle against the federal government to forge a new nation. Second Ed. Illus. Map. 352 pp. Paper. University of Nebraska Press, 2009. $19.95.

COYOTE WAS GOING THERE: INDIAN LITERATURE OF THE OREGON COUNTRY
Jarold Ramsey, Compiler & Editor; Myths & tales of the Oregon Indians, Tillamook, Coos, Nez Perce, Klamath, Paiute. Illus. Map. 336 pp. Paper. University of Washington Press, 25.

*COYOTE & THE WINNOWING BIRDS: A TRADITIONAL HOPI TALE
as told by Eugene Sekaquaptewa; edited & translated by Emory Sekaquaptewa & Barbara Pepper; A traditional Hopi tale. Grades 1-4. Illus. 100 pp. 1995. Paper. Amazon.com. $9.95.

COYOTE WISDOM: THE POWER OF STORY IN HEALING
Lewis Mehl-Madrona, MD, PhD; The therapeutic & transformative powers of storytelling in Native American & other cultures. Includes healing stories from Native American traditions. Illus. 240 pp. Paper. Iner Traditions, 2005. $16.

COYOTE'S COUNCIL FIRE: CONTEMPORARY SHAMANS ON RACE, GENDER, & COMMUNITY Loren Cruden; Leading Native American and non-Native members of the American shamanic community share their thoughts on bringing shamanism into the modern era. Illus. 176 pp. Paper. Inner Traditions, $14.95.

*COYOTE'S POW-WOW
Hap Gilliland
Grades K-4. 31 pp. Paper. Council for Indian Education, 1972. $8.95; paper, $2.95.

COYOTES & CANARIES: CHARACTERS WHO MADE THE WEST WILD & WONDERFUL! Larry Brown; Illus. 287 pp. High Plains Press, 2002. $35; paper, $17.95.

CRAFT MANUAL OF ALASKAN ESKIMO
George M. White; Eskimo culture and handcraft. 80 pp. paper. White Publishing, $5.55.

*CRAFT MANUAL OF NORTH AMERICAN INDIAN FOOTWEAR
George M. White; Grades 4 and up. Includes 28 moccasin designs and patterns, sewing instructions. 72 pp. Paper. White Publishing, 1992. $6.

CRAFT MANUAL OF NORTHWEST INDIAN BEADING
George M. White; Beading methods. Photos. 164 pp. Paper. White Publishing, $17.55.

CRAFT MANUAL OF YUKON TLINGIT
George M. White; Instructions for making dolls, snowshoes, moosehide boats, woodcarvings & bonework. Short history. 56 pp. Paper. White Publishing, $4.85.

*CRAFTS OF FLORIDA'S FIRST PEOPLE
Robin Brown; Grades 5 and up. Illus. 64 pp. Paper. Pineapple Press, 2003. $9.95.

*CRAFTS OF THE NORTH AMERICAN INDIANS: A CRAFTSMAN'S MANUAL
Richard C. Schneider
Grades 9 and up. Reprint of 1972 edition. Illus. 325 pp. Paper. Written Heritage, $26.95.

CRANIOMETRIC RELATIONSHIPS AMONG PLAINS INDIANS: CULTURAL, HISTORICAL & EVOLUTIONARY IMPLICATIONS
Patrick J. Key; 204 pp. Paper. Amazon.com, 1983. $21.

CRASHING THUNDER: THE AUTOBIOGRAPHY OF AN AMERICAN INDIAN
Paul Radin, Editor; 256 pp. Paper. University of Michigan Press, 1999. $19.95.

CRAZY HORSE
Larry McMurtry
Biography. 191 pp. Amazon.com, 1999. Lt. ed. $29.95. Amazon.com, $19.95.

*CRAZY HORSE
Judith St. George; An account of the Sioux Wars and the character of the Plains people; and the life story of Crazy Horse. Grades 6 and up. Illus. 192 pp. Putnam, 1994. $16.95.

CRAZY HORSE: THE BOOK & SCREENPLAY
David Seals; Illus. 295 pp. Sky & Sage Books, 1996. $25.

CRAZY HORSE CALLED THEM WALK-A-HEAPS
Neil Baird Thompson
The story of the foot soldier in the Prairie Indian Wars. Illus. Amazon.com, $9.95.

CRAZY HORSE & CUSTER: THE PARALLEL LIVES OF TWO AMERICAN WARRIORS
Stephen E. Ambrose; Illus. 554 pp. Paper. Doubleday Publishing, 1996. $15.95.

CRAZY HORSE, HOKA HEY: IT IS A GOOD TIME TO DIE!
Vinson Brown; Personal study of Crazy Horse. 192 pp. Paper. Naturegraph, $9.95.

CRAZY HORSE & KORCZAK: THE STORY OF AN EPIC MOUNTAIN CARVING
Robb DeWall; Illus. 154 pp. Crazy Horse Memorial Foundation, $15.95; paper, $7.95.

CRAZY HORSE, A LAKOTA LIFE
Kinglsey M. Bray; Documentary biography. Illus. 528 pp. University of Oklahoma Press, 2008. $34.95; paper, $24.95.

CRAZY HORSE: THE LIFE BEHIND THE LEGEND
Mike Sajna; Illus. 384 pp. John Wiley & Sons, 2000. $27.95.

CRAZY HORSE MEMORIAL, 40TH ANNIVERSARY
Illus. Crazy Horse Memorial Foundation.

CRAZY HORSE & THE REAL REASON FOR THE BATTLE OF THE LITTLE BIG HORN
A.C. Ross; Paper. Wiconi Waste, 2000. $10.

CRAZY HORSE: SACRED WARRIOR OF THE SIOUX
Illus. 52 pp. Sterling, 1989. $12.95.

CRAZY HORSE: THE STRANGE MAN OF THE OGLALAS
Mari Sandoz
50th Anniversary Edition. Illus. Map. 512 pp. Paper. U. of Nebraska Press, 1992. $15.95.

THE CRAZY HORSE SURRENDER LEDGER
Thomas R. Buecker, Editor; Illus. Paper. Amazon.com, 1994.

CRAZY HORSE'S PHILOSOPHY OF RIDING RAINBOWS
Louis Hooban; Indian Amazon.com, 2001.

*CRAZY HORSE'S VISION
Joseph Bruchac; Grades K-4. Lerner Publications, 2012. $29.95.

CRAZY WEATHER
Charles L. McNichols; 195 pp. Paper. University of Nebraska Press, 1994. $12.95.

CREATING CHRISTIAN INDIANS: NATIVE CLERGY IN THE PRESBYTERIAN CHURCH
Bonnie Sue Lewis; Illus. Maps. 304 pp. University of Oklahoma Press, 2003. $34.95.

CREATING & USING THE LARGER NATIVE AMERICAN FLUTES
Lew P. Price; Illus. Paper. Lew Paxton Price, 1998. $10.

CREATING & USING THE LARGEST NATIVE AMERICAN FLUTES
Lew P. Price; Illus. Paper. Lew Paxton Price, 1998. $10.

CREATING & USING THE NATIVE AMERICAN CONCERT FLUTE
Lew P. Price; Illus. 54 pp. Paper. Lew Paxton Price, 1996. $10.

CREATING & USING THE NATIVE AMERICAN LOVE FLUTE
Lew P. Price; Illus. Paper. Lew Paxton Price, 1994. $10.

CREATING & USING THE VERY SMALL NATIVE AMERICAN FLUTES
Lew P. Price; Illus. Paper. Lew Paxton Price, 1998. $12.

CREATION OF A CALIFORNIA TRIBE: GRANDFATHER'S MAIDU INDIAN TALE
Paper. Amazon.com, $6.95.

*CREATION TALES FROM THE SALISH
W.H. McDonald; Grades 3-9. Paper. Council for Indian Education, 1973. $1.95.

CREATION'S JOURNEY: NATIVE AMERICAN IDENTITY & BELIEF
Tom Hill & Richard W. Hill, Sr.; Draws on the vast collections of the National Museum of the American Indian to retell the story of native life from the Arctic to the Tierra del Fuego. Illus. 256 pp. NMAI Press & Amazon.com, 1994. $45.

CREATIVE ALLIANCES: THE TRANSNATIONAL DESIGNS OF INDIGENOUS WOMEN'S POETRY Molly McGlennen
230 pp. Paper. University of Oklahoma Press, 2014. $24.95

CREATOR'S GAME: LACROSSE, IDENTITY, AND INDIGENOUS NATIONHOOD
Allan Downey; UBC Press, 2017. $95.

CREATORS OF THE PLAINS
Thomas E. Mails; Anthony Meisel, Editor
Illus. 96 pp. Paper. Council Oaks Books, 1997. $10.95.

CREATURE TEACHERS: A GUIDE TO THE SPIRIT ANIMALS OF THE NATIVE AMERICAN TRADITION Twylah Nitsch; Illus. 104 pp. Paper. Amazon.com, 1997. $14.95.

CREATURE TOTEMS: NATURE TEACHER MEDICINE
Twylah H. Nitsch; Albert F. Rinehold, Ed.; Illus. 130 pp. Paper. Amazon.com, 1991. $16.

THE CREE LANGUAGE STRUCTURE - A CREE APPROACH
Freda Ahenakew; Cree language. Paper. Pemmican, $13.95

CREE LEGENDS & NARRATIVES FROM THE WEST COAST OF JAMES BAY
told by Simeon Scott, et al; edited & tr. by C. Douglas Ellis
Annotated texts in James Bay Cree. University of Toronto Press & Michigan State University Press, 1995. $75. Set of 6 cassette tapes, $65.

CREE NARRATIVE: EXPRESSING THE PERSONAL MEANING OF EVENTS
Richard J. Preston; 2md Ed. Illus. 350 pp. McGill-Queen's University Press, 2002.

*THE CREEK
Michael D. Green; Grades 5 and up. Illus. 104 pp. Chelsea House, 1989. $17.95.

*CREEK CAPTIVES & OTHER ALABAMA STORIES
Helen F. Blackshear; Illus. by Thomas Raymond; Actual events fro the early American (Southeastern Indians) frontier and told from the viewpoint of a fictional young boy. Grades 5-12. Illus. 112 pp. Paper. Amazon.com, 1995. $9.95.

CREEK COUNTRY: THE CREEK INDIANS & THEIR WORLD
Robbie Ethridge; Illus. Maps. Table. 384 pp. University of North Carolina Press, 2003. $78.95; paper, $26.95.

THE CREEK FRONTIER, 1540-1783
David H. Corkran; Illus. Maps. 368 pp. Paper. U. of Oklahoma Press, 2016. $19.95

CREEK INDIAN HISTORY: A HISTORICAL NARRATIVE OF THE GENEALOGIES, TRADITIONS & DOWNFALL OF THE ISPOCOGA OR CREEK INDIAN TRIBE OF INDIANS BY ONE OF THE TRIBE George Stiggins; Virginia Pounds Brown, Editor
Illus. 176 pp. Paper. University of Alabama Press, 2003. $34.95.

CREEK INDIAN MEDICINE WAYS: THE ENDURING POWER OF MVSKOKE RELIGION
David Lewis, Jr. & Ann T. Jordan
Illus. 224 pp. University of New Mexico Press, $29.95; paper, $21.95.

CREEK (MUSKOGEE) NEW TESTAMENT CONCORDANCE
Lee Chupco, Rev. Ward Coachman, et al
The first New Testamint Concordance printed for an American Indian language. 167 pp. Indian University Press, 1982. $11, postpaid.

CREEK PATHS & FEDERAL ROADS: INDIANS, SETTLERS, AND SLAVES & THE MAKING OF THE AMERICAN SOUTH
Angela Pulley Hudson; Focuses on the creation & mapping of boundaries between Creek Indian lands & the states that grew up around them. Illus. Maps. 272 pp. University of North Carolina Press, 2010. $65; paper, $24.95.

CREEK RELIGION & MEDICINE
John R. Swanton; intro. by James T. Carson
Reprint. Illus. 213 pp. Paper. University of Nebraska Press, 2000. $45.

THE CREEK VERB
Henry O. Harwell & Deloris T. Harwell; A linguistic study of the Creek (Muskogee) verb & grammar. 57 pp. Indian University Press, 1981. $8.50, postpaid.

THE CREEK WAR OF 1813 & 1814
T.H. Ball & H.S. Halbert; Illus. 400 pp. Paper. U. of Alabama Press, 1995. $29.95.

A CREEK WARRIOR FOR THE CONFEDERACY: THE AUTOBIOGRAPHY OF CHIEF G.W. GRAYSON G.W. Grayson; W. David Baird, Editor
Illus. Maps. 182 pp. Paper. University of Oklahoma Press, 1988. $15.95.

CREEKS & SEMINOLES: THE DESTRUCTION & REGENERATION OF THE MUSCOGULGE PEOPLE
J. Leitch Wright, Jr.; Illus. Maps. 383 pp. Paper. U. of Nebraska Press, 1987. $19.95.

CREEKS & SOUTHERNERS: BICULTURISM ON THE EARLY AMERICAN FRONTIER
Andrew K. Frank; Illus. 202 pp. Paper. University of Nebraska Press, 2005. $30.

THE CRESCENT HILLS PRHISTORIC QUARRYING AREA
David J. Ives; 36 pp. Paper. Museum of Anthropology, U. of Missouri, 1975. $1.80.

CRIES FROM A METIS HEART
Lorraine Mayer; Poetry & prose. The author's struggle as a Metis woman, mother & academic; and the Metis people's quest for recognition. Pemmican, 2008. $20.95.

*CRICKETS & CORN: FIVE STORIES ABOUT NATIVE NORTH AMERICAN CHILDREN
Peg Black; Five Native American children make important discoveries about it means to be Native people. paper. Friendship Press, $3.50.

CRIME & NATIVE AMERICANS
David Lester; 192 pp. Amazon.com, 1999. $41.95; paper, $28.95.

CRIMINAL GANGS IN INDIAN COUNTRY: CONGRESSIONAL HEARING
Orrin G, Hatchm Ed.; Reprint. Illus. 70 pp. Paper. Amazon.com, 1997. $25.

CRIMINAL JURISDICTION ALLOCATION IN INDIAN COUNTRY
Ronald B. Flowers; 126 pp. Associate Faculty Press, 1983. $17.50.

CRIMINAL JUSTICE IN NATIVE AMERICA
Marianne O. Nielsen & Robert A. Silverman
H\Overview of how the American justice system impacts Native Americans on both sides of the law. 248 pp. Paper. University of Arizona Press, 2009. $34.95.

CRITICAL INDIGENOUS & AMERICAN INDIAN STUDIES
Andrew Jolivette, Series Editor;   3   volumes: Vol. 3 - Indian Agents: Rulers of the Reserves by John Steckley, 125 pp. $89.95; Vol. 2 - American Indian Women of Proud Nations: Essays on History, Language, and Education by Cherry Maynor Beasley, Mary Ann Jacobs & Ulrike Wiethaus, Vol. 1, 2016. 198 pp. $78.95; Injustice in Indian Country: Jurisdiction, American Law, and Sexual Violence Against Native Women by Amy L. Casselman. Vol. 1, 216 pp. 2016. $76.95.

CRITICAL INUIT STUDIES: AN ANTHOLOGY OF CONTEMPORARY ARCTIC ETHNOGRAPHY Pamela Stern & Lisa Stevenson
Illus. Maps. 302 pp. University of Nebraska Press, 206. $65; paper, $29.95.

CRITICAL ISSUES IN INDIGENOUS STUDIES
Paper. University of Arizona Press, 2015. $35. E-Book available.

CRITICAL NEUROPHILOSOPHY & INDIGENOUS WISDOM
Tito E. Naranjo; Sense Publishing, 2009.

CRITICALLY SOVEREIGN: INDIGENOUS GENDER, SEXUALITY & FEMINIST STUDIES   Joanne Barker, Editor; Jessica Perea, Jodi Byrd, Jennifer Nez Denetdale, et al, contributors; Illus. 288 pp. Duke University Press, 2017. $94.95; paper, $25.95.

GEORGE CROGHAN & THE WESTWARD MOVEMENT 1741-1782
Albert T. Volwiler; Croghan was an Indian trader then promoted an Indian uprising against the French. Acted as George Washington's Indian agent on his Fort Necessity campaign of 1754. Illus. 368 pp. Wennawoods Publishing, $29.95.

THE CROOKED BEAK OF LOVE
Duane Niatum; Poetry. 80 pp. Paper. University of New Mexico Press, $8.95.

CROOKED RIVER COUNTRY: WRANGLERS, ROGUES, AND BARONS
David Braly; North Central Oregon's hostile country. Illus. Map. 344 pp. Paper. WSU Press, 2007. $24.95.

THE CROOKED STOVEPIPE: ATHAPASKAN FIDDLE MUSIC & SQUARE DANCING IN NORTHEAST ALASKA & NORTHWEST CANADA
Craig Mishler; Illus. 248 pp. University of Illinois Press, 1993. $29.95.

CROOKED TREE: INDIAN LEGENDS OF NORTHERN MICHIGAN
John Wright; Reprint. 2nd edition. Illus. 170 pp. Paper. Amazon.com, 1996. $15.95.

THOMAS CROSBY & THE TSIMSHIAN: SMALL SHOES FOR FEET TOO LARGE
Clarence R. Bolt; Missionary in northwestern British Columbia, Canada in 1874. 160 pp. University of Washington Press, 1992. $43.95.

CROSS-CULTURAL COLLABORATION: NATIVE PEOPLES & ARCHAEOLOGY IN THE NORTHEASTERN U.S.
Jordan E. Kerber, Editor; Anthology of essays. Illus. Maps. 384 pp. University of Nebraska Press, 2006. $59.95; paper, $24.95.

CROSS-CULTURAL PERFORMANCE & ANALYSIS OF WEST AFRICANS, AFRICAN AMERICAN, NATIVE AMERICAN, CENTRAL JAVANESE & SOUTH INDIAN DRUMMING Royal J. Hartigan; Vol. 1. 372 pp. Edwin Mellen Press, 1998. $79.95.

CROSSBLOODS: BONE COURTS, BINGO, & OTHER REPORTS
Gerald Vizenor; From reservation treaties to cultural schizophrenia & rise of the American Indian Movement. Illus. 335 pp. U. of Minnesota Press, 1990. $34.95; paper, $14.95.

CROSSCURRENTS ALONG THE COLORADO: THE IMPACT OF GOVERNMENT POLICY ON THE QUECHEN INDIANS Robert Bee
184 pp. Paper. University of Arizona Press, 1981. $7.50.

CROSSING BETWEEN WORLDS: THE NAVAJO OF CANYON DE CHELLY, 2ND ED.
Jeanne M. Simonelli, with Lupita McClanahan
Second Ed. Illus. 138 pp. Paper. School of American Research Press, 2008. $15.50.

*CROSSING BOK CHITTO: A CHOCTAW TALE OF FRIENDSHIP & FREEDOM
Tim Tingle; illus. by Jeanne Rorex Bridge; Picture book. Grades K-2. Amazon.com, 2006

CROSSING MOUNTAINS: NATIVE AMERICAN LANGUAGE EDUCATIONN IN PUBLIC SCHOOLS Phyllis Ngai; 298 pp. AltaMira Press, 2012. $99; eBook, $97.99.

CROSSING THE POND: THE NATIVE AMERICAN EFFORT IN WORLD WAR II
Jere Bishop Franco; Photos. 336 pp. Texas A&M University Press, 1999. $29.95.

THE CROSSING OF TWO ROADS: BEING CATHOLIC & NATIVE IN THE U.S.
Marie T. Archambeault, et al, Eds.; Illus. 254 pp. Orbis Books, 2003. $50; paper, $30.

CROSSROADS ALASKA, NATIVE CULTURES OF ALASKA & SIBERIA
Valerie Chaussonnet; Photos. 112 pp. Paper. Smithsonian Institution Press, 1995. $24.95.

CROSSROADS OF EMPIRE: INDIANS, COLONISTS, & ALBANY CONGRESS OF 1754
Timothy J. Shannon; Illus. 320 pp. Paper. Cornell U. Press, 1999. $45; paper, $17.95.

*THE CROW
Frederick E. Hoxie; Grades 5 and up. Illus. Chelsea House, 1989. $17.95.

*THE CROW
Ruth Hagman; Grades K-4. Illus. 50 pp. Childrens Press, 1990. $14.60; paper, $4.95.

*THE CROW
Craig & Katherine Doherty; Grades 4-8. 32 pp. Amazon.com, 1994. $22.60.

*CROW CHIEF
Paul Goble; Grades PS-3. Illus. 32 pp. Amazon.com, $15.

*CROW CHILDREN & ELDERS TALK TOGETHER
Barrie E. Kavasch; Grades 4 and up. Rosen Group, 1998. $18.

CROW DOG: FOUR GENERATIONS OF SIOUX MEDICINE MEN
Leonard Dog & Richard Erdoes; Illus. 272 pp. Paper. HarperCollins, 1996. $13.

CROW DOG'S CASE: AMERICAN INDIAN SOVEREIGNTY, TRIBAL LAW & U.S. LAW IN THE 19TH CENTURY Sidney Harring; Illus. 317 pp. Paper. Cambridge U. Press, 1994. $27.

THE CROW & THE EAGLE: A TRIBAL HISTORY FROM LEWIS & CLARK TO CUSTER
Keith Algier; Relates the saga of the Crow Nation in the 1800s. Illus. Maps. Biblio. 399 pp. Paper. The Caxton Press, 1994. $14.95.

CROW INDIAN ART: PAPERS PRESENTED AT THE CROW INDIAN ART SYMPOSIUM SPONSORED BY THE CHANDLER INSTITUTE R. Pohrt, Jr. and B. Lanford; F. Dennis Lessurd, Editor; Illus. 68 pp. Paper. Chandler Institute, 1984. $12.

CROW INDIAN BEADWORK
William Wildschut & John C. Ewers; A descriptive and historical study. Second edition. Illus. 95 pp. Paper. Eagles View & Written Heritage, $10.95.

CROW INDIAN MEDICINE BUNDLES
William Wildschut; John C. Ewers, Editor; Reprint of 1960 edition. Illus. 187 pp. Paper. National Museum of the American Indian, $9.95.

CROW INDIAN PHOTOGRAPHER: THE WORK OF RICHARD THROSSEL
Peggy Albright; 80 photos. Biblio. 247 pp. U. of New Mexico Press, $75; paper, $37.95.

THE CROW INDIANS
Robert H. Lowie; intro by Phenocia Bauerle
Reprint of 1935 edition. Illus. 384 pp. Paper. University of Nebraska Press, 2004. $17.95.

CROW IS MY BOSS: ORAL LIFE HISTORY OF A TANACROSS ATHABASKAN ELDER
Kenny Thomas, Sr.; edited by Craig Mishler; Provides insight into the traditional & contemporary culture of Tanacross Athabaskans in Alaska. Illus. 288 pp. University of Oklahoma Press, 2006. $32.95.

CROW JESUS: PERSONAL STORIES OF NATIVE RELIGIOUS BELONGINGS
Mark Clatterbuck; foreword by Jace Weaver
Illus. 280 pp. Paper. University of Oklahoma Press, 201. $29.95.

CROW MAN'S PEOPLE: THREE SEASONS WITH THE NAVAJO
Nigel Pride; Illus. 222 pp. Amazon.com, 1985. $15.

CROWFOOT: CHIEF OF THE BLACKFEET
Hugh A. Dempsey; Reprint of 1972 edition. Illus. Maps. 226 pp. Paper. University of Oklahoma Press, $13.95.

CRY FOR LUCK: SACRED SONG & SPEECH AMONG THE YUROK, HUPA & KAROK INDIANS FO NORTHWESTERN CALIFORNIA
Richard Keeling; University of California Press, 1992. $45.

A CRY FROM THE EARTH: MUSIC OF THE NORTH AMERICAN INDIANS
John Bierhors; Illus. 113 pp. Paper. Amazon.com, 1992. $15.95. Cassette, $10.95.

CRY OF THE EAGLE: ENCOUNTERS WITH A CREE HEALER
David Young & Grant Ingram; University of Toronto Press, $22.50; paper, $14.95.

CRY OF THE THUNDERBIRD: THE AMERICAN INDIAN'S OWN STORY
Charles Hamilton; Reprint of 1971 edition. Illus. Paintings by George Catlin. Map. Biblio. 284 pp. Paper. University of Oklahoma Press, $18.95.

CRYING FOR A DREAM: THE WORLD THROUGH NATIVE AMERICAN EYES
Richard Erdoes; Focus is on the natural & sacred world of North America's indigenous peoples, includes elements of the Sioux ceremonial cycle & portraits of native peoples from the plains, mesas, and deserts. Describe the sun dance, sacred pipe, yuwipi, the vision quest. Reprint. Illus. 128 pp. Paper. Inner Traditions, 2001. $24.95.

*THE CRYING FOR A VISION
Walter Wangerin, Jr.; Saga of Wask Mani - a Lakota orphan with a mysterious past and powers. Grades 7 and up. 288 pp. Simon & Schuster, 1994. $15.

CRYING FOR A VISION: A ROSEBUD SIOUX TRILOGY 1886-1976
John Anderson, Eugene Buechel, S.J. & Don Doll, S.J.; Photos cover nearly a century of life in the Rosebud country of South Dakota. Illus. Amazon.com, $19.95.

CRYSTALS IN THE SKY: AN INTELLECTUAL ODYSSEY INVOLVING CHUMASH ASTRONOMY, COSMOLOGY AND ROCK ART
Travis Hudson & Ernest Underhay; Illus. 165 pp. Paper. Ballena Press, 1978. $18.95.

CUCKOO FOR KOKOPELLI
Dave Walker; The secrets behind the phenomenon of the symbol of the image. Illus. 40 color photos. 64 pp. Paper. Northland, $4.95.

DELFINA CUERO: HER AUTOBIOGRAPHY & HER ETHNOBOTANIC CONTRIBUTIONS
Florence Shipek; Includes "The Autobiography of Delfina Cuero." Illus. 98 pp. Malki-Ballena Press, 1991. $16.50.

CULTIVATED LANDSCAPES OF NATIVE NORTH AMERICA
William E. Doolittle; Paper. Oxford University Press, 2002. $120.

CULTIVATING A LANDSCAPE OF PEACE: IROQUOIS-EUROPEAN ENCOUNTERS IN 17TH-CENTURY AMERICA
Matthew Dennis; Illus. 336 pp. Amazon.com, 1993. $57.95, paper, $19.95.

CULTIVATING THE ROSEBUDS: THE EDUCATION OF WOMEN AT THE CHEROKEE FEMALE SEMINARY, 1851-1909
Devon A. Mihesuah; 240 pp. Paper. University of Illinois Press, 1997. $17.95.

CULTURAL CHANGE AND CONTINUITY ON CHAPIN MESA
Arthur H. Rohn; Illus. 330 pp. University Press of Kansas, 1977. $29.95.

CULTURAL DIVERSITY & ADAPTATION: THE ARCHAIC, ANASAZI & NAVAJO OCCUPATION OF THE SAN JUAN BASIN Lori S. Reed & Paul F. Reed, Editors
Illus. 182 pp. Amazon.com, 1992. $8.

CULTURAL ENCOUNTERS IN THE EARLY SOUTH: INDIAN & EUROPEANS IN ARKANSAS Jeannie M. Whayne; Illus. 240 pp. U. of Arkansas Press, 1995. $39.95.

CULTURAL & ENVIRONMENTAL HISTORY OF CIENEGA VALLEY, SOUTHEASTERN ARIZONA Frank W. Eddy & Maurice Cooley. 62 pp. U. of Arizona Press, 1983. $7.95.

A CULTURAL HISTORY OF NATIVE PEOPLES OF SOUTHERN NEW ENGLAND: VOICES FROM PAST & PRESENT Frank Waabu O'Brien (Moondancer) & Julianne Jennings (Strong Woman); 236 pp. Illus. Bauu Institute Press, 2007. $28.95.

CULTURAL MASKS: ETHNIC IDENTITY & AMERICAN INDIAN HIGHER EDUCATION
Terry E. Huffman; 195 pp. Stone Creek Press, 1999.

CULTURAL PERSISTENCE: CONTINUITY IN MEANING & MORAL RESPONSIBILITY AMONG THE BEARLIKE ATHAPASKANS Scott Rushforth with James Chisholm
Ethnographic description of Athapaskan-speaking Indians of Canada's Northwest Territories. 187 pp. University of Arizona Press, 1991. $42.

CULTURAL POLITICS & THE MASS MEDIA: ALASKA NATIVE VOICES
Patrick Daley & Beverly A. James; Illus. 256 pp. University of Illinois Press, 2004. $37.

CULTURAL PROPERTY LAW: A PRACTITIONER'S GUIDE TO THE MANAGEMENT, PROTECTION, AND PRESERVATION OF HERITAGE RESOURCES
2nd Ed. American Bar Association, 2017.

THE CULTURAL TRANSFORMATION OF A NATIVE AMERICAN FAMILY & ITS TRIBE, 1763-1995: A BASKET OF APPLES
Joel H. Spring; 248 pp. Amazon.com, 1996. $45.

CULTURE, CHANGE & LEADERSHIP IN A MODERN INDIAN COMMUNITY: THE COLORADO RIVER INDIAN RESERVATION
Katherine E. Blossom; 101 pp. Paper. Cherokee Publications, 1979. $6.00.

CULTURE & CUSTOMS OF THE APACHE INDIANS
Veronica E. Velarde Tiller; Illus. 172 pp. ABC-CLIO, 2010. $49.95.

CULTURE & CUSTOMS OF THE CHOCTAW INDIANS
Donna L. Akers; Illus. 205 pp. ABC-CLIO, 2013. $50.

CULTURE & CUSTOMS OF THE SIOUX INDIANS
Gregory O. Gagnon; Illus. 208 pp. Paper. University of Nebraska Press, 2012. $19.95.

A CULTURE'S CATALYST: HISTORICAL ENCOUNTERS WITH PEYOTE & THE NATIVE AMERICAN CHURCH IN CANADA
Fannie Kahan; Erika Dyck, Editor; Paper. Michigan State University Press, 2016. $27.95.

CULTURES IN CONTACT: THE EUROPEAN IMPACT ON NATIVE CULTURAL INSTITUTIONS IN EASTERN NORTH AMERICA A.D. 1000-1800
William W. Fitzhugh, Editor
Illus. 326 pp. Paper. Smithsonian Institution Press, 1985. $29.95; paper, $17.95.

CULTURICIDE, RESISTANCE & SURVIVAL OF THE LAKOTA (SIOUX NATION)
James V. Fenelon; Illus. 440 pp.Garland, 1998. $105.

CUMMING'S VOCABULARY OF SHAWNEE
Richard W. Cummings; 47 pp. Amazon.com, 2001. $28.

CURRENT RESEARCH IN INDIANA ARCHAEOLOGY & PREHISTORY: 1987 & 1988
Christopher S. Peebles; Illus. 51 pp. Paper. Indiana Historical Society, 1989. $2.75.

CURRICULA MATERIALS FOR THE FIRST CAROLINIANS: THE LIFE & TIMES OF NATIVE PEOPLES IN THE PALMETTO STATE Chicora Foundation Staff & SC State Museum Staff; Illus. 94 pp. Spiral bound. Chicora Foundation, 2000. $20.

EDWARD S. CURTIS
Barry Pritzker; 112 pp. World Publications, 2003. $14.99.

EDWARD S. CURTIS: COMING TO LIGHT
Anne Makepeace; 2nd Ed. Illus. 200 pp. Amazon.com, 2002. $35.

EDWARD S. CURTIS: THE GREAT WARRIORS
Edward S. Curtis; Illus. 128 pp. Amazon.com. $35.

CURTIS INDIANS
Taschen Staff; Digtal Manga Publishing, 1999. $12.99.

EDWARD S. CURTIS: THE NORTH AMERICAN INDIAN
Hans Christian Adam; Illus. Photos. 768 pp. Taschen American, LLC, 2003. $19.99.

EDWARD S. CURTIS & THE NORTH AMERICAN INDIAN PROJECT IN THE FIELD
Mick Gidley, Ed. & Intro.; Illus. 224 pp. University of Nebraska Press, 2003. $49.95. 342 pp. Paper. Cambridge University Press, 2000. $23.

EDWARD CURTIS: SITES & STRUCTURES
Dan Solomon, et al; Illus. 144 pp. Amazon.com, 2000. $65.

EDWARD SHERIFF CURTIS: VISIONS OF A VANISHING RACE
Florence Curtis Graybill & Victor Boesen
Reprint. Illus. 111 pp. Paper. University of New Mexico Press, 2000. $29.95.

CUSHING AT ZUNI: THE CORRESPONDENCE & JOURNALS OF FRANK HAMILTON CUSHING, 1879-1884 Jesse Green, Editor
Illus. 450 pp. University of New Mexico Press, 1990. $45.

CUSTER & THE BATTLE OF THE LITTLE BIGHORN: AN ENCYCLOPEDIA OF THE PEOPLE, PLACES, EVENTS, INDIAN CULTURE & CUSTOMS, INFORMATION SOURCES, ART & FILMS Thom Hatch; Photos. Maps. 248 pp. McFarland, 1996. $45.

CUSTER BATTLEFIELD, A HISTORY & GUIDE TO THE BATTLE OF THE LITTLE BIGHORN Robert M. Utley; Illus. 112 pp. Paper. U.S. GPO, 1988. $4.75.

CUSTER, BLACK KETTLE, & THE FIGHT ON THE WASHITA
Charles J. Brill; foreword by Mark L. Gardner
Illus. Maps. 328 pp. Paper. University of Oklahoma Press, 2002. $19.95.

CUSTER & THE CHEYENNE: GEORGE A. CUSTER'S WINTER CAMPAIGN ON THE SOUTHERN PLAINS Louis Kraft; Illus. 212 pp. Amazon.com, 1995. $65.

CUSTER, CODY & THE LAST INDIAN WARS: A PICTORIAL HISTORY
Jay Kimmel; Illus. 214 pp.Paper. Amazon.com, 1994. $25.

THE CUSTER COMPANION: A COMPREHENSIVE GUIDE TO THE LIFE & CAMPAIGNS OF GEORGE ARMSTRONG CUSTER
Thom Hatch; Illus. 290 pp. Paper. Amazon.com, 2002. $29.95.

CUSTER & COMPANY: WALTER CAMP'S NOTES ONTHE CUSTER FIGHT
Bruce R. Liddic & Paul Harbaugh, Editors; Illus. Maps. 189 pp. Paper. Amazon.com, $13.

*CUSTER & CRAZY HORSE
Jim Razzi; Grades 3-7. Paper. Amazon.com, 1989. $2.75.

CUSTER DIED FOR YOUR SINS: AN INDIAN MANIFESTO
Vine Deloria, Jr.; Federal Indian policy from a Native American perspective. Reprint of 1988 edition. 292 pp. Paper. University of Oklahoma Press, $24.95.

THE CUSTER LEGACY
Bruce T. Clark; 640 pp. Four Winds Publishing, 1997. $24.95.

CUSTER & THE LITTLE BIGHORN: A COLLECTION OF WALTER MASON CAMP'S RESEARCH PAPERS ON GENERAL GEORGE A. CUSTER'S LAST FIGHT
Richard G. Hardorff; Illus. 135 pp. Amazon.com, 1997. $50.

THE CUSTER MYTH: A SOURCE BOOK OF CUSTERIANA
Col. W.A. Graham; A complete account of what happened at Little Bighorn with narrative Indian and soldier accounts. Reprint of 1953 ed. Photos. Maps. High-Lonesome Books, $25.

CUSTER: A PHOTOGRAPHIC BIOGRAPHY
Bill & jan Moeller; Illus. 256 pp. Amazon.com, 2004. 24.

THE CUSTER READER
Paul A. Hutton; foreword by Robert M. Utley; First-person narratives, essays, and photos. Illus. Maps. 608 pp. Paper. University of Oklahoma Press, 2004. $26.95.

THE CUSTER STORY: THE LIFE & INTIMATE LETTERS OF GENERAL GEORGE A. CUSTER & HIS WIFE ELIZABETH
Marguerite Merington, Editor; Reprint of 1950 edition. 340 pp. Chatham Pres, $9.95.

THE CUSTER TRAGEDY: EVENTS LEADING UP TO & FOLLOWING THE LITTLE BIG HORN CAMPAIGN OF 1876
Fred Dustin; Reprint of 1939 edition. Illus. 310 pp. Amazon.com, $45.

CUSTEROLOGY: THE ENDURING LEGACY OF THE INDIAN WARS & GEORGE ARMSTRONG CUSTER Michael A. Elliott
Illus. 344 pp. University of Chicago Press, 2007. $25; paper, $16. E-book, $7-16.

CUSTER'S CHIEF OF SCOUTS: THE REMINISCENCES OF CHARLES A. VARNUM
Charles A. Varnum; John M. Carroll, Editor
Illus. 192 pp. University of Nebraska Press, 1987. $18.95; paper, $6.95.

CUSTER'S DEFEAT & OTHER CONFLICTS IN THE WEST
Illus. 110 pp. Paper. Amazon.com, 1979. $15.

CUSTER'S FALL: THE NATIVE AMERICAN SIDE OF THE STORY
David H. Miller; Presents an interpretation of the Battle of the Little Big Horn, and of the death of General Custer. Illus. 288 pp. Paper. Penguin USA, $10.

CUSTER'S LAST CAMPAIGN: MITCH BOYER & THE LITTLE BIGHORN
John S. Gray; Illus. Maps. 446 pp. Paper. Amazon.com, $17.95.

CUSTER'S LAST FIGHT: THE STORY OF THE BATTLE OF THE LITTLE BIG HORN
David C. Evans; Illus. 605 pp. Amazon.com, 1999. $85.

***CUSTER'S LAST STAND**
Quentin Reynolds; Grades 5-9. Illus. 160 pp. Random House, 1964. $8.99; paper, $2.95.

CUSTER'S LUCK
Edgar I. Stewart; Illus. Map. 538 pp. Paper. University of Oklahoma Press, 1980. $29.95.

CUSTER'S PRELUDE TO GLORY
Herbert Krause & Gary Olson; Illus. 280 pp. Amazon.com, $75.

CUSTER'S SEVENTH CAVALRY & THE CAMPAIGN OF 1873
Lawrence A. Frost; Illus. 255 pp. Amazon.com, 1986. $45.

***A CYCLE OF MYTHS: NATIVE LEGENDS FROM SOUTHEAST ALASKA**
John E. Smelcer, Editor
Grades 7 and up. Illus. 116 pp. Paper. Salmon Run, 1993. $12.95.

CYCLES OF CONQUEST: THE IMPACT OF SPAIN, MEXICO & THE U.S. ON INDIANS OF THE SOUTHWEST, 1533-1960
Edward H. Spicer; More than 400 years of cultural history of some 25 Southwestern tribes. Illus. 609 pp. Paper. University of Arizona Press, 1962. $45.

CYCLES OF LIFE
Time-Life Eds.; Illus. 184 pp. Time-Life, Inc., 1994.

CYCLORAMA OF GEN. CUSTER'S LAST FIGHT: A REPRODUCTION OF THE ORIGINAL DOCUMENT COMPLETE IN ALL RESPECTS
John M. Carroll, intro by; Reprint of 1889 edition. Illus. 104 pp. Amazon.com, $30.

D

DAHCOTAH: OR, LIFE & LEGENDS OF THE SIOUX AROUND FORT SNELLING
Mary H. Eastman; Reprint. Illus. 240 pp. Amazon.com, $29.

DAILY AFFIRMATIONS FROM THE DIVINE CREATOR
Willie C. Hooks; 75 pp. Paper. Amazon.com, 1990. $7.95.

DAILY LIFE DURING THE INDIAN WARS
Clarissa W. Confer; Illus. 223 pp. Greenwood Press, 2011. Paper, ebook available.

***DAILY LIFE IN A PLAINS INDIAN VILLAGE, 1868**
Michael Bad Hand Terry
Grades 3 to 5. 130 color photos. 48 pp. Paper. Written heritage, 1999. $9.95.

DAILY LIFE OF THE INUIT
Pamela R. Stern; Illus. Maps. 216 pp. Greenwood Publishing, 2010. $49.95.

***THE DAKOTA**
Brief history of the Dakota. Grades 6 and up. Illus. 32 pp. Minnesota Historical Society Press, 1984. $3.50.

DAKOTA CROSS-BEARER: THE LIFE & WORLD OF A NATIVE AMERICAN BISHOP
Mary E. Cochran; intro by Raymond Bucko & Martin Brokenleg
Biography of Harold S. Jones, the first Native American bishop. Illus. 264 pp. Paper. University of Nebraska Press, 2000. $17.95.

A DAKOTA-ENGLISH DICTIONARY
Stephen R. Riggs
Reprint of 1852 edition. 680 pp. Paper. Minnesota Historical Society Press, $24.95.

DAKOTA ETHNOGRAPHY
Stephen R. Riggs; 88 pp. Paper. Lakota Books, 1998. $18.95.

DAKOTA GRAMMAR, TEXTS & ETHNOLOGY
Stephen R. Riggs; Edited by James Owen Dorsey
Reprint of 1893 edition. 232 pp. Amazon.com, $30.

DAKOTA IN MINNESOTA: THE PEOPLE OF MINNESOTA
Gwen Westerman; Illus. Paper. Minnesota Historical Society Press, $16.95; eBoo, 9.99.

***DAKOTA INDIANS COLORING BOOK**
Chet Kozlak; Grades 1-3. Map. 32 pp. Paper. Minnesota Historical Society Press, $3.50.

DAKOTA LIFE IN THE UPPER MIDWEST
Samuel W. Pond; Illus. 192 pp. Paper. Minnesota Historical Society Press, 2002. $14.95.

***DAKOTA & OJIBWE PEOPLE IN MINNESOTA**
Frances Densmore
Grades 6 and up. Illus. 55 pp. Paper. Minnesota Historical Society Press, 1977. $3.50.

THE DAKOTA OR SIOUX IN MINNESOTA: AS THEY WERE IN 1834
Samuel W. Pond; 192 pp. Paper. Minnesota Historical Society Press, 1986. $8.95.

DAKOTA ORATORY: GREAT MOMENTS IN THE RECORDED SPEECH OF THE EASTERN SIOUX, 1695-1874 compiled & illus. by Mark Diedrich; Illus. Biblio. 102 pp. Paper. Coyote Books, 1989. $18.95.

DAKOTA PANORAMA
J. Leonard Jennewein & Jane Boorman; Illus. 468 pp. Paper. Amazon.com, $14.95.

DAKOTA PHILOSOPHER: CHARLES EASTMAN & AMERICAN INDIAN THOUGHT
David Martinez; Illus. Minnesota Historical Society Press, 2009.

DAKOTA SIOUX INDIAN DICTIONARY
Paul Warcloud; English to Sioux translations of over 4,000 words. Developed for beginners interested in the Sioux language by artist and author Paul Warcloud. 192 pp. Paper. Center for Western Studies, $5.95.

DAKOTA: A SPIRITUAL GEOGRAPHY
Kathleen Norris; An evokation of the Great Plains, this book weaves together the lives of farmers, townsfolk, Native Americans, and a community of Benedictine monks. 224 pp. Paper. Amazon.com, 1994. $9.95.

DAKOTA TEXTS
Ella C. Deloria; Reprint. 280 pp. Paper. University of Nebraska Press, $15.95.

THE DAKOTA WAR OF 1862
Kenneth Carley; Illus. 112 pp. Paper. Minnesota Historical Society Press, 2001. $12.95.

THE DAKOTA WAR: THE U.S. ARMY VS. THE SIOUX, 1862-1865
Michael Clodfelter; Illus. 280 pp. McFarland, 1998. $42.50.

DAKOTA WAY OF LIFE SERIES
Incorporates Indian legends & culture with Christian teaching. using Indian designs, Indian art & photographs of Indian people. Pre-school, Teacher's Guide, $7.50; Grades 1-12, Student text, $2.50; Teacher Guide, $4.75. Amazon.com.

DAKSI
An introductory multicultural educational resource which challenges the ethnocentric cultural stereotypes. David Michael Wolfe.

DAMMED INDIANS: PICK-SLOAN PLAN & THE MISSOURI RIVER SIOUX, 1944-1980
Michael L. Lawson; Reprint of 1982 edition, with a new preface by the author, and a new foreword by Vine Deloria, Jr. Illus. 262 pp. Paper. University of Oklahoma Press, $15.95.

DANCE ASSOCIATIONS OF THE EASTERN DAKOTA
Robert H. Lowie; 39 pp. Paper. Lakota Books, 1993. $9.95.

DANCE CEREMONIES OF THE NORTHERN RIO GRANDE PUEBLOS
Kathryn Huelster & Dick Huelster; Paper. University of New Mexico Press, 2017. $11.95

THE DANCE HOUSE: STORIES FROM ROSEBUD
Joseph Marshall, III (Sicangu Lakota); Essays & short stories based on incidents or events which took place on the Rosebud (Sicangu Lakota) Indian Reservation in South Dakota. 214 pp. Paper. Amazon.com, 1998. $13.95.

DANCE LODGES OF THE OMAHA PEOPLE: BUILDING FROM MEMORY
Mark Awakuni-Swetland
Illus. Figures & tables. 214 pp. Paper. University of Nebraska Press, 2008, $19.95.

THE DANCES OF THE METIS - LI DAWNS DI MICHIF
Metis Resource Centre; Traditional dances & fiddling music of the Metis people of Canada. Pemmican, $24.95 (DVD).

DANCES OF THE TEWA PUEBLO INDIANS: EXPRESSIONS OF LIFE
Jill D. Sweet; Illus. 100 pp. Paper. School for Advanced Research, 1985. $9.95.

DANCES WITH WOLVES
Blake; Plains Indian struggle for survival during the late 1800s.
Illus. Center for Western Studies, 1989. $16.95.

DANCING COLORS: PATHS OF NATIVE AMERICAN WOMEN
C.J. Brafford & Laine Thom; Illus. 120 pp. Amazon.com, 1992. $29.95; paper, $18.95.

DANCING THE DREAM: SEVEN SACRED PATHS OF HUMAN TRANSFORMATION
Jamie Sams; Illus. 288 pp. Paper. Amazon.com, 1999. $14.95.

*DANCING DRUM: A CHEROKEE LEGEND
Terri Cohlene; Grades 4-8. Illus. 48 pp. Amazon.com, 1990. $16.95; paper, $10.15

DANCING GHOSTS: NATIVE AMERICAN & CHRISTIAN SYNCRETISM IN MARY AUSTIN'S WORK Mark Hoyer; 224 pp. University of Nevada Press, 1998. $34.95.

DANCING GODS: INDIAN CEREMONIALS OF NEW MEXICO & ARIZONA
Erna Fergusson; The Corn, Deer and Eagle Dances as well as various dances at Zuni; also describes the Hopi bean-planting and Niman Kachina ceremonies, the Snake Dance, the Navajo Mountain Chant & Night Chant, and Apache ceremonies. Illus. 314 pp. Paper. University of New Mexico Press, 2001. $19.95.

THE DANCING HEALERS: A DOCTOR'S JOURNEY OF HEALING WITH NATIVE AMERICANS Carl Hammerschlag; 128 pp. HarperCollins, 1988. $14.45.

DANCING IN THE PATHS OF THE ANCESTORS; BOOK TWO OF THE PUEBLO CHILDREN OF THE EARTH MOTHER Thomas E. Mails; Overview of the Pueblo Indians of New Mexico and Arizona. Illus. 544 pp. Amazon.com, 1998. $46.50; paper, $29.95.

DANCING ON COMMON GROUND: TRIBAL CULTURES & ALLIANCES ON THE SOUTHERN PLAINS Howard L. Meredith; Photos. Maps. 288 pp. University Press of Kansas, 1995. $29.95.

DANCING ON THE RIM OF THE WORLD: AN ANTHOLOGY OF CONTEMPORARY NORTHWEST NATIVE AMERICAN WRITING
Andrea Lerner, Editor; 266 pp. Paper. University of Arizona Press, 1990. $19.95.

A DANCING PEOPLE: POWWOW CULTURE ON THE SOUTHERN PLAINS
Clyde Ellis; Photos. 232 pp. Paper. University Press of Kansas, 2003. $17.95.

*DANCING TEPEES: POEMS OF AMERICAN INDIAN YOUTH
Virginia Sneve; Grades K-3. Illus. 32 pp. Holiday House, 1989. $15.95; paper, $5.95.

DANCING WITH INDIANS
Angela Shelf Medearis; An African-American family attends a Seminole celebration & participants. Illus. 32 pp. Holiday House, 1991. $14.95; paper, $5.95.

DANGEROUS PASSAGE: THE SANTA FE TRAIL & THE MEXICAN WAR
William Y. Chalfant; Tells the story of the Santa Fe Trail and the Indians who onces lived on it. Ilus. Photos. Biblio. University of Oklahoma Press, 1994. $29.95.

A DANISH PHOTOGRAPHER OF IDAHO INDIANS
Benedict Wrensted; by JoannaCohan Scherer; Photos. biographical data; ethnographic analysis. 160 pp. University of Oklahoma Press, 2007. $29.95.

DANNY BLACKGOAT: DANGEROUS PASSAGE
Tim Tingle; Fiction. Navajos in 1860s. 160 pp. Paper. Book Publishing Co., 2017. $9.95.

DARING DONALD McKAY: OR, THE LAST WAR TRIAL OF THE MODOCS
Keith and Donna Clark, Editors; Illus. Paper. Oregon Historical Society, 1971. $2.95.

*DARK ARROW
Lucille Mulcahy; Illus. by Herbert Danska; Prehistoric cliff-dwelling people. Grades 4 and up. Illus. 210 pp. Paper. University of Nebraska Press, 1995. $7.95.

DARK LADY DREAMING
Amy Cordova; A contemporary Native American/Hispanic artist discusses the methods & spiritual commitments inher work. Illus. 15 pp. Amazon.com, $5.95.

DARK RIVER
Louis Owens; 296 pp. Paper. University of Oklahoma Press, 2000. $19.95.

*THE DARK SIDE OF THE MOON
Tom Kovach; Grades 1-4. Illus. 32 pp. Council for Indian Education, $8.45; paper, $2.45.

DARK THIRTY
Santee Frazier (Cherokee); Poetry. 96 pp. Paper. U. of Arizona Press, 2009. $15.95.

THE DARKEST PERIOD: THE KANZA INDIANS & THEIR LAST HOMELAND, 1846-1873 Ronald D. Parks; 336 pp. University of Oklahoma Press, 2014. $34.95.

THE DARKEST TEARS ON THE TRAILS - TO GRANDMA'S HOUSE
Gloria L. Smith; 50 pp. Paper. Trailstones Heritage Adventures, 1995. $8.

DAUGHTER OF THE WIND: INDIAN LEGENDS & FAMILY TALES
Ernestine Thompson; Illus. 208 pp. Paper. Amazon.com, 2003. $15.

DAUGHTERS OF THE BUFFALO WOMEN: MAINTAINING THE TRIBAL FAITH
Beverly Hungry Wolf; First hand accounts of reservation life. Photos. 144 pp. Paper. The Book Publishing Co., 1997. $9.95.

DAUGHTERS OF THE EARTH
Carolyn Niethammer; Illus. 450 pp. Paper. Simon & Scuster, 1995. $17.

ROBERT DAVIDSON: EAGLE OF THE DAWN
Ian Thorn, Editor; On the works of Davidson, master carver of masks and totems, print maker, painter, and jeweler. Illus. 104 pp. Paper. NMAI Press & University of Washington Press, 2013. $40.

JEFF DAVIS'S OWN: CAVALRY, COMANCHES, & THE BATTLE FOR THE TEXAS FRONTIER James R. Arnold; Illus. 384 pp. John Wiley & Sons, 2000. $40.

THE DAWES COMMISSION & THE ALLOTMENT OF THE FIVE CIVILIZED TRIBES, 1893-1914 Kent Carter; Ancestry, 1998. $29.95.

DAWN IN ARCTIC ALASKA
Diamond Jenness; Ethographic details of the Eskimos. Reprint of 1957 ed. Illus. Maps. 224 pp. Paper. University of Chicago Press, 1984. $16.

DAWN LAND
Joseph Bruchac; First novel by a Native American storyteller. 332 pp. Fulcrum Publishing, 1992. $19.95; paper, $12.95. Also on audiocassettes, $16.95.

THE DAWN OF THE WORLD: MYTHS & TALES OF MIWOK INDIANS OF CALIFORNIA
C. Hart Merriam, Editor; Illus. Maps. 273 pp. Paper. U. of Nebraska Press, 1993. $21.95.

*DAWN RIDER
Jan Hudson; Details of tribal life. Fiction. Grades 4-8. 192 pp. Philomel, 1990. $14.95.

DAWNLAND ENCOUNTERS: INDIANS & EUROPEANS IN NORTHERN NEW ENGLAND Colin Calloway; Illus. 311 pp. Paper. U. Press of New England, 1991. $27.95.

THE DAY GERONIMO SURRENDERED
Ron Swartley; History of Geronimo's final period on the loose after breaking out from his confinement at the Fort Apache Reservation in 1885. Illus. 50 pp. Paper. Frontier Image Press, 2005. $6.95.

*THE DAY OF THE OGRE KACHINAS: A HOPI INDIAN FABLE
Peggy Spence; Grades 1-6. Illus. 48 pp. Paper. Council for Indian Education & Roberts Rinehart, 1994. $4.95.

*A DAY WITH A CHEYENNE
Franco Meli; illus. by Giorgio Bacchin
Grades 4-7. Illus. Color photos. 48 pp. Lerner, 1998. $19.95.

*A DAY WITH A CHUMASH
Franco Meli; illus. by Giorgio Bacchin
Grades 4-7. Illus. Color photos. 48 pp. Lerner, 1998. $19.95.

*A DAY WITH A MIMBRES
Franco Meli; illus. by Giorgio Bacchin
Grades 5-7. Illus. Color photos. 48 pp. Lerner, 1998. $22.60.

*A DAY WITH A PUEBLO
Franco Meli; illus. by Giorgio Bacchin
Grades 4-7. Illus. Color photos. 48 pp. Lerner, 1998. $19.95.

DE GRAZIA'S BORDERLANDS SKETCHES
Elizabeth Shaw; Illus. 80 pp. Amazon.com, 1997. $16.95.

DE RELIGIONE: TELLING THE 17TH CENTURY JESUIT STORY IN HURON THE IROQUOIS John Steckley; Illus. 224 pp. University of Oklahoma Press, 2004. $34.95.

HERNANDO DE SOTO & THE INDIANS OF FLORIDA
Jerald T. Milanich & Charles Hudson; Illus. 312 pp. U. Press of Florida, 1993. $39.95.

DEAD TOWNS OF ALABAMA
W. Stuart Harris; 176 pp. Ilus. University of Arizona Press, 1977. $10.95.

DEAD VOICES: NATURAL AGONIES IN THE NEW WORLD
Gerald Vizenor; Using tales drawn from traditional tribal stories, this book illuminates the centuries of conflict between American Indians & Europeans. 144 pp. Paper. University of Oklahoma Press, 1992. $19.95.

DEADLIEST ENEMIES: LAW & MAKING OF RACE RELATIONS ON & OFF ROSEBUD RESERVATION Thomas Biolsi; Illus. 280 pp. University of California Press, 2001. $50. Paper. University of Minnesota Press, 2007. $22.50.

DEADLIEST INDIAN WAR IN THE WEST: THE SNAKE CONFLICT, 1864-1868
Gregory Michno; Native Americans fight for survival inthe Great Basin between the Rockies and the Sierras. The Snake War's four years battle on the high desert of Idaho, Nevada, Utah, Oregon, & Northern California. 400 pp. Paper. 2007. Amazon.com, $18.95.

DEADLY INDIAN SUMMER
Leonard A. Schonberg; Navajo medicine men. 184 pp. Sunstone Press, 1997. $24.95.

DEADLY LANDSCAPES: CASE STUDIES IN PREHISTORIC SOUTHWESTERN WARFARE Glen E. Rice & Steven A. LeBlanc; Illus. 320 pp. U. of Utah Press, 2001. $45.

DEADLY MEDICINE: INDIANS & ALCOHOL IN EARLY AMERICA
Peter C. Mancall; Illus. 296 pp. Paper. Cornell University Press, 1997. $24.95.

DEADLY POLITICS OF GIVING: EXCHANGE & VIOLENCE AT AJACAN, ROANOKE, AND JAMESTOWN Seth Mallios; Analyzes Contact Period relations between North American Middle Atlantic Algonquian Indians and the Spanish Jesuits. Anthropological and ethnohistorical study of how European violations of Algonquian gift-exchange systems led to intercultural strife during he late 1500s and early 1600s. Illus. 168 pp. University of Alabama Press, 2006. $44.75; paper, $21.50. E-Book available.

DEAR CHRISTOPHER: LETTERS TO CHRISTOPHER COLUMBUS BY CONTEMPORARY NATIVE AMERICANS Darryl Wilson & Barry Joyce, Eds. 211 pp. Paper. University of California, Native American Studies, 1992. $14.95.

DEATH IN THE DESERT: THE FIFTY YEARS' WAR FOR THE GREAT SOUTHWEST
Paul Wellman; Illus. 318 pp. University of Nebraska Press, 1987. $27.95; paper, $8.95.

THE DEATH OF BERNADETTE LEFTHAND
Ron Querry; Alcohol & witchcraft and a mysterious murder in Navajo territory. 232 pp. Amazon.com, 1993, $23.95; paper, $12.95. Poster available.

THE DEATH OF CRAZY HORSE: A TRAGIC EPISODE IN LAKOTA HISTORY
edited by Richard G. Hardorff; Interviews describe the surrender and death of Crazy Horse in 1877. Illus. Maps. 288 pp. University of Nebraska Press, 2001. $15.95.

THE DEATH OF JIM LONELY
James Welch; Novel about a modern American Indian, with no tribe and no real home. 192 pp. Paper. Penguin USA, $8.

*THE DEATH OF JIMMY LITTLEWOLF: AN INDIAN BOY AT BOYS RANCH
R.L. Templeton; Grades 4-7. Eakin Publications, 1980. $6.95.

DEATH ON THE PRAIRIE: THE THIRTY YEARS' STRUGGLE FOR THE WESTERN PLAINS Paul I. Wellman; Illus. 322 pp. U. of Nebraska Press, 1987. $27.95; paper, $8.95.

THE DEATH & REBIRTH OF THE SENECA
Anthony F. Wallace; 416 pp. Paper. Random House, 1972. $6.36.

DEATH STALKS THE YAKAMA: EPIDEMIOLOGICAL TRANSITIONS & MORALITY ON THE YAKAMA INDIAN RESERVATION, 1888-1964
Clifford E. Trafzer; Illus. 220 pp. Paper. Michigan State University Press, 1997. $24.95.

DEATH, TOO, FOR THE HEAVY-RUNNER
Ben Bennett; Illus. 192 pp. Paper. Mountain Press, 1982. $7.95.

DEATH & VIOLENCE ON THE RESERVATION: HOMICIDE, FAMILY VIOLENCE, & SUICIDE IN AMERICAN INDIAN POPULATION
Robert Bachman; Illus. 192 pp. Greenwood, 1992. $78.95.

DEBATING DEMOCRACY: NATIVE AMERICAN LEGACY OF FREEDOM
Bruce E. Johansen; Chapters by Donald A. Grinde, Jr. & Barbara A. Mann. The Iroquois Confederacy and its influence on the founding fathers of the U.S. 224 pp. Amazon.com, 1995. $24.95; paper, $14.95.

DEBERT: A PALEO-INDIAN SITE IN CENTRAL NOVA SCOTIA
George MacDonald; Third revised edition. Illus. 205 pp. Paper. Persimmon, 1985. $13.95.

ANGIE DEBO: PIONEERING HISTORIAN
Shirley A. Leckie; Illus. 256 pp. U. of Oklahoma Press, 2000. $19.95; paper, $14.95.

DECEMBER'S CHILD: A BOOK OF CHUMASH ORAL NARRATIVES
Thomas Blackburn, Editor; 360 pp. Paper. Univerity of California Press, 1980. $26.95.

DECEPTION ON ALL ACCOUNTS
Sara Sue Hoklotubbe; Native American (Oklahoma Cherokee) mystery novel. 210 pp. Paper. University of Arizona Press, 2003. $14.95.

DECIPHERING ANASAZI VIOLENCE: WITH REGIONAL COMPARISONS TO MESO AMERICAN & WOODLAND CULTURES
Peter Bullock, et al; Illus. 150 pp. Paper. Historical Research & Mapping, 1998. $20.

DECONSTRUCTING THE CHEROKEE NATION: TOWN, REGION, AND NATION AMONG 18TH CENTURY CHEROKEES Tyler Boulware; Explores how village and regional affiliations shaped Cherokee life. Examines the tribe's life during the 18th century, up to the Removal. Illus. Maps. 256 pp. U. Press of Florida, 2011. $69.95; paper, $21.95..

DECORATIVE ART OF THE SOUTHWESTERN INDIANS
Dorothy S. Sides; Reprint of 1962 edition. Illus. 100 pp. Paper. Dover, $5.95.

DECORATIVE ARTS OF THE SIOUX INDIANS
Clark Wissler; Illus. 70 pp. Paper. Amazon.com, 1998. $18.95.

DEEP WATERS: THE TEXTUAL CONTINUUM IN AMERICAN INDIAN LITERATURE
Christopher B. Teuton; Examines four key works of contemporary American Indian literature by Momaday, Vizenor, Young Bear, and Conley. 245 pp. University of Nebraska Press, 2010.

DEEPER THAN GOLD: A GUIDE TO INDIAN LIFE IN THE SIERRA REGION
Brian Bibby; Illus. 190 pp. Paper. Heyday Books, 2001. $16.

DEEPER THAN GOLD: INDIAN LIFE ALONG CALIFORNIA'S HIGHWAY 49
Brian Bibby; photos/Dugan Aguilar; Photos. 192 pp. Paper. Heyday Books, 1999. $18.95.

DEER DANCER: YAQUI LEGENDS OF LIFE
Stan Padilla; Traditional Yaqui myths and legends. Illus. 112 pp. Paper. Book Publishing Co. & Amazon.com, $11.95.

DEER TRACK: A LATE WOODLAND VILLAGE IN THE MISSISSIPPI VALLEY
Charles McGimsey & Michael Conner, Editors
Illus. 134 pp. Paper. Center for American Archaeology, 1985. $7.95.

DEER WOMAN AND OTHER POEMS
William K. Powers; 47 pp. Paper. Lakota Books & Amazon.com, 1994. $10.

DEERSKINS & DUFFELS: THE CREEK INDIAN TRADE WITH ANGLO-AMERICA, 1685-1815, 2nd Edition Kathryn E. Holland Braund
Illus. Maps. 336 pp. Paper. University of Nebraska Press, 2008. $19.95.

DEFAMILIARIZING THE ABORIGINAL: CULTURAL PRACTICES & DECOLONIZATION IN CANADA
Julia V. Emberley; 207 pp. University of Toronto Press, 2009. $69; paper, $32.95.

*THE DEFENDERS
Ann McGovern; Grades 3-7. Illus. 128 pp. Paper. Amazon.com, 1987. $2.50.

DEFENDING THE DINETAH: PUEBLITOS IN THE ANCESTRAL NAVAJO HEARTLAND
Ronald H. Towner
Explores the origins of the Navaho. Illus. 208 pp. University of Utah Press, 2004. $35.

DEFENDING MOTHER EARTH: NATIVE AMERICAN PERSPECTIVES ON ENVIRONMENTAL JUSTICE
Jace Weaver, Editor; 220 pp. Paper. Orbis Books, 1996. $24.

DEFENDING WHOSE COUNTRY? INDIGENOUS SOLDIERS IN THE PACIFIC WAR
Noah Riseman; Illus. Maps. 336 pp. University of Nebraska Press, 2012. $50.

DEFYING MALISEET LANGUAGE DEATH: EMERGENT VITALITIES OF LANGUAGE, CULTURE, AND IDENTITY IN EASTERN CANADA Bernard C. Perley; Ethnographic study examining the role of the Maliseet language and its survival in Maliseet identity processes. Map. 256 pp. U. of Nebraska Press, 2011. $60; paper, $30..

THE DELAWARE
Raymond Bial; Marshall Cavendish Corp., 2004.

DELAWARE-ENGLISH / ENGLISH-DELAWARE DICTIONARY
John O-Meara
A dictionary of 7,100 Munsee Delaware words. 650 pp. Amazon.com. $65.

DELAWARE-INDIAN & ENGLISH SPELLING BOOK
David Zeisberger; Includes over 3,000 words with pronunciation guides. 116 pp. Paper. Amazon.com, $12.

THE DELAWARE INDIANS: A BRIEF HISTORY
E.J. Adams; History, language, legends, government. Reprint of 1906 edition. 80 pp. Paper. Amazon.com & Alibris.com, $8.95.

THE DELAWARE INDIANS: A HISTORY
C.A. Weslager; 570 pp. Paper. Amazon.com, 1990. $19.95.

THE DELAWARE LANGUAGE: A PRELIMINARY DRAFT
Lucy Blalock, Bruce Pearson, James Rementer
Basic Delaware language grammar. 88 pp. Paper. Amazon.com, $12.

DELAWARE REFERENCE GRAMMAR
John O'Meara; 168 pp. University of Toronto Press, 1998. $30.

THE DELAWARE & SHAWNEE ADMITTED TO CHEROKEE CITIZENSHIP & THE RELATED WYANDOTTE & MORAVIAN DELAWARE Toni Jollay Prevost
Contains information on migration patterns; missionary school data; 1860 & 1870 federal census of Wyandotte County, Kansas. 129 pp. Paper. Amazon.com, 1992. $21.50.

DELAWARE TRAILS: SOME TRIBAL RECORDS, 1842-1907
transcribed by Fay Louise Smith Arellano; Collection of records pertaining to the Delaware Indians.Illus. 527 pp. Paper. Amazon.com., 1996. $55.

DELAWARE TRIBE IN A CHEROKEE NATION
Brice Obermeyer; Studies how the federal recognition process works and the effects it has on tribal members & tribal relations. Photo. Maps. Tables & figures. 352 pp. University of Nebraska Press, 2009. $45.

THE DELAWARES: A CRITICAL BIBLIOGRAPHY
C.A. Weslager; Paper. Amazon.com & Alibris.com, 1978. $4.95.

DELGAMUUKW: SUPREME COURT OF CANADA DECISION ON ABORIGINAL TITLE
Canada Supreme Court Staff; 142 pp. Paper. U. of Washington Press, 2000. $16.95.

DELIBERATE ACTS: CHANGING HOPI CULTURE THROUGH THE ORAIBI SPLIT
Peter M. Whiteley; 373 pp. University of Arizona Press, 1988. $52.

DELIGHT MAKERS
Adolph F. Bandelier
A fictional reconstruction of prehistoric Indian culture in the American Southwest by a 19th century archaeologist. Illus. 490 pp. Paper. Amazon.com, 1971. $12.95.

DEMANDING THE CHEROKEE NATION: INDIAN AUTONOMY & MERICAN CULTURES, 1830-1900
Andrew Denson; 344 pp. University of Nebraska Press, 2004. $55; paper, $30.

THE DEMOGRAPHICS OF AMERICAN INDIANS
Harold L. Hodgkinson, et al; 30 pp. Paper. Institute for Human Development, 1991. $1.50.

THE DEMON OF THE CONTINENT: INDIANS & THE SHAPING OF AMERICAN LITERATURE Joshua D. Bellin
272 pp. University of Pennsylvania Press, 2000. $55; paper, $24.95.

DENA'INA LEGACY K'TL'EGH'I SUKDU: THE COLLECTED WRITINGS OF PETER KALIFORNSKY Peter Kalfornsky; edited by James Kari & Alan Boraas
Illus. Photos. Maps. 485 pp. Paper. CIRI & Alaska Native Language Center, 1991. $16.

DENA'INA NOUN DICTIONARY
James Kari, Compiled by; Illus. 355 pp. Paper. Alaska Native Language Center, 1977. $8.

DENE NATION: THE COLONY WITHIN
Mel Watkins; Paper. University of Toronto Press, 1977. $12.95.

DENE TS'UKEGHAI TENE RAHESI/DENE SPRUCE ROOT BASKETRY: REVIVAL OF A TRADITION Suzan Marie & Judy Thompson
Illus. Map. 48 pp. Paper. University of Washington Press, 2003. $14.95.

DENETSOSIE
B. Johnson and S.M. Callaway, Editors
Revised edition. Illus. 51 pp. Rough Rock School Press, 1974. $5.

DENNY'S VOCABULARY OF SHAWNEE
Ebenezer Denny; 51 pp. Amazon.com, 1999. $28.

FRANCES DENSMORE & AMERICAN INDIAN MUSIC
Charles Hofmann; 127 pp. Paper. National Museum of the American Indian, 1968. $5.

THE DEPT. OF THE INTERIOR'S DENIAL OF THE WISCONSIN CHIPPEWA'S CASINO APPLICATIONS: HEARINGS BEFORE THE COMMITTEE ON GOVERNMENT REFORM & OVERSIGHT, HOUSE OF REPRESENTATIVES, 150TH CONGRESS, 2ND SESSION
U.S. Staff; U.S. Government Printing Office, 1998.

DEPREDATION & DECEIT: THE MAKING OF THE JICARILLA & UTE WARS IN NEW MEXICO Gregory F. Michno; Illus. 336 pp. University of Oklahoma Press, 2017. $32.95.

DESCENDANTS OF NANCY WARD: A WORKBOOK FOR FURTHER RESEARCH
David K. Hampton; 448 pp. Paper. Arc Press, 1997. $60.

DESCRIPTION -- NATURAL HISTORY OF THE COASTS OF NORTH AMERICA
N. Denys; W.F. Ganong, Editor; Reprint of 1908 edition. Greenwood Press, $42.

A DESCRIPTION OF NEW NETHERLAND
Adriaen van der Donck; Charles T. Gehring & William Starna, Editors; translated by Dierderik Willem Goedhuys; First-hand account of the lives & world of Dutch colonists & northeastern Native communities in the 17th century. Map. 208 pp. University of Nebraska Press, 2008. $40.

DESERT IMMIGRANTS: THE MEXICAN OF EL PASO, 1880-1920
Mario T. Garcia; Illus. 328 pp. Yale University Press, 1981. $32.50; paper, $11.95.

DESERT INDIAN WOMAN: STORIES & DREAMS
Frances Manuel (Tohono O'odham); Deborah Neff, Editor
Illus. 240 pp. Paper. University of Arizona Press, 2001. $17.95.

THE DESERT IS NO LADY: SOUTHWESTERN LANDSCAPES IN WOMEN'S WRITING & ART Vera Norwood & Janice Monk, Editors
Reprint of 1987 edition. Illus. 340 pp. Paper. University of Arizona Press, $24.95.

THE DESERT LAKE: THE STORY OF NEVADA'S PYRAMID LAKE
Sessions S. Wheeler; Prehistory and history of the basin, including its famous Indian battles. Illus. Biblio. 139 pp. Paper. The Caxton Press, $7.95.

DESERT LIGHT: MYTHS & VISIONS OF THE GEAT SOUTHWEST
John Miller, Editor; Illus. 120 pp. Paper. Amazon.com, 1990. $18.95.

THE DESERT SMELLS LIKE RAIN: A NATURALIST IN PAPAGO INDIAN COUNTRY
Gary P. Nabhan; 176 pp. Paper. Amazon.com, 1987. $8.95.

DESERT INDIAN WOMAN: STORIES & DREAMS
Frances Manuel & Deborah Neff; Basket weaver, storyteller, and tribal elder, Frances Manuel is a living preserver of Tohono O'odham culture. Speaking in her own words, she shares the story of her life and tells of O'odham culture and society. Illus. 240 pp. Paper. University of Arizona Press, 2001. $17.95.

THE DESERT SMELLS LIKE RAIN: A NATURALIST IN O'ODHAM COUNTRY
Gary Paul Nabhan; The everyday life and perseverance of the Tohono O'odham. Originally published in 1982. Illus. 148 pp. Paper. U. of Arizona Press, 2002. $16.95.

DESIGNING WITH THE WOOL
Noel Bennett; Illus. 128 pp. Paper. Northland, 1979. $8.95.

DESIGNS & FACTIONS: POLITICS, RELIGION, & CERAMICS ON HOPI THIRD MESA
Lydia Wyckoff; Illus. 210 pp. Paper. University of New Mexico Press, 1990. $24.95.

DESIGNS OF THE NIGHT SKY
Diane Glancy; Fiction. Cherokee theme. 157 pp. U. of Nebraska Press, 2002. $24.95.

DESIGNS ON PREHISTORIC HOPI POTTERY
Jesse W. Fewkes; Reprint. Illus. 290 pp. Paper. Dover, 1973. $9.95.

PATRICK DESJARLAIT: CONVERSATIONS WITH A NATIVE AMERICAN ARTIST
First person narrative, recorded before his death in 1972, Patrick tells of his boyhood as a reservation Indian on the Red Lake Ojibwe reservation of northern Minnesota; also, his experience in art school & his life as a commercial artist. 56 pp. Lerner Publications, $21.50.

DESTROYING DOGMA: VINE DELORIA, JR. & HIS INFLUENCE ON AMERICAN SOCIETY Collection of essays by prominent scholars & intellectuals all sharing Deloria's notion that dogma is the enemy of critical thinking. 240 pp. Paper. Fulcrum Publishing, 2005. $28.95.

THE DESTRUCTION OF AMERICAN INDIAN FAMILIES
Steven Unger, Editor; Paper. Amazon.com, 1977. $4.25.

THE DESTRUCTION OF CALIFORNIA INDIANS
edited by Robert F. Heizer; intro. by Albert Hurtado; Reveals how thousands of California natives died from 1847 to 1865. Illus. 321 pp. Paper. U. of Nebraska Press, 1993. $27.95.

THE DESTRUCTION OF THE PEOPLE
Coyote Man; The history of the Maidu people, from the Indians' point of view. Amazon.com, $15.95.

DEVELOPING REHABILITATION RESEARCHERS IN THE AMERICAN INDIAN COMMUNITY: A TECHNICAL REPORT OF CONSUMER-RESEARCHER TRAINING
C.A. Marshall & George S. Gotto; Paper. Amazon.com, 1998. $10.

THE DEVELOPMENT OF CAPITALISM IN THE NAVAJO NATION: A POLITICAL-ECONOMIC HISTORY
Lawrence D. Weiss; 180 pp. Amazon.com, 1984. $29.95; paper, $10.95.

THE DEVELOPMENT OF SOUTHEASTERN ARCHAEOLOGY
Jay K. Johnson, Editor; 352 pp. Paper. University of Alabama Press, 1993. $29.95.

THE DEVIL IN THE NEW WORLD: THE IMPACT OF DIABOLISM IN NEW SPAIN
Fernando Cervantes; Reveals how Native American reinterpreted the view of Christianity presented to them. He deals with the social history of the interaction between the two cultures. Illus. 192 pp. Yale University Press, 1994. $22.50.

DEVIL SICKNESS & DEVIL SONGS: TOHONO O'ODHAM POETICS
David L. Kozak & David L. Lopez
Illus. Maps. 224 pp. Smithsonian Institution Press, 1999. $45.

DEZBA, NAVAJO WOMAN OF THE DESERT
Gladys A. Reichard; Illus. 220 pp. Paper. Rio Grande Press, $12.

DIABETES AMONG THE PIMA: STORIES OF SURVIVAL
Carolyn Smith-Morris; In-depth ethnographic study of diabetes among the Pima in the Gila River Indian community. 248 pp. Paper. University of Arizona Press, 2006. $22.95.

DIABETES EPIDEMIC HEARING BEFORE THE COMMITTEE ON INDIAN AFFAIRS, U.S. SENATE, 105TH CONGRESS
USGPO staff; 1st Session on Diabetes Epidemic Among American Indians & Others in the Gallup Area, April 4, 1997, Gallup, NM. 33 pp. Paper. USGPO, 1998.

DIALOGUES WITH ZUNI POTTERS
Milfred Nahohai & Elisa Phelps; Illus. 102 pp. Paper. U. of New Mexico Press, $19.95.

THE DIARIES OF JOHN GREGORY BOURKE, 5 VOLS.
Charles Robinson; Texas A&M Univdersity Press, 2009. $55. each

DIARIO OF CHRISTOPHER COLUMBUS'S FIRST VOYAGE TO AMERICA 1492-1493
trans. by Oliver Dunn & James Kelley, Jr.
Illus. 492 pp. University of Oklahoma Press, 1989. $70; paper, $27.95.

DIARY OF DAVID ZEISBERGER: A MORAVIAN MISSIONARY AMONG THE INDIANS OF OHIO Eugene F. Bliss; Reprint. Vol. 2. Kessinger Publishing. $42.30.

DICTIONARY OF THE ALABAMA LANGUAGE
Cora Sylestine, Heather Hardy & Timothy Montler
The language of the Alabama-Coushatta Indian Reservation in Polk County, Texas. Over 8,000 entries. 765 pp. University of Texas Press, 1993. $35.

DICTIONARY OF THE AMERICAN INDIAN
John Stoutenburgh, Jr.
Sourcebook of American Indian history and lore. 480 pp. Cherokee Publications, $9.95.

DICTIONARY CATALOG OF THE EDWARD E. AYER COLLECTION OF AMERICANA & AMERICAN INDIANS Newberry Library Staff
16 Volumes and First Supplement. G.K. Hall, 1970. $1,280.00; First Supplement, $365.

DICTIONARY OF THE CHINOOK JARGON: ENGLISH-CHINOOK
Frederick J. Long, Ed.; 48 pp. Paper. Coyote Press, $5.50.

DICTIONARY OF THE CHOCTAW LANGUAGE
Cyrus Byington; 611 pp. 1995. Amazon.com. $31.95; paper, $13.95.

DICTIONARY OF CREEK/MUSKOGEE
Jack B. Martin & Margaret McKane Mauldin
Illus. Map. 359 pp. University of Nebraska Press, 2000. $65.

DICTIONARY OF DAILY LIFE OF INDIANS OF THE AMERICAS
2 vols. 2,000 pp. American Indian Publishers, 1982. $165. per set.

DICTIONARY OF INDIAN TRIBES OF THE AMERICAS
2nd edition. 3 vols. Illus. 2,000 pp. American Indian Publishers, 1981. $375 per set.

DICTIONARY OF JICARILLA APACHE
Wilhelmina Phone, Maureen Olson, Matilda Martinez; with eds.
Over 5,000 entries; grammatical sketch of the language; Apache to English and English to Apache index; lexicon. 500 pp. University of New Mexico Press, $125.

DICTIONARY OF MESA GRANDE DIEGUENO
Ted Couro & Christina Hutcheson; First dictionary published of a Yuman Indian language. Reprint of 1979 ed. Paper. Malki-Ballena Press, 2004. $25.

DICTIONARY OF NATIVE AMERICAN HEALING
William S. Lyon; Explores the various aspects of Native American healing. Includes Canadian and Eskimo cultures. 360 pp. ABC-CLIO, 1996. $70.

DICTIONARY OF NATIVE AMERICAN LITERATURE
Andrew Wiget, Ed.; 616 pp. Amazon.com, $160.

DICTIONARY OF NATIVE AMERICAN MYTHOLOGY
Sam D. Gill & Irene F. Sullivan; Describes past & present rituals, traditions, and myths of over 100 Native American cultures. Biblio. 425 pp. ABC-Clio, 1992. $69.50.Paper. Illus. 456 pp. Oxford University Press, $18.95.

DICTIONARY OF THE OJIBWAY LANGUAGE
Frederica Baraga; Compiled nearly 150 years ago. Reprint of 1878 edition.
736 pp. Paper. Minnesota Historical Society Press, $24.95.

DICTIONARY OF THE OSAGE LANGUAGE
Francis La Flesche; 406 pp. 1994. Amazon.com, $39.95; paper, $27.95.

A DICTIONARY OF PAPAGO USAGE
M. Mathiot; 504 pp. Amazon.com, $50.

A DICTIONARY OF IOWA PLACE-NAMES
Tom Savage; 192 pp. Paper. U. of Iowa Press, 2008. $19.95; e-book, $10 or $19.95.

DICTIONARY OF POWHATAN
William Strachey; Frederic Gleach, Editor; Reprint. 107 pp. Amazon.com, 1999. $36.

A DICTIONARY OF SKIRI PAWNEE
Douglas R. Parks & Lulu Nora Pratt; 4,500 entries arranged alphabetically by English glosses and by Skiri words & stems. 568 pp. University of Nebraska Press, 2008. $85.

A DIFFERENT MEDICINE: POSTCOLONIAL HEALING IN THE NATIVE AMERICAN CHURCH Joseph Calabrese; Oxford University Press, 2013. $125; paper, $33.95.

DIGEST OF AMERICAN INDIAN LAW: CASES & CHRONOLOGY
H. Barry Holt & Gary Forrester; 140 pp. Amazon.com, 1990. $35.

DIMENSIONS OF NATIVE AMERICA: THE CONTACT ZONE
Jehanne Teilhet-Fisk; Illus. 144 pp. Paper. Amazon.com, 1998. $20.

DINE BAHANE': THE NAVAJO CREATION STORY
Paul G. Zolbrod; 443 pp. Paper. University of New Mexico Press, 1984. $24.95.

DINE BIZAAD BINAHOO'AAH: REDISCOVERING THE NAVAJO LANGUAGE
Evangeline Parsons Yazzie & Margaret Speas; Navajo language textbook. Illus. 448 pp.
$89.95; teacher's edition, electronic PDF CD-ROM, $140; workbook, $39.95.

DINE BIBLIOGRAPHY TO THE 1990s: A COMPARISON TO THE NAVAJO BIBLIOGRAPHY OF 1969 Howard M. Bahr; Contains over 6,300 entries covering Navajo literature from 1970 to 1990, as well as newly discovered literature. Includes health-related, artistic, economic, religious, social, scientific, other literature on the Navajo. 776 pp. Scarecrow Press, 1999. $124.30.

*DINE BIZAAD: SPEAK, READ, WRITE NAVAJO
Irvy Goossen; narrated Peter Thomas; Grades 3-8. Improves Navajo speaking, reading, & writing skills. Paper. Amazon.com, 2008. Book, $44.95. CDs, $60 each, 30 lessons

DINE: A HISTORY OF THE NAVAJOS
Peter Iverson; Winner of the Western Writers of America 2003 Spur Award for Nonfiction-Contemporary. Illus. 3 maps. 432 pp. Paper. University of New Mexico Press, 2003. $24.95.

*DINE, THE NAVAJO
Suan L. Shaffer, Editor; Grade 6. Illus. Includes 30 student booklets, one teacher's resource binder which includes transparencies, color slides & audiocassette. Heard Museum, 1987. $295.

DINE' PERSPECTIVES: REVITALIZING & RECLAIMING NAVAJO THOUGHT
Lloyd L. Lee, Editor; foreword by Gregory Cajete; A collection of essays incorporating the Dine past into the present. 208 pp. Illus. Paper. University of Arizona Press, 2014. $29.95.

DINEJI NA'NITIN: NAVAJO TRADITIONAL TEACHINGS & HISTORY
Robert S. McPherson; Illus. 220 pp. Paper. University Press of Colorado, 2012. $24.95; Ebook, $19.95.

DINETAH: AN EARLY HISTORY OF THE NAVAJO
Lawrence D. Sundberg
A chronicle of the early band Navajo people. 128 pp. Paper. Sunstone Press, $12.95.

DINETAH: NAVAJO HISTORY
Robert A. Roessel; T.L. McCarty, Editor
Volume III. Illus. 180 pp. Rough Rock School Press, 1983. $15.

DIPLOMACY & THE INDIAN GIFTS: THE FRENCH-ENGLISH RIVALRY FOR INDIAN LOYALTIES DURING THE FRENCH & INDIAN WAR YEARS 1748-1763
Wilbur R. Jacobs; Reprint. Illus. 208 pp. Wennawoods Publishing, $19.95.

DIPLOMATS IN BUCKSKINS: A HISTORY OF INDIAN DELEGATIONS IN WASHINGTON CITY Herman J. Viola; foreword by Ben Nighthorse Campbell
Originally published in 1981. Illus. 58 photos. 234 pp. U. of Oklahoma Press, 1996. $19.95.

DIRECTORY OF AMERICAN INDIAN LAW ATTORNEYS
150 pp. Amazon.com, 1990-91. $35.

DIRECTORY OF NATIVE AMERICAN PERFORMING ARTISTS
Lists artists & groups available for booking & performances. Includes storytellers, musicians, dancers, poets, singers, & craft demonstrators. Atlatl, 1991. $3.

THE DIRT IS RED HERE: ART & POETRY FROM NATIVE CALIFORNIA
Margaret Dubin, Editor
California Indian artists & poets. Paper. Heyday Books. $16.95.

DISCIPLINED HEARTS: HISTORY, IDENTITY & DEPRESSION IN AN AMERICAN INDIAN COMMUNITY
Theresa Deleane O'Neil; Illus. 265 pp. Paper. U. of California Press, 1996. $27.95.

*DISCOVER AMERICAN INDIAN WAYS: A CARNEGIE ACTIVITY BOOK
Pamela Soeder; Grades 2-6. Illus. 28 pp. Roberts Rinehart, 1998. $4.95.

DISCOVER INDIAN RESERVATIONS: A VISITOR'S WELCOME GUIDE
Veronica Tiller; Lists reservations by state, providing a tribal profile, location, sites, events, etc. for each. Paper. Council Publications, 1992. $19.95.

DISCOVERED LANDS, INVENTED PASTS: TRANSFORMING VISIONS OF THE AMERICAN WEST Jules David Prown, et al; Presents a major reinterpretation of western American art of the past three centuries. Includes depictions of Indians by early explorers. Illus. 232 pp. Yale University Press, 1992. $40; paper, $25.

DISCOVERY OF THE YOSEMITE & THE INDIAN WAR OF 1851 WHICH LED TO THE EVENT Lafayette H. Bunnell; Original source history of Yosemite Valley. Reprint of 1911 edition. 340 pp. Paper. Amazon.com, $9.95.

DISCOVERING NORTH AMERICAN ROCK ART
Lawrence Loendorf, Christopher Chippindale, David Whitley, Editors
Illus. 336 pp. University of Arizona Press, 2005. $55.

DISCOVERING TOTEM POLES: A TRAVELER'S GUIDE
Aldona Jonaitis; Illus. 144 pp. Paper. University of Washington Press, 2015 $18.95.

DISEASE CHANGE & THE ROLE OF MEDICINE: THE NAVAJO EXPERIENCE
Stephen J. Kunitz
232 pp. Paper. University of California Press, 1989. $26.95. E-Book available.

DISEASE & DEMOGRAPHY IN THE AMERICAS
John W. Verano & Douglas Ubelaker
Illus. 352 pp. Paper. Smithsonian Institution Press, 1992. $34.95.

DISEASE, DEPOPULATION & CULTURE CHANGE IN NORTHWESTERN NEW SPAIN, 1518-1764 Daniel T. Reff; Illus. 415 pp. University of Utah Press, 1990. $30.

DISMEMBERED: NATIVE DISENROLLMENT & THE BATTLE FOR HUMAN RIGHTS
David Wilkins & Shelly Hulse Wilkins
Illus. 227 pp. University of Washington Press, 2017. $80; paper, $25.

THE DISPOSSESSED: CULTURAL GENOCIDE OF THE MIXED-BLOOD UTES, AN ADVOCATE'S CHRONICLE
Parker M. Nielson; Illus. Maps. Biblio. 384 pp. U. of Oklahoma Press, 1998. $34.95.

DISPOSSESSING THE AMERICAN INDIAN: INDIAN & WHITES ON THE COLONIAL FRONTIER
Wilbur R. Jacobs; Illus. Maps. 246 pp. Paper. U. of Oklahoma Press, 1972. $15.95.

DISPOSSESSING THE WILDERNESS: INDIAN REMOVAL & THE MAKING OF THE NATIONAL PARKS
Mark D. Spence; Illus. 210 pp. Oxford University Press, 1999. $94; paper, $28.95.

DISPOSSESSION BY DEGREES: INDIAN LAND & IDENTITY IN NATICK, MA, 1650-1790 Jean M. O'Brien; Illus. Maps. 224 pp. Cambridge University Press, 1997. $65. Paper. University of Nebraska Press, 2003. $29.95.

THE DISPOSSESSION OF THE AMERICAN INDIAN, 1887-1934
Janet A. McDonnell; Illus. 176 pp. Amazon.com & Alibris.com, 1991. $24.95.

THE DISPOSSESSION OF THE AMERICAN INDIANS – & OTHER KEY ISSUES IN AMERICAN HISTORY
Dwight D. Murphey; 135 pp. Paper. Washington Summit Publishers, 1995. $16.

DISPUTED WATERS: NATIVE AMERICA & THE GREAT LAKE FISHERY
Robert Doherty; 184 pp. Amazon.com, 1990. $24.

DISRUPTING SAVAGISM: INTERSECTING CHICANO, MEXICAN IMMIGRANT, & NATIVE AMERICAN STRUGGLES FOR SELF-REPRESENTATION
Arturo J. Aldama; Illus. 208 pp. Duke University Press, 2001. $64.95; paper, $19.95.

DISSONANT WORLDS: ROGER VANDERSTEENE AMONG THE CREE
Earle H. Waugh; Illus. 344 pp. Paper. Wilfred Laurier University Press, 1996.

DISTANT RELATIONS: HOW MY ANCESTORS COLONIZED NORTH AMERICA
Victoria Freeman; Illus. 568 pp. Amazon.com, 2002. $35. Paper.

DISTINGUISHED NATIVE AMERICAN POLITICAL & TRIBAL LEADERS
Duane Champagne & Delia Salvatierra
Illus. 344 pp. Greenwood Publishing, 2000. $69.95.

DISTINGUISHED NATIVE AMERICAN SPIRITUAL PRACTITIONERS & HEALERS
Troy R. Johnson; Illus. 304 pp. Greenwood, 2002. $69.95.

DISTORTED IMAGES OF THE APPALACHIAN MOUNTAIN CHEROKEE
A bibliographic historic & ethnologic survey of the Eurocentric stereotyping of original AniYunwiya history, identity, culture and social mechanisms concerning the original people of Appalachian mountains @ 1500 B.C. to the present historic era. David Michael Wolfe.

DIVERSITY & DIALOGUE: THE EITELJORG FELLOWSHIP FOR NATIVE AMERICAN FINE ART, 2007 James H. Nottage; Honors James Luna (Luiseno) & five Fellows: Gerald Clarke (Cahuilla), Dana Claxton (Lakota), Sonya Kelliher-Combs (Inupiaq/Athapascan), Larry Tee Harbor Jackson McNeil (Tlingit/Nisga'a) & Will Wilson (Dine). Illus. 120 pp. Paper. University of Washington Press, 2009. $25.

THE DIVIDED GROUND: INDIANS, SETTLERS, & THE NORTHERN BORDERLAND OF THE AMERICAN REVOLUTION Alan Taylor; Illus. 560 pp. Amazon.com, 2007. $16.95.

DIVIDING THE RESERVATION: ALICE FLETCHER'S NEZ PERCE ALLOTMENT DIARIES & LETTERS, 1889-1892
Nicole Tonkovich; Illus. Maps. 376 pp. Paper. WSU Press, 2016. $29.95.

DIVING FOR NORTHWEST RELICS
James S. White; Illus. Binfort-Metropolitan, 1979. $8.95; paper, $6.50.

DIVISIVENESS & SOCIAL CONFLICT: AN ANTHROPOLOGICAL APPROACH
Alan R. Beals and Bernard J. Siegel; 185 pp. Amazon.com & Alibris.com, 1966. $19.50.

DO ALL INDIANS LIVE IN TIPIS? QUESTIONS & ANSWERS FROM THE NATIONAL MUSEUM OF THE AMERICAN INDIAN
National Museum of the American Indian; Intro. By Wilma Mankiller
Illus. 240 pp. Paper. NMAI Press & HarperCollins & Amazon.com, 2007. $14.99.

DO THEM NO HARM
Zoa L. Swayne; Illus. Legacy House, 1990. $25.95.

DO YOU SEE WHAT I MEAN? PLAINS INDIAN SIGN TALK & THE EMBODIMENT OF ACTION Brenda Farnell; Illus. 107 figures. Maps. Tables. 400 pp. U. of Texas Press, 1995. $40. Paper. University of Nebraska Press, 2009. $25.

A DOCTOR AMONG THE OGLALA SIOUX TRIBE: THE LETTERS OF ROBERT H. RUBY, 1953-54 Robert H. Ruby, MD; Cary C. Collins & Charles V. Mutschuler, Editors
Details Oglala Lakota people and their culture. Photos. Maps. Figures. 424 pp. University of Nebraska Press, 2010. $45.

DOCTORS OF MEDICINE IN NEW MEXICO: A HISTORY OF HEALTH & MEDICAL PRACTICE, 1886-1986 Jake W. Spidle, Jr.
Illus. 400 pp. University of New Mexico Press, 1986. $29.95.

DOCUMENTARY EVIDENCE FOR THE SPANISH MISSIONS OF ALTA CALIFORNIA
Julia Costello, Ed.; Illus. 565 pp. Garland, 1992. $42.

DOCUMENTARY EVIDENCE FOR THE SPANISH MISSIONS OF TEXAS
Arthur R. Gomez, Ed,; Illus. 504 pp. Garland, 1991. $42.

DOCUMENTS OF AMERICAN INDIAN DIPLOMACY: TREATIES, AGREEMENTS, & CONVENTIONS, 1775-1979 Vine Deloria, Jr. & Raymond DeMallie
Biblio. 1,536 pp. 2 vols. University of Oklahoma Press, 1999. $125.

DOCUMENTS OF U.S. INDIAN POLICY
Francis P. Prucha, Editor; Selection of primary documents important in Indian-white relations. 3rd Edition. 396 pp. University of Nebraska Press, 2000. $50; paper, $25.

*DOG PEOPLE: NATIVE DOG STORIES
Joseph Bruchac; illus. by Murv Jacob
Grades 3 and up. Illus. 64 pp. Fulcrum Publishing, $14.95.

DOG SOLDIER SOCIETIES OF THE PLAINS
Thomas E. Mails; Account of the warrior societies and cults of the Plains Indians.
Illus. 384 pp. Marlowe & Co., $46.50; paper, $29.95.

THE DOG'S CHILDREN: ANISHINAABE TEXTS
told by Angeline Williams; Leonard Bloomfield, Editor; In Ojibwe, with English translations by Bloomfield. Ojibwe-English glossary. Paper. U. of Toronto Press, 1991. $37.50.

DOING BUSINESS ON ARIZONA INDIAN LANDS
(Center for American Indian Economic Development)
Guide for both Native and non-Native people who want to do business on Arizona Indian Reservations. Includes statistics, tourism activities, tribal resources, key tribal contacts, etc. Amazon.com. CD-ROM. $49.95.

DOING FIELDWORK: WARNINGS & ADVICE
Rosalie H. Wax; Reprint of 1971 edition. 396 pp. Paper. University of Chicago Press, $20.

DOLLS & TOYS OF NATIVE AMERICA: A JOURNEY THROUGH CHILDHOOD
Don & Debra McQuiston; Reprint. Indian dolls of North American including Alaska.
Historic color & b&w photos. 119 pp. Paper. Amazon.com, 2001. $20.

DOMESTIC SUBJECTS: GENDER, CITIZENSHIP, AND LAW IN NATIVE AMERICAN LITERATURE Beth H. Piatote
Illus. 248 pp. Yale University Presss, 2013. $50; paper, $26.

DOMINION & CIVILITY: ENGLISH IMPERIALISM, NATIVE AMERICA & THE FIRST AMERICAN FRONTIERS, 1585-1685
Michael L. Oberg; Illus. 256 pp. Amazon.com, 1999. $44.50; paper, $24.95.

DON'T BLAME THE INDIANS: NATIVE AMERICANS & THE MECHANIZED DOORS OF PERCEPTION Aldous Huxley; Paper. HarperCollins, 1970. $3.95.

DON'T LET THE SUN STEP OVER YOU: A WHITE MOUNTAIN APACHE FAMILY LIFE, 1860-1975 Eva Tulene Watt, with Keith Basso; 340 pp. U. of Arizona Press, 2004. $50; paper, $24.95.

*THE DOUBLE LIFE OF POCAHONTAS
Jean Fritz; Dispels myths & describes the life of the girl whose active conscience made her a pawn, exploited by her own people and the white world. Grades 4-8. Illus. 96 pp. Putnam, 1983. $13.95.

DOUBLE WOMAN
Michele Burger; Lakota art & myth. Illus. 99 pp. Paper. Lakota Books & Amazon.com, 1999. $21.95.

THE DOVE ALWAYS CRIED: NARRATIVES OF INDIAN SCHOOL LIFE
Marguerite Bigler Stoltz; Author's experiences as a teacher in schools for Indian children in the 1920s-30s, plus tales by some of her pupils. 36 photos, 7 maps. Paper. Amazon.com & Alibris.com, 1994. $9.95.

DR. JOHN McLOUGHLIN, MASTER OF FORT VANCOUVER, FATHER OF OREGON
Nancy Wilson; Bert Webber, Editor; Treatment of Indians is included. Illus. Maps. Biblio. Paper. Webb Research Group, $12.95.

DOWN COUNTRY: THE TANO OF THE GALISTEO BASIN, 1250-1782
Lucy R. Lippard; photos by Edward Ranney
History of five centuries of the Southern Tewa Pueblo Indian culture in the Galistea Basin, 22 miles south of Santa Fe. Illus. 388 pp. Museum of New Mexico Press, 2010. $50.

EDWARD P. DOZIER: THE PARADOX OF THE AMERICAN INDIAN ANTHROPOLOGIST Marilyn Norcini; Interprets Dozier's career within American anthropology & the Pueblo Indian culture. 208 pp. University of Arizona Press, 2007. $45.

DRAGONFLY'S TALE
Kristina Rodanas; Native American folklore. Paper. Clarion Books, 1993. $14.95.

DRAMATIC ELEMENTS IN AMERICAN INDIAN CEREMONIALS
Virginia S. Heath; Paper. Haskell House, 1970. $22.95.

DRAWING BACK CULTURE: THE MAKAH STRUGGLE FOR REPATRIATION
Ann M. Tweedie; Illus. Maps. 208 pp. University of Washington Press, 2002. $34.95.

DRAWINGS OF THE SONG ANIMALS; NEW & SELECTED POEMS
Duane Niatum; Poetry. Drawing on his native heritage, Niatum interweaves the themes of aging and human community. 136 pp. Holy Cow! Press, 1994. $18.95; paper, $10.95.

DREAM CATCHERS: HOW NATIVE AMERICAN SPIRITUALITY WENT MAINSTREAM
Philip Jenkins; 320 pp. Oxford University Press, 2004. $29.95.

DREAM CATCHERS: LEGEND, LORE & ARTIFACTS
Carl Oberholtzer; Illus. 152 pp. paper. Firefly Books & Amazon.com, 2017. $19.95

*DREAM FEATHER
Stan Padilla; Story of a young boy's spiritual awakening. Grades 5 and up.
Illus. 60 pp. Paper. The Book Publishing Co., 1991. $11.95.

THE DREAM OF A BROKEN FIELD
Diane Glancy; Narrative of Native American cosmology and a Christian upbringing, of Native American boarding schools and Indigenous writers. Illus. 256 pp. Paper. University of Nebraska Press, 2011. $30.

*DREAM QUEST: STORIES FROM SPIRIT BAY
Amy J. Cooper; Grades 3 to 7. Illus. 128 pp. Amazon.com, 1996. $7.95; paper, $4.95.

THE DREAM SEEKERS: NATIVE AMERICAN VISIONARY TRADITIONS OF THE GREAT PLAINS Lee Irwin; Demonstrates the central importance of visionary dreams as sources of empowerment & innovation in Plains Indian religion. Biblio. 320 pp. University of Oklahoma Press, 1994. $28.95; paper, $14.95.

DREAM SONGS & CEREMONY: REFLECTIONS ON CALIFORNIA INDIAN DANCE
Frank LaPena; Illus. 48 pp. Amazon.com, 2004. $25.

*DREAMCATCHER
Audrey Osofsky; illus. by Ed Young
Free verse text with glimpses of Ojibwe life. Grades PS-3. Illus. 32 pp. Amazon.com, $15.

DREAMING THE DAWN: CONVERSATIONS WITH NATIVE ARTISTS & ACTIVISTS
E.E. Caldwell, Editor; Collection of interviews with twelve leading artists and activists. Illus. 146 pp. University of Nebraska Press, 1998. $30.

*DREAMPLACE
George Ella Lyon ; When a young girl visits the Pueblo where the Anasazi lives, she sees images of its past inhabitants' history. Grades PS-3. Illus. 32 pp. Amazon.com, $16.

DREAMER-PROPHETS OF THE COLUMBIA PLATEAU: SMOHALLA & SKOLASKIN
Robert Ruby & John Brown; Illus. Maps. 272 pp. Paper. University of Oklahoma Press, 1989. $19.95.

DREAMERS WITH POWER: THE MENOMINEE
George & Louise Spindler
Reprint of 1971 edition. Illus. 208 pp. Paper. Waveland Press, 1984. $9.95.

DREAMING THE COUNCIL WAYS: TRUE NATIVE TEACHINGS FROM RED LODGE
Ohky Simine Forest; Illus. 350 pp. Paper. Red Wheel/Weiser, 2000. $18.95.

DREAMING OF THE DAWN: CONVERSATIONS WITH NATIVE ARTISTS & ACTIVISTS
E.K. Caldwell; Illus. 145 pp. University of Nebraska Press, 1999. $30.

DREAMING OF SHEEP IN NAVAJO COUNTRY
Marsha L. Weisiger; History of Navajo (Dine) pastoralism. Illus. Maps. 418 pp. University of Washington Press, 2009. $35; paper, $25.

DREAMING WITH THE WHEEL: HOW TO INTERPRET YOUR DREAMS USING THE MEDICINE WHEEL
Sun Bear & Wabun Wind; 320 pp. paper. Simon & Schuster, 1994. $12.

DREAMS OF FIERY STARS: TRANSFORMATIONS OF NATIVE AMERICAN FICTION
Catherine Rainwater; 222 pp. University of Pennsylvania Press, 1998. $18.50.

DREAMS & THUNDER: STORIES, POEMS, AND THE SUN DANCE OPERA
Zitkala-Sa; edited by P. Jane Hafen; Zitkala-Sa (Red Bird)(1876-1938), a Yankton Sioux teacher, artist, activist, and violin soloist presents previously unpublished material. Illus. 174 pp. University of Nebraska Press, 2001. $22.95.

DRESS CLOTHING OF THE PLAINS INDIANS
Ronald P. Koch; Illus. 220 pp. Paper. University of Oklahoma Press, 1977. $15.95.

DRESS & DECORATION OF THE AMERICAN INDIAN
George Catlin; Amazon.com, 1999. $19.95.

DRESSING IN FEATHERS: THE CONSTRUCTION OF THE INDIAN IN AMERICAN POPULAR CULTURE Elizabeth S. Bird, Editor
Illus. 336 pp. Paper. Westview Press, 1996. $48.

DRIFTING THROUGH ANCESTOR DREAMS
Ramson Lomatewama; Poetry. Illus. 72 pp. Amazon.com, $9.95.

DRINKING BEHAVIOR AMONG THE SOUTHWESTERN INDIANS: AN ANTHROPOLOGICAL PERSPECTIVE Jack Waddell & Michael Everett, Editors
248 pp. Paper. U. of Arizona Press, 1980. $19.50.

DRINKING CAREERS: A 25-YEAR STUDY OF THREE NAVAJO POPULATIONS
Stephen J. Kunitz & Jerrold E. Levy; Illus. 296 pp. Yale University Press, 1994. $32.50.

DRINKING CAREERS: A 25-YEAR STUDY OF THREE NAVAJO POPULATIONS
Stephen J. Kunitz & Jerrold E. Levy; First long-term follow-up study of alcohol use among Native Americans. 300 pp. Yale University Press, 1994. $28.50.

DRINKING, CONDUCT DISORDER & SOCIAL CHANGE: NAVAJO EXPERIENCE
Stephen J. Kunitz & Jerrold E. Levy; Illus. 280 pp. Oxford University Press, 2000. $49.

DRINKING & SOBRIETY AMONG THE LAKOTA SIOUX
Beatrice Medicine; 193 pp. AltaMra Press, 2006. $89; paper, $34; eBook, $32.99.

DRIVEN WEST: ANDREW JACKSON'S TRAIL OF TEARS TO THE CIVIL WAR
A.J. Langguth; Traces the contributions pf Presdoents Monroe, Jackson, Van Buren and Polk while covering the debates over native American rights, Manifest Destiny expansion and the events that led up to the Civil War. Illus. 466 pp. Simon & Schuster, 2010.

DROWNING IN FIRE
Craig S. Womack; Novel of sexual and cultural identity.
294 pp. University of Arizona Press, 2001. $35; paper, $17.95.

DRUM SONGS: GLIMPSES OF DENE HISTORY
Kerry Abel; Examines the history of the Dene, one of the aboriginal peoples of Canada's western subarctic. Illus. Maps. McGill-Queen's U. Press, 1993. $44.95; paper, $19.95.

*DRUMBEAT....HEARTBEAT: A CELEBRATION OF THE POWWOW
Susan Braine; Grades 4-8. Illus. 50 pp. Lerner Publications & Meadowlark Communications, $6.95.

DRUMBEATS FROM MESCALERO: CONVERSATIONS WITH APACHE ELDERS, WARRIORS, AND HOUSEHOLDERS
H Henrietta Stockel with Marlan Kelley; Texas A&M University Press, $29.95.

DRUMS ALONG THE ISLETA
Dan Kubiak; Cherokee Indians and Texas struggle for Independence in the earli 1800's. Paper. Fort Tumbleweed, $12.95.

DRUMS ALONG THE MOHAWK
Walter D. Edmonds; 616 pp. Paper. Syracuse University Press, $19.95.

DRY BONES, DAKOTA TERRITORY REFLECTED
John & Pauline Gregg; Ancient diseases in the northern Plains; problems concerning the prehistory of the Great Plains Native populations. Paper. Amazon.com, 1987. $25.

DRY BONES & INDIAN SERMONS: PRAYING INDIANS IN COLONIAL AMERICA
Kristina Bross; Illus. 256 pp. Paper. Amazon.com, 2004. $21.95.

THE DULL KNIFES OF PINE RIDGE: A LAKOTA ODYSSEY
Joe Starita; An account of four generations of Lakota Sioux family. Illus. Map. 392 pp. Paper. University of Nebraska Press, 2002. $19.95.

DURING MY TIME: FLORENCE EDENSHAW DAVIDSON, A HAIDA WOMAN
Margaret B. Blackman with Florence Edenshaw Davidson; Illus. Map. Revised & enlarged edition. 228 pp. Paper. University of Washington Press, 1992. $16.95.

THE DUST ROSE LIKE SMOKE: THE SUBJUGATION OF THE ZULU & THE SIOUX
James O. Gump; Illus. Maps. 180 pp. University of Nebraska Press, 1994. $45.

THE DUTCH, THE INDIANS AND THE QUEST FOR COPPER-PAHAQUARRY AND THE OLD MINE ROAD Herbert C. Kraft; Reprint. Illus. Maps. 183 pp. Paper. Lenape Lifeways, Amazon.com & Alibris.com, $10.

THE DUTCH & THE IROQUOIS
Rev. C.H. Hall; Reprint of 1882 edition. 55 pp. paper. Amazon.com, $8.95.

THE DUTY TO CONSULT: NEW RELATIONSHIPS WITH ABORIGINAL PEOPLES
Dwight G. Newman; Canada. 128 pp. Paper. University of Washington Press, 2017. $30.

DWELLERS AT THE SOURCE: SOUTHWESTERN INDIAN PHOTOGRAPHS OF A.C. VROMAN William Webb & Robert Weinstein
Illus. 223 pp. University of New Mexico Press, 1987. $42.50; paper, $27.50.

*DWELLINGS: A SPIRITUAL HISTORY OF THE LIVING WORLD
Linda Hogan; 16 essays. Grades 7 and up. Oyate, 1995. $21.

DYNAMIC CHICKASAW WOMEN
Phillip Carroll Morgan & Judy Goforth Parker; Biographies of chosen dynamic women from the histories of Indian Removal, Indian Territory, and early Oklahoma statehood. Illus. 192 pp. Published by Chickasaw Press. Distributed by University of Oklahoma Press, 2011. $24.

DYNAMIC SYMMETRY & HOLISTIC ASYMMETRY IN NAVAJO & WESTERN ART & COSMOLOGY Gary Witherspoon & Glen Peterson
192 pp. Paper. Amazon.com, 1995. $27.95.

THE DYNAMICS OF GOVERNMENT PROGRAMS FOR URBAN INDIANS IN THE PRAIRIE PROVINCES
Raymond Breton and Gail Grant; 628 pp. Paper. Gower, 1984. $19.95.

THE DYNAMICS OF NATIVE POLITICS: THE ALBERTA METIS EXPERIENCE
Joe Sawchuk; 314 pp. University of Washington Press, 2017. $26.

DYNAMICS OF SOUTHWEST PREHISTORY
Linda Cordell & George Gumerman, Edis; Illus. 390 pp. Smithsonian Press, 1989. $39.95.

E

E'AAWIYAANG (WHO WE ARE)
Marsha MacDowell & Charmaine Benz, Editors; Illus. 58 pp. Paper. Amazon.com, 1999.

EAGLE DOWN IS OUR LAW: THE WITSUWIT'EN LAND CLAIMS
Antonia Mills; 238 pp. paper. University of Washington Press, 1994. $32.95.

*EAGLE DRUM
Robert Crum; Grades 3 to 5. A 9-year-old boy's involvement in powwows as he changes from traditional dancing to grass dancing. Meadowlark Communications, $16.95.

*EAGLE FEATHER FOR A CROW
Alice Durland Ryniker
Grades Grades 2-6. A Crow Indian boy growing up. Illus. 80 pp. Amazon.com, $9.95.

AN EAGLE NATION
Carter Revard; Poetry. 125 pp. Paper. University of Arizona Press, 1993. $15.95.

THE EAGLE RETURNS: THE LEGAL HISTORY OF THE GRAND TRAVERSE BAND OF OTTAWA & CHIPPEWA INDIANS Matthew L.M. Fletcher
288 pp. Michigan State University Press, 2012. $29.95; eBook, $23.95.

EAGLE TRANSFORMING: THE ART OF ROBERT DAVIDSON
Robert Davidson; Illus. 175 pp. University of Washington Press, 1994. $39.95.

THE EAGLE'S GIFT
Carlos Castaneda; Jane Roseman, Ed.; 320 pp. Paper. Simon & Schuster, 1991. $14.

*THE EARLIEST AMERICANS
Helen Roney Sattler; Grades 5-9. Illus. 125 pp. Paper. Amazon.com, 2001. $

EARLIEST HISPANIC - NATIVE AMERICAN INTERACTION IN AMERICAN SOUTHEAST Jerald T. Milanich, Editor; 528 pp. Amazon.com, 1991. $30.

EARLIEST HISPANIC-NATIVE AMERICAN INTERACTIONS IN THE CARIBBEAN
William F. Keegan; Illus. 432 pp. Amazon.com, 1991. $37.

EARLY AMERICAN CIVILIZATION & EXPLORATION - 1607
Brenda Stalcup, Ed.; Illus. 220 pp. Gale Group, 2003. $43.70; paper, $27.45.

EARLY AMERICAN INDIAN DOCUMENTS: TREATIES & LAWS, 1607-1789
Alden T. Vaughan; 20 vols. 7,000 pp. Amazon.com, 1987. $2,435/set.

EARLY AMERICAN WRITINGS
Giles Gunn, Editor; Includes writings from Cherokee, Hopi, and other Amerindian genesis legends. 720 pp. Penguin USA, 1994. $12.95.

EARLY ART OF THE SOUTHEASTERN INDIANS: FEATHERED SERPENTS & WINGED BEINGS Susan C. Power; Illus. University of Georgia Press, 2004. $39.95.

EARLY ENCOUNTERS - NATIVE AMERICANS & EUROPEANS IN NEW ENGLAND FROM THE PAPERS OF W. SEARS NICKERSON Delores Bird Carpenter, Editor
19 essays from the papers of Warren Sears Nickerson (1880-1966), New England historian, antiquarian, and genealogist. Illus. 200 pp. Michigan State U. Press, $28.85.

THE EARLY ETHNOGRAPHY OF THE KUMEYAAY
M. Steven Shackley, Ed.
Illus. Photos. 336 pp. Paper. University of Washington Press, 2004. $30.

EARLY EXPLORERS OF NORTH AMERICA
C. Keith Wilbur, MD, Editor; Recreates the clash of two dissimilar cultures.
144 pp. Paper. Gobe Pequot Press, $11.95.

EARLY FUR TRADE ON THE NORTHERN PLAINS: CANADIAN TRADERS AMONG THE MANDAN & HIDATSA INDIANS, 1738-1818
W. Raymond Wood & Thomas D. Thiessen
Reprint. Illus. Maps. Biblio. 376 pp. Paper. University of Oklahoma Press, 2000. $29.95.

EARLY HISTORY OF THE CREEK INDIANS & THEIR NEIGHBORS
John R. Swanton; Reprint. 508 pp. Paper. University Press of Florida, 1998. $29.95.

THE EARLY HISTORY OF WESTERN PENNSYLVANIA
I.D. Rupp; Causes that led to the French & Indian War; treaty with Indians; the battle of Tippecanoe. 776 pp. Wennawoods Publishing, $39.95.

*EARLY INDIAN PEOPLE
Roots Magazine back issue; Petroglyphs, tools and bone fragments how early Indians before European arrivals lived. Grades 4 & up. Illus. 32 pp. Minnesota Historical Society Press, 1979. $3.50.

EARLY INUIT STUDIES: THEMES & TRANSITIONS, 1850s-1980s
Igor Krupnik; 15 papers on the intellectual history of Eskimology—known today as Inuit studies. Smtihsonian Institution Press, 2016. Amazon.com, $49.95.

THE EARLY KACHEMAK PHASE ON KODIAK ISLAND AT OLD KIAVEK
Donald W. Clark; Reprint. Illus. 130 pp. Paper. U. of Washington Press, 1997. $25.

EARLY LATE WOODLAND OCCUPATIONS IN THE FALL CREEK LOCALITY OF THE MISSISSIPPI VALLEY David T. Morgan & C. Russell Stafford, Editors
Illus. 145 pp. Paper. Center for American Archaeology, 1987. $7.95.

EARLY MAN IN THE NEW WORLD
Richard J. Shutler, Jr., Editor; Illus. 200 pp. Sage, 1983. $32.00; paper, $16.95.

EARLY NATIVE LITERACIES IN NEW ENGLAND: A DOCUMENTARY & CRITICAL ANTHOLOGY Kristina Bross & Hilary E. Wyss, Editors
Illus. 256 pp. University of Massachusetts Press, 2008. $98; paper, $29.95.

EARLY 19TH CENTURY CONTRIBUTIONS TO AMERICAN INDIAN & GENERAL LINGUISTICS Pierre Swiggers & Charles Boewe; Amazon.com, 1994.

AN EARLY PALEO-INDIAN SITE NEAR PARKHILL, ONTARIO
Christopher Ellis & D. Brian Deller
Illus. Tables. 313 pp. Paper. University of Washington Press, 2001. $29.95.

EARLY POTTERY IN THE SOUTHEAST: TRADITION & INNOVATION IN COOKING TECHNOLOGY
Kenneth E. Sassaman; Illus. 304 pp. Paper. U. of Alabama Press, 1993. $36. E-Book.

EARLY PREHISTORIC AGRICULTURE IN THE AMERICAN SOUTHWEST
W.H. Wills; Illus. 196 pp. School of American Research, $27.50.

EARLY PUEBLOAN OCCUPATIONS: TESUQUE BY-PASS & UPPER RIO GRANDE VALLEY Charles McNutt; Illus. Paper. Amazon.com, 1969. $16.

EARLY SPANISH, FRENCH & ENGLISH ENCOUNTERS WITH AMERICAN INDIANS
Anne Paolucci, et al; Henry Paolucci, Editor
Illus. 192 pp. Paper. Amazon.com, 1997. $14.95.

AN EARLY & STRONG SYMPATHY: THE INDIAN WRITINGS OF WILLIAM GILMORE SIMMS William G. Simms; John C. Guilds & Charles M. Hudson, Editors
Illus. 664 pp. Amazon.com, 2003. $49.95.

EARLY TREATIES WITH THE SOUTHERN CHEYENNE & ARAPAHO
Raymond J. DeMallie; 35 pp. Institute for the Development of Indian Law, $10.

EARLY VOCABULARIES OF CATAWBA, VOL. 38
John L. Miller & Benjamin S. Barton; 50 pp. Amazon.com, 2004. $28.

EARLY WHITE INFLUENCE UPON PLAINS INDIAN PAINTING: GEORGE CATLIN & CARL BODMER AMONG THE MANDAN, 1832-34
John C. Ewers; Illus. Paper. Territorial Press, 1989. $4.50.

THE EARLY YEARS OF NATIVE AMERICAN ART HISTORY: THE POLITICS & SCHOLARSHIP OF COLLECTING Janet Catherine Berlo, Editor
Anthology of academic essays on the development of Native American artifact collections and the historiography of Native American material culture. Reprint. Ilus. 256 pp. University of Washington Press, 1992. $48.95.

EARNEST GENEALOGY: INDIAN EVE & HER DESCENDANTS, AN INDIAN STORY OF BEDFORD CO. Emma A. Replogle; Reprint. Illus. 128 pp. Paper. Amazon.com, $31.

EASY-TO-DUPLICATE NORTH AMERICAN INDIAN BORDERS
Charlene Tarbox; Illus. 48 pp. Paper. Dover, 1996. $5.95.

EARTH ALWAYS ENDURES: NATIVE AMERICAN POEMS
Neil Philip, Editor; Reprint edition. Illus. 93 pp. Amazon.com, $20.

*EARTH DAUGHTER: ALICIA OF ACOMA PUEBLO
George Ancona; Follows Alicia and her family as they make pottery. Grades Preschool and up. Illus. 40 pp. Simon & Schuster & Oyate, 1995. $16.

EARTH ELDER STORIES
Alexander Wolfe; Stories by a Salteaux leader who lived in Canada's Northwest Territories and the U.S. Great Plains in the 1800s. Amazon.com, $9.95.

EARTH FIRE: A HOPI LEGEND OF THE SUNSET CRATER ERUPTION
E. Malotki & M. Lomatuway'ma; Illus. 150 pp. Paper. Northland, 1987. $19.95.

THE EARTH IS FASTER NOW: INDIGENOUS OBSERVATIONS OF ARCTIC ENVIRONMENTAL CHANGE Igor Krupnik & Dyanna Jolly, Editors; Amazon.com

EARTH IS MY MOTHER, SKY IS MY FATHER: SPACE, TIME & ASTRONOMY IN NAVAJO SANDPAINTING Trudy Griffin-Pierce; Illus. 8 color photos, 50 drawings. Paper. University of New Mexico Press, $24.95.

THE EARTH IS OUR MOTHER: A GUIDE TO THE INDIANS OF CALIFORNIA, THEIR LOCALES & HISTORIC SITES
Dolan Eargle, Jr.; 4th Ed. Illus. Photos. Maps. 200 pp. Paper. Amazon.com, 1996. $10.

EARTH MAGIC: SKY MAGIC: NORTH AMERICAN INDIAN TALES
Rosalind Kerven; Illus. 95 pp. Cambridge University Press, 1991. $12.95; paper, $7.95.

EARTH MEDICINE: ANCESTOR'S WAYS OF HARMONY FOR MANY MOONS
Jamie Sams; 364 daily offerings organized according to the cycles of the moon. Insights into the spirituality of the earth. Illus. 400 pp. Paper. Amazon.com, 1994. $15.95.

EARTH MEDICINE: EXPLORE YOUR INDIVIDUALITY THROUGH THE NATIVE AMERICAN MEDICINE WHEEL
Kenneth Meadows; 320 pp. Paper. Amazon.com, 2002. $9.99.

EARTH PIGMENTS & PAINT OF THE CALIFORNIA INDIANS: MEANING & TECHNOLOGY Paul Douglas Campbell; Photos. 19th century Indians. Text on the cave paintings & body paint of California's Indians.

EARTH POWER COMING: SHORT FICTION IN NATIVE AMERICAN LITERATURE
Simon J. Ortiz; Contemporary fiction by 30 contemporary Native American writers. Paper. Amazon.com, $18.30.

THE EARTH SHALL WEEP: A HISTORY OF NATIVE AMERICA
James Wilson; 496 pp. Paper. Grove-Atlantic, 1999. $16.

EARTH SONG, SKY SPIRIT: SHORT STORIES OF THE CONTEMPORARY NATIVE AMERICAN EXPERIENCE
Clifford E. Trafzer; 512 pp. Paper. Doubleday Publishing, 1997. $12.76

EARTH SONGS, MOON DREAMS: PAINTINGS BY AMERICAN INDIAN WOMEN
Patricia Janis Broder; Illus. 286 pp. St. Martins Press, 1999. $60.

THE EARTH'S BLANKET: TRADITIONAL TEACHINGS FOR SUSTAINABLE LIVING
Nancy J. Turner; Ecological knowledge encoded in Northwest Coast Native American stories & lifeways. Illus. 304 pp. Paper. U. of Washington Press, 2005. $40; paper, $24.95.

EARTH'S MIND: ESSAYS IN NATIVE LITERATURE
Roger Dunsmore, et al; Illus. 241 pp. Paper. University of New Mexico Press, $35.

EARTHDIVERS: TRIBAL NARRATIVES ON MIXED DESCENT
Gerald Vizenor; A series of stories that convey the oral tradition of modern American Indian life. Illus. 195 pp. University of Minnesota Press, 1981. $14.95.

*EARTHMAKER'S LODGE: NATIVE AMERICAN FOLKLORE, ACTIVITIES & FOODS
E. Barrie Kavasch; Grades PS-4. Illus. 160 pp. Paper. Cobblestone, $17.50.

EARTHQUAKE WEATHER
Janice Gould; Work by a California Maidu Indian. 96 pp. Paper. University of Arizona Press, 1996. $12.95.

EARTH'S MIND: ESSAYS IN NATIVE LITERATURE
Roger Dunsmore; Paper. University of New Mexico Press, $35.

THE EARTHSHAPERS
Karen Speerstra; Details of daily life, great tribal gfestivals, and reasons behind the gigantic mounds. Illus. 80 pp. Paper. Naturegraph, 1977. $6.95.

EASTERN BAND CHEROKEE WOMEN: CULTURAL PERSISTENCE IN THEIR LETTERS & SPEECHES Virginia Moore Carney; Illus. University of Tennessee Press Alibris.com, Amazon.com & Cherokee Publications, 2005. $34.95.

THE EASTERN BAND OF CHEROKEES, 1819-1900
John R. Finger; Reprint of 1984 ed. Illus. 304 pp. Paper. U. of Tennessee Press. $22.95.

EASTERN CHEROKEE BY BLOOD, 1906-1910, 2 VOLS.
Jeff Bowen; 1906-1910, Vol. 1, 276 pp, Vol. 2, 267 pp. Paper. Genealogical Publishing Co., 2005-2006. $29.50 each.

EASTERN CHEROKEE CENSUS, CHEROKEE, N.C., 1915-1922, TAKEN BY AGENT JAMES E. HENDERSON, VOL. 1
Jeff Bowen; 150 pp. Paper. Genealogical Publishing Co., 2004. $21.50.

EASTERN CHEROKEE FISHING
Heidi M. Altman; Cherokee identity as revealed in fishing methods & materials...revealed from interviews by Cherokee and non-Cherokee people in the Qualla Boundary in the last 75 years. Illus. 168 pp. U. of Alabama Press, 2006. $42.50; paper, $22.95. E-Book.

EASTERN OJIBWA-CHIPPEWA-OTTAWA DICTIONARY
Richard Rhodes; 623 pp. Amazon.com, $125.

THE EASTERN SHAWNEE TRIBE OF OKLAHOMA: RESILIENCE THROUGH ADVERSITY Stephen Warren; Illus. 384 pp. University of Oklahoma Press, 2017. $34.95.

EASTERN SHORE INDIANS OF VIRGINIA & MARYLAND
Helen C. Rountree & Thomas E. Davidson
352 pp. Amazon.com, 1998. $49.50; paper, $16.95.

EASTERN WOODLAND INDIAN DESIGNS
Caren Calloway; Illus. 48 pp. paper. Paper. Stemmer House, $5.95.

EASTMAN JOHNSON'S LAKE SUPEROR INDIANS
Patricia Condon Johnson; Paintings and drawings of the native Ojibwe at Lake Superior in 1856 & 1857. Illus. 72 pp. Johnston Publishing, $12.95.

SETH EASTMAN: A PORTFOLIO OF NORTH AMERICAN INDIANS
Sarah E. Boehme; Illus. 196 pp. Amazon.com, 2004. $39.

EASY GUIDE TO INDIAN ART & LEGENDS OF THE SOUTHWEST
James R. Cunkle; Illus. 32 pp. Paper. Primer Publishers, $1.50.

EASY GUIDE TO SOUTHWESTERN PETROGLYPHS
Elizaeth C. Welsch; Native rock carvings are illustrated and discussed,
along with preservation. Illus. 32 pp. Paper. Primer Publishers, $1.50.

EASY GUIDE TO ROCK ART SYMBOLS OF THE SOUTHWEST
Rick Harris; Illus. 32 pp. Paper. Primer Publishers, $1.50.

***EASY-TO-MAKE PLAINS INDIANS TEEPEE VILLAGE**
A.G. Smith; Grades 2-5. Illus. 12 pp. Paper. Dover Publications, 1990. $6.99.

***EASY-TO-MAKE PUEBLO VILLAGE**
A.G. Smith; Grades 2-5. Illus. 12 pp. Paper. Dover Publications, 1990. $5.95.

**EATING THE LANSCAPE: AMERICAN INDIAN STORIES OF FOOD, IDENTITY &
RESILIENCE** Enrique Salmon; Paper. Illus. University of Arizona Press, 2010. $17.95.

BRUMMETT ECHOHAWK: PAWNEE THUNDERBIRD & ARTIST
Kristin M. Youngbull; Illus. 224 pp. University of Oklahoma Press, 2014. $24.95

**ECOCIDE OF NATIVE AMERICA: ENVIRONMENTAL DESTRUCTION OF INDIAN
LANDS & PEOPLES** Donald A. Grinde, Jr. & Bruce E. Johansen; environmental
perspectives through the testimony of Native North Americans. Illus. 224 pp. Paper.
Amazon.com, 1997. $14.95.

**ECOCRITICISM & THE CREATION OF SELF & PLACE IN ENVIRONMENTAL
& AMERICAN INDIAN LITERATURES**
Donelle N. Dreese; 131 pp. Paper. Amazon.com, 2001. $24.95.

**AN ECOLOGICAL ANALYSIS INVOLVING THE POPULATION OF SAN JUAN
PUEBLO, NM** Richard I. Ford; Illus. 360 pp. Garland, 1992, $10.

THE ECOLOGICAL INDIAN: MYTH & HISTORY
Shepard Krech, III; A look at historical truths & romantic falsehoods
about Native Americans and nature. Illus. 320 pp. Sagebrush Education, $25.70.

**ECOLOGY, SOCIOPOLITICAL ORGANIZATION & CULTURAL CHANGE ON
THE SOUTHERN PLAINS: A CRITICAL TREATISE IN THE SOCIOCULTURAL
ANTHROPOLOGY OF NATIVE NORTH AMERICA**
Michael G. Davis; 214 pp. Truman State University Press, 1996. $45.

ECONOMIC DEVELOPMENT ON AMERICAN INDIAN RESERVATIONS
Roxanne D. Ortiz, Editor
157 pp. Paper. University of New Mexico, Native American Studies, 1979. $8.95.

**THE ECONOMICS OF SAINTHOOD: RELIGIOUS CHANGE AMONG THE RIMROCK
NAVAJOS** Kendall Blanchard; Illus. 244 pp. Fairleigh Dickinson, 1976. $22.50.

EDGAR HEAP OF BIRDS
Bill Anthes; Biography. Native American art. Illus. 232 pp. Duke University Press, 2015.
$89.95; paper, $24.95.

THE EDGE OF THE WOODS: IROQUOIA, 1534-1701
Jon Parmenter; Illus. Maps. 474 pp. Michigan State University Press, 2010.

**EDUCATION & THE AMERICAN INDIAN:
THE ROAD TO SELF-DETERMINATION SINCE 1928**
Margaret C. Szasz; Illus. 3rd Ed. 336 pp. Paper. U. of New Mexico Press, 1999. $29.95.

**EDUCATION AT THE EDGE OF EMPIRE: NEGOTIATING PUEBLO IDENTITY
IN NEW MEXICO'S INDIAN BOARDING SCHOOLS**
John R. Gram; Illus. 260 pp. University of Washington Press, 2015. $45.

EDUCATION & CAREER OPPORTUNITIES HANDBOOK
The CIRI Foundation; Lists over 200 scholarships, grant & loan programs
for which Alaska Natives may be eligible. Annual. CIRI, $5.

**EDUCATION FOR EXTINCTION: AMERICAN INDIAN & THE BOARDING SCHOOL
EXPERIENCE, 1875-1928**
David Wallace Adams; Illus. University Press of Kansas, 1995. $40; paper, $17.95.

**EDUCATION & LANGUAGE RESTORATION: ASSIMILATION VERSUS
CULTURAL SURVIVAL** Jon Allan Reyhner; Chelsea House Publishers, 2004.

***THE EDUCATION OF LITTLE TREE**
Forrest Carter; Foreword by Rennard Strickland
A moving account of a Cherokee as he grows up with his grandparents. Grades 3 and up.
25th Anniversary Reprint. 228 pp. University of New Mexico Press, $24.95; paper, $14.95.

***AN EDUCATIONAL AMERICAN INDIAN COLORING BOOK**
Reginald Oxendine; Grades PS-3. Illus. 31 pp. Paper. Arrow Publishing, 1994. $5.95.

**AN ECONOMY OF COLOUR: VISUAL CULTURE & THE NORTH ATLANTIC WORLD,
1660-1830** Geoff Quilley & Kay Dian Kriz, Eds.
Illus. 272 pp. Amazon.com, 2003 $74.95; paper, $24.95.

**THE EFFECT OF EUROPEAN CONTACT & TRADE ON THE SETTLEMENT
PATTERN OF INDIANS IN COASTAL NEW YORK, 1524-1665**
Lynn Ceci; 360 pp. Amazon.com, 1991. $10.

EFFECTIVE PRACTICES IN INDIAN EDUCATION
Floy Pepper; 211 pp. Teacher's Monograph, 211 pp. $14.80; Curriculum Monograph,
186 pp. $24.45; and Administration Monograph, 86 pp. $11.30. Amazon.com.

EHANAMANI: WALKS AMONG
A.C. Ross; Illus. 226 pp. Wiconi Waste, 1993. $12.

EIGHTEENTH-CENTURY WESTERN CREE & THEIR NEIGHBORS
Dale R. Russell; Maps. 248 pp. Paper. University of Washington Press, 1991. $24.95.

THE 1870 GHOST DANCE
Cora Du Bois; Ethnographic record of Native Californian cultures. Illus. Maps. 368 pp.
Paper. University of Nebraska Press, 2007. $19.95.

THE 1890 CHEROKEE NATION CENSUS, INDIAN TERRITORY
Barbara L. Benge; 2 Vols. Amazon.com, 2002.

THE ELDERS: PASSING IT ON
Essays, art, photos, and poetry by Native American artists about their elders.
Illus. 31 pp. Paper. Amazon.com, $5.95.

ELDERBERRY FLUTE SONG, CONTEMPORARY COYOTE TALES
Peter Blue Cloud; Illus. Amazon.com, $10.

THE ELDERS ARE WATCHING
Dave Bouchard; illus. by Roy H. Vickers
Environmental message. Illus. 66 pp. Paper. Fulcrum Publishing, 1993. $12.95.

JOHN ELIOT'S INDIAN DIALOGUES: A STUDY IN CULTURAL INTERACTION
J. Eliot; H.W. Bowden & J. Rhonda, Eds; Illus. 173 pp. Greenwood Publishing, 1980. $35.

JOHN ELIOT'S MISSION TO THE INDIANS BEFORE KING PHILIP'S WAR
Richard W. Cogley; Illus. 352 pp. Harvard University Press & Amazon.com, 1999. $52.

THE ELKUS COLLECTION: SOUTHWEST INDIAN ART
Dorothy K. Washburn, Editior
Illus. 222 pp. Paper. California Academy of Sciences, 1986. $19.95.

ELLIOT'S VOCABULARY OF CAYUGA
Adam Elliot; Reprint. 47 pp. Amazon.com, 2000. $28.

ELLIOT'S VOCABULARY OF MOHAWK
Adam Elliot; Reprint. 45 pp. Amazon.com, 2000. $28.

ELNGUQ
Anna W. Jacobson; The first novel written in Yup'ik. Reflects a traditional Native
Alaskan way of life. 114 pp. Alaska Native Language Center, $13.50, postpaid.

ELSIE'S BUSINESS
Frances A. Washburn; 216 pp. Paper. University of Nebraska Press, 2006. $17.95.

EMBRACING FRY BREAD: CONFESSIONS OF A WANABE
Roger Welsch; Native American culture. 272 pp. Paper.
University of Nebraska Press, 2012. $19.95.

**THE EMERGENCE OF THE MOUNDBUILDERS: THE ARCHAEOLOGY OF TRIBAL
SOCIETIES IN SOUTHEASTERN OHIO** Elliot M. Abrams & AnnCorinne Freter
Illus. 264 pp. Amazon.com, 2005. $55; paper, $28.95.

EMERGENCE OF NATIVE AMERICAN NATIONALISM IN THE COLUMBIA PLATEAU
Jeffrey Reichwein; Reprint edition. Illus. 416 pp. Garland, 191. $80.

EMERGENT COMPLEXITY: THE EVOLUTION OF INTERMEDIATE SOCIETIES
Jeanne F. Arnold, Editor; Illus. 128 pp. Paper. Amazon.com, 1996. $24.

EMERGING FROM THE MIST: STUDIES IN NORTHWEST COAST CULTURE HISTORY
R.G. Matson, Gary Coupland, Quentin Mackie
Illus. Maps. Tables. 336 pp. University of Washington Press, 2004. $105; paper, $43.95.

THE EMIGRANT INDIANS OF KANSAS: A CRITICAL BIBLIOGRAPHY
William E. Unrau; Illus. 96 pp. Paper. Amazon.com & Alibris.com, 1980. $4.95.

**EMINENT DOMAIN: THE 400 YEAR BATTLE AGAINST NATIVE AMERICANS
FOR EVERY SQUARE MILE OF NORTH AMERICA**
Dudley C. Gould; 96 pp. Paper. Amazon.com, 1008.

**EMOTIONAL EXPRESSION AMONG THE CREE INDIANS: THE ROLE OF PICTORIAL
REPRESENTATIONS IN THE ASSESSMENT OF PSYCHOLOGICAL MINDEDNESS**
Nadia Ferrara; Amazon.com, 1998 $59.95; paper, $26.95.

**EMPIRE OF FORTUNE: CROWNS, COLONIES, & TRIBES IN THE SEVEN YEARS WAR
IN AMERICA** Francis Jennings; W.W. Norton & Co., 1988. $27.

**EMPIRE OF SAND: THE SERI INDIANS & THE STRUGGLE FOR SPANISH SONORA,
1645-1803** Thomas E. Sheridan; 493 pp. University of Arizona Press, 1997. $70.

**EMPOWERING NORTHERN & NATIVE COMMUNITIES FOR SOCIAL, POLITICAL
& ECONOMIC CONTROL: AN ANNOTATED BIBLIOGRAPHY OF RELEVANT
LITERATURE** M.G. Stevenson, C.G. Hickey; Inuit literature on models for community
empowerment. 64 pp. Paper., CCI, 1994. $15.

**EMPOWERMENT OF NORTH AMERICAN INDIAN GIRLS: RITUAL EXPRESSIONS
AT PUBERTY** Carol A. Markstrom; Female puberty rituals in four communities: Navajo,
Apache, Lakota & Ojibwe. Illus. Tables. 480 pp. University of Nebraska Press, 2008. $50.

EMPTY BEDS: STUDENT HEALTH AT SHERMAN INSTITUTE, 1902-1922
Jean A. Keller
Illus. 352 pp. Michigan State University Press, 2002. $59.95; paper, $24.95.

EMPTY NETS: INDIANS, DAMS, & THE COLUMBIA RIVER
Roberta Ulrich; The Columbia River Indians' fight to maintain their livelihood and culture. 2nd Edition. Photos. Maps. 264 pp. Paper. Oregon State University Press, 2007. $19.95.

THE ENCHANTED MOCCASINS, AND OTHER NATIVE AMERICAN LEGENDS
Henry Schoolcraft, Editor. Paper. Eagle'ss View Publishing, $8.5.

ENCHANTING NEW MEXICO CALENDAR: WILLIE MURPHY–HEADING HOME, PAINTINGS OF THE NAVAJO NATION 2009
Paintings of Navajo life & lands. University of New Mexico Press, 2009. $12.95.

ENCOUNTERING THE NEW WORLD, 1493 TO 1800
Susan Danforth; Illus. 108 pp. Paper. John Carter Brown Library, 1991. $25.

ENCOUNTER ON THE GREAT PLAINS: SCANDANAVIAN SETTLERS AND THE DISPOSSESSION OF DAKOTA INDIANS, 1890-1930
Karen V. Hansen; Oxford University Press, 2013. $38.95; paper, $29.95.

ENCOUNTERS ON THE PASSAGE: INUIT MEET THE EXPLORERS
Dorothy Harley Eber; Present day Inuit tell the stories that have been passed down from their ancestors of the first encounters with European explorers. University of Toronto Press, 2010. $45; paper, $21.95.

ENCOUNTERS WITH THE PEOPLE: WRITTEN & ORAL ACCOUNTS OF NEZ PERCE LIFE TO 1858 Dennis Baird, Diane Mallickan & Wiliam Swagerty
Illus. Map. 544 pp. WSU Press, 2015. $50.

ENCYCLOPEDIA OF AMERICAN INDIAN BIOGRAPHY
Donald A. Grinde, Jr. & Bruce E. Johansen; Paper. Da Capo Press, 1997. $22.50

ENCYCLOPEDIA OF AMERICAN INDIAN CIVIL RIGHTS
James S. Olson, et al, Editors; 448 pp. Greenwood, 1997. $65.

ENCYCLOPEDIA OF AMERICAN INDIAN CONTRIBUTIONS TO THE WORLD
Emory Dean Keoke & Kay Marie Porterfield; 15,000 Years of Inventions & Innovations. Illus. Maps. Bibliography. 400 pp. Facts on File, 2002. $65.

ENCYCLOPEDIA OF AMERICAN INDIAN COSTUME
Josephine Paterek
Illus. Biblio. 536 pp. Paper. W.W. Norton & Co., 1996. $24.95. Written Heritage, $19.95.

ENCYCLOPEDIA OF AMERICAN INDIAN ISSUES TODAY
Russell M. Lawson, Editor; Features subjects commonly discussed, including reservations, poverty, sovereignty, lives of urban Indians, among other contemporary issues. Two Volumes. 792 pp. Greenwood Press, 2013. $189.

ENCYCLOPEDIA OF THE AMERICAN INDIAN MOVEMENT
Bruce E. Johansen; Describes the people, events, and issues that changed the lives of Native Americans during the 1960s & 1970s. 384 pp. Greenwood Press, 2013. $89.

ENCYCLOPEDIA OF THE AMERICAN INDIANN IN THE 20TH CENTURY
Alexander Ewen & Jeffrey Wollock
Profiles. Illus. Maps. 552 pp. University of New Mexico Press, $95.

ENCYCLOPEDIA OF AMERICAN INDIAN REMOVAL
Daniel F. Littlefield, Jr. & James W. Parins, Editor
Presents the removal process as a political, economic, and tribally complicit affair. Two Volumes. 615 pp. Greenwood Press, 2011. $165.

ENCYCLOPEDIA OF AMERICAN INDIAN WARS, 1492-1890
Jerry Keenan; Illus. 278 pp. Paper. W.W. Norton & Co., 1999. $18.95.

ENCYCLOPEDIA OF FRONTIER BIOGRAPHY
Dan L. Thrapp, Editor; Contains over 5,500 biographies of the men & women who have played major roles in frontier history. From the earliest European explorers to contemporary historians. Includes Indians & Indian agents. 4 vols. The Arthur H. Clark Co. Original 3 vol. work published in 1988. $195; paper, $60. Vol. 4, Supplemental, 1993. $65.

ENCYCLOPEDIA OF THE GREAT PLAINS INDIANS
David J. Wishart; Photos. Maps. 254 pp. Paper. U. of Nebraska Press, 2007. $24.95.

ENCYCLOPEDIA OF MULTICULTURALISM
Examines American history & society through the experiences of ethnic groups, including Native Americans. 6 Vols. More than 2,000 entries. Cross-referenced. Illus. 2,500+ pp. Bibliographies. Marshall Cavendish Corp., 1998. $214. Available from Amazon.com.

ENCYCLOPEDIA OF NATIVE AMERICA
Trudy Griffin-Pierce; Illus. 192 pp. Paper. Amazon.com, 1995. $25.

ENCYCLOPEDIA OF NATIVE AMERICAN BIOGRAPHY: 600 LIFE STORIES OF IMPORTANT PEOPLE, FROM POWHATAN TO WILMA MANKILLER
Donald A. Grinde & Bruce E. Johansen; Illus. 512 pp. Amazon.com, 1998. $50.

ENCYCLOPEDIA OF NATIVE AMERICAN BOWS, ARROWS, & QUIVERS: NORTHEAST, SOUTHEAST, & MIDWEST Steve Alley & Jim Hamm; 100 historic bows, scores of arrows, and quivers from 38 tribes. Illus. 144 pp. Written Heritage, $29.95.

ENCYCLOPEDIA OF NATIVE AMERICAN CEREMONIES
Michelene Pesantubbee; ABC-Clio, 1996. $65.

THE ENCYCLOPEDIA OF NATIVE AMERICAN ECONOMIC HISTORY
Bruce E. Johansen; Illus. 320 pp. Greenwood Publishing, 1999. $99.95.

ENCYCLOPEDIA OF NATIVE AMERICAN HEALING
William S. Lyon; Explores, explains, and honors the healing practices of Native Americans throughout North America. Illus. Maps. 416 pp. Paper. W.W. Norton, 1998. $21.95.

*ENCYCLOPEDIA OF NATIVE AMERICAN HISTORY
Peter C. Mancall
Grades 9 and up. 3 Vols. Illus. 1068 pp. Facts on File, 2011. $300. eBook available.

THE ENCYCLOPEDIA OF NATIVE AMERICAN LEGAL TRADITION
Bruce E. Johansen, Ed.; Illus. 424 pp. Greenwood, 1998. $109.95.

ENCYCLOPEDIA OF NATIVE AMERICAN MUSIC OF NORTH AMERICA
Elaine Kellor, Tim Archambault, John M.H. Kelly
A reference resource of musical expressions of the First Peoples' cultures of North America, both past & present. 420 pp. Greenwood Press, 2013. $89.

ENCYCLOPEDIA OF NATIVE AMERICAN RELIGIONS
Arlene Hirschfelder & Paulette Molin; Ceremonies, individuals, places & concepts from Native American groups across America. Contains more than 1,200 cross-referenced entries. Includes biographies of religious leaders & Christian missionaries. Updated edition. Illus. 400 pp. Facts on File, 2000. $75.

ENCYCLOPEDIA OF NATIVE AMERICAN SHAMANISM: SACRED CEREMONIES OF NORTH AMERICA William S. Lyon; 512 pp. ABC-Clio, 1998. $65.

ENCYCLOPEDIA OF NATIVE AMERICAN TRIBES
Carl Waldman; illus. by Molly Braun; Revised 3rd edition. History and culture of more than 200 Indian tribes in the U.S., Canada, and Mexico; glossary of terms, bibliography. Illus. 384 pp. Facts on File, 2006. $75.

ENCYCLOPEDIA OF NATIVE AMERICAN WARS & WARFARE
William B. Kessel & Robert Wooster, Eds.; More than 600 cross-referenced entries. Illus. Maps. Chronology & bibliography. 416 pp. Facts On File, 2005. $75.

THE ENCYCLOPEDIA OF NATIVE MUSIC: MORE THAN A CENTURY OF RECORDINGS FROM WAX CYLINDER TO THE INTERNET
Brian Wright-McLeod; 464 pp. University of Arizona Press, 2005. $55; paper, $26.95.

THE ENCYCLOPEDIA OF NORTH AMERICAN INDIAN WARS, 1607-1890
Spencer C. Tucker, Editor; Three Volumes. 1,318 pp. ABC-CLIO. 2011. $310.

ENCYCLOPEDIA OF NORTH AMERICAN INDIANS: NATIVE AMERICAN HISTORY, CULTURE, & LIFE FROM PALEO-INDIANS TO THE PRESENT
Frederick E. Hoxie, Editor; Reprint edition. Illus. 768 pp. Teacher edition. & Text edition. Amazon.com, $40.

ENCYCLOPEDIA OF NATIVE TRIBES OF NORTH AMERICA
Michael Johnson; Illus. 336 pp. Firefly Books, 2014. $49.95.

THE END OF INDIAN KANSAS: A STUDY OF CULTURAL REVOLUTION, 1854-1871
H. Craig Miner & William E. Unrau;
Illus. 182 pp. Paper. U. Press of Kansas, 1977. $12.95.

ENDGAME FOR EMPIRE: BRITISH-CREEK RELATIONS IN GEORGIA & VICINITY, 1763-1776 John T/ Juricek; Illus. 338 pp. University Press of Florida, 2015. $74.95.

ENDANGERED PEOPLES OF NORTH AMERICA: STRUGGLES TO SURVIVE & THRIVE Tom Greaves, Ed.; Illus. 288 pp. Greenwood Press, 2001. $46.95.

ENDING DENIAL: UNDERSTANDING ABORIGINAL ISSUES
Wayne Warry; Promotes assimilation integration as the solution to Aboriginal marginalization. 220 pp. Paper. University of Toronto Press, 2008. $27.95.

ENDURING CONQUESTS: RETHINKING THE ARCHAEOLOGY OF RESISTANCE TO SPANISH COLONIALISM IN THE AMERICAS
Matthew Liebmann & Melissa S. Murphy, Editors
Presents new interpretations of Native American experiences under Spanish colonialism focusing on the Native side of the colonial equation. Illus. Maps. Tables. 344 pp. Paper. School for Advanced Research, 2011. $34.95.

ENDURING CULTURE: A CENTURY OF PHOTOGRAPHY OF THE SOUTHWEST INDIANS Marcia Keegan; 88 photos, 44 color Illus. 120 pp. Amazon.com, 1991. $29.95.

THE ENDURING INDIANS OF KANSAS: A CENTURY & A HALF OF ACCULTURATION
Joseph B. Herring; Illus. 248 pp. Paper. University Press of Kansas, 1990. $12.95.

ENDURING LEGACIES: NATIVE AMERICAN TREATIES & CONTEMPORARY CONTROVERSIES Bruce E. Johansen; 384 pp. Greenwood Press, 2004. $49.95.

ENDURING NATIONS: NATIVE AMERICANS IN THE MIDWEST
R. David Edmunds, Editor; document how tribal peoples have adapted to cultural change while shaping midwestern history. Illus. 296 pp. U. of Illinois Press, 2008. $95; paper, $28.

THE ENDURING NAVAHO
Laura Gilpin; Illus. 243 photos. 321 pp. U. of Texas Press, 1968. $70; paper, $34.95.

ENDURING SEEDS: NATIVE AMERICAN AGRICULTURE & WILD PLANT CONSERVATION Gary P. Nabhan; Native ecology, seeds, and roots. Reprint of 1989 edition. 225 pp. Paper. University of Arizona Press, 2002. $19.95.

THE ENDURING SEMINOLES: FROM ALLIGATOR WRESTLING TO ECOTOURISM
Patsy West; Illus. 192 pp. University Press of Florida, 1998. $24.95.

THE ENDURING STRUGGLE
George H. Phillips, Jr.; N. Hundley and John Schutz, Editors
Illus. 110 pp. Paper. Boyd & Fraser, 1981. $6.95.

ENDURING TRADITIONS: ART OF THE NAVAJO
Lois Essary Jacka; photos by Jerry Jacka; Presents modern-day crafts from
192 Navajo artists. 205 full-color photos. 200 pp. Amazon.com, 1994. $55.

ENDURING VISIONS: ONE THOUSAND YEARS OF SOUTHWESTERN INDIAN ART
D. Erdman and P.M. Hortstein, Editors
Illus. Paper. Amazon.com, 1979. $12.95.

ENGENDERED ENCOUNTERS: FEMINISM & PUEBLO CULTURES, 1879-1934
Margaret D. Jacobs; Explores changing relationships between Anglo-American women
and Pueblo Indians before and after the turn of the century. Illus. Map. 284 pp. University
of Nebraska Press, 1999. $55; paper, $27.50.

**ENDURING HARVESTS: NATIVE AMERICAN FOODS & FESTIVALS FOR
EVERY SEASON** E. Barrie Kavasch; Illus. 352 pp. Paper. Globe Pequot, 1995. $24.50.

**ENGAGED RESISTANCE: AMERICAN INDIAN ART, LITERATURE,
AND FILM FROM ALCATRAZ TO THE NMAI**
Dean Rader; Illus. 297 pp. University of Texas Press, 2011. $60; paper, $27.95.

ENGLISH--CHEYENNE DICTIONARY
163 pp. Paper. Council for Indian Education, 1976. $14.95.

ENGLISH-DAKOTA DICTIONARY
John P. Williamson; Reprint of 1902 edition. 288 pp. Paper.
Minnesota Historical Society Press, $12.95.

ENGLISH--ESKIMO, ESKIMO--ENGLISH DICTIONARY
PAmazn.com, $24.50; thumb-index edition, $29.50.

ENGLISH-ESKIMO, ESKIMO-ENGLISH DICTIONARY
A. Thibert; Revised edition. Paper. Amazon.com, $18.75.

ENGLISH TO CHOCTAW & CHOCTAW TO ENGLISH DICTIONARIES
Cyrus Byingtons; Choctaw Museum.

ENGLISH-ESKIMO & ESKIMO-ENGLISH VOCABULARIES
R. Wells, Compiler; John Kelly, Translator; 72 pp. Paper. Charles E. Tuttle, 1982. $6.95.

ENGLISH-MICMAC DICTIONARY
Silas T. Rand; 286 pp. Amazon.com, 1994. $62.50.

*ENGLISH-NAVAJO CHILDREN'S PICTURE DICTIONARY
Roman de los Santos: illus. by Raymond Johnson
Selected words and phrases. Grades 4-8. Paper. Amazon.com. $24.95.

ENJOYING THE NATIVE AMERICAN-STYLE FLUTE
Henry R. Hermann; Written primarily for the beginning flute player and includes CDs,
videos, websites, and over 300 companies to assist beginners. Illus. 112 pp. paper.
Naturegraph Publishers, 2004. $10.95.

ENJU: THE LIFE & STRUGGLE OF AN APACHE CHIEF FROM THE LITTLE RUNNING
Sinclair Browning; Illus. 165 pp. Paper. Amazon.com & Alibris.com, 2000. $11.95.

'ENOUGH TO KEEP THEM ALIVE: INDIAN SOCIAL WELFARE IN CANADA, 1873-1965
Hugh Shewell; Illus. 384 pp. Paper. University of Toronto Press, 2003.

ENWHISTEETKWA: WALK IN WATER
Jeanette Armstrong; An Okanagan child of 11 in 1860 encounters non-Indian people.
Grades K-4. Illus. 44 pp. Paper. Theytus, 1982. $5.95.

EPA'S INDIAN POLICY AT TWENTY-FIVE
James M. Grijalva; Americn Bar Association, 2010. $19.95.

**EPHEMERAL BOUNTY: WICKIUPS, TRADE GOODS, AND THE FINAL YEARS
OF THE AUTONOMOUS UTE** Curtis Martin
Illus. 192 pp. Paper. University of Utah Press, 2016. $45; eBook, $36.

**EPIDEMICS & ENSLAVEMENT: BIOLOGICAL CATASTROPHE
IN THE NATIVE SOUTHEAST, 1492-1715**
Paul Kelton; Indian slave trade and spread of Old World diseases.
Tables. Maps. 314 pp. Paper. University of Nebraska Press, 2007. $24.95.

EPISODES FROM "LIFE AMONG THE INDIANS" & "LAST RAMBLES"
George Catlin; Marvin C. Ross, Ed. & Intro.
Reprint. Illus. 368 pp. Paper. Dover Publications, $16.95.

EPISODES IN THE RHETORIC OF GOVERNMENT-INDIAN RELATIONS
Janice E. Schuetz; 340 pp. Greenwood Publishing, 2002. $82.95.

LOUISE ERDRICH
David Stirrup; Oxford University Press, 2012. $95; paper, $29.95.

THE ERMANTINGERS: A 19TH-CENTURY OJIBWA-CANADIAN FAMILY
W. Brian Stewart; A fur trader marries an Ojibwa woman, Contrasts European commercial
& trading society with the Ojibwa hunter/warrior values. 224 pp. University of Washington
Press, 2007. $94; paper, $33.95.

THE EROSION OF TRIBAL POWER: THE SUPREME COURT'S SILENT REVOLUTION
Dewl Ioen Ball; 400 pp. University of Oklahoma Press, 2016. $39.95.

ESCAPE FROM INDIAN CAPTIVITY
John Ingles; Roberta Steele, Editor; 39 pp. Paper. Amazon.com, 1982. $3.50.

*ESCAPE TO THE EVERGLADES
Annelle Rigsby & Edwina Raffa; Seminole Indian story. 112 pp. Paper.
Pineapple Press, $9.95. Teacher's Activity Guide, 31 pp. $6.

ESCAPE TO REALITY: THE WESTERN WORLD OF MAYNARD DIXON
Linda Jones Gibbs, et al; Illus. 185 pp. Dist. for Bringham Young University.
University of Chicago Press, 2000. $44.95; paper, $27.95.

*THE ESKIMO
Jean Aigner; Grades 5 and up. Illus. Chelsea House, 1989. $17.95.

*THE ESKIMO
Alice Osinski; Grades 2-3. Illus. 45 pp. Childrens Press, $13.27; paper, $4.95.

THE ESKIMO ABOUT BERING STRAIT
Edward W. Nelson; The Alaskan Eskimos of the 19th century. Reprint of 1899 edition.
Illus. 520 pp. Paper. Smithsonian Institution Press, $29.95.

**ESKIMO ARCHITECTURE: DWELLING & STRUCTURE IN THE EARLY
HISTORIC PERIOD**
Molly Lee & Gregory L. Reinhardt; Illus. Maps. Biblio. 200 pp. U. of Alaska Press, 2002.

*THE ESKIMO: ARCTIC
Jean S. Aigner; Grades 5 and up. Illus. Chelsea House, 1989. $17.95.

ESKIMO ARTISTS
Hans Himmelheber; The cultural & artistic heritage of the Yup'ik Eskimo in southwestern
Alaska during the late 1930s. Illus. Photos. Map. 90 pp. Paper. University of Alaska Press,
1993. $15.

ESKIMO CAPITALISTS: OIL, POLITICS & ALCOHOL
Samuel Z. Klausner & Edward Foulks; Illus. 360 pp. Rowman & Littlefield, 1982. $43.50.

ESKIMO DOLLS
Suzi Jones; with an essay by Susan W. Fair; photos by Rob Stapleton & Chris Arend
Doll-making styles of the Inupiaq, Siberian Yup'ik and Yup'ik cultural regions of Alaska.
Amazon.com, $12.

ESKIMO ESSAYS: YUP'IK LIVES & HOW WE SEE THEM
Ann Fienup-Riordan; Illus. 232 pp. Amazon.com, 1990. $30; paper, $15.

*AN ESKIMO FAMILY
Bryan and Cherry Alexander; Grades 2-5. Illus. 39 pp. Amazon.com, 1985. $8.95.

*THE ESKIMO: INUIT & YUPIK
Grades K-4. Illus. 48 pp. Childrens Press, $11.45.

ESKIMO LIFE OF YESTERDAY
Revellion Freres; 48 pp. Paper. Hancock House, $3.95.

ESKIMO MEDICINE MAN
Otto George; Illus. 324 pp. Paper. Oregon Historical Society, 1979. $7.95.

ESKIMO OF NORTH ALASKA
Norman A. Chance; Paper. Holt, Rinehart & Winston, 1966. $9.95.

**ESKIMO SCHOOL ON THE ANDREAFSKY: A STUDY OF EFFECTIVE
BICULTURAL EDUCATION** Judith S. Kleinfeld
209 pp. Amazon.com, 1979. $36.95.

THE ESKIMO STORYTELLER: FOLKTALES FROM NOATAK, ALASKA
Edwin S. Hall, Jr.; Illus. 510 pp. Originally published by the U. of Tennessee
Press, 1975. Paper. University of Alaska Press, 1999. $24.95.

THE ESKIMOS
Ernest S. Burch, Jr.; photos by Werner Forman
Illus. Map. 128 pp. 302 p. University of Oklahoma Press, 1988. $29.95.

*ESKIMOS
Kate Petty; Grades 1-3. Illus. 32 pp. Franklin Watts, 1987. $10.40.

*ESKIMOS
Derek Fordham; Grades 5 and up. Amazon.com, $13.96.

ESKIMOS & ALEUTS
Don E. Dumond; Illus. 180 pp. Paper. Thames & Hudson, 1977. $11.95.

ESKIMOS: AN EDUCATIONAL COLORING BOOK
Grades 1-8. Illus. 32 pp. Paper. Spizzirri Publishing, 1981. Read & Coloring Book,
$1.95; Cassette/book, $6.95.

ESKIMOS & EXPLORERS
Wendell H. Oswalt
2nd Edition. Illus. Maps. 341 pp. Paper. University of Nebraska Press, 1999. $19.95.

*ESKIMOS - THE INUIT OF THE ARCTIC
J.H. Smith; Grades 4-8. Illus. 48 pp. Amazon.com, 1987. $12.66.

THE ESKIMOS OF BERING STRAIT, 1650-1898
Dorothy Jean Ray; Oral tradition of this region. Quotes & details of cross-cultural contact for the past 250 years. Reprint of 1976 ed. Illus. Maps. 360 pp. Paper. University of Washimgton Press, 1991. $27.50.

ESKIMOS, REVISED
Jill Hughes; Illus. 32 pp. Franklin Watts, 1984. $11.90.

ESSAY OF A DELAWARE-INDIAN & ENGLISH SPELLING BOOK
David Zeisberger; Reprint. 115 pp. Paper. Amazon.com, 1991. $13.95.

AN ESSAY TOWARDS AN INDIAN BIBLIOGRAPHY
Thomas Field; Reprint. Illus. Amazon.com, 1999. $26.95.

ESSAYS IN NORTH AMERICAN INDIAN HISTORY
Gillis; 255 pp. Paper. Kendall-Hunt, 1990. $24.95.

ESSAYS ON THE ETHNOGRAPHY OF THE ALEUTS
R.G. Liapunova; Illus. Photos. Map. 256 pp. Paper. U. of Alaska Press, 1996. $18.

ESSAYS ON NATIVE MODERNISM: COMPLEXITY & CONTRADICTION IN AMERICAN INDIAN ART Symposium by NMAI in 2005; Illus. 112 pp. Paper. NMAI Press, 2006. $20.

ESSIE'S STORY: THE LIFE & LEGACY OF A SHOSHONE TEACHER
Esther Burnett Horne & Sally McBeth; Infomative narrative about education and identity. Illus. Map. 275 pp. Paper. University of Nebraska Press, 1998. $13.95.

ESTHETIC RECOGNITION OF ANCIENT AMERINDIAN ART
George Kubler; Illus. 300 pp. Yale University Press, 1991. $32.50.

ESTIYUT OMAYAT: CREEK WRITING
Lewis Oliver; Illus. 17 pp. Paper. Indian University Press, 1985. $3.60, postpaid.

ETERNAL ONES OF THE DREAM: MYTH & RITUAL, DREAMS & FANTASIES – THEIR ROLE IN THE LIVES OF PRIMITIVE MAN
Geza Roheim; Paper. Amazon.com, $19.95.

ETHICAL CONCEPTIONS OF THE OGLALA
Helen Blish; 68 pp. Paper. Amazon.com, 2003. $18.95.

ETHICS: ATTORNEY VS. TRIBE, WHO'S IN CONTROL
Panel discussion materials discuss ethical considerations of representing Indian tribes from the tribal perspective. 75 pp. Federal Bar Association, 1988. $15.

ETHNIC CLEANSING AND THE INDIAN: THE CRIME THAT SHOULD HAUNT AMERICA
Gary Clayton Anderson; 472 pp. Paper. University of Oklahoma Press, 2014. $21.95.

ETHNIC HERITAGE IN MISSISSIPPI
Barbara Carpenter, Editor
Essays. Illus. 192 pp. Amazon.com, 1993. $35; paper, $15.95.

THE ETHNOBOTANY OF THE COAHUILLA INDIANS OF SOUTHERN CALIFORNIA
David P. Barrows; Reprint of 1900 edtition. Paper. Malki-Ballena Press, $12.

ETHNOBOTANY OF THE GITKSAN INDIANS OF BRITISH COLUMBIA
Harlan I. Smith; Brian D. Compton, et al, Editors
Illus. 216 pp. Paper. University of Washington Press, 1997. $30.

ETHNOBOTANY OF THE HOPI
Alfred E. Whiting; Reprint. Amazon.com, $85.

ETHNOBOTANY OF THE MENOMINEE INDIANS
Huron H. Smith; Reprint of 1923 edition. Greenwood, $35.

ETHNOBOTANY OF THE RAMAH NAVAHO
Paul A. Vestal; Reprint of 1952 edition. Paper. Redwood Seed, $9.50.

ETHNOBOTANY OF WESTERN WASHINGTON: THE KNOWLEDGE & USE OF INDIGENOUS PLANTS BY NATIVE AMERICANS Erna Gunther
Revised 1945 edition. Illus. 74 pp. Paper. University of Washington Press, 1973. $13.95.

ETHNOGRAPHIC BIBLIOGRAPHY OF NORTH AMERICA
J. O'Leary; supplement by Martin & O'Leary
5 vols. of original publication by geographic areas, subdivided by tribe. 1975. Supplement is arranged by author, with extensive subject and tribal indexes. 1990. Alibris.com.

AN ETHNOGRAPHY OF DRINKING & SOBRIETY AMONG THE LAKOTA
Beatrice Medicine, Editor; University of Nebraska Press, 1994.

ETHNOGRAPHY & FOLKLORE OF THE INDIANS OF NORTHWESTERN CALIFORNIA: A LITERATURE REVIEW & ANNOTATED BIBLIOGRAPHY Joan Berman; G. Breschini & T. Haversat, Editors; 120 pp. Paper. Coyote Press, 1986. $7.45.

ETHNOGRAPHY OF FRANZ BOAS: LETTERS & DIARIES OF FRANZ BOAS WRITTEN ON THE NORTHWEST COAST FROM 1886-1931
Franz Boas; Ronald P. Rohner, Editor; Reprint. Illus. University of Chicago Press, $16.

AN ETHNOGRAPHY OF THE HURON INDIANS, 1615-1649
Elisabeth Tooker; Reprint of 1964 edition. 195 pp. Syracuse University Press, $39.95; paper, $15.95.

ETHNOGRAPHY OF THE NORTHERN UTES
Anne M. Smith; Illus. Paper. Museum of New Mexico Press, 1974. $14.95.

ETHNOGRAPHY OF THE TANAINA
Cornelius Osgood; A study of the Tanaina of Cook Inlet, Alaska. Reprint of 1937 edition. Illus. 229 pp. Paper. Amazon.com, $15.

ETHNOHISTORY IN THE ARCTIC: THE BERING STRAITS ESKIMO
Dorothy J. Ray; Richard A. Pierce, Editor; Illus. 280 pp. Amazon.com, 1983. $27.

ETHNOLOGICAL RESULTS OF THE POINT BARROW EXPEDITION
John Murdock; The only major early ethnography of northern Alaskan Eskimos. Reprint of 1892 9th Annual Report of the BIA. Illus. 480 pp. Paper. Smithsonian Institution Press, $29.95.

ETHNOLOGY OF THE ALTA CALIFORNIA INDIANS, VOL. 1: PRECONTACT
Lowell J. Bean & Sylvia Vane, Eds.; Illus. 928 pp. Amazon.com, 1992. $70.

ETHNOLOGY OF THE INDIANS OF SPANISH FLORIDA
David H. Thomas, Editor; Reprint. Illus. 416 pp. Garland, 1991. $42.

THE ETHNOLOGY OF THE SALINAN INDIANS
J. Alden Mason; Reprint of 1912 edition. 143 pp. Paper. Coyote Press, $15.63.

ETHNOLOGY OF THE TEXAS INDIANS
Thomas R. Hester; Reprint. Illus. 420 pp. Garland, 1991. $32.

ETHNOLOGY OF THE YUCHI INDIANS
Frank G. Speck; intro by Jason Baird Jackson
Reprint. Illus. 192 pp. Paper. University of Nebraska Press, 2004. $29.95.

ETHNOPHILOSOPHICAL & ETHNOLINGUISTIC PERSEPCTIVES ON THE HURON INDIAN SOUL Michael Pomedli; Illus. 200 pp. Edwin Mellon Press, 1991. $79.95.

THE EUROPEAN CHALLENGE
Time-Life Books Editors; 176 pp. Amazon.com, 1993. $19.95.

THE EUROPEAN & THE INDIAN: ESSAYS IN THE ETHNOHISTORY OF COLONIAL NORTH AMERICA
James Axtell; Illus. 256 pp. Oxford University Press, 1982. $27.50; paper, $9.95.

EUROPEAN & NATIVE AMERICAN WARFARE
Armstrong Starkey; Illus. Biblio. 160 pp. University of Oklahoma Press, 1998. $39.97; paper, $17.95.

*EUROPEANS & NATIVE AMERICANS
Jim Corrigan; Grades 4-9. Illus. 64 pp. Mason Crest Publishers, 2003. $19.95.

EVA: AN ARCHAIC SITE
Thomas Lewis and Madeline Lewis; Illus. Paper. U. of Tennessee Press, 1961. $5.95.

THE EVACUATION OF SHEKOMEKO & THE EARLY MORAVIAN MISSIONS TO NATIVE NORTH AMERICANS
Karl-Wilhelm Westmeier; Illus. 468 pp. Paper. Edwin Mellen Press, 1995. $109.95.

THE EVERLASTING SKY
Gerald Vizenor; 165 pp. Paper. Minnesota Historical Society Press, 2001. $12.95.

EVERY DAY IS A GOOD DAY: REFLECTIONS BY CONTEMPORARY INDIGENOUS WOMEN Wilma Mankiller; 19 prominent Native women share what it's like to a Native American woman in the early 21st century. Illus. 256 pp. Paper. Fulcrum Publishing, 2004. $16.95.

EVERY DAY EXPOSURE: INDIGENOUS MOBILIZATION & ENVIRONMENTAL JUSTICE Sarah Marie Wiebe; UBC Press, 2017. $95; paper, $32.95; eBook, $32.95.

EVERYDAY LAKOTA: AN ENGLISH-SIOUX DICTIONARY FOR BEGINNERS
Joseph S. Karol & Stephen L. Rozman; Tape & dictionary of 3,800 entries, 300 phrass, idiom drills, expressions of time, coinage, native birds, etc.Intended to enable speakers of English to begin to learn Lakota. 122 pp. Paper. VIP Publishing. $29.95.

EVERYDAY LIFE AMONG THE AMERICAN INDIANS, 1800-1900: GUIDE FOR WRITERS, STUDENTS & HISTORIANS Candy Moulton; Detailed information on tribal life from 1800-1900. 300 pp. Illus. Amazon.com, 2001. $16.99.

*EVERYDAY LIFE OF THE NORTH AMERICAN INDIAN
Jon M. White; Grades 6 and up. Illus. 256 pp. Paper. Dover Publications, 1979. $9.95.

EVERYTHING YOU KNOW ABOUT INDIANS IS WRONG
Paul Chaat Smith; Essays on American Indian culture & history. Illus. 208 pp. University of Minnesota Press, 2009. $21.95.

Everything You Wanted to Know About Indians But Were Afraid to Ask
Anton Treuer; Illus. Paper. Minnesota Historical Society Press, $17.95; eBook, $9.99.

EVOLUTION, CREATIONISM & OTHER MODERN MYTHS: A CRITICAL INQUIRY
Vine Deloria, Jr.; Incorporates Western and Native American ideas. Illus. 320 pp. Paper. Fulcrum Publishing, 1999. $18.95.

THE EVOLUTION OF THE CALUSA: A NON AGRICULTURAL CHIEFDOM ON THE SOUTHWEST FLORIDA COAST
Randolf J. Widmer; Illus. 393 pp. Paper. University of Alabama Press, 1988. $18.95.

THE EVOLUTION OF NORTH AMERICAN INDIANS
David Hurst Thomas, Editor; A 31-volume series of outstanding dissertations. Amazon.com, $2,230 per set; also sold separately.

EVOLUTION OF THE ONONDAGA IROQUOIS: ACCOMODATING CHANGE, 1500-1655
James Bradley; Illus. 288 pp. Syracuse University Press, 1987. $24.95.

EXCAVATING OCCANEECHI TOWN: ARCHAEOLOGY OF AN 18TH CENTURY INDIAN VILLAGE IN NORTH CAROLINA (CD-ROM)
R.P. Stephen Davis, Jr., Patrick Livingood, Trawick Ward & Vincas Steponaitus
With 8-page booklet. CD-ROM. University of North Carolina Press, 1998. $62.95.

EXCAVATING VOICES: LISTENING TO PHOTOGRAPHS OF NATIVE AMERICANS
Michael Katakis, Editor; 25 pp. U. Museum Publications, 1998. $39.95; paper, $24.95.

EXCAVATIONS AT MAGIC MOUNTAIN
Cynthia Irwin-Williams; Paper. Denver Museum, 1966. $4.95.

EXCAVATION OF MAIN PUEBLO AT FITZMAURICE RUIN
Franklin Barnett; Illus. 178 pp. Paper. Museum of Northern Arizona, 1974. $7.50.

EXCAVATIONS AT SNAKETOWN: MATERIAL CULTURE
Harold S. Gladwin, et al; Reconstructs the building of the Hohokam civilization. Reprint of 1965 edition. 305 pp. University of Arizona Press, $19.95.

EXCAVATIONS, 1940, AT UNIVERSITY INDIAN RUIN
Julian Hayden; Illus. Maps. 234 pp. Paper. Western National Parks Assn., 1957. $2.

EXCLUSION & EMBRACE: A THEOLOGICAL EXPLORATION OF IDENTITY, OTHERNESS, AND RECONCILIATION
Miroslav Volf; Histories of slavery and of the decimation of Native American populations. Paper. Abingdon Press, $28.99 E-Book, $28.99.

EXECUTIVE ORDERS ESTABLISHING THE PAPAGO RESERVATIONS – WITH A BRIEF CHRONOLOGICAL HISTORY
Lynn Kickingbird & Curtis Berkey; 57 pp. Institute for the Development of Indian Law, $12.

EXECUTIVE ORDERS RELATING TO INDIAN RESERVATIONS FROM 1855-1912; AND FROM 1912-1922 Reprint of 1922 ed. Two vols. in one. Amazon.com & Alibris.com, $45.

EXEMPLAR OF LIBERTY: NATIVE AMERICAN & THE EVOLUTION OF AMERICAN DEMOCRACY Donald A. Grinde, Jr & Bruce E. Johansen
320 pp. Paper. UCLA, American Indian Studies Center, 1991. $15.

EXILED IN THE LAND OF THE FREE: DEMOCRACY, THE INDIAN NATIONS & THE U.S. CONSTITUTION 8 essays - Oren Lyons, John Mohawk, Vine Deloria, Jr., Laurence Hauptman, Howard Berman, Donald Grinde, Jr., Curtis Berkey, and Robert Venables. Preface by Sen. Daniel K. Inouye; Foreword by Peter Matthiessen. Illus. Maps. 427 pp. Amazon.com, 1992. $24.95; paper, $14.95.

EXILED: THE TIGUA INDIANS OF YSLETA DEL SUR
Randy L. Eickhoff; 300 pp. Paper. Wordware Publishing, 1996. $12.95.

EXPANDING THE VIEW OF HOHOKAM PLATFORM MOUNDS: AN ETHNOGRAPHIC PERSPECTIVE
Mark D. Elson; Illus. 160 pp. paper. University of Arizona Press, 1998. $16.95.

EXPANSION & AMERICAN INDIAN POLICY, 1783-1812
Reginaldø Horsman; Reprint. 210 pp. Paper. U. of Oklahoma Press, 1992. $16.95.

EXPEDITION TO THE SOUTHWEST: AN 1845 RECONNAISSANCE OF COLORADO, NEW MEXICO, TEXAS & OKLAHOMA
James William Albert; Map. 144 pp. Paper. University of Nebraska Press, 1999. $10.

EXPERIENCE MAYHEW'S INDIAN CONVERTS: A CULTURAL EDITION
Laura Arnold Leibman, Editor; History of the Wampanoag Indians on Martha's Vineyard. The lives of four generations of native Americans in colonial America. Illus. 432 pp. University of Massachusetts Press, 2008. $98; paper, $29.95.

EXPLORATION OF ANCIENT KEY DWELLERS' REMAINS ON THE GULF COAST OF FLORIDA
Frank H. Cushing; Reprint. Illus. 120 pp. Paper. University Press of Florida, 2000. $29.95.

EXPLORATION OF THE ETOWAH SITE IN GEORGIA
Warren K. Moorehead; Illus. 178 pp. Paper. University Press of Florida, 2000. $29.95.

EXPLORATION INTO WORLD CULTURES: AN "ORAL HISTORY" BIOGRAPHY OF HAP GILLILAND Heather Logan; The author's experiences with Yanoamo Indians of Venzuela, the Cheyenne of Montana, and the Papuans of New Guinea. 112 pp. Council for Indian Education, 1995. $9.95.

EXPLORATIONS IN NAVAJO POETRY & POETICS
Anthony K. Webster; Paper. University of New Mexico Press, $24.95.

EXPLORE THE RIVER: BULL TROUT, TRIBAL PEOPLE, AND THE JACKO RIVER
Confederated Salish & Kootenai Tribes Staff
Illus. Paper. University of Nebraska Press, 2011. Interactive DVD, $24.95.

EXPLORERS OF THE NEW WORLD
Jake Mattox, Ed.; Paper. Gale Group, 2004. $22.45.

EXPLORING ANCIENT NATIVE AMERICA: AN ARCHAEOLOGICAL GUIDE
David H. Thomas; Illus. 336 pp. John Wiley & Sons, 1994. $25.

EXPLORING COAST SALISH PREHISTORY: THE ARCHAEOLOGY OF SAN JUAN ISLAND   Julie K. Stein; Illus. 126 pp. Paper. U. of Washington Press & Amazon.com, 2000. $19.95.

EXPLORING IOWA'S PAST: A GUIDE TO PREHISTORIC ARCHAEOLOGY
Lynn M. Alex; Illus. 180 pp. Paper. University of Iowa Press, 1980. $8.95.

EXPLORING NATIVE AMERICAN WISDOM & LORE, TRADITIONS & RITUALS THAT CONNECT US Fran Dancing Feather &Rita Robinson; 224 pp. Career Press, 2002. $13.99

EXPLORING THE OUTDOORS WITH INDIAN SECRETS
Allan A. Macfarlan; Illus. 224 pp. Paper. Stackpole, 1982. $12.95.

EXPLORING THE WEST
Herman J. Viola; Story of those who risked everything to open upo the West. Includes the Lewis & Clark Expedition. Illus. 256 pp. Smithsonian Books, $24.96.

EXPLORING YOUR CHEROKEE ANCESTRY: A BASIC GENEALOGICAL RESEARCH GUIDE Tom Mooney; 58 pp. Paper. Cherokee Publications, $15.

EXTERMINATE THEM: WRITTEN ACCOUNTS OF THE MURDER, RAPE & ENSLAVEMENT OF NATIVE AMERICANS DURING THE CALIFORNIA GOLD RUSH, 1848-1868 Clifford E. Trafzer; Paper. Michigan State University Press, 1999. $22.95.

*EXTRAORDINARY AMERICAN INDIANS
Grades 4 and up. Illus. Biblio. 150 pp. Childrens Press, $22.95.

THE EXTRAORDINARY BOOK OF NATIVE AMERICAN LISTS
Arlene Hirschfelder & Paulette Fairbanks Molin
Illus. 584 pp. The Scarecrow Press, 2012. $83. eBook, $82.99.

*THE EYE OF THE NEEDLE: BASED ON A YUP'IK TALE TOLD BY BETTY HUFFMAN
Teri Sloat, retold by & Illus.; Grades Preschool-4. E.P. Dutton, 1990. $13.95.

THE EYES OF CHIEF SEATTLE
The Suquamish Museum
The lives & experiences of the original inhabitants of northwest Washington state. Color & bxw photos. 56 pp. Paper. Book Publishing Co. & Amazon.com, $16.95.

EYEWITNESS AT WOUNDED KNEE
Richard E. Jensen, R. Eli Paul, and John E. Carter
Assesses some 150 photos that were made before and immediately after the massacre. 163 Illus. Maps. 224 pp. Paper. University of Nebraska Press, 2011. $29.95.

EYEWITNESS TO THE FETTERMAN FIGHT: INDIAN VIEWS
John H. Monnett; Illus. 248 pp. University of Oklahoma Press, 2017. $29.95.

EYEWITNESSES TO THE INDIAN WARS, 1865-1890
Peter Cozzens, Editor; Illus. 4 Vols. Vol. I: The Struggle for Apacheria. 720 pp. 2001. $49.95; Vol. II: The Wars for the Pacific Northwest. 736 pp. 2002. $49.95. Vol. III: Conquering the Southern Plains. 848 pp. 2003. $54.95. Vol. IV: The Long War for the Northern Plains. 656 pp. 2004. $69.95. Amazon.com.

F

FACE
Sherman Alexie; Poetry. 160 pp. Paper. Amazon.com, 2009. $18.

A FACE IN THE ROCK: THE TALE OF A GRAND ISLAND CHIPPEWA
Loren R. Graham; Illus. 172 pp. Paper. University of California Press, 1998. $22.95.

FACES IN THE MOON
Betty Louise Bell; Story of three generations of Cherokee women.
192 pp. University of Oklahoma Press, 1994. $19.95; paper, $10.95.

*FACES IN THE FIRELIGHT
Joh L. Peyton; Legends and traditional life ways of the northern Ojibway. Grades 6 to 8. Illus. 267 pp. Paper. University of Nebraska Press, 1992. $14.95.

FACES IN THE FOREST: FIRST NATIONS ART CREATED ON LIVING TREES
Michael D. Blackstock; Illus. 235 pp. McGill-Queens University Prfess, 2001.

FACES OF A RESERVATION: A PORTRAIT OF THE WARM SPRINGS INDIAN RESERVATION
Cynthia D. Stowell; Illus. 220 pp. Oregon Historical Society, 1987. $29.95.

FACING EAST FROM INDIAN COUNTRY: A NATIVE HISTORY OF EARLY AMERICA
Daniel K. Richter; Reprint. 336 pp. Harvard University Press & Amazon.com, 2001. $26; paper, $15.95.

FACING THE FUTURE: THE INDIAN CHILD WELFARE ACT AT 30
Matthew L.M. Fletcher, Wenona T. Singel, Kathryn E. Fort
300 pp. Paper. Michigan State University Press, 2009. $39.95; eBook, 31.95.

FACING WEST: THE METAPHYSICS OF INDIAN HATING & EMPIRE-BUILDING
Richard Drinnan; Makes connection between suppression of native nations and suppression of liberation movements throughout the world. Illus. 608 pp. Paper. University of Oklahoma Press, 1997. $19.95.

FAITH, FOOD, & FAMILY IN A YUPIK WHALING COMMUNITY
Carol Zane Jolles; with Elinor Mikaghaq Oozeva, Elder Advisor
Illus. Maps. 364 pp. Paper. University of Washington Press, 2002. $26.95.

FAITH IN PAPER: THE ETHNOHISTORY & LITIGATION OF UPPER GREAT LAKES INDIAN TREATIES Charles E. Cleland; with Bruce Greene, Marc Clonim, et al
Maps. Tables. 360 pp. University of Michigan Press, 2010. $95; paper, $40.95.

FAITH IN THE WILDERNESS: THE STORY OF THE CATHOLIC INDIAN MISSIONS
Margaret Bunson & Stephen Bunson
Illus. 450 pp. Paper. Our Sunday Visitor, Publishing Division, 2000. $17.95.

THE FAITHFUL HUNTER & OTHER ABENAKI STORIES
Joseph Bruchac; Abenaki traditional legends. Illus. Amazon.com, $7.95.

FAITHFUL TO THEIR TRIBE & FRIENDS
Dennis W. Baird, Editor; Samuel Black's 1829 Fort Nez Perce report.
Illus. 84 pp. Paper. University of Idaho Press, 2006. $10.

THE FALCON: A NARRATIVE OF THE CAPTIVITY & ADVENTURES OF JOHN TANNER Louise Erdrich, Editor; John Tanner was captured by the Shawnee Indians in 1789 and ultimately sold to and adopted by the Ojibwas. 304 pp. Penguin USA, 1993. $12.50.

THE FALL OF NATURAL MAN: THE AMERICAN INDIAN & THE ORIGINS OF COMPARATIVE ETHNOLOGY
Anthony Pagden; 272 pp. Cambridge University Press, 1982. $49.50.

THE FALSE FACES OF THE IROQUOIS
William N. Fenton; Illus. 522 pp. Paper. University of Oklahoma Press, 1991. $44.95.

*FAMILY, CLAN, NATION
Grades 4-5. 50 pp. Amazon.com, 1989. $10.95.

FAMILY MATTERS, TRIBAL AFFAIRS
Carter Revard; Osage writer. 202 pp. Paper. University of Arizona Press, 1998. $17.95.

FAMILY ORIGIN HISTORIES: THE WHALING INDIANS, WEST COAST LEGENDS & STORIES Edward Sapir, et al.; Part II of the Sapir-Thomas Nootka Texts, Told by Tyee Bob, Sa:ya:ch'apis, Illus. Maps. 400 pp. Paper. U. of Washington Press, 2009. $39.95.

*FAMINE WINTER
John W. Schultz; Grades 4-10. Paper. Council for Indian Education, 1984. $1.00.

*FAMOUS AMERICAN INDIAN LEADERS
Bearl Brooks; Grades 4-6. 24 pp. ESP. Workbook, $5.

FAMOUS DAKOTA CHIEFS
Mark Diedrich; Revised Edition. Illus. 148 pp. Paper. Coyote Books, 1999. $24.95.

FAMOUS FLORIDA! SEMINOLE INDIAN RECIPES
Marina Polvay & Joyce LaFray; 29 pp. Amazon.com, 1996. $5.95.

FAMOUS INDIAN TRIBES
William Moyers & David C. Cook; Reprint of 1954 edition. Illus.
Native American culture & history. Fort Tumbleweed, $29.95.

FANTASIES OF THE MASTER RACE: LITERATURE, CINEMA & THE COLONIZATION OF AMERICAN INDIANS Ward Churchill; Examines the connection between culture & genocide in the 500 years since Columbus. Essays on Tony Hillerman's novels, Sun Bear and Dances With Wolves. Revised edition. 192 pp. Paper. City Lights, 1998. $16.95.

THE FAR WEST & THE GREAT PLAINS IN TRANSITION, 1859-1900
Rodman W. Paul; Paper. University of Oklahoma Press, 1998. $17.95.

FAREWELL MY NATION: THE AMERICAN INDIAN & THE U.S., 1820-1890
Philip Weeks; 2nd Ed. Illus. 266 pp. Paper. Amazon.com, 2000. $14.95.

FARMERS, HUNTERS, & COLONISTS: INTERACTION BETWEEN THE SOUTHWEST & THE SOUTHERN PLAINS
Katherine A. Spielmann, Editor; 217 pp. University of Arizona Press, 1991. $40.

FASCINATING CHALLENGES: STUDYING MATERIAL CULTURE WITH DOROTHY BURNHAM Judy Thompson, Judy Hall & Leslie Tepper; with Dorothy K. Burnham Eight papers on the ethnographic collections from the Northern Athabaskan, Arctic, Plateau, & Eastern Woodlands regions of North America. Illus. 290 pp. Paper. University of Washington Press, 2001. $29.95.

FAST CARS & FIREBREAD: REPORTS FROM THE REZ
Gordon Johnson; Essays about fiestas with frybread & beans, storytelling, dancing, etc. Paper. Amazon.com. $12.95.

THE FAST RUNNER: FILMING THE LEGEND OF ATANARJUAT
Michael Robert Evans; Takes readers behind the cameras, introducing them to the culture, history, traditions, and people that made this movie extraordinary. The first feature film written, directed, and acted entirely in Inuktitut, the language of Canada's Inuit people. Photos. Map. Table. 176 pp. Paper. University of Nebraska Press, 2010. $19.95.

FATHER FRANCIS M. CRAFT, MISSIONARY TO THE SIOUX
Thomas W. Foley; Illus. Maps. 198 pp. Paper. U. of Nebraska Press, 2002. $17.95.

FATHER MEME
Gerald Vizenor; Modern fable of sin, sacrifice & survivance in a Native American mission in Minnesota. University of New Mexico Press, $39.95.

FATHER PETER JOHN DE SMET: JESUIT IN THE WEST
Robert C. Carriker; Illus. Maps. 266 pp. 290 p. University of Oklahoma Press, 1995. $34.95; paper, $17.95.

A FATHERLY EYE: INDIAN AGENTS, GOVERNMENT POWER, & ABORIGINAL RESISTANCE IN ONTARIO, 1918-1939 Robn Brownie; Illus. 204 pp. Paper. University of Toronto Press, 2003.

FATHERS & CROWS: VOL. 2 OF SEVEN DREAMS: A BOOK OF NORTH AMERICAN LANDSCAPES William T. Vollmann; Fictional history of the clash of Indians & Europeans in the New World. 1,008 pp. Paper. Penguin USA, $14.

A FEAST FOR EVERYONE
Grades 4-5. 50 pp. Amazon.com, 1989. $10.95.

FEAST OF THE DEAD: ABORIGINAL OSSUARIES IN MARYLAND
Dennis Curry; 110 pp. Paper. Division of Historical & Cultural Programs/Maryland Historical Trust Press, 1999. $15.

FEAST OF SOULS: INDIANS & SPANIARDS IN THE 17TH CENTURY MISSIONS OF FLORIDA & NEW MEXICO Robert C. Galgano; Native responses to the imposition of Spanish spiritual & secular practices in North America. Paper. U. of New Mexico Press, 2001. $30.

FEASTING WITH CANNIBLAS: AN ESSAY ON KWAKIUTL COSMOLOGY
Stanley Walens; Illus. 236 pp. Amazon.com, 1981. $20.00.

FEASTING WITH MINE ENEMY: RANK & EXCHANGE AMONG NORTHWEST COAST SOCIETIES
Abraham Rosman & Paula Rubel; Illus. 221 pp. Paper. Waveland Press, 1986. $9.95.

THE FEATHERED SUN: PLAINS INDIANS IN ART & PHILOSOPHY
Frithjof Schuon; 165 pp. World Wisdom Books, 1990. $37.50; paper, $25.

FEATHERING CUSTER
W.S. Penn; W.S. Penn, a noted Nez Perce fiction writer and critic, considers how modern scholarship has affected the ways Native Americans and others see themselves and their world. 240 pp. University of Nebraska Press, 2001. $35.

FEATHERS COSTUME
William K. Powers; Evolution of the classic Oklahoma fancy dance costume.
Illus. 19 pp. Paper. Amazon.com, 1994. $10.95.

*FEATHERS IN THE WIND: THE STORY OF OLIVE OATMAN
Lillian M. Fisher; Account of capture of two young pioneer girls by Apaches.
Grades 5-10. Illus. Biblio. 184 pp. Paper. Amazon.com, 1992. $12.95.

FEDERAL CONCERN ABOUT CONDITIONS OF CALIFORNIA INDIANS 1853-1913: EIGHT DOCUMENTS Robert F. Heizer; Paper. 152 pp. Ballena Press, 1979. $7.95.

FEDERAL FATHERS & MOTHERS: A SOCIAL HISTORY OF THE U.S. INDIAN SERVICE, 1869-1933
Cathleen D. Cahill; Illus. Maps. Biblio. 384 pp. U. of North Carolina Press, 2010. $45.

FEDERAL INDIAN LAW: CASES & MATERIALS
David H. Getches; Charles F. Wilkinson & Robert A. Williams, Eds.
3rd & 4th editions. Illus. 1,055 pp. & 1100 pp. West Publishing, 1993 & 1998. $54 & $89.

*FEDERAL INDIAN POLICY
Lawrence C. Kelly; Grades 5 and up. Illus. Chelsea House, 1989. $17.95.

FEDERAL INDIAN POLICY IN THE KENNEDY & JOHNSON ADMINISTRATION, 1961-1969 Thomas Clarkin; Illus. 392 pp. University of New Mexico Press, 2001. $45.

FEDERAL INDIAN TAX RULES: COMPILATION OF IRS RULES RELATING TO INDIANS
Hans Walker, Jr.; 240 pp. Paper. Institute for the Development of Indian Law, 1989. $50.

THE FEDERAL-INDIAN TRUST RELATIONSHIP
Institute for Development of Indian Law, 1981. $12.

FEDERAL PERSONNEL: PUBLIC HEALTH SERVICE COMMISSIONED CORPS OFFICERS' HEALTH CARE FOR NATIVE AMERICANS
Larry H. Endy; Illus. 59 pp. Paper. Amazon.com, 1998. $25.

FEDERAL PROGRAMS OF ASSISTANCE TO AMERICAN INDIANS: A REPORT PREPARED FOR THE SENATE SELECT COMMITTEE ON INDIAN AFFAIRS OF THE U.S. SENATE Roger Walke, Editor; 335 pp. U.S. GPO, 1991. No charge.

FEMINIST READINGS OF NATIVE AMERICAN LITERATURE: COMING TO VOICE
Kathleen M. Donovan; Analyzes texts of well-known writers, N. Scott Momaday, Joy Harjo, Paula Gunn Allen, and others. 182 pp. Paper. U. of Arizona Press, 1998. $17.95.

WILLIAM FENTON: SELECTED WRITINGS
William N. Fenton; William Starna & Jack Campisi, Editors
Fenton's most influential writings on the Iroquois. Illus. Map. 368 pp. Paper.
University of Nebraska Press, 2007. $40.

FERTILITY SYMBOLS OF THE WESTERN INDIANS
Carrol B. Howe; Paper. Amazon.com, 1997. $6.95.

THE FETISH CARVERS OF ZUNI
Marian E. Rodee & James Ostler; Revised 1995 ed. Illus. 112 pp.
Paper. University of New Mexico Press, 18.95.

FETISHES & CARVINGS OF THE SOUTHWEST
Oscar T. Branson; Illus. Paper. Treasure Chest & Hothem House, 1976. $9.95.

FICTION INTERNATIONAL 20: AMERICAN INDIAN WRITERS
Harold Jaffe & Larry McCaffrey, Eds.
Illus. 219 pp. Paper. San Diego State University Press, 1991. $7.

FIDUCIARY FOR SEVEN GENERATIONS: THE TRIBAL COLLEGE TRUSTEE
Gregory O. Gagnon; Illus. 81 pp. Paper. University of North Dakota Press, 2004. $4.95.

FIELD GUIDE TO THE FLINT ARROWHEADS & KNIVES OF THE NORTH AMERICAN INDIAN Tully; Illus. 175 pp. Paper. Hothem House, 1997. $9.95.

A FIELD GUIDE TO MYSTERIOUS PLACES OF THE WEST
Salvatore Michael Trento
Includes many Native American sites. Illus. 256 pp. Paper. Pruett Publishing, 1994. $18.95.

FIELD GUIDE TO PROJECTILE POINTS OF THE MIDWEST
Noel D. Justice & Suzanne Kudlaty
Small stone tools & arrow points. Illus. Amazon.com & Alibris.com, 2001. $35.

FIELD GUIDE TO SOUTHWEST INDIAN ARTS & CRAFTS
Jake & Susanne Page; Paper. Random House, 1998. $17.

FIELD GUIDE TO STONE ARTIFACTS OF TEXAS INDIANS
Ellen Sue Turner & Thomas R. Hester; 394 pp. Paper. Amazon.com, 2002. $18.95.

*FIELD MOUSE GOES TO WAR
Edward Kennard; illus. by R. Kabotie
Traditional Hopi stories. Grades 2-5. Illus. 74 pp. Paper. Amazon.com & Alibris.com, $5.

FIELD OF HONOR
D.L. Birchfield; A novel about a secret underground civilization of Choctaws, deep beneath the Ouachita Mountains of southeastern Oklahoma. 224 pp. University of Oklahoma Press, 2004. $27.95.

FIELDS OF VISION: ESSAYS ON THE TRAVELS OF WILLIAM BARTRAM, 1739-1823
Kathryn E. Holland Braund & Charlotee M. Porter
William Bartram, a naturalist & artist's travel accounts of the Seminole, Creek & Cherokee peoples. Illus. 288 pp. U. of Alabama Press, 2010. $50; paper, $29.95. E-Book available.

FIFTEEN FLOWER WORLD VARIATIONS: A SEQUENCE OF SONGS FROM THE YAQUI DEER DANCE Jerome Rothenberg
Illus. 60 pp. Paper. Membrane Press, 1985. $12.00.

FIFTH ANNUAL INDIAN LAW SEMINAR
Federal Bar Association Conference of 1980. 100 pp. Federal Bar Association, $15.

THE FIFTH GENERATION: A NEZ PERCE TALE
Linwood Laughy; A novel. Illus. 266 pp. Amazon.com, $23.95.

THE FIFTH WORLD OF FORSTER BENNETT: PORTRAIT OF A NAVAJO
Vincent Crapanzano; Ethnographic account of the author's time spent with a Navajo man and his community. 245 pp. Paper. University of Nebraska Press, 2003. $15.95.

FIFTY EVENTS THAT SHAPED AMERICAN INDIAN HISTORY: AN ENCYCLOPEDIA OF THE AMERICAN MOSAIC; Donna Martinez (Cherokee) & Jennifer Williams Bordeaux (Sicangu Lakota/Yankton Dakota)**;** 2 Volumes. 825 pp. ABC-CLIO, 2017, $189. eBook.

FIFTY YEARS AFTER THE BIG SKY: NEW PERSPECTIVES ON THE FICTION & FILMS OF A.B. GUTHRIE, JR. William W. Bevis &William E. Farr, Eds.
Illus. 330 pp. Paper. Montana Historical Society Press, 2001. $18.95.

FIFTY YEARS BELOW ZERO
Charles D. Brower; Reprint of 1942 edition. Illus. Dodd-Mead, $12.95.

FIG TREE JOHN: AN INDIAN IN FACT & FICTION
Peter G. Beidler; 152 pp. Paper. University of Arizona Press, 1977. $4.95.

*THE FIGHT FOR FREEDOM, 1750-1783
N. Farr & D. Postert; L. Block, Editor
Grades 4-12. Illus. Pendulum, 1976. $2.95; paper, $1.25.

FIGHTIN': NEW & COLLECTED STORIES
Simon Ortiz; Collection of contemporary short stories. Amazon.com, 1983. $6.95.

THE FIGHTING CHEYENNES
George F. Grinnell; Reprint of 1956 edition. Illus. Map. 468 pp.
Paper. University of Oklahoma Press, 1997. $24.95.

FIGHTING MEN OF THE INDIAN WARS: A BIOGRAPHICAL ENCYCLOPEDIA OF THE MOUNTAIN MEN, SOLDIERS, COWBOYS, & PIONEERS WHO TOOK UP ARMS DURING AMERICA'S WESTWARD EXPANSION
Bill O'Neal. Illus. 272 pp. Western Publications, 1992. $26.95.

FIGHTING TUSCARORA: THE AUTOBIOGRAPHY OF CHIEF CLINTON RICKARD
Barbara Graymont, Editor
Reprint of 1973 edition. Illus. Maps. 328 pp. Paper. Syracuse University Press, $15.95.

A FINAL PROMISE: THE CAMPAIGN TO ASSIMILATE THE INDIANS, 1880-1920
Frederick E. Hoxie; Originally published in 1984. 350 pp. Paper.
University of Nebraska Press. New preface edition, 2001. $19.95.

FINAL REPORT OF THE U.S. DE SOTO EXPEDITION COMMISSION
John R. Swanton; Report of the Indians' and Spaniards' actions, their societies, and the ecology; early southeastern American life. Reprint of 1939 congressional committee report. 12 maps. 400 pp. Smithsonian Institution Press, $29.95.

FINAL ROLLS OF CITIZENS & FREEDMEN OF THE FIVE CIVILIZED TRIBES IN INDIAN TERRITORY & INDEX TO FINAL ROLLS
Dawes Commission; Reprint. 2 Vols. 1,270 pp. Genealogical Publishing, 2003. $125.

FINAL YEAR EXCAVATIONS AT THE EVANS MOUND SITE
Walter A. Dodd; Paper. University of Utah Press, $15.

FINANCIAL AID FOR NATIVE AMERICANS
Gail Schlachter & R. David Weber
A list of scholarships, fellowships, loans, grants, awards, and internships open primarily or exclusively to Native Americans. 510 pp. Reference Service Press, 1999-2001. $45.

FINDING CHIEF KAMIAKIN: THE LIFE & LEGACY OF A NORTHWEST PATRIOT
Richard D. Scheuerman & Michael O. Finley; photos by John Clement; Story of a prominent chief of the Yakamas. Illus. Maps. 288 pp. Paper. WSU Press, 2008. $34.95.

FINDING DAHSHAA: SELF-GOVERNMENT, SOCIAL SUFFERING, & ABORIGINAL POLICY IN CANADA Stephanie Irlbacher-Fox
Illus. Maps. 216 pp. University of Washington Press, 2009. $94; paper, $35.95.

FINDING SAND CREEK: HISTORY, ARCHAEOLOGY, & THE 1864 MASSACRES SITE
Jerome A. Greene & Douglas D. Scott
Illus. Maps. 242 pp. University of Oklahoma Press, 2005. $29.95; paper, $19.95.

FINDING THE CENTER: THE ART OF THE ZUNI STORYTELLER
Dennis Tedlock, tr.; Translated from live performances in Zuni by Andrew Peynetsa and Walter Sanchez. 2nd Ed. Illus. Maps. 337 pp. University of Nebraska Press, 1998. $55; paper, $16.

FINDING THE WEST: EXPLORATIONS OF LEWIS & CLARK
James Ronda; Illus. 156 pp. Paper. University of New Mexico Press, $24.95.

FINDING YOUR NATIVE AMERICAN ROOTS: A GUIDE TO RESEARCHING YOUR ETHNIC-AMERICAN CULTURAL HERITAGE
Robert D. Reed & Danek S. Kaus; Diane Parker, Ed.
Paper. R & E Publishers, 1993. $4.50.

FINDING A WAY HOME: INDIAN & CATHOLIC SPIRITUAL PATHS OF THE PLATEAU TRIBES
Patrick J. Twohy; Reprint. Illus. 296 pp. Paper. Patrick J. Twohy, 1990. $12.

THE FINE ART OF CALIFORNIA INDIAN BASKETRY
Brian Bibby, Editor; Presents 62 baskets in full color. 128 pp. Paper. Heyday Books, Alibris.com & Malki-Ballena Press, $22.50.

FINE INDIAN JEWELRY OF THE SOUTHWEST: THE MILLICENT ROGERS MUSEUM COLLECTION Shelby Tisdale; Navajo & Zuni silver & turquoise; Hopi silverwork, and Pueblo stone & shell jewelry made during the late 1940s & early 1950s. Illus. Photos. 216 pp. Paper. Museum of New Mexico Press, 2009. $34.95.

FINGER WEAVING: INDIAN BRAIDING
Alta R. Turner; Illus. 48 pp. Paper. Book Publishing Co. & Cherokee Pubns, 1989. $4.95.

FINGERWEAVING BASICS
Gerald Findley; Illus. Paper. Crazy Crow Publications.

FIRE ALONG THE SKY
Robert Moss; 350 pp. Bedford/St. Martin's Press, $19.95.

FIRE IN THE MIND: SCIENCE, FAITH & THE SEARCH FOR ORDER
George Johnson; Illus. 400 pp. Paper. Amazon.com, 1996. $15.

FIRE LIGHT: THE LIFE OF ANGEL DE CORA, WINNEBAGO ARTIST
Linda M. Waggoner; De Cora's life & artistry...memories of her Nebraska Winnebago childhood. Illus. 352 pp. University of Oklahoma Press, 2010. $34.95.. $21.95.

FIRE, NATIVE PEOPLES, & THE NATURAL LANDSCAPE
Thomas R. Vale, Ed.; Illus. 240 pp. Island Press, 2002. $50; paper, $25.

FIRE ON THE PLATEAU: CONFLICT & ENDURANCE IN THE AMERICAN SOUTHWEST Charles Wilkinson; Illus. 415 pp. Island Press, 1999. $28.

FIRE & THE SPIRITS: CHEROKEE LAW FROM CLAN TO COURT
Rennard Strickland
Reprint of 1975 ed. Illus. Maps. 280 pp. Paper. University of Oklahoma Press, $16.95.

FIRESTICKS: A COLLECTION OF STORIES
Diane Glancy
Drama, poetry & Cherokee history. 148 pp. University of Oklahoma Press, 1993. $12.95.

FIREWATER
History of whiskey sales and the Blackfoot Nation. Paper. Amazon.com, $17.95.

FIRST AMERICAN ART: THE CHARLES & VALERIE DIKER COLLECTION OF AMERICAN INDIAN ART Bruce Bernstein, Gerald McMaster, Donald Kuspit, Margaret Dubin**;** Works from many tribal traditions across Canada and the U.S. Illus. 272 pp. NMAI Press & U. of Washington Press, 2004. $60.

THE FIRST AMERICANS
William H. Goetzmann; compiled by Owen Andrews
Illus. Photos from The Library of Congress. 144 pp. Fulcrum Publishing, $34.95.

THE FIRST AMERICANS
Timothy D. Roe; Illus. 54 pp. Amazon.com, 1999. Delux Ed., $65.75.

THE FIRST AMERICANS
Time-Life Books Editors; Illus. 185 pp. Amazon.com, 1992.

THE FIRST AMERICANS: FROM THE GREAT MIGRATION TO THE SPLENDID CITIES OF THE MAYA Anthony F. Aveni; Amazon.com, 2005.

THE FIRST AMERICANS: IN PURSUIT OF ARCHAEOLOGY'S GREATEST MYSTERY
James Adovasio & Jack Page; Illus. 352 pp. Paper. Random House, 2003. $14.95.

THE FIRST AMERICANS: THE PLEISTOCENE COLONIZATION OF THE NEW WORLD
Nina G. Jablonski; Illus. 330 pp. University of California Press, 2002. $65; paper, $35.

*THE FIRST AMERICANS COLORING BOOK
William Sauts & Netamuxwe Bock; Grades 3-5. Illus. Paper. 64 pp. Amazon.com, $4.95.

THE FIRST AMERICANS: RACE, EVOLUTION & THE ORIGIN OF NATIVE AMERICANS
Joseph F. Powell; 250 pp. Paper. Cambridge University Press, 2005. $110.

*FIRST AMERICANS SERIES, 8 Vols.
Provides an overview of Native American history & culture. Each volume covers a region of the U.S. Grades 3-6. Illus. @100 pp. each. Facts on File, 1990-92. $26.35 per volume.

*THE FIRST AMERICANS: TRIBES OF NORTH AMERICA
Jane W. Watson; Grades 1-4. Illus. Pantheon, 1980. $6.95.

*FIRST BOOKS
A series of books for Grades 3-5 covering history & culture of various tribes. Titles are: The Chippewa, by Jacqueline D. Greene; The Inuits, by Shirlee P. Newman; The Pawnee, by Arthur Myers; The Pueblos, by Suzanne Powell; and The Zunis, by Craig & Katherine Doherty. Illus. Franklin Watts, 1993.

THE FIRST CANADIANS
Pauline Comeau & Aldo Santin
2nd revised edition. 220 pp. Paper. Amazon.com, 1995. $19.95.

FIRST COASTAL CALIFORNIANS
Lynn Gamble, Editor; paper. University of New Mexico Press, $24.95.

FIRST CROSSING: ALEXANDER MCKENZIE, HIS EXPEDITION ACROSS NORTH AMERICA & THE OPEINING OF THE CONTINENT
Derek Hayes; Illus 320 pp. Amazon.com, 2003. $40.

FIRST ENCOUNTERS: NATIVE VOICES ON THE COMING OF THE EUROPEANS
Howard B. Leavitt, Editor; Includes 42 accounts of native peoples describing their initial encounters with Eueopean explorers, conquerors & settlers. 266 pp. Greenwood Press, 2010. $85.

FIRST ENCOUNTERS: SPANISH EXPLORATIONS IN THE CARIBBEAN & THE U.S., 1492-1570 Jerald T. Milanich & Susan Milbrath, Editors
Illus. Maps. Biblio. 222 pp. University Press of Florida, 1989. $49.95; paper, $22.95.

FIRST FAMILIES: A PHOTOGRAPHIC HISTORY OF CALIFORNIA INDIANS
L. Frank & Kim Hogeland; Paper. Heyday Books, 2007. $27.50.

FIRST FISH, FIRST PEOPLE: SALMON TALES OF THE NORTH PACIFIC RIM
Judith Roche & Meg Mehutchison; 204 pp. Paper. U. of Washington Press, 1998. $24.95.

FIRST HORSES: STORIES OF THE NEW WEST
Robert Franklin Gish; Collection of original short stories on multi-ethnic complexities of the 1950s and 1960s in Albuquerque, NM. Illus. 134 pp. University of Nevada Press, 1993. $19.95; paper, $10.95.

FIRST HOUSES: NATIVE AMERICAN HOMES & SACRED STRUCTURES
Ray Williamson & Jean Monroe; Illus. 160 pp. Amazon.com, 1993. $16.

FIRST HUNTERS - OHIO'S PALEO-INDIAN ARTIFACTS
Lar Hothem; Photos & sites. 163 pp. Paper. Hothem House, 1990. $13.95.

THE FIRST IMMIGRANTS FROM ASIA: A POPULATION HISTORY OF THE NORTH AMERICAN INDIANS
A.J. Jaffe & C. Sperber; Illus. 360 pp. Perseus Publishing, 1992. $47.50.

FIRST IMPRESSIONS: A READER'S JOURNEY TO ICONIC PLACES OF THE AMERICAN SOUTHWEST
David J. Weber & William deBuys; Illus. 368 pp. Yale University Press, 2017. $30.

THE FIRST ANGELINOS: THE GABRIELINO INDIANS OF LOS ANGELES
William McCawley; Study of the pre-mission Gabrielino's religious beliefs & practices, the structure of their society, political system, the ways they made a living and their arts & crafts. Illus. Maps. Malki-Ballena Press, 1996. $49.95; paper, $34.95.

THE FIRST KOSHARE
Alicia Otis; Story of Koshare clown figure in Native American humor.
128 pp. Paper. Sunstone Press, $8.95.

FIRST LESSONS IN MAKAH
William H. Jacobsen, Jr.; Revised ed. Makah Cultural & Research Center, 1999.

FIRST MAN WEST
A. Mackenzie; W. Sheppe, Editor
Reprint of 1962 edition. Illus. 366 pp. Greenwood, $35.

FIRST NATIONS CULTURAL HERITAGE & LAW: CASE STUDIES, VOICES, & PERSPECTIVES Catherine Belland Val Napoleon
544 pp. University of Washington Press, 2008. $94; paper, $37.95.

FIRST NATIONS EDUCATION POLICY IN CANADA: PROGRESS OR GRIDLOCK?
Jerald Paquette & Gerald Fallon
Illus. University of Toronto Press, 2010. $85; paper, $39.95.

FIRST NATIONS, FIRST THOUGHTS: THE IMPACT OF INDIGENOUS THOUGHT IN CANADA Annis May Timpson, Editor
Illus. 336 pp. University of Washington Press, 2009. $94; paper, $35.95.

FIRST NATIONS GAMING IN CANADA
Yale D. Belanger, Editor; 320 pp.Paper. Michigan State University Press, 2011. $31.95.

FIRST NATIONS, IDENTITY, AND RESERVE LIFE: THE MI'KMAQ OF NOVA SCOTIA
Simone Poliandri; 376 pp. University of Nebraska Press, 2011. $65.

FIRST NATIONS OF BRITISH COLUMBIA: AN ANTHROPOLOGICAL SURVEY
Robert J. Muckle
Second Ed. Illus. 160 pp. Paper. University of Washington Press, 2006. $22.95.

FIRST NATIONS SACRED SITES IN CANADA'S COURTS
Michael Lee Ross; 256 pp. University of Washington Press, 2005. $105; paper, $37.95.

FIRST NATIONS TRIBAL DIRECTORY
Canadian aboriginal directory of tribal groups & organizations. Includes U.S. tribal listings, gaming and internet listings. Irregular. 650 pp. Paper. Amazon.com, $49.

THE FIRST OREGONIANS, 2nd EDITION
Laura Berg; A view of Oregon's Native peoples from the past to the present. Includes essays from scholrs exploring federal-Indian relations. Photos. Paper. Oregon State University Press, 2007. $22.95.

*FIRST PEOPLE: THE EARLY INDIANS OF VIRGINIA
Keith Egloff & Deborah Woodward, Editors
Grades 5-8. Illus. 68 pp. Paper. Amazon.com, 1992. $11.95.

FIRST PEOPLE OF MICHIGAN
Wilbert B. Hinsdale; Reprint of 1930 edition. Paper. George Wahr Publishing, $12.95.

FIRST PEOPLES
Colin G. Calloway; 2nd Ed. Illus. 590 pp. Bedford/St. Martin's, 2003. $38.

FIRST PEOPLES & CHEROKEE REMOVAL
Colin G. Calloway; 2nd Ed. Paper. Bedford/St. Martin's, 2003. $45.

FIRST PEOPLES & CHEROKEE REMOVAL & TALKING BACK TO CIVILIZATION
Colin G. Calloway; 2nd Ed. Illus. Paper. Bedford/St. Martin's, 2003. $51.

FIRST PEOPLES: A DOCUMENTARY SURVEY OF AMERICAN INDIAN HISTORY
Colin Galloway; Amazon.com, $61.

FIRST PEOPLES, FIRST CONTACTS: NATIVE PEOPLES OF NORTH AMERICA
J.C.H. King; Illus. 288 pp. Paper. Harvard University Press & Amazon.com, 1999. $24.95.

THE FIRST PEOPLES: A HISTORY OF NATIVE AMERICANS AT THE PASS OF THE NORTH Oscar J. Martinez; Illus. 24 pp. Paper. Amazon.com, 2000. $7.

FIRST PEOPLES: INDIGENOUS CULTURES & THEIR FUTURES
Jeffrey Sissons; Illus. 176 pp. Paper. University of Chicago Press, 2005. $19.95.

FIRST PEOPLES & VICTORS & VANQUISHED
Colin G. Calloway; Paper. Bedford/St. Martins Press, 2003. $43.65.

FIRST PERSON, FIRST PEOPLES: NATIVE AMERICAN COLLEGE GRADUATES TELL THEIR LIFE STORIES Andrew Garrod & Colleen Larimore, Editors'
Contains stories of Native American college students struggling for survival.
250 pp. Paper. Cornell University Press, 1997. $19.95.

FIRST SCALP FOR CUSTER: A SKIRMISH AT WARBONNET CREEK, NEBRASKA, JULY 17, 1876 Paul L. Hedrin
Illus. 106 pp. University of Nebraska Press, 1981. $12.95; paper, $5.95.

*THE FIRST STRAWBERRIES
Joseph Brychac; Anna Vojtech, Illus.
Cherokee Legend. Grades K-4. Illus. 32 pp. Paper. Amazon.com, 1998.

*THE FIRST THANKSGIVING
Jean Craighead George; Its hero is Squanto, a Pawtuxet man, once kidnapped by European traders. Grades PS-3. Illus. 32 pp. Philomel, 1993. $15.95.

FIRST TO FIGHT
Henry Mihesuah; edited by Devon Abbott Mihesuah; The life story of Henry Mihesuah, a Comanche of the Quahada band. Illus. 118 pp. University of Nebraska Press, 2002. $26.95.

FIRST VOICES: AN ABORIGINAL WOMEN'S READER
Patricia Monture & Patricia McGuire, Editors; Collection of articles examining struggles that Aboriginal women have faced. Paper. Amazon.com, 2009. $39.95.

THE FIRST WE CAN REMEMBER: COLORADO PIONEER WOMEN TELL THEIR STORIES Lee Schweninger, Editor with Intro.; Narratives of white American-born, European, and Native American women contending with different circumstances & geographical challenges. Illus. Maps. 408 pp. Paper. University of Nebraska Press, 2011. $35. E-Book available.

FIRST WHITE FROST: NATIVE AMERICANS & UNITED METHODISM
Homer Noley; 276 pp. Paper. Abingdon, 1991. $17.99

*FIRST WOMAN & THE STRAWBERRY: A CHEROKEE LEGEND
Terri Cohlene; Grades 1-5. Illus. Paper. Amazon.com, 1992. $4.95.

FIRSTING & LASTING: WRITING INDIANS OUT OF EXISTENCE IN NEW ENGLAND
Jean M. O'Brien; Illus. 270 pp. Paper. University of Minnesota Press, 2010.

FISH DECOYS OF THE LAC DU FLAMBEAU OJIBWAY
Art & Brad Kimball; Illus. 96 pp. Paper. Aardvark Publications, 1988. $19.50.

FISH IN THE LAKES, WILD RICE & GAME IN ABUNDANCE: TESTIMONY ON BEHALF OF MILLE LACS OJIBWE HU
James McClurken, et al; Illus. 570 pp. Paper. Michigan State U. Press, 1999. $34.95.

THE FISHERMEN'S FRONTIER: PEOPLE & SALMON IN SOUTHEAST ALASKA
David F. Arnold; History of Southeastern Alaska fishery & the people. Illus. Charts. Map. 296 pp. University of Washington Press, 2008. $35; paper, $25.

FISHING AMONG THE INDIANS OF NORTHWESTERN CALIFORNIA
A.L. Kroeber & S.A. Barrett; J.H. Rowe, etal, Editors
Reprint of 1960 edition. Illus. 216 pp. Paper. Coyote Press, $23.

THE FIVE CIVILIZED TRIBES
Grant Foreman; Documents the removal of the Cherokee, Choctaw, Chickasaw, Creek & Seminole tribes from their ancestral homes in the southeast to the Indian territory west oif the Mississippi. Reprint. 478 pp. Paper. The Choctaw Store, University of Oklahoma Press & Wennawoods Publishing, 2001. $19.95.

THE FIVE CIVILIZED TRIBES: A BIBLIOGRAPHY
Library Resources Div.; Paper. Oklahoma Historical Society, 1991. $5.

THE FIVE CROWS LEDGER: BIOGRAPHIC WARRIOR ART OF THE FLATHEAD INDIANS James D. Keyser; Series of 13 ledger-art drawings described and annotated by Fr. Pierre-Jean De Smet. Illus. Map. 120 pp. University of Utah Press. $24.95.

500 NATIONS: AN ILLUSTRATED HISTORY OF NORTH AMERICAN INDIANS
Alvin M. Josephy; Illus. 480 pp. Random House Value Publishing, 2002. $29.99.

500 NATIONS CD-ROM
Interactive version of mini-series produced by Kevin Costner. VIP Publishing. $39.

FIVE INDIAN TRIBES OF THE UPPER MISSOURI: SIOUX, ARICKARAS, ASSINIBOINES, CREES & CROWS Edwin T. Denig; Reprint of 1961 edition. Illus. Map. 260 pp. Paper. University of Oklahoma Press, 2001. $19.95.

THE FIVE NATIONS CITIZENS LAND REFORM ACT
U.S. Senate Committee on Indian Affairs
120 pp. 107th Congress, 2nd Session. U.S. GPO, 2003.

FLAG & EMBLEM OF THE APSAALOOKA NATIVE
Mickey Old Coyote Lloyd G. & Helene Smith
Illus. 75 pp. Paper. MacDonald-Sward, 1995. $14.95.

THE FLAG IN AMERICAN INDIAN ART
Toby Herbst & Joel Kopp
Illus. 120 pp. University of Washington Press, 1993. $40; paper, $24.95.

FLAGS OF THE NATIVE PEOPLES OF THE U.S.: THEIR DESIGN, HISTORY, & SYMBOLISM Donald T. Healy; Details the story of the flags of 135 sovereign American Indian nations. 242 pp. Photo of each flag. Paper. Written Heritage, $24.95.

FLANDREAU PAPERS TREASURE TROVE FOR MIXED BLOOD DAKOTA INDIAN GENEALOGY Alan Woolworth & Charles E. Flandreau
Paper. Amazon.com, 1997. $15.95.

FLAT PEYOTE STITCH
Michael W. Owl; Jason Aberbach & Michael McCluhan, Eds.
Illus. 70 pp. White Owl Publications, 1993. $19.95.

THE FLEETWOOD TESTIMONIES: THE TRANSCRIBED TESTIMONIES OF THE FLEETWOOD FAMILY & THEIR CLAIM TO CHEROKEE CITIZENSHIP
Jennifer Cain Sparks; Illus. 124 pp. Paper. Arc Press, 2001. $22.

THE FLIGHT OF THE NEZ PERCE
Mark H. Brown; Illus. 408 pp. Paper. University of Nebraska Press, 1982. $10.95.

*FLIGHT OF THE NEZ PERCE
Bill Schneider; Grades 4 and up. Illus. 33 pp. Paper.
Council for Indian Education & Falcon Press, 1988. $5.95.

FLIGHT OF THE SEVENTH MOON: THE TEACHING OF THE SHIELDS
Lynn F. Andrews; Illus. 208 pp. HarperCollins, 1984. $13.50.

*FLINT'S ROCK
Hap Gilliland; A young Cheyenne boy must leave his home on the Montana reservation to live with his sister in the city. Grades 4-8. 87 pp. Paper. Council for Indian Education & Roberts Rinehart, 1995. $8.95.

*THE FLOOD
Grades 3-12. Paper. Council for Indian Education, 1976. $2.95.

FLORIDA'S FIRST PEOPLE: 12,000 YEARS OF HUMAN HISTORY
Robin C. Brown; Illus. 262 pp. Pineapple Press, 1994. $29.95.

FLORIDA'S FRONTIERS
Paul E. Hoffman; 300 years of Florida history...settlement of Florida from 1565-1860; the Seminoles, Miccosuki, British & Spanish influences. Illus. Maps. Amazon.com & Alibris.com, 2002. $13.20.

FLORIDA'S INDIANS FROM ANCIENT TIMES TO THE PRESENT
Jerald T. Milanich; Illustrated history of native Americans in Florida. Illus. Maps. 224 pp. University Press of Florida, 1998. $45; paper, $19.95.

FLORIDA INDIANS & THE INVASION FROM EUROPE
Jerald T. Milanich; Illus. Map. 304 pp. Paper. University Press of Florida, 1998. $19.95.

FLORIDA PLACE-NAMES OF INDIAN ORIGIN & SEMINOLE PERSONAL NAMES
William A. Read; A compendium of Indian-derived names from the three languages of the Muskhogean family-Seminole, Hitchiti, and Choctaw. 112 pp. Paper. University of Alabama Press, 2003. $16.95. E-Book, $16.95.

THE FLORIDA SEMINOLE & THE NEW DEAL, 1933-1942
Harry Kersey, Jr.; Illus. Biblio. 230 pp. University Press of Florida, 1989. $25.95.

FLORIDA'S PREHISTORIC STONE TECHNOLOGY: A STUDY OF THE FLINTWORKING TECHNIQUES OF EARLY FLORIDA STONE IMPLEMENT-MAKERS
Barbara Purdy; Illus. 165 pp. University Press of Florida, 1981. $31.95.

FLORIDA'S SEMINOLE INDIANS
Wilfred Neill & E. Ross Allen; Illus. Photos. 128 pp. Paper. Great Outdoors, 1965. $4.95.

FLORIDA'S TIMUCUA INDIANS: A PICTORIAL HISTORY
Donald W. Spencer, et al; Illus. 140 pp. Camelot Publishing, 2003.$24.95.

FLUTE MAGIC: AN INTRODUCTION TO THE NATIVE AMERICAN FLUTE
Tim R. Crawford; Kathleen Joyce-Grendahl, Ed.; 2nd Unabridged edition. 1999. Illus. 100 pp.; 3rd Ed. 2004. 195 pp. Paper. Rain Dance Publications, 2004. $24.95 each.

*THE FLUTE PLAYER: AN APACHE FOLKTALE
Michael Lacapa
Picture book. Ages 6-8. Illus. 48 pp. Paper. Northland Press & Amazon.com, 1990. $7.95.

FLUTES OF FIRE: ESSAYS ON CALIFORNIA INDIAN LANGUAGES
Leanne Hinton
Collection of essays on Native California languages. 274 pp. Heyday Books, 1994. $18.

*FLYING WITH THE EAGLE, RACING THE GREAT BEAR: STORIES FROM NATIVE NORTH AMERICA
Joseph Bruchac; Grades 5-8. Illus. 144 pp. Bridgewater, $13.95; paper, $5.95.

JOSEPHINE FOARD & THE GLAZED POTTERY OF LAGUNA PUEBLO
Dwight P. Lanmon, Lorraine Lanmon, Dominique Coulet du Gard
Illus. 17 color photos; 25 halftones. 272 pp. University of New Mexico Press, $50.

FOCUS ON FEATHERS: A COMPLETE GUIDE TO FEATHER CRAFT
J. Andrew Forsythe; Covers every facet of producing top quality feather work; with comprehensive instructions for a dozen projects. Illus. Color photos. 96 pp. Paper. Written Heritage, $19.95.

FOLK MAMMALOGY OF THE NORTHERN PIMANS
Amadeo M. Rea; Knowledge held about animals by Pima-speaking Native Americans. Illus. 285 pp. University of Arizona Press, 1998. $50.

FOLK MEDICINE OF THE DELAWARE & RELATED ALGONKIAN INDIANS
Gladys Tantaquidgeon; Reprint 1972 ed. Illus. 145 pp. Paper. The Mohegan Tribe, $9.95.

FOLK-TALES OF THE COAST SALISH
collected & edited by Thelma Adamson
Illus. Map.. University of Nebraska Press & Amazon.com, 2009. $56.95; paper, $25.

FOLKLORE OF THE WINNEBAGO TRIBE
David Lee Smith; The oral tradition of the Winnebago, or Ho-Chunk, people ranges from creation myths to Trickster stories and histories of the tribe. 224 pp. University of Oklahoma Press, 1997. $22.95.

FOLLOWING THE GAME: HUNTING TRADITIONS OF NATIVE CALIFORNIA
Malcolm Margolin; Illus. 192 pp. Heyday Books, $27.95; paper, $18.

FOLLOWING THE GUIDON: INTO THE INDIAN WARS WITH GENERAL CUSTER & THE SEVENTH CAVALRY
Elizabeth B. Custer; Covers the period between 1867 to 1869 when Custer engaged in extensive military activity against the Plains Indians. Reprint of 1967 edition. Illus. 368 pp. Paper. University of Oklahoma Press, $12.95.

FOLLOWING THE INDIAN WARS: THE STORY OF THE NEWSPAPER CORRESPONDENTS AMONG THE INDIAN CAMPAIGNERS
Oliver Knight; Illus. Maps. 364 pp. Paper. University of Oklahoma Press, $18.95.

FOLLOWING THE NEZ PERCE TRAIL: A GUIDE TO THE NEE-ME-POO NATIONAL HISTORIC TRAIL WITH EYEWITNESS ACCOUNTS
Cheryl Wilfong; Chronicles the heartbreaking retreat of Chief Joseph and his people. Second revised & expanded edition. Illus. Maps. Biblio. Paper. Oregon State University Press, 2006. $29.95.

FOLLOWING THE SUN & MOON: HOPI KACHINA TRADITION
Alph H. Secakuku; Presents the Hopi kachina ceremonial calendar.
120 color photos. 152 pp. Northland, $19.95.

FOOD IN CALIFORNIA INDIAN CULTURE
Ira Jacknis, Editor; Illus. Photos. 490 pp. Paper. U. of Washington Press, 2004. $35.

FOOD PLANTS OF COASTAL FIRST PEOPLES
Nancy J. Turner; Illus. 176 pp. Paper. UBC Press, 1996. $24.95.

FOOD PLANTS OF INTERIOR FIRST PEOPLES
Nancy J. Turner; Illus. 176 pp. Paper. UBC Press, 1997. $24.95.

FOOD PLANTS OF THE SONORAN DESERT
Wendy C. Hodgson; Information on 540 edible plants used by over 50 traditional
cultures of the Sonoran desert. Illus. 313 pp. University of Arizona Press, 2001. $75.

FOOD PRODUCTS OF THE NORTH AMERICAN INDIANS
Edward Palmer & Jack C. Thompson; 56 pp. Paper. Amazon.com, 2000. $8.95.

FOODS OF THE AMERICAS: NATIVE RECIPES & TRADIITIONS
Fernando & Marlene Diivina, et al
Illus. 240 pp. Paper. NMAI Press & Amazon.com, 2004. $28.

FOOLS CROW
James Welch; Novel. Illus. Paper. Penguin USA, $10.

FOOLS CROW: WISDOM & POWER
Thomas E. Mails; Teton Sioux holy man Frank Fools Crow describes his life.
Illus. Maps. 294 pp. Paper. University of Nebraska Press, 1990. $15.95.

**FOOTPATHS & BRIDGES: VOICES FROM THE NATIVE AMERICAN WOMEN
PLAYWRIGHTS ARCHIVE** Shirley A. Huston-Findley & Rebecca Howard, Editors
Anthology of writings by Native American women, including Moniique Mojica, Marcie
Rendon, Marie Clements, Martha Kreipe de Montano, et al. 304 pp. Paper. University of
Michigan Press, 2008. $41.95.

FOOTPRINTS STILL WHISPERING IN THE WIND
Margie Testerman; Poetry. Chickasaw people. 80 pp. The Chickasaw Press.
Distributed by the University of Oklahoma Press, $20.

**FOOTSTEPS OF THE CHEROKEES: A GUIDE TO THE EASTERN HOMELANDS
OF THE CHEROKEE NATION** Vicki Rozema; Explores through photography many of the
historic Eastern Cherokee sites. 2nd Ed. Illus. 150 b&w photos. Maps. 400 pp. Paper. John
H. Blair, Publisher, 1995. $21.95.

FOR AN AMERINDIAN AUTOHISTORY
Georges E. Sioul; The author, a Huron, presents guidelines for the study of Native history
from an Amerindian point of view. McGill-Queen's University Press, 1992. $29.95.

FOR GOD & LAND: BROWN EARTH: A DAKOTA INDIAN COMMUNITY, 1876-1892
Elwin E. Rogers; Illus. 112 pp. Paper. Amazon.com, 2002.

FOR INDIGENOUS EYES ONLY: A DECOLONIZATION HANDBOOK
Waziyatawin A. Wilson & Michael Yellow Bird, Editors
Indigenous liberation strategies, indigenous intellectuals create hands-on suggestions &
activities to enable indigenous communities to decolonize themselves. Covers indigenous
governance, education, language, oral tradition, repatriation, stereotypes, et al. Illus. 224
pp.Paper. School for Advanced Research, 2005. $19.95.

FOR JOSHUA: AN OJIBWAY FATHER TEACHES HIS SON
Richard Wagamese; 240 pp. Paper. Random House, 2003.

FOR LOVE OF HIS PEOPLE: THE PHOTOGRAPHY OF HORACE POOLAW
Nancy Marie Mithio, Editor; Illus. 184 pp. NMAI Press, 2014. $49.95.

**FOR OUR NAVAJO PEOPLE: NAVAJO LETTERS, SPEECHES & PETITIONS,
1900-1960** Peter Iverson, Ed.; Illus. 300 pp. Paper. U. of New Mexico Press, 2002. $24.95.

FOR THIS LAND: WRITINGS ON RELIGION IN AMERICA
Vine J. Deloria; James Treat, Ed.; 320 pp. Amazon.com, $90; paper, $25.95.

FOR THOSE WHO COME AFTER: STUDY OF NATIVE AMERICAN AUTOBIOGRAPHY
Arnold Krupat; Paper. University of California Press, 1989. $26.95.

FOR WHICH WE STAND: THE LIFE & PAPERS OF RUFUS EASTON
Bruce Campbell Adamson & William Foley
3rd limited ed. Illus. 240 pp. Bruce Adamson Books, 1996. $25.

FORAGERS OF THE TERMINAL PLEISTOCENE IN NORTH AMERICA
Renee B. Walker & Boyce N. Driskell, Editors
Sourcebook & guide to latest research on first humans in North America.
Illus. Tables. 328 pp. University of Nebraska Press, 2007. $59.95.

**FORCED FEDERALISM: CONTEMPORARY CHALLENGES
TO INDIGENOUS NATIONHOOD** Jeff Corntassel & Richard C. Witmer II
272 pp. Paper. U. of Oklahoma Press, 2009. $19.95.

**FORCED TO ABANDON OUR FIELDS: THE 1914 CLAY SOUTHWORTH
GILA RIVER PIMA INTERVIEWS** David H. DeJong
Illus. Maps.192 pp. Paper. University of Utah Press, 2011. $24.95; eBook, $28.

A FOREST OF TIME: AMERICAN INDIAN WAYS OF HISTORY
Peter Nabokov; Illus. 256 pp. Cambridge University Press, 2002. $60; paper, $22.

FOREVER ISLAND
Patrick D. Smith
Seminole Indian boy. Fiction. Illus. 202 pp. Paper. Pineapple Press, 1987. $14.95.

**FORGING A FUR EMPIRE: EXPEDITIONS IN THE SNAKE RIVER COUNTRY,
1809-1824** John Phillip Reid; Explores interaction between the diverse cultures of
the Pacific Northwest, as recorded by early pioneer, Alexander Ross. Illus. Map. 240 pp.
University of Oklahoma Press, 2011. $29.95.

THE FORGOTTEN ARTIST: INDIANS OF ANZA-BORREGO & THEIR ROCK ART
Manfred Knaak; Rose Houk & Harry Daniel, Editors
Illus. 128 pp. Amazon.com, 1988. $36.95; paper, $24.95.

**THE FORGOTTEN CENTURIES: INDIANS & EUROPEANS IN THE AMERICAN SOUTH,
1521-1704** Charles Hudson & Carmen Chaves Tesser, Editors; 17 Essays of the history of
the early South. Illus. Maps. 496 pp. University of Georgia Press, 1994. $50; paper, $25.

FORGOTTTEN FIRES: NATIVE AMERICANS & THE TRANSIENT WILDERNESS
Omer C. Stewart; Native hunter-gatherers and their uses of fire. Originally published in
1955. Illus. 352 pp. University of Oklahoma Press, 2003. $39.95; paper, $24.95.

THE FORGOTTEN PEOPLE
Tony Williams; Studies the history of Madoc, a 12th century prince of Wales and his
interactions with the Sioux people in North American lands before the time of Columbus.
Photos. 203 pp. Paper. Beekman Books, $20.95.

**THE FORGOTTEN TRIBES, ORAL TALES OF THE TENINOS & ADJACENT
MID-COLUMBIA RIVER INDIAN NATIONS** Donald M. Hines; Umatilla, Tenino,
and Cascades Indians' myths, legends & tales. Illus. 176 pp. Amazon.com. $10.95.

**FORGOTTEN TRIBES: UNRECOGNIZED INDIANS & THE FEDERAL
ACKNOWLEDGEMENT PROCESS (FAP)** Mark Edwin Miller
Examines the FAP as viewed by four once unrecognized tribal communities and their
battles to gain indigenous rights under federal law. Map. 356 pp. Paper. University of
Nebraska Press, 2004. $34.95.

FORGOTTEN VOICES: DEATH RECORDS OF THE YAKAMA, 1888-1964
Clifford Trafzer & Robert R. McCoy; Focuses on the causes of death on
American Indian reservations. Illus. 206 pp. Scarecrow Press, 2009. $72. eBook, $59.99.

THE FORK-IN-THE-ROAD INDIAN POETRY STORE
Phillip Carroll Morgan; Poetry. Illus. 110 pp. Paper. Amazon.com, 2006.

**FORKED TONGUES: SPEECH, WRITING & REPRESENTATION
IN NORTH AMERICAN INDIAN TEXTS**
David Murray, Editor; 188 pp. Paper. Amazon.com & Alibris.com, 1991. $5.50.

**FORLORN HOPE: THE BATTLE OF WHITEBIRD CANYON AND THE BEGINNING
OF THE NEZ PERCE WAR** John D. McDermott; Illus. 230 pp. Idaho State Historical
Society, 1978. $9.95; paper, $4.95.

**FORMAL EDUCATION IN AN AMERICAN INDIAN COMMUNITY:
PEER SOCIETY & THE FAILURE OF MINORITY EDUCATION**
Murray Wax, Rosalie Wax & Robert Dumont, Jr.
Revised edition. 145 pp. Paper. Waveland Press, 1989. $8.95.

THE FORMATIVE CULTURES OF THE CAROLINA PIEDMONT
J.L. Coe; Reprint of 1964 edition. Amazon.com, $12.

FORMULATING AMERICAN INDIAN POLICY IN NEW YORK STATE, 1970-1986
Laurence Hauptman
Illus. 288 pp. State University of New York Press, 1988. $57.50; paper, $19.95.

FORT CHIPEWYAN HOMECOMING: A JOURNEY TO NATIVE CANADA
Morningstar Mercredi; 12-year-old boy learns about the traditional ways of the
Chipewyan, Cree & Metis of Canada. Photos by Darren McNally. Paper.
Meadowlark Communications, $6.95.

**FORT CHIPEWYAN & THE SHAPING OF CANADIAN HISTORY, 1788-1920s:
WE LIKE TO BE FREE IN THIS COUNTRY** Patricia A. McCormack
Illus. Maps. 408 pp. University of Washington Press, 2011. $99; paper, $43.95.

**FORT CLARK AND ITS INDIAN NEIGHBORS: A TRADING POST ON THE UPPER
MISSOURI** W. Raymond Wood, William J. Hunt, Jr., Randy H. Williams
A history of the fur trade, between 1830 and 1860, at this historic site, including the latest
archaeological findings. Illus. Maps. 328 pp. University of Oklahoma Press, 2011. $34.95.

FORT ELLSWORTH KANSAS
Jim Gray; Illus. 68 pp. Paper. Amazon.com, 1998. $7.95.

FORT GIBSON HISTORY
Grant Foreman; A brief history of Fort Gibson in Indian Territory. The Five Civilized Tribes
Museum. Booklet, $2.50.

FORT GIBSON: TERMINAL ON THE TRAIL OF TEARS
Brad Agnew
Reprint of 1980 edition. Illus. Maps. 274 pp. Paper. University of Oklahoma Press, $13.95.

FORT LARAMIE & THE GREAT SIOUX WAR
Paul L. Hedren; Paper. University of Oklahoma Press, 1998. $15.95.

FORT LARAMIE & THE SIOUX
Remi Nadeau; Illus. 375 pp. Paper. University of Nebraska Press, 1982. $9.95.

FORT LAURENS 1778-9: THE REVOLUTIONARY WAR IN OHIO
Thomas Piper & James Gidney
Illus. Maps. 97 pp. Paper. Wennawoods Publishing, $9.95.

FORT LIMHI: THE MORMON ADVENTURE IN OREGON TERRITORY, 1855-1858
David L. Bigler; Includes Indian battles; & proselyting among the Shoshone, Bannock, Nez Perce, & other tribes. Illus. Maps. Paper. Utah State University Press, 2004. $24.95.

FORT MEADE & THE BLACK HILLS
Robert Lee; An authoritative history of the fort that served the northern plains from the Indian Wars until World War II. 321 pp. Center for Western Study. $40.

FORT PECK INDIAN RESERVATION
Kenny D. Shields, Jr.; Paper. Amazon.com, 1998. $19.

FORT RENO AND THE INDIAN TERRITORY
Stan Hoig; Illus. 320 pp. Paper. University of Arkansas Press, $19.95.

FORT SUPPLY, INDIAN TERRITORY: FRONTIER OUTPOST ON THE PLAINS
Robert Carriker; Illus. Maps. 258 pp. U. of Oklahoma Press, 1970. $26.95; paper, $13.95.

FOUNDATIONS OF ANASAZI CULTURE: THE BASKETMAKER-PUEBLO TRANSITION
edited by Paul F. Reed; Illus. University of Utah Press. $60; paper, $30.

FORTY MILES A DAY ON BEANS & HAY: THE ENLISTED SOLDIER FIGHTING THE INDIAN WARS Don Rickey, Jr.
Reprint of 1963 edition. Illus. Maps. Paper. U. of Oklahoma Press, $16.95.

*FOUR ANCESTORS: STORIES, SONGS, & POEMS FROM NATIVE NORTH AMERICA
Joseph Bruchac; Stories and songs of the four elements: fire, earth, water and air. Grades 2-5. Illus. 96 pp. Amazon.com, 1996. $14.21.

THE FOUR CORNERS ANASAZI: A GUIDE TO ARCHAEOLOGICAL SITES
Rose Houk; Illus. 225 pp. Paper. Amazon.com & Alibris.com, 1994. $17.95.

THE FOUR CORNERS: TIMELESS LANDS OF THE SOUTHWEST
Kathleen Bryant; Arizona, New Mexico, Colorado & Utah and the traditional cultures that inhabited it. Illus. Paper. Northalnd Publishing, $9.95.

FOUR DAYS IN A MEDICINE LODGE
Walter McClintock; Facsimile reprint. 21 pp. Paper. Amazon.com, $2.95.

THE FOUR GOSPELS & SELECTED PSALMS IN CHEROKEE
Ruth Bradley Holmes; A Companion to the Syllabary New TestamentIllus. 400 pp. Paper. University of Oklahoma Press, $27.95.

FOUR GREAT RIVERS TO CROSS: CHEYENNE HISTORY, CULTURE & TRADITIONS
Patrick M. Mendoza, et al; Illus. 131 pp. Amazon.com, 1998. $20.

THE FOUR HILLS OF LIFE: NORTHERN ARAPAHO KNOWLEDGE & LIFE MOVEMENT
Jeffrey D. Anderson; Figures, tables, map. 376 pp. Paper. University of Nebraska Press, 2008. $29.95.

400 YEARS: ANGLICAN/EPISCOPAL MISSION AMONG AMERICAN INDIANS
Owanah Anderson; Illus. 416 pp. Paper. Forward Movement, 1997. $12.95.

FOUR MASTERWORKS OF AMERICAN INDIAN LITERATURE: QUETZALCOATL, THE RITUAL OF CONDOLENCE, CUCEB, THE NIGHT CHANT John Bierhorst, Editor
Reprint 1974 ed. 371 pp. Paper. University of Arizona Press, 1984. $24.95.

FOUR SEASONS OF CORN: A WINNEBAGO TRADITION
Sally M. Hunter; photos by Joe Allen; A photographic essay where a 12-year-old Ho Chunk (Winnebago) boy learns the traditions of corn from his grandfather. Illus. 40 pp. Amazon.com & Alibris.com, 1997. $20.95; paper, $6.95.

FOUR SQUARE LEAGUES: PUEBLO INDIAN LAND IN NEW MEXICO
Malcolm Ebright, Rick Hendricks, Richard Hughes
Illus. 464 pp. Paper. University of New Mexico Press, 2015. $34.95.

FOUR WINDS: POEMS FROM INDIAN RITUALS
Gene M. Hodge; 36 pp. Paper. Sunstone Press, 1979. $4.95.

FOUR WINDS GUIDE TO AMERICAN INDIAN ARTIFACTS
Preston F. Miller & Carolyn Corey
Illus. 775 color photos, 7 b&w photos. 192 pp. Paper. Written Heritage, 1998. $29.95.

FOURTEEN FAMILIES IN PUEBLO POTTERY
Rick Dillingham; Introduced seven new families and explores the development of the craft. Illus. 275 color plates; 209 halftones. 309 pp. Paper. U. of New Mexico Press. $39.95.

1491: NEW REVELATIONS OF THE AMERICAS BEFORE COLUMBUS
Charles C. Mann; Illus. 541 pp. Paper. Random House, 2006. $29.95.

FOURTH BIENNIAL NATIVE AMERICAN FINE ARTS INVITATIONAL, OCTOBER 21, 1989-SPRING 1990 Margaret Archuleta
Illus. 32 pp. Paper. The Heard Museum, 1989. $5.

FOURTH CORRECTIONS & ADDITIONS TO POCAHONTAS' DESCENDENTS
Stuart E. Brown & Lorraine Myers; 4th Ed. Illus. 40 pp. Paper. Amazon.com, 2001. $9.95.

THE FOURTH WORLD: FEMINISM & ABORIGINAL WOMEN'S ACTIVISM
Grace Ouellette; Illus. 103 pp. Paper. Amazon.com

THE FOURTH WORLD OF THE HOPIS: THE EPIC STORY OF THE HOPI INDIANS AS PRESERVED IN THEIR LEGENDS & TRADITIONS
Harold Courlander; Illus. 239 pp. Paper. U. of New Mexico Press, 1987. $18.95.

FOURTH WORLD RISING: NEO-MODERN INDIAN LITERATURE
Mario Bengay, et al.; 224 pp. Paper. Institute of American Indian Arts, 2002. $10.

*FOX SONG
Joseph Bruchac; illus. by Paul Morin; Story of a modern Abenaki child learning to accept death. Grades PS-3. Illus. 32 pp. Oyate & Philomel, 1993. $14.95.

THE FOX WARS: THE MESQUAKIE CHALLENGE TO NEW FRANCE
R. David Edmunds & Joseph L. Peyser; The Foxes occupied central Wisconsin, where for a long time they had warred with the Sioux. Struggling to maintain their identity in the face of colonial New France, the Foxes were eventually defeated & took sanctuary among the Sac Indians. Illus. Maps. 282 pp. University of Oklahoma Press, 1993. $29.95.

FRAMING THE SACRED: THE INDIAN CHURCHES OF EARLY COLONIAL MEXICO
Eleanor Wake; University of Oklahoma Press, 2009. $65.

FRAMING THE WEST: RACE, GENDER & THE PHOTOGRAPHIC FRONTIER ON THE NORTHWEST COAST
Carol Williams; Illus. 232 pp. Oxford University Press, 2003. $65; paper, $21.95.

BENJAMIN FRANKLIN, PENNSYLVANIA, AND THE FIRST NATIONS: THE TREATIES OF 1736-62 Susan Kalter, Editor; British colonial relations with the Native peoples of eastern North America. Illus. 472 pp. University of Illinois Press, 2005. $47.

FREE TO BE MOHAWK: INDIGENOUS EDUCATION A THE AKWESASNE FREEDOM SCHOOL Louellyn White
Illus. Maps. 196 pp. Paper. University of Oklahoma Press, 2015. $19.95.

FREE PELTIER: A DRAMATIC HISTORY OF THE AMERICAN INDIAN MOVEMENT
David Seals; Illus. 200 pp. Paper. Sky & Sage Books, 1996. $13.95.

FREEDOM ON THE BORDER: THE SEMINOLE MAROONS IN FLORIDA, THE INDIAN TERRITORY, COAHUILA & TEXAS
Kevin Mulroy; Illus. 256 pp. Texas Tech University Press, 2003. $19.95.

THE FREEING OF THE DEER & OTHER NEW MEXICO INDIAN MYTHS
Carmen Espinosa; Illus. 93 pp. Paper. University of New Mexico Press, 1985. $9.95.

THE FREMONT CULTURE: A STUDY IN CULTURE DYNAMICS ON THE NORTHERN ANASAZI FRONTIER James H. Gunnerson; Paper. Peabody Museum, 1969. $15.

FRENCH & INDIAN WAR
Historical overviews, biographical entries & primary source material on this war. Includes maps, graphs, charts, photos & bibliography. 200 pp. Amazon.com, 2003. $58.

THE FRENCH & INDIAN WAR 1754-1760
Daniel Marston; Illus. 96 pp. Paper. Wennawoods Publishing, $15.95.

FRENCH & INDIAN WAR BATTLESITES: A CONTROVERSY
Bob Bearor; New York French & Indian War sites. Paper. Smoke & Fire Co., $17.50.

THE FRENCH & INDIAN WAR AND THE CONQUEST OF NEW FRANCE
William R. Nester; An account of the war from the French perspective. Illus. Maps. 400 pp. University of Oklahoma Press, 2014. $34.95.

THE FRENCH & INDIAN WAR IN PENNSYLVANIA, 1753-1763
Louis M. Waddell & Bruce D. Bomberger; List of all the forts built during that time period. Illus. Maps. Paper. Smoke & Fire Co., $14.95.

THE FRENCH & INDIANS IN THE HEART OF NORTH AMERICA, 1630-1815
Robert Englebert & Guillaume Teasdale; 256 pp. Paper. Michigan State University Press, 2013. $25.95.eBook, $20.95.

*FRIDAY, THE ARAPAHO BOY: A TRUE STORY FROM HISTORY
Marc Simmons; Grades 3-5. Illus. 56 pp. University of New Mexico Press, 2004. $18.95.

A FRIEND AMONG THE SENECAS: THE QUAKER MISSION TO CORNPLANTER'S PEOPLE
David Swatzler & Henry C. Simmons; Illus. 336 pp. Amazon.com, 2000. $24.95.

A FRIEND OF THEIR OWN: WOMEN & AMERICAN INDIAN HISTORY, 1830-1941
John M. Rhea; Illus. 312 pp. University of Oklahoma Press, 2016. $34.95.

FRIENDS OF THUNDER: FOLKTALES OF THE OKLAHOMA CHEROKEES
Jack F. & Anna G. Kilpatrick; 202 pp. Paper. University of Oklahoma Press, 1995. $12.95.

*FROM ABENAKI TO ZUNI: A DICTIONARY OF NATIVE AMERICAN TRIBES
Evelyn Wolfson; Grades 4-7. Illus. 216 pp. Paper. Available from amazon.com. $9.95.

*FROM THE ASHES
Pat Ramsey Beckman; Brothers are abducted and raised separately by the Shawnee in 1794. Grades 4-10. 160 pp. Council for Indian Education. $9.95.

FROM THE BELLY OF MY BEAUTY
Esther Belin; Poetry. 104 pp. Paper. University of Arizona Press, 2008. $15.95.

FROM CHICAZA TO CHICKASAW: THE EUROPEAN INVASION & THE TRANSFORMATION OF THE MISSISSIPPIAN WORLD, 1540-1715
Robbie Ethridge; Illus. Maps. 360 pp. University of North Carolina Press, 2010. $37.50.

FROM COCHISE TO GERONIMO: THE CHIRICAHUA APACHES, 1874-1886
Edwin R. Sweeney; 720 pp. Paper. University of Oklahoma Press, $24.95.

FROM DANIEL BOONE TO CAPTAIN AMERICA: PLAYING INDIAN IN AMERICAN POPULAR CULTURE
Chad A. Barbour; Illus. 208 pp. University Press of Mississippi, 2012. $65.

FROM THE DEEP WOODS TO CIVILIZATION: CHAPTERS IN THE AUTOBIOGRAPHY OF AN INDIAN
Charles A. Eastman; Illus. 255 pp. Paper. University of Nebraska Press, 1977. $14.95.

FROM DOMINANCE TO DISAPPEARANCE: THE INDIANS OF TEXAS & THE NEAR SOUTHWEST, 1786-1859
F. Todd Smith; 320 pp. Paper. University of Nebraska Press, 2008. $24.95

FROM DROUGHT TO DROUGHT
Florence H. Ellis; Illus. 220 pp. Paper. Sunstone, 1988. 1988. $14.95.

FROM THE EARTH TO BEYOND THE SKY: AN ETHNOGRAPHIC APPROACH TO FOUR LONGHOUSE IROQUOIS SPEECH EVENTS
Michael K. Foster; 460 pp. Paper. University of Washington Press, 1974. $24.95.

*FROM THE EARTH TO BEYOND THE SKY: NATIVE AMERICAN MEDICINE
Evelyn Wolfson; Grades 4-8. Illus. 96 pp. Amazon.com, 1993. $16.

FROM FINGERS TO FINGER BOWLS
Helen Walker Linsenmeyer; History of California cooking, including Indian cooking, with recipes and lore. Illus. 152 pp. Paper. EX Nature Books. $14.95.

FROM FORT MARION TO FORT SILL: A DOCUMENTARY HISTORY OF THE CHIRICAHUA APACHE PRISONERS OF WAR, 1886-1913
Alicia Delgadillo, Editor; Illus. Maps. 456 pp. University of Nebraska Press, 2013. $70.

FROM THE GLITTERING WORLD: A NAVAJO STORY
Irvin Morris ; Navajo creation story. 272 pp. Paper. U. of Oklahoma Press, 1997. $24.95

FROM THE HEART OF CROW COUNTRY
Joseph Medicine Crow; foreword by Herman J. Viola; The Crow Indians' own stories. Illus. Photos. 138 pp. Paper. U. of Nebraska Press, 2000. $10.

FROM THE HEART: VOICES OF THE AMERICAN INDIAN
Lee Miller, Editor; 428 pp. Paper. Vintage/Random House, 1996. $20.

FROM HOMELAND TO NEW LAND: A HISTORY OF THE MAHICAN INDIANS, 1600-1830 William A. Starna; Illus. Maps. 320 pp. U. of Nebraska Press, 2013. $60.

FROM INDIAN LEGENDS TO THE MODERN BOOKSHELF
Edith Mosher & Nella Williams; Reprint 1931 ed. Paper. George Wahr Publishing, $12.95.

FROM INDIANS TO CHICANOS: THE DYNAMICS OF MEXICAN-AMERICAN CULTURE
James D. Virgil; Illus. 245 pp. Paper. Waveland Press, $9.95.

FROM THE LAND: TWO HUNDRED YEARS OF DENE CLOTHING
Judy Thompson; Illus. Maps. 150 pp. Paper. U. of Washington Press, 1994. $29.95.

FROM MASSACRE TO MATRIARCH: SIX WEEKS IN THE LIFE OF FANNY SCOTT
Clara Talton Fugate; Illus. 50 pp. 3 maps. Paper. Amazon.com, 1989. $8.95.

FROM THE LAND OF SHADOWS: THE MAKING OF GREY OWL
Donald Smith; Paper. University of Washington Press, $17.95.

FROM THE LAND OF THE TOTEM POLES: THE NORTHWEST COAST INDIAN ART COLLECTION AT THE AMERICAN MUSEUM OF NATURAL HISTORY
Aldona Jonaitis; Illus. 272 pp. Paper. University of Washington Press, 1988. $40.

FROM MISSION TO METROPOLIS: CUPENO INDIAN WOMEN IN LOS ANGELES
Diana Meyers Bahr; Illus. 184 pp. University of Oklahoma Press, 1993. $24.95.

FROM REVIVALS TO REMOVALS: JEREMIAH EVERTS, THE CHEROKEE NATION & THE SEARCH FOR THE SOUL OF AMERICA
John A. Andrew; Illus. 432 pp. University of Georgia Press, 1992. $45.

FROM SAND CREEK
Simon J. Ortiz; 96 pp. Paper. University of Arizona Press, 2000. $12.95.

FROM THE SANDS TO THE MOUNTAIN: A STUDY OF CHANGE & PERSISTENCE IN A SOUTHERN PAIUTE COMMUNITY
Pamela Bunte & Robert Franklin; 350 pp. University of Nebraska Press, 1987. $22.95.

FROM SAVAGE TO NOBLEMAN: IMAGES OF NATIVE AMERICANS IN FILM
Michael Hilger; Covers over 800 films, including many silents and all relevant sound films. Index. Reprint edition. 289 pp. Paper. Scarecrow Press, 2002. $44.55.

FROM THIS EARTH: THE ANCIENT ART OF PUEBLO POTTERY
Stewart Peckham; Illus. 180 pp. Museum of New Mexico Press, 1990. $39.95.

FROM TIME IMMEMORIAL: INDIGENOUS PEOPLES & STATE SYSTEMS
Richard J. Perry; Illus. Maps. 318 pp. Paper. University of Texas Press, 1993. $30.

FROM VILLAGE, CLAN & CITY
Alyce Sadongei, Editor; A chapbook of eleven Native American writers. Includes poetry and short stories. ATLATL, 1989. $3.

FROM WOODEN PLOUGHS TO WELFARE: WHY INDIAN POLICY FAILED IN THE PRAIRIE PROVINCES Helen Buckley; 225 pp. Paper. CUP Services, 1993. $18.95.

FROM YORKTOWN TO SANTIAGO WITH THE SIXTH U.S. CAVALRY
W.H. Carter; Reprint of 1900 edition. Illus. 335 pp. Amazon.com, $24.95.

FRONTIER CHILDREN
Linda Peavy & Ursula Smith; Illus. Photos. 176 pp. U. of Oklahoma Press, 1999. $24.95.

FRONTIER DAY: THE ARMY IN NORTHERN IDAHO, 1853-1876
Donna M. Hanson, Editor; Illus. Maps. Paper. University of Idaho Press, 2006. $14.95.

FRONTIER DIPLOMATS: ALEXANDER CULBERTSON & NATOYIST-SIKSINA' AMONG THE BLACKFEET Lesley Wischmann; Dual biography. Illus. Map. 400 pp. Arthur H. Clark, 2000. $39.95. Paper. University of Oklahoma Press, 2004. $24.95.

A FRONTIER DOCUMENTARY: SONORA & TUCSON, 1821-1848
Kieran McCarty, Editor; 165 pp. University of Arizona Press, 1997. $32.

FRONTIER FORTS OF IOWA: INDIANS, TRADERS, AND SOLDIERS, 1682-1862
William E. Whittaker; Illus. Photos. Drawings. Maps. 288 pp. Paper. University of Iowa Press, 2008. $29.95. Available e-book, $10 (120 days) or $29.95.

FRONTIER ILLINOIS
James E. Davis; From the earliest Indian settlements to the end of the frontier period. Illus. Paper. Amazon.com & Alibris.com, $10.

THE FRONTIER IN AMERICAN CULTURE
Richard White & Patricia Nelson Limerick; James Grossman, Editor
Illus. Paper. University of California Press, 1994. $28.95.

FRONTIER INDIANA
Andrew R.L. Clayton; From the earliest Indian settlements to the end of the frontier period. Illus. Paper. Amazon.com & Alibris.com, $10.

THE FRONTIER NEWSPAPERS & THE COVERAGE OF THE PLAINS INDIAN WARS
Hugh J. Reilly; Illus. 162 pp. Paper. ebook. Amazon.com, 2010.

FRONTIER PATROL: THE ARMY & THE INDIANS IN NORTHEASTERN CALIF., 1861
Loring White; 28 pp. Association of Northern California Records, 1974. $4.

FRONTIER REGULARS: THE U.S. ARMY & THE INDIAN, 1866-1891
Robert M. Utley; Reprint of 1977 ed. Illus. 500 pp. Paper. U. of Nebraska Press, $12.95.

FRONTIER SOLDIER: AN ENLISTED MAN'S JOURNAL OF THE SIOUX & NEZ PERCE CAMPAIGNS 1877 William F. Zimmer; Jerome A. Greene, Ed.
Illus. 238 pp. Teacher edition. Montana Historical Scoiety Press, $32.

FRONTIERS OF HISTORICAL IMAGINATION: NARRATING THE EUROPEAN CONQUEST OF NATIVE AMERICA, 1890-1990 Kerwin Lee Klein; Explores the traditions through which historians, philosophers, anthropologists, and literary critics have understood America's origin story. 388 pp. Paper. U. of California Press, 1999. $21.95.

FRY BREADS , FEAST DAYS & SHEEPS
Kris Hotvedt; 48 pp. Paper. Sunstone, 1987. $6.95.

FUGITIVE POSES: NATIVE AMERICAN INDIAN SCENES OF ABSENCE & PRESENCE
Gerald Vizenor; Essays. 240 pp. Paper. University of Nebraska Press, 1998. $16.95.

FULL-COURT QUEST: THE GIRLS FROM FORT SHAW INDIAN SCHOOL BASKETBALL CHAMPIONS OF THE WORLD
Linda Peavy & Ursula Smith; Illus. 496 pp. University of Oklahoma Press, 2008. $29.95.

FUNCTION & TECHNOLOGY OF ANASAZI CERAMICS FROM BLACK MESA, ARIZONA Marion F. Smith, Jr., Editor; Illus. 254 pp. Paper. Amazon.com, 1994. $40.

FUNNY, YOU DON'T LOOK LIKE ONE: OBSERVATIONS FROM BLUE-EYED OJIBWAY Drew H. Taylor; 132 pp. Paper. Amazon.com, 1997. $10.95.

*FUR TRADE
Roots Mag. back issue; How fur compames and their trade with Indians helped shape Minnesota's history. Grades 6 and up. Illus. 32 pp. Minnesota Historical Society Press, 1981. $3.50.

FUR TRADE & EXPLORATION: OPENING THE FAR NORTHWEST, 1821-1852
Theodore J. Karamanski
Illus. Maps. Biblio. 330 pp. Paper. University of Oklahoma Press, 1983. $17.95.

THE FUR TRADE IN CANADA
Harold A. Innis; Social history through the clash between colonial and aboriginal cultures. 496 pp. Paper. University of Toronto Press, 1999. $24.95.

*FUR TRAPPERS & TRADERS: THE INDIANS, THE PILGRIMS & THE BEAVER
Beatrice Siegel; Grades 3-7. Illus. 64 pp. Walker & Co., 1981. $11.85.

FURS & FRONTIERS IN THE FAR NORTH: THE CONTEST AMONG NATIVE & FOREIGN NATIONS FOR THE BERING STRAIT FUR TRADE
John R. Bockstace; Illus. Maps. 496 pp. Yale University Press, 2010. $30.

THE FUS FIXICO LETTERS: A CREEK HUMORIST IN EARLY OKLAHOMA
Alexander Posey; Edited by Daniel F. Littlefield & Carol A. Pretty Hunter; foreword by A. LaVonne Brown Ruoff; Humorous articles by Posey, the Creek political humorist. Reprint. Illus. Map. 352 pp. Paper. University of Oklahoma Press, 2002. $19.95.

THE FUTURE OF INDIGENOUS PEOPLES: STRATEGIES FOR SURVIVAL & DEVELOPMENT Duane Champagne & Ismael Abu-Saad
272 pp. UCLA American Indian Studies Center Publications, 2003. $60; paper, $20.

THE FUTURE OF THE PAST: ARCHAEOLOGISTS, NATIVE AMERICANS & REPATRIATION Tamara L. Bray; Illus. 272 pp. Amazon.com, 2001. Text, $80.

G

THE GABRIELINO
Bruce W. Miller; A historical look at the Indians of the Los Angeles Basin. Illus. 120 pp. Paper. Amazon.com, $7.95.

GAGIWDULAT: BROUGHT FORTH TO RECONFIRM THE LEGACY OF A TAKU RIVER TLINGIT CLAN Elizabeth Nyman & Jeff Leer; Ancient legends & traditional stories of the Tlingit of the Taku region. Illus. Photos. 261 pp. Alaska Native Language Center, $26.95.

GAH-BACH-JHAGWAH-BUK, THE WAY IT HAPPENED: A VISUAL CULTURE HISTORY OF THE LITTLE TRAVERSE BAY BANDS OF ODAWA James M. McClurken; Suzanne Caltrider, Ed. Illus. 130 pp. Michigan State University Press, 1991. $22.95; paper, $16.95.

KATIE GALE: A COAST SALISH WOMAN'S LIFE ON OYSTER BAY
Llyn De Danaan; Illus. Map. University of Nebraska Press, 2013. $29.95.

GALE ENCYCLOPEDIA OF NATIVE AMERICAN TRIBES
Sharon Malinowski; Essays on the history, culture & current status of about 400 federally recognized Native American groups. In 4 Vols. Vol. 1: Northeast & Southeast; Vol. 2: Great Basin & Southwest; Vol. 3: Arctic, Subarctic, Plateau & Great Plains; Vol. 4: Pacific Northwest & California. Thompson Gale, 1998. 1st Ed. 2,064 pp. $450 per set.

GALENA & ABORIGINAL TRADE IN EASTERN NORTH AMERICA
John A. Walthall; Illus. 66 pp. Paper. Illinois State Museum, 1981. $2.50.

GALL: LAKOTA WAR CHIEF
Robert W. Larson
Biography. Illus. 320 pp. University of Oklahoma Press, 20007. $24.95; paper, $19.95.

GALVANIZED YANKEES ON THE UPPER MISSOURI: THE FACE OF LOYALTY
Michele Butts; Illus. 320 pp. University Press of Colorado, 2003. $29.95.

GAMBLER WAY: INDIAN GAMING IN MYTHOLOGY, HISTORY & ARCHAEOLOGY IN NORTH AMERICA Kathryn Gabriel
Reprint. Illus. 250 pp. Paper. Amazon.com, 1999. $18.

GAMBLING & SURVIVAL IN NATIVE NORTH AMERICA
Paul Pasquaretta; Explores the impact of reservation gambling on the development of contemporary tribal communities and the survival of indigenous cultural traditions. 200 pp. University of Arizona Press, 2003. $45.

***THE GAME OF SILENCE**
Louise Erdrich
The story of an Ojibwe family. Grades 4 to 8. HarperCollins, 2005. Available on audio CD.

GAMES OF THE NORTH AMERICAN INDIANS
Stewart Culin; Reprint of 1907 edition. Two vols. Illus. 402 pp. Vol. 1: Games of Chance; Illus. 490 pp. Vol. 2: Games of Skill. Paper. U. of Nebraska Press, 1992. $15.95 each.

GAMES OF TETON DAKOTA CHILDREN
J. Owen Dorsey; 16 pp. Paper. Amazon.com, 1991. $9.95.

GATEWOOD & GERONIMO
Louis Kraft; Illus. 304 pp. Paper. University of New Mexico Press, 2000. $22.95.

GATHERING THE DESERT
Gary Paul Nabhan; illus. by Paul Mirocha; Reveals how Southwestern desert peoples have used indigenous plants over the centuries. 209 pp. Paper. University of Arizona Press, 1985. $19.95.

GATHERING HOPEWELL: SOCIETY, RITUAL, & RITUAL INTERACTION
Christopher Carr & D. Troy Case; Paper. Amazon.com, 2004.

GATHERING MOSS: A NATURAL & CULTURAL HISTORY OF MOSSES
Robin Wall Kimmerer; Illus. 168 pp. Paper. Oregon State University Press, 2003. $18.95.

GATHERING NATIVE SCHOLARS: UCLA'S 40 YEARS OF AMERICAN INDIAN CULTURE & RESEARCH Kenneth Lincoln, Editor
Collection of articles. UCLA American Indian Studies Center, 2009. Paper. $38.

A GATHERING OF RIVERS: INDIANS, METIS, & MINING IN THE WESTERN GREAT LAKES, 1737-1832 Lucy Eldersveld Murphy; Traces the history of Indian, multi-racial, and mining communities in the western Great Lakes region, 1737-1832. Illus. Maps. 231 pp. University of Nebraska Press, 2000. $50.

A GATHERING OF SPIRIT: WRITING & ART BY NORTH AMERICAN INDIAN WOMEN
Beth Brant, Editor; Illus. 240 pp. Paper. Sinister Wisdom Books, 1984. $9.50.

A GATHERING OF STATESMEN: RECORDS OF THE CHOCTAW COUNCIL MEETINGS, 1826-1828
Peter P. Pitchlyn; 176 pp. Paper. University of Oklahoma Press, $29.95.

GATHERING OF WISDOMS: TRIBAL MENTAL HEALTH–A CULTURAL PERSPECTIVE
Jennifer F. Clarke, Editor; Illus. 514 pp. Paper. Swinomish Indian, 1991. $19.95.

GATHERING PLACES: ABORIGINAL & FUR TRADE HISTORIES
Carolyn Podruchny & Laura Peers; Essays of British traders & Ojibwwe hunters; Metis, fur trade, and First Nations of Canada's history. Illus. Map. 352 pp. University of Washington Press, 2010. $99; paper, $37.95.

GATHERINGS II
Greg Young-Ing, Editor; Features the works of several high profile First Nations' authors and artists. Illus. 240 pp. Paper. Theytus, 1991. $12.95.

GATHERINGS III
Greg Young-Ing, Editor; Features a wide array of work by First Nation authors from across North America. Illus. 240 pp. Paper. Theytus, 1992. $12.95.

GATHERING THE POTAWATOMI NATION: REVITALIZATION & IDENTITY
Christopher Wetzel; Illus. 215 pp. Paper. University of Oklahoma Press, 2015. $19.95.

GATHERING TOGETHER: THE SHAWNEE PEOPLE THROUGH DIASPORA & NATIONHOOD, 1600-1870 Sami Lakomaki; Illus. 344 pp. Yale U. Press, 2014. $40.

GATHERINGS: GREAT LAKES NATIVE BASKET & BOX MAKERS
Marsha MacDowell, et al; Illus. 50 pp. Paper. Michigan State U. Museum, 1999. $14.95.

GATHERINGS IV: RE-GENERATION: EXPANDING THE WEB TO CLAIM OUR FUTURE
Don Fiddler, Editor; Poetry, short fiction, essays, songs, oratory, pictograph writing, drama, criticism, biography, artworks and cartoons. 250 pp. paper. Theytus, 1993. $12.95.

GENDER & SEXUALITY IN INDIGENOUS NORTH AMERICA, 1400-1850
Sandra Slater & Fay A. Yarbrough, Editors
Essays that discuss he complex attitudes & expressions concerning gender & sexual roles in Native American culture. Probes gender identification, labor roles, and political authority within Native American societies. 200 pp. University of South carolina Press, 2011. $34.95.

THE GENEALOGY OF THE FIRST METIS NATION
D.N. Sprague & R.P. Frye; Detailed account fo the original Metis who settled the Red River district. Paper. Pemmican, $20.95.

GENERAL & AMERINDIAN ETHNOLINGUISTICS: IN REMEMBRANCE OF STANLEY NEWMAN Mary Key & Henry Hoenigwald, Editors; 500 pp. Amazon.com, 1989. $125.

GENERAL CROOK IN THE INDIAN COUNTRY
John G. Bourke & F. Remington; Two accounts of soldiers of the Indian wars, written by contemporary observers. Reprint of 1974 edition. Illus. 44 pp. Paper. Amazon.com & Alibris.com, $4.

GENERAL DISCUSSION OF SHAMANISTIC & DANCING SOCIETIES
Clark Wissler; 23 pp. Paper. Amazon.com, 1993. $8.95.

GENERAL GEORGE WRIGHT: GUARDIAN OF THE PACIFIC COAST, 1803-1865
Carl P. Schlicke; Illus. Maps. Biblio. University of Oklahoma Press, 1988. $34.95

GENERAL REQUIREMENTS & PARAMETERS FOR VENDOR LICENSING
Casino & Industry Relations Dept. of NIGA
Directed to the Gaming Commissions and companies who wish to do business with Indian Nations. Offers general parameters and guidelines for issuance of vendor licensees. National Indian Gaming Association (NIGA), $20, members; $40, non-members.

GENERAL STAND WATIE'S CONFEDERATE INDIANS
Frank Cunningham; Illus. 272 pp. Paper. University of Oklahoma Press, 1998. $19.95.

GENERAL TERRY'S LAST STATEMENT TO CUSTER
John Manion; Illus. 182 pp. Amazon.com, 2000. $37.50.

GENERATION TO GENERATION
Edward Benton-Benai; Ojibway traditional teaching story. Illus. 24 pp. Indian Country Communication, 1991. $6.

THE GENETIC RELATIONSHIP OF THE NORTH AMERICAN INDIAN LANGUAGES
Paul A. Radin; Reprint of 1919 edition. 13 pp. Paper. Coyote Press, $1.88.

THE GENIUS OF SITTING BULL: 13 HEROIC STRATEGIES FOR TODAY'S BUSINESS LEADERS Emmett C. Murphy with Michael Snell
Illus. 340 pp. Prentice Hall, 1993. $18.95.

GENOCIDE AGAINST THE INDIANS: ITS ROLE IN THE RISE OF U.S. CAPITALISM
George Novak; Reprint of 1970 edition. 31 pp. Booklet. Amazon.com, $3.

GENOCIDE OF THE MIND: NEW NATIVE AMERICAN WRITING
edited by Marijo Moore (Cherokee); foreword by Vine Deloria, Jr.
Collection of essays, stories & poetry that describes the struggles of American Indian to maintain an authentic identity within an evolving world. Paper. Amazon.com, 2003. $16.95.

GENUINE NAVAJO RUGS: HOW TO TELL
Noel Bennett
2nd revised edition. Illus. 36 pp. Paper. Amazon.com & Alibris.com, 2000. $3.95.

GEOGRAPHICAL NAMES OF THE KWAKIUTL INDIANS
Franz Boas; Reprint of 1934 edition. Illus. 124 pp. Paper. Coyote Press, $13.75.

GEOGRAPHY OF BRITISH COLUMBIA: PEOPLE & LANDSCAPES IN TRANSITION
Brett McGillvray; Traces the province's historical geography, including First Nations ways of life. Illus. 320 pp. Paper. University of Washington Press, 2011. $60.

GEORGE WASHINGTON GRAYSON & THE CREEK NATION, 1853-1920
Mary Jane Warde; Illus. Maps. Biblio. 384 pp. U. of Oklahoma Press, 1999. $25.95.

GEORGIA VOICES, Vol. Two: Nonfiction
Hugh Ruppersburg, Editor; Includes selections from Native American writers.
592 pp. University of Georgia Press, 1994. $40; paper, $19.95.

GERANIUMS FOR THE IROQUOIS: A FIELD GUIDE TO AMERICAN INDIAN MEDICINAL PLANTS
Daniel E. Moerman; Keith Irvine, Editor; Illus. Reference Publications, 1982. $24.95.

GERMAN ARTIST ON THE TEXAS FRONTIER: FRIEDRICH RICHARD PETRI
William K. Newcomb, Jr.; Illus. 250 pp. University of Texas Press, 1978. $35.

GERMAN PIONEER ACCOUNTS OF THE GREAT GERMANS & INDIANS: FANTASIES, ENCOUNTERS, PROJECTIONS Colin G. Calloway, Gerd Gemunden & Susanne Zantop
Historical and cultural roots of the interactions between Germans and Indians.
Illus. Maps. 351 pp. University of Nebraska Press, 2002. $70; paper, $29.95.

GERONIMO
Robert M. Utley; Illus. Maps. 376 pp. Paper. Yale University Press, 2013. $20.

GERONIMO
Alexander B. Adams; Illus. 380 pp. Amazon.com, $14.95.

*GERONIMO
Russell Shorto; Grades 5-7. Illus. 144 pp. Amazon.com, 1989. $11.98; paper, $7.95.

GERONIMO CAMPAIGN
Odie B. Faulk; Illus. Oxford University Press, 1969. $27.95.

GERONIMO & THE END OF THE APACHE WARS
C.L. Sonnichson, Editor; Illus. 141 pp. Paper. U. of Nebraska Press, 1990. $14.95.

GERONIMO: HIS OWN STORY
Geronimo, as told to S.M. Barrett
Revised ed. Illus. 210 pp. Paper. Penguin Group, 1996. $15.

GERONIMO: LAST RENEGADE OF THE APACHE
Jason Hook; Illus. 52 pp. Sterling, 1989. $12.95.

GERONIMO: THE MAN, HIS TIME, HIS PLACE
Angie Debo; Reprint of 1976 edition. Illus. Maps. 500 pp. Paper. University of Oklahoma Press, 2002. $24.95.

GERONIMO: MY LIFE
S.M. Barrett; Reprint of 1906 ed. 144 pp. Paper. Dover. $8.95.

GERONIMO'S KIDS: A TEACHER'S LESSONS ON THE APACHE RESERVATION
Robert S. Ove & H. Henrietta Stockel
Photos. 200 pp. Texas A&M University Press, $26.95.

GERONIMO! STORIES OF AN AMERICAN LEGEND
Sharon S. Magee; Illus. 144 pp. Paper. Arizona Highways, 2002. $7.95.

GERONIMO'S STORY OF HIS LIFE
Geronimo; S.M. Barrett, Editor; Illus. 216 pp. Paper. Amazon.com, 1991. $17.95.

GETTING GOOD CROPS: ECONOMIC & DIPLOMATIC SURVIVAL STRATEGIES OF THE MONTANA BITTEROOT SALISH INDIANS, 1870-1891
Robert J. Bigart; 304 pp. University of Oklahoma Press, $39.95.

GETTING SENSE: THE OSAGES & THEIR MISSIONARIES
James D. White; Illus. 389 pp. Paper. Sarto Pres, 1997. $21.95.

GHOST DANCE
David H. Miller; Illus. 325 pp. University of Nebraska Press, 1985. $27.95; paper, $8.95.

THE GHOST DANCE: ETHNOHISTORY & REVITALIZATION, 2ND ED.
Alice B. Kehoe; Illus. 186 pp. Paper. Waveland Press, 2006. $17.50.

GHOST DANCE MESSIAH: THE JACK WILSON STORY
Paul Bailey; Westernlore, $12.95.

GHOST DANCE RELIGION
Alice B. Kehoe; 190 pp. Paper. Amazon.com, 1989. $23.50.

GHOST-DANCE RELIGION & THE SIOUX OUTBREAK OF 1890
James Mooney; Anthony Wallace, Editor
Reprint. Illus. Maps. 483 pp. University of Nebraska Press, 1991. $80; paper, $39.95.

THE GHOST-DANCE RELIGION & WOUNDED KNEE
James Mooney; Explores messianic cult behind Indian resistance.
Reprint. Illus. 544 pp. Paper. Dover, $12.95.

GHOST DANCES & IDENTITY: PROPHETIC RELIGION & AMERICAN INDIAN ETHNOGENESIS IN THE 19TH CENTURY Gregory E. Smoak
Examines the origins of Shoshone & Bannock ethnicity. 304 pp. University of California Press, 2006. $60; paper, $26.95. E-book available.

GHOST DANCES IN TE WEST: AN EYEWITNESS ACCOUNT
Warren C. Moorhead; intro. By William K. Powers
Illus. 40 pp. Paper. Amazon.com, 1998. $18.95.

GHOST DANCING THE LAW: THE WOUNDED KNEE TRIALS
John W. Sayer; 320 pp. Paper. Harvard University Press & Amazon.com, 1997. $21.50.

GHOST VOICES
Donald M. Hines; Yakama Indian myths, legends, humor and hunting stories.
Illus. 435 pp. Biblio. Amazon.com, 1993. $23.95.

*GIANTS OF THE DAWNLAND: ANCIENT WABANAKI TALES
Alice Mead & Arnold Neptune, Editors
Grades 4 and up. Illus. 76 pp. Paper. Loose Cannon, 2000, $8.

GIDEON'S PEOPLE: BEING A CHRONICLE OF AN AMERICAN INDIAN COMMUNITY IN COLONIAL CONNECTICUT & THE MORAVIAN MISSIONARIES WHO SERVED THERE Corinna Dally-Starna & William A. Starna, Edited & translated
Photos. Maps. Two Vols. 1,376 pp. University of Nebraska Press, 2009. $170.

THE GIFT OF AMERICAN NATIVE PAINTINGS FROM THE COLLECTION OF EDGAR WILLIAM & BERNICE CHRYSLER GARBISCH
Illus. 68 pp. Paper. Chrysler Museum,1975. $5.00.

*THE GIFT OF CHANGING WOMAN
Tryntje Van Ness Seymour; Describes the Apache girl's puberty ceremony.
Grades 5-9. Illus. 40 pp. Amazon.com., 1995. $16.95.

THE GIFT OF THE GILA MONSTER: NAVAJO CEREMONIAL TALES
Introduced & retold by Gerald Hausman; Mythology/ceremonial songs of the Navajo.
Illus. 224 pp. Paper. Simon & Schuster, 1993. $11.

GIFT OF POWER: THE LIFE & TEACHINGS OF A LAKOTA MEDICINE MAN
Chief Archie Fire Lame Deer & Richard Erdoes
Illus. 304 pp. Paper. Inner Traditions, 1992. $20.

*THE GIFT OF THE SACRED DOG
Paul Goble; Grades K-4. Illus. 32 pp. Paper. Aladdin, 1984.

THE GIFT OF THE SACRED PIPE: BASED ON BLACK ELK'S ACCOUNT OF THE SEVEN RITES OF THE OGLALA SIOUX Vera L. Drysdale, Ed. & Illus. by
Originally recorded & edited by Joseph Epes Brown. Illus. 128 pp. Paper.
University of Oklahoma Press, 1995. $27.95.

GIFT OF SPIDERWOMAN: SOUTHWESTERN TEXTILES, THE NAVAJO TRADITION
Joe B. Wheat; Illus. 48 pp. Paper. University of Pennsylvania, 1984. $14.95.

GIFTS OF PRIDE & LOVE: KIOWA & COMANCHE CRADLES
Barbara Hail, Editor; History of the origins of latice cradles and essays by cradle makers.
Originally published by Smithsonian Press in hardcover in 2000. Illus. 136 pp. Paper. University of Oklahoma Press, 2004. $29.95.

*GIFTS OF THE SEASON: LIFE AMONG THE NORTHWEST INDIANS
Carol Batdorf; Grades 1-6. Illus. 25 pp. Hancock House, 1990. $5.95.

GIGYAYK VO JKA! (WALK STRONG!) YUMAN POETRY WITH MORPHOLOGICAL ANALYSIS Lucille Watahomigie & Akira Yamamoto, Editors
Poetry. Reprint. Illus. 141 pp. Paper. Malki-Ballena Press, 1983. $20.

THOMAS GILCREASE
Carole Klein, April Miller, et al; Illus. 192 pp. Paper. U. of Oklahoma Press, 2010. $24.95.

GIRL CAPTIVES OF THE CHEYENNES: A TRUE STORY OF THE CAPTURE & RESCUE OF FOUR PIONEER GIRLS, 1874
Grace E. Meredith; Reprint. Illus. 176 pp. Paper. Amazon.com, $16.95.

GIRL FROM THE GULCHES: THE STORY OF MARY RONAN
Mary Ronan & Margharet Ronan; Ellem Baumler, Ed.
Illus. 264 pp. Paper. Montana Historical Society Press, 2003. $17.95.

*THE GIRL WHO MARRIED THE MOON: TALES FROM NATIVE NORTH AMERICA
Told by Joseph Bruchac & Gayle Ross
Grades 5-8. 127 pp. Amazon.com, 1994. $10.46; paper, $5.95.

THE GIRL WHO SANG TO THE BUFFALO: A CHILD, AN ELDER, AND THE LIGHT FROM AN ANCIENT SKY Kent Nerburn; 408 pp. Paper. New World Lirary, $17.95.

GIVE ME EIGHTY MEN: WOMEN & THE MYTH OF THE FETTERMAN FIGHT
Shannon D. Smith; Illus. 262 pp. University of Nebraska Press, 2008. $39.95.

GIVE OR TAKE A CENTURY: AN ESKIMO CHRONICLE
Joseph E. Senungetuk; The first professional, full-length work to be published by an Eskimo author. Illus. Map. 206 pp. Paper. Amazon.com, 1971. $6.

GIVING: OJIBWAY STORIES & LEGENDS FROM THE CHILDREN OF CURVE LAKE
Curve Lake Reserve, Canada; Paper. Amazon.com, $7.95.

*GIVING THANKS: A NATIVE AMERICAN GOOD MORNING MESSAGE
Jake Swamp; Reprint. Grades K-5. Illus. 24 pp. Paper. Lee & Low Books, 1997. $5.95.

GIVING VOICE TO BEAR: NORTH AMERICAN INDIAN MYTHS, RITUALS, & IMAGES OF THE BEAR David Rockwell; Stories, both oral and written, in which rituals describe the bear as central to initiation, shamanic rites, healing & hunting ceremonies, and New Year celebrations. Revised ed. Illus. 240 pp. Paper. Roberts Rinehart Publishers, 2003. $19.95.

THE GLACIAL KAME INDIANS
Converse; Photos of shell and slate artifacts.159 pp. Hothem House, 1979. $20.

GLASS TAPESTRY: PLATEAU BEADED BAGS FROM THE ELAINE HORWITCH COLLECTION Gloria Lomahaftewa; Illus. 56 pp. Paper. The Heard Museum, 1993. $15.

GLASS TRADE BEADS OF THE NORTHEAST & INCLUDING ABORIGINAL INDUSTRIES Gary L. Fogelman, Ed; Reprint. Illus. 44 pp. Paper. Amazon.com, 1991. $15.

GLEN CANYON: AN ARCHAEOLOGICAL SUMMARY
Jesse D. Jennings; A valuable perspective on Pueblo culture. Illus. Maps. Paper. University of Utah Press, $14.95.

GLEN CANYON REVISITED
Phil R. Geib; Illus. Paper. University of Utah Press, $34.50.

GLIMPSES OF THE ANCIENT SOUTHWEST
David E. Stuart; Describes the prehistoric life in Chaco Canyon, Folsom, esa Verde, Bandelier, Mibres, and other sites. Illus. Maps. 128 pp. Paper. Amazon.com, $10.95.

GLIMPSES OF HISTORY: THE SAN GORGONIO PASS IN THE 19TH CENTURY
Netty Kikumi Meltzer & Louis Doody; Focuses on the story of the Cahuilla people of Southern California's San Gorgonio Pass. 30 pp. Paper. Malki-Ballena Press, 2010. $9.95.

GLITTERING WORLD: NAVAJO JEWELRY OF THE YAZZIE FAMILY
Loiis Sherr Dubin; Illus. 272 pp. NMAI Press, 2014. $50.

THE GLORIOUS QUEST OF CHIEF WASHAKIE
Mary H. Tillman & Ralph Tillman
Illus. 60 pp. Paper. Amazon.com & Alibris.com, 1998. $8.95.

GO SEEK THE POW WOW ON THE MOUNTAIN: & OTHER INDIAN STORIES OF THE SACANDAGA VALLEY
Don Bowman; Illus. 116 pp. Paper. Amazon.com, 1993. $12.95.

GOALS & PRIORITIES OF SOUTH DAKOTA TRIBES: HEARING BEFORE THE COMMITTEE ON INDIAN AFFAIRS
107th U.S. Congress, 2nd Session; 115 pp. U.S. GPO, 2003.

GOD IS RED: A NATIVE VIEW OF RELIGION
Vine Deloria, Jr.; new foreword by George Tinker & Leslie Marmon Silko
Native American religious views. 2003 revised ed. 325 pp. Paper. Fulcrum Publishing, $50.

GODS OF PROPHETSTOWN: THE BATTLE OF TIPPECANOE AND THE HOLY WAR FOR THE AMERICAN FRONTIER Adam Jortner; Oxford University Press, 2011. $27.95.

GOING INDIAN
James Hamill; Explores Indian ethnic identity among Native American people in Oklahoma through their telling, in their own words, of how they became Indian and what being Indian means to them today. Illus. 232 pp. Paper. U. of Illinois Press, 2006. $21.

GOING NATIVE
Tom Harmer; Illus. 283 pp. Paper. University of New Mexico Press, 2001. $24.95.

GOING NATIVE: AMERICAN INDIAN COOKERY
165 pp. Paper. Seattle Indian Services Commission, 1991. $14.95.

GOING NATIVE OR GOING NAÏVE? WHITE SHAMANISM & THE NEO-NOBLE SAVAGE Dagmar Wernitznig; 146 pp. Paper. University Press of America, Dist. By Rowman & Littlfield, 2003. $50.99.

GOING NATIVE: INDIANS IN THE AMERICAN CULTURAL IMAGINATION
Shari M. Huhndorf; Illus. 240 pp. Paper. Cornell University Press, 2001. $23.95.

THE GOLDEN WOMAN: THE COLVILLE NARRATIVE OF PETER J. SEYMOUR
Anthony Mattina, Editor; Northwest Indian version of a European folktale. 357 pp. University of Arizona Press, 1985. $34.95.

A GOOD CHEROKEE, A GOOD ANTHROPOLOGIST: PAPERS IN HONOR OF ROBERT K. THOMAS edited by Steve Pavlik; Collection of essays and personal anecdotes that illuminate the writings and life of Bob Thomas. 390 pp. Amazon.com, 1998. $40; paper, $25.

A GOOD INDIAN
E.J. Rath; Reprint of 1927 edition. Novel. Paper. Fprt Umbleweed, $14.95.

GOOD INTENTIONS GONE AWRY: EMMA CROSBY & THE METHODIST MISSION ON THE NORTHWEST COAST Jan Hare & Jean Barman; A mission among the Tsimshian people. 344 pp. Paper. University of Washington Press, 2007. $94; paper, $33.95.

A GOOD MEDICINE COLLECTION; LIFE IN HARMONY WITH NATURE
Adolph Hungry Wolf; Legends, lore, and spiritual seeking of North America's Native people. Illus. 200 pp. Paper. The Book Publishing Co., 1990. $9.95.

*THE GOOD RAINBOW ROAD
Simon J. Ortiz; illus. by Michael Lacapa
Story of two boys and how they saved their village. In the tradition of Native American oral storytelling. Grades 3 and up. Illus. 80 pp. University of Arizona Press, 2004. $16.95.

THE GOOD RED ROAD: PASSAGES INTO NATIVE AMERICA
Kenneth Lincoln & Al L. Slagle; Illus. 286 pp. Paper. U. of Nebraska Press, 1997. $13.

A GOOD YEAR TO DIE: THE STORY OF THE GREAT SIOUX WAR
Charles M. Robinson, III
Illus. Maps. Photos. Biblio. 428 pp. Paper. University of Oklahoma Press, 1996. $16.95.

*GOODBIRD THE INDIAN: HIS STORY
Edward Goodbird as told to Gilbert L. Wilson
Reprint of 1914 edition. Mandan/Hidatsa on Fort Berthold Reservation. Grades 7 and up. Illus. 110 pp. Paper. Fort Tumbleweed, $29.95.

GOVERNMENT TO GOVERNMENT: MODELS OF COOPERATION BETWEEN STATES & TRIBES Susan Johnson; 88 pp. Amazon.com, 2002. $20.

GRENVILLE GOODWIN AMONG WESTERN APACHE: LETTERS FROM THE FIELD
Morris E. Opler, Editor
Reprint of 1973 ed. 104 pp. University of Arizona Press, $19.95.

R.C. GORMAN'S ENGAGEMENT CALENDAR
10.5 x 12.5". RCGormanGifts.com, $12.

R.C. GORMAN'S NUDES & FOODS: IN GOOD TASTE
R.C. Gorman; compiled & edited by Virginia Dooley
Cookbook. 55 color art reproductions. 142 pp. Amazon.com, 1993. $34.95.

*THE GOSPEL OF THE GREAT SPIRIT
Joshua M. Bennett; Grades 8 and up. Illus. Morning Star Publishing, 1990. $21.

THE GOSPEL OF THE REDMAN, A WAY OF LIFE
Ernest T. Seton; Reprint of 1930 edition. Compilation of Indian thought & culture. Illus. 112 pp. Paper. Naturegraph, $6.95.

GOVERNING GAMBLING
John Lyman Mason & Michael Nelson
Illus. 132 pp. Paper. The Century Foundation, 2001. $13.95.

A GRAMMAR & DICTIONARY OF THE TIMUCUA LANGUAGE
Julian Granberry; Describes the grammar and lexicon of the extinct 17th-century Timucua language of Central and North Florida. 352 pp. Paper. U. of Alabama Press, 1993. $29.95.

A GRAMMAR OF BELLA COOLA
Philip W. Davis & Ross Saunders; Describes the major syntactic and morphological patterns of Bella Coola (NuXalk), a Salishan laguage of British Columbia. 190 pp. paper. Amazon.com, 1997. $20.

A GRAMMAR OF COMANCHE
Jean Ormsbee Charney; 275 pp. University of Nebraska Press, 1994. $55.

A GRAMMAR OF CREEK (MUSKOGEE)
Jack B. Martin; Illus. Maps. 504 pp. University of Nebraska Press, 2011. $75.

A GRAMMAR OF CROW
Randolph Graczyk; Detailed description of the Crow language in a contemporary linguistic framework. Illus. 474 pp. University of Nebraska Press, 2007. $75.

A GRAMMAR OF DELAWARE SEMANTICS, MORPHO-SYNTAX, LEXICON, & PHONOLOGY Bruce L. Pearson; A PhD dissertation providing detailed information on the Lenape language. 236 pp. Paper. Amazon.com, $31.95.

GRAMMAR OF THE LANGUAGE OF THE LENNI LENAPE, OR DELAWARE INDIANS
David Zeisberger; Peter S. Du Ponceau, Tr.; Reprint. Amazon.com, $23.95; paper, $7.95.

A GRAMMAR OF THE MASSACHUSETTS INDIAN LANGUAGE 1822
John Eliot; Reprint. Illus. Paper. Kessinger Publishing, 2005. $20.95.

A GRAMMAR OF MISANTLA TOTONAC
Carolyn MacKay; Grammar of the Totonac-Tepehua language in English. Illus. Maps. University of Utah Press. $55.

GRAND ENDEAVORS OF AMERICAN INDIAN PHOTOGRAPHY
Paula Richardson Fleming & Judith Lynch Luskey
Illus. Smithsonian Institution Press, $39.95.

GRAND MOUND
Michael K. Budak; Minnesota historic site of Woodland people 2,500 years ago. Photos. 32 pp. Paper. Minnesota Historical Society Press, 1995. $7.50.

THE GRAND PORTAGE STORY
Carolyn Gilman; History of legendary fur-trade crossroads in northern Minnesota. Illus. Photos. Maps. Biblio. 168 pp. Paper. Minnestoa Historical Society Press, $9.95.

*GRANDCHILDREN OF THE LAKOTA
LaVera Rose; Young readers learn how Lakota children live. Grades 3-6. Color photos. Lerner, 1999. $16.95.

*GRANDFATHER GREY OWL TOLD ME
Althea Bass; Grades 4 and up. Paper. Council on Indian Education, 1973. $1.95.

GRANDFATHER: A NATIVE AMERICAN'S LIFELONG SEARCH FOR TRUTH & HARMONY WITH NATURE Tom Brown; 210 pp. Paper. Amazon.com, 2001. $12.95.

*GRANDFATHER & THE POPPING MACHINE
Henry Tall Bull & Tom Weist
Grades 2-12. 32 pp. Council for Indian Education, 1970. $8.95; paper, $2.95.

*GRANDFATHER ORIGIN STORY: THE NAVAJO INDIAN BEGINNING
Richard Redhawk; Grades 3-6. 34 pp. Paper. Sierra Oaks, 1988. $6.95.

THE GRANDFATHERS SPEAK: NATIVE AMERICAN FOLK TALES OF THE LENAPE PEOPLE Hitakonanulaxk
160 pp. Amazon.com, 1994. $24.95; paper, $11.95.

GRANDMA WAS AN INDIAN PRINCESS
Donna Akers; Illus. Paper. University of Nebraska Press, 2012.

*GRANDMOTHER FIVE BASKETS
Lisa Larrabee & Lori Sawyer; 12-year old Anna finds it fun to help Grandmother Five Baskets basket weave (Poarch Creek). Grades 3-7. 64 pp. Amazon.com, $14.95; paper, $9.95.

GRANDMOTHER, GRANDFATHER, & OLD WOLF
Clifford E. Trafzer; Collection of oral literature presented by Plateau Indian men & women. Michigan State University Press, 1997.

*GRANDMOTHER SPIDER BRINGS THE SUN: A CHEROKEE STORY
Geri Keams; Illus. by James Bernardin
Picture book. Ages 5-8. Illus. Paper. Northland Press & Amazon.com, 1992. $7.95.

*GRANDMOTHER STORIES: NORTHWESTERN INDIAN TALES
Nashone; Grades 5-12. Illus. Paper. Sierra Oaks, 1987. $5.95.

*GRANDMOTHER'S CHRISTMAS STORY: A TRUE QUECHAN INDIAN STORY
Grades 3-7. Illus. Paper. Amazon.com, $6.95.

GRANDMOTHER'S GRANDCHILD: MY CROW INDIAN LIFE
Alma Hogan Snell; edited by Becky Matthews
Illus. Maps. 215 pp. Paper. University of Nebraska Press, 2001. $14.95.

GRANDMOTHERS OF THE LIGHT: A MEDICINE'S WOMAN'S SOURCEBOOK
Paula Gunn Allen; 250 pp. Paper. Amazon.com, 1991. $19.95.

GRANDPA LOLO'S NAVAJO SADDLE BLANKET: LA TILMA DE ABUELITO LOLO
Nasario Garcia; photos by Richard Moeller
Bilingual tale. Paper. University of New Mexico Press, $19.95

GRANDPA WAS A COWBOY & AN INDIAN & OTHER STORIES
Virginia Driving Hawk Sneve; A Lakota storyteller and stories based on oral traditions. 116 pp. Paper. University of Nebraska Press, 2000. $11.95.

GRASS DANCE COSTUME
William K. Powers; Illus. 16 pp. Paper. Lakota Books & Amazon.com, 1994. $10.95.

GRASS DANCE OF THE SPIRIT LAKE DAKOTA
Louise Garcia with Mark Dietrich; Illus. 189 pp. Lakota Books, 2014. $24.95.

GRASS GAMES & MOON RACES: CALIFORNIA INDIAN GAMES & TOYS
Jeannine Gendar; Dozens of traditional games are described through personal accounts, anecdotes, photographs, and drawings. Photos. Illus. 128 pp. Paper. Heyday Books & Malki-Ballena Press, $14.95.

GRASS HEART: A NOVEL
M.M.B. Walsh; In 1837, a smallpox epidemic devastated the Mandan Indians of the Great Plains. This novel shows the horrifying reality of the epidemic Sioux slavery, cultural plundering by anthropologists, and exile. 176 pp. U. of New Mexico Press, 2001. $22.95.

GRASSHOPPER PUEBLO: A STORY OF ARCHAEOLOGY & ANCIENT LIFE
Jefferson Reid & Stephanie Whittlesley; Life & times of Mogollon community of the 14th century in the American Southwest. Illus. 192 pp. U. of Arizona Press, 1999. $16.95.

GRAVE CONCERNS, TRICKSTER TURNS: THE NOVELS OF LOUIS OWENS
Chris LaLonde; Illus. 240 pp. University of Oklahoma Press, 2002. $25.95.

GRAVE INJUSTICE: AMERICAN INDIAN REPATRIATION MOVEMENT & NAGPRA
Kathleen S. Fine-Dare; Illus. 250 pp. U. of Nebraska Press, 2002. $60; paper, $19.95.

*GRAY WOLF'S SEARCH
Bruce Swanson; illus. by Gary Peterson; Grades 1-4. 24 pp. Amazn.com, 2007. $16.95.

GREAT AMERICAN INDIAN BIBLE
Homer "Louis" Hooban, Editor; Indian Amazon.com, 1990.

*GREAT BALL GAME OF THE BIRDS & ANIMALS
Deborah L. Duvall; illus. by Murv Jacob; Vol. 1 of the Grandmother Stories. Cherokee history & legend. Winner of the 2003 Oklahoma Book Award for Design and Illustration. All ages. Illus. 32 pp. University of New Mexico Press, $14.95.

GREAT BASIN ATLATL STUDIES
T.R. Hester; R.F. Heizer, Editor; Illus. 60 pp. Paper. Ballena Press, 1974. $6.95.

GREAT BASIN INDIAN POPULATION FIGURES (1873 TO 1970) & THE PITFALLS THEREIN BOUND WITH BIG SMOKEY VALLEY SHOSHONI
Joy Leland; Illus. 276 pp. 2 Vols. University of Nevada Systems, 1976. $11.00 per set.

*THE GREAT CHANGE
White Deer of Autumn (Gabriel Horn); A tale of a wise grandmother explaining a meaning of death to her questioninf granddaughter. Grades 3 and up. Illus. 36 pp. Levite of Apache & Beyond Words Publishing, 1992. $14.95.

*THE GREAT CHIEFS
B. Capps; Grades 7-12. Illus. Amazo.com, 1975. $19.94.

THE GREAT CHIEFS
William W. Johnson; Illus. 240 pp. Amazon.com, 1975. $14.95.

THE GREAT CONFUSION IN INDIAN AFFAIRS: NATIVE AMERICANS & WHITES IN THE PROGRESSIVE ERA Tom Holm; The attempt of the U.S. Government to assimilate Native Americans. 264 pp. Paper. University of Texas Press, 2005. $21.95

GREAT CRUELTIES HAVE BEEN REPORTED: THE 1544 INVESTIGATIONS OF THE CORONADO EXPEDITION
Richard Flint; Illus. 665 pp. Paper. University of New Mexico Press, , 2001. $65.

THE GREAT ENCOUNTER: NATIVE PEOPLES & EUROPEAN SETTLERS IN THE AMERICAS Jayme A. Sokolow; Illus. 310 pp. M.E. Sharpe, 2002. $68.95; paper, $25.95.

GREAT EXCAVATIONS: TALES OF EARLY SOUTHWESTERN ARCHAEOLOGY, 1888-1939 Melinda Elliott; Stories of the early Southwestern archaeologists. Illus. 230 pp. School of American Research, 1995.

THE GREAT FATHER: THE U.S. GOVERNMENT & THE AMERICAN INDIANS
Francis Paul Prucha; Detailed chronological overview of the interaction between the federal government and Indian tribes. Abridged edition. Illus. Maps. 426 pp. Paper. University of Nebraska Press, 1986. $36.95.

GREAT FLORIDA SEMINOLE TRAIL: COMPLETE GUIDE TO SEMINOLE INDIAN HISTORIC & CULTURAL SITES Doug Alderson
240 pp. Paper. Pineapple Press, $14.95.

GREAT HOUSE COMMUNITIES ACROSS THE CHACOAN LANDSCAPE
John F. Kantner; Illus. 192 pp. Paper. University of Arizona Press, 2000. $17.95.

*GREAT INDIAN CHIEFS
50 stories of the great chiefs. Grades 3-5. Illus. Paper. Bellerophon, $3.95.

*GREAT INDIANS OF CALIFORNIA
Maurice Vallejo, et al.
Coloring book. Grades K-3. 48 pp. Paper. Bellerophon, 1981. $4.95.

THE GREAT JOURNEY: THE PEOPLING OF ANCIENT AMERICA
Brian Fagan; Illus. 288 pp. Paper. Thames & Hudson, 1987. $12.95.

THE GREAT KIVA
Phillips Kloss; Poetry. Illus. 112 pp. Paper. Sunstone Press, $14.95.

GREAT LAKES INDIAN ACCOMMODATION & RESISTANCE DURING THE EARLY RESERVATION YEARS, 1850-1900 Edmund Jefferson Danziger, Jr.
Photos. Maps. 336 pp. University of Michigan Press, 2009. $60.

GREAT LAKES INDIANS
Amazon.com, 2004. $14.99.

THE GREAT LAW & THE LONGHOUSE: A POLITICAL HISTORY OF THE IROQUOIS CONFEDERACY
William N. Fenton; Illus. Maps. 808 pp. Paper. U. of Oklahoma Press, 1998. $49.95.

*GREAT NATIVE AMERICANS COLORING BOOK
Peter F. Copeland; Grades K-2. 48 pp. Paper. Dover, $2.95.

THE GREAT PEACE: CHRONICLE OF A DIPLOMATIC SAGA
Alain Beaulieu & Roland Viau; Negotiations between the French, their Native allies, and the Iroquois. Illus. 128 pp. Paper. University of Washington Press, 2002. $35.

THE GREAT PEACE OF MONTREAL OF 1701: FRENCH-NATIVE DIPLOMACY IN THE 17TH CENTURY
Gilles Havard; Illus. 310 pp. McGill-Queens University Press, 2001.

GREAT PLAINS: NATIVE NATIONS
Christopher Cardozo; Robert Janjigan, Editor
Illus. 96 pp. Callaway Editions, 1997. $13.95.

A GREAT PLAINS READER
Zitkala-Sa, Editor; Illus. Paper. University of Nebraska Press, 2003.

GREAT SALT LAKE TRAIL
H. Inman and W.F. Cody; Reprint of 1897 edition. Illus. Amazon.com, $15.

THE GREAT SIOUX NATION: SITTING IN JUDGMENT ON AMERICA
Roxanne Dunbar Ortiz; Illus 232 pp. Paper. University of Nebraska Press, 2013. $21.95.

THE GREAT SIOUX TRAIL
Joseph Altsheler; 1990. Reprint. Amazon.com, $21.95.

THE GREAT SIOUX UPRISING, VOL. 3
C.M. Oehler; Reprint. Illus. 290 pp. Paper. Amazon.com, 1997. $17.50

GREAT SIOUX UPRISING: REBELLION ON THE PLAINS, AUGUST-SEPT.. 1862
Jerry Kennan; Illus. 104 pp. Paper. Amazon.com, 2003. $17.95.

THE GREAT SIOUX WAR: THE BEST FROM MONTANA, THE MAGAZINE OF WESTERN HISTORY Paul L. Heden
Illus. 330 pp. Montana Historical Society Press, 1991. $27.50; paper, $11.95.

GREAT SIOUX WAR ORDERS OF BATTLE: HOW THE U.S. ARMY WAGED WAR ON THE NORTHERN PLAINS, 1876-1877
Paul L. Hedren; Illus. Map. Tables. 240 pp. University of Oklahoma Press, 2011. Leatherbound, $150. Hardbound available.

THE GREAT SOUTHWEST OF THE FRED HARVEY COMPANY & THE SANTA FE RAILWAY Marta Weigle & Barbara Babcock, Editors
Illus. 270 pp. Paper. University of Arizona Press, 1996. $24.95.

GREAT SPEECHES BY NATIVE AMERICANS
Bob Blaisdell, Editor; Paper. Eagle's View Publishing, $2.95.

GREAT SPIRIT: NORTH AMERICAN INDIAN PORTRAITS
Edward McAndrews; Illus. 105 pp. Paper. Amazon.com, 1997. $20.

GREAT SPIRIT: NORTH AMERICAN INDIAN PORTRAITS
Edward McAndrews; Illus. 104 pp. Paper. Amazon.com, 1997. $20.

GREAT WESTERN INDIAN FIGHTS
Potomac Coral of the Westerners
Illus. 352 pp. Paper. University of Nebraska Press, 1966. $7.95.

GREATFUL PREY: ROCK CREE HUMAN-ANIMAL RELATIONSHIPS
Robert Brightman; 410 pp. Univesity of California Press, 1993. $55.

GREENGRASS PIPE DANCERS: CRAZY HORSE'S PIPE BAG & A SEARCH FOR HEALING Lionel Little Eagle; Story of trips to sundances with Crazy Horse's pipe bag. 256 pp. Paper. Naturegraph, 1999. $14.95.

GREY HAWK
John Tanner; 340 pp. Paper. Amazon.com 2004. $20.95.

GREY OWL: THE MYSTERY OF ARCHIE BELANEY
Armand G. Ruffo; Illus. 224 pp. Paper. Coteau Books, 1997.

GROS VENTRE OF MONTANA
Regina Flannery; Reprint of 1956 edition. Two volumes: Volume 1: Social Life; Volume 2: Religion and Ritual. Illus. Gros Ventre Treaty, $21.00 per set.

*GROWING UP IN SIOUXLAND
Arthur R. Huseboe & Sandra Looney
Grades 4 and up. Illus. 74 pp. Paper. Center for Western Studies, $5.

*GROWING UP INDIAN
Evelyn Wolfson; illus. by William Sauts Bock; Grades 4-8. Illus. 96 pp. Paper. Walker & Co., 1986. Available on Amazon.com & Barnes & Noble.com. $8.95.

GROWING UP NATIVE AMERICAN: AN ANTHOLOGY
Patricia Riley, Editor; foreword by Ines Hernandez
Stories of Oppression & Survival of Heritage Denied & Reclaimed. Black Elk, Louis Erdrich, N. Scott Momaday, Linda Hogan, Michael Doris,. 336 pp. Amazn.com, 1993. $18.55.

GROWING UP NATIVE IN ALASKA
Alexandra J. McClanahan; Illus. 389 pp. Todd Communications, 2001. $19.95.

*GUARDIAN SPIRIT QUEST
Ella Clark; Grades 5-10. 36 pp. Paper. Council for Indian Education,1974. $4.95.

GUESTS NEVER LEAVE HUNGRY: THE AUTOBIOGRAPHY OF JAMES SEWID, A KWAKIUTL INDIAN James Sewid; James P. Spradley, Editor
Reprint of 1969 edition. Illus. 310 pp. University of Toronto Press, 1969. $16.95.

GUIDE TO AMERICAN INDIAN DOCUMENTS IN THE CONGRESSIONAL SERIAL SET: 1817-1899 Steven L. Johnson; 503 pp. N. Ross, 1977. $35.

A GUIDE TO AMERICA'S INDIANS: CEREMONIALS, RESERVATIONS & MUSEUMS
Arnold Marquis; Illus. Maps. 268 pp. Paper. University of Oklahoma Press, 1974. $19.95.

A GUIDE TO THE ANASAZI & OTHER ANCIENT SOUTHWEST INDIANS
Eleanor Ayer; Illus. Map. 48 pp. Paper. Renaissance House, 1991. $4.95.

A GUIDE TO CHEROKEE DOCUMENTS IN FOREIGN ARCHIVES
William L. Anderson and James A. Lewis; 768 pp. Scarecrow Press, 1983. $40.

A GUIDE TO CHEROKEE DOCUMENTS IN THE NORTHEASTERN U.S.
Paul Kutsche; 541 pp. Scarecrow Press, 1986. $109.45.

A GUIDE TO COMMUNITY EDUCATION
Institute of the Development of Indian Law, $7.50.

GUIDE TO CONTEMPORARY SOUTHWEST INDIANS
Bernard Fontana; Illus. 96 pp. Paper. Western National Parks Assn., 1999. $10.95.

GUIDE TO THE CULIN ARCHIVAL COLLECTION
Deirdre E. Lawrence & Deborah Wythe, Editors; The Brooklyn Museum, 1996.

GUIDE TO FEDERAL FUNDING FOR GOVERNMENTS & NONPROFITS: NATIVE AMERICAN EDITION Describes general assistance funds for which Native Americans are eligible. Covers federal programs that are relevant to Indian Tribal governments, Indian villages, nonprofits serving Native American needs, and state and local governments encompassing Native American populations. 3 Volumes. 2,456 pages. Amazon.com. $329.95, includes 12 monthly grant updates.

GUIDE TO FEDERAL INITIATIVES FOR URBAN ABORIGINAL PEOPLE
Canada Privy Council Office Staff; Amazon.com, 1997.

GUIDE TO THE 400 BEST CHILDREN'S & ADULT'S MULTICULTURAL BOOKS OF PEOPLE OF NATIVE AMERICAN DESCENT
Anna D. Friedler; 60 pp. Spiral bound. Amazon.com, 1997. $29.95

GUIDE TO HOHOKAM POTTERY
Jan Barstad; Illus. 48 pp. Paper. Western National Parks Assn., 1999. $4.95.

GUIDE TO INDIAN ARTIFACTS OF THE NORTHEAST
Roger W. Moeller; Illus. 32 pp. Paper. Hancock House, 1984. $3.95.

GUIDE TO INDIAN HERBS
Ray Stark; Margaret Campbell; Illus. 48 pp. Paper. Hancock House, 1984. $7.95.

GUIDE TO INDIAN JEWELRY OF THE SOUTHWEST
Georgiana K. Simpson; Illus. 32 pp. Paper. Western National Parks Assn, 1999. $4.95.

GUIDE TO INDIAN QUILLWORKING
C. Ann Hensler; Illus. 64 pp. Paper. Hancock House, 1989. $8.95.

GUIDE TO INDIAN ROCK CARVINGS OF THE PACIFIC NORTHWEST COAST
Illus. 48 pp. Paper. Hancock House, 1984. $5.95.

A GUIDE TO THE INDIAN TRIBES OF THE PACIFIC NORTHWEST
Robert H. Ruby, John A. Brown, Cary Collins
Illus. Maps. 448 pp. 3rd edition. Paper. University of Oklahoma Press, 2010. $26.95.

A GUIDE TO THE INDIAN TRIBES OF OKLAHOMA
Muriel H. Wright
Reprint of 1951 edition. Illus. 320 pp. Paper. University of Oklahoma Press, 1997. $19.95.

A GUIDE TO THE INDIAN TRIBES OF THE PACIFIC NORTHWEST
Robert Ruby & John Brown
Third Edition. Illus. Maps. 304 pp. Paper. University of Oklahoma Press, 1986. $26.95.

A GUIDE TO THE INDIAN WARS OF THE WEST
John D. McDermott; Illus. Map. 211 pp. Paper. U. of Nebraska Press, 1998. $19.95.

THE GUIDE TO IOWA'S STATE PRESERVES
Ruth Herzbeeg & John Pearson; Native American relics & Indian mounds.
Maps. 214 pp. Paper. University of Iowa Press, 2001. $19.

GUIDE TO MULTICULTURAL RESOURCES, 1995-96
Alex Boyd, Editor; Current information on multicultural organizations, services and trends. Lists over 3,000 organizations including many Native American associations, institutions, and government agencies. 512 pp. Paper. Highsmith Press, $49.

GUIDE TO NATIVE AMERICAN MUSIC RECORDINGS
Greg Gombert, Ed.; Lists thousands of available recordings. Cassettes & CDs. 128 pp. Paper. Multi Culture Publishing, 1994. $12.95.

GUIDE TO NATIVE NORTH AMERICAN ARTISTS
Profiles 400 prominent artists of the 20th century. Includes a bibliography of books, galleries & museums with artist collections. 1st Ed. 690 pp. Amazon.com, 1999. $150.

GUIDE TO NAVAJO RUGS
Susan Lamb; Describes and depicts the 17 most common Navajo rug styles and includes quotes by some of the weavers. Color photos. 48 pp. Paper. Amazon.com, $4.95.

GUIDE TO NAVAJO RUGS
Kent McManis & Robert Jeffries
Illus. over 50 rug types available to the collector today. Illus. Paper. Amazon.com, $9.95.

GUIDE TO NAVAJO SANDPAINTINGS
Mark Bahti & Eugene Joe
2nd revised Ed. Illus. 56 pp. Paper. Treasure Chest Books, 2004. $9.95.

GUIDE TO THE NORTH AMERICAN ETHNOGRAPHIC COLLECTIONS AT THE UNIVERSITY OF PENNSYLVANIA
Lucy Fowler Williams; Illus. 96 pp. U. Museum Publications, 2003. $29.95; paper, $14.95.

A GUIDE TO OREGON SOUTH COAST HISTORY: TRAVELING THE JEDADIAH SMITH TRAIL Nathan Douthit; Overview of South Coast history with in depth look at the region's native peoples; Indian-white warfare. Paper. Oregon State University Press, 1999. $22.95.

GUIDE TO THE PALAEO-INDIAN ARTIFACTS OF NORTH AMERICA
Richard M. Gramly; 2nd revised edition. An authoritative treatment of the variety of stone, bone, ivory and antler artifacts at North American Palaeo-Indian sites from Alaska to Florida. Illus. 90 pp. Paper. Amazon.com & Hothem House, 1992. $15.95.

GUIDE TO PREHISTORIC RUINS OF THE SOUTHWEST
Oppelt; Surveys many prehistoric sites, and provides background facts.
Illus. 208 pp. Paper. Pruett Publishing, $12.95.

A GUIDE TO PROJECTILE POINTS OF IOWA, PARTS 1 & 2
Joseph A. Tiffany; photos by Christian A. Driver; Part 1: Paleoindian, Late Paleoindian, Early Archaic, & Middle Archaic Points; Part 2: Middle Archaic, Late Archaic, Woodland, & Late Prehistoric Points. Laminated fold-out guide. Illus. Photos. University of Iowa Press, 2009. $9.95 each.

A GUIDE TO PROPOSAL WRITING
Institute of the Development of Indian Law, $7.50.

A GUIDE TO PUEBLO POTTERY
Susan Lamb; Color photos and full descriptions of the 18 most collectible pottery styles of the Southwest. 48 pp. Paper. Amazon.com, $3.95.

GUIDE TO THE RECORDS AT THE NATIONAL ARCHIVES-LOS ANGELES BRANCH
GUIDE TO RECORDS IN NATIONAL ARCHIVES RELATING TO AMERICAN INDIANS
Edward E. Hill, Compiler; Illus. 468 pp. & 368 pp. Smithsonian Institution Press, 1981. $25.

GUIDE TO THE RECORDS OF THE THE MORAVIAN MISSION AMONG THE INDIANS OF NORTH AMERICA 111 pp. Paper. Primary Source Media, 1983. $80.

GUIDE TO RESEARCH ON NORTH AMERICAN INDIANS
Arlene B. Hirschfelder; A basic guide to the literature for general readers, students, and scholars interested in the study of American Indians. 340 pp. American Library Association, 1983. $75.

GUIDE TO ROCK ART OF THE UTAH REGION: SITES WITH PUBLIC ACCESS
Dennis Slifer; Illus. Photos. 46 maps. 255 pp. Paper. Amazon.com, 2002. $16.95.

THE GUIDE TO TRADING POSTS & PUEBLOS
Gian Mercurio & Max Peschel; Illus. 72 pp. Paper. Amazon.com, 1994. $8.95.

A GUIDE TO UNDERSTANDING CHIPPEWA TREATY RIGHTS
Booklet. GLIFWC, 1991. No charge

A GUIDE TO ZUNI FETISHES & CARVING
Kent McManis; Vol. 1: The Animals & the Carvers. Color photos. 56 pp. Vol. 2: The Materials & the Carvers. Photos. 64 pp. Paper. Treasure Chest Books, 2003. $8.95 each.

GUIDING YOUR CHILD IN SPEAKING THE LAKOTA LANGUAGE
Three years with CD, $17.95 each year. Lakota Books.

GULF COAST ARCHAEOLOGY: THE SOUTHEASTERN U.S. & MEXICO
Nancy Marie White; Illus. 432 pp. University Press of Florida, 2005. $65.

GUNBOAT FRONTIER: BRITISH MARITIME AUTHORITY & NORTHWEST COAST INDIANS, 1846-1890 Barry M. Gough; Indian-white relations in the 19th-century British Columbia. Illus. 320 pp. University of Washington Press, 1984. $83.

GUNS ACROSS THE LOXAHATCHEE: AN ARCHAEOLOGICAL INVESTIGATION OF SEMINOLE WAR SITES Illus. 200 pp. Paper. Richard J. Procyk, 1999. $17.95.

GUNS ON THE EARLY FRONTIERS: A HISTORY OF FIREARMS FROM COLONIAL TIMES THROUGH THE YEARS OF THE WESTERN FUR TRADE
Carl P. Russell; 395 pp. University of Nebraska Press, 1980. $28.95.

GUNS OF THE WESTERN INDIAN WAR
Dorsey; Examines Indian weapons from a base collection of 410. Photos. 220 pp. Paper. Hothem House, 1995. $30.

GYAEHLINGAAY: TRADITIONS, TALES, & IMAGES OF THE KAIGANI HAIDA
Carol M. Eastman & Elizabeth A. Edwards; Provides the historical, cultural, and linguistic background of each story. Illus. 138 pp. Paper. University of Washington Press, $22.50.

H

HAA AANI, OUR LAND: TLINGIT & HAIDA LAND RIGHTS & USE
Walter Goldschmidt; Thomas F. Thornton, Ed.
Illus. Maps. 260 pp. Paper. University of Washington Press, 1999. $37.95.

HAA KUSTEEYI, OUR CULTURE: TLINGIT LIFE STORIES
Nora Marks & Richard Dauenhauer, Editor
Introduction to Tlingit social & political history featuring biographies and life histories of 50+ men & women. Illus. 600 pp. Paper. University of Washington Press, 1994. $44.95.

HAA SHUKA, OUR ANCESTORS: TLINGIT ORAL NARRATIVES
Nora Marks & Richard Dauenhauer
A Tlingit author tells stories that deal with "coming of age, alienation, identity and self concept," etc. Illus. 532 pp. Paper. University of Washington Press, 1987. $37.95.

HAA TUWUNAAGU YIS, FOR HEALING OUR SPIRIT: TLINGIT ORATORY
Nora Marks & Richard Dauenhauer, Editor; Tlingit texts with English translations & detailed annotations; biographies of the elders. Illus. Biblio. 606 pp. Paper. University of Washington Press, 1991. $32.95.

HABOO: NATIVE AMERICAN STORIES FROM PUGET SOUND
Vi Hilbert, Editor & Translator; Stories & legends of the Lushootseed-speaking people of Puget Sound. Illus. Map. 228 pp. Paper. University of Washington Press, 1985. $27.95.

HAIDA ART
George F. MacDonald; Illus. 256 pp. University of Washington Press, 1996. $60.

HAIDA GWAII: HUMAN HISTORY & ENVIRONMENT FROM THE TIME OF LOON TO THE TIME OF THE IRON PEOPLE
Daryl W. Fedje & Rolf W. Mathews, Editors; The past environment & culture of Haida Gwaii. Illus. Tables. 352 pp. University of Washington Press, 2005. $105; paper, $39.95.

HAIDA MONUMENTAL ART: VILLAGES OF THE QUEEN CHARLOTTE ISLANDS
George F. MacDonald; Includes about 300 photos of houses & totem poles constructed by the Haida Indians of the Queen Charlotte Islands, British Columbia during the late 19th century. Illus. 240 pp. Paper. University of Washington Press, 1996. $39.95.

HAIDA: THE QUEEN CHARLOTTE ISLAND INDIANS: THEIR ART & CULTURE
Leslie Drew; Illus. 112 pp. Paper. Hancock House, 1996. $9.95.

HAIDA SYNTAX
John Enrico; Description of the syntax of two Haida dialects. Two vols. Map. 1,387 pp. University of Nebraska Press, 2003. $200.

HAIDA TEXTS & MYTHS: SKIDEGATE DIALECT
John R. Swanton, Editor
Reprint. 448 pp. Native American Book Publishing, $69; paper, $49.

HAIDA: THEIR ART & CULTURE
Leslie Drew; Illus. 111 pp. Paper. Hancock House, $7.95.

THE HAKO: SONG, PIPE, & UNITY IN A PAWNEE CALUMET CEREMONY
Alice Fletcher; Illus. 390 pp. Paper. University of Nebraska Press, 1996. $4.25.

HALFBREED CHRONICLES
Wendy Rose; Paper. University of New Mexico Press, $19.95.

HALF MOON WAY: THE PEYOTE RITUAL OF CHIEF WHITE BEAR
James H. Howard; Illus. 39 pp. Paper. Amazon.com, $14.95

HALF-SUN ON THE COLUMBIA: A BIOGRAPHY OF CHIEF MOSES
Robert H. Ruby & John A. Brown
Reprint of 1965 edition. Illus. Maps. 390 pp. Paper. University of Oklahoma Press, $18.95.

HALFBREED
Maria Campbell; A Canadian Metis tells you what it is like to be a half breed woman. 157 pp. Paper. University of Nebraska Press, 1982. $10.95.

THE HALL OF THE NORTH AMERICAN INDIAN
Hillel Burger & Ian Brown; Barbara Isaac, Editor
Illus. 135 pp. Paper. Peabody Museum, 1990. $25.

HALLMARKS OF THE SOUTHWEST: WHO MADE IT?
Indian Arts & Crafts Association Staff; Illus. 244 pp. Schiffer, 1989. $45.

JACOB HAMBLIN: HIS LIFE IN HIS OWN WORDS
Jacob Hamlin; Autobiography of a diplomat among Native Americans...his eye-witness life story. 172 pp. Paper. 1995. Amazon.com, $10.95.

THE HAN INDIANS: A COMPILATION OF ETHNOGRAPHIC & HISTORICAL DATA ON THE ALASKA--YUKON BOUNDARY AREA
Cornelius Osgood; Paper. Yale University, Anthropology, 1971. $7.50.

THE HAND OF THE ANCIENT ONE
Juanita P. Fike; 285 pp. UIM International, 2003. $5.

HAND TREMBLING, FRENZY WITCHCRAFT, & MOTH MADNESS: A STUDY OF NAVAJO SEIZURE DISORDERS
Jerrold E. Levy, et al; 176 pp. Paper. University of Arizona Press, 1987. $21.95.

HANDBOOK OF THE AMERICAN FRONTIER – FOUR CENTURIES OF INDIAN-WHITE RELATIONSHIPS, 5 Vols. J. Norman Heard; Vol. I: The Southeastern Woodlands - 421 pp. 1987. $66; Vol. II: The Northeastern Woodlands - 417 pp. 1990. $47.30; Vol. III: The Great Plains - 280 pp. 1993. $47.30; Vol. IV: The Far West - 400 pp. 1997. $77; Chronology, Bibliography, Index - 336 pp. 1998. $74.25. Scarecrow Press.

HANDBOOK OF AMERICAN INDIAN GAMES
Allan & Paulette Macfarlan; 150 authentic Indian games. Illus. 288 pp. Paper. Dover & Cherokee Publications, 1985. $7.95.

HANDBOOK OF THE AMERICAN INDIAN LANGUAGES
Franz Boas; 920 pp. U. of Chicago Press, Facs. ed. Reprint ed. Amazon.com, $35.

HANDBOOK OF AMERICAN INDIAN RELIGIOUS FREEDOM
Christopher Vecsey; 175 pp. Paper. Crossroad Publishing, 1991. $17.95.

A HANDBOOK OF CREEK (MUSCOGEE) GRAMMAR
Anna Bosch; Vocabulary, spelling, and pronunciation. 35 pp. Paper. Indian University Press, 1994 second printing. $7, postpaid.

HANDBOOK OF THE DELAWARE INDIAN LANGUAGE: THE ORAL TRADITION OF A NATIVE PEOPLE Scott Hayes Wenning; Reprint. 3,000 word vocabulary-grammar & pronunciation guide. Illus. 144 pp. Paper. Wennawoods Publishing, $9.95.

HANDBOOK OF FEDERAL INDIAN LAW
Felix S. Cohen, Editor; Standard reference work on federal Indian law. Reprint of 1942 edition. 662 pp. Amazon.com S. Hein, $95.

HANDBOOK OF FEDERAL INDIAN LAW WITH REFERENCE TABLES & INDEX
Felix S. Cohen; Reprint of 1941 edition. 686 pp. Amazon.com, $75.

HANDBOOK OF THE INDIANS OF CALIFORNIA
A. L. Kroeber; Reprint 1925 ed. Illus. 995 pp. Paper. Hothem House & Dover, $20.95.

HANDBOOK OF NATIVE AMERICAN HERBS
Alma R. Hutchens; Illus. 200 pp. Paper. Random House, 1992. $12.95.

HANDBOOK OF NATIVE AMERICAN LITERATURE
Andrew Wiget, Editor; Essays by over 40 Native American writers provides a guide to the oral & written literatures of Native Americans. Biblio. 616 pp. Paper. Garland, 1996. $24.95.

HANDBOOK OF NATIVE AMERICAN MYTHOLOGY
Dawn E. Bastian & Judy Mitchell
Paper. Oxford University Press & Amazon.com, 2008. $27.95.

HANDBOOK OF NORTH AMERICAN INDIANS
William C. Sturtevant & Wilcomb Washburn, Editors
A 20-volume encyclopedia summarizing knowledge about all Native peoples north of Mesoamerica, including cultures, history, languages, prehistory, and human biology. Vol. 4: History of Indian-White Relations, 852 pp., 1989, $51; Vol. 5: Arctic, 862 pp., 1984, $52; Vol. 6: Subarctic, 853 pp., 1981, $51; Vol. 7: Northwest Coast, 795 pp., 1990, $51; Vol. 8: California, 800 pp., 1978, $51; Vol. 9: Southwest - Puebloan Peoples, 701 pp., 1980, $49;

Vol. 10: Southwest - Non-Puebloan People, 868 pp., 1983, $52; Vol. 11: Great Basin, 868 pp., 1986, $52; Vol. 12: Plateau, 816 pp., 1998. $67; Vol. 13: Plains. 1392 pp., 2001. $101; Vol. 15: Northeast, 924 pp., 1979, $53 (also available from Hothem House, $58.50 postpaid); Vol. 17: Languages, 957 pp., 1997. $74. Volumes 1-3, 13-14, 16, & 18-20 are not yet published. Illus. Maps. Published by the Smithsonian Institution Press. Available from Rowman & Littlefield & Amazon.com.

A HANDBOOK OF NORTHEASTERN INDIAN MEDICINAL PLANTS
James A. Duke; Illus. 212 pp. Quarterman, 1986. $30.

HANDBOOK OF YOKUTS INDIANS
Frank F. Latta; 50th Anniversary reprint of 2md ed. Illus. 800 pp. Bear State Books, $75.

HANDGAME!
Bill Rathbun; A booklet describing the Indian gambling game.
Includes gambling and other songs. Amazon.com, $7.95.

THE HANDS FEEL IT: HEALING & SPIRIT PRESENCE AMONG A NORTHERN ALASKAN PEOPLE Edith Turner; Illus. 240 pp. paper. Amazon.com, 1996. $20.

THE HANDSOME PEOPLE: A HISTORY OF THE CROW INDIANS & THE WHITES
Charles Crane Bradley
Grades 8-adult. 310 pp. Council for Indian Education, $20.95; paper, $14.95.

HANO: A TEWA INDIAN COMMUNITY IN ARIZONA
Edward P. Dozier; Illus. 114 pp. Paper. Amazon.com, 1966. $29.99.

HAPPY HUNTING GROUNDS
Stanley Vestal; illus. by Frederick Weygold
Illus. 240 pp. Paper. University of Oklahoma Press, 2012. $19.95.

THE HARDIN WINTER CUNT
David Finster; Illus. 58 pp. Paper. Amazon.com, 1995. $21.95.

HARMONY BY HAND: ART OF THE SOUTHWEST INDIANS
Patrick Houlihan; Illus. 108 pp. Paper. Amazon.com, 1987. $16.95.

HARPER'S ANTHOLOGY OF TWENTIETH CENTURY NATIVE AMERICAN POETRY
Duane Niatum, Editor
Anthology of poetry by 30+ Native Americans. 432 pp. Paper. Amazon.com, 1988. $22.

LaDONNA HARRIS: A COMANCHE LIFE
LaDonna Harris; edited by H. Henrietta Stockel
Mrs. Harris discusses the importance of her Comanche values and life experiences.
Illus. 160 pp. Map. University of Nebraska Press, 2000. $30; paper, $16.95.

HART'S PREHISTORIC PIPE RACK
Hart; Covers prehistoric Indian pipes for the Mississippi River into the Eastern U.S.
Illus. 272 pp. Hothem House, 1978. $52, postpaid.

HARVEST OF SOULS: THE JESUIT MISSIONS IN NORTH AMERICA, 1632-1650
Carole Blackburn; Illus. 184 pp. CUP Services, 2000. $60.

HASINAI: A TRADITIONAL HISTORY OF THE CADDO CONFEDERACY
Vynola Newkumet & Howard Meredith; Illus. 168 pp. Texas A&M U. Press, 1988. $16.95.

THE HASINAIS: THE SOUTHERN CADDOANS AS SEEN BY THE EARLIEST EUROPEANS
Herbert Bolton; Illus. Maps. 208 pp. Paper. University of Oklahoma Press, 1987. $14.95.

A HAUNTING REVERENCE: MEDITATIONS ON A NORTHERN LAND
Kent Nerburn; Reprint. 192 pp. Paper. University of Minnesota Press, 1999. $14.95.

EMIL W. HAURY'S PREHISTORY OF THE AMERICAN SOUTHWEST
Emil W. Haury; J. Reid & D. Doyel, Editors
506 pp. Paper. University of Arizona Press, 1986. $ 28.95.

HAVASUPAI LEGENDS: RELIGION & MYTHOLOGY OF THE INDIANS OF GRAND CANYON Carma Smithson & Robert Euler; Illus. Paper. U. of Utah Press, 1994. $15.95.

*HAVASUPAI YEARS
Madge Knobloch; Journal of teacher teching on the Havasupai reservation in the bottom of the Grand Canyon in 1931-33. Grades 6 and up. 124 pp. Paper. Council for Indian Education, $8.95.

HAVSUW BAAJA: PEOPLE OF BLUE GREEN WATER
Lois Hurst; Revised 1985 edition. Havasupai Council, $18.

*JOHN HAWK: A SEMINOLE SAGA
Beatrice Levin; A novel recounting the horror and the hostilities of the Seminole wars. Grades 7 and up. Illus. 182 pp. Paper. Council for Indian Education & Roberts Rinehart, 1994. $9.95.

THE HAWK IS HUNGRY; & OTHER STORIES
D'Arcy McNickle; Birgit Hans, Editor; 16 stories by McNickle, one of the most influential Native Americans of this century. 180 pp. Paper. U. of Arizona Press, 1992. $17.95.

HAWK WOMAN DANCING WITH THE MOON
Tela S. Lake; Illus. 255 pp. Paper. M. Evans & Co., 1997. $14.95.

HE WALKED THE AMERICAS
L. Taylor Hansen; Illus. Amherst Press, 1963. $13.95.

HEAD & FACE MASKS IN NAVAHO CEREMONIALISM
Berard Haile; foreword by James Faris
Reprint of 1947 edition. Illus. Paper. University of Utah Press, $15.95.

HEADED UPSTREAM: INTERVIEWS WITH ICONOCLASTS
Jack Loeffler; Illus. 168 pp. Paper. Amazon.com, 1989. $10.95.

THE HEALING BLANKET: STORIES, VALUES & POETRY FROM OJIBWE ELDERS & TEACHERS Blackwolf Jones & Gina Jones; Paper. Amazon.com, 2001, $15.

HEALING HERBS OF THE UPPER RIO GRANDE: TRADITIONAL MEDICINE OF THE SOUTHWEST L.M.S. Curtin; Illus. 280 pp. Paper. Mountain Press. $14.95.

HEALING & MENTAL HEALTH FOR NATIVE AMERICANS: SPEAKING IN RED
Ethan Nebelkopf & Mary Phillips; 11th Ed. 240 pp. AltaMira Press, 2004. $94; paper, $36; eBook, $34.99.

A HEALING PLACE: INDIGENOUS VISIONS FOR PERSONAL EMPOWERMENT & COMMUNITY RECOVERY
Kayleen M. Hazelhurst; Reprint. Illus. 274 pp. Accents Publications, 1996. $29.95.

HEALING PLANTS: MEDICINE OF THE FLORIDA SEMINOLE INDIANS
Alice Micco Snow & Susan Enns Stans
Illus. Photos. 192 pp. University Press of Florida, 1999. $24.95.

HEALING TRADITIONS: THE MENTAL HEALTH OF ABORIGINAL PEOPLES IN CANADA Laurence J. Kirmayer & Gail Guthrie Valaskakis, Editors
Illus. Maps. 464 pp. UBC Press. Distributed by the University of Washington Press, 2008. $105; paper, $43.95.

HEALING WAYS: NAVAJO HEALTH CARE IN THE TWENTIETH CENTURY
Wade Davies; Illus. 256 pp. Paper. University of New Mexico Press, 2001. $30.

HEALING WITH PLANTS IN THE AMERICAN & MEXICAN WEST
Margarita Artschwager Kay; Description of 100 plants commonly used today by Native Americans and Mexican Americans of the Southwest. 330 pp. Paper. University of Arizona Press, 1996. $19.95.

HEALTH & THE AMERICAN INDIAN
Priscilla A. Day & Hilary N. Weaver, Eds.
88 pp. Amazon.com & Alibris.com, 1999. $49.95.

THE HEALTH OF NATIVE AMERICANS TOWARDS A BIOCULTURAL EPIDEMIOLOGY
T. Kue Young; Illus. 288 pp. Oxford University Press, 1994. $71.

HEALTH OF NATIVE PEOPLE OF NORTH AMERICA: A BIBLIOGRAPHY & GUIDE TO RESOURCES, 1970-1994 Sharon A. Gray; Lists peer-reviewed journals, texts, and reference books. Includes association publications, dissertations, reports, audiovisual materials, and book chapters related to health of native peoples. 400 pp. Scarecrow Press, 1996. $82.50.

HEAR ME MY CHIEFS: NEZ PERCE LEGEND & HISTORY
Lucullus V. McWhorter; Reprint of 1952 edition. Illus. Maps. Biblio. 640 pp.
The Caxton Press, $27.95; paper. $19.95.

THE HEARD MUSEUM: HISTORY & COLLECTIONS
Ann Marshall & Mary Brennan; Illus. 50 pp. Paper. Alibris.com, 1989. $8.95.

HEART AS A DRUM: CONTINUANCE & RESISTANCE IN AMERICAN INDIAN POETRY
Robin R. Fast; Illus. 264 pp. University of Michigan Press, 2000. $75.

HEART BAGS & HAND SHAKES: THE STORY OF THE COOK COLLECTION
Dorothy Cook Meade; By the granddaughter of Capt." James H. Cook describes the unique friendships which Cook forged with Sioux & Cheyenne families in western Nebraska from the late 1800s to the 1940. Illus. 60 pp. Paper. Amazon.com, 1994. $10.95.

*HEART BUTTE: A BLACKFEET INDIAN COMMUNITY
John Reyhner; Grades K-4. 18 pp. Paper. Council for Indian Education, 1984. $1.95.

*A HEART FULL OF TURQUOISE: PUEBLO INDIAN TALES
Joe Hayes; illus. by Lucy Jelinek
Grades 4 and up. Illus. 80 pp. Paper. Amazon.com, 1988. $11.95.

THE HEART IS FIRE: THE WORLD OF THE CAHUILLA INDIANS OF SOUTHERN CALIFORNIA Deborah Dozier; Five Cahuilla elders provides an Indian interpretation of the Cahuilla world, past and present. Photos. Illus. Biblio. 169 pp. Paper. Heyday Books & Malki-Ballena Press, $16.

HEART OF THE DRAGONFLY
Allison Bird; Discusses the development and history of the cross necklaces worn by Pueblo & Navajo Indians. Illus. Photos. 208 pp. Paper. Amazon.com, $39.95.

*HEART OF NASOAQUA
Katherine Von Ahnen; In 1823 the Mesquakie Indians are forced to find a new home west of the Mississippi. Nasoaqua is a 12-year-old girl. Grade 4-10. 160 pp. Council for Indian Education. $9.95.

HEART OF THE ROCK: THE INDIAN INVASION OF ALCATRAZ
Adam Fortunate Eagle with Tim Findley
Illus. 232 pp. University of Oklahoma Press, 2002. $29.95; paper, $19.95.

THE HEARTBEAT OF THE PEOPLE: MUSIC & DANCE OF NORTHERN POW-WOW
Tara Browner; Illus. 210 pp. Paper. University of Illinois Press, 2002. $21.

HEARTBEAT, WARBLE, AND THE ELECTRICPOWWOW: AMERICAN INDIAN MUSIC
Craig Harris: Illus. 280 pp. Paper. University of Oklahoma Press, 2016. $24.95.

**HEARTS FELL TO THE GROUND: REBUILDING OLD COMMUNITIES
& SOCIAL CLASS & LBJ**
Colin G. Calloway, et al, Eds.; Paper. Bedford/St. Martin's Press, 2000. $42.75.

HECKEWELDER'S VOCABULARY OF NANTICOKE, VOL. 31
John Heckewelder; Reprint. 34 pp. Amazon.com, 2004. $24.

**HEEDING THE VOICES OF OUR ANCESTORS: KAHNAWAKE MOHAWK
POLITICS & THE RISE OF NATIVE NATIONALISM**
Gerald R. Alfred; Illus. 232 pp. Paper. Oxford University Press, 1995. $32.

*HEETUNKA'S HARVEST: A TALE OF THE PLAINS INDIANS
retold by Jennifer Berry Jones; Grades 1-6. Illus. 32 pp. Roberts Rinehart, 1994. $15.95.

HEILTSUKS: DIALOGUES OF CULTURE & HISTORY ON THE NORTHWEST COAST
Michael E. Harkin; Maps. 195 pp. University of Nebraska Press, 1997. $50; paper, $24.

THE HEIRS OF COLUMBUS
Gerald Vizenor; 198 pp. Paper. Wesleyan University Press.
Distributed by University Press of New England, 1991. $17.95.

HELL WITH THE FIRE OUT: A HISTORY OF THE MODOC WAR
Arthur Quinn; Amazon.com, U.K. 1997. Distributed by Amazon.com. $30.

**HER MOTHER BEFORE HER: WINNEBAGO WOMEN'S STORIES
OF THEIR MOTHERS & GRANDMOTHERS: A RESOURCE GUIDE**
Jocelyn Riley; 114 pp. Paper. Amazon.com, 1995. $20.

HERALDIC POLE CARVERS: 19TH CENTURY NORTHERN HAIDA ARTISTS
Robin K. Wright; Illus. 300 pp. University of Washington Press, 2000.

HERBAL REMEDIES OF THE LUMBEE INDIANS
Arvis Locklear & Loretta O. Oxendine; Illus. 190 pp. Paper. McFarland & Co., 2002. $35.

HERE FIRST: AUTOBIOGRAPHICAL ESSAYS BY NATIVE AMERICAN WRITERS
Arnold Krupat & Brian Swan, Editors; 450 pp. Paper. Random House, 2000. $23.

HERE, NOW, & ALWAYS: VOICES OF THE FIRST PEOPLES OF THE SOUTHWEST
Joan O'Donnell; Foreword by Rina Swentzell; Preface by Bruce Bernstein
Tells the story of the Southwest's oldest communities. Contributors: Carlotta Penny Bird,
Tony Chavarria, Anthony Dorame, Gloria Emerson, Michael Lacapa, Tessie Naranjo, et al.
Illus. 96 pp. Museum of New Mexico Press, 2001. $24.95.

HERE THEY ONCE STOOD: THE TRAGIC END OF THE APALACHEE MISSIONS
Mark F. Boyd, et al; Illus. 240 pp. Paper. University Press of Florida, 1999. $29.95.

*THE HERITAGE
Nancy Armstrong et al; Grades 3-6. Council for Indian Education, 1977. $2.95.

THE HERITAGE OF KLICKITAT BASKETRY: A HISTORY & ART PRESERVED
Nettie Kuneki and Marie Teo; Illus. 48 pp. Paper. Oregon Historical Society, 1982. $4.95.

**HERMANITOS COMANCHITOS: INDO-HISPANO RITUALS OF CAPTIVITY
& REDEMPTION** Enrique R. Lamadrid; photos by Miguel Gandert
Festival of defiance & tribute to the Comanches by the Pueblo & Hispano groups of the
Southwest. Illus. 78 halftones, 3 maps. 312 pp. Includes 70-minute CD. University of New
Mexico Press, $45; paper, $27.95.

**THE HERNANDO DE SOTO EXPEDITION: HISTORY, HISTORIOGRAPHY,
& "DISCOVERY" IN THE SOUTHEAST**
Patricia Galloway, Ed.; Essays. Illus. Maps. 457 pp. U. of Nebraska Press, 1997. $75.

HERNANDO DE SOTO & THE INDIANS OF FLORIDA
Jerald T. Milanich & Charles Hudson
Illus. 42 maps. Biblio. 307 pp. University Press of Florida, 1993. $39.95.

THE HERO TWINS: A NAVAJO-ENGLISH STORY OF THE MONSTER SLAYERS
Jim Kristofic; Nolan Karras James, Illustrator
Illus. 52 pp Paper. University of New Mexico Press, $19.95.

***HEROES & HEROINES IN TLINGIT-HAIDA LEGENDS: & THEIR COUNTERPARTS
IN CLASSICAL MYTHOLOGY**
Mary L. Beck; Grades 8+. Illus. 120 pp. Paper. Alaska Northwest, 1989. $12.95.

*HEROES & HEROINES, MONSTERS & MAGIC
Retold by Joseph Bruchac; Daniel Burgevin; A collection of 30 tales told in the
Longhouses of the Iroquois Indians. Grades 3-7. Illus. 200 pp. Paper. The Crossing Press,
1991. $12.95.

HEYOKA: LAKOTA RITES OF REVERSAL
W.D. Wallis; 114 pp. Paper. Amazon.com, 1996. $25.95.

**HIAPSI WAMI SEEWAM: FLOWERS OF LIFE : A CURRICULUM GUIDE OF
YAQUI CULTURE & ART**
Octaviana V. Trujillo; Wendy Weston-Ben, Editor; Illus. Paper. Atlatl, 1995.

*HIAWATHA
Megan McCiard & George Ypsilantis
Grades 5-7. Illus. 144 pp. Amazon.com, 1989. $11.98; paper, $7.95.

**HIAWATHA: AND OTHER LEGENDS OF THE WIGWAMS OF THE RED AMERICAN
INDIANS** Henry R. Schoolcraft; Reprint of 1882 edition by W.S. Sonnenscheinm & Co.
Illus. 344 pp. Paper. Available from AbeBooks.com or Amazon.com.

*THE HIDATSA
Mary J. Schneider; Grades 7-12. Illus. 112 pp. Chelsea House, 1989. $17.95.

HIDATSA SOCIAL & CEREMONIAL ORGANIZATION
Alfred W. Bowers; Extensive personal and ritual narratives.
Illus. 530 pp. Paper. University of Nebraska Press, 1992. $15.95.

HIDDEN FACES: NATIVE NATIONS
Christopher Cardozo; Robert Janjigan, Ed.; Illus. 96 pp. Callaway Editions, 1997. $13.95.

THE HIDDEN HALF: STUDIES OF PLAINS INDIAN WOMEN
Patricia Albers and Beatrice Medicine
286 pp. University Presses of Ameica, 1983. $31.50; paper, $15.

**HIDDEN IN PLAIN SIGHT: CONTRIBUTIONS OF ABORIGINAL PEOPLES
TO CANADIAN IDENTITY & CULTURE, VOL. 1** David Newhouse & Cora J. Voyageur
420 pp. University of Toronto Press, 2005. $79; paper, $41.95.

**THE HIDDEN LANGUAGE OF THE SENECA: LANGUAGE OF THE STONES;
LANGUAGE OF THE TREES; ENTERING THE SILENCE THE SENECA WAY;
CHANTS & DANCES** Twylah Nitsch; Scriptorium Press, 1987.

**HIDDEN TREASURES OF THE AMERICAN WEST: MURIEL WRIGHT, ANGIE DEBO,
ALICE MARRIOTT** Patricia Loughlin; Biographies of three women public historians of the
1930s & 1940s; Oklahoma historigraphies. Covers federal Indian policy & American Indian
cultures. Illus. Maps. Paper. University of New Mexico Press, 2008. $24.95.

HIDE: SKIN AS MATERIAL & METAPHOR
Kathleen Ash-Milby (Navajo); Essays. Illus. 136 pp. Paper. NMAI Press, 2009. $23.95.

HIGHLANDER IN THE FRENCH & INDIAN WAR
Ian McPherson McCulloch; Full color picture book. Story of the Scottish Highland
Regiments in the F&I War. Illus. Maps. 64 pp. Wennawoods Publishing, 2007. $18.95.

**THE HILL CREEK HOMESTEAD AND THE LATE MISSISSIPPIAN SETTLEMENT
IN THE LOWER ILLINOIS VALLEY** Michael D. Connor, Editor
Illus. 239 pp. Paper. Center for American Archaeology, 1985. $9.95.

**TONY HILLERMAN'S NAVAJOLAND: HIDEOUTS, HAUNTS, & HAVENS IN THE
JOE LEAPHORN & JIM CHEE MYSTERIES**
Laurance D. Linford; foreword by Tony Hillerman
Illus. Map. 360 pp. Paper. University of Utah Press, 2011. $21.95; eBook, $15.

HINDU FESTIVALS IN A NORTH INDIAN VILLAGE
Stanley & Ruth Freed; Illus. 380 pp. Paper. U. of Washington Press, 1998. $34.95.

HIPPIES, INDIANS, AND THE FIGHT FOR RED POWER
Sherry L. Smith; Oxford University Press, 2012. $38.95; paper, $28.95.

HIROSHIMA BUGI: ATOMU 57
Gerald Vizenor; Kabuki novel draws on samurai and native traditions to confront
the nuclear age. 224 pp. University of Nebraska Press, 2003. $26.95.

HISTORIC ARCHAEOLOGY OF HERITAGE SQUARE
Mark R. Hackbarth; Illus. 428 pp. Paper. Pueblo Grande Museum, 1995. $30.

**HISTORIC CONTACT: INDIAN PEOPLE & COLONISTS IN TODAY'S
NORTHEASTERN U.S. IN THE 16TH THROUGH 18TH CENTURIES**
Robert S. Grumet; Illus. Maps. Biblio. 544 pp. U. of Oklahoma Press, 1995. $49.95.

HISTORIC INDIAN TOWNS IN ALABAMA, 1540-1838
Amos J. Wright, Jr.; Illus. Maps. 192 pp. Paper. University of Alabama Press, 2003.
$49.95; paper, $24.95. E-Book, $24.95.

THE HISTORIC INDIAN TRIBES OF LOUISIANA: FROM 1542 TO THE PRESENT
Fred B. Kniffen, et al; Illus. 344 pp. Louisiana State University Press, 1987. $24.95.

HISTORIC NATIVE PEOPLES OF TEXAS
William C. Foster; Illus. Maps. 366 pp. U. of Texas Press, 2008. $60; paper, $24.95.

HISTORIC NAVAJO WEAVING, 1800-1900: THREE CULTURES-ONE LOOM
Tyrone Campbell; Revised edition. Illus. 40 pp. Paper. Avanyu, 1987. $14.75.

HISTORIC POTTERY OF THE PUEBLO INDIANS, 1600-1800
Larry Frank & Francis Harlow; Illus. 175 pp. Schiffer, 1989. $35.

HISTORIC ZUNI ARCHITECTURE & SOCIETY
T.J. Ferguson; Illus. 175 pp. Paper. University of Arizona Press, 1996. $17.95.

HISTORICAL ATLAS OF THE AMERICAN WEST
Warren A. Beck & Ynez D. Haase; Includes a section on aboriginal settings and Native
American tribes, European contacts and settlements, etc. 78 maps. 158 pp. Paper.
University of Oklahoma Press, 1989. $19.95.

HISTORICAL ATLAS OF ARIZONA
Henry P. Walker & Don Bufkin; Includes a section on aboriginal settings & Native
American tribes. Maps. Biblio. 146 pp. U. of Oklahoma Press, 1979. $37.95; paper, $19.95.

HISTORICAL ATLAS OF ARKANSAS
Gerald T. Hanson & Carl H. Moneyhon; Includes a section on Arkansas' aboriginal setting and Native American tribes, etc. 71 maps. 156 pp. Paper. University of Oklahoma Press, 1989. $19.95.

HISTORICAL ATLAS OF CALIFORNIA
Warren A. Beck & Ynez D. Haase; Includes a section on aboriginal settings and Native American tribes, etc. Maps. 231 pp. Paper. University of Oklahoma Press, 1974. $23.95.

HISTORICAL ATLAS OF COLORADO
Thomas J. Noel, et al; Includes a section on Colorado's aboriginal setting and Native American tribes, etc. 60 maps. Biblio. 192 pp. Paper. U. of Oklahoma Press, 1994. $19.95.

HISTORICAL ATLAS OF LOUISIANA
Charles R. Goins & John M. Caldwell; Includes a section on Louisiana's aboriginal setting and Native American tribes, European contacts & settlements, etc. 99 maps. 198 pp. University of Oklahoma Press, 1995. $65; paper, $29.95.

HISTORICAL ATLAS OF MISSOURI
Milton D. Rafferty; Includes a section on Missouri's aboriginal setting and Native American tribes, European contacts & settlements, etc. 113 pp. of maps. 248 pp. University of Oklahoma Press, 1982. $29.95.

HISTORICAL ATLAS OF NEW MEXICO
Warren A. Beck & Ynez D. Haase; Includes a section on aboriginal settings and Native American tribes, etc. Reprint of 1969 edition. Maps. 144 pp. Paper. University of Oklahoma Press, 1969. $19.95.

A HISTORICAL ATLAS OF NORTH AMERICA BEFORE COLUMBUS
Fred Ramen; Rosen Publishing, 2004.

HISTORICAL ATLAS OF OKLAHOMA
Charles R. Goins & Danny Goble; Includes a section on Oklahoma's aboriginal setting & Native American tribes, European contacts & settlements, etc. 4th edition. Maps. 190 pp. University of Oklahoma Press, 2009. $39.95.

HISTORICAL ATLAS OF TEXAS
A. Ray Stephens & William M. Holmes; Includes a section on Texa's aboriginal setting and Native American tribes, European contacts and settlements, etc. 64 maps. 132 pp. University of Oklahoma Press, 1989. $39.95; paper, $19.95.

HISTORICAL ATLAS OF WASHINGTON
James W. Scott & Roland L. De Lorme
Maps. 180 pp. University of Oklahoma Press, 1988. $27.95.

HISTORICAL BACKGROUND OF THE GILA RIVER RESERVATION
R.J. DeMallie; 66 pp. Institute for the Development of Indian Law, $14.

HISTORICAL BACKGROUND OF THE SANTA ANA PUEBLO
Tom Luebben; 25 pp. Institute for the Development of Indian Law, $8.50.

HISTORICAL BACKGROUND TO CHIPPEWA TREATIES
Robert Keller; 25 pp. Institute for the Development of Indian Law, $12.50.

AN HISTORICAL CHRONOLOGY OF THE KIOWA TRIBE
John Belindo; 12 pp. Institute for the Development of Indian Law, $5.50.

HISTORICAL COLLECTIONS OF GEORGIA
George White; Reprint of 1920 edition. 787 pp. Genealogical Publishing, $35.

THE HISTORICAL DEVELOPMENT OF THE CONCEPT OF NUNAVUT:
AN ANNOTATED BIBLIOGRAPHY OF THE LITERATURE SINCE THE 1930'S
R.L. Minion; Paper. CCI, 1994. $15.

HISTORICAL DICTIONARY OF EARLY NORTH AMERICA
Cameron B. Wesson; Illus. Maps. 700 dictionary entries. Bibliography. Appendix of museums & archaeological sites that allow tours by the public. 240 pp. Scarecrow Press, 2004. $79.20.

HISTORICAL DICTIONARY OF THE INUIT
Pamela R. Stern; Overview of the Inuit peoples of the North. Information on traditional Inuit culture. Maps. 248 pp. Scarecrow Press, 2004. $68.20.

HISTORIAL DICTIONARY OF NATIVE AMERICAN MOVEMENTS, 2ND EDITION
Todd Leahy & Nathan Wilson; Bibliography & cross-referenced dictionary entries on important people, places & events. Illus. 336 pp. Rowman & Littlefield, 2016. $90; eBook, $89.99.

HISTORICAL DICTIONARY OF NORTH AMERICAN ARCHAEOLOGY
Edward Jelks & Juliet Jelks; An alphabetical listing of over 1,800 entries providing descriptions for cultures, mounds, ruins, & archaeological sites. Sources of information, and list of references. Biblio. 760 pp. Greenwood, 1988. $95.

AN HISTORICAL JOURNAL OF THE CAMPAIGNS IN NORTH AMERICA IN THE YEARS 1757-1760 A.G. Doughty
Facsimile of 1916 edition. 2 vols. Greenwood, $125 per set.

A HISTORICAL LOOK AT THE SHASTA NATION
Betty Lou Hall & Monica Jae Hall; Illus. 128 pp. Paper. Malki-Ballena Press, $19.95.

HISTORICAL MAP OF PENNSYLVANIA: WITH A HISTORY OF INDIAN TREATIES & LAND TITLES P.W. Schaefer & R.R. Wenning
Illus. Map. Wennawoodds Publishing, 2007. $24.95.

HISTORICAL SKETCH OF THE FLATHEAD INDIAN NATION
Peter Ronan; Reprint of 1890 edition. 108 PP. Amazon.com, $15.

HISTORICIZING CANADIAN ANTHROPOLOGY
Julia Harrison & Regna Darnell
352 pp. U. of Washington Press, 2007. $94; paper, $37.95.

HISTORY & ANNOTATED BIBLIOGRAPHY OF AMERICAN RELIGIOUS PERIODICALS & NEWSPAPERS ESTABLISHED FROM 1730 THROUGH 1830
Gaylor P. Albaugh; 2 vols. 1,550 pp. Oak Knoll, 1994. $125.

HISTORY & CULTURE OF IROQUOIS DIPLOMACY: AN INTERDISCIPLINARY GUIDE TO THE TREATIES OF THE SIX NATIONS & THEIR LEAGUE
Francis Jennings & William Fenton, Editors
Illus. Maps. 296 pp. Paper. Syracuse University Press, 1995. $19.95.

HISTORY, ETHNOLOGY, & ANTHROPOLOGY OF THE ALEUT
Waldemar Jochelson; Aleut society 100 years ago. Illus. Paper. U. of Utah Press. $14.95.

HISTORY, EVOLUTION & THE CONCEPT OF CULTURE: SELECTED PAPERS BY ALEXANDER LESSER Sidney W. Mintz; 192 pp. Cambridge U. Press, 1989. $34.50.

HISTORY IS IN THE LAND: MULTIVOCAL TRIBAL TRADITIONS IN ARIZONA'S SAN PEDRO VALLEY T.J. Ferguson; Chip Colwell-Chanthaphonh; Combines archaeological & ethnographic persepctives of four tribes: Tohono O'odham, Hopi, Zuni and San Carlos Apache. 336 pp. Illus. University of Arizona Press, 2006. $60; paper, $35.

HISTORY, MYTHS & SACRED FORMULAS OF THE CHEROKEES
James Mooney; Primary source book on Cherokee contains 126 legends obtained on the Cherokee Reservation in N.C. in 1887-88. Illus. Paper. Amazon.com, $17.95.

HISTORY OF AMERICAN INDIANS: EXPLORING DIVERSE ROOTS
Robert R. McCoy & Steven M. Fountain; 257 pp. ABC-CLIO, 2017. $58. eBook available.

HISTORY OF THE AMERICAN INDIAN
Jerry R. Baydo; 175 pp. Paper. Gregory Publishing, 1992. $15.

THE HISTORY OF THE AMERICAN INDIANS
James Adair; edited by Kathryn E. Holland Braun; Details the cultures of five southeastern American Indian tribes during the Contact Period. Adair was British and lived and traded among the southeastern tribes for more than 30 years, from 1735-1768. Illus. Maps. 608 pp. University of Alabama Press, 2005; $69.95; paper, $39.95. E-Book, $39.95.

HISTORY OF BAPTIST INDIAN MISSIONS
Isaac McCoy; Reprint. Illus. Paper. Amazon.com, 1999. $35.95.

HISTORY OF THE CATHOLIC MISSIONS AMONG THE INDIAN TRIBES OF THE U.S.
John Shea; Reprint. Illus. Paper. Amazon.com, 1999. $32.95.

HISTORY OF THE CENTRAL BROOKS RANGE: GAUNT BEAUTY, TENUOUS LIFE
William E. Brown; History of the Koyukuk Region of Alaska and its rich cultural heritage. Illus. 180 halftones. 230 pp. Dist. for the University of Alaska Press by University of Chicago Press, 2008. $45; paper, $24.95.

HISTORY OF THE CHOCTAW, CHICKASAW AND NATCHEZ INDIANS
H.B. Cushman; Paper. The Choctaw Store, 1999. $24.95.

HISTORY OF THE EARLY SETTLEMENT OF THE JUNIATA VALLEY
U.J. Jones; Pioneer life on the Pennsylvania frontier.
Reprint of 1866 ed. Paper. Wennawoods Publishing, $31.

HISTORY OF AN EXPEDITION AGAINST FORT DUQUESNE IN 1755 VOL. 9: AN ACCOUNT OF BRADDOCK CAMPAIGN IN 1755
Winthrop Sargent; 425 pp. Wennawoods Publishing, 1997.

HISTORY OF THE BACKWOODS
A.W. Patterson; From Western Pennsylvania into Ohio.
Illus. Maps. Wennawoods Publishing, 2007. $44.95.

HISTORY OF BEADS: FROM 30,000 B.C. TO THE PRESENT
Lois Sherr Dubin; 350 illus. 254 color plates. 8 pp. fold-out time line. 364 pp. Written Heritage, $59.95.

HISTORY OF THE BUREAU OF INDIAN AFFAIRS & ITS ACTIVITIES AMONG INDIANS
Curtis E. Jackson and Marcia J. Galli; Paper. R & E Research Associates, 1977. $15.

HISTORY OF CANADA, OR NEW FRANCE
F. Du Creaux; J.B. Conacher, Editor
Reprint 1951 ed. Two vols. Greenwood, $26.75 each.

HISTORY OF THE CHEROKEE INDIANS & THEIR LEGENDS & FOLKLORE
Emmet Starr; 2009 reprint of the 1921 edition. Illus. Indexed. 680 pp. Paper. Cherokee Publications & Genealogical Publishing, 2009. $40.

*A HISTORY OF THE CHEYENNE PEOPLE
Tom Weist; Grades 6 and up. Illus. 227 pp. Paper. Council for Indian Education, 1977. $14.95; paper, $9.95.

HISTORY OF THE CHOCTAW, CHICKASAW & NATCHEZ INDIANS
H.B. Cushman; edited by Angie Debo; Reprint of 1961 abridged edition by Angie Debo. 503 pp. Paper. University of Oklahoma Press, $24.95.

HISTORY OF THE EARLY SETTLEMENT & INDIAN WARS OF WEST VIRGINIA
William DeHass; Illus. Maps. Paper. Wennawoods Publishing, $16.95.

HISTORY OF THE INDIANS OF CONNECTICUT FROM THE EARLIEST KNOWN PERIOD TO 1850 John W. De Forest; Reprint. 536 pp. Amazon.com, 1991. $79.

A HISTORY OF JONATHAN ALDER: HIS CAPTIVITY & LIFE WITH THE INDIANS
Henry Clay Alder; Larry L. Nelson, Ed. & compiled by
215 pp. Amazon.com, 2002. $34.95; paper, $14.95.

HISTORY OF THE FIVE INDIAN NATIONS OF CANADA
Cadwallader Colden; Reprint. Paper. Amazon.com.

HISTORY OF THE GIRTY'S
C.W. Butterfield; Original source history of the Lord Dunmore's War, the western border war during the Revolution and the Indian wars of the 1790s through the eyes of the Girty brothers. Reprint of 1890 ed. Illus. Maps. 310 pp. Wennswoods Publishing, 2006. $21.95.

HISTORY OF INDIAN ARTS EDUCATION IN SANTA FE
Winona Garmhausen; Illus. 144 pp. Paper. Sunstone Press, 1988. $15.95.

A HISTORY OF INDIAN EDUCATION
Jon Reyhner & Jeanne Eder; Overview from first missionaries to present.
150 pp. Paper. Council for Indian Education. $8.95.

A HISTORY OF INDIAN POLICY: SYLLABUS
Judith Bachman; Paper. National Book, $6.75; cassette recording, $146.10.

HISTORY OF THE INDIAN TRIBES OF NORTH AMERICA
Thomas McKenney; Reprint. Illus. Paper. Amazon.com, 1999. $39.95.

A HISTORY OF INDIAN VILLAGES & PLACE NAMES OF PENNSYLVANIA
George A. Donehoo; 312 pp. Paper. Wennawoods, 1998. $19.95.

HISTORY OF THE INDIAN WARS
Samuel Penhallow; Reprint of 1726 edition. 208 pp. Corner House, $18.50.

HISTORY OF THE INDIAN WARS IN NEW ENGLAND, FROM THE FIRST SETTLEMENT TO THE TERMINATION OF THE WAR WITH KING PHILIP IN 1677
William Hubbard
Reprint of 1865 edition. 3 vols. in one. 595 pp. Map. Paper. Heritage Books, $35.

HISTORY OF INDIAN-WHITE RELATIONS, Vol. 4
William Sturtevant; Wilcomb E. Washburn, Editor; Illus. 852 pp. Smithsonian, 1989. $47.

HISTORY OF THE INDIANS OF CONNECTICUT FROM THE EARLIEST KNOWN PERIOD TO 1850 John W. DeForest; Reprint. 536 pp. Paper. Somerset Publishers, $69.

HISTORY OF THE INDIANS OF THE UNITED STATES
Angie Debo; Reprint of 1970 ed. Illus. Maps. 450 pp. Paper.
University of Oklahoma Press, 2000. $26.95.

HISTORY OF THE IROQUOIS CONFEDERACY
William H. Fenton; Illus. Maps. Biblio. 808 pp. University of Oklahoma Press, 1998. $70.

A HISTORY OF JONATHAN ALDER: HIS CAPTIVITY & LIFE WITH THE INDIANS
Henry Clay Alder; Larry L. Nelson, Ed.
215 pp. University of Akron, 2002. $34.95; paper, $14.95.

HISTORY OF THE NATIVE AMERICANS
Alvin Josephy, Editor; Six biographies of Native American leaders and the tribes theyu represent. Includes separate books for Hiawatha, King Philip, Geronimo, Sitting Bull, Sequoyah & Tecumseh. Illus. Maps. 128 -144pp each. Amazon.com, 1993. $10.95 each; paper, $7.95. $65.70/set; paper, $47.70/set.

A HISTORY OF THE NATIVE PEOPLE OF CANADA VOL. I (10,000-1,000 B.C.)
James V. Wright; The first of 3 vols. on the history of Canada's Native people as revealed by the archaeological evidence. Reprint of 1995 ed. Illus. 564 pp. Paper. University of Washington Press, 2007. $45.

A HISTORY OF THE NATIVE PEOPLE OF CANADA VOL. II (1,000 B.C.-A.D. 500)
James V. Wright; Second of 3 vols. examining the 12,000 years of Native history which preceded the arrival of Europeans in Canada. Illus. Maps. Biblio. 640 pp. Paper. University of Washington Press, 2004. $45.

HISTORY OF NATIVE PEOPLE OF CANADA VOL. III
(A.D. 500-EUROPEAN CONTACT) James V. Wright; The third of 3 vols. examining the 12,000 years of Native history which preceded the arrival of Europeans in Canada. Illus. Maps. Biblio. 507 pp. Paper. University of Washington Press, 1999. $45.

HISTORY OF THE NAVAJOS: THE RESERVATION YEARS
Garrick & Roberta Bailey
Illus. 376 pp. Paper. School for Advanced Research, 1999. $24.95.

HISTORY OF NEW FRANCE
Marc Lescarbot; Reprint of 1907 ed. Three vols. Greenwood, $27.50, $37.75, & $35.25.

HISTORY OF THE NEW YORK INDIANS & INDIANS OF THE PRINTUP FAMILY
A.D. Printup; Illus. 89 pp. DeWitt & Sheppard, 1985. $66.66.

HISTORY OF NORTHERN AMERICAN INDIANS
Rev. David Zeisberger; Reprint. Moravian missionary account of Indian life as he witnessed it in what is now Ohio in the late 1700s. 189 pp. Paper. Amazon.com, $12.95.

HISTORY OF THE OJIBWAY PEOPLE
William W. Warren; First hand descriptions & stories from tribal leaders et al. Reprint of 1885 ed. Illus. 411 pp. Paper. Minnesota Historical Society Press, 1984. $12.95.

THE HISTORY OF OKLAHOMA
Arrell M. Gibson; Illus. Maps. 242 pp. University of Oklahoma Press, 1984. $19.95.

HISTORY OF THE ORIGINAL PEOPLES OF NORTHERN CANADA
Keith J. Crowe; Revised edition. 264 pp. Paper. McGill-Queen's University Press; Dist. by CUP Services, 1991. $19.95.

A HISTORY OF THE OSAGE PEOPLE
Louis F. Burns; 2nd Ed. Illus. 632 pp. University of Alabama Press, 2004. $80; paper, $39.95. E-Book available.

HISTORY OF PHILIP'S WAR, COMMONLY CALLED THE GREAT INDIAN WAR OF 1675 & 1676. ALSO OF THE FRENCH & INDIAN WARS AT THE EASTWARD IN 1689, 1690, 1692, 1696, & 1704 Thomas Church, Esq.; notes by Samuel G. Drake
Reprint. 360 pp. Paper. Amazon.com, $23.50.

HISTORY OF THE SANTEE SIOUX: U.S. INDIAN POLICY ON TRIAL
Roy W. Meyer
Reprint 1967 ed. Illus. Maps. 507 pp. Paper. University of Nebraska Press, $17.95.

HISTORY OF THE SECOND SEMINOLE WAR, 1835-1842
John K. Mahon; Revised 1967 ed. Illus. Biblio. 391 pp. Paper. U. Press of Florida, $15.95.

HISTORY OF THE TIMUCUA INDIANS & MISSIONS
John H. Hann; Illus. 400 pp. University Press of Florida, 1996. $49.95.

HISTORY OF THE TRIUMPHS OF OUR HOLY FAITH AMONGST THE MOST BARBAROUS & FIERCE PEOPLES OF THE NEW WORLD
Andres Perez De Ribas; trans. by Daniel T. Reff, Maureen Ahern & Richard K. Danford
Colonial encounter in southwestern North America. 761 pp. University of Arizona Press, 1999. $89.

A HISTORY OF US: THE FIRST AMERICANS: PREHISTORY-1600
Joy Hakim; 3rd revised edition. Oxford University Press, 2006. $24.95; paper, $15.95.

A HISTORY OF UTAH'S AMERICAN INDIANS
Forrest S. Cuch, Editor; Chapters on each of six tribes.
Illus. 416 pp. Paper. Utah State University Press, 2000. $29.95. E-book, $20.

HISTORY OF THE WYANDOTT MISSION
James Finley; Reprint. Illus. Paper. Amazon.com, 1999. $26.95.

HISTORY & PRESENT DEVELOPMENT OF INDIAN SCHOOLS IN THE U.S.
Solomon R. Ammon; Reprint of 1935 edition. Paper. R & E Associates, $10.95.

HISTORY'S SHADOW: NATIVE AMERICANS & HISTORICAL CONSCIOUSNESS IN THE 19TH CENTURY Steven Conn
Illus. 288 pp. University of Chicago Press, 2004. $40; paper, $25. E-book, $7 to $25.

HITTING THE JACKPOT: THE INSIDE STORY OF THE RICHEST INDIAN TRIBE IN HISTORY Brett Duval Fromson; 256 pp. Amazon.com, 2003. $24; paper, $15.

HIV PREVENTION IN NATIVE AMERICAN COMMUNITIES: A MANUAL FOR NATIVE AMERICAN HEALTH & HUMAN SERVICE PROVIDERS
Updates AIDS: The Basics. It highlights Native American HIV prevention educators and programs. Includes overviews of HIV and AIDS. National Native American AIDS Prevention Center, $20.

HIWASSEE ISLAND: AN ARCHAEOLOGICAL ACCOUNT OF FOUR TENNESSEE INDIAN PEOPLES Thomas N. Lewis and Madeline Kneberg
Reprint of 1984 ed. Illus. 328 pp. Amazon.com. $18.95.

HO-CHUNK POWWOWS & THE POLITICS OF TRADITION
Grant Arndt; Illus. 352 pp. University of Nebraska Press, 2016. $60.

THE HOE & THE HORSE ON THE PLAINS: A STUDY OF CULTURAL DEVELOPMENT AMONG NORTH AMERICAN INDIANS
Preston Holder; An ethnological study; fieldwork with the Arikara; Plains ethnography.
Illus. Maps. 186 pp. Paper. University of Nebraska Press, 1970. $16.95.

THE HOGAN
Scott Thybony; Illus. 8 pp. Paper. Western National Parks Association, 1998. $2.95.

HOGANS: NAVAJO HOUSES & HOUSE SONGS
David & Susan McAllester; Reprint. Illus. 115 pp. Paper. Amazon.com. $15.95.

THE HOHOKAM: ANCIENT PEOPLE OF THE DESERT
David Grant Noble
Illus. Maps. 88 pp. Paper. School of American Research, 1989. $10.95.

HOHOKAM ARTS & CRAFTS
Barbara Granemann; Linda Gregonis, Editor
Reprint. Grades 4 and up. Illus. 48 pp. Paper. Southwest Learning SDources, 1994. $7.95.

HOHOKAM MARINE SHELL EXCHANGE & ARTIFACTS
Richard S. Nelson; Illus. 110 pp. Paper. Amazon.com, 1991. $12.95.

HOHOKAM & PATAYAN: PREHISTORY OF SOUTHWESTERN ARIZONA
R. McGuire and M. Schiffer, Editors; Amazon.com, 1982. $49.50.

HOKAHEY! A GOOD DAY TO DIE! THE INDIAN CASUALTIES OF THE CUSTER FIGHT
Richard G. Hardorff; Identifies the fallen Indians, by name and the location where they were killed. Illus. 174 pp. Paper. University of Nebraska Press, 1999. $12.95.

THE HOKO RIVER ARCHAEOLOGICAL SITE COMPLEX
Dale R. Croes; Native American site on Washington's Olympic Peninsula. Illus. Maps. Biblio. 272 pp. Paper. WSU Press, 1996. $37.50.

*HOKSILA & THE RED BUFFALO
Moses N. Crow; Grades 3 and up. Illus. 40 pp. Paper. Tipi Press, 1991. $5.95.

HOLD EVERYTHING! MASTERWORKS OF BASKETRY & POTTERY FROM THE HEARD MUSEUM COLLECTION
Jody Folwell; Illus. 72 pp. Amazon.com & Alibris.com, 2001.

HOLDING STONE HANDS: ON THE TRAIL OF THE CHEYENNE EXODUS
Alan Boye; Moving account of the Cheyennes' struggle to return to Montana. Illus. 348 pp. Paper. University of Nebraska Press, 1998. $16.

*HOLE-IN-THE-DAY: CHIPPEWA NATIVE AMERICAN INDIAN STORIES
Robert M. Kvasnicka]; Grades 4 and up. Demco, 1996. $10.15.

HOLLOW JUSTICE: A HISTORY OF INDIGENOUS CLAIMS IN THE U.S.
David E. Wilkins; 272 pp. Yale University Press, 2013. $85.

HOLLOW VICTORY: THE WHITE RIVER EXPEDITION OF 1879 & THE BATTLE OF MILL CREEK
Mark E. Miller; Illus. 224 pp. University Press of Colorado, 1997. $27.50.

HOLLYWOOD'S INDIAN: THE PORTRAYAL OF THE NATIVE AMERICAN IN FILM
Peter C. Rollins & John E. O'Connor, Eds. Illus. 264 pp. Exp. ed. Paper. Amazon.com, 2003. $22.

GARY HOLY BULL, LAKOTA YUWIPI MAN
Gary Holy Bull; Bradford Keeney, Editor Illus. 100 pp. Ringing Rocks Press, 2000. $39.95, includes audio CD.

HOLY WIND IN NAVAJO PHILOSOPHY
James K. McNeley; 115 pp. Paper. University of Arizona Press, 1981. $16.95.

HOME IS THE HUNTER: THE JAMES BAY CREE & THEIR LAND
Hans M. Carlson; Illus. Maps. 320 pp. U. of Washington Press, 2008. $94; paper, $37.95.

HOME PLACES: CONTEMPORARY NATIVE AMERICAN WRITING FROM SUN TRACKS Larry Evers & Ofelia Zepeda; Stories, songs, poems and other writings. 97 pp. Paper. University of Arizona Press, 1995. $12.95.

HOME TO MEDICINE MOUNTAIN
Chiori Santiago; illus. by Judith Lowry; Story of 2 young brothers separated and sent to live at a government-run Indian residential school in 1930s. Illus. Meadowlark Communications, $15.95.

HOME: NATIVE PEOPLE IN THE SOUTHWEST
Ann Marshall; Univefsity of New Mexico Press, $50; paper, $35.

HOMELAND FOR THE CREE: REGIONAL DEVELOPMENT IN JAMES BAY, 1971-1981
Richard F. Salisbury; Shows how the first James Bay project was negotiated between the Cree and the Quebec government. McGill-Queen's University Press, 1986. $19.95.

*HOMES OF THE NATIVE AMERICANS
Colleen Madonna Flood Williams Grades 4-9. Illus. 64 pp. Mason Crest Publishers, 2003. $19.95.

HOMOL'OVI: AN ANCIENT HOPI SETTLEMENT CLUSTER
E. Charles Adams; Illus. 304 pp. University of Arizona Press, 2002. $50.

HOMOL'OVI II: ARCHAEOLOGY OF AN ANCESTRAL HOPI VILLAGE, ARIZONA
E. Charles Adams & Kelley Ann Hays, Editors Excavations. 139 pp. Paper. University of Arizona Press, 1992. $19.95.

HONNE, THE SPIRIT OF THE CHEHALIS
Zitkala-Sa; Illus. 216 pp. Paper. University of Nebraska Press, 2013. $17.95.

HONOR DANCE: NATIVE AMERICAN PHOTOGRAPHS
John Running; Illus. 176 pp. Paper. University of Nevada Press, 1985. $24.95.

HONOR THE GRANDMOTHERS: DAKOTA & LAKOTA WOMEN TELL THEIR STORIES
Sarah Penman, Ed. Illus. 145 pp. Minnesota Historical Society Press, 2000. $29.95; paper, $14.95.

HONORING THE MEDICINE: ESSENTIAL GUIDE TO NATIVE AMERICAN HEALING
Ken Cohen; Illus. 448 pp. Ballantine Books, 2003. $26.95.

HONORING THE WEAVERS
Gregory Schaaf; Illus. 200 pp. Center for Indigenous Arts & Cultures Press, 1996. $40.

HONOUR EARTH MOTHER
Basil Johnston; Illus. Paper. University of Nebraska Press, 2004. $13.95.

THE HOOP OF PEACE
Jan Havnen-Finley; Illus. by Ken Edwards; Kevin Locke, a Lakota, is one of a few hoop dancers. He depicts the sacred Great Hoop of Peace. Illus. Photos. 48 pp. Paper. Naturegraph, $7.95.

JOHN HOOVER: ART & LIFE
Julie Decker; Illus. 183 pp. Paper. University of Washington Press, 2002. $35.

*HOPE & HAVE: FANNY GRANT AMONG THE INDIANS
Oliver Optic; Reprint. Grades 3-7. Illus. 264 pp. Paper. Amazon.com, 1997. $14.95.

HOPEWELL SETTLEMENT PATTERNS, SUBSISTENCE, & SYMBOLIC LANDSCAPES
A. Martin Byers & DeeAnne Wymer Essays examine the cultural & social nature of the well-known Ohio Hopewell monumental earthworks. Scholars discuss the purpose, meaning, and role of earthworks & other artifacts. Illus. Maps. 416 pp. University Press of Florida, 2010. $75.

HOPEWELL VILLAGE: A SOCIAL & ECONOMIC HISTORY OF AN IRON-MAKING COMMUNITY J.E. Walker; University of Pennsylvania Press, 1966. $26.50; paper, $14.95.

HOPEWELLIAN STUDIES
Joseph Caldwell and Robert Hall, Editors Facsimile edition. Illus. 156 pp. Illinois State Museum, 1977. $4.

HOPI
Susanne and Jake Page; Photos of Hopi elders, their land and certain ceremonies. Illus. 240 pp. Paper. Harry N. Abrams, 1982. $29.98.

*THE HOPI
Ann Tomchek; Grades K-4. Illus. 48 pp. Childrens Press, 1987. $11.45.

· THE HOPI
Barry Pritzker; Paul Rosier, Series Editor Grades 6-12. Illus. 122 pp. Chelsea House, 2011. $35.

*THE HOPI
Nancy Bonvillain; Part of the Indians of North America series. Grades 4 and up. Illus. 112 pp. Paper. Chelsea House, 1991. $7.95.

*THE HOPIAmazon.com, 1997. Set V, $21.27

*THE HOPI
Elaine Landau; Tells the story of the Hopi way of life. Part of the Indian of Americas seriesFull-color illustrations. Grades 3 and up. 64 pp. Paper. Franklin Watts, 1994. $5.95.

HOPI ANIMAL STORIES
edited & compiled by Ekkehart Malotki Illus. 261 pp. Paper. University of Nebraska Press, 2001. $16.95.

HOPI ANIMAL TALES
edited & compiled by Ekkehart Malotki; Illus. 524 pp. U. of Nebraska Press, 1998. $50.

THE HOPI APPROACH TO THE ART OF KACHINA DOLL CARVING
Erik Bromberg Presents the diversity of Hopi kachina dolls. Illus. 94 pp. Paper. Schiffer, $9.95.

HOPI BASKET WEAVING: ARTISTRY IN NATURAL FIBERS
Helga Teiwes; Illus. 200 pp. University of Arizona Press, 1996. $50; paper, $22.95.

HOPI COOKERY
Juanita Tiger Kavena; Includes over 100 authentic Hopi recipes. 115 pp. Paper. University of Arizona Press, 1980. $15.95.

HOPI COYOTE TALES: ISTUTUWUTSI
Ekkehart Malotki & Michael Lomatuway'ma Illus. 343 pp. Paper. University of Nebraska Press, 1984. $29.95.

*HOPI, THE DESERT FARMERS
Susan L. Shaffer, Editor; Grade 3. Illus. Includes 30 student booklets and teacher's manual with transparencies, slides & audiocassette. The Heard Museum. $295.

HOPI DICTIONARY: HOPI-ENGLISH, ENGLISH-HOPI, GRAMMATICAL APPENDIX
P. David Seaman; 208 pp. Paper. Amazon.com, 1996. $27.

HOPI DWELLINGS: ARCHITECTURAL CHANGE AT ORAYVI
Catherine M. Cameron Hopi & Pueblo history. Illus. 162 pp. U. of Arizona Press, 1999. $42.

HOPI & HOPI-TEWA POTTERY
32 pp. Paper. Museum of Northern Arizona, 1982. $4.

HOPI INDIAN ALTER ICONOGRAPHY
Armin W. Geertz; Illus. 39 pp. Paper. Brill Academic, 1987. $39.

HOPI KACHINA DOLLS & THEIR CARVERS
Theda Bassman; Illustrates contemporary kachina dolls and the lives of the 25 carvers who make them. Illus. 192 pp. Schiffer, $59.95.

HOPI KACHINA DOLLS WITH A KEY TO THEIR IDENTIFICATION
Harold S. Colton; Revised edition. Illus. 14 color photos; 33 halftones. 160 pp. Paper. University of New Mexico Press, 2002. $18.95.

HOPI KACHINAS
Edwin Earle and Edward A. Kennard; Second edition. Illus. 50 pp. National Museum of the American Indian, 1971. $12.50. Portfolio of 28 color plates from the book, $3.50.

HOPI KACHINAS: THE COMPLETE GUIDE TO COLLECTING KACHINA DOLLS
Barton Wright; Includes buying tips and the history of the cultural roles played by the various figures. Illus. 30 color photos. 152 pp. Amazon.com, $14.95.

HOPI KACHINAS: A POSTCARD COLLECTION
Cliff Bahnimptewa, illustrator; 20 full-color postcards. Illus. Amazon.com, $7.95.

HOPI KATCINAS
Jesse W. Fewkes; Reprint of 1903 edition. Illus. 150 pp. Rio Grande Press, $25.
Paper. Hothem House & Dover, $8.95.

HOPI KATSINA SONGS
Emory Sekaquaptewa, Kenneth C. Hill, Dorothy K. Washburn
440 pp. University of Nebraska Press, 2015. $65. E-Book available.

HOPI MUSIC & DANCE
Robert Rhodes; Illus. 36 pp. Paper. Amazon.com, $3.25.

*HOPI MYSTERIES
Jack Woolgar and Barbara J. Rudnicki
Grades 5-9. 32 pp. Council for Indian Education, 1974. $8.95; paper, $2.95.

HOPI ORAL TRADITION & THE ARCHAEOLOGY OF IDENTITY
Wesley Bernardino; 250 pp. University of Arizona Press, 2005. $50.

HOPI POTTERY SYMBOLS
Alex Patterson; Based on work by Alexander M. Stephen. Includes tentative meanings
and a glossary of Hopi words. Illus. 308 pp. Paper. Johnson Books, $17.95.

HOPI QUILTING: STITCHED TRADITIONS FROM AN ANCIENT COMMUNITY
Carolyn O. Davis; Illus. 128 pp. Paper. Amazon.com, 1997. $27.95.

HOPI RUIN LEGENDS: KIQOTUTUWUTSI
Michael Lomatuway'ma, et al; Ekkehart Malotki, Ed. & tr.
Illus. 510 pp. University of Nebraska Press, 1993. $70.

*HOPI SHIELDS & THE BEST DEFENSE
Eugene L. Hartley; Hopi boy learns about their traditional shields and their tradition
of peace. Grades 2-6. 32 pp. Paper. Council for Indian Education, $3.95.

HOPI SILVER: THE HISTORY & THE HALLMARKS OF HOPI SILVERSMITHING
Margaret Nickelson Wright; Revised edition. Illus. 24 color photos; 29 halftones.
160 pp. Paper. University of New Mexico Press, 2003. $19.95.

HOPI SNAKE CEREMONIES
Jesse Walter Fewkes; An eyewitness account. Illus. 40 halftones. 160 pp.
Paper. University of New Mexico Press. $24.95.

**HOPI SOCIAL HISTORY: ANTHROPOLOGICAL PERSPECTIVES ON
SOCIOCULTURAL PERSISTENCE & CHANGE**
Scott Rushforth & Steadman Upham; Illus. 320 pp. Paper.
University of Texas Press, 1992. $18.95.

HOPI STORIES OF WITCHCRAFT, SHAMANISM, & MAGIC
Ekkehart Malotki & Ken Gary; Illus. 290 pp. University of Nebraska Press, 2001. $29.95.

**HOPI SURVIVAL KIT: THE PROPHECIES, INSTRUCTIONS & WARNINGS
REVEALED BY THE LAST ELDERS** Thomas E. Mails
Reprint. 376 pp. Amazon.com, 1997. $15.

HOPI TALES OF DESTRUCTION
collected, trans, ed. by Ekkehart Malotki; narrated by Michael Lomatuway'ma, et al
Seven tales about ancient Hopi villages describing village destruction.
288 pp. Paper. University of Nebraska Press, 2002. $27.95.

HOPI-TEWA POTTERY: 500 ARTIST BIOGRAPHIES
Gregory Schaaf; Richard M. Howard, Editor
Illus. 200 pp. Center for Indigenous Arts & Cultures (CIAC) Press, 1999. $65.

HOPI TIME
E. Malotki; A linguistic analysis of the temporal concepts in the Hopi Language.
677 pp. Amazon.com, $125.

HOPI TRADITIONAL LITERATURE
David Leedom Shaul; 246 pp. University of New Mexico Press, 2002. $49.95.

THE HOPI VILLAGES: ANCIENT PROVINCE OF TUSAYAN
John W. Powell; Powell describes his 1870 journey and observations
of the Hopi way of life. Illus. Maps. 48 pp. Paper. Amazon.com & Alibris.com, 1972. $4.

THE HOPI WAY: AN ODYSSEY
Robert Boissiere; Illus. 90 pp. Paper. Sunstone Press, $8.95.

THE HOPI WAY: TALES FROM A CHANGING CULTURE
Mando Sevillano; drawings by Mike Castro
Illus. 102 pp. Paper. Amazon.com, 1986. $12.95.

HOPITUY
Heather Ahtone & Mark Bahti; 96 pp. University of Oklahoma Press, $15.95.

TOM HORN, GOVERNMENT SCOUT & INDIAN INTERPRETER
Tom Horn; Reprint of 1904 edition. A first-hand account of the Apache Indian wars
of the American Southwest. 318 pp. Paper. The Rio Grande Press, $12.

HORSE, FOLLOW CLOSELY: NATIVE AMERICAN HORSEMANSHIP
GaWaNi Pony Boy; Illus. 144 pp. Amazon.com, 1998. $39.95.

THE HORSE IN BLACKFOOT INDIAN CULTURE
John C. Ewers; Bound with comparative material from other western tribes. Reprint.
Illus. 374 pp. Paper. Smithsonian Institution Press, $21.

*HORSE OF SEVEN MOONS
Karen Taschek; Story of a 16 year old Apache boy, a 14 year old Anglo girl, and the horse
they share, unbeknownst to each other. Paper. U. of New Mexico Press, 2004. $12.95.

*THE HORSE & THE PLAINS INDIAN
Raymond Schuessler & Tom Weist
Grades 4-10. 32 pp. Council for Indian Education, $8.95; paper, $2.95.

**THE HORSEMEN OF THE AMERICAS: AN EXHIBITION FROM THE HALL OF THE
HORSEMEN OF THE AMERICAS** Sheila Ohlendorf and William D. Wittliff
Illus. Paper. University of Texas, Humanities, 1968. $5.

HORSES OF THEIR OWN MAKING: AN EQUESTRIAN HISTORY OF NATIVE AMERICA
Steven M. Fountain; Illus. University of Washington Press, 2017.

*HOSKILA & THE RED BUFFALO
Moses Big Crow
A story from Lakota Sioux traditions. Grades 3 and up. Illus. Paper. Tipi Press, $5.95.

HOSTEEN KLAH: NAVAHO MEDICINE MAN & SAND PAINTER
Franc J. Newcomb
Reprint of 1964 edition. Illus. Map. 227 pp. Paper. University of Oklahoma Press, $17.95.

HOSTILES? THE LAKOTA GHOST DANCE & BUFFALO BILL'S WILD WEST
Sam A. Madra; Illus. 288 pp. University of Oklahoma Press, 2007. $24.95.

HOTEVILLA: HOPI SRINE OF THE COVENANT/MICROCOSM OF THE WORLD
Thomas E. Mails & Dan Evehema; Illus. 577 pp. Amazon.com, 1996. $40; paper, $25.

HOTLINE HEALERS: AN ALMOST BROWNE NOVEL
Gerald Vizenor; Collection of stories set on the White Earth Reservation draws upon the
trickster tradition in Native America culture. 182 pp. Wesleyan University Press, 1997.
Distributed by University Press of New England, 1997. $22.95.

HOUSE MADE OF DAWN
N. Scott Momaday; Pulitzer Prize winning first novel. Reprint of 1968 edition.
192 pp. University of Arizona Press, 1996. $35.

HOUSE OF SHATTERING LIGHT: LIFE AS AN AMERICAN INDIAN MYSTIC
Joseph Rael; Illus. 216 pp. Paper. Council Oak Books, 2003. $15.

**HOUSEHOLDS & HEGEMONY: EARLY CREEK PRESTIGE GOODS,
SYMBOLIC CAPITAL, AND SOCIAL POWER** Cameron B. Wesson
Illus. Maps. 256 pp. Paper. University of Nebraska Press, 2013. $30.

**HOUSEHOLDS & FAMILIES OF THE LONGHOUSE IROQUOIS
AT SIX NATIONS RESERVE**
Merlin G. Myers; Illus. Maps. 260 pp. University of Nebraska Press, 2006. $75.

**HOUSEHOLDS & HEGEMONY: EARLY CREEK PRESTIGE GOODS,
SYMBOLIC CAPITAL, AND SOCIAL POWER**
Cameron B. Wesson; Illus. Maps. Tables. 256 pp. U. of Nebraska Press, 2008. $55.

ALLAN HOUSER
Barbara H. Perlman; The art of Allan Houser. 133 color & 183 bxw illus. 266 pp.
Smithsonian Institution Press, 1991. $75.

ALLAN HOUSER: AN AMERICAN MASTER - CHIRICAHUA APACHE, 1914-1991
W. Jackson Rushing & Allan Houser; Illus. 256 pp. Harry N. Abrams, 2004. $60.

ALLAN HOUSER DRAWINGS: THE CENTENNIAL EXHIBITION
W. Jackson Rushing III & Hadley Jerman
Illus. 108 pp. Paper. University of Oklahoma Press, $15.95.

**HOUSES BENEATH THE ROCK: THE ANASAZI OF CANYON DE CHELLY
& NAVAJO NATIONAL MONUMENT**
David Noble, Editor; Illus. Maps. Photos. 56 pp. Paper. Amazon.com, 1992. $8.95.

*HOUSES OF BARK: TIPI, WIGWAM, & LONGHOUSE
Grades 3-7. Illus. 25 pp. Amazon.com, 1990. $12.95.

HOUSES & HOUSE-LIFE OF THE AMERICAN ABORIGINES
Lewis Henry Morgan; Illus. Paper. University of Utah Press. $19.95.

HOUSING PROBLEMS & NEEDS OF AMERICAN INDIANS & ALASKA NATIVES
C. Thomas Kingsley, et al; Illus. 162 pp. Paper. Amazon.com, 1997. $40.

*HOW THE BABY DEER GOT SPOTS: A STORY BASED ON INDIAN LEGEND
Steven A. Roy; Grades 3 and up. Illus. 17 pp. Paper. Tipi Press, 1996. $3.95.

HOW CAN ONE SELL THE AIR? CHIEF SEATTLE'S VISION
Eli Gifford & R. Michael Cook
New edition. Illus. Photos. 96 pp. Paper. The Book Publishing Co., 1993. $9.95.

**HOW CHOCTAWS INVENTED CIVILIZATION & WHY CHOCTAWS
WILL CONQUER THE WORLD**
D.L. Birchfield; Illus. Maps. 382 pp. University of New Mexico Press, 2002. $27.95.

*HOW COYOTE STOLE THE SUMMER: A NATIVE AMERICAN FOLKTALE
Stephen Krensky; Grades K-4. Illus. 48 pp. Amazon.com & Alibris.com, 2008.

*HOW FIRE GOT INTO THE ROCKS & TREES: A STORY BASED ON INDIAN LEGEND
Steven A. Roy; Grades 3 and up. Illus. 17 pp. Paper. Tipi Press, 1996. $3.95.

*HOW FOOD WAS GIVEN: AN OKANAGAN LEGEND
illus. by Barb Marchand; Grades K-6. Illus. Paper. Theytus, 1991. $12.95.

HOW INDIANS USE WILD PLANTS FOR FOOD, MEDICINE & CRAFTS
Frances Densmore; Focuses on about 200 plants used by the Chippewa.
Reprint of 1926-27 edition. Photos. 155 pp. Paper. Dover Publications, $7.95.

HOW IT IS: THE NATIVE AMERICAN PHILOSOPHY OF V.F. CORDOVA
Kathleen Dean Moore, Kurt Peters, Ted Jojola, Amber Lacy, Editors
Essays on the life and work of the first Native American woman PhD in philosophy.
272 pp. University of Arizona Press, 2007. $45; paper, $19.95.

HOW LIFE CAME TO BE
Long Standing Bear Chief
Blackfoot stories. Illus. by Melvin Tail Feathers. Amazon.com, $7.95.

*HOW MARTEN GOT HIS SPOTS & OTHER KOOTENAI INDIAN STORIES
Kootenai Culture Committee
Traditional Kootenai animal stories. Also, includes a description of how Kootenai tipis are constructed. Grades 3-4. 48 pp. Paper. SKC Press, $6.

*HOW MEDICINE CAME TO THE PEOPLE: A TALE OF THE ANCIENT CHEROKEES
Deborah L. Duvall; illus. by Murv Jacob; Vol. 2 of the Grandmother Stories...Cherokee
history & legend. All ages. Illus. University of New Mexico Press, 2002. $14.95.

*HOW NAMES WERE GIVEN: AN OKANAGAN LEGEND
Illus. by Barb Marchand; Grades K-6. Illus. Paper. Theytus, 1991. $12.95.

*HOW THE PLAINS INDIANS LIVED
George Fichter; Grades 6 and up. David McKay, 1980. $10.95.

*HOW RABBIT LOST HIS TAIL: A TRADITIONAL CHEROKEE LEGEND
Deborah L. Duvall; illus. by Murv Jacob; Vol. 3 of the Grandmother Stories...
Cherokee history & legend. All ages. Illus. University of New Mexico Press, 2003. $14.95.

*HOW RABBIT STOLE THE FIRE: A NORTH AMERICAN INDIAN FOLK TALE
Joanna Troughton, retold by and illus by
Preschool-2. Illus. 28 pp. Amazon.com, 1986. $13.95.

*HOW RAVEN STOLE THE SUN
Maria Williams (Tlingit); illus. by Felix Vigil (Jicarilla pache/Jemez Pueblo)
Tlingit sory. Grades 3 to 8. Illus. 32 pp. NMAI Press & Abbeville Press, 2001. $14.95.

*HOW THE STARS FELL INTO THE SKY: A NAVAJO LEGEND
Jerrie Oughton; Grades K-3. Illus. 32 pp. Amazon.com, 1996. $16; paper, $5.95.

HOW TO COLLECT NORTH AMERICAN INDIAN ARTIFACTS
Robert F. Brand; Illus. 151 pp. Amazon.com, $11.95.

HOW TO ENROLL IN AN INDIAN/ALASKA NATIVE TRIBE
A step-by-step plan for an individual who is interested in enrolling in a tribe.
Includes forms and instructions. Amazon.com, 1994. $19.95.

**HOW TO KEEP YOUR LANGUAGE ALIVE:
A GUIDE TO ONE-ON-ONE LANGUAGE LEARNING**
Leanne Hinton, with Matt Vera & Nancy Steele
A master-apprentice language program. Paper. heyday Books. $17.95.

HOW TO MAKE CHEROKEE CLOTHING
Donald Sizemore; Detailed instructions and illustrations. Illus. 304 pp.
Paper. Book Publishing Co. & Cherokee Publications, $23.95.

HOW TO RESEARCH AMERICAN INDIAN BLOOD LINES
Cecilia S. Carpenter; Illus. 110 pp. Paper. Amazon.com, 1987. $9.

HOW TO TAKE PART IN LAKOTA CEREMONIES
William Stolzman; A step-by-step guide to the Pipe, Sweatbath, Vision Quest, Yuwipi,
Lowanpi, and Sundance ceremonies of the Lakota (Sioux). Illus. 72 pp. Paper. VIP
Publishing, $7.95.

HOW TO TAN SKINS THE INDIAN WAY
Evard H. Gibby; Explains brain tanning as it was done by Native Americans. Photos.
37 line drawings. 32 pp. Paper. Eagle's View Publishing & Written Heritage, 1991. $7.95.

**HOW TO TEACH ABOUT AMERICAN INDIANS: A GUIDE FOR THE SCHOOL
LIBRARY MEDIA SPECIALIST**
Karen D. Harvey, et al; 240 pp. Greenwood, 1995. $35.

**HOW TO TELL THE DIFFERENCE: A GUIDE TO EVALUATING
CHILDREN'S BOOKS FOR ANTI-INDIAN BIAS**
Beverly Slapin, et al; Revised edition. Illus. Paper. Oyate, 1995. $11.

*HOW TURTLE SET THE ANIMALS FREE: AN OKANAGAN LEGEND
illus. by Barb Marchand; Grades K-4. Illus. Paper. Theytus, 1991. $12.95.

*HOW WOULD YOU SURVIVE AS AN AMERICAN INDIAN
Scott Steedman
History of the American Indian. Grades 3 and up. Illus. Paper. Amazon.com, $7.95.

**HOZHO?WALKING IN BEAUTY: NATIVE AMERICAN STORIES
OF INSPIRATION, HUMOR, AND LIFE**
Paula Gunn Allen & Carolyn Dunn Anderson; 256 pp. Paper. McGraw-Hill, 2001. $16.95.

HUBBELL TRADING POST: TRADE, TOURISM, AND THE NAVAJO SOUTHWEST
Erica Cottam; Illus. maps. 368 pp. University of Oklahoma Press, 2015. $29.95.

HUICHOL ART & CULTURE: BALANCING THE WORLD
Melissa S. Powell & C. Jill Grady; Art & essays from Huichol scholars.
Illus. Photos. 176 pp. Paper. Museum of New Mexico Press, 2010. $39.95.

HUICHOL INDIAN CEREMONIAL CYCLE
Jay C. Fikes, PhD; 120 pp. Millenia Press, 1997.

HUICHOL INDIAN SACRED RITUALS
Mariano Valadez; Revised edition. 112 pp. Paper. Amber Lotus, 1998. $24.95.

HUICHOL MYTHOLOGY
Jay C. Fikes, Phil Weigand, Acelia Garcia de Weigand, Eds.
Illus. University of Arizona Press, 2004.

HUMAN & CULTURAL DEVELOPMENT
J.T. Robinson, et al. 66 pp. paper. Indiana Historical Society, 1974. $2.75.

HUMOR ME: AN ANTHOLOGY OIF HUMOR BY WRITERS OF COLOR
John McNally, Editor; Sherman Alexie's humor and Jim Northrup's satire
in their stories.232 pp. Paper. University of Iowa Press, 2002. $21.

*THE HUNT
Samuel Stanley and Pearl Oberg
Grades 5-9. 32 pp. Paper. Council for Indian Education, 1976. $1.95.

THE HUNT FOR WILLIE BOY: INDIAN-HATING & POPULAR CULTURE
James A. Sandos & Larry E. Burgess
The story of the Paiute-Chemehuevi Indian, Willie Boy, and his flight from justice.
Illus. 182 pp. Map. Biblio. University of Oklahoma Press, 1994. $19.95; paper, $12.95.

HUNTED LIKE A WOLF: THE STORY OF THE SEMINOLE WAR
Milton Meltzer; Illus. 186 pp. Pineapple Press, 2004. $16.95.

*THE HUNTER & THE RAVENS
Mary Holthaus; Eskimo legends. Grades K-3. 32 pp.
Council for Indian Education, 1976. $8.95; paper, $2.95.

*THE HUNTER & THE WOODPECKER
Christine Crowl; Grades Preschool-6. Illus. 12 pp. Paper. Tipi Press, 1990. $2.50.

**HUNTER-GATHERER MORTUARY PRACTICES
DURING THE CENTRAL TEXAS ARCHAIC**
Leland C. Bement; Illus. 176 pp. University of Texas Pres, 1994. $37.50.

**HUNTERS AT THE MARGIN: NATIVE PEOPLE & WILDLIFE
CONSERVATION IN THE NORTHWEST TERRITORIES**
John Sandlos; 352 pp. University of Washington Press, 2007. $94; paper, $37.95.

**HUNTERS & BUREAUCRATS: POWER, KNOWLEDGE, & ABORIGINAL-STATE
RELATIONS IN THE SOUTHWEST YUKON** Paul Nadasdy
Illus. Maps. 328 pp. University of Washington Press, 2004. $105; paper, $37.95.

**HUNTERS, CARVERS, AND COLLECTORS: THE CHAUNCEY C. NASH COLLECTION
OF INUIT ART** Maija M. Lutz; Illus. Paper. Peabody Museum, $21.95

HUNTERS OF THE BUFFALO
R. Stephen Irwin; Illus. 52 pp. Paper. Hancock House, 1984. $3.95.

HUNTERS OF THE EASTERN FOREST
R. Stephen Irwin; 52 pp. Paper. Hancock House, 1984. $3.95.

HUNTERS OF THE ICE
R. Stephen Irwin; Illus. 84 pp. Paper. Hancock House, 1984. $5.95.

HUNTERS OF THE NORTHERN FOREST
R. Stephen Irwin; Illus. 52 pp. Paper. Hancock House, 1984. $3.95.

**HUNTERS OF THE NORTHERN FOREST: DESIGNS FOR SURVIVAL
AMONG THE ALASKAN KUTCHIN** Richard K. Nelson
Illus. 320 pp. Second edition. Paper. University of Chicago Press, 1986. $12.95.

HUNTERS OF THE NORTHERN ICE
Richard K. Nelson; Illus. Paper. University of Chicago Press, 1972. $12.95.

HUNTERS OF THE SEA
R. Stephen Irwin; Illus. 52 pp. Hancock House, 1984. $3.95.

HUNTING BY PREHISTORIC HORTICULTURISTS IN THE AMERICAN SOUTHWEST
C.R. Szuter; Illus. 475 pp. Amazon.com, 1991. $80.

**HUNTING FOR HIDES: DEERSKINS, STATUS, AND CULTURAL CHANGE IN THE
PROHISTORIC APPALACHIAN** Heather A. Lapham
Changes in Native American communities as they adapted to advancing Europeans.
Illus. 200 pp. University of Alabama Press, 2006. $60; paper, $29.95. E-Book available.

**HUNTING SACRED - EVERYTHING LISTENS: A PUEBLO INDIAN MAN'S
ORAL TRADITION LEGACY**
Larry Littlebird; Illus. 128 pp. Paper. Western Edge Press, 2001. $10.95.

HUNTING A SHADOW: THE SEARCH FOR BLACK HAWK
Crawford Thayer; Illus. 496 pp. Paper. Thayer Associates, 1984. $9.95.

HUNTING TRADITION IN A CHANGING WORLD: YUP'IK LIVES IN ALASKA TODAY
Ann Fienup-Riordan, et al; Illus. 320 pp. Paper. Amazon.com, 2000. $22.

*HUNTING WITH THE NATIVE AMERICANS
Rob Staeger; Grades 4-9. Illus. 64 pp. Mason Crest Publishers, 2003. $19.95.

HUUPUK"ANUM: THE ART, CULTURE & HISTORY OF NUU-CHAH-NULTH PEOPLE
Alan L. Hoover; 110 photos & Illus. 400 pp. UBC Press, 1999. $39.95.

*THE HURON
Craig & Katherine Doherty; Grades 4-8. 32 pp. Amazon.com, 1994. $22.60.

HURON: FARMERS OF THE NORTH
Bruce G. Trigger; Illus. 176 pp. Paper. Amazon.com, 2002. $9.95.

*THE HURON: GREAT LAKES
Nancy Bonvillain; Grades 5 and up. Illus. Chelsea House, 1989. $17.95.

HURON-WENDAT: THE HERITAGE OF THE CIRCLE
Georges E. Sioui & Jane Brierly; Revised edition. 280 pp. UBC Press, 1999.

HUSK OF TIME: THE PHOTOGRAPHS OF VICTOR MASAYESVA
Victor Masayesva, Jr.; intro by Beverly R. Singer; The author navigates his personal associations with Hopi subject matter in varied investigations of biology, ecology, humanity & history. 128 pp. University of Arizona Press, 2006. $40; paper, $24.95.

I

*I AM THE EAGLE FREE (SKY SONG): A SIX NATIONS LEGEND AS INTERPRETED BY SIMON PAUL-DENE Grade K-4. Illus. 36 pp. Paper. Theytus, 1992. $10.95.

I AM ESKIMO: AKNIK MY NAME
Paul Green & Abbe Abbott
Reprint of 1959 ed. Illus. 86 pp. Paper. Alaska Northwest, $12.95.

I AM THE GRAND CANYON: THE STORY OF THE HAVASUPAI PEOPLE
Stephen Hirst; 276 pp. Paper. University of Arizona Press, 2007. $18.95.

I AM HERE; TWO THOUSAND YEARS OF SOUTHWEST INDIAN CULTURE
Stewart Peckham; Museum of New Mexico Press, 1988. $34.95; paper, $24.95.

I AM LOOKING TO THE NORTH FOR MY LIFE: SITTING BULL, 1876-1881
Joseph Manzione; What happened to the Sioux after the Little Bighorn. Illustrates how two countries, the U.S. & Canada, struggled to control their potentially explosive common border. Illus. 184 pp. Paper. University of Utah Press, 1991. $17.95; eBook, $14.95.

*I AM REGINA
Sally Keehn; illus. by Jan Schoenherr; Fictionalized account of a girl held captive by the Delaware Indians from 1755 to 1764. Grades 4-8. Illus. 240 pp. Philomel, 1991. $15.95.

I BECOME PART OF IT: SACRED DIMENSIONS IN NATIVE AMERICAN LIFE
D.M. Dooling & Paul Jordan-Smith, Eds.; Illus. 304 pp. Paper. Parabola, 1989. $14.95.

I CHOOSE LIFE: CONTEMPORARY MEDICAL & RELIGIOUS PRACTICES IN THE NAVAJO WORLD
Maureen Trudelle Schwarz; 384 pp. U. of Oklahoma Press, 2010. $50; paper, $24.95.

I DREAM OF YESTERDAY & TOMORROW: A CELEBRATION OF JAMES BAY CREE
Illus. 200 pp. Paper. University of Toronto Press, 2003. $26.99.

I FOUGHT WITH GERONIMO
Jason Betzinez & Wilbur Nye
Illus. 214 pp. University of Nebraska Press, 1987. $19.95; paper, $7.95.

I HAVE COME TO STEP OVER YOUR SOUL: A TRUE NARRATIVE OF MURDER & INDIAN JUSTICE Charles W. Sasser; 298 pp. Amazon.com, 1987. $17.95.

I HAVE SPOKEN: AMERICAN HISTORY THROUGH THE VOICES OF THE INDIANS
Virginia I. Armstrong, Editor; Reprint. 230 pp. Paper. Amazon.com, 1971. $15.95.

I HEAR THE TRAIN: REFLECTIONS, INVENTIONS, REFRACTIONS
Louis Owens; Illus. 288 pp. University of Oklahoma Press, 2001. $19.95.

*I'ISHIYATAM (DESIGNS): A CAHUILLA WORD BOOK
Katherine Siva Saubel & Anne Galloway
Cahuilla basket designs, with the words in Cahuilla & English. Age 10 and up. Reprint. Illus. Booklet. Malki-Ballena Press, 1978. $5.50.

I SEND A VOICE
Evelyn Eaton; A first person account of what actually transpires inside of an Amerindian Sweat Lodge. Illus. 180 pp. Amazon.com, 1978. $12.95; paper, $4.95.

I, THE SONG: CLASSICAL POETRY OF NATIVE NORTH AMERICA
A.L. Soens; Illus. Paper. University of Utah Press, 1999. $19.95.

I STAND IN THE CENTER OF THE GOOD: INTERVIEWS WITH CONTEMPORARY NATIVE AMERICAN ARTISTS
Lawrence Abbott; Illus. 330 pp. University of Nebraska Press, 1994. $65.

I SWALLOW TURQUOISE FOR COURAGE
Hershman R. John; Poetry. 96 pp. Paper. University of Arizona Press, 2005. $15.95.

I TELL YOU NOW: AUTOBIOGRAPHICAL ESSAYS BY NATIVE AMERICAN WRITERS
Brian Swann & Arnold Krupat; 283 pp. Paper. University of Nebraska Press, 1987. $12.

"I WILL BE MEAT FOR MY SALISH": THE BUFFALO & THE MONTANA WRITERS PROJECT INTERVIEWS ON THE FLATHEAD INDIAN RESERVATION
Bon I. Whealdon; Robert Bigart, Ed.
Illus. 288 pp. Paper. Montana Historical Society Press & Amazon.com, 2002. $18.95

I WILL FIGHT NO MORE FOREVER: CHIEF JOSEPH & THE NEZ PERCE WAR
Merrill D. Beal; Reprint. Illus. 384 pp. Paper. U. of Washington Press, 2003. $17.95.

I WILL TELL OF MY WAR STORY: PICTORIAL ACCOUNT OF THE NEZ PERCE WAR
Scott M. Thompson; Illus. 122 pp. Paper. University of Washingtpn Press, 2000. $26.95.

ICE WINDOW: LETTERS FROM A BERING STRAIT VILLAGE 1898-1902
edited by Kathleen Loop Smith & Verbeck Smith
A teacher and a student helping a generation of Native Inupiat adjust to the white culture being thrust upon them while learning their language and lifeways. Illus. Maps. Photos. 392 pp. University of Alaska Press, 2002. $34.95; paper, $24.95.

ICHISHKIIN SINWIT YAKAMA / YAKIMA SAHAPTIN DICTIONARY
Virginia Beavert & Sharon Hargus; essays by Bruce Rigsby
Dictionary documents the dialect of Sahaptin that is spoken by the Yakama people. Illus. 576 pp. Paper. University of Washington Press, 2010. $60.

ICON OF POWER: FELINE SYMBOLISM IN THE AMERICAS
Nicholas J. Saunders; Illus. 310 pp. Amazon.com, 1998. $75.

THE ICONIC NORTH: CULTURAL CONSTRUCTIONS OF ABORIGINAL LIFE IN POSTWAR CANADA Joan Sangster
UBC Press, 2016. $95; paper, $34.95; eBook, $34.95.

IDA ANN BELOVED BANNOCK PAPOOSE: A CIVIL WAR EPISODE
Carole G. Sorenson; Illus. 145 pp. Paper. Copa Publishing, 1997. $14.95.

IDENTIFYING OUTSTANDING TALENT IN AMERICAN INDIAN & ALASKAN NATIVE STUDENTS Illus. 84 pp. Amazon.com, 1995. $30.

IDENTIITY BY DESIGN
National Museum of the American Indian
Illus. 160 pp. NMAI Press & HarperCollins, 2007. $24.95.

IDENTITY, FEASTING, & THE ARCHAEOLOGY OF THE GREATER SOUTHWEST
Barbara J. Mills, Ed.; Illus. 360 pp. U. Press of Colorado, 2004. $65; paper, $26.95.

IDENTITY POLITICS OF DIFFERENCE: THE MIXED-RACE AMERICAN INDIAN EXPERIENCE Michelle R. Montgomery
168 pp. University Press of Colorado, 2017. $48; eBook, $38.

IDONAPSHE, LET'S EAT: TRADITIONAL ZUNI FOODS
A:shiwi A:wan Museum & Heritage Center
Illus. Paper. University of New Mexico Press, 1999. $16.95.

IF YOU KNEW THE CONDITIONS: A CHRONICLE OF THE INDIAN MEDICAL SERVICE AND AMERICAN INDIAN HEALTH CARE, 1908-1955 David H. DeJong
Illus. 198 pp. Paper. Lexington Books, 2008. $80; paper, $32.99; eBook, $32.99.

*IF YOU LIVED WITH THE HOPI INDIANS
Anne Kamma & Linda Gardner
Grades 2+. Illus. 80 pp. Paper. Amazon.com, 1999. $5.99.

*IF YOU LIVED WITH THE IROQUOIS
Ellen Levine; Grades 2 and up. Illus. 85 pp. Paper. Amazon.com, $8.49.

*IF YOU LIVED WITH THE SIOUX INDIANS
Ann McGovern; Grades K-3. Illus. 96 pp. Paper. Amazon.com, 1974. $5.99.

IF YOU POISON US: URANIUM & NATIVE AMERICANS
Peter H. Eichstaedt; Story of how America's frantic entry into the nuclear age impacted Native American communities. Illus. 32 color photos. 272 pp. University of New Mexico Press, 1994. $19.95.

IF YOU TAKE MY SHEEP...THE EVOLUTION & CONFLICTS OF NAVAJO PASTORALISM, 1630-1868 Lynn R. Bailey; Illus. 304 pp. Westernlore, 1980. $14.95.

IGNITING KING PHILIP'S WAR: THE JOHN SASSAMON MURDER TRIAL
Yasuhide Kawashima; Map. 192 pp. Paper. University Press of Kansas, 2004. $14.95.

IGNOBLE SAVAGE: AMERICAN LITERARY RACISM, 1790-1890
Louise Barnett; 220 pp. Greenwood, 1976. $29.95.

*IKTOMI & THE BERRRIES: A PLAINS INDIAN STORY
Paul Goble; Grades PS-3. Illus. 32 pp. Amazon.com, 1989. $15.

*IKTOMI & THE BOULDER
Paul Goble; Grades PS-3. Illus. 32 pp. Amazon.com, 1990. $15.

*IKTOMI & THE BUFFALO SKULL: A PLAINS INDIAN STORY
Paul Goble, as told by & Illus.; Grades PS-3. Illus. 32 pp. Amazon.com, 1991. $15.

*IKTOMI & THE DUCKS
Paul Goble; Grades PS-3. Illus. 32 pp. Amazon.com, 1992. $15.

IKTOMI & THE DUCKS & OTHER SIOUX STORIES
Zitkala-Sa; 3rd Ed. 225 pp. Paper. University of Nebraska Press, 2004. $11.95.

*IKWA OF THE MOUND-BUILDER INDIANS
Margaret Zehmer Searcy
Story of a young Indian girl living in the Southeastern U.S. before colonization.
Grades 3-8. Illus. Map. Photos. 800 pp. Amazon.com, $13.95; paper, $6.95.

I HEAR THE TRAIN: REFECTIONS, INVENTIONS, REFRACTIONS
Louis Owens; Illus. 265 pp. University of Oklahoma Press, 2001. $29.95.

I'LL GO & DO MORE: ANNIE DODGE WAUNEKA, A NAVAJO LEADER & ACTIVIST
Carolyn Niethammer; The story of Annie Dodge Wauneka (1918-1997). Illus. Map. 291 pp. University of Nebraska Press, 2001. $29.95.

I'LL SING 'TIL THE DAY I DIE: CONVERSATIONS WITH TYENDINAGA ELDERS
Beth Brant; Elders speak social and political history to Mohawk author, Beth Brant. Illus. 180 pp. Paper. McGilligan Books, $12.95.

ILIMPA'CHI' (WE'RE GONA EAT!): A CHICKASAW COOKBOOK
JoAnn Ellis & Vicki Penner; More than 40 recipes; reminiscences, & lessons in Chickasaw lifeways. Stories reveal the organic connections between food, family, & Chickasaw Nation history. Illus. 160 pp. Chickasaw Press. Distributed by the University of Oklahoma Press, 2011. $30.

THE ILLINOIS & INDIANA INDIANS
H.W. Beckwith; Reprint of 1884 edition. Paper. Arno Press, 1975. Amazon.com.

AN ILLUSTRATED HISTORY OF THE ARTS IN SOUTH DAKOTA
Arthur R. Huseboe; With a major section on Sioux arts by leading Lakota artist Arthur Amiotte. Illus. 396 pp. Center for Western Studies, $24.95.

ILLUSTRATED MYTHS OF NATIVE AMERICA: THE SOUTHWEST, WESTERN RANGE, PACIFIC NORTHWEST & CALIFORNIA
Tim McNeese; Illus. 160 pp. Blandford Press, 1999. $27.95.

IMAGERY & CREATIVITY: ETHNOAESTHETICS & ART WORLDS IN THE AMERICAS
Dorothea S. Whitten & Norman E. Whitten, Jr.
377 pp. University of Arizona Press, 1993. $34.95; paper, $24.95.

IMAGES FROM THE INSIDE PASSAGE: AN ALASKAN PORTRAIT BY WINTER & POND Vicoria Wyatt; A catalog for an exhibition documenting the work of Lloyd Winter and E. Percy Pond. Includes photos of Alaskan natives, landscapes and village scenes. 144 pp. University of Alaska Press, 1989. $40; paperback, $19.95.

IMAGES FROM THE REGION OF THE PUEBLO INDIANS OF NORTH AMERICA
Aby M. Warburg; Michael P. Steinberg, tr.; Illus. 136 pp. Cornell U. Press, 1995. $36.50.

IMAGES IN OSAGE: AN ILLUSTRATED GUIDE TO THE SYLVESTER J. TINKER COLLECTION Diane L. Good; Paper. Kansas State Historical Society, 1990. $5.95.

IMAGES OF A PEOPLE: TLINGIT MYTHS & LEGENDS
Mary Helen Pelton & Jacqueline DiGennaro, Editors
22 Tlingit legends. Illus. 150 pp. Amazon.com, 1992. $22.

IMAGES OF THE OTHER: A GUIDE TO MICROFORM MANUSCRIPTS ON INDIAN-WHITE RELATIONS Polly S. Grimshaw; 200 pp. University of Illinois Press, 1991. $27.50.

IMAGES OF A VANISHED LIFE: PLAINS INDIAN DRAWINGS FROM THE COLLECTION OF THE PENNSYLVANIA ACADEMY OF FINE ARTS
John C. Ewers, et al; Illus. 50 pp. Pennsylvania Academy of Art, 1985.

IMAGINING GERONIMO: AN APACHE ICON IN POPULAR CULTURE
William M. Clements; 320 pp. University of New Mexico, $39.95; paper, $24.95.

IMAGINING HEAD-SMASHED-IN: ABORIGINAL BUFFALO HUNTING ON THE NORTHERN PLAINS
Jack W. Brink; Illus. Maps. 60 pp. U. of Washington Press, 2008. $94; paper, $39.95.

IMAGINING INDIANS IN THE SOUTHWEST: PERSISTENT VISIONS OF THE PRIMITIVE PAST Leah Dilworth
Illus. 304 pp. Smithsonian Institution Press, 1996. $34.95; paper, $16.95.

IMAGINING SOVEREIGNTY: SELF-DETERMINATION IN AMERICAN INDIAN LAW & LITERATURE
David J. Carlson; 242 pp. Paper. University of Oklahoma Press, 2016. $$29.95.

JOSEPH IMHOF: ARTIST OF THE PUEBLOS
Nancy Hopkins Reily; Biography of a famous painter in the American Southwest. Illus. 448 pp. Sunstone Press, 1999. $60.

*THE IMMIGRANT EXPERIENCE
David Reimers; Grades 5 and up. Illus. 112 pp. Chelsea House, 1989. $17.95.

IMMIGRATION & POLITICAL ECONOMY OF HOME: WEST INDIAN BROOKLYN & AMERICAN INDIAN MINNEAOLIS, 1945-1992
Rachel Buff; Illus. 255 pp. University of California Press, 2001. $50; paper, $19.95.

THE IMPACT OF DISLOCATION: THE AMERICAN INDIAN LABOR FORCE AT THE CLOSE OF THE 20th CENTURY
Patricia Kasari; Revised edition. 200 pp. Amazon.com, 1999. $65.

IMPERFECT VICTORIES: THE LEGAL TENACITY OF THE OMAHA TRIBE, 1945-1995
Mark R. Scherer; Details the postwar federal legislation that transferred control over Indian affairs to state authorities. Illus. 166 pp. Paper. U. of Nebraska Press, 1999. $19.95.

THE IMPERIAL OSAGES: SPANISH--INDIAN DIPLOMACY IN THE MISSISSIPPI VALLEY Gilbert Din and Abraham P. Nasatir
Illus. Maps. 432 pp. University of Oklahoma Press, 1983. $49.95.

IMPLEMENTATION OF THE INDIAN GAMING REGULATORY ACT: SURVEY & AUDIT REPORTS Harold Bloom, Editor; Illus. 62 pp. Paper. Amazon.com, 1998. $25.

IMPLEMENTING THE NATIVE AMERICAN GRAVES PROTECTION & REPATRIATION ACT (NAGPRA) Roxana Adams; Amzon.com, 2001.

IMPRISONED ART, COMPLEX PATRONAGE: PLAINS DRAWINGS BY HOWLING WOLF & ZOTOM AT THE AUTRY NATIONAL CENTER
Joyce M. Szabo; Two small books of drawings...images by the Southern Cheyenne warrior artist, Howling Wolf and Zotom, a Kiowa man. The study of Plains Indian ledger art. Illus. Photos. 224 pp. School for Advanced Research, 2011. $60; paper, $30.

IMPROVING AMERICAN INDIAN HEALTH CARE: THE WESTERN CHEROKEE EXPERIENCE William C. Steeler; Illus. Map. 168 pp. U. of Oklahoma Press, 2001. $19.95.

IN THE ABSENCE OF THE SACRED: THE FAILURE OF TECHNOLOGY & THE SURVIVAL OF THE INDIAN NATIONS
Jerry Mander; Reprint. 458 pp. Paper. Amazon.com, 1992. $16.95.

IN A BARREN LAND: AMERICAN INDIAN DISPOSSESSION & SURVIVAL
Paula M. Marks; Illus. 451 pp. Paper. Amazon.com, 1999. $15.95.

IN THE BEAR'S HOUSE
N. Scott Momaday; Explores themes of loneliness, sacredness, and aggression through the author's depiction of the Bear. Illus. 96 pp. University of New Mexico Press, $24.95.

IN BEAUTY I WALK: THE LITERARY ROOTS OF NATIVE AMERICAN WRITING
Jarold Ramsey & Lori Burlingame, Eds.; Anthology of both oral & traditional texts. 416 pp. Paper. University of New Mexico Press, $29.95.

IN THE BELLY OF A LAUGHING GOD: HUMOUR & IRONY IN NATIVE WOMEN'S POETRY Jenifer Andrews
Examines how eight contemporary Native women poets in Canada & U.S. employ humour & irony in their poetry. Illus. University of Toronto Press, 2010. $55.

*IN THE BEGINNING
Ella Clark, Editor; Grades 5-12. Paper. Council for Indian Education, 1977. $2.95.

IN THE BEGINNING: THE NAVAJO GENESIS
Jerrold E. Levy; Navajo religion, myths & rituals. 325 pp. Paper. University of California Press, 1998. $28.95.

IN BITTERNESS & IN TEARS: ANDREW JACKSON'S DESTRUCTION OF THE CREEK & SEMINOLES Sean Michael O'Brien; Illus. 290 pp. Greenwood, 2003. $49.95.

*IN A CIRCLE LONG AGO: A TREASURY OF NATIVE LORE FROM NORTH AMERICA
Nancy Van Laan; Grades PS-3. Illus. 128 pp. Random House, 1995. $21.95.

IN COMPANY: AN ANTHOLOGY OF NEW MEXICO POETS AFTER 1960
Edited by Lee Bartlett, V.B. Price & Dianne Edwards
Collection of poetry including poetry of: Joy Harjo, Jimmy Santiago Baca, N. Scott Momaday, and Arthur Sze. 544 pp. University of New Mexico Press, 2004. $34.95.

IN THE COURTS OF THE CONQUEROR: THE 10 WORST INDIAN LAW CASES EVER DECIDED Walter R. Echo-Hawk
Case studies from a Native American perspective. 576 pp. FulcrumPublishing, 2010. $35.

IN THE DAYS OF VICTORIO: RECOLLECTIONS OF A WARM SPRINGS APACHE
Eve Ball; Records an Apache's own account of their history from 1878-1886. Reprint of 1970 edition. Illus. 222 pp. Paper. University of Arizona Press, 1970. $15.95.

IN DEFENSE OF THE INDIANS: THE DEFENSE OF THE MOST REVEREND LORD, DON FRAY BARTOLOME DE LAS CASAS
Bartolome de Las Casas; Illus. 412 pp. Paper. Northern Illinois U. Press, 2003. $18.

IN DEFENSE OF MOHAWK LAND: ETHNOPOLITICAL CONFLICT IN NATIVE NORTH AMERICA
Linda Pertusati; Illus. 166 pp. State U. of New York Press, 1997. $44.50; paper, $14.95.

IN DIVIDED UNITY: HAUDENOSAUNEE RECLAMATION AT GRAND RIVER
Theresa McCarthy
Illus. 432 pp. Paper. University of Arizona Press, 2017. $35. eBook, $35.

IN THE FIFTH WORLD: PORTRAIT OF THE NAVAJO NATION
Adriel Heisey & Kenji Kawano; Illus. 110 pp. Paper. Treasure Chest Books, 2001. $21.95.

IN THE HANDS OF THE GREAT SPIRIT: THE 20,000 YEAR HISTORY OF THE AMERICAN INDIANS Jake Page
Reprint. Illus. 480 pp. Simon & Schuster, 2003. $30; paper, $16.

IN THE HANDS OF THE SENECAS
Walter D. Edmonds; 233 pp. Paper. Syracuse University Press, $14.95.

IN HONOR OF EYAK: THE ART OF ANNA NELSON HARRY
Michael E. Krauss
Illus. 157 pp. Paper. Alaska Native Language Center, 1982. $10; two cassettes, $9.

IN HONOR OF MARY HAAS: FROM THE HAAS FESTIVAL CONFERENCE ON NATIVE AMERICAN LINGUISTICS William Shipley, Editor; 826 pp. Amazon.com, 1988. $175.

IN THE LAND OF THE GRASSHOPPER SONG: TWO WOMEN IN THE KLAMATH RIVER INDIAN COUNTRY 1908-1909
Mary Ellicott Arnold and Mabel Reed
Second edition. Illus. Map. 344 pp. Paper. Naturegraph, 2011. $19.95.

IN MAD LOVE AND WAR
Joy Harjo; Poetry. Illus. 79 pp. Paper. Wesleyan University Press, 1990. Distributed by University Press of New England. $14.95.

IN THE MAELSTROM OF CHANGE: THE INDIAN TRADE & CULTURAL PROCESS IN THE MIDDLE CONNECTICUT RIVER VALLEY, 1635-1665
Peter A. Thomas; Illus. 568 pp. Garland, 1991. $32.

IN MOHAWK COUNTRY: EARLY NARRATIVES ABOUT A NATIVE PEOPLE
Dean R. Snow, Charles T. Gehring & William A. Starna, Editors
38 narratives written between 1634 and 1810 about the Mohawk Valley and its Iroquois residents. Maps. Biblio. Syracuse University Press, 1998. $39.95; paper, $16.95.

IN THE NAME OF THE SALISH & KOOTENAI NATION: THE 1855 HELL GATE TREATY & THE ORIGIN OF THE FLATHEAD INDIAN RESERVATION
Robert Bigart & Clarence Woodcock, Eds.
Includes text of the treaty & full transcript. 176 pp. Paper. SKC Press, $11.

IN NEZ PERCE COUNTRY
compiled & edited by Lynn & Dennis Baird
Collection of first hand accounts of the Nez Perce Tribe spanning more than 100 years of history. 325 pp. Paper. University of Idaho Press, 2006. $16.95.

IN THE PRESENCE OF THE SUN: STORIES & POEMS, 1961-1991
N. Scott Momaday; Illus. 184 pp. University of New Mexico Press, 2009. $18.95.

IN PURSUIT OF THE NEZ PERCES
reported by Gen. O.O. Howard, Duncan McDonald, & Chief Joseph
Reprint of 1881 ed. Illus. Maps. 307 pp. Paper. Amazon.com, $17.95.

IN PURSUIT OF THE PAST: AN ANTHROPOLOGICAL & BIBLIOGRAPHIC GUIDE TO MARYLAND & DELAWARE Frank W. Porter, III; 268 pp. Scarecrow, 1986. $27.50.

*IN A SACRED MANNER I LIVE: NATIVE AMERICAN WISDOM
Neil Philip, Editor; Grades 6 and up. Illus. 96 pp. Amazon.com, 1997. $20.

IN A SACRED MANNER WE LIVE: PHOTOGRAPHS OF THE AMERICAN INDIAN AT THE BEGINNING OF THE TWENTIETH CENTURY
Don D. Fowler; Illus. 196 pp. Paper. Barre, 1972. $5.95.

IN SEARCH OF NEW ENGLAND'S NATIVE PAST: SELECTED ESSAYS BY GORDON M. DAY Michael F. Foster & William Cowan
Essays on the history of the Western Abenakis and the Indian history of Northwestern New England. Illus. 392 pp. University of Massachusetts Press, 1998. $70; paper, $22.95.

IN SEARCH OF THE WILD INDIAN: PHOTOGRAPHS & LIFE WORKS BY CARL & GRACE MOON
Tom Driebe; 230+ color & 200 bxw photos. 432 pp. Maurose Publishing, $85.

IN THE SHADOW OF MOUNTAINS: TRADITIONAL STORIES OF THE COPPER RIVER INDIANS OF ALASKA
Illus. 102 pp. http://www.native-languages.org/ahtna-legends.htm, 1997. $10.

IN THE SHADOW OF THE SUN: CONTEMPORARY CANADIAN INDIAN & INUIT ART
Gerhard Hoffmann; Illus. 600 pp. University of Chicago Press, 1989. $60.

IN THE SPIRIT OF THE ANCESTORS: CONTEMPORARY NORTHWEST COAST ART AT THE BURKE MUSEUM Robin K. Wright & Kathryn Bunn-Marcuse, Editors
Illus. 168 pp. Paper. University of Washington Press, 2015. $34.95.

IN THE SPIRIT OF CRAZY HORSE
Peter Matthiessen; American Indian Movement and the Leonard Peltier case. 688 pp. Paper. Penguin USA, 1992. $17.95.

IN THE SPIRIT OF MOTHER EARTH: NATURE IN NATIVE AMERICAN ART
Jeremy Schmidt & Laine Thom; Illustrates the relationship between art and nature. 100 full-color & 15 bxw photos. 120 pp. Amazon.com, 1994. $35; paper, $19.95.

IN THE SPIRIT OF TAHLEQUAH: GHOST STORIES FROM THE CHEROKEE NATION
Leslie D. Hannah; 96 pp. Paper. Leslie D. Hannah, 1997. $5.

IN SUN'S LIKENESS & POWER: CHEYENNE ACCOUNTS OF SHIELD & TIPI HERALDRY by James Mooney
2 Vol. set. Illus. Photos. 1320 pp. University of Nebraska Press, 2013. $250.

IN THIS WE ARE NATIVE: MEMOIRS & JOURNEYS
Annick Smith; Paper. 310 pp. Paper. Amazon.com, 2004. $14.95.

IN THE TRAIL OF THE WIND: AMERICAN INDIAN POEMS & RITUAL ORATIONS
John Bierhorst, Ed.; Reprint. 1993. Amazon.com, $49; paper, $5.

IN VAIN I TRIED TO TELL YOU: ESSAYS IN NATIVE AMERICAN ETHNOPOETICS
Dell Hymes; Showcases the methodology and theory of ethnopoetics focusing on Native storytelling traditions of the Pacific Northwest. Reprint of 1981 edition. 424 pp. Paper. University of Nebraska Press, 2004. $29.95.

IN THE VALLEY OF THE ANCIENTS: A BOOK OF NATIVE AMERICAN LEGENDS
Lou Cuevas; Illus. 65 pp. Paper. Western National parks Assn., 1997. $5.95.

IN THE WORDS OF THE ELDERS: ABORIGINAL CULTURES IN TRANSITION
Peter Kulchyski, Don McCaskill & David Newhouse
First Nations cultures. Illus. 480 pp. University of Toronto Press, 1999. $70; paper, $29.95.

INCOME & HEALTH IN A NORTH INDIAN VILLAGE
Mike Shepperdson; Illus. 520 pp. Amazon.com, 1995. $119.95.

INCONSTANT COMPANIONS: ARCHAEOLOGY & NORTH AMERICAN INDIAN ORAL TRADITIONS Ronald J. Mason; Explores the tension between aboriginal oral traditions and the practice of archaeology in North America. 312 pp. University of Alabama Press, 2006. $55; paper, $29.95. E-Book, $27.95.

INCONSTANT SAVAGE: ENGLAND & THE NORTH AMERICAN INDIANS, 1500-1660
H.C. Porter; 588 pp. Biblio Distribution Centre, 1979. $34.95.

*THE INCREDIBLE ESKIMO
Raymond Coccola & Paul King; J. Cameron, Editor; Life among the Barren Land Eskimo. Grade 9. Illus. 435 pp. Paper. Hancock House, 1986. $16.95.

*INDE, THE WESTERN APACHE
Susan L. Shaffer; Grades 5 and up. Illus. Includes 30 student booklets and teacher's resource binder with overhead transparencies, slides, audiocassette. The Heard Museum, 1987. $295.00.

INDEH: AN APACHE ODYSSEY
Eve Ball, et al; Illus. Maps. 360 pp. Paper. University of Oklahoma Press, 1988. $24.95.

INDEX TO THE DECISIONS OF THE INDIAN CLAIMS COMMISSION
Norman A. Ross; 168 pp. N. Ross, 1973. $25.

INDEX TO THE EXPERT TESTIMONY BEFORE BEFORE THE INDIAN CLAIMS COMMISSION: THE WRITTEN REPORTS Norman A. Ross; 112 pp. Amazon.com, 2001.

INDEX TO LITERATURE ON THE AMERICAN INDIAN
Jeanette Henry, Editor; Four vols. Paper. Amazon.com, 1975. $12 each.

INDEX TO THE RECORDS OF THE MORAVIAN MISSION AMONG THE INDIANS OF NORTH AMERICA
Carl J. Fliegel, Compiler; 4 vols. 1,400 pp. Research Publications, 1970. $400 per set.

INDIAN AFFAIRS
Larry Woiwode; 320 pp. Amazon.com, 1991. $18.95.

INDIAN AFFAIRS & THE ADMINISTRATIVE STATE IN THE 19TH CENTURY
Stephen Rockwell; 362 pp. Cambridge University Press, 2010.

INDIAN AFFAIRS IN COLONIAL NEW YORK: THE 17TH CENTURY
Allen W. Trelease; Illus. Maps. 381 pp. Paper. U. of Nebraska Press, 1997. $16.95.

INDIAN AFFAIRS: LAWS & TREATIES: U.S. LAWS, STATUTES, ETC.
Charles J. Kappler, Editor; Reprint. 7 vols. 6,000 pp. Amazon.com, $550.

INDIAN AGENTS OF THE OLD FRONTIER
Flora W. Seymour; Reprint of 1941 edition. Octagon Books, 1973. $27.50.

INDIAN AGENTS: RULERS OF THE RESERVES
John Steckley; Vol. 3 of Critical Indigenous & American Indian Studies series: Indian Agent System in Canada. 195 pp. Peter Lang Publishing, 2016. $89.95;

INDIAN AGRICULTURE IN AMERICA: PREHISTORY TO THE PRESENT
R. Douglas Hurt; Photos. 290 pp. Paper. University Press of Kansas, 1988. $17.95.

INDIAN ALLIANCES & THE SPANISH IN THE SOUTHWEST, 750-1750
William B. Carter; History of the Southwest's Native peoples and their alliances. 328 pp. paper. University of Oklahoma Press, 2007. $24.95.

INDIAN AMERICA: A GEOGRAPHY OF NORTH AMERICAN INDIANS
M. Wallace Ney
Illus. Maps. 56 pp. Paper. VIP Publishing & Cherokee Publications, 1977. $6.

INDIAN AMERICANS: UNITY & DIVERSITY
Murray L. Wax; Prentice-Hall, 1971. $21.

INDIAN ANTIQUITIES OF THE KENNEBEC VALLEY
Charles Willoughby; Arthur E. Spiess, Ed.; Illus. 160 pp. Maine State Museum, 1980. $22.

INDIAN ARROWHEADS - IDENTIFICATION & PRICE GUIDE
Overstreet & Peake; 5th edition. Illus. 950 pp. Hothem House, 1997. $24, postpaid.

INDIAN ART
Richard O. Winstedt; Alibris.com

INDIAN ART & CONNOISSEURSHIP: ESSAYS IN HONOUR OF DOUGLAS BARRETT
John Guy; Illus. 360 pp. Paper. Amazon.com, 1995. $55.

INDIAN ART & CULTURE OF THE NORTHWEST COAST
Della Kew and P.E. Goddard
Reprint of 1978 second edition. Illus. 96 pp. Paper. Hancock House, $12.95.

INDIAN ART IN THE ASHMOLEAN MUSEUM
J.C. Harle & Andrew Topsfield
Illus. 128 pp. University of Chicago Press, 1988. $50; paper, $22.50.

INDIAN ART OF ANCIENT FLORIDA
Barbara Purdy; Illus. 152 pp. University Press of Florida, 1996. $34.95.

INDIAN ART TRADITIONS ON THE NORTHWEST COAST
Roy L. Carlson, Editor; Illus. 214 pp. Paper. U. of Washington Press, 1984. $14.95.

INDIAN ARTIFACTS
Russell; Flint & stone artifacts, with identification & classification.
Illus. 170 pp. Hothem House, 1981. $14.45, postpaid.

INDIAN ARTIFACTS OF THE EAST & SOUTH: AN ID GUIDE
Swope; Many clkasses are described and hundreds of artifacts are shown.
148 pp. Paper. Hothem House, 1982. $14.

INDIAN ARTIFACTS OF THE MIDWEST
Lar Hothem; Reprint. Vol. 2. Illus. 288 pp. Paper. Collector Books, 1994. $19.95.

INDIAN ARTIFACTS OF THE MIDWEST
Lar Hothem; Vol. 5. Illus. 448 pp. Paper. Collector Books. 2003. $21.95.

INDIAN ARTISTS AT WORK
Ulli Steltzer; Illus. 144 pp. University of Washington Press, 1977. $30; paper, $14.95.

INDIAN ARTS & CRAFTS BOARD - SOURCE DIRETORY
A directory of Native American owned & operated businesses located throughout the U.S. that market a wide range of authentic contemporary Native American arts & crafts. Illus. 48 pp. Indian Arts & Crafts Board. Free.

*THE INDIAN AS A SOLDIER AT FORT CUSTER, MONTANA, 1890-1895:
LT. SAMUEL C. ROBERTSON'S FIRST CAVALRY CROW INDIAN CONTINGENT
Richard Upton; Grades 7-12. Illus. 147 pp. Upton Sons, 1985. $27.50.

INDIAN ASSISTANCE HANDBOOK: MARKET SEGMENT UNDERSTANDING
Paper. Athena Information Management, 1996. $25.

THE INDIAN AWAKENING IN LATIN AMERICA
Yves Materne, Editor; Friendship Press, $5.95.

INDIAN AXES & RELATED STONE ARTIFACTS
Lar Hothem; 2nd edition. Illus. 214 pp. Paper. Hothem House, 1993. $24.50, postpaid.

INDIAN BASKET WEAVING
Navajo School of Indian Basketry; Illus. 104 pp. Paper. Written Heritage, $8.95.

INDIAN BASKETMAKERS
Larry Dalrymple; Two-volume slipcased set containing Indian Basketmakers of California and the Great Basin and Indian Basketmakers of the Southwest. 244 pp. Paper. Museum of New Mexico Press, 2001. $60.

INDIAN BASKETMAKERS OF CALIFORNIA & THE GREAT BASIN:
THE LIVING ART & FINE TRADITION Larry Dalrymple; Features the baskets and basketmakers of the Hupa, Yurok, Karuk, Tolowa, Western Mono or northern California, and the Great Basin tribes including the Western Shoshoni, Northern Paiute, Washoe and Chemehuevi. Illus. Map. 80 pp Paper. Museum of New Mexico Press, 2001. $29.95.

INDIAN BASKETMAKERS OF THE SOUTHWEST: THE LIVING ART & FINE
TRADITION Larry Dalrymple**;** Features the baskets and basketmakers of the Hualapai, Havasupai, Yavapai, Western Apache; Jicarilla Apache, the Ute, San Juan Paiute, Navajo, Tohono O'odham; Pueblos of New Mexico and Hopi of Arizona. Illus. Map. 156 pp. Paper. Museum of New Mexico Press, 2001. $29.95.

INDIAN BASKETRY
George W. James; Reprint. Illus. 271 pp. Paper. Hothem House & Dover, $7.95.

INDIAN BASKETRY ARTISTS OF THE SOUTHWEST:
DEEP ROOTS, NEW GROWTH Susan Brown McGreevy
Illus. 96 pp. Paper. School of American Research Press, 2001. $19.95.

INDIAN BASKETS
Sarah & William Turnbaugh
3rd revised edition. Illus. 256 pp. Paper. Schiffer Publishing, 2004. $29.95.

INDIAN BASKETS & CURIOS
Repro. of 1902 Frohman Trading Co. Illus. 28 pp. Catalog. Paper. Binford & Mort, $6.50.

INDIAN BASKETS OF CENTRAL CALIFORNIA
Ralph Shanks; edited by Lisa Woo Shanks
Art, Culture & History: Native American Basketry from San Francisco Bay & Monterey Bay North to Mendocino & East to the Sierras. 190 color Illus. 176 pp. University of Washington Press & Malki-Ballena Press, 2006. $45.

INDIAN BASKETS OF THE PACIFIC NORTHWEST & ALASKA
Lobb; photos by Al Wolfe ; Illus. 130 pp. Amazon.com, 1990. $29.50.

INDIAN BATTLES ALONG THE ROGUE RIVER: ONE OF AMERICA'S WILD
AND SCENIC RIVERS Frank K. Walsh
Second edition. Illus. 32 pp. Paper. Te-Cum-Tom, 1972. $4.95.

INDIAN BATTLES, MURDERS, SEIGES, AND FORAYS IN THE SOUTHWEST:
THE NARRATIVE OF COLONEL JOSEPH BROWN Joseph Brown
Illus. Paper. Territorial Press of Tennessee, 1989. $4.50.

*INDIAN BEAD--WEAVING PATTERNS: CHAIN WEAVING DESIGNS
& BEAD LOOM WEAVING--AN ILLUSTRATED HOW--TO GUIDE

Horace R. Goodhue; 4th revised editrion. Grades 3-12. Illus. Photos. 80 pp.
Paper. Book Publishing Co. & Amazon.com, 1993. $9.95.

THE INDIAN BILL OF RIGHTS
John R. Wunder, Editor; Reprint of 1968 edition. 344 pp. Garland, $70.

INDIAN BIOGRAPHY: NORTH AMERICAN NATIVES
DISTINGUISHED AS ORATORS, WARRIORS, STATESMEN
Samuel Drake; Reprint. Illus. Paper. Amazon.com, 1999. $22.95.

INDIAN BLANKETS & THEIR MAKERS
George W. James; Reprint. Illus. Biblio. 352 pp. The Rio Grande Press, $40.
Paper. Hothem House & Dover, $10.95.

INDIAN BLUES: AMERICAN INDIANS & THE POLITICS OF MUSIC, 1890-1934
John W. Troutman; Native music & dance in the early 1900s.
Illus. 320 pp. Paper. University of Oklahoma Press, 2010. $24.95.

*INDIAN BOYHOOD
Charles A. Eastman; Grades 3 to 7. Chronicles first 15 years in life of a native Santee Sioux Indian in mid-19th century. Illus. 289 pp. Paper. Dover, $9.95.

*INDIAN CANOEING
Pierre Pulling with Hap Gilliland
Grades 6 and up. Illus. 55 pp. Paper. Council for Indian Education, 1976. $4.95.

INDIAN CAPTIVITES: OR, LIFE IN THE WIGWAM
Samuel Drake; Reprint. Illus. 395 pp. Paper. Amazon.com, $29.

THE INDIAN CAPTIVITY OF O.M. SPENCER
O.M. Spencer; 112 pp. Paper. Dover, $6.95.

INDIAN CEREMONIAL & TRADE SILVER
Gibb; Illus. 168 pp. Paper. Hothem House, 1980. $29, postpaid.

*INDIAN CHIEFS
H. Upton; Grades 3-8. Illus. 32 pp. Amazon.com, 1990. $17.26.

*INDIAN CHIEFS
Russell Freedman; Six western chiefs. Grades 4-6. Illus.
Photos. Map. 160 pp. Holiday House, 1987. $18.95; paper, $9.95.

INDIAN CHIEFS OF PENNSYLVANIA: THE STORY OF THE PART
PLAYED BY THE AMERICAN INDIAN IN PENNSYLVANIA HISTORY
C. Hale Sipe; Reprint of 1927 edition. Illus. 569 pp. Paper. Wennawoods Publishing, 2000. $19.95. Available from AbeBooks.com.

INDIAN CHIEFS OF SOUTHERN MINNESOTA
Thomas Hughes; Reprint. Amazon.com, $10.

INDIAN CHILD PROTECTION & FAMILY VIOLENCE PREVENTION ACT
U.S. Senate Committee on Indian Affairs
104th Congress. U.S. Government printing Office, 1997.

INDIAN CHILD WELFARE ACT: UNTO THE SEVENTH GENERATION,
CONFERENCE PROCEEDINGS Troy Johnson, Ed.
448 pp. Paper. University of California, American Indian Studies Center, $12.

THE INDIAN CHILD WELFARE ACT: A CULTURAL & LEGAL EDUCATION PROGRAM
John G. Richardson; Amazon.com, 1997.

THE INDIAN CHILD WELFARE ACT HANDBOOK: A LEGAL GUIDE
TO THE CUSTODY & ADOPTION OF NATIVE AMERICAN CHILDREN
B.J. Jones; 248 pp. Paper. American Bar Association, 1995. $79.95.

*INDIAN CHILDREN PAPER DOLLS
Phyllis Hughes; Author and artist Phyllis Hughes has drawn Pueblo, Navajo and Apache boys and girls in authentic detail. A brief text shows the closeness of Indian families in daily and ceremonial life. Grades PS-2. Illus. Paper. Amazon.com. $5.95.

THE INDIAN CHRONICLES
Jose Barreiro; Historical novel that recounts the invasion of the Americas by the Spaniards as seen by Christopher Columbus's adopted Indian son. 303 pp. Amazon.com, $19.95.

THE INDIAN CIVIL RIGHTS ACT AT FORTY
Kristen A. Carpenter, Matthew L.M. Fletcher, Angela R. Riley
358 pp. Paper. UCLA, American Indian Studies Center Publications, 2012. $40.

INDIAN CLOTHING BEFORE CORTES: MESOAMERICAN COSTUMES
FROM THE CODICES Patricia R. Anawalt
Illus. 232 pp. University of Oklahoma Press, 1981. $65; paper, $39.95.

INDIAN CLOTHING OF THE GREAT LAKES: 1740-1840
Sheryl Hartman; Monte Smith, Editor
Illus. 140 pp. Eagles View, Written Heritage, & Smoke & Fire Co., 1988. $14.95.

INDIAN COOKING
Traditional recipes. Illus. 64 pp. Paper. Cherokee Publications, $3.50.

INDIAN CORN OF THE AMERICAS: GIFT TO THE WORLD
Jose Barreiro, Editor; Explores the meaning of corn to Indian people through tradition, myth, agriculture, economics, histry, and language. Akwe:kon Press, $10.

*INDIAN COSTUMES
Robert Hofsinde (Gray-Wolf); Grades 3-7. Illus. 96 pp. William Morrow, 1968. $11.80.

INDIAN COUNTRY
Gwendolen Cates, photos by; Illus. 210 pp. Paper. Amazon.com, 2001. $49.95.

INDIAN COUNTRY
Peter Matthiessen; 350 pp. Paper. Penguin USA, $11.

INDIAN COUNTRY: THE ART OF DAVID BRADLEY
Valerie K. Verzuh; University of New Mexico Press, $34.95.

INDIAN COUNTRY, GOD'S COUNTRY: NATIVE AMERICANS & THE NATIONAL PARKS Philip Burnham; Illus. 384 pp. Island Press, 2000. $14.

INDIAN COUNTRY: A GUIDE TO NORTHEASTERN ARIZONA
Tom Dollar; Provides an overview of Indian arts & crafts. Illus. Maps. 64 pp. Paper. University of Arizona Press, 1993. $9.95.

*INDIAN COUNTRY: A HISTORY OF NATIVE PEOPLE IN AMERICA
Karen D. Harvey & Lisa D. Harjo; Excerpts from Ada Deer and M. Scott Momaday. Complete lesson plans utilizing a whole-language approach. Grades 4-9. Illus. 360 pp. Paper. Fulcrum Publishing, 1998. $26.95; Teacher's Guide - additional lesson plans and support materials including maps, graphs, documents. $12.95.

INDIAN COUNTRY: INSIDE ANOTHER CANADA
Larry Krotz; Portrait of a new generation of Aboriginal leaders. Pemmican, $16.95.

INDIAN COUNTRY, L.A. MAINTAINING ETHNIC COMMUNITY IN A COMPLEX SOCIETY Joan Weibel-Orlando
2nd revised Ed. Illus. 384 pp. Paper. University of Illinois Press, 1999. $19.95.

INDIAN COUNTRY: NEW MEXICO
Ron Swartley; A guide to all 25 Indian reservations in New Mexico. Illus. 84 pp. Frontier Image Press, 1996. High-Lonesome Books, $11.

INDIAN COUNTRY: TELLING A STORY IN A DIGITAL AGE
Victoria L. LaPoe & Benjamin Rex LaPoe; 146 pp. Paper. Michigan State University Press, 2017. $29.95. eBook, $23.95.

INDIAN COUNTRY: TRAVELS IN THE AMERICAN SOUTHWEST, 1840-1935
Martin Padget; Analyzes the works of Anglo writers & artists who encountered American Indians in the course of their travels in the Southwest during a 100 year period. Illus. 320 pp. Paper. University of New Mexico Press, 2004. $24.95.

INDIAN CRAFT & SKILLS
David R. Montgomery; Illus. 221 pp. Horizon Publishers, 2001. $17.95.

*INDIAN CRAFTS
Janet and Alex D'Amato; Grades 1-4. Illus. Lion Press, $11.95.

INDIAN CRAFTS & LORE
W. Ben Hunt; How-to book with illustrated projects and instructions. Illus. 112 pp. Paper. Written Heritage, $16.95.

THE INDIAN CRAFTS OF WILLIAM & MARY COMMANDA
David Gidmark; Illus. 144 pp. Paper. Stackpole Press, 1995. $15.95.

INDIAN CULTURE & EUROPEAN TRADE GOODS: THE ARCHAEOLOGY OF THE HISTORIC PERIOD IN THE WESTERN GREAT LAKES REGION
George I. Quimby
Reprint of 1966 edition. Illus. 232 pp. Paper. University of Wisconsin Press, 2004. $24.95.

INDIAN DANCES OF NORTH AMERICA: THEIR IMPORTANCE TO INDIAN LIFE
Reginald & Gladys Laubin; Reprint of the 1977 edition. Illus. 538 pp. Paper. University of Oklahoma Press, 1997. $24.95.

*INDIAN DANCING COLORING BOOK
Connie Asch; Grades 2-4. Illus. 32 pp. Paper. Amazon.com, 2001. $3.50.

INDIAN DAYS OF LONG AGO
Edward S. Curtis
Reprint of 1978 edition. Illus. 221 pp. Amazon.com, $8.95; paper, $5.95.

INDIAN DEPREDATION CLAIMS, 1796-1920
Larry C. Skogen; Illus. 290 pp. University of Oklahoma Press, 1996. $35.95.

INDIAN DEPREDATIONS IN TEXAS
J.W. Wilbarger; Reprint. Illus. 690 pp. Amazon.com, $37.95; paper, $16.95. Kindle, $2.95.

INDIAN DEPREDATIONS IN UTAH
Peter Gottfredson; Illus. 392 pp. Paper. 2002. Amazon.com, $21.86.

INDIAN DESIGNS
David & Jean Villasenor; Shows quilt patterns, applique, needlepoint, stitchery, fabric painting, etc. Illus. 48 pp. Paper. Naturegraph, 1983. $9.95.

*INDIAN DESIGNS STAINED GLASS COLORING BOOK
John Green; Grades K-3. 32 pp. Paper. Dover, $3.95.

INDIAN DOCTOR: NATURE'S METHOD OF CURING & PREVENTING DISEASE ACCORDING TO THE INDIANS
Poisons, Ailments & Herbs. Plants to use for treatment and how to prepare; dictionary of herbs and what to use them for. Reprint. Illus. 60 pp. Paper. Amazon.com, $7.50.

INDIAN EDUCATION
Jack Rudman; 3 vols. ElementaryTeacher, Secondary Teacher & Guidance Counselor. Paper. Amazon.com, 1994. $27.95 each.

INDIAN EDUCATION IN AMERICA: EIGHT ESSAYS BY VINE DELORIA, JR.
Vine Deloria, Jr.
70 pp. Paper. American Indian Science & Engineering Society, 1991. $10.95.

INDIAN EDUCATION IN THE AMERICAN COLONIES, 1607-1783
Margaret Connell Szasz; Illus. Maps. 360 pp. Paper. U. of Nebraska Press, 2007. $24.95.

INDIAN EMPLOYMENT, TRAINING & RELATED SERVICES DEMONSTRATION ACT
U.S. Governemnt; 157 pp. U.S. Government Printing Office, 1998.

INDIAN, ESKIMO & ALEUT BASKETRY OF ALASKA
Gogol; Basketry items of the Attu, Yakutat, Tlingit, Haida and Tsimshian. Vol. 6 of American Indian Basketry, 1982. Illus. 34 pp. Hothem House, $7.95, postpaid.

INDIAN, ESKIMO, ALEUT OWNED & OPERATED ARTS BUSINESSES SOURCE DIRECTORY Indian Arts & Crafts Board.

INDIAN & ESKIMO ARTIFACTS OF NORTH AMERICA
Reginald P. Bolton; Amazon.com, 1981. $9.98.

INDIAN & EUROPEAN CONTACT IN CONTEXT: THE MID-ATLANTIC REGION
Dennis B. Blanton & Julia A. King, Editors; Archaeological & ethnohistorical perspectives of contact between the 16th & 19th centuries. Illus. 368 pp. U. Press of Florida, 2004. $65.

THE INDIAN, A FACT BOOK
Indiana Business Research Center Staff
450 pp. Paper. Amazon.com & Alibris.com, 1994. $39.95.

*INDIAN FAIRY TALES
Jacobs; Grades 3 and up. Amazon.com.

INDIAN FIGHTERS TURNED AMERICAN POLITICIANS: FROM MILITARY SERVICE TO PUBLIC OFFICE Thomas G. Mitchell; Illus. 264 pp. Greenwood, 2003. $49.95.

INDIAN FIGHTS & FIGHTERS
Cyrus Brady; Illus. 495 pp. University of Nebraska Press, 1971. $33.95; paper, $8.95.

INDIAN FIGHTS: NEW FACTS ON SEVEN ENCOUNTERS
J.W. Vaughan; Illus. 464 pp. Paper. University of Oklahoma Press, 2001. $24.95.

INDIAN FISHING: EARLY METHODS ON THE NORTHWEST COAST
Hilary Stewart; Illus. 450 drawings, 75 photos. 182 pp. Paper. University of Washington Press, 1977. $24.95.

INDIAN FLINTS OF OHIO
Lar Hothem; Covers prehistoric tools and weapons of the eastern Midwest. 165 artifact types with names and descriptions. Illus. 188 pp. Paper. Hothem House, $11.95.

*INDIAN FOLK TALES FROM COAST TO COAST
Jessie Marsh; Grades 3-6. Illus. Paper. Council for Indian Education, 1978. $1.95.

THE INDIAN FRONTIER, 1763-1846
R. Douglas Hurt; Illus. 35 halftones. 10 maps. 318 pp. Paper. University of New Mexico Press, 2001. $24.95.

THE INDIAN FRONTIER OF THE AMERICAN WEST, 1846-1890
Robert M. Utley; Revised edition. 90 bxw Illus. 344 pp. Paper. University of New Mexico Press, 2003. $24.95.

INDIAN GAMES & DANCES WITH NATIVE SONGS
Alice Fletcher; Reprint. Musical scores. Illus. 140 pp. Paper. University of Nebraska Press, 1994. $15.

INDIAN GAMES: NORTH AMERICAN INDIAN SPORTS
Andrew Davis; Facs. ed. 84 pp. Amazon.com, 2003. $7. Coyote Press, $9.69.

INDIAN GAMING: FOLLOWING A NEW PATH
Donald C. Caldwell; 192 pp. AltaMira Press, 2003. $70.

THE INDIAN GAMING HANDBOOK
Levine & Associates; Portable briefcase/desk reference on Indian gaming. In two vols. Vol. I: The Little Red Book" - The Indian Gaming Regulatory Act (IGRA); Vol. II: "The Little Yellow Book" - The National Indian Gaming Commission (NIGC) bulletins, advisory opinions, management contract and background investigation requirements, etc. National Indian Gaming Association, $50 each, $90 per set.

INDIAN GAMING & THE LAW
Judy Cornelius & William Eadington, Editors
2nd edition. Reprint. 298 pp. Paper. University of Nevada, 1998. $14.95.

INDIAN GAMING: TRIBAL SOVEREIGNTY & AMERICAN POLITICS
W. Dale Mason; Illus. 330 pp. University of Oklahoma Press, 2000. $29.95.

INDIAN GAMING & TRIBAL SOVEREIGNTY: THE CASINO COMPROMISE
Steven Light & Kathryn R.L. Rand; 240 pp. Paper. U. Press of Kansas, 2007. $17.95.

INDIAN GAMING: WHO WINS?
edited by Angela Mullis & David Kamper; Explores American Indian gaming practices on many U.S. Indian reservations today. 189 pp. Paper. UCLA, American Indian Studies Center, 2000. Also available from Amazon.com & Alibris.com. $15.

INDIAN GIVERS: HOW INDIANS OF THE AMERICAS TRANSFORMED THE WORLD
Jack M. Weatherford; Native Americans "gave" Europeans food, the idea of a federal government system, and many other innovations that are thought of as European. 272 pp. Crown, 1989. $18.95; paper, $9.95. Paper. Amazon.com, $10.

INDIAN GIVING: ECONOMIES OF POWER IN EARLY INDIAN-WHITE EXCHANGES
David Murray; Illus. 272 pp. U. of Massachusetts Press, 2000. $50; Paper, $24.95.

INDIAN GRAMMAR BEGUN
John Eliot; Reprint. A basis for teaching the Algonquian-speaking people to read the bible. Illus. Paper. Amazon.com, 2002. $12.95.

THE INDIAN GREAT AWAKENING: RELIGION AND THE SHAPING OF NATIVE CULTURES IN EARLY AMERICA
Linford D. Fisher; Oxford University Press, $38.95; paper, $28.95.

INDIAN HANDCRAFTS
C. Keith Wilbur, M.D.; How to craft dozens of practical objects using traditional Indian techniques. Illus. 144 pp. Paper. Globe Pequot, 1989. $14.95.

INDIAN HEALING: SHAMANIC CEREMONIALISM IN THE PACIFIC NORTHWEST TODAY W.G. Jilek; Reprint. Illus. 184 pp. Paper. Hancock House, $17.95.

INDIAN HEALTH SERVICE: IMPROVEMENTS NEEDED IN CREDENTIALING TEMPORARY PHYSICIANS
Indian Health Service; Illus. 43 pp. Paper. Amazon.com, 1996. $25.

INDIAN HERBALOGY OF NORTH AMERICA
Hutchens; An illustrated encyclopedic guide to over 200 medicinal plants found in North America. Reprint. 1992. 424 pp. Paper. Amazon.com, $22.

INDIAN HERITAGE OF AMERICA
Alvin M. Josephy, Jr.; Enlarged 1968 edition. 464 pp. Paper. Amazon.com, 1991. $16.

THE INDIAN HERITAGE OF AMERICANS
John Frank Phillips; The tools of the American Indians are examined; some achievements of the American Indians. 54 pp. Paper. Amazon.com, 1981. $2.95.

THE INDIAN HERITAGE OF NEW HAMPSHIRE & NORTHERN NEW ENGLAND
Thaddeus Piotrowski; Illus. 231 pp. McFarland, 2002. $39.95.

***INDIAN HEROES & GREAT CHIEFTAINS**
Charles A. Eastman; Grades 3 to 7. Reprint of 1918 ed. Illus. 254 pp. Paper. University of Nebraska Press, 1991. $19.95.

THE INDIAN HISTORY OF AN AMERICAN INSTITUTION: NATIVE AMERICANS & DARTMOUTH Colin G. Calloway; Tells the story of Dartmouth's historical & ongoing relationship with Native Americans. Illus. Map. 280 pp. Paper. Dartmouth College Press, 2010. Distributed by University Press of New England. $24.95. E-book, $35.

THE INDIAN HISTORY OF BRITISH COLUMBIA
Wilson Duff; Illus. Paper. University of Washington Press, 1997. $14.95.

THE INDIAN HISTORY OF THE MODOC WAR
Jeff C. Riddle; Reprint. Illus. 320 pp. Amazon.com, 2004. $19.95.

THE INDIAN HOUSEHOLD MEDICINE GUIDE
J.I. Lighthall; 152 pp. Paper. Fly Eagle, 1996. $14.95.

THE INDIAN HOW BOOK
Arthur C. Parker; Authentic history & information on American Indian crafts, customs, food, clothing, religion & recreation. Reprint. Illus. 335 pp. Paper. Hothem House, Cherokee Publications & Dover, $6.95.

INDI'N HUMOR: BICULTURAL PLAY IN NATIVE AMERICA
Kenneth Lincoln; Illus. 170 pp. Oxford University Press, 1993. $155.

THE INDIAN HUNTERS
R. Stephen Irwin, MD; illus. by J.B. Clemens; The lives of the first North American hunters. 296 pp. Paper. Hancock House, 1994. $16.95.

INDIAN HUNTING, TRAPPING & FISHING RIGHTS IN THE PRAIRIE PROVINCES OF CANADA Kent McNeil; 64 pp. University of Saskatchewan, 1983. $20.00.

INDIAN HUNTS & INDIAN HUNTERS OF THE OLD WEST
F. Hibben; as told to him by Juan de Dios
An account of the old West as told to him by Juan de Dios, a Navajo captured by the Spanish in a slaving raid. Reprint. Illus. Photos. 228 pp. Amazon.com, 1989. $24.95.

THE INDIAN IN AMERICA
Wilcomb Washburn; Illus. 330 pp. Amazon.com, 1975. $19.45; paper, $8.95.

THE INDIAN IN AMERICAN HISTORY
William T. Hagan; 32 pp. Paper. Amazon.com, 1971. $3.50.

***THE INDIAN IN THE CUPBOARD**
Lynne Reid Banks; Grades 4 and up. Illus. 224 pp. Paper. Amazon.com, 1995. $4.95.

INDIAN IN SPANISH AMERICA: CENTURIES OF REMOVAL, SURVIVAL & INTEGRATION, VOL. 1
Jack J. Himelblau; Illus. 480 pp. Paper. Amazon.com, 1995. $17.50.

AN INDIAN IN WHITE AMERICA
Mark Monroe; edited by Carolyn Reyer; Autobiography of Mark Monroe, A Lakota Sioux Indian who overcame his personal struggles to help his communty. Illus. 256 pp. Amazon.com, 1994. $49.95; paper, $18.95.

INDIAN INTERNATIONAL MOTORCYCLE DIRECTORY
Gregory Frazier; Paper. Whole Earth Motorcycle Center, 2001.

INDIAN ISSUES
E.B. Eiselein; Presents a brief introduction to current issues facing both urban and reservation Indians. Spiral bound. Amazon.com, 1993. $12.

INDIAN JEWELRY OF THE AMERICAN SOUTHWEST
William & Sarah Turnbaugh; Revised edition. Illus. 96 pp. Paper. Schiffer, 1996. $12.95.

INDIAN JEWELRY ON THE MARKET
Peter Schiffer; Price guide. Color photos. 144 pp. Paper. Schiffer Books. $19.95.

THE INDIAN JOURNALS, 1859-1862
Lewis Henry Morgan; L. White & C. Walton, Editors; Morgan's researches among the tribes of Kansas & Nebraska. Reprint of 1958 edition. Paper. Dover, $10.95.

INDIAN JUSTICE: A CHEROKEE MURDER TRIAL AT TAHLEQUAH IN 1840
John Howard Payne; First newspaper account of an Indian trial in Indian Territory. First published in "The New York Journal of Commerce" on April 17 & April 29, 1841. Illus. Map. 136 pp. Paper. University of Oklahoma Press, 2002. $19.95.

INDIAN KILLER
Sherman Alexie
Novel by a Spokane/Coeur d'Alene writer. Grades 9 and up. Oyate, 1996. $22.

INDIAN KNOLL
William S. Webb; Artifacts & settlement patterns of the Indian Knoll Culture along Green River & Cyporess Creek in Kentucky. Reprint. Paper. Amazon.com, $32.

INDIAN LAND CONSOLIDATION ACT
U.S. Senate Committee on Indian Affairs; 108th Congress, 1st Session
125 pp. U.S. GPO, 2003.

INDIAN LAND TENURE: BIBLIOGRAPHICAL ESSAYS & A GUIDE TO THE LITERATURE Irme Sutton; 300 pp. Illus. N. Ross, 1975. $25.

INDIAN LANDS
Malcom Rosholt; Illus. 352 pp. Paper. Amazon.com, $17.50.

INDIAN LAW CONFERENCE SERIES
Federal Bar Assn. Editors; Material includes annual updates of legislation & litigation; jurisdictional issues, bibliographies, etc. 1977-92. Federal Bar Association.

INDIAN LAW - RACE LAW: A FIVE HUNDRED YEAR HISTORY
James E. Falkowski; Illus. 192 pp. Greenwood Publishing, 1992. $45.

THE INDIAN LAWYER
James Welch; A young American Indian lawyer is torn between the trappings of his profession and his Indian heritage. Illus. 352 pp. Paper. Penguin USA, $8.95.

INDIAN LEADERSHIP IN THE WEST
Walter Williams, Editor; 92 pp. Paper. Amazon.com, 1984. $15.00.

INDIAN LEGACY OF CHARLES BIRD KING
Herman J. Viola; Illus. 152 pp. Smithsonian, 1976. $27.50.

***INDIAN LEGENDS**
Johanna R. Lyback; Grades 3 and up. Reprint. Illus. 279 pp. Paper. Tipi Press, $7.95.

INDIAN LEGENDS & THE BOOK OF MORMON
John Rutkowski; Paper. Star Bible & Tract Corp., 2000. $6.95.

INDIAN LEGENDS FROM THE NORTHERN ROCKIES
Ella E. Clark
Reprint of 1966 edition. Illus. Map. 356 pp. Paper. University of Oklahoma Press, $19.95.

INDIAN LEGENDS FROM THE NORTHWEST
Arthur Griffin; T.J. Griffin, Editor
Illus. 64 pp. Paper. Hancock House Publishers, 1990. $7.95.

INDIAN LEGENDS OF THE PACIFIC NORTHWEST
Ella E. Clark; 238 pp. Paper. University of California Press, 2003. $19.95.

INDIAN LIFE AT THE OLD MISSIONS
Edith B. Webb; Reprint of 1952 edition. Illus. 385 pp. University of Nebraska Press, $35.

***INDIAN LIFE IN PRE-COLUMBIAN NORTH AMERICA**
John Green; Grades K-3. 48 pp. Paper. Dover, $2.95.

INDIAN LIFE & INDIAN HISTORY
George Copway; Reprint. Illus. Paper. Amazon.com, 1999. $18.95.

INDIAN LIFE OF THE YOSEMITE REGION: MIWOK MATERIAL CULTURE
S.A. Barrett & E.W. Gifford; Study of the Miwok Indian culture based upon data obtained from Miwok informants shortle after 1900. Reprint of 1933 edition. Illus. Maps. Biblio. 261 pp. Paper. Heyday Books & Amazon.com, $14.95.

INDIAN LIFE ON THE UPPER MISSOURI
John C. Ewers; Reprint of 1968 edition. Illus. 228 pp. Paper. University of Oklahoma Press, 1968. $14.95.

INDIAN LIFE: TRANSFORMING AN AMERICAN MYTH
William Savage, Editor; Illus. 286 pp. Paper. University of Oklahoma Press, 1977. $14.95.

INDIAN LIVES: ESSAYS ON 19th & 20th CENTURY NATIVE AMERICAN LEADERS
L.G. Moses & Raymond Wilson; Illus. 232 pp. University of New Mexico Press, 1985. $19.95; paper, $10.95.

INDIAN LIVES: A PHOTOGRAPHIC RECORDS FROM THE CIVIL WAR TO WOUNDED KNEE Ulrich W. Hiesinger; Illus. 140 pp. te Neues Publishing, 1994. $35.

INDIAN LODGE-FIRE STORIES
Frank B. Linderman; Illus. 96 pp. Paper. Homestead Publishing, 1998. $12.95.

INDIAN-MADE: NAVAJO CULTURE IN THE MARKETPLACE, 1868-1940
Erika Marie Bsumek; Photos. 304 pp. U. Press of Kansas, 2008. $34.95; paper, $22.50..

THE INDIAN MAN: A BIOGRAPHY OF JAMES MOONEY
L.G. Moses; Illus. 290 pp. Paper. University of Nebraska Press, 2002. $29.95.

INDIAN MEDICINE POWER
Brad Steiger; Marah Ren, Editor; 224 pp. Schiffer Publishing & Cherokee Publications, 1984. $12.95.

INDIAN METROPOLIS: NATIVE AMERICANS IN CHICAGO, 1945-75
James B. LaGrand; American Indian life in Chicago. Focuses on Chicago's twentyfold increase of American Indian population from 1970 to 2000. Illus. 312 pp. Paper. University of Illinois Press, 2005. $26.

INDIAN MINIATURE PAINTINGS & DRAWINGS: THE CLEVELAND MUSEUM OF ART CATALOGUE OF ORIENTAL ART
L. York Leach; Part One. Illus. 350 pp. Indian University Press, 1986. $65.

INDIAN MOTIFS
Carol Belanger Grafton; Illus. Paper. Dover, 1993. $1.

INDIAN MOUNDS OF THE ATLANTIC COAST
Jerry McDonald & Susan Woodward; A guide to the prehistoric mounds and mound-like features of the Atlantic Coast region. 2nd Edition. Illus. Photos. Maps. 200 pp. Paper. Amazon.com, 2000. $16.95.

INDIAN MOUNDS OF THE MIDDLE OHIO VALLEY: A GUIDE TO MOUNDS & EARTHWORKS OF THE ADENA, HOPEWELL, AND LATE WOODLAND PEOPLE
Jerry McDonald & Susan Woodward
Adena and Hopewell Mounds and earthworks of the region. 2nd Edition. Illus. Maps. Photos. 200 pp. Paper. University of Nebraska Press, 2001. $19.95.

INDIAN MOUNDS OF WISCONSIN
Robert A. Birmingham & Leslie E. Eisenberg; An overview of the remaining @4,000 mounds in Wisconsin. Illus. 264 pp. Paper. University of Wisconsin Press, 2000. $18.95.

INDIAN MOUNDS YOU CAN VISIT: 165 ABORIGINAL SITES ON FLORIDA'S WEST COAST I. Mac Perry; Illus. Photos. 320 pp. Paper. Amazon.com, 1995. $12.95.

INDIAN MYTH & LEGEND
D. Mackenzie; Reprint of 1913 edition. Longwood, $50.

INDIAN MYTH & WHITE HISTORY
Pamela Winchester; Lit Verlag, 1997.

*INDIAN MYTHS FROM THE SOUTHWEST
Beatrice Levin; Grades 4-12. Council for Indian Education, 1974. $1.95.

INDIAN MYTHS & LEGENDS FROM THE NORTH PACIFIC COAST OF AMERICA
Franz Boas; Randy Bouchard & Dorothy Kennedy, Eds.
Illus. 704 pp. Translation of the 1895 edition. University of Toronto Press, 2004. $45.

INDIAN NAMES IN MICHIGAN
Virgil J. Vogel; Illus. 224 pp. Paper. University of Michigan Press, 1986. $19.95.

INDIAN NAMES ON WISCONSIN'S MAP
Virgil J. Vogel; Photos. Maps. 342 pp. Paper. Reprint of 1991 ed. University of Wisconsin Press, 2005. $24.95.

INDIAN NATION
Homer "Louis" Hoban; 55 pp. Paper. Amazon.com, 1991. $10.

INDIAN NATION: NATIVE AMERICAN LITERATURE & 19TH CENTURY NATIONALISM
Cheryl Walker; Illus. 264 pp. Duke University Press, 1`997. $49.95.

INDIAN NATIONS
Larry McMurtry; photos by Danny Lyon
Illus. 108 pp. Twin Palms Publishers, 2002. $60. Limited ed. $90.

INDIAN NATIONS OF NORTH AMERICA
Illus. 384 pp. National Geographic Society, 2010. $40.

INDIAN NATIONS OF WISCONSIN: HISTORIES OF ENDURANCE & RENEWAL
Patty Loew; Illus. 160 pp. Wisconsin Historical Society, 2001. $39.95; paper, $21.95.

INDIAN NEW ENGLAND BEFORE THE MAYFLOWER
Howard S. Russell; Describes how New England Indians lived when European settlers first met them. Illus 296 pp. Paper. University Press of New England, 1980. $22.95.

INDIAN NOTES & MONOGRAPHS: A REPORT FROM NATCHITOCHES IN 1807
John Sibley; Annie H. Abel, Editor; Reprint. 105 pp. Paper. Amazon.com, $15.

INDIAN OLD MAN STORIES: MORE SPARKS FROM WAR EAGLE'S LODGE-FIRE
Frank B. Linderman; Stories collected from Blackfeet, Chippewa and Cree elders and first published in 1920. Illus. 170 pp. Paper. University of Nebraska Press, 1996. $12.95.

INDIAN ORATORY: FAMOUS SPEECHES BY NOTED INDIAN CHIEFTAINS
W.C. Vanderwerth
Reprint of 1971 edition. Illus. 291 pp. Paper. University of Oklahoma Press, $16.95.

INDIAN ORPHANAGES
Marilyn Irvin Holt; Photos. 326 pp. Paper. University of Kansas Press, 2001. $25.

INDIAN OUTBREAKS
Daniel Buck; Reprint of 1965 edition. Amazon.com, $12.50.

THE INDIAN PAPERS OF TEXAS & THE SOUTHWEST, 1825-1916
Dorman H. Winfrey & James M. Day, Editors; Reprint. 5 vols. Illus. Texas A&M University Press & Texas State Historical Association, 1995. $95.

INDIAN PEACE MEDALS IN AMERICAN HISTORY
Francis Paul Prucha; Reprint of 1971 edition. illus. 186 pp. Paper. Hothem House, Written Heritage & University of Oklahoma Press, $19.95.

THE INDIAN PEOPLES OF EASTERN AMERICA: A DOCUMENTARY HISTORY OF THE SEXES James Axtell, Editor
Illus. 256 pp. Paper. Oxford University Press, 1981. $54.95.

INDIAN PLACE NAMES IN ALABAMA
William A. Read; James B. McMillan, revised by
Illus. 128 pp. Paper. University of Alabama Press, 1984. $24.95. E-Book, $19.96.

INDIAN PLACE NAMES IN AMERICA
Sandy Nestor; Illus. 248 pp. McFarland & Co., 2003. $45.

INDIAN PLACE NAMES IN ILLINOIS
Virgil J. Vogel; Paper. Illinois State Historical Society, 1963. $2.00.

INDIAN PLACE NAMES OF NEW ENGLAND
John C. Huden; 408 pp. Paper. National Museum of the American Indian, 1962. $7.50.

INDIAN PLACE-NAMES: THEIR ORIGINS, EVOLUTION, & MEANINGS, COLLECTED IN KANSAS FROM THE SIOUAN, ALGONQUIAN, SHOSHONEAN, CADDOAN, IROQUOIAN, AND OTHER TONGUES
John Rydjord; Illus. Maps. 380 pp. Paper. University of Oklahoma Press, $19.95.

INDIAN PLAY: INDIGENOUS IDENTITIES AT BACON COLLEGE
Lisa K. Neuman; Illus. Maps. 392 pp. University of Nebraska Press, 2014. $50.

INDIAN POPULATION DECLINE: THE MISSIONS OF NORTHWESTERN NEW SPAIN, 1687-1840 R. Jackson; 241 pp. Paper. University of New Mexico Press, 1995. $16.95.

INDIAN PORTRAITS OF THE PACIFIC NORTHWEST
George M. Cochran; Third edition. Illus. 64 pp. Paper. Binford & Mort, 1987. $5.95.

INDIAN POTTERY
Toni Roller; Step-by-step photographs and explanations of traditional Santa Clara Pueblo pottery making. Photos. 64 pp. paper. Sunstone Press, $12.95.

INDIAN POTTERY BY TONI ROLLER OF SANTA CLARA PUEBLO: A GUIDE
Toni Roller; Illus. 64 pp. Sunstone Press, 1997. $12.95.

INDIAN POTTERY OF THE SOUTHWEST: A SELECTED BIBLIOGRAPHY
Marcia Muth; Illus. 35 pp. Paper. Sunstone Press, 1991. $6.95.

INDIAN PROGRAMS: TRIBAL PRIORITY ALLOCATIONS DO NOT TARGET THE NEEDIEST TRIBES Jennifer Duncan; Illus. 48 pp. Amazon.com, 1999. $20.

INDIAN PROVISIONS CONTAINED IN THE TOBACCO SETTLEMENT: CONGRESSIONAL HEARING
Ben Nighthorse Campbell; Reprint. 66 pp. Paper. Amazon.com, 2000. $20.

INDIAN PUEBLO COLOR BOOK
O.T. Branson; 32 pp. Paper. Treasure Chest, 1984. $1.95.

INDIAN QUILLWORKING
Christy A. Hensler; Illus. 64 pp. Paper. Hancock House, $6.95.

*INDIAN READING SERIES
A supplementary reading program for elementary classrooms representing the oral tradition of 16 Northwest tribes in Idaho, Montana, Oregon & Washington. Contains 99 booklets written at six reading levels, teacher's manuals, and a parent/teacher guide. Stories and legends. Education Northwest. $403 (postpaid) for series.

INDIAN RECIPE BOOK
United Tribes Technical College; Authentic recipes. Illus. Arrow Graphics, $6., postpaid.

THE INDIAN REFORM LETTERS OF HELEN HUNT JACKSON, 1879-1885
Helen Hunt Jackson; Illus. Map. 400 pp. University of Oklahoma Press, 1998. $39.95.

INDIAN REGALIA OF NORTHWEST CALIFORNIA
Hearst Museum of Anthropology; Illus. Photos. 23 pp. Paper. Hearst Museum of Anthropology, 1993. $9.

INDIAN RELICS OF NORTHEAST ARKANSAS & SOUTHEAST MISSOURI
Dethrow; Summary of prehistoric artifacts in stone, bone, etc. Also pottery. Illus. 152 pp. Hothem House, 1985. $20.

INDIAN REMOVAL: THE EMIGRATION OF THE FIVE CIVILIZED TRIBES OF INDIANS
Grant Foreman; foreword by Angie Debo; Reprint of 1932 ed. Illus. 423 pp. University of Oklahoma Press & Cherokee Publications, 2001. $19.95. 415 pp. Paper text. Amazon.com, 2003 reprint. $29.

INDIAN REORGANIZATION ACT: CONGRESS & BILLS
Vine Deloria, Jr.; 464 pp. University of Oklahoma Press, 2002. $75.

INDIAN RESERVATION ROAD PROGRAM: HEARING BEFORE THE COMMITTEE ON INDIAN AFFAIRS, U.S. SENATE, 108TH CONGRESS
U.S. Senate Committe on Indian Affairs; Proposals to amend The Indian Reservation Roads Program. Illus. 212 pp. U.S. GPO, 2003.

INDIAN RESERVATION ROADS & THE TRANSPORTATION EQUITY ACT OF THE 21ST CENTURY U.S. Senate Committe on Indian Affairs
Hearing before the 106th Congress, 1999. Illus. 240 pp. U.S. GPO.

INDIAN RESERVATIONS IN THE U.S.
Klaus Frantz; Illus. 57 halftones. 30 tables. Maps. 400 pp. Paper. University of Chicago Press, 1999. $27.50.

INDIAN RESERVATIONS: A STATE & FEDERAL HANDBOOK
Confederation of American Indians Staff; Alpha-geographical listing of reservations with information on land status, culture, govern-ment, facilities, recreation, and vital statistics for each. 330 pp. McFarland & Co., 1986. $45.

INDIAN RESERVED WATER RIGHTS: THE WINTERS DOCTRINE IN ITS SOCIAL & LEGAL CONTEXT, 1880s-1930s John Shurts; Illus. Maps. 350 pp. Paper. University of Oklahoma Press, 2003. $24.95; paper, $21.95.

INDIAN RIGHTS MANUALS
A Manual for Protecting Indian Natural Resources, 151 pp., $25; A Self-Help Manual for Indian Economic Development, 300 pp., $35; A Manual on Tribal Regulatory Systems, 110 pp., $25; Handbook of Federal Indian Laws, 130 pp., $15. Native American Rights Fund.

INDIAN RESISTANCE: THE PATRIOT CHIEFS
Juan Strousa; Amazon.com, 1994. $39.

INDIAN ROCK ART IN WYOMING
Mary H. Hendry; Illus. 240 pp. Amazon.com, 1983. $25.

INDIAN ROCK ART OF THE COLUMBIA PLATEAU
James D. Keyser; Illus. 140 pp. Paper. University of Washington Press, 1992. $22.50.

INDIAN ROCK ART OF THE SOUTHWEST
Polly Schaafsma; Reprint of 1980 edition. Illus. Color & bxw photos. Maps. 390 pp. Paper. University of New Mexico Press, $49.95

INDIAN ROCK CARVINGS
Beth Hill; Illus. 50 pp. Paper. Hancock House, 1990. $4.95.

INDIAN ROOTS OF AMERICAN DEMOCRACY
Jose Barreiro, Editor; Book version of best selling special issue of Akwe:kon Journal. Explores the influence of the Iroquois Great Law of Peace on the formation of U.S. democracy. New & previously published works by Donald Grinde, Richard Hill, Sally Roesch Wagner and others. 195 pp. Paper. Akwe:kon Press, 1992. $12.

INDIAN RUNNING: NATIVE AMERICAN HISTORY & TRADITION
Peter Nabokov; 2nd edition. Illus. Map. 208 pp. Paper. Amazon.com, 1987. $15.95.

INDIAN SANDPAINTING OF THE GREATER SOUTHWEST
David Villasenor
Excerpt from Tapestries in Sand. Illus. 32 pp. Paper. Naturegraph. $4.95.

INDIAN SCHOOL DAYS
Basil H. Johnston; Map. 256 pp. Paper. University of Oklahoma Press, 1989. $19.95.

INDIAN SCOUT CRAFT & LORE
Charles Eastman; Reprint. Illus. 190 pp. Paper. Dover, $5.95.

INDIAN SELF-DETERMINATION & EDUCATION ASSISTANCE ACT
P.L. 93-638, as amended; This handbook is a comprehensive overview of the ISDEAA, covering Titles I, II, IV, V and VI, and includes applicable regulations and selected legislative history. The handbook, which is updated annually, provides useful information for tribal leaders and others working with tribes and tribal organizations on self-determination and self-governance matters. Hobbs, Straus, Dean & Walker, LLP. $20.

INDIAN SELF RULE: FIRST HAND ACCOUNTS OF INDIAN-WHITE RELATIONS FROM ROOSEVELT TO REAGAN
Kenneth R. Philp, Editor; Illus. 350 pp. Paper. Utah State University Press, 1985. $24.95.

*INDIAN SIGN LANGUAGE
William Tomkins; More than 525 signs, developed by the Sioux, Blackfoot, Cheyenne, Aarapahoe, et al. 290 pictographs of the Sioux & Ojibway tribes. Grades 4-7. Illus. 111 pp. Paper. Dover Publications, $5.95.

THE INDIAN SIGN LANGUAGE
W.P. Clark; Map. 443 pp. Paper. University of Nebraska Press, 1982. $21.95.

*INDIAN SIGN LANGUAGE
Robert Hofsinde (Gray-Wolf); Shows how to form more than 500 words in Indian sign language; 200 drawings. Grades 5 and up. 96 pp. William Morrow, 1956. $11.88.

INDIAN SIGN LANGUAGES
William Tomkins; Original title: Universal Sign Language of the Plains Indians of North America. Reprint of 1969 ed. Illus. 108 pp. Paper. VIP Publishing & Cherokee Publications, $4.95.

INDIAN SILVER JEWELRY OF THE SOUTHWEST, 1868-1930
Larry Frank, Millard Holbroo, II; Color photos. Illus. 224 pp. Paper. Schiffer, 1989. $19.95.

INDIAN SKETCHES TAKEN DURING AN EXPEDITION TO THE PAWNEE & OTHER TRIBES OF AMERICAN INDIANS, 2 VOLS.
John Irving; Reprint. Illus. Paper. Amazon.com, 1999. $18.95 each.

INDIAN SLAVE TRADE: THE RISE OF THE ENGLISH EMPIRE IN THE AMERICAN SOUTH, 1670-1717 Alan Galley; Illus. 464 pp. Yale University Press, 2003. $30.

INDIAN SLAVE TRADE IN THE SOUTHWEST: A STUDY OF SLAVE-TAKING & THE TRAFFIC IN INDIAN CAPTIVES FROM 1700-1935
L.R. Bailey; Reprint of 1963 edition. Illus. Westernlore, $19.95.

INDIAN SLAVERY IN COLONIAL AMERICA
Alan Gallay, Editor; Essays examines American Indian enslavement & slave-taking in colonial America. 520 pp. Paper. University of Nebraska Press, 2009. $30.

INDIAN SLAVERY IN THE PACIFIC NORTHWEST
Robert H. Ruby & John A. Brown
Illus. Maps. Biblio. 336 pp. The Arthur H. Clark Co., $37.50.

INDIAN SLAVERY, LABOR, EVANGELIZATION, AND CAPTIVITY IN THE AMERICAS: AN ANNOTATED BIBLIOGRAPHY Russell M. Magnaghi; Focuses on the history of the imposition of policies upon Native Americans by the governments of other people. 768 pp. Scarecrow Press, 1998. $146.30.

INDIAN SOLDIER, SETTLER: EXPERIENCES IN THE STRUGGLE FOR THE AMERICAN WEST Robert M. Utley; Reprint. Illus. 85 pp. Amazon.com, 1992. $9.95.

THE INDIAN SOUTHWEST, 1580-1830: ETHNOGENESIS & REINVENTION
Gary Clayton Anderson; Illus. Maps. Biblio. Paper. U. of Oklahoma Press, 2009. $24.95.

INDIAN SPIRIT
Michael Oren Fitzgerald, Editor; Illus. 152 pp. Paper. World Wisdom Books, 2004. $12.95.

"INDIAN" STEREOTYPES IN TV SCIENCE FICTION: FIRST NATIONS' VOICES SPEAK OUT Sierra S. Adare; 160 pp. Paper. University of Texas Press, 2005. $25.

INDIAN STORIES: AHTNA INDIAN STORIES FROM CANTWELL, ALASKA
Jake Tansy; James Kari, Tr.; Reprint. 2nd Ed. Illus. 96 pp. Paper. Website: http://www.native-languages.org/ahtna-legends.htm, 1997 $10.

INDIAN STORIES FROM THE PUEBLOS: TALES OF NEW MEXICO & ARIZONA
Frank Applegate
Reprint of 1929 edition. Illus. 198 pp. Paper. Amazon.com, 1999. $10.95.

INDIAN STORY & SONG FROM NORTH AMERICA
Alice C. Fletcher; Illus. 126 pp. Paper. University of Nebraska Press, 1995. $6.95.

INDIAN STREAM REPUBLIC: SETTLING A NEW ENGLAND FRONTIER, 1785-1842
Daniel Doan; Illus. 287 pp. University Press of New England, 1996. $45; paper, $23.95.

INDIAN SUMMER: THE FORGOTTEN STORY OF LOUIS SOCKALEXIS, THE FIRST NATIVE AMERICAN IN MAJOR LEAGUE BASEBALL
Brian McDonald; Illus. 256 pp. Rodale Press, 2003. $21.95.

INDIAN SUMMER: A NATIVE AMERICAN VIEW OF NATURE
Betsy Wyckoff; Illus. 64 pp. Paper. Station Hill Press, 1995. $18.95.

INDIAN SUMMER: TRADITIONAL LIFE AMONG THE CHOINUMNE INDIANS OF CALIFORNIA'S SAN JOAQUIN VALLEY
Thomas Jefferson Mayfield; Photos. Illus. Maps. 144 pp. Paper. Heyday Books, $13.95.

INDIAN SUMMERS
Eric Gansworth; Concerns issues of identity for Native Americans. 200 pp. Paper. Michigan State University Press, 1998. $22.95.

INDIAN SUMMERS: WASHINGTON STATE COLLEGE & THE NESPELEM ART COLONY, 1937-41 J.J. Creighton
Illus. Photos. Map. 88 pp. Paper. WSU Press, 2000. $22.95.

INDIAN SURVIVAL ON THE CALIFORNIA BORDERLINE FRONTIER, 1819-60
Albert Hurtado; Illus. 332 pp. Yale University Press, 1988. $29.

*INDIAN TALES
J. De Angulo; Reprint of 1962 ed. Grades 5-12. Illus. 256 pp. Paper. Heyday Books, $12.95.

INDIAN TALES FROM PICURIS PUEBLO
John P. Harrington, Editor; Illus. Photos. 104 pp. Paper. Amazon.com, 1989. $11.95.

INDIAN: TALES & LEGENDS
J.E. Gray; Illus. 230 pp. 35 stories. Amazon.com, AbeBooks.

***INDIAN TALES OF THE NORTHERN PLAINS**
Sally Old Coyote and Joy Yellow Tail Toineeta
Grades 2-5. Council for Indian Education, 1972. $1.95.

INDIAN TALES & OTHERS
John G. Neihardt; 306 pp. Paper. University of Nebraska Press, 1988. $22.

***INDIAN TALK: HAND SIGNALS OF THE NORTH AMERICAN INDIANS**
Iron Eyes Cody; Hand signals for 246 words. A silent language developed by the Plains tribes. Grades 1-12. Illus. Photos. 144 pp. Paper. Naturgraph, 1970. $9.95.

INDIAN TERMS OF THE AMERICAS
Lotsee Patterson & Mary Ellen Snodgrass; Defines a variety of terms from Native American history; a compendium of vocabulary, people, places and events. Illus. 275 pp. Amazon.com, 1994. $37.

THE INDIAN TERRITORY JOURNALS OF COLONEL RICHARD IRVING DODGE
Wayne R. Kime, Editor; Illus. 486 pp. University of Oklahoma Press, 2000. $55.

INDIAN TERRITORY SCHOOL: THE STORY OF HOFFMAN COMMON SCHOOL IN OKMULGEE COUNTY Mike Martin; Illus. 496 pp. Fowble Press, 2001.

INDIAN TERRITORY & THE U.S., 1866-1906: COURTS, GOVERNMENT, & THE MOVE FOR OKLAHOMA STATEHOOD Jeffrey Burton; Shows how the U.S. used judicial reform to surpress the Five Tribes' governments and clear the way for Oklahoma statehood. Illus. 334 pp. Maps. University of Oklahoma Press, 1995. $29.95; paper, $13.95.

THE INDIAN TESTIMONY
Amiya Chakravarty; Paper. Amazon.com, 1983. $2.50.

THE INDIAN TEXANS
James Smallwood; Illus. Texas A&M University Press, $29.95; paper, $10.95.

THE INDIAN TIPI: ITS HISTORY, CONSTRUCTION & USE
Reginald & Gladys Laubin
Reprint of 1977 2nd ed. Illus. 384 pp. Paper. University of Oklahoma Press, 2001. $26.95.

INDIAN TRADE GOODS
Arthur Woodward; Trade goods used in exchange with Indians of the Pacific Northwest, and the way natives adapted these to their own use. Second edition. Illus. 40 pp. Paper. Binford & Mort, $5.95.

INDIAN TRADE GOODS & REPLICAS
Miller & Corey; Color photos of historic era artifacts and goods from the fur trade period. Illus. 192 pp. Paper. Hothem House, 1998. $29.95.

INDIAN TRADER: THE LIFE & TIMES OF J.L. HUBBELL
Martha Blue; Illus. 356 pp. Kiva Publishing, 2000. $32.50; paper, $24.50.

THE INDIAN TRADERS
Frank McNitt; 393 pp. Paper. Amazon.com, 2003. $29.

INDIAN TRADERS ON THE MIDDLE BORDER: THE HOUSE OF EWING, 1827-1854
Robert A. Trennert, Jr.; Illus. 280 pp. University of Nebraska Press, 1981. $23.95.

INDIAN TRADERS OF THE SOUTH-WESTERN SPANISH BORDER LANDS: PANTON & FORBES CO. 1783-1847
W.S. Coker & T.D. Watson; Illus. Maps. Biblio. 448 pp. U. Press of Florida, 1985. $44.95.

THE INDIAN TRIAL: THE COMPLETE STORY OF THE WARREN WAGAN TRAIN MASSACRE & THE FALL OF THE KIOWA NATION
Charles Robinson; Illus. 210 pp. Arthur H. Clark, 1997. $27.50.

INDIAN TRAILS & GRIZZLY TALES
Bud Cheff; Paper. Stoneydale Press, 1994. $14.95.

INDIAN TRAINS
Erika T. Wurth; Poems are tribute to mixed blood Indians of modern America, Paper. University of New Mexico Press, $11.95.

INDIAN TREATIES
Institute for the Development of Indian Law, 1980. $12.

INDIAN TREATIES, 1778-1883
C.J. Kappler, Editor; Contains a listing of every treaty and agreement made between the U.S. & Native Americans. Reprint of 1904 edition. Illus. Map. 1,100 pp. Interland, $75.

INDIAN TREATY-MAKING POLICY IN THE U.S. & CANADA, 1867-1877
Jill St. Germain; Illus. Maps. 253 pp. U. of Nebraska Press, 2001. $45; paper, $29.95.

INDIAN TRIBAL CLAIMS DECIDED IN THE COURT OF CLAIMS OF THE U.S.: BRIEFED & COMPILED JUNE 30, 1947
E.B. Smith, Editor; 2 Volumes. Greenwood, 1976. $65 each.

INDIAN TRIBES AS SOVEREIGN GOVERNMENTS: A SOURCEBOOK ON FEDERAL-TRIBAL HISTORY, LAW & POLICY
Charles F. Wilkinson and The American Indian Resources Institute; 2nd Edition. 228 pp. Paper. American Indian Lawyer Training Program, 2010. $25.

***INDIAN TRIBES OF THE AMERICAS**
Archaeological searches for the ruins of Chaco Canyon.
Grades 4 and up. Photos. 120 pp. Chelsea House, $19.95.

THE INDIAN TRIBES OF OHIO: HISTORICALLY CONSIDERED 1600-1840
Warren K. Moorehead
Reprint. Illus. 110 pp.Paper. Amazon.com, 1992. Library ed., $29.80; paper, $8.30.

INDIAN TRIBES OF HUDSON'S RIVER
E. M. Ruttenber; Reprint. Two vols. Vol. I to 1700...all NY tribes-origins, legends, history, 200 pp. Vol. II to 1850, with 100 appendix of language & bios. 240 pp. Paper. Amazon.com, $12.95 each.

INDIAN TRIBES OF THE LOWER MISSISSIPPI VALLEY & ADJACENT COAST OF THE GULF OF MEXICO
John R. Swanton; Reprint. Illus. 387 pp. Amazon.com., $42. Paper. Dover, $14.95.

INDIAN TRIBES OF THE NEW ENGLAND FRONTIER
Michael Johnson; Illus. 48 pp. Paper. Wennawoods Publishing, $15.95.

INDIAN TRIBES OF NORTH AMERICA
John R. Swanton; Reprint of the 1952 ed. Guide to the Indian tribes of North America, covering all groupings such as nations, confederations, tribes, clans, bands. Formatted as a dictionary. 726 pp. Paper. Genealogical Publishing Co., 2003. $75.

***INDIAN TRIBES OF NORTH AMERICA: COLORING BOOK**
Peter F. Copeland; Grades K-2. 48 pp. Paper. Dover, $2.95.

INDIAN TRIBES OF THE NORTHERN ROCKIES
Adolf & Beverly Hungrywolf; Illus. 144 pp. The Book Publishing Co., 1991. $9.95.

INDIAN TRIBE OF THE NORTHWEST
Reg Ashwell; Illus. 64 pp. Paper. Hancock House, 1990. $8.95.

INDIAN TRIBES OF NORTH AMERICA
Joseph Sherman; Todtri Book Puiblishers, 1998. $14.95.

INDIAN TRIBES OF NORTH AMERICA WITH BIOGRAPHICAL SKETCHES & ANECDOTES OF THE PRINCIPAL CHIEFS
McKenney & Hall; 3 vols. Paper. 1974. Amazon.com, $32.

INDIAN TRIBES OF THE NORTHERN ROCKIES
Adolf Hungry Wolf; Illus. Maps. Biblio. 144 pp. Paper. The Book Publishing Co., $9.95.

INDIAN TRIBES OF OHIO
Warren King Moorehead; History starts in the mid-15th century and ends with the War of 1812. Paper. Smoke & Fire Co., $10.50.

INDIAN TRIBES OF OKLAHOMA: A GUIDE
Blue Clark (Muscogee Creek); A guide to nearly 40 Oklahoma's American Indian tribes. Illus. 416 pp. Paper. University of Oklahoma Press, 2010. $19.95.

INDIAN TRIBES OF THE UPPER MISSISSIPPI VALLEY
Emma H. Blair, Ed. & Tr.
2 vols. in one. Illus. 414 pp. Paper. University of Nebraska Press, 1996. $25.

INDIAN UPRISING ON THE RIO GRANDE: THE PUEBLO REVOLT OF 1680
Franklin Folsom; 144 pp. Paper. University of New Mexico Press, $16.95.

INDIAN USE OF THE SANTA FE NATIONAL FOREST: A DETERMINATION FROM ETHNOGRAPHIC SOURCES Eva Friedlander & Pamela Pinyan
Illus. Maps. 51 pp. Amazon.com, 1980. $8 (postpaid).

INDIAN USES OF NATIVE PLANTS
Describes the uses and documents the plants, giving detailed descriptions and methods of preparation. Includes traditional recipes, dictionary of plants. Illus. 81 pp. Paper. Cherokee Publications, $6.95.

INDIAN VIEWS OF THE CUSTER FIGHT: A SOURCE BOOK
Richard C. Hardorff; Lakota & Cheyenne Indian views of the Battle of the Little Bighorn. Illus. Paper. University of Oklahoma Press, $14.95.

INDIAN VILLAGES OF THE ILLINOIS COUNTRY: HISTORIC TRIBES & SUPPLEMENT
Wayne C. Temple; Facsimile ed. Illus. 218 pp. Paper. Illinois State Museum, 1977. $5. Supplement ed., 160 pp. 39 maps. $20.

INDIAN VILLAGES & PLACE NAMES OF PENNSYLVANIA
George Donehoo; 290 pp. Paper. Wennewoods Publishing, 1999. $19.95.

INDIAN VOICES: THE NATIVE AMERICAN TODAY
Jeanette Henry, Editor; The Second Convocation of Indian Scholars, 1971, discussing education, health and medicine, communications, etc. of American Indians. 250 pp. Paper. Amazon.com, 1974. $9.95.

INDIAN WAR SITES: A GUIDEBOOK TO BATTLEFIELDS, MONUMENTS & MEMORIALS, STATE BY STATE WITH CANADA & MEXICO
Steve Rajtar; Illus. 352 pp. Mcfarland & Co., 1999. $39.95, boxed set.

INDIAN WAR IN THE PACIFIC NORTHWEST: THE JOURNAL OF LT. LAWRENCE KIP
Lawrence Gip; intro. by Clifford E. Trafzer
Map. 151 pp. paper. University of Nebraska Press, 1999. $9.95.

INDIAN WARS, 1850-1890
Richard H. Dillon; Photos. Illus. 128 pp. High-Lonesome Books, 1984. $18.

THE INDIAN WAR OF 1864
Capt. Eugene F. Ware; Illus. Center for Western Studies, $25.

INDIAN WARFARE IN WESTERN PENNSYLVANIA & NORTH WEST VIRGINIA AT THE TIME OF THE AMERICAN REVOLUTION
Jared C. Lobdell, Ed.; 155 pp. Paper. Amazon.com, 1992. $16.50.

*INDIAN WARRIORS & THEIR WEAPONS
Robert Hofsinde (Gray-Wolf)
Grades 4-7. Illus. 96 pp. William Morrow, 1965. $11.88.

INDIAN WARS
Duane Lund; 134 pp. Paper. Amazon.com, 1995. $9.95.

*THE INDIAN WARS
Richard B. Morris; illus. by Leonard E. Fisher
Grades 5 and up. Illus. 74 pp. Lerner, 1985. $13.50.

INDIAN WARS
Robert Utley & W. Washburn
Illus. 317 pp. Paper. Cherokee Publications, 1985. $10.95.

THE INDIAN WARS: BATTLES, BLOODSHED, AND THE FIGHT FOR FREEDOM ON THE AMERICAN FRONTIER Anton Treuer
Illus. 320 pp. National Geographic Society, 2017. $40.

THE INDIAN WARS: STEPHEN F. AUSTIN'S TEXAS COLONY, 1822-1835
Allen G. Hatley; Illus. 150 pp. Paper. Amazon.com, $9.95.

INDIAN WARS & PIONEERS OF TEXAS, 1685-1892
John H. Brown; Reprint. 1993. Amazon.com, $67.

INDIAN WARS OF NEW ENGLAND
Herbert M. Sylvester; R.H. Kohn, Editor; Reprint. 3 vols. Vol. I, 528 pp., 1998. $37; Vol. II, 625 pp., 1998. $42; Vol. III, 705 pp., 1999. $46.50. Paper. Heritage Books.

INDIAN WARS OF PENNSYLVANIA
C. Hale Sipe; Reprint. Illus. 908 pp. Paper. Wennawoods Publishing. $39.95.

INDIAN WARS OF THE RED RIVER VALLEY
William Leckie; Illus. 135 pp. Paper. Sierra Oaks, 1987. $11.95.

INDIAN WARS OF THE WEST & FRONTIER ARMY LIFE, 1862-1898: OFFICIAL HISTORIES & PERSONAL NARRATIVES
Robert Lester, et al; Amazon.com, 1998.

INDIAN WARS & PIONEERS OF TEXAS
John H. Brown; Reprint of 1896 edition. Illus. 775 pp. Amazon.com, $100.

INDIAN WATER, 1985: COLLECTED ESSAYS
Richard B. Collins, et al
137 pp. Paper. American Indian Lawyer Training Program, 1986. $6.

INDIAN WATER RIGHTS: CONGRESSIONAL HEARING
Ben Nighthorse Campbell, Ed.; Reprint. Illus. 280 pp. Amazon.com, 2000. $45.

*INDIAN WAY: LEARNING TO COMMUNICATE WITH MOTHER EARTH
Gary McLain; Grades 3 and up. Illus. 110 pp. Paper. John Muir, 1990. $9.95.

INDIAN WEAVING, KNITTING, AND BASKETRY OF THE NORTHWEST COAST
Elizabeth Hawkins; Illus. 32 pp. Paper. Hancock House, 1978. $3.50.

INDIAN--WHITE RELATIONS IN THE U.S.: A BIBLIOGRAPHY OF WORKS PUBLISHED, 1975-1980 Francis P. Prucha
180 pp. Paper. University of Nebraska Press, 1982. $12.

INDIAN-WHITE RELATIONS: A PERSISTENT PARADOX
Jane Smith & Robert Kvasnicka, Editors
Reprint. 278 pp. Paper. Amazon.com, 2003. $27.95.

INDIAN--WHITE RELATIONSHIPS IN NORTHERN CALIFORNIA, 1849-1920
Norris Bleyhl; 109 pp. Association of Northern California Records, 1978. $12.

INDIAN & WHITE: SELF--IMAGE & INTERACTION IN A CANADIAN PLAINS COMMUNITY
Niels W. Braroe; Illus. 206 pp. Amazon.com, 1975. $22.50; paper, $7.95.

INDIAN & THE WHITEMAN IN CONNECTICUT
Chandler Whipple; Illus. 95 pp. Paper. The Berkshire Traveller, 1972. $3.50.

INDIAN WHY STORIES: SPARKS FROM WAR EAGLE'S LODGE-FIRE
Frank B. Linderman; Illus. 290 pp. Paper. Eagle's View Publishing, 2004. $5.95.

INDIAN WILLS, 1911-1921
Jeff Bowen; Records of the Bureau of Indian Affairs. Book One consists of 96 verbatim wills and references about 2,000 individuals from a number of tribes. 199 pp. Paper. 2005. Book Two transcribes an additional 101 verbatim wills. 196 pp. Paper. 2006. Genealogical Publishing Co., $24.95 each.

*AN INDIAN WINTER
Russell Freedman; The culture of the Mandan & Hidatsa. Grades 4-6.
Illus. 96 pp. Holiday House, 1992. $21.95.

INDIAN WISDOM & ITS GUIDING POWER
Brad & Sherry Steiger; Illus. 176 pp. Paper. Schiffer, 1991. $12.95.

INDIAN WOMEN CHIEFS
Carolyn T. Foreman; Reprint of 1954 edition. Zenger, $15.95.

INDIAN WOMEN & FRENCH MEN: RETHINKING CULTURAL ENCOUNTER IN THE WESTERN GREAT LAKES Susan Sleeper-Smith
Illus. 256 pp. U. of Massachusetts Press, 2001. $45; paper, $24.95.

INDIAN WOMEN SPIRITUALITY & SOCIAL CHANGE
Liste-Ghoode Peace Foundation Women's Delegation
Illus. 54 pp. Paper. Common Ground, 1990. $5.

INDIAN YELL: THE HEART OF AN AMERICAN INSURGENCY
Michael Blake; Profiles military & Indian battles & the sacrifice & tragic misdeeds of real people involved. Maps. Paper. Northland, $21.95.

INDIANCRAFT
Chief McIntosh & Harvey Shell
Concise instruction in the art of Indian craft. Illus. 144 pp. Paper. Naturegraph, $9.95.

INDIANOLOGY: DISCOVERING OUR INDIAN HERITAGE
Frederick J. Goshe; Illus. 128 pp. Paper. Amazon.com., 2002.

INDIANPRENEURSHIP: A NATIVE AMERICAN JOURNEY INTO BUSINESS
A small business training curriculum for the Native American entrepreneur. Story-based illustrations. 2005. Onaben, P.O. Box 231116, Tigard, OR 97223 (503) 968-5000 Fax 968-1548. Website: www.onaben.org. $19.95.

*INDIANS
Teri Martini; Grades K-4. Illus. 48 pp. Childrens Press, 1982. $11.45.

*THE INDIANS
Ben Capps; Grades 7 and up. Illus. Amazon.com, $14.95.

*INDIANS
Edwin Tunis; Revised 1959 edition. Grades 5-12. Illus. Amazon.com, $24.89.

INDIANS
Rich Steber; Illus. 60 pp. Paper. Bonanza, 1987. $4.95.

INDIANS & ALCOHOL IN EARLY AMERICA
Peter C. Mancall; Explores the liquor trade's devastating impact on the Indian communities of colonial America. Amazon.com, 1995. $29.95.

INDIANS, ALCOHOL, AND THE ROADS TO TAOS & SANTA FE
William E. Unrau; Illus. 208 pp. University Press of Kansas, 2013. $39.95.

INDIANS ALONG THE OREGON TRAIL: THE TRIBES OF NEBRASKA, WYOMING, IDAHO, OREGON, WASHINGTON IDENTIFIED Bert Webber; Includes village locations, language groups, populations to 1989. Illus. Biblio. 208 pp. Paper. Webb Research, 1989 expanded edition. $17.95.

INDIANS, THE AMERICAN HERITAGE LIBRARY
William Brandon
Chronicles 20,000 years of Indian history. 420 pp. Paper. Cherokee Publications, $10.95.

INDIANS & THE AMERICAN WEST IN THE 20TH CENTURY
Donald L. Parman; Follows the Indians' continuing struggle to hold on to their land, their resources, and their identity. Illus. 256 pp. Paper. Amazon.com & Alibris.com, 1994. $17.95.

INDIANS, ANIMALS, & THE FUR TRADE: A CRITIQUE OF KEEPERS OF THE GAME
Shepard Krech, Editor; 210 pp. Paper. University of Georgia Press, 1981. $10.

INDIANS & ANTHROPOLOGISTS: VINE DELORIA, JR. & THE CRITIQUE OF ANTHROPOLOGY Thomas Biolsi & Larry Zimmerman, Editors
Essays examining how the relationship between anthropologists and Indians have changed in the past 25 years since Vine Deloria, Jr.'s book, "Custer Died for Your Sins" was published. 240 pp. University of Arizona Press, 1997. $48; paper, $21.95.

INDIANS & ARCHAEOLOGY OF MISSOURI
Chapman & Chapman; Revised edition. Paper. Amazon.com, $17.95.

INDIANS & ARTIFACTS IN THE SOUTHEAST
Bierer; Over 1,000 illustrations, many artifact types. Includes trails, maps, and tribal data. 506 pp. Paper. Hothem House, 1980. $28.50.

INDIANS AS MASCOTS IN MINNESOTA SCHOOLS
Pat Stave Helmberger; Illus. 95 pp. Paper. Friends of the Bil of Rights Foundation, 1999.

INDIANS AT HAMPTON INSTITUTE, 1877-1923
Donald F. Lindsey; 336 pp. University of Illinois Press, 1994. $39.95.

THE INDIANS' BOOK
Natalie Curtis; Lore, music, narratives, drawings by Indians. 149 songs in full notation. Reprint. Illus. 584 pp. Paper. Dover & Cherokee Publications, $14.95.

INDIANS & BRITISH OUTPOSTS IN 18TH CENTURY AMERICA
Daniel Ingram; Illus. 272 pp. University Press of Florida, 2012. $69.95; paper, $22.95.

INDIANS & BUREAUCRATS: ADMINISTERING THE RESERVATION POLICY DURING THE CIVIL WAR Edmund J. Danziger, Jr.; 250 pp. U. of Illinois Press, 1974. $22.95.

INDIANS, BUREAUCRATS & LAND: THE DAWES ACT & THE DECLINE OF INDIAN FARMING Leonard A. Carlson; 231 pp. Greenwood Press, 1981. $35.00.

*THE INDIANS & THE CALIFORNIA MISSIONS
Linda Lyngheim ; Grades 4-6. Illus. Revised edition. 160 pp. Langtry Publications, 1990. $14.95; paper, $10.95.

INDIANS & A CHANGING FRONTIER: THE ART OF GEORGE WINTER
Sarah E. Cooke & Rachel Ramadhyani, Eds; Watercolors & drawings of the Potawatomi Indians in northern Indiana just before their removal west of the Mississippi in the mid 1800's. Illus. 270 pp. Amazon.com & Alibris.com, 1993. $24.95.

INDIANS & COLONISTS AT THE CROSSROADS OF EMPIRE: THE ALBANY CONGRESS OF 1754 Timothy J. Shannon; Cornell U. Press, 1999. $45; paper, $17.95.

INDIANS & CRIMINAL JUSTICE
Laurence French, Editor; 224 pp. Rowman & Littlefield, 1982. $23.95.

INDIANS & EMIGRANTS: ENCOUNTERS ON THE OVERLAND TRAILS
Michael L. Tate; Illus. 352 pp. Paper. University of Oklahoma Press, $21.95.

INDIANS & ENERGY: EXPLOITATION & OPPORTUNITY IN AMERICAN SOUTHWEST
Sherry L. Smith & Brian Frehner; Explores the way people have transformed natural resources in the American Southwest into fuel supplies. Native Americans possess large percentage of total acreage of natin';s coal, oil, & uranium resources. Illus. Maps. 336 pp. School for Advanced Research, 2010. $$34.95.

INDIANS & ENGLISH: FACING OFF IN EARLY AMERICA
Karen Ordahl Kupperman; Paper. Amazon.com, 2000. $18.95.

INDIANS & EUROPE: AN INTERDISCIPLINARY COLLECTION OF ESSAYS
edited by Christian F. Feest; Essays on the relationship between European and Native peoples. Illus. Map. 643 pp. Paper. University of Nebraska Press, 1999. $33.

INDIANS, FIRE & LAND IN THE PACIFIC NORTHWEST
Robert Boyd, Editor; Illus. Maps. 320 pp. Paper. Oregon State U. Press, 1999. $34.95.

INDIANS, FRANCISCANS, AND SPANISH COLONIZATION: THE IMPACT OF THE MISSION SYSTEM ON CALIFORNIA INDIANS Robert H. Jackson & Edward Castillo Illus. 222 pp. Paper. University of New Mexico Press, 1999. $24.95.

INDIANS FROM NEW YORK IN WISCONSIN & ELSWHERE: GENEALOGY REFERENCE Toni J. Prevost; 228 pp. Paper. Heritage Book, 1995. $27.

INDIANS ILUSTRATED: THE IMAGES OF NATIVE AMERICANS IN THE PICTORIAL PRESS John M. Coward
Illus. 240 pp. University of Ilinois Press, 2016. $95; paper, $29.95; eBook, $26.95.

INDIANS IN AMERICAN HISTORY: AN INTRODUCTION
Frederick Hoxie & Peter Iverson; 2nd Ed. Illus. 304 pp. Amazon.com, 1998. $16.95.

INDIANS IN AMERICAN SOCIETY: FROM REVOLUTIONARY WAR TO THE PRESENT
Francis Paul Prucha; Paper. U. of California Press, 1988. $19.95. E-Book available.

INDIANS IN EDEN: WABANAKIS & RUSTICATORS ON MAINE'S MT. DESERT ISLAND
Bunny McBride & Harald Prins; 128 pp. Paper. Down East Books, c/o Rowman & Littlefield, 2009. $16.95; eBook, 15.99.

INDIANS IN THE FUR TRADE: THEIR ROLES AS TRAPPERS, HUNTERS & MIDDLEMEN IN THE LANDS SOUTHWEST OF HUDSON BAY, 1660-1870
Arthur J. Ray
Revised edition. Illus. 320 pp. University of Toronto Press, 1998. $50; paper, $21.95.

INDIANS IN THE MAKING: ETHNIC RELATIONS & INDIAN IDENTITIES AROUND THE PUGET SOUND
Alexandra Harmon; Illus. Maps. 405 pp. Paper. U. of California Press, 2000. $26.95.

INDIANS IN MINNESOTA
Kathy Favis Graves & Elizabeth Ebbott, Editors; Survey of contemporary experience of Ojibway & Dakota Indians on and off the reservations in Minnesota. 5th Ed. Illus. Maps. 352 pp. University of Minnesota Press, 2007. $60; paper, $19.95.

*INDIANS IN NEW YORK STATE
Kenneth Job; Bernard Whitman, Editor
Grades 4-7. Illus. 50 pp. Paper. IN Education, Inc., 1989. $5.

THE INDIANS IN OKLAHOMA
Rennard Strickland; Reprint of 1980 edition. Illus. Maps. 187 pp.
Paper. University of Oklahoma Press, 2002. $19.95.

INDIANS IN OVERALLS: & TWO OTHER ACHUMAWI TALES
Jaime De Angulo; Revised edition.120 pp. Paper. City Lights, 1990. $8.95.

INDIANS IN PENNSYLVANIA
Paul A. Wallace; Illus. 200 pp. Amazon.com, 1981. $8.95; paper, $5.95.

INDIANS IN PRISON: INCARCERATED NATIVE AMERICANS IN NEBRASKA
Elizabeth S. Grobsmith; Illus. 215 pp. University of Nebraska Press, 1994. $55.

INDIANS IN 17th CENTURY VIRGINIA
Ben C. McCary; Reprint of 1957 ed. 93 pp. Paper. University Presses of Virginia, $3.95.

INDIANS IN THE FUR TRADE
Arthur J. Ray; Illus. 320 pp. Paper. University of Toronto Press, 1998. $21.95.

INDIANS IN THE MAKING: ETHNIC RELATIONS & INDIAN IDENTITIES AROUND PUGET SOUND
Alexandra Harmon; 405 pp. Paper. University of California Press, 1999. $29.95.

INDIANS IN UNEXPECTED PLACES
Philip J. Deloria; Photos. 312 pp. Paper. University Press of Kansas, 2004. $18.95.

INDIANS IN THE U.S. & CANADA: A COMPARATIVE HISTORY
Roger L. Nichols; Illus. Maps. 393 pp. Paper. University of Nebraska Press, 1998. $22.

INDIANS IN YELLOWSTONE NATIONAL PARK
Joel C. Janetski; Revised ed. Illus. Map. 152 pp. Paper. University of Utah Press. $15.95.

INDIANS & INDIAN AGENTS
George H. Phillips; The origins of the reservation system in California, 1849-1852. Illus. Maps. 238 pp. University of Oklahoma Press, 1997. $27.95.

INDIANS, INDIAN TRIBES & STATE GOVERNMENT: MAJOR LEGAL ISSUES
79 pp. Paper. Amazon.com, 1994. $30.

THE INDIANS & INTRUDERS IN CENTRAL CALIFORNIA, 1769-1849
George H. Phillips; Illus. Maps. 224 pp. University of Oklahoma Press, 1993. $27.95.

THE INDIANS' LAND TITLE IN CALIFORNIA: A CASE IN FEDERAL EQUITY, 1851-1942 Ruth C. Dyer; Paper. R & E Research Associates, 1975. $10.95.

INDIANS, MISSIONARIES & MERCHANTS: THE LEGACY OF COLONIAL ENCOUNTERS ON THE CALIFORNIA FRONTIERS Kent G. Lightfoot
Illus. Maps. Tables. 355 pp. Paper. U. of California Press, 2004. $28.95. E-Book available.

INDIANS' NEW SOUTH: CULTURAL CHANGE IN THE COLONIAL SOUTHEAST
James Axtell
Illus. 120 pp. Paper. Louisiana State University Press, 1997. $22.95; paper, $11.95.

THE INDIAN'S NEW WORLD: CATAWBAS & THEIR NEIGHBORS FROM EUROPEAN CONTACT THROUGH THE ERA OF REMOVAL
James H. Merrell; Illus. 382 pp. Paper. W.W. Norton, 1991. $14.70.

*INDIANS OF AMERICA
PS-12. Aerial Photography. $2.85.

*INDIANS OF AMERICA SERIES
Indian Crafts; Indian Festivals; Indian Homes; Indians of the Eastern Woodlands; Indians of the Plains; and Indian of the West. Grades 4-6. Paper. VIP Publishing. $5 each.

*INDIANS OF AMERICA: GERONIMO, CRAZY HORSE, OSCEOLA, PONTIAC, SQUANTO, CHIEF JOSEPH
Dan Zadra; Grades 2-4. 6 vols. Paper. Creative Education, 1987. $14.95 each.

INDIANS OF THE AMERICAN SOUTHWEST
Steven Walker; Discusses different prehistoric & present day cultures. Photos & Illus. 64 pp. Paper. Treasure Chest, $8.95.

INDIANS & THE AMERICAN WEST IN THE 20TH CENTURY
Donald L. Parman; 256 pp. Amazon.com & Alibris.com, 1994. $35; paper, $14.95.

THE INDIANS OF THE AMERICAS
John Collier; Reprint. 326 pp. Amazon.com, $80; paper, $39.

INDIANS OF THE AMERICAS
National Geographic Society; An illustrative record of Indians like the Navajo, Tarascan, Eskimo, et al. Illus. Photos. 430 pp. High-Lonesome Books, $10.

*INDIANS OF THE AMERICAS COLORING BOOK
Connie Asch; Grades K6. Illus. 32 pp. Paper. Treasure Chest, 1987. $1.95.

INDIANS OF THE AMERICAS: SELF-DETERMINATION & INTERNATIONAL HUMAN RIGHTS Roxanne D. Ortiz; 360 pp. Praeger, 1984. $38.95; paper, $13.95.

INDIANS OF ARIZONA: A GUIDE TO ARIZONA'S HERITAGE
Eleanor H. Ayer; Illus. Map. 48 pp. Paper. Renaissance House, 1990. $4.95.

THE INDIANS OF ARIZONA & NEW MEXICO: 19TH CENTURY ETHNOGRAPHIC NOTES OF ARCHBISHOP JOHN BAPTIST SALPOINTE
Patricia Fogelan Lange, Louis A, Hieb, Thomas J. Steele
Illus. 392 pp. Paper. Amazon.com, $19.95; Rio Grande Books, 2010. eBook, $4.99.

INDIANS OF CALIFORNIA: THE CHANGING IMAGE
James J. Rawls; Illus. 310 pp. Paper. University of Oklahoma Press, 1984. $21.95.

THE INDIANS OF CALIFORNIA: A CRITICAL BIBLIOGRAPHY
Robert F. Heizer; Paper. 80 pp. Amazon.com & Alibris.com, 1976. $4.95.

THE INDIANS OF CANADA
Diamond Jenness; Sixth Edition. Paper. University of Toronto Press, 1963. $17.95.

INDIANS OF CANADA: CULTURAL DYNAMICS
J. Price; Illus. 262 pp. Paper. Sheffield, Wisc., 1979. $8.95.

INDIANS OF CENTRAL & SOUTH FLORIDA, 1513-1763
John H. Hahn; Illus. 256 pp. University Press of Florida, 2003. $39.95.

INDIANS OF THE CHICAGO AREA
Terry Straus; 2nd Edition. 185 pp. Paper. American Indian Press, 1990. $16.95.

THE INDIANS OF CONNECTICUT
Harold C. Bradshaw; 64 pp. Paper. Fawcett, $8.95.

INDIANS OF THE FEATHER RIVER: TALES & LEGENDS OF THE CONCOW MAIDU OF CALIFORNIA   Donald P. Jewell; Sylvia Vane & Lowell Bean, Editors
Illus. 184 pp. Paper. Malki-Ballena Press, 1987. $13.95.

INDIANS OF THE FOUR CORNERS: THE ANASAZI & THEIR PUEBLO DESCENDANTS, A HISTORY OF YOUNG ADULTS
Alice Marriott; Account of the Anasazi culture, including accounts of everyday life. Illus. 48 drawings. Map. 187 pp. Paper. Amazon.com, $13.95.

INDIANS OF THE GREAT BASIN: A CRITICAL BIBLIOGRAPHY
Omer C. Stewart; 152 pp. Paper. Amazon.com & Alibris.com, 1982. $5.95.

THE INDIANS OF THE GREAT PLAINS
Norman Bancroft-Hunt; photos by Werner Foreman
Presents a vivid image of the lives of the the Great Plains Indians. Reprint of 1982 edition. Ilus. 128 pp. Paper. University of Oklahoma Press, $24.95.

*INDIANS OF THE GREAT PLAINS STENCILS
Mira Bartok & Christine Ronan; Five easy-to-do art projects that explore the myths, legends & festivals of Plains Indians. Grades 3 & up. 32 pp. Paper. Amazon.com & Alibris.com, $9.95.

*INDIANS OF THE GREAT PLAINS: TRADITIONS, HISTORY, LEGENDS & LIFE
Courage Book Staff; Grades 4 and up. Illus. 64 pp. Courage Books, 1997. $9.98.

INDIANS OF GREATER SOUTHEAST: HISTORIC ARCHAEOLOGY & ETHNOHISTORY
Bonnie G. McEwan, Ed.; Illus. 335 pp. University of Florida Press, 2000. $55.

INDIANS OF THE HIGH PLAINS: FROM THE PREHISTORIC PERIOD TO THE COMING OF EUROPEANS   George E. Hyde
Reprint of 1959 edition. Illus. Maps. 230 pp. Paper. Amazon.com, 2003. $29.

THE INDIANS OF HUNGRY HOLLOW
Bill Dunlop & Marcia Fountain-Blacklidge
Illus. 236 pp. Paper. Amazon.com & University of Michigan Press, 2004. $19.95.

THE INDIANS OF IOWA
Lance M. Foster; Illus. Maps. 160 pp. Paper. U. of Iowa Press, 2009. $16.95. E-Book, $10.95.

INDIANS OF KANSAS: THE EURO-AMERICAN INVASION & CONQUEST OF INDIAN KANSAS   William E. Unrau
2nd Ed. Illus. 112 pp. Paper. Kansas State Historical Society, 1995. $10.95.

*THE INDIANS OF LENAPEHOKING
Herbert C. Kraft & John T. Kraft
Grades 7-8. Illus. Maps. 54 pp. Paper. Lenape Lifeways & Amazon.com, $10.

*THE INDIANS OF LOUISIANA
Fred B. Kniffen; Legends and tales. A list of tribes in Louisiana, a glossary of state Indian names are included with the history. Grades 3-8. Illus. 112 pp. Amazon.com, $13.95.

INDIANS OF THE LOWER HUDSON REGION: THE MUNSEE
Julian Harris-Salomon; Illus. 95 pp. Amazon.com, 1983. $15.95; paper, $8.95.

THE INDIANS OF MAINE & THE ATLANTIC PROVINCES: A BIBLIOGRAPHIC GUIDE
Roger B. Ray; Reprint of 1972 edition. Paper. Amazon.com, $5.

THE INDIANS OF MANHATTAN ISLAND & VICINITY
Alanson B. Skinner; Reprint. Facs. ed. Illus. 56 pp. Paper. Coyote Press, $6.99.

THE INDIANS OF NEW ENGLAND: A CRITICAL BIBLIOGRAPHY
Neal Salisbury; 128 pp. Paper. Amazon.com & Alibris.com, 1982. $4.95.

THE INDIANS OF NEW JERSEY
Gregory E. Dowd; Amazon.com, 1992. $9.

*THE INDIANS OF NEW JERSEY: DICKON AMONG THE LENAPE
M.R. Harrington; Grades 4-6. Illus. 352 pp. Paper. Rutgers U. Press, 1963. $12.95.

INDIANS OF NEW MEXICO
Richard C. Sandoval & Ree Sheck, Eds
Color photos. 182 pp. Paper. Amazon.com, $14.95.

THE INDIANS OF NIPMUCK COUNTRY IN SOUTHERN NEW ENGLAND, 1630-1750
Dennis A. Connole; Illus. 315 pp. McFarland, 2000. $55.

*THE INDIANS OF NORTH AMERICA SERIES
Dr. Frank W. Porter, III, Editor; Grades 4 and up. Illus. Maps. 96-144 pp. each. Chelsea House, 1987. 49 hardcover titles, $19.95 each, $977.55 per set; 21 paper titles, $9.95 each; $208.95 per set.

INDIANS OF NORTH AMERICA
Marigold Coleman, Compiler; Amazon.com, $39.

INDIANS OF NORTH AMERICA
Harold E. Driver
2nd revised edition. Illus. 650 pp. Paper. University of Chicago Press, 1969. $45.

INDIANS OF NORTH AMERICA
Geoffrey Turner; Illus. 280 pp. Paper. Sterling Publishing, 2004. $14.95.

INDIANS OF NORTH AMERICA - LIFE, HEALTH, CULTURE & DISEASE CONDITIONS: INDEX OF NEW INFORMATION WITH AUTHORS, SUBJECTS & BIBLIOGRAPHICAL REFERENCES   Swedlo A. Sampos; 150 pp. Paper. Abbe Publishers Assn., 1996. $47.50.

INDIANS OF NORTH AMERICA: SURVEY OF TRIBES THAT INHABIT THE CONTINENT   Paula Franklin; Illus. David McKay, 1979. $12.95.

*INDIANS OF THE NORTH AMERICAN PLAINS
Virginia Luling; Grades 6 and up. 64 pp. Amazon.com, $13.96.

INDIANS OF THE NORTH PACIFIC COAST
Tom McFeat, Editor; Examines the culture of the Tlingit, the Haida, the Tsimshian, the Bella Coola, the Kwakiutl, the Nootka, and the Salish peoples of the Northwest Coast. 286 pp. Paper. University of Washington Press, $17.95.

INDIANS OF NORTH & SOUTH AMERICA: BIBLIOGRAPHY BASED ON THE COLLECTION AT THE WILLARD E. YAGER LIBRARY - MUSEUM, HARTWICK COLLEGE, ONEONTA, NY
Carolyn E. Wolf & Yager Library-Museum Staff; 496 pp. Scarecrow Press, 1997. $82.50.

INDIANS OF THE NORTHEAST
Karin Badt; Illus. 60 pp.Paper. Amazon.com, 1997. $5.95.

INDIANS OF NORTHEAST NORTH AMERICA
Christian F. Feest; Illus. 50 pp. Paper. Brill Academic, 1986. $48.

*INDIANS OF THE NORTHEAST: TRADITIONS, HISTORY, LEGENDS & LIFE
Courage Book Staff; Grades 4 and up. Illus. 64 pp. Courage Books, 1997. $9.98.

INDIANS OF THE NORTHWEST
Rochelle Cashdan, Editor; Illus. 64 pp. Paper. Amazon.com, 1998. $6.95.

*INDIANS OF THE NORTHWEST
Coloring book. Grades K-3. Paper. Bellerophon, $4.95.

*INDIANS OF NORTHWEST CALIFORNIA
Title V program staff & tribal resource people; A curriculum book of Native American culture; information on tribal groups in Northwest California which can be integrated into language, literature, social studies, science & math curriculum. Videos available. Grades K-5. Illus. 325 pp. binder. Amazon.com. $49.95, institutions; $39.95, individuals.

INDIANS OF THE NORTHWEST COAST
D. Allen; Photographic study of the northwest people, their land, houses, dances, totem poles, and artifacts. 32 pp. Paper. Hancock House, $4.95.

INDIANS OF THE NORTHWEST COAST
Peter R. Gerber & Max Bruggmann; Covers the Tlingit, Haida, Nootka, Coast Salish, Tsimshian, Kwakiutl, and other tribes, detailing each group's history, culture, language, religion, and art forms. Illus. 232 pp. Facts on File, 1989. $45.

INDIANS OF THE NORTHWEST COAST
Pliny Goddard; The material culture, social & political organization, religion and art of the Indians of the Northwest Coast. Reprint of 1924 edition. Photos. Illus. Maps. 76 pp. High-Lonesome Books, $22.

*INDIANS OF THE NORTHWEST: TRADITIONS, HISTORY, LEGENDS & LIFE
Courage Book Staff; Grades 4 and up. Illus. 64 pp. Courage Books, 1997. $9.98.

*INDIANS OF OKLAHOMA
Lucilia Wise; Illus. Amazon.com. $1.

*INDIANS OF THE PACIFIC NORTHWEST
Karen Liptak; Grades 5-8. Illus. 96 pp. Facts on File, 1990. $18.95.

INDIANS OF THE PACIFIC NORTHWEST: A HISTORY
Robert H. Rubie and John A. Brown
Illus. Maps. 304 pp. Paper. University of Oklahoma Press, 1981. $32.95.

INDIANS OF THE PACIFIC STATES
Speaks Lightning; A Winter Count of the Indian Nations of Washington, Oregon & California. Lists the important dates & events in the history & culture of the Indians in those states. Amazon.com, $12.

INDIANS OF PECOS PUEBLO
Ernest A. Hooton; Elliots Books, 1930. $200.

INDIANS OF THE PIKE'S PEAK REGION
Irvin Howbert; An account of the Sand Creek massacre of 1864, with material on the Ute Indians of the area east of the Rockies. Reprint of 1914 edition. Illus. Maps. 262 pp. Rio Grande Press, $15.

*INDIANS OF THE PLAINS
Elaine Andrews; Grades 5-8. Illus. 96 pp. Facts on File, 1991. $18.95.

*INDIANS OF THE PLAINS
Ruth Thompson; Grades K-4. Illus. 32 pp. Franklin Watts, 1991. $11.40.

INDIANS OF THE PLAINS
Robert H. Lowie; Reprint of the 1982 edition. Illus. 232 pp.
Paper. University of Nebraska Press. $17.95.

*INDIANS OF THE PLATEAU & THE GREAT BASIN
Victoria Sherrow; Describes the lifeways and surroundings of the Native American groups in the region. Grades 3-6. Illus. Maps. 96 pp. Facts on File, 1992. $26.35.

THE INDIANS OF PUGET SOUND: THE NOTEBOOKS OF MYRON EELS
Myron Eels; George Castile, Editor; Illus. 496 pp. U. of Washington Press, 1985. $40.

INDIANS OF THE RIO GRANDE DELTA: THEIR ROLE IN THE HISTORY OF SOUTHERN TEXAS & NORTHEASTERN MEXICO
Martin Salinas; Maps. 207 pp. Paper. University of Texas Press, 1990. $25.

INDIANS OF THE SOUTH
Maxine Alexander, Editor; Illus. 120 pp. Paper. Institute of Southern Studies, 1985. $4.

*INDIANS OF THE SOUTHEAST
Richard E. Mancini; Describes the lifeways and surroundings of the Native American groups in the region. Grades 3-6. Illus. Maps. 96 pp. Facts on File, 1992. $26.35.

INDIANS OF THE SOUTHEASTERN U.S.
John Swanton; Reprint of 1946 edition. Illus. 13 maps. 1,068 pp. Greenwood Publishing, $59.50. Paper. Smithsonian Institution Press, $29.95.

INDIANS OF THE SOUTHEASTERN U.S. IN THE LATE 20TH CENTURY
J. Anthony Paredes, Editor
Surveys American Indian communities still surviving in the southeastern U.S. from Virginia to Florida. 256 pp. Paper. University of Alabama Press, 1992. $21.95.

THE INDIANS OF SOUTHERN CALIFORNIA IN 1852
B.D. Wilson; John W. Cauphey, Ed.; Illus. 154 pp. Paper. U. of Nebraska Press, 1995. $9.

INDIANS OF SOUTHERN ILLINOIS
Irvin Peithman; Photocopy spiral edition. Illus. 172 pp. Amazon.com, 1964. $14.50.

*INDIANS OF THE SOUTHWEST
Karen Liptak; Grades 3-6. Illus. 96 pp. Facts on File, 1990. $18.95.

INDIANS OF THE SOUTHWEST
Pliny E. Goddard; Reprint of 1913 edition. 248 pp. The Rio Grande Press, $20.

INDIANS OF THE SOUTHWEST: A CENTURY OF DEVELOPMENT UNDER THE U.S.
Edward E. Dale; Reprint of 1949 ed. Illus. Maps. Paper. U. of Oklahoma Press, $16.95.

*INDIANS OF THE SOUTHWEST: TRADITIONS, HISTORY, LEGENDS & LIFE
Courage Book Staff; Grades 4 and up. Illus. 64 pp. Courage Books, 1997. $9.98.

THE INDIANS OF THE SUBARCTIC: A CRITICAL BIBLIOGRAPHY
June Helm; 104 pp. Paper. Indiana Unviersity Press, 1976. $6.95.

THE INDIANS OF TEXAS: AN ANNOTATED RESEARCH BIBLIOGRAPHY
Michael L. Tate; 514 pp. Scarecrow Press, 1986, $82.50.

THE INDIANS OF TEXAS: FROM PREHISTORIC TO MODERN TIMES
W.W. Newcomb, Jr.; Reprint of 1961 ed. Illus. 440 pp. Paper. Amazon.com, $24.95.

*INDIANS OF THE TIDEWATER COUNTRY: MD, VA, DE & NC
Thelma Ruskin; Carol Buchanan & Robert Ruskin, Editors
Grades 4-5. Illus. 132 pp. Amazon.com, 1986. $15.00.

INDIANS OF THE U.S.: FOUR CENTURIES OF THEIR HISTORY & CULTURE
Clark Wissler; Reprint. Illus. 364 pp. Paper. Amazon.com, 1940. $29.95.

INDIANS OF THE UPPER TEXAS COAST
Laurence Aten; 338 pp. Amazon.com, 1983. $125.00

INDIANS OF WASHINGTON
Donald B. Ricky; An overview of early history of the state & region. Contains dictionary of tribal articles & biographies. Somerset Publisher, 1999, Distributed by North American Book Distributors, $95.

INDIANS OF THE WESTERN GREAT LAKES, 1615-1760
W. Vernon Kinietz
Reprint of 1965 edition. 440 pp. Paper. University of Michigan Press, $19.95.

THE INDIANS OF YELLOWSTONE PARK
Joel Janetski; Illus. 116 pp. Paper. University of Utah Press, 1987. $8.95.

INDIANS: OR, NARRATIVES OF MASSACRES & DEPREDATIONS ON THE FRONTIER IN WAWASINK AND ITS VICINITY DURING THE AMERICAN REVOLUTION
Abraham G. Bevier; Reprint of 1846 edition. 90 pp. Paper. Amazon.com, $4.50.

INDIANS, SETTLERS, & SLAVES IN A FRONTIER EXCHANGE ECONOMY: THE LOWER MISSISSIPPI VALLEY BEFORE 1783
Daniel H. Usner, Jr.; Examines the economic and cultural interactions among the Indians, Europeans & slaves of colonial Louisiana. 320 pp. University of North Carolina Press, 1991. $32.50; paper, $12.95.

THE INDIANS & THEIR CAPTIVES
James Levermier and Henry Cohen, Editors; Greenwood Press, 1977. $35.

THE INDIANS & THE U.S. CONSTITUTION
Institute for the Development of Indian Law, $7.95.

INDIANS & THE U.S. GOVERNMENT
Institute for the Development of Indian Law, 1977. $12.

*INDIANS WHO LIVED IN TEXAS
Betsy Warren; Reprint of 1970 edition. Grades 2-12. Illus. 48 pp. Hendrick-Long, $9.95.

INDIGENIETY IN THE COURTROOM: LAW, CULTURE, AND THE PRODUCTION OF DIFFERENCE IN NORTH AMERICAN COURTS Jennifer A. Hamilton
Focuses on the legal deployment of indigenous difference in U.S. & Canadian courts in the late 20th century & early 21st. 130 pp. Routledge & Amazon.com, 2008. $81.

INDIGENIZING THE ACADEMY: TRANSFORMING SCHOLARSHIP & EMPOWERING COMMUNITIES Devon A. Mihesuah & Angela Cavender Wilson, Eds.
Anthology. 256 pp. University of Nebraska Press, 2004. $50; paper, $19.95.

INDIGENOUS AESTHETICS: NATIVE ART, MEDIA, & IDENTITY
Steven Leuthold; Illus. 240 pp. Paper. University of Texas Press, 1998. $19.95.

INDIGENOUS AMERICAN WOMEN: DECOLONIZATION, EMPOWERMENT, ACTIVISM
Devon Abbott Mihesuah, Ed.; Anthology. 288 pp.
Paper. U. of Nebraska Press, 2003. $16.95.

INDIGENOUS ARCHAEOLOGIES: A READER ON DECOLONIZATION
Margaret Bruchac. Siobhan Hart, H. Martin Wobst, Editors
Indigenous authors & articles. Illus. 304 pp. U. of Arizona Press, 2008. $75; paper, $34.95.

INDIGENOUS ARCHAEOLOGY: AMERICAN INDIAN VALUES & SCIENTIFIC PRACTICE Joe S. Watkins; Illus. 220 pp. AltaMira Press, 2000. $72; paper. $26.95.

INDIGENOUS COMMUNITY-BASED EDUCATION
Stephen May, Editor; Collection provides examples of indigenous community-based initiatives from around the world. Includes programs among Native Americans in the U.S. & Canada. 182 pp. University of Toronto Press, 1999. $59.95.

INDIGENOUS CULTURES IN AN INTERCONNECTED WORLD
Claire Smith & Graeme K. Ward; Challenges that globalization presents for Indigenous peoples everywhere. Illus. 284 pp. Paper. University of Washington Press, 2001. $32.95.

INDIGENOUS DANCE & DANCING INDIAN: CONTESTED REPRESENTATION IN THE GLOBAL ERA Matthew Krstal; Comparison of indigenous dance practices representing traditional dance, powwow, folkloric dance, and dancing sports mascots. Illus. Tables. 360 pp. University Press of Colorado, 2011. $70. Ebook, $60.

INDIGENOUS ECONOMICS: TOWARD A NATURAL WORLD ORDER
Jose Barreiro, Editor; Iroquois, Anishnabe, Algonquin, Dene Indian, among other, viewpoints are represented in this book that features Fourth World analysis of environment & developmnent issues. Akwe:kon Press, $10.

INDIGENOUS FILMS (Series)
Randolph Lewis & David Delgado Shorter, Editors; This series explores and illuminates individual films produced by and/or about indigenous peoples around the globe. Each book focuses on one film, addressing key issues raised by the film. U. of Nebraska Press.

INDIGENOUS INTELLECTUAL PROPERTY RIGHTS: LEGAL OBSTACLES & INNOVATIVE SOLUTIONS
Mary Riley; Textbook. 320 pp. AltaMira Press, 2004. $96; paper, $36; eBook, $34.99.

INDIGENOUS KNOWLEDGE & EDUCATION: SITES OF STRUGGLE, STRENGTH, AND SURVIVANCE Malia Villegas, Sabina Neugebauer & Kerry Vnegas, Editors
Articles & essays by Marie Battiste, Gregory Cajete, Bryan Brayboy, et al.
360 pp. Paper. Harvard Education Press & Amazon.com, 2008. $32.95

INDIGENOUS LANDSCAPES & SPANISH MISSION: NEW PERSPECTIVES FROM ARCHAEOLOGY & ETHNOHISTORY Lee M. Panich & Tsim D. Schneider, Editors
Holistic view on the consequences of missionization and the active negotiation of missions by indigenous peoples. 256 pp. Illus. University of Arizona Press, 2014. $55.

INDIGENOUS LANGUAGES OF THE AMERICAS: A BIBLIOGRAPHY OF DISSERTATIONS & THESES
Robert Singerman; Compiled citations to over 1,600 dissertations and master's theses from American, Canadian & British institutions. Illus. 346 pp. Scarecrow Press, 1996. $99.

INDIGENOUS LEGAL TRADITIONS
Law Commission of Canada, Editor
192 pp. University of Washington Press, 2007. $94; paper, $37.95.

INDIGENOUS LITERACIES IN THE AMERICAS: LANGUAGE PLANNING FROM THE BOTTOM UP Nancy H. Hornberger; Illus. 395 pp. Amazon.com., 1997.

INDIGENOUS METHODOLOGIES: CHARACTERISTICS, CONVERSATIONS, & CONTEXTS Margaret Kovach; 207 pp. University of Toronto Press, 2009. $45.

INDIGENOUS MOTIVATIONS: RECENT ACQUISITIONS FROM THE NATIONAL MUSEUM OF THE AMERICAN INDIAN Illus. 80 pp. Paper. NMAI Press, 2006. $19.95.

INDIGENOUS PEOPLES & AUTONOMY: INSIGHTS FOR A GLOBAL AGE
Mario Blaser, Ravi De Costa, Deborah McGregor & William D. Coleman
The negative effect of globalization on the lives of Indigenous peoples. 312 pp.
University of Washington Press, 2010. $94; paper, $35.95.

INDIGENUS PEOPLES AND THE MODERN STATE
Karen Torjesen & Susan Steiner; Duane Champagne, Editor
Textbook. 208 pp. AltaMira Press, 2005. $94; paper, $36; eBook, $34.99.

INDIGENOUS PEOPLES: RESOURCE MANAGEMENT & GLOBAL RIGHTS
Svein Jentoft, Henry Minde, Ragnar Nilsen
328 pp. Paper. Univesity of Chicago Press, 2003. $27.50.

INDIGENOUS PEOPLES: SELF-DETERMINATION, KNOWLEDGE & INDIGENEITY
Henry Minde; 296 pp. Paper. University of Chicago Press, 2008. $40.

INDIGENOUS PEOPLES & TROPICAL FOREST: MODELS OF LAND USE & MANAGEMENT FROM LATIN AMERICA
Jason Clay; 116 pp. Cultural Survival, 1988. $19.95; paper, $8.

INDIGENOUS POP: NATIVE AMERICAN MUSIC FROM JAZZ TO HIP HOP
Jeff Berglund, Jan Johnson, Kimberli Lee; Paper. UBC Press, 2016. $39.95

INDIGENOUS STORYWORK: EDUCATING THE HEART, MIND, BODY, AND SPIRIT
Jo-Ann Archibald; 192 pp. University of Washington Press, 2008. $94; paper, $32.95.

INDIGENOUS WOMEN & FEMINISM: POLITICS, ACTIVISM, CULTURE
Cheryl Suzack, et al., Editors
Illus. 344 pp. University of Washington Press, 2011. $94; paper, $37.95.

INDIGENOUS WOMEN'S HEALTH BOOK, WITHIN THE SACRED CIRCLE
edited by Charon Asetoyer, Katharine Cronk, Samanthi Hewakapuge
Assists Native American women in developing self-advocacy skills; healthcare choices, policies, and politics. 323 pp. Paper. Amazon.com, $32.95.

INDIGENOUS WOMEN & WORK: FROM LABOR TO ACTIVISM
Carol Williams, Editor
Illus. 320 pp. University of Illinois Press, 2012. $95; paper, $30; eBook, $27.

INDIVIDUALITY INCORPORATED: INDIANS & THE MULTICULTURAL MODERN
Joel Pfister; Illus. 352 pp. Duke University Press, 2004. $84.95; paper, $23.95.

INDIVISIBLE: AFRICAN-NATIVE AMERICAN LIVES IN THE AMERICAS
Gabrielle Tayac (Piscataway); Essays. Illus. 256 pp. NMAI Press, 2009. $19.95.

INFINITY OF NATIONS: ART & HISTORY IN THE COLLECTIONS OF THE NATIONAL MUSEUM OF THE AMERICAN INDIAN
Cecile R. Ganteaume, Editor; Illus. 320 pp. NMAI Press & HarperCollins, 2010. $29.99.

AN INFINITY OF NATIONS: HOW THE NATIVE NEW WORLD SHAPED EARLY NORTH AMERICA Michael Witgen; Illus. 448 pp. University of Pennsylvania Press, 2012. $45.

INGALIK MATERIAL CULTURE
C. Osgood; Reprint of 1940 edition. Illus. Biblio. 500 pp. Paper. Amazon.com, $25.

INHABITED WILDERNESS: INDIANS, ESKIMOS & NATIONAL PARKS IN ALASKA
Catton; 285 pp. Paper. University of New Mexico Press, 1997. $35.

INHERITING THE PAST: THE MAKING OF ARTHUR C. PARKER & INDIGENOUS ARCHAEOLOGY Chip Colwell-Chanthaphonh; Examines Parker's career path and asks why it has taken generations for Native peoples to follow in his footsteps. 296 pp. University of Arizona Press, 2009. $40; paper, $24.95.

THE INHUMAN RACE: RACIAL GROTESQUE IN AMERICAN LITERATURE & CULTURE Leonard Cassuto; Illus. 288 pp. Columbia U. Press, 1996. $105; paper, $35.

INIGIO OF RANCHO POSOLMI: THE LIFE & TIMES OF A MISSION INDIAN
Laurence H. Shoup & Randall T. Milliken; The life of a Santa Clara Mission Indian and the history of his land grant rancho. Illus. 182 pp. Malki-Ballena Press, 1999. $29.95; paper, $19.95.

***ININATIG'S GIFT OF SUGAR: TRADITIONAL NATIVE SUGARMAKING**
Laura Waterman Wittstock; photos by Dale Kakkak
Grades 3-7. Photos. Paper. Lerner Publications & Meadowlark Communications, $6.95.

INJUN JOE'S GHOST: THE INDIAN MIXED-BLOOD IN AMERICAN WRITING
Harry J. Brown; 296 pp. Amazon.com, 2004. $47.50.

'INJUNS!' NATIVE AMERICANS IN THE MOVIES
Edward Buscombe; Examines cinematic depictions of Native Americans from a global perspective. Illus. 272 pp. Paper. University of Chicago Press, 2006. $16.

INJUSTICE IN INDIAN COUNTRY: JURISDICTION, AMERICAN LAW, AND SEXUAL VIOLENCE AGAINST NATIVE WOMEN Amy L. Casselman. Vol. 1, in series, Critical Indigenous & American Indian Studies. 216 pp. Peter Lang Publishing, 2016. $76.95.

INKPADUTA: DAKOTA LEADER
Paul N. Beck
Biography of a Santee Sioux leader. 176 pp. U. of Oklahoma Press, $24.95.

INKPADUTA - THE SCARLET POINT: TERROR OF THE DAKOTA FRONTIER & SECRET HERO OF THE SIOUX Maxwell Van Nuys
Illus. 460 pp. Paper. Amazon.com, 1998. $25.

THE INLAND WHALE: NINE STORIES RETOLD FROM CALIFORNIA INDIAN LEGENDS Theodora Kroeber
Illus. 212 pp. University of California Press, 2006. $18.95. E-book available.

INSECTS AS FOOD: ABORIGINAL ENTOMOPHAGY IN THE GREAT BASIN
Mark Q. Sutton; Thomas Blackburn, Ed.; Illus. 115 pp. Paper. Ballena Press, 1988. $17.95.

INSIDE DAZZLING MOUNTAINS: SOUTHWEST NATIVE VERBAL ARTS
David L. Kozak, Editor; Illus. 696 pp. Paper. University of Nebraska Press, 2013. $65.

INSIDE THE EAGLE'S HEAD: AN AMERICAN INDIAN COLLEGE
Angelle A. Khachadoorian
An account of the Southwestern Indian Polytechnic Institute in Albuquerque, NM. Illus. 256 pp. Paper. University of Alabama Press, 2010. $29.95 E-Book, $23.96.

INSIDE PASSAGE: LIVING WITH KILLER WHALES, BALD EAGLES & KWAKIUTL INDIANS Michael Modzelewski; Illus. 215 pp. Amazon.com, 1991. $19.95.

INSIGHT GUIDE: NATIVE AMERICA
A travel guide to Indian reservations, historic sites, festivals and ceremonies. Amazon.com, $19.95.

THE INSISTENCE OF THE INDIAN: RACE & NATIONALISM IN 19TH CENTURY AMERICAN CULTURE Susan Scheckel
184 pp. 492 pp. Amazon.com, 1998. $49.50; paper, $16.95.

THE INSTITUTE OF AMERICAN INDIAN ARTS, ALUMNI EXHIBITION
Intro. by Lloyd K. New; Illus. 72 pp. Paper. Amon Carter Museum, 1974. $3.25.

INSTITUTE OF AMERICAN INDIAN ARTS: MODERNISM & U.S. INDIAN POLICY
Joy L. Gritton; Illus. 200 pp. University of New Mexico Press, 2000. $45; paper, $22.95.

INSURING INDIAN COUNTRY: THE INTERSECTION OF TORT, INSURANCE, AND FEDERAL INDIAN LAW Gabriel S. Galanda; American Bar Association, 2005. $19.95.

INTELLECTUAL PROPERTY RIGHTS FOR INDIGENOUS PEOPLES: A SOURCE BOOK
Tom Greaves, Editor; 274 pp. Paper. Society of Appllied Anthropology, 1994. $18.

INTERCULTURAL DISPUTE RESOLUTION IN ABORIGINAL CONTEXTS
Catherine Bell & David Kahane, Editors; Essays on dispute resolution involving Inuit & Arctic peoples, Cree, Metis, Navajo, et al. 384 pp. University of Washington Press, 2004. $94; paper, $43.95.

INTERDEPENDENCE IN THE PREHISTORIC SOUTHWEST: AN ECOLOGICAL ANALYSIS OF PLAINS-PUEBLO INTERACTION
Katherine A. Spielmann; Reprint. Illus. 370 pp. Garland, 1991. $70

INTERIOR LANDSCAPES: AUTOBIOGRAPHICAL MYTHS & METAPHORS
Gerald Vizenor; Illus. 280 pp. University of Minnesota Press, 1995. $17.95.

INTERIOR SALISH TRIBES OF BRITISH COLUMBIA: PHOTOGRAPHIC COLLECTION
Leslie H. Tepper; Illus. 277 pp. Paper. University of Washington Press, 1987. $19.95.

INTERMEDIATE CREEK: MVSKOKE EMPONVKV HOKKOLAT
Pamela Innes, Linda Alexander & Bertha Tilkens; Language & culture of the Muskogee (Creek) & Seminole Indians. 352 pp. Paper. University of Oklahoma Press, 2009. $29.95.

INTERNATIONAL LAW & INDIGENOUS KNOWLEDGE: INTELLECTUAL PROPERTY, PLANT BIODIVERSITY, AND TRADITIONAL MEDICINE
Chidi Oguamanam; 416 pp. University of Toronto Press, 2006. $72.

INTERPRETATIONS OF NATIVE NORTH AMERICAN LIFE MATERIAL CONTRIBUTIONS TO ETHNOHISTORY Michael S. Nassaney & Eric S. Johnson
Illus. 455 pp. University Press of Florida, 2000. $59.95.

INTERPRETING THE INDIAN: 20TH CENTURY POETS & THE NATIVE AMERICAN
Michael Castro; Reprint. 242 pp. Paper. University of Oklahoma Press, 1991. $19.95.

INTERPRETING THE LEGACY: JOHN NEIHARDT & BLACK ELK SPEAKS
Brian Holloway; Illus. 256 pp. University Press of Colorado, 2002. $29.95.

INTERPRETING NATIVE AMERICAN HISTORY & CULTURE AT MUSEUMS & HISTORIC SITES
Raney Bench; 148 pp. Rowman & Littlefield, 2014. $79; paper, $31. eBook, $30.99.

INTERTRIBAL NATIVE AMERICAN MUSIC IN THE U.S.: EXPERIENCING MUSIC, EXPRESSING CULTURE
John-Carlos Perea; Paper. Oxford University Press, 2013. $49.95.

INTERVENTIONS: NATIVE AMERICAN ART FOR FAR-FLUNG TERRITORIES
Judith Ostrowitz; Illus. 240 pp. University of Washington Press, 2009. $45.

INTIMATE GRAMMARS: AN ETHNOGRAPHY OF NAVAJO POETRY
Annthny K. Webster; Illus. 208 pp. University of Arizona Press, 2015. $45.

INTO THE AMERICAN WOODS: NEGOTIATORS ON THE PENNSYLVANIA FRONTIER
James H. Merrill; Illus. 320 pp. W.W. Norton, 1999. $27.95; paper, $14.95.

INTO THE CANYON: SEVEN YEARS IN NAVAJO COUNTRY
Lucy Moore; A memoir of an Anglo-American's life in Navajo country (Chinle, Arizona) from 1968-1975. 236 pp. Illus. Paper. University of New Mexico Press, 2004. $19.95.

INTO THE FRAY: EITELJORG FELLOWSHIP FOR NATIVE AMERICAN FINE ART, 2005 James H. Nottage, Editor; The art of distinguished artist, sculptor John Hoover (Aleut), and fellow artists: Harry Fonseca (Maidu), James Lavador (Walla Walla), C. Maxx Stevens (Seminole/Muskogee), Tanis Maria S'eilton (Tlingit), and MarieWatt (Seneca).

INTRODUCTION TO AMERICAN INDIAN ART
O. LaFarge, et al
Reprint of 1932 edition. 2 vols. in one. Illus. 200 pp. Paper. The Rio Grande Press, $17.50.

INTRODUCTION TO CHEROKEE: A CHEROKEE LANGUAGE STUDY COURSE
Sam Hider; Teaches the fundamental of the language using tapes and work book. Also a history of the language. 44 pp. CD OR 2 cassette tapes. VIP Publishing, $19.95.

INTRODUCTION TO CHICKASAW: SPEAK, READ, WRITE CHICKASAW
Gregg Howard; Rick Eby, et al, Eds.; 52 pp. Paper. VIP Publishing, 1994. $44.95.

INTRODUCTION TO CHOCTAW: A CHOCTAW LANGUAGE STUDY COURSE
Sam Hider; Teaches the fundamental of the language using tapes and work book. Also a history of the language. 44 pp. CD or 2 cassette tapes. VIP Publishing, $19.95.

INTRODUCTION TO CRIMINAL JURISDICTION IN INDIAN COUNTRY
Gilbert L. Hall; 52 pp. Paper. American Indian Lawyer Training Program, 1981. $6.

INTRODUCTION TO HANDBOOK OF AMERICAN INDIAN LANGUAGES & INDIAN LINGUISTIC FAMILIES OF AMERICA NORTH OF MEXICO
Franz Boas & J.W. Powell; intro. By Michael Silverstein
New edition. 248 pp. Paper. University of Nebraska Press, 2017. $20.

INTRODUCTION TO HOPI POTTERY
Francis H. Harlow; 32 pp. Illus. Paper. Museum of Northern Arizona, 1978. $2.50.

AN INTRODUCTION TO THE LUISENO LANGUAGE
Villiana Hyde; Paper. Malki Museum Press, 1979. $8.

AN INTRODUCTION TO NATIVE NORTH AMERICA
Mark Q. Sutton; 2nd Ed. Illus. 430 pp. Paper. Amazon.com, 2003. $56.80.

AN INTRODUCTION TO THE PREHISTORY OF INDIANA
James H. Kellar
Revised 1983 edition. Illus. Biblio. 78 pp. Paper. Indiana Historical Society, $4.95.

AN INTRODUCTION TO THE SHOSHONI LANGUAGE: DAMMEN DAIQWAPE
Drusilla Gould & Christopher Loether
A basic information on the phonology & grammar of the language. University of Utah Press. $50; paper, $24.95; 4 cassettes, $20; paperback & cassettes, $39.95.

INTRODUCTION TO THE STUDY OF SOUTHWESTERN ARCHAEOLOGY
Alfred V. Kidder; Illus. Paper. Yale University Press, 1962. $16.95.

*INTRODUCTION TO TRIBAL GOVERNMENT
Yerington Paiute Tribe
Grades 9-12. 94 pp. Paper. Yerington Paiute Tribe Publications, $13.

INTRODUCTION TO TRIBAL LEGAL STUDIES, 3rd EDITION
Justin B. Richland & Sarah Deer
Illus. 536 pp. Rowman & Littlefield, 2015. $120; paper, $59; eBook, $57.99,

INTRODUCTION TO WISCONSIN INDIANS: PREHISTORY TO STATEHOOD
Carol I. Mason; Illus. 321 pp. Paper. Amazon.com, 1988. $15.50.

AN INTRODUCTORY GUIDE TO ENTREPRENEURSHIP FOR AMERICAN INDIANS
Enid, et al, Editors; 50 pp. American Assn for Community & Junior Colleges, 1990. $11.

THE INTRUDERS: THE ILLEGAL RESIDENTS OF THE CHEROKEE NATION,1866-1907
Nancy N. Sober; 3rd Edition. Illus. 222 pp. Amazon.com, 1991. $24.95.

*INTRUDERS WITHIN: PUEBLO RESISTANCE TO SPANISH RULE & THE REVOLT OF 1680 Louis Baldwin; Grades 7-12. Illus. 128 pp. Franklin Watts, 1995. $24.

INUA: SPIRIT WORLD OF THE BERING SEA ESKIMOS
William Fitzhugh & Susan Kaplan
Illus. 296 pp. Smithsonian, 1982. $35.00; paper, $19.95.

*INUIT
Elizabeth Hahn; Grades 5-8. Illus. 32 pp. Amazon.com, 1990. $13.26.

INUIT ARTISTS PRINT WORKBOOK
Sandra B. Barz, Editor; Illus. 324 pp. Paper. Arts and Culture of the North, 1981. $58.

INUIT EDUCATION & SCHOOLS IN THE EASTERN ARCTIC
Heather E. McGregor
Illus. Map. 224 pp. University of Washington Press, 2010. $94; paper, $35.95.

THE INUIT: GLIMPSES OF AN ARCTIC PAST
David Morrison & George Hebert Germain
Illus. 160 pp. University of Washington Press, 1995. $27.95.

INUIT IMAGINATION: ARCTIC MYTH & SCULPTURE
Harold Seidelman & James Turner; 224 pp. Paper. U. of Washington Press, 2001. $45.

INUIT KAYAKS IN CANADA: REVIEW OF HISTORICAL RECORDS & CONSTRUCTION
E.Y. Arima; Illus. 244 pp. Paper. U. of Washington Press, 1987. $19.95.

*INUIT MYTHOLOGY
Evelyn Wolfson; Grades 2-5. 150 pp. Paper. Amazon.com, 2001.U. Press, 2003. $29.95.

THE INVASION OF INDIAN COUNTRY IN THE 20TH CENTURY: AMERICAN CAPITALISM & TRIBAL NATURAL RESOURCES, 2ND Edition Donald Fixico
Illus. 306 pp. Paper. University Press of Colorado, 2011. $26.95; eBook, $21.95.

THE INVENTION OF PROPHECY: CONTINUITY & MEANING IN HOPI INDIAN RELIGION Armin W. Geertz; Illus. 39 pp. Paper. Amazon.com, 1987. $54.50.

THE INVENTIVE MIND: PORTRAITS OF RURAL ALASKA TEACHERS
G. Williamson McDiarmid, Judith S. Kleinfeld & Wm. H. Parrett
180 pp. Paper. University of Alaska Press, 1988. $10.

AN INVENTORY OF THE MISSION INDIAN AGENCY RECORDS
James Young, Dennis Moristo & G. David Tanenbaum
66 pp. Paper. UCLA, American Indian Studies Center, 1976. $5.

AN INVENTORY OF THE PALA INDIAN AGENCY RECORDS
James Young, Dennis Moristo and G. David Tanenbaum
66 pp. Paper. UCLA, American Indian Studies Center, 1976. $5.

THE INVINCIBLE CHEROKEE: AN OVERVIEW
Joy Love; Illus. Paper. Wonder Words Publishing, 2001. $20.

THE INVISIBLE CULTURE: COMMUNICATION IN CLASSROOM & COMMUNITY ON THE WARM SPRINGS INDIAN RESERVATION Susan Urmston Philips
A classic in the field of educational anthropology & socio-linguistics.
Reprint of revised edition. 147 pp. Paper. Waveland Press, 1993. $16.50.

INVISIBLE INDIGENES: THE POLITICS OF NONRECOGNITION
Bruce Granville Miller; Maps. 248 pp. Paper. University of Nebraska Press, 2003. $24.95.

THE INVISIBLE MUSICIAN
Ray A. Young Bear
Poetry. Draws upon ancient traditions while creating dramatic versions of the harshness of modern tribal life. 120 pp. Holy Cow! Press, $15; paper, $8.95.

INVISIBLE NATIVE AMERICANS MAGIC PICTURE BOOK
Pat Stewart; Illus. 32 pp. Paper. Dover, 2001. $1.50.

INVISIBLE NATIVES: MYTH & IDENTITY IN THE AMERICAN WEST
Armando Jose Prats; Paper. Cornell University Press, 2002. $34.95.

INVISIBLE REALITY: STORYTELLERS, STORYTAKERS, AND THE SUPERNATURAL WORLD OF THE BLACKFEET
Rosalyn R. LaPier; Illus. 246 pp. University of Nebraska Press, 2017. $50.

INVOLVEMENT OF CANADIAN NATIVE COMMUNITIES IN THEIR HEALTH CARE PROGRAMS: A REVIEW OF THE LITERATURE SINCE THE 1970'S
D.E. Young & L.L. Smith; Identifies ovber 60 models of Native community involvement in health care in Canada. 90 pp. paper. CCI, 1993. $15.

IOWA HISTORY READER
Marvin Bergman, Editor; Includes Native Americans. Illus. Maps. 470 pp. Paper. University of Iowa Press, 2008. $39.95

IOWA INDIANS
O.J. Fargo; Two vols. Book 1, 51 pp.; Book 2, 71 pp. Paper. Amazon.com, 1988. $1.50 each.

IOWA'S ARCHAEOLOGICAL PAST
Lynn Marie Alex; Photos. Drawings. Maps. 364 pp. Paper. U. of Iowa Press, 2008. $31.

THE IOWAY INDIANS
Martha R. Blaine; Illus. Maps. 364 pp. Paper. U. of Oklahoma Press, 1979. $19.95.

IOWAY LIFE: RESERVATION & REFORM, 1837-1860
Greg Olson; Illus. 184 pp. University of Oklahoma Press, 2016. $29.95.

IROQUOIAN COSMOLOGY
John Hewitt; Reprint. Amazon.com, $15.

THE IROQUOIAN WOMEN: THE GANTOWISAS
Barbara A. Mann; Illus. 540 pp. Paper. Amazon.com, 2000. $34.95.

THE IROQUOIS
Dean R. Snow; Illus. 288 pp. Paper. Amazon.com, 1998. $29.95.

THE IROQUOIS
Frank G. Speck; Second edition. Illus. 95 pp. Paper. Cranbrook Institute, 1955. $4.50.

*THE IROQUOIS
Barbara Graymont; Grades 7+. Illus. 104 pp. Chelsea House, 1989. $17.95; paper, $9.95.

*THE IROOQUOIS
Bruce Johansen; Paul Rosier, Series Editor
Grades 6-12. Illus. 128 pp. Chelsea House, 2010. $35.

*THE IROQUOIS
Craig & Katherine Doherty; Grades 4-8. 64 pp. Franklin Watts, 1994. $22; paper, $6.95.

*THE IROQUOIS
Barbara McCall; Grades 5-8. Illus. 32 pp. Amazon.com, 1989. $13.26.

THE IROQUOIS
Sheila Wyborny; Amazon.com, 2004.

IROQUOIS: ART & CULTURE
Carrie Lyford; Illus. 100 pp. Paper. Hancock House, $6.95.

IROQUOIS ART, POWER, AND HISTORY
Neal B. Keating; Illus. 360 pp. University of Oklahoma Press, $55.

THE IROQUOIS BOOK OF RITES
Horatio Hale; Reprint. Illus. Paper. Kessinger Publishing, 2004. $22.95.

THE IROQUOIS CONFEDERACY: HISTORY & LEGENDS
Emerson Klees; Illus. 185 pp. Paper. Amazon.com, 2003. $16.95.

IROQUOIS CORN IN A CULTURE-BASED CURRICULUM
Carol Cornelius; Illus. 288 pp. State U. of New York Press, 1998. $65; paper, $21.95.

IROQUOIS CRAFTS
Carrie A. Lyford; Reprint of 1945 edition. Illus. Photos. 98 pp. Paper. R. Schneider, Publishers & Written Heritage, $5.95.

IROQUOIS CULTURE & COMMENTARY
Doug George-Kanentiio; Perspectives on the life, traditions, and current affairs of the peoples of the Iroquois Confederacy. Illus. Photos. 224 pp. Amazon.com, $14.95.

THE IROQUOIS EAGLE DANCE: AN OFFSHOOT OF THE CALUMET DANCE
William N. Fenton; Reprint. Illus. 324 pp. Paper. Syracuse University Press, 1991. $19.95.

THE IROQUOIS & THE FOUNDING OF THE AMERICAN NATION
Donald A. Grinde, Jr.; UCLA, American Indian Studies Center, 1992.

IROQUOIS IN THE AMERICAN REVOLUTION
Barbara Graymont; Illus. Maps. 370 pp. Paper. Syracuse University Press, 1972. $16.95.

THE IROQUOIS IN THE CIVIL WAR: FROM BATTLEFIELD TO RESERVATION
Laurence M. Hauptman; The ware and effects of the war on the Iroquois families at home. Illus. Maps. 240 pp. Paper. Syracuse University Press, 1993. $29.95.

THE IROQUOIS IN THE WAR OF 1812
Carl Benn; Illus. Maps. 596 pp. University of Toronto Press, 1998. $50; paper, $21.95.

IROQUOIS INDIANS: DOCUMENTARY HISTORY—GUIDE TO MICROFILM COLLECTION Mary Druke, Editor; 718 pp. Research Publications, 1985. $180.

IROQUOIS JOURNEY: AN ANTHROPOLOGIST REMEMBERS
William N. Fenton; Jack Campisi & William Starna, Eds.; Memoir of William N. Fenton, 1908-2005. Photos. 223 pp. University of Nebraska Press, 2007. $55; paper, $24.95.

IROQUOIS LAND CLAIMS
Christopher Vecsey & William Starna, Editors Illus. Maps. 240 pp. Syracuse University Press, 1988. $45; paper, $16.95.

IROQUOIS MEDICAL BOTANY
James W. Herrick & Dean R. Snow; A guide to understanding the use of herbal medicines in traditional Iroquois culture. Illus. 240 pp. Syracuse U. Press, 1994. $29.95; paper, $19.95.

IROQUOIS MUSIC & DANCE: CEREMONIAL ARTS OF TWO SENECA LONGHOUSES
Gertrude P. Kurath; Reprint. Illus. 320 pp. Paper. Amazon.com $6.98.

THE IROQUOIS & THE NEW DEAL
Laurence Hauptman; Illus. 276 pp. Syracuse U. Press, 1988. $24.95; paper, $10.95.

IROQUOIS ON FIRE: A VOICE FROM THE MOHAWK NATION
Douglas M. George-Kanentiio (Mohawk) Study of the historical & social issues raised during the Iroquois' long struggle over disputed territorial titles. 168 pp. Paper. University of Nebraska Press, 2008. $16.95.

IROQUOIS: PEOPLE OF THE LONGHOUSE
Michael Johnson; Illus. 160 pp. 2013. Firefly Books & Amazon.com. $28; paper, $9.

THE IROQUOIS RESTORATION: IROQUOIS DIPLOMACY ON THE COLONIAL FRONTIER, 1701-1754
Richard Aquila; Illus. Maps. 285 pp. Paper. University of Nebraska Press, 1997. $18.95.

THE IROQUOIS: THE SIX NATIONS CONFEDERACY
Mary Englar; Illus. Paper. Amazon.com, $7.95.

AN IROQUOIS SOURCEBOOK
Elisabeth Tooker, Ed; Reprint. Three vols. Vol. 1, Political & Social Organization, 400 pp. $55; Calendric Rituals, 292 pp. $40; & Medicine Society Rituals, 360 pp. $50. Garland Pubg.

IROQUOIS STUDIES: A GUIDE TO DOCUMENTARY & ETHNOGRAPHIC RESOURCES FROM WESTERN NEW YORK & THE GENESEE VALLEY
Russell A. Judkins, Editor; Illus. 98 pp. Paper. Amazon.com.

THE IROQUOIS STRUGGLE FOR SURVIVAL: WORLD WAR II TO RED POWER
Laurence Hauptman; 44 photos. Maps. 344 pp. Paper. Syracuse U. Press, 1986. $16.95.

IROQUOIS SUPERNATURAL: TALKING ANIMALS & MEDICINE PEOPLE
Michael Bastine & Mason Winfield; Collection of tales & beliefs; Iroquois legends of supernatural beings, places, and customs of the Iroquois live on in contemporary paranormal experience. Illus. 384 pp. Inner Traditions, 2011. $20.

THE IROQUOIS TRAIL: DICKON AMONG THE ONONDAGAS & SENECAS
Mark Harrington; 215 pp. Paper. Amazon.com, 1991. $9.95.

IROQUOIS WARS: EXTRACTS FROM THE JESUIT RELATIONS & PRIMARY SOURCES, 1535-1650
Claudio Salvucci & Anthony Schiavo; Illus. 432 pp. Amazon.com, 2003. $85.

THE IROQUOIS WARS I
Claudio Salvucci; Illus. 432 pp. Wennawoods Publishing, $85.

THE IROQUOIS WARS II
Claudio Salvucci; Illus. 432 pp. Wennawoods Publishing, $85.

IOWA'S ARCHAEOLOGICAL PAST
Lynn M. Alex; Illus. 333 pp. University of Iowa Press, 2000. $49.95; paper, $29.95.

IRREDEEMABLE AMERICA: THE INDIANS' ESTATE & LAND CLAIMS
Imre Sutton; Illus. University of New Mexico Press, 1985.

*IS MY FRIEND AT HOME? PUEBLO FIRESIDE TALES
John Bierhorst; Grades 3-8. Illus. 32 pp. Simon & Schuster Childrens, $14.95.

ISHI IN THREE CENTURIES
Edited by Karl Kroeber & Clifton Kroeber Illus. 440 pp. Paper. University of Nebraska Press, 2008. $29.95.

ISHI IN TWO WORLDS: A BIOGRAPHY OF THE LAST WILD INDIAN IN NORTH AMERICA Theodora Kroeber; Karl Kroeber, Editor; 50th anniversary edition. Illus. 304 pp. Paper. U. of California Press, 2011. $19.95. Delux Illus. edition, 286 pp. 2004. $29.95.

*ISHI: THE LAST OF HIS PEOPLE
Grades 2-4. Illus. 32 pp. Childrens Press, $10.95.

ISHI, THE LAST YAHI: A DOCUMENTARY HISTORY
Robert F. Heizer & Theodora Kroeber; Illus. Maps. 251 pp. Paper. U. of California Press, 1979. $18.95.

ISHI MEANS MAN
Thomas Merton; Five essays about Native American Indians. Illus. 75 pp. Unicorn, 1976. $17.50; paper, $6.95.

ISHI'S JOURNEY--FROM THE CENTER TO THE EDGE OF THE WORLD
James A. Freeman Ishi tale, the last Yahi Indian. Illus. Photos. 224 pp. Paper. Naturegraph, $10.95.

ISKWEKWAK - KAH' KI YAW NI WAHKOMA-KANAK: NEITHER INDIAN PRINCESS NOR SQUAW DRUDGES Janice Acoose; 126 pp. Paper. Woman's Press, 1995. $14.95.

ISLAND BETWEEN
Margaret E. Murie; Fiction. Saga of Toozak the Eskimo, his people, his early years, marriage and manhood. Illus. 228 pp. University of Alaska Press, 1977. $9.95.

THE ISLAND CHUMASH: BEHAVIORAL ECOLOGY OF A MARITIME SOCIETY
Douglas J. Kennett; Illus. 310 pp. U. of California Press, 2005. $65. E-Book available.

ISLAND IMMIGRANTS
J.D. Cleaver; 40 pp. Paper. Oregon Historical Society, 1986. $2.95.

ISLAND OF THE ANISHNAABEG: THUNDERERS & WATER MONSTERS IN THE TRADITIONAL OJIBWE LIFE-WORLD
Theresa S. Smith; Illus. 248 pp. Paper. University of Nebraska Press, 2012. $25.

ISLANDS OF TRUTH: THE IMPERIAL FASHIONING OF VANCOUVER ISLAND
Daniel W. Clayton; Native people of Vancouver Island's early encounters with Europeans. Illus. 256 pp. UBC Press, 1999. $75.

ISSUES FOR THE FUTURE OF AMERICAN INDIAN STUDIES
Susan Guyette; 267 pp. Paper. UCLA, American Indian Studies Center, 1985. $10.

ISSUES IN NATIVE AMERICAN CULTURAL IDENTITY
Michael K. Green; 310 pp. Paper. Amazon.com, 1998. $29.95.

IT IS A GOOD DAY TO DIE: INDIAN EYEWITNESSES TELL THE STORY OF THE BATTLE OF THE LITTLE BIG HORN
Herman J. Viola, with Jan Shelton Danis; Accounts of Crow, Lakota, & Cheyenne warriors who triumphed at Little Bighorn. Illus. Maps. Paper. U. of Nebraska Press, 2001. $12.95.

IT WILL LIVE FOREVER: TRADITIONAL YOSEMITE ACORN PREPARATION
Bev Ortiz; Photos. Biblio. 160 pp. Paper. Heyday Books, $14.95.

IT'S YOUR MISFORTUNE & NONE OF MY OWN: A NEW HISTORY OF THE AMERICAN WEST Richard White
Illus. Maps. 664 pp. U. of Oklahoma Press, 1991. $45; paper, $26.95.

ITCH LIKE CRAZY
Wendy Rose; Poetry which addresses concerns with personal identity. Illus. 121 pp. University of Arizona Press, 2002. $15.95.

J

ANDREW JACKSON & HIS INDIAN WARS
Robert V. Remini; 336 pp. Paper. Amazon.com, 2002. $15.

HELEN HUNT JACKSON & HER INDIAN REFORM LEGACY
Valerie Sherer Mathes; Conflict in Indian policy and reform of the period. Illus. Map. 253 pp. U. of Texas Press, 1990. $27.95. Paper. U. of Oklahoma Press, 1997. $19.95.

WILLIAM JACKSON, INDIAN SCOUT
James W. Schultz; Reprint of 1976 edition. 200 pp. Amazon.com, $19.95.

JACKSONLAND: PRESIENT ANDREW JACKSON, CHEROKEE CHIEF JOHN ROSS AND A GREAT AMERICAN LAND GRAB
Steve Inskeep; Illus. Cherokee Publications, $29.95.

THE JAILING OF CECELIA CAPTURE
Janet Campbell Hale; Novel of urban Indian life. Paper. U. of New Mexico Press, $19.95.

*JAMES AT WORK
Looks at reservation life through the eyes of a Choctaw Indian boy. Grades PS-3. 14 pp. Choctaw Heritage Press, $2.75.

THE NATIVE AMERICAN ART COLLECTION: SELECTED WORKS
Christina E. Burke, W. Jackson Rushing III, Rennard Strickland, et al.
Illus. 240 pp. University of Oklahoma Press, $60; paper, $29.95

JAMES RIVER CHIEFTDOMS: RISE OF SOCIAL INEQUALITY IN THE CHESAPEAKE
Martin D. Gallivan; Explores the Powhatan & Monacan societies met by Jamestown colonists in 1607. Illus. 320 pp. Univerity of Nebraska Press, 2003. $55.

***JAMES JOE**
as told to Susan Thompson; Autobiography of a present-day Navajo medicine man. Grades 4 and up. 32 pp. Paper. Council for Indian Education, 1995. $4.95.

THE JAMESTOWN S'KLALLAM STORY: REBUILDING A NORTHWEST COAST INDIAN TRIBE Joseph H. Straus; Illus. Map. Jamestown S'Klallam Tribe, 2002.

THE JAR OF SEVERED HANDS: THE SPANISH DEPORTATION OF APACHE PRISONERS OF WAR, 1770-1810
Mark Santiago; Explores colonial Spanish-Apache relations in the Southwest borderlands. Illus. Maps. 264 pp. University of Oklahoma Press, 2011. $29.95.

JEFFERSON'S AMERICA: 1760-1815
Norman Risjord; 350 pp. Madison House, 1991. $32.95; paper, $17.95.

THOMAS JEFFERSON & THE CHANGING WEST: FROM CONQUEST TO CONSERVATION James P. Ronda; U. of New Mexico Press, $29.95; paper, $16.95.

MR. JEFFERSON'S HAMMER: WILLIAM HENRY HARRISON & THE ORIGINS OF AMERICAN INDIAN POLICY
Robert M. Owens; 344 pp. University of Oklahoma Press, 2009. $34.95.

JEFFERSON & THE INDIANS: THE TRAGIC FATE OF THE FIRST AMERICANS
Anthony F.C. Wallace; Illus. Maps. 416 pp. Harvard University Press & Amazon.com, 2001. $31.95; paper, $19.95.

JEFFERSON & SOUTHWESTERN EXPLORATION: THE FREEMAN & VUSTIS ACCOUNTS OF RED RIVER EXPEDITION OF 1806 Thomas Freeman & Peter Custis
Illus. Maps. Biblio. 386 pp. Paper. University of Oklahoma Press, 1984. $18.95.

MARY JEMISON: WHITE WOMAN OF THE SENECA
Rayna M. Gangi; True story of the famous Indian captive. 152 pp. Amazon.com, 1996. $22.95; paper, $12.95.

THE JEROME AGREEMENT BETWEEN THE KIOWA, COMANCHE & APACHE TRIBES & THE U.S. R.J. DeMalle; 38 pp. Institute for the Development of Indian Law, $11.

THE JESUIT MISSION TO THE LAKOTA SIOUX: PASTORAL MINISTRY & THEOLOGY, 1885-1945 Ross A. Enochs; 180 pp. Paper. Sheed & Ward, 2004. $12.95.

THE JESUS ROAD: KIOWA, CHRISTIANITY, & INDIAN HYMNS
Luke Lassiter, Clyde Ellis, Ralph Kotay; Christian faith among the Kiowas of southwestern Oklahoma. Illus. 152 pp. University of Nebraska Press, 2002. $65; paper, $24.95.

JEWELRY BY SOUTHWEST AMERICAN INDIANS: EVOLVING DESIGNS
Nancy Schiffer; Illus. 256 pp. Schiffer, 1990. $59.95.

JEWELS OF THE NAVAJO LOOM: THE RUGS OF TEEC NOS POS
Ruth K. Belikove; Illus. 38 pp. Paper. Museum of New Mexico Press, 2000. $14.95.

THE JICARILLA APACHE: A PORTRAIT
Veronica E. Velarde Tiller; Nancy Hunter Warren, Photographer
University of New Mexico Press, $45; paper, $29.95.

THE JICARILLA APACHE TRIBE: A HISTORY, 1846-1970
Veronica E. Velarde Tiller; Revised edition. Illus. Photos. Maps. 300 pp.
Paper. University of New Mexico Press, 1991. $24.95.

THE JICARILLA APACHES: A STUDY IN SURVIVAL
Dolores Gunnerson; Illus. 327 pp. Amazon.com, 1973. $22.

***JOHANAA'EI: BRINGER OF THE DAWN**
Veronica Tsinajinnie; illus. by Ryan Singer; Grades K-5. Amazon.com, 2008. $17.95.

JOHNSON OF THE MOHAWKS
Arthur Pound & Richard E. Day; Reprint. 568 pp. 1993. Amazon.com, $5.50.

DOUGLAS JOHNSON: A PAINTER'S ODYSSEY
Robert A. Ewing; Illus. 112 pp. Amazon.com, 1997. $39.95.

***PHILIP JOHNSTON & THE NAVAJO CODE TALKERS**
Syble Lagerquist; Grades 4+. 32 pp. Paper. Council for Indian Education, 1990. $4.95.

JORDAN'S POINT, VIRGINIA: ARCHAEOLOGY IN PERSPECTIVE, PREHISTORIC TO MODERN TIMES Martha W. McCartney; In 1607, when the first European colonists saw it, the area was home to Natives they would call the Weyanoke.

JOSANIE'S WAR: A CHIRICAHUA APACHE NOVEL
Karl H. Schlesier; University of Oklahoma Press, 1998. $22.95

***JOSEPH: CHIEF OF THE NEZ PERCE**
Dean Pollock; Grades 5 and up. Illus. 64 pp. Paper. Binford & Mort, 1990. $7.95.

***ALVIN JOSPEHY'S HISTORY OF THE NATIVE AMERICANS SERIES**
Alvin M. Josephy, Jr.; Grades 5-7. Six books. Illus. 864 pp. Amazon.com, 1989. $71.88 per set; paper, $47.70 per set.

THE JOURNAL & ACCOUNT BOOK OF PATRICK GASS: MEMBER OF THE LEWIS & CLARK EXPEDITION
Carol Lynn MacGregor, Ed.; Illus. Maps. 384 pp. Mountain Press, 1997. $30; paper, $18.

JOURNAL OF THE ADVENTURES OF MATTHEW BUNN
Matthew Bunn; Reprint. 36 pp. New Library Pr. Net, 2003. $88.

JOUNRAL OF AN INDIAN TRADER: ANTHONY GLASS AND THE TEXAS TRADING FRONTIER, 1790-1810
Dan L. Flores, Editor; Illus. Paper. Texas A&M University Press, 2000. $16.95.

JOURNAL OF CALIFORNIA & THE GREAT BASIN ANTHROPOLOGY
Vol. 30.2. Malki-Ballena Press, 2010. $30.

JOURNAL OF CHEROKEE STUDIES
Issues of the Journal (official publication of the Museum of the Cherokee) 1976-1986. Illus. 4 Vols. 1,200 pp. Cherokee Publications, $125/set.

JOURNAL OF THE INDIAN WARS
Vol. One, No. 1: Custer at the Washita & Little Big Horn
Vol. One, No. 2: Battles & Leaders East of the Mississippi
Vol. One, No. 3: The Indian Wars' Civil War
Vol. One, No. 4: Famous Fighting Units
Vol. Two, No. 1: Books on the Indian Wars. Amazon.com.

THE JOURNAL OF...NARRATING AN ADVENTURE FROM ARKANSAS THROUGH INDIAN TERRITORY, ETC. Jacob Fowler; A trip from Arkansas to New Mexico and encounters with the Cherokee, Kiowa, Pawnee & Arapaho. Reprint of 1898 edition. 183 pp. Ross Haines, $15.

A JOURNAL OF SIBLEY'S INDIAN EXPOSITION DURING THE SUMMER OF 1863 & RECORD OF THE TROOPS EMPLOYED
Arthur M. Daniels; Reprint. Illus. 154 pp. Thueson, $30.

THE JOURNALS OF THE LEWIS & CLARK EXPEDITION
Meriweather Lewis & William Clark; Gary Moulton, Editor
Three vols. Illus. University of Nebraska Press, 1987. $40 each.

JOURNALS OF JOSEPH N. NICOLLET: 1836-1837
Martha Bray; Andre Fertey, Translator
Illus. 288 pp. Minnesota Historical Society Press, 1970. $16.50.

JOURNALS OF THE MILITARY EXPEDITION OF MAJOR GENERAL JOHN SULLIVAN: AGAINST THE SIX NATIONS OF INDIANS IN 1779
Maj. Gen. John Sullivan; Reprint. Illus. 612 pp. Paper. Amazon.com, 2000. $34.

JOURNEY FROM PRINCE OF WALES' FORT IN HUDSON'S BAY TO THE NORTHERN OCEAN, 1769-1772 Samuel Hearne; Reprint of 1795 edition. Illus. Maps. 437 pp. Charles E. Tuttle, $20; Greenwood Press, $32.75.

A JOURNEY INTO MOHAWK & ONEIDA COUNTRY, 1634-1635: THE JOURNAL OF HARMEN MEYNDERTSZ VAN DEN BOGAERT
Charles Gehring; Illus. 120 pp. Paper. Syracuse University Press, 1988. $16.95.

THE JOURNEY OF NATIVE AMERICAN PEOPLE WITH SERIOUS MENTAL ILLNESS: FIRST NATIONAL CONFERENCE
A. Marie Sanchez & Frank D. McGuirk; Illus. 137 pp. Paper. Amazon.com, 1996. $35.

THE JOURNEY OF NAVAJO OSHLEY: AN AUTOBIOGRAPHY & LIFE HISTORY
Robert S. McPherson, Editor; Oshley's narrative is woven with vivid and detailed portraits of Navajo culture. Illus. 235 pp. Utah State University Press, 2000. $25.95; paper, $25.95.

THE JOURNEY OF TAI-ME
N. Scott Momaday; Illus. 104 pp. University of New Mexico Press, 2010. $21.95.

JOURNEY SONG: A SPIRITUAL LEGACY OF THE AMERICAN INDIAN
Celinda Reynolds Kaelin; Illus. 250 pp. Paper. Amazon.com, 1998. $14.95.

JOURNEY TO THE ANCESTRAL SELF: TAMARACK SONGS
Teaches that the lifeways of all native peoples are essentially one. Illus. 224 pp. Paperback. Amazon.com, $14.95. With voice cassette, $26.

JOURNEY TO THE ANCESTRAL SELF: THE NATIVE LIFEWAY GUIDE TO LIVING IN HARMONY WITH EARTH MOTHER
Tamarack Song; 264 pp. Paper. Station Hill Press, 1994. $14.95.

***JOURNEY TO CAHOKIA**
Iseminger, Steele; Story about Ancient Cahokia (A.D. 1200) as seen through the eyes of a young boy. Grades 4-6. Illus. 32 pp. Paper. Amazon.com, 1995. $2.95.

***JOURNEY TO CENTER PLACE**
Viola R. Gates; Anasazi life through a 12-year-old Anasazi girl. Grades 3-7. 144 pp. Council for Indian Education, $10.95.

JOURNEY TO THE FOUR DIRECTIONS: TEACHINGS OF THE FEATHERED SERPENT
Jim Berenholtz; Ceremoial musician & visionary traveler Jim Berenholtz shares the story of his mystical awakening & remarkable training. Illus. Map. 288 pp. Paper. Inner Traditions International, $14.95.

JOURNEY TO THE WEST: THE ALABAMA & COUSHATTA INDIANS
Sheri Marie Shuck-Hall; Illus. 304 pp. U. of Oklahoma Press, 2009. $34.95.

JOURNEYS HOME: REVEALING A ZUNI-APPALACHIA COLLABORATION
Dudley Cocke, Donna Porterfield, Edward Wemytewa, Editors

Artists from two traditions and bilingual play. Illus. 112 pp. Paper. University of New Mexico Press, $19.95, with CD

JOY BEFORE NIGHT: EVELYN EATON'S LAST YEARS
Terry Eaton; Illus. 173 pp. Paper. Amazon.com, 1988. $6.95.

THE JUAN PARDO EXPEDITION; EXPLORATION OF THE CAROLINAS & TENNESSEE, 1566-1568 Charles Hudson, Editor
Illus. 354 pp. Smithsonian Institution Press, 1990. $42.

JUH, AN INCREDIBLE INDIAN
Dan L. Thrapp; Juh was a chief and Geronimo only a war leader. The full account of his Apache shadowy life and career. Illus. Map. 42 pp. Paper. Texas Western Press, 1993. $12.50.

THE JUMANOS: HUNTERS & TRADERS OF THE SOUTH PLAINS
Nancy Parrott Hickerson; Describes encounters with Native North Americans by Spanish explorers. Illus. Maps. 340 pp. Paper. University of Texas Press, 1994. $24.95.

THE JUNE RISE
William Tremblay; The story of Joseph Antoine Janis's visionary transformation from a Missouri farmboy to an advisor to Lakota chief, Red Cloud. 240 pp. Fulcrum Publishing, 2000. $22.95.

JUNG & THE NATIVE AMERICAN MOON CYCLES
Michael Owen; Illus. 288 pp. Paper. Amazon.com, 2002. $22.95.

*THE JUNIOR LIBRARY OF AMERICAN INDIANS
Grades 2 and up. Illus. 72-80 pp. each. Chelsea House Publishers, 1992. 30 hardcover titles, $16.95 each, $508.50 per set; 12 paperback titles, $9.95 each, $119.40 per set.

*JUST A WALK
Jordan Wheeler; illus. by Bill Cohen
Children's stories by a Cree author. Grades K-4. Illus. 50 pp. Paper. Theytus, 1994. $8.95.

JUSTICE FOR NATIVES: SEARCHING FOR COMMON GROUND
Andrea P. Morrison, Ed.; Illus. 350 pp. Paper. McGill-Queens University Press, 1994.

JUVENILE JUSTICE IN INDIAN COUNTRY ACT
U.S. Senate Committee on Indian Affairs
105th Congress. Illus. U.S. Government Printing Office, 1997.

K

*KA-HA-SI & THE LOON: AN ESKIMO LEGEND
Terri Cohlene; Grades 1-5. Illus. Paper. Amazon.com, 1992. $4.95.

FRED KABOTIE: HOPI INDIAN ARTIST
Fred Kabotie and Bill Belknap
Illus. 150 pp. Museum of Northern Arizona, $24.95; Northland Press, 1977. $35.00.

KACHINA CEREMONIES & KACHINA DOLLS
Martina M. Jacobs; Illus. 72 pp. Paper. Carnegie, 1980. $1.50.

THE KACHINA & THE CROSS: INDIANS & SPANIARDS IN THE EARLY SOUTHWEST
Carroll Riley; History of the conflict between the Pueblos and the Franciscan Order in the 17th century. Illus. Maps. 352 pp. Paper. University of Utah Press, 1999. $16.95.

*THE KACHINA DOLL BOOK I & II
Donna Greenlee; Grades 1-5. I - Explains the meaning of 14 ceremonial dolls of the Hopi Indians. II - tells about 13 more Hopi dolls with two special pages of Indian symbols. Illus. 32 pp. Paper. Amazon.com, $4.95 each.

KACHINA DOLLS: THE ART OF HOPI CARVERS
Helga Teiwes; Provides an understanding of the secular contexts of contemporary Hopi kachina wood sculpture. Illus. 161 pp. U. of Arizona Press, 1991. $34.95; paper, $29.95.

*KACHINA DOLLS: AN EDUCATIONAL COLORING BOOK
Grades 1-8. Illus. 32 pp. Paper. Spizzirri Publishing, 1981. Read & Coloring Book, $1.95;

THE KACHINA DOLLS OF CECIL CALNIMPTEWA: THEIR POWER, THEIR SPLENDOR
Theda Bassman; photos by Gene Balzer; Features 127 dolls in full-color. Includes a biography of the author. Illus. 112 pp. Treasure Chest, 1993. $70.

KACHINA: A SELECTED BIBLIOGRAPHY
Marcia Muth
Over 100 references to kachinas and an essay. Illus. 32 pp. Paper. Sunstone Press, $4.95.

KACHINA TALES FROM THE INDIAN PUEBLOS
Gene Meany Hodge, Editor; Illus. 96 pp. Paper. Sunstone Press, $8.95.

KACHINAS: A HOPI ARTIST'S DOCUMENTARY
Barton Wright; illus. by Cliff Bahnimptewa
237 color plates. Illus. 272 pp. Paper. Amazon.com, 1973. $29.95.

KACHINAS IN THE PUEBLO WORLD
edited by Polly Schaafsma; 14 scholars examine the vital role of kachinas in the cultures of the Rio Grande, Zuni, and Hopi Pueblos. Illus. Paper. University of Utah Press. $19.95.

KACHINAS: A SELECTED BIBLIOGRAPHY
Marcia Muth; Illus. 32 pp. Paper. Sunstone Press, $4.95.

KACHINAS: SPIRIT BEINGS OF THE HOPI
Neil David, Sr, J. Brent Ricks & Alexander E. Anthony, Jr.; Based on 79 paintings

by Neil David, Sr., Hopi Indian artist & Kachina carver. Illus. Photos. 200 pp. Paper. Amazon.com, 1993. $35.

KAHBE NAGWIWENS - THE MAN WHO LIVED IN THREE CENTURIES
Carl A. Zapffe; Illus. 100 pp. Paper. Historical Heart Associates, 1975. $10.

KAHNAWAKE: FACTIONALISM, TRADITIONALISM & NATIONALISM IN A MOHAWK COMMUNITY Gerald F. Reid; Illus. 235 pp. Paper. U. of Nebraska Press, 2004. $24.95.

KAHTNUHT'ANA QENAGA: THE KENAI PEOPLE'S LANGUAGE
Peter Kalifornsky; James Kari, Editor
Second edition. Illus. 140 pp. Paper. Alaska Native Language Center, 1982. $6.

PAUL KANE, THE COLUMBIA WANDERER: SKETCHES, PAINTINGS & COMMENT, 1846-1847
Thomas Vaughan, Editor; Illus. 80 pp. Paper. Oregon Historical Society, 1971. $3.95.

PAUL KANE'S GREAT NOR-WEST
Diane Eaton & Sheila Urbanek; Canadian artist documents Native people of the Northwest before contact with white settlers. Illus. Photos. 176 pp. University of Washington Press, 1995. $72; paper, $32.95.

KANIENKEHAKA (MOHAWK NATION): STATE POLICIES & COMMUNITY RESISTANCE Donna Goodleaf; Account of the "Oka Crisis" with Mohawkl perspective of the issues & events. 250 pp. Paper. Theytus, 1993. $12.95.

THE KANSA INDIANS: A HISTORY OF THE WIND PEOPLE
William E. Unrau; Illus. 280 pp. Paper. University of Oklahoma Press, 2000. $21.95.

KANSAS INDIANS: A HISTORY OF THE WIND PEOPLE, 1673-1873
William E. Unrau
Illus. Maps. 262 pp. Paper. University of Oklahoma Press, 1971. $16.95.

THE KARANKAWA INDIANS OF TEXAS: AN ECOLOGICAL STUDY OF CULTURAL TRADITION & CHANGE
Robert A. Ricklis; Illus. Maps. Tables. 236 pp. Paper. U. of Texas Press, 1996. $25.

KARNEE: A PAIUTE NARRATIVE
Lalla Scott; Story of Northern Paiute Indian life in Nevada as told by Annie Lowry, a Paiute/Caucasion woman who lived with the Paiute tribe near Lovelock, Nevada. 168 pp. Paper. University of Nevada Press, 1966. $11.95.

KARUK INDIAN MYTHS
John P. Harrington; 100 pp. http://soda.sou.edu/awdata/030310a1.pdf 1995. $69.

KARUK: THE UPRIVER PEOPLE
Maureen Bell; The history of the Karuk; also present-day Karuk life & culture are presented. Photos. 144 pp. Paper. Naturegraph, $9.95.

KASHAYA POMO PLANTS
Jennie Goodrich, Claudia Lawson, Vana Parrish Lawson
Describes 150 common plants growing in Kashaya Pomo territory that have long been an important part of the tribe's culture. Illus. Glossary. 176 pp. Paper. Heyday Books, $12.95.

KASKA INDIANS: AN ETHNOGRAPHIC RECONSTRUCTION
John J. Honigmann; 163 pp. Paper. HRAFP, 1964. $15.

KATIE GALE: A COAST SALISH WOMAN'S LIFE ON OYSTER BAY
Llyn De Danaan; Amazon.com, 2013. $24; Kindle edition, $16.

THE KAW INDIAN CENSUS & ALLOTMENTS
Bradford Koplowitz; 100 pp. Paper. Amazon.com, 1996. $19.

K'ETAALKKAANEE: THE ONE WHO PADDLED AMONG THE ANIMALS
Catherine Attla; University of Alaska Press, $12.

KE-MA-HA: THE OMAHA STORIES OF FRANCIS LA FLESCHE
Francis La Flesche; Daniel Littlefield & James Parins, Eds.
134 pp. Paper. University of Nebraska Press, 1995. $10.

THOMAS VARKER KEAM, INDIAN TRADER
Laura Graves; Illus. 368 pp. University of Oklahoma Press, 1998. $29.95.

KEEPER OF THE DELAWARE DOLLS
Lynette Perry & Manny Skolnick; The Delaware culture and dollmaking craft. Illus. Map. Paper. University of Nebraska Press, 1999. $12.

*KEEPER OF FIRE
James Magorian; Grades 4-12. Illus. 78 pp. Paper. Council for Indian Ed., 1984. $6.95.

*KEEPERS OF THE ANIMALS: NATIVE AMERICAN STORIES & WILDLIFE ACTIVITIES FOR CHILDREN Michael Caduto & Joseph Bruchac; illus. by John Kahionhes Fadden
Grades 1-7. Illus. 286 pp. Paper. Fulcrum Publishing, 1991. $19.95. Native American Animal Stories, Illus. 160 pp. paper, $12.95; Teacher's Guide, 66 pp. paper, $9.95; 2 audiocassettes, $16.95.

KEEPERS OF THE CENTRAL FIRE ISSUES IN ECOLOGY FOR INDIGENOUS PEOPLES Stephen Kunitz & Jerrold Levy; Illus. 191 pp. U. of Arizona Press, 1991. $39.

KEEPERS OF THE CULTURE: WOMEN IN A CHANGING WORLD
Janet Mancini Billson; Explores women's lives in seven distinct & intact North American cultures: Iroquois, Inuit, Blood, Mennonite, West Indian, Chinese & Ukranian. 350 pp. Lexington Books, 1995. $23.

KEEPERS OF THE DREAM
Patricia Wyatt; Illus. 72 pp. Pomegranate, 1995. $24.

*KEEPERS OF THE EARTH: NATIVE AMERICAN STORIES & ENVIRONMENTAL ACTIVITIES FOR CHILDREN
Michael Caduto & Joseph Bruchac; illus. by John Kahiones Fadden
Grades K-12. Illus. 240 pp. Paper. Fulcrum Publishing, 1988. $21.95. Native American Stories, Illus. 160 pp. paper, $12.95; Teacher's Guide, 52 pp. paper, $9.95; two audiocassette, $16.95.

KEEPERS OF THE GAME: INDIAN-ANIMAL RELATIONSHIPS & THE FUR TRADE
Calvin Martin; Illus. Paper. University of California Press, 1982. $24.95.

*KEEPERS OF LIFE: DISCOVERING PLANTS THROUGH NATIVE AMERICAN STORIES & EARTH ACTIVITIES FOR CHILDREN
Michael Caduto & Joseph Bruchac; illus. by John Kahiones Fadden
Grades K-12. Illus. 288 pp. Paper. Fulcrum Publishing, 1994. $19.95. Native Plant Stories, 160 pp. paper, $12.95; Teacher's Guide, 48 pp. paper, $9.95; 2 audiocassette, $16.95.

*KEEPERS OF THE NIGHT: NATIVE AMERICAN STORIES & NOCTURNAL ACTIVITIES FOR CHILDREN   Michael Caduto & Joseph Bruchac
illus. by John Kahiones FaddenGrades K-12. Illus. 168 pp. Paper.
Fulcrum Publishing, $19.95.

KEEPERS OF THE TOTEM
Time-Life Book Eds.; Illus. 192 pp. Amazon.com, 1993.

KEEPING THE CAMPFIRES GOING: NATIVE WOMEN'S ACTIVISM IN URBAN COMMUNITIES Susan Applegate Krouse & Heather A. Howard
Essays of Native women activists in American & Canadian cities. 232 pp. Paper. University of Nebraska Press, 2009. $30.

KEEPING THE CIRCLE: AMERICAN INDIAN IDENTITY IN EASTERN NORTH CAROLINA, 1885-2004
Christopher Arris Oakley; 196 pp. Paper. University of Nebraska Press, 2007. $19.95.

KEEPING HEART ON PINE RIDGE: FAMILY TIES, WARRIOR CULTURE, COMMODITY FOODS, REZ DOGS, AND THE SACRED
Vic Glover; Stories depicting contemporary life with the Lakota people on Pine Ridge Indian Reservation, near the Black Hills of South Dakota. Illus. 160 pp. Paper. Book Publishing Co., $9.95.

KEEPING IT LIVING: TRADITIONS OF PLANT USE & CULTIVATION ON THE NORTHWEST COAST OF NORTH AMERICA
Douglas Deur & Nancy Turner, Editors
Illus. 384 pp. University of Washington Press, 2005. $35.

KEEPING PROMISES: WHAT IS SOVEREIGNTY & OTHER QUESTIONS FROM INDIAN COUNTRY Betty Reid & Ben Winton
Illus. 40 pp. Paper. Western National Parks Association, 2004. $8.95.

KEEPING SLUG WOMAN ALIVE: HOLISTIC APPROACH TO AMERICAN INDIAN TEXTS Greg Sarris; Eight essays on cross-cultural communication. 214 pp. Paper. University of California Press, 1993. $26.95.

KEEWAYDINOQUAY, STORIES FROM MY YOUTH
Keewaydinoquay Peschel; Illus. University of Michigan Press, 2006. $55; paper, $22.95.

KENEKUK, THE KICKAPOO PROPHET
Joseph B. Herring; Photos. Maps. 170 pp. University Press of Kansas, 1988. $19.95.

KENNEWICK MAN: PERSPECTIVES ON THE ANCIENT ONE
Heather Burke, Claire Smith, Dorothy Lippert, et al, Editors
Tribal leaders, archaeologists & others offer views. Illus. 320 pp. University of Arizona Press, 2008. $65; paper, $29.95.

KENTUCKY ARCHAEOLOGY
R. Barry Lewis, Editor; Illus. Amazon.com, $35. E-book, $35.

A KEY INTO THE LANGUAGE OF AMERICA
Roger Williams; Reprint. 232 pp. Paper. Applewood, $12.95.

A KEY INTO THE LANGUAGE OF WOODSPLINT BASKETS
Ann McMullen & Russell Handsman, Editors
Illus. 196 pp. Paper. The Mohegan Tribe, 1987. $22.50.

*THE KEY TO THE INDIAN
Lynn R. Banks; Grades 2-5. Paper. Avon, 1999. $4.95.

KICKAPOO INDIANS, THEIR HISTORY & CULTURE: ANNOTATED BIBLIOGRAPHY
Phillip M. White; Illus. 152 pp. Greenwood Publishing, 1999. $68.95.

THE KICKAPOOS: LORDS OF THE MIDDLE BORDER
Arrell M. Gibson; History of the tribe. Reprint. Illus. Map. Biblio.
408 pp. Paper. University of Oklahoma Press, $25.95.

KIIKAAPOA: THE KANSAS KICKAPOO
Donald D. Stull; Illus. 214 pp. Paper. Kickapoo Tribal Press, 1984. $12.

KILIWA DICTIONARY
Mauricio J. Mixco; 207 pp. Paper. University of Utah Press, 1985. $25.

KILIWA TEXTS: WHEN I HAVE DONNED MY CREST OF STARS
Mauricio J. Mixco; Illus. 250 pp. Paper. University of Utah Press, 1983. $25.

KILLING CUSTER
James Welch & Paul Stekler; Illus. 320 pp. W.W. Norton & Co., 1994. $25.

KILLING THE INDIAN MAIDEN: IMAGES OF NATIVE AMERICAN WOMEN IN FILM
Elise Marubbio; Illus. 200 pp. Paper. Amazon.com, 2006.

THE KILLING OF CHIEF CRAZY HORSE
Robert A. Clark, Editor; Three eyewitness accounts of the killing of Crazy Horse.
Illus. 152 pp. Paper. University of Nebraska Press, 1988. $14.95.

THE KILLING OF CRAZY HORSE
Thomas Powers; Illus. Map. 568 pp. Amazon.com, 2010.

KILLING TIME WITH STRANGERS
W.S. Penn; Nez Perce's family's struggle to fit into a white world.
283 pp. Paper. University of Arizona Press, 2000. $16.95.

KILLING US QUIETLY: NATIVE AMERICANS & HIV/AIDS
Irene S. Vernon; Discusses prevention strategies and educational resources.
Illus. 147 pp. University of Nebraska Press, 2001. $35; paper, $14.95.

KILLING THE WHITE MAN'S INDIAN: REINVENTING NATIVE AMERICANS AT THE END OF THE CENTURY
Fergus M. Bordewich; 400 pp. Paper. Anchor/Knopf Publishing, 1997. $15.95.

KINAALADA: A NAVAJO PUBERTY CEREMONY
Shirley M. Begay and Verna Clinton-Tullie
Illus. 171 pp. Rough Rock School Press, 1983. $15; paper, $25.

KINAALDA: A STUDY OF THE NAVAHO GIRL'S PUBERTY CEREMONY
Charlotte Johnson Frisbie; Illus. Paper. University of Utah Press, 1993. $24.95.

KING ISLAND TALES - UGIUVANGMIUT QULIAPYUIT
Eskimo history & legends from the Bering Strait. University of Alaska Press, $19.95.

KING OF THE DELAWARES: TEEDYUSCUNG, 1700-1763
Anthony F.C. Wallace
Reprint of 1949 edition. 328 pp. Maps. Paper. Syracuse University Press, $16.95.

KING PHILIP'S WAR: CIVIL WAR IN NEW ENGLAND, 1675-1676
James D. Drake; Illus. 272 pp. U. of Massachusetts Press, 2000. $50; paper, $22.95.

KINSHIP, CAPITALISM, CHANGE: THE INFORMAL ECONOMY OF THE NAVAJO, 1868-1995 Michael J. Francisconi; Illus. 284 pp.Garland, 1997. $90.

KINSHIP & THE DRUM DANCE IN A NORTHERN DENE COMMUNITY
M.L. Asch; Illus. 113 pp. CCI, $25; paper, $15.

KINSMEN OF ANOTHER KIND: DAKOTA–WHITE RELATIONS IN THE UPPER MISSISSIPPI VALLEY, 1650-1862
Gary C. Anderson; Reprint. 383 pp. Paper. Minnesota Historical Society, 1997. $15.95.

KINSMEN THROUGH TIME: AN ANNOTATED BIBLIOGRAPHY OF POTAWATOMI HISTORY R. David Edmunds; 237 pp. Scarecrow Press, 1987. $65.45.

KIOWA, APACHE, & COMANCHE MILITARY SOCIETIES: ENDURING VETERANS, 1800 TO THE PRESENT
William C. Meadows; Photos. Tables. 528 pp. Paper. U. of Texas Press, 1999. $34.95.

KIOWA BELIEF & RITUAL
Benjamin R. Kracht; Illus. 402 pp. University of Nebraska Press, 2017. $75.

KIOWA ETHNOGEOGRAPHY
William C. Meadows; Examines the place names, geographical knowledge, & cultural associations of the Kiowa from earliest recorded history to the present. Illus. Maps. 380 pp. Paper. University of Texas Press, 2008. $30.

*THE KIOWA: GREAT PLAINS
John Wunder; Grades 5 and up. Illus. Chelsea House, 1989. $17.95.

KIOWA HUMANITY & THE INVASION OF THE STATE
Jacki Thompson Rand; Photos. Tables. 210 pp. U. of Nebraska Press, 2005. $45.

KIOWA HYMNS
sung by Ralph Kotay ; 2 CDS. 44 pp. U. of Nebraska Press, 2005. $14.97.

KIOWA MEMORIES: IMAGES FROM INDIAN TERRITORY, 1880
Ron McCoy; Illus. 67 pp. Amazon.com, 1987. $21.

KIOWA MILITARY SOCIETIES: ETHNOHISTORY & RITUAL
William C. Meadows; Illus. 472 pp. University of Oklahoma Press, 2010. $75.

A KIOWA'S ODYSSEY: A SKETCHBOOK FROM FOR MARION
edited by Phillip Earenfight; Drawings which chronicles the experiences of 72 Southern Plains Indians captured by the U.S. Army. Illus. Maps. 256 pp. Paper. University of Washington Press, 2007. $40.

THE KIOWA TREATY OF 1853
R.J. DeMallie; 60 pp. Institute for the Development of Indian Law, $12.50.

*KIOWA VOICES: CEREMONIAL DANCE, RITUAL & SONG
Maurice Boyd
Grades 3 and up. Illus. 165 pp. Paper. Texas A&M University Press, 1981. $29.95.

*KIOWA VOICES: MYTHS, LEGENDS & FOLKTALES
Maurice Boyd
Grades 3 and up. Volume II. Illus. 323 pp. Texas A&M University Press, 1983. $39.95.

KIOWA: A WOMAN MISSIONARY IN INDIAN TERRITORY
Isabel Crawford; Illus. 241 pp. Paper. University of Nebraska Press, 1998. $12.

THE KIOWAS
Mildred P. Mayhall; Reprint. Illus. Map. 365 pp. Paper. Amazon.com, $29.

KITCHI-GAMI: LIFE AMONG THE LAKE SUPERIOR OJIBWAY
Johann G. Kohl; trans. by L. Wraxall
Illus. 477 pp. Paper. Minnesota Historical Society Press, 1985. $12.95.

KITCHIGAMIG ANISHINABEG: THE PEOPLE OF THE GREAT LAKES
Bucko Teeple, with photos by Alan R. Kamuda; Illus. Photos. Michigan Indian Press, $25.

KIUMAJUT (TALKING BACK): GAME MANAGEMENT & INUIT RIGHTS, 1950-70
Peter Kulchyski & Frank Tester; Examines Inuit relations with the Canadian state.
328 pp. University of Washington Press, 2008. $94; paper, $37.95.

KIVA ART OF THE ANASAZI AT POTTERY MOUND, N.M.
Frak Hibben; Illus. 145 pp. KC Publications, 1975. $35; paper, $14.95.

KIVA, CROSS, & CROWN: THE PECOS INDIANS & NEW MEXICO, 1540-1840
John L. Kessell; Illus. 304 pp. Paper. Amazon.com, $19.95.

KLALLAM GRAMMAR
Timothy Montler; Illus. Map. 409 pp. University of Washington Press, 2015. $60.

KLAMATH HEARTLANDS: GUIDE TO THE KLAMATH RESERVATION FOREST PLAN
Edward C. Wolf; The Tribe's plan for an ecological & cultural restoration of the
Western forests. Photos. Maps. 56 pp. Paper. Oregon State University, 2004. $19.95.

KLEE WYCK
Emily Carr; Illus. 144 pp. Amazon.com, 2004. $19.95.

THE KLICKITAT INDIANS
Selma M. Neils; Illus. 240 pp. Paper. Binford & Mort, 1985. $12.95.

KNOWLEDGE OF THE ELDERS: THE IROQUOIS CONDOLENCE CANE TRADITION
A study guide designed for high school students. Looks at a living tradition of the Eastern
Woodlands as told by Jacob Thomas, and elder of Cayuga Nation. Akwe:kon Press, $8.

KNOWLEDGE & SECRECY IN AN ABORIGINAL RELIGION
Ian Keen; Illus. 368 pp. Paper. Oxford University Press, 1998. $29.95.

KOASATI DICTIONARY
Geoffrey Kimball; 407 pp. University of Nebraska Press, 1994. $60.

KOASATI GRAMMAR
Geoffrey Kimball; Illus. 640 pp. University of Nebraska Press, 1991. $95.

KOASATI TRADITIONAL NARRATIVES
translated by Geoffrey D. Kimball; Collection of oral literature of the Koasati Indians.
Photos. 328 pp. University of Nebraska Press, 2010. $65.

KOKOPELLI CEREMONIES
Stephen W. Hill; Illus. 64 pp. Kiva Publishing, 1995. $24.95; paper, $16.95.

KOKOPELLI: FLUTE PLAYER IMAGES IN ROCK ART
Dennis Slifer & Jim Duffield; Extensive survey of rock art depictions of the humpbacked
flute player. Photos, Illus. Paper. 210 pp. Amazon.com, 1994. $16.95.

KOKOPELLI: THE MAKING OF AN ICON
Ekkehart Malotki; Story of the mythical flute player. Illus. 200 pp.
University of Nebraska Press, 2000. $35; paper, $19.95.

KOKOPELLI'S COOKBOOK: AUTHENTIC RECIPES OF THE SOUTHWEST
James R. Cunkle & Carol Cunkle; 112 pp. Golden West Publishing, 1997. $9.95.

KOMANTCIA
Harold Keith; A tale of captivity by the Comanche Indians. 300 pp. Levite of Apache, $17.

KONAWA, INDIAN TERRITORY: TWO PIONEER FAMILIES, HAMMONS & TROBAUGH
Chester Kennedy; Illus. 225 pp. Amazon.com, 1993. $36.95.

KOOTENAI WHY STORIES
Frank B. Linderman; Illus. 173 pp. Paper. University of Nebraska Press, 1997. $9.95.

KORCZAK: STORYTELLER IN STONE
The biography of Korczak Ziolkowski, the sculpture of Crazy Horse from Thunderhead
Mountain. Illus. 80 pp. Paper. Crazy Horse Memorial Foundation, $3.25.

KOSSATI GRAMMAR
Geoffrey Kimball; Illus. 640 pp. University of Nebraska Press, 1991. $70.

KOSTER: AMERICANS IN SEARCH OF THEIR PREHISTORIC PAST
Stuart Struever & Felicia Antonelli Holton
Illus. 258 pp. Paper. Waveland Press, 1979. $25.95.

*KOU-SKELOWH "WE ARE THE PEOPLE"
Barb Marchand, Editor & Illus.; Entirely done by Okanagan First Nation people.
Grades K-4. Illus. 28 pp. Paper. Theytus, 1990. $12.95.

KTUNAXA LEGENDS
Kootenai Culture Committee
Legends from the Confederated Salish & Kotenai Tribes. Paper. SKC Press, 1997. $21.

MORT KUNSTLER'S OLD WEST: INDIANS
Mort Kunstler; Illus. 192 pp. Amazon.com, 1998. $ 12.95.

*KUNU: WINNEBAGO BOY ESCAPES
Kenneth Thomasma; Jack Brouwer. Illus.; Historical novel of forced migration of
Winnebago Indians in 1863. Grades 4 & up. Illus. Amazon.com, $10.99; paper, $6.99.

KUSIQ: AN ESKIMO LIFE HISTORY FROM THE ARCTIC COAST OF ALASKA
Waldo Bodfish, Sr.; Illus. Photos. Maps. 330 pp. Paper. U. of Alaska Press, 1991. $21.

*THE KWAKIUTL
Stanley Walens; Grades 5 and up. Illus. Chelsea House, 1989. $17.95.

KWAKIUTL ART
Audrey Hawthorn; Illus. Maps. 292 pp. Paper. University of Washington Press, 1979. $35.

KWAKIUTL ETHNOGRAPHY
Franz Boas; Helen Codere, Editor; Illus. University of Chicago Press, 1967. $30.

THE KWAKIUTL: INDIANS OF BRITISH COLUMBIA
Ronlad P. Rohner & Evelyn C. Bettauer; 111 pp. Paper. Waveland Press, 1970. $15.50.

KWAKIUTL STRING FIGURES
Julia Averkieva & Mark Sherman; Study of 112 string figures & tricks collected among the
Kawkiutl Indians by Averkieva. Illus. 164 drawings. 232 pp. U. of Washington Press, $35.

A KWAKIUTL VILLAGE & SCHOOL
Harry F. Wolcott; Reprint. Illus. 192 pp. Paper. AltaMira Press, 2003. $19.95.

KWAKWAKA'WAKW SETTLEMENT SITES, 1775-1920
Robert Galois; Demographics & settlement patterns of the Kawakiutl in British Columbia
betweem 1775 and 1920. 60 maps. 350 pp. University of Washington Press, $60.

*KWULASULWUT: STORIES FROM THE COAST SALISH
Ellen White; illus. by David Neel; Grades K-6. Illus. 76 pp. Paper. Theytus, 1992. $12.95.

*KWULASULWUT: SALISH CREATION STORIES
Ellen White; illus. by David Neel; Grades K-6. Illus. 25 pp. Paper. Theytus, 1995. $9.95.

L

OLIVER LA FARGE & THE AMERICAN INDIAN: A BIOGRAPHY
Robert A. Hecht; Illus. Photos. 255 pp. Scarecrow Press, 1991. $50; paper, $29.50.

LA HARPE'S POST: TALE OF FRENCH-WICHITA CONTACT ON EASTERN PLAINS
George H. Odell; Illus. 370 pp. paper. University of Alabama Press, 2002. $29.95.

LA LAWNG: MICHIF PEEKISHKWEWIN - VOL. ONE: (METIS) LANGUAGE PRACTICE
Lawrence Barkwell, Rita Flamand, Norman Fleury, Editors
Basics of the Michif (Metis) language. Paper. Pemmican, $14.95.

LA LAWNG: MICHIF PEEKISHKWEWIN - VOL. TWO: (METIS) LANGUAGE PRACTICE
Lawrence Barkwell, Rita Flamand, Norman Fleury, Editors
Deeper explanation of the Michif (Metis) language. Paper. Pemmican, $19.95.

**LABORING IN THE FIELDS OF THE LORD: SPANISH MISSIONS
& SOUTHEASTERN INDIANS** Jerald T. Milanich
Photos. Maps. 224 pp. Paper. University Press of Florida, 2006. $24.95.

**LACHLAN McGILLIVRAY, INDIAN TRADER: THE SHAPING OF THE SOUTHERN
COLONIAL FRONTIER** Edward J. Cashin; The career of the Indian trader from
1736 to 1776. 352 pp. University of Georgia Press, $45.

THE WINONA LADUKE READER: A COLLECTION OF ESSENTIAL WRITINGS
Winona LaDuke; 304 pp. Voyager Press, 2002. $16.95.

LADY BLACKROBES: MISSIONARIES IN THE HEART OF INDIAN COUNTRY
Irene Mahoney; An attempt to convert Native Americans in Montana to Christianity.
344 pp. Paper. Fulcrum Publishing, $16.95.

LAGUNA PUEBLO: A PHOTOGRAPHIC HISTORY
Lee Marmon & Tom Corbett; University of New Mexico Press, 2014. $39.95.

LAKE COUNTY (CA) INDIAN LORE
Henry Mauldin, Editor; Compiled from articles on lake County Indian culture & early
beliefs; also, interviews with local Native Americans. Reprint of 1977 ed. Paper.
Amazon.com, $6.50

LAKE PERTHA & THE LOST MURALS OF CHIAPAS
J. David Wonham; Illus. 19 pp. Paper. Pre-Columbian Art, 1985. $10.

LAKOTA BELIEF & RITUAL
James R. Walker; Illus. 369 pp. Paper. University of Nebraska Press, 1980. $19.95.

LAKOTA CEREMONIAL SONGS
Book & tape. VIP Publishing. $19.95.

LAKOTA CEREMONIES
Alice C. Fletcher; Ills. 48 pp. Paper. Lakota Books, 1993. $12.95.

LAKOTA & CHEYENNE: INDIAN VIEWS OF THE GREAT SIOUX WAR, 1876-1877
Jerome A. Greene, Editor; Illus. Map. 164 pp. U. of Oklahoma Press, 1994. $26.95.

LAKOTA COSMOS: RELIGION AND THE REINVENTION OF CULTURE
William K. Powers; Illus 50 pp. Paper. Lakota Books, $16.95.

LAKOTA CULTURE, WORLD ECONOMY
Kathleen Ann Pickering; Interviews with residents of Pine Ridge and Rosebud
Reservations to present an in-depth look at the modern economy of the Lakotas.
Illus. Maps. 179 pp. University of Nebraska Press, 2000. $45; paper, $19.95.

*LAKOTA & DAKOTA ANIMAL WISDOM STORIES
Mark W. McGinnis; Grades 6 and up. Illus. 24 pp. Paper. Tipi Press, 1994. $11.98.

LAKOTA DICTIONARY: LAKOTA-ENGLISH/ENGLISH-LAKOTA
compiled & edited by Eugene Buechel & Paul Manhart
Over 30,000 entries, examples of word usage; overview of Lakoat grammar.
564 pp. University of Nebraska Press, 2002. $65; paper, $27.95.

THE LAKOTA GHOST DANCE OF 1890
Rani-Henrik Andersson
Illus. Photos. Maps. 462 pp. Paper. University of Nebraska Press, 2008. $35.

LAKOTA GRAMMAR & HANDBOOK
Jan Ullrich with Ben Black Bear, Jr.; 624 pp. A pedagogically oriented self-study reference
& practice book for beginner to upper-intermediate students. 624 pp. Lakota Language
Consortium & Lakota Books, $49.95.

LAKOTA GRIEVING: A PASTORAL RESPONSE
Stephen Huffstetter; 157 pp. Paper. Tipi Press, 1998. $7.95.

LAKOTA HEALER
Marco Ridomi; Illus. 96 pp. Paper. Station Hill Press, 1998. $19.95.

LAKOTA LIFE
Ron Zeilinger; Illus. 74 pp. Paper. Tipi Press, 1986. $3.95.

LAKOTA MYTH
James R. Walker; edited by Elaine A. Jahner
Second edition. 428 pp. Paper. University of Nebraska Press, 2006. $18.95.

LAKOTA NAMING: A MODERN-DAY HUNKA CEREMONY
Marla N.Powers; History of the Hunka and a description of a contemporary
Naming ceremony. Illus. 37 photos. 48 pp. Paper. Lakota Books, 1991. $17.50.

LAKOTA NOON: THE INDIAN NARRATIVE OF CUSTER'S DEFEAT
Gregory Michno; 325 pp. Mountain Press, $30; paper, $16.

LAKOTA OF THE ROSEBUD: A CONTEMPORARY ADAPTATION
Elizabeth Grobsmith; Illus. 160 pp. Paper. Amazon.com, 1981. $29.99.

**LAKOTA PERFORMERS IN EUROPE: THEIR CULTURE AND THE ARTIFACTS
THEY LEFT BEHIND** Steven Friesen; foreword by Walter Littlemoon
Illus. 304 pp. University of Oklahoma Press, 2017. $39.95.

**LAKOTA RECOLLECTIONS OF THE CUSTER FIGHT: NEW SOURCES
OF INDIAN-MILITARY HISTORY** Richard G. Hardorff, Editor; A collection of sixteen
interviews with participants in the Battle of the Little Big Horn. Illus. Maps. 211 pp. Paper.
University of Nebraska Press, 1997. $15.95.

**THE LAKOTA RITUAL OF THE SWEAT LODGE: HISTORY & CONTEMPORARY
PRACTICE** Raymond A. Bucko; Illus. 340 pp. Paper. U. of Nebraska Press, 1998. $17.95.

·THE LAKOTA SIOUX
Frank Rzeczkowski; Paul Rosier, Series Editor
Grades 6-12. Illus. 144 pp. Chelsea House, 2011. $35.

*LAKOTA SIOUX CHILDREN & ELDERS TALK TOGETHER
Barrie E. Kavasch; Grades 4 and up. Rosen Group, 1998. $18.

LAKOTA SOCIETY
James R. Walker; Raymond J. DeMallie, Editor
Illus. 243 pp. Paper. University of Nebraska Press, 1982. $15.95.

LAKOTA SONGS
Isaac Brave Eagle; 100 pp. Sky & Sage Books, 1996. $17 includes audio cassette.

THE LAKOTA SWEAT LODGE CARDS: SPIRITUAL TEACHINGS OF THE SIOUX
Chief Archie Fire Lame Deer & Helene Sarkis; The powerful imagery & sacred wisdom of
the inipi--the sweat lodge ceremony used for centuries by the Lakota people for healing
and purification. Boxed set: 192-page book & 50 full-color cards. Inner Traditions, $29.95.

LAKOTA TALES & TEXTS IN TRANSLATION
Eugene Buechel & Paul Manhart; 2 vols. Tipi Press, 1998. $39.95.

**A LAKOTA WAR BOOK FROM THE LITTLE BIGHORN: THE PICTOGRAPHIC
"AUTOBIOGRAPHY OF HALF MOON"**
Castle McLaughlin; Illus. 368 pp. Paper. Peabody Museum of Archaeology, $50.

LAKOTA WARRIOR: A PERSONAL NARRATIVE
Joseph White Bull; James H. Howard, Editor/Translator
Illus. 108 pp. Paper. University of Nebraska Press, 1998. $22.

THE LAKOTA WARRIOR TRADITION
William K. Powers; Three essays on the significance of warfare in the Lakota tradition.
Illus. Paper. Lakota Books, $22.95.

**THE LAKOTA WAY: STORIES & LESSONS FOR LIVING/NATIVE AMERICAN
WISDOM ON ETHICS & CHARACTER** Joseph Marshall, II
256 pp. Paper. Penguin Group, 2002. $14.

LAKOTA WOMAN
Mary Crow Dog; Illus. 275 pp. Paper. Amazon.com, 1991. $9.95.

THE LAKOTAS & THE BLACK HILLS: THE STRUGGLE FOR SACRED GROUND
Jeffrey Ostler; Map. 238 pp. Viking Press, 2010.

**LAKOTAS, BLACK ROBES, & HOLY WOMEN: GERMAN REPORTS
FROM THE HOLY MISSIONS IN SOUTH DAKOTA, 1886-1900**
Karl Markus Kreis; Photos. Map. 338 pp. University of Nebraska Press, 2007. $55.

LAMAR ARCHAEOLOGY: MISSISSIPPIAN CHIEFDOMS IN THE DEEP SOUTH
Mark Williams & Gary Shapiro, Eds; 256 pp. Paper. U. of Alabama Press, 1990. $20.95.

LAME DEER: SEEKER OF VISIONS: THE LIFE OF A SIOUX MEDICINE MAN
John Fire/Lame Deer and Richard Erdoes; Chief Lame Deer, the chief medicine man for
the western Sioux tribes, tells of the modern Indian experience. Paper. Simon & Schuster,
1972. $11.

LAMENT FOR A FIRST NATION: THE WILLIAMS TREATIES OF SOUTHERN ONTARIO
Peggy J. Blair; 352 pp. University of Washington Press, 2009. $94; paper, $37.95.

*LANA'S LAKOTA MOONS
Virginia Driving Hawk Sneve
Grades 3 and up. Illus. 127 pp. Paper. University of Nebraska Press, 2007. $12.95.

THE LANCE & THE SHIELD: THE LIFE & TIMES OF SITTING BULL
Robert M. Utley; Biography of a great Sioux leader. Reprint. Illus. 430 pp.
Paper. Ballantine Books, 1994. $16.95.

**THE LAND BETWEEN THE RIVERS: THOMAS NUTTALL'S ASCENT OF THE
ARKANSAS 1819** Russell M. Lawson; Illus. 160 pp. U. of Michigan Press, 2004. $27.

**THE LAND HAS MEMORY: INDIGENOUS KNOWLEDGE, NATIVE LANDSCAPES,
AND THE NATIONAL MUSEUM OF THE AMERICAN INDIAN**
Duane Blue Spruce (Laguna) & Tanya Thrasher (Cherokee); Essays by Smithsonian staff
and others involved in the museum's creation. Details 150 native plant species. Illus. 184
pp. NMAI press & University of North Carolina Press, 2009. $45; paper, $24.95.

THE LAND LOOKS AFTER US: A HISTORY OF NATIVE AMERICAN RELIGION
Joel W. Martin; Paper. Amazon.com & Oxford University Press, 2001. $14.99

LAND OF THE FOUR DIRECTIONS
Frederick J. Pratson; A photographic portrayal of American Indians of Maine.
Illus. 140 pp. Paper. Chatham Press, $3.95.

LAND OF NAKODA
Federal Writers' Project Staff; Illus. 240 pp. Paper. Riverbend Publishing, 1004. $19.95.

THE LAND OF THE OJIBWE
MHS Education Dept.; Describes the movement of the Ojibwe throughout the Western
Great Lakes region and beyond. Maps. 48 pp. Paper. Minnesota Historical Society Press,
1973. $1.50.

THE LAND OF PREHISTORY: A CRITICAL HISTORY OF AMERICAN ARCHAEOLOGY
Alice B. Kehoe; 256 pp. Routledge, 1998. $80; paper, $22.99.

THE LAND OF RED CLOUD: AMONG NORTH AMERICA'S INDIANS
Peter Korniss; 136 pp. Amazon.com, 1982. $19.95.

LAND OF THE SLEEPING DINOSAURS
Native American tale about the creation of the Rocky Mountains, given life by the beliefs,
traditions, lore & culture of the Blackkfoot Nation. Amazon.com, $7.95.

LAND OF THE SPOTTED EAGLE: PORTRAITS OF THE RESERVATION SIOUX
Luther Standing Bear; intro. to new Amazon.com Ed. by Joseph Marshall III
New edition. Illus. 276 pp. Paper. University of Nebraska Press, 2006. $15.95.

**LAND OF THE TEJAS: NATIVE AMERICAN IDENTITY & INTERACTION IN TEXAS,
A.D. 1300 TO 1700** John Wesley Arnn, III; Illus. 300 pp. U. of Texas Press, 2012. $55.

LAND RIGHTS OF INDIGENOUS CANADIAN PEOPLES
Brian Slattery; 478 pp. University of Saskatchewan, 1979. $70.

LAND TOO GOOD FOR INDIANS: NORTHERN INDIAN REMOVAL
John P. Bowes; Illus. 328 pp. Paper. University of Oklahoma Press, 2016. $24.95.

THE LAND WAS THEIRS: A STUDY OF NORTH AMERICAN INDIANS
Sharlotte K. Neely & Wendell H. Oswalt ; Amazon.com, 1996 & 1999 edition.

LAND, WIND, & HARD WORDS: A STORY OF NAVAJO ACTIVISM
John W. Sherry; 256 pp. Paper. University of New Mexico Press, 2002. $40.

LANDFILL MEDITATION: CROSS BLOOD STORIES
Gerald Vizenor; 14 stories using his crossblood characters with the comic pleasures of
tribal tricksters. 211 pp. Paper. Wesleyan University Press, 1991. Distributed by University
Press of New England. $17.95.

LANDING NATIVE FISHERIES: INDIAN RESERVES & FISHING RIGHTS IN BRITISH COLUMBIA Douglas C. Harris
Illus. Maps. 256 pp. U. of Washington Press, 2008. $94; paper, $37.95.

LANDLORD TENENT RELATIONS
Institute for the Development of Indian Law, $3.50.

LANDMARK INDIAN LAW CASES
National Indian Law Library Staff; Revised ed. 950 pp. Alibris.com, 2002. $95.

LANDSCAPE OF THE SPIRITS: HOHOKAM ROCK ART AT SOUTH MOUNTAIN PARK
Todd W. Bostwick; photos by Peter Krocek
Illus. 252 pp. University of Arizona Press, 2002. $60; paper, $27.95.

LANDSCAPE TRAVELED BY COYOTE & CRANE: THE WORLD OF THE SCHITSU'UMSH (COEUR D'ALENE INDIANS)
Rodney Frey & tribe; foreword by Ernie Stensgar
Illus. Map. 340 pp. Paper. University of Washington Press, 2001. $22.50.

LANDSCAPES OF FRAUD: MISSION TUMACACORI, THE BACA FLOAT, & THE BETRAYAL OF THE O'ODHAM Thomas E. Sheridan; Examines of the O'odham culture was fragmented by the arrival of the Spanish in the Upper Santa Cruz Valley of southern Arizona. 316 pp. University of Arizona Press, 2006. $35; paper, $19.95.

LANDSCAPES OF ORIGIN IN THE AMERICAS
Jessica Joyce Christie, Editor; Focuses on creation narratives in the Americas. Illus. 280 pp. University of Alabama Press, 2009. $48.50; paper, $28.95. E-Book, $23.16.

LANDSCAPES OF POWER: POLITICS OF ENERGY IN THE NAVAJO NATION
Dana E. Powell; Illus. 336 pp. Duke University Press, 2018. $94.95; paper, $26.95.

LANDSCAPES OF SOCIAL TRANSFORMATION IN THE SALINAS PROVINCE & THE EASTERN PUEBLO WORLD Katherine A. Spielmann, Editor
Illlus. 260 pp. University of Arizona Press, 2017. $65. eBook available.

LANGUAGE & ART IN THE NAVAJO UNIVERSE
Gary Witherspoon; Studies Navajo culture. Illus. Photos.
244 pp. Paper. University of Michigan Press, 1977. $27.95.

LANGUAGE, CULTURE & HISTORY: ESSAYS BY MARY R. HAAS
Mary R. Haas; Anwar S. Dil, Editor; 398 pp. Amazon.com, 1978. $32.50.

LANGUAGE ENCOUNTERS IN THE AMERICAS, 1492-1800: COLLECTION OF ESSAYS Edward G. Gray & Norman Fiering, Eds.
Illus. 370 pp. Paper. Berghahn Books, 2001. $49.95.

LANGUAGE EXTINCTION & THE STATUS OF NORTH AMERICAN INDIAN LANGUAGES Phoebe R. Hunter
Illus. 65 pp. Paper. Iowa State University, Center for Indigenous Knowledge, 1994. $8.

LANGUAGE, HISTORY, & IDENTITY: ETHNOLINGUISTIC STUDIES OF THE ARIZONA TEWA Paul V. Kroskrity; 289 pp. University of Arizona Press, 1993. $60.

LANGUAGE & LITERACY TEACHING FOR INDIGENOUS EDUCATION: A BILINGUAL APPROACH Norbert Francis & Jon Allan Reyhner
260 pp. Paper. University of Toronto Press, 2002. $89.95.

THE LANGUAGE OF NATIVE AMERICAN BASKETS: FROM THE WEAVERS' VIEW
Bruce Bernstein; Illus. 80 pp. Paper. NMAI Press, 2003. $19.95.

LANGUAGE OF THE ROBE: AMERICAN INDIAN TRADE BLANKETS
Robert W. Kapoun with Charles Lohrmann; Resource for trade blanket owners and collectors. Reprint. Color photos. 192 pp. Smith, Gibbs Publisher, 1997. $29.95.

THE LANGUAGE OF THE SALINAN INDIANS
J. Alden Mason; Reprint of 1918 edition. 154 pp. Paper. Coyote Press, $16.88.

A LANGUAGE OF OUR OWN: THE GENESIS OF MICHIF, THE MIXED CREE-FRENCH LANGUAGE OF THE CANADIAN METIS
Peter Bakker; Illus. 336 pp. Oxford University Press, 1997. $80.

LANGUAGE RENEWAL AMONG AMERICAN INDIAN TRIBES
Robert N. St. Clair and William L. Leap
176 pp. Paper. National Clearinghouse Bilingual Education, 1982. $8.95.

LANGUAGE SAMPLER SERIES
Western Cherokee Language; Eastern Cherokee Language; Choctaw Language; Chickasaw Language. 12 pp. Paper. VIP Publishing. $5 each.

LANGUAGE SHIFT AMONG THE NAVAJOS: IDENTITY POLITICS & CULTURAL CONTINUITY Deborah House; 121 pp. U. of Arizona Press, 2002. $35.

LANGUAGES
Ives Goddard, Ed.; Illus. 957 pp. Smithsonian Institution Press, 1997. $74.

LANGUAGES OF THE ABORIGINAL SOUTHEAST: AN ANNOTATED BIBLIOGRAPHY
Karen M. Booker; 265 pp. Scarecrow Pres, 1991. $37.50.

THE LANGUAGES OF THE COAST OF CALIFORNIA NORTH OF SAN FRANCISCO
A.L. Kroeber; Reprint of 1911. 164 pp. Paper. Coyote Press, $11.56.

THE LANGUAGES OF THE COAST OF CALIFORNIA SOUTH OF SAN FRANCISCO
A.L. Kroeber; Reprint of 1911. 103 pp. Paper. Coyote Press, $11.56.

THE LANGUAGES OF NATIVE AMERICA: HISTORICAL & COMPARATIVE ASSESSMENT
Lyle Campbell and Marianne Mithun, Editors; 1,040 pp. U. of Texas Press, 1979. $35.

LANGUAGES OF THE TRIBES OF THE EXTREME NORTHWEST: ALASKA, THE *THE LAST CHEROKEE WARRIORS
Phillip Steele; Grades 6-12. 2nd ed. Illus. 111 pp. Paper. Amazon.com, 1978. $7.95.

LANTERNS ON THE PRAIRIE: THE BLACKFEET PHOTOGRAPHS OF WALTER McCLINTOCK
Steven L. Grafe, Editor; 336 pp. University of Oklahoma Press, 2009. $60; paper, $34.95.

THE LAST CONTRARY: THE STORY OF WESLEY WHITEMAN (BLACK BEAR)
Warren Schwartz; Illus. 146 pp. Center for Western Studies, 1990. $12.95.

THE LAST CROSSING: BLACK HAWK'S FIGHT AGAINST THE U.S.
Ronald J. Baldwin; Story of Black Hawk, Sauk war chief and his fight to remain on their tribal lands in northwestern Illinois. Also about Sauk family life and tribal customs. 320 pp. Ronald Baldwin, 2005.

LAST CRY: NATIVE AMERICAN PROPHECIES; TALE OF THE END TIMES
Robert Ghostwolf; 319 pp. Paper. Wolf Lodge, 1997. $21.95.

LAST DAYS OF THE SIOUX NATION
Robert M. Utley; Historical study of the reaction of the Sioux to the reservation system in the mid 1800s. 2nd Edition. Illus. Maps. Biblio. 370 pp. Paper. Yale University Press, 2004. $34.

THE LAST FIELD NOTES OF FRANKLIN R. JOHNSON'S LIFE & WORK
Franklin R. Johnson; Bill Yenne, Editor; Illus. 200 pp. Amazon.com, 1998. $22.95.

THE LAST FREE CHIEF OF THE MODOC NATION: AN ALLEGORY
Patricia Boyer; 213 pp. Paper. Amazon.com, 2001. $19.95.

THE LAST FRENCH & INDIAN WAR
Denis Vaugeois; Illus. 104 pp. McGill-Queen's University Press, 2002.

THE LAST GHOST DANCE: A GUIDE FOR EARTH MAGES
Brooke Medicine Eagle; Illus. 430 pp. Paper. Ballantine Books, 2000. $23.

THE LAST LIGHT BREAKING: LIVING AMONG ALASKA'S INUPIAT ESKIMOS
Nick Jans; Map. 224 pp. Graphic Arts Center, 1994. $21.95.

THE LAST OF THE INDIAN WARS, THE SPANISH AMERICAN WAR, THE BRINK OF THE GREAT WAR, 1881-1916
Randy Steffen; Illus. 268 pp. Paper. University of Oklahoma Press, 1978. $39.95.

*THE LAST OF THE MOHICANS
James Fenimore Cooper; illus. by N.C. Wyeth
Grades 5 and up. Illus. 400 pp. Paper. Center for Western Studies, $5.95.

THE LAST OF THE OFOS
Geary Hobson; Story. 115 pp. Paper. University of Arizona Press, 2007. $13.95.

THE LAST SHALL BE FIRST
Murray Angus; 96 pp. Paper. University of Toronto Press, 1991. $9.95.

THE LAST STAND: CUSTER, SITTING BULL, & THE BATTLE OF LITTLE BIGHORN
Nathaniel Philbrick; Illus. Maps. 466 pp. Amazon.com, 2010.

*THE LAST WARRIOR
Suzanne Pierson Ellison; Story of a young warrior apprentice to Geronimo.
Ages 12 and up. 240 pp. Northland, $12.95; paper, $6.95.

THE LAST WARRIOR: PETER MACDONALD & THE NAVAJO NATION
Peter MacDonald; Crown Publishing, 1993. $25.

THE LAST WORLD: THE TAOIST & NATIVE AMERICAN PHILOSOPHIES AS A WAY OF LIVING IN HARMONY Richard Spiegel; 200 pp. Paper. Amazon.com, 2002. $14.95.

THE LAST YEARS OF SITTING BULL
Herbert Hoover; Paper. VIP Publishing. $4.95.

LASTING IMPRESSION: COASTAL, LITHIC, & CERAMIC RESEARCH IN NEW ENGLAND ARCHAEOLOGY Jordan E. Kerber, Ed.
Illus. 296 pp. Greenwood Publishing, 2002. $69.95; paper, $27.95.

THE LASTING OF THE MOHEGANS: THE STORY OF THE WOLF PEOPLE
Melissa J. Fawcett; 2nd Ed. Illus. 68 pp. Paper. The Mohegan Tribe, 1995. $10.

THE LASTING OF THE MOHICANS: HISTORY OF AN AMERICAN MYTH
Martin Barker & Roger Sabin
Illus. 224 pp. University Press of Mississippi, 1996. $45; paper, $25.

LATE WOODLAND SITES IN THE AMERICAN BOTTOM UPLANDS
Charles Bentz, et al; Illus. Paper. University of Illinois Press, 1988. $17.50.

LATE WOODLAND SOCIETIES: TRADITION & TRANSFORMATION ACROSS THE MIDCONTINENT edited by Thomas E. Emerson, Dale L. McElrath & Andrew C. Fortier
Sites, artifacts, and prehistoric cultural practices of Late Woodland lifestyle across the Midwest. Illus. Maps. 736 pp. Paper. University of Nebraska Press, 2000. $29.95.

LAUGHING BOY
Oliver La Farge; A novel about a young Navajo lover & his mate.
Winner of the 1929 Pulitzer Prize. 192 pp. Paper. Penguin USA, $4.95.

THE LAUREL CULTURE IN MINNESOTA
James B. Stoltman; Illus. 146 pp. Paper. Minnesota Historical Society, 1973. $5.50.

LAW & THE AMERICAN INDIAN: READINGS, NOTES AND CASES
Monroe E. Price and Robert Clinton; 2nd edition. 800 pp. Michie Co., 1983. $28.50.

LAW ENFORCEMENT ON INDIAN RESERVATIONS AFTER OLIPHANT V. SUQUAMISH INDIAN TRIBES Institute for the Development of Indian Law, $2.

LAWS & JOINT RESOLUTIONS OF THE CHEROKEE NATION
Reprint of 1975 edition. Amazon.com & Alibris.com, $22.

LAWS & JOINT RESOLUTIONS OF THE NATIONAL COUNCIL, PASSED 1870 & 1876
Reprint of 1975 edition. Amazon.com & Alibris.com, $12 each.

LAWS OF THE CHEROKEE NATION: PASSED 1845
Reprint of 1975 edition. Amazon.com & Alibris.com, $12.

LAWS OF THE CHICKASAW NATION
Reprint of 1975 edition. Amazon.com & Alibris.com, $12.

LAWS OF THE CHOCTAW NATION
Reprint of 1975 edition. Amazon.com & Alibris.com, $12.

LAWS & SOCIETIES IN THE CANADIAN PRAIRIE WEST, 1670-1940
Louis A. Knofla & Jonathan Swainger, Editors
Examines the legal history of the Canadian northwest frontier.
360 pp. University of Washington Press, 2006. $105; paper, $37.95.

A LAWYER IN INDIAN COUNTRY: A MEMOIR
Alvin J. Ziontz; Alvin Ziontz reflects on his more than 30 years representing
Indian tribes. Illus. 328 pp. University of Washington Press, 2009. $27.95.

LEADERS & LEADING MEN OF THE INDIAN TERRITORY
H.F. O'Beirne; Joe Goss & Phillip Sperry, Eds.
Reprint. Illus. 326 pp. Amazon.com, 1994. $49.95.

*LEARN ABOUT...TEXAS INDIANS
Georg Zappler; illus. by Elena T. Ivy; Grades 4 and up. Reprint of 1985 ed.
Illus. 48 pp. Paper. University of Texas Press, 2007. $10.95.

LEARNING BY DESIGNING: PACIFIC NORTHWEST COAST NATIVE INDIAN ART
Jim Gilbert & Karin Clark; Illus. 224 pp. Paper. Raven Publishing, 2001.

LEARNING JOURNEY ON THE RED ROAD
Floyd Looks for Buffalo Hand; Mark A. Huminilowycz, Ed.
112 pp. Paper. Amazon.com, 1998. $14.95.

LEARNING & TEACHING TOGETER: WEAVING INDIGENOUS WAYS OF KNOWING INTO EDUCATION
Michelle TD Tanaka; UBC Press, 2017. $95; paper, $34.95; eBook, $34.95.

LEARNING TO BE AN ANTHROPOLOGIST & REMAINING "NATIVE": SELECTED WRITINGS Dr. Beatrice Medicine; Sue-Ellen Jacobs, Editor
Illus. Tables. 400 pp. Paper. University of Illinois Press, 2002. $29.

LEARNING TO WRITE "INDIAN": THE BOARDING SCHOOL EXPERIENCE & AMERICAN INDIAN EXPERIENCE
Amelia V. Katansky; Illus. 288 pp. University of Oklahoma Press, $24.95.

LEASING INDIAN WATER: UPCOMING CHOICES IN THE COLORADO RIVER BASIN
Gary Weatherford & Mary Wallace; 66 pp. Paper. Conservation Forum, 1988. $10.50.

LEAVING EVERYTHING BEHIND: THE SONGS & MEMORIES OF A CHEYENNE WOMAN Bertha Little Coyote & Virginia Giglio; Illus. 192 pp. U. of Oklahoma Press, 1997. $29.95; compact disc, $12.95; book and CD, $40.

LEDFEATHER
Stephen Graham Jones; A novel about a boy set on the Blackfeet Indian Reservation in Montana. 216 pp. Paper. University of Alabama Press, 2008. $17.50.

LEDGER NARRATIVES: THE PLAINS INDIAN DRAWINGS OF THE LANSBURGH COLLECTION AT DARTMOUTH COLLEGE
Colin G. Calloway, Editor; 296 pp.Paper. University of Oklahoma Press, $29.95.

A. ROBERT LEE: NATIVE AMERICAN WRITING
A. Robert Lee; 4 Vol. set. 1,736 pp. Routledge, 2011. $1,080.

LEFT HANDED, SON OF OLD MAN HAT: A NAVAHO AUTOBIOGRAPHY
By Left Handed; recorded by Walter Dyk
Anthropological study. 378 pp. Paper. University of Nebraska Press, 1967. $18.95.

THE LEGACY OF ANDREW JACKSON: ESSAYS ON DEMOCRACY, INDIAN REMOVAL & SLAVERY Robert Remini
120 pp. Paper. Louisiana State University Press, 1990. $6.95.

THE LEGACY OF MARIA POVEKA MARTINEZ
Richard L. Spivey; photos by Herbert Lotz; Illus. 198 four-color photos.
208 pp. Museum of New Mexico Press, 2001. $60; paper, $39.95.

LEGACY OF A MASTER POTTER: NAMPEYO & HER DESCENDANTS
Mary Ellen Blair & Laurence Blair
Illus. 340 pp. Paper. Treasury Chest Books, 2004. $29.95.

THE LEGACY OF SHINGWAUKONSE: A CENTURY OF NATIVE LEADERSHIP
Janet E. Chute; Examines the careers of the Ojibwa chief Shingwaukonse and of two of his sons. Illus. 359 pp. University of Toronto Press, 1998. $60; paper, $24.95.

LEGACY: SOUTHWEST INDIAN ART AT THE SCHOOL OF AMERICAN RESEARCH
Duane Anderson; N. Scott Momaday, Ed.; Illus. 224 pp. Paper.
School of American Research Press, 1998. $49.95; collector's edition, $300.

THE LEGACY: TRADITION & INNOVATION IN NORTHWEST COAST INDIAN ART
Peter Macnair, Alan Hoover & Kevin Neary
Illus. 194 pp. Paper. University of Washington Press, $36.95.

LEGAL CODES & TALKING TREES: INDIGENOUS WOMEN'S SOVEREIGNTY IN THHE SONORAN & PUGET SOUND BORDERLANDS, 1854-1946
Katrina Jagodinsky; Illus. 352 pp. Yale University Press, 2016. $30.

THE LEGAL IDEOLOGY OF REMOVAL: THE SOUTHERN JUDICIARY & THE SOVEREIGNTY OF NATIVE AMERICAN NATIONS
Tim Alan Garrison; 330 pp. University of Georgia Press, 2002. $39.95.

LEGAL INFORMATION SERVICE
32 vols. on Canadian Indian legal affairs. See U. of Saskatchewan for titles and prices.

LEGAL ISSUES IN NATIVE AMERICAN HISTORY
Ben Nighthorse Campbell, Ed.; 214 pp. Pearson Custom Publishing, 2001. $30.50.

LEGAL ISSUES IN INDIAN JURISDICTION
63 pp. National Attorney's General, 1976. $3.50.

LEGAL PROCESS & THE RESOLUTION OF INDIAN CLAIMS
Eric Golvin; Studies in Canadian aboriginal rights. 29 pp.
University of Saskatchewan, 1981. $6.50.

LEGALIZED RACISM: FEDERAL INDIAN POLICY & THE END OF EQUAL RIGHTS FOR ALL AMERICANS
A.R. Eguigueren; Illus. 244 pp. Paper. Amazon.com, 2000. $14.95.

*A LEGEND FROM CRAZY HORSE CLAN
Big Crow & Moses Nelson; Daniel Long Soldier, Illus; Renee S. Flood, Editor
Grades 3 and up. Illus. 36 pp. Paper. Oyate, Tipi Press & Center for Western Studies, 1987. $4.95.

*THE LEGEND OF THE BLUEBONNET, retold
Tomie dePaola; An old tale of Texas..a courageous little Comanche girl sacrifices her most beloved possession, Grades PS-3. Illus. 32 pp. Putnam, 1983. $14.95; paper, $5.95.

*THE LEGEND OF THE INDIAN PAINTBRUSH, retold
Tomie dePaola; An Indian brave dreams of creating a painting that will capture the beauty of a sunset. Grades PS-3. Illus. 40 pp. Paper. Putnam, 1996. $14.95.

THE LEGEND OF NATURAL TUNNEL
Clara Talton Fugate; illus. by Caren Ertman
A tale of love and war and Indian customs, set in the southern Appalachians before white settlement. Illus. 40 pp. 16 drawings, 3 maps. Paper. Amazon.com, 1986. $5.95.

*THE LEGEND OF TOM PEPPER & OTHER STORIES
Arthur Griffin; Grades 2-5. Illus. 100 pp. Bainbridge Press, 1990.

LEGEND OF THE RAINBOW WARRIORS
Steven McFadden; 220 pp. Paper. Amazon.com, 2001. $19.95.

THE LEGEND OF WAPATO: CHIEF CASSINO OF THE MULTNOMAH
Donald & Marilyn Bruner; Illus. 215 pp. Paper. Book Partners, 2001. $16.95.

LEGENDS IN STONE, BONE & WOOD
Tsonakwa; Abenaki legends, history, and photographed works of art.
Amazon.com, $10.95.

THE LEGENDS & LANDS OF NATIVE AMERICANS
David Martinez; Illus. 160 pp. Sterling Publishing, 2003. $24.95.

LEGENDS, LETTERS & LIES: READINGS ABOUT INKPADUTA & THE SPIRIT LAKE MASSACRE Mary Bakeman; Illus. 234 pp. Amazon.com, 2001.

LEGENDS OF AMERICAN INDIAN RESISTANCE
Edward J. Rielly; Presents a timeline of significant events in history & describes the plight of Native Americans from the 17th through the 20th century and the major Indian leaders who resisted the inevitable result. 341 pp. Greenwood Press, 2011. $85.

*LEGENDS OF CHIEF BALD EAGLE
Harry B. Shows and Hap Gilliland
Grades 2-10. Paper. Council for Indian Education, 1977. $2.95.

LEGENDS OF THE COWLITZ INDIAN
Roy I. Wilson; 400 pp. Demco, 1998. Amazon.com, 1998.

LEGENDS OF THE DELAWARE INDIANS & PICTURE WRITING
Richard C. Adams; Edited by Deborah Nichols
Illus. 128 pp. Syracuse University Press, 1998. $25.95.

*LEGENDS OF THE GREAT CHIEFS
Emerson N. Matson; Authentic legends and little-known incidents recalled during first-hand interviews with actual descendants of some of the most famous chiefs. Grades 8-12. Illus. 144 pp. Paper. Storypole, 1972. $5.95.

LEGENDS OF THE IROQUOIS
Tehanetorens; Stories presented in pictograph form with English translation. 112 pp. Paper. Book Publishing Co., $9.95.

LEGENDS OF THE IROQUOIS
William W. Canfield; Yestermorrow Press, 1998. $26.95.

LEGENDS OF THE LAKOTA
James LaPointe; illus. by Louis Amiotte
Illus. 184 pp. Amzon.com, 1975. $11.00; paper, $6.

LEGENDS OF THE LONGHOUSE
Jesse Cornplanter; Iroquois tales told by Jesse Corplanter. Illus. Amazon.com, $10.

LEGENDS OF THE MIGHTY SIOUX
Montana Lisle Reese, Editor; 45 traditional legends of the Sioux written by elders on the Rosebud & Yankton reservations. Reprint of 1941 edition. Center for Western Studies, $14.95; paper, $6.95. Paper. VIP Publishing. $6.95.

LEGENDS OF THE NORTHERN PAIUTE: AS TOLD BY WILSON WEWA
James Gardner, Editor; Paper. UBC Press, 2017. $22.95.

LEGENDS OF OUR NATIONS
Collection of traditional Native tales of Canada & U.S. Paper. Amazon.com, $6.

LEGENDS OF OUR TIMES: NATIVE COWBOY LIFE
Morgan Baillargeon & Leslie Tepper; UBC Press, 1998. $45.

LEGENDS OF THE SEMINOLES
Betty Mae Jumper with Peter Gallagher; Illus. 96 pp. Pineapple Press, $24.95; paper, $18.95.

LEGENDS OF THE YOSEMITE MIWOK
Frank LaPena, Craig D. Bates & Steven P. Medley, Editors
Revised edition. Illus. 64 pp. Paper. Heyday Books & Amazon.com, 1993. $12.95.

LEGENDS & PROPHECIES OF THE QUERO APACHE: TALES FOR HEALING & RENEWAL Maria Yraceburu; 13 teaching tales of the cosmology of the Apaches. Illus. 192 pp. 2002. Inner Traditions, $14.

LEGENDS TOLD BY THE OLD PEOPLE
Adolph Hungrywolf; New expanded edition. Illus. 110 pp. Paper. Cherokee Publications & The Book Publishing Co., 2000. $9.95.

LEGENDS, TRADITIONS & LAWS OF THE IROQUOIS: OR, SIX NATIONS, & HISTORY OF THE TUSCARORA INDIANS Elias Johnson; Reprint. Paper. Amazon.com, $17.99.

LEGIBLE SOVEREIGNTIES: RHETORIC, REPRESENTATIONS, AND NATIVE AMERICAN MUSEUMS Lisa King; Paper. Amazon.com, $19.42.

LEGISLATING INDIAN COUNTRY: SIGNIFICANT MILESTONES IN TRANSFORMING TRIBLISM Laurence Armand French; 192 pp. Paper. Peter Lang Publishing, 2007. $34.95.

LELOOSKA: THE LIFE OF A NORTHWEST COAST ARTIST
Chris Friday; Illus. 304 pp. University of Washington Press, 2003. $24.95.

THE LEMHI: SACAJAWEA'S PEOPLE
Brigham Madsen; Illus. Maps. Biblio. 214 pp. Paper. The Caxton Press, 1980. $7.95.

THE LENAPE
Herbert Kraft; Illus. 300 pp. Amazon.com, 1987. $24.95.

A LENAPE AMONG THE QUAKERS: THE LIFE OF HANNAH FREEMAN
Dawn G. Marsh; Illus. 230 pp. University of Nebraska Press, 2014. $27.95; paper, $17.95

A LENAPE-ENGLISH DICTIONARY
Daniel Garrison Brinton, et al.; 240 pp. Paper. 2009. Amazon.com, $22.99.

LENAPE HISTORY & NUMBERS POSTERS
The Amazon.com, $5 each.

LENAPE INDIAN COOKING WITH TOUCHING LEAVES WOMAN
Delaware or Lenape Indian recipes & historical accounts of Lenape Indian cooking. 32 pp. Paper. Amazon.com, $4.

LENAPE INDIAN TEACHING KIT 2: LENAPE LORE/FOLK MEDICINES
Karen Waldauer
Includes teacher's guide, charts, quizzes. Illus. Amazon.com, $24.95.

THE LENAPE INDIANS
Josh Wilker; Illus. 76 pp. Paper. Chelsea House Publishers, 1993. $8.95.

*THE LENAPE: MIDDLE ATLANTIC
Robert Grumet; Grades 5 and up. Illus. Chelsea House, 1989. $17.95.

THE LENAPE OR DELAWARE INDIAN HERITAGE: 10,000 BC TO AD 2000
Herbert C. Kraft; Illus. 400 photos. 610 pp. Lenape Lifeways., $35.

*THE LENAPE OR DELAWARE INDIANS
Herbert C. Kraft; Grades K-5. Illus. Maps. 64 pp. Lenape Lifeways, $8.

LESBIAN, BISEXUAL & TRANSGENDER MYTHS FROM THE ACOMA TO THE ZUNI: AN ANTHOLOGY Jim Elledge, Ed.; 194 pp. Paper. Amazon.com, 2001. $29.95.

LESCHI, LAST OF THE NISQUALLIES
Cecilia Carpenter; Illus. 56 pp. Paper. Amazon.com, 1986. $5.

LESSONS FROM CHOUTEAU CREEK: YANKTON MEMORIES OF DAKOTA INTRIGUE
Renee Sansom-Flood; Reprint. Illus. Paper. Center for Western Studies, $10.95.

LESSONS FROM AN INDIAN DAY SCHOOL: NEGOTIATING COLONIZATION IN NORTHERN NEW MEXICO, 1902-1907
Adrea Lawrence; Illus. Maps. 320 pp. University Press of Kansas, 2011. $34.95.

LESSONS FROM A QUECHUA STRONGWOMAN: IDEOPHONY, DIALOGUE, AND PERSPECTIVE Janis B. Nuckolls; 248 pp. U. of Arizona Press, 2010. $45.

LESSONS FROM TURTLE ISLAND: NATIVE CURRICULUM IN EARLY CHILDHOOD CLASSROOMS
Guy W. Jones & Sally Moomaw; Illus. 210 pp. Paper. Amazon.com, 2002. $29.95.

LESSONS IN HOPI
Milo Kalectaca; Ronald W. Langacker, Editor; 30 grammar lessons, ten exemplary dialogs, Hopi--English, English--Hopi lexicons. 234 pp. Paper. U. of Arizona Press, 1978. $11.95.

LET ME BE FREE: THE NEZ PERCE TRAGEDY
David Lavender; Illus. Maps/ 432 pp. Paper. University of Oklahoma Press, 1999. $17.95.

*LET ME TELL YOU A STORY
Yerington Paiute Tribe; Grades 2-8. Illus. 95 pp. Paper. Yerington Paiute Tribe Publications, $8. Companion Activity Workbook, 105 pp., $10.

LET MY PEOPLE KNOW: AMERICAN INDIAN JOURNALISM, 1828-1978
James E. & Sharon M. Murphy; 300 pp. Amazon.com, 1979. $19.95.

LET RIGHT BE DONE: ABORIGINAL TITLE, THE CALDER CASE, & THE FUTURE OF INDIGENOUS RIGHTS Hamar Foster, Heather Raven & Jeremy Webber; Canadian Aboriginal title. Illus. Maps. 352 pp. U. of Washington Press, 2011. $99; paper, $37.95.

*LET'S REMEMBER...INDIANS OF TEXAS
Betsy Warren; Grades 3-8. Illus. 32 pp. Paper. Hendrick-Long, $4.50.

LET'S SPEAK CHICKASAW, CHIKASHANOMPA' KILANOMPOLI'
Pamela Munro & Catherione Willmond
Textbook of Chickasaw language. 432 pp. Paper. U. of Oklahoma Press, 2008. $29.95.

LET'S TALK CHEYENNE: AN AUDIO CASSETTE TAPE COURSE OF INSTRUCTION IN THE CHEYENNE LANGUAGE Ted Risingsun & Wayne Leman
57 pp. Paper. WinterSun Press, 1999. $18.95 includes audio.

LET'S WALK WEST: BRAD KAHLHAMER
Susan Krane; Native American artist and his art. Illus. 87 pp. Paper. University of Washington Press, 2005. $24.95.

LETHAL ENCOUNTERS: ENGLISHMEN & INDIANS IN COLONIAL VIRGINIA
Alfred A. Cave; Illus. 216 p. Paper. University of Nebraska Press, 2013. $24.95.

LETHAL LEGACY: CURRENT NATIVE CONTROVERSIES IN CANADA
J.R. Miller; Illus. 320 pp. Random House, 2004. 27.95.

LETTERS FROM INDIAN COUNTRY: NATIVE LETTERS TO EDITORS
Louis Hooban, Ed.; Paper. Amazon.com, 2002. $12.99.

LETTERS FROM WUPATKI
Courtney Reeder Jones; ed. by Lisa Rappoport; Story of National Park Service caretakers in 1938 and their Navajo neighbors. 184 pp. Paper. U. of Arizona Press, 1995. $15.95.

LETTERS FROM THE ROCKY MOUNTAIN INDIAN MISSIONS
Father Philip Rappagliosi; edited by Robert Bigart
Letters from a Jesuit (1841-78) about daily lives, customs, and beliefs of Nez Perces, Kootenais, Salish Flatheads, Coeur d'Alenes, Pend d'Oreilles, Blackfeet, and Canadian Metis. Illus. Map. 156 pp. University of Nebraska Press, 2013. $25.

LETTERS OF THE LEWIS & CLARK EXPEDITION, WITH RELATED DOCUMENTS, 1783-1854
Donald Jackson, Editor; 2nd Ed. 2 vols. 832 pp. University of Illinois Press, 1978. $49.95.

LETTERS & NOTES ON THE MANNERS, CUSTOMS & CONDITIONS OF THE NORTH AMERICAN INDIANS
George Catlin; Reprint. 300 paintings. 572 pp. Paper. 1990. Amazon.com, $16.95.

LETTERS TO HOWARD: INTERPRETATION OF THE ALASKA NATIVE LANDS CLAIM
Fred Bigjim; Collection of 24 letters on critical issues of the Alaska Native Land Claims. Amazon.com, $12.

LUCY M. LEWIS: AMERICAN INDIAN POTTER
Susan Peterson; Illus. 220 pp. Paper. Amazon.com, 2004. $45.

LEWIS & CLARK: ACROSS THE DIVIDE
Carolyn Gilman; Illus. 420 pp. Paper. Smithsonian Intitution Press, $34.95.

LEWIS & CLARK AMONG THE INDIANS
James P. Ronda; Bicentennial edition. Illus. Maps. 310 pp. Paper. University of Nebraska Press, 2002. $18.95.

*THE LEWIS & CLARK EXPEDITION
Patrick McGrath
Grades 5 and up. Illus. 64 pp. Amazon.com, 1985. $14.96; paper, $7.95.

LEWIS & CLARK & THE INDIAN COUNTRY: THE NATIVE AMERICAN PERSPECTIVE
Frederick E. Hoxie & Jay T. Nelson, Editors; Collection of essays & documents. Illus. 376 pp. Paper. University of Illinois Press, 2007. $25.95.

LEWIS & CLARK: LEGACIES, MEMORIES, & NEW PERSPECTIVES
Kris Fresonke & Mark Spence, Editors
Illus. 298 pp. Paper. University of California Press, 2004. $24.95. E-Book available.

LEWIS & CLARK & THE SHAHAPTIAN SPEAKING AMERICANS
Cheryl Halsey & Robert R. Beale; Reprint. Paper. 1983. Amazon.com, $19.99.

LEWIS & CLARK TERRITORY: CONTEMPORARY ARTISTS REVISIT PLACE, RACE, & MEMORY Rock Hushka & Thomas Owl Haukaas; Reevaluates the expedition and its impact on American culture. Includes contemporary works in traditional & innovative Native Americn techniques, such as carving, beadwork, and basketry. Illus. 80 pp. Paper. University of Washington Press, 2004. $21.95.

LEWIS & CLARK THROUGH INDIAN EYES: NINE INDIAN WRITERS ON THE LEGACY OF THE EXPEDITION Alvin M. Josephy, Jr.; 224 pp. Paper. Amazon.com, 2007. $15.

LEWIS & CLARK: VOYAGE OF DISCOVERY
Dan Murphy; Illus. 64 pp. Paper. KC Publications , 1977. $4.50.

LEWIS & CLARK'S WEST: WILLIAM CLARK'S 1810 MASTER MAP OF THE AMERICAN WEST William Clark; Collector's edition. Illus. Maps. University Press of New England, 2004. $50, map only, $14.95.

*MERIWEATHER LEWIS & WILLIAM CLARK: SOLDIERS, EXPLORERS, & PARTNERS IN HISTORY David Petersen & Mark Coburn
Grades 4 and up. Illus. 152 pp. Childrens Press, 1988. $15.95.

LEXICAL ACCULTURATION IN NATIVE AMERICAN LANGUAGES
Cecil H. Brown; 272 pp. Oxford University Press, 1999. $170.

LIBERALISM, SURVEILLANCE, & RESISTANCE: INDIGENOUS COMMUNITIES IN WESTERN CANADA, 1887-1927
Keith D. Smith; Illus. Maps. 324 pp. Paper. U. of Washington Press, 2009. $37.95.

*THE LIBRARY OF NATIVE AMERICANS
Grades 3-6. Illus. 64 pp. each. Set 1 (2003): California - The Luiseno of California; The Chumash of California; The Esselen of California; Set 2 (2003): The Potawatomi of Wisconsin; The Algonquian of New York; The Oneida of Wisconsin. Set 3 (2004): California - The Shasta of California & Oregon; The Modoc of California & Oregon; The Mojave of California & Arizona; The Miwok of California. Set 4 (2005) The Wampanoag of Massachusetts & Rhode Island; The Lenape of Pennsylvania, New Jersey, New York, Delaware, Wisconsin, Oklahoma, & Ontario; The Karankawa of Texas; The Ojibwe of Michigan, Wisconsin, Minnesota, & North Dakota. Rosen Publishing. $21.95 to $29.95 each.

LIBRARY SERVICES TO INDIGENOUS POPULATIONS: VIEWPOINTS & RESOURCES
Kelly Webster, Editor; Bibliography addressing the library & information needs of indigenous people around the world. 76 pp. Paper. American Library Association, 2005. $23.

LICENSE FOR EMPIRE: COLONIALISM BY TREATY IN EARLY AMERICA
Dorothy V. Jones; University of Chicago Press, 1982. $25.

LIES MY TEACH TOLD ME: EVERYTHING YOUR AMERICAN HISTORY TEXTBOOK GOT WRONG James W. Loewen
Illus. 384 pp. Amazon.com, 1995. $24.95. Paper. Simon & Schuster , $15.

LIFE & ADVENTURES OF JAMES P. BECKWOURTH, MOUNTAINEER, SCOUT & PIONEER, AND CHIEF OF THE CROW NATION OF INDIANS
J. Beckwourth; T.D. Bonner, Editor; Reprint of 1856 edition. 650 pp. Paper. University of Nebraska Press, $10.95.

LIFE ALONG THE MERRIMAC: COLLECTED HISTORIES OF THE NATIVE AMERICANS WHO LIVED ON ITS BANKS
John Pendergast, Ed.; Illus. 192 pp. Paper. Merrimac River press, 1996. $19.95.

LIFE AMONG THE APACHES
John C. Cremony; Illus. 322 pp. Paper. University of Nebraska Press, 1983. $29.95.

LIFE AMONG THE INDIANS: FIRST FIELDWORK AMONG THE SIOUX & OMAHAS
Alice C. Fletcher; Joanna C. Scherer & Raymond DeMallie, Editors & Intro. Illus. 448 pp. University of Nebraska Press, 2013. $65.

LIFE AMONG THE MODOCS: UNWRITTEN HISTORY
Joaquin Miller; Reprint of 1873 ed. 460 pp. Paper. Urion Press & Heyday Books. $15.95.

LIFE AMONG THE PAIUTES: THEIR WRONGS & CLAIMS
Sarah Winnemucca Hopkins; Reprint of 1883 edition. Autobiography which deals with her life as a Paiute princess and the plight of the Paiutes. 272 pp. Paper. University of Nevada Press. $13.95.

LIFE AMONG THE TEXAS INDIANS: THE WPA NARRATIVES
David La Vere; Detail about the life among the Kiowas, Comanches, Wichitas, Caddos, Tonkawas, and Lipan Apaches who lived in Texas around 1830. Photos. 288 pp. Texas A&M University Press, Amazon.com, Alibris.com, 1999. $29.95.

LIFE AMONGST THE MODOCS: UNWRITTEN HISTORY
Joaquin Miller; Paper. Heyday Books. $18.95.

LIFE & ART OF THE NORTH AMERICAN INDIAN
John Warner; Amazon.com, 1990. $15.98.

LIFE AT THE KIOWA, COMANCHE, AND WICHITA AGENCY: THE PHOTOGRAPHS OF ANNETTE ROSS Kristina L. Southwell & John R. Lovett
Illus. Map. 256 pp. University of Oklahoma Press, 2010. $34.95.

LIFE & DEATH IN MOHAWK COUNTRY
Bruce E. Johansen; illus. by John Kahionhes Fadden ; Disputed land claims along the U.S. & Canadian border. Illus. 202 pp. Amazon.com, 1992. $23.95.

THE LIFE I'VE BEEN LIVING
Moses Cruikshank; Biography of Moses Cruikshank, an Athabaskan elder and skilled storyteller from Interior Alaska. Reprint of 1986 edition. Illus. 132 pp. Paper. University of Alaska Press, $9.95.

LIFE IN CUSTER'S CAVALRY: DIARIES & LETTERS OF ALBERT & JENNIE BARNITZ, 1867-1868 Albert & Jennie Barnitz; Robert Utley, Editor
Illus. 302 pp. Paper. University of Nebraska Press, 1987. $7.95.

LIFE IN THE PUEBLO: UNDERSTANDING THE PAST THROUGH ARCHAEOLOGY
Kathryn Kamp; Illus. 224 pp. Paper. Waveland Press, 1998. $23.95.

LIFE IN THE PUEBLOS
Ruth Underhill; edited by Willard Beatty; Interprets Pueblo lifestyles for the general public. Illus. Maps. 168 pp. Paper. Amazon.com, $15.95.

LIFE'S JOURNEY-ZUYA: ORAL TEACHINGS FROM ROSEBUD
Albert White Hat, Sr. & John Cunningham
224 pp. University of Utah Press, 2012. $49.95; paper, $24.95; eBook, $20.

LIFE, LETTERS & SPEECHES
George Copway; The biography of a Canadian Ojibwe writer and lecturer. Map. 255 pp. Paper. University of Nebraska Pres, 1997. $29.95.

LIFE STORY OF ROSE MITCHELL: A NAVAJO WOMAN, 1874-1977
Rose G. Mitchell; Charlotte J. Frisbie, Editor
Illus. 552 pp. University of New Mexico Press, 2001. $65; paper, $29.95.

LIFE LIVED LIKE A STORY: LIFE STORIES OF THREE YUKON NATIVE ELDERS
Julie Cruikshank; Illus. Maps. 424 pp. Paper. U. of Washington Press, 1991. $39.95.

LIFE OF GEORGE BENT: WRITTEN FROM HIS LETTERS
George E. Hyde; Savoie Lottinville, Editor
Reprint of 1968 edition. Illus. Maps. 390 pp. Paper. University of Oklahoma Press, $19.95.

LIFE OF BLACK HAWK
Black Hawk; 128 pp. Dover, $6.95.

THE LIFE OF BLACKHAWK, DICTATED BY HIMSELF
J.B. Patterson
Enlarged facsimile of the 1834 edition. 156 pp. Paper. Amazon.com, $10.95.

LIFE OF PUSHIMATAHA
Gideon Lincecum; Biography of Choctaw Chief Pushimataha who was born in 1764. 136 pp. Paper. University of Alabama Press, 1996. $21.95.

LIFE OF ROBERT HALL: INDIAN FIGHTER & VETERAN OF THREE GREAT WARS: ALSO, SKETCHES OF BIG FOOT WALLACE
Brazos; Illus. 160 pp. Paper. Amazon.com, 1992. $14.95.

THE LIFE OF HAROLD SELLERS COLTON: PHILADELPHIA BRAHMIN IN FLAGSTAFF Jimmy Herbert Miller; Paper. Amazon.com, 1991. $15.95.

LIFE OF SITTING BULL: HISTORY OF THE INDIAN WAR OF 1890-1891
W. Fletcher Johnson; Reprint. Illus. 544 pp. Amazon.com, 2000. $39.95.

LIFE OF TECUMSEH & HIS BROTHER THE PROPHET: A HISTORY OF THE SHAWNEE B. Drake; Reprint. 236 pp. Paper. Wennawoods Publishing, $9.95.

LIFE OF TEN BEARS: COMANCHE HISTORICAL NARRATIVES
Francis Joseph Attocknie; edited by Thomas W.. Kavanagh
252 pp. University of Nebraska Press, 2016. $65.

LIFE OF TOM HORN, GOVERNMENT SCOUT & INTERPRETER, WRITTEN BY HIMSELF, TOGETHER WITH HIS LETTERS & STATEMENTS BY HIS FRIENDS: A VINDICATION Tom Horn; 272 pp. Paper. University of Oklahoma Press, 1964. $12.95.

LIFE ON THE RIVER: THE ARCHAEOLOGY OF AN ANCIENT NATIVE AMERICAN CULTURE W.R. Hildebrandt & M. Darcangelo
California Native American history. Paper. Heyday Books, 2008. $13.95.

THE LIFE STORY OF ROSE MITCHELL: A NAVAJO WOMAN, 1874-1977
Rose G. Mitchell; Charlotte J. Frisbie, Ed.
Illus. 550 pp. University of New Mexico Press, 2001. $65; paper, $29.95.

THE LIFE & TIMES OF LEWIS WETZEL
C.B. Allman; Illus. 244 pp. Paper. Wennawoods Publishing, 25.50

THE LIFE & TIMES OF LITTLE TURTLE: FIRST SAGAMORE OF THE WABASH
Harvey L. Carter; Illus. 296 pp. University of Illinois Press, 1987. $24.95.

**LIFE & TIMES OF DAVID ZEISBERGER: THE WESTERN PIONEER
& APOSTLE OF THE INDIANS**
Edmund De Schweinitz; Reprint of 1870 ed. Paper. Kessinger Publishing, 2007. $34.95.

**LIFE & TRADITIONS OF THE RED MAN: A REDISCOVERED TREASURE OF
NATIVE AMERICAN LITERATURE** Joseph Nicolar; Annette Kolodny, Editor
Illus. 240 pp. Duke University Press, 2007. $89.95; paper, $24.95.

LIFE UNDER THE SUN
Charles Lovato
Lithograph art. Illus. Sunstone Press, $35; signed & numbered hard cover edition, $125.

LIFE WITH THE ESKIMO
Illus. 16 pp. Paper. Hancock House, $2.95.

LIFE WOVEN WITH SONG
Nora Marks Dauenhauer; Prose, poetry and plays from a woman from Alaska.
139 pp. Paper. University of Arizona Press, 2000. $19.95.

LIFE & WRITINGS OF BETSY CHAMBERLAIN: NATIVE AMERICAN MILL WORKER
Judith Ranta; Illus. 304 pp. Paper. Northeastern U. Press, 2003. $47.95; paper, $19.95.

**LIGHT FROM ANCIENT CAMPFIRES: ARCHAEOLOGICAL EVIDENCE
FOR NATIVE LIFEWAYS ON THE NORTHERN PLAINS**
Trevor R. Peck; 526 pp. Paper. University of Washington Press, 2011. $44.95.

LIGHT FROM A BULLET HOLE:POEMS NEW AND SELECTED, 1950-2008
Ralph Salisbury
Poetry. Cherokee culture. 177 pp. Paper. Silverfish Review Press, 2009.
Amazon.com & Alibris.com, $19.95.

LIGHT ON THE INDIAN WORLD: THE ESSENTIAL WRITINGS OF OHIYESA
Charles Eastman; Michael Oren Fitzgerald, Ed.
Illus. 240 pp. Paper. World Wisdom, 2002. $17.95.

LIGHT ON THE LAND
Art Davidson; photos by Art Wolfe; Landscape photography with essays & Native writings
from around the world. Illus. 100 photos. 196 pp. Beyond Words Publishing, 1994. $75.

**LIGHT ON THE PATH: THE ANTHROPOLOGY & HISTORY OF THE
SOUTHEASTERN INDIANS** Thomas J. Pluckhahn & Robbie Ethridge
Illus. 296 pp. University of Alabama Press, 2006. $60; paper, $34.95.

THE LIGHT PEOPLE: A NOVEL
Gordon Henry, Jr.; A young Chippewa boy is trying to learn the whereabouts
of his parents. 226 pp. Paper. University of Oklahoma Press, 1994. $13.95.

**LIGHTING THE SEVENTH FIRE: THE SPIRITUAL WAYS, HEALING, AND SCIENCE OF
THE NATIVE AMERICAN** F. David Peat; 322 pp. Amazon.com, 1994. $19.95.

*LIGHTNING INSIDE YOU: & OTHER NATIVE AMERICAN RIDDLES
John Bierhorst, Editor; Grades 2 and up.William Morrow, 1992. $14.

THE LIGHTNING STICK: ARROWS, WOUNDS, AND INDIAN LEGEND
H. Henrietta Stockel; History of the bow & arrow; brings together a broad range of
significant people and events, spiritual usages, medicinal treatments. Illus. 176 pp. U. of
Nevada Press, 1995. $24.95.

THE LIGHTNING WITHIN
Alan R. Velie, Editor; An Anthology of Contemporary American Indian fiction: N. Scott
Momaday, James Welch, Louise Erdich, and Michael Doris. 170 pp. Paper. University of
Nebraksa Press, 1991.$12.

**LIKE BEADS ON A STRING: A CULTURE HISTORY OF THE SEMINOLE INDIANS
IN NORTH PENINSULA FLORIDA**
Brent Weisman; Illus. 216 pp. Paper. University of Alabama Press, 1989. $15.95.

LIKE A BROTHER: GRENVILLE GOODWIN'S APACHE YEARS, 1928-1939
Neil Goodwin; Unpublished field notes, diaries, and letters. Illus. 280 pp.
Paper. University of Arizona Press, 2004. $19.95.

LIKE A DEER CHASED BY THE DOGS: THE LIFE OF CHIEF OSHKOSH
Scott Cross; Biography of Chief Oshkosh of the Menominee. Illus. Photos.
68 pp. Paper. University of Wisconsin Press, 2005. $9.95

LIKE A HURRICANE: INDIAN MOVEMENT FROM ALCATRAZ TO WOUNDED KNEE
Paul C. Smith & Robert A. Warrior; An account of a defining period of
Native American radical protest. 360 pp. Amazon.com, 1996. $25.

**LIKE A LOADED WEAPON: THE REHNQUIST COURT, INDIAN RIGHTS,
& THE LEGAL HISTORY OF RACISM IN AMERICA**
Robert A. Williams, Jr.; Exposes the Supreme Court's racism against Native Americans.
312 pp. Paper. University of Minnesota Press, 2005. $18.95.

THE LILLOOET LANGUAGE: PHONOLOGY, MORPHOLOGY, SYNTAX
Jan VanEijk; 279 pp. University of Washington Press, 1997. $75.

**THE LIMITS OF MULTICULTURALISM: INTERROGATING THE ORIGINS
OF AMERICAN ANTHROPOLOGY** Scott Michaelsen; Traces anthropology's
Native American roots. 280 pp. Paper. University of Minnesota Press, 1999. $24.

LINCOLN & THE INDIANS: CIVIL WAR POLICY & POLITICS
David A. Nichols; Illus. 232 pp. Paper. University of Illinois Press, 2000. $15.95.

*LINDA'S INDIAN HOME
Grades 3-7. Illus. Binford & Mort, 1969. $6.95.

LINGERING ECHOES IN THE LAND OF THE CHEROKEE
Rus L. Brown; Marilee Smede, Ed.; Paper. Rus L. Brown Enterprises, $10.

**LINKING ARMS TOGETHER: AMERICAN INDIAN TREATRY VISIONS OF LAW &
PEACE, 1600-1800** Rob Williams, Jr.; Illus. 208 pp. Oxford University Press, 1997. $100.

THE LIPAN APACHES IN TEXAS
Thomas F. Schilz; Illus. 58 pp. Texas Western, 1987. $10; paper, $5.

THE LIPAN APACHES: PEOPLE OF WIND & LIGHTNING
Thomas A. Britten; Illus. University of New Mexico Press, 2002. $24.95.

*LISTEN & READ FAVORITE NORTH AMERICAN INDIAN LEGENDS
Philip Smith, Editor; Grades 5 and up. 96 pp. Dover, 1997. $5.95 includes audiotape.

LISTEN TO THE DRUM: BLACKWOLF SHARES HIS MEDICINE
Gina & Blackwolf Jones
Illus. 194 pp. Paper. Amazon.com & Educational Services, 2000. $12.95.

**LISTENING TO THE LAND: NATIVE AMERICAN LITERARY RESPONSES
TO THE LANDSCAPE**
Lee Schweninger; Examines works by the following: N. Scott Momaday, Louise Erdrich,
Vine Deloria, Jr., Gerald Vizenor & Louis Owens, regarding Native American philosophy
regarding the land. 256 pp. University of Georgia Press, 2008. $59.95; paper, $24.95.

**LISTENING TO OUR ANCESTORS: THE ART OF NATIVE LIFE ALONG
THE NORTH PACIFIC COAST** Intro. By Robert Joseph ; Illus. 192 pp. Paper.
NMAI Press & National Geographic Books, 2005. $24.

**LISTENING TO OUR GRANDMOTHER'S STORIES: THE BLOOMFIELD ACADEMY
FOR CHICKASAW FEMALES, 1852-1949**
Amanda J. Cobb; Tells the story of the school and its students. American Book Award
from the Before Columbus Foundation. Illus. Maps. 192 pp. University of Nebraska Press,
2000. $30.

LITERACY AND INTELLECTUAL LIFE IN THE CHEROKEE NATION, 1820-1906
James W. Parins; 296 pp. University of Oklahoma Press, $34.95.

LITERATURE BY & ABOUT THE AMERICAN INDIAN: ANNOTATED BIBLIOGRAPHY
Anna L. Stensland, Compiler; Describes more than 775 books on Native American
experiences, new and old. Second edition. 382 pp. Paper. Amazon.com English, 1979.
$10.95.

LITERATURE OF CALIFORNIA, VOL. 1: NATIVE AMERICAN BEGINNINGS TO 1945
edited by Jack Hicks, James Houston, Maxine Hong Kingston & Al Young
Ranges from Native American origin myth to Hollywood novels dissecting the American
dream. Illus. Map. 653 pp. University of California Press, 2000. $60; paper, $24.95.

LITTLE BIG HORN DIARY: CHRONICLE OF THE 1876 INDIAN WAR
James Willert; Second Edition. Illus. 520 pp. J. Willert, 1982. $60.

**LITTLE BIG HORN REMEMBERED, THE UNTOLD INDIAN STORY OF CUSTER'S
LAST STAND** Herman J. Viola; Smithsonian Institution Press, 1999.

LITTLE BIG MAN
Thomas Berger; 480 pp. Amazon.com, $30.95; Paper. Dell, $13.95.

LITTLE BIT KNOW SOMETHING: STORIES IN A LANGUAGE OF ANTHROPOLOGY
Robin Ridington; Illus. 300 pp. Paper. University of Iowa Press, 1990. $21.

A LITTLE BIT OF WISDOM: CONVERSATIONS WITH A NEZ PERCE ELDER
Horace Axtell & Margo Aragon; Illus. 217 pp. Amazon.com, 1997. $25.
Paper. University of Oklahoma Press, 2000. $12.95.

*LITTLE BOY WITH THREE NAMES: STORIES OF TAOS PUEBLO
Ann Nolan Clark; Reprint. Grades 3 and up. Illus. 80 pp. Paper. Amazon.com, $8.95.

LITTLE CROW, SPOKESMAN FOR THE SIOUX
Gary Anderson; Illus. Photos. Maps. 259 pp. Paper.
Minnesota Historical Society Press, 1986. $10.95.

*LITTLE FIREFLY: AN ALGONQUIAN LEGEND
Terri Cohlene; Grades 4-7. Illus. 48 pp. Paper. Amazon.com, $4.95.

*LITTLE HERDER IN AUTUMN
Ann Nolan Clark; Reprint. Grades 3 and up. Illus. 96 pp. Paper. Amazon.com, $9.95.

*LITTLE (SOUTHWEST/PLAINS/SOUTHEAST) INDIAN GIRLS PAPERDOLL
Kathy Allert; Outfits represent Navajo, Pueblos, & Apache tribes.
Grades 3 and up. 16 pp. Paper. Dover, $1.

*LITTLE WATER & THE GIFT OF THE ANIMALS: A SENECA LEGEND
C.J. Taylor; Grades 5 and up. Illus. 24 pp. Paper. Amazon.com, 1997. $6.95.

THE LITTLE WATER MEDICINE SOCIETY OF THE SENECAS
William N. Fenton; Ceremonies of the medicine society of the Iroquois Indians of western New York. Illus. 256 pp. University of Oklahoma Press, 2003. $24.95.

THE LIVING ARCTIC: HUNTERS OF THE CANADIAN NORTH
Hugh Brody; Illus. 270 pp. Paper. University of Washington Press, 1990. $16.95.

LIVING HISTORIES: NATIVE AMERICANS & SOUTHWESTERN ARCHAEOLOGY
Chip Colwell-Chanthaphonh; 212 pp. AltaMira Press, 2010. $83; paper, $33; eBook, $32.99.

LIVING HOMES FOR CULTURAL EXPRESSION: NORTH AMERICAN NATIVE PERSPECTIVES ON CREATING COMMUNITY MUSEUMS
Karen Coody Cooper (Cherokee) & Nicolasa I. Sandoval (Chumash) Illus. 120 pp. Paper. NMAI Press, 2006. $12.95.

LIVING IN BALANCE: THE UNIVERSE OF THE HOPI, ZUNI, NAVAJO & APACHE
Dorothy K. Washburn
Illus. 92 pp. Paper. University of Pennsylvania Museum Publications, 1995. $12.95.

LIVING IN THE LAND OF DEATH: THE CHOCTAW PEOPLE, 1830-1860
Donna Akers; The story of Choctaw survival and the evolution of the Choctaw people in Indian Territory in the 19th century. Illus. 220 pp. Paper. Michigan State U. Press, 2004.

LIVING IN TWO WORLDS: THE AMERICAN INDIAN EXPERIENCE ILLUSTRATED
Charles Alexander Eastman (Ohiyesa); Illus. Maps. 207 pp. Paper. World Wisdom, 2010.

LIVING INDIAN HISTORIES: LUMBEE & TUSCARORA PEOPLE IN NORTH CAROLINA
Gerald Sider; Illus. 332 pp. Paper. University of North Carolina Press, 2003. $31.95.

LIVING & LEAVING: A SOCIAL HISTORY OF REGIONAL DEPOPULATION IN 13TH CDNTURY MESA VERDE
Donna Glowacki; Illus. 312 pp. University of Ariizona Press, 2015. $60.

LIVING LIFE'S CIRCLE: MESCALERO APACHE COSMOVISION
Claire R. Farrer; Illus. Paper. University of New Mexico Press, $21.95.

LIVING LIKE INDIANS: A TREASURY OF NORTH AMERICAN INDIAN CRAFTS, GAMES & ACTIVITIES Allan A. Macfarlan; Illus. 320 pp. Paper. Dover, 1999. $8.95.

LIVING ON THE LAND: INDIGENOUS WOMEN'S UNERSTANDING OF PLACE
Nathalie Kermoal & Isabel Altamirano-Jimenez
Paper. UBC Press, 2017. $27.95.

LIVING OUR LANGUAGE: OJIBWE TALES & ORAL HISTORIES
Cyrus Thomas
Illus. 320 pp. Minnesota Historical Society Press, 1995. $29.95; paper, $19.95.

LIVING SIDEWAYS: TRICKSTERS IN AMERICAN INDIAN ORALTRADITIONS
Franchot Ballinger; Illus. 228 pp. University of Oklahoma Press, $19.95.

LIVING THE SKY: THE COSMOS OF THE AMERICAN INDIAN
Ray A. Williamson; Illus. Maps. 382 pp. Paper. U. of Oklahoma Press, 1987. $24.95.

LIVING STORIES OF THE CHEROKEE
Barbara Duncan & Davey Arch
Illus. 272 pp. University of North Carolina Press, 1998. $29.95; paper, $16.95.

LIVING THE SPIRIT: A GAY AMERICAN INDIAN ANTHOLOGY
Will Roscoe, Editor; Illus. 240 pp. St. Martin Press, 1988. $16.95.

LIVING THROUGH THE GENERATIONS: CONTINUITY & CHANGE IN NAVAJO WOMEN'S LIVES Joanne McCloskey
Ethnographic interviews with 77 women in Crownpoint, NM; on behavior, beliefs and values. 240 pp. University of Arizona Press, 2007. $50; paper, $24.95.

THE LIVING TRADITION OF MARIA MARTINEZ
Susan Peterson; Revised edition. Illus. 300 pp. Kodansha, 1989. $70; paper, $34.95.

LIVING WISDOM: NATIVE NORTH AMERICA
Larry Zimmerman; Illus. 184 pp. Paper. Amazon.com., 1997. $15.95.

*LIVING WITH THE ESKIMOS
Grades K-5. Illus. 40 pp. Childrens Press, $11.45.

LIVING WITH THE NEZ PERCE
Eddy L. Harris; The Amazon.com, 2005. $24.95.

*LIVING WITH THE SENECAS: A STORY ABOUT MARY JEMISON
Susan Bivin Aller; Illus. by Laurie Harden
Grades 4-8. Paper. Lerner Publications, 2007. $8.99.

LIVING WITH STRANGERS: THE 19TH CENTURY SIOUX & THE CANADIAN-AMERICAN BORDERLANDS David G. McCrady
Illus. Maps. 176 pp. University of Nebraska Press, 2006. $45. 200 pp. Paper. University of Toronto Press, $21.95.

THE LIVINGSTON INDIAN RECORDS, 1666-1723
Lawrence H. Leder, Editor; Reprint of 1956 edition. 240 pp. E.M. Coleman, $25.

LOGS OF THE CONQUEST OF CANADA
W. Wood, Editor; Reprint of 1909 edition. Greenwood, $29.

THE LONE RANGER & TONTO FISTFIGHT IN HEAVEN
Sherman Alexie; Short stories. Re-release of 1993 edition with two new stories. 272 pp. Paper. Amazon.com, 2005. $13.

LONE WOLF V. HITCHCOCK: TREATY RIGHTS & INDIAN LAW AT THE END OF THE 19TH CENTURY Blue Clark; Places the Kiowas at center stage in the drama, as prime movers in determining their own fate. Illus. 198 pp. Paper. University of Nebraska Press, 1995. $18.95.

LONG-AGO PEOPLE'S PACKSACK: DENE BABICHE BAGS: TRADITION & REVIVAL
Suzan Marie & Judy Thompson; Describes the role of babiche bags in Dene lives...the craft of making babiche bags. Illus. 47 pp. Paper. U. of Washington Press, 2004. $14.95.

LONG BEFORE COLUMBUS: HOW THE ANCIENTS DISCOVERED AMERICA
Hans Holzer; Illus. 160 pp. Paper. Inner Traditions International, $12.95.

THE LONG BITTER TRAIL: ANDREW JACKSON & THE INDIANS
Anthony F. Wallace; 144 pp. Paper. Amazon.com, 1993. $7.95.

THE LONG DEATH: THE LAST DAYS OF THE PLAINS INDIANS
Ralph K. Andrist; The subjugation of the Plains Indians. Illus. 415 pp. Paper. University of Oklahoma Press, 2001. $24.95.

LONG JOURNEY HOME: ORAL HISTORIES OF CONTEMPORARY DELAWARE INDIANS James W. Brown & Rita Kohn; photos by James W. Brown Illus. Photos. 448 pp. Amazon.com & Alibris.com, $21.

LONG JOURNEY TO THE COUNTRY OF THE HURONS
G. Sagard-Theodat; George M. Wrong, Editor
Reprint of 1939 edition. Greenwood, $29.25.

LONG LANCE
Chief Buffalo Child Long Lance (Sylvester Long); intro. by Donald Smith
A fictional account of the Blackfoot Indians' last days of freedom. 320 pp. Amazon.com, 1995. $45; paper, $16.95.

LONG LANCE: THE TRUE STORY OF AN IMPOSTER
Donald B. Smith; Illus. 325 pp. Paper. University of Nebraska Press, 1983. $8.95.

LONG LIFE, HONEY IN THE HEART
Martin Prechtel; 370 pp. Paper. Amazon.com, 2004. $14.95.

LONG RIVER
Joseph Bruchac
Novel. Sequel to "Dawn Land." 312 pp. Fulcrum Publishing, 1996. $19.95.

*THE LONG SEARCH
Richard A. Boning; Grades 5-11. Illus. 48 pp. B. Loft, 1972. $7.95.

*LONG SHADOWS: INDIAN LEADERS STANDING IN THE PATH OF MANIFEST DESTINY 1600-1900
Jack Jackson; Grades 6 and up. Illus. 128 pp. Paramount, 1985. $17.95.

A LONG & TERRIBLE SHADOW: WHITE VALUES & NATIVE RIGHTS IN THE AMERICAS SINCE 1492 Thomas R. Berger; Surveys and examines the history of the Americas since their discovery by Europeans. Illus. 200 pp. Paper. U. of Washington Press, 1999. $17.95.

THE LONG WALK: HISTORY OF THE NAVAJO WARS, 1846-1868
Lynn Robinson Bailey; Illus. 300 pp. Westernlore, 1981. $10.95.

A LONG WAY FROM HOME: THE TUBERCULOSIS EPIDEMIC AMONG THE INUIT
Pat S. Grygier; Illus. 272 pp. Paper. CUP Services, 1997. $19.95.

LOOK TO THE MOUNTAIN: AN ECOLOGY OF INDIGENOUS EDUCATION
Gregory Cajete, PhD; Studies indigenous educational philosophy by a Native American scholar. Looks to Indian education for tomorrow and into the 21st century. Illus. Biblio. 248 pp. Paper. Amazon.com, 1994. $16.95.

LOOKING AT INDIAN ART OF THE NORTHWEST COAST
Hilary Stewart; Reprint of 1979 ed. Illus. 112 pp. Paper. U. of Washington Press. $17.95.

LOOKING AT THE LAND OF PROMISE: PIONEER IMAGES OF THE PACIFIC NORTHWEST William H. Goetzmann; Contains the work of many important early artists who painted and drew scenes in the Pacific Northwest. Some of the artists recorded th customs of the American Indians. Illus. Biblio. 122 pp. WSU Press, 1988. $35; paper, $20.

LOOKING AT TOTEM POLES
Hilary Stewart; Guide to totem poles in outdoor locations accessible to tourists and interested viewers; with legends most often associated with the poles. Illus. 100 drawings, 30 photos. 192 pp. Paper. University of Washington Press, 1993. $17.95.

LOOKING AT THE WORDS OF OUR PEOPLE
Jeanette Armstrong, Editor
An anthology of First Nation literary criticism. 150 pp. paper. Theytus, 1993. $12.95.

LOOKING BOTH WAYS: HERITAGE & IDENTITY OF THE ALUTIIQ PEOPLE
edited by Aron L. Cromwell, Amy F. Steffian & Gordon L. Pullar
Illus. Maps. Biblio. 266 pp. U. of Alaska Press, 2001. $49.95; paper, $24.95.

LOOKING FOR LOST BIRD: A JEWISH WOMAN'S DISCOVERY OF HER NAVAJO ROOTS Yvette Melanson & Claire Safran; 240 pp. Paper. Avon, 2000. $12.95.

LOOKING HIGH & LOW: ART & CULTURAL IDENTITY
Brenda Jo Bright & Liza Bakewell, Editors; Essays on Native American art & culture.
208 pp. University of Arizona Press, 1995. $43; paper, $18.95.

LOOKING TO THE FUTURE: THE LIFE & LEGACY OF SENATOR DANIEL K. INOUYE
Illus. 160 pp. NMAI Press, 2016. $21.95.

LOON LEGENDS
Corrine A. Dwyer; Illus. Amazon.com, $9.95.

LOON: MEMORY, MEANING, & REALITY IN A NORTHERN DENE COMMUNITY
Henry S. Sharp; Aspects of Chipewyan life in the Northwest Territories of Canada.
216 pp. Paper. University of Nebraska Press, 2001. $29.95.

LOOTING SPIRO MOUNDS: AN AMERICAN KING TUT'S TOMB
David La Vere; Archaeology of the Spiro Mounds in Oklahoma.
Paper. University of Oklahoma Press, 2007. $24.95.

LORD OF THE ANIMALS: A MIWOK INDIAN CREATION MYTH
Fiona French; Grades K-3. Illus. 32 pp. Amazon.com, 1997. $22.50.

LORE OF THE GREAT TURTLE: INDIAN LEGENDS OF MACKINAC RETOLD
Dirk Gringhuis; Illus. 96 pp. Paper. Amazon.com, 1970. $3.75.

LOS COMANCHES: THE HORSE PEOPLE, 1751-1845
Stanley Noyes; Paper. University of New Mexico Press, $16.95.

THE LOST BAND: A NOVEL
Don Coldsmith; 272 pp. University of Oklahoma Press, 2000. $24.95

LOST BIRD OF WOUNDED KNEE: SPIRIT OF THE LAKOTA
Renee S. Flood; Reprint. Illus. 392 pp. Paper. Amazon.com, $18.

LOST CITIES OF THE ANCIENT SOUTHEAST
Mallory M. O'Connor; Illus. 192 pp. University Press of Florida, 1995. $49.95.

LOST COPPER
Wendy Rose; intro by N. Scott Momaday
Poetry. Reprint. Illus. 127 pp. Paper. Malki-Ballena Press, 1992. $15.95.

LOST CREEKS: COLLECTED JOURNALS
Alexander Posey; edited by Matthew Wynn Sivils; Autobiographical works of Alexander Posey (Muscogee-Creek). Photo. 200 pp. University of Nebraska Press, 2009. $45.

THE LOST FIELD NOTES OF FRANKLIN R. JOHNSTON'S LIFE & WORK AMONG THE AMERICAN INDIANS Franklin Johnston; Reprint. Illus. 200 pp. First Glance, 1997. $22.95.

LOST HARVESTS: PRAIRIE INDIAN RESERVE FARMERS & GOVERNMENT POLICY
Sarah Carter; 350 pp. University of Toronto Press, 1990. $34.95.

LOST LABORERS IN COLONIAL CALIFORNIA: NATIVE AMERICANS & THE ARCHAEOLOGY OF RANCHO PETALUMA
Stephen W. Silliman; 250 pp. Illus. U. of Arizona Press, 2004. $39.95; paper, $24.95

LOST TRIBES OF THE INTERIOR: EXTRACTS FROM THE JESUIT RELATIONS & PRIMARY SOURCES Claudio R. Salvucci; 300 pp. Amazon.com, 2004. $75.

THE LOST UNIVERSE: PAWNEE LIFE & CULTURE
Gene Weltfish; Illus. 525 pp. University of Nebraska Press, 1977. $35; paper, $10.95.

LOUD HAWK: THE U.S. VERSUS THE AMERICAN INDIAN MOVEMENT
Kenneth S. Stern; Explains what happened to the American Indian Movement (AIM). Documents official government misconduct on the Pine Ridge Reservation in 1975. Illus. 374 pp. Paper. University of Oklahoma Press, 2002. $19.95.

LOUDON'S INDIAN NARRATIVES
Archibald Loudon; Reprint. Illus. 658 pp. Wennawoods Publishing, 1992. $44.95.

LOUIS - SON OF THE PRAIRIES
Noelle Pauld-Pelletier; History of early Metis life on the prairies..account of early years of Louis Riel. Grades 6-10. Paper. Pemmican, $9.95.

LOUISIANA INDIAN STUDIES: A SELECTED BIBLIOGRAPHY
Michael J. Foret
284 pp. University of Louisiana at Lafayette, Center for Louisiana Studies, 1995. $ $25.

*LOUISIANA INDIAN TALES
Elizabeth Butler Moore & ASlice Wilbert Couvillon; Tales for children to learn of Louisiana Indian heritage. Grades 3-8. Illus. 112 pp. Amazon.com, $11.95.

LOUISIANA'S NATIVE AMERICANS: A MOURNFUL MEMORY - WRITTEN IN BLOOD
Margot Soule; Margaret Thornton, Ed.; Illus. 200 pp. Nashoba tek Press, 1998. $24.95.

LOUISIANA PLACE NAMES OF INDIAN ORIGIN: A COLLECTION OF WORDS
William A. Read; George Riser, Editor & intro.
Illus. 168 pp. Paper. University of Alabama Press, 2008. $18.95. E-Book, $15.16.

*LOVE FLUTE
Paul Goble; Story of a shy young man, incorporating the traditional Native American flute, Plains Indian culture, and the beauty of a legend. Paintings. Grades K-3. Illus 32 pp. Amazon.com, $15.95.

LOVE & HATE IN JAMESTOWN: JOHN SMITH, POCAHONTAS, & THE HEART OF A NEW NATION David Price; Illus. 320 pp. Paper. Vintage/Knopf, 2005. $16.

LOWER UMPQUA TEXTS: NOTES ON THE KUSAN DIALECTS
Leo J. Frachtenberg; Reprint. 221 pp. Paper. Coyote Press, $23.75.

LT. CHARLES GATEWOOD & HIS APACHE WARS MEMOIR
Charles B. Gatewood; Louis Kraft, Editor; Primary source & chronicle of Apache life in the early reservation era. Illus. Map. 328 pp. Paper. U. of Nebraska Press, 2009. $17.95.

LUBICON LAKE NATION: INDIGENOUS KNOWLEDGE & POWER
Dawn Hill; Indigenous rights. Analyzes the Canadian government's actions vis-a-vis the rights of the Lubicon people, a small Cree nation in northern Alberta. 208 pp. University of Toronto Press, 2008. $50; paper, $25.

*LUCY LEARNS TO WEAVE: GATHERING PLANTS
Virginia Hoffman; Grades 1-4. Illus. 46 pp. Paper. Navajo Studies Center, 1974. $2.75.

THE LUISENO INDIANS OF SOUTHERN CALIFORNIA
Malki Museum Press; Booklet of excerpts from Aboriginal Society in Southern California by William Duncan Strong; and from An Introduction to the Luiseno Language by Villiana Hyde. Describes Luiseno background, territories, clan names, myths, and language sounds. Illus. Booklet. Malki-Ballens Press, 2002. $5.50.

LULU LINEAR PUNCTATED: ESSAYS IN HONOR OF GEORGE IRVING QUIMBY
Robert Dunnell & Donald Grayson
Illus. 354 pp. Paper. University of Michigan, Museum of Anthropology, 1983. $12.

*THE LUMBEE
Karen Blu; Grades 5 and up. Illus. Chelsea House, 1989. $17.95.

LUMBEE INDIAN HISTORIES: RACE, ETHNICITY & INDIAN IDENTITY IN THE SOUTHERN U.S. Gerald M. Sider; 336 pp. Paper. Cambridge U. Press, 1994. $18.95.

LUMBEE INDIANS IN THE JIM CROW SOUTH: RACE, IDENTITY, AND THE MAKING OF A NATION Malinda Maynor Lowery
Crafting an identity as a people, a race, a tribe, and a nation. Illus. Maps. 368 pp. University of North Carolina Press, 2010. $65; paper, $21.95.

THE LUMBEE PROBLEM: THE MAKING OF AN AMERICAN INDIAN PEOPLE
Karen I. Blu; Illus. 298 pp. Paper. University of Nebraska Press, 2001. $24.95.

LUMINARIES OF THE HUMBLE
Elizabeth Woody; Collection of poems focusing on the land & people of the Pacific Northwest. 128 pp. Paper. University of Arizona Press, 1994. $17.95.

CHARLES F. LUMMIS: THE CENTENNIAL EXHIBITION
Daniela P. Moneta, Editor; Illus. 82 pp. Paper. Southwest Museum, 1985. $14.95.

JAMES LUNA: EMENDATIO
Truman T. Lowe (Ho-Chunk) & Paul Chaat Smith (Comanche)
Illus. 112 pp. Paper. NMAI Press, 2005. $20.

LURE OF THE ARCTIC
Bernice Chappel; Marjorie Klein, tr; Illus. 256 pp. Paper. Wilderness Adventure.

LUSHOOTSEED CULTURE & THE SHAMANIC ODYSSEY: AN ANCHORED RADIANCE
Jay Miller; Overview of the Native people of Puget Sound. Illus. Map. 185 pp. University of Nebraska Press, 1999. $50.

LUSHOOTSEED DICTIONARY
Dawn Bates, Thom Hess & Vi Hilbert, Editors; Update of Thom Hess's Dictionary of Puget Salish (1976). 406 pp. Paper. University of Washington Press, $40.

LUSHOOTSEED READER WITH INTRODUCTORY GRAMMAR
Thomas M. Hess; 4 stories from Edward Sam. Vol. 1. 200 pp. U. of Montana , 1995. $20.

LUSHOOTSEED TEXTS: AN INTRODUCTION TO PUGET SALISH NARRATIVE AESTHETICS Crisca Bierwert, Ed. & Tr.; Illus. 325 pp. U. of Nebraska Press, 1996. $60.

M

MAASAW: PROFILE OF A HOPI GOD
E. Malotki & M. Lomatuway'ma
Illus. 275 pp. University of Nebraska Press, 1987. $24.95; paper, $14.95.

CORBETT MACK: THE LIFE OF A NORTHERN PAIUTE
Michael Hittman; Illus. 398 pp. University of Nebraska Press, 1996. $55; paper, $18.

MACMILLAN ENCYCLOPEDIA OF NATIVE AMERICAN TRIBES
Michael Johnson, Contributor; History of Native American people from the Canadian Arctic to the Rio Grande. Contemporary & rare historical photographs, regional maps. Illus. 2nd Ed. 256 pp. Amazon.com, 1999. $150.

MAD BEAR: SPIRIT, HEALING, AND THE SACRED IN THE LIFE OF A NATIVE AMERICAN MEDICINE MAN Doug Boyd; Profiles Mad Bear, a Tuscarora Indian, renowned medicine man, and dynamic Indian-rights activist during the 1960s and 1970s. He died in 1985. 352 pp. Paper. Simon & Schuster, 1994. $12.

MADCHILD RUNNING
Keith Egawa; A novel about a young girl caught up in urban violence. The author is a Lummi Indian from Seattle, Wash. 200 pp. Amazon.com, 1999. $23.95; paper, $14.95.

MADONNA SWAN: A LAKOTA WOMAN'S STORY
as told through Mark St. Pierre
Biography of a Lakota Sioux woman from the Cheyenne River Sioux Reservation.
Illus. Maps. 210 pp. Paper. University of Oklahoma Press, 2019. $19.95.

MAGIC IMAGES: CONTEMPORARY NATIVE AMERICAN ART
Edwin Wade and Rennard Strickland
Illus. 125 pp. Paper. University of Oklahoma Press, 1982. $16.95.

MAGIC IN THE MOUNTAINS, THE YAKAMA SHAMAN: POWER & PRACTICE
Donald M. Hines; Account of the Yakama shaman observed from 1872 to 1882;
first-hand accounts from shamans or their patients. Illus. 253 pp. Amazon.com. $17.95.

***THE MAGIC LAKE: A MYSTICAL HEALING LAKE OF THE CHEROKEE**
Tom Underwood; Grades 1-3. Illus. 20 pp. Cherokee Publications, 1982. $5.

***THE MAGIC WEAVER OF RUGS**
Jerrie Oughton; Grades K-3. Illus. 32 pp. Amazon.com, 1994. $14.95.

THE MAGIC WORLD: AMERICAN INDIAN SONGS & POEMS
William Brandon; Reprint of 1971 ed. 168 pp. Paper. Ohio U. Press, 1991. $19.95.

MAGICAL CRITICISM: THE RESOURCE OF SAVAGE PHILOSOPHY
Christopher Bracken; Native American land disputes. 1 drawing. 256 pp.
University of Chicago Press, 2007. $50; paper, $20. E-nook, from $5 to $20.

MAGICAL PASSES: THE PRACTICAL WISDOM OF THE SHAMANS
Carlos Castaneda; Illus. 240 pp. Paper. Harper Trade, 1999. $14.

MAHUTS & ANNWM AVAL: 2 FULL-LENGTH VIDEO THEATRE PLAYS
David Seals; Illus. Paper. Sky & Sage Books, 1996. $17, Includes audiocassette.

THE MAIDU INDIAN MYTHS & STORIES OF HANC'IBYJIM
William Shipley, editor & translator; 192 pp. Paper. Heyday Books, $12.95.

MAIDU MYTHS & TALES
Hanc'ibyjim; Illus. Heyday Books, $12.

MAIDU TEXTS
Ronald Dixon; Reprint. 245 pp. Paper. Coyote Press, $25.95.

THE MAIN STALK: A SYNTHESIS OF NAVAJO PHILOSOPHY
John R. Farella; 221 pp. Paper. University of Arizona Press, 1984. $18.95.

***MAISONS D'ENCORE: TIPI, WIGWAM ET LONGUE MAISON**
Bonnie Shemie; Grades 3-7. Illus. 25 pp. Amazon.com, 1990. $12.95.

MAJOR COUNCIL MEETINGS OF AMERICAN INDIAN TRIBES: PART ONE & TWO
Robert E. Lester, compiler; Microfilm. Part One - Section I (1914-1956); Section II
(1911-1956). Part Two - Section 1 (1957-1971); Section 2 (1957-1971). 35 pp.
Amazon.com, 1982.

MAJOR RICHARDSON'S SHORT STORIES
David Beasley, Editor
Ottawa Indian novelist of the mid-1800s. 134 pp. Paper. Theytus, 1985. $6.95.

THE MAKAH INDIANS
Elizabeth Colson; Reprint of 1953 edition. Illus. 308 pp. Greenwood, $25.

MAKE A BEAUTIFUL WAY: THE WISDOM OF NATIVE AMERICAN WOMEN
Barbara Alice Mann, Editor; foreword by Winona LaDuke
152 pp. Paper. University of Nebraska Press, 2008. $14.95.

MAKE PRAYERS TO THE RAVEN
Richard Nelson; Ethnographic study of the Koyukon Athabascan people.
292 pp. Paper. University of Chicago Press, 1983. $19.

MAKERS & MARKETS: THE WRIGHT COLLECTION OF TWENTIETH-CENTURY NATIVE AMERICAN ART
edited by Penelope Ballard Drooker; Paper. University of New Mexico Press, $30.

***MAKIAWISUG: THE GIFT OF THE LITTLE PEOPLE**
Melissa Jane Fawcett & Joseph Bruchac; A traditional children's tale of the magical little
people (Makiawisug) who inhabit the Mohegan homeland and thei relationship to the earth.
Grades K-3. Illus. Paper. The Mohegan Tribe.

MAKING ARROWS THE OLD WAY
Doug Wallentine; How to make Native American arrows. Illus.
28 pp. Paper. Eagle's View Publishing, & Smoke & Fire Co., $4.50.

MAKING THE ATTIKAMEK SNOWSHOE
Henri Vaillancourt; Describes the design, construction, & use of the Attikamek snowshoe.
Illus. Photos. 176 pp. Amazon.com, 1995. $34, postpaid.

MAKING DICTIONARIES: PRESERVING INDIGENOUS LANGUAGES OF THE AMERICAS William Frawley, et al. Editors
Illus. 495 pp. University of California Press, 2002. $65; paper, $34.95.

MAKING HISTORY: ALUTIIQ/SUGPIAQ LIFE ON THE ALASKA PENINSULA
Patricia Partnow; Illus. Photos. Maps. Biblio. University of Alaska Press, 2002.

MAKING INDIAN BOWS & ARROWS...THE OLD WAY
Doug Wallentine; Explores in detail acquiring tools & wood, designing, and making Native
American bows & arrows. Illus. 98 pp. Paper. Eagle's View Publishing & Smoke & Fire Co.,
$12.95.

MAKING INDIAN LAW: THE HUALAPAI LAND CASE & THE BIRTH OF ETHNOHISTORY
Christian W. McMillen; Mas. 304 pp. Paper. Yale University Press, 2009. $32.

MAKING IT THEIR OWN: SEVEN OJIBWE COMMUNICATIVE PRACTICES
Lisa P. Valentine; Illus. 272 pp. Amazon.com, 1995. $55; paper, $19.95.

MAKING LAMANITES: MORMONS, NATIVE AMERICANS, AND THE INDIAN STUDENT PLACEMENT PROGRAM, 1947-2000
Matthew Garrett; 384 pp. Uniersity of Utah Press, 2016. $44; paper, $29.95.

MAKING THE MISSISSIPPIAN SHATTER ZONE: THE COLONIAL INDIAN SLAVE TRADE & REGIONAL INSTABILITY IN THE AMERICAN SOUTH
Robbie Ethridge & Sheri M. Shuck-Hall; Interactions of American Indian & European
colonists in the South. Photo. Maps. 552 pp. Paper. U. of Nebraska Press, 2009. $35.

MAKING NATIVE AMERICAN POTTERY
Michael Simpson; How indigenous people gathered & processed clay; designs,
finishes, firing pottery, etc. Photos. 80 pp. Paper. Naturegraph, $9.95.

MAKING NATIVE SPACE: COLONIALISM, RESISTANCE, & RESERVES IN BRITISH COLUMBIA
Cole Harris; Illus. Photos. 448 pp. U. of Washington Press, 2003. $94; paper, $37.95.

MAKING PEACE WITH COCHISE: THE 1872 JOURNAL OF CAPTAIN JOSEPH ALTON SLADEN Edwin R. Sweeney, Editor; Chiricahua Apache lifeways. Illus.
Maps. 208 pp. Paper. University of Oklahoma Press, 2009. $19.95.

THE MAKING OF SACAGAWEA: A EURO-AMERICAN LEGEND
Donna J. Kessler; 260 pp. Paper. University of Alabama Press, 1998. $19.95.

MAKING SPACE ON THE WESTERN FRONTIER: MORMONS, MINERS, & SOUTHERN PAIUTES W. Paul Reeve; Exploring the cultural interactions on the southern rim of the
Great Basin in the last half of the 19th century. Illus. 248 pp. U. of Illinois Press, 2007. $37.

MAKING TWO WORLDS ONE & THE STORY OF ALL-AMERICAN INDIAN DAYS
Hila Gilbert; Illus. 60 pp. Paper. Amazon.com, 1986. $8.

MAKING WAWA: THE GENESIS OF CHINOOK JARGON
George Lang, Editor; Maps. 160 pp. U. of Washington Press, 2009. $94; paper, $33.95.

MAKUK: A NEW HISTORY OF ABORIGINAL-WHITE RELATIONS
John Sutton Lutz; Illus. Maps. 448 pp. Paper. U. of Washington Press, 2007. $37.95.

***MALI NPNAGS: THE STORY OF A MEAN LITTLE OLD LADY**
Johnny Arlee; Written in Salish & English. Grades 3-5. 64 pp.
Paper. SKC Press, $10. CD-ROM with sound effects & flute music, $8.

MALINCHE, POCAHONTAS, AND SACAGAWEA: INDIAN WOMEN AS CULTURAL INTERMEDIARIES & NATIONAL SYMBOLS
Rebecca Kay Jager; Illus. Maps. 358 pp. Paper. U. of Oklahoma Press, 2015. $24.95.

MALKI MUSEUM'S NATIVE FOOD TASTING EXPERIENCES
Alice Kotzen; Booklet on the collecting & preparing of plants, fruits, seeds, and game.
Includes contributions from Katherine Siva Sauvel, a Cahuilla elder. 4th Ed. Revised.
Photos. Malki-Ballena Press, 2003. $5.50.

THE MAMMOTH BOOK OF NATIVE AMERICANS: THE STORY OF AMERICA'S ORIGINAL INHABITANTS IN ALL IT'S BEAUTY, MAGIC, TRUTH & TRAGEDY
Jon E. Lewis; 512 pp. Paper. Avalon Publishing, 2004. $12.95.

MAN CORN: CANNIBALISM & VIOLENCE IN THE AMERICAN SOUTHWEST & MEXICO Jacqueline A. Turner; Illus. Maps. University of Utah Press, 1998. $65.

MAN OF THE CANYON: AN OLD INDIAN REMEMBERS HIS LIFE
Richard G. Emerick & Mark Hanna; Illus. 192 pp. Paper. Northern Lights, 1993. $12.95.

MAN OF MANA: MARIUS BARBEAU, A BIOGRAPHY
Laurence Nowry; Illus. 740 pp. Paper. University of Toronto Press, 1998. $27.95.

MAN OF THE PLAINS: RECOLLECTIONS OF LUTHER NORTH, 1856-1882
Luther North; Donald Danker, Editor; Illus. 350 pp. U. of Nebraska Press, 1961. $25.

A MAN OF DISTINCTION AMONG THEM: ALEXANDER MCKEE & BRITISH-INDIAN AFFAIRS ALONG THE OHIO COUNTY FRONTIER, 1754-1799
Larry L. Nelson; Amazon.com, 1999. $35.

MAN OF MANA: MARIUS BARBEAU, A BIOGRAPHY
Laurence Nowry; His research on the North pacific Coast and studies of totem poles and
fieldwork with the Tsimshian, Haida and Tlingit. Illus. Photos. 448 pp. University of
Washington Press, 1998. $27.95.

THE MAN TO SEND RAIN CLOUDS
Kenneth Rosen, Editor; 18 stories, including the work of Leslie Marmon Silko, Simon J.
Ortiz, Anna Lee Walters, and Larry Littlebird & members of the Circle Films. 192 pp. Paper.
Penguin USA, $9.

MAN WHO KILLED THE DEER
Frank Waters; Reprint of 1974 edition. 266 pp. Ohio U. Press, $9.95; paper, $6.95.

THE MAN WHO KNEW THE MEDICINE: THE TEACHINGS OF BILL EAGLE FEATHER
Henry Niese; Eagle Feather is Sun Dance chief and medicine man of the Rosebud Sioux.
Reveals personal accounts of important Native American rituals. Illus. 216 pp. Paper. Inner
Traditions, 2002. $16.

MANAGED CARE IN AMERICAN INDIAN & ALASKA NATIVE COMMUNITIES
Mim Dixon; 195 pp. Amazon.com, 1998. $10.

MAN'S KNIFE AMONG THE ESKIMO: A STUDY IN THE COLLECTION OF THE U.S. NATIONAL MUSEUM Otis Mason; Reprint. Illus. 20 pp. Paper. Shorey's Bookstore, $10.

MAN'S KNIFE AMONG THE NORTH AMERICAN INDIANS: A STUDY IN THE COLLECTION OF THE U.S. NATIONAL MUSEUM
Otis Mason; Reprint of 1897 edition. Illus. 20 pp. Paper. Amazon.com, $16.95.

MAN'S KNIFE AMONG THE NORTH AMERICAN INDIANS: A STUDY IN THE MAN'S RISE TO CIVILIZATION: THE CULTURAL ASCENT OF THE INDIANS OF NORTH AMERICA Peter Farb; Illus. Maps. Biblio. 336 pp. Paper. Penguin USA, $16.95.

MAN'S RISE TO CIVLIZATION: THE CULTURAL ASCENT OF THE INDIANS OF NORTH AMERICA Peter Farb
Illus. Photos. Maps. Biblio. 336 pp. Paper. Penguin USA, $12.95.

*THE MANDANS
Emilie Lepthien; Grades K-4. 50 pp. Childrens Press, 1989. $11.45.

MANHATTAN TO MINISINK: AMERICAN INDIAN PLACE NAMES OF GREATER NEW YORK & VICINITY Robert S. Grumet; 296 pp. University of Oklahoma Press, $34.95.

MANIFEST DESTINY & AMERICAN TERRITORIAL EXPANSION: A BRIEF HISTORY WITHDOCUMENTS Amy S. Greenberg; Amazn.com, $18.

MANIFEST MANNERS: NARRATIVES OF POSTINDIAN SURVIVANCE
Gerald Vizenor; 191 pp. Paper. University of Nebraska Press, 1999. $15.

*WILMA MANKILLER
Linda Lowery; Illus. by Janice Lee Porter; Grades 1-3. Illus. 56 pp. Lerner, 1996. $11.95.

*WILMA MANKILLER
Gini Holland; Grades 4 and up. Illus. 32 pp. Amazon.com, 1997. $21.40.

*WILMA MANKILLER: CHIEF OF THE CHEROKEES
Grades 2-4. Illus. 32 pp. Childrens Press, $10.95.

MANKILLER: A CHIEF & HER PEOPLE
Wilma Mankiller & Michael Wallis; An autobiography by the Principal Chief of the Cherokee Nation. 293 pp. Bedford/St. Martin's Press, 1993. $22.95; paper, $13.95.

*WILMA P. MANKILLER: CHIEF OF THE CHEROKEE
Biography of her childhood to the present, 1992. Includes list of important dates and an index. Grades 3-7. Illus. 20 pp. Cherokee Publications, $3.

RAY MANLEY'S COLLECTING SOUTHWESTERN INDIAN ARTS & CRAFTS
Clara L. Tanner, et al; Third revised edition. Illus. Paper. Ray Manley, 1979. $6.

RAY MANLEY'S "THE FINE ART OF NAVAJO WEAVING"
Steve Getzwiller; Illus. Paper. Ray Manley, 1984. $9.95.

RAY MANLEY'S HOPI KACHINA
Clara L. Tanner; Illus. Paper. Ray Manley, 1980. $6.

RAY MANLEY'S INDIAN LANDS
Clara L. Tanner; Illus. Ray Manley, 1979. $10; paper, $7.95.

MANUAL FOR THE PEACEMAKER: IROQUOIS LEGEND TO HEAL SELF & SOCIETY
Jean Houston; Illus. 177 pp. Paper. Amazon.com, 1997. $12.

A MANUAL OF FINGER WEAVING
Robert J. Austin; How-to book with traditional Indian patterns, weaving techniques & materials. Illus. Photos. 64 pp. Paper. Book Publishing Co., $12.95.

THE MANY FACES OF EDWARD SHERRIFF CURTIS: PORTRAITS & STORIES FROM NATIVE NORTH AMERICA Steadman Upham & Nat Zappia
80 reproductions of Curtiss portraits of Native Americans with original stories recorded in sessions in the field. Illus. 160 pp. University of Washington Press, 2006. $60; paper, $40.

MANY FACES OF GENDER: ROLES & RELATIONSHIPS THROUGH TIME IN INDIGENOUS NORTHERN COMMUNITIES Lisa Frink, et al. Editors
Illus. 232 pp. U. Press of Colorado, 2002. $45; paper, $19.95.

THE MANY FACES OF MATA ORTIZ
Lowell, Hills, Quintana, Parks, Wisner
The ancient art of ceramics. 260 color photos. 208 pp. Paper. Amazon.com, $19.95.

*MANY NATIONS: AN ALPHABET OF NATIVE AMERICA
Joseph Bruchac; illus. by Robert Goetzl; From Anishinabe artists making birch bark bowls to Zuni elders saying prayers. Grades PS-2. Illus. 32 pp. Paper. Amazon.com, $5.95.

MANY NATIONS: A LIBRARY OF CONGRESS RESOURCE GUIDE FOR THE STUDY OF INDIAN & ALASKA NATIVE PEOPLES OF THE U.S.
Patrick Frazier, Ed.; Illus. 334 pp. Paper. Amazon.com, 1997. $50.

MANY SMOKES, MANY MOONS: A CHRONOLOGY OF AMERICAN INDIAN HISTORY THROUGH INDIAN ART Jamake Highwater; 130 pp. Amazon.com, 1978. $15.95.

MANY TENDER TIES: WOMEN IN FUR-TRADE SOCIETY, 1670-1870
Sylvia Van Kirk; Reprint of 1983 edition. Illus. Map. 314 pp. Paper. University of Oklahoma Press, 2000. $24.95.

MANY TRAILS: INDIANS OF THE LOWER HUDSON VALLEY
Catherine C. Brawer, Editor
Illus. 112 pp. Paper. Publishing Center for Cultural Research, 1983. $14.50.

*MANY WINTERS
Nancy Winters; Grades 6-12. Illus. 80 pp. Doubleday, 1974. $13.95.

A MAP OF VIRGINIA: THE PROCEEDINGS OF THE ENGLISH COLONIE IN VIRGINIA
John Smith; Reprint of 1612 edition. 164 pp. Walter J. Johnson, $18.50.

MAP'N'FACTS: NATIVE PEOPLES OF NORTH AMERICA
Two maps show "then" and "now" in the life of Native North Americans.
Friendship Press, $4.50.

THE MAP OF WHO WE ARE: A NOVEL
Lawrence R. Smith; 320 pp. University of Oklahoma Press, 1997. $24.95.

THE MAPMAKER'S EYE: DAVID THOMPSON ON THE COLUMBIA PLATEAU
Jack Nesbet; Explorer surveys the 1250 mile course of the Columbia River.
Illus. Maps. 192 pp. Paper. WSU Press, 2005. $29.95.

MAPPING IDENTITY: THE CREATION OF THE COEUR D'ALENE INDIAN RESERVATION, 1805-1902
Laura Woodworth-Ney; Map. 264 pp. University Press of Colorado, 2004. $34.95.

MAPPING INDIGENOUS PRESENCE: NORTH SCANDINAVIAN NORTH AMERICAN PESPECTIVES Kathryn Shanely & Bjorg Evjen, Editors
Maps. 320 pp. University of Arizona Press, 2015. $35. E-Book available.

MAPPING THE MISSISSIPPIAN SHATTER ZONE: THE COLONIAL INDIAN SLAVE TRADE & REGIONAL INSTABILITY IN THE AMERICAN SOUTH
Robbie Ethridge & Sheri M. Shuck-Hall; Anthology examines the shatter zone created in the colonial South through the interactions of American Indians & European colonists. Illus. Maps. 536 pp. Paper. University of Nebraska Press, 2009. $35.

MAPS & DREAMS: INDIANS & THE BRITISH COLUMBIA FRONTIER
Hugh Brody; Illus. Maps. 294 pp. Waveland Press, 1981. $24.95.

MAPS OF EXPERIENCE: THE ANCHORING OF LAND TO STORY IN SECWEPEMC DISCOURSE Andie Diane Palmer
Illus. 260 pp. University of Toronto Press, 2006. $67; paper, $31.95.

THE MARCH OF THE MONTANA COLUMN: A PRELUDE TO THE CUSTER DISASTER
James Bradley; Reprint of 1961 edition. Illus. Map. 216 pp. Paper.
University of Oklahoma Press, $11.95.

MARIA
Richard L. Spivey; San Ildefonso potter Maria Martinez developed her legendary black-on-black ware around 1919. Illus. Biblio. 176 pp. Amazon.com, 1989 revised & expanded edition. $19.95.

MARIA MAKING POTTERY
Hazel Hyde; Illus. 32 pp. Paper. Sunstone Press, $4.95.

*MARIA MARTINEZ: PUEBLO POTTER
Grades 2-4. Illus. 32 pp. Childrens Press, $10.95.

VIOLA MARTINEZ, CALIFORNIA PAIUTE: LIVING IN TWO WORLDS
Diana Meyers Bahr; Biography. Illus. 224 pp. University of Oklahoma Press, $29.95.

MARIA: THE POTTER OF SAN ILDEFONSO
Alice Marriott; Reprint of 1948 edition. Illus. 294 pp. University of Oklahoma Press & Amazon.com, $27.95; paper, $16.95.

*MARK OF OUR MOCCASINS
Colleen Reece; Grades 5-12. Paper. Council for Indian Education, 1982. $2.95.

VIOLA MARTINEZ, CALIFORNIA PAIUTE: LIVING IN TWO WORLDS
Diana Meyers Bahr; Illus. Map. 210 pp. University of Oklahoma Press, 2003. $29.95.

MARTYRS OF THE OBLONG & LITTLE NINE
Defost Smith; Reprint of 1948 edition. Brown Book Co., $6.

THE MARU CULT OF POMO INDIANS: A CALIFORNIA GHOST DANCE SURVIVAL
Clement W. Meighan and Francis A. Riddele; 134 pp. Southwest Museum, 1972. $12.50.

THE MARVELOUS COUNTRY
Samuel Cozzens; Cochise & the Apaches; Indian life, struggles & customs.
Reprint of 1874 edition. 532 pp. Amazon.com, $20.

MARY & I: FORTY YEARS WITH THE SIOUX
Stephen Riggs; Reprint of 1971 edition. 412 pp. Amazon.com, $15.

*MARY QUEQUESAH'SLOVE STORY
Pete Beaverhead
Story of a young Salish woman. Grade 5. 32 pp. Paper. SKC Press, $5.

MARXISM & NATIVE AMERICANS
Ward Churchill, Editor; 250 pp. Amazon.com, 1984. $20; paper, $12.50.

MASCOUTENS OR PRAIRIE POTAWATOMI INDIANS: SOCIAL LIFE & CEREMONIES
Alanson Skinner; Reprint of 1924 edition. Greenwood Press, $35.

MASHKIKI: OLD MEDICINE NOURISHING THE NEW
Edwin Haller & Larry Aitken; Examines learning by American Indian & Alaskan Native students. 214 pp. Amazon.com, 1992. $68.

THE MASHPEE INDIANS: TRIBE ON TRIAL
Jack Campisi; Illus. 188 pp. Paper. Syracuse University Press, 1991. $15.95.

THE MASK MAKER
Diane Glancy; Novel. 160 pp. University of Oklahoma Press, 2004. $12.95.

MASKED GODS: NAVAHO & PUEBLO CEREMONIALISM
Frank Waters; Reprint of 1950 edition. 432 pp. Paper. Amazon.com, $18.95.

MASKS OF THE SPIRIT: IMAGE & METAPHOR IN MESOAMERICA
Roberta & Pter Markman; Illus. 375 pp. University of California Press, 1989. $75.

MASSACRE!
Frank Laumer; Illus. Maps. Biblio. 188 pp. Paper. U. Press of Florida, 1968. $14.95.

MASSACRE ALONG THE MEDICINE ROAD: A SOCIAL HISTORY OF THE INDIAN WAR OF 1864 IN NEBRASKA TERRITORY Ronald Becher; Paper. Caxton, 1999. $22.95.

MASSACRE AT BAD AXE
Crawford Thayer; Illus. 544 pp. Paper. Thayer Associates, 1981. $9.95.

MASSACRE AT CAMP GRANT: FORGETTING & REMEMBERING APACHE HISTORY
Chip Colwell-Chanthophonh; A multivocal narrative of the events in 1871. 176 pp. University of Arizona Press, 2007. $40; paper, $17.95.

MASSACRE AT FORT BULL: DELERY EXPEDITION AGAINST ONEIDA CARRY, 1756
Gilbert Hagerty; Illus. Mowbray, 1971. $8.

MASSACRE AT FORT WILLIAM HENRY
David R. Starbuck; Illus. 150 pp. Paper. University Press of New England, 2002. $16.95.

MASSACRE AT SAND CREEK: HOW METHODISTS WERE INVOLVED IN AN AMERICAN TRAGEDY Gary L. Roberts; Paper. Abingdon Press, 2106. $19.99.

THE MASSACRE AT SAND CREEK: NARRATIVE VOICES
Bruce Cutler; The massacre of over 200 Cheyennes in southeast Colorado Territory. 252 pp. Paper. University of Oklahoma Press, 1994. $11.95.

MASSACRE AT THE YUMA CROSSING: SPANISH RELATIONS WITH THE QUECHANS, 1779-1782
Mark Santiago; 220 pp. Paper. University of Arizona Press, 1998. $19.95.

MASSACRE ON THE LORDSBURG ROAD: A TRAGEDY OF THE APACHE WARS
Marc Simmons; Illus. 256 pp. Texas A&M University Press & Amazon.com, 1997. $29.95.

MASSACRE: THE TRAGEDY AT WHITE RIVER
Marshall Sprague; Illus. 365 pp. U. of Nebraska Press, 1980. $28.95; paper, $8.95.

MASSACRES OF THE MOUNTAINS VOL. 1: A HISTORY OF THE INDIAN WARS OF THE FAR WEST
J.P. Dunn, Jr.; Reprint. 2 vols. Illus. 375 pp. Paper. Amazon.com, 2000. $19.95.

MASTERPIECES OF AMERICAN INDIAN LITERATURE
Willis G. Regier, Editor; Illus. 623 pp. Paper. U. of Nebraska Press, 2005. $17.95.

MASTERWORKS FROM THE HEARD MUSEUM
Heard Museum Staff
In 3 vols. Illus. 300 pp. Heard Museum & Museum of New Mexico Press, $55.

THE MASTERWORKS OF CHARLES M. RUSSELL: A RETROSPECTIVE OF PAINTINGS & SCULPTURE Joan Carpenter Troccoli, Editor
Companion volume to Charles M. Russell: A Catalogue Raisonne, by B. Byron Price; Showcases many of the artist's best-known works & chronicles the sources & evolution of his style. 304 pp. University of Nebraska Press, 2009. $65; paper, $39.95.

MATERIAL CULTURE OF THE CROW INDIANS
Robert H. Lowie; Illus. 70 pp. Paper. Lakota Books, 1996. $19.95.

MATERIAL CULTURE & THE STUDY OF AMERICAN LIFE
Ian M. Quimby; Illus. Paper. W.W. Norton & Co., 1978. $7.95.

JOHN JOSEPH MATHEWS: LIFE OF AN OSAGE WRITER
Michael Snyder; ; foreword by Russ Tall Chief
Illus. 280 pp. University of Oklahoma Press, 2017. $34.95.

MATRONS & MAIDS: REGULATING INDIAN DOMESTIC SERVICE IN TUCSON, 1914-1934 Victoria K. Haskins
Tohono O'odham. 240 pp. Paper. University of Arizona Press, $35; eBook, $35.

ISAAC MCCOY - APOSTLE TO THE INDIANS
George M. Ella; Illus. 680 pp. Amazon.com. 2002. $42.

ISAAC McCOY – APOSTLE TO THE WESTERN TRAIL
George M. Ella; 2nd revised ed. Illus. 650 pp. Amazon.com. 2003. $42.

TOMMY McGINTY'S NORTHERN TOUCHTONE STORY OF CROW: A FIRST NATION ELDER RECOUNTS THE CREATION OF THE WORLD
Dominique Legros; Tales of Crow from inland northwestern Canada. Map. Biblio. 268 pp. Paper. University of Washington Press, 1999. $27.95.

VALENTINE T. MCGILLYCUDDY: ARMY SURGEON, AGENT TO THE SIOUX
Candy Moulton; 296 pp. University of Oklahoma Press, $34.95; paper, $19.95

McINTOSH & WEATHERFORD, CREEK INDIAN LEADERS
Benjamin W. Griffith; Illus. 336 pp. Paper. University of Alabama Press, 1998. $22.50.

*JAMES McKAY - A METIS BUILDER OF CANADA
Agnes Grant; History of Manitoba and expert guide, James McKay.
Grades 7-10. Paper. Pemmican, $12.95.

MABEL McKAY: WEAVING THE DREAM
Greg Sarris; Illus. Paper. University of California Press, 1997. $18.95.

THE McKENNEY-HALL PORTRAIT GALLERY OF AMERICAN INDIANS
Portraits of famous American Indians. First published in 1836, this new volume includes historical materials & biographical profiles. Illus. 370 pp. Cherokee Publications, $14.95.

D'ARCY McNICKLE'S THE HUNGRY GENERATIONS: THE EVOLUTION OF A NOVEL
Birgit Hans, Editor; Social document providing insight into Indian-White marriages at the turn of the 20th century. Illus. 340 pp. University of New Mexico Press, $34.95.

ME & MINE: THE LIFE STORY OF HELEN SEKAQUAPTEWA
as told to Louise Udall; 262 pp. Paper. University of Arizona Press, 1969. $15.95.

*ME RUN FAST GOOD: BIOGRAPHIES OF TEWANIMA (HOPI), CARLOS MONTEZUMA (APACHE) & JOHN HORSE (SEMINOLE)
Beatrice Levin and Marjorie Vanderveld
Grades 5-9. 32 pp. Paper. Council for Indian Education, 1983. $1.95.

THE MEANING OF ICE: PEOPLE & SEA ICE IN THREE ARCTIC COMMUNITIES
Shari Gearheard, Lene Kielsen Holm, Henry Huntington, et al
The Inuit, Inupiat, and Inughuit. Illus. Maps. 416 pp. Paper.
University Press of New England, 2017. $30.

MECHANISMS & TRENDS IN THE DECLINE OF THE COSTANOAN INDIAN POPULATION OF CENTRAL CALIFORNIA: NUTRITION & HEALTH IN PRE-CONTACT CALIFORNIA & MISSION PERIOD ENVIRONMENTS
Ann Stodder: Gary Breschini & Trudy Harverset, Editors
Illus. 78 pp. Paper. Coyote Press, 1986. $6.20.

MEDIA & ETHNIC IDENTITY: HOPI VIEWS ON MEDIA, IDENTITY, & COMMUNICATION
Ritva Levo-Henriksson; Illus. 246 pp. Paper. Routledge, 2009. $35.96.

MEDIATING KNOWLEDGES: ORIGINS OF A ZUNI TRIBAL MUSEUM
Gwyneira Isaac; Examines, by using in-depth interviews, how Zunis developed their A:shiwi A:wan Museum & Heritage Center to mediate between Zuni & Anglo-American values of history & culture. 272 pp. Illus. University of Arizona Press, 20007. $50.

MEDIATION IN CONTEMPORARY NATIVE AMERICAN FICTION
James Ruppert; Focuses on novels by six major contemporary Native American writers: N. Scott Momaday, James Welch, Leslie Silko, Gerald Vizenor, D'Arcy McNickle, & Louise Erdrich. 174 pp. University of Oklahoma Press, 1995. $29.95; paper, $11.95.

THE MEDICAL HISTORY OF ISHI
Saxton T. Pope; Facsimile edition. Illus. 38 pp. Coyote Press, $4.38.

MEDICINAL FLORA OF THE ALASKA NATIVES
Ann Garibaldi; 200 pp. Todd Communications, 1999. $25.

MEDICINAL & OTHER USES OF NORTH AMERICAN PLANTS
Charlotte Erichsen-Brown; Historical citations document uses of plants with special reference to the Eastern Indian tribes. Illus. 544 pp. Paper. Dover, $12.95.

MEDICINAL PLANTS USED BY NATIVE AMERICAN TRIBES IN SOUTHERN CALIFORNIA Donna Largo, Daniel McCarthy & Marcia Roper; A resource guide for medical & traditional health care practitioners. Illus. 57 pp. Malki-Ballena Press, 2007. $14.95

MEDICINAL USES OF PLANTS BY INDIAN TRIBES OF NEVADA
Percy Train, et al; Reprint of 1957 edition. Quarterman, $30.

MEDICINAL WILD PLANTS OF THE PRAIRIE: AN ETHNOBOTANICAL GUIDE
Kelly Kindscher; Illus. 336 pp. Paper. University Press of Kansas, 2004. $14.95.

MEDICINE BAGS & DOG TAGS: AMERICAN INDIAN VETERANS FROM COLONIAL TIMES TO THE SECOND IRAQ WAR
Al Carroll; Illus. 296 pp. U. of Nebraska Press, 2008. $45.

MEDICINE BEAR
Menunqua; 72 pp. Paper. Amazon.com, 1997. $10.95.

THE MEDICINE BOWS: WYOMING'S MOUNTAIN COUNTRY
Scott Thybony, et al; The region was an important fur trading center and one of the last refuges of the Cheyenne, Arapaho, and Sioux Indians. Illus. Biblio. 180 pp. Paper. The Caxton Press, $7.95.

MEDICINE BUNDLE: INDIAN SACRED PERFORMANCE & AMERICAN LITERATURE, 1824-1932 Joshua D. Bellin; Examines the complex issues surrounding Indian sacred performance in its manifold & intimate relationships with texts & images by both Indian & whites. Illus. University of Pennsylvania Press, 2007. $40.

MEDICINE CARDS: THE DISCOVERY OF POWER THROUGH THE WAYS OF ANIMALS
Jamie Sams & David Carson; 224 pp. Inner Traditions International, 1988. $26.95.

THE MEDICINE CREEK TREATY OF 1854
Lynn Kickingbird & Curtis Berkey; 31 pp. Institute for the Development of Indian Law, $10.

MEDICINE GROVE: A SHAMANIC HERBAL
Loren Cruden
Herbal listings describing the plants and its uses, especially in Native American & shamanic herbal traditions. Illus. 224 pp. Paper. Inner Traditions, 1997. $16.95.

MEDICINE HAT: A NOVEL
Don Coldsmith; A love story and the tale of a daring search for spiritual meaning in the American West of the 1700s. 272 pp. University of Oklahoma Press, 1997. $24.95

*MEDICINE MAN
Grades 4-5. Illus. 48 pp. Amazon.com, 1989. $10.95.

MEDICINE MEN: OGLALA SIOUX CEREMONY & HEALING
Thomas H. Lewis; Describes traditional healing practices of the Oglala Sioux of Pine Ridge Reservation. Illus. 221 pp. Paper. University of Nebraska Press, 1990. $19.95.

MEDICINE MEN OF THE APACHE, A PAPER FROM THE NINTH ANNUAL REPORT OF THE BUREAU OF AMERICAN ETHNOLOGY (1887-1888)
John Bourke; Reprint of 1970 edition. Illus. 187 pp. The Rio Grande Press, $22.50.

MEDICINE OF THE CHEROKEE: THE WAY OF RIGHT RELATIONSHIP
J.T. Garrett & Michael Tlanusta Garrett; Stories of the Four Directions & Universal Circle offer wisdom on circle gatherings, natural herbs and healing, and ways to reduce stress. Illus. 240 pp. Paper. Inner Traditions, 1996. $14.

MEDICINE RIVER
Thomas King; Breaks down stereotypes about Indians. A young Blackfoot Indian returns to his birthplace in Alberta. 480 pp. Paper. Penguin USA, $11.

A MEDICINE STORY: THE RETURN TO NATIVE AMERICAN CONSCIOUSNESS
Karen Degenhart; Reprint. Illus. 284 pp. Paper. Thunderbird Publications, 1996. $15.95.

MEDICINE THAT WALKS: MEDICINE, DISEASE & CANADIAN PLAINS ABORIGINAL PEOPLE, 1880-1945 Maureen Lux; Illus. 600 pp. University of Toronto Press, 2001.

MEDICINE TRAIL: THE LIFE & LESSONS OF GLADYS TANTAQUIDGEON
Melissa Jayne Fawcett; Autobiography of Gladys Tanataquidgeon (100 year-old medicine woman) with Mohegan traditional knowledge & ways of life. Illus. 179 pp. Paper. University of Arizona Press, 2000. $17.95. The Mohegan Tribe.

MEDICINE TRAILS: A LIFE IN MANY WORLDS
Mavis McCovey & John F. Salter; Illus. Paper. Heyday Books. $21.95.

MEDICINE WAY: HOW TO LIVE THE TEACHINGS OF THE NATIVE AMERICAN MEDICINE WHEEL: A SHAMANIC PATH TO SELF-MASTERY
Kenneth Meadows; 256 pp. Paper. Amazon.com, 1997. $17.95.

MEDICINE WHEEL: EARTH ASTROLOGY
Sun Bear & Wabun; Learn about the different moons, totems, powers of the directions and elemental clans. Illus. 228 pp. Paper. Simon & Schuster, $10.

MEDICINE WHEEL CEREMONIES: ANCIENT PHILOSOPHIES FOR USE IN MODERN DAY LIFE Vicki May & Cindy Rodberg; Illus. 48 pp. Paper. Naturegraph, 1995. $9.95.

THE MEDICINE WHEEL: EARTH ASTROLOGY
Sun Bear & Wabun; Illus. 203 pp. Paper. Cherokee Publications, $8.95.

MEDICINE WHEELS: NATIVE AMERICAN VEHICLES OF HEALING
Roy I. Wilson; 154 pp. Paper. Crossorad Publishing, 1994. $14.95.

THE MEDICINE WOMAN INNER GUIDEBOOK
Carol Bridges; Illus. 256 pp. Paper. U.S. Games Systems, 1992. $12.95.

MEDICINE WOMEN, CURANDERAS & WOMEN DOCTORS
Bobette Perrone, et al; Illus. 272 pp. Paper. U. of Oklahoma Press, 1989. $19.95.

A MEDICINE WOMAN SPEAKS: AN EXPLORATION OF NATIVE AMERICAN SPIRITUALITY Cinnamon Moon; Illus. 224 pp. Career Press, 2001. $14.95.

MEDITATIONS WITH ANIMALS: A NATIVE AMERICAN BESTIARY
Gerald Hausman; Shows the healing roles animals have played since the beginning. Illus. 144 pp. Paper. Inner Traditions, 1986. $9.95.

MEDITIATIONS WITH THE CHEROKEE: PRAYERS, SONGS & STORIES OF HEALING & HARMONY J.T. Garrett; Illus. 144 pp. Paper. Inner Traditions, 2001. $12.95.

MEDITATIONS WITH THE HOPI
Robert Boissiere; The author's interpretation of the essence of Hopi experience. Illus. 144 pp. Paper. Inner Traditions, 1984. $12.95.

MEDITATIONS WITH THE LAKOTA: PRAYERS, SONGS & STORIES OF HEALING & HARMONY Paul Steinmetz; New edition of songs & thoughts of the Lakota, along with a section on the Native American Church & Christian influences. Illus. 144 pp. Paper. Inner Traditions, 2001. $12.95.

MEDITATIONS WITH NATIVE AMERICAN ELDERS: THE FOUR SEASONS
Don L. Coyhis (Mohican); Day-at-a-time book qith a quotation by an elder for each day. 476 pp. Paper. DVD, audiocassette. Coyhis Publishing/White Bison, Inc. 2007. $25.

MEDITATIONS WITH THE NAVAJO: PRAYERS, SONGS & STORIES OF HEALING & HARMONY Gerald Hausman & Richard Erdoes
Illus. 144 pp. Paper. Inner Traditions International, 2001. $12.95.

*MEET CHRISTOPHER: AN OSAGE INDIAN BOY FROM OKLAHOMA
Genevieve Simermeyer (Osage); photos by Katherine Fogden (Mohawk)
Grades 3-8. Illus. 48 pp. NMAI Press & Council Oak Books, 2008. $15.95.

MEET CREE: A GUIDE TO THE CREE LANGUAGE
C.H. Wolfart and J.F. Carroll; 120 pp. University of Nebraska Press, 1981. $12.50.

MEET THE LAKOTA, VOL. ONE: THE PEOPLE
Rose LaVera; An introduction to the Lakota, written in English & in Lakota by Alvin Horse Looking. Illus. Paper. Amazon.com, $5.95.

*MEET LYDIA: A NATIVE GIRL FROM SOUTHEAST ALASKA
Miranda Belarde-Lewis (Tlingit/Zuni); photos by John Harrington (Siletz)
Life of a Tlingit girl. Grades 4 to 8. Ilus. 48 pp. NMAI Press & Council Oak Books, 2004. $15.95.

*MEET MINDY: A NATIVE GIRL FROM THE SOUTHWEST
Susan Secakuku (Hopi); photos by John Harrington (Siletz); A Hopi girl story. Grades 4 to 8. Illus. 48 pp. NMAI Press & Council Oak Books, 2003. $15.95.

*MEET NAICHE: A NATIVE BOY FROM THE CHESAPEAKE BAY AREA
Gabrielle Tayac (Piscataway); photos by John Harrington (Siletz)
Grades 4 to 8. Illus. 48 pp. NMAI Press & Council Oak Books, 2003. $15.95.

*MEET THE NORTH AMERICAN INDIANS
Elizabeth Paine; Grades 2-6. Illus. Random House, 1965. $8.99; paper, $5.95.

MEMOIRS OF A CHICKASAW SQUAW: A JOURNAL OF THE CHICKASAW REMOVAL
Velma Taliaferro; Molly Griffis, Editor; Illus. 65 pp. Paper. Amazon.com, 1987. $5.

THE MEMOIRS OF LT. HENRY TIMBERLAKE: THE STORY OF A SOLDIER, ADVENTURER, AND EMISSARY TO THE CHEROKEES, 1756-1765
Henry Timberlake; Duane H. King, Editor
Illus. Photos. Maps. 216 pp. Paper. U. of North Carolina Press, 2007. $45; paper, $19.95.

MEMOIRS OF A WHITE CROW INDIAN
Thomas Leforge; Thomas Marquis, Narrator
356 pp. Paper. University of Nebraska Press, 1974. $29.95.

MEMOIRS, OFFICIAL & PERSONAL
Thomas L. McKenney; Herman J. Viola, Editor; Insight into Indian affairs by Thomas McKenney, Director of Indian Affairs, 1816-1830. 340 pp. Paper. University of Nebraska Press, 1973. $6.95.

MEMORIES COME TO US IN THE RAIN & THE WIND: ORAL HISTORIES & PHOTOGRAPHS OF NAVAJO URANIUM WORKERS & THEIR FAMILIES
Doug Brugge, et al; Reprint. Illus. 62 pp. Paper. Amazon.com, 2002. $15.

MEMORIES OF LAC DU FLAMBEAU ELDERS; WITH A BRIEF HISTORY OF WAASWAAGONING OJIBWEG
Elizabeth M. Tornes; Brief History by Leon Valliere, Jr.; photos by Greg Gent
Photos. 250 pp. Paper. University of Wisconsin Press, 2004. $24.95.

MEMORY ETERNAL: TLINGIT CULTURE & RUSSIAN ORTHODOX CHRISTIANITY THROUGH TWO CENTURIES
Sergei Kan; Illus. 696 pp. University of Washington Press, 1999. $36.95.

MEMORY & VISION: ARTS, CULTURE, AND LIVES OF PLAINS INDIAN PEOPLES
Emma L. Hansen, et al; 300 Illus. 250 in color. Contemporary paintings & sculptures. 256 pp. University of Washington Press, 2008. $75; paper, $45.

MEN & WOMEN IN THE PREHISPANIC SOUTHWEST: LABOR, POWER & PRESTIGE
Patricia L. Crown, Ed.; Illus. 520 pp. School of American Research Press, 2001. $60.

MEN AS WOMEN, WOMEN AS MEN: CHANGING GENDER IN NATIVE AMERICAN CULTURES
Sabine Lang; Illus. Maps. Tables. 416 pp. Paper. U. of Texas Press, 1998. $19.95.

MEN ON THE MOON: COLLECTED SHORT STORIES
Simon J. Ortiz; 26 stories drawn from Ortiz's Acoma Pueblo experience. 216 pp. Paper. University of Arizona Press, 1999. $18.95.

MENDING THE CIRCLE: A NATIVE REPATRIATION GUIDE
Jack Trope, et al; Includes articles on NAGPRA, the Smithsonian Institution's repatriation policies and strategies for the private sector. 167 pp. AIRORF, 1997. $40. Supplement. 57 pp. $8.

*THE MENOMINEE
Patricia Ourada; Grades 5 and up. Illus. Chelsea House, 1989. $17.95.

MENOMINEE DRUMS: TRIBAL TERMINATION & RESTORATION, 1954-1974
Nicholas C. Peroff; Illus. 296 pp. Paper. University of Oklahoma Press, 2006. $19.95.

THE MENOMINI INDIANS OF WISCONSIN: A STUDY OF THREE CENTURIES OF CULTURAL CONTACT & CHANGE
Felix Keesing; 272 pp. Paper. University of Wisconsin Press, 1987. $30; paper, $22.95.

MENTAL HEALTH
Dubray; Paper. West Publishing, 1993. $16.75.

MENTASTA REMEMBERS
Cynthia L. Ainsworth, et al; Illus. 95 pp. Amazon.com, 2002.

MEREJILDO GRIJALVA, APACHE CAPTIVE, ARMY SCOUT
 Edwin R. Sweeney; Presents a detailed acount of his life. Illus. Map.
Biblio. Paper. Texas Western Press, 1993. $12.50.

MESA VERDE NATIONAL PARK
 Ruth Radlauer; Updated edition. Grades 3 and up. Illus. 50 pp.
Childrens Press, 1984. $14.60; paper, $4.50.

MESA VERDE ANCIENT ARCHITECTURE
 Jesse W. Fewkes; 3 essays on the daily lives of the cliff dwellers of Mesa Verde.
Illus. 240 pp. Paper. University of New Mexico Press & Amazon.com, 1999. $16.95.

MESA VERDE: THE STORY BEHIND THE SCENERY
 Linda Martin; Archaeological sites of Anasazi culture. Photos. Maps.
48 pp. Paper. KC Publications, $6.95.

MESCALERO APACHES
 C.L. Sonnichsen; 2nd ed. Illus. Maps. 340 pp. Paper. U. of Oklahoma Press, 1973.
$19.95.

**THE MESKWAKI & ANTHROPOLOGISTS: ACTION ANTHROPOLOGY
RECONSIDERED** Judith M. Daubenmier; How ethnographic fieldwork affected the
Meskwaki Indians of Iowa between 1948 and 1958. 574 pp. University of Nebraska Press,
2008. $55.

**MESSAGES FROM FRANK'S LANDING: A STORY OF SALMON, TREATIES,
& THE INDIAN WAY** Charles Wilkinson; Indian fishing rights in the Pacific Northwest.
Illus. Photos. Maps. 128 pp. Paper. University of Washington Press, 2000. $22.50.

MESSAGES FROM MOTHER EARTH: DAILY AFFIRMATIONS
 Willie Hooks; 60 pp. Paper. Amazon.com, 1989. $6.95.

MESSINGERS OF THE WIND: NATIVE AMERICAN WOMEN
 Jane Katz; 336 pp. Paper. Ballantine Books, 1996. $19.

METAL WEAPONS, TOOLS & ORNAMENTS OF THE TETON DAKOTA INDIANS
 James A. Hanson; Illus. 118 pp. University of Nebraska Press, 1975. $16.50.

**METAPHORS OF DISPOSSESSION: AMERICAN BEGINNINGS
& THE TRANSLATION OF EMPIRE, 1492-1637**
 Gesa mackenthun; Illus. 370 pp. University of Oklahoma Press, 1997. $32.95.

*THE METIS - CANADA'S FORGOTTEN PEOPLE
 D. Bruce Sealey & Antoine Lussier
Grades 8-12. History of the origins of the Metis. Illus. Paper. Pemmican, $14.95.

METIS LEGACY I
 Lawrence J. Barkwell, Leah Dorion & Darren Prefontaine, Editors
Metis history & culture. Pemmican, $69.95.

METIS LEGACY II
 Lawrence J. Barkwell, Leah Dorion & Darren Prefontaine, Editors
Delineates Metis culture, including folklore, storytelling, medicines & healing traditions,
spirituality, housing, clothing, etc. Paper. Pemmican, $45.

*METIS SPIRITS
 Deborah L. Delaronde; Metis stories. Grades 4-8. Paper. Pemmican, $14.95.

THE MEXICAN KICKAPOO INDIANS
 Felipe & Dolores Latorre; Illus. Map. 416 pp. Paper. Dover, $11.95.

MEXICO'S INDIGENOUS COMMUNITIES: THEIR LANDS & HISTORIES, 1500-2010
 Ethelia Ruiz Medrano; Russ Davidson, translator; Illus. Maps. Tables. 400 pp. Paper.
University Press of Colorado, 2011. $26.95. E-book, $50. 30-day rental, $9.99.

THE MIAMI-ILLINOIS LANGUAGE
 David J. Costa
Overview of the Miami-Illinois language. 566 pp. University of Nebraska Press, 2003. $75.

THE MIAMI INDIANS
 Bert Anson; Reprint. Illus. Maps. 352 pp. Paper. University of Oklahoma Press
& Wennswoods Publishing, $29.95.

THE MIAMI INDIANS OF INDIANA: A PERSISTENT PEOPLE, 1654-1994
 Stewart Rafert; Illus. 358 pp. Indian Historical Society, 1996. $29.95; paper, $14.95.

*MI'CA: BUFFALO HUNTER
 Jane Bendix; Sioux life in the 1740's. Grades 4 and up. 188 pp.
Council for Indian Education. $14.95; paper, $9.95.

MICHIF CONVERSATIONAL LESSONS FOR BEGINNERS
 Metis Resource Centre
Lesson guide to Michif language (Metis). Paper. Pemmican, $45 (book & two audio CDs).

MICHIGAN: THE GREAT LAKES STATE, AN ILLUSTRATED HISTRY
 George S. May & Joellen Vinyard; Illus. Photos. 300 pp. Michigan Indian Press, $34.95.

MICHILIMACKINAC: A TALE OF THE STRAITS
 David A. Turrill; Historical novel of the events and occupants of Fort Michilimackinac
during the French & Indian War. Includes the Ottawa, Potawatomie and Ojibway tribes
along with the French. Illus. 466 pp. Paper. Wilderness Adventure Books, $14.95.

MICMAC DICTIONARY
 Albert D. DeBlois; 98 pp. Paper. University of Washington Press, 1997. $29.95.

MICMAC MEDICINES: REMEDIES & RECOLLECTIONS
 Laurie Lacey; Illus. 128 pp. Paper. Amazon.com, 1993.

MICMAC QUILLWORK
 Ruth H. Whitehead
Illus. 230 pp. Nova Scotia Museum. Distributed by Amazon.com, 1991. $29.95.

THE MICROFILM EDITION OF THE WASHINGTON MATTHEWS PAPERS & GUIDE
 Wheelwright Museum Staff
Illus. 126 pp. University of New Mexico Press, 1985. $15. Microfilm (ten rolls), $400.

**MID-APPALACHIAN FRONTIER: A GUIDE TO HISTORIC SITES OF THE FRENCH &
INDIAN WAR** Robert B. Swift; Paper. Smoke & Fire Co., 1999. $17.95.

THE MIDDLE FIVE: INDIAN SCHOOLBOYS OF THE OMAHA TRIBES
 Francis La Flesche; Illus. Map. 152 pp. Paper. U. of Nebraska Press, 1978. $14.95.

**THE MIDDLE GROUND: INDIANS, EMPIRES, & REPUBLICS IN THE GREAT LAKES
REGION, 1650-1815**
 Richard White; Illus. 560 pp. Cambridge University Press, 1991. $75; paper, $25.

**MIDNIGHT & NOONDAY: OR THE INCIDENTAL HISTORY OF SOUTHERN KANSAS
& THE INDIAN TERRITORY, 1871-1890** G.D. Freeman; Richard L. Lane, Editor
Illus. Maps. Biblio. University of Oklahoma Press, 1984. $37.95.

MIDWINTER RITES OF THE CAYUGA LONG HOUSE
 Frank G. Speck; Illus. 210 pp. Paper. University of Nebraska Press, 1995. $8.95.

MIGRATION TEARS
 Michael Kabotie (Lomawywesa); Poems dealing with separation, transition, and loss.
54 pp. Paper. UCLA American Indian Studies Center& Alibris.com, 1987. $10.

MIGRATIONS: NEW DIRECTIONS IN NATIVE AMERICAN ART
 Marjorie Devon, Editor; Work of six contemporary artists: Tom Jones (Ho Chunk),
Steven Deo (Creek), Larry McNeil (Tlingit), Ryan Lee Smith (Cherokee), Star Wallowing
Bull (Chippewa/Arapaho), and Marie Watt (Seneca); and the master printers at Tamarind
Institute of UNM. Illus. 54 color photos. 143 pp. Paper. U. of New Mexico Press, $29.95.

**MI'KMAG HIEROGLYPHIC PRAYERS: READINGS IN NORTH AMERICA'S
FIRST INDIGENOUS SCRIPT**
 David L. Schmidt & Murdena Marshall; Illus. 150 pp. Paper. Amazon.com, 1995.

MI'KMAQ & MALISEET CULTURAL & ANCESTRAL MATERIAL
 Stephen J. Augustine; National Collection from the Canadian Museum of Civilization.
850 color Illus. 260 pp. Paper. University of Washington Press, 2006. $45.

MI'KMAQ: RESISTANCE, ACCOMMODATION, AND CULTURAL SURVIVAL
 Harald E.L. Prins; Illus. 272 pp. Paper. Amazon.com, 2002. $39.99.

BARTLEY MILAM: PRINCIPAL CHIEF OF THE CHEROKEE NATION
 Howard Meredith; 157 pp. Paper. Indian University Press, 1985. $5.

THE MILITARY & THE U.S. INDIAN POLICY, 1865-1903
 Robert Wooster; 268 pp. Paper. University of Nebraska Press, 1988. $10.95.

MILLENIUM: TRIBAL WISDOM & THE MODERN WORLD
 David Maybury-Lewis; Illus. Penguin USA, $45.

MIMBRES ARCHAEOLOGY AT THE NAN RANCH RUIN
 Harry J. Shafer; New information and interpretations of the rise and disappearance of the
ancient Mimbres culture. Illus. 176 halftones, 5 maps. 304 pp. Paper. University of New
Mexico Press, 2003. $45.

THE MIMBRES, ART & ARCHAEOLOGY
 Jesse Walter Fewkes; into. by J.J. Brody; Reprint of 1914 edition. Illus.
182 pp. Paper. University of New Mexico Press & Amazon.com, $16.95.

**MIMBRES CLASSIC MYSTERIES: RECONSTRUCTING A LOST CULTURE THROUGH
ITS POTTERY** Tom Steinbach, Sr.; illus. by Tom Steinbach, Jr. & Peter Steinbach
A visual history of the Mimbres people. Illus. 184 pp. Paper. Museum of New Mexico
Press, 2001. $29.95.

MIMBRES INDIAN TREASURE: IN THE LAND OF BACA
 Roy Evans, R. Evelyn & Lyle Ross; Illus. 352 pp. Amazon.com, 1985. $29.95.

**MIMBRES LIFE & SOCIETY: THE MATTOCKS SITE OF SOUTHWESTERN
NEW MEXICO** Patricia Gilman & Steven LeBlanc
Illus. 656 pp. University of Arizona Press, 2017. $80.

**MIMBRES MOGOLLON ARCHAEOLOGY: CHARLES C. DI PESO'S EXCAVATIONS
AT WIND MOUNTAIN**
 Anne I. Woosley & Allan J. McIntyre; Illus. 480 pp. U. of New Mexico Press, 1996. $34.95.

MIMBRES MYTHOLOGY
 Pat Carr; Illus. 78 pp. Texas Western Press, 1989. $12; paper, $7.50.

MIMBRES MYTHOLOGY: TALES FROM THE PAINTED CLAY
 James R. Cunkle; Illus. 150 pp. Paper. Amazon.com, 2000. $19.95.

MIMBRES PAINTED POTTERY
 J.J. Brody; Revised edition. Updates discussion since the fieldwork done from the original
publication in 1977, with village life and wider issues. Illus. Maps. 264 pp. School for
Advanced Research, 2005. $65; paper, $34.95.

MIMBRES POTTERY: ANCIENT ART OF THE AMERICAN SOUTHWEST
J.J. Brody, Catherine Scott, Steven LeBlanc, et al; Illus. 132 pp. Amazon.com, $35.

MINDING A SACRED PLACE
Sunnie Empie & Robin Beaver; Illus. 210 pp. Boulder House Publishers, 2001. $60.

MINERS OF THE RED MOUNTAIN: INDIAN LABOR IN POTOSI, 1545-1650
Peter Bakewell; Paper. University of New Mexico Press, $30.

MINIATURE ARTS OF THE SOUTHWEST
Nancy Schiffer; Arts of American Indian tribes in the Southwest are occasionally made in miniature. This book presents a wide array of these miniatures of all the major craft styles of the region. Illus. 64 pp. Paper. Schiffer, $12.95.

MINING, THE ENVIRONMENT, & INDIGENOUS DEVELOPMENT CONFLICTS
Saleem H. Ali; Examines environmental conflicts between mining companies and indigenous communities. Illus. 254 pp. University of Arizona Press, 2003. $50.

MINISTER TO THE CHEROKEES: A CIVIL WAR AUTOBIOGRAPHY
James Anderson Slover; edited by Barbara Cloud; in 1857 James Anderson Slover rode into Indian Territory as the first Southern Baptist missionary to the Cherokee Nation. Illus. 212 pp. University of Nebraska Press, 2001. $50.

THE MINNESOTA ETHNIC FOOD BOOK
Anne Kaplan, Marjorie Hoover, Willard Moore
Includes Ojibway recipes. Illus. 449 pp. Minnesota Historical Society Press, 1986. $14.95.

MINNESOTA'S INDIAN MOUNDS & BURIEL SIGHTS: A SYNTHESIS OF PREHISTORIC & EARLY HISTORIC ARCHAEOLOGICAL DATA
Constance Arzigian & Katherine Stevenson; Minnesota Office State Archaeologist, 2003.

THE MI'KMAQ: RESISTANCE, ACCOMMODATION, & CULTURAL SURVIVAL
Harald E.L. Prins; Explores the historical dynamics that have marked Mi'kmaq culture over the last 500 years. Paper. 184 pp. Amazon.com, 1996.

MINOR VOCABULARIES OF HURON, VOL. 32
Jean De Brebeuf, et al; 50 pp. Amazon.com, 2004. $28.

MINOR VOCABULARIES OF NANTICOKE CONOY, VOL. 37
Thomas Jefferson; 50 pp. Amazon.com, 2004. $28.

THE MINUTES OF THE MICHIGAN COMMISSION ON INDIAN AFFAIRS, 1956-1977
James R. Hillman, Ed.; 2 Vols. 850 pp. Hillman Publications, 1991. $89.95.

MIRACLE HILL: THE STORY OF A NAVAJO BOY
Blackhorse Mitchell; An account of a Navajo boy's struggle to learn, and his enrolling at the Institute of American Indian Arts in Santa Fe. 248 pp. Paper. University of Arizona Press, 2005. $17.95.

MIRROR & PATTERN: GEORGE LAIRD'S WORLD OF CHEMEHUEVI MYTHOLOGY
Carobeth Laird; Myths of the Chemehuevi. Reprint of 1984 ed. Illus. 373 pp. Malki-Ballena Press, $44.95.

*THE MISHOMIS BOOK, THE VOICE OF THE OJIBWAY
Edward Benton-Banai; Ojibway traditions, culture and ceremonies. Grades 4 and up. Illus. Indian Country Communication, 1988. $19.95. Also, The Mishomis Coloring Book Series - 5 history coloring books. $4.25 each.

MISHWABIK, METAL OF RITUAL: METALURGY IN PRECONTACT EASTERN NORTH AMERICA   Amelia M. Trevelyan; Illus. 368 pp. University Pres of Kentucky, 2003. $50.

MISSION AMONG THE BLACKFEET
Howard L. Harrod; Examines the effects of Catholic & Protestant missionary activity upon the Blackfeet from the 1840s through the 1960s. Reprint. Illus. Map. Biblio. 240 pp. Paper. University of Oklahoma Press, $19.95.

MISSION TO LITTLE GRAND RAPIDS: LIFE WITH THE ANISHINABE, 1927-1938
Luther L. Schuetze; Illus. 298 pp. Paper. Amazon.com, 2001.

*THE MISSIONS: CALIFORNIA'S HERITAGE
Mary Null Boule; 21 individual booklets of detailed facts of each Mission's history. Grades 4-6. Illus. Meerant Publishers.

MISSIONS & THE FRONTIERS OF SPANISH AMERICA
Robert H. Jackson; A comparative study of the impact of environmental, economic, political & socio-cultural variations on the Missions in the Rio de la Plata region and on the northern frontier of New Spain. Illus. 19 maps. 592 pp. U. of New Mexico Press, 2008. $24.95.

MISSIONS, MISSIONARIES, AND NATIVE AMERICANS: LONG-TERM PROCESSES & DAILY PRACTICES   Maria F. Wade; From the 1600s through the 1800s, Spanish missionaries came to America to convert Native Americans. Illus. Maps. 320 pp. Paper. U. Press of Florida, 2008. $32.95.

THE MISSIONS OF CALIFORNIA, A HISTORY OF GENOCIDE
Rupert Costo & Jeanette Henry; Paper. Amazon.com, $12.50.

THE MISSIONS OF NORTHERN SONORA: A 1935 FIELD DOCUMENTATION RELATING PIMAN INDIANS TO THE MATERIAL CULTURE OF THE HISPANIC SOUTHWEST
Buford Pickens, Notes; Illus. 200 pp. U. of Arizona Press, 1993. $31.95; paper, $17.95.

THE MISSIONS OF SPANISH FLORIDA
David H. Thomas; Reprint. Illus. 536 pp. Garland, $42.

MISSIONS & PUEBLOS OF THE OLD SOUTHWEST
Earle R. Forrest; Reprint of 1929 edition. 398 pp. Paper. The Rio Grande Press, $12.

MISSIONS TO THE COLUSA
John H. Hann, Ed. & tr.; Illus. 560 pp. University Press of Florida, 1991.

MISSISSIPPI ARCHAEOLOGY Q & A
Evan Peacock; Illus. University Press of Mississippi, 2006. $50; paper, $22.

MISSISSIPPI CHOCTAWS AT PLAY: THE SERIOUS SIDE OF LEISURE
Kendall Blanchard; 248 pp. University of Illinois Press, 1981. $22.95.

THE MISSISSIPPIAN EMERGENCE
Bruce D. Smith, Editor; Collection of 11 essays examines the evolution of ranked chiefdoms in the midwestern and southeastern U.S. from 700-1220 A.D. Illus. 272 pp. Smithsonian Institution Press, 1990. $45.

MISSISSIPPIAN MORTUARY PRACTICES
Goldstein; Covers burial details and Indian social organization. Illus. 196 pp. Paper. Amazon.com, 1980. $12.50, postpaid.

MISSISSIPPIAN POLITICAL ECONOMY
Jon Muller; Illus. 472 pp. Paper. Perseus Publishing, 1997. $47.

MISSISSIPPIAN STONE IMAGES IN ILLINOIS
Thomas E. Emerson; Illus. 50 pp. Paper. Univerity of Illinois Archaeology, 1982. $3.75.

MISSISSIPPIAN TOWNS & SACRED SPACES: SEARCHING FOR AN ARCHITECTURAL GRAMMAR
R. Barry Lewis; Paper. University of Alabama Press, 1999. $29.95.

MISSISSIPPIAN VILLAGE TEXTILES AT WICKLIFFE (KY)
Drooker
Prehistoric weavings. Illus. 291 pp. Paper. Hothem House, 1992. $19.95 postpaid.

MITAKUYE OYASIN: WE ARE ALL RLATED
Allen C. Ross; Comparative culture studies. Illus. 215 pp. Paper.
Bear & Center for Western Studies, $12.

MITSITAM CAFÉ COOKBOOK: RECIPES FROM THE SMITHSONIAN'S NATIONAL MUSEUM OF THE AMERICAN INDIAN
Richard Hetzler; Illus. 192 pp. NMAI Press, 2010. $25.

MIWOK MATERIAL CULTURE
S.A. Barrett and E.W. Gifford; Illus. 257 pp. Paper. Yosemite, $6.95.

MIXEDBLOOD MESSAGES: LITERATURE, FILM, FAMILY & PLACE
Louis Owens; Illus. 277 pp. Paper. University of Oklahoma Press, 1998. $14.95.

MIXED BLOOD INDIANS: RACIAL CONSTRUCTION IN THE EARLY SOUTH
Theda Perdue; Illus. 144 pp. University of Georgia Press, 2002. $24.95.

MIXED-BLOODS, APACHES, & CATTLE BARONS
Thomas R. McGuire; Documents for a history of the livestock economy on the White Mountain Apache Reservation, Arizona. 227 pp. Paper. U. of Arizona Press, 1980. $13.95.

MIXED-BLOODS & TRIBAL DISSOLUTION: CHARLES CURTIS & THE QUEST FOR INDIAN IDENTITY
William Unrau; Photos. Maps. 244 pp. University Press of Kansas, 1989. $27.50.

MOBILIAN JARGON: LINGUISTIC & SOCIOHISTORICAL ASPECTS OF A NATIVE AMERICAN PIDGIN   Emanuel J. Drechsel; Oxford University Press, 1997. $280.

MOBILITY & ADAPTATION: THE ANASAZI OF BLACK MESA, ARIZONA
Shirley Powell; 304 pp. Amazon.com, 1983. $29.95.

MOCASSINS ON PAVEMENT: THE URBAN INDIAN EXPERIENCE, A DENVER PORTRAIT   Michael Taylor, et al; Illus. Paper. Denver Museum, 1978. $2.50.

MOCASSINS & RED SHOES
Paula Sundet, Ed.; Illus. 104 pp. Paper. Amazon.com, 1997. $2.95.

MODEL COURT DEVELOPMENT PROJECT: FULL FAITH & CREDIT FOR INDIAN COURT JUDGEMENTS   National Center for State Courts Staff
750 pp. Amazon.com, manuscript - $3.12.

MODELS FOR THE MILLENNIUM: GREAT BASIN ANTHROPOLOGY TODAY
Charlotte Beck, Editor; Illus. Maps. 464 pp. University of Utah Press, 1999. $65.

MODERN AMERICAN INDIAN LEADERS
Dean Chavers; Profiles 87 Indian leaders of the modern age.
792 pp. Two vols. Mellen Press, 2007. $159.95.

MODERN AMERICAN INDIAN TRIBAL GOVERNMENT & POLITICS: AN INTERDISCIPLINARY STUDY   Howard Meredith; 169 pp. Paper. Amazon.com. $16.95.

MODERN BLACKFEET: MONTANANS ON A RESERVATION
Malcolm McFee; Illus. Maps. 144 pp. Paper. University of Nebraska Press, 2014. $20.

MODERN BY TRADITION: AMERICAN INDIAN PAINTING IN THE STUDIO STYLE
Bruce Bernstein & W. Jackson Rushing; Reproduces over 90 paintings by prominent artists such as Pablita Velarde, Joe H. Herrera, Allan Houser, and Opo Chalee. Illus. 176 pp. Paper. Museum of New Mexico Press, 2000. $29.95.

THE MODERN FANCY DANCER
C. Scott Evans & J. Rex Reddick; Traces the evolution of the Fancy dance style, with instructions to make an entire dance outfit. Color photos. Illus. 64 pp. Paper. Book Publishing Co., Meadowlark Communications & Written Heritage, $15.95.

MODERN INDIAN PSYCHOLOGY
John F. Bryde; Paper. Dakota Press, 1971. $9.

MODERN MAN IN NATIVE AMERICA: AN ABBREVIATED CHRONOLOGY OF SELECTED EVENTS, PEOPLE & PLACES Illus. 95 pp. Amazon.com, 1999. $16.95.

MODERN SPIRIT: THE ART OF GEORGE MORRISON
W. Jackson Rushing III & Kristin Makholm
Illus. 182 pp. University of Oklahoma Press & NMAI Press, 2013., $29.95.

MODERN TRANSFORMATIONS OF MOENKOPI PUEBLO
Shuichi Nagata; Illus. 350 pp. Paper. University of Illinois Press, 1970. $10.95.

MODERN TRIBAL DEVELOPMENT: PATHS TO SELF-SUFFICIENCY & CULTURAL INTEGRITY IN INDIAN COUNTRY
Dean Howard Smith; 167 pp. Paper. AltaMira Press, 2000. $72.

MODOC: THE TRIBE THAT WOULDN'T DIE
Cheewa James; History of the Modoc from ancestral times to the present day. Covers the Modoc War of 1873. Illus. Photos. 352 pp. Paper. Naturegraph, 2008. $19.95.

THE MODOC
Odie & Laura Faulk; Illus. 104 pp. Chelsea House, 1988. $17.95.

MODOCS & THEIR WAR
Keith A. Murray; Reprint of 1959 edition. Illus. Map. 358 pp.
Paper. University of Oklahoma Press, 2001. $29.95.

MOGOLLON CULTURE IN THE FORESTDALE VALLEY, EAST-CENTRAL ARIZONA
Emil W. Haury; Reprint. 454 pp. University of Arizona Press, 1985. $54.

MOHAVE ETHNOPSYCHIATRY & SUICIDE: PSYCHIATRIC KNOWLEDGE & THE PSYCHIC DISTURBANCES OF AN INDIAN TRIBE
George Devereux; 586 pp. 1995. Amazon.com, 1995. $64.95; paper, $49.95.

A MOHAVE WAR REMINISCENCE, 1854-1880
A.L. Kroeber & G.B. Kroeber; Illus. 109 pp. Paper. Dover, $7.95.

*THE MOHAWK
Grades K-4. Illus. 48 pp. Children's Press, $11.45.

*THE MOHAWK
Samuel Crompton; Paul Rosier, Series Editor
Grades 6-12. Illus. 136 pp. Chelsea House, 2010. $35.

MOHAWK FRONTIER: THE DUTCH COMMUNITY OF SCHENECTADY, NEW YORK, 1661-1710 Thomas E. Burke, Jr.; Explores Schenectady's origins and its destruction in 1690. The story of Indians, French & African slaves. 264 pp. Cornell U. Press, $36.95.

MOHAWK INTERRUPTUS: POLITICAL LIFE ACROSS THE BORDERS OF SETTLER STATES Audra Simpson; Illus. 280 pp. Duke U. Press, 2014. $89.95; paper, $24.95.

MOHAWK, ONE THOUSAND USEFUL WORDS
David K. Maracle; 158 pp. Paper. Amazon.com, 1992. $12.95.

MOHAWK SAINT: CATHERINE TEKAKWITHA & THE JESUITS
Allan Greer; Illus. 256 pp. Paper. Oxford University Press, 2004. $23.95..

THE MOHAWK THAT REFUSED TO ABDICATE
David P. Morgan; Amazon.com, 1975. $25.

THE MOHAWK TRAIL - HISTORIC AUTO TRAIL GUIDE: MASS ROUTE 2 FROM BOSTON TO WILLIAMSTOWN
Muddy River Press Staff; Illus. 48 pp. Muddy River Press, 2002. $9.

MOHEGAN CHIEF: THE STORY OF HAROLD TANTEQUIDGEON
Virginia Frances Voight; Reprint of 1965 edition. Chronicles the last 24 years of Chief Tantaquidgeon's life. The Mohegan Tribe.

*MOHEGAN FUN & LEARN BOOK
Anita Page; illus. by Dan Kerwin; A young children's guide to Mohegan culture through games, stories & art. Both Page & Kerwin are Mohegan tribal members. Mohegan Tribe.

MOHEGAN INDIAN MAPS OF MONTVILLE, CT
Allen V. Polhemus; Illus. 84 pp. Nutmeg Publishers, 1993. $42.95.

THE MOHICAN WORLD, 1680-1750
Shirley W. Dunn; Illus. 375 pp. Paper. Purple Mountain Press, Ltd., 2000. $24.

THE MOHICANS OF STOCKBRIDGE
Patrick Frazier; The ethnohistory of the colonial Northeast.
Illus. Map. 307 pp. Paper. University of Nebraska Press, 1992. $25.

THE MOHICANS & THEIR LAND: 1609-1730
S.W. Dunn; Ilus. 350 pp. Paper. Amazon.com, 1994. $24.

MOJAVE POTTERY, MOJAVE PEOPLE: THE DILLINGHAM COLLECTION OF MOJAVE CERAMICS
Jill Leslie Furst; 256 pp. School of American Research Press, $45; paper, $24.95.

MOKI SNAKE DANCE
Walter Hough; Travel guide published in 1899 describes the drama of Snake Dance ceremonial of the Moki (Hopi) Indians of Arizona. Includes the Snake Legend. Illus. Photos. 80 pp. Paper. Amazon.com, $5.95.

MOLDED IN THE IMAGE OF CHANGING WOMAN: NAVAJO VIEWS ON THE HUMAN BODY & PERSONHOOD
Maureen Trudelle Schwarz; 320 pp. U. of Arizona Press, 1997. $50; paper, $22.95.

MOLLY MOLASSES & ME: A COLLECTION OF LIVING ADVENTURES
Ssipsis & Georgia Mitchell; Illus. 2nd edition. 75 pp. Paper. Amazon.com, $8.

MOLLY SPOTTED ELK: A PENOBSCOT IN PARIS
Bunny McBride; Illus. 384 pp. U. of Oklahoma Press, 1997. $34.95; paper, $19.95.

N. SCOTT MOMADAY: THE CULTURAL & LITERARY BACKGROUND
Matthias Schubnell; 336 pp. University of Oklahoma Press, 1985. $29.95.

N. SCOTT MOMADAY: REMEMBERING ANCESTORS, EARTH, & TRADITIONS; AN ANNOTATED BIBLIOGRAPHY Kenneth Lincoln & Phyllis S. Morgan
Illus. Map. 400 pp. University of Oklahoma Press, 2010. $60.

MOMADAY, VIZENOR, ARMSTRONG: CONVERSATIONS ON AMERICAN INDIAN WRITING Hartwig Isernhagen; 304 pp. U. of Oklahoma Press, 1999. $34.95.

THE MONACAN INDIAN NATION OF VIRGINIA
Rosemary Clark Whitlock; foreword by Anthony Paredes
Illus. 248 pp. University of Alabama Press, 46.50; paper, $24.95. E-Book, $19.96.

MONACANS & MINERS: NATIVE AMERICAN & COAL MINING COMMUNITIES IN APPALACHIA Samuel R. Cook
Illus. Maps. 337 pp. U. of Nebraska Press, 2000. $65; paper, $14.97.

*THE MONEY GOD
Dolly Hildreth, et al; Grade 6. Paper. Council for Indian Education, 1972. $1.95.

THE MONGREL: A STORY OF LOGAN FONTANELLE OF THE OMAHA INDIANS
Anthony J. Barak; Jim Reisdorff, Ed.; Illus. 145 pp. Paper. Amazon.com, 1988. $9.95.

JESSE MONONGYA: OPAL BEARS & LAPIS SKIES
Lois Sherr Dubin; photos by Togashi; Illus. 182 pp. Amazon.com, $50.

*MONSTORS & MAGIC: MYTHS OF NORTH & SOUTH AMERICA
Stewart Ross; Grades 5 and up. Illus. 44 pp. Amazon.com, 1998. $23.90.

MONSTERS, TRICKSTERS & SACRED COWS: ANIMAL TALES & AMERICANIDENTITIES A. James Arnold, Ed.; 290 pp. Paper. Amazon.com, 1996. $18.

THE MONTANA CREE: A STUDY IN RELIGIOUS PERSISTENCE
Verne Dusenberry; Illus. Maps. Biblio. 296 pp. Paper.
University of Oklahoma Press & Written Heritage, 1996. $15.95.

MONTANA NATIVE PLANTS & EARLY PEOPLES
Jeff Hart; Reprint ed. Illus. 152 pp. Paper. Montana Historical Society Press, 1996. $9.95.

MONTANA 1911: A PROFESSOR & HIS WIFE AMONG THE BLACKFEET
Mary Eggermont-Molenaar, Edited & trans.
Illus. Map. 418 pp. Paper. University of Nebraska Press, 2006. $35.

MONTANA MEMORIES: THE LIFE OF EMMA MAGEE IN THE ROCKY MOUNTAIN WEST, 1866-1950 Ida S. Patterson, with a biography of author by Grace Patterson McComas; Illus. 144 pp. Paper. University of Nebraska Press, 2012. $10.95.

MONTANA'S INDIANS: YESTERDAY & TODAY
William Bryan; Profiles each of Montana's seven reservations and the nations residing there. Illus. 142 pp. 1986 edition distributed by Meadowlark Communications, $24.95.

THE MONTAUKETT INDIANS OF EASTERN LONG ISLAND
John A. Strong; Illus. 212 pp. Syracuse University Press, 2001. $26.95.

MONTEREY IN 1786: THE JOURNAL OF JEAN FRANCOIS DE LA PEROUSE
Intro by Malcolm Margolin; Account of Carmel Mission and the relations between the missionaries and the Indian neophytes, shortly after the death of Junipero Sera. Illus. 104 pp. Paper. Heyday Books, $8.95.

CARLOS MONTEZUMA AND THE CHANGING WORLD OF AMERICAN INDIANS
Peter Iverson; Biography of a Yavapai Indian called Wassaja.
Illus. 238 pp. Maps. University of New Mexico Press, 2006. $29.95; paper, $29.95

CARLOS MONTEZUMA, M.D., A YAVAPAI AMERICAN HERO: THE LIFE & TIMES OF AN AMERICAN INDIAN Leon Speroff; Illus. 560 pp. Amica Publishing, 2003. $34.95.

MONUMENT VALLEY: THE STORY BEHIND THE SCENERY
K.C. DenDooven; The story of the Navajo who lived there, the Gouldings who established the trading post, and a young photographer in 1937. Illus. Photos. 48 pp. Paper. KC Publications, $6.95.

MOON DASH WARRIOR: THE STORY OF AN AMERICAN INDIAN IN VIETNAM, A MARINE FROM THE LAND OF THE LUMBEE
Delano Cummings; Illus. 266 pp. Signal Tree, 1998. $22.

MOON OF POPPING TREES
Rex Alan Smith; The tragedy of Wounded Knee and the end of the Indian wars, 1851-1891. Maps. 219 pp. Paper. University of Nebraska Press, 1981. $16.95.

JAMES MOONEY'S HISTORY, MYTHS & SACRED FORMULAS OF THE CHEROKEES
James Mooney; Illus. 410 pp. Paper. Book Publishing Co., 1992. $18.95.

MOONLIGHT DRAINING OUT OF THE VALLEY: NEW WORK FROM THE INSTITUTE OF AMERICAN INDIAN ARTS
Ramona Crofoot, et al.Illus. 122 pp. Paper. Institute of American Indian Arts, 2000. $8.

THE MORAVIAN SPRINGPLACE MISSION TO THE CHEROKEES
Rowena McClinton, Editor; Two volume set which documents Cherokee daily life at the Mission from 1805 to 1821. Photos. Maps. 566 pp. U. of Nebraska Press, 2007. $99.95. Abridged Edition, 184 pp. Paper. $30.

MORE AH MO: INDIAN LEGENDS FROM THE NORTHWEST
Tren J. Griffin; New Edition of Ah Mo. Illus. 64 pp. Paper. Hancock House, 1994. $7.95.

LEWIS H. MORGAN ON IROQUOIS MATERIAL CULTURE
Elisabeth Tooker; A collection of 500 Iroquois objects, researched in 1849-50, provides information on Irqouois culture. Illus. 400 pp. U. of Arizona Press, 1994. $76; paper, $45.

LEWIS HENRY MORGAN'S LEAGUE OF THE IROQUOIS: THE ETHNOGRAPHIC CORE Russell A. Judkins; Amazon.com, 2004.

MORE TECHNIQUES OF BEADING EARRINGS
Deon DeLange; Illus. 80 pp. Paper. Eagle's View Publishing, $9.95.

***MORNING GIRL**
Michael Dorris; Grades 3 and up. Illus. Paper. Hyperion. $3.50.

MORNING STAR DAWN: THE POWDER RIVER EXPEDITION & THE NORTHERN CHEYENNES, 1876 Jerome A. Greene; Illus. 304 pp. U. of Oklahoma Press, $34.95.

MORNING STAR QUILTS
Florence Pulford ; Illus. 80 pp. Dover, $9.95.

THE MORNING THE SUN WENT DOWN
Darryl Babe Wilson
A memoir of rural Native American life. 190 pp. Paper. Heyday Books, $13.95.

MOST INDISPENSIBLE ART: NATIVE FIBER INDUSTRIES FROM EASTERN NORTH AMERICA
James B. Peterson, Editor; Illus. 240 pp. Amazon.com, 1996. $45.

MOST SERENE REPUBLICS: EDGAR HEAP OF BIRDS
Kathleen Ash-Milby (Navajo) & Truman T. Lowe (Ho-Chunk)
Illus. 96 pp. Paper. NMAI Press, 2009. $20.

A "MOST TROUBLESOME SITUATION," THE BRITISH MILITARY & THE PONTIAC UPRISING OF 1763-64
Tim Todish & Todd Harburn; Illus. 221 pp. Paper. Wennawoods Publishing, $20.

MOTHER EARTH: AN AMERICAN STORY
Sam D. Gill; 206 pp. Paper. University of Chicago Press, 1991. $17.

MOTHER EARTH, FATHER SKY: NATIVE AMERICAN WISDOM
Felicia S. Wiggins; Illus. 80 pp. Paper. Amazon.com, 1999. $4.95.

MOTHER EARTH, FATHER SKY: PUEBLO & NAVAJO INDIANS OF THE SOUTHWEST
Marcia Keegan; Reprint of 1974 edition. Illus. 112 pp. Amazon.com, 1974. $29.95.

MOTHER EARTH, FATHER SKYLINE: A SOUVENIR BOOK OF NATIVE NEW YORK
Duane Blue Spruce (Laguna/Ohkay Owingeh), Editor
Essays. Ilus. 64 pp. Paper. NMAI Press, 2006. $9.95.

MOTHER EARTH SPIRITUALITY: NATIVE AMERICAN PATHS TO HEALING OURSELVES & OUR WORLD
Ed McGaa & Eagle Man; Illus. 304 pp. Paper. Amazon.com, 1990. $14.95.

THE MOUNDBUILDERS
Robert Silverberg; Illus. 276 pp. Paper. Amazon.com, 1986. $14.95.

THE MOUNDBUILDERS: ANCIENT PEOPLES OF EASTERN NORTH AMERICA
George R. Milner; Illus. 224 pp. Paper. Thames & Hudson, 2005. $24.95

MOUND BUILDERS & CLIFF DWELLERS
Time-Life Editors; Illus. 168 pp. Amazon.com, 1993. $25.95.

MOUNDBUILDERS & MONUMENT MAKERS OF THE NORTHERN GREAT LAKES, 1200-1600 Meghan C.L. Howey; 320 pp. University of Oklahoma Press, $45.

MOUNDS FOR THE DEAD
Dragoo; Study of the Adena (Early Woodland) Indians; their lifeway, mounds, burial pratice, artifacts. Reprint of 1963 edition. Illus. 315 pp. Paper. Hothem House, $15.95.

MOUNDS OF EARTH & SHELL
Bonnie Shemie; Amazon.com, 1993. $13.

MOUNDVILLE
John H. Blitz; Pocket travel guide. Illus. 50 color photos, maps & figures. Alabama's prehistoric metropolis. 152 pp. Paper. University of Alabama Press, 2008. $19.95.

MOUNDVILLE'S ECONOMY
Paul D. Welch; Illus. 248 pp. Paper. University of Alabama Press, 1991. $34.95.

THE MOUNTAIN CHANT: A NAVAJO CEREMONY
Washington Matthews; A nine-day Navajo healing ceremony. Contains the story of the wandering hero and describes each of the days, with original song texts and translations. Reprint of 1897 ed. Illus. 120 pp. Paper. University of Utah Press. $14.95.

MOUNTAIN LEGACY: A STORY OF RABUN GAP - NACOOCHEE SCHOOL WITH EMPHASIS ON THE JUNIOR COLLEGE YEARS
Frances P. Statham; Illus. 384 pp.Amazon.com, 1999. $40.

THE MOUNTAIN MEADOWS MASSACRE
Juanita Brooks; Story of a wagon train in southern Utah was attacked by Indians & Mormans. Reprint of 1962 edition. Illus. Maps. 352 pp. Paper. University of Oklahoma Press, 2000. $19.95.

MOUNTAIN SPIRIT: THE SHEEP EATER INDIANS OF YELLOWSTONE
Lawrence Loendorf & Nancy Medaris Stone
Illus. 242 pp. University of Utah Press, 2006. $50; paper, $19.95

MOUNTAIN TOWN: FLAGSTAFF'S FIRST CENTURY
Platt Cline; History of Flagstaff. 175 historic photos. 672 pp. Northland, $35.

MOUNTAIN WINDSONG: A NOVEL OF THE TRAIL OF TEARS
Robert J. Conley; A love story and the Cherokee Removal of 1835-1838 from their traditional lands in North Carolina. 218 pp. Paper. U. of Oklahoma Press, 2001. $19.95.

MOUNTAIN WOLF WOMAN, SISTER OF CRASHING THUNDER: THE AUTOBIOGRAPHY OF A WINNEBAGO INDIAN
Nancy Oestrich Lurie, Editor; Illus. 164 pp. Paper. U. of Michigan Press, 1961. $15.95.

THE MOUNTAINWAY OF THE NAVAJO
Leland Wyman; The examination of a Navajo song ceremonial and its various branches, phases and ritual. Illus. 286 pp. University of Arizona Press, 1975. $35.

MOURNING DOVE: A SALISHAN AUTOBIOGRAPHY
Mourning Dove; edited by Jay Miller
Illus. Map. 267 pp. Paper. University of Nebraska Press, 1990. $15.95.

MOVEMENT, CONNECTIVITY, & LANDSCAPE CHANGE IN THE ANCIENT SOUTHWEST Margaret C. Nelson & Colleen A. Strawhacker
448 pp. University Press of Colorado, 2011. $75. E-book, $65; 30-day rental, $9.99.

MOVEMENT FOR INDIAN ASSIMILATION, 1860-1890
Henry E. Fritz; Reprint of 1963 edition. Illus. 244 pp. Greenwood Press, $35.

MOVING ABORIGINAL HEALTH FORWARD: DISCARDING CANADA'S LEGAL BARRIERS
Yvonne Boyer; 224 pp. Paper. University of Washington Press, 2017. $35.

MOVING ENCOUNTERS: SYMPATHY & THE INDIAN QUESTION IN ANTEBELLUM LITERATURE Laura L. Mielke; Discourse in texts that focus on Native Americans. 328 pp. University of Massachusetts Press, 2008. $80; paper, $26.95.

MOVING WITHIN THE CIRCLE: CONTEMPORARY NATIVE AMERICAN MUSIC & DANCE Bryan Burton; Features songs, dances, and flute tunes of the Haliwa-Saponi Dancers, R. Carlos Nakai, the Porcupine Singers, and more. Illus. 176 pp. World Music Press, Book & CD or Book & Tape Set, $29.95; with optional slides, $63.

***MUCKWA: THE ADVENTURES OF A CHIPPEWA INDIAN BOY**
Wilson G. Dietrich; Illus. Winston-Derek, $6.95.

***THE MUD FAMILY**
Betsy James; illus. by Paul Morin; Story depicting the lives of the Anasazi, ancestor of the Pueblo peoples of the Southwest. Grades PS-3. Illus. 32 pp. Putnam, 1994. $15.95.

***THE MUD PONY**
Caron Lee Cohen; Shonto Begay, Illus.; Native American tale about a young boy and his magical mud pony that comes top life. Grades K-4. Illus. 32 pp. Amazon.com, 1989.

MUD WOMAN: POEMS FROM THE CLAY
Nora Naranjo-MorsePoetry by a noted Pueblo potter. Illus. 127 pp.
Paper. University of Arizona Press, 1992. $17.95.

MUKAT'S LAST GIFT : MORTUARY CUSTOMS AMONG THE CAHUILLA INDIANS
Lowell J. Bean; Ilus. Paper. Malki-Ballena Press

MUKAT'S PEOPLE: THE CAHUILLA INDIANS OF SOUTHERN CALIFORNIA
Lowell J. Bean; Reprint of 1974 edition. 300 pp. Paper. University of California Press & Malki-Ballena Press, $24.95.

MULEWETAM: THE FIRST PEOPLE
Jane H. Hill & Rosinda Nolasquez; Collection of oral histories, myths accounts of old religious ceremonies, stories for children, & songs of the Cupeno people of Southern California. Reprint. Illus. Paper. Malki-Ballena Press, 2005. $40.

MULTICULTURAL AMERICAN LITERATURE: COMPARATIVE BLACK, NATIVE, LATINO/A, AND ASIAN AMERICAN FICTIONS A. Robert Lee; A comparative anaysis of recent ethnic writing. 320 pp. University Press of Mississippi, 2007. $50; paper, $25.

MULTICULTURAL COMICS: FROM ZAP TO BLUE BEETLE
Frederick Luis Aldama, Editor; 13 essays look at comic books by and about race & ethnicity. Includes Native American Anishnaabe-related comics. Illus. 271 pp. University of Texas Press, 2010. $55.

MULTICULTURAL RESOURCE BOOK & APPOINTMENT CALENDAR
Detailed entries marking birthdays, historical/cultural events, & days of religious observance associated ith over 30 different cultural and religious tradition, including 30 entries dealing with Native Americans. Book, 6"X9"; Resource Calendar, 11"x17". Biblio. Index. Annual. Amherst Educational Publishing, $21.95 each.

MULTIDISCIPLINARY RESEARCH AT GRASSHOPPER PUEBLO, ARIZONA
W.A. Longacre and S.J. Holbrook, Editors
138 pp. Paper. University of Arizona Press, 1982. $12.95.

MUMIGCISTET KALIKAIT: A YUP'IK LANGUAGE TERM BOOK
Oscar Alexie, et al, Editors; 175 pp. Paper. University of Alaska, Fairbanks Center, 1990.

THE MUNSEE INDIANS: A HISTORY
Robert S. Grumet; Illus. Maps. 464 pp. University of Oklahoma Press, 2009. $45.

MURDER ON THE RESERVATION: AMERICAN INDIAN CRIME FICTION
Ray Broadus Browne; 304 pp. University of Wisconsin Press, 2004. $65; paper, $19.95.

MURDER STATE: CALIFORNIA'S NATIVE AMERICAN GENOCIDE, 1846-1873
Brendan C. Lindsay; Illus. 456 pp. University of Nebraska Press, 2012. $70; paper, $35.

MUSCOGEE DAUGHTER: MY SOJOURN TO THE MISS AMERICA PAGEANT
Susan Supernaw; foreword by Geary Hobson; Supernaw's story of finding a Native American identity. Illus. 264 pp. Universitry of Nebraska Press, 2010. $24.95

*MARY MUSGRAVE: GEORGIA INDIAN PRINCESS
Helen Todd; Grades 6-12. 152 pp. Paper. Cherokee, 1981. $6.95.

MUSIC & DANCE OF THE AMERICAN INDIAN
Ruth DeCesare; Paper. Amazon.com, 1997. $21.95 includes audio CD.

MUSIC & DANCE RESEARCH ON THE SOUTHWESTERN INDIANS
Charlotte Frisbie; 109 pp. Harmonie Park Press, 1977. $18.

MUSIC OF THE FIRST NATIONS: TRADITION & INNOVATION IN NATIVE NORTH AMERICA
Tara Browner, Editor; Illus. 184 pp. University of Illinois Press, 2009. $39; eBook, $30.

MUSIC OF THE NATIVE NORTH AMERICAN FOR FLUTE & RECORDER
Daniel Chazanoff; Music notation book with spiral binding; includes melodies from the Great Lakes & Eastern Woodlands Indians, Southeast, Plains, Southwestern, Pueblo, Great Basin-Plateau, Northwest & California Indians. 32 pp. $9.95. Canyon Records & Indian Arts. See Audio-Visual Distributors under CAN.

MUSIC OF THE NORTH AMERICAN INDIANS FOR ACOUSTIC GUITAR
Steven Zdenek Eckels; 48 pp. Paper. Mel Bay Publications, 2000. $17.95, includes CD.

MUSKOGEE (CREEK) ENGLISH DICTIONARY
B. Frank Belvin, Editor; Contains complete pronunciation guide & explanations of verb variations. 236 pp. Paper. VIP Publishing, 1964. $19.95.

MUSQUEAM REFERENCE GRAMMAR
Wayne Suttles; One of 23 languages that belong to the Salish family. 496 pp. UBC Press & University of Washington Press, 2004. $125.

MUSTANG EYES: TALES OF THE NEZ PERCE
Emma Rose Lee; Fiction. Paper. Amazon.com, $11.95.

MUTING WHITE NOISE: NATIVE AMERICAN & EUROPEAN AMERICAN NOVEL TRADITIONS James H. Cox
Illus. 352 pp. University of Oklahoma Press, 2007. $29.95; paper, $24.95.

MY ADVENTURES IN ZUNI
Frank H. Cushing; Hist story of life in the Zuni Pueblo in 1867. Illus. 58 pp. Amazon.com & Alibris.com, 1967. $8; paper, $5.

MY CAPTIVITY AMONG THE SIOUX INDIANS
Fanny Kelly; Paper. Amazon.com, 2002. $5.95.

*MY CHILDREN ARE MY REWARD - THE LIFE OF ELSIE SPENCE
Alix Harpelle; Traditional ways of the Metis in Manitoba in the mid-20th century. Grades 7-12. Paper. Pemmican, $17.95.

MY CHOCTAW ROOTS
Judy Shi Connally & Lawana Tomlinson Dansby; Illus. by Norma Howard The Choctaw Store, 2016. $17.99

MY ELDERS TAUGHT ME: ASPECTS OF WESTERN GREAT LAKES AMERICAN INDIAN PHILOSOPHY
John Boatman; 84 pp. Paper. Amazon.com, 1993. $41.

MY FAMILY TELLS THIS STORY
Snow Flower; Illus. 156 pp. Paper. Heritage Press, 1999. $19.

MY FIRST YEARS IN THE FUR TRADE: THE JOURNALS OF 1802-1804
George Nelson; Laura Peers & Theresa Schenk, Eds. Illus. 234 pp. Minnesota Historical Society Press, 2002. $29.95.

MY FRIEND THE INDIAN
James McLaughlin; Illus. 475 pp. Paper. U. of Nebraska Press, 1989. $11.50.

MY GRANDFATHER'S HOUSE: TLINGIT SONGS OF DEATH & SORROW
David Cloutier; Illus. 40 pp. Paper. Holmgangers, 1980. $3.

MY HEART SOARS
Chief Dan George; Illus. 96 pp. Paper. Hancock House, $7.95.

MY INDIAN BOYHOOD
Chief Luther Standing Bear; intro. by Delphine Red Shirt New edition. Illus. 198 pp. Paper. University of Nebraska Press, 2006. $14.95.

MY LEGACY TO YOU
Alice Reardon & Marie Meade; edited by Ann Fienup-Riordan Documents the elder Frank Andrew, Sr. (1917-2006) about Yup'ik life on the Bering Sea coast. Illus. Map. 360 pp. University of Washington Press, 2008. $25.

*MY LIFE AS AN INDIAN: THE STORY OF A RED WOMAN & A WHITE MAN IN THE LODGES OF THE BLACKFEET James W. Schultz
Reprint. Grades 6 and up. Illus. 335 pp. Paper. Dover Publications, 1997. $9.95.

*MY LIFE AS A NATIVE AMERICAN
Ann H. Matzke; Grades K-2. Illus. 24 pp. Paper. Rourke Educational Media, $8.95.

MY LIFE IN SAN JUAN PUEBLO: STORIES OF ESTHER MARTINEZ
Esther Martinez; Sue-Ellen Jacobs & Josephine Binford, Eds. Illus. 225 pp. paper. University of Illinois Press, 2004. $26.95.

MY LIFE ON THE PLAINS; OR, PERSONAL EXPERIENCES WITH INDIANS
George A. Custer; Milo M. Quaife, Editor; Reprint of 1962 edition. Illus. 418 pp. Paper. University of Nebraska Press or University of Oklahoma Press, $12.95.

*MY NAVAJO SISTER
Eleanor Schick; Grades 3 to 7. A white girl forms a close bond with a Navajo girl. Meadowlark Communications, $16.

MY OLD PEOPLE SAY: AN ETHNOGRAPHIC SURVEY OF SOUTHERN YUKON TERRITORY, PART 1 Catherine McClellan
Reprint of 1975 ed. Illus. Maps. 392 pp. Paper. University of Washington Press, 2001. $35.

MY PEOPLE THE SIOUX
L. Standing Bear; E.A. Brininstool, Editor; intro. by Virginia Driving Hawk Sneve New edition. Illus. 296 pp. Paper. University of Nebraska Press, 2006. $13.95.

MY SPIRIT SOARS
Chief Dan George; Illus. 96 pp. Paper. Hancock House, $7.95.

MY WORK AMONG THE FLORIDA SEMINOLES
James Glenn; Harry Kersey, Jr., Editor Illus. Maps. 121 pp. University Press of Florida, 1982. $16.95.

MYSTERIES OF THE HOPEWELL
William F. Romain; Studies the astronomers, geometers, and magicians of the Eastern Woodlands. The Amazon.com, $44.95; paper, $16.95.

MYSTERIOUS ANCIENT AMERICA: AN INVESTIGATION INTO THE ENIGMAS OF AMERICA'S PRE-HISTORY Paul Devereux
Illus. 190 pp. Paper. Sterling Publishing, $14.95.

*MYSTERY AT ECHO CLIFFS
Kate Abbott; Story for children contains information about Navajo customs and history. Grades 4-9. Illus. 184 pp. Paper. Amazon.com, $11.95.

*MYSTERY OF COYOTE CANYON
Timothy Green; Col. Kit Carson's military campaign against the Navajos, artifacts of the Anasazi, and the ruins of Cliff dwellings in Canyon de Chelly are some of the historical themes in this story. Grades 6 & up. Illus. 150 pp. Paper. Amazon.com, 1994. $12.95.

THE MYSTERY OF THE CRYSTAL SKULLS: UNLOCKING THE SECRETS OF THE PAST, PRESENT & FUTURE Chris Morton & Ceri Louise Thomas
Illus. 425 pp. Paper. Inner Traditions, 2002. $20.

MYSTERY OF E TROOP: CUSTER'S GRAY HORSE COMPANY AT LITTLE BIG HORN
Gregory Michno; 352 pp. Paper. Mountain Press. $16.

*THE MYSTERY OF THE ANASAZI
Leonard E. Fisher; Grades K-4. Illus. 32 pp. Children's Press, 1997. $16.

MYSTERY OF SACAJAWEA: INDIAN GIRL WITH LEWIS & CLARK
Harold P. Howard; Story of Shoshone guide Sacajawea of the Lewis & Clark Expedition. Illus. 200 pp. Paper. Center for Western Studies, $4.95.

*MYSTERY TRACKS IN THE SNOW
Hap Gilliland; Identifies over 100 North American animal tracks. Grades 4 and up. 142 pp. Council for Indian Education, $14.95; paper. $7.95.

THE MYSTIC LAKE SIOUX: SOCIOLOGY OF THE MDEWAKANTONWAN SANTEE
Ruth Landes; Illus. Map. 234 pp. University of Wisconsin Press, 1969. $25.

THE MYSTIC WARRIORS OF THE PLAINS: THE CULTURE, ARTS, CRAFTS, & RELIGION OF THE PLAINS INDIANS Thomas E. Mails; Documents the lifestyles of the Plains Indians. Illus. 620 pp. Paper. Amazon.com, 1995. $29.95.

MYSTICS, MAGICIANS, & MEDICINE PEOPLE
Doug Boyd; Simon & Schuster. $12.

MYTH & MEMORY: STORIES OF INDIGENOUS-EUROPEAN CONTACT
John Sutton Lutz; 284 pp. University of Washington Press, 2007. $94; paper, $37.95.

*MYTH, MUSIC & DANCE OF THE AMERICAN INDIAN
Ruth DeCesare; Sandy Feldstein, et al, Editors; Grades 4-12. Illus. 80 pp. Teacher's edition, $12.95 with cassette, $21.95; cassette only, $9.95; student edition, 16 pp. $3.95; student songbook, 24 pp., $4.95. Amazon.com, 1988.

THE MYTH OF HIAWATHA: AND OTHER ORAL LEGENDS, MYTHOLOGIC & ALLEGORIC, OF THE NORTH AMERICAN INDIANS Henry R. Schoolcraft
Reprint of 1856 ed. by 343 pp. Paper. Available from Abebooks.com or Amazon.com.

THE MYTH & PRAYERS OF THE GREAT STAR CHANT & THE MYTH OF THE COYOTE CHANT Recorded by Mary C. Wheelwright; ed. by David McAllester
Illus. 190 pp. Paper. Amazon.com, 1989. $27.

MYTHIC BEINGS: SPIRIT ART OF THE NORTHWEST COAST
Gary R. Wyatt; Illus. 160 pp. Paper. University of Washington Press, 1999. $28.95.

THE MYTHIC WORLD OF THE ZUNI: AS WRITTEN BY FRANK HAMILTON CUSHING
Barton Wright, Editor; Reprint. Illus. 190 pp. Paper. U. of New Mexico Press, $14.95.

THE MYTHICAL PUEBLO RIGHTS DOCTRINE: WATER ADMINISTRATION IN HISPANIC NEW MEXICO Daniel Tyler
Illus. 65 pp. Texas Western, 1989. $12; paper, $7.50.

MYTHOLOGICAL EXPRESSIONS OF SOUTHWESTERN DESIGNS
Leo J. Korte & Judith Adamson; Illus. 136 pp. Kortes Publishing, $42; paper, $28.

THE MYTHOLOGY OF THE AMERICAS
Brian Molyneaux & David Jones; Illus. 255 pp. Amazon.com, 2003. $35.

MYTHOLOGY OF THE BLACKFOOT INDIANS
by Clark Wissler & D.C. Duvall, compiled & tr.
Second Edition. Illus. 204 pp. Paper. University of Nebraska Press, 2008. $15.95.

MYTHOLOGY OF THE LENAPE: GUIDE & TEXTS
John Bierhorst; Synopsis of 218 Lenape narratives on record.
192 pp. Paper. University of Arizona Press, 1995. $20.95.

MYTHOLOGY OF NATIVE NORTH AMERICA
David Leeming & Jake Page
Illus. Map. 224 pp. University of Oklahoma Press, 1998. $24.95; paper, $14.95.

THE MYTHOLOGY OF NORTH AMERICA: INTRO TO CLASSIC AMERICAN GODS, HEROES & TRICKSTERS
John Bierhorst; Illus. 280 pp. Oxford University Press, 2002. $74; paper, $35.

MYTHOLOGY OF THE OGLALA
Martha W. Beckwith; 103 pp. Paper. Lakota Books, 2003. $24.95.

MYTHOLOGY & VALUES: AN ANALYSIS OF NAVAHO CHANTWAY MYTHS
Katherine Spencer; Reprint of 1957 edition. 248 pp. Paper.
University of Texas Press, 1957. $6.95.

MYTHOLOGY OF THE WICHITA
George A. Dorsey; 354 pp. University of Oklahoma Press, 1995. $13.95.

MYTHS & LEGENDS OF CALIFORNIA & THE OLD SOUTHWEST
Katherine Berry Judson; Zuni, Pima, Paiute Shastika, and Miwok stories of the creation of the universe. Illus. 255 pp. Paper. University of Nebraska Press, 1994. $8.95.

*MYTHS & LEGENDS OF THE HAIDA INDIANS OF THE NORTHWEST
Dr. Reid; Grade 5. Illus. Paper. Amazon.com, 1978. $3.95.

*MYTHS & LEGENDS OF THE INDIANS OF THE SOUTHWEST: HOPI, ACOMA, TEWA, ZUNI
Bertha Dutton and Caroline Olin; Grade 5. Illus. Paper. Bellerophon Books, 1978. $3.95.

*MYTHS & LEGENDS OF THE INDIANS OF THE SOUTHWEST: NAVAJO, PIMA & APACHE
Bertha Dutton and Caroline Olin; Grade 5. Illus. Paper. Bellerophon Books, 1978. $4.95.

MYTHS & LEGENDS OF THE PACIFIC NORTHWEST
Katherine Berry Judson; Klamath, Nez Perce, Tillamook, Modoc, Shastan, Chinook, Flathead, Clatsop and other Northwest tribes' stories of the creation of the universe. Illus. 195 pp. Paper. University of Nebraska Press, 1997. $14.95.

MYTHS & LEGENDS OF THE SIOUX
Marie L. McLaughlin
38 Sioux legends. Illus. 200 pp. Paper. University of Nebraska Press, 1990. $14.95.

MYTHS OF THE CHEROKEE
James Mooney; Reprint of 1900 ed. 126 myths. Illus. Maps. 608 pp.
Paper. Dover, $18.95.

MYTHS OF NATIVE AMERICA
Tim McNeese, Ed.; Illus. 336 pp. Paper. Running Press, 2003. $22.95.

MYTHS OF THE NEW WORLD: A TREATISE ON THE SYMBOLISM & MYTHOLOGY OF THE RED RACE OF AMERICA
Daniel G. Brinton; Reprint of 1876 edition. Illus. 360 pp. Longwood, $30; Greenwood, $35.

THE MYTHS OF THE NORTH AMERICAN INDIANS
Lewis Spence; Anthology of the myths & legends of the Algonquins, Iroquois, Pawnees & Sioux. Illus. 480 pp. Paper. Dover, Smoke & Fire Co., 1989. $12.95.

MYTHS OF PRE-COLUMBIAN AMERICA
Donald A. Mackenzie; Reprint. Illus. 416 pp. Paper. Dover, $9.95.

MYTHS & RECIPES OF THE LAST FRONTIER, ALASKA
Judy Kivi; Alisa B. Oliver, Ed.; Illus. 304 pp. Paper. Amazon.com, 1996. $24.95.

MYTHS & SACRED FORMULAS OF THE CHEROKEES
James Mooney; Obtained on the Cherokee Reservation in NC in 1887-1888 covering daily life and thought of the Cherokee. Reprint. 400 pp. Paper. VIP Publishing & Cherokee Publications, $15.95.

MYTHS & SYMBOLS, OR ABORIGINAL RELIGIONS IN AMERICA
Stephen Peet; Reprint of 1905 edition. Illus. Longwood, $45.

MYTHS & TALES OF THE CHIRICAHUA APACHE INDIANS
Morris E. Opler; into. by Scott Rushforth; Reprint of 1942 edition.
115 pp. Paper. University of Nebraska Press, 1994. $11.95.

MYTHS & TALES OF THE JICARILLA APACHE INDIANS
Morris E. Opler; Reprint of 1938 edition. 407 pp. Paper.
University of Nebraska Press, $14.95; Dover, $9.95.

MYTHS & TALES OF THE SOUTHEASTERN INDIANS
John R. Swanton; 276 pp. Paper. University of Oklahoma Press, 1995. $13.95.

MYTHS & TALES OF THE WHITE MOUNTAIN APACHE
G. Goodwin, Ed.; Reprint of 1938 ed. 223 pp. Paper. University of Arizona Press, 1994. $19.95.

MYTHS & TRADITIONS OF THE ARIKARA INDIANS
Douglas R. Parks; Illus. Maps. 407 pp. U. of Nebraska Press, 1996. $40; paper, $17.95.

N

*NA YO PISA
A noun recognition book for young readers. Includes three scenes from reservation life are shown, home-school-town. Grades K-3. 7 pp. www.choctaw.org, $3.

NAIRNE'S MUSKHOGEAN JOURNALS: THE 1708 EXPEDITION TO THE MISSISSIPPI RIVER Capt. Thomas Nairne; Alexander Moore, Editor
Muskhogean society in Colonial white-Indian relations. 92 pp. Paper.
University Press of Mississippi, 1988. $25.

THE NAKED MAN, VOL. 4: MYTHOLOGIQUES
Claude Levi-Strauss; John & Doreen Weightman, translators
Reprint. 760 pp. Paper. University of Chicago Press, 1990. $21.95.

NAME OF SALISH & KOOTENAI NATION: THE 1855 HELL GATE TREATY & THE ORIGIN OF THE FLATHEAD INDIAN RESERVATION
Robert Bigart; Illus. 180 pp. Paper. University of Washington Press, 1996. $14.95.

THE NAMES
N. Scott Momaday; Reprint of 1977 ed. 170 pp. Paper. U. of Arizona Press, 1987. $15.95.

NAMING CANADA: ESSAYS ON PLACE ANMES FROM CANADIAN GEOGRAPHIC
Alan Rayburn; Native place names are stamped across the entire country, reflecting the First Nations' contributions to Canadian history. Illus. 300 pp. Amazon.com, 1994. $18.95.

NAMPEYO & HER POTTERY
Barbara Kramer; Hopi-Tewa Potter. Reprint of 1996 edition.
Illus. 224 pp. Paper. University of Arizona Press, 2003. $24.95.

NANA'S RAID: APACHE WARFARE IN SOUTHERN NEW MEXICO
Stephen H. Lekson; Illus. 78 pp. Texas Western Press, 1989. $12; paper, $7.50.

NANISE: A NAVAJO HERBAL
Vernon O. Mayes & Barbara Bayless Lacy; Identifies and illustrates 100 plants found today on the Navajo Reservation. Illus. Paper. Amazon.com, $27.

*THE NANTICOKE
Frank Porter; Grades 5 and up. Illus. 104 pp. Chelsea House, 1987. $17.95.

THE NANTICOKE INDIANS
C.A. Weslager; Reprint of 1948 edition. 350 pp. University of Delaware Press, $28.50.

NAPA VALLEY'S NATIVES
Richard H. Dillon 110 pp. Paper. Amazon.com, 2001. $8.95.

*THE NARRAGANSETT
William Simmons; Grades 7-12. Illus. 112 pp. Chelsea House, 1989. $17.95.

*THE NARRAGANSETT
Craig & Katherine Doherty; Grades 4-8. 32 pp. Amazon.com, 1994. $22.60.

NARRATIVE ACROSS MEDIA: THE LANGUAGE OF STORYTELLING
Marie-Laure Ryan; Illus. 400 pp. University of Nebraska Press, 2004. $75.

NARRATIVE CHANCE: POSTMODERN DISCOURSE ON NATIVE AMERICAN INDIAN LITERATURES Gerald Vizenor, Editor; 224 pp. University of New Mexico Press, 1989. $29.95. Paper. University of Oklahoma Press, $17.95.

NARRATIVE OF THE CAPTIVITY OF ISAAC WEBSTER
Isaac Webster; 25 pp. Paper. 1988. Available from Amazon.com, $4.95.

A NARRATIVE OF THE CAPTIVITY & REMOVES OF MRS. JOHNSON
Johnson; Rerint of 1814 edition. Illus. 230 pp. Paper. Heritage Book, $18.50.

A NARRATIVE OF THE CAPTIVITY & REMOVES OF MRS. MARY ROWLANDSON
Mary White Rowlandson; Reprint. Paper. 1974. Available from Amazon.com, $20.

A NARRATIVE OF THE DANGERS & SUFFERINGS OF ROBERT EASTBURN DURING HIS CAPTIVITY IN THE YEARS 1756-1757
Robert Eastburn; French & Indian War captivity account. 50 pp.
Paper. 1996. $8.95. Available from Amazon.com, $24.

A NARRATIVE OF THE EARLY DAYS & REMEMBRANCES OF OCEOLA NIKKANOCHEE, PRINCE OF ECONCHATTI, A YOUNG SEMINOLE INDIAN, et al
Andre G. Welch; Reprint of 1841 edition. Illus. 305 pp. U. Press of Florida, $19.95.

NARRATIVE OF THE EXPEDITION TO THE SOURCE OF ST. PETER'S RIVER
W.H. Keating; Facsimile of 1825 edition. Illus. Amazon.com, $20.

A NARRATIVE OF THE LIFE OF MRS. MARY JEMISON
James E. Seaver; Reprint of 1824 edition. 208 pp. Paper. Syracuse University Press, 1990. $14.95. A new edition edited by June Namias, 208 pp. U. of Oklahoma Press. $16.95.

NARRATIVE OF OCCURENCES IN THE INDIAN COUNTRIES OF NORTH AMERICA
S.H. Wilcocke; Reprint of 1817 edition. Beekman Books, $19.95.

NARRATIVE OF MY CAPTIVITY AMONG THE SIOUX
Fanny Kelly; 285 pp. New Library Pr.Net, 2003. $98.

NARRATIVES OF CAPITIVITY AMONG THE INDIANS OF NORTH AMERICA: A LIST OF BOOKS & MANUSCRIPTS ON THE SUBJECT IN THE EDWARD A. AYER COLLECTION OF THE NEWBERRY LIBRARY
Lists 339 narratives. Reprint of 1912 edition. 185 pp. Amazon.com, $35.

NARRATIVES OF INDIAN CAPTIVITIES: THE STORIES OF ROBERT EASTBURN, THE GILBERT FAMILY, & NENEMIAN HOW
Robert Eastburn, et al.; Reprint. 352 pp. Paper. Heritage Books, $26.50.

NARRATIVES OF INDIAN CAPTIVITY AMONG THE INDIANS OF NORTH AMERICA
Edward E. Ayer; Reprint. 170 pp. Martino Publishing, 1991. $65.

NARRATIVES OF THE INDIAN WARS, 1675-1699
Charles Lincoln, Editor; Reprint of 1913 edition. 312 pp. Barnes & Noble Imports, $21.50.

NARRATIVES OF PIONEER LIFE & BORDER WARFARE, Vol. I & II
Dale Payne, Editor
Reprint. Illus. Maps. 150 pp. ea. Paper. Wennawoods Publishing, $16 each.
THE NATCHEZ INDIANS: A HISTORY TO 1735
James F. Barnett, Jr.; Illus. Maps. 224 pp. University Press of Mississippi, 2011. $40; paper, $28.

NATICK DICTIONARY: A NEW ENGLAND INDIAN LEXICON
James Hammond Trumbull; Dictionary of the Natick language of the Narragansett Indians off the Rhode Island area. 400 pp. Paper. University of Nebraska Press, 2009. $30.

A NATION IN TRANSITION: DOUGLAS HENRY JOHNSTON & THE CHICKASAWS, 1898-1939 Michael Lovegrove; Biography. 256 pp. University of Oklahoma Press & The Choctaw Store, 2009. $24.95.

NATION IROQUOIS: A 17TH CENTURY ETHNOGRAPHY OF THE (ONEIDA) IROQUOIS
edited & trans. by Jose Antonio Brandao with K. Janet Ritch
The original French transcription of "Nation Iroquois" manuscript; its English translation, an overview of Iroquois culture and of Iroquois-French relations. Map. 128 pp. University of Nebraska Press, 2003. $40.

A NATION OF STATESMEN: THE POLITICAL CULTURE OF THE STOCKBRIDGE-MUNSEE MOHICANS, 1815-1972
James W. Oberly; History of the modern-day Mohicans.
352 pp. Paper. University of Oklahoma Press, 2010. $24.95.

NATION-STATES & INDIANS IN LATIN AMERICA
Greg Urban & Joel Sherzer; 370 pp. University of Texas Press, 1991. $37.50.

NATION TO NATION: TREATIES BETWEEN THE U.S. & AMERICAN INDIAN NATIONS
Suzan Shown Harjo (Cheyenne & Muscogee)
Illus. Maps. 272 pp. NMAI Press, 2014. $40.

NATION WITHIN A NATION: DEPENDENCY & THE CREE
Marie-Anik Gagne; Canadian First Nations and their struggle against economic subjection and oppression. 160 pp. Consortium Book, $49; paper, $20.

THE NATIONAL CONGRESS OF AMERICAN INDIANS: THE FOUNDING YEARS
Thomas W. Cowger; A full-length history of the NCAI.
Illus. 223 pp. University of Nebraska Press, 1999. $50; paper, $22.

NATIONAL COUNCIL ON INDIAN OPPORTUNITY: QUIET CHAMPION OF SELF-DETERMINATION
Tomas A. Britten; Illus. 352 pp. University of New Mexico Press, $45.

NATIONAL DIRECTORY OF FOUNDATION GRANTS FOR NATIVE AMERICANS
Phyllis Meiners, et al, Ed.; Profiles over 55 private foundations considered to be the most prominent funders of Native American programs. 205 pp. Paper. Alibris.com, $99.95.

NATIONAL DIRECTORY OF PHILANTHROPY FOR NATIVE AMERICANS
Phyllis A. Meiners, et al. Editors; Profiles about 40 private sector (foundations, corporations, and religious institutions) grant makers; prominent funders of Native American programs. 250 pp. Amazon.com & Alibris.com. $125.

NATIONAL IDENTITY & THE CONFLICT AT OKA: NATIVE BELONGING & MYTHS OF POSTCOLONIAL NATIONHOOD IN CANADA
Amelia Kalant; 320 pp. Routledge, 2004. $90.

NATIONAL INDIAN GAMING ASSOCIATION (NIGA) INDIAN GAMING RESOURCE DIRECTORY The complete desk-top reference guide for tribal representatives, gaming management, Indian gaming suppliers and gaming enthusiasts including listings of regional gaming associations, Indian gaming facilities, gaming regulatory agencies, Indian gaming lawyers and lobbyists, American Indian entertainment, and Indian gaming suppliers. National Indian Gaming Association, $30, members; $55, non-members.

NATIONAL INDIAN GAMING MINIMUM INTERNAL CONTROL STANDARDS FOR INDIAN CASINOS adopted by NIGA/NCAI Tribal Leader Task Force & NIGA Membership Developed by tribal professionals from within the Indian gaming industry as a set of baseline internal control procedures for gaming facilities operated by Indian Nations under the Federal Indian Gaming Regulatory Act, 1998 revised version. National Indian Gaming Association, $30, members; $55, non-members.

THE NATIONAL MUSEUM OF THE AMERICAN INDIAN: CRITICAL CONVERSATIONS
Edited by Amy Lonetree & Amanda J. Cobb; Essays on museum studies; also instructs people planning to make a visit to the National Museum of the American Indian. Photos. 518 pp. Paper. University of Nebraska Press, 2008. $29.95.

NATIONAL MUSEUM OF THE AMERICAN INDIAN: MAP & GUIDE
Illus. 64 pp. Paper. NMAI Press, 2012. $8.95.

NATIONAL MUSEUM OF THE AMERICAN INDIAN, A POSTCARD BOOK
30 full-color photos...images from the book Creation's Journey: Native American Identity & Belief. 33 pp. Running Press, $8.95.

NATIONAL MUSEUM OF THE AMERICAN INDIAN: A SOUVENIR BOOK
Illus. 64 pp. Paper. NMAI Press, 2004. $9.95.

THE NATIONAL UNCANNY: INDIAN GHOSTS & AMERICAN SUBJECTS
Renee L. Bergland; 211 pp. Paper. Dartmouth College Press, 2000.
Distributed by the University Press of New England. $22.95.

NATIONS REMEMBERED: AN ORAL HISTORY OF THE CHEROKEES, CHICKASAWS, CHOCTAWS, CREEKS, & SEMINOLES, 1865-1907
Theda Perdue; Illus. Maps. 222 pp. Paper. University of Oklahoma Press, 1993. $19.95.

NATIONS WITHIN A NATION: HISTORICAL STATISTICS OF AMERICAN INDIANS
Paul Stuart; Historical statistics on Native American tribes. Biblio. 251 pp. Greenwood, 1987. $45.

THE NATIONS WITHIN: THE PAST & FUTURE OF AMERICAN INDIAN SOVEREIGNTY
Vine Deloria, Jr. & Clifford Lytle
Reprint of 1984 edition. 304 pp. Paper. University of Texas Press, 1998. $22.95.

NATIVE ACTIVISM IN COLD WAR AMERICA: THE STRUGGLE FOR SOVEREIGNTY
Daniel M. Cobb; Illus. 318 pp. University of Kansas Press, $34.95; paper, $19.95.

NATIVE ACTS: INDIAN PERFORMANCE, 1603-1832
Joshua D. Bellin & Laura L. Mielke; Essays chronicle of the performance of "Indianess" by Natives in North America from the 17th to 19th centuries. Illus. 344 pp. Paper. University of Nebraska Press, $35. E-Book available.

NATIVE ACTS: LAW RECOGNITION, AND CULTURALL AUTHENTICITY
Joanne Barker; Illus. 250 pp. Duke University Press, 2011. $94.95; paper, $25.95.

NATIVE AMERICA
John Gattuso; A narrative approach to identify and describe the sites and activities of the Native American. Includes discussion of Amerian Indian art, Indians and alcohol, and ancestral grounds. Illus. Biblio. 389 pp. Paper. Prentice-Hall, 1992. $19.95.

NATIVE AMERICA: ARTS, TRADITIONS & CELEBRATIONS
Christine Mather; Illus. Crown Publishers, 1990. $40.

NATIVE AMERICA COLLECTED: THE CULTURE OF AN ART WORLD
Margaret Dubin; Examines the ideas and interactions involved in contemporary collecting. Illus. 192 pp. University of New Mexico Press, 2001. $29.95.

NATIVE AMERICA, DISCOVERED & CONQUERED: THOMAS JEFFERSON, LEWIS & CLARK, AND MANIFEST DESTINY
Robert J. Miller; Policies of Doctrine of Discover led to Manifest Destiny and how Native people's rights stood in the way. 240 pp. Paper. University of Nebraska Press, 2008. 18.95.

NATIVE AMERICA & THE EVOLUTION OF DEMOCRACY
Bruce E. Johansen; 184 pp. Greenwood Publishing, 1999. $65.

NATIVE AMERICA IN THE 20TH CENTURY: AN ENCYCLOPEDIA
Mary B. Davis, Editor; Contains 282 signed articles (written by historians, anthropologists, and other specialists - 40% of whom are Native American) on present-day tribal groups providing information on 20th-century American Indians & Alaska Natives. Illus. 75 photos. 25 maps. 832 pp. Amazon.com, 1994. $140; paper, $50.

*NATIVE AMERICA MEDICINE: INDIANS OF NORTH AMERICA
Chelsea House Staff; Grades 5 and up. 120 pp. Chelsea House, 1997. $9.95.

NATIVE AMERICA: PORTRAIT OF THE PEOPLES
Duane Champagne, Editor; A selection of articles covering Native American history, religion, arts, language & present-day lifeways & issues; with biographies. Illus. 200 photos & drawings. Illus. Maps. 818 pp. Paper. Amazon.com, $24.95.

NATIVE AMERICA AND THE QUESTION OF GENOCIDE
Alex Alvarez; 222 pp. Rowman & Littlefield, 2015. $44; paper, $32; eBook, $31.99.

NATIVE AMERICA: A STATE-BY-STATE HISTORICAL ENCYCLOPEDIA
Daniel S. Murphree, Editor; Comprises 50 chapters offering interpretations of Native American history through the lens of the states in which Indians lived or helped shape. Three Volumes. 1,393 pp. Greenwood Press, 2012. $294.

NATIVE AMERICAN AFFAIRS & THE DEPT. OF DEFENSE
Donald Mitchell & David Rubenson; Released from RAND the National Defense Research Institute. 76 pp. Paper. Amazon.com., 1996. $15.

NATIVE AMERICAN AIDS STATISTICS
Statistics from the U.S. CDC on reported cases of AIDS among Native Americans. Graphs. National Native American AIDS Prevention Center. No charge.

THE NATIVE AMERICAN ALMANAC: A PORTRAIT OF NATIVE AMERICA TODAY
Arlene Hirschfelder & Martha Kreipe de Montano; Includes history of Native-white relations, the location & status of tribes, religious traditions & ceremonies, language & literature, & contemporary performers & artists; organizations, Native American landmarks, museums & cultural centers. Illus. 340 pp. The Book Publishing Co., $14.95.

NATIVE AMEICAN ANARCHISM: STUDY OF LEFT WING AMERICAN INDIVIDUALISM
Eunice Minette Schuster. Paper. Da Capo Press, 1970. $40.

NATIVE AMERICAN ANCESTORS: EASTERN TRIBES
Arlene H. Eakle; 50 pp. Paper. Amazon.com, 1996. $16.50.

*NATIVE AMERICAN ANIMAL STORIES
told by Joseph Bruchac; 24 stories. Grades K-5. Illus. 160 pp. Paper. Fulcrum Publishing, 1991. $12.95. Audiocassette, $16.95.

NATIVE AMERICAN ANNUAL, Vol. I
Margaret Clark-Price; Illus. 100 pp. Native American Publishing, 1985. $8.95.

NATIVE AMERICAN ARCHITECTURE
Peter Nabaokov & Robert Easton; 307 photos. Illus. 432 pp. Oxford University Press, 1988. $99; paper, $59.95.

NATIVE AMERICAN ARCHIVES: AN INTRODUCTION
John A. Fleckner; 72 pp. Paper. Amazon.com, 1985. $7.

NATIVE AMERICAN ART
David W. Penney & George C. Longfish; Traces the development of American Indian art from the handmade tools of the Archaic Period to contemporary creations. 290 full-color black & white photos, 320 pp. Levin Associates, 1994. $85.

NATIVE AMERICAN ART
William C. Ketchum, Jr.; Illus. 128 pp. Paper. Amazon.com, 1998. $16.95.

NATIVE AMERICAN ART: COLLECTIONS OF ETHNOLOGICAL MUSEUM, BERLIN
Bolz & Sanner; Illus. 240 pp. Paper. University of Washington Press, 2000. $40.

THE NATIVE AMERICAN ART LOOK BOOK
Dawn Weiss and Barbara Zaffran, Editors; An activity book from The Brooklyn Museum. Presents objects from the museum's collection of Native American art--pottery, basketry, and wood carvings. Illus. 48 pp. Paper. W.W. Norton & Co., 1993. $14.95.

NATIVE AMERICAN ART MASTERPIECES
David W. Penney; Illus. 120 pp. Levin, Hugh Lauter Associates, 1996. $35.

NATIVE AMERICAN ART AT PHILBROOK
Philbrook Art Center; Paper. Philbrook Art Center,1980. $9.95.

NATIVE AMERICAN ART & THE NEW YORK AVANTE-GARDE
W. Jackson Rushing; The influence Native American art had on American modernist art of 1910-1950. Illus. 272 pp. University of Texas Press, 1994. $39.95.

NATIVE AMERICAN ART IN THE 20TH CENTURY
W. Jackson Rushing; Illus. 252 pp. Routledge, 1999. $110.

NATIVE AMERICAN ARTS & CULTURE
Mary Connors & Dona Herweck; Illus. 176 pp. Amazon.com, 1994. $15.99.

NATIVE AMERICAN ARTS & CULTURES
Anne D'Alleva; Illus. 136 pp. Davis Publications, 1994. $26.95.

NATIVE AMERICAN AUTOBIOGRAPHY: AN ANTHOLOGY
Arnold Krupat, Editor; Illus. 560 pp. U. of Wisconsin Press, 1994. $49.95; paper, $23.95.

NATIVE AMERICAN ARTISANS SURVEY
A survey of American Indian artists in Arizona. Atlatl, 1992. $5.

NATIVE AMERICAN BASKETRY
Sarah P. Turnbaugh; Illus. Paper. Amazon.com, 1992. $20.

NATIVE AMERICAN BASKETRY: AN ANNOTATED BIBLIOGRAPHY
Frank W. Porter, III, compiled by; 1,000+ entries on all aspetcs of Native American basketmaking. 249 pp. Greenwood, 1988. $39.95.

NATIVE AMERICAN BASKETRY OF THE SENECA & TLINGIT
Richard C. Schneider, Editor; Reprint of 1941 edition. Illus. Photos. 120 pp. Paper. R. Schneider, Publishers & Written Heritage, $9.95.

NATIVE AMERICAN BEAD WEAVING
Lynn Garner; Illus. 112 pp. Paper. Sterling Publishing, 2003. $14.95.

NATIVE AMERICAN BEADWORK
William C. Orchard; Illus. 192 pp. Paper. Dover Publications, 2002. $9.95.

NATIVE AMERICAN BEADWORK
George J. Barth; Covers all aspects of traditional Indian beadwork. Illus. 220 pp. R. Schneider, Publishers, 1993. $29.95; paper, $23.95. Paper. Written Heritage, $23.95; Crazy Crow Publications, $24..

NATIVE AMERICAN BEADWORK: PROJECTS & TECHNIQUES FROM THE SOUTHWEST Theresa Flores Geary; Illus. 128 pp. Sterling Publishing, 2003. $19.95.

NATIVE AMERICAN BIBLIOGRAPHY SERIES
Jack W. Marken, General Editor; Begun in 1980, titles in this series have focused on individual tribes, geographic areas, literature, languages, and collections of documents. See publisher for titles & prices. Scarecrow Press.

*NATIVE AMERICAN BIOGRAPHIES
3 biographies: Sacajawea, Pocahontas, Sitting Bull. Grades 3-7. Illus. 48 pp. each. Amazon.com, $3.50 each.

*NATIVE AMERICAN BIOGRAPHIES
Series of six biographies: Dennis Banks, 112 pp. Maria Tallchief, 128 pp. Geronimo, 128 pp. Scagawea, 128 pp. Jim Thorpe, 128 pp. & Siting Bull, 112 pp. Grades 6 and up. Illus. Photos. Amazon.com, 1997. $17.95 each, $107.70 per set.

NATIVE AMERICAN BOARDING SCHOOLS
Mary A. Stout; Illus. 214 pp. Greenwood Press, 2012. $58.

NATIVE AMERICAN BOLO TIES: VINTAGE & CONTEMPORARY ARTISTRY
Diana F. Pardue with Norman L. Sandfield; 200+ examples of bolo ties, Western neckties or string tie. Primarily created by Zuni, Hopi and Navajo artists & silversmiths. Published in association with the Heard Museum. Illus. 160 pp. Museum of New Mexico Press, 2012. $29.95.

*THE NATIVE AMERICAN BOOK OF CHANGE
White Deer of Autumn; illus. bu Shonto Begay
Chronicles the struggles of the American Indians since Europeans came into their world. Grades 3-7. Illus. 88 pp. Paper. Beyond Words or Amazon.com & Alibris.com, 1992. $5.95.

*THE NATIVE AMERICAN BOOK OF KNOWLEDGE
White Deer of Autumn; Grades 3-7. Paper. Amazon.com, $5.95.

*THE NATIVE AMERICAN BOOK OF LIFE
White Deer of Autumn; Grades 3-7. Paper. Amazon.com, $5.95.

*THE NATIVE AMERICAN BOOK OF WISDOM
White Deer of Autumn; Grades 3-7. Paper. Amazon.com, $5.95.

NATIVE AMERICAN BUSINESS DEVELOPMENT, TRADE PROMOTION & TOURISM ACT U.S. Senate Committee on Indian Affairs105th Congress, 2nd Session Illus. U.S. GPO, 1999.

NATIVE CANADIANA: SONGS FROM THE URBAN REZ
Gregory Scofield; 125 pp. Paper. Raincoast Book Distribution, 1996.

NATIVE AMERICAN CAPITAL FORMATION & ECONOMIC DEVELOPMENT ACT
U.S. Senate Committee on Indian Affairs
108th Congress, 1st Session. Illus. U.S. GPO, 2003.

NATIVE AMERICAN CASINOS
Melanie Dellas, Editor; Annual. Paper. Amazon.com, $50.

NATIVE AMERICAN CHECKLIST
Barbara Beaver, Compiler; Contains over 900 titles relating to Native Americans. Covers art, history, literature, religion, travel, & women's studies; audiovisual materials and children's books. 20 pp. Paper. Amazon.com. Free to schools and lbraries.

NATIVE AMERICAN & CHICANO LITERATURE OF THE AMERICAN SOUTHWEST: INTERSECTIONS OF INDIGENOUS LITERATURES
Christina M. Hebebrand; 192 pp. Text. Routledge, 2004. $70.

*NATIVE AMERICAN CHIEFS & WARRIORS
William R. Sanford
Seven book series. Grades 4-12. Illus. Enslow Publishers, 2013. $22.60 each.

NATIVE AMERICAN CLOTHING: AN ILLUSTRATED HISTORY
Theodore Brasser; Illus. 368 pp. Firefly Books, 2009. $65.

NATIVE AMERICAN COLLECTIBLES
Dawn E. Reno; Covers baskets, clothing, jewelry, photographs and pottery. Illus. 512 pp. Paper. Hothem House, 1994. $16.95 postpaid.

NATIVE AMERICAN COMMUNITIES IN WISCONSIN, 1600-1960
Robert E. Bieder; Illus. Maps. 272 pp. Paper. U. of Wisconsin Press, 1995. $18.95.

*NATIVE AMERICAN CONFEDERACIES
Anna Carew-Miller; Grades 4-9. Illus. 64 pp. Mason Crest Publishers, 2003. $19.95.

*NATIVE AMERICAN COOKING
Anna Carew-Miller; Grades 4-9. Illus. 64 pp. Mason Crest Publishers, 2003. $19.95.

NATIVE AMERICAN COURTSHIP & MARRIAGE
Leslie Gourse; Includes the Hopi, Navajo, Iroquois, and Oglala Sioux love, courtship, marriage and family traditions. Illus. Photos. 160 pp. Paper. Book Publishing Co., $11.95.

NATIVE AMERICAN CRAFT INSPIRATIONS
Janet & Alex D'Amato; Illus. 224 pp. Paper. M. Evans, 1992. $11.95.

NATIVE AMERICAN CRAFTS
Suzanne McNeill; Sterling, 1997.

NATIVE AMERICAN CRAFTS DIRECTORY
Diane L. McAlister; A guide for locating craft shops and craft suppliers. Over 1,000 entries to help you locate hard-to-find Native American products, organizations, and resources. 136 pp. 2nd Edition. The Book Publishing Co., 1998. $9.95.

NATIVE AMERICAN CRAFTS OF CALIFORNIA, THE GREAT BASIN & THE SOUTHWEST Judith Hoffman-Corwin; Amazon.com, 1999.

NATIVE AMERICAN CRAFTS OF THE NORTHWEST COAST, THE ARCTIC & THE SUBARCTIC Judith Hoffman-Corwin; Amazon.com, 1999.

NATIVE AMERICAN CRAFTS & SKILLS: A FULLY ILLUSTRATED GUIDE TO WILDERNESS LIVING & SURVIVAL
David Montgomery; Illus. 215 pp. Paper. Amazon.com, 2000. $14.95.

NATIVE AMERICAN CROSS STITCH
Julie Hasler; Illus. 128 pp. Paper. Amazon.com, 2001. $19.95

NATIVE AMERICAN CULTURAL & RELIGIOUS FREEDOMS
John R. Wunder; Reprint. 392 pp. Garland, $75.

NATIVE AMERICAN CULTURES IN INDIANA: PROCEEDINGS OF THE FIRST MINNETRISTA COUNCIL FOR GREAT LAKES NATIVE AMERICAN STUDIES
Ronald Hicks, Ed.; Illus. 135 pp.Paper. Amazon.com, 1992. $15.

*NATIVE AMERICAN CULTURES: A STUDY UNIT TO PROMOTE CRITICAL & CREATIVE THINKING Rebecca Stark; Grades 4-8. 80 pp. Student edition, 1991. $12.95; Book & Poster, 1998. $12.95. Amazon.com.

NATIVE AMERICAN DANCE: CEREMONIES & SOCIAL TRADITIONS
Charlotte Heth, General Editor; Collection of essays on Native American dance traditions & their meaning, origin, and evolution. 192 full-color photos & illus. 208 pp. NMAI Press & Fulcrum Publishing, 1992. $45.

NATIVE AMERICAN DANCE STEPS
Bessie & May Evans; 112 pp. Paper. Dover, 2003. $8.95.

NATIVE AMERICAN DESIGNS
Caren Caraway; Combines five regional books: Eastern Woodland Indian Designs, Northwest Indian Designs, Plains Indian Designs, Southeastern Woodland Indian Designs, and Southwest American Indian Designs. Illus. 240 pp. Paper. Stemmer House, 1993. Collected Edition, $27.95. Regional books, $5.95 each.

NATIVE AMERICAN DESIGNS FOR QUILTING
Joyce Mori; 80 pp. Paper. Collector Books, 1998. $14.95.

NATIVE AMERICAN DIRECTORY: ALASKA, U.S. & CANADA
Fred Synder, Editor; 2nd edition. 375 pp. Paper. Amazon.com, 1996. $59.95.

NATIVE AMERICAN DIRECTORY: VITAL RECORDS OF MAINE, MASS., RI, CT, NY & WI Lorraine Henry; 131 pp. Paper. Amazon.com, 1998. $15.

NATIVE AMERICAN DISCOURSE: POETICS & RHETORIC
Joel Sherzer & Anthony Woodbury
Illus. 256 pp. Cambridge University Press, 1987. $44.50.

*NATIVE AMERICAN DOCTOR: THE STORY OF SUSAN LaFLESCHE PICOTTE
Jeri Ferris; Grades 4-7. Biography. Photos. Lerner, 1991. $17.95; paper, $6.95.

NATIVE AMERICAN & THE EARLY REPUBLIC
Frederick Hoxie, et al; Amazon.com, 2000.

THE NATIVE AMERICAN ENCYCLOPEDIA
Donna Hightower-Langston; Illus. 455 pp. John Wiley & Sons, 2002. $40.

NATIVE AMERICAN ENCYCLOPEDIA: HISTORY, CULTURE & PEOPLES
Barry M. Pritzker; Illus. 624 pp. Oxford University Press, 2000. $99; paper, $49.95.

NATIVE AMERICAN ESTATE: THE STRUGGLE OVER INDIAN & HAWAIIAN LANDS
Linda S. Parker; 256 pp. University of Hawaii Press, 1989. $24.

NATIVE AMERICAN ETHNOBOTANY
Daniel E. Moerman; A database of plants used as foods, drugs, dyes, fibers, and more by native peoples of North America. Illus. 925 pp. Amazon.com, 1998. $79.95.

THE NATIVE AMERICAN EXPERIENCE
Lelia Wardwell; Carter Smith, Ed.; Illus. 300 pp. Ring binder. Facts on File, 1991. $140.

NATIVE AMERICAN EXPRESSIVE CULTURE
Akwe:kon Press Editors; Essays from 28 Native American writers. 1213 bxw photos. 176 pp. Paper. NMAI Press & Akwe:kon Press, Cornell University, 1996. $17.95.

NATIVE AMERICAN FAITH IN AMERICA
Michael T. Garrett & J.T. Garrett; Illus. 128 pp. Facts on File, 2003. $30.

*NATIVE AMERICAN COOKING
Anna Carew-Miller; Grades 4-9. Illus. 64 pp. Mason Crest Publishers, 2003. $19.95.

*NATIVE AMERICAN FAMILY LIFE
Colleen Madonna Flood Williams
Grades 4-9. Illus. 64 pp. Mason Crest Publishers, 2003. $19.95.

NATIVE AMERICAN FASHION: MODERN ADAPTATIONS OF TRADITIONAL DESIGNS
Margaret Wood; 2nd revised ed. Illus. 128 pp. Paper. Amazon.com, 1997. $21.95.

*NATIVE AMERICAN FESTIVALS & CEREMONIES
Jenna Glatzer; Grades 4-9. Illus. 64 pp. Mason Crest Publishers, 2003. $19.95.

NATIVE AMERICAN FETISH CARVINGS OF THE SOUTHWEST
Kay Whittle; Illus. 160 pp. Paper. Schiffer Publishing, 1998. $14.95.

NATIVE AMERICAN FLAGS
Donald T. Healy & Peter J. Orenski; Revised edition of Flags of the Native Peoples of the U.S. Illus. 325 pp. Paper. University of Oklahoma Press, 2003. $29.95.

THE NATIVE AMERICAN FLUTE - UNDERSTANDING THE GIFT: AN INTERACTIVE GUIDE FOR LEARNING TO PLAY John Vames; Sherry Fields-Vames, Ed. Illus. 104 pp. Paper. Amazon.com, 2003. $24.95, with audio CD.

NATIVE AMERICAN FOLKLORE IN 19TH-CENTURY PERIODICALS
William M. Clements; 21 essays covers all aspects of oral literature, including dance and ritual. 295 pp. Amazon.com, 1986. $39.95.

*NATIVE AMERICAN FOODS
Raven Hail; Coloring book showing many of the world's staple foods that came from Indian America. Grades K-2. Illus. 21 pp. Paper. Amazon.com, 1986. $3.95.

NATIVE AMERICAN FREEMASONRY: ASSOCIATIONALISM & PERFORMANCE IN AMERICA Joy Porter; Explores its meaning for many of the key Native leaders. Illus. 368 pp. University of Nebraska Press, 2011.$60.

*NATIVE AMERICAN GAMES & STORIES
James & Joseph Bruchac
Grades 4 and up. Illus. 96 pp. Paper. Fulcrum Publishing, 2001. $12.95.

NATIVE AMERICAN GARDENING: STORIES, PROJECTS & RECIPES FOR FAMILIES
Michael J. Caduto & Joseph Bruchac; Explores the Native American approach to gardening. Illus. 176 pp. Paper. Fulcrum Publishing, $15.95.

NATIVE AMERICAN GENEALOGICAL SOURCEBOOK
Paula K. Byers, Editor; 250 pp. Amazon.com, 1995. $69.

NATIVE AMERICAN HEALING
Howard Bad Hand; 160 pp. Paper. McGraw-Hill, 2001. $14.95.

NATIVE AMERICAN HERITAGE, Third Ed.
Merwyn Garbarino & Robert F. Sasso; A text providing a broad overview of the diversity of American Indian cultures. In 4 parts: prehistory, the construct of culture areas; various culture traits, & exploring the interactions between Native Americans & non-Natives. Illus. Maps.557 pp. Paper. Waveland Press, 1994. $37.95.

NATIVE AMERICAN HIGHER EDUCATION IN THE U.S.
Cary M. Carney; 226 pp. Amazon.com, 1999. $32.95.

NATIVE AMERICAN HISTORICAL DEMOGRAPHY: A CRITICAL BIBLIOGRAPHY
Henry Dobyns; 104 pp. Paper. Indian University Press, 1982. $4.95.

NATIVE AMERICAN HISTORY
Colin G. Calloway; 575 pp. Paper. Bedford/St. Martin's, 1999. $38.

NATIVE AMERICAN HISTORY: A CHRONOLOGY OF THE VAST ACHIEVEMENTS OF A CULTURE & THEIR LINKS TO WORLD EVENTS
Judith Nies; Illus. 430 pp. Paper. Ballantine Books, 1996. $15.

*NATIVE AMERICAN HORSEMANSHIP
Clarissa Aykroyd; Grades 4-9. Illus. 64 pp. Mason Crest Publishers, 2003. $19.95.

NATIVE AMERICAN HUNTING & FIGHTING SKILLS
Colin Taylor; Illus. 128 pp. Amazon.com, 2003. $22.95.

NATIVE AMERICAN HUNTING, FIGHTING & SURVIVAL TOOLS
Monte Burch; Illus. 256 pp. Amazon.com, 2004. $24.95.

NATIVE AMERICAN IDENTITIES: FROM STEREOTYPE TO ARCHETYPE IN ART & LITERATURE Scott B. Vickers; Illus. 200 pp. paper. U. of New Mexico Press, 1998. $25.

THE NATIVE AMERICAN IDENTITY IN SPORTS: CREATING & PRESERVING A CULTURE Frank A. Salamone, Editor
Monograph. 222 pp. Rowman & Littlefield, 2012. $76; paper, $35. eBook, $34.99.

NATIVE AMERICAN IN AMERICAN LITERATURE: A SELECTIVELY ANNOTATED BIBLIOGRAPHY Roger O. Rock; 225 pp. Greenwood Press, 1985. $36.95.

THE NATIVE AMERICAN IN LONG FICTION: AN ANNOTATED BIBLIOGRAPHY
Joan Beam & Barbara Branstad; Lists, in 2 vols., novel-length fictional works by and about Native Americans of the U.S. published between the 1890s & 1990s. 384 pp.

Scarecrow Press, 1996. (thru 1994), $59.95. Vol. 2: 400pp. Supplement, 1995-2002, 2003. $73.65.

THE NATIVE AMERICAN INDIAN ARTIST DIRECTORY
Robert Painter; Lists over 1,200 artists, sculptors, potters, rug weavers, basket makers, kachina carvers, bead workers, clothing designers, silversmiths, jewelry makers and other craftspeople from over 100 tribes across America. Includes names, addresses, phone numbers, e-mail addresses, tribal affiliations, web sites. 280 pp. Paper. First Nations Art Publisher, 1999. Available from amazon.com & e-bay.com. $19.95.

NATIVE AMERICAN INDIAN SONGS TAUGHT BY LOUIS W. BALLARD: GUIDEBOOK WITH AUDIO CDS Louis W. Ballard; Amazon.com, 2004. Ring Binder, $100.

NATIVE AMERICAN INTERNET GUIDE & ADDRESS BOOK
Barry Klein, Editor; Lists the websites, e-mail and postal addresses and phone numbers of more than 10,000 Native American groups, associations, organizations, institutions, tribal nations, businesses & individuals. 120 pp. Todd Publications, $95.

NATIVE AMERICAN ISSUES
Paul C. Rosier; Illus. 208 pp. Greenwood, 2003. $45.

NATIVE AMERICAN ISSUES: A REFERENCE HANDBOOK
ABC-Clio staff; 288 pp. ABC-Clio, 1996. $39.50.

NATIVE AMERICAN JUSTICE
Laurence French; Paper. Burnham, 2002. $23.95.

NATIVE AMERICAN LANGUAGE IDEOLOGIES: BELIEFS, PRACTICES, AND STRUGGLES IN INDIAN COUNTRY Edited by Paul V. Kroskrity & Margaret C. Field Samples the language ideologies of a wide range of Native American communities from Canada to Central America, including Cherokee, Northern Arapaho, Kiowa, Paiute, et al. . 336 pp. Illus. University of Arizona Press, 2008. $49.95.

*NATIVE AMERICAN LANGUAGES
Bethanne Kelly Patrick; Grades 4-9. Illus. 64 pp. Mason Crest Publishers, 2003. $19.95.

NATIVE AMERICAN LANGUAGES ACT
U.S. Senate Committee on Indian Affairs
108th Congress,1st Session. Illus. 165 pp. U.S. GPO, 2003.

NATIVE AMERICAN LAW & COLONIALISM BEFORE 1776 TO 1903
John R. Wunder, Editor; Reprint. Illus. 352 pp. Garland, 1996. $100.

*NATIVE AMERICAN LEADERS
Profiles 25 great leaders of North American Indian tribes mostly in the 19th century. Grades 4 and up. Illus. 64 pp. Chelsea House, $17.95.

*NATIVE AMERICAN LEADERS OF THE WILD WEST
William R. Sanford; 7 biographies: Chief Joseph, Crazy Horse, Geronimo, Quanah Parker, Red Cloud, Sitting Bull, and Osceola. Grades 4-10. Illus. Maps. Biblio. 48 pp. each. Enslow Publishing, 1994. $14.95 each; $104.65 per set.

NATIVE AMERICAN LEGENDS
131 legends from many North American Indian tribes and information and background of each legend. Six book set. Illus. 288 pp. Paper. Amazon.com, 1990, $89.70.

NATIVE AMERICAN LEGENDS OF THE GREAT LAKES & THE MISSISSIPPI VALLEY
Katherine Berry Judson; Illus. 204 pp. Northern Illinis U. Press, 2000. $38; paper, $18.

NATIVE AMERICAN LEGENDS & LORE LIBRARY
Troll Book Staff; Paper. Amazon.com, 1999. $12.

NATIVE AMERICAN LEGENDS OF THE SOUTHEAST: TALES FROM THE NATCHEZ, CADDO, BILOXI, CHICKASAW, AND OTHER NATIONS
George E. Lankford
2nd Ed. Illus. 272 pp. Paper. University of Alabama Press, 2011. $26.50. E-Book, $21.20.

NATIVE AMERICAN LIBERATION THEOLOGY: HEALING FOR BOTH THE OPPRESSES & THE OPPRESSOR Roy I. Wilson; Paper. CSS Publishing, 1997.

NATIVE AMERICAN LIFE-HISTORY NARRATIVES: COLONIAL & POSTCOLONIAL NAVAJO ETHNOGRAPHY
Susan Berry Brill de RamArez; 287 pp. University of New Mexico Press, $39.95.

NATIVE AMERICAN LITERATURE: A VERY SHORT INTRODUCTION
Sean Teuton; Paper. Oxford University Press, 2018. $11.95.

NATIVE AMERICAN IN LONG FICTION: AN ANNOTATED BIBLIOGRAPHY
Joan Beam & Barbara Branstad; 385 pp. Scarecrow Press, 1996. $76.95.

NATIVE AMERICAN MASCOT CONTROVERSY: A HANDBOOK
C. Richard King, Editor
290 pp. Rowman & Litlefield, 2010. $58; paper, $28; eBook, $27.99..

NATIVE AMERICAN MATHEMATICS
Michael P. Closs; 13 essays of mathematical development among cultures of Ojibway, the Inuit (Eskimo), and Nootka, Chumash of California, Aztec & Maya. Illus. 439 pp. Paper. University of Texas Press, 1986. $35.

*NATIVE AMERICAN MEDICINE
Tamra Orr; Grades 4-9. Illus. 64 pp. Mason Crest Publishers, 2003. $19.95.

NATIVE AMERICAN MONUMENTS
Brian Innes; 48 pp. Steck-Vaughn, 1999. $6.95.

NATIVE AMERICAN MUSIC DIRECTORY
Greg Gombert; 1,600 listings of traditional flute, vocal, pow wow, peyote, rock, and country songs in print and available for purchase in the U.S. and Canada. 2nd Ed. Illus. 176 pp. Amazon.com, 1999. $14.95, with audio CD.

NATIVE AMERICAN MYTH & LEGEND: AN A-Z OF PEOPLE & PLACES
Mike Dixon-Kennedy; Illus. 304 pp. Paper. Sterling, 1996. $27.95; paper, $17.95.

NATIVE AMERICAN MYTHOLOGY A TO Z
Patricia Ann Lynch; Facts on File, 2004. $35.

NATIVE AMERICAN MYTHS
Diana Ferguson; Illus. 160 pp. Paper. Sterling Publishing, 2001. $24.95.

NATIVE AMERICAN MYTHS & MYSTERIES
Vincent H. Gaddis
Reprint. Paper. Borderland Sciences Research Foundation, 1991. $12.95.

THE NATIVE AMERICAN ORAL TRADITION: VOICES OF THE SPIRIT & SOUL
Lois J. Einhorn, contributor; Illus. 192 pp. Greenwood Publishing, 2000. $85.

NATIVE AMERICAN ORAL TRADITIONS: COLLABORATION & INTERPRETATION
Larry Evers & Barre Toelken, Editors; Native American oral texts with commentary. 256 pp. University Press of Colorado & Utah State U. Press, 2001. $41.95; paper, $26.95;

NATIVE AMERICAN PAINTED BUFFALO HIDES
George P. Horse Capture, Anne Vitart, and Richard West, Editors   .
Collection of 100 photos of painted buffalo hides. Includes introductory & historical essays by two Native American art experts. Illus. 168 pp. W.W. Norton & Co., 1993. $35.

NATIVE AMERICAN PEDAGOGY & COGNITIVE-BASED MATHEMATICS INSTRUCTION Judith T. Hankes; 168 pp. Amazon.com, 1998. $65.

*NATIVE AMERICAN PEOPLE
Rita D'Apice, et al; Grades 5-8. Illus. 6 book set. 192 pp. Amazon.com, $59.70 per set.

NATIVE AMERICAN PERIODICALS & NEWSPAPERS, 1828-1982: BIBLIOGRAPHY, PUBLISHING RECORD & HOLDINGS
James Danky, Editor; Maureen Hady, Compiler; Lists 1,200 Native American periodicals in 146 libraries in North America. Illus. 565 pp. Greenwood, 1983. $50.95.

NATIVE AMERICAN PERSPECTIVES
Illus. 225 pp. McDougal Littell, 2001. $13.50.

NATIVE AMERICAN PERSPECTIVES ON THE HISPANIC COLONIZATION OF ALTA CALIFORNIA   Edward D. Castillo, Ed.; 520 pp. Garland, 1992. $30.

NATIVE AMERICAN PERSPECTIVES ON LITERATURE & HISTORY
Alan R. Velie; 136 pp. Paper. University of Oklahoma Press, 1995. $14.95.

NATIVE AMERICAN PICTURE BOOKS OF CHANGE: HISTORIC CHILDREN'S BOOKS
Rebecca C. Benes; Story of children's books of the last century documenting four decades of these picture books in a readers' series for Pueblo, Navajo, and Lakota/Dakota children. Illus. 106 color plates. 176 pp. Museum of New Mexico Press, 2004. $45.

NATIVE AMERICAN PLACE-NAMES OF CONNECTICUT
R.A. Douglas-Lithgow; 96 pp. Paper. Amazon.com, 2000. $9.95.

NATIVE AMERICAN PLACE-NAMES OF INDIANA
Michael McCafferty; A linguistic history of Native American place-names in Indiana. Illus. 336 pp. University of Illinois Press, 2008. $52.

NATIVE AMERICAN PLACE-NAMES OF MAINE, NEW HAMPSHIRE & VERMONT
R.A. Douglas-Lithgow; 96 pp. Paper. Amazon.com, 2000. $9.95.

NATIVE AMERICAN PLACE NAMES OF MASSACHUSETTS
R.A. Douglas-Lithgow; 96 pp. Paper. Amazon.com, 2000. $9.95.

NATIVE AMERICAN PLACE NAMES IN MISSISSIPPI
Keith A. Baca; Illus. Map. 160 pp. University Press of Mississippi, 2011. $50; paper, $22.

NATIVE AMERICAN PLACE-NAMES OF RHODE ISLAND
R.A. Douglas-Lithgow; 96 pp. Paper. Amazon.com, 2000. $9.95.

NATIVE AMERICAN PLACENAMES OF SOUTHWEST: HANDBOOK FOR TRAVELERS
William Bright; 174 pp. Paper. University of Oklahoma Press, $19.95.

NATIVE AMERICAN PLACE-NAMES OF THE U.S.
William Bright; Dictionary of American placenames derived from Native languages; details the history and culture found in American Indian placenames. 608 pp. University of Oklahoma Press, 2004. $59.95.

NATIVE AMERICAN POETRY: NATIVE AMERICAN ANTHOLOGY OF POETRY
Louis Hooban, Editor; 100 pp. Paper. Amazon.com, 1998. $19.95.

NATIVE AMERICAN POLITICAL SYSTEMS & THE EVOLUTION OF DEMOCRACY: AN ANNOTATED BIBLIOGRAPHY Bruce E. Johansen; 184 pp. Greenwood, 1996. $67.95.

NATIVE AMERICAN PORTRAITS
Nancy Hathaway; Illus. 120 pp. Paper. Amazon.com, 1990. $16.95.

NATIVE AMERICAN POSTCOLONIAL PSYCHOLOGY
Eduardo Duran & Bonnie Duran
227 pp. Paper. State University of New York Press, 1995. $27.95.

NATIVE AMERICAN POWER IN THE U.S., 1783-1795
Celia Barnes; Illus. 256 pp. Amazon.com, 2003. $47.50.

NATIVE AMERICAN PRESS IN WISCONSIN & THE NATION: PROCEEDINGS OF THE CONFERENCE, APRIL, 1982 James P. Danky and Maureen B. Hady
197 pp. Paper. Amazon.com, 1982. $6.50.

NATIVE AMERICAN PROFILES
Gene Machamer; Illus. 170 pp. Paper. Carlisle Press, 1996. $10.

NATIVE AMERICAN PROPHECIES: HISTORY, WISDOM & STARTLING PREDICTIONS
Scott Peterson; 2nd revised edition. 454 pp. Amazon.com, 1999. $15.95.

NATIVE AMERICAN READER: STORIES, SPEECHES & POEMS
Anthology of stories. Amazon.com, $25.

NATIVE AMERICAN REFERENCE COLLECTION: DOCUMENTS COLLECTED BY THE OFFICE OF INDIAN AFFAIRS Amazon.com, 1994. $3,695.

NATIVE AMERICAN RELIGION
Joel W. Martin; 144 pp. Oxford University Press, 1999. $32.95.

*NATIVE AMERICAN RELIGIONS
Rob Staeger; Grades 4-9. Illus. 64 pp. Mason Crest Publishers, 2003. $19.95.

NATIVE AMERICAN RELIGIONS
Sam Gill; 2nd Ed. Illus. 210 pp. Paper. Amazon.com, 2004. $45.95.

NATIVE AMERICAN RELIGIONS
Paula Hartz; Facts on File, 2004.

NATIVE AMERICAN RELIGIONS: A GEOGRAPHICAL SURVEY
John J. Collins; Illus. 394 pp. Edwin Mellen Press, 1991. $99.95.

NATIVE AMERICAN RELIGIONS: AN INTRODUCTION
Denise Lardner Carmody & John Tully Carmody
Surveys major aspects of the traditional religious lives of native peoples in all parts of the Americas. Illus. 288 pp. paper. Amazon.com, 1993. $14.95.

NATIVE AMERICAN RELIGIONS: NORTH AMERICA
Lawrence Sullivan; Macmillan, 1989. $15.95.

*NATIVE AMERICAN RELIGIONS: WORLD RELIGIONS
Paula R. Hartz; Grades 6 and up. Illus. 128 pp. Facts on File, 1997. $21.95.

NATIVE AMERICAN RELIGIOUS IDENTITY: UNFORGOTTEN GODS
Jace Weaver, Ed.; 280 pp. Paper. Orbis Books, 1998. $18.

NATIVE AMERICAN RENAISSANCE
Kenneth Lincoln; 320 pp. Paper. University of California Press, 1985. $28.95.

THE NATIVE AMERICAN RENAISSANCE: LITERARY IMAGINATION & ACHIEVEMENT
Alan R. Velie & A. Robert Lee, Editors
368 pp. Paper. University of Oklahoma Press, $29.95.

NATIVE AMERICAN REPRESENTATIONS: FIRST ENCOUNTERS, DISTORTED IMAGES, & LITERARY APPROPRIATIONS
Edited by Gretchen M. Bataille; Leading critics examine images in a wide range of media. 265 pp. University of Nebraska Press, 2001. $75; paper, $29.95.

NATIVE AMERICAN RESEARCH INFORMATION SERVICE
William Carmack, et al
292 pp. Paper. UCLA, American Indian Studies Center, 1983. $15.

NATIVE AMERICAN RESOURCE HANDBOOK
Kansas Lewis & Clark Bicentennial Commission 2003
Provides information on cultural protocol and communications, a list of Kansas' historic and resident tribes with contact information, and other resources. Free and available by e-mailing the Kansas Lewis & Clark Bicentennial Commission. E-mail: kslewisandclark@charter.net.

NATIVE AMERICAN RESURGENCE & RENEWAL: A READER & BIBLIOGRAPHY
Robert N. Wells, Jr.; Native American self determination. Treaty rights & tribal sovereignty. Illus. 671 pp. Scarecrow Press, 1994. $88.

*NATIVE AMERICAN RIGHTS
Tamara L. Roleff, Editor; Grades 5-12. 208 pp. Greenhaven, 1997. $26.50; paper, 16.20.

THE NATIVE AMERICAN RIGHTS MOVEMENT
Mark Grossman & ABC-Clio Staff; Follows the efforts to preserve and recover the civil rights of American Indians in the U.S. Illus. 400 pp. ABC-CLIO, 1996. $60.

NATIVE AMERICAN SACRED PLACES: HEARING BEFORE THE COMMITTEE ON INDIAN AFFAIRS Senate Committee on Indian Affairs Staff
107th Congress, 2nd Session/ Illus. U.S. GPO, 2002.

NATIVE AMERICAN SADDLERY & TRAPPINGS: A HISTORY IN PAPER DOLLS
J.K. Oliver; Illus. 32 pp. Paper. Texas Tech University Press, 2002. $10.95.

NATIVE AMERICAN SON: THE LIFE & SPORTING LEGEND OF JIM THORPE
Kate Buford; Illus. 528 pp. Paper. University of Nebraska Press, 2010. $24.95.

NATIVE AMERICAN SONGS FOR PIANO SOLO
Gail Smith; 48 pp. Paper. Mel Bay Publications, 1995. $6.95. with audio CD, $21.95.

NATIVE AMERICAN SONGS & POEMS
Swann, Editor; 64 pp. Paper. Dover, $1.

NATIVE AMERICAN SOVEREIGNTY
John R. Wunder, Ed.; 400 pp. Paper. Garland, 1999. $32.

NATIVE AMERICAN SOVEREIGNTY ON TRIAL: A HANDBOOK WITH CASES, LAWS & DOCUMENTS Bryan H. Wildenthal; Illus. 360 pp. ABC-CLIO, 2003. $55.

NATIVE AMERICAN SPEAKERS OF THE EASTERN WOODLANDS: SELECTED SPEECHES & CRITICAL ANALYSES
Barbara Alice Mann, Editor; Illus. 300 pp. Greenwood Publishing, 2001. $91.95.

NATIVE AMERICAN SPIRITUALITY
Speaks Lightning; A glimpse into the diverse religious/spiritual beliefs & practices of the North American Indians. Amazon.com, $6.95.

NATIVE AMERICAN SPIRITUALITY: EXTRACTS FROM THE JESUIT RELATIONS
Claudio R. Salvucci, Ed.; Illus. 400 pp. Amazon.com, 2005. $85.

NATIVE AMERICAN SPIRITUALITY: A CRITICAL READER
Lee Irwin; Essays that explore the problems and prsoepcts of understanding and writing about Native American spirituality in the 21st century. 334 pp. Paper. University of Nebraska Press, 2000. $24.95.

*NATIVE AMERICAN SPORTS & GAMES
Rob Staeger; Grades 4-9. Illus. 64 pp. Mason Crest Publishers, 2003. $19.95.

*NATIVE AMERICAN STORIES
Joseph Bruchac; illus. by John Kahiuonhes Fadden; 25 myths. Grades 4 and up. 1160 pp. Paper. Fulcrum Publishing, $12.95; audio tape, $16.95.

NATIVE AMERICAN STORYTELLING: A READER OF MYTHS & LEGENDS
Karl Kroeber
Illus. 144 pp. Amazon.com, 1991. $79.95; paper, $24.95. E-book available

NATIVE AMERICAN STUDIES
Clara Sue Kidwell & Alan Velie, Editors
Illus. Maps. 162 pp. Paper. University of Nebraska Press, 2005. $19.95.

NATIVE AMERICAN STUDIES FORM: MODELS FOR COLLABORATION BETWEEN UNIVERSITIES & INDIGENOUS NATIONS
Duane Champagne & Jay Staus, Eds.; Illus. 272 pp. U. of Arizona Press, Amazon.com, Alibris.com, 2002. $72; paper, $26.95.

NATIVE AMERICAN STUDIES: A GUIDE TO REFERENCE & INFORMATION SOURCES
Sara Heitshu & Thomas H. Marshall; 300 pp. Amazon.com, 2004.

NATIVE AMERICAN STUDIES: NEW NATIVE AMERICAN STORYTELLERS
Clifford E. Trafzer; 496 pp. Paper. Doubleday, 1996. $14.95.

THE NATIVE AMERICAN STRUGGLE: CONQUERING THE RULE OF LAW: A COLLOQUIUM Margaret A. Gilbert-Temple, Managing Editor
Speeches, articles and review essays. 226 pp. Paper. New York U., Review of Law & Social Change. Volume XX, 1993. $7.

NATIVE AMERICAN STYLE
Elmo Baca & M.J. Van Deventer; Collection of Native & native-inspired designs in art, architecture & interior design. Includes history & tradition of Native American craftsmanship & profiles of modern artisans & craftspeople. Illus. Color photos. 145 pp. Gibbs Smith, Publisher, 1999. $39.95.

THE NATIVE AMERICAN SUN DANCE RELIGION & CEREMONY: AN ANNOTATED BIBLIOGRAPHY
Phillip M. White; Illus. 144 pp. Greenwood Publishing, 1998. $62.95.

NATIVE AMERICAN SURVIVAL SKILLS
W. Ben Hunt; Survival & craft instructions for moccasin making, beadwork items, bows & arrows, et al. Illus. 280 pp. Paper. Written Heritage, $14.95.

NATIVE AMERICAN SWEAT LODGE: HISTORY & LEGENDS
Joseph Bruchac; Explains the history, the meaning and the use of the sweat lodge. Illus. 146 pp. Paper. The Crossing Press, 1993. $12.95.

NATIVE AMERICAN TALES - COYOTE
Richard Erdoes; David McKay, 1992.

*NATIVE AMERICAN TALKING SIGNS
The sign language of the North American Indians is explained and placed into context. Grades 4 and up. Illus. 64 pp. Chelsea House, $17.95.

NATIVE AMERICAN TAROT INTERPRETED
Donna Shaw; Reprint. 2nd Ed. Illus. 272 pp. Paper. Lazuli Productions, 1993. $20.

*NATIVE AMERICAN TESTIMONY: AN ANTHOLOGY OF INDIAN & WHITE RELATIONS, FIRST ENCOUNTER TO DISPOSSESSION
Peter Nabokov, Editor; Grades 7-and up. Illus. 220 pp. Amazon.com, 1992. $25.

NATIVE AMERICAN TESTIMONY: A CHRONICLE OF INDIAN-WHITE RELATIONS FROM PROPHECY TO THE PRESENT, 1492-2000, REVISED EDITION
Peter Nabokov, Editor
Collection of essays by Native Americans. 512 pp. Paper. Penguin USA, 1999. $19.95.

NATIVE AMERICAN THEOLOGY
Clara Sue Kidwell, et al; 210 pp. Paper. Orbis Books, 2001. $21.95.

THE NATIVE AMERICAN TODAY
Joan Isom & Claude Noble, Editors; 118 pp. Paper. Northeastern State U., 1986. $6.95.

*NATIVE AMERICAN TOOLS & WEAPONS
Rob Staeger; Grades 4-9. Illus. 64 pp. Mason Crest Publishers, 2003. $19.95.

NATIVE AMERICAN TRADITIONS
Arthur Versluis; Paper. Element Press, 1993. $9.95.

NATIVE AMERICAN TRIBALISM: INDIAN SURVIVALS & RENEWALS
D'Arcy McNickle; Illus. 120 pp. Paper. Oxford University Press, 1993. $39.95.

NATIVE AMERICAN TRIBES
Norman B. Hunt; Illus. 96 pp. Amazon.com, 1997. $12.98.

NATIVE AMERICAN TRIBES: THE HISTORY & CULTURE OF THE IROQUOIS CONFEDERACY Charles River Editors; Illus. Paper. 32 pp. Amazon.com, $5.99

NATIVE AMERICAN TRADITIONS
Sam Gill; 200 pp. Paper. Amazon.com, 1983. $12.95.

NATIVE AMERICAN TRANSRACIAL ADOPTEES TELL THEIR STORIES
Rita J. Simon & Sarah Hernandez; Monograph. Lexington Books, c/o Rowman & Littlefield, 2008. $100; paper, $40.99; eBook, $40.99.

NATIVE AMERICAN TRUTHS: PHILOSOPHY OF GOOD MEDICINE
H.M. Byron; Illus. 72 pp. Paper. Dorrance, 1999. $10.

NATIVE AMERICAN VERBAL ART: TEXTS & CONTEXTS
William F. Clements; 252 pp. Paper. University of Arizona Press, 1996. $22.95.

NATIVE AMERICAN VISIONS CALENDAR
12 exquisite Sam English (Ojibwa artist) full-color prints; calendar with 10x14 print and appointment calendar below; and selected quotes from historic & present-day tribal leaders. Available in August for upcoming year. Fulcrum Publishing, $10.95.

NATIVE AMERICAN VOICES
David A. Rausch & Blair Schlepp; Native American history & culture from an evangelical perspective. Describes Native cultures before the coming of the Europeans. 192 pp. Paper. Amazon.com, 1993. $10.99.

NATIVE AMERICAN VOICES: A HISTORY & ANTHOLOGY
Steven Mintz; An anthology of 95 selections which provide an overview of Native American history. Revised 2nd edition. Illus. 264 pp. Paper. Amazon.com, 2000. $31.95.

NATIVE AMERICAN VOICES: A READER
Susan Lobo, Steve Talbot, Traci L. Morris
3rd Ed. Illus. Maps. 525 pp. Prentice Hall PTR, 2010. $50; paper, $25.

THE NATIVE AMERICAN WARRIOR, 1500-1890
Chris McNab; Illus. Maps. 224 pp. Alibris, 2010. $1.50.

*NATIVE AMERICAN WAY OF LIFE
Grades 4-8. 28 pp. Paper. Council for Indian Education, 1997. $1.95.

NATIVE AMERICAN WEAPONS
Colin F. Taylor; Surveys weapons made and used by American Indians north of Mexico from prehistoric times to the late 19th century. Illus. 128 pp. Paper. University of Oklahoma Press, 2001. $19.95.

NATIVE AMERICAN WISDOM
Kristen M. Cleary, Ed.; 64 pp. Amazon.com, 1996. $5.

NATIVE AMERICAN WISDOM
Edward S. Curtis; Reprint edition. Illus. Photos. 128 pp. Running Press, 1993. $4.95.

NATIVE AMERICAN WISDOM
Kent Nerburn & Louise Mengelkoch, Editors; Collection of philosophical and religious thoughts, quotations from Chief Joseph, Sitting Bull, Red Cloud, Black Elk, Ohiyesa, and others. 127 pp. Audiocassette, $10.95. Paper. Amazon.com, $4.95.

NATIVE AMERICAN WISDOM, 3 Vols.
Terry P. Wilson, Text by; Hopi: Following the Path of Peace; Lakota: Seeking the Great Spirit; and Navajo: Walking in Beauty. Illus. 64 pp. each. Amazon.com, 1990. $9.95 each; $29.95/set.

NATIVE AMERICAN WOMEN
Charles Convis; Illus. 64 pp. Paper. Pioneer Press, 1996. $7.95.

NATIVE AMERICAN WOMEN: A BIOGRAPHICAL DICTIONARY
Gretchen M. Bataille, Editor; Profiles more than 200 Native American women born in the U.S. and Canada. Covers both historical and contemporary figures; bibliographies of primary & secondary works. 2nd Ed. Illus. 360 pp. Amazon.com, 1993. $20.

NATIVE AMERICAN WOMEN: A CONTEXTUAL BIBLIOGRAPHY
Rayna Green; 700 entries about or by Native North American women. 128 pp. Amazon.com & Alibris.com, 1983. $25.

THE NATIVE AMERICAN WORLD BEYOND APALACHEE: WEST FLORIDA & THE CHATTAHOOCHEE VALLEY

John H. Hann; Study using Spanish language sources in documenting the original Indian inhabitants of West Florida, focusing on the small tribes: Amacano, Chine, Chacato, Chisca and Pensacola. Illus. Maps. 240 pp. University Press of Florida, 2006. $55.

NATIVE AMERICAN WORLDVIEWS: AN INTRODUCTION
Jerry H. Gill; 293 pp. Paper. Prometheus Books, 2002. $25.

NATIVE AMERICAN WRITERS
Stanley Barkann & Joseph Bruchac; Cross-Cultural Communications, 1991. $75.

NATIVE AMERICAN WRITING IN THE SOUTHEAST: AN ANTHOLOGY, 1875-1935
Daniel Littlefield, Jr. & James Parins, Editors; The first anthology of Native American literature representing tribes of the Southeastern U.S. 232 pp. University Press of Mississippi, 1995. $50; paper, $22.

NATIVE AMERICANS
Donald A. Grinde, Jr.; The political history of Native Americans. Illus. 400 pp. CQ Press, 2002. $180.

NATIVE AMERICANS
Edward S. Curtis; Illus. 192 pp. Paper. Amazon.com, 2001. $9.99.

NATIVE AMERICANS
Frederick Hoxie & Harvey Markowitz; Bibliography. 325 pp. Scarecrow Press, 1991. $42.

NATIVE AMERICANS
Biographies. 480 pp. World Publications, 2003. $25.

*NATIVE AMERICANS
Preschool-8. Illus. 32 pp. Paper. Smithsonian, $29.50.

NATIVE AMERICANS
Norman B. Hunt; Paper. Amazon.com, 1998. $19.98.

*NATIVE AMERICANS
William Dudley, Editor
Grades 5-12. Illus. Paper. Greenhaven Press, 1997. $26.20; paper, $16.20.

NATIVE AMERICANS
Dona Herweck & Mari L. Robbins; Illus. Amazon.com, 1994. $14.95.

NATIVE AMERICANS
E.D. Hirsch, Ed.; Teacher edition. Amazon.com, 2003. $8.95.

THE NATIVE AMERICANS
Carter Smith, Editor; Illus. 288 pp. Facts on File, 1990. $14.50.

THE NATIVE AMERICANS
Robert Spencer & Jesse Jennings; The prehistory & ethnology of the pre-Columbian North American Indian, from the Arctic to Middle America. Reprint of 1965 edition. Illus. Maps. 539 pp. High-Lonesome, $25.

NATIVE AMERICANS
Brendan January; History in Art Series. Steck-Vaughn, 2005.

NATIVE AMERICANS: AN ANNOTATED BIBLIOGRAPHY
Frederick E. Hoxie & Harvey Markowitz; Overview of Native American studies, including introductory texts and popular accounts. 324 pp. Scarecrow Press, 1991. $42.

NATIVE AMERICANS AS SHOWN ON STAGE, 1753-1916
Eugene Jones; 219 pp. Scarecrow Press, 1988. $52.75.

NATIVE AMERICANS & ARCHAEOLOGISTS: STEPPING STONES TO COMMON GROUND Nina Swidler, et al, Editors
Illus. 320 pp. Paper. AtlaMira Press, 1997. $38; eBook, $36.99.

NATIVE AMERICANS AT MISSION SAN JOSE
Randall Milliken; Illus. Maps. 112 pp. Malki-Ballena Press, 2008. $32.95; paper, $19.95.

NATIVE AMERICANS BEFORE 1492: THE MOUNDBUILDING CENTERS OF THE EASTERN WOODLANDS
Lynda N. Shaffer; Illus. 149 pp. M.E. Sharpe, 1992. $68.95; paper, $28.95.

*NATIVE AMERICANS & BLACK AMERICANS
Kim Dramer; Grades 5 and up. 120 pp. Chelsea House, 1997. $9.95.

NATIVE AMERICAN AND THE CHRISTIAN RIGHT
Andrea Smith; 250 pp. Duke University Press.

*NATIVE AMERICANS & CHRISTIANITY
Steve Klotts; Grades 5 and up. 120 pp. Chelsea House, 1996. $19.95; paper, $9.95.

NATIVE AMERICANS, CHRISTIANITY, AND THE RESHAPING OF THE AMERICAN RELIGIOUS LANDSCAPE Joel W. Martin & Mark A. Nicholas, Editors
Essays. Maps. 336 pp. University of North Carolina Press, 2010. $75; paper, $27.95.

NATIVE AMERICANS & THE EARLY REPUBLIC
Frederick E. Hoxie, et al, Eds.
Illus. 390 pp. Paper. Amazon.com, 2000. $19.50.

NATIVE AMERICANS: AN ENCYCLOPEDIA OF HISTORY, CULTURE & PEOPLES
Barry Pritzker; 2 Vols. Illus. 868 pp. ABC-Clio, 1998. $150.

NATIVE AMERICANS & THE ENVIRONMENT: PERSPECTIVES ON THE ECOLOGICAL INDIAN Michael E. Harkin & David Rich Lewis, Editors
Essay. Illus. 370 pp. Paper. University of Nebraska Press, 2007. $24.95.

NATIVE AMERICANS: ETHNOLOGY & BACKGROUNDS OF THE NORTH AMERICAN INDIANS Robert Spencer; Second edition. Illus. Amazon.com, $38.50.

NATIVE AMERICANS IN THE CAROLINA BORDERLANDS: A CRITICAL ETHNOGRAPHY Michael Spivey; Illus. 212 pp. Amazon.com, 2000. $50.

NATIVE AMERICANS IN FICTION: A GUIDE TO 765 BOOKS FOR LIBRARIANS AND TEACHERS, K-9 Vicki Anderson; Works are primarily from 1963-1993. Entries provide author, publisher, date, grade designation and a brief annotation. 180 pp. McFarland, 1994. $31.50.

*NATIVE AMERICANS IN FLORIDA
Dean Quigley, Kevin M. McCarthy, Ted Morris
Grades 4 and up. Illus. 216 pp. Pineapple Press, 2003. $25.95; Teacher's manual, $4.

NATIVE AMERICANS IN THE MOVIES: PORTRAYALS FROM SILENT FILMS TO THE PRESENT Michael Hilger; **464 PP.** Rowman & Littlefield, 2015. $100; eBook, $95.

NATIVE AMERICANS IN THE SATURDAY EVENING POST
Peter G. Beidler & Marion F. Egge; Lists references & provides extensive summaries of many of the writings, and in many of the important articles, the authors have quoted excerpts. Also included are reproductions of the images and illustrations from the magazine. Illus. 400 pp. Scarecrow Press, 1999. $88.

NATIVE AMERICANS IN SPORTS
C. Richard King, Ed.; Illus. 2 Vols. 376 pp. M.E. Sharpe, Inc., 2004. $159.

NATIVE AMERICANS IN THE TWENTIETH CENTURY
James S. Olson & Raymond Wilson; Survey of Native American history from the 1890s to the present. 264 pp. Paper. University of Illinois Press, 1986. $26.

NATIVE AMERICANS: THE INDIGENOUS PEOPLE OF NORTH AMERICA
Taylor & Sturtevant
Illus. Color photos. Artifact spreads. 256 pp. Advantage Publishers, 1991. $24.95.

NATIVE AMERICANS: AN INTEGRATED UNIT
Kathy Rogers; Illus. 80 pp. Paper. Amazon.com, 1993. $12.95.

NATIVE AMERICANS & THE LAW
Gary A. Sokolow; ABC-Clio, 1998. $39.50.

NATIVE AMERICANS & THE LAW: CONTEMPORARY & HISTORICAL PERSPECTIVES ON AMEIRCAN INDIAN RIGHTS, FREEDOM & SOVEREIGNTY
John R. Wunder; 6 vols. Garland, 1997. $406.

NATIVE AMERICANS & THE NEW DEAL: THE OFFICE FILES OF JOHN COLLIER, 1933-1945 Robert Lester, et al, Eds.; 20 pp. Amazon.com, 1993.

NATIVE AMERICANS & NIXON: PRESIDENTIAL POLITICS & MINORITY SELF–DETERMINATION, 1969-1972
Jack D. Forbes; A study of how the Nixon administration dealt with Indian demands. 2nd edition. 148 pp. Paper. UCLA, American Indian Studies Center, 1982. $12.

NATIVE AMERICANS: NORTH AMERICA
Frederick E. Hoxie & Harvey Markowitz; Illus. 324 pp. Scarecrow, 1991. $40.

NATIVE AMERICANS OF CALIFORNIA & NEVADA
Jack D. Forbes; Revised edition. 240 pp. Illus. Photos. Paper. Naturegraph, $16.95.

THE NATIVE AMERICANS OF CONNECTICUT: HOLDING ON & MOVING FORWARD
CT State Dept. of Education; Teacher resource guide; workbook includes readings, activities, & lesson plans to help educators with Native American history curricula.

NATIVE AMERICANS: CRIME & JUSTICE
Marianne Nielsen & Robert A. Silverman, Editors
Illus. 336 pp. Paper. Westview Press, 1996. Available from Amazon.com, $9.95.

NATIVE AMERICANS & THE LEGACY OF HARRY S. TRUMAN
Brian Hosmer, Editor; Covers the end of the Indian New Deal and the start of the policy known as termination, the end of tribalism and the assimilation of all Native Americans and a dismantling of the trust relationship betweem the U.S. Government and Native Nations. Illus. 170 pp. Paper. Truman State University Press, 2010.

NATIVE AMERICANS OF THE NORTHWEST COAST: A CRITICAL BIBLIOGRAPHY
Robert S. Grumet; Illus. 128 pp. Paper. Indiana University Press, 1979. $5.95.

NATIVE AMERICANS OF THE PACIFIC COAST
Vinson Brown; Life as it was 300 years ago along the Pacific Coast. Illus. Photos. 272 pp. Paper. Naturegraph, 1979. $16.95.

NATIVE AMERICANS OF THE SOUTHWEST
Sheila Wyborny; Amazon.com, 2004.

*NATIVE AMERICANS OF THE SOUTHWEST: A JOURNEY OF DISCOVERY
Tito E. Naranjo; Grades 5-9. Running Press, 1993.

NATIVE AMERICANS OF THE SOUTHWEST: THE SERIOUS TRAVELER'S INTRODUCTION TO PEOPLES & PLACES
Zdenek Salzmann & Joy Salzmann; Illus. 176 pp. Paper. Westview Press, 1997. $20.

NATIVE AMERICANS OF TEXAS
Sandra L. Myers; Surveys the history of the Native American people of Texas from prehistoric times to the present. Illus. Map. Biblio. 46 pp. American Press, 1981. $3.95.

THE NATIVE AMERICANS OF THE TEXAS EDWARDS PLATEAU, 1582-1799
Maria F. Wade; maps by Don E. Wade
Illus. Maps. 319 pp. University of Texas Press, 2003. $39.95.

*NATIVE AMERICANS OF WASHINGTON STATE: A CURRICULUM GUIDE FOR THE ELEMENTARY GRADES A guide to aid the elementary classroom teacher in implementing Native American curriculum in classroom. Grades 1-6. 40 pp. Daybreak Star Press, $5.50.

NATIVE AMERICANS OF THE WEST, A SOURCEBOOK ON THE AMERICAN WEST
C. Carter Smith; Amazon.com, 1992. $14.15.

NATIVE AMERICANS ON FILM & VIDEO
Elizabeth Weatherford, with Emilia Seubert, Editors; Detailed descriptions of films and videotapes about Indians and Inuit of the Americas. Two volumes Volume I, 151 pp., 1981; Volume II, 112 pp., 112 pp. Paper. National Museum of the American Indian, $5 & $7.

NATIVE AMERICANS ON NETWORK TV: STEREOTYPES, MYTHS, AND THE "GOOD INDIAN" Michael Ray Fitzgerald; 278 pp. Rowman & Littlefield, 2013. $85; eBook, $84.99.

*NATIVE AMERICANS: THE PEOPLE & HOW THEY LIVED
Eloise Potter & John Funderburg; Grades 4-12. Illus. 80 pp. North Carolina State Museum of Natural Sciences, 1986. $18.95; paper, $14.95.

*NATIVE AMERICANS: A PERSONAL HISTORY BOOK
This interctive workbook includes a chronological overview of the history of an American culture; open-ended exercises for research projects. Index & answer key. SVE, $7.95; package of ten, $69.

NATIVE AMERICANS & POLITICAL PARTICIPATION
Jerry D. Stubben, et al; 310 pp. ABC-CLIO, 2005. $60.

NATIVE AMERICANS & PUBLIC POLICY
Fremont Lyden & Lyman Legters; Illuis. 344 pp. Paper. University of Pittsburgh Press, 1992. $27.95.

THE NATIVE AMERICANS REFERENCE COLLECTION: DOCUMENTS COLLECTED BY THE OFFICE OF INDIAN AFFAIRS August Imholtz; compiled by Paul Kesaris Microfilm. Part I: 1840-1900, 29 reels. Amazon.com. 1995.

*NATIVE AMERICANS & THE RESERVATION IN AMERICAN HISTORY
Anita Louise McCormick; Grades 5 and up. Illus. 128 pp. Amazon.com, 1996. $19.95.

NATIVE AMERICANS: A PORTRAIT: THE ART & TRAVELS OF CHARLES BIRD KING, GEORGE CATLIN & KARL BODMER
Robert J. Moore, Jr.; Illus. 280 pp. Stewart Tabori & Chang, 1997. $60.

NATIVE AMERICANS & PUBLIC POLICY
Fremont J. Lyden & Lyman H. Legters, Editors; 17 essays covering such topics as problems of national policy, questions of legal sovereignty, and Native resources and economy. Illus. 336 pp. University of Pittsburgh, 1992. $49.95.

NATIVE AMERICANS: A RESOURCE GUIDE
Illus. 55 pp. Paper. Amazon.com, 1993. $25.

NATIVE AMERICANS IN THE SCHOOL SYSTEM: FAMILY, COMMUNITY, AND ACADEMIC ACHIEVEMENT
Carol J. Ward; Textbook. 282 pp. AltaMira Press, 2005. $96; paper, $44; eBook, $42.99.

NATIVE AMERICANS: THEIR ENDURING CULTURE & TRADITIONS
Trudy Griffin-Pierce; Illus. 192 pp. Amazon.com, 1996. $24.98.

NATIVE AMERICANS: A THEMATIC UNIT
Leigh Hoven
Grades 3-5. Illus. 80 pp. Amazon.com, 1990. Student edition, $9.95.

NATIVE AMERICANS TODAY: A BIOGRAPHICAL DICTIONARY
Bruce E. Johansen, Editor; A collection of 100 Native American profiles 315 pp. Greenwood Press, 2010. $85.

NATIVE AMERICANS & WAGE LABOR: ETHNOHISTORICAL PERSPECTIVES
Alice Livingston & Martha C. Knack
Illus. Biblio. 368 pp. University of Oklahoma Press, 1996. $32.95.

NATIVE APPARITIONS: CRITICAL PERSPECTIVES ON HOLLYWOOD'S INDIANS
Steve Pavlik, M. Elise Marubbio & Tom Holm, Editors; Indigenous media sovereignty. Illus. 232 pp. Paper. University of Arizona Press, 2017. $32.95.

*NATIVE ARTISTS OF NORTH AMERICA
Reavis Moore; Five Native American artists. Grades 8 and up. Illus. 48 pp. Paper. John Muir, 1991. $14.95.

NATIVE ARTS NETWORK
Atlatl convenes native artists and administrators to discuss issues in the field. Special reports document these biennial conferences. 1986, 1990, 1992, 1994. Atlatl, $5.

NATIVE ARTS OF THE COLUMBIA PLATEAU: THE DORIS SWAYZE BOUNDS COLLECTION OF NATIVE AMERICAN ARTIFACTS Susan E. Harless
Illus. Maps. 176 pp. Paper. University of Washington Press, 1998. $29.95.

NATIVE ARTS OF NORTH AMERICA
Christian F. Feest
Revised edition. Illus. 220 pp. Paper. Amazon.com, 1992. $19.95.

THE NATIVE ARTS OF NORTH AMERICA, AFRICA & THE SOUTH PACIFIC: AN INTRODUCTION George Corbin; Illus. 352 pp. Paper. Amazon.com, 1988. $24.95.

*NATIVE ATHLETES IN ACTION!
Vincent Schilling; 13 short biographies of Native American athletes.
Grades 2-5. 128 pp. Book Publishing Co., 2007. $9.95.

NATIVE BASKETRY OF WESTERN NORTH AMERICA
Joan M. Jones; Illus. 72 pp. Paper. Illinois State Museum, 1979. $2.

NATIVE CALIFORNIA GUIDE: WEAVING PAST & PRESENT
Dolan Eargle; Guide to Native peoples in California, including organizations, reservations, rancherias, tribes. With history of early life and interviews with tribal members. Also event calendars-powwows. Appendices of museums, missions, military posts, traders, gaming, etc. Illus. Maps. 260 pp. paper. Trees Company Press, 2000. $18.

NATIVE CALIFORNIANS: A THEORETICAL RETROSPECTIVE
Lowell J. Bean & Thomas Blackburn; Anthology of 16 papers on Native Californians. Cuyltural dynamics of the original inhabitants of California. Illus. 452 pp. Paper. Ballena Press, 1976. $22.50.

NATIVE CANADIAN ANTHROPOLOGY & HISTORY: A SELECTED BIBLIOGRAPHY
Shepard Krech III; Revised edition. 3,000 sources emphasizes recent publications on Canada's Native peoples. 212 pp. University of Oklahoma Press, 1994. $34.95.

NATIVE CANADIANA: SONGS FROM THE URBAN REZ
Gregory Scofield; 125 pp. Paper. Raincoast Book Distributors, 1996.

NATIVE CAROLINIANS: THE INDIANS OF NORTH CAROLINA
Theda Perdue; Illus. 75 pp. Paper. North Carolina Division of Archives & Cherokee Publications, 1985. $4.50.

NATIVE & CHRISTIAN: INDIGENOUS VOICES ON RELIGIOUS IDENTITY IN THE U.S. & CANADA James Treat, Editor; 248 pp. Routledge, 1996. $75; paper, $19.99.

NATIVE CLAIMS: INDIGENOUS LAW AGAINST EMPIRE, 1500-1920
Saliha Belmessous; Oxford University Press, 2011. $87.

THE NATIVE CREATIVE PROCESS: A COLLABORATIVE DISCOURSE
Douglas J. Cardinal & Jeanette Armstrong; illus. by Greg Young-Ing
Authors share their visions and insights into the creative process from the perspective of their Native ancestry. Illus. 127 pp. Paper. Theytus, 1991. $24.95.

NATIVE CULTURES OF ALASKA: TRADITIONS THROUGH TIME
L.J. Campbell; Illus. 112 pp. Paper. Amazon.com, 1996. $14.95.

*NATIVE DEFENDERS OF THE ENVIRONMENT
Vincent Schilling; The lives of 11 individuals who work to save the environment including: Melina Laboucan-Massimo (Cree), Winona LaDuke (Ojibwe), Clayton Thomas-Muller (Cree), Ben Powless (Six Nations), Tom Goldtooth (Navajo/Dakota), Grace Thorpe)Sac & Fox), et al. Grades 4-8. 128 pp. Paper. Book Publishing Co., 2011. $9.95.

NATIVE FACES; INDIAN CULTURES IN AMERICAN ART
P. Trenton and P.T. Houlihan; Illus. 120 pp. Paper. Southwest Museum, 1984. $15.95.

NATIVE FACES: WINOLD REISS
Peter Riess & Thomas Nygard, Eds.; Illus. 67 pp. Paper. Nygard Publishing, 1997. $25.

NATIVE FAMILY: NATIVE NATIONS
Christopher Cardozo; Robert Janjigan, Ed.; Illus. 96 pp. Callaway Editions, 1996. $13.95.

NATIVE FASHION NOW: NORTH AMERICAN INDIAN STYLE
Published by Prestel. Illus. 144 pp. Distributed by NMAI Press, 2015. $49.95.

THE NATIVE GROUND: INDIANS & COLONISTS IN THE HEART OF THE CONTINENT
Kathleen DuVal; Illus. 336 pp. paper. University of Pennsylvania Press, 2007. $24.95.

NATIVE HARVESTS: RECIPES & BOTANICALS OF THE AMERICAN INDIAN
Barrie Kavasch; Illus. Paper. Amazon.com & Alibris.com, 1979. $7.95.

NATIVE HEALER: INITIATION INTO AN ANCIENT ART
Lake Medicine Grizzlybear; Paper. Amazon.com, 1991. $10.95.

NATIVE HEALING: FOUR SACRED PATHS TO HEALTH
W.F. Peate; Illus. 200 pp. Paper. Treasure Chest Books, 2003. $16.95.

NATIVE HEART: AN AMERICAN INDIAN ODYSSEY
Gabriel Horn (White Deer of Autumn); An autobography. One man's sacred journey as he strugles to live the way of his ancestors in modern America. 304 pp. Paper. Amazon.com, $13.95.

A NATIVE HERITAGE: IMAGES OF THE INDIAN IN ENGLISH-CANADIAN LITERATURE Leslie Monkman; 208 pp. Amazon.com, 1981. $35.

NATIVE HERITAGE: PERSONAL ACCOUNTS BY AMERICAN INDIANS, 1790 TO THE PRESENT Arlene Hirschfelder, Editor; Illus. 310 pp. Paper. Amazon.com, 1998. $15.

NATIVE INDIAN WILD GAME, FISH & WILD FOODS COOKBOOK
David Hunt, Editor; 304 pp. Amazon.com, 1992. $24.95

NATIVE LAND
Mary Ann Wells; Documented chronicle about the lands that became the state of Mississippi. Illus. Maps. 256 pp. University Press of Mississippi, 1995. $50; paper, $25.

NATIVE LAND TALK: INDIGENOUS & ARRIVANT RIGHT THEORIES
Yael Ben-Zvi; Illus. 296 pp. University Press of New England, 2016. $95; paper, $45; eBook, $39.99.

NATIVE LANGUAGES & LANGUAGE FAMILIES OF NORTH AMERICA
compiled by Ives Goddard; A map which shows the locations and distriubution of the known languages spoken by Native peoples across North America at the time of first contact. University of Nebraska Press, $14.95, folded study map; $19.95, wall display map.

NATIVE LAW BIBLIOGRAPHY
Linda Fritz; 100 pp. University of Saskatchewan, 1984. $20.

NATIVE LIBERTY: NATURAL REASON & CULTURAL SURVIVANCE
Gerald Vizenor; Examines singular acts of resistance, natural reason, literary practices, and other strategies of survivance. 320 pp. Paper. U. of Nebraska Press, 2009. $30.

NATIVE LIGHT FOR A DARK WORLD
Donald Matheson; 272 pp. Carlton Press, 1988. $14.95.

*NATIVE MEN OF COURAGE
Vincent Schilling; Biographies of ten outstanding leaders including: Patrick Brazeau (Algonquin), Chief Red Hawk (Choerkee), Ben Nighthorse Campbell (Cheyenne), Chief Tom Porter (Mohawk), et al. Grades 4-8. 132 pp. Book Publishing Co., 2008. $9.95.

NATIVE MODERNISM: THE ART OF GEORGE MORRISON & ALLAN HOUSER
Truman T. Lowe (Ho-Chunk)
Illus. 128 pp. Paper. NMAI Press & University of Washington Press, 2004. $35.

*NATIVE MUSICIANS IN THE GROOVE
Vincent Schilling; Lives & accomplishments of ten musicians include Michael Bucher (Cherokee), Mary Youngblood (Seminole/Aleut), Crystal Shawanda (Ojibwa), Blackfire (Navajo), Leela Gilday (Dene), Four Rivers Drum (variety), Jamie Coon (Creek/Seminole), Mato Nanji (Nakota/Sioux), Shane Yellowbird (Cree), and Gabriel Ayala (Pascua Yaqui). Grades 4-8. 128 pp. Paper. Book Publishing Co., 2009. $9.95.

NATIVE NATIONS: CULTURE & HISTORY OF NATIVE NORTH AMERICA
Nancy Bonvillain
2nd Edition textbook. Illus. 648 pp. Paper. Rowman & Littlefield, 2016. $57.

NATIVE NATIONS: JOURNEYS IN AMERICAN PHOTOGRAPHY
Booth-Clibborn Editions Staff
Illus. 320 pp. Amazon.com, 2000. $39.95. Harry N. Abrams, $39.95.

NATIVE NEW ENGLAND: THE LONG JOURNEY
Charles T. Robinson; Illus. 128 pp. Paper. Amazon.com, 1996. $16.95.

THE NATIVE NEW MEXICO GUIDE: YOUR GUIDE TO NEW MEXICO'S TWENTY-TWO TRIBES & AMERICAN INDIAN EVENTS & ATTRACTIONS
(NM Indian Tourism Program); New Mexico Tourism Dept., 491 Old Santa Fe Trail, Santa Fe, NM 87503 (800) 545-2070. Website: ww.newmexico.org.

NATIVE NORTH AMERICA
Larry J. Zimmerman & Brian Leigh Molyneaux
Illus. 184 pp. Paper. University of Oklahoma Press, 2000. $19.95.

NATIVE NORTH AMERICA: CRITICAL & CULTURAL PERSPECTIVES
Renee Hulan, Ed.; 280 pp. Paper. Amazon.com, 1999. 21.95.

NATIVE NORTH AMERICAN ALMANAC
Duane Champagne, Editor; Covers the range of Native history & culture in the U.S. & Canada. Includes a chronology, demographic & distribution descriptions & histories, and discussions. 2nd Edition. Illus. 1,300 pp. Amazon.com, 2001. $15.

NATIVE NORTH AMERICAN ARMOR, SHIELDS & FORTIFICATIONS
David E. Jones; Illus. 230 pp. Paper. University of Texas Press, 2004. $25.

NATIVE NORTH AMERICAN ART
Janet C. Berlo & Ruth Phillips
Illus. 304 pp. Paper. Oxford University Press, 1998. $27.95; 2nd Edition, 2014. $54.95..

NATIVE NORTH AMERICAN FIRSTS
Karen Swisher & Ancita Benally; Melissa W. Doig, Editor; Identifies & explains about 1,500 significant breakthroughs involving Native North Americans from pre-Columbian times to the present. 1st Ed. Illus. 263 pp. Amazon.com, 1997. $15.

NATIVE NORTH AMERICAN FLUTES
Lew P. Price; Illus. Paper. Lew Paxton Price, $5.

NATIVE NORTH AMERICAN INTERACTION PATTERNS
Regna Darnell & Michael K. Foster
238 pp. Paper. University of Chicago Press, 1992. $19.95.

NATIVE NORTH AMERICAN LITERATURE
Biographical & critical information on Native North Americanauthors from both the written & oral traditions. 1st Ed. 706 pp. Amazon.com, 1994. $135.

NATIVE NORTH AMERICAN MUSIC & ORAL DATA: A CATALOGUE OF SOUND RECORDINGS, 1893-1976 Dorothy S. Lee; 480 pp. Indian University Press, 1979. $25.

NATIVE NORTH AMERICAN SHAMANISM: AN ANNOTATED BIBLIOGRAPHY
Shelley Anne Osterreich; 128 pp. Greenwood Publishing, 1998. $77.95.

NATIVE NORTH AMERICAN SPIRITUALITY OF THE EASTERN WOODLANDS: SACRED MYTHS, DREAMS, VISION SPEECHES, HEALING FORMULAS, RITUALS & CEREMONIES Elisabteh Tooker, Editor; 302 pp. Amazon.com, 1979. $14.95.

NATIVE NORTH AMERICAN VOICES
Deborah A. Straub; 1st Ed. 160 pp. Amazon.com, 1997. $18.

NATIVE NORTH AMERICANS: A SUPPLEMENT TO CHILDCRAFT-THE HOW & WHY LIBRARY World Book Staff; World Book, 2004.

NATIVE NORTH AMERICANS: AN ETHNOHISTORICAL APPROACH
Molly R. Mignon & Daniel Boxberger, Editors
2nd Edition. 508 pp. Paper. Kendall-Hunt, 1997. $42.95.

NATIVE NORTH AMERICANS IN DOCTORAL DISSERTATIONS, 1971-1975: A CLASSIFIED & INDEXED RESEARCH BIBLIOGRAPHY
S. Gifford Nickerson; CPL Biblios, 1977. $7.50.

NATIVE NORTH AMERICANS IN LITERATURE FOR YOUTH: A SELECTED ANNOTATED BIBLIOGRAPHY FOR K-12
Alice Crosetto & Rajinder Garcha; 286 pp. Scarecrow Press, 2013. $105; eBook, $104.99

NATIVE: A NOVEL
William Haywood Henderson; A tale of three gay men ensnared in the politics & prejudices of an isolated ranching town in Wyoming's Wind River Valley; one, Gilbert, a Native American from the Wind River Indian Reservation. 264 pp. Paper. University of Nebraska Press, 2010. $18.95.

NATIVE PATHS: AMERICAN INDIAN ART FROM THE COLLECTION OF CHARLES & VALERIE DIKER Allen Wardwell; Illus. 128 pp. paper. Yale U. Press, 1999. $19.95.

NATIVE PATHWAYS: AMERICAN INDIAN CULTURE & ECONOMIC DEVELOPMENT IN THE 20TH CENTURY Brian Hosmer & Colleen O'Neill, Eds; foreword by Donald Fixico
Illus. Map. 368 pp. Paper. University Press of Colorado, 2004. $27.95; eBook, $26.95.

NATIVE PEOPLE IN CANADA: CONTEMPORARY CONFLICTS
James Frideres; 2nd Edition. 344 pp. Prentice-Hall, 1983.

NATIVE PEOPLE, NATIVE LANDS: CANADIAN INDIANS, INUIT & METIS
Bruce Cox; 300 pp. Paper. Oxford University Press, 1988. $16.95.

*NATIVE PEOPLE, NATIVE WAYS SERIES
White Deer of Autumn (Gabriel Horn); Stories about the Native American experience. In 4 vols. Native American Book of Knowledge (Vol. I): stories - "We Have Always Been Here", & "Prophets, Poets & Peacemakers: Before Columbus"; Native American Book of Life (Vol. II): stories - "The Children, Always the Children," & "By the Magic of the Strawberry Moon"; Native American Book of Change (Vol. III): stories: "Prophets, Poets, & Peacemakers: After the Conquest," & "Dad's Signs, Now Mine"; Native American Book of Wisdom (Vol. IV): stories - "From the Great Mystery: Wakan-Tanka," & "Medicine Man." 96 pp. Paper. Beyond Words Publishing, $4.95 each.

THE NATIVE PEOPLE OF ALASKA
Steve J. Langdon; Introductory guide to the Eskimos, Indians, and Aleuts. Focus is on their life-styles, traditions, and culture. Photos. Maps. Biblio. 90 pp. Revised edition. Paper. Alaska Natural History Association & Amazon.com, 1993. $7.95.

NATIVE PEOPLE OF SOUTHERN NEW ENGLAND, 1650-1775
Kathleen J. Bragdon; Illus. Maps. Biblio. 312 p. U. of Oklahoma Press, 2009. $32.95.

NATIVE PEOPLE OF SOUTHERN NEW ENGLAND, 1500-1650
Kathleen J. Bragdon; Illus. Maps. Biblio. 328 pp.
Paper. U. of Oklahoma Press, 1996. $19.95.

NATIVE PEOPLES A TO Z: A REFERENCE GUIDE TO THE NATIVE PEOPLES OF THE WESTERN HEMISPHERE, 2nd Edition; Eight volume set that recounts the history of Native Peoples. Contains articles on Tribes & Nations, biographies, historica events, treaties, bibliography. Illus. Website: www.thenativepeoples.com. North American Book Distributors, 2012. $995.00.

NATIVE PEOPLES: THE CANADIAN EXPERIENCE
R. Bruce Morrison & C. Roderick Wilson; Paper. Oxford University Press, 2004. $65.

NATIVE PEOPLES & LANGUAGES OF ALASKA
Michael Krauss; Map of 20 Alaska Native languages and and four Eskimo languages in Alaska. 36 x 48" University of Chicago Press, $15.

NATIVE PEOPLES OF ALASKA: A TRAVELER'S GUIDE TO LAND, ART & CULTURE
Jan Halliday & Patricia Petrivelli; 320 pp. Paper. Amazon.com, 1998. $17.95.

*NATIVE PEOPLES OF THE ARCTIC
Stuart A. Kallen; Grades 3-5. Lerner Publications, $24.95; paper, $9.99.

NATIVE PEOPLES OF ATLANTIC CANADA: A HISTORY OF INDIAN-EUROPEAN RELATIONS H.F. McGee, Ed.; 210 pp. Paper. McGill-Queen's University Press.

*NATIVE PEOPLES OF THE GREAT BASIN
Krystyna Poray Goddu
Illus. Grades 3-5. Lerner Publications, 2015. $24.99; paper, $9.99.

NATIVE PEOPLES OF NORTH AMERICA: A HISTORY
Bruce E. Johansen; Illus. 512 pp. Amazon.com, 2008. $26.95.

NATIVE PEOPLES OF NORTH AMERICA: A READER
Loretta Fowler; 148 pp. Kendall/Hunt Publishing, 1999. $40.95.

NATIVE PEOPLES OF THE NORTHEAST WOODLANDS: AN EDUCATIONAL RESOURCE PUBLICATION Judith Brundin
Illus. 255 pp. National Museum of the American Indian, 1990. $29.95.

NATIVE PEOPLES OF THE NORTHWEST: A TRAVELER'S GUIDE TO LAND, ART & CULTURE Jan Halliday & Gail Chehak
Guide for travelers to the Northwest. Maps. 291 pp. Paper. Amazon.com, 1996. $16.95.

NATIVE PEOPLES OF THE OLYMPIC PENINSULA: WHO WE ARE
Jacilee Wray, Editor; Explores the different tribes of Olympic Peninsula. Illus. Maps. University of Oklahoma Press, $29.95; paper, $19.95. Paper. Amazon.com, $19.95.

*NATIVE PEOPLES OF THE PLAINS
Linda Lowery; Grades 3-5. Lerner Publications, 2017. $33.32; paper, $9.99.

NATIVE PEOPLES OF SOUTHERN NEW ENGLAND, 1500-1650
Kathleen J. Bragdon; Illus. 330 pp. U. of Oklahoma Press, 1996. $32.95; paper, $19.95.

NATIVE PEOPLES OF SOUTHERN NEW ENGLAND, 1650-1775
Kathleen J. Bragdon; Illus. 312 pp. U. of Oklahoma Press, 2010. $32.95; paper, $19.95.

NATIVE PEOPLES OF THE SOUTHWEST
Trudy Griffin-Pierce; Scholarly text of the true history of Southwestern American Indians. University of New Mexico Press. $34.95; paper, $34.95.

*NATIVE PEOPLES OF THE SOUTHWEST
Susan L. Shaffer, Editor; Grades 2-6. Illus. Includes 150 student booklets with 5 teacher resource binders with overhead transparencies, slides & audiocassette; artifacts, posters, etc. The Heard Museum, 1987. $1,475.

NATIVE PEOPLES OF THE SOUTHWEST
Linda Lowery; Grades 3-5. Lerner Publications, 2015. $24.99.

NATIVE PEOPLES OF THE SOUTHWEST: NEGOTIATING LAND, WATER, & ETHNICITIES Laurie Weinstein, Editor
Illus. 280 pp. Greenwood Publishing, 2002. $67.95; paper, $23.95.

*NATIVE PEOPLES OF THE SUBARCTIC
Stuart Kallen; Illus. Grades 3-5. Lerner Publications, $24.99; paper, $9.99.

NATIVE PEOPLE OF WISCONSIN
(Patty Loew)
Illus. Photos. Maps. 168 pp. Paper. Wisconsin Historical Socety Press, 2003. $15.95.

NATIVE PERFORMERS IN WILD WEST SHOWS: FROM BUFFALO BILL TO EURO DISNEY Linda McNenly; 280 pp. University of Oklahoma Press, $34.95.

*NATIVE PLANT STORIES
Joseph Bruchac
Grades 4 and up. Illus. 160 pp. Paper. Fulcrum Publishing, 2000. $12.95.

NATIVE PLANTS, NATIVE HEALING: TRADITIONAL MUSKOGEE WAY
Tis Mal Crow; Traditional Native American healing techniques by herb doctor Tis Mal Crow of Cherokee & Hitchiti descent. Examines common wild plants. Illus. 144 pp. Paper. Book Publishing Co., $12.95.

THE NATIVE POPULATION OF THE AMERICAS IN 1492
William M. Denevan; Reprint. Illus. 398 pp. Paper. U. of Wisconsin Press, 1992. $19.95.

NATIVE PRAGMATISM: RETHINKING THE ROOTS OF AMERICAN PHILOSOPHY
Scott L. Pratt; Explores the conections between American pragmatism & Native American thought. Illus. 336 pp. Amazon.com & Alibris.com, 2002. $12; paper, $7.

NATIVE RELIGIONS & CULTURES OF NORTH AMERICA: ANTHROPOLOGY OF THE SACRED Lawrence Sullivan, Ed.; Illus. 276 pp. Amazon.com, 2000. $35.

NATIVE RELIGIONS OF NORTH AMERICA
Ake Hultkrantz; 144 pp. Paper. Waveland Press, 1987. $16.95.

NATIVE RESISTANCE & THE PAX COLONIAL IN NEW SPAIN
Susan Schroeder, Editor; Overview of Native uprisings in New Spain. Maps. 200 pp. University of Nebraska Press, 1998. $50; paper, $25.

NATIVE ROOTS: HOW THE INDIANS ENRICHED AMERICA
Jack Weatherford; Illus. 300 pp. Paper. Amazon.com, $10.

NATIVE SCIENCE: NATURAL LAWS OF INTERDEPENDENCE
Gregory Cajete
The indigenous view of reality. Illus. Photos. 328 pp. Amazon.com, $24.95; paper, $14.95.

NATIVE SEATTLE: HISTORIES FROM THE CROSSING-OVER PLACE
Coll Thrush; Accounts of the lived experiences of Native people in Seattle. 2nd Edition. Illus. 350 pp. Paper. UBC Press & University of Washington Press, 2017. $90; paper, $24.95.

THE NATIVE SOUTH: NEW HISTORIES & ENDURING LEGACIES
Tim Alan Garrison & Greg O'Brien; 306 pp. University of Nebraska Press, 2017. $60

NATIVE SPEAKERS: ELLA DELORIA, ZORA NEALE HURSTON, JOVITA GONZALEZ, AND THE POETICS OF CULTURE
Maria Eugenia Cotera; Illus. 300 pp. Paper. University of Texas Press, 2008. $25.

NATIVE STORIES: FIVE SELECTIONS
Gerald Vizenor, Editor; Anthology. 206 pp. Paper. U. of Nebraska Press, 2009. $25.

NATIVE STUDIES KEYWORDS
Stephanie Nhelani Teves, Andrea Smith & Michelle Raheja, Editors
Illus. 352 pp. Paper. University of Arizona Press, 2015. $35.

NATIVE TIME: AN HISTORICAL TIME LINE OF NATIVE AMERICA
Lee Francis; Illus. 352 pp. St. Martins Press, 1996. $35; paper, $19.95.

THE NATIVE TRIBES OF OHIO
Helen Cox Tregillis; Tells the story from the very beginning of the Eries to the later tribes before their removal west of the Mississippi; brief biographies and list of resources. Illus. 130 pp. Maps. Paper. Amazon.com, $15.50.

NATIVE TITLE & THE TRANSFORMATION OF ARCHAEOLOGY IN THE POSTCOLONIAL WORLD Ian Lilley; Examines recent developments in Native title claims regarding land use, ownership, & cultural patrimony and their effect on the practice of archeology. 192 pp. Paper. University of Arizona Press, 2008. $79. $29.95.

NATIVE TRIBES MAP
Alfred L. Kroeber; Maps. Paper. University of California Press, 1966. $14.95

NATIVE UNIVERSE: VOICES OF INDIAN AMERICA
Gerald McMaster (Plains Cree) & Clifford Trafzer (Wyandot)
Illustrated cultural history of American Indians written exclusively by Native people in collaboration with the new National Museum of the American Indian's opening exhibitions. Illus. 320 pp. Paper. NMAI Press & National Geographic Books (2004), $40. Revised edition. Paper. NMAI Press & National Geograpic Books, 2008. $22.

NATIVE VISIONS: EVOLUTION IN NORTHWEST COAST ART FROM THE 18TH THROUGH THE 20TH CENTURY Steven C. Brown
200 photos. 228 pp. Paper. University of Washington Press, 1998. $40.

NATIVE VOICES: AMERICAN INDIAN IDENTITY & RESISTANCE
Richard A. Grounds, et al, Eds.; 368 pp. Paper. U. Press of Kansas, 2003. $19.95.

NATIVE WATERS: CONTEMPORARY INDIAN WATER SETTLEMENTS & THE SECOND TREATY ERA Daniel McCool; 237 pp. Paper. U. of Arizona Press, 2002. $22.95.

NATIVE WAYS: CALIFORNIA INDIAN STORIES & MEMORIES
Malcolm Margolin & Yolanda Montijo
80 photos. Illus. Map. 128 pp. Paper. Heyday Books, $10.95.

NATIVE WILD GAME: FISH & WILD FOODS COOKBOOK
340+ recipes from many tribes. 283 pp. Cherokee Publications, $19.95.

NATIVE WISDOM
Joseph Bruchac; 112 pp. Paper. Amazon.com, $12.

NATIVE WISDOM: PERCEPTIONS OF THE NATURAL WAY
Eagle Man McGaa, Ed; Sharon Diotte, Ed.; Illus. 260 pp. Paper. Amazon.com, 1995. $15.

NATIVE WOMEN & LAND: NARRATIVES OF DISPOSSESSION & RESURGENCE
Stephanie J. Fitzgerald; Illus. 176 pp. Paper. University of New Mexico Press, $29.95.

*NATIVE WOMEN OF COURAGE
Vincent Schilling; Ten biographies of historic & contemporary Native American women leaders. Grades 4-8. 96 pp. Paper. Book Publishing Co., 2007. $9.95.

NATIVE WOMEN'S HISTORY IN EASTERN NORTH AMERICA BEFORE 1900: A GUIDE TO RESEARCH & WRITING Rebecca Kugel & Lucy Eldersveld Murphy
Anthology to histories of Native women's lives in earlier centuries. Photos. Maps. 503 pp. Paper. U. of Oklahoma Press, 2007. $29.95.

NATIVE WRITERS & CANADIAN WRITING
William H. New; 352 pp. Paper. University of Washington Press, 1991. $32.95.

NATIVE WRITINGS IN MASSACHUSETTS
Ives Goddard & Kathleen Bragdon; Illus. 838 pp. Amazon.com, 1988. $60.

NATIVES & ACADEMICS: RESEARCHING & WRITING ABOUT AMERICAN INDIANS
Devon Abbott Mihesuah, Editor
Anthology. 213 pp. Paper. University of Nebraska Press, 1998. $16.95.

NATIVES & NEWCOMERS: THE CULTURAL ORIGINS OF NORTH AMERICA
James Axtell; Illus. 432 pp. Paper. Oxford University Press, 2000. $65.95.

NATIVES & NEWCOMERS: CANADA'S "HEROIC AGE" RECONSIDERED
Bruce G. Trigger; A tale of Canada's early development that finally gives Native people their rightful place. paper. Amazon.com, 1986. $22.95.

NATIVES & STRANGERS: A HISTORY OF ETHNIC AMERICANS
Leonard Dinnerstein, Roger L. Nichols, David Reimers
6th Ed. Paper. Oxford University Press, 2014. $54.95.

*NATOSI: STRONG MEDICINE
Peter Roop; Blackfeet raiding party captures their first horses from the Crows. Grades 3-8. 32 pp. Council for Indian Education, $8.95; paper, $2.95.

A NATURAL EDUCATION: NATIVE AMERICAN IDEAS & THOUGHTS
Stan Padilla, Editor & Illus.; Collection of quotations from traditional Native Americans on the importance of educating young people to the natural way. Revised edition. Illus. 80 pp. Paper. The Book Publishing Co., 1994. $8.95.

THE NATURAL MAN OBSERVED: A STUDY OF CATLIN'S INDIAN GALLERY
William Truettner; Illus. 323 pp. Smithsonian Institution Press, 1979. $47.50.

*NATURAL WORLD OF THE CALIFORNIA INDIANS
Robert F. Heizer & Albert B. Elsasser
Grades 4 and up. Paper. University of California Press, 1981. $19.95.

A NATURALIST IN INDIAN TERRITORY: THE JOURNALS OF S.W. WOODHOUSE, 1849-50 John S. Tomer & Michael J. Brodhead; A young Philadelphia physician was appointed surgeon-naturalist of two expeditions to survey Creek-Cherokee boundary in Indian Territory. Illus. Maps. 320 pp. Paper. University of Oklahoma Press, 1994. $17.95.

THE NATURE & FUNCTION OF LAKOTA NIGHT CULTS
Eugene Fugle; 37 pp. Paper. Lakota Books, 1994. $21.95.

THE NATURE OF NATIVE AMERICAN POETRY
Norma C. Wilson; Illus. 176 pp. Paper. University of New Mexico Press, 2001. $25.

NATURE RELIGION IN AMERICA: FROM ALGONKIAN INDIANS TO THE NEW AGE
Catherine L. Albanese; Illus. Photos. 284 pp. Paper. U. of Chicago Press, 1991. $27.50.

NATURE'S WEEDS, NATIVE MEDICINES: NATIVE AMERICAN HERBAL SECRETS
Marie Miczak; Illus. 146 pp. Paper. Sterling Publishing, 1997. $10.95.

THE NAVAHO
Clyde Kluckhohn and Dorothea Leighton
Revised 1973 edition. Illus. 365 pp. Amazon.com, $18.50; paper, $8.95.

THE NAVAJO
James F. Downs; The basic themes of their culture and their ability to adjust to new situations & the Anglo culture without losing their identity. Illus. 136 pp. Waveland Press, 1972. $15.95. Paper. High-Lonesome Books, 1984. $9.

*THE NAVAJO
S. Stan; Grades 5-8. Illus. 32 pp. Amazon.com, 1989. $13.26.

*THE NAVAJO
Grades K-4. Illus. 48 pp. Childrens Press, $11.45.

*NAVAJO ABC: A DINE ALPHABET BOOK
Eleanor Schick & Luci Tapahonso
Grades PS and up. Illus. 32 pp. Simon & Schuster, 1995. $16.

NAVAJO ARCHITECTURE: FORMS, HISTORY, DISTRIBUTION
Stephen C. Jett & Virginia E. Spencer; 310 pp. University of Arizona Press, 1981. $50.

NAVAHO ART & CULTURE
George T. Mills; Reprint of 1959 edition. Illus. 273 pp. Greenwood, $41.50.

THE NAVAJO ART OF SANDPAINTING
Douglas Congdon-Martin; Contains over 400 full color photos of sandpaintings. Illus. 64 pp. Paper. Schiffer, 1990. $9.95.

NAVAJO ARTS & CRAFTS
Robert Roessel; Illus. 176 pp. Rough Rock School Press, 1989. $15.

NAVAJO ARTS & CRAFTS
Nancy Schiffer
Photos and explanations of each craft. Illus. 64 pp. Paper. Amazon.com, $12.95.

THE NAVAJO AS SEEN BY THE FRANCISCANS, 1898-1921: A SOURCEBOOK
Howard M. Bahr; Illus. Maps. 656 pp. Scarecrow Press, 2004. $73.70.

THE NAVAJO AS SEEN BY THE FRANCISCANS, 1920-1950: A SOURCEBOOK, 2ND EDITION Howard M. Bahr; Illus. Maps. 682 pp. Scarecrow Press, 2011. $105.

THE NAVAJO ATLAS: ENVIRONMENTS, RESOURCES, PEOPLES & HISTORY OF THE DINE BIKEYAH James Goodman
Illus. Maps. 109 pp. Paper. University of Oklahoma Press, 1982. $19.95.

NAVAJO: BASIC MEDICAL
Alan Wilson; 141 pp. Paper. Amazon.com, 1992. $18.95; $39 includes audio.

NAVAJO BEADWORK: ARCHITECTURES OF LIGHT
Ellen K. Moore; History of Navajo beadwork - belts & hatbands, baskets & necklaces. Illus. 296 pp. Paper. University of Arizona Press, 2003. $50.

NAVAJO BLESSINGWAY SINGER: THE AUTOBIOGRAPHY OF FRANK MITCHELL, 1881-1967 Charlotte Frisbie & David McAllester, Editors
Reprint of 1977 edition. 456 pp. Paper. University of New Mexico Press, $34.95.

NAVAJO, BREAKTHROUGH: AN INTRODUCTORY COURSE
Alan Wilson; 234 pp. Paper. Jeffrey Norton Publishers, $16.95.

A NAVAJO BRINGING-HOME CEREMONY: THE CLAUS CHEE SONNY VERSION OF DEERWAY AJILEE Karl W. Luckert; Illus. 224 pp. Paper. University of Nebraska Press and Museum of Northern Arizona, 1980. $14.95.

*THE NAVAJO BROTHERS & THE STOLEN HERD
Maurine Grammer; illus by Fred Cleveland; Story of two Navajo teenagers who regain their family's sheep from thieves. Grades 4-9. Illus. 120 pp. paper. Amazon.com, $9.95.

NAVAJO: A CENTURY OF PROGRESS, 1868-1968
Martin Link, Editor; Illus. 110 pp. Navajo Tribal Museum, 1968. $6.

NAVAJO CEREMONIAL BASKETS: SACRED SYMBOLS, SACRED SPACE
Georgiana Kennedy Simpson; Illus. 160 pp. The Book Publishing Co., 2004. $19.95.

NAVAJO CHANGES: A HISTORY OF THE NAVAJO PEOPLE
Teresa McCarty and staff, Editors; 107 pp. Rough Rock School Press, 1983. $25.

NAVAHO CHANTWAY MYTHS
Katherine Spencer; Reprint of 1957 edition. 240 pp. Paper. High-Lonesome Books, $20.

*NAVAJO CHILDREN
Nancy Armstrong; Grades 2-6. Paper. Council for Indian Education, 1975. $1.95.

NAVAJO CODE TALKERS
Doris Paul; Story of Navajo platoon during World War II and of the intricate and unbreakable code language they created. Illus. 171 pp. Amazon.com, 1973. $14.50.

*NAVAJO CODE TALKERS: NATIVE AMERIACAN HEROES
Catherine Jones; Grades 6 and up. 31 pp. Paper. Amazon.com, 1997. $7.95.

A NAVAJO CONFRONTATION & CRISIS
Floyd A. Pollock; Traces the development of Navajo-federal relations during the 1930s and 1940s. Amazon.com, $10.

NAVAJO COUNTRY DINE BIKEYAH: A GEOGRAPHIC DICTIONARY OF NAVAJO LANDS IN THE 1930s
A. Richard Van Valkenburgh; 2nd ed. Illus. 140 pp. Amazon.com, 1999. $29.95.

NAVAJO COURTS & NAVAJO COMMON LAW: A TRADITION OF TRIBAL SELF-GOVERNANCE Raymond D. Austin
Details 130 cases the Navajo Nation's courts have handled using customary law. 296 pp. University of Minnesota Press, 2009. $60; paper, $19.95.

*NAVAJO COYOTE TALES
collected by William Morgan
Grades 4 and up. Illus. 53 pp. Paper. Amazon.com, 1989. $9.95.

*NAVAJO COYOTE TALES: THE CURLY TO AHEEDLIINII VERSION
Father Berard Haile
Ages 7-10. Reprint. Illus. 146 pp. Paper. University of Nebraska Press, 1984. $12.95.

A NAVAJO CRISIS & CONFRONTATION
Floyd A. Pollock; Amazon.com, 1984. $15.

*NAVAJO CULTURAL GUIDES, EXPERIENCE STORIES, & CULTURAL READERS
See San Juan District Media Center for titles, prices and grade levels.

*THE NAVAJO DESIGN BOOK
Donna Greenlee; Grades 1-6. The arts & crafts of the Navajo people...weaving, sand painting, and silver design. Illus. 32 pp. Paper. Fun Publications, 1975. $4.95.

NAVAJO DICTIONARY OF DIAGNOSTIC TERMINOLOGY: NAVAJO MEDICAL TERMINOLOGY Dine Center for Human Development; Paper. Amazon.com, 1991. $10.

NAVAJO EDUCATION IN ACTION: THE ROUGH ROCK DEMONSTRATION SCHOOL
Robert A. Roessel, Jr.; 149 pp. Rough Rock School Press, 1977. $10.

NAVAJO EDUCATION, 1948-1978: ITS PROGRESS & PROBLEMS
Robert A. Roessel, Jr.; Illus. 339 pp. Rough Rock School Press, 1979. $14.95.

A NAVAJO/ENGLISH BILINGUAL DICTIONARY: ALCHINI BI NAALTISOOSTSCH
Alyse Naundorf; Reprint of 1983 edition. Intended primarily for navajo children learning to read & write the language in bilingual classrooms. Presents over 1,500 noun and 330 verb entries. 885 pp. 600 line drawings. Paper. University of New Mexico Press, $85.

*NAVAJO-ENGLISH CHILDREN'S PICTURE DICTIONARY
Roman Delos-Santos; Raymond Johnson, illustrator
Grades 4-8. Navajo Community College Press, 1995.

NAVAJO-ENGLISH DICTIONARY
Leon Wall & William Morgan; Includes over 9,000 entries, a section on Navajo pronunciation, everyday expressions, etc. 164 pp. Paper. Amazon.com, $9.95.

THE NAVAHO (OR CORRAL) FIRE DANCE
B. Haile; Reprint of 1946-7 editions. 3 vols. in 1. Paper. St. Michaels, $7.50.

NAVAJO FOLK ART: THE PEOPLE SPEAK
Chuck & Jan Rosenak; Features 41 artists. 90 color photos. Biblio. 176 pp. Paper. Northland Press & Amazon.com, $14.95.

NAVAHO FOLK TALES
Franc Johnson Newcomb; 229 pp. Paper. University of New Mexico Press, $17.95.

NAVAJO FOOD PRACTICES, CUSTOMS & HOLIDAYS
Suzanne Pelican & Karen Bachman-Carter; Paper. Amazon.com, 1992. $10.

NAVAJO FOREIGN AFFAIRS: 1795-1846
Frank D. Reeve; ed. by Eleanor Adams & John Kessell
Paper. 54 pp. Amazon.com, 1983. $5.70.

NAVAJO GRAVES: ARCHAEOLOGICAL REFLECTION OF ETHNOGRAPHIC REALITY
Albert E. Ward; Discusses select Navajo burials from northeastern Arizona and northwestern New Mexico. Illus. 54 pp. Amazon.com, 1980. $8.

THE NAVAJO & HIS BLANKET
Uriah S. Hollister; Reprint of 1903 edition. Illus. 176 pp. The Rio Grande Press, $17.50.

NAVAJO HISTORY
Ethelou Yazi, Editor
Revised edition. Volume I. Illus. 100 pp. Paper. Rough Rock School Press, 1982. $11.

·THE NAVAJO: THE HISTORY & CULTURE OF NATIVE AMERICANS
Jennifer Denetdale;

THE NAVAJO-HOPI LAND DISPUTE: AN AMERICAN TRAGEDY
David M. Brugge; Illus. Maps. 320 pp. Paper. University of New Mexico Press, 1999. $40.

THE NAVAJO HUNTER TRADITION
Karl W. Luckert; Hunter myths and rituals are examined in conjunction with other deities and the rise of shamanism. 248 pp. University of Arizona Press, 1975. $35.

*THE NAVAJO INDIAN BOOK
Donna Greenlee; Grades 1-6. Traditional lifestyles of the navajo. 32 pp. Paper. Fun Publications, 1975. $4.95.

NAVAHO INDIAN MYTHS
Aileen O'Bryan, Editor; Tribal fables & legends recorded in the 1920s from an elderly chief. Reprint. 187 pp. Paper. Dover, $6.95.

THE NAVAJO INDIANS
Henry F. Dobyns & Robert C. Euler; An account of the Navajo Indians, past & present. Illus. Maps. 121 pp. Amazon.con, $8.

*NAVAJO INDIANS
Leigh Hope Wood; Grades 4-8. Demco, 1991. $12.15.

NAVAJO INFANCY: AN ETHNOLOGICAL STUDY OF CHILD DEVELOPMENT
James S. Chisholm; 267 pp. Amazon.com, 1983. $49.95.

NAVAJO JEWELRY: A LEGACY OF SILVER & STONE
Lois Jacka; photos by Jerry Jacka; History of Navajo jewelry-making. 100 color photos. Biblio. 144 pp. Paper. Northland Press & Amazon.com, $14.95.

NAVAJO KINSHIP & MARRIAGE
Gary Witherspoon. Reprint. Illus. 138 pp. Paper. U. of Chicago Press, 1996. $15.

THE NAVAJO LANGUAGE: A GRAMMAR & COLLOQUIAL DICTIONARY
Robert W. Young & William Morgan, Sr., Editors
Definitive dictionary & linguistic resource. University of New Mexico Press, $24.95.

NAVAJO THE LAUGHTER WAY
Alan Wilson; 143 pp. Paper. Amazon.com, 1992. $7.95; with audio, $39.

NAVAJO LAND, NAVAJO CULTURE: THE UTAH EXPERIENCE IN THE 20TH CENTURY Robert S. McPherson; History of the Dine of southeastern Utah. Illus. Map. 300 pp. University of Oklahoma Press, 2004. $21.95; paper, $19.95.

NAVAJO LAND USE: AN ETHNOARCHAEOLOGICAL STUDY
Klara B. Kelley; Amazon.com, 1985. $51.

*THE NAVAJO LANGUAGE: A GRAMMAR & COLLOQUIAL DICTIONARY
Robert W. Young & William Morgan, Sr.
Software. Grades 6-12. Navajo/English. CD-ROM of 1070-page is searchable in Navajo & English. charts for all verb forms. $99.50 each.

NAVAJO LEADERSHIP & GOVERNMENT
Title IV Materials Development Staff; 149 pp. Rough Rock School Press, 1977. $7.50.

A NAVAJO LEGACY: THE LIFE & TEACHINGS OF JOHN HOLIDAY
John Holiday & Robert S. McPherson
Illus. 420 pp. Paper. University of Oklahoma Press, 2006. $24.95.

NAVAHO LEGENDS
Washington Matthews
Reprint of 1897 edition. Illus. 322 pp. Paper. University of Utah Press, $19.95.

NAVAJO LIFEWAYS: CONTEMPORARY ISSUES, ANCIENT KNOWLEDGE
Maureen Trudelle Schwarz; Illus. 292 pp. University of Oklahoma Press, 2001. $29.95.

NAVAJO LIVESTOCK REDUCTION: A NATIONAL DISGRACE
Ruth Roessel, Editors; Illus. 224 pp. Navajo Community College Press, 1974. $15.

*NAVAJO LONG WALK
Nancy Armstrong; In 1864 thousands of Navajo Indians were forced to leave their land in Arizona and march nearly 300 miles east. Grades 4-9. 120 pp. Paper. Council for Indian Education & Roberts Rinehart, 1994. $7.95.

*NAVAHO MAGIC OF HUNTING
Elsie Kreischer; illus. by Jin Paddock; Narrative poem telling of a boy's first deer hunt. Grades 4-9. 32 pp. Paper. Council for Indian Education, 1994. $4.95.

NAVAJO MEDICINE BUNDLES OR JISH: ACQUISITION, TRANSMISSION & DISPOSITION IN THE PAST & PRESENT
Charlotte Frisbie; Illus. 627 pp. University of New Mexico Press, 1987. $42.

NAVAJO MEDICINE MAN SAND PAINTINGS
Gladys Reichard; Reprint. Illus. 132 pp. Paper. Dover, $12.95.

NAVAJO MOUNTAIN & RAINBOW BRIDGE RELIGION
Karl W. Luckert; Translated by I.W. Goosen and H. Bilagody, Jr.
Illus. 164 pp. University of Nebraska Press, 1977. $9.95.

NAVAJO MYTHS PRAYERS & SONGS WITH TEXTS & TRANSLATIONS
Washington Matthews; P.E. Goddard, Editor
Facsimile of 1907 edition. 43 pp. Paper. Coyote Press, $4.69.

THE NAVAJO NATION
Peter Iverson; Illus. 275 pp. Greenwood Press, 1981. $35.00.
Paper. University of New Mexico Press, $9.95.

NAVAJO NATION HEALTH CARE SYSTEM
H. Bishara; Paper. Bista'i Press, 2001.

NAVAJO NATION PEACEMAKING: LIVING TRADITIONAL JUSTICE
Edited by Marlanne O. Nielsen, James W. Zion
240 pp. Paper. University of Arizona Press, 2005. $35.00

NAVAJO NATIVE DYES: THEIR PREPARATION & USE
Nonobah Bryan & Stella Young; How to use native plants of the Southwest to dye yarns
for rug making. Reprint of 1940 edition. Illus. 75 pp. Paper. Amazon.com & Alibris.com, $5.

NAVAJO ORAL HISTORY
Alfred W. Yazzie; Gene and Isaac Johnson, Editors
Illus. 56 pp. Paper. Rough Rock Demonstration School, 1984.

NAVAJO ORAL TRADITIONS
Alfred W. Yazzie; Jeri Eck, Editor; Illus. 72 pp. Paper. Rough Rock School Press, 1984.

THE NAVAJO PEOPLE & URANIUM MINING
Doug Brugge, Timonthy Benally, Esther Yazzie-Lewis, Editors
Story of the early Navajo uranium miners. 232 pp. Illus. Paper.
University of New Mexico Press, 2007. $24.95.

**NAVAJO & PHOTOGRAPHY: A CRITICAL HISTORY OF THE REPRESENTATION OF
AN AMERICAN PEOPLE** James C. Faris; Illus. 408 pp. U. of New Mexico Press, $39.95.
Paper. University of Utah Press, 2003. $24.95.

NAVAJO PLACENAMES & TRAILS OF THE CANYON DE CHELLY SYSTEM, ARIZONA
Stephen C. Jett; Illus. 280 pp. Paper. Amazon.com, 2001. $34.95.

NAVAJO PLACES: HISTORY, LEGEND, LANDSCAPE
Laurance D. Linford; Place-Name guide of the entirety of the traditional Navajo homeland.
Maps. Tables. 360 pp. Paper. University of Utah Press, 2000. $24.95.

NAVAJO PICTORIAL WEAVING 1800-1950
Tyrone Campbell & Joel & Kate Kopp; 178 full color photos of Navajo rugs.
Illus. 128 pp. Paper. University of New Mexico Press, $24.95.

THE NAVAJO POLITICAL EXPERIENCE
David E. Wilkins; Revised edition. Examines legal topics within a cultural context. i.e.
Indian Gaming. 277 pp. Paper. Dine Press, 2000. $45. Revised edition. Illus. 304 pp.
Rowman & Littlefield, 2003. $69; paper, $32.95.

NAVAJO: PORTRAIT OF A NATION
Joel Grimes; Calendar. 12 full-color photos of the people, places,
and landscapes from the Navajo Nation. 14x12". Treasure Chest. $10.95.

NAVAJO POTTERY: TRADITIONS & INNOVATIONS
Russell Hartman & Jan Musial; Illus. Biblio. Paper. Amazon.com, 1987. $12.95.

**THE NAVAJO PROJECT: ARCHAEOLOGICAL INVESTIGATIONS
PAGE TO PHOENIX 500 KV SOUTHERN TRANSMISSION LINE**
Donald Fiero, et al; 282 pp. Museum of Northern Arizona, 1978. $9.95.

NAVAJO & PUEBLO EARRINGS, 1850-1945
Robert Bauer; Illus. 128 pp. Paper. Rio Grande Books & Amazon.com, 2007. $17.95.

NAVAJO & PUEBLO SILVERSMITHS
John Adair; Reprint of 1944 ed. Illus. Maps. Paper. U. of Oklahoma Pres, $15.95.

NAVAHO RELIGION: A STUDY OF SYMBOLISM
Gladys A. Reichard
Reprint of 1963 edition. 856 pp. Paper. Amazon.com, $19.95.

**NAVAJO REPORTER: OFFICIAL REPORTS OF CASES ARGUED & DECIDED
IN THE SUPREME COURT & THE DISTRICT COURTS IN THE NAVAJO NATION**
Volume 5. Amazon.com. $50.

NAVAJO RESOURCES & ECONOMIC DEVELOPMENT
Philip Reno; Formerly, Mother Earth, Father Sky; Illus. 200 pp. Paper.
University of New Mexico Press, and Amazon.com, 1981. $8.95.

NAVAJO RUG STIK-WITHIT NOTECUBES
Self Stick; Full color. 600 sheets, 3.5 x 3". Amazon.com, $12.

NAVAJO RUGS: THE ESSENTIAL GUIDE
Don Dedera; Revised second edition discusses history of the art, outline of the process of
making rugs, and how to choose & care for rugs. Illus. 65 color & 6 bxw photos. 136 pp.
Paper. Amazon.com, $14.95.

NAVAJO RUGS, PAST & PRESENT
Gilbert Maxwell; 100 pp. Paper. Treasure Chest, 1987. $7.

NAVAJO SACRED PLACES
Klara Bonsack Kelley & Harris Francis
Illus. Photos. Maps. 272 pp. Paper. Amazon.com & Alibris.com, 1994. $12.

NAVAJO SADDLE BLANKETS: TEXTILES TO RIDE IN THE AMERICAN SOUTHWEST
Edited by Lane Coulter
Illus. 144 pp. Paper. Museum of New Mexico Press, 2001. $29.95.

NAVAJO SANDPAINTING ART: WHERE THE GODS GATHER
Mark Bahti; Illus. 56 pp. Paper. Treasure Chest Books, 1999. $15.95.

NAVAJO SANDPAINTING: FROM RELIGIOUS ACT TO COMMERCIAL ART
Nancy J. Parezo; 275 pp. Paper. University of New Mexico Press, 1991. $19.95.

NAVAJO SANDPAINTING: THE HUCKEL COLLECTION
Leland C. Wyman; Illus. Paper. Amazon.com, 1971. $5.

NAVAJO SANDPAINTINGS
Mark Bahti, Eugene Baatsoslanii Joe; revised edition. Illus. U. of Arizona Press, 2009.

NAVAJO SANDSTONE: A CANYON COUNTRY ENIGMA
F.A. Barnes; Illus. 96 pp. Paper. Amazon.com, 1999. $7.

NAVAJO SHEPARD & WEAVER
Gladys Reichard; Reprint of 1936 edition. Illus. 280 pp. Paper. Rio Grande Press. $12.

**THE NAVAJO SKINWALKER, WITCHCRAFT & RELATED SPIRITUAL PHENOMENA:
SPIRITUAL CLUES: ORIENTATION TO THE EVOLUTION OF THE CIRCLE**
Joanne Teller & Norman Blackwater; Illus. 256 pp. Paper. Infinity Horn Pubg,
1997.$13.95.

*THE NAVAJO: SOUTHWEST
Peter Iverson; Grades 5 and up. Illus. Chelsea House, 1989. $17.95.

NAVAJO SOVEREIGNTY: UNDERSTANDINGS & VISIONS OF THE DINE PEOPLE
Lloyd L. Lee, Editor; Paper. University of Arizona Press, 2016. $29.95.

NAVAJO SPOONS: INDIAN ARTISTRY & THE SOUVENIR TRADE, 1880-1940
Cindra Kline; Navajo silverwork is explored. 128 pp. Paper. Museum of New Mexico
Press, 2001. $27.50.

NAVAJO STORIES OF THE LONG WALK PERIOD
Compiled by Ruth Roessel; Presents Navajo accounts of the Lonf Walk and the
concentration camp life at Fort Sumner in easter New Mexico from 1864-1868.
Paper. Amazon.com. $20.

**NAVAHO SYMBOLS OF HEALING: A JUNGIAN EXPLORATION OF RITUAL, IMAGE,
AND MEDICINE** Donald Sandner, M.D.; A Jungian-trained psychiatrist explores ancient
Navaho methods of healing that use vibrant imagery to bring the psyche into harmony with
the natural forces. Illus. 8 color plates. 304 pp. Paper. Inner Traditions, 1991. $16.95.

NAVAJO TALKING PICTURE: CINEMA ON NATIVE GROUND
Randolph Lewis; Illus. 248 pp. Paper. University of Nebraska Press, 2012. $30.

NAVAJO TEXTILES: BOOK OF POSTCARDS
Southwest Museum Staff
Illus. 30 pp. Paper. Pomegranate Communications, 1996. $9.95.

**NAVAJO TEXTILES: THE CRANE COLLECTION AT THE DENVER MUSEUM
OF NATURE & SCIENCE** Laurie Webster, Louise Stiver, D.Y. Begay, Lynda Teller Pete
Illus. 400 pp. Paper. University Press of Colorado & Denver Museum of Nature & Science,
2017. $34.95; eBook, $27.95.

NAVAJO TEXTILES: THE WILLIAM RANDOLPH HEARST COLLECTION
Nancy J. Blomberg; Reprint. Illus. 257 pp. Paper. U. of Arizona Press, 1994. $36.95.

NAVAJO & TIBETAN SACRED WISDOM: THE CIRCLE OF THE SPIRIT
Peter Gold; Shows the parallels between cultures. 200 Illus. 350 pp.
Paper. Inner Traditions, 1994. $39.95.

NAVAJO TRADER: ESSAYS ON A REGION & ITS LITERATURE
Gladwell Richardson; edited by Philip Reed Rulon
217 pp. Paper. University of Arizona Press, 1986. $22.95.

NAVAJO TRADING: THE END OF AN ERA
Willow Roberts Powers; Examines trading in the last quarter of the 20th century.
Illus. 320 pp. Paper. University of New Mexico Press, 2001. $17.95.

NAVAJO: TRADITION & CHANGE IN THE SOUTHWEST
Wolfgang Lindig; photos by Helga Teiwes
Illus. Photos. Biblio. 240 pp. Facts on File, 1993. $45.

**NAVAJO TRADITION, MORMON LIFE: THE AUTOBIOGRAPHY & TEACHINGS
OF JIM DANDY** Robert McPherson, Jim Dandy, Sarah Burak
306 pp. Paper. University of Utah Press, $19.95; eBook, $14.

THE NAVAJO TREATY, 1868
K C Publications, 1968. $3.50; paper, $1.

**NAVAJO TRIBAL DEMOGRAPHY, 1983-1986: A COMPARATIVE
& HISTORICAL PERSPECTIVE** Cheryl Howard; Illus. 272 pp. Garland, 1993. $15.

THE NAVAJO VERB: A GRAMMAR FOR STUDENTS & SCHOLARS
Leonard M. Faltz; 470 pp. Paper. University of New Mexico Press, 1996. $45.

THE NAVAJO VERB SYSTEM: AN OVERVIEW
Robert W. Young; 350 pp. University of New Mexico Press, 1996. $55.

NAVAJO WAR DANCE
B. Haile; Reprint of 1946 edition. Paper. St. Michaels, $6.

THE NAVAJO WAY: CEREMONIAL MYTHS OF THE NAVAJO
Hausman; Paper. Prentice Hall PTR, 1992. $11.95.

NAVAJO WEAVERS & SILVERSMITHS
W. Matthews; Facsimile of 1968 edition. Illus. 43 pp. Paper.
Amazon.com & Alibris.com. $4.

NAVAJO WEAVING FROM THE SANTA FE COLLECTION
48 pp. Paper. Amazon.com, 1997. $9.95.

A NAVAHO WEAVING, ITS TECHNIC & HISTORY
Charles A. Amsden; A comprehensive study of primitive textile weaving.
Reprint of 1934 ed. Illus. 460 pp. The Rio Grande Press, $17.50. Paper, Dover, $8.95.

NAVAJO WEAVING IN LATE 20TH CENTURY: KIN, COMMUNITY & COLLECTORS
Ann Lane Hedlund; 147 pp. University of Arizona Press, 2004. $35.

NAVAJO WEAVING, NAVAJO WAYS
Harriet & Seymour Koenig; Betty Himmel, Editor
56 pp. Paper. Katonah Galleries, 1986. $12.

NAVAJO WEAVING: THREE CENTURIES OF CHANGE
Kate Peck Kent; Illus. 150 pp. Paper. School of American Research, 1985. $16.95.

NAVAJO WEAVING TODAY
Nancy Schiffer; Full-color photos of contemporary Navajo blankets and rugs, with text.
Illus. 64 pp. Paper. Schiffer, $12.95.

THE NAVAJO WEAVING TRADITION, 1650 TO THE PRESENT
Alice Kaufman & Christopher Selser; Detailed history and appreciation of the Navajo
weavings. Discusses traders, the weaving process, and contemporary weaving. 200 Illus.
160 pp. Paper. E.P. Dutton & Amazon.com, $29.95.

NAVAJO WEAVING WAY: THE PATH FROM FLEECE TO RUG
Noel Bennett; Illus. 160 pp. Paper. Amazon.com, 1997. $21.95.

NAVAJO WEAVINGS FROM THE ANDY WILLIAMS COLLECTION
Ann L. Hedlund & Zoe A. Perkins; Mary A. Steiner, Ed.
Illus. 72 pp. Paper. Amazon.com, 1997. $24.95.

NAVAJO WEAPON
S. McClain; Jan Kristiansson, Ed.; Illus. 336 pp. Books Beyond Borders, 1994. $29.95.

NAVAJOLAND: FAMILY SETTLEMENT & LAND USE
Clara Kelley & Peter Whitely; Paper. Navajo Community College Press, $14.50.

NAVAJOLAND PLANT CATALOG
Vernon Mayes & James Rominger; List of more than 1,100 plants known to grow on
the Navajo Reservation. 72 pp. Paper. Amazon.com, 1994. $7.

NAVAJOLAND: A PORTFOLIO OF NAVAJO LIFE DURING THE 1940's & 1950's
Ray Manley
A pictorial study, in bxw, of the Navajo people. Illus. 52 pp. Paper. Ray Manley, $9.95.

*THE NAVAJOS
Peter Iverson; Grades 5 and up. Illus. Chelsea House, 1990. $17.95; paper, $9.95.

*THE NAVAJOS
Virginia Driving Hawk Sneve; The creation myth of the Navajos; history, customs,
and facts about the tribe today. Grades 2-6. Illus. 32 pp. Holiday House, 1993. $15.95.

THE NAVAJOS
R. Underhill; Reprint of 1956 edition. Illus. Maps. 304 pp. Paper.
University of Oklahoma Press, 2002. $19.95.

THE NAVAJOS: A CRITICAL BIBLIOGRAPHY
Peter Iverson; Paper. Indian University Press, 1976. $4.95.

THE NAVAJOS IN 1705: ROQUE MADRID'S CAMPAIGN JOURNAL
Rick Hendricks & John P. Wilson; Paper. University of New Mexico Press, $15.95.

THE NAVAJOS' LONG WALK FOR EDUCATION
H. Thompson; Broderick Johnson, Editor
Illus. 248 pp. Navajo Community College Press, 1975. $15.

THE NAVAJOS & THE NEW DEAL
Donald L. Parman; Illus. 320 pp. Yale University Press, 1976. $37.50.

*THE NAVAJOS: PEOPLE OF THE SOUTHWEST
Nancy Bonvillain; Grades 4-6. Illus. 64 pp. Amazon.com, 1995. $21.90.

NAVAJOS WEAR NIKES: A RESERVATION LIFE
Jim Kristofic; Memoir. Illus. 232 pp. Paper. University of New Mexico Press, $19.95.

*NAYA NUKI: SHOSHONE GIRL WHO RAN
Kenneth Thomasma; Eunice Hundley, Illus.; Indian lore, survival skills, and the West
before the white man. Grades 4-9. Illus. Amazon.com, $10.99; paper, $6.99.

**NAVIGATING NEOLIBERALISM: SELF-DETERMINATION
& THE MIKISEW CREE FIRST NATION**
Gabrielle Slowey; 144 pp. University of Washington Press, 2008. $94; paper, $33.95.

NAVIGATING POWER: CROSS-CULTURAL COMPETENCE IN NAVAJO LAND
Gelaye Debebe; 180 pp. Lexington Books, 2012. $84; paper, $39.99; eBook, $39.99.

NCH'I-WANA "THE BIG RIVER" MID-COLUMBIA INDIANS & THEIR LAND
Eugene S. Hunn; Illus. Maps. 384 pp. Paper. U. of Washington Press, 1989. $24.95.

NDAKINNA (OUR LAND): NEW & SELECTED POEMS
Joseph Bruchac; Meditations on the New England Abenaki Indians.
Illus. 96 pp. Paper. University of New Mexico Press, $11.95.

NDN ART: CONTEMPORARY NATIVE AMERICAN ART
Charleen Touchette & Suzanne Deats; Collection of expressions of contemporary
American Indian artists. Illus. 168 photos. 206 pp. Paper. U. of New Mexico Press, $45.

THE NEBRASKA INDIAN WARS READER, 1865-77
R. Eli Paul, Editor
Illus. Maps. 290 pp. Paper. University of Nebraska Press, 1998. $19.95.

**A NECESSARY BALANCE: GENDER & POWER AMONG INDIANS
OF THE COLUMBIA PLATEAU**
Lillian A. Ackerman; Illus. Maps. 296 pp. University of Oklahoma Press, 2003. $42.95.

*NEEKNA & CHEMAI
Jeanette Armstrong; Two little Okanagan girls teach about the seasonal life patterns
of the Okanagan Indian people. Grades 2-8. Illus. Paper. Theytus, 1991. $12.95.

NEETS'AII GWIINDAII: LIVING IN THE CHANDALAR COUNTRY
Katherine Peter; Illus. 108 pp. Paper. Alaska Native Language Center, 1992. $12.

NEGOTIATED EMPIRES: CENTERS & PERIPHERIES IN THE NEW WORLD
Christine Daniels & Leslie Page Moch; 336 pp. Paper. Routledge, 2002. $19.95.

NEGOTIATED SOVEREIGNTY: WORKING TO IMPROVE TRIBAL-STATE RELATIONS
Jeffrey S. Ashley & Secody J. Hubbard; 144 pp. Greenwood Publishing, 2003. $65.

NEGOTIATING TRIBAL WATER RIGHTS: FULFILLING PROMISES IN THE ARID WEST
Bonnie G. Colby, John E. Thorson, Sarah Britton
190 pp. Paper. University of Arizona Press, 2005. $35.

**NEGOTIATION WITHIN DOMINATION: NEW SPAIN'S INDIAN PUEBLOS
CONFRONT THE SPANISH STATE** Ethelia Ruiz Medrano & Susan Kellogg, Editors
Case studies about the relationships between indigenous communities & the Spanish state
in the colonial period. Maps. Tables. University Press of Colorado, 2010. $70. E-book, $60;
30-day rental, $9.99.

**NEGOTIATORS OF CHANGE: HISTORICAL PERSPECTIVES ON NATIVE AMERICAN
WOMEN** Nancy Shoemaker, Editor; Collection of articles on th history of women & gender
in American Indian societies. Illus. 320 pp. Routledge, 1994. $59.95; paper, $17.95.

THE NEHALEM TILLAMOOK: AN ETHNOGRAPHY
Elizabeth D. Jacobs; William Seaburg, Ed.
Illus. 272 pp. Paper. Oregon State University Press, 2003. $21.95.

NEHALEM TILLAMOOK TALES
Melville Jacobs, Editor; 276 pp. Oregon State U. Press, 1990. $29.95; paper, $21.95.

NEITHER RED NOR WHITE & OTHER INDIAN STORIES
George A. Boyce; 96 pp. Paper. Sunstone Press, $12.95.

**NEITHER WOLF NOR DOG: AMERICAN INDIANS, ENVIRONMENT & AGRARIAN
CHANGE** David R. Lewis; Illus. 256 pp. Oxford University Press, 1994. $150.

NEITHER WOLF NOR DOG: ON FORGOTTEN ROADS WITH AN INDIAN ELDER
Kent Nerburn; A journey into the Native American experience.
Reprint. Illus. 350 pp. New American Library & Amazon.com, 1994/2002. $15.

THE NELSON ISLAND ESKIMO: SOCIAL STRUCTURE & RITUAL DISTRIBUTION
Norman Chance; Paper. Holt, Rinehart & Winston, 1966. $9.95.

SADIE BROWER NEAKOK, AN INUPIAQ WOMAN
Margaret B. Blackman; An Eskimo's woman's life story. Illus. Maps.
326 pp. Paper. University of Washington Press, 1989. $23.95.

THE NETSILIK ESMIKO
Asen Balikci; Revised edition. Illus. 264 pp. Paper. Waveland, 1989. $9.50.

THE NETWORKED WILDERNESS: COMMUNICATING IN EARLY NEW ENGLAND
Matt Cohen; Illus. 237 pp. Paper. University of Minnesota Press, 2010.

*NEVADA HISTORY COLORING BOOKS: NEVADA'S NATIVE AMERICANS
Nancy C. Miluck; Grades K-5. Illus. 48 pp. Paper. Dragon Enterprises, 1992. $4.

NEVADA MILITARY PLACE NAMES OF THE INDIAN WARS & CIVIL WAR
Daniel C.B. Rathbun; Illus. 232 pp. Paper. Barbed Wire Publishing, 2002. $13.

*NEVADA TRIBAL HISTORY & GOVERNMENT
Yerington Paiute Tribe; Grades 7-12. An introductory social studies unit about
Nevada Tribes. Illus. 32 pp. Yerington Paiute Tribe Publications, $5.

NEVER COME TO PEACE AGAIN: PONTIAC'S UPRISING & THE FATE OF THE BRITISH EMPIRE IN NORTH AMERICA David Dixon
Illus. Maps. 384 pp. University of Oklahoma Press & Wennawoods Publishing, $34.95.

NEVER GIVE UP! THE LIFE OF PEARL CARTER SCOTT
Paul F. Lambert; Biography. Illus. 278 pp. The Chickasaw Press; distributed by University of Oklahoma Press, 2008. $24.95.

NEVER IN ANGER: PORTRAIT OF AN ESKIMO FAMILY
Jean L. Briggs; Illus. Paper. Amazon.com, 1970. $10.95.

NEVER WITHOUT CONSENT: JAMES BAY CREES STAND AGAINST AN INDEPENDENT QUEBEC Grand Council of the Crees Staff
250 pp. Paper. Amazon.com, 1997. $21.95.

THE NEW AMERICAN STATE PAPERS: INDIAN AFFAIRS, 1789-1860, Subject Set, 13 Vols. Loring B. Priest, Ed.; Thomas C. Cochran, Gen. Ed.
Contains reports of the commissioners of Indian Affairs, personal accounts of Indian life and culture, etc. Facsimile reprint. Illus. Amazon.com & Alibris.com, $750 per set.

NEW CAPITALISTS: ISSUES OF LAW, POLITICS & IDENTITY SURROUNDING CASINO GAMING ON NATIVE AMERICAN LAND
Eve Darian-Smith; 144 pp. Paper. Amazon.com, 2003. $25.95.

THE NEW DEAL & AMERICAN INDIAN TRIBALISM: THE ADMINISTRATION OF THE INDIAN REORGANIZATION ACT, 1934-1945
Graham D. Taylor; 210 pp. University of Nebraska Press, 1980. $18.95.

A NEW DEAL FOR NATIVE ART: INDIAN ARTS & FEDERAL POLICY, 1933-1943
Jennifer McLerrann; Paper. University of Arizona Press, 2012. $35.

NEW DIRECTIONS IN AMERICAN INDIAN HISTORY
Colin Calloway, Ed.; 262 pp. Paper. University of Oklahoma Press, 1988. $15.95.

NEW DIRECTIONS IN FEDERAL INDIAN POLICY: A REVIEW OF AMERICAN INDIAN POLICY REVIEW COMMISSION
edited by Anthony D. Brown; Collection of articles presented as papers at a 1978 conference sponsored by the UCLA, American Indian Studies Center. 150 pp. Paper. UCLA, American Indian Studies Center, 1979. $10.

NEW ECHOTA LETTERS: CONTRIBUTIONS OF SAMUEL L. WORCESTER TO THE CHEROKEE PHOENIX Jack & Anna Kilpatrick, Editors
The Phoenix was the first newspaper printed in part in an American Indian language. A white missionary, Worcester, writes of a crucial period in Cherokee history. 136 pp. SMU Press, 1968. $14.95.

THE NEW ENCYCLOPEDIA OF THE AMERICAN WEST
Howard R. Lamar, Editor; Illus. 1344 pp. Yale University Press, 1998. $95.

THE NEW ENCYCLOPEDIA OF SOUTHERN CULTURE: VOL. 6: ETHNICITY
Celeste Ray, Editor; Illus. Maps. Tables. 296 pp. University of North Carolina Press, 2007. $39.95; paper, $19.95.

NEW ENGLAND FRONTIER: PURITANS & INDIANS, 1620-1675
Alden T. Vaughan; 3rd Ed. Illus. 492 pp. Paper. U. of Oklahoma Press, 1995. $26.95.

THE NEW ENGLAND INDIANS
C. Keith Wilbur, MD; Describes how New England's 18 major Indian tribes actually lived. 2nd revised edition. Illus. Biblio. 130 pp. Paper. Amazon.com, 1996. $16.95.

NEW ENGLAND'S PROSPECT
W. Wood; Alden T. Vaughan, Editor
Reprint of 1634 edition. Illus. 144 pp. Paper. University of Massachusetts Press, $11.95.

NEW HISTORIES FRO OLD: CHANGING PERSPECTIVES ON CANADA'S NATIVE PASTS Ted Binnema & Susan Neylan, Editors
Maps. 304 pp. University of Washington Press, 2008. $94; paper, $37.95.

NEW HOPE FOR THE INDIANS: THE GRANT PEACE POLICY & THE NAVAJOS IN THE 1870s Norman Bender; Illus. 288 pp. University of New Mexico Pres, 1990.

NEW HORIZONS IN AMERICAN INDIAN ART
Illus. 16 pp. Paper. Southwest Museum, 1976. $2.00.

NEW INDIANS, OLD WARS
Elizabeth Cook-Lynn; Illus. 248 pp. University of Illinois Press, 2007. $33.95.

NEW LAKOTA DICTIONARY
Jan F. Ullrich; 2nd Ed. Background of the Lakota language & history of Lakota Lexicography; grammar section; 23,000+ words. 1,112 pp. Paper. Oyate, Amazn.com & Lakota Language Consortium, 2010. $50.

NEW LIGHT ON CHACO CANYON
David Grant Noble, Editor; Illus. 108 pp. Paper. School of American Research, $11.95.

NEW MEXICO ART THROUGH TIME: PREHISTORY TO THE PRESENT
Joseph Traugott; Includes pre-European Native American pottery, baskets, and weavings. Illus. 244 pp. Museum of New Mexico Press, 2012. $50.

NEW MEXICO FRONTIER MILITARY PLACE NAMES
Daniel C. Rathbun; Illus. 280 pp. Paper. Barbed Wire Publications, 2003. $13.

NEW MEXICO INDIAN RUINS
Ron Swartley; Illus. 184 pp. Paper. Frontier Image Press, 1998. $21.95.

NEW MEXICO TREASURES 2011: ENGAGEMENT CALENDAR
New Mexico Dept. of Cultural Affairs; Cultural happenings in New Mexico's urban centers, small towns & Pueblos. Illus. 120 pp. Museum of New Mexico Press, 2010. Wirebinding, $13.95.

NEW NATIVE AMERICAN DRAMA: THREE PLAYS
Hanay Geiogamah, Editor
Reprint of 1980 ed. Illus. 158 pp. Paper. University of Oklahoma Press, 2001. $19.95.

NEW & OLD VOICES OF WAH'KON-TAH
Robert Dodge & Jos. McCullough; 144 pp. Paper. Amazon.com, 1985. $4.95.

A NEW ORDER OF THINGS: PROPERTY, POWER & THE TRANSFORMATION OF THE CREEK INDIANS, 1733-1816
Claudio Saunt; Illus. 310 pp. Cambridge University Press, 1999. $60.

THE NEW PEOPLES: BEING & BECOMING METIS IN NORTH AMERICA
Jacqueline Peterson & Jeniifer S.H. Brown, Eds.
Illus. 290 pp. Paper. Minnesota Historical Society Press, 2001. $19.95.

NEW PERSPECTIVES ON NATIVE NORTH AMERICA: CULTURE, HISTORY, & REPRESENTATIONS Sergie A. Kan & Pauline Turner Strong, Editors
Essays, Illus. Map. 516 pp. University of Nebraska Press, 2006. $65; paper, $35.

NEW PERSPECTIVES ON POTTERY MOUND PUEBLO
Polly Schaafsma, Editor; Essay by contemporary scholars on the Pottery Mound Pueblo's murals, rock art, textiles, & archaeofaunal remains. Illus. 112 color photos, halftones, line drawings, maps. 318 pp. University of New Mexico Press, $55.

NEW PERSPECTIVES ON THE PUEBLOS
Alfonso Ortiz, Editor; Illus. 360 pp. Paper. University of New Mexico Press, 1970. $11.95.

A NEW PICTOGRAPHIC AUTOBIOGRAPHY OF SITTING BULL
Alexis A. Praus; Illus. 11 pp. Paper. Lakota Books, 1995. $12.95.

THE NEW POLITICS OF INDIAN GAMING: THE RISE OF RESERVATION INTEREST GROUPS Kenneth N. Hansen & Tracy A. Skopek, Editors
Collection of case studies outlines in detail the activities and results in states with the highest population of Native Americans. Biblio. 228 pp. University of Nevada Press, 2011.

NEW RELATION TO GASPESIA: WITH THE CUSTOMS & RELIGION OF THE GASPESIAN INDIAN C. Le Clercq; Reprint of 1910 ed. Greenwood, $33.75.

THE NEW RESOURCE WARS: NATIVE & ENVIRONMENTAL STRUGGLES AGAINST MULTINATIONAL CORPORATIONS
Al Gedicks; Illus. 250 pp. Amazon.com, 1994. $35; paper, $15.

A NEW SOUTH DAKOTA HISTORY
Herbert T. Hoover; Illus. Center for Western Studies, 2005.

NEW TRAILS IN MEXICO: AN ACCOUNT OF ONE YEAR'S EXPLORATION IN NORTH-WESTERN SONORA, MEXICO, & SOUTH-WESTERN ARIZONA, 1909-1910
Carl Lumholtz; An early look at the Papagos. Reprint of 1912 edition. 411 pp. Paper. University of Arizona Press, $18.95.

NEW TRIBE: NEW YORK/THE URBAN VISION QUEST
Gerald McMaster (Plains Cree), Editor; Illus. 64 pp. Paper. NMAI Press, 2005. $19.95.

NEW VOICES FROM THE LONGHOUSE: AN ANTHOLOGY OF MODERN IROQUOIS LITERATURE Joseph Bruchac; Amazon.com & Albris.com, 1988. $12.95.

NEW VOICES IN NATIVE AMERICAN LITERARY CRITICISM
Arnold Krupat, Editor; 20 critics explore the oral and textual expressions of Native Americans past and present. 704 pp. Paper. Smithsonian Institution Press, 1993. $34.95.

THE NEW WARRIORS: NATIVE AMERICAN LEADERS SINCE 1900
edited by R. David Edmunds; Profiles American Indian men and women who played a significant role in the affairs of their communities and of the nation in the 20th century. Illus. 356 pp. University of Nebraska Press, 2001. $40.

NEW WORDS, OLD SONGS
Charles E. Blanchard; illus. by Merald Clark
Understanding the lives of ancient peoples in Southwest Florida through archaeology. Illus. 136 pp. Paper. IAPS Book. Amazon.com, $24.95; paper, $14.95.

NEW WORLD ARCHAEOLOGY & CULTURE HISTORY: COLLECTED ESSAYS & ARTICLES Gordon Willey; Illus. 450 pp. University of New Mexico Press, 1990. $39.95.

NEW WORLD BABEL: LANGUAGES & NATIONS IN EARLY AMERICA
Edward G. Gray; Amazon.com, 1999. $35.

NEW WORLDS FOR ALL: INDIANS, EUROPEANS, & THE REMAKING OF EARLY AMERICA
Colin G. Calloway; Illus. 216 pp. Johns Hopkins University Press, 1997. $24.95.

NEW WORLDS OF VIOLENCE: CULTURES & CONQUESTS IN THE EARLY AMERICAN SOUTHEAST
Matthew Jennings; The Eiropean-Native American contact period and the conflicts among indigenous peoples that preceded it. Illus. University of Tennessee Press, 2011. $50.

NEW WRITERS OF THE PURPLE SAGE
Russell Martin, Editor
Includes some Native American writers. 368 pp. Penguin USA, $11.

NEW YORK CITY IN INDIAN POSSESSION
Reginald P. Bolton
2nd Ed. Illus. 170 pp. Paper. National Museum of the American Indian, 1975. $6.

NEW YORK PORTRAIT PHOTOGRAPHER & RED CLOUD: PHOTOGRAPHS OF A LAKOTA CHIEF Frank H. Goodyear III; University of Oklahoma Press, 2005. $29.95.

NEWBERRY LIBRARY/CENTER FOR THE HISTORY OF AMERICAN INDIAN BIBLIOGRAPHICAL SERIES Francis Jennings; A series of bibliographies of Native American groups, geographic areas, and subjects. Amazon.com & Alibris.com, 1976-84.

NEWE HUPIA: SHOSHONI POETRY SONGS
Jon P. Dayley, and Beverly & Earl Crum ; Written texts of songs in Shoshoni & English, packaged with a CD with songs by Earl and beverly Crum. 276 pp. Paper & CD. University Press of Colorado & Utah State University Press, 2001. $24.95. E-book, $22.95.

THE NEWSPAPER INDIAN: NATIVE AMERICAN IDENTITY IN THE PRESS, 1820-1890
John M. Coward; Illus. 272 pp. Paper. University of Illinois Press, 1999. $26.

THE NEWSPAPER WARRIOR: SARAH WINNEMUCCA HOPKIN'S CAMPAIGN FOR AMERICAN INDIAN RIGHTS, 1864-1891
Sarah Winnemucca Hopkins; edited by Cari Carpenter & Carolyn Sorisio
Anthology. Illus. 344 pp. University of Nebraska Press, 2015. $75. eBook available.

***NEZ PERCE**
Kathi Howes; Grades 5-8. Illus. 32 pp. Amazon.com, 1990. $9.95.

***THE NEZ PERCE**
Clifford E. Trafzer; Historical look at the Nez Perce. Grades 7 and up. Illus.
Chelsea House Publishers, 1993. $7.95.

***THE NEZ PERCE**
Nancy Bonvillain; Paul Rosier, Series Editor
Grades 6-12. 144 pp. Chelsea House, 2010. $35.

***THE NEZ PERCE**
Virginia Driving Hawk Sneve; The creation myth of the Nez Perce; their history, customs, and facts about the tribe today. Grades 4-6. Illus. 32 pp. Holiday House, 1994. $15.95; paper, $6.95.

***THE NEZ PERCE**
Alice Osinski; Grade K-4. Illus. 48 pp. Childrens Press, 1984. $11.45.

NEZ PERCE COUNTRY
223 pp. Paper. Nez Perce National Historical Park.

NEZ PERCE COUNTRY
Alvin M. Josephy, Jr.; intro. by Jeremy FiveCrows
Describes the Nimiipuu's attachment to the land in the Columbia Basin and their way of life, religion & culture. Photos. Map. 196 pp. University of Nebraska Press, 2007. $14.95.

NEZ PERCE COYOTE TALES: THE MYTH CYCLE
Deward E. Walker; Illus. Maps. Biblio. Paper. U. of Oklahoma Press, 1998. $13.95.

NEZ PERCE DICTIONARY
Haruo Aoki; Illus. how each word is used by citing examples from Nez Perce oral literature. University of California Press, 1994. $185.

THE NEZ PERCE INDIANS & THE OPENING OF THE NORTHWEST
Alvin M. Josephy, Jr.
Abridged edition. Illus. 683 pp. Paper. University of Nebraska Press, 1979. $14.95.

NEZ PERCE NARRATIVES
Aski Haruo & Deward Walker; Paper. University of California Press, 1989. $64.

THE NEZ PERCE NATION DIVIDED: FIRSTHAND ACCOUNTS OF EVENTS LEADING TO THE 1863 TREATY Dennis W. Baird, et al, Eds.
Illus. 480 pp. U. of Idaho Press, 2002. $49.95.

***THE NEZ PERCE: NORTHWEST**
Peter Nabakov; Grades 5 and up. Illus. Chelsea House, 1989. $17.95.

NEZ PERCE WOMEN IN TRANSITION, 1877-1990
Caroline James; Illus. 274 pp. University of Idaho Press, 1996. $49.95.

THE NEZ PERCES IN THE INDIAN TERRITORY: NIMIIPUU SURVIVAL
J. Diane Pearson; foreword by Patricia Penn Hilden
Illus. 25 b&w . 1 map. 383 pp. University of Oklahoma Press, 2008. $34.95.

THE NEZ PERCES SINCE LEWIS & CLARK
Kate McBeth; Reprint. Illus. 288 pp. Paper. University of Idaho Press, $15.95.

NEZ PERCES: TRIBESMEN OF THE COLUMBIA PLATEAU
Francis Haines; Reprint of 1955 edition. Illus. Paper. U. of Oklahoma Press, $17.95.

NI-KSO-KO-WA: BLACKFOOT SPIRITUALITY, TRADITIONS, VALUES, & BELIEFS
Long Standing Bear Chief; Presents an overview of Blackfoot beliefs from a modern day viewpoint. Amazon.com, 1992. E-book, $9.95.

NICOLAS POINT, S.J.: HIS LIFE & NORTHWEST INDIAN CHRONICLES
Cornelius Buckley; 356 pp. Loyola University Press, 1989. $15.95.

JOSEPH N. NICOLLET ON THE PLAINS & PRAIRIES: THE EXPEDITION OF 1838-39 WITH JOURNALS, LETTERS & NOTES ON THE DAKOTA INDIANS

Joseph N. Nicollet; Edmund & Martha Bray, Ed. & tr.
Illus. 310 pp. Paper. Minnesota Historical Society Press, 1993. $14.95.

THE NIGHT CHANT: A NAVAHO CEREMONY
Washington Matthews
Reprint of 1902 edition. Illus. 376 pp. University of Utah Press, 1998. $45; paper, $19.95.

NIGHT FLYING WOMAN: AN OJIBWAY NARRATIVE
Ignatia Broker; illus. by Steven Premo
Life experiences of author's great-great grandmother from the 1860s through the 1940s. Illus. 135 pp. Paper. Minnesota Historical Society Press, 1983. $8.50.

***THE NIGHT THE GRANDFATHERS DANCED**
Linda Theresa Raczek; Illus. by Katalin Olah Ehling
A tale revolving around a Ute Indian traditional springtime dance. Ages 5-8. Illus. 32 pp. Paper. Northland Press & Amazon.com, $7.95.

THE NIGHT HAS A NAKED SOUL: WITCHCRAFT & SORCERY AMONG THE WESTERN CHEROKEE Alan Kilpatrick
Traditional Cherokee beliefs & practices regarding the occult. Maps. 224 pp. Syracuse University Press, 1998. $29.95; paper, $19.95.

***NIGHT OF THE CRUEL MOON: CHEROKEE REMOVAL AND THE TRAIL OF TEARS**
Stanley Hoig; Grades 5-12. Illus. 144 pp. Facts on File, 1996. $17.95; paper, $9.95.

NIGHT SKY, MORNING STAR
Evelina Zuni Lucero; 229 pp. Paper. University of Arizona Press, $17.95.

NIGHT SPIRITS: THE STORY OF THE RELOCATION OF THE SAYISI DENE
Ila Bussidor & Ustun Bilgen-Reinart; Paper. Michigan State University Press & Amazon.com, 1997. $18.95.

***NIGHT WALKER & THE BUFFALO**
Althea Bass; An old Southern Cheyenne warrior tells stories that relate the old ways to the new. Grades 5-9. 32 pp. Council for Indian Education, $8.95; paper, $2.95.

NIGHTLAND: A NOVEL
Louis Owens; Cherokee ranchers. 224 pp. Paper. U. of Oklahoma Press, $9.95.

THE NIGHTWAY: A HISTORY & A HISTORY OF DOCUMENTATION OF A NAVAJO CEREMONIAL James C. Faris; Paper. University of New Mexico Press, $18.95.

NIHANCAN'S FEAST OF BEAVER: ANIMAL TALES OF THE NORTH AMERICAN INDIANS Edward Lavitt & Robert McDowell
Illus. 120 pp. Paper. Museum of New Mexico Press, 1990. $12.95.

NINE VISITS TO THE MYTHWORLD: GHANDL OF THE QAYAHL LLAANAS
translated by Robert Bringhurst; Myths, legends, and everyday stories of the Haidas. 224 pp. University of Nebraska Press, 2000. $35.

NINE YEARS AMONG THE INDIANS, 1870-1879: THE STORY OF THE CAPTIVITY & LIFE OF A TEXAN AMONG THE INDIAN Herman Lehmann; edited by Marvin Hunter
262 pp. Paper. University of New Mexico Press, $19.95.

19TH CENTURY PLAINS INDIAN DRESSES
Susan Jennys; illus. by Alex Koslov; Historical background & tribal styles, with detailed instructions on making various dress styles. 104 pp. Illus. Color Photos. Paper. Book Publishing Co., 2004. $25.

NINSTINCTS: HAIDA WORLD HERITAGE SITE
George E. MacDonald
Reprint of 1983 ed. Illus. 64 pp. Paper. University of Washington Press, 1998. $19.95.

NISHNAABERNWIN REFERENCE GRAMMAR
Randy Valentine; Amazon.com, 2001. $125; paper, $40.

NO HOME IN A HOMELAND: INDIENOUS PEOPLES & HOMELESSNESS IN THE CANADIAN NORTH Julia Christensen; UBC Press, 2017. $85; eBook, $34.95

NO MORE INDIANS
Ralph Taylor & Bearl Brooks; Grades 4-6. 24 pp. Workbook. ESP, Inc., $5.

NO MORE BUFFALO
Bob Scriver; Illus. 150 pp. Lowell Press, 1982. $35.

NO NEED OF A CHIEF FOR THIS BAND: MARITIME MI'KMAQ & FEDERAL ELECTORAL LEGISLATION, 1899-1951 Martha Elizabeth Walls
Illus. Map. 200 pp. University of Washington Press, 2010. $94; paper, $32.95.

***NO ONE LIKE A BROTHER**
Hap Gilliland
Grades 4-12. 32 pp. Council for Indian Education, 1970. $8.95; paper, $2.95.

NO ONE EVER ASKED ME: WORLD WAR II MEMOIRS OF OMAHA INDIAN SOLDIER
Hollis D. Stabler; edited by Victoria Smith
Biography. 190 pp. Paper. University of Nebraska Press, 2006. $19.95.

NO PAROLE TODAY
Laura Tohe; Prose & poetry where the author describes attending a government school for Indian children. 63 pp. Paper. University of New Mexico Press, $9.95.

NO TURNING BACK: A HOPI INDIAN WOMAN'S STRUGGLE TO LIVE IN TWO WORLDS Polingaysi Qoyawayma; as told to Vada F. Carlson; Biography of a Hopi Indian woman. 187 pp. Paper. University of New Mexico Press, 1977. $19.95.

NO WORD FOR TIME: THE WAY OF THE ALGONQUIN
Evan T. Pritchard; Explores Algonquin myth, history, and philosophy.
114 pp. Paper. Council Oak Books, 2001. $12.95.

NOBLE RED MAN: LAKOTA WISDOMKEEPER MATHEW KING
Harvey Arden, Ed; Reprint. 2nd Ed. Illus. 128 pp. Paper. Beyond Words Pubg, $13.95.

NOBLE, WRETCHED & REDEEMABLE: PROTESTANT MISSIONARIES TO THE INDIANS IN CANADA & THE U.S., 1820-1900
C.L. Higham; 320 pp. University of New Mexico Press, 2000. $39.95.

NOCCALULU: LEGEND, FACT & FUNCTION
Jeffrey R. Jones; Jerry Pogue & David Underhill, Editors
Illus. 72 pp. Jeffrey & Jones, 1989. $17.00; paper, $7.

THE NOONTIDE SUN: THE FIELD JOURNALS OF THE REV. STEPHEN BOWERS, PIONEER CALIFORNIA ARCHAEOLOGIST Arlene Benson
Chumash studies; Chumash settlements. Illus. 288 pp. $36; paper, $27.50.

NORTH ALASKA CHRONICLE: NOTES FROM THE END OF TIME
John Martin Campbell; Presents Eskimo tribesman Simon Paneak's detailed drawings of his native culture and life ways. Illus. 160 pp. Museum of New Mexico Press, 2002. $45; paper, $29.95.

NORTH AMERICA
Bruce G. Trigger & Wilcomb E. Washburn, Eds.; 3 Vols. History of the Native Peoples of the Americas. Illus. 1,072 pp. Cambridge University Press, $140.

NORTH AMERICAN ABORIGINAL HIDE TANNING: THE ACT OF TRANSFORMATION & REVIVAL Morgan Baillargeon; Explores the relationship between Aboriginal peoples (hide tanners in northern Alberta, the Yukon, and the Northwest Territories) and the big game animals killed for food. Illus. 156 pp. Paper. U. of Washington Press, 2011. $29.95.

THE NORTH AMERICAN INDIAN
David Hurst Thomas, Editor; 21-volume set reproducing over 375 articles in facsmilie. Amazon.com.

*NORTH AMERICAN INDIAN ACTIVITY BOOK
Winky Adam
Grades K-3. 32 puzzles, crosswords, coloring, mazes. 64 pp. paper. Written Heritage, $1.

NORTH AMERICAN INDIAN ALMANAC
Duane Champagne, Editor; Information on the civilization and culture of the indigenous peoples of the U.S. and Canada. Documentary excerpts, biographies, and 400 maps and illustrations. 800 pp. Gale Research, 1993. $95.

NORTH AMERICAN INDIAN ANTHROPOLOGY: ESSAYS ON SOCIETY & CULTURE
Raymond J. De Mallie & Alfonso Ortiz; Essay exploring the blending of structural & historical approaches to American Indian anthropology. Illus. Maps. 448 pp. Paper. University of Oklahoma Press, 1996. $24.95.

NORTH AMERICAN INDIAN ART
David W. Penney; Illus. 224 pp. Paper. Thames & Hudson, 2004. $21.95.

NORTH AMERICAN INDIAN ART: MASTERPIECES & MUSEUM COLLECTIONS FROM THE NETHERLANDS
Pieter Hovens & Bruce Bernstein, Editors; 320 pp. University of Oklahoma Press, $39.95.

NORTH AMERICAN INDIAN ARTIFACTS: A COLLECTOR'S ID & VALUE GUIDE
Lar Hothem; Revised 6th edition with 500 new color photos and pricing.
Illus. 496 pp. Paper. Amazon.com, 1998. $26.95 postpaid.

NORTH AMERICAN INDIAN ARTS: A GOLDEN GUIDE FROM ST. MARTINS PRESS
Andrew Hunter Whiteford
Revised ed. Illus. 160 pp. Paper. St. Martins Press, 2001. $6.95.

NORTH AMERICAN INDIAN ARTS: PRICES & AUCTIONS
Laurence & Maurine Smith; Annual. Artlist.

NORTH AMERICAN INDIAN BEADWORK
Smith; Standard text gives good directions on Applique, loom work, lazy stitch, and much more. Illus. Smoke & Fire Co., $13.95.

NORTH AMERICAN INDIAN BEADWORK DESIGNS
Clark Wissler; Illus. 32 pp. Paper. Dover Publications, 1999. $4.95.

NORTH AMERICAN INDIAN BEADWORK PATTERNS
Pamela Stanley-Millner; Illus. 48 pp. Paper. Dover, 1985. $4.95.

NORTH AMERICAN INDIAN BORDERS
Charlene Tarbox; 55 copyright-free forms. 48 pp. Paper. Dover, $5.95.

NORTH AMERICAN INDIAN BURIAL CUSTOMS
H.C. Yarrow; Monte Smith, Editor
Illus. 150 pp. Paper. Cherokee Publications & Eagle's View Publishing. $9.95.

THE NORTH AMERICAN INDIAN: THE COMPLETE PORTFOLIOS
Edward S. Curtis; Illus. 768 pp. Paper. Amazon.com, 1997. $29.99.

*NORTH AMERICAN INDIAN CRAFTS
Peter F. Copeland; Grades K-2. Coloring book. 48 pp. Paper. Dover, $2.95.

NORTH AMERICAN INDIAN DANCES & RITUALS
Copeland; Paper. Dover, 1998. $2.95.

NORTH AMERICAN INDIAN DESIGNS
Caren Caraway; 5 titles: Eastern Woodland Indian Designs, Northwest Indian Designs, Plains Indian Designs, Southeastern Woodland Indian Designs, and Southwest American Indian Designs. 50 pp. each. Paper. Amazon.com, $6.95 each.

261 NORTH AMERICAN INDIAN DESIGNS
Madeline Orban-Szontagh; Illus. 48 pp. Paper. Dover, $4.95.

*NORTH AMERICAN INDIAN DESIGNS COLORING BOOK
Paul C. Kennedy; Grades K-3. 48 pp. Paper. Dover, $2.95

NORTH AMERICAN INDIAN DESIGNS FOR ARTISTS & CRAFTSPEOPLE
Eva Wilson; 360 authentic copyright-free designs adapted from Navajo blankets, painted masks, moccasins, pottery, Sioux buffalo hides, et al. Illus. 128 pp. Paper. Dover, 1987. Written Heritage, $12.95.

NORTH AMERICAN INDIAN DESIGNS IN FULL COLOR FOR NEEDLEPOINTERS & CRAFTSPEOPLE Dorothy P. Story; Illus. 32 pp. Paper. Dover, $5.95.

NORTH AMERICAN INDIAN DESIGNS/STAINED GLASS
John Green; Illus. Paper. Dover, 1995. $3.95.

NORTH AMERICAN INDIAN ECOLOGY
J. Donald Hughes; 2nd Edition. Illus. 222 pp. Paper. Texas Western Press, 1996. $20.

NORTH AMERICAN INDIAN ICONS: A CALENDAR BOOK
Beth Garbo; Illus. 106 pp. Amazon.com, 1998. $12.95.

NORTH AMERICAN INDIAN JEWELRY & ADORNMENT: FROM PREHISTORY TO THE PRESENT Lois Sherr Dubin
1200 photos. 50 maps. Biblio. 608 pp. Harry N. Abrams, 1999. $75; paper, $29.95.

NORTH AMERICAN INDIAN LANDMARKS: A TRAVELER'S GUIDE
George Cantor; Explores more than 300 sites relevant to American Indian history and culture. Illus. 409 pp. Gale, $45. Reprint of 1993 edition. Paper. Amazon.com, $18.

NORTH AMERICAN INDIAN LANGUAGE MATERIALS, 1890-1965: AN ANNOTATED BIBLIOGRAPHY OF MONOGRAPHIC WORKS
G. Edward Evans and Jeffrey Clark; An update of James C. Pilling's nine American Indian linguistic bibliographies published for the U.S. Bureau of Ethnology. 187 entries. 153 pp. Paper. UCLA, American Indian Studies Center, 1979. $5.

NORTH AMERICAN INDIAN LEGENDS
Allan A. MacFarlan, Ed.; 432 pp. Paper. Dover Publications, 2001. $16.95.

NORTH AMERICAN INDIAN LIFE: CUSTOMS & TRADITIONS OF 23 TRIBES
Elsie Clews Parsons, Editor
27 fictionalized essays by noted anthropologistss. Studies by Paul Rodin, Robert Lowie, Stewart Culin, Franz Boas, and Elsie Clews Parson. 480 pp. Paper. Dover, $10.95.

NORTH AMERICAN INDIAN LIVES
Nancy O. Lurie; Illus. 72 pp. Paper. Waveland Press, 1985. $6.95.

*NORTH AMERICAN INDIAN MASKS
Frieda Gates; Grades 5 and up. Illus. 64 pp. Walker & Co., 1982. $8.95.

*NORTH AMERICAN INDIAN MEDICINE PEOPLE
Karen Liptak; Grades 5-8. Illus. 65 pp. Franklin Watts, 1990. $11.90.

NORTH AMERICAN INDIAN MOTIFS: CD-ROM & BOOK
Kate; Provides 391 copyright-free designs printed on one side of glossy pages. 32 pp. book and CD-ROM. Amazon.com & Alibris.com, 1996. $7.95, book; $16.95 CD-ROM & book.

NORTH AMERICAN INDIAN MUSIC: A GUIDE TO PUBLISHED SOURCES & SELECTED RECORDINGS Richard Keeling; 470 pp. Garland, 1997. $105.

NORTH AMERICAN INDIAN MYTHOLOGY
Cottie Burland; Illus. 144 pp. Amazon.com, 1985. $19.95.

NORTH AMERICAN INDIAN POINTS
Lar Hothem; Illus. Second edition. 208 pp. Paper. Amazon.com, 1984. $7.95.

THE NORTH AMERICAN INDIAN PORTFOLIOS FROM THE LIBRARY OF CONGRESS
Bodmer, Catlin, McKenney & Hall; Illus. 272 pp. Paper. Abbeville Press, $11.95.

*NORTH AMERICAN INDIAN STORIES
Gretchen Mayo; Grades 5 and up. 4 titles: Earthmaker's Tales, More Earthmaker's Tales, Star Tales & More Star Tales. Illus. 48 pp. each. Walker & Co., 1991. $5.95 each.

*NORTH AMERICAN INDIAN SURVIVAL SKILLS
Karen Liptak; Grades 5-8. Illus. 65 pp. Fraklin Watts, 1990. $11.90.

NORTH AMERICAN INDIAN TALES
W.T. Larned & John Green; Reprint. Illus. 96 pp. Paper. Amazon.com, $1.50.

NORTH AMERICAN INDIAN TRADE SILVER
Carter; Study of the historic silver objects made for, and treasured by, the Indians. Illus. 256 pp. Paper. Amazon.com, 1996. $16.95.

NORTH AMERICAN INDIAN TRAVEL GUIDE
Ralph & Lisa Shanks; U.S. & Canada's Indian & Eskimo events & places of interest. Over 100 tribal offices; over 900 places and events to visit. 5th Ed. Illus. 295 pp. Paper. Amazon.com, 1993. $19.95, postpaid.

THE NORTH AMERICAN INDIAN: VOL. 12: HOPI
Edward S. Curtis; Frederic Hodge, Ed.
Illus. 450 pp. Paper. Curtis & Forrest Publishing, 1996. $19.95.

NORTH AMERICAN INDIAN WARS
Don Nardo; Greenhaven, 1999. $26.20; paper, $16.20.

NORTH AMERICAN INDIAN WARS - CD-ROM
In the process of being completed. Quanta Press.

*NORTH AMERICAN INDIAN WARS
Grades 6 and up. Illus. Smithmark, $26.95.

NORTH AMERICAN INDIANS
Illus. 32 pp. Paper. Hancock House, $3.

**NORTH AMERICAN INDIANS: PHOTOGRAPHS FROM THE NATIONAL
ANTHROPOLOGICAL ARCHIVES** Smithsonian Institution
96 frames; 96 fiche; 5,000 illustrations. University of Chicago Press, 1974. $105.

NORTH AMERICAN INDIANS
George Catlin; Peter Mathiessen, Editor & intro by.; Collection of George Catlin's letters, illustrated with 50 of his drawings. Reprint. Illus. 560 pp. Paper. Amazon.com, $16.

NORTH AMERICAN INDIANS
Paula Fleming & Judith Luskey; 256 pp. Amazon.com, 1986. $34.50.

NORTH AMERICAN INDIANS - CD-ROM
A database of text and image on the history of Native Americans. Includes information on leadership, tribal heritage, religion, family life, and customs. IBM compatible. Quanta Press, 1991. $69.95.

**NORTH AMERICAN INDIANS & ALASKA NATIVES: ABSTRACTS OF THE
PSYCHOLOGICAL & BEHAVIORAL LITERATURE, 1967-1994**
Joseph E. Trimble & Weldon M. Bagwell, Editors
272 pp. Paper. American Psychological Association, 1995. $27.50.

NORTH AMERICAN INDIANS COLORING ALBUM
Rite Warner, Illustrator; Illus. 32 pp. Paper. Amazon.com, 1978. $3.95.

NORTH AMERICAN INDIANS: A COMPREHENSIVE ACCOUNT
Alice B. Kehoe; 2nd Ed. Illus. 625 pp. Paper. Prentice-Hall, 1992. $56.

NORTH AMERICAN INDIANS: A DISSERTATION INDEX
Alibris.com, 1976. $28.

THE NORTH AMERICAN INDIANS IN EARLY PHOTOGRAPHS
Paula Richardson Fleming & Judith Luskey; Published in 1986 by Dorset Press. Reprint. 256 pp. Illus. Amazon.com & Alibris.com, $79.95.

NORTH AMERICAN INDIANS IN THE GREAT WAR
Susan Applegate Krouse; Documents American Indian experience in World War I. Photos. 272 pp. Paper. University of Nebraska Press, 2007. $24.95.

NORTH AMERICAN INDIANS IN HISTORICAL PERSPECTIVE
Eleanor Burke Leacock & Nancy O. Lurie, Editors
Illus. 498 pp. Paper. Waveland Press, 1988. $18.95.

NORTH AMERICAN INDIANS: MYTHS & LEGENDS   LEWIS SPENCE
Reprint. 474 pp. Kessinger Press, 1997. $26. Paper. Amazon.com, 2002. $20.

*NORTH AMERICAN INDIANS OF ACHIEVEMENT
Dr. Frank W. Porter, III; Grades 4 and up. Includes Sitting Bull, Will Rogers, Jim Thorpe, Sarah Winnemucca, Joseph Brant, Quanah Parker, et al. Illus. 104-128 pp. each. Chelsea House, 21 hardcover titles, $19.95, $418.95 per set; 5 paperback titles, $9.95, $49.75/set.

THE NORTH AMERICAN INDIANS: PHOTOGRAPHS BY EDWARD S. CURTIS
Edward S. Curtis; Illus. 96 pp. Aperture, 1972. $25.

NORTH AMERICAN INDIANS: A VERY SHORT INTRODUCTION
Theda Perdue & Michael D. Green; Stresses the great diversity of indigenous peoples in America and their struggle to maintain their sovereignty.   Illus. Maps. 144 pp. Paper. Oxford University Press, 2010. $11.95

NORTH AMERICAN INDIGENOUS WARFARE & RITUAL VIOLENCE
Edited by Richard J. Chacon, Ruben G. Mendoza; Essays documenting specifics acts of Native American violence. 304 pp. University of Arizona Press, 2007. $50.

*NORTH AMERICAN MYTHS & LEGENDS
Philip Ardagh; Paper. Amazon.com, 1999. $23.

NORTH AMERICAN SUN KINGS: KEEPERS OF THE FLAME
Joseph B. Mahan; 300 pp. ISAC Press, 1992. $30.

NORTH AMERICAN TRIBAL DIRECTORY
Arrowfax Editors; U.S. and Canadian tribal listings. 630 pp. Amazon.com Annual. $50.

NORTH CAROLINA'S STATE HISTORIC SITES
Gary L. McCullough; Chronicles more than six centuries of NC history, from the ancient Native American civilization at Town Creek Indian Mound. 96 pp. Paper. Amazon.com, 2001. $12.95.

**NORTH COUNTRY CAPTIVES: SELECTIVE NARRATIVES OF INDIAN CAPTIVITY
FROM VERMONT & NEW HAMPSHIRE** Colin G. Calloway, Ed.

Illus. 176 pp. Paper. U. Press of New England, 1992. $19.95.

NORTH DAKOTA INDIANS: AN INTRODUCTION
Mary Schneider; 275 pp. Paper. Kendall-Hunt, 1986. $19.95.

FRANK J. NORTH: PAWNEE SCOUT, COMMANDER AND PIONEER
Ruby E. Wilson; Illus. 335 pp. Amazon.com, 1982. $19.95.

NORTH MOUNTAIN MEMENTOS
Henry W. Shoemaker; Early Pennsylvania history, both oral from the Indians & written by the settlers. Illus. Maps. Wennawoods Publishing, 2007. $44.95.

NORTH POLE LEGACY: BLACK, WHITE & ESKIMO
S. Allen Counter. Illus. 236 pp. U. of Massachusetts Press, 1991. $24.95.

NORTH SLOPE INUPIAQ DIALOGUES
Edna MacLean; 13 pp. Paper. Alaska Native Language Center, $2.50.

NORTH, SOUTH, EAST & WEST: AMERICAN INDIANS & THE NATURAL WORLD
Marsha C. Bol; Illus. 160 pp. Roberts Rinehart, 1998. $40; paper, $24.95.

**NORTH SPIRIT: TRAVELS AMONG THE CREE & OJIBWAY NATIONS
& THEIR STAR MAPS** Paulette Jiles; 400 pp. Paper. Amazon.com, 2003.

NORTHEAST INDIAN RESOURCE SECRETS: THE BUYER'S GUIDE
Thomas R. Ford; Illus. 127 pp. Amazon.com, 1997. $15.95.

*NORTHEAST INDIANS
Craig Doherty & Katherine Doherty
Grades 5-8. Illus. 208 pp. 3 Vols. Chelsea House, 2008. $35.

NORTHEAST INDIANS: AN EDUCATIONAL COLORING BOOK
Grades 1-8. Illus. 32 pp. Paper. Spizzirri Publishing, 1981.
Read & Coloring Book, $1.95; Cassette/book, $6.95.

***NORTHEAST INDIANS FACT CARDS: INDIANS OF NEW ENGLAND & THE
NORTHEAST COAST**
Reeve Chace; Grades 4 and up. Illus. 70 pp. Toucan Valley, 1998. $29.

A NORTHEASTERN ALGONQUIAN SOURCEBOOK
Edward S. Rogers, Editor; 364 pp. Amazon.com, 1985. $50.

NORTHEASTERN INDIAN LIVES, 1632-1816
Robert S. Grumet, Editor
Illus. 408 pp. University of Massachusetts Press, 1996. $55; paper, $22.95.

NORTHERN ATHABASCAN SURVIVAL: WOMEN, COMMUNITY & THE FUTURE
Phyllis Ann Fast; Conversations with Athabascan women.
Map. 305 pp. University of Nebraska Press, 2002. $55.

NORTHERN ATHAPASKAN ART: A BEADWORK TRADITION
Kate Duncan; Illus. 272 pp. University of Washington Press, 1988. $45.

A NORTHERN CHEYENNE ALBUM: PHOTOGRAPHS BY THOMAS B. MARQUIS
Margot Liberty, Editor; Photos of tribal people in the early 20th century.
Illus. Photos. 304 pp. Paper. University of Oklahoma Press, 2007. $29.95.

THE NORTHERN CHEYENNE EXODUS IN HISTORY & MEMORY
James N. Leiker & Ramon Powers; The exodus of the Northern Cheyennes in 1878 & 1879, an attempt to flee from Indian Territory to their Montana homeland. Illus. Map. 272 pp. University of Oklahoma Press, 2011. $34.95.

*NORTHERN CHEYENNE FIRE FIGHTERS
Henry Tall Bull & Tom Weist
Grades 4-adult. 39 pp. Paper. Council for Indian Education. $5.95.

THE NORTHERN CHEYENNE INDIAN RESERVATION, 1877-1900
Orlan Svingen; 216 pp. Paper. University Press of Colorado, 1993. $34.95; paper, $22.50.

THE NORTHERN COPPER INUIT: A HISTORY
Richard D. Condon, et al.; Illus. 216 pp. 302 p. U. of Oklahoma Press, 1996. $29.95.

NORTHERN HAIDA MASTER CARVERS
Robin K. Wright; Illus. Maps. 400 pp. University of Washington Press, 2001. $45.

NORTHERN HAIDA SONGS
John Enrico & Wendy B. Stuart; 520 pp. University of Nebraska Press, 1996. $55.

THE NORTHERN MAIDU
Marie Potts; Illus. Map. 48 pp. Paper. Naturegraph, 1977. $7.95.

NORTHERN NAVAJO FRONTIER, 1860-1900: EXPANSION THROUGH ADVERSITY
Robert S. McPherson
Navajo tribal history. 144 pp. Paper. Utah State U. Press, 2001. $20.95. eBook, $15.50

NORTHERN PAIUTE-BANNOCK DICTIONARY
Sven Liljeblad, Catherine S. Fowler, Glenda Powell
972 pp. University of Utah Press, 2011. $100.

THE NORTHERN PAIUTE LANGUAGE OF OREGON
W.L. Marsden; Reprint of 1923 edition. 19 pp. Paper. Coyote Press. $2.50.

**NORTHERN PASSAGE: ETHNOGRAPHY & APPRENTICESHIP AMONG THE
SUBARCTIC DENE** Robert Jarvenpa; Illus. 210 pp. Paper. Waveland Press, 1998. $18.95.

NORTHERN PLAINS INDIAN ILLUSTRATION & BIOGRAPHY INDEX
John Van Balen, compiler; Illus. 407 pp. McFarland & Co., 2003. Library ed., $95.

THE NORTHERN SHOSHONI
Brigham D. Madsen; Illus. 260 pp. Caxton Press, 2000. $18.95.

NORTHERN TALES: TRADITIONAL STORIES OF ESKIMO & INDIAN PEOPLES
Howard Norman, Editor
Illus. Maps. 370 pp. Paper. University of Nebraska Press, 2008. $18.95.

THE NORTHERN TRADITIONAL DANCER
C. Scott Evans & J. Rex Reddick; 2nd Ed.
Illus. 50 pp. Book Publishing Co., Amazon.com & Written Heritage, 1998. $12.95.

NORTHERN VOICES: INUIT WRITING IN ENGLISH
Penny Petrone; Illus. 330 pp. Amazon.com, 1988. $27.50.

WALTER NORTHWAY
Yvonne Yarber & Curt Madison, Editors; Della Northway, et al, trs
Reprint. Illus. 55 pp. Paper. Alaska Native Language Center, 1995. $12.

NORTHWEST CHIEFS: GUSTAV SOHON'S VIEWS OF THE 1855 STEVENS TREATY COUNCILS Paper. Amazon.com, 1986. $9.50.

NORTHWEST COAST INDIAN ART: ANALYSIS OF FORM, 50th Anniversary Edition
Bill Holm; Illus. Map. 144 pp. Paper. University of Washington Press, 2015. $30.

*THE NORTHWEST COAST INDIAN ART SERIES
Nan McNutt; Grades 3-6. Illus. 120 pp. Amazon.com, 1991. $29.85.

NORTHWEST COAST INDIAN DESIGNS
Madeleine Orban-Szontagh; Illus. 48 pp. Paper. Dover, $6.95.

NORTHWEST COAST INDIAN PAINTING: HOUSE FRONTS & INTERIOR SCREENS
Edward Malin; Illus. 200 pp. Amazon.com, 1999. $39.95.

*NORTHWEST COAST INDIANS COLORING BOOK
David Rickman; Grades K-2. 48 pp. Paper. Dover, $2.95.

NORTHWEST COAST NATIVE & NATIVE STYLE ART
Lloyd Averill & Daphne Morris; Illus. 256 pp. Paper. U. of Washington Press, $19.95.

NORTHWEST INDIAN DESIGNS
Caren Caraway; Illus. 48 pp. Paper. Stemmer House, 1996. $6.95.

NORTHWEST INDIAN GUIDE & MAP
Features Native attractions, arts & businesses. Affiliated Tribes of Northwest Indians (ATNI), 1995. $2.

NORTHWEST INDIANS: AN EDUCATIONAL COLORING BOOK
Grades 1-8. Illus. 32 pp. Paper. Spizzirri Publishing, 1981. Read & Coloring Book, $1.95; Cassette/book, $6.95.

NORTHWEST NATIVE AMERICAN BUSINESS DIRECTORY
Onaben editors; Listings for approximaely 350 Native business, casinos, tribes chambers of commerce and business associations in the Northwest. Biennial. 2007. Onaben, P.O. Box 231116, Tigard, OR 97223 (503) 968-1500 Fax 968-1548. Website: www.onaben.org. $25.

NORTHWEST NATIVE HARVEST
Carol Batdorf; 96 pp. Paper. Hancock House, 1990. $7.95.

NORTHWEST PASSAGE: THE GREAT COLUMBIA RIVER
Wiliam Dietrich; The settlers & Native American struggle over these lands.
Maps. 432 pp. Paper. University of Washington Press, 1995. $18.95.

NORTHWESTERN INDIAN IMAGES: A PHOTOGRAPHIC LOOK AT PLATEAU INDIANS Richard Scheuerman; Illus. Paper. Sierra Oaks, 1989. $9.95.

THE NORTHWESTERN INDIAN TRIBES IN EXILE: MODOC, NEZ PERCE, & PALOUSE REMOVAL TO THE INDIAN TERRITORY
Clifford Trafzer; Illus. 137 pp. Paper. Sierra Oaks, 1987. $11.95.

*NORTHWOOD CRADLE SONG - FROM A MENOMINEE LULLABY
Douglas Wood
illus. by Lisa Destimini; Ullus. Paper. Meadowlark Communications, $5.99.

NOT FOR INNOCENT EARS: SPIRITUAL TRADITIONS OF A DESERT CAHUILLA MEDICINE WOMAN Ruby Modesto & Guy Mount; Ethnographic portrait of the spiritual beliefs, healing strategies, personal history & cultural heitage of a Desert Cahuila medicine woman & her people. Illus. 128 pp. Paper. Sweetlight, 1980. $9.95.

NOT FOR SCHOOL, BUT FOR LIFE: LESSONS FROM THE HISTORICAL ARCHAEOLOGY OF THE PHOENIX INDIAN SCHOOL
Owen Lindauer; Amazon.com.

NOT WITHOUT OUR CONSENT: LAKOTA RESISTANCE TO TERMINATION, 1950-59
Edward Charles Valandra; Native Americans' continuing struggle for self-determination against American hegemony. Illus. Tables. 320 pp. University of Illinois Press, 2006. $37.

NOTABLE NATIVE AMERICANS
Sharon Malinowski & George H.J. Abrams, Editors; Biographies of about 270 notable Native Americans from all areas of endeavor, both past & present. 1st Ed. 492 pp. Amazon.com, 1995. $115.

NOTEBOOK ON ART, HISTORY & CULTURE
Stephen Wallace, et al; 80 pp. Rough Rock School Press.

NOTEBOOKS OF ELIZABETH COOK-LYNN
Elizabeth Cook-Lynn; A collection of poetry, prose & politics.
208 pp. Paper. University of Arizona Press, 2007. $16.95.

NOTES FROM THE CENTER OF TURTLE ISLAND
Duane Champagne; Monograph. 208 pp. AltaMira Press, 2010. $55; eBook, $52.99

NOTES FROM INDIAN COUNTRY
Tim Giago; Includes columns on communications, culture, education & athletics, government, health, humor, litigation, politics, religion, and people as observed by Giago. Illus. 419 pp. Paper. Amazon.com, 1999. $25.54.

NOTES FROM A MINER'S CANARY: ESSAYS ON THE STATE OF NATIVE AMERICA
Jace Weaver; Biblio. 460 pp. Paper. U. of New Mexico Press, 2010. $30.

NOTES OF A TWENTY-FIVE YEARS' SERVICE IN THE HUDSON'S BAY TERRITORY
John McLean; W.S. Wallace, Editor; Reprint of 1932 edition. Greenwood Press, $29.50.

NOTES ON EIGHT PAPAGO SONGS
E.G. Stricklen; Reprint. 6 pp. Paper. Coyote Press, $.95.

NOTES ON THE IROQUOIS
Henry Schoolcraft; Reprint. Illus. 500 pp. Paper. Amazon.com &. Michigan State University Press, $25.95.

NOTES ON THE SETTLEMENT & INDIAN WARS OF THE WESTERN PARTS OF VIRGINIA & PENNSYLVANIA FROM 1763 TO 1783 Rev. Dr.Joseph Doddridge
Reprint of the 1912 ed. 320 pp. Paper. Wennawoods Publishing, $16.95.

NOTICES OF EAST FLORIDA: WITH AN ACCOUNT OF THE SEMINOLE NATION OF INDIANS W. Simmons; George Buker, Editor
Reprint of 1822 edition. 123 pp. University Press of Florida, $14.95.

NOTICIAS DE NUTKA: AN ACCOUNT OF NOOTKA SOUND IN 1792
Jose Mozino; Iris Engstrand, Editor
200 pp. Paper. University of Washington Press, 1991. $14.95.

NOW I KNOW ONLY SO FAR: ESSAYS IN ETHNOPOETICS
Dell Hymes; Native North American stories. 512 pp. University of Nebraska Press, 2003. $65; paper, $29.95.

NOW IS THE HOUR: NATIVE AMERICAN PROPHECIES & GUIDANCE FOR EARTH CHANGES Elisabeth Dietz & Shirley Jonas; Illus. 110 pp. Paper. Amazon.com, 1998. $10.

NOW THAT THE BUFFALO'S GONE: A STUDY OF TODAYS AMERICAN INDIANS
Alvin M. Josephy; Illus. 302 pp. Paper. University of Oklahoma, 1984. $18.95.

NOW THE WOLF HAS COME: THE CREEK NATION IN THE CIVIL WAR
Christine Schulz White & Benton R. White; Focuses on teh conflict between the Muskogee bands and the Confederate-allied McIntosh family. Photos. 216 pp. Texas A&M University Press, 1990. $29.95.

NUDES & FOODS, VOLUME II
R.C. Gorman; A new collection of nudes, recipes, and anecdotes by Navajo artist, R.C. Gorman. Illus. 112 pp. Navajo Gallery, 1989. $20.

NUMBERS FROM NOWHERE: THE AMERICAN INDIAN CONTACT POPULATION DEBATE David Henige; 544 pp. U. of Oklahoma Press, 1998. $47.95.

*A NUMU HISTORY-THE YERINGTON PAIUTE TRIBE
Michael Hittman
Grades 7-12. Illus. 68 pp. Paper. Yerington Paiute Tribe Publications, $12.50.

*THE NUMU WAY
Yerington Paiute Tribe; Grades 4 and up. Traditional arts, crafts, food, music, medicine, customs, clothing and games of the Yerington Paiute Tribe. 94 pp. Paper. Yerington Paiute Tribe Publications, $8. Workbook, 71 pp., $10.

NUNAVUT ATLAS
Rick Riewe, Editor; The atlas assisted the Inuit in selecting the lands they retained after the settlement of the Nunavut claim. The relationship between Inuit & the natural environment. Illus. Maps. 259 pp. CCI, $15.

NUNAVUT: RETHINKING POLITICAL CULTURE
Ailsa Henderson; Political life in Nunavut, an Inuit self-government in the Arctic. Illus. Maps. 265 pp. University of Washington Press, 2007. $94; paper, $33.95.

NURTURING NATIVE LANGUAGES
Jon Allan Reyhner; 194 pp. Paper. Northern Arizona U. Center for Excellence, 2003 $15.

NUUCHAHNULTH (NOOTKA) MORPHOSYNTAX
Toshihide Nakayama; 183 pp. Paper. University of California Press, 2002. $32.95.

O

O BRAVE NEW PEOPLE: THE EUROPEAN IMAGE OF NATIVE AMERICANS
John Moffitt & Santiago Sebastian; Illus. 415 pp. U. of New Mexico Press, 1996. $55.

O BRAVE NEW PEOPLE: THE EUROPEAN INVENTION OF THE AMERICAN INDIAN
John Moffitt & Santiago Sebastian
Illus. 408 pp. Paper. University of New Mexico Press, 1998. $24.95.

O BRAVE NEW WORDS: NATIVE AMERICAN LOANWORDS IN CURRENT ENGLISH
Charles L. Cutler; Covers more than one thousand North American Indian, Eskimo, and Aleut words in the English vocabulary. Surveys the thousands of Native American place-names in North America. Map. Biblio. 286 pp. University of Oklahoma Press, 1994. $19.95.

O, MY ANCESTOR: RECOGNITION & RENEWAL FOR THE GABRIELINO-TONGVA PEOPLE OF THE LOS ANGELES AREA
Claudia Jurmain & William McCawley; Illus. Paper. Heyday Books. $21.95.

OBJECTS OF BRIGHT PRIDE: NORTHWEST COAST INDIAN ART FROM THE MUSEUM OF NATURAL HISTORY
Allen Wardwell; 2nd ed. Illus. 130 pp. Paper. Amazon.com, 1988. $30.

OBJECTS OF CHANGE: THE ARCHAEOLOGY & HISTORY OF ARIKARA CONTACT WITH EUROPEANS J. Daniel Rogers; Illus. 336 pp. Smithsonian Press, 1990. $35.

OBJECTS OF MYTH & MEMORY: AMERICAN INDIAN ART AT THE BROOKLYN MUSEUM Diana Fane, Ira Jacknis & Lise Breen
Illus. 320 pp. The Brooklyn Museum, 1991. $60; paper, $29.95.

ALANIS OBOMSAWIN: THE VISION OF A NATIVE FILMMAKER
Randolph Lewis; The story of an Abenaki woman filmmaker. Illus. 262 pp. University of Nebraska Press, 2006. $45; paper, $21.95.

OBSCURE BELIEVERS: THE MORMON SCHISM OF ALPHEUS CUTLER
Biloine Whiting Young; Illus. 196 pp. Amazon.com, 2002. $16.95.

OBSERVATIONS OF THE ETHNOLOGY OF THE SAUK INDIANS
A.B. Skinner; Reprint of 1923-1925 edition. Illus. 180 pp. Greenwood Publishing, $35.

OBSERVATIONS ON THE MAHICAN LANGUAGE
Jonathan Edwards; 45 pp. Amazon.com, 2002. $28.

THE OCCUPATION OF ALCATRAZ ISLAND: INDIAN SELF-DETERMINATION & THE RISE OF INDIAN ACTIVISM
Troy R. Johnson; Illus. 304 pp. University of Illinois Press, 1996. $49.95; paper, $17.95.

OCEAN POWER: POEMS FROM THE DESERT
Ofelia Zepeda; Perceptions of Tohono O'odham woman.
96 pp. Paper. University of Arizona Press, 1995. $13.95.

OCETI WAKAN
Pete S. Catches, Sr. & Retek V. Catches; Cynthia L. Catches, Ed.
Translation of Sacred Fireplace. Illus. 215 pp. Paper. Amazon.com, 1997. $28.

OCMULGEE ARCHAEOLOGY, 1936-1986
David J. Hally; Illus. Maps. 264 pp. University of Georgia Press, 1994. $40.

OCONOMOWOC: BARONS TO BOOTLEGGERS
Barbara & David Barquist; Illus. 335 pp. Barquist Publishing, 1999. $40.

ODE SETL'OGHWNH DA': LONG AFTER I AM GONE
Teddy Charlie; Stories of traditional knowledge and skills by Tanana Athabaskan.
Illus. Map. 30 pp. Alaska Native Language Center, 1992. $6.50

THE ODYSSEY OF CHIEF STANDING BUFFALO & THE NORTHERN SISSETON SIOUX Mark Diedrich; Photos. Maps. Biblio. 119 pp. Paper. Coyote Books, 1988. $18.95.

OF BREATH & EARTH: A BOOK OF DAYS WITH WISDOM FROM NATIVE AMERICA
John Netherton; 42 color photos. 120 pp. Amazon.com, 1995. $14.95.

OF EARTH & ELDERS: VISIONS & VOICES FROM NATIVE AMERICA
Serle Chapman; Traditional & contemporary Native American images, narratives and ideas. 2nd Ed. Illus. 224 pp. Paper. Mountain Press, 2002. $25.

OF EARTH & LITTLE RAIN: THE PAPAGO INDIANS
Bernard L. Fontana; Illus. 170 pp. Paper. University of Arizona Press, 1981. $16.95.

OF LIZARDS & ANGELS: A SAGA OF SIOUXLAND
Frederick Manfred; 625 pp. Paper. University of Oklahoma Press, 1993. $14.95.

OF MOTHER EARTH & FATHER SKY
Fred Bia and T.L. McCarthy; Photos. 69 pp. Paper. Rough Rock School Press, 1983. $10.

OF SACRED LANDS & STRIP MALLS: THE BATTLE FOR PUVUNGNA
Ronald Loewe; 258 pp. Rowman & Littlefield Publishers, 2016. $85. eBook, $84.99.

OF UNCOMMON BIRTH: DAKOTA SONS IN VIETNAM
Mark St. Pierre; Illus. Map. 320 pp. University of Oklahoma Press, 2003. $27.95.

OFF THE MAP: LANDSCAPE IN THE NATIVE IMAGINATION
Kathleen Ash-Milby (Navajo), Editor; Art. Illus. 88 pp. Paper. NMAI Press, 2007. $19.95.

OFF THE RESERVATION: REFLECTIONS ON BOUNDARY-BUSTING, BORDER-CROSSING LOOSE CANNONS
Paula Gunn Allen; Tisha Hooks, Ed.; 272 pp. Amazon.com, 1998. $25.

OFFERING
Diane Glancy; Poetry. Commemorating Indian chief Sequoyah's achievement in absorbing and transforming a foreign language into his own native Cherokee.
88 pp. Paper. Holy Cow! Press, $6.95.

OFFERING SMOKE: THE SACRED PIPE & NATIVE AMERICAN RELIGION
Jordan Paper; Illus. Maps. 192 pp. Paper. University of Idaho Press, 1989. $22.95.

OFFICIAL ENCOURAGEMENT, INSTITUTIONAL DISCOURAGEMENT: MINORITIES IN ACADEMIA - THE NATIVE AMERICAN EXPERIENCE
William G. Tierney; 192 pp. Greenwood Publishing, 1992. $99.95; paperl $42.95.

OFFICIAL INSIGNIA OF NATIVE AMERICAN TRIBES
Q. Todd Dickinson; Reprint. 51 pp. paper. Amazon.com, $20.

THE OFFICIAL OVERSTREET INDIAN ARROWHEADS PRICE GUIDE
Robert M. Overstreet; Illus. 1,344 pp. Pasper. Amazon.com, 2003. $26.

OFFICE OF INDIAN AFFAIRS, 1824-1880: HISTORICAL SKETCHES
Edward E. Hill; 255 pp. N. Ross, 1974. $25.

OGLALA FAIR & FESTIVAL, PINE RIDGE, SD
Souvenir Program of the 62nd Anniversary of the Oglala Fair & Festival.
Illus. 100 pp. Paper. Lakota Books, 1994. $17.50.

OGLALA GAMES
Louis L. Meeker; 24 pp. Paper. Lakota Books, 1993. $9.95.

OGLALA LAKOTA CRAZY HORSE: A PRELIMINARY GENEALOGICAL STUDY & AN ANNOTATED LISTING OF PRIMARY SOURCES
Richard G. Hardorff; Illus. Amazon.com. $17.95; paper, $11.95.

OGLALA PEOPLE, 1841-1879: A POLITICAL HISTORY
Catherine Price; Illus. Maps. 244 pp. Paper. U. of Nebraska Press, 1996. $16.95.

OGLALA RELIGION
William Powers; Illus. 237 pp. Paper. University of Nebraska Press, 1977. $24.95.

THE OGLALA SIOUX: WARRIORS IN TRANSITION
Robert H. Ruby; foreword by Glenn Emmons; BIA physician narrative on the effect of the U.S. Government on the reservation in the 1950s. Illus. 136 pp. Paper. University of Nebraska Press, 1955. $14.95.

OGLALA WOMEN: MYTH, RITUAL & REALITY
Marla N. Powers; Illus. 258 pp. Paper. University of Chicago Press, 1986. $23.

OH WHAT A SLAUGHTER: MASSACRES IN THE AMERICAN WEST 1846-1890
Larry McMurtry; 192 pp. Simon & Schuster, 2005. $25.

THE OHIO COMPANY OF VIRGINIA & THE WESTWARD MOVEMENT, 1748-1792
Kenneth P. Bailey; Founded primarily with the purpose of securing a share of the Indian trade west of the Alleghenies. Illus. Wennawoods Publishing, $29.95.

THE OHIO FRONTIER: CRUCIBLE OF THE OLD NORTHWEST, 1720-1830
R. Douglas Hurt; From the earliest Indian settlements to the end of the frontier period. Illus. Maps. 432 pp. Paper. Amazon.com & Alibris.com, $19.95.

THE OHIO HOPEWELL EPISODE: PARADIGM LOST & PARADIGM GAINED
A Martin Byers; Examines Hopewellian archaeology, symbolism & semantics. Amazon.com, $59.95.

OHIO'S FIRST PEOPLES
James H. O'Donnell, 3rd; From the Hopewell people to the forced removal of the Wyandots in the 1840s. Illus. 216 pp. Paper. Amazon.com, 2004. $17.95.

***OHIO'S FIRST SETTLERS: THE INDIANS - NATIVE AMERICANS**
Nicholas P. Georgiady & Louis G. Romano
Vol. 3, 2nd revised edition. Grades 4-8. Ilus. Paper. Amazon.com, 1998. $4.50.

OHIO'S INDIAN PAST
Lar Hothem; Photos. 165 pp. Paper. Amazon.com, 1996. $14.95.

OHIYESA: CHARLES EASTMAN, SANTEE SIOUX
Raymond Wilson; Illus. 242 pp. University of Illinois Press, 1983. $10.95.

THE OHLONE PAST & PRESENT: NATIVE AMERICANS OF THE SAN FRANCISCO BAY REGION Lowell J. Bean & Sylvia B. Vane, Eds.
Illus. 376 pp. Malki-Ballena Press, 1995. $29.95; paper, $23.95.

THE OHLONE WAY: INDIAN LIFE IN THE SAN FRANCISCO & MONTEREY BAY AREAS Malcolm Margolin; Illus. 182 pp. Paper. Heyday Books, 1978. $16.95.

OIL & GAS
Institute for the Development of Indian Law, 1980. $12.

THE OJIBWA OF BERENS RIVER, MANITOBA: EHNOGRAPHY INTO HISTORY
Jennifer S. Brown & A. Irving Hollowell; Illus. 102 pp. Paper. Amazon.com, 1992. $29.99.

OJIBWA CHIEFS, 1690-1890: AN ANNOTATED LISTING
John A. Ilko, Jr., Compiler
Examines about 800 Ojibwa chiefs. Illus. 79 pp. Paper. Whitston Publishing, 1995. $16.95.

OJIBWA CRAFTS
Carrie A. Lyford; Reprint of 1943 edition. Illus. 216 pp.
Paper. R. Schneider, Publishers & Written Heritage, $12.95.

***THE OJIBWA: GREAT LAKES**
Helen H. Turner; Grades 5 and up. Illus. Chelsea House, 1989. $17.95.

OJIBWA NARRATIVES OF CHARLES & CHARLOTTE KAWBAWGAM & JACQUES PEPIQUE, 1893-1895 Arthur P. Bourgeois, Ed.
Illus. 168 pp. Wayne State University Press, 1994. $34.95; paper, $21.95.

THE OJIBWA OF BERENS RIVER, MANITOBA: ETHNOGRAPHY INTO HISTORY
Jennifer Brown & A. Irving Hallowell; Illus. 180 pp. Paper. Amazon.com, 1992. $20.50.

THE OJIBWA OF SOUTHERN ONTARIO
Peter S. Schmalz; Amazon.com, 1991. $24.95.

THE OJIBWA OF WESTERN CANADA, 1780 TO 1870
Laura Peers
Illus. 320 pp. Maps. Minnesota Historical Society Press, 1994. $32.95; paper, $15.95.

OJIBWA WARRIOR: DENNIS BANKS & THE RISE OF THE AMERICAN INDIAN MOVEMENT Dennis Banks; with Richard Erdoes, Editor
Illus. Photos. 352 pp. Paper. University of Oklahoma Press, 2004. $19.95.

THE OJIBWA WOMAN
Ruth Landes; intro. by Sally Coles; Study of gender relations in a Native society.
Reprint ed. 247 pp. Paper. University of Nebraska Press, 1997. $13.

THE OJIBWAS: A CRITICAL BIBLIOGRAPHY
Helen H. Tanner; 88 pp. Paper. Indiana Univerity Press, 1976. $4.95.

OJIBWAY CEREMONIES
Basil Johnston; Illus. by David Beyer
Reprint. Illus. 188 pp. Paper. Oyate & University of Nebraska Press, 1990. $17.

OJIBWAY CHIEFS: PORTRAITS OF ANISHINAABE LEADERSHIP
Mark Diedrich; Illus. 193 pp. Paper. Coyote Books, 1999. $29.95.

THE OJIBWAY DREAM
Arthur Shilling; Illus. 48 pp. Amazon.com, 1986. $29.95.

OJIBWAY HERITAGE
Basil Johnston; Illus. by David Beyer
Illus. Map. 170 pp. Paper. University of Nebraska Press, 1990. $12.95.

*OJIBWAY INDIANS COLORING BOOK
Chet Kozlak
Grades 1-6. Map. 32 pp. Paper. Minnesota Historical Society Press, $2.50.

OJIBWAY MUSIC FROM MINNESOTA: A CENTURY OF SONG FOR VOICE & DRUM
Thomas Vennum, Jr.
LP record/cassette & booklet. Minnesota Historical Society Press, 1990. $9.95.

OJIBWAY ORATORY
compiled & Mark Diedrich, Illus; Illus. Biblio. 110 pp. Paper. Coyote Books, 1990. $18.95.

OJIBWAY TALES
Basil Johnston; Illus. 188 pp. Paper. University of Nebraska Press, 1993. $13.95.

*THE OJIBWE
Raymond Bial; Grades 5 and up. Illus. 128 pp. Amazon.com, 1999. $22.95.

OJIBWE DISCOURSE MARKERS
Brendan Fairbanks; 222 pp. University of Nebraska Press, 2016. $70; paper, $25.

THE OJIBWE JOURNALS OF EDMUND F. ELY, 1833-1849
Theresa M. Schenck, Editor; Illus. Maps. 520 pp. U. of Nebraska Press, 2012. $65.

OJIBWE LANGUAGE BOOK
Coy Eklund
Ojibwe/English translations & phrases. 272 pp. Amazon.com & Alibris.com, $24.

OJIBWE SINGERS: HYMNS, GRIEF & A NATIVE CULTURE IN MOTION
Michael McNally' Illus. 265 pp. Oxford University Press, 2000. $52.

OJIBWE VOCABULARY FOR BEGINNERS; INTERMEDIATE VOCABULARY; & VOCABULARY FOR ADVANCED LEARNERS Ojibwe Mekana; Tape and booklet.
Amazon.com, Beginners, $22; Intermediate Vocabulary, $21; Advanced Learners, $33.

OJIBWE: WE LOOK IN ALL DIRECTIONS
Thomas D. Peacock & Marlene Wisuri; Illus. 160 pp. Amazon.com, 2004. $29.95.

OKANAGAN SOURCES
Jean Webber, Editor; Essays by First Nation authors providing historical accounts of Okanagan Valley. 206 pp. Paper. Theytus, 1990. $16.95.

OKANOGAN HIGHLAND ALBUM
Mary L. Loe, et al; Illus. 510 pp. Statesman-Examimer, 1990. $19.95.

O-KEE-PA, A RELIGIOUS CEREMONY & OTHER CUSTOMS OF THE MANDAN
George Catlin; Reprint. 1990. Paper. Amazon.com, 1990. $19.75.

*OKEMOS: STORY OF A FOX INDIAN OF HIS YOUTH
George Fox and Lela Puffer; Grades 3-9. Paper. Council for Indian Education, 1976. $1.95.

*OKLA APILACI: COMMUNITY HELPERS
Text in Choctaw with English translation. All participants are Choctaw.
Different professions on reservation are featured. Grades Preschool-3.
14 pp. Website: https://eric.ed.gov/?id=ED253358, $3.50.

OKLA HANNALI
R.A. Lafferty; The history of the Choctaw Indians. 222 pp. Paper.
University of Oklahoma Press, $12.95.

OKLAHOMA: FOOT-LOOSE & FANCY-FREE
Angie Debo; Illus. 266 pp. Paper. University of Oklahoma Press, $12.95.

OKLAHOMA: A HISTORY OF FIVE CENTURIES
Arrell M. Gibson
Reprint of 1981 ed. Illus. Maps. 262 pp. Oklahoma: A History of Five Centuries, $29.95.

OKLAHOMA: A HISTORY OF THE SOONER STATE
Edwin C. McReynolds; Reprint of the revised 1964 edition. Illus. Maps. 477 pp.
University of Oklahoma Press, $24.95.

OKLAHOMA: THE LAND & ITS PEOPLE
Kenny Franks & Paul Lambert; Chronicles the history of Oklahoma, its geography and it people and lore from ancient times to the present. Illus. 104 pp. Paper. University of Oklahoma Press, 1997. $15.95.

OKLAHOMA PLACE NAMES
George H. Shirk; Revised 1974 edition. Maps. Biblio. 268 pp. Paper.
University of Oklahoma Press, 2002. $19.95.

OKLAHOMA SEMINOLES: MEDICINES, MAGIC & RELIGION
James H. Howard and Willie Lena
Illus. 280 pp. Paper. University of Olahoma Press, 1984. $12.95.

OKLAHOMA: THE STORY OF ITS PAST & PRESENT
Edwin C. McReynolds,, Allice Marriott & Estelle Faulconer
Reprint of the 3rd 1971 edition. Illus. Maps. 500 pp. University of Oklahoma Press, $22.95.

OKLAHOMA TRIBAL COURT REPORTS
Dennis W. Arrow, Ed.; 1,800 pp. 3 vols. Oklahoma City University, School of Law, Native American Legal Resource Center, 1994-96. $75 each.

OKLAHOMA'S INDIAN NEW DEAL
Jon S. Blackman; 236 pp. Paper. University of Olahoma Press, $24.95.

*O'KOHOME: THE COYOTE DOG
Hap Gilliland; Grades 4-9. Illus. 47 pp. Paper. Council for Indian Education, 1989. $10.45.

THE OLD AMERICAN: A NOVEL
Ernest Hebert; Set in the period of the French & Indian Wars. 304 pp. Dartmouth College Press, 2000. Distributed by the University Press of New England. $29.95; paper, $16.95.

THE OLD BELOVED PATH: DAILY LIFE AMONG THE INDIANS OF THE CHATTAHOOCHE RIVER VALLEY
William W. Winn; Illus. 304 pp. Paper. University of Alabama Press, 2008. $19.95.

OLD BETSY: THE LIFE & TIMES OF A FAMOUS DAKOTA WOMAN & HER FAMILY
Mark Diedrich; Illus. Photos. Maps. 170 pp. Paper. Coyote Book (MN), 1995. $24.95.

*OLD FATHER STORY TELLER
Pablita Velarde; 6 legends from Santa Clara Pueblo. Grades 3 and up. Illus. 56 pp.
Amazon.com, 1992. $24.95; paper, $14.95.

OLD FORT KLAMATH: AN OREGON FRONTIER POST, 1863-1890
Buena Cobb Stone; Bert Webber, Editor
History of the the many military posts in the west over 100 years ago. Fort Klamath and its part in Modoc Indian War. Biblio. 112 pp. Paper. Webb Research Group, $10.95.

OLD FORTS OF THE APACHE WARS
Ron Swartley; A travel guide to 17 old forts in Arizona, New Mexico, and west Texas.
Illus. 88 pp. Frontier Image Press, 1999. $9.95.

OLD HICKORY'S WAR: ANDREW JACKSON & THE QUEST FOR EMPIRE
David S. Heidler & Jeanne T. Heidler
Illus. 320 pp. Louisiana State University Press, 2003. $24.95; paper, $16.95.

OLD INDIAN DAYS
Charles A. Eastman; Stories of Sioux bands of the Upper Midwest in pre-reservation times. 300 pp. Paper. University of Nebraska, $8.95.

OLD INDIAN LEGENDS
Zitkala-Sa (Red Bird); Illus. 216 pp. Paper. University of Nebraska Press, 2013. $14.95.

OLD INDIAN TRAILS
Walter McClintock; Records the native customs, legends, religious rites, and daily life of the Blackfoot. Illus. 400 pp. Paper. Houghton & Mifflin, 1992. $10.95.

THE OLD LADY TRILL, THE VICTORY YELL: THE POWER OF WOMEN IN NATIVE AMERICAN LITERATURE Patrice Hollrah; 192 pp. Routledge, 2003. $85.

OLD MAN COYOTE
Frank B. Linderman; Illus. 254 pp. Paper. University of Nebraska Press, 1996. $11.95.

THE OLD MAN TOLD US: EXCERPTS FROM MICMAC HISTORY, 1500-1950
Ruth H. Whitehead; Illus. 385 pp. Paper. Amazon.com, 1991.

OLD NAVAJO RUGS: THEIR DEVELOPMENT FROM 1900-1940
Marian E. Rodee; Illus. 96 pp. Paper. University of New Mexico Press, 1981. $15.95.

THE OLD NORTH TRAIL: LIFE, LEGENDS & RELIGION OF THE BLACKFEET INDIANS Walter McClintock; intro by William Farr
Reprint of 1910 edition. Illus. 540 pp. Paper. University of Nebraska Press, 1999. $21.95.

OLD ORAIBI: STUDY OF THE HOPI INDIANS OF THE THIRD MESA
  Mischa Titiev
Reprint of 1944 ed. Illus. Maps. 300 pp. Paper. University of New Mexico Press, $45.

OLD SHIRTS & NEW SKINS
  Sherman Alexie; Poetry. Illus. 100 pp. Paper. University of California, American Indian Studies Center, 1992. $12.

OLD STYLE PLAINS INDIAN DOLLS
  Joanita Kant; Illus. Photos. 50 pp. Paper. Lakota Books, 1994. $25.95.

THE OLDEST MAGIC: THE HISTORY & EARLY INFLUENCE OF MUSIC
  Lew P. Price; Illus. 200 pp. Paper. Lew Paxton Price, 1995. $26.

OLOF THE ESKIMO LADY: A BIOGRAPHY OF AN ICELANDIC DWARF IN AMERICA
  Inga Dora Bjornsdottir; Illus. 256 pp. University of Michigan Press, 2010. $29.95.

OMAHA TRIBAL MYTHS & TRICKSTER TALES
  Roger Welsch; 285 pp. Paper. JAmazon.com., 1994. $14.95.

OMAHA TRIBE
  A. Fletcher and F. LaFlesche; Reprint of 1911 edition. Two vols. Illus. Musical examples. Vol. 1, 312 pp.; Vol. 2, 355 pp. Paper. U. of Nebraska Press, $12.95 each, $25.90 per set.

*OM-KAS-TOE: BLACKFEET TWIN CAPTURES & ELKDOG
  Kenneth Thomasma; Jack Brouwer, Illus.; The Blackfeet tribe in the early 1700s. Grades 4 and up. Illus. Amazon.com, $10.99; paper, $6.99.

ON ABORIGINAL REPRESENTATION IN THE GALLERY
  Lynda Jessup & Shannon Bagg, Editors; Addresses current & provocative issues arising from the production, collection, & exhibition of Aboriginal historical & contemporary art. Illus. 340 pp. Paper. University of Washington Press, 2002. $34.95.

ON THE APACHE INDIAN RESERVATIONS & ARTIST WANDERINGS AMONG THE CHEYENNES Frederic Remington; Two stories written & illustrated by Remington in 1889. Reprint of 1974 edition. Illus. 36 pp. Paper. Amazon.com & Alibris.com, $4.

ON BEHALF OF THE WOLF & THE FIRST PEOPLES
  Joseph Marshall, III (Sicangu Lakota); Essays providing insight on being a Native American in a white man's world. 256 pp. Paper. Amazon.com, 1996. $13.95. Also from the Museum of New Mexico Press, $13.95.

ON THE BLOODY ROAD TO JESUS: CHRISTIANITY & THE CHIRICAHUA APACHES
  H. Henrietta Stockel; Study of the religious legacy of the Chiricahua Apaches annd its inevitable collision with Christianity. Illus. 336 pp. U. of New Mexico Press, 2004. $19.95.

ON THE BLOODY TRAIL OF GERONIMO
  John Bigelow; Reprint of 1986 ed. Illus. 200 pp. Paper. Westernlore, $12.95.

ON THE BORDER WITH CROOK
  John G. Bourke; 490 pp. Paper. University of Nebraska Press, 1971. $11.95.

*ON THE CLIFFS OF ACOME
  John Dressman; Children's story for all ages outlining the history of the celebrated New Mexico cliffs. Illus. 48 pp. Paper. Sunstone Press, $5.95.

ON THE DRAFTING OF TRIBAL CONSTITUIONS
  Felix S. Cohen; David E. Wilkins, Editor
Reprint of 1934-35 edition. 200 pp. University of Oklahoma Press, $34.95.

ON THE EDGE OF SPLENDOR: EXPLORING GRAND CANYON'S HUMAN PAST
  Douglas W. Schwartz; Illus. 80 pp. Paper. School of American Research, $12.95.

ON THE GLEAMING WAY: NAVAJOS, EASTERN PUEBLOS, ZUNIS, HOPIS, APACHES & THEIR LAND, & THEIR MEANING TO THE WORLD
  John Collier; Illus. 163 pp. Paper. Amazon.com, 1962. $5.95.

ON INDIAN GROUND: CALIFORNIA: A RETURN TO INDIGENOUS KNOWLEDGE: GENERATING HOPE, LEADERSHIP, & SOVEREIGNTY THROUGH EDUCATION
  Joely Proudfit, Editor; First in a series. Other titles: On Indian Ground: Bureau of Indian Education; On Indian Ground: Southwestern U.S. Amazon.com, 2015.

ON THE LANDING
  Michael W. Simpson; A book of poems by a young Indian poet. 49 pp. Paper. Indian University Press, 1986. $3.60, postpaid.

ON THE MUSIC OF THE NORTH AMERICAN INDIANS
  Theodore Baker; Ann Buckley, Translator; Amazon.com, 1977. $25.

ON NATIVE GROUND: MEMOIRS & IMPRESSIONS
  Jim Barnes
Poetry & prose. 296 pp. University of Oklahoma Press, 1997. $29.95; paper, $16.95.

ON THE PADRE'S TRAIL
  Christopher Vecsey; 520 pp. University of Notre Dame Press, 1996. $30.

ON THE REZ Ian Frazier; Illus. 320 pp.Paper. Picador, 2001. $14.

ON OUR OWN GROUND: THE COMPLETE WRITINGS OF WILLIAM APESS, A PEQUOT Barry O'Connell, Editor & intro.; An autobiography by a Native American in the early 1800s. 432 pp. University of Massachusetts Press, $50.00; paper, $17.95.

*ON THE POWWOW TRAIL COLORING BOOK
  Garrett J. Schembri; Grades 1-3. Companion to On the Powwow Trail video. Focuses on the preservation of Native American Indian customs, traditional dress & dance. Paper. Meadowlark Communications, $2.99.

ON RECORDS: DELAWARE INDIANS, COLONISTS, & THE MEDIA OF HISTORY & MEMORY Andrew Newman; Illus. Maps. 328 pp. U. of Nebraska Press, 2012. $45.

ON THE REZ
  Ian Frazier; Illus. 320 pp. Paper. Picador, 2001. $14.

ON THE STREETS & IN THE STATE HOUSE: AMERICAN INDIAN & HISPANIC WOMEN & ENVIRONMENTAL POLICYMAKING IN NEW MEXICO
  Diane-Michele Prindeville; 260 pp. Routledge, 2003. $80.

ON THIS SPIRIT WALK: THE VOICES OF NATIVE AMERICAN & INDIGENOUS PEOPLES Henrietta Mann & Anita Phillips; A resource for small group study within the local church. List of Native American United Methodist writers who contributed to this work. Paper. Abingdon Press, 2012. $14.99.

ON TIME FOR DISASTER: THE RESCUE OF CUSTER'S COMMAND
  Edward J. McClernand; Illus. 176 pp. Paper. University of Nebraska Press, 1989. $6.95.

ON THE TRAIL OF SPIDER WOMAN: PETROGLYPHS, PICTOGRAPHS, AND MYTHS OF THE SOUTHWEST
  Carol Patterson-Rudolph; Illus. Charts & Maps. 160 pp. Paper. Amazon.com. $4.95.

ON THE TRAIL TO WOUNDED KNEE: THE BIG FOOT MEMORIAL RIDE
  Guy Le Querrec; Illus. 128 pp. Amazon.com, 2002. $35.

ON THE TRANSLATION OF NATIVE AMERICAN LITERATURES
  Brian Swann, Editor; 23 scholars in linguistics, folklore, English, and anthropology, provide a working introduction to the history, methods, and problems of translating Native American l;iteratures. Illus. 498 pp. Smithsonian Institution Press, 1993. $45; paper, $19.95.

ON THE UPPER MISSOURI: JOURNAL OF RUDOLPH FRIEDRICH KURZ, 1851-1852
  Carla Kelly, Editor; Source of info on the Indians of the Northern Plains. Illus. 352 pp. Paper. University of Oklahoma Press, 21.95.

ONCE THEY MOVED LIKE THE WIND: COCHISE, GERONIMO, AND APACHE WARS
  David Roberts
History of final battlkes of the Indian wars. Illus. 368 pp. Paper. Simon & Schuster. $14.

ONE DEAD INDIAN: THE PREMIER, THE POLICE, & THE IPPERWASH CRISIS
  Peter Edwards; Revised edition. Illus. 305 pp. Paper. Amazon.com, 2003. $15.95.

*ONE GOOD STORY, THAT ONE
  Thomas King (Cherokee); Stories of Native-white relations. Grades 7 and up. Paper. University of Minnesota Press, 1993. $16.95.

ONE HOUSE, ONE VOICE, ONE HEART: NATIVE AMERICAN EDUCATION AT THE SANTA FE INDIAN SCHOOL
  Sally Hyer; Illus. 170 pp. Museum of New Mexico Press, 1990. $29.95; paper, $22.50.

ONE HUNDRED SUMMERS: A KIOWA CALENDAR RECORD
  Candace S. Greene
Pictorial Kiowa calendar. Illus. Map. 286 pp. University of Nebraska Press, 2009. $39.95.

ONE HUNDRED & THREE FIGHTS & SCRIMMAGES: STORY OF GENERAL REUBEN F. BERNARD Don Russell, Intro.; Illus. 208 pp. Paper. Amazon.com, 2003. $14.95.

ONE HUNDRED YEARS OF NATIVE AMERICAN ARTS: SIX WASHINGTON CULTURES Delbert McBride; Penelope Loucas, Editor
Illus. 16 pp. Paper. Amazon.com, 1989. $1.

ONE HUNDRED YEARS OF NAVAJO RUGS
  Marian E. Rodee
Illus. Color & bxw photos. 200 pp. Paper. University of New Mexico Press, $29.95.

ONE HUNDRED YEARS OF OLD MAN SAGE: AN ARAPAHO LIFE
  Jeffrey D. Anderson; Biography of Sherman Sage, an Arapaho.
Illus. Map. 140 pp. Paper. University of Nebraska Press, 2003. $19.95.

*ONE INDIAN & TWO CHIEFS: SHORT FICTION
  Ralph Salisbury; Grades 4 and up. Short stories. Amazon.com, 1993. $14.95.

ONE MORE STORY: CONTEMPORARY SENECA TALES
  Duwayne Bowen
Tales of the supernatural drawn from modern day Seneca life. Illus. Amazon.com, $9.95.

ONE NATION UNDER GOD: TRIUMPH OF THE NATIVE AMERICAN CHURCH
  Huston Smith & Reuben Snake, Editors; Includes testimonies offered by Church members from many different tribes. Describes the prayer meetings, the sacramental use of peyote, and the significance of various practices and objects of the Native American Church which now has more than 80 chapters throughout the country. Illus. 174 pp. Amazon.com, 1996. $24.95; paper, $14.95.

ONE OF THE FAMILY: METIS CULTURE IN 19TH CENTURY NORTHWESTERN SASKATCHEWAN Brenda MacDougall; 320 pp. U. of Washington Press, 2010. $94.

ONE OF THE KEYS: 1676-1776-1976: WAMPANOAG INDIAN CONTRIBUTION
  Milton A. Travers; A list of words and definitions from the language of the historical Indians of southeastern Massachusetts. Illus. 64 pp. Amazon.com, 1975. $8.95.

ONE SHAHAPTON STIRRING ASHES
L. Pearne Robbins; Revised ed. Illus. 135 pp. Paper. Robin Lodges Publishing, 1993. $8.

ONE SMART INDIAN
Robert J. Seidman; Paper. Penguin USA, $13.95.

ONE THOUSAND USEFUL MOHAWK WORDS
Mohawk-English, English-Mohawk dictionary includes words, idioms, and expressions common in everyday speech. 158 pp. Amazon.com, $9.95.

ONE THOUSAND YEARS ON MOUND KEY
R. Schell; Revised 1968 edition. Illus. 125 pp. Shoeless Publishing, 1997.$12.95.

ONE VAST WINTER-COUNT: THE NATIVE AMERICAN WEST BEFORE LEWIS & CLARK
Colin G. Calloway; Illus. Maps. 640 pp. University of Nebraska Press, 2003. $39.95.

ONE VOICE, MANY VOICES: RECREATING INDIGENOUS LANGUAGE COMMUNITIES
T. McCarty & O. Zepeda, Editors; Center for Indian Education, $24.

*THE ONEIDA
Grades K-4. Illus. 48 pp. Childrens Press, $11.45.

THE ONEIDA CREATION STORY
Demus Elm & Harvey Antone; tr. & ed. by Floyd G. Lounsbury & Bryan Gick
Ancient elements of Iroquoian cosmology. Illus. 174 pp. U. of Nebraska Press, 2000. $12.

ONEIDA DICTIONARY
Amost Christjohn & Maria Hinton; 665 pp. Amazon.com, 1999. $45.

THE ONEIDA INDIAN EXPERIENCE
Jack Campisi & Laurence Hauptman; 245 pp. Paper. Syracuse U. Press, 1988. $16.95.

ONEIDA INDIAN JOURNEY: FROM NEW YORK TO WISCONSIN, 1784-1860
Laurence M. Hauptman
Illus. Maps. 225 pp. University of Wisconsin Press, 1999. $40; paper, $21.95.

THE ONEIDA INDIANS IN THE AGE OF ALLOTMENT, 1860-1920
Laurence Hauptman & Gordon McAlester, III, Editors; Oneida Indians of Wisconsin and the Dawes Act of 1887 & the Burke Act of 1906. 368 pp. U. of Oklahoma Press, 2007. $34.95.

THE ONEIDA LAND CLAIMS: A LEGAL HISTORY
George Shattuck; 290 pp. Paper. Syracuse University Press, 1991. $16.95.

ONEIDA LIVES: LONG-LOST VOICES OF THE WISCONSIN ONEIDAS
Herbert S. Lewis & L. Gordon McLester III, Editors
Illus. 428 pp. Paper. University of Nebraska Press, 2005. $32.95.

ONEIDA VERB MORPHOLOGY
Floyd G. Lounsbury; 111 pp. Paper. Amazon.com, 1976. $15.

ONLY APPROVED INDIANS: STORIES
Jack D. Forbes; 188 pp. Paper. University of Oklahoma Press, 1995. $14.95.

ONLY THE EARTH ENDURES: THE SPIRITUAL JOURNEY OF A MANDAN INDIAN
Cedric Red Feather; Illus. 192 pp. Paper. Council Oak Books, 2001. $14.

THE ONLY LAND I KNOW: A HISTORY OF THE LUMBEE INDIANS
Adolph Dial & David Eliades
Illus. Biblio. 206 pp. Paper. Syracuse University Press, 1974. $15.95.

THE ONLY LAND THEY KNEW: AMERICAN INDIANS IN THE OLD SOUTH
J. Leitch Wright, Jr.
Illus. Maps. 388 pp. Paper. University of Nebraska Press, 1999. $19.95.

*ONLY THE NAMES REMAIN: THE CHEROKEES & THE TRAIL OF TEARS
Alex W. Bealer; Grades 3-7. Illus. 96 pp. Paper. Amazon.com, $10. 1972.

THE ONLY ONE LIVING TO TELL: THE AUTOBIOGRAPHY OF A YAVAPAI INDIAN
Mike Burns; Gregory McNamee, Editor; Paper. University of Arizona Press, 2010. $17.95/

*THE ONONDAGA
Grades K-4. Illus. 48 pp. Childrens Press, $11.45.

ONONDAGA IROQUOIS PREHISTORY: A STUDY IN SETTLEMENT ARCHAEOLOGY
James A. Tuck; Illus. 256 pp. Paper. Syracuse University Press, $15.95.

ONONDAGA: PORTRAIT OF A NATIVE PEOPLE
Dennis Connors, Editor; photos by Fred R. Wolcott; Collection of photographs & history of the Onondaga people. Illus. 100 pp. Paper. Syracuse University Press, 1985. $16.95.

O'ODHAM CREATION & RELATED EVENTS: AS TOLD TO RUTH BENEDICT IN 1927 IN PROSE Ruth Benedict; Donald Bahr, Ed.; Origin stories of the O'odham (Pima) Indians of Arizona. 320 pp. The University of Arizona Press, 2001. $45.

*O'ODHAM, INDIANS OF THE SONORAN DESERT
Susan Shaffer; Grades 5 and up. Illus. Includes 30 student booklets and teacher's resource binder with overhead transparanecies, slides, and audiocasstte. The Heard Museum, 1987. Student edition, $149.95; teacher edition, $197.95. Set, $294.43.

OPENING IN THE SKY
Armand Garnet Ruffo; Poetry by an Ojibway person. Explores issues of identity, alienation, liberation, love and loss. Illus. 64 pp. Paper. Theytus, 1994. $9.95.

THE OPOSSUM'S TALE
Deborah L. Duvall; Murv Jacob, Illus.; University of New Mexico Press, 2003. $14.95.

ORACLES: A NOVEL
Melissa Tantaquidgeon Zobel; One Indian family trying to maintain tribal culture in the midst of rapid transformation. 192 pp. University of New Mexico Press, 2004. $14.95.

ORATORY IN NATIVE NORTH AMERICA
William M. Clements; Examines speeches made by Native North Americans as recorded by whites. 186 pp. University of Arizona Press, 2002. $40.

THE ORDEAL OF THE LONGHOUSE: THE PEOPLES OF THE IROQUOIAN LEAGUE IN THE ERA OF EUROPEAN COLONIZATION Daniel K. Richter
Illus. Maps. 450 pp. Paper. University of North Carolina Press, 1992. $19.95.

THE ORDEAL OF RUNNING STANDARD
Thomas Fall; Dramatizes the dilemma of two young Indians, Running Standing (Kiowa) and his Cheyenne wife. 320 pp. Paper. University of Oklahoma Press, 1993. $15.95.

THE ORDERS OF THE DREAMED: GEORGE NELSON ON CREE & NORTHERN OJIBWA RELIGION & MYTH, 1823
Jennifer S.H. Brown & Robert Brightman; Detailed portrayal of Algonquian religion & ceremonies. Paper. Minnesota Historical Society Press, 1989. $15.95.

OREGON ARCHAEOLOGY
C. Melvin Aikens, Thomas J. Connolly & Dennis L. Jenkins
The story of Native American cultures in Oregon from 14,000 years ago to the 19th century. Illus. Photos. Maps. Biblio. 512 pp. Paper. Oregon State U. Press, 2011. $29.95.

THE OREGON & CALIFORNIA TRAIL: DIARY OF JANE GOULD IN 1862
Bert Webber, Editor; Indian massacres. 92 pp. Paper. Webb Research Group, $7.50.

OREGON & THE COLLAPSE OF ILLAHEE: U.S. EMPIRE & THE TRANSFORMATION OF AN INDIGENOUS WORLD, 1792-1859
Gray H. Whaley; Chinook word Illahee (homeland)...examines relations among newcomers & between newcomers & Native peoples. Illus. Maps. 320 pp. University of North Carolina Press, 2010. $65; paper, $24.95.

OREGON INDIANS: CULTURE, HISTORY & CURRENT AFFAIRS; ATLAS & INTRO.
Jeff Zucker & Bob Hogfoss
2nd ed. Illus. 192 pp. Paper. Oregon Historical Society, 1988. $15.95.

OREGON INDIANS: VOICES FROM TWO CENTURIES
Stephen Dow Beckham, Editor; Documentary history of Oregon Indians with first-person accounts. Illus. Maps. 608 pp. Oregon State University Press, 2006. $45.

THE OREGON TRAIL & THE CONSPIRACY OF PONTIAC
Francis Parkman; 951 pp. Amazon.com, 1991. $35.

OREGON'S SALTY COAST
James A. Gibbs; with Bert Webber; Details of the Oregon coast from early explore, from what they found to Indian encounters. Includes all state parks and other places. Illus. Maps. Biblio. Paper. Webb Research Group, $14.95.

THE ORGANIZATION OF NORTH AMERICAN PREHISTORIC CHIPPED STONE TOOL TECHNOLOGIES Philip J. Carr, Ed.
Illus. 136 pp. Paper. Amazon.com, 1994. $30; paper, $18.50.

ORGANIZING THE LAKOTA: THE POLITICAL ECONOMY OF THE NEW DEAL ON THE PINE RIDGE & ROSEBUD RESERVATIONS
Thomas Biolsi; Illus. 245 pp. Paper. University of Arizona Press, 1992. $19.95.

THE ORIGIN & DEVELOPMENT OF THE PUEBLO KATSINA CULT
E. Charles Adams; Examines the concept of the katsina and the religion that developed around it. 253 pp. Paper. University of Arizona Press, 1991. $17.95.

ORIGIN OF ANCIENT AMERICAN CULTURES
Paul Shao; Illus. 375 pp. Iowa State University Press, 1983. $42.75.

*THE ORIGIN OF THE MILKY WAY & OTHER LIVING STORIES OF THE CHEROKEE
Barbara R. Duncan, collected & edited by; 27 stories. Cherokee storytelling traditions. Grades 4 and up. Illus. Map. 144 pp. University of North Carolina Press, 2008. $19.95; paper, $12.95.

THE ORIGIN OF A PACIFIC COAST CHIEFDOM: THE CHUMASH OF THE CHANNEL ISLANDS Jeanne E. Arnold; Illus. 336 pp. University of Utah Press, 2001. $60.

THE ORIGIN OF THE WOLF RITUAL: THE WHALING INDIANS, WEST COAST LEGENDS & STORIES, PART 12 OF THE SAPIR-THOMAS NOOTKA TEXTS
Edward Sapir; editd by Eugene Arima, et al.
Illus. Maps. 286 pp. Paper. University of Washington Press, $45.

THE ORIGINAL VERMONTERS: NATIVE INHABITANTS, PAST & PRESENT
William A. Haviland & Marjory W. Power; Revised edition. Illus. 362 pp. Paper.
The University of Vermont Press, 1994. Distributed by U. Press of New England. $25.95.

THE ORIGINS OF NATIVE AMERICANS: EVIDENCE FROM ANTHROPOLOGICAL GENETICS M.H. Crawford; Illus. 325 pp. Cambridge U. Press, 2001. $80; paper, $29.

THE ORIGINS OF A PACIFIC COAST CHIEFDOM: THE CHUMASH OF THE CHANNEL ISLANDS Jeanne E. Arnold, ed.; Illus. 336 pp. University of Utah Press, 2001. $60.

ORIGINS OF PRE-COLUMBIAN ART
Terence Grieder; Illus. 250 pp. University of Texas Press, 1982. $19.95.

ORIGINS OF PREDICATES: EVIDENCE FROM PLAINS CREE
Tomio Hirose; Illus. 288 pp. Routledge, 2003. $80.

THE ORIGINS OF SOUTHWESTERN AGRICULTURE
R.G. Matson; 356 pp. University of Arizona Press, 1991. $70.

ORNAMENTAL & CEREMONIAL ARTIFACTS OF THE NORTH AMERICAN INDIAN: IDENTIFICATION & VALUE GUIDE Lar Hothem; Covers many classes of higher-grade and top-quality artifacts. Illus. 133 pp. Paper. Amazon.com, 1990. $27, postpaid.

SIMON J. ORTIZ: A POETIC LEGACY OF INDIGENOUS CONTINUANCE
Susan Berry Brill de Ramarez, Editor; Paper. University of New Mexico Press, $29.95.

*THE OSAGE
Terry P. Wilson; Grades 5 and up. Illus. 104 pp. Chelsea House, 1988. $17.95.

THE OSAGE CEREMONIAL DANCE I'N-LON-SCHKA
Alice A. Callahan; Illus. Maps. 12 music examples. 172 pp. Paper. University of Oklahoma Press, 1990. $11.95.

THE OSAGE: CHILDREN OF THE MIDDLE WATERS
John Joseph Matthews; An account of the Sioux Osage tribe from the oral history of his people in the period before the coming of the Europeans to the recorded history since, and his own life among them. Reprint of 1961 edition. Illus. 826 pp. Paper. University of Oklahoma Press, $27.95.

OSAGE DICTIONARY
Carolyn Quintero
Words, phrases & sentences. Illus. 480 pp. University of Oklahoma Press, 2010. $55.00.

OSAGE: AN ETHNOHISTORICAL STUDY OF HEGEMONY ON THE PRAIRIE-PLAINS
Rollings; Paper. Amazon.com, $17.95.

OSAGE IN MISSOURI
Wolferman; Paper. Amazon.com, $9.95.

OSAGE INDIAN BANDS & CLANS
Louis F. Burns; A listing of clans & their members from Jesuit records, U.S. Government annuity rolls, and Osage Mission records. Reprint of the 1984 ed. Illus. Maps. Indexed. Paper. Genealogical Publishing, 2006. $21.95.

OSAGE INDIAN CUSTOMS & MYTHS
Louis F. Burns; Illus. 248 pp. Paper. University of Alabama Press, 2005. $19.95.

THE OSAGE INDIAN MURDERS: A TRUE CRIME STORY
Lawrence J. Hogan; Illus. 296 pp. Paper. Amlex, 1998. $16.95.

OSAGE INDIANS: BANDS & CLANS
Louis F. Burns; 196 pp. The Osage Mission, 1984. $20.

THE OSAGE & THE INVISIBLE WORLD: FROM WORKS OF FRANCIS LA FLESCHE
Francis La Flesche; Garrick A. Bailey, Editor
Illus. Tables. Map. 344 pp. University of Oklahoma Press, 1995. $34.95; paper, $16.95.

AN OSAGE JOURNEY TO EUROPE, 1827-1830: THREE FRENCH ACCOUNTS
Edited & translated by William Least Heat-Moon & James K. Wallace
Illus. 168 pp. Paper. University of Oklahoma Press, $29.95.

OSAGE - LIFE & LEGENDS: EARTH PEOPLE - SKY PEOPLE
Robert Liebert
History of the Osage Tribe. Illus. 144 pp. Paper. Naturegraph, 1987. $8.95.

OSAGE MISSION BAPTISMS, MARRIAGES, & INTERMENTS, 1820-1886
Louis Burns, Editor; 870 pp. The Osage Mission, 1986. $35.

THE OSAGE ROSE
Tom Holm; Detective novel. 256 pp. Paper. U. of Arizona Press, 2008. $15.95.

OSAGE SOCIETY & CULTURE: THE FIRST 125 YEARS OF POST EUROPEAN CONTACT, 1700-1825 Michael Tatham; 23 pp. Paper. Amazon.com, 1999. $7.95.

THE OSAGES, DOMINANT POWER OF LOUISIANA TERRITORY
Wallace T. Talbott; 96 pp. Carlton Press, 1989. $8.95.

OSCEOLA'S LEGACY
Patricia Riles Wickman; A geneology & archaeological study of the Seminole leader and the removal of Florida Indians in the early 1800s. Illus. 400 pp. Paper. University of Alabama Press, 2006. $29.95. E-Book, $23.96.

OTHER COUNCIL FIRES WERE BEFORE BEFORE OURS: A CLASSIC NATIVE AMERICAN CREATION STORY AS RETOLD BY A SENECA ELDER & HER GRANDDAUGHTER Twylah Nitsch & Jamie Sam
Illus. 160 pp. Paper. Harper San Francisco, 1991. $17.

OTHER DESTINIES: UNDERSTANDING THE AMERICAN INDIAN NOVEL
Louis Owens; Critical analysis of novels written between 1854 and today by American Indian authors. Traces how ten Native American authors have come to terms with discovering their identity in contemporary America. Biblio. 304 pp. Paper. University of Oklahoma Press, 1994. $19.95.

THE OTHER MOVEMENT: INDIAN RIGHTS & CIVIL RIGHTS IN THE DEEP SOUTH
Denise E. Bates; Examines the most visible outcome of the Southern Indian Rights Movement: state Indian affairs commissions. Looks specifically at Alabama and Louisiana. Illus. 272 pp. University of Alabama Press, 2012. $35.95. E-Book, $28.76.

THE OTHER SIDE OF THE FRONTIER: ECONOMIC EXPLORATIONS INTO NATIVE AMERICAN HISTORY Linda L. Barrington; Essays by scholars on Native American economic history. Illus. 320 pp. Paper. Westview Press, 1998. $44.

THE OTHER SIDE OF NOWHERE
Peter Blue Cloud
Collection of mythic and rythmic coyote stories. Illus. Amazon.com, $10.

OTHER WORDS: AMERICAN INDIAN LITERATURE, LAW, & CULTURE
Jace Weaver; 381 pp. University of Oklahoma Press, 2001. $24.95.

*OTOKAHEKAGAPI (FIRST BEGINNINGS) SIOUX CREATION STORY
Thomas E. Simms; Grades 5 and up. Illus. 36 pp. Paper. Tipi Press, 1987. $4.50.

OTTAWA & CHIPPEWA INDIANS OF MICHIGAN, 1870-1909
Raymond C. Lantz; Three censuses taken by the BIA. 288 pp. Amazon.com, 1991. $21.

*THE OTTAWAS
Elaine Landau; Grades 5-8. Illus. 64 pp. Franklin Watts, 1996. $22; paper, $6.95.

OUR ART, OUR VOICES: NATIVE AMERICAN CULTURAL PERSPECTIVES
Denni D. Woodward; Illus. 48 pp. Paper. Amazon.com, 1995. $10.

*OUR BIT OF TRUTH - AN ANTHOLOGY OF CANADIAN NATIVE LITERATURE
Agnes Grant, Editor; Voices of Aboriginal people...from mythology & legend to biography. Grades 9-12. Paper. Pemmican, $20.95.

OUR BOX WAS FULL: AN ETHNOGRAPHY FOR THE DELGAMUUKW PLAINTIFFS
Richard Daly; A landmark case and the Gitksan & Witsuwit'en peoples of northwest British Columbia. 384 pp. University of Washington Press, 2005. $105; paper, $37.95.

OUR CENTENNIAL INDIAN WAR & THE LIFE OF GENERAL CUSTER
Frances Fuller Victor; The first account of the successive army operations in 1876 and early 1877. Illus. Maps. University of Oklahoma Press, 2011. $29.95.

OUR CHIEFS & ELDERS: WORDS & PHOTOGRAPHS OF NATIVE LEADERS
David Neel; Series of portraits of Native American chiefs & elders. Illus. 64 duotone photos. 162 pp. Paper. University of Washington Press, $25.95.

OUR ELDERS LIVED IT: AMERICAN INDIAN IDENTITY IN THE CITY
Deborah Davis Jackson; Illus. 210 pp. Northern Illinois U. Press, 2003. $38; paper, $20.

OUR FIRE SURVIVES THE STORM: A CHEROKEE LITERARY HISTORY
Daniel Heath Justice
Illus. Maps. 300 pp. University of Minnesota Press, 2005. $60; paper, $22.50.

OUR FRIENDS: THE NAVAJO
Ruth Roessel, Editor; Formerly Papers on Navajo Life & Culture.
Illus. Paper. Navajo Community College Press, 1976. $8.

OUR HEARTS FELL TO THE GROUND & ERA OF FDR
Colin G. Calloway, et al; Paper. Bedford/St. Martin's, 2001. $28.10.

OUR HEARTS FELL TO THE GROUND: PLAINS INDIAN VIEWS ON HOW THE WEST WAS LOST Colin G. Calloway, et al, Eds.; 224 pp. Amazon.com, $115; paper, $20..

OUR INDIAN WARDS
G.W. Manypenny; Reprint of 1880 edition. Amazon.com, $35.

OUR LIFE AMONG THE IROQUOIS INDIANS
Harriet S. Caswell; Biography of Asher & Laura Wright, mid-19th century Seneca Indians. Illus. Map. 358 pp. Paper. University of Nebraska Press, 2007. $24.95.

OUR LIVES IN OUR HANDS: MICMAC INDIAN BASKETMAKERS
Bunny McBridge; Illus. 96 pp. Paper. Tilbury House, 1991. $10.95.

OUR NATIVE AMERICAN HERITAGE
Reader's Digest Editors; Amazon.com, 1996.

OUR NATIVE AMERICAN LEGACY: PACIFIC NORTHWEST TOWNS WITH INDIAN NAMES Sandy Nestor; Wayne Cornell, Ed.; Illus. 312 pp. Caxton Press, 2001. $17.95.

OUR PEOPLE, OUR LAND, OUR IMAGES: INTERNATIONAL INDIGENOUS PHOTOGRAPHY Hulleah J. Tsinhnahjinnie & Veronica Passalacqua, Editors
Paper. Heyday Books. $27.95.

OUR PEOPLE, OUR JOURNEY: THE LITTLE RIVER BAND OF OTTAWA INDIANS
James W. McClurken; Paper. 394 pp. Michigan State University Press, $24.95.

OUR PRAYERS ARE IN THIS PLACE: CENTURIES OF PECOS PUEBLO IDENTITY
Frances Levine; Illus. Maps. 232 pp. University of New Mexico Press, 1999. $39.95.

OUR RED BROTHERS & THE PEACE POLICY OF PRESIDENT ULYSSES S. GRANT
Lawrie Tatum; Illus. 375 pp. University of Nebraska Press, 1970. $28.95.

OUR SACRED GIFTS: AN OJIBWE PERSPECTIVE IN THE PREPARATION OF PARENTHOOD; AN OJIBWE PERSPECTIVE ON EMBRYO & FETAL DEVELOPMENT; AN OJIBWE PERSPECTIVE ON INFANT DEVELOPMENMT; AN OJIBWE PERSPECTIVE ON TODDLERHOOD Phyllis W. Grouph; 4 Vols. Amazon.com, 1990. $75.

OUR STORIES, OUR LIVES
CIRI Foundation; Collection of personal experiences & traditional stories told by 23 Alaska Native elders--Eskimos, Indians & Aleuts of the Cook Inley region. Illus. 245 pp. Paper. CIRI, $15.95.

OUR STORIES REMEMBER: AMERICAN INDIAN HISTORY, CULTURE & VALUES THROUGH STORYTELLING
Joseph Bruchac; Illus. 192 pp. Paper. Fulcrum Pubnlishing, 2004. $16.95.

OUR TELLINGS: INTERIOR SALISH STORIES FROM THE NLHA KAPMX PEOPLE
Darwin Hanna; Maimie Henry, Ed. & Compiler
Illus. 224 pp. Paper. University of Washington Press, 1995. $35.95.

OUR VAST WINTER COUNT: NATIVE AMERICAN WEST BEFORE LEWIS & CLARK
Colin G. Calloway; Illus. Maps. 631 pp. Paper. U. of Nebraska Press, 2006. $19.95.

OUR VOICES: NATIVE STORIES OF ALASKA & THE YUKON
edited by James Ruppert & John W. Bernet; Showcases 20 storytellers and writers who represent a full range of Athabaskan and related languages of Alaska and the Yukon. Maps. 394 pp. Paper. University of Nebraska Press, 2001. $25.

OUR VOICES: NATIVE STORIES OF ALASKA & THE YUKON
James K. Rupert & John W. Bernet, Eds.
Illus. 395 pp. Paper. University of Nebraska Press, 2001. $25.

OUR VOICES, OUR LAND
Stephen Tribmle, Editor; Photographic collection shows Native Americans in various settings. Illus. 176 pp. Amazon.com, $19.95.

OURAY - CHIEF OF THE UTES
P. David Smith; Illus. 220 pp. Paper. Wayfinder Press, 1986. $15.95.

OUT OF THE MIST: TREASURES OF THE NUU-CHAH-NULTH CHIEFS
Martha Black; The art, culture and history of the Nuu-chah-culth, Ditidaht-Pacheenaht and Makah Nations of British Columbia, Canada. Photos. 112 pp. paper. UBC Press, 1999. $25.

OUT OF THE WEST: EITELJORG MUSEUM OF AMERICAN INDIANS & WESTERN ART Suzan Campbell, Editor; Presents the Gund collection of Western art and biographies of featured artists. Illus. 200 pp. Western Edge Press, 2010. $34.95.

OUT THERE SOMEWHERE
Simon J. Ortiz; Poetry. 158 pp. University of Arizona Press, 2002. $35; paper, $17.95.

OUTBREAK & MASSACRE BY THE DAKOTA INDIANS IN MINNESOTA IN 1862
Don H. Tolzmann; 128 pp. Paper. Amazon.com, 2001. $16.

OUTCROPPINGS FROM NAVAJOLAND
David Levering; Poems. Amazon.com, $5.

AN OUTLINE OF BASIC VERB INFLECTIONS OF OKLAHOMA CHEROKEE
Charles D. Van Tuyl; 79 pp. Paper. Indian University Press, 1994. $15.50, postpaid.

AN OUTLINE OF SENECA CEREMONIES AT COLDSPRING LONGHOUSE
William N. Fenton; Bound with: The Shawnee Female Deity, by C.F. Voegelin; Human Wolves Among the Navaho, by William Morgan; Musical Areas in Aboriginal North America, by Helen H. Roberts; and Rank & Potlatch Among the Haida, by George P. Murdock. Reprint of 1936 edition. Amazon.com, $15.

OVER A CENTURY OF MOVING TO THE DRUM: SALISH INDIAN CELEBRATIONS ON THE FLATHEAD INDIAN RESERVATION
Johnny Arlee; Robert Bigart, Editor
Illus. 104 pp. Paper. SKC Press & Montana Historical Society, 1998. $14.95.

OVER THE EARTH I COME: THE GREAT SIOUX UPRISING OF 1862
Duane Schultz; Illus. 320 pp. Paper. St. Martin's Press, 1993. $14.95.

OVERLAND TO STARVATION COVE: WITH THE INUIT IN SEARCH OF FRANKLIN, 1878-1880 Heinrich Klutschak; William Barr, Ed. & tr. Illus. U. of Toronto Press, 1987. $30.

THE OVERSTREET INDIAN ARROWHEADS: IDENTIFICATION & PRICE GUIDE
Robert M. Overstreet & Howard Peake; 4th Ed. Illus. Paper. Amazon.com, 2005. $20.

LOUIS OWENS: LITERARY REFLECTIONS ON HIS LIFE & WORK
edited by Jacquelyn Kilpatrick; Essays examining Owen's writings. Contributors include: Susan Bernardin, David Brande, Renny Christopher, Neil Harrison, Jesse Peters, et al. Illus. 320 pp. University of Oklahoma Press, 2004. $39.95.

THE OWL IN THE MONUMENT CANYON, & OTHER STORIES FROM INDIAN COUNTRY H. Jackson Clark; Illus. University of Utah Press, $24.95; paper, $14.95.

*OWL IN THE CEDAR TREE
N. Scott Momaday; illus. by Don Perceval; Details of Navaho culture and religious beliefs, and the conflict between traditional and contemporary ways. Grades 4-8. Illus. 125 pp. Paper. University of Nebraksa Press, 1992. $9.95.

*OWL'S EYES & SEEKING A SPIRIT
Kootenai Cultur Committee; illus. by Verna Lefthand
Two Kootenai stories. Grade 4. 32 pp. Paper. SKC Press, $5.

*THE OWL'S SONG: A NOVEL
janet Campbell Hale; Grades 4 and up. Paper. University of New Mexico Press, $12.95.

OYATE CATALOG
Books, videos and recordings about American Indian, Alaska Natives, Native Hawaiians, First nations and Indigeous peoples. Grades 6 and up. Oyate.

OYAWIN: AMERICAN INDIAN EDUCATION: A HISTORY
Jon Allan Reyhner& Jeanne M. Eder; University of Oklahoma Press, 2004. $29.95.

OZARK BLUFF-DWELLERS
Mark R. Harrington
Reprint of 1960 edition. Illus. 185 pp. Paper. National Museum of the American Indian, $5.

OZETTE: EXCAVATING A MAKAH WHALING VILLAGE
Ruth Kirk; Illus. Maps. 120 pp. Paper. University of Washington Press, 015. $34.95.

THE OXFORD HANDBOOK OF AMERICAN INDIAN HISTORY
Frederick E. Hoxie; Oxford University Press, 2014. $150.

THE OXFORD HANDBOOK OF INDIGENOUS AMERICAN LITERATURE
James H. Cox & Daniel Heath Justice; Oxford University Press, 2014. $160.

P

PABLITA VELARDE: PAINTING HER PEOPLE
Marcella J. Ruch; intro. by Joyce M. Szabo
Recorded stories by Pablita Velarde illus. with her paintings. Illus. 75 color plates. 75 pp. University of New Mexico Press, $34.95; paper, $18.95.

*PACHEE GOYO: HISTORY & LEGENDS FROM THE SHOSHONE
Rupert Weeks; Paper. Amazon.com, 1981. $6.

PACIFIC COAST INDIANS OF NORTH AMERICA
Grant Lyons; California Coast Indians. Illus. Fort Tumbleweed, 1983. $29.95.

PACIFIC NORTHWEST AMERICANA
Charles W. Smith, Editor; Bibliography of 11,000+ books, pamphlets, newspapers, speeches & historical documents relating to the history of the Pacific Northwest. Also a listing of libraries. Reprint of 1950 edition. 392 pp. Paper. Supplement, 1949-74 by R.E. Moore & N.H. Purcell, Eds. Binford & Mort, $20 each.

PACIFIC NORTHWEST: ITS DISCOVERY & EARLY EXPLORATION BY SEA, LAND, & RIVER Edward W. Nuffield; 288 pp. Paper. Hancock House, $16.95.

PACIFYING THE PLAINS: GENERAL ALFRED TERRY & THE DECLINE OF THE SIOUX, 1866-1890 John Bailey; Greenwood Press, 1979. $35.

PADDLING TO WHERE I STAND: AGNES ALFRED, KWAKWAKA'WAKW NOBLEWOMAN Agnes Alfred; Martine J. Reid, Editor; Daisy Sewid-Smith, trans. 320 pp. Paper. University of Washington Press, 2004. $104; paper, $37.95.

PAGES FROM HOPI HISTORY
Harry C. James; An authentic account of the Hopi way of life. 258 pp. Paper. University of Arizona Press, 1974. $19.95.

PAINTED JOURNEYS: THE ART OF JOHN MIX STANLEY
Peter Hassrick & Mindy Besaw; 308 pp. University of Oklahoma Press, $54.95; paper, $34.95.

PAINTERS, PATRONS & IDENTITY: ESSAYS IN NATIVE AMERICAN ART TO HONOR J.J. BRODY
Joyce M. Szabo & J.J. Brody; Illus. 306 pp. Paper. U. of New Mexico Press, 2001. $50.

PAINTBRUSHES & PISTOLS: HOW THE TAOS ARTISTS SOLD THE WEST
Sherry Clayton-Taggett & Ted Schwartz; Illus. 288 pp. Paper. John Muir, 1990. $17.95

PAINTED TIPIS BY CONTEMPORARY PLAINS INDIAN ARTISTS
Explores the esthetic qualities and significance of 12 painted tipi covers specially created in 1972-73 by contemporary Plains Indian artists. Illus. Map. 80 pp. Amazon.com, $8,

PAINTING THE DREAM: THE VISIONARY ART OF NAVAJO PAINTER DAVID CHETHLAHE PALADIN
35 full-color fine art reproductions. Paper. Inner Traditions, $24.95.

PAINTING INDIANS & BUILDING EMPIRES IN NORTH AMERICA, 1710-1840
William H. Truettner; Includes major Indian images painted by Euro-American artists. Illus. 176 pp. University of California Press, 2010. $39.95.

PAINTING OF LITTLE CROW
Frank Blackwell Mayer; Reproduction of an oil painting from the Minnesota Historical Society, based on a sketch Mayer made of Chief Little Crow in 1851. 20x30" Minnesota Historical Society Press. $6.95.

PAINTING THE UNDERWORLD SKY: CULTURAL EXPRESSION & SUBVERSION IN ART Mateo Romero; foreword by Suzan Shown Harjo
50 paintings reproduced and the artist's reflections on his own life and the power of Pueblo song & dance. Illus. 108 pp. School for Advanced Research, 2006. $34.95; paper, $29.95.

PAITARKIUTENKA / MY LEGACY TO YOU: MIISAQ / FRANK ANDREW, SR.
Alice Rearden & Marie Meade, translators; Ann Fienup-Riordan, Editor
Yup'ik elders Frank Andrew, Sr. (1917-2006) of southwest Alaska and their ways of life on the Bering Sea coast. Illus. Map. 360 pp. Paper. U. of Washington Press, 2008. $27.95.

THE PAIUTE, INDIANS OF NORTH AMERICA
Pamela Bunte & Robert Franklin; 350 pp. University of Nebraska Press, 1989. $22.95.

*THE PAIUTE: SOUTHWEST
Pamela Bunte & Robert Franklin; Grades 5 and up. Illus. Chelsea House, 1989. $17.95.

THE PALEOINDIAN & EARLY ARCHAIC SOUTHEAST
David G. Anderson & Kenneth E. Sasserman, Editors
Illus. 544 pp. Paper. University of Alabama Press, 1996. $34.95.

PALEO-INDIAN SITE IN EASTERN PENNSYLVANIA: AN EARLY HUNTING CULTURE
John Witthoft; Facsimile of the 1952 edition. Illus. 32 pp. Paper. Amazon.com, $4.95.

PALEOINDIAN GEOARCHAEOLOGY OF THE SOUTHERN HIGH PLAINS
Vance T. Holliday; Illus. Tables. 319 pp. Paper. University of Texas Press, 1997. $30.

EDWARD PALMER'S ARKANSAW MOUNDS
Marvin D. Jeter, Editor; Archaeology of mound research in the Southeast in the late 19th century. Illus. 448 pp. Paper. University of Alabama Press, 2010. $42.50.

PANAMINT SHOSHONE BASKETRY: AN AMERICAN ART FORM
Eva Slater; Paper. Heyday Books. $25.

A PAPAGO GRAMMAR
Ofelia Zepeda; 190 pp. Paper. University of Arizona Press, 1983. $19.95.

THE PAPAGO & PIMA INDIANS OF ARIZONA
Ruth Underhill; Illus. 64 pp. Paper. Alibris.com, 1979. $5.

A PAPAGO TRAVELER: THE MEMORIES OF JAMES McCARTHY
James McCarthy; edited by John Westover
Reprint of 1985 edition. 200 pp. University of Arizona Press, $24.95.

PAPAGO WOMAN
Ruth M. Underhill; Reprint. Illus. 98 pp. Paper. Waveland Press, 1979. $14.50.

PAPER MEDICINE MAN: JOHN GREGORY BOURKE & HIS AMERICAN WEST
Joseph C. Porter; Illus. 370 pp. Paper. University of Oklahoma Press, 1986. $17.95.

PAPER TALK: A HISTORY OF LIBRARIES, PRINT CULTURE, AND ABORIGINAL PEOPLES IN CANADA BEFORE 1960
Brenden Frederick R. Edwards; 248 pp. Paper. Scarecrow Press, 2004. $55.

PAPERS FROM THE AMERICAN INDIAN LANGUAGES CONFERENCES HELD AT THE UNIVERSITY OF CALIFORNIA, SANTA CRUZ, JULY & AUGUST, 1991
J.E. Redden, Ed.; Reprint. Illus. 240 pp. Paper. Coyote Press, $25.95.

JOHN PAPUNHANK, A CHRISTIAN INDIAN OF NORTH AMERICA: A NARRATIVE OF FACTS 1820
John Papunhank; Reprint. Illus. Paper. Kessinger Publishing, 2005. $12.50.

CYNTHIA ANN PARKER: INDIAN CAPTIVE
Catherine T. Gonzales; Eakin Publications, 1980. $6.95.

CYNTHIA ANN PARKER: THE LIFE & LEGEND
Margaret S. Hacker; Recounts her experiences a s a captive of the Comanches (1836-60). Illus. Biblio. 64 pp. Paper. Texas Western Press, 1990. $12.50.

PARKER ON THE IROQUOIS
Arthur Parker; William Fenton, Editor; Bound with The Code of Handsome Lake, the Seneca prophet; The Constitution of the Five Nations; and, Iroquois Uses of Maize and Other Food Plants. Illus. Photos. 482 pp. Paper. Syracuse University Press, 1968. $16.95.

QUANAH PARKER, COMANCHE CHIEF
William T. Hagan; Presents Parker as a man torn between two worlds. Illus. Maps. 160 pp. Paper. University of Oklahoma Press, $19.95.

*QUANAH PARKER: GREAT CHIEF OF THE COMANCHES
Catherine Gonzales; Melissa Roberts, Editor
Grades 1-5. Illus. 48 pp. Alibris, 1987. $9.95.

QUANAH PARKER'S STRANGE ENCOUNTERS: A BIOGRAPHY
Mary R. Dees; Illus. 252 pp. Paper. Amazon.com, 1997. $14.95.

*PAINTEDBRUSHES & ARROWS: A STORY OF ST. AUGUSTINE
M.C. Finotti; Grades 6 and up. Story of a 9 year old Comanche girl.
112 pp. Paper. Pineapple Press, $12.95.

*FRANCIS PARKMAN & THE PLAINS INDIANS
Jane Shuter; Grades 6-8. Illus. 48 pp. Raintree, 1995. $24.25.

PARTIAL JUSTICE: FEDERAL INDIAN LAW IN A LIBERAL CONSTITUTIONAL SYSTEM
Petra Shattuck & Jill Norgren; 223 pp. Berg Publishers, 1991. $50; paper, $15.50.

PARTIAL RECALL: PHOTOGRAPHS OF NATIVE NORTH AMERICANS
Lucy R. Lippard, Editor; Explorations by 12 Native American artists and writers into the images that have shaped our ideas of "Indianness," and the complex relationship of photography to identity. Illus. 100 photos. 200 pp. Paper. W.W. Norton & Co., 1992. $35; paper, $19.95.

PARTNERS IN FURS: A HISTORY OF THE FUR TRADE IN EASTERN JAMES BAY, 1600-1870
Daniel Francis & Toby Morantz; Illus. 205 pp. Paper. U. of Toronto Press, 1982. $17.95.

*THE PASHOFA POLE
Mary M. Frye; Henry Willis, Tr., Norrm Howard, Illus. Choctaw cultural children's book.
The Choctaw Store, 2000. $9.95.

*PASSAGE TO LITTLE BIGHORN
Terry Kretzer-Malvehu; Ages 12 and up. 232 pp. Paper. Northland, $6.95.

PASSAMAQUODDY CEREMONIAL SONGS: AESTHETICS & SURVIVAL
Ann Morrison Spinney; Illus. 272 pp. University of Massachusetts Press, 2010. $65.

PASSAMAQUODDY-MALISEET DICTIONARY
David A. Francis, Robert M. Leavitt, Margaret Apt
University of Maine Press, 2008. $45. (Out-of-Stock)

PASSING THE MOON THROUGH 13 BASKETS: A GUIDE TO THE NATURAL YEAR & NATIVE AMERICAN CELEBRATIONS ON THE WILD REDWOOD COAST
Susan Calla, Sandra Jerabek & Loren Bommelyn
Nature narratives and Native American stories highlight this month-by-month travel companion to 60+ seasonal events and regional festivals on California's northernmost wild redwood coast. Illus. 124 pp. paper. Naturegraph Publishers, 2005. $19.95.

A PASSION FOR THE PAST: PAPERS IN HONOUR OF JAMES F. PENDERGAST
J.V. Wright & Jean-Luc Pilon; 22 articles covering the St. Lawrence Iroquoians, linguistics, cosmology, Native persepctives on archaeology, palaeo-botany, physical anthropology and an original contribution by a late 19th-century archaeologist. Illus. Tables. 485 pp. Paper. University of Washington Press, 2004. $39.95.

A PASSION FOR THE TRUE & JUST: FELIX & LUCY KRAMER COHEN & THE INDIAN NEW DEAL Alice Beck Kehoe; 256 pp. Illus. University of Arizona Press, 2014. $55.

PAST, PRESENT, AND FUTURE: CHALLENGES OF THE NATIONAL MUSEUM OF THE AMERICAN INDIAN Seven contributors: Duane Champagine, Kevin Gover (Pawnee), Suzan Shown Harjo (Cheyenne/Muscogee), Frederick Hoxie, Gerald McMaster (Plains Cree), Rosita Worl (Tlingit), et al.. Illus. 152 pp. Paper. NMAI Press, 2011. $20.

THE PATCHES IN A HISTORY QUILT: EPISCOPAL WOMEN IN THE DIOCESE OF SOUTH DAKOTA, 1868-2000 Ruth Ann Alexander; 136 pp. Paper. Amazon.com, 2003.

PATCHWORK: SEMINOLE & MICCOSUKEE ART & ACTIVITIES
Dorothy Downs; 55 pp. Paper. Pineapple Press, $12.95.

PATH BREAKERS: THE EITELJORG FELLOWSHIP FOR NATIVE AMERICAN FINE ART, 2003 Lucy R. Lippard, et al.; The 3rd volume in a series that brings the work of Native American fine artists to public attention. Honors artist Kay WalkingStick (Cherokee) & five fellows: Corwin "Corky" Clairmont (Salish/Kootenai), Robert Houle (Saulteaux), Nora Narranjo-Morse (Tewa-Santa Clara Pueblo), Nadia Myre (Algonquin), & Hulleah Tsinhnahjinnie (Dine/Seminole/Muscogee). Essays by Lucy Lippard, Margaret Archuleta (Pueblo/Hispanic), Gail Trenblay (Onandaga/Micmac), Bonnie Devine (Ojibway), Patricia Deadman (Tuscarora/Mohawk), Jennifer C. Vigil (Navaho/Latina/Ukranian), & Veronica Passalacqua. Illus. 112 pp. Paper. University of Washington Press, 2004. $22.50.

THE PATH OF HANDSOME LAKE: A MODEL OF RECOVERY FOR NATIVE PEOPLE
Alf H. Walle; Greenwood Publishing, 2003. $64.95. Paper. Amazon.com, 2004.

THE PATH OF POWER
Sun Bear, Wabun & Barry Weinstock; The life story of Sun Bear, medicine teacher of the Ojibwa and founder of the Bear Tribe Medicine Society. Illus. 270 pp. Paper. Cherokee Publications, $9.95.

THE PATH TO HEALING: REPORT OF THE NATIONAL ROUND TABLE ON ABORIGINAL HEALTH & SOCIAL ISSUES 360 pp. Paper. Canadian Government Publishing, Dist. by Amazon.com, 1993.

*PATHKI NANA: KOOTENAI GIRL SOLVES A MYSTERY
Kenneth Thomasma; Jack Brouwer, Illus.
Grades 4-8. Illus. Amazon.com, $10.99; paper, $6.99.

THE PATHS OF KATERI'S KIN
Christopher Vecsey; 416 pp. University of Notre Dame Press, 1997. $40; paper, $18.

PATHS OF LIFE: AMERICAN INDIANS OF THE SOUTHWEST & NORTHERN MEXICO
Thomas E. Sheridan & Nancy J. Parezo, Editor; Living portraits of 15 Native American groups. Illus. 298 pp. Paper. University of Arizona Press, 1996. $22.95.

PATHS OF OUR CHILDREN: HISTORIC INDIANS OF ARKANSAS
George Sabo, III; Illus. 144 pp. Paper. Amazon.com, 1992. $5.

PATHS OF THE PEOPLE: THE OJIBWE IN THE CHIPPEWA VALLEY
Tim Pfaff; Reprint of 1993 ed. Illus. Photos. 100 pp. Paper. University of Wisconsin Press, 2005. Also available from Chippewa Valley Museum Press, $15.

PATHS TO A MIDDLE GROUND: THE DIPLOMACY OF NATCHEZ, BOUKFOUKA, NOGALES, AND SAN FERNANDO DE LAS BARRANCAS, 1791-1795
Charles A. Weeks; Shows how diplomatic relations were established and maintained in the Gulf South between Choctaw, Chickasaw, Creek, and Cherokee chiefs and their Spanish counterparts. Illus. 304 pp. U. of Alabama Press, 2005. $45; paper, $32. E-Book.

PATHWAYS TO SELF-DETERMINATION: CANADIAN INDIANS & THE CANADIAN STATE
Leroy Little Bear, et al, Editors; 192 pp. Paper. Amazon.com, 1984. $12.95.

*PATRICK DES JARLAIT: CONVERSATIONS WITH A NATIVE AMERICAN ARTIST
Neva Williams, Editor
Includes photos of his paintings. Grades 1-3. Illus. 56 pp. Paper. Lerner, 1995. $16.95.

THE PATRIOT CHIEFS: A CHRONICLE OF AMERICAN INDIAN RESISTANCE
Alvin M. Josephy, Jr.; Indian resistance to the white man through the stories of nine outstanding leaders. Revised edition. 384 pp. Paper. Penguin Group, 1993. $15.95.

PATTERNS & CEREMONIALS OF THE INDIANS OF THE SOUTHWEST
Moskowitz & Collier; Reprint. 192 pp. Paper. Dover, $14.95.

PATTERNS OF EXCHANGE: NAVAJO WEAVERS & TRADERS
Teresa J. Wilkins; Traces how the relationships between generations of Navajo weavers & traders affected Navajo weaving. 248 pp. Paper. U. of Oklahoma Press, 2010. $19.95.

*THE PAWNEE
Dennis B. Fradin
Revised edition. Grades 2-4. Illus. 48 pp. Children's Press, 1992. $21; paper, $5.50.

PAWNEE, BLACKFOOT, AND CHEYENNE: HISTORY & FOLKLORE OF THE PLAINS
George Bird Grinnell; Illus. 301 pp. Scribner, 1961.
Available from Amazon.com, books.google.com, & abebooks.com.

THE PAWNEE GHOST DANCE HAND GAME: GHOST DANCE REVIVAL & ETHNIC IDENTITY A. Lesser
Reprint of 1933 edition. Illus. 468 pp. University of Wisconsin, $22.00; paper, $8.95.

PAWNEE HERO STORIES & FOLKTALES WITH NOTES ON THE ORIGIN, CUSTOMS & CHARACTER OF THE PAWNEE PEOPLE George Bird Grinnell
Reprint of 1961 edition. Illus. 417 pp. Paper. University of Nebraska Press, $11.95

THE PAWNEE INDIANS
George E. Hyde; Illus. 372 pp. Paper. University of Oklahoma Press, 1974. $24.95.

PAWNEE & LOWER LOUP POTTERY
Rogert Grange, Jr.; Volume 3. Paper. Amazon.com, 1968. $6.

THE PAWNEE MISSION LETTERS, 1834-1851
edited by Richard E. Jensen; Rev. John Dunbar & Samuel Ellis set up a mission to the Pawnee Indians in Nebraska to convert the tribe. Photos. Map. 712 pp. Paper. University of Nebraska Press, 2010. $60.

THE PAWNEE MYTHOLOGY
George A. Dorsey, Editor; Illus. 546 pp. Paper. University of Nebraska Press, 1997. $22.

THE PAWNEE NATION: AN ANNOTATED RESEARCH BIBLIOGRAPHY
Judith A. Boughter
Detailed examination of the Pawnee. 328 pp. Paper. Scarecrow Press, 2004. $60.50.

PAWNEE PASSAGE: 1870-1875
Martha Blaine; Illus. 346 pp. University of Oklahoma Press, 1990. $31.95.

PAWNEES: A CRITICAL BIBLIOGRAPHY
Martha P. Blaine; Illus. 128 pp. Paper. Amazon.com & Alibris.com, 1981. $4.95.

THE PAYNE-BUTRICK PAPERS
William L. Anderson, Jane L. Brown & Anne F. Rogers, Editors
2 Volumes.Collection of information about traditional Cherokee culture & history. 928 pp. University of Nebraska Press, 2010. $150.

PEACE CAME IN THE FORM OF A WOMAN: INDIANS & SPANIARDS IN THE TEXAS BORDERLANDS Juliana Barr
Illus. Maps. 416 pp. University of North Carolina Press, 2007. $69.95; paper, $22.

THE PEACE CHIEF: A NOVEL
Robert J. Conley
Originally published in 1999. 352 pp. Paper. University of Oklahoma Press, 2002. $5.95.

THE PEACE CHIEFS OF THE CHEYENNES
Stan Hoig; Illus. Paper. University of Oklahoma Press, 1980. $19.95.

PEACE, POWER, RIGHTIOUSNESS: AN INDIGENOUS MANIFESTO
Taiaiake Alfred; 200 pp. Paper. Oxford University Press, 1999. $21.95.

PEACE WEAVERS: UNITING THE SALISH COAST THROUGH CROSS-CULTURAL MARRIAGES Candace Wellman; Paper. WSU Press, $27.95.

PECOS RUINS: GEOLOGY, ARCHAEOLOGY, HISTORY, & PREHISTORY
David Grant Noble
Describes the development of Pecos Pueblo from prehistoric times to the Anglo period of 19th century. Illus. Maps. Photos. 32 pp. Paper. Amazon.com, 1990. $7.95.

PELTS, PLUMES & HIDES: WHITE TRADERS AMONG THE SEMINOLE INDIANS, 1870-1930 Harry Kersey, Jr.; Reprint of 1975 edition. Illus. Map. Biblio. 158 pp. Paper. University Press of Florida, $14.95.

PENDLETON WOOLEN MILLS
intro. by Mike Haggerty; Reprint of the first Pendleton Woolen Mills (of Pendleton, Oreg.) mail order catalog of "Indian" blankets. Illus. 40 pp. Paper. University of New Mexico Press & Amazon.com, $12.95.

PENITENTE SELF-GOVERNMENT: BROTHERHOODS & COUNCILS, 1797-1947
Thomas Steele & Rowena Rivera
Illus. 210 pp. Amazon.com, 1985. $29.95; paper, $12.95.

*WILLIAM PENN'S OWN ACCOUNT OF LENNI LENAPE OR DELAWARE INDIANS
Albert C. Myers, Editor
Grades 7 and up. Illus. 96 pp. Paper. Mid Atlantic Press, 1986. $7.95.

PENNSYLVANIA CHERT: IDENTIFYING SOME OF THE MATERIALS USED BY THE INDIANS IN PENNSYLVANIA & SURROUNDING AREAS
Illus. 72 pp. Paper. Amazon.com, 1999. $22.50.

THE PENNSYLVANIA INDIAN TRILOGY
C. Hale Sipe & George Donehoo; Includes three paperbacks: The Indian Chiefs of Pennsylvania; The Indian Wars of Pennsylvania; and A History of the Indian Villages & Place Names in Pennsylvania. Reprint. Illus. 1,700 pp. Wennawoods Publishing, $89.95.

*THE PENOBSCOT
Jill Duvall; Grades K-3. Illus. Childrens Press, 1993.

*THE PENOBSCOT
Katherine Doherty; Grades 4-6. Reprint. 64 pp. Paper. Franklin Watts, $6.95.

THE PENOBSCOT DANCE OF RESISTANCE: TRADITIONS IN THE HISTORY OF A PEOPLE Pauleena MacDougall; 280 pp. Illus. Paper. University of New Hampshire Press, 2004. Distributed by the University Press of New England. $24.95.

PENOBSCOT MAN
Frank G. Speck; Revised edition. Illus. 404 pp. University of Maine Press, 1997. $35.

THE PEOPLE ARE DANCING AGAIN: THE HISTORY OF THE SILETZ TRIBE OF WESTERN OREGON
Charles Wilkinson; Illus. Maps. 576 pp. University of Washington Press, 2010. $34.95.

THE PEOPLE CALLED APACHE
Thomas Mails; Reprint. Illus. Center for Western Studies, $150.

PEOPLE FROM OUR SIDE: A LIFE STORY WITH PHOTOGRAPHS & ORAL BIOGRAPHY Peter Pitseolak & Dorothy Harley Eber
During his lifetime, photographer Peter Pitseolak witnessed the arrival of missionaries, fur traders, law, government, & alcohol in the eastern Canadian Arctic. Reprint of 1975 ed. Illus. U. of Toronto Press, $39.95; paper, $19.95.

THE PEOPLE HAVE NEVER STOPPED DANCING: NATIVE AMERICAN MODERN DANCE HISTORIES Jacqueline Shea Murphy
Illus. 296 pp. Paper. University of Minnesota Press, 2007. $25.

THE PEOPLE: A HISTORY OF NATIVE AMERICA
Frederick E. Hoxie, R David Edmunds, Neal Salisbury; Amazon.com, 2006.

THE PEOPLE: INDIANS OF THE AMERICAN SOUTHWEST
Stephen Trimble, text & photos; Introduction to the native peoples of the American Southwest. Illus. Maps. 520 pp. Paper. School for Advanced Research, 1994. $47.

THE PEOPLE NAMED THE CHIPPEWA: NARRATIVE HISTORIES
Gerald Vizenor; History of the Chippewa experience based on memoirs, court records, and the oral tradition of the Anishinaabe. Illus. Map. 175 pp. Paper. University of Minnesota Press, 1984. $17.50.

THE PEOPLE: NATIVE AMERICAN THOUGHTS & FEELINGS
Illus. 64 pp. Paper. The Book Publishing Co., $5.95.

PEOPLE OF THE LAKES
Time-Life Editors; Overview of the many Indian groups of Great Lakes region. Historic photos. Color illus of artifacts. 192 pp. Amazon.com, 1994. $22, postpaid.

THE PEOPLE VOL. II: OUR NATIVE AMERICAN LEGACY
Max Ferguson; 234 pp. Paper. Amazon.com, 1997.

PEOPLE OF THE BLUE WATER: A RECORD OF LIFE AMONG THE WALAPAI & HAVASUPAI INDIANS
Flora G. Iliff; Reprint of 1954 edition. 271 pp. Paper. University of Arizona Press. $17.95.

*PEOPLE OF THE BUFFALO
Maria Campbell; Grades 5 and up. Paper. Salem House, $6.95.

PEOPLE OF THE CIRCLE: POWWOW COUNTRY
Chris Roberts; Paper. Amazon.com, 1998. $21.95

PEOPLE OF THE CRIMSON EVENING
Ruth Underhill
Papago life of long ago. Illus. 64 pp. Paper. Amazon.com & Alibris.com, $3.

PEOPLE OF THE DALLES: THE INDIANS OF THE WASCOPAM MISSION
Robert Boyd; History & culture of the Chinookan (Wasco-Wishram) & Sahaptan peoples in Oregon. Illus. Maps. 414 pp. University of Nebraska Press, 1996. $75; paper, $29.95.

THE PEOPLE OF DENEDEH: ETHNOHISTORY OF THE INDIANS OF CANADA'S NORTHWEST TERRITORIES
June Helm, et al; Photos. Maps. Charts & Tables. 412 pp. U. of Iowa Press, 2000. $42.

PEOPLE OF THE DESERT
Time-Life Books Eds.; 176 pp. Amazon.com, 1993. $25.95.

PEOPLE OF THE DESERT & SEA: ETHNOBOTANY OF THE SERI INDIANS
Richard Felger & Mary Moser; Illus. 435 pp. Paper. U. of Arizona Press, 1984. $40.

*PEOPLE OF THE EARTH
W. Michael Gear; Grades 2-5. Demco, 1992. $12.

*PEOPLE OF THE FIRE
W. Michael Gear; Grades 2-5. Demco, 1991. $12.

PEOPLE OF THE HIGH COUNTRY: JACKSON HOLE BEFORE THE SETTLERS
Gary Wright; Illus. 191 pp. Paper. Amazon.com, 1984. $20.

*PEOPLE OF THE ICE: HOW THE INUIT LIVED
Heather Siska; Grades 5 and up. Illus. Paper. Salem House, $6.95.

PEOPLE OF THE ICE & SNOW
Time-Life Books Eds.; Illus. 192 pp. Amazon.com, 1994. $25.95.

PEOPLE OF THE LAKE
Time-Life Books Eds.; Illus. 192 pp. Amazon.com 1994. $25.95.

*PEOPLE OF THE LAKES
W. Michael Gear; Grades 2-5. Demco, 1995. $12.

PEOPLE OF LEGEND: NATIVE AMERICANS OF THE SOUTHWEST
John Annerino; Illus. 144 pp. Amazon.com, 1996. $30.

*PEOPLE OF THE LIGHTNING
Kathleen O'Neal Gear; Grades 2-5. Demco, 1996. $12.

*PEOPLE OF THE LONGHOUSE: HOW THE IROQUOIAN TRIBES LIVED
Jillian & Robin Riddington; Grades 5 and up. Illus. Paper. Salem House, $9.95

PEOPLE OF THE MESA: THE ARCHAEOLOGY OF BLACK MESA, ARIZONA
Shirley Powell & George Gummerman
Illus. 200 pp. Amazon.com, 1987. $19.95.

PEOPLE OF THE MIDDLE PLACE: A STUDY OF THE ZUNI INDIANS
Dorothea Leighton & John Adair; 189 pp. Paper. Amazon.com, 1966. $15.

PEOPLE OF PASCUA
Edward H. Spicer; edited by Kathleen M. Sands & Rosamond B. Spicer
The history & culture of the Tucson area Yaqui. 331 pp. U. of Arizona Press, 1988. $48.

PEOPLE OF THE PEYOTE: HUICHOL INDIAN HISTORY, RELIGION & SURVIVAL
Stacy B. Schaefer & Peter T. Furst
Illus. 123 halftones, 1 map. 576 pp. Paper. University of New Mexico Press, $39.95.

PEOPLE OF THE RED EARTH: AMERICAN INDIANS OF COLORADO
Sally Crum; Revised 1996 edition. The history of the Ute, Shoshone, Comanche, Arapaho, and Cheyenne. Illus. Maps. Photos. 308 pp. Paper. Western Reflections Publishing, $29.95.

*PEOPLE OF THE RIVER
W. Michael Gear; Grades 2-5. Demco, 1993. $12.

PEOPLE OF THE SACRED MOUNTAIN: A HISTORY OF THE NORTHERN CHEYENNE CHIEFS & WARRIOR SOCIETIES, 1830-1879
Peter Powell; Two volumes. Illus. 1,376 pp. HarperCollins, 1981. $125 per set.

THE PEOPLE OF THE SAINTS
George Mills; Illus. Paper. Taylor Museum, 1967. $5.

THE PEOPLE OF SAN MANUEL
Clifford E. Trafzer; San Manuel Tribe, 2003.

*PEOPLE OF THE SEA
W. Michael Gear; Grades 2-5. Demco, 1994. $11.

PEOPLE OF THE SEVENTH FIRE: RETURNING LIFEWAYS OF NATIVE AMERICA
Dagmar Thorpe; A collection of personal stories from 20 Native American leaders. Illus. 237 pp. Paper. Akwe kon Press, 1996. $14.

PEOPLE OF THE SHINING MOUNTAINS: THE UTES OF COLORADO
Charles S. Marsh; Illus. 190 pp. Paper. Pruett Publishing, 1984. $11.95.

PEOPLE OF THE SHOALS: STALLINGS CULTURE OF SAVANNAH RIVER VALLEY
Kenneth E. Sassaman; foreword by Jerald T. Milanich; The rise and fall of the Stallings Island culture who occupied the Savannah River Valley of Georgia and South Carolina. Illus. Map. 224 pp. University Press of Florida, 2006. $39.95.

*PEOPLE OF THE SHORT BLUE CORN, TALES & LEGENDS OF THE HOPI INDIANS
Harold Coulander; Grades 4-7. Amazon.com, 1996. $15.05.

PEOPLE OF THE THREE FIRES
James Clifton, George Cornell & James McClurken; History, culture & dynamics of Michigan's Indigenous peoples: Ottawa, Potawatomi & Ojibway. Amazon.com, $14.95.

PEOPLE OF THE TONTO RIM: ARCHAEOLOGICAL DISCOVERY IN PREHISTORIC ARIZONA
Charles L. Redman, Ed.; Illus. 224 pp. Paper. Smithsonian Institution Press, 1993. $17.95

PEOPLE OF THE TOTEM: THE INDIANS OF THE PACIFIC NORTHWEST
Norman Bancroft-Hunt & Werner Forman
Reprint of 1979 edition. Illus. Map. 128 pp. Paper. University of Oklahoma Press, $24.95.

*PEOPLE OF THE TRAIL: HOW THE NORTHERN FOREST INDIANS LIVED
Jillian & Robin Ridington; Grades 5 and up. Illus. Paper. Salem House, $6.95.

PEOPLE OF THE TWILIGHT
Diamond Jenness; Reprint of 1959 edition. Paper. University of Chicago Press, $9.95.

PEOPLE OF THE WIND RIVER: THE EASTERN SHOSHONES, 1825-1900
Henry E. Stamm, IV; Illus. Maps. 272 pp. Paper. U. of Oklahoma Press, 1999. $19.95.

*THE PEOPLE SHALL CONTINUE
Simon Ortiz; illus. by Sharol Graves; Epic story of Native American peoples, a "teaching story." Grades 4-8. Illus. Amazon.com, 1987. $14.95.

THE PEOPLE SPEAK: NAVAJO FOLK ART
Chuck & Jan Rosenak; photos by Lynn Lown
Guide for collectors of Native American art. Illus. 160 pp. Amazon.com, $40.

THE PEOPLE WHO STAYED: SOUTHEASTERN INDIAN WRITING AFTER REMOVAL
Geary Hobson, Janet McAdams & Kathryn Walkiewicz; Anthology focusing on the literary works of Native Americans who trace their ancestry to "people who stayed" in southeastern states after 1830. 404 pp. Paper. University of Oklahoma Press, 2010. $24.95

THE PEOPLE & THE WORD: READING NATIVE NONFICTION
Robert Warrior; The history & impact of Native American nonfiction. Illus. 280 pp. University of Minnesota Press, 2005. $60; paper, $22.50.

A PEOPLE'S ARMY: MASSACHUSETTS SOLDIERS & SOCIETY IN THE SEVEN YEAR'S WAR Fred Anderson; Illus. 292 pp. U. of North Carolina Press, 1984. $27.50.

A PEOPLE'S DREAM: ABORIGINAL SELF-GOVERNMENT IN CANADA
Dan Russell; 260 pp. University of British Columbia Press, 2000.

A PEOPLE'S ECOLOGY: EXPLORATIONS IN SUSTAINABLE LIVING
Gregory Cajete (Santa Clara Tewa), Editor; Contributors examine the underlying ecology of sustainable living rooted in the historical traditions, environmental practices, and sense of place of Indigenous peoples; and explores possibilities of applying the principles in both non-Native and Native communities. Illus. 283 pp. Amazon.com, 1999. $14.95.

THE PEOPLE'S HEALTH: ANTHROPOLOGY & MEDICINE IN A NAVAJO COMMUNITY
John Adair, et al; Illus. 313 pp. U. of New Mexico Press, 1988. $27.50; paper, $14.95.

PEOPLES OF THE NORTHWEST COAST: THEIR ARCHAEOLOGY & PREHISTORY
Kenneth M. Ames & Herbert D. Maschner; Illus. 272 pp. Amazon.com, 1999. $45.

PEOPLES OF THE PLATEAU: THE INDIAN PHOTOGRAPHS OF LEE MOORHOUSE, 1898-1915 Steven L. Grafe; Pacific Northwest Indians @1900. Illus. 224 pp. Paper. University of Oklahoma Press, $29.95.

PEOPLES OF A SPACIOUS LAND: FAMILIES & CULTURES IN COLONIAL NEW ENGLAND Gloria L. Main; Illus. 336 pp. Amazon.com, 2001. $49.95; paper, $19.95.

PEOPLES OF THE TWILIGHT: EUROPEAN VIEWS OF NATIVE MINNESOTA, 1823-1862 Christian F. Feest; Amazon.com, 1998. $125.

PEOPLING INDIANA: THE ETHNIC EXPERIENCE
Robert Taylor, Jr. & Connie McBirney, Editors; Chapter on Native Americans by Elizabeth Glenn & Stewart Rafert. Illus. 800 pp. Indiana Historical Society, 1996. $39.95.

THE PEQUOT WAR
Alfred A. Cave; Analysis of the Pequot War, 1636-37. 232 pp. Paper. University of Massachusetts Press, 1996. $19.95.

THE PEQUOTS IN SOUTHERN NEW ENGLAND: THE FALL & RISE OF AN AMERICAN INDIAN NATION Laurence Hauptman & James Wherry Illus. Maps. 288 pp. Paper. University of Oklahoma Press, 1993. $21.95.

PERFORMING THE RENEWAL OF COMMUNITY: INDIGENOUS EASTER RITUALS IN NORTH MEXICO & SOUTHWEST U.S. Rosamond B. Spicer & N. Ross Crumrine, Eds. Examines the role of the Easter rituals in the Yaqui way of life in both Arizona & Sonora. 624 pp. Paper. University of Press of America, 1997. $82.50.

*PERIL AT THUNDER RIDGE
Anthony Dorame; Myron, a Native American teenager, conveys his people's philosophy that a balanced environment is crucial to man. Grades 6-10. Illus. 128 pp. Paper. Amazon.com, $9.95.

PERILOUS PURSUIT: THE U.S. CAVALRY & THE NORTHERN CHEYENNE
Stanley Hoig; Illus. 292 pp. University Press of Colroado, 2002. $34.95.

PERISHING HEATHENS: STORIES OF PRTESTANT MISSIONARIES & CHRISTIAN INDIANS IN ANTEBELLUM AMERICA
Julius H. Rubin; Illus. 276 pp. University of Nebraska Press, 2017. $50.

PERSISTENCE IN PATTERN IN MISSISSIPPI CHOCTAW CULTURE
Patti C. Black, Editor; Illus. 44 pp. Paper. Amazon.com, 1987. $9.95.

A PERSISTENT SPIRIT: TOWARDS UNDERSTANDING ABORIGINAL HEALTH IN BRITISH COLUMBIA Peter Stephenson, et al Editors
Illus. 450 pp. Paper. U. of Washington Press, 1996. $25.

A PERSISTENT VISION: ART OF THE RESERVATION DAYS
Richard Conn; Illus. 192 pp. Amazon.com, 1986. $35; paper, $19.95.

PERSONAL NARRATIVE OF JAMES O. PATTIE
James O. Pattie; Richard Batman, Editor; Frontier attitudes toward Indians and Mexicans. Illus. 216 pp. Mountain Press, $24.95; paper, $12.95.

PERSONAL RECOLLECTIONS & OBSERVATIONS OF GENERAL NELSON A. MILES
N.A. Miles; Revised 1896 edition. Illus. Amazon.com, $69.50.

PERSONAL RECOLLECTIONS OF THE SIOUX WAR: WITH THE 8TH MINNESOTA COMPANY F Thomas C. Hodgson; Illus. 55 pp. Paper. Amazon.com, 1999. $12.

PERSPECTIVES ON THE NORTH AMERICAN INDIANS
Mark Nagler, Editor; 302 pp. Paper. Random House, $19.95.

PERSPECTIVES ON NORTHERN NORTHWEST COAST PREHISTORY
Jerome S. Cybulski, Editor
Illus. Tables. Maps. 292 pp. Paper. University of Washington Press, 2001. $29.95.

**PERSPECTIVES ON THE SOUTHEAST: LINGUISTICS, ARCHAEOLOGY,
& ETHNOHISTORY** Patricia B. Kwachka; 11 essays focusing on questions relating to the distribution, organization, and relationships of southeastern Native American groups. Illus. Maps. University of Georgia Press, 1994. $40; paper, $20.

PESTILENCE & PERSISTENCE: YOSEMITE INDIAN DEMOGRAPHY & CULTURE IN COLONIAL CALIFORNIA Kathleen L. Hull; Illus. Map. 392 pp. University of California Press, 2009. $50.

PERVERSIONS OF JUSTICE: INDIGENOUS PEOPLES & ANGLOAMERICAN LAW
Ward Churchill; 300 pp. Amazon.com, 2003. $40; paper, $19.95.

PETROGLYPHS: ANCIENT LANGUAGE / SACRED ART
Sabra Moore; 101 drawings. 192 pp. Amazon.com, $19.95.

PETROGLYPHS OF OHIO
James L. Swauger; illus. by Carol A. Morrison
Illus. Maps. 340 pp. Amazon.com, 1984. $19.95.

PETROGLYPHS OF WESTERN COLORADO & THE NORTHERN UTE INDIAN RESERVATION AS INTERPRETED BY CLIFFORD DUNCAN
Carol Patterson; Illus. 164 pp. American Philosophical Society, $37.

PETROGLYPHS & PUEBLO MYTHS OF THE RIO GRANDE
Carol Patterson-Rudolph; Describes individual rock art symbols focusing on their meaning within the context of a language system. Illus. Photos. 162 pp. Paper. Amazon.com, 1991. $29.95.

THE PEYOTE BOOK: A STUDY OF NATIVE MEDICINE
Guy Mount, Compiler/editor; A collection of ancient legends, healing testimonials, spiritual & philosophical perceptions, songs, stories & illustrations inspired by the Good Medicine. 3rd edition. Illus. Biblio. 144 pp. Sweetlight, 1992. $9.95.

THE PEYOTE CULT
Weston La Barre; 5th Ed. Illus. 334 pp. Paper. U. of Oklahoma Press, 1989. $18.95.

PEYOTE: THE DIVINE CACTUS
Edward F. Anderson; Describes peyote ceremonies and the users' experiences, including use by the Native American Church. 2nd revised ed. Illus. 275 pp. University of Arizona Press, 1996. $55.95; paper, $19.95.

PEYOTE HUNT: THE SACRED JOURNEY OF HUICHOL INDIANS
Barbara Myerhoff; Illus. 285 pp. Paper. Cornell University Press, 1976. $23.95.

PEYOTE RELIGION: A HISTORY
Omer C. Stewart; Encyclopedic history. Illus. Maps. 454 pp. Paper.
University of Oklahoma Press, 1987. $24.95.

THE PEYOTE RELIGION AMONG THE NAVAHO
David F. Aberle; Reprint of 2nd Ed. Illus. Maps. 470 pp.
Paper. University of Oklahoma Press, 1991. $24.95.

PEYOTE RELIGIOUS ART: SYMBOLS OF FAITH & BELIEF
Daniel C. Swan; Illus. 112 pp. Amazon.com, 1999. $35.

THE PEYOTE ROAD: RELIGIOUS FREEDOM & THE NATIVE AMERICAN CHURCH
Thomas C. Maroukis; Examines the history of the Native American Church, including its legal struggles to defend the controversial use of Peyote. Illus. 296 pp. University of Oklahoma Press, 2009. $29.95; Paper, $19.95.

PEYOTE VS. THE STATE: RELIGIOUS FREEDOM ON TRIAL
Garrett Epps; Tracks the landmark case from 1990 when it was handed down to the present. 296 pp. Paper. University of Oklahoma Press, 2007. $19.95.

PEYOTE & THE YANKTON SIOUX: THE LIFE & TIMES OF SAM NECKLACE
Thomas C. Maroukis; Illus. 384 pp. U. of Oklahoma Press, 2004. $39.95; paper, $14.95.

PEYOTISM IN THE WEST: A HISTORICAL & CULTURAL PERSPECTIVE
Omer Stewart, Editor; Illus. 168 pp. Paper. University of Utah Press, 1984. $17.50.

PEYOTISM & NATIVE AMERICAN CHURCH, VOL. 45: ANNOTATED BIBLIOGRAPHY
Phillip M. White; Illus. 168 pp. Greenwood Publishing, 2000. $68.95.

*PHANTOM HORSE OF COLLISTER'S FIELDS
Gail Johnson; Grades 4-12. Paper. Council for Indian Education, 1974. $1.95.

PHOENIX. THE DECLINE & REBIRTH OF THE INDIAN PEOPLE
Wiliam E. Coffer; Illus. 281 pp. Paper. Amazon.com, $8.50.

THE PHOENIX INDIAN SCHOOL: FORCED ASSIMILATION IN ARIZONA, 1891-1935
Robert A. Trennert, Jr.; Illus. 256 pp. University of Oklahoma Press, 1988. $29.95.

PHOENIX RISING: NO EYES' VISION OF THE CHANGES TO COME
Mary Summer Rain; 176 pp. Paper. Hampton Roads Publishing, 1993. $11.95.

THE PHONETIC CONSITUENTS OF THE NATIVE LANGUAGES OF CALIFORNIA
A.L. Kroeber; Reprint of 1911 edition. 12 pp. Paper. Coyote Press, $1.56.

THE PHONETIC ELEMENTS OF THE DIEGUENO LANGUAGE
A.L. Kroeber & J.P. Harrington; Reprint 1911 ed. Illus. 11 pp. Paper. Coyote Press, $1.75.

THE PHONETIC ELEMENTS OF THE MOJAVE LANGUAGE
A.L. Kroeber ; Reprint of 1911 edition. Illus. 52 pp. Paper. Coyote Press, $6.56.

THE PHONETICS ELEMENTS OF THE NORTHERN PAIUTE LANGUAGE
T.T. Waterman; Reprint of 1911 edition. Illus. 33 pp. Paper. Coyote Press, $3.75.

PHOTOGRAPHIC GUIDE TO THE ETHNOGRAPHIC NORTH AMERICAN INDIAN BASKET COLLECTION VOL. 2: PEABODY MUSEUM OF ARCHAEOLOGY & ETHNOLOGY Susan H. Haskell, Ed.
Illus. 108 pp. Peabody Museum of Archaeology & Ethnology, 1998. $20.

PHONOLOGICAL ISSUES IN NORTH ALASKAN INUPIAQ
Lawrence D. Kaplan; 280 pp. Paper. Alaska Native Language Center, 1981. $15.

PHONOLOGICAL VARIATION IN WESTERN CHEROKEE
Lawrence Foley; 250 pp. Garland, 1980. $35.

PHONOLOGY OF ARIZONA YAQUI WITH TEXTS
Lynne S. Crumrine; Reprint of 1961 edition. 46 pp. University of Arizona Press, $19.95.

THE PHOTOGRAPH & THE AMERICAN INDIAN
Alfred L. Bush & Lee Clark Mitchell; Illus. 352 pp. Amazon.com, 1994. $75.

PHOTOGRAPHIC GUIDE TO THE ETHNOGRAPHIC NORTH AMERICAN INDIAN BASKET COLLECTION Susan H. Haskell, Ed.; Illus. 110 pp. Vol. 2. Peabody Museum of Archaeology, Harvard University Publications Dept., 1998. $20.

PHOTOGRAPHING NAVAJOS: JOHN COLLIER, JR. ON THE RESERVATION, 1948-1953 C. Stewart Doty, Dale Sperry Mudge, Herbert John Benally
Photos by John Collier, Jr. Illus. 232 pp. University of New Mexico Press, $39.95.

PIA TOYA: A GOSHUTE INDIAN LEGEND
Retold and illustrated by the children & teachers of Ibapah Elementary School.
University of Utah Press. $11.95.

PICKED APART THE BONES
Rebecca Hatcher Travis; Poetry...memories of author's Chickasaw family & the Oklahoma landscapes. 64 pp. University of Oklahoma Press, 2009. $14.95.

EDMUND PICKENS (OKCHANTUBBY): FIRST ELECTED CHICKASAW CHIEF, HIS LIFE & TIMES Juanita J. Keel Tate; Illus. 108 pp. Published by Chickasaw Press; distributed by the University of Oklahoma Press, 2009. $24.95.

SUSAN LA FLESCHE PICOTTE, M.D. OMAHA INDIAN LEADER & REFORMER
Benson Tong; Illus. 375 pp. University of Oklahoma Press, 1999. $29.95; paper, $18.95.

PICTOGRAPHIC HISTORY OF THE OGLALA SIOUX
Amos Brad Heart Bull and Helen Blish; Illus. 530 pp. U. of Nebraska Press, 1968. $35.

PICTORIAL WEAVINGS OF THE NAVAJOS
Nancy Schiffer; Over 200 photos of pictorial weavings. Paper. Schiffer, $12.95.

*A PICTURE BOOK OF SITTING BULL
David A. Adler; illus. by Samuel Byrd
Grades K-3. Illus. 32 pp. Holiday House, 1993. $15.95.

PICTURE ROCKS: AMERICAN INDIAN ROCK ART IN THE NORTHEAST WOODLANDS Edward J. Lenik
Illus. Tables. 288 pp. Paper. U. Press of New England, 2002. $70; paper, $29.95.

PICTURE-WRITING OF THE AMERICAN INDIANS
Garrick Mallery
Reprint. Two vols. 1,300 Illus. 822 pp. Paper. Dover & Written Heritage, $25.90/set.

PICTURES BRING US MESSAGES: PHOTOGRAPHS & HISTORIES FROM THE KAINAI NATION Alison K. Brown, Laura Peers
Illus. Photos. 420 pp. University of Toronto Press, 2005. $84; paper, $34.95.

PICTURES OF OUR NOBLER SELVES: A HISTORY OF NATIVE AMERICAN CONTRIBUTIONS TO THE MEDIA Mark N. Trahant
Traces the untold story of tribal & mainstream media beginning with the first Native American newspaper, The Cherokee Phoenix. Amazon.com, $10.

PICTURING FAITH: A FACSIMILE EDITION OF THE PICTOGRAPHIC QUECHUA CATECHISM IN THE HUNTINGTON
Barbara H. Jaye; Illus. 77 pp. University of Oklahoma Press, 2000. $24.95; paper, $14.95.

PICTURING INDIANS: PHOTOGRAPHIC ENCOUNTERS & TOURIST FANTASIES IN H.H. BENNETT'S WISCONSIN DELLS
Steven D. Hoelscher; The cultural politics of Ho-Chunk life & labor. Illus. Maps. 212 pp. University of Wisconsin Press, 2008. $39.95; paper, 24.95.

*PIECES OF WHITE SHELL: A JOURNEY TO NAVAJOLAND
Terry T. William; Grades 7-12. Illus. 176 pp. Paper. U. of New Mexico Press, $14.95.

PIEGAN
Richard Lancaster; Recollections of James White Calf (or "Hing Gun"), 109-year-old Chief of the Piegan tribe of the Blackfoot Nation. 359 pp. Paper. Doubleday, 1966.

PIIKANI BLACKFEET: A CULTURE UNDER SEIGE
John C. Jackson; Illus. 256 pp. Montain Press Publishing, 2000. $30.

A PILLAR OF FIRE TO FOLLOW: AMERICAN INDIAN DRAMAS, 1808-1859
Priscilla F. Sears; 149 pp. Bowling Green University Press, 1982. $11.95; paper, $5.95.

PIMA INDIAN BASKETRY: ILLUSTRATED WITH PHOTOGRAPHS FROM THE COLLECTION OF THE HEARD MUSEUM
H. Thomas Cain; Illus. 40 pp. Paper. The Heard Museum, 1962. $5.

PIMA INDIAN LEGENDS
Anna Moore Shaw; Reprint of 1968 edition. 111 pp. Paper. U. of Arizona Press, $13.95.

THE PIMA INDIANS
Frank Russell; The 1908 ethnography. Reprint of the 1975 edition. 496 pp. University of Arizona Press, $40.

THE PIMA INDIANS: PATHFINDERS FOR HEALTH
Jane Demouy, et al, Editors; Illus. 51 pp. Paper. Amazon.com, 1998. $15.

*THE PIMA-MARICOPA: SOUTHWEST
Henry Dobyns; Grades 5 and up. Illus. Chelsea House, 1989. $17.95.

A PIMA PAST
Anna Moore Shaw; 262 pp. Paper. University of Arizona Press, 1994. $17.95.

A PIMA REMEMBERS
George Webb; Recollections of childhood and Pima Indian lifeways. 126 pp. Paper. University of Arizona Press, 1959. $13.95.

PIMAN & PAPAGO RITUAL ORATORY
Donald M. Bahr; The author's personal relationship with the Pima & Papago. Illus. Paper. Amazon.com, 1975. $7.

PINE RIDGE 1890
William Fitch Kelley; An eye-witness account of the events surrounding the fighting at Wounded Knee. Reprint of the 1971 ed. Photos. Map. 267 pp. High-Lonesome Books, $30.

PINE RIDGE RESERVATION: A PICTORIAL DESCRIPTION
Ralph H. Ross, MD; Illus. 70 pp. paper. Lakota Books, 1996. $20.95.

PINE RIDGE RESERVATION: YESTERDAY & TODAY
Greg Gagnon & Karen White Eyes
Illus. 33 pp. Paper. Amazon.com, 1992. $2.95.

PEDRO PINO: GOVERNOR OF ZUNI PUEBLO, 1830-1878
E. Richard Hart; foreword by T.J. Ferguson
Illus. 200 pp. Paper. Utah State University Press, 2001. $17.95. E-book, $14.50.

PIONEER MISSIONARY TO THE BERING STRAIT ESKIMOS
Louis Renner, et al; Illus. Binford-Metropolitan, 1979. $12.50.

PIONEER OF THE MOJAVE: THE LIFE & TIMES OF AARON G. LANE
Richard D. Thompson & Kathryn L. Thompson
Illus. 210 pp. Cenotto Publications, 1995. $34.95.

PIONEERING IN MONTANA: THE MAKING OF A STATE, 1864-1887
Stuart Granville; Paul Phillips, Editor
Reprint of 1977 edition. Illus. 265 pp. U. of Nebraska Press, $21.50; paper, $7.95.

THE PIONEERS OF NEW FRANCE IN NEW ENGLAND
J.P. Baxter; Reprint of 1894 edition. 450 pp. Amazon.com, $25.

PIPE, BIBLE & PEYOTE AMONG THE OGLALA LAKOTA: A STUDY IN RELIGIOUS IDENTITY
Paul Steinmetz; 270 pp. Paper. Syracuse University Press, 1999. $19.95.

THE PIPE & CHRIST: A CHRISTIAN-SIOUX DIALOGUE
William Stolzman; Reprint. Illus. 4th Edition. 222 pp. Paper. Tipi Press & Center for Western Studies, 1992. $7.95.

A PIPE FOR FEBRUARY: A NOVEL
Charles H. Red Corn; Novel set against the turn of the century Osage Indians. Map. 272 pp. Paper. University of Oklahoma Press, 2002. $19.95.

PIPESTONE: MY LIFE IN AN INDIAN BOARDING SCHOOL
Adam Fortunate Eagle & Laurence M. Hauptman
248 pp. Paper. University of Oklahoma Press, 2009. $19.95.

THE PIPESTONE QUEST: A NOVEL
Don Coldsmith; Story of Beaver, a member of the Elk-dog People and his quest to undestand the mystifying power of the red pipestone. 272 pp. University of Oklahoma Press, 2004. $24.95.

PISSKAN: INTERPRETING FIRST PEOPLES BISON KILLS AT HERITAGE PARKS
Leslie Davis & John Fisher; Illus. Paper. University of Utah Press, 2016. $50; eBook, $40.

PITCH WOMAN & OTHER STORIES: THE ORAL TRADITIONS OF COQUELLE THOMPSON, UPPER COQUELLE ATHABASKAN INDIAN
William Seaburg, Editor; collected by Elizabeth Jacobs
Athabaskan Indians from southwestern Oregon. Illus. Photos. Map. 310 pp. Paper. University of Nebraska Press, 2007. $25.

PLACE FOR WINTER: PAUL TIULANA'S STORY
Vivian Senungetuk & paul Tiulane; 2nd ed. Illus. 150 pp. CIRI Foundation, 1989. $17.95.

PLACE NAMES OF ATLANTIC CANADA
William B. Hamilton; Amazon.com, 1996. $60; paper, $24.95.

PLACE NAMES OF ONTARIO
Alan Rayburn; Amazon.com, 1997. $55; paper, $21.95.

PLACE NAMES OF WISCONSIN
Edward Callary; Maps. 320 pp. Paper. University of Wisconsin Press, 2016. $21.95.

PLACE & NATIVE AMERICAN INDIAN HISTORY & CULTURE
Joy Porter; 394 pp. Paper. Peter Lang Publishing, 2007. $$89.95

THE PLACE OF THE PIKE: A HISTORY OF THE BAY MILLS INDIAN COMMUNITY
Charles E. Cleland
Illus. 165 pp. U. of Michigan Press, 2001. $29.95; paper, $19.95.

A PLACE TO BE NAVAJO: ROUGH ROCK & THE STRUGGLE FOR SELF-DETERMINATION IN INDIGENOUS SCHOOLING
Teresa L. McCarty; Illus. 248 pp. Paper. Amazon.com, 2002. $24.95.

PLACE & VISION: THE FUNCTION OF LANDSCAPE IN NATIVE AMERICAN FICTION
Robert W. Nelson; Explores the role of physical landscape in three contemporary Native American novels. 189 pp. Peter Lang, 1994. $39.95.

PLACES OF MEMORIES: WHITEMAN'S SCHOOLS & NATIVE AMERICAN COMMUNITIES Alan Peshkin; 160 pp. Amazon.com, 1997. $39.95; paper, $22.50.

PLAGUES, POLITICS, AND POLICY: A CHRONICLE OF THE INDIAN HEALTH SERVICE, 1955-2008 David H. DeJong; Examines the inadequacies of the healthcare provided to American Indians by the Indian Medical Service. Illus. 200 pp. Lexington Books, 2011.

THE PLAINS ACROSS: THE OVERLAND EMIGRANTS & THE TRANS-MISSISSIPPI WEST, 1840-60 John D. Unruh, Jr.; The overland journey on the Oregon Trail. 592 pp. Paper. University of Illinois Press, 1993. $37.

PLAINS APACHE ETHNOBOTANY
Julia A. Jordan; Documents more than 110 plant species valued by the Plains Apache and their use of these plant species. 240 pp. University of Oklahoma Press, 1997. $34.95.

A PLAINS ARCHAEOLOGY SOURCEBOOK: SELECTED PAPERS OF THE NEBRASKA STATE HISTORICAL SOCIETY Wald R. Wedie, Editor; 314 pp. Garland, 1985. $40.

THE PLAINS CREE: TRADE, DIPLOMACY & WAR, 1790 TO 1870
John S. Milloy; Paper. 178 pp. Paper. Michigan State University Press & Amazon.com, 1990. $28.95.

PLAINS INDIAN ART: THE PIONEERING WORK OF JOHN C. EWERS
Jane Ewers Robinson, Editor; Collection of Ewer's (1909-1997) writings presents studies first published in American Indian Art Magazine and other periodicals between 1968 and 1992. Illus. Map. 224 pp. University of Oklahoma Press, 2011. $39.95.

*THE PLAINS INDIAN BOOK
Donna Greenlee; Grades 1-5. About the Indians that live in tipis and hunt Buffalo. Illus. 32 pp. Paper. Amazon.com, $4.95.

PLAINS INDIAN CULTURE
O.J. Fargo; Illus. 50 pp. Paper. Green Valley Area, 1990. $1.50.

PLAINS INDIAN DESIGNS
Caren Caraway; Illus. 48 pp. Stemmer House, 1984. $5.95.

PLAINS INDIAN DRAWINGS, 1865-1935: PAGES FROM A VISUAL HISTORY
Janet C. Berlo, Ed.; Illus. 240 pp. Harry N. Abrams, 1996. $65.

PLAINS INDIAN HISTORY & CULTURE: ESSAYS ON CONTINUITY & CHANGE
John C. Ewers; Essays on Continuity and Change. Explores the role of women in Plains Indian life. Illus. Maps. 272 pp. U. of Oklahoma Press, 1997. $29.95; paper, $14.95.

PLAINS INDIAN & MOUNTAIN MAN ARTS & CRAFTS I & II: AN ILLUSTRATED GUIDE
Charles W. Overstreet; Vol. I - Explores the arts, crafts and other accoutrements made and used by the Plains Indians and Mountain men in the early 1800's. 45 projects ranging from rawhide to an Arapaho saddle. 100s of photos & drawings. Illus. 160 pp. $13.95; Vol. II - Features 40 projects ranging from a Blackfoot Fish Trap to a Wolf Hat in the style of the Wind River Shoshone. Illus. 112 pp. Paper. Eagle's View & Written Heritage, $13.95.

PLAINS INDIAN MYTHOLOGY
Alice Marriott & Carol Rachlin; A collection of traditional stories gleaned from oral sources, with poetry. Illus. 224 pp. Paper. Penguin USA, 1975. $4.95.

THE PLAINS INDIAN PHOTOGRAPHS OF EDWARD S. CURTIS
Edward S. Curtis
A collection of photos by Curtis. Illus. 175 pp. University of Nebraska Press, 2001. $50.

PLAINS INDIAN PORTRAITS & SCENES: 24 WATERCOLORS FROM THE JOSLYN ART MUSEUM Karl Bodmer; Illus. 16 pp. Paper. Dover Publications, 2004. $5.95.

PLAINS INDIAN RAIDERS: THE FINAL PHASES OF WARFARE FROM THE ARKANSAS TO THE RED RIVER
Wilbur S. Nye; Illus. Maps. 418 pp. Paper. University of Oklahoma Press, 1974. $21.95.

PLAINS INDIAN ROCK ART
James D. Keyser & Michael A. Klassen; Illus. Photos. Line drawings. Maps. 344 pp. Paper. University of Washington Press, 2001. $35.

PLAINS INDIAN SCULPTURE: A TRADITIONAL ART FROM AMERICA'S HEARTLAND
John C. Ewers; Illus. 240 pp. Paper. Smithsonian Books, 1986. $27.50.

*PLAINS INDIAN WARRIOR
R.A. May; Grades 3-8. Illus. 32 pp. Amazon.com, 1990. $14.

*PLAINS INDIANS
Kate Petty; Grades 3 and up. Illus. 32 pp. Franklin Watts, 1988. $10.40.

THE PLAINS INDIANS
Paul H. Carlson; Traces the culture and history of the Plains Indians from 1750 to 1890, relying heavily on Indian voices and an Indian viewpoint. Illus. Maps. 272 pp. Texas A&M University Press, 1999. $29.95; paper, $15.95.

THE PLAINS INDIANS
Colin F. Taylor; Covers the cultural diversity of many different tribes. Includes Blackfoot, Cheyenne, Sioux, Comanche, Crow, and others. 250 full-color and b&w illus. 240 pp. Random House, 1994. $25.

PLAINS INDIANS, A.D. 500-1500: THE ARCHAEOLOGICAL PAST OF HISTORIC GROUPS Karl H. Schlesier, Editor; Traces Indian ethnic continuity & cultural diversity in the Great Plains during the millennium preceding European arrival. Illus. Maps. Biblio. 480 pp. University of Oklahoma Press, 1994. $42.95; paper, $19.95.

*PLAINS INDIANS COLORING BOOK
David Rickman; Grades K-2. 48 pp. Paper. Dover, $2.95.

*PLAINS INDIANS: AN EDUCATIONAL COLORING BOOK
Grades 1-8. Illus. 32 pp. Paper. Spizzirri Publishing, 1981. $1.95.

*PLAINS INDIANS OF NORTH AMERICA
Robin May
Grades 4-8. Illus. 48 pp. 6 book set. Amazon.com, $75.96 per set; $12.66 each.

THE PLAINS INDIANS OF THE 20th CENTURY
Peter Iverson, Editor; 11 essays dealing with the complex cultural problems of the 20th century Plains Indian reservations. Illus. 288 pp. University of Oklahoma Press, 1985. $24.95; paper, $14.95.

*PLAINS INDIANS PUNCH-OUT PANORAMA
A.G. Smith; Construction of tribal settlement; pieces illustrate their way of life. 27 full-color pieces, and 4 b&w diagrams. Grades 3 and up. 12 pp. paper. Dover, $3.95.

PLAINS INDIANS REGALIA & CUSTOMS
Michael "Band Hand" Terry; An original study of Plains Indian cultures of the 19th century. Illus. 260 color photos. Documents the seven major tribes: Blackfeet, Cheyenne, Comanche, Crow, Hidatsa, Mandan & Lakota. 256 pp. Written Heritage, $49.95.

*PLAINS INDIANS WARS
Sherry Marker; Chronicles battles of the second half of the 19th century between Native Americans & the U.S. government. Grades 5-12. Illus. 128 pp. Facts on File, 1996. $17.95.

*PLAINS NATIVE AMERICAN LITERATURE
Grades 6-12. Paper. Teacher Ediition. Globe Fearon Educational Publishing, $8.95.

PLAINS SIOUX & U.S. COLONIALISM FROM LEWIS & CLARK TO WOUNDED KNEE
Jeffrey Ostler; Illus. 400 pp. Cambridge University Press, 2004. $65.

PLANNING FOR BALANCED DEVELOPMENT: A GUIDE FOR NATIVE AMERICAN & RURAL COMMUNITIES Susan Guyette; Uses the creation of the Poeh Center at Pojoaqua Pueblo in northern New Mexico as a case study. Illus. Photos. 324 pp. Amazon.com, 1996. $24.95; paper, $14.95.

PLANNING PROCESS ON THE PINE RIDGE & ROSEBUD INDIAN RESERVATION
Richard E. Brown; University of South Dakota, Government Research Bureau, 1969. $1.

PLANTING TAIL FEATHERS: TRIBAL SURVIVAL & PUBLIC LAW 280
Carolew Goldberg-Ambrose; 246 pp. Paper. UCLA, American Indian Studies Center, 1997. $15. Also available from Amazon.com.

PLANTS OF POWER: NATIVE AMERICAN CEREMONY & THE USE OF SACRED PLANTS Alfred Savinelli; Illus. 128 pp. Paper. The Book Publishing Co., 2002. $9.95.

PLANTS THAT WE EAT
Anore Jones; Guide to edible plant life of northwestern Alaska & the Inupiaq people. Illus. 150 pp. Paper. University of Chicago Press, 2008. $24.95.

PLANTS USED IN BASKETRY BY THE CALIFORNIA INDIANS
Ruth Merrill; Reprint. Illus. Acoma Books, 1980. $2.95.

·PLATEAU INDIANS
Craig & Katherine Doherty
Grades 5-8. Illus. 152 pp. Chelsea House, 2008. $35.

PLATEAU INDIANS & THE QUEST FOR SPIRITUAL POWER, 1700-1850
Larry Cebula; Illus. Maps. 195 pp. Paper. University of Nebraska Press, 2003. $19.95.

PLAY & INTER-ETHNIC COMMUNICATIONS: A PRACTICAL ETHNOGRAPHY OF THE MESCALERO APACHE Claire R. Farrer; Reprint. 205 pp. Garland, $10.

PLAYING THE FISH & OTHER LESSONS FROM THE NORTH
Robert J. Wolfe; Essays on nature, culture, and the human condition. 152 pp. Illus. Paper. University of Arizona Press, 2006. $15.95.

PLAYING INDIAN
Philip J. Deloria; Illus. 264 pp. Paper. Yale University Press, 1998. $23.

PLEASING THE SPIRITS: CATLOGUE OF A COLLECTION OF AMERICAN INDIAN ART Douglas C. Ewing; More than 500 objects of Native American art from across North America, Illus. 402 pp. University of Washington Press, 1992. $90.

THE PLEASURE OF THE CROWN: ANTHROPOLOGY, LAW & FIRST NATIONS
Dara Culhane; 416 pp. Amazon.com, 1998. $29.95.

PLENTY-COUPS, CHIEF OF THE CROWS
Frank B. Linderman; intro by Phenocia Bauerle & Barney Old Coyote, Jr. Reprint of 1962 edition. Illus. Map. 225 pp. Paper. U. of Nebraska Press, 2002. $18.95.

PLUNDER OF THE ANCIENTS: A TRUE STRY OF BETRAYAL, REDEMPTION, AND AN UNDERCOVER QUET TO RECOVER SACRED NATIVE AMERICAN ARTIFACTS, 1ST EDITION Lucinda Schroeder; 264 pp. Amazon.com, 2014. $22.95; eBook, $21.99.

PLUNDERED SKULLS & STOLEN SPIRITS: INSIDE THE FIGHT TO RECLAIM NATIVE AMERICA'S CULTURE Chip Colwell
Illus. 336 pp. The University of Chicago Press, 2017. $30; eBook, $18.

PO PAI MO: THE SEARCH FOR WHITE BUFFALO WOMAN
Robert Boissiere; Illus. 96 pp. Paper. Sunstone Press, 1983. $8.95.

POCAHONTAS
Ingri D'Aulaire; Paper. Doubleday, 1989. $7.95.

POCAHONTAS
Joseph Bruchac; Illus. Paper. Cherokee Publications, $6.99.

POCAHONTAS
Grace Steele Woodward; Reprint of 1969 edition. Illus. Map. Biblio. 228 pp. Paper. University of Oklahoma Press, $19.95.

POCAHONTAS & CO: THE FICTORIAL AMERICAN INDIAN WOMAN IN 19th CENTURY LITERATURE: A STUDY OF METHOD
Asebrit Sundquist; 350 pp. Humanities Press, 1986. $39.95.

*POCAHONTAS COLORING BOOK
Doherty & Kliros; Grades K-3. 48 pp. Paper. Dover, $2.95.

*POCAHONTAS: DAUGHTER OF A CHIEF
Grades K-3. Illus. 48 pp. Childrens Press, $11.95.

*POCAHONTAS, GIRL OF JAMESTOWN
Kate Jassem; Grades 3-7. Illus. 48 pp. Paper. Troll Associates, 1979. $3.50.

POCAHONTAS (In the Words of Her Contemporaries)
Stuart E. Brown, Jr.
Reprint of 1989 ed. Illus. Map. 34 pp. Paper. Genealogical Publishing Co., 2006. $12.95.

POCAHONTAS: THE LIFE & LEGEND
Frances Mossiker; Reprint. Illus. 424 pp. Paper. Amazon.com, $18.

POCAHONTAS: POWHATTAN PEACEMAKER
Anne Holler; Illus. Biblio. 104 pp. Written Heritage, $14.95.

POCAHONTAS' DESCENDANTS
Stuart E. Brown, Jr., et al.
Enlarged revised reprint of 1887 edition. 715 pp. Genealogical Publishing, 2003. $50.

POCAHONTAS'S PEOPLE: THE POWHATAN INDIANS OF VIRGINIA
Helen Rountree; Illus. 416 pp. U. of Oklahoma Press, 1990. $29.95; paper, $14.95.

THE POETRY & POETICS OF GERALD VIZENOR
Deborah L. Madsen, Editor; 280 pp. University of New Mexico Press, $50.

THE POINT ELLIOTT TREATY, 1855
Lynn Kickingbird & Curtis Berkey; 28 pp. Institute for the Development of Indian Law, $9.

THE POINT-NO-POINT TREATY, 1855
Lynn Kickingbird & Curtis Berkey; 29 pp. Institute for the Development of Indian Law, $9.

POINT OF PINES, ARIZONA: A HISTORY OF THE UNIVERSITY OF ARIZONA ARCHAEOLOGICAL FIELD SCHOOL
Emil W. Haury; 140 pp. University of Arizona Press, 1989. $19.95.

POISON ARROWS: NORTH AMERICAN INDIAN HUNTING & WARFARE
David E. Jones; Examines evidence of the use of toxins. Paper. 144 pp. University of Texas Press, 2007. $19.95.

POLICING IN INDIAN COUNTRY
Michael Barker; 150 pp. Paper. Willow Tree Press, 1998. $22.50.

POLICING ON AMERICAN INDIAN RESERVATIONS
Stewart Wakeling; Illus. 86 pp. Paper. Amazon.com, 2002. $25.

POLICING RACE & PLACE IN INDIAN COUNTRY: OVER-AND-UNDER-ENFORCEMENT
Barbara Perry; Monograph. Lexington Books, c/o Rowman & Littlefield, 2009. $75.

THE POLITICAL ECONOMY OF NORTH AMERICAN INDIANS
John H. Moore, Editor; Collection of articles on macroeconomics & intercultural conflict. Illus. 320 pp. University of Oklahoma Press, 1993. $29.95.

THE POLITICAL OUTSIDERS: BLACKS & INDIANS IN A RURAL OKLAHOMA COUNTY Brian F. Rader; Paper. R & E Research Associates, 1978. $13.95.

POLITICAL PRINCIPLES & INDIAN SOVEREIGNTY
Thurman Lee Hester; 144 pp. Garland, 2001. $65.

POLITICAL STRUCTURE & CHANGE IN THE PREHISTORIC SOUTHEASTERN U.S.
John F. Scarry, Editor; Illus. 304 pp. University Press of Florida, 1996. $59.95.

POLITICS & AESTHETICS IN CONTEMPORARY NATIVE AMERICAN LITERATURE: ACROSS EVERY BORDER Matthew Herman; Illus. 142 pp. Routledge, 2009. $85.50.

POLITICS & ETHNICITY ON THE RIO YAQUI: POTAM REVISITED
Thomas R. McGuire; Yaqui culture. 186 pp. University of Arizona Press, 1986. $32.

POLITICS & THE MUSEUM OF THE AMERICAN INDIAN: THE HEYE & THE MIGHTY
Roland W. Force; Illus. 504 pp. Amazon.com, 1999. $45.

THE POLITICS OF ALLOTTMENT ON THE FLATHEAD INDIAN RESERVATION
Burton M. Smith; 32 pp. Paper. SKC Press, $5.

THE POLITICS OF HALLOWED GROUND: WOUNDED KNEE & THE STRUGGLE FOR INDIAN SOVEREIGNTY Mario Gonzalez & Elizabeth Cook-Lynn
Illus. 360 pp. University of Illinois Press, 1998. $49.95; paper, $19.95.

THE POLITICS OF INDIAN REMOVAL: CREEK GOVERNMENT & SOCIETY IN CRISES
Michael D. Green; Illus. 250 pp. University of Nebraska Press, 1982. $22.50.

THE POLITICS OF SECOND GENERATION DISCRIMINATION IN AMERICAN INDIAN EDUCATION INCIDENCE, EXPLANATION & MITIGATING STRATEGIES
David E. Wright, III, et al; 192 pp. Greenwood Publishing, 1998. $49.95.

POLITICS & POWER: AN ECONOMIC & POLITICAL HISTORY OF THE WESTERN PUEBLO Steadman Upham; Amazon.com, 1982. $24.50.

THE POLLEN PATH: A COLLECTION OF NAVAJO MYTHS
Retold by M.S. Link; Reprint of 1956 ed. Illus. 210 pp. Amazon.com, $19.50.

*THE POMO
Suzanne Freedman; Grades 5-8. Illus. 32 pp. Amazon.com, 1997. $21.27

POMO BASKETMAKING - A SUPREME ART FOR THE WEAVER
Elsie Allen; Step-by-step instructions for recreating beautiful & useful baskets. Illus. Photos. 67 pp. Paper. Naturegraph, $9.95.

POMO DOCTORS & POISONERS
L.S. Freeland; Reprint of 1923 edition. 18 pp. paper. Coyote Press, $2.19.

POMO INDIAN BASKETRY
Samuel A. Barrett; illus. intro. by Sherri Smith-Ferri; 2nd Edition. Reprint of 1908 edition. Illus. Photos. 276 pp. Paper. Hearst Museum of Anthropology, 1996. Distributed by University of Washington Press, $30.

*POMO INDIANS OF CALIFORNIA & THEIR NEIGHBORS
Vinson Brown; Albert Alsasser, Editor
Grades 4-12. Illus. 64 pp. Paper. Naturegraph, 1969. $9.95.

POMO LANDS ON CLEAR LAKE
E.W. Gifford; Facsimile edition. 16 pp. Paper. Coyote Press, $2.19.

PONCA SOCIETIES & DANCES
Alanson Skinner; 24 pp. paper. Lakota Books, 1998. $8.95.

THE PONCA TRIBE
James H. Howard; Illus. 215 pp. Paper. University of Nebraska Press, 1995. $17.95.

THE POND DWELLERS: HISTORY OF FRESHWATER PEOPLE OF MASS., 1620-1676
Kelly Savage; 368 pp. Paper. Amazon.com, 1996. $13.95.

*PONTIAC: CHIEF OF THE OTTAWAS
Jane Fleischer; Demco, 1979. $8.70.

PONTIAC'S CONSPIRACY & OTHER INDIAN AFFAIRS: NOTICES ABSTRACTED FROM COLONIAL NEWSPAPERS, 1763-1765
Armand Francis Lucier; 330 pp. Paper. Heritage Books, 2001. $27.50.

PONY TRACKS
F. Remington
Reprint of 1961 edition. Illus. 178 pp. Paper. University of Oklahoma Press, $12.95.

HORACE POOLAW, PHOTOGRAPHER OF AMERICAN INDIAN MODERNITY
Laura E. Smith; foreword by Linda Poolaw
Illus. 232 pp. University f Nebraska Press, 2016. $45.

POPULATION CHANGES AMONG THE NORTHERN PLAINS INDIANS
Clark Wissler; Bound with: "Cultural Relations of the Gila River & Lower Colorado Tribes," by Leslie Spier; "Hopi Huntingn & Hunting Ritual," by Ernest Beaglehole; "Navaho Warfare," by W.W. Hill; "The Economy of a Modern Teton Dakota Community," by Mekeel H. Scudder; and "The Distribution of the Northern Athapaskan Indians." Reprinted from the 1936 edition. Amazon.com, $15.

POPULATION MOBILITY & INDIGENOUS PEOPLES IN AUSTRALASIA & NORTH AMERICA John Taylor & Martin Bell, Editors; Illus. 304 pp. Routledge, 2004. Text, $104.

THE PORCUPINE HUNTER & OTHER STORIES: THE ORIGINAL TSIMSHIAN TEXTS OF HENRY TATE Henry W. Tate; Ralph Maud, Ed.; 176 pp. U of Toronto Press, 1994. $14.95.

THE PORTABLE NORTH AMERICAN INDIAN READER
Frederick W. Turner, III; Third Edition. A collection of myths, tales, poetry, speeches, and passages from Indian autobiographies, and recent writings. 640 pp. Penguin USA, 1977. $9.95.

PORTAGE LAKE: MEMORIES OF AN OJIBWE CHILDHOOD
Maude Kegg; edited & transcribed by John Nichols; A child's view of traditional Anishinaabe lifeways coming into contact with Euro-American settlers. 272 pp. Paper. University of Minnesota Press, 1993. $17.95.

PORTFOLIO II
Kathryn Stewart; Illus. 50 pp. Amazon.com, 1988.

PORTRAIT INDEX OF NORTH AMERICAN INDIANS IN PUBLISHED COLLECTIONS
Patrick Frazier, Library of Congress; Identifies & indexes hundreds of pictures, prints, drawings, and lithographs of Native American portraits contained in 75 sources.Illus. Biblio. 142 pp. Paper. U.S. GPO, $16.

PORTRAITS FROM NORTH AMERICAN INDIAN LIFE: ORIGINAL PORTFOLIO EDITION Edward S. Curtis; BBS Publishing, 1990. $39.99.

PORTRAITS OF NATIVE AMERICANS: PHOTOGRAPHS FROM THE 1904 LOUISIANA PURCHASE EXPOSITION Charles H. Carpenter; Turn-of-the-century images of Native Americans, in a postcard format. Illus. 48 pp. Paper. Amazon.com, 9.95.

PORTRAITS OF THE WHITEMAN
Keith Basso; 130 pp. Paper. Cambridge University Press, 1979. $12.95.

ALEX POSEY: CREEK POET, JOURNALIST, & HUMORIST
Daniel F. Littlefield, Jr.; Illus. Map. 330 pp. Paper. U. of Nebraska Press, 1992. $16.95.

POSEY: THE LAST INDIAN WAR
Dr. Steve Lacy, Pearl Baker; Historical narrative recounts the events that led to the 1923 Indian war between the Ute Indians and the white settlers of the Bluff, Blanding, and San Juan River regions of southeastern Utah. Illus. 208 pp. Paper. Amazon.com, 2007. $18.95.

POSITIONING THE MISSIONARY: JOHN BOOTH GOOD & THE COLONIAL CONFLUENCE OF CULTURES
Brett Christophers; Illus. 224 pp. U. of Washington Press, 1999. $83; paper, $35.95.

POST TRIBAL EPICS: THE NATIVE AMERICAN NOVEL BETWEEN TRADITION & MODERNITY Giorgio Mariani; 280 pp. The Edwin Mellen Press, 1997. $89.95.

POSTCOLUMBIAN CULTURE HISTORY IN THE NORTHERN COLUMBIA PLATEAU A.D. 1500-1900 Sarah K. Campbell; Illus. 246 pp. Garland, 1990. $60.

POSTINDIAN CONVERSATIONS
Gerald Vizenor & A. Robert Lee; Collection of in-depth interviews with Gerald Vizenor and his critical perspectives on important issues affecting Native peoples in the late 20th century. 192 pp. Paper. University of Nebraska Press, 1998. $6.25.

*POTAWATOMI
James A. Clifton; Grades 5 and up. Illus. 105 pp. Chelsea House, 1988. $17.95.

*THE POTAWATOMI: GREAT LAKES
Grades 7-12. Illus. 112 pp. Amazon.com, $16.95.

POTAWAOMI INDIANS OF MICHIGAN, 1843-1904, INCLUDING SOME OTTAWA & CHIPPEWA, 1843-1866, & POTAWATOMI OF INDIANA, 1869 & 1885
Raymond C. Lantz; Covers annuity rolls on the Ottawa, Chippewa & Potawatomi of Michigan and Indiana. Roll numbers are given. 92 pp. Paper. Amazon.com, 1992. $14.

POTAWATOMI TRAIL OF DEATH - INDIANA TO KANSAS
Shirley Willard & Susan Campbell, Editors
448 pp. Maps. Bib. Paper. Amazon.com, 2003. $40.

POTAWATOMIS: KEEPERS OF THE FIRE
R. David Edmunds; Illus. 374 pp. Paper. University of Oklahoma Press, 1978. $24.95.

POTLATCH AT GITSEGUKLA: WILLIAM BEYNON'S 1945 FIELD NOTEBOOKS
Margaret Anderson & Marjorie Halpin, Editors; Covers 5 totem pole raisings at Gitsegukla & the field notes he compiled there. Includes a glossary of Gitksan words. Illus. 256 pp. UBC Press, 1999. $75.

POTLATCH: NATIVE CEREMONY & MYTH ON THE NORTHWEST COAST
Mary G. Beck; Illus. 128 pp. Paper. Amazon.com, 1993. $12.95.

THE POTLATCH PAPERS: A COLONIAL CASE HISTORY
Christopher Bracken
Illus. Photos. Maps. 283 pp. University of Chicago Press, 1997. $62.50; paper, $30.

POTLATCH PEOPLE: INDIAN LIVES & LEGENDS OF BRITISH COLUMBIA
Mildred Valley Thornton; Illus. 320 pp. Paper. Hancock House Publishers, 2001. $19.95.

POTTERY BY AMERICAN INDIAN WOMEN: THE LEGACY OF GENERATIONS
Susan Peterson, et al.; 224 pp. Paper. Abbeville Press, 1997.

THE POTTERY FROM ARROYO HONDO PUEBLO: TRIBALIZATION & TRADE IN THE NORTHERN RIO GRANDE Judith A. Habicht-Mauche
Includes The Stone Artifacts from Arroyo Hondo Pueblo, by Carl J. Phagan. Illus. Maps. Biblio. Paper. School of American Research, 1990. $30.

POTTERY OF THE GREAT BASIN & ADJACENT AREAS
Suzanne Griset; Illus. 170 pp. Paper. University of Utah Press, 1986. $17.50.

THE POTTERY OF SANTA ANA PUEBLO
Francis H. Harlow, Duane Anderson & Dwight Lanmon
Illus. Photos. Museum of New Mexico, 2004. $45.

THE POTTERY OF ZIA PUEBLO
Francis H. Harlow & Dwight Lanmon
Illus. 372 pp. School of American Research Press, 2003. $59.95.

THE POTTERY OF ZUNI PUEBLO
Dwight P. Lanmon & Frances Harlow
Illus. Photos. 616 pp. Museum of New Mexico, 2008. $150.

POTTERY & PEOPLE: A DYNAMIC INTERACTION
James M. Skibo & Gary M. Feinman; Illus. University of Utah Press, $55; paper, $25.

POTTERY & PRACTICE: THE EXPRESSION OF IDENTITY AT POTTERY MOUND & HUMMINGBIRD PUEBLO Suzanne L. Eckertt
Examines decorated pottery and its production in prehistoric New Mexico. Illus. halftones, 6 maps. 216 pp. University of New Mexico Press, $34.95.

POTTERY TECHNIQUES OF NATIVE NORTH AMERICA: AN INTRODUCTION TO TRADITIONAL TECHNOLOGY
John K. White; University of Chicago Press, 1976. $46. Includes four-color text-fiches.

POWER & GENDER IN ONEONTA CULTURE: A STUDY OF A LATE PREHISTORIC PEOPLE Thomas F. Berres; Illus. 265 pp. Paper. Amazon.com, 2003. $35.

POWER IN THE BLOOD: A FAMILY NARRATIVE
Linda Tate; Traces the author's journey to rediscover the Cherokee-Appalachian branch of her family & examines poverty, discrimination, & family violence. 256 pp. Amazon.com, 2009. $37.95; paper, $22.95.

THE POWER OF FOUR: LEADERSHIP LESSONS OF CRAZY HORSE
Joseph Marshall III; Sterling Publishing, 2009.

THE POWER OF HORSES & OTHER STORIES
Elizabeth Cook-Lynn; 144 pp. Paper. University of Arizona Press, 2006. $15.95.

THE POWER OF KIOWA SONG: A COLLABORATIVE ETHNOGRAPHY
Luke E. Lassiter; Illus. 270 pp. Paper. University of Arizona Press, 1998. $18.95.

THE POWER OF NATIVE TEACHERS: LANGUAGE & CULTURE IN THE CLASSROOM
David Beaulieu & Anna Figueira, Editors; Center for Indian Education.

POWER OF A NAVAJO: CARL GORMAN: THE MAN & HIS LIFE
Henry & Georgia Greenberg; intro. by R.C. Gorman; Biography of artist, merchant, patriot, and respected Navajo leaders and spokesman. Illus. 224 pp. Amazon.com, 1996. 24.95; paper, $14.95.

THE POWER OF SILENCE
Carlos Castaneda; Jane Rosenman, Editor; 290 pp. Amazon.com, 1991. $8.95.

THE POWER OF SONG: MUSIC & DANCE IN THE MISSION COMMUNITIES OF NORTHERN NEW SPAIN, 1590-1810
Kristin Dutcher Mann; Study on the music of Franciscan & Jesuit missions in the Northern New Spain frontier territories. Illus. Maps. 300 pp. Stanford University Press & Amazon.com, 2010.

POWER & PERFORMANCE IN GROS VENTRE WAR EXPEDITION SONGS
Orin T. Hatton; Illus. 79 pp. Paper. University of Washington Press, 1990. $14.95.

POWER & PLACE
Daniel Wildcat, Vine Deloria, Jr.; Contains 16 essays examining the issues facing Native American students. 176 pp. Paper. Fulcrum Publishing, $17.95.

THE POWER OF PROMISES: RETHINKING INDIAN TREATIES IN THE PACIFIC NORTHWEST
Alexandra Harmon; Maps. 384 pp. U. of Washington Press, 2008. $65; paper, $29.95.

POWER QUEST: THE JOURNEY INTO MANHOOD
Carol Betdorf; Illus. 224 pp. Paper. Hancock House, $12.95.

POWERFUL IMAGES: PORTRAYALS OF NATIVE AMERICA
Sara E. Boehme; Illus. 160 pp. Paper. University of Washington Press, 1998. $50.

POWHATAN FOREIGN RELATIONS 1500-1722
Helen C. Rountree, Editor; Examines the Powhatans and their relationships with both European & Indian "foreigners". 321 pp. Amazon.com, 1993. $35.

THE POWHATAN INDIANS OF VIRGINIA: THEIR TRADITIONAL CULTURE
Helen Rountree; Illus. Maps. 230 pp. Paper. U. of Oklahoma Press, 1992. $19.95.

POWHATAN LORDS OF LIFE & DEATH: COMMAND & CONSENT IN 17TH CENTURY VIRGINIA Margaret Holmes Williamson
Illus. Maps. 344 pp. Paper. University of Nebraska Press, 2003. $19.95.

*THE POWHATAN TRIBES: MIDDLE ATLANTIC
Christina Feest; Grades 5 and up. Illus. Chelsea House, 1989. $17.95.

POWHATAN'S MANTLE: INDIANS IN THE COLONIAL SOUTHEAST
Peter Wood, Gregory Waselkov & M. Thomas Hatley; Revised & expanded edition. Illus. Maps. 554 pp. Paper. University of Nebraska Press, 1989. $21.95.

POWHATAN'S WORLD & COLONIAL VIRGINIA: A CONFLICT OF CULTURES
Frederic W. Gleach; Illus. 243 pp. University of Nebraska Press, 1997. $70; paper, $22.

POWWOW
Clyde Ellis, Luke Eric Lassiter, Gary Dunham
314 pp. University of Nebraska Press, 2005. $19.95.

POWWOW
A young Indian boy, Red Elk, explains what is happening at the Powwow celebration. Illus. 32 pp. Paper. Cherokee Publications, $3.95.

*POW-WOW
Mimi Chenfeld and Marjorie Vandervelds
Grades 5-12. Paper. Council for Indian Education, 1972. $2.95.

*POWWOW
George Ancona; Grades 3-5. Young Anthony Standing Rock as he participates in the Crow Fair in Montana, as a traditional dancer. Meadowlark Communications, $9.

POWWOW
K.R. Johnstone & Gloria Nahanee; Illus. 144 pp. Hancock House, 2003. $39.95.

*POWWOW ACTIVITY BOOK
Sandy & Jesse Hummingbird; Ages 5-10. Illus. 28 pp. Paper. Amazon.com, $4.95.

POWWOW CALENDAR: DIRECTORY OF NATIVE AMERICAN GATHERINGS IN THE USA & CANADA Liz Campbell, Editor; Lists, month-by-month, Native American powwows, dances, crafts fairs and other cultural events. Annual. Illus. 160 pp. Paper. The Book Publishing Co., $9.95.

POWWOW COUNTRY
Chris Roberts; Overview of the powwow circuit and what it means to Indian people. 100 photos taken at Montana powwows. Text & photos. by Chris Roberts. Paper. Meadowlark Communications, 1993. $19.95.

POWWOW COUNTRY: PEOPLE OF THE CIRCLE
Chris Roberts; A sequal to Powwow Country, 1993. Explores the powwow world. In-depth look at the people, the changes & trends influencing American Indian culture today. Includes powwow events & activities from several major national powwows. 120 color photos. Biblio. 128 pp. Paper. Meadowlark Communications, 1998. $21.95.

POWWOW DANCER'S & CRAFTWORKER'S HANDBOOK
Adolf Hungry Wolf; Historical photos of turn-of-century powwows. Illustrations show step-by-step how to make the outfits worn today. Illus., photos. 144 pp. Paper. Book Publishing Co. & Written Heritage, 1999. $19.95.

THE POWWOW HIGHWAY
David Seals; An up-to-date account of being Indian in America. 304 pp. Paper. Sky & Sage Books, 1996. $17.

POWWOW: ON THE RED ROAD
Fred Synder
Lists over 870 American Indian events in the U.S. & Canada. Native American Co-Op, $25.

POWWOW: & OTHER YAKAMA INDIAN TRADITIONS
Helen Willard; 23 stories. Illus. 128 pp. Roza Run, 1990. $29.95; paper, $19.95.

THE POWWOW TRAIL: UNDERSTANDING & ENJOYING THE NATIVE AMERICAN POW WOW Julia C. White; illus. by Diana E. Stanley; Guide to the activities at pow wows including dances and dancers. Illus. 112 pp. Book Publishing Co. & Amazon.com, $8.95.

*POWWOW: IMAGES ALONG THE RED ROAD
Ben Marra
Grades 4 and up. 105 portraits of powwow dancers. Meadowlark Communications, $16.95.

*POWWOW SUMMER: A FAMILY CELEBRATES THE CIRCLE OF LIFE
Marcie R. Rendon; Cheryl Walsh Bellville, Illus.; Grades 1-5. An Anishinabe (Ojibway) family travel to two powwows. Illus. 48 pp. Lerner, 1996. $7.95.

*POWWOW'S COMING
Linda Boyden; Cut-paper collage illustrations and verse. Grades K-5. 30 color illus. 32. University of New Mexico Press, $17.95.

A PRACTICAL GRAMMAR OF THE ST. LAWRENCE ISLAND: SIBERIAN YUP'IK ESKIMO LANGUAGE
Steven A. Jacobson; 105 pp. Paper. Alaska Native Language Center, 1990. $10.

PRAIRIE CITY: THE STORY OF AN AMERICAN COMMUNITY
Angie Debo; foreword by Rennard Strickland
Reprint. Illus. 276 pp. Paper. University of Oklahoma Press, 1998. $17.95.

PRAIRIE FIRE: A GREAT PLAINS HISTORY
Julie Courtwright; Traces the history of both natural & intentional fires from Native American practices to the current use of controlled burns as an effective land management tool. Illus. Map. 264 pp. University Press of Kansas, 2011. $29.95.

*PRAIRIE LEGENDS
M. Earring, et al; Grades 6-9. Paper. Council for Indian Education, 1978. $2.95.

THE PRAIRIE PEOPLE: CONTINUITY & CHANGE IN POTAWATOMI INDIAN CULTURE, 1665-1965 James A. Clifton
Photos. Drawings. 568 pp. Paper. University of Iowa Press, 1998. $27.50.

THE PRAIRIE WAS ON FIRE: EYEWITNESS ACCOUNTS OF THE CIVIL WAR IN THE INDIAN TERRITORY
Whit Edwards; Illus. 200 pp. Oklahoma Historical Society, 2001. $24.95.

PRAYER ON TOP OF THE EARTH: THE SPIRITUAL UNIVERSE OF THE PLAINS APACHES Kay Parker Schweinfurth; University Press of Colorado, 2002. $29.95.

PRAYER TO THE GREAT MYSTERY: THE UNCOLLECTED WRITINGS & PHOTOGRAPHY OF EDWARD S. CURTIS Gerald Housman & Bob Kapoun, Eds. Ilus. 228 pp. Paper. St. Martin's Press, 1997. $17.95.

PRAYERS & MEDITATIONS OF THE QUERO APACHE
Maria Yraceburu, photos by; Illus. 192 pp. Paper. Inner Traditions, 2004. $15.

*THE PRAYING FLUTE: SONG OF THE EARTH MOTHER
Tony Shearer; Grades 4 and up. 96 pp. Paper. Naturegraph, 1988. $16.95.

A PRAYING PEOPLE: MASSACHUSETTS ACCULTURATION & THE FAILURE OF THE PURITAN MISSION, 1600-1690
Dane Morrison; 2nd revised edition. Paper. Amazon.com, 1998. $32.95.

PRE-COLUMBIAN AMERICA: RITUAL ARTS OF THE NEW WORLD
Octavio Paz; Illus. 408 pp. Abbeville Press, 2000. $67.50.

PRE-COLUMBIAN ART
Elizabeth P. Benson, Editor; University of Chicago Press, 1976. $25.

PRE-COLUMBIAN ART FROM THE LAND COLLECTION
Alana Cordy-Collins & H.B. Nicholson; L. K. Land, Editor
Illus. 275 pp. Paper. California Academy of Sciences, 1979. $25.'

PRE-COLUMBIAN ART & THE POST COLUMBIAN WORLD: ANCIENT AMERICAN SOURCES OF MODERN ART
Barbara Braun; Illus. 340 pp. Paper. Harry N. Abrams, 2000. $34.95.

PRE-COLUMBIAN ARCHITECTURE IN THE EASTERN U.S.
Morgan; A source for information on the major prehistoric earthworks east of the Mississippi. Illus. 272 pp. Paper. University Press of Florida, 1980. $19.95.

PRE-REMOVAL CHOCTAW HISTORY: EXPLORING NEW PATHS
Greg O'Brien, Editor; Essays. 256 pp. University of Oklahoma Press, 2010. $39.95.

PRE-SEMINOLE FLORIDA: SPANISH SOLDIERS, FRIARS & INDIAN MISSIONS, 1513-1763 Robert M. Matter; Reprint. 208 pp. Garland, $10.

PREHISTORIC BIOLOGICAL RELATIONSHIP IN THE GREAT LAKES REGION
Richard Wilkinson
Illus. Paper. University of Michigan, Museum of Anthropology, 1971. $3.50.

PREHISTORIC CULTURE CHANGE ON THE COLORADO PLATEAU: TEN THOUSAND YEARS ON BLACK MESA
edited by Shirley Powell & Francis E. Smiley; Study of the ancestral Puebloan and navajo occupation of the Four Corners region. Illus. 221 pp. U. of Arizona Press, 2002. $50.

PREHISTORIC CULTURES OF THE SOUTHWEST: ANASAZI, HOHOKAM, MOGOLLON, SALADO, SINAGUA Rose Houk
Illus. 5 Vols. 16 pp. each. Paper. Western National Park Association, 1992. $3.95 each.

PREHISTORIC EXCHANGE & SOCIOPOLITICAL DEVELOPMENT IN THE PLATEAU SOUTHWEST Amy A. Douglass; Reprint. Illus. 396 pp. Amazon.com, 1990. $80.

PREHISTORIC HOUSEHOLDS AT TURKEY CREEK PUEBLO, ARIZONA
Julie Lowell; Illus. 95 pp. Paper. University of Arizona Press, 1991. $25.95.

PREHISTORIC HUNTERS OF THE HIGH PLAINS
George Frison; Reprint of 1978 edition. Illus. 2nd Edition. 460 pp. Amazon.com, $73.

PREHISTORIC INDIAN ROCK ART: ISSUES & CONCERNS
Jo Anne Van Tilburg & Clement Meighan, Editors
Illus. 66 pp. Paper. UCLA Institute of Archaeology, 1981. $6.

PREHISTORIC INDIAN TOOLS, POINTS & ARROWHEADS
Gary W. Henschel; Rosalie Henschel & Denise Krebs, Editors
Illus. 102 pp.Paper. Henschel's Indian Museum, 1996. $11.95.

PREHISTORIC INDIANS
Barnes & Pendleton; A guide to understanding the early Indian cultures of the Four Corners (AZ, NM, UT, CO) area. Includes artifacts, cultures, rock art and ruins. Illus. 256 pp. Paper. Amazon.com, 1988. $9.50.

PREHISTORIC INDIANS OF THE SOUTHEAST: ARCHAEOLOGY OF ALABAMA & THE MIDDLE SOUTH John Walthall; Illus. 288 pp. U. of Alabama Press, 1980. $25.

PREHISTORIC INDIANS OF THE SOUTHWEST
H.M. Wormington; Covers the Mogollon, Hohokam & Anasazi cultures. Reprint of 1947 edition. Illus. Photos. Maps. 191 pp. High-Lonesome Books, $10.

PREHISTORIC INDIANS OF WISCONSIN
Robert Ritzenthaler; Third revised edition. Illus. 62 pp. Paper. Amazon.com, 1985. $7.95.

PREHISTORIC LAND USE & SETTLEMENT OF THE MIDDLE LITTLE COLORADO RIVER VALLEY Richard C. Lange; Survey of the Homolovi Ruins State Park. 175 pp. paper. University of Arizona Press, 1998. $17.95.

PREHISTORIC LIFEWAYS IN THE GREAT BASIN WETLANDS
Brian Hemphill & Clark Spencer Larsen, Ed.; Illus. 450 pp. U. of Utah Press, 1999. $45.

PREHISTORIC LITHIC INDUSTRY AT DOVER, TENNESSEE
Richard M. Gramly; An investigation of quarries and workshops used by lithic craftsmen of the Mississippian archaeological culture, the Flintkappers of Dover. Illus. 150 pp. Paper. Amazon.com, $21.95.

PREHISTORIC MAN ON THE GREAT PLAINS
Waldo Wedel; Illus. University of Oklahoma, 1961. $28.95.

PREHISTORIC MESOAMERICA
Richard E.W. Adams
Revised 1991 edition. Illus. Maps. Paper. University of Oklahoma Press, $18.95.

PREHISTORIC NATIVE AMERICAN ART OF MUD GLYPH CAVE
Charles H. Faulkner, Editor; Illus. Paper. Amazon.com, $15.

PREHISTORIC NATIVE AMERICANS & ECOLOGICAL CHANGE: HUMAN ECOSYSTEMS IN EASTERN & NORTH AMERICA SINCE THE PLEISTOCENE
Paul A. Delcourt & Hazell R. Delcourt; Illus. 216 pp. Cambridge U. Press, 2004.$90.

PREHISTORIC PAINTED POTTERY OF SOUTHEASTERN ARIZONA
Robert A. Heckman, et al.; Published by Statistical Research, Inc.
Illus. 197 pp. Paper. Distributed by The University of Arizona Press, 1999. $35.

THE PREHISTORIC PEOPLES OF MINNESOTA
Elden Johnson
Revised edition. Illus. 35 pp. Paper. Minnesota Historical Society Press, 1988. $3.95.

PREHISTORIC PEOPLES OF SOUTH FLORIDA
William E. McGoun; 176 pp. Paper. University of Alabama Press, 1993. $19.95.

PREHISTORIC PIPES
Ahlstrom; Pipes found at northern Ohio's Reeve village site.
Photos. 145 pp. Amazon.com, 1979. $14, postpaid.

PREHISTORIC PUEBLO WORLD, A.D. 1150-1350
Michael A. Adler, Ed.; 278 pp. Paper. University of Arizona Press, 1996. $26.95.

PREHISTORIC ROCK ART
Barnes; Guide to the prehistoric and historic petroglyphs and pictographs of the Four Corners and Great Basin. Illus. 304 pp. Paper. Amazon.com, 1986. $11.25, postpaid.

PREHISTORIC SANDALS FROM NORTHEASTERN ARIZONA: THE EARL H. MORRIS & ANN AXTELL MORRIS RESEARCH
Kelly Ann Hays-Gilpin, Ann Cordy Deegan & Elizabeth Ann Morris
Illus. 168 pp. Paper. University of Arizona Press, 1998. $17.95.

PREHISTORIC SOUTHWESTERNERS FROM BASKETMAKER TO PUEBLO
C.A. Amsden; Reprint of 1949 ed. Illus. Maps. 165 pp. Paper. Southwest Museum, $5.

PREHISTORIC WARFARE IN THE AMERICAN SOUTHWEST
Steven A. LeBlanc; Illus. 400 pp. University of Utah Press, 1999. $45.

PREHISTORIC WARFARE ON THE GREAT PLAINS: SKELETAL ANALYSIS OF THE CROW CREEK MASSACRE P. Willey; Illus. 240 pp. Amazon.com, 1990. $60.

PREHISTORIC WEAPONS IN THE SOUTHWEST
Stewart Peckham; Illus. Paper. Museum of New Mexico Press, 1965. $1.50.

PREHISTORY IN THE NAVAJO RESERVOIR DISTRICT
Frank W. Eddy; Illus. Paper. Museum of New Mexico Press, 1966. Two parts, $8.95 each.

PREHISTORY OF THE AMERICAS
Stuart J. Fiedel; 2nd revised edition. Illus. 420 pp.
Cambridge University Press, 1992. $90; paper, $33.

THE PREHISTORY OF THE BURNT BLUFF AREA
James E. Fitting, Editor; Paper. U. of Michigan, Museum of Anthopology, 1968. $3.

THE PREHISTORY OF THE CHICKAMAUGA BASIN IN TENNESSEE, 2 VOLS.
Thomas Lewis & Madeline Kneberg Lewis; Developed the first comprehensive descriptions of the Native American cultures that lived near what is now the city of Chattanooga before the time of European contact. U. of Tennessee Press, 2005. $50 ea.; paper, $25. each

THE PREHISTORY OF COLORADO & ADJACENT AREAS
Tammy Stone; 214 pp. Univesity of Utah Press, 1999. $17.50.

THE PREHISTORY OF FISHTRAP, KENTUCKY
R.C. Dunnell; Paper. Yale University, Anthropology, 1972. $7.

PREHISTORY OF THE RUSTLER HILLS: GRANADO CAVE
Donny L. Hamilton, Editor; The lifeways of prehistoric peoples of the Northeastern Trans-Pecos region of Texas. Illus. Tables. 316 pp. University of Texas Press, 2001. $55.

PREPARING INDIAN STUDENTS FOR COLLEGE
Dean Chavers, Editor; 127 pp. Catching the Dream. 2002. $39.95.

PRESBYTERIAN MISSIONARY ATTITUDES TOWARD AMERICAN INDIANS, 1837-1893 Michael C. Coleman; Based upon correspondence of missionaries in the field. Illus. 222 pp. Amazon.com, 1985. $32.

PRESENT IS PAST: SOME USES OF TRADITION IN NATIVE SOCIETIES
Marie Mauz, Editor
Collection of essays. Illus. 408 pp. U. of Press of America, 1997. $54.50; paper, $35.

PRESENT STATE OF NEW ENGLAND
Co Mather; Reprint of 1690 edition. Haskell House, $59.95.

PRESERVING THE SACRED: HISTORICAL PERSPECTIVES OF THE OJIBWA MIDEWIWIN Michael Angel
274 pp. Michigan State University Press, 2002. $59.95; paper, 28.95.

PRESERVING TRADITIONAL ARTS: A TOOLKIT FOR NATIVE AMERICAN COMMUNITIES Susan Dyal; 205 pp. UCLA, American Indian Studies Center, 1985. $20.

PRESERVING WHAT IS VALUED: MUSEUMS, CONSERVATION, & FIRST NATIONS
Miriam Clavir; Illus. 320 pp. University of Washington Press, 2002. $105; paper, $35.95.

PRESIDENT POLK'S TREATIES WITH NATIVE AMERICANS
Joy Love; 54 pp. Paper. Wonder Words Publishing, 2001. $12.

PRESIDENT WASHINGTON'S INDIAN WAR: THE STRUGGLE FOR THE OLD NORTHWEST, 1790-1795
Wiley Sword; Illus. 432 pp. University of Oklahoma Press, 1985. $39.95.

PRESSING ISSUES OF INEQUALITY & AMERICAN INDIAN COMMUNITIES
Elizabeth Segal & Keith Kilty, Editors; 98 pp. Amazon.com & Alibris.com, 1998. $29.95.

THE PRETEND INDIANS - IMAGES OF NATIVE AMERICANS IN THE MOVIES: AN ANALYTICAL SURVEY OF 20TH CENTURY INDIAN ENTERTAINERS
Gretchen Bataille & Charles Silent; Iowa State University Press, 1978.

PRETTY-SHIELD
Frank B. Linderman; Reprint. Illus. 256 pp. Amazon.com, 1993. $24.95.

PRETTY-SHIELD, MEDICINE WOMAN OF THE CROWS
Frank B. Linderman; illus by Herbert Morton Stoops; An Indian woman's side of life. Reprint of 1932 edition. Illus. 224 pp. Paper. University of Nebraska Press, 2003. $14.95.

A PRETTY VILLAGE: DOCUMENTS OF WORSHIP & CULTURE CHANGE, ST. IGNATIUS MISSION, MONTANA, 1880-1889
Robert J. Bigart, Editor; The Salish & Kootenai of the Flathead Indian Reservation. Photos. Images. 352 pp. Paper. University of Nebraska Press, 2007. $19.95.

THE PRICE OF A GIFT: A LAKOTA HEALER'S STORY
Gerald Mohatt & Joseph Eagle Elk; Eagle Elk's (1931-91) story of his life, practice, and beliefs. Illus. Map. 230 pp. Paper. University of Nebraska Press, 2000. $14.95.

PRIDE OF THE INDIAN WARDROBE: NORTHERN ATHAPASKAN FOOTWEAR
Judy Thompson; 198 pp. Amazon.com, 1990. $49.50; paper, $25.

THE PRIMAL MIND: VISION & REALITY IN INDIAN AMERICA
Jamake Highwater; Examines Indian ritual, art, oral traditions, architecture, and ceremonial dance and how it comes into contact and conflict with the "civilized" Western world. Reprint edition. 255 pp. Paper. Relplica Books, 1999. $29.95.

PRIMARY CARE OF NATIVE AMERICAN PATIENTS: DIAGNOSIS, THERAPY & EPIDEMIOLOGY James M. Galloway, et al
Illus. 410 pp.Paper. Amazon.com, 1998. $56.95.

PRIMER OF NORTH AMERICAN INDIAN POTTERY & RESTORATION TERMS
Darrel Wilson, Editor; Illus. 24 pp. Paper. Darrel Wilson, 1997. $8.

PRIMITIVE ART
Franz Boas; Reprint. 376 pp. Paper. Dover, $9.95.

PRIMITIVE ARTS & CRAFTS
Roderick U. Sayce; Reprint of 1993 ed. Illus. Biblo-Moser. $24.

PRIMITIVE MAN IN OHIO
W.K. Moorehead; Reprint of 1892 edition. 246 pp. Amazon.com. $46.50, postpaid.

PRIMITIVE PRAGMATISTS: THE MODOC INDIANS OF NORTHERN CALIFORNIA
Verne V. Ray; Illus. University of Washington Press, 1963. $11.50.

*****PRINCESS SCARGO AND THE BIRTHDAY PUMPKIN: NATIVE AMERICAN LEGEND**
Eric Metaxas; Illus. 48 pp. Audiocassette. Amazon.com, 1996.

PRINCIPLES OF NATIVE AMERICAN SPIRITUALITY
Dennis Renault & Timothy Freke; Illus. 160 pp. Paper. Amazon.com, 1996. $11.

PRISON OF GRASS: CANADA FROM A NATIVE VIEWPOINT
Howard Adams; Adams, PhD & leader in the Canadian Native rights movement. Updated edition. Amazon.com & Alibris.com, $18.95.

PRISON WRITINGS: MY LIFE IS MY SUN DANCE
Leonard Peltier; Harvey Arden, Ed.
2nd Ed. Illus. 270 pp. St. Martin's Press, 1999. $23.95; paper, $14.95.

PRIVILEGING THE PAST: RECONSTRUCTING HISTORY IN NORTHWEST COAST ART Judith Ostrowitz; Illus. 264 pp. University of Washington Press, 1999. $40.

THE PROBLEM OF JUSTICE: TRADITION & LAW IN THE COAST SALISH WORLD
Bruce G. Miller; Ethnographic study of the Coast Salish communities along the northwest coast of North America. Illus. 240 pp. U. of Nebraska Press, 2001. $60; paper, $19.95.

PROCEEDINGS OF THE FORT CHIPEWYAN/FORT VERMILLION BICENTENNIAL CONFERENCE, SEPT. 23-24, 1988, EDMONTON, ALBERTA
Patricia McCormack & R. Geoffrey Ironside, Editors
Focuses on the Aboriginal beginnings, histories, present conditions, and future prospects of the regions. Illus. 319 pp. CCI, $25.

PROCEEDINGS OF THE GREAT PEACE CONFERENCE
Institute for the Development of Indian Law, $10.

PROCEEDINGS OF THE 1973 HOHOKAM CONFERENCE
Donald Weaver, Jr., Susan Burton & Minnabell Laughlin, Compilers & Editors
Monograph documenting two days of intensive discussions on Hohokam archaeology. Maps. 105 pp. Amazon.com, $12 (postpaid).

PROCEEDINGS OF THE HOKAN LANGUAGES WORKSHOP
J.E. Reden, Editor; Reprints. Coyote Press.

PROCEEDINGS OF THE HOKAN-YUMAN LANGUAGES WORKSHOP HELD AT THE UNIVERSITY OF CALIFORNIA J.E. Reden, Editor; Reprints. Coyote Press.

PROFILES IN WISDOM: NATIVE ELDERS SPEAK ABOUT THE EARTH
Steven McFadden, Ed.; Illus. 256 pp. Paper. Inner Traditions International, 1991. $12.95.

PROGRESSIVE TRADITIONS: IDENTITY IN CHEROKEE LITERATURE & CULTURE
Joshua B. Nelson; 296 pp. University of Oklahma Press, $34.95.

PROJECTILE POINTS OF THE MIDWEST: A FIELD GUIDE
Noel D. Justice & Suzanne Kudlaty
Illus. 60 pp. Paper. Amazon.com, 1999. $12.

PROJECTILE POINT GUIDE FOR THE UPPER MISSISSIPPI RIVER VALLEY
Robert F. Boszhardt; Illus. 80 pp. Paper. University of Iowa Press, 2003. $14.95.

PROLOGUE TO LEWIS & CLARK: THE MACKEY & EVANS EXPEDITION
W. Raymond Wood; Illus. 235 pp. University of Oklahoma Press, 2003. $34.95.

PROMISES OF THE PAST: A HISTORY OF INDIAN EDUCATION IN THE U.S.
David H. DeJong; 304 pp. Paper. University of Arizona Press, 1993. $19.95.

PROMISING PRACTICES & STRATEGIES TO REDUCE ALCOHOL & SUBSTANCE ABUSE AMONG AMERICAN INDIANS & ALASKA NATIVES
Janet Reno, foreword; Illus. 54 pp. Paper. Amazon.com, 2001. $20.

PROPERTY CONCEPTS OF THE NAVAHO INDIANS
B. Haile; Reprint of 1954 edition. Paper. St. Michaels, $6.

PROPERTY RIGHTS & INDIAN ECONOMIES
Terry L. Anderson, Ed.; 320 pp. Rowman & Littlefield Publishers, 1992. $48.50.

PROPHECY & POWER AMONG THE DOGRIB INDIANS
June Helm; Illus. 173 pp. University of Nebraska Press, 1994. $50.

PROPHECY ROCK
Rob MacGregor; Novel. Visiting his Hopi tribal police chief father, Will Lansa is drawn into an unusual murder investigation that may be linked to a powaqu, a powerful witch, and the mystery brings Will closer to his Hopi heritage. 208 pp. Paper. Random House, Laurel Leaf Books, 1998. $9.95.

PROPHETIC WORLDS: INDIANS & WHITES ON THE COLUMBIA PLATEAU
Christopher L. Miller
Reprint of 1985 edition. Map. 192 pp. Paper. U. of Washington Press, 2003. $22.95.

PROPHETS OF THE GREAT SPIRITS: NATIVE AMERICAN REVITALIZATION MOVEMENTS IN EASTERN NORTH AMERICA
Albert A. Cave; 328 pp. University of Nebraska Press, 2006. $27.95.

PROTECTING ABORIGINAL CHILDREN
Christopher Walmsley; Aboriginal child welfare in British Columbia.
Tables. 176 pp. Paper. University of Washington Press, 2005. $33.95.

THE PROTECTOR DE INDIOS IN COLONIAL NEW MEXICO, 1659-1821
Charles R. Cuttler
Illus. 140 pp. University of New Mexico Press, 1986. $17.50; paper, $8.95.

PROTO-ATHAPASKAN VERB STEM VARIATION: PART ONE: PHONOLOGY
Jeff Leer; 100 pp. Paper. Alaska Native Language Center, 1979. $5.

PROTO-WINTUN
Alice Shepherd; 264 pp. Paper. University of California Press, 2006. $45.

THE PROTOHISTORIC PUEBLO WORLD, A.D. 1275-1600
edited by Charles Adams & Andrew I. Duff; Describes and interprets this period of southwestern history. Illus. 260 pp. University of Arizona Press, 2004. $50.

PROUD TO BE CHICKASAW
Mike Larsen & Martha Larsen; Portraits & essays offer insight into living elders of the Chickasaw Nation. Illus. 130 pp. Published by the Chickasaw Press; distributed by the University of Oklahoma Press, 2010. $25.

THE PROVIDERS
Stephen Irwin; Illus. 296 pp. Paper. Hancock House, 1984. $12.95.

PSYCHOCULTURAL CHANGE & AMERICAN INDIAN: ETHNOHISTORICAL ANALYSIS
Laurence French; Garland, 1987. $34.

PSYCHOLOGICAL RESEARCH ON AMERICAN INDIAN & ALASKA NATIVE YOUTH: AN INDEXED GUIDE TO DISSERTATIONS
Spero M. Manson, et al, Editors; Illus. 230 pp. Greenwood, 1984. $36.95.

PSYCHOLOGY OF INDIANS OF NORTH AMERICA: INDEX OF NEW INFORMATION WITH AUTORS, SUBJECTS & BIBLIOGRAPHIC REFERENCES
Swedlo A. Sampos; 150 pp. Paper. ABBE Publishers, 1996. $47.50; paper, $44.50.

*PTEBLOKA; TALES FROM THE BUFFALO
M. Grant Two Bulls
Grades 3 and up. Illus. 20 cartoons. 24 pp. Paper. Dakota Press, 1991. $3.

PUBLIC INDIANS, PRIVATE CHEROKEES: TOURISM & TRADITION ON TRIBAL GROUND Christina Taylor Beard-Moose; Presents the two faces of the Eastern Cherokee people constructing an ethnohistory of tourism. Illus. 296 pp. University of Alabama Press, 2008. $50.75; paper, $29.95. E-Book, $23.96.

*A PUEBLO
Tito E. Naranjo; Grades 4-9. Runestone Press (Amazon books), 1999.

*PUEBLO
Mary D'Apice; Grades 5-8. Illus. 32 pp. Amazon.com, 1990. $9.95.

*THE PUEBLO
Alfonso Ortiz
A history of the people. Grades 7 and up. Illus. Chelsea House Publishers, 1989. $17.95.

*THE PUEBLO
Charlotte Yue; Grades 4-7. Paper. Amazon.com, 1990. $4.95.

PUEBLO ARCHITECTURE & MODERN ADOBES: THE RESIDENTIAL DESIGNS OF WILLIAM LUMPKINS Joseph Traugott; Pueblo source materials. Illus. 144 pp. Paper. Museum of New Mexico Press, 2000, $29.95.

PUEBLO ARTISTS: PORTRAITS
Toba Pato Tucker; Essays by Alfred L. Bush, Rina Swentzell, and Lonnie Vigil. Lives and traditions of over 140 Pueblo artists. 160 pp. Illus. Museum of New Mexico Press, 2001. $55; paper, $35.

PUEBLO BIRDS & MYTHS
Hamilton A. Tyler; Discusses birds place in Pueblo ritual, ceremony, myth, and folklore. Illus. Biblio. 280 pp. Paper. Northland Press,1979. $19.95.

*PUEBLO BOY: GROWING UP IN TWO WORLDS
Marcia Keegan; Grades 3 and up. Illus. 48 pp. Amazon.com, $14.95.

THE PUEBLO CHILDREN OF THE EARTH MOTHER
Thomas E. Mails; Details the history, customs, and accomplishments of the Pueblo Indians of AZ and NM. Reprint. Illus. 544 pp. Paper. Avalon Publishing, 1998. $29.95.

PUEBLO CRAFTS
Ruth Underhill; Willard Beatty, Editor
Reprint of 1944 edition. Illus. Map. 148 pp. Paper. R. Schneider, Publishers, $7.95.

PUEBLO CULTURES
B. Wright; Illus. 30 pp. Paper. Brill, 1986. $36.75.

PUEBLO DESIGNS: 176 ILLUSTRATIONS OF THE RAIN BIRD
H.R. Mera; drawings by Tom Lea
Reprint of 1970 edition. Illus. 115 pp. Amazon.com.

*PUEBLO GIRLS: GROWING UP IN TWO WORLDS
Marcia Keegan
Grades 3 and up. Illus. 60 color photos. 48 pp. Amazon.com, $14.95.

PUEBLO GODS & MYTHS
Hamilton Tyler; Reprint of 1964 edition. Illus. Map. 312 pp. Paper. University of Oklahoma Press & Amazon.com, $15.95.

PUEBLO, HARDSCRABBLE, GREENHORN: SOCIETY ON THE HIGH PLAINS, 1832-1856 Janet Lecompte
Reprint of 1977 edition. Illus. Maps. 354 pp. Paper. University of Oklahoma Press, $25.95.

PUEBLO IMAGINATION
Lee Marmon; Illus. 160 pp. Amazon.com, 2003. $35.

*PUEBLO INDIAN
Steven Cory; Grades 4-7. Illus. 48 pp. Lerner, 1996. $15.95.

PUEBLO INDIAN AGRICULTURE
James A. Vlasich
History of Pueblo Indian agriculture. Illus. 384 pp. University of New Mexico Press, $45.

PUEBLO INDIAN COOKBOOK
Compiled & edited by Phyllis Hughes
Illus. 64 pp. Paper. Museum of New Mexico Press, $11.95.

PUEBLO INDIAN EMBROIDERY
N.R. Mera; Illus. 80 pp. Paper. Dover, 1975. $6.95.

PUEBLO INDIAN EMBROIDERY ARTISTS: WE DANCE WITH THEM
Marian E. Rodee; Illus. Paper. School of American Research, 2001. $19.95.

PUEBLO INDIAN FOLK-STORIES
Charles F. Lummis; Seven elders tell folk-stories. Illus. 257 pp. Paper. University of Nebraska Press & Amazon.com, 1992. $12.

PUEBLO INDIAN PAINTING:
TRADITIONS & MODERNISM IN NEW MEXICO. 1900-1930
J.J. Brody; Winner of the 1998 Benjamin Franklin Award. Illus. Map. 238 pp. School for Advanced Research, 1997. $60; paper, $34.95.

PUEBLO INDIAN POTTERY
Francis H. Harlow & Jack Silverman; Silverman Museum, 2001.

PUEBLO INDIAN POTTERY: 750 ARTIST BIOGRAPHIES
Gregory Schaaf; Richard M. Howard, Editor
Illus. 200 pp. Center for Indigenous Arts & Cultures (CIAC) Press, 2000. $55.

PUEBLO INDIAN RELIGION
Elsie Clews Parsons; Illus. Map. In 2 vols. Vol. 1, 577 pp., Vol. 2, 760 pp. Paper. University of Nebraska Press, $25 each.

PUEBLO INDIAN REVOLT OF 1696 & THE FRANCISCAN MISSIONS IN NEW MEXICO: LETTERS OF THE MISSIONARIES & RELATED DOCUMENTS
J. Manuel Espinosa, translated & edited ; Portrait of the conflict between Franciscan missionary zeal and the Pueblo holy men. Illus. Maps. 314 pp. Paper. University of Oklahoma Press, $19.95.

PUEBLO INDIAN TEXTILES: A LIVING TRADITION
Kate P. Kent; Illus. 136 pp. Paper. School of American Research & University of Washington Press, 1983. $16.95.

THE PUEBLO INDIANS
Joe Sando; The history of the Pueblos; includes the constitution of the All Indian Pueblo Council. Illus. 246 pp. Paper. Amazon.com, 1976. $12.25.

*PUEBLO INDIANS
Liza N. Burby; Grades 4 and up. Demco, 1994. $13.15.

THE PUEBLO INDIANS OF NORTH AMERICA
Edward P. Dozier; Reprint. Illus. 224 pp. Paper. Waveland Press, 1970. $21.50.

PUEBLO INDIANS & SPANISH COLONIAL AUTHORITY IN 18TH CENTURY NEW MEXICO Tracy L. Brown; 248 pp. Illus. University of Arizona Press, 2013. $55.

PUEBLO & MISSION: CULTURAL ROOTS OF THE SOUTHWEST
Susan Lamb; photos by Chuck Place; The events, practices and iconography of the people of the Southwest. 140 photos. Biblio. 160 pp. Paper. Amazon.com, 1997. $19.95.

PUEBLO MOTHERS & CHILDREN: ESSAYS BY ELSIE CLEWS PARSONS, 1915-1924
Barbara Babcock, Editor; Illus. Maps. 150 pp. Amazon.com, $29.95; paper, $17.95.

PUEBLO: MOUNTAIN, VILLAGE, DANCE
Vincent Scully; Pueblo ceremonial dances. 2nd Ed. Illus. 575 halftones. 430 pp. University of Chicago Press, 1989. $95; paper, $39.

PUEBLO NATIONS: EIGHT CENTURIES OF PUEBLO INDIAN HISTORY
Joe S. Sando; Illus. 49 photos. Maps. 295 pp. Amazon.com, 1991. $24.95; paper, $14.95.

PUEBLO & NAVAJO CONTEMPORARY POTTERY & DIRECTORY OF ARTISTS
Guy Berger & Nancy N. Schiffer
Revised edition. Illus. 170 pp. Paper. Schiffer Publishing, 2004. $29.95.

PUEBLO & NAVAJO INDIAN LIFE TODAY
Kris Hotvedt; Revised ed. of Fry Breads, Feast Days and Sheep. Illus. 64 pp. Paper. Sunstone Press, $8.95.

PUEBLO PEOPLE: ANCIENT TRADITIONS, MODERN LIVES
Marcia Keegan; 417 color photos. 264 pp. Amazon.com, $39.95.

PUEBLO PEOPLES ON THE PAJARITO PLATEAU: ARCHAEOLOGY & EFFICIENCY
David E. Stuart; Focuses on the archaeology of Bandelier National Monument and the surrounding area. Illus. Photos. 224 pp. Paper. U. of New Mexico Press, 2010. $21.95

THE PUEBLO POTTER: A STUDY OF CREATIVE IMAGINATION IN PRIMITIVE ART
Ruth L. Bunzel; Reprint of 1926 edition. Illus. 134 pp. Amazon.com

PUEBLO POTTERY DESIGNS
Kenneth M. Chapman; Illus. 208 pp. Paper. Dover, $9.95.

PUEBLO POTTERY FIGURINES:
THE EXPRESSION OF CULTURAL PERCEPTIONS IN CLAY Patricia Fogelman Lange; Illus. 176 pp. U. of New Mexico Press, 2002. $45.

PUEBLO POTTERY OF THE NEW MEXICO INDIANS
Betty Toulouse; Illus. 150 bxw photos; 11 color plates. 96 pp.
Paper. Museum of New Mexico Press, 1977. $12.95.

PUEBLO PROFILES: CULTURAL IDENTITY THROUGH CENTURIES OF CHANGE
Joe S. Sando; Tells the stories of political leaders, educators, and artists who took part in the events and movements that have shaped Pueblo Indian life from the time of the Pueblo Revolt to the present day. Illus. 320 pp. Paper. Amazon.com, 1994. $24.95; paper, $14.95.

THE PUEBLO REVOLT
Robert Silverberg; intro. by Marc Simmons
Map. 216 pp. Paper. University of Nebraska Press, 1994. $14.95.

**THE PUEBLO REVOLT & THE MYTHOLOGY OF CONQUEST:
AN INDIGENOUS ARCHAEOLOGY OF CONTACT**
Michael V. Wilcox; 334 pp. University of California Press, 2009. $45. E-book available.

THE PUEBLO REVOLT OF 1680: CONQUEST & RESISTANCE IN 17TH CENTURY NEW MEXICO Andrew L. Knaut
Illus. 272 pp. Maps. Paper. University of Oklahoma Press, 1997. $16.95.

PUEBLO SHIELDS FROM THE FRED HARVEY FINE ARTS COLLECTION
Barton Wright; Illus. 96 pp. The Heard Museum, 1976. $9.50.

PUEBLO STORIES & STORYTELLERS
Mark Bahti; 56 pp. Paper. Treasure Chest & Amazon.com, 1988. $12.95.

***PUEBLO STORYTELLER**
Diane Hoyt-Goldsmith; Grades 3-7. Illus. 32 pp. Holiday House, 1991.
$15.95; paper, $6.95.

***A PUEBLO VILLAGE**
Hilda Aragon, Illustrator
Preschool-7. Illus. 8 pp. Paper. Amazon.com, $1982. $4.

PUEBLOAN RUINS OF THE SOUTHWEST
Arthur H. Rohn & William M. Ferguson; A complete picture of Puebloan culture from prehistory to the present. 336 pp. 332 color photos; 47 line drawings; 25 maps. University of New Mexico Press, 2006. $60; paper, $34.95.

***THE PUEBLOS**
Suzanne Powell; Includes maps, a glossary and bibliography. Part of Indians of the Americas series. Illus. Grades 3 and up. 64 pp. Paper. Franklin Watts, $5.95.

PUEBLOS: PREHISTORIC INDIAN CULTURES OF THE SOUTHWEST
Sylvio Acatos & Max Bruggman; Illus. 240 pp. Facts on File, 1990. $45.

**PUEBLOS, PRESIDEOS & MISSIONS: JOURNEY TO SPANISH NORTH AMERICA:
AN INTERACTIVE CURRICULUM UNIT FOR SOCIAL STUDIES**
Denise Jess; Illus. Demco, Inc., 2000.

PUEBLOS, SPANIARDS, AND THE KINGDOM OF NEW MEXICO
John Kessell; Illus. Map. 240 pp. University of Oklahoma Press, 2010. $19.95.

PUHPOWEE FOR THE PEOPLE: A NARRATIVE ACCOUNT OF SOME USES OF FUNGI AMONG THE AHNISHINAABEG
Keewaydinoquay Peschel; Illus. 70 pp. Amazon.com, 1998. $24.95.

PUMPKIN SEED POINT: BEING WITHIN THE HOPI
Frank Waters; Reprint of 1973 ed.175 pp. Paper. Amazon.com, 1992. $9.95.

THE PUNISHMENT OF THE STINGY & OTHER INDIAN STORIES
George Bird Grinnell; Reprint 1901 ed. Illus. 265 pp. Paper. U. of Nebraska Press. $9.95.

PURISIMINO CHUMASH PREHISTORY
Michael A. Glassow; Paper. Amazon.com, 1995. $23.50.

PURITAN JUSTICE & THE INDIAN: WHITE MAN'S LAW IN PURITANS AMONG THE INDIANS: ACCOUNTS OF CAPITIVITY & REDEMPTIONS 1676-1724
Alden Vaughan & Edward Clark; Illus. 352 pp. Amazon.com, 1981. $23.50.

PUSHED INTO THE ROCKS: SOUTHERN CALIFORNIA INDIAN LAND TENURE, 1769-1986 Florence Shipek; Illus. 230 pp. University of Nebraska Press, 1988. $25.95.

***PUSHING THE BEAR: AFTER THE TRAIL OF TEARS**
Diane Glancy (Cherokee); Story of the Cherokees' resettlement in the years after "The Removal." Grades 9 and up. 176 pp. Paper. U. of Oklahome Press, 2010. $14.95.

***PUSHING THE BEAR: A NOVEL OF THE TRAIL OF TEARS**
Diane Glancy (Cherokee); Story of a young woman and her family surviving the numbing punishment of the Trail. Grades 9 and up. Amazon.com, 1996. $22.95.

PUSHMATAHA: A CHOCTAW LEADER & HIS PEOPLE
Gideon Lincecum; intro. by Greg O'Brien; Choctaw history & culture. Illus.
136 pp. Paper. University of Alabama Press, 2004. $14.95. E-Book, $11.96.

PUTREFACTION LIVE
Warren Perkins; Novel about disintegration & rejuvenation among a new generation of Navajo warriers seasoned by a century of culture wars on their homeland. Paper. University of New Mexico Press, 2005. $14.95.

PUTTING A SONG ON TOP OF IT: EXPERSSION & IDENTITY ON THE SAN CARLOS APACHE RESERVATION David W. Samuels
270 pp. Illus. University of Arizona Press, 2004. $39.95.

Q

QALUYAARMIUNI NUNAMTENEK QANEMCIPUT / OUR NELSON ISLAND STORIES: MEANINGS OF PLACE ON THE BERING SEA COAST
translated by Alice Rearden; Ann Finup-Riordan, Editor; Nelson Island Yup'ik elders describe hundreds of traditionally important places in the landscape. Illus. Maps. Paper. University of Washington Press, 2011. $50.

QAWIARAQ INUPIAQ LITERACY MANUAL
Lawrence Kaplan; 50 pp. Paper. Alaska Native Language Center, 1987. $5.

QAYAQ: KAYAKS OF SIBERIA & ALASKA
David W. Zimmerly; Illus. 103 pp. University of Alaska Press, 2000. $16.95.

QUAIL SONG: A PUEBLO INDIAN FOLKTALE
Valerie Carey, retold by; Illus. Putnam, 1990. $14.95.

THE QUALLA CHEROKEE SURVIVING IN TWO WORLDS
Laurence A. French; 252 pp. Edwin Mellon Press, 1998. $89.95.

QUALLA: HOME OF THE MIDDLE CHEROKEE SETTLEMENT
T. Walter Middleton; Illus. 287 pp. WorldComm, 1998. $22.95; paper $16.95.

QUANAH: A PICTORIAL HISTORY OF THE LAST COMANCHE CHIEF
Pauline Durrett Robertson & R. L. Robertson
Unabridged edition. Illus. 230 pp. Paramount Publishing, 2000. $39.95.

***THE QUAPAW INDIANS: A HISTORY OF THE DOWNSTREAM PEOPLE**
W. David Baird
Grades 5 and up. Reprint of 1980 edition. Illus. 104 pp. Chelsea House, $17.95.

THE QUAPAW & THEIR POTTERY
Hathcock; The ceramic output of the Quapaw Indians, 1650-1750.
Illus. 176 pp. Amazon.com, 1983. $53, postpaid.

***THE QUAPAWS**
W.D. Baird. Grades 5 and up. Illus. 105 pp. Chelsea House, 1989. $17.95.

***QU APPELLE**
David Bouchard; Michael Lonechild, Illustrator
Northern Plains legend. Grades K-4. Illus. 32 pp. Raincoast Books, 2002.

QUARTER-ACRE OF HEARTACHE
Claude C. Smith; In the words of Big Eagle of the Golden Hill Tribe, Paugussett Nation, his legal struggle to save the token parcel of land that remain of the original Paugussett reservation. Illus. Maps. 160 pp. Amzon.com, 1985. $21.95; paper, $16.95.

QUAY-LEM U EN-CHOW-MEN: A COLLECTION OF HYMNS & PRAYERS IN THE FLATHEAD-KALISPEL-SPOKANE INDIAN LANGUAGE Thomas E. Connolly, S.J.
Catholic hymns & prayers in the Salish language. 76 pp. Paper. SKC Press, $5.

QUEEN OF DREAMS: THE STORY OF A YAQUI DREAMING WOMAN
Heather Valencia & Rolly Kent; 270 pp. Paper. Simon & Schuster, 1993. $17.25.

THE QUEEN'S PEOPLE: A STUDY OF HEGEMONY, COERCION & ACCOMMODATION AMONG THE OKANAGAN OF CANADA
Peter Carstens; Illus. 416 pp. Amazon.com, 1991. $55.

QUEER INDIGENOUS STUDIES: CRITICAL INTERVENTIONS IN THEORY, POLITICS, AND LITERATURE Qwo-Li Driskill, Chris Finley, Brian Gilley & Scott L. Morgensen, Eds
History of gay & lesbian studies in indigenous communities. 258 pp. Paper.
University of Arizona Press, 2011. $34.95.

QUEESTO: PACHEENAHT CHIEF BY BIRTHRIGHT
Chief Charles Jones with Stephen Bosustow; Memoirs of hereditary Chief of the Pacheenaht people of Vancouver Island's West Coast. 125 pp. Theytus, 1982. $14.95.

THE QUEST FOR CITIZENSHIP: AFRICAN-AMERICAN & NATIVE AMERICAN EDUCATION IN KANSAS, 1880-1935 Kim Cary Warren
Illus. 256 pp. University of North Carolina Press, 2010. $59.95; paper, $24.95.

***QUEST FOR COURAGE**
Stormy Randolph; A lame Blackfeet boy overcomes his handicap by going on a vision quest. Grades 3-17. Illus. 102 pp. Paper. Roberts Rinehart, 1993. $8.95.

***QUEST FOR EAGLE FEATHER**
John Duncklee; Grades 3-7. Illus. Northland Press, 1997. $12.95.

THE QUEST FOR HARMONY: NATIVE AMERICAN SPIRITUAL TRADITIONS
William A. Young; Illus. 400 pp. Paper. Paper. CQ Press, 2001.$26.50.

QUEST FOR THE ORIGINS OF THE FIRST AMERICANS
E. James Dixon; Illus. Maps. 156 pp. Paper. U. of New Mexico Press, 1993. $12.95.

***QUEST FOR QUIVERA**
E. Buford Morgan; Historical novel of an Indian known as "the Turk" and his journeys through the Southwest at the time of the Coronado expedition. Grades 9 and up. 189 pp.
Council for Indian Education. $12.95; paper, $6.95.

QUEST FOR TRIBAL ACKNOWLEDGEMENT: CALIFORNIA'S HONEY LAKE MAIDUS
Sara-Larus Tolley; Illus. 304 pp. University of Oklahoma Press, 2006. $29.95.

QUIET PRIDE: AGELESS WISDOM OF THE AMERICAN WEST
J. Bourge Hathaway; photos by Robert A. Clayton; Collection of photograhs and narration that preserves the stories, wisdom & insight of Native and non-Native American elders. Illus. 80 color photos. 128 pp. Beyond Words Publishing, 1993. $39.95.

QUIET TRIUMPH: FORTY YEARS WITH THE INDIAN ARTS FUND, SANTA FE
Mitchell Wilder; Illus. 18 pp. Paper. Amon Carter Museum, 1965. $2.

QUILL & BEADWORK OF THE WESTERN SIOUX
Carrie A. Lyford; Reprint of 1940 edition. Illus. 85 pp. Paper. R. Schneider, Publishers & Written heritage, $9.95.

A QUILLWORK COMPANION: AN ILLUSTRATED GUIDE TO TECHNIQUES OF PORCUPINE QUILL EMBROIDERY Jean Heinbuch; Describes & illustrates all of the basic and advanced designs used by the American Indian. Also explains birchbark and loom quillwork. Illus. 92 pp. Paper. Eagle's View Publishing, & Smoke & Fire Co., $12.95.

*QUILLWORKER: A CHEYENNE LEGEND
Grades 4-8. Illus. Paper. Troll, Amazon.com, 1992. $16.95; paper, $4.95.

QUILTING & APPLIQUE WITH SOUTHWEST INDIAN DESIGNS
Charlotte Bass; Reprint. Illus. Photos. 96 pp. Paper. Naturegraph, 2003. $15.95.

QUILTING PATTERNS FROM NATIVE AMERICAN DESIGNS
Dr. Joyce Mori
Ready-toUse quilting designs. Illus. 80 pp. Paper. Written Heritage, $12.95.

QUINNIPIAC: CULTURAL CONFLICT IN SOUTHERN NEW ENGLAND
John Menta; Illus. Maps. 264 pp. Paper. Yale University Press, 2010. $29.

QULIAQTUAT MUMIAKRAT ILISAQTUANUN SAVAAKSRIAT
Edna MacLean; Illus. 35 pp. Paper. Alaska Native Language Center, 1986. $4.

QWELM U NCAWMN
compiled by Johnny Arlee; Collection of Salish-language hymns & prayers written in the International Phonetic alphabet. 80 pp. Spiral binding. SKC Press, $6.

R

*RABBIT & THE BEARS
Deborah L. Duvall; illus. by Murv Jacob; Grandmother Stories. Cherokee history and legend. All ages. Color Illus. 32 pp. University of New Mexico Press, 2004. $14.95.

*RABBIT & THE WELL
Deborah L. Duvall; illus. by Murv Jacob; Grandmother Stories. Cherokee history and legend. All ages. Color Illus. 32 pp. University of New Mexico Press,. $18.95.

*RABBIT & THE WOLVES
Deborah L. Duvall; illus. by Murv Jacob; Grandmother Stories. Cherokee history and legend. All ages. Color Illus. 32 pp. University of New Mexico Press, $14.95.

*RABBIT GOES DUCK HUNTING: A TRADITIONAL CHEROKEE LEGEND
Deborah L. Duvall; illus. by Murv Jacob; Grandmother Stories
Cherokee history & legend. All ages. Color Illus. 32 pp. U. of New Mexico Press, $14.95.

*RABBIT GOES TO KANSAS
Deborah L. Duvall; illus. by Murv Jacob; Grandmother Stories. Cherokee history and legend. All ages. Color Illus. 32 pp. University of New Mexico Press, $16.95.

*RABBIT PLANTS THE FOREST
Deborah L. Duvall; illus. by Murv Jacob; Grandmother Stories. Cherokee history and legend. All ages. Color Illus. 32 pp. University of New Mexico Press, $18.95.

A RACE AT BAY: NEW YORK TIMES EDITORIALS ON THE "INDIAN PROBLEM, 1860-1900 Robert G. Hays; 304 pp. Amazon.com, 1997. $39.95.

RACE, CASTE, & STATUS: INDIANS IN COLONIAL SPANISH AMERICA
Robert H. Jackson; Illus. 160 pp. Paper. University of New Mexico Press, 1999. $19.95.

RACE & THE CHEROKEE NATION: SOVEREIGNTY IN THE NINETEENTH CENTURY
Fay A. Yarbrough
Examines how leaders of the Cherokee Nation fostered a racial ideology through the regulation opf interracial marriage. Illus. 200 pp. U. of Pennsylavnia Press, 2007. $55.

RACE, DISCOURSE, & THE ORIGIN OF THE AMERICAS, A NEW WORLD VIEW
Vera Lawrence Hyatt & Rex Nettleford
Collection of essays. Photos. 448 pp. Smithsonian Institution Press, 1994. $29.95.

RACE & THE EARLY REPUBLIC: RACIAL CONSCIOUSNESS & NATION BUILDING IN THE EARLY REPUBLIC Michael Morrison & James Stewart, Eds.
Illus. 192 pp. Rowman & Littlefield Publishers, 2002. $74; paper, $23.95.

RACE, NATION & RELIGION IN THE AMERICAS
Henry Goldschmidt & Elizabeth McAlister, Eds.
Illus. 350 pp. Oxford University Press, 2004. $65; paper, $24.95.

RACE PRIDE & THE AMERICAN IDENTITY
Joseph T. Rhea; 224 pp. Amazon.com Press, 1997. $27.

RACE, RACISM & REPATRIATION
J. Angelo Corlett; Paper. Amazon.com, 2003. $19.95.

*RACE TO THE MOONRISE
Sally Crum; Children's adventures dealing with the early southwestern cultures: the Mogollon of the Mimbres Valley, ancestral Pueblo people of Chaco Canyon, Aztec, Mesa Verde, and Chimney Rock. Grades 4-8. Illus. Map. 100 pp. Paper. Western Reflections Publishing, 2007. $9.95.

*RACE WITH THE BUFFALO & OTHER NATIVE AMERICAN STORIES FOR YOUNG READERS
Richard & Judy Young; Grades 4 amd up. Illus. 176 pp. Amazon.com, 1993. $19.95.

RACHEL'S CHILDREN: STORIES FROM A CONTEMPORARY NATIVE AMERICAN WOMAN
Lois Beardslee; 160 pp. AltaMira Press, 2004. $89; paper, $30; eBook, $28.99.

Racism in Indian Country
Dean Chavers; 248 pp. Paper. Peter Lang Publishing, 2009. $37.95.

A RADIANT CURVE: POEMS & STORIES
Luci Tapahonso (Navajo)
Includes an audio CD. 128 pp. University of Arizona Press, $35; paper, $17.95.

THE RAILROAD AND THE PUEBLO INDIANS: THE IMPACT OF THE ATCHISON, TOPEKA & SANTA FE ON THE PUEBLOS OF THE RIO GRANDE, 1880-1930
Richard H. Frost; 280 pp. University of Utah Press, 2015. $34.95.

RAIN: NATIVE EXPRESSIONS FROM THE AMERICAN SOUTHWEST
Ann Marshall, Ed.; Photos & textual analysis of cultural objects drawn from the Heard Museum's extension collections. Illus. 144 pp. Paper. Museum of New Mexico Press, 2000. $29.95. 160 pp. Roberts Rinehart Publishers, $40; paper, $29.95.

*THE RAINBOW BRIDGE: A CHUMASH LEGEND
Tom & Kerry Nechodom; Grades 4 and up. Illus. 32 pp. Paper. Amazon.com, $6.95.

RAINBOW MEDICINE: A VISIONARY GUIDE TO NATIVE AMERICAN SHAMANISM
Wolf Moondance; Teaches self-worth through ancient ceremonies, using ordinary objects, herbs, and foods. Illus. 192 pp. Paper. Sterling Publishing, $14.95.

RAINBOW SPIRIT JOURNEYS: NATIVE AMERICAN MEDITIATIONS & DREAMS
Wolf Moondance; Illus. 144 pp. Paper. Sterling Publishing, 2000. $14.95.

RAINBOW TRIBE: ORDINARY PEOPLE JOURNEYING ON THE RED ROAD
McGaa Eagle Man; 272 pp. Paper. Amazon.com & Alibris.com, 1992. $17.95.

RAINBOWS OF STONE
Ralph Salisbury; Poems of family tales, tribal history, Cherokee religion. 137 pp. University of Arizona Press, 2000. $16.95.

RAINCOAST SASQUATCH: BIGFOOT, SASQUATCH EVIDENCE FROM INDIAN LORE
Robert Alley; Illus. 228 pp. Hancock House Publishers, 2002. $14.95.

RAINHOUSE & OCEAN: SPEECHES FOR THE PAPAGO YEAR
Ruth M. Underhill, Donald M. Bahr, et al
Reprint of 1979 edition. Illus. 153 pp. Paper. University of Arizona Press, $18.95.

THE RAINMAKERS
E.J. Bird; Illus. 150 pp. Lerner, 1993. $19.95.

RAINY RIVER LIVES: STORIES TOLD BY MAGGIE WILSON
Maggie Wilson; compiled & edited by Sally Cole; Stories of Ojibwe men & women. 24 photos. Maps. Paper. University of Nebraska Press, 2009. $35.

*RAINY'S POWWOW
Linda Theresa Raczek; Picture book. Ages 5-8. Illus. Northland, $15.95.

*RAISING OURSELVES
Velma Wallis; A Gwich'in coming of age story from the Yukon River. Grades 6 and up. Illus. 212 pp. Paper. Amazon.com, 2002. $19.95.

RAIZED ON THE REZ: VIEWS, VISIONS & WISDOM OF THE WEST
Betty Ankrum; Illus. 144 pp. Paper. Amazon.com, 1996.

*THE RAMILUK STORIES: ADVENTURES OF AN ESKIMO FAMILY IN THE PREHISTORIC ARCTIC Eugene Vickery
Grades 5 and up. Illus. 125 pp. Stonehaven Publishers, 1989. $16.00; paper, $10.95.

RAMONA
Helen Hunt Jackson : into. by Michael Dorris; Ethical novel of the Native American struggle, and the horror of the American political past. 384 pp. Paper. Penguin USA, $3.50.

RANCE HOOD: MYSTIC PAINTER
James J. Hester; Rance Hood; Biography of Comanche painter Rance Hood. Illus. 72 color plates, 138 color photos. University of New Mexico Press, $19.95.

THE RANGE SITE: ARCHAIC THROUGH LATE WOODLAND OCCUPATIONS
John Kelly, et al; Illus. 480 pp. University of Illinois Press, 1987. $23.95.

RANGERS & REDCOATS ON THE HUDSON: EXPLORING THE PAST ON ROGERS ISLAND David S. Starbuck; An account of an archaeological investigation at a major French & Indian War military encampment. 168 pp. Illus. Paper. University Press of New England, 2004. $19.95.

RANK & WARFARE AMONG THE PLAINS INDIANS
Bernard Mishkin; Reprint of 1940 edition. 65 pp. Paper. U. of Nebraska Press, $6.95.

THE RAPID CITY INDIAN SCHOOL, 1898-1933
Scott Riney; Illus. Maps. 288 pp. University of Oklahoma Press, 1999. $29.95.

RAPPAHANNOCK ROOTS: A REGIONAL HISTORY, A GENEALOGY, A SPIRITUAL JOURNEY Barbara D. Pickett; Illus. 110 pp. Paper. Amazon.com, 2002. $19.95.

RARE & UNUSUAL ARTIFACTS OF THE FIRST AMERICANS
Ray Parman, Jr.; Illus. 300 pp. Paper. Fred Pruett, 1989. $24.95.

RATIONALIIZING EPIDEMICS: MEANINGS & USES OF AMERICAN INDIAN MORTALITY SINCE 1600
David S. Jones; Illus. 310 pp. Harvard University Press & Amazon.com, 2004. $49.95.

*THE RATTLE & THE DRUM: NATIVE AMERICAN RITUALS & CELEBRATIONS
Lisa Sita; Grades 3-6. Illus. 80 pp. Amazon.com, 1994. $25.90.

*RAVEN BRINGS TO THE PEOPLE: ANOTHER GIFT: A STORY BASED ON NATIVE AMERICAN LEGEND Ann M. Reed
Grades 3 and up. Illus. 18 pp. Tipi Press, 1997. $3.95.

RAVEN EYE
Margo Tamez; Poetry. 96 pp. Paper. University of Arizona Press, $14.95.

THE RAVEN & THE REDBIRD
A play in three acts of Sam Houston (Raven) and his Cherokee wife (Redbird). 103 pp. Paper. VIP Publishing. $5.95.

THE RAVEN SPEAKS
Raven Hail; Cherokee Indian lore in English with some Cherokee. Reprint. 192 pp. VIP Publishing. $7.95.

THE RAVEN STEALS THE LIGHT: DRAWINGS BY BILL REID
Bill Reid & Robert Bringhurst; Haida mythology & oral literature. Illus. 128 pp. Paper. University of Washington Press, 1996 (with new preface). $16.95.

THE RAVEN TALES
Peter Goodchild; Illus. 144 pp. Amazon.com, 1991. $16.95; paper, $9.95.

RAVEN TRAVELLING: TWO CENTURIES OF HAIDA ART
Peter MacNair, Daina AugatisMarionne Jones, Nika Collison, et al
140 Illus. 130 in color. 200 pp. Paper. University of Washington Press, 2006. $39.95.

*RAVEN: A TRICKSTER TALE FROM THE PACIFIC NORTHWEST
Gerald McDermott; Grades K-3. Illus. Amazon.com, 1994. $14.95.

RAVEN'S CRY
Christie Harris; illus. by Bill Reid; Fictionalized retelling of the near destruction of the Haida Nation. Illus. 196 pp. Paper. University of Washington Press, 1992. $22.95.

RAVEN'S GUIDE TO AIDS PREVENTION RESOURCES
Alaska Native Health Board; Designed to provide infomation & resources available for American Indians and Alaska Natives on AIDS and AIDS prevention. Includes agencies, programs & servics, books & periodicals, brochures, videos, posters, and other materials. 42 pp. National Native American AIDS Prevention Center, 1991.

RAVEN'S JOURNEY: THE WORLD OF ALASKA'S NATIVE PEOPLE
Susan A. Kaplan; Illus. 210 pp. U. of Pennsylvania Museum, 1986. $39.95; paper, $24.95.

RAVEN'S TALES
Raven Hail; Collection of 13 ancient Cherokee legends. Illus. 49 pp. Amazon.com. $9.95.

RAVEN'S VILLAGE: THE MYTHS, ARTS, & TRADITIONS OF NATIVE PEOPLE FROM THE PACIFIC NORTHWEST COAST
Nancy Ruddell; Illus. 64 pp. Paper. University of Washington Press, 1995. $8.95.

RAVENSONG: CHEROKEE INDIAN POETRY
Amazon.com; VIP Publishing. Book, $6.95; tape, $9.95; both, $14.95.

RE/ENVISIONING RELATIONSHIPS: ABORIGINAL & NON-ABORIGINAL COALITIONS & ALLIANCES Lynne Davis, Editor; 400 pp. Paper. University of Toronto Press, 2010.

REACHING BOTH WAYS
Helen P. Wolf: Barbara Ketcham, Editor;
llus. 135 pp. Paper. Jelm Mountain, 1989. $9.95.

REACHING JUST SETTLEMENTS: LAND CLAIMS IN BRITISH COLUMBIA
Frank Cassidy; 153 pp. Paper. Amazon.com, 1991.$15.95.

READERS DIGEST - AMERICA'S FASCINATING INDIAN HERITAGE
Amazon.com, $30.

READING BEYOND WORDS: CONTEXTS FOR NATIVE HISTORY
Jennifer S.H. Brown & Elizabeth Vibert, Eds.
2nd Ed. Illus. 546 pp. Paper. Amazon.com, 2003.

READING THE FIRE: THE TRADITIONAL INDIAN LITERATURES OF AMERICA
Jarold Ramsey; 352 pp. Paper. University of Washington Press. $24.95.

READING LOUISE ERDRICH'S LOVE MEDICINE
P. Jane Hafen; 56 pp. Paper. Boise State U., Western Writers Series, 2004. $5.95.

READING NATIVE AMERICAN LITERATURE
Bruce A. Goebel; 309 pp. Teacher edition.Paper. Amazon.com, 2004. $35.95.

READING NATIVE AMERICAN WOMEN: CRITICAL/CREATIVE REPRESENTATIONS
Ines Hernandez-Avila; 320 pp. AltaMira Press, 2003. $70.

READING THE VOICE: NATIVE AMERICAN ORAL POETRY ON THE WRITTEN PAGE
Paul Zolbrod; Explores Native American oral poetics. University of Utah Press, 1995. $25.

READING & WRITING THE LAKOTA LANGUAGE
Albert White Hat, Sr.; edited by Jael Kampfe; The effect of language on both cultural deterioration & survival. University of Utah Press, 1998. $50; paper, $24.95. 2 cassettes, $12.95; paperback & cassettes, $34.95.

READING BEYOND WORDS: CONTEXTS FOR NATIVE HISTORY
Jennifer S.H. Brown & Elizabeth Vibert, Eds; 504 pp. Paper. U. of Toronto Press, 2003.

READINGS IN AMERICAN INDIAN LAW: RECALLING THE RHYTHM OF SURVIVAL
Jo Carillo, Editor; 304 pp. Amazon.com, 1998. $69.95; paper, 29.95.

READINGS FOR NATIVE PEOPLE OF NORTH AMERICA
Richard Jeffries; 256 pp. Kendall/Hunt, 1999. $41.95.

READINGS ON JAMES BAY
Articles on the hydroelectric projects planned for the James Bay region of northern Canada where Cree people live. Akwe;kon Press, $8.

READY TO USE NORTH AMERICAN INDIAN
Maggie Kate; 64 pp. Paper. Dover Publications, 1996. $6.95.

REAL INDIANS: IDENTITY & THE SURVIVAL OF NATIVE AMERICA
Eva Marie Garroutte
Illus. 250 pp. Paper. University of California Press, 2003. $26.95. E-Book available.

"REAL" INDIANS & OTHERS: MIXED-BLOOD URBAN NATIVE PEOPLES & INDIGENOUS NATIONHOOD by Bonita Lawrence; Interviews Canadian mixed-blood, urban Natives from Toronto and reveals the ways in which they understand their identities and their struggle to survive. 320 pp. U. of Nebraska Press, 2004. $55; paper, $29.95.

THE REAL ROSEBUD: THE TRIUMPH OF A LAKOTA WOMAN
Marjorie Weinberg; foreword by Luke Yellow Robe
Illus. 128 pp. University of Nebraska Press, 2004. $19.95.

REASONING TOGETHER: THE NATIVE CRITICS COLLECTIVE
Craig S. Womack, Daniel H. Justice, Christopher B. Teuton
416 pp. Paper. University of Oklahoma Press, 2008. $24.95.

REBELLION FROM THE ROOTS: INDIAN UPRISING IN CHIAPAS
John Ross; 250 pp. Common Courage Press, 1994. $29.95; paper, $14.95.

REBIRTH OF THE BLACKFEET NATION, 1912-1954
Paul C. Rosier; Maps. 346 pp. University of Nebraska Press, 2001. $65.

REBIRTH: POLITICAL, ECONOMIC & SOCIAL DEVELOPMENT IN FIRST NATIONS
Anne-Marie Mawhiney; 11 papers published from the 1992 INORD Conference giving voice to stories about the ways in which First Nations are addressing their own conditions. 256 pp. Paper. Amazon.com, 1993. $18.

REBUILDING NATIVE NATIONS: STRATEGIES FOR GOVERNANCE & DEVELOPMENT Miriam Jorgensen; Produced by the Native Nations Institute for Leadership, Management, and Policy at the University of Arizona and the Harvard Project on American Indian Economic Development. 384 pp. Paper. University of Arizona Press, 2007. $20.

RECENT LEGAL ISSUES FOR AMERICAN INDIANS, 1968 TO THE PRESENT
John R. Wunder; Reprint. 344 pp. Garland, $77.

RECENTLY DISCOVERED TALES OF LIFE AMONG THE INDIANS
James Willard Schultz; Warren L. Hanna, Editor
Collection of stories from Schultz's earliest writings from 1880 to 1894. Illus. 152 pp. Paper. Mountain Press, $10.

RECKONINGS: CONTEMPORARY SHORT FICTION BY NATIVE AMERICAN WOMEN
Hertha D. Sweet Wong, Lauren Stuart Muller, Jana Sequoya Magdaleno
Oxford University Press, 2008. $125; paper, $30.95.

RECLAIMING THE ANCESTORS: DECOLONIZING A TAKEN PREHISTORY OF THE FAR NORTHEAST Frederick Matthew Wiseman
Illus. Tables. 312 pp. Paper. University Press of New England, 2005. $24.95.

RECLAIMING INDIGENOUS VOICE & VISION
Marie Battiste, Editor; How Aboriginal cultural rights in postcolonial societies can be restored. 256 pp. University of Washington Press, 2000. $83; paper, $35.95.

RECLAIMING THE VISION: PAST, PRESENT & FUTURE: NATIVE VOICES FOR THE EIGHTH GENERATION Lee Francis & James Bruchac, Editors
Illus. 120 pp. Paper. Amazon.com, 1996. $15.95.

RECKONING WITH THE DEAD, THE LARSEN BAY REPATRIATION & THE SMITHSONIAN INSTITUTION Tamara L. Bray & Thomas W. Killion, Editor
Presents the Larsen Baym Alaska, repatriation request of the Smithsonian. Illus. 352 pp. Paper. Smithsonian Institution Press, 1994. $34.95.

RECLAIMING DINE HISTORY: THE LEGACIES OF NAVAJO CHIEF MANUELITO & JUANITA Jennifer Nez Denetdale
264 pp. Unversity of Arizona Press, 2007. $45; paper, $19.95.

A RECOGNITION OF BEING: RECONSTRUCTING NATIVE WOMANHOOD
Kim Anderson; 320 pp. Paper. Amazon.co, 2004.

RECOLLECTING: LIVES OF ABORIGINAL WOMEN OF THE CANADIAN NORTHWEST & BORDERLANDS Sarah Carter & Patricia McCormack, Editors; Essays on the lives of Aboriginal women from the late 18th-century to the mid-20th century. 432 pp. Paper. University of Washington Press, 2011. $35.95.

RECOLLECTIONS FROM THE COLVILLE INDIAN AGENCY, 1886-1889
Rickard D. Gwydir; Kevin Dye, Editor & Intro.; 134 pp. Arthur H. Clark Co., 2001. $28.50.

RECOLLECTIONS FROM MY TIME IN THE INDIAN SERVICE, 1935-1942: MARIA MARTINEZ MAKES POTTERY
Alfreda Ward Maloof; Illus. 72 pp. Paper. Amazon.com, 1997. $15.

RECOLLECTIONS OF 60 YEARS ON THE OHIO FRONTIER
John Johnston; Includes accounts of notable Ohio Indians, Shawnee & Wyandotte languages and Manners & Customs of the Tribes. Illus. Maps. 80 pp. Paper. Wennawoods Publishing, $14.95.

RECONCILING THE PAST: TWO BASKETRY KA'AI & THE LEGENDARY LILOA & LONOIKAMAKAHIKI
Roger G. Rose; Anthropological literature. Illus. Paper. Bishop Museum, $12.95.

RECONFGURING THE RESERVATION: THE NEZ PERCES, JICARILLA APACHES & THE DAWES ACT
Emily Greenwald; Illus. 200 pp. University of New Mexico Press, 2002. $39.95.

RECONSTRUCTING THE NATIVE SOUTH: AMERICAN INDIAN LITERATURE & THE LOST CAUSE Melanie Benson Taylor
Examines the diverse body of Native Americn literature in the contemporary U.S. South. Illus. 248 pp. U. of Georgia Press, 2012. $59.95; paper, $24.95.

RECONSTRUCTING 18TH CENTURY NAVAJO POPULATION DYNAMICS IN THE DINETAH Ronald H. Towner & Byron P. Johnson; Archaeological & Deendrochronological Investigations in San Rafael Canyon. 150 pp. Paper. U. of Arizona Press, 1998. $15.95.

RECONSTRUCTION IN INDIAN TERRITORY
M. Thomas Bailey; A story of avarice, discrimination, and opportunism. Associated Faculty Press, 1972. $23.95.

RECORDING THEIR STORY: JAMES TEIT & THE TAHLTAN
Judy Thompson; Describes the life of one of Canada's earliest ethnographers and his work among the Tahltan people of northern British Columbia a century ago. Illus. Maps. 208 pp. University of Washington Press, 2007. $50.

RECORDS OF THE BUREAU OF INDIAN AFFAIRS: CENTRAL CLASSIFIED FILES, 1907-1939 Robert E. Lester; Laura Hanes, compiler; Microfilm. Series A: Indian Delegations to Washington; Series B: Indian Customs & Social Relations; Series C: Health & Medical Matters; Series D: Education. User Guide, 176 pp. Amazon.com, 2006.

RECORDS OF THE MORAVIANS AMONG THE CHEROKEES
C. Daniel Crews & Richard W. Starbuck
Firsthand account of daily life among the Cherokees in the 19th century. Vol. 1: Early Contact & the Establishment of the First Missions, 1752-1802; Vol. 2: Moravian/Cherokee story to 1805; Vol. 3: The Anna Rosina Years, Part 1 - Success in School & Mission, 1805-1810; Vol. 4: The Anna Rosina Years, Part 2 - Warfare on the Horizon, 1810-1816. 624 & 618 pp. respectively. Published by the Cherokee National Press. Distributed by the University of Oklahoma Press, 2010 (Vols. 1 & 2); & 2011 (Vols. 3 & 4). Vols. 5 & 6 forthcoming in 2012. $50 each.

RECORDS OF THE U.S. INDIAN CLAIMS COMMISSION
Robert E. Lester; Laura Hanes, compiler; Microfilm. U. Publications of America, 2004.

RECOVERING HISTORY, CONSTRUCTING RACE: THE INDIAN, BLACK, AND WHITE ROOTS OF MEXICAN AMERICANS
Martha Menchaca; Illus. Maps. Paper. University of Texas Press, 2001. $27.95.

RECOVERING OUR ANCESTOR'S GARDENS: INDIGENOUS RECIPES & GUIDE TO DIET & FITNESS
Devon Abbott Mihesuah; Illus. 218 pp. University of Nebraska Press, 2005. $24.95.

RECOVERING THE WORD: ESSAYS ON NATIVE AMERICAN LITERATURE
Brian Swann & Arnold Krupat, Eds.; 600 pp. University of California Press, 1987. $60.00; paper, $17.95.

RE-CREATING THE CIRCLE: THE RENEWAL OF AMERICAN INDIAN SELF-DETERMINATION Stephen Sachs, Barbara Morris, Deborah Hunt, IaDonna Harris, et al.528 pp. University of New Mexico Press, $75.

RECREATING HOPEWELL
Douglas K. Charles & Jane E. Builstra; Overview of Hopewell archaeology representing more than two decades of new research into the world of moundbuilding. Illus. Maps. 640 pp. University Press of Florida, 2006. $75.

RE-CREATING THE WORD: PAINTED CERAMICS OF THE PREHISTORIC SOUTHWEST Barbara Moulard; Illus. 240 pp. Schenck Southwest Publishing, 2002. $85.

THE RED BIRD ALL-INDIAN TRAVELING BAND
Frances Washburn; A novel. Part mystery, part community chronicle.. The story of Indian Country. 184 pp. Paper. University of Arizona Press, 2014. $16.95.

*RED BIRD SINGS: THE STORY OF ZITKALA-SA, NATIVE AMERICAN AUTHOR, MUSICIAN, AND ACTIVIST Gina Capaldi, Q.L. Pearce; Illus. by Gina Capaldi Grades 3-6. Ilus. Lerner Publications, 2011. $13.46.

RED, BLACK & JEW: NEW FRONTIERS IN HEBREW LITERATURE
Stephen Katz; Charts the ways in which the Native American & African American creative cultures served as a model for works produced within the minority Jewish community. 363 pp. Paper. University of Texas Press, 2009. $30.

RED CAPITALISM: AN ANALYSIS OF THE NAVAJO ECONOMY
Larry Galbreath; 150 pp. Paper. Books on Deamnd, 1973. $41.80.

RED CHILDREN IN WHITE AMERICA
Ann H. Beuf; 168 pp. University of Pennsylvania Press, 1977. $19.95.

*RED CLAY: POEMS AND STORIES
Linda Hogan; Traditional Chickasaw poems and stories. Grades 7 and up. Paper. Amazon.com, 1991. $9.95.

RED CLOUD: PHOTOGRAPHS OF A LAKOTA CHIEF
Frank H. Goodyear, III; Illus. Map. 224 pp. University of Nebraska Press, 2003. $35.

RED CLOUD: WARRIOR STATESMAN OF THE LAKOTA SIOUX
Robert W. Larson
Biography. Illus. Map. 350 pp. Paper. University of Oklahoma Press, 1997. $19.9

RED CLOUD & THE SIOUX PROBLEM
James Olson; Illus. Maps. 375 pp. Paper. University of Nebraska Press, 1965. $29.95.

RED CLOUD'S FOLK: A HISTORY OF THE OGLALA SIOUX INDIANS
George E. Hyde
Reprint of revised 1957 edition. Illus. 362 pp. Paper. University of Oklahoma Press, $16.95.

RED CLOUD'S WAR: THE BOZEMAN TRAIL, 1866-1868, TWO VOLS.
John D. McDermott; Indian wars & the history of the Bozeman Trail. Illus. Maps. 704 pp. University of Oklahoma Press, 2010. Leatherbound, $225.

RED CROW: WARRIOR CHIEF
Hugh A. Dempsey; Illus. 815 pp. Paper. University of Nebraska Press, 1980. $45.

RED CRITICAL THEORY
Sandy Marie Grande; 184 pp. Rowman & Littlefield, 2003. $70; paper, $19.95.

RED DREAMS, WHITE NIGHTMARES: PAN-INDIAN ALLIANCES IN THE ANGLO-AMERICAN MIND, 1763-1815
Robert M. Owens; Illus: 320 pp. University of Oklahoma Press, 2015. $32.95.

RED EARTH: RACE & AGRICULTURE IN OKLAHOMA TERRITORY
Bonnie Lynn-Sherow; Illus. Maps. 176 pp. University Press of Kansas, 2004. $29.95.

RED EARTH, WHITE LIES: NATIVE AMERICANS & THE MYTH OF SCIENTIFIC FACT
Vine Deloria, Jr.; On the conflict between mainstream scientific theory about the world and the ancestral worldview of Native Americans. 288 pp. Paper. Fulcrum Publishing & Amazon.com, $18.95.

RED EAGLE & THE WARS WITH THE CREEK INDIANS OF ALABAMA
George Cary Eggleston; Reprint. Amazon.com, $27.95; paper$7.95.

RED: THE EITELJORG CONTEMPORARY ART FELLOWSHIP 2013
Jennifer Complo McNutt & Ashley Holland, Editor
136 pp. Paper. University of Oklahoma Press, 2013. $30.

RED FOX: BRIG.-GENERAL STAND WATIE'S CIVIL WAR YEARS IN INDIAN TERRITORY Wilfred Knight; Watie was the last Confederate General in the Civil War to surrender. He and his Indian troops fought unsung battles in Indian Territory throughout the war. Illus. Map. Biblio. 320 pp. The Arthur H. Clark Co., $27.50.

*RED FROG MAN: A HOHOKAM LEADER
Charles Fellers; Maxine Hughes, Editor
Grades 1-6. Illus. 64 pp. Paper. Laughing Fox, 1990. $6.95.

WILLIAM WAYNE RED HAT, JR.: CHEYENNE KEEPER OF THE ARROWS
William Wayne Red Hat, Jr.; edited by Sibylle M. Schlesier
Biography. 176 pp. University of Oklahoma Press, 2010. $21.95.

*RED HAWK & THE SKY SISTERS: A SHAWNEE LEGEND
Terri Cohlene; Grades 1-5. Illus. Paper. Amazon.com, 1992. $4.95.

*RED HAWK'S ACCOUNT OF CUSTER'S LAST BATTLE
Paul Goble; Grades 4 and up. Illus. 64 pp. Paper. U. of Nebraksa Press, 1992. $9.95

RED-HEADED RENEGADE -- CHIEF BENGE OF THE CHEROKEE NATION
Clara Talton Fugate; Illus. Paper. Amazon.com, 1994.

RED JACKET & HIS PEOPLE
J.M. Hubbard; Reprint of Col. Wm. Stone's The Life & Times of Red Jacket. 356 pp. paper. Amazon.com. $24.50

RED JACKET: IROQUOIS DIPLOMAT & ORATOR
Christopher Densmore; Biography. Includes his speeches. Illus. Maps. Biblio. 176 pp. Syracuse University Press, 1998. $34.95; paper, $16.95.

RED JACKET: SENECA CHIEF
Arthur Caswell Parker; Illus. Maps. 228 pp. Paper. U. of Nebraska Press, 1998. $10.

THE RED KING'S REBELLION: RACIAL POLITICS IN NEW ENGLAND, 1675-1677
Russell Bourne; Illus. 304 pp. Paper. Oxford University Press, 1991. $12.95.

RED LAKE COURT OF INDIAN OFFENSES: MANAGEMENT AUDIT
52 pp. Amazon.com, 1982. Manuscript, $3.12

RED LAKE COURT OF TRIBAL OFFENSES COURT MANUAL
450 pp. Amazon.com, 1982.

RED LAKE NATION: PORTRAITS OF OJIBWE LIFE
Charles Brill; Illus. 192 pp. University of Minnesota Press, 1992. $29.95.

RED LAND, RED POWER: GROUNDING KNOWLEDGE IN THE AMERICAN INDIAN NOVEL Sean Kicummah Teuton
Illus. 312 pp. Duke U. Press, 2008. $89,95; paper, $24.95.

RED MAN IN THE U.S.
G. Lindquist; Reprint of 1923 edition. Illus. 487 pp. Amazon.com, $45.

RED MAN'S AMERICA: A HISTORY OF INDIANS IN THE U.S.
Ruth Underhill; Revised ed. Illus. Maps. 408 pp. Paper. U. of Chicago Press, 1971. $20.

RED MAN'S LAND - WHITE MAN'S LAW: THE PAST & PRESENT STATUS OF THE AMERICAN INDIAN Wilcomb E. Washburn; Provides a clear discussion of the legal history of Indian-white relations. 2nd edition. Illus. 314 pp. Paper. University of Oklahoma Press, 1995. $21.95.

THE RED MAN'S ON THE WARPATH: THE IMAGE OF THE INDIAN & THE SECOND WORLD WAR R. Scott Sheffield; Re-examines the roles & status of Native people in Canadian society. 240 pp. University of Washington Press, 2004. $105; paper, $37.95.

RED MAN'S RELIGION: BELIEFS & PRACTICES OF THE INDIANS NORTH OF MEXICO Ruth Underhill
Illus. Maps. 350 pp. Paper. University of Chicago Press, 1965. $21.

RED MATTERS: NATIVE AMERICAN STUDIES
Arnold Krupat; Illus. 208 pp. University of Pennsylvania Press, $47.50; paper, $18.95.

RED MEN IN RED SQUARE
Bud Smith & Chief Big Eagle; Story of Chief Big Eagle of the Golden Hill Tribe of Connecticut (Quarter-Acre of Heartache, 1985) and his travel to Russia and discovery of the Indianists-Soviet citizens who study the ways, crafts, and religion of Native American tribes. Illus. Amazon.com, 1994. $21.95; paper, $16.95.

RED ON RED: NATIVE AMERICAN LITERARY SEPARATISM
Craig S. Womack; 352 pp. University of Minnesota Press, 1999. $59.95; paper, $22.50.

RED OVER BLACK: BLACK SLAVERY AMONG THE CHEROKEE INDIANS
R. Halliburton, Jr.; Illus. Greenwood Press, 1977. $35.

RED PAINT PEOPLE: A LOST AMERICAN CULTURE
Bruce Bourque; Illus. 96 pp. Bunker Hill Publishing, 2004. $12.95.

RED POWER: THE AMERICAN INDIANS' FIGHT FOR FREEDOM
Alvin M. Josephy, Jr., Joane Nagel & Troy Johnson, Eds.
Documentary history of the American Indian activist movement. 2nd Ed. Illus. 300 pp. Paper. University of Nebraska Press, 1999. $19.95.

*RED POWER ON THE RIO GRANDE
Franklin Folsom; Pueblo Indian uprising of 1680 against Spanish control in the Southwest. Grades 9 and up. 144 pp. Council on Indian Education, 1989. $12.95; paper, $9.95.

RED POWER RISING: THE NATIONAL INDIAN YOUTH COUNCIL AND THE ORIGINS OF NATIVE ACTIVISM
Bradley Shreve; 288 pp. University of Oklahoma Press, $34.95; paper, $19.95.

THE RED RECORD: THE OLDEST NATIVE NORTH AMERICAN HISTORY
David McCutchen; Illus. 240 pp. Paper. Amazon.com, 1992. $14.95.

RED RIVER CROSSINGS: CONTEMPORARY NATIVE AMERICAN ARTISTS RESPOND TO PETER RINDISBACHER (1806-1834)
Margaret Archuleta, et al.; Illus. 60 pp. Paper. Amazon.com, 2005. $15.

THE RED SWAN: MYTHS & TALES OF THE AMERICAN INDIANS
John Bierhorst, Translator
Reprint of 1976 edition. 386 pp. Paper. University of New Mexico Press, $15.95.

RED TWILIGHT: THE LAST FREE DAYS OF THE UTE INDIANS
Val Fitzpatrick, Dalton Carr, M. Wilson Rankin
Illus. 288 pp. Paper. Amazon.com, 2000. $18.95.

RED, WHITE & BLACK: SYMPOSIUM ON INDIANS IN THE OLD SOUTH
Charles Hudson; Paper. University of Georgia Press, 1971. $8.

RED & WHITE: INDIAN VIEWS OF THE WHITE MAN, 1492-1982
Annette Rosensteil; Illus. 192 pp. Amazon.com, 1983. $14.95.

THE RED WINDOW
Marianne Aweagon Broyles; Poetry. Acknowledges the historic oppression of Native Americans and other peoples. 48 pp. Paper. University of New Mexico Press, $10.95.

RED WORLD & WHITE: MEMORIES OF A CHIPPEWA BOYHOOD
John Rogers; Illus. 176 pp. Paper. University of Oklahoma Press, 1996. $12.95.

REDSKINS, RUFFLESHIRTS, & REDNECKS: INDIAN ALLOTMENTS IN ALABAMA & MISSISSIPPI, 1830-1860
Mary Elizabeth Young; Illus. Maps. 234 pp. University of Oklahoma Press, 2002. $19.95.

THE GEORGE REEVES SITE: LATE ARCHAIC, LATE WOODLAND, EMERGENT MISSISSIPPIAN, & MISSISSIPPIAN COMPONENTS
Dale McElrath & Fred Finney; Illus. 464 pp. Paper. U. of Illinois Press, 1987. $22.95.

REFERENCE LIBRARY OF NATIVE NORTH AMERICA, 3 Vols.
Duane Champagne, Editor; 3 vols. 1,920 pp. The Gale Group, 2000. $199.

REFLECTIONS FROM THE COLVILLE INDIAN AGENCY, 1886-1889
Rickard D. Gwydir; Kevin Dye, Ed. & Intro.; 135 pp. Arthur H. Clark Co., 2001. $28.50.

REFLECTIONS OF LAC DU FLAMBEAU: AN ILLUSTRATED HISTORY OF LAC DU FLAMBEAU, WISCONSIN, 1745-1895
Michael J. Goc; Illus. 160 pp. Amazon.com, 1994. $23.

REFLECTIONS OF THE WEAVER'S WORLD: THE GLORIA F. ROSS COLLECTION OF CONTEMPORARY NAVAJO WEAVING
Ann Lund Hedlund; Illustrates the Denver Art Museum's permanent collection of contemporary Navajo weaving. Illus. 112 pp. Paper. U. of Washington Press, $29.95.

REFLECTIONS ON THE ALASKA NATIVE EXPERIENCE: SELECTED ARTICLES & SPEECHES BY ROY M. HUHNDORF
Roy M. Huhndorf; 21 selections from a series of articles written by Huhndorf, President of Cook Inlet Region, Inc., for the editorial section of the Anchorage Times during the period of 1981 through 1984. 61 pp. CIRI, 1991. No charge.

REFLECTIONS ON AMERICAN INDIAN HISTORY: HONORING THE PAST, BUILDING A FUTURE Albert L. Hurtado, Editor; 176 pp. University of Oklahoma Press, 2010. $29.95.

REFLECTIONS ON CHEROKEE LITERARY EXPRESSION
Mary Ellen Meredith & Howard L. Meredith, Eds.
Illus. 150 pp. Edwin Mellen Press, 2003. $99.95.

REFLECTIONS ON NATIVE-NEWCOMER RELATIONS: SELECTED ESSAYS
J.R. Miller; 12 essays on First Nations & Metis relationships with newcomers in Canada over the decades. Illus. 320 pp. University of Toronto Press, 2004. $65; paper, $27.95.

REGULARS IN THE REDWOODS: U.S. ARMY IN NORTHERN CALIFORNIA, 1852-1861
William F. Strobridge; The clash between settlers and Indians during California's early statehood. Detailed account of the Regular Army's attempts to maintain peace.Illus. Map. Biblio. 283 pp. The Arthur H. Clark Co., $29.95.

REGULATORY ACTIVITIES OF THE NATIONAL INDIAN GAMING COMMISSION
U.S. Senate Committee on Indian Affairs; 104th Congress. Illus. USGPO, 1997.

BILL REID & BEYOND: EXPANDING ON MODERN NATIVE ART
edited by Karen Duffek & Charlotte Townsend-Gault; Haida art & tradition. 19 contributors write from many perspectives. Illus. 280 pp. University of Washington Press, 2004. $37.95.

REIMAGINING INDIANS: NATIVE AMERICANS THROUGH ANGLO EYES, 1880-1940
Sherry Lynn Smith; Illus. 290 pp. Paper. Oxford University Press, 2002. $54.

REINCARNATION BELIEFS OF NORTH AMERICAN INDIANS: SOUL JOURNEYS, METAMORPHOSIS, AND NEAR-DEATH EXPERIENCES
Warren Jefferson; In-depth look at spiritual experiences…Winnebago shaman's, Cherokee's Orpheus myth, Hopi & Inuit. Illus. 208 pp. Book Publishing, 2011. $15.95.

REINTERPRETING A NATIVE AMERICAN IDENTITY: EXAMINING THE LUMBEE THROUGH THE PEOPLEHOOD MODEL Eric Hannel
Illus. 180 pp. Lexington Books, 2015. $80; eBook, $79.99.

REINTERPRETING NEW ENGLAND INDIANS & THE COLONIAL EXPERIENCE
Colin G. Calloway & Neal Salisbury, Eds.
Illus. 380 pp. University Press of New England, 2004. $39.50.

REINVENTING THE ENEMY'S LANGUAGE: CONTEMPORARY NATIVE WOMEN'S WRITINGS OF NORTH AMERICA
Joy Harjo & Gloria Bird, Eds.; 576 pp. Paper. W.W. Norton & Co., 1998. $17.95.

RELIGION & CEREMONIES OF THE LENAPE
Mark Harrington; Reprint. Amazon.com, $30.99; paper, $24.99.

RELIGION & HOPI LIFE
John D. Loftin; 2nd Ed. 210 pp. Amazon.com & Alibris.com, 2003. $39.95; paper, $15.95.

RELIGION IN NATIVE NORTH AMERICAN
Christopher Vecsey; Illus. 210 pp. Paper. University of Idaho Press, 1990. $22.95.

RELIGION, LAW & THE LAND: NATIVE AMERICANS & JUDICIAL INTERPRETATIONS OF SACRED LAND Brian E. Brown; 208 pp. Greenwood Publishing, 1999. $87.95.

RELIGION & PROFIT: MORAVIANS IN EARLY AMERICA
Katherine Carte Engel
Illus. 328 pp. University of Pennsylvania Press, 2011. $39.95; paper, $22.50.

RELIGION & RESISTANCE IN THE ENCOUNTER BETWEEN THE COEUR D'ALENE INDIANS & JESUIT MISSIONARIES
Ted Fortier; Illus. 196 pp. Edwin Mellen Press, 2003. $99.95.

THE RELIGIONS OF THE AMERICAN INDIANS
Ake Hultkrantz; Paper. University of California Press, 1981. $27.95.

RELIGIOUS EXPERIENCE
Wayne Proudfoot; 290 pp. Paper. U. of California Press, 1987. $26.95. E-Book available.

RELIGIOUS FREEDOM & INDIAN RIGHTS: THE CASE OF OREGON VS. SMITH
Carolyn N. Long; 264 pp. University Press of Kansas, 2004. $35; paper, $14.95.

RELIGIOUS MEDICINE: THE HISTORY & EVOLUTION OF INDIAN MEDICINE
Kenneth G. Zysk; 340 pp. Transaction Press, 1992. $49.95.

THE RELUCTANT PILGRIM: A SKEPTIC'S JOURNEY INTO NATIVE MYSTERIES
Roger Welsh; 264 pp. paper. University of Nebraska Press, 2015. $19.95.

REMAINING CHICKASAW IN INDIAN TERRITORY, 1830S-1907
Wendy St. Jean
Illus. Maps. 168 pp. University of Alabama Press, 2011. $32; paper, $15. E-Book, $12.

*REMEMBER MY NAME
Sara H. Banks; Deals with the Cherokee Indian Removal of 1838. An 11-year-old Cherokee, Annie Rising Fawn, shows courage and an adventurous spirit. Grades 4 to 9. Illus. 120 pp. Paper. Council for Indian Education & Roberts Rinehart, 1994. $8.95.

REMEMBER NATIVE AMERICA! THE EARTHWORKS OF ANCIENT AMERICA
Richard Balthazar; Documents and illustrates Indian mounds and other earthworks from 23 states. Paper. Amazon.com, 1993. $14.95.

REMEMBER YOUR RELATIONS: THE ELSIE ALLEN BASKETS, FAMILY & FRIENDS
Suzanne Abel-Vidor, Dot Brovarney, Susan Billy
Pomo Indian Basketry. Full-color photos. 128 pp. Paper. Heyday Books, 1997. $20.

REMEMBER YOUR RELATIVES, YANKTON SIOUX IMAGES,
VOL. 1, 1851-1904; VOL. 2, 1865-1915 Renee Sansom-Flood, et al
Illus. Vol. 1, 55 pp.; Vol. 2, 150 pp. Paper. Yankton Sioux Tribe, 1985 & 1989. $8.50 each.

THE REMEMBERED EARTH: AN ANTHOLOGY OF CONTEMPORARY NATIVE AMERICAN LITERATURE Geary Hobson, Editor; Poetry, essays & short stories by contemporary Native American writers. Illus. 429 pp. Paper. University of New Mexico Press, $39.95.

THE REMEMBERING: A DREAM VISION OF NATIVE AMERICA
Ana Reeves Legare; Illus. 2160 pp. Paper. Station Hill Press, 2006. $14.95.

FREDERICK REMINGTON: ARTIST OF THE AMERICAN WEST
Nancy Plain; Amazon.com, 1999.

REMINISCENCES OF THE INDIANS
Cephas Washburn; Phillip A. Sperry, Ed.
Reprint. Illus. 244 pp. Paper. Amazon.com, $34.95.

REMINGTON & RUSSELL: THE SID RICHARDSON COLLECTION
Brian W. Dippie, Editor
Revised ed. Illus. 240 pp. Amazon.com, 1994. $70; paper, $34.95.

REMIX: NEW MODERNITIES IN A POST-INDIAN WORLD
Gerald McMaster (Plains Cree) & Joe Baker (Choctaw); 15 artists of mixed Native-non-Native heritage. Illus. 96 pp. Paper. NMAI Press, 2007. $19.95.

REMOVABLE TYPE: HISTORIES OF THE BOOK IN INDIAN COUNTRY, 1663-1880
Phillip H. Round; Examines relationship between Native Americans and printed books over a 200-year period. Illus. 296 pp. University of North Carolina Press, 2010. $59.95; paper, $24.95.

REMOVAL AFTERSHOCK: THE SEMINOLES' STRUGGLES TO SURVIVE IN THE WEST, 1836-1866 Jane F. Lancaster; Illus. 248 pp. Paper. Amazon.com, 1994. $17.

THE REMOVAL OF THE CHEROKEE NATION: MANIFEST DESTINY OF NATIOAL DISHONOR Louis Filler and Allen Guttman, Editors
Reprint of 1962 edition. 128 pp. Paper. Krieger Publishing, $9.50; paper, $7.50.

THE REMOVAL OF THE CHOCTAW INDIANS
Arthur H. DeRosier, Jr.; An accurate account of a major Indian removal with the policies, treaties & agonies that were a part of it. Illus. 210 pp. Paper. Cherokee Publications, $9.95.

REMOVALS: 19TH CENTURY AMERICAN LITERATURE & THE POLITICS OF INDIAN AFFAIRS Lucy Maddox; 216 pp. Oxford Unviersity Press, 1991. $155.

THE RENAISSANCE OF AMERICAN INDIAN HIGHER EDUCATION: CAPTURING THE DREAM Maenette K. AhNee-Benham & Wayne Stein
Illus. 296 pp. Amazon.com, 2002. $69.95; paper, $32.50.

A RENDEVOUS WITH CLOUDS
Tim Fleming; Illus. 245 pp. Paper. University of New Mexico Press, 2004. $17.95.

RENEGADE TRIBE: THE PALOUSE INDIANS & THEIR INVASION OF THE INLAND PACIFIC NORTHWEST Clifford Trafzer & Richard Scheuerman, Editor
Illus. Maps. Biblio. 224 pp. Paper. WSU Press, 1986. $17.95.

THE RENEWED, THE DESTROYED & THE REMADE: THE THREE THOUGHT WORLDS OF THE IROQUOIS & THE HURON, 1609-1650
Robert M. Carpenter; Illus. 192 pp. Paper. Michigan State University Press, 2004. $27.95.

RENEWING THE WORLD: PLAINS INDIAN RELIGION & MORALITY
Howard L. Harrod; 213 pp. Paper. University of Arizona Press, 1987. $19.95.

REPATRIATION READER: WHO OWNS AMERICAN INDIAN REMAINS?
Devon A. Mihesuah; Anthology focusing on issues of repatriation of American Indian remains and artifacts. Illus. 335 pp. Paper. University of Nebraska Press, 2000. $20.

REPORT OF CHARLES A. WETMORE, SPECIAL U.S. COMMISSIONER OF MISSION INDIANS OF SOUTHERN CALIFORNIA
Norman Tanis, Editor; Paper. California State University, Northridge, 1977. $10.

REPORT OF THE MOUND EXPLORATIONS OF THE BUREAU OF ETHNOLOGY
Cyrus Thomas; Reprint of 1894 edition. Illus. 786 pp. Paper. Smithsonian Books, $29.95.

REPORT TO THE DEPARTMENT OF THE INTERIOR: POEMS
Diane Glancy; 112 pp. Paper. University of New Mexico Press, $21.95

REPORT TO THE SECRETARY OF WAR OF THE U.S., ON INDIAN AFFAIRS
J. Morse; Reprint of 1822 edition. Illus. 400 pp. Amazon.com, $45.

REPOSSESSION AND YOU
Institute for the Development of Indian Law, $3.50.

REQUIEM FOR A PEOPLE: THE ROGUE INDIANS & THE FRONTIERSMEN
Stephen D. Beckham
Reprint. Illus. 232 pp. Paper. Oregon State University Press, 1996. $16.95.

RESEARCH FOR INDIGENOUS SURVIVAL: INDIGENOUS RESEARCH METHODOLOGIES IN THE BEHAVIORAL SCIENCES
Lori Lambert; Photos. 256 pp. Paper. University of Nebraska Press, 2015. $16.95.

RESEARCH IN HUMAN CAPITAL & DEVELOPMENT: AMERICAN INDIAN ECONOMIC DEVELOPMENT Alan L. Sorkin, Ed.; Vol. 10. 200 pp. Amazon.com, 1996. $78.50.

RESEARCH & WRITING TRIBAL HISTORIES
Duane Kendall Hale; A guide to the process of recording the histories of tribal nations. Paper. Michigan Indian Press, $14.95.

THE RESERVATION
Ted C. Williams; Tales of life on the Tuscarora Indian Reservation in New York State, from the late 1930's to the 1950's. Illus. 256 pp. Paper. Syracuse U. Press, 1976. $15.95.

THE RESERVATION BLACKFEET, 1885-1945: A PHOTOGRAPHIC HISTORY OF CULTURAL SURVIVAL
William E. Farr; Illus. 240 pp. Paper. University of Washington Press, 1984. $19.95.

RESERVATION "CAPITALISM": ECONOMIC DEVELOPMENT IN INDIAN COUNTRY
Robert J. Miler; 220 pp. Paper. University of Nebraska Press, 2013. $24.95.

RESERVATION POLITICS: HISTORICAL TRAUMA, ECONOMIC DEVELOPMENT & INTRATRIBAL CONFLICT
Raymond I. Orr; Illus. 256 pp. University of Oklahoma Press, 2017. $34.95.

RESERVATION REELISM: REDFACING, VISUAL SOVEREIGNTY, AND REPRESENTATIONS OF NATIVE AMERICANS IN FILM
Michelle H. Raheja; Photos. 358 pp. Paper. University of Nebraska Press, 2013. $30.

RESERVE MEMORIES: THE POWER OF THE PAST IN A CHILCOTIN COMMUNITY
David W. Dinwoodie; Examines a Northern Athabaskan community. Map. 120 pp. Paper. University of Nebraska Press, 2002. $19.95.

THE RESETTLEMENT OF BRITISH COLUMBIA: ESSAYS ON COLONIALISM & GEOGRAPHICAL CHANGE Cole Harris
336 pp. UBC Press. Dist. bu University of Washington Press, 1997. $83; paper, $35.95.

RESHAPING THE UNIVERSITY: RESPONSIBILITY, INDIGENOUS EPISTEMES, & THE LOGIC OF THE GIFT Rauna Kuokkanen
An indigenous postcolonial critique of the modern university and proposes a new logic. 284 pp. University of Washington Press, 2007. $94; paper, $37.95.

RESILIENCY IN NATIVE AMERICAN & IMMIGRANT FAMILIES
Hamilton McCubbin, Elizabeth Thompsn, et al.; Paper. CQ Press, 1998. $79.

RESILIENT CULTURES: AMERICA'S NATIVE PEOPLES CONFRONT EUROPEAN COLONIZATION, 1500-1800
John E. Kicza; Illus. 200 pp. Paper. Prentice Hall PTR, 2002. $31.80.

RESPECT FOR THE ANCESTORS: AMERICAN INDIAN CULTURAL AFFILIATION IN THE AMERICAN WEST Peter N. Jones; Bauu Institute Press, 2005. $21.95.

RESPECT FOR LIFE: THE TRADITIONAL UPBRINGING OF THE RESPONSIVE EYE: RALPH T. COE & THE COLLECTING OF AMERICAN INDIAN ART Ralph T. Coe
Illus. 352 pp. Yale University Press, 2003. $65. Paper. Amazon.com, $29.95.

RESTITUTION: THE LAND CLAIM CASES OF THE MASHPEE, PASSAMAQUODDY & PENOBSCOT INDIANS OF NEW ENGLAND
Paul Brodeur; Illus. 160 pp. New England University Press, 1985. $21.95; paper, $9.95.

RESTORING THE CHAIN OF FRIENDSHIP: BRITISH POLICY & THE INDIANS OF THE GREAT LAKES, 1783-1815
Timothy D. Willig; Traces the developments of British-Native interaction & diplomacy. Photos. Maps. 390 pp. University of Nebraska Press, 2008. $50.

RESTORING A PRESENCE: AMERICAN INDIANS & YELLOWSTONE NATIONAL PARK Peter Nabakov & Lawrence Loendorf; Documents the many different rolesIndians have played in the history of the park. Illus. Photos & Maps. U. of Oklahoma Press, 39.95.

RETAINED BY THE PEOPLE: A HISTORY OF AMERICAN INDIANS & THE BILL OF RIGHTS John R. Wunder; Illus. 312 pp. Paper. Oxford U. Press, 1994. $21.95.

RETHINKING AMERICAN INDIAN HISTORY
Donald L. Fixico; 149 pp. Paper. University of New Mexico Press, 1999. $30.

RETHINKING THE FUR TRADE: CULTURES OF EXCHANGE IN AN ATLANTIC WORLD
Susan Sleeper-Smith; Essays on the role of Native Americans in the fur trade. Photos. Maps. Paper. University of Nebraska Press, 2009. $40.

RETHINKING HOPI ETHNOGRAPHY
Peter M. Whitely
Photos. Maps. Illus. 288 pp. Smithsonian Institution Press, 1998. $39.95; paper, $19.95.

RETHINKING PUERTO RICAN PRECOLONIAL HISTORY
Reniel Rodriquez Ramos; Focuses on the successive indigenous cultures of Puerto Rico prior to 1493. Illus. 320 pp. University of Alabama Press, 2010. $49.75; paper, $29.95.

RETURN OF THE BUFFALO: THE STORY BEHIND AMERICA'S INDIAN GAMING EXPLOSION
Estaban E. Torres & Terry L. Pechota; Illus. 240 pp. Paper. Greenwood, 1995. $22.

THE RETURN OF CHIEF BLACK FOOT
Victoria Mauricio; Illus. 140 pp. Paper. Donning Co., 1981. $5.95.

THE RETURN OF THE EAGLE: THE LEGAL HISTORY OF THE GRAND TRAVERSE BAND OF OTTAWA & CHIPPEWA INDIANS
Matthew L.M. Fletcher; Illus. Michigan State University Press, 2011.

RETURN OF THE INDIAN: CONQUEST & REVIVAL IN THE AMERICAS
Phillip Wearne; Chronicles the indigenous resistance in Latin and North America. Illus. 255 pp. Temple University Press, 1996. $69.95; paper, $22.95.

*RETURN OF THE INDIAN SPIRIT
Vinson Brown; Grades 4 and up. A young Indian boy's coming of age through the beliefs and ways of his people. Illus. 60 pp. Paper. Cherokee Publications, $5.95.

THE RETURN OF LITTLE BIG MAN: A NOVEL
Thomas Berger; 448 pp. Amazon.com, $25; paper, $12.95.

THE RETURN OF THE NATIVE: AMERICAN INDIAN POLITICAL RESURGENCE
Stephen E. Cornell; Illus. 288 pp. Paper. Oxford University Press, 1990. $59.

RETURN OF THE SUN: TALES FROM THE NORTHEASTERN WOODLANDS
Joseph Bruchac; Varies tales illustrating both the wealth of humor and depth of respect for life and earth of the indigenous Northeast American people. Illus. Paper. Crossing Press, $12.95. Written Heritage, $9.95.

RETURN TO CREATION: A SURVIVAL MANUAL FOR NATIVE & NATURAL PEOPLE
Medicine Story, pseud.; Illus. 210 pp. Paper. Bear Tribe, 1991. $9.95.

RETURNING THE GIFT: POETRY & PROSE FROM THE FIRST NORTH AMERICAN NATIVE WRITERS' FESTIVAL Joseph Bruchac, Editor; A collection of submissions by 92 writers at the "Returning the Gift Festival" held in 1992. Bruchac comments on the current state of Native literature. 369 pp. Paper. University of Arizona Press, 1994. $20.95.

REVENGE OF THE PEQUOTS: HOW A SMALL NATIVE AMERICAN TRIBE CREATED THE WORLD'S MOST PROFITABLE CASINO
Kim Isaac Eisler; Illus. 267 pp. Paper. University of Nebraska Press, 2002. $13.95.

REVENGE OF THE WINDIGO: THE CONSTRUCTION OF THE MIND & MENTAL HEALTH OF NORTH AMERICAN ABORIGINAL PEOPLES
James B. Waldram; The study of Aboriginal mental health. 414 pp. University of Toronto Press, 2004. $45; paper, $24.95.

REVITALIZING COMMUNITIES: INNOVATIVE STATE & LOCAL PROGRAMS
Kellie J. Dressler, Editor; Illus. 149 pp. Paper. Amazon.com, 1998. $30.

REVOLT: AN ARCHAEOLOGICAL HISTORY OF PUEBLO RESISTANCE & REVITALIZATION N 17TH CENTURY NEW MEXICO Matthew Liebmann
The Pueblo Revolt of 1680. 328 pp. Illus. Paper. University of Arizona Press, 2014. $30.

THE REYNOLDS CAMPAIGN ON POWDER RIVER
J.W. Vaughn; Illus. 268 pp. Paper. University of Oklahoma Press, 2017. $19.95.

THE REZ ROAD FOLLIES: CANOES, CASINOS, COMPUTERS, & BIRCH BARK BASKETS Jim Northrup; 256 pp. Paper. University of Minnesota Press, 1999. $15.95.

RICH INDIANS: NATIVE PEOPLE & THE PROBLEM OF WEALTH IN AMERICAN HISTORY Alexandra Harmon; Examines seven instances of Indian affluence & the dilemmas they presented both for Native Americans and for Euro-Americans. 388 pp. U. of North Carolina Press, 2010. $39.95; paper, $19.95.

THE RICHEY CLOVIS CACHE: EARLIEST AMERICANS ALONG THE COLUMBIA RIVER Richard M. Gramly; Illus. 70 pp. Paper. Amazon.com, $12.95.

RIDE ON THE WING OF THE EAGLE: VIEWING LIFE FROM A HIGHER PERSPECTIVE
Sheila G. Griffin; Illus. 188 pp. Paper. Amazon.com, 1998. $12.

RIDEOUT'S VOCABULARY OF SHAWNEE, VOL. 35
Thomas Rideout; 75 pp. Amazon.com, 2004. $30.

RIDING OUT THE STORM: 19TH-CENTURY CHICKASAW GOVERNORS, THEIR LIVES & INELLECTUAL LEGACY Phillip C. Morgan
The Chickasaw Press. 200 pp. Distributed by the University of Oklahoma Press, $20.

RIDING SHOTGUN INTO THE PROMISED LAND
John Lloyd Purdy; Fiction. 232 pp. Paper. Amazon.com, 2011. $12.95.

THE RISE & FALL OF INDIAN COUNTRY, 1825-1855
William E. Unrau; The true nature of the U.S. Government's policy toward the Indians. Maps. 216 pp. University Press of Kansas, 2007. $29.95.

JOHN ROLLIN RIDGE: HIS LIFE & WORKS
James W. Parins; Illus. 280 pp. University of Nebraska Press, 2003. $55; paper, $22.

RIDING BUFFALOES & BRONCOS: RODEO & NATIVE TRADITIONS IN THE NORTHERN GREAT PLAINS Allison Fuss Mellis; Examines events where American Indians gather to celebrate community and equestrian skills. Illus. Maps. 288 pp. University of Oklahoma Press, 2003. $24.95.

*RIEL'S PEOPLE: HOW THE METIS LIVED
Maria Campbell; Grades 5 and up. Paper. Salem House, $6.95.

RIFLES, BLANKETS & BEADS: IDENTITY, HISTORY, & THE NORTHERN ATHAPASKAN POTLATCH
William E. Simeone; Illus. Maps. 216 pp. Paper. U. of Oklahoma Press, 1995. $19.95.

*RIGHT AFTER SUNDOWN: TEACHING STORIES OF THE NAVAJO
Marilyne Virginia Mabery; Raymond Johnson, Illustrator
12 short stories. Grades 4 and up. Paper. Amazon.com, 1991. $14.95.

THE RIGHTS OF INDIANS & TRIBES: THE BASIC ACLU GUIDE TO THE INDIAN & TRIBAL RIGHTS Stephen L. Pevar
4th edition. Illus. 305 pp. Paper. Oxford University Press, 2012. $26.95

THE RIGHTS OF INDIGENOUS PEOPLES
Lawrence Rosen; Oxford University Press, 2005.

RIGHTS REMEMBERED: A SALISH GRANDMOTHER SPEAKSON AMERICAN INDIAN HISTORY & THE FUTURE Pauline R. Hillaire; Gregory P. Fields, Editor
Illus. 486 pp. University of Nebraska Press, 2016. $65.

*THE RINGS ON WOOT-KEW'S TAIL: INDIAN LEGENDS OF THE ORIGIN OF THE SUN, MOON & STARS
Will Gerber, et al; Grades 3-9. Paper. Council for Indian Education, 1973. $1.95.

RIO DEL NORTE: PEOPLE OF THE UPPER RIO GRANDE FROM EARLIEST TIMES TO THE PUEBLO REVOLT
Carroll L. Riley; Reprint. Illus. Maps. 336 pp. Paper. University of Utah Press. $15.95.

RISE & FALL OF THE CHOCTAW REPUBLIC
Angie Debo; Reprint of 1934 edition. 2nd Edition. Illus. Maps. Biblio. 314 pp. Paper. University of Oklahoma Press, 1995. $19.95.

RISE & FALL OF INDIAN COUNTRY, 1825-1855
William E. Unrau; Illus. 216 pp. University Press of Kansas, 2007. $34.95.

RISE & FALL OF NORTH AMERICA'S INDIANS: FROM PREHISTORY THROUGH GERONIMO William Brandon; 472 pp. Rinehart, Roberts Publishers, 2003. $34.95.

*RISING FAWN & THE FIRE MYSTERY
Marilou Awiakta
Story about the Trail of Tears. Grades 4 and up. Illus. Paper. St. Luke's Press, 1984. $6.95.

RITES OF CONQUEST: THE HISTORY & CULTURE OF MICHIGAN'S NATIVE AMERICANS Charles E. Cleland; Illus. Paper. U. of Michigan Press, 2005. $20.95.

RITUAL & MYTH IN ODAWA REVITALIZATION: RECLAIMING A SOVEREIGN PLACE
Melissa A. Pflug; Illus. Biblio. 304 pp. University of Oklahoma Press, 1998. $28.95.

RITUAL IN PUEBLO ART: HOPI LIFE IN HOPI PAINTING
Byron Harvey, III
Illus. 265 pp. Paper. National Museum of the American Indian, 1970. $10.

A RIVER APART: THE POTTERY OF COCHITI & SANTA DOMINGO PUEBLOS
Valerie K. Verzuh, Editor; Examines the pottery tradition of two pueblos, Cochiti & Santo Domingo. Illus. 192 pp. Museum of New Mexico Press, 2010. $45.

THE RIVER & THE HORSEMEN: A NOVEL OF THE LITTLE BIGHORN
Robert E. Skimin; The story (part fiction, part fact) of Custer, Sitting Bull, and the Battle of the Little Bighorn. 384 pp. Amazon.com, 2007. $19.95.

THE RIVER IS IN US: FIGHTING TOXICS IN A MOHAWK COMMUNITY
Elizabeth Hoover; University of Minnesota Press, 2017. $112; paper, $28.

RIVER OF MEMORY: THE EVERLASTING COLUMBIA
William D. Layman; Illus. 160 pp. U. of Washington Press, 2006. $45; paper, $24.95.

RIVER SONG: NAXIYAMTAMA (SNAKE RIVER-PALOUSE) ORAL TRADITIONS FROM MARY JIM, ANDREW GEORGE, GORDON FISHER & EMILY PEONE
Richard Scheuerman & Clifford Trafzer, Editors
Illus. Map. 228 pp. Paper. WSU Press, 2015. $27.95.

RIVER OF SORROWS - LIFE HISTORY OF THE MAIDU-NISENAN INDIANS
Richard Burrill; Historical fiction reveals their lifeways. Illus. Photos.
Maps. 220 pp. Paper. Naturegraph, 1978. $8.95.

RIVER OF TEARS
Maud Emery
The events of the massacre at Bute Inlet. Illus. 96 pp. Paper. Hancock House, 1994. $9.95.

THE RIVER TRAIL: A SAGA OF THE CHEROKEE REMOVAL
Jane B. Noble, Editor; Illus. 275 pp. Paper. Arc Press, 2001.$24.

RIVERS OF SAND: CREEK INDIAN EMIGRATION, RELOCATION, AND ETHNIC CLEANSING IN THE AMERICAN SOUTH
Christopher D. Haveman; Illus. 438 pp. University of Nebraska Press, 2016. $65.

THE ROAD: INDIAN TRIBES & POLITICAL LIBERTY
Russell Barsh & James Henderson; Paper. University of California Press, 1979. $15.

THE ROAD OF LIFE & DEATH: A RITUAL DRAMA OF THE AMERICAN INDIANS
Paul Radin; Reprint. 368 pp. Paper. Amazon.com, $14.95.

THE ROAD ON WHICH WE CAME - PO'I PENTUN TAMMEN KIMMAPPEH: A HISTORY OF THE WESTERN SHOSHONE
Steven J. Crum; Illus. Maps. 252 pp. Paper. University of Utah Press, 1994. $19.95.

THE ROAD TO DISAPPEARANCE: A HISTORY OF THE CREEK INDIANS
Angie Debo
Reprint of 1941 ed. Illus. 400 pp. Paper. University of Oklahoma Press, 2002. $21.95.

THE ROAD TO LAME DEER
Jerry Mader; Memoir. Little Big Horn, Wounded Knee, cultural survival and modern Cheyenne life. Illus. 216 pp. University of Nebraska Press, 2002. $25.

THE ROAD TO NUNAVUT: THE PROGRESS OF THE EASTERN ARCTIC INUIT SINCE THE SECOND WORLD WAR
R. Quinn Duffy; 376 pp. Amazon.com, 1987. $35.

THE ROAD TO THE SUNDANCE: MY JOURNEY INTO NATIVE SPIRITUALITY
Manny Twofeathers; 240 pp. Paper. Little, Brown & Amazon.com 1997. $11.45.

A ROAD WE DO NOT KNOW: A NOVEL OF CUSTER AT THE LITTLE BIGHORN
Frederick Chiaventone; Paper. University of New Mexico Press, $15.95.

THE ROADS OF MY RELATIONS
Devon A. Mihesuah; 19th century Choctaw family forced from Mississippi to Oklahoma. 237 pp. Paper. University of Arizona Press, 2000. $17.95.

ROADS TO CENTER PLACE: AN ANASAZI ATLAS
Kathryn Gabriel; Illus. 250 pp. Paper. Johnson Books, 1991. $12.95.

ROADS TO THE PAST: HIGHWAY MAP & GUIDE TO NEW MEXICO ARCHAEOLOGY
Eric Blinnman & Dick Huelster
Text, photos, graphics, map. University of New Mexico Press, 2017. $17.95.

ROADSIDE GUIDE TO INDIAN RUINS & ROCK ART OF THE SOUTHWEST
Gordon Sullivan; photos/Cathie Sullivan; Illus. 304 pp. Westcliffe Publishers, 2004. $24.95

ROADSIDE HISTORY OF ARIZONA
Marshall Trimble; Illus. Maps. Photos. 496 pp. Mountain Press, 1994. $30; paper, $18.

ROADSIDE HISTORY OF ARKANSAS
Alan C. Paulson; Illus. Maps. Photos. 480 pp. Mountain Press, 1995. $30; paper, $18.

ROADSIDE HISTORY OF NEBRASKA
Candy Moullton; Illus. Maps. Photos. 450 pp. Mountain Press, 1997. $30; paper, $18.

ROADSIDE HISTORY OF NEW MEXICO
Francis L. & Roberta Fugate
Illus. Maps. Photos. 484 pp. Mountain Press, 1990. $24.95; paper, $16.

ROADSIDE HISTORY OF OKLAHOMA
Francis L. & Robert B. Fugate
Tales of early explorers. Illus. 472 pp. Mountain Press, 1990. $24.95; paper, $15.95.

ROADSIDE HISTORY OF OREGON
Bill Gulick; Illus. Maps. Photos. 452 pp. Paper. Mountain Press, 1993. $18.

ROADSIDE HISTORY OF SOUTH DAKOTA
Linda Hasslestrom; Illus. Maps. Photos. 480 pp. Mountain Press, 1995. $25; paper, $16.

ROADSIDE HISTORY OF WYOMING
Candy Moullton; Illus. 480 pp. Mountain Press, 1990. $24.95; paper, $15.95.

ROANOKE & WAMPUM: TOPICS IN NATIVE AMERICAN HERITAGE & LITERATURES
Ron Wellburn; Illus. 255 pp. Paper. Amazon.com, 2001. $29.95.

THE ROARING OF THE SACRED RIVER
Steven Foster with Meredith Little; The wilderness quest for vision and self-healing. Illus. 240 pp. Paper. Prentice Hall Press, $9.95.

ROBES OF POWER: TOTEM POLES ON CLOTH
Doreen Jensen & Polly Sargent; Oral history about button blankets and their place in the culture of the Northwest Coast. Illus. 96 pp. Paper. U. of Washington Press, 1987. $32.95.

ROBES OF SPLENDOR: NATIVE NORTH AMERICAN PAINTED BUFFALO HIDES
George P. Horse Capture, Anne Vitart & Michael Waldberger; Native American life & artworks. 70 color & bxw photos. 144 pp. Paper. W.W. Norton & Co., $20.

ROCK ART IMAGES OF NORTHERN NEW MEXICO
Dennis Slifer; University of New Mexico Press, $17.95.

ROCK ART IN NEW MEXICO
Polly Schaafsma
Explores prehistoric rock art of the Anasazi, rock art of the Navajo, the desert peoples of southern New Mexico. Illus. 168 pp. Paper. Museum of New Mexico Press, 2000. $29.95.

ROCK ART OF THE AMERICAN INDIAN
Campbell Grant; Illus. 192 pp. Paper. Amazon.com, 1972. $16.95.

ROCK ART OF THE AMERICAN SOUTHWEST
Scott Thybony; photos by Fred Hirschmann; 100 color photos of rock art throughout the Southwest. 128 pp. Graphic Arts Center, 1994. $29.50.

THE ROCK ART OF EASTERN NORTH AMERICA: CAPTURING IMAGES & INSIGHT
Carol Diaz-Granados & james R. Duncan, Editors
Illus. 520 pp. University of Alabama Press, 2004. $34.95.

ROCK ART OF KENTUCKY
Coy, et al; About 60 petroglyph sites are located and described.
Photos. 174 pp. Amazon.com, 1997. $34.95.

ROCK ART OF THE LOWER PECOS
Carolyn E. Boyd; Illus. 160 pp Texas A&M University Press, $45.

THE ROCK ART OF TEXAS INDIANS
W.W. Newcomb, Jr.
Paintings by Forrest Kirkland. Illus. University of Texas Press, 1995. $70; paper, $34.95.

THE ROCK ART OF UTAH
Polly Schaafsma; Illus. Paper. University of Utah Press, 1976. $19.95.

ROCK ART OF WESTERN SOUTH DAKOTA
James D. Keyser & linea Sundstrom; An illustrated compendium of prehistoric petroglyphs and pictographs found in caves and on canyon walls throughout western South Dakota. 220 pp. Paper. Center for Western Studies, $9.95.

ROCK ART STUDIES IN THE GREAT BASIN
Eric Ritter; Illus. 129 pp. Paper. Coyote Press, 1998. $15.65.

ROCK, GHOST, WILLOW, DEER: A STORY OF SURVIVAL
Allison Adelle Hedge Coke; Memoir/narrative.
Illus. Photos. 224 pp. Paper. University of Nebraska Press, 2004. $16.95.

ROCK ISLAND: HISTORICAL INDIAN ARCHAEOLOGY IN THE NORTHERN LAKE MICHIGAN BASIN
Ronald Mason; Illus. 275 pp. Paper. Amazon.com, 1986. $19.95.

ROCK PAINTINGS OF THE CHUMASH
Campbell Grant; Chumash history and culture as well as their rock paintings. Illus. Photos. 186 pp. Amazon.com. $35.

THE ROCKS BEGIN TO SPEAK
LaVan Martineau; Illus. 210 pp. K C Publications, 1973. $17.50.

ROCKY MOUNTAIN WEST IN 1867
Louis Simonin; translated by Wilson Clough; Illus. U. of Nebraska Press, 1966. $16.95.

*WILL ROGERS
Jane A. Schott; Grades 1-3. Illus. Color photos. 64 pp. Lerner, 1996.
$14.95; paper, $5.95.

*WILL ROGERS: AMERICAN HUMORIST
Grades 2-4. Illus. 32 pp. Childrens Press, $10.95.

ROGUE DIAMONDS: THE RUSH FOR NORTHERN RICHES, DENE RIGHTS
Ellen Bielawski; Illus. Maps. 256 pp. Paper. U. of Washington Press, 2004. $24.95.

THE ROGUE RIVER INDIAN WAR & ITS AFTERMATH, 1850-1980
E.A. Schwartz; History of the native peoples of western Oregon.
Illus. Maps. 368 pp. University of Oklahoma Press, 1997. $34.95.

*THE ROLLING HEAD: CHEYENNE TALES
Henry Tall Bull and Tom Weist
Grades 3-9. Paper. Council for Indian Education, 1971. $1.95.

ROLLING THUNDER SPEAKS: A MESSAGE FOR TURTLE ISLAND
Rolling Thunder; edited by Carmen Sun Rising Pope; Summation of his teaching in is own words. 12 photos. 266 pp. Paper. Amazn.com, $14.95.

ROLLING THUNDER: A PERSONAL EXPLORATION INTO THE SECRET HEALING POWER OF AN AMERICAN INDIAN MEDICINE MAN
Doug Boyd; 273 pp. Paper. Dell, 1974. $9.95.

ROMANTIC INDIANS: NATIVE AMERICANS, BRITISH LITERATURE, & TRANSATLANTIC CULTURE, 1756-1830 Tim Fulford; Oxford U. Press, 2006. $165.

THEODORE ROOSEVELT & SIX FRIENDS OF THE INDIAN
William T. Hagan; Describes the efforts by six prominent individuals and two institutions to influence Indian affairs during the Roosevelt administration. Illus. 288 pp. University of Oklahoma Press, 1997. $25.95

ROOTED LIKE THE ASH TREES
Richard Carlson, Editor; Collection of writings by members of New England tribes: the Micmac & Penobscot from Maine, the Paugusset of Connecticut, and the Abenakis of Vermont. Paper. Eagle Wing Press, $5.

THE ROOTS OF DEPENDENCY: SUBSISTENCE, ENVIRONMENT, & SOCIAL CHANGE AMONG THE CHOCTAWS, PAWNEES, & NAVAJOS
Richard White; Illus. Maps. 433 pp. Paper. University of Nebraska Press, 1983. $35.

ROOTS OF THE IROQUOIS
Tehanetorens; Illus. 144 pp. Paper. Book Publishing Co., 2000. $9.95.

ROOTS OF OPPRESSION: THE AMERICAN INDIAN QUESTION
Steve Talbot; 240 pp. International Publishing Co., 1981. $14; paper, $5.25.

ROOTS OF OUR RENEWAL: ETHNOBOTANY & CHEROKEE ENVIRONMENTAL GOVERNANCE Clint Carroll; University of Minnesota Press, 2015. $87.50; paper, $25.

ROOTS OF RESISTANCE: HISTORY OF LAND TENURE IN NEW MEXICO (1680-1980)
Roxanne Dunbar Ortiz; A socio-economic interpretation of the history of northern New Mexico focusing on land tenure patterns and changes. 224 pp. University of Oklahoma Press, $19.95.

ROOTS OF SURVIVAL: NATIVE AMERICAN STORYTELLING & THE SACRED
Joseph Bruchac; Focuses on the relationship of Native traditions to contemporary life. Author traces his own spiritual journey. 224 pp. Fulcrum Publishing, 1997. $24.95.

THE ROOTS OF TICASUK: AN ESKIMO WOMAN'S FAMILY STORY
Emily I. Brown
Illus. Photos. Map. 120 pp. Paper. Alaska Northwest Publishing, 1981. $9.95.

ESTHER ROSS, STILLAGUAMISH CHAMPION
Robert H. Ruby, John A. Brown; Illus. 352 pp. U. of Oklahoma Press, 2003. $19.95.

JOHN ROSS: CHEROKEE CHIEF
Gary E. Moulton; Biography. 292 pp. Paper. University of Georgia Press, $11.95.

ROTTING FACE: SMALLPOX & THE AMERICAN INDIAN
R.G. Robertson; Illus. 350 pp. Caxton Press, 2001. $24.95.

*THE ROUGH-FACE GIRL
Rafe Martin; illus. by David Shannon
An Algonquin tale. Grades PS-3. Illus. 32 pp. Amazon.com, 1992. $15.95.

RUBY OF COCHIN: AN INDIAN WOMAN REMEMBERS
Ruby Daniels & Barbara Johnson
240 pp. Paper. Jewish Publication Society, 2001. $14.95.

RUGS & POSTS: STORY OF NAVAJO WEAVING & THE ROLE OF THE INDIAN TRADER H.L James; Illus. Maps. 160 pp. Paper. Schiffer, 1988. $19.95.

RUINS & RIVALS: THE MAKING OF SOUTHWEST ARCHAEOLOGY
James E. Snead; Illus. 226 pp. Paper. University of Arizona Press, 2004. $17.95.

THE RUMBLLE OF A DISTANT DRUM: THE QUAPAW & OLD WORLD NEWCOMERS, 1673-1804 Morris S. Arnold;
Ilus. 230 pp. University of Arkansas Press & Amazon.com, 2000. $35.

RUNNER IN THE SUN
D'Arcy McNickle; A novel of pre-Hispanic Indian life in the Southwest. Paper. University of New Mexico Press, $19.95.

*RUNNING EAGLE: WOMAN WARRIOR OF THE BLACKFEET
James W. Schultz; Grades 2-10. 24 pp. Council for Indian Education. $3.95.

CHARLES M. RUSSELL: A CATALOGUE RAISONNE
B. Byron Price; Features 170 color reproductions of his greatest works and six essays by Russell experts & scholars. 352 pp. University of Oklahoma Press, $125.

CHARLES M. RUSSELL: MASTERPIECES FROM THE AMON CARTER MUSEUM
Rick Stewart; Illus. 60 pp. Paper. Amon Carter Museum, 1992. $10.

A RUSSIAN AMERICAN PHOTOGRAPHER IN TLINGIT COUNTRY: VINCENT SOBOLEFF IN ALASKA
Sergei Kan; Illus. 284 pp. University of Oklahoma Press, $39.95

RUXTON OF THE ROCKIES
George F. Ruxton; R. LeRoy, Editor
Reprint of 1950 edition. Illus. 326 pp. Paper. University of Oklahoma Press, $14.95.

S

S'ABADEB/THE GIFTS: PACIFIC COAST SALISH ART & ARTIFACTS
Barbara Brotherton; Paper. Amazon.com, 2008. $49.95.

SAAD AHAAH SINIL: DUAL LANGUAGE
Martha A. Austin; Paper. Rough Rock School Press, 1983. $10.

SAANICH, NORTH STRAITS SALISH: CLASSIFIED WORD LIST
Timothy Montler; 184 pp. Paper. University of Washington Press, 1991. $19.95.

SAANII DAHATAAL - THE WOMEN ARE SINGING: POEMS & STORIES
Luci Tapahonso; 95 pp. Paper. University of Arizona Press, 1993. $12.95.

S'ABADEB, THE GIFTS: PACIFIC COAST SALISH ART & ARTISTS
Barbara Brotherton; Illus. 240 pp. Paper. University of Washington Press, 2008. $40.

THE SABIN COLLECTION
Selected Americana from Sabin's dictionary of books relating to America from its discovery to the present time. Includes Bibliotheca Americana-over 100,000 entries dating from 1493 to 1890s. See Research Publications for titles and prices.

THE SAC & FOX INDIANS
W.T. Hagan; Reprint of 1958 edition. Illus. 320 pp. Paper. U. of Oklahoma Press, $15.95.

*SACAGAWEA: BRAVE SHOSHONE GIRL
Sneed B. Collard III; Grades 2-5. Illus. 41 pp. Marshall Cavendish, 2007. $24.95.

*SACAJAWEA: INDIAN INTERPRETER TO LEWIS & CLARK
Grades 4 and up. Illus. 130 pp. Childrens Press, $13.95.

SACAJAWEA
Harold P. Howard; foreword by Joseph Bruchac; Reprint of 1971 edition.
Illus. Maps. 214 pp. Paper. University of Oklahoma Press, 2002. $19.95.

SACAJAWEA
Joseph Bruchac; Illus, Paper. Cherokee Publications, $6.99

SACAGAWEA'S CHILD: LIFE & TIMES OF JEAN-BAPTISTE (POMP) CHARBONEEAU
Susan M. Colby; Details Charbonneau family history. 206 pp. Paper.
University of Oklahoma Press, 2010. $24.95.

SACAJAWEA: A GUIDE & INTERPRETER ON THE LEWIS & CLARK EXPEDITION
Grace Raymond Hebard
Reprint. Illus. 340 pp. Martino Publishing, $45. Paper. Dover Publications, $12.95.

*SACAJAWEA--NATIVE AMERICAN HEROINE
Martha F. Bryant; Story of Sacajawea's entire life. Grades 5 and up.
256 pp. Council for Indian Education. $21.95; paper, $15.95.

SACAJAWEA'S PEOPLE: THE LEMHI SHOSHONES & THE SALMON RIVER COUNTRY John W.W. Mann; Their life before their first contact with non-natives, and their encounter witht the Lewis & Clark Expedition in the early 19th century. Paper. University of Nebraska Press, 2011. $19.95. E-Book, $22.95.

SACAJAWEA SPEAKS: BEYOND THE SHINING MOUNTAINS WITH LEWIS & CLARK
Joyce Badgley Hunsaker; Illus. 170 pp. Amazon.com, 2001. $27.50.

*SACAJAWEA, WILDERNESS GUIDE
Kate Jassem; Grades 4-6. Illus. 48 pp. Amazon.com, 1979. $10.95; paper, $3.50.

SACRED BEAUTY: QUILLWORK OF THE PLAINS INDIANS
Mark J. Halvorson; Color photos of crafted quillwork. Paper. Smoke & Fire Co., $6.95.

SACRED BELIEFS OF THE CHITIMACHA INDIANS
Faye Stouff; Illus.81 pp. Amazon.com, 1995. $12.95.

SACRED EARTH: THE SPIRITUAL LANDSCAPE OF NATIVE AMERICA
Arthur Versluis; Discussion of how Native American religions compare to traditional religions. 176 pp. Paper. Inner Traditions, $12.95.

SACRED BELIEFS OF THE CHITIMACHA INDIANS
Faye Stouff & Smithsonian Archives Staff
Illus. 80 pp. Paper. Amazon.com, 1995. $9.95.

SACRED CIRCLES: TWO THOUSAND YEARS OF NORTH AMERICAN INDIAN ART
Ralph Coe
Illus. 260 pp. Paper. Nelson Atkins, $12.95. University of Washington Press, 1977. $15.

SACRED CLOWNS
Tony Hillerman; Novel. Tribal politics. 305 pp. High-Lonesome Books, 1993. $25.

SACRED EARTH: THE SPIRITUAL LANSDSCAPE OF NATIVE AMERICA
Arthur Versluis; Indigenous rituals & sacred sites; Native American spiritualism.
Illus. 176 pp. Paper. Inner Traditions, 1992. $16.95.

SACRED ENCOUNTERS: FATHER DE SMET & THE INDIANS OF THE ROCKY MOUNTAIN WEST Jacqueline Peterson; with Laura Peers
Displays the similarities and differences between European Christianity & Native American beliefs. 200 color illustrations & 20 bxw photos. 192 pp. U. of Oklahoma Press, 1993. $49.95; paper, $24.95.

SACRED FEATHERS: THE REVEREND PETER JONES (KAHKEWAQUONABY) & THE MISSISSAUGA INDIANS Illus. 390 pp. U. of Nebraska Press, 1987. $22.95.

SACRED FIREPLACE (OCETI WAKAN): LIFE & TEACHINGS OF A LAKOTA MEDICINE MAN Pete S. Catches, Sr.; edited by Peter V. Catches
The life and traditional teachings of Peter Catches, a Lakota healer and teacher. 240 pp. Paper. Amazon.com, 1999. $14.95.

SACRED FOODS OF THE LAKOTA
William & Marla Powers; Descriptions of ceremonies related to eating buffalo meat, wasna, and dog. 168 pp. Paper. Lakota Books, $17.50.

THE SACRED GEOGRAPHY OF THE AMERICAN MOUND-BUILDERS
Maureen Korp; Illus. 170 pp. Edwin Mellen Press, 1990. $69.95.

SACRED GROUND
Ron Zeilinger; Illus. 152 pp. Paper. Tipi Press, 1986. $5.95.

*THE SACRED HARVEST: OJIBWAY WILD RICE GATHERING
Gordon Regguinti; Grades 3-6. Illus. 48 pp. Lerner, 1992. $21.27.

THE SACRED HILL WITHIN: A DAKOTA/LAKOTA WORLD VIEW
Little Crow; 140 pp. Paper. One World Publishing, 1999. $12.95.

SACRED HOOP: RECOVERING THE FEMININE IN AMERICAN INDIAN TRADITIONS
Paula G. Allen; Essays, poetry, keen insights. 328 pp. Paper. Amazon.com, 1987. $12.95.

SACRED IMAGES: A VISION OF NATIVE AMERICAN ROCK ART
Craig Law, et al; Illus. 112 pp. Paper. Smith, Gibbs Publishers, 1996. $24.95.

THE SACRED JOURNEY: PRAYERS & SONGS OF NATIVE AMERICA
Peg Streep; Illus. 104 pp. Amazon.com, 1995. $12.45.

SACRED LAND, SACRED VIEW: NAVAJO PERCEPTIONS OF THE FOUR CORNERS REGION
Robert S. McPherson; 152 pp. Paper. Niversity Press of Colorado, 1992. $12.95.

SACRED LANDS OF INDIAN AMERICA
Jake Page, Ed.; Illus. 144 pp. Harry N. Abrams, 2001. $45.

SACRED LANDS OF THE SOUTHWEST
Harvey Lloyd; 4 vols. Illus. 224 pp. Amazon.com, 1995. $60 each; $240 per set.

SACRED LANGUAGE: THE NATURE OF SUPERNATURAL DISCOURSE IN LAKOTA
William K. Powers; Illus. 248 pp. Paper. Lakota Books, $34.95; Paper. University of Oklahoma Press, 1986. $14.95.

SACRED LEGACY: EDWARD S. CURTIS & THE NORTH AMERICAN INDIAN
Edward S. Curtis, et al; Illus. 192 pp. Simon & Schuster, 2000. $60.

SACRED OBJECTS, SACRED PLACES: PRESERVING TRIBAL TRADITIONS
Andrew Gulliford; Illus. 300 pp. Paper. University Press of Colorado, 1999. $34.95.

THE SACRED ORAL TRADITION OF THE HAVASUPAI: AS RETOLD BY ELDERS & HEADMEN MANAKAJA & SINYELLA, 1918-1921 Frank Tikalsky, Catheine Euler, John Nagel, Editors; Illus. 336 pp. University of New Mexico Press, $29.95.

SACRED PATH CARDS: THE DISCOVERY OF SELF THROUGH NATIVE TEACHINGS
Jamie Sams; Illus. 295 pp. Amazon.com, 1990. $36.

A SACRED PATH: THE WAY OF THE MUSCOGEE CREEKS
Jean Chauhuri & Joyotpaul Chauhuri
191 pp. Paper. Amazon.com & Alibris.com, 2001. $15.

SACRED PATH WORKBOOK: NEW TEACHINGS & TOOLS TO ILLUMINATE YOUR PERSONAL JOURNEY Jamie Sams; Illus. 304 pp. Paper. Amazon.com, 1991. $18.

THE SACRED PIPE: AN ARCHETYPAL THEOLOGY
Paul B. Steinmetz, S.J.; 176 pp. Biblio. Syracuse University Press, 1998. $29.95.

THE SACRED PIPE: BLACK ELK'S ACCOUNT OF THE SEVEN RITES OF OGLALA SIOUX Joseph Epes Brown, Editor
Reprint of 1953 edition. Illus. 152 pp. Paper. University of Oklahoma Press, 2002. $19.95.

SACRED PIPE/BLACK ELK, HOLY MAN OF THE OGLALA
Joseph Epes Brown & Michael F. Steltenkamp
Illus. 210 pp. Fine Communications, 1996. $9.98.

SACRED PLACES: HOW THE LIVING EARTH SEEKS OUR FRIENDSHIP
James Swan; Discusses varieties of Native American sacred places and the dilemma of sacred places in a modern world, and includes a guide to sacred places on public lands throughout the U.S. Illus. 240 pp. Paper. Inner Traditions International, 1990. $14.95.

SACRED PLANT MEDICINE: EXPLORATIONS IN INDIGENOUS HERBALISM
Stephen H. Buhner; Illus. 240 pp. Roberts Rinehart Publishers, 1996. $30; paper, $18.95.

SACRED PLANT MEDICINE: EXPLORATIONS IN THE PRACTICE OF INDIGENOUS HERBALISM Stephen H. Buhner; Illus. 210 pp. Paper. Amazon.com, 2001. $18.95.

SACRED PLANT MEDICINE: THE WISDOM IN NATIVE AMERICAN HERBALISM
Stephen Harrod Buhner; foreword by Brooke Medicine Eagle
Illus. 240 pp. Paper. Inner Traditions, 2006. $16.

SACRED POWERS
Time-Life Books Editors; Amazon.com, 1995. $19.95

SACRED REVOLT: THE MUSKOGEE'S STRUGGLE FOR A NEW WORLD
Joel W. Martin; Illus. 224 pp. Paper. Amazon.com, 1993. $18.

SACRED SAGE: HOW IT HEALS
Silver Wolf Walks Alone; Ceremonial uses of sage to help with physical, mental & spiritual healing. Illus. 32 pp. Paper. Book Publishing Co., $6.

SACRED SCROLLS OF THE SOUTHERN OJIBWAY
Selwyn Dewdney; Amazon.com, 1974. $30.

SACRED SELF, SACRED RELATIONSHIPS: HEALING THE WORLD FOR SEVEN GENERATIONS Leonard Bloomfield; Reprint. Amazon.com, $11.50.

SACRED SITES OF THE INDIANS OF THE AMERICAN SOUTHWEST
Raymond Locke; Illus. 130 pp. Amazon.com, 1992. $29.95.

SACRED SITES & REPATRIATION
Joe Watkins; Amazon.com, 2004.

SACRED SITES, SACRED PLACES
David L. Carmichael, et al., Eds.; Illus. 335 pp. Routledge, 19994. $125.

SACRED SITES: THE SECRET HISTORY OF SOUTHERN CALIFORNIA
Susan Suntree; Illus. Map. 320 pp. University of Nebraska Press, 2010. $34.95.

SACRED SMOKE: THE ANCIENT ART OF SMUDGING FOR MODERN TIMES
Harvest McCampbell; Smudging is the practice of burning herbs for spiritual cleansing. Explains & illustrates this integral part of traditional Native American life. Illus. 128 pp. Paper. Book Publishing Co., $9.95.

*SACRED SONG OF THE HERMIT THRUSH: AN IROQUOIS TALE
by Tehanetorens; Mohawk legend. Grades 3 and up. Illus. 64 pp. Paper. The Book Publishing Co.. $5.95.

SACRED STORIES OF THE SWEET GRASS CREE
Leonard Bloomfield; Reprint. Amazon.com, $67.50.

THE SACRED TREE
Four Worlds Development Project
Reflections on Native American spirituality. Paper. Amazon.com, $9.95.

THE SACRED: WAYS OF KNOWLEDGE, SOURCES OF LIFE
Peggy Beck, Anna Walters & Nia Francisco; Religious concepts of North American Indians. Illus. 384 pp. Amazon.com, 1977. $30.

THE SACRED WHITE TURKEY
Franci Washburn; Fiction. Lakota story. Illus. 175 pp. University of Nebraska Press, 2010.

SACRED WORDS: A STUDY OF NAVAJO RELIGION & PRAYER
Sam Gill; Illus. 283 pp. Greenwood Press, 1981. $35.

SAGA OF CHIEF JOSEPH
Helen Addison Howard; The full story opf Chief Joseph and the Nez Perce War. Illus. Maps. 421 pp. Paper. University of Nebraska Press, 1978 $19.95.

SAGA OF THE COEUR D'ALENE INDIAN NATION
Joseph Seltice; Edward J. Kowrach, Intro by
Illus. Photos. 372 pp. 1990. Amazon.com. New & used from $14.95.

THE SAGA OF SITTING BULL'S BONES: THE UNUSUAL STORY BEHIND SCULPTOR KORCZAK ZIOLKOWSKI'S MEMORIAL TO CHIEF SITTING BULL
Robb DeWall; Illus. 320 pp. Paper. Crazy Horse Foundation, 1984. $9.95.

SAGE DREAMS, EAGLE VISIONS
Danielle M. Hornett; 192 pp. Paper. Michigan State University Press, 2004. $24.95.

SAGEBRUSH SOLDIER: PRIVATE WILLIAM EARL SMITH'S VIEW OF THE SIOUX WAR OF 1876
Sherry Smith; Illus. Maps. 158 pp. University of Oklahoma Press, 1989. $19.95.

SAGEBRUSH TO SHAKESPEARE
Carrol B. Howe; Provides informtion on prehistoric Indian cultures; and the peope who discovered and developed the region of Southern Oregon and Northern California. Illus. 216 pp. Paper. Binford & Mort, 1984. $10.

SAGWITCH: SHOSHONE CHIEFTAIN, MORMON ELDER, 1822-1887
Scott R. Christensen; Leader of the Northwestern Shoshone and survivor of the Bear River Massacre. 272 pp. Paper. Utah State University Press, 1999. $23.95.

SAINTE MARIE AMONG THE IROQUOIS: A LIVING HISTORY MUSEUM OF THE FRENCH & THE IROQUOIS AT ONONDAGA IN THE 17TH CENTURY
Illus. 118 pp. Paper. E Metz, 1995. $9.95.

RAMONA SAKIESTEWA - PATTERNED DREAMS: TEXTILES OF THE SOUTHWEST
Suzanne Baizerman; 52 pp. Paper. Wheelright Museum, 1989. $9.95.

SALINAN INDIAN ROCK PAINTING: LITHOGRAPH
Photo by Al Weber; 16x20 inch lithograph, Laser print. Coyote Press, 1980.

SALINAN INDIANS OF CALIFORNIA & THEIR NEIGHBORS
Betty Brusa; History, vocabulary. Illus. 96 pp. Paper. Naturegraph, 1975. $8.95.

SALINAS: ARCHAEOLOGY, HISTORY, PREHISTORY
David Grant Noble, Editor. Illus. Maps. 40 pp. Paper. Amazon.com, 1990. $8.95.

SALINAS PUEBLO MISSIONS (ABO, QUARIA, GRAN QUIVIRA) NATIONAL MONUMENT, NEW MEXICO Dan Murphy; Tells the story of Estancia Basin from Ice Age geology to Indian villages, to European invasion to designation as a national monument. Illus. 64 pp. Paper. Western National Parks Association, 1993. $9.95.

SALISH BLANKETS: ROBES OF PROTECTION & TRANSFORMATION, SYMBOLS OF WEALTH Leslie Tepper & Janice George
Illus. 224 pp. Paper. University of Nebraska Press, 2017. $40.

*SALISH FOLK TALES
Katheryn Law; Grades 2-8. Paper. Council for Indian Education, 1972. $2.95.

SALISH INDIAN SWEATERS
Priscilla Gibson-Roberts; Dos Tejedoras, 1989. $17.50.

THE SALISH LANGUAGE FAMILY: RECONSTRUCTING SYNTAX
Paul D. Kroeber; Examines the history of an array of important syntactic construction in the Salish language family. Map. 464 pp. University of Nebraska Press, 1999. $60.

SALISH MYTHS & LEGENDS: ONE PEOPLE'S STORIES
M. Terry Thompson & Steven Egesdal
Illus. 4 maps. 2 tables. 498 pp. Paper. University of Nebraska Press, 2008. $28.95.

THE SALISH PEOPLE & THE LEWIS & CLARK EXPEDITION
Confederated Salish & Kootenai Tribes
Illus. Maps. 216 pp. Paper. University of Nebraska Press, 2008. $24.95.

SALMON & HIS PEOPLE VOL. 2: FISH & FISHING IN NEZ PERCE CULTURE
Dan Landeen; Illus. 250 pp. Amazon.com, 2004. $49.95; paper, $29.95.

THE SALT RIVER PIMA-MARICOPA INDIANS
John L. Myers & Robert Gryder; Illus. 176 pp. Heritage Publishers, 1988.

SALTWATER FRONTIER: INDIANS & THE CONTEST FOR THE AMERICAN COAST
Andrew Lipman; 360 pp. Paper. Yale University Press, 2017. $25.

SALVATION & THE SAVAGE: AN ANALYSIS OF PROTESTANT MISSIONS & AMERICAN INDIAN RESPONSE, 1787-1862
R.F. Berkhofer; Reprint of 1965 edition. Greenwood, $35.

SALVATION THROUGH SLAVERY: CHIRICAHUA APACHES & PRIESTS ON THE SPANISH COLONIAL FRONTIER H. Henrietta Stockel
Examines the brutal history f forced conversion & subjection by Spanish priests. University of New Mexico Press, $29.95.

*SAM & THE GOLDEN PEOPLE
Marjorie Vandervelde
Grades 5-9. 40 pp. Council for Indian Education, 1972. $8.95; paper, $2.95.

SAMPLER QUILT BLOCKS FROM NATIVE AMERICAN DESIGNS
Dr. Joyce Mori; Explores the sample quilt blocks adaptedfporm cormn husk bags. Illus. 80 pp. Paper. Written Heritage, $12.95.

SAN DIEGO COUNTY INDIANS AS FARMERS & WAGE EARNERS
Teo Couro; Paper. Acoma Books, $1.

SAN GABRIEL DEL YUNGUE AS SEEN BY AN ARCHAEOLOGIST
Florence H. Ellis; Illus. 96 pp. Paper. Sunstone, 1988. $10.95.

SANAPIA: COMANCHE MEDICINE WOMAN
David E. Jones; Reprint of 1972 edition. 107 pp. Paper. Waveland Press, $15.50.

THE SAND CREEK MASSACRE
Stan Hoag; Reprint of 1961 edition. Illus. Maps. 231 pp. Paper. University of Oklahoma Press, 1998. $19.95.

SAND IN A WHIRLWIND: THE PAIUTE INDIAN WAR, 1860
Ferol Egan; Illus. 316 pp. Paper. University of Nevada Press, 1985. $9.95.

THE SANDAL & THE CAVE: THE INDIANS OF OREGON
Luther S. Cressman; The prehistory of Oregon Indians. Illus. Maps. Biblio. 176 pp. Paper. Oregon State University Press, 1981. $14.95.

SANDPAINTINGS OF THE NAVAJO SHOOTING CHANT
Franc Newcomb & Gladys Reichard; Reprint. Illus. 132 pp. Paper. Eagle's View Publishing, $7.45.

SANTA ANA: THE PEOPLE, THE PUEBLO, AND THE HISTORY OF TAMAYA
Laura Bayer; Traces Santa Ana Pueblo's history from the 16th century to the recent past. Paper. University of New Mexico Press, $14.95.

SANTA CLARA POTTERY TODAY
Betty LeFree; Illus. Photos. 126 pp. Paper. University of New Mexico Press, $14.95.

SANTA FE FANTASY: THE QUEST FOR THE GOLDEN CITY
Elmo Baca; Full of lore on early Pueblo culture and Spanish colonial trading. 145 color illustrations. Photos. 109 pp. Amazon.com, $34.95.

SANTA FE GUIDE
Waite Thompson & Richard GottliebWhere to go, what to see, cultural activities in town and at surrounding Indian Pueblos. 64 pp. Paper. Sunstone Press, $6.95.

SANTA FE: HISTORY OF AN ANCIENT CITY
David Grant Noble; Illus. 168 pp. Paper. School of American Research, 1990. $19.95.

SANTA FE INDIAN MARKET: A HISTORY OF NATIVE ARTS & THE MARKETPLACE
Bruce Bernstein; Paper. University of New Mexico Press, $29.95.

SANTA FE: A MODERN HISTORY, 1880-1990
Henry J. Tobias & Charlkes E. Woodhouse; Focuses on what changes over the past 110 years have meant to the city's inhabitants. Illus. 288 pp. University of New Mexico Press, 2001. $24.95.

SANTA FE & TAOS: THE WRITER'S ERA, 1916-1941
Marta Weigle & Kyle Fiore; Illus. 240 pp. Paper. Amazon.com, 1994. $13.95.

SANTANA: WAR CHIEF OF THE MESCALERO APACHE
Almer N. Blazer; ed. by A.R. Pruit
Photos. 320 pp. Amazon.com, 1996. $24.95; paper, $14.95.

THE SANTEE
James H. Howard; Illus. 20 pp. Paper. Lakota Books, 1998. $12.95.

EDWARD SAPIR: LINGUIST, ANTHROPOLOGIST, HUMANIST
Regna Darnell; Biography. He was first to apply comparative Indo-European methods to the study of American Indian languages, pursuing fieldwork on more than 20 of them. Illus. Maps. 512 pp. Paper. University of Nebraska Press, 2010. $35.

SAPAT'QQAYN: TWENTIETH CENTURY NEZ PERCE ARTISTS
72 pp. Paper. Nez Perce National Historical Park.

SASQUATCH: THE APES AMONG US
John Green; Illus. 492 pp. Paper. Hancock House, $12.95.

SASQUATCH: BIGFOOT: THE CONTINUING MYSTERY
Thomas N. Steenburg; An Indian legend told to early explorers. Illus Maps. 128 pp. Paper. Hancock House, $11.95.

SATANTA: THE LIFE & DEATH OF A WAR CHIEF
Charles M. Robinson, III; Illus. 254 pp. Paper. Texas A&M University Press & Amazon.com, 1998. $27.95; paper, $18.95.;

SATANTA'S WOMAN
Cynthia Haseloff; Reprint. 288 pp. Amazon.com, 2001. $4.50.

SAVAGE FRONTIER: RANGERS, RIFLEMEN & INDIAN WARS IN TEXAS
Stephen L. Moore; 352 pp. Paper. Wordware Publishing, 2002. $19.95.

SAVAGES & CIVILIZATION: WHO WILL SURVIVE?
Jack M. Weatherford; 320 pp. Paper. Ballantine Books, 1995. $19.

SAVAGES OF AMERICA
Roy Harvey Pearce; 252 pp. Paper. Johns Hopkins University Press, 2001. $16.95.

SAVAGES & SCOUNDRELS: THE UNTOLD STORY OF AMERICA'S ROAD TO EMPIRE THROUGH INDIAN TERRITORY
Paul VanDevelder; Illus. 352 pp. Paper. Yale University Press, 2012. $18.

SAVAGISM & CIVILIZATION: A STUDY OF THE INDIAN & THE AMERICAN MIND
Roy Harvey Pearce; forewird by Arnold Krupat
Revised ed. 272 pp. Paper. University of California Press, 1988. $26.95. E-Book available.

THE SAVANAH RIVER CHIEFDOMS: POLITICAL CHANGE IN THE LATE PREHISTORIC SOUTHEAST
David G. Anderson; Illus. 488 pp. Paper. University of Alabama Press, 1994. $39.95.

SAVING THE RESERVATION: JOE GARRY & THE BATTLE TO BE INDIAN
John Fahey; Garry was a Coeur d'Alene Indian, served six terms as president of the National Congress of American Indians in the 1950s. Illus. 240 pp. University of Washington Press, 2001. $26.95.

*SAVINGS
Linda Hogan; Poems by a Chickasaw woman. Grades 7 and up. Oyate, 1988. $10.95.

SAYULA POPOLUCA VERB DERIVATION
Lawrence Clark; 80 pp. Paper. Amazon.com, 1983. $8.50. Microfiche, $2.

SAYNDAY'S PEOPLE: THE KIOWA INDIANS & THE STORIES THEY TOLD
Alice Marriott; Illus. 226 pp. Paper. University of Nebraska Press, 1963. $21.95.

SCALP DANCE: INDIAN WARFARE ON THE HIGH PLAINS, 1865-1879
Thomas Goodrich; Illus. 336 pp.Paper. Amazon.com, 1997. $32.95.

THE SCALP HUNTERS: ABENAKI AMBUSH AT LOVEWELL POND, 1725
Alfred E. Kayworth & Raymond G. Potvin; Adolph Caso, Ed.
Illus. 276 pp. Amazon.com, 2002. $17.95.

THE SCALPEL & THE SILVER BEAR:THE FIRST NAVAJO WOMEN SURGEON COMBINES WESTERN MEDICINE & TRADITIONAL HEALING
Lori Alvord & Elizabeth Van Pelt; 240 pp. Amazon.com, 1999. $23.95.

SCALPING COLUMBUS & OTHER DAMN INDIAN STORIES: TRUTHS, HALF-TRUTHS, AND OUTRIGHT LIES Adam Fortunate Eagle
Collection of short stories. 216 pp. Paper. University of Oklahoma Press, $19.95

A SCAR UPON OUR VOICE
Robin Coffee; Poetry explores growing up as an Indian in modern America. 130 pp. University of New Mexico Press, $24.95.

SCARLET RIBBONS: AMERICAN INDIAN TECHNIQUE FOR TODAYS QUILTERS
Helen Kelley; Reprint of 1987 edition. Illus. 134 color photos. 104 pp. Paper. Book Publishing Co. & Written Heritage, 1987. $21.95.

SCENES FROM THE HIGH DESERT: JULIAN STEWARD'S LIFE & THEORY
Virginia Kerns; Illus. 450 pp. University of Illinois Press, 2003. $45.

SCHMICK'S MAHICAN DICTIONARY
Carl Masthay; 188 pp. Amazon.com, 1992. $30.

SCHOLARS & THE INDIAN EXPERIENCE: CRITICAL REVIEWS OF RECENT WRITINGS IN THE SOCIAL SCIENCES
W.R. Swagerty; 280 pp. Amazon.com & Alibris.com, 1984. $22.50; paper, $9.95.

SCHOLASTIC ENCYCLOPEDIA OF THE AMERICAN INDIAN
James Ciment; Amazon.com, 1996.

FRITZ SCHOLDER: INDIAN/NOT INDIAN - STUDY GUIDES
National Museum of the American Indian; This study guide is for grades 5-8; another is for young people 7 and up and another is titled, "Looking at Fritz Scholder." Illus. 192 pp. Paper. NMAI Press & Prestel Publishing, 2008. $34.95.

SCHOOL FINANCE ON THE NAVAJO RESERVATION
Mark Sorensen & Patrick Graham
ASU & Navajo Nation course. Paper. Rough Rock School Press, 2004. $20.

SCHOOL LAW ON THE NAVAJO RESERVATION
Larry Ruzow
ASU & Navajo Nation course. Paper. Rough Rock School Press, 2004. $20.

THE HENRY ROWE SCHOOLCRAFT COLLECTION: A CATALOGUE OF BOOKS IN NATIVE AMERICAN LANGUAGES IN THE LIBRARY OF THE BOSTON ATHENAEUM
Robert Kruse; Illus. 105 pp. Paper. Boston Athenaeum Library, 1991. $11.95

SCHOOLCRAFT: LITERARY VOYAGER
Philip Mason, Editor; 208 pp. Michigan State University Press, 1962. $5.

SCHOOLCRAFT SERIES
Philip P. Mason, Editor; Schoolcraft was explorer, historian, and Indian agent. Includes three volumes: Schoolcraft's Expedition to Lake Itasca; Schoolcraft's Indian Legends; and Schoolcraft's Narrartive Journal of Travels. Reprints. Michigan State University, $35 each; paper, $16. each

SCHOOLCRAFT'S INDIAN LEGENDS
Henry R. Schoolcraft
Reprint. 322 pp. Michigan State University Press, $35; paper, $19.95.

SCHOOLCRAFT'S VOCABULARY OF ONONDAGA, VOL. 19
Henry R. Schoolcraft & Abraham La Fort; Illus. 37 pp. Amazon.com, 2000. $26.

SCHOOLING AT-RISK NATIVE AMERICAN CHILDREN: A JOURNEY FROM RESERVATION HEAD START TO PUBLIC SCHOOL KINDERGARTEN
Cheryl D. Clay; Revised edition. Illus. 208 pp. Amazon.com, 1998. $75.

SCHOOLS FOR THE CHOCTAWS
James D. Morrison; Joy Culbreath & Kathy Carpenter, Editors
How Choctaw peolle were educated from pre-removal to the American Civil War.
The Choctaw Store, 2016. $64.99; paper, $34.99.

SCIENCE ENCOUNTERS THE INDIAN, 1820-1880: THE EARLY YEARS OF AMERICAN ETHNOLOGY   Robert E. Bieder
Illus. 290 pp. University of Oklahoma Press, 1986. $29.95; paper, $15.95.

SCIENCE & NATIVE AMERICAN COMMUNITIES: LEGACIES OF PAIN, VISIONS OF PROMISE edited by Keith James; Gathering of Native American professionals working in the sciences and adavnaced technology and explores the meeting ground between science and Native American communities. 192 pp. University of Nebraska Press, 2001. $40; paper, $17.95.

SCIENTISTS & STORYTELERS: FEMINIST ANTHROPOLOGISTS AND THE CONSTRUCTION OF THE AMERICAN SOUTHWEST
Catherine Lavender; 256 pp. University of New Mexico Press, $39.95.

SCOORWA: JAMES SMITH'S INDIAN CAPTIVITY NARRATIVE
James Smith; Reprint. Illus. 176 pp. Paper. Amazon.com, $5.95.

SCRAPBOOK OF THE AMERICAN WEST
E. Lisle Reedstrom; Illus. 260 pp. Paper. The Caxton Press, 1989. $17.95.

SCREAMING HAWK: FLYING EAGLE'S TRAINING OF A MYSTIC WARRIOR
Patton Boyle; Illus. 1,240 pp. Paper. Station Hill Press, $13.95.

SCREAMING HAWK RETURNS: FLYING EAGLE TEACHES THE MYSTIC PATHS
Patton Boyle; Illus. 144 pp. Paper. Station Hill Press, $9.95.

SCULPTURING TOTEM POLES
Walt Way; Jack Ekstrom, Editor; Illus. 26 pp. Paper. Vestal, 1985. $5.

THE SEA IS MY COUNTRY: THE MARITIME WORLD OF THE MAKAHS
Joshua L. Reid; Illus. 416 pp. Yale University Press, 2015. $40..

THE SEA WOMAN: SEDNA IN INUIT SHAMANISM & ART IN THE EASTERN ARCTIC
Frederic Laugrand & Jarich Oosten; Examines the role of shamanism in modern Inuit art & culture. Illus. 160 pp. University of Chicago Press, 2009. $49.95; paper, $26.95.

SEAHB SIWASH
Leon L. Stock; Illus. 352 pp. Todd & Honeywell, 1981. $15.

*SEAL FOR A PAL
Paul E. Layman
Grades 4-9. 31 pp. Council for Indian Education, 1972. $8.95; paper, $2.95.

SEARCH FOR AMERICAN INDIAN IDENTITY: MODERN PAN-AMERICAN MOVEMENTS Hazel W. Hertzberg; Illus. 362 pp. Paper. Syracuse U. Press, 1971. $16.95.

SEARCH FOR THE FIRST AMERICANS
David J. Meltzer; Illus. 175 pp. Smithsonian Institution Press, 1996. $24.95.

*SEARCH FOR IDENTITY
Hap Gilliland, et al; 5 stories of Indian youth attempting to find their place in life.
Grades 6-10. Council for Indian Education, 1991. $10.95; paper, $4.95.

SEARCH FOR THE LOST TRAIL OF CRAZY HORSE
Cleve Walstrom; Illus. 340 pp. Paper. Dageforde Publishing, 2003.

SEARCH FOR THE NATIVE AMERICAN PUREBLOODS
Charles B. Wilson; 77 pencil portraits of pureblood American Indians.
3rd edition. Illus. 64 pp. Paper. University of Oklahoma Press, 2000. $14.95.

SEARCHING FOR THE BRIGHT PATH: THE MISSISSIPPI CHOCTAWS FROM PREHISTORY TO REMOVAL
James Taylor Carson; Illus. Maps. 185 pp. Paper. U. of Nebraska Press, 1999. $29.95.

SEARCHING FOR CHIPETA: THE STORY OF A UTE AND HER PEOPLE
Vickie L. Krudwig; Chipeta was a string, wise Ute woman wh played a major role in the history of the Ute Indian tribe and the U.S. in the 19th century. 128 pp. Paper. Fulcrum Publishing, 2003. $12.95.

SEARCHING FOR LOST CITY: ON THE TRAIL OF AMERICA'S NATIVE LANGUAGES
Elizabeth Seay; 272 pp. Amazon.com, 2003. $22.95.

SEARCHING FOR MY DESTINY
George Blue Spruce, Jr. as told to Deanne Durrett; The life story of the first American Indian dentist in the U.S. Illus. 336 pp. Paper. University of Nebraska Press, 2009. $30.

SEARCHING FOR RED EAGLE: A PERSONAL JOURNEY INTO THE SPIRIT WORLD OF NATIVE AMERICA Mary Ann Wells; 256 pp. U. Press of Mississippi, 2009. $30.

SEASONS OF THE KACHINA: PROCEEDINGS OF THE CALIFORNIA STATE UNIVERSITY HAYWOOD CONFERENCES ON THE WESTERN PUEBLOS, 1987-1988
Lowell J. Bean; Illus. 175 pp. Ballena Pres, 1989. $32.95; paper, $21.95.

A SEAT AT THE TABLE: HUSTON SMITH IN CONVERSATION WITH NATIVE AMERICANS ON RELIGIOUS FREEDOM
Huston Smith; Phil Cousineau, Editor; Gary Rhine, contributor
A collection of conversations providing an overview of the critical issues facing the Native American community today. 253 pp. University of California Press, 2005. $45; paper, $21.95. E-Book available.

SEAWEED, SALMON, AND MANZANITA CIDER: A CALIFORNIA INDIAN FEAST
Margaret Dubin & Sara-Larus Tolley; Paper. Heyday Books. $21.95.

SECOND CIVIL WAR: EXAMINING THE INDIAN DEMAND FOR ETHNIC SOVEREIGNTY David Price; 219 pp. Paper. Amazon.com, 1998. $14.95.

THE SECOND LONG WALK: THE NAVAJO-HOPI LAND DISPUTE
Jerry Kammer; 258 pp. Paper. University of New Mexico Press, 1980. $12.95.

THE SECRET GUIDE TO MOHEGAN SUN
Sandra J. Eichelberg, Editor; Melissa J. Fawcett, Translator
Illus. 40 pp. Paper. Amazon.com, 1998. $5.

SECRET INDIAN LEGENDS
Snowbird & Sabbeleu; Illus. 122 pp. Whispering Willows, 1996. $19.95.

SECRET NATIVE AMERICAN PATHWAYS: A GUIDE TO INNER PEACE
Thomas E. Mails; A guide to discovering the power of traditional medicine ways and applying spiritual practices in your daily life. Illus. 312 pp. Paper. Council Oak Books, 1988. $24.95, includes audio.

*THE SECRET OF YOUR NAME: PROUD TO BE METIS
David Bouchard; Dennis Weber, Illus.; John Arcand, Music
Grades K-4. Illus. Music. 32 pp. Amazn.com, 2009.

THE SECRET POWERS OF NAMING
Sara Littlecrow-Russell; Poetry. 96 pp. Paper. University of Arizona Press, 1981. $16.95.

SECRET STORIES IN THE ART OF THE NORTHWEST INDIAN
Oscar Newman; 160 pp. Paper. Catskill Press, 2004. $19.95.

SECRETS FROM THE CENTER OF THE WORLD
Joy Harjo & Stephen Strom; Prose. 75 pp. Paper. U. of Arizona Press, 1989. $13.95.

SECRETS OF ESKIMO SKIN SEWING
Edna Wilder; Instructions, drawings, photographs. 140 pp.
Paper. University of Alaska Press, 1998. $12.95.

SECRETS OF THE KINGS INDIAN
Eduard Gufeld; Illus. 320 pp. Paper. Amazon.com, 2000. $14.95.

SECRETS OF NATIVE AMERICAN HERBAL REMEDIES: A COMPREHENSIVE GUIDE TO THE NATIVE AMERICAN TRADITION OF USING HERBS & THE MIND/BODY/SPIRIT CONNECTION FOR IMPROVING HEALTH & WELLBEING
Anthony J. Chichoke; 336 pp. Paper. Penguin Group, 2001. $17.95.

SECRETS OF THE SACRED WHITE BUFFALO: NATIVE AMERICAN HEALING REMEDIES, RITES & RITUALS Gary Null; Illus. 320 pp. Paper. Prentice Hall, 1997. $15.

SEEDS OF CHANGE: A QUINCENTENNIAL COMMEMORATION
Herman J. Viola & Carolyn Margolis, Editors
Illus. 352 pp. Smithsonian Books, 1991. $39.95.

SEEDS OF EMPIRE: THE AMERICAN REVOLUTIONARY CONQUEST OF THE IROQUOIS Max M. Mintz; Amazon.com, 1999. $29.95.

SEEDS OF EXTINCTION: JEFFERSONIAN PHILANTHROPY & THE AMERICAN INDIAN Bernard Sheehan; 313 pp. Paper. University of North Carolina Press, 1973. $40.

SEEING THE WHITE BUFFALO
Robert B. Pickering; Illus. 160 pp. Paper. Johnson Books, 1997. $16.95.

SEEING WITH THE NATIVE EYE: CONTRIBUTIONS TO THE STUDY OF NATIVE AMERICAN RELIGION Walter H. Capps; Paper. HarperCollins, 1976. $6.95.

SEEKERS & TRAVELERS: CONTEMPORARY ART OF THE PACIFIC NORTHWEST COAST Gary Wyatt; Illus. 160 pp. Paper. University of Washington Press, 2015. $29.95

SEEKING RECOGNITION: THE TERMINATION & RESTORATION OF THE COOS, LOWER UMPQUA, AND SUISLAW INDIANS, 1855-1984
David R. M. Beck; Photos. Map. 352 pp. University of Nebraska Press, 2009. $50.

SELECTED MANUSCRIPTS OF GENERAL JOHN S. CLARK RELATING TO THE ABORIGINAL HISTORY OF THE SUSQUEHANNA
Louise Welles Murray, Editor; Aboriginal history of the Native peoples who inhabited the Susquehanna River Basin from late prehistoric times thru the Colonial Period. Illus. Maps. Wennawoods Publishing, 2008. $39.95.

SELECTED PREFORMS, POINTS & KNIVES OF NORTH AMERICAN INDIANS, VOL. I
Perino; Sketches of over 400 types includes description, age, and distribution range. Reprint of 1985 edition. 404 pp. Amazon.com, $70.50, postpaid.

SELECTED WORKS OF MARIA SABINA
Jerome Rothenberg, Ed.; Illus. 228 pp. University of California Press, $50; paper, $16.95.

SELF-DETERMINATION & THE SOCIAL EDUCATION OF NATIVE AMERICANS
Guy B. Senese; 248 pp. Greenwood, 1991. $52.95.

SELF RELAINCE VS. POWER POLITICS: AMERICAN & INDIAN EXPERIENCES IN GUILDING NATION-STATES J. Ann Tickner; 282 pp. Amazonc.com, 1987. $52.50.

SELF & SAVAGERY ON THE CALIFORNIA FRONTIER: A STUDY OF THE DIGGER STEREOTYPE Allan Lonnberg; Illus. 98 pp. Paper. Coyote Press, 1980. $10.

SELLING THE INDIAN: COMMERCIALIZING & APPROPRIATING AMERICAN INDIAN CULTURE
edited by Carter Jones Meyer & Diana Royer; 8 articles, original contributions that consider the selling of American Indian culture and how it affects the native community. Illus. 279 pp. University of Arizona Press, 2001. $45; paper, $22.95.

SELU: SEEKING THE CORN-MOTHER'S WISDOM
Marilou Awiakta; illus. by Mary Adair; Presents the Corn-Mother's wisdoms as traditionally taught by representative Native peoples. Illus. 352 pp. Paper. Fulcrum Publishing & Amazon.com Light, 1993. $16.95.

THE SEMANTICS OF TIME; ASPECTUAL CATEGORIZATION IN KOYUKON ATHABASKAN
Melissa Axelrod; Athabaskan studies. 200 pp. University of Nebraska Press, 1993. $65.

*THE SEMINOLE
B. Brooks; Grades 5-8. Illus. 32 pp. Amazon.com, 1989. $13.26.

*THE SEMINOLE
Merwin Garbarino; Grades 7-12. Illus. 112 pp. Paper.
Great Outddors Publishing & helsea House Publishers, 1989. $8.95.

*THE SEMINOLE
Emilie U. Lepthien; Grades 2-4. Illus. 48 pp. Childrens Press, 1985. $11.45.

THE SEMINOLE BAPTIST CHURCHES OF OKLAHOMA: MAINTAINING A TRADITIONAL COMMUNITY
Jack M. Schultz; Illus. Map. Biblio. 288 pp. University of Oklahoma Press, 1999. $29.95.

SEMINOLE BURNING: A STORY OF RACIAL VENGEANCE
Daniel F. Littlefield; True stories of mob vengeance on two innocent Indian teenagers in Oklahoma. 3 maps. Biblio. 208 pp. University Press of Mississippi, 1996. $35.

THE SEMINOLE FREEDMEN: A HISTORY
Kevin Mulroy; Examines the history of "Black Seminoles."
480 pp. University of Oklahoma Press, 2010. $36.95.

*THE SEMINOLE
Andrew Frank; Paul Rosier, Series Editor
Grades 6-12. 128 pp. Chelsea House, 2010. $35.

*THE SEMINOLE INDIANS
Phillip Koslow; Large-print book traces the history and culture of the Seminoe Indians from pre-Colombian times. Grades 2-5. Illus. 80 pp. Demco, 1994. $12.15. Paper. Amazon.com, $6.95.

SEMINOLE INDIANS OF FLORIDA, 1850-1874
Raymond C. Lantz; Annuity & per capita rolls of the BIA and National Archives. 415 pp. Amazon.com, 1994. $30.

THE SEMINOLE INDIANS OF FLORIDA
Clay MacCauley; Illus. 530 pp. Paper. University Press of Florida, 2000. $29.95.

A SEMINOLE LEGEND: THE LIFE OF BETTY MAE TIGER JUMPER
Betty Mae Tiger Jumper & Patsy West; Florida Seminole woman's life and family history. Illus. 176 pp. Photos. Maps. University Press of Florida, 2001. $24.95.

THE SEMINOLE & MICCOSUKEE TRIBES: A CRITICAL BIBLIOGRAPHY
Harry A. Kersey, Jr.; Examines 200+ major works ethnohistorical development of the Seminole & Miccosukee tribes of Florida. 116 pp. Paper. Indiana U. Press, 1987. $7.95.

THE SEMINOLE NATION OF OKLAHOMA: A LEGAL HISTORY
L. Susan Work; foreword by Lindsay G. Robertson
Illus. Maps. 376 pp. University of Oklahoma Press, 2010. $45.

SEMINOLE PATCHWORK
Margaret Brandenbourg; Illus. 96 pp. Paper. Sterling, 1987. $10.95.

SEMINOLE PATCHWORK BOOK
Cheryl G. Bradkin; Illus. 48 pp. Paper. Burdett Design, 1980. $7.50.

SEMINOLE PATCHWORK: THE COMPLETE BOOK
Beverly Rush with Lassie Wittman; How-to on Seminole patchwork for decoration and shirt and dress making. Illus. 80 pp. Paper. Writtenm Heritage, $7.95.

THE SEMINOLE SEED
Robert N. Peck; 420 pp. Pineapple Press, 1983. $14.95.

A SEMINOLE SOURCEBOOK
W.C. Sturtevant, Editor; 856 pp. Amazon.com, 1985. $90.

*THE SEMINOLE: SOUTHEAST
Grades 7-12. Illus. 112 pp. Amazon.com, $16.95.

SEMINOLE VOICES: REFLECTIONS ON THEIR CHANGING SOCIETY, 1970-2000
Julian M. Pleasants & Harry A. Kersey, Jr.; Series of interviews of more than 200 Florida Seminole members from 1969-71 and then again 1998-99. Illus. Map. 272 pp. University of Nebraska Press, 2010. $40.

*THE SEMINOLES
Martin Lee; Grades 3 and up. Illus. 64 pp. Paper. Franklin Watts, 1991. $4.95.

*THE SEMINOLES
Virginia Driving Hawk Sneve; The creation myth of the Seminoles; history, customs, and facts about the tribe today. Grades 2-6. Illus. 32 pp. Holiday House, 1994. $15.95.

SEMINOLES
Edwin McReynolds; Reprint 1957 ed. Illus. Maps. Paper. U. of Oklahoma Press, $16.95.

THE SEMINOLES OF FLORIDA
James W. Covington; History of the Florida Seminoles. Illus. Maps. Biblio. 416 pp. University Press of Florida, 1994. $49.95; paper, $18.95.

SENDING MY HEART BACK ACROSS THE YEARS: TRADITION & INNOVATION IN NATIVE AMERICAN AUTOBIOGRAPHY
Hertha Dawn Wong; Oxford University Press, 1992. $140.

*THE SENECA
Grades K-4. Illus. 48 pp. Childrens Press, $11.45.

SENECA FICTION, LEGENDS & MYTHS
Jeremiah Curtin, et al, Eds.
820 pp. Paper. Amazon.com, 2000. $80; CD-ROM, $29.95.

SENECA MYTHS & FOLK TALES
Arthur C. Parker; Reprint. Illus. 485 pp. Amazon.com, $60.95; paper, $26.95.

SENECA POSSESSED: INDIANS, WITCHCRAFT, AND POWER IN THE EARLY AMERICAN REPUBLIC
Matthew Dennis; Examines the ordeal of a Native people in the wake of the American Revolution. Illus. 313 pp. University of Pennsylvania Press, 2010.

SENECA RESTORATION, 1715-1754: AN IROQUOIS LOCAL POLITICAL ECONOMY
Kurt A. Jordan; A detailed reconstruction of daily life in the Seneca community, with an archaeological approach to 18th century Native American settlement patterns. Illus. Maps. 448 pp. University Press of Florida, 2008. $69.95; paper, $32.95.

THE SENECA & TUSCARORA INDIANS: AN ANNOTATED BIBLIOGRAPHY
Marilyn L. Haas, Editor; Citations to journal articles, books, theses, and government documents published up to 1992. 465 pp. Scarecrow Press, 1994. $88.

THE SENECA WORLD OF GA-NO-SAY-YEH
Joseph A. Francello; 225 pp. Peter Lang, 1989. $37.10.

SENTINELS ON STONE: THE PETROGLYPHS OF LOS ALAMOS
Dorothy Hoard; Illus. 75 pp. Paper. Los Alamos Historical Society, 1995. $14.95.

SEPARATE PEOPLES, ONE LAND: THE MINDS OF CHEROKEES, BLACKS, & WHITES ON THE TENNESSEE FRONTIER Cynthia Cumfer
Illus. Maps. 336 pp. University of North Carolina Press, 2007. $59.95; paper, $22.50.

SEPARATE REALITY
Carlos Castaneda; Jane Rosenman; 275 pp. Amazon.com, 1991. $8.95; paper, $4.95

SEQUOYAH
Grant Foreman; The life of the creator of the Cherokee alphabet.
Reprint of 1938 edition. Illus. 90 pp. Paper. University of Oklahoma Press, $9.95.

***SEQUOYAH**
Robert Cwiklik; Nancy Furstinger, Editor
Grades 5-7. Amazon.com, 1989. $11.98; paper, $7.95.

SEQUOYAH & THE CHEROKEE ALPHABET
Robert Cwiklik; Illus. 130 pp. Paper. Cherokee Publications, $7.95.

***SEQUOYAH: THE CHEROKEE MAN WHO GAVE HIS PEOPLE WRITING**
James Rumford; tr. From Cherokee by Anna Sixkiller Huckaby (Cherokee)
Oyate, 2004. $16.

SEQUOYAH - COMPUTERIZED SYLLABARY LEARNING PROGRAM - DOS
Diskette. VIP Publishing. $14.95.

***SEQUOYAH: FATHER OF THE CHEROKEE ALPHABET**
David Petersen
Grades 2-4. Illus. 32 pp. Childrens Press, $10.95. Paper. Cherokee Publications, $3.95.

***SEQUOYAH & HIS MIRACLE**
William Roper; Biography of the Cherokee who invented writing for his people.
Grades 5-12. 32 pp. Council for Indian Education, $8.95; paper, $2.95.

SEQUOYAH & THE INVENTION OF THE CHEROKEE ALPHABET
April R. Summitt; Illus. 164 pp. Greenwood Press, 2012. $37.

SEQUOYAH RISING: PROBLEMS IN POST-COLONIAL TRIBAL GOVERNANCE
Steve Russell; Addresses the democracy deficit in tribal governments directly but from an Indian point of view. Illus. 186 pp. Paper. Amazon.com, 2010. $27.

THE SERPENT & THE SACRED FIRE: FERTILITY IMAGES IN SOUTHWEST ROCK ART Dennis Slifer; Illus. 208 pp. Museum of New Mexico Press, 2000. $35; paper, $16.95.

THE SERPENT'S TONGUE: PROSE, POETRY & ART OF THE NEW MEXICAN PUEBLOS Nancy Wood, Editor; 256 pp. Amazon.com, 1997. $210.

THE SERRANO INDIANS OF SOUTHERN CALIFORNIA
Frank Johnston; Reprint of 1967 ed. Illus. Brochure. Malki-Ballena Press, 1980. $5.

SERRANO SONGS & STORIES
Guy Mount; Recorded at Morongo Indian Reservation in southern California by Sarah Martin, Louis Marcus & Magdalina Nombre. Introduction to Serrano culture is provided by author, Guy Mount. Amazon.com, 1993. $5.

SERVING THE NATION: CHEROKEE SOVEREIGNTY & SOCIAL WELFARE, 1800-1907
Julie L. Reed; Illus. 376 pp. University of Oklahoma Press, 2016. $34.95.

SERVING NATIVE AMERICAN STUDENTS: NEW DIRECTIONS FOR STUDENT SERVICES Mary Jo Tippeconnic Fox, Shelly C. Lowe & George S. McCleelan
Illus. Paper. Jossey-Bass, 2005.

SERVING THE TIES THAT BIND: GOVERNMENT REPRESSION OF INDIGENOUS RELIGIOUS CEREMONIES ON THE PRAIRIES
Katherine Pettipas; Illus. 520 pp. Paper. University of Manitoba Press, 1994. $39.95.

SETTING IT FREE: AN EXHIBITION OF MODERN ALASKAN ESKIMO IVORY CARVING Dinah Larsen & Terry Dickey, Editors
Illus. Map. Paper. U. of Alaska Museum, 1982. $10.

SETTLEMENT PATTERN STUDIES IN THE AMERICAS: FIFTH YEARS SINCE VIRU
Brian Billman & Gary Feinman; Illus. Smithsonian Institution Press, 1999. $65.

SETTLEMENT, SUBSISTENCE, & SOCIETY IN LATE ZUNI PREHISTORY
Keith W. Kintigh; 132 pp. Paper. University of Arizona Press, 1985. $19.95.
SEVEN ARROWS
Hyemeyohsts Storm; The story of the Shield and the Medicine Wheel.
A teaching story. Illus. 375 pp. Paper. Cherokee Publications, $14.95.

SEVEN CLANS OF THE CHEROKEE SOCIETY
Marcelina Reed; Contains clan names, information on the matrilineal system, marriage systems, governments, etc. Reprint. Illus. 32 pp. Paper. Book Publishing Co. & VIP Publishing. $4.95

THE 7 COUNCIL FIRES
David Seals; 200 pp. Sky & Sage Books, 2000. $18.95.

SEVEN EYES, SEVEN LEGS: SUPERNATIONAL STORIES OF THE ABENAKI
Yolakia Wapita'ska; Illus. 111 pp. Kiva Publishing, 2001. $16.95.

SEVEN FAMILIES IN PUEBLO POTTERY
Maxwell Museum of Anthropology; Illus. 116 pp. U. of New Mexico Press, 1974. $7.95.

SEVEN ROCK ART SITES IN BAJA CALIFORNIA
Clement W. Meighan & V.L. Pontoni, Editors
Illus. 236 pp. Paper. Ballena Press, 1979. $10.95.

THE SEVEN VISIONS OF BULL LODGE
As told by his daughter Garter Snake; George Horse Capture, Editor
A record of the spiritual life of Bull Lodge (1802-86). Illus. 171 pp. Paper.
University of Nebraska Press, 1992. $17.95.

SEVENTH GENERATION: AN ANTHOLOGY OF NATIVE AMERICAN PLAYS
Mimi Gisolfi D'Aponte, Editor; Collection of contemporary Native American writing for the theatre. Paper. Amazon.com, 1999. $18.95.

THE SEVENTH GENERATION: IMAGES OF THE LAKOTA TODAY
David Seals; Illus. 144 pp. Amazon.com, 1999. $45.

THE SEVENTH GENERATION: NATIVE STUDENTS SPEAK ABOUT FINDING THE GOOD PATH Amazon.com.

SEVERING THE TIES THAT BIND: GOVERNMENT REPRESSION OF INDIGENOUS RELIGIOUS CEREMONIES ON THE PRAIRIES
Katherine Pettipas; Illus. 336 pp. Paper. Amazon.com, 1994. $19.95.

JULIUS SEYLER & THE BLACKFEET: AN IMPRESSIONIST AT GLACIER NATIONAL PARK William E. Farr, Editor; More than 100 images of the national park & Blackfeet Indians. Illus. 256 pp. University of Oklahoma Press, 2010. $45.

JACK SHADBOLT & THE COASTAL INDIAN IMAGE
Marjorie M. Halpin; Canadian Indian artist and his effect on Native art today.
Illus. 64 pp. Paper. University of Washington Press, 1986. $21.95.

SHADES OF HIAWATHA: STAGING INDIANS, MAKING AMERICANS
Alan Trachtenberg; 464 pp. Amazon.com, 2004. $27.

SHADOW COUNTRY
Paula G. Allen; 149 pp. Paper. UCLA, American Indian Studies Center, 1982. $7.50.

SHADOW DISTANCE: A GERALD VIZENOR READER
Gerald Vizenor; 372 pp. Paper. Wesleyan University Press, 1994.
Distributed by the University Press of New England. $27.95. E-book, $19.99.

SHADOW OF THE HUNTER: STORIES OF ESKIMO LIFE
Richard K. Nelson; Illus. 296 pp. Paper. University of Chicago Press, 1980. $19.

SHADOW OF THE WOLF: AN APACHE TALE
Harry James Plumlee; Historical novel of an Apache Shaman.
Map. 206 pp. University of Oklahoma Press, 1997. $21.95.

SHADOW NATIONS: TRIBAL SOVEREIGNTY & THE LIMITS OF LEGAL PLURALISM
Bruce Duthu; Oxford University Press, 2013. $38.95.

SHADOW TRIBE: THE MAKING OF COLUMBIA RIVER INDIAN IDENTITY
Andrew H. Fisher; History of the Pacific Northwest's Columbia River Indians.
Illus. Maps. 322 pp. Paper. University of Washington Press, 2010. $26.95.

SHADOWCATCHERS
Steve Wall; Teachings of Native American elders from 13 different tribes.
Illus. 288 pp. HarperCollins, 1994. $27.50.

THE SHADOW'S HORSE
Diane Glancy
Collection of poems. 58 pp. Paper. University of Arizona Press, 2003. $15.95.

SHADOWS OF THE BUFFALO: A FAMILY ODYSSEY AMONG THE INDIANS
Adolf and Beverly Hungry Wolf; Pat Golbitz, Editor
Illus. 288 pp. Paper. William Morrow, 1985. $6.95.

SHADOWS OF THE INDIAN: STEREOTYPES IN AMERICAN CULTURE
Raymond Stedman; Illus. 282 pp. U. of Oklahoma Press, 1982. $38.95; paper, $17.95.

SHADOWS ON GLASS: THE INDIAN PHOTOGRAPHS OF BEN WITTICK
Patricia Broder; Illus. 224 pp. Rowman & Littlefield, 1991. $49.95.

SHADOWS ON THE KOYUKUK: AN ALASKAN NATIVE'S LIFE ALONG THE RIVER
Huntington & Rearden; Illus. Map. Paper. Amazon.com, $12.95.

SHAKIN' THE BUSHES
Vietzen; Covers paleo to historic peoples in northern Ohio with excavation results, artifact descriptions, and mound reports. Photos. 277 pp. Amazon.com House, 1976. $52.

SHAKING OUT THE SPIRITS: A PSYCHOLOGIST'S ENTRY INTO THE HEALING MYSTERIES OF GLOBAL SHAMANISM
Bradford P. Keeney; 256 pp. Paper. Station Hill Press, 1994. $13.95

SHAKING THE PUMPKIN: TRADITIONAL POETRY OF INDIAN NORTH AMERICA
Jerome Rothenberg
Reprint of revised edition. 424 pp. Paper. University of New Mexico Press, 1991. $17.95.

SHAKING THE RATTLE: HEALING THE TRAUMAS OF COLONIZATION
Barbara Helen Hill; Illus. 280 pp. Amazon.com, 1996. $12.95.

THE SHAMAN & THE MEDICINE WHEEL
Evelyn Eaton; Illus. 206 pp. Theosophical Publishing, 1982. $13.95.

*THE SHAMAN & THE WATER SERPENT
Jennifer Owings Dewey; Benton Yazzie, Illus.; Grades 4 and up. Early Puebloan peoples relationship with animals. University of New Mexico Press, $16.95.

THE SHAMAN: PATTERNS OF RELIGIOUS HEALING AMONG THE OJIBWAY INDIANS John A. Grim; Reprint of 1983 edition. Illus. Maps. Biblio. Paper. University of Oklahoma Press, 1997. $19.95.

THE SHAMAN'S TOUCH: OTOMI INDIAN SYMBOLIC HEALING
James Dow; Illus. 180 pp. University of Utah Press, 1986. $13.95.

SHAMANIC ODYSSEY: THE LUSHOOTSEED SALISH JOURNEY TO THE LAND OF THE DEAD Jay Miller; Sylvia Vane, Editor
Illus. 217 pp. Paper. Malki-Ballena Press, 1988. $28.95.

SHAMANISM
Piers Vitebsky; Illus. Maps. 184 pp. University of Oklahoma Press, 2001. $19.95.

SHAMANISM IN NORTH AMERICA
Norman Bancroft Hunt; Illus. 232 pp. Amazon.com, 2003. $49.95.

SHAMANS, GODS, & MYTHIC BEASTS: COLUMBIAN GOLD & CERAMICS IN ANTIQUITY Armand J. Labbe; Illus. 215 pp. U. of Washington Press, 1998. $40.

SHAMANS & KUSHTAKAS: NORTH COAST TALES OF THE SUPERNATURAL
Mary Beck; illus. by Oliver; Illus. 128 pp. Paper. Amazon.com, 1991. $12.95.

SHAMANS & RELIGION: ANTHROPOLOGICAL EXPLORATION IN CRITICAL THINKING Alice B. Kehoe; Waveland, 2000.

SHAME & ENDURANCE: THE UNTOLD STORY OF THE CHIRICAHUA APACHE PRISONERS OF WAR
H. Henrietta Stockel; 200 pp. Paper. University of Arizona Press, 2004. $19.95.

SHANDAA: IN MY LIFETIME
told by Belle Herbert; edited by Bill Pfisterer & Jane McGary
19th century life on the upper Yukon River. Stories are in Gwich'in Athabaskan with English translations. Illus. 207 pp. Paper. University of Alaska Press, 1988. $14.95.

*SHANNON: AN OJIBWAY DANCER
Sandra King; Catherine Whipple, Photographer
Grades 3-8. Illus. 48 pp. Paper. Lerner Publications, 1993.

**SHAPERS OF THE GREAT DEBATE ON NATIVE AMERICANS –
LAND, SPIRIT & POWER: A BIOGRAPHICAL DICTIONARY**
Bruce E. Johansen; Illus. 304 pp. Greenwood Publishing, 2000. $77.95.

SHAPESHIFT
Sherwin Bitsui; Poetry with Navajo persepctive. 80 pp. U. of Arizona Press, 2003. $15.95.

THE SHAPING OF AMERICAN ETHNOGRAPHY: THE WILKES EXPLORING EXPEDITION, 1838-1842 Barry Alan Joyce; The story of expedition and the observations of indigenous peoples encountered. Illus. Map. 197 pp. U. of Nebraska Press, 2001. $45.

SHAPING SURVIVAL: ESSAYS BY FOUR AMERICAN INDIAN TRIBAL WOMEN
Lanniko Lee, Florestine Kiyukanpi Renville, Karen Lone Hill & Lydia Whirlwind Soldier; Jack Marken & Charles Woodard, Eds; Illus. 240 pp. Paper. Scarecrow Press, 2002. $25.25.

SHARED IMAGES
Diana F. Pardue; Retrospective of the jewelry of Gail Bird (S. Domingo/Laguna) & Yazzie Johnson (Navajo), among the first rank of Native American artists. Illus. 184 pp. Museum of New Mexico Press, 2010. $45.

SHARED SYMBOLS, CONTESTED MEANINGS: GROS VENTRE CULTURE & HISTORY, 1778-1984 Loretta Fowler; Paper. Cornell University Press, 1987. $29.95.

SHARED SPIRITS
Dennis L. Olson; Illus. 144 pp. Paper. NorthSound Music Group, 1999. $19.95.

SHARED VISIONS: NATIVE AMERICAN PAINTERS & SCULPTORS IN THE TWENTIETH CENTURY Margaret Archuleta & Rennard Strickland, Editors
Presents works by Native American artists influenced by Euro-American conceptions of art. Prepared by The Heard Museum. Illus. 112 pp. Paper. W.W. Norton & Co., 1992. $20.

SHARING THE DESERT: THE TOHONO O'ODHAM IN HISTORY
Winston P. Erickson; Traces the development of relations between the tribe and other peoples. 182 pp. University of Arizona Press, 1994. $37; paper, $19.95.

SHARING THE GIFT OF LAKOTA SONG
R.D. Theisz; Amazon.com, 2003.

SHARING THE HARVEST ON THE ROAD TO SELF-RELIANCE: REPORT OF THE NATIONAL ROUND TABLE ON ABORIGINAL ECONOMIC DEVELOPMENT & RESOURCES 360 pp. Paper. Amazon.com, 1993.

SHARING A HERITAGE: AMERICAN INDIAN ARTS
Charlotte Heth; 214 pp. Paper. UCLA, American Indian Studies Center, 1984. $12.

SHARING OUR KNOWLEDGE: THE TLINGIT & THEIR COASTAL NEIGHBORS
Sergei Kan, Editor; with Steve Henrikson
Illus. 584 pp. University of Nebraska Press, 2015. $65.

SHARING OUR STORIES OF SURVIVAL: NATIVE WOMEN SURVIVING VIOLENCE
Introduction to the social & legal issues involved in acts of violence against Native women. Includes Trainer's manual. Alta Mira Press. $99; paper, $38; $36.99, e-Book.

*SHARING OUR WORLDS
A photographic documentary of children from three families sharing their multicultural experiences. Grades 2-6. Illus. 32 pp. Daybreak Star Press, $4.75.

THE SHARPEST SIGHT: A NOVEL
Louis Owens; Mystery. 272 pp. Paper. University of Oklahoma Press, 1992. $19.95.

THE SHASTA INDIANS OF CALIFORNIA & THEIR NEIGHBORS
Elizabeth Renfro; Shasta origins, shamanism, mythology, philosophy, ceremonies, etc. Illus. Photos. 128 pp. Paper. Naturegraph, $8.95.

THE SHAWNEE
Jerry E. Clark; 120 pp. Amazon.com, 1993. $18.

SHAWNEE: THE CEREMONIALISM OF A NATIVE AMERICAN TRIBE & ITS CULTURAL BACKGROUND
James H. Howard; Reprint. Illus. 470 pp. Paper. Amazon.com, 1981. $23.95.

SHAWNEE HOME LIFE: THE PAINTING OF ERNEST SPYBUCK
Lee Callander and Ruth Slivka
Illus. 32 pp. Paper. National Museum of the American Indian, 1984. $8.95.

THE SHAWNEE INDIANS: AN ANNOTATED BIBLIOGRAPHY
Randolph Noe; Illus. Maps. 768 pp. Scarecrow Press, 2001. $139.70.

THE SHAWNEE PROPHET
R. David Edmunds; Illus. 275 pp. Paper. University of Nebraska Press, 1983. $18.95.

SHAWNEE POTTERY: AN IDENTIFICATION & VALUE GUIDE
Jim & Beverly Mangus; Illus. 256 pp. Collector Books, 1994. $24.95.

THE SHAWNEES & THEIR NEIGHBORS, 1795-1870
Stephen Warren; The myths & histories produced by Shawnee interpreters and their vested interests in moderninzing the tribes. Illus. Maps. 232 pp. Paper. University of Illinois Press, 2005. $23.

SHE HAD SOME HORSES
Joy Harjo; Collection of poetry exploring physical & mythic landscapes. 74 pp. Amazon.com, $15.95; paper, $10.95.

SHE'S TRICKY LIKE COYOTE: ANNIE MINER PETERSON, AN OREGON COAST INDIAN WOMAN
Lionel Youst; Illus. 320 pp. Maps. Paper. University of Oklahoma Press, 1997. $24.95.

THE SHEFFIELD SITE: AN ONEONTA SITE ON THE ST. CROIX RIVER
Guy E. Gibbon; Illus. 62 pp. Paper. Minnesota Historical Society, 1973. $4.

SHELL SHAKER
LeAnne Howe; Novel. Amazon.com, 2002.

SHEM PETE'S ALASKA
James Kari & James Fall, Editors; Geography of the Cook Inlet region of Alaska. Contains over 700 Dena'ina place names of the western Cook Inlet region. 2nd Edition. Illus. Maps. 414 pp. University of Alaska Press, Text, $65; paper, $29.95.

SHERIDAN'S TROOPERS ON THE BORDER: A WINTER CAMPAIGN ON THE PLAINS
De B. Randolph Keim; Illus. 308 pp. Amazon.com, 1999. $29.95; paper, $17.95.

SHIFTING BOUNDARIES: ABORIGINAL IDENTITY, PLURALIST THEORY, & THE POLITICS OF SELF-GOVERNMENT
Tim Schouls; Aboriginal self-government in Canada. 240 pp.
University of Washington Press, 2004. $94; paper, $33.95.

THE SHINDLER CATALOGUE: NATIVE AMERICAN PHOTOGRAPHY AT THE SMITHSONIAN
Paula Richardson Fleming, Ed.; Illus. 410 pp.Smithsonian Institution Press, 1996. $34.95.

*SHINGEBISS: AN OJIBWAY LEGEND
Nancy Van Laan; Grades PS-3. Illus. 32 pp. Amazon.com, 1997. $16.

SHINGWAUK'S VISION: A HISTORY OF NATIVE RESIDENTIAL SCHOOLS
J.R. Miller; Illus. 582 pp. Paper. Amazon.com, 1996. $29.95.

SHOOTING BACK FROM THE RESERVATION: A PHOTOGRAPHIC VIEW OF LIFE BY NATIVE AMERICAN YOUTH Jim Hubbard; A look at the varied worlds of Native American children through their eyes. Paper. Amazon.com, 1994. $17.

A SHORT ACCOUNT OF THE DESTRUCTION OF THE INDIES
Bartlome de las Casas; translated by Nigel Griffin; Eyewitness record & protest of Spanish atrocities in territory of Columbus. Reprint. Illus Maps. 192 pp. Paper. Penguin USA, $9.95.

A SHORT HISTORY OF THE INDIANS OF THE U.S.
Edward H. Spicer; Reprint of 1969 edition. 320 pp. Paper. Amazon.com, $11.95.

A SHORT HISTORY OF NATIVE AMERICANS IN THE U.S.
Meredith Howard; 170 pp. Paper. Amazon.com, 2001. $16.25.

A SHORT HISTORY OF NORTH AMERICAN INDIANS
Frederic Baraga; 250 pp. Michigan State University Press, 2004. $34.95.

A SHORT HISTORY OF THE SACRED CALF PIPE
John L. Smith; Illus. 47 pp. Paper. Lakta Books, 1994. $21.95.

THE SHORT, SWIFT TIME OF GODS ON EARTH: THE HOHOKAM CHRONICLES
Donald Bahr, et al; 352 pp. Paper. University of California Press, 1994. $35.

SHORT-TERM SEDENTISM IN THE AMERICAN SOUTHWEST:
THE MIMBRES VALLEY SALADO Ben Nelson & Steven LeBlanc
Illus. 315 pp. Paper. U. of New Mexico Press, 1986. $35.

*THE SHOSHONI
Alden Carter; Grades 3-5. Illus. 65 pp. Franklin Watts, 1989. $11.90.

*THE SHOSHONI
Dennis Fradin
Revised ed. Grades 2-4. Illus. 48 pp. Paper. Children's Press, 1992. $5.50.

THE SHOSHONE-BANNOCKS: CULTURE & COMMERCE AT FORT HALL, 1870-1940
John W. Heaton; Photos. 352 pp. University Press of Kansas, 2005. $39.95.

THE SHOSHONI - CROW SUN DANCE
Fred W. Voget; Illus. Maps. 348 pp. Paper. University of Oklahoma Press, 1984. $14.95.

THE SHOSHONI FRONTIER & THE BEAR RIVER MASSACRE
Brigham D. Madsen. Ed.
Reprint of 1985 ed. Illus. 312 pp. Paper. University of Utah Press, $17.95.; eBook, $17.95

SHOSHONE GHOST DANCE RELIGION: POETRY SONGS & GREAT BASIN CONTEXT
Judith Vander; 688 pp. University of Illinois Press, 1997. $65.

SHOSHONI GRAMMAR
Jon P. Dayley; Amazon.com, 1993.

SHOSHONE INDIAN WORDS
William White; illus. by Emily Donzie White; Glossary of about 500 of the most frequently used words inthe Shoshone language. 55 pp. Paper. VIP Publishing, $14.95.

*SHOSHONE INDIANS OF NORTH AMERICA
Kim Dramer; Grades 5 and up.120 pp. Paper. Chelsea House, 1996. $9.95.

SHOSHONE TALES
collected & edited by Anne M. Smith, Ed. & Compiler; Collected in 1939, from the Shoshone oral tradition. Illus. Map. 224 pp. Paper. University of Utah Press, 1993. $19.95.

SHOSHONI TEXTS
Jon P. Dayley; Amazon.com, 1997.

SHOSHONEAN PEOPLES & THE OVERLAND TRAIL: FRONTIERS OF THE UTAH SUPERINTENDENCY OF INDIAN AFFAIRS, 1849-1869
Dale L. Morgan; Richard L. Saunders, Editor; With an ethnohistorical essay by Gregory E. Smoak. Illus. Maps. 432 pp. Utah State University Press, 2007. $39.95.

THE SHOSHONIS: SENTINELS OF THE ROCKIES
V. Trenholm and M. Carley
Reprint of 1964 edition. Illus. Maps. Biblio. Paper. University of Oklahoma Press, $19.95.

SHOTO CLAY: FIGURINES & FORMS FROM THE LOWER COLUMBIA
Robert Slocum & Kenneth Matsen; Descriptions and classifications of the clay work done by the little-known Shoto Indians, who once lived in the lower Columbia near Vancouver, Wash. Illus. 32 pp. Paper. Binford & Mort, $5.95.

A SHOVEL OF STARS: MAKING OF THE AMERICAN WEST, 1800 TO THE PRESENT
Ted Morgan; The forced removal of the Indians to reservations in Oklahoma. Illus. Maps. 544 pp. Simon & Schuster, 1995. $30.

SHOWDOWN AT THE LITTLE BIGHORN
Dee Brown
Reprint of 1964 edition. Illus. 224 pp. Paper. University of Nebraska Press, 2004. $13.95.

SIBERIAN YUP'IK ESKIMO: THE LANGUAGE & ITS CONTACTS WITH CHUKCHI
Willem J. de Reuse; Examines a number of interrelated grammatical subsystems of Central Siberian Yup'ik, an Eskimo language, spoken on St., Lawrence Island, Alaska. 424 pp. University of Utah Press, 1994. $50.

SIEGE & SURVIVAL: HISTORY OF THE MENOMINEE INDIANS, 1634-1856
David R.M. Beck; Illus. Maps. 294 pp. University of Nebraska Press, 2002. $49.50.

SIFTERS: NATIVE AMERICAN WOMEN'S LIVES
Theda Perdue, Ed.; 270 pp. Oxford University Press, 2001. $155; paper, $47.95.

SIGN LANGUAGE AMONG NORTH AMERICAN INDIANS COMPARED WITH THAT OF OTHER PEOPLES & DEAF-MUTES
Garrick Mallery, with A.L. Kroeber & C.F. Voegelin; 318 pp. Amazon.com, 1972.

SIGN LANGUAGE: CONTEMPORARY SOUTHWEST NATIVE AMERICA
Skeet McAuley; Illus. 80 pp. Aperture, 1989. $24.95.

SIGN TALK OF THE CHEYENNE INDIANS & OTHER CULTURES
Ernest T. Seton; Illus. 288 pp. Paper. Dover, 2000. $9.95.

SIGNALS IN THE AIR: NATIVE BROADCASTING IN AMERICA
Michael C. Keith; Illus. 200 pp. Greenwood Publishing, 1995. $85.

THE SIGNIFICANT TIES EXCEPTION TO THE INDIAN CHILD WELFARE ACT: JUDICIAL DECISION-MAKING OR INCORPORATING BIAS INTO LAW
Raquelle Myers; Nancy Thorington & Joseph Myers, Editors
Illus. 46 pp. Paper. National Indian Justice, 1998. $10.

SIGNS FROM THE ANCESTORS: ZUNI CULTURAL SYMBOLISM & PERCEPTIONS OF ROCK ART
Jane M. Young; Illus. 333 pp. Paper. University of New Mexico Press, 1988. $24.95.

SIGNS OF CHEROKEE CULTURE: SEQUOYAH'S SYLLABARY IN EASTERN CHEROKEE LIFE Margaret O. Bender
Illus. 208 pp. U. of North Carolina Press, 2002. $73.95; paper, $27.95.

SIGNS OF LIFE: ROCK ART OF THE UPPER RIO GRANDE
Dennis Slifer
200 photos & illus. 287 pp. Amazon.com, 2002. $29.95; paper, $16.95.

*SIGNS OF SPRING
Patrick J. Quinn; A young boy whose family moves from the city to the Minnesota woods. Grades 4-10. 152 pp. Council for Indian Education, 1996. $7.95.

*SILAS & THE MAD-SAD PEOPLE
Grades 1-5. New Seed, 1981. $5.

SILENT ARROWS: INDIAN LORE & ARTIFACT HUNTING
Earl F. Moore; Third Edition. Illus. Tremaine, 1973. $12.95.

SILENT VICTIMS: HATE CRIMES AGAINST NATIVE AMERICANS
Barbara Perry; 176 pp. Paper. University of Arizona Press, 2008. $29.95.

SILKO: WRITING STORYTELLER & MEDICINE WOMAN
Brewster E. Fitz; Examines Silko's award-winning literature. 320 pp. Paper. University of Oklahoma Press, 2005. $19.95.

LESLIE MARMON SILKO'S CEREMONY: A CASEBOOK
Allan Chavkin, Ed.; Illus. 288 pp. Oxford University Press, 2002. $50; paper. $16.95.

LESLIE MARMON SILKO: A COLLECTION OF CRITICAL ESSAYS
edited by Louise K. Barnett & James L. Thorson; 13 essays by a Native American writer. 336 pp. Paper. University of New Mexico Press, 2001. $24.95.

LESLIE MARMON SILKO'S STORYTELLER: NEW PERSPECTIVES
Catherine Rainwater, Editor; Essays. University of New Mexico Press, $55.

SILVER FOX, JOURNEYS OF THE INNER SONGBIRD
Sylvie Avery, Editor; Silver Fox, a Crow Indian and his journey of self discovery. Illus. Paper. Amazon.com, $14.95.

SILVER HORN (1860-1940): MASTER ILLUSTRATOR OF THE KIOWAS
Candace Greene; Biographical portrait of the Kiowa artist. Illus. 360 pp. University of Oklahoma Press, 2004. $34.95.

SILVER IN THE FUR TRADE, 1680-1820
Martha W. Hamilton; Photos & Illus. on 250 trade silver maker's marks and their biographies. Summarizing the historic trading routes of North America. 235 pp. Paper. Amazon.com, 1995. $45.

SILVERFOOT'S SECOND DANCE: THE STORY OF A 21ST CENTURY NATIVE AMERICAN William D. Harrison; 97 pp. Paper. Amazon.com, 2001. $10.95.

SINCE PREDATOR CAME: NOTES FROM THE STRUGGLE FOR AMERICAN INDIAN LIBERATION
Ward Churchill; Illus. 450 pp. AIGIS Publications, 1995. $30; paper, $18.

SINCE THE TIME OF THE TRANSFORMERS: THE ANCIENT HERITAGE OF THE NUU-CHAH-NULTH, DITIDAHT & MAKAH Alan D. McMillan
Illus. Maps. 264 pp. University of Washington Press, 1999. $93.95; paper, $35.95.

SINEWS OF SURVIVAL: THE LIVING LEGACY OF INUIT CLOTHING
Betty Kobayashi Issenman; Illus. UBC Press, 1997. $49.95.

SING: POETRY FROM THE INDIGENOUS AMERICAS
Allison Adelle Hedge Coke, Editor
Paper. University of Arizona Press, 2008. $29.95.

SINGING AN INDIAN SONG: A BIOGRAPHY OF D'ARCY McNICKLE
Dorothy R. Parker; Traces the course of D'Arcy McNickle's life. Illus. 330 pp. University of Nebraska Press, 1992. $35.

THE SINGING BIRD: A CHEROKEE NOVEL
John Milton Oskison; edited by Timothy Powell & Melinda Mullikin
The period between the Trail of Tears & the Civil War. University of Oklahoma Press, 2007.

SINGING FOR POWER: SONG MAGIC OF THE PAPAGO INDIANS OF SOUTHERN AZ
Ruth M. Underhill; Reprint of 1938 edition. 158 pp. Paper. U. of Arizona Press, $12.95.

SINGING FOR A SPIRIT: A PORTRAIT OF THE DAKOTA SIOUX
Vine Deloria, Jr.; True stories, legends, songs, and descriptions of traditional Dakota Sioux life. Illus. 232 p.. Paper. Amazon.com, 2000. $14.95.

SINGING THE SONGS OF MY ANCESTORS: THE LIFE & MUSIC OF HELMA SWAN, MAKAH ELDER Linda J. Goodman
Illus. 368 pp. University of Oklahoma Press, 2002. $24.95.

THE SINGING SPIRIT: EARLY STORIES BY NORTH AMERICAN INDIANS
Bernd Peyer, Editor
Native American fiction. 175 pp. Paper. University of Arizona Press, 1990. $13.95.

THE SIOUAN LANGUAGES
Thaddeus C. Grimm; Illus. 85 pp. lakota Books, $24.95.

SIOUAN SOCIOLOGY
James Owen Dorsey; Illus. 36 pp. Paper. Lakota Books, 1993. $15.

*THE SIOUX
Virginia Driving Hawk Sneve; Their creation myth, history, beliefs & ways of life. Grades 4-6. Illus. 32 pp. Holiday House, 1994. $15.95; paper, $6.95.

*THE SIOUX
B. Brooks; Grades 5-8. Illus. 32 pp. Amazon.com, 1989. $12.67.

THE SIOUX
Royal B. Hassrick; with Dorothy Maxwell & Cile Bach
Illus. Paper. University of Oklahoma Press, $17.95.

*THE SIOUX
Elaine Landau; Grades 3-6. Illus. 64 pp. Franklin Watts, 1989. $22; paper, $6.95.

*THE SIOUX
Alice Osinski; Grades K-4. Illus. 48 pp. Children's Press, 1984. $11.45.

*THE SIOUX
Virginia Driving Hawk Sneve; The creation myth of the Sioux; history, customs, and facts about the tribe today. Grades 2-6. Illus. 32 pp. Holiday House, 1993. $15.95.

A SIOUX CHRONICLE
George E. Hyde. Reprint of 1956 edition. Illus. Maps. 356 pp. Paper. University of Oklahoma Press, $16.95.

SIOUX COLLECTIONS
T. Emogene Paulson, Editor; Dakota Press, 1982. $14.95.

SIOUX COUNTRY: A HISTORY OF INDIAN-WHITE RELATIONS
Herbert T. Hoover & Carol Goss Hoover; Illus. Center for Western Studies, 2000.

SIOUX CREATION STORY
Thomas Simms; Illus. 36 pp. Paper. Tipi Press, 1987. $3.50.

THE SIOUX: THE DAKOTA & LAKOTA NATION
Guy E. Gibbon; Illus. 384 pp. Amazon.com, 2002. $27.95.

SIOUX INDIAN RELIGION: TRADITION & INNOVATION
Raymond DeMallie & Douglas Parks, Editors
Illus. 244 pp. Paper. University of Oklahoma Press, 1987. $19.95.

*THE SIOUX INDIANS: HUNTERS & WARRIORS OF THE PLAINS
Sonia Bleeker; Grades 3-6. Illus. Wiliam Morrow, 1962. $11.88.

SIOUX: LIFE & CUSTOMS OF A WARRIOR SOCIETY
Royal B. Hassrick, et al
Reprint of 1964 edition. Illus. Maps. 394 pp. Paper. University of Oklahoma Press, $24.95.

THE SIOUX OF THE ROSEBUD: A HISTORY IN PICTURES
Henry & Jean Hamilton; Reprint of the 1971 edition. Illus. Maps. 320 pp. Paper. University of Oklahoma Press, $22.95.

THE SIOUX & OTHER NATIVE AMERICAN CULTURES OF THE DAKOTAS: AN ANNOTATED BIBLIOGRAPHY Karen Zimmerman & Christopher J. Hoover, Eds
Illus. 288 pp. Greenwood Publishing, 1993. $90.95.

SIOUX QUILL & BEADWORK
Carrie A. Lyford; Illus. 116 pp. Paper. Eagle's View Publishing, 2002. $19.95.

THE SIOUX UPRISING IN MINNESOTA, 1862: JACOB NIX'S EYEWITNESS HISTORY
Jacob Nix; Don H. Tolzmann, Ed. & Tr.
Reprint. Illus. 175 pp. Paper. Indiana German Heritage Society, $12.80.

THE SIOUX UPRISING OF 1862
Kenneth Carley; Revised edition. Illus. Photos. Map. 102 pp. Paper. Minnesota Historical Society Press, 1976. $8.50.

SIOUX WINTER COUNT, A 131-YEAR HISTORY
Roberta Carkeek Cheney; Indian calendar of 131 years, from 1796 to 1926. Illus. 64 pp. Paper. Naturegraph, 1998. $8.95.

THE SISTER CREEKS SITE MOUNDS: MIDDLE WOODLAND MORTUARY PRACTICES IN THE ILLINOIS RIVER VALLEY Michael C. Meinkoth
Illus. 150 pp. Paper. Amazon.com, 1995. $8.

SISTER NATIONS: NATIVE AMERICAN WOMEN WRITING ON COMMUNITY
Heidi Erdrich & Laura Tohe, Eds.
Illus. 252 pp. Minnesota Historical Society Press, 2002. $24.95.

SISTER TO THE SIOUX: THE MEMOIRS OF ELAINE GOODALE EASTMAN, 1885-1891
Elaine Goodale Eastman; Kay Graber, Ed.
Illus. Map. 200 pp. Paper. University of Nebraska Press, 2004. $12.95.

SISTERS IN SPIRIT: HAUDENOSAUNEE (IROQUOIS) INFLUENCE ON EARLY AMERICAN FEMINISTS
Sally Roesch Wagner; Photos. 128 pp. Paper. Book Publishing Co., $9.95.

SITANKA: THE FULL STORY OF WOUNDED KNEE
Forrest W. Seymour; An account of the major events preceding, during and immediately after the battle of 1890 at Wounded Knee. Christopher Publishing, 1981. $10.75.

SITES OF O'AHU
Elspeth Sterling & Catherine Summer; Study of archaeological & historical sites of O'ahu. Illus. Maps. 372 pp. Paper. Bishop Museum, $29.95.

*SITTING BULL
Sheila Black; Nancy Furstinger, Editor
Grades 5-7. Illus. 144 pp. Amazon.com, $11.98; paper, $7.95.

SITTING BULL, CHAMPION OF THE SIOUX: A BIOGRAPHY
Stanley Vestal
Reprint of 1957 edition. Illus. 370 pp. Paper. University of Oklahoma Press, $24.95.

SITTING BULL: THE COLLECTED SPEECHES
Mark Diedrich; Illus. Map. Biblio. 190 pp. paper. Coyote Books, 1998. $29.95.

SITTING BULL & THE PARADOX OF LAKOTA NATIONHOOD
Gary Clayton Anderson; 192 pp. Paper. Amazon.com, 1997. $25.80.

*SITTING BULL & THE PLAINS INDIANS
John Hook; Grades 4-8. Illus. 65 pp. Frankin Watts, 1987. $12.40.

SITTING BULL, PRISONER OF WAR
Dennis C. Pope; Sitting Bull's day-to-day life in captivity, and how he continued to conduct tribal business and learned to deal with the white officials who had come to control the future of the Lakota people. Illus. 187 pp. Paper. Amazon.com, 2010.

*SITTING BULL: WARRIOR OF THE SIOUX
Jane Fleischer; Grades 4-6. Illus. 48 pp. Paper. Amazon.com, 1979. $3.50.

SITTING BULL'S BOSS: ABOVE THE MEDICINE LINE WITH JAMES MORROW WALSH Ian Anderson; Illus. 240 pp. Paper. Amazon.com, 2000. $16.95.

SITTING ON THE BLUE-EYED BEAR
Gerald Hausman; Navajo mythology & history. Sunstone Press, $10.

SIX MICMAC STORIES
Harold McGee, Illus.; 51 pp. Paper. Amazon.com, 1992.

SIX MONTHS AMONG THE INDIANS
Darius B. Cook
Reprint of 1889 edition. Illus. 101 pp. Paper. Amazon.com, $4.50.

THE SIX NATIONS OF NEW YORK: THE 1892 U.S. EXTRA CENSUS BULLETIN
Henry Carrington; intro. by Robert W. Venables; Includes data, details, and photographs of the Six Nations. A report on the condition of the iroquois in 1892. 90 pp. Illus. Photos. Paper. Cornell University Press, 1996. $19.95.

SIX NATIONS SERIES
The only curriculum overview currently available for 7th through 12th grade units on New York State Indians. Separate guides available for teachers and students. Akwe:kon Press, Teacher's guide, $15. Student's guide, $4.

SIX WEEKS IN THE SIOUX TEPEES
Sarah F. Wakefield; Reprint. Illus. 96 pp. Paper. Amazon.com, $9.95.

SIX WEEKS IN THE SIOUX TEPEES: A NARRATIVE OF INDIAN CAPTIVITY
Sarah F. Wakefield; Bound with other captivity narratives. Reprint of 1863 edition, et al. A fully annotated modern version is edited by June Namias, Illus. Map. 175 pp. University of Oklahoma Press, 1997. $16.95; paper, $14.95.

1676: THE END OF AMERICAN INDEPENDENCE
Stephen Saunders Webb; Presents events from the perspectives of the colonists, Whitehall, and the American Indians. Illus. Maps. 460 pp. Paper. Syracuse University Press, $17.95.

SIXTH ANNUAL INDIAN LAW CONFERENCE: PROCEEDINGS OF THE FEDERAL BAR ASSOCIATION, APRIL 1981
Federal Bar Associatio Staff; 113 pp. Federal Bar Association, 1981. $15.

THE SIXTH GRANDFATHER: BLACK ELK'S TEACHINGS GIVEN TO JOHN G. NEIHARDT Raymond J. De Mallie, Editor
Illus. Maps. 465 pp. Paper. University of Nebraska Press & Amazon.com, 1984. $19.95.

THE SIXTY YEARS' WAR FOR THE GREAT LAKES, 1754-1814
David C. Skaggs & Larry L. Nelson
Illus. 414 pp. Michigan State University, 2001. $49.95.

SKELETAL BIOLOGY IN THE GREAT PLAINS, MIGRATION, WARFARE, HEALTH, & SUBSISTENCE Douglas W. Owsley & Richard L. Jantz
Illus. 408 pp. Smithsonian Institution Press, 1994. $45.

SKETCHBOOK '56 THE FRENCH & INDIAN WAR 1756-1763
Ted Spring; Six vols. of notes, sketches, and dimensions depicting life & artifacts of 1756. Paper. Smoke & Fire Co., $9 each.

SKETCHES OF A TOUR TO THE LAKES
Thomas L. McKenney; A sourcebook of early Indian life among the Ojibwe & the Sioux. Reprint of 1827 edition. Illus. 494 pp. Amazon.com, $25.

SKINS & BONES
Paula Gunn Allen; Poetry. Paper. University of New Mexico Press, $9.95.

SKULKING WAY OF WAR: TECHNOLOGY & TACTICS AMONG THE NEW ENGLAND INDIANS
Patrick Malone; Illus. 145 pp. Amazon.com, 1991. $29.95; paper, $18.95.

SKULL WARS: KENNEWICK MAN, ARCHAEOLOGY, & THE BATTLE FOR NATIVE AMERICAN IDENTITY David H. Thomas; HarperCollins, 1999. $25.

*SKUNNY WUNDY: SENECA INDIAN TALES
Arthur C. Parker, Editor; Illus by George Armstrong; Children's tales handed down by Native American storytellers. Grades 4 and up. Illus. 224 pp. Paper. Syracuse University Press, 1994. $15.95.

THE SKY CLEARS: POETRY OF THE AMERICAN INDIANS
Arthur G. Day, Editor; Reprint of 1964 ed. 204 pp. Paper. U. of Nebraska Press, $19.95.

THE SKY IS MY TIPI
Mody Boatright, Editor
Reprint of 1949 edition. Illus. 254 pp. Amazon.com, $13.95.

*SKY WATCHERS OF AGES PAST
Malcolm E. Weiss; Grades 5-9. Amazon.com, 1982. $7.95.

SKYLARK MEETS MEADOWLARK: REIMAGING THE BIRD IN BRITISH ROMANTIC & CONTEMPORARY NATIVE AMERICAN LITERATURE
Thomas C. Gannon (Lakota); Explores how poets & nature writers in Britain & Native America have incorporated birds into their writings. 464 pp. University of Nebraska Press, 2009. $50.

SKYSCRAPERS HIDE THE HEAVENS: THE HISTORY OF INDIAN-WHITE RELATIONS IN CANADA
J.R. Miller; 3rd Edition. Illus. 500 pp. Paper. Amazon.com, 2000. $29.95.

*SKYWOMAN: LEGENDS OF THE IROQUOIS
Joanne Shenandoah & Douglas M. George; Illus. by John & David Fadden Grades 5 and up. Illus. 128 pp. Amazon.com, 1997. $14.95.

SLASH
Jeannette C. Armstrong; A novel which traces the pain, and the alienation felt by the modern First Nation peoples of Canada. 254 pp. Paper. Theytus, 1990. $12.95.

SLAVERY & THE EVOLUTION OF CHEROKEE SOCIETY, 1540-1866
Theda Perdue
Reprint of 1979 ed. Illus. Maps. 222 pp. Amazon.com. $21.

SLAVERY IN INDIAN COUNTRY: THE CHANGING FACE OF CAPITIVITY IN EARLY AMERICA
Christina Snyder; Illus. Maps. 328 pp. Harvard University Press, 2010. $29.95.

*SLEEPY RIVER
Hannah Bandes; illus. by Jeanette Winter
Grades PS-3. Illus. 32 pp. Philomel, 1993. $14.95.

SLIM BUTTES, 1876: AN EPISODE OF THE GREAT SIOUX WAR
Jerome A. Greene, Editor
Illus. Maps. Biblio. 192 pp. Paper. University of Oklahoma Press, 1982. $14.95.

JOHN SLOCUM & THE INDIAN SHAKER CHURCH
Robert H. Ruby & John A. Brown
Illus. Map. Photos. 300 pp. University of Oklahoma Press, 1996. $34.95.

JOHN SIMPSON SMITH, 1810-1871
Stan Hoig; Reprint of 1974 edition. Illus. 30 pp. Arthur H. Clark, $22.50. Paper. Amazon.com, $3.50.

SM'ALGYAX: A REFERENCE DICTIONARY & GRAMMAR OF THE COAST TSIMSHIAN LANGUAGE
John Asher Dunn, Ed. & Compiler; 262 pp. Paper. U. of Washington Press, 1995. $29.95.

SMALL POX & THE IROQUOIS WARS: AN ETHNOHISTORICAL STUDY OF THE INFLUENCE OF DISEASE & DEMOGRAPHIC CHANGE IN IROQUOIAN CULTURE HISTORY, 1630-1700 Stephen Clark; Illus. 125 pp. Paper. Coyote Press, 1981. $11.25.

SMALL SPIRITS: NATIVE AMERICAN DOLLS FROM THE NATIONAL MUSEUM OF THE AMERICAN INDIAN Mary Jane Lenz; intro. by Clara Sue Kidwell
Illus. 176 pp. Paper. NMAI Press & University of Washington Press, 2004. $24.95.

*SMALL WORLD OF ESKIMOS
Bernard Planche; Sarah Matthews, tr.; Grades K-3. Franklin Watts, 1980. $10.40.

ELLEN SMALLBOY: GLIMPSES OF A CREE WOMAN'S LIFE
Regina Flannery; Illus. 128 pp. Paper. McGill-Queen's University Press, 1995.

SMITH & OTHER EVENTS: TALES OF THE CHILCOTIN
Paul St. Pierre; Collection of short stories of the Chilcotin Indians of British Columbia, Canada. 318 pp. Paper. University of Oklahoma Press, 1994. $12.95.

THE SMITHSONIAN & THE AMERICAN INDIAN: MAKING A MORAL ANTHROPOLOGY IN VICTORIAN AMERICA Curtis M. Hinsley
A guide to changing attitudes and values about Indians.
Illus. 320 pp. Paper. Smithsonian Institution Press, 1981. $17.95.

SMOKE FROM THEIR FIRES: THE LIFE OF A KWAKIUTL CHIEF
Clellan S. Ford; Reprint. Illus. 265 pp. Paper. Waveland, 1996. $16.50.

SMOKE RISING: THE NATIVE NORTH AMERICAN LITERARY COMPANION
Joseph Bruchac, et al. ; Illus. 492 pp. Paper. Amazon.com, $17.95.

SMOKE SIGNALS: NATIVE CINEMA RISING
Joanna Hearne; Illus. 280 pp. Paper. University of Nebraska Press, 2012. $30.

THE SMOKEHOUSE BOYS
Shaunna Oteka McCovery; Karuk creation myth. Paper. Heyday Books. $11.95.

SMOKING TECHNOLOGY OF THE ABORIGINES OF THE IROQUOIS AREA OF NEW YORK STATE Edward S. Rutsch; 252 pp. Amazon.com, 1972. $25.

SMOKY-TOP: THE ART & TIMES OF WILLIE SEAWEED
Bill Holm; Illus. 160 pp. University of Washington Press, 1983. $24.95.

*SNAIL GIRL BRINGS WATER: A NAVAJO STORY
Geri Keams; Picture book. Ages 5-8. Illus. Northland Press & Amazon.com, $15.95.

THE SNAKE DANCE OF THE HOPI INDIANS
Earle Forrest; Reprint of 1982 edition. Illus. 175 pp. Westernlore, $12.95.

REUBEN SNAKE, YOUR HUMBLE SERPENT
As told to Jay C. Fikes; Autobiography. Indian (Winnebago, 1937-1993) visionary and activist as told to Jay Fikes. Photos. 287 pp. Amazon.com, 1996. $24.95; paper, $14.95.

THE SNAKE RIVER-PALOUSE AND THE INVASION OF THE INLAND NORTHWEST
Clifford Trafzer & Richard Sceuerman
Illus. Maps. 292 pp. Paper. WSU Press, 2016. $24.95.

SNOWBIRD CHEROKEES: PEOPLE OF PERSISTENCE
Sharlotte Neely; Examines the Cherokees of Snowbird, North Carolina.
Illus. Maps. 192 pp. Paper. University of Georgia Press, $14.95.

SO, HOW LONG HAVE YOU BEEN NATIVE?: LIFE AS AN ALASKA NATIVE TOUR GUIDE Alexis C. Bunten
Illus. 272 pp. University of Nebraska Press, 2015. $26.95. eBook available.

SO YOU WANT TO WRITE ABOUT AMERICAN INDIANS? A GUIDE FOR WRITERS, STUDENTS, & SCHOLARS Devon Abbott Mihesuah; Guidelines to follow when researching and writing about Natives. Illus. 164 pp. Paper. U. of Nebraska Press, $16.95.

SOCIO & STYLOLINGUISTIC PERSPECTIVES ON AMERICAN INDIAN ENGLISH TEXTS Guillermo Bartelt; Illus. 176 pp. Edwin Mellon Press, 2001. $79.95.

SOCIAL CHANGE & CULTURAL CONTINUITY AMONG NATIVE NATIONS
Duane Champagne; Textbook. 368 pp. AltaMira Press, 2006. $96; paper, $44; eBook, $42.99.

SOCIAL CHANGE IN THE SOUTHWEST, 1350-1880
Thomas D. Hall; Traces the evolution & interaction of Native American groups, Hispanic soldiers & settlers, and American pioneers. Maps. 288 pp. Paper. University Press of Kansas, $15.95.

SOCIAL & ECONOMIC CHANGE AMONG THE NORTHERN OJIBWA
R.W. Dunning; Paper. Amazon.com, 1959. $8.95.

SOCIAL LIFE OF STORIES: NARRATIVE & KNOWLEDGE IN THE YUKON TERRITORY
Julie CruikshankStudy of indigenous oral narratives, exploring the social significance of storytelling of the Circumpolar Native peoples of today. Illus. Maps. 220 pp. University of Nebraska Press, 1998. $60; paper, $22.

SOCIAL ORGANIZATION OF THE WESTERN APACHE: LETTERS FROM THE FIELD
edited by Morris E. Opler; Book on request. 104 pp. U. of Arizona Press, 1969. $50.

SOCIAL ORGANIZATION OF THE WESTERN PUEBLOS
Fred Eggan; Reprint of the 1950 ed. Illus. Paper. University of Chicago Press, 1973. $12.50; paper, $2.95.

A SOCIAL STUDY OF 150 CHIPPEWA INDIAN FAMILIES OF THE WHITE EARTH RESERVATION OF MINNESOTA Inez Hilger; Reprint. Amazon.com, $49.50.

SOCIETIES IN ECLIPSE: ARCHAEOLOGY OF THE EASTERN WOODLANDS INDIANS, A.D. 1400-1700 David S. Brose, et al, Eds.; 256 pp. Smithsonian Institution Press, 2001. $65; paper, $29.95.

SOCIETIES OF THE KIOWA
Robert H. Lowie; 14 pp. Paper. Lakota Books, 1995. $7.95.

SOCIETIES OF THE OGLALA
Clark Wissler; Illus. 99 pp. Paper. Lakota Books, 1993. $21.95.

SOCIOLINGUISTIC CONSTRUCTS OF ETHNIC IDENTITY: THE SYNTATIC DELINEATION OF LUMBEE ENGLISH
Clare J. Dannenberg; Illus. 144 pp. Paper. Duke University Press, 2002. $20.

LOUIS SOCKALEXIS: THE FIRST CLEVELAND INDIAN
David L. Fleitz; Illus. 230 pp. Paper. McFarland, 2002. $28.50.

*SOFT CHILD: HOW RATTLESNAKE GOT ITS FANGS
Joe Hayes & Kay Sather; Tohono O'odham tale. Grades Pre-K-3.
Illus. 32 pp. Paper. Amazon.com, $8.95.

SOFT GOLD: A HISTORY OF THE FUR TRADE IN THE GREAT LAKES REGION & ITS IMPACT OF NATIVE AMERICAN CULTURE
Ted Reese; Illus. 136 pp. Paper. Amazon.com, 2001. $15.50.

*SOFT RAIN: A STORY OF THE CHEROKEE TRAIL OF TEARS
Corneli Cornellison; Grades 3 to 5. Illus. 128 pp. Amazon.com, 1998. $14.95.

SOFT STEP & BRIGHT EYES: A TALE OF NATIVE AMERICAN LIFE
Suzanne Tate; Illus. 32 pp. Paper. Amazon.com, 2000. $4.95.

SOLD AMERICAN: THE STORY OF ALASKA NATIVES & THEIR LAND, 1867-1959 - THE ARMY TO STATEHOOD
Donald C. Mitchell; Illus. Photos. Map. 600 pp. Originally published by University Press of New England, 1997. University of Alaska Press, 2002. $29.95.

SOLDIER, SETTLER, SIOUX: FORT RIDGELY & THE MINNESOTA RIVER VALLEY, 1853-1867 Paul N. Beck; History of one of the most important military posts in the Minnesota and Big Sioux River valleys. Illus. 150 pp. Paper. The Center for Western Studies, 2000. $12.95.

THE SOLDIERS OF AMERICA'S FIRST ARMY, 1791
Richard M. Lytle; 456 pp. Paper. Scarecrow Press, 2004. $65.

THE SOLIDARITY OF KIN: ETHNOHISTORY, RELIGIOUS STUDIES, & THE ALGONQUIN-FRENCH RELIGIOUS ENCOUNTER Kenneth M. Morrison
243 pp. State University of New York Press, 2002. $65.50; paper, $21.95.

SOLOMON SPRING
Michelle Black; Historical mystery novel taking place among the Cheyennes in 1878 Kansas. Illus. 175 pp. Paper. WinterSun Press, $14.95. Amazon.com. Kindle, 2.99.

SOME KIND OF POWER: NAVAJO CHILDREN'S SKIN-WALKER NARRATIVES
Margaret K. Brady; 224 pp. University of Utah Press, 1984. $20.

SOME NEWSPAPER REFERENCES CONCERNING INDIAN–WHITE RELATIONSHIPS IN NORTHEASTERN CALIFORNIA, 1850-1920
Norris Bleyhl; 209 pp. Association of Northern California Records, 1979. $9.

SOME PROTECTIVE DESIGNS OF THE DAKOTA
Clark Wissler; Illus. 38 pp. Paper. Lakota Books, 1998. $12.95.

SOME SEX BELIEFS & PRACTICES IN A NAVAHO COMMUNITY
F.L. Bailey; Reprint of 1950 edition. Paper. Peabody Museum, $10.

SOME THINGS ARE NOT FORGOTTEN: A PAWNEE FAMILY REMEMBERS
Martha Royce Blaine; Illus. Map. 286 pp. Paper. University of Nebraska Press, 1997. $35.

SOME WARMER TONE: ALASKA ATHABASKAN BEAD EMBROIDERY
Kate C. Duncan, Editor; Ilus. Maps. 64 pp. Paper. U. of Alaska Museum, 1984. $12.

SOME WESTERN SHOSHONI MYTHS
Julian H. Steward; paper. Boise State University Publications, $17.59.

*SON OF THE DINE'
J. Walter Wood; Grades 5-9. Paper. Council for Indian Education, 1972. $1.95.

"A SON OF THE FOREST" & OTHER WRITINGS BY WILLIAM APESS, A PEQUOT
William Apess; Barry O'Connell, Editor
176 pp. Paper. University of Massachusetts Press, 1997. $17.95.

SON OF OLD MAN HAT: A NAVAHO AUTOBIOGRAPHY
Walter Dyk & Left Handed, recorded by
380 pp. Paper. University of Nebraska Press, 1967. $10.95.

*SON OF THUNDER
Stig Holmas; The sole survivor of a Mexican Army massacre is adopted by Cochise. Grades 7 and up. 128 pp. Amazon.com, 1993. $16.95; paper, $10.95.

SON OF TWO BLOODS
Vincent L. Mendoza; Half Creek and half Mexican, the author's traces his experience with racism. Illus. 200 pp. Paper. University of Nebraska Press, 1996. $12.

A SONG FOR THE HORSE NATION: HORSES IN NATIVE AMERICAN CULTURES
Emil Her Many Horses, George Horse Capture, Eds.
Illus. 120 pp. Paper. NMAI Press & Fulcrum Publishing, 2005. $12.95.

*SONG OF THE HERMIT THRUSH: AN IROQUOIS LEGEND
Terri Cohlene; Grades 1-5. Illus. Paper. Amazon.com, 1992. $4.95.

THE SONG OF THE LOOM: NEW TRADITIONS IN NAVAJO WEAVING
Frederick J. Dockstader; Illus. 132 pp. Amazon.com, 1987. $39.95.

*SONG OF THE SEVEN HERBS
Walking Night Bear & Stan Padilla; Grades 3 and up. Illus. 60 pp. Paper. Cherokee Publications & The Book Publishing Co., $11.95.

SONG OF THE SKY: VERSIONS OF NATIVE AMERICAN SONG-POEMS
Brian Swann; rev. ed. by Barry O'Connell
Paper. University of Massachusetts Press, 1994. $14.95.

SONG OF THE TURTLE: AMERICAN INDIAN LITERATURE, 1974-1994
Paula Gunn Allen (Laguna/Lakota)
Anthology of American Indian literature. Grades 9 and up. Oyate, 1996. $25.

*SONG OF THE WILD VIOLETS
Peggy Thompson, Writer & Illus.
Grades 3 and up. Illus. 36 pp. Paper. The Book Publishing Co., $5.95.

A SONG TO THE CREATOR: TRADITIONAL ARTS OF NATIVE AMERICAN WOMEN OF THE PLATEAU Lillian J. Ackerman, Editor
Illus. 206 pp. U. of Oklahoma Press, 1996. $34.95; paper, $24.95.

SONGPRINTS: THE MUSICAL EXPERIENCE OF FIVE SHOSHONE WOMEN
Judith Vander
376 pp. Paper. University of Illinois Press, 1996. $19.95; $26.95 includes audio.

SONGS FROM AN OUTCAST
by John E. Smelcer; Collection of poems in both English and Ahtna Athabaskan dealing with Native American themes. 95 pp. Paper. Amazon.com, 2000. $12.

SONGS FROM THIS EARTH ON TURTLE'S BACK: AN ANTHOLOGY OF POETRY BY AMERICAN INDIAN WRITERS
Joseph Bruchac; 300 pp. Paper. Amazon.com, 1983. $9.95.

*SONGS FROM THE LOOM: A NAVAJO GIRL LEARNS TO WEAVE
Monty Roessell; Grades 3-8. Illus. 48 pp. Paper. Lerner Publications, 1995. $6.95.

SONGS OF THE APACHE
Willard Rhodes
Reprint. 14 pp. Paper. Jeffrey Norton Publishers, 1999. $14.95, includes audiocassette.

SONGS OF THE EARTH
Edward S. Curtis & Running Press Staff
Illus. 128 pp. Amazon.com, 2003. $19.98.

SONGS OF INDIAN TERRITORY
Illus. 2nd Edition. Includes recorded tape. Paper. Amazon.com, 1991.

SONGS OF THE KIOWA
Willard Rhodes
Reprint. 21 pp. Paper. Jeffrey Norton Publishers, 1999. $14.95, includes audiocassette.

SONGS OF THE NAVAJO
Willard Rhodes
Reprint. 18 pp. Paper. Jeffrey Norton Publishers, 1999. $14.95, includes audiocassette.

SONGS OF THE OKTAHUTCHE: COLLECTED POEMS
Alexander Posey; edited by Matthew Wynn Sivils
3 photos. 288 pp. Paper. University of Nebraska Press, 2008. $24.95.

SONGS OF OUR GRANDFATHERS: MUSIC OF THE UNAMI DELAWARE INDIANS
Robert H. Adams; Master's thesis discussing the many types of Lenape music.
150 pp. Paper. Amazon.com, $21.95.

*SONGS OF SHIPROCK FAIR
Luci Tapahonso; Navajo Nation fair. Grades 2-4. Illus. Paper. Kiva Publishing, 1999.

SONGS OF THE SPIRIT: SCULPTURE BY DOUG HYDE
Patrick T. Houlihan & Charles Dailey; Essays. 24 pp. Paper. Southwest Museum. $4.95.

SONGS OF THE TETON SIOUX
Harry W. Paige; Illus. Amazon.com, 1969. $20.95.

SONGS OF THE TEWA
Herbert J. Spinden, Editor/Translator
Tewa poetry. Reprint of 1933 edition. Illus. 125 pp. Paper. Sunstone Press, $12.95.

SONGS OF THE WIGWAM
Contains more than a dozen songs portraying native life and thought in the forest around the Great Lakes. 24 pages. 95 each; 65 each, 15 or more. World Around Songs, $2.45

SONORA: A DESCRIPTION OF THE PROVINCE
Ignaz Pfefferkorn; Ethnographic account of the Pima, Opata, and Eudeve Indians of the Sonora region. Reprint of 1949 edition. 329 pp. Paper. University of Arizona Press, $12.95.

SONORA YAQUI LANGUAGE STRUCTURES
John M. Dedrick & Eugene H. Casad; 480 pp. University of Arizona Press, 1999. $49.95.

THE SONS OF THE WIND: THE SACRED STORIES OF THE LAKOTA
D.M. Dooling; Mythology of the Oglala Lakota Sioux. 136 pp. Paper.
Amazon.com & Alibris.com, 1984. $8.95.

*SOOTFACE
Robert San Souci; Ojibwa story. Grades K-4. Illus. 32 pp. Paper. Dragonfly Books, 1997.

A SORROW IN OUR HEART: THE LIFE OF TECUMSEH
Allan W. Eckert; 862 pp. Amazon.com, $27.50.

SOUL CONCEPTS OF THE NAVAHO
Berard Haile; Reprint of 1964 edition. Paper. St. Michaels Historical Museum, $6.50.

SOUL & NATIVE AMERICANS
Ake Hultkrantz; Robert Holland, Editor; Abridged edition of original title: Conceptions of the Soul Among North American Indians. 234 pp. Paper. Spring Publications, 1997. $18.

THE SOUL OF THE INDIAN; & OTHER WRITINGS FROM OHIYESA
Charles Eastman; edited by Kent Nerburn; Ohiyesa, a Dakota Indian, has been described as "the Native American Thoreau." Also known as Charles Alexander Eastman. 64 pp. Paper. Dover, $4.95.

THE SOUL OF THE INDIAN: AN INTERPRETATION
Charles A. Eastman
Reprint. Illus. 190 pp. Paper. University of Nebraska Press, 2001. $10.95.

SOUL OF NOWHERE: TRAVERSING GRACE IN A RUGGED LAND
Illus. 240 pp. Amazon.com, 2003. $22.95.

A SOUL RUNS THROUGH IT
Victoria A. Summers; Illus. 138 pp. Paper. Amazon.com, 1998. $10.

SOUL TALK, SONG LANGUAGE: CONVERSATIONS WITH JOY HARJO
Joy Harjo, Tanaya Winder; Laura Coltelli, foreword; Illus. 164 pp. Wesleyan University Press, 2011. Distributed by the University Press of New England. $24.95, E-book, $12.99.

***SOUN TETOKEN: NEZ PERCE BOY TAMES A STALLION**
Kennth Thomasma; Eunice Hundley; Illus.; Recounts the days of the Nez Perce tribe during the War of 1877. Illus. Amazon.com, $10.99; paper, $6.99.

SOUND: NATIVE TEACHINGS & VISIONARY ART OF JOSEPH RAEL
Joseph Rael; Illus. 264 pp. Council Oak Books, 2009. $30.

THE SOUND OF RATTLES & CLAPPERS: A COLLECTION OF NEW CALIFORNIA INDIAN WRITING Greg Sarris, Editor; Poetry & fiction by 10 Native Americans of California Indian ancestry documents history. 161 pp. Paper. University of Arizona Press, 1994. $17.95.

THE SOUND OF STRINGS
Harold Keith; The Comanches during the mid-1800s. 182 pp. Levite of Apache, $17.

SOURCE MATERIAL FOR THE SOCIAL & CEREMONIAL LIFE OF THE CHOCTAW INDIANS John R. Swanton; foreword by Kenneth H. Carleton Illus. 312 pp. Paper. University of Alabama Press, 2001. $34.95. E-Book, $27.96.

SOURCE MATERIAL ON THE HISTORY & ETHNOLOGY OF THE CADDO INDIANS
John R. Swanton & Helen H. Tanner
Maps. Photos. 352 pp. Paper. University of Oklahoma Press, 1996. $21.95.

SOURCES OF FINANCIAL AID AVAILABLE TO AMERICAN INDIAN STUDENTS
Leslie A. Kedelty, Editor; Major sources of financial aid, and admissions and financial aid process information. Includes program reps, BIA area offices, and job opportunities. 78 pp. Annual. Paper. Amazon.com, $5.

SOURCING PREHISTORIC CERAMICS AT CHODISTAAS PUEBLO, ARIZONA
Maria Nieves Zedeno; Prehistoric pottery identification. Illus. 110 p. Paper. University of Arizona Press, 1994. $12.95.

SOUTH CAROLINA INDIANS, INDIAN TRADERS & OTHER ETHNIC CONNECTIONS: BEGINNING IN 1670 Theresa M. Hicks; Reprint Co., 1997. $39.50.

SOUTH DAKOTA LEADERS: FROM PIERRE CHOUTEAU, JR. TO OSCAR HOWE
Herbert T. Hoover & Larry Zimmerman
Includes biographies of Sitting Bull & Crazy Horse. Paper. Dakota Press, 1989. $27.50.

SOUTH FLORIDA'S VANISHED PEOPLE: TRAVELS IN THE HOMELAND OF ANCIENT CALUSA Byron Voegelin; Island Press, 1977. $6.95.

***SOUTHEAST INDIANS: COLORING BOOK**
Peter F. Copeland; Grades K-3. Illus. 48 pp. Paper. Dover, $2.95.

SOUTHEAST INDIANS: AN EDUCATIONAL COLORING BOOK
Grades 1-8. Illus. 32 pp. Paper. Spizzirri Publishing, 1981.
Read & Coloring Book, $1.95; Cassette/book, $6.95.

SOUTHEASTERN CEREMONIAL COMPLEX, ARTIFACTS & ANALYSIS
Patricia Galloway, Editor; Illus. 400 pp. University of Nebraska Press, 1989. $60.

SOUTHEASTERN CEREMONIAL COMPLEX & ITS INTERPRETATION
J.H. Howard and C.H. Chapman
Illus. 169 pp. Paper. Missouri Archaeological Society, 1968. $4.

SOUTHEASTERN FRONTIERS: EUROPEAN, AFRICANS, & THE AMERICAN INDIANS, 1513-1840: A CRITICAL BIBLIOGRAPHY James H. O'Donnell, Illus
136 pp. Paper. Amazon.com & Alibris.com, 1982. $4.95.

THE SOUTHEASTERN INDIANS
Charles Hudson
Reprint of 1976 ed. Illus. 573 pp. Paper. Amazon.com. $24.95.

SOUTHEASTERN INDIANS LIFE PORTRAITS: A CATALOGUE OF PICTURES 1564-1860 Emma Lila Fundaburk; Illus. 350 photos, p[aintings, drawings, and woodcuts. 136 pp. The Choctaw Store & University of Alabama Press, 2000. $22.50. E-Book, $18.

SOUTHEASTERN INDIANS SINCE THE REMOVAL ERA
Walter Williams, Editor; Illus. 270 pp. Paper. University of Georgia Press, 1979. $12.

SOUTHEASTERN WOODLAND INDIAN DESIGNS
Caren Caraway; Illus. 48 pp. Paper. Stemmer House, 1985. $5.95.

SOUTHERN ATHAPASKAN MIGRATION: A.D. 200-1750
128 pp. Amazon.com, 1987. $10.50.

SOUTHERN CADDO: AN ANTHOLOGY
H.F. Gregory & David H. Thomas, Editors; 550 pp. Garland, 1986. $75.

SOUTHERN CHEYENNE WOMEN'S SONGS
Virginia Giglio; Book & tape set. Illus. Maps. 34 song transcriptions. 274 pp. University of Oklahoma Press, $29.95 (book); tape, $9.95; book & tape set, $35.

SOUTHERN CHEYENNES
Donald Berthrong; Reprint of the 1963 edition. Illus. Maps. Biblio. 442 pp. Paper. University of Oklahoma Press, $18.95.

SOUTHERN FRONTIER, 1670-1732
Verner Crane; Reprint of 1956 edition. Greenwood, $22.50.

SOUTHERN INDIAN MYTHS & LEGEDS
Virginia Borwn & Laurella Owens, Eds Illus. 160 pp. Paper. Amazon.com, 1985. $12.95.

SOUTHERN INDIANS & ANTHROPOLOGISTS: CULTURE, POLITICS & IDENTITY
Lisa J. Lefler & Frederic W. Gleach, Eds.
160 pp. University of Georgia Press, 2002. $39.95; paper, $19.95.

THE SOUTHERN INDIANS & BENJAMIN HAWKINS, 1796-1816
Florette Henri; Illus. Maps. Biblio. 378 pp. U. of Oklahoma Press, 1986. $34.95.

THE SOUTHERN INDIANS: THE STORY OF THE CIVILIZED TRIBES BEFORE REMOVAL R.S. Cotterill
Reprint of 1954 edition. Illus. Maps. 259 pp. Paper. University of Oklahoma Press, $13.95.

SOUTHERN PAIUTE: A PORTRAIT
William Logan Hebner; photos by Michael Plyler
Illus. 208 pp. Utah State University Press, 2010. $36.95. E-book, $28.

SOUTHERN PAIUTES: LEGENDS, LORE, LANGUAGE & LINEAGE
LaVan Martineau; Illus. 336 pp. Amazon.com, 1992. $24.95.

SOUTHERN PLAINS ALLIANCES
Howard Meredith; University Press of Kansas, 1994.

SOUTHERN PLAINS LIFEWAYS: APACHE & WICHITA
Pamphlet on the Apache & Wichita Tribes. Wichita Tribal Office.

SOUTHERN PUEBLO POTTERY: 2,000 ARTIST BIOGRAPHIES
Gregory Schaaf; Richard M. Howard, Editor
Illus. 370 pp. Center for Indigenous Arts & Cultures (CIAC) Press, 2002. $65.

SOUTHERN UTE INDIANS OF EARLY COLORADO
Verner Z. Reed; William Jones, Editor; Illus. Paper. Amazon.com, 1980. $3.95.

SOUTHERN UTE WOMEN: AUTONOMY & ASSIMILATION ON THE RESERVATION, 1887-1934 Katherine M.B. Osburn
Illus. 165 pp. University of New Mexico Press, $1997. $45; paper, $21.95.

SOUTHWEST
Alfonso Ortiz, Editor; Illus. 701 pp. Smithsonian, 1980. $23.

SOUTHWEST AMERICAN INDIAN DESIGNS
Caren Caraway; Illus. 48 pp. Paper. Stemmer House, 1996. $5.95.

SOUTHWEST COOKS! THE TRADITION OF NATIVE AMERICAN CUISINES
Lynn Kirst & Jeanette O'Malley, Editors
Illus. 108 pp. Paper. Southwest Museum, 1991. $14.95.

THE SOUTHWEST: GOLD, GOD & GRANDEUR
Paul R. Walker; Illus. 256 pp. Amazon.com, 2001. $35.

SOUTHWEST: HANDBOOK OF NORTH AMERICAN INDIANS
Illus. 868 pp. Smithsonian, 1983. $25.00.

SOUTHWEST INDIAN ARTS & CRAFTS
Mark Bahti; Illus. 48 pp. Amazon.com, 1983. $12.95;

SOUTHWEST INDIAN CALENDAR
Marcia Keegan; 13 color pictures of life in the Navajo Nation and among the Pueblo Indians of New Mexico. 12.5" x 10.25". Cafepress.com, $12.

SOUTHWEST INDIAN COOKBOOK: PUEBLO & NAVAJO IMAGES, QUOTES & RECIPES Marcia Keegan, Ed.; 44 color photos. 120 pp. Paper. Amazon.com, $12.95.

***SOUTHWEST INDIAN DESIGN STAINED GLASS COLORING BOOK**
Carol Krez; Grades K-2. 32 pp. Paper. Dover, $3.95.

SOUTHWEST INDIAN DESIGNS CD-ROM & BOOK
Illus. 48 pp. CD-ROM, Written heritage, $16.95.

SOUTHWEST INDIAN DESIGNS; WITH SOME EXPLANATIONS
Mark T. Bahti; Recreates about 200 symbols and their variations. Includes are symbols and explanations of Zuni, Navajo, Hopi, Tewa, Acoma, Pueblo, Mimbres, and Hohokam designs. Illus. 32 pp. Paper. Treasure Chest, 1994. $4.95.

SOUTHWEST INDIAN SILVER FROM THE DONEGHY COLLECTION
Louise Lincoln, Editor; Illus. 189 pp. University of Texas Press, 1982. $29.95.

*SOUTHWEST INDIANS COLORING BOOK
Peter Copeland; Ready-to-color depictions and descriptions of Southwest Indians of the past and present, 1840s-1980s. Grades 1 -4. Illus. Paper. Dover, $2.95.

*SOUTHWEST INDIANS: AN EDUCATIONAL COLORING BOOK
Linda Spizzirri, Editor; Grades 1-8. Illus. 32 pp. Paper. Spizzirri Publishing, 1981. Read & Coloring Book, $1.95; Cassette/book, $6.95.

SOUTHWEST INDIANS: A PHOTOGRAPHIC PORTRAIT
Bill Harris; A photographic tour of Native American culture in the Southwest. 100 full-color photos. 128 pp. Random House, $9.95.

SOUTHWEST MUSEUM PUBLICATIONS
Southwest Museum.

SOUTHWEST TRAVELER: A TRAVELERS GUIDE TO SOUTHWEST INDIAN ARTS & CRAFTS
Charlotte S. Neyland; Illus. 48 pp. Paper. Amazon.com, 1992. $5.95.

SOUTHWESTERN AMERICAN INDIAN LITERATURE: IN THE CLASSROOM & BEYOND Conrad Shumaker; paper. 118 pp. Peter Lang Publishing, 2008. $29.95.

SOUTHWESTERN ARTS & CRAFTS PROJECTS
Nancy Krenz & Patricia Byrnes; Arts & crafts of the Indian and Spanish-American cultures. 145 pp. Paper. Sunstone Press, $12.95.

SOUTHWESTERN INDIAN ARTS & CRAFTS
Tom Bahti; updated by Mark Bahti; Come to know silverwork, turquoise, beadwork, pottery, baskets, ironwood carvings, Navajo sandpainting, Zuni fetishes, Hopi kachinas, and Navajo rugs. Illus. Photos. Maps. 48 pp. Paper. KC Publications, 1997. $12.95.

SOUTHWESTERN INDIAN BASKETS: THEIR HISTORY & THEIR MAKERS
Andrew H. Whiteford; Illus. 236 pp. Paper. School of American Research, 1988. $18.95.

SOUTHWESTERN INDIAN CEREMONIALS
Tom Bahti; updated by Mark Bahti
3rd revised ed. Illus. Photos. Map. 64 pp. Paper. KC Publications, 1997. $12.95.

SOUTHWESTERN INDIAN DESIGNS
Madeleine Orban-Szontagh; 250 authentic motifs drawn from Navajo jewelry & rugs, Pueblo pottery, Hopi ceremonial dress, & other sources. Illus. 48 pp. Paper. Dover, $5.95.

SOUTHWESTERN INDIAN POTTERY
Bruce Hucko; Illus. 64 pp. Paper. KC Publications, 1999. $12.95.

SOUTHWESTERN INDIAN RECIPE BOOK
Zora G. Hesse; Favorite foods of many tribes. Illus. 60 pp. Paper. Amazon.com & Alibris.com, $4.

SOUTHWESTERN INDIAN RITUAL DRAMA
Charlotte Frisbie; Illus. 372 pp. Paper. Waveland, 1989. $14.95.

SOUTHWESTERN INDIAN TRIBES
Tom Bahti; updated by Mark Bahti; Covers 32 Southwestern Indian cultures. Illus. Photos. Maps. 72 pp. Paper. KC Publications, 1997. $12.95.

SOUTHWESTERN INDIAN WEAVING
Mark Bahti, Cherie C. Madison, Bruce Hucko, K.C. DenDooven
Illus. 50 pp. KC Publications, 2001. $12.95.

SOUTHWESTERN MINNESOTA ARCHAEOLOGY: 12,000 YEARS IN THE PRAIRIE LAKE REGION Scott F. Anfinson; Illus. 156 pp. Paper. Minnesota Historical Society Press, 1997. $18.

SOUTHWESTERN POTTERY: AN ANNOTATED BIBLIOGRAPHY & LIST OF TYPES & WARES Norman T. Oppelt; Illus. 333 pp. Scarecrow Press, 1988. $35.

SOUTHWESTERN POTTERY: ANASAZI TO ZUNI
Allan Hayes & John Blora; An art, history & reference book showcasing more than 1,100 pots. 130 color photos. Biblio. 200 pp. Paper. Northland Press, $21.95.

SOVEREIGN BONES: NEW NATIVE AMERICAN WRITING
Eric Gansworth, Editor; Authors inclkude Marijo Moore, Louise Erdrich, Alex Jacobs, Heid Erdrich, Simon Ortiz, et al. Paper. Amazon.com, 2007. $17.95.

SOVEREIGN SCREENS: ABORIGINAL MEDIA ON THE CANADIAN WEST COAST
Kristin L. Dowell; Illus. Map. 312 pp. University of Nebraska Press, 2013. $50; paper, $25.

SOVEREIGN SELVES: AMERICAN INDIAN AUTOBIOGRAPHY & THE LAW
David J. Carlson; Explores how American Indian autobiographers' approaches to writing about their own lives have been impacted by American legal systems from the Revolutionary War until the 1920s. 232 pp. Paper. University of Illinois Press, 2006. $31.

SOVEREIGN STORIES & BLOOD MEMORIES: NATIVE AMERICAN WOMEN'S AUTOBIOGRAPHY
Annette Angela Portillo; 192 pp. University of New Mexico Press, 2017. $65.

SOVEREIGNTY FOR SURVIVAL: AMERICAN ENERGY DEVELOPMENT AND INDIAN SELF-DETERMINATION
James Robert Allison III; Illus. 256 pp. Yale University Press, 2015. $45.

THE SOVEREIGNTY & THE GOODNESS OF GOD
Mary Rowlandson, et al; Reprint. Paper. Bedford/St. Martin's Press, 2002. $29.95.

THE SOVEREIGNTY & THE GOODNESS OF GOD, CREATING AMERICA & CHEROKEE
Mary Rowlandson, et al; 2nd Edition. Paper. Bedford/St. Martin's Press, 2003. $39.15.

SOVEREIGNTY MATTERS: LOCATIONS OF CONTESTATION AND POSSIBILITY IN INDIGENOUS STRUGGLES FOR SELF-DETERMINATION;
Joanne Barker, Editor; Illus. 250 pp. University of Nebraska Press, 2005.

SOVEREIGNTY & SYMBOL: INDIAN-WHITE CONFLICT AT GANIENKEH
Gail Landsman; Illus. 250 pp. University of New Mexico Press, 1988. $19.95.

SPACES BETWEEN US: QUEER SETTLER COLONIALISM & INDIGENOUS DECOLONIZATION
Scott Lauria Morgensen; Explores the intimate relationship of non-Native and Native sexual politics in the U.S. 336 pp. University of Minnesota Press, 2011. $75; paper, $25.

SPACES OF THE MIND: NARRATIVE & COMMUNITY IN THE AMERICAN WEST
Elaine A. Jahner; Analysis of Native America oral narrative. 192 pp. Paper. University of Nebraska Press, 2008. $19.95.

SPAIN IN THE SOUTHWEST: A NARRATIVE HISTORY OF COLONIAL NEW MEXICO, ARIZONA, TEXAS & CALIFORNIA
John L. Kessell; Illus. 475 pp. University of Oklahoma Press, 2002. $45.

SPANISH ATTEMPTS TO COLONIZE SOUTHEAST NORTH AMERICA, 1513-1587
Larry R. Clark; Illus. 207 pp. Paper. Mcfarland & Co., 2010.

SPANISH EXPLORERS IN THE SOUTHERN U.S., 1528-1543
Frederick Hodge & Theodore Lewis, Editors
Reprint fo 1907 edition. Illus. 410 pp. Barnes & Noble, $21.50.

SPANISH-AMERICAN BLANKETRY: ITS RELATIONSHIP TO ABORIGINAL WEAVING IN THE SOUTHWEST H.P. Mera
Reprint of 1948 edition. Illus. 96 pp. Paper. School of American Research, $14.95.

SPANISH FRONTIER IN NORTH AMERICA
David J. Weber; Definitive history of the Spanish colonial period in North America. Describes the influences by the Spaniards and the effect of Native North Americans on the Spanish settlers from Florida to California. Illus. 600 pp. Paper. Yale U. Press, 1992. $20.

SPANISH-INDIAN RELATIONS IN FLORIDA: A STUDY OF TWO VISTAS, 1657-1678
Fred L. Pearson, Jr.; Reprint. Illus. 336 pp. Amazon.com, 1990. $70.

SPANISH MISSIONS OF NEW MEXICO
John L. Kessell & Rick Hendricks, Eds.; 488 pp. Garland, 1992. $25.

THE SPANISH STRUGGLE FOR JUSTICE IN THE CONQUEST OF AMERICA
Lewis Hanke; Illus. 246 pp. Amazon.com, 2002. $16.95.

*SPARK IN THE STONE: SKILLS & PROJECTS FROM NATIVE AMERICAN TRADITION Peter Goodchild; Grades 5 and up. Illus. 130 pp. Paper. Cherokee Publications & Amazon.com, 1991. $11.95.

*SPARROW HAWK
Meridel le Sueur; illus. by Robert DesJarlait; Fictional look at youth and race relations. Grades 4 and up. 192 pp. Holy Cow! Press, $13.95.

SPEAK LIKE SINGING: CLASSICS OF NATIVE AMERICAN LITERATURE
Kennth Lincoln; 383 pp. University of New Mexico Press, $39.95; paper, $24.95.

SPEAK LAKOTA
Five Levels: Level 1 textbook. 110 pp. Level 2 textbook, 192 pp.; Level 3 Teacher's Guide, $39.95. Level 1 Audio CD, $14.95; 271 Flashcards, $199. Level 2 Audio CD, $14.95; 36 Flash Cards, $49.95. Level 3 Audio CD, $14.95. Level 4Textbook, $39; Audio CD, $14.95; 115 Flashcards, $99.95. Level 5 textbook, 153 pp. $39; Teacher's Guide, 85 pp. 100 Flashcards, $99.95; Lakota Audio Series, $79.95. Lakota Books.

SPEAK TO ME WORDS
edited by Dean Rader & Janice Gould; Essays on contemporary American Indian poetry. 290 pp. Paper. University of Arizona Press, 2003. $24.95..

SPEAKING FOR THE GENERATIONS: NATIVE WRITERS ON WRITING
Simon J. Ortiz, Editor; Includes Gloria Bird & Leslie Marmon Silko describe the influences on their developments as writers. 248 pp. Paper. U. of Arizona Press, 1998. $17.95.

SPEAKING FOR OURSELVES: ENVIRONMENTAL JUSTICE IN CANADA
Julian Agyeman, et al. Editors
Illus. 292 pp. Paper. U. of Washington Press, 2010. $32.95.

SPEAKING OF INDIANS
Ella Deloria; intro by Vine Deloria, Jr.; Describes traditional values, costumes, kinship patterns and religious attitudes of the Sioux. Reprint of 1944 edition. 163 pp. Paper. University of Nebraska Press, 1998. $12.95.

SPEAKING WITH AUTHORITY: THE EMERGENCE OF THE VOCABULARY OF FIRST NATIONS' SELF-GOVERNMENT
Michael W. Posluns; Chronicled through a study of the testimony of First Nations & aboriginal witnesses. Illus. 338 pp. Paper. Routledge, 2010. $35.96.

A SPECIAL GIFT: THE KUTCHIN BEADWORK TRADITION
Kate Duncan & Eunice Carney; Illus. 104 pp. Paper. U. of Alaska Press, 1998. $19.95.

THE SPECTER OF THE INDIAN: RACE, GENDER, AND GHOSTS IN AMERICAN SEANCES, 1848-1890 Kathryn Troy 200 pp. State U. of New York Press, 2017. $85.

SPECULATORS IN EMPIRE: IROQUOIA AND THE 1768 TREATY OF FORT STANWIX William J. Campbell; 296 pp. Paper. University of Oklahoma Press, $24.95.

SPEECH OF CHIEF SEATTLE
Chief Seattle; 24 pp. Amazon.com, $9.95.

THE SPELL OF CALIFORNIA'S SPANISH COLONIAL MISSIONS:
A GUIDEBOOK & HISTORY
Donald Francis Tomey; Illus. 272 pp. Paper. Sunstone Press, 2001. $24.95.

*SPIDER SPINS A STORY
Jill Max; illus. by Robert Annesley, et al; Collection of 14 legends from native America. Ages 8-12. Illus. 72 pp. Northland Press & Amazon.com, $16.95.

SPIDER WOMAN STORIES: LEGENDS OF THE HOPI INDIANS
G.M. Mullett; Hopi mythology. 142 pp. Paper. University of Arizona Press, 1979. $13.95.

SPIDER WOMAN: A STORY OF NAVAJO WEAVERS & CHANTERS
Gladys Reichard; Reprint of 1934 edition. Illus. 319 pp. Paper.
University of New Mexico Press & Amazon.com, $19.95.

SPIDER WOMAN WALKS THIS LAND: TRADITIONAL CULTURAL PROPERTIES
& THE NAVAJO NATION
Kelli Carmean; Illus. 336 pp. AltaMira Press, 2002. $70; paper, $24.95.

SPIDER WOMAN'S GIFT: 19TH CENTURY DINE TEXTILES
Shelby J. Tisdale, Editor; Essays by Joyce Begay-Foss and Marian E. Rodee. Presents Dine textiles and basketry weavings created between 1850s and the 1890s. Illus. 96 pp. Museum of New Mexico Press, 2012. $24.95.

SPIDERWOMAN'S DREAM
Alicia Otis; Southwestern Indian mythology. Illus. 64 pp. Paper. Sunstone Press, $7.95.

SPIDERWOMAN'S GRANDDAUGHTERS: TRADITIONAL TALES & CONTEMPORARY WRITING BY NATIVE AMERICAN WOMEN
Paula G. Allen, Editor; 256 pp. Paper. Fawcett, 1990. $11.95.

THE SPIRAL OF MEMORY: INTERVIEWS
Joy Harjo; Laura Coltelli, Editor
Illus. 152 pp. University of Michigan Press, 1996. $60; paper, $14.95.

SPIRIT CAPTURE: PHOTOGRAPHS FROM NATIONAL MUSEUM OF THE AMERICAN INDIAN Tim Johnson, Editor; Foreword by W. Richard West; 200 images from the Museum with essays from Native American historians, anthropologists, and curators. 25 color photos. 206 pp. NMAI Press, 1998. $60; paper, $34.95.

SPIRIT DANCE AT MEZIADIN: CHIEF JOSEPH GOSNELL & THE NISGA'A TREATY
Alex Rose; Illus. 216 pp. Paper. Harbour Publishing, 2000.

SPIRIT FACES: CONTEMPORARY MASKS OF THE NORTHWEST COAST
Gary Wyatt; Illus. Map. 144 pp. Paper. University of Washington Press, 1994. $28.95.

THE SPIRIT & THE FLESH: SEXUAL DIVERSITY IN AMERICAN INDIAN CULTURE
Walter L. Williams; Illus. 364 pp. Paper. Amazon.com, 1992. $21.

SPIRIT HEALING: NATIVE AMERICAN MAGIC & MEDICINE
Mary Dean Atwood; illus. by Bert Seabourn; A self-help guide to the Native American spiritual growth process. 160 pp. Paper. Sterling, 1992. $12.95.

SPIRIT HERBS: NATIVE AMERICAN HEALING
Mary Atwood; 160 pp. Paper. Sterling, 2000. $12.95.

SPIRIT IN THE ROCK: THE FIERCE BATTLE FOR MODOC HOMELANDS
Jim Compton; photos by Bill Stafford; Illus. Paper. WSU Press, 20017. $27.95.

SPIRIT IN THE STONE: A HANDBOOK OF SOUTHWEST INDIAN
ANIMAL CARVINGS & BELIEFS Mark Bahti, Linnea Gentry; Recounts stories and legends associated with the animals and other figures represented by these fetish forms. Illus. 192 pp. Paper. Treasure Chest Books, 2004. $15.95.

SPIRIT MEDICINE: NATIVE AMERICAN TEACHINGS TO AWAKEN THE SPIRIT
Wolf Moondance; Illus. 160 pp. Paper. Sterling, 1995. $12.95.

SPIRIT MOUNTAIN: AN ANTHOLOGY OF YUMAN STORY & SONG
Leanne Hinton and Lucille Watahomigie, Editors
344 pp. University of Arizona Press, 1984. $45; paper, $24.95.

SPIRIT MOVES: THE STORY OF SIX GENERATIONS OF NATIVE WOMEN
Loree Boyd; Illus. 448 pp. Paper. Amazon.com, 1997. $17.95.

SPIRIT OF THE ALBERTA INDIAN TREATIES
Richard Price; 3rd Ed. 236 pp. Paper. University of Alberta Press, 2000. $12.95.

SPIRIT OF BLACK HAWK: A MYSTERY OF AFRICANS & INDIANS
Jason Berry; photos by Syndey Byrd; The mystery of how a legendary Indian became one of the patron saints of a sect of African-American churches in New Orleans. Illus. 128 pp. Amazon.com, 1995. $25.

SPIRIT OF THE FIRST PEOPLE: NATIVE AMERICAN MUSIC TRADITIONS OF
WASHINGTON STATE Willie Smyth & Esme Ryan; intro. by Vi Hilbert
Illus. Map. 224 pp. Paper. University of Washington Press, $29.95.

SPIRIT OF HAIDA GWAII: BILL REID'S MASTERPIECE
Ulli Steltzer; Illus. 64 pp. Paper. University of Washington Press, 1997. $12.95.

SPIRIT OF THE HARVEST: NORTH AMERICAN INDIAN COOKING
Beverly Cox & Marvin Jacobs; Recipes. Illus. 255 pp. Center for Western Studies & Written Heritage, 1991. $29.95. Amazon.com, $35.

SPIRIT OF NATIVE AMERICA: BEAUTY & MYSTICISM IN AMERICAN INDIAN ART
Anna Lee Walters; Illus. 120 pp. Paper. Amazon.com, 1990. $18.95.

SPIRIT OF A NATIVE PLACE: BUILDING THE NATIONAL MUSEUM OF THE
AMERICAN INDIAN Duane Blue Spruce (Laguna/Ohkay Owingeh)
Illus. 192 pp. Paper. NMAI Press, 2004. $24.

SPIRIT OF THE NEW ENGLAND TRIBES: INDIAN HISTORY & FOLKLORE, 1620-1984
William S. Simmons; Map. 343 pp. Paper. U. Press of New England, 1986. $27.95.

SPIRIT OF THE OJIBWE: IMAGES OF LAC COURTE OREILLES ELDERS
James R. Bailey, et al; 176 pp. Paper. Holy Cow! Press, 2003. $24.95.

THE SPIRIT OF PLACE: A WORKBOOK FOR SACRED ALIGNMENT
Loren Cruden; An awareness of that sacred relationship opens a direct path to spiritual understanding. The author is respectful of the integrity of Native American ways. Illus. 232 pp. Inner Traditions, 1995. $18.95.

*SPIRIT OF THE WHITE BISON
Beatrice Culleton; Plains Nations sory of the deliberate destruction of the bison. Grades 4 and up. Illus. 64 pp. Book Publishing Co., 1989. $5.95.

*SPIRIT QUEST: THE INITIATIONS OF AN INDIAN BOY
Carol Batdorf; Grades 4 and up. Illus. 160 pp. Paper. Hancock House, $9.95.

SPIRIT & REASON: THE VINE DELORIA, JR. READER
Barbara Deloria, Kristen Foehner & Sam Scinta, Editors
An anthology of his works. 400 pp. Paper. Fulcrum Publishing, 1999. $16.95.

SPIRIT RED: VISIONS OF NATIVE AMERICAN ARTISTS FROM THE
RENNARD STRICKLAND COLLECTION
Rennard Strickland; 124 pp. University of Oklahoma Press, $15.95.

SPIRIT SINGS: ARTISTIC TRADITIONS OF CANADA'S FIRST PEOPLES
Glenbow Museum Staff; Illus. 265 pp. Amazon.com, 1990. $50.

THE SPIRIT AND THE SKY: LAKOTA VISIONS OF THE COSMOS
Mark Hollabaugh; Illus. 276 pp. University of Nebraska Press, 2017. $50.

SPIRIT SONG: THE INTRODUCTION OF NO-EYES
Mary Summer Rain; 160 pp. Paper. Hampton Roads Publishing, 1993. $10.95.

SPIRIT VISION OF A GRANDMOTHER
Barbara Pray; Sandra Talkington, Ed.
Illus. 42 pp. Paper. Dream Weavers Publishing, 2001. $10.95.

SPIRIT VISIONS, VOL. 1: THE OLD ONES SPEAK
Dennison & Teddi Tsosie; Illus. 384 pp. Dolphin Publishing, 1997. $19.95.

SPIRIT WARS: NATIVE NORTH AMERICAN RELIGIONS IN THE AGE OF NATION
BUILDING Ronald Niezen & Kim Burgess; Illus. 274 pp. Paper. U. of California Press, 2000. $26.95.

SPIRIT WIND
Jon L. Gibson; Fictional approach to Chitimacha tribal mythology.
Map. 200 pp. Paper. University of Alabama Press, 2010. $21.95.

THE SPIRIT WITHIN: ENCOURAGING HARMONY & HEALTH IN
AMERICAN INDIAN CHILDREN: A PRESCHOOL GRADE 3 CURRICULUM
Lenore Franzen; 128 pp. Student Edition. Amazon.com, 1992. $90.

THE SPIRIT WORLD
Time-Life Book Eds.; Illus. 185 pp. Amazon.com, 1992. $19.95.

SPIRITED ENCOUNTERS: AMERICAN INDIAN PROTEST MUSEUM
POLICIES & PRACTICES Karen Coody Cooper
224 pp. AltaMira Press, 2007. $94; paper, $36; eBook, $34.99.

SPIRITED RESISTANCE: THE NORTH AMERICAN INDIAN STRUGGLE
FOR UNITY, 1745-1815 Gregory Evans Dowd
288 pp. The Johns Hopkins University Press, 1991. $26.95; paper, $16.95..

SPIRITS IN THE ART: FROM THE PLAINS & SOUTHWEST INDIAN CULTURES
James A. Hanson; Over 900 objects are illustrated. 262 color photos.
262 pp. Nedra Matteucci's Galleries, 1994. $95.

SPIRITS OF THE AIR: BIRDS & THE AMERICAN INDIANS IN THE SOUTH
Shepard Krech III; Illustrated tour of Southeastern Indian ethnoornithology. Examines the complex & changeable influences of birds on the Native American worldview. Illus. Maps. 264 pp. University of Georgia Press, $44.95.

SPIRITS OF BLOOD, SPIRITS OF BREATH: THE TWINNED COSMOS
OF INDIGENOUS AMERICA
Barbara Alice Mann; Oxford University Press, 2016. $105; paper, $31.95.

SPIRITS OF EARTH: THE EFFIGY MOUND LANDSCAPE OF MADISON
& THE FOUR LAKES Robert Birmingham

Illus. Maps. 280 pp. Paper. University of Wisconsin Press, 2009. $24.95

SPIRITS OF THE EARTH: A GUIDE TO NATIVE AMERICAN SYMBOLS, STORIES & CEREMONIES Bobby Lake-Thom; Illus. 224 pp. Paper. Penguin Group, 1997. $16.

SPIRITS OF OUR WHALING ANCESTORS: REVITALIZING MAKAH & NUU-CHAH-NULTH TRADITIONS Charlotte Cote
Covers the issues involving indigenous whaling, past & present. Illus. Maps. 288 pp. Paper. University of Washington Press, 2010. $26.95.

SPIRITS OF THE WATER: NATIVE ART COLLECTED ON EXPEDITIONS TO ALASKA & BRITISH COLUMBIA
Steven C. Brown, Ed.; Illus. 207 pp. Paper. University of Washington Press, 2000. $45.

SPIRITUAL DIMENSIONS OF HEALING: FROM NATIVE SHAMANISM TO CONTEMPORARY HEALTH CARE Stanley Krippner & Patrick Welch
Illus. 302 pp. Irvington Publishers, 1992. $19.95; with audio, $39.95.

SPIRITUAL ENCOUNTERS: INTERACTION BETWEEN CHRISTIANITY & NATIVE RELIGIONS IN COLONIAL AMERICA Nicholas Griffiths & Fernando Cervantes, Editors
304 pp. Paper. University of Nebraska Press, 1999. $27.50.

SPIRITUAL LEGACY OF THE AMERICAN INDIAN
Joseph Epes Brown; Reprint 1964 ed. Illus. 135 pp. Paper. Crossroad Publishing, $14.95.

SPIRITUAL WISDOM OF THE NATIVE AMERICANS
John Heinerman; Illus. 170 pp. Paper. Cassandra Press, 1989. $9.95.

SPLENDID HERITAGE: PERSPECTIVES ON AMERICAN INDIAN ARTS
Jhn Warnock, Marva Warnock, Clinton Nagy, Robert Redford
207 pp. University of Utah Press, 2009, $75; paper, $49.95.

SPLENDID LAND, SPLENDED PEOPLE: THE CHICKASAW INDIANS TO REMOVAL
James R. Atkinson
Illus. 456 pp. University of Alabama Press, 2003. $65; paper, $38.50. E-Book, $27.96.

THE SPOKANE INDIANS: CHILDREN OF THE SUN
Robert H. Ruby & John A. Brown; Reprint of 1970 edition. Illus. Maps. Biblio. 346 pp. Paper. University of Oklahoma Press, $24.95.

SPOKEN CREE: WEST COAST OF JAMES BAY
C. Douglas Ellis; 715 pp. Paper. University of Nebraska Press, 1983. $21.

*SPORTS & GAMES THE INDIANS GAVE US
Alex Whitney; Grades 7 and up. David McKay, 1977. $7.95.

*SPOTTED EAGLE & BLACK CROW: A LAKOTA LEGEND
Emery Bernhard; Betrayed by his brother, a warrior is rescued by eagles. Grades K-3. Illus. 32 pp. Holiday House, 1993. $15.95.

*THE SPOTTED HORSE
Henry Tall Bull
Grades 2-10. 32 pp. Council for Indian Education, 1970. $8.95; paper, $2.95.

SPOTTED TAIL'S FOLK: A HISTORY OF THE BRULE SIOUX
George E. Hyde; Reprint of 1961 edition. Illus. Maps. Biblio. 361 pp. Paper. University of Oklahoma Press, $25.95.

SPRING SALMON, HURRY TO ME!: THE SEASONS OF NATIVE CALIFORNIA
Margaret Dubin & Kim Hogeland; Paper. Heyday Books. $16.95.

SPRUCE ROOT BASKETRY OF THE HAIDA & TLINGIT
Sharon J. Busby; photos by Ronald H. Reeder; illus. by Margaret Davidson
Examines the history & evolution of spruce-root basketry. Illus. 160 pp. University of Washington Press, 2003. $55.

SQUAMISH-ENGLISH DICTIONARY
Squamish Nation Dictionary Project; One of ten Coast Salish languages. Map. 390 pp. Paper. University of Washington Press, 2011. $40.

*SQUANTO & THE FIRST THANKSGIVING
Joyce K. Kessel; illus. by Lisa Donze; Grades 1-3. Illus. 56 pp. Amazon.com, 1996.

*SQUANTO, FRIEND OF THE PILGRIMS
Clyde Bulla; Grades 4-6. Reprint. 110 pp. Paper. Demco, $9.

STABILITY & VARIATION IN HOPI SONG
George List; 205 pp. Amazon.com, 1993. $28.

STAGING RITUAL: HOPEWELL CERMONIALISM AT THE MOUND HOUSE SITE, GREENE COUNTY, IL Jane E. Buikstra
Illus. 216 pp. Paper. Center for Archaeology Press, 1998. $ 20.

STALKING THE WILD AGAVE: A FOOD & FIBER TRADITION
Deborah Dozier; Describes traditional uses of Yucca & Agave. Photos. 24 pp. Malki-Ballena Press, 2003. $5.50.

THE STANDING BEAR CONTROVERSY: PRELUDE TO INDIAN REFORM
Valerie S. Mathes & Richard Lowitt; Illus. 240 pp. U. of Illinois Press, 2003. $29.95.

STANDING BEAR IS A PERSON: THE TRUE STORY OF A NATIVE AMERICAN'S QUEST FOR JUSTICE
Stephen Dando-Collins; Biography of a Ponca Chief. Paper. Amazon.com, 2005. $ 18.

STANDING BEAR & THE PONCA CHIEFS
Thomas H. Tibbles; Kay Graber, Editor
143 pp. Paper. University of Nebraska Press, 1995. $13.95.

*STANDING BEAR OF THE PONCA
Virginia Driving Hawk Sneve
Ages 8 and up. Illus. 56 pp. Paper. University of Nebraska Press, 2013. $14.95.

STANDING FLOWER: THE LIFE OF IRVING PABANALE, AN ARIZONA TEWA INDIAN
Robert Black, Editor; Illus. Maps. 279 pp. University of Utah Press. $24.95.

STANDING GROUND: YUROK INDIAN SPIRITUALITY, 1850-1990
Thomas C. Buckley
337 pp. Univesity of California Press, 2002. $50; paper, $25.95. E-Book available.

STANDING IN THE LIGHT: A LAKOTA WAY OF SEEING
Severt Young Bear & R.D. Theisz
Illus. Biblio. Map. 210 pp. Paper. University of Nebraska Press, 1994. $16.95.

STANDING ROCK SIOUX
Donovin Arleigh Sprague; Illus. 130 pp. Paper. Amazon.com, 2004. $19.99.

STANDING TALL: THE LIFEWAY OF KATHRYN JONES HARRISON
Kristine Olson; Biography of Oregon tribal leader of the Grand Rondes. Illus. 288 pp. Paper. University of Washington Press, 2006. $23.95.

THE STANISLAUS INDIAN WARS
Thorne B. Gray; 302 pp. Paper. McHenry Museum Press, 1993. $29.95.

STAR ANCESTORS: EXTRATERRESTRIAL CONTACT IN THE NATIVE AMERICAN TRADITION Nancy Red Star; Explores the long-standing contact between American Indian tribes & extraterrestrial visitors through interviews with the tribes' spiritual leaders. Illus. 208 pp. Paper. Inner Traditions, 2012. $18.

STAR ANCESTORS: INDIAN WISDOMKEEPERS SHARE THE TEACHINGS OF THE EXTRATERRESTRIALS
Nancy Red Star; Interviews with American Indian spiritual leaders concerning the long-standing contact that has existed between their tribes & extraterrestrial visitors. Illus. 208 pp. Paper. Inner Traditions, 2000. $19.47.

THE STAR LAKE ARCHAEOLOGICAL PROJECT: ANTHROPOLOGY OF A HEADWATERS AREA OF CHACO WASH, NEW MEXICO
Walter Wait & Ben Nelson, Editors; Illus. 480 pp. Amazon.com, 1983. $24.95.

STAR MEDICINE: NATIVE AMERICAN PATH TO EMOTIONAL HEALING
Wolf Moondance; Illus. 192 pp. Paper. Sterling, 1997. $12.95.

STAR QUILT
Roberta Hill Whiteman; Poetry. Illus. 92 pp. Paper. Holy Cow! Press, $6.95.

STAR ANCESTORS: INDIAN WISDOMKEEPERS SHARE THE TEACHINGS OF THE EXTRATERRESTRIALS Nancy Red Star; Illus. 210 pp. Paper. Inner Traditions, 2000. $29.95.

THE STAR QUILT: SYMBOL OF LAKOTA IDENTITY
Marla N. Powers; Illus. 10 pp. Paper. Lakota Books, 1990. $8.95.

STAR-SPIDER SPEAKS: THE TEACHINGS OF THE NATIVE AMERICAN TAROT
Magda W. Gonzalez & J.A. Gonzalez
Illus. 205 pp. Paper. U.S. Games Systems, 1992. $9.95.

*STAR TALES: NORTH AMERICAN INDIAN STORIES ABOUT THE STARS
Gretchen Mayo; Grades 5 and up. 96 pp. Walker & Co., 1987. $11.95.

STAR WARRIOR: THE STORY OF SWIFTDEER
Bill Wahlberg; The story of Harley SiftDeer Reagan, a medicine teacher, leader of the Deer Tribe Metis Medicine Society. Illus. 196 pp. paper. Inner Traditions Int'l, 1993. $12.95.

THE STARS ABOVE, THE EARTH BELOW: AMERICAN INDIANS & NATURE
Marsha Bol & Carnegie Museum; Illus. 276 pp. Paper. Robets Rinehart, 1998. $19.95.

STARS OF THE FIRST PEOPLE: NATIVE AMERICAN STAR MYTHS & CONSTELLATIONS Dorcas S. Miller; Guide to Native American constellations and folklore. 75 star charts, 9 regional mapos, bxw illus. 344 pp. Paper. Amazon.com, $19.95.

THE STARS WE KNOW: CROW INDIAN ASTRONOMY & LIFEWAYS
Timothy P. McCleary; Illus. 127 pp. Paper. Waveland Press, 1997. $15.95.

STARTING FROM HERE: DAKOTA POETRY, POTTERY, & CARING
Jerome W. Freeman; Illus. 95 pp. Paper. Ex Machina, 1996. $12.95.

STARTING YOUR OWN SUCCESSFUL INDIAN BUSINESS
Steve Robinson & Stephen Hogan; 160 pp. Paper. Thornsbury Bailey Brown, 1991. $45.

STATE INDIAN ENCYCLOPEDIAS
A History of state related tribes, biographies of noteworthy indigenous peoples, along with articles on the customs & ways. All States included. North American Book Distributors, LLC. Prices range from $50 to $165.

THE STATE OF NATIVE AMERICA: GENOCIDE, COLONIZATION & RESISTANCE
M. Annette Jaimes, Editor; Essays by Native American authors and activists on contemporary Native issues including the quincentenary. 480 pp. Amazon.com, 1991. $40; paper, $20.

THE STATE OF THE NATIVE NATIONS: CONDITIONS UNDER U.S. POLICIES OF SELF-DETERMINATION Harvard Project on American Indian Economic Development Covers tribal government & jurisdiction; relations between tribal government & federal & state governments; and topics: environment, gaming, health, culture & education. 448 pp. Paper. Oxford University Press, 2007. $54.95.

THE STATE OF SEQUOYAH: AN IMPRESSIONISTIC LOOK AT EASTERN OKLAHOMA Jerald C. Walker; Daisy Decazes, photos by Traces the background of what is now eastern Oklahoma. The story of Indian removal, "Trail of Tears", and the development of the state. Illus. 120 pp. Amazon.com, $25.

STATE & RESERVATION: NEW PERSPECTIVES ON FEDERAL INDIAN POLICY George P. Castile & Robert L. Bee, Eds.; Essays focus on the rise, change, and persistence of the Native American reservation system. 259 pp. University of Arizona Press, 1992. $46; paper, $23.50.

STATE-TRIBAL RELATIONS: INTO THE 21st CENTURY Judy Zelio & James Reed; Analysis of government-to-government relations; describes the issues and discusses agreements. Case studies. 120 pp. Ammazon.com, 1993. $25.

STATE-TRIBAL RELATIONSHIPS - REPORTS "1991 State Legislation Relating to Native Americans," Report, Vol. 16, No. 9 - 19 pp. $5; "State-Tribal Transportation Agreements," Report No. 14, No. 4 - 1989. $5; "States and the Indian Gaming Regulatory Act," Report Vol. 17, No. 16 - 1992, 18 pp. $5; "Promoting Effective State-Tribal Relations: A Dialogue" - examines how states and tribes can work together. 1990. 19 pp. $10; "Jurisdiction Over Nuclear Waste Transportation on Indian Tribal Lands: State-Tribal Relationships," Report Vol. 16, No. 4. 1991. 11 pp. $5. Amazon.com.

STATES & THE INDIAN GAMING REGULATION ACT Pam Greenburg & Judy Zelio 17 pp. Paper. National Conference of State Legislators, 1992. $5.

STATISTICAL RECORD OF NATIVE NORTH AMERICANS Marlita A. Reddy, Editor; Statistics on all aspects of Native American family life, education, business & industry. Compiled from government records, & private associations. Includes 1,000 charts, graphs, and tables; 200 current and extinct tribes are detailed. 3rd Edition. Illus. 1,250 pp. Gale Group, 1998. $115.

JOHN ROGERS STATUARY Paul & Meta Bleir; Illus. 224 pp. Paper. Schiffer Publishing, 2001. $29.95.

STATUS & HEALTH IN PREHISTORY: A CASE STUDY OF THE MOUNDVILLE CHIEFDOM Mary Lucas Powell; Illus. 352 pp. Smithsonian Institution Press, 1988. $40.

STATUS TERMINOLOGY & SOCIAL STRUCTURE OF NORTH AMERICAN INDIANS Munro S. Edmonson; 84 pp. Paper. Amazon.com & Alibris.com, 2003. $29.

STATUS OF TRIBAL FISH & WILDLIFE MANAGEMENT PROGRAMS U.S. Senate Committee on Indian Affairs 108th Congress, First Session. Illus. 196 pp. U.S. GPO, 2003.

STE. MADELEINE: A COMMUNITY WITHOUT A TOWN – METIS ELDERS IN INTERVIEW Ken & Victoria Zeilig; A Metis settlement was uprooted in the 1930s to accommodate government development. Paper. Pemmican, $13.95.

STEALING THE GILA: THE PIMA AGRICULTURAL ECONOMY & WATER DEPRIVATION, 1848-1921 David H. DeJong; Illus. 200 pp. Paper. University of Arizona Press, 2009.

STEALING INDIAN WOMEN: NATIVE SLAVERY IN THE ILLINOIS COUNTRY Carl J. Ekberg; Based on orignal source documents...overviw of Indian slavery in the Mississippi Valley. Illus. Maps. Tables. 256 pp. Paper. U. of Illinois Press, 20010. $27.

STEP-BY-STEP BRAIN TANNING THE SIOUX WAY Larry Belitz Reprint of 1973 edition. Illus. 16 pp. Paper. Writen Heritage, $3.95. DVD available.

A STOLEN LIFE: THE JOURNEY OF A CREE WOMAN Rudy Wiebe & Yvonne Johnson ; 470 pp. Paper. Amazon.com, 2000. $16.95.

*THE STOMACHACHE TREE Mary M. Frye; Choctaw cultural children's book. The Choctaw Store, 2002. $20.

STONE AGE IN THE GREAT BASIN Emory Strong; Illus. 280 pp. Paper. Binford & Mort, 1967. $12.95.

STONE AGE ON THE COLUMBIA RIVER Emory Strong; Illus. Photos and maps. 256 pp. Paper. Binford & Mort, 1967. $9.95.

STONE AGE SPEAR & ARROW POINTS OF CALIFORNIA & THE GREAT BASIN Noel D. Justice; Illus. 450 pp. Amazon.com & Alibris.com, 2002. $59.95.

STONE AGE SPEAR & ARROW POINTS OF THE MIDCONTINENTAL & EASTERN U.S. Noel D. Justice A modern survey & reference. Illus. 302 pp. Amazon.com & Alibris.com, 1988. $37.95.

STONE ARTIFACTS OF TEXAS INDIANS - A FIELD GUIDE Turner & Hester; Points & knivfe types, stone tools and ornaments. 200 sketches. 308 pp. paper. Hothem House, 1985. $14.95.

*THE STONE CANOE & OTHER STORIES John L. Peyton; 12 stories told by the People of the Rapids, the northernmost Ojibway. Grades 2 to 5. Illus. 151 pp. Paper. U. of Nebraska Press, 1989. $24.95; paper, $14.95.

*THE STONE CUTTER & THE NAVAJO MAIDEN Vee F. Browne; illus. by Johnson Yazzie Grades K-5. Early reader. Amazon.com, 2010. $17.95.

STONE EFFIGIES OF THE HIGH PLAINS HUNTERS James L. Gaskins; Illus. Amazon.com, 2000.

STONE HEART: A NOVEL OF SACAJAWEA Diane Glancy; Illus. University of Nebraska Press, 2002.

STONE MAGIC OF THE ANCIENTS: TE PETROGLYPHS & SHRINE SITES OF THE UPPER LITTLE COLORADO REGION James R. Cunkle, et al; Illus. Paper. Amazon.com, 1995. $14.95.

STONE PEOPLE MEDICINE: A NATIVE AMERICAN ORACLE Manny Twofeathers; Reprint. 2nd Ed. Illus. 144 pp. Amazon.com, 2001. $19.95.

STONE SONGS ON THE TRAIL OF TEARS Pat Musick; Illus. 120 pp. University of Arkansas Press, 2005. $29.95.

STONE TOOL TRADITIONS IN THE CONTACT ERA Charles R. Cobb, Editor; Illus. 272 pp. U. of Alabama Press, 2003. $60; paper, $34.95.

STONE TOOLS & MOBILITY IN THE ILLINOIS VALLEY George H. Odell; Illus. 420 pp. Amazon.com, 1996. $78; paper, $49.50.

STORIED COMMUNITIES: NARRATIVES OF CONTACT & ARRIVAL IN CONSTITUTING POLITICAL COMMUNITY Hester Lessard, Rebecca Johnson, Jeremy Webber; Storytelklers & scholars in Aboriginal identities. 384 pp. University of Washington Press, 2011. $99; paper, $37.95.

STORIED STONE: INDIAN ROCK ART IN THE BLACK HILLS COUNTRY Linea Sundstrom; Illus. 288 pp. U. of Oklahoma Press, 2004. $44.95; paper, $24.95.

STORIED VOICES IN NATIVE AMERICAN TEXTS: HARRY ROBINSON, THOMAS KING, JAMES WELCH & LESLIE MARMON SILKO Blanca Schorcht; 192 pp. Routledge, 2003. $65.

STORIES FIND YOU, PLACES KNOW: YUP'IK NARRATIVES OF A SENTIENT WORLD Holly Cusack-McVeigh; Illus. 336 pp. Paper. U. of Utah Press, $24.95; eBook, $20.

STORIES FROM THE LAND 32 pp. Paper. Museum of Northern Arizona, 1981. $3.

STORIES FOR FUTURE GENERATIONS/QULIRAT QANEMCIT-LLU KINGUVARCIMALRIIT: THE ORATORY OF YUP'IK ESKIMO ELDER PAUL JOHN trans. by Sophie Shield; edited by Ann Fienup-Riordan Yup'ik tales and personal experiences of Paul John. Text in Yup'ik & English. Illus. 856 pp. Paper. University of Washington Press, 2004. $37.95.

STORIES & STONE: WRITING THE ANCESTRAL PUEBLO HOMELAND Reuben Ellis, Ed.; Includes essays, stories, travelers' reports, poems, and images of the stone ruins, cliff dwellings, pot shards, and peyroglyphs. Illus. Map. 244 pp. Paper. University of Arizona Press, 2004. $19.95.

*STORIES ON STONE: ROCK ART: IMAGES FROM THE ANCIENT ONES Jennifer Owings Dewey; Introduces young readers to the history and mystery of rock art in the Southwest. Grades 2 and up. Illus. 32 pp. U. of New Mexico Press, 2003. $16.95.

STORIES OF AWE & ABUNDANCE Jose Hobday; 128 pp. Paper. Continuum, 1999. $9.95.

STORIES OF MAASAW, A HOPI GOD Ekkehart Malotki & Michael Lomatuway'ma Illus. 275 pp. University of Nebraska Press, 1987. $24.95; paper, $14.95.

STORIES FROM OLD-TIME OKLAHOMA David Dary; Collection of tales from Indian Territory and the Sooner State. Illus. Maps. 288 pp. University of Oklahoma Press, 2011. $24.95.

*STORIES OF OUR BLACKFEET GRANDMOTHERS Mary C. Boss-Ribs & Jenny Running-Crane Grades 1-6. Paper. Council for Indian Education, 1984. $1.45.

STORIES OF OUR WAY: AN ANTHOLOGY OF AMERICAN INDIAN PLAYS edited by Hanay Geiogamah & Jaye T. Darby; Anthology of over 30 years of American Indian theater, including the 1930s classic The Cherokee Night and 11 other plays. 503 pp. University of California, American Indian Studies Center, 1999. $60; paper, $20.

STORIES OF THE PEOPLE: NATIVE AMERICAN VOICES Six diverse cultures and their origin. Illus. 80 pp. NMAI Press, 1997. $18.95

STORIES OF THE ROAD ALLOWANCE PEOPLE Maria Campbell; Collection of short stories about Metis political movement. 127 pp. Paper. Theytus, 1994. $12.95.

STORIES OF THE SIOUX Luther Standing Bear; intro. by Frances Washburn New edition. Illus. 82 pp. Paper. University of Nebraska Press, 2006. $9.95.

STORIES OF SURVIVAL: CONVERSATIONS WITH NATIVE NORTH AMERICANS
Remmelt & Kathleen Hummelen; Stories that depicty concerns of Native peoples in Northeastern cities, Arctic communities, prairie towns, and reservations. Paper. Friendship Press, $5.95.

STORIES THAT MAKE THE WORLD: ORAL LITERATURE OF THE INDIAN PEOPLES OF THE INLAND NORTHWEST: AS TOLD BY LAWRENCE ARIPA, TOM YELLOWTAIL, AND OTHER ELDERS Rodney Frey, Editor
Illus. Map. 256 pp. University of Oklahoma Press, 1995. $24.95; paper, $14.95.

STORIES WE LIVE BY / BAAK'AATUGH TS'UHUNITY
Catherine Attla; University of Alaska Press, $18.

*STORM BOY
Paul Owen Lewis; Grades K-2. Illus. 30 pp. Beyond WordsPublishing, 1995.

STORM IN THE MOUNTAIN
Vernon Crow; Story of William H. Thomas' Legion of Cherokee Indians formed during the Civil War. Illus. Photos. Maps. 300 pp. Paper. Cherokee Publications, $7.95.

STORM PATTERNS: POEMS FROM TWO NAVAJO WOMEN
Della Frank & Roberts D. Joe; 20 poems. Illus. Amazon.com, 1993. $12.

STORMS BREWED IN OTHER MEN'S WORLDS: THE CONFRONTATIONS OF INDIANS, SPANISH, AND FRENCH IN THE SOUTHWEST, 1540-1795
Elizabeth A.H. John; Illus. Maps. 806 pp. Paper. U. of Oklahoma Press, 1981. $24.95.

A STORY AS SHARP AS A KNIFE: THE CLASSICAL HAIDA MYTHTELLERS & THEIR WORLD Robert Bringhurst
Illus. Maps. 527 pp. University of Nebraska Press, 2000. $50; paper, $24.95.

THE STORY OF THE BLACKFOOT PEOPLE: NITSITAPIISINNI
The Glenbow Museum; Illus. 104 pp. paper. Firefly Books, 2013. $1.95.

*THE STORY OF BLUE ELK
Gerald Hausman; illus. by Kristina Rodanas
Grades 3-5. Color illus. 32 pp. Amazon.com, $15.

THE STORY OF THE CHEROKEE PEOPLE
Tom B. Underwood; Reprint of 1961 edition. Illus. 48 pp. Paper.
Book Publishing Co., VIP Publishing & Cherokee Publications, $5.95.

THE STORY OF CYNTHIA ANN PARKER: SUNSHINE ON THE PRAIRIE
Jack C. Ramsay, Jr.; Took into captivity, she had a son, the "white Indian," Quanah, the last and most famous of the Comanche war chiefs. Illus. 225 pp. Amazon.com, $5.95.

STORY OF DEEP DELIGHT
Thomas McNamee; Relates the life stories of three young men - the last Chickasaw Indian chief, a mid-19th century slave, and a present-day artist. 480 pp. Paper. Penguin USA, $11.

*THE STORY OF GERONIMO
Grades 3-6. Illus. 32 pp. Childrens Press, $9.95.

*THE STORY OF LITTLE BIG HORN
R.C. Stern; Grades 3-6. Illus. 32 pp. Childrens Press, 1983. $9.95.

THE STORY OF THE LITTLE BIG HORN: CUSTER'S LAST FIGHT
W.A. Graham; Illus. Maps. 284 pp. Paper. Amazon.com, $13.95.

THE STORY OF LYNX
Claude Levi-Straus; Nez Perce myth. Illus. Maps. 276 pp. University of Chicago Press, 1995. $24.95; paper, $17.95.

THE STORY OF OKLAHOMA
W. David Baird & Danney Goble; The up-to-date history of the Sooner State, including a collection of primary sources on life in Indian Territory. Illus. Maps. Biblio. 512 pp. University of Oklahoma Press, 1994. $28.95.

THE STORY OF THE MEADOWLARK
Scott B. Smith; Illus. 47 pp. Stump Publishing, 1986. $15.

A STORY OF SEVEN SISTERS: A TONGVA PLEIDES LEGEND
Pamela Marx; illus. by Debra Vodhanel; The original people of the greater Los Angeles & Orange County areas of California, about 5,000 living in as many as 100 settlements, neighbors to the Chumash. Illus. 36 pp. Paper. Malki-Ballena Press, 2010. $14.95.

*THE STORY OF THE TRAIL OF TEARS
R. Conrad Stein; Grades 3-6. Illus. 32 pp. Childrens Press, 1985. $9.95.

*THE STORY OF WOUNDED KNEE
R.C. Stein; Grades 3-6. Illus. 32 pp. Childrens Press, 1983. $9.95.

*A STORY TO TELL: TRADITIONS OF A TLINGIT COMMUNITY
Richard Nichols; Grades 3-6. Lerner Publications, 1998. $23.99

STORYPOLE LEGENDS
Emmerson H. Matson; Folk stories, fables and legends from the Indians of the Puget Sound area. 108 pp. Council for Indian Education, 1996. $8.95.

STORYTELLERS & OTHER FIGURATIVE POTTERY
Douglas Congdon-Martin; In 1964, Helen Cordero of Cochiti Pueblo created the first storyteller, a clay image of her grandfather with five children clinging to him. This book

presents over 400 pieces, by nearly 150 artists, in full color and organized by pueblo. Illus. 144 pp. Paper. Schiffer, $19.95.

STRAIGHT WITH THE MEDICINE: NARRATIVES OF WASHOE FOLLOWERS OF THE TIPI WAY Warren L. D'Azevedo; Narratives compiled in the 1950s from seven followers of the Native American Church. Illus. 64 pp. Paper. Heyday Books, 1985. $12.95.

STRANGE BUSINESS
Rilla Askew; Short story collection of Choctaw Indians' place in the fictitious town of Cedar, Okla. 192 pp. Paper. Penguin USA, $10.

STRANGE EMPIRE
Joseph Kinsey Howard
Story of the Metis. Illus. 601 pp. Minnesota Historical Society Press, 1994. $16.95.

STRANGE JOURNEY: VISIONS OF A PSYCHIC INDIAN WOMAN
Louise Lone Dog; illus. by Chester Kahn; Illus. 105 pp. Paper. Naturegraph, $8.95.

A STRANGE LIKENESS: BECOMING RED & WHITE IN 18TH CENTURY NORTH AMERICA Nancy Shoemaker; Illus. 225 pp. Oxford University Press, 2004. $29.95.

A STRANGE MIXTURE
Sascha T. Scott; Pueblo art & architecture. 280 pp. University of Oklahoma Press, $45.

A STRANGER IN HER NATIVE LAND: ALICE FLETCHER & THE AMERICAN INDIANS
Joan Mark; Illus. 428 pp. Paper. University of Nebraska Press, 1988. $20.

STRANGERS IN BLOOD: FUR TRADE COMPANY FAMILIES IN INDIAN COUNTRY
Jennifer S.H. Brown; Reprint of 1953 edition. Illus. 152 pp. 302 p.
University of Oklahoma Press, 1996. $28.95; paper, $10.95.

STRANGERS IN A STOLEN LAND: AMERICAN INDIANS IN SAN DIEGO
Richard L. Carrico; Illus. Paper. Sierra Coaks, 1987. $10.95.

STRANGERS IN THEIR OWN LAND: A CHOCTAW PORTFOLIO
Photos by Carole Thompson; A booklet of 30 b&w photos with text showing daily life rituals of the Mississippi Choctaw. 40 pp. Paper. Amazon.com, 1983. $4.95.

STRANGERS IN THEIR OWN LAND: AN AMERICAN INDIAN HISTORY GUIDE
Sandra Sheffield & Jude Urich; 55 pp. Paper. Amazon.com, 1988. $6.95.

STRANGERS TO RELATIVES: THE ADOPTION & NAMING OF ANTHROPOLOGISTS IN NATIVE NORTH AMERICA edited by Sergei Kan; Leading anthropologists in the U.S. & Canada focus on the cases of such prominent earlier scholars as Lewis Henry Morgan & Franz Boas. Illus. Map. 270 pp. U. of Nebraska Press, 2001. $50; paper, $24.95.

STRATEGIES FOR SURVIVAL: AMERICAN INDIANS IN THE EASTERN U.S.
Frank W. Porter, III, Editor; 248 pp. Greenwood, 1986. $36.95.

STRENGTHENING THE CIRCLE: CHILD SUPPORT FOR NATIVE AMERICAN CHILDREN Barry Leonard, Ed.; Reprint. Illus. 57 pp. Paper. Amazon.com, 2000. $20.

STRONG HEART SONG: LINES FROM A REVOLUTIONARY TEXT
Lance Henson; Poetry. 79 pp. Paper. University of New Mexico Press, $8.95

STRONG HEARTS: NATIVE AMERICAN VISIONS & VOICES
Illus. 128 pp. Aperture, 1995. $44.95.

STRONG HEARTS, WOUNDED SOULS: NATIVE AMERICAN VETERANS OF THE VIETNAM WAR
Tom Holm; The role of military traditions and the warrior ethic in the mid-20th century American Indian life. 254 pp. Paper. University of Texas Press, 1996. $25.

STRUCTURAL CONSIDERATIONS OF METIS ETHNICITY: AN ARCHAEOLOGICAL, ARCHITECTURAL & HISTORICAL STUDY David Burley, Gayle Horsfall & John Brandon
Illus. Dakota Press, 1992. $44.95; paper, $25.95.

THE STRUCTURE OF TWANA CULTURE: WITH COMPARATIVE NOTES ON THE STRUCTURE OF YUROK CULTURE
William Elmendorf & A.L. Kroeber; An account of Washington's Twana Indians of the southern coast Salish region. Illus. Maps. Biblio. 576 pp. Paper. WSU Press, 1992. $18.75.

A STRUCTURED APPROACH TO LEARNING THE BASIC INFLECTIONS OF THE CHEROKEE VERB
Durbin D. Feeling; 190 pp. Paper. Indian University Press, 1994. $29, postpaid.

STRUCTURING SOVEREIGNTY: CONSTITUTIONS OF NATIVE NATIONS
Melissa Tatum, Miriam Jorgensen, Mary Guss, Sarah Deer
Guide for communities engaged in the process of drafting a constitution and for students who are studying that process. Paper. UCLA American Indian Studies Center Publications, 2014. $40. E-mail: sales@aisc.ucla.edu

STRUGGLE FOR THE LAND: INDIGENOUS RESISTANCE TO GENOCIDE, ECOCIDE & EXPROPRIATION IN CONTEMPORARY NORTH AMERICA
Ward Churchill; preface by Winona LaDuke
2nd Ed. Essays. Illus. 460 pp. Amazon.com, 2002. $40; paper, $19.95.

THE STRUGGLE FOR RECOGNITION: CANADIAN JUSTICE & THE METIS NATION
Manitoba Metis Federation; Essays & research articles on the Metis struggle to develop a legal system. Pemmican, $21.95; paper, $19.95.

THE STRUGGLE FOR SELF-DETERMINATION: HISTORY OF THE MENOMINEE INDIANS SINCE 1854
David R.M. Beck; 296 pp. Paper. University of Nebraska Press, 2007. $24.95.

THE STRUGGLE FOR WATER: POLITICS, RATIONALITY & IDENTITY IN THE AMERICAN SOUTHWEST Wendy Nelson Espeland
One chapter devoted to the building of a dam and the effects on the Yavapai Tribe. Illus. Map. 300 pp. U. of Chicago Press, 1998. $60; paper, $23.

JOHN STUART & THE SOUTHERN COLONIAL FRONTIER: A STUDY OF INDIAN RELATIONS, WAR, TRADE, LAND PROBLEMS IN THE SOUTHERN WILDERNESS, 1754-1775 J. Alden; Reprint of 1944 edition. Illus. 384 pp. Amazon.com, $40.

JOHN STUART & THE STRUGGLE FOR EMPIRE ON THE SOUTHERN FRONTIER
J. Russell Snapp; Illus. 288 pp. Louisiana State University Press, 1996. $42.50.

THE STUDENT'S DICTIONARY OF LITERARY PLAINS CREE
H.C. Wolfart & Freda Ahenakew
Cree Dictionary making full use of orthography. Paper. Pemmican, $26.

THE STUDENTS OF SHERMAN INDIAN SCHOOL: EDUCATION & NATIVE IDENTITY SINCE 1892 Diana Meyers Bahr; 192 pp. Paper. U. of Oklahoma Press, 2014. $19.95

STUDIES IN AMERICAN INDIAN ART: A MEMORIAL TRIBUTE TO NORMAN FEDER
Christian F. Feest; Essays explore topics relating to Feder's interests in Native American art. Illus. Map. 208 pp. Paper. University of Washington Press, 2001. $35.

STUDIES IN AMERICAN INDIAN LANGUAGES: DESCRIPTION & THEORY
Leanne Hinton & Pamela Munro; 292 PP. Paper. U. of California Press, 1998. $45.

STUDIES IN AMERICAN INDIAN LITERATURE: CRITICAL ESSAYS & COURSE DESIGNS Paula G. Allen; 385 pp. Amazon.com, 1983. $35; paper, $18.

STUDIES IN CAHUILLA CULTURE
A.L. Kroeber & Lucile Hooper; Illus. Map. Malki-Ballena Press, 1978. $25.

STUDIES IN CHEROKEE BASKETRY: INCLUDING A REPRINT OF DECORATIVE ART & BASKETRY OF THE CHEROKEE by Frank G. Speck
Betty J. Duggan & Bret H. Riggs, Eds.
60 pp. Paper. University of Tennessee-Knoxville, Frank H. McClung Museum, 1991. $10.

STUDIES IN SOUTHEASTERN INDIAN LANGUAGES
James Crawford, Editor; 463 pp. Brown Book & Cherokee Publications, 1975. $25.

THE STUDY OF AMERICAN INDIAN RELIGIONS
Ake Hultkrantz; Illus. 142 pp. Amazon.com, 1983. $26.95.

A STUDY OF THE DELAWARE INDIAN BIG HOUSE CEREMONY
Frank G. Speck; Reprint. Paper. 192 pp. with CD-ROM, Amazon.com, $19.95.

A STUDY OF DELAWARE INDIAN MEDICINE PRACTICE & FOLK BELIEFS
Gladys Tantaquidgeon; Reprint. Amazon,com, $22.95; paper, #19.75.

A STUDY OF THE HOUSES OF THE AMERICAN ABORIGINES
Lewis Henry Morgan; Reprint. 80 pp. Amazon.com, 1999. $27.95; paper, $17.95.

A STUDY OF OMAHA INDIAN MUSIC
Alice C. Fletcher; Reprint of 1893 edition. Includes Omaha songs and scores as well as native words for the songs. 160 pp. Paper. Written Heritage, $5.95.

STUDY OF PUEBLO ARCHITECTURE: TUSAYAN & CIBOLA, 8TH ANNUAL REPORT
Victor Mindeleff; Reprint. Illus. 428 pp. Paper. Coyote Press, 1989. $44.38.

A STUDY OF SIOUAN CULTS: DAKOTA & ASSINIBOINE
J. Owen Dorsey; 76 pp. Paper. Lakota Books, 1999. $24.95.

STUDYING NATIVE AMERICA: PROBLEMS & PROSPECTS
Russell Thornton; Illus. 450 pp. Paper. University of Wisconsin Press, 1998. $27.95.

STYLIZED CHARACTERS' SPEECH IN THOMPSON SALISH NARRATIVE
Steven M. Egesdal; 126 pp. Amazon.com, 1992. $7.

THE SUBARCTIC ATHAPASCANS: A SELECTED, ANNOTATED BIBLIOGRAPHY
Arthur E. Hippler and John R. Wood
380 pp. Paper. University of Alaska Institute of Social Sciences, 1974. $15.

SUBJUGATION & DISHONOR: A BRIEF HISTORY OF THE TRAVAIL OF THE NATIVE AMERICANS
Philip Weeks and James B. Gidney; 160 pp. Paper. Amazon.com, 1981. $8.50.

SUBSISTENCE & CULTURE IN THE WESTERN CANADIAN ARCTIC: A MULTICONTEXTUAL APPROACH
Matthew W. Betts; Illus. 312 pp. Paper. University of Washington Press, 2008. $34.95.

SUMMER IN THE SPRING: ANISHINAABE LYRIC POEMS & STORIES
Gerald Vizenor; New edition. Anthology. Includes translations & a glossary of the Anishinaabe (Chippewa) words in which the poems & stories originally were spoken. Illus. with tribal pictomyths. Illus. 166 pp. Paper. University of Oklahoma Press, $9.95.

SUMMER MEDITATIONS WITH NATIVE AMERICAN ELDERS
Don Coyhis; Reprint. 106 pp. Paper. Moh-He-Con-Nuck, $9.95.

SUMMER OF THE BLACK WIDOWS
Sherman Alexie (Spokane/Coeur d'Alene); Poetry. Grades 9. Paper. Oyate, 1996. $13.50.

SUMMER PEOPLE, WINTER PEOPLE: A GUIDE TO PUEBLOS IN THE SANTA FE, NEW MEXICO AREA Sandra A. Edelman; Illus. 32 pp. Sunstone Press, $4.95.

*A SUMMER'S TRADE: SHIIGO NA'IINI'
Deborah W. Trotter; illus. by Irving Toddy
Grades K-5. Navajo/English. Amazon.com, 2008. $17.95.

SUMMONING THE GODS: SANDPAINTING OF THE NATIVE AMERICAN SOUTHWEST
Ronald McCoy; Illus 32 pp. Paper. Museum of Northern Arizona, 1988. $4.95.

SUN BEAR: THE PATH OF POWER
Sun Bear, et al; Illus. 272 pp. Paper. Bear Tribe, 1984. $9.95.

THE SUN CAME DOWN: TRADITIONAL BLACKFEET STORIES
Percy Bullchild; Illus. 384 pp. Paper. HarperCollins, 1985. $12.95.

SUN CHIEF: THE AUTOBIOGRAPHY OF A HOPI INDIAN
Don C. Talayesva; Leo W. Simmons, Editor
Revised 1963 edition. Illus. 520 pp. Paper. Yale University Press, $12.95.

SUN CIRCLES & HUMAN HANDS: THE SOUTHEASTERN INDIAN'S ART & INDUSTRIES Emma L. Fundaburk & Mary D. Fundaburk Forman
Illus. 240 pp. Paper. University of Alabama Press, 2001. $29.95. E-Book, $23.96

*SUN DANCE FOR ANDY HORN
Shelly Frome
Grades 9-12. 124 pp. Council for Indian Education, 1990. $12.95; paper, $7.95.

THE SUN DANCE OF THE CANADIAN DAKOTA
W.D. Wallis; 61 pp. Paper. Lakota Books, 1993. $14.95.

THE SUN DANCE OF THE KIOWA
Leslie Spier; 17 pp. Paper. Lakota Books, 1995. $7.95.

THE SUN DANCE OF THE OGLALA
J.R. Walker; Lakota religion. Ten narratves of the creation of the universe, et al. 169 pp. Paper. Lakota Books, 1993. $21.95.

THE SUN DANCE & OTHER CEREMONIES OF THE OGLALA DIVISION OF THE TETON DAKOTA J.R. Walker; Reprint. Amazon.com, $23.95; paper, $9.23.

THE SUN DANCE RELIGION: POWER FOR THE POWERLESS
Joseph G. Jorgensen; Illus. 372 pp. Paper. University of Chicago Press, 1972. $14.95.

SUN DANCER
David London; Describes Native American spirituality. 320 pp. Paper. University of Nebraska Press, 1998. $14.95.

SUN DANCING: A SPIRITUAL JOURNEY ON THE RED ROAD
Michael Hull; Illus. 232 pp. Paper. Inner Traditions International, 2000. $16.95.

SUN DOGS & EAGLE DOWN: THE INDIAN PAINTINGS OF BILL HOLM
Steven C. Brown & Lloyd J. Averill; Illus. 200 pp. U. of Washington Press, 2000. $40.

THE SUN GIRL
E. White, pseud.; Reprint of 1941 ed. Illus. 52 pp. Museum of Northern Arizona. $4.75.

THE SUN GOD'S CHILDREN: THE HISTORY, CULTURE, AND LEGENDS OF THE BLACKFEET INDIANS
James Willard Schultz; 260 pp. Paper. Riverbend Publishing, $19.95.

THE SUN HORSE: NATIVE VISIONS OF THE NEW WORLD
Gerald Hausman; Illus. 140 pp. Paper. Lotus Press, 1992. $14.95.

*SUN JOURNEY: A STORY OF ZUNI PUEBLO
Ann Nolan Clark; Grades 8 and up. Illus. 96 pp. Paper. Amazon.com, 1988. $9.95.

SUN MEN OF THE AMERICAS
Grace Cooke; 120 pp. Paper. De Vorss & Co., 2003. $9.95.

SUN, MOON & STARS
Coyote Man; Creation stories and legends of the Maidu people of the foothills and mountains of northern California. Amazon.com, $15.95.

SUN TRACKS
Ofelia Zepeda, Editor; American Indian literary series sponsored by the American Indian Studies Program, Dept. of English, University of Arizona.

SUNDANCING AT ROSEBUD & PINE RIDGE
Thomas E Mails; Reprint. Illus. Center for Western Studies, Delux edition, $125.

SUNDANCING: THE GREAT SIOUX PIERCING CEREMONY
Thomas E. Mails; Illus. 1,324 pp. Paper. Council Oak Books, 1997. $32.95.

SUNDOGS
Lee Maracle; Novel about a young First Nation's family during 1992 and the Meech Lake Accord and the "Oka Crisis." 214 pp. Paper. Theytus, 1992. $12.95.

SUNDOWN
John Joseph Mathews; A novel of life in the Osage. Illus. 312 pp. Paper. University of Oklahoma Press, 1988. $15.95.

*SUNFLOWER'S PROMISE: A ZUNI LEGEND
Terri Cohlene; Grades 1-5. Illus. Paper. Amazon.com, 1992. $4.95.

*SUNPAINTERS: ECLIPSE OF THE NAVAJO SUN
Baje Whitehorne, Writer/Illustrator; Insight into how Native Americans have traditionallu honored natural phenomena. Picture book. Ages 5-8. Illus. 32 pp. Amazon.com, $14.95.

SUNSET TO SUNSET: A LIFETIME WITH MY BROTHERS, THE DAKOTAS
Thomas L. Riggs, Editor; 226 pp. Paper. Amazon.com, 1997. $14.95.

A SUPPLEMENT GUIDE TO MANUSCRIPTS: RELATING TO THE AMERICAN INDIANS IN THE LIBRARY OF THE AMERICAN PHILOSOPHICAL SOCIETY
Daythal Kendall; Amazon.com, 1983. $15.

SUPPLEMENT TO THE HANDBOOK OF MIDDLE AMERICAN INDIANS, Vol. 1: ARCHAEOLOGY Victoria R. Bricker & Jeremy A. Sabloff, Editors
Illus. 475 pp. University of Texas Press, 1981. $55.

SUPPLEMENT TO THE HANDBOOK OF MIDDLE AMERICAN INDIANS, Vol. 2: LINGUISTICS
Victoria Bricker & Munro Edmonson, Editors; 224 pp. Amazon.com, 1984. $35.

SUPPLEMENT TO THE HANDBOOK OF MIDDLE AMERICAN INDIANS, Vol. 3: LITERATURE
Victoria Bricker & Munro Edmonson, Editors; 207 pp. Amazon.com, 1985. $35.

SUPPORTING INDIGENOUS CHILDREN'S DEVELOPMENT: COMMUNITY-UNIVERSITY PARTNERSHIPS Jessica Ball & Alan R. Pence
128 pp. University of Washington Press, 2006. $94; paper, $37.95.

SUPPRESSING AMERICAN INDIAN SPIRITUALITY: A WINTER COUNT
4th Ed. 128 pp. Western Textbook, 2002. $17.

THE SUPREME COURT & TRIBAL GAMING: CALIFORNIA V. CABAZON BAND OF MISSION INDIANS Ralph A. Rossum; The case and historical grounding for the case. 216 pp. University Press of Kansas, 2011. $34.95; paper, $16.95.

*SUQUAMISH TODAY
A documentary on the Suquamish of Port Madison Reservation, Washington. Teacher's guide. Grades 4-8. Illus. 21 pp. Daybreak Star Press, $4.50.

THE SURROUNDED
D'Arcy McNickle; A novel set on the Flathead Indian Reservation in Montana. 315 pp. Paper. University of New Mexico Press, $19.95.

SURVIVAL ARTS OF THE PRIMITIVE PAIUTES
Margaret Wheat; Illus. 140 pp. Paper. University of Nevada Press, 1967. $14.95.

SURVIVAL: LIFE & ART OF THE ALASKAN ESKIMO
The Newark Museum; Text by Barbara Lipton; Text and photographs of Alaska and objects: tools, utensils, dress, art created by the Eskimo. Illus. 96 pp. Paper. Newark Museum Publications, 1977. $7.95.

THE SURVIVAL OF THE BARK CANOE
John McPhee; Illus. 146 pp. Paper. Farrar, Straus & Grioux, 1975. $7.95.

SURVIVAL OF THE SPIRIT: CHIRICAHUA APACHES IN CAPTIVITY
H. Henrietta Stockel; Relates the struggle for survival of the Chiricahua Apaches after being moved from the Southwest to Florida and Alabama then Oklahoma. Illus. 360 pp. University of Nevada Press, 1993. $24.95.

SURVIVAL & REGENERATION: DETROIT'S AMERICAN INDIAN COMMUNITY
Edmund Jefferson Danziger, Jr.; Illus. 262 pp. Wayne State U. Press, 1991. $34.95.

SURVIVAL SKILLS OF NATIVE CALIFORNIA
Paul D. Campbell; Over 1,000 instructional illus. 2,000+ skills. 400 pp. Paper. Gibbs Smith, Publisher. 2000. $39.95.

SURVIVAL SKILLS OF THE NORTH AMERICAN INDIANS
Peter Goodchild; Illus. 244 pp. Paper. Amazon.com, 1999. $17.95.

SURVIVANCE, SOVEREIGNTY, AND STORY: TEACHING AMERICAN INDIAN RHETORICS, 1ST Edition Lisa King, Rose Gubele, Joyce Ran Anderson, Editors
240 pp. Utah State University Press, 2015. Amazon.com $24.95

SURVIVING ARTS: TRADITIONAL SKILLS OF THE FIRST CALIFORNIANS
Mike Shine; Illus. 256 pp. Paper. Heyday Books, $17.95.

SURVIVING AS INDIANS: THE CHALLENGE OF SELF-GOVERNMENT
Menno Bolt; 384 pp. Paper. Amazon.com, 1994. $19.95.

SURVIVING CONQUEST: A HISTORY OF THE YAVAPAI PEOPLES
Timothy Braatz; Maps. 301 pp. Paper. University of Nebraska Press, 2003. $29.95.

SURVIVING DESIRES: MAKING & SELLING NATIVE JEWELRY IN THE AMERICAN SOUTHWEST Henrietta Lidchi; 272 pp. Paper. University of Oklahoma Press, $34.95.

SURVIVING IN TWO WORLDS: CONTEMPORARY NATIVE AMERICAN VOICES
Lois Crozier-Hogle & Darryl Babe Wilson photos by Giuseppe Saitta;
 edited by Jay Leibold; Interviews 26 Native American leaders, such as: Oren Lyons, Arvol Looking Horse, John Echohawk, William Demmert, Cliford Trafzer, Greg Sarris and Roxanne Swentzell. Illus. Photos. 288 pp. University of Texas Press, 1997. $30.

SURVIVING THROUGH THE DAYS: TRANSLATIONS OF NATIVE CALIFORNIA STORIES & SONGS Herbert W. Luthin, Ed.
Illus. 651 pp. University of California Press, 2002. $29.95. E-Book available.

SUSPECT RELATIONS: SEX, RACE & RESISTANCE IN COLONIAL NORTH CAROLINA
Kirsten Fischer; Illus. 290 pp. Paper. Cornell University Press, 2001. $24.95.

*SUSETTE LA FLESCHE: ADVOCATE FOR NATIVE AMERICAN RIGHTS
Grades 4 and up. Illus. 120 pp. Childrens Press, $13.95.

SUSQUEHANNA'S INDIANS
Barry C. Kent
Illus. 438 pp. Pennsylvania Historical and Museum Commission, 1984. $15.95.

SUSTAINING THE CHEROKEE FAMILY: KINSHIP & THE ALLOTMENT OF AN INDIGENOUS NATION Rose Stremlau; During late 19th & early 20th centuries, the federal government sought to forcibly assimilate Native Americans into American society through systematic land allotment. Illuminates the impact of this policy on the Cherokee Nation of northeastern Oklahoma. Illus. Map. 336 pp. University of North Carolina Press, 2011. $65; paper, $24.95.

SWAMP SAILORS IN THE SECOND SEMINOLE WAR, 1835-1842
George Buker; Reprint ed. Illus. 150 pp. University Presses of Florida, 1997. $16.95.

SWAN AMONG THE INDIANS: LIFE OF JAMES G. SWAN, 1818-1900
Lucile McDonald
A record of the Makah Indian culture and artifacts. Illus. 280 pp. Binford & Mort, $14.95.

JAMES SWAN, CHATIC OF THE NORTHWEST COAST: DRAWINGS & WATERCOLORS FROM THE FRANZ & KATHRYN STENZEL COLLECTION OF WESTERN AMERICAN ART
George A. Miles, et al; Illus. 160 pp. Amazon.com & Alibris.com, 2003. $35.

MADONNA SWAN: A LAKOTA WOMAN'S STORY
Mark St. Pierre, Editor
Illus. Maps. 224 pp. Paper. University of Oklahoma Press, 1991. $19.95.

THE SWEET GRASS LIVES ON: FIFTY CONTEMPORARY NORTH AMERICAN INDIAN ARTISTS Jamake Highwater; Illus. 192 pp. HarperCollins, 1980. $35.

SWEET MEDICINE: THE CONTINUING ROLE OF THE SACRED ARROWS, THE SUN DANCE, & THE SACRED BUFFALO HAT IN NORTHERN CHEYENNE HISTORY
Peter J. Powell
Illus. Maps. 2 vols. 994 pp. Paper. University of Oklahoma Press, 1969. $55.

SWEET MEDICINE: SITES OF INDIAN MASSACRES, BATTLEFIELDS & TREATIES
Drex Brooks; Illus. 164 pp. Paper. U. of New Mexico Press, 1995. $26.95.

THE SWEET SMELL OF HOME: THE LIFE & ART OF LEONARD F. CHANA
Leonard F. Chana, Susan Lobo, Barbara Chana; Autobiographical details Tohono O'odham life in his art. 176 pp. University of Arizona Press, 2005. $40; paper, $21.95.

*SWEETGRASS
Jan Hudson
A novel set in the 19th century western Canadian prairie. 160 pp. Philomel, 1989. $13.95.

SWEETWATER WISDOM: A NATIVE AMERICAN SPIRITUAL WAY
Wendy Crockett; 110 pp. Paper. Crossroad Publishing, 1997. $13.95.

ROXANNE SWENTZELL: EXTRA ORDINARY PEOPLE
Gussie Fountleroy; Illus. 96 pp. Amazon.com, 2002. $38.95.

SWEPT UNDER THE RUG: A HIDDEN HISTORY OF NAVAJO WEAVING
Kathy M'Closkey; Illus. 336 pp. U. of New Mexico Press, $34.95; paper, $24.95.

LUKE SWETLAND'S CAPTIVITY
Edward Merrifield; Collection of stories about Wyoming Valley of Pennsylvania during the 1760's and 1770's. Includes documentation on Indian culture during his captivity. Reprint. Illus. 66 pp. Paper. Wennawoods Publishing, $8.95.

SWIMMER MANUSCRIPTS: CHEROKEE SACRED FORMULAS & MEDICINAL PRESCRIPTIONS
James Mooney; Reprint. 1995. 320 pp. Amazon.com, $26.50; paper, $13.95.

SWITCHBACKS: ART, OWNERSHIP, AND NUXALK NATIONAL IDENTITY
Jennifer Kramer; Examines the Nuxalk of Bella Coola, British Columbia. 192 pp. University of Washington Press, 2006. $94.

GEORGE SWORD'S WARRIOR NARRATIVES: COMPOSITIONAL PROCESSES IN LAKOTA ORAL TRADITION
Delphine Red Shirt; 360 pp. University of Nebraska Press, 2017. $65; paper, $35.

SYMBOL & SUBSTANCE IN AMERICAN INDIAN ART
Zena Mathews; Amy Hobar, Editor; 24 pp. Paper. Amazon.com, 1984. $2.95.

SYMBOLIC IMMORTALITY: THE TLINGIT POTLATCH OF THE 19TH CENTURY
Secnd Edition; Sergei Kan; The first comprehensive analysis of the mortuary practices of the Tlingit Indians of southeastern Alaska. Illus. Maps. 432 pp. Paper. UBC Press & University of Washington Press, 2015. $45.

SYMBOLS OF NATIVE AMERICA
Heike Owusu; Paper. Sterling, 1999. $13.95.

SYMPOSIUM ON LOCAL DIVERSITY IN IROQUOIS CULTURE
William N. Fenton; Reprint. Illus. 187 pp. Native American Book Publishing, 1990. $49.

SYNTAX & SEMANTICS: THE SYNTAX OF NATIVE AMERICAN LANGUAGES
Eung-Do Cook and Donna B. Gerdts
Volume 16 of Syntax and Semantics. Amazon.com. 1984. $75.

SYSTEMS OF CONSANGUINITY & AFFINITY OF THE HUMAN FAMILY
Lewis Henry Morgan; Examines the kinship systems of over 100 cultures.
Illus. 604 pp. Paper. University of Nebraska Press, 1997. $40.

T

TACACHALE: ESSAYS ON THE INDIANS OF FLORIDA & SOUTHEASTERN GEORGIA DURING THE HISTORIC PERIOD J.T. Milanich & Samuel Proctor, Editors
Illus. Maps. 217 pp. University Press of Florida, 1978. $23.95.

MARGARET TAFOYA: A TEWA POTTER'S HERITAGE & LEGACY
Mary Ellen & Laurence Blair; Susan McDonald, Editor; Illus. 200 pp. Schiffer, 1986. $45.

TAINO INDIAN MYTH & PRACTICE: THE ARRIVAL OF THE STRANGER KING
William F. Keegan; Taino society, myth, and archaeology at the dawn of the Spanish colonial period, applying the legend of the "stranger king" to Caonabo, the mythologized Taino chief of the Hispaniola settlement Columbus invaded in 1492. Illus. 256 pp. University Press of Florida, 2007. $39.95.

THE TAINO INDIAN: A NATIVE AMERICAN EXPERIENCE
Saul Torres; 50 pp. Paper. Biblos Press, 1996. $10.

TAINO: PRE-COLUMBIAN ART & CULTURE FROM THE CARIBBEAN
Ricrado E. Alegria, et al. ; Illus. 56 pp. Paper. Amazon.com, 1997. $15.

*THE TAINOS: THE PEOPLE WHO WELCOMED COLUMBUS
Francine Jacobs; illus. by Patrick Collins; Describes the early beginnings of the Tainos' culture. Grades 6 and up. Illus. 112 pp. Putnam, 1992. $15.95.

TAITADUHAAN: WESTERN MONO WAYS OF SPEAKING
Paul V. Kroskrity, Rosalie Bethel, Jennifer F. Reynolds
CD-ROM providing an introduction to the language & culture of the Western Mono Indians of Central California. $29.95. Paper. University of Oklahoma Press, $19.95.

TAKE MY LAND, TAKE MY LIFE: THE STORY OF CONGRESS'S HISTORIC SETTLEMENT OF ALASKA NATIVE LAND CLAIMS, 1960-1971
Donald Craig Mitchell
Illus. Photos. Map. Biblio. Paper. University of Alaska Press, 2001. $39.95.

TAKHOMA: ETHNOGRAPHY OF MOUNT RAINER NATIONAL PARK
Allan H. Smith; Illus. Map.208 pp. Paper. WSU Press, 2006. $22.95.

TAKING ASSIMILATION TO HEART: MARRIAGES OF WHITE WOMEN & INDIGENOUS MEN IN THE U.,S. & AUSTRALIA, 1887-1937
Katherine Ellinghaus; Illus. 312 pp. Paper. University of Nebraska Press, 2006. $24.95.

TAKING CHARGE: NATIVE AMERICAN SELF-DETERMINATION & FEDERAL INDIAN POLICY, 1975-1993
George Pierre Castile; 168 pp. University of Arizona Press, 2006. $35.

TAKING CONTROL: POWER & CONTRADICTION IN FIRST NATIONS ADULT EDUCATION
Celia Haig-Brown; 256 pp. University of Washington Press, 1994. $35.95.

TAKING INDIAN LANDS: THE CHEROKEE (JEROME) COMMISSION, 1889-1893
William T. Hagan; Illus. Maps. 296 pp. Paper. U. of Oklahoma Press, 2011. $19.95.

TAKING MEDICINE: WOMEN'S HEALING WORK & COLONIAL CONTACT IN SOUTHERN ALBERTA, 1880-1930
Kristin Burnett; Illus. Map. 248 pp. U. of Washington Press, 2011. $94; paper, $35.95.

TALES THE ELDERS TOLD: OJIBWAY LEGENDS
Basil H. Johnston; illus. by Shirley Cheechoo
Illus. 64 pp. Amazon.com, $15.95.

*TALES FROM THE CHEROKEE HILLS
Jean Starr; 33 Cherokee folktales. 94 pp. Paper.
Amazon.com & Cherokee Publications, $8.95.

TALES FROM THE DENA: INDIAN STORIES FROM THE TANANA, KOYUKUK & YUKON RIVERS Frederica De Laguna, Ed.
Illus. 375 pp. University of Washington Press, 2003. $45; paper, $24.95.

TALES FROM INDIAN COUNTRY: AUTHENTIC STORIES & LEGENDS FROM THE GREAT UINTA BASIN George E. Stewart, Jr.; Maryellen Gardner, Ed.
250 pp. Paper. Amazon.com, 1997. $19.95.

TALES FROM MALISEET COUNTRY: THE MALISEET TEXTS OF KARL V. TEETER
Philip S. LeSourd, Editor & translator; Maliseet language of the Algonquian family.
200 pp. University of Nebraska Press, 2007. $40; paper, $19.95.

TALES FROM THE TRIBES, VOL. 1: FOLKLORE OF THE EASTERN WOODLANDS INDIANS Jack Rushing; 80 pp. Dragon Press, 1999. $19.95; paper, $9.95.

TALES FROM WIDE RUINS: JEAN & BILL COUSINS, TRADERS
Jean & Bill Cousins; Illus. 264 pp.Texas Tech University Press, 1996. $29.95.

TALES OF THE ANISHINAUBACK: OJIBWAY LEGENDS
Basil H. Johnston; illus. by Maxine Noel
Native myths. Illus. 80 pp. Amazon.com & Alibris.com, $24.95.

TALES OF APACHE WARFARE
James M. Barney; True stories of massacres, fights and raids in Arizona & New Mexico. Reprint fo 1933 edition. 45 pp. Paper. High-Lonesome Books, $7.

TALES OF THE BARK LODGES
Bertrand N.O. Walker (Hen-Toh); 12 traditional animal tales that preserve elements of Wyandot culture. Illus. 160 pp. Paper. Amazon.com, 1995. $22.

TALES OF THE BLACK HILLS
Helen Rezatto; Collection of legends, including legends by the Sioux.
Illus. 288 pp. Paper. Center for Western Studies, $9.95.

TALES OF THE COCHITI INDIANS
Ruth Benedict; Reprint. 256 pp. Amazon.com, 1995. $20; paper, $10.95.

TALES OF AN ENDISHODI: FATHER BERARD HAILE & THE NAVAJOS, 1900-1961
Fr. Murray Bodo, Editor
Illus. 264 pp. University of New Mexico Press, 1998. $45; paper, $24.95.

TALES OF GHOSTS: FIRST NATIONS ART IN BRITISH COLUMBIA, 1922-61
Ronald W. Hawker
Illus. 248 pp. University of Washington Press, 2003. $105; paper, $35.95.

TALES OF KANKAKEE LAND
C.H. Bartlett; Reprint of 1907 edition. Amazon.com, $7.50.

TALES OF NATIVE AMERICA
Edward W. Huffstetler; Illus. 112 pp. Michael Friedman Publishing, 1996. $16.

*TALES OF NORTH AMERICA, GRADES PRESCHOOL-3: NATIVE AMERICANS
Irene Handberg; Revised edition. 8 pp. Teacher Ed. Amazon.com, 1995. $24.95

TALES OF THE NORTH AMERICAN INDIANS
Stith Thompson, Editor; Illus. 416 pp. Paper. Amazon.com & Alibris.com, 1966. $16.95.

TALES OF THE NORTHWEST: ON SKETCHES OF INDIAN LIFE & CHARACTER
W.J. Snelling; Collection of short stories on Plains Indians. Reprint of 1830 edition.

TALES OF THE OLD INDIAN TERRITORY & ESSAYS ON THE INDIAN CONDITION
John Milton Oskison; Lionel Larre, Editor
680 pp.Paper. University of Nebraska Press, 2012. $60.

*TALES OF A PUEBLO BOY
Lawrence J. Vallo; Stories of growing up in an Indian Pueblo.
Grades 3-9. Illus. 48 pp. Paper. Sunstone Press, $5.95.

TALES OF A SHAMAN'S APPRENTICE
Mark Plotkin, PhD; Penguin USA, $22.

TALES OF THE TEPEE
Edward Everett Dale; 119 pp. paper. University of Nebraska Press, 1998. $8.

TALES OF TICASUK: ESKIMO LEGENDS & STORIES
Emily Ivanoff Brown; Illus. 135 pp. University of Alaska Press, 1987. $15; paper, $8.95.

TALKING BACK TO CIVILIZATION: INDIAN VOICES FROM THE PROGRESSIVE ERA
Frederick Hoxie, Editor; Amazon.com, 2001.

TALKING BOOKS: ETHNOPOETICS
Kenneth Mendoza; 114 pp. Camden House, 1993. $45.

TALKING CHICKASAW DICTIONARY
Vinnie May Humes (Chickasaw Speaker); 7,000+ words on CD-ROM. VIP, 2002, $34.95.

TALKING LEAVES: CONTEMPORARY NATIVE AMERICAN SHORT STORIES, AN ANTHOLOGY Craig Lesley, Editor; Anthology of 38 contemporary Native American short stories. 385 pp. Amazon.com, $20.

TALKING MYSTERIES: A CONVERSATION WITH TONY HILLERMAN
Tony Hillerman & Ernie Bulow; Author details his early years in Oklahoma, first encounters with Navajo culture and his life as journalist and author. Illus. 144 pp. Paper. University of New Mexico Press. $13.95.

TALKING POEMS: CONVERSATIONS WITH POETS
Eunice de Souza; Illus. 145 pp. Oxford University Press, 2001. $22.

TALKING ROCKS: GEOLOGY & 10,000 YEARS OF NATIVE AMERICAN TRADITION IN THE LAKE SUPERIOR REGION
Ron Morton & Carl Gawboy
Illus. 272 pp. Paper. University of Minnesota Press, 2000. $17.95.

TALKING TAINO: CARIBBEAN NATURAL HISTORY FROM A NATIVE PERSPECTIVE
William F. Keegan & LisabethA. Carlson
Illus. 208 pp. University of Alabama Press, 2008. $59; paper, $29.95.

TALKING TO THE MOON: WILDLIFE ADVENTURES ON THE PLAINS & PRAIRIES OF OSAGE COUNTRY John Joseph Matthews; Keen & intimate observations of nature; Native American comparisons, cowboy reflections & humor. U. of Oklahoma Pres, $16.

TALKING WITH THE CLAY: THE ART OF PUEBLO POTTERY IN THE 21ST CENTURY
Stephen Trimble; 20th Anniversary Revised edition. Illus. Map. 160 pp. Paper.
School for Advanced Research, 2007. $40; paper, $19.95.

TALL WOMAN: LIFE STORY OF ROSE MITCHELL, A NAVAJO WOMAN, @ 1874-1977
Rose Mitchell; edited by Charlotte Frisbie
Illus. Maps. 606 pp. Paper. University of New Mexico Press, 2000. $34.95.

TAMMARNLIT (MISTAKES) INUIT RELOCATION IN THE EASTERN ARCTIC,
1939-1963 Frank Tester & Peter Kulchyski
Illus. 437 pp. University of Washington Press, 1994. $83; paper, $35.95.

TANAINA TALES FROM ALASKA
Bill Vaudrin; Reprint of 1969 edition. Illus. 127 pp. Paper. U. of Oklahoma Press, $11.95.

TANGIBLE VISIONS: NORTHWEST INDIAN SHAMANISM & ITS ART
Allen Wardell; Illus. 352 pp. Monacelli Press, 1996. $85.

TANGLED WEBS OF HISTORY: INDIANS & THE LAW IN CANADA'S PACIFIC COAST
FISHERIES Diane Newell; Illus. 600 pp. U. of Toronto Press, 1993. $40; paper, $18.95.

THE TAOS INDIANS
Blanche C. Grant; Reissue of 1925 edition. Illus. 198 pp. Paper. Rio Grande Press, $10.

THE TAOS INDIANS & THE BATTLE FOR BLUE LAKE
R.C. Gordon-McCutchan; Story of the Taos Indians' 60 year struggle to regain their
sacred tribal lands. Reprint of 1991 ed. Illus. 256 pp. Paper. Museum of New Mexico
Press, $9.95.

TAOS: PEOPLE, LAND, SPIRIT: THE PHOTOGRAPHY OF BARBARA SPARKS
Barbara Sparks; University of New Mexico Press, $45.

TAOS PUEBLO & ITS SACRED BLUE LAKE
Marcia Keegan; Documents the celebration in 1971 when Taos Pueblo
got the sacred lake back. 53 photos. 63 pp. Amazon.com, $14.95.

TAOS: 1847: THE REVOLT IN CONTEMPORARY ACCOUNTS
Michael McNierney, Editor; 102 pp. Paper. Johnson Books, 1980. $4.95.

TAOS ARTISTS & THEIR PATRONS, 1898-1950
Dean A. Porter, Teresa Hayes Ebie & Susan Campbell; U. of New Mexico Press, $65.

TAOS SOCIETY OF ARTISTS
Robert R. White, Editor; University of New Mexico Press, $16.95.

TAOS TALES
Elsie Clews Parsons; Reprint. 192 pp. Paper. Dover, $7.95.

THE TAOS TRAPPERS: THE FUR TRADE IN THE FAR SOUTHWEST, 1540-1846
David J. Webber; Reprint of the 1971 edition. Illus. Maps. 263 pp.
Paper. University of Oklahoma Press, $16.95.

TAPESTRIES IN THE SAND: THE SPIRIT OF INDIAN SANDPAINTING
David Villasenor; Chiricahua Sun Sandpainting. Illus. 112 pp. Paper. Naturegraph, $8.95.

A TASTE OF HERITAGE: CROW INDIAN RECIPES & HERBAL MEDICINES
Alma Hogan Snell
Illus. Map. 200 pp. Paper. University of Nebraska Press, 2006. $17.95.

TATL'AHWT'AENN NENN' THE HEADWATERS PEOPLE'S COUNTRY
James Kari, et al, Editors
Illus. 220 pp. Paper. Alaska Native Language Center, 1986. $10.

TE ATA: CHICKASAW STORYTELLER, AMERICAN TREASURE
Richard Green; Illus. 368 pp. Paper. University of Oklahoma Press, 2006. $19.95.

TEACH YOURSELF NATIVE AMERICAN MYTHS
Steve Eddy; 160 pp. Paper. McGraw-Hill, 2001. $10.95.

A TEACHER'S GUIDE TO HISTORICAL & CONTEMPORARY KUMEYAAY CULTURE
Geralyn Marie Hoffman & Lynn H. Gamble, PhD
For 3rd & 4th grade teachers. Illus. Malki-Ballena Press, $12.

A TEACHER'S GUIDE TO THE LENAPE
Karen Waldauer, Editor; Three separate kits: 1. Introduction to the Lenape, $22.50; 2.
Lenape Lore/Folk Medicines, $15.50; 3. Lenape Lore/Clothing, Shelter, Crafts, Weapons,
Tools & Specialties, $15.50. Illus. Charts, quizzes, posters. The Amazon.com.

TEACHING ABOUT NATIVE AMERICANS
Karen D. Harvey, Lisa D. Harjo, Jane K. Jackson
82 pp. Paper. Amazon.com, $10.95 (members); $12.95 (non-members).

TEACHING AMERICAN INDIAN HISTORY
Terry P. Wilson; 66 pp. Paper. Amazon.com, 1993. $8.

TEACHING AMERICAN INDIAN HISTORY: AN INTERDISCIPLINARY APPROACH
Larry L. Vantine; Paper. R & E Research Associates, 1978. $11.95.

TEACHING AMERICAN INDIAN STUDENTS
Jon Reyhner, Editor; Summarizes the latest research on Indian education, and provides
practical suggestions for teachers, and resources. Map. Biblio. 328 pp. Paper. University of
Oklahoma Press, 1992. $19.95.

TEACHING GUIDE FOR INDIAN LITERATURE
Diana Campbell; Volume I, 110 pp. Grades 4-6; Volume II, 55 pp. Grades 6 and up.
Rough Rock School Press, 1983. $4.50 each.

TEACHING INDIGENOUS STUDENTS: HONORING PLACE, COMMUNITY,
AND CULTURE
Jon Reyhner; Illus. 256 pp. Paper. University of Oklahoma Press, 2015. $24.95.

TEACHING THE NATIVE AMERICAN
Hap Gilliland; A guide to adapting instruction to the needs of American Indian students.
4th Edition. 306 pp. Amazon.com, 1999. $22.95.

TEACHING OREGON NATIVE LANGUAGES
Joan Gross, Editor; The effort to revitalize Oregon's first languages.
Photos. Map. 176 pp. Paper. Oregon State University Press, 2007. $24.95.

TEACHING SPIRITS: UNDERSTANDING NATIVE AMERICAN RELIGIOUS
TRADITIONS Joseph Epes Brown & Emily Cousins
Illus. 170 pp. Paper. Oxford University Press, 2010. $28.95.

TEACHING VIRTUES: BUILDING CHARACTER ACROSS THE CURRICULUM
Donald Trent Jacobs & Jessica Jacobs-Spencer
Illus. 175 pp. Paper. Scarecrow Press, 2001. $35.

TEACHINGS FROM THE AMERICAN EARTH: INDIAN RELIGION & PHILOSOPHY
Dennis & Barbara Tedlock, Editors
Revised edition. Illus. 304 pp. Paper. Amazon.com, 1992. $14.95.

THE TEACHINGS OF DON JUAN: A YAQUI WAY OF KNOWLEDGE
Carlos Castaneda; 40th Anniversary edition
225 pp. University of California Press, 2008. $39.95; paper, $22.95.

TEACHINGS OF NATURE
Adolf Hungry Wolf
Knowledge of the old ways. Illus. 94 pp. Paper. The Book Publishing Co., $8.95.

TEAM SPIRITS: THE NATIVE MASCOTS CONTROVERSY
C. Richard King & Charles Fruehling Springwood, Editors
356 pp. University of Nebraska Press, 2001. $27.50.

TEARS OF REPENTANCE: CHRISTIAN INDIAN IDENTITY & COMMUNITY
IN COLONIAL SOUTHERN NEW ENGLAND
Julius H. Rubin; Illus. 424 pp. Univdersity of Nebraska Press, 2013. $75.

TECHNIQUE OF NORTH AMERICAN INDIAN BEADWORK
Monte Smith; Features examples and photos of beadwork from 1835 to the present time.
200 Illus. Biblio. 106 pp. Paper. Eagle's View Publishing, $10.95.

TECHNIQUE OF PORCUPINE QUILL DECORATION AMONG THE INDIANS
OF NORTH AMERICA William C. Orchard; Monte Smith, Editor
Revised 1917 edition. Illus. 88 pp. Paper. Eagles View Publishing, Written Heritage,
Hothem House, Smoke & Fire Co., $9.95.

TECHNIQUES OF BEADING EARRINGS
Deon DeLange; Illus. 72 pp. Paper. Eagle's View Publishing, $9.95.

*TECUMSEH
Grades 3-6. Illus. 32 pp. Childrens Press, $11.45.

*TECUMSEH
Russell Shorto; Nancy Furstinger, Editor
Grades 5-7. Illus. 145 pp. Amazon.com, 1989. $11.98; paper, $7.95.

TECUMSEH: A LIFE
John Sugden; Illus. 448 pp. Amazon.com, 1999. $15.95.

TECUMSEH'S LAST STAND
John Sugden; maps by Frank O. Williams
Illus. Maps. Biblio. Paper. University of Oklahoma Press, 1985. $19.95.

TECUMSEH! A PLAY
Allan W. Eckert; 192 pp. Paper. Amazon.com, 2000. $13.95.

TECUMSEH & THE QUEST FOR INDIAN LEADERSHIP
R. David Edmunds; Paper. Scott Foresman & Co., 1984. $7.95.

TECUMSEH & THE SHAWNEE CONFEDERACY
Rebecca Stetoff; Grades 5 and up. Illus. 144 pp. Facts on File, 1998. $19.95.

TECUMSEH: VISIONARY CHIEF OF THE SHAWNEE
Jason Hook; Illus. 52 pp. Sterling, 1989. $12.95.

TEEPEE NEIGHBORS
Grace Coolidge; Patricia Trautman, Ed.; 3rd Ed. 150 pp. Mortimore Publishing, 2001. $15.

TEEPEES ARE FOLDED: AMERICAN INDIAN POETRY
Sally Old Coyote; Council for Indian Education, 1991. $5.95.

TEJANO ORIGINS IN 18TH CENTURY SAN ANTONIO
Gerald Poyo & Gilberto Hinojoso; Illus. 200 pp. University of Texas Press, 1991. $19.95.

KATERI TEKAKWITHA: THE LILY OF THE MOHAWKS
Lillien M. Fisher; Illus. 128 pp. Paper. Amazon.com, 1996. $5.95.

TELL ME AHNA: ESKIMO FOLKTALES
Susan Towne DeBree; Stories. Illus. 32 pp. Paper. White Publishing, $3.45.

TELL THEM WE ARE GOING HOME: THE ODYSSEY OF THE NORTHERN CHEYENNES John H. Monnett; Illus. Maps. 288 pp. Paper. University of Oklahoma Press, 2001. $19.95.

TELLICO ARCHAEOLOGY
Jefferson Chapman; 12,000 years of Native American occupation in the Little Tennessee and Tellico Rivers region of Tennessee. Illus. 142 pp. Paper. Hothem House & Amazon.com, 1985. $15.95.

TELLINGS FROM OUR ELDERS: LUSHOOTSEED SYEYEHUB, VOLUME 2: TALES FROM THE SKAGIT VALLEY
David Beck & Thom Hess; UBC Press, 2015. $165.

TELLING A GOOD ONE: THE PROCESS OF A NATIVE AMERICAN COLLABORATIVE BIOGRAPHY Theodore Rios & Kathleen Mullen Sands
Sands draws on her partnership with the late Theodore Rios, a Tohono O'odham narrator and the influence of Tohono O'odham culture and its tradition of storytelling on Rios's actions and words. Illus. Map. 378 pp. U. of Nebraska Press, 2000. $60; paper, $29.95.

TELLING NEW MEXICO
Marta Weigle, with Frances Levine & Louise Stiver, Editors
Essays & articles of New Mexico history including Native American & Chicano studies. Illus. 480 pp. Paper. Museum of New Mexico Press, 2010. $29.95.

THE TELLING OF THE WORLD: NATIVE AMERICAN STORIES & ART
W.S. Penn, Editor; Reprint. Illus. 240 pp. Amazon.com, 2000. $45.

TELLING OUR STORIES: OMUSHKEGO LEGENDS & HISTORIES FROM THE HUDSON BAY
Louis Bird; Illus. 269 pp. Paper. University of Toronto Press, 2005. $27.95.

TELLING OURSELVES: ETHNICITY & DISCOURSE IN SOUTHWESTERN ALASKA
Chase Hensel; 232 pp. Paper. Oxford University Press, 1996. $28.

TELLING THE STORIES: ESSAYS ON AMERICAN INDIAN LITERATURES & CULTURES Elizabeth Hoffman Nelson & Malcolm A. Nelson, Editors
186 pp. Paper. Peter Lang Publishing & Amazon.com, 2001. $24.95.

TELLING STORIES IN THE FACE OF DANGER: LANGUAGE RENEWAL IN NATIVE AMERICAN COMMUNITIES
Paul V. Kroskrity; 288 pp. Paper. University of Oklahoma Press, $24.95.

TELLING STORIES THE KIOWA WAY
Gus Palmer, Jr.; Explores the traditional art of storytelling still practiced by the Kiowas. 145 pp. University of Arizona Press, 2003. $35; paper, $17.95.

TEMALPAKH: CAHUILLA INDIAN KNOWLEDGE & USAGE OF PLANTS
Lowell J. Bean & Katherine Siva Saubel
Reprint of 1972 ed. Illus. 225 pp. Paper. Malki-Ballena Press, 2001. $20.

TEMPLES OF THE CAHOKIA LORDS: PRESTON HOLDER'S 1955-1956 EXCAVATIONS OF KUNNEMANN MOUND Timothy R. Pauketat, et al.
Illus. Paper. University of Michigan, Museum of Anthropology, 1993. $28.

THE TEMPTATIONS OF BIG BEAR: A NOVEL
Rudy Wiebe; Plains Cree of Canada and their struggle for survival. Illus. 456 pp. Paper. Amazon.com, 2000. $16.95.

THE TEN GRANDMOTHERS: EPIC OF THE KIOWAS
A. Marriott
Reprint of 1945 edition. Illus. Map. 305 pp. Paper. U. of Oklahoma Press, $15.95.

***10 LITTLE WHITEPEOPLE**
Beverly Slapin & Annie Esposito; Grades 9 and up. Illus. Paper. Oyate, 1995. $5.

TEN'A TEXTS & TALES: FROM ANVIK, ALASKA
John W. Chapman; Franz Boas, Ed. fac. Ed; Reprint. 236 pp. Paper. Coyote Press, $25.

TENDERFOOT IN TOMBSTONE, THE PRIVATE JOURNAL OF GEORGE WHITWELL PARKSONS: THE TURBULENT YEARS, 1880-1882
Lynn R. Bailey; Illus. Westernlore, 1996. $36.95.

TENDING THE FIRE: NATIVE VOICES & PORTRAITS
Photos by Christopher Felver; intro. By Linda Hogan; foreword by Simon Ortiz
Celebrates indigenous American authors. Ilus. 248 pp. U. of New Mexico Press, $49.95.

***TENDING THE FIRE: THE STORY OF MARIA MARTINEZ**
Juddi Morris; Biography of Maria Martinez, Navajo potter. Ages 8-12. Illus. 120 pp. Northland, $12.95; paper, $6.95.

TENDING THE TALKING WIRE: A BUCK SOLDIER'S VIEW OF INDIAN COUNTRY, 1863-1866 William E. Unrau; 382 pp. Paper. University of Utah Press, 2002. $19.95.

TENDING THE WILD: NATIVE AMERICAN KNOWLEDGE & THE MANAGEMENT OF CALIFORNIA'S NATURAL RESOURCES M. Kat Anderson;; Maps. 555 pp. Malki-Ballena Press, $39.95. Paper. University of California Press, 2006. $24.95.

***TENDOY, CHIEF OF THE LEMHIS**
David Crowder; Grades 5-9. Illus. Paper. Caxton, 1969. $2.75.

TENNESSEE FRONTIERS: THREE REGIONS IN TRANSITION
John R. Finger; Chronicles the formation of Tennesse from indigenous setlements to the closing of the frontier in 1840, beginning with an account of the prehistoric frontiers and a millennia-long habitation by Native Americans. Illus. Photos. Indiana U. Press, 2001. $10.

TENNESSEE'S INDIAN PEOPLES: FROM WHITE CONTACT TO REMOVAL,1540-1840
Ronald N. Satz; Illus. 110 pp. U. of Tennessee Press, 1979. $9.95; paper, $3.50.

TENSION & HARMONY: THE NAVAJO RUG
32 pp. Paper. Museum of Northern Arizona, 1982. $4.

TENTING ON THE PLAINS; OR, GENERAL CUSTER IN KANSAS & TEXAS
Elizabeth B. Custer; Portrays the aftermath of the Civil War in Texas, and life in Kansas. Detailed descriptions of an army officer's home life on the frontier during this major period of Indian unrest. Reprint. Illus. Maps. 388 pp. Paper. U. of Oklahoma Press, $12.95.

TEPEE COOKERY: OR, LET'S CHEW THE FAT INDIAN STYLE: A COOKBOOK
Gwen Fisher; Illus. 74 pp. Paper. Amazon.com, 1986. $12.

TERMINATION & RELOCATION: FEDERAL INDIAN POLICY, 1945-1960
Donald L. Fixico; Illus. 286 pp. Paper. University of New Mexico Press, $14.95.

TERMINATION REVISITED: AMERICAN INDIANS ON THE TRAIL TO SELF-DETERMINATION, 1933-1953
Kenneth R. Philp; Illus. 265 pp. Paper. University of Nebraska Press, 1999. $24.95.

TERMINATION'S LEGACY: THE DISCARDED INDIANS OF UTAH
R. Warren Metcalf; The reality of identity politics in Indian Country. Illus. Maps. 311 pp. Paper. University of Nebraska Press, 2002. $12.47.

TERRIBLE JUSTICE: SIOUX CHIEFS & U.S. SOLDIERS ON THE UPPER MISSOURI, 1854-1868 Doreen Chaky; 408 pp. Paper. University of Oklahoma Press, 2014. $21.95.

HOWARD TERPNING: SPIRIT OF THE PLAINS PEOPLE
Don Hedgpeth; Illus. 180 pp. Teacher Ed. Amazon.com, 2003. $85.

TESTIMONY TO WOUNDED KNEE: A COMPREHENSIVE BIBLIOGRAPHY
William K. Powers & Marla N. Powers; Major works on the Ghost Dance and Wounded Knee Massacre. 60 pp. Paper. Lakota Books, 1994. $24.95.

THE TETON OR WESTERN DAKOTA
James H. Howard; Illus. 24 pp. Paper. Lakota Books, 1996. $12.95.

***THE TETON SIOUX**
Nancy Bonvillain; Grades 4 and up. Chelsea House Publishers, 2004.

TETON SIOUX MUSIC & CULTURE
Frances Densmore; Reprint. Explores the role of music in all aspects of Sioux life. Illus. 560 pp. Paper. University of Nebraska Press, $40.

TEWA TALES
Esie Clews Parsons; Collection of more than 100 tales. Reprint of 1926 edition. 304 pp. Paper. University of Arizona Press, $19.95.

TEWA WORLD: SPACE, TIME, BEING, AND BECOMING IN A PUEBLO SOCIETY
Alfonso Ortiz; 198 pp. Paper. University of Chicago Press, 1969. $14.

THE TEXAS CHEROKEES: A PEOPLE BETWEEN FIRES, 1819-1840
Dianna Everett; Illus. Maps. 174 pp. Paper. University of Oklahoma Press & Cherokee Publications, 1990. $19.95.

TEXAS INDIAN MYTHS & LEGENDS
Jane Archer; Illus. 250 pp. Paper. Wordware Publishing, 2000. $18.95.

TEXAS INDIAN TRAILS: A ROADSIDE GUIDE TO NATIVE AMERICAN LANDMARKS
Daniel J. Gelo & Wayne Pate; 250 pp. Paper. Wordware Publishing, 2003. $18.95.

THE TEXAS INDIANS
David La Vere; Illus. Paper. Texas A&M University Press, 2013. $19.95.

THE TEXAS KICKAPOO: KEEPERS OF TRADITION
Bill Wright & E. John Gesick, Jr.; Illus. Photos. 213 pp. Texas Western Press, 1996. $45.

TEXTBOOKS & THE AMERICAN INDIAN
Jeanette Henry & Rupert Costo, Eds; 269 pp. Paper. Amazon.com, 1969. $5.

TEXTILES IN SOUTHWESTERN PREHISTORY
Lynn S. Teague; University of New Mexico Press, $45.

THE TEXTURE OF CONTACT: EUROPEAN & INDIAN SETTLER COMMUNITIES ON THE FRONTIERS OF IROQUOIA, 1667-1783 David L. Preston
Study of Iroquois & European communities & coexistence in eastern North America before the American Revolution. Ills. 12 figures, 3 maps, 3 tables.464 pp. Paper. University of Nebraska Press, 2009. $25.

THANKSGIVING: A NATIVE PERSPECTIVE
Sourcebook of essays, speeches, poetry, stories and activities will help teachers and students think critically about what has been taught as the "first" thanksgiving. Illus. 93 pp. Paper. Oyate, 1996. $8.

THAT ALL PEOPLE MAY BE ONE PEOPLE, SEND RAIN TO WASH THE FACE OF THE EARTH Chief Joseph; As spoken by Chief Joseph, 1879. Illus. 53 pp. Paper. Amazon.com, 1995. $12.95.

THAT DREAM SHALL HAVE A NAME: NATIVE AMERICAN REWRITING AMERICA
David L. Moore; 488 pp. Paper. University of Nebraska Press, 2014. $45.

THAT THE PEOPLE MIGHT LIVE: NATIVE AMERICAN LITERATURES & NATIVE AMERICAN COMMUNITY Jace Weaver; Paper. Oxford University Press, 1997. $54.

THAT'S WHAT SHE SAID: CONTEMPORARY POETRY & FICTION BY NATIVE AMERICAN WOMEN
Rayna Green, Editor; Illus. 352 pp. Paper. Amazon.com & Alibris.com, 1984. $24.95.

THAT'S WHAT THEY USED TO SAY: REFLECTIONS ON AMERICAN INDIAN ORAL TRADITIONS Donald L. Fixico; Illus. 272 pp. University of Oklahoma Press, 2017. $34.95.

THE THEFT OF FIRE: A CURRICULUM UNIT
Title V program staff & tribal resource people; A currciulum book featuring the traditional story theme of stealing fire fromthe sun. Activities highlight the complex Native American technology of creating fire without matches; 14-minute videos available. Grades 6-8. Illus. 24 pp. booklet. Amazon.com. $10, institutions; $7, individuals.

THE THEFT OF THE SPIRIT: THE JOURNEY TO SPIRITUAL HEALING WITH NATIVE AMERICANS
Carl A. Hammerschlag; Reprint. 176 pp. Paper. Simon & Schuster, 1994. $12.

THEIR BEARING IS NOBLE & PROUD
James F. O'Neil, II; Collection of unique narratives regarding the appearance of Natives from 1740-1815. Two vols. Smoke & Fire Co., $18.95 each.

THEIR FIRES ARE COLD
Vietzen; Prehistoric artifacts and metal trade items like axes, pipe-tomahawks, pipes, knives. Photos & sketches. 192 pp. Hothem House, 1984. $60.

THEIR NATURAL RESOURCES FAIL: NATIVE PEOPLE & THE ECONOMIC HISTORY OF NORTHERN MANITOBA, 1870-1930
Frank Tough; Illus. 384 pp. University of Washington Press, 1997. $65; paper, $29.95.

THEIR NUMBER BECOME THINNED: NATIVE AMERICAN POPULATION DYNAMICS IN EASTERN NORTH AMERICA
Henry F. Dobyns; Illus. 382 pp. U. of Tennessee Press, 1983. $34.95; paper, $16.95.

THEIR OWN FRONTIER: WOMEN INTELLECTUALS RE-VISIONING THE AMERICAN WEST Shirley A. Leckie & Nancy J. Parezo, Editors
Essays honoring ten pioneering women scholars of the early American West, pioneers in the writing of Indian-centered history, ethnology & folklore. Illus. 414 pp. Paper. University of Nebraska Press, 2008. $27.95.

THEIR SECRETS: WHY NAVAJO INDIANS NEVER GET CANCER
De Lamar Gibbons; 125 pp. Paper. Academy of Health, 811 N. 100 West 33-10, Blanding, UT 84511 (435) 678-7853. 1998. $10.

THEIR STORIES OF LONG AGO
Belle Deacon; A bilingual collection of traditional Athabascan tales from Alaska. Illus. Alaskan Native Language Center, $10.

THEMES IN SOUTHWEST PREHISTORY
George J. Gumerman, Editor
Illus. 350 pp. Paper. School of American Research Press, 1994. $24.95.

A THEOLOGY OF IN-BETWEEN: THE VALUE OF SYNCRETIC PROCESS
Carl F. Starkloff; 178 pp. Paper. Marquette University Press, 2002. $20.

THEORETICAL PERSPECTIVES ON AMERICAN INDIAN EDUCATION: TAKING A NEW LOOK AT ACADEMIC SUCCESS & THE ACHIEVEMENT GAP
Terry Huffman; Monograph. 278 pp. AltaMira Press, 2010. $72; eBook, $54.99

THEORETICAL PERSPECTIVES ON NATIVE AMERICAN LANGUAGES
Donna Gerdts & Karin Michelson, Editors
Illus. 290 pp. State University of New York Press, 1989. $24.50; paper, $12.95.

THEORIIZING NATIVE STUDIES
Audra Simpson; Andrea Smith, Editor; contributors
Essays. Illus. 352 pp. Duke University Press, 2014. $99.95; paper, $27.95.

THERAPEUTIC NATIONS: HEALING IN THE AGE OF INDIGENOUS HUMAN RIGHTS
Dian Million; 240 pp. Illus. Paper. University of Arizona Preee, 2010. $26.95.

*THERE STILL ARE BUFFALO
Ann Nolan Clark; Willard Beatty, Editor; illus. by Steve Tongier
Grades 1-6. Illus. 50 pp. Paper. Amazon.com, 1992. $8.95.

THESE ARE THE PEOPLE: THOUGHTS IN POETRY & PROSE
William N. Fenton; Illus. 90 pp. Paper. Ah-tee-noh-eh Press, 1991. $9.

*THESE WERE THE SIOUX
Marie Sandoz; The philosophy & practical wisdom of the Sioux Indians, including their beliefs & customs. Reprint of 1961 ed. Grades 6-12. Illus. 118 pp. Paper. University of Nebraska Press, 1985. $11.95.

THESE WERE THE UTES: THEIR LIFESTYLE, WARS & LEGENDS
Madoline Cloward Dixon; A collection of historical & biographical tales of the Ute Indians of central Utah. Illus. 184 pp. Published by Press Publishing Limited, 1983. Available from Amazon.com, $9.95.

THEY CALL ME AGNES: A CROW NARRATIVE BASED ON THE LIFE OF AGNES YELLOWTAIL DEERNOSE
Fred W. Voget; Illus. Maps. 256 pp. Paper. University of Oklahoma Press, 1993. $19.95.

THEY CALLED IT PRAIRIE LIGHT: THE STORY OF CHILOCCO INDIAN SCHOOL
K. Tsianina Lomawaima
Illus. Maps. 215 pp. Paper. University of Nebraska Press, 1995. $14.95.

THEY CALLED ME SWEETGRASS
Bernice Q. Estes; Reprint. Illus. 80 pp. Paper. Amazon.com, 1994. $9.95.

THEY DIED WITH CUSTER: SOLDIER'S BONES FROM THE BATTLE OF LITTLE BIGHORN Douglas D. Scott, P. Willey & Melissa A. Conner
Illus. Map. University of Oklahoma Press, 1998. $29.95.

THEY HAVE NO RIGHTS
Walter Ehlich; 266 pp. Paper. Jefferson National, 1979. $7.95.

THEY KNOW WHO THEY ARE: ELDERS OF THE CHICKASAW NATION
Mike Larsen & Martha Larsen; Illus. 144 pp. The Chickasaw Press. Distribted by the University of Oklahoma Press, 2008. $29.95.

THEY LED A NATION
Virginia Driving Hawk Sneve; N. Jane Hunt, Editor; A pictorial and biographical documentation of 20 historic Sioux leaders. llus. 46 pp. Paper. Amazon.com, 1975. $5.95.

"THEY MADE US MANY PROMISES" THE AMERICAN INDIAN EXPERIENCE SINCE 1524 Philip Weeks; 2nd Ed. Illus. 300 pp. Paper. Amazon.com, 2002. $21.95.

THEY SANG FOR HORSES: THE IMPACT OF THE HORSE ON NAVAJO & APACHE FOLKLORE LaVerne Harrell Clark; illus. by Ted DFeGrazier; The weaving of the horse into existent mythology of the Navajo and Apache tribes. Reprint of 1966 ed. Illus. 225 pp. Paper. University Press of Colorado, 2001. $26.95.

THEY SAY THE WIND IS RED: THE ALABAMA CHOCTAW LOST IN THEIR OWN LAND Jacqueline Anderson Matte & Vine Deloria, Jr.
The past and present of a Southeastern Indian Tribe. Contains a how-to section on researching Indian genealogy. Illus. 256 pp. Paper. Amazon.com, 2002. $19.95.

"THEY TREATED US JUST LIKE INDIANS": THE WORLDS OF BENNETT CO., SD
Paula L. Wagoner; The story of Bennett County, divided by residents into three groups - "whites," "fullbloods," and "Mixedbloods." Illus. Maps. 156 pp. University of Nebraska Press, 2002. $12.50; paper, $9.97.

THEY WALKED BEFORE: THE INDIANS OF WASHINGTON STATE
Cecilia Carpenter; Illus. Revised edition. 75 pp. Paper. Tahoma Publications, 1989. $10.

THE THINKING INDIAN: NATIVE AMERICAN WRITERS, 1850S-1920S
Bernd C. Peyer; 384 pp. Paper. Peter Lang Publishing, 2007. $88.95.

THINKING IN INDIAN: A JOHN MOHAWK READER
Jose Barreiro, Editor; Essays by an elder of the Seneca Nation and deeply rooted Iroquois traditionalist. 290 pp. Paper. Fulcrum Publisher, 2010.

THE THIRD ARROW: A STORY OF MOSHULATUBBEE, CHOCTAW CHIEF
Maxine W. Barker; 166 pp. Paper. Amazon.com, 1977. $18.

THE THIRD SPACE OF SOVEREIGNTY: THE POSTCOLONIAL POLITICS OF U.S.-INDIGENOUS RELATIONS
Kevin Bruyneel; Struggle between indigenous resistance & American colonialism. 1 photo. 320 pp. University of Minnesota Press, 2007. $67.50; apper, $24.50.

THIRTEEN DAYS OF TERROR: THE RUFUS BUCK GANG IN INDIAN TERRITORY
Glenn Shirley; Illus. 109 pp. Western Publications, 1996. $22.95.

THIRTEEN MOONS ON TURTLE'S BACK
Joseph Bruchac & Jonathan London; illus. by Thomas Locker
Retelling of Native American legends. Storytelling poems. Illus. 30 pp. Amazon.com & Philomel Press, 1992. $14.95.

THE THIRTEEN ORIGINAL CLAN MOTHERS: YOUR SACRED PATH TO DISCOVERING THE GIFTS, TALENTS & ABILITIES OF THE FEMININE THROUGH THE ANCIENT TEACHINGS OF THE SISTERHOOD
Jamie Sams; Reprint. Illus. 336 pp. Paper. Amazon.com, 1994. $19.

*THIRTY INDIAN LEGENDS OF CANADA
Margaret Bemister; Grades 3-7. Illus. 158 pp. Paper. Publishers Group, 1991. $9.95.

THIS DAY IN NORTH AMERICAN INDIAN HISTORY: EVENTS IN THE HISTORY OF NORTH AMERICA'S NATIVE PEOPLES
Philip Konstantin; Illus. 480 pp. Amazon.com, 2002. $35.

THIS FOOL HISTORY, AN ORAL HISTORY OF DAKOTA TERRITORY
Sylvia G. Wheeler; A play representing the meeting of Indian and white cultures in Dakota Territory. Dakota Press, 1991. $19.95.

THIS IS NOT A PEACE PIPE: TOWARDS A CRITICAL INDIGENOUS PHILLOSOPHY Dale Turner; 200 pp. U. of Toronto Press, 2006. $62; paper, $29.95.

THIS IS OUR LAND
Val J. McClellan
2 Vols. Vol. 1, 902 pp. 1977. Vol. 2, 927 pp. 1979. Illus. Amazon.com, $99.57.

THIS IS WHAT THEY SAY: STORIES
Francois Mandeville; tr. by Ron Scollon; Traditional life & thought in the northern Athapaskan world. Illus. Paper. 288 pp. University of Washington Press, 2009. $25.

*THIS LAND IS MY LAND
George Littlechild
Grades 1-6. Story by a Canadian Plains Cree. Illus. Amazon.com, $15.95.

THIS LAND WAS THEIRS: A STUDY OF NATIVE AMERICANS
Wendell H. Oswalt; 9th edition. Illus. 576 pp. Paper. Oxford U. Press, 2008. $99.95.

THIS PATH WE TRAVEL: CELEBRATIONS OF CONTEMPORARY NATIVE AMERICAN CREATIVITY National Museum of the American Indian, Smithsonian Institution
Combining photography with collected observations, this book documents a group of Native American artists examining the relationships between native and contemporary and traditional and innovative artistic endeavors. Illus. 126 pp. NMAI Press & Fulcrum Publishing, 1994. $24.95; paper, $18.95.

COQUELLE THOMPSON, ATHABASKAN WITNESS: A CULTURAL BIOGRAPHY
Lionel Youst, William R. Seaburg; Illus. 320 pp. U. of Oklahoma Press, 2003. $34.95.

THE THOMPSON LANGUAGE
Laurence C. Thompson & M. Terry Thompson; 253 pp. Amazon.com, 1992. $20.

THOMPSON RIVER SALISH DICTIONARY
Laurence C. Thompson & M. Tewrry Thompson; 1,410 pp. U. of Montana, 1996. $45.

THOREAU & THE AMERICAN INDIANS
Robert F. Sayre; Amazon.com, 1977. $29.50; paper, $13.50.

THOREAU'S INDIAN OF THE MIND
Elizabeth I. Hanson; 148 pp. Edwin Mellen Press, 1992. $69.95.

*JIM THORPE: WORLD'S GREATEST ATHLETE
Grades 4 and up. Illus. 130 pp. Childrens Press, $13.95.

THOSE TREMENDOUS MOUNTAINS: THE STORY OF THE LEWIS & CLARK EXPEDITION David Hawke; Illus. 290 pp. Paper. W.W. Norton & Co., 1985. $7.70.

THOSE WHO CAME BEFORE: SOUTHWESTERN ARCHAEOLOGY IN THE NATIONAL PARK SYSTEM Robert & Florence Lister
Prehistoric cultures of the American Southwest as preserved and interpreted by the NPS in over 37 sites. Photos. 232 pp. Paper. Amazon.com, $16.95.

THOSE WHO REMAIN: PHOTOGRAPHER'S MEMOIR OF SOUTH CAROLINA INDIANS Gene J. Crediford
Illus. 248 pp. University of Alabama Press, 2009. $51.75; paper, $28.95. E-Book, $23.16.

A THOUSAND YEARS OF AMERICAN INDIAN STORYTELLING
Rupert Costo & Jeanette Henry Costo
Collection of Native American tales. Amazon.com & Alibris.com, $12.

THREE CENTURIES OF WOODLANDS INDIAN ART
J.C.H. King & Christian F. Feest, Editors
152 color Illus. 208 pp. Paper. University of Nebraska Press, 2007. $19.95.

THREE FIRES UNITY: THE ANISHNAABEG OF THE LAKE HURON BORDERLANDS
Phil Bellfy; Comprehensive cross-border history of the Anishnaabeg over 400 years in the Lake Huron area. Illus. Maps. Tables. 256 pp. University of Nebraska Press, 2011. $35.

THREE INDIAN CAMPAIGNS
Wesley Merritt; Reprint. 24 pp. Paper. Shorey's Bookstore, $10.

THREE NATIVE AMERICAN LEARNING STORIES: WHO SPEAKS FOR WOLF, WINTER WHITE & SUMMER GOLD, & MANY CIRCLES
Paula Underwood; Jeanne Slobod, Ed.; Illus. 160 pp. Amazon.com, 2002.

THREE PICTOGRAPHIC AUTOBIOGRAPHIES OF SITTING BULL
M.W. Stirling; Illus. 57 pp. Paper. Lakota Books, 1995. $21.95.

THREE PLAYS: THE INDOLENT BOYS, CHILDREN OF THE SUN, & THE MOON IN TWO WINDOWS N. Scott Momaday; Interweaving oral & literary traditions. Illus. 224 pp. University of Oklahoma Press, 2007. $24.95.

THREE STRANDS IN THE BRAND: A GUIDE FOR ENABLERS OF LEARNING
Paula Underwood; Illus. 78 pp. Paper. Amazon.com, $12.

THREE YEARS AMONG THE COMANCHES: THE NARRATIVE OF NELSON LEE, THE TEXAS RANGER Nelson Lee; Reprint edition. Illus. 190 pp. Paper. Amazon.com, $10.95.

THREE YEARS ON THE PLAINS: OBSERVATIONS OF INDIANS, 1867-1870
Edmund B. Tuttle
Illus. Maps. 216 pp. Paper. University of Oklahoma Press, 2003. $29.95; paper, $19.95.

A THRILLING NARRATIVE OF INDIAN CAPTIVITY: DISPATCHES FROM THE DAKOTA WAR Mary Butler Renville; edited by Carrie Reber Zeman, et al
Illus. Maps. 408 pp. University of Nebraska Press, 2012. $60.

THROUGH DAKOTA EYES: NARRATIVE ACCOUNTS OF THE MINNESOTA INDIAN WAR OF 1862
Gary Anderson; Alan Woolworth, Editor; Illus. Photos. Maps. 316 pp. Minnesota Historical Society Press, 1988. $24.95; paper, $11.95.

THROUGH THE EYE OF THE DEER: AN ANTHOLOGY OF NATIVE AMERICAN WOMEN WRITERS Edited by Carolyn Dunn and Carol Comfort; Amazon.com, 2003.

THROUGH THE EYE OF THE FEATHER: NATIVE AMERICAN VISIONS
Gail Tuchman; The symbolism of the feather in prose and photographs. Photos. 95 pp. Paper. Written Heritage, $19.95.

THROUGH INDIAN EYES: THE NATIVE EXPERIENCE IN BOOKS FOR CHILDREN
Beverly Slapin & Doris Seale, Editors; Articles, stories, poetry, and reviews of books dealing with Native Americans. Bibliography. 246 pp. Paper. Oyate, 1991. $24.95. Also available from Amazon.com.

THROUGH INDIAN EYES: OUR NATIONS PAST AS EXPERIENCED BY NATIVE AMERICANS Reader's Digest Eds; Illus. 400 pp. Reader's Digest Association, 1996. $40.

THROUGH INDIAN SIGN LANGUAGE: THE FORT SILL LEDGERS OF HGH LENOX SCOTT & ISEEO, 1889-1897 William C. Meadows, Editor
Illus. Maps. 520 pp. University of Oklahoma Press, 2015. $55.

THROUGH AN INDIAN'S LOOKING-GLASS: A CULTURAL BIOGRAPHY OF WILLIAM APESS, PEQUOT Drew Lopenzina
Illus. 310 pp. University of Massachusetts Press, 2017. $90; paper, $29.95

THROUGH NAVAJO EYES: AN EXPLORATION IN FILM COMMUNICATION & ANTHROPOLOGY Sol Worth and John Adair
Illus. 320 pp. Paper. University of New Mexico Press, 1996. $14.95.

THROUGH THE NORTHERN LOOKING GLASS: BREAST CANCER STORIES OF NORTHERN NATIVE WOMEN Lorelai Anne Lambert Colomeda
Illus. 200 pp. Paper. Amazon.com, 1996. $17.95.

THROWING FIRE AT THE SUN, WATER AT THE MOON
Anita Endrezze; 205 pp. University of Arizona Press, 2000. $32; paper, $17.95.

THE THUNDER BEFORE THE STORM: THE AUTOBIOGRAPHY OF CLYDE BELLECOURT Clyde Bellecourt; as told to Jon Lurie
Minnesota Historical Society Press, $27.95; eBook, $9.99.

THUNDER & HERDS: ROCK ART OF THE HIGH PLAINS
Lawrence L. Loendorf
Clues to interpret rock art. 240 pp. University of Arizona Press, 2008. $65; paper, $29.95.

THUNDER IN THE MOUNTAINS: THE STORY OF THE NEZ PERCE WAR
Ronald K. Fisher; Merle Wells, Ed.; Illus. 345 pp. Paper. Alpha Omega, 1992. $12.95.

THUNDER IN MY SOUL: A MOHAWK WOMAN SPEAKS
Patricia Monture-Angus; 275 pp. Paper. Eiron, 1995. $19.95.

THUNDER OVER THE OCHOO, 4 Vols.
Andrew Gale Ontko; The Shoshoni Indian history in 5 vols: Vol. I - The Gathering Storm, 436 pp. Covers hundreds of years from pre-Columbian times to the collapse of the world fur trade in 1840, Vol. I meets the Shoshoni Indians before arrival of the Europeans; Vol. II - Covers the 20 year period between 1840 & 1860; Vol. III - Covers between 1860 and 1869; Vol. IV - Covers the 45 year interval between 1867 & 1912; Vol. V - And the Juniper Trees Bore Fruit, 392 pp. Illus. 5 Vols. 2,000+ pp. @400 pp. ea. Paper. Amazon.com, 2008. $19.95 each.

THUNDER RIDES A BLACK HORSE: MESCALERO APACHES & THE MYTHIC PRESENT Claire F. Farrer; A 4-day, 4-night Mescalero Apache girls' puberty ceremonial. 124 pp. Waveland Press, 1996. $15.95.

*THUNDER WATERS: EXPERIENCES OF GROWING UP IN DIFFERENT INDIAN TRIBES Frances Snow, et al; Grades 3-8. Council for Indian Education, 1975. $7.95; paper, $1.95.

THUNDER'S GRACE: WALKING THE ROAD OF VISIONS WITH MY LAKOTA GRANDMOTHER Mary Elizabeth Thunder
Illus. 288 pp. Paper. Station Hill Press, 1999. $16.95.

THUNDERS SPEAK: BIOGRAPHIES OF NINE SPECIAL ORIGINAL PEOPLE
James P. Dowd; Illus. 178 pp. Paper. Amazon.com, 1999. $20.50.

TIES THAT BIND: THE STORY OF AN AFRO-CHEROKEE FAMILY IN SLAVERY & FREEDOM
Tiya Miles; Illus. Maps. 329 pp. University of California Press, 2005. $45; paper, $23.95.

THE TIGUAS: PUEBLO INDIANS OF TEXAS
Bill Wright; Illus. Photos. Biblio. 179 pp. Texas Western Press, 1993. $40.

TILLAMOOK INDIANS OF THE OREGON COAST
John Sauter and Bruce Johnson; Illus. Binford-Metropolitan, 1974. $9.95; paper, $6.95.

TILLER'S GUIDE TO INDIAN COUNTRY: ECONOMIC PROFILES OF AMERICAN INDIAN RESERVATIONS
Veronica Tiller, Editor; Summarizes the history, language, culture, natural resource base, industries, enterprises, etc. for more than 560 reservations in 33 states including Alaska. 3rd revied edition. Illus. Maps. 1,120 pp. Bow Arrow Publishing, 2012. Tiller Research, Inc. Distributed by University of New Mexico Press, $325. Also available as a CD-ROM, $199.

TIME AMONG THE NAVAJO: TRADITIONAL LIFEWAYS ON THE RESERVATION
Kathy Hooker
Illus. 100 pp. Paper. Museum of New Mexico Press, 1991. $24.95.

A TIME BEFORE DECEPTION: TRUTH IN COMMUNICATION, CULTURE, AND ETHICS
Thomas W. Cooper; Describes the practices of tribal culture worldwide and examines the communication ethic of the Dine (Navajo) of northern Arizona and the Shuswap people of British Columbia. Illus. 224 pp. Amazon.com, 1995. $24.95.

TIME BEFORE HISTORY: THE ARCHAEOLOGY OF NORTH CAROLINA
H. Trawick Ward & R.P. Stephen Davis, Jr.
Illus. Maps. 368 pp. Paper. University of North Carolina Press, 1999. $24.95.

A TIME BEFORE NEW HAMPSHIRE: THE STORY OF A LAND & NATIVE PEOPLES
Michael J. Caduto; Illus. 284 pp. Paper. University of New Hampshire Press, 2003. Distributed by the University Press of New England. $22.95.

A TIME OF LITTLE CHOICE: A DISINTEGRATION OF TRIBAL CULTURE IN THE SAN FRANCISCO BAY AREA, 1769-1810
Randall Milliken; Describes the Native American nations that lived in the Bay Area and their reaction to the Spanish influence. Reprint. Illus. Paper. Malki-Ballena Press, $24.95.

A TIME OF VISIONS: INTERVIEWS WITH NATIVE AMERICAN ARTISTS
Table of Contents: Rick Bartow, Sara Bates, Patricia Deadman, Joe Feddersen, Anita Fields, Harry Fonseca, Bob Haozous, Melanie Printup Hope, Bobby Martin, Gerald McMaster, George Morrison, Shelley Niro, Joanna Osburn-Bigfeather, Diego Romero, Mateo Romero, Bently Spang, Ernie Whiteman, Richard Ray Whitman, Alfred Young Man. Available on the web site: www.britesites.com/native_artist_interviews

TIME: SPACE & TRANSITION IN ANASAZI PREHISTORY
Michael S. Berry. 112 pp. University of Utah Press, 1982. $20.

TIME'S FLOTSAM: OVERSEAS COLLECTIONS OF CALIFORNIA
Thomas Blackburn & Travis Hudson
Illus. 226 pp. Santa Barbara Museum of Natural History, 1990. $34.95.

TIMELESS TEXTILES: TRADITIONAL PUEBLO ARTS 1840-1940
Tyrone D. Campbell. Illus. Paper. Museum of New Mexico Press, 2002. $14.95.

TIMELESS WISDOM OF THE NATIVE AMERICANS
Steve Eddy. Illus. 96 pp. Paper. Amazon.com, 2000. $11.95.

*A TIMELINE HISTORY OF THE TRAIL OF TEARS
Alison Behnke; Grades 5-8. Lerner Publications, 2016. $22.99; paper, $9.99.

TIMELINES OF NATIVE AMERICAN HISTORY
Susan Hazen-Hammond
From 1492-1990s. Illus. Maps. 352 pp. Paper. Amazon.com, 1997. $16.

TIMUCUA INDIAN MOUNDS OF NORTHEAST FLORIDA: AN ILLUSTRATED ENCYCLOPEDIA Donald D. Spencer. Illus. 140 pp. Camelot Publishing, 2003. $24.95.

THE TIMUCUAN CHIEFDOMS OF SPANISH FLORIDA
John E. Worth. 2 Vols. Vol. I: Assimilation. 288 pp. Vol. II: Resistance & Destruction. 336 pp. University Press of Florida, 1998. $49.95 each.

TIPAI ETHNOGRAPHIC NOTES
William D. Hohenthal, Jr.; Information on the Tipai/Diegueno communities of northern Baja California during the late 1940s.Illus. 378 pp. Malki-Ballena Press, 2001. $27.50.

TIPI: HERITAGE OF THE GREAT PLAINS
Nancy B. Rosoff & Susan Kennedy Zeller
Reveals the history & significance of its architectural form from the 1830s to the present. Illus. Map. 256 pp. University of Washington Press, 2011. $60.

TIPI LIVING: A SIMPLE LIVING BOOK
Patrick Whitefield. Illus. 48 pp. Paper. Chelsea Green Publishing, 2001. $7.95.

THE TIPI: TRADITIONAL NATIVE AMERICAN SHELTER
Adolf Hungrywolf; Photos & historical texts presents an overall view of tipi life. Illus. Photos. 224 pp. Paper. Book Publishing Co., $17.95.

TIPIS & YURTS: AUTHENTIC DESIGNS FOR CIRCULAR SHELTERS
Blue Evening Star Staff; Leslie Dierks, Ed.. Illus. 128 pp. Amazon.com, 1995. $24.95.

TIYOSPAYE: THE NATURE OF THE LAKOTA BAND
William K. Powers, Ed.; Illus. 50 pp. Paper. Lakota Books, $21.95.

*TJATJAKIYMATCHAN (COYOTE)
Alex O. Ramirez; A legend from Carmel Valley. Illus. 12 pp. Paper. Oyate, 1995. $6.

TLAPACOYA POTTERY IN THE MUSEUM COLLECTION
Muriel Weaver
Illus. 48 pp. Paper. National Museum of the American Indian, 1967. $3.50.

*THE TLINGIT
Grades K-4. Illus. 48 pp. Childrens Press, $11.45.

TLINGIT, THE ALASKA INDIAN: THEIR ART, CULTURE & LEGEND
Dan & Nan Kaiper
Reprint. Illus. 96 pp. Paper. Hancock House Publishers, 1997. $9.95.

TLINGIT ART & CULTURE
Don Kaiper; Illus. 95 pp. Hancock House, 1990. $4.95.

THE TLINGIT: AN INTRODUCTION TO THEIR CULTURE & HISTORY
Wallace M. Olson; 3rd Ed. Illus. 111 pp. Paper. Amazon.com, 1997. $12.50.

TLINGIT INDIANS OF ALASKA
Anatoli Kamenski; translated by Sergei Kan; Marvin Falk, Editor
Illus. Biblio. 166 pp. Paper. University of Alaska Press, 1985. $15.

THE TLINGIT INDIANS
George Thornton Emmons; Frederica de Laguna, Editor
Illus. 65 drawings, 127 photos. 530 pp. University of Washington Press, $80.

THE TLINGIT INDIANS IN RUSSIAN AMERICA, 1741-1867
Andrei Val'terovich Grinev; Outlines a picture of traditional Tlingit society before contact with Europeans and then analyzes interaction between them. 388 pp. Paper. University of Nebraska Press, 2008. $24.95.

THE TLINGIT INDIANS: OBSERVATIONS OF AN INDIIGENOUS PEOPLE OF SOUTHEAST ALASKA, 1881-1882
Aurel Krause; Erna Gunther tr.
306 pp. Paper. Amazon.com & Epicenter Press, 2013. $24.95.

TLINGIT MYTHS & TEXTS
John R. Swanton; Reprint. 451 pp. Amazon.com, $69; paper, $49.

TLINGIT TALES: POTLATCH & TOTEM POLES
Lorle K. Harris; told by Robert Zuboff; Illus. 48 pp. Paper. Naturegraph, $6.95.

TO THE AMERICAN INDIAN: REMINISCENCES OF A YUROK WOMAN
Lucy Thompson; Photos. Revised edition. 325 pp. Paper. Heyday Books, $14.95.

TO BE INDIAN: THE LIFE OF IROQUOIS-SENECA ARTHUR CASWELL PARKER
Joy Porter; Illus. 320 pp. University of Oklahoma Press, 2003. $19.95.

TO BE AN INDIAN: AN ORAL HISTORY
Joseph Cash & Herbert Hoover, Eds.; Collection of personal accounts presents the contemporary Northern Plains Native Americans' view of themselves, their history, and their world. 1971 reissue. Photos. 239 pp. Minnesota Historical Society Press, 1995. $11.95.

TO BECOME A HUMAN BEING: THE MESSAGE OF TADODAHO CHIEF LEON SHENANDOAH: AN INTERACTION BETWEEN A SEER & A SAGE
Steve Wall; 112 pp. Paper. Hampton Roads Publishing, 2001. $16.95.

TO THE ARCTIC BY CANOE
C. Stuart Houston; The journal & paintings of Robert Hood, midshipman with Sir John Franklin, Arctic explorer. Reveals the adverse effects on Native peoples & their environment of the coming of the Europeans. Illus. 280 pp. Paper. Amazon.com, 1994. $22.95.

TO BE INDIAN: THE LIFE OF IROQUOIS-SENECA ARTHUR CASWELL PARKER
Joy Porter; Illus. 310 pp. University of Oklahoma Press, 2001. $34.95.

TO BE THE MAIN LEADERS OF OUR PEOPLE: A HISTORY OF MINNESOTA OJIBWE POLITICS, 1825-1898
Rebecca Kugel; Illus. 230 pp. Paper. Michigan State University Press, 1998. $24.95.

TO BE A WARRIOR
Robert Barlow Fox
Navajo boy taught the old ways of his people. 128 pp. Paper. Sunstone Press, $12.95.

TO CHANGE THEM FOREVER: INDIAN EDUCATION AT THE RAINY MOUNTAIN BOARDING SCHOOL, 1893-1920
Clyde Ellis; Kiowa reservation boarding school. Maps. Biblio. 288 pp. Paper. University of Oklahoma Press, 2008. $21.95.

TO THE CHUKCHI PENINSULA & TO THE TLINGIT INDIANS 1881/1882: JOURNALS & LETTERS BY AUREL & ARTHUR KRAUSE
translated by Margot Krause McCaffrey; Studies & observations of the region's natural history, art and ethnography. Illus. Maps. 230 pp. Paper. U. of Alaska Press, 1993. $17.50.

TO DIE GAME: THE STORY OF THE LOWRY BAND, INDIAN GUERILLAS OF RECONSTRUCTION
William McKee Evans; Indian guerilla warfare against the Confederates and Klu Klux Klan during the Civil War. 310 pp. Paper. Syracuse University Press, $15.95.

TO DIE IN DINETAH: THE DARK LEGACY OF KIT CARSON
John A. Truett; Kit Carson's involvement with the relocation of the Navajo and the "Long Walk." 256 pp. Paper. Sunstone Press, $14.95.

TO DO GOOD TO MY INDIAN BRETHREN: THE WRITINGS OF JOSEPH JOHNSON
Laura J. Murray, Editor
344 pp. University of Massachusetts Press, 1998. $60; paper, $24.95.

TO FISH IN COMMON: THE ETHNOHISTORY OF LUMMI INDIAN SALMON FISHING
Daniel L. Boxberger; Illus. 237 pp. Paper. University of Washington Press, 1989. $19.95.

TO HARVEST, TO HUNT: STORIES OF RESOURCE USE IN THE AMERICAN WEST
Judith L. Li; Weaves a tapestry of cultures and voices - from Pueblo tribes in the Southwest to Native Alaskans and Mexican, European, and Asian immigrants. Photos. Paper. Oregon State University Press, 2007. $18.95.

TO HAVE THIS LAND: THE NATURE OF INDIAN/WHITE RELATIONS, SOUTH DAKOTA, 1888-1891 Philip S. Hall; Illus. Paper. Dakota Press, 1991. $10.95.

TO HONOR & COMFORT: NATIVE QUILTING TRADITIONS
Edited by Marsha L. MacDowell & C. Kurt Dewhurst; Native quilters in North America & the Hawaiian Islands featuring more than 80 quilts, essays, photos & profiles of quilters. Illus. 240 pp. Museum of New Mexico Press, 2001. $50; paper, $35.

TO IMAGE & TO SEE: CROW INDIAN PHOTOGRAPHS BY EDWARD S. CURTIS & RICHARD THROSSEL, 1905-1910 Tamara Northern & Wendi-Starr Brown
Illus. Hood Museum of Art & Amazon.com, 1993. $6.

TO INTERMIX WITH OUR WHITE BROTHERS: INDIAN MIXED BLOODS IN THE U.S. FROM EARLIEST TIMES TO THE INDIAN REMOVALS
Thomas N. Ingersoll; Examines the origins and early history of mixed bloods in North America. Illus. 472 pp. University of New Mexico Press, $45.

TO LIVE & DIE IN THE WEST: THE AMERICAN INDIAN WARS, 1860-1890
Jason Hook & Martin Pegler; Illus. 164 pp. Amazon.com, 2002. $45.

TO LIVE IN TWO WORLDS: AMERICAN INDIAN YOUTH TODAY
Brent Ashabranner; Grades 7-11. Illus. Amazon.com, $13.95.

TO LIVE HEROICALLY: INSTITUTIONAL RACISM & AMERICAN INDIAN EDUCATION
Delores J. Huff; 211 pp. State University of New York Press, 1997. $54.50; paper, $17.95.

TO LIVE ON THIS EARTH: AMERICAN INDIAN EDUCATION
Estelle Fuchs and Robert Havighurst
Revised 1983 edition. 408 pp. Paper. University of New Mexico Press, $11.95.

TO LIVE TO SEE THE GREAT DAY THAT DAWNS: PREVENTING SUICIDE BY AMERICAN INDIANS & ALASKA NATIVE YOUTH & YOUNG ADULTS
U.S. Dept. of Health & Human Services, Substance Abuse & Mental Health Services Administration, Center for Mental Health Services. Website: www.samhsa.gov

TO PLEASE THE CARIBOU: PAINTED CARIBOU-SKIN COATS WORN BY THE NASPAKI, MONTAGNAIS, & CREE HUNTERS OF THE QUEBEC-LABRADOR PENINSULA Dorothy K. Burnham; Description and illustrations of 60 painted caribou-skin coats. Illus. 763 drawings, photos. 328 pp. U. of Washington Press, $60; paper, $35.

TO PRESERVE A CULTURE: THE TWENTIETH-CENTURY TO RUN AFTER THEM: CULTURAL & SOCIAL BASES OF COOPERATION IN A NAVAJO COMMUNITY
Louise Lamphere; Reprint of 1977 edition. 246 pp. University of Arizona Press, $22.50.

TO REMAIN AN INDIAN: LESSONS IN DEMOCRACY FROM A CENTURY OF NATIVE AMERICAN EDUCATION K. Tsianina Lomawaima & T. McCarty, Editors
240 pp. Amazon.com, 2006. $70; paper, $30.95.

TO SHOW HEART: NATIVE AMERICAN SELF-DETERMINATION & FEDERAL INDIAN POLICY, 1960-1975
George P. Castile; 227 pp. Paper. University of Arizona Press, 1998. $18.95.

TO SHOW WHAT AN INDIAN CAN DO: SPORTS AT NATIVE AMERICAN BOARDING SCHOOLS
John Bloom; Illus. 176 pp. University of Minnesota Press, 2005. $54; paper, $17.95.

TO SING OUR OWN SONGS: COGNITION & CULTURE IN INDIAN EDUCATION
Paper. Amazon.com, 1985. $2.50.

TO TOUCH THE PAST: THE PAINTED POTTERY OF THE MIMBRES PEOPLE
J.J. Brody & Rina Swentzel; Illus. 120 pp. Paper. Amazon.com, 1996. $29.95.

TO TOUCH THE WIND: AN INTRODUCTION TO NATIVE AMERICAN PHILOSOPHY & BELIEFS
Edward Morton; 128 pp. Paper. Kendall-Hunt, 1988. $13.95.

TO AN UNKNOWN GOD: RELIGIOUS FREEDOM ON TRIAL
Garrett Epps; Illus. 290 pp. St. Martin's Press, 2001. $24.95.

TO WALK IN BEAUTY: A NAVAJO FAMILY'S JOURNEY HOME
Stacia Spragg-Braude, photos & text; Portrait of the Begay family of Jeddito Wash, Arizona, on the Navajo Reservation. Illus. 200 pp. Museum of New Mexico Press, 2010. $45.

TO YOU WE SHALL RETURN: LESSONS ABOUT OUR PLANET FROM THE LAKOTA
Joseph M. Marshall III; 192 pp. Sterling Publishing, 2010.

TOBA TUCKER: A SHINNECOCK PORTRAIT
John Strong & Madeleine Burnside; Illus. 25 pp. Paper. Guild Hall, 1987. $7.

TOBACCO AMONG THE KARUK INDIANS OF CALIFORNIA
John P. Harrington; Reprint of 1932 edition. Illus. 357 pp. Coyote Press, $37.50.

TOBACCO, PEACE PIPES & INDIANS
Louis Seig; History of the ceremonial use of tobacco. Illus. Maps. 51 pp. Paper. Amazon.com & Alibris.com, 1971. $4.

TOBACCO, PIPES & SMOKING CUSTOMS OF THE AMERICAN INDIANS
G.A. West; Reprint of 1934 edition. Greenwood Press, $57.50.

TOBACCO USE BY NATIVE NORTH AMERICANS: SACRED SMOKE & SILENT KILLER
Joseph C. Winter; Illus. 512 pp. Univesity of Oklahoma Press, 2000. $65.

A TOHONO O'ODHAM GRAMMAR
Ofelia Zepeda; 190 pp. Paper. University of Arizona Press, 1983. $21.95

TOHONO O'ODHAM/PIMA TO ENGLISH, ENGLISH TO TOHONO O'ODHAM/PIMA DICTIONARY Dean & Lucille Saxton, Susie Enos; 2nd Edition. 5,000+ entries, plus appendixes on culture. 145 pp. Paper. University of Arizona Press, 1983. $20.95.

TOM-KAV: A LATE LUIS REY SITE IN NORTHERN SAN DIEGO CO., CALIF.
D.L. True, R. Pankey, C.N. Warren; Monograph describing the setting, features, and artifacts of late prehistoric settlements in the San Luis Rey River Basin of norhern San Diego Co. Illus. Paper. University of California Press, 1991. $45.

TOMAHAWK & CROSS: LUTHERAN MISSIONARIES AMONG NORTHERN PRAIRIE INDIANS, 1858-1866
Gerhard Schmutterer; Illus. 220 pp. Paper. Center for Western Studies, 1989. $12.95.

TOMAHAWKS ILLUSTRATED
Kuck; Illus. 112 pp. Paper. Hothem House, 1977. $11.

TOMAHAWKS - PIPE AXES - OF THE AMERICAN FRONTIER
Baldwin; Pipe axes' & tomahawks' origins and distributions. Illus. 128 pp. Hothem House & Written Heritage, 1995. $69.95.

TOMOCHICHI: INDIAN FRIEND OF THE GEORGIA COLONY
Helen Todd; Illus. 208 pp. Cherokee Publishing, 1977. $12.95.

TONKAWA, AN INDIAN LANGUAGE OF TEXAS
Harry Hoijer; Paper. J.J. Augustin, Inc., Publisher, $15.

THE TONKAWA PEOPLE: A TRIBAL HISTORY FROM EARLIEST TIMES TO 1893
Deborah Newlin; Gale Richardson, Editor; Illus. 120 pp. Paper. West Texas Museum, $5.

TONTO'S REVENGE: REFLECTIONS ON AMERICAN INDIAN CULTURE & POLICY
Rennard Strickland
Essays on Native American identity. 190 pp. Paper. University of New Mexico Press, $30.

TOP OF THE HILL
Morris Taylor
Tale that crosses generations and cultures. 64 pp. Paper. Naturegraph, $4.95.

*TOTEM POLE
Diane Hoyt-Goldsmith; The background of totem poles & the creation of one. Grades 4-6. Illus. 32 pp. Holiday House, $15.95; paper, $6.95.

TOTEM POLE CARVING: BRINGING A LOG TO LIFE
Vickie Jensen; Illus. 185 pp. Paper. University of Washington Press, 2004. $26.95.

A TOTEM POLE HISTORY: THE WORK OF LUMMI CARVER JOE HILLAIRE
Pauline Hillaire; Gregory Fields, Editor
Illus. Maps. 344 pp. University of Nebraska Press, 2013. $40.

*TOTEM POLE INDIANS OF THE NORTHWEST
Don E. Beyer; Grades 3 and up. Illus. 64 pp. Paper. Franklin Watts, 1991. $4.95.

THE TOTEM POLE: AN INTERCULTURAL HISTORY
Aldona Jonaitis & Aaron Glass; Essays illustrating the various relationships that people have with the totem pole. Illus., Maps. 360 pp. University of Washington Press, 2010. $50.

*TOTEM POLES
Put the parts together and you will have a pole from floor to ceiling. Grades 3-5. Paper. Bellerophon, $4.95.

TOTEM POLES: AN ILLUSTRATED GUIDE
Marjorie M. Halpin
Illus. 64 pp. Paper. UBC Press. Distributed by U. of Washington Press, 1981. $18.95.

TOTEM POLES OF THE NORTHWEST
D. Allen; Illus. 32 pp. Paper. Hancock House, $4.95.

TOTEM POLES OF THE PACIFIC NORTHWEST COAST
Edward Malin; photos by David Woodcock
Presents totem poles from the Tlingit settlements of Alaska to the Kwakiutl villages of Vancouver Island. 54 historic photos, and 14 color photos of contemporary poles; 199 line drawings. 195 pp. Paper. Amazon.com, $14.95.

TOTEM POLES & TEA
Hughina Harold; 220 pp. Paper. Midpoint Trade Books, 1996. $17.95.

*TOTEM POLES TO COLOR & CUT OUT, VOL. 2: TLINGIT; VOL. 3: KWAKIUTL
Grades 3-5. Paper. Bellerophon, $4.95 each.

TOTEMISM
C. Levi-Strauss; Paper. Amazon.com, 1963. $9.95.

TOTEMLAND: TOTEMIC SYMBOLISM OF THE NORTHWEST COAST INDIANS
Dorie A. Erickson; Illus. 16 pp. Spiral bound. Amazon.com, 1995. $4.95.

TOTKV MOCVSE · NEW FIRE: CREEK FOLKTALES
Earnest Gouge; edited & trans. by Jack B. Martin, Margaret McKane Mauldin & Juanita McGirt; foreword by Craig Womack
Illus. 160 pp. University of Oklahoma Press, 2004. $49.95; paper, $29.95; DVD, $29.95.

TOUCH THE EARTH: A SELF-PORTRAIT OF INDIAN EXISTENCE
T.C. McLuhan; Statements and writings by North American Indians. Reprint of 1971 edition. 185 pp. High-Lonesome Books, $12.

TOUCHING THE FIRE: BUFFALO DANCERS, THE SKY BUNDLE, & OTHER TALES
Roger L. Welsch; Illus. 272 pp. Paper. University of Nebraska Press, 1997. $12.

TOUCHWOOD: A COLLECTION OF OJIBWAY PROSE
Gerald Vizenor, Ed.; 2nd Ed. Illus. 188 pp. Paper. New River Press, 1993. $16.95.

TOURISM & GAMING ON AMERICAN INDIAN LANDS
Alan A. Lew & George A. Van Otten, Eds.
275 pp. Paper. Cognizant Communication Corp., 1998. $35.

TOVANGER (WORLD): A GABRIELINO WORD BOOK
Anne Galloway; 36 pp. Booklet. Paper. Malki-Ballena Press, 1978. $5.

TOWARD A NATIVE AMERICAN CRITICAL THEORY
Elvira Pulitano; 264 pp. University of Nebraska Press, 2003. $50.

TOWARDS ABORIGINAL SELF-GOVERNMENT: RELATIONS BETWEEN STATUS INDIAN PEOPLES & THE GOVERNMENT OF CANADA
Anne-Marie Mawhiney; 160 pp. Garland, 1993. $24.95.

TOWN CREEK INDIAN MOUND: A NATIVE AMERICAN LEGACY
Joffre Lanning Coe; An archaeologist's view of a temple mound and mortuary at Town Creek in Montgomery County, North Carolina. Illus. 338 pp. University of North Carolina Press, 1995. $45, cloth; $18.95, paper.

TOWN & TEMPLES ALONG THE MISSISSIPPI
David Dye & Cheryl Cox, Editors; Illus. 280 pp. Paper. U. of Alabama Press, 1990. $22.95.

TOWNSITE SETTLEMENT & DISPOSSESSION IN THE CHEROKEE NATION, 1866-1907 Brad A. Bays; Illus. 290 pp. Garland, 1998. $90.

TRACING ANCESTORS AMONG THE FIVE CIVILIZED TRIBES: SOUTHEASTERN INDIANS PRIOR TO REMOVAL
Guide book for genealogists, providing general information about how to research and locate material. Reprint. 156 pp. Genealogical Publishing Co., $2005. $24.95.

TRACK OF THE COYOTE
Todd Wilkinson; Illus. 144 pp. Paper. Creative Publishing International, 1995. $16.95.

TRACKING ANCIENT FOOTSTEPS: WILLIAM D. LIPE'S CONTRIBUTIONS TO SOUTHWESTERN PRHISTORY & PUBLIC ARCHAEOLOGY
R.G. Matson & Timothy A. Kohler, Editors
Illus. Photos. Maps. 200 pp. Paper. WSU Press, 2006. $22.95.

TRACKING PREHISTORIC MIGRATIONS: PUEBLO SETLERS AMONG THE TONTO BASIN HOHOKAM Jeffrey J. Clark; Evaluates Puebloan migration into the Tonto Basin of east-central Arizona during the early Classic period (A.D. 1200-1325). Illus. 124 pp. Paper. The University of Arizona Press, 1999. $16.95.

TRACKS THAT SPEAK: THE LEGACY OF NATIVE AMERICAN WORDS IN NORTH AMERICAN CULTURE Charles L. Cutler; Illus. 272 pp. Amazon.com & Alibris.com, 2002. Teacher's edition, $22; paper, $14.

THE TRADE GUN SKETCHBOOK
Full-size plans to build seven different Indian trade guns from the Revolution to the Indian Wars. Illus. 48 pp. Paper. Thr Fur Press, $2.

TRADE ORNAMENT USAGE AMONG THE NATIVE PEOPLES OF CANADA: A SOURCE BOOK Karlis Karlins; Illus. 244 pp. Paper. Amazon.com, 1992. $15.25.

TRADERS OF THE WESTERN MORNING: ABORIGINAL COMMERCE IN PRECOLUMBIAN NORTH AMERICA
John U. Terrell; Illus. Maps. 145 pp. Southwest Museum, 1967. $12.50.

TRADERS TALES: NARRATIVES OF CULTURAL ENCOUNTERS IN THE COLUMBIA PLATEAU, 1807-1846
Elizabeth Vibert; Illus. Maps. 366 pp. University of Oklahoma Press, 1997. $29.95.

TRADING BEYOND THE MOUNTAINS: THE BRITISH FUR TRADE ON THE PACIFIC, 1793-1843 Richard S. Mackie; Illus. Paper. UBC Press, 1997. $29.95.

TRADING GAZES: EURO-AMERICAN WOMEN PHOTOGRAPHER & NATIVE NORTH AMERICANS, 1880-1940
Susan Bernardin, et al; Illus. 240 pp. Amazon.com, 2003. $60.

TRADING IDENTITIES: THE SOUVENIR IN NATIVE NORTH AMERICAN ART FROM THE NORTHEAST, 1700-1900
Ruth B. Phillips; Illus. Map. 352 pp. Paper. University of Washington Press, $45.

TRADING POST GUIDEBOOK: WHERE TO FIND THE TRADING POSTS, GALLERIES, AUCTIONS, ARTISTS, & MUSEUMS OF THE FOUR CORNERS REGION
Patrick Eddington & Susan Makov; Illus. Biblio. 264 pp. Paper. Northland, $17.95.

TRADITION & CHANGE ON THE NORTHWEST COAST: THE MAKAH, NUU CHAH-NULTH, SOUTHERN KWAKIUTL & NUXALK Ruth Kirk
Illus. 200 photos. maps. 256 pp. Paper. University of Washington Press, 1988. $32.95.

TRADITION & INNOVATION: A BASKET HISTORY OF THE INDIANS OF THE YOSEMITE-MONO LAKE REGION Craig D. Bates & Martha J. Lee; Study of the history and basketry of the Miwok and Paiute people. Illus. 252 pp. Yosemite Assn, 1991. $49.95.

TRADITION & INNOVATION: THE POTTERY OF NEW MEXICO'S PUEBLOS
Linda B. Eaton; Illus. 34 pp. Paper. Amazon.com, 1993. $5.95.

TRADITIONAL CLOTHING OF THE NATIVE AMERICANS
Edward H. Gibby; Patterns & ideas for making authentic traditional clothing, modern buckskin clothing, and a section on tanning buckskin and furs. Illus. Paper. Smoke & Fire Co. & Written Heritage, $17.95.

*TRADITIONAL CRAFTS FROM NATIVE NORTH AMERICA
Florence Temko; Grades 2-5. Illus. Color photos. Lerner Publishing, 1996. $22.60.

TRADITIONAL DRESS: KNOWLEDGE & METHODS OF OLD-TIME CLOTHING
Adolph Hungry Wolf; 2nd revised edition. Illus. 130 pp. Paper. The Book Publishing Co. & Written Heritage, 2003. $9.95.

TRADITIONAL ECOLOGICAL KNOWLEDGE & NATURAL RESOURCE MANAGEMENT
Charles R. Menzies, Editor; Examines how traditional ecological knowledge is taught & practiced today among Native communities. Illus. 274 pp. University of Nebraska Press, 2006. $45; paper, $19.95.

TRADITIONAL INDIAN BEAD & LEATHER CRAFTS
Monte Smith & Michele Van Sickle; Illus. 100 pp. Paper. Eagle's View Publishing, Written Heritage & Smoke & Fire Co., 1987. $12.95.

TRADITIONAL INDIAN CRAFTS
Monte Smith; Illus. 96 pp. Paper. Eagle's View Publishing, 1987. $9.95.

TRADITIONAL LITERATURES OF AMERICAN INDIAN: TEXTS & INTERPRETATIONS
Karl Kroeber, Editor; 2nd ed. Illus. 161 pp. U. of Nebraska Press, 1997. $50; paper, $14.

TRADITIONAL NARRATIVES OF THE ARIKARA INDIANS, 4 Vols.
Douglas Parks; Vol. 1, Stories of Alfred Morsette, 684 pp; Vol. 2, Stories of Other Narrators, 660 pp. University of Nebraska Press, 1991. $125 per set. Audiocassette, $20. Vols. 3 & 4, Free Translations. Illus. Maps. 400 pp. & 320 pp. $75.

*TRADITIONAL NATIVE AMERICAN ARTS & ACTIVITIES
Arlette N. Braman; Grades 4 and up. Easy-to-follow projects, recipes, and games. Illus. 128 pp. Amazon.com, $12.95.

TRADITIONAL NATIVE AMERICAN HEALING & CHILD SEXUAL ABUSE
David W. Lloyd, Editor; 62 pp. Paper. Amazon.com, 1994. $30.

THE TRADITIONAL NORTHERN DANCER
C. Scott Evans
Features dancers at powwows. Color photos. Illus. 48 pp. Paper. Written Heritage, $11.95.

TRADITIONAL OJIBWA RELIGION & ITS HISTORICAL CHANGES
Christopher Vecsey; Amazon.com, 1983. $12.

TRADITIONAL PLANT FOODS OF CANADIAN INDIGENOUS PEOPLES: NUTRITION, BOTANY & USE Harriet V. Kuhnlein; 633 pp. Gordon & Breach, 1991. $118.

TRADITIONS: BEADWORK OF THE NATIVE AMERICAN
Lynn Harrison; 20 pp. Paper. Paper. Amazon.com, 1990. $9.95.

TRADITIONS IN TRANSITION: CONTEMPORARY BASKET WEAVING OF THE SOUTHWESTERN INDIANS
Barbara Maudlin; Illus. 64 pp. Paper. Museum of New Mexico Press, 1984. $8.95.

TRADITIONS OF THE ARAPAHO
George A. Dorsey & A.L. Kroeber
Reprint of 1903 edition. Illus. 488 pp. Paper. University of Nebraska Press, $22.

TRADITIONS OF THE CADDO
George A. Dorsey
Reprint of 1905 edition. Illus. 132 pp. Paper. University of Nebraska Press, 1997. $10.95.

TRADITIONS OF THE NORTH AMERICAN INDIANS
J.A. Jones; 168 pp. Paper. Amazon.com, $9.99.

TRADITIONS OF THE OSAGE: STORIES COLLECTED & TRANSLATED BY FRANCIS LA FLESCHE
Garrick Bailey; Illus. Map. 216 pp. University of New Mexico Press, $34.95.

THE TRANSFORMING IMAGE: PAINTED ARTS OF NORTHWEST COAST FIRST NATIONS
Bill McLennan & Karen Duffek; Illus. 304 pp. Paper. U. of Washington Press, 2000. $50.

THE TRAGEDY OF THE BLACKFOOT
W. McCluntock; Reprint of 1930 edition. Illus. 53 pp. Southwest Museum, $5.

*TRAGEDY OF TENAYA
Allan Shields
Grades 6-and up. 60 pp. Paper. Council for Indian Education, 1974. $9.95; paper, $3.95.

TRAGEDY OF THE WAHKSHUM: THE DEATH OF ANDREW J. BOLON...; ALSO, THE SUICIDE OF GENERAL GEORGE A. CUSTER AS TOLD BY OWL CHILD, EYEWITNESS Lucullus V. McWhorter; ed. by Donald Hines
Illus. Maps. 105 pp. Amazon.com. $10.95.

TRAGIC SAGA OF THE INDIANA INDIANS
Harold Allison; 350 pp. Amazon.com, 1987. $15.

THE TRAIL OF MANY SPIRITS: PAWS - HOOVES - MOCCASINS
Serle Chapman; Illus. 218 pp. Paper. Mountain Press, 1999. $24.95.

TRAIL OF TEARS
Julia Coates; Illus. 210 pp. Amazon.com, 2013. $58.

THE TRAIL OF TEARS
John Ehle; Portrays the Cherokee Nation filled with legend, lore and religion.
424 pp. Paper. VIP Publishing & Cherokee Publications, $14.95.

*THE TRAIL OF TEARS
Joseph Bruchac; Grades 4 and up. Illus. Random House, 1999. $11.99; paper, $3.99.

THE TRAIL OF TEARS
Gloria Jahoda; 224 pp. Random House, 1995. $9.99.

TRAIL OF TEARS ACROSS MISSOURI
Joan Gilbert; Illus. 136 pp. Paper. Amazon.com, 1995. $8.95.

TRAIL OF TEARS: AMERICAN INDIANS DRIVEN FROM THEIR LANDS
Jeanne Williams; Reprint. Illus. 192 pp. Hendrick-Long, $16.95.

TRAIL OF TEARS: NATIONAL HISTORIC TRAIL
Elliot West; Illus. 16 pp. Western National Parks Association, 1999. $3.95.

TRAIL OF TEARS: THE RISE & FALL OF THE CHEROKEE NATION
John Ehle; 430 pp. Doubleday, 1988. $19.95. Paper. Cherokee Publications, $10.95.

*THE TRAIL ON WHICH THEY WEPT: THE STORY OF A CHEROKEE GIRL
Dorothy and Thomas Hoobler; pictures by S.S. Burrus; The Trail of Tears through the eyes of a young Cherokee girl. Grades 3-5. Illus. 64 pp. Amazon.com, 1992. $7.95; paper, $3.95.

TRAIL TO WOUNDED KNEE: THE LAST STAND OF THE PLAINS INDIANS, 1860-1890
Herman Viola; Illus. 210 pp. Paper. Amazon.com & Alibris.com, 2004. $16.

TRAILHEAD OF THE AMERICAN INDIAN COURTING FLUTE
Jeff Ball & Bruce A. Whitten; Illus. 22 pp. Paper. Amazon.com, 1999. $11.

TRAILING GERONIMO
Anton Mazzanovich; 278 pp. Paper. Amazon.com, 2004. $17.95.

TRAILS TO TIBURON: THE 1894 & 1895 FIELD DIARIES OF W.J. McGEE
transcribed by Hazel McFeely Fontana; Journals of McGees expedition to the Papagos (Tohono O'odham). 170 pp. University of Arizona Press, 2000. $36.

TRAITS OF AMERICAN INDIAN LIFE & CHARACTER
Peter S. Ogden; Reprint. 2nd Edition. 128 pp. Dover & Amazon.com, $34.50.

TRANSATLANTIC VOICES: INTERPRETATIONS OF NATIVE NORTH AMERICAN LITERATURES Elvira Pulitano, Editor; Critical essays by European scholars.
336 pp. Paper. University of Nebraska Press, 2007. $26.95.

THE TRANSFORMATION OF BIGFOOT: MALENESS, POWER, & BELIEF AMONG THE CHIPEWYAN Henry S. Sharp; 192 pp. Smithsonian Institution Press, 1988. $30.

THE TRANSFORMATION OF THE SOUTHEASTERN INDIANS
Robbie Ethridge & Charles Hudson, Editors; Essays by Charles Hudson, Helen Rountree, Stephen Davis, et al., on how Southeastern Indian culture and society evolved. 416 pp. University Press of Mississippi, 2002. $50; paper, $30.

THE TRANSFORMING IMAGE: PAINTED ARTS OF NORTHWEST COAST FIRST NATIONS Bill McLellan & Karen Duffek
904 Illus. 193 in color. 304 pp. Paper. University of Washington Press, 2007. $50.

TRANSFORMING IMAGES: THE ART OF SILVER HORN & HIS SUCCESSORS
Robert G. Donnelley, Candace S. Green, Janet Berlo
Kiowa art. Illus. 75 color plates, 15 b&w photos. 216 pp. Paper.
University of Chicago Press, 2001. $45.

THE TRANSIT OF EMPIRE: INDIGENOUS CRITIQUES OF COLONIALISM
Jodi A. Byrd; Explores how indigeneity functions as transit, a trajectory of movement serving as precedent within U.S. imperial history. 320 pp. University of Minnesota Press, 2011. $75; paper, $25.

TRANSMISSION DIFFICULTIES: FRANZ BOAS & TSIMSHIAN MYTHOLOGY
Ralph Maud; Illus. 176 pp. University of Toronto Press, 2004. $14.95.

TRANSNATIONAL INDIANS IN THE NORTH AMERICAN WEST
Clarisa Confer , Andrae Marak & Laura Tuerneman, Editors
Essays. Texas A&M University Press, 2012. $45.

*TRAPPERS & TRADERS
Gail Stewart; Grades 3-8. Illus. 32 pp. Amazon.com 1990. $17.26.

TRAUMA & RESILIENCE IN AMERICAN INDIAN & AFRICAN AMERICAN SOUTHERN HISTORY Anthony S. Parent & Ulrike Wiethaus
Illus. 309 pp. Peter Lang Publishing, 2013. $89.95.

TRAPS OF THE AMERICAN INDIANS: A STUDY IN PSYCHOLOGY & INVENTION
Otis T. Mason; Reprint. Illus. 15 pp. Paper. Amazon.com, $2.95.

A TRAVEL GUIDE TO THE PLAINS INDIAN WARS
Stan Hoig; Narratives of the Plains Indian conflicts & directions to battle sites.
Illus. Maps. 232 pp. Paper. University of New Mexico Press, $21.95.

A TRAVELER IN INDIAN TERRITORY: THE JOURNAL OF ETHAN ALLEN HITCHCOCK
Ethan Allen Hitchcock
Illus. Maps. Photos. 288 pp. Paper. University of Oklahoma Press, 1996. $17.95.

TRAVELER'S GUIDE TO THE GREAT SIOUX WAR: THE BATTLEFIELDS, FORTS, & RELATED SITES OF AMERICA'S GREATEST INDIAN WAR
Paul L. Hedren
Illus. 130 pp. Montana Historical Society Press, 1996. $70; paper. $10.95.

A TRAVELERS GUIDE TO SOUTHWEST INDIAN ARTS & CRAFTS
Charlotte Smith Neyland; Illus. Map. 48 pp. Paper. Renaissance House, 1992. $4.95.

TRAVELS AMONG THE DENA OF ALASKA'S YUKON VALLEY
Frederica de Laguna; Illus. Maps. 368 pp. University of Washington Press, 1999. $29.95.

TRAVELS IN THE GREAT WESTERN PRAIRIES
T.J. Farnham; Reprint of 1843 edition. 2 vols. in 1. 612 pp. Amazon.com, $25.

TRAVELS IN NORTH AMERICA, INCLUDING A SUMMER WITH THE PAWNEES
C. Murray; Reprint of 1839 Second Edition. 878 pp. Amazon.com, $25.

TRAVELS IN A STONE CANOE: THE RETURN TO THE WISDOMKEEPERS
Harvey Arden & Steve Wall; Illus. 320 pp. Simon & Schuster, 1998. $25.

TRAVELS & INQUIRIES IN NORTH AMERICA, 1882-1883
Herman F. Ten Kate; Peter Hovins, et al, Eds.
Illus. 480 pp. University of New Mexico Press, 2004. $55.

TRAVELS & RESEARCHES IN NORTH AMERICA, 1882-1883
Herman ten Kate; tr. from the Dutch & edited by Pieter Hovens, William Orr, Louis Hieb
Dutch traveler, Ten Kate's studies of the Pima, Hopi, Apache, and Zuni people. Illus. 480 pp. University of New Mexico Press, 2004. $65.

TRAVELS WITH FRANCES DENSMORE: HER LIFE, WOK, AND LEGACY IN NATIVE AMERICAN STUDIES Joan M. Jensen & Michelle Wick Patterson, Editors
Photos. 496 pp. University of Nebraska Press, 2015. $75.

TREADING IN THE PAST: SANDALS OF THE ANASAZI
Kathy Kankainen, Editor; Essays. 256 color photos. U. of Utah Press. $50; paper, $29.95.

A TREASURED HERITAGE: WORKS OF MASTERS & APPRENTICES
Exhibition catalog featuring biographies and the works of 54 Alaska Native master artists and their apprentices. Illus. 64 pp. Paper. Institute of Alaska Native Arts, 1988. $12.50.

TEASURES OF GILCREASE: SELECTIONS FROM THE PERMANENT COLLECTION
Anne Morand, kevin Smith, Daniel C> Swan, Sarah Erwin; Collections of the Gilcrease Museum. Illus. 200 pp. University of Oklahoma Press. $39.95; paper, $19.95.

TREASURES OF THE HOPI
Theda Bassman; The history and art of the Hopi. Illus. 110 color photos.
116 pp. Paper. Amazon.com & Alibris.com, 2003. $12.95.

TREASURES OF THE MOUND BUILDERS
Lar Hothem; Covers 135 Adena and Hopewell mounds in Ohio, with name, location, when and by whom excavated, artifacts found. Illus. 146 pp. Paper. Hothem House, 1989. $11.95.

TREASURES OF THE NATIONAL MUSEUM OF THE AMERICAN INDIAN
W. Richard West, Jr., et al; Overview of the collection of art from the museum.
Illus. 320 pp. NMAI Press & Abbeville Press, 1996. $11.95.

TREASURES OF THE NAVAJO
Theda Bassman; The history and art of the Navajo. Illus. 105 color photos.
124 pp. Paper. Amazon.com & Alibris.com, 2003. $12.95.

TREASURES OF THE ZUNI
Theda Bassman; The history and art of the Zuni. Illus. 104 color photos.
116 pp. Paper. Amazon.com & Alibris.com, 2003. $12.95.

A TREASURY OF OUR WESTERN HERITAGE: THE FAVELL MUSEUM OF WESTERN ART & INDIAN ARTIFACTS Illus. Favell Museum, 1986. $19.75.

TREATIES & AGREEMENTS OF THE INDIAN TRIBES OF THE PACIFIC NORTHWEST Institute for the Development of Indian Law, $12.

TREATIES ON TRIAL: THE CONTINUING CONTROVERSY OVER NORTHWEST INDIAN FISHING RIGHTS
Fay G. Cohen, et al; Illus. 280 pp. Paper. University of Washington Press, 1986. $11.95.

TREATIES WITH AMERICAN INDIANS: AN ENCYCLOPEDIA OF RIGHTS, CONFLICTS & SOVEREIGNTY Donald L. Fixico, Ed.; 3 Vols. 1,200 pp. ABC-CLIO, 2004. $285.

TREATISE ON THE HEATHEN SUPERSTITIONS THAT TODAY LIVE AMONG THE INDIANS NATIVE TO THIS NEW SPAIN, 1629
Ruiz de Alarcon; J. Richard Andrews & Ross Hassig, Editors
Illus. Map. 406 pp. Paper. University of Oklahoma Press, 1984. $24.95.

A TREATISE ON LOVESICKNESS: AN OFFSHOOT OF THE CALUMET DANCE
Jacques Ferrand; Beecher & Ciavolella, Eds.
Reprint. Illus. 742 pp. Paper. Syracuse University Press, $19.95.

TREATMENT OF INDIANS BY THE CRIMINAL JUSTICE SYSTEM
51 pp. paper. Amazon.com, 1993. $25.

TREATY MANUSCRIPTS SERIES
A series of treaties. See Institute for the Development of Indian Law for titles and prices.

TREATY OF CANANDAIGUA 1794: 200 YEARS OF TREATY RELATIONS BETWEEN THE IROQUOIS CONFEDERACY & THE U.S.
edited by G. Peter Jemison & Anna M. Schein; Tells the story of the Six Nations and their relationship with the U.S. Among the contributors are Chief Irving Powless, Jr., Chief Leon Shenandoah, Chief Oren Lyons, Chief Bernard Parker, Chief Jake Swamp, et al. Illus. Photos. 352 pp. Paper. Amazon.com, $14.95.

THE TREATY OF FORT STANWIX, 1784
Henry S. Manley & Edward C. Ball; Amazon.com, 2003.

TREATY TALKS IN BRITISH COLUMBIA: BUILDING A NEW RELATIONSHIP
Christopher McKee; 3rd Ed. Recent treaties with Maa-nulth First Nations on the west coast of vancouver Island. Maps. 200 pp. Paper. U. of Washington Press, 2009. $33.95.

TREE OF DREAMS: A SPIRIT WOMAN'S VISION OF TRANSITION & CHANGE
Lynn Andrews; 256 pp. Paper. Penguin Group, 2003. $12.95.

TREEHOUSES
David Pearson, Editor; Illus. 96 pp. Chelsea Green Publishing, 2001. $16.95.

TREKWAYS OF THE WIND
Nils-Aslak Valkeapaa; trans. by Ralph Salisbury, et al
Studies Native American poetry. 300 pp. University of Arizona Press, 1994. $20.

TRENDS IN INDIAN HEALTH
Indian Health Service; Annual compendium of tables and charts that describe the IHS program, and health ststaus of American Indian & Alaska Natives. Paper. U.S. Government Printing Office. No charge.

WILLIAM TRENT & THE WEST
Sewell Elias Slick; An Indian trader and diplomat, land speculator and a soldier of fortune in the French & Indian War. Reprint. Illus. 200 pp. Wennawoods Publishing, $29.95.

THE TRIAL OF DON PEDRO LEON LUJAN: THE ATTACK AGAINST INDIAN SLAVERY & MEXICAN TRADERS IN UTAH
Sondra Jones; Illus. Maps. 208 pp. University of Utah Press, 2000. $27.50.

THE TRIAL OF "INDIAN JOE": RACE & JUSTICE IN THE 19TH CENTURY WEST
Clare V. McKanna, Jr.; Illus. 159 pp. Paper. University of Nebraska Press, 2003. $19.95.

THE TRIAL OF LEONARD PELTIER
Jim Messersmith; Paper. Amazon.com, 1991. $12.

TRIBAL ASSETS: THE REBIRTH OF NATIVE AMERICA
Robert White; Amazon.com, 1990. $24.95.

TRIBAL BOUNDARIES IN THE NASS WATERSHED
Neil J. Sterritt, et al.; Illus. Paper. UBC Press,, 1998. $27.95.

TRIBAL CONTRACTING: UNDERSTANDING & DRAFTING BUSINESS CONTRACTS WITH AMERICAN INDIAN TRIBES
M. Brent Leonhard; American Bar Association, 2009. $89.95.

TRIBAL CRIMINAL LAW & PROCEDURE, 2ND EDITION
Carrie Garrow & Sarah Deer
Illus. 429 pp. Alta Mira Press, $99; paper, $55; $54.99, e-Book..

TRIBAL CULTURAL RESOURCE MANAGEMENT: THE FULL CIRCLE TO STEWARDSHIP Darby C. Stapp, et al; Illus. 208 pp. Paper. AltaMira Press, 2002. $70.

TRIBAL DISPOSSESSION & OTHER OTTAWA INDIAN UNIVERSITY FRAUD
William E. Unrau & H. Craig Miner
Illus. Maps. 212 pp. University of Oklahoma Press, 1985. $32.95.

TRIBAL ENERGY SELF-SUFFICIENCY ACT & THE NATIVE AMERICAN ENERGY DEVELOPMENT & SELF-DETERMINATION ACT
U.S. Senate Committee on Indian Affairs
108th Congress, 1st Session. Illus. U.S. GPO, 2003.

THE TRIBAL FIRES CATALOG
Zango Music; Native American music. 500 titles: cassettes, CDs, albums, etc. Over 200 album reviews. Wholesale only. Zango Music, No charge.

TRIBAL GOVERNMENT: A NEW ERA
Includes Choctaw Tribal constitution and all Choctaw treaties with U.S. Government. Website: https://eric.ed.gov/?id=ED232837, $6.

TRIBAL GOVERNMENT OF THE OGLALA SIOUX OF PINE RIDGE, SD
Ira Grinnell; University of South Dakota, Government Research Bureau, 1967. $5.

TRIBAL GOVERNMENT TEXTBOOK
National Congress of American Indians.

TRIBAL GOVERNMENT TODAY: POLITICS ON MONTANA INDIAN RESERVATIONS
James J. Lopach, Margery Hunter Brown & Richmond L. Clow
Revised edition. Illus. 285 pp. University Press of Colorado, 1998. $45.

TRIBAL GOVERNMENT: WIND RIVER RESERVATION
Janet Flynn & Scott Ratliff; Pat Trautman, Editor
2nd revised edition. Illus. 90 pp. Paper. Mortimore Publishing, 1998. $14.95.

*TRIBAL LAW
Scott Prentzas; Grades 4-8. 64 pp. Amazon.com, 1994. $25.27.

TRIBAL LIBRARIES, ACHIVES, AND MUSEUMS: PRESERVING OUR LANGUAGE, MEMORY, AND LIFEWAYS Loriene Roy, Editor; Anijali Bhasin & Sarah K. Arriaga; 268 pp. Scarecrow Press, 2011. Paper, $61.

THE TRIBAL MOMENT IN AMERICAN POLITICS: THE STRUGGLE FOR NATIVE AMERICAN SOVEREIGNTY Christine K. Gray
Monograph. Rowman & Littlefield, 2013. 232 pp. $99; paper, 35. eBook, $34.99.

TRIBAL NATIONS & THE U.S.: AN INTRODUCTION
National Congress of American Indians

TRIBAL POLICING: ASSERTING SOVEREIGNTY, SEEKING JUSTICE
Eileen Luna-Firebaugh; Tribal government & law enforcement in America.
168 pp. Paper. University of Arizona Press, 2007. $29.95.

TRIBAL SECRETS: RECOVERING AMERICAN INDIAN INTELLECTUAL TRADITIONS
Robert Allen Warrior; A narrative account of the literary productions and political & cultural interactions of American Indian writers of the 20th century. 192 pp. Paper. University of Minnesota Press, 1994. $19.50.

TRIBAL SOVEREIGNTY & THE HISTORICAL IMAGINATION: CHEYENNE-ARAPAHO POLITICS Loretta Fowler; Illus. Maps. 368 pp. U. of Nebraska Press, 2002. $27.50.

*TRIBAL SOVEREIGNTY: INDIAN TRIBES IN U.S. HISTORY
Four scholarly papers which consider the issue of tribal sovereignty. Papers by: Dr. Fay Cohen, Dr. D'Arcy McNickle, Dr. Roger Buffalohead, and Dr. Mary Young. Studies the impact of non-Indian settlement and U.S. Government policy. Teacher's guide. Grades7-12. Illus. 60 pp. Daybreak Star Press, $5.50.

TRIBAL STRENGTHS & NATIVE EDUCATION: VOICES FROM THE RESERVATION
Terry Huffman; 192 pp. University of Massachusetts Press, 2017. $90; paper, $27.95.

THE TRIBAL TERRITORY, SOVEREIGNTY & GOVERNANCE: A STUDY OF THE CHEYENNE RIVER & LAKE TRAVERSE INDIAN RESERVATIONS
Erin H. Fouberg; Illus. 250 pp. Amazon.com, 2000. $80.

TRIBAL THEORY IN NATIVE AMERICAN LITERATURE: DAKOTA & HAUDENOSAUNEE WRITING & INDIGENOUS WORLDVIEWS
Penelope Myrtle Kelsey
Photos. 190 pp. U. of Nebraska Press, 2008. $45; paper, $24.95.

TRIBAL WARS OF THE SOUTHERN PLAINS
Stan Hoig; Indian conflicts from the Spaniards in the 16th century through the U.S.-Cheyenne Battle of the Sand Hills in 1875. Illus. Maps. 344 pp. University of Oklahoma Press, 1993. $34.95.

TRIBAL WATER RIGHTS: ESSAYS IN CONTEMPORARY LAW, POLICY, AND ECONOMICS John E. Thorsen, Sarah Britton, Bonnie G. Colby
As a follow-up-to Negotiating Tribal Water Rights, this volume provides more in-depth treatment of the issues. 304 pp. University of Arizona Press, 2006. $50.

TRIBAL WRITERS: THE CORRESPONDENCE GUIDE FOR NATIVE AMERICANS
Linda J. Rasmussen; 2nd edition reprint. 196 pp. Paper. Amazon.com, 1995. $22.95.

TRIBALLY CONTROLLED COLLEGES: MAKING GOOD MEDICINE
Wayne J. Stein; History of the early years of the American Indian tribally controlled college movement. 180 pp. Amazon.com, 1992. $35.95.

TRIBALLY CONTROLLED INDIAN COLLEGE
Norman T. Oppelt
History of American Indian higher education. Paper. Amazon.com, 1991. $20.

TRIBES, LAND & ENVIRONMENT
Sarah Krakoff & Ezra Rosser, Editors; Amazon.com, 2012.

TRIBES OF CALIFORNIA
Stephen Powers; Covers American Indian ethnography of California. 1976 revised edition. Illus. 482 pp. Paper. University of California Press, $31.95.

TRIBES OF THE EXTREME NORTHWEST, ALASKA, THE ALEUTIANS & ADJACENT TERRITORIES
George Gibbs, et al; Reprint. Illus. 156 pp. Paper. Shorey Bookstore, $10.

TRIBES OF THE IROQUOIS CONFEDERATION
Michael Johnson; illus. by Jonathan Smith
Illus. 48 pp. Paper. Wennawoods Publishing, $15.95

TRIBES OF THE SIOUX NATION
Michael Johnson & Jonathan Smith; Illus. 50 pp. Paper. MBI Distribution, 2001. $14.95.

TRIBES OF THE SOUTHERN WOODLANDS
Time-Life Books; Amazon.com, 1994.

TRIBES & THE STATES: GEOGRAPHIES OF INTERGOVERNMENTAL INTERACTION
Brad Bays & Erin H. Fouberg; Illus. 240 pp. Paper. Rowman & Littlefield, 2002. $70.

TRIBES THAT SLUMBER: INDIANS OF THE TENNESSEE REGION
T. Lewis and M. Kneberg; Reprint of 1958 edition. Illus. 208 pp.
Paper. Hothem House & Amazon.com & Alibris.com, $16.95.

TRIBES, TREATIES, & CONSTITUTIONAL TRIBULATIONS
David E. Wilkins & Vine Deloria, Jr.; Fishing Rights of the Indian people who live alng the Columbia River between Washington & Oregon. Examines relationship between Indians and the U.S. Constitution. Illus. 221 pp. Paper. Amazon.com, $19.95.

TRIBES & TRIBULATIONS: MISCONCEPTIONS ABOUT AMERICAN INDIANS & THEIR HISTORIES
Laurence M. Hauptman; 165 pp. Paper. University of New Mexico Press, 1995. $30.

THE TRICKSTER IN THE FRONT YARD: STILL SEMI-NATIVE
Jim Belshaw; Paper. University of New Mexico Press, $19.95.

THE TRICKSTER OF LIBERTY: NATIVE HEIRS TO A WILD BARONAGE
Gerald Vizenor; Novel of a traditional tribal trickster figure; moves from oral stories into contemporary narrative. Illus. 160 pp. Paper. University of Oklahoma Press, 1988. $14.95.

THE TRICKSTER SHIFT: HUMOUR & IRONY IN CONTEMPORARY NATIVE ART
Allan J. Ryan; 160 Illus. 320 pp. University of Washington Press, 1999. $60.

TRICKSTER: STUDY IN AMERICAN INDIAN MYTHOLOGY
Paul Radin; Reprint of 1956 edition. 223 pp. Greenwood, $35.
New edition. 223 pp. Paper. Shocken Books, 1972. $6.95.

*THE TRICKSTER & THE TROLL
Virginia Driving Hawk Sneve
Grades 4 and up. Illus. 110 pp. Paper. University of Nebraska Press, 1997. $8.

TRICKY TRIBAL DISCOURSE: THE POETRY, SHORT STORIES & FUS FIXICO LETTERS OF CREEK WRITER ALEX POSEY
Alexa M. Kosmider; 116 pp. University of Idaho Press, 1998. $24.95.

*A TRIP TO A POW WOW
Grades 3 and up. Paper. Amazon.com, $6.95.

TROOPERS WITH CUSTER: HISTORIC INCIDENTS OF THE BATTLE OF THE LITTLE BIG HORN E.A. Brininstool; 343 pp. Paper. Amazon.com, $13.95.

TROUBLED TRAILS: THE MEEKER AFFAIR & THE EXPULSION OF UTES FROM COLORADO
Robert Silbernagel; Illus. Maps. 304 pp. Paper. University of Utah Press, 2011. $24.95.

THE TRUE SPIRIT & ORIGINAL INTENT OF TREATY 7
Walter Hildebrant, et al.; Illus. 430 pp. McGill-Queen's University Press, 1995.

TRUE STORIES OF NEW ENGLAND CAPTIVES CARRIED TO CANADA DURING THE OLD FRENCH & INDIAN WARS
Alice C. Baker; Illus. 420 pp. Paper. Heritage Books, 1991. $27.50.

TRUST IN THE LAND: NEW DIRECTIONS IN TRIBAL CONSERVATION
Beth Rose Middleton; Examines new and innovative ideas concerning Native land conservancies, providing advice on land trusts, collaborations, and conservation groups. 352 pp. Paper. University of Arizona Press, 2011. $35.

TRUSTEESHIP IN CHANGE: TOWARD TRIBAL AUTONOMY IN RESOURCE MANAGEMENT Richmond Clow & Imre Sutton, Eds.
Illus. 354 pp. University Press of Colorado, 2001. $59.95; paper, $24.95.

THE TRUTH ABOUT GERONIMO
Britton Davis; M.M. Quaife, Editor
Illus. 293 pp. Paper. University of Nebraska Press, 1976. $18.95.

THE TRUTH ABOUT STORIES: A NATIVE NARRATIVE
Thomas King; The relationship between story telling and the Native North American experience. 184 pp. University of Minnesota Press, 2008. $60; paper, $19.95.

TRUTH OR CONSEQUENCES: A NATIVE AMERICAN VIEW OF SOCIETY
David Two Bears; Illus. 108 pp. Paper. Amazon.com. 2001. $10.95.

TSAWALK: A NUU-CHAH-NULTH WORLDVIEW
E. Richard Atleo; Hereditary chief Umeek introduces an alternative indigenous worldview - an ontology drawn from the Nuu-cha-nulth origin stories. 160 pp. University of Washington Press, 2004. $94; paper, $33.95.

TSONAKWA & YOLAIKIA: LEGENDS IN STONE, BONE & WOOD
Gerard Rancourt Tsonakwa; Indian stories discussing Native American beliefs about the earth and shared life. Illus. 64 pp. Amazon.com, $10.95.

TSEE-MA'HEONE-NEMEOTOTSE: CHEYENNE SPIRITUAL SONGS
David Graber, Editor; 227 pp. Faith & Life, 1982. $29.95.

TSEYI / DEEP IN THE ROCK: REFLECTIONS ON CANYON DE CHELLY
Laura Tohe; photos by Stephen E. Strom
Photos. 72 pp. Paper. University of Arizona Press, 2005. $15.

TS'ILIIYAZHI SPUDS BAA HANE
Marie Lewis & Navajo Language Program; Pamphlet. Amazon.com. $2.95.

TSIMSHIAN CULTURE: A LIGHT THROUGH THE AGES
Jay Miller; Illus. 204 pp. Paper. University of Nebraska Press, 1997. $28.50.

THE TSIMSHIAN: IMAGES OF THE PAST; VIEWS FOR THE PRESENT
Margaret Seguin, Editor; Illus. 364 pp. Paper. University of Washington Press, $20.

THE TSIMSHIAN & THEIR NEIGHBORS OF THE NORTH PACIFIC COAST
Jay Miller & Carol Eastman, Editors; Illus. 366 pp. U. of Washington Press, 1985. $35.

TSIMSHIAN TREASURES: THE REMARKABLE JOURNEY OF THE DUNDAS COLLECTION Donald Ellis, Steven Clay Brown, Bill Holm, et al
Essays on Northwest Coast art. Illus. 176 pp. University of Washington Press, 2007. $45.

TULALIP FROM MY HEART: AN AUTOBIOGRAPHICAL ACCOUNT OF A RESERVATION COMMUNITY Hariette Sjelton Dover
Illus. Maps. 344 pp. Paper. University of Washington Press, 2015. $30.

*TUL-TOK-A-NA: THE SMALL ONE
Kathleen Allan Myer
A Yosemite Indian legend. Grades 1-5. 32 pp. Council for Indian Education, 1991. $4.95.

TULAPAI TO TOKAY: A BIBLIOGRAPHY OF ALCOHOL USE & ABUSE AMONG NATIVE AMERICANS OF NORTH AMERICA
David R. McDonald & Pat Mail; 372 pp. HRAFP, 1981, $25.

*THE TUNICA-BILOXI: SOUTHEAST
Jeffrey Brain; Grades 5 and up. Illus. Chelsea House, 1989. $17.95.

THE TURN TO THE NATIVE: STUDIES IN CRITICISM & CULTURE
Arnold Krupat; 168 pp. Paper. University of Nebraska Press, 1996. $13.

*TURQUOISE BOY: A NAVAJO LEGEND
Grades 4-7. Illus. 48 pp. Paper. Amazon.com, 1992. $9.15; paper, $4.95.

TURQUOISE - THE GEM OF THE CENTURIES
Branson; Turquoise types and different kinds of Southwestern Indian jewelry. Illus. 62 pp. Paper. Hothem House, 1975. $7.95.

TURQUOISE & THE INDIAN
Bennett; Study of raw gem materials, turquoise mines & locations, and the beginning of gem-working & Indian jewelry style. Reprint. Illus. 152 pp. Hothem House, $9.95.

TURQUOISE JEWELRY
Nancy Schiffer; Full color photos of a variety of Southwest Indian-made jewelry with many types of turquoise. Illus. 64 pp. Paper. Schiffer, $9.95.

TURQUOISE & THE NAVAJO
Lee Hammons; Illus. 32 pp. Paper. Primer Publishers, $1.95.

THE TURQUOISE TRAIL: NATIVE AMERICAN JEWELRY & CULTURE OF THE SOUTHWEST
Photos by Jeffrey J. Foxx; Illus. Photos. 216 pp. Harry N. Abrams, 1993. $49.50.

TURTLE BOY: A NOVEL
Joel Monture
Covers traditional Mohawk culture. 304 pp. Paper. University of Oklahoma Press, $14.95.

TURTLE DREAM
Gerald Hausman; Illus. Mariposa Print, 1989. $9.95.

TURTLE ISLAND ALPHABET: A LEXICON OF NATIVE AMERICAN SYMBOLS & CULTURE
Gerald Hausman; Reprint. Illus. 204 pp. Paper. St. Martin's Press, 1999. $13.95.

TURTLE LUNG WOMAN'S GRANDDAUGHTER
Delphine Red Shirt; Stories of Red Shirt's mother, Lone Woman and her grandmother Turtle Lung Woman, a medicine woman. 242 pp. Paper. U. of Nebraska, 2002. $14.95.

TURTLE MEAT & OTHER STORIES
Joseph Bruchac
18 stories, myths and legends reveal the transforming power Native American writing in a contemporary world. Illus. 128 pp. Holy Cow! Press, 1993. $18.95; paper, $10.95.

TURTLES, WOLVES & BEARS: A MOHAWK FAMILY HISTORY
Barbara J. Sivertson; 344 pp. Paper. Amazon.com, 1996. $29.

TUSAYAN KATCINAS & HOPI KATCINA ALTARS
Jesse Walter Fewkes; Discusses the ceremonies of the Tusayan (Hopi) Indians and the Cibola (Zuni) Indians. Illus. 120 pp. Paper. Amazon.com, 1991. $17.95.

*THE TUSCARORA
Grades K-4. Illus. 48 pp. Childrens Press, $11.45.

TUSCARORA-ENGLISH, ENGLISH-TUSCARORA DICTIONARY
Blair A. Rudes; 382 pp. Amazon.com, 1998.

THE TUSCARORA LEGACY OF J.N.B. HEWITT: MATERIALS FOR THE STUDY OF THE TUSCARORA LANGUAGE & CULTURE
Blair Rudes & Dorothy Crouse; 670 pp. Paper. University of Chicago Press, 1988. $39.95.

TUSCARORA NATION, NY (IMAGES OF AMERICA)
Bryan Printup & Neil Patterson, Jr.; Paper. Amazon.com, 2007. $15.95

THE TUSCARAWAS VALLEY IN INDIAN DAYS, 1750-1797
Russell H. Booth, Jr., Editor
329 pp. Hothem House & Wennawoods Publishing, 1994. $29.95.

THE TUTELO LANGUAGE
Horatio Hale; 110 pp. Amazon.com, 2002. $36.

THE TUTOR'D MIND: INDIAN MISSIONARY-WRITERS IN ANTEBELLUM AMERICA
Bernd C. Peyer; Traces the development of American Indian literature from 17th century to the eve of the Civil War. 408 pp. U. of Massachusetts Press, 1997. $70; paper, $24.95.

TWANA GAMES
A handbook of games played by Twana people of the Skokomish Reservation in western Washington State. Illus. 20 pp. Daybreak Star Press, $3.50.

TWANA NARRATIVES: NATIVE HISTORICAL ACCOUNTS OF A COAST SALISH CULTURE William D. Elmendorf
375 pp. University of Washington Press & Amazon.com, 1993. $40.

TWELVE THOUSAND YEARS: AMERICAN INDIANS IN MAINE
Bruce J. Bourque; Reveals how Penobscot, Abenakis, Passamaquoddies, Maliseets, Micmacs, and other Native communities lived and survived ove the centuries. Illus. Maps. 369 pp. University of Nebraska Press, 2001. $45; paper, $19.95.

THE TWENTIETH CENTURY FICTIONAL AMERICAN INDIAN WOMAN & FELLOW CHARACTERS: A STUDY OF GENDER & RACE
Asebrit Sundquist; 304 pp. Humanities Press, 1991, $39.95.

TWENTY-FIVE YEARS AMONG THE INDIANS AND BUFFALO: A FRONTIER MEMOIR
William D. Street; Warren R. Street, Editor

TWENTY THOUSAND MORNINGS: AN AUTOBIOGRAPHY
John Joseph Mathews; 20th Century Native American literature. 352 pp. University of Oklahoma Press, $29.95.

*TWILIGHT BOY
Timothy Green; Navajo story. Ages 12 and up. 240 pp. Northland, $12.95; paper, $6.95.

TWILIGHT OF EMPIRE
Allan W. Eckert; Illus. 590 pp. Paper. Amazon.com, 2004.

THE TWILIGHT OF THE SIOUX
John Neihardt; Reprint of 1971 edition. Vol. II of, "A Cycle of the West." 292 pp. Paper. University of Nebraska Press, $22.

*TWO BEAR CUBS: A MIWOK LEGEND FROM CALIFORNIA'S YOSEMITE VALLEY
Daniel San Souci, Illus.; Grades K-4. Heyday Books & Yosemite Assn, 1997. $14.95.

TWO CROWS DENIES IT: A HISTORY OF CONTROVERSY IN OMAHA SOCIOLOGY
R.H. Barnes; Illus. 288 pp. University of Nebraska Press, 1984. $24.95.

TWO EARLY HISTORIC IROQUOIAN SITES IN WESTERN NEW YORK
Michael Gramly; Paper. Amazon.com, 1996. $12.95.

TWO FEATHERS: SPIRITUAL SEED PLANTER
Kevin Laughing Hawk; Illus. 120 pp. Paper. Amazon.com, 2003. $15.

TWO GREAT SCOUTS & THEIR PAWNEE BATTALION: THE EXPERIENCES OF FRANK J. NORTH & LUTHER H. NORTH Georghe Griorest.
Told with an ecological perspective. Grades 6 and up. Illus. 160 pp. Amazon.com, $16.95. Paper. Alaska Natural History Association, $9.

TWO OLD WOMEN
Velma Wallis
The elderly & their value in Alaskan society. Illus. Amazon.com, $16.95.

TWO RAVENS: THE LIFE & TEACHINGS OF A SPIRITUAL WARRIOR
Louis Two Ravens Irwin & Robert Liebert
Illus. 176 pp. Paper. Destiny Books, 1996. Available from Iner Traditions, $12.95.

TWO SPIRIT PEOPLE: AMERICAN INDIAN LESBIAN WOMEN & GAY MEN
Lester B. Brown; 120 pp. Paper. Amazon.com & Alibris.com, 2003. $16.95.

TWO-SPIRIT PEOPLE: NATIVE AMERICAN GENDER IDENTITY, SEXUALITY, AND SPIRITUALITY Sue-Ellen Jacobs, Wesley Thomas & Sabine Lang, Editors
Explores gender and sexuality issues as they relate to lesbian, gay, transgendered, and other "marked" Native Americans. Illus. 352 pp. Paper. U. of Illinois Press, 1997. $25.

TWO SPIRITS: A STORY OF LIFE WITH THE NAVAJO
Walter L. Williams & Toby Johnson; Historical fiction on Navajo philosophy & spirituality. Demonstrates gender variance as a source of spiritual power and documents "same-sex marriage" as indigenous to the American continent. Paper. 332 pp. Amazon.com & Alibris.com, 2006. $18.

TWO TOMS: LESSONS FROM A SHOSHONE DOCTOR
Thomas H. Johnson & Helen S. Johnson; Details the Shoshone culture & chronicles the story between two men of different backgrounds. Illus. Map. 104 pp. Paper. University of Utah Press, 2011. $15.95; eBook, $10.

TWO WORLDS: THE INDIAN ENCOUNTER WITH THE EUROPEAN, 1492-1509
S. Lyman Tyler; 275 pp. University of Utah Press, 1988. $25.

U

UGIUVANGMIUT QULIAPYUIT KING ISLAND TALES
Lawrence D. Kaplan; Eskimo history and legends from Bering Strait. Illus. Maps. 258 pp. Paper. University of Alaska Press, 1988. $19.95.

UKOMNO'M: THE YUKI INDIANS OF NORTHERN CALIFORNIA
Virginia P. Miller; Illus. 108 pp. Paper. Malki-Ballena Press, 1979. $8.95.

ULTIMATE AMERICANS - POINT HOPE, ALASKA: 1826-1909
Tom Lowenstein; Examines the first encounters between the native Tikigaq people and Anglo-Americans during the 19th century. Illus. 368 pp. University of Chicago Press, 2009. $49.95; paper, $36.95.

UMATILLA DICTIONARY: CONFEDERATED TRIBES OF THE UMATILLA INDIAN RESERVATION Noel Rude, Ed; Illus. 640 pp. U. of Washington Press, 2015. $50.

UNAFFECTED BY THE GOSPEL: OSAGE RESISTANCE TO THE CHRISTIAN INVASION, 1673-1906: A CULTURAL VICTORY Willard Hughes Rollings
Illus. 4 maps. 255 pp. University of New Mexico Press, $45; paper, $22.95.

*THE UNBREAKABLE CODE
Sara Hoagland Hunter; illus. by Julia Miner
Picture book. Ages 6-8. Illus. Amazon.com & Malki-Ballena Press, $15.95.

UNBROKEN CIRCLES: TRADITIONAL ARTS OF CONTEMPORARY WOODLAND PEOPLES; Looks at the preservation of culture through the artistic media that have been used by Native people since before Columbus. Akwe:kon Press, $10.

THE UNBROKEN THREAD: CONSERVING THE TEXTILE TRADITIONS OF OAXACA
Kathryn Klein, Editor; Illus. 176 pp. Amazon.com, 1998. $55; paper, $39.95.

UNCAS: FIRST OF THE MOHEGANS
Michael Leroy Oberg; Illus. 270 pp. Amazon.com, 2003. $27.50.

UNCERTAIN ACCOMMODATION: ABORIGINAL IDENTITY & GROUP RIGHTS IN THE SUPREME COURT OF CANADA
Dimitrios Panagos; UBC Press, $85; paper, $27.95; eBook, $27.95.

UNCERTAIN ENCOUNTERS: INDIANS & WHITES AT PEACE & WAR IN SOUTHERN OREGON, 1820S-1860S
Nathan Douthit; Illus. 256 pp. Paper. Oregon State University Press, 2002. $17.95.

UNCLE SAM'S STEPCHILDREN: THE REFORMATION OF U.S. INDIAN POLICY, 1865-1887; L.B. Priest; Reprint of 1942 ed. 310 pp. Paper. U. of Nebraska Press, $6.95.

AN UNCOMMON ENEMY
Michelle Black; An historical novel on Custer's and the 1868 attack on a Cheyenne village presided over by Chief Black Kettle, called the Washita Massacre. Illus. 180 pp. Paper. WinterSun Press, 2008. $14.95. Available from amazon.com. Kindle, $2.99.

UNCOMMON THREADS: WABANAKI TEXTILES, CLOTHING, AND COSTUME
Bruce J. Bourque & Laureen A. Labar; Textile traditions of four tribes: Penobscots, Passamaquoddies, Maliseets & Micmacs. Illus. Map. 192 pp. Paper. University of Washington Press, 2009. $45.

THE UNCONQUERED HEARTS
Ruby H. Happel-Holtz; Illus. 412 pp. Vantage Press, 2003. $19.95.
Available from Amazon.com & books.google.com

UNCONQUERED PEOPLE: FLORIDA'S SEMINOLE & MICCOSUKEE INDIANS
Brent R. Weisman; foreword by Jerald T. Milanich; Guide to Seminole history & culture. Illus. Maps. 184 pp. Paper. University Press of Florida, 1999. $19.95.

THE UNCOVERED PAST: ROOTS OF NORTHERN ALBERTA SOCIETIES
Patricia A. McCormack & R. Geoffrey Ironside, Editors
Illus. Maps. 290 pp. CCI, $30; paper, $20.

UNDER THE EAGLE: SAMUEL HOLIDAY, NAVAJO CODE TALKER
Samuel Holiday & Robert S. McPherson; 288 pp. Paper. U. of Oklahoma Press, $19.95

*UNDER THE INDIAN TURQUOISE SKY
Rosemary Davey
Animal fables. Grades 4 and up. Illus. 92 pp. Amazon.com, 1985. $8.95.

UNDER THE PALACE PORTAL: NATIVE AMERICAN ARTISTS IN SANTA FE
Karl A. Hoerig; A history of the Portal and the Native American Vendors Program. Illus. Map. 320 pp. University of New Mexico Press, 2003. $19.95.

UNDER THE RATTLESNAKE: CHEROKEE HEALTH & RESILIENCY
Lisa J. Lefler, Editor; foreword by Susan Leading Fox; Portrait of Cherokee health issues. Illus. 200 pp. University of Alabama Preee, 2009. $46.75; paper, $26.95. E-Book, $21.56.

UNDER SACRED GROUND: A HISTORY OF NAVAJO OIL, 1922-1982
Kathleen P. Chamberlain; Illus. 177 pp. Paper. U. of New Mexico Press, 2000. $30.

THE UNDERGROUND RESERVATION: OSAGE OIL
Terry P. Wilson; Illus. 263 pp. University of Nebraska Press, 1985. $22.95.

UNDERSTANDING THE ANASAZI OF MESA VERDE & HOVENWEEP
David Noble, Editor; Illus. Maps. 40 pp. Paper. Amazon.com, 1992. $8.95.

UNDERSTANDING DISABILITIES IN AMERICAN INDIAN & ALASKA NATIVE COMMUNITIES: TOOLKIT GUIDE
Martina Whelshula, Ed.; Illus. 194 pp. Paper. Amazon.com, 2003. $40.

UNDERSTANDING NORTHWEST COAST ART: A GUIDE TO CRESTS, BEINGS & SYMBOLS Cheryl Shearar; A dictionary-style reference guide to identifying & understanding the symbols, crests, & beings depicted in Northwest Coast Native American works of art such as the totem poles, masks, and prints. Illus. Map. 192 pp. Paper. University of Washington Press, 2000. $22.50.

UNDERSTANDING TOLOWA HISTORIES: WESTERN HEGEMONIES & NATIVE AMERICAN RESPONSES James Collins; 240 pp. Routledge, 1997. $95; paper, $30.

THE UNDYING WEST: STORIES FROM MONTANA'S CAMAS PRAIRIE
Carlene Cross; History of western Montana's Camas Prairie. The Salish, Kootenai, Nez Perce, & Iroquois Indians. 50 bxw photos. 176 pp. Paper. Fulcrum Publishing, 1999. $16.95.

UNEARTHING GOTHAM: THE ARCHAEOLOGY OF NEW YORK CITY
Anne-Marie E. Cantwell; Illus. 384 pp. Yale University Press, 2003. $39.95; paper, $20.

UNEARTHING INDIAN LAND: LIVING WITH THE LEGACIES OF ALLOTMENT
Kristin T. Ruppel; Covers the issues of Indianland ownership.
240 pp. Paper. University of Arizona Press, 2008. $35.

UNEVEN GROUND: AMERICAN INDIAN SOVEREIGNTY & FEDERAL LAW
David E. Wilkins & K. Tsianina Lomawaima
336 pp. Paper. University of Oklahoma Press, 2002. $26.95.

UNHALLOWED INTRUSIONS, A HISTORY OF CHEROKEE FAMILIES IN FORSYTH CO., GA Don L. Shadburn
Illus. Maps. 806 pp. Amazon.com, 1993. Limited 3rd printing, $65.

UNITING THE TRIBES: THE RISE & FALL OF PAN-INDIAN COMMUNITY ON THE CROW RESERVATION
Frank Rzeczkowski; Illus. 294 pp. University Press of Kansas, 2012. $39.95.

THE UNITED KEETOOWAH BAND OF CHEROKEE INDIANS IN OKLAHOMA
Georgia R. Leeds; 320 pp. Amazon.com, 1997. $49.95.

U.S. CONGRESS, SENATE & HOUSE COMMITTEES ON INDIAN AFFAIRS, PROCEEDINGS U.S. Government Printing Office

U.S. FISCAL YEAR BUDGET HEARING BEFORE THE COMMITTEE ON INDIAN AFFAIRS, U.S. SENATE U.S. Government Printing Office.

UNIVERSITIES AND INDIAN COUNTRY: CASE STUDIES IN TRIBAL-DRIVEN RESEARCH Dennis Norman & Joseph Kalt, Editor
Illus. 216 pp. University of Arizona Press, 2015. $29.95. e-Book available.

UNIVERSITY OF CALIFORNIA ANTHROPOLOGICAL RECORDS
A series of 30 facsimile reprints. See Coyote Press for titles and prices.

UNIVERSITY OF CALIFORNIA, ARCHAEOLOGICAL REPORTS
A series of 74 facsimile reprints. See Coyote Press for titles and prices.

UNIVERSITY OF CALIFORNIA, PUBLICATIONS IN AMERICAN ARCHAEOLGY & ETHNOLOGY A series of 49 facsimile reprints. See Coyote Press for titles and prices.

UNJUST RELATIONS: ABORIGINAL RIGHTS IN CANADIAN COURTS
Peter Kulchyski, Editor; 380 pp. Paper. Oxford University Press, 1994. $32.

THE UNKECHAUG INDIANS OF EASTERN LONG ISLAND: A HISTORY
John A. Strong; Traces the history of the Indians of the Poospatuck Reservation.
Illus. Maps. 352 pp. University of Oklahoma Press, 2011. $29.95.

UNLEARNING "INDIAN" STEREOTYPES, A TEACHING UNIT FOR ELEMENTARY TEACHERS & CHILDREN'S LIBRARIANS
Racism & Sexism Resource Center for Educators
Council on Interracial Books for Children, 1981. $39.95. Teaching Guide, $4.95.

UNLEARNING THE LANGUAGE OF CONQUEST: SCHOLARS EXPOSE ANTI-INDIANISM IN AMERICA
Four Arrows (Don Trent Jacobs); Illus. 300 pp. Paper. U. of Texas Press, 2006. $21.95.

UNLIKELY ALLIANCES: NATIVE NATIONS AND WHITE COMMUNITIES JOIN TO DEFEND RURAL LANDS Zoltan Grossman; Paper. UBC Press, 2017. $34.50.

UNLOCKING THE PAST: CELEBRATING HISTORICAL ARCHAEOLOGY IN NORTH AMERICA Lu Ann De Cunzo & John H. Jameson, Jr., Editors
Illus. 256 pp. University Press of Florida, 2005. $39.95.

UNNATURAL SELECTION: THE YANOMAMI, THE KAYAPO & THE ONSLAUGHT OF CIVILIZATION
Linda Rabben; Illus. 250 pp. Paper. U. of Washington Press, 1998. $18.95.

THE UNRATIFIED TREATY BETWEEN THE KIOWAS, COMANCHES & APACHES & THE U.S. OF 1863 R.J. DeMallie; 8 pp. Institute for the Development of Indian Law. $5.

UNRAVELLING THE FRANKLIN MYSTERY: INUIT TESTIMONY
David C. Woodman; Examination of Sir John Franklin's final Arctic expedition (1845) reconsyructs events surrounding the mysterious loss of both ships and all hands by giving credence to the testimony of Inuit witnesses. Paper. U. of Toronto Press, 1991. $19.95.

UNSCRIPTED AMERICA: INDIGENOUS LANGUAGES AND THE ORIGINS OF A LITERARY NATION Sarah Rivett; Oxford University Press, 2017. $39.95.

UNSETTLED PAST, UNSETTLED FUTURE: THE STORY OF MAINE INDIANS
Neil Rolde; Paper. Tilbury House Publishers, 2004. $20.

UNSETTLING AMERICA: THE USES OF INDIANNESS IN THE 21ST CENTURY
C. Richard King; 164 pp. Rowman & Littlefield, 2013. $76; paper, $30.. eBook, $29.99.

UNSETTLING ENCOUNTERS: FIRST NATIONS IMAGERY IN THE ART OF EMILY CARR Gerta Moray; 283 Illus. 83 in color. 400 pp. U. of Washington Press, 2006. $83.

UNSETTLING THE SETTLER WITHIN: INDIAN RESIDENTIAL SCHOOLS, TRUTH TELLING, AND RECONCILIATION IN CANADA
Paulette Regan; foreword by Taiaiake Alfred; Relations between indigenous peoples & Canadians. 316 pp. University of Washington Press, 2011. $94; paper, $37.95.

AN UNSPEAKABLE SADNESS: THE DISPOSSESSION OF NEBRASKA INDIANS
David J. Wishart; Illus. Maps. 311 pp. Paper. University of Nebraska Press, 1995. $23.95.

*UNSUNG HEROES OF WORLD WAR II: STORY OF THE NAVAJO CODE TALKERS
Deanne Durrett
Grades 6 and up. Illus. Maps. 136 pp. Paper. University of Nebraska Press, 2009. $14.95.

UP FROM THE HILLS: MEMORIES OF A CHEROKEE BOYHOOD
Leonard Carson Lambert, Jr.; as told to Michael Lambert; What it was like to grow up during the 1930s & 1940s in the mountains of western North Carolina and on a sharecropper's farm in eastern Tennessee. 240 pp. Paper. University of Nebraska Press, 2011. $18.95.

UPPER CHEHALIS DICTIONARY
M. Dale Kinkade; 378 pp. Amazon.com, 1991. $20.

UPON OUR RUINS: A STUDY IN CHEROKEE HISTORY & GENEALOGY
Don L. Shadburn; Illus. 786 pp. Cottonpatch Press, 2011. $55.

UPRISING! WOODY CRUMBO'S INDIAN ART
Robert Perry; Illus. 256 pp. Published by Chickasaw Press;
distributed by the University of Oklahoma Press, 2009. $29.95.

UPSIDE DOWN: SEASONS AMONG THE NUNAMIUT
Margaret B. Blackman; Essays about the people and the life of Anaktuvuk Pass in northern Alaska. Illus. 224 pp. University of Nebraska Press, 2004. $27.95.

THE UPSTREAM PEOPLE: AN ANNOTATED RESEARCH BIBLIOGRAPHY OF THE OMAHA TRIBE Michael L. Tate, Editor; Illus. 480 pp. Scarecrow Press, 1991. $75.

THE UPWARD MOVING & EMERGENCE WAY; THE GISHIN BIYE VERSION
Father Berard Haile, O.F.M.; Illus. 250 pp. University of Nebraska Press, 1981. $11.95.

UPWHERE BELONG
Buffy Sainte-Marie; 224 pp. Paper. LPC InBook, 1998. $15.95.

URBAN INDIAN EXPERIENCE IN AMERICA
Donald L. Fixico; Illus. 265 pp. Paper. University of New Mexico Press, 2000. $27.95.

*URBAN INDIANS
Donald Fixico; Grades 5 and up. Illus. Chelsea House, 1989. $17.95.

URBAN INDIANS
Center for the History of the American Indian Staff; 185 pp. Amazon.com, 1981. $4.

URBAN INDIANS: DRUMS FROM THE CITIES
Gregory W. Frazier; Describes the plight of over one-half of the Alaska Native & American Indian population. Illus. 500 pp. Paper. Amazon.com, 1994. $22.95.

URBAN INSTITUTIONS & PEOPLE OF INDIAN ANCESTRY
Raymond Breton and Gail Akian; 52 pp. Paper. Gower Publishing, 1978. $3.

URBAN VOICES: THE BAY AREA AMERICAN INDIAN COMMUNITY
Susan Lobo, Editor; Essays, photos, stories, and art on the American Indian urban experience. Illus. 180 pp. University of Arizona Press, 2002. $21.95.

URBANIZING FRONTIERS: INDIGENOUS PEOPLES & SETTLERS IN 19TH-CENTURY PACIFIC RIM CITIES
Penelope Edmonds; Explored the lives of Indigenous peoples & newcomers in two Pacific Rim cities - Victoria, British Columbia & Melbourne, Australia. Illus. 328 pp. University of Washington Press, 2010. $94; paper, $39.95.

URBANIZATION OF AMERICAN INDIANS: A CRITICAL BIBLIOGRAPHY
Russell Thornton, et al; 96 pp. Paper. Amazon.com & Alibris.com, 1982. $4.95.

THE URINE DANCE OF THE ZUNI INDIANS OF NEW MEXICO
John G. Bourke; 15 pp. Amazon.com, 1989. $9.95.

USES OF PLANTS BY THE INDIANS OF THE MISSOURI RIVER REGION
Melvin R. Gilmore
Enlarged edition. Illus. 165 pp. Paper. University of Nebraska Press, 1991. $12.95.

UTAH PLACE NAMES
John W. Van Cott; Paper. University of Utah Press, $14.95.

UTAH'S BLACK HAWK WAR
John Alton Peterson; An account of the "secret" war between a band led by Ute tribal leader Black Hawk and the Mormons. University of Utah Press, $59.95; paper, $19.95.

*THE UTE
Craig & Katherine Doherty; Grades 4-8. 32 pp. Amazon.com, 1994. $22.60.

UTE INDIAN ARTS & CULTURE: FROM PREHISTORY TO THE NEW MILLENNIUM
William Wroth, Editor; Includes interviews and essays by Alden B. Naranjo, Terry G. Knight, Sr., James A. Goss, Richard N. Ellis, Catherine S. Fowler, Craig D. Bates, and

Cathy L. Wright. Illus. 256 pp. Paper. Colorado Springs Fine Arts Center, 2000. Also available from the University of New Mexico Press, $45.

UTE INDIANS OF COLORADO IN THE 20TH CENTURY
Richard K. Young; Comparative history of the Southern Ute and Ute Mountain Ute peoples. Illus. Maps. 384 pp. University of Oklahoma Press, 1997. $29.95

THE UTE INDIANS OF SOUTHWESTERN COLORADO
Helen Sloan Daniels; Jan & P. David Smith, Editors; Revised 1941 edition.The Ute history, culture & artifacts. Illus. 180 pp. Paper. Western Reflections Publishing, $17.95.

THE UTE INDIANS OF UTAH, COLORADO, AND NEW MEXICO
Virginia McConnell Simmons; Illus. 325 pp. Paper. U. Press of Colorado, 2001. $24.95.

UTE LAND RELIGION IN THE AMERICAN WEST, 1879-2009
Brandi Denison; Illus. 330 pp. University of Nebraska Press, 2017. $55.

UTE LEGENDS
Celinda Kaelin; Illus. 209 pp. University of Idaho Press-Caxton Press, 2016. $16.

UTE MOUNTAIN UTES
Robert Delaney; Illus. 150 pp. University of New Mexico Press, 1990.

UTE TALES
collected by Anne M. Smith; foreword by Joseph G. Jorgensen
Illus. Map. Paper. University of Utah Press. $19.95.

*THE UTES
Alice Flanagan; Grades 2-4. 48 pp. Children's Press, 1997. $21.

THE UTES: A FORGOTTEN PEOPLE
Wilson Rockwell; The history of the Ute Indians of western Colorado and Utah. Reprint of the 1956 edition. Illus. 307 pp. Paper. Western Reflections Publishing, $21.95.

UTES: THE MOUNTAIN PEOPLE
Jan Pettit; Revised edition. 225 pp. Paper. Johnson Books, $12.95.

THE UTES MUST GO! AMERICAN EXPANSION & THE REMOVAL OF A PEOPLE
Peter R. Decker; Illus. 256 pp. Paper. Fulcrum Publishing, 2004. $19.95.

UTMOST GOOD FAITH: PATTERNS OF APACHE-MEXICAN HOSTILITIES IN NORTHERN CHICUAHUA BORDER WARFARE, 1821-1848
William Griffen; Illus. 336 pp. University of New Mexico Press, 1989. $37.50.

UTOPIAN LEGACIES: A HISTORY OF CONQUEST & OPPRESSION IN THE WESTERN WORLD John Mohawk; Philosophical analysis of Western history in light of patterns of utopian thinking. 296 pp. Amazon.com, $24.95; paper, $14.95.

V

THE VAIL SITE: A PALEO-INDIAN ENCAMPMENT IN MAINE
Richard M. Gramley. Ilus. 170 pp. Paper. Amazon.com, $13.95.

VALLEY OF THE MISSISSIPPI
Henry Lewis; Bertha Heilbron, Editor
Illus. 423 pp. Minnesota Historical Society, 1967. $39.75; uncut edition, $50.

VALLEY OF THE SPIRITS: UPPER SKAGIT INDIANS OF WESTERN WASHINGTON
June Collins; Illus. 282 pp. University of Washington Press, 1974. $20; paper, $9.95.

VANISHED IN HIAWATHA: THE STORY OF THE CANTON ASYLUM FOR INSANE INDIANS Carla Joinson; Illus. 424 pp. University of Nebraska Press, 2016. $29.95.

THE VANISHING AMERICAN: THE EPIC OF THE INDIAN
Zane Grey; Paper. Amazon.com, 1982. $3.50.

THE VANISHING AMERICAN: WHITE ATTITUDES & U.S. INDIAN POLICY
Brian W. Dipple; Photos. 438 pp. Paper. University Press of Kansas, 1982. $15.95.

VANISHING HERITAGE
Hooge & Lepper; Archaeology & culture history of Licking County, Ohio. Covers moundbuilders, including the famous Newark Earthworks. Illus. 100 pp. Hothem House, 1992. $22.50.

THE VANISHING RACE & OTHER ILLUSIONS: PHOTOGRAPHS OF INDIANS BY EDWARD S. CURTIS Christopher M. Lymans
Illus. 158 pp. Smithsonian Institution Press, 1982. $24.95. Paper. Pantheon, $14.95.

THE VANISHING RACE: SELECTIONS FROM EDWARD S. CURTIS' THE NORTH AMERICAN INDIAN
Mick Gidley, Editor; Reprint 1977 ed. Illus. Paper. U. of Washington Press, $14.95.

VAST DOMAIN OF BLOOD
Don Schellie; 289 pp. Westernlore, 1968. $9.95.

VECTORS OF DEATH: THE ARCHAEOLOGY OF EUROPEAN CONTACT
Ann Ramenofsky; Illus. 360 pp. University of New Mexico Press, 1987. $27.50.

*VEHO
Henry Tall Bull & Tom Weist
Grades 2-6. Paper. Council for Indian Education, 1971. $1.95.

THE VENGEFUL WIFE & OTHER BLACKFOOT STORIES
Hugh A. Dempsey
Illus. Maps. 304 pp. U. of Oklahoma Press, 2003. $24.95; paper, $14.95.

VERBAL ART IN SAN BLAS: KUNA CULTURE THROUGH ITS DISCOURSES
Joel Sherzer; 281 pp. Paper. University of New mexico Press, 1998. $21.95.

*THE VERY FIRST AMERICANS
Cara Ashrose; illus. by Byrna Waldman; How first Americans lived. Illus. with paintings depicting clothing, dwellings, art , tools, & other artifacts. Grades PS-3. Illus. 32 pp. Paper. Grosset & Dunlap, 1993. $2.25.

VESPERS: CONBTEMPORARY AMERICAN POEMS OF RELIGION & SPIRITUALITY
Virgil Suarez & Ryan G. Van Cleave
Includes Native American poems. 178 pp. Paper. University of Iowa Press, 2003. $21.

A VICTORIAN EARL IN THE ARCTIC: THE TRAVELS & COLLECTIONS OF THE FIFTH EARL OF LONSDALE, 1888-89 Shepard Krech III; Examination and analysis of a collection of native artifacts gathered during an early expedition in Canada & Alaskan Arctic. Illus. 216 pp. University of Washington Press, $35.

VICTORIO: APACHE WARRIOR & CHIEF
Kathleen P. Chamberlain; The story of this 19th-century Warm Springs Apache warrior. 272 pp. University of Oklahoma Press, $24.95.

VICTORIO & THE MIMBRES APACHES
Dan L. Thrapp; Illus. Maps. 394 pp. Paper. University of Oklahoma Press, 1980. $14.95.

THE VICTORY WITH NO NAME: THE NATIVE AMERICAN DEFEAT OF THE FIRST AMERICAN ARMY
Colin G. Galloway; Oxford University Press, 2014. $24.95; paper, $17.95.

VIET CONG AT WOUNDED KNEE: THE TRAIL OF A BLACKFEET ACTIVIST
Woody Kipp; Story of Woody Kipp from the Blackfeet Reservation & culture to Vietnam to activism at Wounded Knee. 176 pp. Paper. University of Nebraska Press, 2004. $12.95.

A VIEW FROM BLACK MESA: THE CHANGING FACE OF ARCHAEOLOGY
George Gumerman; A synopsis of Anasazi prehistory & cultural ecology. 184 pp. Paper. University of Arizona Press, 1984. $16.95.

VIEW FROM THE MEDICINE LODGE: STORIES FROM THE AMERICAN INDIAN'S SOUL Jim Great Elk Waters; Illus. 272 pp. Paper. Amazon.com, 2002. $16.95.

THE VIEW FROM OFFICERS' ROW: ARMY PERCEPTIONS OF WESTERN INDIANS
Sherry L. Smith; 263 pp. Paper. University of Arizona Press, 1990. $17.95.

VIEW FROM THE SHORE: AMERICAN INDIAN PERSPECTIVES ON THE QUINCENTENARY Jose Barreiro, Editor
A collection of articles, interviews, and essays exploring the effects of Columbus's arrival on Indigenous people. Akwe:kon Press, 1992. $12.

VIEWS FROM THE APACHE FRONTIER: REPORT ON THE NORTHERN PROVINCES OF NEW SPAIN, 1799 Jose Cortes; Elizabeth John, Editor & John Wheat, tr. Illus. Maps. 192 pp. Paper. University of Oklahoma Press, 1989. $13.95.

VIEWS OF A VANISHING FRONTIER
John C. Ewers, et al; Illus. 150 pp. U. of Nebraska Press, 1984. $29.95. Paper. Joslyn Art, $14.95.

THE VILLAGE INDIANS OF THE UPPER MISSOURI: THE MANDANS, HIDATSAS & ARIKARAS Roy W. Meyer; Illus. 355 pp. University of Nebraska Press, 1977. $27.50.

VILLAGERS: ATHABASKAN INDIAN LIFE ALONG THE YUKON RIVER
Claire Fejes; Drawings & text. 224 pp. Amazon.com & Epicenter Press, 2016. $18.95.

VILLAGES OF HISPANIC NEW MEXICO
Nancy Hunter Warren; Illus. 136 pp. Paper. School of American Research, 1987. $14.95.

VINEYARDS & VAQUEROS: INDIAN LABOR & THE ECONOMIC EXPANSION OF SOUTHERN CALIFORNIA, 1771-1877
George Harwood Phillips; How American Indians contributed to the making of greater Los Angeles. Illus. Maps. 384 pp. University of Oklahoma Press, 2010. $45.

VINTAGE NATIVE AMERICAN POSTCARDS
W.W. Norton & Co., 2003. $15.95.

VIOLENCE OVER THE LANDS: INDIANS & EMPIRES
Ned Blackhawk; Illus. 384 pp. Paper. Harvard University Press, 2006. $13.99.

VIOLENCE, RESISTANCE, & SURVIVAL IN THE AMERICAS: NATIVE AMERICANS & THE LEGACY OF CONQUEST William B. Taylor & Franklin Pease G.Y.; Documents a variety of roles played by Native Americans in the westernization of the Americas. Illus. 336 pp. Smithsonian Institution Press, 1994. $49.

VIOLENT ENCOUNTERS: INTERVIEWS ON WESTERN MASSACRES
Deborah Lawrence, Jon Lawrence; Historians talk about their study of violence in the West during the 19th century. Illus. Maps. 224 pp. U. of Oklahoma Press, 2011. $34.95.

VIRGINIA'S WESTERN WAR 1775-1786
Neal Hammon & Richard Taylor; Illus. Maps. 352 pp. Wennawoods Publishing, $29.95.

*THE VISION OF THE SPOKANE PROPHET
Rebecca Egbert; Hap Gilliland, Editor
Grades 4 and up. Illus. 36 pp. Paper. Council for Indian Education, 1989. $5.95.

VISION QUEST
Steven Foster & Meredith Little; Personal transformation in the wilderness.
Revised edition. Illus. 235 pp. Paper. Prentice Hall Press, $9.95.

VISION, SPACE, DESIRE: GLOBAL PERSPECTIVES & CULTURAL HYBRIDITY
Natioal Museum of the American Indian; Illus. 180 pp. Paper. NMAI Press, 2006. $20.

VISIONS OF CHIMNEY ROCK
Chimney Rock Interpretive Association; Chimney Rock was a special place for the
ancestors of the Pueblo people, the Anasazi. The purpose of the site is explored. Illus.
136 pp. Paper. Western Reflections Publishing, 2005. $19.95.

VISIONS OF A HUICHOL SHAMAN
Peter T. Furst; Illus. 112 pp. University Museum Publications, 2003. $29.95.

VISIONS OF THE NORTH: NATIVE ARTS OF THE NORTHWEST COAST
Don & Debra McQuiston; Illus. 120 pp. paper. Amazon.com, 1995. $19.95.

VISIONS OF OUR NATIVE AMERICAN HERITAGE
Jay Stock; Illus. 192 pp. Jays, Inc., 1994. $79.95.

**VISIONS OF SOUND: MUSICAL INSTRUMENTS OF FIRST NATION COMMUNITIES IN
NORTHEASTERN AMERICA** Beverly Diamond, M. Sam Cronk, Franziska von Rosen
Study of musical instruments of native peoples in Northeastern North America. Focuses on
interpretations by elders and consultants from Iroquois, Wabanaki, Innuat, and Anishnabek
communities. Illus. 28 color, 132 halftones. 240 pp. University of Chicago Press, 1995. $70.

VISIONS & VOICES: AMERICAN INDIAN ACTIVISM & THE CIVIL RIGHTS MOVEMENT
Kurt Peters & Terry Straus, Editors; Illus. 468 pp. Paper. Albatross Press, 2009. $20.

**VISIONS & VOICES: NATIVE AMERICAN PAINTING FROM THE PHILBROOK
MUSEUM OF ART** Lydia L. Wyckoff, Editor
146 color Illus. 363 halftone photos. University of New Mexico Press, $70; paper, $37.

VISITING WITH THE ANCESTORS: BLACKFOOT SHIRTS IN MUSEUM SPACES
Laura Peers & Alison K. Brown; Paper. UBC Press, 2016. $39.95.

*THE VISUAL DICTIONARY OF ANCIENT CIVILIZATIONS
Includes early Native American civilizations. Tribal artifacts & crafts.
Grades 3 and up. Illus. 64 pp. Amazon.com, 1994. $15.95.

VISUAL TESTAMENT & THE ISRAELITE INDIAN
Tom Cryer; Illus. 432 pp. Paper. Amazon.com, 1999. $24.95.

**VISUALIZING THE SACRED: COSMIC VISIONS, REGIONALISM, AND THE ART OF
THE MISSISSIPPIAN WORLD** George E. Lankford, F. Kent Reilly, III, James F. Garber
Illus. Tables. Map. University of Texas Press, 2011. $60.

VITAL SOULS: BORORO COSMOLOGY, NATURAL SYMBOLISM & SHAMANISM
J. Christopher Crocker; 380 pp. University of Arizona Press, 1985. $29.95.

GERALD VIZENOR: WRITING IN THE ORAL TRADITION
Kimberly M. Blaeser; 260 pp. University of Oklahoma Press, 1996. $31.95.

GERALD VIZENOR: TEXTS & CONTEXTS
A Lee & Deborah Madsen; Illus. 448 pp. University of New Mexico Press, $50.

A VOCABULARY OF STOCKBRIDGE MAHICAN
Benjamin Smith barton, et al; 50 pp. Amazon.com, 2004. $28.

A VOCABULARY OF MOHEGAN-PEQUOT
J. Dyneley Prince & Frank Speck
Reprint. 60 pp. Amazon.com, 1998. $16.

VOCABULARY OF NEW JERSEY DELAWARE
James A. Madison; 50 pp. Amazon.com, 1998. $16.

VOCABULARY OF THE SHOSHONE LANGUAGE
George W. Hill; Reprint. 2nd edition. 40 pp. Paper. Amazon.com, $11.75.

A VOCABULARY OF THE TUSCARORA
John A. Lawson; Amazon.com, 1998. $16.

A VOCABULARY OF WOCCON
John A. Lawson; 33 pp. Amazon.com, 1998. $24.

**VOCATIONAL READINESS IN AMERICAN INDIAN LEARNING DISABLED
ADOLESCENTS** J.M. Dodd, et al; 89 pp. Paper. Northern Arizona U., 1992. $8.25.

**THE VOCATIONAL REHABILITATION OF AMERICAN INDIANS
WHO HAVE ALCOHOL OR OTHER SUBSTANCE ABUSE DISORDERS**
R.M. Schacht & L. Gaseoma; 45 pp. Amazon.com, 1993. $6.

A VOICE IN HER TRIBE: A NAVAJO WOMAN'S OWN STORY
Irene Stewart; Illus. 90 pp. Paper. Malki-Ballena Press, 1980. $8.95.

**THE VOICE OF THE CRANE ECHOES AFAR: THE SOCIOPOLITICAL
ORGANIZATION OF THE LAKE SUPERIOR OJIBWA, 1640-1855**
Theresa M. Schenck; Illus. 142 pp. Garland, 1997. $65.

THE VOICE OF THE DAWN: AN AUTOHISTORY OF THE ABENAKI NATION
Frederick M. Wiseman; Illus. 325 pp. Paper. U. of New England Press, 2001. $24.95.

**VOICE OF INDIGENOUS PEOPLES: A PLEA TO THE WORLD: NATIVE PEOPLE
ADDRESS THE UNITED NATIONS** compiled & edited by Alexander Ewen for The Native
American CouncilWith the U.N. Draft Declaration of Indigenous Peoples Rights. In an
epilogue, Chief Oren Lyons describes events of the International Year of Indigenous
People, 1993. 19 Photos. Maps. 120 pp. Paper. Amazon.com, 1994. $12.95.

VOICE OF THE GREAT SPIRIT
Kaiser; Paper. Random House, $10.

**VOICE OF THE OLD WOLF: LUCULLUS VIRGIL McWHORTER
& THE NEZ PERCE INDIANS** Steven Ross Evans
Illus. Photos. Maps. Biblio. 250 pp. WSU Press, 1996. $32; paper, $19.95.

*VOICE OF THE PAIUTES: A STORY ABOUT SARAH WINNEMUCCA
Jodie Shull; Illus. by Keith Birdsong; Grades 4-8. Paper. Lerner Publications, 2007. $8.99.

THE VOICE OF THE TURTLE: AMERICAN INDIAN LITERATURE, 1900-1970
Paula G. Allen, Editor; 336 pp. Paper. Amazon.com, 1995. $12.50.

THE VOICE THAT WAS IN TRAVEL: STORIES
Diane Glancy; 20 stories reveal insights into contemporary American Indian life.
128 pp. University of Oklahoma Press, 1999. $19.95.

VOICES FROM THE DELAWARE BIG HOUSE CEREMONY
Robert S. Grumet, Ed.; Illus. 240 pp. University of Oklahoma Press, 2002. $19.95.

**VOICES FROM FOUR DIRECTIONS: CONTEMPORARY TRANSLATIONS
OF THE NATIVE LITERATURES OF NORTH AMERICA**
edited by Brian Swann; Stories & songs from 31 Native groups in North America.
632 pp. University of Nebraska Press, 2002. $70; paper, $27.50.

VOICES FROM HASKELL: INDIAN STUDENTS BETWEEN TWO WORLDS, 1884-1928
Myriam Vuckovic; Examines educational experience of Native children at Haskell Indian
school. Photos. 320 pp. University Press of Kansas, 2008. $34.95.

*VOICES FROM THE ICE
John L. Peyton; A glimpse of Ojibway life during the early 20th Century.
Grades 1-4. Illus. 52 pp. Paper. University of Nebraska Press, 1990. $9.95.

VOICES FROM THE TRAIL OF TEARS
Vicki Rozema, Ed.; The author drom from letters, military & medical recods, and journal
excerpts to provide insight into what actually happened. Illus. 176 pp. Paper.
Amazon.com, 2003. $11.95.

VOICES FROM WOUNDED KNEE, 1973, IN THE WORDS OF THE PARTICIPANTS
Akwesasne Notes
History of American Indian Movement (AIM). Illus. Amazon.com, 1974.

VOICES IN THE CANYON
Viele; The story of a Navajo National Monument's amazing cliff dwellings written for
laymen and reviewed by professionals. Illus. 50 color photos. Maps. 76 pp. Paper. Western
National Parks Assn., $6.

VOICES IN CLAY: PUEBLO POTTERY FROM THE EDNA M. KELLY COLLECTION
Bruce Bernstein & J.J. Brody
Illus. 116 pp. Miami Univerity Art Museum, 2002. $49.95; paper, $24.95.

VOICES IN THE STONE: LIFE LESSONS FROM THE NATIVE WAY
Kent Nerburn; 184 pp. Paper. New World Library, $16.

VOICES IN THE WATERFALL
Elizabeth Cuthand; Poetry. Rhythms & traditions of First Nations people.
New edition featuring ten new poems. 80 pp. Paper. Theytus, 1992. $11.95.

**VOICES OF AMERICAN INDIAN ASSIMILATION & RESISTANCE:
HELEN HUNT JACKSON, SARAH WINNEMUCCA & VICTORIA HOWARD**
Siobhan Senier; Illus. Map. 272 pp. U. of Oklahoma Press, 2004. $29.95; paper, $17.95.

VOICES OF THE AMERICAN INDIAN EXPERIENCE
James E. Seely, Jr. & Steven A. Littleton, Editors
Provides insights into American Indian history by focusing on Indian accounts instead
of relying on other sources. Two Volumes, 800 pp. Greenwood Press, 2012. $189.

VOICES OF THE AMERICAN WEST
Eli S. Ricker; Richard E. Jensen, Editor; 2 Volumes. Vol. 1: The Indian Interviews of Eli S.
Ricker, 1903-1919. Illus. 544 pp. Paper. Vol. 2: The Settler & Soldier Interviews of Eli S.
Ricker, 1903-1919. Illus. 498 pp. Paper. University of Nebraska Press, 2012. $34.95 each.

VOICES OF CHEROKEE WOMEN
Carolyn Ross Johnston; Illus. 256 pp. Paper. Cherokee Publications, $12.95.

VOICES OF EARTH & SKY
Vinson Brown
The vision life of the Native Americans. Illus. 184 pp. Paper. Naturegraph, 1976. $8.95.

VOICES OF NATIVE AMERICA: NATIVE AMERICAN INSTRUMENTS & MUSIC
Douglas Spotted Eagle; Includes information and explanations of traditional and
contemporary music. Photos. Illus. Music sheets. 120pp. paper. Eagle's View, 1999.
$17.95.

VOICES OF NATIVE AMERICA: NATIVE AMERICAN MUSIC
Douglas Spotted Eagle; Monte Smith, Editor
Includes information and explanations of traditional and contemporary music.
Photos. Illus. Music sheets. 120 pp. Paper. Eagle's View, 1997. $17.95.

VOICES OF THE RAINBOW: CONTEMPORARY POETRY OF NATIVE NORTH AMERICA Kenneth H. Rosen, Editor; 232 pp. Paper. Arcade Publishing, 1993. $11.95.

VOICES OF RESISTANCE & RENEWAL: INDIGENOUS LEADERSHIP IN EDUCATION Dorothy Aguilera-Black Bear & John W. Tippeconnic III Illus. 224 pp. Paper. University of Oklahoma Press, 2015, $24.95.

VOICES OF A THOUSAND PEOPLE: THE MAKAH CULTURAL & RESEARCH CENTER Patricia Pierce Erikson; Illus. Map. 264 pp. University of Nebraska Press, 2002. $22.50.

VOICES OF THE WIND: NATIVE AMERICAN FLUTE SONGS Bryan Burton; Illus. 36 pp. World Music Press, 1998. $20.95 includes CD-ROM/

VOICES OF THE WIND: NATIVE AMERICAN LEGENDS Margot Edmonds & Ella Clark; Illus. 385 pp. Facts on File, 1989. $27.95.

VOICES OF THE WIND: POLYNESIAN MYTHS & CHANTS Katherine Luomala The oral traditions of the region is examined. Illus. 209 pp. Paper. Bishop Museum, $15.95.

VOICES OF WOUNDED KNEE edited by William S.E. Coleman; Brings together all of the available sources -- Lakota, military, and civilian -- using accounts of participants and observers, and reconstructs the massacre. Illus. Maps. 446 pp. Paper. University of Nebraska Press, 2000. $19.95.

VOICES THROUGH THE AGES: A NATIVE AMERICAN ANTHOLOGY Written by ITEPP Students at Humboldt State University from 1982-1998. Includes writings from "Our People Speak." 1999. Amazon.com.

*VOICES UNDER ONE SKY Trish Fox Roman Contemporary Native literature. Illus. 224 pp. Paper. The Crossing Press, 1997. $12.95.

*VOSTAAS: THE STORY OF MONTANA'S INDIAN NATIONS White Buffalo & Maxine Ruppel Covers present day life of seven Montana tribes and other Plains Indians. Grades 4-10. Paper. Council for Indian Education, 1970 ed. 68 pp. $4.95; 1990 ed. 80 pp. $6.95.

A VOYAGE TO THE NORTHWEST SIDE OF AMERICA: THE JOURNALS OF JAMES COLNETT, 1786-89 Robert Galois; The fur trade on the Northwest Coast and the first encounters with the Tsimshian and southern Heiltsuk, and the first land on the southern Queen Charlotte Islands. 448 pp. University of Washington Press, 2003. $105.

W

WABANAKI HOMELAND & THE NEW STATE OF MAINE: THE 1820 JOURNAL & PLANS OF SURVEY OF JOSEPH TREAT Micah A. Pawling; Illus. 320 pp. University of Massachusetts Press, 2007. $34.95.

THE WABANAKIS OF MAINE & THE MARITIMES: A RESOURCE BOOK ABOUT PENOBSCOT, PASSAMOQUODDY, MALISEET, MICMAC & ABENAKI INDIANS Contains over 50 lesson plans for grades 4-8. Illus. 510 pp. Paper. Amazon.com, $20.

WABANSI: FIEND OR FRIEND? Alice F. Zeman; Illus. 118 pp. Amazon.com, 1991. $14.75.

WACCAMAW LEGACY: CONTEMPORARY INDIANS FIGHT FOR SURVIVAL Patricia Lerch Illus. 184 pp. University of Alabama Press, 2004. $57.50; paper, $29.95. E-Book, $23.96.

THE WAGON BOX FIGHT: AN EPISODE OF RED CLOUD'S WAR Jerry Keenan; 160 pp. Paper. Amazon.com, 2000. $14.95.

WAHEENEE: AN INDIAN GIRL'S STORY Gilbert L. Wilson; Illus. 190 pp. University of Nebraska Press, 1981. $17.95; paper, $5.95.

THE WAKE OF THE UNSEEN OBJECT: TRAVELS THROUGH ALASKA'S NATIVE LANDSCAPES Tom Kizzia; Illus. Map. 280 pp. Paper. University of Nebraska Press, 1998. $15.

WAKEMAP MOUND: A STRATIFIED SITE ON THE COLUMBIA RIVER Emory Strong, Editor; Illus. 40 pp. Paper. Binford & Mort, $5.95.

WAKING A SLEEPING GIANT Theodore Kouba; Vantage Pres, 1987. $14.95.

WAKINYAN: LAKOTA RELIGION IN THE 20TH CENTURY Stephen E. Feraca; Illus. 104 pp. Paper. University of Nebraska Press, 1998. $12.

WALAPAI (HUALAPAI) TEXTS Werner Winter; Paper. Amazon.com & Albris.com, 1998.

WALK FOR JUSTICE: ONE MAN'S SACRIFICE FOR ANOTHER MAN'S FREEDOM Harry Kindness; Illus. 200 pp. Paper. Wo-Pila Publishing, 1999. $19.95.

WALK IN BALANCE: THE PATH TO HEALTHY, HAPPY, HARMONIOUS LIVING Sun Bear, Crysalis Mulligan, Peter Nufer & Wabun; A holistic pathway to personal enrichment & health. A personal survival manual. 171 pp. Paper. Prentice Hall Press, $8.95.

WALK IN BEAUTY: THE NAVAJO & THEIR BLANKETS Anthony Berlant & Mary Kahlenberg; Illus. 225 pp. Paper. Gibbs Smith, 1991. $29.95.

*WALK IN PEACE: LEGENDS & STORIES OF THE MICHIGAN INDIANS Simon Otto; M.T. Bussey, Editor; Selection of legends and stories in the Anishnabe (Odawa/Ojibwe) oral tradition. Grades 3-4. 2nd edition. Illus. 56 pp. Paper. Michigann Indian Press & University of Nebraska Press, 1992. $9.95.

WALK IN YOUR SOUL: LOVE INCANTATIONS OF THE OKLAHOMA CHEROKEES Jack and Anna Kilpatrick; Reprint of 1965 edition. Illus. 174 pp. Paper. Amazon.com, $6.95.

WALK SOFTLY, THIS IS GOD'S COUNTRY: 66 YEARS ON THE WIND RIVER INDIAN RESERVATION Beatrice Crofts & Elinore Markley Illus. 160 pp. Paper. Mortimore Publishing, 1997. $9.95.

*WALKER OF TIME Helen Hughes Vick; Native American mythology & mystery combined in a tale for young readers. Grades 7 and up. 192 pp. paper. Amazon.com, 1994. $9.95.

WALKING IN INDIAN MOCCASINS: THE NATIVE POLICIES OF TOMMY DOUGLAS & THE CCF R. Laurie Brown; Illus. 288 pp. University of Washington Press, 1997. $24.95.

WALKING ON THE WIND: CHEROKEE TEACHINGS FOR HARMONY & BALANCE Michael Tlanusta Garrett; Illus. 204 pp. Paper. Inner Traditions, 1998. $14.

WALKING THE CLOUDS: AN ANTHOLOGY OF INDIGENOUS SCIENCE FICTION Grace L. Dillon, Editor; Paper. University of Arizona Press, 2010. $24.95.

WALKING THE MAZE: THE ENDURING PRESENCE OF CELTIC SPIRIT Loren Cruden; Equates Celtic customs with Native American traditions & rituals. Presents a vision of the ancient Celtic path as it can be lived today. Illus. 256 pp. Paper. Inner Traditions, 1998. $14.95.

THE WALKING PEOPLE: A NATIVE AMERICAN ORAL HISTORY Paula Underwood; Barbara McNeill & Jeanne Slobod, Editors Illus. 839 pp. Amazon.com, 1993. $48; paper, $28.

WALKING THUNDER: DINE MEDICINE WOMAN Bradford Keeney; Illus. 200 pp. Paper. Leete's Island Books, 2002. $18.95.

WALKING THE TRAIL: ONE MAN'S JOURNEY ALONG THE CHEROKEE TRAIL OF TEARS Jerry Ellis; Map. 256 pp. Paper. University of Nebraska Press, 2001. $17.95.

WALKING WHERE WE LIVED: MEMOIRS OF A MONO INDIAN FAMILY Gaylen D. Lee; Illus. Maps. 224 pp. Paper. University of Oklahoma Press, 1999. $14.95.

WALKING WITH GRANDFATHER: THE WISDOM OF LAKOTA ELDERS Joseph Marshall III; Illus. 230 pp. Paper. Amazon.com, 2005. $14.95.

KAY WALKINGSTICK: AN AMERICAN ARTIST Kathleen Ash-Milby (Navajo) & David W. Penney; Illus. 208 pp. NMAI Press, $50.

*WALKS IN BEAUTY Hazel Krantz; Navajo story. Ages 12 and up. 192 pp. Northland, $12.95; paper, $6.95.

WALKS IN THE SUN Don Coldsmith; Illus. 245 pp. Amazon.com, $12.50.

*WALKS TWO WORLDS: A NAVAJO BOY'S COMING OF AGE Robert B. Fox; Grades 4 and up. 62 pp. Paper. Sunstone Press, $6.95.

THE WALLEYE WAR: THE STRUGGLE FOR OJIBWE SPEARFISHING & TREATY RIGHTS Larry Nesper; Spearfishing conflict on the Lac du Flambeau Reservation in Wisconsin. Illus. Map. 245 pp. University of Nebraska Press, 2002. $60; paper, $21.95.

WALLEYE WARRIORS: THE CHIPPEWA TREATY RIGHTS STORY Rick Whaley & Walter Bresette 2nd Ed. Illus. 289 pp. Paper. Writers Publishing Cooperative, 1999. $25.

*THE WAMPANOAG Laurie Weinstein-Farson; Grades 5 and up. Illus. 104 pp. Chelsea House, 1988. $17.95.

*THE WAMPANOAG Katherine Doherty; Grades 4-6. Reprint. 64 pp. Paper. Franklin Watts, $6.95.

WAMPANOAG GENEALOGICAL HISTORY OF MARTHA'S VINEYARD, MASS. Jerome D. Segel; Illus. Genealogical Publishing, 2003.

*WAMPANOAG INDIANS Bill Lund; Grades K-3. Illus. 24 pp. Children's Press, 1997. $14.

*THE WAMPANOAGS Alice Flanagan; Grades 2-4. Illus. 48 pp. Children's Press, 1997. $21; paper, $6.95.

THE WAMPANOAGS OF MASHPEE Russell M. Peters; Historical & cultural portrayal of the Wampanoags of Mashpee, Mass. Illus. Amazon.com, $16.

WAMPUM BELTS OF THE IROQUOIS Tehanetorens; The history of the Iroquois Confederacy, its treaties, chiefs, important events, etc. Illus. Photos. 96 pp. Book Publishing Co., $9.95.

WAMPUM BELTS & PEACE TREES: GEORGE MORGAN, NATIVE AMERICANS & REVOLUTIONARY DIPLOMACY
Gregory Schaaf; Illus. 304 pp. Fulcrum Publishing, 1990. $27.95.

WAMPUM AND THE ORIGINS OF AMERICAN MONEY
Marc Shell; A Thoughtful Exploration of the Meanings & Metaphors of American Money. 168 pp. University of Illinois Press, 2013. $37.

WAMPUM, WAR & TRADE GOODS WEST OF THE HUDSON
Gilbert W. Hagerty; Illus. 310 pp. Heart of the Lakes, 1987. $40.

WANDERINGS OF AN ARTIST AMONG THE INDIANS OF NORTH AMERICA
Paul Kane; 384 pp. Paper. Dover, $10.95.

WANGKA: AUSTRONESIAN CANOE ORIGINS
Edwin Doran, Jr.; Illus. 121 pp. Texas A & M University Press, 1981. $15.

WAPATO HERITAGE: THE HISTORY OF THE CHELAN & ENTIAT INDIANS
Tom R. Hackenmiller; 192 pp. Paper. Amazon.com, 2001. $17.95.

THE WAPPO: A REPORT
Yolande S. Beard; Paper. Malki-Ballena Press, 1979. $8.50.

WAR CHIEFS
Bill Dugan; A series of five books: Geronimo, Chief Joseph, Crazy Horse, Quanah Parker, and Sitting Bull. Paper. HarperCollins, 1991-94. $4.99 each.

WAR DANCE AT FORT MARION: PLAINS INDIAN WAR PRISONERS
Brad D. Lookingbill; Kiowa, Cheyenne, Comanche & Arapaho chiefs & warrior prisoners from 1875-1878, partake in an educational experiment. Illus. 352 pp. Paper. University of Oklahoma Press, $21.95.

WAR DANCE: PLAINS INDIAN MUSICAL PERFORMANCE
William K. Powers; 199 pp. Paper. University of Arizona Press, 1990. $14.95.

*WAR DRUMS AT EDEN PRAIRIE
Gladys Nelson; Fictionalized account of Sioux uprising of 1862. Grades 6-8. Illus. Amazon.com, $5.95.

WAR EAGLE'S FACT OF LIFE
Gary D. Bromley (War Eagle); Teachings by the author of the ancient red road. Gary D. Bromley, P.O. Box 1629, Fontana, CA 92334-1629.

WAR EAGLE: A LIFE OF GENERAL EUGENE A. CARR
James T. King; Illus. 325 pp. University of Nebraska Press, 1964. $27.95.

WAR IN THE TRIBAL ZONE: EXPANDING STATES & INDIGENOUS WARFARE
R. Brian Ferguson & Neil Whitehead, Editors
Native warfare. Illus. 350 pp. School of American Research, 1989. $35; paper, $15.95.

THE WAR IN WORDS: READING THE DAKOTA CONFLICT THROUGH THE CAPTIVITY LITERATURE Kathryn Zabelle Derounian-Stodola
Studies 24 of the captivity & confinement narratives generated by the Dakota Conflict of 1862. Photos. Map. 398 pp. University of Nebraska Press, 2009. $60.

THE WAR NOBODY WON: THE MODOC WAR FROM THE ARMY'S POINT OF VIEW
Edward E. Hathaway; Illus. 135 pp. Paper. Amazon.com, 1995. $11.95.

WAR OF A THOUSAND DESERTS: INDIAN RAIDS & THE U.S. MEXICAN WAR
Brian DeLay; Exploring Mexican, American, and Indian sources and the economic, cultural, and political developments within Native communities affected 19th-century nation-states. The Lamar Series in Western History. 496 pp. Paper. Yale University Press & Amazon.com, $30.

WAR PAINT: BLACKFOOT & SARCEE PAINTED BUFFALO ROBES IN THE ROYAL ONTARIO MUSEUM Arni Brownstone
Blackfoot tradition, art, and culture as told through six historic buffalo robes. Illus. 96 pp. Paper. University of Toronto Press, $24.95.

WAR PARTY IN BLUE: PAWNEE SCOUTS IN THE U.S. ARMY
Mark Van de Logt; Illus. Maps. 350 pp. University of Oklahoma Press, 2010. $34.95.

WAR UNDER HEAVEN: PONTIAC, THE INDIAN NATIONS, & THE BRITISH EMPIRE
Gregory Evans Dowd; Illus. 384 pp. Johns Hopkins U. Press, 2002. $32; paper, $19.95.

WAR WOMAN: A NOVEL
Robert J. Conley; Cherokee based. 368 pp. Paper. University of Oklahoma Press, $5.95.

WARBONNETS
Rod Peate; Short history and how-to manual in making a warbonnet. Illus. 17 pp. Paper. Book Publishing Co., Amazon.com & Written Heritage, 1995. $6.95.

THE WARING PAPERS: THE COLLECTED WORKS OF ANTONIO J. WARING
Stephen Williams; Paper. Peabody Museum, 1977. $22.50.

WARLORDS OF THE WEST: A STORY OF THE COMANCHE
Preston Harper; Borderlands Pres, 1990. $14.95.

WARM SPRINGS MILLENNIUM VOICES FROM THE RESERVATION
Michael Baughman & Charlotte Hadella
Illus. 181 pp. Paper. University of Texas Press, 2000. $25.

WARPATH & BIVOUAC: CONQUEST OF THE SIOUX
John F. Finerty; Detailed account of the Dakota Indian wars of 1876 & the Nez Perce Indian wars of 1877. Reprint. Illus. Map. 360 pp. Paper. University of Oklahoma Press, $14.95. Reprint. Illus. 460 pp. Amazon.com, 2000. $34.50.

WARPATH: THE TRUE STORY OF THE FIGHTING SIOUX TOLD IN A BIOGRAPHY OF CHIEF WHITE BULL
Stanley Vestal; Illus. Maps. 291 pp. Paper. University of Nebraska Press, 1984. $19.95.

WARPATH & CATTLE TRAIL
Hubert E. Collins, et al, Editors; Illus. 296 pp. University Press of Colorado, 1998. $34.95.

WARPATHS: INVASIONS OF NORTH AMERICA
Ian K. Steele; Reprint. Illus. 304 pp. Paper. Oxford University Press, $25.95.

WARPATHS! TRAVELS OF A MILITARY HISTORIAN IN NORTH AMERICA
John Keegan; Illus. 370 pp. Amazon.com, 1998. $26.

WILLIAM W. WARREN: THE LIFE, LETTERS & TIMES OF AN OJIBWE LEADER
Theresa M. Schenck
Biography. Illus. Maps. 224 pp. Paper. University of Nebraska Press, 2007. $19.95.

THE WARREN WAGONTRAIN RAID
B. Capps; Illus. 328 pp. SMU Press, 1974. $10.95.

CLYDE WARRIOR: (1939-1968) TRADITION, COMMUNITY, AND RED POWER
Paul R. McKenzie-Jones
Biography of the Ponca leader. Illus. 256 pp. University of Oklahoma Press, 2014. $29.95.

A WARRIOR I HAVE BEEN: PLAINS INDIAN CULTURES IN TRANSITION
The Richard Green Collection of Plains Indian Art. Illus. 273 color plates, 35 b&w photos. 2 maps. 208 pp. Paper. Whispering Wind, $29.95.

WARRIOR IN THE RING: THE LIFE OF MARVIN CAMEL, NATIVE AMERICAN WORLD CHAMPION BOXER Brian D'Ambrosio
248 pp. Riverbend Publishing, 2016. $29.95; paper, $15.95. eBook, $9.99.

WARRIOR IN TWO CAMPS: ELY S. PARKER, UNION GENERAL & SENECA CHIEF
William H. Armstrong; 256 pp. Paper. Syracuse University Press, $15.95.

WARRIOR MAIDEN: A HOPI LEGEND
Ellen Schecter; Grades PS-3. Ilus. 48 pp. Paper. Amazon.com, 1992. $3.99.

WARRIOR NATIONS: THE U.S. AND INDIAN PEOPLES
Robert L. Nichols; 256 pp. Paper. University of Oklahoma Press, $19.95.

WARRIOR, SHIELD & STAR: IMAGERY & IDEOLOGY OF PUEBLO WARFARE
Polly Schaafsma; Illus. 216 pp. Paper. Western Edge Press, 1999. $24.95.

WARRIOR WOMAN: THE STORY OF LOZEN, APACHE WARRIOR & SHAMAN
Paul Aleshire; 336 pp. St. Martin's Press, 2001. $24.95.

*THE WARRIORS
Joseph Bruchac; Grades 4-6. Paper. Carolhoda Books & Lerner Publications, $4.99.

WARRIORS & CHIEFS OF THE OLD WEST
Charles L. Convis; Illus. 64 pp. Paper. Pioneer Press, 1996. $8.95.

WARRIORS IN UNIFORM: THE LEGACY OF AMERICAN INDIAN HEROISM
Herman J. Viola; intro. by Ben Nighthorse Campbell
Native Americans in the U.S. military. Illus. 216 pp. National Geographic, 2008. $30.

WARRIORS - NAVAJO CODE TALKERS
Photos by Kenji Kawano; Photos & quotes from 75 of the surviving Navajo code talkers. 105 pp. Paper. Northland Press, $19.95

*WARRIORS OF THE RAINBOW: STRANGE & PROPHETIC DREAMS OF THE INDIAN PEOPLE William Willoya & Vinson Brown; Grades 4-12. Revised & expanded 1962 edition. Illus. 96 pp. Paper. Naturegraph, 2009. $12.95.

WARRIORS OF THE WORLD: THE NATIVE AMERICAN WARRIOR
Chris McNab; Examines the various tribes that fought both themselves and the various European colonizers across North America. Illus. 224 pp. St. Martin's Press, 2010. $29.95.

WARRIORS ON THE LITTLE BIG HORN, 1876
Richard Hook; Illus. 50 pp. Paper. MBI Distribution Services, 2004. $14.95.

WARS FOR EMPIRE: APACHES, THE U.S., AND THE SOUTHWEST BORDERLANDS
Janne Lahti; Illus. 328 pp. Map. University of Oklahoma Press, 2017. $34.95.

THE WARS OF THE IROQUOIS: A STUDY IN INTERTRIBAL TRADE RELATIONS
George T. Hunt
Reprint of 1940 edition. Map. 218 pp. Paper. University of Wisconsin Press, $24.95.

WASASE: INDIGENOUS PATHWAYS OF ACTION & FREEDOM
Taiaiake Alfred; 313 pp. Paper. University of Toronto Press, 2005.

WASHINGTON STATE PLACE NAMES
Paper. University of Washington Press, $12.95.

WASHINGTON STATE PLACE NAMES: FROM ALKI TO YELM
Doug Brokenshire; Paper. The Caxton Press, 1994. $14.95.

WASHAKIE, CHIEF OF THE SHOSHONES
Grace Raymond Hebard; Illus. Maps. 325 pp. Paper. U. of Nebraska Press, 1995. $12.

THE WASHAKIE LETTERS OF WILLIE OTTOGARY: NORTHWESTERN SHOSHONE JOURNALIST & LEADER, 1908-1929 Matthew E. Kreitzer, Editor; Letters describing a society in cultural transition. Illus. 352 pp. Paper. Utah State University Press, 2000. $15.95.

GEORGE WASHINGTON'S WAR ON NATIVE AMERICA
Barbara Alice Mann; Recounts the events on the forgotten western front of the American Revolution. Maps. 316 pp. Paper. University of Nebraska Press, 2004. $17.95.

WASHITA MEMORIES: EYEWITNESS VIEWS OF CUSTER'S ATTACK ON THE BLACK KETTLE'S VILLAGE Richard G. Hardorff; Presents firsthand testimonies of the Battle of the Washita. Illus. 464 pp. University of Oklahoma Press, $34.95.

WASHITA: THE U.S. ARMY & THE SOUTHERN CHEYENNES, 1867-1869
Jerome A. Greene; Illus. Maps. 304 pp. University of Oklahoma Press, 2004. $29.95.

THE WASHO LANGUAGE OF EAST CENTRAL CALIFORNIA & NEVADA
A.L. Kroeber; Reprint oif 1907 edition. 66 pp. Paper. Coyote Press, $7.8l.

WASHO SHAMANS & PEYOTISTS: RELIGIOUS CONFLICT IN AN AMERICAN INDIAN TRIBE Edgar E. Siskin; Illus. 300 pp. University of Utah Press, 1983. $25.

WASI'CHU: THE CONTINUING INDIAN WARS
Bruce Johansen & Roberto Maestro; Chronicles the history of Native struggles in the U.S. Illus. 270 pp. Paper. Amazon.com, 1980. $10.

WASTELANDING: LEGACIES OF URANIUM MINING IN NAVAJO COUNTRY
Traci Brynne Voyles; University of Minnesota Press, 2015. $87.50; paper, $25.

WATER ON THE PLATEAU
Paper. Museum of Northern Arizona, 1981. $3.

*WATERLESS MOUNTAIN
Laura A. Armer; Reprint of 1931 edition. Grades 5-8. Illus. Amazon.com, $11.95.

WATERLILY
Ella Cara Deloria; New edition. A novel of a Sioux woman's life.
288 pp. Paper. University of Nebraska Press, 1988. $14.95.

THE WATERS BETWEEN: A NOVEL OF THE DAWN LAND
Joseph Bruchac; Story of pre-contact Native Americans, 10,000 years ago, Lake Champlain and the Abenaki communities. 310 pp. Paper. University Press of New England, 1998. $15.95.

WATERWAY
B. Haile; Reprint. Illus. 155 pp. Paper. University of Nebraska Press, $12.95.

WAUBA YUMA'S PEOPLE: THE COMPARATIVE SOCIO-POLITICAL STRUCTURE OF THE PAI INDIANS OF ARIZONA Henry F. Dobyns & Robert C. Euler; Describes Pai socia structure prior to U.S. reservation policy that created the contemporary Walapai and Havasupai groups. Illus. Map. 98 pp. Amazon.com, 1970. $30.

THE WAY IT WAS: AN INDIAN GIRL LIVING THRU THE DEPRESSION
Wanda S. Brookshire; Jean Starr, Ed.; Illus. 56 pp. Brooks Publishing, 1999. $10.

THE WAY OF THE DEAD INDIANS: GUARJIRO MYTHS & SYMBOLS
Michael Perrin; Michael Fineberg, tr.
Illus. 230 pp. University of Texas Press, 1987. $30; paper, $12.95.

A WAY OF LIFE THAT DOES NOT EXIST: CANADA & THE EXTINGUISHMENT OF THE INNU Colin Samson; Illus. 386 pp. Verso, 2003. $27.

THE WAY OF THE MASKS
Claude Levi-Strauss; translated by Sylvia Modelski; Study of Northwest Coast Indians and Strauss's approach to their tribal art & culture. Reprint of 1982 edition. Illus. Maps. 276 pp. Paper. UBC Press. Distributed by University of Washington Press, $22.50.

THE WAY OF THE PIPE: ABORIGINAL SPIRITUALITY & SYMBOLIC HEALING IN CANADIAN PRISONS
James B. Waldram; 233 pp. Paper. Amazon.com, 1997.

THE WAY OF THE SPIRIT
Time-Life Books Editors; Illus. 228 pp. Amazon.com, 1997. $29.95.

THE WAY OF THE WARRIOR
Time-Life Books Eds.; Amazon.com, 1993.

THE WAY OF THE WARRIOR: STORIES OF THE CROW PEOPLE
Phenocia Bauerle, Editor; Illus. 135 pp. Paper. U. of Nebraska Press, 2003. $12.47.

THE WAY TO INDEPENDENCE: MEMORIES OF A HIDATSA INDIAN FAMILY, 1840-1920 Carolyn Gilman, et al; Account of the evolving culture & environment of Buffalo Bird Woman's family & her tribe. Illus. Photos. Biblio. 371 pp. Minnesota Historical Society Press, 1987. $24.95; paper, $14.95.

THE WAY TO KNOWLEDGE
Carole Yazzie-Shaw; illus by William Yazzie; Pamphlet. Amazon.com. $5.

THE WAY TO MAKE PERFECT MOUNTAINS: NATIVE AMERICAN LEGENDS OF SACRED MOUNTAINS Leonard F. Chana; 64 pp. Paper. Cinco Puntos, 1997. $9.95.

THE WAY TO RAINY MOUNTAIN
N. Scott Momaday; An account of the historic trek of the Kiowa Indians to Oklahoma. Reprint of 1969 edition. Illus. 90 pp. Paper. University of New Mexico Press, $14.95.

THE WAY TO THE WEST: ESSAYS ON THE CENTRAL PLAINS
Elliott West; The great migrations of the Cheyennes and Anglo pioneers onto the Central Plains. Illus. 5 maps. 254 pp. Paper. University of New Mexico Press, $24.95.

THE WAY TO THE WESTERN SEA: LEWIS & CLARK ACROSS THE CONTINENT
David Lavender; Illus. 415 pp. HarperCollins, 1988. $22.95.

*THE WAY WAS THROUGH WOODS: THE STORY OF TOMO-CHI-CHI
Sara H. Banks; Story of a Creek man who adopted what he could from the white settlers, insuring peace with them. Grades 7 and up. Illus. 92 pp. Paper. Roberts Rinehart, 1994. $7.95.

THE WAY WE GENUINELY LIVE: MASTERWORKS OF YUP'IK SCIENCE & SURVIVAL
Ann Fienup-Riordan; Yup'ik tools & items of everyday use; cosmology & traditional spiritual values. 360 Illus. 320 in color. drawings. 376 pp. Paper. University of Washington Press, 2007. $45.

THE WAY WE LIVED: CALIFORNIA INDIAN STORIES, SONGS & REMINISCENCES
Malcolm Margolin, Editor; Reprint. Photos. Maps. 260 pp. Paper. Heyday Books, 1981. $16.95.

THE WAY WE MAKE SENSE
Dawn Karima Pettigrew; Amazon.com, 2002.

ANTHONY WAYNE, A NAME IN ARMS
Anthony Wayne; Richard Knopf, Editor; An account of the third campaign of the Indian Wars, 1790-1795, tp;d through the correspondence of major General Anthony Wayne. Reprint of 1959 edition. Illus. 610 pp. Paper. Universitry of Pittsburgh Press, $32.95.

WAYS OF THE HUMAN BEING
Calvin Luther Martin; 256 pp. Yale University Press, 2000. $34.

WAYS OF INDIAN MAGIC
Teresa VanEtten; Pueblo Indian legends. 91 pp. Paper. Sunstone, 1985. $8.95.

WAYS OF INDIAN WISDOM
Teresa VanEtten; Pueblo Indian legends. 120 pp. Paper. Sunstone, 1987. $10.95.

WAYS OF KNOWING: EXPERIENCE, KNOWLEDGE, & POWER AMONG DENE THA
Jean-Guy A. Goulet; Athabaskan ethnology...the study of the Dene Tha of northern Canada. Illus. Map. 334 pp. University of Nebraska Press, 1998. $70; paper, $30.

THE WAYS OF MY GRANDMOTHERS
Beverly H. Wolf; 224 pp. Paper. Amazon.com, 1980. $9.95.

*WAYS OF THE LUSHOOTSEED PEOPLE: CEREMONIES & TRADITIONS OF THE NORTHERN PUGET SOUND INDIANS Readings. Written in English & Lushootseed. Grades 7-12. Illus. 56 pp. Daybreak Star Press, $6.

WAYTA'YAWA' (ALWAYS BELIEVE)
Dorothy Ramon & Eric Elliott; Documents the language & culture of the Serrano people. Illus. 894 pp. Paper. Malki-Ballena Press, 2000. $30.

WE ARE AN INDIAN NATION: A HISTORY OF THE HUALAPAI PEOPLE
Jeffrey P. Shepherd; Focuses on the historical construction of the Hualapai Nation in the face of modern American colonialism. 320 pp. Universitry of Arizona Press, 2010. $45; paper, $24.95.

"WE ARE NOT SAVAGES" NATIVE AMERICANS IN SOUTHERN CALIFORNIA & THE PALA RESERVATION, 1840-1920
Joel R. Hyer; Illus. 352 pp. Michigan State University Press, 2001. $39.95.

WE ARE NOT YET CONQUERED: THE HISTORY OF THE NORTHERN CHEROKEE NATION OF THE OLD LOUISIANA TERRITORY
Beverly Baker Northup; Illus. 272 pp. Turner Publishing, 2001. $49.95.

WE ARE NOT YOU: FIRST NATIONS & CANADIAN MODERNITY
Claude Denis; 208 pp. Paper. Amazon.com, 1997.

WE ARE OUR LANGUAGE: AN ETHNOGRAPHY OF LANGUAGE REVITALIZATION IN A NORTHERN ATHABASKAN COMMUNITY
Barbra A. Meek; 240 pp. University of Arizona Press, 2010. $49.95.

WE ARE A PEOPLE IN THIS WORLD: THE LAKOTA SIOUX & THE MASSACRE AT WOUNDED KNEE
Conger Beasley, Jr.; 172 pp. Paper. University of Arkansas Press, 2003. $19.95.

WE ARE STILL HERE! THE ALGONQUIAN PEOPLES OF LONG ISLAND TODAY
John A. Strong; 105 pp. Heart of the Lakes Publishing, 1996. $12.

WE ARE STILL HERE: AMERICAN INDIANS IN THE 20TH CENTURY
Peter Iverson; 255 p. Paper. Amazon.com, 1998. $12.95.

*WE ARE STILL HERE: NATIVE AMERICANS TODAY
A series of books examining Native American cultural traditions and customs. Titles are: Children of Clay: A Family of Pueblo Potters; Clambake: A Wampanoag Tradition; Ininatig's Gift of Sugar: Traditional Native Sugarmaking; Kinaalda: A Navajo Girl Grows Up; The Sacred Harvest: Ojibway Wild Rice Gathering; and Shannon: An Ojibway Dancer; Drumbeat...Heartbeat: A Celebration of the Powwow; Four Seasons of Corn: A Winnebago Tradition; Fort Chipewyan Homecoming: A Journey to Native Canada; Songs from the

Loom: A Navajo Girl Learns How to Weave; A Story to Tell: Traditions of a Tlingit Community; Weaving a California Tradition: A Native American Basketmaker. Grades 3-6. Illus. Photos. 48 pp. Lerner, 1992-1998. $15.95 each; paper, $6.95 each.

WE BECAME AS MOUNTAINS: POEMS OF THE PUEBLO CONQUEST
Nancy Wood; Illus. 96 pp. Paper. Western Edge Press, 2010. $14.95.

WE CAME NAKED & BAREFOOT: THE JOURNEY OF CABEZA DE VACA ACROSS NORTH AMERICA
Alex D. Krieger, et al; Illus. 335 pp. University of Texas Press, 2002. $39.95.

WE, THE FIRST AMERICANS
Dwight Johnson; Illus. 28 pp. Paper. U.S. Government Printing Office, 1989. $1.75.

WE GET OUR LIVING LIKE MILK FROM THE LAND
Okanagan Rights Committee; Historical overview of the Okanagan Nation of Canada. Illus. Maps. 175 pp. Paper. Theytus, 1993. $9.95.

*WE HAVE ALWAYS BEEN HERE
Grades 4-5. 48 pp. Amazon.com, 1989. $10.95.

WE HAVE A RELIGION: THE 1920S PUEBLO INDIAN DANCE CONTROVERSY & AMERICAN RELIGIOUS FREEDOM Tisa Wenger
Illus. Map. 360 pp. University of North Carolina Press, 2009. $59.95; paper, $22.95.

WE HAVE THE RIGHT TO EXIST: A TRANSLATION OF ABORIGINAL THOUGHT: THE FIRST BOOK EVER PUBLISHED FROM AN AHNISHINABEOTJIBWAY PERSPECTIVE
Wub-e-ke-niew; Illus. 420 pp. Paper. Black Thistle Press, 1995. $16.

WE HOLD THE ROCK: INDIAN OCCUPATION OF ALCATRAZ ISLAND, 1969--1971
Troy Johnson
Illus. 64 pp. Paper. Golden Gate National Parks Conservancy, 1997. $9.95.

WE INTERRUPT THIS PROGRAM: INDIGENOUS MEDIA TACTICS IN CANADIAN CULTURE Miranda Brady & John Kelly; UBC Press, 2017. $75.

*WE LIVE ON AN INDIAN RESERVATION
Hap Gilliland; Grades 1-6. 31 pp. Paper. Council for Indian Education, 1981. $4.95.

WE KNOW WHO WE ARE: METIS IDENTITY IN A MONTANA COMMUNITY
Martha Harroun Foster; Illus. 304 pp. University of Oklahoma Press, 2007. $29.95

WE, THE PEOPLE: OF EARTH & ELDERS
Serle L. Chapman, Ed.; Vol. 2. Illus. 350 pp. Amazon.com, $29.95.

*WE RODE THE WIND: RECOLLECTIONS OF NATIVE AMERICAN LIFE
Jane B. Katz, Editor; The writings of eight notable Native Americans who grews up on the Great Plains. Grades 6-9. Illus. Color photos. Glossary. 128 pp. Lerner, 1995. $16.95.

WE TALK, YOU LISTEN: NEW TRIBES, NEW TURF
Vine Deloria, Jr.; intro. by Suzan Shown Harjo
221 pp. Paper. University of Nebraska Press, 2007. $19.95.

WE TALK YOU YAWN
Fred Bigjim; Native education in Alaska; problems & concerns, as well as solutions. Amazon.com, $9.95.

WE WERE NOT THE SAVAGES: A MI'KMAQ PERSPECTIVE ON THE COLLISSION BETWEEN EUROPEAN & NATIVE AMERICAN CIVILIZATIONS
Daniel N. Paul; 21st Edition. Illus. 400 pp. Paper. Eiron, 2000.

WE WILL ALWAYS BE HERE: NATIVE PEOPLES ON LIVING & THRIVING IN THE SOUTH Denise E. Bates, Editor; Illus. 248 pp. University Press of Florida, 2016. $39.95.

WE'RE STILL HERE: ART OF INDIAN NEW ENGLAND
Joan Lester; 86 pp. Paper. Consortium Books, 1987. $9.95.

WE'VE BEEN HERE BEFORE: WOMEN IN CREATION MYTHS & CONTEMPORARY LITERATURE OF THE NATIVE AMERICAN SOUTHWEST
Maria Moss; 212 pp. Paper. Westview Press, 1994. $35.50.

WE'LL BE IN YOUR MOUNTAINS, WE'LL BE IN YOUR SONGS: A NAVAJO WOMAN SINGS Ellen McCullough-Brabson & Marilyn Help
Illus. 165 pp. University of New Mexico Press, 2001. $19.95, includes CD-ROM.

WE WILL DANCE OUR TRUTH: YAQUI HISTORY IN YOEME PERFORMANCES
David Delgado Shorter; Yaqui (Yoeme) culture of the Sonora & Arizona borderlands. Illus. Photos. 448 pp. University of Nebraska Press, 2009. $45.

A WEALTH OF THOUGHT: FRANZ BOAS ON NATIVE AMERICAN ART
Franz Boas; Aldona Jonaitis, Editor
Illus. 380 pp. Paper. University of Washington Press, 1995. $37.95.

WEARING THE MORNING STAR: NATIVE AMERICAN SONG-POEMS
Brian Swann; 182 pp. Paper. University of Nebraska Prss, 2005. $22.

THE WEAVER'S PATHWAY: A CLARIFICATION OF THE "SPIRIT TRAIL" IN NAVAJO WEAVING Noel Bennett; 64 pp. Paper. Northland, 1974. $9.95.
WEAVER'S TALES Romona Bradley
Collection of Cherokee legends. Illus. 36 pp. Paper. Cherokee Publications, $3.50.

WEAVERS OF TRADITION & BEAUTY: BASKETMAKERS OF THE GREAT BASIN
Mary Lee Fulkerson; photos by Kathleen Curtis
Illus. 128 pp. Paper. University of Nevada Press, 1995. $19.95.

WEAVING ARTS OF THE NORTH AMERICAN INDIAN
Frederick J. Dockstader; Revised edition. Survey of the textile artistry of the Indian tribes of North America. Illus. 224 pp. HarperCollins, 1994. $22.50.

WEAVING A CALIFORNIA TRADITION: A NATIVE AMERICAN BASKETMAKER
Linda Yamane; photos by Dugan Aguilar; California Indian basketmaking. Illus. 48 pp. Oyate & Lerner Publications, 1996. $14.95; paper, $6.95.

WEAVING THE DANCE: NAVAJO YEIBICHAI TEXTILES, 1910-1950
Rebecca M. & Jean-Paul Valette; Illus. 72 pp. Paper. Amazon.com, 2000. $19.95.

WEAVING IS LIFE: NAVAJO WEAVINGS FROM THE EDWIN L. & RUTH E. KENNEDY SOUTHWEST NATIVE AMERICAN COLLECTION Edited by Jennifer McLerran
40 color Illus. 80 pp. Paper. University of Washington Press, 2007. $19.95.

WEAVING A LEGACY: INDIAN BASKETS & THE PEOPLE OF OWENS VALLEY, CALIFORNIA Sharon E. Dean, Peggy Ratcheson, Judith Finger, Ellen Daus, Craig Bates
Illus. 190 pp. University of Utah Press, 2005. $55.

WEAVING A NAVAJO BLANKET
Gladys Reichard; Reprint of 1936 edition. Illus. 225 pp. Paper. Dover, $6.95.

WEAVING NEW WORLDS: SOUTHEASTERN CHEROKEE WOMEN & THEIR BASKETRY
Sarah H. Hill; Illus. 414 pp. Paper. University of North Carolina Press, 1997. $34.95.

WEAVING OF THE SOUTHWEST
Marian Rodee; Both traditional & modern weaving styles are identified & explained. Discussion of family styles among weavers today. Illus. 248 pp. Schiffer, $39.95; paper, $29.95.

WEAVING OURSELVES INTO THE LAND: CHARLES GODFREY LELAND, INDIANS & THE STUDY OF NATIVE AMERICAN RELIGIONS
Thomas C. Parkhill; Illus. 238 pp. Paper. University of New York Press, 1997. $21.95.

WEAVING WILDLY: MATS & BASKETS THE CHOCTAW WAY
Mary L. Stahl; Illus. 80 pp. Paper. Amazon.com, 1997. $15.95.

WEAVING A WORLD: TEXTILES & THE NAVAJO WAY OF SEEING
Paul G. Zolbrod & Roseann Willink
Features 70 rugs. 100 color plates. 132 pp. Paper. Museum of New Mexico Press, $29.95.

WEAVING WOMEN'S LIVES: THREE GENERATIONS IN A NAVAJO FAMILY
Louise Lamphere, Eva Price, Carole Cadman & Valerie Darwin
Illus. 344 pp. Paper. University of New Mexico Press, $29.95.

ANSELM WEBER, O.F.M. MISSIONARY TO THE NAVAJO
Robert Wilken; Reprint of 1955 edition. St. Michaels Press, $12.50.

WEBS OF KINSHIP: FAMILY IN NORTHERN CHEYENNE NATIONHOOD
Christina Gish Hill; Illus. Maps. 400 pp. University of Oklahoma Press, 2017. $34.95.

CONRAD WEISER 1696-1760, FRIEND OF COLONIST & MOHAWK
Paul A. Wallace
Pennsylvania's Indian ambassador. 2nd Ed. Illus. Wennawoods Publishing, $44.95.

THE WEISER INDIANS: SHOSHONI PEACEMAKERS
Hank Corless; Reprint. Illus. 170 pp. Paper. Caxton Press, 1996. $14.95.

WELCOME TO THE OGLALA NATION: A DOCUMENTARY READER IN OGLALA LAKOTA POLITICAL HISTORY
Akim D. Reinhardt, Editor; Map. 306 pp. University of Nebraska Press, 2015. $60.

THE WENATCHEE VALLEY & ITS FIRST PEOPLES: THRILLING GRANDEUR, UNFULFILLED PROMISE
Richard Scheuermann; photos by John Clement
The Native peoples of the mid-Columbia and the Wenatchee Valley. Illus. 168 pp. WSU Press, 2009. $36.95.

THE WEST AS AMERICA: REINTERPRETING IMAGES OF THE FRONTIER
William H. Truettner, Editor; How the 19th & early 20th century artists depicted and romanticized the often brutal, conflict-ridden history of the westward expansion. 408 pp. Smithsonian Books, $49.96.

THE WEST POLE
Diane H. Glancy; Illus. 216 pp. University of Minnesota Press, 1997. $18.95.

WEST TO THE PACIFIC: THE STORY OF THE LEWIS & CLARK EXPEDITION
Ronald Fisher; Merle Wells, Editor; Illus. 152 pp. Paper. Alpha & Omega, 1989. $9.95.

WESTERN ABENAKI DICTIONARY: VOL. 1: ABENAKI-ENGLISH
Gordon M. Day; 612 pp. Paper. University of Washington Press, 1994. $34.95.

THE WESTERN ABENAKIS OF VERMONT, 1600-1800: WAR, MIGRATION & THE SURVIVAL OF AN INDIAN PEOPLE
Colin G. Calloway; Illus. Maps. 346 pp. Paper. U. of Oklahoma Press, 1990. $19.95.

WESTERN AMERICAN INDIAN: CASE STUDIES IN TRIBAL HISTORY
Richard N. Ellis, Editor; Indian-White relations from 1850 to the present. Maps. 203 pp. Paper. University of Nebraska Press, 1972. $17.

WESTERN APACHE-ENGLISH DICTIONARY: A COMMUNITY-GENERATED BILINGUAL DICTIONARY
Dorothy Bray, Editor; 528 pp. Paper. Biling Review Press, 1998. $20.

WESTERN APACHE HERITAGE: PEOPLE OF THE MOUNTAIN CORRIDOR
Richard J. Perry; Illus. Maps. 314 pp. University of Texas Press, 1991. $37.50.

WESTERN APACHE LANGUAGE & CULTURE: ESSAYS IN LINGUISTIC ANTHROPOLOGY
Keith H. Basso; Reprint. Illus. 195 pp. Paper. University of Arizona Press, 1990. $17.95.

WESTERN APACHE MATERIAL CULTURE: GOODWIN & GUENTHER COLLECTIONS
Alan Ferg, Editor; Illus. 176 pp. Paper. University of Arizona Press, 1987. $28.95.

WESTERN APACHE RAIDING & WARFARE
Grenville Goodwin; edited by Keith Basso; Personal narratives of six Western Apaches. Also discusses weapons, taboos, leadership, and other aspects of Apache raiding. Reprint edition. Illus. 330 pp. Paper. University of Arizona Press, 1994. $18.95.

WESTERN APACHE WITCHCRAFT
Keith H. Basso, Editor; Reprint of 1969 edition. 80 pp. Paper. U. of Arizona Press, $21.95.

WESTERN INDIAN BASKETRY
Joan Jones; Illus. 56 pp. Paper. Hancock House, 1990. $7.95.

WESTERN MILITARY FRONTIER, 1815-1846
H.P. Beers; Reprint of 1935 edition. Illus. 230 pp. Amazon.com, $25.

THE WESTERN ODYSSEY OF JOHN SIMPSON SMITH: FRONTIERSMAN & INDIAN INTERPRETER Stan Hoig; Smith served as interpreter for major treaty negotiations and accompanied three delegatons of chiefs to Washington, DC to visit presidents. Illus. 256 pp. Paper. University of Oklahoma Press, 2004. $21.95.

THE WESTERN PHOTOGRAPHS OF JOHN K. HILLERS: MYSELF IN THE WATER
Don Fowler; Illus. 160 pp. Smithsonian Press, 1989. $24.95.

WESTERN POMO PREHISTORY: EXCAVATIONS AT ALBION HEAD, NIGHTBIRDS' RETREAT, & THREE CHOP VILLAGE, MENDOCINO COUNTY, CALIFORNIA
Thomas Layton; Illus. 230 pp. Paper. University of California, Los Angeles, Institute of Archaeology, 1990. $17.50.

WESTERN PUEBLO IDENTITIES: REGIONAL INTERACTION, MIGRATION, & TRANSFORMATION Andrew I. Duff; Illus. 233 pp. U. of Arizona Press, 2002. $48.

WESTERN SHOSHONI GRAMMAR
John P. Dayley; Boise State University, 1993.

WESTERN WAYS OF BEING RELIGIOUS: AN ANTHOLOGY
Gary E. Kessler; 230 pp. Paper.McGraw-Hill, 2001. $37.95.

MARIETTA WETHERILL: LIFE WITH THE NAVAJOS IN CHACO CANYON
Kathryn Gabriel, Editor; Primitive life in Chaco Canyon at the turn of the century. Illus. 256 pp. Paper. University of New Mexico Press, 1995. $19.95.

LEWIS WETZEL, INDIAN FIGHTER
C.B. Allman; Revised 1961 edition. Illus. Devin-Adair, $16.95.

LEWIS WETZEL: THE LIFE & TIMES OF A FRONTIER HERO
C.B. Allman; Illus. 238 pp. William Hintzen Publishers, 2002.

FREDERICK WEYGOLD: ARTIST & ETHNOGRAPHER OF NORTH AMERICAN INDIANS Christian F. Feest, C. Ronald ald Corum, Editors
Illus. 272 pp. University of Oklahoma Press, 2017. $29.95.

THE WHALING INDIANS: WEST COAST LEGENDS & STORIES, LEGENDARY HUNTERS Edward Sapir, et al.; Part 9: Sapir-Thomas Nootka Texts, Told by Sa:ya:ch'apis, William, Frank Williams, Big Fred, Captain Bill, and Qwishanishim. 28 accounts of traditional huting life among the Nuu-chah-nulth...oral history gathered between 1910 and 1923. Illus. Maps. 456 pp. Paper. University of Washington Press, 2004. $45.

WHAT CAN TRIBES DO? STRATEGIES & INSTITUTIONS IN AMERICAN INDIAN ECONOMIC DEVELOPMENT Stephen Cornell & Joseph P. Kalt, Eds.
A guide to successful self-determined economic development on Indian reservations. 336 pp. Paper. Amazon.com, 1992. $15.

*WHAT NATIVE AMERICANS WORE
Colleen Madonna Flood Williams
Grades 4-9. Illus. 64 pp. Mason Crest Publishers, 2003. $19.95.

WHAT THIS AWL MEANS: FEMINIST ARCHAEOLOGY WAHPETON DAKOTA VILLAGE Janet D. Spector; Focuses on Little Rapids, a 19th-century Eastern Dakota (Sioux) planting village near present-day Minneapolis. Illus. 370 pp. Paper. Minnesota Historical Society Press, 1993. $15.95.

WHAT WE LEARNED: TWO GENERATIONS REFLECT ON TSIMSHIAN EDUCATION
Helen Raptis; UBC Press, 2016. $95; paper, $32.95; eBook, $32.95.

WHAT YOU SEE IN CLEAR WATER: INDIANS, WHITES, & A BATTLE OVER WATER IN THE AMERICAN WEST Geoffrey O'Gara; 304 pp. Paper. Random House, 2002. $14.

*WHAT'S YOUR STORY, SEQUOYH
Jody Jensen Shaffer; Grades K-3. Lerner Publications, $19.99; paper, $8.99.

WHATEVER HAPPENED TO PROFESSOR COYOTE? A JOURNEY TO THE HEART OF THE HANDGAME Bill Rathbun; Teaches the handgame through stories & song. Includes Maidu BearDance; gambling songs and other power songs. Amazon.com, 1999. $15.95. $10.95, multimedia CD.

WHAT'S AN INDIAN WOMAN TO DO? AND OTHER PLAYS
Mark Anthony Rolo; UCLA American Indian Studies. Drama. 2010. Paper. $16.

WHEN THE ANIMALS WERE PEOPLE
Kay Sanger; illus. by Tom Sanger; Collection of stories of mythology of the Chumash Indians. Reprint. Illus. 41 pp. Paper. Malki-Ballena Press, 1997. $12.95.

WHEN BRER RABBIT MEETS COYOTE: AFRICAN-NATIVE AMERICAN LITERATURE
Jonathan Brennan, Editor; Explores the literature, history, and culture of people of mixed African-Native American descent. 328 pp. University of Illinois Press, 2003. $42.

WHEN BUFFALO RAN
George Grinnell; Story of Wikis, a Plains Indian who grew up in the mid-1800s as part of the last generation before the white changed the plains forever. Reprint. Illus. Paper. Hancock House, $9.95.

*WHEN CLAY SINGS
Byrd Baylor; illus by Tom Bahti; Grades P-3. Illus. 32 pp. Charles Scribner'sSons, $12.95.

WHEN CULTURES MEET
Papers given by Florence Ellis, Myra Ekken Jenjins, Richard Ford, Marc Simmons, Orlando Romero, and Jim Sagel at the 1984 Conference at San Juan Pueblo. Illus. 96 pp. Paper. Sunstone Press, $9.95.

WHEN DID INDIANS BECOME STRAIGHT: KINSHIP, THE HISTORY OF SEXUALITY, AND NATIVE SOVEREIGNTY
Mark Rifkin; Oxford University Press, 2011. $125; paper, $40.95.

WHEN DID THE SHOSHONI BEGIN TO OCCUPY SOUTHERN IDAHO: ESSAYS ON LATE PREHISTORIC CULTURAL REMAINS FROM THE UPPER SNAKE & SALMON RIVER COUNTIES B. Robert Butler
30 pp. Paper. Idaho Museum of Natural History & Amazon.com, 1981. $5.

WHEN THE EARTH WAS LIKE NEW: WESTERN APACHE SONGS & STORIES
Chesley Goseyun Wilson, Ruth Longcor-Harnish Wilson & Bryan Burton
Includes 17 musical transcriptions of social traveling and game sngs and Apache violin pieces; 38 archival and contemporary photographs of instruments, ceremonies and social life; traditional legends. Illus. 128 pp. World Music Press, 1994. Book & CD or Book & Tape Set, $29.95.

WHEN GERONIMO RODE
Forrestine C. Hooker; Fictionalized account of Geronimo's campaign. Reprint of 1924 edition. 325 pp. High-Lonesome Books, $20.

*WHEN THE GREAT CANOES CAME
Mary Louise Clifford; A series of conversations between Cockacoeske, the queen of the Pamunkey Indians, and the adolescents of her tribe. Grades 5 to 9. Illus. Map. Biblio. 144 pp. Amazon.com, 1990. $12.95.

WHEN THE GREAT SPIRIT DIED: THE DESTRUCTION OF THE CALIFORNIA INDIANS, 1850-1860 William B. Secrest
Illus. 352 pp. Paper. Word Dancer Press, 2002. $15.95.

WHEN THE HORSES ARE GONE: A STORY OF THE NEZ PERCE INDIAN TRIBE
Alan Venable; Jerry Stemach, Ed.
Don Johnston, Inc., 2001. $50; with audio & CD-ROM, $65.

WHEN I WAS SMALL - I WAN KWIKWAS: A GRAMMATICAL ANALYSIS OF ST'AT'IMC ORAL NARRATIVES Lisa Matthewson, Editor; Life histories of four female St'at'imc elders...among the last remaining fluent speakers of St'at'imcets, an imperilled Northern Interior Salish langauge, also known as Lillooet and spoken in the southwest interior of British Columbia. Illus. 552 pp. University of Washington Press, 2006. $138.

WHEN INDIANS BECAME COWBOYS: NATIVE PEOPLES & CATTLE RANCHING IN THE AMERICAN WEST Peter Iverson; Indian cattle ranching focusing on the Northern Plains & the Southwest. Illus. Map. 266 pp. University of Oklahoma Press, 1994. $26.95; paper. $15.95.

WHEN IS A KIVA: & OTHER QUESTIONS ABOUT SOUTHWESTERN ARCHAEOLOGY
Watson Smith; Raymond H. Thompson, Editor
273 pp. Paper. University of Arizona Press, 1990. $19.95.

WHEN JESUS CAME, THE CORN MOTHERS WENT AWAY: MARRIAGE, SEXUALITY & POWER IN NEW MEXICO, 1500-1846
Ramon Gutierrez; 456 pp. Amazon.com, 1991. $49.50; paper, $16.95.

WHEN THE LAND WAS YOUNG: REFLECTIONS ON AMERICAN ARCHAEOLOGY
Sharman Apt Russell; Illus. Map. 230 pp. Paper. U. of Nebraska Press, 2001. $14.95.

WHEN THE MISSISSIPPI RAN BACKWARDS
Jay Feldman; Empire, Intrigue, Murder, and the New Madrid Earthquakes at the time of Shawnee Chief Tecumseh. 305 pp. Amazon.com, 2005. $27.

WHEN NAVAJOS HAD TOO MANY SHEEP: THE 1940's
George A. Boyce; Jeanette Henry, Editor; Stock overgrazing led to rapidly eroding farmland. Illus. Map. 288 pp. Paper. Amazon.com, 1974. $12.50.

WHEN NICKELS WERE INDIANS: AN URBAN, MIXED-BLOOD STORY
Patricia Penn Hilden;Discusses folk imagery of blood quantum that defines people's lives. Examines the idea that Native America is once more the destination of souls lost in a "New Age." Photos. 260 pp. Paper. Smithsonian Institution Press, 1997. $17.95.

WHEN THE NIGHTBIRD SINGS
Joyce Sequichie Hifler
Reprint. BxW line drawings. 268 pp. Paper. Council Oak Books, 2000. $11.95.

WHEN OLD WORLDS MEET
Peter Wood; Eric Bates, Ed.; Illus. 64 pp. Paper. Amazon.com, 1992. $5.

WHEN NO ONE IS LOOKING
Red Hawk – Pipikwass; 50 pp. Paper. Amazon.com, 1990. $7.

WHEN OUR WORDS RETURN: WRITING, HEARING, & REMEMBERSING ORAL TRADITIONS OF ALASKA & THE YUKON
Phyllis Morrow & William Schneider, Editors; Collection of essays on Native oral traditions from the North. 264 pp. Utah State University Press, $36.95; paper, $19.95.

WHEN RAIN GODS REIGNED: FROM CURIOS TO ART AT TESUQUE PUEBLO
Duane Anderson; Illus. 156 pp. Museum of New Mexico Press, 2002. $45; paper, $29.95.

*WHEN RAIN SINGS: POEMS BY YOUNG NATIVE AMERICANS
Intro. By Elizabeth Woody (Confederated Tribes of Warm Springs)
Garades 4-8. Illus. 64 pp. Paper. NMAI Press & Simon Schuster, 1999. $14.95.

WHEN THE RAINBOW TOUCHES DOWN
Tryntje Van Ness Seymour; The artists and stories behind the Apache, Navajo, Rio Grande Pueblo, and Hopi paintings in the William and Leslie Van Ness Denman Collection. Illus. Maps. Biblio. 396 pp. University of Washington Press, 1989. $50.

WHEN THE RIVER RAN WILD! INDIAN TRADITIONS ON THE MID-COLUMBIA & THE WARM SPRINGS RESERVATION George W. Aguilar, Sr.
Personal memoir & tribal history...the Kiksht-speaking Eastern Chinookans. Stories of their change since meeting Lewis & Clark expedition in 1805 on the Columbia River. Illus. 272 pp. Paper. University of Washington Press, 2005. $22.50.

WHEN STARS CAME DOWN TO EARTH: COSMOLOGY OF THE SKIDI PAWNEE INDIANS OF NORTH AMERICA
Von Del Chamberlain; Illus. 272 pp. Paper. Malki-Ballena Press, 1982. $17.95.

*WHEN THUNDERS SPOKE
Virginia Driving Hawk Sneve; illus. by Oren Lyons; Indian story. Grades 5 and up. Illus. 95 pp. Paper. University of Nebraska Press, 1993. $9.95.

WHEN THE CHENOO HOWLS: NATIVE AMERICAN TALES OF HORROR
James & Joseph Bruchac; Grades 3-7. Illus. 128 pp. Walker & Co., 1998. $17.85.

WHEN WAR EAGLE SPEAKS
Gary D. Bromley (War Eagle); Teachings by the author of the ancient red road. 36 pp. Paper. Gary D. Bromley, P.O. Box 1629, Fontana, CA 92334. 2003. $19.99.

*WHEN WE WENT TO THE MOUNTAINS
Hap Gilliland, et al
Grades 1-9. 40 pp. Paper. Council for Indian Education, 1991. $9.95; paper, $3.95.

WHEN THE WOLF CAME: THE CIVIL WAR & THE INDIAN TERRITORY
Mary Jane Warde; Illus. 440 pp. University of Arkansas Press, 2016. $34.95.

*WHEN THE WORLD ENDED, HOW HUMMINGBIRD GOT FREE, HOW PEOPLE WERE MADE Linda Yamane
Rumsien Ohlone stories. Grades 2-5. Illus. 46 pp. Paper. Oyate, 1995. $10.

WHEN YOU SING IT NOW, JUST LIKE NEW: FIRST NATIONS POETICS, VOICES, AND REPRESENTATIONS Robin & Jillian Ridington; Essays. Athapaskan. Illus. 346 pp. University of Nebraska Press, 2007. $49.95; paper, $24.95.

WHERE CLOUDS ARE FORMED
Ofelia Zepeda (Tohono O'odham)
Poetry. 96 pp. University of Arizona Press, 2008. $29.95; paper, $14.95.

WHERE COURAGE IS LIKE A WILD HORSE: THE WORLD OF AN INDIAN ORPHANAGE Sharon Skolnick & Manny Skolnick; Story of an Apache Indian orphan. 148 pp. Paper. University of Nebraska Press, 1997. $11.95.

WHERE CUSTER FELL: PHOTOGRAPHS OF THE LITTLE BIGHORN BATTLEFIELD THEN & NOW James S. Brust, Brian C. Pohonka, & Sandy Barnard
Illus. Maps. 240 pp. University of Oklahoma Press, $39.95; paper, $26.95..

WHERE THE ECHO BEGAN: & OTHER ORAL TRADITIONS FROM SOUTHWESTERN ALASKA
Recorded by Hans Himmelheber; edited by Ann Fienup-Riordan
Illus. 262 pp. University of Washington Press & U. of Alaska Press, 2000. $39.95.

WHERE A HUNDRED SOLDIERS WERE KILLED: THE STRUGGLE FOR THE POWDER RIVER COUNTRY IN 1866 AND THE MAKING OF THE FETTERMAN MYTH
John . Monnett; Illus. Maps. 352 pp. Paper. University of New Mexico Press, $24.95.

*WHERE INDIANS LIVE: AMERICAN INDIAN HOUSES
Nashone; Grades K-6. Illus. 37 pp. Paper. Sierra Oaks, 1989. $6.95.

WHERE LEGENDS LIVE
Douglas Rossman; Illus. Photos. 48 pp. Paper. Book Publishing Co., VIP Publishing & Cherokee Publications, 1988. $5.95

WHERE THE PAVEMENT ENDS: FIVE NATIVE AMERICAN PLAYS
William S. Yellow Robe, Jr.; Based on the author's experiences on the Fort Peck Indian Reservation. 192 pp. U. of Oklahoma Press, 2009. $24.95; paper, $16.95.

WHERE THE PEOPLE GATHER: CARRVING A TOTEM POLE
Vickie Jensen; Documents the entire process of carving a totem pole. Illus. Photos. 194 pp. University of Washington Press, $29.95.

WHERE THE TWO CAME TO THEIR FATHER: A NAVAJO WAR CEREMONIAL GIVEN BY JEFF KING Maud Oakes, Editor; commentary by Joseph Campbell
Illus. 120 pp. Paper. Amazon.com, 1991. $90; paper, $14.95.

WHERE THERE IS NO NAME FOR ART: THE ART OF TEWA PUEBLO CHILDREN
Bruce Hucko; Illus. 128 pp. Paper. School of American Research Press, 1996. $20.

WHERE TWO WORLDS MEET: THE GREAT LAKES FUR TRADE
Carolyn Gilman; History of the fur trade, and essays on various aspects of the early cross-cultural contacts between Indians and whites. Illus. Photos. Maps. 136 pp. Paper. Minnesota Historical Society Press, & Smoke & Fire Co., 1982. $18.95.

WHERE THE WATERS DIVIDE: NEOLIBERALISM, WHITE PRIVILEGE, & ENVIRONMENTAL RACISM IN CANADA Michael Mascarenhas
Advances an empirical understanding of Canada's contemporary "Indian" problem. 178 pp. Lexington Books, 2012. $84; paper, $39.99; eBook, $39.99.

*WHERE WE LIVE: A PUZZLE BOOK OF AMERICAN INDIAN ART
Grades 4-8. Illus. NMAI Press, 2011. $15.95.

WHERE THE WEST BEGINS: ESSAYS ON MIDDLE BORDER & SIOUXLAND WRITING Arthur Huseboe & William Geyer, Editors
Illus. Paper. Center for Western Studies, 1978. $3.95.

WHILE THE LOCUST SLEPT: A MEMOIR
Peter Razor; Illus. 210 pp. Paper. Minnesota Historical Society Press, 2002. $10.95.

A WHIRLWIND PASSES: NEWS CORRESPONDENTS & THE SIOUX INDIAN DISTURBANCES OF 1890-1891
George R. Kolbenschlag; Illus. Paper. Dakota Press, 1990. $9.95.

WHISKEY PEDDLER: JOHNNY HEALY, NORTH FRONTIER TRADER
William R. Hunt; 263 pp. Paper. Mountain Press. $12.

WHISKEY TRADE OF THE NORTHWESTERN PLAINS: MULTIDISCIPLINARY STUDY
Margaret A. Kennedy; 208 pp. Amazon.com, 1998. $39.95.

*WHISPERS FROM THE FIRST CALIFORNIANS: A STORY OF CALIFORNIA'S FIRST PEOPLE Gail Faber & Michele Lasagna; Grades 4-8. Revised edition. Illus. 355 pp. Amazon.com, 1994. Teacher edition. $34.95; student edition, 268 pp. paper, $14.95.

WHISPERS OF THE ANCIENTS: NATIVE TALES FOR TEACHING & HEALING IN OUR TIME Tamarack Song & Moses (Amik) Beaver
Illus. 272 pp. University of Michigan Press, 2010. $80; eBook available.

*THE WHISTLING TREE
Audrey Penn; illus. by Barbara Gibson; Grades 3 and up. Chronicles a young girl's search for her Cherokee identity. 32 pp. Amazon.com, 2004. $16.95.

*WHITE BUFFALO WOMEN
Christine Crowl; Grade 6 and up. Illus. 18 pp. Paper. Tipi Press, 1991. $3.95.

WHITE CAPTIVES: GENDER & ETHNICITY ON THE AMERICAN FRONTIER
June Namias; Illus. 378 pp. Paper. University of North Carolina Press, 1993. $24.95.

WHITE CLOUD - LAKOTA SPIRIT: LEGENDS
Cecilia Brownlow & Leslie Wilner
Native American shamanism. Illus. 94 pp. Paper. Sunstone Press, $10.95.

*THE WHITE DEER: & OTHER STORIES TOLD BY THE LENAPE
John Bierhorst, Editor
Grades 7 and up. Illus. 160 pp. William Morrow & Amazon.com, 1995. $15.

WHITE EAGLE MEDICINE WHEEL: NATIVE AMERICAN WISDOM AS A WAY OF LIFE
Wa-Na-Nee-Che; Illus. 132 pp. St. Martin's Press, 1997. $24.99.

WHITE EARTH NATION: RATIFICATION OF A NATIVE DEMOCRATIC CONSTITUTION
Gerald Vizenor & Jill Doerfler; 112 pp. paper. University of Nebraska Press, 2012. $16.

THE WHITE EARTH TRAGEDY: ETHNICITY & DISPOSSESSION AT A MINNESOTA ANISHINAABE RESERVATION, 1889-1920
Melissa L. Meyer; Illus. Maps. 333 pp. Paper. U. of Nebraska Press, 1994. $18.95.

WHITE ENOUGH TO BE AMERICAN? RACE MIXING, INDIGENOUS PEOPLE, & THE BOUNDARIES OF STATE & NATION
Lauren L. Basson; Illus. 256 pp. U. of North Carolina Press, 2008. $59.95; paper, $22.50.

WHITE EYES, LONG KNIVES & RENEGADE INDIANS
Dr. V. Keith Thorne; General Crook's U.S. Army campaigns against the Yavapai & Apache Indians in the Verde Valley of Arizona during the late 1800s. Illus. 40 pp. Paper. Primer Publishers, $3.95.

WHITE GRIZZLY BEAR'S LEGACY: LEARNING TO BE INDIAN
Lawney L. Reyes; Early life in the Indian village of Inchelium, destroyed by the building of the Grand Coulee Dam in 1942. Illus. 216 pp. U. of Washington Press, 2002. $23.95.

WHITE INDIAN BOY
Charles Wilson & Trilba Redding; Revised edition. Bound with The Return of the White Indian. Illus. 395 pp. Charles A. Wilson, 1988. $32.50.

WHITE LIES ABOUT THE INUIT
John Steckley; 168 pp. Paper. University of Toronto Press, 2008. $22.95.

WHITE MAN'S CLUB: SCHOOLS, RACE, & STRUGGLE OF INDIAN ACCULTURATION Jacqueline Fear-Segal; Examines schools for Native children in the late 19th century. Photos. 422 pp. University of Nebraska Press, 2007. $55; paper, $24.95.

THE WHITE MAN'S GONNA GETCHA: THE COLONIAL CHALLENGE TO THE CREES IN QUEBEC Toby Morantz; Illus. 370 pp. Paper. McGill-Queen's University Press, 2001.

THE WHITE MAN'S INDIAN: IMAGES OF THE AMERICAN INDIAN FROM COLUMBUS TO THE PRESENT Robert Berkhofer, Jr.; Illus. Paper. Random House, 1979. $6.26.

WHITE MAN'S LAW: NATIVE PEOPLE IN 19TH CENTURY CANADIAN JURISPRUDENCE Sidney L. Harring
First Nations legal traditions and culture. 488 pp. University of Toronto Press, 1998. $45.

WHITE MAN'S MEDICINE: GOVERNMENT DOCTORS & THE NAVAJO, 1863-1955
Robert A. Trennert, et al; 290 pp. U. of New Mexico, School of Medicine, 1998. $39.95.

WHITE MAN'S WATER: THE POLITICS OF SOBRIETY IN A NATIVE AMERICAN COMMUNITY Erica Prussing; Analysis of Cheyenne views of sobriety and the politics of the 12-Step Program of Alcoholics Anonymous. 288 pp. U. of Arizona Press, 2011. $49.95.

WHITE MAN'S WICKED WATER: THE ALCOHOL TRADE & PROHIBITION IN INDIAN COUNTRY, 1802-1892 William Unrau
Illus. University Press of Kansas, 1996. $34.95; paper, $16.95.

WHITE MOTHER TO A DARK RACE: SETTLER COLONIALISM, MATERNALISM, & THE REMOVAL OF INDIGENOUS CHILDREN IN THE AMERICAN WEST & AUSTRALIA, 1880-1940 Margaret D. Jacobs
Photos. Maps. 592 pp. University of Nebraska Press, 2009. $60.

WHITE MOUNTAIN REDWARE: A POTTERY TRADITION OF EAST-CENTRAL ARIZONA & WESTERN NEW MEXICO Roy L. Carlson

WHITE ON RED: IMAGES OF THE AMERICAN INDIAN
Nancy B. Black & Bette S. Weidman, Editors; Associated Faculty Press, 1976. $26.50.

WHITE PEOPLE, INDIANS, AND HIGHLANDERS: TRIBAL PEOPLE & COLONIAL ENCOUNTERS IN SCOTLAND & AMERICA Colin G. Calloway
Paper. Oxford University Press, 2008. $125.

WHITE ROBE'S DILEMMA: TRIBAL HISTORY IN AMERICAN LITERATURE
Neil Schmitz; The Mesquakie peoples of present-day Iowa and the encounter with the French in the Great Lakes region. 192 pp. University of Massachusetts Press, 2001. $40; paper, $21.95.

WHITE ROOTS OF PEACE: THE IROQUOIS BOOK OF LIFE
Paul A.W. Wallace; The story of the founding of the Iroquois League of Nations.

WHITE WEATHER UNIVERSE: NAVAJO SILVER FROM FRED HARVEY COLLECTION
Byron Harvey, III, et al; Illus. 53 pp. Paper. Heard Museum, 1981. $5.

WHITE WOLF WOMAN
40+ myths from 30 tribes. 168 pp. Paper. Cherokee Publications, $8.95.

BERNIE WHITEBEAR: AN URBAN INDIAN'S QUEST FOR JUSTICE
Lawney L. Reyes; 160 pp. Paper. University of Arizona Press, 2006. $17.95.

WHITEHALL & THE WILDERNESS: THE MIDDLE WEST IN BRITISH COLONIAL POLICY, 1760-1775 Jack Sosin; Reprint of 1961 edition. Illus. 318 pp. Greenwood, $38.50.

WHITESTONE HILL: THE INDIANS & THE BATTLE
Clair Jacobson; Story of the bloodiest battle ever fought in eastern Dakota Territory, involving the Yanktonai & Hunkpatina Sioux and the U.S. Army under General Sully. Illus. 120 pp. Center for Western Studies, $11.95.

JIM WHITEWOLF: THE LIFE OF A KIOWA APACHE INDIAN
Charles S. Brant, Editor; Autobiography of Jim Whitewolf. Reprint of 1969 edition. 144 pp. Map. Paper. High-Lonesome Books, $7.

*WHO WAS SITTING BULL? AND OTHER QUESTIONS ABOUT THE BATTLE OF LITTLE BIGHORN
Judth Pinkerton Josephson. Grades 4-6. Lerner Publications, 2011. $34.99.

WHO'S WHO IN INDIAN RELICS
The top collectors and artifact assemblages across the country. 9th Edition. Published once every 4 years. Illus. 400 pp. Hothem House, 1997. $43, postpaid.

THE WHOLE COUNTRY WAS... 'ONE ROBE'": THE LITTLE SHELL TRIBE'S AMERICA
Co-published by the Little Shell Tribe of Chippewa Indians of Montana and Drumlumon Institute. Illus. 504 pp. Riverbend Publishing, 2015. $

WHOSE LAND IT IT ANYWAY?
Ruth Roessel; Grades 6 and up. Navajo studies. Rough Rock School Press, 2003. $5.

*WHY BUFFALO ROAM
L. Michael Kershen; Original tale in the Comanche oral tradition, written by a ten year old boy. Grades 3-7. Illus. 32 pp. Stemmer House, 1993. $15.

*WHY DID THE CHEROKEES MOVE WEST? AN OTHER QUESTIONS ABOUT THE TRAIL OF TEARS Judith Josephson
Illus. Grades 4-6. Lerner Publications, 2011. $22.95; paper, $9.99.

WHY DON'T THEY GIVE THEM GUNS? THE GREAT AMERICAN INDIAN MYTH
Stephen E. Feraca; Illus. 325 pp. Amazon.com, 1990. $71.

WHY GONE THOSE TIMES? BLACKFOOT TALES
James Willard Schultz; edited by Eugene Lee Silliman; Schultz's experience with the Blackfeet from 1877 to 1947. Illus. 288 pp. Paper. U. of Oklahoma Press, 2002. $19.95.

WHY I CAN'T READ WALLACE STEGNER & OTHER ESSAYS: A TRIBAL VOICE
Elizabeth Cook-Lynn; 172 pp. Paper. University of Wisconsin Press, 1996. $17.95.

*WHY THE POSSUM'S TAIL IS BARE: & OTHER NORTH AMERICAN INDIAN NATURE TALES James E. Connolly, Editor
Grades 3-12. Illus. 64 pp. Stemmer House, 1985. $15.95; paper, $7.95.

THE WICHITA INDIANS: TRADERS OF TEXAS & THE SOUTHERN PLAINS, 1540-1845
F. Todd Smith; Illus. 206 pp. Texas A&M University Press, 2000. $32.95.

*WHO CAME DOWN THAT ROAD?
George Ella Lyon; Story takes children on a journey through time. Grades PS-3. Illus. 32 pp. Amazon.com, 1993. $16.

WHO LIVED IN THIS HOUSE? A STUDY OF KOYUKUK RIVER SEMISUBTERRANEAN HOUSES A. McFayden Clark; Illus. 282 pp. Paper. U. of Washington Press, 1996. $24.95.

WHO SPEAKS FOR WOLF: A NATIVE AMERICAN LEARNING STORY
Paula Underwood; A story of one people's struggle to live within their environment. Amazon.com, $8.95.

WHO WAS WHO IN NATIVE AMERICAN HISTORY: INDIANS & NON-INDIANS FROM FIRST CONTACTS THROUGH 1900 Carl Waldman
1,000 brief biographical sketches of Indian and non-Indians active in Indian affairs, culture, and history up to 1900. Illus. 416 pp. Facts on File & Written Heritage, 1990. $49.95.

WHO WERE THE FIRST AMERICANS? PROCEEDINGS OF THE 58TH ANNUAL BIOLOGY COLLOQUIUM Robson Bonnichsen, Ed.
Illus. Paper. The Center for the Study of the First American, 2003. $24.

WHO'S LOOKING FOR WHOM IN NATIVE AMERICAN ANCESTRY
Laurie B. Duffy; 155 pp. Paper. Amazon.com, 1997. $16.

THE WICHITA INDIANS
F. Todd Smith; Texas A&M University Press, $32.95.

WICHITA MEMORIES
Pamphlet on the Wichita Tribe. Wichita Tribal Office.

THE WICHITA PEOPLE
W.W. Newcomb, Jr.; Published by Indian Tribal Series, Phoenix, 1976. Available at the Wichita Tribal Office, $25.

WIDE RUINS: MEMORIES FROM A NAVAJO TRADING POST
Sallie Wagner; Illus. 150 pp. Paper. University of New Mexico Press, 1997. $30.

WIDENING THE CIRCLE: CULTURALLY RELEVANT PEDAGOGY FOR AMERICAN INDIAN CHILDREN
Beverly J. Klug & Patricia T. Whitfield; Illus. 336 pp. Paper. Routledge, 2002. $26.95.

THE WIECHQUAESKECK INDIANS OF SOUTHWESTERN CONNECTICUT IN THE 17TH CENTURY John A. Buckland; Illus. 300 pp. Paper. Amazon.com, 2002. $20.95.

WIGWAM EVENINGS: SIOUX TALES RETOLD
Charles Eastman & Elaine Goodale Eastman
Traditional Sioux legends. Illus. 255 pp. Paper. U. of Nebraska Press, 1990. $12.95.

*THE WIGWAM & THE LONGHOUSE
Charlotte & David Yue; Grades 4-8. Amazon.co, 1999.

*WILD BROTHERS OF THE INDIANS: AS PICTURED BY THE ANCIENT AMERICANS
Alice Wesche; Grades 3-8. Illus. Paper. Treasure Chest, 1977. $4.95.

WILD INDIANS & OTHER CREATURES
Adrian C. Louis; Collection of short fiction. 200 pp. U. of Nevada Press, 1996. $20.

WILD JUSTICE: THE PEOPLE OF GERONIMO VS. THE U.S.
Michael Lieder & Jake Page; 336 pp. Paper. University of Oklahoma Press, 1999. $16.95

WILD PLANTS & NATIVE PEOPLES OF THE FOUR CORNERS
William W. Dunmire & Gail D. Tierney
Illus. Paper. Museum of New Mexico Press, 2008. $22.50.

WILD RICE & THE OJIBWAY PEOPLE
Thomas Vennum, Jr.; Illus. Photos. Biblio. 358 pp. Minnesota Historical Society Press, 1988. $29.95; paper, $14.95.

WILD WEST SHOWS & THE IMAGES OF AMERICAN INDIANS, 1883-1933
L.G. Moses; Examines the lives of Show Indians from their own point of view. Illus. 384 pp. Paper. University of New Mexico Press, 1999. $24.95.

WILDERNESS EMPIRE
Allan Eckert; Illus. Little, Borwn & Co., 1969. $25.

THE WILDERNESS OF THE SOUTHWEST: CHARLES SHELDON'S QUEST FOR DESERT BIGHORN SHEEP & ADVENTURES WITH THE HAVASUPAI & SERI INDIANS
Neil Carmony & David Brown, Editors; Illus. Paper. University of Utah Press, $14.95.

WILDERNESS POLITICS & INDIAN GIFTS: THE NORTHERN COLONIAL FRONTIER, 1748-1763 Wilbur Jacobs; Reprint. Illus. 208 pp. Paper. U. of Nebraska Press, $4.95.

THE WILDERNESS TRAIL
Charles Hanna
Reprint of 1911 edition. Illus. 2 vols. 840 pp. Wennwoods Publishing, $79.95 per set.

WILDERNESS WAR ON THE OHIO
Alan Fitzpatrick; Details the British-Indian alliance during the Revolutionary War in Ohio country. Revised 2nd Ed. Paper. Wennawoods Publishing, 2006. $ 24.95.

WILDFLOWERS OF IOWA WOODLANDS
Sylvan T. Runkel & Alvin F. Bull
2nd Edition. Photos. 280 pp. Paper. University of Iowa Press, 1980. $29.95.

'WILL THE CIRCLE BE UNBROKEN?': ABORIGINAL COMMUNITIES, RESTORATIVE JUSTICE, AND THE CHALLENGES OF CONFLICT & CHANGE
Jane Dickson-Gilmore & Carol La Prairie
320 pp. University of Toronto Press, 2005. $72; paper, $36.95.

WILL THE TIME EVER COME? A TLINGIT SOURCE BOOK
Andrew Hope & Thomas F. Thornton, Editors; Illus. 160 pp. Paper. Amazon.com, 2001. $15.

A WILL TO SURVIVE: INDIGENOUS ESSAYS ON THE POLITICS OF CULTURE, LANGUAGE, AND IDENTITY Stephen Greymorning
Illus. 1st Ed. 256 pp. Paper. McGraw-Hill, 2004.

WILLIE BOY: A DESERT MANHUNT
Harry Lawton; Paper. Malki-Ballena Press, 1979. $20; paper, $15.95.

JOHN P. WILLIAMSON, A BROTHER TO THE SIOUX
Winifred W. Barton; Reprint of 1919 edition. Illus. 308 pp. Sunnycrest, $10.

THE WILLIAMSON SITE
Peck; Covers the most important early-man paleolithic site in the Southeast (Virginia). Illus. 203 pp. Paper. Hothem House, 1985. $25.

WILLOW STORIES: UTAH NAVAJO BASKETS
Carol A. Edison, et al.; Illus. 32 pp. Paper. Utah Arts Council, 1996. $8.

*WILLY WHITEFEATHER'S OUTDOOR SURVIVAL HANDBOOK FOR KIDS
Willy Whitefeather; Outdoor survival guidebook. Grades 3 and up. Illus. 104 pp. Paper. Amazon.com & Alibris.com, $9.95.

*WILLY WHITEFEATHER'S RIVER BOOK FOR KIDS
Willy Whitefeather; Grandfather teaches a young Cherokee how to make it on the river of life. Grades 3 and up. 128 pp. Paper. Amazon.com, $11.95.

WIND FROM AN ENEMY SKY
D'Arcy McNickle; 269 pp. Paper. University of New Mexico Press. $19.95.

THE WIND IS MY MOTHER: THE LIFE & TEACHINGS OF AN AMERICAN SHAMAN
Bear Heart & Molly Larkin; 272 pp. Paper. Amazon.com, 1998. $14.

WIND & HARD WORDS: A STORY OF NAVAJO ACTIVISM
John W. Sherry; 256 pp. 256 pp. University of New Mexico Press, 2002. $29.95.

*THE WIND IS NOT A RIVER
Arnold Griese; Illus. by Glo Coalson
Grades 1-4. Illus. Boyds Mills Press, 1996 reissue. $7.95.

WIND WOLF WOMAN: THE STORY OF A MEDICINE WOMAN
Mahinto; 590 pp. Tate Publishing, 2001. $24.95.

THE WIND WON'T KNOW ME: THE HISTORY OF THE NAVAJO-HOPI LAND DISPUTE
Emily Benedek; Illus. Map. 480 pp. Paper. University of Oklahoma Press, 1998. $19.95.

WINDHORSE WOMAN: A MARRIAGE OF SPIRIT
Lynn V. Andrews; 210 pp. Paper. Warner Books, 1990. $13.99.

THE WINDING TRAIL: THE ALABAMA–COUSHATTA INDIANS
Vivien Fox; Illus. Eakin Publications, 1983. $7.95.

A WINDOW ON THE PAST: EARLY NATIVE AMERICAN DRESS FROM THE JOHN PAINTER COLLECTION John W. Painter; Cincinnati Art Museum, 2002. $25.

WINDOW ON THE WEST: CHICAGO & THE ART OF THE NEW FRONTIER, 1890-1940
Judith A. Barter & Andrew Walker; Illus. 184 pp. Amazon.com, $50.

THE WINDS ERASE YOUR FOOTPRINTS
Shiyowin Miller; illus. by Chester Kahn
Authentic account of Navajo history. Illus. 325 pp. Naturegraph, $16.95.

WINDS OF CHANGE
Robert Ghost Wolf & the Mountain Brotherhood; Collective view of Native American prophecies. Illus. 219 pp. Paper. Amazon.com, 1998. $12.95.

THE WINDS OF INJUSTICE: AMERICAN INDIANS & THE U.S. GOVERNMENT
Laurence A. French; 288 pp. Amazon.com, 1994. $20.

WINDS OF THE PAST: GUIDE TO PLAYING THE NATIVE AMERICAN FLUTE
By Choctaw/Cherokee flutemaker and recording artist Paul Hacker. Illus. 30 pp. Paper. The Choctaw Store & Amazon.com, $20.

WINDSONG: TEXAS CHEROKEE PRINCESS
Raven Hail; Illus. 140 pp. Paper. Alibris.com & VIP Publishing, 1986. $9.95.

THE WINGED SERPENT: AMERICAN INDIAN PROSE & POETRY
Margot Astrov, Editor; Songs, chants, prayers, myths, and speeches from over 50 native nations throughout North, South & Central America. 392 pp. Paper. Amazon.com, $16.

WINGED WORDS: AMERICAN INDIAN WRITERS SPEAK
Laura Coltelli, Editor; Paula Gunn Allen, Michael Dorris, Joy Harjo, Simon Ortiz, N. Scott Momaday, Gerald Vizenor, and othjers. Illus. 215 pp. Paper. University of Nebraska Press, 1990. $9.95.

WINGS IN THE DESERT: A FOLK ORNITHOLOGY OF THE NORTHERN PIMANS
Amadeo M. Rea; Identifies how birds are incorporated into Piman legends, song, art, religion & ceremonies. 320 pp. Illus. University of Arizona Press, 2007. $70.

THE WINNEBAGO TRIBE
Paul Radin; Reprint of the 1970 ed. Illus. 575 pp. Paper. U. of Nebraska Press, $29.95.

SARAH WINNEMUCCA
Sally Zanjani; Illus. Maps. 366 pp. University of Nebraska Press, 2001. $29.95.

SARAH WINNEMUCCA OF THE NORTHERN PAIUTES
Gae Whitney Canfield; Illus. Maps. 336 pp. Paper. U. of Oklahoma Press, 1983. $14.95.

WINNERS OF THE WEST: A CAMPAIGN PAPER PUBLISHED IN THE INTERESTS OF THE VETERANS OF ALL INDIAN WARS, THEIR WIDOWS & ORPHAN CHILDREN
Reprint of 1944 edition. 2,040 pp. Amazon.com, Microfiche only, $197.

WINNING THE DUST BOWL
Carter Revard; Growing up on the Osage Reservation during Oklahoma Dust Bowl times. 212 pp. Paper. University of Arizona Press, 2001. $17.95.

WINNING THE WEST WITH WORDS: LANGUAGE & CONQUEST IN THE LOWER GREAT LAKES James J. Buss; Explores the ways 19th century Anglo-Americans used language, rhetoric, & narrative to claim culturl ownership of the region that comprises present-day Ohio, Indiana & Illinois. Illus. 336 pp. U. of Oklahoma Press, 2011. $34.95.

WINTER COUNT
Dallas Chief Eagle; Originally published in 1967. Historical novel set during turbulent years leading up to the infamous Wounded Knee Massacre of 1890. Map. 230 pp. Paper. University of Nebraska Press, 2003. $14.95.

A WINTER COUNT OF THE OGLALA
William K. Powers; 11 pp. Paper. Lakota Books, 1962. $12.95

*THE WINTER HUNT
Henry Tall Bull & Tom Weist; Grades 3-9. Paper. Council for Indian Education, 1971. $2.

WINTER IN THE BLOOD
James Welch
A novel set on a Blackfoot reservation in Montana. 192 pp. Paper. Penguin USA, $8.

WINTER OF THE HOLY IRON
Joseph Marshall, III (Sicangu Lakota)
Novel about the winter of 1750, a holy iron (flintlock rifle) and 2 Frenchmen are thrust into the lives of the Wolf Tail Band of Sicangu Lakota. 304 pp. Paper. Amazon.com, 1994. $19.95. Poster available. Also available from Museum of New Mexico Press.

THE WINTU & THEIR NEIGHBORS: A VERY SMALL WORLD-SYSTEM IN NORTHERN CALIFORNIA
Christopher Chase-Dunn & Kelly M. Mann; Case study to compare and contrast systematically an indigenous Native American society with the modern world at large. Illus. 310 pp. University of Arizona Press, 1998. $38.

THE WINTUN INDIANS OF CALIFORNIA & THEIR NEIGHBORS
Peter Knudtson; Ethnographic study. Illus. 96 pp. Paper. Naturegraph, 1977. $9.95.

WIPING THE WAR PAINT OFF THE LENS: NATIVE AMERICAN FILM & VIDEO
Beverly R. Singer; Illus. 136 pp. University of Minnesota Press, 2001. $56.95; paper, $20.

WISCONSIN CHIPPEWA MYTHS & TALES & THEIR RELATION TO CHIPPEWA LIFE
Victor Barnouw; A collection of traditional Chippewa legends from Lac Court Oreilles & Lac du Flambeau reservations in Wisconsin between 1941 & 1944. 304 pp. Maps. Paper. University of Wisconsin Press, 1979. $26.95.

WISCONSIN'S COUNTY FORESTS: CONFLICT OVER INDIAN TIMBER RIGHTS
Michael F. Sohasky; 100 pp. Amazon.com, 1994. $9.

THE WISCONSIN FRONTIER
Mark Wyman; From the earliest Indian settlements to the end of the frontier period. Illus. Paper. Amazon.com & Alibris.com, $10.

WISCONSIN INDIAN LITERATURE: ANTHOLOGY OF NATIVE VOICES
Kathleen Tigerman; foreword by Jim Ottery
Photos. Maps. 336 pp. University of Wisconsin Press, 2006. $75; paper, $26.95.

WISDOM OF THE ELDERS: NATIVE TRADITIONS ON THE NORTHWEST
Ruth Kirk; Illus. Amazon.com, 1988. $10.

WISDOM OF THE ELDERS: SACRED NATIVE STORIES OF NATURE
David Suzuki & Peter Knudtson; Synthesis of Native ecological knowledge & western scientific insights. Illus. 274 pp. Paper. Amazon.com, $19.

THE WISDOM OF THE GREAT CHIEFS
Kent Nerburn, Editor; Includes the Soul of an Indian and Other Writings Ohiyesa and the Great Speeches of Chief Red Jacket, Chief Joseph and Chief Seattle, documenting Native perception and philosophy. 96 pp. Amazon.com, $12.95.

WISDOM OF THE NATIVE AMERICANS: INCLUDING THE SOUL OF AN INDIAN & OTHER WRITINGS FROM OHIYESA & THE GREAT SPEECHES OF CHIEF RED JACKET Kent Nerburn; 242 pp. New World Library, 1999. $17.95.

WISDOM SITS IN PLACES: LANDSCAPE & LANGUAGE AMONG THE WESTERN APACHE Keith H. Basso; Illus. 172 pp. Paper. U. of New Mexico Press, 1996. $23.95.

WISDOM'S DAUGHTERS: CONVERSATIONS WITH WOMEN ELDERS OF NATIVE AMERICA Steve Wall; Interviews with Native American spiritual leaders, giving voice to women who discuss their ancestyral knowledge, philosophies and traditions. 100+ b&x photos. Illus. 320 pp. Paper. HarperCollins, $17.

WISDOMKEEPERS: MEETINGS WITH NATIVE AMERICAN SPIRITUAL ELDERS
Steve Wall & Harvey Arden; Spirit journey into the lives, minds, and natural-world philosophy of Native American spiritual elders representing 17 tribes. 128 pp. Beyond Words Publishing, 1990. $39.95; paper, $19.95. Two-tape audio, $16.95.

WISHRAM TEXTS: WASCO TALES & MYTHS
Edward Sapir; Vol. II. Facs. ed.. 330 pp. Paper. Coyote Press, $34.95.

THE WITCH OF GOINGSNAKE & OTHER STORIES
Robert J. Conley; Stories reflect the range of Cherokee culture. 166 pp. Paper. University of Oklahoma Press, $12.95.

THE WITCH PURGE OF 1878: ORAL & DOCUMENTARY HISTORY IN THE EARLY NAVAJO RESERVATION YEARS Martha Blue; Paper. Amazon.com. $4.75.

WITCHCRAFT IN SOUTHWEST: SPANISH & INDIAN SUPERNATURALISM ON THE RIO GRANDE Marc Simmons; Illus. 185 pp. Paper. U. of Nebraska Press, 1980. $5.95.

WITCHCRAFT & SORCERY OF THE NORTH AMERICAN NATIVE PEOPLE
Deward E. Walker, Editor; Revised ed. 336 pp. Paper. U. of Idaho Press, 1989. $23.95.

THE WITCHES OF ABIQUIU: THE GOVERNOR, THE PRIEST, THE GENIZARO INDIANS, AND THE DEVIL Malcolm Ebright & Rick Hendricks
A priest's charges of witchcraft among Indians in the mid 18th century New mexico and how the Spanish government rejected the charges in the effort to achieve peace with their Native subjects. Paper. Amazon.com, Alibris & University of New Mexico Press, $24.95.

WITH EAGLE TAIL
Hugh Dempsey & Colin Taylor; Illus. 128 pp. Amazon.com, 1999. $12.98.

WITH GOOD HEART: YAQUI BELIEFS & CEREMONIES IN PASCUA VILLAGE
Muriel Painter; Ed Spicer & WilmaKaemlein, Editors
Illus. 533 pp. University of Arizona Press, 1986. $50.95.

WITH GOOD INTENTIONS: EURO-CANADIAN & ABORIGINAL RELATIONS IN COLONIAL CANADA Celia Haig-Brown & David A. Nock, Editors; The colonization of native peoples in Canada through missionary work. Illus. 400 pp. U. of Washington Press, 2006. $94; paper, $37.95.

WITH MY OWN EYES: A LAKOTA WOMAN TELLS HER PEOPLE'S HISTORY
Susan Bordeaux Bettelyoun & Josephine Waggoner; Tells the histoy of the 19th century Lakotas. Illus. Maps. 200 pp. Paper. University of Nebraska Press, 1998. $16.95.

WITH THE NEZ PERCES: ALICE FLETCHER IN THE FIELD, 1889-1892
E. Jane Gay; Frederick E. Hoxie and Joan T. Mark, Editors
Illus. Map. 226 pp. Paper. University of Nebraska Press, 1981. $10.95.

WITH PEN & PENCIL ON THE FRONTIER IN 1851: THE DIARY & SKETCHES OF FRANK BLACKWELL MAYER
Frank Blackwell Mayer; Presents the signing of the Treaty of Traverse des Sioux. Illus. 256 pp. Minnesota Historical Society Press, 1986. $9.95.

WITHOUT QUARTER: THE WICHITA EXPEDITION & THE FIGHT ON CROOKED CREEK William Y. Chalfant; The story of the first major U.S. army expedition against the Comanches along Texas frontier. Illus. Maps. 184 pp. University of Oklahoma Press, 1991. $24.95.

WITNESS: A HUNKPAPHA HISTORIAN'S STRONG-HEART SONG OF THE LAKOTAS
Josephine Waggoner; Emily Levine, Editor & Intro. Illus. Maps. 824 pp. University of Nebraska Press, 2013. $85.

WITSUWIT'EN GRAMMAR: PHONETICS, PHONOLOGY, MORPHOLOGY
Sharon hargus; A First Nation's Athapaskan language spoken in western-central British Columbia. 850 pp. University of Washington Press, 2007. $165.

WIVES & HUSBANDS: GENDER & AGE IN SOUTHERN ARAPAHO HISTORY
Loretta Fowler; 400 pp. University of Oklahoma Press, $39.95

WIYAXAYXT / WIYAAKAA'AWN / AS DAYS GO BY: OUR HISTORY, OUR LAND, OUR PEOPLE - THE CAYUSE, UMATILLA, AND WALLA WALLA
Jennifer Karson, Editor
Illus. Maps. 320 pp. Paper. University of Washington Press, 2006. $23.95.

WIYOT GRAMMAR & TEXTS
Gladys Reichard; Reprint fo 1925 edition. 215 pp. Paper. Coyote Press, $23.13.

WIYUTA: ASSINIBOINE STORYTELLING WITH SIGNS CD
Brenda Farnell; University of Texas Press, 1995. $100.

WOKINI LAKOTA: A LAKOTA JOURNEY TO HAPPINESS & SELF-UNDERSTANDING
Billy Mills & Nicholas Sparks; Billy Mills, (Sioux) Olympic gold medalist, teaches of his personal journey to happiness and self-understanding. Amazon.com $12.95.

WO'WAKITA: RESERVATION RECOLLECTIONS
Emily H. Lewis; A people's history of the Allen Issue Station District on the Pine Ridge Reservation of South Dakota. Illus. 294 pp. Center for Western Studies, $19.95.

THE WOLF & THE BUFFALO
Elmer Kelton; 570 pp. G.K. Hall, 1989. $19.95.

THE WOLF AT TWILIGHT: AN INDIANN ELDER'S JOURNEY THROUGH A LAND OF GHOSTS & SHADOWS Kent Nerburb; 368 pp. Paper. New Wrld Library, $16.95.

*WOLF DOG OF THE WOODLAND INDIANS
Margaret Zehmer Searcy; Experiences that propel the young Indian boy quickly into manhood. Grades 3-8. Illus. 112 pp. paper. Amazon.com, $6.95.

THE WOLF & THE RAVEN: TOTEM POLES OF SOUTHEASTEN ALASKA
Viola E. Garfield & Linn A. Forrest
Reprint of 1948 ed. Illus. 161 pp. Paper. University of Washington Press, 1961. $14.95.

*WOLF STORIES: MYTHS AND TRUE-LIFE TALES FROM AROUND THE WORLD
Susan Strauss; Grades 1-7. 48 pp. Paper. Beyond Words. $11.95; paper, $7.95.

*WOLF TALES: NATIVE AMERICAN CHILDREN'S STORIES
edited & adapted for children by Mary Powell
Grades 3 and up. Illus. 48 pp. Paper. Amazon.com, 1992. $9.95.

WOLF THAT I AM: IN SEARCH OF THE RED EARTH PEOPLE
Fred McTaggart; Biblio. 202 pp. Paper. University of Oklahoma Press, 1984. $14.95.

WOLFSONG: A NOVEL
Louis Owens; 256 pp. Paper. University of Oklahoma Press, 2002. $19.95.

WOLLASTON: PEOPLE RESISTING GENOCIDE
Miles Goldstick; Natives' struggle in northern Saskatchewan to protect their homes from the effects of uranium mining. Illus. Photos. 315 pp. Paper. U. of Toronto Press, 1987. $17.

WOLVES FOR THE BLUE SOLDIERS: INDIAN SCOUTS & AUXILLIARIES WITH THE U.S. ARMY, 1860-1890
Thomas Dunlay; Illus. Maps. 320 pp. Paper. University of Nebraska Press, 1982. $25.

THE WOLVES OF HEAVEN: CHEYENNE SHAMANISM, CEREMONIES, & PREHISTORIC ORIGINS
Karl H. Schlesier; Illus. Maps. 232 pp. Paper. University of Oklahoma Press, 1987. $14.95.

WOMAN OF THE GREEN GLADE: THE STORY OF AN OJIBWAY INDIAN LADY
Virginia Soetebier; Illus. 88 pp. Paper. University of Nebraska Press, 1999. $14.95.

A WOMAN OF THE PEOPLE
Benjamin Capps; Captivity tale. 248 pp. paper. Texas A&M U. Press, 1966. $15.95.

WOMAN WALKING AHEAD: IN SEARCH OF CATHERINE WELDON & SITTING BULL
Eileen Pollack; Illus. 368 pp. Paper. University of New Mexico Press, 2004. $12.95.

THE WOMAN WHO LOVED MANKIND: THE LIFE OF A TWENTIETH-CENTURY CROW ELDER Lillian Bullshows Hogan told to Barbara Loeb & Mardell Hogan Plainfeather. Illus. Maps. 496 pp. University of Nebraska Press, 2012. $60.

THE WOMAN WHO WATCHES OVER THE WORLD: A NATIVE MEMOIR
Linda Hogan; 225 pp. Paper. W.W. Norton & Co., Inc., 2002. $13.95.

WOMEN ELDERS' LIFE STORIES OF THE OMAHA TRIBE: MACY, NEBRASKA 2004-2005 Wynne L. Summers; Female elders, Eleanor Baxter, Alice Saunsoci & Hawate (Wenona Caramony), focus on traditional culture and modern success. Photos. Map. University of Nebraska Press, 2010. $35.

WOMEN ETHNOGRAPHERS & NATIVE WOMEN STORYTELLERS
Susan Berry Brill de Ramirez; Focuses on the collaborative work between Native women storytellers and their female ethnographers and/or editors; also cultural authenticity, & storytelling signification & meaning. 216 pp. Rowman & Littlefield, Lexington Books, 2007. $80; eBook, $79.99.

*WOMEN IN AMERICAN INDIAN SOCIETY
Rayma Green; Grades 5 and up. Ill. Chelsea House, 1989. $17.95.

WOMEN IN PREHISTORY: NORTH AMERICA & MESOAMERICA
Cheryl Classen & Rosemary Joyce, Editors
Illus. 288 pp. University of Pennsylvania Press, 1996. $39.95; paper, $18.50.

WOMEN & INDIANS ON THE FRONTIER, 1825-1915
Glenda Riley; Illus. 350 pp. Paper. University of New Mexico Press, 1984. $19.95.

WOMEN IN NAVAJO SOCIETY
Ruth Roessel; Illus. 184 pp. Rough Rock School Press, 1981. $20.

WOMEN IN PREHISTORY: NORTH AMERICA & MESOAMERICA
Cheryl Classen & Rosemary Joyce, Eds.
Illus. 290 pp. University of Pennsylvania Press, 1996. $39.95; paper, $18.50.

WOMEN & MEN IN THE PREHISTORIC SOUTHWEST: LABOR, POWER & PRESTIGE
Patricia L. Crown, Editor
Illus. 520 pp. School of American Research Press, $60; paper, $24.95.

WOMEN OF THE APACHE NATION: VOICES OF TRUTH
H. Henrietta Stockel; Interviews of Chiricahua Apache women emphasizes the importance of storytelling and ritual in preserving Apache heritage. Illus. 226 pp. Paper. University of Nevada Press, 1993. $14.95.

WOMEN OF COLOR: MOTHER-DAUGHTER RELATIONSHIPS IN 20TH CENTURY LITERATURE Elizabeth Brown-Guillory, Editor; Includes essay on Native Americans by Leslie Marmon Silko. 263 pp. Paper. University of Texas Press, 1996. $25.

WOMEN OF THE DAWN
Bunny McBride; Stories of four Wabanaki Indian women. Friends of American Writers Literary Award. Illus. Map. 160 pp. Paper. University of Nebraska Press, 1999. $12.95.

WOMEN OF THE EARTH LODGES: TRIBAL LIFE ON THE PLAINS
Virginia Bergman Peters; Examines the influence and vitality of Plains Indian women. Illus. Map. 250 pp. Shoe String Press, $39.50. Paper. U. of Okla. Press, 2002. $19.95.

WOMEN OF THE FIRST NATIONS: POWER, WISDOM & STRENGTH
Christine Miller & Patricia Chuchryk, Editors; Paper. U. of Toronto Press, 1996. $19.95.

WOMEN OF THE NATIVE STRUGGLE: PORTRAITS & TESTIMONY OF NATIVE AMERICAN WOMEN Ronnie Farley, Ed. & photos by; Direct record of author's travels across America based on her photographs of native women in their different environments and her interviews with them. Paper. Crown Publishing Group, $1993. 25.

WOMEN & POWER IN NATIVE NORTH AMERICA
Lilian Ackerman & Laura Klein, Editors
Map. 294 pp. Paper. University of Oklahoma Press, 1995. $19.95.

WOMEN'S RIGHTS IN NATIVE NORTH AMERICA: LEGAL MOBILIZATION IN THE U.S. & CANADA Judith H. Aks; 256 pp. LFB Scholarly Publishing, 2004. $65.

WOMEN ON THE RUN
Janet Campbell Hale; Short fiction of contemporary Native & non-Native American women living & surviving outside of mainstream America. 186 pp. U. of Idaho Press, $16.95.

THE WOMEN'S WARRIOR SOCIETY
Lois Beardslee; Stories of Native American women. 160 pp. University of Arizona Press, 2008. $29.95; paper, $16.95.

WOOD BURNERS
Daniel Mihalyo; Illus. 112 pp. Paper. Princeton Architectural Press, 1997. $21.95.

WOODEN LEG: A WARRIOR WHO FOUGHT CUSTER
Thomas Marquis, Tr. Illus. Maps. 416 pp. Paper. U. of Nebraska Press, 2003. $14.95.

WOODLAND FEAST: NATIVE AMERICAN FOODWAYS OF 17TH & 18TH CENTURIES
Carolyn Raine; Illus. 90 pp. Paper. Amazon.com, 1997. $15.

***WOODLAND INDIANS**
Cleary & Taylor; Grades 3-6. Teacher Illus. 48 pp. Paper. Amazon.com, 1995. $5.95.

WOODLAND INDIANS OF THE WESTERN GREAT LAKES
Robert & Pat Ritzenthaler; 2nd Ed. Illus. 154 pp. Paper. Waveland Press, 1983. $16.50.

WOODLAND PEOPLES: AN EDUCATIONAL UNIT
Nicholas L. Clark; 32 pp. Paper. Minnetrista, 1993.

WOODLAND POTTERS & ARCHAEOLOGICAL CERAMICS OF THE NORTH CAROLINA COAST Joseph M. Herbert; Illus. 352 pp. U. of Alabama Press, 2009. $60; paper, $36.95.

WOODLAND TRAPPERS: HARE INDIANS OF NORTHWSTERN CANADA
Harold Broch; 225 pp. Paper. Barber Press, 1987. $10.95.

***WOODLANDS INDIANS: COLORING BOOK**
Peter F. Copeland; Grades K-2. 48 pp. paper. Dover, $2.95.

WOODSMEN, OR THOREAU & THE INDIANS: A NOVEL
Arnold Krupat; 134 pp. Paper. University of Oklahoma Press, 1994. $10.95.

WORD WAYS: THE NOVELS OF D'ARCY McNICKLE
John Lloyd Purdy; 167 pp. University of Arizona Press, 1989. $30.95.

WORDARROWS: INDIANS & WHITES IN THE NEW FUR TRADE
Gerald Vizenor; Focuses on the cultural word wars which dominate the relations of Indians and whites. 170 pp. Paper. University of Minnesota Press, 1978. $12.95.

WORDARROWS: NATIVE STATES OF LITERARY SOVEREIGNTY
Gerald Vizenor; Modern Native American life and the different ways that Native Americans & whites interact, and resolve their conflicts. 164 pp. Paper. U. of Nebraska Press, 2003. $4.

WORDS IN THE BLOOD: CONTEMPORARY INDIAN WRITERS OF NORTH & SOUTH AMERICA Jamake Highwater; 416 pp. Paper. Amazon.com, 1984. $9.95.

WORDS OF POWER: VOICES FROM INDIAN AMERICA
Norbert S. Hill, Jr., Editor; Collection of quotations, illustrates views & values. Illus. 72 pp. Paper. Fulcrum Publishing & Amazon.com, 1994. $9.95.

WORDS OF THE REAL PEOPLE: ALASKA NATIVE LITERATURE IN TRANSLATION
Ann Fienup-Riordan & Lawrence D. Kaplan; Collection of life stories, poetry, and oral literature of the Yup'ik, Inupiaq, and Aluutiq peoples of Alaska. Illus. Maps. 320 pp. University of Chicago Press, 2007. $49.95; paper, $21.95.

THE WORK OF SOVEREIGNTY: TRIBAL LABOR RELATIONS & SELF-DETERMINATION AT THE NAVAJO NATION
David Kamper; Explores the political, economic & cultural forces that structure & influence indigenous economic development. In-depth look at the ways labor relations play out in Indian Country. 272 pp. Paper. School for Advanced Research, 2010. $34.95.

WORKING IN INDIAN COUNTRY: BUILDING SUCCESSFUL BUSINESS RELATIONSHIPS WITH AMERICAN INDIAN TRIBES Larry D. Keown
Illus. Paper. Amazon.com. $19.95.

WORKING THE NAVAJO WAY: LABOR & CULTURE IN THE 20TH CENTURY
Colleen O-Neill; History of Navajo labor through accounts of Navajo coal miners, weavers, et al. Photos. 224 pp. Paper. University Press of Kansas, 1977. $22.50.

WORKING ON THE RAILROAD, WALKING IN BEAUTY: NAVAJOS, HOZHO, AND TRACK WORK Jay Youngdahl; Navajo involvement in railroad labor and underlying cultural values interface. 208 pp. University Press of Colorado & Utah State University Press, 2011. $34.95, E-book, $27.

WORKING TOGETHER: NATIVE AMERICANS & ARCHAEOLOGISTS
Kurt E. Dongoske, et al, Editors; Illus. 237 pp. Society for American Archaeology, 2000.

THE WORLD BEGINS HERE: AN ANTHOLOGY OF OREGON SHORT FICTION
Glen Love; Stories of Oregon, ranging from a Nez Perce story of Coyote to stories of work, courage, and relationships between people. Illus. 288 pp. Oregon State University Press, 1993. $39.95; eBook, $27.

THE WORLD OF THE AMERICAN INDIAN
Jules B. Billard, National Geographic Editor
Revised edition. Illus. 398 pp. Amazon.com, 1993. $29.95.

THE WORLD OF CHIEF SEATTLE: HOW CAN ONE SELL THE AIR?
Warren Jefferson; Chief Seattle's life and brief history of the Puget Sound area of the State of Washington. Illus. photos. maps. 128 pp. Book Publishing Co., $13.95.

THE WORLD OF THE CROW INDIANS: AS DRIFTWOOD LODGES
Rodney Frey; Illus. Maps. 194 pp. Paper. University of Oklahoma Press, 1987. $13.95.

A WORLD OF FACES: MASKS OF THE NORTHWEST COAST INDIANS
Edward Malin; Classic study of Native American masks from the Pacific Northwest. Explores the rcihes of this ancient tradition, showing outstanding old masks. 8 color photos, 49 b&w photos. 158 pp. Paper reprint of 1978 edition. Amazon.com. $17.95.

THE WORLD OF FLOWER BLUE: POP CHALEE: AN ARTISTIC BIOGRAPHY
Margaret Cesa; Portrait of a unique Native American artist. Illus. 40 color plates. 288 pp. Amazon.com, 1999. $49.95.

***WORLD OF THE SOUTHERN INDIANS**
Virginia Brown & Laurella Owens
Grades 6-9. Illus. 176 pp. Paper. Amazon.com, 1983. $15.95.

WORLD OF WAKARA
Conway Ballantyne Sonne; illus. by Tom Jones & George Hughey
Illus. 235 pp. Naylor Co., 1962. Amazon.com. $11.95.

THE WORLD TURNED UPSIDE DOWN: INDIAN VOICES FROM EARLY AMERICA
Colin G. Calloway, Editor; Illus. 224 pp. Paper. Bedford/St. Martin's, 1994.

WORLD WAR II & THE AMERICAN INDIAN
Kenneth W. Townsend; Illus. 284 pp. Paper. University of New Mexico Press, $35.

THE WORLD'S RICHEST INDIAN: JACKSON BARNETT
Tanis C. Thorne; Illus. 312 pp. Oxford University Press, 2003. $35.

THE WORLD'S RIM: GREAT MYSTERIES OF THE NORTH AMERICAN INDIANS
Hartley Alexander; Illus. 300 pp. Paper. Dover Publications, 1967. $8.95.

WORLDS BETWEEN TWO RIVERS: PERSPECTIVES ON AMERICAN INDIANS IN IOWA Gretchen Bataille, et al, Editors
Reprint of 1987 ed. Photos. Drawings. 208 pp. Paper. University of Iowa Press, 2000. $21.

WOUNDED KNEE 1973: A PERSONAL ACCOUNT
Stanley David Lyman; Illus. Map. 196 pp. Paper. U. of Nebraska Press, 1991. $16.

WOUNDED KNEE II
Rolland Dewing; 230 pp. Amazon.com, 1995. $21.95; paper, $10.95.

WOUNDED KNEE & THE GHOST DANCE TRAGEDY
Jack Utter; Account of events leading to and includng the infamous massacre at Wounded Knee, SD, in 1890. 29 pp. Illus. Maps. Paper. Amazon.com, 1991. $3.95.

***WOUNDED KNEE: AN INDIAN HISTORY OF THE AMERICAN WEST**
Dee Brown; Grades 7 and up. 192 pp. Paper. Dell, 1974. $1.50.

WOUNDED KNEE: LEST WE FORGET
Alvin M. Josephy, Jr. & Trudy Thomas; Attempts to tell the true story of the history of Wounded Knee and the practice of Ghost Dance religion by the Sioux. Illus. 64 pp. Paper. University of Washington Press, $21.95.

THE WOUNDED KNEE MASSACRE: FROM THE VIEWPOINT OF THE SIOUX
James H. McGregor; Reprint. Illus. 131 pp. paper. Center for Western Studies, $5.95.

WOUNDED KNEE: THE MEANING & SIGNIFICANCE OF THE SECOND INCIDENT
Rolling Dewing; 417 pp. Irvington, 1984. $49.50; paper, $19.95.

WOUNDED KNEE: PARTY POLITICS AND THE ROAD TO AN AMERICAN MASSACRE
Heather Cox Richardson; Narrative tracing the story from a political point of view. Illus. Map. Biblio. 363 pp. Amazon.com, 2010.

WOUNDED WARRIORS: A TIME FOR HEALING
Doyle Arbogast; 330 pp. Paper. Amazon.com, 1995. $22.

WOVEN BY THE GRANDMOTHERS
Eulalie H. Bonar, Editor; 19th century Navajo textiles from the National Museum of the American Indian. Illus. 215 pp. Smithsonian Institution Press, 1996. $34.95.

WOVEN STONE: THE AUTOBIOGRAPHY OF SIMON J. ORTIZ
Simon J. Ortiz; 350 pp. University of Arizona Press, 1992. $51; paper, $22.95.

WOVEN WORLDS: BASKETRY FROM THE CLARK FIELD COLLECTION
edited by Lydia L. Wyckoff; Weavers and their baskets from eight major cultural areas. A color map in each chapter with historical information and a discussion with some interviews. Amazon.com. Illus. Maps. 246 pp. University of New Mexico Press, 2001. $75; paper, $39.95.

WOVOKA & THE GHOST DANCE: A SOURCE BOOK
Expanded edition by Michael Hittman; edited by Don Lynch; The known research about Wovoka (Jack Wilson) as the Ghost Dance Prophet. Illus. Map. 370 pp. Paper. University of Nebraska Press & Yerington Paiute Tribe Publications, 1997. $22.95.

WOVOKA POSTER
16 1/2" x 23" poster of the Northern Paiute Ghost Dance Prophet. $5.

WRITE IT ON YOUR HEART: WORLD OF AN OKANAGAN STORYTELLER
Harry Robinson; Okanagan stories. Amazon.com, $18.95.

WRITERS OF THE PURPLE SAGE: AN ANTHOLOGY OF RECENT WESTERN WRITING Russell Martin & Marc Barash, Editors
Includes some Native American writers. 368 pp. Paper. Penguin USA, $9.95.

WRITING CHEROKEE
Syllabary practice book. 28 pp. VIP Publishing. $5.

WRITING THE CIRCLE: NATIVE WOMEN OF WESTERN CANADA-AN ANTHOLOGY
Jeanne Perreault & Sylvia Vance; Anthology of contemporary Native Canadian women's writings. 288 pp. Paper. Amazon.com, 1993. $14.95.

WRITING INDIAN, NATIVE CONVERSATIONS
John Lloyd Purdy; Conversations on traditions of Native American fiction with personal reflections on the last 30 years of work in the genre. Includes Paula Gunn Allen, Simon Ortiz, Gerald Vizenor, Sherman Alexie, and Louis Owens. 352 pp. University of Nebraska Press, 2009. $45.

WRITING INDIAN NATIONS: NATIVE INTELLECTUALS & THE POLITICS OF HISTORIOGRAPHY, 1827-1863
Maureen Konkle; Illus. 384 pp. Paper. University of North Carolina Press, 2003. $27.95.

WRITING INDIANS: LITERACY, CHRISTIANITY & NATIVE COMMUNITY IN EARLY AMERICA Hilary E. Wyss; Focuses on New England missionary settlements from the mid 17th century to the early 19th century. 224 pp. University of Massachusetts Press, 2000. $32.50; paper, $22.95.

WRITING THE SOUTHWEST
David King Dunaway & Sara Spurgeon; Includes interviews, bibliographies, excerpts, and criticism on 14 of the Southwest's most important authors, including Joy Harjo, Tony Hillerman, Linda Hogan, Simon Ortiz, et al. Revised edition. 320 pp. University of Arizona Press, 2003. $39.95; paper, $17.95. Includes 74 min. CD.

WRITING TO CREATE OURSELVES: NEW APPROACHES FOR TEACHERS, STUDENTS, & WRITERS T.D. Allen; Describes nearly two decades of experience in teaching writing to Navaho & Eskimo students. 253 pp. U. of Oklahoma Press, 1982. $22.95.

WRITINGS IN INDIAN HISTORY, 1985-1990
Jay Miller, Colin G. Calloway & Richard A. Sattler
Bibliography. 216 pp. University of Oklahoma Press, 1995. $28.95; paper, $12.95

WRITINGS OF DAVID THOMPSON, VOL. 1: THE TRAVELS, 1850 VERSION
William E. Moreau, Editor; Life inthe fur trade from 1784 to 1812 from the Great Lakes to the Rockies. Illus. Maps. 432 pp. University of Washington Press, 2008. $40.

THE WSANEC & THEIR NEIGHBOURS: DIAMOND JENNESS ON THE COAST SALISH
Diamon Jenness & Barnett Richling; Paper. Amazon.com, $19.95.

WUPATKI & WALNUT CANYON: NEW PERSPECTIVES ON HISTORY, PREHISTORY, AND ROCK ART David Grant Noble, Editor; Reveals the remains of the Sinagua culture & contains sketches of the Navajo who live in Wupatki today. Illus. Maps. Photos. 48 pp. Paper. Amazon.com, 1990. $8.95.

WYNEMA: A CHILD OF THE FOREST
S. Alice Callahan; edited by A. LaVonne Brown Ruoff; Originally published in 1891. Illus. Map. 120 pp. Paper. University of Nebraska Press, 1997. $19.95.

NED WYNKOOP & THE LONELY ROAD FROM SAND CREEK
Louis Kraft; Biography. His career as a soldier and then U.S. Indian agent after the Sand Creek Massacre. Illus. Maps. 336 pp. University of Oklahoma Press, 2011. $34.95.

WYOMING PLACE NAMES
Mae Urbanek; 238 pp. Paper. Amazon.com, $10.

X

X-MARKS: NATIVE SIGNATURES OF ASSENT
Scott R. Lyons; Explores contemporary Indian identity & current debates among Indians about traditionalism, nationalism, & tribalism. Biblio. 220 pp. U. of Minnesota Press, 2010.

Y

*THE YAKAMA: NORTHWEST
Helen Schuster; Grades 5 and up. Illus. Chelsea House, 1989. $17.95.

YAKAMA, PALOUSE, CAYUSE, UMATILLA, WALLA WALLA, & WANAPUM INDIANS: AN HISTORICAL BIBLIOGRAPHY
Clifford E. Trafzer, Editor; Map. 263 pp. Scarecrow Press, 1992. $65.95.

YAKAMA RISING: INDIGENOUS CULRURAL REVITALIZATION, ACTIVISM, & HEALING Michelle M. Jacob; 152 pp. Illus. Paper. U. of Arizona Press, 2010. $24.95.

YAKAMA SAHAPTIN DICTIONARY
Virginia Beavert & Sharon Hargus; with essays by Bruce Rigsby
Illus. CD. 576 pp. Paper. University of Washington Press, 2010. $60.

THE YAKAMAS: A CRITICAL BIBLIOGRAPHY
Helen H. Schuster; 168 pp. Paper. Amazon.com & Alibris.com, 1982. $5.95.

THE YAMASEE WAR: A STUDY OF CULTURE, ECONOMY & CONFLICT IN THE COLONIAL SOUTH
William L. Ramsey; Tables. Maps. 324 pp. University of Nebraska Press, 2008. $50.

YAMORIA THE LAWMAKER: STORIES OF THE DENE
George Blondin; Illus. 264 pp. Amazon.com, 1997.

THE YANKTON
James H. Howard; 28 pp. paper. Lakota Books, 1998. $12.95.

*THE YANKTON SIOUX
Herbert Hoover; Grades 5 and up. Illus. 104 pp. Chelsea House, 1988. $17.95.

YANKTONAI SIOUX WATER COLORS: CULTURAL REMEMBRANCES OF JOHN SAUL Martin Brokenleg & Herbert T. Hoover; John Saul was a Minnesota Sioux (1878-1971). His family was removed to the Dakota Territory after the Minnesota Dakota war of 1862. Includes 23 of his drawings in full color; and includes chapters on Sioux customs, the Yanktonai and their Sioux relatives, a photographic essay on John Saul, and more. Illus. 66 pp. Center for Western Studies, $12.95.

YAQUI DEER SONGS: A NATIVE AMERICAN POETRY
Larry Evers & Felipe Molina; 239 pp. Paper. University of Arizona Press, 1986. $19.95. Audiocassette of deer songs, $12.95.

A YAQUI EASTER
Muriel Thayer Painter
Introduction to the ceremony. 40 pp. Paper. University of Arizona Press, 1971. $8.95.

YAQUI HOMELAND & HOMEPLACE: THE EVERYDAY PRODUCTION OF ETHNIC IDENTITY Kristin C. Erickson; 208 pp. U. of Arizona Press, 2008. $50; paper, $24.95.

A YAQUI LIFE: THE PERSONAL CHRONICLE OF A YAQUI INDIAN
Rosalio Moises, et al; Illus. 251 pp. U. of Nebraska Press, 1977. $23.95; paper, $5.95.

YAQUI MYTHS & LEGENDS
Ruth Warner Giddings
61 tales narrated by Yaquis. 180 pp. Paper. University of Arizona Press, 1968. $14.95.

YAQUI RESISTANCE & SURVIVAL: THE STRUGGLE FOR LAND & AUTONOMY, 1821-1910 Evelyn Hu-DeHart
Maps. 320 pp. Paper. University of Wisconsin Press, 2016. $29.95.

YAQUI WOMEN: CONTEMPORARY LIFE HISTORIES
Jane Holden Kelley; Illus. 265 pp. University of Nebraska Press, 1978. $32.50.

THE YAQUIS: A CULTURAL HISTORY
Edward H. Spicer; Reprint of 1980 edition. 406 pp. University of Arizona Press, $35.

THE YAVAPAI: SEDONA'S NATIVE PEOPLE
Kate Ruland-Thorne; A history of the Yavapai people in Arizona written from their persepctive. Illus. 90 pp. Paper. Primer Publishers, $6.95

YEAR IN NAM: A NATIVE AMERICAN SOLDIER'S STORY
Leroy TeCube; TeCube, a Jicarilla Apache, spent a year in Vietnam in 1968 as an infantryman in the U.S. Army. Illus. 288 pp. Universityt of Nebraska Press, 1999. $30; paper, $14.95.

THE YEAR OF THE HOPI
Tyrone Stewart, et al; Illus. 96 pp. Paper. Rizzoli International, 1982. $14.95.

THE YEARS THE STARS FELL: LAKOTA WINTER COUNTS AT THE SMITHSONIAN
Candace C. Greene & Russell Thornton, Editors
Illus. Map. 377 pp. University of Nebraska Press, 2007. $45.

YELLOW DIRT: AN AMERICAN STORY OF A POISONED LAND AND A PEOPLE BETRAYED Judy Pasternak; A rare voice to Navajo perceptions of the world, their own complicated involvement with uranium mining, and their political coming-of-age. Illus. Map. Biblio. 317 pp. Amazon.com, 2010.

*YELLOW SHIRT & BLACK NECKLACE
Long Standing Bear Chief
Grades pre K-3. Illus. by Tom Gilleon. Paper. Amazon.com, $8.95.

YELLOW WOLF: HIS OWN STORY
L.V. McWhorter
Nez Perce War. Illus. Map. Biblio. 328 pp. The Caxton Press, $19.95; paper, $15.95.

YELLOWTAIL, CROW MEDICINE MAN & SUN DANCE CHIEF: AN AUTOBIOGRAPHY
Thomas Yellowtaill Illus. Map. 242 pp. Paper. U. of Oklahoma Press, 1991. $19.95.

YELLOW WOLF: HIS OWN STORY
L. McWhorter; Reprint. Illus. 325 pp. Caxton Press, $19.95; paper, $14.95.

YERINGTON PAIUTE DICTIONARY
118 pp. Paper. Yerington Paiute Tribe Publications, $15.

YERINGTON PAIUTE LANGUAGE GRAMMAR
168 pp. Paper. Yerington Paiute Tribe Publications, $15.

YOEME-ENGLISH, ENGLISH-YOEME STANDARD DICTIONARY
David L. Shaul; Reprint. 350 pp. Paper. Amazon.com, $14.95.

YOKUTS DIALECT SURVEY
A.L. Kroeber; J.H. Rowe, et al, editors
Reprint of 1963 edition. 83 pp. Paper. Coyote Press, $9.38.

THE YOKUTS LANGUAGE OF SOUTH CENTRAL CALIFORNIA
A.L. Kroeber; Reprint of 1907 edition. 213 pp. Paper. Coyote Press, $9.38.

YOKUTS & PAIUTE SONGS & CULTURE
Alfred Pitroforte
25 songs. Illus. 64 pp. Paper. Naturegraph Publishers, 2006. $15.95, includes audio CD.

YOKUTS TEXTS
Geoffrey Gamble, Ed.; Illus. 110 pp. Paper. Amazon.com, 1994.

YONDER MOUNTAIN: A CHEROKEE LEGEND
Teacher Edition; Paper. Amazon.com, 1999.

YOSEMITE INDIANS
Elizabeth Godfrey; Revised ed. Illus. 36 pp. Paper. Amazon.com, 1977. $2.95.

YOU ARE ON INDIAN LAND: ALCATRAZ ISLAND, 1969-1971
Troy R. Johnson, Ed.; 160 pp. Paper. UCLA, American Indian Studies Center, 1995. $12.

*YOU ARE NOW ON INDIAN LAND: THE AMERICAN INDIAN OCCUPATION OF ALCATRZ ISLAND, CALIFORNIA, 1969
Margaret J. Goldstein; Grades 9-12. Lerner Publications, 2011. $28.99

YOU & THE UTILITY COMPANY
Institute for the Development of Indian Law, $3.50.

YOUNG CHILD, OLD SPIRIT: PRESCHOOL CHEMICAL DEPENDENCY CURRICULUM
Phyllis Gough; 119 pp. Student Ed. Minn. Indian Women's Resource Center, 1990. $85.

*YOUNG POCAHONTAS, INDIAN PRINCESS
Anne Benjamin; Grades K-3. Illus. 32 pp. Paper. Amazon.com, 1992. $3.50.

YOUR FYRE SHALL BURN NO MORE: IROQUOIS POLICY TOWARD NEW FRANCE & ITS ALLIES TO 1701 Jose Antonio Brandao; Historiography of the colonial Northeast. Illus. 377 pp. Paper. University of Nebraska Press, $19.95.

YOUR NAME IN CHEROKEE
Prentice Robinson; 1,000 names listed in English with Cherokee phonetics, the English phonetics & Cherokee syllabary. 25 pp. Paper. Cherokee Publications, $6.

YOUR RIGHTS AS AMERICAN INDIANS
Institute for the Development of Indian Law, $7.50.

YOUROWQUAINS, A WYANDOT INDIAN QUEEN: THE STORY OF CATY SAGE
Bill Bland; Rhoda Catron, Ed.; Illus. 288 pp. Amazon.com, 1992. $19.95.

YUCHI CEREMONIAL LIFE: PERFORMANCE, MEANING, & TRADITION IN A CONTEMPORARY AMERICAN INDIAN COMMUNITY
Jason Baird Jackson; Illus. Maps. 350 pp. University of Nebraska Press, 2003. $37.50.

THE YUCHI GREEN CORN CEREMONIAL: FORM & MEANING
W.L. Ballard; 81 pp. Paper. UCLA, American Indian Studies Center, 1978. $7.50.

YUCHI INDIAN HISTORIES BEFORE THE REMOVAL ERA
Jason Baird Jackson, Edi.; Illus. Maps. 280 pp. Paper. U. of Nebraska Press, 2012. $30.

YUKON BIBLIOGRAPHY - UPDATE SERIES
G.A. Cooke, Series Editor; CCI.

YUKON-KOYUKUK SCHOOL DISTRICT BIOGRAPHY SERIES
Curt Madison & Yvonne Yarber, Editors; Interviews of selected individuals and describes the events of their lives in their own words. Includes historical and contemporary photos. See Spirit Mountain Press for complete list of individuals profiled and prices.

*THE YUMA: CALIFORNIA
Robert L. Bee; Grades 5 and up. Illus. Chelsea House, 1989. $17.95.

YUMAN TRIBES OF THE GILA RIVER
Leslie Spier; Reprint of 1933 edition. Illus. 435 pp. Paper. Dover, $8.95.

YUP'IK ELDERS AT THE ETHNOLOGISCHES MUSEUM BERLIN: FIELDWORK TURNED ON ITS HEAD Ann Fienup-Riordan; Norwegian, Johan Adrian Jacobsen collected 2,000+ Yup'ik objects during his travels in Alaska in 1882 & 1883...now housed the Berlin Museum. Illus. 352 pp. Paper. University of Washington Press, 2005. $54.95.

YUP'IK ESKIMO DICTIONARY
Steven Jacobson; Illus. 755 pp. Paper. Alaska Native Language Center, 1984. $18.

YUP'IK ESKIMO GRAMMAR
Irene Reed, et al; 330 pp. Paper. Alaska Native Language Center, 1977. $7.50.

YUP'IK ESKIMO PROSODIC SYSTEMS: DESCRIPTIVE & COMPARATIVE STUDIES
Michael Krauss, et al. Illus. 215 pp. Paper. Alaska Native Language Center, 1985. $15.

THE YUP'IK ESKIMOS AS DESCRIBED IN THE TRAVEL JOURNALS & ETHNOGRAPHIC ACCOUNTS OF JOHN & EDITH KILBUCK
Ann Fienup-Riordon; Illus. Amazon.com, 1988. $30.

THE YUQUOT WHALERS' SHRINE
Aldona Jonaitis; research contributions by Richard Inglis; Materials from Nootka peoples of Yuquot on west coast Vancouver Island. Illus. 260 pp. University of Washington Press, 1999. $40.

YUROK AFFIXES
T.T. Waterman; Reprint of 1923 edition. 20 pp. Paper. Coyote Press, $2.50.

YUROK-KAROK BASKET WEAVERS
Lila M. O'Neale; Reprint of the 1932 ed. Illus. Photos. 184 pp. Hearst Museum of Anthropology, 1995. Paper. Distributed by the University of Washington Press, $29.

YUROK MYTHS
A.L. Kroeber; Study of Yurok Indians. Reprint. 460 pp. U. of Calif., $37.50; paper, $10.95.

YUUNGNAQPIALLERPUT / THE WAY WE GENUINELY LIVE: MASTERWORKS OF YUP'IK SCIENCE & SURVIVAL Ann Fienup-Riordan.
Illus. 376 pp. Paper. University of Washington Press, 2007. $45.

YUUYARAQ: THE WAY OF THE HUMAN BEING
Harold Napolean; Alaska Natives from 1770s to the 40s. Illus. 66 pp. Paper. University of Chicao Press, 1996. $5.95.

YUWIPI: VISION & EXPERIENCE IN OGLALA RITUAL
William K. Powers; Illus. Maps. 113 pp. Paper. U. of Nebraska Press, 1982. $12.95.

Z

ZEALOUS IN ALL VIRTUES: DOCUMENTS OF WORSHIP & CULTURE CHANGE, ST. IGNATIUS MISSION, MONTANA, 1890-1894 Robert J. Bigart, Editor
The Salish & Kootenai of the Flathead Indian Reservation. Photos.
Illus. 324 pp. Paper. University of Nebraska Press, 2007. $19.95.

DAVID ZEISBERGER & HIS BROWN BRETHREN
William H. Rice; Paper. Kessinger Publishing, 2005. $14.

DAVID ZEISBERGER'S HISTORY OF THE NORTH AMERICAN INDIANS IN 18TH CENTURY OHIO, NEW YORK & PENNSYLVANIA
Archer Hulbert William N. Schwarze; Reprint of 1910 ed. Illus. 190 pp. Kessinger Publishing, 1999. $28.95; Paper, $17.95. Paper. Wennawoods Publishing, $19.95.

DAVID ZEISBERGER: A LIFE AMONG THE INDIANS
Earl P. Olmstead & David Zeisberger; Amazon.com, 1997. $39.

ZEISBERGER'S INDIAN DICTIONARY: ENGLISH, GERMAN, IROQUOIS – THE ONONDAGA & ALGONQUIN - THE DELAWARE
David Zeisberger; Reprint. 248 pp. Kessinger Publishing, $31.95; paper, $20.48.

•THE ZUNI
Nancy Bonvillain; Paul Rosier, Series Editor
Grades 6-12. Illus. 156 pp. Chelsea House, 2011. $35.

A ZUNI ARTIST LOOKS AT FRANK HAMILTON CUSHING
Phil Hughte; Illus. 125 pp. Paper. University of New Mexico Press, $24.95.

A ZUNI ATLAS
T.J. Ferguson and E. Richard Hart
Illus. Maps. 168 pp. Paper. University of Oklahoma Press & Amazon.com, 1985. $21.95.

*ZUNI CHILDREN & ELDERS TALK TOGETHER
Barrie E. Kavasch; Grades 4 and up. Rosen Group, 1998. $18.

ZUNI CONTEMPORARY POTTERY
Marian Rodee & Jim Ostler; Illus. 92 pp. Paper. Maxwell Museum, 1987. $9.95.

ZUNI & THE COURTS: A STRUGGLE FOR SOVEREIGN LAND RIGHTS
E. Richard Hart, Editor; Photos. 415 pp. University Press of Kansas, 1995. $40.

ZUNI COYOTE TALES
Frank H. Cushing; Reprint. of 1901 ed. 104 pp. Paper. U. of Arizona Press, $9.95.

ZUNI & EL MORO: PAST & PRESENT
David Grant Noble & Richard Woodbury. Illus. 40 pp. Paper. Ancient City Pr., 1990. $8.95.

THE ZUNI ENIGMA
Nancy Y. Davis; Illus. 352 pp. W.W. Norton, 2000. $26.95.

ZUNI FETISHES
F.H. Cushing; Illus. 43 pp. Paper. KC Publications, 1966. $4; Expanded Edition, $12.95..

ZUNI FETISHES: USING NATIVE AMERICAN SACRED OBJECTS FOR MEDITATION, REFLECTION, & INSIGHT Hal Zina Bennett; Guide to the fetishes used by the Zuni people of New Mexico. Illus. 192 pp. paper. Amazon.com, $19.

ZUNI FETISHISM
Ruth Kirk; Study 25 pieces from the Museum of New Mexico. Illus. 72 pp. Paper. Amazon.com, 1988. $4.75.

ZUNI INDIAN TRIBE WATER SETTLEMENT ACT
U.S. Senate Committee on Indian Affairs; 107th Congress. Illus. 100 pp. USGPO, 2002.

THE ZUNI INDIANS: THEIR MYTHOLOGY, ESOTERIC FRATERNITIES & CEREMONIES
M.C. Stevenson; Reprint of 1904 edition. Illus. 685 pp. Rio Grande Press, $60.

THE ZUNI INDIANS & THEIR USES OF PLANTS
Matilda Coxe Stevenson. Reprint of 1908 report. 80 pp. Paper. Dover, $5.95.

ZUNI JEWELRY
Theda & Michael Bassmann; Presents jewelry of the Zuni Indians of New Mexico. Both traditional and new styles are shown in full color. Illus. 64 pp. Paper. Schiffer, $12.95.

ZUNI KATCHINAS
Ruth Bunzel. Reprint of 1932 edition. Illus. 358 pp. Rio Grande Press, $40.

A ZUNI LIFE: A PUEBLO INDIAN IN TWO WORLDS
Virgil Wyaco; J.A. Jones, Ed.; Illus. 153 pp. Paper. U. of New Mexico Press, $19.95.

THE ZUNI MAN-WOMAN
Will Roscoe. Illus. Map. 325 pp. Paper. University of New Mexico Press, 1992. $24.95.

ZUNI POTTERY
Marian Rodee & Jim Ostler. Illus. 92 pp. Paper. Schiffer, 1987. $9.95.

ZUNI: SELECTED WRITINGS OF FRANK HAMILTON CUSHING
F.H. Cushing; Jesse Green, Editor
Illus. 450 pp. University of Nebraska Press, 1979. $31.50; paper, $10.95.

ZUNI: A VILLAGE OF SILVERSMITHS
James Ostler, Marian Rodee; U. of New Mexico Press, $45; paper, $29.95.

*THE ZUNIS
Alice Flanagan; Grades 2-4. Illus. 48 pp. Children's Press, 1997. $21; paper, $6.95.

*THE ZUNIS
Katherine M. Doherty & Craig A. Doherty; Includes maps, a glossary and bibliography. Part of Indians of the Americas series. Full-color illustrations. Grades 3 and up. 64 pp. Paper. Franklin Watts, $5.95.

THE ZUNIS: SELF-PORTRAYALS
The Zuni People; translated by Alvina Quam; 46 stories from oral literatre of the Zuni Indians of New Mexico. Illus. 272 pp. Paper. University of New Mexico Press, 2015. $24.95.

SUBJECT CLASSIFICATIONS

In this section, titles annotated in the alphabetically arranged bibliography are grouped under one or more subject headings.

ABENAKI INDIANS

*The Abenaki
*Abenaki Captive
Abenaki Warrior, The Life & Times of Chief Escumbuit
The Abnakis & Their History
The Faithful Hunter & Other Abenaki Stories
*Fox Song
*From Abenaki to Zuni: A Dictionary of Native American Tribes
Legends in Stone, Bone & Wood
In Search of New England's Native Past: Selected Essays by Gordon M. Day
Alanis Obomsā: The Vision of a Native Filmmaker
Rooted Like the Ash Trees
The Scalp Hunters: Abenaki Ambush at Lovelwell Pond, 1725
Seven Eyes, Seven Legs: Supernatural Stories of the Abenaki
Twelve Thousand Years: American Indians in Maine
The Voice of the Dawn: An Autobiography of the Abenaki Nation
The Wabankis of Maine & the Maritimes
Western Abenaki Dictionary
The Western Abenakis of Vermont, 1600-1800
The Wind Eagle

ACTIVISM

Acts of Rebellion: The Ward Churchill Reader
Against the Black Panther Party & the American Indian Movement
Agents of Repression Vol. 7: The FBI's Secret Wars Against the American Indian Movement
  & the Black Panther Party
Alcatraz! Alcatraz!: The Indian Occupation of 1969-1971
Alcatraz: Indian Land Forever
American Indian Activism: Alcatraz to the Longest Walk
American Indian Mafiar: An FBI agent's True Story About Wounded Knee, Leonard Peliter,
  and the American Indian Movement (AIM)
Black Panther Party & the American Indian Movement
Blood of the Land: The Government and Corporate War Against the
  American Indian Movement
Custer Died for Your Sins: An Indian Manifesto
Encyclopedia of the American Indian Movement
Fantasies of the Master Race
Free Peltier: A Dramatic History of the American Indian Movement
Ghost Dancing the Law: The Wounded Knee Trails
Heart of the Rock: The Indian Invasion of Alcatraz
The Indian Civil Rights Act At Forty
Legends of American Indian Resistance
Like a Hurricane: The Indian Movement from Alcatraz to Wounded Knee
Loud Hawk: The U.S. versus the American Indian Movement
Marxism & Native Americans
The Occupation of Alcatraz Island
Ojibwa Warrior: Dennis Banks & the Rise of the American Indian Movement
Perversions of Justice: Indigenous Peoples & Angloamerican Law
Prison Writings: My Life is My Sun Dance
Since Predator Came: Notes from the Struggle for American Indian Liberation
Struggle for the Land
Visions & Voices: American Indian Activism & the Civil Rights Movement
Where White Men Fear to Tread: Autobiography of Russell Means
You Are On Indian Land: Alcatraz Island, 1969-1971

AGRICULTURE & FARMING

Agricultural Origins & Development in the Midcontinent
Agriculture of the Hidatsa Indians
Anasazi Harvest
At the Desert's Green Edge: An Ethnobotany of the Gila River Pima
Before the Wilderness: Environmental Management by Native Californians
Biodiversity & Native America
Buffalo Bird Woman's Garden: Agriculture of the Hidatsa Indians
Corn Among the Indians of the Upper Missouri
Early Prehistoric Agriculture in the American Southwest
Enduring Seeds: Native American Agriculture & Wild Plant Conservation
Indian Agriculture in America: Prehistory to the Present
Indians, Bureaucrats & Land: The Dawes Act & the Decline of Indian Farming
Iroquois Corn in a Culture-Based Curriculum
Neither Wolf Nor Dog: American Indians, Environment & Agrarian Change
The Origins of Southwestern Agriculture
Pima & Papago Indian Agriculture
Plains Apache Ethnobotany
Pueblo Indian Agriculture
Red Earth: Race & Agriculture in Oklahoma Territory

ALABAMA-COUSHATTA INDIANS

The Alabama-Coushatta Indians
Dictionary of the Alabama Language
Historic Indian Towns in Alabama, 1540-1838
Journey to the West: The Alabama & Coushatta Indians
The Winding Trail: The Alabama-Coushatta Indians

ALASKA NATIVES - ESKIMOS

The A to Z of the Inuit
Across Arctic America, Narrative of the Fifth Thule Expedition
Across the Shaman's River: John Muir, the Tlingit Stronghold, and the Opening of the North
*Across the Tundra
Against Culture: Development, Politics, & Religion in Indian Alaska
Ahtna Athabaskan Dictionary
Alaska At 50: The Past, Present, and Next 50 Years of Alaska Statehood
Alaska Days With John Muir
Alaska Eskimo Footwear
The Alaska Eskimos: A Selected, Annotated Bibliography
Alaska 1899: Essays from the Harriman Expedition
Alaska: A History
Alaska: A History of the 49th State
Alaska History Series
*Alaska in the Days That Were Before
Alaska Native Allotment Subdivision Act
Alaska Native Arts & Crafts
Alaska Native Claims Settlement Act, 1991, & Tribal Government
Alaska Native Land Rights
Alaska Native Language Center Publications
Alaska Native Languages: Past, Present & Future
Alaska Native Parents in Anchorage: Perspectives on Childrearing
Alaska Native Policy in the 20th Century
Alaska Native Political Leadership & Higher Education
Alaska Native Policy in the 20th Century
Alaska Native Ways: What the Elders have Taught Us
Alaska Natives & American Laws
Alaska Natives: A Guide to Current Reference Souces in the Rasmuson Library
Alaska: Reflections on Land & Spirit
Alaska's Daughter: An Eskimo Memoir of the Early Twentieth Century
Alaska's Native People
Alaska's Southern Panhandle
Alaska's Totem Poles
Alaskameut '86
Alaskan Eskimo Life in the 1890s: As Sketched by Native Artists
*Alaskan Igloo Tales
Alaskan Native Food Practices, Customs & Holidays
Aleut Dictionary
Aleut Tales & Narratives
Aleuts: Survivors of the Beping Land Bridge
Always Getting Ready, Upterrlainarluta: Yup'ik Eskimo Subsistence in Southwest Alaska
American Indian & Alaska Native Health: Bibliography: Jan. 1990 Through Sept. 1996
The American Indian & Alaska Native Higher Education Funding Guide
American Indian & Alaskan Native Newspapers & Periodicals, 1826-1924
American Indian Alaska Native Resource Directory for the Puget Sound &
  Olympic Peninsula
American Indian & Alaskan Native Traders Directory
American Indians in the Marketplace: Persistence & Innovation Among the
  Menominees & Metlakatlans, 1870-1920
An Aleutian Ethnography
*Anna's Athabaskan Summer
An Annotated Bibliography of American Indian & Eskimo Autobiographies
Anooshi Lingit Aani Ka / Russians in Tlingit America: The Battles of Sitka, 1802 & 1804
Anthologia Anthropologica: The Native Races of America
Anthropological Papers of University of Alaska
The Archaeology of Cape Nome, Alaska
Arctic Art: Eskimo Ivory
Arctic Dreams
Arctic: Handbook of North American Indians, Vol. 5
Arctic Journeys Ancient Memories: Sculpture by Abraham Anghik Ruben
Arctic Life: Challenge to Survive
Arctic Memories
Arctic Schoolteacher: Kulukak, Alaska, 1931-1933
The Arctic Sky: Inuit Astronomy, Star Lore & Legend
Arctic Transformations: The Jewelry of Denise & Samuel Wallace
Arctic Village
Art & Eskimo Power: The Life & Times of Alaskan Howard Rock
Art of the Far North: Inuit Sculpture, Drawing & Printmaking
The Artists Behind the Work
Artists of the Tundra and the Sea
At Home With the Bella Coola Indians
Athabaskan Stories from Anvik
Athabaskan Verb Theme Categories: Ahtna
The Athabaskans: People of the Boreal Forest
Authentic Alaska: Voices of Its Native Writers
Bad Girl & the Man Who Followed the Sun: An Athabaskan Indian Legend from Alaska
Baleen Basketry of the North Alaskan Eskimo
Bashful No Longer: An Alaskan Eskimo Ethnohistory, 1778-1988
Being in Being
Being In Place Among the Tlingit
Bird Girl & the Man Who Followed the Sun: An Athabaskan Indian Legend from Alaska
Book of the Eskimo
Books on American Indians and Eskimos
Boundaries & Passages: Rule & Ritual in Yup'ik Eskimo Oral Tradition
Breaking New Ground for AmericanIndian & Alaska Native Youth At Risk:
The Canoe Rocks: Alaska's Tlingit & the Euramerican Frontier, 1800-1912
The Cape Alitak Petroglyphs
Catalogue Raisonne of the Alaska Commercial Company Collection
Celebration: Tlingit, Haida, Tsimshian Dancing on the Land
The Central Eskimo
Cev'armiut Qanemciit Qulirait-llu: Eskimo Narratives & Tales from Chevak, Alaska
*Chief Stephen's Parky: One Year in the Life of an Athapascan Girl

ALGONQUIAN INDIANS

AMERICAN INDIAN RHETORIC

ANASAZI CULTURE

ANTIQUITIES-ARCHAEOLOGY

754   BIBLIOGRAPHY – SUBJECT/PUBLISHER INDEX

APACHE INDIANS

ARAPAHO
(See CHEYENNE & ARAPAHO)

ARCHITECTURE-DWELLINGS

ARMS & ARMOR

ART

ARTIFACTS

ATHABASKAN

BASKETRY

The Language of Native American Baskets
Lewis & Clark Territory
Mabel McKay: Weaving the Dream
The Native American Art Look Book
Native American Basketry
Native American Basketry: An Annotated Bibliography
Native American Basketry of the Seneca & Tlingit
Native Basketry of Western North America
Navajo Ceremonial Baskets: Sacred Symbols
North American Indian Designs for Artists and Craftspeople
Northwest Coast Indian Art
*The Northwest Coast Indian Art Series
Northwest Coast Indian Designs
Our Lives in Our Hands: Micmac Indian Basketmakers
Panamint Shoshone Basketry: An American Art Form
Passing the Moon Through 13 Baskets
Photographic Guide to the Ethnographic North American Indian Basket Collection
Pima Indian Basketry
Plants Used in Basketry by the California Indians
Pomo Basketmaking - A Supreme Art for the Weaver
Pomo Indian Basketry
Reconciling the Past
Remember Your Relations
Southwestern Indian Baskets
Southwestern Indian Weaving
Spruce Root Basketry of the Haida & Tlingit
Studies in Cherokee Basketry
Tradition & Innovation
Traditions in Transition: Contemporary Basket Weaving of the Southwestern Indians
Weavers of Tradition & Beauty: Basketmakers of the Great Basin
Weaving Arts of the North American Indian
Weaving a California Tradition: A Native American Basketmaker
Weaving A Legacy
Weaving New Worlds: Southeastern Cherokee Women & Their Basketry
Weaving of the Southwest
Western Indian Basketry
Willow Stories: Utah Navajo Baskets
Woven Worlds: Basketry from the Clark Field Collection
Yurok-Karok Basket Weavers

BEADWORK

American Indian Beadwork
Applique Patterns From Native American Beadwork Designs
Beads & Beadwork of the American Indians
Beads: Their Use by Upper Great Lakes Indians
A Beadwork Companion
Beadwork Techniques of the Native American
Beadworking With Today's Materials
Big Book of Indian Beadwork
The Complete Guide to Traditional Native American Beadwork
Craft Manual of Northwest Indian Beading
Crow Indian Beadwork
How to Bead Native American Style
Manual of Beading Techniques (Four Winds)
Native American Beadwork
North American Indian Beadwork Designs
North American Indian Beadwork Patterns
Navajo Beadwork: Architectures of Light
Northern Athapaskan Art: A Beadwork Tradition
Quill & Beadwork of the Western Sioux
A Quillwork Companion
Sioux Quill & Beadwork
A Special Gift: The Kutchin Beadwork Tradition
Techniques of Beading Earrings & More Techniques of Beading Earrings
The Techniques of North American Indian Beadwork
Traditional Indian Bead & Leather Crafts
Traditions: Beadwork of the Native American

WILLIAM M. BEAUCHAMP

Aboriginal Occupation of New York
Aboriginal Use of Wood in New York
Horn & Bone Implements of the New York Indians
Iroquois Fol Lore
Wampum & Shell Articles Used By the New York Indians

BIBLIOGRAPHIES

Against Borders: Promoting Books for a Multicultural World
Alaska Natives: A Guide to Current Reference Sources in the Rasmuson Library
The American Indian in Graduate Studies: A Bibliography of Theses and Dissertations
American Indian Literatures: An Introduction, Bibliographic Review,
 & Selected Bibliography
American Indian Reference Books for Children & Young Adults
The American Indian in Short Fiction: An Annotated Bibliography
American Indian: Language and Literature
American Indian Sovereignty & Law: An Annotated Bibliography
American Indian Stereotypes in the World of Children: A Reader & Bibliography
American Indian Studies: A Bibliographic Guide
American Indian Women: A Guide to Research
American Indians: A Select Catalog of National Archives Microfilm Publications
The American West in the Twentieth Century: A Bibliography

An Annotated Bibliography of American Indian and Eskimo Autobiographies
Annotated Bibliography of American Indian Paintings
Annotated Bibliography of Federal & Tribal Law: Print & Internet Sources
The Apaches: A Critical Bibliography
A Bibliographical Guide to the History of Indian-White Relations in the U.S.
Bibliography: Native American Arts & Crafts of the U.S.
A Bibliography of the Athapaskan Languages
Bibliography of the Blackfoot
Bibliography of the Catawba
Bibliography of the Chickasaw
Bibliography of the Constitution & Laws of the American Indians
A Bibliography of Contemporary North American Indians
Bibliography of the Indians of San Diego County
Bibliography of Language Arts Materials for Native North Americans
Bibliography of the Languages of Native California
Bibliography of Native American Bibliographies
Bibliography of Native North Americans on Disc - CD-ROM
Bibliography of North American Indian Mental Health
Bibliography of the Osage
Bibliography of the Sioux
Bibiliography of Native American Writers, 1772-1925
Black Indians: Bibliography of Materials on Relationships Between American Indians
 & African Americans
A Bookman's Guide to the Indians of the Americas
Books on American Indians and Eskimos
Books Without Bias: Through Indian Eyes
Canadian Indian Policy: A Critical Bibliography
Catalogue of the Library Belonging to Mr. Thomas W. Field
Cherokee Bibliography
The Cheyennes, Ma heo o's People: A Critical Bibliography
Chippewa & Dakota Indians: A Subject Catalog
The Chumash & Their Predecessors: An Annotated Bibliography
The Delawares: A Critical Bibliography
The Demon of the Continent: Indians & the Shaping of American Literature
Dictionary Catalog of the Edward E. Ayer Collection of Americana & American Indians
Dine Bibliography to the 1990s
The Emigrant Indians of Kansas: A Critical Bibliography
Encyclopedia of American Indian Issues Today
An Essay Towards An Indian Bibliography
Ethnographic Bibliography of North America
Fifty Years After the Big Sky: New Perspectives on the Fiction & Films of A.B. Guthrie, Jr.
The Five Civilized Tribes: A Bibliography
From Savage to Nobleman: Images of Native Americans in Film
A Guide to Cherokee Documents in Foreign Archives
A Guide to Cherokee Documents in the Northeastern U.S.
Guide to the 400 Best Children's & Adult's Multicultural Books of People of
 Native American Descent
Guide to Records in the National Archives Relating to American Indians
Health and Diseases of American Indians North of Mexico: A Bibliography, 1800-1969
Health of Native People of North America
History & Annotated Bibliography of American Religious Periodicals & Newspapers
Images of the Other: Guide to Microform Manuscripts on Indian-White Relations
In Pursuit of the Past: An Anthropological & Bibliographic Guide to Maryland & Delaware
Index to Literature on the American Indian
Indian Land Tenure: Bibliographical Essays
Indian Slavery, Labor, Evangelization, and Captivity in the Americas:
 An Annotated Bibliography
Indian-White Relations in the U.S.
The Indians of California: A Critical Bibliography
Indians of the Great Basin: A Critical Bibliography
The Indians of Maine and the Atlantic Provinces: A Bibliographic Guide
The Indians of New England: A Critical Bibliography
Indians of North & South America: Bibliography
The Indians of the Subarctic: A Critical Bibliography
The Indians of Texas: An Annotated Research Bibliography
Indigenous Films
Indigenous Languages of the Americas
'Injuns!' Native Americans in the Movies
Iroquois Indians: A Documentary History-Guide to the Microfilm Collection
Kinsmen Through Time: An Annotated Bibliography of Potawatomi History
Languages of the Aboriginal Southeast: An Annotated Bibliography
Library Services to Indigenous Population: Viewpoints & Resources
Literature By and About the American Indian: An Annotated Bibliography
Louisiana Indian Studies: A Selected Bibliography
N. Scott Momaday: Remembering Ancestors, Earth & Traditions: An Annotated Bibliography
Narrative Chance: Postmodern Discourse on Native American Indian Literatures
Narratives of North American Indian Captivity: A Selective Bibliography
The National Uncanny: Indian Ghosts & American Subjects
Native American Archives: An Introduction
Native American Historical Demography: A Critical Bibliography
The Native American in American Literature: A Selectively Annotated Bibliography
The Native American in Long Fiction: An Annotated Bibliography
Native American Resurgence & Renewal: A RTeader & Bibliography
Native American Studies: A Guide to Reference & Information Sources
Native American Women: A Contextual Bibliography
Native Americans
Native Americans: An Annotated Bibliography
Native Americans in Fiction
Native Americans in the Movies: Portrayals from Silent Films to the Present
Native Americans: North America--An Annotated Bibliography
Native Americans of the Northwest Coast: A Critical Bibliography
Native Canadian Anthropology & History: A Selected Bibliography
Native North American Reference Library
Native North American Reference Library: Cumulative Index

Native North Americans in Doctoral Dissertations, 1971-1975: A Classified & Indexed Research Bibliography
Native North Americans in Literature for Youth: A Selected Annotated Bibliography for K-12
Newberry Library/Center for the History of the American Indian Bibliographical Series
North American Indian Language Materials, 1890-1965
Northeast Indian Resource Secrets: The Buyer's Guide
Office of Indian Affairs, 1824-1880: Historical Sketches
The Ojibwas: A Critical Bibliography
The Pawnee Nation: An Annotated Research Bibliography
Pawnees: A Critical Bibliography
Peyotism & the Native American Church, Vol. 45: Annotated Bibliography
Recovering the Word: Essays on Native American Literature
Resource Reading List
Selected Americana from Sabin's Dictionary of Books Relating to America From Its Discovery to the Present Time
The Seneca & Tuscarora Indians: An Annotated Bibliography
The Shawnee Indians: An Annotated Bibliography
The Sioux & Other Native American Cultures of the Dakotas: An Annotated Bibliography
The Subarctic Athapascans: A Selected, Annotated Bibliography
A Supplement to a Guide to Manuscripts Relating to the American Indian in the Library of the American Philosophical Society
Traditional Literatures of the American Indians: Texts and Interpretations
Tulapai to Tokay: A Bibliography of Alcohol Use and Abuse Among Native Americans of North America
The Upstream People: An Annotated Research Bibliography of the Omaha Tribe
Winged Words: American Indian Writers Speak
Writings in Indian History, 1985-1990
Yakama, Palouse, Cayuse, Umatilla, Walla Walla, and Wanapum Indians: An Historical Bibliography
The Yakamas: A Critical Bibliography

BIOGRAPHIES

A to Z of Native American Women
Abenaki Warrior, the Life & Times of Chief Escumbuit: Big Island Pond, 1665-1727
Adventures With a Saint: Kateri Tekawitha, "Lily of the Mohawks"
Alijca, Son of Mashpee: Reflections of Chief
Sherman Alexie: A Collection of Critical Essays
American Indian Autobiography
American Indian Baskets: 1,200 Artist Biographies
American Indian Intellectuals of the 19th & 20th Century
American Indian Jewelry I: 1,200 Artist Biographies
American Indian Textiles: 2,000 Artist Biographies
American Indian Leaders: Studies in Diversity
American Indian Lives Series
American Indian Painters: A Biographical Directory
American Indian Prophecies: Conversations With Chasing Deer
*American Indian Stories
American Indian Textiles: 2,000 Artist Biographies
American Puritanism & the Defense of Mourning: Mary White Rowlandson's Captivity Narrative
An Annotated Bibliography of American Indian & Eskimo Autobiographies
Apache Agent: The Story of John P. Clum
The Art of the Native American Flute - R. Carlos Nakai
The Art of Native North America
At Standing Rock & Wounded Knee: The Journals & Papers of Father Francis M. Craft, 1888-1890
The Autobiography of a Kiowa Apache Indian-Jim Whitewolf
Autobiography of Red Cloud
The Autobiography of a Winnebago Indian
*Dennis Banks: Native American Activist
Bartley Milam: Principal Chief of the Cherokee Nation
Being & Becoming Indian: Biographical Studies of North American Frontiers
Being Indian Is: The Humor of Reuben Snake
Bernie Whitebear: An Urban Indian's Quest for Justice
Between Worlds
Beyond the Hundredth Meridian
Big Bear: The End of Freedom
Bighorse the Warrior
A Biobibliography of Native American Writers, 1772-1924: A Supplement
Biographical Dictionary of American Indian History to 1900
Biographical Dictionary of Indians of the Americas
Biographical & Historical Index of American Indian & Persons Involved in Indian Affairs
Biographical Portraits of 108 Native Americans
Black Elk & Flaming Rainbow
Black Elk: Holy Man of the Oglala
Black Elk Lives: Conversations with the Black Elk Family
*Black Elk: A Man With Vision
The Black Elk Reader
Black Elk: The Sacred Ways of a Lakota
Black Elk Speaks
Black Elk's Religion
Black Elk's World (Website)
The Black Hawk War, Including a Review of Black Hawk's Life
Black Kettle: The Cheyenne Chief Who Sought Peace But Found War
Black Sun of the Miwok
Bloodlines: Odyssey of a Native Daughter
The Blossoming: Dramatic Accounts in the Lives of Native Americans
*Blue Jacket: War Chief of the Shawnees
Blue Jacket: Warrior of the Shawnees
The Book of Mazakute: A Life Story of a Sioux Family
Borderlander: The Life of James Kirker, 1793-1852
Born a Chief: The Nineteenth Century Hopi Boyhood of Edmund Nequatewa
Born Cree: The Life of Pete Hawley, of Sitting Horse Drum

Born of Fire (Margaret Tafoya)
Henry Boucha - Star of the North
Elias Cornelius Boudinot: A Life on the Cherokee Border
Joseph Brant, 1743-1807: A Man of Two Worlds
Molly Brant: A Legacy of Her Own
Brave Are My People: Indian Heroes Not Forgotten
Building Native American Nations: The Lives & Work of Modern Tribal Leaders
Natalie Curtis Burlin: A Life in Native & African American Music
Ben Nighthorse Campbell
T.C. Cannon: He Stood in the Sun
Kit Carson & His Three Wives: A Family History
Kit Carson: Indian Fighter or Indian Killer?
Kit Carson & the Indians
Chainbreaker: The Revolutionary War Memoirs of Governor Blacksnake
Kenneth Milton Chapman: A Life Dedicated to Indian Arts & Artists
Cherokee National Treasures: In Their Own Words
Cherokee Sister: The Collected Writings of Catherine Brown, 1818-1823
Chevato: The Story of the Apache Warrior Who Captured Herman Lehmann
Cheyenne Autumn
Chief Bender's Burden: The Silent Struggle of a Baseball Star
Chief Bowles & the Texas Cherokees
Chief - Champion of the Everglades: A Biography of Seminole Chief James Billie
Chief Cornplanter (Gy-Ant-Wa-Kia) of the Senecas
Chief Joseph: Guardian of the Nez Perce
*Chief Joseph of the Nez Perce Indians: Champion of Liberty
*Chief Joseph's Own Story As Told by Chief Joseph in 1879
Chief Junaluska of the Cherokee Indian Nation
Chief Left Hand: Southern Arapaho
Chief Logan: An Anthology
Chief Marin: Leader, Rebel, & Legend
*Chief Plenty Coups: Life of the Crow Indian Chief
Chief Pocatello, the "White Plume"
Chief Sarah: Sarah Winnemucca's Fight for Indian Rights
Chief Washakie
Child of the Fighting Tenth: On the Frontier With the Buffalo Soldiers
Chipeta: Queen of the Utes
Jesse Chisholm: Ambassador of the Plains
Jesse Chisholm: Texas Trail Blazer & Peacemaker
Civilian. Military. Native Anerican: Portraits of Fort Phil Kearney
William Clark: Jeffersonian Man on the Frontier
Coach Tommy Thompson & the Boys of Sequoyah
Cochise: Chiricahua Apache Chief
Cold River Spirits: The Story of an Athabascan-Irish Family in Twentieth Century Alaska
The Collected Works of Benjamin Hawkins
Mangas Coloradas: Chief of the Chiricahua Apaches
"Come, Blackrobe" De Smet & the Indian Tragedy
Confederate Colonel & Cherokee Chief: The Life of William Holland Thomas
Contemporary Native American Authors: A Biographical Dictionary
Converting the West: A Biography of Narcissa Whitman
Corbett Mack: The Life of a Northern Paiute
*Counting Coup: Becoming a Crow Chief on the Reservation and Beyond
Coyotes & Canaries: Characters Who Made the West Wild & Wonderful!
Crashing Thunder: The Autobiography of an American Indian
Crazy Horse
*Crazy Horse
Crazy Horse: The Book & Screenplay
Crazy Horse & Custer: The Parallel Lives of Two American Warriors
Crazy Horse, Hoka Hey: It Is a Good Time to Die!
Crazy Horse, A Lakota Life
Crazy Horse: The Life Behind the legend
Crazy Horse & the Real Reason for the Battle of the Little Big Horn
Crazy Horse: Sacred Warrior of the Sioux
Crazy Horse: The Strange Man of the Oglalas
Crazy Weather
Crow Dog: Four Generations of Sioux Medicine Men
Crow Indian Photographer: The Work of Richard Throssel
Delfina Cuero: Her Autobiography
Edward Sheriff Curtis: Visions of a Vanishing Race
The Custer Story: Life & Intimate Letters of General George A. Custer & His Wife Elizabeth
*The Defenders
Dakota Cross-Bearer: The Life & World of a Native American Bishop
Dakota Philosopher: Charles Eastman & American Indian Thought
Daughter of the Wind: Indian Legends & Family Tales
The Day Geronimo Surrendered
Angie Debo: Pioneering Historian
Desert Indian Woman: Stories & Dreams
Diary of David Zeisberger: A Moravian Missionary Among the Indians of Ohio
Distinguished Native American Political & Tribal Leaders
*The Double Life of Pocahontas
Edward P. Dozier
Dreamer-Prophets of the Columbia Plateau: Smohalla & Skolaskin
During My Time: Florence Edenshaw Davidson, A Haida Woman
Eagle Transforming: The Art of Robert Davidson
*Charles Eastman: Physician, Reformer, and Native American Leader
Edgar Heap of Birds
The Education of Little Tree
Ehanamani: Walks Among
Encyclopedia of Frontier Biography
Encyclopedia of Native American Biography
Enju: The Life & Struggle of an Apache Chief from the Little Running
Louise Erdrich
Exploration Into World Cultures
*Extraordinary American Indians
The Extraordinary Book of Native American Lists

The Way It Was: An Indian Girl Living Thru the Depression
The Way of the Warrior: Stories of the Crow People
The Way Was Through Woods: The Story of Tomo-chi-chi
Conrad Weiser 1696-=1760, Friend of Colonists & Mohawk
We'll Be in Your Mountains, We'll Be in Your Songs: A Navajo Woman Sings
The Western Odyssey of John Simpson Smith: Frontiersman & Indian Interpreter
Marietta Wetherill: Life With the Navajos in Chaco Canyon
Frederick Weygold: Artist & Ethnographer of North American Indians
When the Night Bird Sings
When No One Was Looking
Where White Men Fear to Tread: Autobiography of Russell Means
While the Locust Slept: A Memoir
White Indian Boy
The Wind Is My Mother: The Life & Teachings of American Shaman
Wind Wolf Woman: The Story of a Medicine Woman
Who Was Who in Native American History
The Wind Is My Mother: The Life & Teachings of American Shaman
Winning the Dust Bowl
With Eagle Tail
Sarah Winnemucca
Sarah Winnemucca of the Northern Paiutes
Woman Walking Ahead: In Search of Catherine Weldon & Sitting Bull
The Woman Who Loved Mankind: The Life of a Twentieth-Century Crow Elder
The Woman Who Watches Over the World: A Native Memoir
The World of Chief Seattle
The World of Flower Blue: Pop Chalee: An Artistic Biography
The World's Richest Indian: Jackson Barnett
Woven Stone: Autobiography of Simon J. Ortiz
Writing Indians: Literacy, Christianity & Native Community in Early America
Ned Wynkoop & the Lonely Road From Sand Creek
A Yaqui Life: The Personal Chronicle of a Yaqui Indian
Yellowtail: Crow Medicine Man & Sun Dance Chief: An Autobiography
*Young Pocahontas, Indian Princess

BLACK ELK

Black Elk & Flaming Rainbow
Black Elk: Holy Man of the Oglala
Black Elk Lives
*Black Elk: A Man With Vision
Nicholas Black Elk: Medicine Man, Missionary, Mystic
Black Elk's Religion
Black Elk: The Sacred Ways of a Lakota
Black Elk Speaks
Black Elk's World (Website)
Native American Wisdom
The Sacred Pipe: Black Elk's Account of the Seven Rites of Oglala Sioux
The Sixth Grandfather: Black Elk's Teachings

BLACK HAWK WAR

Black Hawk: An Autobiography
Black Hawk's Autobiography
Black Hawk & Jim Thorpe
The Black Hawk War, 1831-1832
The Black Hawk War of 1832
The Black Hawk War, Including a Review of Black Hawk's Life
The Black Hawk War, Why?
The Last Crossing: Black Hawk's Fight Against the U.S.
Life of Black Hawk
The Sauks & Black Hawk War
The Spirit of Black Hawk: A Mystery of Africans and Indians

BLACKFEET INDIANS

•The Blackfeet
The Blackfeet: Artists of the Northern Plains
Blackfeet & Buffalo: Memories of Life Among the Indians
Blackfeet Crafts
Blackfeet IndianStories
The Blackfeet: Raiders on the Northwestern Plains
Blackfeet Tales From Apikuni's World
Blackfeet Tales of Glacier National Park
Bleed Into Me: A Book of Stories
Crowfoot: Chief of the Blackfeet
Frontier Diplomats: Alexander Culbertson & Natoyist-Siksina' Among the Blackfeet
*Heart Butte: A Blackfeet Indian
Invisible Reality: Storytellers, Storytakers, and the Supernatural World of the Blackfeet
Lanterns on the Prairie: The Blackfeet Photographs of Walter McClintock
Ledfeather
Mission Among the Blackfeet
Modern Blackfeet: Montanans on a Reservation
Montana 1911: A Professor & Hs Wife Among the Blackfeet
Montana's Indians: Yesterday & Today
The Old North Trail: Or, Life, Legends and Religion of the Blackfeet Indians
Piikani Blackfeet: A Culture Under Seige:
Rebirth of the Blackfeet Nation, 1912-1954
The Reservation Blackfeet, 1885-1945: A Photographic History of Cultural Survival
*Running Eagle: Woman Warrior of the Blackfeet
The Sun God's Children: The History, Culture, and Legends of the Blackfeet Indians
Viet Cong at Wounded Knee: The Trail of a Blackfeet Activist
Why Gone Those Times? Blackfoot Tales

BLACKFOOT INDIANS

The Amazing Death of Calf Shirt & Other Blackfoot Stories
Bibliography of the Blackfoot
*Blackfoot Children & Elders Talk Togerther
The Blackfoot Confederacy ,1880-1920: A Comparative Study of Canada & U.S. Indian Policy
Blackfoot Craftworker's Book
Blackfoot Grammar
Blackfoot Indian Portraits
Blackfoot Lodge Tales
The Blackfoot Moonshine Rebellion of 1881
Blackfoot Musical Thought
Blackfoot Redemption: A Blood Indian's Story of Murder, Confinement, and Imperfect Justice
A Blackfoot Sourcebook
Blackfoot War Art: Pictographs of the Reservation Period, 1880-2000
Horse in Blackfoot Indian Culture
How Life Came to Be
Long Lance
Medicine River
Mythology of the Blackfoot Indians
Ni-Kso-Ko-Wa: Blackfoot Spirituality, Traditions, Values & Beliefs
Old Indian Trails
Pawnee Blackfoot, & Cheyenne
Piegan
The Plains Indians
The Return of Chief Black Foot
The Story of the Blackfoot People: Nitsitapiisinni
The Tragedy of the Blackfoot
The Unconquered Hearts
The Vengeful Wife & Other Blackfoot Stories
Visitng With the Ancestors: Blackfoot Shirts in Museum Spaces
War Paint: Blackfoot & Sarcee Painted Buffalo Robes in the Royal Ontario Museum
Why Gone Those Times? Blackfoot Tales
Winter in the Blood
Wooden Leg: A Warrior Who Fought With Custer

FRANZ BOAS

Franz Boas
Franz Boas As Public Intellectual, Vol. 1: Theory, Ethnography, Activism
Franz Boas: The Early Years, 1858-1906
The Central Eskimo
Coeur D'Alene, Okanogan & Flathead Indians
Constructing Cultures Then & Now
Ethnography of Franz Boas
Geographical Names of the Kwakiutl Indians
Haida Songs & Tsimshian Texts
Handbook of the American Indian Languages
Indian Myths & legends from the North Pacific Coast of America
Introduction to Handbook of American Indian Languages
Kwakiutl Ethnography
North American Indian Life
Primitive Art
Strangers to Relatives
Ten'a Texts & Tales: From Anvik, Alaska
Transmission Difficulties: Franz Boas & Tsimshian Mythology
A Wealth of Thought: Franz Boas on Native American Art

BOATS & CANOES

The Algonquin Birchbark Canoe
Bark Canoes: The Art & Obsession of Tappan Adney
The Bark Canoes and Skin Boats of North America
The Birch: Bright Tree of Life & Legend
Birchbark Canoe: Living Among the Algonquin
Birchbark Canoes of the Fur Trade
Building a Chippewa Indian Birchbark Canoe
California Indian Watercraft
The Canoe: An Illustrated History
Canoeing With the Cree
*Indian Canoeing
Qayaq: Kayaks of Siberia & Alaska
The Survival of the Bark Canoe
Wangka: Austronesian Canoe Origins

BUFFALO-BISON

The American Buffalo in Transition
Blackfeet & Buffalo
Buckskin & Buffalo: The Artistry of the Plains Indians
Buffalo, Inc.: American Indians & Economic Development
Buffalo Country: America's National Bison Range
Buffalo Country: A Northern Plains Narrative
Buffalo Hearts
*Buffalo Hunt
The Buffalo Hunters
*Buffalo & Indians on the Great Plains
Buffalo Nation: American Indian Efforts to Restore the Bison
The Buffalo: The Story of American Bison & Their Hunters
I Will Be Meat for My Salish: The Buffalo & the Montana Writers Native American Painted Buffalo Hides

American Indian Life Skills Development Curriculum
American Indian Stereotypes in the World of Children
American Indian & White Children: A Sociopsychological Investigation
Breaking New Ground for American Indian & Alaska Native Youth At Risk:
    Program Summaries
A Broken Flute: The Native Experience in Books for Children
Childhood & Folklore: A Psychoanalytic Study of Apache Personality
Childhood & Youth in Jicarilla Apache Society
Children of the Dragonfly: Native American Voices on Child Custody
    & Education Advocate Project
Children of the Circle
Children of Cottonwood
*Children of the Earth & Sky
Children of the First People
Children Indian Captives
Children of the Salt River
Children of the Tlingit
Chippewa Child Life and Its Cultural Background
Crickets & Corn: Five Stories About Native North American Children
Criminal Gangs in Indian Country: Congressional Hearing
*The Death of Jimmy Littlewolf: An Indian Boy at Boys Ranch
Dolls & Toys of Native America
Empowerment of North American Indian Girls: Ritual Expressions at Puberty
*Indian Boyhood
*Indian Children Paper Dolls
Indian Child Protection & Family Violence Prevention Act
The Indian Child Welfare Act: A Cultural & Legal Education Program
Indian Orphanages
Juvenile Justice in Indian Country: hearings Before the Congress,
    Senate Committee on Indian Affairs
Native American Transracial Adoptees Tell Their Stories
Navajo Infancy: An Ethological Study of Child Development
Our Sacred Gifts: An Ojibwe Perspective in the Preparation of Parenthood, et al
Overcoming Obstacles and Improving Outcomes
Play & Inter-Ethnic Communications
Red Children in White America
Respect for Life: The Traditional Upbringing of
Schooling At-Risk Native American Children
Shooting Back from the Reservation
*Thunder Waters: Experiences of Growing Up in Different Indian Tribes
*To Live In Two Worlds: American Indian Youth Today
*The Trail on Which They Wept: The Story of a Cherokee Girl
Where Courage is Like a Wild Horse: The World of an Indian Orphanage
Widening the Circle: Culturally Relevant Pedagogy for American Indian Children

CHIPPEWA (See OJIBWE)

CHOCTAW INDIANS

Acts & Resolutions, Constitution & Laws of the Choctaw
    (See Constitution & Laws of the American Indian Tribes Series)
Chahta Anumpa: A Grammar of the Choctaw Language (CD-ROM)
*The Choctaw
The Choctaw Academy: Official Correspondence, 1825-1841
*A Choctaw Anthology, I & II
Choctaw-Apache Foodways
The Choctaw Before Removal
1830 Choctaw Census "Armstrong Roll"
Choctaw & Chickasaw Early Census Records
Choctaw Crime & Punishment, 1884-1907
Choctaw Genesis, 1500-1700
Choctaw Hymns
Choctaw Language Awareness Teachers Manual
Choctaw Language & Culture: Chahta Anumpa
Choctaw Language Dictionary
Choctaw Language Sampler
The Choctaw Laws
Choctaw Legends with Teacher's Guide
Choctaw Music & Dance
Choctaw Nation Dictionary
Choctaw Nation: A Story of American Indian Resurgence
The Choctaw of Oklahoma
Choctaw Prophecy: A Legacy of the Future
A Choctaw Reference Grammar
The Choctaw Revolution: Lessons for Federal Indian Policy
Choctaw Tales
Choctaw Verb Agreement & Universal Grammar
Choctaw Women in a Chaotic World
Choctaws at the Crossroads
The Choctaws in Oklahoma: From Tribe to Nation, 1855-1970
Choctaws & Missionaries in Mississippi, 1818-1918
The Choctaws in a Revolutionary Age, 1750-1830
Culture & Customs of the Apache Indians
Field of Honor: A Novel
A Gathering of Statesmen: Records of the Choctaw Council Meetings, 1826-1828
History of the Choctaw, Chickasaw & Natchez Indians
How Choctaws Invented Civilization & Why Choctaws
    Will Conquer the World
Intruders Into the Choctaw & Chickasaw Nations, 1884-1890
Life of Pushmataha
Living in the Land of Death: The Choctaw People, 1830-1860
Mississippi Choctaws at Play: The Serious Side of Leisure
My Choctaw Roots

Nations Remembered: An Oral History of Cherokees, Chickasaws,
    Choctaws, Creeks, and Seminoles, 1865-1907
Okla Hannali
*The Pashofa Pole
Persistence of Pettern in Mississippi Choctaw Culture
Pre-Removal Choctaw History: Exploring New Paths
The Removal of the Choctaw Indians
Rise & Fall of the Choctaw Republic
The Roads of My Relations
Schools for the Choctaws
Searching for the Bright Path: The Mississippi Choctaws
Source Material for the Social & Ceremonial Life of the Choctaw Indians
*The Stomachache Tree
Stranges in Their Own Land: A Choctaw Portfolio
They Say the Wind Is Red: The Alabama Choctaw Lost in Their Own Land
Tribal Government: A New Era

CHUMASH INDIANS

*California's Chumash Indians
*The Chumash
Chumash Healing
Chumash
*The Chumash
The Chumash & Costanoan Languages
Chumash Ethno-botany: Plant Knowledge Among the Chumash People
    of Southern California
Chumash Healing
*Chumash Indian Games
The Chumash Indians of Southern California
The Chumash People
Chumash: A Picture of Their World
The Chumash & Their Predecessors: An Annotated Bibliography
The Chumash World at European Contact
Crystals in the Sky: Chumash Astronomy, Cosmology and Rock Art
*A Day With a Chumash
December's Child: A Book of Chumash Oral Narratives
The Island Chumash: Behavioral Ecology of a Maritime Society
The Origins of a Pacific Coast Chiefdom: The Chumash of the Channel islands
Purisimo Chumash Prehistory
Rock Painting of the Chumash
When the Animals Were People

CINEMA/FILM

The American Indian in Film
American Indians in Silent Films
American Indians on Film & Video
Celluloid Indians: Native Americans & Film
Engaged Resistance: American Indian Art, Literature, and Film from Alcatrax to the NMAI
From Savage to Nobleman: Images of Native Americans in Film
Hollywood's Indian: The Portrayal of the Native American in Film
Indians Ilustrated: The Images of Native Americans in the Pictorial Press
Killing the Indian Maiden: Images of Native American Women in Film
Mixedblood Messages: Literature, Film, Family & Place
Native Americans on Film & Video
Navajo Talking Picture: Cinema on Native Ground
Reservation Reelism: Redfacing, Visual Sovereignty, and Representations
    of Native Americans in Film
Smoke Signals: Native Cinema Rising
Sovereign Screens: Aboriginal Media on the Canadian West Coast
Wiping the War Paint Off the Lens: Native American Film & Video

CIVIL RIGHTS

Aboriginal Law Handbook
American Indian Politics & the American Political System
Contemporary Native American Political Issues
Encyclopedia of American Indian Civil Rights
Great Cruelties Have Been Reported: The 1544 Investigations of the Coronado Expedition
Hippies, Indians, and the Fight for Red Power
The Indian Civil Rights Act At Forty
The Indian Reform Letters of Helen Hunt Jackson, 1879-1885
Helen Hunt Jackson & Her Indian Reform Legacy
The Nations Within: The Past and Future of American Indian Sovereignty
Native Activism in Cold War America: The Struggle for Sovereignty
Native American Cultural & Religious Freedoms
Native American Transracial Adoptees Tell Their Stories
The Newspaper Warrior: Sarah Winnemucca Hopkin's Campaign for
    American Indian Rights, 1864-1891
Ojibwa Warrior: Dennis Banks & the Rise of the American Indian Movement
The Other Movement: Indian Rights & Civil Rights in the Deep South
Race & the Early Republic: Racial Consciousness & Nation Building in the Early Republic
Red Power Rising: The National Indian Youth Council and the Origins of Native Activism
Religious Freedom & Indian Rights: The Case of Oregon vs. Smith
The Rights of Indians & Tribes: The Authoritative ACLU Guide to Indian & Tribal Rights
The Second Civil War: Examining the Indian Demand for Ethnic Sovereignty
Sovereignty Matters: Locations of Contestation and Possibility in Indigenous Struggles
    for Self-Determination
The Tribal Moment in American Politics: The Struggle for Native American Sovereignty
Tribes, Treaties, and Constitutional Tribulations

CLIFF DWELLERS

The Cliff Dwellers of the Mesa Verde, Southwestern Colorado
Cliff Dwellings of the Mesa Verde
*Dark Arrow
The Land of the Cliff-Dwellers
Mesa Verde Ancient Architecture
Mesa Verde National Park
Mesa Verde: The Story Behind the Scenery
Mound Builders & Cliff Dwellers
The Ozark Bluff Dwellers
The Village of Blue Stone
Voices in the Canyon

COEUR D'ALENE INDIANS

Analysis of Coeur D'Alene Indian Myths
Background History of the Coeur D'Alene Indian Reservation
Bloodlines: Odyssey of a Native Daughter
Coeur D'Alene Indian Myths
The Coeur d'Alene Indian Reservation
Coeur d'Alene, Okanogan & Flathead Indians
Landscape Traveled by Coyote & Crane: The World of the Schitsu'umsh
  (Coeur d'Alene Indians)
Mapping Identity: The Creation of the Cooeur d'Alene Indian Reservation, 1805-1902
Religion & Resistance in the Encounter Between the Coeur D'Alene
  Indians & Jesuit Missionaries
Saga of the Coeur D'Alene Indian Nation
Saving the Reservation: Joe Garry & the battle To Be Indian

COMANCHE INDIANS

Archaeological Investigations of the Kiowa & Comanche
Being Comanche
Buffalo Hump and the Penateka Comanches
Census of the Comanche Tribe
*The Comanche
Comanche Census
Comanche Dictionary & Grammar
The Comanche Empire
Comanche Ethnology
Comanche Indian Research and History with Biographies,
  Book Reviews & Cemetaries
Comanche Lessons (Language)
Comanche Moon
Comanche Picture Dictionary
Comanche Political History
Comanche Song Book
Comanche Talking Dictionary
Comanche Treaties During the Civil War
Comanche Treaties: Historical Background
Comanche Treaties (1835, 1846, 1850, 1851, 1853) with the U.S.
Comanche Treaties with the Republic of Texas
Comanche Vocabulary
*Comanche Warbonnet
The Comanchero Frontier
The Comanches: A History, 1706-1875
Comanches in the New West, 1895-1908: Historic Photographs
The Comanches: Lords of the South Plains
Comanches & Mennonites on the Oklahoma Plains
Expedition to the Southwest
First to Fight
Gifts of Pride & Love; Kiowa & Comanche Cradles
A Grammar of Comanche
LaDonna Harris: A Comanche Life
The Jerome Agreement Between the Kiowa, Comanche, and Apache Tribes of the U.S.
Kiowa, Apache, and Comanche Military Societies
Komantcia
The Legend of the Bluebonnet, retold
Life Among the Texas Indians
Life At the Kiowa, Comanche, and Wichita Agency: The Photographs of Annette Ross
Life of Ten Bears: Comanche Historical Narratives
Los Comanches: The Horse People, 1751-1845
New Comanche Dictionary
Cynthia Ann Parker: The Life & Legend
The Plains Indians
Quanah Parker: Comanche Chief
*Quanah Parker: Great Chief of the Comanches
Quanah: A Pictorial History of the Last Comanche Chief
Rance Hood: Mystic Painter
Sanapia: Comanche Medicine Woman
The Sound of Strings
The Story of Cynthia Ann Parker
Three Years Among the Comanches
Warlords of the West: A Story of the Comanche
*Why Buffalo Roam
Without Quarter: The Wichita Expedition & the Fight on Crooked Creek

CRAZY HORSE

American Indian Warrior Chiefs
Crazy Horse
*Crazy Horse

Crazy Horse Called Them Walk-A-Heaps
Crazy Horse & Custer
Crazy Horse, Hoka Hey: It Is A Good Time To Die
Crazy Horse & Korczak: The Story of an Epic Mountain Carving
Crazy Horse, A Lakota Life
Crazy Horse: The Life Behind the Legend
Crazy Horse Memorial, 40th Anniversary
Crazy Horse & the Real Reason
  for the Battle of the Little Big Horn
Crazy Horse: Sacred Warrior of the Sioux
Crazy Horse: The Strange Man of the Oglalas
The Crazy Horse Surrender Ledger
Crazy Horse's Philosophy of Riding Rainbows
*Custer & Crazy Horse
The Death of Crazy Horse
Famous Indians of Northwest Nebraska
Greengrass Pipe Dancers
In The Spirit of Crazy Horse
Indians of America: Crazy Horse.....
The Journey of Crazy Horse: A Lakota History
The Killing of Chief Crazy Horse
The Killing of Crazy Horse
Korczak: Storyteller in Stone
*A Legend From Crazy Horse Clan
*Native American Leaders of the Wild West
Oglala Lakota Crazy Horse
The Power of Four: Leadership Lessons of Crazy Horse
Search for the Lost Trail of Crazy Horse
South Dakota Leaders
War Chiefs

CREE INDIANS

Acaoohkiwina & Acimowina: Traditional Narratives of the Rock Cree Indians
Born Cree: The Life of Pete Hawley
Bringing Home Animals: Religious Ideology & Mode of Production
  of the Mistassini Cree Hunters
Broken Treaties: U.S. & Canadian Relations with the Lakotas & the Plains Cree, 1868-1885
Canoeing With the Cree
The Counselling Speeches of Jim Ka-Nipitehtew
The Cree Language Structure - A Cree Approach
Cree Legends & Narratives from the West Coast of James Bay
Cree Narrative
Cry of the Eagle: Encounters With a Cree Healer
Dissonant Worlds: Roger Vandersteene Among the Cree
Emotional Expression Among the Cree Indians
Fort Chipewyan Homecoming: A Journey to Native Canada
Greatful Prey: Rock Cree Human-Animal Relationships
A Homeland for the Cree: Regional Development in James Bay, 1971-1981
I Dream of Yesterday & Tomorrow: A Celebration of the James Bay Cree
Indian Old Man Stories
*Just a Walk
A Language of Our Own
Meet Cree: A Guide to the Cree Language
The Montana Cree: A Study in Religious Persistence
Nation Witin a Nation: Dependency & the Cree
Navigating Neoliberalism: Self-Determination & the Mikisew Cree First Nation
Notes on the Eastern Cree and Northern Salteaux
The Orders of the Dreamed
Origins of Predicates: Evidence From Plains Cree
The Plains Cree: Trade, Diplomacy & War, 1790 to 1870
Plains Cree Texts
Readings on James Bay
Sacred Stories of the Sweet Grass Cree
Ellen Smallboy: Glimpses of a Cree Woman's Life
Spoken Cree: West Coast of James Bay
A Stolen Life: The Journey of a Cree Woman
The Student's Dictionary of Literary Plains Cree
*This Land Is My Land
To Change Them Forever
To Please the Caribou

CREEK INDIANS

African Americans & Native Americans in the Cherokee & Creek Nations, 1830s to 1920s
African Creeks
Africans & Creeks: From the Colonial Period to the Civil War
Beginning Creek: Myskoke Emponvkv
Bryant: A Creek Indian Nation Townsite
Camp, Clan & Kin, Among the Cow Creek Seminole of Florida
The Collected Works of Benjamin Hawkins
The Color of the Land: Race, Nation, and the Politics of Landownership
  in Oklahoma, 1832-1929
*The Creek
*Creek Captives & Other Alabama Stories
Creek Country: The Creek Indians & Their World
The Creek Frontier, 1540-1783
Creek Indian History
Creek Indian Medicine Ways
Creek (Muskogee) New Testament Concordance
Creek Paths & Federal Roads: Indians, Settlers, and Slaves & the Making
  of the American South
Creek Religion & Medicine

The Creek Verb
The Creek War of 1813 & 1814
A Creek Warrior for the Confederacy: The Autobiography of Chief G.W. Grayson
Creeks & Seminoles: The Destruction & Regeneration of the Muscogulge People
Creeks & Southerners: Biculturalism on the Early American Frontier
Deerskins & Duffels: The Creek Indian Trade with Anglo-America, 1685-1815
Early History of the Creek Indians & Their Neighbors
Estiyut Omayat: Creek Writings
The Fus Fixico Letters: A Creek Humorist in Early Oklahoma
A Grammar of Creek (Muskogee)
George Washington Grayson & the Creek Nation, 1853-1920
Handbook of Creek (Muscogee) Grammar
Handbook of the Creek Langauge
Households & Hegemony: Early Creek Prestige Goods,
  Symbolic Capital & Social Power
The Invention of the Creek Nation, 1670-1763
Lost Creeks: Collected Journals
McIntosh & Weatherford, Creek Indian Leaders
Nations Remembered: An Oral History of Cherokees, Chickasaws, Choctaws,
  Creeks, and Seminoles, 1865-1907
A New Order of Things: Property, Power & the Transformation
  of the Creek Indians, 1733-1816
Now the Wolf Has Come: The Creek Nation in the Civil War
The Politics of Indian Removal: Creek Government and Society in Crises
Red Eagle & the Wars With the Creek Indians of Alabama
Rivers of Sand: Creek Indian Emigration, Relocation, and Ethnic Cleansing
  in the American South
The Road to Disappearance: A History of the Creek Indians
A Sacred Path: The Way of the Muscogee Creek
Sacred Revolt: The Muskogee's Struggle for a New World
Songs of the Oktahutche: Collected Poems
Totkv Mocvse • New Fire: Creek Folktales

CROW INDIANS

*Absaloka: Crow Children's Writing
Absaraka: Home of the Crows
Jim Beckwourth: Black Moutnain Man & War Chief of the Crows
*Chief Plenty Coups: Life of the Crow Indian Chief
*The Crow
*Crow Children & Elders Talk Together
The Crow & the Eagle: A Tribal History
Crow Indian Art
Crow Indian Beadwork
Crow Indian Medicine Bundles
Crow Indian Photography
The Crow Indians
From the Heart of Crow Country
A Grammar of Crow
The Handsome People: A History of the Crow Indians and the Whites
*The Indian as a Soldier at Fort Custer, Montana, 1890-1895
Life and Adventures of James P. Beckwourth
Memoirs of a White Crow Indian
Myths & Traditions of the Crow
Plenty-Coups, Chief of the Crows
Pretty-Shield, Medicine Woman of the Crows
The Shoshini-Crow Sun Dance
Silver Fox, Journeys of the Inner Songbird
The Stars We Know: Crow Indian Astronomy & Lifeways
The Sun Dance of the Crow Indians
A Taste of Heritage: Crow Indian Recipes & Herbal Medicines
They Call Me Agnes
To Image & To See: Crow Indian Photographs by Edward S. Curtis & Richard Throssel
Two Crows Denies It: A History of Controversy in Omaha Sociology
Two Leggings: The Making of a Crow Warrior
Uniting the Tribes: The Rise & Fall of Pan-Indian Community on the Crow Reservation
The Way of the Warrior: Stories of the Crow People
The Woman Who Loved Mankind: The Life of a Twentieth-Century Crow Elder
The World of the Crow Indians: As Driftwood Lodges

CULTURAL ASSIMILATION, INTERACTION & SURVIVAL

Acculturation in Seven Indian Tribes
America's Second Tongue: American Indian Education & the Ownership of English
American Indian Education: A History
The American Indian in Film
American Indian Nations From Termination to Restoration, 1953-2006
American Indian Policy & American Reform: Case Studies of the Campaign
  to Assimilate the American Indians
American Indian Policy & Cultural Values: Conflict & Accommodation
American Indian Societies: Strategies & Conditions of Political & Cultural Survival
American Indian Stereotypes in the World of Children: A Reader & Bibliography
American Indian Stories
American Indian: A Cultural Geography
American Indians in the Marketplace: Persistence & Innovation Among the
  Menominees & Metlakatlans, 1870-1920
Apache Reservation: Indigenous Poeples and the American State
Around the Sacred Fire: Native Religious Activism in the Red Power Era
As We Are Now: Mixedblood Essays on Race & Identity
Assimilation's Agent: My Life As a Supt. in the Indian Boarding School System
Bad Fruits of the Civilized Tree: Alcohol & the Sovereignty
  of the Cherokee Nation
Beginning & End of Rape: Confronting Sexual Violence in Native America

Being and Becoming Indian
Between Indian & White Worlds: The Cultural Broker
Biodiversity & Native America
Blood Struggle: The Rise of Modern Indian Nations
Blood Will Tell: Native Americans & Assimilation Policy
Bullying the Moqui
Celluloid Indians: Native Americans & Film
Changing Culture of an Indian Tribe
Cherokee Diaspora: An Indigenous History of Migration, Resettlement, and Identity
The Cherokee Ghost Dance
Cherokees and Missionaries, 1789-1839
Chief Joseph, Yellow Wolf & the Creation of Nez Perce History in the Pacific Northwest
Children of the Dragonfly: Native American Voices on Child Custody & Education
The Chiricahua Apache Prisoners of War, Fort Sill, 1894-1914
City Indian: Native American Activism in Chicago, 1893-1934
Coming To Stay: A Columbia River Journey
Conflict and Schism in Nez Perce Acculturation: A Study of Religion & Politics
Confederate Colonel & Cherokee Chief: The Life of William Holland Thomas
Confounding the Color Line: The Indian-Black Experience in North America
Contested Ground
Thomas Crosby & the Tsimshian: Small Shoes for Feet Too Large
Cultural Persistence: Continuity in Meaning & Moral Responsibility
  Among the Bearlake Athapaskan
The Cultural Transformation of a Native American Family & Its Tribe, 1763-1995
Cultures in Contact: The European Impact on Native Cultural Institutions in Eastern
  North America, 1000-1800 A.D.
Daksi
Deadly Politics of Giving: Exchange & Violence at Ajacan, Roanoke, and Jamestown
Defamiliarizing the Aboriginal: Cultural Practices & Decolonization in Canada
Devil Sickness & Devil Songs: Tohono O'odham Poetics
Disciplined Hearts
Dispossession By Degrees
Dress Clothing of the Plains Indians
Early White Influence Upon Plains Indian Painting: George Catlin & Carl Bodmer
  Among the Mandan, 1832-1834
Education & Language Restoration: Assimilation Versus Cultural Survival
Education for Extinction
Emergence of Native American Nationalism in the Columbia Plateau
Ending Denial: Understanding Aboriginal Issues
Farmers, Hunters & Colonists
Engaged Resistance: American Indian Art, Literature, and Film from Alcatrax to the NMAI
A Final Promise: The Campaign to Assimilate the Indians, 1880-1920
Florida Indians & the Invasion from Europe
From Savage to Nobleman: Images of Native Americans in Film
Fugitive Poses: Native American Indian Scenes of Absence & Presence
Gambling & Survival in Native North America
Genocide of the Mind: New Native American Writing
Geographical Names of the Kwakiutl Indians
Germans & Indians: Fantasies, Encounters, Projections
The Good Red Road'
Hippies, Indians, and the Fight for Red Power
The Hunt for Willie Boy: Indian-Hating & Popular Culture
Hunting for Hides: Deerskins, Status, and Cultural Change in the Prohistoric Appalachian
In Defense of Mohawk Land
In the Path of an Avalanche: A True Story
Indian Country, L.A. Maintaining Ethnic Community in a Complex Society
Indian Culture and European Trade Goods: The Archaeology of the Historic Period
  in the Western Great Lakes Region
Indian Givers: How the Indians of the Americas Transformed the World
Indian Metropolis: Native Americans in Chicago, 1945-75
Indian Play: Indigenous Identities at Bacon College
Indian Police & Judges: Experiments in Acculturation & Control
The Indian Reform Letters of Helen Hunt Jackson, 1879-1885
Indians Are Us?
Indians Ilustrated: The Images of Native Americans in the Pictorial Press
The Indians in American Society
Indians in Prison
Indians in Unexpected Places
Indians R Us: Culture & Genocide
Indigenizing the Academy
Individuality Incorporated: Indians & the Multicultural Modern
IndiVisible: African-Native American Lives in the Americas
Institute of American Indian Arts: Modernism & U.S. Indian Policy
The Invented Indian: Cultural Fictions & Government Policies
Issues in Native American Cultural Identity
Mr. Jefferson's Hammer: William Henry Harrison & the origins of American Indian Policy
Killing the Indian Maiden: Images of Native American Women in Film
Learning to Write "Indian"
Legends of American Indian Resistance
Lost Bird of Wounded Knee: Spirit of the Lakota
Lumbee Indians in the Jim Crow South: Race, Identity, and the Making of a Nation
Making Space on the Western Frontier: Mormons, Miners, and Southern Paiutes
The Miami Indians
Mining, the EPA's Indian Policy at 25, and Indigenous Development Conflicts
Mixed Blook Indians: Racial Construction in the early South
Mixedblood Messages: Literature, Film, Family & Place
Mixed-Bloods and Tribal Dissolution: Charles Curtis & the Quest for Indian Identity
Mother Earth, Father Skyline: A Souvenir Book of Native New York
The Movement for Indian Assimilation, 1860-1890
Multicultural Comics: From Zap to Blue Beetle
Muscogee Daughter: My Sojourn to the Miss America Pageant
Native Activism in Cold War America: The Struggle for Sovereignty
Native American Ethnobotany
Native American Identities: From Stereotype to Archetype in Art & Literature

Native American Mascot Controversy: A Handbook
Native American Perspectives on Literature & History
Native American Renaissance
The Native American Renaissance: Literary Imagination & Achievement
Native American Representations: First Encounters, Distorted Images,
  & Literary Appropriations
Native American Transracial Adoptees Tell Their Stories
Native American Writing in Southeast: An Anthology, 1875-1935
Native Americans & the Environment
Native Americans & the Legacy of Harry S. Truman
Native Americans on Network TV: Stereotypes, Myths, and the "Good Indian"
Native Roots: How the Indians Enriched America
Natives & Newcomers: The Cultural Origins of North America
Navajo Infancy: An Ethological Study of Child Development
New Worlds of Violence: Cultures & Conquests in the Early American Southeast
North American Indian Lives
Not for School, But for Life
Off the Reservation
A Passion for the True & Just: Felix & Lucy Kramer Cohen and the Indian New Deal
The Phoenix Indian School: Forced Assimilation in Arizona, 1891-1935
Pipestone: My Life in an Indian Boarding School
Plains Apache Ethnobotany
Playing Indian
Plundered Skulls & Stolen Spirits: Inside the Fight to Reclaim Native America's Culture
A Praying People: Massachusetts Acculturation & the Failure
  of the Puritan Mission, 1600-1690
Race & the Cherokee Nation: Sovereignty in the Nineteenth Century
Rebellion From the Roots: Indian Uprising in Chiapas
Red Power Rising: The National Indian Youth Council and the Origins of Native Activism
Restoring the Chain of Friendship: British Policy & the Indians
  of the Great Lakes, 1783-1815
Riding Buffalos & Broncos: Rodeo & Native Traditions in the Northern Great Plains
The Round Valley Indians of California
Savages & Civilization: Who Will Survive?
Savages of America
Separate Peoples, One Land: The Minds of Cherokees, Blacks, and Whites
  on the Tennessee Frontier
Silent Victims: Hate Crimes Against Native Americans
Smoke Signals: Native Cinema Rising
Sovereignty & Symbol: Indian-White Conflict at Ganienkeh
Spirit Wars: Native North American Religions in the Age of Nation Building
Storied Communities: Narratives of Contact & Arrival in Constituting Political Community
Stories of the People: Native American Voices
Strong Hearts: Native American Visions & Voices
Struggles for the Land
Taking Assimilation to Heart
Tammarnlit (Mistakes) Inuit Relocation in the Eastern Arctic, 1939-1963
Team Spirits: The Native American Mascots Controversy
They Treated Us Just Like Indians
To Change Them Forever: Indian Education at the Rainy Mountain
  Boarding School, 1893-1920
To Harvest, To Hunt: Stories of Resource Use in the American West
To Intermix With Our White Brothers: Indian Mixed Bloods in the U.S.
The Transit of Empire: Indigenous Critiques of Colonialism
The Tribal Moment in American Politics: The Struggle for Native American Sovereignty
Tribal Writers: The Correspondence Guide for Native Americans
Unaffected by the Gospel: Osage Resistance
Unconquered People: Florida's Seminole & Miccosukee Indians
Unnatural Selection: The Yanomamim the Kayapo & the Onslaught of Civilizations
Urban Indian Experience in America
Urban Indians
Urban Indians: Drums From the Cities
Urban Voices: The Bay Area American Indian Community
Urbaniztion of American Indians
The Vanishing American: White Attitudes & U.S. Indian Policy
Voices of American Indian Assimilation & Resistance
Wasi'chu: The Continuing Indian Wars
The Way We Make Sense
We Are Not You: First Nations & Canadian Modernity
A Will to Survive: Indigenous Essays on the Politics of Culture, Language, and Identity
White Enough to Be American? Race Mixing, Indigenous People, & the Boundaries
  of State & Nation
White Man's Club
White People, Indians, and Highlanders: Tribal People & Colonial Encounters
  in Scotland & America
Wordarrows: Indians & Whites in the New Fur Trade
Wordarrows: Native States of Literary Sovereignty
World of Wakara
World War II & the American Indian

CULTURE

Acculturation in Seven Indian Tribes
The Age of Manufactures, 1700-1820
Alaska in the Days That Were Before
Alaska's Totem Poles
All Roads Are Good: Native Voices on Life & Culture
America - Land of the Rising Sun
American Indian Cultural Heroes & Teaching Tales: Evenings with Chasing Deer
American Indian Culture & Research Journal: Vol. 40, No. I
American Indian Ethnic Renewal: Red Power & the Resurgence of Identity & Culture
American Indian Grandmothers
American Indian DNA & Chromosome Genetic Data, and the Peopling of North America
American Indian Rhetorics of Survivance: Word Medicine, Word Magic

American Indians: The First of This Land
American Indians and the Mass Media
American Indians in a Modern World
American Indians, Time, and the Law: Native Societies in a Modern
  Constitutional Democracy
Ancestor's Footsteps
Ancient Buriel Practices in the American Southwest
Ancient Drums, Other Moccasins: Native North American Cultural Adaptation
The Anguish of Snails: Native American Folklore in the West
Apache Odyssey
Apachean Culture: History & Ethnology
Arboretum America: A Philosophy of the Forest
Arizona Traveler: Indians of Arizona
Around the Sacred Fire: Native Religious Activism inthe Red Power Era
Art & Environment in Native America
Art of the American Indian Frontier: A Portfolio
Basic Call to Consciousness
Becoming Brave: The Path to Native American Manhood
Between Indian & White Worlds: The Cultural Broker
Between Sacred Mountains: Navajo Stories & Lessons from the Land
Beyond the Vision: Essays on American Indian Culture
Beyond White Ethnicity: Developing a Sociological Understanding of
  Native American Identity Reclamation
Biodiversity & Native America
Bread & Freedom
The Brothers of the Pine
Captured Heritage: The Scramble for the Northwest Coast Artifacts
Caring for American Indian Objects: A Practical & Cultural Guide
Carving Traditions of Northwest California
Catlin's North American Indian Portfolio
Ralph T. Coe & the Collecting of American Indian Art
Changing Culture of an Indian Tribe
The Changing Presentation of the American Indian: Museums & Native Cultures
Cherokee Dance and Drama
Clay, Copper & Turquoise: The Museum Collection of Chaco Culture
  National Historical Park
The Collecting Passions of Dennis & Janis Lyon
Collecting the Pre-Columbian Past
Colonial Discourses, Collective Memories
Colonial Intimacies: Indian Marriage in Early New England
Contesting Knowledge: Museums & Indigenous Perspectives
The Covenent Chain: Indian Ceremonial and Trade Silver
Coyote's Council Fire
Creation's Journey" Native American Identity & Belief
Critical Neurophilosophy & Indigenous Wisdom
Crossbloods: Bone Courts, Bingo, and Other Reports
Cultural Diversity & Adaptation
The Cultural Transformation of a Native American Family & Its Tribe
Culture, Change & Leadership in a Modern Indian Community:
  The Colorado River Indian Reservation
Cultures in Contact: The European Impact ...
Culturicide, Resistance & Survival of the Lakota (Sioux Nation)
Cycles of Conquest: The Impact of Spain, Mexico & the U.S. on Indians
  of the Southwest, 1533-1960
Dakota Life in the Upper Midwest
Deliberate Acts: Changing Hopi Culture Through the Oraibi Split
The Desert Smells Like Rain: A Naturalist in Papago Indian Country
*Discover American Indian Ways
Discovering Totem Poles: A Traveler's Guide
Dreaming the Dawn
Earth Medicine: Ancestor's Ways of Harmony for Many Moons
Earthdivers: Tribal Narratives on Mixed Descent
Embracing Fry Bread: Confessions of a Wanabe
Enduring Culture: A Century of Photography of the Southwest Indians
*Europeans & Native Americans
The False Faces of the Iroquois
Family Matters: Tribal Affairs
The Fighting Cheyennes
Finding the Center: The Art of the Zuni Storyteller
First American Art: The Charles & Valerie Diker Collection of American Indian Art
First Horses: Stories of the New West
First Peoples: Indigenous Cultures & Their Futures
For Those Who Come After: A Study of Native American Autobiography
The Fremont Culture: A Study in Culture Dynamics on the Northern Anasazi Frontier
From Daniel Boone to Captain America: Playing Indian in American Popular Culture
Fugitive Poses: Native American Indian Scenes of Absence and Presence
Gathering Hopewell: Society, Ritual, & Ritual Interaction
Gathering Native Scholars: UCLA's 40 Years of American Indian Culture & Research
*The Gift of Changing Woman
The Girl Who Sang to the Buffalo
Going Indian
Going Native: Indians in the American Cultural Imagination
The Gospel of the Redman
The Great Mystery Explained
Growing Up Native American
Guide to Contemporary Southwest Indians
Guide to the North American Ethnographic Collection at the University of Pennsylvania
Haida Art
Haida: Their Art & Culture
Handbook of the American Frontier - Four Centuries of Indian-White Relationships:
  The Southeastern Woodlands
Handbook of Yokuts Indians
Hidatsa Social & Ceremonial Organization
The Heiltsuks: Dialogues of Culture & History on the Northwest Coast

A Will to Survive: Indigenous Essays on the Politics of Culture,
 Language, and Identity
The Wintu & Their Neighbors
Wisdom's Daughters: Conversations with Women Elders of Native America
Women in Prehistory
The World of the American Indian
Wovoka & the Ghost Dance
X-marks: Native Signatures of Assent

EDWARD S. CURTIS

Edward S. Curtis: Coming to Light
Edward S. Curtis: The Great Warriors
Curtis Indians
Edward S. Curtis: The North American Indian
Edward S. Curtis & the North American Indian Project in the Field
Edward Curtis: Sites & Structures
Edward Sheriff Curtis: Visions of a Vanishing Race
Indian Days of Long Ago
The Many Faces of Edward Sherriff Curtis
Native American Wisdom
Native Americans
The North American Indian
The North American Indian: The Complete Portfolio
The North American Indians: Photographs by Edward S. Curtis
The North American Indian, Vol. 12: Hopi
The Photography of Edward S. Curtis
The Plains Indian Photographs of Edward S. Curtis
Portraits from North American Indian Life: Original Portfolio Edition
Prayer to the Great Mystery: The Uncollected Writings & Photography
 of Edward S. Curtis
Sacred Legacy: Edward S. Curtis & the North American Indian
To Image & To See: Crow Indian Photographs by Edward S. Curtis
 & Richard Throssel, 1905-1910
The Vanishing Race & Other Illusions: Photographs of Indians by Edward S. Curtis
The Vanishing Race: Selections from Edward S. Curtis' The North American Indian

CUSTER & THE LITTLE BIGHORN

The Arikara Narrative of Custer's Campaign & the Battle of the Little Bighorn
The Army & Navy Journal on the Battle of the Little Bighorn & Related Matters, 1876-1881
Battle of the Little Bighorn
Bloody Knife: Custer's Favorite Scout
Boots & Saddles: Or, Life in Dakota With General Custer
Camp, Custer & the Little Bighorn
Cavalier in Buckskin
Cheyenne Memories
The Custer Album
Custer & the Battle of the Little Bighorn
Custer Battlefield, A History & Guide to the Battle of the Little Bighorn
Custer, Black Kettle, & the Fight on the Washita
Custer & the Cheyenne: George A. Custer's Winter Campaign on the Southern Plains
Custer, Cody & the Last Indian Wars: A Pictorial History
Custer & Company
Custer & Crazy Horse
Custer Died for Your Sins
The Custer Legacy
Custer & the Little Bighorn
The Custer Myth
Custer: A Photographic Biography
The Custer Reader
The Custer Story
The Custer Tragedy
Custerology: The Enduring Legacy of the Indian Wars
Custer's Chief of Scouts
Custer's Defeat & Other Conflicts in the West
Custer's Fall: The Native American Side of the Story
Custer's Last Campaign
Custer's Last Fight: The Story of the Battle of the Little Big Horn
Custer's Last Stand
Custer's Luck
Custer's Prelude to Glory
Custer's Seventh Cavalry & the Campaign of 1873
The Day the World Ended at Little Bighorn: A Lakota History
Hokahey! A Good Day to Die
Indian Views of the Custer Fight: A Source Book
It Is a Good Day to Die: Indian Eyewitnesses Tell the Story of the Battle of the Little Bighorn
Killing Custer
Lakota Recollections of the Custer Fight: New Sources of Indian-Military History
The Last Stand: Custer, Sitting Bull, and the Battle of the Little Bighorn
Mystery of E Troop: Custer's Gray Horse Company at Little Big Horn
Our Centennial Indian War & the Life of General Custer
Showdown at the Little Bighorn
Soldiers Falling Into Camp: The Battles
 at the Rosebud & the Little Bighorn
*The Story of Little Big Horn
The Story of the Little Big Horn: Custer's Last Fight
General Terry's Last Statement to Custer
They Died With Custer
Troopers With Custer
An Uncommon Enemy

Voices of Wounded Knee
Warriors on the Little Big Horn, 1876
Where Custer Fell: Photographs Of the Little Bighorn Battlefield Then and Now

DANCE (See MUSIC & DANCE)

DELAWARE/LENAPE INDIANS

Blackcoats Among the Delaware: David Zeisberger on the Ohio Frontier
Complete Delaware Roll 1898
The Delaware
Delaware-English / English-Delaware Dictionary
Delaware-Indian & English Spelling Book
The Delaware Language: A Preliminary Draft
The Delaware Indians: A Brief History
The Delaware Indians: A History
Delaware Reference Grammar
The Delaware & Shawnee Admitted to Cherokee Citizenship
Delaware Trails: Some Tribal Records, 1842-1907
Delaware Tribe in a Cherokee Nation
The Delawares: A Critical Bibliography
The Dutch, the Indians and the Quest for Copper-Pahaquarry and the Old Mine Road
Essay of Delaware-Indian & English Spelling Book
*The First Americans Coloring Book: Lenape Indian Drawings
Folk Medicine of the Delaware & Related Algonkian Indians
A Grammar of Delaware Semantics, Morpho-Syntax, Lexicon, & Phonology
Grammar of the Language of the Lenni Lenape, or Delaware Indians
Handbook of the Delaware Indian Language: The Oral Tradition of a Native People
*I Am Regina
*The Indians of Lenapehoking
*The Indians of New Jersey: Dickon Among the Lenapes
Keeper of the Delaware Dolls
King of the Delawares: Teedyuscung, 1700-1763
Legends of the Delaware Indians & Picture Writing
The Lenape
Lenape History & Numbers Posters
Lenape Indian Cooking With Touching Leaves Woman
Lenape Indian Teaching Kit 2
The Lenape Indians
The Lenape: Middle Atlantic
The Lenape or Delaware Indian Heritage: 10,000 BC to AD 2000
*The Lenape or Delaware Indians
Long Journey Home: Oral Histories of Contemporary Delaware Indians
The Munsee Indians: A History
Mythology of the Lenape
*The Nanticoke
The Nanticokke Indians
Oklahoma Delaware Ceremonies
On Records: Delaware Indians, Colonists, and the Media of History & Memory
*William Penn's Own Account of the Lenni Lenape or Delaware Indians
Religion & Ceremonies of the Lenape
Songs of Our Grandfathers: Music of the Unami Delaware Indians
A Study of Delaware Indian Medicine Practice & Folk Beliefs
A Teacher's Guide to the Lenape
Vocabulary of New Jersey Delaware
Voices From the Delaware Big House Ceremony
The White Deer & Other Stories Told by the Lenape
Zeisberger's Indian Dictionary

VINE DELORIA, JR.

American Indian Policy in the 20th Century
American Indians, American Justice
Behind the Trail of Broken Treaties
Custer Died for Your Sins: An Indian Manifesto
Destroying Dogma
Documents of American Indian Diplomacy
Exiled In the Land of the Free
For This Land: Writings on Religion in America
God Is Red: A Native View of Religion
Indian Education in America: Eight Essays by Vine Deloria, Jr.
Indian Reorganization Act: Congress & Bills
Indians & Anthropologists: Vine Deloria, Jr. & the Critique of Anthropology
The Nations Wiithin: The Past & Future of American Indian Sovereignty
Red Earth, White Lies: Native Americans & the Myth of Scientific Fact
Singing for a Spirit: A Portrait of the Dakota Sioux
Spirit & Reason: The Vine Deloria, Jr. Reader
They Say the Wind Is Red: The Alabama Choctaw Lost In Their Own Land
Tribes, Treaties, & Constitutional Tribulations

FRANCES DENSMORE

Cheyenne & Arapaho Music
*Chippewa Customs
Choctaw Music
*Dakota & Ojibwe People in Minnesota
Frances Densmore & American Indian Music
How Indians Use Wild Plants for Food, Medicine & Crafts
Teton Sioux Music & Culture
Travels With Frances Densmore: Her Life, Wok, and Legacy in Native American Studies

DIRECTORIES, BIBLIOGRAPHIES & REFERENCE BOOKS

The A to Z of Native American Movements
Access First Nations
AIDS Regional Directory: Resources in Indian Country
The American Indian & Alaska Native Traders Directory
American Indian/Alaska Native Tribal & Village HIV-1 Policy Guidelines
American Indian Culture & Research Journal: Vol. 40, No. I
American Indian Encyclopedia CD-ROM
American Indian Facts of Life
American Indian Index: A Directory of Indian Country
American Indian Literatures
American Indian Reference Books for Children & Young Adults
American Indian Religious Freedom Act: A Legislative History of Public Law No. 95-341
American Indian Resource Manual for Public Libraries
American Indian Women
American Indians in Silent Films
American Indians on Film & Video
Atlas of American Indian Affairs
Atlas of the North American Indian
Bibliography of Articles and Papers on North American Indian Art
Bibliography of Native North Americans on Disc - CD-ROM
Biographical Directory of Native American Painters
Cahuilla Dictionary
Celluloid Indians
*Children's Atlas of Native Americans
Church Philanthropy for Native Americans & Other Minorities
Comanche Vocabulary
Contemporary Native American Authors: A Biographical Dictionary
Corporate and Foundation Fundraising Manual for Native Americans
Demographics of American Indians
Digest of American Indian Law
Directory of American Indian Law Attorneys
Directory of Native American Performing Artists
Discover Indian Reservations USA - A Visitor's Guide
E-Mail Names for Indian Country
Education Assistance for American Indians & Alaska Natives
Encyclopedia of American Indian Biography
Encyclopedia of American Indian Issues Today
Encyclopedia of the American Indian Movement
Encyclopedia of American Indian Removal
Encyclopedia of Frontier Biography
Encyclopedia of Multiculturism
*Encyclopedia of Native American Healing
Encyclopedia of Native American History
Encyclopedia of Native American Religions
*Encyclopedia of Native American Tribes
Encyclopedia of World Cultures
Federal Programs of Assistance to Native Americans
Financial Aid for Native Americans
First Americans Series
First Nations Tribal Directory
From Savage to Nobleman: Images of Native Americans in Film
Guide to American Indian Documents
Guide to America's Indians
Guide to the Anasazi & Other Ancient Southwest Indians
Guide to Cherokee Documents in Foreign Archives
Guide to Cherokee Documents
Guide to Community Education
Guide to Federal Funding for Governments & Nonprofits
Guide to the 400 Best Children's & Adults Multicultural Books
Guide to Multicultural Resources, 1995-96
Guide to Research on North American Indians & Others
Guide to Indian Artifacts of the Northeast
Guide to Indian Herbs
Guide to Indian Jewelry of the Southwest
Guide to Indian Quillworking
Guide to Indian Rock Carvings of Pacific Northwest
Guide to Indian Tribes of Oklahoma
Guide to Indian Tribes of the Pacific Northwest
Guide to Multicultural Resources
Guide to Native American Music Recordings
Guide to Navajo Rugs
Guide to Navajo Sandpainting
Guide to Palaeo-Indian Artifacts of North America
Guide to Prehistoric Ruins of the Southwest
Guide to Proposal Writing
Guide to the Records at the National Archives
The Guide to Trading Posts & Pueblos
Handbook of American Indian Games
Handbook of American Indian Languages
Handbook of American Indian Religious Freedom
Handbook of Creek Grammar
Handbook of Federal Indian Law
Handbook of the Indians of California
Handbook pf Native American Literature
Handbook of North American Indians
Handbook of Northeastern Indian Medicinal Plants
Historial Dictionary of Native American Movements
Historical Dictionary of North American Archaeology
Hopi Dictionary: Hopi-English, English-Hopi, Grammatical Appendix
Indian Country Address Book
Indian International Motorcycle Directory
The Indian Question CD-ROM

Indian Reservations: A State & Federal Handbook
Indian Tribes of North America
Indians of Arizona: A Guide to Arizona's Heritage
Indians of the Northwest Coast
Indigenous Methodologies: Characteristics, Conversations, and Contexts
Medicinal Plants Used by Native American Tribes in Southern California
National Directory of Minority-Owned Businesses
National Directory of Corporate Philanthropy for Native Americans
National Directory of Foundation Grants for Native Americans
National Directory of Philanthropy for Native Americans
National Directory of Seed Money Grants for American Indian Projects
National Indian Gaming Association (NIGA) Indian Gaming Resource Directory
Nations Within a Nation
Native America
Native American Bibliography Series
Native American Biographies
Native American Casinos
Native American Checklist
Native American Crafts Directory
Native American Directory: Alaska, U.S. & Canada
Native American Directory: Vital Records of ME, MA, RI, CT, NY & WI
The Native American Indian Artist Directory
Native American Internet Guide & Address Book
Native American Music Directory
Native American Wisdom
Native American Women
Native Americans in the Saturday Evening Post
Native Americans Information Directory
Native Americans: A Resource Guide
Native California Guide: Weaving Past & Present
The Native New Mexico Guide
The Native North American Almanac
Native Peoples A to Z: A Reference Guide to the Native Peoples
  of the Western Hemisphere
Navajo Dictionary on Diagnostic Terminology
New Mexico Treasures 2011
North American Indian Landmarks: A Traveler's Guide
North American Indian Travel Guide
North American Indian Wars - CD-ROM
North American Indians - CD-ROM
Notable Native Americans
Pacific Northwest Americana
Portrait of North American Indians in Published Collections
Pow Wow Calendar
Pow-Wow On the Red Road
Raven's Guide to AIDS Prevention Resources
Research and Writing Tribal Histories
Resource Reading List
Sources of Financial Aid to American Indian Students
Spirit & Reason: The Vine Deloria, Jr. Reader
State Indian Encyclopedias
Talking Chickasaw Dictionary
Tiller's Guide to Indian Country: Economic Profiles of American Indian Reservations
A Travelers Guide to Southwest Indian Arts & Crafts
Trends in Indian Health
Ukwehu-Wehnaha Tekawxnate?neyse: An Oneida Dictionary
Who Was Who in Native American History
Who's Who in Indian Relics

DRAMA

Alternatives
American Gypsey: Six Native American Plays
American Indian Performing Arts: Critical Directions
American Indian Theater in Perfromance: A Reader
Celluloid Indians
Chairs
Cherokee Dance & Drama
Dance Unto Death
Dramatic Elements in American Indian Ceremonials
Indian Nation
Mahuts & Annwm Aval: 2 Full-Length Video Theatre Plays
Native Americans as Shown on the Stage, 1753-1916
New Native American Drama: Three Plays
A Pillar of Fire To Follow: American Indian Dramas, 1808-1859
The Powwow Highway
Seventh Generation: Anthology of Native American Plays
Stories of Our Way: An Anthology of American Indian Plays
Tecumseh! A Play
What's an Indian Woman To Do? and Other Plays

EARTH ASTROLOGY

The American Indian: Secrets of Crystal Healing
Cherokee Astrology: Animal Medicine in the Stars
Compass of the Heart: Embodying Medicine Wheel Teachings
Earth Medicine: Ancestor's Way's of Harmony for Many Moons
Medicine Wheel Ceremonies
Medicine Wheel: Earth Astrology
Star Ancestors: Extraterrestrial Contact in the Native American Tradition
Star Ancestors: Indian Wisdomkeepers Share the Teachings of the Extraterrestrials
Star Warrior: The Story of Swiftdeer
Stars of the First People
*Star Tales

CHARLES EASTMAN (OHIYESA)

Between Worlds: Interpreters, Guides, & Survivors
*Charles Eastman: Physician, Reformer, & Native American Leader
From the Deep Woods to Civilization: Chapters in the Autobiography of an Indian
*Indian Boyhood
*Indian Heroes & great Chieftains
Indian Scout Craft & Lore
Light on the Indian World: The Essential Writings of Ohiyesa
Ohiyesa: Charles Eastman, Santee Sioux
Old Indian Days
The Soul of an Indian; & Other Writings from Ohiyesa
The Soul of an Indian: An Interpretation
Wigwam Evenings: Sioux Tales Retold

ECONOMIC CONDITIONS

Aboriginal Economic Development Forum
Aboriginal Slavery on the Northwest Coast of North America
Alternatives to Social Assistance in Indian Communities
American Indian Ecology
American Indian Energy Resources and Development
American Indians & the Fight for Equal Voting Rights
American Indian Inventions
American Indian Policy: Self-Governance & Economic Development
An Apache Life-Way: The Economic, Social & Religious Institutions
  of the Chiricahua Indians
Before the Wilderness: Environmental Management by Native Californians
Beyond the Village: A Colonial Parkway Guide to the Local Indians' Use
  of Natural Resources
Breaking the Iron Bonds: Indian Control of Energy Development
Buffalo, Inc.: American Indians & Economic Development
The Caddo Chiefdoms: Caddo Economics & Politics, 1700-1835
The Campo Indian Landfill War: The Fight for Gold in California's Garbage
The Canadian Fur Trade in the Industrial Age
Challenges to Assessing & Improving Telecommunications For Native Americans
  on Tribal Lands
The Cherokee Strip Live Stock Association
The Cheyenne in Plains Indian Trade Relations, 1795-1840
Commerce By a Frozen Sea: Native Americans & the European Fur Trade
A Community Guide to Money
Contemporary Alaskan Native Economies
Culture, Change and Leadership in a Modern Indian Community:
  The Colorado River Indian Reservation
Corporate & Foundation Fundraising Manual for native Americans
Defending Mother Earth: Native American Perspectives on Environmental Justice
The Development of Capitalism in the Navajo Nation: Political-Economic History
Doing Business on Arizona Indian Lands
Ecocide of Native America: Environmental Destruction of Indian Lands & Peoples
Economic Development on American Indian Reservations
The Effect of European Contact & Trade on the Settlement Pattern
  of Indians in Coastal New York
Emergent Complexity: The Evolution of Intermediate Societies
The Encyclopedia of Native American Economic History
EPA's Indian Policy at 25
Federal Indian Tax Rules
Financial Aid for Native Americans
The Four Hills of Life
The Future of Indigenous Peoples: Strategies for Survival & Development
Gambling & Survival in Native North America
Housing Problems & Needs of American Indians & Alaska Natives
If You Poison Us: Uranium & Native Americans
The Impact of Occupational Dislocation: The American Indian
  Labor Force at the Close of the 20th Century
Income and Health in a North Indian Village
Indian Assistance Handbook: Market Segment Understanding
Indian Gaming & Tribal Sovereignty: The Casino Compromise
Indian Giving: Economies of Power in Early Indian-White Exchanges
Indian-Made: Navajo Culture in the Marketplace, 1868-1940
Indigenous Knowledge & Education
Invasion of Indian Country in the 20th Century
Kinship, Capitalism, Change: The Informal Economy of the Navajo, 1868-1995
Lakota Cutlure, World Economy
Making Native Space: Colonialism, Resistance & Reserves in British Columbia
Mining, the Environment, and Indigenous Development Conflicts
Modern Tribal Development: Paths to Self-Sufficiency & Cultural Integrity in Indian Country
A Nation Within a Nation
National Directory of Corporate Philanthropy for Native Americans
National Directory of Foundation Grants for native Americans
National Directory of Philanthropy for Native Americans
National Directory of Seed Money Grants for American Indian Projects
National Indian Gaming Association - Indian Gaming Resource Directory
National Indian Gaming Minimum Internal Control Standards for Indian Casinos
Native American Business Development, Trade Promotion & Tourism ACT of 1999
Native American Capital Formation & Economic Development ACT
Native Ameriacn Issues
Native Americans & Wage Labor
Navajo Energy Resources
Navajo Land, Navajo Culture: The Utah Experience in the 20th Century
Navajo Land Use: An Ethnoarchaeological Study
Navajo Resources & Economic Development
The New Politics of Indian Gaming
The New Resource Wars: Native and Environmental Struggles Against Multinational
Corporations

The Other Side of the Frontier: Economic Explorations Into Native American History
A People's Ecology: Explorations in Sustainable Living
*Peril at Thunder Ridge
Planning for Balanced Development: A Guide for Native American and Rural Communities
The Political Economy of North American Indians
Political Structure & Change in the Prehistoric Southeastern U.S.
Pressing Issues of Inequality & American Indian Communities
Property Concepts of the Navaho Indians
Property Rights & Indian Economies
The Re-Establishment of the Indians in Their Pueblo Life Through the Revival
  of Their Traditional Crafts: A Study in Home Extension Education
Rebuilding Native Nations: Strategies for Governance & Development
Red Capitalism: An Analysis of the Navajo Economy
Regulatory Activities of the National Indian Gaming Commission
Research in Human Capital & Development: American Indian Economic Development
Reservation "Capitalism": Economic Activity in Indian Country
Reservation Politics: Historical Trauma, Economic Development & Intratribal Conflict
Rich Indians: Native People & the Problem of Wealth in American History
The Roots of Dependency: Subsistence, Environment, & Social Change
  Among the Choctaws, Pawnees, & Navajos
The Roots of Oppression: The American Indian Question
Roots of Resistance: Land Tenure in New Mexico (1680-1980)
San Diego County Indians As Farmers and Wage Earners
Science & Native American Communities: Legacies of Pain, Visions of Promise
Sharing the Harvest on the Road to Self-Reliance:...
Soft Gold: A History of The Fur Trade in the Great Lakes
  Region & Its Impact of Native American Culture
The State of the Native Nations
Survival & Regeneration: Detroit's American Indian
  Community
Survival Skills of the North American Indians
Tending the Wild: Native American Knowledge & the Management
  of California's Natural Resources
The Texture of Contact
Their Natural Resources Fail: Native People & the Economic History of Northern Manitoba
Tiller's Guide to Indian Country: Economic Profiles of American Indian Reservations
Traditional Ecological Knowledge & Natural Resource Management
Tribal Contracting: Understanding & Drafting Business Contracts
  With American Indian Tribes
Tribal Energy Self-Sufficiency ACT & the Native American Energy Development
  & Self-Determination ACT
Trusteeship in Change: Toward Tribal Autonomy in Resource Management
Under Sacred Ground: A History of Navajo Oil
The Underground Reservation: Osage Oil
The Vocational Rehabilitation of American Indians Who Have Alcohol
  or Other Substance Abuse Disorders
Wampum and the Origins of American Money
What Can Tribes Do? Strategies & Institutions in American Indian Economic Development
When Indians Became Cowboys
The Wintu & Their Neighbors
Women in Prehistory: North America & Mesoamerica
Working In Indian Country: Building Successful Business Relationships
  With American Indian Tribes
Working the Navajo Way: Labor & Culture in the 20th Century
You Are On Indian Land: Alcatraz Island, 1969-1971

EDUCATION (STUDY & TEACHING)

*ABC's The American Indian Way
Administration in Navajo Reservation Schools
Alaska Native Political Leadership & Higher Education
America's Blacks & Tribal Colleges
America's Indians: Unit Study Outline
America's Second Tongue: American Indian Education & the Ownership
  of English, 1860-1910
The American Indian & Alaska Native Higher Education Funding Guide
American Indian & Alaskan Natives in Postsecondary Education
American Indian Education: A History
American Indian Higher Educational Experiences: Cultural Visions & Personal Journeys
American Indian Issues in Higher Education
The American Indian Mind in a Linear World
The American Indian Reader
The American Indian Reader: Education
American Indian Reference Books for Children
American Indian Stereotypes in the World of Children: A Reader and a Bibliography
Amerian Indian Studies: An Interdisciplinary Approach to Contemporary Issues
The American Indian: Yesterday, Today & Tomorrow
American Indians, the irish, & Government Schooling: A Comparative Study
Annals of Shawnee Methodist Mission & Indian Manual Labor
Anti-Indianism in Modern America: A Voice From Tatekeya's Earth
The Art of Americaniztion at the Carlisle Indian School
Away From Home: American Indian Boarding School Experiences, 1879-2000
Bacone Indian University
Battlefield & Classroom: Four Decades with the American Indian, 1867-1904
Boarding School Blues
Boarding School Seasons: American Indian Families, 1900-1940
Braiding Histories
A Broken Flute: The Native Experience in Books for Children
Capturing Education: Envisioning & Building the First Tribal Colleges
Changing the Faces of Mathematics
Children of the Dragonfly: Native American Voices on Child Custody & Education
Classroom Activities in Chippewa Treaty Rights
Classroom Activities on Wisconsin Indian Treaties & Tribal Sovereignty
Clearing a Path: Theoretical Approaches to the Past in Native American Studies

Young Child, Old Spirit: A Preschool Chemical Dependency Curriculum

ENVIRONMENT & ECOLOGY

Arboretum America: A Philosophy of the Forest
American Indian Ecology
The Animals Came Dancing: Native American Sacred Ecology & Animal Kinship
The Cherokee Excavations: Holocene Ecology & Human Adaptations in Northwestern Iowa
Cultivated Landscapes of Native North America
Ecology, Sociopolitical Organization & Cultural Change on the Southern Plains
EPA's Indian Policy at 25
Hollocene Human Ecology in Northeastern North America
Indians & Energy: Exploitation & Opportunity in the American Southwest
The Island Chumash: Behavioral Ecology of a Maritime Society
Keepers of the Central Fire: Issues in Ecology for Indigenous Peoples
*Native Defenders of the Environment
North American Indian Ecology
The River Is in Us: Fighting Toxics in a Mohawk Community
Roots of Our Renewal: Ethnobotany & Cherokee Environmental Governance
Trust in the Land: New Directions in Tribal Conservation
Wastelanding: Legacies of Uranium Mining in Navajo Country

RICHARD ERDOES

American Indian Myths & Legends
*American Indian Trickster Tales
Crow Dog: Four Generations of Sioux Medicine Men
Crying for a Dream: The World Through Native American Eyes
Lame Deer: Seeker of Visions: The Life of a Sioux Medicine Man
Native American Tales - Coyote
Ojibwa Warrior: Dennis Banks & the Rise of the American Indian Movement

LOUISE ERDRICH

American Indian Literature, Environmental Justice, & Ecocriticism
*The Birchbark House
The Chippewa Landscape of Louise Erdrich
Conversations With Louise Erdrich & Michael Doris
The Falcon: A Narrative of the Captivity & Adventures of John Tanner
*The Game of Silence
Meditation in Contemporary Native American Fiction
Reading Louise Erdrich's Love Medicine

ETHICS

American Indian Environmental Ethics: An Ojibwa Case Study
The Circle Without End: A Sourcebook of American Indian Ethics
I Have Come to Step Over Your Soul: A True Narrative of Murder & Indian Justice
Time Before Deception: Truth in Communication, Culture & Ethics

ETHNIC IDENTITY

Against Culture: Development, Politics & Religion in Indian Alaska
The Alabama-Coushatta Indians
All My Sins Are Relative
American Indian Cultural Heroes & Teaching Tales: Evenings with Chasing Deer
As We Are Now: Mixedblood Essays on Race & Identity
At the Risk of Being Heard: Identity, Indigenous Rights, and Postcolonial States
Blood Matters: The Five Civilized Tribes & the Search for Unity in the Early 20th Century
Blood Politics: Race, Culture, & Identity in the Cherokee Nation of Oklahoma
Blood Struggle: The Rise of Modern Indian Nations
The Caddos, the Wichitas, & the U.S., 1846-1901
Cartographies of Desire
Children of the Dragonfly
Columbus & Beyond: View From Native Amerians
Confronting Race
Contemporary Native American Cultural Issues
Cultural Politics & the Mass Media: Alaska Native Voices
D'Arcy McNickle's The Hungry Generations
Disrupting Savagism: Intersecting Chicano, Mexican Immigrant, & Native American
   Struggles for Self-Representation
Endangered Peoples of North America: Struggles to Survive & Thrive
The Enduring Seminoles
The First Americans: Race, Evolution & the Origin of Native Americans
From Mission to Metropolis: Cupeno Indian Women in Los Angeles
Growing Up Native in Alaska
Heart of the Rock: The Indian Invasion of Alcatraz
Media & Ethnic Identity: Hopi Views on Media, Identity, and Communication
How to Tell the Difference: A Guide to Evaluating Children's Books for Anti-Indian Bias
Huron-Wendat: The Heritage of the Circle
Identity, Feasting, & the Archaeology of the Greater Southwest
Immigraption of Dislocation: Economy
In Defense of Mohawk Land
Injun Joe's Ghost: The Indian Mixed-Blood in American Writing
'Injuns!' Native Americans in the Movies
Interpretations of Native North American Life Material Contributions to Ethnohistory
Issues in Native American Cultural Identity
Language, History, & Identity: Ethnolinguistic Studies of the Arizona Tewa
Lost Bird of Wounded Knee: Spirit of the Lakota
The Lumbee Problem
Mixed Blood Messages: Literature, Film, Family, Place
The Morning the Sun Went Down

National Identity & the Conflict at Oka
Native American Identities
Native American Perspectives on Literature & History
Native American Resurgence & Renewal: A Reader & Bibliography
Native Americans in the Carolina Borderlands: A Critical Ethnography
Native Americans in the Movies: Portrayals from Silent Films to the Present
Native Apparitions: Critical Perspectives on Hollywood's Indians
Native Peoples of the Southwest: Negotiating Land, Water, & Ethnicities
Native Voices: American Indian Identity & Resistance
Our Elders Lived It: American Indian Identity in the City
A Place to Be Navajo
Playing Indian
Present Is Past: Some Uses of Tradition in Native Societies
Pueblo Profiles: Cultural Identity Through Centuries of Change
The Qualla Cherokee Surviving in Two Worlds
Race Pride & the American Identity
Real Indians: Identity & the Survival of Native America
Remix: new Modernities in a Post-Indian World
Reservation X: The Power of Place in Aboriginal Contemporary Art
Riding Buffalos & Broncos: Rodeo & Native Traditions in the Northern Great Plains
Ritual & Myth in Odawa Revitalization: Reclaiming a Sovereign Place
Sacred Objects & Sacred Places: Preserving Tribal Traditions
Savages & Civilization: Who Will Survive?
Science & Native American Communities: Legacies of Pain, Visions of Promise
Strong Hearts: Native American Visions & Voices
Teaching American Indian Students
Teaching the Native American, 4th Ed.
Termination Revisited: American Indians on the Trail to Self-Determination
Unlearning the Language of Conquest: Scholars Expose Anti-Indianism in America
War Under Heaven: Pontiac, the Indian Nations, & the British Empire
Wiping the War Paint Off the Lens: Native American Film & Video
World War II & the American Indian

ETHNOBOTANY

At the Desert's Green Edge: An Ethnobotany of the Gila River Pima
By the Prophet of the Earth: Ethnobotany of the Pima
Chumash Ethnobotany: Plant Knowledge Among the Chumash People of Southern Calif.
Ethnobotany of the Coahuilla Indians of Southern California
Ethnobotany of the Gitksan Indians of British Columbia
Ethnobotany of the Hopi
Ethnobotany of the Menomini Indians
Ethnobotany of Western Washington: The Knowledge & Use of Indigenous Plants
   by Native Americans
Gathering Moss: A Natural & Cultural History of Mosses
Hunting by Prehistoric Horticulturists in the American Southwest
Keeping It Living: Traditions of Plant Use & Cultivation on the Northwest Coast
   of North America
Native American Ethnobotany
People of the Desert & Sea: Ethnobotany of the Seri Indians
Wildflowers of Iowa Woodlands

WILLIAM FENTON

The False Faces of the Iroquois
William Fenton: Selected Writings
The Great Law & the Longhouse: A Political History of the Iroquois Confederacy
History of the Iroquois Confederacy
Interdisciplinary Guide to the Treaties of the Six Nations & Their League
The Iroquois Eagle Dance
Iroquois Journey: An Anthropologist Remembers
The Little Water Medicine Society of the Senecas
An Outline of Seneca Ceremonies at Coldspring Longhouse
Parker on the Iroquois
Symposium on Local Diversity in Iroquois Culture
These Are the People: Thoughts in Poetry & prose

FICTION

All My Relations: An Anthology of Contemporary Canadian Native Fiction
Almanac of the Dead
Alone in the Wilderness
The American Indian in Short Fiction: An Annotated Bibliography
American Indian Life
Ancestral Voice
Apache Autumn
Bearheart: The Heirship Chronicles
The Bingo Palace
Bone Game: A Novel
The Book of One Tree
Bone Game
Butterfly Lost
Ceremony
Chancers: A Novel
Cherokee Dragon: A Novel
Cogewea, The Half-Blood
Comanche Warbonnet
Critical Fictions: The Politics of Imaginative Writings
Danny Blackgoat: Dangerous Passage
Daring Donald McKay: Or, The Last War Trial of the Modocs
Dawn Land
The Death of Bernadette Lefthand
The Death of Jim Lonely

Deception on All Accounts
Designs of the Night Sky
Drowning in Fire
Earth Power Coming: Short Fiction in Native American Literature
Elnguq
Elsie's Business
Faces in the Moon
Fathers & Crows
Field of Honor
Firesticks: A Collection of Stories
Fools Crow
Four Masterworks of American Indian Literature
The Fus Fixico Letters
A Good Indian
Hiroshima Bugi: Atomu 57
House Made of Dawn
The Indian Lawyer
Ishi Means Man
Laughing Boy
The Light People: A Novel
The Lightning Within
Long River
The Lost Band: A Novel
Man Who Killed the Deer
The Map of Who W Are: A Novel
Medicine Hat: A Novel
Medicine River
Mountain Windsong: A Novel of the Trail of Tears
The Native American in Long Fiction
Nightland" A Novel
One Indian and Two Chiefs
Oracles: A Novel
The Pipestone Quest: A Novel
The Portable North American Indian Reader
The Powwow Highay
The Punishment of the Stingy
Ramona
The Red Bird All-Indian Traveling Band
The Sacred White Turkey
Sage Dreams, Eagle Vision
The Sharpest Sight: A Novel
Smith & Other Events: Tales of the Chilcotin
A Story of Deep Delight
Strange Business
The Trickster in the Front Yard: Still Semi-Native
The Trickster of Liberty
Turtle Belly: A Novel
War Woman: A Novel
Waterlily
Winter in the Blood
Winter of the Holy Iron
The Wolf and the Buffalo
Wolfsong: A Novel
A Woman of the People
Woodsmen, or Thoreau & the Indians: A Novel
Woven Stone
Charlie Young Bear

FIRST CONTACT WITH EUROPEANS

The Ambiguous Iroquois Empire
American Encounters: Natives & Newcomers from European Contact
  to Indian Removal, 1500-1850
American Indian History: Conquest of a Continent, 1492-1783
Aristocratic Encounters: European Travelers & North American Indians
Colonial Encounters in a Native American Landscape: The Spanish &
  Dutch in North America
Colonial Writing & the New World, 1583-1671: Allegories of Desire
Conquistador in Chains: Cabeza de Vaca & the Indians of the Americas
Cultural Encounters in the Early South: Indians & Europeans in Arkansas
Hernando de Soto & the Indians of Florida
Deadly Medicine: Indians & Alcohol in Early America
Deadly Politics of Giving: Exchange & Violence at Ajacan, Roanoke, and Jamestown
Earliest Hispanic - Native American Interaction in the American Southeast
Early Spanish, French, & English Encounters with the American Indians
The Effect of European Contact & Trade On the Settlement Pattern of Indians
  in Coastal New York, 1524-1665
Enduring Conquests: Rethinking the Archaeology of Resistance to
  Spanish Colonialism in the Americas
The European Challenge
*Europeans & Native Americans
Explorers of the New World
Facing East from Indian Country: A Native History of Early America
First Peoples, First Contacts: Native Peoples of North America
Great Cruelties Have Been Reported
Hunting for Hides: Deerskins, Status, and Cultural Change in the Prohistoric Appalachian
Indian & European Contact in Context: The Mid-Atlantic Region
Indian Giving: Economies of Power in Early Indian-White Exchanges
Indian Women & French Men: Rethinking Cultural Encounter in the Western Great Lakes
Indians of Central & South Florida, 1513-1763
The Invention of the Creek Nation, 1670-1763
La Harpe's Post: A Tale of French-Wichita Contact on the Eastern Plains
Love & Hate in Jamestown: John Smith, Pocahontas, & the Heart of a New Nation
Myth & Memory: Stories of Indigenous-European Contact

Natives & Newcomers: The Cultural Origins of North America
New Worlds of Violence: Cultures & Conquests in the Early American Southeast
The Ordeal of the Longhouse: The Peoples of the Iroquois League
  in the Era of European Colonization
Paths of Our Children: Historic Indians of Arkansas
Pocahontas: The Life & the Legend
Pueblos, Presidios & Missions
Societies in Eclipse: Archaeology of the Eastern Woodlands Indians, A.D. 1400-1700
Spain in the Southwest
Stone Tool Traditions in the Contact Era
A Strange Likeness: Becoming Red & White in 18th Century North America
The Texture of Contact: European & Indian Settler Communities on the Frontiers
  of Iroquoia, 1667-1783
Warpaths: Invasions of North America, 1513-1765

FIVE CIVILIZED TRIBES

The American Indian Treaty Series
Are You In There Grandpar? Beginning Black Indian Beginning Black Indian
  History & Genealogy - The Cherokees
Beginning Black Indian History & Genealogy - The Seminoles
Blood Matters: The Five Civilized Tribes & the Search for Unity in the Early 20th Century
Buckskin Hollow Reflections
Cherokees, An Illustrated History
The Chickasaws
The Darkest Tears on the Trails - To Grandma's House
The Dawes Commission & the Allotment of the Five Civilized Tribes, 1893-1914
Five Civilized Tribes
The Five Civilized Tribes: A Bibliography
*14 Flags Over Oklahoma
Fort Gibson History
Fort Gibson: Terminal on the Trail of Tears
Indian Removal: The Emigration of Five Civilized Tribes of Indians
*Indians of Oklahoma
Muskogee City & County
Nations Remembered: An Oral History of the Five Civilized Tribes, 1865-1907
Notices of East Florida; With An Account of the Seminole Nation of Indians
Pow Wow Chow
Reconstruction in Indian Territory
The Southern Indians: The Story of the Civilized Tribes Before Removal
Stories From Old-Time Oklahoma
Tracing Ancestors Among the Five Civilized Tribes
*West of Yesterday

FOOD-COOKING

Alaskan Native Food Practices, Customs & Holidays
American Indian Cooking
American Indian Cooking & Herblore
*American Indian Foods
The Art of American Indian Cooking
Artistic Tastes: Favorite Recipes of Native American Artists
The Buckskinner's Cookbook
Cherokee Cooklore
Cherokee Plants
Choctaw-Apache Foodways
Cooking With Spirit
Corn Recipes from the Indians
Eating the Landscape: American Indian Stories of Food, Identity & Resilience
*Earthmaker's Lodge
Enduring Harvests: Native American Foods & Festivals for Every Season
Ethno-Botany of the Gosiute Indians of Utah
Famous Florida! Seminole Indian Recipes
Food in California Indian Culture
Food Plants of Coastal First Peoples
Food Plants of Interior First Peoples
Food Plants of the Sonoran Desert
Food Products of the North American Indians
Foods of the Americas: Native Recipes & Tradiitions
From Fingers to Finger Bowls
Going Native: American Indian Cookery
R.C. Gorman's Nudes & Foods
Guide to Indian Herbs
Handbook of Native American Herbs
Heard in the Kitchen: The Heard Museum Guild Cookbook
Hopi Cookery
How Indians Use Wild Plants for Food, Medicine & Crafts
Identity, Feasting, & the Archaeology of the Greater Southwest
Idonapshe, Let's Eat: Traditional Zuni Foods
Ilimpa'chi' (Let's Eat): A Chickasaw Cookbook
Indian Cooking
Indian Corn of the Americas, Gift to the World
Indian Recipe Book
Indian Foods and Fibers of Arid America
Indian Uses of Native Plants
Insects As Food: Aboriginal Entomophgy in the Great Basin
Kokopelli's Cookbook
Malki Museum's Native Food Tasting Experiences
Mechanisms & Trends in the Decline of the Costanoan Indian Population of Central
  California: Nutrition & Health in Pre-Contact California & Mission Period Environments
The Minnesota Ethnic Food Book
Mitsitam Café Cookbook: Recipes from the Smithsonian's National Mueum
  of the American Indian

*Native American Cooking
*Native American Foods
Native American Gardening
Native Harvests: Recipes & Botanicals of the American Indian
Native Indian Wild Game, Fish & Wild Foods Cookbook
Native Wild Game: Fish & Wild Foods Cookbook
Navajo Food Practices, Customs & Holidays
Plants That We Eat
Pow Wow Chow
Pueblo Indian Cookbook
Recovering Our Ancestor's Gardens: Indigenous Recipes & Guide to Diet & Fitness
Seaweed, Salmon, and Manzanita Cider: A California Indian Feast
Southwest Cooks! The Tradition of Native American Cuisines
Southwest Indian Cookbook
Southwestern Indian Recipe Book
Spirit of the Harvest: North American Indian Cooking
Stalking the Wild Agave: A Food & Fiber Tradition
Tepee Cookery
Traditional Plant Foods of Canadian Indigenous Peoples
A Woodland Feast

FRENCH & INDIAN WAR, 1753-1763

America's First First World War: The French & Indian War, 1754-1763
*The American Revolutionaries: A History in Their Own Words
George Croghan & the Westward Movement 1741-1782
Diplomacy & the Indian Gifts: The French-English Rivalry for Indian Loyalties
   During the French & Indian War Years 1748-1763
Empire & Liberty: American Resistance to British Authority, 1755-1763
Empire of Fortune: Crowns, Colonies, & Tribes in the Seven Years War in America
*Fawn
*The Fight for Freedom, 1750-1783
French & Indian War
The French & Indian War 1754-1760
French & Indian War Battlesites: A Controversy
The French & Indian War and the Conquest of New France
The French & Indian War in Pennsylvania, 1753-1763
Highlander in the French & Indian War
An Historical Journal of the Campaigns in North America for the Years 1757-1760
History of an Expedition Against Fort DuQuesne in 1755 Vol. 9:
   An Account of Braddock Campaign in 1755
The History of the Indian Wars in New England
The History of Philip's War
*The Indian Wars
Jeferson's America: 1760-1815
The Last French & Indian War
*The Last of the Mohicans
Logs of the Conquest of Canada
Major General Adam Stephen & the Cause of American Liberty
Manuscript Records of the French & Indian War
Massachusetts Officers & Soldiers in the French & Indian Wars, 1755-56
Massacre at Fort Bull: The Delery Expedition Against Oneida Carry, 1756
Memoirs of Lt. Henry Timberlake
Michilimackinac: A Tale of the Straits
Mid-Appalachian Frontier: A Guide to Historic Sites of the French & Indian War
Military Affairs in North America, 1748-1765
Military Journals of Two Private Soldiers, 1758-1775
Montcalm and Wolfe
Narrative of the Captivity of Mrs Johnson
New England Captives Carried to Canada
The Ohio Company of Virginia & the Westward Movement, 1748-1792
Ohio Valley in Colonial Days
A People's Army: Massachusetts Soldiers & Society in the Seven Years War
Pioneers of New France in New England
Rangers & Redcoats on the Hudson
Sketchbook '56 The French & Indian War 1756-1763
Shipping and the American War, 1755-1783: A Study of British Transport Organization
Slim Buttes, 1876: An Episode of the Great Sioux War
*Struggle for a Continent: The French & Indian Wars, 1690-1760
William Trent & the West
True Stories of New England Captives Carried to Canada During
   the Old French & Indian Wars
Wilderness Empire
Wilderness Politics and Indian Gifts: The Northern Colonial Frontier, 1748-1763

GAMES/SPORTS

*American Indian Games
American Indian LaCrosse
American Indian Sports Heritage
Anetso, the Cherokee Ball Game: At the Center of Ceremony & Identity
*Chumash Indian Games
Contesting Constructed Indian-ness: The Intersection of theFrontier, Masculinity,
   and Whiteness in Native American Mascot Representations
Creator's Game: Lacrosse, Identity, and Indigenous Nationhood
Exploring the Outdoors With Indian Secrets
Full-Court Quest: The Girls from Fort Shaw Indian School Basketball Champions
   of the World
Games of the North American Indians
Grass Games & Moon Races: California Indian Games & Toys
Handbook of American Indian Games
*Indian Games & Crafts
Indian Games & Dances With Native Songs
Indian Games: North American Indian Sports

The Native American Identity in Sports: Creating & Preserving a Culture
*Native American Sports & Games
Native Ameriacns in Sports
*Native Athletes In Action!
The Pawnee Ghost Dance Hand Game
*Sports & Games the Indians Gave Us
To Show What an Indian Can Do: Sports at Native American Boarding Schools
Twana Games

GAMING

The Bingo Palace
Code of Federal Regulations, Title 25: Indians
First Nations Tribal Directory
Gambler Way: Indian Gaming in Mythology, History & Archaeology in North America
Gambling & Survival in Native North America
General Requirements & Parameters for Vendor Licensing
Governing Gaming
Implementation of the Indian Gaming Regulatory Act
Indian Gaming: Following a New Path
The Indian Gaming Handbook
Indian Gaming & the Law
Indian Gaming: Tribal Sovereignty & American Politics
Indian Gaming & Tribal Sovereignty: The Casino Compromise
Indian Gaming: Who Wins?
National Indian Gaming Association-NIGA Indian Gaming Resource Directory
National Indian Gaming Minimum Internal Control Standards for Indian Casinos
The Navajo Political Experience
New Capitalists: Issues of Law, Politics & Identity Surrounding Casino Gaming
   on Native American Land
Regulatory Activities of the National Indian Gaming Commission
Return of the Buffalo: The Story Behind America's Indian Gaming Explosion
State-Tribal Relationships-Reports
States & the Indian Gaming Regulation Act
The Supreme Court & Tribal Gaming: California v. Cabazon Band of Mission Indians
Tax Policy: A Profile of the Indian Gaming Industry
Tourism & Gaming on American Indian Lands

GENEALOGY

American Indian Marriage Record Directory for Ashland Co., Wisc.
Are You In There Grandpar? Beginning Black Indian Genealogy:
   A Look At Those Other Cousins
Beginning Black Indian History & Genealogy - The Cherokees
Beginning Black Indian History & Genealogy - The Seminoles
Black Elk Lives: Conversations with the Black Elk Family
Black Indian Genealogy Research
Catawba Indian Genealogy
Census of the Blackfeet, Montana, 1897-1898
Cherokee By Blood: Records of Eastern Cherokee Ancestry in the
   U.S. Court of Claims, 1906-1910
Cherokee Connections
Cherokee Proud: A Guide to Tracing & Honoring Your Cherokee Ancestors
Cherokee Connections
Cherokee Roots
Choctaw & Chickasaw Early Census Records
Choctaw Claimants & Their Heirs
Complete Delaware Roll 1898
The Darkest Tears on the Trails - To Grandma's House
Descendants of Nancy Ward: A Workbook for Further Research
Earnest Genealogy: Indian Eve & Her Descendants, an Indian Story of Bedford Co.
Eastern Cherokee By Blood, 1906-1910, 2 Vols.
Eastern Cherokee Census
The 1890 Cherokee Nation Census, Indian Territory
Final Rolls of Citizens & Freedmen of the Five Civilized Tribes in Indian Territory
   & Index to Final Rolls
Finding Your Native American Roots
Flandreau Papers Treasures Trove for Mixed Blood Dakota Indian Genealogy
Fourth Corrections & Additions to Pocahontas' Descendents
How to Research American Indian Blood Lines
Index to the Cherokee Freedmen Enrollment Cards of the Dawes Commission
Indian Wills, 1911-1921
Indians from New York in Wisconsin & Elsewhere: A Genealogy Reference
Native American Ancestors: Eastern Tribes
Native American Directory: Vital Records of ME, MA, RI, CT, NY & WI
Native American Genealogical Sourcebook
Native American Records
Ojibwa Chiefs, 1690-1890: An Annotated Listing
Osage Indian Bands & Clans
Pocahontas' Descendants
South Carolina Indians, Indian Traders & Other Ethnic Connections: Beginning in 1670
Tracing Ancestors Among the Five Civilized Tribes
Turtles, Wolves & Bears: A Mohawk Family History
Unhallowed Intrusions, a History of Cherokee Families in Forsyth Co., GA
The Wampanoag Genealogical History of Martha's Vineyard, Massachusetts
Warrior In the Ring: The Life of Marvin Camel, Native American World Champion Boxer
We Are Not Yet Conquered: History of Northern Cherokee Nation
Who's Looking for Whom in Native American Ancestry

GERONIMO

Bloody Trail of Geronimo
The Day Geronimo Surrendered

GHOST DANCE

GOVERNMENT RELATIONS

Termination Revisited
Termination's Legacy: The Discarded Indians of Utah
Theodore Roosevelt & Six Friends of the Indian
They Have No Rights
The Third Space of Sovereignty
The Timucuan Chiefdoms of Spanish Florida
To Fish in Common
To Have This Land: The Nature of Indian/White Relations in South Dakota, 1888-1891
To Preserve a Culture: The 20th Century Fight Over Indian Reorganization
To Show Heart: Native American Self-Determination and Federal Indian Policy, 1960-1975
Tonto's Revenge
The Trail of Tears
The Treatment of the Indians by the Colonists
Tribal Assets: The Rebirth of Native America
Tribal Government: The Wind River Reservation
The Tribal Moment in American Politics: The Struggle for Native American Sovereignty
*Tribal Sovereignty: Indian Tribes
The Tribes & the States: Geographies of Intergovernmental Interaction
The True Spirit & original Intent of Treaty 7
Two Worlds: The Indian Encounter with the European, 1492-1509
Uncle Sam's Stepchildren: The Reformation of U.S. Indian Policy, 1865-1887
Understanding Tolowa Histories
Unearthing Indian Land: Living With the Legacies of Allotment
Unsettling America: The Uses of Indianess in the 21st Century
The View from Officers' Row: Army Perceptions of Western Indians
Voices From the Trail of Tears
Voices from Wounded Knee, 1973, In the Words of the Participants
Walking in Indian Moccasins
The Walleye War
Walleye Warriors
Wampum Belts of the Iroquois
Wampum Belts & Peace Trees
Wampum and the Origins of American Money
We Were Not the Savages
The Weiser Indians: Shoshoni Peacemakers
Western American Indian: Case Studies in Tribal History
The Western Military Frontier, 1815-1846
The Western Odyssey of John Simpson Smith: Frontiersman & Indian Interpreter
A Whirlwind Passes
The White Man's Gonna Getcha: The Colonial Challenge to the Crees in Quebec
Who Was Who in Native American History
Why Don't They Give Them Guns? The Great American Indian Myth
Wilderness Politics & Indian Gifts: The Northern Colonial Frontier, 1748-1763
The Wind Won't Know Me: History of the Navajo-Hopi Land Dispute
Wounded Knee II
Writing Indian Nations
Yellow Dirt: An American Story of a Poisoned Land and a People Betrayed

HAIDA INDIANS

Against Culture
Alaska Native Language Center Publications
Alaska Native Languages
Alaska's Southern Panhandle
Being in Being
Chief of the Sea & Sky: Haida Heritage Sites of the Queem Charlotte Islands
During My Time: Florence Edenshaw Davidson, A Haida Woman
Gyaehlingaay: Traditions, Tales, & Images of the Kaigani Haida
Haa Aani, Our Land: Tlingit & Haida Land Rights & Use
Haida Art
Haida Gwaii
Haida Monumental Art
Haida: The Queen Charlotte Island Indians
Haida Songs & Tsimshian Texts
Haida Syntax
Haida Texts & Myths
Haida: Their Art & Culture
Heraldic Pole Carvers: 19th Century Northern Haida Artists
*Heroes & Heroines in Tlingit-Haida Legends
Indian, Eskimo & Aleut Basketry of Alaska
Indians of the North Pacific Coast
Indians of the Northwest Coast
*Indians of the Pacific Northwest
Indians of the Pacific Northwest: A History
*Myths & Legends of the Haidas Indians of the Northwest
Nine Visits to the Mythworld: Ghandl of the Qayahl Llaanas
Ninstincts: Haida World Heritage Site
Northern Haida Master Carvers
Northern Haida Songs
Raven's Cry
The Raven Steals the Light: Drawings by Bill Reid
Raven Travelling: Two Centuries of Haida Art
Raven's Village
Bill Reid & Beyond: Expanding on Modern Native Art
Spirit of Haida Gwaii: Bill Reid's Masterpiece
Spruce Root Basketry of the Haida & Tlingit
A Story As Sharp As a Knife: The Classical Haida Mythtellers & Their World

HAVASUPAI INDIANS

Havasupai Habitat
Havasupai Legends: Religion & Mythology of the Indians of the Grand Canyon
Havasupai Years
Havsuw Baaja: People of Blue Green Water

I Am the Grand Canyon: The Story of the Havasupai People
Indian Basketmakers of the Southwest
People of the Blue Water
The Sacred Oral Tradition of the Havasupai: As Retold By Elders & Headmen
  Manakaja & Sinyella, 1918-1921
Wauba Yuma's People
The Wilderness of the Southwest

HEALTH (MENTAL HEALTH)

Aboriginal Health in Canada: Historical, Cultural, & Epidemiological Perspectives
AIDS Regional Directory: Resources in Indian Country
Alcohol Problems in Native America
American Indian & Alaska Native Health
American Indian Family Support Systems
American Indian Medicine
American Indian Task Force Report on the Year 2000
Bibliography of North American Indian Mental Health
Changing Numbers, Changing Needs: American Indian Demography & Public Health
Community Health & Mental Health Care Delivery for North American Indians
Counseling American Indians
Coyote's Council Fire
Crow Indian Medicine Bundles
Death Stalks the Yakama
Diabetes Epidemic Hearing Before the Committee on Indian Affairs
Diabetes in Native Americans: The Eastern Tribes
Diagnosis & Treatment of Prevalent Diseases of North American Indian Populations, I & II
Disciplined Hearts: History, Identity & Depression in an American Indian Community
Disease & Demography in the Americas
Doctors of Medicine in New Mexico: A History of Health & Medical Practice, 1886-1986
Drinking Careers: A 25-Year Study of Three Navajo Populations
Early Intervention with American Indian Families: An Annotated Bibliography
Empty Beds: Student Health at Sherman Institute
Encyclopedia of Native American Healing
Federal Personnel: Public Health Service
Firewater
Folk Medicine of the Delaware and Related Algonkian Indians
Gathering of Wisdoms: Tribal Mental Health - A Cultural Perspective
Geraniums for the Iroquois: A Field Guide to American Indian Medicinal Plants
The Growing Path
Guide to Indian Herbs
Healing Herbs of the Upper Rio Grand: Traditional Medicine of the Southwest
Healing & Mental Health for Native Americans: Speaking in Red
Healing Traditions: The Mental Health of Aboriginal Peoples in Canada
Healing Ways: Navajo Health Care in the Twentieth Century
Health & the American Indian
Health & Diseases of American Indians North of Mexico: A Bibliography, 1800-1969
The Health of Native Americans Towards a Biocultural Epidemiology
Health of Native People of North America: A Bibliography & Guide to Resources,
  1970 to 1994
HIV Prevention in Native American Communities: A Manual
If You Knew the Conditions: A Chronicle of the Indian Medical Service
  and American Indian Health Care, 1908-1955
Income & Health in a North Indian Village
Indian Healing: Shamanic Ceremonialism in the pacific Northwest Today
Indian Health Service: Improvements Needed in Credentialing Temporary Physicians
Indian Medicine Power
The Journey of Native American People With Serious Mental Illness:
  First National Conference
Keepers of the Central Fire: Issues in Ecology for Indigenous Peoples
Killing Us Quietly: Native Americans & HIV/AIDS
Lakota Belief and Ritual
A Long Way from Home: Tuberculosis Epidemic Among the Inuit
Managed Care in American Indian & Alaska Native Communities
Mashkiki: Old Medicine Nourishing the New
Medicinal Uses of Plants by Indian Tribes of Nevada
Medicine That Walks: Medicine, Disease & Canadian Plains Aboriginal People, 1880-1945
Native American AIDS Statistics
Navajo Dictionary on Diagnostic Terminology
Navajo Medicine Man Sand Paintings
The Path to Healing: Report of the National Round Table on Aboriginal
  Health & Social Issues
A Persistent Spirit: Towards Understanding Aboriginal Health in British Columbia
Perspectives on Health Care Delivery Systems for American Indian Families
The Pima Indians: Pathfinders for Health
Piman Shamanism and Staying Sickness: Ka: Cim Mumkidag
Plagues, Politics, and Policy: A Chronicle of the Indian Health Service, 1955-2008
Pretty-Shield, Medicine Woman of the Crows
Primary Care of Native American Patients
Profiles in Wisdom: Native Elders Speak About the Earth
Promising Practices & Strategies to Reduce Alcohol & Substance Abuse
  Among American Indians & Alaska Natives
Rationalizing Epidemics: Meanings & Uses of American Indian Mortality Since 1600
Restoring Balance: Community-Directed Health Promotion for American Indians
  & Native Alaskans
Revenge of the Windigo: The Construction of the Mind & Mental Health
  of North American Aboriginal Peoples
Rolling Thunder: A Personal Exploration Into the Secret Healing Power
  of an American Indian Medicine Man
Sanapia: Comanche Medicine Woman
The Shaman & the Medicine Wheel
Smallpox and the Iroquois Wars
A Study of Delaware Indian Medicine Practice & Folk Beliefs
Survival Skills of the North American Indians

Taking Medicine: Women's Healing Work & Colonial Contact In Southern Alberta, 1880-1930
Their Secrets: Why Navajo Indians Never Get Cancer
To Live to See the Great Day That Dawns: Preventing Suicide by American Indians & Alaska Native Youth & Young Adults
Tobacco Use by Native North Americans: Sacred Smoke & Silent Killer
Under the Rattlesnake: Cherokee Health & Resiliency
Vectors of Death: The Archaeology of European Contact
The Vocational Rehabilitation of American Indians Who Have Alcohol or Other Substance Abuse Disorders
White Man's Medicine: Government Doctors & The Navajo, 1863-1955

HISTORY

The A to Z of Early North America
The A to Z of Native American Movements
An Account of the History, Manners & Customs of the Indian Nations Who Once Inhabited Pennsylvania & the Neighboring States 1819
Acoma: Pueblo in the Sky
Across a Great Divide: Continuity & Change in Native North American Societies, 1400-1900
Adventures on the Western Frontier
Africans & Creeks
Africans & Indians
Africans & Native Americans: The Language of Race & the Evolution of Red-Black Peoples
Africans & Seminoles
After King Philip's War: Presence & Persistence in Indian New England
After Removal: The Choctaw in Mississippi
All Roads Are Good: Native Voices on Life & Culture
Alpine Centinels: A Chronicle of the Sheep Ester Indians
Also Called Sacajawea: Chief Woman's Stolen Identity
Always A People: Oral Histories of Contemporary Woodland Indians
America A.D. 1000: The Land & the Legends
America Before the European Invasions
America Firsthand & Pueblo
America On Paper, The First Hundred Years
America's Fascinating Indian Heritage
American Beginnings
*American Bison
The American Buffalo in Transition
American Carnage: Wounded Knee, 1890
American Colonial History: Clashing Cultures & Faith
The American Discovery of Europe
American Encounters
American Encounters: Natives & Newcomers from European Contact to Indian Removal, 1500-1850
The American Indian
American Indian Education: A History
The American Indian As Slaveholder & Successionist
The American Indian & the End of the Confederacy, 1863-1866
*The American Indian Experience
American Indian History
American Indian History: Conquest of a Continent, 1492-1783
American Indian History Day by Day
American Indian Holocaust & Survival
The American Indian in the Civil War, 1862-1865
American Indian Mafia: An FBI Agent's True Story About Wounded Knee, Leonard Peliter, and the American Indian Movement (AIM)
American Indian: Past & Present
American Indian Policy
American Indian Policy in the 20th Century
American Indian Population Recovery in the 20th Century
American Indian Quotations
American Indian Reader
American Indian Resource Materials in the Western History Collection
American Indian Studies
American Indian Treaties: The History of a Political Anomaly
American Indian & the U.S.
American Indian Warrior Chiefs
The American Indian Wars
The American Indian: Yesterday, Today & Tomorrow
American Indians
*The American Indians
*The American Indians in America--Volume II: The Late 18th Century to the Present
American Indians in American History, 1870-2001: A Companion Reader
American Indians/American Presidents
The American Indian and the Problem of History
American Indians & State Law: Sovereignty, Race & Citizenship, 1790-1880
American Indiann and the Study of U.S. History
American Indians in U.S. History
American Indians & World War II
American Indians in World War I
The American Military Frontiers: The U.S. Army in the West, 1783-1900
American Nations: Encounters in Indian Country, 1850 to the Present
The American Revolution in Indian Country
The American West
Among the Apaches
Ancient American Inscriptions: Plowmarks or History?
Ancient Peoples of the American Southwest
Annals of the Susquehannocks & Other Indian Tribes of Pennsylvania
The Appalachian Indian Frontier
Appalachian Mountain AniYunwiya
Arizona: A History
Art for an Undivided Earth: The American Indian Movement Generation

As If the Land Owned Us: The Ethnohistory of the White Mesa Utes
As Long As the Grass Shall Grow and the Rivers Flow: A History of Native Americans
At the Crossroads: Indians & Empires on a Mid-Atlantic Frontier, 1700-1763
Atlas of American Indian Affairs
Atlas of Great Lakes Indian History
Atlas of Indians of North America
Attitudes of Colonial Powers Toward the American Indian
Avenging the People: Andrew Jackson, the Rule of Law, and the American Nation
Bacavi: A Hopi Village
The Backbone of History
Bad Men & Bad Towns
Battle for the BIA
Battlefield & Classroom: Four Decades With the American Indian, 1867-1904
Battles & Skirmishes of the Great Sioux War, 1876-1877: The Military View
Bayonets in the Wilderness: Anthony Wayne's Legion in the Old Northwest
Bear Chief's War Shirt
John Beargrease: Legend of Minnesota's North Shore
Beauty, Honor & Tradition: The Legacy of Plains Indian Shirts
John Beeson's Plea for the Indians
*Before Columbus
*Before Columbus: The Americas of 1491
Before the Storm: American Indians Before Columbus
Betraying the Omaha Nation, 1790-1916
Beyond the Covenant Chain
Beyond the Hundredth Meridian
The Birth of America
Bitter Feast: Amerindians & Europeans in Northeastern North America, 1600-1664
Bitterness Road: The Mojave, 1604-1860
Black, Brown & Red
Black, Red and Deadly: Black and Indian Gunfighters of the Indian Territories
Black, White, and Indiian
Blackfeet Indian Stories
The Blackfoot Moonshine Rebellion of 1881: The Indian War That Never Was
Blood At Sand Creek: The Massacre Revisited
Blood of the Land: The Government and Corporate War Against the American Indian Movement
Franz Boas: The Early Years, 1858-1906
Both Sides of the Billpen: Navajo Trade & Posts
Bound for Santa Fe: The Road to New Mexico & the American Conquest, 1806-1848
Brave Winds: Native American Experiences
Bread & Freedom
Brief History of King Philip's War
Brief History of the Quapaw Tribe of Indians
A Brief History of the Seneca-Cayuga Tribe
Broken Landscape: Indians, Indian Tribes, and the Constitution
The Broken Ring: The Destruction of the California Indians
The Brothertown Nation of Indians: Land Ownership & Nationalism in Early America, 1740-1840
Buffalo Hearts
Buried Roots & Indestructible Seeds
Bulwark of the Republic: The American Militia in Antebellum West
Bury My Heart at Wounded Knee: An Indian History of the American West
The Caddo Indians: Where We Came From
Call for Change: The Medicine Way of American Indiann History, Ethos, and Reality
Cambridge History of the Native Poeples of the Americas
Captive Histories: English, French, and Native Narratives of the 1704 Deerfield Raid
Captors & Captives: The 1704 French & Indian Raid on Deerefield
Cartographies of Desire
The Catholic Calumet: Colonial Conversions in French & Indian North America
Celebrate Native America! An Aztec Book of Days
Chainbreaker: The Revolutionary War Memoirs of Governor Blacksnake
Challenge: The South Dakota Story
The Changing Nature of Racial & Ethnic Conflict in U.S. History: 1492 to the Present
Cherokee Americans Eastern Band of Cherokees in the 20th Century
Cherokee Chronicles: From First Contact to the Trail of Tears
The Cherokee Freedmen: From Emancipation to American Citizenship
The Cherokee Indian Nation: A Troubled History
The Cherokee People
The Cherokee Removal
Cherokee Removal: The William Penn Essays and Other Writings by Jeremiah Evarts
Cheyenne Dog Soldiers: A Ledgerbook History of Coups & Combat
The Chicago American Indian Community, 1893-1988
Chiefs & Challengers
Chinigchinich
The Chippewa and Their Neighbors: A Study in Ethnohistory
The Choctaw Academy: Official Correspondence, 1825-1841
Choctaw Genesis, 1500-1700
Christian Harvest
Chronology of the American Indian
Chronology of American Indian History
Chronology of Native North American History From Pre-Columbian Times to the Present
Colonial Genocide in Indigenous North America
Colonial Intimacies: Indian Marriage in Early New England
The Color of the Land: Race, Nation, and the Politics of Landownership in Oklahoma, 1832-1929
The Columbia Guide to American Indians of the Southwest
The Comanches: A History, 1706-1875
Common & Contested Ground: A Human & Environmental History of the Northwestern Plains
A Companion to American Indian History
Comparative Indigeneities of the Americas: Toward a Hemisphereic Approach
The Complete Idiot's Guide to Native American History
Confronting Race: Women & Indians on the Frontier, 1815-1915
Conquest By Law: How the Discovery of America Dispossessed Indigenous

HISTORY, SOURCES

HOPEWELL CULTURE

HOPI INDIANS

Hopi Time
Hopi Traditional Literature
The Hopi Villages
The Hopi Way: Tales From a Changing Culture
Hopi & Zuni Ceremonialism
Hopis, Tewas, and the American Road
Hopituy
Hotevilla: Hopi Shrine of the Covenant/Microcosm of the World
Husk of Time: The Photographs of Victor Masayesva
*If You Lived With the Hopi Indians
Introduction to Hopi Pottery Lessons in Hopi
Kachina Dolls: The Art of Hopi Carvers
Kachina Tales From the Indian Pueblos
Kachinas: Spirit Beings of the Hopi
Language, History, & Identity
Maasaw: Profile of a Hopi God
Ray Manley's Hopi Kachina
Me & Mine: The Life Story of Helen Sekaquaptewa
Media & Ethnic Identity: Hopi Views on Media, Identity, and Communication
Meditiations With the Hopi
Moki Snake Dance
Nampeyo and Her Pottery
The Navajo-Hopi Land Dispute: An American Tragedy
No Turning Back: A Hopi Indian Woman's Struggle to Live in Two Worlds
Oraibu Maru Ceremony
Pages From Hopi History
Prehistoric Hopi Pottery Designs
Pumpkin Seed Point: Being Within the Hopi
Religion & Hopi Life
Rethinking Hopi Ethnography
Ritual in Pueblo Art: Hopi Life in Hopi Painting
The Snake Dance of the Hopi Indians
Spider Woman Stories: Legends of the Hopi Indians
Stories of Maasaw, a Hopi God
Sun Chief: The Autobiography of a Hopi Indian
Treasures of the Hopi
The Wind Won't Know Me: History of the Navajo-Hopi Land Dispute
The Year of the Hopi

HUALAPAI INDIANS

Camp Beale's Springs and the Hualapai Indians
Making Indian Law: The Huaapai Land Case & the Birth of Ethnohistory
We Are An Indian Nation: A History of the Hualapai People

HUICHOL INDIANS

Huichol Art & Culture: Balancing the World
Huichol Indian Ceremonial Cycle
Huichol Indian Sacred Rituals
Huichol Mythology
Peyote Hunt: The Sacred Journey of Huichol Indians
People of the Peyote: Huichol Indian History, Religion & Survival
Visions of a Huichol Shaman

HUNTING & FISHING

Always Getting Ready, Upterrlainarluta: Yup'ik Eskimo Subsistence
 in Southwest Alaska
Apauk: Caller of Buffalo
Archaic Hunters & Gatherers in the American Midwest
Bringing Home Animals
The Buffalo Hunters
The Buffalo: the Story of American Bison & Their Hunters
Disputed Waters: Native Americans & the Great Lakes Fishery
Don't Blame the Indians: Native Americans & the Mechanized Destruction
 of Fish & Wildlife
Early Fur Trade on the Northern Plains
Eastern Cherokee Fishing
Encyclopedia of Native American Bows, Arrows & Quivers:
 Northeast, Southeast, & Midwest
First Fish, First People: Salmon Tales of the North Pacific Rim
Fish Decoys of the Lac du Flambeau Ojibway
Fishing Among the Indians of Northwestern California
Following the Game: Hunting Traditions of Native California
Forging A Fur Empire: Expeditions in the Snake River Country, 1809-1824
Fort Clark and Its Indian Neighbors: A Trading Post On the Upper Missouri
*Fur Trappers & Traders: The Indians, The Pilgrims, and the Beaver
The Horse in Blackfoot Indian Culture
*The Hunt
Hunters of the Buffalo
Hunters of the Eastern Forest
Hunters of the Ice
Hunters of the Northern Forest
Hunters of the Sea
*Hunting With the Native Americans
Indian Fishing: Early Methods of the Northwest Coast
Indian Hunts & Indian Hunters of the Old West
Messages From Frank's Landing: A Story of Salmon, Treaties, & the Indian Way
Native American Hunting & Fighting Skills
Native American Hunting, Fighting & Survival Tools
North American Aboriginal Hide Tanning: The Act of Transformation & Revival
Salmon & His People Vol. 2: Fish & Fishing in Nez Perce Culture

Snares, Deadfalls & Other Traps of the Northern Algonquian & Northern Athapaskans
Status of Tribal Fish & Wildlife Management Programs
Survival Skills of North American Indians
Traps of the American Indians: A Study in Psychology & Invention
Treaties on Trial: The Continuing Controversy Over Northwest Indian Fishing Rights
A Voyage to the Northwest Side of America: The Journals of James Colnett, 1786-89
The Walleye War: The Struggle for Ojibwe Spearfishing & Treaty Rights
Walleye Warriors: The Chippewa Treaty Rights Story
The Whaling Indians: West Coast Legends & Stories, Legendary Hunters
*The Winter Hunt

IMPLEMENTS

Ancient Art of Ohio
Clovis Blade Technology
Collecting Indian Knives
Collector's Guide to Indian Pipes: Identification & Values
Encyclopedia of Native American Bows, Arrows & Quivers: Northeast,
 Southeast, & Midwest
Field Guide to Stone Artifacts of Texas Indians
Florida's Prehistoric Stone Technology
A Guide to Projectile Points of Iowa: Parts 1 & 2
Horn & Bone Implements of the New York Indians
Metal Weapons, Tools & Ornaments of the Teton Dakota Indians
North American Indian Points
The Organization of North American Prehistoric Chipped Stone Tool Technologies
The Origins of a Pacific Coast Chiefdom
The Overstreet Indian Arrowheads: Identification & Price Guide
Projectile Point Guide for the Upper Mississippi River Valley
Projectile Points of the Midwest: A Field Guide
Southwestern Minnesota Archaeology: 12,000 Years in the Prairie Lake Region
Stone Age Spear & Arrow Points of California & the Great Basin
Stone Tool Traditions in the Contact Era
Stone Tools & Mobility in the Illinois Valley

INDIAN BOARDING SCHOOL

Assimilation's Agent: My Life As a Supt. in the Indian Boarding School System
Away From Home: American Indian Boarding School Experiences, 1879-2000
Boarding School Blues
Boarding School Seasons: American Indian Families, 1900-1940
Education for Extinction: American Indianns & the Boarding School Experience, 1875-1928
Learning to Write "Indian": The Boarding School Experience
Mountain Boarding School, 1893-1920
Native American Boarding Schools
Pipestone: My Life in an Indian Boarding School
To Show What an Indian Can Do: Sports at Native American Boarding Schools
Voices From Haskell: Indian Students Between Two Worlds, 1884-1928
White Man's Club: Schools, Race, & the Struggle of Indian Acculturation

INDIAN PLACE-NAMES

Archaeologies of Placemaking: Monuments, Memories, & Engagement
 in Native North America
By Canoe & Moccasin: Some Native Place-Names of the Great Lakes
The Cahuilla Landscape
A Dictionary of Iowa Place-Names
Florida Place-Names of Indian Origin & Seminole Personal Names
Geographical Names of the Kwakiutl Indians
Indian Names in Michigan
Indian Names on Wisconsin's Map
Indian Place-Names in Alabama
Indian Place-Names in America
Indian Place-Names in Illinois
Indian Place-Names in Mexico & Central America
Indian Place-Names of New England
Indian Place-Names of the Penobscot Valley & the Maine Coast
Indian Place Names: Their Origins, Evolution & Meanings
Indian Villages & Place Names of Pennsylvania
Manhattan to Minisink: American Indian Place Names of Greater New York & Vicinity
Names of the American Indian
Native American Place-Names of Connecticut
Native American Place-Names of Indiana
Native American Place Names of Maine, New Hampshire & Vermont
Native American Place-Names of Massachusetts
Native American Place Names in Mississippi
Native American Place-Names of Rhode Island
Native American Placenames of the Southwest: A Handbook for Travelers
Native American Place-Names of the U.S.
Navajo Places
Nevada Military Place-Names of the Indian Wars & Civil War
New Mexico Frontier Military Place-Names
O Brave New Words
Oklahoma Place Names
Our Native American Legacy: Pacific Northwest Towns With Indian Names
Place Names of Atlantic Canada
Place Names of Ontario
Place Names of Wisconsin
Study in the Etymology of the Indian Place Name
Utah Place Names
Washington State Place Names

INDIAN SLAVERY

Aboriginal Slavery on the Northwest Coast of North America
Analysis of Aboriginal Slavery on the Northwest Coast of North America
Indian Slavery in the Pacific Northwest
Indian Slavery, Labor, Evangelization & Captivity in the Americas:
  An Annotated Bibliography
Mapping the Mississippian Shatter Zone: The Colonial Indian Slave Trade
  & Regional Instability in the American South
Red Over Black: Black Slavery Among the Cherokee Indians
Slavery & the Evolution of Cherokee Society, 1540-1866
Stealing Indian Women: Native Slavery in the Illinois Country
Ties That Bind: The Story of an Afro-Cherokee Family in Slavery & Freedom
The Trial of Don Pedro Leon Lujan: The Attack Against Indian Slavery

INDIAN TRAILS

The Great Sioux Trail
The Good Red Road: Passages Into Native America
Indians Along the Oregon Trail; The Tribes Identified
Old Indian Trails
Indians & Emigrants: Encounters on the Overland Trails
The Iroquois Trail
Many Trails: Indians of the Lower Hudson Valley
The Mohawk Trail - Historic Auto Trail Guide: Mass Route 2 from Boston to Williamstown
Navajo Placenames & Trails of the Canyon de Chelly System, Arizona
The Old North Trail: Life, Legends & Religion of the Blackfeet Indians
*Oregon Trail

INDIANS OF CALIFORNIA

Aboriginal Society in Southern California
*Adopted by Indians: A True Story
Alaawich
Alcatraz! Alcatraz!: The Indian Occupation of 1969-1971
American Genocide: The U.S. and the California Indian Catastrophe, 1846-1873
Ancient Modocs of California & Oregon
Ararapikva: Traditional Karuk Indian Literature from Northwestern California
Archives of California Prehistory
An Artist's Portfolio: The California Sketches of Henry B. Brown, 1851-1852
Basket Weavers for the California Curio Trade
The Bear Shaman Tradition of Southern California Indians
Before the Wilderness: Environmental Management by Native Californians
Bibliography of the Languages of Native California
Black Sun of the Miwok
Bringing Them Under Subjection: California's Tejon Indian Reservation
  & Beyond, 1852-1864
The Broken Ring: The Destruction of the California Indians
Cahuilla Dictionary
Cahuilla Grammar
The Cahuilla Indians
The Cahuilla Indians of Southern California
The Cahuilla Landscape: The Santa Rosa & San Jacinto Mountains
California
California Archaeology
California Indian Baskets
California Indian Country: The Land & the People
California Indian Cradle Baskets & Childbirth Traditions
California Indian Folklore
California Indian Nights Entertainment
California Indian Shamanism
California Indian Watercraft
*California Indians
*California Indians: An Educational Coloring Book
California Indians & the Environment
California Indians: Primary Resources
The California Indians: A Source Book
California Indians & Their Environment: An Introduction
*California Missions
The California Missions Source Book
*The California Native American Tribes
California Place Names
1500 California Place Names: Their Origin & Meaning
*California Tribes
*California's Chumash Indians
California's Gabrielino Indians
California's Indians & the Gold Rush
Carving Traditions of Northwest California
A Case Study of a Northern California Indian Tribe: Cultural Change to 1860
The Chemehuevi Indians of Southern California
Chemehuevi: People of the Coachilla Valley
Chemehuevi Song: The Resilience of a Southern Paiute Tribe
Chem'ivillu: Let's Speak Cahuilla
Chief Marin: Leader, Rebel, & Legend
Chiefs & Challengers: Indian Resistance & Cooperation in Southern California, 1769-1906
Chimariko Grammar: Areal & Typological Perspective
Chinigchinix, An Indigenous California Indian Religion
*The Chumash
Chumash Healing
Chumash
*The Chumash
The Chumash & Costanoan Languages
Chumash Ethnobotany: Plant Knowledge Among the Chumash People
  of Southern California

Chumash Healing
*Chumash Indian Games
The Chumash Indians of Southern California
The Chumash People
Chumash: A Picture of Their World
The Chumash & Their Predecessors
The Chumash World at European Contact
The Classification and Distribution of the Pit River Indian Tribes of California
The Conflict Between the California Indian & White Civilization
Conquests & Historical Identities in California, 1769-1936
Converting California Indians & Franciscans in the Missions
The Costanoan/Ohlone Indians of the San Francisco & Monterey Bay Area:
  A Research Guide
Crystals in the Sky: Chumash Astronomy, Cosmology and Rock Art
*A Day With a Chumash
December's Child: A Book of Chumash Oral Narratives
Deeper Than Gold: Indian Life Along California's Highway 49
Delfina Cuero: Her Autobiography
The Destruction of California Indians
Dictionary of Mesa Grande Diegueno
The Diegueno Indians
The Dirt Is Red Here: Art & Poetry from Native California
Discovery of the Yosemite and the Indian War of 1851 Which Led to That Event
The Early Ethnography of the Kumeyaay
The Earth Is Our Mother: A Guide to the Indians of California
Earthquake Weather
Earth Pigments & Paint of the California Indians: Meaning & Technology
The Ethno-Botany of the Coahuilla Indians of Southern California
Ethnography and Folklore of the Indians of Northwestern California
The Ethnology of the Salinan Indians
Federal Concern About Conditions of California Indians, 1853-1913
The Fine Art of California Indian Basketry
The First Angelinos: The Gabrielino Indians of Los Angeles
First Coastal Californians
First Families: A Photographic History of California Indians
Food in California Indian Culture
From Fingers to Finger Bowls
Gabrielino
Gigyayk Vo:jka
Glimpses of History: The San Gorgonio Pass in the 19th Century
Grass Games & Moon Races: California Indian Games & Toys
*Great Indians of California
Guide to the Records at the National Archives-Los Angeles Branch
Handbook of the Indians of California
The Heart Is Fire: The World of the Cahuilla Indians of Southern California
A Historical Look at the Shasta Nation
I'isniyatam (Designs): A Cahuilla Word Book
Indian Baskets of Central California
Indian Life of the Yosemite Region: Miwok Material Culture
Indian Regalia of Northwest California
Indian Summer: Traditional Life Among the Choinumne Indians
  of California's San Joaquin Valley
Indian Survival on the California Borderland Frontier, 1819-60
Indian Tales
Indian-White Relationships in Northern California, 1849-1920
Indians and Indian Agents
Indians, Franciscans, and Spanish Colonization: The Impact
  of the Mission System on California Indians
Indians & Intruders in Central California, 1769-1849
The Indians' Land Title in California: A Case in Federal Equity, 1851-1942
Indians, Missionaries & Merchants: The Legacy of Colonial Encounters
  on the California Frontiers
Indians of California: The Changing Image
Indians of California: A Critical Bibliography
Indians of the Feather River: Tales & Legends of the Concow
The Indians of Southern California in 1852
Indigenous Landscapes & Spanish Mission: New Perspectives from
  Archaeology & Ethnohistory
Inigio of Rancho Posolmi: The Life & Times of a Mission Indian
The Inland Whale: Nine Stories Retold from California Indian Legends
An Introduction to the Luiseno Language
Ishi in Two Worlds: A Biography of of the Last Wild Indian in North America
Ishi's Journey from the Center to the Edge of the World
Ishi, the Last Yahi: A Documentary History
The Island Chumash: Behavioral Ecology of a Maritime Society
It Will Live Forever: Traditional Yosemite Acorn Preparation
Journal of California & the Great Basin Anthropology
Karuk: the Upriver People
Kashaya Pomo Plants
Kiliwa Texts: "Whe I Have Donned My Crest of Stars"
Legends of the Yosemite Miwok
Life Amongst the Modocs: Unwritten History
Life on the River: The Archaeology of an Ancient Native American Culture
The Literature of California, Vol. 1: Native American Beginnings to 1945
Lost Copper
Lost Laborers in Colonial California: Native Americans & the Archaeology
  of Rancho Petaluma
The Luiseno Indians of Southern California
The Maidu Indian Myths & Stories of Hanc'ibyjim
Maidu of California
Malki Museum's Native Food Tasting Experiences
Medicinal Plants Used by Native American Tribes in Southern California
Viola Martinez, California Paiute: Living in Two Worlds
Massacre at the Yuma Crossing

INDIANS OF FLORIDA

INDIANS OF THE GREAT LAKES REGION (NORTHWEST, OLD)

INDIANS OF THE GREAT PLAINS
(See Lakota, Cheyenne, Comanches, Blackfeet, Blackfoot, Cherokee of Oklahoma, Kiowa, Omaha)

Marquis de Miores at War in the Bad Lands
Memory & Vision: Arts, Culture, and Lives of Plains Indian Peoples
Midnight & Noonday
My Life on the Plains
The Mystic Warriors of the Plains
Joseph N. Nicollet on the Plains & Prairies
19th Century Plains Indian Dresses
Noble Red Man: Lakota Wisdomkeeper Mathew King
North Dakota Indians: An Introduction
Northern Plains Indian Illustration & Biography Index
Northwest Indian Images: A Photographic Look at Plateau Indians
Of Uncommon Birth: Dakota Sons in Vietnam
Oklahoma: Foot-Loose & Fancy-Free
Oklahoma: A History of Five Centuries
Oklahoma: A History of the Sooner State
Oklahoma: The Land & Its People
Oklahoma Place Names
Oklahoma Seminoles
Oklahoma: The Story of Its Past & Present
Oklahoma's Indian New Deal
On the Rez
Origins of Predicates: Evidence From Plains Cree
Our Hearts Fell to the Ground
Pacifying the Plains
Painted Tipis by Contemporary Plains Indian Artists
Paleoindians Geoarchaeology of the Southern High Plains
*Francis Parkman & the Plains Indians
Pawnee, Blackfoot, and Cheyenne: History & Folklore of the Plains
A Plains Archaeology Sourcebook
Plains Indian Art: The Pioneering Work of John C. Ewers
*The Plains Indian Book
The Plains Cree
The Plains Indian Book
Plains Indian Culture
Plains Indian Designs
Plains Indian Drawings, 1865-1935
Plains Indian History & Culture
Plains Indian & Mountain Arts & Crafts I & II
Plains Indian Mythology
The Plains Indian Photographs of Edward S. Curtis
Plains Indian Portraits & Scenes
Plains Indian Raiders
Plains Indian Rock Art
Plains Indian Sculpture
*Plains Indian Warrior
*Plains Indians
The Plains Indians
Plains Indians, A.D. 500-1500
*Plains Indians Coloring Book
*Plains Indians: An Educational Coloring Book
The Plains Indians & New Mexico
*The Plains Indians of North America
The Plains Indians of the 20th Century
Plains Indians Portraits & Scenes: 24 Watercolors From the Joslyn Art Museum
*Plains Indians Punch-Out Panorama
Plains Indians Regalia & Customs
*Plains Indians Wars
*Plains Native American Literature
The Plains Sioux & U.S. Colonialism from Lewis & Clark to Wounded Knee
The Plains Wars, 1757-1900
The Planning Process on the Pine Ridge & Rosebud Indian Reservations
•The Plateau Indians
Political Organization of the Plains Indians
Population Changes Among the Northern Plains Indians
Power & Gender in Oneonta Culture: A Study of a Late Prehistoric People
Prairie Fire: A Great Plains History
Prehistoric Lifeways in the Great Basin Wetlands
Prehistoric Man on the Great Plains
Prehistoric Warfare on the Great Plains: Skeletal Analysis of the Crow Creek Massacre
The Quest for Citizenship: African-American & Native American Education
  in Kansas, 1880-1935
Rank & Warfare Among the Plains Indians
Renewing the World: Plains Indian Religion & Morality
The Sac & Fox Indians
Search for the Lost Trail of Crazy Horse
Seminole Burning
Sister to the Sioux
Sitting Bull & the Plains Indians
Skeletal Biology in the Great Plains
Southern Plains Alliances
Southern Plains Lifeways
*Spirit of the White Bison
Spirits in the Art
Stone Effigies of the High Plains Hunters
Stories From Old-Time Oklahoma
Tales of the Northwest: On Sketches of Indian Life & Character
Talking to the Moon
Tenting on the Plains
Howard Terpning: Spirit of the Plains People
The Teton Sioux
They Treated Us Just Like Indians: The Worlds of Bennett Co., SD
*This Land Is My Land
Three Years Among the Comanches
Three Years on the Plains: Observations of Indians, 1867-1870

Through Dakota Eyes
Tipi: Heritage of the Great Plains
To Be An Indian: An Oral History
Trail to Wounded Knee: The Last Stand of the Plains Indians, 1860-1890
A Travel Guide to the Plains Indian Wars
The Tribal Government of the Oglala Sioux of Pine Ridge, SD
The Tribal Territory, Sovereignty & Governance: A Study of the Cheyenne River & Lake
Traverse Indian Reservations
Tribal Wars of the Southern Plains
*Vostaas: The Story of Montana's Indian Nations
War Dance: Plains Indian Musical Performance
*We Rode the Wind: Recollections of Native American Life
When Buffalo Ran
When Indians Became Cowboys
The Whiskey Trade of the Northwestern Plains
The Wichita Indians
Wolf That I Am: In Search of the Red Earth People
Women of the Earth Lodges: Tribal Life on the Plains

INDIANS OF IOWA

Art of the Red Earth People: The Mesquakie of Iowa
The Cherokee Excavations: Holocene Ecology & Human Adaptations
  in Northwestern Iowa
A Dictionary of Iowa Place-Names
Frontier Forts of Iowa: Indians, Traders, and Soldiers, 1682-1862
The Guide to Iowa's State Preserves
Guide to Projectile Points of Iowa, Parts 1 & 2
The Indians of Iowa
Iowa History Reader
Iowa Indians
Iowa's Archaeological Past
The Ioway Indians
Ioway Life: Reservation & Reform, 1837-1860
The Meskwaki & Anthropologists
The Prairie People: Potawatomi
White Robe's Dilemma: Tribal History in American Literature
Wildflowers of Iowa Woodlands
Worlds Between Two Rivers: Perspectives on American Indians in Iowa

INDIANS OF KANSAS

The Emigrant Indians of Kansas: A Critical Bibliography
The End of Indian Kansas
The Enduring Indians of Kansas
Fort Ellsworth Kansas
History of Neosho County, Kansas
Kenekuk, the Kickapoo Prophet
The Kickapoo Indians, Their History & Culture: An Annotated Bibliography
The Kickapoos: Lords of the Middle Border
Kiikaapou: The Kansas Kickapoo
The Quest for Citizenship: African-American & Native American Education
  in Kansas, 1880-1935
*Rabbit Goes to Kansas
Tenting on the Plains; Or, General Custer in Kansas & Texas

INDIANS OF MINNESOTA

Brackett's Battalion: Minnesota Cavalry in the Civil War & Dakota War
Dakota in Minnesota
*Dakota Indians Coloring Book
Dakota Life in the Upper Midwest
*Dakota & Ojibwe People in Minnesota
The Dakota or Sioux in Minnesota As They Were in 1834
Dakota War Whoop; Or, Indian Masscres & War in Minnesota
Indian in Minnesota, 4th Edition
Indians As Mascots in Minnesota Schools
Minnesota's Indian Mounds & Burial Sites
Ojbway Music from Minnesota
Ojibway Oratory
Ottawa & Chippewa Indians of Michigan, 1870-1909
Outbreak & Massacre by the Dakota Indians in Minnesota in 1862
Paths of the People: The Ojibwe in the Chippewa Valley
The People Named the Chippewa
Peoples of the Twilight: European Views of Native Minnesota, 1823-1862
Portage Lake: Memories of an Ojibwe Childhood
Red Lake Nation: Portraits of Ojibway Life
The Sioux Uprising in Minnesota, 1862
A Social Study of One Hundred Fifty Chippewa Indian Families
  of the White Earth Reservation of Minnesota
Through Dakota Eyes: Narrative Accounts of the Minnesota Indian War of 1862
The Thunder Before the Storm: The Autobiography of Clyde Bellecourt

INDIANS OF NEW ENGLAND

*The Abenaki
After King Philip's War: Presence & Persistence in Indian New England
The Archaeology of New England
Becoming Brothertown
Beothuk & Micmac
Beyond Conquest: Native Peoples & the Struggle for History in New England
Captive Histories: English, French, and Native Narratives of the 1704 Deerfield Raid
Captors & Captives: The 1704 French & Indian Raid on Deerfield

INDIANS OF NORTH AMERICA-GENERAL

Red Men in Red Square
Reference Library of Native North America, 4 Vols.
Reflections on American Indian History: Honoring the Past, Building a Future
Research and Writing Tribal Histories
The Return of the Native: American Indian Political Resurgence
Science Encounters the Indian, 1820-1880
Secrets of the Kings Indian
Shades of Hiawatha: Staging Indians, Making Americans
Shadow Country
Shadow Distance: A Gerald Vizenor Reader
Signals in the Air: Native Broadcasting in America
Six Months Among the Indians
The Southeastern Indians
Southeastern Indians Since the Removal Era
Southern Athapaskan Migration: A.D. 200-1750
The Spanish Borderlands Sourcebooks
Spanish Explorers in the Southern U.S.
Spirit Capture: Photographs from the National Museum of the American Indian
A Spirited Resistance: The North American Indian Struggle for Unity, 1745-1815
The State of Native America: Genocide
, Colonization and Resistance
State Indian Encyclopedias
Strangers to Relatives: The Adoption & Naming of Anthropologists in Native North America
Structuring Sovereignty: Constitutions of Native Nations
Sun Bear: The Path of Power
Recently Discovered Tales of Life Among the Indians
Teaching About Native Americans
Tennessee's Indian Peoples: From White Contact to Removal, 1540-1840
Their Bearing Is Noble & Proud
Theoretical Perspectives on Native American Languages
This Path We Travel: Celebrations of Contemporary Native American Creativity
Toward a Native American Critical Theory
*Traditional Crafts from Native North America
Treasures of the National Museum of the American Indian
Tribal Libraries, Achives, and Museums: Preserving Our Language, Memory, and Lifeways
Tulapai to Tokay: A Bibliography of Alcochol Use & Abuse Among Native Americans
   of North America
Urban Indians
Urban Indians: Drums From the Cities
Urbanization of American Indians: A Critical Bibliography
The Vanishing Race: Selections from Edward S. Curtis' the North American Indian
Views of a Vanishing Frontier
Voice of Indigenous Peoples: Native People Address the U.N.
*The Wampanoag
Wanderings of an Artist Among the Indians of North America
Warriors in Uniform: The Legacy of American Indian Heroism
*We Live on an Indian Reservation
We, The First Americans
When Nickels Were Indians: An Urban, Mixed-Blood Story
The White Man's Indian
Words in the Blood: Contemporary Indian Writers of North and South America
Words of Power: Voices from Indian America
World of American Indian
World War II & the American Indian
The World's Rim: Great Mysteries of the North American Indians

INDIANS OF THE NORTHEAST

Accessing the Past: The iroquois Gas Transmission System Pipeline
   Archaeological Collection
An Account of the History, Manners & Customs of the Indian Nations Who
   Once Inhabited Pennsylvania & the Neighboring States 1819
Akwesane Historical Postcards
*Algonkian: Lifestyle of the New England Indians
The Algonquian Peoples of Long Island: From Earliest Times to 1700
*The Algonquians
American Indians in Connecticut
American Native History Brief Study
Amerlnds & Their Paleoenvironments in Northeastern North America
Annals of the Susquehannocks & Other Indian Tribes of Pennsylvania, 1500-1763
Anthropological Studies of the Quichua & Machiganga Indians
Apologies to the Iroquois
Archaeology of Eastern North America: Papers in Honor of Stephen Williams
Archaic of the Far Northeast
Beyond the Covenant Chain: The Iroquois & Their Neighbors in Indian North America
Biography & History of the Indians of North America
Bitter Feast: Amerindians & Europeans in Northeastern North America, 1600-1664
A Brief History of the Seneca-Cayuga Tribe
Blackcoats Among the Delaware: David Zeisberger on the Ohio Frontier
*The Cayuga
A Clan Mother's Call: Reconstructing Haudenosaunee Cultural Memory
The Columbia Guide to American Indians of the Northeast
The Common Pot: The Recovery of Native Space in the Northeast
Connecticut's Indigenous Peoples: What Archaeology, History, and Oral Traditions
   Teach Us About Theiir Communities and Cultures
The Constitution of the Five Nations
Count Zinzindorf & the Indians 1742 (Philadelphia area)
Cross-Cultural Collaboration: Native Peoples & Archaeology in Northeastern U.S.
The Delaware
The Delaware Indians: A Brief History
The Delaware Indians: A History
Delaware Reference Grammar
The Delaware & Shawnee Admitted to Cherokee Citizenship
Delaware Trails

The Delawares: A Critical Bibliography
A Description of New Netherland
Distorted Images of the Appalachian Mountain Cherokee
Dominion & Civility: English Imperialism, Native America & the First Frontiers, 1585-1685
Drums Along the Mohawk
The Dutch & the Iroquois
The Early History of Western Pennsylvania
The Edge of the Woods: Iroquoia, 1534-1701
Elliot's Vocabulary of Cayuga
An Ethnography of the Huron Indians, 1615-1649
Evolution of the Onondaga Iroquois
Experience Mayhew's Indian Converts: A Cultural Edition
William Fenton: Selected Writings
Fighting Tuscarora: The Autobiography of Chief Clinton Rickard
First People: The Early Indians of Virginia
Five Civilized Tribes
The Great Law & the Longhouse
Guide to Indian Artifacts of the Northeast
*Heroes & Heroines, Monsters & Magic
The Hidden Language of the Seneca
Historical Map of Pennsylvania; with History of Indian Treaties & Land Titles
History of the Backwoods (Western PA & OH)
History of the Early Settlement of the Juniata Valley
A History of Indian Villages & Place Names of Pennsylvania
History of New York Indians and the Printup Family
Horn and Bone Implements of the New York Indians
*The Huron
The Huron: Farmers of the North
Huron: Farmers of the North
In Defense of Mohawk Land
In Divided Unity: Haudenosaunee Reclamation at Grand River
In the Hands of the Senecas
In Mohawk Country: Early Narratives About A Native People
Indian Chiefs of Pennsylvania
Indian Tribes of Hudson's River
Indian Villages & Place Names of Pennsylvania
Indian Wars of Pennsylvania
Indians In Eden: Wabanakis & Rusticators on Maine's Mt. Desert Island
Indians in Pennsylvania
The Indians of Greater New York and the Lower Hudson
Indians of the Lower Hudson Region: The Munsee
The Indians of Manhattan Island & Vicinity
The Indians of New Jersey
*The Indians of New Jersey: Dickon Among the Lenapes
The Indians of Nimuck Country in Southern New England, 1630-1750
Indians of the Northeast
Indians of the Northeast North America
*Indians of the Northeast: Traditions, History, Legends & Life
Iroquois
*Indians of Tidewater Country: MD, VA, DE & NC
An Infinity of Nations: How the Native New World Shaped Early North America
Iroquoian Women: The Gantowisas
Iroquois: Art & Culture
The Iroquois Eagle Dance
The Iroquois & the Founding of the American Nation
Iroquois in the American Revolution
The Iroquois in the Civil War
Iroquois Indians: A Documentary History
Iroquois Land Claims
Iroquois Music and Dance
The Iroquois & the New Deal
Iroquois On Fire: A Voice from the Mohawk Nation
The Iroquois Restoration
An Iroquois Sourcebook
Iroquois Studies
The Iroquois Struggle for Survival: World War II to Red Power
The Iroquois Trail
Iroquois Wars
Iroquois Wars I & II
Journals of the Military Expedition of Major General John Sullivan
A Journey Into Mohawk & Oneida Country, 1634-1635
King of the Delawares: Teedyuscung, 1700-1763
Land of the Four Directions
Legends of the Delaware Indians & Picture Writing
Legends of the Iroquois
The Lenape
*The Lenape: Middle Atlantic
Lenape History & Numbers Posters
The Lenape Indians
Life & Death in Mohawk Country
*Living With the Senecas: A Story About Mary Jemison
Long Journey Home: Oral Histories of Contemporary Delaware Indians
Manhattan to Minisink: American Indian Place Names of Greater New York & Vicinity
Many Trails: Indians of the Lower Hudson Valley
Martyrs of the Oblong & Little Nine
Midwinter Rites of the Cayuga Long House
*The Mohawk
The Mohawk That Refused to Abdicate, and Other Tales
Mohegan Indian Maps of Montville, CT
The Mohican World, 1680-1750
The Mohicans & Their Land: 1609-1730
The Montaukett Indians of Eastern Long Island
Mother Earth, Father Skyline: A Souvenir Book of Native New York
Moving Encounters: Sympathy & the Indian Question in Antebellum Literature

*The Nanticoke
The Nanticoke Indians
Nation Iroquois: A 17th Century Ethnography of the Native American Ancestors: Eastern Tribes
Native American Speakers of the Eastern Woodlands
Native North American Spirituality of the Eastern Woodlands
The Native Peoples of the Northeast Woodlands: An Educational Resource Publication
Native Peoples of Southern New England, 1500-1650
Native Peoples of Southern New England, 1650-1775
The Native Population of the Americas in 1492
New York City in Indian Possession
North Mountain Mementos (Pennsylvania)
*Northeast Indians
*Northeast Indians Fact Cards
Northeastern Indian Lives, 1632-1816
Notes on the Iroquois
One Thousand Years on Mound Key
*The Oneida
The Oneida Creation Story
Oneida Dictionary
The Oneida Indian Experience
Oneida Indian Journey
The Oneida Land Claims
Oneida Verb Morphology
*The Onondaga
Onondaga Iroquois Prehistiry
Onondaga: Portrait of a Native People
The Ordeal of the Longhouse
Our Life Among the Iroquois Indians
An Outline of Seneca Ceremonies at Coldspring Longhouse
Parker on the Iroquois
Passamaquoddy Ceremonial Songs: Aesthetics & Survival
Passamaquoddy-Maliseet Dictionary
William Penn's Own Account of Lenni Lenape or Delaware Indians
Pennsylvania's Indian Relations to1754
The Pennsylvania Indian Trilogy
Quinnipiac: Cultural Conflict in Southern New England
Reclaiming the Ancestors: Decolonizing a Taken Prehistory of the far Northeast
Red Jacket & His People
Red Jacket: Iroquois Diplomat & Orator
Red Jacket: Seneca Chief
Religion & Ceremonies of the Lenape
The Reservation
Return of the Sun: Native American Tales From the Northeast Woodlands
Return to Creation
The River Is in Us: Fighting Toxics in a Mohawk Community
Sainte Marie Among the Iroquois
Schoolcraft's Vocabulary of Onondaga
Searching for Lost City: On the Trail of America's Native Languages
Selected Manuscripts of General John S. Clark Relating to Aboriginal History of the Susquehanna
*The Seneca
Seneca Myths & Folk Tales
The Seneca & Tuscarora Indians: An Annotated Bibliography
The Seneca World of Ga-No-Say-Yeh
The Six Nations of New York
Smallpox & the Iroquois Wars
Storied Voices in Native American Texts
A Study of Delaware Indian Big House Ceremony
A Study of Delaware Indian Medicine Practice & Folk Beliefs
Susquehanna's Indians
Their Number Become Thinned
Three Centuries of Woodlands Indian Art
To Be Indian: The Life of Iroquois-Seneca Arthur Caswell Parker
To Do Good to My Indian Brethren: The Writings of Joseph Johnson, 1751-1776
Travels
Toba Tucker: A Shinnecock Portrait
Trading Identities: The Souvenir in Native North American Art From the Northeast
Turtles, Wolves & bears: A Mohawk Family History
*The Tuscarora
Tuscarora-English, English-Tuscarora Dictionary
The Tuscarora Legacy of J.N.B. Hewitt
The Tuscarawas Valley in Indian Days, 1750-1797
Twana Narratives: Native Historical Accounts of a Coast Salish Culture
Uncas: First of the Mohegans
A Vocabulary of Mohegan-Pequot
A Vocabulary of New Jersey Delaware
A Vocabulary of the Tuscarora
Voices From the Delaware: Big House Ceremony
Wampum and the Origins of American Money
Wampum & Shell Articles Used by the New York Indians
Warrior in Two Camps: Ely S. Parker, Union General & Seneca Chief
The Wars of the Iroquois
We Are Still Here! The Algonquian Peoples of Long Island Today
Conrad Weiser & the Indian Policy of Colonial Pennsylvania
Women of the Dawn
Writing Indians: Literacy, Christianity, and Native Community in Early America

INDIANS OF THE NORTHWEST, PACIFIC

Aboriginal Slavery on the Northwest Coast of North America
An Account of the origin & Early Prosecution of the Indian War in Oregon
Analysis of Aboriginal Slavery on the Northwest Coast of North America
Coeur D'Alene Indian Myths

Ancient Modocs of California and Oregon
Ancient Tribes of the Klamath Country
Anooshi Lingit Aani Ka / Russians in Tlingit America: The Battles of Sitka, 1802 & 1804
Approaching Footsteps: Puget Sound Indians - Bainbridge Island Sawmills
Archaeology in Washington
Art of the Northwest Coast
Artifacts of the Northwest Coast Indians
Answering Chief Seattle
Art of the Northwest Coast Indians, 2nd Ed.
As Days Go By: Our History, Our Land, Our People - The Cayuse, Umatilla, and Walla Walla
Background History of the Coeur D'Alene Indian Reservation
Bartering With the Bones of Their Dead: The Colville Confederated Tribes & Termination
Becoming Tsimshian
Being Cowlitz: How One Tribe Renewed & Sustained Its Identity
Bibliography of the Blackfoot
Bitterroot Crossing: Lewis & Clark Across the Lolo Trail
The Blackfeet: Raiders on the Northwestern Plains
Blackfeet: Their Art & Culture
Franz Boas
Franz Boas: The Early Years, 1858-1906
Breaking Ground: The Lower Elwha Klallam Tribe & the Unearthing of Tse-whit-zen Village
Bri nging Indians to the Book
Brushed by Cedar, Living by the River: Coast Salish Figures of Power
Captain Jack, Modoc Renegade
Captured Heritage: The Scramble for Northwest Coast Artifacts
Carvings & Commerce: Model Totem Poles, 1880-2010
A Case Study of a Northern California Indian Tribe: Cultural Change to 1860
Cathlamet on the Columbia
Caw Pawa Laakni / They Are Not Forgotten: Sahaptian Place Names Atlas of the Cayuse, Umatilla, and Walla Walla
The Cayuse Indians
Cedar: Tree of Life to the Northwest Coast Indians
Chief Joseph Country: Land of the Nez Perce
Chief Joseph & the Nez Perces: A Photographic History
Chief Joseph's Allies: The Palouse Indians and the Nez Perce War of 1877
Children of the Fur Trade: Forgotten Metis of the Pacific Northwest
*Chinook
Chinook: A History and Dictionary
The Chinook Indians
*The Chinook - Northwest
Chinookan Peoples of the Lower Columbia
Coast Salish
The Coast Salish of British Columbia
*The Coast Salish Peoples
The Coeur d'Alene Indian Reservation
Coming Full Circle: Spirituality & Wellness Among Native Commnities in the Pacific Northwest
The Coming of the Spirit Pestilence
Coming To Stay: A Columbia River Journey
Contemporary Coast Salish Art
Content & Style of an Oral Literature: Clackamas Chinook Myths and Tales
Contributions to the Ethnography of the Kutchin
Converting the West: A Biography of Narcissa Whitman
*Coyote & Kootenai
Coyote Warrior: One Man, Three Tribes, & The Trial That Forged A Nation
Creation Tales from the Salish
Crooked River Country: Wranglers, Rogues, and Barons
Dictionary of the Chinook Jargon: English-Chinook
Discovering Totem Poles: A Traveler's Guide
Diving for Northwest Relics
Dreamer-Prophets of the Columbia Plateau
The Earth's Blanket
Eighteenth-Century Western Cree & Their Neighbors
Emerging From the Mist: Studies in Northwest Coast Culture History
Empty Nets: Indians, Dams, and the Columbia River
Ethnography of Franz Boas
The Eyes of Chief Seattle
Faces of a Reservation: A Portrait of the Warm Springs Indian Reservation
Feasting With Cannibals: An Essay on Kwakiutl Cosmology
Feasting With Mine Enemy
Finding Chief Kamiakin: The Life & Legacy of a Northwest Patriot
The First Oregonians
The Five Crows Ledger: Biographic Warrior Art of the Flathead Indians
Folk Tales of the Coast Salish
Following the Nez Perce Trail
Forging A Fur Empire: Expeditions in the Snake River Country, 1809-1824
The Forgotten Tribes, Oral Tales of the Teninos & Adjacent Mid-Columbia River Indian Nations
Fort Clark and Its Indian Neighbors: A Trading Post On the Upper Missouri
Four Days in a Medicine Lodge
From the Land of Shadows: The Making of Grey Owl
From the Land of the Totem Poles: The Northwest Coast Indian Art Collection at the American Museum of Natural History
Frontier Day: The Army in Northern Idaho, 1853-1876
Fur Trade & Exploration: Opening the Far Northwest, 1821-1852
Katie Gale: A Coast Salish Woman's Life on Oyster Bay
Ghost Voices: Yakama Indian Myths, Legends, Humor and Hunting Stories
Gifts of the Season: Life Among the Northwest Indians
Good Intentions Gone Awry
A Guide to the Indian Tribes of the Pacific Northwest
A Guide to Oregon South Coast History
Haida: Their Art and Culture

INDIANS OF THE SOUTHWEST
(See Apache, Yavapai, Hopi, Navajo,& Pueblo Indian Classifications)

The Western Photographs of John K. Hiller
When Clay Sings
White Eyes, Long Knives & Renegade Indians
Wild Plants & Native Peoples of the Four Corners
Wind Won't Know Me: The History of the Navajo-Hopi Land Dispute
Witchcraft in the Southwest
The Zunis: Self-Portrayals

INDIANS OF TEXAS

The Alabama-Coushatta Indians
Apache Reservation
Apache, The Sacred path to Womanhood
Apache Shawdows
Apache Voices
Apache Wars
Apache Women Warriors
Apachean Culture History & Ethnology
Apaches at War & Peace
The Apaches: A Critical Bibliography
The Apaches: Eagles of the Southwest
Apaches: A History & Culture Portrait
*The Apaches & Navajos
The Archaeology of the Caddo
Blessed Assurance: At Home with the Bomb in Amarillo, Texas
Border Wars of Texas
The Buffalo Soldier Tragedy of 1877
The Caddo Indians: Tribes at the Convergence of Empires, 1542-1854
The Caddos, the Wichitas, and the U.S., 1846-1901
Chief Bowles & the Texas Cherokees
Drums Along the Isleta
Jesse Chisholm: Ambassador of the Plains
Jesse Chisholm: Texas Trail Blazer & Peacemaker
*The Comanche
Comanche Code Talkers of World War II
Comanche Moon
Comanche Society
The Conquest of the Karankawas & the Tonkawas, 1821-1859
The Conquest of Texas: Ethnic Cleansing in the Promised Land, 1820-1875
Documentary Evidence for the Spanish Missions of Texas
Drumbeats from Mescalero: Conversations with Apache Elders, Warriors,
  and Householders
Ethnology of the Texas Indians
Exiled: The Tigua Indians of Ysleta del Sur
Field Guide to Stone Artifacts of Texas Indians
From Dominance to Disappearance: The Indians of Texas & the Near Southwest,
  1786-1859
Hasinai: A Traditional History of the Caddo Confederacy
The Hasinai: The Southern Caddoans As Seen by the Earliest Europeans
Historic Native Peoples of Texas
Historical Atlas of Texas
Indian Depredations in Texas
The Indian Papers of Texas & the Southwest, 1825-1916
The Indian Texans
Indian Wars & Pioneers of Texas, 1685-1892
The Indian Wars: Stephen F. Austin's Texas Colony, 1822-1835
Indians of the Rio Grande Delta
The Indians of Texas: An Annotated Research Bibliography
The Indians of Texas: From Prehistoric to Modern Times
Indians of the Upper Texas Coast
*Indians Who Lived in Texas
Jounral of an Indian Trader: Anthony Glass and the Texas Trading Frontier, 1790-1810
Juh, An Incredible Indian
The Jumanos: Hunters & Traders of the South Plains
The Karankawa Indians of Texas
Kiowa, Apache, and Comanche Military Societies
Kiowa Ethnogeography
Land of the Tejas: Native American Identity & Interaction in Texas, A.D. 1300 to 1700
*Learn About Texas Indians
*The Legend of the Bluebonnet
Legendary Texans, Vol. 2
*Let's Remeber...Indians of Texas
Life Among the Texas Indians: The WPA Narratives
The Lipan Apaches in Texas
Merejildo Grijalva, Apache Captive, Army Scout
Mimbres Mythology
Native Americans of Texas
The Native Americans of the Texas Edwards Plateau, 1582-1799
Paleoindian Geoarchaeology of the Southern High Plains
Cynthia Ann Parker: The Life & Legend
Peace Came in the Form of a Woman: Indians & Spaniards in the Texas Borderlands
Prehistory of the Rustler Hills: Granado Cave
The Rock Art of Texas Indians
Stone Artifacts of Texas Indians - A Field Guide
The Story of Cynthia Ann Parker
Tejano Origins in 18th Century San Antonio
Tenting on the Plains; Or, General Custer in Kansas & Texas
The Texas Cherokees
Texas Indian Myths & Legends
Texas Indian Trails: A Roadside Guide to Native American Landmarks
The Texas Indians
The Texas Kickapoo: Keepers of Tradition
Three Years Among the Comanches
The Tiguas: Pueblo Indians of Texas

Tonkawa, an Indian Language of Texas
The Tonkawa People: A Tribal History from Earliest Times to 1893
Transnational Indians in the Noth American West
The Way of the Dead Indians: Guarjiro Myths & Symbols
We Came Naked & Barefoot: The Journey of Cabeza de Vaca Across North America
Western Apache Heritage
Western Apache Language & Culture
Western Apache Material Culture
Western Apache Raiding & Warfare
Western Apache Witchcraft
The Wicita Indians
The Wichita Indians: Traders of Texas & the Southern Plains, 1540-1845
Windsong: Texas Cherokee Princess

INDIANS OF WISCONSIN

The Aboriginal Pipes of Wisconsin
All That Remains: A West Virginia Archaeologist's Discoveries; The Antiiquities
  of Wisocnsin, As Surveyed & Described
Chief Daniel Bread & the Oneida Nation of Indians of Wisconsin
Chippewa Treaty Rights: The Reserved Rights of Wisconsin's Chippewa Indians
Classroom Activities on Wisconsin Indian Treaties & rial Sovereignty
The Dept. of the Interior's Denial of the Wisconsin Chippewa's Casio Applications
The Fox Wars: The Mesquakie Challenge to New France
Indian Culture & European Trade Goods
Indian Mounds of Wisconsin
Indian Names on Wisconsin's Map
Indian Nations of Wsconsin
Indians of New York in Wisconsin & Elsewhere
Introduction to Wisocnsin Indians: Prehistory to Statehood
The Library of Native Americans
Like a Deer Chased by the Dogs: The Life of Chief Oshkosh
Memories of lac du Flambeau Elders
The Menomini Indians of Wisconsin
Native American Communitiies in Wisconsin, 1600-1960
Native American Press in Wisocnsin & the Nation
Native People of Wisconsin
The Oneida Indian Journey: From New York to Wisconsin, 1784-1860
The Oneida Indians in the Age of Allotment, 1860-1920
Oneida Lives: Long-Lost Voices of the Wisconsin Oneidas
Paths of the people: The Ojibwe in the Chippewa Valley
Picturing Indians
Prehistoric Indians of Wisconsin
Reflections of Lac du Flambeau: An Illustrated History of Lac du Flambeau, WI, 1745-1895
The Walleye War:The Struggle for Ojibwe Searfishing & Treaty
Walleye Warriors: The Chippewa Treaty Rights Story
Wisconsin Chippewa Myths & Tales & Their Relation to Chippewa Life
Wisconsin's County Forests: Conflict Over Indian Timber Rights
The Wisconsin Frontier
Wisconsin Indian Literature: Anthology of Native Voices

INDIGENOUS SEXUALITY

Bedbugs' Night Dance & Other Hopi Tales of Sexual Encounter
Gender & Sexuality in Indigenous North America, 1400-1850
The Indian Peoples of Eastern America: A Documentary History of the Sexes
Queer Indigenous Studies: Critical Interventions in Theory, Politics, and Literature
The Spirit & the Flesh: Sexual Diversity in American Indian Tradition
Suspect Relations: Sex, Race & Resistance in Colonial North Carolina
Two Spirit People: American Indian Lesbian Women & Gay Men
Two-Spirit People: Native American Gender Identity, Sexuality & Spirituality
Two Spirits: A Story of Life With the Navajo
When Did Indians Become Straight: Kinship, the History of Sexuality, & Native Sovereignty

INDIGENOUS STUDIES

Comparative Indigeneities of the Americas: Toward a Hemisphereic Approach
Mapping Indigenous Presence
Native Studies Keywords
Universities and Indian Country

INDUSTRIES

Algonquin Apprentice
American Indian Arts & Crafts Source Book
American Indian Counted Cross-Stitch
American Indian Craft Book
American Indian Design & Decoration
American Indian Jewelry: 1,200 Artist Biographies
American Indian Textiles: 2,000 Artist Biographies
*American Indian Tools & Ornaments
*American Indian Utensils: How to Make Baskets, Pottery & Woodenware
  with Natural Materials
The Ancestors: Native American Artisans of the Americas
And Eagles Sweep Across the Sky: Indian Textiles of the North American West
Approaching Footsteps: Puget Sound Indians - Bainbridge Island Sawmills
Arapaho Women's Quillwork: Motion, Life & Creativity
The Arbitrary Indian: The Indian Arts & Crafts Act of 1990
The Art of Simulating Eagle Feathers
Artifacts of the Northwest Coast Indians
Arts & Crafts of the Cherokee
Applique Patterns From Native American Beadwork Designs
Authentic Indian Designs

INUT

Canadian Prehistory Series
Cape Dorset Sculpture
Case & Agreement in Inuit
Critical Inuit Studies
Daily Life of the Inuit
Empowering Northern & Native Communities for Social, Political & Economic Control
Encounters on the Passage: Inuit Meet the Explorers
*The Eskimo: Inuit & Yup'ik
*Eskimos: The Inuit of the Arctic
The Fast Runner: Filming the Legend of Atanarjuat
*First Books
The First Canadians
Historical Dictionary of the Inuit
Human Ecology: Issues in the North
*Inuit
Inuit Artists Print Workbook
Inuit Education & Schools in the Eastern Arctic
The Inuit: Glimpses of an Arctic Past
Inuit Imagination: Arctic Myth & Sculpture
Inuit Kayaks in Canada
The Inuit Life As It Was
*Inuit Mythology
Inuit: The North in Transition
The Inuit Print, L'Estampe Inuit
Inuit Stories/Legendes Inuit
Inuit Women Artists
Inuit Youth
Keepers of the Culture
Kiumajut (Talking Back): Game management & Inuit Rights, 1950-70
A Long Way From Home: The Turberculosis Epidemic Among the Inuit
Native American Mathematics
Native Americans on Film & Video
Native People, Native Lands: Canadian Indians, Inuit & Metis
The Northern Copper Inuit: A History
Northern Voices: Inuit Writing in English
Nunavut Atlas
Nunavut: Rethinking Political Culture
Overland to Starvation Cove: With the Inuit in Search of Franklin, 1878-1880
People From Our Side: A Life Story (Peter Pitseolak) With Photos & Oral Biography
*People of the Ice: How the Inuit Lived
The Sea Woman: Sedna in Inuit Shamanism & Art in the Eastern Arctic
Sinews of Survival: The Living Legacy of Inuit Clothing
Tammarniit (Mistakes): Inuit Relocation in the Eastern Arctic, 1939-63
White Lies About the Inuit

IROQUOIS INDIANS

The Ambiguous Iroquois Empire
Apocalypse of Chiokoyhikoy: Chief of the Iroquois
The Caddoan, Iroquoian & Siouan Languages
A Clan Mother's Call: Reconstructing Haudenosaunee Cultural Memory
Concerning the League
Conservatism Among the Iroquois at the Six Nations Reserve
Conspiracy of Interests: Iroquois Dispossession & the Rise of New York State
The Constitution of the Five Nations
Cultivating A Landscape of Peace: Iroquois-European Encounters in 17th-Century America
De Religione: Telling the 17th Century Jesuit Story in Huron the Iroquois
Debating Democracy: Native American Legacy of Freedom
The Dutch & the Iroquois
The Edge of the Woods: Iroquoia, 1534-1701
Evolution of the Onondaga Iroquois
Extending the Rafters: Interdisciplinary Approaches to Iroquois Studies
The False Faces of the Iroquois
From the Earth to Beyond the Sky: An Ethnographic Approach to
 Four Longhouse Iroquois Speech Events
The Great Law & the Longhouse: A Political History of the Iroquois Confederacy
*Heroes & Heroines, Monsters & Magic
Historic Zuni Architecture & Society
The History & Culture of Iroquois Diplomacy
History of the Five Indian Nations
History of the Five Indian Nations in Canada
History of the Iroquois Confederacy
Households & Families of the Longhouse Iroquois at Six Nations Reserve
Hunting Tradition in a Changing World: Yup'ik Lives in Alaska Today
*If You Lived With the Iroquois
In Divided Unity: Haudenosaunee Reclamation at Grand River
In Mohawk Country
Iroquoian Cosmology
The Iroquoian Women
The Iroquois
*The Iroquois
Iroquois: Art & Culture
Iroquois Art, Power, and History
The Iroquois Book of Rites
The Iroquois Confederacy: History & Legends
Iroquois Corn in a Culture-Based Curriculum
Iroquois Crafts
Iroquois Culture & Commentary
The Iroquois Eagle Dance
The Iroquois & the Founding of the American Nation
Iroquois in the American Revolution
The Iroquois in the Civil War From Battlefield to Reservation
The Iroquois in the War of 1812
Iroquois Indians: A Documentary History

Iroquois Journey: An Anthropologist Remembers
Iroquois Land Claims
Iroquois Medical Botany
Iroquois Music & Dance
The Iroquois & the New Deal
Iroquois On Fire: A Voice from the Mohawk Nation
Iroquois: People of the Longhouse
The Iroquois Restoration
The Iroquois: The Six Nations Confederacy
An Iroquois Sourcebook
Iroquois Studies
The Iroquois Struggle for Survival
The Iroquois Trail
The Iroquois Wars I & II
Iroquois Wars: Extracts from the Jesuit Relations & Primary Sources, 1535-1650
Knowledge of the Elders: The Iroquois Condolence Cane Tradition
Legends of the Iroquois
Legends, Traditions & Laws of the Iroquois
Little Water Medicine Society of the Senecas
Manual for the Peacemaker: An Iroquois Legend to Heal Self & Society
Lewis H. Morgan on Iroquois Culture
Lewis Henry Morgan's League of the Iroquois
Nation Iroquois: A 17th Century Ethnography of the (Oneida) Iroquois
Native American Tribes: The History & Culture of the Iroquois Confederacy
Notes on the Iroquois
Oneida Verb Morphology
Onondaga: Portrait of a Native People
The Ordeal of the Longhouse
Our Life Among the Iroquois Indians
Parker on the Iroquois
A Passion For the Past: Papers in Honour of James F. Pendergast
Red Jacket & His People
Red Jacket: Iroquois Diplomat & Orator
Red Jacket: Seneca Chief
The Roots of the Iroquois
Sainte Marie Among the Iroquois
Seeds of Empire: The American Revolutionary Conquest of theIroquois
Selected Manuscripts of General John S. Clark Relating to Aboriginal History
 of the Susquehanna
The Seneca Restoration, 1715-1754: An Iroquois Local Political Economy
Sisters in Spirit: Iroquois Influence on Early American Feminists
The Six Nations of New York
Samllpox and the Iroquois Wars
Smoking Technology of the Aborigines of the Iroquois Area of New York State
*Skywoman: Legends of the Iroquois
Speculators in Empire: Iroquoia and the 1768 Treaty of Fort Stanwix
Symposium on Cherokee & Iroquois Culture
Symposium on Local Diversity in Iroquois Culture
Thinking In Indian: A John Mohawk Reader
To Be Indian: The Life of Iroquois-Seneca Arthur Caswell Parker
Traditions and Laws of the Iroquois
Treaty of Canandaigua 1794
Tribes of the Iroquois Confederation
Two Early Historic Iroquoian Sites in Western New York
Wampum Belts of the Iroquois
White Roots of Peace: Iroquois Book of Life
Your Fyre Shall Burn No More: Iroquois Policy to New France & Its Native Allies to 1701

JEWELRY - COSTUME & ADORNMENT

Adventures In Creating Earrings
American Indian Beadwork
American Indian Design & Decoration
American Indian Jewelry: Artist Biographies
Applique Patterns of from Native American Beadwork Designs
Arctic Transformations: The Jewelry of Denise & Samuel Wallace
Authentic Indian Designs
Be Dazzled! Masterworks of Jewelry & Beadwork from the Heard Museum
Beading in the Native American Tradition
Beads & Beadwork of the American Indian
Beads to Buckskins
A Beadwork Companion
The Beauty of Hopi Jewelry
Big Book of Indian Beadwork Designs
Chain of Friendship: North American Indian Trade Silver
*Cherokee Clothing & Activity Book
Complete Book of Seminole Patchbook
Complete Guide to Traditional Native American Beadwork
Costumes of the Plains Indians
Crow Indian Beadwork
Dress Clothing of the Plains Indians
Dress & Decoration of the American Indian
Encyclopedia of American Indian Costume
Feminine Fur Trade Fashions
Fine Indian Jewelry of the Southwest
Flat Peyote Stitch
Glass Tapestry: Plateau Beaded Bags from the Elaine Horwitch Collection
Glass Trade Beads of the Northeast & Including Aboriginal Industries
Glittering World: Navajo Jewelry of the Yazzie Family
Guide to Indian Jewelry of the Southwest
Guide to Indian Quillworking
Head & Face Masks in Navaho Ceremonialism
Heart of the Dragonfly
Hide: Skin as Material & Metaphor

History of Beads
How to Make Cherokee Clothing
How to Tan Skins the Indian Way
Indian Bead-Weaving Patterns
Indian Clothing Before Cortes
Indian Clothing of the Great Lakes: 1740-1840
*Indian Costumes
Indian Jewelry of the American Southwest
Indian Jewelry on the Market
Indian Silver Jewelry of the Southwest, 1868-1930
Jewelry by Southwest American Indians: Evolving Designs
Language of the Robe: American Indian Trade Blankets
Making Arrows the Old Way
Making Indian Bows & Arrows
More Techniques of Beading Earrings
Native American Bead Weaving
Native American Beadwork
Native American Beadwork: Projects & Techniques from the Southwest
Native American Bolo Ties
Native American Clothing: An Illustrated History
Native American Fashion
Native Fashion Now: North American Indian Style
Navajo Beadwork: Architectures of Light
Navajo Jewelry: A Legacy of Silver & Stone
Navajo & Pueblo Earrings, 1850-1945
Navajo & Pueblo Silversmiths
Navajo Spoons: Indian Artistry and the Souvenir Trade, 1880-1940
Navajo Weavers & Silversmiths
19th Century Plains Indian Dresses
North American Indian Beadwork Designs
North American Indian Beadwork Patterns
North American Indian Jewelry & Adornment
Pennsylvania Chert: Identifying Some of the Materials Used by the Indians
  in Pennsylvania & Surrounding Areas
Pueblo Indian Embroidery
Quill & Beadwork of the Western Sioux
A Quillwork Companion
Sacred Beauty: Quillwork of the Plains Indians
Salish Indian Sweaters
Shared Images
Sioux Quill & Beadwork
A Special Gift: The Kutchin Beadwork Tradition
Stone Ornaments Used by Indians in the U.S. & Canada
Surviving Desires: Making & Selling Native Jewelry in the American Southwest
Techniques of Beading Earrings
The Technique of North American Indian Beadwork
The Technique of Porcupine Quill Decoration Among the Indians of North America
Traditional Clothing of the Native Americans
Traditional Dress
Traditional Indian Bead & Leather Crafts
Traditional Indian Crafts
Traditions: Beadwork of the Native American
Treading in the Past: Sandal of the Anasazi
Turquoise Jewelry
The Turquoise Trail: Native American Jewelry of the Southwest
War Paint: Blackfoot & Sarcee Painted Buffalo Robes in the
Royal Ontario Museum
Warbonnets
*What the Native Americans Wore
Zuni Jewelry
Zuni: A Village of Silversmiths

ALVIN M. JOSEPHY, JR.

America in 1492
Chief Joseph's People & Their War
500 Nations: An Illustrated History of North American Indians
History of the Native Americans
Indian Heritage of America
*Alvin Joseph's History of the native Americans Series
The Nez Perce Indians & the Opening of the Northwest
Now That the Buffalo's Gone
The Patriot Chiefs: A Chronicle of American Indian Resistance
Red Power: The American Indians' Fight for Freedom
Wounded Knee: Lest We Forget

JOURNALISM

The American Indian & the Media
Let My People Know: American Indian Journalism, 1828-1978
Native American Press in Wisconsin and the Nation
Native American Representations: First Encounters, Distorted Images & Literary
Appropriations
The Newspaper Indian: Native American Identity In the Press, 1820-1890
Notes From the Center of Turtle Island
Pictures of Our Nobler Selves: A History of Native American Contributions to the Media

JUVENILE LITERATURE

*Across the Tundra
*Algonquian
*All About Arrowheads & Spear Points
*Allapattah

*American Indian Arts & Crafts Source Book
*The American Indian in America
*American Indian Music & Musical Instruments
*American Indians
*American Indians Today
*Anasazi Legends
*An Anasazi Welcome
*The Animals' Ballgame
*Ancient Indians: The First Americans
*Anna's Athabaskan Summer
*ANPAO: An American Indian Odyssey
*Apache
*The Apaches & Navajos
*Approaches to Teaching Momaday's "The Way to Rainy Mountain"
*Arctic Hunter
*Arctic Memories
*Around the World in Folktale & Myth: American Indian
*At the Mouth of the Luckiest River
*Atariba and Niguayona
*Aunt Mary, Tell Me Stories
*Authentic North American Indian Clothing Series
*Authentic North American Indian Cradleboards Series
*Baby Rattlesnake
*A Bag of Bones
*The Beaded Moccasins
*Beauty Beside Me, Stories of My Grandmother's Skirts
*Beaver Steals Fire /Fire on the Land
*Beaver Steals Fire: A Salish Coyote Story
*The Bentwood Box
*Between Earth & Sky: Legends of Native American Sacred Places
*Bill Red Coyote Is a Nut
*The Birchbark House
*Black Elk: A Man with a Vision
*Blackfeet Crafts
*Blue Jacket: War Chief of the Shawnees
*Blue Thunder
*Boat Ride With Lillian Two Blossom
*The Boy Who Dreamed of an Acorn
*The Boy Who Lived With the Seals
*Brave Bear & the Ghosts: A Sioux Legend
*Brave Wolf and the Thunderbird
*A Breeze Swept Through
*Broken Ice
*Brother Eagle, Sister Sky
*Buffalo Hunt
*Buffalo Hunter
*Buffalo & Indians on the Great Plains
*The Buffalo Jump
*Building A Bridge
*Butterfly Dance *The Cahuilla
*California Indians
*California Indians: An Educational Coloring Book
*California's Indians & the Gold Rush
*The California Native American Tribes
*The Catawbas
*The Cedar Plank
*Ceremony in the Circle of Life
*Chant of the Red Man
*Charlie Young Bear
*The Charm of the Bear Claw Necklace
*The Cherokee
*Cherokee Legends & the Trail of Tears
*Cherokee Summer
*Cheyenne
*The Cheyenne
*Cheyenne Legends of Creation
*Cheyenne Short Stories
*Cheyenne Warriors
*The Chichi Hoohoo Bogeyman
*The Chickasaw
*Chief Hawah's Book of Native Americann Indians
*Chief Joseph
*Chief Joseph's Own Story As Told By Chief Joseph in 1879
*Chief Sarah: Sarah Winnemucca's Fight for Indian Rights
*Chief Stephen's Parky
*The Children, Always the Children
*Children of the Morning Light
*Chinook
*The Chinook: Northwest
*Chocolate Chipmunks & Canoes
*The Choctaw
*The Chumash
*Circle of Thanks
*Circle of Wonder: A Native American Christmas Story
*Clamshell Boy: A Makah Legend
*Cloudwalker: Contemporary Native American Stories
*Clues from the Past: A Resource Book on Archaeology
*Columbus Day
*The Comanche
*Comanche Warbonnet
*Come to Our Salmon Feast
*The Coming of Coyote
*Concise Encyclopedia of the American Indian
*Cottontail and Sun

KACHINAS

KICKAPOO INDIANS

KIOWA INDIANS

KOKOPELLI

KOOTENAI (See SALISH & KOOTENAI INDIANS)

KWAKIUTL INDIANS

LAKOTA/DAKOTA (SIOUX) INDIANS

LAND CESSIONS, TENURES, TRANSFERS & DISPUTES

Land, Wind & Hard Words: A Story of Navajo Activism
Making Indian Law: The Huaapai Land Case & the Birth of Ethnohistory
The Montaukett Indians of Eastern Long Island
Murder State: California's Native American Genocide, 1846-1873\
A Nation Within a Nation: Dependency & the Cree
Native American Estate
*Native Americans & the Reservation in American History
Native Peoples of the Southwest: Negotiating Land, Water & Ethnicities
Navajo Land, Navajo Culture: The Utah Experience in the 20th Century
Navajo Land Use: An Ethnoarchaeological Study
The New Resource Wars
Of Sacred Lands & Strip Malls: The Battle for Puvungna
One Dead Indian:The Premier, the Police, & the Ipperwash Crisis
The Oneida Land Claims
*Only the Names Remain: The Cherokees and the Trail of Tears
The Pleasure of the Crown: Anthropology, Law & First Nations
Prehistoric Pueblo World, A.D. 1150-1350
The Protohistoric Pueblo World, A.D. 1275-1600
Pueblo Indian Land Grants of the "Rio Abajo", NM
Pushed Into the Rocks: Southern California Indian Land Tenure
Qualla: Home of the Middle Cherokee Settlement
Reaching Just Settlements: Land Claims in British Columbia
Reconfiguring the Reservation
Reconstruction in Indian Territory
Red Lake Nation: Portraits of Ojibwe Life
Redskins, Ruffleshirts and Rednecks
The Removal of the Cherokee Nation: Manifest Destiny or National Dishonor
Rogue Diamonds: The Rush for Northern Riches, Dene Rights
Roots of Resistance: Land Tenure in New Mexico (1680-1980)
Sacred Lands of Indian America
Savages & Scoundrels: The Untold Story of America's Road to Empire
  through Indian Territory
Searching for the Bright Path
The Second Long Walk: Navajo-Hopi Land Dispute
Sold American: The Story of Alaska Natives & Their Land, 1867-1959
Spirit Dance at Meziadin: Chief Joseph Gosnell & the Nisga'a Treaty
*The Story of the Trail of Tears
Sustaining the Cherokee Family: Kinship & the Allotment of an Indigenous Nation
The Taos Indians & the Battle for Blue Lake
Territorial Subdivision & Boundaries of the Wampanoag, Massachusett and Nauset Indians
Townsite Settlement & Dispossession in the Cherokee Nation, 1866-1907
The Trail of Tears
Unearthing Indian Land: Living With the Legacies of Allotment
Unsettled Past, Unsettled Future: The Story of Maine Indians
An Unspeakable Sadness: The Dispossession of the Nebraska Indians
The Weiser Indians: Shoshoni Peacemakers
The Wind Won't Know Me: A History of the Navajo-Hopi Land Dispute
*You Are Now on Indian Land: The American Idian Occupation of Alcatraz island, 1969
You Are On Indian Land: Alcatraz Island, 1969-71
Zuni & the Courts: A Struggle for Sovereign land Rights

LANGUAGES, DICTIONARIES, GLOSSARIES, ETC.

A Is For American: Letters & Other Characters in the Newly U.S.
Absaloka: Crow Chilren's Writing
Ahtna Athabaskan Dictionary
Alaawich
Alaska Native Language Center Publications
Aleut Dictionary
America's Second Tongue: American Indian Education & the Ownership of English
American Indian English
American Indian: Language & Literature
American Indian Language: The Historical Linguistics of Native America
American Indian Language Series
American Indian Languages, Vol. 5
American Indian Languages: Cultural & Social Contexts
American Indian Linguistics & Ethnography in Honor of Laurence C. Thompson
American Indian Linguistics & Literature
American Indian Rhetorics of Survivance: Word Medicine, Word Magic
An Ancient New Jersey Indian Jargon, Vol. 5
Arapaho Dialects
The Arapaho Language
Athabaskan Language Studies: Essays in Honor of Robert W. Young
The Athabaskan Languages: Perspective on a Native American Language Family
Athapaskan Linguistics
The Bearer of This Letter: Language Ideologies, Literacy Practices
  & the Fort Belknap Indian Community
Beginning Cherokee
Beginning Creek: Myskoke Emponvkv
Beginning Washoe
Bibliography of Language Arts Materials for Native North Americans, 1965-1974
Bibliography of the Languages of Native California
Blackfoot Grammar
Born in the Blood: On Native American Translation
Caddo Verb Morphology
Cahuilla Dictionary
California Indian Languages
The Calusa: Linguistic & Cultural Origins & Relationships
The Canadian Michif Language Dictionary (Metis)
Carry Forth the Stories: An Ethnographer's Journey Into Native Oral Tradition
Case & Agreement in Inuit
Castiglioni's Vocabulary of Cherokee, Vol. 33
Chahta Anumpa: A Grammar of the Choctaw Language (CD-ROM)
Chem'ivillu: Let's Speak Cahuilla

*Cherokee ABC Coloring Book
Cherokee Dictionary
Cherokee-English Dictionary
Cherokee-English Interliner, First Epistle of John of the New Testiment
Cherokee Glossary
Cherokee Language Workbook
Cherokee Reference Grammar
The Cherokee Syllabary
Cherokee Words
Chew's Vocabulary of Tuscarora
Cheyenne Indians: Sketch of the Cheyenne Grammar
Chickasaw: An Analytical Dictionary
Chickasaw Glossary
Chimariko Grammar: Areal & Typological Perspective
Chinook Jargon
Choctaw Language Awareness Teachers Manual
Choctaw Language & Culture: Chahta Anumpa
Choctaw Language Dictionary
Choctaw Nation Dictionary
The Chumash & Costanoan Languages
The Collected Works of Edward Sapir
Colloquial Navajo: A Dictionary
Comanche Dictionary & Grammar
Comanche Talking Dictionary
Comparative Chukoto-Kamchatkan Dictionary
Comparative Hokan-Coahuiltecan Studies
Comparative Studies in Amerindian Languages
A Comparative Study of Lake-Iroquoian Accent
A Concise Dictionary of Minnesoita Ojibwe
A Concise Dictionary of Indian Tribes of North America
The Concise Lakhota Dictionary: English to Lakhota
A Concise Nuxalk-English Dictionary
The Cree Language Structure - A Cree Approach
Creek (Muscogee) New Testament Concordance
The Creek Verb
Crossing Mountains: Native American Language Educationn in Public Schools
Cumming's Vocabulary of Shawnee
Dakota-English Dictionary
Dakota Grammar, Texts & Ethnology
Dakota Philosopher: Charles Eastman & American Indian Thought
Dakota Sioux Indian Dictionary
Defying Maliseet Language Death: Emergent Vitalities of Language, Culture,
  and Identity in Eastern Canada
Delaware-English / English-Delaware Dictionary
Delaware-Indian & English Spelling Book
The Delaware Language: A Preliminary Draft
Delaware Reference Grammar
Denny's Vocabulary of Shawnee
Dictionary of the Alabama Language
Dictionary of the American Indian
Dictionary Catalog of the Edward E. Ayer Collection
Dictionary of the Chinook Jargon: English-Chinook
Dictionary of the Choctaw Language
Dictionary of Creek/Muskogee
Dictionary of Daily Life of Indian of the Americas
Dictionary of Indian Tribes of the Americas
Dictionary of Jicarilla Apache
Dictionary of Mesa Grande Diegueno
Dictionary of Native American Healing
Dictionary of Native American Mythology
Dictionary of the Ojibway Language
Dictionary of the Osage Language
Dictionary of Papago Usage
Dictionary of Powhatan
A Dictionary of Skiri Pawnee
Dine Bizaad Binahoo'aah: Rediscovering the Navajo Language
Dine Bizaad: Speak, Read, Write Navajo
Do You See What I Mean? Plains Indian Sign Talk & the Embodiment of Action
The Dog's Children: Anishinaabe Texts
Drinking & Sobriety Among the Lakota Sioux
Early 19th Century Contributions to American Indian & General Linguistics
Early Vocabulary of Catawba
Eastern Ojibwa-Chippewa-Ottawa Dictionary
Education & Language Restoration
Elliot's Vocabulary of Cayuga
Elliot's Vocabulary of Mohawk
Elnguq
English-Cheyenne Dictionary
English-Eskimo & Eskimo-English Vocabularies
English-Micmac Dictionary
English-Navajo Children's Picture Dictionary
Essay of Delaware-Indian & English Spelling Book
The Ethnology of the Salinan Indians
Everyday Lakota: An English-Sioux Dictionary for Beginners
The Fast Runner: Filming the Legend of Atanarjuat (Inuktitut)
First Lessons in Makah
Flutes of Fire: Essays on California Indian Languages
Forked Tongues: Speech, Writing & Representation in North American Indian Texts
General & Amerindian Ethnolinguistics
Grammar & Dictionary of the Timucua Language
A Grammar of Bella Coola
A Grammar of Comanche
A Grammar of Creek (Muskogee)
A Grammar of Crow

The Student's Dictionary of Literary Plains Cree
Studies in American Indian Languages
Studies in Southeastern Indian Languages
Stylized Characters' Speech in Thompson Salish Narrative
*A Summer's Trade: Shiigo Na'iini'
Supplement to the Handbook of Middle American Indians: Linguistics
Syntax & Semantics: The Syntax of Native American Languages
Taitaduhaan: Western Mono Ways of Speaking
Talking Chickasaw Dictionary
Teaching Oregon Native Languages
Telling Stories in the Face of Danger: Language Renewal in Native American Communities
Ten'a Texts & Tales: From Anvik, Alaska
Theoretical Perspectives on Native American Languages
The Thompson Language
Thompson River Salish Dictionary
Tlingit Verb Dictionary
A Tohono O'odham Grammar
Tohono O'odham/Pima to English, English to Tohono
Tonkawa, An Indian Language of Texas
Totkv Mocvse • New Fire: Creek Folktales
Tovangar
Tracks That Speak: The Legacy of Native American Words in North American Culture
Traditional Narratives of the Arikara Indians
Tribal Theory in Native American Literature
Turtle Island Alphabet
Tuscarora-English, English-Tuscarora Dictionary
The Tutelo Language
Umatilla Dictionary: Confederated Tribes of the Umatilla Indian Reservation
Unscripted America: Indigenous Languages and the Origins of a Literary Nation
Upper Chehalis Dictionary
A Vocabulary of Stockbridge Mahican
A Vocabulary of Mohegan-Pequot
Vocabulary of New Jersey Delaware
Vocabulary of the Shoshone Language
Vocabulary of the Tuscarora
A Vocabulary of Woccon
The Washo Language of East Central California & Nevada
We Are Our Language: An Ethnography of Language Revitalization in a Northern Athabaskan Community
Western Abenaki Dictionary, Vol. 2: English-Abenaki
Western Apache-English Dictionary
Western Apache Language/Culture: Essays in Linguistic Anthropology
Western Abenaki Dictionary: Abenaki-English
When I Was Small - I Wan Kwikwas: A Grammatical Analysis of St'at'imc Oral Narratives
Where the West Begins: Essays on Middle Border and Siouxland Writing
Wisdom Sits in Places: Landscape & Language Among the Western Apache
*Wisdom Weaver: Bina'nitin Bidziilgo Atlohi
Wishram Texts: Together With Wasco Tales & Myths
Writing Cherokee
Wiyot Grammar & Texts
Yakama Sahaptin Dictionary
Yerington Paiute Dictionary
Yerington Paiute Language Grammar
Yoeme-English, English-Yoeme Standard Dictionary
Yokuts Dialect Survey
The Yokuts Language of South Central California
Yup'ik Eskimo Dictionary
Yurok Affixes
Zeisberger's Indian Dictionary: English, German, Iroquois – the Onondaga & Algonquin - the Delaware

LEGAL, LAWS, ETC.

Aboriginal Law handbook
Aboriginal Peoples & Government Responsibility: Exploring Federal & Provincial Roles
Aboriginal Title & Indigenous Peoples: Canada, Australia & New Zealand
Acts & Resolutions (of National Tribal Councils)
Alaska Natives & American Laws
All Indians Do Not Live in Teepees (or Casinos)
All Our Relations: Native Struggles for Land & Life
American Indian Constitutional Reform & the Rebuilding of Native Nations
American Indian & Crime, 1992-2002
American Indian Law
The American Indian Law Deskbook
American Indian Law In a Nutshell
American Indian Religious Freedom Act: A Legislative History of Public Law No. 95-341
The American Indian in Western Legal Thought: The Discourse of Conquest
The American Indian in the White Man's Prisons: A Story of Genocide
The American Indian Law Series
American Indian Legal Materials: A Union List
American Indian Legal Studies Teacher's Manual & Text
The American Indian Occupation of Alcatraz Island: Red Power & Self-Determination
American Indian Policy in the 20th Century
American Indian Sovereignty & Law: An Annotated Bibliography
American Indian Sovereignty & the U.S. Supreme Court: The Masking of Justice
American Indian Tribal Courts
American Indian Water Rights & the Limits of the Law
American Indians, American Justice
American Indians, Time and the Law
American Indians & World War II
Annotated Bibliography of Federal & Tribal Law: Print & Internet Sources
Anthropologists & Indians in the New South
The Arbitrary Indian: The Indian Arts & Crafts Act of 1990

Arguing With Tradition: The Language of Law in Hopi Tribal Court
Bartering With the Bones of Their Dead: The Colville Confederated Tribes & Termination
Basic Guide to Indian Community Advocacy
John Beeson's Plea for the Indians
Behind the Trail of Broken Treaties
Bibliography of the Constitution & Laws of the American Indians
Bibliography of the English Colonial Treaties With the American Indians
Braid of Feathers:American Indian Law & Contemporary Tribal Life
Bread & Freedom
Broken Treaties: U.S. & Canadian Relations with the Lakotas & the Plains Cree, 1868-1885
Call to Justice: The Life of a Federal Trial Judge
The Case of the Seneca Indians in the State of New York
The Cherokee Cases: Two Landmark Federal Decisions in the Fight for Sovereignty
Cherokee Nation Code: Annotated
Cherokee Nation vs. Georgia: Native American Rights
The Cheyenne Way: Conflict and Case Law in Primitive Jurisprudence
Claiming Turtle Mountain's Constitution: The History, Legacy, and Future of a Tribal Nation's Founding Documents
The Constitution and Laws of the American Indian Tribes
Felix S. Cohen's Handbook of Federal Indian Law
Conquest By Law: How the Discovery of America Dispossessed Indigenous Peoples of Their Lands
Conservation & Indian Rights
Consolidated Native Law Statutes, Regulations & Treaties
Constitutionalism & Native Americans, 1903-1968
Constitutions, Treaties, and Laws Series
Consulting With Tribes for Off-Reservation Projects
The Consumer's Rights Under Warranties
Contemporary Native American Political Issues
Contracts & You
Coyote Warrior: One Man, Three Tribes & the Trial That Forged a Nation
Criminal Jurisdiction Allocation in Indian Country
Criminal Justice in Native America
Crow Dog's Case: American Indian Sovereignty...
Cultural Property Law: A Practitioner's Guide to the Management, Protection, and Preservation of Heritage Resources, 2nd Ed.
Deadliest Enemies: Law & Making the Race Relations On & Off Rosebud Reservation
Digest of American Indian Law: Cases & Chronology
Diplomates in Buckskin
Directory of American Indian Law Attorneys
Intercultural Dispute Resolution in Aboriginal Contexts
Documents of American Indian Diplomacy
Documents of U.S. Indian Policy, 3rd Ed.
Doing Things the Right Way
Early American Indian Documents: Treaties & Laws, 1607-1789
Encyclopedia of American Indian Civil Rights
Encyclopedia of Native American Legal Traditions
Enduring Legacies: Native American Treaties & Contemporary Controversies
Tne Encyclopedia of Native American Legal Tradition
Exiled in the Land of the Free: Democracy, Indian Nations & the U.S. Constitution
Federal Indian Law, Cases & Material
The Federal-Indian Trust Relationship
Fifth Annual Indian Law Seminar
A Final Promise: The Campaign to Assimilate the Indians, 1880-1920
Forgotten Tribes: Unrecognized Indians & the Federal Acknowledgement Process
The Future of the Past: Archaeologists, Native Americans & Repatriation
Grave Injustice: The American Indian Repatriation Movement & NAGPRA
Guide to American Indian Documents in the Congressional Serial Set: 1817-1899
Handbook of American Indian Religious Freedom
Handbook of Federal Indian Law
Hollow Justice: A History of Indigenous Claims in the U.S.
Igniting King Philip's War: the John Sassamon Murder Trial
Imperfect Victories: The Legal Tenacity of the Omaha Tribe, 1945-1995
Implementing the Native American Graves Protection and Repatriation Act (NAGPRA)
In the Courts of the Conqueror: The 10 Worst Indian Law Cases Ever Decided
Indian Affairs & the Administrative State in the 19th Century
Indian Affairs: Laws & Treaties
The Indian Bill of Rights
The Indian Child Welfare Act Handbook
The Indian Civil Rights Act At Forty
Indian Court Judgements
Indian Employment, Training & Related Services Demonstration Act
Indian Gaming & the Law
Indian Gaming: Who Wins?
Indian Justice: A Cherokee Murder Trial at Tahlequah in 1840
Indian Law Conferences Series
Indian Law - Race Law: A Five Hundred Year History
The Indian Lawyer
Indian Orphanages
Indian Police and Judges: Experiments in Acculturation and Control
The Indian Reorganization Act: Congress & Bills
Indian Reserved Water Rights
Indian Rights Manual
Indian Roots of American Democracy
Indian Territory & the U.S., 1866-1906
Indian Treaty-Making Policy in the U.S. & Canada, 1867-1877
Indian Water, 1985: Collected Essays
Indian Water Rights: Congressional Hearing
Indians & Criminal Justice
The Indians & the U.S. Constitution
Indians, Indian Tribes & State Government: Major Legal Battles
Indigeniety in the Courtroom: Law, Culture, and the Production of Difference in North American Courts
Indigenous Intellectual Property Rights: Legal Obstacles & Innovative Solutions

Insuring Indian Country: The Intersection of Tort, Insurance, and Federal Indian Law
Intellectual Property Rights for Indigenous Peoples: A Source Book
Introduction to Criminal Jurisdiction in Indian Country
Introduction to Tribal Legal Studies, 3rd Edition
Issues in Native American Cultural Identity
Jicarilla Apache Tribal Code
Justice for Natives: Searching for Common Ground
Keeping Promises: What Is Sovereignty & Other Questions from Indian Country
Labor Laws, Union, and Indian Self-Determination
Landlord Tenant Relations
Landmark Indian Law Cases
Law and the American Indian: Readings, Notes and Cases
Law Enforcement on Indian Reservations After Oliphant v. Suquamish Indian Tribes
Law & Identity: Lawyers, Native Americans and Legal Practice
Law & Status Among the Kiowa Indians
A Lawyer In Indian Country: A Memoir
Laws of the Cherokee Nation
Laws & Joint Resolutions
Leasing Indian Water
Legal Conscience, Selected Papers
The Legal Ideology of Removal
Legal Issues in Native American History
Legal Structures for Indian Business Development on Reservations
Legalized Racism: Federal Indian Policy & the End of Equal Rights for All Americans
Legends, Traditions & Laws of the Iroquois: Or, Six Nations, & History
   of the Tuscarora Indians
Like a Hurricane: The Indian Movement from Alcatraz to Wounded Knee
Like a Loaded Weapon
Linking Arms Together: American Indian Treaty Visions of Law & Peace
The Livingston Indian Records, 1666-1723
Long & Terrible Shadow: White Values & Native Rights
Major Council Meetings of American Indian Tribes: Part One & Two
Making Indian Law: The Huaapai Land Case & the Birth of Ethnohistory
Mending the Circle: A Native Repatriation Guide
Model Court Development Project
Nation to Nation: Treaties Between the U.S. & American Indian Nations
Native Acts: Law Recognition, and Culturall Authenticity
Native American Affairs & the Dept. of Defense
Native American Cultural & Religious Freedoms
Native American Issues
Native American Issues: A Reference Handbook
Native American Justice
Native American Law & Colonialism Before 1776 to 1903
*Native American Rights
The Native American Rights Movement
Native American Sovereignty
Native American Sovereignty on Trial
The Native American Struggle: Conquering the Rule of Law A Colloquium
Native American Transracial Adoptees Tell Their Stories
Native Americans: Crime & Justice
Native Americans & the Law
Native Americans & Nixon: Presidential Politics & Minority Self-Determination, 1969-1972
Native Americans & Public Policy
The Native Americans Reference Collection: Documents Collected
   by the Office of Indian Affairs
Native Claims: Indigenous Law Against Empire, 1500-1920
Native People in Canada: Contemporary Conflicts
Native Waters: Contemporary Indian Water Settlements & the Second Treaty Era
Navajo Courts & Navajo Common Law, A Tradition of Tribal Self-Governance
The Navajo-Hopi Land Dispute: An American Tragedy
Navajo Nation Peacemaking: Living Traditional Justice
Navajo Tribal Code
Negotiated Sovereignty: Working to Improve Tribal-State Relations
Never Without Consent; The james Bay Cree Stand Against an Independent Quebec
New Capitalists: Issues of Law, Politics & Identity Surrounding Casino Gaming
   on Native American Land
The New Deal & American Indian Tribalism
A New Order of Things: Property, Power & the Transformation
   of the Creek Indians, 1733-1816
Not Without Our Consent: Lakota Resistance to Termination, 1950-59
Notes From a Miner's Canary: Essays on the State of Native America
Oil & Gas
Oklahoma Tribal Court Reports
Organizing the Lakota
Other Words: American Indian Literature, Law & Culture
Partial Justice" Federal Indian Law in a Liberal-Constitutional System
A Passion for the True & Just: Felix & Lucy Kramer Cohen and the Indian New Deal
The Patriot Chiefs: A Chronicle of American Indian Resistance
Perversions of Justice: Indigenous Peoples & Angloamerican Law
Planting Tail Feathers: Tribal Survival & Public Law 280
The Pleasure of the Crown: Anthropology, Law & First Nations
Policing in Indian Country
Policing on American Indian Reservations
Policing Race & Place in Indian Country: Over-and-Under-enforcement
The Politics of Hallowed Ground: Wounded Knee & the Struggle for Indian Sovereignty
The Potlatch Papers: A Colonial Case History
The Problem of Justice: Tradition & Law in the Coast Salish World
Property Rights & Indian Economies
Puritan Justice & the Indian: White Man's Law in Massachusetts, 1630-1763
Recent Legal Issues for American Indians, 1968 to the Present
Quarter-Acre of Heartache
Readings in American Indian Law
Real Indians: Identity & the Survival of Native America
Records of the Bureau of Indian Affairs: Central Classified Files, 1907-1939

Red Lake Court of Tribal Offenses Court Manual
Red Man's Land, White Man's Law: The Past & Present Status of the American Indian
Reflections on the Alaska Native Experience
Religion, Law & the Land: Native Americans & the Judicial Interpretations of Sacred Land
Repatriation Reader: Who Owns American Indian Remains?
Repossession & You
The Return of the Eagle: The Legal History of the Grand Traverse Band
   of Ottawa & Chippewa Indians
The Rights of Indians & Tribes: The Basic ACLU Guide
The Rights of Indigenous Peoples
Sacred Sites & Repatriation
Sharing Our Stories of Survival: Native Women Surviving Violence
The Significant Ties Exception to the Indian Child Welfare Act
Sixth Annual Indian Law Conference
Skull Wars: Kennewick Man, Archaeology, & the Battle For Native American Identity
Sovereign Selves: American Indian Autobiography & the Law
The Spanish Struggle for Justice in the Conquest of America
Standing Bear Controversy: Prelude to Indian Reform
*Standing Bear of the Ponca
Standing Bear & the Ponca Chiefs
Structuring Sovereignty: Constitutions of Native Nations
Struggle for the Land: Native North American Resistance to Genocide,
   Ecocide, & Colonization
The Supreme Court & Tribal Gaming: California v. Cabazon Band of Mission Indians
Tangled Webs of History
"They Treated Us Just Like Indians"
Tonto's Revenge: Reflections on American Indian Culture & Policy
Towards Aboriginal Self-Government
Treaties on Trial
Treatment of Indians by the Criminal Justice System
The Trial of "Indian Joe"
Tribal Contracting: Understanding & Drafting Business Contracts
   With American Indian Tribes
Tribal Courts Directory
Tribal Criminal Law & Procedure
*Tribal Law
The Tribal Moment in American Politics: The Struggle for Native American Sovereignty
Tribes, Land & Environment
Tribes, Treaties, and Constitutional Tribulations
Trusteeship in Change: Toward Tribal Autonomy in Resource Management
Uneven Ground: American Indian Sovereignty & Federal Law
Unjust Relations: Aboriginal Rights in Canadian Courts
Voice of Indigenous Peoples: A Plea to the World
Walk for Justice
The Walleye War
Walleye Warriors
When Did Indians Become Straight: Kinship, the History of Sexuality, & Native Sovereignty
Wisconsin's County Forests: Conflict Over Indian Timber Rights
The World's Richest Indian: Jackson Barnett
You and the Utility Company
Your Rights As American Indians

LEGENDS & LORE

Acaoohkiwina & Acimowina: Traditional Narratives of the Rock Cree Indians
Aleut Tales & Narratives
*Algic Researches: North American Indian Folktales & Legends
Algonquin Legends of New England
American, African, and Old European Mythologies
The American Eagle
American Indian Genesis
American Indian Legends
American Indian Linguistics & Literature
American Indian Mythology
*American Indian Mythology
American Indian Myths & Legends
The American Indian Oral History Manual: Making Many Voices Heard
American Indian Stories
*American Indian Trickster Tales
American Indians: Folk Tales & Legends
American Indians' Kitchen-Table Stories
Anasazi Legends
Ancient Voices, Current Affairs: The Legend of the Rainbow Warriors
*And It Is Still That Way: Legends Told by Arizona Indian Children
*Apache Legends: Songs of the Wild Dancer
Arrow Creek Stories
Artistry in Native American Myths
As My Grandfather Told It: Traditional Stories of the Koyukuk
Bad Girl & the Man Who Followed the Sun: An Athabaskan Indian Legend from Alaska
Bad Medicine & Good: Tales of the Kiowas
Badger & Coyote Were Neighbors: Melville Jacobs on Northwest Indian Myths & Tales
The Basket Woman
The Bear Knife: And Other American Indian Tales
The Bear That Turned White; & Other Native Tales
*Beaver Steals Fire /Fire on the Land
*Beaver Steals Fire: A Salish Coyote Story
Bedbugs' Night Dance & Other Hopi Tales of Sexual Encounter
Before The Horse: Indian Myths & Legends
Being Dakota: Tales & Traditions of the Sisseton & Wahpeton
Being In Being (Haida myth)
Bird Girl & the Man Who Followed the Sun
Birds of Algonquin Legend
Blackfoot Lodge Tales
The Blind Man and the Loom: The Stpry of a Tale

Whispers of the Ancients: Native Tales for Teaching & Healing in Our Time
The White Canoe and Other Legends of the Ojibways
White Wolf Woman
Who Speaks for Wolf? A Native American Learning Story
Wigwam Evenings
Willow Stories: Utah Navajo Baskets
The Wind Eagle
Wisconsin Chippewa Myths & Tales
Wisdom of the Elders: Native Traditions on the Northwest
Wisdom of the Elders: Sacred Native Stories of Nature
The Wisdom of the Great Chiefs
Wisdom of the Native Americans
Wishram Texts: Wasco Tales & Myths
The Witch of Goingsnake & Other Stories
Write It On Your Heart: World of an Okanagan Storyteller
Wiyot Grammar & Texts
Yamoria the Lawmaker: Stories of the Dene
Yokuts Texts
Yonder Mountain: A Cherokee Legend
Zuni Coyote Tales

LEWIS & CLARK EXPEDITION

Among the Sleeping Giants
Bitterroot Crossing: Lewis & Clark Across the Lolo Trail
Do Them No Harm
Exploring the West
Finding the West: Explorations of Lewis & Clark
The Incredible Journey of Lewis & Clark
The Journal & Account Book of Patrick Gass
The Journals of the Lewis & Clark Expedition
Letters of the Lewis & Clark Expedition
Lewis & Clark: Across the Divide
Lewis & Clark Among the Indians
*The Lewis & Clark Expedition
Lewis & Clark & the Indian Country: The Native American Perspective
Lewis & Clark: Legacies, Memories, & New Perspectives
Lewis & Clark & the hehaptian Speaking Americans
Lewis & Clark Territory: Contemporary Artists Revisit Place, Race, & Memory
Lewis & Clark Through Indian Eyes: Nine Indian Writers on the Legacy of the Expedition
Lewis & Clark: Voyage of Discovery
Lewis & Clark's West
Meriwether Lewis & William Clark: Soldiers, Explorers, & Partners in History
Native America, Discovered & Conquered: Thomas Jefferson, Lewis & Clark, and Manifest Destiny
Sacajawea: A Guide & Interpreter on the Lewis & Clark Expedition
Sacagawea: Indian Interpreter to Lewis & Clark
Sacajawea's People: The Lemhi Shoshones & the Salmon River Country
The Salish People and the Lewis & Clark Expedition
*The Story of the Lewis & Clark Expedition
Those Tremendous Mountains
The Way to the Western Sea
West to the Pacific: The Story of Lewis & Clark Expedition

LITERATURE

Algonquian Spirit: Contemporary Translations of the Algonquian Literatures of North America
Sherman Alexie: A Collection of Critical Essays
All My Relations
All My Relatives
All That Remain: Varieties of Indigenous Expression
American Indian Linguistics & Literature
American Indian Literary Nationalism
American Indian Literature: An Anthology
American Indian Literature, Environmental Justice, & Ecocriticism
American Indian Literature & the Southwest: Contexts & Dispositions
American Indian Literatures
American Indian Nonfiction
American Indian Rhetorics of Survivance: Word Medicine, Word Magic
American Indian Stories
American Indian Themes in Young Adult Literature
American Lazarus: Religion & the Rise of African-American & Native American Literatures
The Ancient Child
Ararapikva: Traditional Karuk Indian Literature from Northwest California
Art As Performance: Reflections on Native Literary Aesthetics
Authentic Alaska" Voices of Its Native Writers
Back to the Blanket: Recovered Rhetorics & Literacies in American Indian Studies
Bear Island: The War at Sugar Point
Being in Being: The Collected Works of Skaay of the Qquuna Qiighawaay
Beyond Bounds: Cross-Cultural Essays on Anglo, Americann Indian & Chicano Literature
Black Silk Handkerchief
Bleed Into Me: A Book of Stories
Blood Brother
Blue Horses Rush In: Poems & Stories
Book of the Fourth World: Reading the Native Americas Through Their Literature
Born in the Blood: On Native American Translation
Briefcase Warriors: Stories for the Stage
The Broken Circle
The Broken Cord
Captivity & Sentiment: Cultural Exchange in American Literature, 1682-1861
Captured in the Middle: Tradition & Experience in The Cherokee Night & Other Plays
Chair of Tears

Cherokee Reference Grammar
Chihuly's Pendletons
Chikasha Stories, 3 Vols.
The Chippewa Landscape of Louise Erdrich
A Circle of Nations: Voices & Visions of American Indians
The Cold-and-Hunger Dance
The Collected Writings of Samson Occum, Mohegan
The Colour of Resistance: Contemporary Collection of Writing by Aboriginal Women
Columbus, Shakespeare & the Interpretation of the New World
Comeuppance At Kicking Horse Casino & Other Stories
Coming to Light: Contemporary Translations of the Native Literatures of North America
The Common Pot: The Recovery of Native Space in the Northeast
The Complete Seymour: Colville Storyteller
Contemporary American Indian Literatures & the Oral Traditions
Contemporary American Indian Writing: Unsettling Literature
Contemporary Native American Literature
Conversations With Louise Erdrich & Michael Dorris
Conversations With Leslie marmon Silko
Cries From a Metis Heart
Dancing on the Rim of the World
Dark River
Dawn Land
Dead Voices: Natural Agonies in the New World
Deadly Indian Summer
Deep Waters: The Textual Continuum in American Indian Literature
Destroying Dogma: Vine Deloria, Jr. & His Influence on American Society
Dictionary of Native American Literature
*Dog People: Native Dog Stories
Domestic Subjects: Gender, Citizenship, and Law in Native American Literature
The Dream of a Broken Field
Dreams of Fiery Stars: The Transformations of Native American Fiction
Dreams & Thunder: Stories, Poems, & The Sun Dance Opera
Dry Bones & Indian Sermons: Praying Indians in Colonial America
Early American Writings
Earth Power Coming: Short Fiction in Native American Literature
Earth Song, Sky Spirit: Short Stories of the Contemporary Native American Experience
Earth's Mind: Essays in Native Literature
Ecocriticism & the Creation of Self & Place in Environmental & American Indian Literatures
Elsie's Business
Louise Erdrich
Feathering Custer
Feminist Readings of Native American Literature
Fiction International 20: American Indian Writers
Fire Sticks: A Collection of Stories
Folk-Tales of the Coast Salish
Footpaths & Bridges: Voices from the Native American Women Playwrights Archive
For Those Who Come After: A Study of Native American Autobiography
Forever Island & Allapattah
Forked Tongues
Four Masterworks of American Indian Literature
Fourth World Rising: Neo-Modern Indian Literature
From the Glittering World: A Navajo Story
From Sand Creek
The Girl Who Married the Moon: Tales from Native North America
The Golden Woman: The Colville Narrative of Peter J. Seymour
Grandmother, Grandfather, & Old Wolf
Grave Concerns, Trickster Turns: The Novels of Louis Owens
A Great Plains Reader
Handbook of Native American Literature
Happy Hunting Grounds
The Hawk is Hungry and Other Stories
Heart as a Drum: Continuance & Resistance in American Indian Poetry
Tony Hillerman's Navajoland
Home Places: Contemporary Native American Writing from Sun Tracks
Hopi Traditional Literature
Hotline Healers: An Almost Browne Novel
Hundred in the Hand
I Hear the Train: Reflections, Inventions, Refractions
Iktomi and the Ducks and Other Sioux Stories
In Beauty I Walk: The Literary Roots of Native American Writing
Index to Literature on the American Indian
Imagining Indians in the Southwest: Persistent Visions of a Primitive Past
Indian Land Tenure
Indian Nation: Native American Literature & 19th Century Nationalism
Indian Old Man Stories
Indian Why Stories
The Inhuman Race: The Racial Grotesque in American Literature & Culture
Injun Joe's Ghost: The Indian Mixed-Blood in American Writing
Inside Dazzling Mountains: Southwest Native Verbal Arts
Interpreting the Indian: 20th century Poets & the native American
Inventing the American Primitive: Politics, Gender & the Representation of Native American Literary Traditions, 1789-1936
The Invention of Native American Literature
The Jailing Of Cecelia Capture
Ke-Ma-Ha: The Omaha Stories of Francis La Flesche
Kootenai Why Stories
Landfill Meditation: Cross blood Stories
The Last of the Ofos
The Lasting of the Mohicans: History of an American Myth
A. Robert Lee: Native American Wiritng
Life Woven With Stone
The Lightning Within
Listening to the Land: Native American Literary Responses to the Landscape & Literary Masters

Women of Color: Mother-Daughter Relationships in 20th Century Literature
A Woman of the People
Word Ways
Words of the Real People: Alaska Native Literature in Translation
The World Begins Here: An Anthology of Oregon Short Fiction
Woven Stone
Write It On Your Own Heart
Writers of the Purple Sage
Writing the Circle
Writing Indian, Native Conversations
Writing Indians: Literacy, Christianity & Native Community in Early America
Writing the Southwest
Writing to Create Ourselves
Writings in Indian History
Wynema: A Child of the Forest

LUMBEE INDIANS

Herbal Remedies of the Lumbee Indians
Living Indian Histories: Lumbee & Tuscarora People in North Carolina
*The Lumbee
Lumbee Indian Histories
Lumbee Indians in the Jim Crow South: Race, Identity, and the Making
  of a Nation
The Lumbee Problem
Moon Dash Warrior
The Only Land I Know: A History of the Lumbee Indians
Reinterpreting a Native American Identity: Examining the Lumbee
  Through the Peoplehood Model
Sociolinguistic Constructs of Ethnic Identity

MAGIC

Breath of the Invisible
The Eagle's Gift
Invisible Reality: Storytellers, Storytakers, and the Supernatural World of the Blackfeet
Magic in the Mountains: The Yakama Shaman: Power & Practice
The Navajo Skinwaler, Witchcraft & Related Spiritual Phenomena
The Night Has a Naked Soul: Witchcraft & Sorcery Among the Western Cherokee
Sacred Bundles of the Sac & Fox Indians
Spirit Healing: Native American Magic & Medicine
Witchcraft in the Southwest: Spanish & Indian Supernaturalism on the Rio Grande
Zuni Fetishism

MAIDU INDIANS

Creation of a California Tribe: Grandfather's Maidu Indian Tale
The Destruction of the People
Earthquake Weather
Handgame!
Indians of the Feather River
Maidu Indian Myths & Stories of Hanc'ibyjim
Maidu Myths & Tales
Maidu Texts
The Northern Maidu
Quest for Tribal Acknowledgement: California's Honey Lake Maidus
River of Sorrows - Life History of the Maidu-Nisenan Indians
Sun, Moon and Stars
Whatever Happened to Professor Coyote? A Journey to the Heart of the Handgame

MAKAH INDIANS

Drawing Back Culture: The Makah Struggle for Repatriation
First Lessons in Makah
The Makah Indians
Ozette: Excavating a Makah Whaling Village
The Sea Is My Country: The Maritime World of the Makahs
Singing the Songs of My Ancestors: The Life & Music of Helma Swan, Makah Elder
Spirits of Our Whaling Ancestors: Revitalizing Makah & Nuu-chah-nulth Traditions
Tradition & Change on the Northwest Coast: The Makah, Nuu-chah-nulth,
  Southern Kwakiutl & Nuxalt
Voices of a Thousand People: The Makah Cultural & Research Center
The Whaling Indians: West Coast Legends & Stories, Legendary Hunters

MANDAN & HIDATSA INDIANS

Agriculture of the Hidatsa Indians
Becoming & Remaining a People
Buffalo Bird Woman's Garden: Agriculture of the Hidatsa Indians
*A Coloring Book of Hidatsa Indian Stories
Early Fur Trade on the Northern Plains
Ethnography and Philology of the Hidatsa Indians
*Goodbird the Indian: His Story
Grammar & Dictionary of the Languages of the Hidatsa
*The Hidatsa
Hidatsa Social & Ceremonial Organization
*The Mandans
Only the Earth Endures: The Spiritual Journey of a Mandan Indian
The Village Indians of the Upper Missouri: The Mandans, Hidatsas & Arikaras
The Way to Independence: Memories of a Hidatsa Indian Family, 1840-1920
White Influence Upon Plains Indian Painting: George Catlin & Carl Bodmer
  Among the Mandan, 1832-34

MASKS

Agayul?Our Way of Making Prayer
The False Faces of the Iroquois
Head & Face Masks in Navaho Ceremonialism
*North American Indian Masks
Spirit Faces: Contemporary Masks of the Northwest Coast
A World of Faces: Masks of the Northwest Coast Indians

MEDICINE/SHAMANISM

After the First Full Moon in April: A Sourcebook of Herbal Medicine
  from a California Indian Elder
American Indian/Alaska Native Tribal & Village HIV-1 Policy Guidelines
American Indian Healing Arts: Herbs, Rituals & Remedies....
American Indian Medicine
American Indian Medicine Ways: Spiritual Power, Prophets, and Healing
Apache Medicine-Men
At the Desert's Green Edge: An Ethnobotany of the Gila River Pima
Basic Medical Navajo
The Beauty of the Primitive: Shamanism & Western Imagination
Blackfoot Physics
Breath of the Invisible
The Broken Cord
Buffalo Woman Comes Singing: The Spirit Song of a Rainbow Medicine Woman
California Indian Shamanism
The Cherokee Full Circle: A Practical Guide to Ceremonies & Traditions
The Cherokee Herbal: Native Plant Medicine from the Four Directions
Cherokee Medicine, Colonial Germs: An Indigenous Nation's Fight
  Against Smallpox. 1518-1824
Cherokee Medicine Man
Cherokee Plants
The Circle Is Sacred: A Medicine Book for Women
Columbus & the New World: Medical Implications
Coming Full Circle: Spirituality & Wellness Among Native Commnities
  in the Pacific Northwest
Coyote Healing: Miracles in Native Medicine
Coyote Medicine
Coyote Wisdom: The Power of Story in Healing
Creek Indian Medicine
Creek Religion & Medicine
Crow Dog: Four Generations of Sioux Medicine Men
Crow Indian Medicine Bundles
Creature Totems: Nature Teacher Medicine
Cry of the Eagle: Encounters with a Cree Healer
Deadly Indian Summer
Devil Sickness & Devil Songs: Tohono O'odham Poetics
The Dancing Healers: A Doctor's Journey of Healing with Native Americans
Diabetes Among the Pima: Stories of Survival
Dictionary of Native American Healing
Disease Change and the Role of Medicine: The Navajo Experience
Drinking Careers: A 25-Year Study of Three Navajo Populations
Earth Medicine: Explore Your Individuality Through the Native American Medicine Wheel
Encyclopedia of Native American Healing
Folk Medicine of the Delaware and Related Algonkian Indians
Fools Crow: Wisdom & Power
Forgotten Voices: Death Records of the Yakama, 1888-1964
*From the Earth to Beyond the Sky: Native American Medicine
Gathering the Desert
Gathering of Wisdoms: Tribal Mental Health-A Cultural Perspective
Geraniums for the Iroquois
Gift of Power: The Life & Teachings of a Lakota Medicine Man
Grandmothers of Light: A Medicine Woman's Sourcebook
Guide to Indian Herbs
Hand Trembling, Frenzy Witchcraft, & Moth Madness
A Handbook of Northeastern Indian Medicinal Plants
The Hands Feel It: Healing & Spirit Presence Among a Northern Alaskan People
Healing Herbs of the Upper Rio Grande
A Healing Place: Indigenous Visions for Personal Empowerment & Community Recovery
Healing Ways: Navajo Health Care in the Twentieth Century
Healing With Plants in the American and Mexican West
Health & the American Indian
Health Plants: Medicine of the Florida Seminole Indians
Honoring the Medicine: The Essential Guide to Native American Healing
How Indians Use Wild Plants for Food, Medicine & Crafts
"I Choose Life" Contemporary Medical & Religious Practices in the Navajo World
Indian Doctor
Indian Herbalogy of North America
The Indian Household Medicine Guide
Indian Medicine Power
Indian Uses of Native Plants
Indian Wisdom & Its Guiding Power
Indigenous Women's Health Book, Within the Sacred Circle
Introduction to Navajo Chant Practice
Iroquois Medical Botany
Iroquois Supernatural: Talking Animals & Medicine People
Lakota Belief & Ritual
Lame Deer: Seeker of Visions
Lenape Indian Teaching Kit 2: Lenape Lore/Folk Medicines
Listen to the Drum: Blackwolf Shares His Medicine
The Little Water Medicine Society of the Senecas
Lushootseed Culture and the Shamanic Odyssey
Mad Bear
Magic in the Mountains: The Yakama Shaman: Power & Practice

The Man Who Knew the Medicine: The Teachings of Bill Eagle Feather
The Medical History of Ishi
Medicinal Flora of the Alaska Natives
Medicinal & Other Uses of North American Plants
Medicinal Plants Used by Native American Tribes in Southern California
Medicinal Uses of Plants by Indian Tribes of Nevada
Medicine Bundle: Indian Sacred Performance & American Literature, 1824-1932
Medicine Cards: The Discovery of Power Through the Ways of Animals
Medicine Grove: A Shamanic Herbal
*Medicine Man
The Medicine Men: Oglala Sioux Ceremony & Healing
Medicine Men of the Apache
Medicine of the Cherokee: The Way of Right Relationship
Medicine That Walks: Medicine, Disease & Canadian Plains Aboriginal People, 1880-1945
Medicine Trail: The Life & Lessons of Gladys Tantaquidgeon
Medicine Trails: A Life in Many Worlds
Medicine Way: How to Live the Teachings...
Medicine Wheels: Native American Vehicles of Healing
Medicinal Wild Plants of the Prairie: An Ethnobotanical Guide
Medicine Women, Curanderas & Women Doctors
Medicine Woman Inner Guidebook
A Medicine Woman Speaks: An Exploration of Native American Spirituality
Micmac Medicines: Remedies & Recollections
Mohave Ethnopsychiatry & Suicide
Mystics, Magaicians, & Medicine People
Nanise: A Navajo Herbal
Native American Healing
*Native American Medicine
*Native American Medicine: Indians of North America
Native Healer: Initiation into an Ancient Art
Native Healing: Four Sacred Paths to Health
Native North American Shamanism: An Annotated Bibliography
Native Plants, Native Healing: Traditional Muskogee Way
Nature's Weeds, Native Medicines: Native American Herbal Secrets
Navajo: Basic Medical
Navajo Classification of Their Song Ceremonials
Navajo Dictionary of Diagnostic Terminology: Navajo Medical Terminology
A Navajo Legacy: The Life & Times of John Holiday
Navajo Medicine Bundles or Jish
Navajo Medicine Man Sand Paintings
Navajo Nation Health Care System
Navaho Symbols of Healing
The Night Chant: A Navaho Ceremony
*North American Indian Medicine People
Ohiyesa: Charles Eastman, Santee Sioux
The People's Health: Anthropology & Medicine in a Navajo Community
The Peyote Book: A Study of Native Medicine
Piman Shamanism and Staying Sickness
Plants of Power: Native American Ceremony & the Use of Sacred Plants
Pomo Doctors & Poisoners
Pretty Shield, Medicine Woman of the Crows
The Price of a Gift: A Lakota Healer's Story
Puhpowee for the People: A Narrative Account of Some Uses of Fungi
   Among the Ahnishinaabeg
Rainbow Medicine: A Visionary Guide to Native American Shamanism
Raven's Guide
Religious Medicine: The History & Evolution of Indian Medicine
A Rendeous With Clouds
Rolling Thunder
Sacred Fireplace: Life & Teachings of a Lakota Medicine Man
Sacred Plant Medicine: Explorations in Indigenous Herbalism
Sacred Plant Medicine: Explorations in the Practice of Indigenous Herbalism
Sacred Plant Medicine: The Wisdom in Native American Herbalism
Sanapia: Comanche Medicine Woman
The Scalpel & the Silver Bear: The First Navajo Women Surgeon
Secrets of Native American Herbal Remedies
Secrets of the Sacred White Buffalo: Native American Healing
   Remedies, Rites & Rituals
The Shaman & the Medicine Wheel
Sacred Plant Medicine: Explorations in the Practice of Indigenous Herbalism
The Shaman: Patterns of Religious Healing Among the Ojibway Indians
The Shaman's Touch: Otomi Indian Symbolic Healing
Shamanic Odyssey
Shamanism
Song of the Seven Herbs
Spirit Healing: Native American Magic & Medicine
Spirit Herbs: Native American Healing
The Spirit of Place: A Workbook for Sacred Alignment
Spiritual Dimensions of Healing: From Native Shamanism
   to Contemporary HealthCare
Star Medicine: Native American Path to Emotional Healing
A Study of Delaware Indian Medicine Practice & Folk Beliefs
Swimmer Manuscripts: Cherokee Sacred Formulas & Medicinal Prescriptions
Tales of a Shaman's Apprentice
Tangible Visions: Northwest Coast Shamanism & Its Art
A Taste of Heritage: Crow Indian Recipes & Herbal Medicines
The Theft of the Spirit
Traditional Native American Healing & Child Sexual Abuse
Turtle Lung Woman's Granddaughter
Walking the Maze: The Enduring Presence of Celtic Spirit
Walking Thunder: Dine Medicine Woman
Washo Shamans & Peyotists
Wild Plants & Native Peoples of the Four Corners
The Wind Is My Mother: The Life & Teachings of an American Shaman

The Wolves of Heaven: Cheyenne Shamanism, Ceremonies, & Prehistoric Origins

MENOMINEE INDIANS

American Indians in the Marketplace: Persistence & Innovation Among the
   Menominees & Metlakatlans, 1870-1920
Dreamers With Power: The Menominee
Ethnobotany of the Menomini Indians
Like a Deer Chased By the Dogs: The Life of Chief Oshkosh
*The Menominee
Menominee Drums: Tribal Termination & Restoration, 1954-1974
Menomini Indians of Wisconsin
*Northwood Cradle Song - From a Menominee Lullaby
Siege & Survival: History of the Menominee Indians, 1634-1856
The Struggle for Self-Determination: History of the Menominee Indians Since 1854

METIS

The Canadian Michif Language Dictionary (Metis)
Children of the Fur Trade: Forgotten Metis of the Pacific Northwest
Contours of a People: Metis Family, Mobility, and History
Cries From a Metis Heart
The Dances of the Metis - Li Dawns di Michif
A Gathering of Rivers: Indians, Metis & Mining in the Western Great Lakes, 1737-1832
The Genealogy of the First Metis Nation
La Lawng: Michif Peekishkwewin - 2 Vols. (Metis) Language Practice
Louis - Son of the Prairies (Metis)
*James McKay - A Metis Builder of Canada
*The Metis - Canada's Forgotten People
Metis Legacy I & II
*Metis Spirits
*My Children Are My Reward - The Life of Elsie Spence (Metis)
Native People, Native Lands: Canadian Indians, Inuit & Metis
The New Peoples: Being & Becoming Metis in North America
One of the Family: Metis Culture in 19th-Century Northwestern Saskatchewan
*Riel's People: How the Metis Lived
*The Secret of Your Name: Proud to Be Metis
Ste. Madeleine: A Community Without a Town-Metis Elders in Interview
We Are Not You: First nations & Canadian Modernity
We Get Our Living Like Milk From the Land
We Know Who We Are: Metis Identity in a Montana Community

MIMBRES

Art of a vanished Race: The Mimbres Classic Black-on-White
A Day With a Mimbres
Mimbres Archaeology at the Nan Ranch Ruin
The Mimbres, Art & Archaeology
Mimbres Classic Mysteries
Mimbres Indian Treasure: In the Land of Baca
Mimbres Life & Society: The Mattocks Site of Southwestern New Mexico
Mimbres Mythology
Mimbres Mythology: Tales From the Painted Clay
Mimbres Pottery: Ancient Art of the American Southwest
Short-Term Sedentism in the American Southwest
Southwest Indian Designs
To Touch the Past: The Painted Pottery of the Mimbres People
Victorio & the Mimbres Apaches

MISSIONS & MISSIONARIES

American Indians & Christian Missions
Annals of Shawnee Methodist Mission and Indian Manual Labor School
The Apalachee Indians & Mission San Luis
Black Elk, Holy Man of the Oglala
Black Robe for the Yankton Sioux
The Brainerd Journal: A Mission to the Cherokees, 1817-1823
Bringing Indians to the Book
Catechism & Guide: Navaho-English
The Catholic Calumet: Colonial Conversions in French & Indian North America
Champions of the Cherokees: Evan & John B. Jones
Cherokees & Missionaries, 1789-1839
Chiefs & Change in the Oregon Country
Christianity & Native Traditions
Churchmen & the Western Indians, 1820-1920
Columbus & Las Casas: The Conquest & Christianization of America, 1492-1566
Converting California Indians & Franciscans in the Missions
Thomas Crosby & the Tsimshian: Small Shoes for Feet Too Large
The Crossing of Two Roads: Being Catholic & Native in the U.S.
De Religione: Telling the 17th Century Jesuit Story in Huron the Iroquois
Disease, Depopulation & Culture Change in Northwestern New Spain, 1518-1764
Documentary Evidence for the Spanish Missions of Alta California
Documentary Evidence for the Spanish Missions of Texas
John Eliot's Indian Dialogues
John Eliot's Mission to the Indians Before King Philip's War
The Evacuation of Shekomeko & the Early Moravian Missions to Native North Americans
Faith in the Wilderness: The Story of the Catholic Indian Missions
Father Francis M. Craft, Missionary to the Sioux
Father Meme
Father Peter John de Smet: Jesuit in the West
Feast of Souls: Indians & Spaniards in the 17th Century
   Missions of Florida & New Mexico

MIWOK INDIANS

MIXED DESCENT

MODOC INDIANS

MOHAWK INDIANS

Mohawk Interruptus: Political Life Across the Borders ofSettler States
Mohawk, One Thousand Useful Words
Mohawk Saint: Catherine Tekakwitha & the Jesuits
The Mohawk That Refused to Abdicate
The Mohawk Trail
*Sacred Song of the Hermit Thrush: An Iroquois Tale
Kateri Tekakwitha: The Lily of the Mohawks
The River Is in Us: Fighting Toxics in a Mohawk Community
Thunder In My Soul: A Mohawk Woman Speaks
Turtle Boy: A Novel
Turtles, Wolves & Bears: A Mohawk Family History

MOHEGAN NATION

Folk Medicine of the Delaware & Related Algonkian Indians
A Key Into the Language of Woodsplint Baskets
The Lasting of the Mohegans
*Makiawisug: The Gift of the Little People
Medicine Trail: The Life & Lessons of Gladys Tantaquidgeon
Mohegan Chief: The Story of Harold Tantaquidgeon
*Mohegan Fun and Learn Book
Mohegan Indian Maps of Montville, CT
The Native Americans of Connecticut: Holding On & Moving Forward
The Secret Guide to Mohegan Sun
To Do Good to My Indian Brethren: The Writings of Joseph Johnson, 1751-1776
Uncas: First of the Mohegans
A Vocabulary of Mohegan-Pequot

MOHICAN INDIANS
(STOCKBRIDGE-MUNSEE MOHICANS)

The Last of the Mohicans
The Lasting of the Mohicans
Markings on Earth
The Mohican World, 1680-1750
The Mohicans of Stockbridge
The Mohicans & Their Land: 1609-1730
A Nation of Statesmen: The Political Culture of the
  Stockbridge-Munsee Mohicans, 1815-1972

N. SCOTT MOMADAY

*Approaches to Teaching Momaday's "The Way to Rainy Mountain"
House Made of Dawn
In the Bear's House
In Company: An Anthology of New Mexico Poets After 1960
In the Presence of the Sun: Stories & Poems, 1961-1991
Indian Country: A History of Native People in America
The Journey of Tai-Me
Legacy: Southwest Indian Art at the School of American Research
The Lightning Within
Mediation in Contemporary Native American Fiction
N. Scott Momaday: The Cultural & Literary Background
N. Scott Momaday: Remembering Ancestors, Earth & Traditions:
  An Annotated Bibliography
Momaday, Vizenor, Armstrong: Conversations on American Indian Writing
The Names
*Owl in the Cedar Tree
Three Plays: The Indolent Boys, Children of the Sun, and The Moon in Two Windows
The Way To Rainy Mountain
Winged Words: American Indian Writers Speak

MOUNDS, MOUNDBUILDERS

Aboriginal Monuments of the State of New York
Ancestral Mounds: Vitality & Volatility of Native America
The Ancient Mounds of Poverty Point: Place of Rings
Angel Site
Bioarchaeology of Virginia Burial Mounds
Burial Mounds of the Red River Headwaters
Cahokia: City of the Sun
Cahokia: Domination & Ideology in the Mississippian World
Cahokia, The Great Native American Metropolis
Cahokia: Mirror of the Cosmos
*Children's Atlas of Native Americans
The Earthshapers
The Enmergence of the Miundbuilders: The Archaeology of Tribal Societies
  in Southeastern Ohio
Expanding the View of Hohokam Mounds
Final Year Excavations at the Evans Mound Site
Grand Mound
Historical Dictionary of North American Archaeology
*Ikwa of the Mound-Builder Indians
Indian Mounds of the Atlantic Coast
Indian Mounds of the Middle Ohio Valley
Indian Mounds of Wisconsin
Indian Mounds You Can Visit: 165 Aboriginal Sites on Florida's West Coast
*Journey to Cahokia
Minnesota's Indian Mounds & Burial Sites
Mound Builders & Cliff Dwellers
The Moundbuilders
Moundbuilders & Monument Makers of the Northern Great Lakes, 1200-1600

Mounds for the Dead
Mounds of Earth & Shell
Moundville's Economy
Native Americans Before 1492
North Carolina's State Historic Sites
One Thousand Years on Mound Key
Edward Palmer's Arkansaw Mounds
Remember Native America!
Report of the Mound Explorations of the Bureau of Ethnology
The Sacred Geography of the American Mound-Builders
Shakin' the Bushes
Spirits of Earth: The Effigy Mound Landscape of Madison & the Four Lakes
Staging Ritual: Hopewell Cermonialism at the Mound House Site, Greene County, IL
Status & Health in Prehistory: A Case Study of the Moundville Chiefdom
Temples of Cahokia Lords
Timucua Indian Mounds of Northeast Florida
The Timucuan Chiefdoms of Spanish Florida
Town Creek Indian Mound
Treasures of the Mound Builders
Vanishing Heritage
Wakemap Mound

MUSIC & DANCE

American Indian Ballerinas
American Indian Poetry
American Indian Songs
*American Indian Music & Musical Instruments
The American Indians & Their Music
The Art of the Native American Flute
Blackfoot Musical Thought: Comparative Perspectives
Natalie Curtis Burlin: A Life in Native & African American Music
Ceremonies of the Pawnee
Cherokee Dance: Ceremonial Dances & Costumes
Cherokee Dance & Drama
The Cherokee Ghost Dance
Cherokee Psalms: A Collection of Hymns
Cheyenne & Arapaho Music
The Chilkat Dancing Blanket
Choctaw Music
Choctaw Music & Dance
Creating & Using the Larger Native American Flutes
Creating & Using the Largest Native American Flutes
Creating & Using the Native American Concert Flute
Creating & Using the Native American Love Flute
Creating & Using the Very Small Native American Flutes
The Crooked Stovepipe: Athapaskan Fiddle Music & Square Dancing
Cross-Cultural Performance & Analysis of West Africans,
  African American, Native American...
Cry for Luck: Sacred Song & Speech Among the Yurok, Hupa & Karok Indians
  of Northwestern California
A Cry From the Earth: Music of the North American Indians
Dance Ceremonies of the Northern Rio Grande Pueblos
Dance Lodges of the Omaha People
The Dances of the Metis - Li Dawns di Michif
Dances of the Tewa Pueblo Indians: Expressions of Life
Dancing Gods: Indian Ceremonials of New Mexico & Arizona
Frances Densmore and American Indian Music
Dream Songs & Ceremony: Reflections on California Indian Dance
Encyclopedia of Native American Music of North America
The Encyclopedia of Native Music
Enjoying the Native American-Style Flute
Fifteen Flower World Variations: A Sequence of Songs from the Yaqui Deer Dance
Flute Magic: An Introduction to the Native American Flute
Guide to Native American Music Recordings
The Heartbeat of the People: Music & Dance of the Northern Pow-Wow
Heartbeat, Warble, and the ElectricPowwow: American Indian Music
The Hoop of Peace
Hopi Katsina Songs
Hopi Snake Ceremonies
In Vain I Tried to Tell You: Essays in Native American Ethnopoetics
Indian Blues: American Indians & the Politics of Music, 1890-1934
Indian Dances of North America: Their Importance to Indian Life
*Indian Dancing Coloring Book
Indian Games & Dances with Native Songs
Indian Regalia of Northwest California
Indians' Book
Indian Story & Song from North America
Indigenous Dance & Dancing Indian: Contested Representation in the Global Era
Indiigeous Pop: Native American Music from Jazz to Hip Hop
Intertribal Native American Music in the U.S.: Experiencing Music, Expressing Culture
The Iroquois Eagle Dance
Iroquois Music & Dance: Ceremonial Arts of Two Seneca Longhouses
Kiowa Hymns
Kokopelli Ceremonies
Kokopelli: Flute Player Images in Rock Art
Kokopelli: The Making of an Icon
Lakota Songs
*Love Flute
The Magic World: American Indian Songs & Poems
The Modern Fancy Dancer
Moki Snake Dance
Mother Earth, Father Sky: Ancient Chants by Pueblo & Navajo Indians of the Southwest
Moving Within the Circle: Contemporary Native American Music & Dance

Music & Dance of the American Indian
Music & Dance Research of the Southwestern Indians
Music of the Native North American for Flute & Recorder
The Maru Cult of the Pomo Indians
Myth, Music & Dance of the American Indian
Music & Dance Research of the Southwestern Indians
Music of the North American Indian
Myth, Music & Dance of the American Indian
Native American Dance: Ceremonies & Social Traditions
Native American Dance Steps
The Native American Flute - Understanding the Gift:
   An Interactive Guide for Learning to Play
Native American Indian Songs Taught By Louis W. Ballard: Guidebook With Audio CDs
Native American Music Directory
Native American Songs for Piano Solo
Native American Songs & Poems
The Native American Sun Dance Religion & Ceremony
Native Canadiana: Songs from the Urban Rez
*Native Musicians In the Groove
The Native North American Flutes
Native North American Music & Oral Data: A Catalogue of Sound Recordings, 1893-1976
The Navajo (Or Corral) Fire Dance
Navajo Myths Prayers & Songs with Texts & Translations
Navajo War Dance
Newe Hupia: Shoshoni Poetry Songs
North American Indian Dances & Rituals
North American Indian Music: A Guide to Published Sources & Selected Recordings
Northern Haida Songs
The Northern Traditional Dancer
Notes on Eight Papago Songs
Observations on the Thunder Dance of the Bear Gens of the Fox Indians
The Oldest Magic: The History & Early Influence of Music
Ojibwe Singers: Hymns, Grief & a Native Culture in Motion
On the Music of the North American Indians
The Osage Ceremonial Dance I'n-Lon-Schka
Papago Music
Passamaquoddy Ceremonial Songs: Aesthetics & Survival
The Pawnee Ghost Dance Hand Game: Ghost Dance Revival & Ethnic Identity
The People Have Never Stopped Dancing
The People: Native American Thoughts & Feelings
Plains Indians Regalia & Customs
Powwow Dancer's & Craftworkers Handbook
The Power of Kiowa Song
The Power of Song: Music & Dance In the Mission Communities
   of Northern New Spain, 1590-1810
Power & Performance in Gros Ventre War Expedition Songs
Pueblo: Mountain, Village, Dance
The Sacred Journey: Prayers & Songs of Native America
Sharing the Gift of Lakota Song
The Shoshoni-Crow Sun Dance
Shoshone Ghost Dance Religion: Poetry Songs & Great Basin Context
Singing for Power: The Song Magic of the Papago Indians of Southern Arizona
The Snake Dance of the Hopi Indians
Song of the Sky
Songprints: The Musical Experience of Five Shoshone Women
Songs of the Apache
Songs of Indian Territory
Songs of the Kiowa
Songs of the Navajo
Songs of the Teton Sioux
Songs of the Tewa
Songs of the Wigwam
Southern Cheyenne Women's Songs
Spirit of the First People
Spirit Mountain: An Anthology of Yuman Story & Song
Spirit of the First People: Native American Music Traditions of Washington State
Stability & Variation in Hopi Song
A Study of Omaha Indian Music
The Sun Dance & Other Ceremonies of the Oglala Division of the Teton Dakota
The Sun Dance of the Crow Indians
Sun Dancing: A Spiritual Journey on the Red Road
Surviving Through the Days: Translations of Native California Stories & Songs
Teton Sioux Music & Culture
The Traditional Northern Dancer
A Treatise on Lovesickness: An Offshoot of the Calumet Dance
The Tribal Fires Catalog
Tsee-Ma'Heone-Nemeototse: Cheyenne Spiritual Songs
The Tsimishian: Their Arts & Music
Upwhere Belong
Visions of Sounds: Musical Instruments of First Nation Communities
   in Northeastern America
Voices of Native America: Native American Instruments & Music
Voices of the Wind: Native American Flute Songs
War Dance: Plains Indian Musical Performance
We'll Be In Your Mountains, We'll Be in Your Songs: A Navajo Woman Sings
Winds of the Past: Guide to Playing Native American Flute
Yaqui Deer Songs/Maso Bwakam
Yokuts & Paiute Songs & Culture

NATIVE LAND CLAIMS

The Alaska Native Claims Settlement Act, 1991 & Tribal Government
Bay Mills Indian Community Land Claims Settlement Act
The Case of the Seneca Indians in the State of New York

The Cherokee Cases: Two Landmark Federal Decisions in the Fight for Sovereignty
Eagle Down Is Our Law: The Witsuwit'en Land Claims
Haa Aani, Our Land: Tlingit & Haida Land Rights & Use
Hollow Justice: A History of Indigenous Claims in the U.S.
Index to the Expert Testimony Before the Indian Claims Commission: The Written Reports
Indian Claims Commission Act
Indian Depredation Claims, 1796-1920
Indian Reserved Water Rights
Indian Tribal Claims Decided in the Court of Claims of the U.S.
The Miami Indians of Indiana: A Persistent People, 1654-1994
Mining, the Environment & Indigenous Development Conflicts
Native Claims & Political Development
Native Title & the Transformation of Archeology in the Postcolonial World
Reaching Just Settlements: Land Claims in British Columbia
Restitution: The Land Claims of the Mashpee, Passamaquoddy
   & Penobscot Indians of New England
We Hold the Rock: The Indian Occupation of Alcatraz Island, 1969--1971
Zuni & the Courts: A Struggle for Sovereign Land Rights
Zuni Indian Tribe Water Settlement Act

NAVAJO (DINE) INDIANS

Administration in Navajo Reservation Schools
Along Navajo Trails: Recollections of a Trader, 1898-1948
American Indian Tribal Government & Politics
The Army and the Navajo
Apaches de Navajo
Basic Medical Navajo
*Beauty Beside Me, Stories of My Grandmother's Skirts
Beyond the Four Corners of the World
The Big Missionary: A Story of One Man's Compassion for the Navajo
Bighorse the Warrior
Bitter Water: Dine Oral Histories of the Navajo-Hopi Land Dispute
Black Sheep, White Crow and Other Windmill Tales: Stories from Navajo Country
Blessingway
Blood & Voice: Navajo Women Ceremonial Practitioners
The Book of the Navajo
Border Towns of the Navajo Nation
Bosque Redondo: A Study of Cultural Stress at the Navajo Reservation
Both Sides of the Billpen: Navajo Trade & Posts
A Breeze Swept Through: Poetry
A Cannoneer in Navajo Country
Canyon De Chelly: The Story Behind the Scenery
Circles, Consciousness & Culture
Colloquial Navajo: A Dictionary
*Colors of the Navajo
Common Threads: Pueblo & Navajo Textiles
   in the Southwest Museum
Contemporary Navajo Affairs
Crossing Between Worlds: The Navajos of Canyon de Chelly
Crow Man's People: Three Seasons with the Navajo
Danny Blackgoat: Dangerous Passage
Defending the Dinetah
Denetsosie
The Development of Capitalism in the Navajo Nation: A Political-Economic History
Defending Whose Country? Indigenous Soldiers in the pacific War
Dine Bahane', The Navajo Creation Story
Dine Bibliography to the 1990s
Dine Bizaad Binahoo'aah: Rediscovering the Navajo Language
Dine Bizaad: Speak, Read, Write Navajo
Dine: A History of the Navajos
Dine' Perspectives: Revitalizing & Reclaiming Navajo Thought
Dinetah: An Early History of the Navajo
Dinetah: Navajo History
Disease Change and the Role of Medicine: The Navajo Experience
Dreaming of Sheep in Navajo Country
Drinking Careers: A 25-Year Study of Three Navajo Populations
Drinking, Conduct Disorder & Social Change: Navajo Experience
Earth Is My Mother, Sky Is My Father
The Economics of Sainthood: Religious Change
   Among the Rimrock Navajos
The Enduring Navaho
Enduring Traditions: Art of the Navajo
Explorations in Navajo Poetry & Poetics
The Fifth World of Forster Bennett: Portrait of a Navajo
From the Glittering World: A Navajo Story
From the Land: Two Hundred Years of Dene Clothing
Genuine Navajo Rugs: How to Tell
The Gift of the Gila Monster: Navajo Ceremonial Tales
The Gift of Spiderwoman: Southwestern Textiles, The Navajo Traditions
Grandpa Lolo's Navajo Saddle Blanket: La tilma de Abuelito Lolo
Guide to Navajo Rugs
A Guide to Navajo Weavings
Hand Trembling, Frenzy Witchcraft, & Moth Madness
Head and Face Masks in Navaho Ceremonialism
Healing Ways: Navajo Health Care in the Twentieth Century
The Hero Twins: A Navajo-English Story of the Monster Slayers
Historic Navajo Weaving: 1800-1900: Three Cultures-One Loom
History of the Navajos: The Reservation Years
Hogans: Navajo Houses and House Songs
Holy Wind in Navajo Philosophy
Hosteen Klah: Navaho Medicine Man and Sand Painter
*How the Stars Fell Into the Sky: A Navajo Legend
Hubbell Trading Post: Trade, Tourism, and the NavajoSouthwest

NEZ PERCE INDIANS

OJIBWE (CHIPPEWA) INDIANS

Osage Indian Bands & Clans
Osage Indian Customs & Myths
The Osage Indian Murders: A True Crime Story
Osage Indians: Bands & Clans
The Osage & the Invisible World
An Osage Journey to Europe, 1827-1830: Three French Accounts
Osage - Life & Legends: Earth People - Sky People
Osage Mission Baptisms, Marriages and Interments, 1820-1886
Osage Society & Culture: The First 125 Years of Post European Contact, 1700-1825
The Osages, Dominant Power of the Louisiana Territory
A Pipe for February: A Novel
Talking to the Moon
Traditions of the Osage
Unaffected by the Gospel: Osage Resistance
War Ceremony & Peace Ceremony of the Osage Indians
Winning the Dust Bowl

PAIUTE INDIANS

Beneath These Red Cliffs: An Ethnohistory of the Utah Paiutes
Boundaries Between: The Southern Paiutes, 1775-1995
The Chemehuevi Indians of Southern California
Chemehuevi: People of the Coachilla Valley
Chemehuevi Song: The Resilience of a Southern Paiute Tribe
Coyote Tales & Other Paiute Stories
From the Sands to the Mountain
Karnee: A Paiute Narrative
Legends of the Northern Paiute: As Told by Wilson Wewa
*Let Me Tell You a Story & Workbook
Life Among the Paiutes
Corbett Mack: The Life of a Northern Paiute
Making Space on the Western Frontier: Mormons, Miners, and Southern Paiutes
Viola Martinez, California Paiute: Living in Two Worlds
Northern Paiute-Bannock Dictionary
The Northern Paiute Indians of California
A Numu History - The Yerington Paiute Tribe
*The Numu Way & Workbook
The Paiute, Indians of North America
Southern Paiute: A Portrait
Southern Paiutes: Legends, Lore, Language & Lineage
Survival Arts of the Primitive Paiute
*Voice of the Paiutes: A Story About Sarah Winnemucca
Warm Springs Millennium: Voices from the Reservation
Weaving a Legacy: Indian Baskets & the People of Owens Valley, California
Sarah Winnemucca of the Northern Paiutes
Wovoka & the Ghost Dance: A Source Book
Wovoka Poster
Yerington Paiute Dictionary
Yerington Paiute Language Grammar
*Yerington Paiute Tribe Coloring Book

PAWNEE INDIANS

Ceremonies of the Pawnee
A Dictionary of Skiri Pawnee
The Dubar-Allis Letters on the Pawnee
Brummett Echohawk: Pawnee Thunderbird & Artist
The Hako: Song, Pipe and Unity in a Pawnee Calumet Ceremony
Indian Sketches Taken During an Expedition to the Pawnee &
   Other Tribes of American Indians, 2 Vols.
The Lost Universe: Pawnee Life and Culture
Frank J. North: Pawnee Scout, Commander and Pioneer
*The Pawnee
Pawnee, Blackfoot, and Cheyenne: History & Folklore of the Plains
Pawnee Ghost Dance Hand Game
Pawnee Hero Stories & Folktales
The Pawnee Indians
Pawnee Indians of North America
Pawnee & Kansa (Kaw) Indians
Pawnee & Lower Loup Pottery
The Pawnee Mission Letters 1834-1851
The Pawnee Mythology
The Pawnee Nation: An Annotated Research Bibliography
Pawnee Passage, 1870-1875
Pawnees: A Critical Bibliography
Some Things Are Not Forgotten
Travels in North America, Including a Summer with the Pawnees
Two Great Scouts & Their Pawnee Battalion
When Stars Came Down to Earth: Cosmology of the Skidi War Party in Blue:
   Pawnee Scouts in the U.S. Army

PERIODICALS

American Indian
American Indian & Alaska Native Newspapers & Periodicals, 1826-1924 & 1971-1985
Let My People Know: American Indian Journalism, 1828-1978
Schoolcraft: Literary Voyager

PEYOTE, PEYOTISM

The Attraction of Peyote
Doors of Perception
One Nation Under God

People of the Peyote
The Peyote Book: A Study of Native Medicine
The Peyote Cult
Peyote: The Divine Cactus
Peyote Hunt: The Sacred Journey of Huichol Indians
The Peyote Religion: A History
Peyote Religion Among the Navaho
Peyote Religious Art: Symbols of Faith & Belief
The Peyote Road: Religious Freedom and the Native American Church
Peyote vs. the State: Religious Freedom on Trial
Peyote & the Yankton Sioux: The Life & Times of Sam Necklace
Peyotism in the West: A Historical & Cultural Perspective
Peyotism & the Native American Church
Pipe, Bible & Peyote Among the Oglala Lakota: A Study in Religious Identity
Washo Shamans & Peyotists: Religious Conflict in an American Indian Tribe

PHILOSOPHY

The American Indian Mind in a Linear World
American Indian Thought
An American Urphilosophie: An American Philosophy-BP (Before Pragmatism)
An Analysis of Navajo Temporality
The Bear Tribe's Self-Reliance Book
Being & Vibration
Black Holes & Tepee Rings On Cosmic Mysteries & Spiritual Mythology
Blackfoot Physics: A Journey Into the Native American Universe
The Book of Ceremonies
Catch the Whisper of the Wind
Center of the World: Native American Spirituality
Classification and Development of North American Indian
Cultures: A Statistical Analysis of the Driver-Massey Sample
Crazy Horse's Philosophy of Riding Rainbows
*Crazy Horse's Vision
Cree Narrative: Expressing the personal Meaning of Events
Critical Neurophilosophy & Indigenous Wisdom
Daily Affirmations from the Divine Creator
Dakota Philosopher: Charles Eastman & American Indian Thought
Earth Medicine: Ancestor's Ways of Harmony for many Moons
Ethnophilosophical & Ethnolinguistic Perspectives on the Huron Indian Soul
Feasting with Cannibals: An Essay on Kwakiutl Cosmology
Fire in the Mind: Science, Faith & the Search for Order
A Haunting Reverence: Meditations on a Northern Land
Headed Upstream: Interviews with Iconoclasts
Holy Wind in Navajo Philosophy
Honour Mother Earth
How It Is: The Native American Philosophy of V.F. Cordova
The Indian Testimony
Joy Before Night: Evelyn Eaton's Last Years
Jung & the Native American Moon Cycles
The Last World: The Taoist & Native American Philosophies as a Way of Living in Harmony
Listening to the Land: Native American Literary Responses to the Landscape
   & Literary Masters
Living in Balance: The Universe of the Hopi, Zuni, Navajo & Apache
Magical Criticism: The Resource of Savage Philosophy
The Main Stalk: A Synthesis of Navajo Philosophy
Meditations With Native American Elders: The Four Seasons
Messages from the Divine Creator
Messages from Mother Earth: Daily Affirmations
Molded In the Image of Changing Woman: Navajo Views on the Human Body & Personhood
Mother Earth, Father Sky: Native American Wisdom
Native American Predictions
Native American Prophecies
Native American Wisdom
Native American Worldviews: An Introduction
Native Americans: A Portrait
Native Light for a Dark World
Native Pragmatism
Navajo & Tibetan Sacred Wisdom: The Circle of the Spirit
Neither Wolf Nor Dog: On Forgotten Roads With an Indian Elder
One Shahapton Stirring Ashes
Our Chiefs & Elders: Words & Photographs of Native Leaders
The Path of Power
The Primal Mind: Vision & Reality in Indian America
Profiles in Wisdom: Native Elders Speak Out About the Earth
The Roaring of the Sacred River
Shadowcatchers
Shaping Survival: Essays by Four American Indian Tribal Women
The Soul of an Indian; and Other Writings from Ohiyesa
The Soul of the Indian: An Interpretation
Spirit Healing: Native American Magic & Medicine
Spiritual Wisdom of the Native Americans
Teachings from the American Earth: Indian Religion & Philosophy
Thinking In Indian: A John Mohawk Reader
To Image & To See: Crow Indian Photographs
To Touch the Wind: An Introduction to Native American Philosophy & Beliefs
Truth or Consequences: A Native American View of Society
Vision Quest
Walk in Balance
Ways of Knowing
White Roots of Peace: Iroquois Book of Life
The Wisdom of the Great Chiefs

PICTURE-WRITING

Coffee in the Gourd
Legends of the Delaware Indians & Picture Writing
Picture-Writing of the American Indians

PICTURES, PHOTOGRAPHS & PORTRAITS

Ada, Oklahoma, Queen City of the Chickasaw Nation
Always a People: Oral Histories of Contemporary Woodland Indians
America on Paper: The First Hundred Years
The American Indian: Bronze Sculpture by Griffin
*Among the Plains Indians
Anasazi Places: The Photographic Vision of William Current
Arapaho Journeys: Photographs & Stories From the Wind River Reservation
Art From Fort Marion: The Silberman Collection
Marius Barbeau's Photographic Collection: The Nass River
Becoming Brave: The Path to Native American Manhood
O.E. Berninghaus - Taos, New Mexico: Master Painter of American Indians & Frontier West
Beyond the Reach of Time & Change: Native American Reflections on the
  Frank A. Rinehart Photograph Collection
Blackfoot Indian Portraits
Karl Bodmer's North American Prints
Karl Bodmer's Studio Art: The Newberry Library Bodmer Collection
Carving the Native American Face
Catlin's North American Indian Portfolio
George Catlin's Souvenirs of the North American Indians: A Facsimile of the Original Album
Children of the First People: A Photographic Essay
Michael Coleman
Comanches in the New West, 1895-1908: Historic Photographs
Crazy Horse & Korczak
Crow Indian Photographer
Crying for a Dream: The World Through Native American Eyes
Edward S. Curtis
Edward S. Curtis: Coming to Light
Edward S. Curtis: The Great Warriors
Edward S. Curtis: The North American Indian
Edward S. Curtis & the North American Indian Project in the Field
Edward Sheriff Curtis: Visions of a Vanishing Race
Crow Indian Photographer: The Work of Richard Throssel
Crying for a Dream: The Earth Is Our Mother
Crying for a Vision: A Rosebud Sioux Trilogy 1886-1976
A Danish Photographer of Idaho Indians
De Grazia's Borderlands Sketches
Deeper Than Gold: A Guide to Indian Life in the Sierra Region
Dwellers at the Source: Southwestern Indian Photographs of A.C. Vroman, 1895-1904
Seth Eastman: Pictorial Historian of the Indian
Easy-to-Duplicate North American Indian Borders
An Economy of Colour: Visual Culture & the North Atlantic World, 1660-1830
Enduring Culture: A Century of Photography of the Southwest Indians
Escape to Reality: The Western World of Maynard Dixon
Excavating Voices: Listening to Photographs of Native Americans
Florida's Timucua Indians: A Pictorial History
Framing the West: Race, Gender & the Photographic Frontier on the Northwest Coast
German Artist on the Texas Frontier: Friedrich Richard Petri
Grand Endeavors of American Indian Photography
Great Spirit: North American Indian Portraits
Honor Dance: Native American Photographs
The Horsemen of the Americas
Husk of Time: The Photographs of Victor Masayesva
I Will Tell of My War Story: A Pictorial Account of the Nez Perce War
Imagining Indians in the Southwest: Persistent Visions of a Primitive Past
In the Fifth World: Portrait of the Navajo Nation
In a Sacred Manner We Live
Indian Country
The Indian Legacy of Charles Bird King
Indian Lives: A Photographic Records from the Civil War to Wounded Knee
Indian Motifs
Indian Nations
Indian Portraits of the Pacific Northwest
Indian Spirit
Indians of the American Southwest
Indians & A Changing Frontier: The Art of George Winter
The Interior Salish Tribes of British Columbia
Invisible Native Americans Magic Picture Book
Keepers of the Dream
Korczak, Storyteller In Stone
Lakota Healer
Land of the Spotted Eagle: Portrait of the Reservation Sioux
Lanterns on the Prairie: The Blackfeet Photographs of Walter McClintock
Life At the Kiowa, Comanche, and Wichita Agency: The Photographs of Annette Ross
The Masterworks of Charles M. Russell: A Retrospective of Paintings & Sculpture
Native American Portraits: 1865-1918
Native American Profiles
Native Americans
Native Nations: Journeys in American Photography
The Natural Man Observed: A Study of Catlin's Indian Gallery
New Indian Sketches
The North American Indian: The Complete Portfolios
North American Indian Portfolios
The North American Indian Vol. 12: Hopi
North American Indians
North American Indians Coloring Album
The North American Indians: Photographs by Edward S. Curtis
A Northern Cheyenne Album: Photographs of Thomas B. Marquis
On the Trail to Wounded Knee: The Big Foot Memorial Ride

Our Chiefs & Elders: Words & Photographs of Native Leaders
Our People, Our Land, Our Images: International Indigenous Photography
Partial Recall: Photographs of Native North Americans
People of Legend: Native American of the Southwest
Peoples of the Plateau: The Indian Photographs of Lee Moorhouse, 1898-1915
Peoples of the Twilight: European Views of Native Minnesota, 1823-1862
The Photograph & the American Indian
Pictographic History of the Oglala Sioux
Picture-Writing of the American Indians
Plains Indian Art: The Pioneering Work of John C. Ewers
The Plains Indian Photographs of Edward S. Curtis
Plains Indian Raiders: The Final Phases of Warfare from the Arkansas to the Red River
Plains Indians Portraits & Scenes: 24 Watercolors From the Joslyn Art Museum
Horace Poolaw, Photographer of American ndian Modernity
Portrait Index of North American Indians in Published Collections
Portraits from North American Indian Life: Original Portfolio Edition
Portraits of Native Americans
Powerful Images: Portrayals of Native America
Prayer to the Great Mystery: The Uncollected Writings & Photography of Edward S. Curtis
Pueblo Imagination
Quanah: A Pictorial History of the Last Comanche Chief
Frederick Remington: Artist of the American West
The Reservation Blackfeet, 1885-1945: A Photographic History of Cultural Survival
Charles M. Russell: A Catalogue Raisonne
Charles M. Russell: Masterpieces from the Amon Carter Museum
A Russian American Photographer in Tlingit Country: Vincent Soboleff in Alaska
Sacred Legacy: Edward S. Curtis & the North American Indian
The Saga of Sitting Bull's Bones
Search for the Native American Purebloods
The Seventh Generation: Images of the Lakota Today
Julius Seyler & the Blackfeet: An Impressionist at Glacier National Park
Shadows on Glass: The Indian Photographs of Ben Wittick
*Sharing Our Worlds
The Shindler Catalogue: Native American Photography at the Smithsonian
Songs From the Earth
Southeastern Indians Life Portraits: A Catalogue of Pictures 1564-1860
Southwest Indians: A Photographic Portrait
John Rogers Statuary
Spirit Capture: Photographs from the National Museum of the American Indian
The Story of the Meadowlark
Sun Dogs & Eagle Down: The Indian paintings of Bill Holm
Sweet Medicine: Sites of Indian Massacres, Battlefields & Treaties
Those Who Remain: A Photographer's Memoir of South Carolina Indians
To Image & To See: Crow Indian Photographs by Edward S. Curtis &
  Richard Throssel, 1905-1910
Trading Gazes: Euro-American Women Photographer & Native North Americans,
  1880-1940
Traditions & Change on the Northwest Coast
The Turquoise Trail: Native American Jewelry & Culture of the Southwest
The Vanishing Race & Other Illusions: Photographs of Indians by Edward S. Curtis
Vintage Native American Postcards
Visions of Our Native American Heritage
Where Custer Fell: Photographs
With Eagle Tail

POETRY

Above the Line: New Poems
After & Before the Lightning
Akwe:kon Literary Issue
All My Relations: A Native's Thoughts, Poems & Prayers
America the Beautiful: Last Poems
American Indian Poetry: An Anthology of Songs & Chants
American Indian Prayers & Poetry
Ants & Orioles: The Art of Pima Poetry
Asylum in the Grasslands
The Athabaskans
Autobiography of a Yaqui Poet
Blessingway
Blood of Our Earth: Poetic History of the American Indian
The Blue God: An Epic pf Mesa Verde
Blue Horses Rush In: Poems & Stories
Bone Dance: New & Selected Poems, 1965-1993
Breathtracks
A Breeze Swept Through: Poetry
Buckskin Hollow Reflections
The Business of Fancydancing
Cedar Smoke on Abalone Mountain
Chasers of the Sun
Cherokee Psalms
The Circle of Thanks: Native American Poems and Songs of Thanksgiving
Columbus Day
Coming to Light
Connotations
A Coyote Reader
Creative Alliances: The Transnational Designs of Indigenous Women's Poetry
The Crooked Beak of Love
*Dancing Tepees
Dark Thirty
Devil Sickness & Devil Songs: Tohono O'odham Poetics
The Dirt Is Red Here: Art & Poetry from Native California
Drawings of the Song Animals: New & Selected Poems
Dreams & Thunder: Stories, Poems, and The Sun Dance Opera
Drifting Through Ancestor Dreams

An Eagle Nation
Earth Always Endures: Native American Poems
The Elders: Passing It On
Explorations in Navajo Poetry & Poetics
Face
Firesticks: A Collection of Stories
Flood Song
The Fork-in-the-Road Indian Poetry Store
Footprints Still Whispering in the Wind
Four Ancestors: Stories, Songs, & Poems from Native North America
Four Winds: Poems from Indian Rituals
From the Belly of My Beauty
From Sand Creek
From Village, Clan & City
From the Western Door to the Lower West Side
Gatherings IV: Re-Generation: Expanding the Web to Claim Our Future
Genocide of the Mind
Gigyayk Yo JKA!
The Great Kiva
Harper's Anthology of Twentieth Century Native American Poetry
The Healing Blanket
Hear the Creator's Song
Heart As a Drum
Home Places: Contemporary Native American Writing from Sun Tracks
I, the Song: Classical Poetry of Native North America
I Swallow Turquoise for Courage
In Company: An Anthology of New Mexico Poets After 1960
In Mad Love and War
In the Trail of the Wind: American Indian Poems & Ritual Orations
In Vain I Tried to Tell You
Indian Trains
Interpreting the Indian
Intimate Grammars: An Ethnography of Navajo Poetry
The Invisible Musician
Itch Like Crazy
*Just Talking About Ourselves: Voices of Our Youth, Vol. 2
Life Woven With Song
Light From a Bullet Hole:Poems New and Selected, 1950-2008
Lost Copper
Luminaries of the Humble
The Magic World: American Indian Poems & Songs
The Mama Poems
*Many Winters
Maria: The Potter of San Ildefonso
Markings on Earth
Migration Tears
Mud Woman: Poems from the Clay
Ndakinna (Our Land): New & Selected Poems
Sarojini Naidu: An Introduction to Her Life, Work & Poetry
Native American Discourse: Poetics & Rhetoric
Native American Poetry: Native American Anthology of Poetry
Native American Reader: Stories, Speches & Poems
Native American Songs & Poems
Native Wisdom
The Nature of Native American Poetry
*Navaho Magic of Hunting
New and Old Voices of Wah'kon-Tah
Newe Hupia: Shoshoni Poetry Songs
No Parole Today
Notebooks of Elizabeth Cook-Lynn
Now I Know Only So Far: Essays in Ethnopoetics
Ocean Power: Poems from the Desert
Offering: Poetry & Prose
Old Shirts & New Skins
On the Landing
On Native Ground: Memories & Impressions
Opening in the Sky
Simon J. Ortiz: A Poetic Legacy of Indigenous Continuance
Out There Somewhere
Outcroppings from Navajoland
Picked Apart the Bones
Plains Indian Mythology
The Portable North American Indian Reader
Alex Posey: Creek Poet, Journalist & Humorist
A Radiant Curve: Poems & Stories
Rainbows of Stone
Raven Eye
Ravensong: Cherokee Indian Poetry
Reading the Voice: Native American Oral Poetry on the Written Page
*Red Clay: Poems and Stories
Red Willow People
The Red Window
Report to the Department of the Interior: Poems
Returning the Gift: Poetry & Prose...
John Rollin Ridge: His Life & Works
Saanii Dahataal / The Women Are Singing
The Sacred Hoop
*Savings
A Scar Upon Our Voice
The Secret Powers of Naming
Selected Works of Maria Sabina
The Serpent's Tongue: Prose, Poetry & Art...
The Shadow's Horse
Shaking the Pumpkin: Traditional Poetry of Indian North America

Shapeshift
She Had Some Horses
Shoshone Ghost Dance Religion: Poetry, Songs...
Sing: Poetry from the Indigenous Americas
Skins & Bones
The Sky Clears: Poetry of the American Indians
Song of the Sky
Songs
Songs From an Outcast
Songs From This Earth on Turtle's Back
Songs of the Oktahutche: Collected Poems
Songs of the Tewa
Soul Talk, Song Language: Conversations With Joy Harjo
The Sound of Rattles & Clappers
Speak to Me Words
Star Quilt
Starting From Here: Dakota Poetry, ...
Stories & Stone
Storm Patterns: Poems From Two Navajo Women
Strong Heart Song
Summer In the Spring: Anishinaabe Lyric Poems & Stories
Summer of the Black Widows
Talking Books: Ethnopoetics
Talking Poems: Conversations With Poets
Teepees Are Folded: American Indian Poetry
Thanksgiving: A Native Perspective
That's What She Said: Contemporary Poetry & Fiction by Native American Women
That's What They Used to Say: Reflections on American Indian Oral Traditions
These Are the People: Thoughts in Poetry & Prose
Thirteen Moons on Turtle's Back
Through Indian Eyes: The Native Experience
Trekways of the Wind
Tricky Tribal Discourse
The Twilight of the Sioux
Vespers: Contemporary American Poems of Religion & Spirituality
The Vision: Poetry of Native Americans
Voices in the Waterfall
Voices of the Rainbow: Contemporary Poetry of Native North America
We Became As Mountains: Poems of the Pueblo Conquest
Wearing the Morning Star: Native American Song-Poems
When No One Is Looking
*When Rain Sings: Poems by Young Native Americans
Where Clouds Are Formed
The Winged Serpent: American Indian Prose & Poetry
Woven Stone
Writing the Circle
Yaqui Deer Songs/Maso Bwakam: A Native American Poetry
Yuman Poetry with Morphological Analysis

POLITICS & GOVERNMENT

AFL to Arrowhead: Four Decades of Chiefs History & Trivia
After the Trail of Tears: The Cherokee's Struggle for Sovereignty, 1839-1880
Alaska Native Policy in the 20th Century
Alcatraz! Alcatraz: The Indian Occupation of 1969-71
Alcatraz: Indian Land Forever
Alternative Leadership Strategies in the Prehispanic Southwest
American Indian Constitutional Reform & the Rebuilding of Native Nations
American Indian Policy: Self-Governance & Economic Development
American Indian Politics & the American Political System
American Indian Tribal Government & Politics
American Indians: Answers to Todays Questions
American Indians & the Fight for Equal Voting Rights
American Indians & U.S. Politics: A Companion Reader
The Ascent of Chiefs: Cahokia & Mississippian Politics in Native North America
An Assumption of Sovereignty: Social & Political Transformation
  Among the Florida Seminoles
Beyond Red Power: American Indian Politics & Activism Since 1900
Blood Struggle: The Rise of Modern Indian Nations
Building Native American Nations: The Lives & Work of Modern Tribal Leaders
The Caddo Chiefdoms: Caddo Economics & Politics, 700-1835
The Cahokia Chiefdom: The Archaeology of a Mississippian Society
Cash, Color, & Colonialism: The Politics of Tribal Acknowledgement
The Chaco Anasazi
The Chaco Meridian
Chief Daniel Bread & the Oneida Nation of Indians of Wisconsin
Chiefdoms & Chieftaincy in the Americas
The Choctaw Laws
The Choctaw Revolution: Lessons for Federal Indian Policy
The Choctaws in Oklahoma: From Tribe to Nation, 1855-1970
Competing Voices From Native America: Fighting Words
Conservatism Among the Iroquois at the Six Nations Reserve
Conspiracy of Interests: Iroquois Dispossession
The Constitution & Laws of the Choctaw Nation
Constitution, Laws & Treaties of the Chickasaws
The Constitution of the Five Nations
Constitutionalism & Native Americans, 1903-1968
Constitutions & Laws of the American Indian Tribes
Contemporary Native American Political Issues
Controlling Consulting: A Manual for Native American Governments & Organization
Coosa: The Rise & Fall of a Southeastern Mississippian Chiefdom
Crossroads of Empire: Indians, Colonists, & the Albany Congress of 1754
Dancing on Common Ground: Tribal Cultures & Alliances on the Southern Plains
Debating Democracy: Native American Legacy of Freedom

Distinguished Native American Political & Tribal Leaders
Ecocide of Native America: Environmental Destruction of Indian Lands & Peoples
The Ecological Indian: Myth & History
Ecology, Sociopolitical Organization & Cultural Change on the Southern Plains
Encyclopedia of Minorities in American Politics
Episodes in the Rhetoric of Government-Indian Relations
The Erosion of Tribal Power: The Supreme Court's Silent Revolution
Exemplar of Liberty: Native America & the Evolution of Democracy
Exiled in the Land of the Free
Famous Dakota Chiefs
Federal Indian Policy in the Kennedy & Johnson Administrations, 1961-1969
The First Canadians
For Indigenous Eyes Only: A Decolonization handbook
Forced Federalism: Contemporary Challenges to Indigenous Nationhood
The Four Hills of Life: Northern Arapaho Knowledge & Life Movement
The Fox Wars: The Mesquakie Challenge to New France
Benjamin Franklin, Pennsylvania, and the First Nations: The Treaties of 1736-62
Government-to-Government: Models of Cooperation Between States & Tribes
Governments of the Western Hemisphere
The Great Confusion in Indian Affairs: Native Americans & Whites in the Progressive Era
The Great Law & the Longhouse: A Political History of the Iroquois Confederacy
Imagining Sovereignty: Self-Determination in American Indian Law & Literature
In Bitterness & In Tears: Andrew Jackson's Destruction of the Creeks & Seminoles
In Defense of Mohawk Land: Ethnopolitical Conflict in Native North America
In the Spirit of Crazy Horse
Indian Gaming: Who Wins?
Indian Programs: Tribal Priority Allocations Do Not Target the Neediest Tribes
Indian Reorganization Act: Congress & Bills
Indian Self-Determination & Education Assistance Act
Indian Self Rule
Indian Treaty-Making Policy in the U.S. & Canada, 1867-1877
Indian Tribes As Sovereign Governments
Indian Tribes of North America With Biographical Sketches
Indians & the American West in the 20th Century
Indians, Indian Tribes & State Government: Major Legal Issues
Indigenous Peoples: Resource Management & Global Rights
Into the American Woods: Negotiators on the Pennsylvania Frontier
The Invention of the Creek Nation, 1670-1763
Keeping Promises: What is Sovereignty & Other Questions from Indian Country
Landscapes of Power: Politics of Energy in the Navajo Nation
Last Cry: Native American Prophecies; Tale of the End Times
The Last Warrior: Peter MacDonald & the Navajo Nation
The Laws of the Chickasaw Nation
The Laws of the Choctaw Nation
Legible Sovereignties: Rhetoric, Representations, and Native American Museums
*Long Shadows
Mankiller: A Chief & Her People
*Wilma Mankiller
The Minutes of the Michigan Commission on Indian Affairs, 1956-1977
Modern American Indian Tribal Government & Politics: An Interdisciplinary Study
Modern Tribal Development: Paths to Self-Sufficiency & Cultural Integrity
A Nation of Statesmen: The Political Culture of the Stockbridge-Munsee Mohicans, 1815-1972
The National Congress of American Indians: The Founding Years
National Identity & the Conflict at Oka: Native Belonging & Myths of Postcolonial Nationhood in Canada
The Nations Within: The Past & Future of American Indian Sovereignty
Native America & the Evolution of Democracy
Native American Affairs & the Dept. of Defense
Native American Political Systems & the Evolution of Democracy: An Annotated Bibliography
Native American Power in the U.S., 1783-1795
The Native American Rights Movement
Native Americans & the Environment
Native Americans & Political Participation
Native Voices: American Indian Identity & Resistance
Navajo Foreign Affairs, 1795-1846
The Navajo Political Experience
Navigating Power: Cross-Cultural Competence in Navajo Land
Negotiated Sovereignty: Working To Improve Tribal-State Relations
New Capitalists: Issues of Law, Politics, & Identity Surrounding Casino Gaming on Native American Land
The New Resource Wars
The New Warriors: Native American Leaders Since 1900
Notebooks of Elizabeth Cook-Lynn
The Occupation of Alcatraz Island
Oglala People, 1841-1879: A Political History
Oklahoma Tribal Court Reports, Vol. 3
*One Indian & Two Chiefs: Short Fiction
Organizing the Lakota: The Political Economy of the New Deal on the Pine Ridge & Rosebud Reservations
Our Chiefs & Elders: Words & Photographs of Native Leaders
Peace, Power, Righteousness: An Indigenous Manifesto
Policing in Indian Country
The Political Economy of North American Indians
The Political Outsiders: Blacks & Indians inn a Rural Oklahoma County
Political Principles & Indian Sovereignty
Political Structure & Change in the Prehistoric Southeastern U.S.
Politics & Ethnicity on the Rio Yaqui
Politics & the Museum of the American Indian: The Heye & the Mighty
The Politics of Hallowed Ground
The Politics of Indian Removal
The Politics of Second Generation Discrimination in American Indian Education
Politics & Power: An Economic & Political History of the Western Pueblo Identities

The Queen's People
Re-creating the Circle: The Renewal of American Indian elf-Determination
"Real" Indians & others: Mixed-Blood Urban Native Peoples & Indigenous Nationhood
Red Critical Theory
Red Jacket: Iroquois Diplomat & Orator
Removals: 19th Century American Literature & the Politics of Indian Affairs
Reservation Politics: Historical Trauma, Economic Development & Intratribal Conflict
The Roads of My Relations
Saving the Reservation: Joe Garry & the Battle To Be Indian
The Savanah River Chiefdoms: Political Change in the Late Prehistoric Southeast
The Second Civil War: Examining the Indian Demand for Ethnic Sovereignty
Self Relaince vs. Power Politics
Settlement Pattern Studies in the Americas
Shadow Nations: Tribal Sovereignty & the Limits of Legal Pluralism
Since Predator Came: Notes From the Struggle for American Indian Liberation
Sitting Bull & the Paradox of Lakota Nationhood
State & Reservation: New Perspectives on Federal Indian Policy
Surviving As Indians: The Challenge of Self-Government
"They Made Us Many Promises": The American Indian Experience Since 1524
Thinking In Indian: A John Mohawk Reader
To Be the Main Leaders of Our People
To Show Heart: Native American Self-Determination & Federal Indian Policy, 1960-1975
Survivance, Sovereignty, and Story: Teaching American Indian Rhetorics
Tribal Cultural Resource Management: The Full Circle To Stewardship
Tribal Government Today: Politics on Montana Indian Reservations
The Tribal Moment in American Politics: The Struggle for Native American Sovereignty
Tribal Policing: Asserting Sovereignty, Seeking Justice
Tribal Sovereignty & the Historical Imagination: Cheyenne-Arapaho Politics
The Tribes & the States: Geographies of Intergovernmental Interaction
Trusteeship In Change: Toward Tribal Autonomy in Resource
The United Keetoowah Band of Cherokee Indians in Oklahoma
Unsettling America: The Uses of Indianess in the 21st Century
The Voice of the Crane Echoes Afar
Wounded Knee II
Wounded Knee: Party Politics and the Road to an American Massacre
You Are On Indian Land: Alcatraz Island, 1969-1971
Your Fyre Shall Burn No More: Iroquois Policy to New France

POMO INDIANS

*Coyote & the Grasshoppers: A Pomo Legend
Kashaya Pomo Plants
Mabel McKay: Weaving the Dream
*The Pomo
Pomo Basketmaking
Pomo Doctors & Poisoners
Pomo Indian Basketry
*Pomo Indians of California & Their Neighbors
Pomo Lands on Clear Lake
The Maru Cult of the Pomo Indians: A California Ghost Dance Survival
Western Pomo Prehistory

PONCA INDIANS

The Ponca Tribe
The Standing Bear Controversy
Standing Bear Is a Person: The Tru e Story
Standing Bear & the Ponca Chiefs
Clyde Warrior: (1939-1968) Tradition, Community, and Red Power

PONTIAC

A "Most Troublesome Situation," The British Military & the Pontiac Uprising
Never Come to Peace Again: Pontiac's Uprising
Oregon Trail & the Conspiracy of Pontiac
*Pontiac: Chief of the Ottawas
Pontiac's Conspiracy & Other Indian Affairs
Squanto, Pontiac, Chief Joseph

POTAWATOMI INDIANS

Gathering the Potawatomi Nation: Revitalization & Identity
Indians and a Changing Frontier: The Art of George Winter
Kinsmen Through Time: An Annotated Bibliography of Potawatomi History
Mascoutens of Prairie Potawatomi Indians
*Potawatomi
Potawatomi Trail of Death - Indiana to Kansas
The Potawatomis: Keepers of the Fire
The Prairie People: Continuity & Change in Potawatomi Indian Culture, 1865-1965

POTLATCH

Bags of Friendship
Chiefly Feasts: The Enduring Kwakiutl Potlatch
Feasting With Mine Enemy: Rank & Exchange Among Northwest Coast Societies
Potlatch at Gitsegukla
Potlatch: Native Ceremony & Myth on the Northwest Coast
Potlatch Papers: A Colonial Caser History
Potlatch People: Indian Lives & Legends of British Columbia
Rifles, Blankets & Beads
Symbolic Immortality: The Tlingit Potlatch of the 19th Century
Tlingit Tales: Potlatch & Totem Poles

POTTERY

Acoma & Laguna Pottery
Adventures in Physics & Pueblo Pottery
All That Glitters: The Emergence of Native American Micaceous Art Pottery
  in Northern New Mexico
American Indian Pottery
American Indian Pottery: An Identification & Value Guide
Anasazi Painted Pottery in the Field Museum
Anasazi Pottery
Ancient Indian Pottery of the Mississippi River Valley
Art of Clay: Timeless Pottery of the Southwest
Art of a Vanished Race: The Mimbres Classic Black-0n-White
Artists in Clay
Beauty From the Earth: Pueblo Indian Pottery from the University Museum
  of Archaeology & Anthropology
Born of Fire (Margaret Tafoya)
Catawba Indian Pottery: The Survival of a Folk Tradition
*Children of Clay: A Family of Pueblo Potters
Collections of Southwestern Pottery
Decorative Art of the Southwestern Indians
Designs & Factions: Politics, Religion, & Ceramics on the Hopi Third Mesa
Designs on Prehistoric Hopi Pottery
Dialogues With Zuni Potters
Early Pottery in the Southeast
*Earth Daughter: Alicia of Acoma Pueblo
Fourteen Families in Pueblo Pottery
From This Earth: The Ancient Art of Pueblo Pottery
Guide to Hohokam Pottery
Function & Technology of Anasazi Ceramics from Black Mesa, Arizona
A Guide to Pueblo Pottery
Historic Pottery of the Pueblo Indians, 1600-1800
Hold Everything! Masterworks of Basketry & Pottery from the Heard Museum Collection
Hopi & Hopi-Tewa Pottery
Hopi Pottery Symbols
Hopi-Tewa Pottery: 500 Artist Biographies
In the Belly of a Laughing God: Humour & Irony in Native Women's Poetry
Indian Pottery
Indian Pottery by Toni Roller of Santa Clara Pueblo: A Guide
Indian Pottery of the Southwest: A Selected Bibliography
Introduction to Hopi Pottery
Josephine Foard & The Glazed Pottery of Laguna Pueblo
Lasting Impression: Coastal, Lithic, & Ceramic Research
  in New England Archaeology
The Legacy of Maria Poveka Martinez
Legacy of a Master Potter: Nampeyo & Her Descendants
Legacy: Southwest Indian Art at the School of American Research
The Living Tradition of Maria Martinez
Making Native American Pottery
Maria
Maria Making Pottery
Maria Martinez: Pueblo Potter
Maria: The Potter of San Ildefonso
The Mimbres: Art & Archaeology
Mimbres Classic Mysteries: Reconstructing a Lost Culture Through Its Pottery
Mimbres Painted Pottery
Mimbres Pottery: Ancient Art of the American Southwest
Mojave Pottery, Mojave People: The Dillingham Collection of Mojave Ceramics
Mud Woman
Nampeyo and Her Pottery
Navajo Pottery: Traditions & Innovations
New Perspectives on Pottery Mound Pueblo
Pottery by American Indian Women: The Legacy of Generations
The Pottery From Arroyo Hondo Pueblo
Pottery of the Great Basin and Adjacent Areas
The Pottery of Santa Ana Pueblo
The Pottery of Zia Pueblo
The Pottery of Zuni Pueblo
Pottery & People: A Dynamic Interaction
Pottery & Practice: The Expression of Identity at Pottery Mound
Pottery Techniques of Native North America
Prehistoric Hopi Pottery Designs
Prehistoric Painted Pottery of Southeastern Arizona
Primer of North American Indian Pottery & Restoration Terms
Pueblo: Mountain, Village, Dance
Pueblo Indian Pottery
Pueblo Indian Pottery: 750 Artist Biographies
Pueblo & Navajo Contemporary Pottery: And Directory of Artists
The Pueblo Potter: A Study of Creative Imagination in Primitive Art
Pueblo Pottery Designs
Pueblo Pottery Figurines: The Expression of Cultural Perceptions in Clay
Pueblo Pottery of the New Mexico Indians
The Quapaw and Their Pottery
Recollections from My Time in the Indian Service, 1935-1942:
  Maria Martinez Makes Pottery
Re-Creating the Word: Painted Ceramics of the Prehistoric Southwest
A River Apart (Pueblo pottery)
Santa Clara Pottery Today
Seven Families in Pueblo Pottery
Shawnee Pottery: An Identification & Value Guide
Southern Pueblo Pottery: 2,000 Artist Biographies
Southwestern Indian Pottery
Southwestern Pottery: An Annotated Bibliography & List of Types & Wares
Southwestern Pottery: Anasazi to Zuni

Starting From Here: Dakota Poetry, Pottery & Caring
Storytellers & Other Figurative Pottery
Margaret Tafoya: A Tewa Potter's Heritage and Legacy
Talking With the Clay: The Art of Pueblo Pottery
*Tending the Fire: The Story of Maria Martinez
Tlapacoya Pottery in the Museum Collection
To Touch the Past: The Painted Pottery of the Mimbres People
Tradition & Innovation: The Pottery of New Mexico's Pueblos
Two Hundred Years of Historic Pueblo Pottery: The Gallegos Collection
Visions of Chimney Rock
Voices in Clay: Pueblo Pottery From the Edna M. Kelly Collection
*When Clay Sings
White Mountain Redware
Woodland Potters & Archaeological Ceramics of the North Carolina Coast
Zuni Pottery

POWHATAN INDIANS

Before & After Jamestown: Virginia's Powhatans & Their Predecessors
Chapters of the Ethnology of the Powhatan Tribes of Virginia
Dictionary of Powhatan
Encyclopedia of Native American Biography
James River Chiefdoms
Pocahontas (In the Words of Her Contemporaries)
Pocahontas's People: The Powhatan Indians of Virginia Pocahontas: Powhatan
Peacemaker
Powhatan Foreign Relations 1500-1722
Powhatan Indians of Virginia: Their Traditional Culture
Powhatan Lords of Life & Death
Powhatan Tribes: Middle Atlantic
Powhatan's Mantle: Indians in the Colonial Southeast
Powhatan's World & Colonial Virginia

POWWOWS

California Powwows
Celebrating the Powwow
A Dancing People: Powwow Culture on the Southern Plains
Drumbeat...Heartbeat: A Celebration of the Powwow
*Eagle Drum
Heartbeat of the People: Music & Dance of the Northern Powwow
Ho-Chunk Powwows & The Politics of Tradition
*On the Powwow Trail Coloring Book
People of the Circle: Powwow Country
Powwow
*Powwow
Powwow
*Powwow
*Powwow Activity Book
Powwow Calendar
Powwow Chow
Powwow Country
Powwow Country: People of the Circle
The Powwow Highway
Powwow: On the Red Road
Powwow: & Other Yakama Indian Traditions
The Powwow Trail
*Powwow
*Powwow Activity Book
Powwow Country
Powwow Country: People of the Circle
Powwow Dancer's & Craftworker's Handbook
The Powwow Highway
*Powwow: Images Along the Red Road
Powwow: On the Red Road
Powwow: & Other Yakama Indian Traditions
*Powwow Summer
The Powwow Trail: Understanding & Enjoying the Native American Powwow
*Powwow Summer: A Family Celebrates the Circle of Life
*Powwow's Coming
*Rainy's Powwow
The Traditional Northern Dancer
*A Trip to a Pow Wow

PSYCHOLOGY

The American Indian Mind in a Linear World
American Indian & White Children
Bibliography of North American Indian Mental Health
Chippewa Child Life & Its Cultural Background
Choosing Life: Special Report on Suicide Among Aboriginal People
Disciplined Hearts: History, Identity & Depression In an American Indian Community
Emotional Expression Among the Cree Indians
Indian Nation
Lesbian, Bisexual & Transgender Myths from the Acoma to the Zuni: An Anthology
Many Faces of Gender: Roles & Relationships Through Time
  in Indigenous Northern Communities
Modern Indian Psychology
Mohave Ethnopsychiatry & Suicide
Molded In the Image of Changing Woman
North American Indians & Alaska Natives: Abstracts of the Psychological
  & Behavioral Literature, 1967-1994
Psychocultural Change and the American Indians: An Ethnohistorical Analysis

Psychology of Indians of North America
Psychosocial Research on American Indian and Alaska Native Youth
Research for Indigenous Survival: Indigenous Research Methodologies
  in the Behavioral Sciences
Revenge of the Windigo: The Construction of the Mind & Mental Health
  of North American Aboriginal Peoples
Vanished in Hiawatha: The Story of the Canton Asylum for Insane Indians

PUEBLO INDIANS

Acoma: Pueblo in the Sky
Advocates for the Oppressed: Hispanos, Indians, Genizaros and Their Land in New Mexico
All Indians Do Not Live in Teepees (or Casinos)
All My Relations - Mitakuye Oyasin: The Sioux, The Pueblo & the Spirit World
America Firsthand & Pueblo
*American Pueblo Indian Activity Books
The Archaeology & History of Pueblo San Marcos: Change & Stability
Architecture of Acoma Pueblo
The Architecture of Social Integration in Prehistoric Pueblos
Before Santa Fe
Born a Chief
Born of Fire (Margaret Tafoya)
Kenneth Milton Chapman: A Life Dedicated to Indian Arts & Artists
*Children of Clay: A Family of Pueblo Potters
Cochiti: A New Mexico Pueblo
Common Threads: Pueblo & Navajo Textiles in the Southwest Museum
Conquest & Catastrophe: Changing Rio Grande Pueblo Settlement Patterns
  in the 16th & 17th Centuries
Coyote Tales from the Indian Pueblos
Cushing at Zuni
Dance Ceremonies of the Northern Rio Grande Pueblos
Dances of the Tewa Pueblo Indians
Dancing in the Paths of the Ancestors
*A Day With a Pueblo
Deliberate Acts: Changing Hopi Culture Through the Oraibi Split
*Earth Daughter: Alicia of Acoma Pueblo
Earth Fire: A Hopi Legend of the Sunset Crater Eruption
An Ecological Analysis Involving the Population of San Juan Pueblo, NM
*Easy-to-Make Pueblo Village
Education at the Edge of Empire: Negotiating Pueblo Identity in New Mexico's
  Indian Boarding Schools
Engendered Encounters: Feminism & Pueblo Cultures, 1879-1934
Excavation of Main Pueblo at Fitzmaurice Ruin
The First Koshare
Four Square Leagues: Pueblo Indian Land in New Mexico
Fourteen Families in Pueblo Pottery
The Fourth World of the Hopis
The Freeing of the Deer and Other New Mexico Indian Myths
Glen Canyon: An Archaeological Summary
A Guide to Pueblo Pottery
A Guide to Zuni Fetishes & Carvings
Hano: A Tewa Indian Community in Arizona
Historic Pottery of the Pueblo Indians, 1600-1880
Historical Background of the Santa Ana Pueblo
Historical Introduction to Studies Among the Sedentary Indians of New Mexico
Hopi Indian Altar Iconography
Hopi Katcinas
*Hopi Mysteries
The Hopi Photographs
Hopi Snake Ceremonies
The Hopi Way: Tales from a Vanishing Culture
Hopis, Tewas, and the American Road
Idonapshe, Let's Eat: Traditional Zuni Foods
Images from the Region of the Pueblo Indians of North America
Indian Uprising on the Rio Grande: The Pueblo Revolt of 1680
Indian Stories from the Pueblos
Indian Tales from Picuris Pueblo
Indians of Pecos Pueblos
Josephine Foard & The Glazed Pottery of Laguna Pueblo
Kiva, Cross, & Crown: The Pecos Indians & New Mexico, 1540-1840
The Kachina & the Cross: Indians & Spaniards in the Early Southwest
Laguna Pueblo: A Photographic History
Landscapes of Social Transformation in the Salinas Province & the Eastern Pueblo World
Language, History, & Identity
Life in the Pueblo: Understanding the Past Through Archaeology
Life in the Pueblos
*Little Boy with Three Names: Stories of Taos Pueblo
Maasaw: Profile of a Hopi God
Masked Gods: Navaho and Pueblo Ceremonialism
Meditations with the Hopi
Men on the Moon: Collected Short Stories
Modern Transformation of Moenkopi Pueblo
Mother Earth, Father Sky: Ancient Chants by Pueblo and Navajo Indians of the Southwest
My Adventures in Zuni
My Life in San Juan Pueblo: Stories of Esther Martinez
The Mythical Pueblo Rites Doctrine
Navajo & Pueblo Earrings, 1850-1945
Negotiation Within Domination: New Spain's Indian Pueblos Confront the Spanish State
New Perspectives on Pottery Mound Pueblo
New Perspectives on the Pueblos
*Old Father Story Teller
The Origin & Development of the Pueblo Katsina Cult
Our Prayers Are In This Place
Painting the Underworld Sky: Cultural Expression & Subversion in Art

People of the Middle Place: A Study of the Zuni Indians
Petroglyphs & Pueblo Myths of the Rio Grande
Pottery & Practice: The Expression of Identity at Pottery Mound & Hummingbird Pueblo
Prehistoric Households at Turkey Creek Pueblo, Arizona
Pedro Pino: Governor of Zuni Pueblo, 1830-1878
*A Pueblo
*The Pueblo
The Protohistoric Pueblo World, A.D. 1275-1600
Pueblo Architecture & Modern Adobes
Pueblo Artists: Portraits
Pueblo Birds & Myths
*Pueblo Boy: Growing Up in Two Worlds
The Pueblo Children of the Earth Mother
Pueblo Crafts
Pueblo Cultures
Pueblo Designs
*Pueblo Girls: Growing Up in Two Worlds
Pueblo Gods and Myths
Pueblo, Hardscrabble, Greenhorn
Pueblo Imagination
*Pueblo Indian
Pueblo Indian Agriculture
Pueblo Indian Cookbook
Pueblo Indian Embroidery
Pueblo Indian Embroidery Artists
Pueblo Indian Folk-Stories
Pueblo Indian Painting: Traditions & Modernism in New Mexico. 1900-1930
Pueblo Indian Pottery
Pueblo Indian Pottery: 750 Artist Biographies
Pueblo Indian Religion
The Pueblo Indian Revolt of 1696 and the Franciscan Missions in New Mexico
Pueblo Indian Textiles
The Pueblo Indians
*Pueblo Indians
The Pueblo Indians of North America
Pueblo Indians & Spanish Colonial Authority in 18th Century New Mexico
Pueblo & Mission: Cultural Roots of the Southwest
Pueblo Mothers & Children
Pueblo: Mountain, Village, Dance
Pueblo Nations: Eight Centuries of Pueblo Indian History
Pueblo & Navajo Contemporary Pottery & Directory of Artists
Pueblo & Navajo Indian Life Today
Pueblo People: Ancient Traditions, Modern Lives
Pueblo Peoples on the Pajarito Plateau: Archaeology & Efficiency
The Pueblo Potter
Pueblo Pottery Designs
Pueblo Pottery of the New Mexico Indians
Pueblo Profiles: Cultural Identity Through Centuries of Change
The Pueblo Revolt
The Pueblo Revolt & the Mythology of Conquest
The Pueblo Revolt of 1680
Puebloan Ruins of the Southwest
Pueblo Shields from the Fred Harvey Fine Arts Collection
*The Pueblo: Southwest
Pueblo Stories & Storytellers
*A Pueblo Village
*The Pueblos
Pueblos: Prehistoric Indian Cultures of the Southwest
Pueblos, Spaniards, and the Kingdom of New Mexico
The Railroad and the Pueblo Indians: The Impact of the Atchison, Topeka & Santa Fe
  on the Pueblos of the Rio Grande, 1880-1930
The Re-Establishment of the Indians in Their Pueblo Life Through the Revival
  of Their Traditional Crafts
Rethinking Hopi Ethnography
Revolt: An Archaeological History of Pueblo Resistance
  & Revitalization n 17th Century New Mexico
Ritual in Pueblo Art: Hopi Life in Hopi Painting
A River Apart (Pueblo pottery)
Salinas Pueblo Missions National Monument
Santa Ana: The People, the Pueblo, and the History of Tamaya
Searching for My Destiny
The Serpent's Tongue: Prose, Poetry & Art of the New Mexican Pueblos
Seven Families in Pueblo Pottery
Signs from the Ancestors: Zuni Cultural Symbolism and Perceptions of Rock Art
Social and Ceremonial Organization of Cochiti
Social Organization of the Western Pueblos
Songs of the Tewa
Standing Flower: The Life of Irving Pabanale, an Arizona Tewa Indian
Stories of Maasaw, a Hopi God
Stories & Stone: Writing the Ancestral Pueblo Homeland
A Strange Mixture
A Study of Pueblo Architecture
Talking With the Clay: The Art of Pueblo Pottery in the 21st Century
Taos Artists & Their Patrons, 1898-1950
The Taos Indians
The Taos Indians & the Battle for Blue Lake
Taos Pueblo and Its Sacred Blue Lake
Taos Society of Artists
The Taos Trappers
Tewa Tales
Tewa World
The Tiguas: Pueblo Indians of Texas
Tracking Prehistoric Migrations: Pueblo Settlers Among the Tonto Basin Hohokam
Trends in Pueblo Pottery

Warrior, Shield & Star Imagery & Ideology of Pueblo Warfare
We Became As Mountains: Poems of the Pueblo Conquest
We Have a Religion: The 1920s Pueblo Indian Dance Controversy
  & American Religious Freedom
Western Pueblo Identities
When Cultures Meet
When Rain Gods Reigned: From Curios to Art at Tesuque Pueblo
Where There is No Name for the Art: The Art of Tew a Pueblo Children
A Zuni Atlas
Zuni Bread Stuff
Zuni Contemporary Pottery
Zuni Coyote Tales
Zuni & El Moro
The Zuni Enigma
Zuni Fetishes
Zuni Fetishism
The Zuni Indians
The Zuni Indians & Their Uses of Plants
Zuni Jewelry
Zuni Katchinas
Zuni Katcinas
Zuni Kin and Clan
A Zuni Life: A Pueblo Indian in Two Worlds
The Zuni Man-Woman
Zuni Pottery
Zuni: Selected Writings of Frank Hamilton Cushing
Zuni: A Village of Silversmiths
The Zunis

QUAPAW INDIANS

Brief History of the Quapaw Tribe of Indians
The Quapaws
The Quapaw Indians: A History of the Downstream People
The Rumble of a Distant Drum: The Quapaw & Old World Newcomers, 1673-1804
The Quapaw and Their Pottery

RED CLOUD (LAKOTA CHIEF)

Autobiography of Red Cloud
The Land of Red Cloud: Among North America's Indians
New York Photographer & Red Cloud: Photographs of a Lakota Chief
Red Cloud: Photographs of a Lakota Chief
Red Cloud & the Sioux Problem
Red Cloud: Warrior Statesman of the Lakota Sioux
Red Cloud's Folks: A History of the Oglala Sioux Indians
Red Cloud's War: The Bozeman Trail, 1866-1868
The Wagon Box Fight: An Episode of Red Cloud's War

RELIGION & MYTHOLOGY

All My Relations - Mitakuye Oyasin: The Sioux, The Pueblo & the Spirit World
Amerindian Rebirth: Reincarnation Belief Among North American Indians & Inuit
American, African, and Old European Mythologies
The American Indian Ghost Dance, 1870 & 1890: An Annotated Bibliography
American Indian Mythology
American Indian Prayers & Poetry
American Indian Prophets: Religious Leaders & Revitalization Movements
American Indian Religious Freedom Act: A Legislative History of Public Law No. 95-341
American Indian Religious Traditions: An Encyclopedia
American Indian Traditions & Ceremonies
American Indians: The First Nation: Native North American Life, Myth & Art
American Lazarus: Religion & the Rise of African-American & Native American Literatures
Analysis of Coeur D'Alene Indian Myths
Anasazi Legends: Songs of the Wind Dance
The Ancestors' Path: A Native American Oracle for Seeking Guidance
  from Nature & Spirit Helpers
Ancient Spirit Wisdom: An Elder's Guidebook To Native Spirituality & Beyond
The Animals Came Dancing: Native American Sacred Ecology & Animal Kinship
Answered Prayers
Apache Medicine-Men
An Archaeology of the Soul: North American Indian Belief & Ritual
Around the Sacred Fire: Native Religious Activism in the Red Power Era
Artistry in Native American Myths
At Home on the Earth
The Attraction of Peyote
Becoming & Remaining a People: Native American Religions on the Northern Plains
Before the Great Spirit: The Many Faces of Sioux Spirituality
Before the Horse: Indian Myths & Legends
Beyond the Lodge of the Sun: Inner Mysteries of the Native American Way
The Big Missionary: A Story of One Man's Compassion for the Navajo
Birds, Beads & Bells: Remote Sensing of a Pawnee Sacred Bundle
Black Elk & Flaming Rainbow
Black Elk: Holy Man of the Oglala
Black Elk Lives
*Black Elk: A Man with a Vision
Black Elk's Religion: The Sun Dance & Lakota Catholicism
Black Elk: The Sacred Ways of the Lakota
Black Hills: Sacred Hills
Black Elk Speaks
Black Elk's World
Blessingway
The Book of Ceremonies: A Native Way of Honoring & Living the Sacred

The Boy Who Made Dragonfly: A Zuni Myth
Bringing Indians to the Book
The Brothertown Nation of Indians: Land Ownership & Nationalism
  in Early America, 1740-1840
Brushed by Cedar, Living by the River: Coast Salish Figures of Power
The Burial Ground
By the Power of the Dreams: Songs, Prayers & Sacred Shields of the Plains Indians
California Indian Nights
Can You Feel the Mountains Tremble? A Healing the Land Handbook
Carlos Castaneda, Academic Opportunism, and the Psychedelic Sixties
The Chant of Life: Liturgical Inculturation & the People of the Land
*Chant of the Red Man
Chants & Prayers: A Native American Circle of Beauty
Cherokee Folk Zoology
The Cherokee Full Circle: A Practical Guide to Ceremonies & Traditions
The Cherokee Ghost Dance
Cherokee New Testament
A Cherokee Prayerbook
Cherokee Psalms, A Collection of Hymns
The Cherokee Sacred Calendar: A Handbook of the Ancient Native American Tradition
Cherokee Vision of Eloh'
The Cherokees and Christianity, 1794-1870
Children of Cottonwood
Chinigchinix, An Indigenous California Indian Religion
Christian Indians & Indian Nationalism, 1855-1950
Christianity and Native Traditions
Circles, Consciousness, and Culture
Clowns of the Hopi: Tradition Keepers & Delight Makers
Comanches & Mennonites on the Oklahoma Plains
Coming Down From Above: Prophecy, Resistance, and Renewal
  in Native American Religions
The Complete Book of Natural Shamanism
A Coyote Reader
Creating Christian Indians: Native Clergy in the Presbyterian Church
*Creation Tales from the Salish
Creation's Journey: Native American Identity & Belief
Creators of the Plains
Creek Indian Medicine Ways
Creek (Muskogee) New Testament Concordance
Creek Religion & Medicine
Thomas Crosby & the Tsimshian: Small Shoes for Feet Too Large
The Crossing of Two Roads: Being Catholic & Native in the U.S.
Crow Jesus: Personal Stories of Native Religious Belongings
Crying for a Dream: The World Through Native American Eyes
Dakota Cross-Bearer: The Life & World of a Native American Bishop
Dance Ceremonies of the Northern Rio Grande Pueblos
Dancing the Dream: The Seven Sacred Paths of Human Transformation
Dancing Ghosts: Native American & Christian Syncretism in Mary Austin's Work
Dancing Gods: Indian Ceremonials of New Mexico & Arizona
Daughters of the Buffalo Women: Maintaining the Tribal Faith
The Devil in the New World
The Dawn of the World: Myths & Tales of the Miwok Indians of California
Devil Sickness & Devil Songs: Tohono O'odham Poetics
Dictionary of Native American Mythology
A Different Medicine: Postcolonial Healing in the Native American Church
Distinguished Native American Spiritual Practitioners & Healers
Dramatic Elements in American Indian Ceremonials
Dream Catchers: How Native American Spirituality Went Mainstream
Dream Catchers: Legend, Lore & Artifacts
The Dream Seekers: Native American Visionary Traditions of the Great Plains
Dream Songs & Ceremony: Reflections on California Indian Dance
Dreaming the Council Ways: True Native Teachings from the Red Lodge
Dreaming With the Wheel: How to Interpret Your Dreams Using the Medicine Wheel
Dry Bones & Indian Sermons: Praying Indians in Colonial America
Earth Fire: A Hopi Legend of the Sunset Crater Eruption
The Economics of Sainthood: Religious Change Among the Rimrock Navajos
Empowerment of North American Indian Girls: Ritual Expressions at Puberty
Encyclopedia of Native American Religions
Encyclopedia of Native American Shamanism
Exploring Native American Wisdom: Lore, Tradition & Rituals That Connect Us All
Evolution, Creationism & Other Modern Myths: A Critical Inquiry
The False Faces of the Iroquois
The Feathered Sun: Plains Indians in Art & Philosophy
Finding a Way Home: Indian & Catholic Spiritual Paths of the Plateau Tribes
Flight of the Seventh Moon: The Teaching of the Shields
First White Frost: Native Americans & United Methodism
Following the Sun & Moon: Hopi Kachina Tradition
Fools Crow: Wisdom & Power
For This Land: Writings on Religion in America
The Four Gospels & Selected Psalms in Cherokee
Framing the Sacred: The Indian Churches of Early Colonial Mexico
The Freeing of the Deer and Other New Mexico Indian Myths
The 1870 Ghost Dance
Ghost Dance
Ghost Dance Messiah: The Jack Wilson Story
Ghost Dance Religion
Ghost-Dance Religion & the Sioux Outbreak of 1890
The Ghost-Dance Religion & Wounded Knee
*Giving Thanks: A Native American Good Morning Message
Giving Voice to Bear: Native American Myths, Images, and
  Rituals of the Bear
God Is Red: A Native View of Religion
Going Native
The Gospel of the Great Spirit

REMOVAL/RELOCATION

REPATRIATION

RESERVATIONS

RITES & CEREMONIES

Agayul/Our Way of Making Prayer
American Indian Ceremonies: A Practical Workbook & Study Guide
  to the Medicine Path Hawk Medicine
American Indian Religious Traditions: An Encyclopedia
American Indian Traditions & Ceremonies
Apache Medicine Men
Apache: Sacred Path to Womanhood
An Archaeology of the Soul: North American Indian Belief & Ritual
The Attraction of Peyote
Becoming & Remaining a People
Black Elk: Holy Man of the Oglala
Catlinite Pipes
Ceremonies of the Pawnee
Colonial Intimacies: Indian Marriage in Early New England
Crying for a Dream: The World Through Native American Eyes
Dakota Life in the Upper Midwest
Dancing Gods: Indian Ceremonials of New Mexico & Arizona
Discovering Totem Poles: A Traveler's Guide
Dramatic Elements in American Indian Ceremonials
The Dream Seekers: Native American Visionary Traditions of the Great Plains
Dream Songs & Ceremony: Reflections on California Indian Dance
Encyclopedia of Native American Ceremonies
Exploring Native American Wisdom & Lore, Traditions & Rituals That Connect Us
Feast of the Dead: Aboriginal Ossuaries in Maryland
Fertility Symbols of the Western Indians
First Houses: Native American Homes & Sacred Structures
*Flying With the Eagle, Racing the Great Bear
The Forgotten Artist
Gathering Hopewell: Society, Ritual & Ritual Interaction
The Gift of the Sacred Pipe: Based on Black Elk's Account
  of the Seven Rites of the Oglala Sioux
Giving Voice to Bear: North American Indian Myths, Rituals, & Images of the Bear
The Great Law & the Long House: A Political History of the Iroquois Confederacy
Greengrass Pipe Dancers: Crazy Horse's Pipe Bag & a Search for Healing
*Guardian Spirit Quest
A Guide to Navajo Sandpaintings
A Guide to Zuni Fetishes & Carving
The Hako: Song, Pipe and Unity in a Pawnee Calumet Ceremony
Head & Face Masks in Navaho Ceremonialism
Healing Ways: Navajo Health Care in the 20th Century
Hidatsa Social & Ceremonial Organization
Hogans: Navajo Houses & House Songs
Hopi Snake Ceremonies
How to Take Part in Lakota Ceremonies
Huichol Indian Sacred Rituals
Huichol Mythology
Hunter-Gatherer Mortuary Practices During the Central Texas Archaic
I Send a Voice
In the Trail of the Wind: American Indian Poems & Ritual Orations
Indian Games & Dances with Native Songs
Indian Myth & Legend
The Iroquois Eagle Dance
An Iroquois Sourcebook: Medicine Society Rituals
Journey to the Ancestral Self: The Native Lifeway Guide to Living in Harmony
  With Earth Mother
Kachinas: A Hopi Artist's Documentary
Kinaalada: A Navajo Puberty Ceremony
*Kiowa Voices: Ceremonial Dance, Ritual and Songs
Lakota Belief & Ritual
Lakota Grieving: A Pastoral Response
Lakota Life
Learning Journey on the Red Road
The Little Water Medicine Society of the Senecas
Lushootseed Culture & the Shamanic Odyssey: An Anchored Radiance
Making Two Worlds One and the Story of All-American Indian Days
Medicine Wheel Ceremonies
Medicine Wheels: Native American Vehicles of Healing
Midwinter Rites of the Cayuga Long House
Mishwabik, Metal of Ritual: Metallurgy in Precontact Eastern North America
Mitakuye Oyasin: We Are All Related
The Moki Snake Dance
Mother Earth, Father Sky: Ancient Chants by Pueblo & Navajo Indians of the Southwest
The Mountain Chant: A Navajo Ceremony
Myths & Symbols, or Aboriginal Religions in America
*Native American Religions
Native American Religious Identity: Unforgotten Gods
Native American Worldviews: An Introduction
Native North American Spirituality of the Eastern Woodlands
The Native American Sun Dance Religion & Ceremony: An Annotated Bibliography
Native American Sweat Lodge: History & Legend
Native North American Shamanism: An Annotated Bibliography
A Navajo Bringing-Home Ceremony
Navajo Ceremonial Baskets: Sacred Symbols, Sacred Space
Navajo Mountain & Rainbow Bridge Religion
Navajo Sandpainting Art: Where the Gods Gather
Navajo Sandpaintings
The Navajo Way: Ceremonial Myths of the Navajo
The Night Chant: A Navaho Ceremonial
The Night Has a Naked Soul
The Nightway: A History & a History of Documentation of a Navajo Ceremonial
North American Indian Dances & Rituals
North American Indian Travel Guide

Oceti Wakan
Offering Smoke: The Sacred Pipe & Native American Religion
Ojibway Ceremonies
O-Kee-Pa, A Religious Ceremony & Other Customs of the Mandan
Oklahoma Delaware Ceremonies: Feats & Dances
On the Gleaming Way
One Nation Under God: The Triumph of the Native American Church
Only the Earth Endures: The Spiritual Journey of a Mandan Indian
The Osage Ceremonial Dance I'n-Lon-Schka
The Osage & the Invisible World
Patterns & Ceremonials of the Indians of the Southwest
The Peyote Cult
Peyote: The Devine Cactus
Peyote Hunt: The Sacred Journey of Huichol Indians
Peyote Religion: A History
Peyote Religious Art: Symbols of Faith & Belief
The Peyote Road: Religious Freedom and the Native American Church
Peyotism & the Native American Church
Phoenix Rising: No Eyes' Vision of the Changes to Come
The Pipe & Christ
Plants of Power: Native American Ceremony & the Use of Sacred Plants
Potlatch: Native Ceremony & Myth on the Northwest Coast
Powwow: And Other Yakama Indian Traditions
The Power of Kiowa Song: A Collaborative Ethnography
*The Praying Flute
Pueblo Indian Religion
Rainhouse & Ocean: Speeches for the Papago Year
The Rattle & the Drum: Native American Rituals & Celebrations
Religion & Ceremonies of the Lenape
Rig Veda Americanus
Ritual & Myth in Odawa Revitalization
The Road of Life & Death: A Ritual Drama of the American Indians
The Road to Sundance: My Journey Into Native Spirituality
Rolling Thunder: A Personal Exploration Into the Secret Healing Power
  of an American Indian Medicine Man
Rolling Thunder Speaks
Sacred Ground
The Sacred Pipe: An Archetypal Theology
The Sacred Pipe: Black Elk's Account of the Seven Rites of Oglala Sioux
Scalp Ceremonials of Zuni
Secret Native American Pathways
Secrets of the Sacred White Buffalo: Native American Healing Remedies, Rites & Rituals
The Serpent & the Sacred Fire: Fertility Images in Southwest Rock Art
The Seven Visions of Bull Lodge
Severing the Ties That Bind
Shaking the Rattle: Healing the Traumas of Colonization
The Shoshoni - Crow Sun Dance
The Sister Creeks Site Mounds
Source Material for the Social & Ceremonial Life of the Choctaw Indians
The Southeastern Ceremonial Complex, Artifacts & Analysis
Southwestern Indian Ceremonials
Southwestern Indian Ritual Drama
Spirit Medicine
Spirit Song: The Introduction of No-Eyes
The Spirit World
Spirits of the Earth
Staging Ritual: Hopewell Ceremonialism at the Mound House Site, Greene County, IL
Standing in the Light: A Lakota Way of Seeing
The Story of the Meadowlark
The Sun Dance & Other Ceremonies of the Oglala Division of the Teton Dakota
Sun Dancing
Sundancing: The Great Sioux Piercing Ceremony
Sweetwater Wisdom: A Native American Spiritual Way
Teaching Spirits: Understanding Native American Religious Traditions
Tobacco, Peace Pipes & Indians
Totem Pole Carving: Bringing a Log to Life
Totem Poles & Tea
A Treatise on Lovesickness: An Offshoot of the Calumet Dance
The Urine Dance of the Zuni Indians of New Mexico
War Ceremony & Peace Ceremony of the Osage Indians
*Ways of the Lushootsed People: Ceremonies & Traditions of the
  Northern Puget Sound Indians
Weaving the Dance: Navajo Yeibichai Textiles, 1910-1950
Witchcraft & Sorcery of the North American Native Peoples
Witchcraft in the Southwest
The Witches of Abiquiu
With Good Heart: Yaqui Beliefs & Ceremonies in Pascua Village
The World's Rim: Great Mysteries of the North American Indians
Yuchi Ceremonial Life
The Yuchi Green Corn Ceremonial
Yuwipi: Vision and Experience in Oglala Ritual
Zuni Fetishes
Zuni Festishes: Using Native American Sacred Objects for Meditation, Reflection, & Insight
Zuni Fetishism
The Zuni Indians: Their Mythology, Esoteric Fraternities & Ceremonies

ROCK ART-PETROGLYPHS

Ancient Visions: Petroglyphs & Pictographs
The Art of the Shaman: Rock Art of California
Art of the Warriors: Rock Art of the American Plains
Blackfoot War Art: Pictographs of the Reservation Period, 1880-2000
Canyon de Chelly: Its People and Rock Art
Crystals in the Sky

Cuckoo for Kokopelli
Discovering North American Rock Art
The Forgotten Artist: Indians of Anza-Borrego & Their Rock Art
Guide to Indian Rock Carvings of the Pacific Northwest Coast
Guide to Rock Art of the Utah Region: Sites With Public Access
Indian Rock Art in Wyoming
Indian Rock Art of the Columbia Plateau
Indian Rock Art of the Southwest
Indian Rock Carvings
Kokopelli: Flute Player Images in Rock Art
Landscape of the Spirits: Hohokam Rock Art
Marks of the Ancestors
Petroglyphs: Ancient Language/Sacred Art
Petroglyphs of Ohio
Peroglyphs of Western Colorado & the Northern Ute Indian Reservation
Petroglyphs & Pueblo Myths of the Rio Grande
Picture Rocks: American Indian Rock Art in the Northeast Woodlands
Plains Indian Rock Art
Prehistoric Rock Art
Roadside Guide to Indian Ruins & Rock Art of the Southwest
Rock Art Images of Northern New Mexico
Rock Art in New Mexico
Rock Art of the American Indian
Rock Art of the American Southwest
The Rock Art of Eastern North America: Capturing Images & Insight
Rock Art of Kentucky
Rock Art of the Lower Pecos
The Rock Art of Texas Indians
The Rock Art of Utah
Rock Art of Western South Dakota
Rock Art Studies in the Great Basin
Rock Paintings of the Chumash
The Rocks Begin to Speak
The Sacred Geography of the American Moundbuilders
Sacred Images: A Vision of Native American Rock Art
Salinan Indian Rock Painting: Lithograph
The Serpent and the Sacred Fire: Fertility Images in Southwest Rock Art
Seven Rock Art Sites in Baja California
Signs From the Ancestors: Zuni Cultural Symbolism & Perceptions of Rock Art
Signs of Life: Rock Art of the Upper Rio Grande
Storied Stone: Indian Rock Art in the Black Hills Country
Stories & Stone: Writing the Ancestral Pueblo Homeland
*Stories in Stone: Rock Art: Images From the Ancient Ones
Thunder & Herds: Rock Art of the High Plains

SAC, FOX & IOWA INDIANS

Expedition Against the Sauk & Fox Indians, 1832
Observations of the Ethnology of the Sauk Indians
The Sac & Fox Indians
Sacred Bundles of the Sac & Fox Indians
The Sauks & the Black Hawk War

SACAGAWEA, 1786-1884

The Bird Woman: Sacajawea, Guide to Lewis & Clark
Bird Woman: Sacagawea's Own Story
The Making of Sacagawea: A Euro-American Legend
Mystery of Sacajawea
Sacajawea
*Sacagawea: Brave Shoshone Girl
Sacagawea's Child: The Life & Times of Jean-Baptiste (Pomp) Chabonneau
Sacajawea: A Guide & Interpreter on the Lewis & Clark Expedition
Sacajawea: Indian Interpreter to Lewis & Clark
*Sacajawea--Native American Heroine
Sacagawea of the Lewis & Clark Expedition
Sacajawea's People: The Lemhi Shoshones & the Salmon River Country
Sacajawea Speaks: Beyond the Shining Mountains with Lewis & Clark
Sacajawea, Wilderness Guide
Stone Heart: A Novel of Sacajawea
*The Value of Adventure: The Story of Sacajawea

SALISH & KOOTENAI INDIANS

Be of Good Mind: Essays on the Coast Salish
*Beaver Steals Fire: A Salish Coyote Story
Beginnings – A Meditation on Coast Salish Lifeways
Brushed by Cedar, Living by the River: Coast Salish Figures of Power
Bull Trout's Gift: Confederated Salish & Kootenai Tribes
A Century of Coast Salish History: Media Companion to the Book "Rights Remembered"
Coming Back Slow: The Importance of Preserving Salish Indian Culture & Language
Coast Salish
The Coast Salish of British Columbia
Coast Salish Essays
The Coast Salish People
The Coast Salish Peoples
Coast Salish Spirit Dancing: The Survival of an Ancestral Religion
Coast Salish Totem Poles: Media Companion at "A Totem Pole History"
Contemporary Art on the Northwest Coast: Salish, Nuu-Chah-Nulth, Makah
Contemporary Coast Salish Art
The Contemporary Coast Salish: Essays
*Coyote Stories of the Montana Salish Indians
*Creation Tales from the Salish

A Dictionary of Puget Salish
Explore the River: Bull Trout, Tribal People, and the Jacko River
  Exploring Coast Salish Prehistory
Folk-Tales of the Coast Salish
Folk-Tales of the Salishan & the Sahaptin Tribes
Katie Gale: A Coast Salish Woman's Life on Oyster Bay
Getting Good Crops: Economic & Diplomatic Survival Strategies
  of the Montana Bitterroot Salish Indians, 1870-1891
Historical Sketch of the Flathead Nation
*How Marten Got His Spots
"I Will Be Meat for My Salish"
In the Name of the Salish & Kootenai Nation: The 1855 Hell Gate Treaty
  & the Origin of the Flathead Indian Reservation
Indians of the North Pacific Coast
Indians of the Northwest Coast
Indians of the Northwest
Indians of the Pacific Northwest
Indians of the Pacific Northwest: A History
The Interior Salish Tribes of British Columbia
Kootenai Why Stories
Ktunaxa Legends
*Kwulasulwut: Stories from the Coast Salish
*Kwulasulwut: Salish Creation Stories
Letters from the Rocky Mountain Indian Missions
Lushootseed Dictionary
Lushootseed Texts
*Mali Npnags: The Story of Mean Little Old Lady
Mary Quequasah's Love Story
Name of Salish & Kootenai Nation
Our Tellings: Interior Salish Stories
Over a Century of Moving to the Drum: Salish Indian Celebrations
  on the Flathead Indian Reservation
*Owls Eyes and Seeking a Spirit
Peace Weavers: Uniting the Salish Coast Through Cross-Cultural Marriages
The Politics of Allotment on the Flathead Indian Reservation
A Pretty Village: Documents of Worship & Culture Change, St. Ignatius Mission,
  Montana, 1880-1889
The Problem of Justice: Tradition & Law in the Coast Salish World
Quay-Lem U En-Chow-Men: A Collection of Hymns & Prayers in the
  Flathead-Kalispel-Spokane Indian Language
Qwelm u Ncawmn
Rights Remembered: A Salish Grandmother Speakson American Indian History
  & the Future
Saanich, North Straits Salish: Classified Word List
S'abadeb, The Gifts: Pacific Coast Salish Art & Artists
Salish Blankets: Robes of Protection & Transformation, Symbols of Wealth
*Salish Folk Tales
Salish Indian Sweaters
The Salish Language Family
Salish Myths & Legends: One People's Stories
The Salish People and the Lewis & Clark Expedition
The Sanpoil & Nespelem: Salishan Peoples of Northeastern Washington
Salish, or Flat-Head Grammar
Shamanic Odyssey: the Lushootseed Salish
Stylized Characters' Speech in Thompson Salish Narrative
Thompson River Salish Dictionary
Twana Narratives: Native Historical Accounts of a Coast Salish Culture
The Undying West: Stories from Montana's Camas Prairie
The WSANEC & Their Neighbours: Diamond Jenness on the Coast Salish
  of Vancouver Island
Zealous In All Virtues: Documents of Worship & Culture Change,
  St. Ignatius Mission, Montana, 1890-1894

SANDPAINTING

Earth Is My Mother, Sky Is My Father
Hosteen Klah: Navaho Medicine Man and Sand Painter
Indian Sandpainting of the Southwest
The Navajo Art of Sandpainting
Navajo Medicine Man Sandpaintings
Navajo Sandpainting Art: Where the Gods Gather
Navajo Sandpainting From Religious Act to Commercial Art
Navajo Sandpainting: The Huckel Collection
Navajo Sandpaintings
Sandpaintings of the Navajo Shooting Chant
Summoning the Gods: Sandpainting of the Native American Southwest
Tapestries in Sand - The Spirit of Indian Sandpainting

SCULPTURE

The American Indian: Bronze Sculpture by Griffin
American Indian Painting & Sculpture
American Indian Sculpture
Arctic Journeys Ancient Memories: Sculpture by Abraham Anghik Ruben Art of the Far
North: Inuit Sculpture, Drawing & Printmaking
Cape Dorset Sculpture
Contemporary Indian Sculpture: An Algebra of Figuration
Inuit Imagination: Arctic Myth & Sculpture
Plains Indian Sculpture
Sculpturing Totem Poles
Plains Indian Sculpture

SELF DETERMINATION

The American Indian Occupation of Alcatraz Island: Red Power & Self-Determination
Blood Struggle: The Rise of Modern Indian Nations
Dismembered: Native Disenrollment & the Battle for Human Rights
Implementation of the Native American Housing Assistance
  & Self Determination ACT of 1996
Indians of the Americas: Self Determination & International Human Rights
Indigenous Peoples: Self-Determination, Knowledge & Indigeneity
Labor Laws, Union, and Indian Self-Determination
Native American & the Legacy of Harry S. Truman
Native Americans & Nixon: Presidential Politics & Minority Self-Determination
Navajo Courts & Navajo Common Law, A Tradition of Tribal Self-Governance
Pathways to Self-Determination: Canadian Indians and the Canadian State
A Place to Be Navajo: Rough Rock & the Struggle for Self-Determination
  in Indigenous Schooling
Self-Determination & the Social Education of Native Americans
Sovereignty for Survival: American Energy Development & Indian Self-Determination
The Struggle for Self-Determination: History of the Menominee Indians Since 1854
Taking Charge: Native American Self-Determination & Federal Indian Policy, 1975-1993
Therapeutic Nations: Healing in the Age of Indigenous Human Rights
To Show Heart: Native American Self-Determination and Federal Indian Policy, 1960-1975
Tribal Energy Self-Sufficiency ACT & the Native American Energy Development
  & Self-Determination ACT
X-marks: Native Signatures of Assent

SEMINOLE INDIANS

Africans & Seminoles: From Removal to Emancipation
*Allapattah
America's Hundred Years' War: U.S. Expansion tot he Gulf Coast
  & the Fate of the Seminole, 1763-1858
An Assumption of Sovereignty
Big Cypress: A Changing Seminole Community
The Black Seminoles: History of a Freedom-Seeking People
The Black Seminoles: The Little-Known Story of the First Seminoles
Complete Book of Seminole Patchwork
Creeks and Seminoles
*Dancing with the Indians
The Enduring Seminoles: From Alligate Wrestling to Ecotourism
*Escape to the Everglades, with Teacher's Guide
The Florida Seminole and the New Deal, 1933-1942
Florida's First People – 12,000 Years of Human History, Revised edition
Florida's Seminole Indians
*Forever Island
Freedom on the Border: The Seminole Maroons in Florida,
  the Indian Territory, Coahuila & Texas
Great Florida Seminole Trail
Guns Across the Loxahatchee: An Archaeological
  Investigation of Seminole War Sites
Healing Plants: Medicine of the Florida Seminole Indians
History of the Second Seminole War, 1835-1842
*John Hawk: A Seminole Saga
Hunted Like a Wolf: The Story of the Seminole War
Legends of the Seminoles
My Work Among the Florida Seminoles
Nations Remembered
Native Americans in Florida, with Teacher's Manual
Oklahoma Seminoles: Medicines, Magic and Religion
*Paintbrushes & Arrows: A Stry of St. Augustine
Patchwork: Seminole & Miccosukee Art & Activities
Pelts, Plumes and Hides
Removal Aftershock
*The Seminole
The Seminole
The Seminole Baptist Churches of Oklahoma
Seminole Burning: A Story of Racial Vengeance
The Seminole Freedmen: A History
*The Seminole Indians
The Seminole Indians of Florida
Seminole Indians of Florida, 1850-1874
A Seminole Legend: The Life of Betty Mae Tiger Jumper
The Seminole & Miccosukee Tribes
The Seminole Nation of Oklahoma: A Legal History
Seminole Patchwork
Seminole Patchwork Book
Seminole Patchwork: The Complete Book
The Seminole Seed
A Seminole Sourcebook
*The Seminole: Southeast
The Seminole Wars: America's Longest Indian Conflict
Seminole Voice: Reflections on Their Changing Society, 1970-2000
*The Seminoles
Seminoles
The Seminoles of Florida

SENECA INDIANS

The Allegany Senecas and Kinzua Dam
A Brief History of the Seneca-Cayuga Tribe
The Case of the Seneca Indians in the State of New York
Chief Cornplanter (Gy-Ant-Wa-Kia) of the Senecas
The Death and Rebirth of the Seneca

A Friend Among the Senecas: The Quaker Mission to Cornplanter's People
The Hidden Language of the Seneca
In the Hands of the Senecas
Iroquois Music & Dance: Ceremonial Arts of Two Seneca Longhouses
The Iroquois Trail: Dickon Among the Onondagas & Senecas
Mary Jemison: White Woman of the Seneca
*Little Water & Gift of the Animals: A Seneca Legend
Native American Basketry of the Seneca & Tlingit
One More Story: Contemporary Seneca Tales
Other Council Fires Were Before Ours: A Classic Native American Creation Story
  As Retold by a Seneca Elder & Her Granddaughter
An Outline of Seneca Ceremonies at Coldspring Longhouse
Parker on the Iroquois
Red Jacket: Seneca Chief
The Seneca
Seneca Fiction, Legends & Myths
Seneca Myths & Folk Tales
Seneca Possessed: Indians, Witchcraft, and Power in the Early American Republic
The Seneca Restoration, 1715-1754: An Iroquois Local Political Economy
The Seneca & Tuscarora Indians: An Annotated Bibliography
The Seneca World of Ga-No-Say-Yeh
*Skunny Wundy: Seneca Indian Tales
Thinking In Indian: A John Mohawk Reader
To Be an Indian: The Life of Iroquois-Seneca Arthur Caswell Parker
Warrior in Two Camps: Ely S. Parker, Union General & Seneca Chief

SEQUOYAH

The Cherokee Syllabary: Writing the People's Perseverance
Sequoyah
*Sequoyah
Sequoyah & the Cherokee Alphabet
*Sequoyah (Cherokee Hero)
*Sequoyah: The Cherokee Man Who Gave His people Writing
Sequoyah - Computerized Syllabary Learning Program - DOS
Seqouyah: Father of the Cherokee Alphabet
*Sequoyah & His Miracle
Sequoyah & the Invention of the Cherokee Alphabet
Sequoyah Rising: Problems in Post-Colonial Tribal Governance
Signs of Cherokee Culture: Sequoyah's Syllabary in Eastern Cherokee Life
The State of Sequoyah

SHAMANISM

The Art of the Shaman: Rock Art of California
The Bear Shaman Tradition of Southern California Indians
California Indian Shamanism
Call of the Great Spirit: The Shamanic Life & Teachings of Medicine Grizzly Bear
The Complete Book of Natural Shamanism
Coyote's Council Fire: Contemporary Shamans on Race, Gender & Community
Encyclopedia of Native American Shamanism
Giving Voice to Bear: North American Indian Myths, Rituals & Images of the Bear
Hopi Stories of Witchcraft, Shamanism, & Magic
Indian Healing: Shamanic Ceremonialism in the Pacific Northwest Today
Lushootseed Culture & the Shamanic Odyssey: An Anchored Radiance
Magic in the Mountains, the Yakama Shaman: Power & Practice
Magical Passes: The Practical Wisdom of the Shamans
Medicine Way: How To Live the Teachings of the Native American Medicine Wheel:
  A Shamanic Path to Self-Mastery
Native North American Shamanism: An Annotated Bibliography
The Navajo Hunter Tradition
Rainbow Medicine: A Visionary Guide to Native American The Sea Woman:
  Sedna in Inuit Shamanism & Art in the Eastern Arctic
Shaking Out the Spirits: A Psychologist's Entry Into the Healing Mysteries of Global
  Shamanism
Shamanism
Shadow of the Wolf: An Apache Tale
The Shaman & the Medicine Wheel
The Shaman: Patterns of Religious Healing Among the Ojibway Indians
The Shaman's Touch
*The Shaman & the Water Serpent
Shamanic Odyssey: The Lushootseed Salish Journey to the Land of the Dead
Shamanism
Shamanism in North America
Shamans, Gods, & Mythic Beasts: Columbian Gold & Ceramics in Antiquity
Shamans & Kushtakas: North Coast Tales of the Supernatural
Shamans & Religion: An Anthropological Exploration in Critical Thinking
The Shamans Touch
The Shasta Indians of California & Their Neighbors
The Specter of the Indian: Race, Gender, and Ghosts in American Seances, 1848-1890
Spiritual Dimensions of Healing
Tales of a Shaman's Apprentice
Tangible Visions: Northwest Indian Shamanism & Its Art
Visions of a Huichol Shaman
Vital Souls: Bororo Cosmology, Natural Symbolism & Shamanism
Warrior Woman: The Story of Lozen, Apach Warrior & Shaman
Washo Shamans & Peyotists: Religious Conflict in an American Indian Tribe
White Cloud - Lakota Spirit: Legends
The Wind Is My Mother: The Life & Teachings of an American Shaman
The Wolves of Heaven: Cheyenne Shamanism, Ceremonies
  & Prehistoric Origins

SHAWNEE INDIANS

SHOSHONE INDIANS

SIGN LANGUAGE

SITTING BULL - DAKOTA CHIEF, 1834-1890

SOCIAL CONDITIONS, LIFE & CUSTOMS

Sharing Our Stories of Survival: Native Women Surviving Violence
Sheridan's Troopers on the Border: A Winter Campaign on the Plains
Shooting Back from the Reservation: A Photographic View of Life by Native American Youth
Silent Arrows
Singing the Songs of My Ancestors: The Life & Music of Helma Swan, Makah Elder
Sister to the Sioux: The Memoirs of Goodale Eastman, 1885-1891
The Sioux: The Dakota & Lakota Nations
Smallpox & the Iroquois Wars
Snowbird Cherokees: People of Persistence
Social & Ceremonial Organization of Cochiti
Social Change in the Southwest, 1350-1880
Social Organization of the Western Pueblos
A Social Study of 150 Chippewa Indian Families of the White Earth Reservation of Minnesota
Son of Old Hat: A Navaho Autobiography
Source Material on the History & Ethology of the Caddo
Source Material for the Social & Ceremonial Life of the Choctaw Indians
Southwestern Indian Ceremonials
Spanish-Indian Relations in Florida: A Study of Two Vistas, 1657-1678
Spider Woman Walks This Land: Traditional Cultural Properties & the Navajo Nation
The Spirit & the Flesh: Sexual Diversity in American Indian Tradition
Spirit Moves: The Story of Six Generations of Native Women
Spirit & Reason: The Vine Deloria, Jr. Reader
*Sports & Games the Indians Gave Us
*Squanto & the First Thanksgiving
Status Terminology & the Social Structure of North American Indians
*The Story of Wounded Knee
Strangers in Blood
Strangers to Relatives
Strengthening the Circle: Child Support for Native American Children
Subjugation & Dishonor: A Brief History of the Travail of the Native Americans
Survival & Regeneration: Detroit's American Indian Community
Surviving As Indians: The Challenge of Self-Government
Suspect Relations: Sex, Race & Resistance in Colonial North Carolina
Symbolic Immortality, The Tlingit Potlatch of the 19th Century
Symposium on Cherokee & Iroquois Culture
Tales of the Endishodi: Father Berard Haile & the Navajos, 1900-1961
Tales of the Tepee
Talking Leaves
Team Spirits: The Native American Mascots Controversy
Themes in Southwest Prehistory
Theoriizing Native Studies
They Call Me Agnes: A Crow Narrative based on the Life of Agnes Yellowtail Deernose
They Say the Wind Is Red: The Alabama Choctaw Lost in Their Own Land
Thinking In Indian: A John Mohawk Reader
Three Native American Learning Stories
*To Live In Two Worlds: American Indian Youth Today
Tobacco, Peacepipes and Indians
Tobacco, Pipes & Smoking Customs of the American Indians
Trade Ornament Usage Among the Native Peoples of Canada: A Source Book
Traditions of the Arapaho
Traditions of the Caddo
Traditions of the North American Indians
Traditions of the Osage
Trailhead of the American Indian Courting Flute
Traits of American Indian Life & Character
Travels & Inquiries in North America, 1882-1883
Travels in North America, Including a Summer with the Pawnees
Treaties With American Indians: An Encyclopedia of Rights, Conflicts & Sovereignty
The Treatment of the Indians by the Colonists
The Trial of "Indian Joe": Race & Justice in the 19th Century West
Tribal Secrets: Recovering American Indian Intellectual Traditions
Tribes of the Southern Woodlands
Truth or Consequences: A Native American View of Society
Turquoise & the Navajo
The Turquoise Trail: Native American Jewelry & Culture of the Southwest
Twana Narratives
Two Crows Denies It: A History of Controversy in Omaha Sociology
Two Leggings: The Making of a Crow Warrior
Two Spirit People: American Indian Lesbian Women & Gay Men
Two Spirits: A Story of Life With the Navajo
The Underground Reservation: Osage Oil
Understanding Disabilities in American Indian & Alaska Native Communities: Toolkit Guide
Universities and Indian Country: Case Studies in Tribal-Driven Research
Unnatural Selection: The Yanomami, the Kayapo & the Onslaught of Civilization
Unsettled Past, Unsettled Future: The Story of maine Indians
Urban Indian Experience in America
*Urban Indians
Urban Indians
Urban Indans: Drums from the Cities
Urban Institutions & People of Indian Ancestry
Urban Voices: The Bay Area American Indian Community
Urbanization of American Indians: A Critical Bibliography
The Ute Indians of Colorado in the 20th Century
Vocational Rehabilitation Projects: Final Report
Valley of the Spirits: The Upper Skagit Indian of Western Washington
Visual Testament & the Israelite Indian
Voices in the Stone: Life Lessons from the Native Way
The Wake of the Unseen Object: Travels Through Alaska's Native Landscapes
Walk in Your Soul: Love Incantations of the Oklahoma Cherokees
Warriors on the Little Big Horn, 1876
The Way of the Dead Indians
The Way of the Warrior

The Way We Live: California Indian Reminiscences, Stories & Songs
Ways of Knowing: Experience, Knowledge & Power Among the Dene Tha
We Are Not You: First Nations & Canadian Modernity
We Are a People In This World: The Lakota Sioux & the Massacre at Wounded Knee
We, The People: Of Earth & Elders
Marietta Wetherill: Life With the Navajos in Chaco Canyon
Whatever Happened to Professor Coyote: A Journey to the Heart of the Handgame
When Jesus Came, the Corn Mothers Went Away
When Nickels Were Indians
Where Courage Is Like a Wild Horse
White Grizzly Bear's Legacy: Learning to Be Indian
White Man's Water: The Politics of Sobriety in a Native American Community
White Man's Wicked Water: The Alcohol Trade & Prohibition in Indian Country
Why I Can't Read Wallace Stegner & Other Essays: A Tribal Voice
Wide Ruins: Memories from a Navajo Trading Post
Wild West Shows & the Images of American Indians, 1883-1933
Will the Time Ever Come? A Tlingit Source Book
Winds of Change
The Winds of Injustice
The Wintu & Their Neighbors
Without Reserve: Stories from Urban Natives
Women of the Dawn
Women of the Native Struggle: Portraits & Testimony of Native American Women
The Women's Way
Woodland Indians of the Western Great Lakes
Wounded Warriors: A Time for Healing

FRANK G. SPECK

Chapters on the Ethnology of the Powhatan Tribes of Virginia
Cherokee Dance & Drama
Ethnology of the Yuchi Indians
The Iroquois
Midwinter Rites of the Cayuga Long House
Penobscot Man
Studies in Cherokee Basketry
Territorial Subdivisions & Boundaries of the Wampanoag, Massachusetts & Nauset Indians
We Talk, You Listen: New Tribes, New Turf
A Vocabulary of Mohegan-Pequot

SUN DANCE

The Native American Sun Dance Religion & Ceremony
The Road to the Sundance
Shoshoni-Crow Sun Dance
*Sun Dance for Andy Horn
The Sun Dance & Other Ceremonies of the Oglala Division of the Teton Dakota
The Sun Dance Religion: Power for the Powerless
Sun Dancer
Sun Dancing: A Spiritual Journey on the Red Road
Sundancing at Rosebud & Pine Ridge
Sundancing: The Great Sioux Piercing Ceremony

SUQUAMISH INDIANS

*Brother Eagle, Sister Sky
*Suquamish Today
Law Enforcement on Indian Reservations After Oliphant v. Suquamish Indian Tribes
The Wisdom of the Great Chiefs

JOHN SWANTON

Creek Religion & Medicine
Early History of the Creek Indians & Their Neighbors
Final Report of the U.S. De Soto Expedition Commissionxw
Haida Texts & Myths
Indian Tribes of the Lower Mississippi Valley
Indian Tribes of North America
Indians of the Southeastern U.S.
Myths & Tales of Southeastern Indians
Source Material for the Social & Ceremonial Life of the Choctaw Indians
Tlingit Myths & Texts

SWEAT LODGE

The Lakota Ritual of the Sweat Lodge: History & Contemporary Practice
The Lakota Sweat Lodge Cards
The Native American Sweat Lodge: History & Legends

TAINO INDIANS

Cave of the Jagua: The Mythological World of the Tainos
Rethinking Puerto Rican Precolonial History
Taino Indian Myth & Practice: The Arrival of the Stranger King
The Taino Indian: A Native American Experience
Taino: Pre-Columbian Art & Culture
The Tainos: The People Who Welcomed Columbus
Talking Taino

TAOS PUEBLO

O.E. Berninghaus – Taos, N.M., Master Painter of American Indians & Frontier West
Chinle to Taos
*Little Boy With Three Names: Stories of Taos Pueblo
Paintbrushes & Pistols: How the Taos Artists Sold the West
Santa Fe & Taos: The Writer's Era, 1916-1941
The Taos Indians
The Taos Indians & the Battle for Blue Lake
Taos: People, Land Spirit
Taos Pueblo & Its Sacred Blue Lake
Taos: 1847: The Revolt in Contemporary Accounts
Taos Artists & Their Patrns, 1898-1950
Taos Society of Artists
Taos Tales
The Taos Trappers

TECUMSEH

The Life of Tecumseh & His Brother The Prophet: A History of The Shawnee
A Sorrow In Our Heart: The Life of Tecumseh
American Indian Warrior Chiefs: Tecumseh, Crazy Horse, Chief Joseph, Geronimo
*Tecumseh
Tecumseh: A Life
Tecymseh's Last Stand
Recumseh! A Play
Tecumseh & the Quest for Indian Leadership
Tecumseh & the Shawnee Confederacy
Tecumseh: Visionary Chief of the Shawnee
When the Mississippi Ran Backwards

TEXTILE INDUSTRY; CLOTHING
FABRICS & FOOTWEAR

American Indian Textiles: 2,000 Artist Biographies
And Eagles Sweep Across the Sky: Indian Textiles of the North American West
*Authentic North American Indian Clothing Series
Blanket Weaving in the Southwest
A Burst of Brilliance: Germantown, PA & Navajo Weaving
Chasing Rainbows: Collecting American Indian Trade & Camp Blankets
The Chilkat Dancing Blanket
Collecting the Navajo Child's Blanket
Collecting the Weaver's Art: The William Claflin Collection of Southwestern Textiles
CommonThreads: Pueblo & Navajo Textiles in the Southwest Museum
Complete Book of Seminole Patchwork
Contemporary Navajo Weaving
Designing with the Wool
Dress Clothing of the Plains Indian
Encyclopedia of American Indian Costume
From the Land: Two Hundred Years of Dene Clothing
The Gift of Spiderwoman: Southwestern Textiles, the Navajo Tradition
Guide to Navajo Rugs
A Guide to Navajo Weavings
Historic Navajo Weaving, 1800-1900: Three Cultures-One Loom
Honoring the Weavers
How to Make Cherokee Clothing
Identity By Design
*Indian Bead-Weaving Patterns
Indian Blankets and Their Makers
Indian Clothing Before Cortes: Mesoamerican Costumes from the Codices
Indian Clothing of the Great Lakes, 1740-1840
Indian Designs
Indian Foods and Fibers of Arid America
Jewels of the Navajo Loom: The Rugs of Teec Nos Pos
Language of the Robe: American IndianTrade Blankets
Learning by Designing: Pacific Northwest Coast Native Indian Art
Micmac Quillwork
The Navajo Design Book
Ray Manley's "The Fine Art of Navajo Weaving"
Most Indispensible Art: Native Fiber Industries from Eastern North America
Native American Fashion: Modern Adaptations of Traditional Designs
Navajo Native Dyes: Their Preparation and Use
Navajo Pictorial Weaving, 1800-1950
The Navajo Rug
Navajo Rugs: The Essential Guide
Navajo Rugs, Past & Present
Navajo Saddle Blankets: Textiles to Ride in the American Southwest
Navajo Shepherd & Weaver
Navajo Textiles: Book of Postcards
Navajo Textiles: The Crane Collection at the Denver Museum of nature & Science
Navajo Textiles: The William Randolph Hearst Collection
Navajo Weavers & Silversmiths
Navajo Weaving from the Santa Fe Collection
Navaho Weaving, Its Technic & History
Navajo Weaving, Navajo Ways
Navajo Weaving: Three Centuries of Change
Navajo Weaving Today
The Navajo Weaving Tradition, 1650 to the Present
Navajo Weaving: Three Centuries of Change
Navajo Weaving Way
19th Century Plains Indian Dresses
North American Indian Arts: A Golden Guide from St. Martins Press
Northwest Coast Indian designs

Old Navajo Rugs: Their Development from 1900 to 1940
One Hundred Years of Navajo Rugs
Patterns and Sources of Navajo Weaving
Pictorial Weavings of the Navajos
Pride of the Indian Wardrobe
Pueblo Indian Textiles: A Living Tradition
Ramona Sakiestewa - Patterned Dreams: Textiles of the Southwest
Rugs & Posts: The Story of Navajo Weaving
Scarlet Ribbons: American Indian Technique for Today's Quilters
Seminole Patchwork
The Seminole Patchwork Book
Sinews of Survival: The Living Legacy of Inuit Clothing
The Song of the Loom: New Traditions in Navajo Weaving
Spider Woman: A Story of Navajo Weavers & Chanters
Spider Woman's Gift: 19th Century Dine Textiles
Swept Under the Rug: A Hidden History of Navajo Weaving
Textiles in Southwestern Prehistory
Timeless Textiles: Traditional Pueblo Arts 1840-1940
Traditional Clothing of the Native Americans
Traditional Dress: Knowledge & Methods of Old-Time Clothing
The Unbroken Thread: Conserving the Textile Traditions of Oaxaca
Uncommon Thrteads: Wabanaki Textiles, Clothing, & Costume
Walk in Beauty: The Navajo and Their Blankets
Weaving Arts of the North American Indian
Weaving the Dance: Navajo Yeibichai Textiles, 1910-1950
Weaving a Navajo Blanket
Weaving Wildly: Mats & Baskets the Choctaw Way
Weaving a World: Textiles & the Navajo Way of Seeing
Weaving of the Southwest
A Window on the Past: Early Native American Dress from the John Painter Collection
Woven by the Grandmothers

JIM THORPE

Black Hawk & Jim Thorpe
Native American Son: The Life & Sporting Legend of Jim Thorpe
*Jim Thorpe
*Jim Thorpe: World's Greatest Athlete

TLINGIT INDIANS

Across the Shaman's River: John Muir, the Tlingit Stronghold, and the Opening of the North
Against Culture: Development, Politics & Religion in Indian Alaska
Alaska's Southern Panhandle
Alaskameut '86
Being In Place Among the Tlingit
Blonde Indian: An Alaska Native Memoir
The Canoe Rocks: Alaska's Tlingit & the Euroamerican Frontier, 1800-1912
Celebrations: Tlingit, Haida, Tsimshian Dancing on the Land
*Children of the Tlingit
Gagiwdulat: Brought Forth to Reconfirm The Legacy of a Taku River Tlingit Clan
Haa Aani, Our land: Tlingit & Haida Land Rights & Use
Haa Kusteeyi, Our Culture: Tlingit Life Stories
Haa Shuka, Our Ancestors: Tlingit Oral Narratives
Haa Tuwunaagu Yis, for Healting Our Spirit: Tlingit Oratory
*Heroes & Heroines in Tlingit-Haida Legends
Images of a People: Tlingit Myths & Legends
Indians of the North Pacific Coast
Memory Eternal: Tlingit Culture & Russian Orthodox Christianity through Two Centuries
My Grandfather's House: Tlingit Songs of Death & Sorrow
Sharing Our Knowledge: The Tlingit and Their Coastal Neighbors
Spruce Root Basketry of the Haida & Tlingit
*A Story to Tell: Traditions of a Tlingit Community
Symbolic Imortality, The Tlingit Potlatch of the 19th Century
*The Tlingit
Tlingit Art & Culture
The Tlingit Indians
The Tlingit Indians in Russian America, 1741-1867
Tlingit Indians of Alaska
The Tlingit Indians: Observations of an Indiigenous People of Southeast Alaska, 1881-1882
The Tlingit Indians: Results of a Trip to the Northwest Coast of America & the Bering Straits
The Tlingit: An Introduction to Their Culture & History
Tlingit Myths & Texts
Tlingit Tales: Potlatch & Totem Poles
To the Chukchi Peninsula & to the Tlingit Indians 1881/1882
Totem Poles of the Pacific Northwest
Will the Time Ever Come? A Tlingit Source Book

TOHONO O'ODHAM
(PAPAGO & PIMA INDIANS)

At the Boders of Empires: The Tohono O'odham, Gender, and Assimilation, 1880-1934
At the Desert's Green Edge: An Ethnobotany of the Gila River Pima
Basketry of the Papago and Pima Indians
By the Prophet of the Earth: Ethnobotany of the Pima
Desert Indian Woman: Stories & Dreams
The Desert Smells Like Rain: A Naturalist in O'odham Country
Devil Sickness, Devil Songs, Tohono O'odham Poetics
Diabetes Among the Pima: Stories of Survival
Folk Mammalogy of the Northern Pimans
Forced to Abandon Our Fields: The 1914 Clay Southworth Gila River Pima Interviews
Gathering the Desert
Landscapes of Fraud: Mission Tumacacori, the Baca Float, & the Betrayal of the O'odham

TOTEMS, TOTEMISM

TRAIL OF TEARS

TRAILS

TRANSPORTATION

TRAVEL GUIDES

TREATIES

The History & Culture of Iroquois Diplomacy
In the Name of the Salish & Kootenai Nation: The Hell Gate Treaty
Indian Affairs, Laws & Treaties
Indian Law - Race Law: A Five Hundred Year History
Indian Treaties
Indian Treaties, 1778-1883
Indian Treaties by Tribe
Indian Treaty-Making Policy in the U.S. & Canada, 1867-1877
Indian Tribal Claims Decided in the Court of Clains of the U.S.
Indians, Superintendents, and Councils: Northwestern Indian Policy, 1850-1855
The Jerome Agreement Between the Kiowa, Comanche & Apache Tribes & the U.S.
The Kiowa Treaty of 1853
The Last French & Indian War
A Lawyer in Indian Country: A Memoir
Legalized Racism: Federal Indian Policy & the End of Equal Rights for All Americans
License for Empire: Colonialism by Treaty in Early America
Lone Wolf v. Hitchcock: Treaty Rights & Indian Law at the End of the 19th Century
The Medicine Creek Treaty of 1854
Name of Salish & Kootenai Nation: The 1855 Hell Gate Treaty & the Origin
   of the Flathead Indian Reservation
Nation to Nation: Treaties Between the U.S. & American Indian Nations
The Navajo Treaty, 1868
Northwest Chiefs: Gustav Sohon's Views of the 1855
Stevens Treaty Councils
The Point Elliott Treaty, 1855
The Point-No-Point Treaty, 1855
The Power of Promises: Rethinking Indian Treaties in the Pacific Northwest
Proceedings of the Great Peace Commissions
Redskins, Ruffleshirts & Rednecks: Indian Allotments in Alabama & Mississippi, 1830-1860
Spirit Dance at Meziadin: Chief Joseph Gosnell & the Nisga'a Treaty
The Spirit of the Alberta Indian Treaties
Treaties, Agreements & Proceedings of the Tribes & Bands of the Sioux Nation
Treaties & Agreements of the Chippewa Indians
Treaties & Agreements of the Five Civilized Tribes
Treaties & Agreements of the Indian Tribes of the Great Lakes Region
Treaties & Agreements of the Indian Tribes of the Northern Plains
Treaties & Agreements of the Indian Tribes of the Pacific Northwest
Treaties & Agreements of the Indian Tribes of the Southwest
Treaties for the 1860s with the Southern Cheyenne & Arapaho
The Treaties of Puget Sound, 1854-1855
Treaty Manuscript Series
The Treaty of 1842 Between the U.S. & Chippewa Indians
The Treaty of 1836 Between the Ottawa & Chippewa Nations of Indians & the U.S.
The Treaty of Fort Stanwiix, 1784
The Treaty of Medicine Lodge, 1867
Treaty of Medicine Lodge: A Programmed Text
The Treaty on the Little Arkansas River, 1865
Treaty Talks in British Columbia
Treaty With the Makah
Treaty With the Quinault & Quileute Indians
Tribes of the Extreme Northwest, Alaska, the Aleutians & Adjacent Territories
The True Spirit & Original Intent of Treaty 7
The U.S.-Chippewa Treaty at La Pointe, 1854
The U.S.-Seneca Treaty, 1842
The U.S. Treaty With the Sioux Brule, Oglala, et al.
U.S. Treaty With the Walla Walla
The Unratified Treaty Between the Kiowas, Comanches & Apaches & the U.S. of 1863
Voices From the Trail of Tears
The Walleye War
Walleye Warriors: The Chippewa Treaty Rights Story
Western Washington Treaty Proceedings
Writing Indian Nations: Native Intellectuals & the Politics of Historiography, 1827-1863

TRIBAL GOVERNMENT

The Alaska Native Claims Settlement Act, 1991 & Tribal Government
American Indian Tribal Governments
American Indian Tribal Courts: The Costs of Separate Justice
Indian Tribes of North America
Introduction to Tribal Government
*Long Shadows
The Nations Within: The Past and Future of American Indian Sovereignty
Native Brotherhoods: Modern Intertribal Organizations on the Northwest Coast
Nevada Tribal History and Government
Penitente Self-Government: Brotherhoods & Councils, 1797-1947
Political History of the Navajo Tribe
Political Organization & Law-Ways of the Comanche Indians
Political Organization of the Plains Indians
The Politics of Indian Removal: Creek Government and Society in Crisis
Politics and Power
The Road: Indian Tribes & Political Liberty
Tribal Government: A New Era
Tribal Government Textbook
Tribal Government Today: Politics on Montana's Indian Reservations
The Tribal Moment in American Politics: The Struggle for Native American Sovereignty
Tribal Sovereignty: Indian Tribes in U.S. History

TSIMSHIAN INDIANS

Alaska's Southern Panhandle
Becoming Tsimshian: The Social Life of Names
Canadian Prehistory Series
Thomas Crosby & the Tsimshian: Small Shoes for Feet Too Large
Good Intentions Gone Awry

Indian, Eskimo & Aleut Basketry of Alaska
Indians of the North Pacific Coast
The Porcupine Hunter & Other Stories: The Original Tsimshian
Texts of Henry Tate
Transmission Difficulties: Franz Boas & Tsimshian Mythology
Tsimshian Culture
The Tsimshian: Images of the Past; Views for the Present
The Tsimshian & Their Neighbors of the North Pacific Coast
The Tsimshian & Their Neighbors of the Northwest Coast
Tsimshian Texts
Tsimshian Treasures: The Remarkable Journey of the Dundas Collection

TUSCARORA INDIANS

Chew's Vocabulary of Tuscarora
Fighting Tuscarora: Autobiography of Chief Clinton Rickard
Legends, Traditions & Laws of the Iroquois: Or, Six Nations,
   & History of the Tuscarora Indians
Life of a Native American Medicine Man
The Reservation
The Seneca & Tuscarora Indians
*The Tuscarora
Tuscarora-English, English-Tuscarora Dictionary
The Tuscarora Legacy of J.N.B. Hewitt
Tuscarora Nation, NY
The Tuscarawas Valley in Indian Days, 1750-1797
Vocabulary of the Tuscarora

UTE INDIANS

American Indians in Colorado
As If the Land Owned Us: The Ethnohistory of the White Mesa Utes
Blue Sky, Night Thunder: The Utes of Colorado
Bull Creek
Chipeta: Queen of the Utes
Depredation & Deceit: The Making of the Jicarilla & Ute Wars in New Mexico
The Dispossessed: Cultural Genocide of the Mixed-Blood Utes
Ephemeral Bounty: Wickiups, Trade Goods, and the Final Years of the Autonomous Ute
Ethnography of the Northern Utes
Indians of the Pike's Peak Region
Ouray, Chief of the Utes
People of the Red Earth
People of the Shining Mountains: The Ute Indians of Colorado
Posey: The Last Indian War
Red Twilight: the Last Free Days of the Ute Indians
Searching for Chipeta: The Story of a Ute and Her People
Southern Ute Indians of Early Colorado
These Were the Utes: Their Lifestyle, Wars & Legends
Troubled Trails: The Meeker Affair & the Expulsion of Utes From Colorado
Utah's Black Hawk War
*The Ute
The Ute Indians of Colorado in the 20th Century
The Ute Indians of Southwestern Colorado
The Ute Indians of Utah, Colorado, and New Mexico
Ute Land Religion in the American West, 1879-2009
Ute Legends
Ute Mountain Utes
Ute Tales
*The Utes
Utes: A Forgotten People
The Utes: The Mountain People

ROBERT M. UTLEY

Battlefield & Classroom: Four Decades with the American Indian, 1867-1904
Cavalier in Buckskin: George Armstrong Custer
Custer Battlefield, A History & Guide to the Battle of the Little Bighorn
Frontier Regulars: The U.S. Army & the Indian, 1866-1891
The Indian Frontier of the American West, 1846-1890
Indian Soldier, Settler: Experiences in the Struggle for the American West
Indian Wars
The Lance & the Shield: The Life & Times of Sitting Bull
Last Days of the Sioux Nation
Life in Custer's Cavalry

HERMAN J. VIOLA

After Columbus
American Indians
Ben Nighthorse Campbell
The Commissioners of Indian Affairs, 1824-1977
Diplomates in Buckskins
Exploring the West
From the Heart of Crow Country
Indian Legacy of Charles Bird King
It Is A Good Day to Die
Little Big Horn Remembered
Memoirs, Official & Personal
Seeds of Change: A Quincentennial Commendation
Trail to Wounded Knee: The Last Stand of the Plains Indians, 1860-1890
Warriors in Uniform: The Legacy of American Indian Heroism

GERALD VIZENOR

Bear Heart: The Heirship Chronicles
Bear Island: The War at Sugar Point
Chair of Tears
Chancers: A Novel
Crossbloods: Bone Courts, Bingo, & Other Reports
Dead Voices: Natural Agonies in the New World
Deep Waters
Earthdivers: Tribal Narratives on Mixed Descent
The Everlasting Sky
Father Meme
Fugitive Poses: Native American Indian Scenes of Absence & Presence
The Heirs of Columbus
Hiroshima Bugi: Atomu 57
Hotline Healers: An Almost Browne Novel
Interior Landscapes: Autobiographical Myths & Metaphors
Landfill Meditation: Crossblood Stories
Listening to the Land
Manifest Manners: Narratives of Postindian Survivance
Mediation in Contemporary Native American Fiction
Momaday, Vizenor, Armstrong: Conversations On American Indian Writing
Narrative Chance: Postmodern Discourse on Native American Indian Literatures
Native Liberty: Natural Reason & Cultural Survivance
Native Stories: Five Selections
The People Named the Chippewa: Narrative Histories
The Poetry & Poetics of Gerald Vizenor
Postindian Conversations
Shadow Distance: A Gerald Vizenor Reader
Summer in the Spring: Anishinaabe Lyric Poems & Stories
Survivance: America's First Warriors: Native Americans & Iraq
Touchwood: A Collection of Ojibway Prose
The Trickster of Liberty: Native Heirs to a Wild Baronage
Gerald Vizenor: Texts & Contexts
Gerald Vizenor: Writing in the Oral Tradition
The White Earth Nation
Winged Words: American Indian Writers Speak
Wordarrows: Indians & Whites in the New Fur Trade
Wordarrows: Native States of Literary Sovereignty
Writing Indian, Native Conversations

WARS

American Indian Wars
The American Indian Wars, 1860-1890
Americans Woodland Indians
An Apache Nightmare: The Battle at Cibecue Creek
Apache Wars
Apache Women Warriors
Battles & Leaders: The Indian Wars East of the Mississippi
The Bear River Massacre
Books on the Indian Wars
Border Wars of Texas
A Brief of the Pequot War
Buffalo Soldiers, Braves, & the Brass: The Story of Fort Robinson, Nebraska
Bury My Heart at Wounded Knee: An Indian History of the American West
Campaigning with King
A Cannoneer in Navajo Country
Changing Military Patterns of the Great Plains Indians
Cheyenne Dog Soldiers: A Ledgerbook History of Coups & Combat
*Cheyenne Warriors
Children of Sacred Ground: America's Last Indian War
Chronoloigcal List of Engagements Between the Regular Army of the
  U.S. & Various Tribes of Hostile Indians, 1790-1898
A Clash of Cultures on the Warpath of Nations: The Colonial Wars
  in the Hudson-Champlain Valley
The Conflict Between the California Indian & White Civilization
Crazy Horse Called Them Walk-A-Heaps: The Story of the Foot Soldier
  in the Prairie Indian Wars
Commanders & Chiefs: A Brief History of Fort McDowell, Arizona, 1865-1890
Dakota War Whoop; Or, Indian Masscres & War in Minnesota
Deciphering Anasazi Violence
Deadly Landscapes: Case Studies in Prehistoric Southwestern Warfare
Death in the Desert: The Fifty Years' War for the Great Southwest
Depredation & Deceit: The Making of the Jicarilla & Ute Wars in New Mexico
The Dust Rose Like Smoke: The Subjugation of the Zulu & the Sioux
Encyclopedia of American Indian Wars, 1492-1890
Encyclopedia of Native American Wars & Warfare
Encyclopedia of North American Indian Wars, 1607-1890
European & Native American Warfare, 1675-1815
Fighting Men of the Indian Wars
Following the Indian Wars: The Story of the Newspaper Correspondents Among the Indian
Forlorn Hope: The Battle of White Bird Canyon & the Beginning of the Nez Perce War
The Fox Wars: The Mesquakie Challenge to New France
From Yorktown to Santiago with the Sixth U.S. Cavalry
Frontier Soldier
Galvanized Yankees on the Upper Missouri: The Face of Loyalty
General Crook in the Indian Country
*The Great Chiefs
Great Western Indian Fights
A Guide to the Indian Wars of the West
Hasinai: A Traditional History of the Caddo Confederacy
History of the Early Settlement & Indian Wars of West Virginia
History of the Girty's

History of the Indian Wars
History of the Indian Wars in New England
Indian Battles Along the Rogue River: One of America's Wild & Scenic Rivers
Indian Battles, Murders, Sieges, & Forays in the Southwest
Indian Depredations in Texas
Indian Depredations in Utah
Indian Fighters Turned American Politicians
Indian Fights: New Facts on Seven Encounters
The Indian Frontier, 1763-1846
Indian War Sites: A Guidebook to Battlefields, Monuments & Memorials
Indian Warfare in Western Pennsylvania & North West Virginia
  at the Time of the American Revolution
*Indian Warriors & Their Weapons
Indian Wars
Indian Wars & Pioneers of Texas, 1685-1892
Indian Wars of New England
Indian Wars of Pennsylvania
Indian Wars of the Red River Valley
Indian Wars of the West & Frontier Army Life, 1862-1898
Inkkpaduta - The Scarlet Point: Terror of the Dakota Frontier & Secret Hero of the Sioux
Iroquois Wars I: Extracts from the Jesuit Relations & Primary Sources, 1535-1650
Journal of the Indian Wars
Journals of the Military Expedition of Major General John Sullivan
Kiowa, Apache, and Comanche Military Societies
*The Last of the Cherokee Warriors
Legends, Letters & Lies: Readings About Inkpaduta & the Spirit Lake Massacre
Loudon's Indian Narratives
Massacres of the Mountains Vol. 1: A History of the Indian Wars of the far West
Memoir of Indian Wars & Other Occurrences
The Military & the U.S. Indian Policy, 1865-1903
Morning Star Dawn: The Powder River Expedition & the Northern Cheyennes, 1876
The Native American Warrior, 1500-1890
Native North American Armor, Shields & Fortifications
Navajo Roundup
Nevada Military Place Names of the Indian Wars & Civil War
New Mexico Frontier Military Place Names
North American Indian Wars
*North American Indian Wars
North American Indians in the Great War (World War I)
North American Indigenous Warfare & Ritual Violence
Oh What a Slaughter: Massacres in the American West, 1846-1890
Origin Legend of the Navaho Enemy Way
Our Indian Wards
The Papers of the Order of the Indian Wars
Plains Indian Raiders
*Plains Indian Warrior
The Plains Wars, 1757-1900
Poison Arrows: North American Indian Hunting & Warfare
Prehistoric Warfare in the American Southwest
President Washington's Indian War
Red Cloud: Warrior Statesman of the Lakota Sioux
Red Eagle & the Wars With the Creek Indians of Alabama
The Reynolds Campaign on Powder River
The Sac & Fox Indians
Sacred Revolt: The Muskogee's Struggle for a New World
Savage Frontier: Rangers, Riflemen, & the Indian Wars in Texas
Scenes & Adventures in the Army: Or, Romance of Military Life
The Second Civil War: Examining the Indian Demand for Ethnic Sovereignty
The Seminole Wars: America's Longest Indian Conflict
The Shoshoni Frontier & the Bear River Massacre
Skulking Way of War: Technology & Tactics Among the New England Indians
The Soldiers of America's First Army
Struggle for the Land
Tenderfoot in Tombstone, the Private Journal of George Whitwell Parksons
Three Indian Campaigns
Tribal Wars of the Southern Plains
Twilight of Empire
The Unconquered Hearts
Vision & Valor: General Oliver O. Howard - a Biography
War in the Tribal Zone: Expanding States and Indigenous Warfare
Warpaths! Travels of a Military Historian in North America
Warrior, Shield & Star Imagery & Ideology of Pueblo Warfare
Warriors in Uniform: The Legacy of American Indian Heroism
The Wars of the Iroquois
George Washington's War on Native America
The Way of the Warrior
Western Apache Raiding & Warfare
What You See in Clear Water: Indians, Whites, & A Battle Over Water in the American West
Wilderness War on the Ohio
The Wind Won't Know Me: A History of the Navajo-Hopi Land Dispute
*Wounded Knee: An Indian History of the American West

WARS, 1600-1800
See (French & Indian War)

Africans and Creeks: From Colonial Period to the Civil War
Anza's 1779 Comanche Campaign
At the Crossroads: Michilimackinac During the American Revolution
Bayonets in the Wilderness: Anthony Wayne's Legion in the Old Northwest
Blacks, Indians & Women In America's War of Independence
The Bloodstained Field: A History of the Sugarloaf Massacre, Sept. 11, 1780
Cheyennes & Horse Soldiers
Chronicles of Border Warfare
A Clash of Cultures on the Warpath of Nations: The Colonial Wars

in the Hudson-Champlain Valley
Connecticut Unscathed: Victory in the Great Narragansett War, 1675-1676
Daily Life During the Indian Wars
Empire of Fortune: Crowns, Colonies, & Tribes in the Seven Years War in America
European & Native Ameican Warfare, 1675-1815
*The Fight for Freedom, 1750-1783
Fort Laurens 1778-9: The Revolutionary War in Ohio
French & Indian War
French & Indian War Battlesites: A Controversy
The French & Indian War in Pennsylvania, 1753-1763
Frontier Forts of Iowa: Indians, Traders, and Soldiers, 1682-1862
History of an Expedition Against Fort DuQuesne in 1755 Vol. 9:
  An Account of Braddock Campaign in 1755
History of the Indian Wars in New England
The History of Philip's War
Indian Fighter
Indian Uprising on the Rio Grande: The Pueblo Revolt of 1680
Indians: Or Narratives of Massacres & Depredations
Journal of the Adventures of Mathew Bunn
Journals of the Military Expedition of Major General John Sullivan
King Philip
King Philip's War
King Philip's War: Civil War in New England, 1675-1676
Life of Robert Hall: Indian Fighter & Veteran of Three Great Wars: Also,
  Sketches of Big Foot Wallace
Loudon's Indian Narratives
A Man of Distinction Among Them: Alexander Mckee & British-Indian Affairs
Narratives of the Indian Wars, 1675-1699
Navajos in 1705: Roque Madrid's Campaign Journal
Never Come to Peace Again: Pontiac's Uprising
Notes on the Settlement & Indian Wars of the Western Parts of VA & PA from 1763 to 1783
The Old Indian Chronicle
On Time for Disaster
The Pequot War
Present State of New England
President Washington's Indian War
The Pueblo Revolt
The Pueblo Revolt & the Mythology of Conquest
The Red King's Rebellion: Racial Politics in New England, 1675-1677
Redeemed Captive Returning to Zion
*Mary Rowlandson & King Philip's War
The Scalp Hunters: Abenaki Ambush at Lovewell Pond, 1725
The Sixty Years' War for the Great Lakes, 1754-1814
So Dreadful a Judgement: Puritan Responses to King Philip's War, 1667-1677
The Southern Frontier, 1670-1732
Tecumseh & the Quest for Indian Leadership
Thunder in the Mountains: The Story of the Nez Perce War
Virginia's Western War 1775-1786
War Under Heaven: Pontiac, the Indian Nations, & the British Empire
Warpaths: Invasions of North America, 1513-1765
Anthony Wayne, A Name in Arms
Wept of Wish-Ton-Wish
Lewis Wetzel, Indian Fighter
Lewis Wetzel: The Life & Times of a Frontier Hero
Wilderness Empire
Wilderness War on the Ohio
Winners of the West
The Yamasee War

WARS, 1800-1900

An Account of the Origin & Early Prosecution of the Indian War in Oregon
Amidst A Storm of Bullets: The Diary of Lt. Henry Prince in Florida, 1836-1842
An Apache Campaign in the Sierra Madre
An Apache Nightmare: The Battle of Cibecue Creek
Apache Days & After
Apache Wars
Apaches At War & Peace: The Janos Presidio, 1750-1858
Archaeology, History, & Custer's Last Battle
Arikara Narrative of Custer's Campaign & the Battle of the Little Bighorn
The Arikara War: The First Plains Indian War, 1823
The Army & Navy Journal on the Battle of the Little Bighorn & Related Matters, 1876-1881
Battle at Sand Creek: The Military Perspective
The Battle of Beecher Island & the Indian War of 1867-1869
Battle of the Loxahatchee River: The Seminole War
Battle of the Little Bighorn
Battle of the Rosebud
Battle Rock, The Hero's Story
Battlefield & Classroom: Four Decades With the American Indian, 1867-1904
Battles of the Red River War
Battles & Skirmishes of the Great Sioux War, 1876-1877
The Bear River Massacre
The Bear River Massacre & the Making of History
Before the Little Big Horn
The Black Hawk War, Why?
Black Kettle: The Cheyenne Chief Who South Peace but Found War
Bloody Knife: Custer's Favorite Scout
The Blue, the Gray, & the Red: Indian Campaigns of the Civil War
Blue Jacket: Warrior of the Shawnees
Blue Water Creek & the First Sioux War, 1854-1856
Bound To Have Blood: Frontier Newspapers & the Plains Indian Wars
Brackett's Battalion: Minnesota Cavalry in the Civil War & Dakota War
Brave Eagle's Account of the Fetterman Fight
Buffalo Soldiers, Braves, & the Brass

Buffalo Soldiers in the Old Southwest
The Buffalo War: The History of the Red River Indian Uprising of 1874-1875
Bury My Heart at Wounded Knee: An Indian History of the American West
Camp, Custer & the Little Bighorn
Campaigns in the West, 1856-1861: The Journal & Letters
A Cannoneer in Navajo Country: Journey of Private Josiah M. Rice, 1851
Kit Carson: Indian Fighter or Indian Killer?
Cavalier in Buckskin: George Armstrong Custer & the Western Military Frontier
Centennial Campaign: The Sioux War of 1876
Chasing Shadows: Apaches & Yaquis Along the U.S. - Mexico Border, 1876-1911
Cheyenne Memories of the Custer Fight: A Source Book
Cheyennes & Horse Soldiers
Child of the Fighting Tenth: On the Frontier With the Buffalo Soldiers
Children of Grace: The Nez Perce War of 1877
Chiricahua Apache Prisoners of War: Fort Sill, 1894-1914
Chronology of the Indian War Battles
Circle of Fire: The Indian War of 1865
Columns of Vengeance: Soldiers, Sioux, and the Punitive Expeditions, 1863-1864
The Conflict Between the California Indian & White Civilization
Conquest of Apacheria
The Conquest of the Karankawas & the Tonkawas, 1821-1859
The Conquest of Texas: Ethnic Cleansing in the Promised Land, 1820-1875
Copper Paladin: The Modoc Tragedy
The Creek War of 1813 & 1814
Custer & the Battle of the Little Bighorn
Custer Battlefield
Custer, Black Kettle, & the Fight on the Washita
Custer & the Cheyenne: George A. Custer's Winter Campaign on the Southern Plains
The Custer Companion
Custer & Company
*Custer & Crazy Horse
Custer Died for Your Sins
The Custer Legacy
Custer & the Little Bighorn
The Custer Story
The Custer Tragedy
Custerology: The Enduring Legacy of the Indian Wars
Custer's Chief of Scout
Custer's Defeat & Other Conflicts in the West
Custer's Fall: The Native American Side of the Story
Custer's Last Campaign
Custer's Last Fight
Custer's Last Stand
Custer's Prelude to Glory
Custer's Seventh Cavalry & the Campaign of 1873
The Dakota War of 1862
Jeff Davis's Own: Cavalry, Comanches, & the Battle for the Texas Frontier
Deadliest Indian War in the West: The Snake Conflict, 1864-1868
Death in the Desert: The Fifty Years' War for the Great Southwest
Death on the Prairie: The Thiry Years' Struggle for the Western Plains
Death, Too, For the Heavy-Runner
Discovery of the Yosemite & the Indian War of 1851
Dog Soldier Societies of the Plains
Eyewitness at Wounded Knee
Eyewitnesses to the Fetterman Fight: Indian Views
Eyewitnesses to the Indian Wars, 1865-1890
The Fighting Cheyennes
Finding Sand Creek: History, Archaeology, and the 1864 Massacre Site
First Scalp for Custer
The Florida Wars
Following the Guidon: Into the Indian Wars with General Custer & the Seventh Cavalry
Following the Indian Wars
Forlorn Hope: The Battle of Whitebird Canyon & the Beginning of the Nez Perce War
Fort Ellsworth Kansas
Fort Gibson History
Fort Gibson: Terminal on the Trail of Tears
Fort Laramie & the Great Sioux War
Fort Laramie of the Sioux
Fort Limhi: The Mormon Adventure in Oregon Territory, 1855-1858
Fort Meade & the Black Hills
Fort Supply, Indian Territory
Forty Miles a Day on Beans & Hay: The Enlisted Soldier Fighting the Indian Wars
From Fort Marion to Fort Sill: A Docmentary History of the Chiricahua Apache Prisoners
  of War, 1886-1913
Frontier Day: The Army in Northern Idaho, 1853-1876
The Frontier Newspapers & the Coverage of the Plains Indian Wars
Frontier Regulars: The U.S. Army & the Indian, 1866-1891
German Pioneer Accounts of the Great Sioux Uprising of 1862
Geronimo! Stories of an American Legend
Geronimo's Story of His Life
Ghost-Dance Religion & the Sioux Outbreak of 1890
Gods of Prophetstown: The Battle of Tippecanoe and the Holy War
  for the American Frontier
A Good Year to Die: The Story of the Great Sioux War
The Great Sioux Uprising, Vol. 3
Great Sioux Uprising: Rebellion on the Plains, Aug.-Sept. 1862
The Great Sioux War
Great Sioux War Orders of battle: How the U.S. Army Waged War
  on the Northern Plains, 1876-1877
Guns Across the Loxahatchee: An Archaeological Investigation of Seminole War Sites
History of the Second Seminole War, 1835-1842
Hokahey! A Good Day to Die! The Indian Casualties of the Custer Fight
Hunted Like a Wolf: The Story of the Seminole War
I Will Fight No More Forever: Chief Joseph & the Nez Perce War

WASHO

WATER RIGHTS

WICHITA INDIANS

WOMEN

Waheenee: An Indian Girl's Story
Walking Thunder: Dine Medicine Woman
Warrior Woman: the Story of Lozen, Apache Warrior & Shaman
Waterlily
The Way It Was: An Indian Girl Living Thru the Depression
The Ways of My Grandmothers
Weaving New Worlds: Southeastern Cherokee Women & Their Basketry
Weaving Women's Lives: Three Generations in a Navajo Family
What This Awl Means: Feminist Archaeology at a Wahpeton Dakota Village
What's an Indian Woman To Do? and Other Plays
White Mother to a Dark Race: Settler Colonialism, Maternalism, and the Removal
  of Indigenous Children in the American West & Australia, 1880-1940
Sarah Winnemucca
Sarah Winnemucca of the Northern Paiutes
Wisdom's Daughters: Conversations With Women Elders of Native America
With My Own Eyes: A Lakota Woman Tells Her People's History
Woman of the Green Glade
A Woman of the People
Woman Walking Ahead
The Woman's Way
Women Elders' Life Stories of the Omaha Tribe: Macy, Neb. 2004-05
*Women in American Indian Society
Women in Navajo Society
Women in Prehistory: North America & Mesoamerica
Women & Indians on the Frontier, 1825-1915
Women & Men in the Prehistoric Southwest: Labor, Power & Prestige
Women & Power in Native North America
Women of the Apache Nation: Voices of Truth
Women of Color: Mother-Daughter Relationships in 20th Century Literature
Women of the Dawn
Women of the Earth Lodges: Tribal Life on the Plains
Women of the First Nations
Women of the Native Struggle
Women & Power in Native North America
Women's Rights in Native North America: Legal Mobilization in the U.S. & Canada
The Women's Warrior Society
The Women's Way
Writing the Circle: Native Women of Western Canada, an Anthology
Wynema: A Child of the Forest
Yaqui Women: Contemporary Life Histories

WOUNDED KNEE

American Carnage: Wounded Knee, 1890
Call to Justice: The Life of a Federal Trial Judge
Eyewitness at Wounded Knee
Free Peltier: A Dramatic History of the American Indian Movement
The Ghost Dance Religion & Wounded Knee
Ghost Dancers in the West: The Sioux at Pine Ridge & Wounded Knee in 1891
Ghost Dancing the Law: The Wounded Knee Trails
Like a Hurricane: The Indian Movement from Alcatraz to Wounded Knee
Lost Bird of Wounded Knee: Spirit of the Lakota
Viet Cong at Wounded Knee: The Trail of a Blackfeet Activist (Woody Kipp)
Voices from Wounded Knee, 1973, In the Words of the Participants
Voices of Wounded Knee
Wounded Knee 1973
Wounded Knee & the Ghost Dance Tragedy
Wounded Knee, Leonard Peliter, and the American Indian Movement (AIM)
Wounded Knee: Lest We Forget
Wounded Knee Massacre: From the Viewpoint of the Sioux
Wounded Knee: The Meaning & Significance of the Second Incident
Wounded Knee: Party Politics and the Road to an American Massacre

YAKAMA INDIANS

Death Stalks the Yakama
Forgotten Voices: Death Records of the Yakama, 1888-1964
Ghost Voices: Yakama Indian Myths, Legends, Humor and Hunting Stories
Ichishkiin Sinwit Yakama / Yakima Sahaptin Dictionary
Magic in the Mountains: The Yakama Shaman: Power & Practice
Pow Wow: & Other Yakama Indian Traditions
*The Yakama: Northwest
Yakama, Palouse, Cayuse, Umatilla, Walla Walla, and Wanapum Indians:
  An Historical Bibliography
Yakama Rising: Indigenous Culrural Revitalization, Activism, and Healing
Yakama Sahaptin Dictionary
The Yakamas: A Critical Bibliography
*The Yakama: Northwest

YAQUI INDIANS

Autobiography of a Yaqui Poet
Chasing Shadows: Apaches & Yaquis Along the U.S.-Mexican Border, 1876-1911
Deer Dancer: Yaqui Legends of Life
Pascua
People of Pascua
Phonology of Arizona Yaqui with Texts
Politics & Ethnicity on the Rio Yaqui
Sonora Yaqui Language Structures
The Teachings of Don Juan: A Yaqui Way of Knowledge
We Will Dance Our Truth: Yaqui History in Yoeme Performances
With Good Heart: Yaqui Beliefs & Ceremonies in Pascua Village
Yaqui Deer Songs: A Native American Poetry

A Yaqui Easter
Yaqui Homeland & Homeplace: The Everyday Production of Ethnic Identity
A Yaqui Life
Yaqui Myths & Legends
Yaqui Resistance & Survival: The Struggle for Land & Autonomy, 1821-1910
Yaqui Women: Contemporary Life Histories
The Yaquis: A Cultural History

YAVAPAI
(see Indians of the Southwest)

Indian Basketmakers of the Southwest
Carlos Montezuma and the Changing World of American Indians
Carlos Montezuma, M.D., A Yavapai American Hero
The Only One Living to Tell: The Autobiography of a Yavapai Indian
The Struggle for Water
Surviving Conquest: A History of the Yavapai Peoples
Whte Eyes, Long Knives & Regeade Indians
The Yavapai: Sedona's Native People

ZUNI INDIANS

The Beautiful and the Dangerous: Encounters With the Zuni Indians
The Blue God: An Epic of Mesa Verde
The Boy Who Made Dragonfly: A Zuni Myth
Classic Hopi & Zuni Kachina Figures
Cushing at Zuni
Dialogues With Zuni Potters
The Fetish Carvers of Zuni
Finding the Center: The Art of the Zuni Storyteller
*From Abenaki to Zuni
A Guide to Zuni Fetishes & Carvings
Historic Zuni Architecture & Society
Idonapshe, Let's Eat: Traditional Zuni Foods
Journeys Home: Revealing a Zuni-Appalachia Collaboration
Mediating Knowledges: Origins of a Zuni Tribal Museum
Migrations: New Directions in Native American Art
Music of the Acoma, Isleta, Cochiti & Zuni Pueblos
My Adventures in Zuni
The Mythic World of the Zuni
On the Gleaming Way
People of the Middle Place: A Study of the Zuni Indians
The Pottery of Zuni Pueblo
Settlement, Subsistence & Society in Late Zuni Prehistory
Signs From the Ancestors: Zuni Cultural Symbolism & Perceptions of Rock Art
*Sun Journey: A Story of Zuni Pueblo
Treasures of the Zuni
The Urine Dance of the Zuni Indians of New Mexico
•The Zuni
A Zuni Artist Looks At Frank Hamilton Cushing
A Zuni Atlas
*Zuni Children & Elders Talk Together
Zuni Contemporary Pottery
Zuni & the Courts: A Struggle for Sovereign Land Rights
Zuni Coyote Tales
Zuni & El Moro: Past & Present
Zuni Fetishes
Zuni Fetishism
Zuni Indian tribe Water Settlement Act
Zuni Indians: Their Mythology, Esoteric Fraternities & Ceremonies
Zuni Indians & Their Use of Plants
Zuni Jewelry
Zuni Katchinas
A Zuni Life: A Pueblo Indian in Two Worlds
The Zuni Man-Woman
Zuni Pottery
Zuni: Selected Writings of Frank Hamilton Cushing
Zuni: A Village of Silversmiths
*The Zunis
The Zunis: Self-Portrayals

PUBLISHERS INDEX

Lists publishers whose books appear in the bibliography.
Entries are arranged alphabetically, with complete
zip-coded addresses, websites & e-mails and phone numbers.

A

Aardvark Publications
P.O. Box 252 • Boulder Junction, WI 54512 (715) 385-2862

Abbeville Press
116 West 23 St. • New York, NY 10011
(800) 278-2665; (646) 375-2136 Fax 375-2359
Website https://www.abbeville.com; E-mail: abbeville@abbeville.com

ABC-CLIO
Customer Service, P.O. Box 1911 • Santa Barbara, CA 93116
(800) 368-6868; Fax (866) 270-3856; (805) 968-1911 Fax 685-9685
E-mail: customerservice@abc-clio.com; Website: www.abc-clio.com

Abingdon Press
P.O. Box 801 • Nashville, TN 37202
(800) 251-3320 Fax (800) 836-7802; (615) 749-6409 Fax 749-6056
Website: www.abingdonpress.com; E-Mail: info@abingdon.org

Harry N. Abrams
195 Broadway, 9th Fl. • New York, NY 10007
(800) 345-1359; (212) 206-7715 Fax 519-1210
Website: www.abramsbooks.com; E-mail: abrams@abramsbooks.com

Affiliated Tribes of Northwest Indians
6636 NE Sandy Blvd. • Portland, OR 97213 (503) 249-5770 Fax 249-5773
Website: www.atnitribes.org; E-mail: atni@atnitribes.org

Alaska Geographic Society - See Alaska Northwest Books

Alaska Native Language Center
University of Alaska, P.O. Box 757680 • Fairbanks, AK 99775
(907) 474-7874 Fax 474-6586;
Website: www.uaf.edu/anlc; E-mail: fyanip@uaf.edu

Algonquin Books of Chapel Hill
Div. of Workman Publishing Co.

AltaMira Press
Div. of Rowman & Littlefield Publishing
15200 NBN Way • Blue Ridge Summit, PA 17214
(717) 794-3800 Fax (717) 794-3803; (800) 338-4550
Website https://rowman.com/Altamira; E-mail: orders@rowman.com

American Academy of Political & Social Sciences
Distributed by Sage Publications

American Bar Association
321 N. Clark St. • Chicago, IL 60654
(312) 988-5561 Fax 988-6030
Website: www.shop.americanbar.org; E-mail: service@abanet.org

American Indian Publishers
177F Riverside Ave. • Newport Beach, CA 92663

American Library Association
Review copies: 50 E. Huron St. • Chicago, IL 60611
(800) 545-2433; (312) 280-2425 Fax 944-8085
ALA Order Fulfillment: P.O. Box 932501 • Atlanta, GA 31193
(866) 746-7252 Fax 280-4155
Website: www.alastore.org; E-mail: editionsmarketing@ala.org

American Philosophical Society
104 S. Fifth St. • Philadelphia, PA 19106
(800) 821-7823; (215) 440-3425 Fax 440-3450
Website: www.amphilsoc.org; E-mail: acadsvc@aaol.com

Anthropology Resource Center
Distributed by Cultural Survival

B

Bellerophon Books
P.O. Box 21307 • Santa Barbara, CA 93121
(800) 253-9943 Fax (805) 965-8286
Website: www.bellerophonbooks.com
E-Mail: info@bellerophonbooks.com

John F. Blair, Publisher
1406 Plaza Dr. • Winston-Salem, NC 27103
(800) 222-9796; (336) 768-1374 Fax 768-9194
Website: www.blairpub.com; E-mail: blairpub@blairpub.com

Boise State University Publications
Rediscovered Books, 180 N. 8th St. • Boise, ID 83702
(208) 376-4229 Fax 426-4373
Website: www.boisestate.edu; E-mail: mmyoung@boisestate.edu

Book Publishing Co./Native Voices
P.O. Box 99 • Summertown, TN 38483
(888) 260-8458; (800) 695-2241; (931) 964-3571 Fax 964-3518
Website: www.nativevoices.com; E-mail: info@bookpubco.com

Brooklyn Museum
Publications & Marketing Services
200 Eastern Pkwy. • Brooklyn, NY 11238
(718) 638-5000 ext. 308; E-mail: bklnmus2@metgate.metro.org

C

Callaway Editions
41 Union Square West, Suite 1101 • New York, NY 10003
(212) 929-5212 Fax 929-8087; Website: www.callaway.com
E-mail: nicholas@callaway.com

Cambridge University Press
100 Brook Hill Rd. • W. Nyack, NY 10994
(800) 872-7423; (845) 353-7500 Fax 353-4141
Website: www.cup.org; E-mail: orders@cup.org

Caxton Press
312 Main St. • Caldwell, ID 83605
(800) 657-6465; (208) 459-7421 Fax 459-7450
Website: www.caxtonpress.com
E-mail: wcornell@caxtonpress.com

Center for Indigenous Arts & Cultures
(CIAC) Press - Div. of Southwest Learning Center
P.O. Box 8627 • Santa Fe, NM 87504 (505) 473-5375 Fax 424-1025
E-mail: greg@indianartbooks.com; Website: www.indianartbooks.com

Center for Western Studies
Box 727, Augustana College • Sioux Falls, SD 57197
(800) 727-2844; (605) 274-4007 Fax 274-4999
Website: www.inst.augie.edu; E-mail: cws@inst.augie.edu

Center for American Indian Economic Development
College of Business Administration - Northern Arizona University
Box 15066 • Flagstaff, AZ 86011 (928) 523-732 Fax 523-5990
Website: www.cba.nau.edu/caied

Chelsea House Publishers
Div. of Main Line Book Co.
2080 Cabot Blvd. W., Suite 201 • Langhorne, PA 19047-1813
(800) 848-2665; Fax (877) 780-7300
E-mail: info@chelseahouse.com
Website: www.chelseahouse.com

Cherokee Publications
P.O. Box 430 • Cherokee, NC 28719
(828) 488-8856 Fax 488-6934
Website: www.cherokeepublications.net
E-mail: cpubl@aol.com

Chickasaw Press
Chickasaw Nation Div. of History & Culture
(580) 622-7130; Website: www.chickasawpress.com
Order From: University of Oklahoma Press

Children's Press
Div. of Scholastic Library Publishing

Chilton Book Co.
Dist. by Krause Publications

Chippewa Valley Museum Press
P.O. Box 1204 • Eau Claire, WI 54702
(715) 834-7871 Fax 834-6624; Website: www.cvmuseum.com
E-mail: info@cvmuseum.com

The Choctaw Store
1882 Hwy. 69/75 • Colbert, OK 74733
(580) 296-2672; (855) 865-7854
Website: www.choctawstore.com

Chu-Nan-Nee Books
P.O. Box 127 • Somerville, TN 38068
(901) 465-9426 Fax 853-9049; Website: www.cherokeeproud.com
E-mail: cheroproud@aol.com

Church Publishing, Inc.
445 Fifth Ave. • New York, NY 10016
(800) 242-1918; (212) 592-1800 Fax 779-3392
Website: www.churchpublishing.org; E-mail: churchpublishing@cpg.org

Cincinnati Art Museum
953 Eden Park Dr. • Cincinnati, OH 45202
(513) 639-2995 Fax 721-0129; Website: www.cincinnatimuseum.org

Cinco Puntos Press
701 Texas Ave. • El Paso, TX 79901
(800) 566-9072; (915) 838-1625 Fax 838-1635
Website: www.cincopuntos.com; E-mail: bbyrd@cincopuntos.com

Circle of Nations Publishing
P.O. Box 12017 • Grand Forks, ND

The CIRI Foundation
2600 Cordova St., #206 • Anchorage, AK 99503
(907) 263-5582 Fax 279-8836

City Lights Books, Inc.
261 Columbus Ave. • San Francisco, CA 94133
(415) 362-1901 Fax 362-4921; Website: www.citylights.com
E-mail: staff@citylights.com

Clarity Press, Inc.
3277 RoswellRd., NE, #469 • Atlanta, GA 30305
(877) 613-1495 Fax (877) 613-7868; Fax (404) 231-3899
Website: www.claritypress.com; E-mail: clarity@islandnet.com

Arthur H. Clark Co.
P.O. Box 14707 • Spokane, WA 99214
(800) 842-9286; (509) 928-9540 Fax 928-4364
Website: www.ahclark.com; E-Mail: clarkbks@soar.com

Client Distribution Services
387 Park Ave. So. • New York, NY 10016
(212) 340-8100 Fax 340-8195; Website: www.cdsbooks.com
E-mail: tflowers@cdsbooks.com

Columbia University Press
61 W. 62nd St. • New York, NY 10023
(212) 459-0600 Fax 459-3678

Comanche Language & Cultural Preservation Committee
1375 N.E. Cline Rd. • Elgin, OK 73538
(877) 492-4988; (580) 492-5126 Fax 492-5119
Website: www.comanchelanguage.org
E-mail: clcpc@comanchelanguage.org

Cornell University Press
P.O. Box 6525 • Ithaca, NY 14850 (607) 277-2211 Fax (800) 688-2877
E-mail: cupresssales@cornell.edu; Web site: www.cornellpress.cornell.edu

Cotsen Institute of Archaeology of UCLA
Box 951510, A163 Fowler Bldg. • Los Angeles, CA 90095
(866) 628-2895; (310) 825-7411 Fax (310) 206-4723; E-mail: ioapubs@ucla.edu

Cottonpatch Press
P.O. Box 762 • Cumming, GA 30028 (770) 887-1626
Website: www.donshadburn.com; E-mail: donshadburn@webtv.net

Council Oak Books; Dist. By IPG Books
2822 Van Ness Ave. • San Francisco, CA 94109
E-mail: orders@ipgbook.com; E-mail: marketing@counciloakbooks.com

Coyhis Publishing/White Bison, Inc.
6455 N. Union Blvd., Suite 102 • Colorado Springs, CO 80918
(877) 871-1495; (866) 518-5275; (719) 548-1000 Fax 548-9407
Website: www.whitebison.org; E-mail: info@whitebison.org

Coyote Press
P.O. Box 3377 • Salinas, CA 93912
(831) 422-4912 Fax 422-4913
E-mail: orders@coyotepress.com

CQ Press - Division of Sage Publishing
2455 Teller Rd. • Thousand Oaks, CA 91320
(800) 818-7243 Fax (805) 499-9774
E-mail: orders@sagepub.com

Crazy Horse Memorial Foundation
The Black Hills, Ave. of the Chiefs • Crazy Horse, SD 57730
(605) 673-4681 Fax 673-2185

Crown Publishers - Division of Random House

Cultural Survival, Inc.
215 Prospect St. • Cambridge, MA 02138
(617) 441-5400 Fax 441-5417
Website: www.cs.org; E-mail: culturalsurvival@cs.org

D

Da Capo Press; hatchette Book Group
185 N. Mt. Zion Rd. • Lebanon,, IN 46052
(800) 759-0190 Fax (800) 331-1664
E-mail: orders@hbgusa.com

David & Charles
Dist. by Sterling Publishing

Delacourte Press - See Bantam/Dell

Dell Publishing - See Bantam/Dell

Doubleday - See Random House

Dover Publications
31 E. Second St. • Mineola, New York 11501
(800) 223-3130; (516) 294-7000 Fax (516) 742-5049
Website: www.doverpublications.com

Duke University Press
905 W. Main St., Suite 18B• Durham, NC 27701
(919) 688-5134 Fax 688-2615; (888) 651-0122 Fax 651-0124
Website: www.dukepress.edu; E-mail: orders@dukeupress.edu

E

Eagle's View Publishing
Subs. of Westwind, Inc., 6756 North Fork Rd. • Liberty, UT 84310
(800) 547-3364; (801) 393-4555 Fax (801) 745-0903
Website: www.eaglesviewpub.com; E-mail: eglcrafts@aol.com

Education Northwest
101 SW Main, Suite 500 • Portland, OR 97204
(800) 547-6339; (503) 275-9500
Website: www.educationnorthwest.org

Enslow Publishers, Inc.,
Box 398, 40 Industrial Rd., Dept. F61 • Berkeley Heights, NJ 07922
(800) 398-2504; (908) 771-9400 Fax 771-0925
Website: www.enslow.com; E-mail: customerservice@enslow.com

Epicenter Press
P.O. Box 82368 • Kenmore, WA 98028
(800) 950-6663; (425) 458-6822 Fax (425) 481-8253
Website: www.epicenterpress.com; E-mail: sales@epicenterpress.com

F

Facts on File, Inc.
132 W. 31st St., 16th Floor • New York, NY 10001-2006
(800) 322-8755 Fax (800) 678-3633
Website: www.factsonfile.com; E-mail: custserv@factsonfile.com

Favell Museum of Western Art & Indian Artifacts
125 W. Main • Klamath Falls, OR 97601 (541) 882-9996 Fax 850-0125
Website: www.favellmuseum.org; E-mail: info@favellmuseum.org

Federal Bar Association
2215 M St., NW • Washington, DC 20037 (202) 785-1614 Fax 785-1568
Website: www.fedbar.org; E-mail: pubs@fedbar.org
Firefly Books, Ltd.
66 Leek Crescent, Richmond Hill • ON, Canada L4B 1H1
(800) 387-5085 Fax (800) 565-6034
in Canada (800) 387-6192 Fax (800) 450-0391
(416) 499-8412 Fax 499-8313; Website: www.fireflybooks.com
E-mail: service@fireflybooks.com

First Peoples: New Directions in Indigenous Studies
355 S. Euclid Ave., Suite 103 • Tucson, AZ 85719 (520) 626-8484
Website: www.firstpeoplesnewdirections.org; E-mail: nvarner@uspress.arizona.edu

The Five Civilized Tribes Museum
Agency Hill on Honor Hts. Dr. • Muskogee, OK 74401
(918) 683-1701 Fax 683-3070

Four Winds Indian Books
823 Don Diego Ave. • Santa Fe, NM 87505
(505) 989-9590 Fax 989-9519
Website: www.fourwindsindianbooks.com; E-mail: fourwind@megavision.com

Fulcrum Publishing
4690 Table Mountain Dr. #100 • Golden, CO 80403
(800) 992-2908; (303) 277-1623 Fax (800) 726-7112; (303) 279-7111
Web site: www.fulcrum-books.com; E-mail: dianneh@fulcrum-books.com

G

Genealogical Institute
c/o Family History World, P.O. Box 129 • Tremonton, UT 84337
(800) 377-6058; (435) 257-3185 Fax (435) 257-8622
Website: genealogical-institute.com; E-mail: genealogy@utahlinx.com

Greenwood Press - Imprint of ABC-CLIO

Gros Ventre Treaty Committee
Fort Belknap Agency-BIA, RR 1, Box 980 • Harlem, MT 59526
(406) 353-2901 Ext 23 Fax 353-2886

H

Hafner Press c/o Macmillan Publishing

G.K. Hall & Co. - Imprint of Thomson Gale

Hancock House Publishers
1431 Harrison Ave. • Blaine, WA 98231
(800) 938-1114 Fax (800) 983-2262 (604) 538-1114 Fax 538-2262
Website: www.hancockhouse.com; E-mail: sales@hancockhouse.com

Leslie D. Hannah
715 James Ct. • Reno, NV 89503 E-mail: hannah@netsites.net

HarperCollins Publishers
1000 Keystone Industrial Park • Scranton, PA 18512
(800) 242-7737; (570) 941-1500 Fax (800) 822-4090
Website: www.harpercollins.com

Harvard Education Press
8 Story St., 1st Fl. • Cambridge, MA 02138
Sales: (888) 437-1437 Fax (978) 348-1233
Editorial: (617) 495-3432 Fax 496-3584; Website: www.hepg.org

Harvard Project on American Indian Economic Development
John F. Kennedy School of Government, 79 JFK St. • Cambriidge, MA 02138
(617) 495-1480 Fax 496-3900; Website: www.ksg.harvard.edu/paied

Harvard University Press
c/o Triliteral LLC, 100 Maple Ridge Dr. • Cumberland, RI 02864
(800) 405-1619 Fax (800) 406-9145 (401) 531-2800 Fax 531-2801
E-mail: orders@triliteral.org; customer.care@triliteral.com
Editorial: 79 Garden St. • Cambridge, MA 02138 (617) 495-2600 Fax 495-5898
E-mail: contact_hup@harvard.edu; Website: www.hup.harvard.edu

Havasupai Tribal Council
P.O. Box 10 • Supai, AZ 86435 (928) 448-2961 Fax 448-2551

The Heard Museum
2301 N. Central Ave. • Phoenix, AZ 85004
(602) 252-8840 fax 252-9757; Website: www.heard.org

Hearst Museum of Anthropology
Distributed by University of Washington Press

William S. Hein & Co.
2350 N. Forest Rd. • Getzville, NY 14068
(800) 828-7571 Fax (716) 883-8100
Website: www.wshein.com; E-mail: mail@wshein.com

Heritage Books, Inc.
1540 E. Pointer Ridge Pl. • Bowie, MD 20716
(800) 398-7709; (301) 390-7708 Fax (800) 276-1760
Website: www.heritagebooks.com; E-mail: info@heritagebooks.com

Heyday Books
P.O. Box 9145 • Berkeley, CA 94709
(510) 549-3564 Fax 549-1889
Website: www.heydaybooks.com; E-mail: ncc@heydaybooks.com

High-Lonesome Books
P.O. Box 878 • Silver City, NM 88062 (800) 380-7323 Fax (505) 388-5705
E-mail: high-lonesomebooks@zianet.com; Website: www.high-lonesome books.com

Hobbs, Straus, Dean & Walker, LLP
Publications Dept., 851 S.W. Sixth Ave., Suite 1650
Portland, OR 97204 (503) 242-1745
E-mail: publications@hsdwdc.com; Website: www.hsdwlaw.com/publications.htm

Holiday House
425 Madison Ave. • New York, NY 10017 (212) 688-0085 Fax 688-0395
Website: www.holidayhouse.com; E-mail: bwalsh@holidayhouse.com

Henry Holt & Co. - Division of Holtzbrinck Publishers

Holy Cow! Press
Box 3170 • Duluth, MN 55803 (218) 724-1653 (phone & fax)
Website: www.holycowpress.org

Hood Museum of Art
Dartmouth College • Hanover, NH 03755
(603) 646-2808 Fax 646-1400
Website: www.dartmouth.edu; E-mail: hood.museum@dartmouth.edu

Horizon Publishers
P.O. Box 490 • Bountiful, UT 84011
(800) 453-0812; (801) 295-9451 Fax (801) 295-0196
Website: www.horiizonpublishers.com; E-mail: horizonp@burgoyne.com

I

Idaho Museum of Natural History
Campus Box 8096, Idaho State University
Pocatello, ID 83209 (208) 236-3168

Indian Arts & Crafts Board
USDI, 1849 C St., NW, MS: 2058 MIB • Washington, DC 20240
(888) ART-FAKE; (202) 208-3773 Fax 208-5196

Indian University Press
Bacone College, 2299 Old Bacone Rd. • Muskogee, OK 74403
(918) 683-4581 Fax 687-5913

Indiana Historical Society
315 W. Ohio St., Rm. 350 • Indianapolis, IN 46202
(800) 447-1830; (317) 232-1882 Fax 233-0857
E-mail: rvaught@indianahistory.org; Website: www.indianahistory.org

Ingram Publisher Service
(844) 841-0257; E-mail: ips@ingramcontent.com

Institute for the Development of Indian Law
Oklahoma City U., School of Law
2501 N. Blackwelder • Oklahoma City, OK 73106
(405) 531-5337 Fax 208-5185

Institute of Alaska Native Arts
P.O. Box 70769 • Fairbanks, AK 99707
(907) 456-7491 Fax 451-7268

J

Jamestown S'Klallam Tribe
1033 Old Blyn Hwy. • Sequim, WA 98382
(360) 683-1109; E-mail: info@jamestowntribe.org
Website: www.jamestowntribe.org;

K

KC Publications
P.O. Box 98118 • Las Vegas, NV 89193
(800) 626-9673; (702) 433-3415 Fax 456-5334

Kessinger Publishing Co.
P.O. Box 4587 • Whitefish, MT 59937 (406) 756-0167
E-Mail: sales@kessinger.net; Website: www.kessinger.net

L

Lakota Books
P.O. Box 140 • Kendall Park, NJ 08824
(908) 421-0485 Fax (732) 940-9429; Website: www.lakotabooks.com

Lakota Language Consortium
2620 N. Walnut St., Suite 1280 • Bloomington, IN 47404
(888) 525-6828 Fax (812) 961-0141
Website: www.lakhota.org; E-mail: help@lakhota.org

Peter Lang Publishing
29 Broadway, 18th Floor • New York, NY 10006
(800) 770-5264; (212) 647-7706 Fax 647-7707
Website: www.peterlang.com; E-mail: newyork@plang.com

Lenape Lifeways, Inc.
P.O. Box 239 • Stanhope, NJ 07874
(973) 691-2316 (phone & fax)
Website: www.lenapelifeways.org; E-mail: lenapelifeways@nac.net

Lerner Publications
1251 Washington Ave. N. • Minneapolis, MN 55401
(800) 328-4929 Fax (800) 332-1132; (612) 332-3344 Fax 204-9208
E-mail: custserv@lernerbooks.com; Website: www.lernerbooks.com

Library of Congress
Motion Picture, Broadcasting & Recorded Sound Division
Washington, DC 10540-4800 (202) 707-5840 Fax 707-2371

Louisiana State University LSU Press
P.O. Box 25053 • Baton Rouge, LA 70894
(800) 861-3477 Fax (800) 305-4416 (225) 388-6695 Fax 388-6461
E-mail: lsupress@lsu.edu; Website: www.lsu.edu

M

Makah Cultural & Research Center
Makah Indian Tribe, P.O. Box 115 • Neah Bay, WA 98357
(360) 645-2201 Fax 645-2788

Malki-Ballena Press
Malki Museum, Inc., P.O. Box 578 • Banning, CA 92220
(951) 849-7289 Fax 849-3549; E-mail: malkipress@malkimuseum.org

Mason Crest Publishers
450 Parkway Dr., Suite D • Broomall, PA 19008
(866) 627-2665 Fax (610) 543-3878; Website: www.masoncrest.com

Meadowlark Communications
P.O. Box 7218 • Missoula, MT 59807
(888) 728-2180; (406) 728-2180 Fax 549-3090
E-mail: info@powwowcountry.com; Web site: www.powwowcountry.com

The Edward Mellen Press
240 Portage Rd. • Lewiston, NY 14092
(716) 754-2266 Fax 854-4056
Website: www.mellenpress.com; E-mail: editor@mellenpress.com

Michigan Indian Press
531 Ashmun St. • Sault Ste. Marie, MI 49783
(800) 793-0660; (906) 632-6398 Fax 635-4969
E-mail: slucas@saulttribe.net; Website: www.legislativeimpact.com/book.htm

Michigan State University Press
1405 S. Harrison Rd., Suite 25 • East Lansing, MI 48823
(517) 355-9543 Fax 432-2611; E-mail: msupress@msu.edu
Website: www.msupress.msu.edu

Minnesota Historical Society Press
Distributed by Ingram Publisher Service

The Mohegan Tribe - See Little People Publications

Montana Historical Society Press
P.O. Box 201201 • Helena, MT 59620
(800) 243-9900 Fax (406) 444-2696 Fax 444-2696
E-Mail: cwhitehorn@state.mt.us; Website: www.montanahistoricalsociety.org

Muddy River Press
P.O. Box 865 • Brookline, MA 02446 (617) 739-7978
E-Mail: publisher@muddyriverpress.com
Museum of New Mexico Press
725 Camino Lejo • Santa Fe, NM 87504
(800) 249-7737 Fax (800) 622-8667 (505) 272-2777 Fax 272-7778
E-mail: custserv@upress.unm.edu; Website: www.mnmpress.org

Museum of Northern Arizona Press
3101 N. Fort Valley Rd. • Flagstaff, AZ 86001
(928) 779-1527; E-mail: lyazzi@mna.mus.az.us

Mystic Moon Publishing
551 W. Cordova Rd., Suite 550, Santa Fe, NM 87501
(888) 843-8408; (505) 820-6190 Fax 982-3785

N

National Congress of American Indians
1516 P St., Ave. NW • Washington, DC 20005
(202) 466-7767 Fax 466-7797
E-mail: ncai@ncai.org; Website: www.ncai.org

National Geographic Society
1145 17th St., N • Washington, DC 20036
(800) 437-5521; (801) 783-2144
E-mail: ngs@genealogy.org; Website: www.nationalgeographic.com

National Indian Gaming Association (NIGA)
224 Second St., SE • Washington, DC 20003
(202) 546-7711 Fax 546-1755
E-mail: sjohns@indiangaming.org; Website: www.indiangaming.org

NMAI Press - National Mseum of the American Indian Press
4th St. & Independence Ave. SW • Washington, DC 20580
(800) 242-6624; (202) 633-6985; E-mail: nmaipressoffice@si.edu
Website: www.nmai.si.edu/press; E-mail: nmai-info@si.edu

National Native American AIDS Prevention Center
1031 33rd St., Suite 270 • Denver, CO 80205
(720) 382-2244
E-mail: information@nnaapc.org; Website: www.nnaapc.org

Native Law Centre - University of Saskatchewan
101 Diefenbaker Place, Saskatoon, SK, Canada S7N 5B8
(306) 966-6189 Fax 966-6207; E-mail: K10tz@duke.usak.ca

NativeStudy.com
P.O. Box 908 • Hixon, TN 37343 (423) 870-5960 Fax 870-1796
E-mail: nativestudy@nativestudy.com; Website: www.nativestudy.com

Naturegraph Publishers
P.O. Box 1047 • Happy Camp, CA 96039
(800) 390-5353; (530) 493-5353 • Fax 493-5240
E-mail: nature@sisqtel.net; Website: www.naturegraph.com

Navajo Gallery
P.O. Box 1756 • Taos, NM 87571 (505) 758-3250

New Library Pr.Net
P.O. Box 130 • Murrieta, CA 92564

New World Library
14 Pamaron Way • Novato, CA 94949

(800) 972-6657 (415) 884-2100 Fax 884-2199
E-mail: escort@nwlib.com; Website: www.nwlib.com

Newberry Library
60 W. Walton St. • Chicago, IL 60610
(312) 943-9090 Fax 255-3513; Website: www.newberry.org

Nez Perce National Historical Park
39063 US Hwy. 95 • Lapwai, ID 83540 (208) 843-7009

North American Book Distributors, LLC
P.O. Box 510 • Hamburg, MI 48139
(810) 231-3728 Fax 231-8910
Website: www.www.nabdllc.com; E-mail: nabdllc@gmail.com

W.W. Norton & Co., Inc.
800 Keystone Industrial Park • Scranton, PA 18512
(800) 233-4830; (570) 346-2020 Fax 346-1442
E-mail: orders@wwnorton.com; Website: www.wwnorton.com

O

Oklahoma City University, School of Law
Native American Legal Resource Center,
2501 N. Blackwelder • Oklahoma City, OK 73106 (405) 521-5188

Oregon State University Press
121 The Valley Library • Corvallis, OR 97331
(800) 621-27736; (541) 754-3166 Fax 737-3170
E-mail: osu.press@oregonstate; Website: www.osu.orst.edu

Oxford University Press
198 Madison Ave. • New York, NY 10016
Customer Service: 2001 Evans Rd. • Cary, NC 27513
(800) 445-9714 Fax (919) 677-1303
Website: www.oup-usa.org; E-mail: custserv.us@oup.com

Oyate
330 E. Thomson Ave. • Sonoma, CA 95476
(707) 996-6700 Fax 935-9961
Website: www.oyate.org; E-mail: orders@oyate.org

P

Peabody Museum of Archaeology & Ethnology
Harvard University-Publications Dept.
11 Divinity Ave. • Cambridge, MA 02138 (617) 495-3938 Fax 495-7535
E-mail: ddickens@fas.harvard.edu; Website: harvard.edu/publications

Pineapple Press
P.O. Box 3899 • Sarasota, FL 34230
(800) 746-3275; (941) 359-0886 Fax (941) 351-9988
E-mail: info@pineapplepress.com; Website: www.pineapplepress.com

Lew Paxton Price
P.O. Box 88 • Garden Valley, CA 95633 (530) 333-9470
Website: www.lewpaxtonprice.us

Primer Publishers; American Traveler Press
5738 N. Central • Phoenix, AZ 85012
(800) 521-9221; (602) 234-1574 Fax (602) 234-3062
E-mail: info@americantravelerpress.com
Website: www.primerpublishers.com

R

Rio Grande Books
925 Salamanca NW • Los Ranchos de ALB, NM 87107
(505) 344-9382 Fax 345-5129; E-mail: info@nmsantos.com
Website: www.nmsantos.com

Riverbend Publishing
P.O. Box 5833 • Helena, MT 59604
(866) 787-2363; (406) 449-0200 Fax 449-0330
E-Mail: info@riverbendpublishing.com
Website: www.riverbendpublishing.com

Rough Rock School Press
Navajo Curriculum Center; Rough Rock Community School
Rough Rock Trading Post, P.O. Box 5000-PTT • Chinle, AZ 86503
(928) 728-3501 Fax 728-3502; Website: www.roughrock.k12.az.us/bookstore.htm

Rourke Education Media
P.O. Box 643328 • Vero Beach, FL 32964
(800) 394-7055; (772) 234-6001 Fax 234-6622
E-mail: rourke@rourkepublishing.com; Website: www.rourkepublishing.com

Routledge; c/o Taylor & Francis Group
7625 Empire Dr. • Florence, KY 41042 (800) 634-7064 Fax (800) 248-4724
E-mail: orders@taylorandfrancis.com
Website: https://www.routledge.com/culturalstudies

Rowman & Littlefield Publishers
P.O. Box 191 • Blue Ridge Summit, PA 17214
(800) 462-6420 Fax (800) 338-4550; (717) 794-3800 Fax 794-3801
Website: www.rowmanlittlefield.com

S

John Sabella & Associates
190 E. Uncas Rd. • Port Townsend, WA 98368
(360) 379-1668 Fax 379-5148
Website: www.johnsabella.com; E-mail: info@johnsabella.com

San Juan District Media Center
Curriculum Division, P.O. Box 804 • Blanding, UT 84511 (801) 678-2281

San Manuel Tribe
P.O. Box 266, Patton, CA 92369 (909) 864-8933 Fax 864-3370

Scarecrow Press
Div. of Rowman & Littlefield Publishing, 15200 NBN Way, P.O. Box 191
Blue Ridge Summit, PA 17214 (800) 462-6420 Fax (800) 338-4550
E-mail: orders@scarecrowpress.com; Website: www.scarecrowpress.com

Schiffer Publishing
4880 Lower Valley Rd. • Atglen, PA 19310 (610) 593-1777 Fax 593-2002
E-mail: schifferii@aol.com; Website: www.schifferbooks.com

School for Advanced Research - SAR Press
P.O. Box 2188 • Santa Fe, NM 87504
(888) 390-6070; (505) 954-7206 Fax 954-7241
Website: www.sarweb.org; E-mail: bkorders@sarsf.org

Simon & Schuster
100 Front St. • Riverside, NJ 08075 (800) 223-2336 Fax (800) 943-9831
E-mail: ssonline_feedback@simonsays.com
Website: www.oasis.simonanschuster.com

SKC Press
Box 117 • Pablo, MT 59855 (406) 275-2830 Fax 275-2831
Website: www.charkoosta.com/features.html

Sky & Sage Books
918 Fourth St. • Rapid City, SD 57701
(605) 343-5176 E-Mail: libyad817@aol.com

Smithsonian Institution Press
P.O. Box 960 • Herndon, VA 20172 (800) 782-4612 Fax (202) 287-3637
E-mail: inquiries@sipress.si.edu; Website: www.sipress.si.edu

Smithsonian Videos (800) 322-0344

Smoke & Fire Co., 27 N. River Rd. • Waterville, OH 43522
(800) 766-5334; (419) 878-8535 Fax 878-3653
Website: www.smoke-fire.com; E-mail: store@smoke-fire.com

Southwest Museum
234 Museum Dr. • Los Angeles, CA 90065 (323) 221-2164 Fax 224-8223
E-mail: info@southwestmuseum.org; Website: www.southwestmuseum.org

Spirit Mountain Press - Dist. by University of Alaska Press

Stanford University Press
1450 Page Mill Rd. • Palo Alto, CA 94304 (650) 723-9434 Fax 725-3457
Website: www.sup.org

State University of New York Press
P.O. Box 960 • Herndon, VA 20172
(877) 204-6073; Fax (877) 204-6074; (703) 661-1575 Fax 996-1010
E-mail: suny@presswarehouse.com; Website: www.sunypress.edu

Station Hill Press
120 Station Hill Rd. • Barrytown, NY 12507 (845) 758-5293 Fax 758-8163
E-mail: buun@stationhill.org; Website: www.stationhill.org

Sunstone Press
Box 2321 • Santa Fe, NM 87504
(800) 243-5644; (505) 988-4418 Fax 988-1025
E-mail: jsmith@sunstonepress.com; Website: www.sunstonepress.com

Syracuse University Press
621 Skytop Rd., #110 • Syracuse, NY 13244
(315) 443-2597 Fax (315) 443-5545; E-mail: supress@syr.edu
Website: www.syracuseuniversitypress.syr.edu

T

Texas A&M University Press
John H. Lindsey Bldg., Lewis St., 4354 TAMU • College Station, TX 77843
(800) 826-8911 (979) 845-1436 Fax 847-8752
E-mail: gec@tampress.tamu.edu; Website: www.tamu.edu/upress

Texas Western Press - Dist. by University of Texas Press
P.O. Box 7819 • Austin, TX 79968 (800) 252-3206 Fax (800) 687-6046
Website: www.utexas.edu/utpress/

Thames & Hudson
Div. of W.W. Norton, 500 Fifth Ave. • New York, NY 10110
(800) 233-4830; (212) 354-3763 Fax 398-1252
E-Mail: bookinfo@thames.wwnorton.com; Website: www.thamesandhudsonusa.com

Time-Life
P.O. Box 85026 • Richmond, VA 23285 (800) 449-2010 Fax (800) 449-2011
E-mail: education@timelifecs.com; Website: timelifeedu.com

Tipi Press
St. Joseph's Indian School • Chamberlain, SD 57326
(800) 229-5684 Fax (605) 734-3480; Website: www.stjo.org

Todtri Book Publishers
254 W. 31st St. #13th Fl. • New York, NY 10001 (800) 696-7299 Fax (800) 696-7482
Website: www.todtri.com; E-mail: todtri@mindspring.com

Treasure Chest Books
P.O. Box 5250 • Tucson, AZ 85703
(800) 969-9558 Fax (800) 715-5888 (520) 623-9558 Fax 624-5888
Website: www.treasurechestbooks.com; E-mail: info@treasurechestbooks.com

Truman State University Press
100 E. Normal St. • Kirksville, MO 63501 (800) 916-6802 Fax (660) 785-4480
E-mail: tsup@truman.edu; Website: tsup.truman.edu

U

UBC Press - University of British Columbia Press
6344 Memorial Rd. • Vancouver, BC Can. V6T 1Z2
Website: www.ubcpress.ca; E-mail: info@ubcpress.ca
Orders to: UNIpresses, 34 Armstrong Ave. • Georgtown, ON L7G 4R9
(877) 864-8477 Fax (877) 864-4272 (905) 873-9781 Fax 873-6170
E-mail: orders@gtwcanada.com; Website: www.ubcpress.ubc.ca

U.S. Government Accountability Office
441 G St., NW • Washington, DC 20548 (202) 612-8000 Fax 612-8081
Website: www.gao.gov

U.S. GPO (Government Printing Office)
P.O. Box 371954 • Pittsburgh, PA 15250
(866) 512-1800; (202) 512-1800 Fax 512-2250
E-mail: orders@gpo.gov; Website: www.access.gpo.gov/su_docs/

University of Alabama Press
Box 870380 • Tuscaloosa, AL 35487-0380
(800) 621-2736; (205) 348-5180 Fax 348-9201
E-Mail: jkramer@uapress.ua.edu; Website: www.uapress.ua.edu

University of Alaska Press
P.O. Box 756240 • Fairbanks, AK 99775
(888) 252-6657; (907) 474-5831 Fax 474-5502
E-Mail: fypress@uaf.edu; Website: www.uaf.edu/uapress
For orders outside Alaska: Chicago Distribution Center
(800) 621-2736 Fax (800) 621-8476; E-mail: orders@press.uchicago.edu

The University of Arizona Press
Main Library Bldg., 5th Floor, 1510 E. University Blvd.
P.O. Box 210055 • Tucson, AZ 85719
(800) 621-2736 Fax (800) 621-8476
E-m ail: orders@uapress.arizona.edu; Website: www.uapress.arizona.edu

The University of Arkansas Press
105 McIlroy Ave. • Fayetteville, AR 72701
(800) 626-0090; (479) 575-3246 Fax 575-6044
E-Mail: uaprinfo@cavern.uark.edu; Website: www.uark.edu/~uaprinfo

UCLA, American Indian Studies Center Publications Unit
3220 Campbell Hall • Box 951548 • Los Angeles, CA 90095-1548
(310) 206-7508 Fax 206-7060; E-Mail: sales@aisc.ucla.edu

University of California Press
California/Princeton Fulfillment Services, 1445 Lower Ferry Rd., Ewing, NJ 08618
(800) 777-4726 Fax (800) 999-1958 (609) 883-1759 Fax 883-7413
E-Mail: orders@cpfs.pupress.princeton.edu; Website: www.ucpress.edu

University of Chicago Press
1426 E. 60th St. • Chicago, IL 60637
(800) 621-2736 Fax (800) 621-8476; (773) 702-7700 Fax 702-9756
E-mail: sales@press.uchicago.edu; Website: www.press.uchicago.edu

University of Georgia Press
330 Research Dr. • Athens, GA 30602
(800) 266-5842 (706) 369-6148 Fax 425-3061
E-mail: books@ugapress.uga.edu; Website: www.ugapress.org

University of Idaho Press – The Caxton Press
See Longleaf Services, Inc., 116 S. Boundary St. • Chapel Hill, NC 27514
(800) 848-6224 Fax 272-6817; E-Mail: customerservice@longleafservices.org

University of Illinois Press
c/o Chicago Distribution Center, 11030 S. Langley Ave. • Chicago, IL 60628
(800) 621-2736 Fax 621-8476 (773) 702-7000 Fax 702-7212
E-mail: orders@press.uchicago.edu; Website: www.press.uillinois.edu

University of Iowa Press
119 W. Park Rd., 100 Kuhl House • Iowa City, IA 52242-1000
(319) 335-2000 Fax 335-2055; (800) 621-2736 Fax (800) 621-8476
E-mail: uipress@uiowa.edu; Website: www.uiowapress.org

University of Louisiana at Lafayette Center for Louisiana Studies
P.O. Box 40831 • Lafayette, LA 70504 (337) 482-6027 Fax 482-6028
E-mail: labiche@louisiana.edu; Website: www.louisiana.edu

University of Maine Press
5729 Fogler Library • Orono, ME 04473 (207) 581-1652 Fax 866-2084
E-mail: umpress@umi.maine.edu;

University of Massachusetts Press
P.O. Box 429 • Amherst, MA 01004 (413) 545-2219
E-mail: orders@umpress.umass.edu; Website: www.umass.edu/umpress

University of Michigan-Museum of Anthropology
Publications Dept., 4009 Museum Bldg., 1109 Geddes • Ann Arbor, MI 48109
(734) 764-0482 Fax 763-7783; E-mail: shorv@umich.edu
Website: www.umich.edu/~umma

University of Michigan Press
Website: www.press.umich.edu
c/o Chicago Distribution Center, 11030 S. Langley Ave. • Chicago, IL 60628
(800) 621-2736 Fax (800) 621-8476; (773) 702-7000 Fax 702-7212
E-mail: orders@press.uchicago.edu

University of Minnesota Press
111 3rd Ave. So., #290 • Minneapolis, MN 55401
(800) 621-2736 (Customer Service); (612) 627-1970 Fax 627-1980
E-mail: ump@staff.tc.umn.edu; Website: www.upress.umn.edu

University of Nebraska Press
1111 Lincoln Mall • Lincoln, NE 68588
(402) 472-3581 Fax 472-6214;
E-mail: pressmail@unl.edu; Website: www.nebraskapress.unl.edu
Ordering: (800) 848-6224 Fax (800) 272-6817
(919) 966-7449 Fax 962-2704; E-mail: orders@longleafservices.org

University of Nevada Press
Mail Stop 166 • Reno, NV 89557-0076 (877) 682-6657; (775) 784-6573 Fax 784-6200
E-mail: nvinfo@nvbooks.nevada.edu; Website: www.nvbooks.nevada.edu

University of New Mexico Press
1312 Basehart Rd. SE • Albuquerque, NM 87106
(800) 249-7737 Fax (800) 622-8667 (505) 272-7777 Fax 272-7778
E-mail: unmpress@unm.edu; E-mail: custserv@unpress.unm.edu
Website: www.unmpress.com

University of North Carolina Press
P.O. Box 2288 • Chapel Hill, NC 27514
(800) 848-6224; (919) 966-3561 Fax 966-3829
E-mail: uncpress@unc.edu; Website: www.uncpress.org

University of Oklahoma Press
OU Press Distribution Center, 2800 Venture Dr. • Norman, OK 73069
(800) 627-7377 Fax (800) 735-0476 (405) 325-2000 Fax 364-5798
Website: www.oupress.com

University of Pennsylvania Press
3905 Spruce St. • Philadelphia, PA 19104 (215) 898-6261 Fax 898-0404
E-mail: custserv@pobox.upenn.edu; Website: www.upenn.edu/pennpress
Orders to: Hopkins Fulfillment Services
P.O. Box 50370 Hamppdon Station • Baltimore, MD 21211
(800) 537-5487; Fax (410) 516-6998
E-mail: hfscustserv@preess.jhu.edu

University of Pittsburgh Press
3400 Forbes Ave. • Pittsburgh, PA 15260
(800) 666-2211; (412) 383-2456 Fax 383-2466
E-Mail: press+@pitt.edu; Website: www.upress.pitt.edu

University of South Carolina Press
718 Devine St. • Columbia, SC 29208
(800) 768-2500 Fax (800) 868-0740 (803) 777-1774 Fax 777-0026
E-mail: cdibble@sc.edu; Website: www.sc.edu/uscpress

University of Tennessee Press
11030 S. Langley Ave. • Chicago, IL 60628
(800) 621-2736 Fax (800) 621-8476 (773) 568-1550 Fax 660-2235
E-mail: hannah@utpress.org; Website: www.utpress.org

University of Texas Press
P.O. Box 7819 • Austin, TX 78713
(800) 252-3206 Fax (512) 232-7178
(800) 687-6046 (512) 471-7233 Fax 320-0668
E-mail: info@utpress.utexas.edu; Website: https://utpress.utexas.edu/

University of Toronto Press
5201 Dufferin St. • Downsview, ON M3H 5T8
Canada (800) 565-9523 Fax (800) 221-9985
E-Mail: utpbooks@gpu.utcc.utoronto.ca

University of Utah Press
1795 E. South Campus Dr. #101 • Salt Lake City, UT 84112
(800) 773-6672; (801) 581-6771 Fax (801) 581-3365
E-mail: info@upress.utah.edu; Website: www.upress.utah.edu
c/o Chicago Distribution Center, 11030 S. Langley Ave. • Chicago, IL 60628
(800) 621-2736 Fax (800) 621-8476; (773) 702-7000 Fax 702-7212
E-mail: orders@press.uchicago.edu

University of Washington Press
P.O. Box 50096 • Seattle, WA 98145 (800) 441-4115 Fax (800) 669-7993
Foreign: (206) 543-8870 Fax 543-3932; E-mail: uwpord@u.washington.edu
Website: www.washington.edu/uwpress/
Orders to: Hopkins Fulfillment Services
P.O. Box 50370 Hamppdon Station • Baltimore, MD 21211
(800) 537-5487; Fax (410) 516-6998
E-mail: hfscustserv@preess.jhu.edu

University of Wisconsin Press
11030 S. Langley • Chicago, IL 60628
(800) 621-2736 Fax (800) 621-8476 (773) 568-1550 Fax 660-2235
E-mail: uwiscpress@uwpress.wisc.edu; Website
c/o Chicago Distribution Center, 11030 S. Langley Ave. • Chicago, IL 60628
(800) 621-2736 Fax (800) 621-8476; (773) 702-7000 Fax 702-7212
E-mail: orders@press.uchicago.edu

University Press of Colorado
5589 Arapahoe Ave., #206C • Boulder, CO 80303
(800) 621-2736 Fax (720) 406-8849

University Press of Florida
15 NW 15th St. • Gainesville, FL 32611
(800) 226-3822; (352) 392-1351 Fax (800) 680-1955; (352) 392-7302
E-mail: press@upf.com; Website: www.upf.com

University Press of Kansas
2502 Westbrooke Circle • Lawrence, KS 66049;
(785) 864-4155 Fax 864-4586; E-mail: upress@ku.edu

University Press of Mississippi
3825 Ridgewood Rd. • Jackson, MS 39211
(800) 737-7788; (601) 432-6205 Fax 432-6217
E-mail: kerr@ihl.state.ms.us; Website: www.upress.state.ms.us

University Press of New England (UPNE)
One Court St. • Lebanon, NH 03766
(800) 421-1561 Fax (603) 448-9429
E-mail: university.press@dartmouth.edu; Website: www.upne.com

Utah State University Press
3078 Old Main Hill • Logan, UT 84322
(800) 239-9974; (435) 797-1362 Fax 797-0313
E-mail: brooke.bigelow@usu.edu; Website: www.usu.edu/usupress
Orders: (800) 621-2736 Fax (720) 406-8849

V

VIP Publishing - Various Indian Peoples
P.O. Box 1540 • Tahlequah, OK 74465
(800) 776-0842 Fax (918) 457-5843
E-mail: vipublish@earthlink.net; Website: www.nativelanguages.com

W

Walker & Co.
Distributed by www.amazon.com

Franklin Watts, Inc. - See Scholastic Library Publishing

Waveland Press
4180 Rt. 83, #101 • Long Grove, IL 60047 (847) 634-0081 Fax 634-9501
E-mail: info@waveland.com; Website: www.waveland.com

Wayfinder Press
P.O. Box 217 • Ridgway, CO 81432 (970) 626-5452 Fax 626-4233
E-mail: wayfinderpress@ouraynet.com; Website: www.wayfinderpress.us

Wayne State University Press
Leonard N. Simons Bldg., 4809 Woodward Ave. • Detroit, MI 48201
(800) 978-7323; (313) 577-6120 Fax 577-6131
E-mail: bookorders@wayne.edu; Website: www.wsupress.wayne.edu

Webb Research Group
P.O. Box 314 • Medford, OR 97501
(800) 866-9721; (541) 664-5205 Fax 664-9131
E-Mail:anybody@pnwbooks.com; Website: www.pnwbooks.com

Welcome Rain Publishers
532 LaGuardia Pl. #473 • New York, NY 10012
(212) 889-0088 Fax 889-0869; Dist. by National Book Network

Wennawoods Publishing
RR#2 Box 529C • Lewisburg, PA 17837
(800) 796-1702; (570) 523-9218 (phone & fax)
E-Mail: wennapub@csrlink.net; Website: www.wennawoods.com

West Publishing Co. - Div. of Thomson Learning; Dist. by Thomson Gale Group

Western Edge Press
126 Candelario St. • Santa Fe, NM 87501 (505) 988-7214
E-Mail: westernedge@santa-fe.net; Website: www.westernedgepress.com

Western National Parks Association
12880 N. Vistoso Village Dr. • Tucson, AZ 85737 (520) 622-1999 Fax 623-9519
E-mail: abby@wnpa.org; Website: www.wnpa.org

Western Reflections Publishing Co.
P.O. Box 1149 • Lake City, CO 81235 (970) 944-0110 Fax 944-0273
Website: www.westernreflectionspublishing.com
E-mail: publisher@westernreflectionspublishing.com

Westernlore Publications
11860 N. Tami Pl. • Tucson, AZ 85737

Westview Press - See Perseus Book Group

Wheelwright Museum of the American Indian
P.O. Box 5153 • Santa Fe, NM 87502 (505) 982-4636 Fax 989-7386
Website: www.wheelwright.org

Whispering Willows, Ltd.
P.O. Box 890294 • Oklahoma City, OK 73189
(800) 368-1053; (405) 239-2531 Fax 236-0502
E-Mail: wwillows@telepath.com

White Crane Books
c/o White Crane Institute, 172 Fifth Ave. • Brooklyn, NY 11217
Website: www.whitecranebooks.org; E-Mail: info@whitecranebooks.org

White Mane Publishing
P.O. Box 708 • Shippensburg, PA 17257
(888) 948-6263; (717) 532-2237 Fax 532-6110
E-mail: marketing@whitemane.com; Website: www.whitemane.com

White Pine Press
P.O. Box 236 • Buffalo, NY 14201 (716) 627-4665 (phone & fax)
Website: www.whitepine.org; E-mail: wpine@whitepine.org

White Publishing
P.O. Box 342 • Arlee, MT 59821 (406) 726-3627

White Owl Publications
124 N. Norris Ave. • Tucson, AZ 85719 (520) 792-9283 Fax 624-1992

Whitston Publishing Co.
P.O. Box 38263 • Albany, NY 12203 (518) 869-5110 Fax 452-2154
E-mail: whitston@capital.net; Website: www.whitston.com

Whole Earth Motorcycle Center
P.O. Box 102125 • Denver, CO 80250
(303) 715-9292 Fax 733-8625; E-mail: gregfrazier@yahoo.com

Wichita Tribal Office
P.O. Box 729 • Anadarko, OK 73005 (405) 247-2425 Fax 247-2005

Wiconi Waste
7892 W. First Pl. • Lakewood, CO 80226 (303) 238-3420 Fax 238-0323

Wilderness Adventure Books
P.O. Box 856 • Manchester, MI 48158
(800) 852-8652; (734) 433-1595 Fax (206) 339-6597
E-Mail: sales@wildernessbooks.org; Website: www.wildernessbooks.org

John Wiley & Sons
1 Wiley Dr. • Somerset, NJ 08875
(732) 469-4400 Fax 302-2300 (800) 225-5945 Fax 597-3299
E-mail: bookinfo@wiley.com; Website: www.wiley.com

Willow Tree Press
P.O. Box 249 • Monsey, NY 10952 (845) 354-9139 Fax 362-8376
E-mail: cjpress109@aol.com; Website: www.criminaljusticepress.com

WinterSun Press
P.O. Box 2626 • Overland Park, KS 66221 (413) 691-2928
E-Mail: books@wintersunpress.com; Website: www.wintersunpress.com

Wisconsin Academy of Sciences, Arts & Letters
1922 University Ave. • Madison, WI 53705
(800) 443-6159; (608) 263-1692 Fax 265-3039

Wisconsin Dept. of Public Instruction
P.O. Drawer 179 • Milwaukee, WI 53293
(800) 243-8782; (608) 266-2188 Fax 267-9110
E-mail: pubsales@dpi.wi.us; Website: www.dpi.wi.us

Wisconsin Historical Society
816 State St. • Madison, WI 53706 (608) 264-6482 Fax 264-6486
E-mail: dtjohnson@whs.wisc.edu; Website: www.wisconsinhistory.org

David Michael Wolfe
4167 Timberlane Dr. • Allison Park, PA 15101
(412) 487-7093 E-Mail: wahya@usaor.net

Wolf Moon Press - See WinterSun Press

Wolfe Publishing Co.
P.O. Box 8036 • Fernandina Beach, FL 32035
(904) 277-0555 Fax 321-0417
E-Mail: wolfepub@net-magic.net; Website: www.wolfepublishing.com

Woman's Press
600 F Cathedral Rd. #1107 • Philadelphia, PA 19128

Wo-Pila Publishing
P.O. Box 8966 • Erie, PA 16505
(888) 567-8267; (814) 868-5331 Fax 864-3823
E-Mail: wopila2@aol.com; Website: www.mannytwofeathers.com

Word Dancer Press
Div. of Quill Driver Books
1831 Industrial Way #101 • Sanger, CA 93657
(800) 497-4909; E-mail: sbm12@csufresno.edu

Wordware Publishing
2320 Los Rios Blvd. #200 • Plano, TX 75074
(800) 229-4949; (972) 423-0090 Fax 881-9147
E-Mail: info@wordware.com; Website: www.wordware.com

Workbooks Press
P.O. Box 8504 • Atlanta, GA 30306
(888) 427-4260; (404) 892-5169 Fax 875-1103
E-Mail: jimgibsn@mindspring.com

Workman Publishing Co.
708 Broadway • New York, NY 10003
(800) 722-7202 Fax (800) 521-1832; (212) 254-5900 Fax 614-7783
E-Mail: mged@workman.com; Website: www.workman.com

World Around Songs
5790 Hwy. 80 S. • Burnsville, NC 28714 (704) 675-5343

World Book, Inc. - Div. of Scott Fetzer Co.
233 N. Michigan, #2000 • Chicago, IL 60601
(800) 975-3250 Fax (800) 433-9330; (312) 729-5800 Fax 729-5600
Website: www.worldbook.com

World Music Press
P.O. Box 26627 • Wauwatosa, WI 53226
(888) 283-5273; (203) 748-1131 Fax 748-3432
E-Mail: info@worldmusicpress.com
Website: www.worldmusicpress.com

World Vision International
800 W. Chestnut Ave. • Monrovia, CA 91016
(818) 303-8811; E-Mail: wvpp@wvi.org; Website: www.wvi.org

World Wisdom, Inc.
P.O. Box 2682 • Bloomington, IN 47402
(888) 992-6651; (812) 330-3232 Fax 333-1642
E-Mail: info@worldwisdom.com; Website: www.worldwisdom.com

WorldComm
65 Macedonia Rd. • Alexander, NC 28701
(800) 472-0438 Fax (828) 252-9515 Fax 255-8719
E-mail: sales@abooks.com; Website: www.abooks.com

Writer's Digest Books - See F&W Publications

Written Heritage, Inc.
P.O. Box 1390 • Folsom, LA 70437-1390
(800) 301-8009; (985) 796-5433 Fax 796-9236; E-Mail: whiswind@i-55.com

WSU Press - Washington State University Press
P.O. Box 645910 • Pullman, WA 99164
(800) 354-7360; (509) 335-3518 Fax 335-8568
E-mail: wsupress@wsu.edu; Website: www.wsu.edu/wsupress

Y

Yale University Press
c/o Triliteral LLC, 100 Maple Ridge Dr. • Cumberland, RI 02864
(800) 405-1619 Fax 406-9145; (401) 531-2800 Fax 531-2801
E-mail: yupmkt@yale.edu; Website: www.yale.edu/yup/

A

ABBOTT, STEVEN
(director for recruitment & student affairs)
Affiliation & Address: Director, Recruitment & Student Affairs, Harvard University Native American Program, 14 Story St., 4th Floor, Cambridge, MA 02138 (617) 495-9058. *Other professional post*: Council Executive Board Member, National Institute for Native Leadership in Higher Education, University of Northern Colorado, Greeley, CO.

ABEITA, ANDY P. (Isleta Pueblo) 1963-
(artist-stone sculptor)
Born July 24, 1963, Chicago, Ill. *Principal occupation*: Artist-stone sculptor. *Home address*: 2 N. Park Lane, Peralta, NM 87042 (505) 869-8148; (800) 638-7791 (work). *Affiliations*: Co-owner, Laboraex Enterprises, Peralta, NM, 1986-; co-owner Laboraex Enterprises, Denver, CO, 1992-; co-owner, Andy Abeita's Bear Fetish Studio, Santa Fe, NM, 1992-present. *Memberships*: Indian Arts & Crafts Association; Heard Museum Guild; American Indian Art Council; Gallup Ceremonial Association; Indian Arts Foundation; Council for Indigenous Arts & Culture (president). *Interests*: "My wife, Roberta and I are Native American artisans – stone sculptors & fetish carvers. We have traveled extensively promoting our artwork and our culture. We average 30 gallery appearances a year and ten wholesale shows annually. In recent years, I have become quite involved with educational & environmental functions held in many parts of the country. I am also a recognized lecturer/speaker by the Native American Art Council."

ABEITA, ISIDOR (Pueblo of Isleta)
(Pueblo 2nd lt. governor)
Affiliation & Address: 2nd Lt. Governor, Isleta Pueblo Council, P.O. Box 1270, Isleta, NM 87022 (505) 869-3111.

ABEITA, JAMES (Pueblo)
(BIA agency supt.)
Affiliation & Address: Supt., Northern Pueblos Agency, Bureau of Indian Affairs, P.O. Box 4269, Fairview Station, Espanola, NM 87533 (505) 753-1400.

ABEITA, ROBERTA (Ramah Navajo)
(artist-stone sculptor)
Born August 13, 1951, Rehobeth, N.M. *Principal occupation*: Artist-stone sculptor. *Address*: 2 N. Park Lane, Peralta, NM 87042 (505) 869-8148; (800) 638-7791 (work). *Affiliation*: Co-owner, Laboraex Enterprises, Peralta, NM, 1986-present. *Memberships*: Indian Arts & Crafts Association; Heard Museum Guild; American Indian Art Council; Gallup Ceremonial Association; Indian Arts Foundation (advocacy for nature conservancy). *Interests*: "My husband Andy and I are Native American artisans - stone sculptors & fetish carvers. Andy & I travel roughly 50,000 miles a year promoting our artwork and our culture. We average 30 gallery appearances a year and 10 wholesale shows annually. In recent years, I have become quite involved with educational & environmental functions held in many parts of the country. I'm also a recognized lecturer/speaker by the Native American Art Council."

ABEITA, ZELDA (Santo Domingo Pueblo)
(artist)
Address: P.O. Box 566, Santo Domingo, NM 87052 (505) 269-3092. E-mail: abeitaz@hotmail.com. *Membership*: Indian Arts & Crafts Association.

ABEYTA, JOSEPH, JR. (Pueblo)
(Indian school supt.)
Affiliation: Santa Fe Indian School, P.O. Box 5340, Santa Fe, NM 87501 (505) 989-6300.

ABEYTA, LESTER (Pueblo)
(artist)
Address: P.O. Box 591, Santo Domingo, NM 87052 (505) 465-2473. E-mail: lesterabeyta@aol.com. *Membership*: Indian Arts & Crafts Association.

ABEYTA, SHARON (Pueblo)
(artist)
Address: P.O. Box 712, Santo Domingo, NM 87052 (505) 465-2473. E-mail: sharonabeyta@gmail.com. *Membership*: Indian Arts & Crafts Association.

ABINANTI, ABBY (Yurok)
(chief judge; board president)
Education: Humboldt State University, BA; and holds a juris doctorate from the University of New Mexico School of Law, JD. *Affiliation & Address*: Chief Judge Yurok Tribal Wellness Court, 190 Klamath Blvd., P.O. Box 1027, Klamath, CA 95548 (707) 482-1350. *Other professional post*: Board President (2012-present), Friendship House of American Indians, San Francisco, CA. *Past

professional posts: In 1987, Abby served as corporate attorney for Friendship House, San Francisco, CA. She was in private practice for 15 years ending in 1992, served as the Legal Director and Director of the Lesbian Rights, and as Directing Attorney for California Indian Legal Services in Eureka. In 1994 she became the first American Indian to be appointed as a Commissioner for the Superior Court of the City and County of San Francisco; and she currently serves as a Duty Officer for that Court. *Membership*: California Bar Assn.

ABNEY, DON (Sac & Fox)
(former tribal 2nd chief)
Address & Affiliation: Former 2nd Chief, Sac & Fox Nation of Oklahoma Business Committee, Rt. 2, Box 246, Stroud, OK 74079 (918) 968-3526. E-mail: secondchief@sacandfoxnation-nsn.gov

ABOUREZK, CHARLES (Oglala Lakota)
(attorney; newspaper columnist; adjunct professor)
Affiliation: Adjunct professor, Oglala Lakota College, Graduate Studies Program, P.O. Box 490, Kyle, SD 57752 (605) 455-6000. *Other professional post*: Contributing editor, Native Nations Magazine. *Past professional posts*: Founder of KILI Radio on the Pine Ridge Reservation; former director & producer of nationally syndicated "First Person Radio," and former Minority Affairs Producer for South Dakota Public Television. He is an expert on treaties, federal Indian law and tribal law. He is also a human rights specialist who represented the International Indian Treaty Council at the United Nations Commission on Human Rights for five years.

ABRAMS, GEORGE H.J. (*Ha-doh-jus*) (Seneca) 1939-
(museum director; anthropologist)
Born May 4, 1939, Allegany Indian Reservation, Salamanca, N.Y. Education: SUNY, Buffalo, BA, 1965, MA, 1967; University of Arizona, PhD program, 1968-1971. *Past professional posts*: Past-president, Association of Indigenous Anthropologists, Arlington, VA; director, Yager Museum, Hartwick College, Oneonta, NY, 1998-2004; special assistant to the Director, National Museum of the American Indian, Heye Foundation, New York, NY; member, Board of Directors, American Indian Development, Inc., Denver, CO; member, American Indian Advisory Board, Denver Museum of Natural History, Denver, CO; member, Board of Trustees, Museum of the American Indian-Heye Foundation, New York, New York; chairman, Ad Hoc Committee on the New York State Indian, New York State Archaeological Assn, Rochester, NY; chairman, North American Indian Museums Assn, Salamanca, NY, 1978-89; member, Board of Directors, New York Iroquois Conference, Inc., Buffalo, NY, 1979-81; member, advisory board, Center for the History of the American Indian, The Newberry Library, Chicago, 1980-87. *Community activities*: Seneca Nation Library, NY (member); Johnson O'Malley (JOM) Local Indian Education Committee, Allegany Indian Reservation; Mohawk-Caughnawaga Museum, Fonda, NY (member). *Awards, honors*: John Hay Whitney Fellow, 1968-1969; American Indian Graduate Scholarship Program Grant, School of Law, University of New Mexico, 1971. *Interests*: Teaches contemporary American Indian anthropology; American Indian education; applied anthropology; ethno-history, museology, Iroquois Indians. *Published works*: The Cornplanter Cemetary (Pennsylvania Archaeologist, 1965); Moving of the Fire: A Case of Iroquois Ritual Innovation (Iroquois Culture, History & Prehistory, 1967); Red Jacket (The World Book Encyclopedia, 1976); The Seneca People (Indian Tribal Series, Phoenix, 1976); The Directory of Indian Museums.

ABRAMSON, CATHY (Sault Ste. Marie Chippewa)
(tribal secretary; board chairperson)
Affiliation & Address: Treasurer, Sault Ste. Marie Tribe of Chippewa Indians, 423 Ashmun St., Sault Ste. Marie, MI 49783 (906) 322-3823, E-mail: cabramson@saulttribe.net. She served as Secretary to the Board of Directors for five terms. *Other professional posts*: Chairperson & Bemidji Area Representative (Michigan, Wisconsin & Minnesota), National Indian Health Board, Washington, DC. Cathy is actively involved with United Tribes of Michigan and the Midwest Alliance of Sovereign Tribes (MAST). She also serves on the Tribe's Traditional Living & Foods Program Planning Committee, Conservation Committee, and has served as an advisor for the Sault Ste. Marie Chippewa Tribal Youth Council.

ABRAMSON, GREGORY (Spokane)
(tribal chairperson)
Affiliation & Address: Spokane Indian Tribe, P.O. Box 100, Wellpinit, WA 99040 (509) 458-6500.

ACEBEDO, LEON (LEE) (Kumeyaay Diegueno)
(executive director)
Education: California Lutheran College; Kansas State University, BA (Psychology). *Affiliation & Address*: Executive Director, California Nations Indian Gaming Association, 2150 River Plaza Dr., Suite 120, Sacramento, CA 95833 (916) 448-8706. E-mail: lee@cniga.com. *Past professional posts*: Director of Behavioral & Mental Health Programs, 1989-92, Salt River Pima Maricopa Indian Community in Arizona; State of Arizona's Tribal Liaison for the

Dept. of Health, 1992-96; sales manager for a waste water consulting firm, 1996-99; tribal administrator, Rincon Band of Luiseno Indians, 1999-2001; In May 2002, Leon was selected to participate as part of a Master/Apprentice Team, along with a Jamul Tribal elder, by the Advocates for Indigenous California Language Survival; chairperson, Jamul Indian Village, Jamul, CA, 2003-2007. *Military service*: U.S. Army (six years, Vietnam Vet). *Awards, honors*: Leon was selected as a speaker at "Bridging the Health Care Network for HIV/AIDS," a major national healthcare forum in 1991; In May 2002, he was selected to participate as part of a Master/ Apprentice Team, along with a Jamul Tribal Elder, by the Advocates for Indigenous California Language Survival.

ACEVEDA, CASIMERO A. (Eskimo)
 (Alaskan village president)
Affiliation: Organized Village of Kake, P.O. Box 316, Kake, AK 99830 (907) 785-6471.

ACKLEY, ARLYN, JR. (Mole Lake Ojibwe)
 (tribal vice chairperson)
Affiliation & Address: Vice Chairperson, Sokaogon (Mole Lake) Band of Lake Superior Chippewa, 3051 Sand Lake Rd., Crandon, WI 54520 (715) 478-7500.

ACKLEY, WILLARD L. (Mole Lake Ojibwe)
 (tribal chief)
Affiliation: Chief, Sokaogon (Mole Lake) Band of Lake Superior Chippewa, 3051 Sand Lake Rd., Crandon, WI 54520 (715) 478-7500. Website: www. sokaogonchippewa.com.

ACUNA, BERNIE (Gabrielino/Tongva)
 (tribal chairperson)
Affiliation & Address: Chairperson, Gabrielino/Tongva San Gabriel Band of Mission Indians, 1999 Avenue of the Stars, Suite 1100, Los Angeles, CA 90067 (310) 428-5690 E-mail: bacuna1@gabrielinotribe.org

ADAIR, JOHN WILLIAM (Cherokee-Deer Clan) 1942-
 (company president)
Born June 6, 1942, Sequoyah County, Okla. *Education*: Bacone College, Muskogee, OK, AA, 1962; Northeastern State University, Tahlequah, OK, BA, 1964, MA, 1973. *Principal occupation*: Oil/gas exploration; real estate development. *Address*: 8309 S. 241st E. Ave., Broken Arrow, OK 74014 (918) 357-1745. jwacherokeegas@cox.net. *Affiliations*: President, OK Land Development Co., Inc., Broken Arrow, OK, 1975-1988; President, Adair Oil Co., Tulsa, OK, 1988-present. *Other professional posts*: Chairperson, Cherokee Nation Election Commission; trustee, Cherokee Nation Museum. *Military service*: Naval Air Reserve, active duty, 1964-71; Reserves, 1971- (Captain; Commanding Officer of Naval Reserves of Nuclear Aircraft Carrier USS Carl Vinson CVN-70; flew 225 combat missions in Vietnam-14 Air Medals, two Navy Commendation Medals with Combat V, Air Gallantry Cross, Vietnamese Air Gallantry Medal, Vietnam Service Medal with four Bronze Stars). *Interests*: "Descendant of prominent Cherokee family - father was Walthal Corrigan Adair, an original enrollee, grandfather was Oscar F. Adair, a Cherokee Veteran of the Civil War under Cherokee General Stand Watie. Cherokees were last to surrender in War. Oscar F. was later judge of Sequoyah District. Great grandson of Judge John Thompson Adair, the Chief Justice of the Supreme Court of the Cherokee Nation."

ADAIR, MARY (Cherokee) 1936-
 (artist)
Born July 2, 1936, Sequoyah County, Okla. *Education*: Bacone Indian Junior College, AA, 1955; Northeastern Oklahoma State University, BA, 1957; Tulsa University , BFA, 1967; Northeastern State University, Tahlequah, OK, MF, 1983. *Principal occupation*: Artist. *Address*: Rt. 2, Box 287, Sallisaw, OK 74955 (918) 775-5785. *Affiliations*: Murrow Indian Children's Home, Muskogee, OK (child care-residence care institution) (executive director, 1973-79); Cherokee Nation of Oklahoma, Tahlequah, OK (education & health positions, 1979-88); Cherokee Nation art and Native American crafts teacher, 1988-2001; artist (in paint and Native crafts), 2001-present. *Other professional posts*: Artist in residence, State Arts Council of Oklahoma, Oklahoma City. *Community activities*: Presbyterian Church; Community Council (board member); Indian Parent Committee; Soroptimist Club; American Baptist Indian Caucus; Oklahoma Association of Children's Institutions & Agencies (secretary-treasurer). *Memberships*: North American Indian Women's Association (past secretary); Daughters of the Earth (a group of eight Indian women artists who displayed their work together in gallery & museum shows); National Indian Education Assn (past secretary); Descendants of Nancy Ward Association (board member); Goingsnake Historical Assn; Trail of Tears Assn; Sequoyah County Historical Society (treasurer) Adair Reunion (treasurer); McCoy Cemetery Association (treasurer). *Awards, honors*: Painting and crafts awards and entries in the following shows: Philbrook Museum - Indian Annual Art Show; Five Tribes Museum - Annual Art Show; Cherokee National Museum Show; Bacone Indian Art Competition; American Indian Exposition

Competition; Red Cloud Indian Art Show; Heard Museum; Tsa-La-Gi Museum; Santa Fe Indian Market and others. *Interests*: "I have interest in contemporary American Indian affairs, history, education and art. (I) Have traveled to a number of traditional Indian communities and reservation areas for business and fellowship. I have spent the last 18 years serving the Cherokee Nation of Oklahoma in several areas of interest. A highlight was being able to attend the first joint meeting of the eastern and Oklahoma Cherokee councils, and two later meetings; genealogy, Native American crafts." *Published works*: Illustrations in "Women of Power" magazine, 1989; Selu: Seeking the Corn Mother's Wisdom, book by Marilou Awiakta (Fulcrum, 1993); illus. in Native American Gardening by M. Caduto & Joseph Bruchac.

ADAMS, ANDREW, III (Muscogee Creek)
 (attorney)
Education: University of Michigan, BA, 1996, MA, 1999; University of Wisconsin School of Law, JD, 2006. *Affiliation & Address*: Founding Partner, Hogen Adams PLLP, 1935 W. County Road B2, Suite 460, St. Paul, MN 55113 (651) 842-9100. E-mail: aadams@hogenadams.com. *Other professional posts*: Chief Justice for the Muscogee (Creek) Nation Supreme Court; board member, Minnesota American Indian Bar Association; treasurer, Federal Bar Association, Indian Law Section; board member, State Bar of Wisconsin Indian Law Section; Chair, Federal Bar Association. Andrew has regularly lectured on Indian-law issues at seminars and conferences nationally. Chief Justice of the Santee Sioux Nation of Nebraska Supreme Court. Andrew also serves on the Board of Directors for the Native American Community Development Institute and the Tiwahe Foundation. He regularly lectures on Indian-law issues at seminars & conferences across the country. *Past professional posts*: Staff Attorney (2010-13), The Jacobson Law Group, St. Paul, MN; Associate General Counsel & General Counsel for the St. Croix Chippewa Indians of Wisconsin. *Practice areas*: Federal Indian law, tribal constitutional law, tribal governance, gaming law, tax issues related to tribal governments & individual tribal members, employment law, treaty hunting, fishing & gathering law; and government relations.

ADAMS, ANNA MARIA (*Henu*) (Winnebago) 1961-
 (certified art teacher)
Born April 4, 1961, Washington, D.C. *Education*: Institute of American Indian Arts, AFA, 1981; Oklahoma State University, 1982-83; University of Oklahoma, BFA, 1984. *Principal occupation*: Certified art teacher. *Address*: 7629 Hunt Rd., Ponca City, OK 74604 (580) 765-5086. *Affiliations*: Art teacher, Ponc City High School; art club. *Other professional posts*: Owner, Adams & Adams Farms (Registered Paint Horses), Ponca City, OK, 1990-present; owner, Adams Studios, Ponca City, OK, 1986-present. *Community activities*: Standing Bear Education Committee, Standing Bear Park, Ponca City, OK, 1996-present; Pawnee Bill Wild West Show Actor, 1995-99; Parent Coalition, Title VII Program, Ponca City High School; Native American Powwows. *Membership*: Ponca City Art Association; Ponca City Art Center; Paint Horse Association; Oklahoma Arts Council Master/Apprentice Program. *Awards, honors*: Who's Who in American Junior Colleges; 1st Miss IAIA Powwow Princess; 1996 "Outstanding Patron" Hideaway Pizza Collage 2001-2004 - An Oklahoma Centennial Project. *Interests*: "I have displayed artwork in New York, Santa Fe, NM, and Oklahoma; training and breeding American Paint Horses; raising & breeding Manx cats; four wheelers ATV; boating & fishing. Work in Progress: Working on a book of "Ribbonwork & Ribbonwork Designs" of the Native Americans.

ADAMS, BERT (Tlingit-Haida)
 (Alaskan village president)
Affiliation: Native Village of Yakutat, P.O. Box 418, Yakutat, AK 99689 (907) 784-3932.

ADAMS, DONALD (Athapascan)
 (Alaskan village president)
Affiliation: Native Village of Tetlin, Box TTL, Tetlin, AK 99779 (907) 324-2130.

ADAMS, E. CHARLES 1947-
 (professor of archaeology; head of research)
Born November 27, 1947, Denver, Colo. *Education*: University of Colorado, BA, 1970, MA, 1973, PhD, 1975. *Affiliation & Address*: Professor of Archaeology & Head of Research, Arizona State Museum, University of Arizona, P.O. Box 210026, Tucson, AZ 85721 (520) 621-2093. E-mail: ecadams@email.arizona.edu (1985-present; director, Homolovi Research Program). *Military service*: Army National Guard, 1966-72 (Sergeant). *Community activities*: President, Arizona Archaeological Council, 1978-80. *Memberships*: Society for American Archaeology; American Anthro-pological Association; Arizona Archaeological Council; Arizona Archaeological & Historical Society. *Awards, honors*: Earl Morris Award (presented to the outstanding archaeology graduate student in the Department of Anthropology, University of Colorado, 1975). *Interests*: The prehistory & history of the Colorado Plateau with emphasis on the Pueblo Indians, especially the Hopi. "I have directed several research expeditions for the Museum of Northern Arizona, Flagstaff, and the

Arizona State Museum, Tucson, on the Plateau. "I direct an archaeological research project at the University of Arizona excavating 600-700 year-old pueblos that are ancestral to the Hopi Indians. I have worked with the Hopi Tribe over the years on these research projects & employ Hopi high school students." *Published works*: Walpi Archaeological Project: Synthesis & Interpretation (Museum of Northern Arizona, 1982); Homol'ovi II: The Archaeology of an Ancestral Hopi Village (U. of Arizona Press, 1991); The Origin & Development of the Pueblo Katsina Cult (U. of Arizona Press, 1991); with Vincent LaMotta, The Protohistoric Pueblo World: A.D. 1275 to 1600. (U. of Arizona Press, 2004);. New Perspectives on an Ancient Religion: Katsina Ritual and the Archaeological Record. In *Religion in the Prehispanic Southwest*, edited by Christine S. VanPool and Todd VanPool, pp. 53-66. (AltaMira Press., 2006); Hopi History Prior to 1600. In *The Oxford Handbook of the Archaeology of the American Southwest*, edited by Barbara J. Mills and Severin Fowles (Oxford University Press, 2014).

ADAMS, EDMUND S. (Pamunkey)
(tribal chief)
Affiliation: Upper Mattaponi Indian Tribe, P.O. Box 182, King William, VA 23086 (804) 769-0041.

ADAMS, EDWARD J. (Athapascan)
(former Alaskan village president)
Affiliation: Native Village of Nunam Iqua, P.O. Box 27, Sheldon's Point, AK 99666 (907) 498-4184.

ADAMS, GORDON (Lummi)
(tribal vice chairperson)
Affiliation: Lummi Nation, 2616 Kwina Rd., Bellingham, WA 98226 (360) 384-1489.

ADAMS, KENNETH (Upper Mattaponi)
(tribal chief)
Affiliation: Upper Mattaponi Tribe, P.O. Box 174, King William, VA 23086 (804) 898-3310.

ADAMS, MICHAEL (Powhatan Renape)
(tribal chairperson)
Affiliation: Powhatan Renape Nation, P.O. Box 225, Rancocas, NJ 08073 (609) 261-4747.

ADAMS, VIVIAN M. (Yakama, Puyallup, Suquamish, Quinault) 1943-
(tribal library administrator)
Born March 21, 1943, Toppenish, Wash. *Education*: Institute of American Indian Art, Santa Fe, NM, 1981. *Address & Affiliation*: Yakama Nation Library, P.O. Box 151, Toppenish, WA 98948 (509) 865-2800 ext. 4721. *Community activities*: Yakama Agency Employees Club (secretary-treasurer); IAIA Student Senate Representative; Yakama Women's Investor's Club. *Memberships*: Washington State Folklife Council; American Association of State & Local History; Toppenish Chamber of Commerce; Washington Museum Association; National Trust for Historic Preservation; Native American Task Force, Washington State Centennial; Washington State Native American Task Force, Native American Consortium. *Awards, honors*: Outstanding Artistic & Academic Achievement, 1980-81; Institute of American Indian Art President's Award; Who's Who Among Students, American Junior Colleges, 1981; Scholastic Achievement Award, Yakama Nation Education, 1982. *Interests*: "My main interest is two-dimensional art (sketching, pen and ink). I love to work with Indian artifacts--those items that are hand made of natural materials. Plus, it is a joy to design ways to display these items that teach a lesson in an aesthetic manner. It is important to present our cultural history & traditions from our (Native American) point of view to promote a better understanding by other cultures--and to learn from them. Oral history and elders input into telling our ways is extremely important to accomplishing those goals of the museum. Therefore, museology is my second interest, my financial base to a sporadic art career! But being a curator allows me the time to work with objects of art-- my main love. My third interest is pursuing conservation techniques: recognizing and maintaining basket weaving, textile weaving, restoration techniques, time allowing I hope to accomplish conservator's training."

ADAMS DONEY, MEL L. (Gros Ventre, Assiniboine)
(former tribal vice president)
Affiliation: Fort Belknap Community Council, Rt. 1, Box 66, Harlem, MT 59526 (406) 353-2205.

ADAMS, HENRY LYLE (HANK) (Assiniboine Sioux) 1943-
(rights activist)
Born on the Fort Peck Indian Reservation in Montana on May 16, 1943. *Affiliation & Address*: Leader (1968-present), Survival of American Indian Associations, 7803-A Samurai Dr., SE, Olympia, WA 98503 (360) 459-2679.. Hank has been trying to better the lives of Native Americans for most of his adult life. In 1964, he helped organize the march on Olympia in Washington

State protesting the State''s attack on Indian fishing rights. While he was in college, he spent much of his time on the Quinault Reservation helping to fix a suicide problem they had there. He became Special Projects Director of the National Indian Youth Council, a radical Native American institution at the time. He took the role of leader of the Survival of American Indians Association in 1968. He fought against state fishing regulations on the Nisqually River in Washington State. Negotiated a settlement between AIM occupation of Bureau of Indian Affairs offices in Washington in 1972 Adams created a Twenty Point Proposal which the Nixon Administration considered in exchange for the evacuation of the offices. It ultimately led to Native American rights to interpret treaties, and abolish laws which threatened Indian sovereignty & life. At the Wounded Knee incident, he was the intermediary between the head of the Lakota Occupation and the U.S. Government. He produced a documentary film entitled "As Lng As the River Runs" between 1968 and 1970.

ADAMS-BLACKEYE, KATHY (Shoshone)
(tribal council member)
Affiliation & Address: Former Vice Chairperson, Duckwater Shoshone Tribe, P.O. Box 140068, Duckwater, NV 89314 (775) 863-0227. *Past tribal post*: Vice Chairperson.

ADAMSON, REBECCA L. (Eastern Cherokee) 1949-
(association founder/president; economist)
Education: Southern New Hampshire University, MS (Economic Development). *Affiliation & Address*: Founder & President (1997-present), First Peoples Worldwide, 857 Leland Rd., Fredericksburg, VA 22405 (540) 899-6545. Rebecca has worked directly with grassroots tribal communities, and nationally as an advocate of local tribal issues, since 1970. She has worked to establish a new field of culturally appropriate, values-driven development to establish the first reservation-based microenterprise loan fund in the U.S., the first tribal investment model, a national movement for reservation land reform, and legislation that established new standards of accountability regarding federal trust responsibility for Native Americans. *Past professional post*: Founder & president, First Nations Development Institute, Fredericksburg, VA, 1980-97. *Community activities*: Board member - The Bay & Paul Foundations, the Calvert Social Investment Fund, & the Calvert Group Governance Committee; co-chairs the Calvert Social Investment Fund Audit Committee; columnist, Indian Country Today, Canastota, NY. *Awards, honors*: 2004 Schwab Outstanding Social Entrepreneur and a Doctor in Humane Letters degree from Dartmouth College; honored in the National Women's History Project; chosen as one of America's most influential women as part of the PBS program MAKERS: Women Who Make America. Makers will premiere in early 2013. *Published work*: Co-authored, "The Color of Wealth," 2006.

ADDISON, ANTHONY (Arapahoe)
(former tribal chairperson)
Affiliation: Arapahoe Tribe, P.O. Box 396, Fort Washakie, WY 82514 (307) 332-6120.

ADKINS, A. LEONARD (Chickahominy)
(tribal chief)
Affiliation: Chickahominy Indian Tribe, RFD 1, Box 299, Providence Forge, VA 23140 (804) 829-2186.

ADKINS, PRESTON
(dance troops coordinator)
Affiliation: Native American Dance Troops, Chickahominy Red Men Dancers, P.O. Box 473, Providence Forge, VA 23140 (804) 829-2152.

AGLI, ANDREA (Aleut)
(shareholder administrator)
Affiliation: Bristol Bay Native Corporation, 800 Cordova St., Suite 200, Anchorage, AK 99501 (907) 278-3602. E-mail: andria@bbnc.net . *Membership*: Americans for Indian Opportunity.

AGNASSAGA, GEORGE (Eskimo)
(AK village council president)
Affiliation: Wainwright Traditional Council, P.O. Box 184, Wainwright, AK 99782 (907) 763-2726.

AGNUS, SIMON (Umkumiut)
(AK village council president)
Affiliation: Umkumiut Village Council, General Delivery, Nightmute, AK 99690 (907) 647-6213.

AGOYO, HERMAN (Pueblo)
(former pueblo governor)
Affiliation: Pueblo of San Juan, P.O. Box 1099, San Juan Pueblo, NM 87566 (505) 852-4400; *Past professional post*: Chairperson, All Indian Pueblo Council, Albuquerque, NM.

AGOYO, PAMELA (Dine')
(director of American Indian student services)
Affiliation & Address: Director & Special Assistant to the President for American Indian Affairs; University of New Mexico, 1119 Mesa Vista Hall MSC06 3800, 1-University of New Mexico, Albuquerque, NM 87131 (505) 277-6343 E-mail: pagoyo@unm.edu

AGOYO, TAILINH (Narragansett/Blackfeet)
(public relations, marketing, programming)
Education: Dartmouth College, BA (Anthropology/Native American Studies). *Affiliation & Address*: Director of Public Relations, Marketing & Programming (2010-present), Southwestern Association for Indian Arts, P.O. Box 969, Santa Fe, NM 87504 (505) 983-5220. E-mail: tailinh@swaia.org. She is the daughter of renowned artist Tchin and led his marketing efforts & assisted at national art shows throughout his career. In 2007, she moved to New mexico and started her own social media marketing web and grahic design business.

AGTUCA, JACQUELINE (Eastern Cherokee)
(director of public policy)
Education: J.D. *Affiliation & Address*: Public Policy Director, Clan Star, Inc., P.O. Box 1630, Cherokee, NC 28719 (828) 497-5507. *Other professional post*: Founding member, National Congress of American Indians Task Force on Violence Against Native Women; Policy Advisor for the Task Force & editor of its *Restoration of Safety & Sovereignty Magazine*, 2003-present. *Past professional posts*: Staff attorney, Legal Assistance Foundation of Chicago, 1984-88; director, San Francisco District Attorney's Office of Family Violence Project, 1988-90; director, Criminal Justice Advocacy Unit for the Family Violence Prevention Fund, 1990-95; in 1995, Jacqueline helped to open the newly created Violence Against Women Office of the USDOJ, 1995; Deputy Director, and then Acting Director of the USDOJ Office of Tribal Justice, 1999-2001; appointed Chief of Staff, National Indian Gaming Commission, 2001-2007; from 2008-2010, she served as a member of the USDOJ National Baseline Study Federal Advisory Committee; In November of 2010, Jacqueline attended on behalf of the NCAI Task Force the UN Periodic Review of the U.S.

AGUCHAK, FRANK (Eskimo)
(Alaskan village president)
Affiliation: Native Village of Scammon Bay Traditional Council, P.O. Box 110, Scammon Bay, AK 99662 (907) 558-5425.

AGUILAR, GABE (Mescalero Apache)
(tribal vice president)
Affiliation & Address: Vice President (2015-present), Mescalero Apache Tribal Council, P.O. Box 227, Mescalero, NM 88340 (505) 671-4494.

AGUILAR, MICHELLE PENOZIEQUAH (Pueblo)
(executive director)
Affiliation: Governor's Office of Indian Affairs, 1515 S. Cherry St., Box 40909, Olympia, WA 98504 (206) 753-2411.

AGUILAR, PAULITA (Pueblo)
(associate professor of Libraries & Learning Sciences)
Affiliation & Address: Associate Professor, Indigenous Nations Library Program, College of Libraries & Learning Sciences, University Libraries, MSC05 3020, 1 University of New meico, Albuquerque, NM 87131. *Awards, honors*: Library Leadership Award, New Mexico Library Associationm Oct. 23, 2014. She is an advocate for library services to students of color, and serves as a mentor to library graduate students. *Past professional post*: President, American Indian Library Association (2015-16).

AGUILAR, TEMET (Pauma Band Luiseno)
(tribal chairperson)
Affiliation & Address: Chairperson, Pauma Band of Luiseno Mission Indian, 110 Reservation Rd., P.O. Box 369, Pauma Valley, CA 92061.

AGUILAR, TERRY (San Ildefonso Tewa)
(former Pueblo governor)
Affiliation & Address: San Ildefonso Pueblo Council, Rt. 5 Box 315-A, Santa Fe, NM 87501 (505) 455-2273.

AGUINO, MARCELINO (Pueblo-Ohkay Owingeh)
(Pueblo governor)
Affiliation & Address: Governor, Ohkay Owingeh (San Juan Pueblo), P.O. Box 1099, San Juan Pueblo, NM 87566 (505) 852-4400.

AHGOOK, TIMOTHY (Eskimo)
(Alaskan village president)
Affiliation: President, Village of Anaktuvuk Pass, P.O. Box 21065, Anaktuvuk Pass, AK 99721 (907) 661-2575.

AHHAITTY, PERRI (Iowa)
(tribal vice chairperson)
Affiliation: Iowa Tribe of Oklahoma, Rt. 1 Box 721, Perkins, OK 74059 (405) 547-2402. E-mail: pahhaitty@iowanation.org.

AHKINGA, ORVILLE (Eskimo)
(former Alaskan village president)
Affiliation: Native Village of Diomede (aka Inalik), P.O. Box 7099, Diomede, AK 99762 (907) 686-3021.

AHTONE, DEBORAH (Kiowa) 1947-
(editor)
Born July 2, 1947, Carnegie, Okla. *Education*: Bacone College, AAm 1967; Rocky Mountain College, BA, 1970; University of Oklahoma, Graduate School, 1970-71. *Address*: P.O. Box 397, Mountain View, OK 73062 (405) 347-2875. *Affiliations*: Editor, Kiowa Indian News, Carnegie, OK, 1982-; editor/owner, Feather Review News, Mountain View, OK, 1989-. *Other professional posts*: Official photographer for Kiowa Tribe; member, Kiowa Tribal Museum Commission; Instructor, traditional techniques, Institute of American Indian Art (one year); instructor, Indian studies, Dawson College, Glendive, MT (two years). *Community activities*: Volunteer to Kiowa Tribal Museum & Kiowa Senior Citizen Center; photographer for 1992 Sovereignty Symposium, Oklahoma City. *Memberships*: Southern Plains Museum Assn (chairperson, 1990; treasurer, 1992); Native American Journalists Assn; Southwestern Assn on Indian Affairs; National Congress of American Indians. *Awards, honors*: First Place, Scottsdale Indian Art Show-Mixed Media; Promising New Artist, Rose State College, 1978. *Interests*: Photography; "Interest in Indian affairs - led to appointment as editor of Kiowa News, which led to the establishment of statewide newspaper, "The Feather Review." Business trips for Dawson College led to contacts with other tribes and tribal leaders throughout the U.S. These contacts have remained crucial in networking the "Feather Review" with news from the tribes. Tribal leaders bestowed nickname "Scoop" to me because I am always out searching for news and in attendance of inter-tribal meetings both in Okla. and other states."

AHTONE, TRISTAN (Kiowa)
(journalist, reporter)
Education: Institute of American Indian Arts, BA (Creative Writing), 2006; Columbia School of Journalism, MA (Journalism), 2008. *Affiliation & Address*: Poverty & Public Health Reporter, KUNM-FM Radio, 1 University of New Mexico, Albuquerque, NM 87131 (505) 277-4806. E-mail: tristanahtone@kunm.org. *Other professional post*: Board Treasurer, Native American Journalists Assn, Norman, OK. Since 2008, Tristan has specialized in covering Native American, environmental & healthcare issues, and has worked with the Newshour with Jim Lehrer, National Native News, Frontline, Indian Country Today, Sirius Satellite Radio, NPR and the Fronteras Desk.

AIKMAN, SUSANNE (Eastern Cherokee)
(publisher; radio & TV producer)
Address: Owner, Morning Flower Press and Path of the Sun Images, P.O. Box 11443, Denver, CO 80211 (303) 477-8442. E-mail: producer@alterNative Voices.orgAffiliation: Producer, "alter•Native Voices" - weekly Native radio program aired on KUVO-FM 89.3 in Denver & syndicated on American Indian Radio on Satellite Network (Website: www.airos.org).

AINSLEY, KATHY (Seneca) 1952-
(librarian)
Born January 21, 1952, Youngstown, Ohio. *Education*: BFA, MLS. Principal occupation: Librarian. *Address*: 17536 Afton Ave., Lake Milton, OH 44429 (330) 633-4345. E-mail: rememberearth@yahoo.com. *Memberships*: American Indian Library Association; Wordcraft Circle of Native Writers & Storytellers.

AITKEN, GARY, JR. (Kootenai)
(tribal chairperson)
Affiliation & Address: Chairperson, Kootenai Tribe of Idaho, P.O. Box 1269, Bonners Ferry, ID 83805 (208) 267-3519.

AITKEN, LARRY P. (Ojibwe)
(college president)
Affiliation: Leech Lake Tribal College, 6530 U.S. Hwy. 2 NW, Cass Lake, MN 56633 (218) 335-4220.

AITKEN, ROBERT (Ojibwe)
(tribal executive director)
Affiliation: Leech Lake Band of Ojibwe, 115 Sixth St., NW, Suite E, Cass Lake, MN 56633 (218) 335-8200.

AKELKOK, SR., LUKI (Eskimo)
(Alaskan village president)
Affiliation: Ekwok Village, P.O. Box 70, Ekwok, AK 99580 (907) 464-3336. E-mail: ekwokvill@aol.com.

AKERS, BAMBI (Eskimo)
(AK village president)
Affiliation: Native Village of Chuloonawick, P.O. Box 245, Chuloonawick, AK 99581 (907) 949-1345.

AKERS, DONNA L. (Oklahoma Choctaw)
(associate professor of history & ethnic studies)
Education: University of California, Riverside, PhD, 1997. *Affiliation & Address*: Professor, Native American History & Culture, Institute for Ethnic Studies, Native American Studies (2005-present), University of Nebraska, Lincoln, 642 Oldfather Hall, Lincoln, NE 68588 (402) 617-6378; office: (402) 472-2414. E-mail: dakers2@unl.edu. *Past professional posts*: Director of Native American Studies Program, California State University, Northridge, CA; assistant professor of history, Purdue University; marketing executive (15 years). *Research Interests*: American Indian studies, Indigenous women, global Indigenous peoples, Native peoples of North America, human trafficking, race, gender, ethnicity, and decolonization studies. *Published works*: Living In the Land of Death: The Choctaw People, 1830-1860 (Michigan State University Press, 2004); Culture & Customs of the Choctaw Indians (Greenwood Publishing, 2010); Grandma Was an Indian Princess (University of Nebraska Press, 2012); articles, book chapters & book reviews..

AKOOTCHOOK, ISAAC K. (Eskimo)
(Alaskan village president)
Affiliation: Kaktovik Village, P.O. Box 130, Kaktovik, AK 99747 (907) 640-2042.

ALBANY, JAMES (Lenni Lenape)
(historical society president)
Address & Affiliation: President, Lenni Lenape Historical Society & Museum, 2825 Fish Hatchery Rd., Allentown, PA 18103 (610) 797-2121. E-mail: lenape@lenape.org.

ALBERS, PATRICIA
(professor of anthropology & American Indian Studies)
Education: University of Wisconsin, BA, MA, PhD (Anthropology). *Address & Affiliation*: American Indian Studies Dept. (Dept. Chair), University of Minnesota, Twin Cities Campus, College of Liberal Arts, 72 Pleasant St. SE, 214 Scott Hall, Minneapolis, MN 55455 (612) 625-8050. E-mail: alber033@umn.edu. *Interests*: American Indian history; Native American culture; Native American tribes & nations; Anthropology, Gender, Ethnicity & Intertribal relations; Ethnohistory. *Published work*: "Home of the Bison: An Ethnographic Study of Cultural Affiliations to Wind Cave National Park," an ethno-historical Studies for the National Park Service, 2006.

ALBERT, ANGELIQUE (Confederated Salish & Kootenai)
(executive director of Indian center)
Education: Salish & Kootenai College, BA (Human Services); Gonzaga University, MBA (Entrepreneurship). *Affiliation & Address*: Executive Director, American Indian Graduate Center, 3701 San Mateo Blvd. NE, Albuquerque, NM 87110 (505) 881-4584 Fax 884-0427; E-mail: angelique@aigcs.org. *Past professional post*: Associate Director, American Indian Business Leaders (AIBL), Missoula, MT.

ALBERT, ROBERT STEPHEN (*Sakhomenewa*) (Hopi) 1964-
(artist)
Born March 27, 1964, Ganado, Ariz. *Education*: Institute of American Indian Arts, AFA, 1986; National Indian Center, Phoenix, Commercial Arts Degree, 1990. Resides in Tucson, AZ (602) 770-1921. *Art*: Kachina doll carver (12 years) and watercolor painter. Gallery and Indian Market Shows include: Heard Museum, Mesa Southwest Museum, Museum of North Arizona, Tohono Chul Park, Gallup Ceremonial. *Awards, honors*: "Artist of the Year Award" from Council for Tribal Employment Rights, 1988, for original Acrylic on Canvas painting; Best of Show, categories - Kachina Doll, watercolor painting, et al.

ALBIETZ, JUDITH KAMMINS
(attorney)
Education: University of Michigan, MPA; University of the Pacific, McGeorge School of Law, JD. *Address & Affiliation*: President, Albietz Law Corporation, 2001 N St., Suite 100, Sacramento, CA 95814 (916) 442-4241. *Other professional posts*: Co-chair of the Natural Resources Subsection of the Real Property Section, California State Bar, 1994-96' co-chair, State Bar of California Sacramento Real Property Roundtable, 1996-97. Ms. Albietz has been involved for over 25 years with environmental, Federal and State public agency law, and real property matters in the private law firm setting and the public sector. Her experience with the Federal government includes environmental, Indian law, and land & energy-related experience. She was Chief of the Division of Conveyances to Alaskan Natives for the Bureau of Land Management ("BLM") in Alaska. *Awards, honors*: Received the "Arthur S. Flemming Award (one of the highest honors in the Federal civil service) for her work on behalf of Alaskan Natives in conveying over 22 million acres of land.

ALBRO, JANICE (Sisseton-Wahpeton Dakota)
(artist, shop owner)
Born at Claremore, OK Indian Hospital. *Affiliation*: Artist/Owner, Visions of Eyahotanka, RR 3 Box 7820, Bartlesville, OK 74003 (918) 336-4110. E-mail: janicealbro@netzero.net. Her paintings & sculptures are in many private collections & museums. Janice has traveled to many states throughout the country dancing in Jingle Dress competition and has been honored to serve as head Lady Dancer at numerous powwows.

ALCHESAY-NACHU, CARLA (Navajo)
(director-Indian hospital)
Affiliation: Director, Whiteriver Indian Hospital, P.O. Box 860, Whiteriver, AZ 85941 (602) 338-4911.

ALEK, VIRGINIA (Eskimo)
(Alaskan village president)
Affiliation: President, Chignik Lake Village, P.O. Box 33, Chignik Lake, AK 99548 (907) 845-2212.

ALEGRIA, REBECCA (Menominee)
(tribal researcher)
Affiliation & Address: Menominee Tribal Researcher, Menominee Indian tribe, P.O. Box 910, Keshena, WI 54135 (715) 799-5258. E-mail: black3@frontiernet.net. *Membership*: Americans for Indian Opportunity. *Interest*: Historical preservation, research.

ALEJANDRE, ANDREW (Paskenta Nomlaki)
(tribal chairperson)
Affiliation & Address: Chairperson (2016-present), Paskenta Band of Nomlaki Indians, 2625 Everett Freeman Way, P.O. Box 709, Corning, CA 96021 (530) 528-3538; E-mail: alejandre@paskenta.org

ALEXANDER-JUAREZ, CARLA M. (*Wandering Spirit Woman*)
(Ramapough Lenape) 1962-
(director of Indian education)
Born November 3, 1962, Bourne, Mass. *Education*: BS in Criminal Justice. *Principal occupation*: Director of Indian education. *Address*: 266 Sloatsburg Rd., Ringwood, NJ 07456 (973) 962-7029. *Affiliation*: Director of Indian Education, Ringwood Borough Schools, Ringwood, NJ. *Community activities*: Tribal member; Sunday school teacher for Brook Presbyterian Church; choir member; Hillburn Homework Club director. *Associations*: American Indian Community House (New York, NY); Association on American Indian Affairs.

ALEXANDER, KAREN WILKINS (Miami) 1954-
(library director)
Born March 21, 1954, Ardmore, Okla. *Education*: University of Science & Arts of Oklahoma (Chickasha), BA 1975; MA in Library & Information Studies, University of Oklahoma, Norman, 1997. *Affiliation & Address*: Library Director (1989-present), Miami Tribe of Oklahoma, P.O. Box 1326, 202 S. Eight Tribes Trail, Miami, OK 74355 (918) 542-4505; E-mail: kalexander@myaemia.org.

ALEXANDER, MERLE C. (Tsimshian, Kitasoo Xai'xais First Nation-
aka Klemtu)
(attorney-Indigenous Resource Lawyer)
Education: University of Victoria, LLB & BA (Law & Political Science), 1999; University of Toronto, LLB, Law – Dean's Transfer, 1999. *Affiliation & Address*: Indigenous Resource Lawyer, Partner, Leader of Indigenous Law Group, Gowling WLG Canada LLP, 550 Burrard St., Suite 2300, Bentall 5, Vancouver, BC V6C 2B5 Can (604) 891-2271. E-mail: merle.alexander@gowlingwlg.com. *Practice Area*: Indigenous People's title & rights, their economic development participation & environmental sustainable management within their Territories. He advises on negotiations & implementation of impact-benefit agreements, resource revenue-sharing arrangements & a variety of interim agreements. Merle commodifies Indigenous economic rights by structuring business ventures, limited partnerships limited liability partnerships & corporations. He also has significant experience negotiating government-to-government agreements, including strategic engagement, interim treaty, forestry consultation, mining revenue-sharing & other reconciliation agreements, representing clients in British Columbia, Yukon, & Newfoundland & Labrador. A professional and personal interest of Merle's is the protection of Indigenous intellectual property rights, particularly traditional knowledge. He has negotiated treaty chapters on cultural heritage resources, drafted traditional knowledge protocols & represented national Indigenous organizations in various international forums. Consequently, Merle is knowledgeable on protective mechanisms of Indigenous knowledge both domestically & internationally. *Past professional posts*: Co-chair Aboriginal Practice Group, Boughton Law Corp., 2003-10; partwner & Co-Leader of Aboriginal Group, Norton Rose Fulbright, 2010-13; director & VP of Legal Affairs, Nacho Nyak Dun Development Corporation, 2010-12; Industry Council for Aboriginal Business, director; Vancouver Native Housing Society, director & treasurer;

West Coast Environmental Law, director; Vancouver Aboriginal Child & Family Services, president & director. *Community service*: Langara College, Academic Program Review Self Study Committee, Department of Aboriginal Studies; St'at'imc Eco Resources Ltd., Director; Vancouver Native Community Health Foundation, Director & President; Eagle Eye Ventures Ltd., Director, Aboriginal Equity & Joint Venture Entity; Coast Opportunity Fund,

ALEXANDER, PAUL
(attorney)
Education: Georgetown University Law Center, JD, 1967, LLM, 1970. *Address & Affiliation*: Alexander, Berkey, Williams & Weathers, LLP, 2000 Center St., Suite 308, Berkeley, CA 94704 (510) 548-7070. Website: www.abwwlaw.com. E-mail: palexander@abwwlaw.com. *Areas of Practice*: Indian Gaming, Finance, Economic Development, Taxation, Jurisdiction, Self-Governance, Indian Health Care. *Past professional posts*: U.S. Commission on Civil Rights, 1972-75, directed several hearings in Arizona & New Mexico and supervised the resulting report of the Commission in 1973 "Southwest Indian Report." He also produced the 1975 report entitled, "The Navajo Nation: An American Colony"; In 1975, he joined the Congressional American Indian Policy Review as Special Counsel to the Jurisdiction Task Force. With others, he wrote the Jurisdiction Task Force Report and the Special Report on the Alaskan Native Claims Settlement Act; he was instrumental in developing the American Indian Child Welfare Act; in 1977 he once again joined the Commission and help develop & produce the Commission's classic works on Indian Affairs. In 1981 & 1982 he served as the General Counsel of the Commission; In 1983-85, he was staff director of the Senate Select Committee on Indian Affairs. He has played a significant role in development & progress of the Indian Gaming Regulatory Act (IGRA), the Tribal Self-Governance Demonstration Project and the Self-Governance portion of the Indian Self-Determination Act Amendments of 1995, the Indian Forestry Resource Act, and the model Self-Governance compact & funding agreement. He was one of the senior tribal attorneys for the development of Self-Governance regulations for the Dept. of the Interior. Recently, he was involved in the drafting & passage of the permanent Self-Governance legislation for the Indian Health programs. His work has involved assistance to tribes in all aspects of their internal organizational development and in their legislative needs.

ALEXIA, TONY (Athapascan)
(Alaskan village chief)
Affiliation: Nikolai Village, P.O. Box 9105, Nikolai, AK 99691 (907) 293-2311.

ALEXIE, ANDREW (Athapascan)
(school chairperson)
Affiliation: Tuluksak IRA Contract School, Tuluksak, AK 99679 (907) 695-6212.

ALEXIE, JOSEPH (Athapascan))
(Alaskan community president)
Affiliation: Tuluksak Native Community, P.O. Box 95, Tuluksak, AK 99679 (907) 695-6420.

ALEXIE, OSCAR (Athapascan)
(professor of Yup'ik language)
Affiliation & Address: Assistant Professor of Yup'ik Language, University of Alaska, Kuskokwim Campus, 201 Akiak Dr., Bethel, AK 99559 (907) 543-4580. E-mail: lfofa@uaf.edu. *Other professional post*: Teaches Yup'ik language, Alaska Native Language Center, Fairbanks, AK.

ALEXIE, SOPHIE (Athapascan)
(instructor of Yup'ik language)
Affiliation & Address: Instructor of Yup'ik Language, University of Alaska, Kuskokkwim Campus, 201 Akiak Dr., Bethel, AK 99559 (907) 543-4580. E-mail: lfsaa@uaf.edu. *Other professional post*: Teaches Yup'ik language, Alaska Native Language Center, Fairbanks, AK.

ALEXIE, SHERMAN J., JR. (Spokane/Coeur d'Alene) 1966-
(writer, poet)
Born October, 1966, Spokane Indian Reservation in Wellpinit, Wash. *Education*: Washington State University, BA (American Studies) 1990. *Address*: Falls Apart Productions, PMB 2294, 10002 Aurora Ave. North #36, Seattle, WA 98133. E-Mail: info@fallsapart.com. Website: www.fallsapart.com. *Published works*: Poetry - The Business of Fancydancing, 1991; I Would Steal Horses, 1993; Old Shirts & New Skins, 1993; First Indian on the Moon, 1993; Seven Mourning Songs for the Cedar Flute I Have Yet to Learn to Play, 1993; Water Flowing Home, 1996; The Summer of Black Widows, 1996; The Man Who Loves Salmon, 1998; One Stick Song, 2000; Dangerous Astronomy, 2005; Face, 2009. Poetry published by Hanging Loose Press, 231 Wyckoff St., Brooklyn, NY 11217 Website: www.hangingloosepress.com. Books - The Lone Ranger & Tonto Fistfight in Heaven (Grove/Atlantic, 1993, 2005); Reservation Blues (Atlantic Monthly Press, 1995; paperback, Warner Books, 1996); The Toughest Indian in the World (stories, 2000); The Little Indians (stories, 2003); Dangerous Astronomy, a poetry chapbook; Anthologies, 1994-99, 2000-

present; The Absolutely True Diary of a Part-Time Indian, a novel, 2008; numerous essays & articles. *Music*: Readings and stand-up performances with musician Jim Boyd, collaborated to record album, "Reservation Blues," 1995. *Film credits*: Wrote screenplay, "Smoke Signals," 1998; wrote screenplay & directed, "The Business of Fancydancing" (independently released in 2002; Wellspring, 2003); wrote screenplay, "49?" (produced independently in 2003). *Awards, honors*: Washington State Arts Commission Poetry Fellowship, 1991; National Endowment for the Arts Poetry Fellowship, 1992; PEN/Hemingway Award for Best First Book of Fiction, 1993, for The Lone Ranger & Tonto Fistfight in Heaven; Lila Wallace-Reader's Digest Writers' Award, 1993; was a member of the 2000 & 2001 independent Spirit Awards Nominating Committees and has served as a creative adviser to the Sundance Institute Writers Fellowship Program & the independent Feature Films West Screenwriters Lab; Alexie received the Washington State University's Regents Distinguished Alumnus Award in Oct. 2003; among others.

ALEXIE, WASSILY B. (Iqurmiut-Eskimo)
(Alaskan tribal president)
Affiliation: Iqurmiut Tribe, P.O. Box 09, Russian Mission, AK 99657 (907) 584-5511.

ALFRED, GERALD TAIAIAKE (Bear Clan Mohawk) 1964-
(professor of Indigenous Governance)
Born in Montreal, Quebec, Canada in 1964 and was raised in the Kahnawake Mohawk Territory. He now lives on Snake Mountain in Wsanec Nation Territory on the Saanich Peninsula. *Education*: Concordia University, BA; Cornell University, MA & PhD (Political Science). *Affiliation & Address*: Professor (1994-present) & Director, Indigenous Governance Program, Faculty of Human & Social Development, University of Victoria, 3800 Finnerty Rd., HSD Bldg., Rm. A260, Victoria, BC V8W 2Y2 (250) 721-6438. *Other professional posts*: Advisor to many First Nation governments & organizations. *Current Research*: Studying the effects of environmental contamination on Indigenous cultural practices, with a special focus on the Mohawk community of Akwesasne. *Awards, honors*: Canada Research Chair; National Aboriginal Achievement Award in the field of education; Native American Journalists Association award for best column writing. *Miltary service*: U.S. Marine Corps. *Published works*: Hearing the Voices of Our Ancestors (Oxford University Press, 1995); Peace, Power, Righteousness (Oxford University Press, 1999, 2009); Wasase (Broadview Press, 2005); Numerous scholarly articles, essays in newspapers, magazines & journals; stories; book-length research reports for First Nations & government clients.

ALLAN, CHIEF JAMES (Coeur D'Alene) 1972-
(tribal chairperson)
Born in Spokane, Wash. *Education*: Eastern Washington University, BA (Political Science), 1996. *Address & Affiliation*: Chairperson (2005-present), Coeur D'Alene Tribe, 850 A St., P.O. Box 408, Plummer, ID 83851 (208) 686-5803. *Past Affiliations*: Legislative Associate, National Congress of American Indians, Washington, DC, 2000-2001; Coeur D'Alene Tribe (Administrative Director, 2001-03, Vice Chairperson, 2003-05).

ALLAN, GABRIELLE (Dine'/Turtle Mountain Chippewa)
(Indian program coordinator)
Affiliation & Address: Program Coordinator, Native American Center, Fort Lewis College, 1000 Rim Dr., Durango, CO 81301 (970) 247-7225; E-mail: gallan@fortlewis.edu

ALLARD, JEANINE (Flathead-Confederated Salish & Kootenai)
(museum director)
Affiliation & Address: Flathead Indian Museum, Flathead Indian Reservation, 1 Museum Lane, St. Ignatius, MT 59865 (406) 745-2951.

ALLARD, L. DOUG (*Anteh*) (Flathead-Confederated Salish & Kootenai) 1931-
(Indian trader & auctioneer)
Born August 30, 1931, St. Ignatius, Mont. *Education*: Montana State University, BA, 1956. *Principal occupation*: American Indian art dealer. *Address*: P.O. Box 460, St. Ignatius, MT 59865 (406) 745-2951. *Affiliations*: Founder, owner & curator, Flathead Indian Museum & Doug Allard Trading Post, St. Ignatius, MT (24 years). *Other professional post*: Owner, Allard Indian Auctions (30 years). *Military service*: U.S. Marine Corps, 1950-53 (Korean War Ribbon, U.N. Medal, two Battle Stars, Good Conduct Medal). *Community activities*: Chairman, Flathead Reservation Powwow Committee; chairman, Flathead Constitution Convention Committee; former tribal secretary, Confederated Salish & Kootenai Tribes. *Memberships*: National Association of Appraisers; Indian Arts & Crafts Assn (charter member, board of directors); V.F.W.; American Legion; National Auctioneers Assn; Salish-Kootenai College Foundation (chairperson). *Interests*: Tribal culture; avid collector of Indian artifacts; consultant to many museums & Indian groups. Nationally known appraiser & auctioneer of American Indian material. *Biographical source*: Who's Who in the West. *Published works*: Numerous articles.

ALLEN, BEULAH (Navajo)
(medical director)
Education: BA (Anthropology); MD. *Affiliation & Address*: Medical Director, Tsaile Indian Health Center, P.O. Box 467, Tsaile, AZ 86556 (928) 724-3600. Other professional post: Vice Chairperson, National Indian Youth Leadership project, Albuquerque, NM. *Interests*: Dr. Allen has worked with the Indian Health Service for more than 22 years. She is interested in traditional healing, ranching, hunting, conservation & reading.,

ALLEN, CHADWICK (Chickasaw)
(professor of English, Associate Dean, Div. of Arts & Humanities)
Education: Harvard University, BA, 1987; Washington University, St. Louis, MFA, 1990; University of Arizona, PhD (Comparative Cultural & Literary Studies), 1997. *Affiliation & Address*: Professor of English; Associate Dean, Division of Arts & Humanities; Director of Dversity & Identity Studies Collective (DISCO); Professor & Coordnator of American Indian Studies, Dept. of English, 1164 W. 17th Ave., 114 University Hall, The Ohio State University, Columbus, OH 43210 (614) 247-7988. E-mail: allen.559@osu.edu. *Research & Teaching Interests*: Global Indigenous literary studies, American Indian & New Zealand & Maori literatures & cultures. *Other professional post*: Editor, for the journal SAIL: Studies in American Indian Literatures (2011-present). His areas of research & teaching interest are in global Indigenous literary studies; American Indian and New Zealand Maori literatures and cultures; literatures of Oceania; postcolonial literatures & theory; & frontier studies & the popular western. He has published articles on the World Council of Indigenous Peoples, on postcolonial theory and the discourse of treaties, on the trope "blood memory," on the construction of contemporary indigeneity, on Indigenous aesthetics, & on western series, *The Lone Ranger*. Awards, honors: Awarded Fulbright Fellowships to Aotearoa as a graduate student and as a senior scholar, he participated in a Lannan Summer Institute in American Indian Studies at the Newberry Library in Chicago, and he participated in an NEH Summer Institute on Indigenous cultures in the Pacific at the University of Hawai'i. *Membership*: Native American & Indigenous Studies Association (president, 2013-14). *Published works*: Blood Narrative: Indigenous Identity in American Indian & Maori Literary & Activist Texts (Duke U. Press, 2002); Trans-Indigenous: Methodologies for Global Native Literary Studies (U. of Minnesota Press, 2012); co-editor, with Alice Te Punga Somerville, of a special issue of JNZL devoted to Comparative Approaches to Indigenous Literary Studies (2007) and, with Beth Piatote, of a special combined issue of the journals SAIL and AIQ devoted to The Society of American Indians and Its Legacies (forthcoming 2013); numerous articles on the World Council of Indigenous Peoples.

ALLEN, CINDY (Catawba)
(craftsperson)
Address: 1815 Baskins Rd., Rock Hill, SC 29730 (803) 324-5088. *Artwork*: Traditional 19th century-style Catawba pottery.

ALLEN, CHIEF JAMES (Coeur D'Alene) 1972-
(tribal chairperson)
Born in Spokane, Wash. in 1972. *Education*: Eastern Washington University, BA (Political Science), 1996. *Affiliation & Address*: Chair (2005-present), Coeur D'Alene Tribe, P.O. Box 408, Plummer, ID 83851 (208) 686-1800. *Past tribal posts*: Legislative director, 1996-2000; Administrative director, 2001-2003; tribal council, 2003-2005.

ALLEN, JESSICA (San Carlos Apache)
(administrator)
Affiliation & Address: Operations Director, The Tribal Law & Policy Institute (TLPI), 8235 Santa Monica Blvd., Suite 211, West Hollywood, CA 90046 (323) 650-5467. E-mail: Jessica@tlpi.org. Jessica is responsible for the financial management, human resources and overall administrative operations of TLPI. *Other professional post*: Operations Director, NRC4Tribes, National Child Welfare Resource Center for Tribes, Helena, MT.

ALLEN, JUDY (Choctaw of Oklahoma)
(executive director of tribal public relations)
Affiliation & Address: Executive Director of Public Relations (1999-present), Choctaw Nation of Oklahoma, P.O. Box 1210, Durant, OK 74702 (405) 924-8280. *Past professional post*: Editor, Bishinik (tribal newspaper), 1986-99. Judy is a member and Ambassador for Class XXV of Leadership Oklahoma. Judy is also is on the Board of Directors of the Choctaw Code Talkers Association, Creative Oklahoma and the Women's Foundation of Oklahoma. She is a member of the Board of Advocates for the Oklahoma Children's Hospital. Judy serves on committees for Choctaw Nation Natural Resources, PAC and Employee Benefits. Past honors include awards for Preservation of Choctaw Culture from the Okla Chahta Clan (2000) and the Meritorious Service Award from the DFW Native American Chamber of Commerce (2009). She was also honored to serve as Faculty in Residence in 2012 for the National Education for Women's Leadership Initiative. She was one of the Oklahoma women chosen in 2012 for the 50 Making a Difference and nominated for 2012 Journal

Record Woman of the Year. Rating high among Judy's past accomplishments is being on the leadership team to obtain recognition through the U.S. Congress for Native American Code Talkers. Other achievements include leading teams to begin the first Choctaw Commemorative Trail of Tears Walk and Choctaw Veterans Ceremony, both of which are now annual events. Another honor for Judy and her team at Choctaw Nation was the organization and successful implementation of the first tribal festival at the Smithsonian National Museum of the American Indian (NMAI) in Washington, D.C. The occasion was such a success that the Smithsonian NMAI requested the Choctaw festival become an annual event, & launched a campaign to request other tribes across the United States to host celebrations at the museum.

ALLEN, MICHAEL, SR. (Lake Superior Chippewa)
(tribal vice president)
Affiliation & Address: Vice President, Lac du Flambeau Tribal Council, P.O. Box 67, Lac du Flambeau, WI 54538 (715) 588-3303.

ALLEN, PAULA GUNN (Laguna Pueblo)
(writer)
Address: 3940 Rose Court, Seal Beach, CA 90740 (310) 493-6493.

ALLEN, RICHARD P. (Santee Sioux)
(former tribal president)
Affiliation: President, Flandreau Santee-Sioux Tribe, P.O. Box 283, Flandreau, SD 57028 (605) 997-3891.

ALLEN, SUSAN L. (Rosebud Lakota)
(attorney)
Education: Augsburg College, BA (Ecocnomics), 1992; University of New Mexico School of Law, JD, & Certificate of Indian Law, 1995; LL.M. in Taxation, William Mitchell College of Law, 2000. *Affiliation & Address*: Attorney, The Jacobson Law Group, 335 Atrium Office Bldg., 1295 Bandana Blvd., St. Paul, MN 55108 (651) 644-4710. E-mail: sallen@thejacobsonlawgroup.com . *Past professional post*: Attorney, BlueDog Olson & Small, PLLP, Bloomington. *Practice areas*: Federal Indian law, tax, gaming, employment, commercial transactions. *Memberships*: American Bar Assn; Minnesota Bar Assn; Minnesota American Indian Bar Assn. Susan joined the firm in 2013, bringing substantial experience representing tribal governments, gaming enterprises and tribal business entities on a full range of matters, including tribal and corporate governance, commercial transactions, contracts, & tax issues. Susan is an enrolled member of the Rosebud Sioux Tribe. She has a comprehensive background in transactional work. Over the years, handling numerous business & corporation matters for tribes, including structuring & negotiation of mergers, acquisitions, dispositions, management transactions, construction agreements, business formation, economic development, tax planning, & many other business matters. In the area of taxation, Susan regularly advises tribes on the scope of state taxing authority and tribal tax immunity. She also represents and trains tribal tax commissions regarding the development & administration of tax codes & has significant knowledge regarding negotiation of tribal-state tax agreements. In addition, Susan has a masters in tax law and is very familiar with federal tax laws applicable to tribal activities, including such matters as executive compensation, employment taxes and tax exemptions. In addition to practicing law, Susan was elected to the Minnesota House of Reps in 2012. She is the first American Indian women to be elected to the Minnesota Legislature. Susan is also an active member of various professional and community organizations, including the Indigenous Peoples Task Force, ICWA Law Center and the Minnesota American Indian Bar Assn. In addition, Susan speaks regularly at lawyer's seminars on tax issues. *Honors & Awards:* Minneapolis Community & Technical College, Distinguished Alumni Award, 2012; West Award for Excellence in Indian Law, 1995; Honors in Clinical Law, U. of NM School of Law, 1995.

ALLEN, W. (WILLIAM) RON (Jamestown S'Klallam)
(tribal chairperson, chief executive director)
Born December 14, 1947, Port Angeles, Wash. *Education*: Peninsula College, AA & AAA, 1978; University of Washington, BA (Political Science/Economics), 1982. *Address*: 1033 Old Blyn Highway, Sequim, WA 98382 (360) 681-4621 (work). *Affiliation*: Chairperson (1977-present) & Executive Director, Jamestown Band of S'Klallam Tribe, Sequim, WA, 1978-present. As executive director, Ron is responsible for the administration of all the tribe's programs. *Other professional posts*: Senior Strategist, Blue Stone Strategy Group, Phoenix, AZ; Chairperson & Executive Director, Tribal Leadership Forum, The Institute for Tribal Government, Hatfield School of Government, Portland, OR; chairperson, Washington Indian Gaming Assn. *Community activities*: Affiliated Tribes of Northwest Indians (Treasurer, 1984-90, Delegate, 1977-present); National Indian Policy Center (Co-chairman, 1990-96); president (1995-99), Treasurer (1989-93; 2001-present), National Congress of American Indians (1977-present); Point No Point Treaty Council (1981-present); Washington Indian Gaming Assn (2002-present); Washington Coalition for Tribal Self-Reliance (co-chair, 2002-present); Assn of Washington Tribes (delegate).

Awards, honors: Student of the Year, Peninsula College; Dedicated Service, Northwest Indian Fisheries Commission. *Published works*: Determining the True Cost of Contracting Federal Programs for Indian Tribes (Affiliated Tribes of Northwest Indians, 1987). Chairman Allen is widely recognized at the national, state and local level for his strong commitment to improving the quality, financing and delivery of healthcare services for American Indians and Alaska Natives. His commitment is shown through the multiple organizations in which he has participated and continues to participate, including the National Congress of American Indians, Centers for Medicare and Medicaid Services Tribal Technical Advisory Group, Washington Indian Gaming Association and many more.

ALLERY, CHRIS (Anishinabe)
(attorney; executive Director)
Education: University of North Dakota School of Law, JD, 1999. *Affiliation & Address*: Staff Attorney & Co-Executive Director (2005-present), Anishinabe Legal Services, P.O. Box 157, Cass Lake, MN 56633 (218) 335-2223. Chris is a licensed attorney in the State of Minnesota, as well as the tribal courts of Mille Lacs, White Earth, Leech Lake, Red Lake, and Bois Forte.

ALLERY, VIRGINIA (Anishinabe)
(American Indian studies department coordinator)
Affiliation & Address: Coordinator, American Indian Studies Deparrment, CB 115, Minneapolis, MN 55454 (612) 330-1661. E-mail: alleryv@augusburg.edu.

ALLIS, KEVIN J. (Forest County Potawatomi)
(attorney; executive director)
Education: Louisiana State University; University of Baltimore, BS, 1999; JD, 2004. *Affiliation & Address*: Executive Director, Native American Contractors Association, 1514 P St., NW, Suite 2, Washington, DC 20005 (202) 756-2676. *Other professional post*: Chairperson, Board of Directors, Potawatomi Business Development Corporation, Milwaukee, WI. *Past professional post*: Attorney, Piliero Mazza PLLC, Washington, DC (provided legal advice to Alaska Native Corporations, Native Hawaiian Organizations, and other tribal entities participating in the SBA 8(a) program). *Professional interests*: Kevin primarily concentrates in management labor & employment law. He also advises on various aspects of government contracting with concentration on small & disadvantaged businesses; and conducts workshops & supervisory training across the country for employers on various labor & employment topics. Kevin works closely with several Native American tribes, tribal enterprises, & Native American associations on labor & employment law issues impacting Indian Country.

ALLISON, ARTHUR P. (Dine'-Navajo)
(business owner; Dine corporation chairperson)
Born & raised in Tohatchi, NM. *Education*: Brigham Young University, BS; Ball State University, MBA. *Affiliations*: CEO & president, Five-Star Security, Farmington, NM (20+ years); chairperson (2006-present), Dine Development Corporation, P.O. Box 307, Window Rock (Navajo Nation), AZ 86515 (505) 879-1533. *Past professional posts*: Director, Navajo Division of Economic Development, Window Rock, AZ, 1995-98; planning director & general manager, Navajo Agricultural Products Industry (eight years).

ALLISON, SHERRY (Dine')
(Indian college president)
Affiliation & Address: President, Southwestern Indian Polytechnic Institute (SIPI), 9169 Coors Rd., NW, Albuquerque, NM 87184 (505) 346-4087. E-mail: sherry.allison@bie.edu

ALLISON, HARVEY DALE (Dine'-Navajo)
(school principal)
Affiliation: Principal, Na'Neelzhiin Ji'Olta (Torreon), HCR 79, Box 9, Cuba, NM 87013 (505) 731-2272.

ALLISON, MICHAEL (Dine'-Navajo)
(Native American liaison)
Education: University of New Mexico, MBA, 1974; University of Arizona, MPH, 2003. *Affiliation & Address*: Native American Liiaison, Arizona Department of Health Services, Office of the Director, 150 N. 18th Ave, Suite 595, Phoenix, AZ 85007 (6002) 364-1041. Michael has thirty-four years of management work experience in small business development, tribal economic development, health care management, and public health. Former positions held by Michael include: Executive Director, Navajo Division of Economic Development; Executive Vice President, National Center for American Indian Enterprise Development; and Executive Director, Native American Community Health Center, Inc. Representing the Department, Michael serves as an Ex-Officio Board Member of the Arizona Commission on Indian Affairs and as a member of the Arizona Advisory Council on Indian Health Care.

ALLISON, SHERRY (Dine'-Navajo)
(Indian college president)
Education: New Mexico State University, BA (Social Work); Northern Arizona University, MA Education), 1984, PhD (Educational Leadership), 1994. *Affiliation & Address*: President (2009-present), Southwestern Indian Polytechnic Institute (SIPI), 9169 Coors Rd. NW, Albuquerque, NM 87184 (505) 346-2348. E-mail: sherry.allison@bie.edu. *Past professional posts*: served 10 years with the Office of Indian Education Programs, now the Bureau of Indian Education, in the Interior Department where she worked in programs dealing with residential treatment & education services to students in juvenile detention centers, professional development & special education. She served details on the Navajo Nation reservation as the Education Line Officer for the Bureau of Indian Affairs' Northern Navajo Agency in Shiprock, N.M. (June-October 2004) and the Fort Defiance Agency in Fort Defiance, Ariz. (October 2005-May 2006). From February to August 2007, she served as acting chief for the BIE's performance & accountability division in Albuquerque. *Awards, honors*: Allison has been nominated for and is the recipient of numerous honors for her work including: Honorary Commander (for community service), Kirtland Air Force Base (1999); induction into the Council for Exceptional Children Hall of Fame, New Mexico Chapter, Division of Linguistically Diverse Exceptional Learners (1999); YWCA Woman on the Move nominee, Albuquerque (1998); University of Oklahoma Faculty Leadership Institute Fellowship recipient (1997); U.S. Department of Education Patricia Roberts Harris Academic Fellowship recipient – doctoral program (1992-1994); National Native American Honor Society (1993-1994); Who's Who in American Colleges: Recognition for Scholastic Achievement (1994) and the National Bojack Humanitarian Award, Flagstaff, Ariz. (1991).

ALLSTON, LYNETTE (Nottoway of Virginia)
(tribal chief & chairperson)
Affiliation & Address: Chairperson & Chief, Nottoway Indiann Tribe of Virginia, P.O. Box 246, Capron, VA 23829 (434) 658-4454.

ALLWOOD, ADOLPH A. (*The Eagle Among Us*) (Cherokee) 1943-
(marketing/public relations consultant)
Born November 11, 1943, Buffalo, N.Y. Education: City College of New York, BA (Economics); Fordham University, MBA (Marketing-Management). *Address*: 119-30 199th St., St. Albans, NY 11412 (718) 341-6457. E-mail: aaallwood@earthlink.net. *Affiliation*: Affective Marketing Management Consultants, St. Albans, NY. *Other professional posts*: Public relations, marketing, management planning, training & development with the following companies: New York Post, The New York Times, Ziff Davis Publishing Co. *Interests*: Adolph has competed as an artist working with sculpture, copper, and painting. Primarily self-taught, all themes are core to the Native American culture. The most pronounced dimension of Adolph's involvement with Native American culture has been directing traditional Native American dance groups. He organized an intertribal dance troupe called, International Native American Performers. They perform before various audiences throughout the state. Adolph provides his expertise to audiences as a lecturer or writer about history & varied cultures of Native Americans. He served as the Native Core Economist of a community publication - The Long Island Courier, as a researcher to the late Professor E.L. Gilmore's, Institute of Cherokee Studies, Tahlequah, Oklahoma. Professor Gilmore's great, great grandfather was the first Chief of the Reformed Movement - John Ross.

ALMEIDA, DEIRDRE A.
(director of American Indian studies)
Education: University of Massachusetts, Amherst, BA, EdD; Stanford University, MA. *Affiliation & Address*: Director (2001-present), American Indian Studies Program, Eastern Washington University, Longhouse MS-21EC, Cheney, WA 99004 (509) 359-6242. E-mail: dalmeida@ewu.edu.

ALOYO, SOPHIE (Eskimo)
(Alaskan tribal council president)
Affiliation: Pilot Point Tribal Council, P.O. Box 449, Pilot Point, AK 99649 (907) 797-2208.

ALPHONSE, DENNIS
(Indian band chief)
Affiliation: Cowichan Indian Band, Box 880, Duncan, British Columbia, Canada V9L 3Y2 (604) 748-3196.

ALSTROM, GAIL (Yupiit)
(Alaskan tribal president)
Affiliation: President, Yupiit of Andreafski, P.O. Box 88, St. Mary's, AK 99658 (907) 438-2312.

ALTHER, DOROTHY (Oglala Lakota)
(attorney; executive director)
Education: University of South Dakota, BA; Northeastern University, JD. *Affiliation & Address*: Senior Staff Attorney & Executive Director, California Indian Legal Services, 609 S. Escondido Blvd., Escondido, CA 92025 (760) 746-8941. Dorothy has been an attorney with CILS for over 15 years and was in the Bishop CILS Office until she relocated to the Escondido Office in 2003. Her current work focuses on tribal issues including environmental law, housing law, tribal ordinance development, land acquisition, she serves as legal counsel for several Tribes and tribal entities and has worked on tribal court development and a variety of other tribal matters. Ms. Alther has been a trainer on Public Law 280, the Indian Child Welfare Act, housing law and civil and criminal jurisdiction in Indian Country. Ms. Alther served as Managing Attorney at DNA's People's Legal Services in Crownpoint, New Mexico prior to coming to CILS and has acted as Tribal Attorney for the Suquamish Tribe in Washington.

ALVAREZ, STEVEN (*Wounded Deer*)
(Mescalero Apache/Yaqui/Upper Tanana Athabascan)
(storyteller, musician, vocalist, stage actor)
Education: San Jose State University, BA (Music Education & History, minor in Philosophy). Resides in Anchorage, Alaska. Steven currently performs with the Anchorage Symphony Orchestra, the Anchorage Opera & Anchorage Concert Chorus, & recording artists medicine Dream, Pamyua, & Joy Harjo. Recently, he co-founded Theater Artists United, an Anchorage-based Theater Company, where he is presently the musical director of "Hair." "*Connections*" is a Steven Alvarez production of three traditional stories about Native people reconnecting or staying connected with their culture. Contact Steven c/o Susan Vargo, The Charles Agency (602) 547-0708 E-mail: info@thecharlesagency. com.

ALVIDREZ, ALBERT (Tigua)
(pueblo governor; tribal enterprise manager)
Affiliations: Ysleta Del Sur Pueblo Council, P.O. Box 17579, Ysleta Sta., El Paso, TX 79917 (915) 859-7913; manager, Thur-Shan Arts & Crafts Center, 305 Yaya Lane, El Paso, TX 79907 (915) 859-5287.

ALVIDREZ, LAURA (Tigua)
(program manager)
Affiliation & Address: Program Manager, Intertribal Timber Council, 1112 NE 21st Ave., Suite 4, Portland, OR 97213 (503) 282-4296.

ALVORD, LORI (Navajo-Dine') 1958-
(physician-surgeon)
Born in Crownpoint, N.M. in 1958. *Education*: Dartmouth College, BA; Stanford University School of Medicine, MD. First Dine' woman to be board certified in surgery. Dr. Alvord uses new techniques that bring together Navajo healing techniques and modern Western medicine. After studying medicine at Stanford University, Dr. Alvord returned to her Navajo reservation in New Mexico only to learn that, despite the importance of her technical proficiency in surgery, simply "fixing" the physical problem was not sufficient to fully cure a patient. Addressing the psychological and spiritual aspects of healing was important as well. This led to a more holistic approach to medicine that took into account the patient's environment and relationships, and also incorporated artwork and nature into the hospital's design. *Past professional posts*: From 1991-1997, Dr. Alvord practiced as a surgeon with the Indian Health Service, at one of its facilities in Gallup. Alvord was also the associate dean for student affairs at Dartmouth Medical School as well as assistant professor of surgery and psychiatry at Dartmouth from 1997-2009. From 2003 onwards, Dr. Alvord served as an Associate Faculty member for the Center for American Indian Health at Johns Hopkins School of Public Health From 2008-2010, Dr. Alvord served on the National Advisory Council for Complementary and Alternative Medicine (NACCAM), the principal advisory body to the National Center for Complementary and Alternative Medicine (NCCAM), a component of the National Institutes of Health. From 2010-2012, Dr. Alvord served as the Associate Dean of the Central Michigan University College of Medicine, which opened during the Fall 2013 semester. She played an instrumental role in developing the new medical school. She was also the associate dean of student affairs and admissions at the University of Arizona College of Medicine, in Tucson, Arizona from 2012-2014. *Awards, honors*; In 2001, Dr. Alvord received an honorary degree from Albany Medical College. In 2006, Dr. Alvord received an honorary degree from Drexel University. In 2009, Dr. Alvord was bequeathed an honorary degree from Pine Manor College. In 1992, Dr. Alvord was the recipient of Governor's Award for Outstanding New Mexico Women, from former governor of New Mexico, Bruce King. In 1999, Dr. Alvord was the recipient of the American Medical Writers Association the 2000 Will Solimene Award of Excellence, for the publication "Warp and Weft", an excerpt from The Scalpel and the Silver Bear.[16] In 2000, Dr. Alvord was the recipient of Circles Book Award from Georgia College and State University for her autobiography, *The Scalpel and the Silver Bear*. In 2003, Dr. Alvord was the recipient of Veterans Affairs Federal Appreciation Award, The White River Junction Veterans Affairs Medical Center; 2013 nominee for U.S. Surgeon General. *Published work*: Her autobiography, *The Scalpel and the Silver Bear*, has brought increased attention to her career as a surgeon and has sold over 50,000 copies.

AMBLER, ALLEN W. (Paiute) 1962-
(tribal chairperson)
Born March 7, 1962, Reno, Nev. *Education*: University of Nevada, Reno. *Principal occupation*: management consultant; programs administrator. *Affiliation & Address*: Winnemucca Indian Colony, P.O. Box 1370, Winnemucca, NV 89446 (775) 623-0888. *Past professional posts*: Chairperson, Lovelock Paiute Tribal Council, Lovelock, NV, 1996-2007; secretary of Executive Board, Inter Tribal Council of Nevada; president, Nevada Indian Environmental Coalition, 1997-present; chairperson, Board of Directors, 1st Momentum, Inc., 1997-present. *Community activities*: Head Start Committee; Child Protection Team; Education Committee; Chamber of Commerce; volunteer for Special Olympics; Youth Mentor Program; Stop Domestic Violence Team.

AMBROSIA, ALEX (Eskimo)
(Alaskan village president)
Affiliation: Native Village of Ouzinkie, P.O. Box 130, Ouzinkie, AK 99644 (907) 680-2259.

AMDUR-CLARK, NATHANIEL H. (Citizen Potawatomi)
(attorney; policy advisor)
Education: Harvard University, BA, 2009; Harvard Law School, JD, 2014; Harvard Kennedy School, MPP, 2014. *Affiliation & Address*: Policy Advisor, Sonosky, Chambers, Sachse, Endreson & Perry, LLP, 1425 K St., NW, Suite 600, Washington, DC 20005 (202) 682-0240. Email: nclark@sonosky.com. Nathaniel joined the firm's DC office as a Policy Advisor in 2014 after working as a summer associate and law clerk in 2012 and 2014. He works in all areas of the firm's practice. He is a member of the Alaska Bar and pending in the District of Columbia. Nathaniel graduated from Harvard Law School in 2014, where he was involved in the Harvard Native American Law Students Association and served on the Board of the National Native American Law Students Association. During law school, he was active on the Harvard Law and Policy Review and interned at the Office of Tribal Justice and Civil Appellate Division at the U.S. Department of Justice. In addition to his law degree, Nathaniel has a Master in Public Policy Degree from the Harvard Kennedy School, where he was a Harvard Kennedy School Native American Public Service Fellow.

AMERMAN, ROGER E. (Choctaw of OK)
(artist)
Address: 109 N. 55th Ave., Yakima, WA 98908. E-mail: chains04@msn.com. Artwork: Beadwork and Choctaw cultural attire.

AMIOTTE, ARTHUR DOUGLAS (*Good Eagle Center*) (Oglala Sioux) 1942-
(artist, author, educator)
Born March 25, 1942, Pine Ridge, S.D. *Education*: Northern State University, BsEd, 1964; Montana State University, MIS (Master of Interdisciplinary Studies), 1983; Honorary doctorates from Oglala Lakota College & Brandon University in Manitoba, Can. *Principal occupation*: Artist; author; educator. Mr. Amiotte has studied traditional Lakota arts techniques with Christina Standing Bear, 1969-75; Lakota Sacred Traditions with Peter Cathces, Sr. (novice apprentice, 1972-76; assistant, 1977-82. *Address*: P.O. Box 471, Custer, SD 57730 (605) 673-4373. *Affiliations*: Art teacher, Woodrow Wilson Jr. High School, Sioux City, IA, 1964-66; instructor of art, Northern State College, Aberdeen, SD, 1966-69; Lakota arts/creative writing teacher, Porcupine Day School, BIA, Porcupine, SD, 1969-71; director of curriculum development, BIA, Aberdeen Area Office, 1971-74; Lakota Studies & art specialist, Little Eagle Day School, BIA, 1975-77; chairperson, Lakota Studies Dept., Standing Rock Community College, Fort Yates, SD, 1977-80; Dept. of Native Studies, Brandon University, Brandon, Manitoba, Canada (visiting assistant professor, 1982-85; adjunct professor of Native Studies, 1985-); artist, writer, consultant on Indian Cultures of the Northern Plains, White Horse Creek, Ltd., Custer, SD, 1985-. Exhibitions, commissions, published art and research, and lectures, too numerous to mention. *Awards, honors*: Recipient of "Outstanding Contribution to Indian Education" Award by State of South Dakota Indian Education Association, 1976; appointed member of the Presidential Advisory Council for the Performing Arts, Kennedy Center, Washington, DC by President Jimmy Carter, 1979-81; recipient of "Excellence in Teaching Award," Native Studies, Standing Rock Community College, Fort Yates, ND, 1980; recipient of State of South Dakota Governor's Award, Biennial Award for Outstanding Creative Achievement in the Arts, Pierre, SD, 1980; recipient of the Bush Leadership Fellowship for advanced study in Native American Sacred Traditions and Native Art History, Bush Foundation, 1980-83; recipient of Distinguished Alumni Award, Northern State College, June 1988; presenter of Richard Thompson Memorial Lecture, Iowa State University, June 1988; appointed four year member of Board, National Foundation for Advancement in the Arts, Miami, FL, June 1988; appointed member of Board of Directors, National Native American Art Studies Association (June 1988); appointed member of

Board of Directors, Arts Midwest, Minneapolis, MN (June 1988); appointed member of Planning Committee for Northern Tier States Centennial Symposium Project, Montana State Historical Society, Helena, (June 1988); appointed Commissioner of Indian Arts and Crafts Board (a five commissioner board) by U.S. Secretary of the Interior (June 1988); awarded Honorary Doctorate of Lakota Studies by Oglala Lakota College, June 1988; awarded 14th Annual Artistic Achievement Citation by Board of Trustees, SD Art Museum, April 1989; appointed member of National Board of Directors, Center for Western Studies, Augustana College, Sioux Falls, SD, (Nov. 1990); appointed Senior Advisor to Director, Foundation for the Arts in South Dakota, Rapid City, (Oct. 1990); appointed member of Board of Directors, National Museum of the American Indian, Smithsonian Institute, Washington, DC, (Oct. 1990); co-curator, Plains Section of North American Indian Hall, Museum of Natural History, Smithsonian Institute, Washington, D.C., 1991-; One of 25 artists selected from Western Hemisphere to create a collaborative exhibition, "Celebrations" for the 1993-94 opening of the new National Museum of the American Indian, George Gustave Heye Center, Smithsonian Institute, New York, NY, 1992-; Lifetime Achievement Award as Artist & Scholar from the Native American Art Studies Association. His work is included in 26 public & nearly 200 private collections.

AMMON, DANIEL (Tsnungwe/South Fork Hupa)
(Hupa language/math/computer science instructor)
Address: P.O. Box 368, Salyer, CA 95563 (916) 629-4159. E-mail: ammon@cs.stanford.edu. *Affiliations*: DQ University, Davis, CA, 1995-present; Hoopa Tribal Education Association, Hoopa, CA, 1994-95. *Community activities*: Master/Apprentice Hupa Language Project. *Memberships*: California Professional AISES; National Council of Teachers of Mathematics.

AMOS, HOWARD T. (Eskimo)
(Alaskan village president)
Affiliation: Native Village of Mekoryuk, P.O. Box 66, Mekoryuk, AK 99630 (907) 827-8828.

AMYLEE (Iroquois - Mohawk-Seneca) 1952-
(consultant, artist, writer)
Born in 1952. *Education*: State University of New York, 1976-1979; Kent State University, 1970-1980 (concurrent). *Principal occupation*: Director of Indian organization. *Address*: 3225 S. McLeod, Suite 100, Las Vegas, NV 89121. E-mail: talon@tusco.net. *Affiliations*: Founder & director, American Indian Rights Association, Kent State University, 1970-1983; Licensed Raptor (Bird of Prey) Rehabilitator (ongoing); Medicine Woman Initiate (ongoing). *Other professional posts*: Member of the Board (past director), lecturer and artist for the Native American Indian Resource Center (NAIRC). *Memberships*: National Wildlife Rehabilitators Association; Earthwalker Learning Lodge. *Awards, honors*: Numerous awards for artistic achievement; her work can be found in selected galleries and at festivals celebrating women's culture. *Interests*: AmyLee has appeared with Native American leaders & dignitaries including Sakokwenonk-was of Akwesasne, Mad Bear, Rolling Thunder, Sun Bear, Grandfather Sky Eagle and Vernon Bellecourt. She has also had the opportunity to serve as a script consultant for the Smithsonian Institution and a character actress in the Public Broadcast System's film, Americas Ethnic Symphony. As member of the board for NAIRC, AmyLee travels over 50,000 miles annually offering lectures, workshops and retreats. She donates and devotes time to Native & nature projects including a drug & crime rehabilitation facility for recovering Indian youth. Biographical sources: Chapter-long interview in recently released, Profiles in Wisdom by Steven McFadden; excerpts from her writing and lectures appears in Wabun Wind's, Lightseeds, Kay Gardner's, Sounding the Inner Landscape; to MS. Magazine (November 1991). *Published works*: The Pathfinder Directory: A Guide to Native Americans in the Ohiyo Country (Indian House, 1982); When One Foot Wears the Moccasin, 2000; several articles. Presently, she is currently working on two book manuscripts regarding Native women's spirituality and politics.

ANAWAK, JACK (Nunatsiaq)
(parliament member)
Affiliation: Parliament Bldgs., Ottawa, ON, Canada K1A 0A4 (613) 992-4587.

ANAYA, S. JAMES (Parasco Apache)
(attorney-professor of law)
Education: University of New Mexico, BA, 1980; Harvard Law School, JD, 1983. *Affiliation & Address*: Regents' & James J. Lenoir Professor of Human Rights Law & Policy (1999-present), Indigenous Peoples Law & Policy Program, James E. Rogers College of Law, University of Arizona, P.O. Box 210176, Tucson, AZ 85721 (520) 626-6341. E-mail: sjanaya@email.arizona.edu. *Other professional post*: United Nations Special Rapporteur on the Rights of Indigenous Peoples. Professor Anaya has advised numerous indigenous and other organizations from several countries on matters of human rights & indigenous peoples, representing indigenous groups from many parts of North & Central America in landmark cases before courts & international organizations. He participated in the drafting of the UN's

Declaration on the Rights of Indigenous Peoples and was the lead counsel for the indigenous parties in the case of Awas Tingni v. Nicaragua, in which the Inter-American Court of Human Rights for the first time upheld indigenous land rights as a matter of international law. *Past professional posts*: Professor, University of Iowa College of Law, Iowa City, IA, 1988-99; staff attorney, National Indian Youth Council, Albuquerque, NM & practiced law in Albuquerque, NM, 1983-88. *Awards, honors*: John O'Connor Human Rights Award for "Outstanding Achievement in Promoting the Rights of Indigenous peoples," by Cultural Survivial, May 2002; Haywood Burns/Shanara Gilbert Award for"Outstanding Service to the Recipient's Community," by the Northeast People of Color Conference, October 2009; named Regents Professor, effective June 2010, the "highest of faculty ranks" at the University of Arizona. *Published works*: Indigenous Peoples in International Law (Oxford University Press, 1996, 2nd ed. 2004); International Human Rights & Indigenous Peoples (Aspen Publisher/Wolters Kluwer Law & Business, 2009); International Human Rights: Problems of Law, Policy & Practice (Aspen Publisher, 5th Ed. 2011) with Hurst Hannum & Dinah Shelton (an edited compilation of materials with extensive original commentary); numerous reorts written as UN Special Reporteur on the rights of indigenous peoples. The reports are available at: http://unsr.jamesanaya.org/.

ANDALIO, CINDY
(American Indian graduate program manager)
Affiliation & Address: Director, American Indian Graduate Program, University of California, 327 Sproul Hall #5900, Berkeley, CA 94720 (510) 642-3228.

ANDARY, CAROL (Ojibwe)
(tribal chief judge)
Address & Affiliation: Bay Mills Tribal Court, Rt. 1, Box 313, Brimley, MI 49715 (906) 248-3241.

ANDERSON, CRAIG (Sisseton Wahpeton Sioux)
(organization president & executive director)
Affiliation: President/Executive Director (past vice president & treasurer), American Indian Chamber of Commerce of Wisconsin, 10809 W. Lincoln Ave. #201, West Allis, WI 53227 (414) 604-2044. E-mail: craiga@aiccw.org. *Past professional posts*: Co-founder & executive vice president, Links Networks (3 years); co-owner & executive vice president, Dakota Technology Systems, Inc.

ANDERSON, CURTIS F., JR. (Pomo)
(rancheria vice chairperson)
Affiliation & Address: Vice Chairperson, Robinson Rancheria, 1545 E. Hwy. 20, Nice, CA 95464 (707) 275-0527.

ANDERSON, CURTIS (Paiute)
(former tribal chairperson)
Affiliation: Las Vegas Indian Colony, One Paiute Dr., Las Vegas, NV 89106 (702) 386-3926.

ANDERSON, ERIC GARY
(Indian program director & associate professor
of American Indian studies)
Affiliation & Address: Director & Associate Professor of American Indian literatures, U.S. and global Southern studies, Native American and Indigenous Studies, American fiction from the beginnings to the 21st century, multi-ethnic American literatures, Office of Diversity, Inclusion and Multicultural Education, College of Humanities & Social Sciences, 405C Robinson Hall A, MS 3E4, Fairfax, VA 22030 (703) 993-1160; E-mail: eandersond@gmu.edu. From 2012-14, he served as President of The Society for the Study of Southern Literature. At Mason, he coordinates the interdisciplinary minor in Native American & Indigenous Studies and serves as faculty advisor for the GMU Native American and Indigenous Alliance. Awards, honors: In 2014, Eric Gary Anderson won a University Teaching Excellence Award with special acknowledgment of his contributions to General Education at Mason. Published works: In addition to his book, *American Indian Literature and the Southwest: Contexts and Dispositions* (University of Texas Press, 1999), he has published more than twenty essays in edited vols & journals, including pieces in *PMLA*, *American Literary History*, *Early American Literature*, *Southern Spaces*, *Mississippi Quarterly*, and *South to a New Place*. With Taylor Hagood and Daniel Cross Turner, he is a co-editor of *Undead Souths: The Gothic and Beyond in Southern Literature and Culture*, a collection of essays available now from Louisiana State University Press. He is working on two book projects: a monograph that brings together Indigenous Studies & Southern Studies and an edited collection, *Swamp Souths: Literary and Cultural Ecologies* (with co-editors Kirstin L. Squint, Taylor Hagood, and Anthony Wilson). Other current works in progress include an essay on queer native southern transmissions in the film *The Doe Boy* and another essay on William Faulkner's *Light in August* and Stephen Graham Jones's native southern werewolf novel *Mongrels*. *Undead Souths: The Gothic and Beyond in Southern Literature and Culture*. Co-edited by Eric Gary Anderson, Taylor Hagood, and Daniel Cross Turner. Baton Rouge: Louisiana State University Press, 2015.

ANDERSON, ESTHER L. (Arapaho) 1950-
(business owner)
Born September 20, 1950, Casper, Wyo. *Education*: Casper College (Associate of Science, 19710. *Address*: 5003 Alcova Rte. #20, Casper, WY 82604 (307) 237-7985 (home); (307) 235-0002 (office). *Affiliation*: Member, Equal Opportunity & DBE Committee for the Associated General Contractors of Wyoming. *Community activities*: Former county coordinator for Farm Bureau, ten years as election clerk. *Membership*: Associated General Contractors of Wyoming, 1985-.

ANDERSON, GENEAL (Paiute)
(tribal chairperson)
Affiliation: Paiute Indian Tribe of Utah, 600 North 100 East, Paiute Dr., Cedar City, UT 84720 (801) 586-1111.

ANDERSON, GREG (Southern Paiute)
(tribal vice chairperson)
Affiliation & Address: Vice Chairperson, Moapa Band of Paiute Indians, P.O. Box 340, Moapa, NV 89025 (702) 865-2787. E-mail: mbop.vicechair@mvdsl.com

ANDERSON, JEREMY (Eskimo)
(Alaskan village president)
Affiliation: Native Village of Chignik Lagoon, P.O. Box 57, Chignik Lagoon, AK 99565 (907) 840-2281.

ANDERSON, JoELLEN (Ojibwe)
(Native American studies lecturer)
JoEllen grew up on the Fort Peck Indian Reservation in Montana. *Education*: Oregon State University, BS; Stanford University, MA, PhD. *Affiliation & Address*: Lecturer, Ethnic Studies Dept., Native American Studies Program, College of Letters & Science, 540 Barrows Hall, Berkeley, CA 94720 (510) 643-0796. E-mail: andersonje@berkeley.edu. *Other professional posts*: Co-director, The Joseph A. Myers Center for Research on Native American Issues, Institute for the Study of Societal Issues, University of California, Berkeley; lecturer, Native American Studies, Stanford University, Stanford, CA. *Past professional post*: Taught at the University of Michigan, Ann Arbor, MI. *Research Interests*: Tribal histories, Native American Film & Literature, Contemporary Native Americans. *Awards, honors*: University Award, Native American Community at Stanford University; Outstanding Mentor to American Indian, Alaska Native & Native Hawaiian Students at Stanford. *Published works*: Cowboys & Indians, the Perceptions of Western Films Among American Indians & Anglos; Fort Peck Indian Reservation.

ANDERSON, KEITH B. (Mdewakanton Sioux)
(tribal vice chairperson)
Affiliation & Address: Vice Chairperson, Shakopee Mdewakanton Sioux Community, 2330 Sioux Trail, NW, Prior Lake, MN 55372 (952) 445-8900.

ANDERSON, KENNY (Paiute)
(Indian colony chairperson)
Affiliation: Las Vegas Indian Colony Council, One Paiute Dr. Las Vegas, NV 89106 (702) 386-3926.

ANDERSON, KIERSTIN (Yaqui)
(tribal attorney)
Education: Washburn University School of Law, JD, 2003. *Affiliation & Address*: Managing Attorney, Legal Services Office, Salt River Pima-Maricopa Indian Community, 10005 E. Osborn Rd., Scottsdale, AZ 85256 (480) 362-5670. E-mail: kierstin.anderson@srpmic-nsn.gov. *Past professional post*: Staff Attorney, Pascua Yaqui Tribe.

ANDERSON, LARRY (Fond du Lac Lake Superior Chippewa)
(tribal college president)
Education: University of Wisconsin, Superior, BS & MSE (Counseling). *Affiliation & Address*: President (2008-present), Fond du Lac Tribal & Community College, 2101 14th St., Cloquet, MN 55720 (218) 879-0804. E-mail: larrya@fdltcc.edu. *Past professional posts*: Director, American Indian Programs, Arrowhead Economic Opportunities Agency; Talent Search counselor, Minnesota Chippewa Tribe; Upward Bound/Student Support Services director, College of St. Scholastica (three years); vice president of administration & student services, Fond du Lac Tribal & Community College, 1995-2008. *Awards, honors*: Administrator of the Year in 1999 by the Minnesota Indian Education Association; elected to the Independent School District #2142 Board of Directors, 1984-1999, chair for four years.

ANDERSON, LAURA (Cherokee)
(instructor of Native American studies)
Affiliation: Native American Studies Program, University of Oklahoma, 455 W. Lindsey, Rm. 804, Norman, OK 73019 (405) 325-2312.

ANDERSON, MARJORIE (MARGE) (Ojibwe) 1932-
(former tribal chief executive)
Born April 21, 1932 on the Mille Lacs Reservation, Onamia, Minn. *Affiliation & Address*: Chief Executive (1991-2000; 2008-2012), Mille Lacs Band of Ojibwe, 43408 Oodena Dr., Onamia, MN 56359 (320) 532-4181. *Past tribal affiliations*: District I Rep., 1976-87; Secretary/treasurer, 1987-91; served as the Minnesota's Chippewa Tribe's (MCT) vice president; also served on the MCT's education, housing & economic development & legislative committees. *Interests*: She has become an authority on the history, traditions and culture of her people and is fluent in the Ojibwe language. *Awards, honors*: Indian Child Advocate of the Year award in 1994 for her leadership on the effort to change the income & residency guidelines for the national Indian Head Start program; recognized by the Native American Finance Officers Association in 1994 with the lifetime achievement award for her dedication to opening doors to economic opportunity for Indian tribes.

ANDERSON, MARK A. (Bois Forte Chippewa)
(attorney)
Education: Gustavus Adolphus College (St. Peter, MN), BA, 1971; University of Minnesota Law School, JD, 1974. *Affiliation & Address*: Partner (1994-present), The Jacobson Law Group; Jacobson, Magnuson, Anderson & Halloran, P.C., 1295 Bandana Blvd., St. Paul, MN 55108 (651) 644-4710. E-mail: manderson@thejacobsonlawgroup.com. For 20 years, Mr. Anderson advised & represented the U.S. Dept. of the Interior at the Office of the Solicitor in Minnesota. He has acquired a national reputation for his work in the areas of Indian tribal authority & rights, natural resources protection & development, and land tenure in Indian Country. Mark also has extensive experience advising tribal business on a daily basis regarding management and personnel issues. He has been the principal advisor to a tribal enterprise client that has realized asset growth of over $25 million over a six-year period and has negotiated contracts for financing, construction, infrastructure, and provision of services to the enterprise & tribe. He has further represented tribal employers in administrative and judicial proceedings involving grievances and complaints arising under tribal and federal law, represented tribal employees in grievances and Merit Systems Protection Board matters arising under federal law, and has served as a hearing officer in tribal administrative processes covering appeals from disciplinary actions. Mr. Anderson also has counseled tribal employers in the development of comprehensive employee handbooks & personnel policies & has advised tribal human resources personnel on the administration of employee benefit plans, and has addressed FLSA, OSHA and ERISA issues arising under tribal benefit plans. He is a frequent lecturer on Indian law and natural resource issues throughout the United States.

ANDERSON, MICHAEL J. (Muscogee (Creek)/Choctaw)
(attorney)
Education: Georgetown University, JD, 1984. *Address & Affiliation*: Owner, Anderson Indian Law, 418-B C St. NE, Washington, DC 20002 (202) 543-5000. E-mail: info@mjaindianlaw.com. His practice areas include advocacy before federal agencies, legislative advocacy, counseling on all facets of the Indian Gaming Regulatory Act, trust land acquisition; tribal gaming commission counseling, and National Environmental Policy Act (NEPA) counseling. *Past professional posts*: Litigation Associate, Calkins, Kramer, Grimshaw & Harring, Denver, CO, 1984-85; Associate, Reed, Smith, Shaw & McClay, 1985-87; Associate, McKenna & Cueno, 1987-92; tribal planner, Muscogee (Creek) Nation; Associate Counsel & General Counsel, U.S. Senate Committee on Indian Affairs, Special Committee on Investigations; Associate Solicitor-Indian Affairs, U.S. Dept. of the Interior, 1993-95; Deputy Assistant Secretary-Indian Affairs, Dept. of the Interior, Washington, DC, 1995-2001; coordinator of the White House Working Group on American Indian & Alaska Natives; adjunct faculty at American University; co-founder, AndersonTuell, LLP; partner, Monteau & Peebles, LLP, Omaha, NE. At the Department, he provided counseling and policy advice on matters including: recognition of Alaska Native governments as federally recognized tribes; litigation support in hunting and fishing rights cases including the favorable result by the United States Supreme Court in Minnesota v. Mille Lacs Band of Chippewa Indians; chaired the Self Governance Negotiated Rulemaking Committee and testified before Congress two dozen times. served as General Counsel to the United States Senate Committee on Indian Affairs, Special Committee on Investigations. *Memberships*: Muskogee (Creek) Nation; National Congress of American Indians (executive director, 1991-92); Federal Bar Association; American Bar Association; Colorado Bar Association; District of Columbia Bar Association; Nebraska Bar Association. *Awards, honors*: Named in 2009 in Global Gaming Business Magazine as one of the "Ten Most Influential People in Gaming."

ANDERSON, MICHELLE N. (Athabascan)
(operation specialist/program officer)
Affiliation: U.S. Dept. of Housing & Urban Development (HUD), c/o Denali Commission, 510 L St., Suite 410, Anchorage, AK 99501 (907) 271-1542. E-mail: manderson@denali.gov. *Membership*: Americans for Indian Opportunity. *Interests*: Government-to-government relations.

ANDERSON, NORMAN (Aleut)
(AK village council president)
Affiliation: Naknek Native Village, P.O. Box 106, Naknek, AK 99633 (907) 246-4210.

ANDERSON, OWANAH (Choctaw)
(secretary-board of directors)
Affiliation: Secretary, Board of Directors, Association on American Indian Affairs, P.O. Box 268, Sisseton, SD 57262 (605) 698-3998.

ANDERSON, PATRICK M. (*Daakudein*) (Tlingit-Alutiiq) 1953-
(attorney; executive director)
Education: Princeton University Woodrow Wilson School of Public & International Affairs, 1975; University of Michigan Law School, JD, 1978. *Affiliation & Address*: Chugachmiut Natives, Inc. 1840 Bragaw St., Suite 110, Anchorage, AK 99508 (907) 562-4155. *Other professional posts*: Serves on the boards of Sealaska Corporation & the Alaska Native Justice Center (chairperson); commissioner, Alaska Justice & Law Enforcement Commission; co-chair, Alaska Federation of Natives, Human Resource Committee; and as Parliamentarian, National Congress of American Indians and the Alaska Federation of Natives; treasurer, Native American Children's Alliance, Muskogee, OK. *Past professional posts*: Anchorage's municipal lobbyist; director, Alaska Economic Development Center; assistant professor of Public Administration & Law Science, University of Alaska Southeast. *Awards, honors*: Outstanding Young Man of America in 1988. *Interests*: Coaches baseball as an NPA certified pitching coach; collects books on Alaska history & culture; occasionally makes jewelry as a hobby.

ANDERSON, PHYLISS J. (Mississippi Choctaw)
(tribal chief)
Affiliation & Address: Chief, Mississippi Band of Choctaw Indians, 101 Industrial Rd., Choctaw, MS 39350 (601) 656-5251. Chief Anderson, fluent in the Choctaw language, has more than 26 years of experience with tribal government management including eight years as tribal council representative and four years as Secretary-Treasurer of the Tribe.

ANDERSON, ROBERT (Bois Forte Ojibwe)
(professor of law)
Education: Bemidji State Univesity, BA, 1980; University of Minnesota Law School, JD, 1983. *Affiliation & Address*: Professor of Law & Director (2001-present), Native American Law Center, University of Washington, William H. Gates Hall, Box 353020, Seattle, WA 98195 (206) 685-2861. E-mail: boba@uw.edu. *Other professional posts*: Oneida Nation Visiting Professor of Law, Harvard Law School, Cambridge, MA, 2010-. Robert teaches the course, Federal Indian Law as it applies to Alaska Natives at The Institute for Tribal Government, The Hatfield School of Government, College of Urban & Public Affairs, Portland State University, Portland, OR; Of Counsel, Kanji & Katzen, Seattle, WA. *Past professional posts*: Senior Staff Attorney for the Native American Rights Fund (NARF), 1983-1995; Associate Solicitor for Indian Affairs, and as Counselor to the Secretary on legal and policy matters, 1995-97, and Counselor to the Secretary of the Interior, 1995-2001, Dept. of the Interior under Secretary Bruce Babbitt. *Awards, honors*: Students have selected Professor Anderson as a Professor of the Year three times at the UW. In 2008, he was co-lead of the Obama Transition team for the Department of the Interior; named to the National Commission on Indian Trust Administration & Reform by Secretary of the Interior Ken Salazar; Washington Law Review, Outstanding Faculty Contribution Award, 2011. *Published works*: Co-author & member of the Board of Editors of "Cohen's Handbook of Federal Indian Law" (2005); co-author of Anderson, Berger, Frickey & Krakoff, "American Indian Law: Cases & Commentary" (Second Edition, 2010).

ANDERSON, RODNEY (Eskimo)
(AK village council president)
Affiliation: Native Village of Chignik Lagoon, P.O. Box 57, Chignik Lagoon, AK 99565 (907) 840-2206.

ANDERSON, WILLIAM (Paiute)
(former tribal chairperson)
Affiliation & Address: Moapa Band of Paiutes, P.O. Box 340, Moapa, NV 89025 (702) 865-2787.

ANDERSON, WILLIAM, III (Inuit)
(association president)
Affiliation: President, Labrador Inuit Association, P.O. Box 70, Nain, Labrador, Canada A0P 1L0 (709) 922-2942.

ANDREAS, CHERYL (Paiute)
(tribal council chairperson)
Affiliation: Big Pine Reservation, P.O. Box 700, Big Pine, CA 93513 (619) 938-2003.

ANDREAS, MARY ANN (Cahuilla)
(tribalvice chairperson)
Affiliation & Address: Vice Chairperson, Morongo Band of Mission Indians, 12700 Pumarra Rd., Banning, CA 92220 (951) 849-4697.

ANDREAS, MARY ANN (Cahuilla)
(tribal vice-chairperson)
Education: Harvard University, special program for government leaders at the John F. Kennedy School of Government. *Affiliation & Address*: Vice-chairperson, Tribal Council, Morongo Band of Mission Indians, 12700 Pumarra Rd., Banning, CA 92220 (951) 849-4697. E-mail: martinandreas1@aol.com. *Other professional post*: 1st Vice Chair, Native American Caucus of the California Democratic Party, Sacramento, CA. *Past professional posts*: Served as a commissioner for the All Mission Indian Housing Authority, delegate to the San Bernardino County Board of Indian Health, and a board member of the Malki Museum, which is dedicated to preserving the cultures & traditions of Southern California Indian tribes. *Awards & honors*: She was the first member of her tribe to attend Harvard University, where she graduated from a special program for senior executives in state & local government. Mary Ann was a Super Delegate to the 1996 Democratic National Convention, and has served as a delegate in every subsequent national convention since. In 2008, she was a member of the National Convention Credentials Committee. Named Tribal Leader of the Year by the National Indian Gaming Association.

ANDREW, MARTIN (Eskimo)
(Alaskan village president)
Affiliation: Organized Village of Kwethluk, P.O. Box 130, Kwethluk, AK 99621 (907) 757-6714.

ANDREW, TREFIM (Athapascan)
(AK village council president)
Affiliation: Iguigig Village Council, P.O. Box 4008, Iguigig, AK 99613 (907) 533-3211.

ANDREWS, SCOTT (Cherokee)
(American Indian studies director)
Education: University of Oklahoma, BA, 1987; University of California, Riverside, MA, 1993, PhD, 2000. *Affiliation & Address*: Director, American Indian Studies Program, College of Humanities, 730 Sierra Tower, CSU Northridge, 18111 Nordhoff St., Northridge, CA 91330 (818) 677-3418. E-mail: scott.andrews@csun.edu. Scott teaches American & American Indian literatures in the English Dept. and American Indian Studies Program's course on popular culture. *Published works*: Book reviews, essays, fiction, and poetry.

ANDREWS-MALTAIS, CHERYL (Wampanoag)
(tribal chairperson)
Affiliation & Address: Chairperson, Wampanoag Tribe of Gay Head (Aquinnah), 20 Black Brook Rd., Aquinnah, MA 02535 (508) 645-9265.

ANELON, HARVEY (Athapascan)
(Alaskan village president)
Affiliation: Native Village of Iliamna, P.O. Box 286, Iliamna, AK 99606 (907) 571-1246.

ANGAIAK, THEODORE (Eskimo)
(Alaskan village president)
Affiliation: Native Village of Tunanuk, P.O. Box 77, Tununak, AK 99681 (907) 652-6527.

ANGASAN, SR., RALPH (Eskimo)
(Alaskan tribal president)
Affiliation: King Salmon Tribe, P.O. Box 68, King Salmon, AK 99613 (907) 246-3553.

ANGELO, LARRY (Ottawa)
(tribal chief)
Affiliation: Ottawa Tribe of Oklahoma, P.O. Box 110, Miami, OK 74355 (918) 540-1536.

ANGLE, HARVEY (Maidu)
(rancheria chairperson)
Affiliation: Enterprise Rancheria, 1940 Feather River Blvd., Suite B, Oroville, CA 95965 (530) 532-9214.

ANOATUBBY, BILL (Chickasaw) 1945-
(tribal governor)
Born November 8, 1945, Tishomingo, Okla. *Education*: Murray State College, AS, 1970; East Central University, BS, 1972. *Affiliation & Address*: Governor, Chickasaw Nation, P.O. Box 1548, Ada, OK 74821 (580) 436-2603. *Affiliations*: Chickasaw Nation (health services director, 1975; director of accounting dept.,

1976-78; special assistant to governor & controller, 1978-79; lieutenant governor, 1979-87; governor, 1987-). *Other professional post*: Member, Board of Directors, American Indian Graduate Center, Albuquerque, NM. *Military service*: U.S. Army National Guard, 1963-71 (staff Sgt.). *Community activities*: chairman, Advisory Council to the Special Trustee for American Indians, U.S. Dept. of the Interior; United Indian Nations in Oklahoma; Creative Oklahoma Board of Directors (member). *Past Leadership roles*: Ada Area Chamber of Commerce (board of directors); Oklahoma City University (board of trustees); Oklahoma State Chamber of Commerce & Industry (board of directors); Five Who Care (board of directors); Trail of Tears National Historic Trail Advisory Committee. *Memberships*: National Congress of American Indians; Inter-Tribal Council of the Five Civilized Tribes; Oklahoma Foundation for Excellence; Oklahoma Academy of State Goals. *Awards, honors*: Appointed to the Oklahoma Indian Affairs Commission, 1987, by Oklahoma Governor Henry Bellmon and re-appointed by Governor David Walters in 1991; appointed by President Bill Clinton to the board of trustees of the Morris K. Udall Scholarship & Excellence in National Environmental Policy Foundation, 1995; Leadership Oklahoma Class III; A+ Award, City of Ada, 1997; 1997 Governor's Arts Award, Oklahoma Arts Council; 1998 Honoree during Literacy Recognition Banquet, for his work in promoting adult literacy in Oklahoma; 2004 Oklahoma Hall of Fame Inductee; awarded the "Most Honored One' and "Friend of the Court" by the Oklahoma Supreme Court; 2007 "Centennial Leadership Award for Preservation of State & Local History," by the Oklahoma Heritage Assn; 2007 "Minority Advocate of the Year," by the U.S. Small Business Administration; 2007 Oklahoma Institute for Child Advocacy, "Outstanding Service to Oklahoma's Children Award"; 2007 Red Earth Ambassador. *Biographical source*: Who's Who in America; Who's Who in the South & Southwest.

ANSEL, ERYNNE
(museum director)
Affiliation: Iroquois Indian Museum, P.O. Box 7, Caverns Rd., Howes Cave, NY 12092 (518) 296-8949.

ANSPACH, ALLEN J. (Blackfeet) 1951-
(BIA regional director)
Born October 25, 1951, Lander, Wyo. *Education*: University of Arizona, BS, 1975. *Address & Affiliation*: Director, Bureau of Indian Affairs, Western Regional Office, P.O. Box 10, Phoenix, AZ 85001 (602) 379-6600 (2006-present). *Past professional posts*: Supt. Pawnee Agency, BIA, 1985-88; Supt., San Carlos Agency, BIA, San Carlos, AZ, 1988-93; Supt., Colorado River Agency, BIA, Parker, AZ, 1993-2005; Fort Apache Agency, BIA, 2005-06. *Other professional posts*: Vocational agricultural instructor, tribal operations specialist, land operations officer.

ANTELL, JUDITH A. (White Earth Ojibwe)
(director emerita of American Indian studies program)
Education: University of California, Berkeley, PhD (Ethnic Studies). *Affiliation & Address*: Director Emerita (1993-present), American Indian Studies Program, College of Arts & Sciences, University of Wyoming, Ross Hall 114, Anthropology Bldg., Laramie, WY 82701 (307) 766-6521. E-mail: antell@uwyo.edu.

ANTELL, LEE (White Earth Ojibwe)
(organization president & CEO)
Affiliation: President & CEO, American Indian Opportunities Industrialization Center (AIOIC), 1845 East Franklin Ave., Minneapolis, MN 55404 (612) 341-3358. E-mail: info@aioic.org.

ANTIQUIA, CLARENCE (Tlingit) 1940-
(federal government administrator)
Born April 16, 1940, Sitka, Alaska. *Education*: Sheldon Jackson Junior College, Sitka, Alaska, 1958-59. *Principal occupation*: Federal government administrator. *Address*: Box 1111, Juneau, Alaska 99802. *Affiliations*: Area director, Bureau of Indian Affairs, Juneau, Alaska, 1965-1975. *Awards, honors*: Outstanding Performance Awards, B.I.A., 1965, 1967, 1970. *Interests*: Public administration, government, race relations, Indian affairs.

ANTOINE, MINONQUA (*Greta Gigi*) (Odawa/Oneida) 1934-
(writer, singer)
Born March 5, 1934, Depauville, N.Y. *Education*: High schooll, some college. Principal occupation: Writer, singer. *Address*: Odawa Mukwa Dodem, 06185 Behling Rd., East Jordon, MI 49727 (231) 536-2162. E-mail: minonqua2000@yahoo.com. *Published work*: Medicine Bear; Minokahmeh.

ANTONE, DONALD R., SR. (Tohono O'odham)
(tribal council governor)
Affiliation: Gila River Indian Community Council, P.O. Box 97, Sacaton, AZ 85247 (520) 562-6000.

ANTONE, FRANCES G. (Tohono O'odham)
(tribal legislative council representative)
Affiliation & Address: Legislative Council Representative, Tohono O'odham Nation, P.O. Box 837, Sells, AZ 85634 (520) 383-2028. *Other professional post*: Tucson Area Rep., National Indian Health Board, Washington, DC.

ANTONE, MARTIN, SR. (Tohono O'odham)
(former tribal chairperson)
Affiliation: Ak Chin Indian Community Council, 42507 N. Peters & Nall Rd., Maricopa, AZ 85239 (602) 568-2227.

ANTONIO, CHRISTINE (Laguna Pueblo)
(associate director)
Affiliation: Office of Tribal Activities, Albuquerque Area Indian Health Services, 505 Marquette Ave., NW, Suite 1502, Albuquerque, NM 87102 (505) 766-2151.

ANTONIO, HARRY A. (Laguna Pueblo)
(former Pueblo Lt. governor)
Affiliation & Address: Former Lt. Governor, Pueblo of Laguna, P.O. Box 194, Laguna, NM 87026 (505) 552-6654.

ANTONIO, JOHN E. (Laguna Pueblo)
(former Pueblo governor)
Affiliation: Pueblo of Laguna, Box 194, Laguna, NM 87026 (505) 552-6654.

ANUNGAZUK, KELLY J. (Eskimo)
(Alaskan village president)
Affiliation: Native Village of Wales, Box 549, Wales, AK 99783 (907) 664-3062.

ANYON, ROGER (Zuni Pueblo)
(archaeology program director)
Affiliation: Zuni Archaeology Program, Pueblo of Zuni, P.O. Box 339, Zuni, NM 87327 (505) 782-4814.

ANYWAUSH, JOELLEN (Dakota)
(health director)
Affiliation: White Earth Band Clinic, P.O. Box 418, White Earth, MN 56591 (218) 983-3285.

ANYWAUSH, MARISA (Dakota)
(tribal vice chairperson)
Affiliation & Address: Vice Chairperson, Upper Sioux Community of Minnesota, P.O. Box 147, Granite Falls, MN 56241 (320) 564-2360.

APACHITO, GEORGE (Navajo)
(school chairperson)
Affiliation: Alamo Navajo School, P.O. Box 907, Magdalena, NM 87825 (505) 854-2543.

APACHITO, PATSY (Navajo)
(radio station manager)
Affiliation: KABR - 1500 AM, Alamo Navajo School Board, P.O. Box 907, Magdalena, NM 87825 (505) 854-2632.

APAREZUK, JOSEPH (Eskimo)
(Alaskan village chairperson)
Affiliation: Chair, Native Village of Bill Moore's Slough, P.O. Box 20288, Kotlik, AK 99620 (907) 899-4232.

APPLE, LESLIE (Oglala Lakota)
(development & grants coordinator)
Affiliation & Address: Development & Grants Coordinator, Tiwahe Foundation, 2801 21st Ave. South, Suite 132F, Minneapolis, MN 55407 (612) 722-0999. E-mail: lapple@tiwahefoundation.org.

APPLEBY, NANCY J.
(attorney; Indian law)
Affiliation & Address: Principal, Appleby Law PLLC (2009-present), 333 N. Fairfax St., Suite 302, Alexandria, VA 22314 (703) 837-0001. E-mail: nancy@applebylawpllc.com. Nancy is a nationally recognized expert in real estate and project development on tribal land. Her strength and reputation are the result of a number of factors, including 30 years experience and expertise in commercial real estate, lending, Indian law and the Indian Financing Act, and her strong relationships and credibility with tribal counsel and with counsel and staff at the Department of Interior. *Other professional post*: Member, Board of Directors, Tribal Business Opportunities, Albuquerque, NM; frequent speaker at American & State Bar Association meetings on real estate & Indian law; arbitrator, mediator & settlement facilitator for Indian & non-Indian claims.

Past professional posts: Rodey, Dickason, Sloan, Akin & Robb, PA, Albuquerque, NM, 1982-2005; Bracewell & Giuliani LLP, Washington, DC, 2005-09. *Awards, honors*: In 2004, Nancy was one of the first federal Indian law attorneys in the U.S. to be recognized by hambers USA – Best Lawyers in America as one of the the premier Indian law attorneys in America based on evaluations by peers & clients. She has earned a top ranking every year since.

AQUALLO, ALAN LECHUSA (Luiseno/Maidu)
  (professor of American Indian studies)
Education: California State University, Long Beach, B.A. (Music); University of California, Irvine M.F.A. and a Ph.D. in Critical Studies/Experimental Practices (CS/EP) PhD focusing upon Native American Hip Hop, Identity and Native American contemporary culture from the University of California, San Diego. *Affiliation & Address*: Professor, American Indian Studies Program, American Studies Department, Palomar Community College, 1140 W. Mission Rd., San Marcos, CA 92069 (619) 744-1150. E-mail: aaquallo@palomar.edu Dr. Lechusza Aquallo's academic focus is on Native/Indigenous music and the multi-media arts in addition to his work as a multi-genre composer and installation/performing artist.

ARAGON, ARNOLD (Crow-Pueblo) 1953-
  (artist, shop owner)
Born July 9, 1953, Crow Agency, Mont. *Education*: American Indian Art Institute, Santa Fe, N.M. (Art/Sculpture), 1979 graduate; University of Nevada, Reno, 1980-84. *Principal occupation*: Professional artist & shop owner. *Address*: P.O. Box 64, Walker River Reservation, Schurz, NV 89427. *Affiliation*: Aragon native Sculpture, P.O. Box 64, Schurz, NV 89427 (775) 773-2542. *Other professional posts*: Rites of Passage Wilderness Camp, Schurz, Nevada; art consultant, board member, Nevada Urban Indians--Earth Window. *Interests*: Sculpturing using hand tools. His art includes watercolors, pastels & pencil drawings. Arnold's sculptures are in various galleries and museums throughout the West as well as private collections throughout the country. He enjoys travel and the outdoors.

ARAGON, RALPH (San Felipe Pueblo)
  (artist)
Education: Institute of American Indian Arts, Santa Fe, NM. Ralph resides in the Pueblo of Zia, NM. *Affiliation*: Zia pottery, rock art images and patterns, paint shields, pottery & gourds.

ARAGON, VIDAL (Santo Domingo Pueblo)
  (pueblo council governor)
Affiliation: Santo Domingo Pueblo Council, P.O. Box 99, Santo Domingo, NM 87052 (505) 465-2214.

ARAUJO, JAELEEN (Tlingit)
  (vice president & general counsel)
Education: Stanford University, BA; University of New Mexico School of Law, JD. *Affiliation & Address*: Vice President & General Counsel, Sealaska Corporation, One Sealaska Plaza, #400, Juneau, AK 99801. (907) 586-2304.

ARCHAMBAULT, DAVE LEON (Standing Rock Sioux)
  (consultant; educational administrator)
Education: Black Hills State College, Spearfish, SD, BS (Secondary Education), 1976; Pennsylvania State University, MS (Educational Administration), 1982. *Principal occupation*: Educational administrator. *Address*: P.O. Box 519, Fort Yates, ND 58538 (701) 854-7246. E-mail: hotspit@westriv.com, dave.archambault@aibl.org. *Affiliations*: Assistant principal & Jr. High Principal, Little Wound School, Kyle, SD (eight years); acting recreation director, United Tribes Technical College, Bismarck, ND (three years); president, Standing Rock College, Fort Yates, ND, 1987-. *Other professional posts*: American Indian Higher Education Consortium, (1972-; president, 1989); chair, American Indian Business Leaders (www.aibl.org), University of Montana, Missoula, MT. *Community activities*: Board member, American Indian College Fund; board member, North Dakota Humanities Council; secretary, Sitting Bull Historical Society. *Memberships*: National Indian Activities Association, (Board of Directors, 1972-82 & 1987); National Indian Education Association; American Association of Colleges & Junior Colleges. *Awards, honors*: South Dakota Cross Country Coach of the Year, 1980; South Dakota Indian Educator of the Year, 1982; National Indian Basketball Coach of the Year, 1980. *Interests*: "Most interested in educational reform. Masters degree work was done on rationale and justification to change K-12 systems to better meet the needs of Indian learners. (I am an) advocate of the literacy work done by Paulo Freire, author of "Pedogogy of the Oppressed."

ARCHAMBAULT, DAVE LEON, II (*Tokala Ohitika*) (Standing Rock Sioux)
  (tribal chairperson)
Born in Denver, Colo. Education: North Dakota State University, BS (Business Administration); University of Mary, MS (Management). *Affiliation & Address*: Chairperson (2013-present), Standing Rock Sioux Tribe, P.O. Box D, Fort Yates, ND 58538 (701) 854-8500.

ARCHAMBEAULT, DWIGHT (Standing Rock Sioux)
  (former BIA regional supt.)
Affiliation & Address: Supt., Bureau of Indian Affairs, Standing Rock Agency, P.O. Box E, Fort Yates, ND 58538 (701) 854-3433 E-mail: Dwight.archambault@bia.gov

ARCHAMBAULT, JOALLYN (Standing Rock Sioux) 1942-
  (anthropologist, program director)
Born February 13, 1942, Claremore, Okla. *Education*: University of California, Berkeley, BA, 1970, MA, 1971, PhD, 1984 (Dissertation topic: "The Gallup Ceremonial," A study of patronage within a contemporary context of Indian-white relationships). *Affiliation & Address*: Director of American Indian Programs (1986-present), National Museum of Natural History, NHB 112, Smithsonian Institution, Washington, DC 20560 (202) 357-4760 (work). *Past professional posts*: Lecturer in Native American Studies, University of California, Berkeley, 1976-1979; Department chairperson & lecturer in Ethnic Studies Program, California College of Arts & Crafts, 1979-1983; research associate, Center for the Study of Race, Crime & Social Policy of Cornell University, 1980-82; field ethnographer, Sonoma State Foundation, 1983-1984; assistant professor in anthropology, University of Wisconsin, Milwaukee, 1983-1986. *Community activities*: Board member: California Indian Education Association, 1967-70; Native American Scholarship Fund, Inc., 1976-77; City of Berkeley Minority Elder Project, 1976-77; Committee to Stop Hanta Yo, 1979-82; advisory council member, Foundation for Illinois Archaeology, Native American Studies Program, 1980-81. *Memberships*: American Anthropological Association; Native American Art Studies Association (vice-president, 1982-85); Society for Applied Anthropology; American Ethnological Society; Anthropology Society of Washington. *Awards, honors*: Ford Foundation Fellowship; National Endowment for the Humanities Travel Grant; numerous art awards dating from 1969 through 1980; art exhibits (group and one-man shows); examples of art in permanent collection of the Heard Museum, the Navajo Tribal Museum, the Indian Arts & Crafts Board, the Red Cloud Cultural Center, and numerous private collections. *Interests*: "Art & material culture, political anthropology, ethnic relations, Indian-white relations. I curated an exhibit titled Plains Indian Arts - Change & Continuity for the National Museum of Natural History. The exhibit traveled nationally in 1989." *Published works*: Articles; An Annotated Bibliography of Sources on Plains Indian Art (G.K. Hall & Co.); and The Uses of Non-Visual Sacred Material in Museums by Contemporary Native Americans (Buffalo Bill Historical Center).

ARCHAMBEAU, MADONNA (Yankton Sioux)
  (tribal chairperson)
Affiliation: Yankton Sioux Tribal Business Committee, P.O. Box 248, Marty, SD 57361 (605) 384-3804.

ARCHULETA-DEAN, ALAINA (Kaibab Paiute)
  (communications coordinator)
Born & raised in Denver, Colo. *Education*: University of Northern Colorado, BA (Communi-cations). *Affiliation & Address*: Communications Coordinator & Executive Assistant, First Nations Development Institute, 351 Coffman St., Suite 200, Longmont, CO 80501 (303) 774-7836. *Past professional posts*: National Indian Gaming Association (NIGA), Washington, DC; National Indian Education Association (NIEA).

ARCHULETA, GARY (Koncow-Maidu)
  (rancheria chairperson)
Affiliation & Address: Chairperson, Mooretown Rancheria, 1 Alverda Dr., Oroville, CA 95965 (530) 533-3625.

ARCHULETA, MANUEL (Picuris Pueblo)
  (Pueblo governor)
Affiliation & Address: Governor, Picuris Pueblo, P.O. Box 127, Penasco, NM 87553 (575) 587-2519.

AREVGAQ JOHN, THERESA (Yup'ik) 1957-
  (associate professor of indigenous studies)
Education: University of Alaska, Fairbanks, BA, 1983, MEd (Cross-cultural Education), 1992, PhD (Indigenous Studies, 2010. *Affiliation & Address*: Professor (2001-present), Dept. of Alaska Native Studies & Rural Development, University of Alaska, Fairbanks, 319 Brooks Bldg., P.O. Box 756500, Fairbanks, AK 99775 (907) 474-1539. E-mail: tjohn@alaska.edu. *Past professional posts*: Village administrator, City of Toksook Bay, 1976-77; commercial fisher, in Bristol Bay & Nelson Island, 1977-2002; Instructor, Alaska Native Studies Department, University of Alaska, 1989-92; assistant professor, Alaska Native Studies & Theatre Dept., University of Alaska, Fairbanks, 1992-97; Native teacher mentor, Alaska Native Teachers for Excellence Project, The CIRI Foundation, 1998-1999; assistant professor of Alaska Native Studies & Liberal Arts, Alaska Pacific University, 1999-2000; adjunct professor, Kuskokwim Community College, 2001. *Community activities*: Founder, director, script writer, choreographer, cast member, dancer, singer, Tuma Theatre, 1980; Panel member, Traditional Native Arts Panel,

Alaska State Council on the Arts, 1985-86; executive board member, Dancing Bear Productions, 1985-87; UAF Chancellors Advisory Committee on Native Education, 1993-97; executive board member, Institute of Alaska Native Arts, 1992-98; member, Alaska Native/Rural Education Consortium, 1995-present; ANHC Yup'ik/Cup'ik Cultural Advisory Committee, 1997-present. *Areas of Interest*: Cross-cultural education, Yup'ik language & culture, preserving historical Alaskan films, Alaska Native dance, history & culture of Alaska Natives, Alaska Native theatre, preserving cultural knowledge from elders.

ARIAS, RONALD (Havasupai)
(Indian school principal)
Affiliation: Havasupai School, P.O. Box 40, Supai, AZ 86435 (520) 448-2901.

ARKEKETA, BENNETT (Ponca)
(tribal chairperson; technical programs manager)
Affiliations: Chairperson, Ponca Tribe of Oklahoma Business Committee, 20 White Eagle Dr., Ponca City, OK 74601 (580) 762-8104; technical programs manager, Native Americans in Biological Sciences, 306 Life Sciences East, Oklahoma State University, Stillwater, OK 74078 (405) 744-6802.

ARKEKETA, SUSAN M. (Otoe-Missouria/Muscogee Creek) 1954-
(humanities chair)
Born September 5, 1954, Tulsa, Okla. *Education*: University of Oklahoma, BA (Journalism), 1978, MA (Communications), 1983. *Principal occupation*: Humanities chair. *Address*: 155 Indian Ave., Lawrence, KS 66046 (913) 749-8431 (work). *Affiliations*: Director, Native American Journalists Association, 1987-90; writer/editor, Native American Rights Fund, Boulder, CO, 1985-91; Haskell Indian Nations University, Lawrence, KS (journalism instructor1991-.94; Humanities Chair, 1994-present) *Other professional posts*: Advisory Board, Winds of Change, Boulder, CO; freelance writer; consultant-proposal writer; writer/editor. *Community activities*: Lawrence Arts Commission, Lawrence KS; Three Sisters Festival. *Memberships*: Kansas Indian Education Assn; Native American Journalists Assn; American Assn of University Women. *Awards, honors*: Miss Indian America, 1978; Outstanding Young Woman of America, 1982, 1986 & 1987; Indian National Finals, Rodeo Trade Fair.

ARMAGOST, JAMES GRAYHAWK (Mohican) 1945-
(silversmith & lapidary; shop owner)
Born July 8, 1945, Johnstown, Penn. *Education*: Accredited GRE - two year college. Address: Unknown. *Affiliation & Address*: Owner, Silver Phoenix Trading Post, 1371 Caverns Rd., Quicksburg, VA 22847 (540) 477-9616. The Silver Phoenix has been promoting Native American crafts for 15 years. *Military service*: U.S. Army Special Forces. *Community activities*: American Indian Inter-Tribal Cultural Organization (member, board of directors.) *Memberships*: American Indian Society of Washington, DC; American Indian Intertribal Cultural Association. *Awards, honors*: Numerous first place and Best of Show Awards for his jewelry in assorted regional competitions (Native American and non-Native American). *Art form*: His Navajo leafwork & multi-level chizeled boarders are some of the cleanest to be found. The geometrics in his overlay styles are crisp and exact, and his animals, plants and people are nearly animated. He has also produced breathtaking pieces blending inlaid stone & highly polished metal with flawless skill. He has walked away with top prizes in every competition he has ever entered. Annual powwow.

ARMENTA, VINCENT (Chumash)
(former tribal chairperson)
Affiliation & Address: Santa Ynez Band of Chumash Indians, P.O. Box 517, Santa Ynez, CA 93440 (805) 688-7997.

ARMER, CHRISTINE (Cherokee)
(Cherokee language instructor)
Affiliation & Address: Cherokee Language Instructor, Native American Language Program, Department of Anthropology, College of Arts & Sciences, The University of Oklahoma, 455 W. Lindsey, Cate 4 Room 202, Norman, OK 73019 (405) 325-2615. E-mail: carmer@ou.edu.

ARMSTRONG, DAVID
(attorney; Indian law office director)
Education: University of North Carolina-Asheville, BA, 2004; Northern Illinois University College of Law, JD, 2007. *Affiliation & Address*: Director, Indian Law Office, Judicare Wisconsin, Inc., P.O. Box 6100, Wausau, WI 54402 (715) 842-1681. *Other professional post*: Reviewer, Indigenous Policy Journal, 2008-present. *Memberships*: U.S. Distrct Courts, Eastern & Western Wisconsin; Ho-Chunk Nation Supreme Court; Menominee Tribal Court.

ARMSTRONG, RICHARD J. (Yakama)
(attorney)
Education: University of California, Davis, BA, 1993; Arizona State University, JD, 1996; Naval Justice School (Judge Advocate 197); Marine Corps University - Command & Staff Course, 2014. Affiliation & Address: Of Counsel, Rosette, LLP, 193 Blue Ravine Rd. #255, Folsom, CA 95630 (916) 353-1084.

E-mail: Armstrong@rosettelaw.com. Mr. Armstrong has over twenty years of experience in federal Indian Law. As a descendant of Confederated Tribes and Bands of the Yakama Indian Nation, he has maintained close ties to the Native American Indian community his entire life. Mr. Armstrong began his legal career as an intern with the Office of Legal Counsel for the Confederated Tribes and Bands of the Yakama Indian Nation in 1993. Mr. Armstrong was active in the Native American Student Union and received a minor in Native American Studies from the University of California Davis between 1988 and 1993. Mr. Armstrong was also active in the Native American Law Student Association at the Arizona State University College of Law while in law school between 1993 and 1996, & serving as President in 1996. His primary areas of practice have been gaming related and include advising tribal governments on compact related matters, establishing tribal gaming agencies in order to implement provisions of gaming ordinances & compacts, advising tribal gaming agencies with regard to gaming regulation development, licensing & administrative hearing procedures. Mr. Armstrong's extensive experience includes working with the National Indian Gaming Commission (NIGC), Governor's Office for the State of California, California Attorney General's Office, Bureau of Gambling Control, California Gambling Control Commission (CGCC), and the Tribal-State Association on tribal & gaming commission matters. Mr. Armstrong has provided numerous regulatory updates to the membership of California Nations Indian Gaming Association (CNIGA) and has been an invited speaker at numerous National Indian Gaming Association (NIGA) gaming commission training courses throughout the country. Mr. Armstrong has honorably served our country in the United States Marine Corps for twenty-six years and continues to serve as a Major and Judge Advocate in the United States Marine Corps Reserves. He enlisted in 1987 & was commissioned as an officer in 1993. Most recently, Mr. Armstrong is currently assigned as a Regional Judge Advocate & provides legal services to Marines and Marine commands throughout the western United States. He completed six years on active duty as a Judge Advocate performing Trial Counsel, Defense Counsel & Legal Assistance Officer duties, as well as a tour as a Marine instructor at the Naval Justice School Detachment in San Diego, California. He has extensive trial experience as a prosecutor and trial defense counsel at General & Special Courts-martial, as well as administrative proceedings. Mr. Armstrong's military awards & decorations include the United States Marine Corps Commandant's Trophy (Honor Graduate at Officer Candidate School), Navy & Marine Corps Commendation Medal with Gold Star, National Defense Service Medal with Bronze Star, a Meritorious Unit Citation and the Global War on Terrorism Service Medal.

ARNETT, HOWARD
(attorney)
Education: Stanford University, BA (Political Science), 1970; London School of Economics, MSc, 1971; University of Oregon School of Law, JD, 1977. Affiliation & Address: Partner, Karnopp Peterson LLP, 360 SW Bond St., Suite 400 Bend, OR 97702 (541) 382-3011. *Practice Areas*: Indian Law; Natural Resources & Energy; Strategies. Howard joined Karnopp Petersen in 1980, after working as a legal services attorney on the Navajo Indian Reservation in Arizona following law school. He has concentrated his practice in the area of Federal Indian law, especially with representation of the Confederated Tribes of the Warm Springs Reservation of Oregon as well as other tribes, on matters involving treaty rights, tribal sovereignty, tribal law development, government-to-government relations,and gaming. Howard has additional expertise in civil litigation & appellate practice. *Professional and Community Activities*: He is active in Oregon's statewide legal community. He has served as a member of the Oregon State Board of Bar Examiners, the Bar Examiners' Review Board, and as a past member of the Executive Committee of the Appellate Practice, Indian Law and Legal Services sections of the Oregon State Bar. He also served as Lawyer's Representative to the Ninth Circuit Judicial Conference. Howard served as President of the Oregon Law Foundation Board for 2013 and currently serves as the statewide Co-Chair of the Lawyers' Campaign for Equal Justice and is a member of the CEJ Board. Howard also is an adjunct professor at the University of Oregon School of Law. He teaches the survey course on American Indian Law as well as advanced seminars on Tribal Law and Tribal Courts, Contemporary Issues in American Indian Law and Comparative Law of Indigenous Peoples. Previously, he was an adjunct professor at the Lewis & Clark Law School teaching the survey course and advanced seminars on Federal Indian Law.

ARNOLD, GREIG W. (Makah)
(tribal vice chairperson)
Affiliation & Address: Vice Chairperso, Makah Indian Tribal Council, P.O. Box 115, Neah Bay, WA 98357 (360) 645-2201.

ARNOLD, LINDA J. (Dine')
(attorney)
Affiliation & Address: In-house counsel (2003-present), Pinnacle West Capital Corporation, Law Department, 400 N. 5th St., MS 8695, Phoenix, AZ 85004 (602) 250-3633. Linda serves with co-counsels to provide pro bono legal services to help shape and/or reform the laws & regulations that will help

assure the religious rights of Native Americans. *Other professional posts*: President, Board of Directors, Phoenix Indian Center; founding member & secretary, National Native American Bar Association, Tempe, AZ; member, State Bar of Arizona Selection Committee for the Bar Leadership Institute. *Past professional posts*: Arizona Public Service Co.; served on the State Bar's Diversity Task Force. *Awards, honors*: Received the 2009 Hal Israel award from the State Bar of Arizona acknowledging her generous commitment of time & knowledge to the community through Bar-sponsored programs & initiatives.

ARNOLD, RICHARD W. (Southern Paiute)
(Indian Center director)
Education: Mt. San Antonio College (Walnut, CA) AA (Police Science), 1973; Cal-State University, Long Beach, BS (Criminal Justice/Administration, Certificate & Minor in American Indian Studies), 1975, MS (Educational Psychology & Counseling), 1977. *Address & Affiliation*: Executive director (1977-present), Las Vegas Indian Center, 2300 W. Bonanza Rd., Las Vegas, NV 89106 (702) 647-5842. *Other professional posts*: Nevada State Steering Committee on Indian Education; U.S. Senate appointed Delegate to the White House Conference on Indian Education; Commissioner, Nevada Indian Commission; consultant to: U.S. Dept. of Labor Division of Indian & Native American Programs & U.S. Dept. of Energy; member, Board of Trustees, Nevada Business Services, Nevada State Board of Social Workers-Advisory Committee on Continuing Education; Minority Outreach Council; Delegate to the White House Conference on Indian Education; Chairperson, Nevada State Education Steering Committee; Consultant to Yucca Mountain Cultural Resources Program & Nevada Test Site-American Indian Religious Freedom Act Compliance Program. *Community activities*: Clark County Police Community Relations Board; Preservation Association of Clark County; Federal Emergency Management Board of Clark County; Comprehensive Housing Affordability Strategy Task Force, City of Las Vegas & Clark County; American Red Cross Long Range Planning Committee, Clark County; Overall Economic Development Plan Committee & Training Conference; Fair Housing Task Force - City of Las Vegas; Affirmative Action Advisory Committee. *Memberships*: National Adult Indian Education Assn; Nevada State Board of Social Workers; National Indian Education Assn; National Indian Employment & Training Assn; National Urban Indian Council. *Awards, honors*: Letters of Commendation: City of Las Vegas, Clark County, Governor-State of Nevada, U.S. Dept. of Energy, National Indian & Native American Employment & Training Conference, Las Vegas Chamber of Commerce; Boulder City Rotary Club. *Interests*: Community development - major area of vocational interest, including facilitating motivational seminars for American Indians; enjoy public speaking & representing American Indian interests in associated issues; enjoy traveling, collecting & restoring antiques.

ARQUERO, J. LEROY (Cochiti Pueblo)
(pueblo governor)
Affiliations & Address: Governor, Pueblo of Cochiti, P.O. Box 70, Cochiti, NM 87072 (505) 465-2244.

ARQUETTE, DAVID (Mohawk) 1963-
(environmentalist)
Born August 29, 1963, Rochester, N.Y. *Education*: Canton (NY) Agricultural & Technical College, AAS, 1984; Rochester Institute of Technology, B.T., 1991. *Affiliation*: Environmentalist, St. Regis Mohawk Tribe, Hogansburg, NY, 1991-. *Memberships*: American Indian Science & Engineering Society (AISES); American Society of Civil Engineers. *Awards, honors*: A.T. Anderson Award, AISES; Frederick Douglas Scholarship, Minority Student Affairs Office, R.I.T.; Merit Award for Excellence in Leadership and Community Service, R.I.T. *Interests*: First National People of Color Environmental Conference, Washington, DC - protecting the rights of minorities and the environment; James Bay II - involved in helping the Cree & Inuit people protect their lands & culture from degradation of dams being built by Hydro-Quebec.

ARQUETTE, T. LULANI (Hawaiian)
(foundation president & CEO)
Education: University of Hawaii, BA (Drama & Theatre), MA (Political Science). *Affiliation & Address*: President/CEO, Native Arts & Cultures Foundation, 11109 NE 14th St., Vancouver, WA 98684 (360) 314-2421. Lulani has more than 25 years experience in all phases of operations including strategic visioning & planning, resource development, building partnerships, & program development. She is a strong advocate of Native self-determination and was involved in developing the first for-profit subsidiary of ALU LIKE, Inc., the largest multi-service organization in Hawaii serving Native Hawaiians.

ARROW, DENNIS WAYNE (Cheyenne-Arapaho) 1949-
(professor of law; center associate director)
Born July 27, 1949, Chicago, Ill. *Education*: George Washington University, BA, 1970; California Western School of Law, JD, 1974; Harvard University, LL.M, 1975. *Address & Affiliation*: Associate Director, Native American Legal Resource Center, 1988-, Oklahoma City University, 2501 N. Blackwelder, Oklahoma City, OK 73106 (405) 208-5179 (Professor of Law, 1975-associate

director, 1988-; associate justice, Supreme Court of the Cheyenne-Arapaho Tribes, Concho, OK, 1995-. E-mail: darrow@okcu.edu. *Other professional posts*: Associate director, Center for the Study of State Constitutional Law & Government, Oklahoma City University School of Law; editor-in-chief, Oklahoma Tribal Court Reports. *Community activities*: Oklahoma Assn of Scholars (president); Oklahoma Constitution Revision Commission (member). *Memberships*: Oklahoma Indian Bar Assn (president, Oklahoma City Chapter, 1989-90); American Indian Bar Assn. *Awards, honors*: Outstanding Graduate-Level Professor, Oklahoma City University, 1990. *Interests*: American Indian law (sovereignty issues); constitutional law (state and federal); U.S. Supreme Court litigation. *Published works*: Contributing Editor, Oklahoma Tribal Court Reports (eight vols. to date); Indian Country, Indian Lands, Indian Jurisdiction, in 22 Sovereignty Symposium (Oklahoma Supreme Court, et al., 2009) 73 pp.

ARROYO, ANGELINA (Habematolel Pomo)
(tribal vice chairperson)
Affiliation & Address: Chairperson (2008-present), Habematolel Pomo of Upper Lake Rancheria, P.O. Box 516, Upper Lake, CA 95485 (707) 275-0737.

ARROYO de WALKER, CANDACE J.
(WRG president)
Affiliation & Address: President, Walker Research Group (WRG), Ltd., P.O. Box 4147, Boulder, CO 80306 (303) 492-6719. Website: www.walkerresearch group.com. Mrs. Arroyo de Walker is majority stockholder in WRG, Ltd. She has extensive research experience in the Hispanic cultures of Colorado and the greater U.S. Southwest, and has served as cultural consultant & official interpreter in a variety of capacities and is of both Hispanic and American Indian descent. She is an expert in the graphic, plastic, and textile arts of the Indigenous cultures of the Southwest.

ARRUM, DARLENE (Paiute)
(tribal band chairperson)
Affiliation & Address: Kanosh Band of the Paiute Indian Tribe of Utah, P.O. Box 116, Kanosh, UT 84637 (435) 383-3283.

ARTERBERRY, BETTY (Pomo)
(tribal vice chairperson)
Affiliation & Address: Vice Chairperson, Dry Creek Rancheria Band of Pomo Indians, P.O. Box 1607, Geyserville, CA 95441 (707) 431-4090.

ARTMAN, CARL J. (Oneida of Wisconsin)
(professor & program director)
Education: Columbia College (Missouri), B.A.; University of Wisconsin-Madison, M.B.A.; Washington University School of Law, J.D.; University of Denver, LL.M. in Natural Resources & Environmental Law. *Affiliation & Address*: Professor of Practice (2009-present), Director, College of Law's Economic Development in Indian Country Program, Sandra Day O'Connor College of Law, Armstrong Hall, Arizona State University (ASU), Box 877906, Tempe, AZ 85287 (480) 965-4085. E-mail: carl.artman@asu.edu. *Past professional posts*: Assistant Secretary-Indian Affairs, U.S. Dept. of the Interior, Washington, DC 2007-09); Interior Department's Associate Solicitor for Indian Affairs; chief legal counsel & director of Federal Affairs, Oneida Tribe of Indians of Wisconsin; COO of an Oneida tribe-owned telecommunications venture; member, Board of Directors for the Library of Congress's American Folk Life Center, Oneida Nation Electronics, et al; member, Board of the Presidential Board of Advisors on Tribal Colleges & Universities; worked on the staff of Rep. Michael Oxley, R-Ohio. As the 10th Assistant Secretary-Indian Affairs, Mr. Artman was responsible to carry out the Department's trust responsibilities regarding the management of tribal & individual Indian trust lands & assets, and was responsible for promoting the self-determination & economic self-sufficiency of the nation's 565 federally recognized American Indian & Alaska Native tribes and their almost two million members.

ARVISO, DANA (Navajo)
(executive director)
Born & raised on the Bishop Paiute-Shoshone Indian Reservation in California. *Education*: California State University, Sacramento, BA (Child Development); University of Washington, MA (Education); 2008 granduate of First Nations Development Institute's Seattle LEAD Program. *Affiliation & Address*: Executive Director, Potlatch Fund, 801 Second Ave., Suite 34, Seattle, WA 98104 (206) 624-6075. E-mail: dana@potlatchfund.org. *Other professional posts*: Board member, Native Americans in Philanthropy, Minneapolis, MN; board member, Social Justice Fund Northwest; board member, Longhouse Media. *Interests*: Dana has dedicated her life to combating the social & economic disparities that affect all communities of color in Pacific Northwest.

ARVISO-ALVORD, LORI, M.D. (Navajo)
(surgeon, professor & associate dean)
Born in Crownpoint, N.M. *Education*: Dartmouth College, BA; Stanford University Medical School, MD, 1985. *Address & Affiliation*: Affiliate Faculty, University of Arizona College of Medicine, Family & Community Medicine,

1642 E. Helen St., Room 106, Tucson, AZ 85719 (520) 626-6216. E-mail: lalvord@medadmin.arizona.edu. *Other professional posts*: Dr. Alvord performs clinical research in surgical outcomes in American Indian populations, and is funded by a National Institute of Health grant from the National Institute of Aging. She is also a member of the NIH's National Advisory Council for the National Institute of Complementary & Alternative Medicine. *Past professional post*: Surgeon, Navajo & Zuni Tribes, Indian Health Service, Gallup, NM, 1991-97; served on the Advisory Council for Complementary & Alternative Medicine (NACCAM), a component of the national Institutes of Health; Professor & Associate Dean of Student & Multicultural Affairs, Office of Multicultural Affairs, Dartmouth Geisel School of Medicine, Hanover, NH. *Published work*: Co-author, with Elizabeth Cohen Van Pelt, "The Scalpel and the Silver Bear: The First Navajo Surgeon Combines Western Medicine & Traditional Healing." *Interests*: Dr. Alvord is the first Navajo woman surgeon, and an advocate for the use of Native healing philosophies & practices in modern medicine. *Awards, honors*: Outstanding Women in Medicine Award from the University of Missouri-Kansas City School of Medicine; Governor's Award for Outstanding Women from the State of New Mexico.

ARVISO, TOM, JR. (Navajo)
(publisher & CEO)
Born & raised in Window Rock, Ariz. *Education*: Mesa Community College; Arizona State University, BA (Journalism); Stanford University (Newspaper Management) John S. Knight Fellowship in 2000-01. *Affiliation & Address*: Editor, 1988-993, Publisher & CEO, 1993-present, Navajo Times Publishing Co., Inc., P.O. Box 310, Window Rock, AZ 86515 (928) 871-7359. E-mail: tarviso@navajotimes.com. *Other professional post*: President & CEO, Unity: Journalists of Color, Inc., McLean, VA. *Past professional posts*: Sportswriter & news reporter, Navajo Times Today, 1984-86; wrote for "The Arizona Indian" (monthly), Phoenix, AZ. *Memberships*: Native American Journalists Association (former vice president & treasurer). *Awards, honors*: NAJA's "Wassaja Award" in 1997, for extraordinary service to Native journalism; 1998 "Freedom of Information Award," Arizona Newspaper Association. He is the only full-blood Native American to have been selected for a Knight Fellowship,

ASETOYER, CHARON (Comanche) 1951-
(executive director)
Born March 24, 1951, San Jose, Calif. *Education*: School of International Training (Masters of International Administration & Masters of International Management), 1983. *Address & Affiliation*: Executive Director (1988-present), Native American Women's Health Education Resource Center, Native American Community Board, P.O. Box 572, Lake Andes, SD 57356 (605) 487-7072. E-mail: charon@charles-mix.com. *Other professional post*: Editor, Wicozanni Wowapi, newsletter. *Memberships*: National Women's Network (executive board); South Dakota Coalition of Violence & Sexual Assault, Advisory Committee for Girls, Inc. *Awards, honors*: "Women of Vision Award," by Ms Foundation. *Interests*: Reproductive rights for indigenous women. *Published works*: Women, AIF+DS & Activism (collection of works by women) (South End Press, 1990).

ASHBY, RICKIE (Eskimo)
(AK village council president)
Affiliation: Native Village of Noatak, P.O. Box 89, Noatak, AK 99761 (907) 485-2173.

ATAUMBI, KERI (Kiowa)
(artist)
Address: 76 Camino Tocido, Santa Fe, NM 87507 (505) 424-3207. E-mail: ataumbi@msn.com. *Artwork*: Jewelry, paintings, and sculpture.

ATCHAK, ROY J. (Eskimo)
(Alaskan village chief)
Affiliation: First Chief, Chevak Native Village, P.O. Box 140, Chevak, AK 99563 (907) 858-7428.

ATCITTY, R. THREEHAWK (Dine'-Navajo)
(artisan, shop owner)
Address: Mizhoni Keyah, Inc., Orlando, FL (407) 293-4757. E-mail: info@ nizhonikeyah.com. *Art forms*: Designer silver, bone & natural mineral jewelry & chokers, breastplates, drums & carvings.

ATCITTY, SHENAN R. (Dine'-Navajo)
(attorney; board president)
Education: University of New Mexico, BA, 1988; University of New Mexico School of Law, JD, 1993. *Address & Affiliation*: Partner, Sr. Counsel, Holland & Knight, LLP, 2099 Pennsylvania Ave., NW, Suite 100, Washington, DC 20006 (202) 457-7128; E-mail: shenan.atcitty@hklaw.com. Shenan focuses on representing Indian tribal governments before Congress & Federal Agencies. *Other professional post*: President, Board of Directors, American Indian Graduate Center, Albuquerque, NM. *Past professional posts*: Ms. Atcitty began her legal career clerking and later serving as a contract attorney for the U.S.

attorney's office, District of New Mexico in Albuquerque, N.M. where she focused on Indian water rights adjudications & settlements, as well as protection of Indian lands in the Southwest. Following her work with the U.S. attorney's office, she joined a small firm in Albuquerque which handled all of the Navajo Nation's complex litigation. While working there, she second-chaired the successful litigation and settlement of a class action lawsuit filed on behalf of all Navajo allottees against the federal government for beneficial title to the minerals underlying their allotments. When the federal government broke apart the eastern portion of the Navajo Reservation in the early 1900's under the allotment policy, the Department of the Interior wrongfully reserved the minerals under the authority of general public lands laws, which had no legal application to Indian trust lands. Sixty years later, the class action (Mescal litigation) was filed on behalf of the severely impoverished allottees who had experienced years of federal neglect and abuse of their land rights, while watching burgeoning energy development on their lands without any financial return or benefit to them. After more than 13 years in federal court and a year of settlement negotiations, Ms. Atcitty & lead attorney Paul Frye, successfully settled the case, resulting in the allottees sharing in the revenue stream of existing leases and providing a mechanism for the federal government to provide the allottees title to the minerals that had been wrongfully reserved. Also on behalf of the Navajo Nation, Ms. Atcitty conducted the trial work in the longstanding Navajo Nation v. United States breach of trust case involving the Department of the Interior's wrongful collusion with Peabody Coal Company to undervalue the coal leases on the Navajo Nation. Her work provided the foundation for the successful reconsideration by the U.S. Court of Appeals for the Federal Circuit in ruling the federal government liable for money damages to the Navajo Nation for breach of trust in colluding with the energy company.

ATKINS, HERMAN (Shoshone/Paiute)
(tribal administrator)
Affiliation: Shoshone-Paiute Tribes of the Duck Valley Indian Reservation, P.O. Box 219, Owyhee, NV 89832 (208) 759-3100.

ATKINSON, LISA L. (Cherokee/Osage)
(attorney; tribal judge)
Education: University of Washington, JD, 1999. *Affiliation & Address*: Law Offices of Lisa L. Atkinson, PLLC, 611 Main St., Suite B-1, Edmonds, WA 98020 (425) 778-2421. E-mail: info@lisaatkinsonpllc.com. Website: www.lisaatkinsonpllc.com. *Other professional posts*: Judge, Jamestwn S'Klallam Tribal Court, Sequim, WA; treasurer, Northwest Indian Bar Association, Edmonds, WA. *Past professional posts*: Prosecutor, Northwest Intertribal Court System, Mountainlake Terrace, WA; Of Counsel, National Indian Gaming Commission, Washington, C, 1999-2000.

ATOLE, LEONARD (Jicarilla Apache)
(tribal council president)
Affiliation: Jicarilla Apache Tribal Council, P.O. Box 507, Dulce, NM 87528 (505) 759-3242.

ATTEBERY, RUSSELL (Karuk)
(tribal chairperson)
Affiliation & Address: Chairperson, Karuk Tribe of California, P.O. Box 1016, Happy Camp, CA 996039 (530) 493-1600. E-mail: rattebery@karuk.us. *Other professional post*: Commissioner, California Native American Heritage Commission, Sacramento, CA (2014-present) appointed by Governor Brown.

ATTI, WILLIE (Eskimo)
(AK village council president)
Affiliation: Kwigillingok Native Village, P.O. Box 49, Kwigillingok, AK 99622 (907) 588-8114.

ATWELL, CLARENCE, JR. (Yokut)
(tribal chairperson)
Affiliation: Santa Rosa General Council, P.O. Box 8, Lemoore, CA 93245 (209) 924-1278.

ATWINE, RUBY (Ute)
(tribal chairperson)
Affiliation: Uintah & Ouray Tribal Business Council, P.O. Box 190, Fort Duchesne, UT 84026 (801) 722-5141.

AUBREY, JOHN
(committee chairperson)
Affiliation: Committee on Library Services for American Indian People, American Indian Library Association, American Library Association, Office of Outreach Services, 50 East Huron St., Chicago, IL 60611 (312) 944-6780.

AUSTIN, JACK, JR. (Choctaw of Oklahoma)
(tribal assistant chief)
Education: MEd. *Affiliation & Address*: Chief (2014-present), Choctaw Nation of Oklahoma, P.O. Drawer 1210, Durant, OK 74702 (580) 924-8280. *Past*

professional post: Program director for the Choctaw Nation Recovery Center. *Military service*: U.S. Army.

AUSTIN, MATTHEW (Caddo)
  (attorney)
Education: University of Wisconsin-Madison, BS, 2002; University of Oregon, MS (Ecoomics), 2007; University Wisconsin Law School, JD, 2012. *Affiliation & Address*: Staff Attorney (2013-present), Wisconsin Judicare, Inc., P.O. Box 6100, Wausau, WI 54402 (715) 842-1681. E-mail: maustin@judicare.org. Matthew handles our Criminal Clinic at the Menominee Tribal Court. He is also involved with our NAEOP outreach and general case work.

AUSTIN, RAYMOND D. (Dine'-Navajo) 1958-
  (professor of law)
Born in northeastern Arizona. *Education*: Arizona State University, BS, 1979; University of New Mexico Law School, JD, 1983; University of Arizona, PhD (American Indian Studies), 2007. *Affiliation*: Affiliated Faculty, American Indian Studies Program, University of Arizona, Rountree Hall 313, Tucson, AZ 85721. E-mail: rdaustin@email.arizonaa.edu. Jurist Austin teaches Federal Indian Law. *Other professional post*: Distinguished Jurist in Residence for the Indigenous Peoples Law & Policy Program, James E. Rogers College of Law, University of Arizona. *Past professional posts*: Served on the Navajo Nation Supreme Court, 1985-2001; Judge pro term, Arizona Court of Appeals, Div. 1, 1993-94; Distinguished Visiting Professor of Law, Stanford Law School, Spring 1995; Solicitor to the Pascua Yaqui Tribe Court of Appeals, 2005-07; taught courses as visiting professor at the Harvard Law School, Arizona State University College of Law, University of Utah College of Law; taught seminars on Indian law and tribal law & judicial systems to members of the bars of Arizona, Utah, and New Mexico and to other legal associations. He is a past member of the board of directors for the National Indian Justice Center, National American Indian Court Judges Association, and the Advisory Council on Indian Legal Programs at the Arizona State University College of Law. *Military service*: U.S. Army (Vietnam Era Veteran). Areas of Interest: Tribal courts; tribal law; tribal customary law; tribal constitutions & governments; Federal Indian law. *Memberships*: Navajo Nation Bar Association; state bars of Arizona & Utah. *Published works*: Navajo Courts & Navajo Common Law, A Tradition of Tribal Self-Governance (University of Minnesota Press, 2009).

AVERY, CHARLENE, M.D. (Navajo)
  (physician; director, IHS office)
Education: Harvard University, BA (Ethnomedicine of the American Southwest); University of Arizona College of Medicine, MD, 1991. *Affiliation & Address*: Director (2010-present), Office of Clinical & Preventive Services, Indian Health Service (IHS), 801 Thompson Ave., Rockville, MD 20852 (301) 443-1083. *Past professional posts*: Key Contact, Chronic Care Initiative & Chief of the Diabetes Dept., Gallup Indian Medical Center, Gallup, NM. Dr. Avery began working with the National Diabetes Education Program (NDEP) in 1998-2002 as the chair of the very first American Indian/Alaskan Native Work Group. *Memberships*: American Medical Association; Member, Association of American Indian Physicians (secretary, treasurer; president, 2010-2011). *Published works*: Articles on American Indian health & culture in the Journal of American Medical Association, The Diabetes Educator, and Diabetes Care.

AVILIA, TRACEY (Pomo)
  (former tribal chairperson)
Affiliation & Address: Former chairperson, Robinson Rancheria of Pomo Indians, P.O. Box 4015, Nice, CA 95453 (707) 275-0527.

AVRITT, MICHAEL D. (San Felipe Pueblo) 1949-
  (mechanical engineer)
Born August 30, 1949, Albuquerque, NM. *Education*: University of New Mexico, BS, 1973. *Address*: 118 Crestview Ct., Louisville, CO 80027. *Affiliation*: Staff engineer, Pennant Systems Co. (An IBM Co.), Tucson, AZ, 1974-. *Memberships*: American Indian Science & Engineering Society (current board member; chairperson, 1987-88; vice-chairperson, 1985-87). *Awards, honors*: Informal Awards, IBM, 1977 & 1980; First Invention Achievement Level, IBM Corp, 1980; Second Invention Achievement Level, IBM, 1988; named on five patents. Interests: Temporary assignment in Boeblingen, Germany for IBM, Dec. 1988 through June 1990; June 1984 to June 1985 IBM loaned executive to American Indian Science & Engineering Society to coordinate annual conference held in Los Angeles, CA. *Biographical source*: AISES role model publication, 1987. *Published works*: Various articles in IBM Technical Disclosure Bulletin; various poems published in Winds of Change magazine and used in AISES brochures.

AWAKUNI-SWETLAND, MARK (Uthixide) 1956-
  (professor of anthropology & Native American studies)
Born April 7, 1956, Lincoln, Neb. *Education*: University of Oklahoma, BA, 1994, MA (Anthropology), 1996, PhD, (Anthropology), 2003. *Affiliation & Address*: Professor of Anthropology & Native American Studies, University of Nebraska, Dept. of Anthropology, Bessey Hall 132, Lincoln, NE 68588-0368 (402) 472-

3455. E-mail: mawakuni-swetland2@unl.edu. A joint appt in Anthropology & Ethnic Studies (Native American Studies) where he is teaching a 4-semester series of Omaha language classes with the assistance of local Omaha speakers. *Past professional posts*: DOI, National Park Service, Yosemite, CA, 1983-90; Kalaupapa, HI; lecturer, University of Nebraska, Lincoln, 1990-1996, 1999-present. *Community activities*: Public speaking on Native American & Great Plains topics, powwows, hand games, Master of Ceremony duties; Traditional War Dancer; Southern Plains Gourd Dancer; Museum exhibit consultant. *Memberships*: Nebraska State Historical Society; Hawaiian Historical Society; Arizona Memorial Museum Assn; Omaha Tia Piah Society. *Interests*: Native language & culture maintenance and revitalization; teaching Omaha language; oral histories; material culture replication. *Published works*: Mark compiled & published an Omaha vocabulary in 1977; Dance Lodges of the Omaha: Building From Memory - monograph (Routledge, 2001); Umo'ho' Iye of Elizabeth Staber: with an Omaha to English Lexicon (John Mangan Printing, Macy, NE, 1991).

AWIAKTA, MARILOU (Cherokee)
  (writer, poet, storyteller)
Born in Oak Ridge, Tenn. *Address*: 35 Belleair Dr., Memphis, TN 38104 (901) 726-4639. *Awards, honors*: Distinguished Tennessee Writer Award in 1989; Outstanding Contribution to Appalachian Literature Award in 1991; profiled in the 1994 Oxford Companion to Women's Writing in the U.S. *Published works*: Abiding Appalachia: Where Mountain & Atom Meet; Rising Fawn and the Fire Mystery; Selu: Seeking the Corn-Mother's Wisdom (Fulcrum Publishing, 1994).

AYALA, NANCY (Chukchansi)
  (tribal chairperson)
Affiliation & Address: Picayune Rancheria of the Chukchansi Indians, 46575 Road 417, Coursegold, CA 93614 (559) 683-6633.

AYER, LINDA (Southern Paiute)
  (tribal chairperson)
Affiliation & Address: Chairperson, Winnemucca Indian Colony, P.O. Box 1370, Winnemucca, NV 89446. (775) 623-0888.

AYRES, SONJA K. (Cherokee) 1946-
  (professional artist)
Born May 26, 1946, Fort Smith, Ark. *Education*: High school. *Principal occupation*: Professional artist. *Address*: Unknown. *Affiliation*: Sonjya K. Ayres Studio, Muldrow, OK, 1970-. *Collection*: "Red Earth & Fire" - a unique collection of traditional clay art forms using ancient Native American techniques that capture the mystique & lore of great Woodland Indian Tribes. Art shows/awards: "Night of the First Americans" John F. Kennedy Center, Washington, DC, 1982; Smithsonian Institute, Washington, DC, 1982; Annual Trail of Tears Arts Show, Tahlequah, OK (Merit Awards, 1984, 1988); Annual Five Civilized Tribes Museum Art Competition, Muskogee, OK (Division II Award, 1986; Cherokee Heritage Award, 1988; 2nd Place, 1989; Merit Award, 1990); Cherokee National Holiday Art Show, Tahlequah, OK, Honor Award, 1987; Five Civilized Tribes Museum (Poster Artist, Art Under the Oaks, Indian Market, 1989; Craft Show: 2nd Place, 1990; 1st, 2nd & Honorable Mention, 1991; Solo Exhibit, 1991); Red Cloud Indian Art Show, Pine Ridge, SD, Woodward Award, 1990; Five Civilized Tribes Museum Art & Craft Competitions, awards for clay pipes & pottery, 1992 & 1993; Cherokee Heritage Art Show, Cherokee, NC, 1992; Cherokee Nation History Art Show, 1992 & 1993 awards for Pottery & Graphics; Illustrator of "A Time for Native Americans" 48 playing card portraits, Aristoplay, LTD. Educational Games. *Interests*: Sonja spends most of her time in her studio and personally attends only select major & one-woman shows each year. She spends much of her time researching Native American customs & history.

AZULE, DEAN (Gila River Pima)
  (coordinator of student services-student affairs)
Affiliation & Address: Coordinator, Diversity & Multicultural Student Services-Student Affairs, Portland State University, 140 NASCC MC: NAC, P.O. Box 751, Portland, OR 97207 (503) 725-5348. E-mail: azuled@pdx.edu.

AZURE, F. SAM (Turtle Mountain Ojibwe) 1953-
  (school principal)
Born July 25, 1953, Rolette, N.D. *Education*: University of North Dakota, BS, 1974; University of South Dakota, Masters in Administrative Education, 1980. *Principal occupation*: Elementary school principal. *Address*: Theodore Jamison Elementary School, 3315 University Dr., Bismarck, ND 58504 (701) 255-3285. *Affiliations*: Teacher, elementary school, Eagle Butte, SD, 1974-81; Federal Program Coordinator, BIA, Billings, MT, 1981-83; BIA Adult Education, teacher of physical education, math, science, Theodore Jamerson Elementary School, Belcourt, ND, 1983-91; principal, Theodore Jamerson Elementary School, Bismarck, ND, 1991-present. *Other professional post*: Tribal Adult Education, Belcourt, ND, 1991-. *Community activities*: Chairperson of Health Board, Turtle Mountain; Board of Directors, Turtle Mountain Community College.

Memberships: North Dakota Assn of Elementary School Principals. *Interests*: High school official for boys & girls basketball & football, & weekend musician.

AZURE, FLOYD (Assniboine Sioux)
(tribal chairperson)
Affiliation & Address: Chairperson, Fort Peck Tribe, P.O. Box 1027, Poplar, MT 59255 (406) 768-2300. E-mail: fazure@fortpecktribes.org

AZURE, JANE (Turtle Mountain Ojibwe)
(special education coordinator)
Affiliation: Cheyenne River Agency, Bureau of Indian Affairs, P.O. Box 2020, Eagle Butte, SD 57625 (605) 964-8722.

AZURE, JANICE (Turtle Mountain Ojibwe)
(tribal secretary-treasurer)
Affiliation: Turtle Mountain Band of Chippewa Indians, P.O. Box 900, Belcourt, ND 58316 (701) 477-2600.

AZURE, LANE (Turtle Mountain Ojibwe)
(vice president of academic affairs)
Affiliation & Address: Vice President of Academics, Candeska Cikana Community College, P.O. Box 269, Fort Totten, ND 58335 (701) 766-1309. E-mail: lane.azure@littlehoop.edu. *Other professional post*: Math instructor, Candeska Cikana Community College.

AZURE, MARK (Chippewa-Cree)
(culture consultant)
Affiliation & Address: Culture Consultant, Sacred Circle, P.O. Box 21451, Keizer, OR 97307 (971) 239-5697. E-mail: markazure@comcast.net.

AZURE, MARK L. (Assiniboine)
(tribal president)
Affiliation & Address: President, Fort Belknap Community Council, RR 1, Box 66, Harlem, MT 59526 (406) 353-8303. E-mail: ching@ftbelknap-nsn-gov.

AZURE, SAM (Turtle Mountain Ojibwe)
(school principal)
Affiliation: Theodore Jamerson Elementary School, United Tribes Technical College, 3315 University Dr., Bismarck, ND 58504 (701) 255-3285.

AZURE, TONY (Santee Sioux)
(economic development director)
Education: Washington State University, BS (Business Administration). *Affiliation & Address*: Economic Development Director, Ketchikan Indian Community, 2960 Tongass Ave., Ketchikan, AK 99901 (907) 228-5230. E-mail: tazure@kictribe.org. Tony has been involved in the Alaska tourism industry for over 30 years. *Other professional post*: Alaska Region Representative, American Indian & Alaska Native Tourism Association, Albuquerque, NM.

AZUYAK, TONY (Eskimo)
(AK village president)
Affiliation: Native Village of Old Harbor, P.O. Box 62, Old Harbor, AK 99643 (907) 286-2215.

B

BABCOCK, BARBARA
(regents professor of English & American Indian studies)
Education: University of Chicago, PhD, 1975. Address: Esquire Apts., 1230 N. Park Ave., Tucson 85721 (520) 626-7014. E-mail: bbabcock@email.arizona.edu. *Affiliation*: Regents Professor of English, Graduate Advisor of the Program in Comparative Cultural & Literary Studies; American Indian Studies Program, University of Arizona, Tucson, AZ. *Interests*: Folklore; Cultural Studies; Feminist Theories; Southwest Indian cultures, especially Pueblo. *Published works*: She has authored, co-authored, & edited numerous publications on southwestern anthropology, on the invention of the Southwest, and Pueblo art & culture, notably The Pueblo Storyteller: Development of a Figurative Ceramic Tradition (1986), Daughters of the Desert Women Anthropologists & The Native American Southwest (1988); Pueblo Mothers & Children: Essays by Elsie Clews Parsons, 1915-1924 (1991). She is presently completing "Stories Told in Clay," a study of the art & experience of Helen Cordero, & "Mudwomen & Whitemen," a collection of critical essays on the politics of representation, in addition to editing Elsie Clews Parsons' unpublished personal essays about her first years of Pueblo fieldwork in the Southwest.

BABCOCK, W. KENNETH (Narragansett)
(tribal council chief sachem)
Affiliation: Chief Sachem, Narragansett Indian Tribal Council, P.O. Box 268, Charleston, RI 02813 (401) 364-1100.

BACA, JOE (*Seng Weng*) (Santa Clara Tewa) 1940-
(gallery owner)
Born September 10, 1940, Dulce, N.M. *Education*: Highlands University, B.A., 1963; University of New Mexico, MBA, 1975. *Address*: Rt. 5, Box 472-C, Espanola, NM 87532 (505) 753-9663 (work). *Affiliation*: Owner, Singing Water Gallery, Espanola, NM. *Military service*: U.S. Army, 1963-65 (PFC).

BACA, KIM (Navajo-Santa Clara Pueblo)
(journalist)
Education: University of New Mexico, BA (Journalism; minor in Native American Studies). *Address & Affiliation*: Interim Executive Director, Native American Journalists Association, 555 N. Dakota St., Vermillion, SD 57069 (605) 677-5282. E-mail: kimbaca@naja.com. *Past professional posts*: Communications specialist & legislative assistant on Capitol Hill; general & beat reporting for the Associated Press, the El Paso Times & Santa Fe New Mexican; Policy Analyst for the New Mexico Office of Indian Affairs.

BACA, LAWRENCE R. (Pawnee)
(attorney)
Education: University of California, Santa Barbara, BA, 1973; Harvard Law School, JD, 1976. Baca was one of the first American Indians to graduate from Harvard. *Affiliation & Address*: Board member & treasurer (2013-15), National Native American Bar Association, P.O. Box 11145, Tempe, AZ 85284. *Past professional posts*: Deputy Director, Office of Tribal Justice, U.S. Dept. of Justice, Washington, DC 20530 (1977-2008); professor, Native American Legal Resource Center, Oklahoma City University Law School, Oklahoma City, OK; chairperson, Indian Law Section, Federal Bar Association, Washington, DC. *Awards, honors*: Lawrence was the first American Indian ever hired through the Department of Justice's Honor Law Program; 1988 Distinguished Alumni Award by the UCSB; in 2008, the Indian Law Section of the Federal Bar Association created the Lawrence R. Baca Lifetime Achievement Award for Excellence in Federal Indian Law to honor his career & contributions to the Federal Bar Association. He was the first recipient. Baca also received the American Bar Association Spirit of Excellence Award in 2008 recognizing his work in mentoring minority attorneys & opening doors & opportunities for Native American attorneys at the U.S. Department of Justice.

BACA, LORENZO (Isleta Pueblo-Mescalero Apache) 1947-
(visual/literary/performing artist; educator)
Born September 9, 1947, Morenci, Ariz. *Education*: California State University, Long Beach, BA (Art), 1972; UCLA, MA (American Indian Studies), 1986. *Principal occupation*: Visual/literary/performing artist; educator. *Address*: P.O. Box 4353, Sonora, CA 95370 (209) 532-1573. *Affiliations*: Arts/graphics consultant: Sierra Audio Systems, Sonora, CA; Image Maker, James, CA; The Woodwright Shop, Twaine Harte, CA. *Other professional posts*: Artist-in-Residence: Tri-County Consortium of Special Education, Tuolumne County Schools, Sonora, CA, 1986-88; Twaine Harte Elementary School, Twaine Harte, CA, 1988-92. Shows/Exhibits: Stanford Powwow, Stanford, CA, May 1991; Chaw Se Invitational, Chaw Se State Park, Volcano, CA, Aug. 1991; Buff Show, Anne Saunders Gallery, Jamestown, CA, Feb. 1991, 1992; California Spirit, Calaveras County Arts Council, San Andreas, CA, Feb. 1992; among many others dating back to 1986. *Commissions*: Indian Nations At Risk Task Force, U.S. Office of Education, Washington, DC, March 1991; D. Fregeau, Harmony Center, Graphics, Twaine Harte, CA, Sept. 1991; M. Pelletier, Silver Pendant Design, Truckee, CA, Jan. 1992; B. Lopez, Silver Designs, Sutter Creek, CA, Feb. 1992. Numerous workshops & performances. *Awards, honors*: 1st Place awards: sculpture-Twaine Harte Annual Art Show, 1987; sculpture-Chaw Se Indian Grinding Rock, 1987; photography-Central Sierra Arts Council, 1987; pottery-Durfee Gallery, Scottsdale, AZ, Nov. 1985; among others. *Interests*: "His works, which include fine art, sculpture, poetry, acting & video, are often a contemporary expression of the native traditions of his Southwestern heritage of storytelling, dance, song and art."

BAD HEART BULL, JAY THOMAS (Standing Rock/Oglala Sioux)
(president & CEO)
Affiliation & Address: President & CEO (2012-present), Native American Community Development Institute, 1414 East Franklin Ave., Minneapolis, MN 55404 (612) 235-4976. Past professional posts: Vice president, Little Earth of United Tribes, Minneapolis, MN, 2009-12.

BAD MILK, RICHARD (Rosebud Lakota)
(school superintendent)
Affiliation: School Supt., Sicangu Oyate Ho., Inc., Sicangu Oyate Ho., Inc (St. Francis Indian School), P.O. Box 379 HCR 59 Box 1A, St. Francis, SD 57572 (605) 747-2297.

BAD MOCCASIN, DONALD "BRUCE" (Crow Creek Sioux) 1949-
(health care administration)
Born February 3, 1949, Chamberlain, S.D. *Education*: South Dakota School of Mines & Technology, BSCE, 1972, MSCE, 1981. *Affiliations*: Engineer, Bureau of Indian Affairs, Aberdeen, SD (four years); engineer, Indian Health Service,

Oklahoma City, OK, 1977-79, Aberdeen Area, 1979-91, and Phoenix Area, 1991-93; Aberdeen Area Office, 1993-. *Military service*: U.S. Army (commissioned 2nd lieutenant, 1972), 1977-present, currently on active duty with the U.S. Public Health Service with rank of Captain (06). *Memberships*: American Water Works Assn. 1985-; Commissioned Officers Association (associate recruiter for PHS with emphasis in recruitment of minorities into the I.H.S.) *Awards, honors*: Outstanding Service Medal, USPHS, 1989; Area Excellence Award-Phoenix, 1992; Employee-of-the-Year, Aberdeen Area, IHS, 1983. *Interests*: "I am interested in early architecture & woodworking. My hobbies are bowling, basketball, and other sports activities involving running. Recently relocated back to Northern Plains area with IHS. Changed career track from engineering management to health care administration. Currently responsible for directing a comprehensive health care delivery system for American Indians throughout North & South Dakota, Nebraska and Iowa."

BADBEAR, FAITH G. (*One Who Cares for Children*) (Crow) 1959-
(assistant curator of ethnology)
Born February 23, 1959, Dallas, Tex. *Education*: BSED Art K-12. *Affiliation & Address*: Assistant curator of ethnology, Science Museum of Minnesota, 120 W. Kellogg Blvd., St. Paul, MN 55102 (651) 221-9432. E-mail: badbear@ smm.org. *Past professional posts*: Buffalo Bill Historical Center, Cody, WY, 1989-92; National Museum of the American Indian, 1992-93; Canadian Museum of Civilization, Hull, Quebec, Canada, 1994; St. Louis Historical Society, St. Louis, MO, 1995; Duluth Children's Museum, Duluth, MN, 1995. *Community activities*: Diabetes Walkathon, Toys for Tots, Ain Dah Yung (support Indian group home); volunteer to give lectures at schools & companies in Minnesota on Indian awareness & women in science. *Memberships*: AAM - Keepers of the Treasurers. *Interests*: Cultures of the World, Native American Graves Protection; Repatriation Act & Museum Management; teaches Indian people aspects of handling & running a museum.

BAHE, CATHY L. (Navajo-Dine')
(Dine' College, Chinle Center director)
Education: Northern Arizona University, BA. *Affiliation & Address*: Director, Dine' College Chinle Center, P.O. Box 1997, Chinle, AZ 86503 (928) 724-3319. E-mail: clbahe@dinecollege.edu

BAHE, ELIZABETH
(director of Native American programs)
Affiliation & Address: Director, Native American Program, American Ethnic Studies, Willamette University, College of Liberal Arts, 900 State St., Salem, OR 97301 (503) 370-6960. E-mail: ebahe@willamette.edu.

BAILEY, ADAM (Choctaw of Oklahoma)
(attorney & board president)
Education: Harvard College, BA, 2001; UCLA School of Law, JD, 2011. *Affiliation & Address*: Associate, Hobbs, Straus, Dean & Walker LLP, Sacramento, CA (916) 442-9444. E-mail: abailey@hobbsstraus.com. At UCLA School of Law, Adam was a Senior Editor of the UCLA Law Review; and a student clerk at the Hopi Tribal Appellate Court and the Hualapai Tribal Court of Appeals. He focused on tribal & Indian law, and received a specialized degree in critical race studies. Prior to law school, Mr. Bailey was a legislative specialist for Hobbs, Straus, Dean, & Walker and a legislative associate for the National Congress of American Indians. *Other professional post*: Board President, California Indian Law Association. *Past professional post*: Associate, Sheppard Mullin Richter & Hampton, San Francisco, CA.

BAILEY, DEREK J. (Grand Traverse Ottawa) 1972-
(former tribal chairperson)
Born in Traverse City, Mich. *Education*: Grand Valley State University, BA, 1995, MSW, 1998. *Affiliation & Address*: Council member, 2004-08, Chairperson, 2008-12, Grand Traverse Band of Ottawa & Chippewa Indians, Peshawbestown, MI. *Other professional post*: Adjunct Professor, Grand Valley State University, Social Work Program. *Past professional post*: Director of Substance Abuse, Saginaw Chippewa Indian Tribe; Health Department Manager, Grand Traverse Band of Ottawa & Chippewa Indians. *Awards, honors*: Received a Presidential appointment (November 2012) by President Obama to the National Advisory Council on Indian Education.

BAINBRIDGE, BRYAN (Red Cliff Ojibwe)
(former tribal chairperson)
Affiliation & Address: Former Chairperson, Red Cliff Band of Lake Superior Chippewa Indians of Wisconsin, 88385 Pike Rd., Hwy. 13, Bayfield, WI 54814 (715) 779-3700.

BAINES, DAVID, M.D. (*Nei Goot*) (Tlingit/Tsimshian) 1955-
(clinical professor; family physician)
Born April 26, 1955 in Mt. Edgecumbe, Alaska. *Education*: Mayo Medical School. *Affiliation & Address*: Providence Family Medicine Center, 1201 E. 36th St., Anchorage, AK 99508 (907) 562-9229. *Other professional posts*: Faculty at the Alaska Family Medicine Residency; Iliuliuk Family & Health Services Clinic,

Unalaska, AK; Assistant Clinical Professor of Family Medicine, University of Washington School of Medicine. *Past professional posts*: private practice (14 years) on the Coeur d'Alene Indian Reservation; clinical director, Nez Perce Tribal Clinic in Kamiah, ID (1 year); affiliate faculty, Idaho State University Family Practice Residency Program; clinical faculty, University of Nevada, Reno, School of Medicine; staff, St. Maries Family Medicine; fight doctor (professional boxing), Coeur D'Alene Tribal Casino; board member, National Native News Program, "Native America Calling." *Community activities*: Chairperson-Ad Hoc Committee for Minority Populations, National Heart, Lung and Blood Institute, National Institutes of Health; member, Clinical Laboratory Improvement Act Advisory Committee at Centers for Disease Control and Prevention. *Awards, honors*: 1993 Searle Pharmaceutical Co.'s "Gentle Giants of Medicine" award; appointed by the Clinton Administration to a six-member screening committee that selected the new Indian Health Services director; member, Environmental Justice Committee at the Institute of Medicine, National Academy of Sciences, convened by Executive Order (President Clinton) #12898; 2012 Association of American Indian Physicians' Physician of the Year. *Memberships*: Association of American Indian Physicians (member-at-large, 2009-2010; past president); American Academy of Family Physicians (past chairperson); American Medical Association. *Published works*: Special Health Problems of Native Americans (chapter 37) in "Principles & Practices of Clinical Preventive Medicine," edited by Richard S. Lang, MD, MPH (Mosby Medical Books, 1992); Native American Women & health Care (chapter IV.12) in "Behavioral Medicine for Women: A Comprehensive Handbook," edited by Elaine Ann Blechman & Kelly Brownell (Guilford Publications, 1997).

BAIRD, BRUCE RICHARD (Ojibway/Oneida)
(administrator, teacher)
Affiliation & Address: Administrator, teacher (1980-present), Office of Indian Education, ISD 316, Greenway High School, P.O. Box 520, Coleraine, MN 55722 (218) 245-1199. *Past professional posts*: Univac Corp., 1962-65; Control Data Corp., 1965-69; ISD, Minneapolis, MN, 1969-70; University of South Dakota, 1970-80. *Other professional posts*: Teach part time in community college; video/film producer. *Military service*: U.S. Navy, 1958-62. *Community activities*: Chairman, local Indian council. *Memberships*: American Legion, VFW.

BAIRD-OLSON, KARREN (Wyandot)
(American Indian studies program instructor)
Education: Montana State University, BS, 1962; University of Montana, MA, 1984; University of New Mexico, PhD, 1994. *Affiliation & Address*: Instructor, American Indian Studies Program, College of Humanities, Sierra Hall 194, CSU Northridge, 18111 Nordhoff St., Northridge, CA 91330 (818) 677-6762. E-mail: karren.bairdolson@csun.edu. Karren teaches American Indian studies courses & criminology courses in the Dept. of Sociology. Her publications include articles on American Indian women's spiritual practices, victimization, and activism.

BAKER, BILL JOHN (Cherokee)
(principal chief)
Education: Northeastern State University, BS (Political Science & History), 1972. *Affiliation & Address*: Principal Chief (2011-present), Cherokee Nation of Oklahoma, P.O. Box 948, Tahlequah, OK 74465 (918) 456-0671. E-mail: bill-baker@cherokee.org. *Past professional posts*: Tribal Council (12 years), Cherokee Nation of Oklahoma.

BAKER, JACK D. (Cherokee)
(tribal council member; association president)
Address: 1102 Marlboro Lane, Oklahoma City, OK 73116. E-mail: jackdbaker@cox.net. *Affiliations*: Council Member-at-Large, Cherokee Nation of Olahoma, Tahlequah, OK. E-mail: jack-baker@cherokee.org; president, Trail of Tears Association, Little Rock, AR.

BAKER, JOE (*Waim-Me-Ke-Mon*) (Delaware) 1946-
(artist/associate professor)
Born January 14, 1946, in Okla. *Education*: University of Tulsa, BFA, 1968, MFA, 1978. *Address*: 277 E. Tuckey Lane, Phoenix, AZ 85012 (602) 279-1318. *Affiliations*: Colorado College, Colorado Springs, CO., Visual Arts Faculty, The Marie Walsh Sharpe Foundation, 1986-91; Visiting Associate Professor of Art, 1992-; curator of fine arts, The Heard Museum, Phoenix, AZ, 2003-. *Other professional posts*: *Military service*: U.S. Air Force, 1968-78. *Community activities*: Minority Coalition, United Parents. *Membership*: College Art Association. *Awards, honors*: Arizona Commission of the Arts, Phoenix, AZ (Visual Arts Panelist, 1982-84; Bi-cultural Arts Representative to Mexico, 1983-84); Visual Arts Representative, Western States Arts Foundation, Santa Fe, NM, 1983-84; Nominee, Regional Arts Panelist, national Endowment for the Arts, Washington, DC, 1983-84; Arts Panelist, Idaho Commission on the Arts, Boise, ID, 1986; Arts Panelist, Wyoming Council on the Arts, Cheyenne, WY, 1987. *Exhibitions*: Numerous solo & group exhibitions from 1977 to the present. *Biographical sources*: California Art Review, Los Angeles, CA, 1983; The Complete Book of Country Swing & Western Dance and a Bit About

Cowboys, by Peter Livingston (Doubleday, 1981); Love Medicine, by Louise Erdrich (Rowohlt Publishing, Germany, 1984); Signale: Indianischer Kunstler, by Katrina Hartje (Berlinger, Kunstblatt, 1984); The American West: The Modern Vision (New York Graphics Society, 1984); A History & Selections from the Permanent Collections, by Colorado Springs Fine Arts Center (Williams Publishing, 1986); "Art & Life," Calendar (Design Graphics, Phoenix, 1992); "Joe Baker, The Painter," by Eileen Baily (Arizona Trends, Apr. 1992); Joe Baker: The Carolina Series," Catalyst (The Colorado College, 1992); New Art of the West 3, Eiteljorg Museum (Benham Press, 1992). Numerous public collections, such as: Metropolitan Museum of Art, Heard Museum, Smithsonian Institution, Phoenix Art Museum, Fine Arts Museum of New Mexico.

BAKER, MEL (Southern Ute)
(tribal vice chairperson)
Affiliation & Address: Vice Chairperson, Southern Ute Tribe, P.O. Box 737, Ignacio, CO 81137 (970) 563-0100.

BAKER-DEMARAY, TWYLA (Mandan, Hidatsa, Arikara)
(Indian college president)
Education: University of North Dakota, BS (Environmental Geology & Technology), MS (Education General Studies), PhD (Research Methodologies-in progress). *Affiliation & Address*: President, Fort Berthold Community College, P.O. Box 490, New Town, ND 58763 (701) 627-4738 ext. 248. *Past professional posts*: Research Analyst & Project Director (2006-2013), National Resource Center on Native American Aging, Center for Rural Health, The University of North Dakota (UND), School of Medicine & Health Sciences (SMHS), Grand Forks, ND; Principal investigator, National Indigenous Elder Justice Initiative (NIEJI), UND, SMHS, Grand Forks, ND; Sequoyah Fellow, American Indian Science & Engineering Society; Bush Foundation/Native Nations Institute Rebuilder Fellow. *Awards, honors*: Named a Native American Top 40 Under 40 honoree by the National Center for American Indian Enterprise Development.

BAKER-JOSEPH, RHONDA (Athabascan)
(association president)
Affiliation & Address: President, Fairbanks Native Association, 605 Hughes Ave., Suite 100, Fairbanks, AK 99701 (907) 452-1648.

BALDERAS, RUBEN (Yavapai)
(former tribal president)
Affiliation: Fort McDowell Yavapai Nation, P.O. Box 17779, Fountain Hills, AZ 85269 (480) 837-5121.

BALDWIN, DARYL (Miami)
(Indian center/project director)
Born & raised around the Great Lakes area. *Education*: University of Montana, MA (with emphasis In Native American linguistics), 1999. *Affiliation & Address*: Director, Myaamia Center, Miami University, 200 Bonham House, Oxford, OH 45056 (513) 529-5648. E-mail: myaamiaproject@muohio.edu. Since 1995, he has worked with the Myaamia people developing culture and language based educational materials & programs for the tribal community. The Myaamia Center is a joint venture between the Miami Tribe of OK and Miami University.

BALLARD, JOYCE (Shoshone-Bannock)
(museum director)
Affiliation & Address: Director, Shoshone-Bannock Tribal Museum, P.O. Box 793, Fort Hall, Idaho 83203 (208) 237-9791.

BALLENGEE-MORIS, CHRISTINE (Cherokee-Appalachian)
(professor & program director of American Indian Studies)
Education: Miami University (OH), BS, 1980, MA (Art Education, 1992; Penn State University, PhD (Art Education), 1995. Affiliation & Address: Professor in the Arts Administration, Educationn & Policy Department and Professor & Coordinator of the American Indian Studies Program, The Ohio State University, 1961 Tuttle Park Place, Columbus, OH 43210. E-mail: moris.390@osu.edu. Christine was the founding director of The Multicultural Center at OSU. *Other professional post*: Performs flatfoot dance with her musician husband, David Morris, and son, Jack. *Past professional posts*: Twenty years as an artist-in-residence in public schools and five countries, higher education since 1992, and international teaching. *Awards, honors*: 2013 June King McFee Award for her work around diversity; 2012 National Art Education Fellow Award; the 2008 National Art Education Higher Education Western Division Award; 2007 Ziegfeld Award for Diversity; 2006 National Art Education Grigsby Award; 2000 OSU-Newark research & service award. *Published works*: Co-author, Interdisciplinary Approaches to Teaching Art in High School (NAEA Publications, 2007); Standing Up for a Change: Voices of Arts Educators, 2013, with Kevin Tavin.

BALLENGER, ROBIN FLINT (Cherokee)
(chief executive officer; foundation president)
Middlebury College, BA (Philosophy); University of Southern California, MA (Gerontology). *Affiliation & Address*: CEO (2001-present), Flintco, 1624 W. 21st St., Tulsa, OK 74107 (918) 587-8451. *Other professional posts*: Board President, The Cherokee Nation Foundation, Tahlequah, OK; member, Cherokee Nation Education Corporation; board member, Tulsa Library Trust; member, American Indian Resource Center's American Indian Author Award Selection Committee; member, The Flint Family Foundation, Tulsa, OK. Flintco, founded in 1908, is a family-run business which was ranked one on the top 100 Native American companes by Diversity Business.

BALLEW, TIM, III (Lummi)
(tribal chairperson)
Affiliation & Address: Chairperson, Lummi Nation, 2616 Kwina Rd., Bellingham, WA 98226 (360) 384-1489.

BALLOUE, JOHN (Cherokee) 1948-
(professional artist)
Born April 19, 1948, Richmond, Calif. *Education*: Chabot College, Hayward, CA, 1971-73; California State University, Hayward, BA (Art), 1975. *Address*: 26838 Grandview Ave., Hayward, CA 94542 (510) 538-4003. *Affiliations*: American Indian Traders Guild, Fresno, CA, 1991-; *Military service*: U.S. Army, 1968-69 (Specialist-4, Vietnam Vet; National Defense Service Medal, Vietnam Service Medal, Vietnam Campaign Medal, Army Commendation Medal). *Memberships*: Indian Arts & Crafts Assn; Southwestern Assn for Indian Arts. *Awards, honors*: 1992 Indian Arts & Crafts Assn, Artist of the Year; over 25 awards for various (Indian & non-Indian) juried art shows. *Interests*: "Photography is closely related to much of my work. I've tried to illustrate dance, costumes, and traditions of contemporary Native America. I attend powwows & various social events, photograph and later translate them into artwork. My work is evolving from a purdy photo - Realistic Nature, to that of images that are more spiritual and historical in nature."

BANKS, DENNIS J. (*Nowa Cumig*) (Anishinabe)
(lecturer, author, activist)
Born on the Leech Lake Reservation in northern Minnesota. *Education*: DQ University, A.A. *Address*: Nowa Cumig Institute, 5450 Mapleton Rd., Baxter, MN 56425. Website: www.nowacumig.org. *Affiliations*: Co-founder & presently National Field Director, American Indian Movement, 1968-present; founder & director, Sacred Run Foundation (website: www.sacredrun.org), 1978-present. *Military service*: U.S. Air Force, 1954-58 (active duty-four years, inactive duty-8 years). *Awards, honors*: Autobiography, "Sacred Soul," won the non-fiction "Book of the Year Award." *Activities*: In 1968, Dennis co-founded the American Indian Movement (AIM), and established it to protect the traditional ways of Indian people and to engage in legal cases protecting treaty rights of natives - such as hunting & fishing, trapping, wild ricing. Among other activities, he participated in the occupation of Alcatraz Island where demands were made that all federal surplus property be returned to Indian control. In 1972, he organized & led the Trail of Broken Treaties' caravan across the U.S. to Washington DC calling attention to the plight of Native Americans. Mr. Banks spearheaded the move on Pine Ridge Reservation in South Dakota in 1973 to oust corruption and the U.S. appointed tribal chairman. This led to the occupation of Wounded Knee and a siege of 71 days that received national attention. He was the principal negotiator and leader of the Wounded Knee forces. Under the leadership of Dennis Banks, AIM led a protest in Custer (SD) in 1973 against the judicial process that found a white man innocent of murdering an Indian. As a result of his involvement in Wounded Knee & Custer, Banks and 300 others were arrested and faced trial. He was acquitted of the Wounded Knee charges, but was convicted of riot and assault at Custer. Refusing the prison term, Banks went underground, later receiving amnesty in California by then Governor Jerry Brown. In California, from 1976-1983, Dennis earned an Associates of Arts degree at Davis University and taught at DQ University (an all Indian-controlled Institution), where he became the first American Indian chancellor. He also established the first spiritual run from Davis to Los Angeles, CA in 1978 (now an annual event) & organized the Longest Walk from Alcatraz to Washington, DC that same year. This 3,600-mile walk was successful in its purpose: to gather enough support to halt purposed legislation abrogating Indian treaties with the U.S. government. In the spring of 1979, he taught at Stanford University. After Governor Brown left office, Banks received sanctuary on the Onondaga Nation in upstate New York in 1984. It was while living there that Banks organized the Great Jim Thorpe Longest Run from New York City to Los Angeles, California. A Spiritual run, this event ended in Los Angeles to begin the Jim Thorpe Memorial Games where the gold medals Thorpe had won at the 1912 Olympics were restored to the Thorpe family. In 1985, Banks left Onondaga to surrender to law enforce-ment officials in South Dakota and served 18 months in prison. When released, he worked as a drug & alcohol counselor on the Pine Ridge Indian Reservation. During 1987, grave robbers in Uniontown, Kentucky were halted in their digging for artifacts after they had destroyed over 1,200 American Indian gravesites. Banks was called in to organize the reburial ceremonies for

the uncovered remains. His activities in this state resulted in Kentucky & Indiana passing strict legislation against grave desecration. He revived the idea of traditional spiritual running in 1978 when he began Sacred Run. Since then it has become a multi-cultural, international event with participants from around the world joining Native American runners to carry the message of the sacredness of all Life and of humankind's relationship to the planet, Mother Earth. To date, In addition to leading and organizing Sacred Runs, Dennis Banks stays involved with American Indian issues, AIM activities, and travels the globe lecturing, providing drug & alcohol counseling, teaching Native traditions, and sharing his experiences. In 1994, Banks led the four-month, "Walk for Justice," from Alcatraz Island in San Francisco to Washington, DC. The purpose was to bring public awareness to current Native issues. Banks agreed to head the "Bring Peltier Home" Campaign in 1996 bringing Native Americans and other supporters together in a national drive for executive clemency for political prisoner Leonard Peltier. A musical tape "Still Strong" featuring Banks' original work as well as traditional Native American songs was completed in 1993 and a musical video with the same name was released in 1995. His autobiography, the "Longest Walk," is in writing now...the publication date is unknown at this time. Key roles in the following movies: "War Party", "The Last of the Mohicans", & "Thunderheart". *Published works*: Sacred Soul (autobiography, Ashai, Japan, 1988); forewords to "Native America: Portrait of Peoples;" "Shooting Back From the Reservation;" "Of Earth Elders."

BANKS, JOHN (Penobscot)
(director of tribal natural resources)
Education: University of Maine, BS (Forest Protection). *Affiliation & Address*: Director (1980-present), Department of Natural Resources, Penobscot Indian Nation, Community Bldg. - Indian Island, 6 River Rd., Indian Island, ME 04468 (207) 827-7776. E-mail: jbanks@penobscotnation.org. *Other professional post*: Member, Maine Indian Tribal-State Commission. *Past professional posts*: Board member: National Tribal Environmental Council, Native American Fish & Wildlife Society, National Indian Policy Center, Tribal Operations Committee with USEPA.

BARBER, RUSSELL "RUSTY" (Lac Courte Oreilles Ojibwe)
(tribal vice chairperson)
Affiliation & Address: Vice Chairperson, Lac Courte Oreilles Band of Ojibwe Indians, 13394 W. Trapania Rd., Bldg. #1, Hayward, WI 54843 (715) 634-8934. E-mail: rbarber@lco-nsn.gov.

BARBERO, CAROL L.
(attorney)
Education: Allegheny College, BA; Georgetown University Law School, J.D., 1978. *Address & Affiliation*: Hobbs, Straus, Dean & Walker, LLP (Associate, 1982-86; Partner, 1987-present), 2120 L St., NW, Suite 700, Washington, DC 20037 (202) 822-8282. E-mail: cbarbero@hsdwdc.com. She has represented tribal schools and Indian education organizations throughout her tenure with the Firm, and is one of a few attorneys in the country who specializes in Indian education law. She served as one of the lead advocates for the Indian-related amendments to the Elementary and Secondary Education Act in 1988 & 1994, and has been an active participant in the ESEA reauthorization effort in the 106th Congress. Ms. Barbero also has expertise in Indian self-determination law, and Indian health care. Past professional posts: Legislative assistant, House of Representatives (six years); associate, Wilkinson, Cragun & Barker. *Memberships*: District of Columbia Bar Association; American Bar Association.

BARBRY, EARL, SR. (Tunica-Biloxi)
(former tribal chairperson)
Born on Avoyelles Parish & raised on the Tunica-Biloxi Reservation in Marksville, LA. *Affiliation & Address*: Chairperson (1978-2014), Tunica-Biloxi Indian Tribe, 151 Melacon Dr., Marksville, LA 71351 (318) 253-9767. Chairman Barbry was elected Tribal Chairman in 1978 and was appointed as Tribal Administrator that same year. Barbry serves in those capacities to this day and under his leadership, and that of Council members, tribal members have seen modern housing development, a Tribal Administrative Office, a Health Department and Social Services Office, Gaming Board and Gaming Commission Office, and Tribal Police and Court Building. Tribal landholdings have also signifiantly increased during Barbry's tenure as Chairman.

BARCENA, BERNARD F., JR. (Lipan Apache)
(tribal chairperson)
Affiliation: Lipan Apache Tribe of Texas, P.O. Box 8888, Corpus Christi, TX 78468 (361) 215-5121. E-mail: bbarcena@lipanapache.org.

BARCUS, JOHNEL (Blackfeet)
(executive director)
Born & raised on the Blackfeet Reservation. *Education*: Montana State University, EdD, 1997. *Affiliation & Address*: Executive Director, Montana Indian Business Alliance, P.O. Box 2222, Colstrip, MT 59323. *Other professional post*: Owner & Lead Principle Investigator, Sage Quest Consulting.

BAREHAND, SHANA GREENBERG (Mono/Chicana)
(tribal liaison; board treasurer)
Education: California State University, Long Beach, BA (psychology); Arizona State University School of Law's Indian Law Program, JD. *Affiliations*: Liaison to Tribal Governments, Office of Intergovernmental Affairs, Consumer & Governmental Affairs Bureau of the Federal Communications Commission (FCC); founding board member & treasurer, Society of American Indian Government Employees (SAIGE), P.O. Box 7715, Washington, DC 20044 (202) 564-0375. E-mail: shana.barehand@gmail.com. The Office of Intergovernmental Affairs administers the Commission's Indian Telecommunications Initiatives (ITI), a comprehensive FCC program designed to increase access to telecommunications services on tribal reservations & to promote understanding, cooperation & trust among the FCC & other government agencies, the telecommunications industry & Native American tribal organizations & Alaska Native communities. *Other professional posts*: Treasurer, National Native American Bar Assn. *Past professional posts*: Enforcement attorney in the Toxics & Pesticides Enforcement Compliance Assurances of the U.S. Environmental Protection Agency, Washington, DC. *Community activities*: Shana is pre-ICWA adoptee whose non-Indian adoptive parents kept her in touch with her American Indian heritage through involvement in local Indian community and Indian educational programs in the schools. She worked for Southern California Indian Center as a tutor for American Indian youth, youth employment coordinator, and career advisor & counselor for Indian Education Program in Long Beach (CA) School District.

BARKER, DEBRA K.S.
(program director of American Indian Studies; professor of English)
Education: Ball State University, BS (English), 1976, PhD (English/Composition), 1989; University of Missouri-Columbia, MA (English), 1978. *Affiliation & Address*: Associate Professor of English & Program Director, American Indian Studies Program, Hibbard Humanities Hall 426, University of Wisconsin, Box 4004, Eau Claire, WI 54702 (715) 836-6045. E-mail: barkerdk@uwec.edu. *Teaching areas*: American Indian literature, American literature, rhetoric & composition. *Published works*: Numerous articles in scholarly journals; presentations.

BARKER, JOANNE (Lenni-Lenape)
(associate professor)
Education: University of California, Santa Cruz, PhD, 2000. *Affiliation & Address*: Associate Professor, American Indian Studies, Ethnic Studies & Psychology Bldg. 106, San Francisco State University, 1600 Holloway Ave., San Francisco, CA 94132 (415) 338-7062. E-mail: jmbarker@sfsu.edu. *Other professional post*: Serves on the Nomination's Committee of the Native American & Indigenous Studies Association, 2010-2013. *Awards, honors*: Ford Foundation Fellowship with an association at the Center for Race & Gender, University of California, Berkeley, 2005-06; SFSU Presidential Sabbatical Award, Spring 2010; visiting scholarship in the American Indian Studies Center, University of California, Los Angeles, 2010-2011. *Awards, honors*: She has been the recipient of fellowships from the University of California, the Rockefeller Foundation, and the Ford Foundation. *Published works*: Editor, Sovereignty Matters: Locations of Contestation & Possibility In Indigenous Struggle for Self-Determination (University of Nebraska Press, 2005); Native Acts: Law, Recognition, & Cultural Authenticity (Duke University Press, 2011; Editor, Critically Sovereign: Indigenous Gender, Sexuality, and Feminist Studies (Duke University Press, 2017). She is currently working on a book monograph addressing issues of debt in Native America. She has published articles in the *American Indian Quarterly, Wicazo Sa Review, Cultural Studies, Meridians*, and several other peer reviewed journals including the inaugural issue of the *Critical Ethnic Studies Journal*.

BARKER, NATHAN "PAT" (Snoqualmie Coast Salish)
(tribal chief)
Affiliation & Address: Chief, Snoqualmie Indian Tribe, P.O. Box 969, Snoqualmie, WA 98065. (425) 888-6551.

BARNARD, ROGER (*Yonv Unega-White Bear*) (Amonsoquath Cherokee) 1949-
(spiritual leader, publisher, artist)
Born October 16, 1949, Carrolton, Mo. *Education*: Daytona Beach Community College; Universal Life Church (theology). *Affiliation & Address*: Spiritual Advisor/Leader-Chief, President, Pan American Indian Association, 8335 Sevigny Dr., N. Fort Myers, FL 33917 (239) 543-7727. E-mail: panamia@msn.com. *Military service*: U.S. Navy, 1969-71. *Community activities*: Adopt-a-Road, Lee County, FL; conduct regular Asi ceremonies, weddings, funeral and other special requests; teen and novice program to introduce individuals to the basic understanding of the American Indian spiritual path of learning to respect, "We are Related, We are One." *Memberships*: Pan American Indian Association (chief); Native American Church; American Indian Defense; Universal Life Church; American Indian Medicine Society; Amonsoquath Cherokee Tribe of Missouri. *Published work*: "Quest of the Shield" & "Basic Instruction for Individual Learning Toward Ceremonie" (self-published).

BARND, NATCHEE
(professor of Native American studies)
Education: Sonoma State University, BA (Ethnic Studies & Philosophy with minor in Native American Studies); UCLA, MA (American Indian Studies); UC San Diego, PhD & MA (Ethnic Studies. *Affiliation & Address*: Assistant Professor of Native American Studies (2014-present), Department of Ethnic Studies, Oregon State University, 260 Waldo Hall, 2250 SW Jefferson Way, Corvallis, OR 97331 (541) 737-1113. E-mail: natchee.barnd@oregonstate.edu. *Past professional posts*: Worked with several cultural centers throughout California, with special emphasis on combining scholarship, mentoring, and community building. California College of Arts, 2009-14; San Francisco State University (American Indian studies), UC San Diego (ethnic studies), Sacramento State University (ethnic studies), Laney College (American Indian studies), and Sonoma State University (American multicultural studies).

BARNES, ALLAN (Lenni Lenape)
(tribal manager)
Affiliation & Address: Tribal Manager, Delaware Tribe of Indians, 170 NE Barbara, Bartlesville, OK 74006 (918) 337-6593. E-mail: abarnes@delawaretribe.org

BARNES, BEN (Shawnee)
(tribal 2nd chief)
Affiliation & Address: 2nd Chief, Shawnee Tribe, P.O. Box 189, Miami, OK 74355 (918) 542-2441; or, P.O. Box 860114, Shawnee, KS 66286 (913) 284-6635. E-mail: benbarnes@gmail.com

BARNES, HARRY (Blackfeet)
(tribal chairperson)
Affiliation & Address: Blackfeet Reservation, 1 Agency Square, Browning, MT 59417 (406) 338-7521.

BARNETT, D'SHANE (Mandan/Arikara)
(executive director-NCUIH)
Affiliation & Address: Executive Director, National Council of Urban Indian Health (NCUIH), 924 Pennsylvania Ave., SE, Washington, DC 20003 (202) 544-0344. E-mail: dbarnett@ ncuih.org. *Past professional posts*: Director of Planning & Policy, Native American Health Center, Oakland, CA; program coordinator, Inter-Tribal Council of California, Sacramento, CA; program coordinator, Native American Youth Association, Portland, OR. Mr. Barnett was a founding member & president of the California Consortium for Urban Indian Health (CCUIH).

BARNETT, JAMES F., JR.
(director-historic landmark site)
Affiliation & Address: The Grand Village of the Natchez Indians, 400 Jefferson Davis Blvd., Natchez, MS 39120 (601) 446-6502.

BARNETT, ROGER (Muscogee Creek)
(tribal second chief)
Affiliation & Address: Second Chief, Muscogee (Creek) Nation, P.O. Box 580, Okmulgee, OK 74447 (918) 732-7620.

BARREIRO, KATSI COOK (Mohawk) (writer)
Address: 226 Blackman Hill Rd., Berkshire, NY 13736 (607) 657-8112.

BARRETT, BOBBY L. (Viejas Band of Kumayaay Diegueno)
(executive director)
Affiliation & Address: Executive Director (2010-present), Viejas Community Relations Dept., Viejas Enterprises, 5000 Willows Rd., Suite 115, Alpine, CA 91901 (619) 659-5400. E-mail: community@viejas.com. *Other professional post*: Board member, Blue Stone Strategy Group, Irvine, CA & Phoenix, AZ. *Past professional posts*: Viejas Casino (10 years in management); Viejas Band of Kumeyaay Indians (vice chairperson, six years; chairperson, four years), Alpine, CA; chair of the California Tribal Business Alliance (CTBA), created to protect the tribal government gaming industry, and to create strategic alliances with a wide group of businesses & industries; and founded the Bobby Barrett Foundation (community welfare).

BARRETT, JOHN ADAMS "ROCKY", JR. (Citizen Potawatomi) 1944-
(tribal chairperson; corporate president, cattle breeder)
Born March 25, 1944, Shawnee, Okla. *Education*: Princeton University, 1962-64; University of Oklahoma, 1964-65; Oklahoma City University, BS, 1968, MS, 1986; St. Gregory's University, PhD (hon.) Commercial Sciences, 2000. *Affiliation & Address*: Chairperson, Citizen Potawatomi Nation, 1601 Gordon Cooper Dr., Shawnee, OK 74801 (405) 275-3121. E-mail: rbarrett@ potawatomi.org. *Past professional posts*: U.S. Plywood Corp., Oklahoma City, 1966-69; Greenbriar Development Co., Memphis, TN, 1969-70; Barrett Construction Co., Southaven, MS, 1970-71; Central Tribes of the Shawnee Area (CTSA), 1971-74; Vice-Chairman, Citizen Potawatomi Nation, 1971-74; Barrett Drilling Corp., 1974-82; Barrett Refining Co., 1985-96; BLC Angus

Ranch, 1989-present; Barrett Drilling Co. (oil & gas production, gaming technology, land development), 1989-present; tribal chairperson, Citizen Potawatomi Nation, 1985-present. *Other professional posts*: Registered Lobbyist in Oklahoma Legislature for Oklahoma Home Builders Assn, 1968-69; Board of Directors - United Tribes of Western Oklahoma & Kansas; City of Shawnee Mayor's Advisory Board; Shawnee Service Unit of Indian Health Service; Oklahoma Indian Health Service Advisory Board; National Indian Action Contractor's Assn (president); Delegate to the National Tribal Chairman's Assn; National Congress of American Indians; Commissioner - Oklahoma Indian Affairs Commission (Governor's appointment), 2000-04, 2004-present; Board of Directors - St. Gregory's University, 1998-present; Delegate to the United Nations Conference on the Rights of Indigenous People, Geneva, Switzerland, 2002. Delegate to Tribal Self-Governance Advisory Council, 2004-present; Board of Directors - Native Nations Institute, Morris Udall Foundation, Tucson, AZ, 2003-present.

BARRIOS, RUBEN (Tachi Yokut)
(tribal chairperson)
Affiliation & Address: Chairperson, Tachi-Yokut Tribe of the Santa Rosa Rancheria, P.O. Box 8, Lemoore, CA 93245 (559) 924-1278. E-mail: rbarrios@tachi-yokut.com

BARSH, RUSSELL L.
(consultant, teacher, writer)
Education: JD. *Affiliation & Address*: Center for the Study of Coast Salish Environments, 2108-G Fisherman Bay Rd., Lopez, WA 98261 (360) 468-2808. E-mail: rlbarsh@gmail.com. Russell has been involved in Indigenous advocacy as a litigator in disputes over sacred sites & ceremonies, as a diplomatic agent for the Mi'kmaq Grand Council, as a consultant with international agencies, and above all as a teacher & writer. *Other professional post*: Instructor, International Institute for Indigenous Resource Management, Portland, OR. *Past professional posts*: He was involved in a four-year study of conflicts between multinational corporations and indigenous peoples worldwide funded by the MacArthur Foundation and the United Nations, and the book, Effective Negotiation by Indigenous Peoples: An Action Guide," written with Krisma Bastien. He has taught at the University of Washington and University of Lethbridge (Alberta, Canada), and as a visitor at Harvard Law School, New York University Law School, and Dartmouth College.

BARTGIS, JAMI (Cherokee)
(director of technical assistance & research)
Education: Oklahoma State University, PhD (Clinical Psychology); University of South Florida, Florida Mental Health Institute, APA predoctoral internship. *Affiliation & Address*: Director of Technical Assistance & Research, National Council of Urban Indian Health (NCUIH), 924 Pennsylvania Ave., SE, Washington, DC 20003 (202) 544-0344. E-mail: jbartgis@ncuih.org. Dr. Bartgis has spent the last ten years providing behavioral health services to both tribal & urban Indian individuals & communities. She currently works to provide technical assistance support to the Urban Indian health programs across the U.S. to both improve quality of care and to expand the capacity to provide health services to American Indians & Alaska Natives living in cities. *Past professional posts*: Clinical practice, Indian Health Care Resource Center, Tulsa, OK (three years); co-chair of the Tribal/State Relations Workgroup through Oklahoma Governor, Brad Henry's Mental Health Transformation Advisory Board. She worked with Indian youth & families both in direct patient care and in the development & advocacy of mental health systems for the patients she served.

BARTON, LOUISE ANN (*Wind Walks Woman*) (Cherokee-Mohawk) 1934-
(educator, author, performer)
Born November 21, 1934, New York, NY. *Education*: Rutgers, Master Gardner Certification, 2003; New York University, MA, 1981; Herbert Lehman College, BA, 1978; Bronx Community College, AAS, 1973. *Address*: 4A Hancock Dr., Whiting, NJ 08759 (732) 849-1892. E-mail: windwalker732@yahoo.com. *Affiliations*: Retired from various NYC Board of Education-teaching/coordinator posts. She worked with the Native American Education Program (NYC), & the Liberty Correctional Institution's Native Awareness Program (FL). *Community activities*: Native American storytelling & lectures in NYC & NJ colleges, public schools and libraries, senior residences, and private organizations; affiliated with The Gatherer Institute. *Memberships*: Southeastern Cherokee Confederacy; chairperson of Wind Walker Productions (non-profit, theatrical organization specializing in Native American folk arts presentations) and The Lyme Tyx (variety shows). *Awards, honors*: Artistic Community Enrichment Award, 1993-94, from a subsidiary of the NYC State Council on the Arts; grants awarded for Native American Storytelling in NYC public branch libraries, and other projects; scholastic honor societies: Kappa Delta Pi & Delta Pi Epsilon. *Interests*: "A master storyteller from a family of storytellers, telling Native & other tales in public schools, libraries, & colleges; working to improve education, preserve the ecology, inform people about Native American cultures and political problems, and lobbying to change laws. Engaged in multicultural activities, bringing people from all backgrounds together in common projects to

enrich their communities. Enjoy writing, lecturing & performing. I've taught Business Education & computer skills at both secondary & college levels, I have worked in community theater in all capacities, and have appeared at Shakespeare Festivals and at Medieval Fairs." *Published works*: Tales of the Pine Barrens, with Donna Lee Sharp Albertson; Fiction, non-fiction, Native stories, children's stories, poetry, plays, newspaper articles, CD covers, artist's books, information pamphlets & packets; also, co-author of scholastic mission statements & city-wide guidelines for computer training.

BASS, BARRY W. (*Big Buck*) (Nansemond)
(former tribal chief)
Affiliation & Address: Chief, Nansemond Indian Tribe, P.O. Box 2515, Suffolk, VA 23432 (757) 986-3354.

BASS, VINCENT (Winnebago)
(tribal vice chairperson)
Affiliation & Address: Winnebago Tribal Council, P.O. Box 687, Winnebago, NE 68071(402) 878-3102. E-mail: vince.bass@winnebagotribe.com.

BASSETT, FRANCES C. (Cherokee)
(attorney)
Education: University of New Mexico, BA, 1974, JD, 1980. Board of Editors, Natural Resource Journal, 1978-80. *Affiliation*: Partner, Fredericks Peebles & Morgan, LLC, 1900 Plaza Dr., Louisville, CO 80027 (303) 815-1720. E-mail: fbassett@ndnlaw.com. *Practice areas*: Natural resources; water & environmental law; commercial transactions; civil litigation & appellate advocacy. Ms. Bassett is experienced in transactional work, litigation & appellate advocacy. She also has broad experience in water, natural resources & environmental law. *Past professional posts*: Staff attorney, New Mexico Court of Appeals, 1985-87, Colorado Court of Appeals, 1988-95; private practice, New Mexico, 1995-2002; Assistant Attorney General, New Mexico, Division of Water, Environmental & Utilities, 2003-08.

BATAILLE, GRETCHEN M. 1944-
(university president)
Born September 28, 1944, Mishawaka, Ind. *Education*: Purdue University, 1962-1965; California State Polytechnic University, B.S., 1966, M.A., 1967; Drake University, D.A., 1977. *Address*: University of North Texas, Denton, TX. *Affiliations*: Instructor (1967-86) & professor (1986-90), Dept. of English, Iowa State University, Ames, Iowa; Associate Dean, College of Liberal Arts and Sciences, 1990-2000, Arizona State University, Tempe, AZ; Sr. V.P. for Academic Affairs, University of North Carolina System, Chapel Hill, NC, 2000-2006; President, University of North Texas, Denton, TX, 2006-present. She's a recognized scholar of Native American literature. *Memberships*: National Association for Ethnic Studies; Assn for the Study of American Indian Literature; Modern Language Assn. *Interests*: "I am interested in American Indian literature as a reflection of the culture, history, and world view of diverse peoples. *Published works*: The Worlds Between Two Rivers: Perspectives on American Indians in Iowa (Iowa State University Press, 1978); The Pretend Indians: Images of Native Americans in the Movies (Iowa State University Press, 1980); American Indian Literature: A Selected Bibliography for Schools and Libraries (NAIES, Inc., 1981); American Indian Women: Telling Their Lives (University of Nebraska Press, 1984); Images of American Indians in Film: An Annotated Bibliography (Garland Publishing, 1985); American Indian Women: A Guide to Research (Garland, 1991); Native American Women: A Biographical Dictionary (Garland, 1993).

BATCHELOR, WANDA (Washoe)
(former tribal chairperson)
Affiliation & Address: Stewart Indian Community, Gardnerville, NV 89410 (775) 883-8600. E-mail: wand.batchelor@ washoetribe.us.

BATES, T. ERIC
(instructor of anthropology)
Education: Northern Kentucky University, BA, BS, MA; Union Institute & University, PhD. *Affiliation & Address*: Instructor, Dept. of Anthropology, 216 Landrum, Highland Heights, KY 41099 (859) 572-6112. E-mail: batesth@ nku.edu *Research and Teaching Interests*: Cultural anthropology; North American Indians (especially Blackfoot); contemporary Native Americans and Christianity; religion and critical contextualization; ethnicity; Appalachia; cultural and social geography; communication and speech. *Current Research*: My doctoral research focused on the intersections of Pentecostalism and Native Identity formation on the Blackfeet Indian reservation in Browning, Montana. After years of gathering ethnographic data on the reservation, I propose that the Pentecostal experience has had substantial effects on Blackfeet Indian thus producing unique and multifaceted identities that interrogate both Pentecostal and Indian modes of existence. Although these points of convergence may disrupt typical Native identity formation, it is my position that Blackfeet Pentecostals continue to maintain their Native identity. Using theories of ethnic boundaries, I contend that Blackfeet Pentecostals employ cultural signals in order to maintain boundaries around which their Indian identity is produced. *Published works*: Native American Identity, Christianity, and Critical Contexualization (Cherohala Press, 2013).

BATTISE, JO ANN (Alabama Coushatta)
(tribal administrator)
Affiliation: Alabama-Coushatta Indian Museum, Rt. 3, Box 640, U.S. Hwy. 190, Livingston, TX 77351 (713) 563-4391.

BATTISE, KEVIN (Alabama-Coushatta)
(tribal chairperson)
Affiliation & Address: Chairperson, Alabama-Coushatta Tribe, Rt. 3, Box 659, Livingston, TX 77351 (936) 563-1100.

BATTISE, JO ANN (Alabama-Coushatta of Texas)
(tribal chairperson)
Affiliation & Address: Chairperson, Alabama-Coushatta Tribe of Texas, 571 State Park Rd., Livingston, TX 77351 (936) 563-1100.

BATTISE, NITA (Alabama-Coushatta of Texas)
(former tribal chairperson)
Affiliation & Address: Former Chairperson, Alabama-Coushatta Tribe of Texas, 571 State Park Rd., Livingston, TX 77351 (936) 563-1100.

BATTISE, LAWRINE (Alabama-Coushatta)
(tribal elder, cultural preservation specialist)
Affiliation: American Indian Resource Center, 4914 Nuthatch, San Antonio, TX 78217 (210) 655-1300; Alabama-Coushatta Tribe, Rt. 3, Box 659, Livingston, TX 77351 (936) 563-1100.

BATTON, GARY (Choctaw of Oklahoma)
(tribal chief)
Education: Southeastern Oklahoma State University, BS (Business management), 1989, *Affiliation & Address*: Chief (2014-present), Choctaw Nation of Oklahoma, P.O. Drawer 1210, Durant, OK 74702 (580) 924-8280. *Past professional posts*: Gary began his career with the Choctaw Nation in 1987 as a clerk in the Purchasing Department while he was attending Southeastern Oklahoma State University. Upon graduating with a Bachelor's Degree in Business Management in 1989, he accepted the position of Deputy Director at the Choctaw Nation Housing Authority. While at Housing, he was responsible for the management of Housing Authority operations & established several programs including the Choctaw Nation Drug Elimination Program, Family Investment Center Program and the Choctaw Nation Boys and Girls Club. In 1997, he was appointed to the position of Executive Director of Health. His first undertaking after stepping into the role was replacing the Choctaw Nation Hospital, a former Tuberculosis Center constructed in the 1930s, with the state-of-the-art Choctaw Nation Health Care Center, the first tribally funded health facility in the United States. He continued to expand and improve the Choctaw health system by adding clinics in Idabel, Stigler and Atoka and replacing or expanding outdated, inadequate clinics in Hugo, Broken Bow and McAlester. He constructed a new facility for adult inpatient alcohol and drug treatment and a hospitality house for patients traveling long distances for appointments at the health care center in Talihina. Concerned by the fact that some tribal businesses were not profitable and impressed with the growth and improvements to the health system, Chief Pyle appointed Gary to the position of Assistant Chief in May 2007. Gary immediately took action to grow the businesses & improve the profitability for the benefit of Choctaw members. As the Assistant Chief, Gary's focus changed from improving the health system for tribal members to growing and improving the entire Choctaw Nation for the benefit of tribal members. Among his numerous duties, he served as Chairman of the Choctaw Nation Business Committee where his first initiative was the development of an economic plan that would boost the economy in the 10½ counties and creat more than 700 jobs for the area. Under his guidance, the profitability for all tribal businesses improved with an overall increase of 69%.

BAUM, DAWN STURDEVANT (Ojibwe/Menominee)
(attorney)
Education: Beloit College, BA (Religious Studies), 1998; University of Wisconsin Law School, JD, 2001; University of Tulsa College of Law, LLM, 2005. *Affiliation & Address*: Attorney Advisor (2016-present), Office of Tribal Justice, U.S. Department of Justice, 950 Pennsylvania Ave., NW, Washington, DC 20530 (202) 514-8812. *Past professional posts*: Senior Attorney, Intern Coordinator, Department of the Interior-Office of the Solicitor, 2012-16; Staff Attorney, National Indian Gaming Commission, Washington, DC, 2010-12; Staff Attorney, Native American Rights Fund, Washington, DC, 2006-10

BAUR, DONALD
(attorney)
Education: Trinity College, BA (History), 1976; University of Pennsylvania Law School, JD, 1979. *Affiliation & Address*: Co-chair & Partner, Native American Law & Policy Group, Perkins Coie, 700 Thirteenth St., NW • Washington, DC 20005 (202) 654-6234. E-mail: dbaur@perkinscoie.com Throughout his 30-

year legal career, Don has engaged in a broad-based environmental & natural resources practice. He has been involved in the full range of legal issues arising under the laws dealing with Native Americans, ranging from Alaska Native Corporations & subsistence rights, to Native Hawaiian land disputes, to Indian gaming, trust land, tribal acknowledgment, natural resource & energy development, wildlife conservation business transactions, & cultural resource protection matters, from Alaska to California to Florida to New England. He is co-chair of the Perkins Coie Native American Law group, which is nationally-ranked by Chambers. One of the principal elements of Don's Native American law practice has been the successful negotiation of precedent-setting agreements between local governments and Indian gaming tribes such as the Seminole, Mashpee Wampanoag, Menominee, Mohegan, Narragansett, and Shakopee Mdewakanton Sioux Tribes & their local government neighbors. His work with the Town of Montville and Mohegan Tribe led to the federal Mohegan Nation of Connecticut Land Claims Settlement Act of 1994. He also has represented energy, timber, real estate, water utility, irrigation districts and mining entities in transactional work for access to tribal lands and use of tribal resources, including business activities on Indian reservations throughout the country. Don has worked directly for Tribes & Alaska Native corporations and entities on numerous matters, including Endangered Species Act compliance & Indian religious practices. He works with Tribes and parties dealing with Tribes to ensure full consultation on federal actions affecting historic, cultural, & religious properties and artifacts. In addition to environmental compliance and natural resource use and development, Don practices in all areas of federal Indian law, including gaming, trust land acquisition, tribal acknowledgment, & business transactions. *Other professional posts*: Vermont Law School, Adjunct Professor, Environmental Law Center, 1998 – present; Environmental Law Institute, Instructor, Environmental Law Boot Camp, 2002 – present.

BAUERLE, PHENOCIA (Crow)
(writer/editor)
Publication: Editor, "The Way of the Warrior: Stories of the Crow People" (University of Nebraska Press, 2003).

BAZAN, S. NICOLE (Rosebud Sioux)
(attorney)
Education: Stanford University, BA (Native American Political History & Law, an individually designed major), 1995; Harvard Law School, JD, 1999. *Address & Affiliation*: Hobbs, Straus, Dean & Walker, LLP (Associate, 1999-present), 2120 L St., NW, Suite 700, Washington, DC 20037 (202) 822-8282. E-mail: nbazan@hsdwdc.com. While at Harvard, she was an officer in the Native American Law Students Association, La Alianza, and the Coalition for Cross-Cultural Unity (the umbrella organization for student groups of color). She also served as an editor for the Harvard Blackletter Law Journal, a research assistant in American Indian Law, and a member of the Harvard Legal Aid Bureau. Nicole participated in a treaty-drafting clinic with the Carrier-Sekani Bands of British Columbia & wrote her thesis (Dine Bi Beehaz'aanii: Customary Law in Navajo Nation) for the Navajo Supreme Court. Areas of concentration: Indian Self-Determination and Education Assistance Act; tribal sovereignty; tribal government; Indian health care. *Memberships*: Native American Bar Assn; New York Bar Assn; Sicangu Oyate (Rosebud Sioux) Bar Assn.

BEAL, ALVIN G "CHIP" (Choctaw of Oklahoma/Chickasaw/Cherokee)
(professor of First Nations Studies)
Education: Southeastern Oklahoma State niversity, BS (Biology & Psychology); Northeastern State University, M.Ed. (Counseling); University of Wisconsin-Superior, Post Masters in School Psychology. *Affiliation & Address*: Assistant Professor, First Nationns Studies, Human Behavior, Justice & Diversity Department, Swenson Hall 3103, Belknap & Catlin, Superior, WI 54880 (715) 394-8297. E-mail: abeal@uwsuper.edu. He is also the Diversity Coordinator within the Office of Multicultural Affairs. *Teaching & Research Interests*: First Nations Survey course; First Nations history, myths & legends; exploring ways to increase Native American student retention at both K-12 and university levels. *Resources*: First Nations Center.

BEANE, TAMARA (Cherokee-Choctaw) 1958-
(potter)
Born April 15, 1958, Idaho Falls, Idaho. *Education*: Jacksonville State University, Jacksonville, AL, BS, 1979. *Affiliation & Address*: Tammy Beane Pottery, 3589 County Road 822, Collinsville, AL 35961 (256) 523-5849.. *Community activities*: Presents programs for museums, archaeological societies, state & other parks. *Memberships*: Southeastern Archaeological Conference; Primitive Society; Alabama Archaeological Society. *Interests*: "I reproduce southeastern prehistoric & historic Native American pottery. "I travel, visit archaeological sites, museums, & labs doing research."

BEAR, CANDACE (Goshute)
(tribal chairperson)
Affiliation & Address: Chairperson, Skull Valley Band of Goshute Indians, 1198 N. Main St., Tooele, UT 84029 (435) 882-4532.
E-mail: candaceb@svgoshutes.com

BEAR, HENRY JOHN (Houlton Maliseet)
(Maine state representative)
Affiliation & Address: Maine State Rpresentative, 41 Elm St., Houlton, ME 04730 (207) 532-8368. E-mail: bearlaw2@yahoo.com. *Committee*: Health & Human Services. Maliseet Rights Advocate

BEAR, WILFORD
(education)
Affiliation & Address: Director, Vocational Rehabilitation Program, Fort Peck Tribes, P.O. Box 1027, Poplar, MT 59255 (406) 768-5136. E-mail: asrvp@nemontel.net.

BEAR DON'T WALK, ELDENA (Crow)
(director of Indian law clinic)
Education: University of Montana, BS (Sociology), MPA, JD; University of Arizona, Rogers College of Law, LLM (Indigenous People's Law & Policy). *Affiliation & Address*: Adjunct Professor & Director (2014-15), Margery Hunter Brown Indian Law Clinic, University of Montana School of Law, Law 112, 32 Campus Dr., Missoula, MT 59812 (406) 243-2544. E-mail: eldena. beardon'twalk@mso.umt.edu. Eldena has co-taught Tribal Courts/ Tribal Law and is often a guest lecturer on the Indian Child Welfare Act(ICWA), election issues, and other current legal issues facing Indian Country. She has presented numerous workshops on ICWA, Tribal Courts, judicial ethics and the development of tribal codes. She began her legal career as a public defender for the State of Montana working on the Confederated Salish & Kootenai Indian Reservation, which is a PL-280 reservation. Her private practice includes all aspects of Indian law. As a second generation Indian lawyer & judge, she has invested her career in bettering Indian Country. She is the Chief Justice of the Confederated Salish and Kootenai Appellate Court. She sits as an Associate Appellate Justice for the Chippewa Cree Tribe. Professor Bear Don't Walk also sits as an associate appellate justice for the Ponca Tribe of Nebraska on its inaugural appellate court panel and was the first female Chief Justice of the Crow Tribe. Professor Bear Don't Walk has sat pro tem as an administrative law judge for the Fort Belknap Indian Community and as an appellate justice and constitutional court justice for the Northern Cheyenne Tribe. She has written over 60 appellate opinions. She is a member of the State Bar of Montana and currently, serves as Chair of the Indian Law Section.

BEAR EAGLE, JENNIFER (Oglala Lakota)
(attorney)
Education: University of Nebraska, BA (English), 2002, and College of Law, JD, 2008. *Affiliation & Address*: Associate (2009-present), Fredericks Peebles & Morgan, LLP, 3610 North 163rd Plaza, Omaha, NE 68116 (402) 333-4053. E-mail: jbeareagle@ndnlaw.com. *Practice areas*: Federal Indian law; tribal sovereignty & self-determination; economic development; trial & appellate advocacy; employment law & administrative law; alternative dispute resolution. *Past professional posts*: Law Clerk, Nebraska Attorney General's Office - Dept. of Roads; Law Clerk, Native American Rights Fund. *Memberships*: Commissioner, Executive Committee member, Nebraska Commission on Indian Affairs; board secretary, Planning & Development Committee Chair, Indian Center, Inc.

BEAR SHIELD, WAYNE (Rosebud Lakota Sioux)
(tribal general operations director)
Affiliation & Address: General Operations Director, Rosebud Sioux Tribal Council, P.O. Box 430, Rosebud, SD 57570 (605) 747-2381.

BEARD, ANNA
(museum curator)
Affiliation & Address: Curator, Tonkawa Tribal Museum, P.O. Box 70, Tonkawa, OK 74653 (405) 628-5301.

BEARDT, LEE ANN (Rosebud Lakota)
(BIA agency supt.)
Affiliation & Address: Supt., Bureau of Indian Affairs, P.O. Box 228, Mission, SD 57555 (605) 747-2224. E-mail: leeann.beardt@bia.gov.

BEARHEART, STUART (St. Croix Ojibwe)
(tribal secretary/treasurer)
Affiliation & Address: Secretary/Treasurer & Maple Plain Community Representative, St. Croix Chippewa Indians of Wisconsin, 14633 Angeline Ave., Webster, WI 54893 (715) 349-2195. *Past tribal post*: Tribal chairperson.

BEATTY, JOHN J. (*Tewahnitaneken*) (Mohawk) 1939-
(anthropologist)
Born September 5, 1939, Brooklyn, N.Y. *Education*: Brooklyn College, BA, 1964; University of Oklahoma, MA, 1966; City University of New York, PhD (Anthropology), 1972. *Address*: 2983 Bedford Ave., Brooklyn, N.Y. 11210. E-mail: profbeatty@hotmail.com. *Affiliations*: Teaching assistant, University of Oklahoma, 1964-65; instructor, Long Island University, 1966-67; professor, Dept. of Anthropology, 1966-2002, professor emeritus, Anthropology/Film, Film

Dept., 2002-present, Brooklyn College, CUNY. Other professional posts: Founder & director, American Indian Institute of City University of New York; private investigator, Phoenix Investigative Associates, 1982-. *Military service*: New York Guard (captain.) *Major research work*: Ethnographic & linguistic: American Indians in Urban Areas (major U.S. cities) 1963-; Tlingit Language & Culture (in New York & Alaska) 1964-67; Totonac Language & Culture (in New York & Mexico) 1964-67; Kiowa-Apache Language & Culture (Anadarko, Oklahoma) 1965-; Mohawk Language & Culture (New York City & various Mohawk Reserves) 1964-; Japanese & Japanese Americans: Language & Culture, 1973-; Scots & Scottish Americans, 1974-; Cross Cultural Perspectives on Police, 1978-*Memberships*: American Anthropological Association (Fellow); New York Academy of Sciences (Fellow); American Indian Community House. Awards, honors: National Science Foundation Training Grant, University of Oklahoma, 1965 (for research with the Kiowa-Apache); City University of New York and National Science Foundation Dissertation Year Fellowships, 1971 (for research with Mohawk languages); National Science Foundation Grant (U.S. - Japanese Co-operative Program, 1973); Brooklyn College Faculty Award, 1973, for research with Japanese macaques; Faculty Research Award Program, CUNY, 1974 & 1975, for research with chimpanzees & for research on sexual behavior; Department of Health, Education & Welfare: Office of Native American Programs, 1975 grant to work with urban American Indians in New York State; National Endowment for the Arts, 1977, for filming Iroquois social dances; Rikkyoo University (Japan) Research Fellowship, 1986-87, for research on solidarity; Certificate of Appreciation, New York Academy of Sciences; Sigma Xi. *Interests*: Anthropology; linguistics, symbolic anthropology - American Indians; Asia; theatre; forensics; lecture series on American Indians & Japanese culture, 1969-; coach, Brooklyn College Wrestling Team. *Published works*: Kiowa-Apache Music and Dance (Museum of Anthropology, University of Northern Colorado, 1974); Mohawk Morphology (Museum of Anthropology, University of Northern Colorado, 1974); A Guide to New York for Japanese: An Ethnographic Approach (Gloview Press, Tokyo, 1985); Kujira! The Whale in Japanese Culture (AJSU, Japan, 1988); Intercultural Communication (2001); numerous articles. *Recording*: Music of the Plains Apache (Folkways Records). *Films*: Iroquois Social Dances, Two parts, with Nick Manning, 1979; and others. Videotapes: The American Indian Art Center, 1978; American Indians at Brooklyn College, 1978; Scottish Highland Dances, 1979; Custer Revisited, 1980.

BEAUDET, MATTHEW W. (Montaukett)
  (attorney)
Education: Loyola University Chicago, BS, 1985; The John Marshall Law School, JD, 1989; Federal Emergency Management Institute, 2008-09. *Affiliation & Address*: First Deputy Commissioner, Chicago Department of Buildings, 121 N. LaSalle St., Room 906, Chicago, IL 60602 (312) 744-6585. *Other professional post*: Attorney-at-Law, Law Offices of Matthew W. Beaudet, Chicago, IL, 1989-present; tribal consultant, Montaukett Indian Nation, 2012-present. Past professional posts: Of Counsel, Rubinstein & Rubinstein, 1995-97; Assistant Director, City of Chicago, Department of Administrative Hearings, 1997-2003; General Counsel, Montaukett Tribe of Long Island, 2000-09; Commissioner, Illinois Supreme Court, Committee on Character & Fitness, 2000-09; President, Illinois Native American Bar Association, 2000-02, 2010-12; Chief of Electronic Tolling, Illinois State Toll Highway Authority, 2003-08; Assistant Director, Illinois Department of Central Management Service, 2008-09; 1ˢᵗ Deputy Health Commissioner, City of Chicago, 2009-11;

BEAULIEU, DAVID (White Earth Ojibwe)
  (professor)
Education: University of Minnesota, PhD (Education Administration); Post Doctorate Fellow of the D'Arcy McNickle Center for the History of the American Indian, Newberry Library, Chicago, IL. *Affiliation & Address*: Professor & Director, Center for Indian Education, Mary Lou Fulton College of Education, Arizona State University, P.O. Box 871311, Tempe, AZ 85287 (480) 965-6292. E-mail: david.beaulieu@asu.edu. *Other professional post*: President, Board of Directors, National Indian Education Association. *Past professional posts*: Electa Quinney Professor of American Indian Education, University of Wisconsin-Milwaukee School of Education, and a professor in the Department of Educational Policy & Community Studies; director, Office of Indian Education, U.S. Dept. of Education, 1997-2001; appointed Commissioner, Department of Human Rights, State of Minnesota, 1991, and re-appointed in 1995; faculty positions held at Moorehead State University, University of Illinois, Chicago; Associate Professor & Chairperson of the Department of American Indian Studies, University of Minnesota, Minneapolis, MN. *Awards, honors*: Dr. Beaulieu was the first American Indian to be appointed as a Commissioner in State Government for Minnesota.

BEAUTY, THOMAS (Yavapai-Apache)
  (former tribal chairperson)
Affiliation & Address: Chairperson, Yavapai-Apache Nation, 2400 W. Datsi St., Camp Verde, AZ 86322 (928) 567-3649.

BEAUVAIS, ARCHIE BRYAN (Rosebud Sioux) 1948-
  (educational administrator/instructor)
Born December 30, 1948, Rosebud, S.D. *Education*: Northern Arizona University, Flagstaff, B.S. (Education), 1974, M.A. (Education), 1976; Harvard University, EdD, 1982. *Principal occupation*: Education administrator/instructor. Home *Address*: P.O. Box 426, Mission, S.D. 57555. E-mail: abeaux@post.harvard.edu. *Affiliation*: Bilingual Director/Grant Writer, St. Francis Indian School, St. Francis, SD 57572 (605) 747-2299 (2002-present). *Past professional posts*: Dean, Academic Affairs & Chair, Graduate Education Program, Sinte Gleska University, Rosebud, SD, 1984-02; consultant, South Dakota Board of Regents for Title II math & science; consultant-evaluator, North Central Association, Chicago, IL. *Military service*: U.S. Army, 1967-1970 (Vietnam, 1968-1969, Specialist Fifth Class, Army Commendation Medal.) *Community activities*: Doctoral representative to Student Association Cabinet, Harvard Graduate School of Education. *Memberships*: School Administrators of South Dakota; Ducks Unlimited; Harvard Chapter of Phi Delta Kappa; South Dakota Indian Education Association, South Dakota Council for Social Studies. *Awards, honors*: 1988 Alumni Achievement Award, Northern Arizona University, Flagstaff, AZ; Jubilee Year Distinguished Alumnus Award, Northern Arizona University, Flagstaff, AZ, 1990; Executive Proclamation, Office of the Governor, State of South Dakota, Feb. 1991; Trio Achiever, National Council of Educational Opportunity Associations, Sept. 1991; Certificate of Appreciation, Rosebud Sioux Tribe, 2002. *Interests*: "Major interest is developing new & innovative programs which will significantly impact reservation, tribal, and other native communities." *Published works*: Article, "A Unique Masters Program" (Harvard Graduate School of Education - Alumni Bulletin, 1989).

BEAVER, B. TOM (Muscogee Creek)
  (director of public information)
Born in Muskogee, Okla. *Education*: University of Kansas, B.S., 1972, M.S., 1974. Resides in Minneapolis, MN (612) 626-7280. *Affiliations*: WCCO TV, Minneapolis, MN (anchor, producer, reporter, 1973-79; public service director, 1981-86); Special Assistant, Assistant Secretary for Indian Affairs, Dept. of the Interior, Washington, DC, 1979-81; public information officer, Regional Transit Board, St. Paul, MN, 1987-88; host & board member, First Americans Update, KTCI-TV, St. Paul, MN & Westmarc Cable, St. Cloud, MN, 1991-; director of public information, University of Minnesota, Office of the Associate Provost & Associate Vice President for Academic Affairs, Minneapolis, MN, 1988-. *Other professional posts*: Freelancer, 1985-; columnist, "The Lakota Times," Martin, SD, 1985-86. *Community activities*: Work with community groups to define relevant issues and translate those issues into media events; serves on a variety of commissions, panels & boards of non-profit agencies. *Awards, honors*: Indian Media Award for Outstanding Achievement in Television, Native American Public Broadcasting Consortium, 1984; Volunteer of the Year, Minneapolis Junior League, 1985; Distinguished Service Award, City of Minneapolis, MN, 1986.

BEAVER, JOHN (Muscogee Creek)
  (museum director/curator)
Education: University of Oklahoma, BA (Anthropology, Archaeology, Allied Health), 1999; University of Illinous at Chicago, MA (Anthropology, Archaeology, Museum Studies)), 2002, PhD Candidate (Anthropology, Museoogy, Museum Administration/Collections Management). *Affiliation & Address*: Director/Curator (2009-present), Muscogee (Creek) Nation Museum & Cultural Center & Archives, 2950 N. Wood Dr., Okmulgee, OK 74447 (800) 482-1979. Other professional post: Member, Committee on Museums, Collections, and Curattion, Society for American Archaeology, 20l1-present. *Past professional posts*: Research Fellow, National Science Foundation, 1999-2003; Repatriation Research Specialist, 2003-05, Repatriation/Cultural Protocols Program Specialist & Curatorial Council, 2005-07, National Museum of the American Indian, Smithsonian Instituteion, 2003-05; Committee on Native American Relations, Society for American Archaeology, 2004-07; Heritage Management Journal, Editorial Board, Left Coast Press, 2007-10.

BEAVER, R. PERRY (Muscogee Creek)
  (principal chief)
Address & Affiliation: Principal Chief, Muscogee Creek Nation of Oklahoma, P.O. Box 580, Okmulgee, OK 74447 (918) 756-8700.

BEBO, NAOMI Y. (Ho-Chunk/Menominee)
  (attorney)
Education: University of California, Los Angeles, JD/MA Program in Law & American Indian Studies, 2009. Her thesis paper concerned cultural property protection and the Indian Arts & Crafts Act. *Affiliation & Address*: Associate, Nordhaus Law Firm, LLP, 405 Dr. Martin Luther King, Jr. Ave. NE, Albuquerque, NM 87102 (505) 243-4275. *Past professional posts*: Alexander, Berkey, Williams & Weathers, Berkeley, CA serving tribal clients regarding native land rights, environmental & cultural resource protection, Indian child dependency, tribal law & litigation. Ms. Bebo previously clerked for two tribal courts, the Eastern Band of Cherokee Indians and the Hopi Supremem Court, and the Arizona Court of Appeals; also worked for the American Indian Higher

Education Consortium, the Native American Rights Fund, & Sonosky, Chambers, Sachse & Endreson. *Memberships*: Native American Bar Assn and the California Indian Law Assn.

BECENTI, DELORIS (Navajo-Dine')
(dean of student services)
Education: Navajo Community College, AA; Fort Lewis College, BA (Political Science); Western New Mexico University, MA (Educational Leadership). *Affiliation & Address*: Dean of Student Services, Navajo Technical University, P.O. Box 849, Crownpoint, NM 87313 (505) 786-4104. E-mail: dbecenti@navajotech.edu.

BECENTI, FRANCIS D. (Navajo-Dine') 1952-
(higher education administrator)
Born May 18, 1952, Fort Defiance, Ariz. *Education*: Navajo Community College, A.A., 1973; University of California, Berkeley, B.A., 1975. *Principal occupation*: Higher education administrator. *Address*: Native American Student Services, Colorado State University, 312 Student Services, Fort Collins, CO 80523 (303) 491-1101. *Affiliations*: Director of financial aid, Navajo Community College, 1975-1979; director of financial aid, University of Albuquerque, 1980-1981; director of student services, College of Ganado, 1981-1984; director, Native American Student Services, Colorado State U., Fort Collins, 1984-.

BECK, DAVID R.M. 1956-
(professor of Native Ameriacn studies)
Born July 14, 1956, Evanston, Ill. Education: Northwestern University, BA, 1979; University of Illinois, Chicago, MA, 1987, PhD, 1994. *Affiliation & Address*: Professor of History (2000-present), The Payne Family Native American Center, Room 112, Native American Studies Dept., University of Montana, 32 Campus Dr., Missoula, MT 59812 (406) 243-6097. E-mail: dave.beck@mso.umt.edu. *Past professional posts*: Chair, Dept. of Native American Studies, University of Montana, Missoula; NAES College, Chicago, IL (director, Tribal Research Center, 1992-97; dean & senior resident faculty, 1997-2000). *Community activities*: Archivist, NAES College, 1987-92; consultant, Menominee Tribe Historic Preservation Dept.; advisor, Americans for Indian Opportunity; advisor, Piegan Institute, Browning, MT; Missoula American Indian Parent Education Committee, 2000-03. *Memberships*: American Historical Association; Wisconsin Historical Society; Montana Historical Society; Natural Resources Defense Council. *Awards, honors*: Listed in Outstanding Young Men of America, 1988; University Fellowship, University of Illinois at Chicago, 1990-92; Certification of Recognition, Americans for Indian Opportunity Ambassador Program, 1993; Wisconsin Historical Society Book Awards of Merit for "Seige & Survival," 2002 & "The Struggle of Self-Determination," 2005. *Interests*: Teaching & writing history; travelling. *Published works*: Editor: Contemporary Issues, Reader One (NAES College Press, 1981); The Chicago American Indian Community, 1983-1988, Annotated Bibliography & Guide to Sources in Chicago (NAES College Press, 1988); Siege & Survival: Menominee Indian History, 1634-1856 (U. of Nebraska Press, 2002); The Struggle for Self-Determination: Menominee Indian History Since 1854 (U. of Nebraska Press, 2005); Seeking Recognition: The Termination & Restoration of the Coos, Lower Umpqua & Suislaw Indians, 1855-1984 (U. of Nebraska Press, 2009).

BEDARD, IRENE (Inupiat Eskimo/Metis Cree) 1967-
(actress, TV & film producer)
Born & raised in Anchorage, Alaska, July 22, 1967. *Education*: The University of the Arts in Philadelphia, PA (Musical Theatre). *Affiliation & Address*: Founder & President (with Thom Denomme, CEO), Sleeping Lady Films & Waking Giants Productions, P.O. Box 110918, Anchorage, AK 99518 (403) 612-5402. E-mail: sleepyladywalkinggiants@gmail.com Her first role was as Mary Crow Dog in the television production, Lakota Woman: Siege at Wounded Knee, which depicted the 1970s standoff between police & Native Americans at Wounded Knee, SD. She is probably best known as the voice of the eponymous heroine in the Disney anmated film Pocahontas & its direct-to-video sequal Pocahontas II: Journey to a New World. Ms. Bedard was also the physical model for the character. She appeared in a different take of the story in the 2005 film, The New World, as Pocahontas' mother whose name was Nonoma Winanuske Matatiske. In 2005, she was cast in the television mini-series, Into the West, portraying the half-Lakota, half-white adult Margaret "Light Shines" Wheeler. She was chosen as one of People magazine's 50 Most Beautiful People for 1995. TV & Movie Credits (partial): Lakota Woman: Siege at Wounded Knee, 1994; Squanto: A Warrior's Tale, 1994; The Marshal (1 episode), 1995; Pocahontas (voice), 1995; Grand Avenue, 1996; Crazy Horse, 1995; True Women, 1997; Smoke Signals, 1998; Two for Texas, 1998; Pocahontas II: Journey t a New World (direct-to-video, voice), 1998; Wildfires, 1999; Blood Money, 1998; The Lost Child, 2000; The Outer Limits (1 episode), 2001; Edge of America, 2003; Into the West (3 episodes), 2005; Love's Long Journey, 2005; The New World, 2005; The pectacular Spider-Man (4 episodes), 2008-09; Young Justice:Invasion (1 episode), 2012. *Awards, honors*: Nominated for a Golden Globe, for Best Performance by an Actress in a Mini-Series or TV Movie, for Lakota Woman: Siege at Wounded Knee; Western Heritage Awards for Lakota Woman (1995), Two for Texas (1999), Into the West (2006); American Indian LA Film & TV Awards for Best Lead Actress in a Feature Film for Greesewood Flat, 2004; NAMIC Vision Awards for Best Dramatic Performances for Into the West, 2006.

BEDEL, MARK (Shoshone)
(tribal executive director)
Affiliation: Northwestern Band of Shoshone Nation, 707 N. Main St., Brigham City, UT 84302 (800) 310-8241.

BEETSO, CHIA HALPERN (Spirit Lake Dakota)
(tribal court specialist)
Education: University of California, Berkeley, BA (Political Science), 2005; Arizona State University College of Law, JD, 2008. Affiliation & Address: Tribal Court Specialist (2011-present), Tribal Law & Policy Institute, 8235 Santa Monica Blvd. #211, West Hollywood, CA 90046 (323) 650-5467. E-mail: chia@tlpi.org. *Past professional posts*: Deputy Prosecutor, Salt River Pima-Maricopa Indian Community, 2008; Program manager for the Native American Congressional Internship, Udall Foundation, 2009-11;.

BEGAY, ADRIANN, M.D. (Navajo-Dine')
(physician; association president-elect)
Affiliation & Address: President-elect (2012-13), Association of American Indian Physicians, 1225 Sovereign Row #103, Oklahoma City, OK 73108 (405) 946-7072.

BEGAY, CARLYLE (To'tsohnii) (Navajo-Dine')
(Arizona State Senator)
Education: University of Arizona, BS, 2003; Arizona State University, W.P. Carey School of Business, MS (Health Sector Management), 2004-06. *Affiliation & Address*: Ariizona State Senator (Democrat), District 7 (2013-present), 1700 W. Washingtonn, Room 315, Phoenix, AZ 85007 (602) 926-5862. E-mail: cbegay@azleg.gov. *Committees*: Education, Government & Environment, Natural Resources & Rural Affairs. *Other professional posts*: Chai, Community Advisory Board Member, 2012-present; member, Board of Directors, Arizona American Indian Chamber of Commerce, 2009-presnt; VP & Chief Development Officer, AIHMP, Inc., 2006-present. *Past professional posts*: Vice President of Business Development, American Indian Health & Management Policy, Phoenix, AZ; AmeriChoice, United Health Group; health policy congressional fellow, Barbara Jordan Health Policy Scholars Program of the Kaiser Family Foundation, Washington, DC.

BEGAY, CATHERINE T. (Navajo-Dine')
(school principal)
Affiliation & Address: Principal, Greasewood/Toyei Consolidated Boarding School, Ganada, AZ 86505 (602) 654-3331.

BEGAY, D.Y. (Navajo-Dine') 1953-
(weaver, textile consultant)
Born September 3, 1953, Ganado, Ariz. *Education*: Rocky Mountain College, 1974; Arizona State University, BA, 1978. *Principal occupation*: Weaver, textile consultant. *Address*: 6929 E. Jenan Dr., Scottsdale, AZ 85254 (480) 922-9232. E-mail: dybegay@cox.net. *Affiliation*: Owner/Manager, D.Y. Begay's Weaving Studio, Scottsdale, AZ; owner, Navajo Textiles & Arts, Chinle, AZ, 1984-. *Other professional posts*: Textile instructor, lecturer. *Memberships*: Palisades Guild; Indian Education; Museum of Natural History, Museum of the American Indian; Handweavers Guild of America. *Interests*: Have done extensive traveling (Canada, Mexico, Europe and U.S.) All my interest is in the field of textiles (Navajo weaving). *Biographical sources*: A Navajo Weaver (N.Y. Times); Navajo Weaving (Bergen Record). *Published works*: Co-editor, The Sheep (documentary film), 1982.

BEGAY, EDWARD T. (Navajo-Dine')
(former speaker - Navajo Nation)
Affiliation & Address: (3rd Speaker, 1999-2003), Navajo Nation, P.O. Box 9000, Window Rock, AZ 86515 (928) 871-6352.

BEGAY, HAROLD (Navajo-Dine')
(school director)
Affiliation & Address: Director, Greyhills High School, P.O. Box 160, Tuba City, AZ 86045 (602) 283-6271.

BEGAY, JASON (Navajo-Dine' Nation)
(assistant professor & project director)
Education: University of Montana, BA (Journalism), 2002. *Affiliation & Address*: Assistant Professor & Director of Native American Journalism Projects, University of Montana School of Journalism, Don Anderson Hall, 32 Campus Dr., Missoula, MT 59812 (406) 243-4001. E-mail: jbegay@naja.com. *Other professional post*: Board Vice President, Native American Journalists Association, Norman, OK. Jason has worked at the New York Times, The Oregonian, and Navajo Times (six years).

BEGAY, JIMMIE C. (Navajo-Dine') 1948-
  (Indian school director)
Born September 4, 1948, Rough Rock, Ariz. *Education*: New Mexico Highlands University, A.S., 1969, B.A., 1972, M.A., 1974. *Affiliation & Address*: Board President, Navajo Nation Board of Education, Department of Dine Education, P.O. Box 670, Window Rock, AZ 86515 (928) 871-7475. *Past professional posts*: Director, Rock Point Community School, Rock Point, AZ. Native American Studies teacher; coordinator, Black Mesa Day School; president, board of directors, Association of Community Tribal Schools, Inc., Vermillion, SD. *Community activities*: Navaho Culture Organization (chairman); originator of Navaho psychology classes; sponsor of Black Mesa five mile run. *Memberships*: National Association of Secondary School Principals; Smithsonian Institution; Harvard Education Review; Dine Biolta Association. *Honors & awards*: Outstanding Accomplishments, Rough Rock School Board. *Interests*: Betterment in education programs, especially for Indians; travel. (I) would like to pursue higher educational goals. *Biographical sources*: Principals & Views About Indian Education, (Rough Rock News); Candidate for NACIE (Navajo Times); History of Rough Rock, by Robert Roessell. *Published works*: Navajo Culture Outline, and Navajo Philosophy of Education.

BEGAY, JOHNNY C. (Navajo-Dine')
  (Indian school principal)
Affiliation & Address: Aneth Community School, P.O. Box 600, Montezuma Creek, UT 84534 (801) 651-3271.

BEGAY, JONES (Navajo-Dine')
  (Indian school chairperson)
Affiliation & Address: Black Mesa Community School, P.O. Box 97, Pinon, AZ 86510 (520) 674-3632.

BEGAY-FOSS, JOYCE (Navajo-Dine')
  (center director; artist, business owner)
Address: Box 1322 · San Juan Pueblo, NM 87566 (505) 852-4882. Website: www.begayfossdesigns.com *Artwork*: Navajo custom order saddle blankets & textiles. *Affiliation & Address*: Director, Living Traditions Education Center, Museum of Indian Arts & Culture/Laboratory of Anthropology, Box 2087, Santa Fe, NM 87504 (505) 476-1250. E-mail: joyce.begay-foss@state.nm.us.

BEGAY, JUDI (Navajo-Dine')
  (college instructor)
Affiliation & Address: Navajo Community College, P.O. Box 580, Shiprock, NM 87420 (505) 368-5291.

BEGAY, KAREN FRANCIS (Navajo-Dine')
  (student affairs)
Affiliation & Address: Director, Native American Student Affairs, University of Arizona, 1212 E. University Blvd., Nugent Bldg., Rm. 203, Tucson, AZ 85721 (520) 621-3835.

BEGAY, KRISTI (Wells Band of Te-Moak Western Shoshone)
  (tribal vice chairperson)
Affiliation & Address: Vice Chairperson, Wells Band Colony, P.O. Box 809, Wells, NV 89835 (775) 752-3045.

BEGAY, LISA (Navajo-Dine')
  (Indian program administrator)
Born in Fort Defiance on the Navajo Reservation. *Education*: Arizona State University, BS in Communications and a Certificate in Native American Justice Studies. *Affiliation & Address*: Indian program administrator, Council of Indian Nations, P.O. Box 1800, Apache Junction, AZ 85217 (800) 811-6955. E-mail: info@cinprograms.org. Website: www.cinprograms.org. *Other professional post*: Southwest Program Director for the National Relief Charities. She administers all of the programs for both the Southwest Indian Relief Council and the Council of Indian Nations. *Community activities*: While in high school, she was president of the Native American Youth Leadership Council and vice president & secretary of the United National Indian Tribal Unit. While in college, she started Native American Students United, an organization that was tailored to meet the needs of individual students. One of the projects was to match children from urban schools, with an A.S.U. student of a similar cultural background. The A.S.U. student taught the child various things about their shared culture including language, customs, and traditions so the urban school student would learn more about their cultural ties. Upon graduation from college, Lisa worked as a project coordinator for the Department of Youth Services in Chinle, AZ.

BEGAY, LORENZO J. (Navajo-Dine')
  (business consultant)
Education: Northern Arizona University, BS; University of Phoenix, MBA & Doctorate in Business Administration. *Affiliation & Address*: Sr. Principal Consultant, Tselani Business Consulting Services, P.O. Box 2171, Chinle, AZ

86503 (480) 980-0211. E-mail: ljbegay@tpbcs.com. *Past professional posts*: CEO, Navajo Nation Shopping Centers, Inc.; CEO, ATLATL, Inc.; former Dean of Navajo Nation's Dine College; consulting work with various organizations, government agencies, and tribal and community colleges.

BEGAY, LORRAINE C. (Navajo-Dine')
  (college instructor)
Affiliation & Address: Instructor, Navajo Community College, Tsaile Rural Post Office, Tsaile, AZ 86556 (602) 724-3311.

BEGAY, MANLEY A., JR. (Navajo-Dine')
  (senior lecturer/associate social scientist)
Born in Fort Defiance, Navajo Nation (AZ) & raised in Tuba City via Wheatfields, Navajo Nation (AZ). *Education*: Navajo Community College, AA, 1975; University of Arizona, BA, 1977; Brigham Young University, MEd, 1984, Ed.Spec., 1985; Harvard Graduate School of Education, MEd, 1989, EdD, 1997. *Affiliation & Address*: Professor, Applied Indigenous Studies Department, SBS West Bldg. 70 Rm #224, Northern Arizona University, P.O. Box 15020, Flagstaff, AZ 86011 (928) 523-6437; E-mail: manley.begay-jr@nau.edu *Other professional posts*: Member of faculty in the College of Education and W.A. Franke College of Business, Northern Arizona University, Flagstaff, AZ; Co-Director (2000-present), Native Nations Institute for Leadership, Management & Policy (NNI), Udall Center for Studies in Public Policy; senior lecturer/associate social scientist, American Indian Studies Program, The University of Arizona, Tucson, AZ; Co-director, Harvard Project on American Indian Economic Development (HPAIED), John F. Kennedy School of Government, Harvard University, Cambridge, MA; As Senior lecturer/associate social scientist in the American Indian Studies Program at The University of Arizona, he teaches courses on nation-building, curriculum development, & indigenous education; faculty member, Institute for Planet Earth, The University of Arizona; member, Aboriginal Program Advisory Committee (co-chair); member, Aboriginal Leadership & Self-Government Program, The Banff Centre for Management, Banff, Alberta, Canada; member, Native American Sports Council Curriculum Committee, Denver, CO; Coordination Team member, Native Network, U.S. Institute for Environmental Conflict Resolution, Tucson, AZ; member, Governing Council, National Institute for Native Leadership in Higher Education, University of New Mexico, Albuquerque, NM. *Past professional posts*: Principal, Navajo Nation Schools; high school teach on the White Mountain Apache Reservation. *Interests*: Tribal economic development, educational leadership; served as member of the Board of Trustees, National Museum of the American Indian, Washington, DC; consultant, First Nations & bands in Canada, American Indian nations, University of Auckland in New Zealand, federal agencies in the U.S. & Canada, curriculum development specialist & researcher, and reviewer for several major textbook publishing & film companies.

BEGAY, MEREDITH MAGOOSH (Mescalero Apache) 1937-
  (medicine woman)
Born May 2, 1937, Mescalero, N.M. *Address*: 410 Yucca Dr., P.O. Box 91, Mescalero, NM 88340 (505) 671-4344. *Community activities*: Miss Mescalero Apache Committee; Bent-Mescalero School P.T.A.; Mescalero Indian Health Service (hospital board member); National Federation of Federal Employees Local 1472. *Award*: Bureau of Indian Affairs Special Achievement & Tribal Award. *Interests*: "I am active in my traditional religion & application of holistic medicine for my own tribal people. I have been a "medicine woman" for over twenty years. I'm trying to keep up the tribal tradition, culture & heritage, along with other medicine men & women, including the school children. Presently give workshops on traditional medicine in cohesion with Western medicine."

BEGAY, NOTAH, III (Navajo/Pueblo) 1972-
  (professional golfer; business consultant)
Born September 14, 1972, Albuquerque, N.M. *Education*: Stanford University, B.S. (Economics). *Affiliation & Address*: Founder & President, NB3 Consulting, LLC, 290 Prairie Star Rd., Santa Ana Pueblo, NM 87004 (505) 867-0775. Website: www.notah.com; E-mail: info@nb3f.org. Notah started NB3 to serve Native American communities looking to develop golf properties. He writes, "I am very proud that NB3 Consulting is a Native American owned business that always acts in the best interest of the community." *Community activities*: Founder, The Notah Begay III Foundation which delivers sustainable sports programming for Native American youth; programs that have been designed specifically by Natives for Native youth. *Honors, awards*: 3-time All American golfer at Stanford University and won an NCAA title in 1994 where he shot a 62 in the second round, a score which still stands today; Notah was named one of the Top 100 Worldwide Sports Educators by the Institute for International Sport in a three year study that the Institute performed. *Interests*: Mr. Begay is the only full-blooded Native American on the PGA Tour having earned his PGA Tour Card in 1998. In 1999 & 2000, he won four PGA Tour events & represented the U.S. as a member of the 2000 President's Cup Team. In 2001, he suffered an injury and was not able to play for almost seven years. Recently, he has resumed his professional golfing career.

BEGAY, PAULINE M. (Navajo-Dine')
(supt. of schools)
Education: PhD. Address & Affiliation: Supt. of Schools, Apache County Schools, P.O. Box 548, St. Johns, AZ 85936 (928) 337-7539. E-mail: pmmrshllb@yahoo.com. Pauline is the fiscal & education service agent for 11 public schools districts, which includes five on the Navajo Nation Reservation. Other professional post: Member, Board of Directors, Treasurer, National Indian Education Association (chair, Education Research Committee), Washington, DC.

BEGAY, PHYLLIS T. (Navajo-Dine')
(Dine' College, Tuba City director)
Education: Northern Arizona University, MEd. Affiliation & Address: Director, Dine' College, Tuba City Center, P.O. Box 1716, Tuba City, AZ 86045 (928) 283-5113. E-mail: ptbegay@dinecollege.edu.

BEGAY, RUTH TRACY (Navajo-Dine') 1940-
(family nurse practitioner)
Born May 14, 1940, Ganado, Ariz. Education: Loretto Heights College, School of Nursing, Denver, Colo., BSN, 1978. Affiliation: Director, Navajo Community College Health Center, Tsaile, AZ, 1978-90. Other professional posts: Member, Navajo Health Authority, Office of Nursing Education Board; member, Navajo Community College Nursing Program Board. Memberships: Arizona Nurses Association (council on practice); Arizona Public Health Association; Pacific Coast College Health Association; Awards, honors: Two documentary films on Nurse Practitioner on Navajo Reservation by NBC and University of Arizona, School of Medicine, 1973; Navajo Community College 1978 Student Service Employee of the Year Award; Outstanding Young Woman of the Year, 1977. Interests: Involvement in local community health-social work among the Navajo people. Travel locally, regionally in college health service & nurses association. Interested in continual growth & development in cross-cultural aspects of a different society integrated with our own Navajo Society.

BEGAY, SARAH J. (Navajo-Dine')
(artist)
Address: 244 W. Indigo St. • Mesa, AZ 85201 (480) 835-8405. E-mail: vazdibe@msn.com. Works: Sarah produces Navajo rugs, jewelry, arts & crafts.

BEGAY, SARARESA "SARA" (Navajo-Dine')
(project coordinator)
Education: Northern Arizona University, B.S. (Public Relations). Address & Affiliation: Project coordinator, Native American Public Telecommunications (NAPT) for Native Radio Theatre, 1800 North 33rd St., Lincoln, NE 68583 (402) 472-3522. E-mail: native@unl.edu. Sara will develop radio theatre productions, NAPT. Past professional posts: Smithsonian's National Museum of the American Indian, Washington, DC.

BEGAY, TINA (Navajo-Dine')
(business instructor)
Education: Salish Kootenai College, AA; University of Montana, BS & MBA. Affiliation & Address: Business Instructor, Business Management/ Entrepreneurship Program, Salish Kootenai College, P.O. Box 70, Pablo, MT 59855 (406) 275-4800. Community activities: Tina is the advisor for the SKC AIBL Chapter & coordinates the Volunteer Income Tax Assistance (VITA) Program. Other professional posts: Owner, Redtail Enterprises, specializing in business consulting, QuickBooks, & workforce development; interim executive director, American Indian Business Leaders (AIBL), Missoula, MT. Past professional post: Executive director, American Indian Business Leaders (AIBL), Missoula, MT.

BEGAY, TOMMY K., JR. (Navajo-Dine')
(lecturer of health education)
Affiliations: Program director for the Special Education Program for Teachers & Administrators Program, and lecturer of Health Education, Division of Health Promotion Sciences; Coordinator of Service Learning Curriculum, Division of Community & Environmental Health Policy & Practice, College of Public Health, University of Arizona, 2231 E. Speedway Blvd., P.O. Box 245158, Tucson, AZ 85719 (520) 321-7777 ext. 23. Mr. begay is a doctoral candidate in the Dept. of Language, Reading & Culture, College of Education, U. of Arizona.

BEGAYE, ENEI (Dine'-Tohono O'odham)
(senior advisor, grant writing support)
Born & raised on the Navajo Reservation, Shonto, AZ. Education: Stanford University, BS (Geological & Environmental Sciences). Affiliation & Address: Senior Advisor, Grant Wrriting Support (former executive director), Black Mesa Water Coalition, P.O. Box 613, Flagstaff, AZ 86002 (928) 213-5909. E-mail: eneibegaye@mac.com. Other professional post: Co-founder, Native Movement Collective. Past professional posts: Water campaigner for the Indigenous Environmental Network (IEN). Awards, honors: Arizona's Native American "Woman of Our Community" award; Southwest's "Water Guardian" award. Interests: Enei is a recognized advocate of Indigenous peoples rights, youth,

and the environment. She is an active speaker, strategist, writer, & organizer. Her experience includes work within the United Nations as well as national & local governments, representing Indigenous environmental interests.

BEGAYE, KELSEY A. (Navajo-Dine')
(tribal president)
Affiliation & Address: President, Navajo Nation, P.O. Box 9000, Window Rock, AZ 86515 (928) 871-66352.

BEGAYE, RAY (Navajo-Dine')
(NM state representative)
Address: Box 609, Shiprock, NM 87420 (505) 215-3197. E-mail: ray.begaye@nmleg.gov. Affiliation: Representative, NM District 4 (San Juan) Legislature. Committee memberships: Chair, Behavioral Health Subcommittee; member, Indian Affairs Committee. Other professional post: Consultant.

BEGAYE, RUSSELL (Navajo-Dine')
(tribal president)
Affiliation & Address: President (2015-present), Navajo Nation, P.O. Box 7440, Window Rock, AZ 86515 (928) 871-7000.

BEGAYE, TIMOTHY (Navajo-Dine')
(assistant professor)
Education: Harvard University, EdD. Address & Affiliation: Assistant Professor of Education Leadership & Policy Studies, College of Education, Arizona State University, P.O. Box 872411, Tempe, AZ 85287 (480) 965-4670. E-mail: tim.begaye@asu.edu. Other professional post: Board member, National Indian Education Association, Washington, DC. Past professional posts: Research Associate, Harvard Project on American Indian Economic Development and a Teaching Fellow at the JFK School of Government, Harvard University, Cambridge, MA.

BEGICH, MARK P.
(president & CEO)
Affiliation & Address: President & CEO, Northern Compass Group, LLC, 310 K St., Suite 401, Anchorage, AK 99501 (907) 264-6621. E-mail: markbegich@ northerncompassgroup.com. Mark, the former U.S. Senator from Alaska, has built an impressive record of accomplishments on some of the most complicated & important issues: fisheries, travel & tourism, transportation, resource development, tribal & Alaska Native interests, the Arctic, education, veterans, commerce, housing and more. During his tenure as U.S. Senator for Alaska, Mark Begich earned the reputation of a hard-working, pragmatic problem-solver who was willing to work across party lines to get things done. Defying party labels and drawing daily on his business background, Begich broke down bureaucratic barriers to get things done. Quickly rising to leadership positions, Begich chaired both the Steering and Outreach Committee and the Oceans Subcommittee. He also served on other influential committees including Appropriations, Commerce, Veterans, Homeland Security & Governmental Affairs, Armed Services, & Indian Affairs. In addition, Begich was appointed to the President's Export Council, the national advisory board to the White House on important export and trade policy. Begich was also named Chair of the bipartisan U.S.-China Inter-parliamentary Group aimed at improving trade relations between the U.S. and China. Prior to serving in the Senate, Begich was the Mayor of Anchorage for six years and served on the Anchorage Assembly for ten years.

BEHELER, JOHN (Lower Brule Sioux)
(executive director)
Affiliation & Address: Executive Director, Dakota Indian Foundation, 209 N. Main St., Box 340, Chamberlain, SD 57325 (605) 734-5472.

BEIRISE, JOHN H.
(president & CEO)
Education: Northwestern University, BS; University of Michigan, MBA. Address: 999 18th St., Suite 2460, Denver, CO 80202 (303) 988-2727. E-mail: beirise@nabna.com. Website: www.nabna.com. Affiliation: President & CEO, Native American Bank (NAB), Denver, CO, 1999-present. Past professional posts: Continental Bank, Chicago, IL, 1968-92; Mercantile Bancorp., St. Louis, MO, 1992-98.

BELANGER, YALE
(professor of Native American studies)
Education: University of Lethbridge, Alberta, BA (Native American Stduies), 1998; Univerfsity of Manitoba, Winnipeg, MA (Political Science, Nati ve American Studies & Anthropology), 2000; Trent University, Peterborough, Ontario, Canada, PhD (Indigenous Studies), 2006. Affiliation & Address: Associate Professor of Native American Studies, Adjunct Associate Professor of Health Sciences, University of Lethbridge, A452 University Hall, Lethbridge, AB T1K 3M4 Canada (403) 382-7101. E-mail: belayd@uleth.ca. His doctoral work focused on the emergence & evolution of Aboriginal political organizations in the late 19th and early 20th century Canada. Published works:

Gambling With the Future: The Evolution of Aboriginal Gaming in Canada (Purich Publishing, 2006); Editor, Aboriginal Self-Government in Canada: Current Issues & Trends, 3rd Ed. (Purich Publishing, 2008); Ways of Knowing: An Intrduction to Native Studies in Canada (Nelson Education, 1st Ed., 2010; 2nd Ed. 2014); First Nations Gaming in Canada (University of Manitoba Press, 2011); Editor, with P.W. Lackenbauer, Blockades or Breakthroughs? Aboriginal Peoples Confront the Canadian State (McGill-Queen's University Press, 2014); numerous chapters, articles.

BELCOURT, ERNESTINE
(executive director)
Affiliation & Address: Executive Director, Indian Family Health Clinic, 1220 Central Ave., Great Falls, MT 59401 (406) 268-1510. E-mail: execdirector@ indianfamilyhealth.org. *Past professional post*: Administrative Officer, Rocky Boy's PHS Indian Health Center, Box Elder, MT.

BELCOURT, TONY (Chippewa-Cree)
(state legislator)
Affiliation: Montana House of Representatives, Helena, MT. *Address*: P.O. Box 192, Box Elder, MT 59521 (406) 352-5000. E-mail: tbelcourt@hotmail. com.

BELGARDE, PETER, JR. (Sisseton-Wahpeton Sioux)
(tribal chairperson)
Affiliation: Devil's Lake Sioux Tribal Council, Sioux Community Center, Fort Totten, ND 58335 (701) 766-4221.

BELINDO, JON EDWIN (*Gui-tain*) (Kiowa/Pawnee/Choctaw/ Navajo) 1963-
(educator, artist)
Born August 4, 1963, Oklahoma City, Okla. *Education*: East Central University (Ada, OK), BA, 1986; Oklahoma City University, M.Ed., 1994. *Address*: P.O. Box 501, Arkansas City, KS 67005. E-mail: jon_468@mail.com. *Affiliations*: Gifted Facilitator, Cowley County Special Services COOP/USD 465, Winfield, KS, 1995-present. *Past professional posts*: Program facilitator, Lawton Johnson O'Malley Program, Lawton, OK, 1986-87; art teacher, Stratford High School, Stratford, OK, 1987-90; art teacher, Tuttle High School, Tuttle, OK, 1990-93; Gifted Facilitator, Putnam City West High School, Oklahoma City, OK, 1994 State Director, Indian Education, Oklahoma State Dept. of Education, Oklahoma City, OK, 1994-95. *Community activities*: Coach, Sunday school teacher; F.C.A. director. *Memberships*: Kansas Assn of Gifted, Talented and Creative, 2004-present; National Education Assn, 1987-present; Assn for Supervision & Curriculum Development, 1987-present. *Community activities*: Tuttle Chamber of Commerce; sign & mural painter; church activity; Little League coach. *Awards, honors*: Susan Peters Art Award, 1981; recognized by ECU faculty (art dept.) as top senior of 1986; ECU Fine Arts Award, 1986; Adolf Van Pelt Scholarship Award for graduate studies in education; Oklahoma Fall Arts Institute Award & Alumnus, 1992; AITTP Scholarship (American Indian Teacher Training Program) for American Indian Research & Development (AIRD) - Full scholar-ship to get MEd in Gifted Education, 1993; Outstanding Student Educator, Oklahoma City University, 1994; Five Year Service Award, Winfield Public Schools, 2000; One Man Art Show, Winfield Arts & Humanities Center, 2002; Winfield Art in the Park-Exhibitor Award, 2003-04.

BELL, BILLY A. (Paiute)
(tribal chairperson)
Affiliation & Address: Chairperson, Fort McDermitt Paiute & Shoshone Tribe, P.O. Box 457, McDermitt, NV 89421 (775) 532-8259.

BELL, HARVEY (*Spotted Eagle-Gishwash*) (Batchewana Ojibway) 1946-
(cultural teacher; traditional medicines; pipe-maker)
Born January 20, 1946, Sault Ste. Marie, Ontario, Canada. *Address*: 35 Pontiac St., Sault Ste. Marie, Ontario, Canada P6A-5K9 (705) 253-4610. *Affiliation*: Batchewana First Nation of Ojibways (counsel-six years; chief-six years). *Community activities*: Founded Nog-da-win-da-min, 1987 (shelter for women & children); member, chiefs of Ontario. *Interests*: "Picking and making medicines, pipe carving and making, fire-keeping at lodges or 4-day fires. Work with wife Elisabeth Dietz-Bell with young people and elders."

BELL, JOSEPH T. (Lumbee)
(family practitioner; medical director)
Education: University of North Carolina, Chapel Hill Medical School, MD, 1986. *Affiliation & Address*: Medical Director, Pembroke Pediatrics, 812 Candy Park Rd., Pembroke, NC 28372 (910) 521-0201. *Other professional posts*: Pediatrition, Catawba Indian Health Service, Catawba Indian Reservation, Pembroke, SC; chair, North Carolina American Indian Health Board, Wnston-Salem, NC. *Past professional posts*: Member, Executive Committee, Native American Child Health & North Carolina Pediatric Society; past president, Assn of American Indian Physicians. *Awards, honors*: 2013 Native American Child Health Advocacy Award from the American Academy of Pediatrics.

BELL, KATHRYN (Cheyenne)
(film producer/writer)
Address: P.O. Box 875, Beggs, OK 74421 (918) 267-4940.

BELL, NICOLE (Anishnaabe First Nation)
(professor of Indigenous Studies)
Education: Trent University, BA, PhD Candidate; Queen's University, B.Ed. & M.Ed. *Affiliation & Address*: Part-time Faculty, Indigenous Studies Department, Trent University, OC 148, 1600 Westband Dr., Pterborough, ON K9J 7B8. E-mail: nicolebell@trentu.ca. Nicole is a grassroots community worker and is the founder of Anishnaabe Bimaadizwin Cultural Healing & Learning Program, an Anishnaabe culture-based school for Aboriginal children (K-12).

BELL, RONNY A. (Lumbee)
(professor; center director)
Born & raised in Robeson County, N.C. *Education*: University of North Carolina, Chapel Hill, BS (Public Health Nutrition); Wake Forest School of Medicine, MS (Epidemiology), University of North Carolna, Greensboro, PhD (Nutrition). *Affiliations & Address*: Professor, Department of Epidemiology, Division of Public Health Sciences, Wake Forest School of Medicine; Director, Maya Angelou Center for Health Equity, Medical Center Blvd., Winston-Salem, NC 27157 (336) 713-7600. *Other professional post*: Board Chairperson, North Carolina American Indian Health Board, Winston-Salem, NC.

BELL, THERESA HAYWARD (*Wildflower*) (Mashantucket Pequot) 1952-
(museum director)
Born May 28, 1952, Camp Lejeune, N.C. *Education*: High school. *Address & Affiliation*: Executive Director, Mashantucket Pequot Museum & Cultural Research Center, 110 Pequot Trail, Mashantucket, CT 06338 (860) 396-7073. E-mail: tbell@mptn-nsn.gov. Website: www.pequotmuseum.org. *Awards, honors*: Harriet Tubman Award; Mashantucket Pequot Tribal Representative on the Governor's Task Force on Indian Affairs. *Membership*: National Register's Who's Who in Executives & Professionals.

BELLECOURT, CLYDE H. (Anishinabe-Ojibwe)
(Indian organization founder & director)
Affiliation: Co-founder & director, American Indian Movement, P.O. Box 13521, Minneapolis, MN 55414 (612) 721-3914. Clyde was a major figure in the occupation of Wounded Knee in 1973 and played a founding role in an ongoing Indian School System, Legal Rights Center and the International Indian Treaty Council. He is also directing the Peacemaker Center for Indian youth and the AIM Patrol that provided security for the Minneapolis Indian community. He is an organizer of the National Coalition on Racism in Sports and the Media. Also, founder and currently Chairperson of the Board of American Indian OIC (Opportunities, Industrialization Centers), an innovative job program that has moved over 14,000 people from welfare to full-time employment.

BELLON, RICHARD (Chehalis)
(tribal administrator)
Affiliation & Address: Administrator, Confederated Tribes of the Chehalis Reservation, P.O. Box 536, Oakville, WA 98568 (360) 273-5911.

BELLSON, SHIRLEY L. (Zuni)
(artisan, shop owner)
Address: Owner, J/S Bellson Jewelry, P.O. Box 397, Zuni, NM 87327 (505) 782-2448. *Artwork*: Handmade silver women's jewelry.

BELONE, CECILIA A. (Navajo)
(IHS director)
Affiliation & Address: Director, Indian Health Service, P.O. Box 358, Crownpoint, NM 87313 (505) 786-5291 E-mail: Cecilia.belone@ihs.gov; president, National Indian Youth Council, Albuquerque, NM.

BELONE, DEBORAH (Navajo)
(Indian school principal)
Affiliation: Cove Day School, P.O. Box 2000, Red Valley, AZ 86505 (928) 653-4457. E-mail: Deborah.belone@bie.edu

BELLONGER, BRENDA J. (Sisseton-Wahpeton Sioux
& White Earth Ojibwe)
(attorney, board president)
Address & Affiliation: President, North American Indian legal Services, Inc., 1710 S. Balsam St., Lakewood, CO 80232 (720) 840-5438. E-mail: bellonger@ gmail.com. *Other professional posts*: She is attorney & project director of the Indian Child Welfare & Juvenile Justice Advocacy Project.

BELT, ROSEANNA S. (Eastern Cherokee)
(former Indian center director)
Education: University of Colorado, BA (History); Harvard University, MA (Counseling & Consulting Psychology); Western Carolina University, (Certificate in School Counseling). *Affiliation & Address*: Former Director

(2001-16), Cherokee Center, Western Carolina University, Cherokee, NC. E-mail: rbelt@email.wcu.edu. Her goal is to prepare more Cherokees for college and to encourage them to attend. *Other professional posts*: Clinical faculty member at Western's College of Education & Allied Professions, co-teaching "Education In a Diverse Society." She serves on several university committees related to diversity & minority issues & works closely with the Sequoyah Distinguished Professor in building the Cherokee Studies program at Western. Roseanna also serves on the Yogi Crowe Memorial Scholarship" board; board member for Jackson County REACH, and recently called to serve on the State Advisory Council on Indian Education in Raleigh, NC. *Past professional post*: Counselor, U. of Colorado, Boulder, CO (10 years); school counselor, Cherokee Elementary School (13 years).

BELT, TOM (Cherokee)
(Cherokee language program coordinator)
Education: University of Oklahoma, University of Colorado. *Affiliation & Address*: Coordinator, Cherokee Language Program, Cherokee Center, Western Carolina University, 1594 Acquoni Rd., Cherokee, NC 28719 (828) 227-2721. E-mail: tbelt@email.wcu.edu. Mr. Belt teaches the first four semesters of Cherokee language and he co-teaches courses on Cherokee grammar and Cherokee language literature. He works closely with speakers from the Eastern Band of Cherokee Indians to produce culturally-based Cherokee language learning material. *Past professional posts*: Counselor's aide in a local treatment center for native youths with chemical dependencies; he taught the Cherokee language at the Cheokee elementary school in Cherokee, NC; consultant to various archives & indigenous language programs in public schools and post-secondary level.

BELTRAN, DANIEL D. (Koi-Pomo)
(former tribal chairperson)
Affiliation & Address: Lower Lake Rancheria Koi Nation, P.O. Box 3162, Santa Rosa, CA 95402 (707) 575-5586.

BELTRAN, DARIN (Koi-Pomo)
(tribal chairperson)
Affiliation & Address: Chairperson, Lower Lake Rancheria Koi Nation, P.O. Box 3162, Santa Rosa, CA 95402 (707) 575-5586. Darin has been a Business Development Director for the tribe for over five years now. Recently joining the Tribal Council as Chairman, Darin strongly feels that he will bring much integrity, honor, and respect to the position in which he was voted into. He has been in the Commercial Construction Industry for over twenty-five years and believes that his leadership skills in that position would compliment his sworn duties as a Chairman for the Koi Nation. Darin is extremely committed to encourage the youth of the tribe as well as the adults to embrace their culture.

BELTRAN, DRAKE (Koi-Pomo)
(tribal vice chairperson)
Affiliation & Address: Vice Chairperson, Lower Lake Rancheria Koi Nation, P.O. Box 3162, Santa Rosa, CA 95402 (707) 575-5586.

BEN, DEON (Navajo)
(Native American program associate)
Born in Tohatchi, N.M. *Education*: Northern Arizona University, BS (Environmental Studies). *Affiliation & Address*: Native American Program Associate (2009-present), Grand Canyon Trust, 2601 N. Fort Valley Rd., Flagstaff, AZ 86001 (928) 774-7488. He focuses on environmental conservation in surrounding tribal communities & nations throughout the Southwest.

BEN, HARRISON (Mississippi Choctaw)
(former tribal vice chief)
Affiliation: Vice Miko, Mississippi Band of Choctaw Indians, 101 Industrial Rd., Choctaw, MS 39350 (601) 656-5251.

BENAI, EDWARD BENTON (Lac Courte Orielles Ojibway)
(spiritual teacher; Indian school founder)
Education: MA (Education. *Affiliation*: Spiritual Teacher, Lac Court Orielles Band of Ojibway Nation, 418 Little Pine Rd., P.O. Box 67, Lac du Flambeau, WI 54538 (715) 588-3303. Founder of Red School House, an Indian-controlled school with 150, K through 12 math students. Co-founder of the American Indian Movement. He is a pioneer in culture-based curriculum & Indian alternative education who believes that education should be built on identity, spirituality, music, heritage & pride. Eddie believes, "It is time to talk with our Brothers & Sisters of other nations, colors & beliefs. The ideas & philosophies of yesterday may be the key to the world family's future." *Publication*: The Mishomis Book (Indian Country Press). The culture, history & philosophy of the Ojibway Nation and his life within the family circle.

BENALLY, EVA M. (Dine'-Navajo)
(Indian school principal)
Affiliation: Red Rock Day School, P.O. Drawer 10, Red Valley, AZ 86544 (602) 653-4456.

BENALLY, HERBERT (Dine'-Navajo)
(college instructor)
Affiliation & Address: Navajo Community College, P.O. Box 580, Shiprock, NM 87420 (505) 368-5291.

BENALLY, JONES (FAMILY) (Dine'-Navajo)
(entertainment)
Born on Big Mountain, Ariz. *Education*: Traditional Navajo. *Principal occupation*: Native American dance & music. *Address*: P.O. Box 1492, Flagstaff, AZ 86002 (928) 527-1041. E-mail: tacoho@hotmail.com. Website: www.blackfire.net. *Affiliations*: Indigenous Action Media, 2001-present. *Community activities*: President (Dine Bi Naal Gloosh Baa Ahaa Yaa) a 501-c3 dedicated to preserving cultural heritage; president of Grand Canyon Schools Indian Parent Association, 1988-90; president, Flagstaff Arts Council, 1992-95. *Interests*: "The Jones Benally family is a traditional Native American Dance Troupe consisting of Jones, his daughter Jeneda and sons Klee & Clayson Benally. The family also has an original rock band called Blackfire. Their philosophy is that you can live in both worlds and never lose your heritage or identity." *Awards, honors*: Jones Benally is the first traditional consultant for Winslow Indian Hospital ever, and is the only traditional consultant for IHS at this time; Klee Benally was the youngest "Best of Show" winner at the Museum of Northern Arizona in 1992; the family has done numerous film, television and commercial work; nominated for 1999 NAMI "Best Independent Album.". *Published works*: Albums -Tanz und Fest Compilation 92 (Hei-Deck Records, 1992); Soundtrack to Geronimo (Columbia Records, 1993); Navajo Reflections (Canyon Records, 1994); Blackfire 1994 & 1998 (Tacoho Records); One Nation Under. Film documentaries: Rockin Warriors, '96; Bethel '97.

BENALLY, LINDA DAYISH (Dine'-Navajo)
(attorney)
Born in Shiprock, N.M. *Education*: Arizona State University; Arizona State University School of Law, JD. *Affiliation & Address*: In-House Counsel, Pinnacle West Capital Corp., 400 North 5th St., P.O. Box 53999, Phoenix, AZ 85004 (602) 250-1000. *Other professional post*: President-Elect, National Native American Bar Association, 2013-15. Past professional posts: Phoenix Indian Center; Arizona Commission of Indian Affairs.

BENALLY, SUZANNE (Dine'Navajo/Santa Clara Tewa)
(executive director)
Affiliation & Address: Executive Director (2010-present), Cultural Survival, 215 Prospect St., Cambridge, MA 02139 (617) 441-5400. E-mail: sbenally@cs.org. *Past professional posts*: Deputy director & director of education programs at the American Indian Science & Engineering Society; director of the Institute on Ethnic Diversity at the Western Interstate Commission for Higher Education; associate provost for institutional planning & assessment & associate vice president for academic affairs, Naropa University, Boulder, CO, 1999-2010. She has been a teacher at the university level and has served as a consultant to philanthropic foundations, nonprofits, & many higher education institutions. She has worked with American Indian communities. *Interests*; Teaching; relationship between land, spirituality, & people as reflected in stories; environmental issues & indigenous rights.

BENALLY, TIMOTHY (Dine'Navajo)
(assistant superintendent of schools)
Affiliation & Address: Assistant Superintendent of Schools, Department of Dine' Education, P.O. Box 670, Window Rock, AZ 86515 (928) 871-7475.

BENDER, JUDITH (Meskwaki Sac & Fox)
(tribal council member-education; former tribal chairperson)
Affiliation & Address: Council member (Education), Sac & Fox of the Mississippi in Iowa Meswaki Nation, 349 Meskwaki Rd.,Tama, IA 52339 (641) 484-4678.

BENDER, PAUL
(professor of law; dean emeritus)
Education: Harvard College, BA, 1954; Harvard Law School, 1957. *Affiliation & Address*: Professor of Law, Dean Emeritus, Indian Legal Program, Sandra Day O'Connor College of Law, Arizona State University, Box 877906, Tempe, AZ 85287 (480) 965-2556. E-mail: paul.bender@asu.edu. *Other professional posts*: Chief Justice of the Fort McDowell Nation Supreme Court, and the San Carlos Apache Court of Appeals. *Past professional posts*: Professor of Law (24 years), University of Pennsylvania Law School; principal deputy solicitor General of the U.S., 1993-97; dean, College of Law, ASU, 1984-89, during which time he was instrumental in starting its Indian Legal Program; past member, Hopi Tribe's Court of Appeals. *Awards, honors*: He has argued more than 20 cases before the U.S. Supreme Court, and actively participates in constitutional litigation in federal and state courts.

BENDICKSON, WAYNE J. (*Sisoka Duta*) (Sisseton Wahpeton Oyate)
(Dakota language instructor)
Affiliation & Address: Teaching Specialist, Dakota Language, Deartment of American Indian Studies, 110 Scott Hall, 72 Pleasant St. SE, Minneapolis, MN 55455 (612) 625-2021. E-mail: bendi001@umn.edu. His undergraduate work focused on Dakota language, culture and history. Following graduation, he worked with two fluent Dakota/Lakota speakers for four years to improve his language skills. Prior to his current position, he taught Dakota language for three years at the Shakopee Mdewakanton Sioux Community.

BENDREMER, JEFFREY C.
(professor of history)
Education: University of Connecticut, MA (Education), 1984, MA (Anthropology), 1986, PhD (Anthropology), 1993. *Affiliation & Address*: Professor of History, Native American Studies Dept., Salish Kootenai College, P.O. Box 70, Pablo, MT 59855 (406) 675-4942. E-mail: jeffrey_bendremer@skc.edu. *Other professional posts*: Affiliate faculty, Anthropology Dept., University of Montana, Missoula, MT; lead faculty member developing a Tribal Historic Preservation degree under a grant from the National Endowment for the Humanities. *Past professional posts*: Manager, Tribal Historic Preservation Program, Mohegan Tribe of Connecticut; assistant professor of anthropology, Indiana University; assistant professor, Eastern Connecticut State University; visiting professor, Connecticut College. *Published works*: Article, "Mohegan Oral Tradition, Archaeology & the Legacy of Uncas," written with the Mohegan Tribal Linguist & Mohegan Archivist.

BENEDICT, PATRICIA (Abenaki) 1956-
(executive director)
Born August 11, 1956, Waterbury, Conn. *Education*: Mattatuck Community College, Waterbury, CT., A.S. (Alcohol and Drug Counseling), 1980. *Address & Affiliation*: Executive director, American Indians for Development, Meriden, CT (203) 238-4009 (social worker, 1975-81; executive director, 1986-present). *Other professional post*: Co-editor of American Indians for Development Newsletter; editor of May Wutche Aque'ne, American Indians for Development Journal. *Community activities*: American Indians for Development (past chairman, board of directors); member, Energy Assistance Program Policy Making Board, Meriden, Conn.; member, Federal Regional Support Center, American Indian Committee, New Haven, CT.; chairperson, A.I.D./Eagle Wing Press Powwow Committee; organized Waterbury Indian community into an organization. *Membership*: Title IV Indian Education Committee, Waterbury, CT. (chairperson); Governor appointee of Connecticut Legislative Task Force o Indian Affairs; member and one of the incorporators of New England Indian Task Force. *Awards, honors*: Award for work performed on behalf of the Connecticut Indian Community, given by the Connecticut River Powwow Society. *Interests*: Attending & participating in Native American cultural activities.

BENEDICT, SALLI (Mohawk)
(writer)
Address: P.O. Box 35, Rooseveltown, NY 13683 (613) 932-0230.

BENAVIDES, BEN (Apache)
(board chairperson)
Affiliation & Address: Board Chairperson, Marin American Indian Alliance, P.O. Box 150565, San Rafael, CA 94915.

BENGE, GEORGE (Cherokee)
(news executive)
Address: c/o Native American Journalists Association (NAJA), 3359 36th Ave. South, Minneapolis, MN 55406 (612) 729-9244. E-mail: benge@naja.com. *Affiliation*: News executive with Gannett Co., Inc. In addition to his corporate news role, he writes columns on American Indian and diversity issues for Gannett News Service. *Other professional post*: Member-board of directors, Native American Journalists Association. *Past professional posts*: Executive editor of Gannett newspapers in Asheville, NC, Lafayette, Ind., and Muskogee, OK; & managing editor in Springfield, MO; editing & management positions at The Sun-Sentinel in Fort Lauderdale, The Dallas Morning News, The Miami Herald, & The Detroit News. *Membership*: Society for Newspaper Design (past president). *Awards, honors*: McCormick Foundation Fellow in the Advanced Executive Program of the Media Management Center; Pulitzer Prize juror.

BENGOCHIA, MONTY (Paiute)
(tribal vice chairperson)
Affiliation: Bishop Indian Tribal Council, 50 Tu Su Lane, Bishop. CA 93514 (760) 873-3584. E-mail: monty.bengochia@bishoppaiute.org.

BENJAMIN, DELBERT (Wintun)
(tribal chairperson)
Affiliation: Colusa Rancheria, P.O. Box 8, Colusa, CA 95932 (916) 458-8231.

BENJAMIN, MELANIE A. (Mille Lacs Ojibwe)
(tribal chief executive)
Education: Bemidji State University, B.S. (Business Administration), 1988. *Affiliation & Address*: Chief Executive (2000-08, 2012-present), Mille Lacs Band of Ojibwe Indians, 43408 Oodena Dr., Onamia, MN 56359 (320) 532-4181 ext. 7486. *Past tribal posts*: Business Development Specialist & Assistant Program Director, Mille Lacs Band's Indian Business Development Center, 1988-89; hired in 1989 by the Band's late chairman Arthur Gabhow to serve as Commissioner of Administration for the Band, the highest appointed position in Band government. Melanie served a dual purpose; she served as chief of staff to the chief executive and as the head administrator of the reservation, a position she held for eight years. In 1990, Melanie was appointed by Minnesota Governor Anne Carlson to serve a two-year term on the citizen board of the Roundtable for Sustainable Development. In 1995, she served as senior vice president of Administration & Finance for Grand Casino Hinkley. When the Band further diversified its economy by opening Woodlands National Bank, Melanie played a lead role in the bank and served on its board of directors. In 2005, as Chief Executive, she helped create the Minnesota Tribal Government Foundation for the purpose of providing economic development grants to other tribes in Minnesota. In 2006, she was appointed to Affordable Housing Advisory Council of the Federal Home Loan Bank of Des Moines; she's a founding member & treasurer of Women Empowering Women for Indian Nations (WEWIN); a board member of the Indian Law Resource Center and the National Indian Gaming Association (NIGA); Vice Chair of Tribal Executive Committee of Mille Lacs Band & Chair of Housing Subcommittee.

BENNETT, GEORGE E. (Ottawa)
(tribal chairperson)
Affiliation & Address: Chairperson, Grand Traverse Band of Ottawa & Chippewa Indians, Peshawbestown Community Center, 2605 NW Bay Shore Dr., Suttons Bay, MI 49682 (231) 271-3538. E-mail: gbennett@gtbindians.com.

BENNETT, HAROLD (Karuk)
(former tribal chairperson)
Affiliation & Address: Former chairperson, Quartz Valley Indian Reservation, 13601 Quartz Valley Rd., P.O. Box 24, Fort Jones, CA 96032 (530) 468-5907.

BENNETT, FRIEDA (Karuk)
(tribal chairperson)
Affiliation & Address: Chairperson, Quartz Valley Indian Reservation, 13601 Quartz Valley Rd., P.O. Box 24, Fort Jones, CA 96032 (530) 468-5907.

BENNETT, RUTH (Shawnee) 1942-
(ethnographic researcher/technical writer)
Born December 12, 1942. Education: Indiana University, B.A., 1964; University of Washington, M.A. (English), 1968; California State University, San Francisco, Standard Secondary Teaching Credential (Multi-Cultural Education), 1973; University of California, Berkeley, Ph.D. (language & reading development with a specialization in bilingual education), 1979. *Affiliation & Address*: Ethnographic researcher/technical writer, Humboldt State University, The Center for Community Development, Arcata, CA 95521 (707) 826-3711. E-Mail: rsb3@axe.humboldt.edu. *Other professional posts*: Resource teacher, Hoopa Elementary School, 1976-; field director, Native Language & Culture Program, 1978-1979, assistant director, 1980-, Center for Community Development; director, Title VII, Institute of Higher Education Training Grant, Bilingual Emphasis Program, Center for Community Development, 1981-; teacher, Department of Education, Humboldt State University, 1981-. evaluator/consultant, Hupa Valley Tribe, Johnson O'Malley K-12 Program, 1994-; language program consultant, Cahto Tribe, Laytonville Rancheria, 1996; phonetics chart consultant, Wiyot Tribe, Table Bluffs Rancheria, 1996. *Community activities*: Volunteer research & curriculum preparation, Indian tribes of Northwest California: Hupa, Yurok, Karuk. *Memberships*: Phi Delta Kappa, Phi Beta Kappa, Alpha Lambda Delta, Alpha Omicron Pi; University of California & Indiana University Alumni Associations. *Interests*: Ruth has conducted innovative curriculum work for 15 years, leading to computer uses for curriculum. *Published works*: Downriver Indians' Legends, 1983; Let's Go Now, 1983; 1983 Hupa Calendar, 1982; Karuk Fishing, 1983; Look Inside and Read, 1982; Unifon Update, 1983; 1983-1984 Yurok Unifon Calendar, 1983; Origin of Fire; Songs of a Medicine Woman; Hupa Spelling Book; Legends and Personal Experiences; Ceremonial Dances; Yurok Spelling Book; What Is An Indian?; Karuk Vocabulary Book; Karuk Fishing; Basket Weaving Among the Karuk; Tolowa Legends; Tolowa/English Lesson Units; Ya:na:'a'awh, Four Hupa Songs by Alice Pratt, Elementary School Level, High School Level, Higher Education & Adult Level, 1994; and others (all published by The Center for Community Development, Humboldt State University; numerous articles, including PhD dissertation, Hoopa Children's Storytelling, University of California, Berkeley.

BENOIT, JOAN (Chippewa of the Thames First Nation)
(executive director)

Affiliation & Address: Executive Director (1999-present), Native American Aids Project, 1540 Market St., Suite 130, San Francisco, CA 94102 (415) 431-6227. Joan has over 20 years of experience in the HIV care and prevention field. She has developed and implemented HIV care and prevention programs within Native American communities, integrating traditional Native approaches with western interventions to create effective & innovative programming to meet the needs of the most at-risk populations in American Indian communities.Joan has served as an HIV Regional Consultant for the Centers for Disease Control & Prevention, was a member of the Native American HIV Dialogue Group for the CDC and Indian Health Service and a member of the San Francisco HIV Prevention Planning Council. Since 2008, Joan served on the National Minority AIDS Council, American Indian Policy Advisory Group. As part of her ongoing training as HIV/AIDS specialist & leader in the Non-profit Community, Joan is currently participating in the National Minority AIDS Council's Nonprofit Executive Leadership Academy, after being selected through a national competitive selection process. Joan has been on many Boards of Directors for non-profit organizations throughout the San Francisco Bay Area, has served on a few Federal grant review committees & provided professional consultation for National Native American AIDS Prevention Center, as well as participated in planning committees for local & national HIV prevention & care conferences.

BENSON, DIANE E. (*Lxeis*) (Tlingit) 1959-
(freelance writer, talent agent, stage director)

Born October 17, 1959, Yakima, Wash. *Education*: University of Alaska, B.A., 1985. *Principal occupation*: Free-lance writer, talent agent, stage director. *Address*: P.O. Box 770369, Eagle River, AK 99577 (907) 688-1370. *Affiliations*: Alaska Film Group, Anchorage, AK; Chugiak/Eagle River Chamber of Commerce, Eagle River, AK. *Other professional posts*: Founder, Alaska Native performance & Film Commission, 1993; Artist in the Schools Residency Program, 1993-; National Museum of the American Indian Consultant, 1991-92. *Community activities*: Board member, Arctic Moon Stage Co.; Chugiak Dog Mushers Club, Junior Club Chute Judge; founder, Kookeena Improv Troupe, 1985; Out North Theatre (member & guest artist - Anchorage); Artist in the Schools Residency Program, 1993-. *Memberships*: Alaska Press Women; National Congress of American Indians; National Association of the Self-Employed; American Indian Register, 1989-93. *Awards, honors*: University of Alaska Outstanding Alumni, 1990; race marshall, Chugiak Junioir Dog Musher's Club, 1993. *Interests*: Traditional dancing & singing - Tlingit & Haida Dancers of Anchorage, 1987-. First Alumni & first Native American to direct UAA Mainstage, 1993. Public speaking on theater, alcohol & drug recovery & motivation; workshop facilitation in acting & theater & combining cultural concepts, writing, poetry, research. Attended International Native American Writers, Festival in Oklayoma, 1992; travel to Central America. *Biographical sources*: "Goose Girl Lives in Many Worlds" (Tundra Times, 7/6/83); "Fire in Her Heart" (Anchorage Time, 2/25/90). *Published works*: Raven Tells Stories: An Anthology, edited by Joseph Bruchac (Greenfield Review Press, 1991); Native American Literatures: A Special Issue, 1994. "I am currently writing for Gale Research, Multicultural Encyclopedia." Films: Sacajawea -animated film received national & international awards (FilmFair Communications, Los Angeles, 1989); White Fang (Disney, 1989). Sister Warrior (feature film) script. Performed in many other local television spots, training video's and radio drama's, in addition, stage acting for 15 years.

BENSON-TAYLOR, MELANIE (Herring Pond Wampanoag) 1977-
(assistant professor of English & Native American Studies)

Born on Cape Cod, Mass. in 1977. *Education*: Smith College, BA, 1998; Boston University, MA, 1999; PhD, 2005. *Affiliation & Address*: Assistant professor of English & Native American Studies, Dartmouth College, 37 N. Main St., The Sherman House, Hanover, NH 03755 (603) 646-3530. Melanie is a literary & cultural studies scholar. Her work explores the effects of capitalist & colonialist logic on the lives, language, and cultural productions of marginalized peoples throughout the Americas. Presently, she is conducting research on Plains Indian ledger drawings as frustrated attempts to overwrite and subvert colonial-capitalist paradigms & materials. As a student of Wopanaak, a revitalized dialect in the Algonquian language family, she is committed to Supporting Native language reclamation efforts nationwide. *Memberships*: Society for the Study of Southern Literature (member, executive council). *Published works*: Disturbing Calculations: The Economics of Identity in Postcolonial Southern Literature, 1912-2002 (University of Georgia Press, 2008); Reconstructing the Native South: American Indian Literature & the Lost Cause (University of Georgia Press, 2012); A Beautiful Nothing (in progress).

BENTLEY, REGINA GASCO (Odawa)
(acting tribal chairperson)

Affiliation & Address: Acting Chairperson, Little Traverse Bay Bands of Odawa Indians, 7500 Odawa Circle, Harbor Springs, MI 49740 (231) 838-2081.

BENTON, MARIA (Zia Pueblo) 1944-
(health educator)

Born July 17, 1944, Zia Pueblo, N.M. *Education*: Parks College, San Jose, CA (1 Yr.); University of New Mexico, Albuquerque (288 hrs.) Certified Chemical Dependency Health Educator. *Principal occupation*: Health educator. *Address*: Zia Route, Box 3, San Ysidro, N.M. 87053 (505) 766-8418. *Affiliation*: Health educator, Southwestern Indian Polytechnic Institute, Albuquerque, NM, 1989-. *Awards, honors*: Community Service Award, Jemez Springs Municipal School Boards; Dedication & Excellence in Health Delivery Service, Five Sandoval Indian Pueblos.

BENTON, SHERROLE DAWN (*Ay-nah-wayne-shee-Quay*)
(Oneida/Ojibwe) 1956-
(editor, Native news)

Born December 1, 1956, Green Bay, Wisc. *Education*: University of Wisconsin, Green Bay, BA (Communications & the Arts), 1985. *Principal occupation*: Editor, Native news. *Affiliation & Address*: Editor, Regional Native News, WOJB-FM, 13386W Trepania Rd., Hayward, WI 54843 (715) 634-4070. *Other professional post*: Production coordinator, Regional Native News, WOJB-FM. *Community activities*: Parent Advisory Committee, LCO Ojibwe School, Hayward, WI*Awards, honors*: Best Radio Feature; Outstanding American Indian Reporter. *Interests*: "My major vocational goal is to provide communication & cultural exchanges between Native American people & mainstream American society to encourage understanding, dialogue, respect & dignity among the different culture groups."

BENYSHEK, DANIEL C. 1963-
(professor)

Born July 11, 1963, Belleville, Kans. *Education*: PhD in Anthropology. *Address & Affiliation*: Assistant Professor, Dept. of Anthropology & Ethnic Studies, 4505 Maryland Pkwy., Box 455003, University of Nevada, Las Vegas, NV 89154-5003 (702) 895-2070. E-mail: daniel.denyshek@ccmail.nevada.edu. Website: www.nevada.edu/~benyshek/. *Professional activities*: His academic areas of expertise include medical & nutritional anthropology, ethno-medicine, and Native North America. His primary research interests focus on the political ecology & etiology of type 2 Diabetes, the impact of Diabetes on Native American populations & community-based interventions generated in response to epidemic of type 2 diabetes among American Indians. Dr. Benyshek has spent over a decade working with the Havasupai Indian Tribe of northern Arizona in an effort to understand the etiology of diabetes in the community, document local attitudes about the disease, assess community resources to combat the problem, and assess the social, political & economic factors which may be impeding the maintenance of healthy bodyweight and blood glucose levels in the community. He consulted on a multi-year, diabetes prevention/control grant proposal submitted by the Havasupai Tribe and funded (June 1998) by the Indian Health Service, (IHS Special Diabetes Program for Indians) and has helped organize a tribal diabetes task force to oversee the Indian Health Service grant. *Published works*: Numerous articles on these topics in the Journal of American Dietetic Association.

BERCIER, SANDRA (Turtle Mountain Ojibwe)
(training director)

Born & raised on the Turtle Mountain Reservation. *Education*: University of Mary, BS (Social Work); Gonzaga University, MBA. *Affiliation & Address*: Training Director, Native American Training Institute, 3333 E. Broadway Ave., Bismarck, ND 58501 (701) 255-66374. E-mail: sandra@nativeinstitute.org.

BERESKIN, JOE (Yup'ik Eskimo)
(Alaskan village president)

Affiliation & Address: President, Native Village of Akutan, P.O. Box 89, Akutan, AK 99553 (907) 698-2300.

BERG, TIMOTHY J.
(attorney)

Affiliation & Address: Director of the Indian Program, Fennemore Craig Attorneys, 2394 E. Camelback Rd., Suite 600, Phoenix, AZ 85016 (602) 916-5421. E-mail: tberg@fclaw.com.

BERGEN, RONALD J. (Oglala Sioux) 1946-
(educator)

Born July 8, 1946, Pine Ridge, S.D. *Education*: National College (Rapid City, SD), B.S., 1979. *Principal occupation*: Educator. *Address & Affiliation*: Director, Indian Education/Peer Tutorial Programs, Hot Springs Public Schools, 1609 University Ave., Hot Springs, SD 57747 (605) 745-4145, 1984-. *Military service*: S.D. National Guard, 1964-68; U.S. Army, 1968-70; U.S. Navy, 1971-73. *Community activities*: Board of Directors, Southern Hills Developmental Services; secretary/treasurer, Hot Springs Child Protection Team; Hot Springs Public Schools Strategic Planning Committee; Hot Springs Youth Soccer Coordinator. *Memberships*: Disabled American Veterans; Veterans of Foreign Wars (life member).

BERGMAN, GORDON (Athapascan)
(Alaskan village chief)
Affiliation & Address: First Chief, Allakaket Village, Box 30, Allakaet, AK 99720 (907) 968-2237.

BERKEY, CURTIS
(attorney, Indian law firm partner)
Education: Eastern Mennonite College, BS, 1974; Columbus School of Law at Caholic University, JD, 1979. *Affiliation & Address*: Founding Partner, Berkey Williams LLP, 2030 Addison St., Suite 410 • Berkeley, CA 94704 (510) 548-7070. Mr. Berkey specializes in the areas of tribal water rights, land conservation transactions, cultural resource protection, land claims & environmental protection. He has worked in the field of Indian law his entire legal career, from 1979 to the present. He was a staff attorney at the Indian Law Resource Center in Washington, D.C. from 1979 to 1990, where he litigated many significant Indian land claims cases. In 1990, Mr. Berkey became the Washington Director of the Indian Law Resource Center, a position he held for five years. In 1995, Mr. Berkey joined the U.S. Justice Department as a senior trial lawyer in the Indian Resources Section of the Environment and Natural Resources Division. In that capacity, he litigated a number of environmental cases and complex water cases for Indian tribes. In 1997, he received the Department of Justice's Meritorious Award for his efforts in litigating and settling a multi-million dollar groundwater contamination case on behalf of the Sac and Fox Nation of Oklahoma. In 1997, Mr. Berkey entered private practice with an exclusive focus on Indian law. He represented the Pueblo of Santa Clara in reacquiring a significant portion of its ancestral lands from private owners, which for the first time in 140 years gave the Pueblo complete control and ownership of an important watershed and traditional use area. He represented the Yurok Tribe in several significant victories in federal court establishing their fishing & water rights in the Klamath River. He represented a consortium of Northern California tribes in securing the right to continue traditional harvesting and gathering within marine protected areas set up by California. Mr. Berkey is a frequent speaker at conferences on Indian law and has published widely in professional journals. He is co-author of the critically acclaimed book *Exiled in the Land of the Free: Democracy, Indian Nations and the U.S. Constitution* (1992).

BERNAL, JACOB (Chemehuevi)
(executive Director)
Affiliation & Address: Executive Director, Tucson Indian Center, P.O. Box 2307, Tucson, AZ 85702 (520) 884-7131.

BERNARDIS, TIMOTHY A. (Crow)
(Indian college library director)
Education: University of California, Berkeley, BA (History & Native American Studies), 1981; Montana State University, MEd, 1987. *Affiliation & Address*: Director (1985-present), Little Big Horn College Library, P.O. Box 721, Crow Agency, MT 59022 (406) 638-3113. E-mail: tim@lbbhc.edu.

BERNSTEIN, BRUCE
(museum curator)
Affiliation & Address: Assistant Director of Cultural Resources, National Museum of the American Indian Cultural Resources Center, 4220 Silver Hill Rd., Suitland, MD 20746 (238-1454.

BERREY, JOHN L. (Quapaw)
(tribal chairperson)
Affiliation & Address: Quapaw Tribe of Oklahoma, P.O. Box 765, Quapaw, OK 74363 (918) 542-4694. E-mail: jberrey@ogahpah.com.

BERRY, ANGELA (Choctaw)
(project manager)
Affiliation & Address: Executive Director, California Indian Environmental Alliance, P.O. Box 2128, Berkeley, CA 94702 (510) 848-2043. E-mail: angela@cieaweb.org.

BERRYHILL, ALFRED (Muscogee Creek)
(tribal 2nd chief)
Born and resides in Okmulgee County, Okla. *Education*: Sequoyah Indian High School & Haskell Institute; Oklahoma State University, majored in Business Administration. *Affiliation*: Muscogee Creek Nation, P.O. Box 580, Okmulgee, OK 74447 (918) 756-8700. *Other professional posts*: Sits on several boards including the Muscogee Nation Business Enterprise Board, and the Five Civilized Tribes Museum Board. He is currently overseeing the development of a Ministerial Alliance of Muscogee (Creek) Churches and is part of the MCN Legal Services Commission, and Museum Oversight Committee. Also, he initiated the official Muscogee (Creek) Nation annual calendar. *Past professional posts*: Administrative Intern for the BIA in Washington, DC; former Administrative Assistant, Okmulgee Indian Health Center.

BERTRAM, SHALEENA L. (Lummi, Quileute & Nooksack)
(mental health counselor)
Education: University of Washington, BA (Psychology), MSW. *Address*: Shaleena L. Bertram, LA, 2530 Kwina Rd., Bellingham, WA 98226 (360) 384-2373. Ms. Bertram works with American Indian youth in helping to combat the residual influences of historical trauma in her community. Her objective is to encourage her clients to find their strengths & become empowered in shaping their futures. Her counseling approach incorporates nutrition, lifestyle changes, and the importance of exercise in working toward holistic wellness. She has been working with youth for about ten years in tribal schools, hospitals, homeless shelters, treatment centers, et al.

BESAW, GARY (Menominee)
(tribal chairperson)
Affiliation & Address: Chairpeson, Menominee Indian Tribe of Wisconsin, P.O. Box 910, Keshena, WI 54135 (715) 799-5100. E-mail: gbesaw@mitw.org

BETHEL-FINK, ELAINE (Mono)
(tribal vice chairperson)
Affiliation & Address: Vice Chairperson, North Fork Rancheria of Mono Indians, P.O. Box 929, North Fork, CA 93643 (559) 877-2461.

BETTEGA, CARLINO (Wailaki/Yuki)
(Indian community vice president)
Affiliation & Address: Vice President, Covelo Indian Community of the Round Valley Reservation, P.O. Box 448, Covelo, CA 95428 (707) 983-6126. E-mail: vicepresident@rvit.org.

BETTENBERG, WILLIAM D.
(attorney-Indian law)
Education: University of Washington, BA, MA (Political Science), graduate study in natural resources & public policy; University of Wisconsin School of Law, JD. *Affiliation & Address*: Principal (2003-present). Homer Law, 1730 Rhode Island Ave., NW Suite 501, Washington, DC 20036 (202) 955-5601; E-mail: bbettenberg@homerlaw.com. *Past professional posts*: Department of the Interior where he focused on natural resource & environmental policy & management, tribal issues, and effective governance. He helped in negotiating the first six self-governance compacts between Interior and tribes, establishing the basic government-to-government pattern for compacts & funding agreements under which 230+ tribes now manage resources, establish priorities, and design programs previously managed by the Bureau of Indian Affairs. He established the Office of Self-Governannce & proposed the Office of American Indian Trust. At Homer Law, he has concentrated on National Indian Gaming Commission & BIA regulatory policy, tribal regulations of gaming activities, fee-to-trust actions, environmental impact analysis, and tribal water & economic issues. He served stints as the Deputy Assistant Secretary for Indian Affairs.

BIANCHI, ELEANOR LEFTHAND (Arapaho)
(online store owner)
Affiliation & Address: Owner, A Gallery of Nations, 454 Elm St., Phoenix, OR 97535. Website: www.agalleryofnations.com. E-mail: info@agalleryofnations. com. Online store features Zuni fetishes, turquoise & silver jewelry and pottery.

BIBLE, ROBERT (Muscogee-Creek)
(tribal college president)
Affiliation & Address: President, College of the Muscogee Nation, P.O. Box 917, Okmulgee, OK 74447 (918) 549-2800. E-mail: robertb@muscogeenation-nsn.gov

BIELECKI, PAUL MICHAEL
(Indian law practice group principal)
Education: Arizona State University, BA, 1986. *Affiliation & Address*: Principal, Lewis Roca Rotherberger Christi LLP, Tribal Affairs & Gaming Practice Group, 201 E. Washington St., Suite 1200, Phoenix, AZ 85004 (602) 262-5354. E-mail: mbielecki@lrrc.com. Mr. Bielecki works with the Government Relations, Tribal Affairs & Litigation practice groups. He represents clients before federal, state and local governments in legislative, contract and regulatory matters. He also represents & advises Tribal governments on a wide range of public policy issues. He has represented corporate & tribal clients facing challenges with state & local governments. His varied experience inside & outside government & his range of contacts has provided the basis of his effectiveness in various industry sectors. Mr. Bielecki has assisted Tribal leadership with a wide range of issues. From gaming development projects, health care system challenges, economic development efforts, to Tribal-state tax issues and defending Tribal rights, he has effectively supported Tribes in achieving their goals. He has assisted Tribes with compact negotiations, public relation programs, issue advocacy before state legislatures & regulators, & generated local government support for Tribal goals. Mr. Bielecki understands tribal issues and has a deep respect for Tribal leaders who represent their people.

BIETZ, DORE A. (Me-wuk)
(Indian lands consultant)
Address: P.O. Box 328, Tuolumne, CA 95379 (209) 928-5627. E-mail: sugarbtz@aol.com. *Membership*: Americans for Indian Opportunity. *Interest*: Land.

BIGFOOT, DOLORES SUBIA (Caddo Nation of Oklahoma)
(psychologist; assistant professor; health program director)
Education: PhD (Psychology). *Principal occupation*: Psychologist; assistant professor. *Affiliation & Address*: Director, Indian Country Child Trauma Center, University of Oklahoma Health Sciences Center, College of Public Health, Dept. of Pediatrics, P.O. Box 26901, Oklahoma City, OK 73190 (405) 271-8858; E-mail: dee-bigfoot@ouhsc.edu. Website: www.ouhhsc.edu. *Affiliation*: Assistant Professor of Research, Dept. of Pediatrics, OU Health Sciences Center, Oklahoma City, OK. She is Project Director, Project Making Medicine, Center on Child Abuse & Neglect, OU Health Sciences Center, Oklahoma City, OK. The project is a national training program for mental health providers in the treatment of child physical & sexual abuse and the newly funded Indian Country Child Trauma Center that is part of the National Child Traumatic Stress Network. *Other professional post:* Board member, National Indian Youth Project; Board member, Parents Assistance Center. *Memberships*: American Psychological Association, American Professional Society on the Abuse of Children, National Indian Child Welfare Association. *Interests*: Storytelling, history, museum, historical and fiction writing. *Published works*: Upon the Back of a Turtle; Project Making Medicine, Training Manual; Head Start curriculum - Prevention of Child Abuse and Neglect.

BIGHEART, DEIRDRE (Osage)
(tribal director of operations)
Affiliation & Address: Director of Operations, Osage Nation of Oklahoma, P.O. Box 1449, Pawhuska, OK 74056 (918) 287-5555.

BIGHORN, PRAIRIE (Fort Peck Sioux)
(executive director)
Education: Rocky Mountain College, BS (Business); University of Montana, MBA. Affiliation & Address: Executive Director, American Indian Business Leaders, Gallagher Business Bldg. #366, Missoula, MT 59812 (406) 243-2298 E-mail: prairie.bighorn@aibl.org. Before joining the AIBL team, she worked in Washington DC, providing accounting & contract management services to help support economic development within American Indian communities. She has also served as the comptroller for the Northern Cheyenne Tribe in Montana and worked for an auditing firm specializing in governmental compliance. Awards, honors: In 2011, she was a recipient of the National Center for American Indian Economic Development's 40 Under 40 Awards.

BIGHORSE, AMBER J. (Cheyenne & Arapaho)
(attorney)
Education: Oklahoma City University, JD, 2008. *Affiliations*: Managing Attorney, Mayo & Bighorse, 2313 Paul Ct., Norman, OK 73071 (405) 808-5891. E-mail: abighorse.law@gmail.com. Family Law Attorney, 2016-present. *Past professional posts*: Lieutenant Governor, Cheyenne & Arapaho Tribes, 2012-14, Concho, OKla.; Associate Attorney, Hobbs, Straus Dean & Walker, 2010-11, Oklahoma City, OK; In-House Counsel, Cheyenne & Arapaho Tribes, 2008-10, Concho, Okla.

BIGHORSE, SCOTT (Osage)
(tribal assistant principal chief)
Born in Pawhuska, Okla. *Education*: Haskell Indian College. *Affiliation*: Osage Nation of Oklahoma, P.O. Box 779, Pawhuska, OK 74056 (918) 287-5555.

BIGLER, GREGORY H.
(tribal attorney general)
Affiliation & Address: Attorney General, Kickapoo Tribe of Oklahoma, P.O. Box 70, McLoud, OK 74851 (405) 964-2075; E-mail: gdbigler@swbell.net Past professional post: Judge, Prairie Band Potawatomi Nation Tribal Court, Mayetta, KS.

BILL, CRAIG A. (Colville/Choctaw)
(executive director)
Education: Central Washington University, BA (Political & Social Science). *Affiliation & Address*: Executive Director (2005-present), Washington State Governor's Office of Indian Affairs (GOIA), P.O. Box 40909, Olympia, WA 98504 (360) 902-8827. *Past professional posts*: Director of Intergovernmental Affairs and Advisor to the tribal chairperson for the Lummi Nation tribal government located in Bellingham, WA. *Membership*: Enrolled member of the Swinomish Tribe.

BILLIE, CARRIE L. (Navajo-Dine')
(attorney; president & CEO of Indian organization)
Education: University of Arizona, BA; Georgetown University Law Center, JD. Affiliation & Address: President & CEO, American Indian Higher Education Consortium, 121 Oronoco St., Alexandria, VA 22314 (703) 838-0400.

BILLIE, COLLEY (Miccosukee Seminole)
(tribal chairperson)
Affiliation & Address: Chairperson, Miccosukee Indian Tribe, Box 440021, Tamiami Sta., Miami, FL 33144 (305) 223-8380.

BILLIE, JAMES E. (Seminole of Florida)
(former tribal chairperson)
Affiliation & Address: Former Chairperson, Board of Directors, Seminole Tribe of Florida (STOF), 6300 Stirling Rd., Hollywood, FL 33024 (954) 966-6300.

BILLINGS, OSCAR "TYKE" (Hoopa)
(tribal vice chairperson)
Affiliation & Address: Vice Chairperson, Hoopa Valley Tribe, P.O. Box 1348, Hoopa, CA 95546 (530) 625-4211

BILINSKI, YVONNE (Dine'-Navajo)
(Native American center director)
Affiliation & Address: Director, Native American Center, Fort Lewis College, 1000 Rim Dr., Durango, CO 81301 (970) 247-7222; E-mail: bilinski_y@fortlewis.edu

BILLY, CARRIE L. (Navajo)
(attorney; president & CEO)
Education: University of Arizona, BA; Georgetown University Law School, JD. *Affiliation & Address*: President & CEO (2008-present), American Indian Higher Education Consortium, 121 Oronoco St., Alexandria, VA 22314 (703) 838-0400. E-mail: cbilly@aihec.org.

BILLY, CHARMAIN (*Me-tigh*) (Ponca of Oklahoma)
(executive director)
Born in Ponca City, Okla. *Education*: University of Oklahoma, B.A., 1985. *Principal occupation*: Executive director. *Address & Affiliation*: Executive Director, Lawrence Indian Center, 1423 Haskell Ave., Lawrence, KS 66044, (913) 841-7202 (work), 1993-present. *Other professional post*: Director, Child Welfare Program, Ponca Tribe of Oklahoma, 1985-86. *Community activities*: Indian Education/Parent Committee (vice-president, secretary, historian), 1980-; Native American Law Enforcement Task Force, 1993-94. *Memberships*: Up With People (Alumni, 1968-); Oklahoma University Native American Alumni Association; Chilocco Alumni Association; Haskell Indian Nations University Alumni Association. *Awards, honors*: Full scholarships to attend "Summer Institute on American Indian Affairs, University of Colorado, Boulder; "Clyde Warrior Institute on American Indian Affairs", Stout University, Menominee, WI. *Interests*: Educational and legal matters as they affect Native Americans. Travels with "Up With People" included countries of Germany, France, Austria, Spain, Japan, and Korea. *Biographical source*: "Journal World", July 25, 1993.

BILLY, LISA (Chickasaw)
(R-Purcell, OK state representative)
Affiliation: Co-chair, Native American Caucus of the Oklahoma House of Representatives, c/o Oklahoma Indian Affairs Commission, 4545 N. Lincoln Blvd., Suite 282, Oklahoma City, OK 73105 (405) 521-3828; Website: www.ok.gov/oiac/. Rep. Billy, a former legislator for the Chickasaw Nation, is the Majority Caucus Vice Chair and Deputy Majority Whip of the House. She also serves as Chairperson of the International, Federal & Tribal Relations Committee, through which the Oklahoma Indian Affairs Commission funding passes, as well as a member of the General Government & Transportation Committee; Human Services Committee; and Committee for Children & Families. Lisa also serves as Co-chairperson of the Economic Development Committee for the National Native American Caucus.

BINNEY, ALLISON C. (Pomo)
(attorney)
Education: California State University, Chico, BA, 1997; Arizona State University Law School, J.D. (Certificate in Indian Law), 2000. Her substantial paper for the certificate program focused on repatriation issues for unrecognized tribes. *Address & Affiliation*: Partner, Akin Gump Straus Hauer & Feld, LLP, Robert E. Straus Bldg., 1333 New Hampshire Ave. NW, Washington, DC 20036 (202) 887-4326; E-mail: abinney@akingump.com. Allison advises clients regarding American Indian law & policy. *Past professional posts*: Coordinator, Indian Legal Program, Arizona State University College of Law, Tempe, AZ, 1999-2000; law clerk, Native American Rights Fund, Washington, DC, 1998-2000; associate, Hobbs, Straus, Dean & Walker, LLP, Washington, DC, 2000-03; U.S. Senate Select Committee on Indian Affairs, Washington, DC (general counsel, 2005—07; chief counsel, 2007-11. While at the committee, she oversaw & assisted in efforts to enact

laws impacting Native Americans, oversaw congressional invesigations & versight of federal agencies that interact with American Indian, Alaska Natives and Native Hawaiians. Current work includes the areas of Indian education, housing, & legislation affecting Indian tribes & tribal organizations. *Awards, honors*: Chambers USA: America's Leading Lawyers for Business in the area of Native American law; *Financial Times*, "Most Innovative North American Law Firms 2015" competition, "Protecting Clients Business" category; National Center for American Indian Enterprise Development's "Native American 40 under 40" award.

BIOLSI, THOMAS
(professor of Native American studies)
Education: Hofstra University, BA (Anthropology), 1975; Columbia University, PhD (Anthropology), 1987. *Address & Affiliation*: Professor & Chair of Ethnic Studies Dept., College of Letters & Science, 578 Barrows Hall, Berkeley, CA 94720 (510) 643-0796. E-mail: biolsit@berkeley.edu. *Research Interests*: Native Americans & other indigenous peoples; political economy; racemaking & racisms. *Awards, honors*: Visiting Fellow, Research Institute for the Comparative Study of Race & Ethnicity, Stanford University, 2003-04. *Published works*: Organizing the Lakota: The Political Economy of the New Deal on Pine Ridge & Rosebud Reservations (University of Arizona Press, 1992); Indians & Anthropologists: Vine Deloria, Jr., & the Critique of Anthropology, edited with Larry W. Zimmerman (University of Arizona Press, 1997); Deadliest Enemies: Law & Race Relations On & Off Rosebud Reservation (University of Minnesota, 2001, 2007); Rural Modernities: Space & Time in the American Heartland (in progress); numerous book chapters and articles in journals.

BIRCHFIELD, D.L. (Choctaw, Chickasaw)
(poet, writer, editor)
Education: University of Oklahoma, MA, 1972, JD, 1975. *Address*: 5024 Drexel, Oklahoma City, OK 73119 (405) 681-4886. *Affiliations*: News From Indian Country, Hayward, WI; contributing editor, "Moccasin Telegraph," Fairfax, VA. *Awards, honors*: Won the North American Native Authors first book award for "Oklahoma Basic Intelligence Test," from the Native Writers' Circle of the Americas at the U. of Oklahoma. *Published works*: Oklahoma Basic Intelligence Test; Field of Honor: A Novel (U. of Oklahoma Press, 2004).

BIRCHIM, JAMES, JR. (Shoshone)
(former tribal chairperson)
Affiliation & Address: Former Chairperson, Yomba Shoshone Tribe, HC61, Box 6275, Austin, NV 89310 (775) 964-2463.

BIRD, KERRY (Lumbee/Sisseton-Wahpeton Oyate)
(society president)
Education: University of North Carolina at Chapel Hill, BA; Washington University in St. Louis, Missouri, MSW. *Past professional posts*: Development Officer at UNC Chapel Hill, a former President of the National Indian Education Association, served as the interim Executive Director for both Native Americans in Philanthropy and the National Native American AIDS Prevention Center, and previously worked for the N.C. Commission of Indian Affairs.

BIRD, MICHAEL E. (Santo Domingo-San Juan Pueblo)
(Native Ameican public health)
Education: University of Utah, MSW; University of California, Berkeley, MPH, 1983. Resides in Albuquerque, NM. *Affiliations*: Director, Region 6 for Native Americans with Value Options - New Mexico (VONM), a national for-profit behavioral health company; *Other professional posts*: Board president, Seva Foundation, Berkeley, CA; member, Robert Wood Johnson Foundation Urban Indian Health Commission; member, Board of Directors, American Indian Graduate Center, Albuquerque, NM. *Past professional post*: Executive director, National Native American AIDS Prevention Center, Oakland, CA, 2001-05; 20 years with the USPHS, Indian health Service (IHS), and agency of the U.S, Dept. of Health & Human Services; director of Preventive Health Programs for the Santa Fe Service Unit & Albuquerque Area Office; Office of Tribal Activities & Office of Planning Evaluation. *Memberships*: American Public Health Association (president, 2000-01); New Mexico Public Health Assn (past president); fellow in the USPHS Primary Care Policy Fellowship. *Awards, honors*: The first Native Ameican to be elected to the position of president of the American Public Health Association; Healthcare Hero Award from the Congressional Native American Caucus, U.S. House of Representative.

BIRD, PEGGY (Santo Domingo Pueblo)
(attorney)
Resides in Albuquerque, NM (505) 368-4377 (work). *Memberships*: NM Indian Bar Assn (president); Native American Bar Assn; American Bar Assn.

BISULKA, PAUL (Penobscot)
(commission chair)
Education: U.S. Military Academy, 1970. *Address & Affiliation*: Chairperson (2005-present), Maine Indian Tribal-State Commission, P.O. Box 186, Hudson,

ME 04449 (207) 394-2045. E-mail: biscula@verizon.net. *Past professional posts*: Chairperson, Penobscot Nation Hydro Committee, 1992-95; elected (1995-2005) as the Penobscot Nation Tribal Representatives serving in the 117th & 118th Legislatures. *Military service*: U.S. Army, 1970-90.

BITSOIE, FREDERIC J. (FREDDIE) (Dine' Navajo) 1972-
(Native American chef, lecturer, host)
Born in Monticello, Utah in 1972 & raised in the four corners of Utah, Arizona, New Mexico & Colorado. *Education*: University of New Mexico-Gallup, 1998-2001; Le Cordon Bleu College of Culinary Arts, Scottsdale, AZ. *Affiliation & Address*: FJBits Concepts & Designn, Scottsdale, AZWebsite: www.fjbits.com. E-mail: freddie@fjbits.com. *TV Production*: "Rezervations Not Required," hosted by Freddie Bitsoie (Sleeping Lady Films/Giants Waking Productions, 2012-present). *Awards, honors*: Smithsonian's 2013 Native chef competition.

BLACK, AMOS EARL, III (Sac & Fox) 1943—2016 ()
(attorney)
Education: Oklahoma State University, BS (Business); University of Tulsa, JD. Amos served in Vietnam from 1970-1971 & was honorably discharged as a 2nd Lieutenant. 1971, serving as the assistant district attorney in Anadarko, before going into private practice. Amos was a member of the Bear Clan, within the Sac & Fox Nation of Oklahoma, serving as the tribal attorney and chief justice of the tribal supreme court.

BLACK, DARLA (Oglala Lakota)
(tribal vice president)
Affiliation & Address: Vice President, Oglala Sioux Tribal Executive Committee, P.O. Box 2070, Pine Ridge, SD 57770 (605) 867-4009. E-mail: darla@ oglala.org.

BLACK, MARY A. (Iroquois) 1955-
(attorney)
Born May 4, 1955, Tulsa, Okla. *Education*: University of Oklahoma, BS, 1978; Oklahoma City University Law School, JD, 1981. *Principal occupation*: Attorney. Resides in Shawnee, OK (405) 275-0123 (office). *Affiliation*: Attorney, Private Practice, Shawnee, OK, 1982-. *Other professional posts*: District Judge, Absentee Shawnee Tribe; Supreme Court Justice, Sac & Fox Nation. *Memberships*: American Indian Bar Assn; Oklahoma Indian Bar Assn (secretary, 1991-92); Oklahoma Bar Assn; Oklahoma Trial Lawyers Assn; American Trial Lawyers Assn; American Bar Assn; Lawyer-Pilot Bar Assn; Pottawatomie County Bar Assn (secretary, 1990; treasurer, 1991, 1992; Law Day Committee, 1984-). *Interests*: "Private practice in law with emphasis in personal injury and Indian law."

BLACK, MICHAEL S. (Oglala Lakota)
(acting Assistant Secretary-Indian Affairs)
Education: South Dakota School of Mines & Technology, BS (Mechanical Engineering), 1986. *Affiliation & Address*: Acting Assistant Secretary - Indian Affairs (2017-present), U.S. Department of the Interior, 1849 C St., NW MS-4606-MIB, Washington, DC 20240 (202) 208-5116. *Past professional posts*: Acting Director, Bureau of Indian Affairs, Washington, DC (2010-16); Prior to becoming acting BIA director, Black had served since July 20, 2008, as Regional Director of the BIA's Great Plains Regional Office in Aberdeen, S.D., following an eight-month appointment starting in June 2007 as the acting regional director. The office oversees 12 agencies serving 16 federally recognized tribes in Nebraska, North Dakota & South Dakota. Black began his federal career in 1987 with the BIA's Aberdeen Area Office (now the Great Plains Regional Office) as General Engineer in the Branch of Facilities Management. From 1992 to 2001, he worked in the BIA's Billings Area Office (now the Rocky Mountain Regional Office) as Regional Facility Manager where he was responsible for facilities construction and operations & maintenance programs. In December 2001, he was named Chief of the Office's Division of Engineering, where he was responsible for regional facility management, road construction, and road maintenance and safety programs. In January 2004, Black was promoted to the Rocky Mountain Regional Office's post of Deputy Regional Director-Indian Services, where he was responsible for the management and oversight of Road Construction, Road Maintenance, Tribal Government Services, Credit, Housing, Self-Determination, Social Services, Safety, & Environmental & Cultural Resources Management programs.

BLACK, SHERRY SALWAY (Oglala Lakota)
(executive director)
Education: University of Pennsyvania, Wharton School, MBA. *Affiliation & Address*: Director, Partnership for Tribal Governance, National Cngress of American Indians, Embassy of Tribal Nations, 1516 P St., NW, Washington, DC 20005 (202) 466-7767. E-mail: sherry_black@ncai.org. *Other professional post*: Member, Board of Directors, Council on Foundations, Johnson Scholarship Foundation, Trilliuum Asset Management Corp., and the Hopi Education Endowment Fund; Member of Advisory Committee, National Cngress of American Indians; *Past professional posts*: Senior vice-president, First Nations Development Institute, Fredericksburg, VA (1986-2005);

Executive Director (2005-12), Ovarian Cancer National Alliance, Washington, DC; Vice-chair, American Indian Business Leaders, Missoula, MT.

BLACK EAGLE, CEDRIC (Crow)
(former tribal chairperson)
Affiliation & Address: Crow Tribe (Apsaalooke Nation), P.O. Box 159, Crow Agency, MT 59022 (406) 638-3700.

BLACK HORSE, BREE R. (Seminole of Oklahoma)
(attorney)
Education: Seattle Pacific University, BA (Political Science), 2010; Seattle University School of Law, JD, 2013. *Affiliation & Address*: Associate, Galanda Broadman, 8606 35th Ave. NE, Suite L1, P.O. Box 15146, Seattle, WA 98115 (206) 735-0448. Email: bree@galandabroadman.com. Her practice focuses on federal court and tribal court litigation involving tribal governments, enterprises and businesses. Bree recently completed a clerkship with Judge Brian M. Morris in the United States District Court for the District of Montana Great Falls Division, which has civil and criminal jurisdiction over several Indian reservations. She regularly encountered federal procedural and jurisdictional issues involving tribal parties, including tribal sovereign immunity and tribal court jurisdiction. Prior to her federal court clerkship, Bree served as a youth advocate and case manager at the United Indians of All Tribes Foundation's Labateyah Youth Home in Seattle, where she advanced the interests of formerly homeless young adults.

BLACKBIRD, DONALD (Omaha)
(school principal)
Education: University of Nebraska, Lincoln, BA; Creighton University, MA. *Affiliation & Address*: Prncipal, St. Augustine Indian Mission School, 1 Mission Road South, Winnebago, NE 68071 (402) 878-2242. E-mail: dnblackbird@archomaha.org.

BLACKCLOUD, PAUL (Hunkpapa Lakota)
(physician)
Education: Dartmouth College, BA (Environmental Studies), 2002; Columbia University College of Physicians & Surgeons, MD, 2016. After spending a few years in an unrelated field, I am happy to now be pursuing a life in medicine. I am currently a fourth year medical student at Columbia University in New York City, and I hope to pursue a career in dermatology following graduation. My primary interest in regards to native health is in growing the number of native physicians through mentorships with high school and undergraduate students interested in medicine, to ensure they get the support & guidance they need. *Activities*: President (2015-16, Association of Native American Medical Students.

BLACKDEER, GREGORY S. (Ho-Chunk)
(tribal vice president)
Education: Haskell Indian Junior College, AA, 1986; University of Wisconsin-Stevens Point, BS (Resource Management, minor in Environmental Law Enforcement), 2004. *Affiliation & Address*: Vice President, Ho-Chunk Nation, P.O. Box 667, Black River Falls, WI 54615 (715) 284-9343. E-mail: gblackdeer @ho-chunk.com *Past professional posts*: Manager, Division of Natural Resources, Ho-Chunk Nation, 2006-09.

BLACKHAWK, JOHN (Winnebago of Nebraska)
(former tribal chairperson)
Affiliation & Address: Chairperson, Winnebago Tribe of Nebraska, P.O. Box 687, Winnebago, NE 68071 (402) 878-3103. E-mail: jblackhawk@aol.com. *Other professional post*: Executive Director, Nebraska State Commission on Indian Affairs, Lincoln, NE.

BLACKHAWK, NED (Te-Moak Western Shoshone)
(professor of history & American Indian studies)
Born in Detroit. *Education*: McGill University, BA (History), 1992; UCLA, MA (History), 1994; University of Washington, PhD, 1999. *Affiliation & Address*: Professor of History & American Studies (2009-present), Department of American Studies & History, Native American Cultural Center, Yale University, 26 High St., P.O. Box 208201, New Haven, CT 06520 (203) 432-8530. *Past professional post*: Professor of History & American Indian Studies, (1999-2009), History Dept., U. of Wisconsin-Madison, Madison, WI. *Memberships*: American Studies Association; Western History Association; American Society for Ethnohistory; Association of American Indian & Alaska Native Professors. *Awards, honors*: His book, *Violence over the Land: Indians & Empires in the Early American West* (Harvard, 2006), a study of the American Great Basin which received the Frederick Jackson Turner Prize from the Organization of American Historians. Serves on the editorial boards of American Quarterly and Ethnohistory, Professor Blackhawk has led the establishment of two fellowships, one for American Indian Students to attend the Western History Association's annual conference, the other for doctoral students working on American Indian Studies dissertations at Yale named after Henry Roe Cloud

(Winnebago, Class of 1910). *Published works*: Violence Over the Land: Indians & Empires (Harvard U. Press, 2006); numerous articles in journals.

BLACKMON, WADE T.
(attorney)
Education: Stanford University, BA, 1987; New York University School of Law, JD, 1990. *Affiliation & Address*: Counsel, Kilpatrick Townsend & Stockton, LLP, The Grace Bldg., 1114 Avenue of the Americas, New York, NY 10036 (212) 775-8775. Prior to joining the firm, Wade served as legal counsel tp the Mashantucket Pequot Tribal Nation's Foxwoods Resort Casino since 1998. He advised & represented Foxwoods' officials in all legal aspects of its resort/casino operations with a focus on contract negotiations & drafting. *Admissions*: Mshantucket Pequot Tribal Court.

BLACKOWL, ELIZABETH (Pawnee)
(tribal committee member)
Education: Oklahoma Baptist University, BS, 1957; University of Oklahoma, MS, 1976. *Affiliation & Address*: President (1995-97), vice president (1997-99), second council member (2003-present), Pawnee Tribal Business Committee (PBC), P.O. Box 470, Pawnee, OK 74058 (918) 762-3621. *Other professional post*: PBC representative on the Pawnee Nation College Board of Trustees, 2005-present.

BLACKWELL, WILLIAM (Grand Portage Lake Superior Chippewa)
(director of Indian resource center)
Education: Bemidji State University, BA. *Affiliation & Address*: Director, American Indian Resource Center, Bemidji State University, 1500 Birchmont Dr. NE #21, Bemidji, MN 56601 (218) 755-2032; E-mail: wblackwell@bemidjistate.edu. *Past professional posts*: After spending the last three years at Leech Lake Tribal College. Since 2014, Blackwell has served as the college's director of institutional advancement. In that role, he directed the institution's private and public fundraising activities, which included capital campaigns, planned giving, major gifts and annual gift programs. Blackwell also managed the college's grant writing and reporting efforts and its marketing and public relations activities. Before overseeing the college's advancement efforts, he was an admissions and outreach coordinator. He implemented outreach activities and helped Leech Lake Tribal College to an 11-percent increase in student retention. He also managed a project to revamp the college's marketing and electronic communication materials.

BLAESER, ROBERT A. (White Earth Ojibwe) 1953-
(judge)
Born December 31, 1953, White Earth, Minn. *Education*: Concordia College, BA, 1976; University of Minnesota Law School, JD, 1979. *Principal occupation*: Judge. *Address*: Minnesota Judicial Center, 25 Rev. Martin Luther King, Jr. Blvd., St. Paul, MN 55155 (651) 297-7650. *Affiliation*: Appointed Judge, 4th Judicial District Court, Hennepin County, MN, 1995; elected to post in 1996 & 2002. *Other professional posts*: Member, Minnesota Supreme Court Judicial Education Advisory Committee, 1996-present; Minnesota Tribal State Court Committee, 1997-present; Fourth Judicial District Executive Committee, 1997-present; Chief Judge, Juvenile Court, 2000-present. *Past professional post*: Senior partner, Robert A. Blaeser & Associates, Minneapolis, MN, 1980-95. *Memberships*: American Bar Association, 1979-present; Minnesota American Indian Bar Association (board of directors, founding member, and past officer); Minnesota State Bar Association (board of governors): Hennepin County Bar Association (governing council). *Interests*: He is nationally known for his expertise on racial bias in the justice system and the Indian Child Welfare Act. Judges around the country use him as a resource and for conducting training sessions. He has written numerous articles & given seminars & presentations on topics including racial bias, the Indian Child Welfare Act, domestic abuse, truancy & the concept of family conferencing.

BLAKE, GEORGE N. (Hupa-Yurok)
(craftsperson)
Address: George Blake's Studio, P.O. Box 1304, Hoopa, CA 95546 (530) 625-4619. George makes jewelry with California basket designs, precious & semi-precious stones, pottery, ceramic sculpture, wood carvings.

BLAKE, RICHARD C. (Hupa-Yurok)
(attorney; chief judge)
Affiliation & Address: Chief Judge (2002-present), Hoopa Valley Tribal Court, P.O. Box 1389, Hoopa, CA 95546 (530) 625-4305. *Other professional post*: Contractual Judge, Smith River Rancheria Tribal Court & the Redding Rancheria Tribal Court First Vice President, National American Indian Court Judges Association, Boulder, CO. Judge Blake is the founder of the Northern California Tribal Court Coalition.

BLAKE, SANDRA L. (Ojibwe)
(tribal representative)
Born and raised on the Mille Lacs Reservation, *Education*: College of St. Scholastica BA (Organizational Development); working toward a Master's

degree in Education. *Affiliation & Address*: District I Representative, Mille Lacs Band of Ojibwe, 43408 Oodena Dr., Onamia, MN 56359 (320) 532-4181.Blake was elected Mille Lacs Band District I Representative in 2008 and again in 2012; she previously served as District I Representative from 2000-2004. Blake most recently served as executive director of education for the Mille Lacs Band of Ojibwe. She has also held numerous positions within the Minnesota Historical Society at the Mille Lacs Indian Museum, et al.

BLANCHARD, ROBERT (Bad River Ojibwe)
(tribal chairperson)
Affiliation & Address: Chairperson, Bad River Band of Lake Superior Chippewa Tribe, P.O. Box 39, Odanah, WI 54861 (715) 682-7111.

BLANCHARD, VICTOR (*Singing Eagle* (Potawatomi)
(poet, teacher)
Address & Affiliation: Dept. of English, Eastern Washington University, MS 25G, Cheney, WA 99004 (509) 359-7081.

BLANKENSHIP, BOB (*Oo-Ga-Nast*) (Eastern Cherokee) 1938-
(organization director)
Education: North Carolina State University, BS, 1960; Western Carolina University, MBA, 1972. *Affiliation & Address*: Director, Cherokee Roots, P.O. Box 525, Cherokee, NC 28719 (928) 497-9709. *Other professional post*: President, Museum of the Cherokee Indian. *Military service*: U.S. Army (retired-30 years Colonel; paratrooper, Vietnam War). *Published works*: 1924 Baker Roll: Eastern Band of Cherokee Indians - North Carolina (Cherokee Roots, $45; 1898 Dawes Roll "PLUS" (Cherokee Roots, $35); Guion Miller Roll "PLUS" (Cherokee Roots, $40).

BLEDSOE-DOWNES, ANN MARIE (Winnebago of Nebraska)
(deputy assistant secretary-US/DOI Indian Affars)
Affiliation & Address: Deputy Assistant Secretary – Indian Affairs for Policy & Economic Development & Acting Director of the Bureau of Indian Affairs, U.S. Department of the Interior, 1849 C St., NW, MS-3658-MIB, Washington, DC 20240 (202) 208-3710. She was appointed to the Obama Administration on September 2, 2014. The DAS-PED oversees the Office of Indian Energy and Economic Development and the Office of Self-Governance. The BIE Director oversees the management, policies, procedures and the supervision of all Indian Education programs at the Department of the Interior. Prior to joining the Department, Ms. Bledsoe Downes had been since December 2013 executive director of the Indian Legal Program (ILP) at Arizona State University's Sandra Day O'Connor College of Law in Tempe. She has served as director of ILP's graduate and academic programs (August 2005 to May 2010), as the ILP's interim executive director (October 2011 to October 2012), and as an ILP faculty associate since October 2012. She also served briefly as executive director of the National Native American Bar Association from October 2012 to March 2013. In September 2003, Ms. Bledsoe Downes joined Arizona Governor Janet Napolitano's administration as Policy Advisor for Tribal Affairs, a post she held until the following September. From June 2000 to September 2003, Ms. Bledsoe Downes served as president of Little Priest Tribal College, an institution of higher learning chartered by the Winnebago Tribe of Nebraska in 1996, and again from May to July 2013 as interim president. In December 1996, Ms. Bledsoe Downes was named to the Hoopa Valley Tribal Gaming Commission, an appointment she held until April 1998. Ms. Bledsoe Downes has been a member of the Ho-Chunk, Inc., board of directors since 2008 and a member of the Little Priest Tribal College Board of Trustees since 2012. She also served as a member of the White House Initiative on Tribal Colleges and Universities Advisory Board from 2002 to 2005. She received a Bachelor of Arts degree in Social Sciences Education from Wayne State College in 1991 and a Juris Doctorate from ASU in 1994.

BLEVINS, WIN (Cherokee) 1938-
(novelist, book editor)
Born October 21, 1938, Little Rock, Ark. *Education*: M.A., post-doctoral diploma. *Address*: P.O. Box 223, Bluff, UT 84512 (435) 672-2459. E-mail: win@winblevins.com. Website: www.winblevins.com. *Memberships*: Wordcraft Circle; Pen-America; Western Writers of America; Mystery Writers of America. *Awards, honors*: Spur Award for best novel of the West, 1996; Mountains and Plains Booksellers Award for Best Fiction, 1996, nominated for Pulitzer Prize for "Stone Song, 1995; Wordcraft Circle Writer of the Year, 2003. *Published works*: 13 books - Give Your Heart to the Hawks; Dictionary of the American West; Stone Song; Raven Shadow; Charbonneau; Misadventures of Silk & Shakespeare; So Wild a Dream, et al.

BLOOD, BROOKTYNN M. (Omaha)
(attorney)
Education: Brigham Young University, BA, 2004; BYU Reuben Clark Law School, 2008. *Affiliation & Adress*: Associate, Tribal Affairs & Gaming Group, Lewis & Roca, LLP, 40 N. Central Ave., Suite 1900, Phoenix, AZ 85004 (602) 262-5342. E-mail: bblood@llrlaw.com. Her area of practice focuses on researching & writing legal memoranda to assist tribal governments with federal & administrative court proceedings, providing legal & strategic advice to Tribal Governments & Tribal enterprise clients & assisting Tribal clients in securing tribal-state gaming compacts and in renegotiating existing compacts. Her experiences also includes drafting tribal ordinances & resoliutions, and land-into-trust acquisitions. *Bar Admissions*: Arizona, 2008; Rincon Tribe, 2010; Shingle Springs Tribe, 2011; Navajo Nation, 2012.

BLUE EYES, FAYE (Navajo-Dine')
(Indian school director)
Affiliation & Address: Shiprock Northwest High School, Shiprock Alternative Schools, P.O. Box 1799, Shiprock, NM 87420 (505) 368-2070.

BLUE SPRUCE, GEORGE, JR. (*Fon-Tem-Dey-Sten*)
(Laguna/San Juan Pueblo/Ohkay-Owingeh) 1931-
(assistant dean for American Indian Affairs)
Born January 16, 1931, Santa Fe, N.M. *Education*: Creighton University, D.D.S., 1956; University of California School of Public Health, M.P.H., 1967; Federal Executive Institute, Certificate, 1973. *Affiliation & Address*: Assistant Dean for American Indian Affairs. Arizona School of Dentistry & Oral Health, Arizona State University, 5850 E. Still Circe, Mesa, AZ 85206 (480) 219-6000. *Other professional posts*: President emeritus & founder (1990-present), Society of American Indian Dentists (SAID), Menifree, CA; chairperson, Intra-Departmental Council on Indian Affairs (DHEW); chairperson, Health Manpower Opportunity Advisory Committee; chairperson, Feasibility Study Team for Project: Center for Health Professions Education (Navajo Reservation, Arizona); special consultant, Special Committee for the Socio-economically Disadvantaged, American Dental Hygienist's Assn; regional director, Indian Health Service, USPHS; president, Society of American Indian Dentists, 1990-. *Military service*: U.S. Navy, 1956-58 (Navy Citation Medal-dentist for Atomic Submarine "Nautilus" prior to underwater/ North Pole journey). *Community activities*: Was on the Phoenix City Council; Phoenix Indian Center Board of Directors; president, North American Indian Tennis Assn. *Memberships*: National Indian Education Assn (board of directors); Health Education Media Assn (board of directors, Minority Affairs); American Indian Bank (board of directors); American Fund for Dental Education (member, Selection Committee); Task Force for Medical Academic Achievement Program; Students American Veterinary Medicine Assn (member, Selection Committee; Health Manpower Study for American Indians (member, Advisory Committee); Navajo Health Authority (member, board of commissioners, Kellogg Scholarship Committee, Dean Selection Committee, Health Professions Education Committee); American Indian School of Medicine - Feasibility Study (member, Advisory Council); Health Professions Education System, Rockville, MD (board of directors); USPHS Commissioned Officers' Assn; American Public Health Assn; American Indian Physicians' Assn; American Dental Assn; American Assn of Dental Schools; New Mexico State Dental Society; North American Indian Tennis Assn (president); U.S. Lawn Tennis Assn; Society of American Indian Dentists; American Indian Science & Engineering Society. *Awards, honors*: Outstanding American Indian for 1972, American Indian Exposition, Inc., Anadarko, OK; Outstanding American Indian Achievement Award, 1974, American Indian Council Fire, Inc., Washington, DC; Award of Merit, presented by the Association of American Indian Physicians for: Significant Contributions Towards Raising the Level of Health Care of the American Indian and Alaskan Native, August 1980; Alumni of the Year, presented by Creighton University (Omaha, NE) in May 1984, for his distinguished service to his fellow man and his alma mater while keeping with the finest traditions of the University; Annual Assn of American Medical Colleges Award for Health Professional contributing to the health of American Indians; Annual Award for Most Outstanding American Indian Health Professional by the American Indian Science and Engineering Society; inducted into the American Indian Athletic Hall of Fame in 1996 and is the first & only male tennis player to be inducted. *Interests*: "Have been visiting instructor on health care administration for St. Francis College (Joliet, IL) and Northern Michigan University (Marquette, MI). I'm presently a consultant to the Federal Government in the review of grants for medical schools and Centers of Excellence in dental & pharmacy schools." *Published works*: Numerous articles.

BLUEDOG, KURT V. (Sisseton-Wahpeton Sioux) 1950-
(attorney)
Born & raised on the Sisseton-Wahpeton Indian Sioux Reservation in Agency Village, S.D. *Education*: University of South Dakota, BA, 1972; University of Minnesota School of Law, JD, 1977. *Address & Affiliation*: Foundng Partner, BlueDog Paulson & Small, PLLP, 5001 West 80th, Bloomington, MN 55437 (952) 893-1813. Mr. BlueDog has been in private practice for about 15 years and is currently involved in litigation, administrative & legislative activity representing tribal concerns, with emphasis in the area of tribal commercial law, corporate law, gaming, & economic development. *Past professional posts*: Staff attorney, Native American Rights Fund; adjunct professor at William Mitchell College of Law & the Hamline Law School, St. Paul, MN; Chief Judge (ten years), Fond du Lac Reservation Tribal Court; Executive Committee (15 years), National Indian Gaming Association. *Military service*: U.S. Army, 1972-

74. *Memberships*: American Bar Association; Minnesota Bar Association; Wisconsin Bar Association; Minnesota Indian Bar Association; several Tribal Courts; the U.S. Supreme Court & Federal District & Appellate Courts.

BLUEHOUSE, MILTON, SR. (Navajo)
(former tribal president)
Affiliation & Address: (4th President 1999), Navajo Nation, P.O. Box 9000, Window Rock, AZ 86515 (928) 871-6352.

BLUEHOUSE, RANDELLA (Navajo)
(executive director)
Affiliation & Address: Executive Director, National Indian Council on Aging, 10501 Montgomery Blvd. NE, Suite 210, Albuquerque, NM 87111 (505) 292-2001.

BLUEWOLF, JAMES DON (*Csimu Muppah*) (Oklahoma Choctaw) 1950-
(ANA language grant executive coordinator)
Born March 19, 1950, in Okla. *Principal occupation*: ANA language grant executive coordinator. *Address*: 750 North High St., Lakeport, CA 95453 (707) 263-1099. Website: www.anoliscircle.com. Affiliation: Big Valley band of Pomo Indians, 11/03 to present. *Other professional posts*: Producer/programmer of Native music and other on Lake County community radio, KPFZ 104.5 FM. *Awards, honors*: Poet Laureate of Lake County, Calif. 2002-2003. *Community activities*: Board member, Lucy Moore Foundation; member of KPFZ, Lake County Community Radio. *Membership*: Regional caucus leader for the Wordcraft Circle of Native Writers & Storytellers. Interests: Writing, language, radio, music, family. *Published works*: "Sitting By His Bones," 1999, Earthen Vessel (poetry); "Grandpa Says - Stories for a Seventh Generation," 2000, Earthen Vessell (stories).

BLUMER, THOMAS J. (*Fallsapart*) 1937-
(archivist; consultant)
Born July 7, 1937, Freeport, N.Y. *Education*: University of Mississippi, BA, 1967, MA, 1968; University of South Carolina, PhD, 1976. *Affiliation & Address*: Archivist, consultant, P.O. Box 302, Edinburg, VA 22824 (540) 984-3922. E-mail: tblumer@shentel.net. Archivist & *Consulting work*: consultant, Native American Rights Fund, Boulder, Colo., 1980-; consultant, McKissick Museums, University of South Carolina, 1984-; consultant, Schiele Museum of Natural History, Gastonia, NC, 1984-; editor, American Indian Libraries Newsletter, American Library Association, Chicago, IL, 1984-87; consultant, Pamunkey Indian Museum, King William, Va., 1985-; historian, Catawba Nation Restoration of Justice Project, Catawba Nation, Rock Hill, SC, 1989-. *Community activities*: Civilian Conservation Corp. Legacy Board, 2001-04. *Military service*: U.S. Navy, 1956-60. *Memberships*: South Carolina Historical Association, 1986-; Cherokee Indian Historical Association, 1980-; York County Genealogical & Historical Society, 1989-. *Interests*: Southeastern Indians, Catawba Indian history, Pamunkey Indian history, Southern Indian pottery traditions (Catawba, Cherokee, Pamunkey); lectures. *Published works*: Bibliography of the Catawba (Scarecrow Press, 1987); "History as a Tool in a Folklife Study of the Catawba Indians of South Carolina" (New York Journal of Folklore, 1983); "Wild Indians and the Devil: The Contemporary Catawba Indian Spirit World" (American Indian Quarterly, 1985); "Catawba Indian Influence on the Cherokee Indian Pottery Tradition" (Appalachian Journal, 1987); Catawba Indian Pottery: The Survival of a Folk Tradition (University of Alabama Press, 2003); Catawba Indian Nation of the Carolinas (Arcadia Publishing, 2004); Catawba Nation: Treasures in History, with E. Fred Sanders (History Press, 2007).

BLUMM, MICHAEL
(professor of law – Indian law program)
Education: Williams College, BA, 1972; George Washington University Law School, JD, 1976, LL.M., 1979. *Affiliation & Address*: Jeffrey Bain faculty Scholar & Professor of Law, Indian Program, Lewis & Clark Law School, 10015 S.W. Terwilliger Blvd., Portland, OR 97219 (503) 768-6824; E-mail: blumm@lclark.edu. Professor Blumm is one of the architects of the Law School's acclaimed Environmental and Natural Resources Law Program. He has been teaching, writing, and practicing in the environmental and natural resources law field for thirty-five years. He came to the law school after practicing with an environmental group and the U.S. Environmental Protection Agency in Washington, D.C., where he helped draft the EPA's first wetland protection regulations. Blumm's chief interests are in the restoration of the Pacific Northwest salmon runs, the preservation of the West's public lands and waters, the management of natural resources by Indian tribes, the modern use of the public trust doctrine, and governmental authority to regulate private property for public purposes. Professor Blumm was instrumental in the founding of the Law School's pioneering Externship Program, which began in 1979 as part of the environmental law program and over the years has expanded to include all legal subjects. The Externship Program has sponsored over 600 students who spend a semester gaining practical experience working for government agencies, non-profit organizations, and law firms. For over a decade during the 1980s, Blumm edited the Natural

Resources Law Institute's Anadromous Fish Law Memo. He then spent seven years during the 1990s co-directing the Northwest Water Law and Policy Project. He has co-authored casebooks on Natural Resources Law, Public Trust Law, and Native American Natural Resources Law. Blumm is a prolific scholar, with well over one-hundred published articles, book chapters, and monographs on salmon, water, public lands, wetlands, environmental impact assessment, public trust law, and constitutional takings law, to name just a few topics. Much of his scholarship includes student co-authors. He also regularly helps students publish on their own. For example, over twenty of his students have authored state analyses in a comprehensive study of the public trust doctrine in the American states. Blumm was visiting professor at the University of Melbourne in 1988, Fulbright Professor at the University of Athens in 1991, and visiting professor at the University of California-Berkeley in 2004. He has lectured on a variety of topics as visiting professor in in law schools in Australia, Canada, Greece, and Brazil, and has been distinguished visitor at Florida State University, the University of Calgary, Vermont Law School, and several Australian law schools. In 2005-07, he was Chair of the American Association of Law School's Natural Resources Law Section. Published works: Natural Resources Law: Private Rights and the Public Interest (West Pub. Co., forthcoming 2015) (co-author); **The Public Trust Doctrine in Environmental and Natural Resources Law** (Carolina Academic Press 2013) (co-author), with teachers manual; *Native American Natural Resources Law: Cases and Materials* (Carolina Academic Press, 1st ed. 2002, 2d ed. 2008, 3d ed. 2013) (with teachers manual and annual teacher's updates) (co-author). **Sacrificing the Salmon: A Legal and Policy History of the Decline of Columbia Basin Salmon** (BookWorld Publications, 2002, republished by Vandeplas Publishing, 2013).

BLYTHE, FRANK (Eastern Cherokee/Dakota)
(founding executive director)
Education: Arizona State University, B.A. *Address & Affiliation*: Executive director, Native American Public Telecommunications, 1800 North 33rd St., Lincoln, NE 68583 (402) 472-3522. E-mail: fblythe@yahoo.com. *Award, honors*: Award for his work in media by the Nebraska Commission on Indian Affairs at the first annual Chief Standing Bear Commemoration Celebration.

BLYTHE, LARRY (Eastern Cherokee)
(former tribal vice chief)
Affiliation & Address: Former Vice Chief, Eastern Band of Cherokee Indians, Qualla Boundary, P.O. Box 455, Cherokee, NC 28719 (828) 497-7000. E-mail: lblythe@nc-cherokee.com.

BOB, DIANA R. (Lummi)
(attorney; association president)
Education: Pitzer College (Claremont, CA), BA (Environmental Studies & Anthropology); Lewis & Clark Law School, JD (with certificate in environmental law). *Affiliation & Address*: Partner, Stoel Rives LLP, 600 University St. #3600, Seattle, WA 98101 (206) 386-7564. E-mail: Diana.bob@stoel.com. *Past professional posts*: Staff Attorney, Lummi Nation, Bellingham, WA 2009-14; Diana works on matters relating to land use, natural resources, water rights & other matters with local governments, Washington state & the U.S.; attorney, National Congress of American Indians, 2008-09; attorney, Northwest Justice Project, 2006-08; law clerk, Hobbs, Straus, et al., 2004-05. *Memberships*: National Native American Bar Association; Northwest Indian Bar Association (president, 2012-13); American Bar Association; Lummi, Colville, Kalispel, & Spokane Tribal Court bars, the Washington state & District of Columbia bar associations, and is admitted to practice in the Western District of Washington.

BOHAM, RUSSELL (Little Shell Chippewa)
(program director; commission member)
Address: P.O. Box 1384, Great Falls, MT 59403 (406) 452-2892. E-mail: rboham@bresnan.net. *Affiliation*: Director, Indian Natural Resource-Science & Engineering Program, Humboldt State University, McMahan House 80, Arcata, CA 95521 (707) 826-4994. *Other professional post*: Member, State Tribal Economic Development Commission (STEDC), c/o Montana Dept. of Commerce, Helena, MT.

BOHAM, SANDRA (Salish)
(Indian college president)
Affiliation & Address: President, Salish Kootenai College, P.O. Box 70, Pablo, MT 59855 (406) 675-4800. E-mail: Sandra_boham@skc.edu. *Other professional post*: Chairperson, Montana Indian Education Association, Great Falls, MT. *Past professional post*: Indian Education Director (eight years), Great Falls Public Schools, Great Falls, MT.

BOHANON, JOSEPH (Pawnee)
(professor of Native American studies)
Education: University of Texas, Arlington, MA (Social Work Administration & Community Planning); University of Southern Mississippi, PhD (Educational Leadership & Administration, Higher Education). *Affiliation & Address*: Co-Owner/Vice President, 2013-present), Native Insights Consulting, LLC, 26370

E. 113th Ct., Coweta, OK 74429 (918) 639-2234. *Other professional post*: Adjunct Faculty, Native American Studies & Psychology, Southeastern Oklahoma State University, Durant, OK (2014-present). *Past professional posts*: President, Pawnee Nation College, Pawnee, OK, 2011-13; faculty, University of Southern Mississippi, 2001-07.

BOHLEN, STACY A. (Sault Ste. Marie Ojibwe)
(executive director)
Education: Oakland University, BA (Political Science); Johns Hopkins University, D.C. (MA (Government). *Affiliation & Address*: Executive Director, National Indian Health Board (NIHB), 926 Pennsylvania Ave., SE, Washington, DC 20003 (202) 507-4070. E-mail: sbohlen@nihb.org. She is responsible for implementing the NIHB strategic plan, fulfilling the organization's mission of advocating on behalf of all tribal governments and American Indians/Alaska Natives in their efforts to provide quality health care. *Past professional post*: Director of Federal Relations, American Indian Higher Education Consortiumm.

BOHNEE, GARY (Hopi)
(staff director)
Address & Affiliation: Staff director, U.S. Senate Select Committee on Indian Affairs, 838 Hart Senate Office Bldg., Washington, DC 20510 (202) 224-2251.

BOINTY, CHARLOTTE (Kiowa)
(secretary/treasurer)
Affiliation & Address: Secretary-Treasurer, Kiowa Indian Tribe, P.O. Box 369, Carnegie, OK 73015 (580) 654-1729.

BOIVIN, LAURIE (Menominee)
(former tribal chairperson)
Affiliation & Address: Menominee Indian Tribe of Wisconsin, P.O. Box 910, Keshena, WI 54135 (715) 799-5100.

BOL, RUTH WAUQUA (Comanche)
(dentist; sociert president)
Raised in Bakersfield, CA. *Education*: Cal-State Bakersfield, BS, 2000; University of the Pacific School of Dentistry, DDS, 2003; UCLA Pediatric Residency, MPH. *Affiliation & Address*: President, Society of American Indian Dentists (SAID), 27180 Newport Rd., Suite 3, Menifee, CA 92584 (951) 306-2092. E-mail: ruthwbol@gmail.com. After graduation, Ruth worked with American Indian tribes as a dentist and dental director at times for four years in Washington State. Her last assignment was with the Navajo Nation in Arizona where she worked only with children on the reservation until she moved to Los Angeles to complete her pediatric residency at UCLA.

BOLAND, LITTLE FAWN (Piro-Manso-Tiwa) 1976-
(attorney; law firm partner)
Born on the San Juan de Guadalupe Pueblo, New Mexico, 1976. *Education*: University of the Pacific, School of International Studies, BA, 1998; University of California, Hastings College of Law, JD, 2005. *Affiliation & Address*: Partner, Ceiba Legal, LLP, (415) 684-77670. *Past professional posts*: Lynch, Gilardi, Grummer, San Francisco, CA, 2001; General Counsel of the Washoe Tribe of Nevada & California, 2006-2007; partner, Rosette, LLP, San Francisco, CA, 2007-10;. Ms. Boland is experienced in multiple practice areas including litigation, tribal administrative & transactional law. As an attorney & professional, she has experience in real estate & business development, corporate & tribal governance, project management, finance, & legislative analysis. "I assist tribes to bring a range of economic development projects to fruition by providing guidance and strategically mapping out the steps and the team needed to make projects a reality. I specialize in negotiating & structuring tribal economic development transactions, negotiating on behalf of tribes with federal, state, and local governments, assisting tribes in the development of necessary legal infrastructure for economic development including taxation and corporate codes, creating functional corporate charters and bylaws, obtaining necessary entitlements, and navigating "Indian Lands Decision" and "Fee-to-Trust" processes. I am currently serving as legal counsel on several gaming and non-gaming projects. I also work for a handful of tribal casinos and gaming commissions. *Memberships*: New Markets advisory board member; San Juan Guadalupe Pueblo in New Mexico. *Awards, honors*: A moot court champion and ranked second in the world at the 2004 Jessup International Moot Court Competition.

BOLTON, TOMMY W. (Choctaw & Lipan Apache) 1949-
(safety representative; former tribal chief/chairperson)
Born August 12, 1949, Converse, La. *Principal occupation*: Offshore drilling safety representative. *Affiliation*: Choctaw-Apache Community of Ebarb Tribe, P.O. Box 1428, Zwolle, LA 71486 (318) 645-2744. *Military service*: U.S. Navy, 1968-74 (Republic of Vietnam Service & Republic of Vietnam Campaign). *Community activities*: Deputy, Sabine Parish Sheriff's Dept.; past administrative chief, North Sabine Fire Prot. District; VFW; American Legion.

BOMBERRY, VICTORIA
(assistant professor)
Education: Stanford University, PhD (Modern Thought & Literature). Her dissertation titled, "Indigenous Memory & Imagination: Thinking Beyond the Nation," is a study of the development of a hemispheric consciousness among indigenous in the Americas and the ways in which indigenous women are contributing to this phenomenon. *Affiliation & Address*: Instructor, Native American Studies Program, Dept. of Ethnic Studies, College of Humanities, Arts & Social Sciences, INTS 4017, Riverside, CA 92521 (951) 827-2531. E-mail: victoria.bomberry@ucr.edu. *Past professional posts*: UC President's Postdoctoral Fellow, Dept. of Native American Studies, UC, Davis, 2001-03; editor, Native Self-Sufficiency, Seventh Generation Fund, Forestville, CA .

BOMMELYN, LOREN J. ME'-LASH-NE (Tolowa)
(former tribal chairperson)
Affiliation & Address: Former chairperson, Tolowa Tribe of the Smith River Rancheria, 140 Rowdy Creek Rd., Smith River, CA 95567 (707) 218-7723. lbommelyn@tolowa. com.

BONGA, DAVID C. (Minnesota Chippewa-White Earth) 1952-
(institute president)
Born June 23, 1952, Monroe, Wash. *Education*: Dartmouth College, B.A., 1974; Gonzaga Law School, J.D., 1982. *Address*: So. 1915 Pierce, Spokane, WA 99206 (509) 445-1147. *Affiliations*: President, Camas Institute, Kalispel Indian Tribe, Usk, WA, 2003-present. *Other professional post*: Member, Board of Directors, National Indian Youth Leadership Project, Albuquerque, NM; Judge pro-tem for Spokane, Colville, Coeur d'Alene, Nez Perce & Quinault Indian tribes; magistrate for Kalispel Tribe; guest lecturer, Eastern Washington University, Indian Studies Department, Cheney, WA. *Past professional post*: Tribal planner; in-house counsel, Kalispel Indian Tribe, Usk, WA, 1985-2003. *Memberships*: Washington State Bar Assn; Northwest Tribal Judges Assn; Intercollegiate Center for Nursing (Native American Advisory Council); University of Idaho President Advisory Council for Native American Studies; Board of Directors, Gonzaga University Legal Assistance. *Interests*: History & Indian law.

BONNEY, RACHEL A. 1939-
(professor of anthropology)
Born March 28, 1939, St. Paul, Minn. *Education*: University of Minnesota, B.A., 1961, M.A., 1963; University of Arizona, Ph.D., 1975. *Affiliation & Address*: Professor, Dept. of Sociology & Anthropology, University of North Carolina, Charlotte, NC 28223 (704) 687-2252; E-mail: rabonney@email.uncc.edu. *Affiliations*: Assistant professor, Tarkio College, Mo., 1965-67; instructor, University of South Florida, 1967-70; graduate teaching associate, University of Arizona, 1971-73; instructor & professor, University of North Carolina at Charlotte, 1973-. *Other professional posts*: Teacher, guidance, B.I.A., Teec Nos Pos Boarding School, Arizona (Navajo), 1964. *Community activities*: Charlotte-Mecklenburg Title IV (Indian Education Act) Indian Parent Committee (ex-officio member, 1975-77); Metrolina Native American Association, Charlotte, N.C.; UNCC Phoenix Society (American Indian Student Organization) & Phoenix Dancer (Indian dance team), (advisor). *Memberships*: American Anthropological Association (Fellow); American Ethnological Society; Southern Anthropological Association; National Congress of American Indians; Anthropological Council on Education; National Indian Education Association; Southeastern Indian Cultural Association. *Awards, honors*: HEW Title IX (ethnic heritage studies) Project Grant, 1977-78. *Interests*: Indian studies; multi-ethnic studies; culture change (Catawba land claims case); Indian powwows; powwows with Phoenix Dancers; archaeological projects in Minnesota, New York, New Mexico, and Austria. *Published works*: American Indian Studies in the Social Studies Curriculum (Proceedings, North Carolina Association for Research in Education, May, 1975); The Role of Women in Indian Activism (The Western Canadian Journal of Anthropology, Vol. VI, No. 3, 1976); The Role of AIM Leaders in Indian Nationalism (American Indian Quarterly, Vol. 3, No. 3, 1977); Indians of the Americas, Courtship Customs (Encyclopedia of Indians of the Americas, Scholarly Press, 1978); Anthropologists & Indians in the New South, with James Paredes (University of Alabama Press, 2001); among others.

BOONE, STEVE (Zuni Pueblo)
(Pueblo lt. governor)
Affiliation & Address: LT. Governor, Pueblo of Zuni, P.O. Box 339, Zuni, NM 87327 (505) 782-7022.

BORAAS, ALAN
(professor of anthropology)
Affiliation & Address: Professor, Dept. of Anthropology, University of Alaska, 3211 Providence Dr., Anchorage, AK 99508 (907) 786-6840. *Interests*: Athapaskan prehistory & ethno-history. E-mail: ifasb@uaa.alaska.edu.

BORCHARDT, JEANNIE (Paiute)
(tribal band chairperson)
Affiliation & Address: Chairperson, Indian Peaks Band, Paiute Indian Tribe of Utah, 940 W. 526 S. Cedar City, UT 84721.

BORCHARDT-SLAYTON, TAMRA (Paiute)
(tribal chairperson)
Affiliation & Address: Chairperson, Paiute Indian Tribe of Utah, P.O. Box 235, Cedar City, UT 84721 (435) 586-1112.

BORDEAUX, LIONEL (Rosebud Lakota Sioux)
(college president)
Affiliation: Sinte Gleska University, P.O. Box 490, Rosebud, SD 57570-0490 (605) 747-2263. *Other professional post*: Editorial Advisory Board, The Independent American Indian Review.

BORDEAUX, ROGER C. (Rosebud Lakota) 1952-
(executive director)
Born August 20, 1952, Valentine, Neb. *Education*: St. Francis Mission, 1970; University of South Dakota, BA (Communications; Indian Studies minor), 1974, MA (Administration), 1988, EdD, 1990. *Address & Affiliations*: Executive director (2006-present), Association of Community Tribal Schools, Inc., P.O. Box 1518, Mission, SD 57555 (605) 838-0424. E-mail: drbourdeaux@acts-tribal.org. *Past professional posts*: Teacher, director, St. Francis Indian School, St. Francis, SD, 1980-90; supt., Tiospa zina Tribal School, P.O. Box 719, Agency Village, SD 57262, 1991-2005. *Memberships*: South Dakota Indian Education Association. *Awards, honors*: M.A. Student of the Year, 1988, University of South Dakota. *Interests*: Golf, softball, fishing.

BORENE, GREG (Maidu)
(rancheria vice chairperson)
Affiliation & Address: Vice Chairperson, Enterprise Rancheria Band of Maidu Indians, 2133 Monte Vista Ave., Oroville, CA 95966 (530) 532-9214. E-mail: gregb@enterpriserancheria.org

BOTSFORD, JAMES (Winnebago)
(attorney)
Education: University of North Dakota, BA, Syracuse University, MA, University of North Dakota Law School, JD. *Address & Affiliation*: Director, Indian Law Office, Wisconsin Judicare, Inc., 300 Third St. #210, Wausau, WI 54403 (800) 472-1638. E-mail: jbotsford@judicare.org. *Other professional post*: Associate Justice of the Supreme Court of the Winnebago Tribe of Nebraska. *Community activities*: Member, Steering Committee of the National Association of Indian Legal Services. *Memberships*: State Bars of Wisconsin & Minnesota.

BOUCHA, HENRY C. (O'Git'chi'Dah) (Ojibway) 1951-
(Indian education director, realtor)
Born June 1, 1951, Warroad, Minn. *Education*: University of Detroit (general business courses); Fond du Lac Community College (Title IX workshops & Johnson O'Malley Workshop) 1993. *Address*: 314 Minnesota Ave., NE, Warroad, MN 56763 (218) 386-2834. E-mail: henryboucha@means.net. *Affiliations*: Real estate agent, Pahlen Realty, Roosevelt, MN 1986-; Indian education director, Warroad Public Schools, Warroad, MN, 1993-. *Other professional posts*: Former National Hockey League player with the Detroit Red Wings & Minnesota North Stars, 1972-75; Hockey coach for Warroad High School, 1989-; Pacific Northwest Hockey School, Lynwood, WA, 1993-. *Military service*: U.S. Army, 1970-72. *Community activities*: Minnesota Indian Education Board of Directors, 1993-95; advisory board - Warroad Community Education; Minnesota's Planning, Evaluation, and Reporting Board; USA's Diversity Hockey Task Force's Board; Warroad's First Nation Board of Directors; chairperson, Warroad's Annual Traditional Powwow (1st weekend in June); chair, Kah-Bay-Kah-Nong, Inc. (non-profit to help young people); chair, United Fund of Roseau County, Inc. (non-profit to help people of Roseau County). *Memberships*: U.S. Olympic Alumni; U.S. National Coaches Assn; Detroit Red Wings & Minnesota North Stars Alumni; NHL Players Assn Alumni; Minnesota Realtors' Assn; National Association of Realtors. *Awards, honors*: 1970 World Hockey Championships - Gold Medal; First American Indian inducted into the U.S. Hockey Hall of Fame, Sept. 16, 1995; honored by the American Indian College Scholarship Fund in Sept. 1995; honored at Gathering of the Nations in Albuquerque, NM as one of ten American Indians ever to play in the Olympics; 1973 Detroit Red Wings Rookie of the Year, broke a 41 year old NHL record, scoring the fastest goal at the start of a NHL game on Jan. 23, 1973; Olympic Silver Medalist, Ice Hockey, Sapporo, Japan in 1972; U.S. National Hockey Teams, 1970 & 1971; inducted into the Warroad Warrior Sports Hall of Fame 1995; number #16 Warroad Warrior Hockey jersey retired. *Interests*: Golf, guitar, fishing, hunting, boating, travel, mountains. *Biographical source*: Subject of an Autobiography, "Henry Boucha, Star of the North," by Mary Halverson Schofield (Snowshoe Press, 2000).

BOUCHARD, KIMBERLY
(BIA regional supt.)
Affiliation & Address: Supt. Bureau of Indian Affairs, Great Lakes Agency, 916 W. Lake Shore Dr., Ashland, WI 54806 (800) 495-4655; (715) 682-4527 E-mail: Kimberly.bouchard@bia.gov

BOULE, MARY NULL
(author, publisher)
Address: c/o Merryant Publishers, Inc., 7615 SW 257th St., Vashon Island, WA 98070 (206) 463-3879. *Affiliations*: California elementary school teacher for 27 years. *Community activities*: Church musician; Island Singers. *Published works*: The Missions: California's Heritage, and The California Native American Tribes; both are written at the 3rd to 5th grade reading level & published by Merryant Publishers; Mission Series, 21 vols.; Native American Series, 26 vols.

BOULLEY, ANGELINE (Sault Ste. Marie Chippewa)
(tribal education director)
Education: Central Michigan University, BS (Psychology; minor in Management), Masters in Public Administration, MPA. *Master's Thesis*: "Tribal Political Empowerment: How Indian Tribes Impact Public Policy at the Local, State & National Levels." Angeline is an alumnus of the UCLA/Johnsonn & Johnson Head Start Management Fellows Program. *Affiliation & Address*: Education Director, Sault Ste. Marie Tribe of Chippewa Indians, 523 Ashmun St., Sault Ste. Marie, MI 49783 (906) 635-7010. E-mail: aboulley@saulttribe.net *Other professional posts*: Board Member, Tribal Education Departments' National Assembly (TEDNA); chairperson, Michigan Tribal Education Directors' Consortium; serves on the Board of Regents for Bay Mils Community College; president, Title VII Indian Education Committee for Sault Area Public Schools.

BOULWARE, TYLER
(professor of history)
Affiliation & Address: Member, Native American Program Committee & Associate Professor of History, Department of History, Eberly College of Arts & Sciences, G3 Woodburn Hall, P.O. Box 6303, Morgantown, WV 26506 (304) 293-9306. E-mail: tyler.boulware@mail.wvu.edu. Dr. Boulware's teaching & research are mainly in early American history dealing with Native Americans, empires, and encounters. He structures his courses to situate indigenous peoples at the center of colonial American history. *Published works*: Deconstructing the Cherokee Nation: Town, Regon, and Nationa Among 18th Century Cherokees (Univerity Press of Floria, 2011); in progress: Next to Kin: Native Americans & Friendship in Early America, reveals how Native Ameican understandingsof friendships helped to solidify personal reationships and inter-group alliances throughout North America.

BOURLAND, GREGG J. (Wanbli Awanyankapi)
(Cheyenne River Sioux) 1956-
(tribal chairperson)
Born December 22, 1956, Ash Butte, S.D. *Education*: Black Hills State University, BS. *Affiliation & Address*: Chairperson, Cheyenne River Sioux Tribe, P.O. Box 590, Eagle Butte, SD 57625 (605) 964-4155. E-mail: eaglwatc@rapidnet.com. *Other professional posts*: The Lakota O'Tipi Group Home in the early 1980s working with children on the reservation; along with his wife Kay, opened one of the only reservation Indian owned businesses in 1985, a video business called Kay's Video World. *Community activities*: Chairman, Cheyenne River Sioux Tribe Industrial Business Development Committee; chairman, Tribal Tax Commission; board member, South Dakota Rural Development Association; board member, Aberdeen Area Tribal Chairman's Health Board; secretary treasurer, Great Plains Tribal Chairmen Association; board member, American Indian Research & Policy Institute; board member, Trustees Presentation College; chairman, Intertribal Monitoring Association on Indian Trust Funds; member of national Indian Policy Center - National Governance Task Force; board member, Morning Star Foundation; board member, Northwest Area Foundation. *Awards, honors*: Served as the only Chairman of the AATCHB Task Force on Health Care Reform; served on Hillary Clinton's panel on health care reform; chosen by his fellow tribal leaders to speak at the White House Tribal Leaders Summit with President Clinton, VP, Al Gore, and the entire Clinton Cabinet on April 29, 1994. He is in constant demand throughout Indian Country and the Nation as a speaker at various functions. He has authored various congressional bills & various congressional appropriations requests.

BOURSAW, JON (Citizen Potawatomi)
(tribal cultural center director)
Affiliation & Address: Executive Director, Citizen Potawatomi Cultural Heritage Center, 1601 S. Gordon Cooper • Shawnee, OK 74801 (405) 275-3121. E-mail: jboursaw@potawatomi.org.

BOW, CORRINA (Paiute)
(former tribal chairperson)
Affiliation & Address: Former Chairperson, Paiute Indian Tribe of Utah, P.O. Box 235, Cedar City, UT 84721 (435) 586-9433. *Past professional post*: Council member, Kanosh Band of Paiute.

BOWANNIE, MARY K. (Zuni/Cochiti)
(lecturer in Native American studies)
Education: University of Colorado, MA (Journalism). *Affiliation & Address*: Lecturer, Native American Studies (NAS) Dept., University of New Mexico, Mesa Vista 3080, Albuquerque, NM 87131 (505) 277-3917. *Other professional posts*: Managing editor, "Dawn of Nations Today," an online news publication produced by students n the Native American Studies program; she also hosts a YouTube channel documenting the voices & images of the NAS program. *Past professional posts*: "Indian Voices," KGNU 88.5 FM - Public Radio, Boulder, CO. Mary covered stories on Native America for various magazines, tribal newspapers & public radio outlets since 1994. She has collaborated with NPR's Next Generation Radio, the Radio & Television News Directors Association, The Navajo Times, & other organizations on media projects & panels. *Awards, honors*: 2006 Recipient of the RTNDF Educator in the Newsroom Fellowship; 2009 Fellow with the Journalism Center on Children & Families Ladder of Success; Covering Early Childhood Learning; 2010 APME News Train/McCormick Foundation Awardee; 2011-12 nominee for the UNM Outstanding Online Teacher of the Year Award; 2012 McCormick Foundation Reporting Institute participant. *Membership*: NM Academic Advising Assn.

BOWECHOP, JANINE (Makah)
(tribal enterprise manager)
Affiliation: Director, Makah Cultural & Research Center, P.O. Box 160, Neah Bay, WA 98357 (360) 645-2711 or 645-2712. E-mail: mcrc@aolypen.com. *Membership*: Americans for Indian Opportunity. *Interest*: Cultural retention.

BOWEN, DUWAYNE LESLIE (*Dah-dah-wen-yae*) (Seneca) 1946-
(museum management)
Born July 7, 1946, Salamanca, N.Y. *Education*: Vale Technical Institute (Blairsville, PA), diploma, 1966; Jamestown (NY) Community College. *Address*: RD Box 71J, Salamanca, NY 14779 (716) 945-2260. *Affiliation*: Seneca-Iroquois National Museum, Salamanca, NY, 1990-. *Community activities*: American Red Cross, Salamanca, NY; Red House Indian Chapel, Jimersontown-Salamanca, NY (trustee); Red House Memorial Church, Jimersontown-Salamanca, NY (secretary-treasurer). *Membership*: Cornplanter Descendants Assn, Allegany Indian Reservation-Salamanca, NY (chairperson, 1990-), *Interests*: Local church; museum/history of Seneca people; public speaker on subjects of Iroquois history; professional storyteller of ghost stories/supernatural; movies/stage/literary. *Published works*: Anthology, New Voices From the Longhouse (Greenfield Review Press, 1990); contributor, A Quaker Promise Kept (Spencer Butte Press, 1990); One More Story (Bowman Books, 1991); short story, "He-Sees-Good" (Akew:kon-Northeast Indian Quarterly, 1991).

BOWERS, ANDREW J., JR. (Cow Creek Seminole)
(tribal representative)
Affiliation & Address: Brighton Reservation Representative, c/o Seminole Agency, 6300 Stirling Rd., Hollywood, FL 33024 (800) 683-7800.

BOWERS, CLINT (Cherokee)
(policy & research associate)
Affiliation & Address: Executive Director, National Indian Education Association (NIEA), 1514 P St., NW, Suite 8, Washington, DC 20005 (202) 544-7290. E-mail: cbowers@niea.org. Clint provides support for the association's Research & Capacity-Building activities. He served his tribe as Legislative Officer for its Washington, DC office, focusing on education, tribal self-governance, & federal funding.

BOWERS, RICHARD J., JR. (Cow Creek Seminole)
(tribal president; council president)
Born & raised on the Brighton Seminole Indian Reservation *Affiliation & Address*: Brighton Representative (2007-present), Tribal Council, Seminole Tribe of Florida, 6300 Stirling Rd., Hollywood, FL 33024 (800) 683-7800. *Other professional posts*: President, Intertribal Agriculture Council, Billings, MT; board member, American Indian Business network, Washington, DC.

BOWES, JOHN P. 1973-
(assistant professor of history)
Born January 15, 1973, Summit, N.J. *Education*: Yale University, BA, 1995; UCLA, MA, 1999, PhD, 2003. *Affiliation & Address*: Assistant professor, Eastern Kentucky University, Department of History, 521 Lancaster Ave., Keith 323, Richmond, KY 40475 (859) 622-1287. E-mail: john.bowes@eku.edu. Dr. Bowes received a National Endowment for the Humanities Summer Stipend award to conduct research & write chapters for book, "Northern Indian Removal: An Unfamiliar History." *Past professional post*: Visiting Professor

(2004-06) Dartmouth College, Native American Studies Program; *Other professional post*: Mellow Postdoctoral Fellow in Native American Studies, Dartmouth College. *Awards, honors*: UCLA Norris Hundley Dissertation Prize, 2004. *Memberships*: American Society for Ethnohistory; Western History Association. *Interests*: 19th Century American Indian history; Indian removal in the Great Lakes; history of the American West. *Published works*: Exiles & Pioneers: Eastern Indians in the Trans-Mississippi West (Cambridge University Press, 2007); Black Hawk & the War of 1832: Removal in the North (Chelsea House, 2007); Trail of Tears: Removal to the South (Chelsea House, 2010); The Choctaw (Chelsea House, 2010); Northern Indian Removal: An Unfamiliar History (Chelsea House, 2012).

BOWMAN, JEFF (Stockbridge Munsee Mohegan)
(bank president)
Affiliation: President, Mitchell Bank, 1039 W. Mitchell St., Milwaukee, WI 53204 (414) 645-0600. *Other professional post*: Board member & past president, American Indian Chamber of Commerce of Wisconsin, West Allis, WI.

BOWMAN, NICOLE R. (Mohican/Munsee)
(company owner)
Education: University of Wisconsin, BA, MEd, PhD (Education Leadership & Policy Analysis). *Affiliation*: President/Owner, Bowman Performance Consulting (BPC), LLC, 271 River Pine Dr., Shawano, WI 54166 (715) 526-9240. E-mail: nbowman@nbowmanconsulting.com. BPC is the only certified Native American & scientific research firm in the country. Provides business & educational consulting services working within tribal communities as well as bridging tribal & non-tribal groups on policy, research, strategic planning, and evaluation topics. *Awards, honors*: U.S. Small Business Administration's Young Entrepreneur of the Year Award, the first time a Native American or WI resident has ever been given this honor; appointed by WI governor Doyle and/or selected by her academic colleagues to serve on numerous boards, national academic journals, & advisory committees for her expertise on Indian education, economic development, evaluation, & community development.

BOWMAN, SHERRIE (Laguna Pueblo)
(administrative coordinator)
Affiliation & Address: Administrative Coordinator (2011-present), American Indian & Alaska Native Tourism Association (AIANTA), 2401 12th St., NW, Albuquerque, NM 87104 (505) 724-3592. *Past professional posts*: Sales Associate, Facilities Coordinator & Special Events Coordinator, Indian Pueblo Cultural Center, 1985-1998; Administrative Assistant, New Mexico Indian Tourism Association, 1998-2000; Administrative Coordinator, Pueblo of Sandia, 2000-2006; Marketing coordinator, Pueblo of Laguna's Dancing Eagle Casino, 2006-2011.

BOXER, MAJEL (Sisseton-Wahpeton Dakota)
(chair & professor of Native American studies)
Education: Washington State University, BA, 2002; University of California, Berkeley, MA, 2004, PhD, 2008. *Affiliation & Address*: Chairperson & Associate Professor, Dept. of Native American & Indigenous Studies, Fort Lewis College, 1000 Rim Dr., Durango, CO 81301 (970) 247-6102. E-mail: boxer_m@fortlewis.edu. *Expertise*: 19th and 20th century Native American history; Indigenous Women's history; Native American oral and written traditions; Native American religions and spirituality; History of tribal museums and indigenous cultural centers; Fort Lewis Indian school; Fort Lewis College Tuition Waiver; Racial discourse and public spaces

BOXLEY, DAVID (Tsimshian)
(Tsimshian carver, performer)
Born & raised in Metlakatla, Alaska in 1952. *Education*: Seattle Pacific University, BS, 1974. *Address*: 34589 Hansville Hwy., Kingston, WA 98346 (360) 638-1748. E-mail: davidboxley@msn.com. David primarily produces his artwork on a commission basis from organizations, individuals, companies and governmental bodies. After college, while teaching in Metlakatla, David began devoting time to the study of traditional Tsimshian carving. Through researching ethnographic material & carvings from museum collections, Boxley has learned the traditional carving methods of his grandfather's people. In 1986, he devoted all of his energies toward carving & researching the legacy of Northwest Coast Indian art. *Commissions*: 1990 Goodwill Games to carve the crown of a "Talking Stick." His carving of a unified American eagle and a Russian bear became a symbol of peace & harmony between the U.S. & Soviet Union. He has taught & demonstrated at numerous museums & institutes. David has been deeply involved in the rebirth of Tsimshian culture through organizing & hosting Potlatches in Alaska & Washington. In 1996, he was responsible for the first Seattle Northwest Coast Potlatch in one hundred years. He has been directly involved in the formation of four successful dance groups: one in his home village of Metlakatla, Alaska, and others in Seattle, Washington. He led the Tsimshian Haayuuk for six years, and now has a new group called the Git-Hoan (people of Salmon). David has written over 40 songs in his Native language, & carved masks, rattles, paddles & other performance items. Numerous exhibitions & completed carved totem poles from 1988-2005.

BOYCE, KATHERINE R.
(attorney)
Education: Wheaton College, BA, 1971; Cathlic University of American Law School, JD, 1979. *Affiliation & Address*: Patton Boggs, LLP, 2550 M St., NW, Washington, DC 20037 (202) 457-6094. Ms. Boyce founded the firm's Native American Law practice and continues to represent Indian tribal governments, Alaskan Native Cororations (ANCs) & tribal-owned and other Native nonprofit organizations, as well as tribal & Indian-owned businesses on federal appropriations and other legislativion affecting tribes and ANCs in the areas of business, economic & community development, procurement policy and health care delivery.

BOYD, COLLEEN 1959-
(assistant professor of anthropology)
Born February 6, 1959, Seattle, Wash. *Education*: Western Washington University, BA, 1988; University of Washington, MA, 1993, PhD (Anthropology), 2001. *Principal occupation*: Ethno-historian & environmental anthropologist. *Address & Affiliation*: Assistant professor of anthropology, director of American Indian Studies Minor Program (2004-present), Ball State University, Dept. of Anthropology, BB 306, Muncie, IN 47306 (765) 285-3568. E-mail: ceboyd@bsu.edu. Married into The Lower Klallam Tribe. *Past professional posts*: Lecturer, American Indian Studies Program & Anthropology, University of Washington, Seattle, WA, 1999-2002; Andrew W. Mellon Postdoctoral Fellowship, Wesleyan University, Middletown, CT, 2002-2004. *Applied Research Positions*: Native American Working Group of the Hanford Environmental Dose Reconstruction Project, U.S. Dept. of Energy, 1990-93; contract researcher for the Stillaguamish Tribe of Indians, Arlington, WA, 2001-2002. *Student Research Projects*: supervised Wesleyan University student service learning project with the Lower Elwha Klallam Tribe, Port Angeles, WA, 2003-2004. *Memberships*: American Anthropological Associa-tion; American Studies Association; American Society for Ethno-history. *Publications*: Edited with Daniel L. Boxberger, Native North Americans: An Ethno-historical Approach (Kendall/Hunt Publishing, 1990); A Working Bibliography on Native Food Consumption, Demography & Lifestyle, edited with Wendy Lee, (Battelle Human Affairs Research Center for the CDC, 1992); First Things First: Strategies for Development of basic Tribal Emergency Response Capability, edited with Edward Liebow, M. Luke Jones & Jill Peters, a report prepared by Battelle Human Affairs Research Center for the U.S. Dept. of Energy, 1993); "That Government Man Tried to Poison All the Clallam Indians": Metanarratives of History & Colonialism on the Central Northwest Coast," in Ethno-history; "Oral Traditions of the Pacific Northwest," In American Indian Religious Traditions: An Encyclopedia (ABC-CLIO, 2005).

BOYD, JAMES (Colville)
(forrmer tribal chairperson & district rep)
Affiliation & Address: Former Chairperson & Inchelium District Representative, Confederated Tribes of the Colville Reservation, P.O. ox 150, Nespelem, WA 99155 (509) 634-2212. E-mail: jim.boyd@colvilletribes.com.

BOYD, LOUIS WAYNE (Rosebud Sioux)
(association VP)
Address & Affiliation: Vice President, Native American Heritage Association, P.O. Box 512, Rapid City, SD 57709 (605) 341-9110. E-mail: wboyd@naha-inc.org

BOYD WILLARD, VANESSA (Cherokee)
(attorney)
Address: 999 18th St., Suite 945, Denver, CO 80202 (303) 312-7312. E-mail: vanessa.boydwillard@usdoj.gov. *Membership*: National Native American Bar Association.

BOYER, LEE R. 1938-
(Professor/author, U.S. Indian history)
Born June 1, 1938, Aliquippa, PA. *Education*: Mount Union College, BA, 1959; University of Notre Dame, MA, 1969, PhD, 1972; University of New Mexico, Indian law student, 1978-79; Plains Indian Museum, Indian studies seminar, 1981. *Address*: 2691 Matteson Lake, Bronson, MI 49028 (313) 487-0053. *Affiliation*: Professor of history, Eastern Michigan University, Ypsilanti, MI, 1972-. *Other professional posts*: Assistant professional specialist, University of Notre Dame, (3 years). *Memberships*: American Association of University Professors; National Council for the Social Studies; Michigan Council for the Humanities. *Awards, honors*: Research grant, Merit award, Eastern Michigan University; experienced Teacher Fellowship, Department of H.E.W. *Interests*: Travel and research to Western states; Federal Indian Reservations - sabbatical study; Neah Bay archaeological dig. *Published works*: Episodes in American History (Ginn, 1972); U.S. Indians: A Brief History (Advocate, 1982).

BOYIDDLE, PARKER (Kiowa/Western Delaware)
(artist/owner)
Affiliation & Address: Owner, Parker Boyiddle Editions, 334 Phantom Rd., Westciff, CO 81252 (719) 783-2590. E-mail: parkerboyiddle@aol.cm. Website:

www.parkerboyiddle.com. *Products*: Steel & stone sculpture, bronze, paintings, drawings, watercolor.

BOYUM, BILL (Eastern Cherokee)
(tribal supreme court justice)
Affiliation & Address: Chief Justice, Tribal Court of the Eastern Band of Cherokee Indians, Qualla Boundary, P.O. Box 455, Cherokee, NC 28719 (828) 497-1064.

BOZSUM, BRUCE (*Two Dogs*) (Mohegan)
(former tribal chairperson)
Affiliation & Address: Chairperson (2010-13), Mohegan Tribe, 5 Crow Hill Rd., Uncasville, CT 06382 (860) 862-6100. *Other tribal posts*: Appointed ceremonial Pipe Carrier. *Past tribal posts*: Mohegan Tribal Council, 2004-09; manager, Cultural & Community Programs, responsible for educational outreach programs, the annual Wigwam Festival and Cultural Week.

BRADFORD, SAM (Cherokee) 1987-
(NFL football player)
Born November 8, 1987. Resides in Oklahoma City, OK. *Education*: University of Oklahoma. *Affiliation*: Quarterback, St. Louis Rams (2010-present), St. Louis, MO. Website: www.sambradford.org.

BRADLEY, CARMEN (Paiute)
(tribal chairperson; organization chairperson)
Affiliation: Kaibab Paiute Tribal Council, HC65, Box 2, Fredonia, AZ 86022 (928) 643-7245. *Other professional post*: Chairperson, Council of Energy Resource Tribes (CERT), 695 S. Colorado Blvd., Suite 10, Denver, CO 80202 (303) 282-7576. E-mail: cert1975@aol.com. Website: www.certredearth.com.

BRADLEY, OMAR C. (Cherokee of OK) 1952-
(BIA regional director)
Education: University of New Mexico, BA (University Studies), 1974; MA (Business Administration), 1975. *Address & Affiliation*: Regional Director, 2007-present, Navajo Regional Office, Bureau of Indian Affairs, P.O. Box 1060, Gallup, NM 87305 (505) 863-8314. *Past professional posts*: Business economic development specialist, All Indian Development Association, 1975-78; realty officer, BIA, Southern Pueblos Agency, 1978-1990; natural resources program administrator, 1990-98 & periodically as acting agency superintendents for various agencies. From 1998-2000, he was the regional water rights protection manager in the Bureau's Albuquerque Area Office (now known as the Southwest Regional Office). In 2000, he was named deputy regional director for the Navajo Regional Office. Following a reorganization of the BIA, his title changed in 2004 to deputy regional director for trust services. His responsibilities included the day-to-day administration and management of the BIA's trust programs servicing the Navajo Nation, 2004-06.

BRADY, DARRYL (Shoshone)
(tribal chairperson)
Affiliation & Address: Chairperson, Yomba Shoshone Tribe, HC61, Box 6275, Austin, NV 89310 (775) 964-2463.

BRAFFORD, C.J. (Kimimi La) (Lakota Oglala Sioux) 1959-
(museum director)
Born October 11, 1959, Pine Ridge Indian Reservation, S.D. *Education*: AFA, BS, Master's Certificate Museum Studies/Anthropology. *Principal occupation*: Museum director. *Address*: 1670 Solar Ct., Montrose, CO 81401. *Affiliation & Address*: Director, Ute Indian Museum (1997-present), 17253 Chipeta Rd., Montrose, CO 81401 (970) 249-3098. E-mail: cj.brafford@state.co.us. *Past affiliation*: Museum curator, Grand Teton National Park Service, 1988-97. *Awards, honors*: Ms. Congeniality - Miss Indian American Pageant, 1986. *Community activities*: Board member of the Visitor Convention Bureau. *Memberships*: American Association of State & Local History (board member); American Indian Museum Association. Published work: "Dancing Colors," Native American Woman Paths.

BRAINARD, BRENDA (Lower Umpqua & Suislaw)
(attorney; storyteller & basketweaver)
Affiliation & Address: Director, NATIVES Indian Education Program, Falmouth Institute, 3702 Pender Dr. #300, Fairfax, VA 22030 (703) 352-2250. For the past 15 years, Brenda has focused on the rights of Indian children in social services & education. *Past professional posts*: For 30 years, she worked in Indian Country as tribal administrator, tribal attorney, and in tribal government services and gaming for the BIA. She has served on many boards, committees & commissions, including the State of Oregon's Commission on Indian Services and various tribal committees. *Interests*: Constitutional development in Indian Country and the implementation of policies, ordinances & procedures for tribes; storytelling & basketweaving.

BRAINARD, RON (Lower Umpqua & Suislaw)
   (tribal council member)
Affiliation & Address: Council member, Confederated Tribes of Coos, Lower Umpqua & Suislaw Indians, 1245 Fulton Ave., Coos Bay, OR 97420 (541) 888-9577. Website: www.ctclusi.org.

BRAINARD, WARREN (Lower Umpqua & Suislaw)
   (tribal chief)
Affiliation & Address: Chief, Confederated Tribes of Coos, Lower Umpqua & Suislaw Indians, 1245 Fulton Ave., Coos Bay, OR 97420 (541) 297-1655. E-mail: wbrainard@ctclusi.org

BRAINE, SUSAN (Assiniboine/Hunkpapa Sioux)
   (National Native News COO)
Grew up on the Northern Cheyenne Reservation in southeastern Montana. Enrolled in the Fort Peck Assiniboine Sioux Tribe. *Affiliation & Address*: Chief Operating Officer-National, National Native News/Native America Calling (Koahnic Broadcasting Corp.), P.O. Box 40164, Albuquerque, NM 87196; or, UNM, Onate Hall, 2nd Fl., Albuquerque, NM 87131; (505) 277-5354. E-mail: sbraine@nativeamericacalling.com. *Past professional posts*: Manager, Zuni Pueblo radio KSHI-FM in Zuni NM; manager, KMXT-FM, Kodiak, AK; manager, KSKO-AM, McGrath, AK. Ms. Braine was instrumental in the on-air debut & initial management of the Three Affiliated Tribes' KMHA-FM in Newtown, ND, also KNBA-FM in Anchorage, AK, and most recently Hopi radio KUYI-FM in northern AZ. Susan has also worked with the Blackfeet, Northern Cheyenne & the Laguna-Acoma Indian communities to help plan local stations for their reservations. She has been a major player in the development of Native radio. She served as the first network manager for AIROS (American Indian Radio on Satellite) and on the boards of the Alaska Public Radio Network, Native American Public Telecommunications, Inc., & the Native American Journalists Association.

BRAITHWAITE, TINA (Paiute)
   (tribal chairperson)
Affiliation & Address: Chairperson, Bentonn Paiute – Utu Utu Gwaitu Paiute Tribe, 555 Yellow Jacket Rd. • Benton, CA 93512 (760) 933-2321. E-mail: t.braithwaite@bentonpaiutereservation.org

BRAMLETTE, ALLAN (Cora-Cherokee-Choctaw)
   (archaeologist/heritage resource specialist)
Education: Sonoma State University, BA, 1981, MA, 1989. *Principal occupation*: Archaeologist/heritage resource specialist. *Address*: The Center for Community Development, Graves Annex #30, Humboldt State University, Arcata, CA 95521 (707) 826-3711. *Affiliations*: Senior staff archaeologist, Anthropological Studies Center, Sonoma State University (two years); currently - archaeologist/heritage resource specialist, The Center for Community Development, Humboldt State Univ. Mr. Bramlette provides archaeological consultancy & cultural resource management assistance to Northern California Indian communities. He provides technical training in development & management of cultural exhibits, interpretive programs & museum collections & facilities. He also serves as liaison between local Indian communities & the professional archaeologists and other heritage resource personnel who work in Northern California. *Other professional post*: Teaches four courses per year in archaeology-related topics in Native American Studies Department of Humboldt State University. *Membership*: Society for California Archaeology.

BRANDT, EDWARD N., II (Chickasaw)
   (attorney)
Address: 820 Spyglass Cir., Louisville, CO 80027. *Membership*: Native American Bar Association (First Amendment Bar Association of Texas Representative).

BRANDT, DR. ELIZABETH A. 1945-
   (anthropological linguist)
Born October 20, 1945, Sanford, Fla. *Education*: Florida State University, BA, 1967; Southern Methodist University, MA, 1969, PhD, 1970. *Address*: 1810 S. Roberts Rd., Tempe, AZ 85281 (602) 965-6213. E-mail: betsy.brandt@asu.edu. *Affiliations*: University of Illinois, Chicago, 1970-74; Anthropological Linguist, Dept. of Anthropology, Arizona State University, Tempe, 1974-present. *Community activities*: AZ Humanities Council (board member); American Indian Institute, ASU (director); ASU American Indian Summer Seminars in the Humanities *Memberships*: Linguistics Society of America, Society for Applied Anthropology, Keepers of the Treasures, 1991; Society for the Study of Indigenous Languages of the Americas; Native American Language Issues Institute. *Interests*: "Assist tribes & traditional elders in researching & preparing nominations to National Register for Traditional Cultural Properties, sacred sites protection, land claims, language presentation and renewal." *Published works*: Speaking, Singing & Teaching, Arizona State University Press, 1979); Bilingualism & Language Contact (Teachers College Press, 1980); Navajo Students At Risk (Navajo Nation, 1986).

BRANHAM, DEAN (Monacan)
   (tribal chief)
Affiliation & Address: Chief, Monacan Indian Nation, P.O. Box 1136, Madison Heights, VA 24572 (804) 946-0389.

BRANT, CHERIE L. (Mohawk)
   (attorney; partner, Indian law section)
Education: University of Waterloo, BA (Environmental Studies, Urban & Regional Planning Program), 1998; University of Toronto School of Law, JD, 2003. *Affiliation & Address*: Member, Partner, Dickinson Wright, Indian Law Section, 199 Bay St. #2200, Commerce Court West, Toronto, ON M5L 1G4 (416) 746-3845. E-mail: cbrant@dickinsonwright.com Cherie has a commercial real estate, renewable energy and Aboriginal law practice. Cherie provides strategic counsel to several First Nations & industry clients seeking to develop projects with First Nations and to understand and address Aboriginal rights and interests. Cherie has been named one of Lexpert magazine's *Rising Stars, Leading Lawyers Under 40*. As a member of Mohawks of the Bay of Quinte and with family from Wikwemikong First Nation on Manitoulin Island, Cherie brings a profound understanding of the opportunities and challenges that both Indigenous people & Industry proponents face in carrying out resource, infrastructure & economic development in Canada. Cherie completed the first 100% First Nation owned windpower project in Ontario and is active in providing both on-going advocacy for renewable energy development proponents. As lead counsel to the First Nations Energy Alliance (a consortium of twenty First Nations) on the Integrated Power System Plan review before the Ontario Energy Board, her counsel was instrumental in promoting Aboriginal participation models for renewable energy procurement.

BRANT, SARAH
   (program manager)
Affiliation & Address: Program Manager, North American Indian Association, 22720 Plymouth Rd., Detroit, MI 48239 (313) 535-2966. E-mail: sbrant@naiadetroit.org.

BRASHEAR, CHARLES R. (Cherokee) 1930-
   (retired professor of English; writer)
Born December 11, 1930, Martin County, Tex. *Education*: Denver University, PhD, 1962. *Principal occupation*: Retired professor of English, writer. *Address*: 1718 Arroyo Sierra Circle, Santa Rosa, CA 95405-7762 (707) 545-3903. E-mail: brashear@mail.sdsu.edu. Website: www.charlesbrashear.com. *Affiliation*: San Diego State University (retired, 1992). *Military service*: U.S. Army, 1953-55. *Memberships*: Wordcraft Circle of Native American Writers; The Writer's League of Texas; California Writers Club; Western Writers of America. *Interests*: Travel, writing, genealogy. *Published works*: The Other Side of Love, 2 novellas (Alan Swallow, 1963); A Snug Little Purchase, How Richard Henderson Bought Kaintuckee from the Cherokees in 1775 (Associated Creative Writers, 1979); Contemporary Insanities (Press of MacDonald & Reineke, 1990); Killing Cynthia Ann, a novel (Texas Christian University Press, 1999); Comeuppance at Kicking Horse Casino, & Other Stories (UCLA, American Indian Studies, 2000); Little Crutches, collected poems (Books Etc., 2005).

BRATT, BENJAMIN (Quechua)
   (actor, producer)
Affiliation: Narrated & produced, "Ghost Riders," (2003) directed by V. Blackhawk Aamodt (Blackfoot/Lakota/Mexican) which documents the participation of Lakota elders and youth in the Bigfoot Memorial Ride, a 300-mile journey on horseback to honor those massacred at Wounded Knee.

BRAUCHLI, ROBERT C. 1945-
   (attorney)
Born November 11, 1945, Morristown, N.J. *Education*: American University, BA, 1967; Howard University Law School, JD, 1970. *Address*: 5800 N. Campbell Ave., Tucson, AZ 85718. E-mail: aztuc158@aol.com. *Office address*: 6650 N. Oracle Rd., Suite 110, Tucson, AZ 85704 (520) 742-2191. *Affiliations*: General counsel, Cibecue Community School, Cibecue, AZ on Fort Apache Indian Reservation, 1981-present; tribal attorney and/or special counsel, White Mountain Apache Tribe, Whiteriver, AZ, 1980-87, 1990-present; General Counsel, Tohono O'odham Community College, Sells, AZ, 1999-present. *Past professional posts*: Maricopa County Legal Aid Society, Phoenix & Tempe, AZ, 1970-73; Deputy County Attorney, Pima County, AZ, 1973-78; director, Consumer Fraud Division, Assistant Attorney General, 1978-80; tribal attorney and/or special counsel, Pascua Yaqui Tribe of Arizona, Tucson, 1988-96; *Awards, honors*: Reginald Heber Smith Fellow, 1970-72. *Memberships*: State Bar of AZ, Indian Law Section, 1990-. *Awards, honors*: Arizona Bar Foundation, State Bar of AZ. *Interests*: Hobbies include: skiing, fishing, hiking, travel, and reading.

BRAUKER, SHIRLEY M. (*Moon Bear*) (Odawa) 1950-
(potter, sculptor, painter)
Born August 11, 1950, Angola, Ind. *Education*: Mid-Michigan Community College, AA, 1979; Central Michigan University, BFA, 1981, MA, 1983; attended the Institute of American Indian Art, Santa Fe, 1990. *Principal occupation*: Potter, sculptor, painter. *Address*: 1048 Silver Rd., Coldwater, MI 49036 (517) 238-5833 E-mail: moonbear@cbpu.com. Website: www.cbpu. com/moonbear *Affiliations*: Secretary, Central Michigan University, 1982-88; taught pottery at continuing education and aboard the traveling "Art Train", 1983; worked on documentary film, "Woodland Traditions - 3 Native Americans", 1983; lectured at Delta College on Native American Art, 1992; participated in Native American Women Artists of the Great Lakes - The Kellogg Project, 1993; owner, Moon Bear Pottery, Coldwater, Mich. *Other professional post*: Teaching art appreciation course at Tri-State University, Angola, IN; taught workshop on "Pottery & Stories" at University of Alaska, Sitka campus, 2004; lectured at Fremont & Angola Libraries, on the "Sitka Influence." *Memberships*: National Collegiate Education of Ceramics; National Honor Society; Phi Kappa Phi; Sisters of the Great Lakes (Indian women artists). *Art Exhibitions*: Bachelor of Fine Arts, Central Michigan University, 1981; Great Lakes Traveling Indian Art Exhibition, Dept. of the Interior, Washington, DC, 1983; Ethnic Art Show, Lansing Art Gallery, 1983; Sacred Circle Gallery, Seattle, WA, American Indian Ceramic Art; Yesterday, Today & Tomorrow Exhibit, 1984; Midland Christmas Arts Festival, 1984; Museum of the Plains Indian, Browning, MT, Contemporary Clay Indian Art exhibit, 1985; Larson Gallery, Grand Rapids, MI; the Hummingbird Gallery at Soaring Eagle Casino, Mt. Pleasant, Mich., the Kalamazoo Valley Art Museum Project "Sky Legends of the 3 Fires" - art donations to Diabetes Association, Santa Fe, 1995-98; Synchronicity Gallery, 2001 Glenn Arbor, MI 1999-01; Indigenous Art Market, 2000, 2001 (Mt. Pleasant, Mich.); Elderhostel Workshop 2001; exhibit: University of Michigan Hospital visitor's gallery, Ann Arbor. *Memberships*: Southwest American Indian Arts; Michigan University Alumni Association. *Awards, honors*: Phi Kappa Phi, Central Michigan University (top 100 students to attend CMU over past 100 years); Mae Beck Indian Artist Scholarship Award, 1982; Potter of the Month, Lansing Art Gallery, 1983; numerous awards for pottery, Eiteljorg Indian Market (Indianapolis, IN), 1993-98; 3rd Place-Pottery & Honorable Mention, Dayton, OH Indian Market; 1st Place in Pottery at Red Earth, Oklahoma City, OK, 1996; numerous awards & prizes at Santa Fe, NM Indian Market, 1996-01; received "Top 100 Alumni" to attend C.M.U. in last 100 years. *Interests*: Indian history, culture and art work; craft work, doll making, quilting, painting, beadwork; travel and guitar - writing children's stories; grant recipient from Kellogg Foundation "25 Native American Women Artists of the Great Lakes" - traveling show & workshops - spanning one year...ending up at the Field Museum, Chicago, IL; Smithsonian Institute; presenter at the First Annual Story Festival, Central Michigan University, Mt. Pleasant, MI, "Story in Sculpture'; 2md & 3rd place, Santa Fe, NM Indian Market, 2003. *Biographical sources*: Documentary film: Woodland Traditions: The Art of Three Native Americans; American Indian Index; Southwest Art Magazine, "Emerging Artists," 1996; and "The Traveler's Guide to American Art"; Who's Who of International Professionals. Moon Bear writes, "My biography will be published later this year (2005)."

BRAUN, SEBASTIAN
(professor & American Indian Studies program director)
Education: Universitaet Basel, Switzerland, Lic. Phil I (Ethnology, History & Philosophy); Indiana University, MA (Anthropology & Folklore), PhD (Anthropology). *Affiliation & Address*: Director, American Indian Studies Program, iowa State University, 324 Curtiss, College of Liberal Arts & Science, Ames, IA 50011 (515) 294-9730; E-mail: sfbraun@iastate.edu. Past professional post: Assoc. Professor/Chair, American Indian Studies, University of North Dakota, Grand Forks, ND. His interests concerned with perspectives & constructions of the environment; the cultural meanings & relationships that people assign to their social, natural, & spiritual environments. *Published works*: Buffalo Inc. American Indians & Economic Development (University of Oklahoma Press, 2008; paper, 2013); he has been writing the chapters on the U.S. for "The Indigenous World" the yearbook of the International Work Group on Indigenous Affairs (IWGIA), since 2004; Editor, Transforming Ethnohistories. Narrative, Meaning, and Community (University of Oklahoma Press, 2013; texts on Native peoples in francophone comics and on the rhetoric of indigenous nationalism.

BRAVE EAGLE, DOROTHY (*Mani wakan win*) (Oglala Lakota) 1940-
(former BIA administrator)
Born April 18, 1940, Red Water Creek, S.D. Education: Western Colorado University, BS, 1972, MA, 1974. *Address*: 7892 W. 1st Pl., Lakewood, CO 80226 (303) 238-3420. *Affiliations*: Supt., Bureau of Indian Affairs, Crow Creek Agency, Fort Thompson, SD, 1986-91; administrative officer, Bureau of Indian Affairs, Golden, CO., 1991-95; *Other professional posts*: Owner, B.E.A.R. Publishing Co.; Director, Denver Indian Center. Community activities: Lakota Arts creator, instructor and presenter; Instructor, White Buffalo Council, officer - March Powwow committee. *Memberships*: American Indian Traders Guild; Roaming Buffalo Indian Arts; President of the Board, Wiconi Waste "Beautiful

Life" (non-profit educational corporation for American Indian culture, history). *Awards, honors*: Selected to display traditional Lakota arts at Santa Fe Indian Market. Interests: Traveled to France, Germany, Belgium, and England to display Lakota Arts; mother of twin daughters, three grandchildren and one great grandson. *Published work*: Ehanamani (walks among) (B.E.A.R., 1992).

BRAVE HEART, BASIL (Oglala Sioux) 1933-
(Lakota elder, teacher, author)
Born October 5, 1933, Pine Ridge, S.D. *Education*: Chadron State College, BS, 1957; University of Minnesota, MA, 1976; St. Mary's Graduate Center, Minneapolis, MA (Psychology & Counseling), 1986. Principal occupation: School administrator. *Address*: Box 83, White Clay, NE 69365 (605) 867-5121 (office). *Past professional posts*: Member, Board of Directors, South Dakota Educational TV, Pierre, S.D. (1 year); National Alcohol & Drug Program, Washington, D.C. (3 years); Agency Supt. for Education, BIA, Pine Ridge, SD, 1988-. *Military service*: U.S. Paratroopers - 187 Regimental Combat Team (11th Airborne Div. Korea, 1951-54; Combat Infantry Badge, Airborne Wings, 3 Combat Citations). *Community activities*: Pine Ridge, SD YMCA Board. *Awards, honors*: Superior Performance Award, by HUD for efforts during the 1972 flood, Rapid City, SD. *Interests*: Travel, Far East & Korea; Korean conflict, 1951-54. Biographical sources: Circle of Life; Teacher Handbook on Cultural Orientation, Minneapolis School System.

BRAVE-HEART, JEREMY (Klamath)
(tribal chief judge)
Affiliation & Address: Chief Judge, Klamath Tribes of Oregon, P.O. Box 436, Chiloquin, OR 97624 (541) 783-2219.

BRAY, ETHEL E. (Seneca)
(library director)
Affiliation: The Seneca Nation Library, 1490 Rte. 438, Irving, NY 14081 (716) 532-9449.

BRAY, KAYLENA (Haudenosaunee/Seneca)
(health program coordinator)
Education: Brown University, BA (Commerce, Organization & Entrepreneurship). *Affiliation & Address*: Program Coordinator, California Indian Environmental Alliance, P.O. Box 2128, Berkeley, CA 94702 (510) 848-2043. E-mail: kaylena@cieaweb.org. Kaylena has six years of experience working as a workshop facilitator and organizer. Her experience includes coordination of workshops & conferences at the United Nations, the Convention on Biological Diversity, COICA, and Rio +20 with global Indigenous leaders and activists aimed at environmental justice, Native health, & building Indigenous resilience to climate change. She has also worked on building food sovereignty, with an emphasis on health and nutrition as part of her work with the Seneca Nation Health Department and The Cultural Conservancy. As part of her work toward environmental justice, she has led community discussions with environmental justice leaders, Indigenous leaders, and activists on environmental health at the Smithsonian National Museum of the American Indian in coordination with the Conversations with the Earth (CWE) multi-media exhibit.

BRAYBOY, BRYAN McKINLEY JONES (Lumbee)
(professor & Indian center co-director)
Affiliation & Address: Borderlands Professor of Indigenous Education and Justice in the School of Social Transformation, Co-Director of the Center for Indian Education and co-editor of the Journal of American Indian Education. Arizona State University, West Hall, 25, Mail Code: 6403, P.O. Box 874902, Tempe, AZ 85287 (480) 965-5327. Email: bryan.brayboy@asu.edu. He also has affiliations with the Mary Lou Fulton Teachers College, American Indian Studies, and the Department of English. In the last 15 years, he and his team have created programs in Alaska, Arizona & Utah that have prepared over 125 Indigenous teachers, most of whom are still teaching in Indian Country. His research focuses on the experiences of Indigenous students, staff, & faculty in institutions of higher education, Indigenous Knowledge Systems, & Indigenous Research Methodologies. *Past professional post*: Visiting President's Professor of Indigenous Education at University of Alaska, Fairbanks, 2007-12.

BRAYBOY, CONNIE (Lumbee)
(editor)
Born in Robeson County, N.C. *Address*: P.O. Box 1075, Pembroke, NC 28372 (910) 521-2826. E-mail: conneebrayboy@hotmail.com. *Affiliation*: Editor, Carolina Indian Voice (weekly Indian newspaper), Pembroke, NC, 1973-. *Publication*: Pembroke, The Twentieth Century.

BREAD, JERRY C. (Kiowa)
(Native American Studies outreach coordinator)
Education: Northeastern State University, BS (Education); MS (Educational Administration), PhD (Educational Administration). *Affiliation & Address*: Outreach Coordinator, Native American Studies Program, College of Arts & Sciences, Ellison Hall 210, University of Oklahoma (OU), Norman, OK 73019

(405) 325-5463. E-mail: jcbread@ou.edu. Jerry is a founding member of the current OU Native American Studies program. *Other professional post*: Advisor to the Kiowa Tribal Cultural Authority, Oklahoma's tribal colleges and many local, state, national & tribal trusts related to the education & welfare of American Indian citizens. *Research & Teaching Interests*: Focus on American Indian participation in education, tribal governance & policy development, history leadership, cultural influence on learning & teaching, language and contemporary American Indian affairs. *Personal Interests*: Tribal languages, tribal business development, ceremony, religion, athletics & psychology of American Indians. *Past professional posts*: Elected representative to the Southwest Indian Polytechnic Institute Board of Regents, Joint Tribes of Oklahoma; assistant director of the Johnson O'Malley Indian Education Program for the Cherokee Nation of Oklahoma; director, OU's American Indian Institute; founder & director, Foundations in Native Educationn Graduate Program, American Indian Teacher Corps & Mentorship Program for Minority Students, OU College of Education.

BRENARD, BARRY (Wiyot-Mattole)
(tribal chairperson)
Affiliation & Address: Chairperson, Bear River Band of the Rohnerville Rancheria, 27 Bear River Rd., Loleta, CA 95551 (707) 733-1900. E-mail: barrybrenard@brb-nsn.gov

BREUNINGER, DANNY, SR. (Mescalero Apache)
(tribal president)
Affiliation & Address: President (2015-present), Mescalero Apache Tribal Council, P.O. Box 227, Mescalero, NM 88340 (505) 671-4494. *Past professional posts*: Supt. Southern Ute Agency, BIA, Ignacio, CO; Supt., Truxton Canon Agency, BIA, Valentine, AZ.

BREWER, BRYAN (Oglala Lakota)
(tribal president)
Affiliation & Address: Oglala Sioux Tribal Executive Committee, Pine Ridge Indian Reservation, P.O. Box 2070, Pine Ridge, SD 57770 (605) 867-5326. *Other professional post*: Founder & director, Lakota Nation Basketball Invitational (held annually in Rapid City, SD in December.)

BRIDGES, SHERRY TREPPA (Pomo)
(tribal chairperson)
Education: University of San Francisco, BS. *Affiliation & Address*: Chairperson, Habematolel Pomo of Upper Lake Rancheria, P.O. Box 516, Upper Lake, CA 95485 (707) 275-0737. *Past tribal positions*: Enrollment Committee, 2001-04; Vice Chairperson of Executive Council, 2004-09. Also served as a member of the Housing Committee, CILS Board of Directors & Tribe's CNIGA delegation.

BRIEN, RUSS (Iowa of Kansas & Nebraska)
(attorney)
Education: University of Kansas, BA (Political Science), 1989; University of Michigan Law School, JD, 1992. *Affiliation & Address*: Owner, Brien Law, LLC, P.O. Box 435, Oskaloosa, KS 66066 (785) 863-3500. E-mail: russ@brienlawllc.com *Other professional post*: Faculty, Falmouth Institute, Fairfax, VA. Russ frequently speaks on Indian law & reservation-based economic development at seminars across the country. *Awards, honors*: Listed in the "Best Lawyers in America for Structured Finance Law."

BRIGGS, KARA (Yakama/Snohomish)
(journalist; media company owner)
Affiliation & Address: Owner, Red Hummingbird Media Corporation, 8825 34th Ave. NE, Suite L-154, Tulalip, WA 98271 (503) 577-0012. *Other professional posts*: Editor, American Indian News Service, Smithsonian's National Museum of the American Indian, Washington, DC. *Past professional post*: Editor, The Oregonian, Portland, OR.

BRIGHTMAN, LEHMAN L.
(director-Indian organization)
Affiliation & Address: Director, United Native Americans, 2434 Faria Ave., Pinole, CA 94564 (415) 758-8160.

BRIGHTMAN, ROBERT 1950-
(anthropologist; professor of Native American studies)
Born April 23, 1950, Chicago, Ill. *Education*: Reed College, Portland, OR, B.A., 1973; University of Chicago, MA, 1976, Ph.D., 1982. *Affiliation & Address*: Greenburg Professor of Native American Studies (1988-present), Dept. of Anthropology, Reed College, Portland, OR 97202 (503) 771-1112. *Past professional posts*: Assistant professor of anthropology, University of Wisconsin-Madison, 1982-88. *Memberships*: American Anthropological Association; Linguistic Society of America; American Society for Ethno-history. *Interests*: North American Indian cultural anthropology & linguistics; Algonquian linguistics; field research: Pokatawagan, Manitoba, 1977-79, 1986

Cree. *Published works*: Orders of the Dreamed (University of Winnipeg, 1988); Acadohkiwina & Acimoina: Traditional Literature of the Rock Cree (Canadian Ethnology Service, 1989); Grateful Prey: Cree Human-Animal Relationships (University of California Press, 1993); numerous book chapters & articles in professional journals.

BRILL, PETER SCOTT
(museum curator of exhibits)
Affiliation & Address: George Gustav Heye Center, National Museum of the American Indian, Smithsonian Institution, 1 Bowling Green, New York, NY 10004 (212) 283-2420.

BRINK, JEANNE A. (Abenaki) 1944-
(Native American educator, consultant, basketmaker)
Born November 12, 1944, Montpelier, Vt. *Education*: Norwich University, MA (with concentration in Native American Studies), 1966. *Principal occupation*: Native American educator, consultant, & ash splint & sweetgrass basketmaker. *Address*: 130 Tremont St., Barre, VT 05641-3126 (802) 479-0594. E-mail: azoniz@aol.com. *Other professional post*: Native American presenter & consultant to various schools & organizations throughout New England & New York, 1987-present. *Past professional posts*: Board of Advisors, Robert Hull Fleming Museum, University of Vermont, Burlington, VT, 1993-2000; Board of Trustees, Vermont Historical Society, Montpelier, VT, 1992-98. *Community activities*: Coordinator for Shelburne Museum Intertribal Powwow; coordinator & member of Western Abenaki Dancers (traditional Western Abenaki social dancers). *Interests*: Her performances are on Western Abenaki history, culture, language, dance, family stories, basketry and oral tradition. *Published work*: Alnobaodwa: A Western Abenaki Language Guide, with Gordon M. Day, 1990.

BRISCOE, KEVIN (Mississippi Choctaw)
(attorney; judge)
Affiliation & Address: Senior Youth Court Judge (ten years), Juvenile Court, Mississippi Band of Choctaw Indians, 101 Industrial Dr., Choctaw, MS 39350. *Other professional post*: Second Vice President, National American Indian Court Judges Association, Boulder, CO; Children's Justice Commission for the State of Mississippi; Forrest County Juvenile & Family Model Court team, Hattiesburg, MS; appointed to the National Council of Juvenile & Family Court Judges Advisory Committee for the Permanency Planning for Children Department.

BROADDUS, MANDY SMOKER (Fort Peck Assiniboine & Sioux)
(educator, poet)
Affiliation & Address: Director, Indian Education Programs & Services Division, 1300 11th Ave., Helena, MT 59620 (406) 444-3013.

BROADMAN, ANTHONY S.
(attorney)
Born & raised in Visalia, Calf. *Education*: Princeton University, BA (English), 2001; University of Arizona College of Law, JD, 2007. *Affiliation & Address*: Partner (2010-present), Galanda Broadman PLLC, 11320 Roosevelt Way NE, Seattle, WA 98125 (206) 691-3631. E-mail: anthony@galandabroadman.com. His Practice focuses on representing tribal governments in taxation, public affairs, & economic development matters, along with tribe and company-critical business litigation. *Other professional post*: Editor-in-Chief of the Washington State Bar Association (WSBA) Indian Law Section's Indian Law Newsletter. *Past professional post*: Associate, Williams Kastner, Seattle, WA, 2007-10; past chair of the WSBA Administrative Law Section. *Membership*: WSBA (former trustee). *Published work*: Administrative Law in Washington Indian Country; paper, "Know Your Enemy: Local Taxation & Tax Agreements in Indian Country," published in Seattle University's, American Indian Law Journal.

BROCKIE, CLARENA (Gros Ventre & Assiniboine)
(Montanan State (D) representative)
Education: University of Arizona, MA (American Indian Studies), 2013. *Affiliation & Address*: Montana State (Democrat) representative, P.O. Box 173, Harlem, MT 59526 (406) 673-3236. E-mail: clarenabrockie@hotmail.com. Committee: State-Tribal Relations.

BRODT, ERIK R., M.D. (Chippewa/Anishinaabe)
(physician-family medicine)
Education: University of Medicine Medical School; Residency in Family Medicine at the Seattle Indian Health Board. *Address*: 1100 Delaplaine Court, Madison, WI 53715 (608) 263-4550. *Affiliations*: Clinical Assistant Professor, Department of Family Medicine, University of Wisconsin School of Medicine & Public Health, Madison, WI. E-mail: erik.brodt@fammed.wisc.edu; Family Medicine, Yahara Clinic, 1050 E. Broadway, Monona, WI 53716 (608) 222-8779. *Hospital Affiliation*: Meriter Hospital. *Other professional post*: Member-at-Large, Association of American Indian Physicians, Oklahoma City, OK.

BROKENLEG, MARTIN (Lakota 'Rosebud Sioux')
(professor of minority studies)
Affiliation & Address: Associate Professor of Minority Studies, Augustana College, Sioux Falls, SD 57197 (605) 336-4007. *Published works*: with Larry Brendtro & Steve Van Bockern, Reclaiming Youth at Risk: Our Hope for the Future (suggests ways in which Native American and European traditions of child-rearing can be merged to help troubled youth); with Herbert T. Hoover, Yanktonai Sioux Water Colors: Cultural Remembrances of John Saul (Center for Western Studies, 1993).

BROKENLEG, PETER (Lakota 'Rosebud Sioux')
(artist)
Address: 195 Winona Ct., Denver, CO 80219. *Art work*: Plains Lakota beadwork, quillwork, carvings, flutes, dance, regalia, moccasins.

BROMLEY, GARY D. (*War Eagle*) (United Lumbee-adopted) 1936-
(retired/author)
Born August 2, 1936, Fort Edward, N.Y. *Education*: Glendale (CA) Community College, 1984. *Principal occupation*: Retired/author. *Address*: P.O. Box 1629, Fontana, CA 92334-1629 (909) 381-9375. *Affiliations*: United Lumbee Nation, 1954-present (chief; director, research & development; former reporter, United Lumbee Times). *Other professional post*: Acting liaison officer to courts for United Lumbee Nation. *Past professional post*: U.S. Dept. of Labor, Bureau of Mine Safety, Health Administration, 1980-95. *Military service*: National (NY State) Guard (Honorable Discharge, Oct. 1953). *Community activities*: "I have been involved in mail-only contacts with prison inmates with the intent to help them find and walk only the straight good path...it does at times work." *Membership*: Native American Wolf Clan InterTribal Society (principal chief). *Awards, honors*: The "Silver Eagle Award," from the United Lumbee Nation for outstanding services to the Lumbee Nation and to the Indian community at large. *Interests*: "I am at this time forming sound goodwill efforts with any tribal leaderships or bands and clans that seriously help or will help elderly and youth. *Published works*: "When War Eagle Speaks," & "War Eagle Speaks True Facts of Life," - numerous teachings of ancient red road upgraded and presented in modern American English. Scheduled for print in Spanish & Canadian French in late 2004.

BROOKS, CHESTER (Lenni Lenape)
(tribal chief; trust chairperson)
Affiliation & Address: Chief & Trust Chairperson, Delaware Tribe of Indians, 170 NE Barbara, Bartlesville, OK 74006 (918) 337-6593. E-mail: cbrooks@delawaretribe.org

BROOKS, FORREST (Oneida of Wisconsin)
(lecturer in First Nations Studies)
Education: MA (Curriculum & Instruction), 2003. *Affiliation & Address*: Academic Advisor & Lecturer, Adult Degree Program, First Nations Studies, CL K206, University of Wisconsin-Green Bay, 2420 Nicolet Dr., Green Bay, WI 54311 (920_ 465-2777. E-mail: brooksf@uwgb.edu. *Past professional posts*: Worked with GED students at the Oneida Career Center and as J'OM director; teacher at Oneida High School; worked on Oneida language curriculum.

BROOKS, LISA (Abenaki)
(Native American Indigenous studies program chair)
Education: Goddard College, BA, 1993; Boston College, MA, 1998; Cornell University, PhD, 2004. *Affiliation & Address*: Advisor, Five College Native American & Indigenous Studies, 97 Spring St., Amherst, MA 01004 (413) 542-5594. E-mail: lbrooks@amherst.edu Lecturer, Engish & American Studies, Amherst College, Aherst, MA. Professor Lisa Brooks teaches courses in Native American studies, early American literature and comparative American Studies. She received her Ph.D. in English, with a minor in American Indian Studies, from Cornell University in 2004. Before coming to Amherst, she was John L. Loeb Associate Professor of the Humanities at Harvard University. Her first book, *The Common Pot: The Recovery of Native Space in the Northeast* (University of Minnesota Press 2008) reframes the historical and literary landscape of the American northeast. Illuminating the role of writing as a tool of community reconstruction and land reclamation in indigenous social networks, *The Common Pot* constructs a provocative new picture of Native space before and after colonization. The Media Ecology Association honored the book with its Dorothy Lee Award for Outstanding Scholarship in the Ecology of Culture for 2011. Although deeply rooted in her Abenaki homeland, Professor Brooks's work has been widely influential in a global network of scholars. She co-authored the collaborative volume, *Reasoning Together: The Native Critics Collective* (University of Oklahoma Press 2008), which was recognized by the Native American & Indigenous Studies Association (NAISA) as one of the Ten Most Influential Books in Native American and Indigenous Studies of the First Decade of the Twenty-First Century. She also wrote the "Afterword" for *American Indian Literary Nationalism* (University of New Mexico Press 2006), which won the Beatrice Medicine Award for Scholarship in American Indian Studies. In 2009, Brooks was elected to the inaugural Council of the Native American and Indigenous Studies Association, and she currently

serves on the Editorial Board of *Studies in American Indian Literatures*. In addition to her scholarly work, Brooks serves on the Advisory Board of Gedakina, a non-profit organization focused on indigenous cultural revitalization, educational outreach, and community wellness in New England. She is currently working on a book project, "Turning the Looking Glass on Captivity and King Philip's War," which places early American texts, including Mary Rowlandson's captivity narrative, within the historical & literary geography of Native space. *Awards, honors*: Native American and Indigenous Studies Association Prize: *Reasoning Together*. Voted one of the ten Most Influential Books in Native American & Indigenous Studies of the First Decade of the Twenty-First Century, 2011; Roslyn Abramson Award for Excellence in Undergraduate Teaching, Harvard University, 2008; Native Americans at Harvard College "Role Model of the Year" Award, 2004. *Published works*: The Common Pot: the Recovery of Native Space in the Northeast, University of Minnesota Press,Indigenous Americas Series, 2008; Digging at the Roots: Locating an Ethical, Native Criticism."*Reasoning Together: The NativeCritics Collective,* University of Oklahoma Press, 2008; Afterword: At the Gathering Place," *American Indian Literary Nationalism,* by Robert Warrior, Jace Weaver, and Craig Womack, with a foreword by Simon Ortiz. University of New Mexico Press, 2006.

BROSSY, JACKSON SLIM (Navajo-Dine')
(executive director)
Education: Stanford University, BA (Public Policy & minor in Native American Studies); Harvard University Kennedy School of Government, MA (Public Policy), 2010; University of Pennsylvania Wharton School, MBA (Finance), 2012. *Affiliation & Address*: Executive Director, Navajo Nation Washington Office, 750 First St. NE #1010, Washington, DC 20002 (202) 682-7390; E-mail: jbrossy@nnwo.org. Past professional post: Senior Strategist, Blue Stone Strategy Group, Phoenix, AZ.

BROUGHTON, NANCY J. 1948-
(library/archives director)
Born December 17, 1948 in Dubuque, Iowa. *Education*: University of Wisconsin-Platteville, BS, 1971; University of Nevada-Reno, MS, 1983; University of Wisconsin-Madison, MA, 1988. *Affiliation & Address*: Director, Ruth A. Meyers Library/Ojibwe Archives (1996-present), Fond du Lac Tribal & Community College, Cloquet, MN 55720 (218) 879-0837. E-mail: sam@ezigaa.fdl.cc.mn.us. *Past professional post*: Idaho State University Library, 1991-95. *Community activities*: Council member, Emanuel Lutheran Church, Brookston, MN. *Memberships*: Western History Assn; Wisconsin Library Assn; Wisconsin Assn of Academic Librarians.

BROWER, PEARL KIYAWN NAGEAK (Inupiaq)
(Indian college president)
Affiliation & Address: President, Ilisagvik College, P.O. Box 749, Barrow, AK 99723 (907) 852-3333.

BROWN, BONNIE M.
(coordinator of Native American Studies program)
Affiliation & Address: Lecturer (2001-present) & Coordinator (2005-present), Native American Studies Program, Eberly College of Arts & Sciences, 207 Knapp Hall, West Virginia University, P.O. Box 6284, Morgantown, WV26506 (304) 293-4626. E-mail: bonniem.brown@mail.wvu.edu. *Academic Interests*: Media representatives of Native Americans and other ethnic minority groups. Bonnie teaches introduction to Native American Studies and has developed courses on Contemporary Native American issues, Native Women in Leadership, Sovereign Tribal Nations, and a seminar with Walter Echo-Hawk (Pawnee Nation) called, "Courts of the Conqueror" (based on his recent book, In the Courts of the Conqueror: Ten Worst Indian Law Cases Ever Decided).

BRINEGAR, DARREN (Ho-Chunk)
(tribal vice president)
Affiliation & Address: Ho-Chunk Nation, P.O. Box 667, Black River Falls, WI 54615 (715) 284-3297. E-mail: darren.brinegar@ho-chunk.com

BROWN, DANIEL A. (Yakama)
(attorney)
Born & raised on the Yakama Indian Reservation in Eastern Washington. *Education*: University of Washingtonn, BA (History), 1989; University of Washington School of Law, JD, 1992. *Affiliation & Address*: Partner, Williams Kastner & Gibbs, PLLC, Two Union St. #4100, Seattle, WA 98101 (206) 233-2949. E-mail: dbrown@williamskastner.com. Daniel focuses his practice on litigation & dispute resolution; Indian Law & Gaming. Mr. Brown is a pro tem tribal court judge for numerous tribes, including the Skokomish, the Tulalip, the Quinault, and the Stiilaguamish. Since 2006, he has also served as a court of appeals judge for NICS (the Northwest Intertribal Court System), a consortium of Indian tribes based in the Puget Sound Region. *Awards, honors*: Selecte by his peers for inclusion in The Best Lawyers in America in 2010 & Washington Suer Lawyers for 2010-13. He has & continues to be Martindale-Hubbell "AV" top-rated by his peers in the legal community.

BROWN, DAVID QUENTIN (*Dotsuwah*) (Chickamauga-Cherokee) 1953-
(raven or war chief)
Born October 7, 1953, Chattanooga, Tenn. *Education*: McKenzie (Chattanooga, TN) ABS. *Principal occupation*: War chief of Tennessee River Band Chickamaugas. *Address*: 7703 Georgetown Rd., Ooltewah, TN 37363 (423) 855-2801. *Affiliation*: War Chief, Tennessee River Band of Chickamauga Cherokees. *Community activities*: Currently conducts teachings & new moon get together/dances; involved in protecting Moccasin Bend Burial Ground Historic Site. *Membership*: Tennessee River Band of Chickamauga Cherokees. *Activities*: Has led various classes in Native American awareness for children & adults, for summer camps & church groups. He is active in the fight against grave desecrations & environmental issues. Involved in initial meetings with the Hamilton County Sheriffs Dept. in forming the Native American Reserve Force that is a deputized group of Native Americans who protect the burial sites at Moccasin Bend from further desecration. This is the first time in history that a group of Native Americans, off reservation, has been deputized to oversee our ancestor's graves. *Published works*: Articles in the "The New Phoenix," "Pan American News," & "Katuah Journal."

BROWN, DONNA (Turtle Mountain Chippewa)
(chief diversity officer)
Education: Sitting Bull College, AA, 1989; University of North Dakota, BS (Business & Vocational Education), 1991; MA (Counseling), 1995, EdD (Educational Leadership), 2002. *Affiliation & Address*: Chief Diversity Officer, American Multicultural Studies Department, Moorhead State University, 1104 7th Ave South, 279 MacLean Hall, Moorhead, MN 56560 (218) 477-2196. While at UND, Donna co-directed the Campus Suicide Prevention Program, coordinated the Indians Into Medicine Program (INMED), and was Assistant Director of American Indian Student Services. In 2007, she joined Minnesota State University, Moorhead in Counseling and Student Affairs, & eventually became Associate Vice President for Diversity, Inclusion & Affirmative Action.

BROWN, DOREEN (Yu'pik/Athabascan)
(Indian education supervisor)
Born in Great Falls, Mont. *Education*: Chaminade University (Honolulu, HI), BA; University of Kansas, MA. *Affiliation & Address*: Supervisor, Anchorage School District, Education Center, 5530 E. Northern Lights Blvd., Anchorage, AK 99504 (907) 742-4445. E-mail: brown_doreen@asdk12.org.

BROWN, DYANI (Shinnecock)
(tribal council chairperson)
Affiliation & Address: Chairperson, Shinnecock Indian Nation, P.O. Box 5006, Southampton, NY 11969 (631) 283-6143.

BROWN, EDDIE F. (Pascua Yaqui/Tohono O'odham)
(emeritus executive director & professor)
Education: Brigham Young University, BS, 1970; University of Utah, MSW, 1972 & PhD (Social Work), 1975. *Affiliation & Address*: Emeritus Executive Director, American Indian Policy Institute, Arizona State University (ASU), Discovery Hall Rm. 356, Tempe, AZ 85287 (480) 727-8690. E-mail: efbrown@asu.edu. *Other professional post*: Member, U.S. President's Board of Advisors on Tribal Colleges & Universities; emeritus Professor/Director, American Indian Studies, School of Social Work, Arizona State University (ASU); Chief, Division of Social Services, Bureau of Indian Affairs, Washington, DC, 1984-86; director, Arizona Dept. of Economic Security, 1987-89; former Assistant Secretary of Indian Affairs, U.S. Dept. of the Interior, Washington, DC, 1989-93; executive director, Dept. of Human Services, Tohono O'odham Nation, 1993-96; associate dean & director, Center for American Indian Studies, George Warren Brown School of Social Work, Washington University, St. Louis, MO, 1996-2003. *Published works*: Numerous articles in scholarly journals. Presentations

BROWN, FRANK, M.D. (Cherokee) 1958-
(physician, geriatric neuropsychiatrist)
Born February 14, 1958, Searcy, Ark. *Education*: BS, MD, MBA. *Principal occupation*: Physician, Geriatric Neuropsychiatrist. *Address*: 1899 E. Gate Dr., Stone Mountain, GA 30087 (404) 728-6690. E-mail: sdpfwb@emory.edu. *Affiliations*: Associate Professor, Emory University, Atlanta, GA; Medical Director, Wesley Woods Geriatric Hospital, Atlanta, GA; Medical Director, Emory Clergy Care, Atlanta, GA. *Military service*: U.S. Army Reserves, 1982-89. *Memberships*: American College of Psychiatrists (Fellow); American Psychiatrists Association; American Association of Geriatric Psychiatrists. *Published works*: Journal articles and book chapters.

BROWN, MICHAEL (Metis)
(professor of Native American studies)
Born & raised in the shadows of the Crow & Northern Cheyenne Reservations of Montana. *Education*: University of Notre Dame, MA; Emory University, PhD (Philosophy). *Affiliation & Address*: Professor of Philosophy, Native American Studies Program, Department of Sociology, Anthropology, and Social Work, College of Arts & Sciences, 2500 California Plaza, Room 437, Omaha, NE

68178 (402) 280-3587. E-mail: mbr@creighton.edu. Dr. Brown specializes in metaphysics, epistemology, and their relation to both literature & religion, especially native, non-Christian religion.

BROWN, GINGER E. (Choctaw of Oklahoma) 1952-
(illustrator, fine artist)
Born November 9, 1952, Oklahoma City, Okla. *Education*: Kansas City Art Institute. *Affiliation & Address*: Illustrator, fine artist. 11407 W. 155th Ter., Overland Park, KS 66221 (913) 897-4873. *Other professional post*: Illustrator of endangered species for World Wildlife Fund, 1992-93. *Memberships*: Choctaw Nation of Oklahoma; Indian Arts & Crafts Association; National Colored Pencil Association; Native American Rights Fund. *Awards, honors*: 1990 Scholarship Award from Kansas City Art Institute. *Interests*: "Depicting & combining wildlife with Native American artifacts and their legends & traditions."

BROWN, KENNEDY (Chickasaw)
(board chairperson)
Affiliation & Address: Chairperson, The Chickasaw Foundation, P.O. Box 1726, Ada, OK 74821 (580) 421-9030. *Other professional posts*: Chairperson, Ada American Red Cross Chapter; board member, Mental Health Services for Southern Oklahoma; board member, Chickasaw Historical Society; board member, Inter-Tribal Council of the Five Civilized Tribes of Oklahoma; active with the Ada Masonic Lodge. *Past professional posts*: Special assistant to Anoatubby of the Chickasaw Nation; former lt. governor of Chickasaw Nation.

BROWN, KEVIN P. (*Red Eagle*) (Mohegan)
(tribal chairperson)
Education: U.S. Military Academy, BS (Aerospace Engineering); Norwich University, MA (Public Diplomacy); Naval Postgraduate School in Monterey, CA, MS (Operational Research & Systems Analysis); Kansas State University (Doctoral Candidacy). *Affiliation & Address*: Chairperson (2013-present), Mohegan Indian Tribe, 13 Crow Hill Rd., Uncasville, CT 06382 (860) 862-6100. E-mail: kbrown@moheganmail.com. *Other professional posts*: Kevin serves as Chairman of the Mohegan Gaming & Entertainment (MGE) Management Board which oversees gaming entities across the country, as well as two professional sports teams. Under his leadership, the Mohegan Tribe has made monumental steps forward in its business growth and expanded its footprint worldwide including the future Inspire Integrated Resort in South Korea and a multi-million dollar non-gaming tourist destination in southeastern Connecticut, creating hundreds of jobs and driving economic growth in the region. Brown serves on the Board of Directors for the Chamber of Commerce of Eastern Connecticut and Channel 3 Kids Camp, and is the Chairman of the American Heart Association Southeastern Connecticut Heart Walk and the forthcoming National Native American Veterans Memorial at the Smithsonian's National Museum of the American Indian. *Awards, honors*: Awarded the National Indian Gaming Association's prestigious John Kieffer Sovereignty Award; both the Military Community Support Award and the Board of Directors Special Award from the Chamber of Commerce of Eastern Connecticut and the Annual Outstanding Leadership Award from the Boy Scouts of America. *Military service*: U.S. Army (25 years). Kevin has served as an analyst at the Pentagon in Washington DC following attainment of a Master of Science in Operational Research and Systems Analysis at the Naval Postgraduate School in Monterey, CA.

BROWN, MARK F. (Mohegan)
(tribal ambassador)
Affiliation: Ambassador (2005-present), Mohegan Indian Tribe, 5 Crow Hill Rd., Uncasville, CT 06382 (860) 862-6100. *Past tribal posts*: Tribal chairperson, 2000-2005; tribal council member, 1995-2000. He currently serves on numerous boards both nationally and also in the local area, and currently serves as the chairperson of the Mohegan Tribal Gaming Authority's Audit Committee. Mark is a direct descendant of the renowned Mohegan Chief Matahga and the son of Tribal Nonner Pauline Brown. He was actively involved in the Mohegan Tribe's efforts to achieve federal recognition.

BROWN, RAYMOND (Washoe)
(senior vice president of bank)
Education: Oregon State University, BS (Business Administration); Golden State University, MBA. *Affiliation & Address*: Senior Vice President, City National Bank, San Francisco, CA. Mr. Brown is active in the economic development activities of the Native American community in the San Francisco Bay area. *Other professional posts*: Treasurer, The National Center for American Indian Economic Development, Oakland, CA; board member, Washoe Development Enterprise, Gardnersville, NV; founder/board chairperson, American Indians in Business, Oakland, CA; board member, St. Paul's Da School, Oakland, CA. *Past professional post*: First Interstate Bank, San Francisco (22 years). *Military service*: U.S. Army, 1967-69.

BROWN, ROY B. (Arapaho)
(tribal chairperson)
Affiliation & Address: Chairperson, Northern Arapaho Tribe, P.O. Box 396, Fort Washakie, WY 82514 (307) 332-6120.

BROWN, STEPHANIE (Pomo)
(tribal vice chairperson)
Affiliation & Address: Vice Chairperson, Sulphur Bank of Pomo Indians, P.O. Box 757 • Lower Lake, CA 95457 (707) 994-3400;
E-mail: s.brown@elemindiancolony.org

BROWN, WAYNE (Meherrin)
(principal chief)
Affiliation & Address: Principal Chief, Meherrin Indian Tribe, P.O. Box 274, Ahoskie, NC 27910 (252) 398-3321. E-mail: chiefbrownmeherrin@yahoo.com

BROWN, WILLIAM F. (Eskimo)
(village president)
Affiliation & Address: Native Village of Eek, P.O. Box 87, Eek, AK 99578 (907) 536-5128.

BROWN THUNDER, JOSEPH (Ho-chunk/Lakota Oglala)
(business owner)
Address & Affiliation: President/Founder, American Indian Search (AIS), 813 Harbor Blvd. #223, West Sacramento, CA 95691 (916) 273-9440 Website: www.a-isearch.com. Directory of American Indian Businesses & Groups.

BROWN-PEREZ, KATHLEEN
(co-chair of Native American & Indigenous studies)
Affiliation & Address: Co-Chairperson, Five College Native American & Indigenous Studies, 97 Spring St., Amherst, MA 01004 (413) 542-5594. E-mail: brown-perez@honors.umass.edu. *Specialties:* federal Indian law, criminal jurisdiction in Indian Country, tribal sovereignty, federal acknowledgement of tribes, identity.

BROWNE, DALLAS L. (*Thundering Hoofs*) (Cherokee/Blackfoot) 1944-
(professor of anthropology)
Born October 9, 1944, Chicago, Ill. Education: University of Illinois, Urbana, PhD (Cultural Anthropology), 1983. *Address & Affiliation*: Professor, Department of Anthropology, Box 1451, Southern Illinois University, Edwardsville, IL 62026 (618) 692-6715. E-mail: dbrowne@siue.edu. *Other professional posts*: President, St. Louis Committee on Foreign Relations, St. Louis, MO; Honorary Consul for Tanzania. *Community activities*: Human Relations Commission, City of Edwardsville, IL; YMCA Board of Directors, Edwardsville, IL.; St. Louis Council on Foreign Relations (board member); American Committee on Foreign Relations (board member), *Memberships*: American Anthropological Assn; Society for Urban Anthropology; Assn of Black Anthropologists; World Affairs Council. *Interests*: Writing; Urban culture, ritual & performance, symbolism, family & kinship, political anthropology, theory & history, African culture, Latin American culture. *Published work*: Discourses on Education in Developing Countries (Nova Sciences Press, 2005)

BROWNE, VEE F. (*Elvita*) (Navajo) 1956-
(educator, writer, poet, test administrator, grant writer)
Born September 4, 1956, Ganado, Ariz. *Education*: Cochise Community College, AA, 1977; Northern Arizona University, BS, 1985; Western New Mexico University, MA, 1990. *Address*: Cottonwood/Tselina, AZ. c/o Salina Bookshelf, Inc., 3120 N. Caden Ct. #4, Flagstaff, AZ 86004. *Affiliations*: Northland Publishing, Flagstaff, AZ, 1991-; journalist, The Navajo-Hopi Observer, Flagstaff, AZ 1991-. *Other professional posts*: National Caucus (member, board of directors) 1994-96; Wordcraft Circle of Native Writers (mentor)/Apprenticeship. *Memberships*: Society of Southwestern Authors; Society of Children's Book Writers; North American Native Authors; Arizona Press Association - The Navajo-Hopi Observer (newspaper); Arizona Interscholastic Athletics Association. *Awards, honors*: Western Heritage 1991 - Cowboy Hall of Fame Award - Juvenile Book of the Year; The Buddy Bo Jack Nationwide Award for Humanitarian, 1992 Children's Book Writer; Society of Southwestern Authors, 1993 Published Work Award. *Interests*: Returning of Gift of North America's Native Authors during July each year; enjoy conferences and writer's workshops. I enjoy attending writer's intensive Institute each year. *Published works*: Monster Slayer (1991), Monster Birds (1993), Neon Powwow Anthology (1993) (Northland Publishing); Maria Tallchief (1993) The Owl (1993) Blue Dawn, Red Earth (1996); Sister Nation (Minnesota Historical Society Press, 2002). Bi-weekly newspaper sports articles - "Observer"; Maria Tallchief (Simon & Schuster).

BROWNEAGLE, DAVID (Spokane)
(tribal vice chairperson)
Affiliation & Address: Vice Chairperson, Spokane Business Council, P.O. Box 100, Wellpinit, WA 99040 (509) 258-4581. E-mail: david.browneagle@spokanetribe.com

BROWNELL, GARY F. (Ho-Chunk)
(attorney)
Education: University of Notre Dame, BA, 1977; Cornell University School of Law, JD, 1980. *Affiliation & Address*: Attorney, Sonosky, Chambers, Sachse, Endreson & Perry, LLP, 500 Marquette Ave., NW, Suite 1310, Albuquerque, NM 87102 (505) 247-0147. E-mail: gbrownell@abqsonosky.com. Before joining the firm as a partner in 2001, Mr. Brownell served in the Dept. of Justice of the Ho-Chunk Nation, first as a tribal attorney and then, from 1997-2001 as Attorney General. In that position, he supervised an eight-lawyer legal department handling a wide range of tribal legal issues, and focused his personal practice in the areas of gaming, economic development, financing, taxation, housing, personnel relations, employee benefits, & code development. Tribal Court Admissions: Ho-Chunk Nation, 1996, Puyallup, 2001, Isleta, 2002.

BROWNER, TARA
(professor of ethnomusicology)
Education: California State University, Sacramento, B.A.; University of Colorado, M.M.; University of Michigan, PhD (Musicology). *Affiliation & Address*: Associate Professor, Department of Ethnomusicology, The UCLA Herb Alpert School of Music, UCLA, 2539 Schoenberg Music Bldg., Los Angeles, CA 90095 (310) 206-3033. E-mail: tbrowner@ucla.edu. Tara teaches courses in Native North American music & dance in the American Indian Studies Dept. at UCLA; Native North American contemporary music; musical imagery of Indians in popular culture; and indigenous concepts of music theory. *Community activities*: She is a powwow dancer in the Women's Southern Cloth tradition and a professional percussionist & timpanist. *Published works*: Heartbeat of the People: Music & Dance of the Northern Powwow (University of Illinois Press, 2002); editor, Music of the First Nations: Tradition & Innovation in Native North American Music (University of Illinois Press, 2009); editor, Songs from "A New Circle of Voices." The 16th Annual Powwow at UCLA - musical edition drawn from powwow performance for the series "Music in the United States of America" (MUSA) (A-R Editions, Madison, Wisc. 2008); various articles in Ethnomusicology, The Journal of Musicological Research, and American Music.

BROZZO, SHIRLEY A. (Keweenaw Bay Anishinaabe) 1956-
(adjunct instructor; university administrator)
Born February 4, 1956, Wakefield, Mich. Education: Northern Michigan University (NMU), BS (Business Administration, 1992), MA (English Writing, 1994). *Affiliation & Address*: Adjunct instructor, Center for Native American Studies, NMU, 1401 Presque Isle Ave., Marquette, MI 49855 (906) 227-1557; E-mail: sbrozzo@nmu.edu. Coordinator, GAP (Gateway Academic Program), Northern Michigan University, 1994-present. *Past professional post*: Past president, NMU Commission for Women, 1997-99. *Community activities*: Storyteller at local schools. Memberships: Wordcraft Circle of Native Writers & Storytellers, 1992-present; NMU Allies (co-founder, 1998-present). *Interests*: Writing, reading, knitting & crocheting, working jigsaw puzzles. *Published work*: "Food for Thought: A Postcolonial Study of Food Imagery in Louis Erdrich's, Antelope Wife," featured in the Missouri Humanities Council Missouri Passages.

BRUCHAC, JAMES (Abenaki) 1966-
(author, storyteller; animal tracker & naturalist; wilderness skills expert)
Born June 24, 1966, Greenfield Center, N.Y. *Address*: 23 Middle Grove Rd., Greenfield Center, NY 12833 (518) 583-9980. Website: www.ndakinna.com. *Professional posts*: Native American Storyteller & youngest member of The Adirondack Liars' Club, Jim has offered programs for hundreds of public & private schools across the U.S. He has also performed at festivals, museums & libraries, including the Smithsonian Discovery Theater in Washington, DC. The Boston Children's Museum, et al. A collection of Jim's animal stories can be found on audio CD, Northeast Native American Animal Stories, and a two-volume audio CD from the book, When the Chenoo Howls, both by Good Mind Records. As animal tracker & naturalist, Jim has done research on just about every animal in North America. As a tracking instructor, he has trained people of all ages & level of expertise. Since 1992, he has led tracking expeditions from the Adirondack Mountains to Yellowstone National Park. He has co-authored two books on tracking, Scats & Tracks of the Northeast & Scats & Tracks of the Southeast, with world-renowned tracker & carnivore ecologist Dr. James Halfpenny. Jim has worked with numerous schools & organizations including the National Wildlife Federation, the National Parks Service, et al. His wilderness prowess has been featured on such television shows as Wild TV on PBS and Ray Mears Ultimate Survival Guide, Travel Channel; founder & director of The Ndakinna Wilderness Project, Greenfield Center, NY. Jim has done survival-based research in all corners of the U.S. & Lower Canada as well as having traveled to places such as West Africa & Central America. When he is not on the road, Jim is running programs at his family's education center & nature preserve in Greenfield Center. *Memberships*: Charter member of The International Society of Professional Trackers (ISPT); The Adirondack Liars' Club; The Wordcraft Circle of Native Writers & Storytellers. *Awards, honors*: 1999 Storyteller of the Year by the Wordcraft Circle; Jim and his father, Joseph Bruchac were awarded the 2004 National Wildlife Federation

Conservation Achievement Award. *Publications*: When the Chenoo Howls, Native Tales of Terror (Walker Books); Native American Games & Stories (Fulcrum Publishing); At How On the Earth (Modern Curriculum Press); three picture books by Dial Publications: How Chipmunk Got His Stripes, Turtle's Race With Beaver & Raccoons Last Race; 2 Falcon field guides to animal tracking: Scats & Tracks of the Northeast, & Scats & Tracks of the Southeast. Jim is working on several wilderness based books including a comprehensive annual tracking & observation guide for kids from Fulcrum Publishing.

BRUCHAC, JESSE (Abenaki)
(education center treasurer; musician & storyteller)
Education: Goddard College, BA. *Affiliation & Address*: Treasurer, The Ndakinna Education Center, 23 Middle Grove Rd., Greenfield Center, NY 12833 (518) 583-9958. Jesse has worked extensively over the past 15-20 years in projects involving the preservation of the Abenaki language, storytelling, music and traditional culture. He is the creator and webmaster of the Abenaki Language site, www.weaternabenaki.com as well as the Greenfield Review Literary Center's site focusing on American Indian writers, www.nativeauthors.com. Mr. Bruchac is a traditional storyteller & musician whose specialty is the native flute. He is the founder of the Dawn Land Singers and has performed American Indian music at festivals and in concerts throughout the U.S. and Canada, and in several European nations. Jesse also performs frequently as a visiting artist in schools.

BRUCHAC III, JOSEPH (Abenaki) 1942-
(writer, storyteller, editor)
Born October 16, 1942, Saratoga Springs, N.Y. *Education*: Cornell University, BA (English), 1965; Syracuse University, MA (Literature, Creative Writing), 1966; Union Institute Graduate School (Yellow Springs, Ohio), PhD (Comparative Literature), 1974. *Principal occupation*: Writer, storyteller, editor. *Address*: P.O. Box 308, Greenfield Center, NY 12833 (518) 584-1728. E-mail: nudatlog@earthlink.net. Website: www.josephbruchac.com. *Affiliations*: Founder & Co-editor of The Greenfield Review Press, Greenfield Center, NY, 1969-present; literary editor of "Studies in American Indian Literature" (SAIL), 1989-present; editor of "The Greenfield Review", 1969-87. *Past professional posts*: Board member, National Association for Storytelling (NAPPS), 1992-94; acting chair, Native Writers Circle of the Americas, 1992-93; advisory board, Wordcraft Circle of Native American Writers, 1992-93; national chair, Returning the Gift Project, 1991-92; board member, Poetry Society of America, 1985-87; COSMEP-National Independent Publishers Association (board member, 1973-74, 1981-85; national chairman, 1984-85; adjunct faculty, SUNY/Albany, 1987-1988; faculty, Hamilton College, 1983, 85, 87; coordinator of program at Great Meadow Prison, 1974-81, editor of "The Prison Writing Review", 1976-85; Skidmore College (English instructor, 1969-73. *Awards, honors*: NEA Creative Writing Fellowship (poetry), 1974; CCLM Editors' Fellowship, 1980; Rockefeller Humanities Fellowship, 1982; New York State CAPS Poetry Fellowships, 1973, 1982; NEA/PEN Syndicated Fiction Award, 1983; American Book Award for "Breaking Silence", 1984; Yaddo Residency Fellowships, 1984, 1985; The Cherokee Nation Award (prose), 1986; New York State Council on the Arts Editors Fellowship, 1986; The Hope S. Dean Memorial Award, 1993; Knickerbocker Award, 1995; Body Mind Spirit Magazine Award of Excellence, 1995; 1998 Storyteller of the Year from Wordcraft Circle of Native Writers & Storytellers; Albany (NY) Public Library Author of the Year, 1998; 1999 Lifetime Achievement Award from the Native Writers Circle of the Americas; 2000 Parents Choice Gold Award for Crazy Horse's Vision; 2001 Parents Guide to Childrens' Media Award for Skeleton Man; National Education Association Civil Rights Award, 2003; 2005 Virginia Hamilton Literary Award; numerous book awards & honors. *Interests*: The Dawnland Singers (Joe, Jim, Jesse, and Marge Bruchac) traditional Native American storytelling, drum songs & chants, contemporary music in Abenaki & English, flute songs, and historical presentations. The group formed in the spring of 1993 for the Abenaki Heritage Festival, and has since performed at the Flynn Theater in Burlington, VT, the Champlain Valley Festival and a number of other locations and festivals. *Published works*: Poems and stories in over 400 magazines; poems & stories anthologized in 150+ anthologies; translations from Abenaki, Ewe, Iroquois, and Spanish in numerous magazines; articles, essays & book reviews in more than 75 magazines & anthologies. *Anthologies edited*: Native Wisdom (1995) Smoke Rising (1995); Returning the Gift (1994); Singing of Earth (with Diana Landau, The Nature Co., 1993); Raven Tells Stories: Contemporary Alaskan Native Writing (1990); New Voices From the Longhouse: Contemporary Iroquois Writing (1989); Songs From This Earth on Turtle's Back: Contemporary American Indian Poetry (1983); among others. *Drama*: Pushing Up the Sky, Seven Native American Plays for Children (Dial, 2000). *Fiction*: Pocahontas (Harcourt, 2003); Foot of the Mountain (Holy Cow Press, 2003); The Warriors (Darby Creek, 2003); The Winter People (Dial, 2002); Skeleton Man (Harper Collins, 2002); Sacajawea (Harcourt, 2000); Heart of a Chief (Harcourt, 1999); Arrow Over the Door (Dial, 1998); Children of the Longhouse (Dial, 1996); Eagle Song (Dial, 1997); Dog People (Fulcrum, 1996); Long River (Fulcrum, 1995); Gluskabe and the Four Wishes (Cobblehill Books, 1994); Returning the Gift (editor, University of Arizona Press, 1994); A Boy Called Slow (Philomel, 1994); The Great Ball Game (Dial, 1994); Dawn

Land (novel, Fulcrum, 1993); Turtle Meat (short stories, Holy Cow Press, 1992); The White Moose (short stories, Blue Cloud Quarterly, 1988); among others. Non-Fiction: Our Stories Remember (Fulcrum, 2003); Navajo Long Walk (National Geographic Society Press, 2002); Native Games & Stories, with James Bruchac (Fulcrum, 2000); Seeing the Circle (Richard C. Owens Publishers, 1999); Bowman's Store, an autobiography (Dial, 1997); Lasting Echoes (Harcourt, 1997); Roots of Survival (Fulcrum, 1996); Native American Gardening, with M. Caduto (Fulcrum, 1996); The Native American Sweat Lodge (The Crossing Press, 1994); Keepers of Life: Discovering Plants Through Native American Stories and Earth Activities for Children, with M. Caduto (Fulcrum, 1994); Keepers of the Night, with M. Caduto (Fulcrum, 1994); The Native American Sweat Lodge in History & Story (The Crossing Press, 1994); Keepers of the Animals: Native American Stories & Wildlife Activities for Children, with Michael Caduto (Fulcrum, 1990); Keepers of the Earth: Native American Stories & Environmental Activities for Children (with Michael Caduto, Fulcrum, 1988); Survival This Way (University of Arizona Press, 1987); among others. Folk Stories: How Chipmunk Got His Stripes, with James Bruchac (Dial, 2002); When the Chenoo Howls, with James Bruchac (Walker, 1998); Makiawisug: The Gift of the Little People, with Melissa Fawcett (Little People, 1997); The Girl Who Married the Moon, with Gayle Ross (Bridgewater, 1994); Native Plant Stories (Fulcrum, 1995); Native American Animal Stories (Fulcrum, 1992); Hoop Snakes,, Hide-Behinds and Sidehill Winders (The Crossing Press, 1991); Native American Stories (Fulcrum, 1991); Return of the Sun (The Crossing Press, 1989); The Faithful Hunter and Other Abenaki Stories (Bowman Books, 1988); Iroquois Stories (The Crossing Press, 1985); among others. Picture Books: Seasons of the Circle (Troll, 2003); Squanto's Story (Harcourt, 2000); Crazy Horse's Vision (Lee & Low, 2000); Many Nations (Bridgewater, 1998); Between Earth and Sky (Harcourt, 1997); among others Poetry: Ndakinna/Our Land (West End Press, 2003); Above the Line (West End Press, 2003); No Borders (Holy Cow Books, 1998); among others. *Audio cassettes*: Dawnland (Fulcrum, 1993); Keepers of the Animals (Fulcrum, 1992); Keepers of the Earth (Fulcrum, 1990), The Boy Who Lived With the Bears (Parabola/Harper Audio, 1990); Gluskabe Stories (Yellow Moon, 1990); Translator's Son (Cross Cultural Communications, 1981). Children's Books: The First Strawberries (Dial Books, 1993; Fox Song (Philomel, 1993); Thirteen Moons on Turtle's Back, with Jonathan London (Philomel, 1992).

BRUCHAC, MARGARET "MARGE" (Abenaki)
(professor of anthropology; native studies program coordinator)
Education: Smith College, BA (History & Theater), 1999; University of Massachusetts, Amherst, MA & PhD (Anthropology), 1999-2007. *Affiliation & Address*: Assistant Professor of Anthropology (2013-present), University of Pennsylvania, Department of Anthropology, 416 Museum, 3260 South St., Philadelphia, PA 19104 (215) 898-6989. E-mail: mbruchac@sas.upenn.edu. coordinator, Faculty Working Group on the Native American Studies Initiative; project director (2014-present), On the Wampum Trail: Restorative Research in NE Museums, Penn Museum, Philadelphia, PA; associate faculty (2014-present) Penn Cultural Heritage Center, University of Pennsylvania Museum of Archaeology & Anthropology, Philaldephia, PA 19104 (215) 898-7461. *Past professional posts*: Postdoctoral Fellowship for Excellence in College & University Teaching, Ford Foundation, 2011-12; Katrin H. Lamon Scholar in Residence, School of Advanced Research, Santa Fe, NM, 2011-12; assistant professor of anthropology & coordinator, Native & Indigenous Studies Program, University of Connecticut, Avery Point Campus, Gorton, CT (2008-12). Marge performs (Ndakinna Education Center) traditionall Algonkian Indian songs, stories and dances with her husband, Justin Kennick as "Hand in Hand," and with her brother Joe and nephews, Jim & Jesse Bruchac, as part of the "Dawnland Singers. She also serves as a Trustee of Plimoth Plantationn, an advisor to the museum's Wampanoag Indigenous Program, & a consultant for many other New England museums. *Published works*: Consorting With Savages: Indigenous Informants & American Anthropologists, University of Arizona Press and the "First Peoples: New Directions in Indigenous Studies" publishing initiative. This book project examines cross-cultural relations among a cadre of highly influential male scholars---including Franz Boas, Frank Speck, William Fenton, & Arthur Parker---who dominated the field of American anthropology during the early 20th century; *Dreaming Again: Algonkian Indian Poems*. Bowman Books, Northeastern Native Authors Series. Greenfield Center, NY: Greenfield Review Press, 2012; with Siobhan Hart, & H. Martin Wobst, eds. *Indigenous Archaeologies: A Reader in Decolonization*. Walnut Creek, CA: Left Coast Press, 2010; with Frederique Apffel-Marglin, *Exorcising Anthropology's Demons*. Dissenting Knowledges Pamphlet Series No. 2. Penang, Malaysia: Multiversity and Citizens International, 2004.

BRUGGE, DAVID M. 1927-
(anthropologist; author)
Born September 3, 1927, Jamestown, N.Y. *Education*: University of New Mexico, BA, 1950. *Affiliation & Address*: Chief, Branch of Curation, Southwest Cultural Resources Center, National Park Service, 1220 S. St. Francis Dr., Box 728, Santa Fe, NM 87504 (505) 988-6766. *Past professional post*: Anthropologist, The Navajo Tribe, Window Rock, AZ, 1958-68. *Other*

professional posts: Archaeologist, Museum of Northern Arizona, Flagstaff, AZ, 1957; director, Navajo Curriculum Center, Rough Rock, AZ, 1968; instructor, College of Ganado, AZ, 1973. *Military service*: U.S. Army, 1945-47. *Community activities*: Sage Memorial Hospital, Ganado, Ariz. (secretary, advisory board); Title I Committee, Ganado Public Schools. *Interests*: "Navajo studies, especially in archaeology, ethno-history & history, and more generally of the greater Southwest. In addition to my work with the Navajos, I have done fieldwork in northwestern Mexico among the Pima Bajo (Lower Pima) of Sonora. My work with the Navajo Tribe involved research for various land disputes such as the Land Claims Case, the Navajo-Hopi boundary dispute, the McCracken Mesa land exchange and Utah school section case and the Huerfano Mesa land exchange." *Published works*: Navajo Pottery & Ethno-history (The Navajo Tribe, 1963); Long Ago in Navajoland (The Navajo Tribe, 1965); Navajo Bibliography, with J. Lee Correll & Edith Watson (The Navajo Tribe, 1967); Navajos in the Catholic Church Records of New Mexico, 1694-1875 (The Navajo Tribe, 1968); Zarcillos Largos, Courageous Advocate of Peace (The Navajo Tribe, 1970); The Story of the Navajo Treaties, with J. Lee Correll (The Navajo Tribe, 1971); Navajo & Western Pueblo History (Tucson Corral of Westerners, 1972); The Navajo Exodus (Archaeological Society of New Mexico, 1972); Hubbell Trading Post National Historic Site (Southwest Parks & Monuments Association, 1993); The Navajo-Hopi Land Dispute: An American Tragedy (University of New Mexico Press, 1999; In Search of Chaco: New Approaches to an Archaeological Enigma (SAR Press, 2004); Navajos in the Catholic Church Records of New Mexico, 1694-1875 (SAR Press, 2010.)

BRUGUIER, LEONARD R. (Yankton Sioux) 1944-
(director of American Indian studies)
Born October 9, 1944, Wagner, S.D. *Education*: University of South Dakota, BA, 1984, MPA, 1986; Oklahoma State University, PhD, 1989. *Affiliation & Address*: Director, Institute of American Indian Studies, University of South Dakota, 414 E. Clark, Vermillion, SD 57069 (605) 677-5209, 1989-. *Other professional post*: Editor, "The Bulletin," Institute of American Indian Studies, University of South Dakota; assistant professor of American history, University of South Dakota; host radio show, "Voices of the Plains," South Dakota Public Radio Network, Vermillion, SD. *Military service*: U.S. Marine Corps, 1963-70 (Sergeant; Combat Action Ribbon, Presidential Unit Citation, Vietnam Service Medal, Vietnam Campaign Ribbon, Armed Forces Expeditionary Medal, National Defense Medal). *Community activities*: Member, Indian Memorial Committee, National Parks Service. *Memberships*: Organization of American Historians, 1986-; Western Historical Association, 1985-; Southern Historical Association, 1988-; Phi Alpha Theta, 1986-; Machinists and Aerospace Workers, 1971-; Vietnam Veterans of America, 1976-. *Awards, honors*: Oklahoma State Regents for Higher Education Minority Doctoral Study Grant; Townsend Memorial Minority Scholarships; Archie B. Gillfillan Award for Creative Writing; History Alumni Award; University of South Dakota Veterans Club. *Interests*: "North & South American comparative studies of "Indians," with a particular interest in plains people & their religion, government, and social institutions. in North America, I am researching the Pipe Religion and its influence in Indian-White relations. Ongoing research of Indian men & women who served in the U.S. Armed Forces and their impact on reservation, government, & social patterns. Demographic & statistical information on Indians, both continents." *Biographical source*: "The Yankton Sioux", Indians of North America Series, by Herbert Hoover. *Published works*: Remember Your Relatives (Marty Indian School, 1985; Yankton Sioux Elderly Board, 1989); Conference on Reburials (American Indian Research Project, 1985); The Yankton Sioux (Chelsea House Publishers, 1988); South Dakota Leaders (University of South Dakota Press, 1989).

BRUNDIN, CLAUDIA (Wiyot-Yurok)
(tribal chairperson)
Born in Blue Lake, Calif. *Education*: Humboldt Business College. *Affiliation & Address*: Chairperson, Blue Lake Rancheria Tribe, P.O. Box 428, Blue Lake, CA 95525 (707) 668-5101. Website: www.bluelakerancheria-nsn.gov. *Other professional posts*: Tribal Government Consultation Committee; California Rural Indian Health Board; manages housekeeping operations for the Blue Lake Casino. *Past professional post*: St. Joseph Hospital in housekeeping & administration for 30 years.

BRUNDIN, JUDITH A. 1949-
(editor, writer)
Born December 18, 1949, Columbus, Ohio. *Education*: University of Colorado, BFA, 1972; Colorado College, MAT, 1978; New York University, Graduate Certificate-Museum Studies, 1983. *Principal occupation*: Museum education department head. Resides in New Jersey E-mail: jbr33333@aol.com. *Professional posts*: Consulting, lectures-presentations; editor of American history publications & writes articles for scholarly journals including those from the NAS. *Past professional posts*: Instructor, BIA, AZ, 1974-77; technician, Tucson Public Schools, 1978-80; exhibitions designer, Navajo Tribe, AZ, 1980-81; Head, Education Dept., National Museum of the American Indian (NMAI), Smithsonian Institution, New York, NY, 1982-95. *Awards, honors*: Letter of Commendation, BIA, presented upon resignation, April 1977; Tribal plaque

from the Navajo Tribe upon completion of the Navajo Tribal Museum's exhibit installation, 1981. *Published works*: Author - American Indian Dolls, An Educational Resource Kit (NMAI, 1986), & The Native People of the Northeast Woodlands, An Educational Resource Publication (NMAI, 1990); articles - "Navajo Sandpainting," Instructor, 87 (Nov. 1977); "On Your Own With Great Native Americans" exhibit guide (NMAI, 1988); "On Your Own With Native American Cultures" exhibit guide (NMAI, 1989); among many other media & journal articles, 1995-present).

BRUNDIN-MILLER, KARA (Tolowa)
(former tribal chairperson)
Affiliation & Address: Tolowa Tribe of the Smith River Rancheria, 140 Rowdy Creek Rd., Smith River, CA 95567 (707) 218-7723. kmiller@tolowa. com.

BRUNELLE, BRIAN (Ojibwe-Chippewa)
(tribal director of administration)
Affiliation & Address: Director of Administration, Minnesota Chippewa Tribe, Box 217, Cass Lake, MN 56633 (218) 335-8581. E-mail: dbrunnelle@ mnchippewatribe.org

BRUNSCH, TAWNEY (Oglala Lakota)
(executive director)
Born & raised on the Pine Ridge Reservation. *Education*: South Dakota State University, BS (Commercial Economics). *Affiliation & Address*: Executive Director, The Lakota Fund, P.O. Box 340, Kyle, SD 57752 (605) 455-2500. E-mail: tbrunsch@lakotafunds.org. *Other professional post*: Member, Board of Directors, Mazaska Owecaso Otipi Financial; chairperson, Lakota Federal Credit Union Steering Committee. Before becoming executive director, Ms. Brunsch served as Loan Portfolio Manager at Lakota Funds, and eight years as Black Hills Federal Credit Union Wall Branch Manager. *Awards, honors*: 2007 Volunteer of the Year by Wall Neighborhood Housing Services,

BRUSHBREAKER, DAVID (Rosebud Lakota)
(board vice president)
Address & Affiliation: Board Vice President, Sicangu Oyate Ho., Inc., St. Francis Indian School, P.O. Box 379 HCR 59 Box 1A, St. Francis, SD 57572 (605) 747-2299.

BRYAN, CATHERINE (Navajo)
(attorney; associate director)
Born & raised in southeastern New Mexico. *Education*: University of Oklahoma, BA, MA; University of New Mexico School of Law, JD, 2004. Graduated with Clinical Honors for her work in the Southwest Indian Law Clinic. *Affiliation & Address*: Associate Director, National Tribal Justice Center, National American Indian Curt Judges Association, 3300 Arapahoe Ave. #206, Boulder, CO 80303 (303) 449-4112. *Past professional posts*: Senior Program Officer, Research, Policy & Asset-Building Programs, First Nations Development Institute, Longmont, CO; Legal Analyst (2004-08), National Tribal Justice Resource Center, Boulder, CO. Her work at the Center focused on tribal child support enforcement (TCSE). She assisted tribes in applying for federal grants to fund TCSE Programs through grant writing, conducting training workshops for tribal court staff, & providing additional technical support to tribes in their development of their TCSE. *Awards, honors*: Recipient of the Mary Beth & W. Richard West, Jr., Award for Excellence in Indian Law.

BRYAN, STEPHANIE A. (Poarch Band of Creek)
(tribal council chair)
Education: Jefferson Davis Community College & Faulkner State Junior College. *Affiliation & Address*: Chairperson (2014-present), Poarch Band of Creek Indians, 5811 Jack Springs Rd., Atmore, AL 36502 (251) 368-9136. E-mail: sbryan@pci-nsn.gov. She served as vice chairperson from June 2006.

BRYANT, CHRISTINA (*Ageya Wahya*)
(Tsalagi Cherokee/Shinnecock) 1948-
(visual artist, puppeteer, poet, teacher, doll artist)
Born March 14, 1948, Kings County, N.Y. *Education*: Pace University (New York, NY) B.A. *Principal occupation*: Storyteller, visual artist, free-lance educator, environmentalist. *Address*: 105 Lincoln Rd., Apt. 5J, Brooklyn, NY 11225 (718) 462-8128. *Affiliation*: Freelance educator - folkways interpreter of Native American culture, environment, recreation therapist, American Indian arts/crafts teacher, storyteller, Huntington Free Library/Heye Foundation & the Smithsonian Institution (American Indian Library); Henry Street Art in Education, Learning Through an Expanded Arts Program (LEAP); Museum of Natural History - Special Education Department & Peoples Center; Arts Horizons, NJ & NY, 1998-. *Community activities*: Teaching Native children about puppetry & use of puppets in theatre setting using Native American stories. *Memberships*: Nuyagi Keetoowah, Inc.; Southeastern Cherokee Confederacy of Georgia; National Outdoor Leadership School; Nitchin Family Awareness Network. *Interests*: Storytelling - speaks annually to hundreds of students in the NYC schools and area private schools; works as free-lance art in education teacher. *Publication*: "Tlanuwa Speaks (book of poetry).

BRYANT, SHARON (Monacan)
(tribal chief)
Affiliation & Address: Chief, Monacan Indian Nation, P.O. Box 1136, Madison Heights, VA 24572 (804) 946-0389.

BRYCELEA, CLIFFORD (Dine') 1953-
(professional artist; painter)
Born September 26, 1953, Shiprock, N.M. *Education*: Fort Lewis College, BA (Art), 1975. *Principal occupation*: Professional artist; painter. *Address*: 1721 Montano St., Santa Fe, NM 87501 (505) 984-8632. *Affiliations*: Toh-Atin Gallery, Durango, CO (16 years); Spirits in the Wind, Golden, CO (eight years); Long Ago & Far Away, Manchester Center, VT (ten years); Skystone N' Silver, Hobart, IN (12 years); Tekakwitha, Helen, GA (eight years); Blue Gem & Gallery, Midland, TX (15 years). *Memberships*: Indian Arts & Crafts Association (IACA), Albuquerque (member, 1980-; board of directors, 1986-91); Southwestern Association on Indian Affairs (Santa Fe), 1980-. *Awards, honors*: 4 Gold Medals, IACA, San Dimas, CA 1981, 1982 & 1986; 1st Place & Memorial Award, Gallup (NM) Ceremonial; Artist-of-the-Year, 1987 by IACA; and City Poster Award, 1991, Santa Fe, NM. *Interests*: "My work is in contemporary and representational style - paintings of various cultures, telling the stories and recall the legends of American Indians. It also depicted the mysticism & magical composition (spiritual meaning.) *Biographical sources*: Beyond Tradition, by Jerry & Lois Jacka; The Art Fever, by James Parsons; American Artist by Les Krantz; story by Julie Pearson, June, 1992, Southwest Art Magazine. *Published works*: illus. - American Way (American Airlines, 1976); illus. - Navajo Painting, by Katherin Chase, 1980; Pieces of White Shell (Charles Scribner's Sons, 1984); illus. - Haunted Mesa (Bantam Books, 1987); illus. Beyond Tradition, by Lois & Jerry Jacka, 1988; cover illus. - "Wildfire" magazine, Fall 1990; cover illus. - "San Francisco Chamber of Commerce Magazine, 1991; illus. - The Talking Wind, by Jack Hawkins, 1994; illus. - Enduring Traditions, by Lois & Jerry Jacka, 1994; cover illus. - Fire in the Mind, by George Johnson, 1995; cover & illus. - Moon and Otter and Frog, by Laura Simms, 1995.

BUBAR, ROE
(associate professor of ethnic studies)
Education: University of New Hampshire, BA; University of Colorado, JD. *Affiliation & Address*: Associate Professor, Department of Ethnic Studies, Colorado State University, 363 Aylesworth Hall SE, Fort Collins, CO 80523 (303) 491-2418. E-mail: roe.bubar@colostate.edu. *Professional Interests*: Roe is a nationally recognized trainer & expert in interviewing indigenous children in child sexual abuse cases & her research interests include sexual violence, child maltreatment in tribal communities. Her current research projects include sexual assault of Indigenous women/children, Native youth & STDs, drug endangered children in tribal communities. She is a licensed mediator and she works with federal, state and tribal agencies; and provides consultation to tribes in Indian Country & Alaska Native communities. *Published works*: Research monographs.

BUCHANAN, BRIAN (*BLUE JAY*) (*Akima Tandaksa*) (Miami of Indiana)
(tribal chief)
Affiliation & Address: Chief, Miami Nation of Indians of Indiana, P.O. Box 41, Peru, IN 46970 (765) 473-9631.

BUCHANAN, RADM. CHRIS (Seminole of Oklahoma)
(acting IHS area director)
Education: University of North Carolina, Chapel Hill, BS (Environmental Health), MPH (Health Policy & Administration). *Affiliation & Address*: Acting Director (2017-present), Indian Health Service, Department of Health & Human Services, 5600 Fishers Lane, Rockville, MD 20857 The IHS is the principal federal health care advocate and provider of health care services for American Indians & Alaska Natives. As Acting Director, CAPT Buchanan has administrative responsibility for 19 service units consisting of seven hospitals and 10 health centers. He manages a varied health program for more than 126,000 American Indian people eligible for IHS services. The Great Plains Area IHS serves 17 Tribes and supports two urban Indian health programs. Chris oversees a unique Indian health system composed of direct health services provided primarily through the IHS owned and operated facilities and through Tribes that have assumed partial or full responsibility for their own health care programs through contractual arrangements with the IHS Great Plains Area under the authority of the Indian Self-Determination & Education Assistance Act. *Past professional posts*: Former Acting Director, Great Plains Area of the Indian Health Service (IHS), Department of Health & Human Services (2011-16). Buchanan began his IHS career in 1993 serving in various environmental health officer positions in the Phoenix, Albuquerque, & Oklahoma City Areas. From 2005-10, he held management positions in the Oklahoma City Area, including serving as the Administrative Officer for Lawton Indian Hospital and the Chief Executive Officer for Haskell Health Center. In 2010, he served as the Administrative Officer of Clinical Services for the Chickasaw Nation's Division of Health in Ada, Oklahoma. He was also an environmental health officer in the U.S. Public Health Service Commissioned

Corps with more than 20 years of active duty. His position of record is the Director, Office of Direct Services & Contracting Tribes for IHS. RADM Buchanan has served on several national IHS workgroups, completed two fellowships, and been deployed to several natural disaster events. *Awards, honors*: He has been the recipient of several professional awards, including the National Council of Chief Executive Officer's Rookie of the Year.

BUCK, JIM
(radio host/producer)
Affiliation & Address: "Sequoyah," WBAI - FM, 505 Eighth Ave., New York, NY 10018 (212) 279-0707.

BUCK, SHELLEY (Mdewankanton Sioux)
(tribal president)
Affiliation & Address: President, Prarie Island Indian Community, 5636 Sturgeon Lake Rd., Welch, MN 55089 (651) 385-2554. E-mail: sbuck@ piic.org. President Shelley Buck is serving her third term on Prairie Island Tribal Council. Prior to being elected Tribal Council President for the 2016-2017 term, Buck held other positions within the Prairie Island Indian Community government, such as the Tribal Council Secretary, enrollment clerk in the Prairie Island Enrollment Office and Tribal Lobbyist. She has also served on the Pow Wow, Constitution Revision and Enrollment Committees. Buck has a bachelor's degree in business accounting from Indiana University and master's degree in Sports Management from Concordia University. She is currently serving as a board member of the Twins Community Fund and has also served as a board member of the Native Vote Alliance of Minnesota.

BUCKLEY, THOMAS 1942-
(writer)
Born May 28, 1942, Louisville, KY. *Education*: Harvard University, BA, 1975; University of Chicago, MA, 1977, PhD, 1982. *Address*: 156 Sabino Rd., West Bath, ME 04530; E-mail: timbuckley@earthlink.net. *Past professional posts*: Anthropology & American Studies, UMass/Boston, MA (professor, 1980-2001; academic director, Native American Resource Center, 1996-2001; director, Native American Studies Concentration, 1997-2001). *Interests*: Fieldwork in Native Northwestern California, among Yurok, Hupa, Karuk and Tolowa Indians, since 1976. Focus is on Yurok language, politics, religion, gender. Serve as consultant and as expert witness in fishing and in land use and religious freedom cases. *Published works*: Editor, Blood Magic (University of California Press, 1988); Standing Ground (University of California Press, 2002); numerous articles on the Yuroks and on A.L. Kroeber.

BUCKO, FR. RAYMOND A.
(professor of anthropology; director of Native American studies)
Education: Fordham University, BA (Anthropology & Philosophy), 1978; Jesuit School of Theology at Berkeley, Master of Divinity, 1983; Regis College, Toronto, Master of Sacred Theology, 1984; University of Chicago, PhD (Anthropology). Dissertation: "Inipi: Historic Transformation & Contemporary Significance of the Sweat Lodge in Lakota Ritual Practice." *Affiliation & Address*: Professor of Anthropology (2000-present) & Chairperson, Dept. of Sociology, Anthropology & Social Work, Creighton University; director, Native American Studies Program, Creighton University, 2500 California Plaza, Omaha, NE 68178 (402) 280-3587. E-mail: bucko@creighton.edu. *Other professional posts*: Member, College ADA Committee; liaison for Native American Outreach, Creighton University; faculty advisor for Hui-o-Hawaii (Hawaiian cultural society on campus). Chaplain. *Past professional posts*: Red Cloud Indian High School, 1978-80; Oglala Lakota College, 1987-89; Native American Education Services, Chicago, IL, 1991-92; instructor, Le Moyne College, 1984-85, 1992-2000). *Published works*: The Lakota Ritual of the Sweat Lodge: History & Contemporary Practice (University of Nebraska Press, 1998); articles, book chapters; book & film reviews; Electronic Publications: Lakota Dakota Comprehensive Bibliography, 2005, www.puffin.creighton. edu/lakota/biblio.html (periodically updated); Lakota Dakota Information Page, 2005 with Martin Brokenleg) www.puffin.creighton.edu/lakota/ (website is periodically updated.

BUFFALO, HENRY M., JR. (Red Cliff Ojibwe)
(attorney)
Education: University of Wisconsin, Milwaukee BS (Criminal Justice), 1978, University of Wisconsin (Madison) School of Law, 1981. *Address & Affiliation*: Law Offices of Henry M. Buffalo, Jr., Energ Park Financial Center, Suite 210, 1360 Energy Park Dr., St. Paul, MN 55108. *Other professional posts*: From 1988-present, Henry has served as Judge on the Tribal Court of the Shakopee Mdewankanton Sioux (Dakota) Community in Minnesota; he speaks regularly at lawyers' seminars & gaming trade conferences on the subjects of gaming development, Federal law, tribal sovereignty. *Areas of practice*: Administrative Law, Civil Litigation, Gaming Law, Government Relations & Regulatory Compliance, Indian/Tribal Law. *Past professional posts*: Partner (1991-2012), Jacobson, Buffalo, Magnuson, Anderson & Hogan, LLP, St. Paul, MN; In-house tribal counsel for the Red Cliff Band of Lake Superior Chippewa, and later for the Fond du Lac Band of Lake Superior Chippewa; he founded &

served as the first executive director of the Great Lakes Indian Fish & Wildlife Commission; served as lead counsel to the National Indian Gaming Association from its inception through the passage & adoption of the Indian Gaming Regulatory Act.

BUFFALOHEAD, ERIC L. (Ojibwe)
(professor & chair of American Indian studies)
Education: University of Minnsota, BA, MA, ABD. *Affiliation & Address*: Associate Professor (1999-present) & Chair of American Indian Studies Program, Augsburg College, Memorial Hall 215, CB 115, Minneapolis, MN 55454 (612) 330-1661. E-mail: buffaloe@augsburg.edu.

BUFFALOHEAD, W. ROGER (Ojibwe)
(Indian center director)
Affiliation: Director, Tribal Research Center, NAES (Native American Educational Services) College, 2838 W. Peterson Ave., Chicago, IL 60659 (773) 761-5000. *Past professional post*: Director, Achievement Through Communications Project, Migizi Communications, Inc., Minneapolis, MN.

BUFORD, BETTIE (*LITTLE DOVE*) (Gttigua Cox)
(Yamasee/ Creek/Cherokee) 1935-
(principal chief)
Born February 20, 1935, Ocoee, Fla. *Principal occupation*: Principal chief. *Address*: P.O. Box 521, Cox-Osceola Seminole Indian Reservation, Orange Springs, FL 32182 (904) 546-5525. *Affiliations*: President, Oklavueha Seminole Trading Post, Orange Springs, FL, 1985-; licensed genealogist & historian (29 years). *Other professional post*: Teacher, Indian culture, Osceola Christian Indian School. *Military service*: American Red Cross Military Hospital, Korean conflict. *Community activities*: Principal chief, Oklavueha Band of Seminole Indians, 1979-; Assistant principal of Coe Harjo's Private Christian Indian School, 1986-. Memberships: Native American Historical Presentation Service, 1991-; National Indian Unity Coalition, 1990-; The Concerned Citizens League of America (president). *Awards, honors*: Marion Education Awards; several awards for teaching Indian culture an crafts. *Interests*: "My major interest is to help improve the lifestyles of my Indian people and to stop some of the prejudice against them. To let all people know what real Indians are, not the stereotypes that they see in the movies and on television. I would like to travel to all tribes." *Published works*: Oklavueha #1-2-3-4-5 Band of Seminoles, 1992-94; Oklawaka People of the River Indians, 1994; Yamasee Indians - Last Known as Oklavueha Band Seminoles, 1994; Oklavuehas Written Language.

BUGBEE, RICHARD (Kumeyaay)
(Indian center director & curator)
Address: P.O. Box 1668, Topanga, CA 90290 (619) 459-9086/ E-mail: hunwut@aol.com. *Affiliations*: Associate director & curator, American Indian Culture Center & Museum, San Diego, CA; director & curator, Kumeyaay Culture Center. *Other professional post*: Board Chairperson, Advocates for Indigenous California Languages, Vallejo, CA. *Interests*: Richard is an active presence in all Native American language revitalization efforts in Southern California, teaching classes, publishing a daily e-mail newsletter, etc.

BULL, BRIAN (Nez Perce)
(radio news director)
Education: Macalester College, B.A. (in Psychology), 1998. *Address & Affiliation*: Assistant News Director, Wisconsin Public Radio (WPR) (2004-present), 821 University Ave., Madison, WI 53706 (608) 263-3970; (800) 747-7444. E-mail: bull@wpr.org. Acting news director for 15 months. Brian has covered a number of issues related to Indian Country, including the significance of Native American veterans, the clout of Indian voters in local & national politics, & a 30-year retrospective of the American Indian Movement. His contribution to multicultural coverage helped WPR win a UNITY Award in 2006. *Other professional posts*: Chair, Vision Maker Media, Lincoln, NE; Reporter, National Native News, Albuquerque, NM. *Past professional posts*: News Director, South Dakota Public Radio, 1999-2004. *Awards, honors*: "Best Overall Radio News Reporting for 2001" Award from the Native American Journalists Association; Feature & documentary work has earned him six Edward R. Murrow Awards, a National Headliner Award, & numerous first place plaques from the Associated Press & Milwaukee Press Club. *Community activities*: Serves on the boards of the Native American Public Telecom-munications and the Radio & Television News Directors Association as an Ex-Officio, and the Northwest Broadcasters News Association. *Interests*: Brian likes public radio for its integrity & balance, plus its kinship to oral tradition, an important practice in Nez Perce culture.

BULLOCK, ED (*Eyes that Shine*) (Wampanoag)
(store owner & powwow dancer & singer)
Affiliation: Owner, The Little Bull, P.O. Box 383, York Beach, ME 03910 (207) 363-7108. E-mail: info@thelittlebull.com. Ed travels extensively, dancing & singing ("101 Singers") at powwows. The Bullock family opened "The Wandering Bull" in Carver, Massachusetts, a Native craft supplier, selling beads, leather, and books. The Little Bull is a combination of fine art gallery &

contemporary trading post carrying handmade Native jewelry and local art such as baskets, flutes, pipes & drums. Also provides educational programs to schools & organizations to teach others about Native life.

BUNCH, JOE (United Keetoowah Cherokee)
(tribal chief)
Affiliation & Address: Chief (2015-present), United Keetoowah Band of Cherokee Indians, P.O. Box 746, Tahlequah, OK 74465 (918) 431-1818.

BUNNER, GRACE (Creek)
(town king-Mekko)
Address & Affiliation: Thlopthlocco Tribal Town, P.O. Box 188, Okemah, OK 74859 (918) 623-2620.

BURDEAU, GEORGE (Blackfeet)
(film producer/director)
Affiliation & Address: Founding Dean of the Communications Department, Institute of American Indian Arts, 83 Avan Nu Po Rd., Santa Fe, NM 87503 (505) 424-2302. *Films produced/directed*: The Pueblo People, 1991; Story-tellers of the Pacific, 1994; The Native Americans/The Plains: Part 1 & 2, 1996; Backbone to the World: The Blackfeet, 1997; Stories Told in the Dark, 1999; Who Owns the Past, 1999. *Past professional posts*: George was the first Native American director in the Directors Guild of America. He served as chairperson of the Indian Arts & Crafts Board; board member of the Institute for the Preservation of the original Languages of Americas; board chair of the Institute of Native Culture & Communication; founding board member of the Native American Public Broadcasting Consortium. *Awards, honors*: Received an Emmy Award for The Native Americans/The Plains; and a Peabody Award for Surviving Columbus.

BURDETTE, VIVIAN L. (Tonto Apache)
(former tribal chairperson)
Affiliation & Address: Former President, Tonto Apache Tribe, 18 Tonto Reservation, Payson, AZ 85541 (928) 474-3988.

BURETTA, SHERI (Aleut)
(Alaska corporation chairperson)
Born in Anchorage, Alaska *Education*: University of Alaska, BS (Accounting). *Affiliation & Address*: Chairperson, Chugach Alaska Corp., 3800 Centerpoint Dr. #601, Anchorage, AK 99503 (907) 563-8866. *Other professional posts*: Member, board of directors of the following organizations: Native American Contractors Assn, Alaska Federation of Natives (1997-present), Prince William Sound Regional Citizens Advisory Council (1999-2012), ANCSA Regional Assn (1999-present), Alaskans Standing Together (2010-present), ROSSIA Russian Orthodox Sacred Sites in Alaska, Inc. (2002-present), Foraker Group Governance Board (2007-present), Tatitlek Corporation Board (treasurer, 2005-present).

BURGESS, MICHAEL (Comanche)
(tribal college interim president)
Affiliation & Address: Interim President, Pawnee Nation College, 861 Little Dee Dr., P.O. Box 470, Pawnee, OK 74058 (918) 762-3363 ext. 11. E-mail: mburgess@pawneenationcollege.org. *Past professional post*: Chairperson, Comanche Nation, Lawton, OK.

BURGOS, ADRIAN, JR.
(Interim director of American Indian studies)
Affiliation & Address: Professor & Interim Director, American Indian Studies, 1204 W. Nevada St. MC-138, Urbana, IL 61801 (217) 265-9870   E-mail: burgosjr@illinois.edu

BURKHART, BRIAN (Cherokee)
(American Indian studies program director)
Education: University of Northern Colorado, BS, 1997; Indiana University, PhD, 2008. *Affiliation & Address*: Faculty, American Indian Studies Program, College of Humanities, Sierra Hall 194, CSU Northridge, 18111 Nordhoff St., Northridge, CA 91330 (818) 677-6762. E-mail: brian.burkhart@csun.edu. He specializes in American Indian intellectual history, environmental philosophy & justice, sacred places & development. *Published work*: Respect for Kinship: Toward an Indigenous Environmental Ethics (PhD dissertation).

BURLEY, SILVIA (Miwok)
(tribal chairperson)
Affiliation & Address: Chairperson, California Valley Miwok Tribe of the Sheep Ranch Rancheria, 4620 Shippee Lane, Stockton, CA 95212 (209) 931-4567. E-mail: s.burley@ cvmt.net

BURNETT, DAVID (Chehalis)
(former tribal chairperson)
Affiliation & Address: Former Chairperson, Confederated Tribes of the Chehalis Reservation, P.O. Box 536, Oakville, WA 98568 (360) 273-5911.

BURNETTE, BERNADINE (Yavapai)
(tribal president)
Affiliation & Address: President, Fort McDowell Yavapai Nation, P.O. Box 17779, Fountain Hills, AZ 85269 (480) 837-5121. E-mail: bburnette@ftmcdowell.org

BURNS, KRISTI K.
(deputy director)
Education: Southern Oregon State College, 1990-92; University of Montana, BA (Anthropology; Native American Studies), 1996. *Affiliation & Address*: Program Director (1998-2012), Deputy Director (2012-present), ONABEN, 6441 SW Canyon Court, Suite 104, Portland, OR 97221 (503) 968-1500. E-mail: kristi@onaben.org. *Other professional post*: Member, Board of Directors, Willowbrook Arts Camp (2011-present).

BURR, DONNA J. (Choctaw)
(educator)
Born in Philadelphia, Miss. *Education*: University of St. Thomas, MA. *Address*: Onamia School District #480, Indian Education Program, 35465 - 125th Ave., Onamia, MN 56359 (320) 532-4174. *Affiliation*: Instructor, Onamia School District #480, Onamia, MN. *Military service*: U.S. Air Force, 1980-86. *Community activities*: Chairperson, Onamia Parent Advisory Committee.

BURRAGE, SEAN (Choctaw of Oklahoma)
(university president)
Born & Raised in Durant, Okla. *Education*: University of Okahoma, BS (Accounting); University of Oklahoma College of Law, JD, 1993. *Affiliation & Address*: President, Southeastern Oklahoma State University, 1405 North 4th, Durant, OK 74701 (580) 745-2000. *Past professional post*: Oklahoma State Senate (two terms, 2006-14). Burrage served as Legislative Director to .S. Senator David Boren in Washington, DC and later as Special Assistant & Director of State Federal Rlations to President Boren at the University of Oklahoma. *Awrads, honors*: "Best Newcomer Legislator of the Year" by the Higher Education Councill, and "2013 Legislator of the Year" by the Oklahoma Association for Justice. In Nov. 2011, he was elected Democratic Floor Leader after serving as Assistant Demcratic Leader for the 52nd Oklahoma Legislature. Also in 2011, he was a member of the Joint Committee on Indian Tribal-State Relations.

BURRUS, S.S. (MS.) (*Going About Grasshopper Sam*) (Cherokee)
(artist)
Born in Okla. *Education*: Central State University, BA. *Principal occupation*: Artist of watercolor, sculpture, fashion designer. *Permanent Collections*: State Trail of Tears Museum - Cape Girardeau, MO, 1987, 1991; A-Eiteljorg Museum - Indianapolis, IN, 1989; Heritage Center - Tahlequah, OK, 1991; Cherokee Museum - Cherokee, NC, 1991; Five Tribes Museum - Muskogee, OK, 1991; Smithsonian - Office of Dr. Rayna Green, 1992; University of Oklahoma - Dr. Rennard Strickland, Director of American Indian Law & Policy Center - Oklahoma City, 1992. *Memberships*: Indian Arts & Crafts Association; Southwestern American Indian Association; Oklahoma Arts Council. *Awards, honors*: Numerous awards including: 1988 - Tulsa Arts Festival, Oklahoma Indian Market; 1989 - Five Tribes Museum, Intertribal Ceremonial; 1990 - Tulsa Indian Festival, Red Earth, Intertribal-Gallup; 1991 - Santa Fe Indian Market, Dallas Market Center, Katowah Intertribal Show, Trail of Tears Art Show; 1992 - Featured Fashion Designer-20th Annual Symposium on the American Indian-March 1992 by N.S.U., Tahlequah, OK. One Woman Shows & Special Exhibits, Invitationals. *Published works*: Prose by S S. Burrus - "Why Do They Whisper" (All My Relations, 1991); five prints (Wintercount Greeting Cards, 1991); cover & content illustrations for "The Trail On Which They Wept" (Cherokee Girl) (Silver/Burdett Press, 1992); 1993 Calendar (Wintercount Greeting Cards 1992); numerous prints and posters.

BURSON, JAMES M.
(attorney)
Education: University of New mexico School of Law, JD. *Affiliation & Address*: Partner, Stetson & Jordan, P.C., 1305 Rio Grande Blvd. NW, Albuquerque, NM 87104 (505) 256-4911. E-mail: jburson@stetsonlaw.com. James found himself drawn to the law field while teaching music at an Indian tribe's reservation school and serving as mayor of a small town in rural New Mexico. He then pursued a law degree from the University of New Mexico, simultaneously clerking with the U.S. District Court for New Mexico and the Department of the Interior's Regional Solicitor's Office, volunteering for the SW Indian Law Clinic, serving as Lead Articles Editor (Nat. Resources J.), and ultimately graduating with certificates in Indian Law & Natural Resources Law. Before joining Stetson Law Offices, he worked for over ten years with the firm of Hobbs, Straus, Dean & Walker, LLP, performing general counsel and gaming counsel services for a number of Oklahoma-based Indian tribes and tribal enterprises. Prior to that he worked with Quinlan, Bloom & Assoc. in New Mexico serving the interests of Mescalero Apache Tribe and Gerald Champion Medical Center. Jim has handled both transactional work & litigation for almost two decades, protecting tribal interests in construction, financing, real estate, economic development,

and vendor relationships. He provides policy advice and development of regulations related to: gaming, ethics, taxation, HIPAA compliance, housing, natural resource development and protection, child welfare, tort & prize claims, and employment matters among others. Licensed to practice law in Oklahoma & New Mexico, he has litigated in the U.S. Supreme Court, 10th Circuit Court of Appeals, Court of Federal Claims, all Federal District Courts for Oklahoma and New Mexico, the Court of Indian Offenses, Osage Nation Court, Muscogee Creek Nation Court, and Absentee Shawnee Tribe Court.

BURT, EUGENE C. 1948-
(managing editor)
Born July 31, 1948, Philadelphia, PA. *Education*: Temple University, BA, 1970; University of Washington, MA, 1973, PhD, 1980. *Principal occupation*: Managing editor, Ethnoarts Index. *Address*: P.O. Box 30789, Seattle, WA 98103 (206) 783-9580. *Affiliation*: Owner, Data Arts, Seattle, WA, 1983-. *Other professional post*: Higher education teaching positions at various institutions. *Interests*: Non-western art history. *Published works*: Bibliography of Tribal Art Bibliographies (Data Arts, 1986); Native American Art: A 5-Year Cumulative Bibliography (Data Arts, 1990).

BUSH, BOBBIE LOUISE (Chehalis)
(poet, writer)
Address: P.O. Box 926, Hoodsport, WA 98548 (360) 426-3990.

BUSH, MITCHELL LESTER, JR. (Onondaga) 1936-
(chief-tribal enrollment, B.I.A.-retired)
Born February 1, 1936, Syracuse, N.Y. *Education*: Haskell Institute, 1951-56. *Principal occupation*: Chief, tribal enrollment, B.I.A. *Address*: 22258 Cool Water Dr., Ruther Glen, VA 22546. *Affiliation*: Chief, Branch of Tribal Enrollment Services, BIA, Washington, DC, 1956-91. *Other professional post*: Editor, American Indian Society (Washington, DC) Newsletter, 1966-. *Military service*: U.S. Army, 1958-61 (Specialist 4th Class). *Community activities*: DC-MD-VA Chapter of VEVITA (board of directors); American Indian Inaugural Ball (committee member, 1969, '73, '77, '81, '85, '89, '93, '97, 2001); American Indian Society, Washington, D.C. (president, 1966-91); Board of Directors, Governors' Interstate Indian Council, 2002-present. *Awards, honors*: American Indian Society Distinguished Service Award, 1971 & 1990; Maharishi Award conferred by the Maharishi University; appointed by Gov. Gerald L. Baliles to Virginia Council on Indians, 1989; reappointed to Virginia Council on Indians by Governor Mark Warner in 2004; Outstanding Public Service to the U.S.A. certificate from the Dept. of the Interior, May, 1990; Mental Health Association Distinguished Service Award; Certificate of Appreciation from MD Governor Hughes; Points of Light Certificate for Outstanding Volunteer Contributions to the U.S.A. issued by Dept. of the Interior; Certificate of Appreciation from the Presidential Inaugural Committee, Jan. 1981. *Interests*: "Lecturer and Indian dancer for American Indian Society; participant, 1990 Census Planning Conference on Race & Ethnic Items sponsored by the Census Bureau; tour leader to Virginia Indian reservations for Resident Associate Program, Smithsonian Institution; honored at the 1982 Nanticoke (Delaware) Powwow; judge at the 1978, '80, '82, '84 & '85 Miss Indian America Pageants held in Sheridan, WY, & Bismarck, ND; photo & bio included in Shadows Caught: Images of Native Americans, by Stephen Gambaro at Gilcrease Institute, Tulsa, Oklahoma. Avocational - roller skating & raising ornamental fowl." *Biographical sources*: To Live in Two Worlds, by Brent Ashabranner; American Indian Wars, by John Tebbel, 1960; Successful Indian Career Profiles, to be published by North American Indian Club, Syracuse, N.Y. *Published works*: Editor, American Indian Society Cookbook (American Indian Society, 1975 & 1984 editions); Movies & Television shows: Lives of the Rich and Famous, segment featuring Connie Stevens; MGM, George Washington TV Mini-Series; Indians, Walt Disney Productions; TNT's "Broken Chain"; New Line Cinemas, "The New World," and numerous television programs.

BUSH, PHIL (Chehalis Confederated Tribes)
(corporation chairperson)
Affiliation & Address: Chairperson, Amerind Risk Management Corp., 502 Cedar Dr., Santa Ana, NM 87004 (505) 404-5000 Website: www.amerind-corp.org. *Other professional posts*: Executive director (1989-present), Modoc Lassen Indian Housing Authority, 401 Peninsula Dr. #6, Lake Almanor, CA 96137 (530) 596-4127; chair, Nevada-California Indian Housing Association, 1991-present; appointed member of the Negotiated Rule Making Committee of the Native American Housing Assistance & Self-Determination Act. *Past professional post*: Three terms as president of the Southwest Indian Housing Association. *Membership*: Confederated Tribes of the Chehalis Reservation.

BUTLER, RODNEY A. (Pequot)
(tribal chairperson)
Born & raised in Montville, Conn. *Education*: University of Connecticut, BS (Finance). *Affiliation & Address*: Chairperson (2010-Present), Mashantuckett Pequot Tribal Nation, 2 Matts Path, P.O. Box 3060, Mashantucket, CT 06338 (860) 396-6100. Mr. Butler is the founding Trustee of the Mashantucket (Western) Pequot Tribe Endowment Trust. *Other professional posts*: He is

currently the Co-Chair for the United Way of Southeastern Connecticut, serves on the Board of Trustees for Roger Williams University, is a Director on the Board of the Mystic Aquarium, and a Board Member for the Southeastern Connecticut Chamber of Commerce. *Past affiliations*: Chair of Tribal Business Advisory Board; tribal council member since 2004; 2005, elected treasurer of tribe (2005-2010); served as chair of the tribe's Housing & Judicial Committee, and chair of Finance Committee; financial analyst at tribe's Foxwoods Resort Casino. Mr. Butler was active in the resort expansion at Foxwoods, as well as Phase VII housing development on the reservation.

BUTLER-WOLFE, EDWINA GEORGE (Absentee-Shawnee)
(tribal governor)
Affiliation & Address: Governor, Absentee-Shawnee Tribe, 2025 S. Gordon Cooper Dr., Shawnee, OK 74801 (405) 275-4030.

BUTTERFIELD, ROBIN A. (Winnebago/White Earth Ojibwa)
(program supervisor)
Education: University of Puget Sound, BA; University of Wisconsin, MA (Curriculum & Instruction); Portland State University (Education Administration Certification). *Affiliation & Address*: Program Supevisor, Office of Native Education, Special Programs & Federal Accountability, Office of Supt. of Public Instruction, Old Capitol Bldg., 600 Washington St. SE, P.O. Box 47200, Olympia, WA 98504 (360) 725-6160. E-mail: robin.butterfield@k12.wa.us. *Past professional posts*: Served five three year terms, and past president, National Indian Education Association, Board of Director; Coordinator, Oregon Dept. of Education, Indian Education, Salem, OR; Professional Development Specialist, Center for School Improvement, Bureau of Indian Affairs, Albuquerque, NM. Recently managed the contracts with 13 tribally controlled community colleges and state universities, providing staff development to BIA funded schools. *Awards, honors*: Appointed by President Geoge Bush and President Obama to serve on the National Advisory Council on Indian Education, which advises the Secretary of U.S. Department of Education, on matters impacting Indian education & reports directly to Congress.

BUTTES, BARBARA F.
(professor)
Affiliation & Address: Professor of American Indian Studies, Dept. of American Studies, Arizona State University, Tempe, AZ 85287 (602) 965-6213. *Interests*: Mdewekanton Sioux of Minnesota; tribal gaming. E-mail: barbara.buttes@asu.edu.

BYARS, TONY (Alabama-Coushatta)
(museum supt.)
Affiliation & Address: Superinentnedent, Alabama-Coushatta Indian Museum, Route 3, Box 640, U.S. Hwy. 190, Livingston, TX 77351 (713) 563-4391.

BYERS, AMBER (Sault Ste. Marie Ojibwe)
(attorney)
Education: University of Washington, BA, 2003; University of New Mexico School of Law: Pre-Law Summer Institute for American Indians, 2005; University of Arizona College of Law, JD, 2008. *Affiliation & Address*: Private practice, Longmont, CO. *Practice areas*: Business, Family, Criminal Defense, Estate Planning, Real Estate, Personal Injury. *Past professional post*: Associate (2010-14), Fredericks Peebles & Morgan, Louisville, CO.

BYRD, JODI A. (Chickasaw)
(professor of American Indian studies & English)
Education: University of Iowa, PhD (English), 2002. *Affiliation & Address*: Associate Professor & Acting Director, American Indian Studies & English, College of Arts & Sciences, University of Illinois, 1204 W. Nevada St., Room 2004, Urbana, IL 61801 (217) 265-9870. E-mail: jabyrd@illinois.edu. Research Interests: Indigenous studies & governance, indigenous & postcolonial literatures, cultural studies, film, theory. *Published works*: The Transit of Empire: Indigenous Critiques of Colonialism (University of Minnesota Press, 2011); numerous articles in journals; book contributions.

BYRD, JOE (Cherokee)
(principal chief)
Address & Affiliation: Cherokee Nation of Oklahoma, P.O. Box 948, Tahlequah, OK 74465 (918) 456-0671.

BYRD, RANDI R.
(community engagement coordinator)
Affiliation & Address: Community Engagement Coordinator, American Indian Center, University of North Carolina, 113A Abernathy Hall, CB 3457, Chapel Hill, NC 27599 (919) 962-5927. E-mail: rrbyrd@email.unc.edu *Other professional post*: Carolinians Network Project Director. She serves as Project Director for the Healthy Native North Carolinians Network. Ms. Byrd works closely with American Indian communities in North Carolina around health and

wellness through a holistic community lens, community grassroots organizing that values indigenous ways of knowing & practices, facilitating & promoting tribally-vetted & culturally appropriate curricula on NC American Indians, affirming tribal self-determination in sustainable planning & fostering mutually beneficial partnerships meaningfully strengthen communities. Ms. Byrd serves as mentor through the American Indian Center for students and Ambassadors particularly interested in opportunities to give back to their communities through service, education and advocacy.

BYRNES, JIM (Navajo)
(Indian school principal)
Affiliation: To'hajiilee-He (Canoncito) School, P.O. Box 438, Laguna, NM 87026 (505) 831-6426.

C

CABAGNOT, JADE
(program coordinator)
Affiliation & Address: Program Coordinator, The D'Arcy McNickle Center for American Indian & Indigenous Studies, The Newberry Library, 60 W. Walton St., Chicago, IL 60610 (312) 255-3552. E-mail: cabagnot@newberry.org.

CABANISS, DONALD, JR. (Apache of Oklahoma)
(former tribal chairperson)
Affiliation & Address: Apache Tribe of Oklahoma, P.O. Box 1330, Anadarko, OK 73005 (405) 247-9493 ext. 121.

CABRAL, DARIEN
(association executive director)
Address & Affiliation: Executive director, Indian Arts & Crafts Association, 4010 Carlisle NE, Suite C, Albuquerque, NM 87107 (505) 265-9149.

CADUE, CHERYL (Kickapoo)
(public information coordinator)
Affiliation: American Indian College Fund, 21 W. 68th St., Suite 1F, New York, NY 10023 (800) 776-3863; (212) 787-6312. E-mail: cadue@collegefund.org.

CADUE, STEVEN (Kickapoo)
(tribal councilman)
Affiliation & Address: Kickapoo Tribe of Kansas, P.O. Box 271, Horton, KS 66439 (785) 486-2131. *Past professional post*: Chairperson, Kickapoo Nation School, Powhattan, KS.

CADUTO, MICHAEL J.
(author, master storyteller, ecologist, educator, poet & musician)
Education: University of Michigan, MS in Natural Resources/Environmental Education. *Affiliation & Address*: P.E.A.C.E., P.O. Box 1052, Norwich, VT 05055 (802) 649-1815. Website: www.p-e-a-c-e.net In 1984, Michael founded a service called P.E.A.C.E. (Programs for Environmental Awareness & Cultural Exchange), promotes understanding, awareness, appreciation & stewardship as the foundation for building a harmonious sustainable relationship between people and Earth, and among the cultures of the world. He has worked with many indigenous peoples during the past 25 years. His programs, performances, keynotes, workshops & residencies are given to children, school groups, teachers, naturalists, storytellers, conferences & general audiences. *Native American Programs*: Native American Thanksgivings: he Circle of Giving & Receiving; Nature in Indian Myths: Earth Stewardship Traditions; Native American Gardening & the Seeds of Life: Preserving Biological & Cultural Diversity; Native American Games; A Time Before New Hampshire & Vermont; The White Roots of Peace Haudenosaunee (Iroquois) Roots of the U.S. Constitution & the True Story of Hiawatha. *Other professional post*: Sr. Education Fellow with the Atlantic Center for the Environment. *Awards, honors*: NAPPA Gold & Silver Awards, National Parenting Publications Award; Brimstone Award for Applied Storytelling, National Storytelling Network; Aesop Prize, American Folklore Society's choice for Best Book of the Year; ALA (American Library Association) Best Books for Young Adults. *Interests*: Travels extensively presenting environmental & cultural programs for adults & children. *Published works*: Keepers of the Animals: Native American Stories & Wildlife Activities for Children; Keepers of the Earth: Native American Stories & Environmental Activities for Children; Keepers of Life: Discovering Plants Through Native American Stories & Earth Activities for Children; Keepers of the Night: Native American Stories and Nocturnal Activities for Children; Native American Gardening; Earth Tales from Around the World, Pond & Brook: A Guide to Nature in Freshwater Environments, A Time Before New Hampshire: The Story of a Land & Native Peoples; Everyday Herbs in Spiritual Life: A Guide to Many Practices; Catch the Wind, Harness the Sun: 22 Supercharged Projects for Kids & Riparia's River (2011) (all "Keepers" books with Joseph Bruchac); also audiocassette, All One Earth: Songs for the Generations (Fulcrum Publishing).

CAGEY, HENRY M. (Lummi)
(foundation chairperson)
Education: Northwest Indian College. *Affiliation & Address*: Chairperson, United Indian of All Tribes Foundation, P.O. Box 99100, Seattle, WA 98199 (206) 285-4425. *Other professional posts*: Board President, National Tribal Development Association, Box Elder, MT; senior strategist, Blue Stone Strategy Group, Irvine, CA. *Past professional posts*: Lummi Nation, for almost 30 years in various roles such as the TERO director, vocational rehabilitation, and economic development director. 16 years on the Lummi Indian Business Council, 12 years serving as tribal chairperson; Affiliated Tribes of Northwest Indians (ATNI), Portland, OR (president & 1st vice president); PTAC director, National Center for American Indian Economic Development. *Military service*: U.S. Navy.

CAHOON, HEATHER (Confederated Salish & Kootenai)
(professor of Native American studies)
Education: University of Montana, BA (English & Native American Studies), 2000, NFA (Poetry), 2001, PhD (History, Anthropology & Native American Studies, 2005. *Affiliation & Address*: Adjunct Faculty, Native American Studies Depatment, NAC 203B, University of Montana, Missoula, NT 59812 (406) 243-5838. E-mail: heather.cahoon@mso.umt.edu. *Awards, honors*: University of Montana Merriam-Frontier Award for Publication of "Elk Thurst," Big Sky Journal, Bozeman, MT, 2005.Membership: Montana Indian Education Association. *Published works*: Poetry; conributions to books; three collections of 16 short stories for children that wewre translated into Salish and used for level 1-3 Salish Language Curriculum at Nikwusmm, the Salish Language Immersion School located on the Flathead Indian Reservation.

CAJERO, JOE (Jemez Pueblo)
(artist, shop owner; former pueblo governor)
Affiliation: Artist/owner, Cajero Sculptures Ltd., P.O. Box 377, Jemez Pueblo, NM 87024 (505) 867-3773. Website: www.cajerosculpture.com. *Artwork*: Limited editions bronze sculptures & one-of-a-kind clay sculptures that reflect Native American Pueblo culture & spirituality. *Past tribal post*: Governor, Jemez Pueblo.

CAJETE, GREGORY A. (Tewa-Santa Clara Pueblo)
(professor of education; director of Native American studies)
Education: New Mexico Highlands University, BA; University of New Mexico, MA; International College - Los Angeles (New Philosophy Program in Social Science Education with emphasis in Native American Studies), PhD. *Affiliation & Address*: Director, Native American Studies Department, University of New Mexico, Mesa Vista 3080, Albuquerque, NM 87131 (505) 277-3917; Associate Professor (1995-present), Division of Language, Literacy & Sociocultural Studies, College of Education, University of New Mexico, Albuquerque, NM. *Past professional posts*: Institute of American Indian Arts, Santa Fe, NM (21 years) as Dean of the Center for Research & Cultural Exchange, Chairperson of Native American Studies & Professor of Ethno-science. He organized & directed the First & Second Annual National Native American Very Special Arts Festival in Santa Fe, NM in 1991 & Albuquerque, NM in 1992. *Awards, honors*: American Indian Graduate Fellowship, US-DOE Office of Indian Education (1977-78); the D'Arcy McNickle Fellowship in American Indian History, Newberry Library, Chicago, IL (1984-85); Katrin Lamon Fellowship in American Indian Art & Education (1985-86) from the School of American Research, Santa Fe, NM. *Published works*: Look to the Mountain: An Ecology of Indigenous Education (Kivaki Press, 1994); Ignite the Sparkle: An Indigenous Science Education Curriculum Model (Kivaki Press, 1999); A People's Ecology: Explorations in Sustainable Living, and Native Science Natural Laws of Interdependence" (Clearlight Publishers, 1999 & 2000); Spirit of the Game: Indigenous Wellsprings (Clearwater Publishers, 2004).

CALCATERA, MARY (Sault Ste. Marie Ojibwe)
(Native American Institute academic specialist)
Education: Michigan State University, BA. *Affiliation & Address*: Academic Specialist, Native American Institute, Justin S. Morrill Hall of Agriculture, Michigan State University, 446 W. Circle Dr., Rm. 406, East Lansing, MI 48824 (517) 353-6632. E-mail: catera@anr.msu.edu.

CALDWELL, ALAN JAMES (Menominee-White Earth Chippewa) 1948-
(education program director)
Born May 27, 1948, Shawano, Wisc. *Education*: University of Wisconsin, Green Bay, BS (History), 1976; University of Wisconsin, Superior, 1979-83; University of Wisconsin, Madison. *Address*: Program Director, Upward Bound, University of Wisconsin, Stevens Point, WI 54481 (715) 346-3337 (office). *Past professional posts*: Principal/teacher, Lac Courte Oreilles Ojibwe Schools, Hayward, WI, 1976-81; business manager, Menominee Positive Youth Development Corp., Keshena, WI, 1981-84; education consultant, Wisconsin Department of Public Instruction, Madison, WI; director-Upward Bound, University of Wisconsin, Stevens Point, WI, 1991; Indian education director, Shawano School District, Shawano, WI. *Military service*: U.S. Army, 1969-71, SP/5. *Community activities*: Wisconsin Humanities Committee, 1983-89; past

member & chair, board of directors, Menominee Tribal Enterprises; (Wisconsin) American Indian Language & Culture Education Board, 1984. Memberships: National Indian Education Association (board of directors, 1977-78); Wisconsin Indian Education Association (former president, board of directors); National Coalition for Sex Equity in Education; National Bilingual Education Association; Wisconsin Bilingual Education Association; Wisconsin Teachers of English to Speakers of Other Languages. *Awards, honors*: 1988 "Wisconsin Indian Educator of the Year Award" from Wisconsin Indian Education Association; "Outstanding Leadership Award" from UW-Green Bay Ethnic Heritage Program, 1976. *Interests*: "Responsible for American Indian education programs established under Wisconsin Act 31 - 1989-91 biennial budget. *Published works*: Articles on American Indian history, culture, education, athletics and youth programs.

CALDWELL-WOOD, NAOMI RACHEL (Ramapough Lenape) 1958-
(associate professor of library & information science)
Born March 31, 1958, Providence, R.I. *Education*: Clarion State College, BS, 1980; Clarion University of Pennsylvania, MSLS, 1982; graduate studies: Texas A&M University, 1986-87, Providence College, 1990-92, School of Ministry, Faith Christian Center (Seekonk, Mass.), Diploma-two year program; University of Pittsburgh, PhD, 2002. *Principal occupation*: Library science. *Affiliation & Address*: Associate Professor, Graduate School of Library & Information Studies, The University of Rhode Island, Rodman Hall, Office 11, Kingston, RI 02881 (401) 874-2278. E-mail: inpeacencw@aol.com. *Past professional posts*: Microtext Reference Librarian, Sterling C. Evans Library, Texas A&M University, College Station, TX, 1985-87; Library Media Specialist, Nathan Bishop Middle School, Providence, RI, 1987-92; American Indian Library Association (secretary, 1987-90; president, 1990-). *Other professional activities*: Editorial Advisory Board & Reviewer, "MultiCultural Review," Greenwood Publishing, 1991-; Professional Reading Reviewer, "School Library Journal" Cahners/R.R. Bowker, 1991-; Advisory Board, OYATE, Berkeley, CA, 1992-; Advisory Board, "Native American Information Directory," Gale Research, 1992; Screening Committee, Native American Public Broadcasting Consortium, 1993-. *Community activities*: Consultant, Brown University, Providence Drug-Free Schools Project, 1987-91; Rhode Island Children's Book Award Committee, 1990-92. *Memberships*: Ramapough Mountain Indian Tribe; American Library Association (OLOS: Library Services for American Indian People Subcommittee, member, 1986-88, 1990-92, chair, 1992-; ALA Council Committee on Minority Concerns, member, 1991-93, 1994-; ALA Councilor-at-Large, 1992-); American Indian Library Association (secretary, 1987-90; president, 1990-present). *Awards, honors*: First American Indian to earn a PhD in library & information sciences; U.S. Board on Books for Young People (member, Discovery Award Committee, 1994-); honorary delegate to White House Conference on Library & Information Services, Washington, DC, 1991; participant, Native American & Alaskan Native Pre-Conference to the White House Conference on Library & Information Services, March 1991; participant, National Indian Policy Center, Forum on Native American Libraries & Information Services, George Washington University, Washington, DC, May 1991. *Interests*: Native American educational materials and books for children; multicultural literature; library & information services. Numerous presentations, including: "Multicultural Books for Children: The Native American Perspective," Library Science Colloquium, Clarion University of Pennsylvania, Jan. 1994; "Native Americans & Children's Books: Evaluation & Selection," Carnegie Library of Pittsburgh Children's Services Meeting, Jan. 1993; "How to Evaluate Native American Books," Texas Library Association, March 1993; Native American Materials for Children," Dept. of Education, Clarion University of Pennsylvania, Oct. 1992. *Published works*: Checklist of Bibliographies Appearing in the Bulletin of Bibliography, 1897-1987, with Patrick Wood (Meckler Corp., 1988). Articles: "I Is Not for Indian: The Portrayal of Native Americans in Books for Young People," with Lisa Mitten, in MultiCultural Review (April 1992); "Native American Images in Children's Books," in School Library Journal (May 1992); "Boxes of Light," in Hungry Mind Review: Children's Review Supplement (Fall 1992).

CALF BOSS RIBS, FORRESTINA "FROSTY" (Blackfeet)
(Montana State (D) representative)
Affiliation & Address: Montana State representative, P.O. Box 20, Heart Butte, MT 59448 (406) 338-2086. E-mail: frostycbr@hotmail.com. *Committee*: State-Tribal Relations. Frosty is the first Blackfeet Indian woman elected to the Montana Legislature.

CALLOWAY, COLIN G. 1953-
(professor, historian)
Born February 10, 1953, Yorkshire, England. *Education*: University of Leeds, England, BA, 1974, PhD, 1978. *Affiliation & Address*: Professor of History & Samson Occom Professor of Native American Studies (1995-present), Dartmouth College, Native American Studies Dept. 37 N. Main St., 204 Sherman House, Hanover, NH 03755 (603) 646-2076; E-mail: colin.calloway@dartmouth.edu. *Past professional posts*: Assistant director/editor, D'Arcy McNickle Center for the History of the American Indian, The Newberry Library, Chicago, IL, 1985-87; professor of history, University of Wyoming, Laramie,

1987-95. *Memberships*: Organization of American Historians; American Society for Ethnohistory; Western History Association. *Awards, honors*: 1993 John P. Ellbogen Meritorious Teaching Award, University of Wyoming; John Sloan Dickey Third Century Professor in the Social Sciences, Dartmouth College, 1996-2001; American Council of Learned Societies Fellowship, 2004-2005. *Interests*: American Indian history; early American history. *Published works*: Crown & Calumet: British-Indian Relations, 1783-1815 (University of Oklahoma Press, 1987); Editor, New Directions in American Indian History (University of Oklahoma Press, 1988); The Abenaki (Chelsea House, 1989); The Western Abenakis of Vermont (University of Oklahoma Press, 1990); Editor, Dawnland Encounters: Indians and Europeans in Northern New England (University Press of New England, 1991); Editor (with Alden T. Vaughn), Early American Indian Documents: Treaties and Laws, 1607-1789: The Confederation Period, 1775-1789 (University Publications of America, 1992); Editor, The World Turned Upside Down: Indian Voices from Early America (Bedford Books, 1994); The American Revolution in Indian Country (Cambridge University Press, 1995); editor, Our Hearts Fell to the Ground: Plains Indian Views of How the West Was Lost (Bedford Books, 1996); editor, After King Philip's War: Presence & Persistence in Indian New England (University Press of New England, 1997); New Worlds for All: Indians, Europeans, and the Remaking of Early America (Johns Hopkins University Press, 1997); First Peoples: A Documentary Survey of American Indian History (Bedford Books, 1999, 2004); editor with Gerd Gemundsen & Susanne Zantop, Germans & Indians (University of Nebraska Press, 2002); editor, Reinterpreting New England Indians & the Colonial Experience (Colonial Society of Massachusetts, 2003); One Vast Winter-Count: The Native American West Before Lewis & Clark (University of Nebraska Press, 2003); The Scratch of a Pen: 1763 & the Transformation of North America (Oxford University Press, 2006); The Shawnees & the War for America (Viking/Penguin, 2007); White People, Indians, & Highlanders: Tribal Peoples & Colonial Encounters in Scotland & America (Oxford University Press, 2008); The Indian History of an American Institution: Native Americans & Dartmouth (University Press of New England, 2010); Pen and Ink Witchraft: Treaties and Treaty Making in American Indian History (2013); The Victory with No Name: The Native American Defeat of the First American Army (2015).

CAMBRA, ROSEMARY (Ohlone/Costanoan Muwekma)
(tribal chairperson)
Affiliation & Address: Chairperson, Ohlone/Costanoan Muwekma Tribe, 2574 Seaboard Ave., San Jose, CA (408) 383-9318. E-mail: rcambra@muwekma.org.

CAMPBELL, ALYSSA D. (Kaw)
(tribal attorney general)
Education: University of Texas, BA, 2001; University of Oklahoma College of Law, JD, 2004; Certification in American Indian Law from the Center for the Study of American Indian Law & Policy, 2004. *Affiliation & Address*: Partner, Legal Advocates for Indian Country, LLP, P.O. Box 2293, Stillwater, OK 74076 (405) 742-0200. E-mail: acampbell@laic-law.com. *Other professional post*: Attorney General, Kaw Nation, Kaw City, OK. *Membership*: Oklahoma Bar Association.

CAMPBELL, BEN (Nighthorse) (Northern Cheyenne) 1933-
(former U.S. Senator; jeweler; rancher)
Born April 13, 1933, Auburn, Calif. *Education*: San Jose State University, 1953-58. *Principal occupation*: Jeweler; rancher; U.S. Senator, D-CO. *Affiliation & Address*: Nighthorse Jewelry, Inc., P.O. Box 639, Ignacio, CO 81137 (970) 563-4623. *Past professional post*: U.S. Senate, Washington, DC; chairman, Senate Select Committee on Indian Affairs. *Military service*: U.S. Air Force, 1951-53 (Airman 2nd Class; Korean Veteran). *Memberships*: American Quarter Horse Association; U.S. Brangus Association; American Paint Horse Association; Indian Arts & Crafts Association; U.S. Olympic Committee (former secretary). *Awards, honors*: U.S. Judo Champion, 1961-63, All-American, 1964; 1963 Gold Medal Winner, Pan American Games; Captain, U.S. Olympic Team, 1964; "have also won over 200 awards in art shows for jewelry design." *Interests*: "Have traveled extensively - 40 countries. I'm now a member of a delegation to North Atlantic Assembly." *Biographical sources*: Autobiography now being published by Smithsonian Press; have been in Woman's Day, Arizona Highways, Empire Magazine Southwest, and USA Today. *Published work*: Judo Drill Training (Zenbei Publishing, 1967).

CAMPBELL, GREGORY R. (Eastern Shawnee) 1955-
(professor of anthropology)
Born August 1, 1955, Cincinnati, Ohio. *Education*: Chaffey Community College, AA, 1976; UCLA, BA (Anthropology & History), 1979; University of Oklahoma, Norman, MA, 1982, PhD (Anthropology), 1987 (Dissertation: The Political Economy of Ill-Health: Changing Northern Cheyenne Health Patterns & Economic Underdevelopment, 1876-1930); Institute of American Cultures, University of California, Los Angeles, Postdoctoral Diploma, 1988. *Address*: 104 Peery Park Dr., Missoula, MT 59803. *Office address*: Professor, Dept. of Anthropology, University of Montana, Missoula, MT 59812 (406) 243-2478. E-

mail: gregory.campbell@mso.umt.edu. *Affiliations*: Professor, Department of Anthropology, U. of Montana, Missoula, MT, 1988-present (Dept. Chair, 1999-05). *Other professional posts*: Curator of Ethnology, Anthropological Collections, Dept. of Anthropology, University of Montana, Missoula, 1988-05; Peer Reviewer, articles & manuscripts for various professional journals & publishers, 1988-05; project director, Glacier National Park NAGPRA Cultural Affiliation Study, National Park Service, Glacier National Park, MT, 2003-05. University & Community Services: Dept. of Anthropology, University of Montana (General Student Advisor, 1988-04; Graduate Student Advisor, 1995-04. *Past professional posts*: Graduate & teaching assistantships, instructor & assistant professor, University of Oklahoma, Dept. of Anthropology, 1979-87; Research associate, Southern Cheyenne Ethno-history Project, Dept. of Anthropology, University of Oklahoma, 1979-82; ethnological curator, Oklahoma Historical Society, State Museum, 1982-85; acting assistant professor, Dept. of Anthropology & American Indian Studies, UCLA, 1987-88; Symposium chair & organizer, Native American Ethnology, Anthropology Program Section Coordinator, 1989 Western Social Science Assn, Albuquerque, NM, 1988-89; (current) Curator of ethnology, Anthropological Collections, Dept. of Anthropology, University of Montana; research affiliate, Center for Population Research, University of Montana; Symposium Chair, "Tribal Preservation & Renewal, 1999, 52nd Annual Northwest Anthropological Conference, Oregon State University, Newport, OR; appointed member (presidential appointment), University of Montana Lewis & Clark Bicentennial Committee, Office of the President, University of Montana, Missoula, 2001-04; Chair Workshop Series, University of Montana, Missoula, 2001-03; Provost Seminar Series "Diversity Within Higher Education," 2002-04. *Ethnographic & Consultation Field Research*: Research Associate, Southern Cheyenne Ethno-history Project, Dept. of Anthropology, University of Oklahoma, 1979-82; Ethnographic Research, Northern Cheyenne Tribe, Lame Deer, MT, 1984-04; Research Ethnologist/Ethno-historian Consultant, Association for American Indian Affairs, 1992-97; Research Ethnologist/ Ethno-historian, Fort Lemhi Indian Community, Inc. Federal Recognition Project, Salmon, Idaho, 1996-98; Research & Demographic Consultant, Confederated Salish & Kootenai Tribes, Tribal & Legal Dept., The Confederated Salish & Kootenai Tribes of the Flathead Reservation, 1997-98, 2002; Ethnographic/Ethno-historical Research, Gila River Indian Community, Sacaton, AZ, 1998-04; Ethnographic Research, Blackfeet Tribe, Browning, MT, 2000-01; Historic Preservation Consultation, Chippewa Cree Tribe of the Rocky Boy Reservation, Box Elder, MT, 2001; Ethnographic & Museum Interpretation Consultant, Sacajawea Interpretive Center, Salmon, ID, 2001-04. *Research Grants & Contracts*: Project Director, NAGPRA Ethnographic Consultation, Glacier National Park, MT, 2003-05; Principal Investigator, "First Nations of the Northwestern Plains: A Cultural History of Persistence & Change After the Lewis & Clark Expedition," National Park Service, Cooperative Agreement Grant. *Awards, honors*: Antiquarian Bookseller's Association of America Award, UCLA, 1979; Counseling Award, Academic Achievement Program, UCLA, 1979; scholarship, Buffalo Bill Historical Center, Cody, WY, 1981; National Endowment for the Arts Grant, 1984-85; Oklahoma Foundation for the Humanities Grant, 1985; Dr. Robert E. Bell Fund Award, Dept. of Anthropology, University of Oklahoma, 1985; University of Oklahoma Associates' Fund, Dissertation Research Grant, 1986; Postdoctoral Scholar, Institute of American Cultures, Native American Studies Center, U.C.L.A., 1987-88; Merit Awards, Teaching & Research, Dept. of Anthropology, University of Montana, Missoula, 1997 & 2001; Publication Awards, The Mansfield Library, University of Montana, Missoula, 1999 & 2002. *Memberships*: American Society for Ethno-history; Plains Anthropological Assn; Northwest Anthropological Society; The International & Infectious Disease Study Group, Society for Medical Anthropology; American Anthropological Assn; National Assn for Ethnic Studies; Museum Association of Montana; American Assn for State & Local History; Lambda Alpa, National Anthropology Honor Society. Research *Interests*: Native North America, race & ethnicity, cultural resource management, cultural heritage studies, political economy, demographic anthropology, social epidemiology, social organization, ethnohistory. *Published works*: Plains Pictographic Art: An Evolving Tradition; Many Americas: Critical Perspectives on Race, Racism, & Ethnicity (Kendall/Hunt, 1998; revised second edition, 2001); An Ethno-historical & Ethnographic Evaluation of Blackfeet Religious & Traditional Cultural Practices in East Glacier National Park and the Surrounding Mountains (Browning: The Blackfeet Nation, 2001); Native Peoples of the Northwestern Plains: An Ethno-history of Cultural Persistence & Change (manuscript in progress, 2004). Articles; numerous reports, book reviews & articles on Native American history & culture; also, conference papers & research presentations.

CAMPBELL, HIRAM O., SR. (Pomo)
(tribal chief)
Affiliation & Address: Chief, Coyote Valley Band of Pomo Indians, P.O. Box 39, Redwood Valley, CA 95470 (707) 485-8723.

CAMPBELL, LETA LOIS (Coeur D'Alene)
(tribal council member)
Address & Affiliation: Coeur D'Alene Tribe, 850 A St., P.O. Box 408, Plummer, ID 83851 (208) 686-1800. *Other professional post*: Medical Records Director,

Benewah Medical Center, 1997-present). *Community activities*: Chairperson, Benewah Medical Center Health Board; delegate, Northwest Portland Area Indian Health Board; member, Idaho Council on Indian Affairs; member, Museum of Art & Culture.

CAMPBELL, MARIA (Metis) 1940-
(writer; visiting academic)
Born & raised in northwestern Saskatchewan. *Education*: University of Saskatchewan, MA (Native Studies); University of Regina, Honorary Doctorate, 1995; Athabasca University, Honorary Doctorate, 2000). *Affiliation & Address*: Visiting Academic, Athabasaca U., Centre for World Indigenous Knowledge & Research, 1 University Dr., Athabasca, AB T9S 3A3 (780) 675-6100. *Awards, honors*: Maria was made an Officer of the Order of Canada in 2008. *Published works*: Many Laws, 1969, (a hand book explaining the laws & problems that confront First Nations people who move to the cities); Half-Breed, 1973; People of the Buffalo, 1975; Little Badger and the Fire Spirit, 1977; Riel's People, 1978; Stories of the Road-Allowance People, 1995; plays & scripts. Her script, The Red Dress (1977) is a film for the National Film Board.

CAMPBELL, MATTHEW L. (Eskimo)
(attorney)
Education: Fort Lewis College, BA; Arizona State University, O'Connor Colege of Lw, JD. *Affiliation & Address*: Staff Attorney, Nat̃ive American Rights Fund (NARF), 1506 Broadway, Boulder, CO 80302 (303) 447-8760. *Past professional posts*: Attorney, Cuddy & McCarthy, LLP, Albuquerque, NM, focusing on Indian law, education, and water law; clerked for the Arizona Court of Appeals.

CAMPBELL, RICHARD H. (Pomo)
(former tribal chief)
Affiliation & Address: Former Chief, Coyote Valley Band of Pomo Indians, P.O. Box 39, Redwood Valley, CA 95470 (707) 485-8723.

CAMPBELL, ROGER (Pomo)
(tribal office director)
Roger was raised on the Rosebud Sioux Reservation and is a member of the Pomo Tribe of the Round Valley Indian Reservation in Covelo, Calif. *Education*: South Dakota State University, BS, 1993. *Military service*: U.S. Marine Corps, 1986-90. *Address & Affiliation*: Office of Tribal Government Relations, Div. of SD Dept. of Tourism & State Development, 711 E. Wells Ave., Pierre, SD 57501 (605) 773-3415. Roger was appointed by Governor Mike Rounds in 2003. *Past professional post*: Executive Director, Oglala Sioux Tribe Partnership for Housing, Inc., Pine Ridge, SD, 1999-2003; Personal Banker, Norwest Banks South Dakota, Rapid City, SD, 1994-99.

CAMPBELL, SUSAN J. (*Shanote*) (Potawatomi/Menominee) 1944-
(author)
Born December 30, 1944, Wichita, Kans. *Education*: Highline Community College, AA, 1964; Seattle Pacific University, BA (Biblical Studies/Theology), 1988. *Address*: 3200-C Wawae Rd., Kalaheo, HI 96741. E-mail: nokmis@yahoo.com. *Affiliations*: Minnestra Center for Great Lakes Native American Studies, Muncie, IN, 1991-95; Museums at Prophetstown, Lafayette, IN, 1996-2000; National Center for Great Lakes Native American Studies, 2001-03; Wordcraft Circle, 2000-present. *Past professional post*: Associate Pastor, Columbia Baptist Church, 1988-92; regional director, Citizen Band Potawatomi, 1992-98. *Awards, honors*: Honored by Seattle Indian community/Grey Eagle, 1997. *Community activities*: Volunteer, American Cancer Society (patient services), Kaua'i. *Membership*: Kauai Orchid Society. *Interests*: Historical research; genealogy; Potawatomi language & cultural recovery; beadwork & quillwork; writing. *Published works*: "One Woman's Family and the Footprints It Left Behind," 2001 (a history of the Vieux family and its Native American and French roots); The Trail of Death: The Potawatomi Removal of 1838, co-authored with Shirley Willard, historian (Fulton Co. Historical Society (Rochester, IN), 2003).

CAMPEAU, PRISCILLA (Metis-Cree)
(First Nations program administrator)
Affiliation & Address: Chair & Program Administrator, Centre for World Indigenous Knowledge & Research, Athabasca University, 1 University Dr., Athabasca, AB T9S 3A3 (780) 675-6100; E-mail: pcampeau@athabascau.ca

CANALES, MARYANNE (Eastern Cherokee)
(director of administration)
Education: University of Maryland, BA (in Legal Studies in progress). *Affiliation & Address*: Director of Administration, Clan Star, Inc., P.O. Box 1630, Cherokee, NC 28719 (828) 497-5507. *Past professional posts*: Volunteer, Michigan Child Abuse Council, 1980-85; Michigan Indian Employment Center, 1986-88; Grand Rapids Inter-Tribal Council, 1988-92; Michigan Indian Health Services, 1992-96. *Awards, honors*: In 1983, Michigan Governor James Blanchard appointed her to the Economic & Social Opportunity Commission.

CANDILLO, JOSEPH (Pascua Yaquii)
(lecturer in Native Ameican Studies)
Education: Appalachian State University, BS (Anthropology); University of Arizona, MA (American Indian Studies); University of Buffalo, PhD candidate. *Affiliation & Address*: Lecturer, Native Ameican Studies Program & lecturer in the Division of Forestry & Natural Resources, Davis College of Agriculture, Natural Resources, and Design, West Virginia University, Office 102, 325 Willey St., P.O. Box 6284, Morgantown, WV 26506 (304) 293-4626. Website: www.jooecandillo.com. *Current Research*: Focuses on Southeastern Woodland material culture & traditions. "I am an advocate of authenticity & traditional Native American artistry."

CANEZ, LEO (Yurok/Karuk/Tohono O'odham)
(language revitalization & restoration)
Address: 3579 Trinity St., Eureka, CA 95501. E-mail: neknewleo@yahoo.com. Leo has dedicated his life to revitalization & restoring the Yurok language by working with the elders in his community & facilitating various language activities. *Affiliation*: Board member, Advocates for Indigenous California Languages, Vallejo, CA.

CANNON, CAROLINE H. (Eskimo)
(AK village council president)
Affiliation: Point Hope Village Council, P.O. Box 109, Point Hope, AK 99766 (907) 368-2330.

CANTRELL, KATRINA (Shoshone)
(women's health specialist; board president)
Affiliation & Address: Clinical Systems Manager (1990-present), University Health Care System, 1350 Walton Way, Augusta, GA 30901. *Other professional post*: Board President, Native American Women's Health Education Resource Center, Native American Community BoardLake Andes, SD. *Past professional post*: Systems Analyst, Augusta Service Co., Inc., Augusta, GA, 1985-90.

CAPPS, LINDA (Citizen Potawatomi)
(tribal vice chairperson)
Affiliation & Address: Vice Chairperson, Citizen Potawatomi Nation, 1601 Gordon Cooper Dr., Shawnee, OK 74801 (405) 275-3121. E-mail: lcapps@potawatomi.org.

CAPTAIN, PETER (Louden)
(first chief)
Affiliation & Address: First Chief (1995-present), Louden Tribe, P.O. Box 244, Galena, AK 99741 (907) 656-1711. *Other professional post*: Member, Yukon River Inter-Tribal Watershed Council.

CARDOZA, MARY (Lummi)
(chief judge/director)
Affiliation & Address: Chief Judge/Director, Lummi Tribal Court, 2665 Kwina Rd., Bellingham, WA 98226 (360) 312-2239.

CARDWELL, TERI (Shawnee/Cherokee)
(clinical social worker)
Education: Anderson University, BA; Indiana University, MSW. Her career spans mental health, addictions, medical social work, & social policy. *Affiliation & Address*: Clinical Social Worker, St.Vincent Hospital, 2001 W. 86th St., Indianapolis, IN 46260 (317) 338-2345. *Other professional posts*: adjunct faculty at IUPUI; chairperson, American Indian Center of Indiana, Indianapolis, IN. In addition, her current community involvement includes her role as vice-chair of the Interagency State Council on Black and Minority Health; the National Association of Social Workers, as a past president of the state chapter and now serving a three year term on the national board of directors that includes chairing the committee on racial and ethnic diversity from 2011-14; and the US Commission on Civil Rights.

CARLISLE, SHIRLEY (Choctaw/Cherokee)
(executive director)
Address & Affiliation: American Indian Chamber of Commerce of Texas, 6900 Anderson Blvd., Suite 215, Fort Worth, TX 76120 (817) 429-2323.

CARLYLE, DELIA M. (Ak Chin)
(tribal council member)
Affiliation & Address: Member, Ak Chin Indian Community Council, 42507 W. Peters & Nall Rd., Maricopa, AZ 85138 (520) 568-1000. *Other professional post*: First Vice Chairperson, National Society of American Indian Elderly, Phoenix, AZ. *Past professional post*: A founding director of Title VI Grants to Native Americans in Arizona.

CARMELO, TONANZTIN (Tongva/Kumeyaay)
(actress)
Education: UC Irvine, BA (Environmental Analysis & Design with a minor in Dance). An award winning, multifaceted actor of the stage, screen and new media. She is best known for her leading roles as Thunder Heart Woman in the emmy-winning Steven Spielberg miniseries Into the West; and the Michael Linn film Imprint for which she was awarded Best Actress at the 2007 American Indian Motion Picture Awards. Her projects this year include a return to the stage at the Denver Center for the Performing Arts as Victoria Roubideux in the world premiere production of Eventide, followed by a leading role in the feature film Shouting Secrets. Some of her other big screen credits include starring roles in the feature films Unearthed, Shadowheart, and King Rikki. She has guest starred in the prime-time television shows Dark Blue, American Dad, CSI Miami, and Dragnet. Awards and nominations include a coveted Screen Actors Guild nomination for Outstanding Performance by a Female Actor in Dreamworks' Into the West; Best Actress awards & nominations for Imprint at the Hoboken International Film Festival (nom), American Indian Film Festival (win), and the Cherokee International Film Festival (win). Her character Kendra Daniels was named one of the Hottest Video Game Babes of 2008 by Maxim Magazine. Carmelo began her career as a native dancer and musician, recording 3 CDs with Canyon Records. She is a member of the LA based professional theater company Native Voices, most recently as Lisa Yellowtree in the world premiere production of Carbon Black. In 2009 she was appointed by L.A. Mayor Antonio Villaraigosa to serve on the Los Angeles City/County Native American Indian Affairs Commission.

CARMEN, ANDREA (Yaqui)
(executive director)
Affiliation & Address: Executive Director, International Indian Treaty Council, 2940 16th St. #305, San Francisco, CA 94103 (415) 641-4482. E-mail: andrea@treatycouncil.org.

CARNEY, VIRGINIA (Eastern Cherokee)
(former tribal college president)
Education: Tennessee Temple University, B.A., 1969; Cleveland (TN) State University, A.D.N. (Nursing), 1978; University of Alaska, Anchorage, M.A. (English), 1990; University of Kentucky, Ph.D. (English), 2000. Past professional post: Vice president of Student Affairs, 2000-07; President, 2007-12, Leech Lake Tribal College, Cass Lake, MN.

CARPENTER, CARI
(professor of English)
Affiliation & Address: Associate Professor of English, Eberly College of Arts & Sciences, West Virginia University, P.O. Box 6296, Morgantown, WV 26506 (304) 293-9709. E-mail: cari.carpenter@mail.wvu.edu. Other professional post: Member, Native American Studies Program Committee. Dr. Carpenter specializes in early Native American women writers & connections between sovereignty, nationalism, & gender. She teaches Literature of Native America, Native American Women Writers, & Multiethnic Literature. Published works: Seeing Red: Anger, Sentimentality, & American Indians (Ohio State University Press, 2008); co-edited a forthcoming collection of newspaper articles by & about the Northern Paiute activist & educator, Sarah Winnemucca Hopkins, published by (University of Nebraska Press, 2014).

CARPENTER, KRISTEN A.
(professor of law & associate dean for research)
Education: Dartmouth College, BA, 1994; Harvard Law School, JD, 1998. Address & Affiliation: Associate Dean for Faculty Development & Council Tree Professor of Law (2009-present), American Indian Law Program, American Indian Law Clinic, University of Colorado Law School, Wolf Law Bldg., 401 UCB, Boulder, CO 80309 (303) 492-6526; E-mail: kristen.carpenter@ colorado.edu. Kristen devotes her teaching & scholarship to Property and American Indian Law. Her research focuses on the legal claims of indigenous peoples, especially with respect to issues of property, religion, culture, and human rights. Her articles have been published in the Yale Law Journal, California Law Review, Texas Law Review, UCLA Law Review, Fordham Law Review and others. Professor Carpenter is also active in pro bono work on American Indian cultural and religious freedoms. She is a graduate of Dartmouth College & Harvard Law School. At Colorado Law, Professor Carpenter teaches courses in Property, Cultural Property, American Indian Law, and Indigenous Peoples in International Law. Professor Carpenter has been awarded the Provost's Award for Faculty Achievement and the Outstanding New Faculty Award. She served as a director of the American Indian Law Program from 2012-2014, as Associate Dean for Faculty Development from 2011-2013, and as Associate Dean for Research from 2014-2015. Past professional posts: Clerked for the Honorable John C. Porfilio on the U.S. Court of Appeals for the 10th Circuit; practiced law at Hill & Barlow, P.VC., Boston, MA; Mashantucket Pequot Tribal Nation's Office of Legal Counsel; private Indian law firms in Colorado & Alaska; Suffolk University

School of Law, 2002-04; University of Denver Sturm College of Law, 2004-09. Memberships: Colorado Indian Bar Association (former board member); Federal Bar Association (Annual Indian Law Conference, 2010 & 2011. Published works: The Indian Civil Rights Act at Forty (with K. Carpenter, M. Fletcher, and A. Riley, Eds.) (UCLA American Indian Studies Center, 2012); Indian Status Is Not Racial: Understanding ICWA as a Matter of Law & Practice (Catāo Unbound, Aug. 2016; One River, Two Canoes: Peace & Respect in Indian Child Welfare (Catao Unbound, Aug. 2016); Standing Tall: The Sioux's Battle Sgainst a Dakota Pipeinne Is a Galvanizing Social Justice Movement for Native Americans, with A. Riley (State.com Sept. 1916. Book chapters: "Repairing Reparations in the American Indian Nation Context," (with S. Krakoff), in Reparations for Indigenous Peoples: International & Comparative Perspectives, F. Lenzerini, Ed. (Oxford University Press, 2008); Lyng v. Northwest Indian Cemetery Protective Association: Challenging the Narrative of Conquest (with A. Bowers, in Indian Law Stories 489 (Foundation Press, 2011); Property & Peoplehood, in The Power of Peoplehood: Regenerating Indigenous Nations, by J. Corntassel & T. Holm, Eds. (University of Texas Press, 2011); numerous articles & book reviews.

CARPENTER, LEAH J. (White Earth Ojibwe)
(tribal college president)
Education: Bemidji Stae University, B.A. (Indian Studies & Political Science), 1985; University of Wisconsin Law School, J.D., 1989; University of Arizona, PhD., 2007. Affiliation & Address: President, Leech Lake Tribal College, 6945 Littlewolf Rd., NW, P.O. Box 180, Cass Lake, MN 56633 (218) 335-4200.

CARPIO, MYLA VICENTI (Jicarilla Apache-Laguna/Isleta Pueblo)
(professor of American Indian studies)
Education: University of New Mexico, BA, 1992; Arizona State University, MA, 1995; PhD, 2001. Affiliation & Address: Graduate Studies Director & Associate Professor (2001-present), American Indian Studies Program, P.O. Box 874603, Arizona State University, Tempe, AZ 85287 (480) 727-7989. E-mail: vicenti@asu.edu. Published works: Indigenous Albuquerque (Texas Tech Press, 2011); co-editor with Dr. Jefffrey Shepherd (UTEP) of the Critical Issues in Indigenous Studies Book Series (University of Arizona Press); numerous articles.

CARRICK, LEVI (Ojibwe)
(tribal chairperson)
Affiliation & Address: Chairperson, Bay Mills Indian Community, 12140 W. Lakeshore Dr., Brimley, MI 49715 (906) 248-3241. Past professional post: Chief Judge, Bay Mills Indian Community.

CARRILLO, ROMAN, JR. (Pomo)
(tribal chairperson)
Education: Santa Rosa Junior College, A.A. Affiliation & Address: Chairperson, Hopland Band of Pomo Indians, 3000 Shanel Rd., Hopland, CA 95449 (707) 744-1647. Past professional posts: Fiscal Officer, 1998-2001, Hopland Band; Controller & CFO, Shokawah Casino, 2001-04, Hopland Band; CFO, Tribal Government & Economic Development Corp., 2005-07, Hopland Band; chairperson, 2007-present.

CARROLL, CLINT (Oklahoma Cherokee)
(instructor of American Indian Studies)
Education: University of Arizona, BA (Anthropology), 2003; University of California, Berkeley, PhD (Environmental Science), 2011. Affiliation & Address: Instructor, Dept. of American Indian Studies, University of Minnesota, 19 Scott Hal, 72 Pleasant St. SE, Minneapolis, MN 55455 (612) 625-3821. carroll@umn.edu. Academic specialties: American Indian environmental issues, political ecology, ethnography, tribal environmental policy & governance, traditional ecological knowledge & politics, American Indian nationalism & politics, Cherokee studies. Professional Interests: "I have been working with Cherokee communities in Oklahoma since the summer of 2004, when I helped launch an applied ethno-botany program in the Cherokee Nation Office of Environmental Services. Future endeavors include an analysis of environmentalism in the Cherokee Nation, as well as an analysis of renewable/ green energy projects throughout Indian country and their significance to tribal sovereignty & self-determination." Memberships: Society for Applied Anthropology, 2002-present; Native American & Indigenous Studies Assn, 2009-present. Awards, honors: Native Investigator Development Program, 2014-16; Ford Fellowship Postdoctoral Fellowship, 2013-14; IDEA Multicultural Research Award, University of Minnesota, Summer 2013; Environmental Public Policy & Conflict Resolution Dissertation Fellowship – Morris K. Udall & Stewart L. Udall Foundation, 2010-2011; National Science Foundation Graduate Research Fellowship, 2007-2010; EPA STAR Graduate Fellowship, 2005-2007. Published work: "Articulating Indigenous Statehood: Cherokee State Formation & Implications for the UN Declaration on the Rights of Indigenous Peoples." In Indigenous Rights in the Age of the UN Declaration, edited by Elvira Pulitano (Cambridge University Press, 2012).

CARROLL, MARGUERITE
(editor)

Born January 31, 1955, Syracuse, N.Y. *Education*: Syracuse University, BA in Journalism. *Address & Affiliation*: Editor, Syracuse Post Standard, 1980-84; editor, American Indian Report, The Falmouth Institute, Inc. (1986-present), 3702 Pender Dr., Suite 300, Fairfax, VA 22030 (703) 352-2250. E-mail: mcarroll@falmouthinst.com. *Community activities*: Ventures in Community, Conference for northern Virginia. *Memberships*: Native American Journalists Association; National Congress of American Indians.

CARSON, DALE (Abenaki)
(writer, artist, business owner)

Address: 110 Duck Hole Rd., Madison, CT 06443 (203) 245-2847. E-Mail: dalecarsonct@aol.com, or nativecooking@aol.com. *Affiliation*: Owner, Indian Country, Madison, CT. *Community activities*: Hammonasset Festival 2005. *Memberships*: Mashantucket Museum & Research Center, National Museum of the American Indian. *Interests*: Native American foods, antiques & art. *Published works*: "New Native American Cooking"; "Native New England Cooking"; "A Dreamcatcher Book."

CARTER, (REV.) DONALD R. (*Speak the Word*) (Coharie) 1946-
(tribal chief)

Affiliation: Chief (2008-present), Coharie Indian Tribe, 7531 N. US Hwy. 421, Clinton, NC 28328 (910) 564-6909. *Other professional post*: Pastor, New Hope Baptist Church of Buckhead, NC, 1980-present. *Past professional post*: United Parcel Service (UPS), 1968-2000. *Military service*: U.S. Army, 1966-68 (Vietnam Vet).

CARTER, PAULA (Turtle Mountain Ojibwe)
(research assistant professor)

Education: University of North Dakota, BS (Psychology with minor in Gerontology), MA (Counseling, 1997, PhD (Counseling Psychology). *Affiliation & Address*: Director, National Resource Center on Native American Aging & Research Assistant Professor at the School of Medicine & Health Sciences, Center for Rural Health, University of Noth Dakota, Roomm 4535, 501 N. Columbia Rd., MS 9037, Grand Forks, ND 58202 (701) 777-3720. E-mail: paula.carter@med.und.edu. Other professional post: Tribal liaison for the Collaborative Research Center on American Indian Health through Sanford Health. Her liaison position brings together UND, CRCAIH, and the Turtle Mountain Band of Chippewa to build research infrastructure in that tribal community. As a Research Assistant Professor & Director, she oversees a national neds assessment for American Indian, Alaska Native, and Native Hawaiian elders. Past professional posts: Research Director, National Indigenous Elder Justice Initiative and a faculty fellow with the Seven Gneration Center of Excellence in Native Behavioral Health at the Center for Rural Health. Prior to joining the CRH, Carter was a mental health researcher with the Veterans Administration, where she developed culturally appropriate mental health resources to be utilized with Native American veterans. She also worked with the Indian Health Service as a mental health provider in rural reservation settings.

CARTER, SUSAN
(educator)

Education: University of New Mexico, PhD (Cultural Studies). Affiliation & Address: Susan Lee Carter, Inc., 1217 Espanola NE, Albuquerque, NM 87110 (505) 508-2232. E-mail: susanleecarter@comcast.net. *Other professional posts*: Evaluation Coordinator (1994-present), National Indian Youth Leadership Project, Albuquerque, NM. *Past professional post*: Research director, Santa Fe Indian School; adjunct professor of human development & learning (13 years), University of New Mexico, Albuquerque, NM *Awards, honors*: Awarded the Excellence in Cultural Studies Award by the U. of New Mexico for her doctoral dissertation research on Navajo college students' experiences.

CARTER, TRACIE (Chickasaw)
(special projects coordinator)

Affiliation & Address: Special Projects Coordinator, The Chickasaw Foundation, P.O. Box 1726, Ada, OK 74821 (580) 421-9030.

CARTER, TRUMAN (Sac & Fox) 1949-
(attorney)

Born January 16, 1949, Pawnee, Okla. *Education*: U.S. Indian Police Academy, 1979; University of Oklahoma, BA, 1980, College of Law, JD, 1987. *Affiliation & Address*: Attorney at Law, P.O. Box 1722, Shawnee, OK 74802 (405) 275-0877. E-mail: tcndnlaw@netscape.com. *Current activities*: Attorney General, Kickapoo Tribe in eastern Oklahoma, 1988-, the Cheyenne-Arapaho Tribes in western Oklahoma, 1988-, Iowa Tribe of Oklahoma, 1992-, and Otoe-Missouria Tribe of Oklahoma, 1993-; Chairperson, Otoe-Missouria Tax Commission, 1990-; special prosecutor, Iowa Tribe of Oklahoma, 1991-; Coordinator, Liaison of Sac & Fox law and order and judicial system, 1984-; Treasurer & Assistant Attorney General (Chief, Criminal Division), Sac & Fox Nation, 1987-; justice, Supreme Court, Kickapoo Tribe of Kansas, 1991-,

Citizen Band Potawatomi of Oklahoma, 1992-; Prosecutor, BIA Court of Indian Offenses, Chickasaw Agency & Wewoka Agency, 1993-. *Accomplishments*: Appeared before the U.S. Supreme Court as designated co-counsel in 1993 landmark case, Oklahoma Tax Commission v. Sac & Fox Nation, where Court ruled 9-0 decision, state cannot impose motor vehicle & income taxes on tribal members; An elected tribal official, served as chief executive financial officer; developed excellent employee compensation & benefit package; provide training, assist Indian tribal governments in development, preparation, administration, & enforcement of tribal laws, policies, and procedures, 1982 to present; organizer & administrator of comprehensive tribal taxation system; negotiated several tribal cooperative agreements with cities, counties & state agencies dealing with business development, law enforcement, fire protection services, & joint road improvement programs; organized & developed tribal court systems, police operations and fire department for the Sac & Fox Tribe in 1984. *Memberships*: Native American Bar Association; Oklahoma Indian Bar Association (treasurer-Indian Law Section); legislation committee); Oklahoma Bar Association; Potawatomie County (OK) Bar Association; National District Attorneys Association; Leadership Oklahoma, Inc.

CARMINE, NATOSHA N. (Nanticoke)
(tribal chief)

Affiliation & Address: Chief, Nanticoke Indian Association, 27073 John J. Williams Hwy., Millsboro, DE 19966. (302) 945-3400.

CASEY, ANDREW M. (Cherokee)
(associate attorney)

Education: University of Oklahoma College of Law, JD, 2015. *Affiliation & Address*: Associate, Stinnett Law, 404 E. Dewey Ave., Suite 202, Sepulpa, OK 74066 (918) 227-1177. Andrew "Andy" joined Stinnett Law as an Associate Attorney in January 2016. While attending the University of Oklahoma College of Law, he served as the Articles Development Editor for the American Indian Law Review, an officer for the Board of Advocates, and competed in the National NALSA Moot Court Championship. During his 2L year, Andy earned the title of Top Speaker/Best Oral Advocate in the country for the 2014 National NALSA Moot Court Championship. An Oklahoma native, Andy grew up in the Sand Springs/Sapulpa area before graduating from Jenks High School in 2004. In 2009, he graduated with a Bachelors Degree in Political Science from the University of Central Oklahoma. While completing his degree, Andy received several awards as a nationally competitive policy debater including being named an All-American as well as advancing into deep elimination rounds at several national debate tournaments. By nature, Andy is a fierce competitor who never lost the drive to out-research and out-work his opponents; he brings that charisma to all of Stinnett Law's cases. Law was not Andy's first career, he began as a debate coach at the University of North Texas in Denton, TX and Heritage Hall in Oklahoma City. For over four years, Andy specialized in conducting policy and legal research while being able to convey his research to high school and college students. To this day, one of the greatest skills he has honed is the ability to break complex legal theories down into practical and easy-to-understand ideas. As a loving father and a lucky fiance, Andy brings dedication to every client centered around in-depth research and a passion for writing. Awards, honors: Top Speaker/Best Oralist, National Native American Law Student Association, 2014.

CASTILLO, EDWARD D. (Cahuilla-Luiseno) 1947-
(professor of Native American studies)

Born August 25, 1947, San Jacinto, Riverside Co., Calif. *Education*: University of California, Riverside, BA, 1969; University of California, Berkeley, MA, 1976, PhD (Anthropology), 1977. *Affiliation & Address*: Professor of Native American Studies, Dept. Chair, Native American Studies Program, Sonoma State University, Rohnert Park, CA 94928 (707) 664-2450. *Past professional posts*: Lecturer, Native American Studies Dept., University of California at Berkeley, 1970-71, 1973-77; Associate professor, director, Native American Studies, University of California, Santa Cruz, 1977-82; project director, Title IV, Laytonville Unified School District, 1985-88; curriculum resource specialist, Parents for the Improvement of Community & Education Services, Ukiah, CA. *Other professional posts*: President-Advisory Council, California Indian Education Association, California State Dept. of Education; Chairperson of Native American Advisory Committee to the California State University Chancellor Office. Memberships: California Historical Society; American Indian Historical Society. *Awards, honors*: National Endowment for the Humanities, History Teacher Training Grant; Meritorious Performance, Professional Promise Award for Research, 1989, California State University system. *Interests*: Reconstruction of California, Far Western, Borderlands; history of Indian tribes, and Hispanic Colonial institutions, i.e. Missions, Presidios, Civilian Hispanic Pueblos. *Published works*: "History of the Impact of Euro-American Exploration & Settlement on the Indians of California (107 pages) & "Recent Secular Movements Among California Indians, 1900-1973 (15 pages). Both chapters appear in Volume 8 of the Smithsonian Institute's Handbook of North American Indians: California; co-author: The California Missions (American Indian History Society Press, 1987); A Bibliography of California Indian History, edited by Robert Heizer (Ballena Press, 1978); Native American

Perspectives on the Hispanic Colonization of Alta California (Garland Publishing, 1990); numerous articles & book reviews.

CASTILLO, JOHN (Fort Sill Apache) 1956-
(administrator)
Born February 14, 1956. *Education*: California State University, Fullerton, BA, 1979; UCLA, MSW, 1981, PhD (Organizational Development), 1984. *Principal occupation*: Executive director. *Affiliation & Address*: Executive Director (1999-present), Walking Shield, Inc., 22541 Aspan St., Suite E, Lake Forest, CA 92630 (949) 639-0472. E-mail: jcastillo@walkingshield.org. *Past professional posts*: Executive Director (nine years), Southern California Indian Center, Fountain Valley, CA; California & National Child & Adolescent Service System Program Advisory Committee for Culturally Competent Service for Children & Families. *Community activities*: Orange County Community Developmental Council; Orange County ESP & FEMA Board-Orange Coast College EDP Board; Huntington Beach Adult Advisory Board. *Memberships*: UCLA Chancellors Community Advisory Commission; Los Angeles County American Indian Commission (chairperson, 1987-89); Indian Child Welfare Task Force (chairperson, 1986-89); Los Angeles County American Indian Mental Health Task Force, 1986-87. *Awards, honors*: 1979 Federal Mediation Council Labor/Management Certificate; 1985 County of Los Angeles Affirmative Action Volunteer of the Year; 1985-88 Kellogg National Fellowship Fellow Group 6; 1991 Freedoms Foundation at Valley Forge George Washington Honor Medal. *Interests*: "International work with indigenous peoples - helping indigenous peoples develop their human & economic resources through the many international programs." *Published works*: Articles: "Spiritual Foundations of Indian Success," in American Indian Culture & Research Journal (1982, Vol. 6 No. 3); "JPTA: American Indian Success Through Group Consensus and Individual Attention," in Occupational Education Forum (1986, Vol. 15 No. 2); "American Indians: An Overview of Their Socio Economic and Education Status," in The Journal for Vocational Needs Educations (1988, Vol. 10 No. 3).

CASTRO, GLORIA (Costanoan {Ohlone} Rumsen-Carmel)
(tribal vice chairperson)
Affiliation: Costanoan Rumsen Carmel Tribe, 240 East 1st St., Pomona, CA 91766 (909) 623-7889. E-mail: rumsen@aol.com

CASTRO, VERNON (Yokut)
(rancheria chairperson)
Affiliation: Table Mountain Rancheria, P.O. Box 410, Friant, CA 93626 (209) 822-2587.

CATA, JUANITA O. (Pueblo-Ohkay Owingeh)
(BIA supt for education)
Affiliation: Northern Pueblos Agency, BIA, P.O. Box 4269, Fairview Station, Espanola, NM 87533 (505) 753-1465.

CATA, PETER (Pueblo-Ohkay Owingeh)
(tribal 1st lt. governor)
Affiliation: Ohkay Owingeh (San Juan Pueblo), P.O. Box 1099, San Juan Pueblo, NM 87566 (505) 852-4400.

CATA, SIMON (San Juan Pueblo)
(pueblo governor)
Affiliation: San Juan Pueblo Council, P.O. Box 1099, San Juan Pueblo, NM 87566 (505) 852-4400.

CAUSLEY, CHERYL A. (Bay Mills Chippewa)
(executive director)
Affiliation & Address: Executive Director, Bay Mills Housing Authority, 3095 S. Towering Pines Rd., Brimley, MI 49715. *Other professional post*: Board Chairperson, National American Indian Housing Council, Washington, DC.

CAVE, RODINA COLE (Quechua of Peru)
(senior policy advisor, Office of the Assistant Secretary – Indian Affairs, U.S. Department of the Interior)
Education: University of Masachusetts, Amherst, BS & MEd.; Arizona State University College of Law, JD (Indian Law). *Affiliation & Address*: Senior Policy Advisor (2013-present), Office of the Assistant Secretary – Indian Affairs, U.S. Department of the Interior, 1849 C St., NW, MS-3658-MIB, Washington, DC 20240 (202) 208-3710. *Past professional posts*: Cave practiced law in New Mexico and Arizona until her appointment to the Assistant Secretary's staff. She had been in practice since 2003 representing Indian tribes & tribal entities in administrative & regulatory proceedings, in environmental matters, on tribal governance issues, and on economic development projects. She worked on several large breach-of-trust cases brought by tribes in Federal courts. In addition to her Indian law practice, she has extensive experience in Federal and state matters involving complex litigation and appeals. Cave also served as an adjunct professor at the University of New Mexico School of Law and taught the Indian law course for the American Indian Law Center Pre-Law Summer Institute in 2011. She is a past chair of the Indian Law Section of the

New Mexico State Bar. Cave was admitted to the State Bar of Arizona in 2003, the State of Bar of New Mexico in 2005, the U.S. District Court for the District of New Mexico in 2005, and the Navajo Nation Bar in 2011.

CEBALLOS, GUADALUPE
(staff attorney)
Affiliation & Address: Staff Attorney, Center for Indian Law & Policy, Seattle University School of Law, Sullivan Hall, 901 12th Ave., P.O. Box 222000, Seattle, WA 98122 (206) 398-4000. E-mail: ceballos@seattleu.edu. Ms. Ceballos primarily focuses on assisting Indian families with all areas of estate planning, encouraging them to make informed decisions about their property & drafting wills to conform to tribal, federal, and state law. *Interests*: Federal Indian law, environmental law, and indigenous rights.

CERDA, TONY (Costanoan {Ohlone} Rumsen-Carmel)
(tribal chairperson)
Affiliation: Costanoan Rumsen Carmel Tribe, 240 East 1st St., Pomona, CA 91766 (909) 623-7889. E-mail: rumsen@aol.com

CHAATSMITH, MARTI (Comanche/Choctaw)
(associate director of Newark Earthworks Center)
Affiliation & Address: Associate Director, Newark Earthworks Center, The Ohio State University at Newark, c/o The American Indian Studies Program, 455 Hagerty Hall, 1775 College Rd., Columbus, OH 43210. E-mail: chaatsmith.1@osu.edu. The Center consults with Ohio's historic American Indian tribes to develop sustainable relationships with tribal governments removed from Ohio on tribal representation in the state, and the protection of Indigenous historic & ancient places.

CHACON, AUTUMN (Dine-Navajo)
(filmmaker)
Born in Albuquerque, NM. I reside on the Navajo Reservation. I am from the Bitterwater Clan. Autumn writes, "I am a videographer by trade yet study & practice many forms of media for purposes of strengthening communication amongst my desert community. The health of my people is my motivation to ensure this communication and conversations."

CHAILLIER, GRACE (Sicangu Lakota)
(adjunct assistant professor)
Education: Northern Michigan University (NMU), BA (English with minor in Native American Studies), 2002; NMU, MFA English Literature), 2004, MFA (Creative Writing), 2008. *Affiliation*: Adjunct assistant professor, Center for Native American Studies, 112G Whitman Hall, Northern Michigan University, 1401 Presque Isle Ave., Marquette, MI 49855 (906) 227-1397. E-mail: grachail@nmu.edu. *Past professional posts*: Taught Native American Literature, Ferris State University, 2004; taught the Native American Experience course at NMU, 2005; she wrote curriculum for & taught the History of Indian Boarding School Education course, NMU, 2007-08. *Published work*: Edited with Rebecca Tavernini, "Voice on the Water: Great Lakes Native America Now," an anthology collaboration of over 80 authors, artists, & writers.

CHALAN, MARY ZUNI (Muskogee Creek)
(tribal executive director)
Affiliation & Address: Executive Director, Thlopthlocco Tribal Town, P.O. Box 188, Okemah, OK 74859 (918) 560-6198.

CHALEPAH, ALONZO (Kiowa Apache)
(tribal vice chairperson)
Affiliation & Address: Vice Chairperson, Apache Tribe of Oklahoma, P.O. Box 1220, Anadarko, OK 73005 (405) 247-9493.

CHAMBERLAIN, JOBA (Winnebago) 1985-
(major league baseball player)
Born Sept. 23, 1985, Lincoln, Neb. *Education*: University of Nebraska. *Affiliation*: Pitcher, New York Yankees, Bronx, NY, 2007-present.

CHAMBERLIN, ROBERT, OWADI (Kwikwasut'inuxw Haxwa'mis)
(Canadian First Nation chief councilor)
Affiliation & Address: Kwikwasut'inuxw Haxwa'mis First Nation, Box 1, Alert Bay, British Columbia, Canada V0N 1A0 (250) 974-8282. E-mail: bobc@khfn.ca Robert was elected Chief Councillor in 2005. Since that time, he has been actively involved in the community's comprehensive community planning process, undertaking major capital development projects and engaging in activities for nation strengthening. Currently, Chief Chamberlin also sits as Chair of the Musgamagw-Tsawataineuk Tribal Council and a serves on the Board of Directors for the Inter Tribal Health Authority. As the elected Vice-President of the Union of BC Indian Chiefs, Chief Chamberlin takes an active role in the defense of Aboriginal Title & Rights & is committed to overcoming the challenges and impacts of fish farms in the Broughton Archipelago. Further, he frequently engages in lobby efforts at both the provincial and federal levels to ensure the protection of First Nations water

rights and safe drinking water for our communities. As the Co-Chair of the First Nation Child Family and Wellness Council, Chief Chamberlin also works to address key issues facing First Nations children & families in British Columbia.

CHAMBERS, CURTIS P. (Ottawa/Chippewa)
(tribal chairperson)
Affiliation & Address: Burt Lake Band of Ottawa & Chippewa Indians, P.O. Box 206, Brutus, MI 49716 (616) 529-6113.

CHAMBERS, LETITIA (Cherokee)
(museum director)
Education: University of Oklahoma, BA; Oklahoma State University, PhD (Educational Research & Curriculum Development). *Affiliation & Address*: Director (2010-present), Heard Museum, 2301 N. Central Ave., Phoenix, AZ 85004 (602) 252-8848. lchambers@heard.org. *Past professional posts*: Founder & CEO, Chambers Associates, Washington, DC, 1980-2000; managing director, Navigant, 2001-04, 2005-08; head, System of Higher Education, State of New Mexico, 2004-05; independent consutant, 2008-10. *Awards, honors*: Appointed by President Clinton, in 1996, as a U.S. Representative to the United Nations General Assembly, a position with ambassadorial rank. Letitia is the first person of American Indian heritage to be appointed as director of the museum; also, the second woman to the founder, Marie Bartlett Heard, to lead the institution.

CHAMBERS, REID PEYTON
(attorney)
Education: Amherst College, BA, 1962; Harvard Law School, JD, 1967. Affiliation & *Address*: Partner, Sonosky, Chambers, Sachse, Endreson & Perry, LLP, 1425 K St., NW, Suite 600, Washington, DC 20005 (202) 682-0240. E-mail: rchambers@sonosky.com. Since joining the firm in 1976, Mr. Chambers has represented tribes or other Alaska Native interests in litigation involving land, timber & water rights, hunting & fishing rights, reservation disestablishment, Alaska tribal rights & immunities, gaming law, tribal jurisdiction & taxation, oil & gas rights, and coal development. He has codified tribal laws, advised Native American corporations on government procurement, and engaged in legislative advocacy on behalf of a variety of tribal interests. In 2003, Mr. Chambers represented the Bishop Paiute Tribe before the U.S. Supreme Court in *Inyo County v. Paiute-Shoshone Indians of the Bishop Community*, 538 U.S. 701. *Other professional posts*: For over 20 years, Mr. Chambers has taught a seminar on federal Indian law at Georgetown University Law School. He has also taught the seminar several times at Yale Law School. *Past professional posts*: Associate Solicitor for Indian Affairs at the U.S. Dept. of the Interior, 1973-76. He was the Depart-ment's chief legal officer with responsibility over Indian & Alaska's Native matters. Mr. Chambers has worked extensively with the Native American Rights Fund. *Publications*: Co-author of the 1982 revised edition of Cohen's landmark treatise on federal Indian law and has published two oft-cited articles in the Stanford Law Review on federal Indian law issues, as well as a number of Indian water rights.

CHAMPAGNE, DUANE W. (Turtle Mountain Ojibway) 1951-
(professor of sociology; consultant)
Born May 18, 1951, Belcourt, N.D. *Education*: North Dakota State University, BA, 1973, MA, 1975; Harvard University, PhD, 1982. *Principal occupation*: Professor; consultant; journal editor. *Address*: 2152 Balsam Ave., Los Angeles, CA 90025. *Affiliations*: Professor of Sociology, member of the Faculty Advisory Committee, UCLA American Indian Studies Center, (1990-2002; 2010-present), 3220 Campbell Hall, Box 951551, Los Angeles, CA 90095-1551 (310) 475-7315. E-mail: champagn@ucla.edu; Series Editor, Contemporary American Indian Issues, AltaMira Press, 1998-present; partner, Champagne & Goldberg Consultants, 2002-present. *Past professional posts*: Research consultant for the Smithsonian Institution-Public Radio & Native American Public Broadcasting Consortium (NAPBC). Developed public radio documentaries for the Quintcentennial of Columbus' landing in the New World, 1989-92; Advisory Board Member for the Harvard Project on American Indian Economic Development, Energy & Environmental Policy Center, Harvard University, John F. Kennedy School of Government, 1988-90; UCLA Native Nations Law & Policy Center, 2003-2010, UCLA Dept. of Sociology, 1984-2010; Honoring Nations, 2000-2010. *Community activities*: National Museum of the American Indian (member of board of trustees), 1987-present; The Los Angeles City/County American Indian Commission (chair, board member), 1990-present; Los Angeles American Indian Commission, 1990-present; Southwest Museum (board member, 1994-96); member, American Indian Women's Health Advisory Board, 1994-96; Project Peace-maker, 1998-present; Public Law 280 Police Enforcement Study, 2000-present; Native Voices at the Autry, 1999-present; Tribal Learning Community & Education Exchange (TLCEE), 2003-present. *Memberships*: American Sociological Assn; International Sociological Assn; American Indian Professors Assn.; Pacific Sociological Assn. *Awards, honors*: American Indian Scholar-ship, 1973-75; American Sociological Assn Minority Fellowship, 1975-78; Rockefeller Postdoctoral Fellowship, 1982-83; University of California Pre-tenure Award, 1986; National Science Foundation (Fellow, 1985-88; Creativity Extension

Grant, 1988-90; Ford Foundation Postdoctoral Fellowship, 1988-89; Master for the College of Humanities & Social Sciences, North Dakota State University, 1996; Honoree, National Center for American Indian Enterprise, 1999; Wordcraft Circle of Native Writers & Storytellers, Writer of the Year, 1999. *Published works*: American Indian Societies: Strategies & Conditions of Political & Cultural Survival, revised 2nd ed. (Cultural Survival, 1989); Social Order & Political Change: Constitutional Governments Among the Cherokee, the Choctaw, the Chickasaw, and the Creek (Stanford U. Press, 1992); The Native North American Almanac (Gale Research, 1994; second edition, 2001); Native America: Portrait of the People (Visible Ink Press, 1994); The Chronology of Native North American History (Gale Research, 1994); American Indian Activism: Alcatraz to the Longest Walk (U. of Illinois Press, 1997) ed. with Troy Johnson & Joanne Nagel; Contemporary Native American Cultural Issues (AltaMira Press, 1999); Native American Studies in Higher Education: Models for Collaboration Between Universities & Indigenous Nations (AltaMira Press, 2002) ed. with Jay Stauss; The Future of Indigenous Studies: Strategies for Survival & Development (UCLA American Indian Studies Center, 2003) ed. with Ismael Abu Saad, 100+ articles & reports.

CHAMPION-SHAW, CHARMAYNE (Southern Cheyenne)
(American Indian program director)
Affiliations & Address: Director, American Indian Programs; Director, Native American & Indigenous Studies; Council Organizer, Native American Faculty Staff Council, Indiana University-Purdue University, IU School of Liberal Arts, 425 University Blvd., Cavanaugh Hall 325, Indianapolis, IN 46202 (317) 274-8356. E-mail: cchampio@iupui.edu

CHANG, DAVID
(professor of history)
Education: University of Wisconsin, PhD, 2002. *Address & Affiliation*: University of Minnesota, Twin Cities Campus, History Dept., 614 Social Sceince Tower, 267 19th Ave. So., Minneapolis, MN 55455 (612) 624-2800. E-mail: dchang@umn.edu. *Research interests*: Native American history. The racial politics of the struggle over land ownership in Indian Territory and Oklahoma. PhD Dissertation: "From Indian Territory to White Man's Country: Race, Nation & the Politics of Land Ownership in Eastern Oklahoma, 1889-1940," University of Wisconsin, 2002. *Published works*: "Where Will the Nation Be At Home?: Race, Nationalisms & Emigration Movements in the Creek Nation," Miles & Holland, Eds., Crossing Waters, Crossing Paths: Black & Indian Journeys in the Americas (Duke University Press, 2004).

CHAPMAN II, DONALD, (*Coqayohomuwok*) (Mohegan)
(senior advisor on Native American affairs)
Education: Norfolk College; University of Maryland. *Affiliation*: President, Uncas Consulting Services LLC, 518 Fortress Circle SE, Leesburg, VA 20175 (410) 340-7027. E-mail: don@donchapman.com. Uncas is a Native American-owned practice which is under contract supporting Tribal representatives serving on the White House National ocean Council in strategic areas of organizational development, facilitation & outreach on ocean policy, and Coastal Marine Spatial Planning. He also advises many Tribally-owned, individually-owned Native businesses, federal agencies, & investment groups concerning energy & other economic development endeavors. *Other professional post*: National Federal Senior Strategist, Blue Stone Strategy Group, Phoenix, AZ. *Past professional posts*: Senior Advisor on Native American Affairs, Office of the Secretary, U.S. Dept. of Commerce, Washington, DC (2010-11); senior executive manager, Wyandotte Tribal Corp.; Chenega Advanced Solutions & Engineering (ANC), & TKC Communications; senior consultant for NCAIED, Washington, DC. Awards, honors: Mr. Chapman was appointed in 2009 by Secretary Gary Locke as the first senior advisor on Native American Affairs.

CHAPMAN, DUANE "DOG" (Cherokee)
(bounty hunter)
Website: www.dogthebountyhunter.com
E-Mail: comments@dogthebountyhunter.com (808) 537-2245.

CHAPMAN, JEFF (Ojibwe)
(teaching specialist)
Address & Affiliation: University of Minnesota, Twin Cities Campus, 262 Applebee Hall, Minneapolis, MN 55455 (612) 625-3376. E-mail: chapman027 @umn.edu.

CHAPMAN, MAUREEN (Skawahlook First Nation)
(chief of Skawahlook First Nation)
Affiliation & Address: Chief, Skawahlook First Nation, 58611A Lougheed Hwy., Agassiz, BC V0M 1A2 (604) 796-9129. E-mail: Maureen@skawahlook.com. Maureen is the hereditary Chief of her Nation and was handed this responsibility in 1999. Skawahlook First Nation practices a matrilineal system and her successor is being mentored for the Chief's position. Maureen participates as a member of the Sto:lo Nations Chief's Council (SNCC), which is comprised of 11 First Nation communities and, 7 of the 11 communities are

currently negotiating a treaty. She has been appointed by the SNCC to represent them, as their political voice, to the First Nations Health Council, as well as participating on a number of committees & boards for the SNCC. Additionally, she is the political Chair for the Aboriginal Children and Families Chiefs Coalition, which is comprised of 13 Chiefs as the Board members, who advocate for programs and services for children and families within their communities.Skawahlook First Nation is a member of the Union of BC Indian Chiefs (UBCIC), the BC Assembly of First Nations (BC AFN) and, the First Nations Summit (FNS). For each of the respective organizations, committees and boards include: for the BC AFN – as a Director, political appointment to the Chiefs Committee on Health and Chiefs Committee on Claims; for the UBCIC – Specific Claims Working Group – Chair and, as the UBCIC Gaming Commissioner; and for the FNS – attends quarterly meetings related to treaty discussions.

CHAPMAN, ROBERT (Pawnee)
(tribal president)
Address & Affiliation: Pawnee Tribe, P.O. Box 470, Pawnee, OK 74058 (918) 762-3621.

CHAPMAN, STEVE (White Earth Chippewa) 1951-
(program administrator)
Born July 3, 1951, Minneapolis, Minn. *Education*: Minneapolis Community College, 1969-70; Augsburg College, BA, 1973; Hamline University, MA, 1993. *Address*: 3625 24th Ave. S., Minneapolis, MN 55406 (612) 722-2080. *Affiliations*: Special Programs, University of Minnesota, Minneapolis, MN, 1973-77; director, American Indian Studies, Minneapolis Community College, 1977-94; Administrator, Indian Education Programs, Minneapolis Public Schools, 1994-. *Other professional posts*: Executive director, American Indian OIC, 1981-82; Instructor: American Indian Art History, Augsburg College, University of St. Thomas. *Community activities*: Commissioner, Minneapolis Public Housing Authority (vice chair); Minneapolis Community Development Agency (former commissioner); Minnesota Commission on Affordable Housing (former commissioner); American Indian Business Development; Minnesota Indian Women's Resource Center. *Memberships*: Minnesota Indian Education Association; National Indian Education Association. *Awards, honors*: First American Indian graduate of Augsburg College; Outstanding Alumni Award, 1986, Minneapolis Community College; Scholarship Award, MAPE; Outstanding American Indian Educator, 1999, Minneapolis, Minn. *Interests*: "Beadwork; American Indian art history; refinishing furniture; lecturing on American Indian culture, and helping out when asked." *Published work*: Urban American Indian Views on the U.S. Constitution (Hamline Law Journal, 1986).

CHAPOOSE, SHAUN (Ute)
(former tribal chairperson & band representative)
Affiliation & Address: Former chairperson, Uncomphgre Band Representative, The Ute Indian Tribe, P.O. Box 190, Fort Duchesne, UT 84026 (435) 722-5141.

CHAPPABITTY, DENNIS G. (Chiricahua Apache & Comanche) 1949-
(attorney)
Born in 1949 at the Indian Hospital in Lawton, Okla. *Education*: Oklahoma State University, BA, 1972. University of New Mexico School of Law, JD, 1981. *Address*: P.O. Box 292122, Sacramento, CA 95829 (916) 682-0575. E-mail: chaplaw@earthlink.net. *Professional activities*: Private Practice (1985-present) in Federal Indian law. Counseling & legal representation of Federal employees before the U.S. Merit Systems Protection Board and Federal Equal Employment Opportunity Commission. *Past professional posts*: Staff attorney, Comanche Tribe, 1981-85. *Military service*: U.S. Army, 1972-75.

CHAPPAROSA, SHANE (Cahuilla)
(tribal spokesman)
Affiliation & Address: Spokesperson, Los Coyotes Band of Cahuilla & Cupeno Indians, P.O. Box 189, Warner Springs, CA 92086 (760) 782-0711.

CHAPUT, REV. CHARLES J. (*Wambli Waste-Good Eagle*, Lakota; *Pyet-ta-sen*, Potawatomi) 1944-
(Roman Catholic Archbishop)
Born September 26, 1944, Concordia, Kans. *Education*: St. Fidelis College, BA, 1967; Capuchin College, MA; University of San Francisco (MA in theology), 1971. Archbishop Chaput was ordained Bishop of Rapid City, South Dakota, on July 26, 1988. Pope John Paul II appointed him Archbishop of Denver on February 18, 1997, and he was installed on April 7 the same year. As a member of the Prairie Band Potawatomi Tribe, Archbishop Chaput was the second Native American to be ordained a bishop in the United States, and the first Native American archbishop. *Pope Benedict XVI appointed him Archbishop of Philadelphia on July 19, 2011.* He was installed as the 13th bishop and ninth archbishop of Philadelphia on September 8, 2011. He served on the U.S. Commission on International Religious Freedom, 2003-2006. Duties included religious freedom fact-finding missions to China and Turkey,

and annual reports monitoring global trends in religious liberty mandated by 1998 federal law. In 2005, he was named a member of the official U.S. delegation to Cordoba, Spain, for the "Conference on Anti-Semitism and Other Forms of Intolerance," sponsored by the Organization for Security and Cooperation in Europe (OSCE). The national Becket Fund for Religious Liberty awarded him the 2009 Canterbury Medal for his work in advancing religious freedom. Archbishop Chaput served on the Board of Directors for The Catholic University of America, Washington, D.C. (1994 – 2009) and the National Catholic Bioethics Center (1993 – 2006). He serves on the board of directors for Eternal Word Television Network, Birmingham, Alabama (1996 – present); The Catholic Foundation of Northern Colorado (1998 – 2011); St. John Vianney Theological Seminary in Northern Colorado (1999 – 2011); Redemptorists Mater Seminary in Northern Colorado (1998 – 2011); The Fellowship of Catholic University Students (2001 – present); Catholic Association of Latino Leaders (2007 – present); World Youth Alliance International (2010 – present). As Archbishop of Philadelphia, he serves as the ex-officio Chairman of the Board of Trustees of Saint Charles Borromeo Seminary *Affiliations*: Archbishop of Philadelphia. *Awards, honors*: "Served as master of ceremonies for 1987 National Tekakwitha Conference with Pope John Paul, !!, Phoenix, AZ. *Interests*: Travel. He is author of two books: Living the Catholic Faith: Rediscovering the Basics (Servant, 2001) and Render Unto Caesar: Serving the Nation by Living Our Catholic Beliefs in Political Life (Doubleday, 2008); articles & pastoral letters. His writings, discourses, & homilies are available www.archphila.org/archbishopchaput/index.htm and www.archden.org/archbishop.

CHARETTE, RENO (Crow)
(director of American Indian outreach)
Education: University of Montana, MA (History), 1997. *Affiliation & Address*: Director (2007-present), American Indian Outreach, Montana State University, Billings, Department of Social Sciences & Cultural Studies, Native American Studies Program, 1500 University Dr., Billings, MT 59101 (406) 657-2144. E-mail: rcharette@msubillings.edu. *Past professional posts*: Coordinator of Indian Affairs, State of Montana, 2004-07; Native American Stuies Coordinator, Montana State University, Billings, MT, 2007-09.

CHARGING, LEONIKA R. (Mandan, Hidatsa, Arikara)
(attorney)
Education: University of Kansas, BA, 1997; University of South Dakota School of Law, JD, 2003. *Affiliation*: Associate, 2007-2010; Partner (2011-present), Fredericks Peebles & Morgan, LLP, 3610 North 163rd Plaza, Omaha, NE 68116 (402) 333-4053. E-mail: lcharging@ndnlaw.com. *Practice areas*: Tribal governance; tribal economic development, administrative law; and Indian gaming. *Past professional posts*: Associate attorney in Omaha, NE with a law firm specializing in Indian law. legal analyst to the Santee Sioux tribe Court; law clerk for Hobbs, Straus, Dean & Walker, Washington, DC.

CHARLES, FRANCES G. (Lower Elwha Klallam)
(tribal chairperson)
Affiliation & Address: Chairperson (16 years) Lower Elwha Klallam Tribe, 2851 Lower Elwha Rd., Port Angeles, WA 98362 (360) 452-8471. *Past professional posts*: Olympic National Forest Service devoting 12 years of service working with the fire crews and earning her way to one of the top crew leaders for our area. Frances played a vital role in the recovery of Tse-whit-zen, one of the largest archaeological recoveries in the Northwest; Frances took a lead role in the negotiation process for the Ancient Klallam Village on behalf of her people and their ancestors, and as a leader for her community she did a great job in upholding Klallam Cultural Values. She has been involved in the culture of the Lower Elwha Klallam Tribe most of her life, she is an active supporter of the annual Tribal Canoe Journey as well as the language program, Indian Education and honoring Tribal Veterans, the youth and the elders of the Tribe.

CHARLES, GEORGE P. (*Kanaqiak*) (Yup'ik Eskimo)
(executive director)
Affiliation & Address: Director, NRC for American Indian, Alaska Native & Native Hawaiian Elders, University of Alaska, Achorage, College of Health, 3211 Providence Dr., Suite 205, Anchorage, AK 99508 (907) 786-4329. E-mail: afgpc1@uaa.alaska.edu.

CHARLES, JAMES (Navajo) 1950-
(archaeologist; park supt.)
Born March 25, 1950, Ganado, Ariz. *Education*: Fort Lewis College, BA, 1974; Northern Arizona University, MA. *Principal occupation*: Archaeologist, park supt.. *Address*: Navajo National Monument, National Park Service, Tonalea, AZ 86044 (520) 672-2366. *Affiliations*: Archaeologist, B.I.A., Phoenix, AZ, 1981-82; archaeologist, B.I.A., Billings, MT, 1982-91; supt., B.I.A., Fort Totten, ND, 1991-96; supt., Navajo National Monument, Tonalea, NM, 1996-. *Membership*: North Dakota Archaeological Society. *Interests*: Archaeology, anthropology, cultural anthropology, Navajo history.

CHARLIE, LYNETTE C. (Navajo) 1966-
(educator)
Born October 28, 1966, Tuba City, Ariz. *Education*: University of New Mexico. *Address*: P.O. Box 1815, Tuba City, AZ 86045 (520) 283-5628. *Affiliation*: Director of Recruiting, Native American Scholarship Fund, Albuquerque, NM, 1990-. *Community activities*: "Currently volunteering my personal time helping young Native students get into college & obtain the financial support to continue their education. *Memberships*: National Association of Female Executives, 1994-; National Coalition for Indian Education (board member, 1991; member, 1991-).

CHARLIE, ROBERT (Athabascan)
(executive director)
Affiliation & Address: Founder & Executive Director (1984-present), Cultural Heritage & Education Institute, P.O. Box 73030, Fairbanks, AK 99707 (907) 451-0923. E-mail: chei@mosquitonet.com. *Other professional posts*: Member, Boreal Forest Council; board member of Fairbanks Family Services.

CHARLO, BOB (Kalispel)
(photographer)
Address: Buffalo River-Fine Art Photography, P.O. Box 1498, Auburn, WA 98071 (360) 825-5752. Website: bcharlofineart.com. Bob's photography is museum quality posters of American Indian dancers, dance regalia.

CHARTRAND, DAVID (Metis)
(Metis Federation president)
Born in Duck Bay, Manitoba. *Affiliation & Address*: President (1996-present), Manitoba Metis Federation, 300-150 Henry Ave., Winnipeg, MB R3B 0J7 (204) 586-8474. Website: www.mmf.mb.ca

CHARTRAND, ELBERT (Metis)
(executive director)
Affiliation: Swan River Indian & Metis Friendship Centre, 723 Main St., Box 1448, Swan River, MB, Canada R0L 1Z0 (204) 734-9301. *Other professional post*: Vice President, NorthWest Metis Council.

CHASE, ELIZABETH (LIBBY) (Wasco/Warm Springs/Yakama/Hoopa)
(organization president-elect)
Education: Brigham Young University (two years). *Affiliation & Address*: President-elect, National Native American Purchasing Association, P.O. Box 1169, Warm Springs, OR 97761 (541) 553-3254. E-mail: lchase@wstribes.org.

CHASING HORSE, NATHAN (Lakota)
(writer)
Address: 1109 Wambli Dr., Rapid City, SD 57701 (605) 343-5820.

CHAUDHURI, JONODEV OSCEOLA (Muscogee Creek)
(commission chairperson)
Education: Dartmouth College, BA; Cornell Law School, JD. *Affiliation & Address*: Acting Chairperson, National Indian Gaming Commission, 1441 L St., NW, Washington, DC 20005 (202) 632-7003. Jonodev served as Senior Counselor to the Department of the Interior's Assistant Secretary for Indian Affairs, where he provided guidance & assistance on a wide range of national policy issues, including Indian gaming, economic development, energy, Alaska affairs, and tribal recognition. He has served as a judge on five different tribal courts, including serving his tribe as Chief Justice of the Muscogee Creek Nation Supreme Court.

CHAUVIN, DOLLIE (Hopi-Tewa)
(project supervisor)
Affiliation & Address: Supervisor, AmeriCorps VISTA Program, National Society of American Indian Elderly (NSAIE), P.O. Box 50070, Phoenix, AZ 85076 (602) 424-0542. *Past professional posts*: Phoenix Indian Center; tribal liaison for the State of Arizona, Department of Labor; served on committees for the Arizona Governor's Office for Children, Youth & Families, Vision of Youth Collaborators; and the Department of Labor's Division of Indian & Native American Program Advisory Council.

CHAVARRIA, J. MICHAEL (Santa Clara Pueblo)
(Pueblo governor)
Affiliation & Address: Governor, Pueblo of Santa Clara, P.O. Box 580, Espanola, NM 87532 (505) 753-7330.

CHAVERS, CATHY (Bois Forte Ojibwe)
(tribal chairperson)
Affiliation & Address: Chairperson, Boise Forte Band of Ojibwe, P.O. Box 16, Nett Lake, MN 55772 (218) 757-3261. E-mail: cchavers@boisforte-nsn.gov

CHAVERS, DEAN (Lumbee) 1941-
(fundraiser)
Born February 4, 1941, Pembroke, N.C. *Education*: University of Richmond, 1960-62; University of California, Berkeley, BA, 1970; Stanford University, MA (Anthropology), 1973, MA (Communications), 1975, PhD (Communications Research), 1976. *Address*: 9710 Camino del Sol, NE, Albuquerque, NM 87111 (505) 823-2914. E-mail: deantonichavers@msn.com. *Affiliations & Address*: Director (1986-present), Catching the Dream (formerly Native American Scholarship Fund), 8200 Mountain Rd., NE #203, Albuquerque, NM 87110 (505) 262-2351. E-mail: ctd4deanchavers@aol.com; founding president, Coalition for Indian Education, Albuquerque, NM, 1987-present (editor, newsletter). *Past professional posts*: Assistant professor, California State University, Hayward, 1972-74; president, Bacone College, Muskogee, OK, 1978-81; president, Dean Chavers & Associates, 1981-85; member, Advisory Panel for Minority Concerns, The College Board, 1980-85; member, Minority Achievement Program, Association of American Colleges, 1980-84; president, MANAGE, Inc., 1985-86. *Military service*: U.S. Air Force, 1963-68 (Navigator, Captain; Distinguished Flying Cross, Air Medal). *Community activities*: Rotary Club, Muskogee & Broken Arrow, OK; Democratic Party of Bernalillo County, NM; chairman, Albuquerque Commission on Indian Affairs, 1993-95. *Memberships*: National Indian Education Assn (board member, 1983-86, 1987-90); Native American Scholarship Fund (president); National Congress of American Indians, 1972-; International Communication Association; Assn of Fund Raising Professionals. *Awards, honors*: Ford Foundation Graduate Fellowship for doctoral study, 1970-74; National Honor Society; Junior Officer of the Quarter, 1971, U.S. Air Force, Travis Air Force Base; 1996 recipient of Human Rights Award, City of Albuquerque, NM. *Interests*: Main interest is Indian education & economic development. Have published 12 books & technical manuals in these areas, as well as some 30 journal articles. Main occupation is providing technical assistance in fundraising, financial management, computer software development, and training for Indian tribes, contract schools, and Indian health clinics. *Published works*: The Feasibility of an Indian University (Bacone College, 1979); How to Write Winning Proposals (DCA Publications, 1983 & 1996); Funding Guide for Native Americans (DCA Publications, 1983 & 1985); Grants to Indians (DCA Publications, 1984); The Status of Indian Education (Journal of Thought, 1984); Tribal Economic Development Directory (DCA Publications, 1985); "The Effects of Testing on American Indians," symposium paper for the National Commission on Testing and Public Policy, 1987; The Indian Dropout (Coalition for Indian Education, 1991); Research in Indian Education (Catching the Dream Publications, 2003); editor, Deconstructing the Myths; Exemplary Programs in Indian Education, 4th Ed. (Catching the Dream Publications, 2004); Indian Students & College Preparation; Indian Teachers & Indian Control; editor, The National Indian Grant Directory (Catching the Dream Publications, 2006); Modern American Indian Leaders (Mellen Press, 2007).

CHAVEZ, EDWARD (*Two Moons*) (Chiricahua Apache)
(tribal president)
Affiliation & Address: Chiricahua Apache Nde Nation, P.O. Box 50955, Albuquerque, NM 87181 (505) 299-2276. Website: www.chiricahuaapache.org.

CHAVEZ, ENA B. (Navajo)
(craftsperson, co-manager)
Affiliation: Co-manager, Crownpoint Rug Weavers' Association, P.O. Box 1630, Crownpoint, NM 87313 (505) 786-5302 or 786-7386. *Product*: Navajo rugs sold at auction.

CHAVEZ-LAMAR, CYNTHIA (San Felipe Pueblo, Hopi/Tewa & Navajo)
(Indian center director)
Born & raised in San Felipe Pueblo, N.M. *Education*: Colorado College, BA; University of California, Los Angeles, MA (American Studies); University of New Mexico, PhD (American Studies), 2001. *Affiliation & Address*: Director (2007-present), Indian Arts Research Center, School for Advanced Research, P.O. Box 2188, Santa Fe, NM 87504 (505) 954-7205. *Past professional posts*: Associate curator, Smithsonian's National Museum of the American Indian (NMAI), 2000-05. Lead in the development of the inaugural exhibition, "Our Lives: Contemporary Life & Identities," which currently remains on exhibit at the museum. Director, Indian Pueblo Cultural Center (IPCC), Albuquerque, NM, 2005-07. *Research Interests*: Contemporary Native arts, issues of representation in museums, and cultural heritage rights of Native peoples. *Awards, honors*: Received an Honorary doctorate from Colorado College in 2008; appointed by former Governor Richardson to the New Mexico Arts Commission in 2009; nominated by President Obama to the Institute of American Indian Arts Board of Trustees in 2010.

CHAVIS-MICKEY, ANGELA YELVERTON (Lumbee) 1950-
(dentist)
Born May 11, 1950, Pembroke, N.C. Education: Pembroke State University, BS, 1971; University of North Carolina, Chapel Hill, School of Dentistry, DDS, 1980. *Affiliation & Address*: Dentist, Lumberton Correctional Institution, P.O. Box 1649, Lumberton, NC 28359 (910) 618-5574. *Community activities*:

Student Health Action Committee; Voter Registration. *Memberships*: North Carolina Association for Preventive Dentistry; American Dental Association. *Awards, honors*: Graduated Cum Laude, Pembroke State University, 1971; scholarship from American Fund for Dental Health, 1976-80. *Interests*: My vocational interest is dentistry. I plan to return to my hometown and work to better the dental health of the Indian people in my town & surrounding community. *Biographical source*: Who's Who Among Students in American Universities & Colleges, 1971.

CHEE, RONALD (Navajo)
(artist)
Address: Ronald Chee Studio, 2914 Ellesmere Ave., Costa Mesa, CA 92626 (714) 549-0148 or 334-9052. E-mail: ronaldcheestudio@sbcglobal.net. *Art medium*: Oil-based ink monotypes; acrylic paintings & limited edition prints; contemporary format dealing with interpretations of traditional Navajo myths & culture.

CHEEK, JOHN W. (Creek)
(Indian education)
Affiliations: Editorial Advisory Board, The Independent American Indian Review, PMB 268, 1840 E. Warner Rd., Suite A105, Tempe, AZ 85284 (480) 839-8355. *Membership*: National Indian Education Assn (former executive director).

CHEHAK, GAIL E. (Klamath)
(executive director)
Address & Affiliation: Executive Director, Indian Arts & Crafts Association (IACA), 4010 Carlisle NE, Suite C, Albuquerque, NM 87107 (505) 265-9149 E-mail: gchehak@iaca.com.

CHEKELELEE, EDNA (Eastern Cherokee)
(storyteller)
Address: Rt. 1 Box 151, Robbinsville, NC 28771 (704) 479-6601. Sharing Cherokee songs and stories, Edna works in all educational settings, elementary through high school. She has performed at powwows & Native American festivals. Edna also specializes in Cherokee arts & crafts workshops.

CHENAULT, VENIDA S. (Priaire Band Potawatomi)
(college president)
Education: Haskell Indian Nations University, 1975, 1984; University of Kansas, BS (Social Work), 1986, MSW, 1990, PhD, 2004. *Affiliation & Address*: President, Haskell Indian Nations University, 155 Indian Ave. P, Larwence, KS 66046 (785) 749-8404. E-mail: vchenault@haskell.edu. *Past professional posts*: In December 2004, Chenault was named Haskell's vice president of academic affairs, which gave her administrative oversight of a $3-$4 million budget & supervisory responsibility for all academic programs, budgets, faculty & staff within the Division of Academic Affairs. In her position she also served as acting vice president for university services from October 2009 to January 2010; acting Haskell president from January to May 2010; and at BIE headquarters in Washington, D.C., from September 2012 to April 2013. While with the Bureau, she helped lead key priority post-secondary education projects, including developing partnership agreements with tribal colleges and universities (TCUs) and working with the Bureau of Indian Affairs' Office of Justice Services and the National Park Service to design professional development curriculum. From 2006 to 2007, she also held consultations and workshops on tribal sovereignty and self-determination as well as academic assessment and research for TCUs. She has given numerous presentations on the subject of violence and substance abuse activity and prevention within the American Indian community, and developed and taught courses on human behavior, community health social work practice, chemical dependency and social work as they relate to Native people. In addition, she has published numerous articles and reports on a variety of topics related to the study of American Indian societies and cultures. *Awards, honors*: Haskell Outstanding Alumni of the Year (Spring 2009) and the Crystal Eagle Indigenous Leadership Award, Center for Indigenous Studies, University of Kansas (Spring 2005). She was named both a Kellogg Minority Serving Institutions Leadership Program Fellow and an American Indian Higher Education Consortium Fellow in 2003, and an American Indian College Fund Mellon Award Fellow in 2004.

CHERUBINI, LORENZO
(Indian centre director)
Affiliation & Address: Director, Tecumseh Centre for Aboriginal Research & Education, Brock University, Welch Hall, University Rd. W., St. Catherines, ON L2S 3A1 Canada (905) 688-5550. E-mail: Lorenzo.cherubini@brocku.ca.

CHESTNUT, PETER
(attorney)
Address: 121 Tijeras Ave., NE #2001, Albuquerque, NM 87102 (505) 842-5864. *Membership*: New Mexico Bar Association (chair, Indian Law Section).

CHEYFITZ, ERIC T.
(professor of American Indian studies)
Affiliation: Director, American Indian Program, Cornell University, 402 Caldwell Hall Hall, Ithaca, NY 14853 (607) 255-1755. E-mail: etc7@cornell.edu. *Interests*: American Indian literature and Federal Indian law. "I publish & lecture widely and teach in both areas. My commentary on Federal Indian law has appeared in Indian Country Today, on public radio and in the award-winning film, "Our Land, Our Life." My most recent publication on these topics is, "The Columbia Guide to American Indian Literatures of the United States Since 1945" (2006), of which I am the editor and the first part of which contains my book-length essay, "The (Post) Colonial Construction of Indian Country: U.S. American Indian Literatures & Federal Indian Law." *Current Research*: "I am writing a book titled, What Is a Just Society? Native American Philosophies and the Limits of Capitalism's Imagination, which analyzes the linked global crises of the environment & poverty from various indigenous perspectives in the Americas.

CHIAGO, ROBERT KEAMS (Navajo-Pima) 1942-
(executive director; tribal planner)
Born June 22, 1942, Los Angeles, Calif. *Education*: Arizona State University, BA, 1965; Northern Illinois University, Dekalb, MS, 1970; University of Utah, 1974-76 (61 hours towards PhD). Resides in Phoenix, AZ. *Past professional posts*: Associate director, American Indian Culture Center, UCLA, 1970; director, Ramah Navajo School Board, Inc., Ramah, N.M., 1970-71; director, Navajo Division of Education, Navajo Nation, Window Rock, AZ, 1971-73; consultant, Mesa Consultants, Albuquerque, NM, 1973; editor & founder, Utah Indian Journal, which was a statewide Indian newspaper in 1976 & 1977; visiting assistant professor of humanities, University of Utah, Salt Lake City, 1976-79; director, Native American Studies, University of Utah, 1973-81; director of Indian Teacher/Counselor Education Programs, University of Utah, 1980-84; president, Western Indian Technologies, Salt Lake City, Utah, 1984-92; founder & coordinator, Western Indian Education Conference; consulting; proposal writing and evaluation; Executive director, National Advisory Council on Indian Education (NACIE), Washington, DC, 1992-2002; tribal planner, Salt River Pima-Maricopa Indian Tribe, Scottsdale, AZ, 1994-2002. *Military service*: U.S. Marine Corps, 1965-68 (Captain, infantry officer; Presidential Unit Citation, Navy Unit Citation, National Defense Service Medal, Vietnam Service Medal & Campaign Medal). *Community activities*: Presidential appointee, National Advisory Council on Indian Education; gubernatorial appointee to the Utah State Board of Indian Affairs; National Congress of American Indians (resolutions committee chairman, 1976-80); advisory committee for the creation of the Native American Rights Fund, 1971-72; member, State of Utah ESEA Title IV Advisory Council, 1977-79; Community Services Council of Utah (board member, 1974-75; director, Minority Economic Development Council. *Memberships*: National Congress of American Indians; Western Indian Education Conference (coordinator, 1983, '84, '86); National Advisory Council on Indian Education, 1983-86. *Interests*: Major areas of interest include education, economic development, and employment.

CHICHARELLO, ELOUISE
(BIA regional director & agency supt.)
Affiliations & Address: Navajo Regional Office, Bureau of Indian Affairs, P.O. Box 1060, Gallup, NM 87305 (505) 863-8314; supt., Western Navajo Agency, BIA, P.O. Box 127, Tuba City, AZ 86045; Chinle Agency, BIA, P.O. Box 7H, Chinle, AZ 86503; supt. Fort Defiance Agency, BIA, Rt. 1, Box 9-C, Fort Defiance, AZ 86504.

CHIEF, SIMON (Navajo-Dine')
(Indian program coordinator)
Affiliation & Address: Coordinator, Native American Student Services, Northern Arizona University, Native American Cultural Center (Bldg. 14, Rm. 100), P.O. Box 5653, Flagstaff, AZ 86011 (928) 523-8061. E-mail: simon.chief@nau.edu

CHILD, BRENDA J. (Red Lake Ojibwe)
(professor; dept. chair)
Education: Bemidji State University, BS (History); University of Iowa, MA & PhD (History). *Affiliation & Address*: Chairperson, Department of American Indian Studies, Dept. of American Studies, 209 Scott Hall, 72 Pleasant St. SE, University of Minnesota, Twin Cities Campus, Minneapolis, MN 55455 (612) 626-5330. E-mail: child 011@umn.edu. Brenda teaches courses in American Indian Studies and History. *Other professional post*: Consultant to the Heard Museum exhibit in Phoenix called "Remembering Our Indian School Days." She is working on several book-length projects. The first project examines Ojibwe history in the 20th Century and the labor practices of men & women associated with traditional wild rice harvest. The second is the comparative study of indigenous leaders from the U.S., Canada & New Zealand. Brenda is also writing a general history of Indian education in the U.S. *Community activities*: Board Member for the Eiteljorg Museum, the Division of Indian Work; Board of Editors of Ethno-history. *Memberships*: Minnesota Historical Society; American Society for Ethno-history. *Awards, honors*: The North American

Indian Prose Award for Boarding School Seasons; 2003 President's Outstanding Community Service Award, University of Minnesota. *Published works*: Boarding School Seasons: American Indian Families, 1900-1940 (University of Nebraska Press, 1998) (the first study to make use of American Indian letters to document the boarding school & assimilation experiences of Native children & families); Away From Home: American Indian Boarding School Experiences, 1879-2000 (The Heard Museum, 2000).

CHILDRESS, DAVID (Cherokee)
  (MIS director)
Address & Affiliation: MIS Director, D-Q University, P.O. Box 409, Davis, CA 95617 (916) 758-0470. *Military service*: U.S. Army, 1965-69. *Memberships*: AAAS; Association for Supervision Curriculum Development, AISES.

CHISCHILLY, ANN MARIE (Dine')
  (executive director)
Born & raised in Shonto/Kayenta, Arizona. *Education*: St. Mary's University School of Law, JD; Vermont Law School, Master's in Environmental Law); Arizona Bar Leadership Institute (graduate). *Affiliation & Address*: Executive Director, Institute for Tribal Environmental Professionals (ITEP), Northern Arizona University, P.O. Box 15004, Flagstaff, AZ 86011 (928) 523-9555. E-mail: ann-marie.chischilly@nau.edu. Ms. Chischilly is responsible for coordinating ITEP's work with NAU, state & federal agencies, tribes & Alaska Native villages. *Past professional posts*: Recently served on the National Tribal Water Council; Senior Assistant General Counsel, Gila River Indian Community, where Ann Marie assisted the tribe in implementing the historic Arizona Water Settlement Act and founded the Gila River Indian Community Renewable Energy Team. *Other professional posts*: he serves on the Arizona Attorney magazine Editorial Board, Indian Law Section of the Arizona State Bar, Native American Connections Board, and Native American Community Service Center Capital Campaign. *Interests*: "I want to listen to tribal needs and work with tribes in developing outstanding educational & technical support."

CHISHOLM, ANITA (Shawnee)
  (administration)
Address & Affiliation: Former Director, American Indian Institute (1975-2008), College of Continuing Education, University of Oklahoma, 555 Constitution St., Suite 237, Norman, OK 73072 (405) 325-4127. E-Mail: achishol@cce.occe.ou. edu. *Published works*: Oklahoma's Indian People: Images of Today, Yesterday & Tomorrow; Culture Through Concepts - Five Tribes; Cultural Curriculum Materials on Indian Tribes in Oklahoma; conference proceedings (derived from the 11th National Native American/First Nations Cultural Curriculum Development Workshop) guides I & II.

CHITTO, RANDALL (Choctaw)
  (artist)
Address: 6777 Camino Rojo, Santa Fe, NM 87507 (505) 986-3479. Website: www.rchitto.com. E-mail: rchitto@aol.com

CHIWIWI, ANTONIO (Pueblo of Isleta)
  (Pueblo 1st lt. governor)
Affiliation & Address: 1st Lt. Governor, Isleta Pueblo Council, P.O. Box 1270, Isleta, NM 87022 (505) 869-3111.

CHRISJOHN, RICHARD (Oneida-Iroquois)
  (artist; tribal leader)
 Address: RD 2, Box 315, Red Hook, NY 13421. *Affiliation*: Oneida Nation of New York, Oneida, NY.

CHRISTENSEN, LISA (Washoe)
  (former tribal chairperson)
Affiliation & Address: Washoe Tribe of the Dresslerville Colony, 1585 Watasheamu, Gardnerville, NV 89460 (775) 265-5645
E-mail: lisa.christensen@washoetribe.us

CHRISTENSEN, ROSEMARY (Bad River Anishinabe-Ojibwe)
  (professor of First Nations Studies)
Born on the Bad River Reservation in Wisconsin. *Education*: Harvard University, MA; University of Minnesota, EdD (Education). *Affiliation & Address*: Assistant Professor, Department of First Nations Studies, UW Green Bay, WI 54311 (920) 465-2158. E-mail: christer@uwgb.edu. Rosemary is a founding member of the National Indian Education Association. "Presently, she is working on a model promoting an American Indian learning & teaching style centered on core American Indian values & elder epistemology, assisting Medicine Elders in curriculum for teaching Ojibwe orally-based life lessons & working with UWGB colleagues in fusing First Nations Studies into Teacher education toward a goal of systemic change in how K-12 teachers provide information about American Indians in their classroom."

CHRISTIAN, RANDY LAVAGHN (*Shield Wolf*)
(Tcinto Sakto Muscogee) 1959-
  (cardiac IUC, RN, PCC)
Born April 12, 1959, Lakeland, Ga. *Education*: Georgia Military College (Milledgeville, GA), AAS-Emergency Medical Technology; Abraham Baldwin Agricultural College (Tifton, GA), AAS Nursing; Valdosta State University, BS, 2001. Principal occupation: Cardiac IUC, RN, PCC. *Address*: 3895 Shelton Rd., Lake Park, GA 31636 (229) 242-3504. *Affiliations*: South Georgia Medical Center, Cardiac ICU patient care coordinator; Emergency department RN for 17 years; paramedic for 25 years. Community activities: Board of Trustees, Valwood School, 1992-94; wildlife rehabilitation for Georgia; bird-of-prey educator, handler & rehabilitator, 1995-present. *Memberships*: Georgia EMT Association, 1982-84; Emergency Nurses Association, 1989-90; B.A.S.S. Federation member; Tcinto Sakto Muscogee member. *Awards, honors*: 1988 Outstanding Young Men of America; Prayer Blanket & Gord Rattle, Red Feather, 1993. *Interests*: Wildlife protection, environmental protection.

CHURCH, ANN (Match-E-Be-Nash-She-Wish band of Potawatomi Indians)
  (IHS acting director, Office of Finance & Accounting)
Education: St. Mary's College of Maryland, BA. *Affiliation & Address*: Acting Director, Office of Financing & Accounting, Indian Health Service (IHS), DHH, 801 Thompson Ave., Rockville, MD 20852 (301) 443-1083. As the Acting Director of the Office of Finance and Accounting, Ms. Church is responsible for Agency budget formulation, execution, and associated systems and policies. She advises the IHS Director and senior management staff on the Agency's financial activities. Ms. Church most recently served as the Director, Division of Financial Operations, in the OFA. In that role, she supported Headquarters budget and payment activities, and managed the agency-wide travel program. Throughout her 16 years of service to the Agency, she performed many functions including support for: previous Headquarters organizational components such as the Office of Management Support's Director, Deputy Director, and Executive Officer; the National Council of Executive Officers; and the IHS Business Plan Workgroup. She has received several HIS Director's Awards and was honored with the Luana Reyes Leadership Award in 2007.

CHURCH, RICHARD M. (Grand Traverse Band-Ottawa/Chippewa Indians)
  (assistant Surgeon General, Indian Health Service)
Education: University of Michigan, BS, College of Pharmacy, Pharm. D. *Affiliation & Address*: Assistant Surgeon General, Indian Health Service, Director (2015-present), DHH, 801 Thompson Ave., Rockville, MD 20852 (301) 443-1083. *Past professional post*: Former Director of Office of Public Health Support (2004-15), Indian Health Service (IHS), 36 years of PHS-IHS - Chief Pharmacist, IHS; director & chief information officer, Division of Information Resources, IHS, Rockville, MD. *Awards, honors*: Surgeon General's Medallion; Distinguished Service Medal; numerous PHS and professional awards.

CLADOOSBY, M. BRIAN (Swinomish)
  (tribal chairperson)
Affiliation & Address: Chairperson (1997-present), Swinomish Indian Tribal Community, P.O. Box 817, LaConnor, WA 98257 (360) 466-7314. *Other professional posts*: President, Association of Washington Tribes; executive board member, Washington Gaming Association; board president (2013-present), National Congress of American Indians, Washngton, DC; co-speaker, Coast Salish gathering, which comproses British Columbia First Nations and Western Washington Tribes. *Past professional post*: Former president, Affiliated Tribes of Northwest Indians (ATNI), Portland, OR. *Awards, honors*: Received the American Indian Tribal Leader Award from the Reservation Economic Summit & American Indian Business Trade Fair, 2011. Brian has been instrumental in the domestic & international emergence of the Northwest Indian country salmon & seafood industry. He shares a vision with the Swinomish Indian Tribal Community members to have strong economic development plan that supports a way of life for today and future generations.

CLAH, HERBERT (Navajo-Dine') 1949-
  (executive director)
Born June 1, 1949, Farmington, N.M. *Education*: Brigham Young University, BS, 1975, MPA, 1981. *Address & Affiliations*: Executive director, Utah Navajo Development Council, P.O. Box 129, Bluff, UT 84512 (801) 678-2285, 1986-present; Dean of Instruction, Navajo Community College, Shiprock, 1990-. *Community activities*: Blanding City Planning Commission; Rural Community Assistance Corporation (board of directors). *Awards, honors*: Outstanding Young Men of America; Jamie Thompson Award; Dean's Leadership Award, BYU; USO National Defense Peace Time Award.

CLAHCHISCHILLIAGE, SHARON (Navajo-Dine')
  (New Mexico State (R) representative)
Affiliation: New Mexico State Representatie (2013-14), District 4, New Mexico Legislature, Albuquerque, NM. *Address*: P.O. Box 585, Kirtland, NM 87417 (505) 258-4342. E-mail: sharon.chahchischilli@nmlegis.gov. *Membeship*: Economic Development Policy Committee, 2013-14, National Caucus of Native State Legislators.

CLAIRMONT, BONNIE (Ho-Chunk)
(victim advocacy specialist)
Affiliation & Address: Tribal Law & Policy Institute, 1619 Dayton Ave., Suite 305, St. Paul, MN 55104 (651) 644-1125. E-mail: bonnie@tlpi.org.

CLAPSADDLE, ANNETTE SAUNOOKE (Eastern Cherokee)
(executive director)
Education: Yale University, BA (American Studies); College of William & Mary, MA (American Studies). *Affiliation & Address*: Executive Director (2013-present), Cherokee Preservation Foundation, P.O. Box 504, Cherokee, NC 28719 (828) 497-5550. E-mail: aclapsaddle@cpfdn.org. She was a member of the programming staff soon after the Foundation was established and then served as assistant to EBCI Principal Chief Michell Hicks and as a National Board Certified teacher.

CLARK, C. BLUE (Muscogee-Creek)
(intertribal governmental affairs & cultural advisor))
Education: University of Oklahoma, BA, MA, PhD. *Affiliation & Address*: Instructor of Law (1988-present), Native American Legal Resource Center, Oklahoma City University, 2501 N. Blackwelder, Oklahoma City, OK 73106. (405) 208-5017. E-mail: bclark@okcu.edu. Dr. Clark has extensive experience in Indian Country. He teaches in the areas of history, legal anthropology & Native American legal issues & religion. *Past professional post*: Administrator, Oklahoma City University. *Published work*: Lone Wolf v. Hitchcock (University of Nebraska Press, 1994; paper, 1999); Indian Tribes of Oklahoma: A Guide (University of Oklahoma Press, 2009).

CLARK, CYNTHIA
(Indian center director)
Affiliation & Address: Director, Center for the Study of Indigenous Lamguage of the West, UCB 295, University of Colorado, Boulder, CO 80309 (303) 492-8456. E-mail: cynthia.clark@colorado.edu.

CLARK, DON (*Edge of the Water*) (Navajo) 1955-
(commercial graphic artist)
Born March 22, 1955, Winslow, Ariz. *Education*: Navajo Community College, 1974-75; Northern Arizona University, BFA, 1980. *Principal occupation*: Commercial graphic artist. *Address*: P.O. Box 3240, Tuba City, AZ 86045 (602) 283-4123. *Other professional post*: Professional jazz guitarist. *Memberships*: Indian Arts & Crafts Association; Inter-tribal Indian Ceremonial Association; SWAIA. *Awards, honors*: 1992 First Place, SWAIA; First Place, Santa Fe Indian Market; First Place in pastel drawings at the Navajo Show, Museum of Northern Arizona; 1993 First Place, Poster Artist Winner at Inter-tribal Indian Ceremonial. among others. *Interests*: A full-time painter since 1986. "I am also known for my, more or less trademark, "blanket series." Each is a portrait of a Native American child or adult wrapped in a colorful Navajo blanket. The background is always black, representing darkness and uncertainty. The blanket means protection and security. It's a symbol of hope, trust and all that is good. One of my goals is to let people know who American Indians are. I'm very proud to American Indian."

CLARK, ERNEST (Cherokee)
(American Indian Institute director)
Affiliation & Address: Director, American Indian Institute, College of Continuing Education, University of Oklahoma, 555 Constitution Ave., Suite 237, Norman, OK 73072-7820 (405) 325-4127. E-mail: erclark@ou.edu. *Past professional post*: Former supt., Yakama Agency, BIA, Toppenish, WA.

CLARK, FERLIN (Navajo-Dine')
(college president)
Born in Crystal, N.M. *Affiliation*: President, Dine College, P.O. Box 126, Tsaile, AZ 86556 (928) 724-3311. Website: www.dinecollege.edu. *Past professional posts*: Director, Dine College, Navajo Nation's Ford Teacher Education Project, 1994-98; vice president for development, Senior Program Coordinator, University of Arizona's Native Nation's Institute, 2001-07.

CLARK, NICHOLAS L. (*Alankwia*) (Potawatomi/Cherokee) 1944-
(historian & museologist & cultural consultant)
Born November 16, 1944, Topeka, Kans. *Education*: Washburn University, BA, 1972, MA, 1976; University of Idaho, MA, 1978. *Principal occupation*: Historian, museologist & cultural consultant. *Affiliation & Address*: Founding President, National Center for Great Lakes Native American Culture, 5401 S. County Rd. 900 E., Lafayette, IN 47905 (765) 296-9943. E-mail: nlclark1@aol.com & nclark@ncglnac.org. *Past professional posts*: Social Studies Chair, St. Mary's High School, St. Mary's, KS, 1973-76; executive director, Heritage Hill State Park, Green Bay, WI, 1978-83; executive director, Southern Oregon Historical Society, 1983-86; founding president, Minnetrista Cultural Center, Muncie, IN, 1986-95; charter member, Governor's Indiana Native American Council; founding director, Museums At Prophetstown, Battle Ground, IN, 1995-2000; president, Clark Associates, 2000-present; founding president, National Center for Great Lakes Native American Culture, 2000-

present. (Clark Associates is a firm that consults with museums, public and private institutions of learning, and government agencies concerning Great Lakes Native American Culture. NCGLNAC is under development and will be a gathering place for those traditions.) *Other professional posts*: Founding Co-Chair, Minnestrista Council for Great Lakes Native American Studies, 1988-95; Founding Chair, Prophetstown Council for Preservation of Great Lakes Native American Culture, 1995-2000; advisor, Miami Nation of Indians of Indiana. Consultant to: Time-Life Publishing, The Arts & Entertainment and History Channels; & Houghton Mifflin Publishing. *Interests*: Networking for Woodland Cultural Projects, promoting Great Lakes Native American artists & craftspeople; & organizing Woodland Native American cultural workshops, symposiums, events & exhibits that promote & raise awareness of Woodland Great Lakes Culture. *Memberships*: American Association of Museums, Midwest Museums Association, Midwest Outdoor Museums Coordinating Council, Association of Indiana Museums, and Public Historians of America.

CLARK, TONY (*Locha*) (Lumbee) 1969-
(religious coordinator)
Born October 26, 1969, Robeson Co., N.C. *Principal occupation*: Native American religious coordinator for North Carolina DOC. *Address*: 5160 Union School Rd., Rowland, NC 28383 (910) 521-9017. *Community activities*: Cultural class teacher; Healing Lodge; fatherhood education; Lumbee elders. *Interests*: Arts & crafts; education of youth; education of others concerning Lumbee people.

CLARK, TRACY (White Earth Ojibwe)
(interim Indian college president
Affiliation & Address: President, White Earth Tribal & Community College, P.O. Box 478, Mahnomen, MN 56557 (218) 935-0417. E-mail: tracy.clark@wetcc.edu

CLARK-PRICE, MARGARET A. (*Tio-ron-ia-te-BrightSky*)
(Wyandotte-Chippewa-Shawnee) 1944-
(motivational speaker, artist)
Born August 2, 1944, Colville Indian Agency, Nespelem, Wash. *Education*: St. Michael's (AZ) High School, 1962; Sierra Nevada College (three years). *Principal occupation*: Motivational speaker, artist. *Address*: P.O. Box 1281, Scottsdale, AZ 85252 (602) 483-8212. *Affiliation*: Legal secretary & researcher, 1966-77; executive director, Native American Press Association, 1985-87; president/director, Native American Communication & Career Development, Ltd. (NACCD), 1987-; associate editor, Native Peoples Magazine, Phoenix, 1988-92; publisher, Native American Annual (Native American Publishing Co.); consultant, Scottsdale Community College, Tribal Management Programs, Scottsdale, AZ. *Other professional posts*: Member, board of education, Scottsdale Native American Indian Cultural Foundation. *Community activities*: Advisory committee member: Association for Retarded Citizens of Arizona, Inc., Phoenix; fundraising activities; among others. *Exhibits*: Her pastels, oils, acrylics, watercolors and pencil works hang in galleries in Arizona, California & Nevada as well as in many private collections throughout the U.S. *Memberships*: National Organization of Native American Women; Association for Education in Journalism & Mass Communications. *Awards, honors*: Six awards and a Grand prize for a large pastel entitled Caught in the Middle, at the 1982 annual Navajo Nation Fair, Window Rock, AZ. *Interests*: "My main interests, obviously, surround the Indian world. I have spent years on my own family genealogy, necessitating journeying across the U.S. and into Canada. I hope to instill such an interest in others through the journey among the pages of the Native American Annual." NACCD, Ltd. focuses on career-development seminars to prepare students for journalism careers as well as fund-raising for schools with Native American students. *Published works*: Native American Annual (Native America Publishing Co., 1985); co-founder & editor, Native Peoples Magazine, 1988-92.

CLARKE, DAMON R. (Hualapai)
(tribal chairperson)
Affiliation & Address: Chairperson, Hualapai Tribal Council, P.O. Box 179, Peach Springs, AZ 86434 (928) 769-2216. E-mail: damon.clarke@hualapai-nsn.gov.

CLARKE, JEROME (Navajo)
(executive director)
Education: University of New Mexico, BS (Business Administration), 2003; Arizona State University College of Law, JD, 2008. *Affiliationn & Address*: Executive Diector, CEO, 1830 West University Dr., Suite 105, Tempe, AZ 85281 (480) 968-9354. E-mail: jclarke@cooknam.org. *Published work*: Co-author, Streamlining the Federal Recognition Process, A report to the Senate on Indian Committee on Indian Affairs, Washington, DC, 2008.

CLARKSON, GAVIN (Choctaw/Cherokee)
(assistant professor of law & Native American studies)
Education: Rice University, BA, MBA; Harvard Business School, doctorate; Harvard Business School, JD. *Affiliation & Address*: Assistant Professor (2003-

present), School of Information, University of Michigan, 4322 North Quad, 105 S. State St., Ann Arbor, MI 48109 (734) 763-2284. E-mail: gsmc@umich.edu. Professor Clarkson conducts research in intellectual property management & tribal economic development, including tribal access to capital markets and the determinants of success for tribal entrepreneurship. *Past professional post*: Computer Science Faculty, Rice University, 1991-98; KPMG Fellow, Harvard Business School, 1998-2003. *Awards, honors*: Gavin recently received the first ever grant from the National Sciences Foundation to study the dynamics of tribal finance. *Interests*: Dr. Clarkson has consulted, written, and published extensively on tribal sovereignty, tribal governance & court systems, tribal economic development, and tribal asset management, and has conducted research on the empirical data underlying the American Indian mascot controversy. *Published work*: Contributing author for the most recent edition of Felix Cohen's Handbook of Federal Indian Law, providing material on tribal finance, tribal corporations, economic development, and intellectual property.

CLARKSON, KAREN (Choctaw)
(artist)
Address: 1044 Broadmoor Blvd., San Leandro, CA 94577. Website: www. clarksonart.com. E-mail: info@clarksonart.com. Karen does oil paintings & graphite drawings of Native Americans.

CLAUSEN, MARILYN (Arapaho)
(Indian education program director)
Affiliation & Address: Director, Arapahoe School, Fremont County School District #38, Indian Education Program, P.O. Box 9211, Arapahoe, WY 82510 (307) 856-9333. E-mail: mclausen@fremont38.k12.wy.us.

CLAY, JULIE ANNA (Omaha) 1958-
(center coordinator)
Born November 2, 1958, Flandreau, S.D. *Education*: University of Oklahoma, BA, 1982; OU-Health Sciences Campus (Oklahoma City, OK), MPH, 1984. *Affiliation*: Coordinator. American Indian Disability Technical Assistance Center (AIDTAC), Center for Excellence in Disability Education, Research & Services, 52 Corbin Hall, University of Montana, Missoula, MT 59801 (406) 243-5467. *Other professional posts*: Advisory Board for research project, "VR Independent Living Counselor Effects on Independent Living Outcomes for American Indians with Disabilities." *Past professional posts*: Research & Training Center on Rural Rehabilitation, University of Montana, Missoula (Project Manager, 1989-92, Program Analyst, 1990-92) Management analyst, Indian Health Service, Rockville, MD, 1992-93; Principal Investigator, Montana University Affiliated Rural Institute on Disabilities, University of Montana, Missoula, MT, 1993-2007. *Memberships*: American Public Health Association (Advisory Committee); American Association of University Affiliated Programs (Minority Affairs Committee); National Congress of American Indians (Disability Issues Committee); member of the Administration on Developmentally Disabled Multicultural Committee; Advisory Council of the Human Services - Rehabilitation Degree Project, Salish Kootenai Tribal College; Training Advisory Committee, Research & Training Center on Public Policy on Independent Living. *Awards, honors*: Indian Health Service Scholarship, Outstanding OU MPH Indian Student, 1984; All American Indian Student Award of Excellence, Americans with Disabilities Act Award. *Interests*: "My major area of interest is to promote communication & education on American Indians with disabilities & all the attendant issues. I enjoy outdoor recreational activities such as skiing, camping, bicycling, attending powwows and other tribal gatherings." *Published works*: A Descriptive Study of Secondary Conditions Reported by a Population of Adults with Physical Disabilities Served by Three Independent Living Centers in a Rural State, by J.A. Clay et al (Journal of Rehabilitation, April/May/June 1994); National Council on Disability - Prevention of Disabilities - Meeting the Unique Needs of Minorities with Disabilities; A report to the President & the Congress, April 1993; numerous articles & presentations.

CLAY, SHAWNA (Oklahoma Choctaw)
(configuration/data manager, U.S. Navy)
Education: LaVerne University (CA), BS (Business Administration), 1992. *Affiliation*: Configuration/Data Manager for Foreign Military Sales (FMS) and with Assault Survivability Equipment (ASE) software, U.S. Dept. of the Navy, Naval Air Warfare Center Weapons Division, for Tactical Aircraft Electronic Warfare Dept., Point Magu, CA (1988-present). *Other professional posts*: Native American/Alaskan Native (NA/AN) Chairperson committee member, 1995-present, Point Magu & China Lake; member, board of trustees, First Americans In the Arts (FAITA), Beverly Hills, CA (1995-present). She scouts out American Indian actors & musicians for nominations for movies, theatrical, or latest music releases on CDs; showcases (with others) an award show every year at the Beverly Hilton Hotel; recruits celebrities to attend & as presenters, and is associate director for clips & videos for FAITA. Vice-chair for Candelaria American Indian Council, Ventura, CA, assisting students attending college for tuition, employment to student graduates; board member, SAIGE (Society for American Indian Governmental Employees, Washington, DC.

CLEAVES, REUBEN CLAYTON (Passamaquoddy)
(tribal governor)
Education: University of Maine, Orono, AA, 1972; HUD Management & Compliance Training, 1998-2004. *Affiliation & Address*: Governor, Passama-quoddy Tribe, P.O. Box 343, Perry, ME 04667 (207) 853-2600. *Past tribal posts*: Director, Housing Authority, 1973-80, 1998-2010; EDA Planner, 1981-84; Tribal Manager, Pleasant Point Reservation, 1984-89, Health Care Planner, 1991-98.

CLEMENTS, RODNEY K. (Mechoopda Maidu)
(training & technical assistance specialist)
Affiliation & Address: Training & Technial Assistance Specialist, National American Indian Indian Housing Council, California Field Office, P.O. Box 25, Tehama, CA 96090 (530) 966-3921. E-mail: rclements@naihc.net.

CLEMMER, JANICE WHITE (Wasco, Shawnee, Delaware) 1941-
(professor of education)
Born February 17, 1941, Warm Springs Reservation, Oregon. *Education*: Brigham Young University, BS, 1964; Dominican College of San Rafael, MA (History), 1975; University of San Francisco, MA (Education), 1976; University of Utah, PhD (Cultural Foundation of Education), 1979, PhD (History), 1980; J. Reuben Clark Law School, BYU, JD, 1993. *Address*: 1445 E. Princeton Ave., Salt Lake City, UT 84105. *Affiliations*: Professor, College of Education, Brigham Young University, Provo, Utah, 1980-. *Other professional posts*: Council member, National Association of Ethnic Studies; departmental and college committees; consultant. *Community activities*: Native American Advisory Board, State of Utah Board of Education (board chairman); Coalition for Minority Affairs, State Office of Education (Board member); Minority Affairs, KUTV-Channel 12 committee member; Utah Endowment for the Humanities (board member); American Indian Services (board member). *Memberships*: SIETAR (Society for Intercultural Education, Training & Research, International Organization); Native American Historians' Assn (founding member); American Studies Assn; OHOYO - National Native American Women's Program; Association for Supervision & Curriculum Development; State of Utah Bilingual Assn; American Historians Western History Assn; Utah State Historical Society; Oregon Historical Society; California Historical Society; National Archives (associate); Jefferson Forum; American Assn for State & Local History. *Awards, honors*: University of Utah Danforth Foundation Fellowship Candidate; Distinguished Teaching Award Candidate, University of Utah; Tribal Archives Conference Award Recipient; Consortium for Native American Archives; OHOYO One Thousand, Native American Women Award Listing; American Indian Alumni Award, Brigham Young University; Lamanite Award, American Indian Services, BYU; D'Arcy McNickle, Newberry Library Fellowship Research Award, Chicago, Ill.; Spencer W. Kimball Memorial Award, Private Corporation Endowment & AIS, BYU; Phi Alpha Theta; Phi Delta Kappa; Phi Kappa Phi; Phi Alpha Delta; first Native American woman in U.S. history to earn three doctorates; J. Reuben Clark Law School Service Awards, 1990-91, 1991-92; Law School student organization awards, 1990-93; 1982 Women's Conference Spotlight, outstanding woman faculty member from the College of Student Life, BYU; Multicultural Week Advisor Awards, BYU; Multicultural Programs Awards, BYU. *Published works*: The Good Guys and the Bad Guys, The Utah Indian, Journal, Spring, 1979; Ethnic Traditions and the Family--The Native Americans, Ethnic Traditions and the Family series, Salt Lake City Board of Education, Fall, 1980; editor, Minority Women Speak Out; co-editor for the Utah Centennial (1996) Tribal History Project sponsored by the state of Utah, the Utah Historical Society, and Utah Office of Indian Affairs; various book reviews pertaining to Native American topics; printed works primarily in-house curriculum development material, Brigham Young University.

CLEVELAND, WILFRID "WILLY" (Ho-Chunk)
(tribal president)
Affiliation & Address: President, Ho-Chunk Nation, P.O. Box 667, Black River Falls, WI 54615 (715) 284-3297. E-mail: wcleveland@ho-chunk.com

CLINE, RAYMOND M. (Delaware Lenni Lenape)
(tribal trust board chairperson)
Education: Oklahoma State University; Northeastern State University. *Affiliation*: Trust Board Chairperson, Delaware Tribe of Indians, 170 NE Barbara, Bartlesville, OK 74006 (918) 336-5272. E-mail: w_stull2006@yahoo. com. *Other professional posts*: President, Nowata County Historical Society, Museum & Glass Mansion; chair, Nowata Educational Endowment Foundation; chair, Nowata Chamber Industrial Foundation; chair, Museum for the Shenadoah Valley. *Military service*: U.S. Army, 1970-72; OK National Guard.

CLINTON, ROBERT N.
(attorney, professor)
Education: University of Michigan, BA, 1968; University of Chicago Law School, JD, 1971. *Address & Affiliation*: Foundation Professor of Law, Sandra Day O'Connor College of Law, 246B Armstrong Hall, Arizona State University (ASU), Box 877906, Tempe, AZ 85287 (480) 389-6814. E-mail: rclinton@

robert-clinton.com. *Other professional posts*: Faculty Advisor on Tribal Engagement, Indian Legal Program, and Faculty Fellow, Center for Law, Science & Innovation, Sandra Day O'Connor College of Law, Arizona State University; Affiliated Faculty, ASU American Indian Studies Program; Chief Justice of the Winnebago Supreme Court & as an Associate Justice of the Cheyenne River Sioux tribal Court of Appeals, the Colorado River Indian Tribes Court of Appeals, the Hualapai Tribal Court of Appeals, and Hopi Court of Appeals. *Past professional posts*: Faculty, University of Iowa College of Law (1973-2000), Iowa City, IA; the Wiley B. Rutledge Professor of Law & Founder & Affiliated Faculty member of the American Indian & Native Studies Program, University of Iowa College of Liberal Arts. *Awards, honors*: 2001-2003 academic years, appointed the Barry Goldwater Chair of American Institutions at Arizona State University. *Published works*: Co-author of casebooks on Indian law & federal courts, "The Handbook of Federal Indian Law" (1982 ed.), multiple editions of "American Indian Law: Native Nations & the Federal System, Colonial & American Indian Treaties" (a collection on CD-ROM), and over 25 major articles on federal Indian law, American constitutional law & history, and federal courts.

CLOUD, ALEX S. (Southern Ute)
(tribal chairperson)
Affiliation & Address: Chairperson, Southern Ute Indian Tribe, 356 Ouray Dr., P.O. Box 737, Ignacio, CO 81137 (970) 563-0100.

CLOUD, CHARLES RILEY (Cherokee) 1932-
(retired chief judge)
Born November 20, 1932, Britton (now Oklahoma City), Okla. *Education*: College of William & Mary, BS, 1957, Marshall-Wythe Law School, JD, 1959. *Address*: 1211 Colonial Ave., Norfolk, VA 23517 (804) 622-6185. *Affiliation*: Retired Chief Judge, Norfolk General District Court. *Other professional posts*: Member, Coordinating Council, Conference of Chief Justices, to resolve disputes between State & Tribal Courts over jurisdiction; co-chairperson, Native American Tribal Courts Committee, National Conference of Special Court Judges, JAD, ABA; trustee, Jamestown-Yorktown Foundation. *Military service*: U.S. Army, 1953-55. *Community activities*: Former chief deputy, Norfolk Commonwealth Attorney's Office; deacon & chairperson of the board, First Christian Church (Disciples of Christ), Norfolk, VA. *Memberships*: National Conference of Special Court Judges, Judicial Administration Division (JAD), American Bar Administration (ABA) (district representative & member of executive committee). *Awards, honors*: Several awards from the ABA, National Conference of Special Court Judges, for outstanding service as Chair of the Native American Tribal Courts Committee, and as a member of the Coordinating Council, Civil Jurisdiction of Tribal Courts & State Courts, and for service to the profession. "Honored by receiving letters of support from Indian leaders, such as Chief Wilma Mankiller and former Chief, Ross Swimmer, Cherokee Nation of Oklahoma; Chief Justices of the Navajo Nation, Chief Justice of Supreme Court of Virginia, and the General Assembly of Virginia leading to nomination as one of two judges of the U.S. to serve on the National Judicial College Board, and as its first Native American member." *Interests*: "Participate in programs, as well as advocating the education of Americans as to the many contributions Native Americans to our Constitutional form of government and Bill of Rights--also, about the part Native Americans played in the Federation of the original colonies and the American Revolution." *Published works*: Foreword to "The Encyclopedia of Native American Legal Tradition," by Bruce Elliott Johansen, Editor.

CLOUTIER, FRANK J. (Saginaw Chippewa)
(tribal chief)
Affiliation & Address: Chief, Saginaw Chippewa Indian Tribe, 7070 E. Broadway, Mount Pleasant, MI 48858 (989) 775-4000.

CLOW, RICHMOND L. 1949-
(professor of Native American studies)
Born May 21, 1949, Sioux Falls, S.D. *Education*: University of South Dakota, BS, 1971, MA, 1972; University of New Mexico, PhD, 1977. *Address*: 311 Skyline, Missoula, MT 59802 (406) 543-7504. E-mail: clowr@mso.umt.edu. *Affiliation*: Associate professor, Department of Native American Studies, University of Montana, Missoula, 1984-. *Memberships*: Organization of American Historians; Western Historical Assn. *Interests*: "I enjoy teaching Native American studies courses which enables me to cover many topics of interest to myself and to my students." *Published works*: Co-author: A Forest in Trust: Three Quarters of a Century of Indian Forestry, 1910-1986, (Washington, D.C.: Litigation Support Services for the Bureau of Indian Affairs, 1986); Tribal Government Today: Politics on Montana's Indian Reservations (Westview Press, 1990; revised updated edition, University Press of Colorado, 1998); edited with Imre Sutton, Trusteeship in Change: Toward Tribal Autonomy in Resource Management (University Press of Colorado, 2001); numerous articles in books.

COATES, JULIA (Cherokee)
(professor; Cherokee historian)
Education: PhD. *Affiliation*: Assistant professor, Dept. of Native American Studies, University of California, Davis, 2417 Hart Hall, One Shields Ave., Davis, CA 95616 (530) 754-6492. Website: www.nas.ucdavis.edu; E-mail: jmcoates@ucdavis.edu. *Address*: P.O. Box 1202, Woodland, CA 95776. Julia is an instructor for the award-winning Cherokee Nation history course, & serves on tribal council of the Cherokee Nation as its "At Large" representative.

COBB-GREETHAM, AMANDA (Chickasaw)
(professor & chair of Native American studies)
Education: The University of Oklahoma, PhD*Affiliation & Address:* Professor & Director of Native American Studies, Department of Anthropology, Ellison Hall 204, The University of Oklahoma, 633 Elm Ave., Norman, OK 73019 (405) 325-0684. E-mail: acobb@ou.edu. *Other professional posts:* Director, Native Nations Center, University of Oklahoma, Norman, OK; Associate Department Head, Department of English, Oklahoma State University, Fall 2013-present; *Areas of Specialization:* Representation/Cultural Production; Chickasaw History & Culture; Sovereignty & Law; Editor, Chickasaw Press, 2007-present. *Past professional post:* Professor of American Studies, University of New Mexico, Albuquerque, NM; Administrator of Chickasaw Nation Division of History & Culture, Chickasaw Nation, Sulphur, OK, 2007-12.. *Membership*: Americans for Indian Opportunity. *Published works*: Listening to Our Grandmother's Stories: The Bloomfield Academy for Chickasaw Females, 1852-1949 (University of Nebraska Press, 2000. Reprinted in 2007). (Winner of the American Book Award and the North American Indian Prose Award); The National Museum of the American Indian: Critical Conversations. Co-edited with Amy Lonetree. (University of Nebraska Press, October 2008); numerous articles.

COBB, DANIEL M.
(professor of history & coordinator of American Indian studies)
Education: Messiah College, BA (History), 1996; University of Wyoming, MA (History), 1998; University of Oklahoma, PhD (History), 2003. *Affiliation & Address*: Professor of History & American Indian Studies (2010-present), American Indian & Indigenous Studies Program, Department of American Studies, Greenlaw Hall 215, CB #3520, University of North Carolina, Chapel, Hill, NC 27599 (919) 962-3654. E-mail: dcobb@unc.edu. *Other professional post*: UNC's liaison to the Newberry Consortium in American Indian Studies. My research & teaching focuses on American Indian history since 1887, political activism, ethnohistorical methods, ethnobiography, memory, & global indigenous rights. Since joining the faculty at UNC, the list has grown to include an introduction to American Indian history; Approaches to American Indian Studies; Native America: The West; Twentieth-Century Native America; The Long 1960s in Native America; and Beyond Red Power: American Indian Activism since 1900. My current research and writing projects continue to explore American Indian political activism broadly conceived and have begun to move into the realm of ethnobiography. My next monograph focuses on the life of Ponca activist Clyde Warrior, a central figure in the American Indian youth movement of the 1960s. In addition to publishing, I enjoy working on projects that engage the public. In 2005, I served as program director for a series of public events at Miami University devoted to Indian politics & culture. In 2007, I was honored to have Della Warrior (Otoe-Missouria) invite me to create and install an exhibit on the life and legacy of her late husband for the Ponca Tribe of Oklahoma's Clyde Warrior Memorial Building. In 2010, I co-organized a public symposium entitled "Memory Matters" as one of the two inaugural John W. Altman Fellows at Miami University's Humanities Center. Over the past few years, I have also been involved in Teaching American History & other professional development programs for public school teachers sponsored by the National Council for History Education, National Underground Railroad Freedom Center, Ohio Historical Society, and Ohio Humanities Council. *Past professional posts*: Faculty member in the History Department at Miami University in Oxford, Ohio and as Assistant Director of the D'Arcy McNickle Center for American Indian and Indigenous Studies at the Newberry Library in Chicago. At my former university, I developed under-graduate courses on the United States since 1877; Native America before 1840; Native America since 1840; the United States since 1933; History, Memory, and Tradition; American Indian History through Film; a Junior Honors Colloquium; and senior seminars on Flathead author/activist D'Arcy McNickle and twentieth-century American Indian political activism. At the graduate level, I taught courses on historical methods, contemporary Native America, & ethnohistory. *Awards, honors*: At Miami University, undergraduates nominated me for the Associated Student Government's Outstanding Professor of the Year Award in four consecutive years (2007-2010), and I was a nominee for the E. Phillips Knox Teaching Award from the Center for the Enhancement of Learning and Teaching in 2008 and 2009. In 2012, I was honored to receive the Tanner Award for Excellence in Undergraduate Teaching at the University of North Carolina. *Published works*: Native Activism in Cold War America: The Struggle for Sovereignty (2008), won the inaugural Labriola Center American Indian National Book Award in 2009. I am the co-editor, with anthropologist

Loretta Fowler, of *Beyond Red Power: American Indian Politics & Activism since 1900* (2007), with Helen Sheumaker, *Memory Matters* (2011). In 2013, the University of Chicago Press will publish my revised and expanded fourth edition of William Hagan's classic work, *American Indians.* Completed forthcoming works include contributions to two edited vols., *Native Diasporas: Indigenous Identities & Settler Colonialism in the Americas;* and *Beyond Two Worlds,* and I am also working on a primary document collection, tentatively titled *Say We're Nations,* devoted to Native rights movements from the late nineteenth century to the present. My essays have appeared in *American Indian Quarterly, American Indian Culture and Research Journal, Western Historical Quarterly,* and *Chronicle of Higher Education.*

COBB, JUDY GENE (Modoc)
(tribal second chief)
Affiliation & Address: Second Chief, Modoc Tribe of Oklahoma, 515 G St. SE, Miami, OK 74354 (918) 542-1190.

COCHRAN, PATRICIA LONGLEY (Inpuiat Eskimo)
(executive director)
Born & raised in Nome, Alaska. *Affliation & Address*: Executive Director, Alaska Native Science Commission (ANSC), 429 L St., Anchorage, AK 99501 (907) 258-2672. E-mail: pcochran@aknsc.org. Other professional posts: Treasurer & Past Chair, American Indian/Alaska Native/Native Hawaiian Caucus of the American Pubic Health Association; Science Advisor to the Arctic Research Commission; member, Alaska Global Change Planning Team; program chair for the Indigenous Program of the International Congress on Circumpolar Health; member, National Native Science Education Advisory Council; board member, American Society for Circumpolar Health, president, Albrecht-Milan Foundation; board member, Native American Cancer Research; et al. Past professional posts: Administrator, Institute for Circumpolar Health Studie at the University of Alaska, Anchorage; executive director, Alska Community Development Corporation; Local Government Program Director, Univefrsity of Alaska, Fairbanks; Director of Employment & Training for the North Pacific Rim Native Corporationn (Chugachmiut).

COCHRAN STEFFANI A. (Chickasaw)
(attorney; member, tribal advocacy group)
Resides in Santa Fe, NM. *Education*: Oklahoma State University, BS (Political Science/Public Affairs); George Mason University, MPA, 1988; American University Washington College of Law, JD, 1996. *Affiliation & Address*: Member, Tribal Aadvocacy Group, Crowell Law Office, 1487 W. 89A, Suite 8, Sedona, AZ 86336 (425) 802-5369. E-mail: scochran@cotag.net. Steffani has devoted over two decades of her professional life to the growth and well-being of Indian Country & the exercise of sovereign rights & self-sufficiency. Steffani was named the Chickasaw Nation's Dynamic Woman of the Year in 2011 for her significant contributions to the Nation and for serving as a role model to other Chickasaw women. Global Gaming Business Magazine named her among the 25 People to Watch in 2014 as part of the next generation of gaming industry leaders and an innovate person willing to take a chance to stay a step ahead in the Indian gaming industry. *Past professional posts*: Judge Pro-Tem, Southwest Intertribal Court of Appeals, 1997-2009; Vice Chairperson (2010-2015), National Indian Gaming Commission, Washington, DC; Special Counsel for Indian Affairs in the New Mexico Attorney General's Office; General Counsel, 2005-09 & Chief General Counsel, 2013-15, Pueblo of Pojoaque.

CODY, ROBERT TREE (Red Cedar Whistle) (Dakota-Maricopa)
(traditional flute player, dancer, actor)
Address: c/o Robert Doyle, Canyon Records, 3131 W. Clarendon Ave., Phoenix, AZ 85017 (602) 266-7835. Robert is an internationally known traditional flute player, dancer and actor. He has traveled extensively and participated in a tour of Asia sponsored by the National Council of Traditional Arts and U.S. Information Service. His programs share music from many native communities including his own Dakota and Maricopa. He is currently under recording contract with Canyon Records.

COFFEY, PETE, JR. (*Bear Charging/Center Feathers/Spirit Eagle*)
(Mandan-Arickara-Hidatsa) 1954-
(public radio broadcasting)
Born October 26, 1954, Garrison, S.D. *Education*: High school. *Address*: P.O. Box 286, Parshall, ND 58770 (701) 862-3058 or 743-4391. *Affiliation*: KMHA-FM, Newtown, ND, 1984-. *Activities*: Chairman of & contributor to Nation Native News, American Public Radio; Coffey programmed & directed operations of KMHA-FM, the first truly native radio station in North Dakota, and is recognized on the national public broadcasting level. He has been in management position at KMHA since inception in 1984 and has served as operations & program manager of KMHA that is looked to by other fledgling Indian communications programs as a model in regard to programming for Native American audiences. *Awards, honors*: Most Outstanding Broadcaster Award given by Fort Berthold Media Association; named to election board for Fort Berthold Tribal Elections, 1988. *Interests*: "Reading and occasionally

writing for local tribal newspaper, The MHA Times & Lakota Times. Other interests include combating the terrible effects of alcohol on the Native Indian population such as serving as speaker at chemical dependency seminars and at forums addressed to youth-young adult audiences. (I am) a follower of Native Spiritual belief system more commonly referred to as "The Red Road" and use the teachings of the Red Road to help combat alcoholism among Native Americans. (I) know that groups such as AA are fine but feel Indian people need help with a program which encompasses Native spirituality as a base."

COFFEE, ROBIN (Cherokee/Creek/Sioux)
(licensed professional counselor)
Born October 5, 1953 in Lawrence, Kans. *Education*: M.S. in Counseling Psychology. *Address*: P.O. Box 124, Tahlequah, OK 74465 (918) 456-1861. *Affiliation*: Cherokee Nation of Oklahoma, Tahlequah, OK, 1995-99. *Membership*: The American Mental Health Counselors Association. *Interest*: Poetry. *Published works*: "Voices of the Heart" (poetry-1990); "The Eagles Path" (poetry-1991); "Sacred Seasons" (poetry-1995); "Vision of the Winter Sleeping Seed" (poetry-1998); "The Eagles Path" (1998-compact disk-music by Tim Veazy, words by Robin Coffee).

COFFEY, WALLACE E. (Comanche)
(former tribal chairperson)
Affiliation & Address: Former Chairperson, Comanche Nation, P.O. Box 908, Lawton, OK 73502 (580) 492-3240. E-mail: wallacec@comanchenation.com. *Past professional post*: Tribal Liaison, Institute of American Indian Arts, Santa Fe, NM.

COFFEY-PILCHER, MAGGIE (Comanche)
(attorney)
Affiliation & Address: General Counsel, New Mexico Department of Cultural Affairs, 407 Galisteo, Suite 260, Santa Fe, NM 87501 (505) 827-6427. E-mail: maggie.coffee-pilch@stte.nm.us. *Other professional post*: Board Member, National Native American Bar Association

COFFIN, JAMES L.
(program head-Native American studies)
Affiliation: Native American Studies Program, Ball State University, Muncie, IN 47306 (317) 285-1575.

COHEN, JAMES E.
(Attorney)
Affiliation: California Indian Legal Services, 120 W. Grand Ave., Suite 204, Escondido, CA 92025 (619) 746-8941.

COHOE, PATSY M. (San Carlos Apache)
(training & technical assistance specialist)
Affiliation & Address: Training & Technial Assistance Specialist, National American Indian Indian Housing Council, Arizona Field Office, P.o. Box 1411, Globe, AZ 85502 (928) 475-3670. E-mail: pcohoe@naihc.net.

COIN, CYNDEE (Hopi)
(institute program manager)
Affiliation & Address: Program Manager, American Indian Policy Institute, Arizona State University, Discovery Hall, Rm. 272E, P.O. Box 872603, Tempe, AZ 85287 (480) 965-5869. E-mail: cyndee.coin@asu.edu. Cyndee has been the Program Manager since May 2006 and has been employed at ASU for 20 years. She is responsible for personnel and financial administrative activity, overseeing day-to-day operations of the Institute & supervising administrative staff and student workers.

COKE, ALLISON HEDGE (Huron/Tsalagi) 1958-
(writer, artist, education)
Born August 4, 1958, Amarillo, Tex. *Education*: MFAW & Postgraduate work. *Address*: c/o SDAC, 804 N. Indiana Ave., Sioux Falls, SD 57103 (605) 338-5058. E-mail: aahedgecoke@ sio.midco.net. Website: www.hedgecoke.org. *Affiliations*: SDAC, Arts Corr. *Community activities*: Director, Literary Arts Mentorship for Incarcerated Youth in South Dakota. *Memberships*: Wordcraft Circle; NWCA. *Interests*: Youth; elders; women's issues; survival. *Awards, honors*: American Book Award, 1998, for "Dog Road Woman;" Mentor of the Year, Wordcraft Circle, 2001; Sioux Falls Mayor's Award, 2003. *Interests*: Youth, elders, women's issues, Native community issues, indigenous representation, mental illness, survival. *Published works*: Dog Road Woman (Coffee House Press, 1997); Rock, Ghost, Willow, Deer (University of Nebraska Press); Off-Season City Pipe (Coffee House Press, forthcoming).

COKER, DENNIS J. (Lenape)
(tribal principal chief)
Affiliation & Address: Principal Chief, Lenape Indian ribe of Delaware, 4164 N. Dupont Hwy., Suite 6, Dover, DE 19901. (302) 730-4601

COLBERT, D. SCOTT (Chickasaw)
(tribal legislature representative)
Affiliation & Address: Tishomingo District (Seat #1) Representative, The Chickasaw Nation, P.O. Box 773, Sulphur, OK 73086 (580) 622-3960. E-mail: scott.colbert@chickasaw.net

COLBERT, J.D. (Chickasaw-Creek)
(association president)
Affiliation & Address: Founder & President, North American Native American Bankers Association (NANBA), 909 S. Meridian Ave., Oklahoma City, OK 73108 (866) 987-4225. Website: www.nanba.org. E-mail: jdcolbert@bank2.biz. *Past professional posts*: Founder of Bank, Oklahoma City, OK (owned by the Chickasaw Nation); head of economic development, Bureau of Indian Affairs, Washington, DC.; speaker at numerous banking conferences.

COLBERT, TIMOTHY (Chickasaw)
(tribal legislature representative)
Affiliation & Address: Tishomingo District (Seat #2) Representative, The Chickasaw Nation, P.O. Box 773, Sulphur, OK 73086 (580) 993-2818. E-mail: tim.colbert@chickasaw.net

COLE, JENNIFER PEREZ (Assiniboine)
(MT State Indian affairs coordinator)
Born & raised on the Fort Belknap Reservation. *Education*: University of Montana, B.A. (Print Journalism), 2001. *Address & Affiliation*: Indian Affairs Coordinator (2007-10), Montana Office of Indian Affairs, P.O. Box 200801, Helena, MT 59620 (406) 444-3703. *Past professional posts*: Reporter, Great Falls Tribune, 2001-03; editor, Fort Belknap News, 2003-07. Appointed by Governor Schweitzer of Montana to the post of Montana State Indian Affairs Coordinator.

COLE, TOM (Chickasaw)
(U.S. Congressman)
Education: Grinnell College, BA; Yale University, MA; University of Oklahoma, PhD. Thomas Watson Fellow and a Fulbright Fellow at the University of London. Resides in Moore, Okla. Member, U.S. House of Representatives (2003-present), (Republican) Oklahoma's 4th District, 2458 Rayburn HOB, Washington, DC 20515 (202) 225-6165. Website: www.cole.house.gov. Appointed to the House Appropriations Committee; Deputy Whip in the House. GOP Steering Committee. Also serves as Republican Co-Chair of the Native American Caucus/ Recently served as Chair of the National Republican Congressional Committee. *Awards, honors*: Serves on the national board of the Fulbright Association; currently the only Native American serving in Congress; Congressional Leadership Award by the National Congress of American Indians; inducted into the Chickasaw Hall of Fame in 2004.

COLE, ZELLA JEANETTE CRAWFORD (*Chief Na-Ye-Hi*) (Cherokee) 1941-
(administrator)
Born January 14, 1941, Clermont, FL. *Education*: Jarvis Christian College, BA, 1983; Northeastern State University, Tahlequah, OK, MA, 1985. *Principal occupation*: Administrator. *Address*: Unknown. *Affiliations*: Education specialist, Hopi Dept. of Education, Kykotsmovi, AZ, 1986-87; executive, Native American Heritage Preserve, Phoenix, AZ, 1988; assistant manager for administration, U.S. Census, Tuscaloosa, AL, 1989. *Other professional posts*: Free-lance writer, 1980-. *Community activities*: Editor of two newsletters; West Blocton Improvement Committee; present programs on Indians at schools and libraries. *Awards, honors*: Presidential Scholar; many awards for writing & presenting papers; achievement in history. Interests: "I have traveled in 22 states & lived in seven." *Published works*: A Comparative Analysis of American Indian Tribes (book); Indians of Northeastern Texas (professional paper-award winner); Mixed Bloods (an award-winning poem); Petroglyphs and Pictographs (book); Profiles of Native American Leaders (book); Problems & Complexities of American Indian Law Enforcement (major paper for Cole's class in Indian law); and many other poems, short stories, and papers.

COLEBUT-JACKSON, MARJORIE (Pequot)
(tribal council secretary)
Affiliation & Address: Secretary (2010-Present), Mashantuckett Pequot Tribal Council, 2 Matts Path, P.O. Box 3060, Mashantucket, CT 06338 (860) 396-6100. *Other professional posts*: Chair for the tribe's Health & Human Services & Judicial Committee, 2005-present, and Co-Chair of the Family Protection & Reunification Team; president of Pequot Pharmaceutical Network; corporator of Lawrence & Memorial Hospital.

COLEGROVE, LEONA T. (Hoopa)
(attorney)
Raised on the Quinault & Yakama Indian Reservations. *Education*: Northwest Indian College, A.A., 1995; University of Washington, BA (Political Science), 1997; University of Washington School of Law, JD, 2000. *Address & Affiliation*: Associate, Williams, Kastner & Gibbs, PLLC, Two Union Square, 601 Union St., Suite 4100, Seattle, WA 98101-2380 (206) 628-6649. E-mail: lcolegrove@

wkg.com. Raised on the Quinault & Yakama Indian Reservations, she is a descendant of the Quinault Tribe in Washington, and an enrolled member of the Hoopa Tribe of Northern California. *Practice areas*: Indian & Gaming Law. Provides legal counsel for the governing body of two Indian tribes, in areas including the enforcement & protection of treaty rights, economic development, environmental protection, civil enforcement, natural & cultural resource protection, state & federal relations, jurisdiction, Indian health, and labor & employment. *Other affiliations*: Law Alumni Ambassador for the University of Washington, 2003-present; admitted to the Bar of Quinault Nation, Chehalis Tribe, Tulalip Tribes. *Memberships*: American Bar Assn, Federal Bar Assn, National Native American Bar Assn, Washington State Bar Assn (chair, Committee for Diversity, 2002-present; Indian Law Section, 2003-present).

COLEGROVE-RAYMOND, ADRIENNE (Yurok/Hoopa)
(ITEPP coordinator/director)
Education: Humboldt State University, BA & MA (Journalism, Public Relations). *Affiliation & Address*: Coordinator (2013-present), Native American Center for Acaemic Excellence, & Director, of ELITE Scholars, Indian Tribal & Educational Personnel Program (ITEPP), Humboldt State University, Curriculum Resource Center (CRC), 1 Harpst St., Brero House #93 • ARCATA, CA 95521 (707) 826-3672. E-mail: abc1@humboldt.edu. *Past professional post*: Director, Student Academic Services Outreach Program, Humboldt State University, Arcata, CA, 2006-13.

COLEMAN, CYNTHIA-LOU (Osage)
(chair of department of communications)
Education: Sonoma State University, BA; Cornell University, MPS; University of Wisconsin-Madiison, PhD. *Affiliation & Address*: Associate Professor & Chair (2001-present), Department of Communication, 23 Neuberger Hall, Portland State University, Portland, OR 97207 (503) 725-5368. E-mail: ccoleman@pdx.edu. Blog: nativescience.wordpress.com. *Other professional post*: Professor of Indigenous Nations Studies, Portland State University. Professor Coleman teaches communication theory & research methods, with areas of inquiry focusing on the social construction of science in mainstream discourse and the effects of framing on biopolitical policies that impact American Indian communities. She has held fellowships with the Centers for Disease Control & Prevention and the Smithsonian National Museum of the American Indian. *Past professional posts*: Assistant Professor, Georgia State Univesity, 1997-2000; assistant professor, University of Oregon, 1993-96. *Published works*: Numerous articles in scholarly journals.

COLEMAN, PENNY
(Indian law attorney)
Education: Northern State University, BS (Education & Lbrary Science), 1975; University of South Dakota School of Law, JD, 1981. *Affiliation & Address*: Principal (2011-present), Coleman Indian Law, 4601 N. Fairfax Dr., Suite 1200, Arlington, VA 22203 (703) 763-5483; Website: www.colemanindianlaw.com; E-mail: colemanindianlaw@gmail.com. Penny represents Tribal Nations' legislative, regulatory & litigation interests before Federal, State & Indian Nation agencies, Congress, universities & organizations. Work with tribal leaders, commissions, and tribal lawyers to improve procedures & revenues and provide advice to tribal program managers as they work to comply with Federal & Indian Nation law. *Other professional post*: Partner, Gwe: Nis Consulting which provides consulting services on Indian gaming, federal recognition, health, education, and other general Indian Nation matters; commissioner, St. Regis Mohawk Judicial Oversight Commission, 2012-present. *Past professional posts*: Counsel, Anderson Indian Law, 2011-13; Acting General Counsel & Deputy General Counsel of the National Indian Gaming Commission, 1994-2010; prior to 1994, she worked for the Division of Indian Affairs, Office of the Solicitor in the Department of the Interior.

COLEMAN, STACI D. (Choctaw of Oklahoma) 1970-
(attorney)
Education: Southern Methodist University, BS (cum laude), 1991; Georgetown University Law School, J.D. (cum laude), 1997. *Principal occupation*: Attorney. *Address & Affiliation*: Hobbs, Straus, Dean & Walker, LLP (2001-present), 117 Park Ave., 2nd Floor, Oklahoma City, OK 73102 (405) 602-9425. E-mail: scoleman@hsdwok.com. *Other professional post*: VP of Board, Oklahoma Indian Legal Services, Oklahoma City, OK, 1999-present. *Past professional posts*: Patton Boggs, LLP, Washington, DC; McAfee & Taft, Oklahoma City, OK. At Georgetown University Law Center, was a member of the Georgetown International Environmental Law Journal; founder & president of the Georgetown chapter of the Native American Law Students Assn. While earning her law degree, Ms. Coleman served as an intern at the White House, Office of Counsel to the President; and at U.S. Dept. of Justice, Office of Tribal Justice; written papers on Native American issues, including one on federal trust responsibility, which won first place in the Oklahoma Sovereignty Symposium Writing Competition; & second place in the American Indian Law Review Writing Competition. *Memberships*: Native American Bar Assn; Oklahoma Bar Assn; & serves as president & member of the board of Oklahoma Indian Legal Services. *Areas interest*: Federal Recognition; Indian gaming; litigation.

COLLEY, BROOK (Eastern Cherokee/Wasco)
(Native American studies chairperson)
Education: University of California, Davis, PhD (Native American Studies). *Affiliation & Address*: Assistant Professor & Native American Studies Program Chairperson, Southern Oregon University, Taylor Hall 018B, 1250 Siskiyou Blvd., Ashland, OR 97520 (541) 552-6751. E-mail: colleyb@sou.edu. *Past professional post*: Adjunct Instructor, Indigenous Nations Studies, Portland, OR 97207. Brook's teaching & research interests include Native American & First Nations film & new media, federal Indian law & policy, Oregon Tribes, intertribal relations & conflict, & community health & healing. She also participates in a wide variety of intertribal & interdepartmental intellectual endeavors and has a long-term record of creating and coordinating successful events & projects. While serving as Visiting Assistant Professor at Willamette University, Brook collaborated with the Indian Country Conversations program to facilitated artist-in-residence visits with award-winning filmmakers including Sterlin Harjo (Seminole/Creek), Lisa Jackson (Anishinaabe) and Andrew Okpeaha MacLean (Iñupiat). Currently, Brook is working on a book project that investigates the emergence of the tribal casino economy & engages a problem-solving approach to intertribal conflict in the tribal casino era. In addition, she is directing & co-producing a documentary film Uneasy Remains, which explores the history of collecting and studying Indigenous human remains, specifically focused on the University of California system.

COLLINS, DANIEL (Shinnecock)
(tribal chairperson)
Affiliation & Address: Chairperson, Board of Trustees, Shinnecock Tribe, P.O. Box 5006, Southampton, NY 11968 (631) 283-6143.

COLLINS, RICHARD B.
(professor of Indian law)
Education: Yale University, BA, 1960; Harvard Law School, LL.B., 1966. *Affiliation & Address*: Professor of Law, University of Colorado Law School, 426 Wolf Law Bldg. 401 UCB, Boulder, CO 80309. (303) 492-5493; E-mail: richard.collins@colorado.edu. Since joining the faculty, he has continued work as a pro bono consultant to NARF and to Native American tribes, including the Southern Ute Indian Tribe. *Past professional posts*: 15 years practicing Indian law with organizations such as California Rural Legal Assistance, California Indian Legal Services, Dinebeiina Nahiilna Be Agaditahe in Window Rock, Arizona, and the Native American Rights Fund (NARF). Professor Collins has continued work as a pro bono consultant to NARF and to Native American tribes, including the Southern Ute Indian Tribe. During the course of his appellate work, he has had a major role in several important Indian law decisions, including United States Supreme Court decisions such as *McClanahan v. Arizona Tax Commission*, 421 U.S. 164 (1973). His scholarship also focuses on constitutional issues, and he was Director of the law school's Byron R. White Center for the Study of American Constitutional Law from 2002 to 2010. Professor Collins has written and lectured on such topics as the religion clauses and their relationship to Indian Tribes, the Commerce Clause, and ballot initiatives and referendums. His recent research projects include a treatise on the Colorado Constitution, written with Dale Oesterle, an article on sacred sites on government lands in the United States, Australia, New Zealand, and Canada, the current revision of Felix Cohen's Handbook of Federal Indian Law, and an article in the Colorado Law Review on lawmaking by citizens' initiatives.

COLLINS, ROBERT KEITH
(professor of American Indian studies)
Education: University of California at Berkeley, BA (Anthropology & Native American Studies); UCLA, MA & PhD (Anthropology). *Affiliation & Address*: Associate Professor & Dept. Chair, American Indian Studies Department, San Francisco State University, 1600 Holloway Ave., EP 103, San Francisco, CA 94132 (415) 338-2013. E-mail: rkc@sfsu.edu. *Area of Expertise*: A four-field trained anthropologist, Dr. Collins uses a person-centered ethnographic approach, his research explores American Indian cultural changes and African and Native American interactions in North, Central, and South America. His recent academic efforts include being a co-curator on the Smithsonian's traveling banner exhibit "IndiVisible: African-Native American Lives in the Americas," an edited volume currently in press with Cognella on "African and Native American Contact in the U.S.: Anthropological & Historical Perspectives", an edited volume for the American Indian Culture & Research Journal at UCLA on "Reducing Barriers to Native American Student Success", & two books in final preparation: "African-Native Americans: Racial Expectations and Red-Black Lived Realities" (University of Minnesota Press) and "Memoirs of Kin that Race Can't Erase: Kinship, Memory, and Self Among African-Choctaw Mixed Bloods" (University of North Carolina Press).

COLLINS, VICTORIA
(executive director)
Affiliation & Address: Executive Director, National Society of American Indian Elderly (NSAIE), P.O. Box 50070, Phoenix, AZ 85076 (602) 424-0542. Victoria has 20+ years experience in direct service, outreach, prevention & project development. She conducts training related to the work of the NSAIE, including project management, resource development, grant writing & volunteer management. She is responsible for the Tribal AmeriCorps VISTA program. The Knowledge Preservation project was developed under her leadership and resulted in the publication of American Indian, Celebrating the Voices, Traditions & Wisdom of Native Americans. *Awards, honors*: Recipient of a lifetime Presidential Volunteer Service Award.

COLMAN, ELLA (Seminole of Oklahoma)
(tribal assistant chief)
Education: Seminole State Junior College, Associates in Business Administration, 1982; Mid-American Christian University, BS, 2009. *Affiliation*: Seminole Nation of Oklahoma, P.O. Box 1498, Wewoka, OK 74884 (405) 257-7205. *Past professional posts*: Soil Conservation Service, Tinker Air Force Base, Indian Health Service at the OKC Area Office as Chief of Contracts Management. She worked at the headquarters in Rockville, MD from 1987-92 before transferring to the BIA Central Office in Washington, DC serving as Chief of the Contracts Operations Branch, Chief of Contracts Policy & Oversight Review Branch & Chief of Construction Contracts Management Branch from 1992-98.

COLOMBI, BENEDICT J.
(professor of American Indian studies; author)
Education: Washington State University, PhD, 2006. *Affiliation & Address*: Professor, American Indian Studies Program, The University of Arizona, 218 Harvill Bldg., P.O. Box 210076, Tucson, AZ 85721 (520) 621-2269. E-mail: bcolombi@email.arizona.edu. *Other professional posts*: Assistant Professor & Program Chair, School of Anthropology, the School of Natural Resources & Environment, The University of Arizona, Tucson, AZ; faculty member, Institute of the Environment, The University of Arizona, Tucson, AZ; Faculty Fellow, Udall Center for Studies in Public Policy, The University of Arizona, Tucson, AZ. *Area of Interest*: Indigenous resource management, sustainability, & globalization. *Published works*: The Nez Perce Tribe & the Extinction of Pacific Salmon: A Social Power Approach (Northwest Indian College Press, 2006); Salmon Nation: Tribal Sovereignty & Climate Change (Left Coast Press, 2009); Indigenous Peoples, large Dams, and Capital-Intensive Energy Development: A View from the Lower Colorado River (School for Advanced Research Press, 2010); Indigenous Peoples & Fish: Culture, History, & Economy in the North Pacific (in press, School for Advanced Research Press); Nation Building Through Salmon: Nez Perce Tribe & Indigenous People as World Citizens (in press, School for Advanced Research Press); Salmon Nation Building: Globalization, and the Future (in press, University of Nebraska Press); Salmon Migrations, Nez Perce Nationality, and the World Economy (in press, Oxford University Press); Declining Salmon, Large Dams, and Power Plays: A Case Study of Biocultural Diversity in the Nez Perce Homeland (in press, UNESCO-Springer Press).

COLONNESE, TOM GRAYSON (Santee Sioux)
(professor & chair, American Indian studies)
Education: Arizona State University, PhD (English). *Affiliation & Address*: Professor (1993-present), American Indian Studies Program, University of Washington, Padelford Hall C-514, Box 354305, Seattle, WA 98195 (206) 543-9082. E-mail: buffalo@u.washington.edu. *Other professional posts*: Co-director of the NASA funded American Indian Science Technology Education Consortium (AISTEC), which has been widely lauded as one of the nation's premier programs for American Indian education in science & math. Also serves as consultant to the Educational Testing Service, the College Board of the Department of Education. *Past professional posts*: English professor at Northern Arizona University (14 years); assistant vice president for minority affairs at University of Washington. *Awards, honors*: Director, Microsoft Tribal Support project; advisor on tribal education to the President of the U.S., Bill Clinton. *Published works*: The Vietnam War in American Literature; American Indian Novelists, with Louis Owens; also write two volumes of the Encyclopedia of the North American Indian; numerous articles & short stories.

COMBRINK, VIRGINIA (Tonkawa)
(tribal council president; museum director)
Affiliation: Tonkawa Business Committee, 1 Rush Buffalo Rd., Tonkawa, OK 74653 (405) 628-2561; Tonkawa Tribal Museum, Tonkawa, OK.

COMELLA, NICHOLAS V. (Cherokee) 1948-
(Indian education)
Born May 5, 1948, Salem, Oreg. *Education*: Canada College (Redwood City, CA) 1 year. *Affiliation & Address*: Director of Indian education, Title IX, Milpitas Unified School District, 1331 E. Calaveras Blvd., Milpitas, CA 95035 (408) 945-2387. E-Mail: wolfn@fuhsd.org. *Other professional posts*: Provides Title IX Indian Education Program Services to Berryessa Union School District, Campbell Union High School District, & Oak Grove Elementary School District *Military service*: U.S. Army, Specialist 4 (Vietnam Service Medal; Army Commendation Medal; Good Conduct Medal). *Community activities*: American Indian Alliance of Santa Clara County - Education Project participant;

contributor to Santa Clara County American Indian Needs Assessment Survey; coordinates New Year's Eve Powwow (Annual) & Homestead Powwow (Annual); annual Title IX Spring Festival; annual American Indian Students/Family Career Day. Memberships: National Indian Education Association; California Indian Education Association; San Francisco Bay Area Title IX Indian Education Council; Santa Clara Title IX Indian Education Coalition. Interests: "Learning about Native cultures & teaching American Indian people & non-Indians about Native cultures. Preservation of American Indian cultures - writing culturally relevant curriculum for American Indian students grades 8-12."

COMMANDER, BRENDA (Maliseet)
(former tribal chief)
Affiliation & Address: Former Chief, Houlton Band of Maliseet Indians, 88 Bell Rd., Littleton, ME 04730 (207) 532-4273. Website: www.maliseets.com

CONCHO, RAYMOND J., JR. (Pueblo of Acoma)
(Pueblo 1st Lt. governor)
Affiliation & Address: 1st Lt. Governor, Pueblo of Acoma, P.O. Box 309, Acomita, NM 87034. (505) 552-6604.

CONDON, LISA KATHLEEN
(attorney-Indian law)
Education: University of California, Irvine, BA; Western State University College of Law, JD. University of California, Santa Cruz, Hazardous Materials management; University of California, Berkeley, Air Quality Management, Affiliation & Address: Attorney, 13428 Maxella Ave., Suite 118, Marina Del Rey, CA 90292 (310) 741-1584 Fax 496-0237. Professional Experience: Biosafety Review Board, UCSF Medical School, Current (six year appointment) Practice Areas: Native American Law; Entertainment & Sports; Personal Injury; Environmental Law..

CONLEY, ROBERT J. (United Keetowah Cherokee) 1940-
(Sequoyah Distinguished Professor in Cherokee Studies; writer)
Born in Cushing, Okla. December 29, 1940. Education: Midwestern University, B.A. (Drama), 1966; M.A. (English), 1968. Affiliation & Address: Sequoyah Distinguished Professor in Cherokee Studies, Western Carolina University, Cullowhee, NC 28723 (828) 227-2306. E-mail: rconley@email.wcu.edu. Past professional posts: Instructor of English at Northern Illinois University and at Southwest Missouri State University; Director of Indian Studies at Eastern Montana College, Bacone College & Morningside College; Associate Professor of English, Morningside College; Assistant Programs Manager, Cherokee Nation of Oklahoma. Memberships: The Wordcraft Circle of Native American Writers & Storytellers; Western Writers of America. Awards, honors: Wordcrafter of the Year, 1997; Wordcraft Circle Writer of the Year, 1999 for War Woman, and in 2000 for Cherokee Dragon; numerous Spur Awards from the Western Writers of America; Cherokee Medal of Honor for 2000; Oklahoma Writers Hall of Fame. Published works: Rattlesnake Band & Other Poems (Indiana University Press, 1984); Back to Malachi (Doubleday, 1986); The Witch of Goingsnake & Other Stories (University of Oklahoma Press, 1988); The Saga of Henry Starr (Doubleday, 1989); Mountain Windsong: A Novel of the Trail of Tears (University of Oklahoma Press, 1992); Geronimo: An American Legend (Pocket Books, 1993); Zeke Proctor: Cherokee Outlaw (Pocket Books, 1994); The War Trail North (Doubleday, 1995); War Woman: A Novel of the Real People (St. Martin's Press, 1997); Incident at Buffalo Crossing (Leisure Books, 1998); The Peace Chief: A Novel of the Real People (St. Martin's Press, 1998); Cherokee Dragon (St. Martin's Press, 2000); A Cherokee Encyclopedia (University of New Mexico Press); The Cherokee Nation: A History (University of New Mexico).

CONNELL, L. DAVID
(attorney, Indian law)
Affiliation & Address: Indian Law - Partner, Chair of Business Development, Ater Wynne LLP, Lovejoy Bldg., 1331 NW Lovejoy, Suite 900, Portland, OR 97209 (503) 226-1191 (503) 226-8605; E-mail: ldc@aterwynne.com

CONNERS, MICHAEL (Karoniatens) (Mohawk)
(tribal chief)
Affiliation & Address: Chief (2017-20), Saint Regis Mohawk Tribe, 412 State Route 37, Akwesasne, NY 13655 (518) 358-2272.

CONNOLLY, DONNA M.
(attorney)
Education: Hunter College, CUNY, BA, 1989; Washington College of Law, American University, JD, 1995. Affiliation & Address: Associate (2005-present), Associate, Rothstein, Donatelli, Hughes, Dahlstrom, Schoenburg & Bienvenu, LLP, 1215 Paseo De Peralta, P.O. Box 8180, Santa Fe, NM 87504 (505) 988-8004. E-mail: dconnolly@rothstenlaw.com. Past professional posts: General Counsel, Pueblo of Pojoaque, 2001-05; Assistant District Attorney, Eleventh Judicial District of New Mexico, 2000-01; attorney, San Juan County Legal Services, 1997-2000. As General Counsel to the Pueblo of Pojoaque, she negotiated contracts, litigated disputes, and advised the Pueblo, its entities & enterprises, and tribal members on egal matters.

CONRAD, BEVERLEY (St. Regis Mohawk) 1950-
(artist/writer, musician)
Born June 13, 1950, Rochester, N.Y. Education: SUNY College at Buffalo, BA, 1973. Principal occupation: Artist/writer, musician. Address: Salem Swamp, RR1 Box 159, Selinsgrove, PA 17870 (717) 374-2647. Community activities: Volunteer at the Joseph Priestly House Museum, North Cumberland, PA (sew reproduction historical clothing & take part in living history exhibitions.) Membership: Indian Arts & Crafts Association. Interests: Reproduction and original Eastern Woodland Indian products. Ms. Conrad makes Corn Husk Faces as a way of keeping a traditional craft alive in her family. "The Iroquois Indians are the only natives in North America that make medicine "masks" out of corn husk." She also grows corn to use for the Husk Faces she makes. Currently, she is writing & illustrating children's books, and works as a portrait artist accepting commissions as they come in. She is active as a musician in the area as a fiddler of American music. Ms. Conrad lectures on the subject of the Corn Husk Face and also on Native American beadwork. Biographical source: "Through the Corn" by Gregory Burgess (Indian Artifacts Magazine, Jan.-March 1992.) Published works: Doggy Tales - Bedtime Stories for Dogs & Kitty Tales - Bedtime Stories for Cats (Dell Publishing, 1980).

CONRAD, DAVID F. (Osage)
(director for tribal & intergovernmental affairs)
Education: Santa Clara University, BS (Political Science); University of Wisconsin-Green Bay, MS (Environmental Science & Policy). Affiliation & Address: Director, Tribal & Intergovernmental Affairs, Office of Congressional & Intergovernmental Affairs, U.S. Department of Energy, Washington, DC. David is responsible for oversight & guidance of the Department's government-to-government relationships with Federally-recognized Indian tribes; as well as strengthening relationships with major cities & other local governments across the Nation. Other professional post: Chairperson, Board of Directors, International Institute for Indigenous Resource Management, Denver, CO. Past professional posts: Director for Intergovernmental Affairs, Osage Nation, 2006-10; director, Environmental Program, Council of Energy Resource Tribes (CERT); executive director, National Tribal Environmental Council (NTEC), Albuquerque, NM; City of Seattle's Tribal & Legislative, Office of Intergovernmental Relations; policy analyst for the Nez Perce Tribe's Department of Environmental Restoration & Waste Management, Lapwai, ID.

CONRAD, JILL A. (Nez Perce)
(attorney)
Address & Affiliation: Dorsey & Whitney LLP, U.S. Bank Centre, 1420 Fifth Ave., Suite 3400, Seattle, WA 98101 (206) 903-8767. E-mail: conrad.jill@dorseylaw.com. Attorney in the Indian Law practice group since 1997. Represents tribes, tribal corporations & tribal members in tribal & state courts.

CONTWAY, BRUCE P. (Wan Mni Awacin)
(Sisseton-Wahpeton Sioux, Chippewa) 1955-
(artist)
Born October 25, 1955, Havre, Mont. Education: Montana State University, BA, 1979. Principal occupation: Artist. Address: P.O. Box 920, Whitehall, MT 59759 (406) 287-5122. Bronze sculptor. A second generation artist, Bruce grew up on the Blackfeet Reservation in Northern Montana where his parents taught school. His work reflects his connection to Northern Plains Indians. Community activities: Donated sculptures to Sheriff's Office for crime stoppers, to benefit the Galatin County group home for disabled citizens, and as a first donation to Murton McKloskey Scholarship Fund for Indian students. Memberships: Professional Rodeo Cowboy Association; Indian Arts & Crafts Association. Awards, honors: 1989 Winner, Calgary Stampede Trophy Bronze Competition; 1989 1st & 2nd Sculpture Division, Colorado Indian Market; 1990 Best of Show, Calgary Stampede Art Show; 1991 & 1994 People's Choice Award, Great Falls Native American Art Show; 2nd Bronze, 1993 Santa Fe Indian Market; Finalist, 1996 Statuary Hall Competition for Wyoming entry, Chief Washakie; 1998 Indian Artist of the Year, Indian Arts & Crafts Association; 2005 Sculpture Juried Exhibition, Sioux Falls, SD Outdoor Sculpture Walk. Major commissions: Atlantic Richfield Corp., Calgary Stampede Rodeo Trophy Bronzes, Montana Pro Rodeo Association. Major honors: Portrait sculpture of U.S. Senator Ben Nighthorse Campbell of Colorado; permanent collection of Calgary Stampede Museum. Interests: "Indian oral history; art-I'm lucky that in going to art shows I get to travel all over the country."

COOCHWYTEWA, JASON (Hopi)
(marketer & promoter; company president)
Education: Arizona State University, BS (Marketing). Affiliation & Address: President, Red Note, Inc., P.O. Box 13426, Phoenix, AZ 85002 (888) 999-6422; (602) 903-4380. E-mail: contact@rednoteinc.com. Red Note works in planning & managing intimate to large-scale event productions & promotions including festivals & headlining music concerts. Other professional posts:

Board of Trustee with the Arizona Science Center; board chairperson, American Indian Camber of Commerce of Arizona, Tempe, AZ; co-founding member of the Phoenix Chapter of the National Association of Record Industry Professionals. *Past professional post*: Executive, Native American casino in New Mexico. *Awards, honors*: 2009 Native American "40 Under 40 in Indian Country" by the National Center for American Indian Enterprise Development; 2011 Outstanding American Indian Man of the Year" by the Native American Recognition Days; 2012 Phoenix "40 Under 40," awarded by the Phoenix Business Journal.

COOEYATE NORMAN (Zuni)
(project manager; cultural liaison)
Born & raised on the Zuni Indian Reservation, N.M. *Education*: University of New Mexico, BA (Native American Studies). *Affiliation & Address*: Project Manager, Division of Pediatric Emergency Medicine, Health Sciences Center, Institute for Indigenous Knowledge & Development, MSC07 4255, 717 Encino Place NE #9 · University of New Mexico, Albuquerque, NM 87102 (505) 925-4439. E-mail: ncooeyate@salud.unm.edu. Mr. Cooeyate currently works at the UNM Health Sciences Center, Institute for Indigenous Knowledge & Development as a Project Manager/Cultural Liaison, and as a Cultural Liaison for the HRSA funded Child Ready Program, under the UNM Pediatric Emergency Department. Mr. Cooeyate still maintains strong ties with the 45 Nations in the Southwest and is still a strong advocate for AI/AN issues and concerns. His Bachelor's degree in Native American Studies emphasized Leadership & Building Native Nations concentration. He plans to pursue a Masters in Public Health & Public Administration. Mr. Cooeyate received his secondary education in Salt Lake City, Utah, continuing his post-secondary education in Biology at the University of New Mexico and was attending the University of New Mexico School of Medicine, when he was approached by the National Institutes of Digestive, Diabetes & Kidney Disorders to assist in researching interventions for preventing or reducing the rates of Diabetes Mellitus, among American Indian/Alaskan Native populations. *Past professional posts*: Managed the Diabetes Prevention Program in his community for 13 years before deciding to turn his interests to politics; Governor, Pueblo of Zuni, 2007 – 2011 (his primary focus was on improving basic living conditions, addressing health & wellness, environmental, sacred sites, and promoting new ideas of economic development & workforce development.) *Awards, honors*: Awarded the National Indian Health Board 2010 Tribal Leadership Impact Award, for his advocacy for American Indian/Alaska Native populations.

COOK, BEVERLY (*Kiohawlton*) (St. Regis Mohawk)
(tribal chief)
Affiliation & Address: Chief (2016-19), St. Regis Mowak Tribe, 3412 State Rt. 37, Akwesasne, NY 13655 (518) 358-2272.

COOK, DAPHNE RICHARDS (Oglala Sioux)
(executive director)
Affiliation & Address: Executive director, Alliance of Tribal Tourism Advocates, 511 7th St., Suite 210, Rapid City, SD 57701 (605) 545-3351. E-mail: daphne_57752@yahoo.com.

COOK, KATSI (Akwesasne Mohawk)
(executive director)
Affiliation & Address: Executive Director, Running Strong for American Indian Youth, 2550 Huntington Ave., #200, Alexandria, VA 22303 (703) 317-9881. Katsi created the First Environment Collaborative of Running Strong. *Past professional posts*: Maternal & Child Health consultant for the Tribal Epidemiology Center at United South & Eastern Tribes (USET, Inc.), Nashville, TN; she was a Mohawk midwife, women's health advocate & activist for environmental restoration in her Tribal community, the Mohawk Nation of Akwesasne. She has written numerous published essays, articles for Indian Country Today, and was featured speaker at Live Earth at the National Museum of the American Indian in Washington, DC in 2007. *Awards, honors*: Recipient of the 2004-05 Indigenous Knowledge Cultural Researcher Award from the Indigenous Health Research Development Program at U. of Toronto.

COOK, SAMUEL R.
(associate professor of American Indian studies)
Education: Radford University, BA (Anthropology); University of Arizona, MA (American Indian Studies), PhD (Comparative Culture). *Affiliation & Address*: Associate Professor & Director, American Indian Studies Program, Virginia Tech University, Department of Sociology, 560 McBryde Hall, Blacksburg, VA 24061 (540) 231-9596. Email: sacook2@vt.edu. *Teaching Interests*: Indigenous Ecologies, Politics & Film; Appalachian Communities. *Honors & awards*: Mooney Award for book, Monacans & Miners, by the Southern Anthropological Society, 2003; Virginia Council on Indians Award for Outstanding Contributions to American Indians, 2002. *Published works*: Monacans & Miners: Native American & Coal Mining Communities in Appalachia (University of Nebraska Press, 2000); numerous book chapters & introductions; articles in refereed journals.

COOK, J.R.
(executive director)
Education: Coffeyville Jr. College, AA; University of Okalhoma, BS; Southwestern Oklahoma State University, MEd. *Address & Affiliation*: Founder & Executive Director (1976-present), United National Indian Tribal Youth, Inc. (UNITY), P.O. Box 800, Oklahoma City, OK 73101 (405) 424-3010. E-Mail: unity@unityinc.org. *Other professional posts*: Director, Upward Bound, Weatherford, OK, 1967-75; coordinator, Native American Program, Oklahoma City University. *Community activities*: Founder, Southwest Indian Cultural Center; organizer/coach, UNITY Eagle's men's basketball team promoting healthy lifestyles; coordinator, Atlanta Hawks success seminars/basketball clinics for Indian youth. *Awards & honors*: Commendation, Southwest Association of Student Assistance for ten years of service to youth; Jefferson Award for Outstanding Public Service; 1995 Sporting Goods Manufacturers Association's "Heroes Award"; participant, Carnegie Council on Adolescent Development, Washington, DC; profile, 1997 Strathmore's Who's Who Registry. *Memberships*: St. Luke's United Methodist Church, Oklahoma City, OK; Oklahoma County Cherokee Organization; National Indian Education Association; National Congress of American Indians; and MADD Commission on Youth

COOK, ROBERT (Oglala Lakota)
(educator)
Education: Black Hills State University, B.A. (Secondary Education), 1990; Oglala Lakota College, M.A. (Education Administration). *Address & Affiliation*: Administrating a ninth grade transition program for American Indian students, Central High School, 433 Mt. Rushmore Rd. N., Rapid City, SD 57701 (605) 394-4023. E-mail: robert.cook@k12.ed.sd.us. Robert has about 20 years of teaching & administrative experience in American Indian education. *Other professional post*: President of Board 2008-2009, National Indian Education Association, Washington, DC. *Past professional posts*: Teaching at Red Cloud Catholic School and on three different reservation schools: Crow Creek Boarding School, Little Wound & Lower Brule BIA schools. *Awards, honors*: Little Wound Educator of the Year, 1998-99; Lower Brule Teacher of the Year, 2000-01; South Dakota's Milkin National Educator, 2005; NIEA's Indian Teacher of the Year, 2006. *Community activities*: SDEA Board of Directors; RCEA Executive Board. *Interests*: Owns business, "Mni Tanka Tours," which provides training & technical assistance to tribal community members in order to promote tribal tourism and economic development through cultural interpretation.

COOK, G. WARREN (Pamunkey)
(former tribal assistant chief)
Affiliation & Address: Former Assistant Chief, Pamunkey-Indian Tribe, 191 Lay Landiing Rd., King William, VA 23086 (804) 769-4767.

COOK-LYNN, ELIZABETH (Crow-Creek Lakota Sioux) 1930-
(editor, essayist, poet, novelist; professor emerita of English)
Born November 17, 1930, Fort Thompson, S.D. *Education*: South Dakota State College, BS, 1952; University of South Dakota, MA, 1970; doctoral work at University of Nebraska, Lincoln. *Principal occupation*: Teacher, writer. *Address*: Resides in Rapid City, SD. *Affiliations*: Newspaper work, editing & writing in S.D., 1952-57; part-time teaching, Carlsbad, NM, 1958-64; secondary teaching, Carlsbad, NM, 1965-68, Rapid City, S.D., 1968-69; Professor Emerita of English & Native American Studies (20 years), Eastern Washington University, Cheney, WA; visiting professor, University of California, Davis, 1990-; among others. *Other professional posts*: Editor, "The Wicazo SA Review," a journal of Native Studies, Eastern Washington University, 1985-. *Professional activities*: Consultant & participant in the curriculum development seminar RMMLA, Flagstaff, Ariz., 1978; project director (planning grant) NEH Media Project: Indian Scholar's Journal; member, National Research Council Panel, National Academy of Science, Washington, DC, 1989. *Memberships*: National Indian Education Association; Writer's Guild; Modern Language Association; Council of Editors of Learned Journals. *Awards, honors*: In 2009, Lifetime Achievement Award from the Native Writers' Circle of the Americas. *Biographical sources*: "Acts of Survival" by Jamie Sullivan, in The Bloomsbury Review, Vol. 13/Issue 1/Feb. 1993; "Bleak & Beautiful Moments" by John Purdy, in American Book Review, 1992-93 (Dec./Jan.). *Published works*: Short stories, poems, and papers: Problems in Indian Education, (South Dakota Review), A Severe Indictment of Our School Systems, and Authentic Pictures of the Sioux? (Great Plains Observer), 1970; Propulsives in Native American Literatures, paper read at National meeting of Conference of College Composition, and Communications, New Orleans, 1973; The Teaching of Indian Literatures, NCTE, Minneapolis, Minn., 1974; The Image of the American Indian in Historical Fiction, RMMLA, Laramie, Wyoming; Delusion: The American Indian in White Man's Fiction, RMMLA, El Paso, Texas; Three, prose & poetry in Prairie Schooner, Fall, 1976; A Child's Story, short story in Pembroke Magazine, 1976; poems published in Sun Tracks (University of Arizona, 1977), and The Ethnic Studies Journal; The Indian Short Story, and bibliography for Encyclopedia of Short Fiction, edited by Walton Beacham (Salem Press, 1980); "The Cure," short

story accepted for Anthology of Native American Literature, edited by Berud Pryor, UCLA, Davis, 1980; two short stories, The Power of Horses, and A Good Chance, accepted by Simon J. Ortiz (Pueblo writer and poet) for inclusion in anthology, The Short Story in Native American Literature (Navajo College Press, 1983); "Then Badger Said This," collection of poems (Ye Galleon Press, 1984); 12 poems, entitled, "Seek the House of Relatives" (Blue Cloud Press, 1983); three poems, Harper's Book of Twentieth Century Native American Poetry, 1986, edited by Duane Niatum; among other short stories, articles, and essays; short story collection, entitled, "The Power of Horses and Other Stories" (Arcade-Little, Brown, 1990); novel, "From the River's Edge" (Arcade-Little, Brown, 1991); essays, "Why I Can't Read Wallace Stegner" (University of Wisconsin Press, 1996); poetry, "I Remember the Fallen Trees" (Eastern Washington University Press, 1997).

COOK-MACARRO, HOLLY (Red Lake Ojibwe)
(consulting partner)
Education: University of North Dakota, BA; University of St. Thomas (St. Paul, MN), MBA. *Affiliation & Address*: Partner, Ietan Consulting, LLC, 1333 New Hampshire Ave., NW, Washington, DC 20036 (202) 419-3527. Ieten Consulting is a federal government relations firm specializing in the representation of tribal governments & tribal business enterprises. Her primary focus areas include federal governmental relations, legislative advocacy, and appropriations issues. *Other professional posts*: Speaker & presenter at tribal conferences & events. *Past professional posts*: Senior public affairs advisor for Holland & Knight, LLP, 1999-2001; director, Office of Native American Affairs at the Democratic National Committee; served in the White House Office of Native American Affairs, 1997-98, where she worked for Lynn Cutler, President Clinton's top person on Indian affairs issues. Holly coordinated the first tribal economic development conference hosted by the White House & several federal agencies in 1998. In 2002, she worked on Senator Tim Johnson's re-election campaign in South Dakota, serving as an organizer on the Pine Ridge Reservation. In 2003-2004, Holly served as the national co-chair of the Native Vote Initiative at the National Congress of American Indians (NCAI). Also, in 2004, she served on the Kerry-Edwards Native American Policy team & was the Native American coordinator for the Democratic Party of New Mexico. In 2006, Holly served on the Minnesota Native Vote team, providing training to staff & coordination of reservation GOTV efforts. In 2007-2008, she served as a key member of Senator Hillary Clinton's Native American Policy Advisory Committee as part of her Presidential campaign. Following the primaries, she was invited to join Barack Obama's Native American Policy Committee as part of his presidential campaign. Holly then served as a national delegate to the Democratic National Convention in Denver, CO in 2008.

COOMBS, LINDA (Aquinnah Wampanoag) 1949-
(Indian program director)
Born August 24, 1949, Oak Bluffs, Mass. *Education*: Lowell State College (now - UMass, Lowell) B.MusicEd., 1971. *Address*: P.O. Box 1554, Mashpee, MA 02649 (508) 477-7240. E-mail: lcoombs@plimoth.org. *Affiliations*: Associate Director, Wampanoag Indian Program, Plimoth Plantation (1975-84, 1988-present), P.O. Box 1620, Plymouth, MA 02362 (508) 746-1622 ext. 8385; Mashpee Indian Education, Title IV, Mashpee, MA, 1984-88; Boston Children's Museum (Native Advisory Committee, 1975-present); Robbins Museum of Archaeology, Middleboro, MA, 1990-present; Aquinnah Cultural Center, Aquinnah, Martha's Vineyard, MA, (board of directors, 1996-present). *Other professional posts*: Visiting Committee, Peabody Museum, Andover, MA, 1997-present. *Community activities*: Museum committee member, Wampanoag Tribe of Gay Head (Aquinnah); member, Wampanoag Nation Singers & Dancers, 1992-present (performance group - traditional Eastern songs). *Interests*: Wampanoag history & culture from traditional times to colonial to present; traditional Wampanoag arts: weaving (bags, mats), clothing (deerskin); beadwork; quilting, embroidery, needle-arts. *Published work*: "Powwow" - contemporary childrens' book (Modern Curriculum Press, 1992); "First Gift of Spring," article in Turtle Quarterly, 1990.

COONS, SHAUNA L. (Lac Courte Oreilles Ojibwe)
(attorney)
Education: University of Minnesota, BA, 20003; William Mitchell Colllege of Law, JD, 2007. *Affiliation & Address*: Associate Attorney, Hogen Adams PLLC, 1935 W. County Rd. B2, Suite 460, St. Paul, MN 55113 (651) 842-9106. E-mail: scoons@hogenadams.com. Shauna is an associate in the firm's Native American Law and Real Estate Sections. She has worked for, and directly with, tribal governments for several years. Shauna focuses her practice on assisting tribal clients with issues pertaining to federal Indian law, tribal law, contract review, tribal code development, tribal land and real estate, economic development, governance, gaming law, gaming regulatory, tribal financing and business law. Shauna is passionate about supporting tribal communities and the prosperity of tribal people. Past professional posts: Best & Flanagan LLP, Minneapolis, MN; Deputy Solicitor General with the Mille Lacs Band of Ojibwe where she worked closely with the Commissioner of Community Development on community planning initiatives. Shauna has experience working on transactions in housing, real estate, community development, public works,

construction and other development and utility infrastructure needs. Shauna has litigated cases related to housing, child protection and criminal violations. Shauna also has experience working as a law clerk, on both civil and criminal matters, in Minnesota's Fourth Judicial District. Shauna chose to pursue a career in law after serving as an Indian Child Welfare Social Worker for the Fond du Lac Band of Lake Superior Chippewa. Professional Associations & Memberships: Minnesota State Bar Association (Real Estate Section); Federal Bar Association; Minnesota American Indian Bar Association (Treasurer, 2008-2009; Scholarship Committee, 2008; Independent School District #728, Early Childhood Family Education Parent Advisory Council (Member, 2010-Present; Co-Chair, 2012-2013; Marketing Committee Member, 2010-2013); National Tribal Land Association. Presentations.

COOPER, ARNOLD (Squaxin Island)
(tribal vice chairperson)
Affiliation & Address: Squaxin Island Tribe, 10 SE Squaxin Lane, Shelton, WA 98584 (360) 426-9781. E-mail: acooper@squaxin.us

COOPER, CASEY (Eastern Cherokee)
(hospital administrator)
Education: Gardner-Webb University, BSN; University of North Carolina, Chape Hill, MBA; Fellow of the American College of Healthcare Executives. *Affiliation & Address*: Chief Executive Officer, Cherokee Indian Hospital, Cherokee, NC 28719 (828) 497-9163 ext. 6403. E-mail: casey.cooper@cherokeehospital.org *Other professional post*: Board member, North Carolina American Indian Health Board, Winston-Salem, NC. Casey has been involved in American Indian health care for 19½ years and has served the Eastern Band of the Cherokee Nation (EBCN) and its community since graduating from nursing school in 1993. He served as a Primary Care Nurse, Community Health Nurse, Nurse Educator and Nursing Manager. As the Health Director of the EBCN from 1999 to 2004, he helped shape public health policy with a focus on chronic disease prevention and lead a community wide initiative to assume the management responsibilities of the CIH from the Indian Health Services through Indian Self-Determination & Self-Governance Agreement. He is a current member of the WNC Health Network, the United South and Eastern Tribes (USET) Health Committee, Board of Directors for Foundation for Nursing Excellence, NC Medical Care Advisory Committee, NC American Indian Health Board, Rotary Club of Cherokee and current member and former Chairman of the Board of Directors for Smoky Mountain Mental Health.

COOPER, JENNIFER (Seneca)
(acting IHS office director)
Education: Colgate University, BA (Ecnomics) & Native American Studies); Cornell Law School, JD; Syracuse University Maxwell School of Citizenship & Public Affairs; MPA. *Affiliation & Address*: Acting Director of the Office of Tribal Self-Governance (OTSG) for the Indian Health Service (IHS). U.S. Department of Health & Human Services, The Reyes Bldg. (RB) 801 Thompson Ave., Suite 400, Rockville, MD 20852. As the Acting Director of the OTSG, Ms. Cooper oversees all aspects of the administration of the Tribal Self-Governance Program authorized by Title V of the Indian Self-Determination & Education Assistance Act. This includes determining eligibility for participation in the IHS Tribal Self-Governance Program & providing information, technical assistance, & policy coordination in support of IHS tribal self-governance activities. The OTSG provides policy analysis & development support to tribal governments and the Director in the evolving area of self-governance & tribal/federal government relationships. Ms. Cooper provides oversight to ensure the IHS meets its requirement for tribal consultation & carries out a wide range of agency functions critical to the working partnership between the HIS and the 567 federally recognized Tribes. Ms. Cooper joined the OTSG in January 2014 as the Deputy Director. *Past professional posts*: Prior to federal service, she served as the Director of Federal Relations & Legislative Director at the National Indian Health Board. She worked closely with tribal leaders & advocates on Indian health policy issues, including the reauthorization of the Indian Health Care Improvement Act (IHCIA).

COOPER, KAREN COODY (Cherokee) 1946-
(museum education)
Born November 10, 1946, Tulsa, Okla. *Education*: Oklahoma College of Liberal Arts, 1965-66; Western Connecticut State University, BA, 1981; University of Oklahoma, MLS, 1996. *Affiliation & Address*: Executive Director, Cherokee National Historical Society, Cherokee Heritage Society, P.O. Box 515, Tahlequah, OK 74465 (918) 456-6007. *Past professional posts*: Coordinator, Museum Training Program, National Museum of the American Indian, Smithsonian Institution, Washington, DC, 1994-2006. *Past professional posts*: American Indian Archaeological Institute, Washington, CT, 1985-89; curator of education, Museum of the Great Plains, Lawton, OK, 1990-93. *Community activities*: Board member, Eagle Wing Press, an American Indian newspaper, 1982-89. *Memberships*: American Association of Museums. *Awards, honors*: Kidger Award, 1987, for Excellence in Museum Education, New England History Teachers Association. *Interests*: Ms. Cooper writes, "I am interested in finger-weaving, an ancient craft of American Indians in the Woodlands, and

have won prizes & written articles; I am a published poet; and enjoy black & white photography." *Published works*: Tribal Museum Directory.

COOPER, TINA M. (Chickasaw)
(medical director)
Education: Cameron University, AD (Nursing), 1979; University of Oklahoma Health Sciences Center, BS (Nursing, 1983), MD, 1995. *Affiliation & Address*: Chief of Staff & Medical Director (2010-present), Sovereign Famiy Practice Clinic, 1007 N. Country Club Rd., Ada, OK 74820 (580) 421-8700. *Other professional post*: Board member (2003-present), The Chickasaw Foundation, Ada, OK. *Past professional post*: Chief of Staff & Family Physician at the Chickasaw Nation Medical Center, 1998-2010. *Memberships*: American Academy of Family Physicians & the OK Academy of Family Physicians. Dr. Cooper also is a fellow of the American Academy of Family Physicians. She serves on the CN Institutional Review Board for research and is a principal investigator for the Oklahoma Native American Research Centers of Health.

CORBINE, ELDRED (Bad River Ojibwe)
(former tribal vice chairperson)
Affiliation & Address: Former Vice Chairperson, Bad River Band of Lake Superior Chippewa Tribe, P.O. Box 39, Odanah, WI 54861 (715) 682-7111.

CORCORAN, DOLORES PURDY (Caddo)
(artist)
Address: 7031 S.W. Queen's Ct., Topeka, KS 66614 (785) 478-4801. Website: www.dolorespurdycorcoran.com. *Art work*: Original transparent watercolors, mixed media paintings, limited edition prints, large gourd pots & masks of Woodland designs.

CORDALIS, RITA JO (Dine') 1954-
(gallery director)
Born March 27, 1954. *Education*: Univesity of Colorado, Boulder, MS (Museum Studies), 2000 *Principal occupation*: Gallery director. *Address*: 1242 County Rd. #205, Durango, CO 81301 (970) 259-1363. E-mail: cordalis_r@fortlewis.edu. Website: www.fortlewis.edu. *Affiliations*: Fort Lewis College, Durango, 1993-; Anasazi Heritage Center, Dolores, CO, 1995-; Gallery 10, Santa Fe, NM, Scottsdale, AZ, 1992-. *Other professional posts*: Instructor, artist. *Membership*: Southwestern Association of Indian Arts (Santa Fe, NM), 1982-present.

CORDELL, COLLEEN HEMINGER (Sisseton Wahpeton Sioux)
(Indian center director)
Affiliations: Director, American Indian Culture Research Center, Blue Cloud Abbey, P.O. Box 98, Marvin, SD 57251 (605) 398-9200; owner, Colleen's Gardens, P.O. Box 68, Marvin, SD 57251 (605) 398-6923. Website: www.indiangifts.com; E-mail: colleen@indiangifts.com.

CORDOVA, SHERRY (Cocopah)
(tribal chairperson)
Affiliation & Address: Chairperson, Cocopah Tribal Council, County 15 & Ave. G, Somerton, AZ 85350 (928) 627-2102.

CORE, M. ALLEN (Osage) 1948-
(attorney)
Born August 4, 1948, Tulsa, Okla. *Education*: University of Oklahoma, BS, 1970, MBA, 1974; University of Oklahoma College of Law, JD, 1988. *Affiliation*: Oklahoma Bar Association, Oklahoma City, OK, 1988-. *Community activities*: Board of Directors of the Tulsa Indian Heritage Center, and Oklahoma Indian Legal Services. *Memberships*: Oklahoma Indian Bar Assn (vice-president); Native American Bar Assn (board member); Federal Bar Assn; Muscogee Bar Assn; Court of Indian Offenses for the Anadarko and Muskogee Area Indian Offices. *Awards, honors*: The Oklahoma Bar Association's Outstanding Senior Law Student, U. of Oklahoma College of Law, 1988.

CORNELIUS, RON (Oneida of Wisconsin)
(IHS area director)
Education: Montana State University, Bozeman, BS (Business Administration). *Affiliation & Address*: Director, Great Plains Area IHS, 115 4th Ave., SE, Aberdeen, SD 57401 (605) 226-7582. E-mail: ron.cornelius@ihs.gov. Mr. Cornelius has administrative responsibility for 19 service units consisting of 7 hospitals and 10 health centers. He manages a varied health program for more than 126,000 American Indian people eligible for IHS services. Great Plains Area IHS serves 17 Tribes & supports 2 urban Indian health programs. The Great Plains Area employs 2,200 employees and has an annual operating budget of more than $359 million. *Past professional posts*: Mr. Cornelius began his career with the IHS in December 1985. He recently served as the Acting Deputy Area Director for Management Operations for the Great Plains Area. He has also served in a number of Great Plains Area leadership roles, including as a standing member of the Great Plains Area Governing Body Committee, the Great Plains Area Senior Leadership Group, & Great Plains

Area Executive Committee. Mr. Cornelius has participated in various national financial leadership roles during his career, most recently as a member of the Great Plains Area Financial Management Officer Advisory Committee Officer.

CORNELL, STEPHEN 1948-
(Indian institute faculty chair)
Born March 30, 1948, Buffalo, NY. *Education*: University of Chicago, PhD, 1980. *Affiliation & Address*: Faculty Chair, Native Nations Institute for Leadership, Management & Policy (NNI), The University of Arizona, 803 E. 1st St., Tucson, AZ 85719 (520) 626-4393; E-mail: scornell@u.arizona.edu. *Other professional posts*: Professor of Sociology and of Public Administration & affiliate faculty member of the American Indian Studies Program, The University of Arizona, Tucson, AZ; co-director, Harvard Project on American Indian Economic Development, Cambridge, MA. *Past professional posts*: Chair, Department of Sociology, University of California, San Diego and at Harvard University where he co-founded (in the mid 80's) the Harvard Project on American Indian Economic Development, Harvard University. *Interests*: He works with indigenous nations in the U.S. & Canada as well as Australia and New Zealand on governance, economic development & related issues; American Indian policy. *Published works*: "The Return of the Native: American Indian Political Resurgence"; co-author (with Douglas Hartmann) of "Ethnicity & Race: Making Identities in a Changing World"; co-editor (with Joseph P. Kalt) of "What Can Tribes Do? Strategies & Institutions in American Indian Economic Development."

CORNSILK, CAROL PATTON (Oklahoma Cherokee) 1949-
(film producer/director/writer/editor)
Born July 8, 1949, Tulsa, Okla. *Education*: University of Texas, BS (Radio-TV-Film), 1973. *Principal occupation*: Film producer/director/writer/editor. *Address*: Unknown. *Affiliations*: "Austin City Limits," PBS (associate producer, 1979-84, associate producer/editor, 1984-85; producer/director, KLRU-TV, Austin, TX, 1985-87; Sr. producer/director, WDCN-TV, Nashville, TN, 1987-95; Director of Programming & Production, Native American Public Telecommunications, Lincoln, NE, 1996-2002. *Community activities*: Member, First Church Unity, Nashville, TN. *Awards, honors*: Certificate of Merit, Chicago International Film/Video Festival 1980 for "Austin City Limits 'Songwriter's Special'" Associate Producer/Publicist; Gold Medal, New York International Film/Video Festival 1982 for Best Network Music Special: "Down Home Country Music" Co-producer; CPB Training Grant, 1984; CPB Professional Development Grants, 1985, 1987; CPB Scriptwriting/Storytelling Fellowship, 1991; Native American Public Broadcasting Consortium Program Screening Panel, 1991; National Endowment for the Humanities Media Panelist, 1991. *Interests*: "Cherokee legends, storytellers and history; travelled extensively in Europe, 1983, 1985, 1987; traveled and lived in the west and southwest - Texas, New Mexico and Colorado. I love music, art, theatre, gardening, travelling, and of late devoting much of my free time to my two-year-old son, James Eagle Pace-Cornsilk."

CORNTASSEL, JEFF (Cherokee)
(associate professor of Indigenous Governance)
Education: University of Arizona, PhD (Political Science), 1998. *Affiliation & Address*: Associate Professor & Graduate Advisor, Indigenous Governance Program, Faculty of Human & Social Development, University of Victoria, 3800 Finnerty Rd., HSD Bldg., Rm. A260, Victoria, BC V8W 2Y2 (250) 721-6438. Website: www.corntassel.net. *Current Research*: Global indigenous rights & indigenous political mobilization/self-determination movements. *Awards, honors*: faculty of Human & Social Development Award for Teaching Excellence. *Published works*: Forced Federalism: Contemporary Challenges to Indigenous Nationhood (University of Oklahoma Press, 2008); The Power of Peoplehood: Regenerating Indigenous Nations, co-edited with Tom Holm (University of Texas Press, 2012).

COSER, PETER R.G. (Muscogee-Creek)
(Indian center program manager)
Education: Oklahoma State University, BA (Political Science); University of Oklahoma, MA (Human Relations). *Affiliation & Address*: Program Manager (2011-present), Buder Center for American Indian Studies, Brown School of Social Work, Washington University, 336 Goldfarb, St. Louis, MO 63130 (314) 935-4804. E-mail: pcoser@gwbmail.wustl.edu. *Past professional posts*: Academic advisor, Tulsa Community College; adjunct instructor, College of the Muscogee Nation.

COTE, CHARLOTTE (*Nuu-chah-nuth*)
(professor of American Indian studies)
Education: Simon Fraser University British Columbia, Canada), BA (Political Science); University of California, Berkeley, MA & PhD (Comparative Ethnic Studies). *Affiliation & Address*: Associate Professor (2001-present), American Indian Studies, Department of American Indian Studies, Padelford Hall C-514, Box 354305, Seattle, WA 98195 (206) 221-6549. E-mail: clotise@u.washington.edu. *Research Interests*: Examines issues around Native governance, politics, law & sovereignty in the U.S. & Canada. *Other professional post*: Chairperson, Project Advisory Committee, University of

Washington's Intellectual House of Knowledge; board member, UW's Graduate Opportunities & Minority Achievement Program. *Community activities*: Member, Potlatch Fund Foundation Bard; executive member, Seattle Art Museum Native Arts Council. *Published works*: Spirits of Our Whaling Ancestors: Revitalizing Makah & Nuu-chah-nulth Traditions (2010); numerous articles on traditional Indian law & justice systems, the Makah & Nuu-chah-nulth whaling tradition & the northwest coast Guardian Spirit Complex.

COTHREN, SUSAN (Comanche)
(tribal vice chairperson)
Affiliation & Address: Vice Chairperson, Comanche Nation, P.O. Box 908, Lawton, OK 73502 (580) 492-3240. E-mail: susanc@comanchenation.com

COULTER, JOE DAN (Citizen Band Potawatomi)
(college program director)
Education: PhD. *Affiliation & Address*: Director, American Indians/Native Americans, Opportunity at Iowa, 1410 Bowen Science Bldg., Iowa City, IA 52242-1109 (319) 335-7766. E-mail: joe-coulter@uiowa.edu.

COULTER, ROBERT T. (Citizen Band Potawatomi) 1945-
(attorney)
Born September 19, 1945, Rapid City, S.D. *Education*: Williams College, BA, 1966; Columbia University Law School, JD, 1969. *Principal occupation*: Lawyer. *Address & Affiliation*: President & Executive Director (1978-present), Indian Law Resource Center, 602 N. Ewing St., Helena, MT 59601 (406) 449-2006. *Memberships*: American Bar Assn; American Society of International Law. *Awards, honors*: Harvard Law School, Shikes Visiting Fellow, 1983. *Interests*: Indian law; international human rights law; avocations: cello & double bass playing. *Published work*: Indian Rights - Human Rights (Indian Law Resource Center, 1984).

COUNTS, SHERRY J. (Hualapai)
(former tribal chairperson)
Affiliation & Address: Hualapai Tribal Council, P.O. Box 179, Peach Springs, AZ 86434 (928) 769-2216.

COURNOYER, DAVID (Sicangu Lakota)
(association secretary/treasurer)
Affiliations & Address: Secretray/Treasurer,First Peoples Fund, P.O. Box 2977, Rapid City, SD 57709 (605) 348-0324. Past professional post: Lumina Foundation, Indianapolis, IN. *Membership*: Americans for Indian Opportunity. *Interests*: Communications, public relations, journalism, education, cultural retention, fundraising.

COURNOYER, FRANK (Yankton Sioux) 1952-
(visual artist, electronic slot technician)
Born December 26, 1952, Wagner, S.D. *Education*: Las Vegas Gaming & Technical School Graduate Certificate, 1992. *Principal occupation*: Visual artist, electronic slot technician. *Affiliatios & Address:* Manager, Yankton Sioux Maintenance, 29896 394th Ave., Wagner, SD 57380 (605) 384-3966. *Other professional posts*: Elementary teacher-art & Indian studies; member, Board of Directors, Dakota Plains Institute of Learning, Marty, SD 57361, 1984-; chairman, Board of Directors, Native American National Arts Council, and Oyate Kin Cultural Society, Marty, S.D., 1984-. *Military service*: U.S. Army, 1971-1974 (Specialist E-4, 82nd Airborne Division) (National Defense Ribbon, Expert Rifleman Badge, Jump Wings). *Community activities*: Dakota Plains Institute of Learning is the higher adult education branch of the Yankton Sioux Tribe. *Awards, honors*: Honorable mention (best of show); sang a song for "Dances With Wolves" the movie. *Interests*: Reviving & promoting cultural & contemporary arts & culture for 15 years; "I write poetry & short stories about life & the aboriginal people of this continent; other interests include clay, wood & stone sculpture, & most importantly, the revival of the planet. I'm concerned about the environment & tribal issues concerning the living conditions of my people. I am a traditional singer, pipe carrier & sundancer. I perform sacred sweatlodge ceremonies on my reservation for the health & lives of the people. I have traveled from coast to coast many times promoting my own and the work of others (Indian art work) and have been active in producing, promoting and marketing Indian art for almost ten years."

COURNOYER, GERALD (Oglala Sioux)
(artist; studio owner)
Education: Institute of American Indian Arts, Santa Fe, NM, 1995; University of South Dakota, BFA, 1999, MA, 2000; University of Oklahoma, MFA candidate. *Address*: Studio 35, 1024 W. Apache, Norman, OK 73070 E-mail: geraldcournoyer.com; E-mail: studio3502@yahoo.com. *Affiliation*: Coordinator & painting instruct, Oscar Howe Summer Art Institute (two-week program in June at the University of South Dakota, Vermillion). *Exhibitions*: Third place in painting at Northern Plains Tribal Art show in Sioux Falls, SD; Fred Jones Museum of Art and the Sam Noble Museum of Natural History, Norman, Oklahoma; and a group show "Connected Voices," in Oklahoma City, OK. Mr. Cournoyer is currently represented by RB Ravens Gallery in Taos, NM to view

his work online go to website: www.rbravens.com or contact the MA Doran Gallery in Tulsa, OK (918) 748-8700.

COURTNEY, DAN (Cow Creek Umpqua)
(tribal chairperson)
Affiliation & Address: Chairperson, Cow Creek Band of Umpqua Tribe of Indians, 2371 N.E. Stevens, Roseburg, OR 97470 (541) 672-9405.

COWAN, CLYDE
(executive director)
Affiliation & Address: Executive Director, North America Indigenous Ministries, P.O. Box 220, Sta. A, Abbotsford, BC V2T 6Z6 Canada (604) 850-3052.

COWAN, GENI D. (Choctaw)
(professor)
Education: PhD. *Affiliation* & Address: Professor, Educational Administration & Policy Studies Deppartment, Eureka Hall 0402A, California State University, Sacramento, 6000 "J" St., Sacramento, CA 95819 (916) 278-6154. E-mail: gcowan@csus.edu. *Other professional post*: Governing Council Executive Board Member, National Institute for Native Leadership in Higher Education, University of Northern Colorado, Greeley, CO.

COWARD, JOHN M.
(professor of communication)
Education: East Tennessee State University, BS, 1972; University of Tennessee-Knoxville, MS, 1981; University of Texas, Austin, PhD (Communication), 1989. *Affiliation & Address*: Associate Professor of Communication, Oliphant Hall 131, Dept. of Communication, University of Tulsa, Tulsa, OK 74104 (918) 631-2542. E-mail: john-coward@utulsa.edu. *Past professional posts*: Emory & Henry College, Emory, VA, 1980-84; University of Oklahoma, Norman, 1989-90. *Membership*: Western History Association. *Awards, honors*: 2000 Finalist, Best Western Nonfiction-Historical, Western Writers of America Awards for "The Newspaper Indian." Best American Journalism Article Award, American Journalism Historians Association, Oct. 2004, for "Selling the Southwestern Indian: Ideology & Image in Arizona Highways, 1925-1940," American Journalism, Spring 2003. *Published works*: The Newspaper Indian: Native American Identity in the Press, 1820-90 (University of Illinois Press, 1999); The Indian Wars (Greenwood, 2005); articles, chapters & book reviews.

COWELL, ANDREW (Algonquin)
(professor of Indigenous languages)
Affiliation & Address: Professor of Linguistics (Allgonquian & Miwok languages), 295 UCB, Dept. of Linguistics, University of Colorado, Boulder, CO 80309-0295 (303) 492-2747. E-mail: james.cowell@colorado.edu.

COWGER, THOMAS W. (Chickasaw)
(director of Native studies & history chair)
Affiliation & Address: History Chair & Director of Native Studies, Department of History & Native American Studies, East Central University, Hayes Native American Studies Center, Horace Mann Bldg. 3rd Floor, 1100 E. 14th St., Ada, OK 74820 (580) 332-8000. E-mail: tcowger@ecok.edu.

COX, BRUCE (Anishinabe)1934-
(professor & executive director)
Born June 29, 1934, Santa Rosa, Calif. *Education*: Reed College, B.A., 1956; University of Oregon, M.A., 1959; University of California at Berkeley, Ph.D., 1968. *Affiliation & Address*: Assistant Professor of Anthropology (1969-present), Carleton University, 140 Kenilworth, Ottawa, Ontario, Canada (613) 788-2604 (office). *Affiliations*: Instructor, Lewis & Clark College, 1964-1965; visiting professor, University of Florida, 1966; assistant professor, University of Alberta, 1967-1969. *Other professional post*: Executive director of Greenpeace Canada. *Memberships*: American Anthropological Association; Canadian Ethnology Association (program chair, 1989 meetings). *Interests*: Dr. Cox writes, "I am interested in the cultural ecology of indigenous North American peoples." *Published works*: Cultural Ecology of Canadian Native Peoples (Carleton Library, 1973); Cultural Ecology: Readings on the Canadian Indians & Eskimos (Institute of Canadian Studies, 1978); Native People, Native Lands (Carleton University, 1988); A Different Drummer: Readings in Anthropology with a Canadian Perspective (Carleton University, 1989); Los Indios del Canada (Mapre Foundation, Madrid, 1992).

COX, DEBORAH LYNN WHITEWOLF (*Unega Waya - White Wolf*) (Tcinto Sakto Muskogee) 1957-
(supervisor of elections)
Born February 1, 1957, Elizabeth County, Ky. *Education*: AS in Criminal Justice, BS in Psychology, MS in Sociology, PhD in Psychology. *Address*: 318 Crestview Dr., Valdosta, GA 31602 (229) 333-5100. E-mail: lcbe@datasys.net. *Affiliations*: Supervisor of Elections, Lowndes County, GA. *Other professional posts*: Native American Artist; assistant manager, Storm of Creations; secretary, Tcinto Sakto Muskogee. *Community activities*: Instructor, Native American Studies. *Military service*: USAF, 1980-91. *Memberships*: American

Taekwondo Association; Georgia Election Officials Association. *Interests*: Native American history & art. *Published works*: Correlates of Correctional Institution Suicide, 1989; Post Traumatic Stress Disorder in Police Officers, 1990; When a Cop Kills, 1992; Learning Cherokee: Workbook Series, 1994.

COX, DONALD D. (*Quiet Storm*) (Tcinto Sakto Muskogee) 1950-
  (police captain)
Born September 16, 1950, Lakeland, Ga. *Education*: Georgia Military College, AA, 1972; South Georgia Tech (2 years). *Address*: 318 Crestview Dr., Valdosta, GA 31602 (229) 244-9104; 293-3099 (work); E-mail: dcox@datasys.net. *Affiliation*: Captain, Administrative Assistant to the Chief, Valdosta Police Department, Valdosta, Ga., 1973-. *Community activities*: Emergency medical instructor; firearms instructor (civilian & police); CPR & first aid instructor; instruct Citizens Police Academy classes - general instruction certificate. *Membership*: Georgia Peace Officers Assn; Police Benevolent Assn (former president); Georgia Police Academy (member, Advisory Board); Firearms Instructors Assn; Red Feather Society; International Association of Bomb Technicians & Investigators. *Award*: Medal of Valor, Valdosta Police Dept., 1995. *Published work*: Firearms for Women - A Practical Guide.

COX, S. DIANE (*Many Cats*) (Tcinto Sakto Muskogee) 1972-
  (curator)
Born November 26, 1972, Valdosta, GA. *Education*: B.S. (English); BS (History), BS (Journalism). *Principal occupation*: Zoo curator. *Address*: 6562 S.W. 92nd Dr., Jasper, FL 32052. *Affiliation*: Curator-birds of prey, primates & big cats, Silver Springs Zoo. *Interests*: Conservation, preservation.

COX, STEPHEN D. 1948-
  (museum administrator/curator)
Born April 24, 1948, Bloomington, Ill. *Education*: Middle Tennessee State University, BS, 1970, MA, 1975. *Affiliation & Address*: Director of Exhibits & Curator, Tennessee State Museum, 505 Deaderick St., Nashville, TN 37243-1120 (615) 741-2692; director of exhibits fabrication/senior curator of Indian collections & manager, Photographic Archives, 1976-present. *Memberships*: Intermuseum Council of Nashville; Tennessee Association of Museums; American Association for State & Local History; Tennessee Historical Society; Historic Nashville, Inc.; National Trust for Historic Preservation; Mid-Cumberland Archaeological Society; Southeastern Archaeological Conference; Kentucky Historical Society; National Trust for Historic Preservation. *Awards, honors*: American Association for State & Local History "Award of Merit" for the exhibition "The First Tennesseans--Tennessee's Prehistoric Indian Cultures" (for which Cox was the supervising curator) and for book, Art & Artisans of Prehistoric Middle Tennessee (for which he was the editor). *Interests*: Prehistoric Indian cultures in Tennessee. "My great grandmother was full-blooded Indian and was born in Canada." *Published work*: Art & Artisans of Prehistoric Middle Tennessee (Tennessee State Museum, 1985).

COX, THOMAS (Iowa)
  (tribal vice chairperson)
Affiliation & Address: Vice Chairperson (2013-), Iowa Nation of Oklahoma, Rt. 1 Box 721, Perkins, OK 74059 (405) 547-2402. E-mail: tcox@iowanation.org

COYHIS, DONALD L. (Mohican)
  (writer; non-profit president)
Affiliation & Address: Coyhis Publishing & White Bison, Inc., 6145 Lehman Dr., Suite 200, Colorado Springs, CO 80918 (719) 548-1000. Website: www.whitebison.org. E-mail: info@whitebison.org. Founder & president of White Bison, Inc., an American Indian non-profit organization based in Colorado Springs, CO. since 1988. Offers sobriety, recovery, addictions prevention and wellness/wellbriety learning resources to the Native American community nationwide. White Bison's mission is to assist in bringing 100 Native American communities into healing by 2010. Wellbriety resources include books, DVDs, audiotapes; holds conferences, specialized community training events and the grassroots "Firestarters" circles of recovery groups across the country. Published works: Recovery From the Heart, A Journey Through the Twelve Steps - Audio, 1990 & Workbook, 1994; Meditations With Native American Elders, 1993; The Red Road to Wellbriety; In the Native American Way, 2002; Meditations With Native American Elders: The Four Seasons, 2007. All published by Coyhis Publishing & White Bison, Inc.

COZZO, DAVID
  (project director; ethnobotanist)
Education: Eastern Kentucky University, BS (Biology); Appalachian State University, MA (Appalachian Studies); University of Georgia, PhD (Anthropology). Doctoral Dissertation: Ethnobotanical Classificationn System and Medical Ethnobotany of the Eastern Band of Cherokee Indians (2004). *Affiliation & Address*: Project Director, Revitalization of Traditional Cherokee Artisan Resources, Cherokee Studies Program, College of Arts & Sciences, McKee Bldg. 105A-C, Western Carolina University, Cullowhee, NC 28723 (828) 554-6856. E-mail: cozzod@email.wcu.edu.

CRAIG, LAURA (Pit River)
  (tribal chairperson)
Affiliation: Lookout Rancheria Council, P.O. Box 1570, Burney, CA 96013 (916) 335-5421.

CRAIG, RONALD (Nashoba Homma) (Chickasaw/Cherokee) 1944-
  (college instructor)
Born October 10, 1944, Louisville, Ky. *Education*: BA in Sociology, MA & PhD in History. *Affiliation & Address*: Chairperson, Native American Studies, Fort Peck Community College (1993-present), P.O. Box 398, Poplar, MT 59255 (406) 768-5551 ext. 22. *Military service*: U.S. Marine Corps, 1962-66, 1974-76; U.S. Air Force, 1966-72. *Community activities*: Sacred site coordinator with Fort Peck Tribal Government and Bureau of Reclamation; advisor to Sioux Treaty Council; Reservation Historical Preservation. *Memberships*: American Indian Professors' Association; Western History Association; Western Outlaw Lawman Historical Association. *Published works*: The Colberts in Chickasaw History, 1783-1818: A Study of Internal Tribal Dynamics (University of New Mexico, 1998); A History of Fort Peck Indian Reservation, 1999.

CRAMBLIT, ANDRE (Yurok)
  (Indian council director; consultant)
Education: Dartmouth College, BA (Education/Sociology), 1986; Humboldt State University, Teacher Credential, 1988. *Affiliation & Address*: Operations Director (1996-present), Northern California Indian Development Council, 241 F St., Eureka, CA 95501 (707) 464-3512. E-mail: andrekar@ncidc.org. Andre's duties include day-to-day oversight of all programs including the Del Norte Indian Education Center and youth & family wellness programs. Also, he researches & writes grants, assists with supervision of all staff, writes & edits newsletters, and prepares required program reports providing technical assistance & training to tribes & American Indian organizations throughout California. *Other professional post*: Consultant to a variety of tribal, Federal & state agencies, 1988-present). *Past professional posts*: Education specialist, Bureau of Indian Affairs, 1990-93; education director, Yurok Tribe, 1993-97.

CRANDELL, E.J. (Pomo)
  (tribal chairperson)
Affiliation & Address: Chairperson (2014-present), Robinson Rancheria of Pomo Indians, P.O. Box 4015, Nice, CA 95453 (707) 275-0527. E-mail: ej@rrrc.com

CRANK, MICHELE (Dine)
  (museum administrator)
Education: University of Phoenix, BS (Business Administration). *Affiliation & Address*: Director of Public Affairs & Government Relations, Heard Museum, 2301 N. Central Ave., Phoenix, AZ 85004 (602) 252-8840. E-mail: publicaffairs75@yahoo.com. *Other professional post*: Southwest Regional Representative, American Indian Alaska Native Tourism Association, Albuquerque, NM.

CRAPPEL, AUGUST (Houma)
  (tribal vice principal chief)
Affiliation & Address: Vice Principal Chief, United Houma Nation, 20986 Hwy. 1, Golden Meadow, LA 70357 (504) 475-6640.

CRAWFORD, ALAN (Umatilla)
  (triball chairperson)
Affiliation & Address: Chairperson, Confederated Tribes of the Umatilla Indian Reservation, Nixyaawii Governance Center, 46411 Timine Way, Pendleton, OR 97801 (541) 429-7378; E-mail: alancrawford@ctuir.org

CRAWFORD, JEFFREY A.
  (attorney)
Address & Affiliation: President, Minnesota American Indian Bar Association, Minneapolis, MN 55401 (612) 540-3728.

CRAWFORD, SUZY (Ottawa of Oklahoma)
  (tribal second chief)
Affiliation & Address: Second Chief, Ottawa Tribe of Oklahoma, P.O. Box 110, Miami, OK 74355 (918) 540-1536.

CRAZY BULL, CHERYL (*Wacinyanpi*) (Sicangu Lakota)
  (Indian college president; tribal educator)
Education: University of South Dakota, BS (Business); South Dakota State University, MA (Educational Leadership); Sinte Gleska University, 2005 Honorary Doctorate. *Affiliation & Address*: President & CEO, American Indian College Fund, 8333 Greenwood Blvd., Denver, CO 80221 (303) 426-8900. E-mail: crazybull@collegefund.org (2012-present). *Past professional posts*: Board chair (fourth term), American Indian Higher Education Consortium (AIHEC); advisory board, National Congress of American Indian Policy Research Center; board of trustees, National Museum of the American Indian; board member, American Indian College Fund; president, Northwest Indian

College, Bellingham, WA, 2002-2012; vice-president (17 years), Sinte GleskaUniversity, Rosebud, SD; executive director, Sicangu Enterprise Center, Mission, SD; chief educational officer (four years), Sicangu Oyate Ho., Inc., St. Francis Indian School, St. Francis, SD.

CRAZY HORSE, ROY (*Chief Nemattanew*) (Powhattan Renape)
(tribal chief)
Affiliation & Address: Chief, Powhattan Renape Nation, P.O. Box 225, Rancocas, NJ 08073 (609) 261-4747. *Other professional post*: New Jersey Governor's Office, Ethnic Advisory Council, State House CN001, 125 W. State St., Trenton, NJ 08625 (609) 292-6000.

CREEL, BARBARA (Pueblo of Jemez)
(professor of law; attorney)
Education: University of Colorado, BA, 1987; University of New Mexico School of Law, JD, 1990. *Affiliation & Address*: Professor of Law (2007-present), Director, Southwest Indian Law Clinic, Henry Weihofen Professorship, MSC11 6070, University of New Mexico School of Law, 1117 Stanford NE, Albuquerque, NM 87131 (505) 277-0907; E-mail: creel@law.unm.edu. *Past professional posts*: National Advisory Council for Indian Education, Washington, DC, 1990-93; Native American Program, Oregon Legal Services, Portland, OR, 1993-95; clinical fellow, Southwest Indian Lw Clinic and associate professor and adjunct in the UNM Clinicla Law Program; appellate public defender with the New Mexico Public Defender's Office, 1995-9; assistant federal public defender in Oregon, 1999-2007. For seven years, she was an assistant federal public defender in the District of Oregon, where she developed a federal habeas corpus & post-conviction expertise. She assisted in the defense of Native American clients on cases from reservations prosecuted under the Major Crimes Act. Creel also worked at the trial level and argued before the 9th Circuit Court of Appeals. Prior to joining the UNM law faculty, she worked as tribal liaison for the Portland District of the U.S. Army Corps of Engineers, fostering government-to-government relations between the federally recognized Indian tribes and the federal government. She worked with tribal leaders, commanding officers and senior civilian managers, as well as the individual tribal members & corps staff, to translate complex Indian law issues among all parties & build relationships. Creel's interest in Indian law began when she worked for the Native American Rights Fund during her undergraduate years at the University of Colorado. Following graduation from the UNM School of Law in 1990, she worked for the National Advisory Council for Indian Education in Washington, D.C. In 1993, she joined the Native American Program of Oregon Legal Services in Portland. Creel returned to the UNM School of Law in 1995, first as a clinical fellow with the Southwest Indian Law Clinic and later as an associate professor and adjunct in the UNM Clinical Law Program. She taught for four years, during which she also spent time as an appellate public defender with the New Mexico Public Defender's Office. In 1999, she became an assistant federal public defender in Oregon. She was a contributing author in the 2005 revision of the FELIX S. COHEN HANDBOOK OF FEDERAL INDIAN LAW. In addition to clinical and Indian law, Creel's academic interests include the intersections of Indian, civil, criminal and constitutional law.

CREWS, NAPOLEON (Kickapoo)
(Indian school administrator)
Affiliation: Kickapoo Nation School, P.O. Box 106, Powhattan, KS 66527 (785) 474-3550.

CRISWELL, STEPHEN
(associate professor of English & Native American studies)
Affiliation & Address: Associate Professor of English & Native American Studies, Native American Studies Center, Room 120, 119 S. Main St., Lancaster, SC 29721 (803) 313-7108; E-mail: criswese@mailbox.sc.edu.

CRITTENDEN, S. JOE (Cherokee)
(deputy principal chief)
Affiliation & Address: Deputy Principal Chief (2011-present), Cherokee Nation of Oklahoma, P.O. Box 948, Tahlequah, OK 74465 (918) 456-0671. E-mail: joe-crittenden@cherokee.org

CROMARTY, DENNIS (Nishnawbe Aski)
(grand chief)
Affiliation: Nishnawbe Aski Nation, 14 College St., 6th Floor, Toronto, ON, Canada M5C 1K2 (416) 920-2376.

CROMWELL, CEDRIC (Mashpee Wampanoag)
(tribal chairperson)
Born & raised on the Mashpee Wampanoag Tribal Community. *Education*: UMass, BS. *Affiliation*: Mashpee Wampanoag Indian tribe, P.O. Box 1048, Mashpee, MA 02649. (508) 477-00208. Member of the tribal council for ten years. *Past professional post*: Fidelity Investments, Boston, MA.

CROSS, RAYMOND (Mandan, Hidatsa, Arikara)
(professor of law)
Education: Yale Law School, JD, 1973. *Affiliation & Address*: Professor of Law, University of Montana School of Law, Law 317, Missoula, MT (406) 243-4816. E-mail: ray.cross@umontana.edu. Professor Cross teaches Federal Indian Law, Comparative Legal Status & Rights of the Indigenous Peoples of Canada, Australia, New Zealand & United States, and Public Land & Natural Resources Law. He advises the Public Land & Resources Law Review, and he coaches the National Native American Law Students' Moot Court team. He works extensively with Indian tribes, Indian organizations, and federal agencies on issues of Indian education, tribal self-determination, and cultural & natural resources preservation. *Past professional posts*: Staff attorney, California Indian Legal Services, Ukiah, CA, 1973-75; Director, Indian Law Support Center, Native American Rights Fund, Boulder, CO, 1975-80; tribal attorney, Mandan, Hidatsa & Arikara Nation, Fort Berthold Indian Reservation, 1981-93. *Biographical source*: Coyote Warrior: One Man, Three Tribes & the Trial That Forged A Nation (Little, Brown Publishing Co., 2004). *Published works*: Numerous articles in scholarly journals.

CROSS, TERRY L. (*Ha-nee-ga-noh*) (Seneca) 1952-
(executive director; adjunct professor)
Born August 20, 1952. *Education*: Grove City College (PA), BA, 1974; Portland State University (OR), MSW, 1977. *Affiliation & Address*: Founder & Executive Director, National Indian Child Welfare Association, (1987-present), 5100 SW Macadam Ave., Suite 300, Portland, OR 97201 (503) 222-4044 ext. 112. E-mail: tlcross@nicwa.org. *Past professional post*: Adjunct professor (1979-94), Portland State University, School of Social Work, Portland, OR; member, SAMHSA National Advisory Council. *Community activities*: Member, Minority Resource Committee; CASSP Technical Assistance Center, Georgetown University; chair of Monograph Sub-Committee, 1988-present; consultant, The Casey Family Program, 1982-present. *Membership*: Association of Certified Social Workers. *Awards, honors*: 2009 Civic Engagement Award for Excellence in Community-Based Research from Portland State University; 2010 finalist for the EcoTrust Indigenous Leadership Award; 2011 Robert F. Kennedy Children's Action Corp' "Embracing the Legacy" award at the Kennedy Presidential Library in Boston. *Published works*: Heritage & Helping: A Model Curriculum for Indian Child Welfare Practice, an 11-manual curriculum for tribal child welfare staff (NWICWI, Parry Center for Children, 1985); Cross-Cultural Skills in Indian Child Welfare: A Guide for the Non-Indian (NWICWI, Parry Center for Children, 1988); Positive Indian Parenting: Honoring Our Children by Honoring Our Traditions (NWICWI, Parry Center for Children, 1987); Towards a Culturally Competent System of Care: A Monograph on Effective Services for Minority Children Who Are Severely Emotionally Handicapped (CASSP Technical Assistance Center, Georgetown U., with Dennis, Bazron, Isaacs & Mason).

CROSS, VIRGINIA (Muckleshoot)
(tribal chairperson)
Affiliation & Address: Chairperson, Muckleshoot Indian Tribe, 39015 172nd St., SE, Auburn, WA 98002 (253) 939-3311. Website: www.muckleshoot.nsn.us.

CROW, JERY (Seneca-Cayuga)
(tribal second chief)
Affiliation & Address: Second Chief, Seneca-Cayuga Tribe of Oklahoma, P.O. Box 1283, Miami, OK 74355 (918) 542-6609.

CROMWELL, CEDRIC (Mashpee Wampanoag)
(tribal chairperson)
Affiliation & Address: Chairperson, Mashpee Wampanoag Indian Tribe, 483 Great Neck Rd., South, P.O. Box 1048, Mashpee, MA 02649 (508) 477-0208

CROWELL, SCOTT D.
(attorney)
Education: Arizona State University, BS (Economics), 1980; Arizona State University Law School, JD, 1984. *Affiliation & Address*: Founder (1991-present), Crowell Law Office, Tribal Advocacy Group, 1487 W. 89A, Suite 8, Sedona, AZ 86336 (425) 802-5369 and in Washington State: 10 N. Post, Spokane, WA 99201 (509) 768-5109. E-mail: scrowell@clotag.net. Scott has given presentations or taught at numerous seminars including: Northwest Gaming Law Summit, 2007-10; 2010 Florida Gaming Summit; 2010 California Indian Law Association, Indian Law Conference; Native American Finance & Economic Development Conference, 2006-07. *Past professional posts*: Attorney, Burch & Cracchiolo, Phoenix, AZ, 1984-88; partner, Spady & Crowell, Seattle, WA, 1989-90; attorney, Dillon Enterprises, Puyallup Tribe, 1990-91; partner, Monteau, Peebles & Crowell, 2000.

CROWFOOT, BERT (Blackfoot/Salteaux) 1953-
(publisher; management)
Born September 19, 1953, Gleichen, Alberta, Can. *Education*: Brigham Young University (three years). *Principal occupation*: Publisher; management.

Address: Unknown. *Affiliation*: Founder & CEO, Aboriginal Multi-Media Society of Alberta (AMMSA), Edmonton, Alberta, 1983-; general manager, CFWE-FM, an Alberta-wide Aboriginal radio network; publisher, Windspeaker (bi-weekly journal), AMMSA (current) Canada's largest publisher of Aboriginal news & information. *Community activities*: Coach - Alberta team for Canada Summer Games. *Memberships*: Native American Journalists Association; National Aboriginal Communications Society; Native, Inuit, Indian, Photographers Association. *Awards, honors*: Merit Award from Government of Canada for Community Contribution; Lifetime Achievement Award from the Province of Alberta; inducted into the Aboriginal Walk of Honor in Edmonton, 2006. *Interests*: Sports psychology, psychology, cultural exchange with republic of S. Korea. *Published works*: Powwow Trail (Bear Ghost Enterprises, 1981); Nation's Ensign, monthly (Society for the Preservation of Indian Identity, 1980-83); Windspeaker, bi-weekly & Sweetgrass, monthly (AMMSA).

CROWFOOT, SAMUEL R.C. (Siksika First Nation Blackfoot)
(attorney)
Education: Brigham Young University, BA, 2007; University of Wisconsin Law School, JD, 2012. *Affiliation & Address*: Chief Judge, Pueblo of Zuni, P.O. Box 339, Zuni, NM 87327 (505) 782-7123 *Past professional posts*: Associate Attorney, Rosette, LLP, Chandler, AZ, 2015-16. Mr. Crowfoot has worked for Native American tribes and is familiar with the needs, values and expectations that Tribes demand from their legal representation. Before joining Rosette, LLP in 2015, Mr. Crowfoot was the Chief Prosecutor for the Hopi Tribe located in northern Arizona. While in the Hopi prosecutor's office, Mr. Crowfoot focused in the areas of family dependency & criminal law where he enjoyed great success implementing the Tribal Law & Order Act. In addition to running the Hopi prosecutor's office, Mr. Crowfoot also oversaw the Hopi Domestic Violence Program and worked extensively with victims of Domestic Violence; his service in this capacity earned him an award of appreciation from the Hop-Tewa Women's Coalition. Mr. Crowfoot has worked for Tribes across the country and has been able to maintain professional relationships via an expansive personal network. He is a graduate from Utah Valley State College, Brigham Young University and the University of Wisconsin Law School. While at Brigham Young University, Mr. Crowfoot worked as an intern for the United Nations in Geneva Switzerland. As a law student Mr. Crowfoot served all three years as an executive board member for the Indigenous Law Students Association and was instrumental in running the Annual Coming Together of People's Conference, the oldest student run Indian law conference in the country. Samuel was raised on – & is an enrolled member of – the Siksika First Nation Indian reserve (Blackfoot) located in Alberta, Canada. Mr. Crowfoot is also of Oneida (Wisconsin), Saulteaux (Ojibwa) & Akwesasne (Mohawk) descent.

CRUM, STEVEN JAMES (Western Shoshone) 1950-
(associate professor)
Born December 29, 1950, Phoenix, Ariz. *Education*: Arizona State University, BA, 1975; University of Arizona, MEd, 1977; University of Utah, PhD, 1983. *Affiliation & Address*: Professor, Dept. of Native American Studies, UC Davis, 2411 Hart Hall, Davis, CA 95616 (530) 752-6488. E-mail: sjcrum@ucdavis.edu. *Past professional posts*: Chairperson, Dept. of Native American Studies, UC Davis; Center for Ethnic & Women's Studies, California State University, Chico (acting coordinator, 1984-85, coordinator, 1985-88, American Indian Studies; lecturer, 1985-85, assistant professor, Dept. of History); associate professor, Native American Studies Department, University of California, Davis, 1990-present. *Memberships*: Western Historical Association; National Indian Education Association; California Indian Education Association; Organization of American Historians. *Awards, honors*: "Outstanding Young Men of America" Award, 1987; "Professional Promise" Award, California State University, Chico, 1988; Ford Foundation Postdoctoral Fellowship for Minorities, Native American Studies, University of California, Davis, 1988-89; Postgraduate Researcher/ Visiting Scholar, University of California President's Fellowship Program, Native American Studies, University of California, Davis, 1989-90; Nick Yengich Editors' Choice Award, 1992, Utah State Historical Society, for best article in the "Utah Historical Quarterly." *Published works*: The Road on Which We Came: A History of the The Western Shoshone (University of Utah Press, 1994); numerous articles.

CRUZ, ROBERT (Tohono O'odham)
(activist, speaker)
Affiliation: Board member, International Indian Treaty Council, P.O. Box 3727, New York, NY 10017. He works extensively at the U.N. *Other professional posts*: Works with the World Archaeological Congress of professionals dedicated to ethical archaeology; Southwest Coordinator, American Indians Against Desecration, he assisted in the passage of the Native American Graves Protection & Repatriation Act. Mr. Cruz helped in recovering the remains of 6,000 Indian ancestors from institutions & private collections for reburial. *Awards, honors*: 1993 recipient of the Bill Wahpepah Memorial Human Rights Award.

CRUZ, VIOLA
(editor)
Affiliation: American Indian Culture & Research Journal, American Indian Studies Center, Room 3220 Campbell Hall, UCLA, 405 Hilgard Ave., Los Angeles, CA 90024 (213) 206-1433.

CRUZAN, DARREN A. (Maimi of Oklahoma)
(deputy Bureau of Indian Affairs director – Justice Services)
Education: Mountain State University (West Virginia), BS (Criminal Justice Administration); graduate of the Federal Burau of Investigation National Academy (FBINA), 2006. *Affiliation & Address*: Deputy Bureau of Indian Affairs Director, Office of Public Affairs – Indian Affairs, U.S. Department of the Interior, 1849 C St., NW, MS-3658-MIB, Washington, DC 20240 (202) 208-3710. He oversees the Bureau's law enforcement, corrections and tribal courts functions and programs that serve the federally recognized tribes. Mr. Cruzan returned to the BIA after serving since 2006 with the U.S. Department of Defense Pentagon Force Protection Agency (PFTA) as the Assistant Special Agent in Charge of the Criminal Investigative and Protective Directorate, where he supervised the day-to-day operations of the agency's Criminal Investigations Division. He also served as the detail leader on dignitary protection missions for senior level department officials, both within the continental United States and overseas. His overseas missions included assignments into Iraq, Beirut, Saudi Arabia, Germany, France, Belgium, The Czech Republic, The United Kingdom, Austria and Japan. He was later appointed by the agency's director as division chief of its Recruitment and Medical Division. Mr. Cruzan's law enforcement career began as a patrolman with the Joplin (Mo.) Police Department in 1992. He went on to serve as a police officer with his tribe until 1995, when he selected to work for the BIA's District II Law Enforcement (now OJS) Office in the Bureau's Eastern Oklahoma Regional Office in Muskogee, Okla. In 1998, Mr. Cruzan was promoted to the rank of Supervisory Police Officer and assigned to the United States Indian Police Academy located at the Federal Law Enforcement Training Center in Artesia, N.M., where he provided law enforcement training to newly hired police, corrections and telecommunications officers working in Indian Country. In 2001, he was promoted to Criminal Investigator and assigned to the BIA's Portland, Ore., field office, where he carried out federal criminal investigations and provided technical law enforcement assistance to the federally recognized tribes in the Pacific Northwest. Mr. Cruzan's next promotion was to the post of Supervisory Special Agent on the Crow Indian Reservation in Montana. During his tenure his department was honored in 2004 by the Secretary of the Interior with DOI's "Customer Service Excellence Award" for their efforts in reducing the number of Driving Under the Influence-related fatalities on the reservation. Also in 2004, Mr. Cruzan accepted a request to serve as the Senior Law Enforcement Advisor to the BIA's Associate Director of Operations at its headquarters in Washington, D.C. While there, he also served as the Indian Country Law Enforcement liaison to the Department. He continued in both capacities until moving to the PFTA in 2006.

CUARA, JANICE (Tachi-Yokut)
(tribal administrator)
Affiliation & Address: Administrator, Tachi-Yokut Tribe of the Santa Rosa Rancheria, P.O. Box 8, Lemoore, CA 93245 (559) 924-1278.

CUBBINS, ELAINE M. (Tohono O'odham)
(Indian college librarian)
Affiliation & Address: Librarian, Tohono O'odam Community College Library , P.O. Box 3129, Sells, AZ 85634 (520) 383-8401

CUCH, CAMERON (Ute/Wampanoag)
(educator)
Address: P.O. Box 872, Fort Duchesne, UT 84026 (435) 722-2331. E-mail: cameronc@utetribe.com. *Other professional post*: Board member, National Indian Education Association, Washington, DC.

CUCH, FORREST S. (Ute) 1951-
(director of Indian affairs)
Born July 8, 1951 on the Uintah & Ouray Ute Indian Reservation in northeastern Utah. *Education*: Westminster College, BA, 1973. *Address & Affiliation*: Utah Division of Indian Affairs, 324 S. State St., Suite 500, Salt Lake City, UT 84111 (801) 538-8788. E-mail: fscuch@dced.state.ut.us. Inter-governmental relations, information & referral, and responsible for repatriation of human remains found on non-federal lands. *Affiliations*: Education director, Ute Indian Tribe, 1973-88; planner for newly recognized tribe, the Wampanoag Tribe of Gay Head (Aquinnah), Gay Head, Mass., 1988, tribal administrator, 1992-94; Social Studies Dept. Head, Wasatch Academy, Mt. Pleasant, UT, 1994-97; executive director, Utah Division of Indian Affairs, Salt Lake City, UT, 1997-2011. *Published works*: A History of the Northern Ute People (University of Utah Press, 1982); A History of Utah's American Indians (Utah State University Press, 2003).

CUCH, IRENE (Ute)
(former tribal chairperson)
Affiliation & Address: Chairperson (2010-2012), The Ute Indian Tribe, P.O. Box 190, Fort Duchesne, UT 84026 (435) 722-5141.

CUDDINGTON, ANA (Gila River Pima)
(American Indian program director)
Affiliation & Address: Director, American Indian Studies Program, Scottsdale Community College, 9000 E. Chaparral St., Scottsdale, AZ 85256 (480) 423-6531. E-mail: ana.cuddington@sccmail.maricopa.edu.

CUEVAS, LOU (Apache) 1946-
(writer)
Address: c/o Naturegraph Publishers, P.O. Box 1047, Happy Camp, CA 96039 (530) 493-5353. He writes about Southwest & Apache legends and culture, and is a member of the First Friday Forum Writer's Group. *Published works*: Anasazi Legends: Songs of the Wind Dancer (Naturegraph Publishers, 2000); Apache Legends: Songs of the Wind Dancer (Naturegraph Publishers, 1991); In the Valley of the Ancients: A Book of Native American Legends (Petroglyph National Monument {Albuquerque, NM}), 1996).

CULTEE, CLIFF (Lummi)
(former tribal chairperson)
Affiliation & Address: Chairperson, Lummi Nation, 2616 Kwina Rd., Bellingham, WA 98226 (360) 384-1489.

CULTEE, ROGER (Quinault)
(ethno-historian; metal-smith; musician)
Education: Institute of American Indian Arts, BA (Creative Writing); University of New Mexico, BA (Art Studio). *Affiliation & Address*: Director, Department of Ancient Decipherments, The Indigenous Research Center, 2103 Eton Ave. SE #4, Albuquerque, NM 87106. E-mail: racultee@yahoo.com. Roger is the first metal-smith to come out of the Quinault Nation. He is also a world reknown guitar player & musician. *Interests*: "I learned to decipher ancient art and it became my passion."

CUMMINGS, VERNON (Omaha)
(chief of tribal operations)
Affiliation & Address: Chief of Tribal Operations, Omaha Tribe, P.O. Box 368, Macy, NE 68039 (402) 837-5391.

CUNHA, AGNES E. (*White Dove*) (Paucatuck Eastern Pequot)
(tribal ambassador)
Affiliation: Paucatuck Eastern Pequot Tribe, P.O. Box 370, North Stonington, CT 06359 (860) 448-0492.

CUNHA, JAMES A. JR. (*Growling Bear*) (Paucatuck Eastern Pequot) 1962-
(tribal chief/treasurer)
Born May 15, 1962, Warwick, RI. *Affiliation & Address*: Chief, treasurer, Paucatuck Eastern Pequot Tribe, P.O. Box 370, North Stonington, CT 06359 (860) 448-0492. E-mail: pepitn@aol.com. *Community activities*: Chairperson, North Stonington Democratic Town Committee; member, Board of Directors, Alliance for the Living; commissioner, North Stonington Planning & Zoning Commission.

CUNNINGHAM, PAM (Penobscot)
(craftsperson)
Address: 208 Old County Rd., Hampden, ME 04444 (207) 941-9373.
Product: Penobscot brown ash and sweetgrass fancy baskets.

CUPP, LORI, MD (Navajo-Dine) 1959-
(surgeon)
Born in Crownpoint, NM. *Education*: Dartmouth College (majored in psychology, sociology & Native American studies), B.A., 1981; Stanford Medical School, M.D., 1990. *Address & Affiliation*: Gallup Indian Medical Center, P.O. Box 1337, Gallup, NM 87305. *Other professional posts*: Crownpoint PHS Indian Hospital, Crownpoint, NM. *Membership*: Association of American Indian Physicians. *Interests*: Dr. Cupp is the first Navajo woman to become a surgeon.

CURE, MICHELLE (Te-Moak Western Shoshone)
(tribal chairperson)
Affiliation & Address: Chairperson, Te-Moak Tribe of Western Shoshone Indians of Nevadad, Wells Band, Box 809, Wells, NV 89835 (775) 752-3045.

CURRIER, JOHN (Luiseno)
(interim director, American Indian Graduate Center))
Education: University of Massachusetts, Boston, BS (Management & Accounting). *Affiliation & Address*: Interim Director, American Indian Graduate Center, University of New Mexico, 3701 San Mateo Blvd. NE #200, Albuquerque, NM 87110 (505) 881-4584. E-mail: joan@aigcs.org. *Other*

professional posts: Joan is an active participant in the organization's community ourtreach activities & represents AIGC Scholars on the GMS Advisory Council & Gates Foundation Domestic Scholarship Provider Partnership; she serves on the Education Advisory Committee for FAFOA, the Native American Finance Officer's Association. *Past professional post*: Controller, American Cancer Society, Massachusetts Division, 1984-93; Chairperson, Rincon Band of Mission Indians, Valley Center, CA; Accounting Manager, Futures for Children in Albuquerque; chief operating officer (2007-present), interim executive director & coordinator, The Executive Search Team in 2000 & 2006, American Indian Graduate Center.

CURTISS, SARAH (Anishinaabe)
(Sacred Hoop tribal coalition coordinator)
Affiliation & Address: Sacred Hoop Tribal Coalition Coordinator, Mending the Sacred Hoop, 202 W. 2nd St., Duluth, MN 55802 (218) 623-HOOP. Sarah trains tribal & urban programs on the unique issues Native women face around domestic violence, and trains programs on how to work with survivors from a holistic cultural perspective. Sarah is on the Circle Keepers, Board of Directors for the Minnesota Indian Women's Sexual Assault Coalition.. She incorporates traditional Ojibwe traditions.

CUSHMAN, HELEN (Cherokee)
(professor of writing, rhetoric & American cultures)
Affiliation & Address: Professor of Writing, Rhetoric & American Cultures, American Indian Studies Program, 277 EBH, East Lansing, MI 48825 (517) 432-2193. E-mail: hcushman@msu.edu. Member of the Cherokee Nation Sequoyah Commission. She is an associate professor of WRAC, has recently published about Indian identity politics and self representation for *College Composition and Communication*. She has received an IRGP grant to finish her book on the Cherokee syllabary, *The Cherokee Syllabary: Writing Linguistic, Historical, and Cultural Perseverance*. She's also working on a book with Tom Holm *Native American History for Beginners*.

CUSTALOW, CHRISTINE (*Rippling Water*) (Mattaponi) 1938-
(potter & teacher)
Born April 28, 1938, Mattaponi Indian Reservation, Virginia. *Education*: Mattaponi Indian School. *Address*: 35 Nee-A-ya Lane, West Point, VA 23181 (804) 769-9331. *Affiliation*: Teach pottery, beadwork, leather, & mask making to Indian children for the schools in King William, VA. *Interests*: "I am very proud to be able to bring back the lost art of my ancestors as I have been interested in crafts. Make pottery, beadwork, leather, and masks for shows and powwows. I became interested in pottery in 1978 after a training program I was in with Eric Callahan, an archaeological teaching old ways of making pottery." Her pottery has been displayed at various craft shows and is on permanent display at the River of High Banks Pottery Shop, Mattaponi Indian Reservation, King William, VA. *Honors, awards*: 3rd Place, Potomac Art League, 1981; 1st Place, Kilmarnock Arts & Crafts Show, 1983; Best in Show, Poquoson Art Show, 1984; Award of Excellence, Poquoson Seafood Festival, 1986.

CUSTALOW, LIONEL (Mattaponi) 1966-
(cabinet maker)
Born December 17, 1966, Richmond, Va. *Address*: Mattaponi Reservation Circle, West Point, VA 23181. *Community activities*: Councilman, Mattaponi Tribe. *Interests*: "I am lead singer of Native American drum group ("Wahunsunacock Drum Group"), singing our song all through our Indian land."

CUSTALOW, WEBSTER (*Little Eagle*) (Mattaponi)
(tribal chief)
Affiliation: Chief, The Upper Mattaponi Indian Tribe, 1467 Mattaponi Reservation Circle, West Point, VA 23181 (804) 769-4508.

CUTBANK, RICHARD (Leech Lake Ojibwe)
(college instructor)
Affiliation: Leech Lake Tribal College, 6530 U.S. Hwy. 2 NW, Cass Lake, MN 56633 (218) 335-4220.

CUTHAIR, HAROLD (Ute Mountain Ute)
(tribal chairperson)
Affiliation & Address: Chairperson, Ute Mountain Ute Tribe, 124 Mike Wash Rd., Towaoc, CO 81334 (970) 565-3751. E-mail: hcuthair@utemountain.org.

CUTS THE ROPE, DELINA (Gros Ventre)
(Indian commission member)
Address: RR #1, Box 66, Harlem, MT 59526 (406) 353-2205. E-mail: delina2 marie@yahoo.com. *Affiliation*: Member, State Tribal Economic Development Commission (STEDC), c/o Montana Dept. of Commerce, Helena, MT.

CYPRESS, BILLY (Miccosukee)
(former tribal chairperson)
Affiliation: Miccosukee Indian Tribe, Box 44021, Tamiami Station, Miami, FL 33144 (305) 223-8380.

CYPRESS, DAVID (Miccosukee-Seminole)
(tribal representative)
Affiliation: c/o Seminole Agency, 6300 Stirling Rd., Hollywood, FL 33024 (800) 683-7800.

CYPRESS, MITCHELL (Florida Seminole)
(tribal chairperson)
Affiliation: Seminole Tribe of Florida, 6300 Stirling Rd., Hollywood, FL 33024 (954) 966-6300.

CYR, JAMES
(Indian center director)
Affiliation: American Indian Center of Indiana, Inc., 406 N. Broadway, Peru, IN 46970 (765) 473-3010.

D

DABODA, DARREN (Paiute)
(tribal chairperson)
Affiliation & Address: Chairperson, Moapa Band of Paiute Indians, P.O. Box 340, Moapa, NV 89025 (702) 865-2787. E-mail: chair.mbop@mvdsl.com

DACON, CHEBON (*Chebon*) (Creek) 1946-
(artist)
Born November 11, 1946, Oklahoma City, Okla. *Education*: University of Oklahoma, 1965-67. *Address*: 907 Hwy. 62W, Mountain Home, AR 72653 (870) 425-8369. His artwork includes detailed pencil drawings, watercolors & acrylics. Specializes in contemporary Western & Indian art. *Community activities*: Celebrities Golf for Indian Education Tournament. *Memberships*: Indian Arts & Crafts Association; SWIWA. *Awards, honors*: High awards & recognition for ceremonial dancing, as well as his talent for art, brought an invitation from the U.S. Dept. of Commerce to act as Good Will Ambassador to Australia. His art has been shown in several European countries and takes its place in museums, galleries, and some private collections throughout the U.S.

DAHLSTROM, ERIC N. 1950-
(attorney)
Education: Beloit College, BA, 1972; University of Wiscosnin Law School, JD, 1976. *Affiliation & Address*: Partner, Rothstein, Donatelli, Hughes, Dahlstrom, Schoenburg & Bienvenu, LLP, 80 E. Rio Salado Parkway, Suite 710, Tempe, AZ 85281 (480) 921-9296. Eric's career has trackd the growth in the practice of Federal Indian law over the past thirty years. He represents tribes in Arizona & Wisconsin and has been involved in nearly every development in the growth of Indian gaming law in both AZ & WI. Also, an active practice in the field of natural resourcces protection & development on behalf of federally recognized Indian tribes & Indian economic enterprises. Mr. Dahlstrom and the firm's other partners were appointed Special Prosecutors by the Navajo Nation's Department of Justice in October 2011 and directed to investigate allegations related to the use of tribal funds. *Past professional posts*: Deputy Attorney General, Navajo Nation, 1987-90; Director, Four Rivers Indian Legal Srrvices, 1979-87; Chair, project dvisory Group, Indian Law Supports Center, 1984-86.

DAILEY, CHARLES 1935-
(faculty emeritus)
Born May 25, 1935, Golden, Colo. *Education*: University of Colorado, BFA-Fine Arts, 1961. Home *Address*: 64 Apache Ridge Rd., RR #3. Santa Fe, NM 87505 (505) 988-6281 ext. 114 (work). *Affiliations*: Curator of Exhibitions, Museum of New Mexico, Santa Fe, NM, 1962-71; Director, Institute of American Indian Arts (IAIA) Museum, Santa Fe, NM, 1971-89; chair, Museum Studies Program, Institute of American Indian Arts College, 1989-2009); Faculty emeritus, IAIA, 2009-present. *Military service*: U.S. Marine Corps, 1953-56 (Sergeant). *Community activities*: Judge for Indian arts & crafts competitions; National Ski Patrol Member, 1960-83; Professional Ski Patrolman, 1962-70. *Memberships*: American Assn for State & Local History, 1956-; MPMA, 1960-80; American Assn of Museums, 1960-; New Mexico Assn of Museums, 1960-85; Native American Museum Assn (charter member). *Awards, honors*: Various artistic painting awards - state & local competitions, 1960-1970; professor of the Year Award from Institute of American Indian Arts, Jr. College, 1974,'76,'82,'86, '90; kayaking - invited to participate in World Championships, Italy, 1961; various whitewater championships, 1958-62; 2009 IAIA Lifetime Achievement Award. *Published works*: Creating a Crowd: Mannikens for Small Museums, El Pacio, MNM Press, 1969; Museum Training Workbooks - IAIA, DOI, BIA, Bureau of Publications, 1973; Art History; Vol. I/II, IAIA, DOI, BIA BOP, 1974; "How to Start an Indian Museum, BIA, IAIA, 1978; Major Influences, Contemporary Indian Art, IAIA, DOI, BOP, 1982; "Museum Theory" BIA, IAIA, 1984; "Museum Problem Solving" BIA, IAIA, 1990; "T.R.C. Cannon", "Bill Soza" IAIA; reviews & articles on various Indian artists, 1978-93.

DAKOTA, FREDERICK (Chippewa)
(tribal councilmember)
Affiliation & Address: Councilperson, Keweenaw Bay Tribal Council, 795 Michigan Ave., Baraga, MI 49908 (906) 353-6623.

DALEY, SEAN M.
(American Indian studies & center director)
Affiliation & Address: Director & Professor of American Indian Studies, Center for American Indian Studies, 12345 College Blvd., Box 36, Overland Park, KS 66210 (913) 469-8500 ext. 4823. E-mail: smdaley@jccc.edu

DALTON, ADAM (Miwok)
(rancheria chairperson)
Affiliation & Address: Chairperson, Jackson Rancheria, P.O. Box 1090, Jackson, CA 95642 (209) 223-1935.

DALTON, MARGARET (Miwok)
(former rancheria chairperson)
Affiliation & Address: Chairperson (30 years), Jackson Rancheria, P.O. Box 1090, Jackson, CA 95642 (209) 223-1935.

DAMES, FATIMA (Pequot)
(tribal vice chairperson)
Education: University of Arizona, BS (Legal Studies; Paralegal Certificate); MA (American Indian Studies with a concentration in Federal Indian Law). *Affiliation & Address*: Vice Chairperson, Mashantuckett Pequot Tribal Nation, 2 Matts Path, P.O. Box 3060, Mashantucket, CT 06338 (860) 396-6100. Ms. Dames is serving her second consecutive term on the Tribal Council, and had previously served on Tribal Council for one term, which began in January 2001. *Other professional posts*: A committed representative for the National Congress of American Indians (NCAI), Ms. Dames is an Alternate Delegate on behalf of the Mashantucket Pequot Tribe; appointed as Alternate Vice President for NCAI's Northeast Caucus. She also serves on the Board of Directors for United South and Eastern Tribes (USET). Ms. Dames is the Chairwoman for the Tribe's Administrative Support and Education Committees, & previously chaired the Economic Development, Judicial, & Natural Resource Protection Committees. *Past professional posts*: Tribal Council Vice Chairwoman, 2012-2014. Prior to serving on Tribal Council, Ms. Dames worked for the Tribal Council as a Special Assistant, with a focus on Legal Affairs; & served as a member of the Tribe's Education & Judicial Committees, Peacemakers Council, Constitution Review Team, and Election Team. She is a strong advocate for Civil Rights, & enjoys spending time with family & friends.

DANA, RALPH (Passamaquoddy)
(tribal chief)
Affiliation & Address: Former Chief, Passamaquoddy Tribe – Pleasant Point, 9 Sakom Rd., P.O. Box 343 • Perry, ME 04667 (207) 853-2600.

DANAY, RICHARD GLAZER (Mohawk of Kahnawake, Canada) 1942-
(retired professor emeritus; artist)
Born August 12, 1942, Coney Island, N.Y. *Education*: California State University, Chico, MA, 1972; University of California, Davis, MFA, 1978. *Address*: 927 Alta Loma Dr., Corona, CA 91720 (714) 735-4347. *Affiliation*: The Rupert Costo Chair in American Indian History, The University of California, Riverside, 1991-93. Retired Professor Emeritus, Dept. of Art & American Indian Studies, California State University, Long Beach, 1985-2006. *Military service*: U.S. Army, Specialist IV, 1961-62; U.S. Army Reserve, 1962-65. *Community activities*: Commissioner, Indian Arts & Crafts Board, U.S. Dept. of the Interior, 1989-. *Memberships*: L'Association Canadienne Des Etudes D'Art Autochtone, 1986-; Native American Art Studies Association, 1983-90; California Indian Education Association, 1970-91. *Awards, honors*: Distinguished Faculty Scholar, California State University, Long Beach, 1990/91. *Interests*: Animal rights activist; exhibited art in over 150 group & one man shows from 1970 to 1992. Art Exhibit/Show Catalogs: "Shared Vision;" Native American Painters and Sculptors in the 20th Century (The Heard Museum, 1991); "Collecting the Twentieth Century," (British Museum, London, 1991-92); "The Human Figure in American Indian Art," (The Institute of American Indian Arts Museum, 1991).

DANFORTH, CRISTINA S. (Oneida of Wisconsin)
(former tribal chairperson)
Affiliation & Address: Former Chairperson, Business Committee, Oneida Nation, P.O. Box 365, Oneida, WI 54155 (920) 869-4354. E-mail: tdanfort@oneidanation. org. *Other professional posts*: Chairperson (2007-present), Native American Bankcorporation. *Past professional posts*: Tribal Treasurer, Business Committee, Oneida Nation; Owner, White Eagle Sports Bar & Grill, Oneida, WI, 2006-10; Gaming Commissioner & Councilperson (1996-2005), Tribal Judge, Oneida Appeals Commission (2007-08), Oneida Nation of Wisconsin, Oneida, WI.

DANFORTH, GERALD (Oneida of Wisconsin)
(former tribal chairperson)
Born on the Oneida Indian Reservation in Wisconsin. *Affiliation*: Former Chairperson (1999-2002, 2005-08), Oneida Nation, P.O. Box 365, Oneida, WI 54155 (920) 869-2214. *Other professional posts*: President, Great Lakes Inter-Tribal Council; delegate, National Indian Gaming Association (NIGA); delegate, National Congress of American Indians. *Past professional posts*: Consultant, National Indian Gaming Association (NIGA). As a special advisor, Mr. Danforth facilitated the design & development of the Indian Gaming National Intelligence Network (www.eagleintel.com); judicial officer, Oneida Appeals Commission, 1995-99. *Military service*: U.S. Navy, 1964-94.

DANFORTH, MELINDA J. (Oneida of Wisconsin)
(tribal vice chairperson)
Affiliation & Address: Vice Chairperson, Business Committee, Oneida Nation of Wisconsin, P.O. Box 365, Oneida, WI 54155 (920) 869-4461. E-mail: mdanforj@oneidanation.org.

DANIELS, JAY (Cherokee)
(BIA realty officer)
Education: Haskell Indian Junior College, 1979-81. *Affiliation & Address*: Realty Officer, Bureau of Indian Affairs (BIA), Midwest Regional Office, 5600 W. American Blvd., Suite 500, Bloomington, MN 55347 (612) 713-4400. *Other professional post*: Faculty, Falmouth Institute, Fairfax, VA. *Past professional posts*: BIA, Rocky Mountain Region, Fort Peck Agency, Poplar, MT, 1985-2005; Western Region, Pima Agency, Sacaton, AZ, 2005-07.

DANIELS, JOHN, JR. (Muckleshoot)
(tribal vice chairperson)
Affiliation & Address: Vice Chairperson, Muckleshoot Tribe, 39015 172nd St., SE, Auburn, WA 98092 (253) 939-3311.

DANKERT, DIANE C.
(editor)
Affiliation & Address: Arizona Tribal Director, Arizona Commission on Indian Affairs, 1645 W. Jefferson, Phoenix, AZ 85007 (602) 255-3123.

DANKS, KAYLA (Three Affiliated Tribes)
(BIA agency supt.)
Affiliation & Address: Supt. Bureau of Indian Affairs, P.O. Box 370, New Town, ND 58763 (627-4707) E-mail: kayla.danks@bia.gov

DANNER, ROBIN (*Puanani*) (Hawaiian)
(Hawaiian council president)
Robin was raised on the Navajo, Hopi and Apache reservations of Arizona and lived 25 years among the Inupiat Eskimo of Alaska. *Affiliation & Address*: Founding President & Chief Executive Officer, Council for Native Hawaiian Advancement (CNHA), 1050 Queen St., Suite 200, Honolulu, HI 96814 (808) 596-8155. The council is a non-profit dedicated to supporting Native Hawaiian communities and the organizations that serve them; operates a public policy center on Native Hawaiian issues, conducts resource development & organizational capacity training, & owns & operates an information technology company in partnership with 11 Indian tribes & Alaska Native firms. *Other professional posts*: Vice chairperson, State Council of Hawaiian Homestead Associations; director, Board of the Inter-Tribal Economic Alliance; serves on the Hawaii Advisory Committee of the Human Rights Commission; overseas the operation of the Native Hawaiian Economic Alliance; member, board of directors, Native American Contractors Association. *Past professional posts*: Vice president, National Bank f Alaska (13 years); executive director, Indian Housing Authority (three years). *Awards, honors*: Received the Alaska Governor's Volunteer of the Year Award and the Small Business Minority Business Advocate of the year from the state of Hawaii. Her expertise is in public & private administration, business & community development with a specialized focus on rural & Native American populations.

DARDAR, THOMAS, JR. (Houma)
(tribal principal chief)
Affiliation & Address: Principal Chief, United Houma Nation, 20986 Hwy. 1, Golden Meadow, LA 70357 (504) 475-6640.

DARDEN, JOHN PAUL (Chitimacha)
(former tribal chairperson)
Affiliation & Address: Chairperson (2009-2015), Chitimacha Tribal Council, P.O. Box 661, Charenton, LA 70523 (337) 924-4973. E-mail: johnp@chitimacha.gov. *Other professional posts*: Memebr of Raintree Market Board of Directors; Inter-Tribal Council, USET Board of Directors. He also weaves Chitimacha baskets and is a Chitimacha historian.

DARDEN, MELISSA (Chitimacha)
(tribal chairperson)
Affiliation & Address: Chairperson (2017-18), Chitimacha Tribal Council,

P.O. Box 661, Charenton, LA 70523 (337) 924-4973. E-mail: melissa.darden@chitimacha.gov

DARDEN, O'NEILL J., JR. (Chitimacha)
(former tribal chairperson)
Affiliation & Address: Chairperson (2016-17), Chitimacha Tribal Council, P.O. Box 661, Charenton, LA 70523 (337) 924-4973. E-mail: oneill.darden@chitimacha.gov.

DARDAR, THOMAS, JR. (Houma)
(tribal principal chief)
Affiliation & Address: Principal Chief, United Houma Nation, 20986 Hwy. 1, Golden Meadow, LA 70357 (985) 475-6640

DARLING, NEDRA (Potawatomi/Cherokee)
(BIA director of public affairs)
Affiliation & Address: Director of Public Affairs, Bureau of Indian Affairs, 1849 C St., NW, MS 4140-MIB, Washington, DC 20240 (202) 208-3711.

DARROW, LELAND MICHAEL (Fort Sill Apache)
(tribal secretary-treasurer; tribal historian)
Education: Univefsity f Oklahoma, 1975-80; Institute of American Indian Arts, 1975-80. *Affiliation & Address*: Secretar-Treasurer (2002-present); Tribal Historian (1986-present), Fort Sill Apache Tribe, Route 2, Box 121 • Apache, OK 73507 (580) 588-2298.

DARTT-NEWTON, DEAN (Coastal Chumash/Californio)
(assistant professor of American Indian studies; museum curator)
Education: University of Oregon, BA, MA, PhD (Cultural Anthropology), Certificate in Museum Studies from the Arts Administration Program. *Affiliation & Address*: Assistant Professor, Department of American Indian Studies, University of Washington, Padelford Hall, C-514, Box 354305, Seattle, WA 98195 (206) 616-9508. E-mail: ddart@u.washington.edu. *Research Interests*: Native American representation in museums, and the role museums play in public or collective memory about Native peoples; California Indian history; revitalization efforts among traditionally marginalized indigenous groups. *Dissertation*: Negotiating the Master Narrative: Museums and the Indian/California Community of California's Central Coast.

DASHENO, WALTER (Santa Clara Pueblo)
(former pueblo governor)
Affiliation & Address: Pueblo of Santa Clara, P.O. Box 580, Espanola, NM 87532 (505) 753-7330.

DAUENHAUER, NORA MARKS (*Keixwnei*) (Tlingit) 1927-
(writer & poet)
Born May 8, 1927, Syracuse, NY. *Education*: Alaska Methodist University, Anchorage, BA, 1976. *Address*: 3740 N. Douglas Hwy., Juneau, AK 99801 (807) 463-4844 (work). *Affiliations*: Tlingit language researcher, Alaska Native Language Center, University of Alaska-Fairbanks, 1972-73; cultural coordinator, Cook Inlet Native Association, Anchorage, AK, 1978-80; translator & principal investigator, Tlingit Text Translation Project, 1980-81; assistant professor, Alaska Native Studies, University of Alaska, Juneau, 1981-82; principal researcher, Language & Cultural Studies, Sealaska Heritage Foundation, 9085 Glacier Hwy., Juneau, AK, 1983-97. *Community activities*: Member and chair, Russian Orthodox Church & Alaska Native Sisterhood; president, Shax'saanikeek' Weavers. *Awards, honors*: Commissioner, Alaska Historical Commission, 1978-81; First Prize in Short Story and Poetry Categories, Southeast Alaska Native Arts Festival, Sitka, AK, 1979; 1980 "Humanist of the Year" by Alaska Humanities Forum (joint award with Richard Dauenhauer); member, Alaska Humanities Forum Committee, 1981-87; 1989 "Governor's Award for the Arts", presented by Alaska Governor Steve Cowper; 1991 American Book Award for Haa Tuwunaagu Yis, for Healing our Spirit: Tlingit Oratory. *Interests*: Tlingit language and literature, poetry, fiction, drama. *Published works*: Beginning Tlingit (Tlingit Readers, 1976) in Tlingit; Co-editor, "Because We Cherish You...": Sealaska Elders Speak to the Future (Sealaska Foundation, 1981) in Tlingit & English; short story anthologized in Earth Power Coming: Short Fiction in Native American Literature, edited by Simon Ortiz (Navajo Community College Press, 1983); Tlingit Spelling Book (revised 3rd edition), with Richard Dauenhauer (Sealaska Heritage Foundation, 1984); poetry anthologized in That's What She Said: Contemporary Poetry & Fiction by Native American Women, edited by Rayna Green (Indiana University Press, 1984); Alaska Native Writers, Storytellers & Orators (special issue of Alaska Quarterly Review, University of Alaska, Anchorage, 1986); Haa Shuka, Our Ancestors: co-editor, Tlingit Oral Narratives (University of Washington Press, 1987); poetry anthologized in Harper's Anthology of 20th Century Native American Poetry, edited by Duane Nitatum (Harper & Row, San Francisco, 1988) in Tlingit & English; The Droning Shaman (The Black Current Press, Haines, AK, 1988) in Tlingit & English; Editor, with Richard Dauenhauer, Haa Tuwunaagu Yis, for Healing our Spirit: Tlingit Oratory (University of Washington Press, 1990) in Tlingit & English; Beginning Tlingit, 3rd Revised

Edition, with Richard Dauenhauer (Sealaska Heritage Foundation, 1991); Haa Kusteeyi, Our Culture (U. of Washington Press, 1994) in Tlingit & English; Life Woven With Song (U. of Arizona Press, 2000); and numerous other writings.

DAUENHAUER, RICHARD 1942-
(poet, writer; retired professor of Alaska Native languages & culture)
Born April 10, 1942, Syracuse, N.Y. Education: Syracuse University, BA, 1964; University of Texas, Austin, MA, 1966; University of Wisconsin, Madison, PhD (Comparative Literature), 1975. *Address*: 3740 N. Douglas Hwy., Juneau, AK 99801 (907) 586-4708. *Affiliations*: Assistant professor, Alaska Methodist University, Anchorage, 1969-75; education specialist, Alaska Native Education Board, Anchorage, 1974-76; staff associate, Alaska Native Foundation, Anchorage, 1976-78; associate professor, Alaska Pacific University, Anchorage, 1979-83; program director, Sealaska Heritage Foundation, Juneau, 1983-97. Richard married into (Nora Marks) and has become an expert on the Tlingit nation of southeastern Alaska. *Community activities*: Reader, parish council officer, St. Nicholas Orthodox Church. *Memberships*: PEN; Poets & Writers. *Awards, honors*: Woodrow Wilson Fellowship, 1964; Fulbright Fellowship, 1966; Named "Humanist of the Year" by Alaska Humanities Forum, 1980 (joint award with Nora Marks Dauenhauer); Poet Laureate of Alaska, 1981-88; 1989 Governor's Award for the Arts, presented by Steve Cowper, Governor of Alaska; 1991 American Book Award for "Haa Tuwunaagu Yis, for Healing our Spirit: Tlingit Oratory"; 2005 President's Professor of Alaka Native Languages & Culture jointly at UAS & UAF; American Book Award for "Russians in Tlingit America"; 2013 recipient of the University of Alaska Founation's Edith R. Bullock Prize for Excellence, in honor of his work in preserving Alaska Native languages, Tlingit in particular. *Interests*: Comparative literature, oral literature, Alaska Native literature, languages & linguistics, poetry. *Published works*: Co-editor, Snow in May: An Anthology of Finnish Writing, 1945-72 (Associated University Presses, Cranbury, NJ, 1978); Glacier Bay Concerto (Poetry) (Alaska Pacific University Press, Anchorage, 1980); co-editor with Nora Marks, "Because We Cherish You...": Sealaska Elders Speak to the Future (Sealaska Heritage Foundation, 1981; The Shroud of Shaawat Seek' (Poetry) (Orca Press, Sitka, AK, 1983); co-editor, Tlingit Spelling Book (Third revised Edition-Sealaska, 1984); co-editor, Alaska Native Writers, Storytellers & Orators (special issue of Alaska Quarterly Review, 1986); Frames of Reference (Poetry) (The Black Current Press, Haines, AK, 1987); co-editor with Nora Marks, Haa Shuka, Our Ancestors: Tlingit Oral Narratives (University of Washington Press, 1987); co-edited with Nora Marks, Haa Tuwunaagu Yis, for Healing our Spirit: Tlingit Oratory (University of Washington Press, 1990; Beginning Tlingit, 3rd revised ed., with Nora Marks Dauenhauer (Sealaska Heritage Foundation, 1991); co-edited with Nora Marks, Haa Kusteeyi, Our Culture: Tlingit Life Stories (University of Washington Press, 1994); with Nora Marks, Russians in Tlingit America: The Battles of Sitka, 1802 & 1804, edited by Lydia T. Black (University of Washington Press, 2008); with Nora Marks, a 4-volume series on Tlingit culture & history.

DAUGHERTY, DANELLE
(BIA deputy regional director)
Affiliation & Address: Deputy Regional Director-Indian Services, Great Plains Regional Office, Bureau of Indian Affairs, 15 4th Ave. Southeast, Suite 400, Aberdeen, SD 57401 (605) 226-7343. E-mail: ddaugherty@bia.gov

DAUGHERTY, JOHN, JR. (Eastern Shawnee/Delaware) 1948-
(health systems administrator)
Born August 9, 1948, Claremore, Okla. *Education*: Northeastern State University, BA, BS, 1976; University of Minnesota, 1984 (certificate in health administration). *Address*: Claremore PHS Indian Hospital, W. Will Rogers & Moore, Claremore, OK 74017 (918) 341-8430. *Affiliation*: Executive director, Native American Coalition of Tulsa, 1978-79; administrator, USPHS Miami Indian Health Center, Miami, OK, 1979-90; Claremore PHS Indian Hospital, Claremore, OK, 1991-. *Military service*: U.S. Air Force, 1969-72 (in Madrid, Spain) (Commendation Medal for Meritorious Service). *Community activities*: Member, Rotary International; chairman, Title IV, Indian Education Parent Committee; officer, Native American Student Assn at Northeast Oklahoma A&M Junior College & Northeastern Oklahoma State University, 1973-76. *Awards, honors*: Who's Who Among Students in American Universities and Colleges, 1976-77; golf team; deans honor roll, 1976, NEOSU, Tahlequah; chosen by University of Minnesota Independent Study Program to give presentation on Indian Health in U.S. during International Health Night, July 17, 1985. *Interests*: "My educational & vocational interest is in health care administration. My goals are to better myself in these areas. Indian cultures and the presentation of my tribal ceremonies are of great concern to me. Participating in tribal activities of other tribes, as well as my tribe and encouraging others to participate are very important to me."

DAUGHETY, SAMUEL
(attorney; Native American law & policy)
Education: Washington University, BA, 2001; University of Arizona, JD, 2004. *Affiliation & Address*: Counsel, Native American Law & Policy Practice,

Dentons LLP, 1301 K St., NW, Washington, DC 20005 (202) 408-6427. E-mail: Samuel.daughety@dentons.com. Sam is a member of Dentons' Public Policy & Regulation practice & Native American Law & Policy practice. Sam has substantial experience advising clients on complex Indian lands and Indian gaming issues, including tribal-state compacts and related agreements, the fee-to-trust process, leasing, regulatory compliance, and tribal governmental and administrative matters. He regularly assists clients in developing viable strategic solutions in the face of legislative and regulatory challenges. He has represented tribal interests in numerous matters before state & federal courts of appeal and in arbitration proceedings. He also has represented national tribal organizations as *amicus curiae* before federal courts on matters with widespread implications for tribal trust lands, federal administrative procedure, and child welfare. Throughout his career, Sam has advised clients on all manner of legal & policy issues related to the Indian Child Welfare Act (ICWA), and has represented tribes and tribal interests in trial and appellate court proceedings involving ICWA in multiple states. Prior to joining Dentons, Sam served as an assistant attorney general for the Tohono O'odham Nation, a federally recognized Indian tribe. In that capacity, he advised the Nation's legislative council, executive branch & departments on a wide variety of matters related to federal Indian law. *Memberships*: Native American Bar Association of Washington, DC; Indian Law Section Executive Council, State Bar of Arizona; Tribal In-House Counsel Association (Associate Member)

DAUT, SHANNON
(executive director)
Education: University of Wisconsin, madison, BA (Film Studies); University of Colorado, Denver, MA (Cmmunications). *Affiliation & Address*: Executive Director (2012-present), Alaska State Council on the Arts, 161 Klevin St., Suite 102, Anchorage, AK 99508 (907) 269-6607. E-mail: shannon.daut@alaska.gov. *Other professional post*: Member of the Governing Board of the National Performance Network. *Past professional posts*: Deputy Director, The Western State Arts Federation (WESTAF), Denver, CO, 2000-2011; co-chair, Create Denver Advisory Committee.

DAVALOS, JOSEPH (Suquamish)
(tribal education superintendent)
Education: La Verne College, BA (History), 1973; Lesley College, MA (Curriculum & Instruction); Seattle Pacific University, MA (Education Leadership). *Affiliation & Address*: Superintendent, Port Madison Suquamish Tribal Education, 5305 Totten Rd., Poulsbo, WA 98370 (360) 394-8566, *Other professional post*: Board member, Tribal Education Departments National Assembly, Boulder, CO.

DAVIES, WADE
(professor & co-chair of Native American studies)
Affiliation & Address: Professor & Co-Chairperson, The Payne Family Native American Center, NAC 203A, Native American Studies Dept., University of Montana, 32 Campus Dr., Missoula, MT 59812 (406) 243-5835. E-mail: wade.davies@mso.umt.edu.

DAVIS, DERRICK SUWAIMA (Hopi, Choctaw)
(artistic director, talent coordinator, singer, dancer)
Derrick is a Plains Indian style singer & dancer. His group, The Living Traditions Dance Troupe, is comprised of various championship artists, each bringing his/her own cultural values & ideals, & expressing them through dance movements. The group involves a variety of dancers, including the following tribes: Hopi, Dine, Lakota, Seminole, Creek, Hidatsa, Apache and Choctaw. All performances are done in a fashion that will educate people & correct misconceptions about Native American music & dance. Dances include Eagle Dance, Fancy Feather Dance, Hoop Dance, and Round Dance. He can be contacted c/o Susan Vargo, The Charles Agency (602) 547-0708. E-mail: info@thecharlesagency.com.

DAVIS, DOUGLAS (Shoalwater Bay)
(former tribal chairperson)
Affiliation & Address: Chairperson, Shoalwater Bay Indian Tribe, P.O. Box 130, Tokeland, WA 98590 (360) 267-6766. E-mail: ddavis@shoalwaterbay-nsn.gov.

DAVIS, GARY "LITEFOOT" (Cherokee)
(entrepreneur; musical performer & actor; author, motivational speaker)
Born March 1, 1969 in Upland, California and raised in Tulsa, Oklahoma. Resides in Seattle, Washington. Website: www.litefoot.com. *Affiliations*: President & CEO, The National Center for American Indian Enterprise Development (NCAIED). Gary traveled to Washington, DC on September 27, 2012 to attend a Business Leaders in Indian Country Forum at the White House. The forum focused on the Obama Administration's programs & initiatives for American Indian & Alaska Native business leaders facing the challenges of doing business in Indian Country and the NCAIED's Native American Global Trade Center (NAGTC). *Other professional posts*: Litefoot produces & hosts his own nationally distributed hip hop & R&B radio show called, "Reach The Rez Radio," (www.reachtherezradio.com) which debuted in

2005. The show is aired weekly through Native Voice One Satellite Network. Litefoot produces several clothing lines the best known being the brand, "Native Style." He tours the U.S. & Canada on music & speaking engagements, "Reach The Rez Tour." He has released ten albums in the past twelve years. His latest CD, "Relentless Pursuit," released in late 2008, had nationwide distribution. Litefoot has also appeared in Hollywood films, such as "The Indian in the Cupboard" (1995), "Mortal Kombat: Annihilation" (1997), "Kull the Conqueror" (1997), and "Adaptation" (2002), and several independent films including, "29 Palms" (2002), "Song of Hiawatha" (1997), and "The Pearl" (2000). He has also appeared on TV programs: "CSI: Miami," "Family Law," and "Any Day Now." *Published work*: The Medicine of Prayer.

DAVIS, JAMES L. (Turtle Mountain Chippewa)
(tribal college president)
Education: Dickinson State University (ND), BA; Penn State University, MEd, DEd; post-doctoral work at the University of California, Los Angeles. *Affiliation & Address*: President, Turtle Mountain Community College, P.O. Box 340, Belcourt, ND 58316 (701) 477-7865. E-mail: jdavis@tm.edu. *Past professional posts*: Dean of Education, United Tribes Technical College, Bismarck, ND; member, Board of Regents, Haskell Indian Nations University, Lawrence, KS; graduate assistant at Penn State University; Assistant Program Director, Native American Leadership Training Program, Penn State University, University Park, PA; Director of Indian Education, ND Dept. of Public Instruction; director of state-wide American Indian Curricular Development Program; Supt. for Education, Turtle Mountain Agency, Bureau of Indian Affairs, Belcourt, ND.

DAVIS, JEFFREY (Turtle Mountain Chippewa)
(assistant U.S. attorney)
Born & raised on a reservation in north central ND. *Education*: University of New Mexico Law School, JD, 1989. *Affiliation & Address*: Assistant U.S. Attorney, Western District of Michigan, P.O. Box 208, Grand Rapids, MI 49501 (616) 456-2404. *Other professional post*: Board member, Native American Children's Alliance, Cleveland, OH.

DAVIS, LYNNE
(director of PhD Indigenous studies program)
Affiliation & Address: Director, PhD Program in Indigenous Studies,, Department of Inigenous Studies, Trent University, 1600 Westbank Dt., Peterborough, ON K9J 7B8 (705) 748-1011. E-mail: lydavis@trentu.ca.

DAVIS, ROBERT E.
(national secretary-organization)
Affiliation & Address: Great Council of U.S. Improved Order of Red Men, P.O. Box 683, Waco, TX 76703 (817) 756-1221.

DAVIS, ROSE-MARIE (Turtle Mountain Chippewa)
(BIE associate deputy director)
Education: University of North Dakota, BA (Social Work, 1975, BS (Elementary Education), 1987, MA (Education), 1982. Completed over 30 doctoral hours in Educational Leadership. She currently holds an Elementary Principal Certification (1993) from Pennsylvania State University and a Superintendent Credential (1998) from the University of North Dakota. *Affiliation & Address*: Associate Deputy Director, Tribally Controlled Schools, Bureau of Indian Education, Department of the Interior, 2001 Killebrew Dr. #122, Bloomington, MN 55425 (952) 851-5427. E-mail: rosemarie.davis@bie.edu. Davis's career in Indian education encompasses nearly 40 years working in public schools, BIE-operated and tribally controlled schools, and tribal colleges and universities. Prior to serving as Acting ADD for Tribally Controlled Schools, Davis served as Acting ADD-East from 2013-2014. From 2011-2012, she was the Education Program Administrator in BIE's Pine Ridge Education Line Office and from 2005-2011 Davis was the Education Program Administrator in BIE's Turtle Mountain Education Line office. She also served as the Field Education Specialist in the Office of Indian Education Programs Turtle Mountain Agency from 2000 to 2005. In addition, Davis has held various positions throughout Indian Country as a school social worker, teacher, special education resource coordinator, principal, and superintendent at White Shield School, Turtle Mountain Elementary and Middle Schools, Ojibwa Indian School, Lame Deer Public School, and Northern Cheyenne School. She has also served as the President of Little Hoop College in Fort Totten, ND and as the Academic Dean at Turtle Mountain Community College in Belcourt, ND.

DAVIS, SCOTT J. (Standing Rock Lakota Hunkpapa/Turtle Mountain Chippewa)
(executive director)
Education: Haskell Indian Jr. College, A.A.; University of Mary, BA, MA. *Affiliation*: Executive Director (2009-present), North Dakota Indian Affairs Commission, 600 East Blvd. Ave. Room 117, Bismarck, ND 58505 (701) 328-2428. E-mail: sjdavis@nd.gov. *Past professional posts*: United Tribes Technical College Development Officer, Wellness Activities Coordinator,

Facilitator & Adjunct Instructor for Introduction to Wellness; Culture Committee Chair &. Powwow Committee Member. Davis also worked for the Standing Rock Sioux Tribe on environmental quality issues and as teacher's aide at the Pierre Indian Learning Center & Turtle Mountain Community High School.

DAVIS, SHERI (Puyallup)
(tribal administrative executive officer)
Affiliation & Address: Administrative Executive Officer, Puyallup Tribe, 3009 E. Portland Ave., Tacoma, WA 98404 (253) 573-7800.

DAVIS, WALLY, JR. (Tonto Apache)
(former tribal vice chairperson)
Affiliation & Address: Former Chairperson, Vice Tribe, #30 Tonto Reservation, Payson, AZ 85541 (928) 474-5000.

DAVIS, YVONNE (Navajo)
(board president)
Affiliation & Address: President, Board of Directors, National Native American AIDS Prevention Center, 436-14th St., Suite 1020, Oakland, CA 94612 (510) 444-2051. E-mail: ydavis@nnaapc.org.

DAVIS-WHITE EYES (Siletz)
(Indian program director)
Education: University of California, Los Angeles, BA & MA; Oregon State University, PhD student of education. *Affiliation & Address*: Director, American Indian Initiatives, Oregon State University, A150 Kerr Administration Bldg., Corvallis, OR 97330 (541) 737-9030. *Other professional post*: Adjunct faculty, Dept. of Ethnic Studies, Oregon State University, Corvallis.

DAWAVENDEWA, SYLVIA (POLACCA) (Hopi-Tewa-Havasupai)
(program facilitator)
Affiliation & Address: The University of Arizona, American Indian Studies, 320A Harvill Bldg., P.O. Box 210076, Tucson, AZ 85721 (520) 626-9110. E-mail: spolacca@email.arizona.edu. Ms. Polacca is responsible for outreach & community development & works with American Indian communities & organizations locally, statewide and nationally.

DAWES, CHARLES (Ottawa)
(tribal chief)
Affiliation & Address: Chief, Ottawa Tribe of Oklahoma, P.O. Box 110, Miami, OK 74355 (918) 540-1536.

DAWSON, RUTH (Eskimo)
(Alaskan village president)
Affiliation & Address: President, Native Village of Afognak, 215 Mission Rd. #212, Kodiak, AK 99615 (907) 486-6014.

DAY, APRIL (Cherokee)
(attorney)
Education: Stanford University, BA (Native American Studies), 2002; Columbia University School of Law, JD, 2007. *Affiliation & Address*: Associate, Kilpatrick Townsend & Stockton, LLP, 607 14th St., NW, Suite 900, Washington, DC 20005 (202) 508-58838. Ms. Day focuses her practice on Native American affairs. She represents tribes in litigation matters in federal, state & tribal courts & federal administrative agencies. April has served as the civil staff attorney for a non-profit tribal corporation and a legal fellow at the Micigan Indian Legal Services. *Admissions*: Shoshone Paiute Tribes Tribal Court; Little River band of Ottawa Indians Tribal Court; Grand Traverse Band of Ottawa & Chippewa Indians Tribal Court.

DAY, DONALD (Ojibwe)
(former Indian college president)
Affiliation & Address: Former President, Leech Lake Tribal College, P.O. Box 180, Cass Lake, MN 56633 (218) 335-4200. E-mail: Donald.day@lltc.edu. *Past professional posts*: President, Fond du Lac Tribal & Community College, Cloquet, MN; director, American Indian Resource Center, Bemidji State University, Bemidji, MN.

DAY, EDNA (Mille Lacs Ojibwe)
(associate administrator)
Affiliation & Address: Associate Administrator, American Indian Studies Department, College of Liberal Arts, 19 Scott Hall, 72 Pleasant St. SE, University of Minnesota, Twin Cities Campus, Minneapolis, MN 55455 (612) 624-7325. E-mail: dsja003@umn.edu.

DAY, KEVIN A. (Miwok)
(tribal chairperson)
Affiliation & Address: Chairperson, Tuolumne Band of Me-wuk Indians, P.O. Box 699, Tuolumne, CA 95379 (209) 928-5300.

DAYLEY, JON P. 1944-
(professor of linguistics)
Born October 8, 1944, Salt Lake City, Utah. *Education*: Idaho State University, BA, 1968, MA, 1970; University of California, Berkeley, MA, 1973, PhD, 1981. *Address*: 5953 Eastwood Place, Boise, ID 83716 (208) 385-1714 (work). *Affiliations*: Visiting lecturer in linguistics, University of California, Berkeley, 1982; professor of linguistics, Boise State University, Boise, ID, 1982-. *Other professional posts*: Linguista - Projecto Linguistico Francisco Marroquin, Guatemala, 1973-78; writer, researcher, Experiment in International Living, Brattleboro, Vt., 1978-79. *Memberships*: Linguistic Society of America; Society of the Study of Indigenous Languages of America; Berkeley Linguistics Society. *Interests*: American Indian languages & cultures: Mayan language--Tzutujil Maya, Uto-Aztecon languages--Shoshone & Panamint; Creole languages; general linguistics. *Published works*: Belizean Creole Handbook, Vols. I-IV (Experiment in International Living, U.S. Peace Corps, 1979); Tzutujil Grammar (U. of California Press, 1985); Tumpisa (Panamint) Shoshone Grammar & Dictionary (two separate books) (U. of California Press, 1989); Western Shoshoni Grammar (Boise State U., 1993); Dictionario Tz'utujil de San Juan la Laguna (Projecto Linguistico Francisco Marroquin, Guatemala, 1994); Shoshoni Texts (Boise State U., 1997); Newe Hupia: Shoshoni Poetry Songs, with Beverly and Earl Crum (Utah State U. Press, 2002); and many articles on Mayan languages, Shoshone & general linguistics.

DEAM, SR., CHUCK (Suquamish)
(tribal vice chairperson)
Affiliation: The Suquamish Tribe, P.O. Box 498, Suquamish, WA 98392 (360) 598-3311. E-mail: cdeam@suquamish.nsn.us.

DEAN, S. BOBO
(attorney)
Education: Yale University, BA, 1954, LLB, 1961; Oxford University (Rhodes Scholar), MA, 1956. *Address & Affiliation*: Co-founder (in 1982), Hobbs, Straus, Dean & Walker, 2120 L St., NW, Suite 700, Washington, DC 20037 (202) 822-8282. E-mail: sdean@hsdwdc.com. *Past professional posts*: Debevoise Plimpton, New York, NY, 1961-65; Strasser, Spiegelberg, Fried, Frank & Kampelman (founded by Felix Cohen whose work in the Indian field was nationally known), 1965-82. His extensive experience in the representation of Indian tribal governments & tribal organizations includes assisting the Miccosukee Tribe of Indians of Florida in negotiating the first contract with the Bureau of Indian Affairs under which an entire BIA agency is administered by a tribal government. Mr. Dean was instrumental in the enactment & implementation of the Indian Self-Determination & Education Assistance Act of 1975, and the 1988 & 1994 amendments to that Act. He served as member of Negotiated Rulemaking Committee that prepared regulations under Title I of the Act as a representative of tribes in Alaska. He has represented Indian tribal & Alaska Native organizations in contracting with federal agencies to operate schools, hospitals, & federal service programs for Indians; he represents tribes & tribal organizations in administrative appeals & litigation to vindicate tribal self-determination rights. He participated in drafting the bill to reauthorize the Indian Health Care Improvement Act that is now under consideration in the Congress.

DEARMAN, JANICE (Cherokee)
(senior director)
Education: Northeastern State University (Tahlequah, Oklahoma), BA & MA (Secondary Education). University of Nevada, Las Vegas, JD. *Affiliation & Address*: Senior Director Diversified Businesses, Cherokee Nation Business LLC, P.O. Box 948, Tahlequah, OK 74465 (918) 384-7474. E-mail: Janice.dearman@cn-bus.com.

DEARMAN, TONY L. (Cherokee)
(director of Bureau of Indian Education)
Born & raised in Oklahoma *Education*: Bacone College, AA, 1989; Northeastern State University (Tahlequah, OK), BS (Education), 1993, MA (School Administration), 2004. *Affiliation & Address*: Director (2017-present), Bureau of Indian Education, Department of the Interior, 1849 C St. NW, MS-3609-MIB, Washington, DC 20240 (202) 208-6123. E-mail: tony.dearman@bie.edu *Past professional posts*: Tony brings over two decades of experience as a teacher, coach, and administrator in BIE operated and tribally controlled schools. He began his career in education in 1993 at Sequoyah High School as a science teacher and coach. Sequoyah is a boarding school operated by the Cherokee Nation of Oklahoma, located in Tahlequah Oklahoma. He served as the principal at Sequoyah High School from 2004-2005. In January of 2006, Dearman accepted the leadership role of Superintendent at Riverside Indian School. Riverside is an offreservation boarding school operated by the Bureau of Indian Education. It serves grades 4-12 and is located in Anadarko, Oklahoma. From 2008-2009 he was the acting Education Line Officer for the Seattle, Washington Office. While in this position, Dearman worked with nine tribally controlled schools and one BIE operated off-reservation boarding school. From 2009-2010 he served as the Education Line Officer for the BIE New Mexico South Office. While serving the New Mexico South office, he worked with four tribally controlled and five BIE operated schools. In 2010,

Dearman returned to Riverside Indian School as the Superintendent. During Mr. Dearman's tenure at Riverside, he participated in the development and planning of a new academic high school building and two residential dormitories. He remained in this position until November of 2015 when he was selected as the Associate Deputy Director of BIE Operated Schools. While serving in this position, he has assisted in the implementation of the BIE Reorganization and Reform. As Associate Deputy Director, he oversaw 17 schools, 4 offreservation boarding schools, and one peripheral dormitory spanning across eight states.

DeBOER, ROY J. (Lummi) 1936-
(retired school principal)
Born July 23, 1936, Bellingham, Wash. *Education*: Olympic Junior College, AA, 1960; Western Washington State University, BA, 1962; University of Puget Sound, Tacoma, Wash., MEd, 1981. *Address*: 3528 S.E. Pine Tree Dr., Port Orchard, WA 98366. *Affiliations*: Director of Indian Education, South Kitsap School District, Port Orchard, WA, 1973-80; principal, Wolfe Elementary School, Kingston, WA, 1981-2012. *Other professional posts*: Seven years on Washington State Advisory Committee, Indian Education to Washington State Supervisor of Schools. *Military service*: U.S. Air Force, 1954-58 (A 1/C). *Community activities*: Pacific Lutheran Theological Seminary (board of directors); Division of Service & Mission in America, American Lutheran Church (board of directors); Chamber of Commerce, Kingston, Wash.; Sons of Norway, Poulsbo, WA. *Memberships*: National Education Assn; Washington Education Assn; ASCD; ESPA. *Awards, honors*: Outstanding Secondary Teacher of America, 1973; Quill & Scroll Adult Leadership Award, 1969. *Interests*: Reading, travel, photography; singing with Twana Dancers, Skokomish traditional dance group.

DeCAMP, LINDA
(Indian education program coordinator)
Affiliation: Big Bay de Noc School, Indian Ed., 1250 N. Oaks St., Davison, MI 48423 (810) 591-3531. E-mail: ldecamp@mail.davison.k12.mi.us.

DeCOLA, JERI (Tonto Apache)
(tribal chairperson)
Affiliation & Address: Tonto Apache Tribe, 18 Tonto Reservation, Payson, AZ 85541 (928) 474-3988.

DeCOTEAU, JERILYN MONETTE (Turtle Mountain Ojibwe)
(attorney; director of policy)
Education: University of Oregon Law School, J.D. *Address & Affiliation*: Director of Policy (2007-president) First Nations Development Institute, The Stores Bldg., 11917 Main St., Fredericksburg, VA 22408 (540) 371-5615. E-mail: jdecoteau@firstnations.org. She will lead First Nation's policy & advocacy work at the tribal, state & federal levels developing policy, with emphasis on articulating a strategy for asset building in Indian Country. *Other professional posts*: Adjunct professor at DU Law School and is a judge on her tribe's appellate court. She has practiced Indian law for 25 years. *Past professional posts*: Staff attorney at the Native American Rights Fund; trial attorney at the Dept. of Justice in the Indian Resources Section; director of the Indian Law Clinic, University of Colorado Law School; counsel for the Turtle Mountain Ojibwe Tribe.

DeCOTEAU, TAMMY (Sisseton-Wahpeton Oyate)
(director of language program)
Affiliation: Association on American Indian Affairs, P.O. Box 509, Agency Village, SD 57262 (605) 698-4400. E-mail: tdc.aaia@verizon.net.

DeCOTEAU, TROY (Turtle Mountain Ojibwe)
(tribal chairperson)
Affiliation: Turtle Mountain Band of Chippewa Indians, P.O. Box 900, Belcourt, ND 58316 (701) 477-2600.

DEER, ADA E. (Menominee) 1935-
(director-Indian studies program)
Born August 7, 1935, Keshena, Wis. *Education*: University of Wisconsin, Madison, BA, 1957; Columbia University, School of Social Work, MSW, 1961. *Affiliation & Address*: Distinguished Lecturer Emerita, American Indian Studies Program, University of Wisconsin, 317 Ingraham Hall, 1155 Observatory Dr. Madison, WI 53706 (608) 263-5501. E-mail: aedeer@wisc.edu. *Other professional post*: Fellow, Harvard Institute of Politics at the John F. Kennedy School of Government, 2000-present. *Past professional posts*: Lecturer, School of Social Work & Native American Studies Program, University of Wisconsin, Madison, WI, 1977-93; assistant secretary, Bureau of Indian Affairs, Washington, DC, 1993-2000; chairperson, Menominee Restoration Committee, 1973-76; vice president & Washington lobbyist, National Committee to Save the Menominee People & Forest, Inc., 1972-73; chairperson, Menominee Common Stock & Voting Trust, 1971-73; chaired the Native American Rights Fund. *Community activities*: American Indian Policy Review Commission (member, 1975-77); Ada helped implement American

Indian participation in the Peace Corps. *Memberships*: National Association of Social Workers; National Organization of Women; Common Cause; Girl Scouts of America; Democratic Party of Wisconsin; National Congress of American Indians. *Awards, honors*: Honorary Doctorates from University of Wisconsin & Ohio State University; Northland College, Ashland, WI; White Buffalo Council Achievement Award, Denver, CO, 1974; Pollitzer Award, Ethical Cultural Society, NY, 1975; Fellow at the Harvard Institute of Politics, John F. Kennedy School of Government, Cambridge, MA, 1977; first member of her tribe to receive a master's degree; she became the first woman chair of the Menominee Nation, first American Indian woman to run for the Congress & Wisconsin's secretary of state; and first woman appointed assistant secretary for Indian Affairs, U.S. Dept. of the Interior. *Interests*: Social work; community organization and social action; minority rights.

DEER CLOUD, SUSAN ANN (*Deer Cloud*) (Mohawk/Seneca/Blackfoot) 1950-
(writer; professor of creative writing)
Born October 20, 1950, Livingston Manor, N.Y. *Education*: Binghamton University, BA, 1980, MA, 1982. *Principal occupation*: Writer; professor of creative writing. *Address*: 45 Vine St., Apt. 2, Binghamton, NY 13903 (607) 723-3816. E-mail: sdeercloud@stny.rr.com. *Affiliation*: Binghamton University, Binghamton, NY. *Community activities*: Do readings & talks at the university & in the community; bring Native people to Binghamton University to perform/read. *Membership*: Poets & Writers, AWP, Wordcraft Circle of Native Writers & Storytellers. *Awards, honors*: New York State Foundation for the Arts Poetry Fellowship, 1993. *Poetry honors*: "Indian Interlude," Honorable Mention in New Letters 1990 Poetry Competition; "Singularities," 1st Prize, Paterson's Poetry Center's International Poetry Contest; "Potato," finalist in Eve of St. Agnes Competition, 1993; Prairie Schooner's Reader's Choice Award, 2003; among others. *Interests*: "Primarily interested in writing both stories & poetry that often contain an interweaving of Indian themes. I started a "tribe" of writers, with the Binghamton Underground Poets, Wild Indians, and Exuberant Others, UNC - we do readings in various venues in Binghamton, NY; I also like photography, reading, hiking, and traveling to just about anywhere. I am also deeply involved with Indian issues, which I try to express in my work." *Published works*: The Sacred Hoop (Blue Cloud Press, 1988); In the Moon When the Deer Lose Their Horns (Chantry Press, 1993).

DEERINWATER, DAN
(BIA regional director)
Affiliation & Address: Director, Southern Plains Regional Office, Bureau of Indian Affairs, P.O. Box 368, Anadarko, OK 73005 (405) 247-6673. E-mail: dan.deerinwater@bia.gov

DEERNOSE, KITTY BELLE (Crow) 1956-
(museum curator)
Born April 14, 1956, Crow Agency, Mont. *Education*: Institute of American Indian Arts, Santa Fe, NM. *Principal occupation*: Museum curator. *Address & Affiliation*: Little Bighorn Battlefield National Monument, P.O. Box 39, Crow Agency, MT 59022 (406) 638-2621. E-mail: kitty-deernose@nps.gov (1990-). *Community activities*: Plenty Coups Museum, Advisory Board member; Little Bighorn College, School-to-Work Governing Board. *Memberships*: American Association of Museums; Museum Assn of Montana; Montana Plains Museum.

DeGROAT, JENNIE (Navajo)
(Bilingual/multicultural education instructor)
Education: University of New Mexico, BA, MA (Bilingual, Multicultural Education). *Affiliation*: Instructor, American Indian Language Development Institute (AILDI), University of Arizona, Dept. of Language, Reading & Culture, College of Education, Rm. 517, 1430 E. Second St., P.O. Box 210069, Tucson, AZ 85721 (520) 621-1068. *Other professional post*: Teaching courses in bilingual/multicultural education at the Northern Arizona University, Flagstaff, AZ. *Memberships*: National Council of Teachers of English; National Association for Bilingual Education; National Indian Education Association. Jennie's work involves educating Native American communities across the country about language loss issues and revitalization in creating speakers.

DeJOLIE, LEROY (Navajo)
(business owner)
Affiliation & Address: Owner, Navajoland Images, 13421 N. 43rd Ave. #2111, Phoenix, AZ 85029 (602) 439-3946. Website: www.imagesofarizona.com. E-mail: info@dejolie.com. Mr. DeJolie is a fine art photographer & holds photo workshops. Member of "Friends of Arizona Highways."

DELA ROSA, VINCE (Oneida of WI)
(tribal councilman)
Affiliation: Councilman, Oneida Nation of Wisconsin, P.O. Box 365, Oneida, WI 54155 (920) 869-4378. E-mail: vdelaro1@oneidanation.org. Website: www.oneidanation.org. *Past professional posts*: Vice chair, Oneida Nation Gaming Commission; president, American Indian Justice Coalition. Vince has helped create a viable small business funding instrument (Oneida Small Business Project 2000) which has helped many Oneida business people pursue their business dreams. *Community activities*: Chairman, Legislative Operating Committee; Joint Tribal State Relations Committee; member, Green Bay Area Chamber of Commerce Board of Directors.

DeLaCRUZ, JOSEPH (Quinault)
(former tribal chairperson)
Address & Affiliation: Quinault Business Committee (chairperson, 1970-94), P.O. Box 189, Taholah, WA 98587 (206) 276-8211.

DeLaTORRE, JOELY (Pechanga Band of Luiseno) 1969-
(associate professor of public administration)
Born March 2, 1969, San Bernardino, Calif. *Education*: California State University, Long Beach, BA, 1993; Northern Arizona University, MA, 1995, PhD (Political Science with emphasis Public Policy & American Indian Studies), 1999. Her dissertation focused on Tribal gaming and was entitled, "Interpreting Power: The Power & Politics of Tribal Gaming in Southern California." *Principal occupation*: Associate professor of Public Administration. *Address*: Dept. of Public Administration, California State University, San Bernardino, CA. E-mail: joely@joelydelatorre.com. *Affiliations*: Associate Professor of Public Administration, California State University at San Bernardino, 2005-present; lecturer of American Politics, Dept. of Political Science, University of San Diego, CA. *Other professional posts*: Owner & Founder of "Naqmayam Communications," a full service California Indian owned & operated public relations agency promoting socially conscious marketing & consumer & cultural education; 2nd Vice Chair, Native American Caucus of the California Democratic Party, Sacramento, CA; serves as executive producer for the documentary entitled, "I Is Not For Indian," which explores the controversy of how Native American curriculum is taught in our public schools. *Past professional posts*: Lecturer, California State University, Long Beach, 1993; lecturer. Northern Arizona University, Flagstaff, AZ, 1995-96; Dept. Chair & Professor of American Indian Studies, San Francisco State University, 1996-2004. *Community activities*: Campaign spokesperson for the "Yes on Proposition 5" Campaign: The Indian Self-Reliance Initiative; board member, California Indian Museum & Cultural Center; served as Special Advisor to California Lt. Governor Bustamonte for California Indian Sovereign nations in 2002. She has testified before state legislators on the California Indian education issues and works side-by-side with tribal leaders & state legislators to implement new legislation to benefit California Indians. *Awards, honors*: First recipient of the American Political Science Association Native Fellows Program; received the California Teachers Association's "Salute to Friends of Education Award," the "Opportunities Unlimited, 2002 Award; the "John F. Kennedy, Jr. Award for Outstanding Public Service"; and recipient of the "National Native American Bo Jack Humanitarian Award." *Memberships*: American Political Science Association; Native American Caucus; executive director of California Indian Professors Association; member, National Congress of American Indians Telecommunications Committee. *Published works*: American Indian Political Power in the New Millennium (University of Texas Press, 2007).

DELABREAU, JOAN (Menominee of Wisconsin)
(tribal chairperson)
Affiliation & Address: Chairperson, Menominee Indian Tribe of Wisconsin, P.O. Box 910, Keshena, WI 54135 (715) 799-5100.

DELANEY II, CHARLES L. (*Megeso-Soaring Eagle*) (Mazipskwik Abenaki) 1957-
(contractor, missisquoi masonry)
Born March, 21, 1957, Burlington, Vermont. *Address*: P.O. Box 5862, Burlington, VT 05402 (802) 863-6002. *Affiliations*: Local #6 Masons, Washington, DC, 1977-81; Federal Government sub-contractor, 1982-89; private & Historic Restoration, State of Vermont, General Contractor, 1990-present. *Other professional posts*: At-large representative, Missisquoi Abenaki Nation; lecturer in anthropology & social history, Abenaki history at the University of Vermont & Community College of Vermont; United Nation's Delegate representing Mazipskik Abenaki at Indigenous Forums. *Awards, honors*: Former ambassador to State of Vermont, U.S. Government, Washington, DC. *Community activities*: Property Committee, Unitarian Universalist Society, Burlington, VT; Red Path member; Burlington-BILWI Sister City program (Vermont-Nicararagua); board of directors, Green Mountain Project; working to promote self-reliance with Abenakis & Moskitia, Mayanga Aboriginals in Nicaragua thru non-profit community projects. *Memberships*: Mazipskwik Abenaki; director, Waubanawin Society; Aboriginal Non-profit Co-op between First Nations peoples. *Interests*: Indian legal affairs - representing Abenakis on state & federal government affairs; traditional, cultural & religious practices of Abenakis; work-training for Moskitia youth in traditional home repairs, construction. *Published works*: Wabanawin Society information pamphlet; non-profit public interest letters.

DeLEON, DEBORAH Odawa)
(tribal vice chairperson)
Affiliation & Address: Vice Chairperson, Little Traverse Bay Bands of Odawa Indians, 7500 Odawa Circle, Harbor Springs, MI 49740 (231) 242-1418.

DELGADO, C. PETE (Tohono O'odham)
(executive director)
Affiliation & Address: Executive Director, Tohono O'odham Ki:Ki, P.O. Box 790, Sells, AZ 85634 (520) 383-2202. E-mail: pdelgado@tokahousing.org.

DELGADO, DALE "CHAD" (Paiute)
(former tribal chairperson)
Affiliation & Address: Bishop Paiute Tribe, 50 Tu Su Lane, Bishop, CA 93514 (760) 873-3584. E-mail: chad.delgado@bishoppaiute.org.

DELGADO, EDWARD (Oneida)
(former tribal chairperson)
Affiliation & Address: Oneida Nation of Wisconsin, P.O. Box 365, Oneida, WI 54155 (920) 869-2214. E-mail: edelgado@oneidanation.org.

DELLINGER, KEVIN W. (Muscogee Creek)
(tribal secretary)
Education: Baker University (Baldwin City, KS), BS in Accounting; Oklahoma City University School of Law, JD. *Affiliation*: First Secretary of the Nation of the Muscogee (Creek) Nation since 2008, P.O. Box 580, Okmulgee, OK 74447 (918) 732-7605. *Past professional post*: Assistant Attorney General for the Muscogee (Creek) Nation, 1996-2008.

DELMAR, CHARISSA (Navajo)
(research specialist)
Education: University of Arizona, College of Fine Arts in Media Arts, BA (with emphasis in Film & Television Studies and a minor in American Indian Studies). *Affiliation & Address*: Research Analyst, Educational Resources Program, Native Nations Institute for Leadership, Management & Policy, Udall Center for Studies in Public Policy, The University of Arizona, 803 East First St., Tucson, AZ 85719 (520) 626-0664. E-mail: cdelmar@email.arizona.edu

DeLORME, EUGENE
(attorney; director)
Education: J.D. *Affiliation & Address*: Director, Indians Into Medicine (INMED), University of North Dakota, School of Medicine & Health Sciences, UNDSMHS. Rm. 2101, Stop 9037, Grand Forks, ND 58202 (701) 777-3037. E-mail: Eugene.delorme@med.und.edu.

DeLONG, LORETTA
(BIA education administrator)
Education: PhD (Education). *Affiliation*: Turtle Mountain Agency, Bureau of Indian Affairs, School St., P.O. Box 30, Belcourt, ND 58316 (701) 477-3463.

DELORIA, ELLA CARA (Standing Rock Lakota)
(author)
Published works: Waterlily (novel); The Dakota Way of Life (Mariah Press, 2009).

DELORIA, PHILIP J. (Standing Rock Lakota)
(historian; professor)
Education: University of Colorado, BME (Music Education), 1982, MA (Journalism & Communications), 1988; Yale University, PhD (History), 1994. *Affiliations & Address*: Professor of American Culture & History & Faculty, Native American Studies; Dept. of History, 2216 LSA, University of Michigan, 435 S. State St., Ann Arbor, MI 48109 (734) 764-6305. E-mail: pdeloria@umich.edu. *Other professional post*: President's Advisory Committee on Culturally Unaffiliated Human, NAGPRA, 2009-present. *Past professional posts*: Former LSA Associate Dean of Undergraduate Education. *Memberships*: American Historical Association; Western Historical Association; Native American & Indigenous Studies Association; American Studies Association (president, 2008-09); Organization of American Historians (council member, 2007-2010; Volunteer Lectureship Program, 1998-present); Smithsonian National Museum of the American Indian (Board of Trustees, 2009-2011). *Awards, honors*: Son of author, Vine Deloria, Jr.; IMPART Award, University of Colorado, 1994; Gustavus Myers Outstanding Book Award, for "Playing Indian," 1999; John C. Ewers Prize for Ethno-historical Writing, Western History Association, 2006 (for "Indians in Unexpected Places"); Michigan Society of Fellows, 2008-2013. *Published works*: Playing Indian (Yale University Press, 1998); Blackwell Companion to Native American History, with Neal Salisbury, Eds. (Blackwell Publishers, 2002); This Land: A History of the U.S., with David Burner, Jack Rakove & Patricia Nelson Limerick (Brandywine Press, 2003); Indians in Unexpected Places (University of Kansas Press, 2004); C.G. Jung & the Sioux Traditions: Dreams, Visions, Nature, and the primitive by Vine Deloria, Jr., c-edited with Jerome Bernstein (Spring Journal Press, May 2009); Crossing the (Indian) Color Line: A Family Memoir with

Philip Deloria (1989 International House Lectures (773) 753-2274). *Video Documentary*: Producer, Director & Editor, "Eyanopapi: Heart of the Sioux," 1989.

DELORIA, PHILIP (SAM) (Standing Rock Lakota)
(former director-American Indian Graduate Center)
Education: Yale University, BA; Yale University Law School, JD. *Affiliation & Address*: Former Director (35 years), American Indian Graduate Center (www.aigcs.org), 3701 San Mateo Blvd. NE #200, Albuquerque, NM 87110 (505) 881-4584 ext. 112. E-mail: sam@aigcs.org. *Past professional post*: Director (35 years), American Indian Law Center, University of New Mexico, School of Law, Albuquerque, NM; founder & first Secretary-General of the World Council of Indigenous People; in 1976, was one of the founders of the Commission on State-Tribal Relations. *Memberships*: National Institutional Review Board for the protection of human subjects of research, established by the Indian Health Service.

DeLOS ANGELES, ANDY (Snoqualmie)
(tribal chief)
Affiliation & Address: Chief, Snoqualmie Indian Tribe, P.O. Box 969, Snoqualmie, WA 98065 (425) 888-6551.

DeLUCIA, CHRISTINE
(assistant professor of history)
Education: Harvard College, BA; Yale University, MA, M.Phil, PhD; University of St. Andrews, Scotland, M.Litt. *Affiliation & Address*: Assistant Professor of History, Mount Holyoke College, 50 College St., 302 Skinner Hall, South Hadley, MA 01075 (413) 538-2451. E-mail: cdelucia@mtholyoke.edu. *Other professional post*: Co-Chairperson, Five College Native American & Indigenous Studies, 97 Spring St., Amherst, MA *Specialties:* federal Indian law, criminal jurisdiction in Indian Country, tribal sovereignty, federal acknowledgment of tribes, identity. Christine specializes in indigenous and colonial histories of North America, particularly in the Northeast/New England. Her current research is on the conflict known as King Philip's War (1675-1678), which violently transformed Algonquian & Euro-American settler communities in the late seventeenth century. This war—one of the formative events of early America—did more than momentarily disrupt these societies. It dramatically altered the balance of power in the Northeast, and shaped how subsequent generations have understood themselves, their entangled histories, and their presence on lands that remain disputed. As DeLucia's work shows, memories of this war & related violences continue to inflect discourses about sovereignty, dispossession, decolonization, & regeneration. DeLucia approaches early American and indigenous histories in an interdisciplinary manner. Besides working extensively in regional & local archives, she also draws upon material & visual culture—such as paintings, household objects, and family heirlooms—archaeological sources, ethnography and oral history, and the land itself. Her goal is to bring into the historical conversation voices, perspectives, and narratives that have tended to be overlooked or marginalized by dominant conceptions of the past, and to stress the dynamic, contested character of history-making. DeLucia has published articles in *The Journal of American History*;*Studies in American Indian Literatures*; *Re-thinking History: The Journal of Theory & Practice*; and *Common-place*. Her first book,*The Memory Frontier: Memorializing King Philip's War in the Native Northeast* is under contract with Yale University Press. Her research has received support from the John Carter Brown Library, American Antiquarian Society, Massachusetts Historical Society, New England Regional Fellowship Consortium, & Phillips Fund for Native American Research from the American Philosophical Society. Other sources of grants & awards include the Newberry Consortium in American Indian Studies, the Council on Library & Information Resources/ Mellon Foundation, Gilder Lehrman Center for the Study of Slavery, Resistance, & Abolition. At Mount Holyoke, DeLucia teaches The American Peoples to 1865; Native American History; Violence in Early North America; Homelands and New Worlds; Cartography and Exploration in North America; and The Atlantic World.

DeMAIN, PAUL (*Oshscabewis*) (Oneida/White Earth Ojibway) 1955-
(editor)
Born October 8, 1955, Milwaukee, Wis. *Education*: University of Wisconsin, Eau Claire, AA, 1975-77. *Affiliation & Address*: Managing Editor & CEO, News From Indian Country, P.O. Box 1500, 8558N County Road K, Hayward, WI 54843 (715) 634-5226 Fax (634-3243. *Affiliations*: Manager, Lac Courte Oreilles Graphic Arts, 1979-80; acting director, Great Lakes Indian News Association, 1980-82; self determination information officer, Lac Courte Oreilles Tribal Government, 1980-82; managing editor, Lac Courte Oreilles Journal, Hayward, WI, 1977-82; advisor on Indian affairs policy to Governor Anthony S. Earl, State of Wisconsin, 1983-87; secretary-treasurer, Native Horizons, 1983-; CEO, Indian Country Communications, 8558N County Road K, Hayward, WI 54843, 1987-. *Other professional posts*: Native American Journalists Association (NAJA) (treasurer, 1991-92; president, board of directors, 1992-); president of UNITY 94 & 99, an alliance of the National Association of African American Journalists, Asian American Journalists

Association, National Association of Hispanic Journalists, and NAJA. 1999 Green Party Vice Presidential Campaign Manager for Winona LaDuke. *Community activities*: Governor's representative, State Council on Alcohol and Other Drug Abuse, 1983-87; lay counselor, Lac Courte Oreilles Tribal Court, 1980-; board member, Lac Courte Oreilles Honor the Earth Education Foundation, 1980-; volunteer, WOJB Radio, Hayward, WI, 1980-; representative, Governor's Council on Minority Business Development, 1983-88; planning committee, National Indian Media Conference; Governor's Interstate Indian Council Executive Board, 1986-88; advisory board, Center for Mining Alternatives, 1980-82; member, Northwestern Wisconsin Mining Impact Committee, 1980-82; member, Governor's Study Committee on Equal Rights, 1977. *Memberships*: National Congress of American Indians (conference planning committee, 1983); Native American Press Assn (Board of Directors, 1986-88). *Published works*: North America's Indian Country Gaming Guide & The Powwow Directory (Indian Country Communications); publisher of "News From Indian Country," a national twice-monthly newspaper located on the Lac Courte Oreilles Ojibway reservation of northern Wisconsin; also, "Explore Indian Country" (Indian Country Communications) a monthly enter-tainment tabloid & distributes native language materials & books.

DeMALLIE, RAYMOND J.
(professor of anthropology; institute co-director; museum curator)
Education: University of Chicago, BA, 1968, MA, 1970, PhD, 1971. *Principle occupation*: Professor of anthropology & American studies; adjunct professor of folklore. *Address & Affiliation*: Co-Director, American Indian Studies Research Institute, Indiana University, 422 N. Indiana Ave., Bloomington, IN 47408 (812) 855-4086. E-mail: demallie@indiana.edu. *Other professional post*: Curator of North American Ethnology, Mathers Museum. *Expertise*: *Fieldwork*: The geographical area of his studies is North America, with emphasis on Plains Indians especially Sioux society & culture; topical areas include kinship & social organization, ritual & belief systems, oral traditions & material culture. Since 1970, he has done fieldwork on reservations in the Dakotas, Montana, and Saskatchewan, Canada, where Sioux and the closely related Assiniboine peoples live. Much of my field study has been linguistics, recording texts of historical traditions, myths & tales. More recently, in collaboration with Douglas R. Parks, Professor DeMallie has become involved in projects to teach the Sioux and Assiniboine languages, both on reservations and at IU. *Published works*: Editor, with Elaine Jahner, Lakota Belief & Ritual by James R. Walker (University of Nebraska Press, 1980, new ed. 1991); The Sixth Grandfather: Black Elk's Teachings Given to John G. Neihardt (University of Nebraska Press, 1984; Sioux Indian Religion: Tradition & Innovation University of Oklahoma Press, 1987 with Douglas R. Parks); North American Indian Anthropology: Essays on Society & Culture, with Alfonso Ortiz (University of Oklahoma Press, 1994); Documents of American Indian Diplomacy: Treaties, Agreements, and Conventions, 1775-1979, 2 vols. (editor, with Vine Deloria, Jr.; University of Oklahoma, 1999); Editor, Handbook of North American Indians, Vol. 13: Plains, William Sturtevant, General Editor (Smithsonian Institution Press, 2001).

DEMARAY-BAKER, TWYLA (Mandan Hidatsa)
(Indian college president)
Education: Bismarck State College, BA; University of North Dakota, PhD. *Affiliation & Address*: President, Nueta Hidatsa Sahnish College (formerly, Fort Berthold Community College), 220 8th Ave. N., P.O. Box 490 • New Town, ND 58763 (701) 627-4738.

DeMEYER, TRACE A. (*Winyan Ohmanisa waste la ke*) (Cherokee) 1956-
(freelance photo-journalist; independent scholar)
Born September 9, 1956, St. Paul, Minn. *Education*: University of Wisconsin-Superior, BFA (Drama/Communications). *Principal occupation*: Freelance photo-journalist, independent scholar. *Address*: 25 Keegan Lane, Unit 8-6, Greenfield, MA 01301 (413) 772-6996. E-mail: tdemeyer@verizon.net. Website: www.quantumdragonfly.com. *Affiliations*: Editor, Ojibwe Akiing (regional Ojibwe newspaper), 1997-1998; staff writer, News From Indian Country (Wisconsin independent Native newspaper), 1996-present; editor, The Pequot Times, Mashantucket Pequot Tribal newspaper), Mashantucket, CT, 2000-present; Wiping the Tears, memoirs of a Native American adoptee, Spring 2005, Talking Stick Newsletter, New York City. *Other professional posts*: Lecture on Native American Journalism, Gateway Community College, 2004; other guest lectures, poetry readings; media interviews. *Community activities*: Growing a Green Community Fair, 2005; Reading is Fundamental volunteer, 2005. *Memberships*: Native American Journalists Association; Mashantucket Pequot Museum & Research Center; National Museum of the American Indian. *Awards, honors*: NAJA Media Award, General Excellence for News From Indian Country, 1996 & 1997; NAJA Media Award - Best News Story Award, Honorable Mention, "Free Peltier"; Presenter on Native Media, 6th Annual (2000) Crime Prevention & Drug Elimination Conference "Catching Our Dreams" at Foxwoods, Mashantucket, CT; NAJA General Excellence Award: Honorable Mention - Pequot Times, 2001; 2001 NAJA Award for Best Feature Writing, The Film "Kusah Hakwaan"; 2002 NAJA Award for Best News Writing Monthly (2nd Place) "America Stands United in the Shadow of

Tragedy" (9-11 coverage); NAJA Award: Pequot Times Best Layout & Design, Tabloid 2002 (1st Place) & 2003 (2nd Place); NAJA Award: Pequot Times Monthly General Excellence (2nd Place), 2003; NAJA Media Award: Best Feature Writing - An Interview with Historic Eastern Pequot Tribe (2nd Place), 2003; Trace's writings is being archived by the Native American Press Archives at the University of Arkansas in Little Rock. Her work is also published and available on the Ethnic Newswatch archives in private and public libraries. Interests: Slavery of Indigenous people (book: First Contact). *Writings*: Contributing author of "Honor Restored, Jim Thorpe's Olympic Medals, The Olympics at the Millennium: Power, Politics and the Games 2000, edited by Shaffer & Smith (Rutgers Press, 2000. Chapter 2, pages 38-50). *Poetry*: Spirit in the Words poetry collection by Native Americans, 1999 & 2004 (Bozelll Worldwide/DaimlerChrysler); Tracy's Journal Collection, circa 1965-2005 (project underway) (Donation to UAR). *Fiction*: All Hearts Beating (in progress); Plays: Apple Anatomy; The Opening; The Sign; William Deer; Children Stories: Red Man, Through the Eyes of Many. *Research*: Power Politics and the Pequot: The Richest Indians in America, presented at the 26th American Indian Workshop, Munich, Germany, April 2005. Ms. DeMeyer's website: www.quantumdragonfly.com, includes her essay "Earth Tribes," poetry, and early draft of "Wiping the Tears."

DEMIENTIEFF, SAMUEL S. (Eskimo)
(former BIA agency supt.)
Addresses & Affiliations: Supt., Fairbanks Agency, Bureau of Indian Affairs, Fairbanks, AK; executive director, Fairbanks Native Association, 310 1st Ave., 2nd Floor, Fairbanks, AK 99701 (907) 452-1648.

DEMPSEY, L. JAMES (*Kitsemonisi - High Otter*) (Blood) 1958-
(historian)
Born September 20, 1958, Calgary, Alberta, Can. *Education*: University of Calgary, BA, 1985, MA, 1987; University of East Angelia (England), 1992- (PhD candidate). *Principal occupation*: Historian. *Address*: 7944 - 85 Avenue, Edmonton, AB, Can. T6C 1C2 (403) 492-2991. *Affiliation*: Director of the School of Native Studies, University of Alberta, Edmonton, AB, Can., 1992-; professor, Saskatchewan Indian Federated College, Saskatoon, SK, Can., 1987-92. *Interests*: As a member of the Blood tribe, my interests have centered on the Northern Plains culture & history with a particular emphasis on Blackfoot Indians & warfare. I have also studied the role of Canadian Indians in World War I & World War II. Currently, I am studying the significance of Blackfoot pictography to warfare. *Published works*: Problems of Western Canadian Indian War Veterans After World War I (Native Studies Review, 1989); editor, Treaty Days (Glenbow Museum, 1991).

DENET, DOROTHY KATHERINE (*Pephise*) (Hopi)
(lecturer, consultant, entrepreneur)
Born in Kearns Canyon, Ariz. *Education*: Northland Pioneer College, AA, 1989. *Principal occupation*: Lecturer, consultant, entrepreneur. *Address*: P.O. Box 210, Polacca, AZ 86042 (602) 737-2534. *Affiliations*: General Manager, Hopi Cultural Center, Second Mesa, AZ; vice-president, Secakuku Enterprises, Second Mesa, AZ; president, Polingyami, Inc., Polacca, AZ, 1992-. *Other professional posts*: lecturer, Northern Arizona University, Elder Hostel Program, Flagstaff, AZ, 1990-; lecturer, Yavapai College Elder Hostel Program, Prescott, AZ, 1990-. *Community activities*: Arizona State Tourism Advisory Council (appointed by Governor, 1988-94); Arizona State Employment & Training Advisory Council (appointed by Governor, 1989-94); Applied Economics/Junior Achievement, Hopi Jr.-Sr. High School (business consultant, 1990-); Arizona Strategic Planning for Economic Development, Native American Coalition & Tourism Cluster, member, 1989-92. *Memberships*: Arizona Coalition for Displaced Homemakers, Governor's Office for Women, 1989-94; Arizona Tribal Private Industry Council (chairperson-member, 1987-89); Hostelling International (America Youth Hostel), Arizona Chapter, Board of Directors, member, 1992-). *Interests*: "Tourism, particularly as related to Indian reservations; economics-cultural compatibility; employment & training - Job Training Partnership Act on tribal reservations and their congruence with the states including women in non-traditional training, jobs; women's issues - cultural impact & changes."

DENETDALE, JENNIFER NEZ (Dine'/Navajo)
(associate professor of American studies)
Affiliation & Address: Associate Professor, Native American Studies, 430 Humanities, Albuquerque, NM 87131 (505) 277-3929. E-mail: jdenet@unm.edu. Jennifer specializes in Navajo history & culture; Native American women, gender, and feminism; and Indigenous nations, colonialism, and decolonization. *Other professional post*: Member, Advisory Board, First Peoples: New Directions in Indigenous Studies, Tucson, AZ. *Awards, honors*: She is the first ever Dine'/Navajo to earn a PhD in history; recently reappointed to the Navajo Nation Human Rights Commission by Johnny Naize, Speaker of the Navajo Nation Council. *Published works*: Reclaiming Dine' History: The Legacies of Navajo Chief Manuelito & Juanita (University of Arizona Press, 2007); The Long Walk: The Forced Exile of the Navajo (Chelsea House, 2007); The Navajo (Chelsea House, 2011).

DENETSOSIE, LOUIS (Dine'/Navajo)
(attorney general-Navajo Nation)
Address & Affiliation: Attorney General, The Navajo Nation, P.O. Box 9000, Window Rock, AZ 86515.

DENNISON, JEAN (Osage)
(professor of anthropology & American Indian studies)
Affiliation & Address: Assistant Professor of Anthropology & American Indian & Indigenous Studies, Department of Anthropology, 409-E Alumni Bldg. CB #3115, University of North Carolina, Chapel Hill, NC 27599 (919) 843-1557. E-mail: jeandennison@unc.edu. "My current research focuses on the implementation of constitutional democracy in the Osage Nation. As a citizen of the Osage Nation, I deeply committed to critically interrogating settler colonial systems of power, as well as indigenous responses to this entanglement." *Published work*: Colonial Entanglement: Constituting a Twenty-First-Century Osage Nation (U. of Noth Carolina Press, 2012); numerous articles.

DENNISON, WALLACE E., III (Ramapough Lenape) 1973-
(tribal administrator)
Born October 18, 1973, in Rockland County, N.Y. Graduated the Pomona (NY) Fire Training Academy. *Affiliation*: Tribal council (2003-present), Ramapough Lenape Indian Nation, P.O. Box 103, Hillburn, NY 10931 (201) 529-1171. *Other professional post*: Member, Hillburn Fire Dept. *Community activities*: Founder & president of Ramapough Family Genealogical & Historical Society that preserves the genealogical & historical presence of all Ramapough Indians and their descendants.

DENNY, RUTH (*Zibiquah*) (Potawatomi/Winnebago/Oneida) 1957-
(newspaper editor)
Born November 11, 1957, in Milwaukee, Wisc. *Education*: University of California, Berkeley. *Address & Affiliation*: Editor, The Circle, Minneapolis American Indian Center, 1530 E. Franklin Ave., Minneapolis, MN 55404 (612) 871-4749. *Membership*: Native American Journalists Association.

DENSON, BEASLEY (Mississippi Choctaw)
(former tribal chief)
Born in the Conhatta Community and raised in the Standing Pine Community. *Education*: Hinds Community College & Mississippi State University. *Affiliation & Address*: Miko, Mississippi Band of Choctaw Indians, 101 Industrial Rd., Choctaw, MS 39350 (601) 656-5251. *Past professional posts*: He served on the tribal council as both secretary/treasurer and vice-chief, and served on numerous boards, the Choctaw Housing Authority Board for ten years, the tribal school board for eight years, the Choctaw Credit Union Board of two years, the Choctaw Gaming Commission Board for two years, the Choctaw Development Enterprise Board, the Choctaw Utility Commission; the National Indian Education Board, and Board of the United South & Eastern Tribes.

DePOE, ROBERT R. (Salish/Kootenai)
(former tribal college president)
Affiliation & Address: Former President, Salish Kootenai College, P.O. Box 70, Pablo, WA 59855 (406) 675-4800. E-mail: Robert_depoe@skc.edu.

DeROIN, DEE ANN, MD (Ioway of Kansas)
(physician)
Education: University of New Mexico, American Indian Graduate Center, BA; University of California, Berkeley, MA; Stanford University, MD. *Affiliations*: Twenty years experience practicing family medicine & health education; consultant in community & women's health since 2001, primarily with the National Indian Women's Health Resource Center, Tahlequah, OK. E-mail: deedoc@earthlink.net. *Other professional posts*: Nominating Chairperson, Board of Directors, Association on American Indian Affairs, Rockville, MD. Website: www.indian-affairs.org; member, Board of Directors, American Indian Graduate Center, Albuquerque, NM 87109.

DEROUEN, ELIZABETH ELGIN (*Eh'La Puti'A - Fying Feather*) (Pomo) 1964-
(rancheria band chairperson; ICWA advocate)
Born February 12, 1964, Santa Rosa, Calif. *Education*: AS/Juvenile Corrections; Court Reporting Graduate. *Principal occupation*: Rancheria Band chairperson; ICWA advocate. *Address*: P.O. Box 607, Geyserville, CA 95441 (707) 431-2388. E-mail: Liz@dry-creek-rancheria.com. *Affiliation*: Dry Creek Rancheria Band of Pomo Indians, Geyserville, CA (vice chair, 1996-2000; chair, 2000-present). *Other professional post*: ICWA advocate, 1994-present; Statewide Tribal Steering Committee member, CNIGA. *Memberships*: NAIC; CNIGA, NIGA. *Interests*: Athletics, music, traditional wellness ceremonies.

DERWIN, TIMOTHY (Sault Ste. Marie Ojibwe)
(Indian youth activities director)
Address: Sault Ste. Marie Tribe JTPA, 1919 14th Ave. N., Escanaba, MI 49829.

DESCHAMPE, DEAN (Ojibwe)
(tribal secretary/treasurer)
Affiliation & Address: Secretary/Treasurer, Grand Portage Band of Lake Superior Chippewa, P.O. Box 428, Grand Portage, MN 55605 (218) 475-2277.

DESCHAMPE, NORMAN W. (Ojibwe)
(tribal president/chairperson)
Affiliations & Address: Chairperson, Grand Portage Band of Lake Superior Chippewa, P.O. Box 428, Grand Portage, MN 55605 (218) 475-2277. E-mail: norman@grandportage.com. *Other professional post*: President, Minnesota Chippewa Tribe, Cass Lake, MN.

DESERLY, ELIZABETH (Kickapoo)
(tribal child welfare specialist)
Affiliation & Address: National Child Welfare Resource Center for Tribes, 501 N. Sanders St., Suite 2, Helena, MT 59601. E-mail: Elizabeth@nrc4tribes.org.

DESERLY, KATHY (Kickapoo)
(associate director)
Affiliation & Address: Associate Director (2009-present), National Child Welfare Resource Center for Tribes, 501 N. Sanders St., Suite 2, Helena, MT 59601. E-mail: kathy@nrc4tribes.org. Founding Board member of the Indian Child & Family Resource Center based in Helena, MT (2004-present); Kathy has provided technical assistance to states & tribes, & assisted in the development of statewide Tribal child welfare associations, She spent 12 years working in tribal communities in So. California, and assistant director of a Native American foster & adoption agency before being a policy analyst & technical assistance specialist for National Indian Child Welfare Assn.

DESIDERIO, DANTE (Sappony)
(executive director)
Affiliation & Address: Executive Director (2007-present), Native American Finance Officers Association, 1101 30th St., NW Suite 500, Washington, DC 20007 (202) 631-2003. E-mail: dante@nafoa.org.

DESJARLAIT, ROBERT (*Akoongiss*) (Red Lake Ojibway) 1946-
(artist, writer)
Born November 18, 1946, Redlake, Minn. *Principal occupation*: Artist, writer. *Address*: 5901 Rhode Island Ave., N., Minneapolis, MN 55428 (612) 535-0091. *Art/cultural consultant*: Minnesota Center for Arts Education, Minneapolis; 1993; Four Winds Ojibwe/French Language School, Minneapolis, MN, 1993; Saturn School of Tomorrow, St. Paul, 1994; Minneapolis Institute of Arts, 1994; American Indian Movement, Minneapolis, 1994; University of Minnesota, - Weisman Gallery, Minneapolis, 1995; Minnesota Historical Society, St. Paul, 1995; Migizi Communications, Side-by-Side Program, Minneapolis, 1996. *Other professional posts*: Art instructor, Heart of the Earth Survival School, Minneapolis, MN, 1989-90; art director & curriculum developer, Northern Winds Community Arts Project, Minneapolis, 1992-95; Native arts history teacher, NAES College, Minneapolis, 1996; traditional arts teacher, American Indian OIC, Minneapolis, 1996; Native arts history teacher, Lac Courte Oreilles Community College, Minneapolis, 1996. *Commissions*: Minnesota Indian Women's Resource Center, Minneapolis, 1991; MN Museum of American Art, St. Paul, 1992; Phillips Gateway Project, Minneapolis, 1993-95; Philips Neighborhood Safe Arts Project, Minneapolis, 1995; Minneapolis Indian Education Program, 1996. *Community activities*: Minneapolis Institute of Arts Advisory Panel on Art of the Americas, 1993; "Promoting Social Change Through the Arts: A Conference for Activists & Artists in Grass Roots Community Organizations," Headwaters Fund, Minneapolis, 1994; Native Arts Circle Advisory Panel on Artists in Education, Minneapolis, 1995. *Awards, honors*: Ojibwe Art Expo, 1985 2nd Place - Drawing, 1987 2nd Place - Painting, 1988 1st Place - Drawing; 1988 Percy Fearing Award - Illustration, Minnesota Council on the Teaching of Foreign Languages; CUE Award, Minneapolis Commission on the Arts, 1995. *Biographical sources*: "DesJarlait Depicts Ojibwe Vision," Red Lake Times, Nov. 1987; "Minnesotan Culturally Diverse Artists," Minnesota Monthly, July 1992; "Interview - Robert DesJarlait," Northern Light and Insights (Video), Minneapolis Public Library Artist/Author Series, 1992; "Patrick DesJarlait & Family: Red Lake Ojibway Tradition," Resources for Indian Schools: Minnesota Indian Artists, 1996. *Published works*: Author - O-do-i-daym Ojibway: Clans of The Ojibway Coloring Book (Minnesota Indian Women's Resource Center Press, 1989); Nimiwin: A History of Ojibway Dance (Anoka-Hennepin Press, 1991). Illustrator - Sparrow Hawk, by Meridel Le Seur (Holy Cow Press, 1987); Cherish The Children (MIWRC Press, 1987); Young Child, Old Spirit (MIWRC, 1990); The Spirit Within - Encouraging Harmony & Health in American Indian Children (Minnesota Indian Women's Resource Center Press, 1992); Rethinking Stereotypes: Native American Imagery in European & Euro-American Art (Anoka-Hennepin Press, 1993); "No-ko-miss Wa-kai-gan," essay in Ojibway Family Life in Minnesota: 20th Century Sketches (Anoka-Hennepin Press, 1993); "Patrick DesJarlait: Art of Tribe & Culture," exhibition catalog, "Patrick DesJarlait and the Ojibway Tradition," Minnesota Museum of American Art, St. Paul, 1994; Art of the Ojibway: Traditional to Contemporary (Northern Winds Desktop Press, 1996);

"Niimiwin: An Ojibway Dance Curriculum Coloring Book (Northern Winds Desktop Press, 1996); "Contest Powwow Vs. Traditional Powwow & the Role of the Native American Community," article in Wicazo Sa Review, U. of Minnesota Press, 1997.

DESMARAIS, MICHELE MARIE (Canadian Metis/Dakota)
(professor of Religious Studies & Native American Studies)
Born & raised in Vancouver, British Columbia, Canada. Education: Simon Fraser University, BA (Psychology); University of British Columbia, MA (Religious Studies), PhD (Asian Studies). Address & Affiliation: Associate Professor of Religious Studies & Native American Studies, 205M AS, University of Nebraska, Omaha, 6001 Dodge St., Omaha, NE 68182-0213 (402) 554-2679. E-mail: mdesmarais@unommaha.edu. Past professional post: Editor of the Journal of Reigion & Film. Awards, honors: Her book, "Changing Minds," was included as one of 250 foundationl texts in the field of Science & Religion by the International Society for Science & Religion. Published work: Changing Minds: Mind, Consciousness & Identity in Petanjali's Yoga-sutra & Cognitive Neuroscience (Motillal Banarsidass, Delhi, India, 2008).

DeSOTO, CLAUDE "LARRY" (Tule River Yokut)
(638 contracts coordinator)
Address: P.O. Box 589, Porterville, CA 93258 (559) 781-4271. Membership: Americans for Indian Opportunity.

DeSOTO, RANDI (Paiute)
(tribal vice chairperson)
Affiliation & Address: Vice Chairperson, Summit Lake Paiute Tribe, 1708 H St., Sparks, NV 89431 (775) 827-9670. E-mail: randi.desoto@summitlaketribe.org

DeVAULT, PENNY
(tribal representative))
Education: Leech Lake Tribal College, AA; Bemidji State University (working towards a B.A. in Indian Studies). Affiliation & Address: District I Representative, Leech Lake Tribal Council, 190 Sailstar Dr. NW, Cass Lake, MN 56633 (218) 335-8200. Other professional post: Recently selected to sit on the Minnesota Chippewa Tribe Health & Human Services & Education Sub-Committee. Past professional posts: Dean of Student Services, Leech Lake Tribal College, Cass Lake, MN. Penny grew up just outside the village of Inger and has spent a majority of her life living & working on the Leech Lake Reservation. Prior to being elected as Representative, Penny worked as Executive Assistant to the District I Representative for six years where she gained valuable experience and vast knowledge of the internal and external operations of the Band; also working hand in hand with the five Local Indian Councils of District I as well as the at-large LIC's Twin Cities & Duluth. Penny has served as Chairperson of the Winnie Dam LIC which allowed her first hand insight into the needs, wishes, and dreams for their communities and the pride each & every community member holds. The office of the District I Representative attends all District I LIC meetings along with all community events & cultural activities. Before beginning her career in Tribal Government, Penny worked at the Leech Lake Tribal College as a federal work study student providing administrative support, to eventually becoming Dean of Student Services. Penny was employed as Office Manager for the Health Division, then Tribal Health Director for the Leech Lake Band of Ojibwe.

DEVERS, CHRISTOBAL C. (Pauma-Yuima Luiseno)
(tribal vice chairperson)
Affiliation: Chairperson (2001-present), Pauma-Yuima Band of Mission Indians, P.O. Box 369, Pauma Valley, CA 92061 (760) 742-1289. Past professional posts: Rural Community Assistance Corporation (2000-2007) - provided technical assistance and training on water & wastewater operation & maintenance to tribal operators; served as Water Master for Pauma Tribe, 1992-2000, assisted the tribe on the development of their water resource management program. Military service: U.S. Army, 1972-76.

DEVINE, DIANA YAZZIE (Navajo-Dine')
(president & CEO)
Education: Arizona State University, MBA; International & State licenses in substance abuse counseling. Affiliation & Address: President & CEO, Native American Connections, 4520 N. Central Ave. #600, Phoenix, AZ 85012 (602) 254-3247. E-mail: d.devine@nativeconnections.org. Diana has been working with Native American urban & tribal entities since 1972 and has been employed by NAC since 1979. She dedicates her time to local, state and national boards/committees including: Founding board member Native Home Capital & People of Color Network; current advisory boards: St. Joseph's Hospital & Medical Center; Maricopa Integrated Health System Audit & Compliance; City of Mesa Housing; Arizona State University Lodestar Center for Phlanthropy & Nonprofit Innovation. Awards, honors: Valley Leadership's Woman of the Year (2003); ONE (Organization for Nonprofit Executives) Executive Director of the Year (2006); YWCA's Tribute to Women – Business

Leader Award (2008); Foothills Magazine's Women Who Move the Valley (2010); Arizona's Centennial Legacy Project – Arizona's 48 Most Intriguing Women (2012) & Phoenix Business Journal's 25 Most Admired CEOs (2012).

DEWEES, SARAH
(senior director of research policy & asset-building programs)
Education: Oberlin College, BA, 1990; Ohio University, MA (Sociology), 1992; University of Kentucky, PhD (Rural Sociology), 1998. Affiliation & Address: Senior Director, Research, Policy & Asset-Building Programs, First Nations Development Institute, 351 Coffman St., Suite 200, Longmont, CO 80501 (303) 774-7836. Past professional posts: Research Project Manager, Center for Civil Society Studies at Johns Hopkins University; Rural Policy Research Institute; taught at the University of Kentucky & Towson University.

DIAMOND, BILLY (Cree) 1949-
(politician)
Born May 17, 1949, at Waskaganish, Quebec, Can. Education: Bawating Collegiate & Vocational High School (5 year arts & science program, graduated in June 1968). Principal occupation: Politician. Address: P.O. Box 9, Waskaganish, Quebec, Can. J0M 1R0 (819) 895-8971. Affiliations: On-the-job-training, Dept. of Indian Affairs & Northern Development, Val D'or, Quebec; band manager, 1969-71; chief, 1970-76, Rupert House Band, Rupert House, Quebec; communications worker, 1972, regional chief, 1972-74, Indians of Quebec Association, Huron Village, Quebec; grand chief, Grand Council of the Crees (of Quebec), Rupert House, Quebec, 1974-84; chairman & school commissioner for Cree Regional Authority, 1976-88; chairman/grand chief, Cree Regional Authority, Val D'or, Quebec, 1978-84; chairman & president, Cree Housing Corporation, 1984-87; president, Air Creebec, Inc., 1982-; proprietor, Diamond Brothers Enterprises Registered, 1983-; chief Waskaganish Band Council, James Bay, Quebec, re-elected 1988-. Other professional posts: Member, Board of Directors, Creeco (Cree Regional Economic Enterprises Co.) & Cree Construction Co., 1980-; president, Native Peoples Television Network, 1982-; chairman, Board of Advisors, National Native Bible College, 1984-; Band councillor, Waskaganish Band Council, P.O. Box 60, Waskaganish, P.Q., James Bay J0M 1R0, 1984-; president, Waskaganish Enterprises Development Corporation (WEDCO), 1985-; member, Board of Directors, Construction Regional Authority, Northern Flood Committee, Manitoba, 1985-; chairman, Cree-Yamaha Motor Enterprises Ltd., 1986-; member, Board of Directors of the Grand Council of the Crees and the Council of the Cree Regional Authority, 1984-. Awards, honors: Inducted as a Knight in the Order of Quebec, Jan. 15, 1987.

DIAMOND, JAMES
(Indian law clinic director; professor of practice)
Affiliation & Address: Director & Professor of Practice, Indigenous Peoples Law & Policy (IPLP) Tribal Justice Clinic, The University of Arizona, James E. Roger College of Law, RH 304, P.O. Box 210176, Tucson, AZ 85721 (520) 626-9762. E-mail: jamesdiamon@email.arizona.edu. Diamond completed his Doctor of Juridical Science (SJD) with IPLP in 2014. His doctoral dissertation focused on reconciliation after mass shootings & the history of criminal dispute resolution among the Red Lake Band of Chippewa Indians & other indigenous communities. His academic publications include research about law enforcement in Indian Country & tribal membership litigation. Prior to earning his SJD, Diamond practiced law for 27 years, including serving as a Connecticut Assistant State's Attorney, managing a law firm, and being a criminal prosecutor & defense attorney. Certified by the National Board of Trial Advocacy as a Criminal Trial Specialist, Diamond has tried more than 30 jury trials to verdict. Over the course of his career he has represented clients in pre-trial hearings, trials, and appeals, defending more than 1,000 criminal cases. He is admitted to practice law in the states of Arizona, New York, & Connecticut, the Pascua Yaqui Tribal Court, the Mashantucket Pequot Tribal Court, and numerous federal trial and appellate courts. In addition to teaching in the Bachelor of Arts in Law and Master of Legal Studies programs at Arizona Law, Diamond is a faculty member at the National Tribal Trial College, a collaboration between the Southwest Center for Law and Policy and the University of Wisconsin School of Law. He advises Indian tribes and has conducted training of tribal court prosecutors, defense lawyers, and judges on trial skills and ethics in tribal courts. "I'm thrilled to join the world class faculty at IPLP," said Diamond. "This faculty has literally written the book on Indian law and international human rights for indigenous peoples. The program is well known for engaging students in cutting edge litigation and advocacy, and I'm looking forward to expanding hands-on casework for our students in the new Tribal Justice Clinic. My career has emphasized two principal forums: the courtroom and the classroom.

DIAZ, VICTORIA (Kumeyaay Diegueno)
(tribal vice chairperson)
Affiliation & Address: Vice Chairperson, San Pasqual Band of Diegueno Indians, P.O. Box 365, Valley Center, CA 92082 (760) 749-3200.

DICK, GEORGIA (Cherokee)
(director of Indian education)
Address & Affiliation: Director of Indian Education, Tahlequah Public Schools, District I-35, P.O. Box 517, Tahlequah, OK 74465 (918) 458-4162, 1990-present. *Community activities*: Sponsor of "Native Reflections," a youth group focused on performing community projects & addressing community needs. Students utilize classroom skills in all their activities; Briggs Community Organization, Tahlequah, OK. *Memberships*: National Indian Education Assn; National Coalition for Indian Education; Oklahoma Council of Indian Education; National Dropout Prevention Network; National Johnson O'Malley Assn; National Service-Learning Assn; Tahlequah Parent-Teacher Assn.

DICK, LEROY S. (Navajo) 1943-
(health systems administrator)
Born December 15, 1943, Shiprock, N.M. *Education*: Loretto Heights College, Denver, BA, 1975; Leslie Graduate School, MA, 1984. *Principal occupation*: Health systems administrator. *Address*: P.O. Box 836, Shiprock, NM 87420 (505) 632-1801. *Affiliation*: Vice-president of Management Board, Navajo Tribal Utility Authority, Ft. Defiance, AZ; director, Dzilth-Na-O-Dith-Hle PHS Indian Health Center, Bloomfield, NM. Other professional post: Counseling psychologist. *Military service*: U.S. Army, 1965-67 (E-5 Sergeant, 7th Division; Outstanding Leadership Award, 12/66 while serving in Korea). *Community activities*: Vice-president, School Board, Central School District 22, 1981-; board member, Four Winds Alcoholic Treatment Center. Memberships: National Institute of Business Management, Inc.; National Rural Electric Co-op Association; American Public Power Association. *Awards, honors*: "I am the only American Indian to receive a 7th Division Outstanding Leadership Award for Outstanding Performance"; Recognition of High Quality of Performance, PHS - Shiprock, NM, 1973; Letter of Commendation for Outstanding Performance, PHS - Shiprock, 1974; Recognition of Appreciation for Outstanding Services in EEO Program by Marlene E. Haffner, M.D., NAIHS, Window Rock, AZ, 1975. *Interests*: " In my spare time, the family will travel to Rock Point, AZ where we manage a small herd of cattle, takes up a lot of our time and something I enjoy doing."

DICKSTEIN, HOWARD
(attorney)
Resides in Sacramento, California. Represents California Indian tribes—cutting deals with governors and paving the way for the state's $7 billion-a-year Indian casino industry. Helped defend about 200 Oglala Lakota and followers of the American Indian Movement against charges stemming from the 71-day occupation of Wounded Knee, South Dakota on the Pine Ridge Indian Reservation—has come under the microscope for amassing great wealth at the expense of his clients. Negotiated the compacts for three of the region's top casinos:Jackson Rancheria Casino & Hotel,Cache Creek Casino ResortandThunder Valley Casino Resort.

DIDESCH, BRUCE
(attorney)
Education: Colorado College, BA (Political Science), 1974; University of Idaho, College of Law, JD, 1980. *Affiliation & Address*: Of Counsel, Crowell Law Office – Tribal Advocacy Group, 10 N. Post, Suite 445, Spokane, WA 99201 (509) 209-6038. Email: bdidesch@att.net. *Other professional post*: Adjunct professor, Indian Law Curriculum, Gonzaga University School of Law, 2003-present. *Past professional posts*: Attorney, Colville Confederated Tribes Legal Office, Nespelem, WA, 1985-95; assistant U.S. attorney, U.S. Attorney's Office, Eastern District of Washington, 1995-2000; general manager, Northern Quest Casino, Kalispel Tribe of Indians, 2000-02; corporate counsel (2003-05), Interim CEO, 2005-07), corporate counsel (2007-09), Colville Tribal Enterprise Corporation, Nespelem, WA.

DIEHL, JOSEPH B.
(attorney; executive director)
Affiliation & Address: Principal, Diehl & Co. LLC, c/o Loveridge Hunt & Co. PLLC, 14725 SE 36th St., Suite 401, Bellevue, WA 98006 (206) 290-5498. E-mail: joseph.diehl@gmail.com. *Other professional post*: Executive Director, Northwest Indian Housing Association, Seattle, WA.

DIETZ, ELISABETH (*Miigiisdeahkwe*) (Sault Ste. Marie Chippewa) 1941-
(art gallery manager)
Born February 16, 1941, Sault Ste. Marie, Mich. *Education*: College. *Principal occupation*: Art gallery manager. *Address & Affiliation*: Manager/resident artist, Bawating Native Art Gallery, 558 East Spruce St., Sault Ste. Marie, MI 49783 (906) 632-0530 ext. 53529. *Community activities & Interests*: Help elders & volunteer with the local Anishnabe (Chippewa) School. "I teach herb gathering and pipe-carving to young people. I am what you call a medicine woman, an artist and a pipe-maker; a published author, and a tribal elder/pipe carrier. *Published works*: Star of Bethlehem (American Federation of Astrologers {Tempe, AZ}; Now Is the Hour (native prophecies) (Blue Dolphin Press {CA}).

DIETZ, JERRY
(editor)
Affiliation: Susquehanna Valley Native American Eagle, P.O. Box 99, Walnut Valley Farm, Loganville, PA 17342 (717) 428-1440.

DIETZ-BELL, ELISABETH (*Miigesiiahkwe*) (Sault Chippewa)
(traditional medicine; pipe-maker)
Address: P.O. Box 1685, Sault Ste. Marie, MI 49783. *Community activities*: Teach traditional arts & crafts in Bawating Art Gallery; storyteller; work with children and elders. *Published work*: Star of Bethlehem; Now Is the Hour: Native Prophecies (Blue Dolphin).

DILLNER, JERRY R. (Seneca-Cayuga)
(tribal chief)
Affiliation & Address: Chief, Seneca-Cayuga Tribes, P.O. Box 1283, Miami, OK 74355 (918) 542-6609.

DILLON, GRACE L. (Anishinaabe)
(professor of English & Native American studies)
Affiliation & Address: Associate Professor, English & Native American Studies, 225 Extended Studies Bldg., Indigenous Nations Studies, Portland State University, P.O. Box 751, Portland, OR 97207 (503) 725-8144. E-mail: dillong@pdx.edu. Grace teaches undergraduate & graduate courses on a range of interests including Native American and Indigenous studies, science fiction, Indigenous cinema, popular culture, race and social justice, and early modern literature. Her work appears in diverse journals including The Journal of Science Fiction Film & Television; Foundation: The International Review of Science Fiction; Extrapolation; The Journal of the Fantastic in the Arts; The Historical Journal of Film, Radio & Television; Science Fiction Studies; and Renaissance Papers. *Published works*: Hive of Dreams: Contemporary Science Fiction From the Pacific Northwest (Oregon State University Press, 2003); editor, Walking the Clouds: An Anthology of Indigenous Science Fiction (University of Arizona Press, 2012); numerous articles in scholarly journals.

DILLON, HESTER M. (Cherokee)
(development director)
Affiliation & Address: Director of Development, Indian Law Resource Center, 602 N. Ewig St., Helena, MT 59601 (406) 449-2006 ext. 105.

DILWEG, RORY (Oneida of Wisconsin) 1972-
(attorney; Indian law firm partner)
Education: University of Wisconsin, BA, 1993; University of Wisconsin Law School, JD, 1996. *Affiliation & Address*: Partner, Tilden McCoy & Dilweg LLP, 13310 Maxella Ave., Unit 10, Marina Del Rey, CA 90292 (213) 915-4172. E-mail: rdilweg@tildenmccoy.com. He represents Indian tribal governments through-out the United States in all aspects of the law; including: gaming, taxation, corporate issues, health care, child welfare, grant writing and compliance, and negotiations with state and local governments. He has participated in gaming compact negotiations in Wisconsin and California, as well as acted as lead negotiator for intergovernmental agreement discussions in both states. He has also successfully assisted Indian tribes navigate the complicated process of funding and operating Tribal Temporary Assistance for Needy Families programs. *Past professional posts*: Prior to joining Tilden McCoy + Dilweg LLP, he started Birch Tree Law, a boutique Indian law firm. Before forming Birch Tree Law, he was a partner in the Indian Law Practice Group at Holland & Knight LLP. At Holland & Knight LLP, he provided tribal governments with expert representation in all areas affecting Indian tribes. Mr. Dilweg assisted tribes in California and Wisconsin with land-into-trust applications, gaming management agreements, & environmental issues associated with large-scale gaming & development projects. Rory worked on discreet issues for individual tribes as well as broad policy issues affecting all of Indian Country. Before joining Holland & Knight LLP, Rory served as in-house counsel for the Oneida Tribe of Indians of Wisconsin for over six years, including two years as Chief Counsel of the Tribe's legal department. As Chief Counsel, Mr. Dilweg managed a seven attorney office and provided day to day legal advice to the government of the Oneida Tribe. Prior to becoming Chief Counsel, he was lead attorney for several tribal departments, including the Oneida Health Center and the Oneida Utilities Department. Rory is currently admitted to the State Bars of Wisconsin and California, and various Federal courts throughout the United States. *Membership*: Federal Bar Assn, the Native America Bar Assn, the Wisconsin Bar Assn, & the California Bar Assn. Mr. Dilweg has been a member of the Wisconsin Bar's Indian Law Section for the past fifteen years and has twice served as an officer. During his career Rory has been a featured speaker at public events on topics ranging from the Indian Child Welfare Act to Indian gaming to Tribal TANF.

DIRACLES, JAMES C. 1948-
(attorney, Indian law)
Education: Colorado College, BA (English), 1970; University of Minnesota, JD, 1973. *Affiliation & Address*: Attorney, Best & Flanagan LLP 60 South Sixth

Street, Suite 2700 Minneapolis, Minnesota 55402 (612) 339-7121. His practice focuses on financing, securities, mergers and acquisitions, general corporate law, and Native American law including tax, financing & business development matters. He serves small to medium-sized public corporations, private businesses, start-ups, real estate developers & Native American clients by offering them an experienced point of view from which to confront the legal issues. His projects include representing both buyers & sellers in corporate acquisitions, a variety of corporate and governmental financings, as well as advising outside board members and special committees on issues such as SEC enforcement actions. Jim's work with Native American tribes has included restructuring trusts for Tribal children to achieve tax-deferred status and obtaining a ruling from the IRS that tribal housing program benefits are not subject to income taxation. As part of his work for Native American tribes, Jim has arranged a wide variety of different financings including financings up to $280 million for casino expansion from a variety of lenders. Awards, honors: Jim has been named a "Super Lawyer" (1999-present) and a "Top Ten Merger and Acquisition Lawyer". In his spare time, he likes to garden, collect coins, and travel.

DIVER, KAREN R. (Lake Superior Chippewa)
(former tribal chairperson)
Affiliation & Address: Former Chairperson, Fond du Lac Band of Lake Superior (Ojibwe) Chippewa, 1720 Big Lake Rd., Cloquet, MN 55720 (218) 879-4593. E-mail: karendiver@fdlrez.com. *Other professional post*: Vice President, Minnesota Chippewa Tribe, Cass lake, MN.

DIXIE, YAKIMA K. (Miwok)
(tribal hereditary spokesperson)
Affiliation & Address: California Valley Miwok Tribe of the Sheep Ranch Rancheria, 11178 Sheep Ranch Rd., Mountain Ranch, CA 95246 (209) 834-0197.

DIXON, JENNIFER
(attorney)
Education: Western Washington State University, BS (Political science); Thomas M. Cooley Law School, JD, 2007. *Affiliation & Address*: Associate Attorney (2009-present), Legal Advocates for Indian Country, LLP, 720 Third Ave., Suite 1900, Seattle, WA 98104 (206) 499-8684. Ms. Dixon focuses her practice on Native American law, criminal law, family law, environmental law, as well as general practice. *Past professional post*: Public defender and policy counsel to the Washington State Senate.

DIXON, PATRICIA ANN (Luiseno)
(Indian studies program chairperson)
Education: University of San Diego, BA & MA (American History), 1971; with minors in Religious Studies and Sociology at the University of San Diego. Beyond the M.A. she has completed course work at the University of New Mexico in law, the University of California at Riverside in American Indian Studies, & St. Thomas Seminary, Denver, CO in Religious Studies. *Affiliation & Address*: Faculty & Department Chairperson, American Indian Studies Program, American Studies Dept., Palomar Community College, 1140 W. Mission Rd., San Marcos, CA 92069 (619) 744-1150. E-mail: pdixon@palomar.edu. Professor Dixon has held various positions on her Pauma Tribal Council including Tribal Chairman. She has executed the Department chair duties for more than fifteen years. Professor Dixon is also a lecturer and consultant on tribal governments and Indian History for local schools and colleges. Research interests are California Indians, tribal law, and Indians in film.

DIXON, STACY (Paiute)
(former tribal chairperson)
Affiliation & Address: Chairperson, Susanville Indian Rancheria, 745 Joaquin St., Susanville, CA 96130 (530) 257-6264.

DOCKTER-PINNICK, LYNN
(college president)
Affiliation & Address: President, Fort Berthold Community College, P.O. Box 490, New Town, ND 58763 (701) 627-3665.

DOCTOR, SHARON (Navajo)
(Native American student services)
Education: Northern Arizona University, BGS (Business Administration), BSBA (Management), MEd (Counseling & Student Affairs). *Afiliation & Address*: Interim Director, Native American Student Services, Northern Arizona University, University Union, Bldg. 30, Rm. 104, P.O. Box 5653, Flagstaff, AZ 86011 (928) 523-6960. E-mail: sharon.doctor@nau.edu.

DODD, MARK (Potawatomi)
(attorney; executive director)
Education: Kilgore College, 1995-97; Brigham Young University, BA (Political Science), 2003; University of Kansas School of Law, JD, 2006. Mark specialized in researching & writing about Native American & property law issues. *Affiliation & Address*: Executive Director (2011-present), Kansas State Gaming Agency, 420 SE 6th, Suite 3000, Topeka, KS 66607 (785) 368-6202. *Other professional posts*: Attorney/Owner, The Law Offices of Mark D. Dodd, P.A., Topeka, KS, 2011-present); Adjunct Professor, School of Business, Haskell Indian Nations U., Lawrence, KS, 2010-present). *Past professional post*: General Counsel/Tribal Attorney for Prairie Band of Potawatomi Nation, 2009-11; Associate Attorney, Hines & Ahlquist, P.A., 2006-09.

DOERFLER, JILL (White Earth Ojibwe)
(American Indian Studies department head)
Education: University of Minnesota-Morris, BA (History), 2001; University of Minnesota, Twin Cities, PhD (American Indian Studies), 2007. *Affiliation & Address*: Head, Department of American Indian Studies, 302 Kirby Plaza, 1208 Kirby Dr., Duluth, MN 55812 (218) 726-7192. E-mail: doerflj@d.umn.edu "My primary area of scholarly interest is American Indian, specifically Anishinaabe, identity with a political focus on citizenship. Growing up on the White Earth reservation, I was all too familiar with the divisions that the use of blood quantum as the sole requirement for tribal citizenship (1961) caused. After a political crisis during the 1990s, there was a growing concern about the vast numbers of Anishinaabeg being excluded under the blood quantum requirement; families were literally divided with some possessing the blood quantum required for citizenship and others lacking it. I felt compelled to research the history of tribal citizenship and blood quantum. My research is premised on my commitment to bridging scholarly efforts with the practical needs of American Indian peoples, communities, and nations. My research draws upon both historical documents and literature to delineate Anishinaabe conceptions of identity in the 20th and 21st centuries. I am especially interested in the ways in which Anishinaabeg resisted pseudo-scientific measures of blood (race/blood quantum) as a means to define identity. One of my newer areas of research dovetails with community service and focuses on the process of constitutional reform. I have been working with the White Earth Nation since 2007 on constitutional reform efforts. I have found working with the White Earth Nation to be rewarding and it has solidified my commitment to partnerships between scholars and Native nations." *Past professional posts*: Chancellor's Postdoctoral Fellow in American Indian Studies at the University of Illinois (2007-08).

DOERING, MAVIS V. (Cherokee)
(artisan, craftsperson)
Address: 211 W. Tierra Buena, Phoenix, AZ 85023 (602) 375-2110. Mavis produces baskets made from buckbrush, honeysuckle, white oak and reeds, with tribal or original designs.

DOHERTY, HELEN (Cherokee of Okla.)
(educator, caucus chair)
Address & Affiliation: Chairwoman, Native American Caucus of the California Democratic Party, 1401 21st St., Suite 100, Sacramento, CA 95814. Website: www.nativeamericacaucus.com. *Other professional posts*: Director of Region 16 for the California Democratic Party, which includes parts of Los Angeles County, Orange County Riverside & San Bernardino County. Recently founded the Kudos For Kids Foundation, a non-profit organization dedicated to the needs of children. Past professional post: Public school teacher for @40 years. *Awards, honors*: Received the California Teachers Association, Human & Civil Rights Award in 2003; The Constitutional Rights Foundation, "Teacher of Distinction" Award; the Bob Mack, "Democrat of the Year" award for grass roots effort.

DOLL, FR. DON, S.J.
(photographer; journalist; instructor in photography)
Education: St. Louis University, BA & MA (English); Rochester Institute of Technology, MFA (Photography). *Affiliation & Address*: Instructor of Photography, Department of Journalism & Mass Communications, Creighton University, Omaha, NE 68178. E-mail: dollsj@creighton.edu. Fr. Don has been featured in National Geographic wit the Yu'pik Eskimos in the "Hunters of the Bering Sea" June, 1984; and "The Athapaskans Along the Yukon," Feb. 1990. *Awards, honors*: In May 1997, he was presented with the Kodak Crystal Eagle Award for his over 20 years of photography among Native Americans. *Published works*: Two books and a CD-ROM on Native Americans. Includes, "Vision Quest: Men, Women, and Sacred Sites of the Sioux Nation" (Random House's Crown Books); the exhibit traveled to 17 cities. Doll was introduced to both photography and to the Lakota people in the 1960s when he was assigned to the Rosebud Reservation in SD as a young Jesuit.

DOLLARHIDE, JASON (Peoria)
(tribal 2nd chief)
Affiliation & Address: 2nd Chief, Peoria Tribe of Indians of Oklahoma, P.O. Box 1527, Miami, OK 74355 (918) 659-8508.

DOLSON, MICHAEL (Salish & Kootenai)
(Native American studies director)
Born & raised in Hot Springs, Mont. *Education*: Thomas Aquinas College, Santa Paula, CA, BA; University of Montana School of Law, JD; Gonzaga University, MBA. *Affiliation & Address*: Chairperson, Native American Studies Dept., Salish Kootenai College, P.O. Box 70, Pablo, MT 59855 (406) 675-4942. E-mail: mike_dolson@skc.edu. Mike came to Salish Kootenai College in 1987 to teach developmental mathematics, which he did until 1994 when he assumed chair of the Native American Studies Dept. His teaching focus has been in Tribal history & government, Federal Indian Policy & Law. *Other professional post*: Board member, Nkwusm Institute (a private, non-private Salish Language School.) *Past professional posts*: Member, Board of Directors: S&K Holding, Inc., Montana Board of Research & Commercialization Technology.

DOMINGUEZ, DAVID (Chumash)
(tribal business committee member; former chairperson)
Affiliation & Address: Business Committee member, Santa Ynez Band of Mission Indians, P.O. Box 317, Santa Ynez, CA 93460 (805) 688-7997. David was elected to serve on the Business Committee for the Santa Ynez Band of Chumash Indians in 2005. He was re-elected to a fifth term in March 2013. Although he was elected to the Business Committee in 2005, he is not a novice in tribal politics. In the early 90s he was elected to the position of Tribal Chairman and spent nearly a decade leading the tribe. Over the years, David has also served on the tribe's Elders Council and has been instrumental in working on tribal cultural projects. Prior to his involvement in tribal leadership, he worked for the City of Santa Barbara for 40 years and also had a plumbing business and a travel agency.

DONAHUE, DEBRA L.
(professor of law & American Indian Studies)
Education: JD. *Affiliation & Address*: Professor of Law, University of Wyoming College of Law, Law Bldg. 204, Laramie, WY 82071 (307) 766-2191. Debra teaches the American Indian Studies course, Federal Indian Law. She has been on the College of Law faculty since 1992, where she teaches Public Land, Environmental Law & Policy, Indian Law, and Native American Natural Resources Law. *Past professional post*: Visiting lecturer/researcher in 2002 at the University of Auckland School of Law & the University of Canterbury School of Forestry in Christchurch, New Zealand. *Awards, honors*: 2000 Wyoming Wildlife Federation's Resource Conservationist f the Year. *Published works*: Articles: "Educationn & Cooperative Management of Tribal Natural Resources," 42 Tulsa L. Rev. 5 (2006); "A Call for Native American Natural Resources in the Law School Curriculum," 24 Land Resources & Environmental Law 211 (2004). Book: The Western Range Revisited: Removing Livestock from Public Lands to Conserve Native Biodiversity (University of Oklahoma Press, 1999); other articles & contributions to books.

DONAHUE, KATHIE M. (*Apv-Whilt-Tin-Toom*) (Okanogan, Rogue River, Shasta) 1946-
(professional genealogist)
Born in 1946, in Spokane, Wash. *Education*: College & professional training. *Principal occupation*: Professional genealogist, accredited for American Indian Research. *Address*: 4516 E. Sixth Ave., Spokane, WA 99212 (509) 535-6821. E-mail: amerindgen@qwest.net. Website: www.amerindgen.com. *Community activities*: Assistant director, Spokane (WA) Family History Center. *Memberships*: International Commission for the Accreditation of Professional Genealogists; Board for Certification of Genealogist. *Published works*: An Irish Chippewa Family of Wisconsin; This Family Morse); My Journey Through the 20th Century (Wolff).

DONALDSON, LAURA E. (Cherokee)
(associate professor)
Education: Guilford College, BA; Emory University, PhD. *Affiliation & Address*: Professor, Dept. of English & Director of Graduate Studies, American Indian Program, Cornell University, 250 Goldwin Smith Hall, Ithaca, NY 14853 (607) 255-6800. E-mail: ld49@cornell.edu. *Interests*: American Indian literature & culture; Indian women's literature; postcolonial theory, religion, gender, race & law.

DONEY, KYLE (Florida Seminole/Gros Ventre)
(deputy executive director)
Education: Florida State University, BA (Political Science). Affiliation & Address: Deputy Executive Director (2011-present), Native Learning Center, Seminole Tribe of Florida, 6363 Taft St., Hollywood, FL 33024 (954) 985-2315. E-mail: kyledoney@semtribe.com. *Other professional post*: Member, National Board of Directors, Florida State Univesity's Alumni Association.

DONEY, MEL L. ADAMS (Gros Ventre)
(tribal vice president)
Affiliation & Address: V.P., Fort Belknap Community Council, RR 1, Box 66, Harlem, MT 59526 (406) 353-8471. E-mail: mel_ftbelknap@yahoo.com.

DONGOSKE, KURT E. 1952-
(Hopi Tribal archaeologist)
Born November 24, 1952, Minneapolis, Minn. *Education*: University of Minnesota, BA, 1976; University of Arizona, MA, 1984. *Principal occupation*: Hopi Tribal archaeologist. *Address*: 104 N. Maricopa Dr., Winslow, AZ 86047 (602) 734-2441 (work). *Affiliation*: The Hopi Tribe, Kykotsmovi, AZ. *Memberships*: American Anthropological Association; American Association of Physical Anthropologists; Society for American Archaeology; Society of Professional Archaeologists; Arizona Archaeological Council; Arizona Archaeological & Historical Society. *Interests*: "Cultural resource management, human osteology, faunal analysis, archaeology & Native American concerns, laser mapping instruments & AutoCad, geographic information systems, and Western US archaeology, and Native American oral tradition, and the Archaeological Record."

DOONKEEN, ALFREDA (Seminole of Oklahoma)
(organization president)
Education: University of Central Oklahoma, BA (Sociology), BS (Business Administration). *Affiliation & Address*: President, Operations at Wind Clan Promotions, Oklahoma City, OK *Other professional post*: Member, Board of Trustees, Pawnee Nation College, P.O. Box 470, Pawnee, OK. *Past professional posts*: Her previous experience includes appointment to represent Texas, Oklahoma and Kansas on the National Indian Health Board's Voluntary Tribal Public Health Accreditation Committee; Chair of the Seminole Nation Health Advisory Board and Chair of the Wewoka Clinic and representative to the Oklahoma City Area InterTribal Health Board; Executive Assistant at the Oklahoma City Indian Clinic; University of Oklahoma Native American Center of Excellence Consortium; appointed to Mental Health Planning and Coordinating Board for three counties; and appointed to Seminole Nation Judgment Fund Committee.

DOONKEEN, EULA NARCOMEY (Seminole of Oklahoma) 1931-
(artist)
Born December 12, 1931, Oklahoma City, Okla. *Education*: Central State College, BA (Education), 1965. *Address*: 1012 N.W. 46th St., Oklahoma City, OK 73118 (405) 326-1515. *Affiliation*: Co-owner, Alco Printing Co., Oklahoma City, OK. *Other professional post*: General Council member, Seminole Nation of Oklahoma, Wewoka, OK. *Military service*: U.S.A.F. Women's Reserve, 1951-55. *Community activities*: Shawnee Area Health Advisory Board; Neighborhood Services Organization, Oklahoma City (secretary, 1972); Oklahoma City Community Council; Oklahoma City Area Health Advisory Board; West Central Neighborhood All Sports Association (vice president). *Memberships*: Seminole General Tribal Council (member; assistant chief); Five Civilized Tribes Inter-Tribal Council (sergeant-at-arms); National Congress of American Indians (area vice president, 1967-68); Kappa Pi; Bacone Alumni Association; Oklahoma Federation of Indian Women; American Indian Center (secretary, 1968); Feathers & Buckskin Society; American Indian Press Association; Indian Development Center, Inc.; Universal Link, Plains Center, Oklahoma City (vice president). *Awards, honors*: Several awards for painting in acrylics. *Exhibits*: Mrs. Doonkeen writes, "I have exhibited at the Smithsonian Institution (but) I paint mainly on commission & rarely enter competitions because I feel most competitions are based on bias & inherent traditional favoritism, & not on realistic approaches." *Interests*: "I have traveled extensively over the U.S. on business for Indian organizations and my own Seminole Nation's business; also travel extensively for my own business, the Alco Printing Co. I am well known all over the country for my greeting card and stationery designs."

DORSCHER, JOYCELYN, MD (Turtle Mountain Ojibwe) 1958-
(physician, center director)
Education: University of Minnesota Medical School, MD, 1994. *Affiliation*: Family Practitioner, 4884 Miller Trunk Hwy., Hermantown, MN 55811 (218) 249-5700. *Other professional post*: Director, Center of American Indian & Minority Health (CAIMH), Duluth School of Medicine, University of Minnesota, Room 182-Med, 1035 University Dr., Duluth, MN 55812-2487 (218) 726-7235 E-mail: jdorsche@d.umn.edu.

DOTSON, DEBORAH (Delaware)
(tribal president)
Affiliation & Address: President, Delaware Nation, P.O. Box 825, Anadarko, OK 73005 (405) 247-2448. E-mail: ddotson@delawarenation.com.

DOUCET, RANDY (Coushatta)
(tribal chief judge; attorney)
Affiliation & Address: Chief Judge, Muckleshoot Tribal Court, 39015 172nd Ave. SE, Auburn, WA 98092 (253) 939-3311 ext. 3203. *Other professional posts*: Chief Judge, Port Gamble S'Klallam, 31912 Little Boston Rd. NE, Kingston, WA 98346 (425) 774-5808; Chief Judge, Stillaguamish Tribal Court, P.O. Box 3067, Arlington, WA 98223 (360) 474-8562. *Past professional post*: Lummi Tribal Court, Bellingham, WA. *Membership*: Americans for Indian Opportunity. *Interests*: Law enforcement, legal issues.

DOUGHERTY, JOHN J.
(professor of Native American studies)

Affiliation & Address: Professor of Native American Studies, American Indian Graduate Program, University of California, 327 Sproul Hall #5900, Berekely, CA 94720 (510) 642-3228.

DOUGHERTY, LAURA (Cherokee)
(attorney)

Address: 4272 W. Pondview Dr., Littleton, CO 80123 (303) 797-0764. E-mail: ladpubear@yahoo.com. *Practice area*: Civil litigation.

DOUGLAS, JERRY L. (Delaware-Lenni Lenape)
(tribal chief)

Education: Tulsa Junior College; Oklahoma School of Accounting. *Affiliation & Address*: Delaware Tribe of Indians, 170 NE Barbara, Bartlesville, OK 74006 (918) 336-5272. E-mail: jldouglas2005@yahoo.com. *Other professional post*: President, Delaware Enterprise Authority. *Past professional posts*: Delaware Indian Tribe (Assistant Chief, 2002-06; Delaware Tribal Committees, 1992-2002). *Military service*: U.S. Air Force.

DOVE, DAWN (Niantic Narragansett)
(cultural center director)

Address & Affiliation: Director, Dovecrest Indian Cultural Center, 390 Summit Rd., Arcadia Village, Exter, RI 02822 (401) 539-7795.

DOWD, GREGORY EVANS
(professor of Native American studies & history)

Education: University of Connecticut, BA, 1978; Princeton University, MA, 1982, PhD, 1986. *Affiliations & Address*: Professor of History & American Culture (2002-present), Director, Program in American Culture (2007-present), Dept. of History, Program in American Culture, University of Michigan, 3672 Haven Hall, University of Michigan, 505 S. State St., Ann Arbor, MI 48109 (734) 936-6872. E-mail: dowdg@umich.edu. *Past professional posts*: Professor of History, University of Notre Dame, 1987-2002; associate dean for Undergraduate Studies, College of Arts & Letters, University of Notre Dame, 2001-2002; director of Native American Studies, Program in American Culture, 2002-06, University of Michigan. *Published works*: A Spirited Resistance: The North American Indian Struggle for Unity, 1745-1815 (Johns Hopkins University Press, 1992); War Under Heaven: Pontiac, The Indian Nations, and the British Empire (Johns Hopkins University Press, 2002).

DOWD, RICK R. (Yurok)
(tribal chairperson)

Affiliation & Address: Chairperson, Resighini Rancheria Coast Indian Community, P.O. Box 529, Klamath, CA 95548 (707) 482-2431. E-mail: rickdowd7@gmail.com

DOWNES, ANN MARIE BLEDSOE (Winnebago of Nebraska) 1973-
(attorney; deputy assistant secretary0Indian Affairs)

Education: Wayne State College, BA, 1991; Arizona State University O'Connor College of Law, JD, 1994. *Address & Affiliation*: Deputy Assistant Secretary – Indian Affairs for Policy & Economic Development (DAS-PED), & Acting Director of the Bureau of Indian Education (BIE), U.S. Department of the Interior, 1849 C St., NW, MS-3658-MIB, Washington, DC 20240 (202) 208-3710. *Past professional posts*: Executive Director, National Native American Bar Association, Tempe, AZ. Executive director, Indian Legal Program, Sandra Day O'Connor College of Law, Arizona State University; Policy Advisor for Tribal Affairs to Arizona Governor, Janet Napolitano; president, Little Priest Tribal College, Winnebago, NE. Ms. Bledsoe Downes has been a member of the Ho-Chunk, Inc., board of directors since 2008 and a member of the Little Priest Tribal College Board of Trustees since 2012. She also served as a member of the White House Initiative on Tribal Colleges & Universities Advisory Board from 2002 to 2005.

DOWNES, BRADLEY G. BLEDSOE (Chickasaw)
(attorney)

Address & Affiliation: Dorsey & Whitney LLP, Center Tower, 650 Town Center Dr, Suite 1850, Costa Mesa, CA 92626-1925 (714) 662-7300. E-mail: downes.bradley@dorseylaw.com. Attorney in the Indian Law practice group since 1999. Practices in the areas of Federal Indian law, gaming law, business law, civil litigation, Indian Child Welfare and Federal Government relations.

DOYLE, CARRIE C.
(attorney; Indian law practice)

Education: M.A. in American History with a focus on the history of the American West. University of Colorado Law School JD (Indian Law Certificate with Honors). *Affiliation & Address*: Associate, Tilden McCoy & Dilweg LLP, 2500 30th St., Suite 207, Boulder, CO 80301 (303) 323-1922 E-mail: ccdoyle@tildenmccoy.com Carrie has represented tribal clients in litigation matters in tribal courts, federal district & appellate courts and in administrative matters. Carrie advises tribal governments on tribal code development and constitution and ordinance interpretation; tribal governance administration including separation of powers issues, judiciary matters, elections, enrollment, housing and employment matters; and gaming development and compliance. Carrie's practice also incorporates her educational background in history and environmental law. She was an editor to her law school's Environmental Law Journal and her law review article was internally awarded "Best Student Note" by this Journal. This expertise allows her to assist tribes with administrative matters pertaining to ta tribe's history, culture & reservation land status. Carrie graduated from the, the American Indian Clinic Award & a Natural Resources Award. Before joining Tilden McCoy + Dilweg LLP, Carrie completed a clerkship at the Colorado Court of Appeals and worked for a family law firm. During her clerkship, she researched and drafted opinions on subjects including statutory interpretation, administrative remedies, summary judgment practice, governmental immunity, contract nondisclosure, & property disputes. Carrie's family law practice included dissolution and post-dissolution matters and appeals.

DOYLE, RICHARD M. (Passamaquoddy)
(tribal governor - Sakom)

Education: University of Maine at Farmington, BS (Community Health Education). *Affiliation*: Pleasant Point Passamaquoddy Tribe, P.O. Box 343, Perry, ME 04667 (207) 853-2600; E-mail: rick@wabanaki.com. *Past tribal posts*: Health Planner; council member; lt. governor; "Site Manager" for the tribe's Health Management Information System.

DOZIER, DEBORAH W.
(professor of anthropology & American Indian studies)

Education: Syracuse University, MFA (Fiber Structure and Interlocking), 1984, and an MFA in Museology, 1990. University of California, Riverside, MA (Anthropology), 1997, PhD (Anthropology), 2000. *Affiliation & Address*: Professor, American Indian Studies Program, American Studies Dept., Palomar Community College, 1140 W. Mission Rd., San Marcos, CA 92069 (619) 744-1150. E-mail: ddozier@palomar.edu She worked for many years as a community organizer and as an activist working for social justice. She has done extensive research and field work in Southern California and in Baja California. Special research interests include the visual arts with an emphasis on textiles and basketry, ethnobotany, and Native technology. She has parallel interests in California Indian history & California Indian resistance movements.

DRAKE, ELROY (Navajo) 1942-
(financial manager)

Born March 20, 1942, Tuba City, Ariz. *Education*: Northern Arizona University, BS, 1972. *Address*: P.O. Box 805, Window Rock, AZ 86515 (602) 871-4705. *Affiliation*: Manager, Navajo Savings Branch of First Federal Savings, Phoenix, AZ, 1975-85; manager, part owner, Window Rock Travel Services, Inc., 1986-. *Other professional post*: College instructor. *Military service*: U.S. Army, 1964-66 (Vietnam Service Medal; SP/4 Class-Military Police). *Community activities*: VFW; helped establish United Way organization on the Navajo reservation (Navajo Way). *Memberships*: Northern Arizona University Indian Club (social manager). *Awards, honors*: 1977 Young Navajo of Year, The Navajo Tribe. *Interests*: Established first Savings & Loan Association on Indian Reservation to promote housing; calligraphy, woodworking, astronomy, restoring VW "bug" sedans, traveling, golfing.

DRAKE, MICHAEL (United Lumbee) 1954-
(publisher)

Born July 30, 1954, Miami, Okla. *Education*: Washburn University, BBA, 1977. *Affiliation*: Owner/Publisher, Talking Drum Publications, Goldendale, WA, 1991-. *Memberships*: (Shago) High Eagle Warrior Society of United Lumbee Nation; Oregon Natural Resources Council; Friends of Enola Hill. *Interests*: "My primary interests include writing, publishing, and drummaking. The drum is the heart of my life & work. I travel throughout the Pacific Northwest presenting lectures & workshops on drumming. I also support the preservation of Native American sacred sites through lectures & articles that raise people's awareness of their cultural & religious significance." *Biographical source*: "Drumming Our Way to Balance" by Robert Mann (The New York Times, July 1993). *Published work*: Shamanic Drum (Talking Drum Publications, 1991).

DRAUGHON, SCOTT (Oklahoma Cherokee) 1952-
(social worker, attorney)

Born June 17, 1952, Muskogee, Okla. *Education*: Oklahoma State University, B.A., 1974; University of Tulsa Law School, J.D., 1977; University of Oklahoma, MSW, 1992. *Affiliation & Address*: Social worker & attorney, Cushing Regional Hospital, 1023 E. Cherry, Tulsa, OK 74129. *Affiliation*: Director of Research/Information, Oklahoma Credit Union, Tulsa, OK, 1990-91; social worker, Tulsa Boys' Home (Aftercare Dept. Coordinator, 1992-94); medical social worker, Olsten Kimberly Quality Care, Tulsa, OK, 1995-; legal counsel, Tulsa City-County Health Department, Tulsa, OK, 1996-; clinical social worker, Cushing Regional Hospital, Cushing, OK, 1996-. *Other professional post*: Attorney in Private Practice, Tulsa, OK, 1979-; Director of

Research/Information, Oklahoma Credit Union League, Tulsa, OK, 1988-91; stockbroker, 1983-93. *Community activities*: Alumnus, Leadership Oklahoma, Inc.; Leadership Tulsa (lifetime member); Phi Delta Phi (lifetime member); Cushing Care Clinic (volunteer); Master Mason, Petroleum Lodge #474; Tulsa Human Rights Commission (past executive board); Indian Affairs Commission of the City of Tulsa (past board); International Council of Tulsa (past Board); Tulsa Senior Services, Inc. (past board). *Memberships*: National Association of Social Workers (past treasurer, executive board - Oklahoma Chapter); Oklahoma Association of Municipal Attorneys; Tulsa Area Human Resources Association (past vice president of Community Relations); Oklahoma Bar Association. *Awards, honors*: Graduate College Fee Waiver Scholarship, University of Oklahoma, Fall 1991; Regional Finalist, White House Fellowship; Leadership Oklahoma, Inc. 1993-94 Class; 1994 nominee, Friends of Children Award, Oklahoma Institute for Child Advocacy.

DREADFULWATER, MARK (Cherokee)
(journalist; newspaper editor)
Affiliation & Address: Multimedia Editor, Cheokee Phoenix (the country's oldest Native American newspaper), P.o. Box 948, Tahlequah, OK 74465 (918) 453-5269. *Other professional post*: Member, Board of Directors, past chair of the Education Commttee, Native American Journalists Association, Norman, OK.

DRIBEN, PAUL 1946-
(anthropologist)
Born May 4, 1946, St. Boniface, Manitoba, Can. *Education*: University of Manitoba, MA, 1969; University of Minnesota, PhD, 1976. *Address*: 166 College St., Thunder Bay, Ontario, Can. P7A 5J7 (807) 343-8568. *Affiliation*: Professor of Anthropology, Lakehead University, Thunder Bay, Ontario, Can., 1974-. *Interests*: Ethnohistory & ethnography of the Ojibway Indians and the Metis. *Published works*: When Freedom Is Lost: The Dark Side of the Relationship Between Government and the Fort Hope and the Fort Hope Band (University of Toronto Press, 1983; We Are Metis: The Ethnography of a Halfbreed Community in Northern Alberta (AMS Press, 1985; Aroland Is Our Home: An Incomplete Victory in Applied Anthropology (AMS Press, 1986; Portrait of Humankind: An Introduction to Human Biology & Prehistoric Culture (Prentice Hall, 1994); Grand Portage Chippewa: Stories and Experiences of Grand Portage Band Members (Grand Portage Tribal Council, 2000).

DRIFT-HILL, TERRI (Anishinaabe)
(cultural services project coordinator)
Education: Itasca Community College, AAS (Human Services); Bemidji State University, BAS (Psychology). *Affiliation & Address*: Cultural Services Project Coordinator (2009-present), Mending the Sacred Hoop – Technical Assistance Project, 202 E. Superior St., Duluth, MN 55802 (218) 623-HOOP. *Other professional post*: Co-facilitates a Native women's healing circle in Duluth, MN for Native women who have experienced sexual violence. *Past professional posts*: Domestic Violence Advocate in Grand Rapids, MN and was licensed to practice chemical dependency counseling in Minnesota; Community Family & Youth Services Director, Mille Lacs Band of Ojibwe, 2003-06, and the Grand Casino Mille Lacs in their Training & Educational Performance area, 2006-07; PR/Communications Director, Bois Forte Reservation Administration, 2007-09.

DRIVING HAWK, JAMES (Lakota)
(HIS acting area director)
Education: Cardinal Stritch University, BS (Business Administration). Affiliation & Address: Acting Director, Great Plains Area Indian Health Service (IHS), 115 4th Ave., SE, Aberdeen, SD 57401 (605) 226-7582. As Acting Director, Mr. Driving Hawk has administrative responsibility for 19 Great Plainsservice units consisting of seven hospitals and 10 health centers. The Great Plains Area also supports two Urban Indian Health Programs. The Indian health system in Iowa, Nebraska, South Dakota & North Dakota serves 17 Tribes and more than 130,000 American Indian people eligible for IHS services. Mr. Driving Hawk oversees this system, which is composed of services provided through IHS federal-government-operated facilities as well as health care services provided by Tribes that have assumed partial or full responsibility for their own health care programs under the authority of the Indian Self-Determination & Education Assistance Act. Before joining the IHS Great Plains Area, Mr. Driving Hawk served as Executive Officer for the IHS Phoenix Area Office. He chairs the IHS National Council of Executive Officers, which is responsible for identifying and disseminating administrative best practices among IHS Executive Officers nationwide and which advises the IHS Director on administrative and management matters. Mr. Driving Hawk also serves IHS as a member of its Labor Management Relations Council, which promotes effective relations between IHS and its unions. With more than 19 years of service to IHS, Mr. Driving Hawk brings deep expertise in financial management, healthcare administration, purchased/referred care, business office operations, and tribal budget consultation to IHS Great Plains Area. He began his career as a Supervisory Operating Accountant, then served IHS Phoenix Area as Budget Officer and later Director of Revenue Enhancement and Director of Field Operations. He also served as Chief Financial Officer for IHS Bemidji Area. Mr. Driving Hawk was Chief Executive Officer for the

Southern Band Health Center in Elko, Nevada from 2002 to 2005 and Chief Executive Officer for the Fort Yuma Hospital from 2005 to 2007.

DRUMMER, KELLY (Oglala Lakota)
(foundation president & CEO)
Education: Minneapolis Community & Technical College, AA, 1993; University of Minnesota, BA (Anthropology), 1996; Saint Mary's University of Minnesota, MA (Philanthropy & Development), 2004. *Affiliation & Address*: President & CEO (2011-present), Tiwahe Foundation, 2801 21st Ave. South, Suite 132F, Minneapolis, MN 55407 (612) 722-0999. kdrummer@tiwahefoundation.org. *Past professional posts*: Development & Endowment Associate, The Family Partnership, 2004-04; Development Officer, Headwaters Foundation for Justice, 2004-07; Development Director, New Foundations, Inc., 2007-11.

DUCHENEAUX, FRANKLIN D. (Cheyenne River Sioux) 1940-
(attorney)
Born January 30, 1940, Cheyenne Agency, S.D. *Education*: University of South Dakota, BS, 1963; University of South Dakota Law School, JD, 1965. *Principal occupation*: Attorney. *Affiliation*: Special Counsel on Indian Affairs, Committee on Interior & Insular Affairs, U.S. House of Representatives, Washington, DC, 1973-92; Partner, Ducheneaux, Taylor & Associates (legislative lobbying & government relations), 1993-present.

DUCHENEAUX, NICOLE (Cheyenne River Sioux; Confederated Salish & Kootenai)
(attorney)
Education: Fort Lewis College, BA, 2003; University of Montana School of Law, JD, 2007. *Affiliation & Address*: Associate, 2012-14; Partner (2015-present), Fredericks Peebles & Morgan, LLP, 3610 North 163rd Plaza, Omaha, NE 68116 (402) 333-4053. E-mail: nducheneaux@ndnlaw.com. *Practice areas*: Trial advocacy; Tribal Government Affairs; Tribal Economic Development; Gaming; Indian Child Welfare Act; et al. *Past professional post*: Staff Attorney, Montana Office of the State Public Defender, 2008-12. *Awards, honors*: 2010 Excellence Award for Professional Excellence & Dedication to the Montana Office of the State Public Defender.

DUCHENEAUX, ROCHELLE (Cheyenne River Sioux)
(tribal supreme court judge)
Education: University of New Mexico, JD. *Affiliation & Address*: Judge, Supreme Court, Mashpee Wampanoag Indian Tribe, P.O. Box 1048, Mashpee, MA 02649 (508) 477-0208. *Memberships*: South Dakota & North Dakota Federal Bars and numerous tribal bars.

DUFFY, PATRICK F. (Crow)
(BIA agency supt.)
Affiliation & Address: Supt., Crow Creek Agency, Bureau of Indian Affairs, P.O. Box 139, Fort Thompson, SD 57339 (605) 245-2311.

DUGAN, JOYCE C. (Eastern Cherokee)
(school director; former tribal chief)
Born August 25, 1948, Cherokee, N.C. *Education*: Bacone Jr. College, 1965-66; Western Carolina University, BS, 1975, MA, 1981. *Principal occupation*: School director; former tribal chief. *Address & Affiliation*: Director, Cherokee Elementary School & Central High School, P.O. Box 134, Cherokee, NC 28719 (704) 497-6370. *Past professional post*: Principal Chief, Eastern Band of Cherokee Tribal Council, Cherokee, NC. *Community activities*: Cheokee Boy's Club Board of Directors; member of Parent Advisory Board for Special Education; served on United South & Eastern Tribes, Inc. *Awards, honors*: Selected a member of the White House Conference on Indian Education, 1992 (appointed to a task force to study & develop improved procedures and forms for special education); was nominated for Citizen of the Year by the Asheville Times - was selected as one of three finalists; selected as one of North Carolina's Most Distinguished Women in Education, 1994. *Interests*: "Great supporter of special programs for special students."

DUGGAN. JESSICA L. (Houma)
(attorney; member, Native American law & policy practice)
Education: Stanford University, BA (Psychology with minor in Native American studies), 2006; Washington University, St. Louis, School of Law, MSW & JD, 2010. *Affiliation & Address*: Managing Associate, Dentons LLP, 525 Market St., 26th Floor, San Francisco, CA 94105 (415) 882-0369. E-mail: jessica.duggan@dentons.com. Jessica is a member of Denton's Energy, Transportation, and Infrastructure and PPP sectors. Her practice includes environmental, land use & natural resources law, with a particular focus on advising project developers, public agencies, Indian tribes & trade associations on National Environmental Policy Act (NEPA) and other environmental impact assessment laws. Jessica's practice also involves all aspects of environmental due diligence & counseling clients on environmental compliance matters in a wide range of corporate transactions. She advises national and multinational clients on compliance with domestic and international hazardous materials laws & regulations including the Comprehensive Environmental Response, Compensation, and Liability Act,

the Clean Air Act, the Clean Water Act and other statutes. She is also active in Dentons' Native American Law & Policy practice, where she is an active member of the firm's tribal litigation practice team. Specializing in tribal sovereignty, sovereign immunity & related jurisdictional issues, she has represented tribal interests in a variety of litigation contexts, both as plaintiff & defendant. Her experience representing tribes includes litigation of numerous appeals at the district court level as well as the Ninth Circuit Court of Appeals. Jessica also has experience litigating patent infringement and intellectual property cases in district courts & before the International Trade Commission.

DUKEPOO, ALVIN "JOE" (Pomo)
(tribal vice president)
Affiliation & Address: Vice President, Round Valley Indian Tribes, 77826 Covelo Rd., Covelo, CA 95428 (707) 983-6126. E-mail: jdukepoo@rvit.org.

DUKEPOO, FRANK C. (Hopi/Laguna) 1945-
(geneticist)
Born in 1945 on the Mohave Reservation. *Education*: Arizona State University (BS in Biology, 1966; MS in Zoology, 1968; and PhD in Zoology, 1973). *Principal occupation*: Geneticist. *Address*: c/o Christine Hollins, 1333 Florence St., Aurora, CO 80010. *Affiliations*: Assistant Professor of Biology, San Diego State University, 1973-77; program manager, National Science Foundation, Washington, DC, 1977-78; executive secretary, National Cancer Institute, NIH, Washington, DC, 1978-80; special assistant to the academic vice president (1980-94) & senior lecturer in the Dept. of Biological Sciences (1990-present), Northern Arizona University, Flagstaff, AZ. *Other professional posts*: Founder & current director, National Native American Honor Society; director, Center for Indian Education, Northern Arizona University, 1980-84; consultant to the BIA, Dept. of Education, NIH, NSF, Southwest Development lab and the Far West Lab; served as consultant to the production of the film, "The Four Corners: A National Sacrifice Area," 1987; served as consultant and featured in the film, The River That Harms," 1988; served as advisor, consultant and starred in "the Frank Duckepoo Story," film was produced as part of the Whizkids Project in 1993. *Memberships*: SACNAS (Society for the Advance of Chicanos & Native Americans in Science (founding member); AISES (founding member); *Awards, honors*: John Hay Whitney & Ford Foundation Fellowships; Bo Jack Humanitarian Award; Iron Eyes Cody Medal of Freedom Award; Outstanding Educator of the Year Award from the National Coalition of Indian Education; 1995 Indian Man of the Year; inducted into the Indian Hall of Fame; listed in "Past & Present Indian leaders" & selected for inclusion in "Bibliographies of Outstanding Native Americans"; 1996 Hopi of the Year & received the "Lifetime Achievement Award" for service to Indian people. He is the first Hopi to have earned a doctorate & one of six Indians nationally who hold earned doctorates in the sciences. He is one of only two Native American geneticists in the country. *Interests*: For the past ten years he has expanded his interest in the area of retention & motivation. In recent years he has gained considerable reputation as on the country's outstanding motivators of Indian students. In addition to retention & motivation studies, his other research interests include the study of birth defects in Southwest Native Americans & albinism & inbreeding among the Hopi Indians of northern Arizona. He is attempting to map the albino gene and has made two films pertaining to his research. The Whizkids production has received the ABC Excellence Award in Children's Programming, Telly Award and the School Library Journal Award. In 1995, the production was accepted for airing by the Minnesota Public Television. Currently, he is developing culturally-relevant science material, science modules & science kits for elementary students. As an amateur magician he gives "Mind, Magic and Motivation" shows to Indian youth. *Published works*: Numerous articles.

DULANEY, JOE (Karuk)
(board chairperson)
Affiliation & Address: Executive Board Secretary & Government Speicalist, Native American Youth & Family Center, 5135 NE Columbia Ave., Portland, OR 97218 (503) 288-8177. *Other professional post*: Member, New Avenues for Youth Ambassador Board. *Past professional post*: Project Manager, Symantec Corporation (18 years).

DULIK, EMMA (Makah)
(chief judge)
Affiliation & Address: Chief Judge, Makah Tribal Court, P.O. Box 117, Neah Bay, WA 98357 (360) 645-3301.

DuMARCE, HARVEY W. (Sisseton-Wahpeton Sioux) 1946-
(Indian college president; attorney)
Born September 5, 1946, Sisseton, S.D. *Education*: University of California, Berkeley, BA, 1976; University of Iowa, College of Law, JD, 1994. *Affiliation & Address*: President, Sisseton-Wahpeton College, P.O. Box 689, Old Agency, Sisseton, SD 57262 (605) 698-3966. *Community activities*: Tribal court, Sisseton-Wahpeton Sioux Reservation (ten years). *Memberships*: Native American Law Student Association; Disabled Law Student Society. *Interests*: "I am interested in American Indian law, voting rights. I would like to work for a

tribe as a judge or legal counsel when I am finished with law school. I have always been active in the field of voting rights for Indian people. I was one of the plaintiffs in a landmark voting rights case in South Dakota captioned Buckanaga v. Sisseton School District. We were the first group of American Indians to file a voting rights act complaint in the U.S. After seven years of litigation, we were able to settle our case out of court, and as a result of our long struggle, we had the old at-large voting system in the Sisseton School District replaced by a cumulative voting scheme. Now for the first time i the history of the Sisseton-Wahpeton Sioux Tribe, Indian parents were able to elect candidates of their choice to sit on the Sisseton School Board. I envision a day soon when an Indian will win an election in South Dakota to the U.S. Senate on the strength of Indian votes."

DUNCAN, CLIFFORD (Ute)
(museum director)
Affiliation & Address: Director, Ute Tribal Museum, P.O. Box 190, Highway 40, Fort Duchesne, UT 84026 (801) 722-4992.

DUNCAN, DOREEN (Arikara, Hidatsa & Mandan)
(museum director)
Education: Arizona State University, College of Education, BA. *Affiliation & Address*: Salt River Pima Maricopa Tribal Museum, 10005 E. Osborn Rd. • Scottsdale, AZ 85256 (480) 850-8191. *Other professional post*: Manager, YellowBird Productions/Yellowbird Indian Dancers, 3827 E. Contessa, Mesa, AZ 85205 (480) 641-7887 E-mail: nsveways@aol.com. *Interests*: Native American cultural interpretation.

DUNCAN, KEN (San Carlos Apache)
(storyteller/lecturer)
Affiliation & Address: Director, Yellow Bird Productions/Yellow Bird Indian Dancers, 3827 E. Contessa, Mesa, AZ 85205 (480) 641-7887. E-mail: apachekidz@hotmail.com. Yellow Bird provides unique & authentic Native American song & dance presentations, including: interactive activities, storytelling & lectures. *Awards, honors*: Nominated candidate as one of Arizona's Culture Keepers 2003. *Interests*: Flute, traditional Apache crafts.

DUNCAN, LENA (Ute)
(administrative director)
Affiliation & Address: Administrative Director, National American Indian Housing Council, 900 2nd St., NE Suite 107, Washington, DC 20002 (202) 789-1754.

DUNCAN, LUKE (Ute)
(tribal chairperson & band representative)
Affiliation & Address: Chairperson & Uncomphgre Band Representative, The Ute Indian Tribe, P.O. Box 190, Fort Duchesne, UT 84026 (435) 722-5141. E-mail: lduncan@utetribe.com

DUNN, FRANK (Eastern Cherokee)
(communications specialist)
Affiliation & Address: Cmmunications Specialist, Natiev Arts & Cultures Foundation, Native Arts & Cultures Foundation, 11109 NE 14th St., Vancouver, WA 98684 (360) 314-2421. *Past professional post*: Communications Director (ten years), Swinomish Indian Tribal Community. Frank is also a professional magician who presents native culture & storytelling through his Native American Magic show.

DUNN, KENNETH EDWARD (*Half Eagle*) (United Lumbee/Creek) 1956-
(freelance writer, historian)
Born December 17, 1956, Santa Barbara, Calif. *Education*: Grossmont Community College (San Diego, CA), GPA. *Principal occupation*: Writer, researcher, book reviewer, historian. *Address*: c/o United Lumbee Nation, P.O. Box 512, Fall River Mills, CA 96028 (619) 670-3396. *Affiliations*: Pan American Indian Assn News (Contributing reporter, 1990-94; staff writer, 1995-2001); staff writer, historian, United Lumbee Nation Times, 1995-. *Memberships*: Pan American Indian Assn; United Lumbee Nation (council member), Red Tailed Hawk Band of Southern California. *Awards, honors*: 1975 Cal Expo Award for racing photo entitled "CMC Shot of Top Southern California Professional IMX Racers at Continial Motor Sports Club Event", Carlsbad, CA. *Interests*: Politics, history, current events, civil rights, film, literature, writing, motor cross/ supercross racing; political & economic participation & access for all people. *Unpublished works*: "Tustennuggee," "Cry for the Mountain," "Autumn Winds," "Season of the Wolf" (history of the Eastern U.S. American Indian); book reviews, essays, historical, semi-genealogical work.

DUNNAGEN, JOHN (Miami of Indiana)
(tribal vice-chief, tribal historian)
Affiliation & Address: Vice Chief & Tribl Historian, Miami Nation of Indians of Indiana, P.O. Box 41, Peru, IN 46970. Website: www.miamiindians.org.

DUNNIGAN, TIMOTHY
(professor of anthropology)
Education: University of Arizona, MA (Anthropology), PhD (Cultural Anthropology & Linguistics). *Address & Affiliation*: Anthropology Dept., University of Minnesota, Twin Cities Campus, 366 HHH Center, 301 19th Ave. So., Minneapolis, MN 55455 (612) 625-0879. E-mail: dunni001@umn.edu. *Interests*: Cultural anthropology, Algonquian, Siouan, and Uto-Aztecan linguistics, kinship & social network analysis, linguistic acculturation.

DUNNAGAN, JOHN (Miami of Indiana)
(tribal vice chief)
Affiliation & Address: Vice Chief, Miami Nation of Indians of Indiana, P.O. Box 41, Peru, IN 46970 (765) 473-9631.

DUNNINGTON, JEAN
(editor)
Affiliation & Address: Editor, Tsa'Aszi' (The Yucca) Magazine of Navajo Culture, Tsa'Aszi Graphics Center, Ramah Navajo School Board, CPO Box 12, Pine Hill, NM 87321 (505) 783-5503.

DUNSMORE, ROGER 1938-
(professor emeritus of liberal & wilderness studies)
Affiliation & Address: Professor Emeritus, Dept. of Liberal Studies, University of Montana, Missoula, MT 59812. Dr. Dunsmore is a student & teacher of Native literature. *Published work*: Earth's Mind: Essays in Native Literature (University of New Mexico Press, 1997).

DUPREE, DOROTHY A. (Assiniboine & Sioux)
(IHS area director)
Education: University of North Dakota, BS (Education); University of Arizona, MBA. *Affiliation & Address*: Director, Billings Area IHS, 2900 4th Ave. North, P.O. Box 36600, Billings, MT 59107 (406) 247-7248. E-mail: Dorothy.dupree@ihs.gov. Ms. Dupree provides leadership to the Billings Area and oversees the delivery of health care to more than 65,000 American Indians and Alaska Natives on seven reservations in Montana and one in Wyoming. The Billings Area has health care facilities ranging from acute care and critical access hospitals on the Blackfeet, Crow, & Fort Belknap reservations to several smaller ambulatory care service units, as well as five urban Indian health programs. *Past professional posts*: Joined the IHS in the late 1980s and later served in a number of leadership roles in the Albuquerque Area, including Executive Officer and Acting Area Director. In 1999, she was detailed to the HHS Centers for Medicare & Medicaid Services (CMS) to serve as the Senior Policy Advisor on Indian Health, where she served for 10 years. While in this position, Ms. Dupree established a Tribal Leaders Advisory Group and a Tribal Affairs Office before returning to the IHS in 2008. Upon her return to IHS, Ms. Dupree served as the Director for the Tucson Area from 2008 to 2010 and the Director for the Phoenix Area from 2010 to 2014. Prior to joining the IHS, Ms. Dupree was the Director of Finance for the Pascua Yaqui Tribe in Tucson. *Awards, honors*: Numerous awards from IHS & CMS, including the HHS Secretary's Award for Distinguished Service, IHS Superior Performance awards, CMS Administrator's Achievement awards, and CMS Superior Performance awards. She has also been recognized by tribal organizations and has been awarded the National Luna Wessel Leadership Award from the California Rural Indian Health Board and the National Impact Award from the National Indian Health Board.

DUPRES, CHRIS (Cowlitz-Cree)
(sustainability officer)
Education: University of Pennsylvania, PhD (Folklore). *Affiliation*: Sustainability Officer, Native American Youth & Family Center, 5135 NE Columbia Blvd., Portland, OR 97218 (503) 288-8177. E-mail: dupresc@nayadx.org. *Past professional posts*: Project coordinator, "Indigenous Ways of Knowing Project," Lewis & Clark Graduate School of Education & Counseling; Chris worked at the Oregon Historical Society on a tribal cultural documentation project. *Interests*: Social justice work; she has considerable experience working with Native communities and populations.

DUPRIS, ANITA (Colville)
(chief justice)
Affiliation & Address: Chief Justice, Colville Tribal Court of Appeals, P.O. Box 150, Nespelem, WA 99155 (509) 634-2507. E-mail: anita.dupris@colvilletribes.com.

DUPUIS, KEVIN R. (Fond du Lac Ojibwe)
(tribal executive committee president)
Affiliation & Address: President, Minnesota Chippewa Tribe, P.O. Box 217, Cass lake, MN 56633 (218) 335-8581; E-mail: kdupuis@mnchippewatribe.org.

DURAN, BONNIE M. (Opealousas/Coushatta)
(director of health research)
Affiliation & Address: Adjunct Associate Professor of Social Work, and Director, Center for Indigenous Health Research, Indigenous Wellness Research Institute, School of Social Work, University of Washington, H-691, 1959 NE Pacific St., Seattle, WA 98195 (206) 685-8223. E-mail: bonduran@u.washington.edu. *Research Interests*: Native American mental health; community-based participatory research.

DURAN, ROMAN (Tesuque Pueblo)
(Pueblo lt. governor)
Affiliation & Address: Lt. Governor, Pueblo of Tesuque, Rt. 5 Box 360-T, Santa Fe, NM 87501 (505) 955-7732.

DURGLO, JOSEPH (Salish & Kootenai)
(former tribal chairperson)
Affiliation & Address: Former Chairperson, Confederated Salish & Kootenai Tribes, P.O. Box 278, Pablo, MT 59855 (406) 675-2700. E-mail: jdurglo@cskt.org. *Past tribal affiliations*: Vice Chairperson, Confederated Salish & Kootenai Tribes; State Tribal Economic Development Commission (STEDC), c/o Montana Dept. of Commerce, Helena, MT.

DURHAM, BARBARA (Timbisha Shoshone) 1955-
(tribal administrator)
Born September 23, 1955, Lone Pine, Calif. *Principal occupation*: Tribal administrator. *Address*: P.O. Box 206, Death Valley, CA 92328 (760) 786-2374. E-mail: timbisha@aol.com. *Affiliation*: Timbisha Shoshone Tribe. *Community activities*: Land restoration team member; chairperson of tribal non-profit center; represents tribe on Toiyabe Indian Health Project. *Membership*: National Congress of American Indians.

DUROCHER, SKIP
(attorney)
Education: Marquette University, BA (Political Scence), 1983; University of Wisconsin Law School, JD, 1986. *Affiliation & Address*: Co-chair, Indian Law Practice Group, Dorsey & Whitney LLP, 50 S. Sixth St., Suite 1500, Minneapolis, MN 55402 (612) 340-7855. E-mail: Durocher.skip@dorsey.com. Represented federally-recognized Indian tribe in federal court litigation against State of Michigan Revenue Officials regarding its attempt to impose ad valorem property taxes against the Tribe and its members on fee land within the Tribe's Reservation. Obtained summary judgment on behalf of the Tribe; affirmed by the 6th Circuit Court of Appeals. Represented federally-recognized Indian tribe and tribal corporation in federal court litigation against Kansas Revenue Officials regarding seizure of tribal corporation's gas tanker truck and attempt to impose fuel tax on sales of fuel to Indian tribes in Kansas. Argued certified question to Kansas Supreme Court. Obtained TRO and preliminary injunction from District Court, affirmed by 10th Circuit. Obtained summary judgment on behalf of Tribe and tribal corporation.

DUSHKIN, ARNOLD (Aleut)
(Alaskan village president)
Affiliation & Address: President, Native Village of Nikolski, P.O. Box 105, Nikolski, AK 99638 (907) 576-2225.

DUTCHER, KIMBERLY A (Navajo-Dine')
(executive director)
Education: Georgetown University, BA (Foreign Service); George Washington University, MEd; Arizona State University, Sabdra Day O'Connor College of Law, JD. *Affiliation & Address*: Executive Director (2015-present), Association onn American Idian Affairs, 966 Hungerford Dr., Suite 12-B, Rockville, MD 20850 (240) 314-7155. Prior to joining AAIA, Ms. Dutcher served the Gila River Indian Community for ten years as Prosecutor, Senior Assistant General Counsel, & most recently as Division Manager providing visionary leadership, direction & guidance to elected leadership as well as seven administrative departments. A champion for innovation & change, Ms. Dutcher was appointed lead for developing the employment sector for a Department of Labor model tribal employment program. Ms. Dutcher also oversaw the largest integrated software application program for the tribe to date. An accomplished writer and speaker, Ms. Dutcher has been called upon to prepare speeches and other executive level communications, including Inaugural and State of the Community addresses, and is often sought out as a conference speaker.

DUTHU, N. BRUCE (Houma) 1958-
(professor of Native American studies)
Born December 30, 1958, Houma, La. *Education*: Dartmouth College, BA, 1980; Loyola University School of Law, JD, 1983. *Affiliation & Address*: Professor & Chair, Native American Studies Program, Dartmouth College, 37 N. Main St., The Sherman House, Hanover, NH 03755 (603) 646-3530. E-mail: n.bruce.duthu@ dartmouth.edu. *Other professional post*: Board of Trustees for Earthjustice, one of the leading environmental non-profit litigation firms in the

country. *Past professional posts*: Vice Dean for Academic Affairs and Professor of Law, Vermont Law School, So. Royalton, VT, 1991-2008; dire tor, VLS-Sun Yat-sen University (Guangzhou, China) Partnership in Environmental Law; visiting professor of law, Harvard Law School, University of Trento (Italy), University of Wollongong (Australia), & University of Sydney (Australia). Community activities: Board member, Native American Program, Brown School of Social Work, Washington University; advisory committee, Hood Museum Repatriation Project, Dartmouth College. *Memberships*: Association of American Law Schools; Louisiana Bar Association; Federal Indian Bar Association; Tucker Foundation of Dartmouth College (board of visitors); Native American Alumni Association of Dartmouth College (National Steering Committee); American Indian Program, Brown School of Social Work, Washington University, St. Louis, MO (board of visitors). *Published works*: American Indians & the Law, with Colin Calloway (Penguin Books, 2009); contributing author, Felix S. Cohen's handbook of Federal Indian Law, 2005; contributed chapters to: Intercultural Dispute Resolution in Aboriginal Contexts: Canadian & International, 2004; and, First Person, First Peoples: Native American College Graduates Tell Their Life Stories, 1997; numerous articles, published commentary, & talks on the rights of Native Americans & Indigenous peoples to audiences throughout the U.S. & other parts of the world.

DUTSCHKE, AMY
(BIA regional director)
Affiliation & Address: Director, Bureau of Indian Affairs, Pacific Regional Office, 2800 Cottage Way, Sacramento, CA 95825 (916) 978-6000.

DWORKIN, JUDITH M.
(attorney, Indian law & tribal relations)
Born in Worcester, Mass. *Education*: Clark University, MA, 1975, PhD, 1978; Arizona State University, JD (cum laude), 1986. *Address & Affiliation*: Head, Indian Law & Tribal Relations Practice Group, Sacks Tierney, P.A., 4250 N. Drinkwater Blvd. #4, Scottsdale, AZ 85251 (480) 425-2615. E-mail: judith.dworkin@sackstierney.com. *Other professional posts*: Adjunct professor, Arizona State University, 1986-present; advisory committee, Indian Legal Program, 2006-present; solicitor, Hualapai Judiciary, Hualapai Indian Tribe. *Past professional posts*: Judge Pro Tem, Tribal Court of the Tohono O'odham Nation, 1995-99. Court & Bar Admissions: Southwest Intertribal Court of Appeals; Courts of the Hualapai, Hopi & Tohono O'odham tribes; State Bar of Arizona; Bar of the Navajo Nation; U.S. Supreme Court. *Awards & honors*: The Best Lawyers in America (Native American Law, Water Law), 2009-2016; Arizona's Finest Lawyers, 2010-present. *Published works*: Numerous articles, including, "Waivers of Sovereign Immunity Key Contracting With Indian Tribes," Southwest Contractor, 2005; "Doing Business With Our Neighbor: The Salt River Pima-Maricopa Indian Community."

DYER, PATRICIA (*Mukwa Odae Kwa*) (Little Traverse Bay Bands of Odawa-Mississippi Choctaw) 1953-
(admissions counselor)
Born February 14, 1953, Charlevoix, Mich. *Education*: Northern Michigan University, B.S.W., 1981; Michigan State University, M.A., 1997. *Principal occupation*: Admissions counselor. *Address*: 3572 Annis Rd., Mason, MI 48854 (517) 589-5065. *Affiliation*: Michigan Association of College Admissions Counselors, 1990-present. *Other professional post*: American Indian historian. *Community activities*: Little Traverse Bay Band of Odawa Tribal Council (Eagle President). *Memberships*: Ethno-history Association; Native American Indian Higher Education Council; Eagle President, an American Indian faculty & staff association at Michigan State University. *Interests*: "I make Michigan Native American art - porcupine quillwork, beadwork, leatherwork." *Published works*: Native American Experience (Michigan Dept. of Education, 1989); WPA Arts & Crafts Project (Michigan History Magazine, 1995); The Northern Michigan Ottawa Association, (MSU, 1997).

DYER, WAYNE K. (Western Shoshone)
(former tribal vice chairperson)
Afiliation & Address: Former Vice Chairperson, Yomba Shoshone Tribe, HC61 Box 6275, Austin, NV 89310 (775) 964-2463.

E

EADIE, BETTY J. (Rosebud Lakota)
(writer)
Address: P.O. Box 25490, Seattle, WA 98109. *Published work*: "Embraced by the Light."

EAGLE, SCOTT (Three Affiliated Tribes)
(tribal vice chairperson)
Affiliation & Address: Vice Chairperson, MHA Nation, Thee Affiliated Tribes, 404 Frontage Rd., New Town, ND 58763 (701) 627-4781.

EAGLE, TOM
(Indian council president)
Affiliation: N.W.T. Council of Friendship Centres, P.O. Box 2859, Yellowknife, NT, Canada X1A 2R2 (403) 920-2288; director, Tree of Peace Friendship Centre, P.O. Box 2667, Yellowknife, NT, Canada X1A 1H0.

EAGLE BULL, TAMARA (Oglala Lakota)
(architect)
Affiliation: The Presnell Group, 6808 Deerwood Dr., Lincoln, NE 68516. E-mail: teaglebull@hotmail.com. *Membership*: Americans for Indian Opportunity.

EAGLE ELK, STACI (Osage)
(public affairs specialist)
Education: University of Central Oklahoma, BA (Journalism Public Relations/Advertising); South Dakota State University (pursuing a Master's degree in Rural Sociology, specializing in Native Community Development). *Affiliation & Address*: Marketing Director, Operations Manager, Public Affairs Specialist (2008-present), American Indian & Alaska Native Tourism Association, 2401 12th St., Albuquerque, NM 87104 (505) 724-3592. *Past professional post*: Tourism Director, Osage Nation, Pawhuska, OK, 2003-07.

EAGLE STAFF, MARY KAY (Lakota/Northern Arapaho/ Northern Cheyenne)
(board secretary; government specialist)
Affiliation & Address: Executive Board Secretary & Government Speicalist, Native American Youth & Family Center, 5135 NE Columbia Ave., Portland, OR 97218 (503) 288-8177.

EAGLE STAFF, ROBERT (*To Wakanhi Wamblee-Blue Lighting Eagle*) (Lakota) 1952-
(educator)
Born December 20, 1952, Dupree, S.D. *Education*: University of South Dakota, B.S., M.S.; University of Washington, 1991- (doctoral candidate). *Affiliation & Address*: American Indian Heritage School, 9600 College Way N., Seattle, WA 98103 (206) 298-7895. *Affiliations*: Principal, Seattle Public Schools, Seattle, WA, 1989-present (206) 298-7801; American Indian Heritage School, Seattle, WA. *Other professional post*: Teacher, consultant, engineering assistant. *Community activities*: Enrolled at the Cheyenne River Sioux Reservation. *Memberships*: National Association of Secondary School Principals; Association of Washington School Principals; Principals Association of Seattle Schools; Lakota Sundancer Society, 1978-. *Awards, honors*: Numerous athletic awards, especially in basketball; numerous academic awards. *Interests*: "I am interested in researching the history of my family at various sites throughout the U.S. I would like to go back thousands of years & document those years."

EAGLE WOMAN, ANGELIQUE (Sisseton-Wahpeton)
(attorney)
Address: 12324E. 86th St. N. #115, Owasso, OK 74055 (918) 636-1427. E-mail: eaglewoman11@aol.com. *Other professional post*: Board Member, National Native American Bar Association.

EAGLEFEATHERS, MOKE (Northern Cheyenne)
(executive director)
Affiliation & Address: Executive director, North American Indian Alliance, 55 E. Galena, Butte, MT 59701 (406) 782-0461. *Other professional post*: Board President, National Council of Urban Indian Health (NCUIH), Region 4.

EAGLESTAFF-JETTY, DONNA (Lakota)
(BIE education program specialist)
Affiliation & Address: Education Program Specialist, Bureau of Indian Education, P.O. Box 215, Fort Yates, ND 58538 (701) 854-3499. E-mail: donna.eaglestaff@bie.edu.

EAGLEWOMAN, ANGELIQUE TOWNSEND (*Wambdi A. WasteWin*) (Sisseton-Wahpeton Dakota Oyate of the Lake Traverse Reservation)
(professor of law; attorney)
Education: Stanford University, BA (Political Science); University of North Dakota School of Law, JD; University of Tulsa College of Law, LL.M. (American Indian & Indigenous Law with Honors). *Affiliation & Address*: Associate Professor of Law & James E. Rogers Fellow in American Indian Law (2008-present), College of Law, University of Idaho, 875 Perimeter Dr. MS 2321, Moscow, ID 883844-2321 (208) 885-7634. E-mail: eaglewoman@ uidaho.edu She teaches in the areas of Native American Law, Native Natural Resources Law, Tribal Ecnomics & Law, & Civil Procedure. *Past professional posts*: Professor EagleWoman was formerly a member of the law faculty at Hamline University School of Law in St. Paul, MN and held a visitorship position at the University of Kansas School of Law & the Indigenous Nations Program. She served as General Counsel to the Sisseton-Wahpeton (Dakota) Oyate of the Lake Traverse Reservation, working as an associate attorney with Sonosky, Chambers, Sachse & Endrson in Washington, DC, and serving as

Tribal Public Defendert for the Kaw Nation & Ponca Nation, both of Oklahoma. *Memberships*: National Native American Bar Association (board member); Bar association of DC, Oklahoma & South Dakota. *Awards, honors*: In the Spring of 2008, Angelique received the University of Kansas Center for Indigenous nation's Crystal Eagle Award; the William F. and Joan L. Boyd Excellence in Teaching Award (January 2010); recognized as one of the twelve national Emerging Scholars by Diverse Issues in Higher Education (January 7, 2010 edition); recognized as a Distinguished Alumni Scholar by Stanford University (May 2010); the Inspiirational Faculty Award by the Univesity of Idaho Office of Alumni Relations (Dec. 2010); and named the Allan G. Shepard Distinguished Professor at the College of Law for 2011-12.

EASTERDAY, ADEL (*Nodiwayqua***) (Seneca) 1954-**
(teacher)
Born Sept. 30, 1954, Hillsdale, Mich. *Education*: Western Michigan University, BS (History), MA (Educational Leadership). *Address*: 6439 Nicolet Rd., Sault Ste. Marie, MI 49783 (906) 632-8611. E-mail: ayooper2@yahoo.com. *Affiliation*: Teacher, Sault Ste. Marie Public Schools, Dept. of Indian Education, 1980-96; Bahweting Tribal School, Sault Ste. Marie, MI, 1997-. *Other professional posts*: Guest lecturer, speaker, and storyteller presenting various workshops, in services & addresses on education, curriculum & topics relative to American Indian history & culture to public schools, colleges & universities, & professional organizations & conferences. *Membership*: American Legion Auxiliary Unit 0053. *Interests*: Writing, fishing, old movies, history, finger weaving, music, beadwork and world politics.

EASTMAN, JANE
(professor of anthropology; director of Cherokee studies)
Education: University of North Carolina, PhD (Anthropology). *Affiliation & Address*: Associate Professor of Anthropology & Director of Cherokee Studies, Western Carolna University, College of Arts & Sciences, McKee Bldg. 105A-C, Cullowhee, NC 28723 (828) 227-3841. E-mail: jeastman@email.wcu.edu. *Research Interests*: Native American societies of the Southeastern U.S., particularly community organization, gender relations, pottery analysis, and culture contact studies. She is working with Roseanna Belt, director of Western Carolina University's Cherokee Center, on a Cherokee Language Preservation Grant from the Cherokee Cultural Preservation Foundation and is an active member of the Cherokee Language Revitalization Committee. In 2003, she was elected president of the North Carolina Chapter of the Trail of Tears Association.

EASTMAN, SHAUN (Sisseton Wahpeton Oyate)
(tribal attorney)
Education: University of South Dakota School of Law, JD. *Affiliation & Address*: Tribal Attorney (2008-present), Sisseton Wahpeton Oyate, Lake Traverse Reservation, P.O. Box 509, Agency Village, SD 57262 (605) 698-3911. E-mail: shaune@swo-nsn.gov. She is a member of the Buffalo Lake District & licensed to practice in the SWO Tribal Court and the State & Federal Courts of South Dakota.

EASTWOOD, LESLIE (Samish)
(tribal general manager)
Affiliation & Address: General Manager, Samish Indian Nation, P.O. Box 217, Anacortes, WA 98221 (360) 293-6404.

EBARB, AMBER D. (Tlingit)
(program manager)
Born & raised in Anchorage, Alaska. Education: Whitman College, BA. *Affiliation*: Program Manager, National Congress of American Indians Policy Research Center, 1301 Connecticut Ave. NW, Suite 200, Washington, DC 20036 (202) 466-7767. E-mail: aebarb@ncai.org. She began working at the Center soon after its launch in 2003. Amber heads the Census Information Center at the center.

EBERHARD, ERIC D. 1945-
(attorney)
Education: Western Reserve University, BA, 1967; University of Cincinnati, School of Law, JD, 1970; George Washington University, LLM, 1972. *Affiliation & Address:* Distinguished Indian Law Practitioner in Residence, Center for Indian Law & Policy, Seattle University School of Law, P.O. Box 222000, Seattle, WA 98122 (206) 398-4284. E-mail: eberhare@seattleu.edu. *Past professional posts*: Legal services on the Navajo, Hopi & White Mountain Apache reservations; and as Deputy Attorney General of the Navajo Nation, 1973-83; executive director, Navajo Nation Washington Office, 1983-85; executive director, Navajo Nation, Washington office, 1985-87; Minority Staff Director & Counsel, Senate Select Committee on Indian Affairs, Washington, D.C., 1987-95; partner, Indian Law Practice Group, Dorsey & Whitney LLP, 1995-2009. Mr. Eberhard has been actively engaged in the practice of Indian affairs law since 1973. His practice has involved all aspects of the representations of Indian tribes & individuals in federal, state, and tribal forums. As Deputy General of the Navajo Nation & Executive Director of the Navajo Nation, Washington Office, he was involved in the development & passage of federal legislation relating to all aspects of tribal self-governance and development.

EBERHART, JOHN
(attorney)
Education: Georgetown University, BA; Columbia University, MA; Seattle University, JD. *Affiliation & Address*: Deputy General Counsel, Tanana Chiefs Conference TCC), 122 First Ave. #600, Fairbanks, AK 99701 (907) 452-8251. John performs legal services & advises tribes, clients, and programs for a 700 employee organization covering 42 villages spread over 235,000 square miles. He mentors the Human Resources Department, oversees corporate compliance & governance. *Other professional posts*: Adjunct lecturer, University of Alaska, Fairbanks; lecturer, Falmouth Institute, Fairfax, VA. *Past professional posts*: In-House Counsel & Director of Human Resources for Fairbanks Native Assn; since 1991, John has served as Arbitrator, Mediator, Hearing Examiner & Hearing Officer with the American Arbitration Association.

ECHO-HAWK, ABIGAIL (Pawnee)
(institute director)
Education: University of Washington, Bothell, BA, 2007; University of Washington, MA (Policy Studies), 2009. *Affiliation & Address*: Director (2016-present), Urban Indian Health Institute, P.O. Box 3364, Seattle, WA 98114 (206) 812-3030. E-mail: abigaile@uihi.org. *Past professional posts*: Co-Diretor, Civic Roots, 2007-08; Chair, Seattle Women's Commission, 2006-13; Associate Director, Tribal Liaison, University of Washington, Seattle, 2009-15; Co-Director, Partnerships for Native Health, Washington State University, Spokane, WA, 2015-16.

ECHO-HAWK, BUNKY (Pawnee/Yakama)
(proactive artist)
Education: Institute of American Indian Arts, AA (Creative Writing). Website: www.bunkyechohawk.com. Featured artist on the current show, *Impacted Nations,* a national traveling art exhibition. *Other professional posts*: Special Events Coordinator, American Indian College Fund; board member, Denver Indian Center; co-founder & executive director, NVision (national non-profit focuses on Native youth development). *Interests*: "I have been painting for years and have exhibited my work throughout the nation and overseas. I also write, mainly poetry, and have had some plays produced. I am also a freelance graphic designer & photographer."

ECHO-HAWK, COLLEEN (Pawnee/Athabascan)
(executive director-Indian club)
Affiliation & Address: Executive Director, Chief Seattle Club, 410 2nd Ave., Ext. S., Seattle, WA 98104 (206) 292-6214. E-mail: colleen.echohawk@ chiefseattleclub.org. *Other professional posts*: Founder, The Coalition to End Urban Native Homelessness; Co-founder and principal at Headwater People Consulting Group; serves on several local boards: KUOW (National Public Radio member station)board chair, Red Eagle Soaring Native Youth Theatre, et al.

ECHO-HAWK, CRYSTAL (Pawnee)
(executive director-consulting)
Education: University of Colorado (two years, History); University of Sussex, BA (History), 1994, MA (Political Science & Sociology), 1996. *Affiliation & Address*: President & CEO (2014-present), Echo Hawk Consulting, (720) 891-9118; E-mail: crystal@echohawkconsulting.com. Crystal is a visionary planner with the ability to identify and manage priorities, communicate effectively & develop key external partnerships throughout identified markets and constituencies. She has a proven track record in developing & implementing innovative organizations, programs and projects that deliver measurable results & fulfill a client's strategic vision in tribal, philanthropic and/or corporate settings. *Past professional posts*: Executive Director (2009-2014), Notah Begay III Foundation; National coordinator, National Commission for Democracy in Mexico, 1997-99; program coordinator, Indigenous Women's Network, 1999-2000; co-director of Indian education, Redwood Valley Schools, 2001-03; executive director, Buffalo Horse Camp, 2000-04; social service advocate, Lower Sioux Social Services, 2003-04; tribal planner, Pawnee Nation of Oklahoma, 2004-06; co-founder & president, NVision, 2006-09; assistant director of development, Native American Rights Fund, 2006-09.

ECHO HAWK, JOHN E. (Pawnee) 1945-
(attorney)
Born August 11, 1945, Albuquerque, N.M. Education: University of New Mexico, BA, 1967; University of New Mexico, School of Law, JD, 1970. *Address & Affiliation*: Native American Rights Fund, 1506 Broadway, Boulder, CO 80302 (303) 447-8760 (research associate, 1970-1972; deputy director, 1972-73, 1975-77; executive director, 1973-75, 1977-). E-mail: jechohawk@ narf.org. *Community activities*: Association on American Indian Affairs (member-board of directors); American Indian Lawyer Training Program (board of directors); National Committee on Responsive Philanthropy (member-board

of directors). *Memberships*: American Indian Bar Association; American Bar Association. *Awards, honors*: Assisted in forming the American Indian Law Student's Association; Americans for Indian Opportunity, Distinguished Service Award; White Buffalo Council, Friendship Award; 1987 National Indian Achievement Award from the Indian Council Fires; National Congress of American Indians, President's Indian Service Award; appointed to the Wayne Morse Chair of Law & Politics at the University of Oregon. *Interests*: Indian law.

ECHO HAWK, LAEL (Pawnee)
(attorney)

Education: University of Washington, BA, 1999; University of Washington School of Law, JD, 2003. *Affiliation & Address*: Of Counsel, Hobbsm Straus, Dean & Walker LLP, 2120 L St., NW, Washington, DC 20037 (202) 822-8282. E-mail: lexhohawk@hobbsstraus.com. *Other professional posts*: Instructor (2008-present), Everett Community College, Everett, WA; member-at-large, Northwest Indian Bar Assn Governing Council, 2012-13; justice, Suquamish Appeals Court, 2014-17. *Past professional posts*: Of Counsel (2012-2015), Indian Law, Garvey Schubert Barer, Washington, DC; Of Counsel, Crowell Law Office, Trial Advocacy Group, Spokane, WA, 2011-12; Tulalip Tribe, Tulalip, WA, 2003-10; Legislative Director (2010), Native American Contractors Assn, Washington, DC; counselor to the hair, National Indian Gaming Commission, Washington, DC. *Memberships*: National Native American Bar Assn (president, 2008-09): Northwest Indian Bar Assn (president, 2011-12; member-at-large, 2012-13).

ECHO HAWK, LARRY J. (Pawnee) 1948-
(attorney; assistant secretary-Indian Affairs)

Born August 2, 1948, Cody, Wyo. Raised in Farmington, New Mexico. *Education*: Brigham Young University, BS, 1970 (football scholarship); University of Utah Law School, J.D., 1973. *Principal occupation*: 11th Assistant Secretary-Indian Affairs. *Affiliation & Address*: Assistant Secretary-Indian Affairs, U.S. Dept. of the Interior, 1849 C St., NW - MS 4160-MIB, Washington, DC 20240 (202) 208-7163. *Other professional post*: Sr. Partner, EchoHawk Law Offices, Pocatello, Idaho. *Past professional posts*: Idaho State House of Representatives, 1983-90; Idaho State Attorney General, Boise, ID, 1991-95; law instructor, Brigham Young University's Clark Law School, 1995-. *Community activities*: Served on the American Indian Services National Advisory Board & Board of trustees; appointed by President Clinton to the Coordinating Council on Juvenile Justice & Delinquency Prevention; served on the Indian Alcoholism Counseling & Recovery Housing Program, and the American Indian Community Resource Center Board. *Awards, honors*: In 1991, Mr. Echo Hawk was awarded the George Washington University's Martin Luther King medal for his contributions to human rights, and was honored as a speaker at the Democratic National Convention. As Idaho's delegation chair, he became the first American Indian to lead a state delegation to a national political convention. *Interests*: Politics. Larry was the first Native American elected to a constitutional statewide office in 1982. He was the Democratic Party's nominee for Governor of Idaho in 1994 (lost).

ECHO HAWK, MARK A. (Pawnee)
(attorney; founding partner)

Education: Idaho State University, BS (Spanish), 1996; Brigham Young University, J. Reuben Clark Law School, JD, 1999. Affiliation & Address: Founding Partner, Echo Hawk & Olsen, PLLC, 505 Pershing Ave., P.O. Box 6119, Pocatello, ID 83205 (208) 478-1624. E-mail: mark@echohawk.com Mark maintains a general litigation practice as the founding partner of Echo Hawk & Olsen, PLLC. After graduating from Idaho State University, Mark studied law at the J. Reuben Clark Law School at Brigham Young University. During law school Mark served as a law clerk for the Idaho Supreme Court. Upon graduating from law school, he clerked for the Honorable Chief United States District Judge B. Lynn Winmill. He then worked as a litigation associate for Cooper & Larsen in Pocatello before starting Echo Hawk Law. He focuses his practice on Indian Law and has represented numerous tribal governments for over a decade. He has extensive experience with tribal land use and zoning, taxation, treaty rights, gaming regulation, jurisdiction, education, easements and rights of way, lobbying, economic development, TEDBs, contracts, tribal court and code revision matters. Mark has represented tribes in State and Federal courts, and has successfully fought for tribal interests in administrative proceedings as well. Additionally, Mark has worked on state and federal legislation affecting tribes. Mark speaks Spanish fluently. *Professional Activities*: Member, Idaho, Utah, & Federal Bar Associations; Member, Idaho Trial Lawyers Association; Member, Shoshone-Bannock Tribal Bar Association; Judge, Shoshone Paiute Tribal Court; Special Prosecutor, Shoshone-Bannock Tribes; Board Member, Federal Public Defender Services of Idaho

ECHO HAWK, PAUL C. (Pawnee)
(attorney)

Education: Brigham Young University, BS, 1995, Clark Law School, JD, 1998. *Affiliation & Address*: Attorney, Echo Hawk Law Office, P.O. Box 6119, Pocatello, ID 83205 (208) 705-9503. E-mail: paulechohawk@gmail.com *Past

professional post: Counsel, Kilpatrick Townsend & Stockton, LLP, Seattle, WA, 2013-14. Represents tribal governments in litigation in federal, state, and tribal courts. Includes water law, environmental regulations, jurisdiction disputes, treaty rights, land use, native religious freedom, gaming, and employment issues. Also represents tribes in drafting & reviewing contracts for commercial transactions as well as in drafting tribal laws & regulations to further tribal sovereignty & self-government. *Past professional posts*: Founding partner, EchoHawk Law Offices, Pocatello, ID; trial attorney, U.S. Department of Justice, Washington, DC; attorney, U.S. Attorney for the District of Idaho and the ative American Rights Fund in its Washington, DC office.

ECHO HAWK, SARAH (Pawnee)
(chief executive officer)

Education: Metropolitan State College, BS (Political Science); Regis University, MNM (Masters of Nonprofit Management); University of Colorado Law School, JD; University of Denver (graduate coursework in the applied communications master's program). *Affiliation & Address*: Chief Executive Officer, American Indian Science & Engineering Society (AISES), P.O. Box 9828, Abuquerque, NM 87119 (505) 765-1052. sechohawk@aises.org. *Other professional posts*: Vice president, First Nations Oweesta Corporation; adjunct professor, Metropolitan State College (teaches "Introduction to Native American Studies"). *Past professional posts*: Vice President, First Nations Development Institute, Longmont, CO; American Indian College Fund (five years); independent consultant offering training seminars & services to American Indian & nonprofit.

ECHO-HAWK, WALTER R., JR. (Pawnee)
(attorney)

Education: Oklahoma State University, BA (Political Science), 1970; University of New Mexico, JD, 1973. *Affiliation & Address*: Of Counsel, Indian Law & Gaming Practice Group, Crowe & Dunlevy LLP, 500 Kennedy Bldg., 321 S. Boston Ave., Tulsa, OK 74103 (918) 592-9874. E-mail: walter.echohawk@crowedunlevy.com *Other professional posts*: Teaches at Lewis & Clark Law School in Portland, OR; member, Supreme Court Justice for the Pawnee Nation; member, Board of Trustees, Pawnee Nation College, 2005-present); board chairperson, Native Arts & Cultures Foundation. *Past professional posts*: Staff Attorney (1973-81), Senior Staff Attorney (1982-2009), Native American Rights Fund, Boulder, CO. *Practice area*: Indian law & gaming; general counsel, Pawnee Nation; national coordinator for American Indian Religious Freedom Act Coalition; member, Board of Trustees, American Indian Ritual Object Repatriation Foundation, New York, NY. *Classes Taught*: Federal Indian Law, U.S. Forest Service, 2005-2009. *Awards, honors*: 2015 Federal Bar Association Lawrence R. Baca Lifetime Achievement Award; 2014 President's Award for his commitment to human right by the International Association of Official Human Rights Agencies; 2010 Oklahoma Governor's Commendation Award for professional contributions on behalf of indigenous cultures throughout the nation; 2009 Federal Bar Association's Judge Sarah Hughes Civil Liberties Award; 2009 Distinguished Native American Alumni, Oklahoma State University; 1998 Martin Luther King Peace Award, Metropolitan College, Denver, Colorado;1995 American Bar Association Spirit of Excellence Award, Commission on Opportunities for Minorities in the Profession; 1992 ACLU of Oregon Civil Liberties Award. *Membership*: Native American Bar Association. Speaking Engagement: Keynote Speaker, "Native Pride & Spirit: Yesterday, Today and Forever," Society of American Indian Government Employees Conference, June 10, 2014, Albuquerque, NM. *Published works*: The Native American Graves Protection and Repatriation Act: Background and Legislative History, 23 Arizona St. L.J. 35, 1992; "Law, Legislation and Native Religion" in American Indian Religious Traditions, Vol. 2, J-P, Suzanne J. Crawford (ed.), Santa Barbara, CA: ARC-CLIO, 2005; Battlefields & Burial Grounds: The Indian Struggle to Protect Ancestral Graves in the U.S. (Lerner, 1994); In the Courts of the Conqueror: The 10 Worst Indian Law Cases Ever Decided (Fulcrum Publishing, 2010); In the Light of Justice (2013),

ECOFFEY, ROBERT (Oglala Lakota)
(BIA deputy regional director)

Born on the Pine Ridge Reservation, S.D. *Address & Affiliation*: Deputy Regional Director, Great Plains Regional Office, Bureau of Indian Affairs, 115 4th Ave., SE, Federal Bldg., Aberdeen, SD 57401 (605) 226-7416 (2004-present). Mr. Ecoffey oversees BIA programs for North & South Dakota, and Nebraska, including social services, transportation, law enforcement & child welfare. *Past professional posts*: Appointed to U.S. Marshall from SD, 1994-96 (first Native American to ever hold that post); Supt., BIA Pine Ridge Agency, Pine Ridge, SD, 1996-2001; Deputy Director of BIA Office of Law Enforcement Services, Albuquerque, NM, 2001-2004.

EDER, JEANNE (Dakota Sioux)
(associate professor)

Born on the Fort Peck Assiniboine & Sioux Reservation, Poplar, MT. *Education*: Carroll College (Helena, MT), BA (American History); Montana State University, MA (American History); Washington, State University, PhD, 2000 (American History & Public History). *Address & Affiliation*: Director of

Alaska Native Studies Program (2001-2005), Associate Professor, Dept. of History, University of Alaska, Anchorage, AK (2005-present). *Published works*: The Dakota Sioux; The Makah; American Indian Education: A History, with Jon Reyhner (University of Oklahoma Press, 2004). *Activities*: Conducts workshops for children on Native American stories, dances, games, dream catchers & toys.

EDGE, JAMES E. 1948-
(health administrator)
Born April 29, 1948, Anacortes, Wash. *Education*: University of Washington, BS, 1971; University of Hawaii, MPH, 1979. *Principal occupation*: Health administrator. *Address*: 1580 Rio Vista Way S., Salem, OR 97302 (503) 399-5937. *Affiliation*: Service Unit Director, Western Oregon Service Unit, Indian Health Service, Salem, OR, 1980-. *Other professional post*: Chairperson, Service Unit Directors' Steering Committee on Health Care Reform, Portland Area Indian Health Service, 1993-. *Military service*: Commissioned Officer, 18 years, USPHS, (Captain). *Memberships*: American College of Healthcare Executives; Association of Military Surgeons of the U.S.; Reserve Officers Association; American Academy of Medical Administrators; Commissioned Officers Association of the U.S. Public Health Service; American Public Health Association; Washington State Pharmaceutical Association. *Awards, honors*: Indian Health Service Long Term Training, 1978-79; USPHS Citation and Ribbon, 1984; USPHS Commendation Medal, 1986; USPHS Outstanding Unit Citation, 1988; USPHS Unit Commendation, 1989; USPHS Outstanding Service Medal, 1991). *Interests*: "Special interest in rural and minority health care. Eighteen years broad based experience in American Indian health care. Extensive travel & consultation in Pacific Island health care; running, skiing, fishing, antique cars." *Biographical sources*: The National Dean's List, 1979-80; Outstanding Young Men of American, 1980; Marquis Who's Who in Finance and Industry, 1992-93.

EDMO, BLAINE J. (Shoshone-Bannock)
(former tribal chairperson)
Education: University of Idaho; Idaho State University (Paralegal Certificate). *Affiliation & Address*: Former chairperson (2015-17), Shoshone-Bannock Tribes, P.O. Box 306, Fort Hall, ID 83203 (208) 478-3805. E-mail: bedmo@sbtribes.com/ Mr. Edmo served six terms on the council and as district representative of Ross Fork District. His areas of focus range from tribal courts, water rights, treaty rights, natural resources, jurisdiction, protection & preservation of tribal land base, tribal economic diversity, language preservation, tribal history and improvement of health care for our community. Prior to serving on the council, Mr. Edmo worked as a tribal prosecutor, trial judge, chief judge & court administrator for various tribal governments ranging from the Shoshone-Paiute, the Te-moak Band, the Fort McDermitt & Fallan band all of Nevada, the Fort Duchesne in Utah, and the Jicarilla Apache in New Mexico.

EDMO, ED, JR. (Shoshoni-Bannock) 1944-
(consultant, poet)
Address: 9430 N.E. Prescott, Portland, OR 97220 (503) 256-2257. *Interests*: Professional Native American story teller who visits schools, libraries, colleges, and museums to present a program of arts & crafts, story telling of legends & myths of various Native American tribes. He is a crafts artist with shows held periodically in cities and towns of the Northwest. He has many published poems and is author of book and magazine materials.

EDMO, SE-AH-DOM (Shoshone-Bannock/Nez Pece/Yakama)
(program coordinator)
Born & raised in the Portland Metro area. *Affiliation & Address*: Coordinator, Indigenous Ways of Knowing Program, Lewis & Clark College, Graduate School of Education & Counseling, Center for Community Engagement, 0615 S.W. Palatine Hill Rd., MSC 85, Portland, OR 97219 (503) 768-6040. E-mail: edmo@lclark.edu. *Community activities*: Serves on the boards of the Oregon Indian Education Association (vice president); Columbia Riverkeeper, the National Indian Women's Health Resource Center, Nak-Nu-Wit (Systems of care Program) at NARA Northwest, and Northwest Indian Storytellers Association; chair, Mascot Project.

EDMO-SUPPAH, LORRAINE P. (Shoshone-Bannock) 1948-
(journalist, program administrator)
Born October 26, 1948, Blackfoot, Idaho. *Education*: University of Montana, BA (Journalism), 1970; University of New Mexico, MA, 1982; University of Missouri, Multi-Cultural Management Program; University of Idaho, School of Communications (Journalist in Residence 2001-2002 through a grant from the Freedom Forum). *Principal occupation*: Journalist, program administrator. *Affiliation & Address*: Editor, Sho-Ban News, P.O. Box 900, Fort Hall, ID 83203 (208) 478-3701. E-mail: edmosup@ida.net. *Past affiliations*: TV News Reporter, 1970-72; resource development specialist, 1972-73, executive director, 1973-75, Idaho Inter-Tribal Board, Inc., Boise, Idaho; technical writer, 1976-79, development officer, 1979-80, Native American Rights Fund, Boulder, CO; executive director, American Indian Graduate Center, Albuquerque, NM,

1984-93; editor, Sho-Ban News (weekly tribal newspaper), 1993-present. *Other professional posts*: Treasurer, Native American Journalists Association. *Community activities*: Warden & treasurer, Episcopal Urban Indian Ministry, Albuquerque, NM, 1986-93; board of directors, UNITY: Journalists of Color, Inc. *Memberships*: Native American Journalists Association (NAJA); National Indian Education Association (executive committee-board of directors, 1989-92; executive director, 1993-99); National Organization of Native American Women (former president); National Congress of American Indians. *Awards, honors*: Selected by the Albuquerque Tribune as one of 12 "Rising Stars" in the education field for 1988; selected as a 1989 Outstanding Young Woman of American, Boulder, CO; 1995 Wassaja Award from NAJA Board of Directors for excellence in Native journalism; numerous awards from NAJA and the Idaho Press Club for her photography and writing. NAJA named the Sho-Ban News the Best Native Weekly in 2000, & honorable mention for General Excellence in 2001. *Interests*: "I am interested in working for the betterment of Indian tribal governments and American Indian people. I attempt to do this through advocacy; service on Board and commissions, writing, etc. I have travelled extensively to visit and work with tribes & Indian organizations throughout the country." *Published work*: "From the Frontlines," essay.

EDMUND, RICK
(editor)
Affiliation: Susquehanna Valley Native American Eagle, Box 99, Walnut Valley Farm, Loganville, PA 17342 (717) 428-1440.

EDMUNDS, JUDITH A. 1943-
(dealer-American Indian jewelry)
Born September 8, 1943, Waltham, Mass. *Education*: Massachusetts College of Pharmacy. *Principal occupation*: Dealer of fine American Indian jewelry and related items. *Address*: Box 788, West Yarmouth, MA 02673. *Affiliation*: President-treasurer, Edmonds of Yarmouth, Inc., 1973-. *Other professional posts*: State chairperson, Indian Arts & Crafts Assn (served on Education & Public Relations Committee; currently chairperson for Massachusetts). *Interests*: Ms. Edmunds writes, "My business is a retail outlet, but my greatest pleasure is educating the general public on the different Indian tribes and their style of work and their living conditions, and to create collectors of fine Indian art. By educating these people - those dealers that are selling fakes and misrepresenting their wares will soon be out of business, I travel to reservations a couple of times a year and spend time in the Hopi Mesas and San Domingo Pueblos, as well as on the Navajo Reservation; we have Indian friends spread out through the various reservations, as well as Anglo friends."

EDWARDS, BRENDA SHEMAYNE (Caddo)
(tribal chairperson)
Affiliation & Address: Chairperson, Caddo Nation, P.O. Box 487, Binger, OK 73009 (405) 656-2344. E-mail: bgedwards@caddonation.org

EDWARDS. CATHERINE (Hoh)
(tribal executive director)
Affiliation & Address: Executive Director, Hoh Tribe, P.O. Box 2196, Forks, WA 98331 (360) 374-6582. E-mail: marial@hohtribe-nsn.gov

EDWARDS, DAVID (Tyme Maidu)
(rancheria chairperson)
Affiliation: Berry Creek Rancheria, 5 Tyme Way, Oroville, CA 95966 (530) 534-3859.

EDWARDS, JAMES (Tyme Maidu)
(rancheria chairperson)
Affiliation & Address: Chairperson, Berry Creek Rancheria, 5 Tyme Way, Oroville, CA 95966 (530) 534-3859. E-mail: jedwards@ berrycreekrancheria.com

EDWARDS, JAMES LEE (Absentee Shawnee)
(tribal governor)
Affiliation & Address: Absentee Shawnee Tribe, 2025 S. Gordon Cooper, Shawnee, OK 74801 (405) 275-4030.

EDWARDS, KENNETH LEE (*Rainbow Cougar*) (Colville) 1956-
(artist, storyteller/speaker/comedian)
Born February 8, 1956, Greenville, S.C. *Education*: Institute of American Indian Arts, AFA, 1977. *Principal occupation*: Artist-painter; storyteller, speaker, comedian. *Address*: 287-H Omak Riverside Eastside Dr., Omak, WA 98841 (509) 826-4744. *Membership*: Indian Arts & Crafts Association, 1984-present. Ken resides on the Colville Indian Reservation and works in a wide variety of media: predominantly watercolor, oil, acrylic, and pen and ink. He is experienced in silversmithing, welding, drafting, photography and beadwork. An additional talent is that of storyteller and oral historian. Ken has traveled to about 100 Indian reservations and memorized more than one thousand stories from many tribes. *Awards, honors*: Participated in the First National Indian Art Show, Nov. 1985, held in Washington, DC; did the painting which was made

into a Porter-Print announcing the first Miss Indian U.S.A. Pageant; his painting, "First Love" was part of a Native American Art Show at the December 1987 International Friendship House, Moscow, USSR. His artwork has been exhibited and sold in fine art shows and galleries across the U.S. He has received several top awards at major shows. His ink drawings and poetry have been published in ten Indian newspapers. *Published works*: Illustrated five children's books - How the Animals Got Their Names, How Food Was Given, Neekna and Chemai, and Turtle and the Eagle - published by Theytus Books, Penticton, B.C., Canada; Wintercount Card Co., Newcastle, CO has purchased 15 of Ken's watercolors and added them to their series of cards by Native American artists.

EDWARDS, TRACY (Pit River)
(rancheria tribal CEO)
Affiliation & Address: CEO, Redding Rancheria, 2000 Redding Rancheria Rd., Redding, CA 96001 (530) 225-8979.

EID, TROY A.
(attorney)
Education: Stanford University, BA, 1986; Univesityof Chicago Law School, JD, 1991. *Affiliation & Address*: Partner & Co-Chair, American Indian Law Practice Group, Greenburg Traurig LLP, 1200 17th St., Suite 2400, Denver, CO 80202 (303) 572-6521. E-mail: eidt@gtlaw.com. The Law Practice Group is one of the top-rated in the U.S. by the "Chambers USA" guide. Chambers features Mr. Eid in both American Indian law & environmental law/natural resources. *Other professional posts*: Adjunct Professor of Law, University of Colorado School of Law, Boulder, CO; chairperson, Indian Law & Order Commission, which advises President Obama and the Congress on criminal justice & public safety issues concerning 566 federally recognized Indian tribes and nations throughout the country. Past professional posts: U.S. Attorney for the District of Colorado, 2006-09; Mr. Eid was appointed as Colorado's U.S. Attorney by Presdient George W. Bush; and was appointed to the Commission by U.S. Senate Majority Leader, Harry Reid (D-NV) & unanimously elected Chairperson by its members. *Admitted to Practice*: Hualapai Indian Tribe and Navajo Nation. *Awards, honors*: "Lawyer of the Year" by Law Week Colorado (2011), in recognition of his role in the $1.5 billion sale of the HealthONE hospital system; "Member of the Year" by the Navajo Nation Bar Association (2012); listed in "Best Lawyers in America." He has also been honored by the FBI, the Drug Enforcement Administration, U.S. Secret Service, the National Congress of American Indians, the U.S. Senate Committee on Indian Affairs, and the U.S. Hispanic Chamber of Commerce.

ELDEMAR, KATHERINE M. (Tlingit)
(attorney)
Affiliation: Judge, Whatcom County Superior Court, 311 Grand Ave., Bellingham, WA 98225 (360) 676-6777 ext. 50039. E-mail: keldemar@co.whatcom.wa.us. *Membership*: Americans for Indian Opportunity. *Interests*: Law enforcement, legal issues.

ELIAS, JENNINE J. (Inupiaq)
(external affairs coordinator)
Born in Anchorage, AK. *Education*: University of Arizona, BA, Pepperdine University, MA (Public Policy & Dispute Resolution). *Affiliation*: External Affairs Coordinator, Native American Contractors Association, 1514 P St., NW #2, Washington, DC 20005 (202) 758-2676. Website: www.nativecontractors.org. *Past professional posts*: Program Associate, National Congress of American Indians, Policy Research Center. She has interned at the Tribal Law & Policy Institute, Rural CAP through the Denali Commission, the Native Nations Institute, and Cook Inlet Region, Inc., as a First Alaskans Institute intern while attending college.

ELLIOTT, JERRY C. (*High Eagle*) (Osage/Cherokee) 1943-
(physicist, author, composer, musician, actor)
Born February 6, 1943, Oklahoma City, Okla. *Education*: BS in Physics, Mathematics. *Affiliation & Address*: High Eagle Productions, Inc., P.O. Box 58182, Houston, TX 77258 (281) 483-0819; E-mail: jchigheagle-2004@yahoo.com; Website: www.ghgcorp.com/higheagl. *Other professional posts*: Deputy chief technologist. NASA Johnson Space Center, Houston, TX. *Awards, honors*: Presidential Medal of Freedom; Medal of Honor from the National Society of Daughters of the American Revolution; Bronze Halo Award for Outstanding Contributions to Humanity, presented by the Southern California Motion Picture Council; AISES, Ely S. Parker Award for Outstanding Technical Accomplish-ments & Community Service; Cherokee Medal of Honor by the Cherokee Nation. Memberships: American Society of Composers; Authors & Publishers (ASCAP) American Indian Science & Engineering Society, Inc. (AISES); Sigma Xi, Scientific Research Society. *Interests*: Music, writing, acting, seminar presenting. *Published works*: Campfire Stories & Legends, Vol. I & II; Soul Fire Odyssey; Lovebeams; Mystic Moods of Love and Life; Four Directions (book).

ELLIOTT, LEROY J. (Kumeyaay Diegueno)
(tribal chairperson)
Affiliation & Address: Chairperson, Manzanita Band of the Kumeyaay Nation, P.O. Box 1302, Boulevard, CA 91905 (619) 766-4930.

ELLIOTT, SONNY J., SR. (Pomo)
(tribal chairperson)
Affiliation & Address: Chairperson, Hopland Band of Pomo Indians, 3000 Shanei Rd., Hopland, CA 95449 (707) 472-2111. E-mail: sjelliott@hoplandtribe.com

ELLIS, A.D. (Muscogee Creek)
(tribal principal chief)
Born in Pawnee, Okla. *Education*: Tulsa Business College. *Affiliation*: Principal Chief, Muscogee Creek Nation, P.O. Box 580, Okmulgee, OK 74447 (918) 756-8700. *Past tribal posts*: He served as second chief from January 2000 to December 31, 2004; and served four consecutive two-year terms as a National Council Representative from the Okmulgee District. *Other professional posts*: Member, Oklahoma Indian Affairs Commission (2007-2010). Military service: U.S. Air Force & Oklahoma National Guard. *Award, honors*: He was appointed, in 2007, to serve a 3-year term on the Oklahoma Indian Affairs Commission by Gov. Brad Henry; received a personal invitation from President George W. Bush, to visit the White House, for a second time.

ELLISON, ROSEMARY
(museum curator)
Affiliations & Address: Curator, Southern Plains Indian Museum, 715 E. Central Blvd., P.O. Box 749, Anadarko, OK 73005 (405) 247-6221.

ELLSBURY, JACOBY McCABE (Navajo) 1983-
(major league baseball player)
Born Sept. 11, 1983 in Madras, Oreg. *Education*: Attended Oregon State University, 2003-05. *Affiliations*: Boston Red Sox, Fenway Park, Boston, MA; he's a registered member of the Colorado River Indian Tribes. *Awards, honors*: 2005 First Team NCAA All-American leading them to two straight (2004 & 2005) College World Series wins. Jacoby is the first Native American of Navajo descent to reach the major leagues; 2011 runner-up for MVP in the American League.

ELLSWORTH, CHRISTINA (Navajo)
(craftsperson, co-manager)
Affiliation: Co-manager, Crownpoint Rug Weavers' Association, P.O. Box 1630, Crownpoint, NM 87313 (505) 786-5302 or 786-7386. *Product*: Navajo rugs sold at auction.

EMERY, STEVEN CHARLES (*Mato Tanka*) (Rosebud Sioux) 1958-
(attorney; secretary of tribal relations)
Born November 14, 1958, in S.D. Education: University of South Dakota, BA, 1986; Harvard Law School, JD, 1989. *Afiliation & Address*: Secretary of Tribal Relations, South Dakota Department of Tribl Reations, 302 E. Dakota, Pierre, SD 57501 (605) 773-3415. *Other professional posts*: Attorney, Cheyenne River Sioux Tribe, Eagle Butte, SD, 1989-; partner, Van Norman & Emery, Eagle Butte, SD, 1989-; General counsel, Marty Indian School, Marty, SD, 1990-. *Community activities*: Cheyenne River Sioux Tribal Police Commission (chairperson, 1989-91); Dakota Plains Legal Services Board of Directors, 1989-91; Cheyenne River Community College Board of Directors (vice-chairperson), 1990-. *Military service*: U.S. Army, 1980—82. *Memberships*: South Dakota Bar Association; Federal Bar Association; American Bar Association; Eighth Circuit Court of Appeals, U.S. *Awards, honors*: McGovern-Abourezk Human Rights Award, USD Political Science/Criminal Justice Dept., 1985; Phi Beta Kappa (Alpha Chapter, USD, 1986); Faculty Appreciation Award, USD Political Science/Criminal Justice Dept., 1986; Who's Who in American Universities & Colleges (1985-86 Edition); Massachusetts Indian Association Fellow (1986-89); U.S. Dept. of Education American Indian Fellowship Recipient (1986-89). *Interests*: "Traditional singer (Itazipco Hoka); singer/songwriter; guitarist; lectures on topics such as: federal Indian law, Lakota/Dakota culture and language." *Published work*: Musical album - Dakota Wakan Cekiye Odowan (collection of ten hymns played & sung by Steve Emery in the Dakota language, June 1986.

EMM, ELWOOD L. (Yerington Paiute)
(tribal councilperson)
Affiliation & Address: Councilperson, Yerington Paiute Tribe, 171 Campbell Lane, Yerington, NV 89447 (775) 463-3301.

EMM. STACI (Yerington Paiute)
(professor & extension educator)
Education: University of Nevada, Reno, BS (Public Relations & Business management); Colorado State University, BS (Agriculture). *Affiliation & Address*: Extension Educator/Associate Professor, University of Nevada Cooperative Extension, Reno, NV *Other professional post*: Vice Chair, Indian

Land Tenure Foundation, Little Canada, MN. *Past professional post*: Newspaper reporter, Federally Recognized Tribes Extension Program Coordintor for Nevada Tribes. Staci also raises registered Black Angus cattle with her father & sister on the family ranch on the Walker iver reservation.

EMMERICH, LISA E.
(American Indian studies coordinator)
Affiliation & Address: Coordinator & Advisor, American Indian Studies Program, Center for Multicultural & Gender Studies & History Department, 611 Butte Hall, California State University, Chico, 400 West First St., Chico, CA 95929 (530) 898-6338. E-mail: lemmerich@csuchico.edu.

EMMONS, NICHLAS (Kispoko Shawnee)
(professor of Native American & Indigenous studies)
Affiliation & Address: Professor, Native American & Indigenous Studies, Fort Lewis College, 1000 Rim Dr., Durango, CO 81301. E-mail: ndemmons@fortlewis.edu.

ENAS, ELDRED (Mohave-Chemehuevi)
(former tribal chairperson)
Affiliation & Address: Former Chairperson, Colorado River Indian Tribes, 26600 Mohave Rd., Parker, AZ 85344 (928) 669-9211. Eldred served about 15 years previousiy on the tribal council, including the position of vice chairperson.

ENCELEWSKI, RICHARD (Kenaitse)
(Alaskan village president)
Affiliation & Address: President, Ninilchik Traditional Council, P.O. Box 39070, Ninilchik, AK 99639 (907) 567-3313. E-mail: masteryoda@alaska.net.

ENDREZZE ANITA (Yaqui) 1952-
(poet, writer, artist, professor)
Born March 15, 1952, Long Beach, Calif. *Education*: BA in English & Secondary Education; Eastern Washington University, MA (Creative Writing). *Principal occupation*: Poet, writer, artist, professor. Resides in Everett, Washington. *Affiliations*: Teach part time in area universities. *Community activities*: Volunteer art teacher for daughter's school. *Awards, honors*: 1992 Bumbershoot / Weyerhauser Award & the Governor's Writing Award for Washington State for "At the Helm of Twilight." *Published works*: The Mountain and the Guardian Spirit (CDR Forlag, Denmark, 1986); At the Helm of Twilight (Broken Moon Press, 1992); Burning the Fields, A Confluence Chapbook (Confluence Press); The North People (Blue Cloud Quarterly Press); The Humming of Stars & Bees & Waves (Making Waves Press, 1998); Throwing Fire at the Sun, Water at the Moon (U. of Arizona Press, 2000).

ENGLAND-AYTES, KATHRYN (Delaware/Cherokee)
(educator; consultant; board secretary)
Affiliation & Address: Lecturer (2007-present), Division of Social, Behavioral & Global Studies, California State University at Monterey Bay, 100 Campus Center, Seaside, CA 93955 (831) 582-3000. *Other professional posts*: Consultant, The Kinship Center, Monterey County, CA; curriculum consultant for the Cherokee Nation, Tahlequah, OK; board secretary, Native American Children's Alliance, Cleveland, OH.

ENGLISH, SHIRLEY (Potawatomi)
(former tribal chairperson)
Affiliation: Huron Potawatomi Indian Council, Pine Creek Reservation, 2221 1.5 Mile Rd., Fulton, MI 49052 (616) 729-5151.

ENICH, JERRY (Snoqualmie Coast Salish)
(tribal head chief)
Affiliation & Address: Chief, Snoqualmie Indian Tribe, P.O. Box 969, Snoqualmie, WA 98065 (425) 888-6551.

ENOS, DIANE (Pima-Maricopa)
(former tribal president; attorney)
Education: Arizona State University, B.A.; ASU Law School, J.D., 1992. *Affiliation & Address*: President, Salt River Pima-Maricopa Indian Community, 10005 E. Osborn Rd., Scottsdale, AZ 85256 (480) 362-7465. *Other professional posts*: Director, Family Advocacy Center of the Salt River Pime-Maricopa Indian Community; Board Vice President, Inter-Tribal Council of Arizona, Phoenix; chair, Arizona Indian Gaming Association; Western Area delegate to the Tribal Justice Advisory Group for the U.S. Dept. of Justice; chairperson, Domestic Violence Committee for the Maricopa Association of Governments. *Past professional posts*: Senior Trial Attorney, Maricopa County Public Defender's Office (11 years); council member, (16 years).

ENOS, TERRY O. (Pima-Papago)
(tribal councilperson)
Affiliation & Address: Ak Chin Indian Community Council, 42507 W. Peters & Nall Rd., Maricopa, AZ 85239 (520) 568-2227.

ENRIIQUEZ, ERIC (Pomo/Wailaki)
(director of operations)
Affiliation & Address: Director of Operations, California Native Health Center, 2020 J St., Sacramento, CA 95811 (916) 341-0576 ext. 2212.

ENUBUZOR, TRISHA L. (Spirit Lake Ojibwe)
(attorney; tribal deputy socilictor general))
Education: University of North Dakota, BS (Criminal Justice), 2009; University of Dakota Law School, JD, 2012. *Affiliation & Address*: Deputy Socilicitor General, Mille Lacs Band of Ojibwe Indians, 43408 Oodena Dr., Onamia, MN 56359.

ENYART, CHARLES D. (Eastern Shawnee)
(tribal chief)
Address & Affiliation: Eastern Shawnee Tribe, P.O. Box 350, Seneca, MO 64865 (918) 666-2435.

EOKER, DANNY (Navajo)
(school principal)
Affiliation & Address: Ch'ooshgai (Chuska) Community School, P.O. Box 321, Tohatchi, NM 87325 (505) 733-2700.

ERASMUS, BILLY (Dene)
(president-Dene Nation)
Affiliation: Dene Nation, Denedeh National Office, P.O. Box 2338, Yellowknife, Northwest Territories, Canada Y1A 2P7 (403) 873-4081.

ERASMUS, GEORGES HENRY (Dene) 1948-
(politician, administration)
Born August 8, 1948, Behchoko, N.W.T., Canada. *Principal occupation*: Co-chair, Royal Commission on Aboriginal Peoples. *Affiliations*: Secretary, Indian Band Council, Yellowknife, NWT, Can., 1969-71; Organizer & chairman, Community Housing Association, Yellowknife, 1969-72; advisor to president, Indian Brotherhood of NWT, 1970-71; fieldworker & regional staff director, Company of Young Canadians, 1970-73; chairman, University Canada North, 1971-75; director, Community Development Program, Indian Brotherhood of Northwest Territories (later the Dene Nation) (director, Community Development Program, 1973-76; president, 1976-83); president, Denedeh Development Corporation, 1976-83; elected Northern vice-chief, Assembly of First Nations, 1983; elected National Chief, Assembly of First Nations, Ottawa, Canada, 1985, re-elected 1988-91; co-chair, Royal Commission on Aboriginal Peoples, Ottawa, ON, 1991-99. *Membership*: Honorary member, Ontario Historical Society, 1990. *Awards, honors*: Representative for Canada on Indigenous Survival International, 1983; Canadian delegate to World Council of Indigenous Peoples International Conferences, 1984-85; appointed director of the World Wildlife Fund of Canada, 1987; appointed to the Order of Canada, 1987; appointed to the Board of the Canadian Tribute to Human Rights, 1987; board member, Energy Probe Research Foundation, Operation Dismantle, 1988; honorary committee member, International Youth for Peace and Justice, 1988; advisory council member, The Earth Circle Foundation, 1988; Honorary Degree of Doctorate of Laws, Queen's University, 1989; board of directors, Earth Day 1990; Board of Directors, SAVE Tour, 1990; art, school, athletic awards. *Biographical sources*: New Canadian Encyclopedia; Who's Who in Canada. *Published work*: Co-author, Drumbeat: Anger and Renewal in Indian Country (Summer Hill Publishers, 1990).

ERDRICH, HEID (Turtle Mountain Chippewa)
(poet)
Address & Affiliation: University of St. Thomas, English Dept. - 30F, St. Paul, MN 55105 (612) 962-5626.

ERDRICH, LOUISE (Turtle Mountain Chippewa)
(writer)
Address: c/o Harper Collins Publishing, 10 E. 53 St., New York, NY 10022 (800) 242-7737.

ERLICH, IAN (Inupiaq)
(president & CEO)
Affiliation & Address: President & CEO (2008-present), Maniilaq Association, P.O. Box 258, Kotzebue, AK 99752 (907) 442-3311.

ESCALANTI, KEENY, SR. (Quechan)
(tribal president)
Affiliation & Address: President, Quechan Tribe, P.O. Box 1899, Yuma, AZ 85366 (760) 572-0213.

ESKOFSKI, M. LOLLIE (New York Oneida) 1949-
(Indian education program coordinator)
Born January 22, 1949, Waukegan, Ill. *Education*: Associates Degree in Communications/English. *Principal occupation*: Indian education program coordinator. *Address & Affiliation*: Title VII coordinator (1991-present), Rapid

River Public Schools, P.O. Box 68, Rapid River, MI 49878 (906) 474-6411 ext. 572. E-Mail: leskofski@rapidriver.k12.mi.us. *Other professional posts*: Senior class advisor; Yearbook advisor. *Community activities*: Eucharistic minister. *Interests*: Gardening, photography, camping, baseball, football, Chicago Cubs.

ESMAILKA, JUSTIN (Eskimo)
(Alaskan village chief)
Affiliation & Address: First Chief, Village of Kaltag, P.O. Box 129, Kaltag, AK 99748 (907) 534-2224.

ESQUERRA, N. LEVI (Chemehuevi)
(Indian center director)
Affiliation & Address: Director, The Center for American Indian Economic Development, Box 15066, Northern Arizona University, Flagstaff, AZ 86011 (928) 523-7320. E-mail: levi.esquerra@nau.edu. *Past professional posts*: Business Development Representative, Arizona Commission of Indian Affairs; tribal chair, council member, planner, Chemehuevi Indian Tribe. *Awards, honors*: In 2009, the U.S. Dept. of State invited Mr. Esquerra to Argentina to lecture on Economic Development for Indigenous Non-Governmental Organizations under the department's Speaker & Specialist Program.

ESQUIVEL, DENNIS (Ottawa-Ojibwe)
(artist, studio owner)
Address: P.O. Box 28804, Santa Fe, NM 87592 (505) 438-2062 E-mail: myingan@yahoo.com. *Artwork*: Fine furniture & woodworking.

ESTABO, ANDREA (*PEPPER*) (Ho-Chunk)
(tribal representative)
Born in California & raised in Blue Wing Village in Tomah, Wisc. *Education*: Upper Iowa University, BS (Business), 2010. *Affiliation & Address*: District 2 Representative, Ho-Chunk Nation, P.O. Box 667, Black River Falls, WI 54615 (715) 284-9343. E-mail: andrea.estabo@ho-chunk.com. *Past tribal posts*: Ho-Chunk Nation (Human Resource Specialist, 1994-96; Residential Services Counselor, Dept. of Housing, 1999-2001; Grants Program Manager, 2006-07; Executive Director of Administration, 2007-11).

ESTES, TERESA
(BIA agency deputy supt. of trust services)
Affiliation & Address: Deputy Supt. of Trust Services, Bureau of Indian Affairs, Minnesota Agency, Federal Bldg., Rm. 418, 522 Minnesota Ave., NW, Bemidji, MN 56601 (218) 751-2011 E-mail: teresa.estes@bia.gov

ESTEVES, PAULINE (Timbisha Shoshone)
(tribal chairperson)
Address & Affiliation: Chairperson, Historic Preservation Committee and Tribal Council, Timbisha Shoshone Tribe, P.O. Box 206, Death Valley, CA 92328 (760) 786-2374. E-mail: timbisha@aol.com. *Community activities*: Alliance to Protect Native Rights in National Parks Historic Preservation Committee; enrollment committee for Timbisha Shoshone Tribe. *Memberships*: National Congress of American Indians; Toiyabe Indian Health Project, Inc.; California Indian Manpower Consortium. *Published work*: The Timbisha Shoshone Tribe & Their Living Valley, written by the Timbisha Historic Preservation Committee.

ESTRADA, STEVEN (Cahuilla)
(tribal chairperson)
Affiliation & Address: Chairperson (2016-present), Santa Rosa Band of Cahuilla Indians, P.O. Box 391820, Anza, CA 92539 (951) 659-2700.

ESTRELLA, LYNDA (Pascua Yaqui/Mexican)
(program manager)
Education: MA (Sociology). *Affiliation & Address*: Program Manager, Education Support Program, Walking Shield, Inc., 22541 Aspan St., Suite E, Lake Forest, CA 92630 (949) 639-0472. E-mail: lestrella@walkingshield.org. Lynda is responsible for the American Indian Access Scholarship Program, the Harvard eLearning Program, and all other aspects relating to students "Journey to College." *Other professional posts*: She is a motivational speaker to students promoting higher education at local colleges and an educational consultant to local tribal Temporary Assistance to Needy Families (TANF) programs.

ETHELBAH, UPTON (*GREYSHOES*)
(Santa Clara Pueblo/White Mountain Apache)
(artist)
Address: 3639 Cameo Dr. SW, Albuquerque, NM 87105 (505) 797-2884 Website: www.greyshoes.com; E-mail: ethelbah1@aol.com. *Artwork*: Native American stone & bronze sculptures inspired by the traditions of the Santa Clara Pueblo and White Mountain Apache.

ETTER, PATRICIA A.
(librarian/archivist)
Born in Winnipeg, Manitoba, Can. *Education*: California State University, Long Beach, BA (Anthropology), 1979; University of Arizona, MLS, 1986. *Principal occupation*: Librarian, archivist. *Address*: 1051 S. Dobson Rd. #218, Mesa, AZ 85202 (480) 965-0270. E-mail: patricia.etter@asu.edu. *Affiliations*: Curator, Labriola National American Indian Data Center & Archivist for Information Services, Dept. of Archives & Manuscripts, Arizona State University, Tempe, AZ, 1988-. *Memberships*: Western History Association; Dwight Smith Award Committee for WHA, 1993-96; past sheriff, Scottsdale Corral, Westerners International & current member of Posse 1986-; member, editorial advisory board, "Overland Journal; Society of Southwestern Archivist; Society of Southwestern Authors; Arizona & California Historical Societies. *Awards, honors*: Outstanding Alumna, Anthropology, California State University, Long Beach, 1992; Beta Pi Mu International Library Honor Society, 1986; & recipient of two Coke Wood Awards from Westerners International for best article on American history published in a journal, 1993 & 1995. *Interests*: "Major area of research & publication is the history of Southwestern trails in Arizona, New Mexico & California in the mid to late 1800s. I don't claim any tribal affiliation though my great, great grandmother was Cree." *Published works*: Editor, American Odyssey (University of Arkansas Press, 1986; numerous journal articles & book reviews dealing with Southwestern topics including Native Americans; author, The Southern Route 1849: An Annotated History & Bibliography (The Arthur H. Clark Co., 1998).

ETTER, TASHINA (Navajo)
(deputy executive director)
Affiliation & Address: Deputy Executive Director, Native American Finance Officers Association, 1101 30th St., NW Suite 500, Washington, DC 20007 (602) 540-0736. E-mail: tashina@nafoa.org.

EVANS, CAROL (Spokane)
(tribal chairperson)
Affiliation & Address: Chairperson, Spokane Business Council, P.O. Box 100, Wellpinit, WA 99040 (509) 258-4581. E-mail: carole@spokanetribe.com

EVANS, GENE H., MD (Pawnee)
(family practitioner)
Education: Abilene Christian University, BS (Biology); University of Kansas, School of Medicine, MD, 1993. *Affiliation & Address*: Family Practitioner, Pawnee Clinic, 535 6th St., Pawnee, OK 74058 (918) 762-3942. *Other professional post*: member (past vice chair), Board of Trustee, Pawnee Nation College, 2008-present. *Past professional post*: President, Pawnee Indian Veterans.

EVANS, MICHAEL C. (*Didahalqid*) (Snohomish)
(tribal chairperson)
Affiliation: Chairperson (2007-present), Snohomish Tribe, 11014 19th Ave. SE, Suite 8, PMB 101, Everett, WA 98208 (425) 744-1855. E-mail: chair@snohomishtribe.com. *Other professional post*: Chair, Small Tribes of Western Washington (STOWW). *Past tribal positions*: Council member, 1993-2007, Snohomish Tribe. *Past professional posts*: Kent (WA) Fire Dept. (30 years).

EVANS, WAYNE H. (Wokopacola) (Rosebud Sioux) 1938-
(associate professor of education)
Born April 19, 1938, Rosebud, S.D. *Education*: Black Hills State College, BS, 1962; University of South Dakota, EdD, 1976. *Principal occupation*: Associate professor of education. *Address*: 24 S. Pine, Vermillion, SD, 57069 (605) 677-5808 (work). *Affiliation*: Associate Professor of Education, University of South Dakota, Vermillion, 1969-. *Other professional post*: Drum keeper, lead singer on drum. *Community activities*: Evening study time lab for Native American children - facilitator. *Memberships*: South Dakota Indian Education Association (former president); South Dakota Indian Counselor's Association. *Awards, honors*: Outstanding Young Man of America. *Interests*: Counseling, guidance; family therapy; values - value orientation. *Biographical sources*: Who's Who Among the Sioux (Institute of Indian Studies, University of South Dakota, 1987). *Published work*: Indian Student Counseling Handbook (Black Hills State College, 1977); Bicultural Teaching Method & Materials (University of South Dakota, 1987); Issues in Undergraduate Education - chapter on: Native Americans in Undergraduate Education (University of South Dakota, 1988).

EVANS-CAMPBELL, TESSA (Snohomish)
(associate professor; associate director)
Education: University of Washington, BA (Art History), 1989; University of California, Los Angeles, MSW, 1994, PhD, 2000. Affiliation & Address: Associate Director, Indigenous Wellness Research Institute (website: www.iwri.org), School of Social Work, 4101 15th Ave. NE, Box 354900, University of Washington (UW), Seattle, WA 98105 (206) 543-6075. E-mail: tecamp@uw.edu. *Other professional posts*: Associate professor & Director, UW School of Social Work, University of Washington, Seattle, WA, (2000-present); Graduate faculty Appointment, UW, 2000-present); Director, Center for Indigenous Child Welfare Research, Institute for Indigenous Wellness Research, University of Washington, 2006-present); dirctor, Institute of Excellence, International Indigenous Health & Child Welfare Research, School of Social Work, University of Washington, 2004-present); Chair, Building on

Strengths Indian Child Welfare Project Advisory Committee, 2003-present); member, Local Indian Child Welfare Advisory Board, Seattle, WA, 2004-present); member, Child Protective Team - Native Unit, Seattle, WA, 2006-present); Editorial Board Member, Social Work, 2007-present); Council on Social Work Education; Society for Social Work & Research; National Association of Social Workers; National Association of American Indian Social Workers; National Indian Education Association. *Research Interests*: Historical trauma, reistnce & healing; cultural buffers of trauma; substance use and mental health; and indigenous family wellness. *Awards, honors*: Community Service Award, Los Angeles American Indian Children's Council, 2000; Student's Choice Teaching Award, UW School of Social Work, 2003; Distinguished Teaching Award, UW, 2004. *Published works*: Numerous journal articles, book chapters, reports, ad hoc reviewer; presentations.

EWAN, ROY S. (Athabascan) 1935-
(Alaskan village council president)
Born February 2, 1935, Copper Center, Alaska. *Address*: P.O. Box 242, Gakona, AK 99586 (907) 822-3476. *Affiliations*: President, Gulkana Village Council, P.O. Box 254, Gulkana, AK 99586 (907) 822-3746. *Other professional post*: Board member, Ahtna Development Corporation. *Past professional posts*: Served as ex-officio member on all corporate committees, and shareholder committees & subsidiary boards. *Military service*: U.S. Army, 1953-55 (Corporal). *Community activities*: Gulkana Village Council (Indian education, past president). *Memberships*: Alaska Federation of Natives (board member); Alaska Native Federation; The Alliance. *Awards, honors*: 1985 AFN Citizen of the Year, Alaska Federation of Natives.

EXENDINE, LEAH
(tribal health director)
Affiliation & Address: Director, Pyramid Lake Health Department, P.O. Box 227, Nixon, NV 89424 (775) 574-1018..

EYRAUD, COLBERT H.
(museum president & chief curator)
Affiliation & Address: President & Chief Curator, Cabot's Old Indian Pueblo Museum, 67-616 E. Desert View Ave., Desert Hot Springs, CA 92240 (619) 329-7610.

EYRE, CHRIS (Cheyenne-Arapaho) 1968-
(film director & producer)
Born in 1968 in Portland, Oreg. *Education*: Mt. Hood Community College, AA (Television production), 1989; University of Arizona. *Address & Affiliation*: c/o Jim Ehrich, The Rothman Brecher Agency, 9250 Wilshire Blvd. Penthouse, Beverly Hills, CA 90212 (310) 247-9898. Website: www.chriseyre.org. *Film credits*: "Smoke Signals," director & producer, 1998; "The Doe Boy," producer, 2001; "Skins," director & producer, 2002; "Skinwalkers," director, 2002; "Edge of America," director & producer, 2003; "A Thief of Time," director, 2004; "A Thousand Roads," director, 2005; "Imprint," producer, 2007; "After the Mayflower," director, 2007; "Tecumseh's Vision," director, 2008; "Trail of Tears," director, 2008; "A Year in Mooring, director," 2011. His films focus on all aspects of contemporary Native American life, while dispelling the usual stereotypes. Chris has directed two episodes of the famed PBS series, "Mystery." In 2008 Eyre directed the first three episodes of "We Shall Remain," a mini-series that establishes Native history as an essential part of American history from PBS's acclaimed history series, "American Experience;" "The Doe Boy," producer, 2010. *Awards, honors*: Won the 1998 Sundance Film Festival, Filmmakers Trophy & the Audience Award for "Smoke Signals"; "Best Film" honors at the 1998 American Indian Film Festival for "Smoke Signals"; "Edge of America" was the 2004 Sundance Film Festival "opening night" film, and won the DGA's award for Outstanding Directorial Achievement in Children's Programs, becoming the first Native American to win the award; "A Thousand Roads," Eyre's short film was the signature film" for the Smithsonian's National Museum of the American Indian, opened in Washington, DC April 10, 2005; he was named a 2007 USA Rockefeller Foundation Fellow & awarded a $50,000 grant by United States Artists, a public charity; in June 2007, won the Bush Foundation's Artists Fellows Program.

EZRA, MIKE
(Native American studies coordinator)
Affiliation & Address: Professor & Coordinator, Sonoma State University, Native American Studies Department, Nichols Hall 214, 1801 East Cotati Ave., Rohnert Park, CA 94928 (664-3293) E-mail: ezra@sonoma.edu.

F

FADDEN, JOHN (*Kahionhes*) (Mohawk-Turtle Clan) 1938-
(art teacher, illustrator; museum curator/director)
Born December 26, 1938, Massena, N.Y. (near Akwesasne, St. Regis Indian Reservation). *Education*: Rochester Institute of Technology, BFA, 1961. *Principal occupation*: Art teacher, artist, illustrator. *Address*: Six Nations Indian Museum, HCR 1, Box 10, Onchiota, NY 12989 (518) 891-2299. *Affiliations*: Art teacher, Saranac Central School District, Saranac, NY, 1961-94; staff curator & director, Six Nations Indian Museum, Onchiota, NY, 1954-present. *Other professional posts*: Museum curator; illustrator, consultant. *Exhibitions*: Six National Indian Museum, 1954-present; Penn State Museum, Harrisburg, 1962; "Art of the Iroquois," Erie County Savings Bank, Buffalo, 1974; New York State Fair, Syracuse, 1977; The Woodland Indian Cultural - Educational Centre, Brantford, Ontario, 1977, '80, '84; American Indian Community House Gallery, New York City, 1977, '80, '82, '84; Akwesasne Museum, Hogansburg, NY, 1980; Schoharie Museum of the Iroquois Indian, 1981-85; Iroquois Indian Festival II, feature artist, Cobleskill, NY 1983; Akwesasne: Our Strength, Our Spirit, World Trade Center, New York City, 1984; "The Iroquois Experience: A Festival of the Arts," North Country Community College, Saranac Lake, NY, 1993; among others. Also numerous illustrations in periodicals, cover & calendar illustrations, and posters. *Community activities*: Advisory Committee, North American Indian Traveling College, Akwesasne Mohawk Territory; Akwesasne Mohawk Board of Education; Cornell University, Ithaca, NY, American Indian Program Advisory Committee; Round Dance Productions, Inc., Thirty Two Acres Oneida Territory, board of directors. *Memberships*: NY State Education Dept. (Native American Social Studies Writers Committee); NY State Museum (Native Peoples of New York Exhibition Advisory Committee); Round Dance Productions (Board of Directors); Tree of Peace Society (Board of Directors); Iroquois Indian Museum; and Viola White Water Foundation (Board of Directors). *Interests*: As John looks back over the years, he sees the 1961-68 period as one of experimentation in which he worked with pen & ink & painted in tempera, selling a few of his works at the family museum (Six Nations Indian Museum), and giving away others. As became more aware of the political changes taking place at Akwesasne, and throughout Native America, he began to make more political statements through his art, mainly through drawings and cover illustrations for Akwesasne Notes, a newspaper published by the Mohawk Nation at Akwesasne. The details of his work typically show native nationalism & political assertiveness based on the traditions of the native peoples. He has illustrated many books and periodicals, and has done cover art for many books; also, calendar art for Akwesasne Notes Calendar, 1972-. He has produced art for films/video: Who Were the Ones (National Film Board of Canada, 1970); Hodenosaunee: People of the Longhouse (Stiles-Akin Films, 1981); The Iroquois Creation Myth (video tape, Image Film, 1982); Why the Bear Clan Know Medicine (Quinn-Sturgeon, 1990); Moyers-Oren Lyons the Faithkeeper (Public Affairs Television, 1991).

FAHLEY, MICHELLE (Luiseno)
(deputy general counsel)
Education: University of Washington, BA, 1998; UCLA, MA (American Indian Studies), 2004; UCLA School of Law, JD, 2003. *Affiliation & Address*: Deputy General Counsel, Pechanga Band of Luiseno Indians, P.O. Box 1477, Temecula, CA 92593 (951) 770-6000. *Other professional posts*: Chairperson, Conference Planning Committee, and vice president, Board of Directors, California Indian Law Association (CILA), Sacramento, CA. *Past professional post*: Staff attorney, Escondido office of California Indian Legal Services (5+ years).

FAILLE, MAXIME
(attorney)
Affiliation & Address: Indigenous Resource Lawyer, Partner, Leader of Indigenous Law Group, Gowling WLG Canada LLP, 550 Burrard St., Suite 2300, Bentall 5, Vancouver, BC V6C 2B5 Canada (604) 891-2733. E-mail: maxime.faille@gowlingwlg.com. Practices in Indigenous law, public law and general litigation. Max currently serves as national leader of Gowling WLG's Indigenous Law Group and co-leader of the firm's Indigenous Tax Service. His clients consist of Indigenous governments and businesses across Canada, as well as private sector interests seeking to do business with Indigenous communities. In addition to legal representation in the courts and in negotiations, Max regularly provides advice on matters of Aboriginal and treaty rights, First Nation taxation, self-government, Aboriginal consultation & accommodation, Impact and Benefit Agreements, and Aboriginal economic development. His advocacy includes representing clients before the Ontario Superior Court and Divisional Court, the Ontario Court of Appeal, the Supreme Court of the Northwest Territories, the Court of Appeal for the Northwest Territories, the Yukon Supreme Court, the Federal Court of Canada, the Federal Court of Appeal, the Tax Court of Canada and the Supreme Court of Canada. Prior to completing his law studies, Max worked on Parliament Hill and as special adviser on United Nations Reform to the office of the Minister of Foreign Affairs. In 1995, he was awarded the Government of Canada Merit Award by the Minister of Foreign Affairs for "Exceptional and Distinguished Contribution to the Effectiveness and Efficiency of the Public Service." From 1988 to 1993, he worked at the United Nations in New York in the areas of human rights, arms control & peacekeeping. Max is frequently invited to present to or chair major national legal conferences in Indigenous law on such topics as Indigenous consultation and accommodation, First Nation taxation, Aboriginal economic development and Impact Benefit Agreements. He is a member of the board of directors of the Canadian Council for Aboriginal

Business. Fluent in both English & French, Max practices in both official languages. Among numerous recognitions & awards for his work in Aboriginal law, Max is recognized as a leading lawyer in Aboriginal Law in *Chambers Canada 2016, Lexpert's Leading Canadian Lawyers in Energy 2015 and Leading Canadian Lawyers in Global Mining, 2015-2016*; named Benchmark Canada's Aboriginal Lawyer of the Year for 2016,

FAIRBANKS, ANTHONY R. (Ojibwe-Chippewa)
(tribal superintendent)
Education: New Mexico State University, EdD. *Affiliation & Address*: Superintendent, Pueblo of Laguna Dept. of Educaton, P.O. Box 207, Laguna, NM 87026 (505) 552-6008. *Past professional posts*: Assistant Professor, New Mexico State University; Native American Development Speialist, University of Wisconsin; elementary school principal, K-12 dean of students; consultant, Blandin Foundation; executive director, American Heart Association for he states of Alaska & Montana.

FAIRBANKS, CHERYL DEMMERT (Tlingit-Tsimpshian)
(attorney; mediator; tribal appellate justice; visiting professor of law)
Born in Ketchikan, Alaska. *Education*: Fort Lewis College, BA, 1969; University of New Mexico, JD, 1987. *Affiliation & Address*: Partner, Cuddy & McCarthy, LLP, P.O. Box 4160, Santa Fe, NM 87502 (505) 988-4476. Her practice concentrates in the areas of Indian Law, State-Tribal Relations, Indian Gaming, Tribal Courts, Mediation, Family, School, and Educational Law. Her experience includes working in the area of Indian Child Welfare tribal courts (specializing in peacemaking and appellate work). As a practioner in Indian law, she was instrumental in the development of a tribal alliance for peace circles including developing a curriculum for the implementation of tribal peacemaking and family conferencing using traditional concepts of justice. *Other professional post*: Visitng Professor, Lewis & Clark Law School, Potland, OR; and University of New Mexico School of Law at the Southwest Indian Law Clinic, Albuquerque, NM; Justice for the Inter Tribal Court of Appeals for Nevada and is adjunct faculty for the National Judicial College. *Past professional posts*: Prior to her law career, Ms. Fairbanks served as a teacher for the Albuquerque Public Schools, Zia Day School, and Administrator for Acomita Day School and the Santa Fe Indian School. Prior to joining the Cuddy Law Firm, Ms. Fairbanks was a partner with the law firm of Roth, VanAmberg, Rogers, Ortiz, Fairbanks & Yepa, LLP, where she specialized in Indian law. Ms. Fairbanks worked with the New Mexico Office of Indian Affairs, as Sr. Policy Analyst, in the area of state-tribal relations. She was instrumental in establishing the Indian Child Welfare Desk, New Mexico Office of Indian Tourism, the University of New Mexico Indian Law Clinic, and the passage of the New Mexico Indian Arts and Crafts Act. *Memberships*: State Bar of New Mexico (Member, Indian Law Section; Co-Director, CLE); Federal Bar Association; New Mexico Indian Bar Association (past President); National American Indian Court Judges Association Family Court Judge, Santa Clara Pueblo, 1992-1994; Chief Justice Yavapai Apache, 1995 - 2005; Associate Justice, Saginaw Band of Chippewa Indians; Member, New Mexico Center for Dispute Resolution.

FAIRBANKS, DEANNA L. (Chippewa-Ojibway) 1949-
(tribal consultant)
Born May 15, 1949, Leech Lake Reservation, Cass Lake, Minn. *Education*: Bemidji State University, B.A., 1985; University of Minnesota, J.D., 1988. *Principal occupation*: Tribal consultant. *Address*: The Leech Lake Reservation, RR 2, Box 227, Cass Lake, MN 56633 (218) 335-6767. *Affiliation*: Self-employed - consultant in specific federal areas, to tribes only. *Other professional posts*: Special Magistrate for the Court of Central Jurisdiction, the Mille Lacs Band of Ojibwe. *Community activities*: Minnesota Environmental Quality Board & the Minnesota Arts Task Force; committee member, American Indigenous Games to be held in Bemidji, MN in 1995. *Awards, honors*: Minnesota Woman of the Year, 1993 - decreed by Governor Arne Carlson. *Interests*: Tribal sovereignty & jurisdiction. The Self-Governance Act, interpretation & implementation; environmental issues, the arts. "I'm an active Democrat & politics consumes me."

FAIRBANKS, DEVERY J. (*Ma in ga nens*) (Anishinaabe-White Earth Ojibwe) 1957-
(educator)
Born May 24, 1957, Minneapolis, Minn. *Education*: Minneapolis Community College, AA, 1984; University of Minnesota, BA, 1988. *Principal occupation*: Educator. Resides in Minnesota *Affiliation*: Admissions officer, American Indian Student Recruiter, University of Minnesota, Minneapolis, MN, 1989-93; Minority Student Services Director, Rainy River Community College, International Falls, MN, 1993-. *Other professional posts*: Free-lance writer, painter, graphic illustrator. *Community activities*: Board member of five American Indian organizations & institutions: Alcohol & Drug treatment Center, Indian Parent Committee, et al. *Memberships*: Minnesota Indian Education Assn; National Indian Education Assn; American Indian Higher Education Consortium; American Indian Science & Engineering Society; UNITY. *Interests*: "Principal American Indian student recruiter for the University of Minnesota; job requires

extensive travel--numerous friendships & acquaintances nationwide in fields of art, publications, powwows, sports, & chemical dependency. Art and literature: wrote & produced one play, "A Long Road for Milo," reviews favorably on both coasts (by Vizenor & Bruchac). Trade, collect, and volunteer at Indian Art Shows in the Southwest, Midwest & Ontario, Canada. Visited over 30 states in the U.S. & Canada; mostly Indian reservations & reserves. Also visited major urban Indian communities." *Biographical source*: Article in the University of Minnesota Counselors Quarterly magazine, March 1992. *Published works*: Articles published in the following periodicals: The Circle (Minneapolis, MN), Anishnabe-Oyate Newsletter (University of Minnesota), the NIEA News (Washington, DC), and The Journal (Hayward, WI).

FAIRBANKS, BRENDAN G. (Kickapoo/Ojibwe-Chippewa)
(professor of Ojibwe language & American Indian studies)
Education: Brigham Young University, BA (Linguistics), 1998; University of Minnesota, MA, 2005, PhD (Linguistics), 2009. *Affiliation & Address*: Assistant Professor of Ojibwe Language, Department of American Indian Studies, 6 Scott Hall, 72 Pleasant St. SE, Minneapolis, MN 55454 (612) 625-2973. E-mail: fair0061@umn.edu.

FAIRCLOTH, SUSAN C. (Cohairie)
(chair of department of educational leadership)
Education: M.Ed in Special Education; EdD in Educational Administration. *Affiliation & Address*: Chairperson & Programm Coordinator, Professor, Department of Educational Leadership, Watson College of Education, University of North Carolina, Wilmington, EB Room 377, 601 S. College Rd., Wilmington, NC 28403 (910) 962-2290. E-mail: faircloths@uncw.edu. Other professional post: Associate Editor, *American Educational Research Journal – Social and Institutional Analysis,* 2013-present . *Past professional post*: Associate Professor, Department of Leadership, Policy, and Adult & Higher Education, North Carolina State University, Raleigh, NC; Associate Professor, Educational Policy Studies Dept.; & Co-Director, Center for the Study of Leadership in American Indian Education, Penn State University, University Park, PA. *Professional interests*: Her research interests include: Indigenous education, the education of culturally & linguistically diverse students with special educational needs, & the moral & ethical dimensions of school leadership. She has been published in such journals as Educational Administration Quarterly, Harvard Educational Review, The Journal of Special Education Leadership, International Studies in Educational Administration, Values and Ethics in Educational Administration, Tribal College Journal of American Indian Higher Education, Rural Special Education Quarterly, and Journal of Disability Policy Studies. Dr. Faircloth is a former Fulbright Senior Scholar to New Zealand, Ford Foundation Postdoctoral scholar with the Civil Rights Project/Proyecto Derechos Civiles at the University of California Los Angeles, and a Fellow with the American Indian/Alaska Native Head Start Research Center at the University of Colorado Denver. Dr. Faircloth currently serves as a senior associate editor of the American Journal of Education and an associate editor of the American Educational Research Journal – Social and Institutional Analysis. She also serves on the editorial boards of the Journal of American Indian Education and American Secondary Education. Published works: Editor, On Indian Ground: The South (Information Age Publishing, 2015).

FAIRCLOTH, WILLARD GENE (*Spotted Eagle*) (Coharie) 1943-
(former tribal chief)
Born March 21, 1943, in Sampson County, N.C. *Address*: 1001 Indian Town Rd., Clinton, NC 28328 (910) 592-5488. E-mail: coharie_chief@yahoo.com. *Affiliation*: Chief, Coharie Indian Tribe, Clinton, NC. *Other professional post*: Appointed Magistrate for Sampson County, NC. *Past professional post*: Was the first and only Native American to serve on the Clinton, NC Police Dept., Roseboro NC Police Dept.; and attain the rank of Sergeant with the Sampson's County Sherriff's Dept.

FAITH, MIKE P. (Standing Rock Sioux)
(tribal councilmember)
Affiliation & Address: Councilmember, Standing Rock Sioux Tribe, P.O. Box D, Fort Yates, ND 58538 (701) 854-8500.

FALCON, AUDREY (*Algunkwe*) (Saginaw Chippewa/Grand River Ottawa) 1953-
(employee relations manager)
Born January 18, 1953, Detroit, Mich. *Education*: Ferris State University (Big Rapids, MI) 1972-74, Registered Nurse, Associate Degree, Health Services Management, 1980-84. *Address*: 7580 Ogemaw Dr., Mt. Pleasant, MI 48858 (517) 775-4034. E-mail: afalcon@sagchip.org. *Affiliations*: Healthadministrator, Nimkee Memorial Wellness Center, Mt. Pleasant, MI, 1977-94; Saginaw Chippewa Indian Tribe, Mt. Pleasant, MI (tribal operations personnel manager, 1994-96, employee relations manager, 1996-). *Community activities*: Saginaw Chippewa Tribal Council (member/treasurer 1990-) Ziibiiwing Cultural Society-Repatriation (board of directors); museum/cultural center planning committee, 1999. *Memberships*: Society for Human Resource Management; Mid Michigan

Human Resource Assn; American Public Health Assn; Michigan Public Health Assn; American Red Cross-Local Chapter. *Award*: Indian Health Service, U.S. Public Health Service, Exceptional Performance Award, Nov. 1988.

FALCON-CHANDLER, CAROLE (Assiniboine/Gros Ventre)
(tribal college president)
Affiliation & Address: President, Aaniiih Nakoda College (Fort Belknap Community College), P.O. Box 159, Harlem, MT 59526 (406) 353-2607. E-mail: cfalcon@hotmail.com.

FALLEY, NANCI (Many Spirits Woman) 1938-
(rancher)
Born October 19, 1938, San Angelo, Tex. *Education*: California Polytechnic Institute (Certificate in Horse Management), 1960. *Principal occupation*: Rancher. *Address & Affiliation*: President, American Indian Horse Registry & Museum, 9028 State Park Rd., Lockhart, TX 78644 (512) 398-6642. *Other professional posts*: President, Indian Horse Hall of Fame, Lockhart, TX; editor, American Indian Horse News.

FARIELLO, ANNA
(associate research professor)
Education: An MFA in visual art and a MA in museum studies and art history. *Affiliation & Address*: Associate Research Professor, Hunter Library, Cherokee Studies Program, Western Carolna University, College of Arts & Sciences, McKee Bldg. 105A-C, Cullowhee, NC 28723 (828) 227-2499. E-mail: fariello@email.wcu.edu. Anna is head of the library's Digital Initiatives Program which builds websites & collections focused on southern Appalachian history & culture. *Cherokee Traditions: From the Hands of Our Elders* is a website focused on Cherokee culture. *Other professional post*: Visual Art Editor for the Encyclopedia of Appalachia; Museology Specialist for the U.S. Fullbright Commission and the board of the World Craft Council. *Past professional posts*: Research Fllow at the Smithsonian Museum of American Art & Archives of American Art, and field researcher for the Smithsonian Folklife Center. *Awards, honors*: 2010 recipient of the Brown Hudson Award from the North Carolina Folklore Society. *Published works*: Objects & Meaning (2003); A Virginia Field Guide to Cultural Sites (2006); Cherokee Basketry (2009); Cherokee Pottery (2011); Cherokee Carving (2013).

FARIS, JAMES C.
(professor emeritus; author)
Education: Cambridge University (England), PhD, 1966. *Address*: Resides in Santa Fe, NM. *Affiliation*: Emeritus Professor of Anthropology, University of Connecticut, Storrs, CT. *Published works*: Visual Rhetoric: Navajo Art & Curing; The Nightway: A History of Documentation of a Navajo Ceremonial; Navajo & Photography: A Critical History of the Representation of an American People (University of New Mexico Press (hardcover), 1990, University of Utah Press (paperback), 2003).

FARLEY, TOM C.
(executive secretary)
Affiliation & Address: Executive Secretary, Idaho State Indian Education Committee, State Department of Education, P.O. Box 83720, Boise, ID 83720 (208) 332-6891. E-mail: tcfarley@sde.state.id.us. Website: www.sde.state.id. us. *Other professional post*: Instructor, Idaho State University.

FARMER, GARY DALE (Cayuga) 1953-
(actor; editor & publisher)
Born June 12, 1953, in Ohsweken, Ontario, Canada. *Education*: Syracuse University & Ryerson Polytechnic University (studied film production & photography). *Affiliation*: The Runner, Native Magazine for the Communicative Arts, c/o ANDPVA, 39 Spadina Rd., 2nd Floor, Toronto, ON M5R 2S9 (416) 972-0871. Quarterly magazine. *Acting Credits*: CBC's Spirit Bay; TV series, Forever Knight; movie role: as a spiritual Native American guide "Nobody" in "Dead Man." a cameo in Ghost Dog: The Way of the Samurai. He played Cowboy Dashee in the 1991 film, The Dark Wind, and Captain Largo in Coyote Waits in 1993, and a Thief of Time in 2004. He was nominated for the Independent Spirit Awards for his roles in the movies Powwow Highway, Dead Man, and Smoke Signals. Farmer also played the role of Fagin in Twist, the 2003 independent film adaptation of the Charles Dickens classic. He also has a band called, "Gary Farmer and the Troublemakers. Also, he was the publisher of Aboriginal Voices magazine; he was one of the founders of Aboriginal Voices Radio Network

FARRELL, RUBY SLIPPERJACK (First Nation Ojibwa)
(professor of Indigenous Learning)
Born in the Fort Hope Indian Band in Ontario, Canada. *Education*: BA (History), 1988; B.Ed, 1989; M.Ed, 1993; University of Western Ontario, PhD. *Affiliation & Address*: Professor, Department of Indigenous Learning, RB 1007, 955 Oliver Rd., Thunder Bay, ON P7B 5E1 (807) 343-8424. E-mail: ruby.farrell@lakeheadu.edu.

FARRELL-SMITH, KA'ILA (Klamath/Modoc)
(adjunct instructor of Indigenous studies)
Affiliation & Address: Director & Professor of Indigenous Nations Studies, P.O. Box 751, Potland State University, Portland, OR 97207 (503) 725-9689.

FARRENKOPF, TINA M. (Passamaquoddy)
(attorney; executive director)
Education: Dartmouth College, BA (Psychology); University of Maine, MBA; University of Maine School of Law, JD. *Affiliation & Address*: Executive Director, National Tribal Justice Resource Center, National American Indian Court Judges Association, 3300 Arapahoe Ave., Suite 206, Boulder, CO 80303 (303) 449-4112. Tina's focus has been in economic development & tribal justice. *Past professional posts*: Tina has served as the Tribal Justice Committee Co-Chair for the United South & Eastern Tribes, Inc.; senior program officer, First Nations Development Institute; member, Advisory Board, BJA Indian Alcohol & Substance Abuse Program.

FARRER, CLAIRE R. 1936-
(independent research professional)
Born December 26, 1936, New York, N.Y. *Education*: University of California, Berkeley, BA, 1970; University of Texas, Austin, MA (Anthropology/Folklore; Thesis: Performances of Mescalero Apache Clowns), 1974, PhD (Anthropology/Folklore; *Dissertation*: Play & Inter-ethnic Communication: A Practical Ethnography of the Mescalero Apache), 1977. *Principal occupation*: Professor of anthropology. *Address*: P.O. Box 50293, Colorado Springs, CO 80949 (719) 536-0307. E-Mail: clairerfarrer@aol.com. *Affiliations*: Weatherford Resident Fellow, School of American Research, Santa Fe, NM, 1977-78; assistant professor of anthropology, University of Illinois - Urbana/Champaign, IL, 1978-85; Dept. of Anthropology, California State University, Chico, CA (associate professor, 1985-89, professor of anthropology, 1989-2001); Visiting Professor of Southwest Studies, Colorado College, 2002-06; Independent Research, 2006-present. *Past professional posts*: Western Folklore, California Folklore Society (book review editor, 1985-89; executive editor, 1994-99); consulting editor for Archaeo-astronomy, 1984-99; Anthropology & Humanism, ed. board member; reader for refereed journals; guest lecturer. *Past field research*: General ethnography & ethno-astronomy with Mescalero Apache, 1976-2001; Individual work with Mescalero Apache Singers of Ceremonies on ritual, religion, medicine, healing, & general ethnographic work, 1990-present; works with Whiteriver (Ft. Apache, AZ) Apaches, 1995-present; ethno-botanical & life history research with Whiteriver Apache healer, 1999-present; archaeo-astronomical research at various Southwestern sites, 2004-present. *Past field research*: Periodically worked with the Warm Springs Confederated Tribe in Oregon in the 1960's & 1970s, and minor work in the 1970s & 1980s at various sites in New Mexico including the pueblos of Laguna, San Juan, Santo Domingo, Tesuque & Zuni. *Memberships*: American Anthropological Assn; American Ethnological Society; American Folklore Society; American Society for Ethno-history; California Folklore Society; Society for Cultural Anthropology; Traditional Cosmology Society (United Kingdom). *Honors, awards*: Invited participant for Southwestern Indian Ritual Drama by School of American Research, Santa Fe, NM; American Philosophical Society, Phillips Fund & University of Illinois-Urbana, $2,500 for transcription/translation of wax cylinders recorded in 1931 at Mescalero, 1982; American Council of Learned Societies grant for ethno-astronomy of the Mescalero Apache; Professional Promise Award & Professional Achievement Award, California State University, Chico, 1987; Student Internship Service Grant to support powwow and other Indian songs taping, California State University, Chico, 1989; private donor grant to work on Southwestern Indian basketry at the Pitt Rivers Museum, University of Oxford, England (summer), 1990; Living Life's Circle (book) chosen as Outstanding Book by CHOICE; also 1st Honorable Mention in Victor Turner Prize for Ethnographic writing; grants also from Thanks Be To Grandmother Winifred Foundation in 1995; The American Philosophical Society in 1996; Master Teacher, CSU-Chico, 1999-2000; named one of 2,000 Outstanding Scientists for 2002 by the Biographical Center of Cambridge University, Cambridge, England; National Endowment for the Humanities, Harry Jack Gray Distinguished Visiting Professor of Humanities, University of Hartford (CT), 2002-03; Jackson Fellowship Summer Stipend to support research project on "Cultural Astronomy of the Southwest, 2004. *Interests*: Language, travel. *Biographical sources*: Who's Who in America, Who's Who of American Women. *Published works*: Books: editor, Women and Folklore (University of Texas Press, 1976; reissue, Waveland Press, 1986); co-editor, with Edward Norbeck, Forms of Play of Native North Americans (West Publishing, 1979); Women & Folklore: Images & Genres (Waveland Press, 1986); editor, Play & Inter-Ethnic Communications: A Practical Ethnography of the Mescalero Apache, in a 31 volume series of outstanding dissertations (Garland, 1990); Living Life's Circle: Mescalero Apache Cosmovision, eight chapters (U. of New Mexico Press, 1991); co-editor, with Ray Williamson, 14 chapters, Earth and Sky: Visions of the Cosmos in Native American Folklore (U. of New Mexico Press, 1992); Thunder Rides a Black Horse: Mescalero, Apaches and the Mythic Present (Waveland Press, 1994; 2nd Ed. 1996); Folklore! In Celebration of Ourselves, & Addressing The Divine: Religion in Anthropological Perspective (Waveland Press); Kaleidoscope Vision & the

Rope of Experience (on shamanism); Not Just the Portrait of a Woman, The Life Story of Gladys Lavender, Whiteriver Apache; Clown Boy and the Mountain Gods: An Apache Tale (children's book) & Hannah's House (children's book); book chapters; monographs; journal, encyclopedic, newspaper & magazine articles; book reviews; and books & articles refereed.

FAT, MARY WEASEL (*Diving Around Woman*) (Blood) 1955-
(journalist)
Born December 12, 1955, Cardston, Alberta, Canada. *Education*: Grant McEwan Community College, Edmonton, Alberta (one Year Certificate, Native Communications Program), 1980. *Address*: Box 181, Cardston, Alberta T0K 0K0 (403) 737-2854.

FATZINGER, AMY 1979-
(professor of American Indian studies)
Education: Cedar Crest College (Allentown, PA), BA, 2000; University of Arizona, MA, 2002, PhD (American Indian Studies), 2008. *Affiliation & Address*: Assistant Professor & Director of Undergraduate Studies, American Indian Studies Program, The University of Arizona, Harvill 235B, Tucson, AZ 85721 (520) 621-8440. E-mail: fatzinge@ email.arizona.edu. Area of *Interest*: American Indian literature; American Indian film; historical biography; women's frontier literature.

FAWCETT, JAYNE GRANDCHAMP (Mohegan) 1936-
(tribal councilor & ambassador)
Born January 6, 1936, New London, Conn. *Education*: University of Connecticut, BA, 1957. *Principal occupation*: Tribal councilor & ambassador. *Affiliations*: Mohegan Nation (councilor & ambassador). *Address*: 5 Crow Hill Rd., Uncasville, CT 06382 (860) 862-6100. *Other professional posts*: Vice-chair, Mohegan Tribal Council, 1995-present; instructor & lecturer on Mohegan culture at Project Learn & various Connecticut schools & universities; lecturer, American Field Studies; member, board of directors & treasurer of the United South & Eastern Tribes, Inc. *Past professional posts*: Teacher, Ledyard Junior High School, Gales Gerry, CT, 1972-99; assistant curator, Tantaquidgeon Indian Museum; curriculum committees for the local multicultural school & the Ledyard & Norwich public schools; chair of the Montville Indian Parent Committee; served on Eastern Connecticut State University's Multicultural Advisory Committee; advisor for the projected Native American Studies Program at the University of Connecticut. *Community activities*: Founding member of the new, constitutionally elected Mohegan Tribal Council, 1978; was elected Chair in 1990 of the Constitutional Review Board, a.k.a. Council of Elders, the tribe's judicial branch; volunteer organist at the Mohegan Church. *Interests*: "Inspired by the travels of my Aunt, Gladys Tantaquidgeon, my family & I have traveled extensively throughout the western part of America visiting as many groups of Native Americans as we were able." *Published works*: Article, with Gladys Tantaquidgeon, on Mohegan basketry in, "A Key to the language of Woodsplint Baskets."

FAYARD, KELLY (Poarch Band Creek)
(assistant dean; director of Native American Cultural Center)
Education: Duke University, BA & MA (Anthropology & Religion); University of Michigan, PhD (Anthropology. *Affiliation & Address*: Assistant Dean, Yale College; Director, Native American Cultural Center, 26 High St., New Haven, CT 06520 (203) 432-2900. Other professional post: Professor, Contemporary Native America,/ *Past professional post*: Taught anthropology for several years at Bowdoin College.

FEATHERLY, WALTER T.
(attorney)
Education: St. John's College, BA, 1977; Harvard Law School, JD, 1980. *Affiliation & Address*: E-mail: Executive Partner & member of the Corporate, M&A & Securities Practice Group, Holland & Knight, 601 West Fifth Avenue, Suite 700, Anchorage, AK 99501 (907) 263-6395. E-mail: walter.featherly@ hklaw.com Mr. Featherly focuses his practice on Alaska Native- and Native American-owned businesses. He regularly counsels boards of directors & executives on matters including corporate law and governance, the Alaska Native Claims Settlement Act, the Alaska National Interest Lands Conservation Act, business transactions, mergers & acquisitions, government contracting, labor and employment, finance and real estate. He also assists Alaska Native Corporation and tribal-owned businesses to navigate the laws and regulations of the Small Business Administration's (SBA) 8(a) Business Development and the Historically Underutilized Business Zones (HUBZone), particularly those related to subcontracting and teaming opportunities. Mr. Featherly regularly speaks on the subjects of corporate governance and compliance, teaming and joint venturing, the requirements of the Federal Acquisition Regulation, the SBA and other laws applicable to small, minority and disadvantaged contractors and the large companies that team with them. *Awards & honors*: Chambers USA - America's Leading Business Lawyers guide, Native American Law, 2013-2016. *Memberships*: Alaska Bar Association; Anchorage Bar Association. *Past professional post*: Managing Partner, Patton Boggs, LLP, Anchorage, AK.

FEDMAN, ALAN
(attorney; Indian program counsel)
Education: Brown University, BA (Political Science), 1969; University of Sussex, MA (Comparative Politics), 1972. *Affiliation & Address*: Counsel, Native American Law & Policy Practice, Dentons LLP, 1301 K St., NW, Washington, DC 20005 (202) 408-3954. E-mail: alan.fedman@dentons.com Alan is the former head of the Firm's Native American Law and Policy practice. He is the former director of enforcement of the National Indian Gaming Commission (NIGC). He represents tribes on NIGC regulatory compliance matters and serves as counsel to a number of tribal gaming commissions. He is well versed in the legal issues involved in NIGC investigations and compliance audits and has substantial experience in handling NIGC administrative appeals. He also represents Indian tribes in matters before the US Department of the Interior. While serving at the NIGC, Alan directed a national field staff regulating 400 Indian gaming operations responsible for protecting the financial integrity of tribal gaming operations and keeping Indian gaming free from criminal influence. In this capacity, he worked closely with the federal agencies responsible for the oversight of Indian gaming. Alan has recently has been involved in a number of tribal-state compact negotiations, and is well versed in tribal Internet gaming issues. In addition, he has extensive experience in gaming project development & in securing the required federal and state approvals related to those projects. Alan served as associate counsel at the US Senate Special Committee on Investigations where he participated in the investigation of the federal government's management of Indian-owned natural resources. He also served as assistant chief counsel for the US Department of Energy, Office of Special Counsel, where he supervised attorneys and auditors responsible for enforcing the crude oil provisions of the Mandatory Petroleum Price Regulations. At the Department of Energy, Alan directed regulatory enforcement actions and represented the department in appeals before the Federal Energy Regulatory Commission. Prior to joining the NIGC, Alan was counsel at Green, Stewart and Farber, were he was part of the firm's regulatory compliance practice. *Awards, honors*: Best Lawyers, 2014, 2016. *Memberships*: Served on the Native American Policy Advisory Committee for the presidential campaign of former Vermont Governor Howard Dean. He has also served as an adjunct professor at the University of Tulsa College of Law.

FEHER-ELSTON, CATHERINE (*Kateri*) (Mohawk) 1953-
(historian, author)
Born July 20, 1953. *Education*: Washington State University; University of Texas at Austin, BA (History/Anthropology); MA (History); PhD candidate (American History/Middle East/Energy Resource Development). *Affiliation & Address*: Instructor of history (1990-present), Northern Arizona University, History Dept., Flagstaff, AZ 86011. E-mail: ravenfair@aol.com or raven@mail.utexas.edu. *Affiliations*: Media Specialist, Navajo-Hopi Task Force, Navajo Tribe, 1982-83; Editor, Navajo-Hopi Observer, 1983-86; founding editor, Hopi Tutu-veh-ni, The Hopi Tribe, 1986-93. *Other professional posts*: Director of Southwest Information (an investigative news and resource agency), 1983-93; news director of the Navajo-Hopi Observer, 1983-85. *Community activities*: Working on building models of sustainable development for the living future of the Colorado Plateau through Canyon Forest Village, 3/97-present; DNA Legal Services, Window Rock, AZ; editor, DNA newsletter; grant proposal writer; Rio Puerco Nuclear Study coordinator. *Awards, honors*: Her book, "Ravensong," won Best Book of 1992 Award from the Rocky Mountain Publishers Association; selected Outstanding Young Woman of America, 1984, for news work with the Navajo-Hopi Observer; selected as an Arizona Humanities Council Scholar, 4/97; selected to present paper at the "Seventh Tampere Conference on North American Studies"; selected to address the "Sixth Maple Leaf & Eagle American Studies Conference" at Helsinki, Finland in May, 1996 - presentation title, "Indians of the Imagination, New Age Hucksterism & Cosmic Profits"; recipient of Southwest Thematic Fellowship for 1997-98; recipient of Graduate Opportunity Fellowship from the University of Texas, 1993-97; recipient of University of Texas Graduate Opportunities Summer Research Award, 1995. *Memberships*: Native American Journalists' Assn; American Historical Assn; Organization of American Historians; Wildlife Rehabilitation Assn; Phi Alpha Theta. *Interests*: "My interests revolve around cultural diversity, understanding changes in lands & peoples as a result of resource development & colonization; environmental history, law & politics. I am interested in cross-cultural conflict resolution & the interface between people, cultures & their governments. Teaching, writing, research, editing & communication are my strong areas. I have been honored by the friendship, trust & confidence of many tribal leaders and friends among the Navajo, Hopi and Apache, and it is my wish to be a bridge between worlds, tribal worlds, international worlds, corporate worlds & the world of man & nature." *Published works*: Children of Sacred Ground (Northland, 1988); Ravensong: A Natural and Fabulous History of Ravens and Crows (Northland, 1992); The Navajo Cookbook (1982, '83, '84); Comanche History (1997); Seeds of Empowerment, Seeds of Divisiveness: Indian Organization, Resource Development & the Transformation of the Colorado Plateau.

FEINSTEIN-TOBY, MARCIA
(administrator, American Indian studies)
Education: She earned a B.A. in fine art at UC Santa Barbara, BA (Fine Art), 1981; University of Washington, MA (French), 1987. *Affiliation & Address*: Administrator (2001-present), Department of American Indian Studies, University of Washington (UW), Seattle, WA 98195 (206) 543-9082. E-mail: maf@u.washington.edu. *Other professional post*: Instructor, Department of Comparative Literature, UW.

FELDMAN, GLENN M.
(attorney; Indian law section)
Education: Georgetown University Law Center, JD, 1973. *Affiliation & Address*: Member, Dickinson Wright, Indian Law Section, 1875 Eye St., NW, Washington, DC 20006 (602) 285-5138. E-mail: gfeldman@dickinsonwright. Com. Glenn's practice is devoted exclusively to Federal Indian Law, with heavy emphasis on Indian gaming and reservation economic development activities. He is counsel to a number of Indian tribes, tribal casinos & tribal business ventures in Arizona, California & other western states. In 1986, Glenn successfully argued the tribal gaming case, California v. Cabazon Band of Mission Indians, before the United States Supreme Court. Since that time, he has also been involved in a variety of other important Indian law cases, including Cabazon Band v. Wilson, 37 F.3d 430 (9th Cir. 1994), United States v. Santa Ynez, 983 F. Supp. 1317 (C.D. Cal. 1997) & Cabazon v. Smith, 388 F.3d 691 (9th Cir. 2004). Glenn has extensive experience in drafting tribal codes & ordinances and has been involved in the negotiation of tribal-state gaming compacts in California, Arizona, Wisconsin, Kansas and Oklahoma. Since 2002, he has been involved in casino financing transactions totaling more than $1 billion, as well as providing legal counsel to a variety of other tribal businesses, including three tribal telephone companies. *Membership*: Arizona State Bar, Past Chair, Indian Law Section

FENELON, JAMES V. (Lakota/Dakota)
(professor of sociology; Indian center director)
Education: Loyola Marymount University, BA; Harvard & the School for International Training, MA; Northwestern University, PhD. *Affiliation*: Professor of Sociology & Director, Center for Indigenous Peoples Studies, California State University, San Bernardino, 5500 University Pkwy., San Bernardino, CA 92407 (909) 537-5000. James teaches race/ethnic relations, urban sociology, social movements, indigenous issues, political sociology, sovereignty, & dedicates his professional life to assisting social justice struggles. *Past professional post*: Director, Sac & Fox Area Field Office, BIA, Tama, IA. *Published works*: Culturicide, Resistance, & Survival of the Lakota (Sioux Nation); Indigenous Peoples & Globalization, with Thomas D. Hall.

FERGUSON, BOB (Choctaw)
(museum director)
Affiliation & Address: Director, Choctaw Museum of the Southern Indian, P.O. Box 6010, Philadelphia, MS 39350 (601) 650-1685.

FERGUSON, CAMILLE (Tlingit)
(economic development)
Affiliation & Address: Executive Director (2013-present), American Indian & Alaska Native Tourism Association (AIANTA), 2401 12th St., NW, Albuquerque, NM 87104 (505) 724-3592. *Past professional posts*: Economic Development Director, Sitka Tribal Enterprise, Sitka, AK, 1996-2012; AIANTA Board of Directors, 2002-12; president of AIANTA Board of Directors, 2003-07; interim executive director of AIANTA from July to December, 2011. *Awards, honors*: The 2011 Denali Award for Professionalism & Leadership; 2012 recipient of the Alaska Coalition's Dan Moreno Award.

FERGUSON, JOHN P. (Iroquois)
(editor)
Affiliation & Address: Editor, "Museum Notes," Iroquois Indian Museum, P.O. Box 7, Howes Cave, NY 12092 (518) 296-8949.

FERGUSON, MARY JANE (Eastern Cherokee)
(board president)
Born & raised in Cherokee, North Carolina. *Education*: Bacone Jr. College, AA; Western Carolina University, BA (Education), MA (Education). *Affiliations*: Director of Marketing & Promotions, Eastern Band of Cherokee Indians, P.O. Box 455, Cherokee, NC 28719 (828) 497-7000. E-mail: maryfer@frontier.com. *Other professional posts*: President, American Indian & Alaska Native Tourism Association (AIANTA), Albuquerque, NM; vice chair, Cherokee Historical Association; member of executive board, Museum of the Cherokee Indians' board member, Sequoyah Birthplace Museum; member, North Carolina Governor's Western Residence Board of Directors. *Past professional posts*: Hotel Operations Manager, Harrah's Cherokee Casino & Hotel. Mary Jane is a Certified Lodging Manager and received the Travel Marketing Professional designation from Southeast Tour-ism Society after completing a 3-year marketing college requirements in 2006.

FERGUSON-BOHNEE, PATRICIA A. (Pointe-au-Chien) 1975-
(attorney; legal clinic director; professor of law)
Born in Louisiana in 1975. *Education*: Stanford University, BA, 1997; Columbia University School of Law, JD, 2001. *Affiliation & Address*: Associate, Indian Law & Tribal Relations Practice Group at Sacks Tierney P.A. 4250 N. Drinkwater Blvd., 4th Floor, Scottsdale, AZ 85251 (480) 425-2637. E-mail: patty.ferguson@sackstierney.com; *Other professional posts*: faculty Director, Indian Legal Clinic; Associate Clinical Professor of Law (2008-present), Sandra Day O'Connor College of Law, Arizona State University, P.O. Box 877906, Tempe, AZ 85287 (480) 727-0420. E-mail: pafergus@asu.edu. *Professional Interests*: Indian law & tribal relations; water, environmental, & natural resources; appeals & civil litigation; election law & policy, voting rights, & status clarification of tribes. She has testified before the U.S. Senate Committee on Indian Affairs and the Louisiana State Legislature regarding tribal recognition. *Professional activities*: State Bar of Arizona: Indian Law Section Executive Council; board president, National Native American Bar Association, Tempe, AZ; serves as the Native Vote Election Protection Coordinator for the State of Arizona. *Past professional posts*: past-president, National Native American Bar Association, 2010-12. *Awards, honors*: As a Fulbright Scholar to France, she researched French colonial relations with Louisiana Indians in the 17th & 18th centuries; Judge Learned Hand Award (Emerging Leadership): American Jewish Committee (Arizona Region), 2011. *Community Leadership*: Miss Indian Arizona Assn. *Court & Bar Admissions*: State Bar of Aizona, 2001; Tohono O'odham Justice Court, 2004; Ak-Chin Indian Community Court, 2007; Fort McDowell Yavapai Nation Court, 2007; Gila River Indian Community Court, 2007; U.S. Supreme Court, 2009. *Memberships*: State Bar of Arizona: Indian Law Section Executive Council; Arizona State, Tribal & Federal Court Forum; Federal Bar Assn: Indian Law Section; Northwest Indian Bar Assn; Native American Bar Assn.

FERNANDEZ, ARNE G. (Laguna Pueblo) 1953-
(storekeeper)
Born June 2, 1953, Albuquerque, N.M. *Education*: University of New Mexico (5 years). *Principal occupation*: Storekeeper, Laguna Pueblo. *Address*: 212 Carlisle, NE, Albuquerque, NM 87106 (505) 268-2662. *Membership*: Indian Arts & Crafts Association, 1986-. *Interests*: "I specialize in finding traditional pottery for clients - top museums & collectors. I was a judge for the 1991 & 1992 Gallup Ceremonials. I have dealt with most major potters and their work from a first name basis for over 20 years."

FERNANDEZ, RON A. (Laguna Pueblo)
(senior strategist)
Affiliation & Address: Senior Strategist, Blue Stone Strategy Group, ITCA/El Canto Bldg., 2214 N. Central Ave., Suite 130, Phoenix, AZ 85004 (602) 307-1994. *Professional interests*: Ron specializes in working with Tribes in the design & organization of successful store policy & procedures. He has worked to help ensure the execution & structure of efficient & effective organization of all operational levels for the facilities. He also assists Tribes with the organization of their C-Store's deli, liquor, and tobacco products.

FERRIS, NEAL L. (Eastern Shoshone)
(project manager & trainer)
Education: Fort Lewis College, BA (Southwest Studies). *Affiliation & Address*: Experiential Manager & Project Venture Replication Trainer, National Indian Youth Leadership Project, 924 Park Ave., Suite A, Albuquerque, NM 87102 (505) 554-2289. E-mail: nferris@niylp.org.

FIDDLER, TANYA (Cheyenne Lakota)
(executive director)
Affiliation & Address: Executive Director (2002-present), Four Bands Community Fund, P.O. Box 932, Eagle Butte, SD 57625 (605) 964-3687. E-mail: tfiddler@fourbands.org. *Awards, honors*: Appointed by President Obama to the Community Development Advisory Board at the U.S. Treasury Dept.

FIELD, MARGARET (Kumeyaay)
(chair of American Indian Studies)
Education: University of Alaska-Fairbanks, B.Ed., 1989; University of California, Santa Barbara, MA, 1993, PhD, 1998. *Affiliation & Address*: Professor & Chair, Department of American Indian Studies, AL-331, San Diego State University, 5500 Campanile Dr., San Diego, CA 92182 (619) 594-2779. E-mail: mfield@mail.sdsu.edu. *Teaching Interests*: American Indian Heritage, oral tradition, languages; American Indian identity; California Indian people; linguistic anthropology. *Published works*: Native American Language Ideologies: Language Veliefs, Practices, and Stuggles in Indian Country, with Paul Kroskrity (University of Arizona Press, 2009); numerous articles.

FIELDS, GREGORY
(professor of American Indian Studies)
Education: University of Hawaii, PhD (Philosophy), 1994. *Affiliation & Address*: Professor of Philosophy & American Indian Studies, Peck Hall, Room 2211, Southern Illinois University   (618) 650-2461. E-mail: gfields@siue.edu.

Research Interests: Native North Pacific Coast culture, philosophy, and language preservation/revitalization. South Asian philosophy & religion. *Teaching Interests*: American Indian studies, Asian studies, philosophy of religion, critical thinking. *Other professional post*: Research Associate, American Indian Studies Research Institute at Indiana University, Bloomington, where he conducted research during his Fall 2012 sabbatical leave. Professor Fields has presented research at the International Conference on Salish & Nieghboring languages. Gregory was among the faculty members who recently founded a minor in Native American Studies. He was awarded SIUE's two-year Hoppe Research Professorship starting in July 2013 for his work involving collaborative publications, audio, and audio-visual media produced with Coast Salish culture-bearers, and for his efforts toward establishing a digital archive to support preservation & revitalization of Native Northwest languages & knowledge-systems. *Published works*: Editor, Totem Pole History: The Work of Lummi Carver Joe Hillaire, by Pauline Hillaire (University of Nebraska Press, 2013); Field's current projects include the audio collection, "Medicine Songs of the Four Seasons From the Straights & Coast Salish (Smithsonian Folkways, 2014); and a second collaboration with Coast Salish elder, Pauline Hillaire, "Rights Remembered: A Salish Grandmother Speaks on American Indian History and the Future (University of Nebraska Press, 2014).

FIELDS, NANCY (Lumbee)
(museum education coordinator)
Education: Institute of American Indian Arts Tribal College, B.A. (Museum Studies.) *Affiliation*: Assistant to Outreach & Public Programs, American Indian Cultural Center & Museum, 900 N. Broadway #100, Oklahoma City, OK 73102 (405) 239-5500. Website: www.aiccm.com. *Past professional posts*: Teacher's Services Coordinator, Education Dept., Smithsonian's National Museum of the American Indian, 2006-2008; Program & Youth Director, Metrolina Native American Association, Charlotte, NC, 2004-06. *Awards, honors*: 2004 American Indian Higher Education Consortium. American Indian College Fund, Institute of American Indian Arts Student of the Year Award/Scholarship.

FIFE, BILL S. (Creek)
(tribal commerce commissioner)
Affiliation & Address: Commerce Commissioner, Muscogee (Creek) Nation of Oklahoma, P.O. Box 158, Okmulgee, OK 74447 (918) 732-7605.

FIFE, GARY D. (Creek, Cherokee) 1950-
(radio producer/host)
Born September 21, 1950, Tulsa, Okla. *Education*: North East State College, Tahlequah, OK, 1968-72 (Journalism; University Without Walls (Westminster College), B.A., 1974. *Affiliation & Address*: Host, Mvskoke Radio, Muscogee Creek Nation of Oklahoma, P.O. Box 158, Okmulgee, OK 74447 (918) 756-1410. *Past professional posts*: Producer/host, Alaska Public Radio Network, Anchorage, AK, 1986-93; One Sky Productions, Ltd., Anchorage, AK 99503 (907) 272-8111, 1993-2010. *Memberships*: Native American Public Broadcasting Consortium (Board member); Alaska Press Club; Native American Press Association. *Awards, honors*: 1983 Nominee for Outstanding Achievement in Radio, by Native American Public Broadcasting Consortium; 1984 Outstanding Young Men of America; 1988 Men of Achievement by International Biographical Center; 1988 National Public Radio Resident in News & Information by National Public Radio. *Interests*: Traveled to Honduras & Nicaragua to cover refugees' stories; also traveled above Arctic Circle to cover Alaska Native issues. *Biographical sources*: We Alaskans (1/4/87); Daily Courier, Grants Pass, OR (2/19/87); Tulsa World (2/20/87); Olympian (WA) (2/22/87; Tulsa Tribune (2/25/87); Anchorage Daily News; The Arctic Sounder (11/3/89).

FIGHTING BEAR (Navajo/Cherokee)
(teacher supervisor & student counselor)
Education: G.E.D. High School Diploma. *Principal occupation*: Teaching supervisor & student counselor with the public schools. *Address*: 1300 S. Fairview Rd., Columbia, MO 65203. *Affiliation*: Aurora Public Schools-Continuing Education, Aurora, CO ("I teach students 14 years old and up). *Other professional posts*: Owner, Fighting Bear Enterprises (American Indian arts & crafts, stained glass, & cultural presentations), Denver, CO. "I give presentations on American Indian history, culture and art to schools, colleges, corporations, recreation and senior centers, private organizations, government agencies, and the public at large." " I have had professionally paid parts in the following: "The Marz Project" a made for TV movie in 1999; "Larger Than Life" with Bill Murray, released in 1997; "Deep Grease" a comedy spoof on contemporary society' "One on One" with Robbi Benson; and "The Mayor." Had roles in various theatrical productions. *Community activities*: Member, Thunderbird Society ('my Aunt Red Squirrel is the founder and chief elder"); member, Cherry Creek School's, Hope of Our People (H.O.O.P.) Program; member, The Denver Indian Center; member, Native American Multicultural Education School (N.A.M.E.S.). *Awards, honors*: 1980 "One of the Outstanding Young Men in America" by the National Jaycees; 1991 Nominated by Aurora Public Schools for National Teacher of the Year; 1995 Nominated for the national, "Cornelius P. Turner Award, sponsored by the American Council on

Education, GED office; 1995 voted by "my people" as the most frequently published American Indian in the greater Denver metro area. *Interests*: " I like to help coordinate powwows; I like to draw; I enjoy visiting other reservations/pueblos during the summer months; I really enjoy and feel honored in being able to spend time with my Aunt Red Quirrel. I get such a great feeling each time I am invited to be a guest speaker at an elementary or high school, a business luncheon or an organizational meeting, so, I do it a lot." *Published works*: Author, The Proud People (an overview of American Indians in the U.S.); poetry in the book, "Suede Milk"; "I won a national poetry writing contest and appear in the book, "The Lasting Joy," published by the National Library of Poetry. Further examples of my poetry can be viewed on the Internet at www.poets.com. I have a picture story in the book, "Algo Dicho, Something Said." I also have picture stories in three national magazines, La Luz, Sports Karate, & Tak Kwon Do Digest."

FIKES, JAY COURTNEY (*Pari Temai*) 1951-
(writer/researcher of Native American issues)
Born June 14, 1951, San Luis Obispo, Calif. *Education*: University of California, Irvine, BA, 1973 (Comparative Culture); University of San Diego, MEd, 1974 (Bilingual Education); University of Michigan, MA, 1977, PhD (Anthropology), 1985. *Address*: P.O. Box 517, Carlsbad, CA 92018. E-mail: jayfikes2004@yahoo.com. *Affiliations*: Owner of Cuatro Esquinas Traders (Mexican Indian art), 1979-present; land use planner & housing consultant to Navajo Nation, 1983; professor of Social Science Research Methods, Marmara University, Istanbul, Turkey, 1985-87; independent writer, Las Vegas, N.M., 1987-89; legislative secretary specializing in Native American issues, Friends Committee on National Legislation, Washington, DC, 1990-91 & 1995; post-doctoral fellow, Smithsonian Institution, 1991-92; president, Institute of Investigation of Inter-Cultural Issues, Carlsbad, CA, 1993-; professor, Dept. of Anthropology, Yeditepe University, Istanbul, Turkey, 1999-present. *Memberships*: Religious Society of Friends. *Awards, honors*: Two academic scholarships from University of Michigan; graduate cum laude from University of California, Irvine; graduated with honors from the University of San Diego in 1974; awarded Smithsonian fellowship, 1988; Smithsonian Post-Doctoral Fellow in Anthropology, 1991-93. *Interests*: "Translating & interpreting songs & "myths" of the Huichol Indians of Mexico; debunking the books of Carlos Castaneda and his academic allies. I am planning to write more autobiographical and biographical works on Native Americans of today. I am learning how to produce documentary films, including one on the Huichol Indian ritual cycle circa 1934." *Published works*: Huichol Indian Identity and Adaptation (University of Michigan microfilms, 1985); Step Inside the Sacred Circle (Wyndham Hall Press, 1989); Carlos Castaneda, Academic Opportunism, and the Psychedelic Sixties (Millenia Press, 1993); Reuben Snake, Your Humble Serpent (Clear Light Publishers, 1996); Huichol Indian Ceremonial Cycle - film available from Pennsylvania State University, 1997; La Mitologia de los Huicholes (Colegio de Michoacan, 1998); The Man Who Ate Honey (Ambrosia Books, 2003); Huichol Mythology, edited with Phil Weigand & Acelia Garcia de Weigand (University of Arizona Press, 2004).

FILLMORE, ELLEN (Washoe)
(tribal secretary/treasurer)
Affiliation & Address: Secretary/Treasurer, Washoe Tribe of the Carson Indian Community, P.O. Box 3269, Carson City, NV 89703 (775) 883-6459. E-mail: ellen.fillmore@washoetribe.us.

FINE-DARE, KATHLEEN
(professor of anthropology)
Education: DePauw University, BA (Anthropology); University of Illinois, Urbana-Champaign), MA (Anthropology), PhD (Anthropology). *Affiliation & Address*: Chairperson & Associate Professor, Dept. of Native American & Indigenous Studies, Fort Lewis College, 1000 Rim Dr., Durango, CO 81301 (970) 247-7438. E-mail: fine_k@fortlewis.edu.

FINKBONNER, JOE (Lummi)
(executive director)
Affiliation & Address: Executive Director, Northwest Portland Area Indian Health Board, 2121 SW Broadway #300, Portland, OR 97201 (503) 228-4185. E-mail: jfinkbonner@npaihb.org.

FINLEY, AMBER (Mandan,Hidatsa, Arikara/Dakota & Lakota)
(executive director)
Education: Fort Berthold Community College, AA, 2004; University of North Dakota, BS (Fsheries & Wildlife), 2006; University of San Francisco, MS (Environmental Management), 2008. Affiliation & Address: Executive Director, Northstar Council, P.O. Box 13969, Grand Forks, ND 58208 (701) 330-1126. E-mail: nstarcouncil@gmail.com. Amber is a Gates Millennium Scholar alum, a lifetime Sequoyah member of the American Indian Science and Engineering Society, and serves as a mentor for several diversity-based organizations. After returning to Grand Forks, Amber worked with other members of the American Indian community, exploring avenues for cultural awareness, development, & expression. In 2010, the group established Northstar Council,

an organization with the mission of empowering indigenous people through research, education, and outreach.

FINLEY, FRANK A. (Salish-Kootenai)
(coordinator of cultural arts)
Education: Salish Kootenai College, BS (Environmental Science); University of Idaho, MA (Education). *Affiliation & Address*: Coordinator, Cultural Arts, Native American Studies Department, Salish Kootenai College, P.O. Bx 70, Pablo, MT 59855 (406) 675-4800. E-mail: frank_finley@skc.edu. *Past professional post*: Instructor & former head, Native American Studies Department, Salish Kootenai College, 1994-2013.

FINLEY, MICHAEL O. (Colville)
(former tribal chairperson)
Affiliation & Address: Colville Business Committee, P.O. Box 150, Nespelem, WA 99155 (509) 634-2208. E-mail: michael.finley@colvilletribes.com.

FINLEY, VERNON (Salish & Kootenai)
(tribal chairperson)
Affiliation & Address: Chairperson, Confederated Salish & Kootenai Tribes, P.O. Box 278, Pablo, MT 59855 (406) 675-2700.

FIRECLOUD, DOROTHY (Rosebud Sioux)
(national monument supt.)
Education: College of Santa Fe, BS; University of New Mexico School of Law, JD. *Affiliations*: Tuzigoot National Monument, P.O. Box 68, Clarkdale, AZ 86324 (602) 634-5564; Montezuma Castle National Monument, P.O. Box 219, Camp Verde, AZ 86322. *Interests*: The field of Indian law with specialization in American Indian water rights issues. *Past professional posts*: Supt., Devis Tower National Monument in Wyoming; Dept. of Justice, U.S. Attorney's Office & BIA Phoenix Office as water rights specialist; U.S. Forest Service, Southwwestern Region, as tribal relations program coordinator; In 2006, she accepted the position as supt. of Devils Tower, the first National Monument in the U.S.

FIRECROW, JOSEPH (Cheyenne)
(musician, flutist)
Address: P.O. Box 173, Winsted, CT 06098 (860) 379-6007. E-mail: joseph@josephfirecrow.com. Website: www.josephfirecrow.com. *Awards, honors*: GRAMMYTM nomination at the 43rd Annual Awards for Cheyenne Nation; 2003 "Songwriter for the Year," and winner of the Indian Summer Music Awards flute category winner for Legend of the Warrior; 2005 "Flutist of the Year," award at the Annual Native American Music Awards for the album, Red Beads; Male Artist 2006 for album, Red Beads; Record of the Year, Song/Single of the Year, & Best New Age Recording, all at NAMMY Awards, 2010 for album, Face the Music. Published works: CDs – The Mist (1994); Rising Bird; FireCrow (1992); Cheyenne Nation, Legend of the Warrior, Red Beads, Face the Music; Night Walk (2012).

FISHER, JOE (Blackfeet) 1943-
(photographer/filmmaker)
November 19, 1943, Santa Monica, Calif. *Education*: Haskell Indian Jr. College, AA, 1964; Northern Montana College, 1964-66; University of Montana, 1973-74; Montana State University, Film/TV Production, 1994. *Principal occupation*: Photographer/filmmaker. *Address*: P.O. Box 944, Browning, MT 59417 (406) 338-7869. *Affiliation*: Historical documenter, photographer, Blackfeet Tribe, Browning, MT. *Community activities*: American Legion; Blackfeet Societies: Rough Rides, Slickfoot, and Crazy Dog. *Military service*: U.S. Army (Sp-5 Engs.) (Vietnam Service Unit Commendation). *Membership*: VFW. Award: The Montana State Alumni Award of Excellence in Film & TV Production, Oct. 1993. *Interests*: Photographic showing, Indian Pride on the Move, in Browning, Missoula, Helena; Blackfeet art slide presentation. Presently working on TV documentaries on the Blackfeet and a Crow Indian elder. *Published work*: Blackfeet Nation, 1977. *Video*: Produced & directed with D. Kipp, "Transitions," 1992.

FISHER, LLEVANDO (*Cowboy*) (Northern Cheyenne)
(former tribal president)
Affiliation & Address: Former president, Northern Cheyenne Tribal Council, P.O. Box 128, Lame Deer, MT 59043 (406) 477-8284.

FISHER, WILLIAM L. (Seneca-Cayuga of Oklahoma)
(tribal chief)
Affiliation & Address: Chief, Seneca-Cayuga Tribe of Oklahoma, 23701 South 655 Road, Grove, OK 74344 (918) 787-5452. E-mail: wfisher@sctribe.com

FITZ GIBBON, KATE
(attorney; author; speaker)
Affiliation: Law Offices of Kate Fitz Gibbon, Esq., 215 West San Francisco St., Suite 202C, Santa Fe, NM 87501 (505) 412-2209. Website: www.fitgibbonlaw.com. E-mail: fitzgibbon.law@gmail.com. *Legal expertise*: Native American & international cultural property & cultural heritage issues; art collection, inheritance & donation. Museum law; gallery-client relations & art and artist contracts. *Other professional posts*: Contributing articles to "The Magazine Antiques"; Kate is a specialist in domestic & international law affecting cultural heritage. *Past professional post*: Member of the Cultural Property Advisory Committee to Presidents Clinton & Bush. Speaker Program: "New Mexico Lawyers for the Arts: Collecting Native American Art Legally," A Talk by Kate Fitz Gibbon. *Publications*: Native American Art and the Law, A Collector's Guide (ATADA Foundation, 2010).

FITZGERRAL, MICHAEL (Pomo)
(former tribal chairperson)
Affiliation & Address: Sherwood Valley Rancheria Band of Pomo Indians, 190 Sherwood Hill Dr., Willits, CA 95490 (707) 459-9690.

FITZPATRICK, ROBIN
(Native American outreach coordinator)
Affiliation & Address: Coordinator, Native American Outreach, Native American Programs, University of Oklahoma Health Sciences Center, College of Public Health, 801 N.E. 13th St., Oklahoma City, OK 73104 (405) 271-8999 ext. 46896. Email: robin-fitzpatrick@ouhsc.edu.

FIXICO, DONALD L. (Shawnee/Sac & Fox/Muscogee Creek/Seminole)
(professor of history)
Affiliation: Distinguished Foundation Professor of History, Affiliate Faculty, American Indian Studies, Arizona State University, Mail Code: 4302, Coor 4576, Tempe, AZ (480) 727-9082. E-mail: donald.fixico@asu.edu. *Past affiliations*: Founding Director, Center for Indigenous Nations Studies Program, University of Kansas; Professor of History, History Dept., Western Michigan University, Kalamazoo, MI. *Published works*: Termination & Relocation: Federal Indian Policy, 1945-1960 (1986); editor, An Anthology of Western Great Lakes Indian History (1988) Urban Indians (1991); editor, Rethinking American Indian History (1997); The Urban Indian Experience in America (University of New Mexico Press, 2000); The American Indian Mind in a Linear World: American Indian Studies & Traditional Knowledge (2003); Daily Life of Native Americans in the 20th Century (2006); editor, Treaties with American Indians: An Encyclopedia of Rights, Conflicts & Sovereignty, 3 Vols. (2007); American Indians In a Modern World (2008); Invasion of Indian Country in the 20th Century: American Capitalism & Tribal Natural Resources, 1st Ed. 1998, & 2nd Ed., 2011 (University Press of Colorado, 2011); Caall for Change: The Medicine Way of American Indian History, Ethos, and Reality (Univerfsity of Nebraska Press, 2013); in progress: textbook on American Indian History for Oxford University Press; That's What They Used to Say: Reflections on American Indian Oral Traditions (University of Oklahoma Press, 2017)

FIXICO, JUNE (Creek)
(tribal town education board chairperson)
Affiliation & Address: Education Board Chairperson, Kialagee Tribal Town, 318 S. Washila, Box 332, Wetumpka, OK 74883 (405) 452-3263.

FLANNERY, MARISSA K. (Tohono O'odham)
(attorney)
Education: Stanford University, BA (American Studies); Stanford University School of Law, JD. *Affiliation & Address*: Sonosky, Chambers, Sachse, Endreson & Perry, LLP, 900 W. Fifth Ave., Suite 700, Anchorage, AK 99501 (907) 258-6377. E-mail: marissa@sonosky.net. Ms. Flannery joined the firm in 2000, and works primarily in the firm's Health Law Practice Group. Her practice includes monitoring & participating in the development of state & federal health care legislation & regulations, & counseling clients on compliance with Joint Commission standards & the Health Insurance Portability & Accountability Act (HIPAA). Ms. Flannery regularly navigates the Indian Health Care Improvement Act, the Indian Health Service regulations, & Indian Self-Determination Act contracts & compacts to assist Tribal health providers in making policy decisions & in drafting eligibility policies for health care services. She frequently assists tribal clients with personnel disputes & with the development of employee handbooks. She has also litigated on behalf of Tribes before state & federal courts, including the Alaska Supreme Court. *Past professional post*: Legislative intern, Mashantucket Pequot Tribal Nation. *Memberships*: American Bar Association; Alaska Bar Association.

FLEMING, DALE
(Indian center program specialist)
Affiliation & Address: Program Specialist, Native American Indian Center, Edison High School, 1425 S. Center, Stockton, CA 95206 (209) 933-7000 ext. 8069. E-mail: dfleming@stockton.k12.ca.us.

FLEMING, ELAINE (Leech Lake Ojibwe)
(college instructor)
Affiliation & Address: Arts & Humanities Department Chairperson & Instructor, Leech Lake Tribal College, P.O. Box 180, Cass Lake, MN 56633 (218) 335-4200.

FLEMING, WALTER C. (Kickapoo Tribe in Kansas (Enrolled) Oneida Tribe and Cherokee Nation Descendent)
(professor of Natie American studies, dept. head)
Born on the Crow Indian Reservation and raised on the Northern Cheyenne Indian Reservation Education: Dawson College, AA, 1973; Eastern Montana College, BS, 1976; Montana State University, MEd, 1979; University of Kansas, PhD (American Studies; Museum Studies minor), 1996. Affiliation & Address: Professor (1979-present) Head (2002-present), Native American Studies Department, College of Letters & Science, Montana State University, 2-181 Wilson Hall, P.O. Box 172340, Bozeman, MT 59717 (406) 994-5260. E-mail: wfleming@montana.edu. Other professional posts: Associate Curator of History, Museum of the Rockies in Bozeman. He currently serves on the Friends of Montana PBS board. Past professional post: President of the Montana Committee for the Humanities (now Humanities Montana). Interests: Traditional native dancer and a member of the Gourd Dance Society, a traditional "warrior" society of the Southern Plains. Native American literature; Montana Indians. Memberships: World's Indigenous Nations Higher Education Consortium Member since 2008 Native American & Alaska Native Professors Association Member since 1995 Native American Studies Association Member since 1999. Published works: A History & Foundation of American Indian Education Policy; Visions of an Enduring People; The Complete Idiot's Guide to Native American History

FLETCHER, LINDSEY (Pechanga Luiseno)
(attorney; board vice president)
Education: UCLA School of Law,joint JD/MA (Americann Indian Studies). Affiliation & Address: Associate General Counsel, Pechanga Band of Luiseno Indians, P.O. Box 1477, Temecula, CA 92593 (951) 676-2768. Other professional post: Board Vice President, California Indian Law Association. While in law school, Ms. Fletcher served as managing editor of the UCLA Law Review; served as Secretary of the National Native American Law Students Association and UCLA's local chapter; clerked for the Hualapai Tribal Court; externed for the Ninth Circuit Court of Appeals; participated in moot court; provided ordinance & constitution drafting assistance to a California tribe; and wrote a Masters thesis titled "Bargaining for Jurisdiction: Tort Liability in Tribal-State Gaming Compacts." Prior to joining Pechanga's Office of General Counsel, Ms. Fletcher was an associate in the Los Angeles office of Sheppard Mullin Richter & Hampton.

FLETCHER, MATTHEW L.M. (Grand Traverse Band Ottawa & Chippewa)
(center director; professor of law)
Education: University of Michigan, BA, 1994; University of Michigan Law School, JD, 1997. Affiliation & Address: Assistant professor, Michigan State University College of Law; director, Indigenous Law & Policy Center, Michigan State University, 405B Law College Bldg., East Lansing, MI 48824 (517) 432-6800. E-mail: matthew.fletcher@law.msu.edu. Other professional posts: He teaches American Indian law courses & Constitutional Law I. Matthew sits as Chief Justice of the Pokagon Band of Potawatomi Indians and the Hoopa Valley Tribe; also sits as an appellate judge for the the Turtle Mountain Band of Chippewa Indians; and consultant to the Seneca Nation of Indians Court of Appeals. Past professional post: Staff Attorney for four Indian Tribes – the Pascua Yaqui Tribe, the Hoopa Valley Tribe, the Suquamish Tribe, and the Grand Traverse Band, and he has been a consultant to the Seneca Nation of Indians Court of Appeals; Co-chair, Federal Bar Association's Annual Indian Law Conference in Albuquerque, NM 2006-08. Published works: American Indian Education: Counternarratves in Racism, Struggle, and the Law (Routledge, 2008); Facing the Future: The Indian Child Welfare Act at 30 with Winona T. Singel & Kathryn Fort (Michigan State University Press, 2009); Co-author of the 6th edition of Cases on Federal Indian Law (Thomson West, 2011) with David Getches, Charles Wilkinson, & Robert Williams; American Indian tribal Law (Aspen, 2011) the first casebook for law students on tribal law; The Return of the Eagle: The Legal History of the Grand Traverse Band of Ottawa & Chippewa Indians (Michigan State University Press, 2012); co-editor The Indian Civil Rights Act at 40, with Kristen A. Carpenter & Angela R. Riley (UCLA American Indian Studies Press, 2012; numerous articles on American Indian law. Professor Fletcher is the primary editor & author of the leading law blog on American Indian law & policy, "Turtle Talk."

FLETCHER, ZEKE (Grand Traverse Ottawa & Chippewa) 1981-
(attorney; law firm associate)
Education: University of Michigan, BA, 2003; University of Wisconsin-Madison Law School, 2006. Address & Affiliation: Associate, Rosette & Associates, PC, 112 E. Allegan St. #600, Lansing, MI 48933 (517) 367-7040. Other professional posts: Chair-elect of the State Bar of Michigan's American Indian Law Section; member, Standing Committee on American Indian Law as appointed by the President of the State Bar of Michigan; member, State Bar of Wisconsin's Indian Law Section. Past professional posts: Grand Traverse Band of Ottawa & Chippewa Indians, Legal Dept. Clerk, 2001-03, 2005; Assistant General Counsel, 2006-07; Law Clerk, Wisconsin Legislative Council, 2004-05; Associate, Honigman Miller Schwartz & Cohen, LLP, 2007-09. Mr. Fletcher is experienced in many areas of Indian law an advises tribal

governments, tribal gaming operations, tribal businesses, and tribal gaming commissions regarding self-governance, gaming, economic development & diversification, child welfare, etc.

FLICK, SHIRLEY
(Indian education program coordinator)
Affiliation: Warroad Public Schools - ISD #690, Indian Education Dept., 510 Cedar Ave., Warroad, MN 56763 (218) 386-1820.

FLORENDO, BRENT (Wasco, Warm Springs)
(programs coordinator & instructor for Native American studies)
Education: Southern Oregon University, BA (Theatre). Affiliation & Address: Academic Programs Coordinator; instructor for Native American Studies, Native American Studies Program, Southern Oregon University, College of Arts & Sciences, Taylor Hall, Room 018, 1250 Siskiyou Blvd., Ashland, OR 97520 (541) 552-6751. E-mail: florendb@sou.edu. Brent is a Native American storyteller and dancer. He has performed with the Oregon Cabaret Theater in Egene, Oregon in the Festival of Musical Theater and the Kena: Peninsula Dancers. He is a leader of the popular Rogue Valley Earth Day performance.

FLORES, AMELIA
(library director)
Affiliation & Address: Director, Colorado River Indian Tribes Public Library/Archives, Tribal Administration Center, Rte. 1, Box 23-B, Parker, AZ 85344 (928) 669-1332.

FLORES, KESNER, JR. (Wintun/Paiute)
(interim executive director)
Affiliation & Address: Interim Executive Director, National Tribal Environmental Council, 4520 Montgomery Blvd. NE, Suite 3, Albuquerque, NM 87109 (505) 242-2175. Past professional posts: Director, Wintun EPA, Cortina Rancheria (ten years). Kesner has done consultant work with tribes on government relations, strategic planning, tribal utility systems, housing & environmental concerns; and lead negotiator for the tribe's economic development committee.

FLOWERS, MARCIA JONES (Paucatuck Eastern Pequot)
(tribal ambassador)
Affiliation & Address: Ambassador, Eastern Pequot Tribal Nation, 640 Lantern Hill Rd., P.O. Box 370, North Stonington, CT 06359 (860) 535-1868.

FLOYD, JAMES (Muscogee Creek)
(tribal principal chief)
Affiliation & Address: Principal Chief, Muscogee (Creek) Nation, P.O. Box 580, Okmulgee, OK 74447 (918) 732-7601.

FLOYD, JAMES
(community & economic development)
Education: Portland State University, BA (Psychology & Economics), MA (Economics), PhD (Economics). Affiliation & Address: Adjunct Faculty, Falmouth Institute, 3702 Pender Dr. #300, Fairfax, VA 22030 (703) 352-2250. Dr. Floyd has over 30 years experience working for Native American organizations. His major area of focus is in community & economic development of tribal communities & Native villages. Most recently, he was part of a design & implementation team that created a comprehensive organizational assessment process for tribal communities that identifies strengths & weaknesses in governmental & economic operations. Jams has directed the creation & operation of Native eDGE for the White House Domestic Policy Council & coordinated the effort with 14 federal agencies. He supervised the transfer of Native eDGE to the National Center for American Indian Enterprise Development (NCAIED). He worked as a consultant to HUD & American Indian & Alaska Native tribes on strategic panning, self-governance, and community & economic development.

FLUTE, DAVID (Sisseton Wahpeton Oyate)
(tribal chairperson)
Affiliation & Address: Chairperson, Sisseton Wahpeton Oyate, Lake Traverse Reservation, P.O. Box 509, Agency Village, SD 57262 (605) 698-3911. E-mail: chairman@swo-nsn.gov.

FLUTE, DEBRA (Sisseton Wahpeton Oyate)
(tribal attorney)
Affiliation & Address: Attorney, Sisseton Wahpeton Oyate, Lake Traverse Reservation, P.O. Box 509, Agency Village, SD 57262 (605) 698-3911. E-mail: debraf@swo-nsn.gov

FLYING HAWK, ROBERT (Yankton Sioux)
(tribal chairperson)
Affiliation & Address: Chairperson, Yankton Sioux Tribe, Box 248, Marty, SD 57361 (605) 384-3804.

FODOR, LEAH (Pottawatomi)
(former tribal chairperson)

Affiliation & Address: Former chairperson (2016-), Match-e-be-nash-she-wish Band of Pottawatomi Indians, 2872 Mission Dr., Dorr, MI 49344 (269) 397-1780. Leah Ardis Sprague-Fodor has been an elected representative on Gun Lake Tribal Council for the Salem Voting District since 2012. Leah was proudly mentored by both her Auntie Ardis and the previous Tribal Chairman, DK Sprague, each for over a decade and has been an essential part of helping the Gun Lake Tribe garner the success and improvement it has seen over that past 20 years. Leah's main priority while on Tribal Council is to protect our assets and the voice for the people she represents. As one of the Gun Lake Tribe's original employees, Leah has spearheaded the Member Services Department for 20+ years and feels blessed to have had the opportunity to be a voice for Tribal Elders. Leah's Tribal involvement doesn't stop there; she has been a part of the Land Use Committee, Michigan Indian Family Olympics planning and the Elder's Committee. Leah continues to be passionate about gaining additional housing resources for citizens, protecting Gun Lake Casino as the Tribal Government's source of income, & enhancing programs & services offered to benefit all Tribal Citizens.

FOGELMAN, GARY L. 1950-
(editor/publisher)

Born January 1, 1950, Muncy, Pa. *Education*: Lock Haven State University, BS, 1972; West Chester State University (two years). *Address*: RD 1, Box 240, Turbotville, PA 17772. *Affiliation*: Editor/publisher, Indian-Artifact Magazine. *Memberships*: Local, state & northeastern archaeological societies; SPA (Chapter No. 8, vice president); IACAP (vice president). *Awards, honors*: Catlin Peace Pipe Award. *Interests*: Collecting Indian artifacts; hunting & fishing. *Published works*: The Muncy Indians (Grit Publishing, 1976); The Pennsylvania Artifact Series (in progress).

FOGELSON, RAYMOND D. (Talageesi) 1933-
(anthropologist)

Born August 23, 1933, Red Bank, N.J. *Education*: Wesleyan University, BA, 1955; University of Pennsylvania, MA, 1958, PhD, 1962. *Address*: 1761 N. Sedgwick, Chicago, IL 60614 (312) 642-7693. *Affiliations*: Assistant professor, University of Washington, Seattle, 1962-65; Department of Anthropology, University of Chicago, 1965-. *Other professional posts*: Book review editor, "American Anthropologist". *Memberships*: American Ethnological Society; American Society for Ethnohistory (president); Central State Anthropological Society (president); Society for Psychological Anthropology; Society for Medical Anthropology. *Interests*: Southeastern Indians, Plateau. *Biographical sources*: Who's Who in America. *Published works*: The Cherokees: An Annotated Bibliography (Indiana U. Press); editor: A.I. Hallowell, Contributions to Anthropology (U. of Chicago Press); editor (with R.N. Adams): Anthropology of Power (Academic Press).

FOGHORN, CARMEN A.
(Indian program director)

Affiliation & Address: Director, American Indian Graduate Program, University of California, 327 Sproul Hall #5900, Berekely, CA 94720 (510) 642-3228.

FOLEY, ROBERT
(president & CEO)

Affiliation & Address: President & CEO, National Native American AIDS Prevention Center, 720 S. Colorado Blvd. #650, Denver, CO 80246 (720) 382-2244 x 303. E-mail: rfoley@nnaapc.org. *Other professional posts*: Member, Board of Directors for several local non-profit & advocacy organizations. *Past professional posts*: Training specialist, Denver STD/HIV Prevention Training Center; research assistant, Tri-Ethnic Center for Prevention Research, Colorado State University.

FOLLIS, BILL GENE (Modoc)
(tribal chief & administrator)

Affiliation & Address: Chief & Administrator, Modoc Tribe of Oklahoma, 515 G St. SE, Miami, OK 74354 (918) 542-1190.

FONSECA, NICHOLAS H. (Miwok)
(tribal chairperson)

Affiliation & Address: Chairperson, Shingle Springs Band of Miwok Indians, P.O. Box 1340, Shingle Springs, CA 95682 (530) 676-6281. E-mail: nfonseca@ssband.org. Since 1998, he has been employed with the Tribe. Prior to serving as chairperson of the tribe council, he worked for the tribe on housing & community development matters.

FOO, JOSEPHINE (Navajo-Dine')
(attorney-Indian law)

Education: Vassar College, BA; Brown University, MFA; University of Pennsylvania, JD. *Affiliation & Address*: Director, Project Attorney, Indian Country Grassroots Support (2015-present), 709 N. Butler Ave., Farmington, NM 87401 *Past professional posts*: Office of the Chief Justice, Window Rock,

AZ, 2006-14; Managing Attorney & Staff Attorney, DNA People's Legal Services, Farmington & Shiprock, NM, 2000-06. *Practice Jurisdictions*: Navajo Nation, 2001-present; New Mexico. *Practice Area*: Native American Law.

FORD, NUBIA (Kumeyaay)
(education director)

Affiliation & Address: Director, Sycuan Education Department, 2 Kwaaypaay Coirt, El Cajon, CA 92019 (619) 659-5897. E-mail: nford@sycuan-nsn.gov.

FORQUERA, RALPH (Juaneno Band of California Mission Indians) 1948-
(healthcare administrator; executive director)

Born July 7, 1948, Delano, Calif. *Education*: MPH. *Principal occupation*: Health care administrator. *Affiliation & Address*: Executive Director (1990-present), Seattle Indian Health Board, 606 - 12th Ave. S., Seattle, WA 98144 (206) 324-9360. E-Mail: ralphf@sihb.org. *Other professional posts*: Clinical faculty, University of Washington School of Public Health. *Past professional posts*: San Diego County Dept. of Public Health, 1979-82; San Diego American Health Center, 1982-89. *Community activities*: Visiting committee-Master's Program in non-profit leadership, Seattle University; advisory board, King County Health Systems/Health Status Committee; commissioner, American Indian Health Commission for Washington State. *Memberships*: American Public Health Association; American Indian, Alaska Native & Native Hawaiian Caucus (chair); Society of Non-Profit Agencies. *Published works*: Health Status of Urban American Indians & Alaska Natives.

FORSMAN, LEONARD (Suquamish) 1962-
(tribal chairperson)

Born January 25, 1962, Bremerton, Wash. *Education*: University of Southern California, 1979-81; University of Washington, BA (Anthropology), 1987. *Affiliation & Address*: The Suquamish Tribe, P.O. Box 498, Suquamish, WA 98392 (360) 598-3311. E-mail: lforesman@suquamish.nsn.us. *Other professional post*: Editor of museum newsletter. *Past professional posts*: Researcher, Suquamish Tribal Cultural Center, Suquamish, WA, 1981-85; director, Suquamish Museum, 1985-2007. *Community activities*: Secretary, Suquamish Tribal Council; member, Kitsap County Council on Human Rights. *Published works*: Eyes of Chief Seattle (Suquamish Museum, 1984); A Time of Gathering (Burke Museum/University of Washington Press, 1990).

FORT, KATHRYN E.
(attorney; adjunct professor of law)

Education: Hollins University (Roanoke, VA), BA (History). Michigan State University College of Law, JD (with the Certificate in Indigenous Law). *Affiliation & Address*: Director, Director of the Indian Child & Welfare Act Appellate Project, Indigenous Law & Policy Center, Michigan State University College of Law, Law College Building, 648 N. Shaw Lane, Rm 405C, East Lansing, MI 48824 (517) 432-6992. Email: fort@law.msu.edu. Ms. Fort joined the Center in 2005 as the Indigenous Law Fellow. She co-teaches an experiential learning class, researches & writes on behalf of Center clients and on topics in Federal Indian law & manages administrative aspects of the Center. She has recently been published in the George Mason Law Review, and the American Indian Law Review.

FORWARD, JEAN S.
(senior lecturer of Native American studies)

Affiliation & Address: Senior Lecturer, Certificate Program in Native American Studies, Anthropology Department, University of Massachusetts, Thompson 4, Amherst, MA 01003 (413) 577-1607. E-mail: jforward@anthro.umass.edu.

FOSTER, CHARLES (Cherokee)
(Cherokee language instructor)

Affiliation & Address: Cherokee Language Instructor, Native American Language Program, Department of Anthropology, College of Arts & Sciences, The University of Oklahoma, 455 W. Lindsey, Cate 4 Room 201, Norman, OK 73019 (405) 325-0179. E-mail: cfoster@ou.edu.

FOSTER, LANCE (Iowa Tribe of Kansas & Nebraska)
(artist-writer; geomancer-psychogeographer; landscape/tribal historian, anthropologist, educator, storyteller, folklorist)

Affiliation & Address: Adjunct Faculty (2007-present), Art & Anthropology/ Archaeology, University of Montana, Helena College of Technology, 1115 N. Roberts St., Helena, MT 59601 (406) 447-6900. *Past professional posts*: Arcchaeologist, USDA Forest Service, 1990-98; Historic Landscape Architect, National Park Service, 199802992; Director of Native Rights, Land & Culture, OHA Office of Hawaiian Affairs, 2003-06. *Interests*: "I have had 30 years plus of cultural & historic preservation & environmental experience, especially focusing on indigenous peoples and the land.

FOSTER, LENNY (Dine-Navajo)
(project director; Indian activist)

Affiliation: Director, Navajo Nation Corrections Project and the Spiritual Advisor for 1,500 Indian inmates in 34 state and federal prisons in the Western U.S. He has co-authored legislation in New Mexico, Arizona and Colorado that allows Native American spiritual & religious practice in prison & results in significant reductions in prison returns. *Other professional post*: Board Member, International Indian Treaty Council, San Francisco, CA. *Interests*: Sun Dancer and member of the Native American Church. He has been with the American Indian Movement since 1969 and has participated in actions including Alcatraz, Black Mesa, the Trial of Broken Treaties, Wounded Knee "73, the Longest Walk and the Big Mountain land struggle, et al. *Awards honors*: 1993 recipient of the City of Phoenix, Dr. Martin Luther Kink Human Rights Award.

FOSTER, MORRIS W. 1960- (professor of anthropology)
Born January 28, 1960 in Alva, Okla. *Education*: University of Oklahoma, BA, 1981; Yale University, MPhil, 1984, PhD, 1988. *Address*: 819 W. Brooks, Norman, OK 73069 (405) 325-2491. *Affiliations & Address*: Instructor & Assistant & Adjunct Associate Professor, Native American Studies Program; Associate Professor of Anthropology, University of Oklahoma, Norman, OK, 1986-present. *Other professional posts*: Faculty Fellow, Science & Public Policy Program, University of Oklahoma, Norman, OK, 1995-present; Adjunct Associate Professor of Pediatrics, University of Oklahoma Health Sciences Center, 2000-present; associate member, Oklahoma Medical Research Foundation, 2001-present. Fieldwork experience: Comanche Community, 1984-present; Creek, Seminole, and Yuchi communities, 1987-present; Plains Apache community, 1991-present; Choctaw community, 1997-present; African American communities in Oklahoma, 1999-present. *Past professional post*: editor, American Indian Quarterly (U. of Nebraska Press), 1993-97. *Memberships*: Society for Linguistic Anthropology, American Anthropological Assn; American Society for Ethnohistory. *Awards, honors*: 1992 Erminie Wheeler Voegelin Prize for best book in ethnohistory, the American Society for Ethnohistory. *Interests*: Anthropology, Native American studies, ethno-history, sociolinguistics, specializing in the people of the Native Plains & Southwest. *Published work*: Being Comanche: The Social History of an American Indian Community (U. of Arizona Press, 1991); book chapters articles.

FOSTER, TONY (Quileute)
(former tribal chairperson)
Affiliation & Address: Quileute Nation, P.O. Box 279, LaPush, WA 98350 (360) 374-6163. E-mail: tony.foster@quileutenation.org.

FOUNTAIN, STEVEN M.
(coordinator of native American programs)
Affiliation & Address: Coordinator & & Clinical Assistant Professor of History, Native American Programs, Washington State University Vancouver, 14204 NE Salmon Creek Ave., Vancouver, WA 98686 (360) 546-9738; E-mail: sfountain@wsu.edu Steven was a Diversity Faculty Fellow for 2013-14 and 2014-15, and received the John Topham and Susan Redd Butler Faculty Research Award from the Redd Center for Western Studies in 2009-2010. He teaches courses in Early American History (HIST 110, 413, 414, & 415), Environmental History (HIST 409 & 494), and Native American History (HIST 308). He also serves as the Faculty Advisor for the WSUV History Club and Phi Alpha Theta (History Honors). *Published work*: Horses of Their Own Making: An Equestrian History of Native America (University of Washington Press, 2016); History of the American Indians: Exploring Diverse Roots (ABC-CLIO, 2017).

FOWLER, ELIZABETH A. (Comanche/Eastern Cherokee)
(IHS deputy director for management operations)
Education: University of Maryland, BS (mathematics). *Affiliation & Address*: Deputy Director for Management Operations, Indian Health Service (HIS), The Reyes Bldg., 801 Thompson Ave. #400, Rockville, MD 20852 (301) 443-1083. As Deputy Director, she is responsible for providing management direction to the IHS program offices, including implementing IHS agency goals & mission; providing overall organization management to improve agency performance; developing strategic plans; and planning, directing, & evaluating the operations of the Headquarters functions, authorities, and responsibilities in support of the Director. *Past professional posts*: Ms. Fowler began her career with IHS in 1990 in the headquarters division of Personnel Management. In December 1990, she moved to the Office of Public Health and worked in positions of increasing responsibility through October 2002, when she became the Deputy Director for Budget Formulation within the Division of Financial Management. In that role, Ms. Fowler was responsible for directing the development of the IHS budget documents from the preliminary phase through the congressional phase & ensuring tribal consultation in the process. Ms. Fowler most recently served as the Director of the Office of Finance and Accounting. *Awards, honors*: HHS Secretary's Award for Distinguished Service, various IHS Director's Awards, and the Luana Reyes Leadership Award.

FOWLER, VERNA M. (Menominee) 1942-
(Indian college president; educational administrator)
Born July 1, 1942, Keshena, Wisc. *Education*: PhD (Educational Admin). *Affiliation & Address*: Founding President, College of the Menominee Nation, P.O. Box 1179, Keshena, WI 54135 (715) 799-4921. E-mail: vfowler@

menominee.edu. *Other professsional posts*: Executive director, National Indian Gaming & Hospitality Institute, College of the Menominee Nation, Keshena, WI; Supt. for Education, Menominee Tribal School, Neopit, WI. *Awards, honors*: Honorary Doctorate from the University of Wisconsin, Oshkosh. *Memberships*: Menominee Indian Tribe of Wisconsin; American Indian College Fund (board member); American Indian Higher Education Consortium. *Published work*: The Menominee (book).

FOWLER-OTTO, CLARA (Menominee)
(headstart director)
Affiliation & Address: Menominee Tribe, P.O. Box 910, Keshena, WI 54135 (715) 799-5100.

FOX, DENNIS R. (Mandan-Hidatsa) 1943-
(BIA-chief, Div. of Education)
Born September 8, 1943, Elbowoods, N.D. *Education*: Dickinson State College, BS, 1966; Penn State University, MEd, 1971, D.Ed, 1977. *Affiliations*: Education program administrator, Johnson O'Malley Program, BIA, Cheyenne River Agency & Aberdeen Area Office, SD, 1975-83; assistant director of education, BIA, Washington, DC, 1983-2008; teacher, worked in BIA higher education grant program. *Memberships*: National Indian Education Association; Phi Delta Kappa. *Awards, honors*: Gave presentation at National School Administration Conference. *Interests*: Educational administration.

FOX, DENNIS RAMON, JR. (*Dog Bear*) (Mandan-Hidatsa) 1968-
(independent contractor – agent; hide painter)
Education: University of Maryland, BA (Fine Arts/Anthropology), 1989. *Address*: P.O. Box 1311, New Town, ND 58763 (701) 627-3173. E-mail: dennisfox2@live.com. *Affiliation*: Independent Contractor-Agent, D. Fox II Creative Solutions, New Town, ND, 2010-present. *Other professional post*: Director of Independence Program, Three Affiliated Tribes, New Town, ND. Dennis is a Northern Plains hide painter and his work is in the collection of the Smithsonian Institution's National Museum of American History. *Past professional posts*: Program Coordinator, Office of Folklife Programs, Smithsonian Institution, 1989-90; curator & special projects coordinator, University of Maryland, 1990-91; consultant & writer, National Museum of the American Indian, Smithsonian Institution, 1993-94; director, First Nations Arts, First Nations Development Institute, 1992-94; director, Tourism & Cultural Programming, Three Affiliated Tribes, New Town, ND, 1994-95; leadership coordinator 1995-97, program director, 1997-2004, YouthBuild Fort Berthold, Fort Berthold Housing; executive director, 2004-09, general manager, 2009-10, Trustland Oilfield Services.

FOX, JOE, JR. (Northern Cheyenne)
(tribal vice chairperson; commission member)
Affiliation & Address: Vice Chairperson, Northern Cheyenne Tribe, P.O. Box 128, Lame Deer, MT 59043 (406) 477-6284. *Other professional post*: Member, State Tribal Economic Development Commission (STEDC), c/o Montana Dept. of Commerce, Helena, MT.

FOX, JOSEPH B. (Gros Ventre)
(tribal council member)
Address & Affiliation: Fort Belknap Community Council, P.O. Box 1019, Harlem, MT 59526.

FOX, MARK (Hidatsa)
(tribal chairperson)
Affiliation & Addresss: Chairperson, MHA Nation, Three Affiliated Tribes, 404 Frontage Rd., New Town, ND 58763 (701) 627-4781. E-mail: chairmanfox@mhanation.com

FOX, MARY JO TIPPECONNIC (Comanche)
(professor of American Indian studies)
Education: University of Arizona, PhD, 1982. *Affiliation*: American Indian Studies Program, The University of Arizona, Harvill 224., P.O. Box 210076, Tucson, AZ 85721 (520) 626-4242. E-mail: foxm@email.arizona.edu. *Other professional posts*: Associate to the President for American Indian Affairs and Ambassador to American Indian Nations, 1999-2006. *Memberships*: National Indian Education Association (NIEA); Western Social Science Association (WSSA) *Interests*: American Indian higher education; American Indian women's issues & roles; Indian gaming. *Published works*: "Serving Native American Students"; monograph, "New Directions for Student Services"; article: "Traditional Feminism."

FOX, PAULA LONG
(Indian foundation chairperson)
Born and raised in rural South Dakota. *Education*: University of South Dakota, BA (History), MA (School Administration & Counseling). *Address & Affiliation*: Chairperson, American Indian Education Foundation, P.O. Box 27491, Albuquerque, NM 87125 (800) 881-8694. *Past professional posts*: Teacher & guidance counselor since 1980, schools majority American Indian enrollment.

FOX, SANDRA J. (HARRELL) (Oglala/Cheyenne River Sioux) 1944-
(BIA education specialist)
Born December 9, 1944, Kadoka, S.D. *Education*: Dickinson State College, BS, 1966; Penn State University, MEd, 1971, D.Ed, 1976. *Affiliation & Address*: Education specialist, Bureau of Indian Affairs, Office of Indian Education Programs, MS: 3512-MIB, 1849 C St., NW, Washington, DC 20240 (202) 273-2382. *Affiliations*: Education specialist, Bureau of Indian Affairs, Aberdeen Area Office, S.D.; education specialist-curriculum, ORBIS, Inc., Washington, D.C., 1985-. *Other professional post*: Education specialist & consultant, B.I.A. *Memberships*: International Reading Association; National Indian Education Association; North American Indian Women's Association. *Awards, honors*: North Dakota Indian Scholarship; invited to join Pi Lambda Theta; given presentations at National Council of Teachers of English Convention, National Reading Conference, & International Reading Association Convention. *Interests*: Elementary & secondary education reading improvement. *Published work*: An Annotated Bibliography of Young People's Books on American Indians (Bureau of Indian Affairs, 1973).

FOX, SHANNON D. (*NeetAhKus na cita Kux*) (Arikara/Santee Sioux)
(college faculty)
Education: University of North Dakota, 1996, MFA BFA (Visual Arts with a major in Mixed Media with emphasis in digital image printing),, 1999; Vocational Certifications, Bismarck State Colege & Valley City State University. *Affiliation & Address*: Faculty. Fort Berthold Community College, 220 8th Ave. N., P.O. Box 490 • New Town, ND 58763 (701) 627-4738. *Military service*: U.S. Air Force, 1987-90. After opening his own company, 3-Foxx Productions now White Pipe, he established a graphic arts program and developed a nine-month certificate program at Fort Berthold Community College. He currently teaches digital imaging, computers, drawing, painting and traditional native arts & crafts. While his own work has received national recognition, he counts his students' successes among his proudest accomplishments. Shannon's work received recognition along with several other Native American artists in the book, Storytelling Time: Native North American Art from the Collections at the University of North Dakota. Several of his mixed media, digital manipulations, and art pieces are featured in this book. Shannon Fox serves on the Board of Directors for the North Dakota Council on the Arts.

FOXWORTH, RAYMOND (Navajo)
(senior program officer)
Education: University of Colorado at Boulder, BA, MA, PhD student (Political Science). *Affiliation & Address*: Senior Programs Officer, Research, Policy & Asset-Building Programs, First Nations Development Institute, 351 Coffman St., Suite 200, Longmont, CO 80501 (303) 774-7836. *Past professional post*: Project officer, American Indian College Fund, Denver, CO.

FRAGUA, CLIFF (Jemez Pueblo)
(artist-sculptor)
Address: E-mail: cfragua55@yahoo.com. *Affiliation*: Board Member, Artist Representative, Indian Arts & Crafts Association (2012-14), Jemez Pueblo, NM. *Past professional posts*: IACA Past President & Past IACA Artist of the Year returns to the IACA Board of Directors. Cliff has served on the board of directors of SWAIA, and the Indigenous Sculptor Society as well. Cliff brings unique insights to the IACA board through his previous board of directors' experience, & unique artist perspectives that are vital to the organization. Since 1974, when he created his first stone sculpture, Cliff has created a significant body of work that keeps evolving with new influences and new interests. His sculptures are featured in such public locations as the U.S. Capitol Building Statuary Hall, and in many private collections throughout the country. He has been included in many invitational exhibitions & one-man shows in leading museums & galleries, & has earned honors & awards for his sculptures.

FRAGUA, MARISHA (Paiute)
(rancheria chairperson)
Affiliation & Address: Cedarville Rancheria, 200 N. Howard St., Cedarville, CA 96101 (530) 2333-3969.

FRAHER, DIANE (Osage/Cherokee)
(writer, filmmaker; founder & director)
Affiliation & Address: Founder & Director, American Indian Artists, Inc. (AMERINDA), 288 E. 10th St., New York, NY 10009 (212) 598-0968. Founded AMERINDA in 1987, a community-based arts organization dedicated to making the indigenous perspective in the arts available to a broad multicultural audience. *Films*: "The Reawakening," is the first feature-length film written & directed by a Native woman and fully produced by Native people. Her film, "The Heart Stays," is currently in development.

FRANCIS, HARTWELL
(director of Cherokee language program)
Education: University of New Mexico, BA; Portland State University, MA (Applied Linguistics); University of Colorado, PhD (Theoretical Linguistics) where he focused on the syntax-semantics in Native American languages. *Affiliation & Address*: Director, Cherokee Language Program, Cherokee Studies, Western Carolina University, Western Carolna University, College of Arts & Sciences, McKee Bldg. 105A-C, Cullowhee, NC 28723 (828) 227-2303. E-mail: hfrancis@email.wcu.edu. Dr. Francis has worked with Cherokee Language Coordinator, Thomas Belt, on the Western Carolina University Cherokee Language curriculum. Together, they have instituted the Cherokee Scholars program, which brings members of the Eastern Band of Cherokee Indians to campus to speak about their experiences as Cherokee language teachers. Hartwell teaches courses on Cherokee grammar, language death, language revitalization, and linguistic anthropology.

FRANCIS, KIRK E. (Penobscot)
(tribal chief)
Affiliation & Address: Chief (2006-present), Penobscot Indian Nation, 12 Wabanaki Way, Indian Island, ME 04468 (207) 817-7350. *Other professional post*: Chairperson, National Tribal Environmental Council, Albuquerque, NM.

FRANCIS, LEE, IV (Laguna Pueblo)
(organization director)
Born in Albuquerque, N.M. *Address & Affiliation*: Wordcraft Circle of Native Writers & Storytellers, 200 Rio Grande SW, Apt. 214, Albuquerque, NM 87104 (505) 842-8425. E-Mail: E-mail: naterealities@yahoo.com. Website: www. wordcraftcircle.org.

FRANCIS, VERA (Passamaquoddy)
(tribal vice chief)
Affiliation & Address: Vice Chief, Passamaquoddy Tribe – Pleasant Point, 9 Sakom Rd., P.O. Box 343 • Perry, ME 04667 (207) 853-2600.

FRANCIS-FOURKILLER, TAMARA (Caddo)
(tribal chairperson)
Affiliation & Address: Chairperson, Caddo Nation, P.O. Box 487, Binger, OK 73009 (405) 656-2344. E-mail: tffourkiller.cn@gmail.com

FRANCKE, JACKIE (Navajo)
(senior projects officer)
Education: New Mexico Institute of Mining & Technology, BS (Mining Engineer). *Affiliation & Address*: Senior Projects Officer, First Nations Development Institute, 351 Coffman St., Suite 200, Longmont, CO 80501 (303) 774-7836. *Past professional posts*: President, Geotechnika, Inc. (as a technical consultant assisting tribal organizations & communities with program development, implementation, and management for tribal programs, projects & grants); senior engineer, Westinghouse Electric Corporation (ten years).

FRANCO, DESIREE (Cahuilla)
(tribal vice chairperson)
Affiliation & Address: Vice Chairperson, Torres Martinez Desert Cahuilla Indians, P.O. Box 1160, Thermal, CA 92274 (760) 397-0300. E-mail: tmdfranco@torresmartinez.org

FRANK, BILLY, JR. (Nisqually) 1931-
(commission chairperson)
Affiliation & Address: Co-founder & chairperson (1975-present), Northwest Indian Fisheries Commission, 6730 Martin Way E., Olympia, WA 98506 (360) 438-1180. With Frank's leadership, the NWIFC and the tribes it serves are working to protect & restore the natural resources for Indians and non-Indians alike. *Other professional post*: Instructor, The Institute for Tribal Government, Portland State University, Portland, OR. *Past professional posts*: Helped to found the Northwest Renewable Resources Center in 1984. *Awards, honors*: 1991 Albert Schweitzer Award for his "achievements as a mediator between opposing interest groups and as a protector of the fragile cultural & environmental heritage that all humanity share"; 2004 Indian Country Today 's first, "American Indian Visionary Award."

FRANK, DAWN TWO-CROW (Oglala Lakota)
(Indian college vice president for instruction)
Education: Oglala Lakota College, BS (Human Services), 2002; MA (Lakota Leadership & Management), 2004; South Dakota State University, PhD (Biological Sciences), 2010. *Affiliation & Address*: Vice President for Instruction & Director & Chair of the Graduate Studies Program, Oglala Lakota College, P.O. Box 490, Kyle, SD 57752 (605) 455-6000. Dawn has worked with the Oglala Sioux Tribe in the Health Administration office & Indian Health Service. In 2001, she became the Project Director of the a program titled Teca Aicibleza Pi Kte meaning Youth Understanding themselves until 2004, where she was appointed as the Executive Director of the Oglala Sioux Tribe under Cecelia Fire Thunders' administration. In the spring of 2005, she began working for the Oglala Lakota College within the Graduate Program as the Coordinator of the Education Administration. She currently serves as Chair for the Institutional Review Board, member of Assessment Committee, has served as a member of the Institutional Affairs Committee for two years, and was a member of the

Piya Wiconi Okola Kiciye - governing body of the Oglala Lakota College, for one term. Dawn is active member of community organizations: Wacante Kiyapi Board of Directors, Tasunke Wakan Okolakiciye, Wakpamni District Task force, and has served as the Calico community president. She founded the annual Mni Huha Wacipi located in Calico, SD. She has been a member of the American Evaluation Assn (AEAS) since 2006, South Dakota Experimental Program to Stimulate Competitive Research (SDEPSCOR), & the Circle of Life Steering Committee through the University of Colorado. She has been a member of the Oglala Sioux Tribe Research and Review Board (OSTRRB) since 2009; appointed to Black Hills Treaty Council on September 19, 2012.

FRANK, EARLE, III (Timbisha Shoshone)
(tribal vice chairperson)
Affiliation & Address: Vice Chairperson, Timbisha Shoshone Tribe, P.O. Box 206, Death Valley, CA 92328 (760) 258-5919.

FRANK, HAROLD "GUS" (Forest County Potawatomi)
(tribal chairperson)
Affiliation & Address: Chairperson, Forest County Potawatomi Community, P.O. Box 340, Crandon, WI 54520 (715) 478-2903.

FRANK, JOEL (Seminole of Florida)
(tribal board of directors)
Born in Fort Lauderdale, Florida & raised on federal reservation lands of the Seminole Tribe of Florida, Hollywood, Fla. *Education*: Dade Community College; St. Thomas University. *Affiliation & Address*: Board Member, Big Cypress Representative, The Seminole Tribe of Florida, 6300 Stirling Rd., Hollywood, FL 33024. E-mail: jfrank@semtribe.com. *Other professional post*: Board member, American Indian Graduate Center, Albuquerque, NM. *Past professional posts*: Executive Director & Chairperson, AMERIND Risk Management Corporation; founding member & president, National Indian Gaming Association; board member, National Center for American Indian Enterprise Development. *Awards, honors*: The 2012 John Kieffer Award (along with Toy Sanchez, Jr.) from the National Indian Gaming Association's 14th Annual Sovereignty Awards Banquet for his four decades of dedication to the furtherance of economic prosperity & the protection of stable governments for American Indians through his participation in organizations such as the National Indian Gaming Association, AMERIND, the United South & Eastern Tribes, the National Center for American Indian Enterprise Development; the Florida Governor's Council on Indian Affairs, & the North American Indigenous Games Council & the Indigenous Language Institute. In 1990, he accepted an appointment to serve on newly formed National Indian Gaming Commission.

FRANK, KATHLEEN (Navajo)
(Indian commission chair)
Education: Northern Arizona University, BS (Business), MA (Administration). *Affiliation & Address*: Chairperson, Commission for Native Americans, Northern Arizona University, P.O. Box 4085, Flagstaff, AZ 86011 (928) 523-9557. E-mail: Kathleen.frank@nau.edu. As Director, Special Programs and Alumni Relations During her many years at NAU, Kathleen Frank has worked in several areas throughout the university, ranging from academic departments to student services. From 2011-2016, Ms. Frank served as Director of the Native American Cultural Center, working to provide a "home away from home" for Native American students while increasing the visibility of Native American cultures and traditions at NAU. She currently serves on the NAU Commission for Native Americans and is a member of the Arizona Indian Education Association, the American Indian Chamber of Commerce of Arizona, and the Arizona 21st Century Community Learning Center (CCLC) Vision Team. Ms. Frank is an enrolled member of the Navajo Nation (Diné) originally from Dennehotso, Arizona. She is of the Towering House Clan (Kinyaa'aanii) and born for the Salt Clan (Ashiihi). Her maternal grandfathers are the Water Edge Clan (Tábaahí) and paternal grandfathers are the Near-to-Water Clan (Tó'áhaní). *Past professional posts*: Director, Native American Cultural Center, Northern Arizona University, 2011-16; Administrative Associate, Institute for Native Americans, 1992-2008; Administrative Associate, Applied Idigneous Studies, Northern Arizona University, 2008-11.

FRANK, NICK (Eskimo)
(Alaskan village president)
Affiliation & Address: President, Native Village of Tuntutuliak, P.O. Box 8086, Tuntutuliak, AK 99680 (907) 256-2128.

FRANK, SHAWN R. (Seneca)
(attorney)
Education: Cornell University, BS, 1991; American University, Washington College of Law, JD, 1994. *Affiliation & Address*: Attorney (2002-present), *Affiliation & Address*: Partner (1994-present), The Jacobson Law Group; Jacobson, Magnuson, Anderson & Halloran, P.C., 1295 Bandana Blvd., St. Paul, MN 55108 (651) 644-4710. E-mail: sfrank@thejacobsoblawgroup.com. *Areas of Practice*: Civil Litigation, Employment Law, Indian/Tribal Law. *Past professional posts*: Assistant Attorney General for the Seneca Nation of

Indians (1994-96). While in house counsel, he worked extensively in the areas of federal self-determination contracts, federal grant administration, employment law, and tribal economic development. From 1996-2000, Shawn was a corporate associate at a Minneapolis law firm; 2000-02, he practiced with Albuquerque, NM law firm practicing Indian law exclusively. *Membership*: Americans for Indian Opportunity. *Interest*: Fundraising. Mr. Frank speaks regularly at lawyers' seminars on the subjects of tribal sovereignty, doing business in Indian Country, the Freedom of Information Act, and administrative appeals through the Department of the Interior. *Bar Admissions:* NY, MN, NM, U.S. Court of Appeals for the Tenth Circuit; U.S. District Court for the District of New Mexico; Ho-Chunk Tribal Court; Lower Sioux Tribal Court; Menominee Tribal Court; Oneida Appeals Commission; Prairie Island Indian Community Tribal Court; Pueblo of Laguna Tribal Court; Tribal Court of the Saginaw Chippewa Indian Tribe of Michigan; Seneca Nation of Indians Peacemaker's Court. *Honors and Awards:* Americans for Indian Opportunity Ambassadors Fellow, 1998; Kellogg National Fellowship, 1998

FRANK, WALLY R. (Tlingit)
(AK village president)
Affiliation & Address: President, Angoon Community Association, P.O. Box 328, Angoon, AK 99820 (907) 788-3411.

FRANK, WILLIE, III (Nisqually)
(tribal councilperson)
Education: Evergreen State College, BA (Native American Studies). *Affiliation & Address*: 7th Councilperson, Nisqually Indian Tribe, 4820 She-Nah-Num Dr., SE, Olympia, WA98513 (360) 456-5221. E-mail: frank.willie@nisqually-nsn.gov. Past tribal post: Vice Chairperson.

FRANKLIN, RENO KEONI (Kashia Pomo)
(tribal chairperson)
Affiliation & Address: Chairperson, Kashia Band of Pomo Indians of Stewarts Point Rancheria, 1420 GuernevilleRd. Suite I, Santa Rosa, CA 95403 (707) 591-0580

FRANKS, JEANNIE (*Shinning Star*) (United Lumbee)
(chief of United Lumbee Black Bear Clan)
Address: 2510 Markwardt, Joplin, MO 64801 (417) 781-0213. *Principal occupation*: Chief of United Lumbee Black Bear Clan. *Address*: 13159 Oakwood Trail, Neosho, MO 64850. *Affiliations*: Manager, Crossways, 1960-65; manager, Steak & Grape, 1965-70; manager, Colony Inn, 1970-74; manager, Howard Johnsons, 1974-80; domestic engineer, 1980-present. *Community activities*: Athletic Boosters; B.P.O. Elks USA; fund raising for various organizations. *Memberships*: United Lumbee Black Bear Clan; B.P.O. Elks USA; Loma Linda Country Club; Golden Hawk Society.

FRANTZ, DONALD G. (Omahkokoyaato'si) 1934-
(linguistic research & consultation; professor emeritus)
Born January 20, 1934, Oakland, Calif. *Education*: University of California, Berkeley, BA, 1960; University of Alberta, PhD. *Principal occupation*: Linguistic research & consultation; professor emeritus. *Address*: 9 Lafayette Crescent, Lethbridge, Alberta, Canada T1K 4B5 (403) 381-0302; E-Mail: frantz@uleth.ca. *Affiliation*: Professor emeritus, Native American Studies Dept., University of Lethbridge, A444 University Hall, Lethbridge, AB, Canada (403) 394-3969. *Military service*: U.S. Coast Guard, 1953-57 (1st Class P.O.). *Memberships*: Linguistics Society of America; Society for the Study of Indigenous Languages of the Americas. *Interests*: Native language research; triathlon participation. *Published works*: "Blackfoot Dictionary," 1989 & 1995, & "Blackfoot Grammar," 1991 (U. of Toronto Press).

FRAZER, GARY (Ojibwe-Chippewa)
(tribal executive director)
Affiliation & Address: Executive Director, Minnesota Chippewa Tribe, Box 217, Cass Lake, MN 56633 (218) 335-8581. E-mail: gfrazer@mnchippewatribe.org.

FRAZIER, CAPT. FRANCIS (Cheyenne River Sioux)
(IHS office director)
Education: Montana State University, BS (Nursing); SUNY, Buffalo, MS (Nursing/Family Nurse Practitioner); University of Utah, MPH. *Affiliation & Address*: Director, Indian Health Service Office of Public Health Support (OPHS) at IHS Headquarters, The Reyes Bldg. (RB) 801 Thompson Ave., Suite 400, Rockville, MD 20852. The IHS, an agency within the Department of Health and Human Services, is the principal federal health care advocate and provider for American Indians and Alaska Natives. OPHS produces statistical information & publications on American Indian and Alaska Native health widely used by policymakers, journalists, and health administrators. OPHS also supports research by IHS staff and external researchers by operating the IHS Institutional Review Board, which reviews and approves proposed studies and papers to ensure patient privacy and compliance. CAPT Frazier most recently served as the Acting Director of the IHS Great Plains Area comprising Iowa, Nebraska, North Dakota, and South Dakota. In this role, he had administrative

responsibility for seven hospitals and 10 health centers that serve 17 Tribes and more than 130,000 American Indian people eligible for IHS services. With more than 20 years of service through the U.S. Public Health Service Commissioned Corps, *Military service*: U.S. Army 82nd Airborne Division. He also has experience on Capitol Hill. Prior to his work as OPHS Director, CAPT Frazier served as Acting Director and Deputy Director of OPHS. *Past professional posts*: CAPT Frazier worked as a nurse practitioner and registered nurse with the Seneca Nation of Indians and with Bristol Bay Health Corporation in Alaska. He also served as a registered nurse in pediatrics and intensive care and a clinical supervisor at Alaska Native Medical Center. He also worked with an Urban Indian Health Program in Salt Lake City as a certified diabetes educator and in the private sector in clinical practice.

FRAZIER, GREGORY W. (Crow) 1947-
(writer/adventurer)

Born September 5, 1947, Richmond, Ind. Education: Earlham College, 1965-67; Temple University, BA, 1972; University of Puget Sound, MBA, 1978, PhD, 1988. *Address*: P.O. Box 427, Englewood, CO 80151. E-mail: gregfrazier@yahoo.com. Website: www.horizonsunlimited.com/gregfrazier. *Affiliations*: President, Whole Earth Motorcycle Center, P.O. Box 102125, Denver, CO 80250; owner, Intracity Properties, Englewood, CO; president/chairman, Indians for United Social Action; president, GAMA, Englewood, CO; president, National Urban Indian Council, Denver, CO. *Other professional posts*: Chairperson, Arrowstar, Yellowtail, MT; Chairperson, Absarokee Investments, Seattle. *Affiliations*: Instructor/consultant, American Indian Management Institute, Albuquerque, N.M., 1972-74; executive director, Seattle Indian Center, Inc., 1974-77; executive director, AL-IND-ESK-A (The 13th Regional Corp.), Seattle, WA, 1977-79; president, National Indian Business Council, Englewood, CO, 1977-89. *Community activities*: Indians for United Social Action (member); National Low Income Housing Coalition (member). *Memberships*: Indian Motorcycle Owners Assn (vice president); American Motorcyclists Assn; America Film Producers Assn; America Writers Guild. *Awards, honors*: Outstanding Contribution Award, CETA Coalition; Individual Personal Achievement Award, IHRC, Inc.; Outstanding Minority Writer, 1985, U.S. Writers Association; Best Business Efforts, Community Chamber of Commerce, 1985; Outstanding Minority Writer of the Year, 1988; Presidential appointee, National Advisory Council on Indian Education; appointee, Secretary's Advisory Group, Department of HUD; appointee, Department of Labor Ad Hoc Advisory Committee. *Interests*: Business & economic development; international economic development; developing countries; political & bureaucratic abuses of authority; fundraising. "Dr. Frazier is a professional motorcycle adventurer, having traveled around the world by motorcycle. He has written extensively about his travel adventures. He has won professional events throughout the U.S. as a BMW and Indian racer. Dr. Frazier is a well-known figure in the motorcycle industry both in Europe and the U.S. Dr. Frazier has long been an advocate for the rights of American Indians and Alaska Natives, having served as president of the National Urban Indian Council from 1977-89. As a registered lobbyist in the U.S. House & Senate, he lobbied for Native rights and funding and is a noted expert on urban Indian policy in America. Dr. Frazier has spent 30 years exposing government abuses, discrimination, and bureaucratic malfeasance in federal agencies. As an Indian activist, he has been responsible for changes in federal laws and regulations that have benefited American Indians & Alaska Natives." *Published works*: While We're At It, Let's Get You a Job (NCIB Press, 1984); American Indian Index (Arrowstar Publishing, 1987); Smoke Signals (Arrowstar Publishing, 1989); American Indian/Alaska Native Higher Education Funding Guild (Arrowstar Publishing, 1989); Urban Indians: Drums from the Cities (Arrowstar); Motorcycle Sex, Or Freud Would Never Understand the Relationship Between Me and My Motorcycle (Arrowstar); Urban Indian Profile in America (Arrowstar); Alaska by Motorcycle, Europe by Motorcylce, Riding South-Mexico, Central America and South America by Motorcycle, and New Zealand by Motorcycle; (Whole Earth Motorcycle Center); BMW Sing Around the World (Whole Earth Motorcycle Center) Indian International Motorcycle Directory (Whole Earth Motorcycle Center).

FRAZIER, HAROLD (Cheyenne River Lakota) 1966-
(tribal chairperson)

Born November 23, 1966 in White Horse, S.D. *Education*: White Horse Day School, 1981; Cheyenne River Butte High School, 1985; Chadron State College, Chadron, Neb; Eastern Wyoming College, AA, 1989. *Principal occupation*: Tribal chairperson. *Affiliation*: Chairperson, Cheyenne River Sioux Tribe, P.O. Box 590, Eagle Butte, SD 57625 (605) 964-4155. *Past professional posts*: Cheyenne River Gas & CATV Co., 1990-98; elected as a District 4 Council Representative representing the communities of White Horse, Timber Lake, Green Grass, and West Eagle Butte. *Memberships*: Great Plains Tribal Chairman's Association (chair); Intertribal Monitoring Assn (chair); National Congress of American Indians (Great Plains Regional Vice-President). *Interests*: Riding & raising horses; singing at the drum with his relatives and friends; & researching the treaties and the history of the Great Sioux Nation.

FRAZIER, TERI
(organization director)

Affiliation & Address: Director, Inter-tribal Indian Ceremonial Association, 206 W. Coal Ave., Gallup, NM 87301 (505) 863-3896. E-mail: ceremonialtf1@gmail.com.

FREDERICKS, CARLA (Manda/Hidatsa & Arikara)
(Indian law program & clinic director)

Education: University of Colorado, BA; Columbia University Law School, JD. *Affiliation & Address*: Associate Clinical Professor & Director of the Indian Law Clinic & Director of the American Indian Law Program (AILP), Colorado Law, University of Colorado, 401 UCB, Wolf Law Bldg., Rm. 105T, Boulder, CO 80309 (303) 492-7079; E-mail: carla.fredericks@colorado.edu. At Colorado Law, Fredericks leads a year-long clinic in which students have the opportunity to represent American Indian tribes, organizations, and individuals in a variety of matters, designed to ready students for the complexities of general counsel work. *Other professional posts*: Counsel to Fredericks, Peebles & Morgan LLP, where she focuses on complex & appellate litigation and Native American affairs, representing Indian tribes and organizations in a variety of litigation & policy matters; Chair of the Board of Trustees for the Mashantucket Pequot (Western) Endowment Trust, and has been appointed by the American Indian College Fund as its representative to the Indian Education Scholarship Holding Fund as part of *Cobell v. Salazar* settlement. *Past professional post*: Taught at Columbia Law School teaching Columbia's Legal Practice seminar, focused on development of research, writing and appellate advocacy skills and working with Columbia's National NALSA moot court competition team. Previously a partner at Milberg LLP in New York, Fredericks founded Milberg's Native American practice and directed the firm's civil/human rights litigation.

FREDERICKS, EVELYN (Hopi)
(sculptor)

Born in Kykotsmovi, Ariz. Hopi Reservation. *Address*: Box 134 · Kykotsmovi, AZ 87039 (928) 734-9377 Website: www.evelynfredericks.com; E-mail: mail@evelynfredericks.com. *Artwork*: Native American stone & bronze sculpture. *Past professional post*: Fine Arts Librarian, Institute of American Indian Arts, Santa Fe, NM, 1973-88.

FREDERICKS, JOHN, III (Mandan, Hidatsa & Arakara)
(attorney)

Born on the Fort Berthold Reservation, N.D. *Education*: Minot State University of Montana, BS, 1984; University of Colorado School of Law, JD, 1987. *Affiliation*: Partner (2007-present), Fredericks Peebles & Morgan LLP, 3730 29th Ave., Mandan, ND 58554 (303) 673-9600. E-mail: jfredericks@ndnlaw.com. *Practice areas*: Federal Indian law; tribal government; housing & taxation law; commercial & business law. Mr. Fredericks has been involved in federal, state & tribal court litigation throughout the country, involving issues of Indian & commercial law, as well as general civil matters. He's an acknowledged expert in Indian housing law; has considerable knowledge and experience in Indian gaming issues; and has extensive experience in tribal tax law & litigation. *Past professional posts*: Associate, Fredericks & Pelcyger, LLC, 1987-92; Partner, Fredericks, Pelcyger & Hester, LLC, 1992-2007. *Legal Authorship*: "Financing Indian Agriculture: Mortgaged Indian Lands and the Federal Trust Responsibility," (14 American Indian Legal Review 105, 1989); "State Regulation in Indian Country: The Supreme Court's Marketing Exemptions Concept, A Judicial Sword Through the Heart of Tribal Self-Determination," (50 Montana Law Review 49, 1989); "America's First Nations: The Origins, History & Future of American Indian Sovereignty," (J.L. & Pol'y 347, 1999.

FREDERICKS, LUCY K. (Mandan, Hidatsa & Arakara)
(director of Indian education)

Affiliation & Address: Director of Indian Education, North Dakota Department of Public Instruction, 600 E. Boulevard Ave., Bismarck, ND 58505 (701) 328-1718. E-mail: lkfredericks@nd.gov.

FREDERICKS, THOMAS W. (Mandan, Hidatsa & Arakara)
(attorney)

Born on the Fort Berthold Reservation, N.D. *Education*: Minot State University, BS, 1965; University of Colorado School of Law, JD, 1972. *Affiliation & Address*: Founding Partner, Fredericks Peebles & Morgan LLP, 1900 Plaza Dr., Louisville, CO 80027 (303) 673-9600. E-mail: tfredericks@ndnlaw.com. Mr. Fredericks joined the firm as a partner in 2007, merging his practice from the law firm that he founded in Colorado in 1979. *Practice areas*: Water & land rights, natural resource development; casino & economic development; inter-governmental affairs; tribal sovereignty & self-determination; land into trust; tribal government; energy & environmental law, et al. Legal experience: Mr. Fredericks has special qualifications to serve Indian Tribes in the capacity of legal counsel. He has served tribal governments in an administrative capacity. As staff attorney and later director of the Native American Rights Fund, Mr. Thomas has considerable expertise in the legal & political relationships that tribes have with the state & federal governments. He has also served as chief legal officer for the Bureau of Indian Affairs (BIAS) and later served as the primary policy official for Indian Affairs within the Dept. of the Interior (DOI). As Associate Solicitor, he was responsible for formulating the position of the U.S. with the lawyers from the Dept. of Justice in all Indian-related cases. As Assistant Secretary for Indian Affairs, he was charged with formulating Indian policy for the Secretary, representing the DOI in transactions with the U.S. Congress. He was instrumental in getting Congress to consider & pass the Indian Mineral Development Act. *Legal Authorship:* Author of the First Solicitor's Opinion dealing with the issue of tribal gaming; formulating the Indian Water Settlement Policy as it relates to Indian Tribal nations; authored the first compact for IGRA (Indian Gaming Regulatory Act.)

FREDERICKS-DUBRAY, MICHELLE CATHERINE (*Pinto Horse Woman*) (Mandan-Hidatsa-Arikara) 1966-
(consultant, grant writer)
Born October 21, 1966, Fort Yates, N.D. *Education:* University of Colorado, BA, 1989. *Principal occupation:* Consultant grant writer. *Affiliation & Address:* Pinto Horse Woman Consulting, HCR 30 Box 32, Mobridge, SD 57601 (605) 733-2387. E-mail: pintohorsewoman@yahoo.com. *Past professional post:* Administrative director, Intertribal Bison Cooperative, Rapid City, SD, 1983-97. *Community activities:* American Indian Ambassador Class of 1994 for Americans for Indian Opportunity. *Interests:* "I am entering into the field of fundraising through my work with the Intertribal Bison Cooperative. In February (1994), I attended a course offered by the Fund Raising School of Indian University's Center on Philanthropy." *Membership:* Americans for Indian Opportunity. *Biographical source:* "Tatanka Returns," by Richard Simonelli, in Winds of Change, Vol. 8, No. 4, Autumn 1993.

FREDERIKSEN, ROBERT DOUGLAS (*Tzuscum Doogie*) (Tsimshian) 1967-
(storyteller, cultural advisor)
Born April 17, 1967, Seattle, Wash. *Education:* Seattle Pacific University, 1985-86; University of Washington, 1992-. *Principal occupation:* Storyteller (ancient Tsimshian legends & parables), cultural advisor. *Affiliation & Address:* Raven Speaker Productions / Ethical Locators, 115 W. Magnolia St., Suite 207, Bellingham, WA 98227 (360) 224-0947 (1988-present). *Other professional post:* Secretary, Tsimshian Tribal Association of Washington; former vice-chairperson & choreographer of Alaska Native Cultural Heritage Association in Washington. *Community activities:* Currently organizing two related organizations, Wisdom, a social research organization dedicated to change, & F.E.E.D. (Foundation for Educational & Economic Development), a trust fund for self-help & education programs. *Interests:* "Pan American Native history; development of self-sustaining solutions to problems facing Natives & other disadvantaged peoples; reading historical fiction, writing; revitalizing hope in an increasingly disenchanted urban youth; constitutional study; economics, market theory. I love to dance, travel & debate."

FREE, KALYN (Choctaw of Oklahoma)
(organization founder & president)
Born & raised in Red Oak, Okla. *Education:* Southeastern Oklahoma State University, BA (Communications), BA (History), 1984; University of Oklahoma, Schoo of Law, JD, 1987. *Affiliation & Address:* President & Founder, Indigenous Democratic Network's (IDN) List (2005-present), 4870 S. Lewis, Suite 204, Tulsa, OK 74105 (918) 583-6100. Website: www.idnslist.org; E-mail: info@indnslist.org. Kalyn is passionate about helping Indians and women run for and win elective office. With the help of INDN's List, 45 tribal members, 11 in Oklahoma, have been elected (and re-elected) since 2006 and are now serving in state & local offices across America. She is most proud to have helped elect the first Indian woman to the Washington State Senate and to statewide office in Montana. *Past professional posts:* After graduating from law school, Kalyn was the youngest lawyer ever hired by the U.S. Dept. of Justice (DOJ). During her ten years with DOJ, she served as Senior Counsel in the Indian Resources Section, where she supervised environmental litigation throughout Indian Country. After leaving the DOJ, Kalyn returned to Southeastern Oklahoma and became the first woman elected District Attorney of Pittsburg & Haskell Counties, 1999-2002. *Awards, honors:* Arthur S. Fleming Award for Outstanding Service to the Federal Government; the American Bar Association's Spirit of Excellence Award for her efforts to increase minority hiring at the DOJ; Oklahoma Institute of Child Advocacy's Friend of Children Award; Oklahoma Coalition Against Domestic Violence & Sexual Assaults Make a Difference Award; the 21st Century Democrats 2006 Rising Star Award; the National Education Association's 2007 Leo Reano Memorial Award; honored by the Women Empowering Women for Indian Nations (WEWIN) for her lifetime devotion to Indian Country; the Charles Chibity Community Service Award; named as one of the Top Fifty Women in Oklahoma by the Journal Record. Kalyn ran for the U.S. Congress in 2004, with the support of endorsement of 117 Indian tribes, AFL-CIO, Sierra Club, et al. Kalyn served as a Super Delegate on the Democratic National Committee from 2005-2009.

FREEMAN, ANDREW (Paskenta Nomlaki)
(former tribal chairperson)
Affiliation & Address: Former chairperson, Paskenta Band of Nomlaki Indians, 2625 Everett Freeman Way, P.O. Box 709, Corning, CA 96021, CA 95963 (530) 528-3538; E-mail: afreeman@paskenta.org

FREEDMAN, HEATHER VALDEZ
(program director)
Education: UCLA, MA (American Indian Studies); Kennedy School of Government at Harvard, MA (with focus on criminal justice policy in Indian country.) *Affiliation & Address:* Program Director (2006-present), Tribal Law & Policy Institute, 8235 Santa Monica Blvd., Suite 211, West Hollywood, CA 90046 (323) 650-5467. E-mail: heather@tlpi.org. Heather provides oversight for programmatic operations, as well as overseeing TLPI's tribal-state collaboration work. She has over 15 years of experience working on policy issues in Indian country with a focus on tribal criminal justice systems. She has researched and written in the areas of tribal legal and community development and California tribal history. Her experience includes serving as project director for several research-related projects in Indian country, including the UCLA Native Nations Law and Policy Center's nationwide assessment of Public Law 280, tribal liaison for tribal court grantees in California, and consultant for the Gabrieleno/Tongva tribal recognition project. She is an instructor for the UCLA Tribal Learning Community and Educational Exchange and the series co-editor of the Tribal Legal Studies textbook series.

FREEMAN, JONATHON (Choctaw)
(program director)
Affiliation & Address: Program Director, Seventh Generation Fund for Indian Development, P.O. Box 4569, Arcata, CA 95518 (707) 825-7640. E-mail: jk@7genfund.org.

FREEMAN, LACY WAYNE (Waccamaw Siouan)
(tribal chief)
Affiliation: Waccamaw Siouan Tribe, P.O. Box 69, Bolton, NC 28423 (910) 655-8778. Website: www.waccamaw-siouan.com.

FREEMAN, LACY WAYNE (Waccamaw Sioux)
(tribal chief)
Affiliation & Address: Chief, Waccamaw Siouan Tribe, P.O. Box 69, Bolton, NC 28423 (910) 655-8778

FREEMAN, RICHARD
(attorney-partner; co-team leader)
Education: Claremont Men's College, BA, 1970; Duke University Law School, JD, 1974. *Affiliation & Address:* Co-Team Leader, Tribal & Indian Law, Sheppard Mullin Richter & Hampton LLP, 12275 El Camino Real, Suite 200, San Diego, CA 92130 (858) 720-8909. E-mail: rfreeman@sheppardmullin.com. Mr. Freeman specializes in Native American issues, including but not limited to sovereign immunity, Tribal sovereignty, Indian water rights, the Indian Gaming and Regulatory Act, Tribal Compacts, Tribal contracts & leases, Indian Tax issues, Indian environmental regulatory and compliance issues and labor and employment issues on tribal lands. *Awards, honors:* He has been named as one of the top Southern California "Super Lawyers." He has been a member of the Board of Governors of the San Diego Association of Business Trial Lawyers. He is listed in Who's Who in American Lawyers. He has spoken before national attorney groups on a variety of subjects including trial issues and employment issues.

FREEMAN, ROBERT LEE (Dakota-Luiseno) 1939-
(artist, cartoonist, muralist, printmaker)
Born January 14, 1939, Rincon Indian Reservation, Calif. *Education:* Palomar College, AA, 1976. *Principal occupation:* Artist, cartoonist, muralist, printmaker. Resides in San Marcos, CA. Website: www.robertfreemanartist.com; E-mail: freemanedwina@yahoo.com. *Affiliation:* Art instructor, Palomar College. *Military service:* U.S. Army, 1957-60 (E-2 Korea, 1959). *Exhibitions:* One-man shows: Schiver Gallery, St. Louis, MO; Sioux Museum, Rapid City, SD; Turtle Mountain Gallery, Philadelphia, PA; Gallery of the American Indian, Sedona, AZ; among others. *Group shows:* U.S. Department of the Interior, Washington, DC; Heard Museum, Phoenix, AZ; Scottsdale National Indian Art Exhibit, AZ; among others. *Murals:* Los Angeles Public Library (45 ft.) and five private murals in homes. Numerous selected public & private collections. *Awards, honors:* 150 national Indian art awards from the following: Scottsdale National Indian Art Exhibit, Heard Museum, Red Cloud Art Show, Southern California Exposition, Gallup Ceremonial, and California State Fair. *Interests:* Mr. Freeman works in several media and has won awards in oil, watercolor, woodcarving, etching, pen and ink, bronze, airbrush and drawing, acrylic & lithography. He has instructed the course Native American Art at Grossmont College, San Diego, and Palomar College, San Marcos, Calif. Travel. *Biographical sources:* Who's Who in Indian Art; International Artists & Writers (Cambridge, England). *Published works:* Mr. Freeman's work has appeared in

such periodicals as Ford Times, Western Horseman, Southwest Art Scene, Indian Voices, Genie, North County Living, Westerner, and Artist of the Rockies. Paintings included in two books, I Am These People, and Contemporary Sioux Paintings. Mr. Freeman has illustrated two books: The Layman's Typology Handbook, and The Luiseno People. He is author and publisher of two cartoon books, For Indians Only, 1971, and War Whoops and All That Jazz, 1973; Robert Freeman Drawings, 1985.

FREESE, ALISON 1951-
(educator, information specialist)
Born August 13, 1951, Washington, DC. *Education*: University of Wisconsin, BA, 1974; University of New Mexico, MA, 1986, PhD, 1991. *Affiliation & Address*: Senior Program Officer, Institute of Museum & Library Services (2003-present), 1800 M St., NW, 9th Floor, Washington, DC 20036 (202) 653-4657. E-mail: afreese@imls.gov. *Past professional post*: Information Specialist, Native American Studies Dept., University of New Mexico, Albuquerque, NM, 1991-98; Tribal Libraries Consultant, New Mexico State Library, Santa Fe, NM, 1998-2003. *Community activities*: Organize speaker series, liaison with Native American organizations; editor of monthly newsletter; computer networking with tribal libraries. *Memberships*: America Society for Ethno-history; American Historical Association; American Library Association, New Mexico Library Association, Phi Kappa Phi Honorary Society. *Interests*: "Pueblo/Spanish relations in 17th century New Mexico; cultural resistance strategies implemented by Native American groups in response to European colonization, particularly in the Pueblo Southwest; ethical issues relating to scholarship in Native American studies. Also interested in facilitating Native American students at UNM and encouraging them to pursue a career in Native American studies through research & writing." *Published works*: UNM Dissertation - "Sacred Clowns" Role in Cultural Boundary maintenance Among the Pueblo Indians; editor, et al, By Force of Arms: The Journals of don Diego de Vargas, New Mexico, 1691-93 (UNM Press, 1992); chapter, "Send in the Clowns: Resistance Strategies Among the Pueblo Indians in 17th Century New Mexico," in The Spanish Missions of New Mexico: A Sourcebook, Vol. 2, by David Hurst Thomas, et al, Editors (Garland Press, 1991).

FREY, RODNEY
(professor of ethnography)
Education: Clorado State University, BA, 1972, MA (Anthropology), 1974; University of Colorado, PhD (Anthropology), 1979. *Affiliation & Address*: Chair, Department of Sociology & Anthropology & Director of the Alfred W. Bowers Laboratory of Anthropology & Professor of Ethnography, University of Idaho, P.O. Box 441110, Moscow, ID 83844 (208) 885-6268. E-mail: rfrey@uidaho.edu Over the past 40 years, Professor Frey has been associated with & has conducted various applied, collaborative projects with the Apsaalooke (Crow) of Montana, the Schitsu'umsh (Coeur d'Alene) and Nimiipuu (Nez Perce) of Idaho, and the Confederated Warm Springs Tribes of Oregon. His current research & writing endeavor is tentatively called "Huckleberries: Stories from the American Indian Experience." Professor Frey states, "It is an attempt to bring together all the lessons I've learned from working with Tribal elders over the last four decades, & offer an ethnographic methodology & pedagogical approach to researching, understanding, presenting & teaching American Indian culture." *Awards, honors*: Research Excellence Award, 2005; UNITY Service Medallion, UNITY Student Organization and the Office of Multicultural ffairs, 2006; Distinguished Humanities Professor, 2011-12, College of Letters, Arts & Social Sciences; Teaching Excellence Award, 2012/ *Published works*: The World of the Crow Indians: As Driftwood Lodges (Universit of Oklahoma Press, 1987; paper, 1993); Stories That Make the World: Oral Literature of the Indian Peoples of the Inland Northwest as Told by Lawrence Aripa, Tom Yellowtail & Other Elders (U. of Oklahoma Press, 1995; paper, 1999); Landscape Traveled by Coyote & Crame: The World of the Schitsu'umsh – Coeur d'Alene Indians, in collaboration with the Schitsu'umsh (University of Washington Press, 2001, 2005); Nez Perce Tribe Lifelong Learning Online Module (Nez Perce Tribe, 2001); Coeur d'Alene Tribe Lifelong Learning Online Module (Coeur d'Alene Tribe, 2002); Confederated Tribes of Warm Springs Lifelong Learning Online Module (Confederated Tribes of Warm Springs, 2003); Religion & Healing in Native America, edited with Suzanne Crawford (Praeger Press, 2008).

FRIAS, HERMINIA (MINNIE) (Pascua Yaqui)
(partnership manager)
Education: University of Arizona, MPH. *Affiliation & Address*: Partnership Manager, Bush Foundation, Native Nations Institute for Leadership, Management, and Policy, 803 E. First St., Tucson, AZ 85719 (520) 626-4661. E-mail: frias@u.arizona.edu. In her role as Partnership Manager she primarily works with the Native nations in Minnesota, North Dakota and South Dakota in areas ranging from executive education on nation building to major constitutional reform initiatives. In 2002, she served as a congressional fellow with Congressman Tom Udall through the Kaiser Family Foundation Native American Health Fellowship program. This experience led her to a career in politics, policy, governance, and leadership. In 2004, she was honored to serve as Chairwoman for her nation, the Pascua Yaqui Tribe. In 2009, she served as

the executive director of a local urban Indian behavioral health center non-profit, Native Images, Inc. She also has worked with the University of Arizona's Indigenous Peoples Law and Policy Program, the Native American Technical Assistance Office, and the Graduate College.

FRICHNER, TONYA GONNELLA (Onondaga)
(attorney; activist; indigenous activist)
Education: St. Johns University, BS; Queens College Law School, JD. *Affiliation & Address*: President & Founder (1989-present), American Indian Law Alliance (AILA), 11 Broadway, 2nd Floor, New York, NY 10004 (212) 598-0100 Ext. 257. E-mal: aila@ailanyc.org. *Other professional posts*: Board chairperson, Seventh Generation Fund for Indigenous Peoples, Inc., Arcata, CA. Tonya has worked most closely with elders from the Haudenosaunee (Iroquois) Confederacy & the Lakota Nation. She has considerable experience in the process of the establishment of the Permanent Forum on Indigenous Issues, and in the negotiation process concerning the draft U.N. Declaration on the Rights of Indgenous Peoples and the Organization of American States Proposed American Declaation on the Rights of Indogenous Peoples. *Awards, honors*: The Spirit Award for International Service from the American Indian Community House, New York, NY; Harriet Tubman Humanitariann Achivement Award; the Female Role Model of the Year of the Ms. Foundation for Women; Thunderbird Indian of the Year Award; the Ellis Island Medal of Honor; NY County Lawyers Association Award for Outstanding Pubic Service; the Alston Bannerman Award.

FRICKE, HERB (Mandan, Hidatsa, Arikara)
(president/chief engineer; board president)
Affiliation & Address: President & CEO, Cooper Zeitz Engineers, 620 SW 5th, Suite 1225, Portland, OR 97204 (503) 253-5429. *Other professional post*: Board President & Chair of the Fund Development Committee, Oregon Native American Chamber (ONAC), Portland, OR. Herb has managed a wide range of projects many for regional Nations & Tribes working to improve their neighborhoods, infrastructure, and community centers. *Community activities*: Herb is committed to improving opportunities for Native American youth and emerging businesses.

FRIDERES, JAMES S.
(Indigenous program coordinator)
Affiliation & Address: Coordinator, International Indigenous Studies Program, Department of Sociology, University of Calgary, 2500 University Dr. NW, Calgary, AB T2N 1N4 (403) 220-5521. E-mail: frideres@ucalgary.ca

FRIEND, BILLY (Wyandotte)
(tribal chief)
Affiliation & Address: Chief, Wyandotte Nation of Oklahoma, P.O. Box 250, Wyandotte, OK 74370 (918) 678-2297. Website: www.wyandotte-nation.org.

FRINKMAN, LAUREN (Cochiti Pueblo)
(tribal law specialist)
Education: UCLA School of Law, JD (studied Tribal & Federal Indian Law). Affiliation & Address: Tribal Law Specialist, Tribal Law & Policy Institute (TLPI) 8235 Santa Monica Blvd. #211, West Hollywood, CA 90046 (323) 650-5467. E-mail: lauren@tlpi.org. *Other professional post*: Secretary, California Indian Law Assn, Sacramento, CA. *Past professional post*: Law Clerk, Native American Rights Fund & the Legal Aid Foundation of Los Angeles. While in law school, she served as president of the Native American Law Students Assn, and as Area 1 Rep. of the National Native American Law Students Assn.

FRITZSCHE, MELANIE PATTEN (Laguna Pueblo)
(attorney; publishing CEO)
Education: Adams State College (Alamosa, CO), BA; University of New Mexico School of Law, JD (with a Certificate in Indian Law & Natural Resources). *Affiliations & Address*: Staff Attorney, American Indian Law Center, Inc., P.O. Box 4456, Albuquerque, NM (505) 277-5462. E-mail: fritzsche@ailc-inc.org. *Other professional posts*: Appellate Judge, Southwest Intertribal Court of Appeals; CEO, Aurora Publishing, Albuquerque, NM, 2004-present; board vice president, American Indian Graduate Center, Albuquerque, NM. *Past professsional posts*: Private practice with a firm specializing in water law; assistant Attorney General for the New Mexico Attorney General's Office (Civil Division); attorney advisor for the Solicitor's Office, U.S. Dept. of the Interior, Southwest Regional Office; judicial law clerk for the Honorable Celia Foy Castillo of New Mexico Court of Appeals; law clerk, U.S. Senate Committee on Indian Affairs, and U.S. Attorney's Office for the District of New Mexico.

FRIZZELL, GEORGE
(head of special collectios)
Education: Western Carolina University, MA (History); University of North Carolina at Greensboro, MLS. *Affiliation & Address*: Head of Special Collections, Hunter Library, Western Carolina University, Cullowhee, NC 28723 (828) 227-7474. E-mail: gfrizzell@email.wcu.edu. George is a recognized expert in the fields of Cherokee and Appalachian history.

FROMAN, JOHN P. (Peoria)
(tribal chief & administrator)
Affiliation & Address: Chief & Administrator (2005-present), Peoria Tribe of Indians of Oklahoma, P.O. Box 1527, Miami, OK 74355 (918) 540-4155. E-mail: jfroman@peoriatribe.com.

FROST, CLEMENT J. (Southern Ute)
(former tribal chairperson)
Affiliation & Address: Former chairperson, Southern Ute Tribe, Box 737, Ignacio, CO 81137 (970) 563-0100.

FRYBERG, DEENA (Tulalip)
(tribal court administrator)
Affiliation & Address: Administrator, Puyallup Tribal Court, 1638 E. 29th St., Tacoma, WA 98404 (253) 680-5589.

FRYBERG, STEPHANIE (Tulalip)
(professor of psychology)
Education: Stanford University, PhD, 2003. *Address*: Professor, University of Arizona, Dept. of Psychology, Rm. 216, Tucson, AZ 85721 (520) 626-9730. E-mail: fryberg@email.arizona.edu. *Affiliations*: Assistant professor, Dept. of Psychology, University of Arizona; affiliate faculty, American Indian Studies, University of Arizona, Tucson, AZ. She teaches undergraduate & graduate courses on cultural & social psychology. *Research interests*: "Focus on how social representations of race, culture, and social class influence psychological well-being, physical health, and educational attainment." *Published works*: "On Being American Indian: Current & Possible Selves," with H.R. Markus, in Journal of Self & Identity); "Racial Ethnic Self-Schemas," with D. Oyserman, et al, in Social Psychology Quarterly; "Models of Education in American Indian, Asian American & European American Contexts," with H.R. Markus; Honor or Harm: The Effects of American Indian Mascotson American Indian Selves," with H.R. Markus, et al.; The Psychology of Engagement with Indigenous Identities: A Cultural Perspective," with G. Adams, et al.; and "The Psychology of Invisibility," with S. Townsend.

FULLER, J.B. (BUTCH), JR., (Creek) 1952-
(cultural educator)
Born August 5, 1952, Wetumpka, Alaska. *Education*: University of Montevallo (AL), 1971-72. *Principal occupation*: Cultural educator. *Address*: 705 Cornelia Rd., Brierfield, AL 35035 (205) 665-5137. *Affiliation*: Alabama Power Co., Birmingham, AL, 1974-96; cultural educator (specializing in Creek Indian history & culture), 1996-present. *Membership*: Founder & president, Southeastern Indian Heritage Association; Native American Resource Center, University of Alabama (advisory board member); Baha's Faith; Native American Teaching Committee. *Awards, honors*: Outstanding Young Men of America, 1981. *Interests*: Reproducing early Southeastern Indian material culture pieces for collectors and museums. "(I'm a) maker of museum-quality Southeastern Indian bows, arrows & tools; (I'm a) demonstrator at museums and educational events; and a freelance magazine writer." *Publication*: Creek Indians of the Early 1800's: A Coloring Book for All Ages.

FULLMER, JAMIE L. (Yavapai-Apache)
(organization chair & CEO)
Education: Southern Utah University, BS; University of Utah, MSW. *Affiliation & Address*: Chairperson & CEO (2007-present), Blue Stone Strategy Group, 19900 MacArthur Blvd., Suite 658, Irvine, CA 92612 (949) 476-8828. Website: www.bluestonestrategy.com. The Group's purpose is to promote economic development & sustainability of Tribal Nations. *Other professional post*: Chairperson & Founder, Fire Mountain Wines, P.O. Box 4120, Cottonwood, AZ 86326 (928) 649-9135. Website: www.firemountainwines.com. Jamie is dedicated to providing thought leadership in Indian Country in maintaining sustainable & efficient Tribal systems & the development of a National Indian Economy. He has spoken at numerous conferences & continues to represent the American Indian Business Network initiative on behalf of the National Indian Gaming Association. *Past professional posts*: Yavapai-Apache Nation (director of health & human services; chairperson for two terms); president, Inter-Tribal Council of Arizona. *Community service*: Board member, National Inter-Tribal Economic Alliance; chairperson, Northern Arizona University's, Institute for Native Americans; board member, Native Home Capital. *Awards, honors*: In 2007, Jamie was recognized for outstanding leadership & contributions to American Indian economic & business development by the National Center for American Indian Enterprise Development (NCAIED).

FUNMAKER-ROMANO, CHRISTINE (Ho-Chunk)
(executive director)
Affiliation & Address: Executive Director, American Indian Community House, 134 W. 29th St., 4th Floor, New York, NY 10001 (212) 598-0100. E-mail: cfr@aich.org.

FURLAN, LAURA N.
(assistant professor of English)
Education: University of Iowa, BA (American Studies);, San Diego State University, MA (English); University of California, Santa Barbara, PhD (English). Affiliation *& Address*: Assistant Professor, English Department, Bartlett Hall, University of Massachusetts, W443 South College, Amherst, MA 01003 (413) 545-5518. E-mail: furlan@english.umass.edu. *Other professional post*: Affiliatd faculty, Five College Native American & Indigenous Studies. Her teaching and research interests include American Indian literary and cultural studies, American Studies, autobiography, and creative nonfiction. Her work has been published in Crossing Lines: Race and Mixed Race across the Geohistorical Divide (AltaMira, 2005), Studies in American Indian Literatures, Intertexts, Yellow Medicine Review, Sentence, and Sovereign Erotics (Arizona, 2011), *and* she co-edited a Special Forum for the Journal of Transnational American Studies, 2012 on transnational Native American Studies. Her book, Indigenous Cities: Urban Indian Fiction and the Histories of Relocation (University of Nebraska Press, 2017).

FURSE, ELIZABETH
(institute director/founder/instructor)
Born in Nairobi, Kenya. *Education*: Evergreen College, BA; Lewis & Clark Law School, JD. *Affiliation & Address*: Founder/Director/instructor, member of Policy Board, The Institute for Tribal Government, Hatfield School of Government, College of Urban & Public Affairs, Portland State University, P.O. Box 751, Portland, OR 97207 (503) 725-9000. *Past professional posts*: Co-founder, National Coalition to Support Indian Treaties, 1970-78; director, Tribal Restoration project for the Native American Program at Oregon Legal Services, 1980-86; founder & director, Oregon Peace Institute, 1986-91; member, U.S. Congress (First District of Oregon), 1992-1999.

G

GABRIEL, RICKY (Colville)
(tribal council member; committee chair)
Affiliation & Address: Nespelem District Representative, Confederated Tribes of the Colville Reservation, P.O. Box 150, Nespelem, WA 99155 (509) 634-2207. E-mail: ricky.gabriel@colvilletribes. com. *Other tribal post*: Chair, Tribal Government Committee.

GACHUPIN, FRANCINE C. (Jemez Pueblo)
(professor of family & community medicine)
University of Washington, MPH (Epidemiology); University of New Mexico, PhD. *Affiliation & Address*: Assistant Professor, Department of Family and Community Medicine, College of Medicine; Assistant Director, Cancer Disparities Institute, Arizona Cancer Center; and Assistant Director of the Native American Research and Training Center, all at the University of Arizona, 1642 E. Helen St., Tucson, AZ 85719 (520) 621-5072. E-mail: fcgachupin@email.ariizona.edu She studies primarily chronic diseases and related behavioral risk factors. Much of her training has been at the National Institutes of Health and most of her work has occurred at four separate tribal based epidemiology centers – Portland Area, Aberdeen Area, Albuquerque Area and Navajo Area. She has worked with two tribal comprehensive cancer control programs in the northern plains and the pacific northwest.

GACHUPIN, NORMAN (Zia Pueblo)
(Pueblo lt. governor)
Affiliation & Address: Lt. Governor, Pueblo of Zia Council, 135 Capitol Square Dr., Zia Pueblo, NM 87053 (505) 867-3304.

GAFFNEY, PAT
(school principal)
Affiliation: Ahfachkee Day School, Star Route, Box 40, Clewiston, FL. *Other professional posts*: Consultant for several tribal colleges including Lac Courte Oreilles Ojibwe College, Leech Lake Tribal College, and Oglala Lakota College. *Past professional posts*: Vice president for Instructional Affairs & instructor in Lakota Studies & General Studies departments at Oglala Lakota College, Pine Ridge, SD (17 years); administrator & faculty member at colleges in New Jersey & Illinois earlier; until 2010, he was a consultant-evaluator & team chair for the Higher Learning Commission of the North Central Assn. *Published works*: Pine Ridge Reservation: Yesterday & Today (Badlands Natural History Assn, 1992); Fiduciary For Seven Generations: The Tribal College Trustee (University of North Dakota, Dept. of Indian Studies, 2004); An Indian Chapbook, 2nd Ed. (University of North Dakota, Dept. of Indian Studies, 2006); In A Good Way: American Indian Studies In the Classroom (Minnesota Humanities Commission, 2006; Culture & Customs of the Sioux Indians (ABC-CLIO, 2011); articles, reviews, teaching material.

GAGNON, GREGORY (Bad Rver Lake Superior Chippewa)
(professor emeritus of history)
Education: University of Maryland, PhD (History), 1970. *Affiliation & Address*: Associate Professor Emeritus of History, Department of American Indian Studies, College of Arts & Sciences, University of North Dakota, 221 Centennial Dr., Stop 7103, Grand Forks, ND 58202 (701) 777-4649. Email: Gregory.gagnon@email.und.edu. Professor Gagnon joined the American Indian Studies Department in 1997 after seventeen years at Oglala Lakota College, Pine Ridge Reservation, where he was academic vice president and teacher. Before 1980, he was an administrator and teacher at colleges in New Jersey and Illinois. Since retirement in 2011, Dr. Gagnon teaches American Indian Law at Loyola University of New Orleans and American Indian Religion at Tulane University. He continues as a consultant for Oglala Lakota College. He also teaches courses for the Oshner Life Long Learning Institute at UND and is an occasional faculty member in the UND Integrated Studies Program *Published works*: Sioux Culture & Society (ABC-Clio 2011; paperback revised edition, University of Nebraska Press, 2013), Pine Ridge Reservation: Yesterday & Today, 2nd edition, 2013), Fiduciary for Seven Generations: The Tribal College Trustee (2004)and articles in the North Dakota Law Review (2014), North Dakota Quarterly (2013 & 2014), & reviews in Choice Magazine and other journals.

GAIASHKIBOS (Lac Courte Oreilles Ojibwe)
(formal tribal chairperson)
Address: 9888 W. Chippewa Flwge Rd., Couderoy, WI 54828 (715) 634-8934. E-mail: gkibos@charerinternet.com. *Affiliation*: Treasurer, National Congress of American Indians, Washington, DC. *Past affiliation*: Former chairperson, Lac Courte Oreilles Tribal Governing Board, Hayward, WI.

GAIASHKIBOS, JUDI M. (Ponca)
(executive director)
Education: Doane College, B.A. (Human Relation), 2000, MA (Management), 2007. *Affiliation*: Executive Director (1995-present), Nebraska State Commission on Indian Affairs, P.O. Box 94981, Lincoln, NE 68509 (402) 471-3475. E-mail: judi.gaiashkibos@nebraska.gov. *Other professional posts*: President (2006-present), Governor's Interstate Indian Council (GIIC); appointed to the University of Nebraska's Presidents Advisory Council in 2008. Lecturer & advisor for the first Native Daughter's Project and currently an adjunct professor for the second Native Daughters Project focusing on Indian women of Oklahoma through the Univesity of Nebraksa, Lincoln. She serves on several state advisory boards including the Nebraska Minority Justice Committee, the P-16 Initiative, and the Nebraska Partners in Prevention Coalition; and a board member of CEDARS Youth Services & Interchurch Ministries/Grants to American Indians in Nebraska (GAIN); member of the Sheldon Museum of Art's Advisory Council. *Awards, honors*: Recipient of the Doulas County Historical Society 2009 Door Keeper Award in recognition of opening new doorways in the spirit of Unity, Equality & Understanding; 2012 recipient of the Nebraska Humanities Sower Award; appointed to the Doane College Board of Trustees in 2012.

GAIKOWSKI, DIXIE (Sisseton-Wahpeton Oyate)
(IHS area director)
Education: South Dakota State University, Brookings, BS. *Affiliation & Address*: Director, Tucson Area Indian Health Service (IHS), 7900 South "J" Stock Rd., Tucson, AZ 85746 (520) 295-2405. E-mail: Dixie.gaikowski@ihs.gov. Ms. Gaikowski is responsible for the Area's financial programs and management. The Tucson Area provides primary & community outreach programs for health services to the Tohono O'odham Nation and the Pascua Yaqui Tribe of Arizona. *Past professional posts*: Dixie began her career with the IHS in March 2001 as the Assistant Director of Nursing at the Woodrow Wilson Keeble Memorial Health Care Center in Sisseton, South Dakota, where she later served as the Director of Nursing and Deputy Chief Executive Officer. She subsequently moved to the Great Plains Area to serve as the Area Managed Care Nurse and Director of Resource Management. In November 2011, Ms. Gaikowski was named Acting Deputy Area Director Field Operations for the Great Plains Area. She has also served as Acting Chief Executive Officer for the Belcourt Service Unit, Rosebud Service Unit, and the Omaha/Winnebago Service Unit. *Awards, honors*: Received numerous local & national awards, including an IHS National Director's Award.

GAINES-GRAY, ELIZABETH (Cherokee/Shawnee)
(newspaper editor)
Affiliation & Address: Editor, Intertribal Times Newspaper, Inter-Tribal Council, Inc., P.O. Box 1308 • Miami, OK 74355 (918) 542-4486

GAJAR, ANNA H. 1943-
(associate professor)
Education: Hunter College, BA, 1964; University of Virginia, MEd, 1973, PhD, 1977. *Principal occupation*: Associate professor of special education. *Address*: 272 Spring St., State College, PA 16801 (814) 237-5473; 863-2284. *Affiliations*: Assistant professor (1977-84), associate professor of special education

(1984-), Dept. of Special Education, Penn State University, 226B Moore Bldg., University Park, PA 16802. Teaches a seminar on Issues in American Indian Special Education. *Other professional posts*: Consulting - evaluation of the American Indian Professional Training Program of the Dept. of Speech & Hearing Sciences, University of Arizona, Tucson, AZ, 1985; external evaluation of a professional degree training program entitled American Indian Professional Training in Speech-Language Pathology & Audiology at the University of Arizona, 1985. *Interests*: Improvement of graduate and undergraduate teacher education in special education (American Indian projects.) *Published works*: American Indian personnel preparation in special education: Needs, program components, programs (refereed) "Journal of American Indian Education," 1985; American Indian Special Education Teacher Training Program (U.S. Dept. of Education, Personnel Preparation (report); American Indian Special Education Personnel Preparation (presentation before CEC International Convention); A Model Program for American Indian Special Education Teacher Training at The Pennsylvania State University (presentation at NIEA Convention).

GALANDA, GABRIEL S. (GABE) (Round Valley Nomlaki-Concow)
(attorney)
Education: Western Washington University, BA (English Literature), 1997; University of Arizona College of Law, JD, 2000. *Affiliation & Address*: Partner, Galanda Broadman, P.O. Box 15146, Seattle, WA 98115 (206) 691-3631. E-mail: gabe@galandabroadman.com. Website: www.galandabroadman.com. *Past professional posts*: Associate, Williams, Kastner & Gibbs, PLLC, Seattle, WA; Office of the prosecutor, Tohono O'odham Nation. *Practice areas*: Indian Law & Gaming, Labor & Employment, Litigation-General. His practice focuses on multi-party commercial & Indian law litigation; *Memberships*: American Bar Association; Federal Bar Association (Indian Law Section); National Native American Bar Association (board member); Washington State Bar Association (past chair, Indian Law Section); founding member, The William L. Dwyer American Inn of Court. *Awards, honors*: National Native American Law Students' Association 2001 Alumnus of the Year. In 2002 & 2003, Mr. Galanda spearheaded the resurgence of the Northwest Indian Bar Association (NIBA) (past president); Washington Law & Politics magazine recognized Gabe as a Rising Star for 2002, 2004 & 2005 and also named him one of Washington's four Leadership Edge Litigators in 2003; awarded the WSBA Young Lawyers Division's Outstanding Young Lawyer Award for 2004; he is one of five attorneys from across the country selected to serve as an ABA Business Law Ambassador for 2004-2006; awarded the "Doug Mason Memorial Award" by the Municipal League of Kings County; recently selected to "The Best Lawyers in America from 2007-2013.

GALINDO, ED
(professor of American Indian studies)
Affiliation & Address: Director, Natural Resources Trbal Cooperative; Professor of American Indian Studies, Aquaculture Research Institute, University of Idaho, P.O. Box 2260, Moscow, ID 83844 (208) 885-5871. E-mail: edg@uidaho.edu.

GALLAGHER, ROXANNE S.
(attorney)
Born in Las Vegas, Nev. *Education*: University of Colorado, BA, 1999; Arizona State University, JD (Certificate in Indian Law), 2002. *Address & Affiliation*: Sacks Tierney, P.A., 4250 N. Drinkwater Blvd. #4, Scottsdale, AZ 85251 (480) 425-2615. E-mail: judith.dworkin@sackstierney.com. *Practice Areas*: Indian Law & Tribal Relations; Business & Corporate Law. Court & Bar Admissions: State Bar of Arizona; Navajo Nation. *Professional activities*: Federal Bar Association: Indian Law Section; Native American Bar Association of Arizona. *Presentations*: "New Economic Development Bonds Available to Indian Tribal Governments," Inter Tribal Council of Arizona, Inc., Phoenix (Aug. 2009); "UCC & Secured Transactions," Navajo Nation Bar Association CLE, St. Michaels, AZ (Aug. 2009); "CLE for Free: Doing Business in Indian Country," Ballard Spahr, Phoenix (March 2009); et al.

GAMBARO, RETHA WALDEN (Muscogee-Creek) 1917-
(sculptor)
Born December 9, 1917, Lenna, Okla. *Education*: Corcoran School of Art, 1969. *Principal occupation*: Sculptor. *Address*: 74 Dishpan Lane, Stafford, VA 22554 (540) 659-0130. E-mail: viagambaro1@aol.com. *Arts specialization*: sculpture wall hangings. *Medium or media*: sculpture in bronze, stone, and wood. Mixed media sculpture. Wall hangings of mixed media only. *Conferences attended or lectures presented*: Gallaudet College, Washington, DC; Eugene O'Neill Center, Waterford, CT; Slater Memorial Museum, Norwich, CT; Williams School, New London, CT; Haverford College, Haverford, PA; Haskell Indian Jr. College, Lawrence, KS; Marywash College. *Exhibitions*: Smithsonian Institution-Museum of Natural History, Kennedy Center (Night of the First Americans), National Cathedral, Howard University, Folger Shakespeare Library, Trinity Episcopal Church, American Spirit Gallery, Art Barn, St. Augustine Chapel, People Life Insurance, Midtown Gallery, and U.S. Safe Deposit (all in Washington, D.C.); Art Institute of Philadelphia; Slater

Museum, Norwich, CT; Coast Guard Academy & Yah Ta Hey Gallery (both in New London, CT); Peabody Museum (Cambridge, MA); Hampton Museum (Hampton, VA); among others. *Major Collections*: U.S. Dept. of Parks, VA; National Arboretum, Gallaudet College, B'Nai B'Rith Museum, Church of the Reformation, Native American Research, Howard University, and the Convention Center (all in Washington, D.C.; Daybreak Art Center, Seattle, WA; among others. *Memberships*: Artists Equity; Indian Arts and Crafts Association; National Museum of Women in the Arts (charter member); National Museum of the American Indian (charter member). Awards, honors: Best in Show at the Art League of Northern Virginia, and Best in Sculpture at the Mystic Harbour Invitational in Connecticut. *Biographical sources*: In publications - "Art Business News, Vol. 9 Issue 3, March 1982; "National American Indian Women's Art Show"; American Artists of Renown, 1981-82; Women At Work; Contemporary American Women Sculptors; Art and the Animal. Video - Born of Fire (28 minute educational film by White Light Productions).

GANJE, LUCY ANNIS 1949-
(professor of graphic arts)
Born December 14, 1949, Eagle Butte, S.D. *Education*: Black Hills State University, BS, 1983; Academy of Art College, MFA, 1984. *Principal occupation*: Professor of graphic arts. *Address*: 419 Princeton St., Grand Forks, ND 58203 (701) 772-9259. *Affiliations*: Instructor, Cheyenne River Sioux Tribe Community College, 1985-86; Assistant professor of graphic arts, Native American Media Center Committee, Indian Programs Committee, University of North Dakota, School of Communication, Grand Forks, ND, 1988-. *Other professional posts*: Manager, Printing Division, Cheyenne River Sioux Tribe Telephone Authority, 1984-88; design consulting. *Professional activities*: Presenter, "Publication Design" Native American Journalists Association, Annual Convention, March 1991; Coordinator, North Dakota Indian Youth Leadership Institute, ND Dept. of Public Instruction, Indian Programs Division, Grand Forks, ND, June 1991; "Press Freedom in Indian Country" panel for Editors-Broadcasters Day, Oct. 1991; among others. *Memberships*: Association for Education In Journalism & Mass Communication; American Advertising Federation; Native American Journalists Association. *Awards, honors*: Invited and designed material for Native American Manufacturers Marketing Conference, February 1989; Curriculum Development Grant for attendance to Native American Journalists Conference, Denver, CO, March 1991. *Creative activity*: Videos - "Rock Art at Pinon Canyon Maneuver Site," Southeastern Colorado, March 1990, produced by the National Rock Art Research Foundation; "Cultural Resources at Pinon Canyon," produced for the National Park Service, Summer 1991-.

GANSWORTH, ERIC (Onondaga)
(writer, visual artist)
Born & raised at the Tuscarora Indian Nation near Niagara Falls, New York. *Education*: SUNY at Buffalo, BA & MA. *Affiliation & Address*: Professor of English & Lowry Writer-in-Residence at Canisius College, CT-902, Department of English, 2001 Main St., Buffalo, NY 14208 (716) 883-2113. E-mail: ganswore@canisius.edu. Teaching Interets: Creative Writing, contemporary Native American literature, film adaptation, contemporary fiction, et al. *Awards, honors*: American Book Award, New Atlantic Independent Booksellers Association, for "Extra Indians"; PEN Oakland-Josephine Miles Award, for "Mending Skins"; National Book Critics Circle's "Good Reads" List for Spring 2008, for "A Half-Life of Cardio-Pulmonary Function." *Published works*: Indian Summers (Michigan State University Press (MSUP), 1998); Smoke Dancing (MSUP, 2004); Mending Skins (Universiy of Nebraska Pres, 2005); Nickel Eclipse: Iroquois Moon (MSUP, 2000); Sovereign Bones (Nation Books, 2007); A Half-Life of Cardio-Pulmonary Function (Syracuse University Press, 2008); From the Western Door to the Lower West Side (White Pine, 2009); Extra Indians (Milkweed Editions, 2010); If Ever I Get Out of Here (Scholastic/Arthur A. Levine, 2013); As a visual artist, Gansworth has exhibited in many grop shows and has had a solo or two-person exhibits at Niagara Univesity, The Stuyvesant Gallary, Canisius College, Bright Hill Center, and Colgate University. He has received theater commissions from SUNY Oneonta and Ohio Northern University and was the recipient of the Individual Artist's Grant for Fiction, from the Constance Saltonstall Foundation.

GANT, JACQUELINE (Oneida Nation of the Thames, ON, Can.)
(executive director)
Education: Michigan State University, BS (Criminal Justice); Harvard University, MA (Education), 1998. *Affiliation & Address*: National Executive Director, Native American Business Alliance (2004-present), 30700 Telegraph Rd., Suite 1675, Bingham Farms, MI 48025 (248) 988-9344. E-mail: jgant@n-a-b-a.org. *Other professional post*: President & CEO, Youth Vision; President, Dreamcatcher Consulting & Event Planning.

GANTT, AMY (Chickasaw)
(recruitment & retention coordinator)
Education: University of North Texas, BFA, 1999; Texas Woman's University, MA, 2004. Holds a Texas Teaching Certificate. *Affiliation & Address*: recruitment & retention coordinator, Native American Center for Student

Success, 1405 North 4th, PMB 2747, Durant, OK 74701-0609 (580) 745-3220. E-mail: agantt@se.edu Amy is a recruitment and retention coordinator for the Chickasaw Nation Education Services Department. She divides her time between the Murray State College & Southeastern Oklahoma State University campuses. Amy's SE office is located in the Native American Center for Student Success in the Hallie McKinney Building. Her office hours are 9:00 a.m. to 3:00 p.m. on Tuesday of each week. As the recruitment and retention coordinator for the Chickasaw Nation, she provides educational services to all Chickasaw students. In particular; Chickasaw student attending Southeastern will work with her to determine eligibility for, and receive tribal grants & scholarships. Higher Education grant & scholarship application may be found here. Amy came on board with the Chickasaw Nation education department in November 2006. Prior to that, she worked in the Division of Heritage Preservation at the Chickasaw Council House Museum as an education specialist. Amy has lived in Oklahoma since 2004 and has worked for the Chickasaw Nation since that time. She is also a citizen of the Chickasaw Nation. Amy enjoys working with clay and learning about the Chickasaw language in her free time.

GARCEAU, DANNY J. (Lake Superior Ojibwe)
(society chairperson)
Affiliation: Conference chair (2008), chairperson (2010-present), Society of American Indian Government Employees (SAIGE), P.O. Box 7715, Washington, DC 20044 (202) 564-0375. E-mail: danjeau@msn.com. *Military service*: 30 years of active duty military service in the Army and Michigan National Guard. *Past professional post*: In 2000 he joined the Michigan National Guard Cultural Diversity Council where he served until his retirement as the Native American SEPM and recruiting advisor; also served as the chair of the Great Lakes Region for the Army National Guard National Recrutiiting Advisory committee.

GARCIA, AGUSTIN (Pomo)
(tribal chairperson)
Affiliation & Address: Chairperson, Sulphur Bank of Pomo Indians, P.O. Box 757 • Lower Lake, CA 95457 (707) 994-3400; E-mail: a.garcia@elemindiancolony.org

GARCIA, ANDREA (Mandan/Hidatsa/Arikara)
(physician)
Born & raised in Los Angeles, Calif. *Education*: UC Berkeley-USCF Joint Medical Program, MD, 2012. Past President, Association of Native American Medical Students.

GARCIA, ARNOLD J. (Nambe Pueblo)
(Pueblo lt. governor)
Affiliation & Address: Lt. Governor, Pueblo of Nambe, Rt. 1 Box 117-BB 8, Nambe Pueblo, NM 87747 (505) 455-2036.

GARCIA, BOB (Lower Umpqua & Suislaw)
(former tribal chairperson)
Affiliation & Address: Former Chairperson, Confederated Tribes of Coos, Lower Umpqua & Suislaw Indians, 1245 Fulton Ave., Coos Bay, OR 97420 (541) 888-9577. E-mail: bgarcia@ctclusi.org

GARCIA, BRUCE (San Felipe Pueblo)
(Pueblo administrator)
Affiliation & Address: Administrator, Pueblo of San Felipe, P.O. Box 4339, San Felipe Pueblo, NM 87001 (505) 867-3381.

GARCIA, CAROLE J. (Tohono O'Odham)
(craftsperson, store owner)
Affiliation & Address: Reservation Creations, 2000 W. San Xavier Loop Rd., P.O. Box 27626, Tucson, AZ 85726 (602) 622-4900. *Other professional post*: Co-director, National Native American Cooperative, P.O. Box 1000, San Carlos, NM 85550.

GARCIA, CARIE LYNN (Cahuilla/Luiseno)
(tribal cultural program manager)
Affiliation & Address: Manager, Cultural Program, Soboba Band of Luiseno Indians, 23906 Soboba Rd., P.O. Box 487, San Jacinto, CA 92583 (951) 654-5544

GARCIA, EMMETT (Santa Ana Pueblo)
(entertainer/composer)
Affiliation & Address: "Shkeme" Native Roots Band, 6909 Porlamar Rd., Albuquerque, NM 87120 (505) 620-8539. *Membership*: Americans for Indian Opportunity.

GARCIA, PETER, JR. (San Juan Pueblo)
(pueblo governor)
Affiliation & Address: Governor, San Juan Pueblo, P.O. Box 1099, San Juan Pueblo, NM 87566 (505) 852-4400.

GARCIA, ROBERT M. (Santa Ana Pueblo)
(museum technician)
Address: 3963 Saxon Ave. #1R, Bronx, NY 10461 (212) 514-3964. E-mail: garciam@ic.si.edu. *Affiliation*: National Museum of the American Indian, Smithsonian Institution, New York, NY. *Membership*: Americans for Indian Opportunity. *Interest*: Cultural retention.

GARCIA, ROBERT T. (Pueblo of Acoma)
(Pueblo 2nd Lt. governor)
Affiliation & Address: 2nd Lt. Governor, Pueblo of Acoma, P.O. Box 309, Acomita, NM 87034. (505) 552-6604.

GARCIA, SAMMY (Santo Domingo Pueblo)
(former Pueblo lt. governor)
Affiliation: Kewa Pueblo, P.O. Box 99, Santo Domingo, NM 87052 (505) 465-2214.

GARCIA, TONY (Yankton Sioux) 1951-
(educational administration, Indian education)
Born October 7, 1951, Pierre, S.D. *Education*: University of South Dakota, EdD., 1991. *Principal occupation*: Educational administration/Indian education. *Affiliation & Address*: Executive Director (2009-present), Yankton Sioux Adult Education, P.O. Box 295, Marty, SD 57361 (605) 384-3997. *Past professional posts*: Director of Indian Education, Rapid City School District, 1991-2005; president, Ihantonwan Community College, Wagner, SD, 2005-09. *Military service*: U.S. Army, 1970-72 (Spec. 4th class; Vietnam Veteran). *Community activities*: Board Member, Big Brothers & Big Sisters. *Memberships*: National Indian Education Association; South Dakota Indian Education Association; National Association of Bilingual Education; South Dakota Bilingual-Bicultural Association. *Awards, honors*: 1993 Dakota Wesleyan Indian Alumna of the Year. Interests: Founder of Ateyapi (Fatherhood) Society for Lakota People, Rapid City, SD. *Published works*: Dissertation - Attitude Difference As Seen by Indian and Non-Indian students Towards Their Teachers, 1991.

GARDIPE, DOUG (Paiute)
(tribal vice chairperson)
Affiliation & Address: Vice Chairperson, Reno-Sparks Indian Colony, 98 Colony Rd., Reno, NV 89502 (775) 329-2936. E-mail: dgardipe@rsic.org.

GARDNER, JERRY (Cherokee)
(attorney; institute founder & executive director)
Education: Antioch School of Law, JD. *Affiliation & Address*: Founding Executive Director (1996-present), Tribal Law & Policy Institute, 8235 Santa Monica Blvd., Suite 211, West Hollywood, CA 90046 (323) 650-5467. E-mail: jerry@tlpi.org. Jerry has more than 35 years of experience working with American Indian/Alaska Native Nations, tribal court systems, and victims of crime in Indian country. *Other professional posts*: Executive Diector, National Child Welfare Resource Center for Tribes, Helena, MT; adjunct professor, UCLA School of Law, and an Appellate Court Judge for the Turtle Mountain Band of Ojibwe Indians in North Dakota. *Past professional posts*: Adjunct Professor, University of California, Berkeley, School of Law, 1995-2000; administrator, National American Indian Court Judges Association, 1998-2000; senior staff attorney, National Indian Justice Center, 1983-96; He previously served as the Administrator for the National American Indian Court Judges Association (NAICJA). He has been an appellate court judge for the Turtle Mountain Band of Chippewa Indians (North Dakota) and Poarch Creek Band (Alabama). He served as the Senior Staff Attorney with the National Indian Justice Center (NIJC) from NIJC's establishment in 1983 until TLPI's founding in 1996. He served as a Professional Staff Member at the U.S. Senate Committee on Indian Affairs in the late 1970s. He also served in legal training positions for the national office of the Legal Services Corporation and the American Indian Lawyer Training Program.

GARDNER, RAY (Chinook) 1956-
(tribal chairperson)
Born in South Bend, Wash. *Affiliation*: Chair (2001-present), Chinook Tribe, P.O. Box 368, Bay Center, WA 98527. *Other professional posts*: Transportation Specialist/Investigator IV, Washington Utilities & Transportation Commission, Satsop, WA. Liaison between WUTC & the Native American tribes of Washington, & City/State/Federal Law Enforcement Agencies. Head Investigator for all fatalities involving the railroad in the state. *Tribal community service*: Chair, Fisheries Committee; vice chair, Health Board.

GARFIELD, RYAN (Yokut)
(tribal vice chairperson)
Affiliation & Address: Vice Chairperson, Tule River Tribal Council, P.O. Box 589, Porterville, CA 93258 (559) 781-4271.

GARRITY, GERALDINE (Navajo)
(college chairperson)
She is To'áheedlíinii & born for To'dichíinii. She was raised & resides in Lukachukai, Arizona. *Education*: Arizona State University, BA (Elementary Education), MA (Education); Doctorate in Educational Leadership & Change with an emphasis in Grounded Theory Study with Fielding Graduate University. Garrity also holds a teaching and administrative certificate with Arizona Department of Education. *Affiliation & Address*: Faculty Chair, Diné College Center for Dne Teacher Education, 6th Floor, Ned Hatathli Center, P.O. Box C-15, Tsaile, AZ 86556 (928) 724-6699 E-mail: ggarrity@dinecollege.edu Garrity teaches variety of educational courses such as Language Arts courses & Structure English Immersion for the Center for Diné Teacher Education. She taught Elementary Education for 7 years and was a School Improvement Specialist for three years at Lukachukai Community School. She is passionate about preserving and maintaining Din4 language through Navajo Nation schools by promoting Navajo culture to her students.

GARROW, CARRIE E. (St. Regis Mohawk)
(attorney; professor of Indiigenous law)
Born & raised at the Akwesasne Territory in New York. *Education*: Dartmouth College, BA; Harvard University (MA (Public Policy from the Kennedy School of Government); Stanford Law School, JD. *Affiliation & Address*: Visiting Assistant Professor of Indigenous Law, Syracuse University College of Law, E263 White Hall, Syracuse, NY 13244 (315) 443-9558. E-mail: cegarrow@law.syr.edu. *Past professional posts*: Deputy district attorney, Chief Judge, St. Regis Mohawk Tribal Courts; consultant for Tribal Law & Policy Institute, the Harvard Project on American Indian Economic Development, and the Native Nations Institute. She has worked with several Indigenous Nations, including the Oglala Sioux Tribe on a participatory evaluation of the federally funded criminal justice initiative, Comprehensive Indian Resources for Community & Law Enforcement & the Grand Traverse Band of Ottawa & Chippewa Indians on juvenile justice reform. *Published work*: Co-author, with Sarah Deer, "Tribal Criminal Law & Procedure" (Google eBook, Rowman Altamira, 2004).

GARZA, JUAN, JR. (Kickapoo of Texas)
(tribal chairperson)
Affiliation & Address: Chairperson, Kickapoo Traditional Tribe of Texas, HC 1 Box 9700, Eagle Pass, TX 78852 (830) 773-2105.

GATES, TODD (Seneca)
(Seneca Nation president)
Address & Affiliation: President, Seneca Nation of Indians, P.O. Box 231, Salamanca, NY 14779 (716) 945-1790. Former president of Seneca Nation

GATEWOOD, TARA (Isleta Pueblo/Navajo-Dine' Nation)
(radio host & producer)
Born & raised in isleta Pueblo. *Affiliation & Address*: Host/Producer, Native America Calling, Koahnic Broadcast Corporation, 4401 Lomas Blvd. NE Suite C, Albuquerque, NM 87110 (505) 999-2440. E-mail: tgatewood@nativeamericacalling.com. Tara hs worked in Indian Country in the arenas of health & community development, and has more than 19 years of experience as a journalist. *Other professional post*: Board member of UNITY: Journalists for Diversity. She has also worked on video documentaries and in music production. Tara is a visual artist and has participated in her family's legacy of Native American jewelry fabrication.

GEER, BRENDA (Eastern Pequot)
(tribal vice chairperson)
Affiliation & Address: Vice Chairperson, Eastern Pequot Tribe, P.O. Box 370, North Stonington, CT 06359 (860) 535-1868.

GEHMAN, DAVID W. (Poarch Band Creek)
(tribal council secretary)
Born & raised in Atmore, Ala. *Education*: Jefferson Davis Communty College, AA; Auburn University, BS (Management). *Affiliation & Address*: Treasurer, 1995-2001; Secretary, 2009-present, Poarch Band of Creek Indians, 5811 Jack Springs Rd., Atmore, AL 36502 (251) 368-9136. E-mail: dwgehman@pci-nsn.gov. He currently serves as a member of the Utilities Authority, the Land and Natural Resources and the Budget and Finance Legislative Committees.

GEHMAN, R. DALE (Poarch Band Creek) 1957-
(radio broadcaster, consulting engineer)
Born June 16, 1957, Carlisle, Penn. *Education*: Alabama Aviation and Technical College, AB, 1976; Jefferson Davis College (Brewton, AL), AAS (Industrial Electronics), 1993; Atmore State Tech. College, 1991-93 (General Electronics). *Affiliation & Address*: President, Gehman Compliance & Consulting, 1242 Main St., Akron, PA 17501 (717) 859-6410. *Past professional posts*: President, chief engineer, Digital Engineering Service, Ephrata, PA,

1992-2005; chief engineer, WIOV AM/FM, Ephrata, PA, 1993-2005; broadcaster, consulting engineer, WASG Radio, Atmore, AL, 1981-92; board member, Alabama Broadcasters Assn; board member, Creek Indian Enterprises (The economic develop-ment arm of the Poarch Band of Creek Indians). *Community activities*: Atmore Chamber of Commerce (director, 1984-90); Gospel Light Church, Inc. (board member, secretary); Creek Indian Arts Council (board member). *Memberships*: Certified Senior Broadcast Engineer by the Society of Broadcast Engineers, 1993-; Alabama Broadcasters Assn, 1987-93; Alabama Emergency Broadcasting System (chairperson, 1993); Poarch Band of Creek Indians Tribal Council (member, 1977-90; Atmore Civitan Club (past president). *Awards, honors*: "Outstanding Young Men of America" 1987. *Interests*: Private pilot at age 16; first class FCC Radio-telephone license at age 16; outdoor camping, skiing; electronics; public service for my community and tribe.

GEIOGAMAH, HANAY (Kiowa/Delaware) 1945-
(playwright; TV/movie producer; professor of theater; artistic director)
Born in Lawton, Oklahoma in 1945. *Education*: University of Oklahoma, BA (Journalism); Indiana University, MA (Theatre). *Address & Affiliation*: Professor, School of of Theatre & Television, UCLA, Los Angeles, CA 90095 (310) 825-7315. E-mail: hgeiog@ucla.edu. *Other professional post*: Serves on The National Film Preservation Board, established in 1988 as an advisory body to the Librarian of Congress' National Film Registry. *Past professional posts*: In 1971, he formed a theater grop at the La MaMa Experiemtnal Theater Club in New York City; founded the 16-member American Indian Theatre Ensemble in New York in 1972, which was the first company to perform Native American plays for Indian people; founder & co-director along with Jaye T. Darby, of Project HOOP (Honoring Our Origins & People). Project HOOP is a national, multi-disciplinary initiative to establish Native theatre as a subject & creative development in tribal colleges, Native communities, K-12 schools, and mainstream institutions; director, UCLA American Indian Studies Center, 2002-09; founder & artistic director, American Indian Dance Theatre, 1987; managing editor for the American Indian Culture & Research Journal. *Theatre Credits*: Plays: "Body Indian," "Foghorn, 49," "Coon Cons Coyote," and "Land Sale," have been performed throughout the U.S. and Europe; co-producer for the TBS project, "The Native Americans: Behind the Legends, Beynd the Myths aired on TNT from 1993-96; co-producer, "The Broken Chain," which told the story of the Iroquois Confederacy during colonial times and also for "Geronimo"'; co-producer for "Lakota Woman: Return to Wounded Knee," 1994; co-producer, "Tecumseh," the story of the Shawnee leader, 1995; co-executive producer for "The Only Good Indian," a 2009 independent Western starring Cherokee actor, Wes Studi. *Published works*: New Native American Drama: Three Plays (University of Oklahoma Press, 1980).

GEMMILL, MICKEY, JR. (Pit River)
(tribal chairperson)
Affiliation & Address: Chairperson, Pit River Tribe, 36970 Park Ave., Burney, CA 96013 (530) 335-5421.

GENEAL, KARLA E. (Mohawk)
(attorney)
Affiliation & Address: Staff Atorney, Indian Law Resource Center (Washington office), 601 E St., SE, Washington, DC 20003 (202) 547-2800. E-mail: dcoffice@indianlaw.org.

GENETT, WARREN DEAN (Potawatomi/Menominee) 1957-
(U.S. Geological Survey)
Born August 20, 1957, Menominee Indian Reservation, Keshena, WI. *Education*: Georgia State University, B.A., 1987. *Principal occupation*: U.S. Geological Survey, Water Resources Division. *Address*: 228 Valleybrook Dr., Woodstock, GA 30188 (404) 926-4531. *Affiliation*: Chairperson, The Native American Center of Georgia, 110 S. Main St., Suite 203, Woodstock, GA 30188 (404) 924-3738, 1993-. *Military service*: U.S. Air Force, 1977-81. *Community activities*: Chair, Atlanta Couples Together, 1987-89; Atlanta Regional Commission, Diversity Collaborative, 1994. *Membership*: American Society for Quality Control, 1993-. *Awards, honors*: Emory University, for Native American History Month, 1994; United Way (Atlanta, GA) for V.I.P. Selection Committee, 1994; U.S. Geological Survey, WRD for Total Quality Management. *Interests*: "Primary focus is to develop a sound organizational structure for the Native American Center of Georgia (formed in 1993) and to promote the organizational success of the Center throughout state of Georgia."

GENIA, JAMES M. (Odawa)
(attorney)
Education: Augsburg College, BA, 1987; William Mitchell College of Law, JD, 1990. *Address & Affiliation*: Partner, Lockridge Grindal Nauen, PLLP, 100 Washington Ave. South, Suite 2200, Minneapolis, MN 55401-2197. E-mail: jmgenia@locklaw.com. Practices extensively in the government relations department and heads the Indian law practice group. His government relations practice focuses on commerce, economic development, environmental & tribal issues, & currently represents a variety of Indian tribes. *Professional*

memberships: Mille Lacs Band of Ojibwe Tribal Court; U.S. District Court, District of Minnesota; U.S. Court of Appeals, 8th Circuit; U.S. Supreme Court. *Other professional posts*: Board member, Johnson Institute Foundation; board member, Minnesota American Indian Chamber of Commerce. *Past professional post*: Solicitor General, Mille Lacs Band of Ojibwe, 1993-1999. *Membership*: Little Traverse Bay Band of Odawa Indians; American Bar Association; Minnesota Indian Bar Association; State Bar of Minnesota. *Awards, honors*: Attorney of the Year by Minnesota Lawyer; William Mitchell College of Law top 100 all-time graduates for its Centennial in 2000.

GENSAW, DAVID (Yurok) (tribal vice chairperson)
Affiliation & Address: Chairperson, Yurok Tribe, P.O. Box 1027, Klamath, CA 95548 (707) 482-1350. E-mail: dgensaw@yuroktribe.org.

GENTRY, BARBARA (Wampanoag) 1948-
(Native American education)
Born October 21, 1948, Utica, N.Y. *Education*: Utah State University, BS, 1974; University of Wyoming, MA, 1975. *Principal occupation*: Native American education. *Affiliations*: School Counselor, Ute Tribe, Fort Duchesne, UT, 1974-76; head counselor/director of para-professional counseling program, University of Wyoming, 1976-77; education unit director, Boston Indian Council, 1977-83; entrepreneur, partnership in family-owned business, 1983-90; multicultural coordinator, Eastern Michigan University, Ypsilanti, MI, 1990-. *Other professional posts*: Consulting in Indian education. *Memberships*: National Indian Education Assn, 1974-86; National Indian Adult Education (Northeast Representative), 1982). *Awards, honors*: 1991 Gold Medallion Award, Eastern Michigan University; "Outstanding Young Woman of America," 1982; "Successful Indian Education Program," by Office of Indian Education, U.S. Dept. of Education, 1980.

GENTRY, DON (Klamath)
(tribal chairperson)
Affiliation & Address: Chairperson, Klamath Tribes of Oregon, P.O. Box 436, Chiloquin, OR 97624 (541) 783-2219. E-mail: don.gentry@klamathtribes.com

GENTRY-LEWIS, JO LYNN (Dine-Navajo)
(board president)
Affiliation & Address: President, Phoenix Indian Center, 2601 North 3rd St. #100, Phoenix, AZ 85004 (602) 264-6768.

GEOIGAMAH, HANAY (Kiowa)
(playwright, movie producer)
Address: 1750 N. Wilcox #223, Los Angeles, CA 90028 (213) 463-8535. Founder of the American Indian Dance Theatre.

GEORGE, DOUGLAS M. (*Kanentiio*) (Mohawk) 1955-
(writer; journalist)
Born February 1, 1955, Akwesasne Mohawk Reservation, N.Y. *Education*: Syracuse University, 1977-80; Antioch School of Law (Washington, DC), 1980-83. *Principal occupation*: Writer; journalist. *Address*: Box 450, Oneida Iroquois Territory, Oneida Castle, NY 13421 (315) 363-1655. E-mail: kanentiiio@aol.com. *Affiliations*: Editor, Akwesasne Notes, Mohawk Nation, Rooseveltown, NY, 1986-92; columnist, Syracuse Newspapers, 1993-94; chairperson, Round Dance Productions, 1992-; Trustee, National Museum of the American Indian, 1996-2002. *Other professional posts*: Chairperson, Round Dance Productions, Inc. (non-profit educational & cultural organization formed for the preservation of Native American culture), 1991-; editor, Indian Time newspaper, 1986-90; in the process of writing for film & book publishers. *Community activities*: Mohawk Nation Land Claims Committee, 1984-91; Mohawk Nation Business Committee, 1984-90; Member of the volunteer Akwesasne emergency team, 1983-91. *Membership*: Akwesasne Communications Society - Radio CKON (board member). Awards, honors: D'Arcy McNickle Fellowship Recipient, 1979, Newberry Library, Chicago, IL; Wassaja Award for Journalism Excellence from the Native American Journalists Association, 1994. *Interests*: Creative writing; travels to Europe, Mid-East, China, India, Thailand, Korea, and extensive travel throughout North America - historical research and writing. *Biographical sources*: Articles - Los Angeles Times, Oct. 1991; Syracuse (NY) Herald Journal, July 1990; Now Magazine (Toronto, ON), May 1990; Gentlemen's Quarterly, Nov. 1993. *Published works*: Skywoman (Clear Light Press, 1999); Syracuse herald columnist - over 40 articles; numerous stories printed in Akwesasne Notes, 1986-.

GEORGE, KELLER (Laluhtay^thos) (Oneida)
(council member; organization president)
Education: Attended Harvard University and earned a certificate from its Senior Managers in Government program. *Address & Affiliation*: Wolf Clan Representative, Oneida Indian Nation Council, P.O. Box 1, Vernon, NY 13476 (315) 361-6300. *Other professional post*: President (serving his sixth term), United South & Eastern Tribes (an organization of 24 federally recognized Indian Nations located east of the Mississippi River which works to assist member tribes and their governments in meeting the needs of their members

and in dealing with public policy issues). *Community activities*: Board member, Four Directions Media, Inc. (publishes the nationally recognized newspaper, Indian Country Today); chairman, Oneida Indian Nation Gaming Commission (oversees gaming & licensing operations at Turning Stone Casino Resort. *Memberships*: National Tribal Development Association (Board of Directors); The Close Up Foundation, Washington, DC (Advisory Committee); National Congress of American Indians (delegate); National Museum of the American Indian (member of Board of Trustees, Jan. 2003).

GEORGE, LEN (Paiute-Shoshone)
(tribal chairperson))
Affiliation & Address: Chairperson, Fallon Paiute-Shoshone Tribe, 565 Rio Vista Rd., Fallon, NV 89406 (775) 423-6075. Email: chairman@fpst.org

GEORGE, MAGGIE (Navajo-Dine')
(former college president)
Born & raised on the Navajo Reservation, Red Valley, Arizona. *Education*: New Mexico Highlands University, BA (Elementary Education), MA (Guidance & Counseling); University of Kansas, PhD (Higher Education). *Affiliation & Address*: Former President, Dine' College, 1 Circle Dr., 6th Floor, Ned Hatathlie Center, Tsaile, AZ 86556 (928) 724-6669. E-mail: mlgeorge@dincecollege. edu. *Other professional post*: Faculty/Chair Administrator for the Center for Dine' Studies at Dine' College. *Past professional posts*: Executive Director for the White House Initiative on Tribal Colleges and Universities in Washington, DC; deputy director, American Indian Science & Engineering Society, Albuquerque, NM; director, American Indian Program, New Mexico State University; director of Educational Equity & Access at the New Mexico Higher Education Department. She was Dean & Academic Vice Presient at Dine' College in Tsaile, Arizona; Dean of the School of Education at Haskell Indian Nations University, Lawrence, KS; She was a consultant-evaluator with the Higher Learning Commission from 2003-09, and an adjunct faculty member at the American Indian Languages Development Institute at the Univesity of Arizona.

GEORGE, RICK D. (Nooksack)
(tribal vice chairperson)
Affiliation & Address: Vice Chairperson, Nooksack Tribe, P.O. Box 157, Deming, WA 98244 (360) 592-5176. E-mail: ngeorge@nooksack-tribe.org.

GEORGE, SHILO (Southern Cheyenne/Arapaho)
(adjunct instructor of Indigenous studies)
Affiliation & Address: Director & Professor of Indigenous Nations Studies, P.O. Box 751, Potland State University, Portland, OR 97207 (503) 725-9689.

GEORGE, WAYNE (Suquamish)
(tribal vice chairperson)
Affiliation & Address: Vice Chairperson, The Suquamish Tribe, P.O. Box 498, Suquamish, WA 98392 (360) 598-3311. E-mail: wgeorge@suquamish.nsn.net.

GERONIMO, RONALD (Tohono O'odham)
(Indian studies director)
Affiliation & Address: Director, Tohono O'odham Studies, Tohono O'odam Community College, P.O. Box 3129, Sells, AZ 85634 (520) 383-8401

GESSNER, JAMES, JR. (Mohegan)
(tribal vice chairperson)
Affiliation & Address: Vice Chairperson, Mohegan Indian Tribe, 13 Crow Hill Rd., Uncasville, CT 06382 (860) 862-6100.

GHEBREGZI, ALEX (Seminole)
(teaching specialist)
Education: University of Minnesota, BA (Italian & American Indian Studies). *Address & Affiliation*: University of Minnesota, Twin Cities Campus, 215 Scott Hall, 72 Pleasant St. SE, Minneapolis, MN 55455 (612) 625-3821. E-mail: gheb0002@umn.edu.

GHOLSON, GEORGE (Timbisha Shoshone)
(tribal chairperson)
Affiliation & Address: Chairperson, Timbisha Shoshone Tribe, P.O. Box 206, Death Valley, CA 92328 (760) 786-2374.

GIAGO, DORIS (Oglala Sioux)
(professor & executive director)
Education: University of Kansas, MA. *Affiliation & Address*: Professor, Journalism & Mass Communications, SDSU, Yeager 228, Box 2235, Brookings, SD 57007 (605) 688-6236. E-mail: doris.giago@sdstate.edu. Professor Giago teaches newswriting & reporting, publicity methods & advanced reporting. *Other professional post*: Registration coordinator, annual Native American Newspaper Career Conference. *Awards, honors*: 2009 First Place for Innovative Outreach to Scholastic Journalism by the Association for Education in Journalism & Mass Communication, Scholastic Journalism

Division; Distinguished Alumnus, SDSU Native American Club. *Memberships*: South Dakota High School Press Association (director); Native American Journalists Association (NAJA).

GIAGO, TIM (*Nanwica Kciji*) (Oglala Sioux) 1934-
(columnist; publisher)
Born July 12, 1934, Pine Ridge Reservation, S.D. *Education*: San Jose Junior College; University of Nevada, Reno; Harvard University (Nieman Fellowship, 1990-91). *Affiliation & Address*: Publisher, Giago Book Publishing, 2218 Jackson Blvd., Suite 9, Rapid City, SD 57702 (605) 388-3313. *Past professional post*: Publisher/owner, Indian Country Today (newspaper), Rapid City, SD, 1981-1998. *Community activities*: U.S. West Communications (state executive board); Multi-Cultural Management Training Program - University of Missouri, Columbia (board of directors); Native Peoples (editorial board). *Awards, honors*: 1985 - H.L. Menkin Award from the Baltimore Sun for Best Column; Civil & Human Rights Award from the National Education Association in 1988; Harvard University Award for Contributions to Minority Journalism in 1990; University of Missouri School of Journalism, Medal of Honor for Distinguished Journalism; inducted into the South Dakota Hall of Fame in 1995; Distinguished Service Award from the Washington Times, and while publisher of newspaper, "Indian Country Today," he received more than 70 awards for excellence; articles featured in "People" magazine, "Denver Post" magazine, "Minnesota Monthly," "Chicago Tribune" magazine; and has appeared on CBS Nightwatch, the Oprah Winfrey Show, and the NBC Nightly News; inducted into the South Dakota Newspaper Hall of Fame in 2007. *Published works*: The Aboriginal Sin (Historian Press, 1978); Notes From Indian Country, Volume I, 1978-82; editor, The American Indian and the Media; Notes From Indian Country (Giago Book Publishing, 1999); writes a weekly column syndicated by Knight Ridder Tribune Service; articles in magazines.

GIAMMARINO, BARBARA (*Mi Ma Ku-Berry Woman*)
(storyteller)
Address: 24 Burt Rd., Springfield, MA 01118 (413) 783-1665. Barbara presents history & culture of American Indian people in a unique program of singing, drumming, dancing, & storytelling. An artistically organized performance to present her collection of authentic Native American articles.

GIBBS, HUGH (Etowah Cherokee)
(tribal chief)
Affiliation & Address: Chief, Etowah Cherokee Nation, 150 9th Ave. N., Cleveland, TN 37203.

GIBSON, BUSTER (Shoshone-Paiute)
(tribal vice chairperson)
Affiliation & Address: Shoshone Paiute Business Council, Duck Valley Reservation, P.O. Box 219, Owyhee, NV 89832 (702) 759-3100 ext. 1231. E-mail: Gibson.buster@shopai.org.

GIBSON, ISAAC (Absentee-Shawnee)
(tribal lt. governor)
Affiliation & Address: Lt. Governor, Absentee-Shawnee Tribe, 2025 S. Gordon Cooper Dr., Shawnee, OK 74801 (405) 275-4030.

GIBSON, WILLIAM (*Wassaja*) (Onondaga) 1932-
(retired account technician)
Born January 20, 1932, Yonkers, N.Y. Education: Manhattan College, 1956-58. *Principal occupation*: Retired account technician - municipal housing authority *Address*: 66 Washington St. #12B, Poughkeepsie, NY 12601. *Affiliation*: Principal Chief & President, Northeastern Native American Association (845) 473-2833. *Other professional posts*: Editor/Publisher, Smoke Signals; editor, Common Ground; editor, Westchester Advocate; security supervisor, Sentry Investigations; security director & account technician, Municipal Housing Authority. *Military service*: U.S. Marine Corps, 1950-52. *Community activities*: Labor & Industry chairman (C.A.C.) NYS Urban Development Commission; labor chairman & national board member of Negro Labor Council, Yonkers Human Rights Commission; chairman, Yonkers Community Action Program; commissioner of deeds, Westchester County, NY; coordinator of 1963 March on Washington. *Membership*: Native American Writers & Artists Association (secretary); Pan American Indian Association; American Indian Community House. *Awards, honors*: 1982 Golden Globe for Poetry; Even Elevan-Man of the Year, 1965; 1986 Silver Scribe (Native American Writers/Artists. *Interests*: Chief Wassaja is also an ordained minister in the Native American Church - ordained 1995. "Goal in life: To be an instrument of peace, to lead, walk beside or follow those who still follow the path of our fathers into the 7th generation. To be loved, respected & needed;" guest columnist with several Native American newspapers.

GIDNER, JEROLD L. (JERRY) (Sault Ste Marie Chippewa)
(government administration; writer)
Education: Michigan State University, BS (Zoology), 1982; University of Michigan, MS (Natural Resources), 1987; University of Michigan Law School,

JD (Environmental Law), 1990. American University – Kogod School of Business, MBA (Entrepreneurship), 2007. *Affiliation & Address*: Deputy Chief Learning Officer (2011-present), Office of Strategic Employee & Organizational Development, U.S. Department of the Interior, 1849 C St., NW, Washington, DC 20240. E-mail: jerrygidner@gmail.com. "As director of the Bureau of Indian Affairs (BIA) (2007-09), I led one of the most complex organizations in the Federal Government; with 4,500 staff in 35 states and a budget of over $3 billion. The BIA has an enormous scope of mission, providing numerous services to tribes, including land & natural resources management, forestry, probate, law enforcement & detention, social services, and roads." *Other professional posts*: "I am working on tribal issues related to the Extractive Industries Transparency Initiative (USEITI), which is being headed up by the Office of Natural Resources Revenue at the Department of the Interior" (May 2014-present); President, Board of Directors, Encore Stage & Studio (children's theater), Arlington, VA, 2012-present; owner, Aardvarks Are Wee (children's book publisher), 2007-present. *Past professional posts*: Director, Bureau of Indian Affairs, U.S. Department of the Interior, Washington, DC, 2007-09; Acting Director, Office of Tribal Government Relations, BIA, Feb. 2014 – May 2014; member, Board of Directors, Encore Stage & Studio, Arlington, VA. Jerry facilitated a strategic plan for the organization, & advocated for expansion of programs and fundraising; and professionalized the board of directors. *Interests*: Besides his interest in children's theater & writing children's books, Jerry's passion is leadership & executive development, & likes to bring people together & drive transformational change. *Published works*: If You Were an Aardvark: An ABC Book Starring Mammals (Aardvarks Are Wee, 2007, Xlibris.com).

GIFFEN, JACK, JR. (Confederated Tribes of Grand Ronde)
(tribal vice chairperson)
Affiliation & Address: Vice Chairperson, Confederated Tribes of the Grand Ronde Community, 9615 Grand Ronde Rd., Grand Ronde, OR 97347 (503) 879-5211.

GIFFORD, ROBERT DONALD, II (Cherokee)
(attorney; tribal court judge; professor)
Education: Southwestern College, BA, 1993; University of Oklahoma College of Law, JD (former editor of American Indian law Review), 1996; U.S. Army War College, MS (Strategic Studies), 2015. *Affiliation & Address*: Gungoll, Jackson, Box & Devoll, P.C., 101 Park Ave., Suite 1400, Oklahoma City, OK 73102 (405) 272-4710. E-mail: Gifford@gungolljackson.com. A former federal prosecutor and now Senior Attorney at Gungoll, Jackson, Box & Devoll with a practice specialty in Native American Law, White Collar/Criminal Defense, Military Law, Government Contracts, and Civil Litigation. Mr. Gifford, a tribal member of the Cherokee Nation, also serves as a tribal court judge for two Native American tribes, a Colonel in the Army Reserves with five years of active duty service, and an adjunct law professor at two law schools teaching Trial Practice, Military Law, Indian Gaming, & National Security Law. *Other professional posts*: Associate Justice, Iowa Nation Supreme Court, 2012-present; Chief Judge, Kaw Nation Tribal Court, 2009-present; Staff Judge Advocate/Commander/Executive Officer, U.S. Army Reserve, 2000-present; Adjunct Law Professor, University of Oklahoma College of Law & Oklahoma City University School of Law; Chief District Court Judge, Kaw Nation, Kaw City, OK. *Past professional posts*: Assistant U.S. Attorney (2006-16), U.S. Attorney's Office, Western District of Oklahoma, Oklahoma City, OK; former Adjunct Law Professor, University of Arkansas School of Law; former Editor, American Indian Law Review. *Military service*: Colonel, U.S. Army Reserves. *Awards, honors*: Justice Cardozo Award, Oklahoma Bar Association's Criminal Law Section, 2016; Recognition for International Human Trafficking Case, FBI, 2015; Proferssional Advocate of the Year, Oklahoma Bar Association, 2013.

GILBERT, MATTHEW SAKIESTEWA (Hopi)
(professor of American Indian studies & history)
Education: University of California, Riverside, MA & PhD; MA in theology from the Talbot School of Theology/Biola University. *Affiliation & Address*: Associate Professor, American Indian Studies & History, College of Liberal Arts & Sciences, Room 2005, 1204 West Nevada St., MC138, University of Chicago, Urbana, IL 61801 (217) 265-9870. E-mail: tewa@illinois.edu. Professor Gilbert centers his research & teaching on Native American history & the history of the American West. He examines the history of American Indian education, the Indian boarding school experience, and American Indians and sports. *Other professional posts*: Serves on the Editorial Board of the History of Education Quarterly, and as a board member of the Hopi Education Endowment Fund. *Past professional posts*: Post-doctoral Research Associate in American Indian Studies at the University of Illinois-Urbana-Champaign, and as an adjunct faculty in history at the University of Redlands, Azusa Pacific University, San Bernardino Valley Community College, and The Master's College. *Awards, honors*: Spur Award for "Marathoner Louis Tewanima and the Continuity of Hopi Runnng, 1908-1912," Best Western Short Nonfiction, Western Writers of America (2013); Helen Corley Petit Scholar Award, College of Liberal Arts & Sciences, University of Illinois at Urbana-Champaign (2013-14). Produced a documentary film -- Beyond the Mesas -- on the Hopi boarding school

experience. *Published works*: Education Beyond the Mesa: Hopi Students at Sherman Institute, 1902-1929 (University of Nebraska Press, 2010); Editor, with Clifford E. Trafzer & Lorene Sisquoc, The Indian School on Magnolia Avenue: Voices & Images from Sherman Institute (Oregon State University Press, 2012); co-edits new series, "Indigenous Confluences," (University of Washington Press, 2013); Hopi Runner: Crossing the Terrain Between Indian & American, 1908-1932 (University Press of Kansas, work-in-progress); numerous articles in scholarly journals and book contributions.

GILBERT, WILLARD (*Sakiestewa*) (Hopi)
(professor of education; dept. chair)
Education: University of New Mexico, EdD. *Affiliation & Address*: Professor of Education & Dept. Chairperson, College of Education, Northern Arizona University (NAU), P.O. Box 5774, Flagstaff, AZ 86011 (928) 523-7107. E-mail: gilbert@nau.edu; His expertise is Curriculum & Instruction, American Indian education and has experience as an administrator, faculty & researcher in higher education. *Other professional posts*: President, Hopi Education Endowment Fund (HEEF). In 2006, HEEF was a Harvard Honoring Nations "High Honors" Award recipient; board member (president, 2007-08), National Indian Education Association (NIEA), Washington, DC. *Past professional posts*: Former chair, Educational Specialties Dept., Northern Arizona University, Flagstaff, AZ; board president, Native Americans for Community Action, Inc., Flagstaff Indian Center, Flagstaff, AZ; Secretary of NIEA (2005-06); vice-president, National Association for Bilingual Education (NABE). *Awards, honors*: American Assn for Higher Education Award, Washington, DC; President's Award from NAU. *Military service*: U.S. Navy.

GILES, ERICK (Muscogee Creek)
(program director)
Education: University of Oklahoma, MS (City Planning & Public Administration); University of Maine (law degree in progress). *Affiliation & Address*: Program Director, Indian land Tenure Foundation & National Indian Carbon Coalition, 62 Old Farm Rd., South Portland, ME 04106 (406) 471-0820. E-mail: egiles@indiancarbon.org. Giles provides education, training & technical assistance to tribes & Indian landowners who are interested in entering the carbon credit market. *Past professional posts*: City Planner for Portland, Maine; city planner for Claremont, New Hampshire; planning coordinator for the Flathead County Planning & Zoning Department; board of directors (seven years) for the Indian Land Tenure Foundation.

GILES, MARCELLA (Muscogee Creek)
(attorney)
Address: 926 Ridge Dr., McLean, VA 22101 (202) 208-6050.
Affiliation: Delegate, Muskogee Creek National Tribal Bar Association.

GILLETTE, JODI A. (Hunkpapa & Oglala Sioux)
(attorney; policy advisor)
Education: Dartmouth College, BA (Government & Native American Studies); University of Minnesota Humphrey's School of Public Affairs, MPP. *Affiliation & Address*: Policy Advisor, Sonosky, Chambers, Sachse, Endreson & Perry, LLP, 1425 K St., NW, Suite 600, Washington, DC 20005 (202) 682-0240. Email: jgillette@sonosky.com. Jodi currently serves as a Policy Advisor for the Firm, after serving at the pleasure of President Barack Obama from 2009-2015. During her tenure under the Administration, Jodi played an integral role in multiple capacities. Most recently, she served as the Special Assistant to the President for Native American Affairs in the White House Domestic Policy Council. Subsequent to this, she served as the Deputy Assistant Secretary to the Assistant-Secretary Indian Affairs in the U.S. Department of the Interior. Additionally, as the Associate Director of Intergovernmental Affairs at the White House, she implemented and institutionalized the President's interactions with the tribes and his Administration. Prior to joining the Obama Administration, Ms. Gillette served as the executive director of the Native American Training Institute in Bismarck, a non-profit offering technical assistance and training to tribal, state and local governments in the area of human service delivery systems. In 2008, Obama for America hired Jodi to direct ND's statewide First American vote efforts. As the longest serving political appointee in the Administration, Jodi was quite influential in advising the President of the United States on policy to improve the lives of Native Americans and strengthen the nation-to-nation relationship between the United States and Indian Tribes. She was instrumental in advancing the protection of Native women and children against violence, ensuring tribes were treated as governments when faced with emergencies, and resolving long-standing legal disputes between tribes and the federal government.

GILLIAND, RICHARD M. (*Ne Mook Na Na*) 1937-
(artist & craftsman)
Born October 9, 1937, Detroit, Mich. *Education*: Michigan State University (2 years). *Principal occupation*: Artist & craftsman. *Address*: Rt. 1, Box 836, Interlochen, MI 49643 (616) 275-6476. *Affiliations*: Ward & Eis Art Gallery, Petoskey, MI (major outlet); Minnetrista Council for Great Lakes Native American Studies, Muncie, IN (recently commissioned for museum work).

Military service: U.S. Army, 1958-60 (E-5; 82nd Airborne Div.; Military Intelligence Det.) Community activities: Lecture to schools & scouting activities on Native American arts and crafts. *Memberships*: Liberty Tree (Black Powder Club) (president, 1981-88); Grand Traverse Metis, 1983-. *Interests*: "My main vocational interests are birch bark ma kuks, quill boxes, medicine drums, trade silver work, flint lock rifles, and any area of arts & crafts of the Eastern Woodland people. I spent 18 years living in the Alaskan bush. Halibut fishing, horse wrangling, guiding, log cabin building. I was closely associated with Indian & Eskimo people in my life there. Currently, I have about 100 pages written on my life there. Also, I'm currently writing for grants to work on book devoted to birch-bark makuks & quill boxes and the people doing them."

GILLILAND, KIMBERLIE (Cherokee)
(executive director)
Affiliation & Address: Executive Director, The Cherokee Nation Foundation, 115 E. Delaware, Tahlequah, OK 74464 (918) 207-0950.

GILMAN, DAVID M.
(bank president)
Affiliations & Address: President & CEO, Native American Bank, N.A., 999 18th St., Suite 2460, Denver, CO 80202 (720) 963-5501. dgilman@nabna.com. *Other professional post*: President & Director, The Native American Bancorporation Co., Past professional post: Chairperson, First National Bank of Colorado, Denver, CO (ten years); executive vice president & chief credit officer, Weststar Bank.

GIOVANNETTI, JOSEPH M. (Tolowa)
(assistant professor)
Born in Eureka, Calif. *Education*: Humboldt State University, BA (Journalism), 1972, MA (Educational Administration), 1979; participant in the Los Angeles-based Center for Leadership Education (CLE) Educational Administration program in 1979; Sierra University, PhD (Psychology), 1987. *Affiliation & Address*: Assistant Professor of Native American Studies, Ethnic Studies Dept., Lower Library Rm. 7, Humboldt State University, Arcata, CA 95521 (707) 826-5572 (1993-present). E-mail: jmgtwo@cox.net. *Past professional posts*: Coordinator, Indian Education Programs, Eureka City Schools, CA, 1979-1993; Tribal Chairman, Tolowa Nation Tribal Council, 1983-85. *Community activities*: Member of the Genealogy Committee & Tribal History committees during the preparation of the Tolowa Nation petition to the Interior Department's Bureau of Acknowledgement & Research (BAR). He testified on behalf of the Tolowa Nation's recognition petition at Congressional hearings in 1988 & 1991. *Membership*: Tolowa - Smith River Rancheria. *Awards, honors*: NCAA Division II Track & Field Championship's finalist, semi-finalist, 800 meter run (1971-72); California State U. Affirmative Action Grant Recipient, Humboldt State U., 1995; Research, Scholarship & Creative Activities Grant Recipient, Humboldt State University, 1996, 1997. *Areas of Expertise*: Psychology, mental health, imagery of Native Americans, Native American athletes, Indian education, Indians in American history, and federal Indian policy. *Interests*: Tolowa culture, history & recognition/status clarification issues since 1979.

GIPP, DAVID M.
(college fund trustee emeritus)
Affiliation & Address; Trustee Emeritus, American Indian College Fund, 8333 Greenwood Blvd. • Denver, CO 80221 (303) 426-8900. Past professional post: Former President, United Tribes Technical College, 3315 University Dr., Bismarck, ND 58501 (701) 255-3285 ext. 293.

GIPP, GERALD E. (Hunkpapa)
(executive director)
Education: Ellendale State Teachers College (ND), BA; Pennsylvania State University, MA & PhD. Contact: E-mail: gegipp1@verizon.net. *Past professional posts*: Executive Director, American Indian Higher Education Consortium (AIHEC), Alexandria, VA; President, Haskell Indian Nations University, Lawrence, KS; Interim Director, National Indian Education Association (NIEA). He served as the first Indian director of the American Indian Leadership Program at Penn State University. With an extensive background in the field of education & federal policy development, including work as a Program Officer for The National Science Foundation, he is also a national and inter-nationally known scholar & has written & presented on such issues as education policy, governance, & economic development. *Published works*: Editor, On Indian Ground: The Northern Plains (Information Age Publishing, 2015).

GIPP, WILLIAM C. (Standing Rock Sioux) 1940-
(BIA agency supt.)
Born November 11, 1940, Fort Yates, N.D. (Standing Rock Sioux Reservation). *Education*: Black Hills State College, BS, 1968; South Dakota State University, MA, 1973. *Affiliation & Address*: Superintendent, Blackfeet Agency, BIA, Browning, MT 59417 (406) 338-7544. *Past professional posts*: Supt., Rosebud Sioux Agency, Rosebud, SD, 1984-87; supt., Blackfeet Agency, BIA, Browning, MT, 1987-. *Other professional post*: Board of directors, Boy Scouts of America,

Minnesota. *Military service*: U.S. Army, 1963-67 (Sergeant E-5, Special Forces, Vietnam Vet). *Memberships*: American Legion; Veterans of Foreign Wars; National Congress of American Indians; South Dakota Teachers Assn.

GIPS, ROBERT L.
(Of counsel on Indian affairs)
Education: Harvard University, BA; Yale University, JD, 1984. *Affiliation & Address*: Special Counsel on Indian affairs & corporate matters, Drummond Woodsum, 84 Marginal Way, Suite 600, Portland, ME 04101 (207) 253-0557. E-mail: rgips@dwmlaw. com. *Professional activities*: Robert has served as legal counsel and as a key business & financial advisor to Indian tribes since 1983. As counsel to the Mashantucket Pequot Tribal Nation, he was instrumental in the creation & development of Foxwoods Resort Casino. He has been counsel or senior advisor for most of the Tribe's major business ventures, including hotel acquisition & resort development activities. Also has counseled the Seminole Tribe of Florida & Seminole Hard Rock Entertainment, the Passamaquoddy & Penobscot Tribes in Maine, the Pokagon Band of Ottawa Indians, and the Grand Traverse band of Ottawa Indians in Michigan, as well as the Guidiville Rancheria in California & the Tulalip Tribes in Washington. *Other professional posts*: Board member, Seminole Hard Rock Entertainment & Seminole Hard Rock International; vice chairperson, Native American Bank, Denver, CO; vice chairperson & Board member, Native American Community Development Corporation, Browning, MT; board member, Passamaquoddy Tribe's Northeastern Blueberry Company. *Awards, honors*: New England Super Lawyers, Native American Law, Business/Corporate, Gaming (2007-2010); Best Lawyers USA, Native American Law (2007-2016); Chambers USA, Nationwide, Native American Law

GISH, ROBERT FRANKLIN (Cherokee) 1940-
(writer, professor emeritus)
Born April 1, 1940, Albuquerque, N.M. *Education*: University of New Mexico, MA, 1967, PhD, 1972. *Principal occupation*: Writer, emeritus professor. *Address*: P.O. Box 12562, Albuquerque, NM 87195. E-mail: robert.gish@uni.edu. *Affiliations*: Distinguished Scholar & Professor of English, University of Northern Iowa, 1967-91; Director, Ethnic Studies Program, Professor of English, English Dept., California Polytechnic State University, San Luis Obispo, CA, 1991-2000; visiting NM writer, U. of New Mexico, 2001-present. *Other professional post*: Contributing editor, "The Bloomsbury Review." *Memberships*: Authors Guild; Pen West; Western Writers of America. *Award*: Distinguished Alumni Award, University of New Mexico. *Biographical sources*: Who's Who in America. *Published works*: First Horses: Stories of the New West (U. of Nevada Press, 1993); Songs of My Hunter Heart (U. of New Mexico Press, 1994); When Coyote Howls (U. of New Mexico Press, 1994); Bad Boys and Black Sheep (U. of Nevada Press, 1996); Beyond Bounds (U. of New Mexico Press, 1997; Dreams of Quivira (Clear Light Publishers, 1998); Beautiful Swift Fox: Erna Ferguson's Southwest (Texas A&M U. Press, 1998); West Bound: Stories of Providence (West End Press, 2005).

GISHEY, LAURENCE
(institute director)
Education: Arizona State University, B.S. (Business Administration). *Address & Affiliation*: Director, Institute for Native Americans, Bldg. 2, Rm. 103, College of Social & Behavioral Sciences, Northern Arizona University, P.O. Box 4085, Flagstaff, AZ 86011 (928) 523-9557. E-mail: laurence.gishey@nau.edu. *Other professional post*: Co-chair, Commission for Native Americans, NAU, Flagstaff, AZ. *Past professional posts*: President, Navajo Community College, Tsaile, AZ;

GISHIE, LEO THOMAS (Navajo) 1941-
(educational administration)
Born April 26, 1941, Tees To Community, Ariz. *Education*: Northern Arizona University, BS, 1973; University of New Mexico, MA, 1984. *Address*: N. Mars Dr., Flagstaff, AZ 86011. *Affiliations*: Assistant to Dean of Instruction, Navajo Community College, Tsaile, AZ (five years); principal, BIA School, Holbrook, AZ, 1987-90; principal, Wide Ruins Boarding School, Chambers, AZ, 1991-93; principal, Lukachukai Boarding School, Lukachukai, AZ, 1993-. *Other professional posts*: AIRCA (president). *Military service*: U.S. Army (Staff Sgt. or E-5, 1963-66; Expert Medal). *Community activities*: Local board member (eight years). *Awards, honors*: Outstanding Award for BIA Service. Interests: Administration; rodeo competition; public work, public speaking; some travel.

GIVENS, THOMAS (Muscogee Creek)
(tribal first warrior)
Affiliation & Address: First Warrior, Kialegee Tribal Town, P.O. Box 332, Wetumka, OK 74883 (405) 452-3262. E-mail: thomas.givens@kialegeetribe.net

GLANCY, DIANE (Cherokee) 1941-
(professor of English, writer)
Born March 18, 1941, Kansas City, Mo. *Education*: University of Missouri, BA (English Literature), 1964; University of Central Oklahoma, MA (English),1983; University of Iowa, MFA, 1988. *Principal occupation*: Professor of English,

writer. *Address*: 261 Brimhall, St. Paul, MN 55105 (651) 690-2174. E-mail: glancy@macalester.edu. *Affiliation*: Professor of English, Macalester College, St. Paul, MN, 1988-present. *Membership*: Wordcraft Circle of Native Writers & Storytellers. *Awards, honors*: Received the 1986 Lakes and Prairies Prize for "One Age in a Dream," poetry book; received the 1988 Capricorn Prize from the Writer's Voice, New York, for "Iron Woman"; received the 1992 Minnesota Book Award for Poetry; 2001 Cherokee Medal of Honor; 2003 National Endowment for the Arts. *Published works*: "Brown Wolf Leaves the Res," poetry book (Blue Cloud Quarterly, 1984); "One Age in a Dream," poetry book (Milkweed Edition, Minneapolis, MN, 1986; "Offering," poetry book (Holy Cow! Press, 1988); "Iron Woman," poetry book (New Rivers Press, Minneapolis, 1990); "Lone Dog's Winter Count," poetry book (West End Press, 1991); "Coyote's Quodlibet," poetry book (Chax Press, 1995); "Boom Town," poetry book (Black Hat Press, 1995); "The Only Piece of Furniture in the House," poetry book (Moyer Bell, Wakefield, RI, 1996); "Pushing the Bear," a novel of the Trail of Tears (Harcourt Brace, 1996); "War Cries," a collection of nine plays (Holy Cow! Press, Duluth, MN, 1996); "A Primer of the Obsolete," poetry book (Chax Press, 1998); "Flutie," poetry book (Moyer Bell, Wakefield, RI, 1998); "(Ado) ration," poetry book (Chax Press, 1999); "The Closets of Heaven," poetry book (Chax Press, Tucson, 1999); "Fuller Man," poetry book (Moyer Bell, Wakefield, RI, 1999); "Cold-and-Hunger Dance," essay (U. of Nebraska Press, 2000); "The Mask Maker," novel (U. of Oklahoma Press, 2001); "Designs of the Night Sky," novel (U. of Nebraska Press, 2002); "The Man Who Heard the Land," novel (Minnesota Historical Society, 2002); "American Gypsy," play (U. of Oklahoma Press, 2002); "Stone Heart: A Novel of Sacajawea" (Overlook Press, 2003); "The Shadow's Horse," poetry book (U. of Arizona Press, 2003); "In-Between Places," essay (U. of Arizona Press, 2004).

GLATKE, THEODORE
(Indian program director)
Affiliation: American Indian Professional Training Program in Speech-Language Pathology & Audiology, University of Arizona, Dept. of Speech & Hearing Sciences, Tucson, AZ 85721 (520) 621-1969.

GLAZE, JAMES E.
(attorney; Indian law)
Affiliation & Address: Partner, Sonoskey, Chambers, Sachse, Endreson & Perry, LLP, 600 West Broadway, Suite 700, San Diego, CA 92101 (619) 546-1306. E-mail: jglaze@sonosky.com. Mr. Glaze joined the firm in 1993. He assists tribal clients on a wide range of legal matters, including litigation and negotiations under the Indian Self-Determination and Education Assistance Act, federal construction and public infrastructure projects (including health clinics, hospitals, schools, tribal justice centers, water treatment and supply systems, road and bridge projects), labor law, employment law and tribal governance matters. He also leads the firm's transportation & public infrastructure practice & regularly is asked to speak at national & regional tribal conferences. Mr. Glaze helped to develop many first-of-their-kind tribal funding agreements, including the first tribal transportation innovative financing agreement, the first IRR Program self-governance compact, the first FHWA IRR Program Agreements & many Tribal-State fund transfer agreements. He served as an attorney advisor to the tribal members of the Indian Reservation Roads (IRR) Negotiated Rulemaking Committee & the IHS Self-Governance Negotiated Rulemaking Committee. He also played a leading national advocacy role in the development of the tribal transportation program and funding provisions included in the Safe, Accountable, Flexible and Efficient Transportation Equity Act: A Legacy for Users (SAFETEA-LU) and the American Recovery & Reinvestment Act (ARRA). Following passage of these laws, Mr. Glaze worked closely with tribal & federal officials to implement new tribal transportation programs within the U.S. Department of Transportation, including the Tribal Transit Grant Program, the Federal Highway Administration-Federal Lands Highways (FHWA-FLH) IRR Program, and the Tribal Scenic Byways Program.

GLAZE, LaVERNE (Karuk/Yurok) 1932-
(Indian basketweaver, elder)
Born April 18, 1932 in Orleans, Calif. *Principal occupation*: Teaching basketweaving, pottery, and regalia making with Karuk language for the past 20 years at the Orleans Elementary School in Orleans, California. *Address*: P.O. Box 295, Orleans, CA 95556 (530) 627-3112. *Other professional posts*: Founding member of the California Indian Basketweavers Association (CIBA). She is available for speaking engagements, demonstrations, and basket identification (Karuk, Yurok, & Hupa. *Community activities*: Works to educate local government agencies on plant management to improve the quality of the natural materials essential to basketweaving. Her efforts to ensure that weavers have the access to the plant materials found on U.S. Forest Service and Bureau of Land Management lands. Dedicated to the success of the "Passport in Time" (PIT) basketweavers camp and "Following the Smoke," an annual basketweaver's event.

GLAZER, JOHN (Paiute)
(tribal chairperson)
Affiliation & Address: Chair, Bridgeport Indian Colony, P.O. Box 37, Bridgeport, CA 93517 (760) 932-7083. E-mail: chair@bridgeportindiancolony.com

GOBERT, JUDY (Blackfeet/Nakota/Salish) 1956-
(college dean; educator, activist)
Education: MS, PhD. *Affiliation & Address*: Dean, Math & Science, Salish Kootenai College, P.O. Box 117, Pablo, MT 59855 (406) 275-4711. E-mail: judy_m_gobert@skc.edu. *Other professional post*: Chairperson of the Board, Indigenous Peoples Council on Biocolonialism, Nixon, NV.

GOBIN, GLEN (Swinomish)
(tribal councilmember)
Affiliation & Address: Councilmember, Swinomish Indian Tribal Community, P.O. Box 817, LaConnor, WA 98257 (360) 466-7314. *Past tribal post*: Vice chairperson.

GOBIN, HENRY
(speaker)
A cultural and historical speaker, Henry is a specialist in languages of the Native American people with background in Museum Studies. He can be reached at (206) 653-4585 ext. 365.

GODFREY, MERRILL C
(attorney, American Indian law)
Education: University of Utah, BA (Political Science), 1995; University of California at Berkeley School of Law, JD, 1998. *Address & Affiliation*: Senior Counsel, Akin Gump Straus Hauer & Feld, LLP, Robert E. Straus Bldg., 1333 New Hampshire Ave. NW, Washington, DC 20036 (202) 887-4326; E-mail: abinney@akingump.com. *Areas of Experience*: American Indian Gaming & Compact Negotiation; American Indian Policy & Regulation; Energy * Renewable Energy for Indian Tribes; Environment, Natural Resources & Land for American Indian Tribes. Merrill advises clients regarding American Indian law & policy. He litigates complex civil matters & appeals. He represents plaintiffs & defendants in federal & state courts & in administrative proceedings. *Practice & Background*: Mr. Godfrey frequently represents Indian tribes and has litigated high-stakes cases in areas such as breach of trust, gaming, oil and gas, water rights, contracts, and elections. He has extensive experience in litigation against the United States & its executive agencies. He was trial counsel in cases that led to the largest settlement ever by an Indian tribe suing the United States.

GOE, DOUGLAS E.
(attorney)
Education: Lewis & Clark College, BA, 1977; Willamette Univerrsity College of Law, JD, 1981. *Affiliation & Address*: Partner, Public Finance, Indian Tribal Finance, 1120 NW Couch St., Suite 200, Portland, OR 97209 (503) 943-4810. E-mail: dgoe@orrick.com For more than 25 years, Doug also has served as bond, underwriter's counsel and bank counsel on a broad range of tribal financings for tribal schools, utilities, justice centers, healthcare, hydroelectric dam facilities, manufacturing and economic development projects. He also has worked on a variety of financings for tribal gaming facilities, resorts and convention facilities. Doug also advises tribal clients on direct investment projects and other investment related matters. Among other tribal clients, Doug serves as bond counsel to The Navajo Nation and The Confederated Tribes of the Warm Springs Reservation of Oregon.

GOES AHEAD, CARLSON (Crow)
(tribal vice chairperson)
Born on the Crow Reservation in St. Xavier, Mont. *Afiliation & Address*: Vice Chairperson, Crow Nation, P.O. Box 129, Crow Agency, MT 59022 (306) 638-3708.

GOFF, RALPH (Diegueno)
(tribal chairperson)
Affiliation & Address: Chairperson, Campo Band of Mission Indians, 36190 Church Rd., Suite 1, Campo, CA 91906 (619) 478-9046. E-mail: rgoff@campo-nsn.gov.

GOGGLES, DEAN (Arapaho)
(former tribal chairperson)
Affiliation & Address: Former Chairperson, Northern Arapaho Tribe, P.O. Box 396, Fort Washakie, WY 82514 (307) 332-6120.

GOGOL, JOHN M. 1938-
(professor; publisher; institute president)
Born August 15, 1938, Westfield, Mass. *Education*: Clark University, BA, 1960; University of Washington, MA, 1965, ABD Doctoral Candidacy, 1969. *Principal occupation*: University professor, publisher. *Address*: P.O. Box 66124, Portland, OR 97266 (503) 233-8131. *Affiliations*: Instructor, Colorado State

University, 1965-68; assistant professor of humanities, Pacific University, Forest Grove, Oregon, 1970-74; publisher, Mr. Cogito Press, Pacific University, 1973-; publisher, American Indian Basketry & Other Native Arts, 1979-; director, Institute for the Study of Traditional American Indian Arts, Portland, OR, 1979-. *Memberships*: Oregon Archaeological Society; Oregon Historical Society; Central States Archaeological Society; Coordinating Council of Literary Magazines; COSMEP. *Awards, honors*: Graves Prize Award in the Humanities, 1971. *Interests*: "In a long teaching career (I) taught German, Russian, comparative literature, American Indian studies, American history, European history, mathematics, physics, and humanities; poet and translator of German, Russian & Polish poetry." *Published works*: Native American Words (Tahmahnawi's Publishers, 1973); Columbus Names the Flowers (Mr. Cogito Press, 1984); articles and other publications in numerous periodicals.

GOINS, WILL M. (*Tsiyohi-Uhayli: Do*) (Eastern Cherokee/Lumbee) 1961-
(executive, artistic director)
Born December 2, 1961, Washington, D.C. *Education*: The George Washington University, BA, 1983; The Pennsylvania State University, MEd, 1989, PhD, 1994. *Principal occupation*: Executive, artistic director. *Affiliations*: CEO, Executive/artistic director, National Native Network of Talent/The Washington's First Americans Theater, Washington, DC, 1982-. *Other professional posts*: Co-editor/contributing writer, Indian Youth Magazine, 1981-83; freelance communications specialist for various private & governmental agencies developing educational, public informational & industrial films, videos, brochures & media, 1984-; freelance writer-correspondent (journalistic articles), 1981-; producer-director, U.S. Indian Health Service, video series for health professionals, 1984-85; professor, The Pennsylvania State University, Dept. of Educational Administration, Policy, Foundations, and Comparative-International Education, "American Indian, Education & Media," 1992-93. *Community activities*: Class Agent for The Columbian College Alumni Assn, The George Washington University, 1990-; Officer, Native American Student Assn of Penn State, 1989-93. *Memberships*: American Anthropological Assn; National Education Assn; American Educational Research Assn; National Indian Educational Assn; AERA-SIG American Indian Sig (Special Interest Group), American Alliance of Health Education, Physical Fitness, Recreation & Dance; American Indian Registry of Performing Arts; National Association for the Advancement of Colored People; National Eagle Scout Association; North Carolina Historical Society; The Gonzaga Dramatics Association. *Awards, honors*: Award of Excellence, Rackley Scholarship, Penn State University, 1988-94; American Indian Leadership Program Fellow, 1988-92; Commendation for Outstanding Service, U.S. Surgeon General, Dr. Everett Rhodes, U.S. Public Health Service, 1984; Outstanding Service Award, Indian Health Service, 1984; Outstanding & Dedicated Service Award, Penn State University, Native American Indian Student Assn, 1993. AFTRA-SAG, 1984-; ASCAP; Native American Journalists Assn, 1983-; American Film Institute, 1980-. *Interests*: Founder, executive artistic director of "The Free Spirit Players," a non-profit collective of Native performing & creative artists & production technicians for the region east of the Mississippi. *Biographical source*: 1980 article in "Indian Youth Magazine," called a Profile. *Published works*: Co-author of play, "Feather in the Wind" (NNT Publishing, 1984); author, "Feathers" the musical (NNT Publishing, 1989; Administering Culturally Specific Health Educational Programs & Curriculum (Penn State, 1989); The Perceptions of Native American Alumni of Graduate Level Educational Degree Programs at the Penn State University (UMI Publishing, 1994).

GOKEE, ANDREW (Ojibwe)
(Native American Center director)
Affiliation & Address: Director, Native American Center, College of Letters & Science, 464 College of Professional Studies, University of Wisconsin, Stevens Point, WI 54481 (715) 346-3576. E-mail: agokee@uwsp.edu.

GOLDBERG, CAROLE E. 1947-
(professor of law; vice chancellor, academic personnel)
Born September 3, 1947, Chicago, Ill. *Education*: Smith College, BA, 1968; Stanford Law School, JD, 1971. *Principal occupation*: Law professor & director of Joint Degree Program in Law & American Indian Studies. *Affiliation & Address*: Professor, UCLA School of Law & American Indian Studies Center, P.O. Box 951476, Los Angeles, CA 90095 (310) 825-4429. E-mail: goldberg@law.ucla.edu. *Affiliations*: Professor, UCLA Law School, 1972-; director of Joint Degree Program in Law & American Indian Studies, American Indian Studies Center, UCLA; Faculty Advisory Committee Chair of the Law School's Native Nations Law & Policy Center; Vice Chancellor, Academic Personnel, for the UCLA campus, 2011-present. *Interests*: "I teach courses in American Indian law and tribal legal systems." *Published works*: Co-editor & co-author, Felix Cohen's Handbook of Federal Indian Law (Michie Co., 1982 & 2005); Planting Tail Feathers: Tribal Survival and Public Law 280, 1997; Co-author of casebook, American Indian Law: Native Nations & the Federal System (6th ed., 2010); Co-author with anthropologist Geyla Frank, Defying the Odds: The Tule River Tribe's Struggle for Sovereignty in Three Centuries (Yale University Press, 2010); Indian Law Stories (Foundation Press, 2011);

Professor Goldberg is currently co-principal investigator of a $1.5 million grant from the National Institute of Justice to study the administration of criminal justice in Indian country..

GOLDING, BRIAN, SR. (Quechan-Yuma)
(economic development administration specialist)
Affiliation: Quechan Indian Tribe, Fort Yuma Indian Reservation, P.O. Box 1899, Yuma, AZ 85366 (760) 572-5270. E-mail: b.golding@quechantribe.com. *Membership*: Americans for Indian Opportunity. Interest: Law.

GOLDMAN, LAWRENCE (Cherokee/Choctaw/Apache)
(business owner/operator)
Address: P.O. Box 465, Mackinaw City, MI 49701 (616) 436-5158. *Affiliations*: President/CEO, Monadnock Trading Co., Inc., 1975-present; president/CEO, Sticks N Stones, Inc., 1984-present. *Community activities*: Chairman, Mackinaw City Downtown Development Authority, 1984-present. *Memberships*: Indian Arts & Crafts Assn; Michigan Retailers Assn; Mackinac Associates. *Published work*: Field Guide to Geology of the Eastern Upper Peninsula of Michigan.

GOLDTOOTH, ANTHONY (Navajo)
(college instructor)
Affiliation & Address: Instructor, Native American Studies, Dine' College, P.O. Box 1924, Window Rock, AZ 86515.

GOLDTOOTH, THOMAS (Dine'-Dakota)
(organization spokesman; environmentalist)
Affiliation & Address: Executive Director, Indigenous Environmental Network, P.O. Box 485, Bemidji, MN 56601 (218) 751-4967. E-mail: ien@igc.org. *Other professional posts*: Coordinator, Red Lake Nation (Minnesota) Environmental Protection Department which is developing an indigenous environmental infrastructure based on traditional eco-knowledge; co-founder, Durban Group for Climate Justice; co-founder, Climate Justice NOW!; co-founder of the U.S. based Environmental Justice Climate Change Initiative; member of the International Indigenous Peoples Forum on Climate Change that operates as the indigenous caucus within the United Nations Framework Convention on Climate Change; policy advisor to Indigenous communities on environmental protection. Tom is involved with local, state, national & International issues directly related to the environmental justice movement; and he advises various science & historical museums on repatriation, reassessment & reburial of human remains and return of cultural items.

GOLLA, VICTOR
(organization secretary)
Affiliations: Society for the Study of the Indigenous languages of the Americas (SSILA), Box 555, Arcata, CA 95518. E-mail: golla@ssila.org; American Indian Languages & Literature Program, Humboldt State University, The Center for Community Development, Arcata, CA 95521 (707) 826-3711.

GOMEZ, CHRISTOPHER (Tigua)
(tribal lt. governor)
Affiliation & Address: Lt. Governor, Ysleta Del Sur Pueblo, P.O. Box 17579, El Paso, TX 79907 (915) 859-8053.

GOMEZ, CYNTHIA (Tule River Yokut)
(executive secretary; tribal advisor)
Education: University of Northern California, JD. *Affiliation & Address*: Tribal Advisor to Governor Brown (2012-present), 915 Capitol Mall, Room 364, Sacramento, CA 95814 (916) 653-4082. *Other professional posts*: Executive Secretary, California Native American Heritage Commission, West Sacramento, CA. *Past professional posts*: Prior to working for the Governor, she served as Chief Judge for the Shingle Springs Tribal Court; In 2010 Judge Gomez was appointed to the California Tribal Court/State Court Coalition by the California Supreme Court Justice, Ronald M. George; Assistant Secretary for Environmental Justice & Tribal Government Affairs for the Office of the Secretary at the California Environmental Protection Agency; Chief for the Native American Liaison Branch. Also srerved as the Chairperson for the National Transportation Research Council.

GOMEZ, DANIEL (Cachil DeHe Wintun)
(tribal chairperson)
Affiliation & Address: Chairperson, Colusa ndian Community, 3730 Hwy. 45, Colusa, CA 95932 (530) 458-8231.

GOMEZ, JOHN A., JR. (Luiseno)
(cultural research supervisor)
Address: 41801 Corte Valentine, Temecula, CA 92592 (951) 541-6612. E-mail: pechangajg@msn.com. *Affiliation*: Pechanga Cultural Research, Pechanga Band of Luiseno Mission Indians. *Membership*: Americans for Indian Opportunity. *Interest*: Law.

GOMEZ, RICHARD (Chumash)
(former tribal vice chairperson)
Education: college courses in business management, as well as seminars in tribal government, leadership and gaming regulations. *Affiliation & Address*: Former Vice Chairperson (1999-2015), Santa Ynez Band of Chumash Mission Indians, P.O. Box 517, Santa Ynez, CA 93440 (805) 688-7997. Website: www.santaynezchumash.org. Richard has served as the tribe's liaison to the state of California in Sacramento and to the federal government in Washington D.C. He completed many An experienced alarm technician, *Past professional post*: He was employed by Sylvester Security Alarms since 1980 and recently retired. *Awards, honors*: Recipient of several award certificates in Radionics Equipment. Richard was selected as an award recipient of the 2010 American Indian Heritage Month Local Leadership Awards. The Leadership Awards recognizes the outstanding accomplishments of American Indian/Alaskan Native men & women who are providing great leadership & making significant contributions to the community.

GOMEZ, TERESA C. (Isleta Pueblo)
(organization president & CEO)
Education: University of New Mexico, MS (Political Science). *Affiliation & Address*: President & CEO, Futures for Children, 9600 Tennyson St. NE, Albuquerque, NM 87122 (505) 821-2828. Teresa worked extensively with tribal governments & various governmental agencies at the federal, state & local level. She has been instrumental in building & strengthening Tribal-State relations & collaboration. Teresa has played a key role in major policy initiatives including the New Mexico Tribal Infrastructure Act, State-Tribal Collaboration Act and the Indian Education Act. *Past professional posts*: Acting Executive Director & Deputy Director of the American Indian Science & Engineering Society (AISES). At AISES, she advocated for policies relating to Indian education, diversity, and equity. In 2006, Ms. Gomez was appointed by Governor Bill Richardson to serve as the Deputy Cabinet Secretary for the New Mexico Indian Affairs Department. She was the first Pueblo woman to hold this post. Teresa also served as the Deputy Cabinet Secretary for the New Mexico Department of Workforce Solutions and as the Deputy CEO for the New Mexico Behavioral Health Purchasing Collaborative. *Published work*: "American Indian Woman Leaders: Public Policy and the Importance of Gender & Ethnic Identity," in the journal, Women & Politics.

GONE, JOSEPH P. (Gros Ventre)
(professor of psychology & Native American studies)
Education: Harvard College, BA, 1992; University of Illinois, Urbana, PhD, 2001. Joseph served as the Charles A. Eastman dissertation fellow at Dartmouth College prior to completing his clinical psychology internship at McLean Hospital/Harvard Medical School. *Affiliation & Address*: Associate Professor of Clinical Psychology, Dept. of Psychology, 2239 East Hall, University of Michigan, 530 East University, Ann Arbor, MI 48109 (734) 647-3958. E-mail: jgone@ umich.edu. *Other professional post*: Associate Professor of American Culture, Native American Studies, U. of Michigan, Ann Arbor. *Past professional posts*: Served on editorial boards of four academic journals. Fields of study: Mental health services for American Indians, cultural psychology, community mental health, sociolinguistics, psychiatric anthropology, narrative & cultural identity, cross-cultural diagnosis of mental disorder, innovative mental health service delivery, wellness, distress, & healing in American Indian lives. *Military service*: U.S. Army & former West Point cadet. *Memberships*: First Nations Behavioral Health Assn (board of directors); Canada's Network for Aboriginal Mental Health Research (international collaborator); Americans for Indian Opportunity. *Interests*: Health, research, social services. *Research projects*: Integrating Traditional Healing & Behavioral Health Services for Urban American Indians; Blackfeet Culture As Substance Abuse Treatment. *Awards, honors*: W.H. Kellogg Fellow in Health Disparities (2003-04); Ford Foundation Postdoctoral Diversity Fellow (2005-06); Katrin H. Lamon Fellow at the School for Advanced Research on Human Experience (2007-08); inaugural recipient of the Henry Tomes Award for exceptional contributions as an emerging leader in ethnic minority psychology; 2013 recipient of the Stanley Sue Award for Distinguished Contrbutions to Diversity in Clinical Psychology from Division 12 of the American Psycholoial Association. Dr. Gone has delivered about 60 invited presentations, and was honored as a Noted Scholar by the Faculty of Education at the U. of British Columbia and as a Distinguished Visitor by the Faculty of Arts at the U. of Alberta; received a Residential Fellowship at the Center for Advanced Study in the Behavioral Sciences at Stanford U. (2010-11). *Published works*: Chapters & Articles: Chapter, Suicide in Native American Communities, with C. Alcantara, pp. 173-199 in book, "Suicide Among Racial & Ethnic Groups," by F.T. Leong & M.M. Leach (Routledge, 2008); article, A Community-Based Treatment for Native American Historical Trauma, pp. 751-762, in Jan. 2009, Journal of Consulting & Clinical Psychology, 77(4); article, Psychotherapy & Traditional Healing for American Indians, pp. 166-235, in 2010, The Clinical Psychologist 38(2); article, The Red Road to Wellness, pp. 187-202, in American Journal of Community Psychology, 47(1-2); article, "American Indian Culture As Substance Abuse Treatment", with P.E. Calf Looking, in Journal Psychoactive Drugs; et al.

GONG, LOUIE (Nooksack)
(educator, artist, activist)
Born & raised in the Nooksack tribal community. *Address*: Resides in Seattle, WA. E-mail: info@eighthgeneration.com. *Past professional posts*: President, MAVIN, co-developer of the Mixed Heritage Center; founder of Eighth Generation, through which he merges traditional Coast Salish art * icons from popular culture to make strong statements about identity, such as his highly south-after, hand-drawn custom shoes. Louie's latest creation is called "Mockups," (www.getmockups.com) a DIY design toy based on his work with youth and his desire to make the experience of personalizing a pair of shoes more accessible. *Video produced*: His unique merger of art & activism is the subject of "Unreserved: The Work of Louie Gong," a Longhouse Media film that is currently screening at film festivals around the world, including Festival De Cannes and National Geographic's All Roads Film Festival. *Awards, honors*: Named to Native Max Magazines "Top 10 Most Inspirational Natives." *Activities*: Presentations & workshops.

GONZALES, ANGELA ANN (Hopi) 1964-
(assistant professor)
Born June 3, 1964, San Bernardino, Calif. *Education*: University of California, Riverside, B.A., 1990; Harvard University, MA (Education), 1994, MA (Sociology), 1996, PhD, 2001. *Dissertation title*: American Indian Identity Matters: The Political Economy of Ethnic Boundaries. *Address*: Cornell University, 339 Warren Hall, Dept. of Development Sociology, Ithaca, NY 14853 (607) 255-1795. E-Mail: aag27@cornell.edu. *Affiliations*: Social Analyst (provided information to congressional staffers on issues concerning Native Americans; & assisted the Senate Select Committee on Indian Affairs in the evaluation of material presented as testimony before the committee), Teaching Fellow, Harvard University, Department of Religious Studies, 1991-95; director, Grants & Scholarship Program, Hopi Tribe, Kykotsmovi, AZ, 1994-95; Department of American Indian Studies, San Francisco State University (lecturer, assistant professor, 1996-; chair of American Indian Studies, 1997-98). *Other professional posts*: External Reviewer, American Indian Culture & Research Journal, 1996-; external reviewer, SIGNS: Journal of Women in Culture & Society, 1998-; Development Committee, American Indian Museum & Culture Center, 1998-. Selected Conference Presentations: Annual National Indian Educators Association Conferences, Nov. 1991-93; panelist at the Leading Ideas in American Indian Studies Conference, U. of Wisconsin, Madison, Sept. 1993; Papers given at the American Indian Graduate Student Conference, University of California, Berkeley, April 1996, American Indian Research Forum, Stanford, Palo Alto, CA, April 1996, the National Academy of Science, Ford Conference of Fellows, U. of California, Irvine, Oct. 1996; and a panelist at the American Academy of Religion, Annual Conference, New Orleans, LA, Nov. 1996; among others. *Awards, honors*: UCR Alumni Award, 1990; Rupert Costo Scholarship, 1990; Hopi Tribal Scholarship, 1988-present; Harvard Prize Fellowship, 1995-present; Ford Foundation, Pre-Doctoral Fellowship, 1992-95; SFSU grants, 1997-99. *Memberships*: American Sociological Assn; Assn of American Indian & Alaskan Native Professors; National Congress of American Indians; American Studies Association. *Interests*: Sociology of identity, U.S. Indian law & policy; indigenous intellectual & cultural property rights.

GONZALES, ANTONIA (Navajo-Dine' Nation)
(radio anchor/producer)
Education: University of New Mexico, BA (Mass Communications & Journalism, with minor in Native American Studies). *Affiliation & Address*: Anchor/Producer, National native News, 4401 Lomas Blvd. NE, Albuquerque, NM 87110 (505) 999-2404. E-mail: agonzales@nativenews.net. Antonia is anchor of Native Voice One (website: www.nv1.org), 90.3 fm KNBA, a five-minute, weekday newcast dedicated to Native issues, that compiles spot news reports from around the country. She has worked for Koahnic Broadcast Corporation (KBC) for more than a decade, starting out as an associate producer for KBC's nationally syndicated talk show, Native America Calling. Before Joining KBC, she was a one-woman-band television reporter for a CBS affiliate in Southeastern New Mexico. *Past professional post*: Former board member, Native American Journalists Association (NAJA).

GONZALES, CLAUDIA (Chukchansi)
(tribal chairperson)
Affiliation & Address: Chairperson, Picayune Rancheria of the Chukchansi Indians, 46575 Road 417 • Coarsegold, CA 93614 (559) 683-6633 E-mail: cgonzales@tcouncil.com

GONZALES, DAVIS (Elko Band of Te-Moak Western Shoshone)
(tribal vice chairperson)
Affiliation & Address: Vice Chairperson, Te-Moak Band of Western Shoshone Indians of Nevada, 525 Sunset St., Elko, NV 89801 (775) 738-8889.

GONZALES, MARIO (Oglala Lakotah)
(tribal attorney)
Affiliation: Attorney, Oglala Sioux Tribe, P.O. Box H, Pine Ridge, SD 57770 (605) 867-2244.

GONZALES, NATHAN (Kickapoo of Oklahoma)
(tribal vice chairperson)
Affiliation & Address: Vice Chairperson, P.O. Box 70, McLoud, OK 74851 (405) 964-2075. E-mail: ngonzales@kickapootribeofokahoma.com

GONZALES, PATRISIA (Kickapoo/Maceual)
(professor of American Indian studies)
Education: University of Wisconsin, PhD, 2007. *Address & Affiliation:* American Indian Studies program, The University of Arizona, Cesar E. Chavez 220, Tucson, AZ 85721 (520) 626-0408. E-mail: pgonza@email.ariizona.edu. *Other professional posts:* She collaborates with the Indigenous Birthworkers Network, & Tewa Women United and is affiliated with the Indigenous Wellness Research Institute at the University of Washington. She is an advisor to the Indigenous Institute of the Americas, a member of the Native American Journalist Association; and former board member of the American Indian Resource Center in San Antonio, TX. Areas of *Interests:* Indigenous communications; Indigenous health systems; Indigenous knowledge. *Published works:* Co-author (with Roberto Rodriguez) The Mud People: Chronicles, Testimonios & Remembrances (Chusma, 2003).

GONZALES, VINCENT, III (Agua Caliente Cahuilla)
(tribal secretary/treasurer)
Affiliation & Address: Secretary/Treasurer, Agua Caliente Band of Cahuilla Indians, 5401 Dinah Shore Dr., Palm Springs, CA 92264 (760) 699-6800.

GONZALEZ, ANGELO (Shoshone-Bannock)
(tribal executive director)
Affiliation & Address: Executive Director, Shoshone-Bannock Tribes, P.O. Box 306, Fort Hall, ID 83203 (208) 478-3721

GONZALEZ, BOBBY (Taino) 1951-
(storyteller, lecturer, poet)
Born September 22, 1951, New York, N.Y. *Education:* Manhattan College. *Principal occupation:* Storyteller, lecturer, poet. *Address:* 3215 Hull Ave. #5C, Bronx, NY 10467 (212) 459-4753. E-mail: bobbyguno@aol.com. *Website:* www.bobbygonzalez.com. *Community activities:* Master of Ceremonies and Event Coordinator for annual Native Harvest Festival held in Riverdale, NY. *Memberships:* Taino Del Norte, 1989-; Native American Heritage Committee, 1990-. *Interests:* (I) "write a monthly column for the publication, "Latino Village News"; (I) "have given presentations on the history & culture of the Taino at the American Museum of Natural History, S.U.N.Y. at Binghamton, the Waterloo Indian Village Museum, Carnegie Hall, the National Museum of the American Indian, and the University of New Mexico." *Published works:* Puerto Rican Indian Wars: Part Two; Song of the American Holocaust: Native Poetry from the South Bronx Reservation.

GONZALEZ, PAUL (Iipay-Diegueno)
(tribal vice chairperson)
Affiliation & Address: Vice Chairperson, Iipay Nation of Santa Ysabel, P.O. Box 130, Santa Ysabel, CA 92070 (760) 765-0846.

GOOD FOX, JULIA (Pawnee)
(college instructor)
Education: University of Oklahoma, BA (English), MA (English), 1995; University of Kansas, PhD candidate. *Affiliation & Address:* Instructor (2005-present), College of Indigenous & American Indian Studies, Haskell Indian Nations University, 155 Indian Ave., Lawrence, KS 66046 (785) 749-8404. *Other professional posts:* Member (2008-present), Board of Trustees, Pawnee Nation College, Pawnee, OK.

GOODEN, CLYDE (Inupiat)
(business development)
Affiliation & Address: Vice President of Business Development, NANA Development Corporation (NDC), P.O. Box 49, Kotzebue, AK 99752 (907) 442-3301. *Other professional post:* Board of Directors, National Center for American Indian Enterprise Development. *Past professional post:* President, NANA, Seattle, WA.

GOODHOUSE, DAKOTA (Standing Rock Sioux) 1974-
(college instructor)
Affiliation & Address: Instructor, United Tribes Technical College, 3315 University Dr., Bismarck, ND 58504. Mr. Goodhouse is helping to revive the "winter count," a traditional practice among Dakota & Lakota Sioux for keeping time by painting pictographs marking the year's memorable events.

GOODMAN, JANEEN
(senior strategist)
Education: University of California (UCI), Irvine, BA (Social Ecology). *Affiliation:* Senor Strategist, Blue Stone Strategy Group, Irvine, CA. Janeen has provided support on more than 100 projects varying in subject, depth, and timing with

Tribal Nations and organizations across Indian Country. Continuing to sharpen her personal and professional skills, Goodman learns from Blue Stone's strong leadership & subject matter experts in providing assistance to Tribal communities, working to ensure that each tribal Nation's unique perspective, processes, history & culture is integrated into each project. She coordinates various strategic planning and economic development projects, assists in information gathering & synthesis, scope/proposal development, logistics coordination, research, deliverable development & project tracking to ensure the needs of the client are met in an efficient and orderly manner; and also assists in the preparation & facilitation of a variety of Blue Stone Strategy Group's unique workshops. During her time at UCI, Goodman worked for the Center for Educational Partnership where she dedicated her time to supporting minorities in their educational pursuits of obtaining a higher education.

GOODMAN, JIMMY K.
(Of counsel)
Education: University of Oklahoma, BA, 1968; Stanford Law School, JD, 1971. *Affiliation & Address:* Of Counsel, Crow Dunlevy LLP, Indian Law & Gaming Practice Group, 324 N. Robinson Ave., Suite 100 • Oklahoma City, O 73102 (405) 235-7717; E-mail: jimmy.goodman@crowedunlevy.com. Jimmy is a senior trial attorney & past president at Crowe & Dunlevy. Since 1973, Goodman has specialized in high-stakes business litigation, product claims and disputes involving tribal compacts, economic development, gaming enterprises and federal Indian law. Goodman has tried cases before state, federal, bankruptcy and tribal courts representing individuals, small businesses and Native American Nations along with Fortune 500 companies.

GOODMAN, LINDA J.
(professor)
Born in Denver, Colo. *Education:* University of Colorado, Boulder, BA, 1966; Wesleyan University, MA, 1968; Washington State University, Pullman, PhD, 1978. *Address:* 4135 Dover St., Wheat Ridge, CO 80033. *Affiliation:* Assistant Professor, Dept. of Music, Colorado College, Colorado Springs, CO, 1979-. *Other professional posts:* Advisor of Native American students at Colorado College; director of tribes program for pre-college Native American students. *Community activities:* Talks on Native American music and culture to various museum groups, tour groups, and Native American groups; have organized various Native American music and dance performances for non-Indian audiences; consultant for Native American music education programs, District II public schools, Colorado Springs, CO; member, Colorado Springs Native Americans Women's Association; organized Native American symposia, art shows, and guest speakers at Colorado College. *Awards, honors:* American Philosophical Society grant, 1967, to work on Pueblo Indian music; 1979 Humanities Division Research Grant from Colorado College, to work on life history of Makah Indian singer; 1980 Mellon Grant, to work on Southwest Indian music, to teach as a new course; 1983 American Council of Learned Societies Fellowship for work on life history of a Northwest Coast musician. *Interests:* "Native American music & culture, especially Northwest Coast & American Southwest. "(I) have spent much time traveling and living on reservations in both areas, studying music & culture, attending ceremonies, learning from the people in those areas. Have lead many field trips of college students to various reservations in the Southwest so that they could see and talk to the people living there and learn from them first-hand. Have led a tour group of older people to the Makah Reservation for the same purpose. I am writing books and articles on Native American music & culture. I am very interested in teaching, counseling, & advising Native American young people, helping them find a way to fit into two worlds. Have worked with a number of Native American students over the years, and I'm interested in Indian singing & dancing, and participate on the few occasions when it is appropriate." *Published works:* Music and Dance in Northwest Coast Indian Life (Navajo Community College Press, 1977); A Makah Biography, in Dalmoma: Digging for Roots (Empty Bowl Press, 1985); Nootka Indian Music, in New Grove Dictionary of Music in the U.S. (Macmillan, 1986).

GOOMBI, JAY (Kiowa-Apache)
(storyteller, author, teacher)
Education: The University of Science & Arts of Oklahoma, Meredith Indigenous Humanities Center, BA, 2000. *Affiliation & Address:* Storyteller, author, teacher of Clemente courses, Meredith Indigenous Humanities Center, The University of Science & Arts of Oklahoma, Davis Hall, Rm. 131, Chickasha, OK 73018 (405) 574-1269. *Membership:* Wordcraft Circle.

GORDON, JAMES (*Spirit Wolf*) (United Lumbee) 1942-
(poet, writer)
Born August 5, 1942, in Calif. *Principal occupation:* Poet, writer. *Address:* P.O. Box 163, McArthur, CA 96056 (530) 336-7307. *Past professional posts:* Steel worker (foundry), CA, 1976-90; transit driver, City of Livermore, CA, 1990-2001. *Membership:* Deer Clan of the United Lumbee Nation. *Interests:* Fishing, outdoor life, photographer. *Published work:* "Old Man River's Book of Poetry," 2004.

GORDON, NATHAN (Red Cliff Ojibwe)
(tribal vice chairperson)
Affiliation & Address: Vice Chairperson, Red Cliff Band of Lake Superior Chippewa Indians of Wisconsin, 88385 Pike Rd., Hwy. 13, Bayfield, WI 54814 (715) 779-3700.

GORDON, PATRICIA TRUDELL (Santee Sioux-Mdewakanton Band) 1943-
(foundation president)
Born August 24, 1943, Woodbury County, Iowa. *Education*: Morningside College, BA, 1977; Boalt Hall School of Law, University of California, Berkeley, JD, 1992. Principal Occupation: Executive Director, Indian Youth of America, Inc. *Address*: P.O. Box 2786, Sioux City, IA 51106 (712) 276-0794 (work). *Affiliations*: Camp Director, Indian Youth Camps in Oregon, Arizona, Idaho, and South Dakota, summer of 1976-90; assistant director, Indian Studies Program, Morningside College, 1977-84; Indian Student Advisor, Student Services, Morningside College, 1975-77; executive director, Indian Youth of America, Sioux City, Iowa, 1978-; president, George Bird Grinnell American Indian Children's Education Foundation, Dover Plains, NY, 1991-. *Community activities*: Iowa Supreme Court Commission on Continuing Legal Education (commissioner, 1984-89); Sioux City Human Rights Commission (commissioner & chairperson, 1982-89); United Way of Siouxland Agency Relations Committee (panel chair, 1981-86, board of directors, 1987-89); Native American Child Care Center, Sioux City, IA, (Co-founder & president, 1980-89; George Bird Grinnell American Indian Children's Educational Foundation, Dover Plains, NY, (co-founder & president, 1988-); Edwin Gould Foundation for Children, New York, NY (trustee & charter member, 1987-). *Memberships*: American Indian Law Students Association, 1989-91. *Awards, honors*: Participant for the Community International Fellows, a program of the International Leadership Development Institute; Robert F. Kennedy Memorial Fellow, 1977-80; Sertoma Service to Mankind Award, 1983; appointed, in 1984, by the Iowa Supreme Court to serve on the State Commission on Continuing Legal Education; Distinguished Alumni Award, Morningside College, 1987; Soroptimist International of Berkeley Award, 1991-92; recently completed an internship at the U.S. Senate Select Committee on Indian Affairs in Washington, D.C. where she reviewed & drafted legislation. *Interests*: "My main concern and interest at this time is working with Indian young people and improving their lives. I am also very interested in the law especially pertaining to American Indians. Women's issues will always be one of my concerns. My work has taken me throughout the U.S. giving lectures and presentations."

GORDON, ROXY (Choctaw)
(poet, writer)
Address: 5476 Oram, Dallas, TX 75206 (214) 827-9309.

GORMAN, GWENDA (Navajo-Dine')
(health promotion director)
Education: Arizona State University, BS (Family Studies & Human Development). *Affiliation & Address*: Health Promotion Director, Inter Tribal Council of Arizona, Inc. (ITCA), Phoenix, AZ. Her primary role in the Program is working with the tribes in Arizona to develop & implement culturally appropriate programs that address teen pregnancy, tobacco, and sexually transmitted infections in their communities. She has been working with ITCA since 2001. *Other professional posts*: Member, Arizona American Indian HIV/AIDS/STD Task Force; bpard member, National Native American HIV/AIDS Prevention Center and member of their Awareness Day committee.

GORMAN. ZONNIE M. (Navajo) 1963-
(historian/lecturer/consultant)
Born May 15, 1963. *Education*: University of Redlands (CA), 1981-82; University of Arizona, 1982-83; Navajo Community College, Spring 1984; University of New Mexico (Gallup), AA (Elementary Education), 1986, AA (Secondary Education, 1987); University of Arizona, BA, 1992. Website: www.zonniegorman.com. E-mail: admin@zonniegorman.com. Zonnie is a recognized historian on the Navajo Code Talkers of World War II. She is the daughter of Carl Gorman, one of the original Code Talkers, and sister to renowned artist, RC Gorman. She lectures at universities, colleges, museums and other institutions, including the Museum of the American Indian in Washington, DC. *Affiliation*: Program coordinator, Gallup Inter-Tribal Indian Ceremonial Association, Church Rock, NM, 1997-present. *Other professional posts*: Indian Country Tour Guide (self-employed) on Amtrak's Southwest Chief, round trips, Gallup-Albuquerque; Sundance Tours, Albuquerque, NM; two-day Navajo Reservation tour; Gallup (NM) Film Festival (associate producer, 1993, 1994; program coordinator, 1995, 1996, 1997). *Community activities*: 1996 UNM Gallup Ambassador, University of New Mexico-Gallup Campus. *Memberships*: Navajo Education & Scholarship Foundation, Window Rock, AZ (member, board of directors, 1995-present); *Awards, honors*: Certificate of Recognition for contribution to the success of Amtrak's Southwest Chief Enhancement Program during the year of introduction, 1985-86; Certificate of Recognition for Indian Country guide service, 1986-89, presented by the Inter-Tribal Indian Ceremonial Association; Award of Excellence, Student Art Exhibition of Northern Arizona, 1989; poetry awards, 1997. *Video*

produced: Co-produced, and main researcher for 16 minute video, "Navajo Code Talkers: The First Twenty-nine," 1992.

GOSHORN, SHAN (Eastern Band Cherokee)
(artist, studio owner)
Address: 1637 S. Delaware Ave., Tulsa, OK 74104 (918) 744-0698. *Products*: Hand-colored black-and-white photographs featuring contemporary native images; large abstract acrylic paintings; posters, note cards.

GOTTFREDSON, PHILLIP B.
(film producer & director)
Address & Affiliation: Owner/director, Black Hawk Productions, LLC, P.O. Box 63, Blachly, OR 97412 (801) 473-6697 Website: www.blackhawkproductions.com. E-mail: moreinfo@blackhawkproductions.com. Phillip began research on the history of the Native people of Utah in 2002. *Film produced*: The Black Hawk War: Utah's Forgotten Tragedy. *Published work*: Indian Depredations in Utah (Fenestra Books, 2002).

GOUDY, JoDe L. (Yakama)
(tribal chairperson)
Affiliation & Address: Chairperson, Yakama Nation, P.O. Box 151, Toppenish, WA 98948 (509) 865-5121.

GOULD, CORRINA (Ohlone)
(Title VII coordinator)
Affiliation & Address: Title VII Coordinator, American Indian Child Resource Center, 522 Grand Ave., Oakland, CA 94610 (510) 208-1870 ext. 319. E-mail: corrina@aicrc.org. Other professional posts: Corrina is also the co-founder and a lead organizer for Indian People Organizing for Change (IPOC), a small Native run organization that works on Indigenous people issues as well as sponsoring an annual Shellmound Peace Walk to bring about education & awareness of the desecration of the sacred sites in the greater Bay Area, 2005-09. She sits on the California Indigenous Environmental Association Board, the Board of Directors for the Oakland Street Academy Foundationn and is the treasurer for the Edes HOA.

GOULD, DRUSILLA (Shoshoni)
(instructor of American Indian studies)
Affiliation & Address: Senior lecturer, Native Language Instructor, American Indian Studies Program, Department of Anthropology, CB 8005, Pocatello, ID 83209 (208) 282-2629. E-mail: gouldrus@isu.edu. Drusilla is a Native Shoshoni speaker who teaches a two-year Shoshoni language curriculum & courses in Native craft traditions.

GOULD, JANICE (Maidu)
(poet, writer)
Address: 515 Fitzpatrick Rd., NW, Albuquerque, NM 87107 (505) 344-7570.

GOULD, MARK M. (Lenni-Lenape)
(tribal chairperson)
Affiliation & Address: Chairperson, Nanticoke Lenni-Lenape Indians of NJ, Inc., P.O. Box 544, Bridgeton, NJ 08302 (856) 455-6910.

GOULD, ROY (Micmac)
(publisher)
Affiliation: Micmac News, Nova Scotia Native Communications Society, P.O. Box 344, Sydney, Nova Scotia, Canada B1P 6H2 (902) 539-0045.

GOURNEAU, BOYD (Lower Brule Sioux)
(tribal chairperson)
Affiliation & Address: Chairperson, Lower Brule Sioux Tribe, P.O. Box 187, Lower Brule, SD 57548 (605) 473-8000. E-mail: chairman@lbst.org.

GOURNEAU, HAVEN (Assiniboine Sioux)
(Indian college president)
Born & raised on the Fort Peck Indian Reservation, Poplar, Mont. *Affiliation & Address*: President, Fort Peck Community College, P.O. Box 398, Poplar, MT 59255 (406) 768-5551 ext. 22. E-mail: hgourneau@fpcc.edu. Helen spent 24 years at FPCC as an administrative assistant, the financial aid director, a faculty member, and eventually as vice president of student services.

GOVER, DAVID L. (Pawnee/Choctaw)
(attorney)
Education: University of Oklahoma, BA, 1997, OU College of Law, JD, 2001. *Affiliation & Address*: Staff Attorney (2005-present), Native American Rights Fund, 1506 Broadway, Boulder, CO 80302 (303) 447-8760. E-mail: dgover@narf.org. David has worked in the areas of water rights, repatriation, Indian gaming, and tribal trust fund matters. Currently, he represents the Klamath Tribes in the Klamath Basin Adjudication. *Past professional posts*: Served as a contributing author to NARF''s publication, "A Practical Guide to the Indian Child Welfare Act"; served as an Assistant

Attorney General for the Muscogee (Creek) Nation and was primarily assigned the natural resource, environmental & water issues of the Nation; served as Legislative Counsel for the Navajo nation Council, 201-04; while attending OU College of Law, as an editor for the American Indian Law Review, an officer of the National & OU Native Ameican Law Student Associations, and clerked for the law firm of Hobbs, Straus, Dean & Walker.

GOVER, KEVIN (Pawnee/Comanche)
(museum director; professor of Indian law)

Education: Princeton University, BA (International Affairs), 1978; University of New Mexico School of Law, JD, 1981. *Affiliation*: Executive Director, National Museum of the American Indian, Fourth St. & Independence Ave. SW, Washington, DC 20560 (202) 633-6700. E-mail: kevin.gover@asu.edu. *Other professional post*: Professor (2002-present), Indian Law Program, Sandra Day O'Connor College of Law, Arizona State University, Tempe, AZ. Serves as a judge for the Tonto Apache Tribal Court of Appeals, and the San Carlos Apache Tribal Court of Appeals, and is on the governing boards of several non-profit educational institutions. *Past professional posts*: Assistant Secretary - Indian Affairs, Dept. of Interior, Bureau of Indian Affairs, Washington, DC, 1997-2002; practiced law with Steptoe & Johnson, where he headed the Indian Practice Group from 1997-2001; co-executive director, American Indian Policy Institute & an affiliate professor in the American Indian Studies program at ASU, Tempe, AZ. Professor Gover, in 1986, formed a law firm in New Mexico, which grew into one of the largest Indian-owned law firms in the country.

GOVER, MARSHALL (Pawnee)
(former tribal president)

Affiliation & Address: Pawnee Nation of Oklahoma, P.O. Box 470, Pawnee, OK 74058 (918) 762-3621. E-mail: mgover@pawneenation.org.

GOWAN, RAY
(editor/publisher)

Affiliation: Indian Books from the Four Winds, P.O. Box 3300, Rapid City, SD 57709 (605) 343-6064.

GRAHAM, JOE L.
(Indian program director)

Affiliation & Address: Director, American Indian Resource Program, University of California (UC), Irvine, 407 Social Science Tower, Irvine, CA 92697 (949) 824-6502. E-mail: jgraham1@uci.edu.

GRAHAM, ROSE (Navajo)
(tribal program director)

Education: Fort Lewis College, BA; Certified Navajo Court Interpreter. *Affiliation*: Director, Office of Navajo Nation Scholarship & Financial Assistance (ONNSFA), Department of Dine' Education, P.O. Box 670, Window Rock, AZ 86515 (928) 871-7475. graham9931@msn.com. *Other professional post*: Secretary-treasurer, Board of Directors, American Indian Graduate Center, Albuquerque, NM. *Past professional post*: Legislative Services Director, Legislative Advisor & Interpreter during Council sessions, Navajo Nation Council (9 years).

GRANDIA, LIZA
(associate director of Native American language center)

Affiliation & Address: Associate Director of Native American Language Center & Director of Indigenous Research Center of the Americas, Department of Native American Studies, University of California, One Shields Ave., 2401 Hart Hall, Davis, CA 95616 (530) 752-0357. E-mail: emgrandia@ucdavis.edu

GRANT, JAMES E. (Otoe-Missouria)
(tribal chairperson)

Address & Affiliation: Otoe-Missouia Tribe, 8151 Hwy. 77, Red Rock, OK 74651 (580) 723-4434.

GRANT, LANA SUE (Sac and Fox-Shawnee) 1942-
(library director & newspaper editor)

Born November 25, 1942, Pawnee, Okla. *Education*: El Reno Junior College, AA, 1968; University of Oklahoma, BS, 1970; University of Oklahoma, MLS, 1977. *Principal occupation*: Library director and newspaper editor. *Address*: 1401 Abbey Dr., Norman, OK 73071 (918) 968-3526 (office). *Affiliations*: Director, Sac and Fox National Public Library, and editor of the "Sac and Fox News", Route 2, Box 246, Stroud, OK 74079, 1982-.

GRANT, TED (Otoe-Missouria)
(tribal vice chairperson)

Affiliation & Address: Vice Chairperson, Otoe-Missouria Tribe, 8151 Hwy. 177, Red Rock, OK 74651 (580) 723-4466 ext. 107. E-mail: tgrant@omtribe.org

GRANT, VERNELDA J. (San Carlos Apache)
(tribal archaeologist)

Affiliation: Director, Historic Preservation & Archaeology, San Carlos Apache Tribe, P.O. Box 653, San Carlos, AZ 85550 (928) 475-2329. E-mail: apachevern@yahoo.com. *Membership*: Americans for Indian Opportunity. *Interest*: Cultural retention.

GRANT-JACKSON, MARLETTE (Hoopa-Yurok) 1968-
(resource coordinator & student services advisor)

Education: Humboldt State University, BA (Native American Studies), 2001. *Affiliation*: Resource Coordinator, 2001-) & Student Services Advisor, 2007-), ITEPP-CRC, Humboldt State University, 1 Harpst St., Brero House #93, Arcata, CA 95521 (707) 826-3672. E-mail: mmj5@humboldt.edu. ITEPP (Indian Teacher & Educational Personnel Program). CRC - Curriculum Research Center.

GRANT-KOTA, SHARON LEONA (Ojibwe) 1946-
(coordinator for Indian education)

Born December 16, 1946, St. Clair County, Mich. *Education*: Wayne State University, B.S., 1973. *Principal occupation*: Coordinator for Indian education. *Address*: 5315 Ravenswood Rd., Kimball, MI 48074 (810) 989-2727. *Affiliations*: Coordinator for Indian Education and assistant director of gifted & talented program, coordinates gifted & talented parent meeting, Destination Imagination & Chess Club, Quiz Bowl and gifted & talented Summer Enrichment School, Port Huron Area School District, Port Huron, MI, 1977-. *Other professional posts*: Indian Education Program, Grant Application Panelist - reader for American Indian Fellowships; reader for Discretionary Proposals. *Community activities*: Chair, American Indian Communities Leadership Council; board member, Southeastern Michigan Indian Center; chair, Michigan Indian Education Association; conference committee, St. Clair County Preschool Group; minority board, St. Clair County Community College; co-chair & treasurer, Blue Water Indian Powwow. *Memberships*: Michigan Association for the Education of Young Children; Blue Water Association for the Education of Young Children (newsletter chairperson); Blue Water Native American Indians; New Detroit, Inc. (race relations committee); Wayne State University Alumni Association. *Awards, honors*: Selected as Michigan Urban Delegate to White House Conference on Indian Education; scholarship recipient, North American Indian Association, 1971-73. *Interests*: "I coordinate a full-time Title IX Indian Education Program for eligible American Indian students. The main aspects of the program are cultural classes, tutoring, counseling & home visits. Conferences, career days, field trips, parent committee meetings and a monthly newsletter are also included in this position. Culture & self-determination are the program's major goals." Attend workshops. Other interests include sports, American Indian literature & professional readings, music, powwows and good friends.

GRAVELINE, FRYE JEAN (Metis Cree)
(professor of First Nations Studies)

Affiliation & Address: Professor, Department of Fist Nations Studies, University of Northern British Columbia, 3333 University Way, Prince George, BC V2N 4ZN Canada (250) 960-5239. Efrye.jeangraveline@unbc.ca. *Research Interests*: Healing through traditional methods: connection to ceremony, land, language, story, art, music & circle. *Published works*: Circle Works: Transforming Eurocentric Consciousness (Fernwood Books, 1998); Healing Wounded Harts: Stories I Tell to Teach (Fernwood Books, 2005),

GRAVELLE, TODD K. (Sault Ojibwe)
(attorney)

Education: Lake Superior State University, BS, 1997; University of Wisconsin, JD, 2000. *Affiliation*: Associate (2008-present), Fredericks Peebles & Morgan, LLP, 1900 Plaza Dr., Louisville, CO 80027 (303) 815-1704. E-mail: tgravelle@ndnlaw.com. *Practice areas*: Tribal economic development; Sovereignty & Self-Determination; Administrative & Gaming Law; Constitutional Law; Employment & Tribal Housing. *Past professional posts*: Staff attorney and Assistant Tribal Prosecutor & General Counsel, Sault Tribe of Chippewa Indians Legal Dept., 2000-2004; elected member, Sault Tribe of Chippewa Indians' Board of Directors, 2004-2008. *Military service*: U.S. Marine Corps (Embassy Security Guard for U.S. State Department American Embassy, Stockholm, Sweden and at the American Embassy in Ouagadougou, Burkina Faso. Later, while in college & law school, he served in the Michigan & Wisconsin National Guard as a Bridge Engineer and as a law clerk in the Wisconsin Army National Guard's Office of Staff Judge Advocate.

GRAVES, ALEX (Shoshone/Cherokee)
(senior program analyst; board president)

Affiliation & Address: Branch Chief, Firearms Division, Federal Law Enforcement Training Center, 1131 Chapel Crossing Rd., Glynco, GA 31524. *Other professional posts*: Board president, Native American Children's Alliance, Ceveland, OH; appointed as a Representative for Indian Country for the American Society for Law Enforcement Trainers (ASLET). *Past professional post*: Law Enforcement Training Specialist, Cangleska, Inc.;

special investigator for the Oglala Lakota Attorney General; detective, Hawaii County Police Department. *Military service*: U.S. Marine Corps (six years).

GRAY, GERALD (Little Shell Chippewa)
(tribal chairperson)
Affiliation & Address: Chairperson, Little Shell Tribe of Chippewa Indians of Montana, 625 Central Ave. W, Suite 100 • Great Falls, MT 59404 (406) 315-2400 Fax 315-2401 E-mail: ggray@gng.net

GRAY, GREGORY GRAYSON (*Mah-She-Hop-Pee*) (Osage) 1947-
(silversmith, business owner)
Born April 4, 1947, Muskogee, Okla. *Education*: Central State University (Edmond, OK), BA, 1991. *Address*: Unknown. *Affiliation*: Owner, Gray Deer Arts, Edmond, OK, 1990- (production & distribution of Native American recordings). *Other professional post*: State trooper, Oklahoma Highway Patrol (retired). *Military service*: U.S. Army Reserve, 1967-75 (Sergeant E-5; National Service Award and Certificate of Commendation for Outstanding Performance of Duty). *Community activities*: Civil Air Patrol; Little League Coach; Art Judge, 1991 Oklahoma Native American High School Art Competition; Red Earth Art Competition Committee, 1992. *Memberships*: Indian Arts & Crafts Assn; Gallup Inter-Tribal Assn; Celebrations of the American Indian, Ormand Beach, FL (board of directors). *Awards, honors*: Awards won: Tulsa Indian Art Festival; Indian Summer, Bartlesville, OK; Edmond (OK) Art Show; Canterbury Art Show, Edmond, OK; Okmulgee (OK) Indian Art Market; Chism Trail Art Show, Yukon, OK. *Interests*: "History of Indian jewelry, gems & stones used in jewelry & legends and lore of Native Americans. Due to the extensive traveling I have done in the past five years throughout the U.S., I have developed an insatiable desire to learn all that I can about my heritage." *Biographical source*: The Source Directory (Indian Arts & Crafts Board, U.S. Dept. of the Interior. *Published works*: Currently writing a book on the history of Southwest jewelry; completed a recording entitled, The History of Southwest Jewelry.

GRAY, JACQUELINE (Choctaw/Cherokee)
(research associate professor & director)
Education: University of Oklahoma, BS (Laboratory Technology), Med (Guidance & Counseling Psychology); Oklahoma State University, PhD (Applied Behavioral Studies with specialty in counseling psychology). *Affiliation & Address*: Research Associate Professor & Director of Indigenous Programs (2004-present), National Resource Center on Native American Aging, National Indigenous Elder Justice Initiative, Center for Rural Health & Department of Pathology, University of North Dakota School of Medicine & Health Sciences, Room 4535, 501 N. Columbia Rd. MS 9037, Grand Forks, ND 58202 (701) 777-3265. E-mail: Jacqueline.gray@med.und.edu. Jacque also directs the Native Research Halth Team and mentors more than 25 Native students on research inIndian Country. Past professional post: Provided conseling, assessment, and program development services through the Creek County Health Department in Oklahoma. She went to North Dakota in 1999 as a visiting professor in the UND Department of Counseling and in 2001 she became a post-doctoral fellow at the Grand Forks Human Nutrition Research Center of the USDA Agrcultural Research Service.

GRAY, JIM ROAN (Osage)
(former tribal principal chief)
Affiliation: Osage Nation of Oklahoma, P.O. Box 779, Pawhuska, OK 74056 (918) 287-5555. *Past professional post*: Co-publisher, Native American Times, Okmulgee, OK.

GRAY, JODY (Lakota-Irish)
(librarian; association board president)
Born on the Cheyenne River Sioux Reservation in S.D. *Education*: University of Wisconsin, MLIS. *Affiliation*: Diversity Outreach Librarian, University of Minnesota, Minneapolis, MN, 2010-present. *Past professional post*: Executive Director (2014-15), American Indian Library Association. Jody had helped to develop the blogs of the Multicultural Center for Academic Excellence (http://blog.lib. umn.edu/mcae/mcae).

GRAY, LYNNE CATHERINE (*Migizi Wi Quay & Ukchevwhoosh*) (Yaqui) 1951-
(television producer/director, president; business consultant)
Born August 21, 1951, Los Angeles, Calif. *Education*: Cypress College, AA, 1973; California State University, Long Beach, BA, 1982, Field Work/Internship, 1982, Gerontology Certificate, 1983, Basic Education/Social Science Credentials, 1989. *Principal occupation*: Television producer/director & president; business consultant. *Affiliations*: Veterinary manager, Bristol Veterinary Clinic, Santa Ana, CA, 1971-77; partner, franchise, L&W Service Co., Norwalk, CA, 1976-83; associate practitioner, Developmental Guidance Services, Inc., Long Beach, CA, 1984-89; assistant director, National Conference of Christians & Jews, Minneapolis, MN, 1990-92; Native American Television, St. Cloud, MN (television producer," First Americans Journal," 1991-; president, 1991-). *Professional activities*: Member, American Indian Media Image Task Force, 1990-; professional member, Women in Broadcast

Technology. Published works: "Broadcast Media: Indian Access & Careers," feature articles in Winds of Change, publication of the American Indian Science & Engineering Society, Summer 1991; managing editor, The American Indian & the Media, a publication of the American Indian Media Image Task Force, Jan. 1992. *Published works*: Stars in the Mouth (children's book).

GRAY, ROBERT (Pamunkey)
(tribal chief)
Affiliation & Address: Chief, Pamunkey Indian Tribe, 191 Lay Landing Rd., King William, VA 23086 (804) 843-2851.

GRAY-PROCTOR, MARGO (Osage)
(company president)
Education: Northeastern State University, Tahlequah, OK; Tuck School of Business, Dartmouth College. *Affiliation & Address*: President, Horizon Engineering Services Co., 1414-A East 71st St., Tulsa, OK 74136 (918) 663-0870. Margo consults with Tribes on transportation planning, gaming/casino developments, project management, research for environmental assessment, scheduling, bidding & negotiations, and construction phase of the project. She also provides coordination between the Tribe/Owner & design team. *Other professional post*: Chairperson, National Center for American Indian Enterprise Development, Mesa, AZ; board member, American Indian Business Network; board member, National Indian Gaming Assn; co-chair, Economic Development Sub-Committee for the National Congress of American Indians; member, Women Empowering Women for Indian Nations. *Community activities*: Board member (2006-present), Oklahoma Aquarium Board; Executive Women's Forum; American Indian Chamber of Commerce of Oklahoma (AICCO); Commissioner for the Oklahoma State Film & Music Advisory Board; Southern Plains Indian Housing Association; Pawnee Nation Academy Advisory Board; member, Oklahoma Federation of Indian Women; Tulsa Indian Arts Festival & Cultural Center, Advisory Board Member. *Memberships*: National American Indian Chamber of Commerce; National Indian Gaming Assn; National Congress of American Indians; American Indian Business Network; Women Impacting Public Policy (WIPP); Women Empowering Women for Indian Nations (WEWIN). *Awards, honors*: 2008 "Badger Award for Tenacity & Perseverance in Business" by the American Indian Business Leaders Assn; 2008 "Georgeann Robinson Humanitarian Award" from the Oklahoma Federation of Indian Women; 2007 State Business of the Year" Awarded by State Board of the IACCO; 2006 "Local Hero" Awarded by the Tulsa Metro Chamber for chairing the local planning committee for National Congress of American Indians annual conference.

GRAYSON, JOSEPH, JR. (Cherokee)
(tribal deputy principal chief)
Born & raised in Cherokee County, Okla. *Affiliation & Address*: Cherokee Nation of Oklahoma, P.O. Box 948, Tahlequah, OK 74465 (918) 453-5000 ext. 3999. E-mail: joe-grayson@cherokee.org. Mr. Grayson participates in Cherokee cultural activities, co-chairing the Cherokee National Holiday, the Tahlequah Public Schools Indian Parent Committee, & served as chairperson of the Cherokee United Way. In 2005, he was elected National Congress of American Indians' Vice President for Eastern Oklahoma. Also, he has volunteered for Help-in-Crisis and the Cherokee Heritage Center. *Military service*: U.S. Army (Vietnam Veteran). *Memberships*: Masonic Lodge; American Legion Post #50.

GRAYSON, MARY-CHARLOTTE (Cherokee)
(volunteer coordinator/artist services)
Education: Fort Lewis College, BS (Sociology); University of Oklahoma, MHR (Masters in Human & Cultural Relations). *Affiliation & Address*: Volunteer Coordinator/Artist Services, Southwestern Association for Indian Arts, P.O. Box 969, Santa Fe, NM 87504 (505) 983-5220. E-mail: mgrayson@swaia.org. *Past professional posts*: Collections Manager for the Cherokee National Museum & Cultural Center, and also working for Cherokee Nation Business Cultural Tourism Department in marketing & PR. While earning her Masters, she focused her research on Tribal Historic Preservation & Cultural Resource Management; exploring & documenting significant historical tribal sites..

GRAYUM, MICHAEL
(executive director)
Affiliation & Address: Executive Director, Northwest Indian Fisheries Commission, 6730 Martin Way E., Olympia, WA 98506 (360) 438-1180. E-mail: grayum@nwifc.org.

GREEN, CANDACE
(anthropologist)
Education: University of Oklahoma, PhD. *Principal occupation*: Anthropologist. *Address & Affiliation*: Specialist for North American Ethnology, Dept. of Anthropology, Smithsonian's National Museum of Natural History, NHB 112, Washington, DC 20560. *Interests*: Specializes in the art & culture of the Southern Plains. She has published widely on Kiowa and Cheyenne drawings. She is now directing a major project for the preservation of 20,000 pieces of

artwork in the National Anthropological Archives, including 2,700 Plains drawings. *Publication*: Silver Horn: Master Illustrator of the Kiowa (University of Oklahoma Press, 1999).

GREEN, EDMORE (Sac & Fox of Missouri)
(former tribal chairperson)
Affiliation & Address: Chairperson, Sac & Fox Nation of Missouri in Kansas & Nebraska, 305 N. Main St., Reserve, KS 66434 (785) 742-0053.

GREEN, GAIL L. (Wiyot)
(tribal chairperson)
Born & raised on the Table Bluff Rancheria. *Affiliation*: Chairperson, Wiyot Tribe of the Table Bluff Rancheria, 1000 Wiyot Dr., Loleta, CA 95551 (707) 733-5055. E-mail: gail@wiyot.us. *Past tribal posts*: Fiscal Dept.; staff member to the Enrollment Committee; headed up the construction project for new houses on reservation; Loleta School District; Loleta School Board member.

GREEN, JESS (Chickasaw) 1952-
(attorney)
Born Sept. 21, 1952, in Ada, Okla. Education: East Central University, BA, 1974; University of Oklahoma School of Law, JD, 1977. *Address*: 301 E. Main St., Ada, OK 74820 (405) 436-1946. *Affiliations*: Private-practice law firm in Ada, OK. *Past professional posts*: Chair, Chickasaw Tribal Legislature; eight years as a state court judge, tribal court prosecutor, tribal court judge & Chickasaw Nation Supreme Court Chief Justice. *Awards, honors*: Numerous awards & citations for his service to the Native American community; 2011 Inductee into the Chickasaw Nation Hall of Fame. *Memberships*: Oklahoma Bar Association (chairperson, Family Law Section; American Bar Association (Judiciary Committee Vice Chair, General Practice Section, 1995-96). *Community activities*: Pontotoc Co. March of Dimes Council, 1986-; National Organization for Victim Assistance Racial Minority Committee; Vice President of TELL, Child Abuse Prevention Organization.

GREEN, JOHN D. (Yurok)
(tribal councilmember)
Affiliation & Address: Councilmember, Elk Valley Tribal Council, P.O. Box 1042, Crescent City, CA 95531 (707) 464-4680. *Other professional post*: Intertribal Bison Cooperative (policy council).

GREEN, MICHAEL DAVID 1941-
(professor of American studies)
Born February 17, 1941, Cedar Rapids, IA. *Education*: Cornell College, BA, 1963; University of Iowa, MA, 1965, PhD, 1973. *Principal occupation*: Professor of American Studies. *Affiliation & Address*: Professor, Dept. of American Studies, CB #3195, Hamilton Hall, University of North Carolina, Chapel Hill, NC 27599. E-mail: mgreen@email.unc.edu. *Past professional posts*: Assistant professor, West Texas State University, 1970-74; assistant professor, 1977-83, associate professor, 1983-92, Dartmouth College. *Other professional post*: Fellow, D'Arcy McNickle Center for the History of the American Indian, The Newberry Library, Chicago, IL. *Memberships*: Western History Association; Organization of American Historians; American Society for Ethno-history (executive committee, 1985-87). *Research Interests*: Native American history, 18th & 19th century Creek history; the period between Creek removal and the establishment of the Creek constitutional government in 1867. *Published works*: The Creeks: A Critical Bibliography (University of Indiana Press, 1979); The Politics of Indian Removal: Creek Government and Society in Crisis (University of Nebraska Press, 1982); The Creeks: Indians of North America (Chelsea House, 1990).

GREEN, RAYNA (Cherokee) 1942-
(museum administrator/program manager)
Born July 18, 1942, Dallas, Tex. *Education*: Southern Methodist University, Dallas, BA, 1963, MA, 1966; Indiana University, Bloomington, Ph.D. (Folklore, American Studies), 1974. *Address*: 814 G St., SE, Washington, DC 20003 (202) 357-2071. *Affiliations*: Program director, American Association for the Advancement of Science, 1975-80; program director, Dartmouth College, Hanover, NH, 1980-83; planner, 1983-85, director, American Indian Program, National Museum of American History, 1985-, Smithsonian Institution, Washington, DC, 1983-. *Other professional posts*: Visiting professor, University of Massachusetts & Yale University; consultant to numerous federal agencies, tribes, tribal/Indian organizations, institutions, museums, & universities. *Community activities*: Ms. Foundation for Women (board member); Indian Law Resource Center, Fund for the Improvement of Post-Secondary Education (board member); Phelps-Stokes Fund (Indian advisory board); American Indian Society of Washington; American Indian Intertribal Cultural Organization. *Memberships*: American Folklore Society (president); American Engineering Society; Society for the Advancement of Native Americans & Chicano Scientists; American Anthropological Association. *Awards, honors*: Smithsonian Fellow, 1970; Ford Foundation, National Research Council Fellow, 1983; Distinguished Service Award, American Indian Society of

Washington. *Interests*: "American folklorist; research on Native American women; Southern women; American material culture; Indian traditional science, technology, & medicine; relations between Indians & museums; Indian energy/minerals development; poetry/short fiction; film/TV script writing; exhibit production." *Published works*: Native American Women: A Contextual Bibliography (Indiana University Press, 1982); That's What She Said: Contemporary Poetry and Fiction by Native American Women (Indiana University Press, 1984); Introduction to Pissing in the Snow: Other Ozark Folktales; Handicrafts in the Southern Highlands; articles & essays in Ms. Magazine, Southern Exposure, Science, Handbook of American Folklore, Handbook of North American Indians, and Signs.

GREENBERG, SHANA (Mono)
(attorney)
Affiliation & Address: U.S. Environmental Protection Agency, 7838 Mayfield Ave., Elkridge, MD 21075 (540) 295-4393. E-mail: greenberg.shana@epa.gov. *Other professional post*: Treasurer, National Native American Bar Association.

GREENE, AUSTIN, JR. . (Wasco)
(tribal chairperson)
Affiliation & Address: Chairperson, Confederated Tribes of the Warm Springs Reservation, 1233 Veterans St.., Warm Springs, OR 97761 (541) 553-1161. E-mail: agreene@wstribes.org

GREENE, BRUCE R.
(attorney)
Education: Uiversity of California, Berkeley, BS, 1964; University of California Hastings College of the Law, JD, 1967. *Affiliation & Address*: Founding Partner (2008-present), Law Offices of Bruce R. Greene & Associates, LLC, 1500 Tamarack Ave., Boulder, CO 80304 (303) 284-8654. E-mail: bgreene@greenelawyer.com. Bruce has specialized in all aspects of Federal Indian law and the representation of Native American Indian tribes for more than 40 years, with special emphasis on treaty rights and in all aspects of Indian gaming. *Past professional posts*: Native American Rights Fund, Boulder, CO (staff attorney, 1971-72); director, Indian Law Support Center, 1975-77; director, California Indian Legal Services, Oakland, CA, 1972-74; director of litigation, Navajo Nation Department of Justice, 1984-86; appointed as Federal Mediator by Hon. Robert H. Coyle, U.S. District Court, 1987-89; founder & managing partner, Greenne, Meyer & McElroy, PC, 1977-2008. *Awards, honors*: Awarded the Tecumseh Peacekeeping Awad by the State Bar of Michigan, for his lifetime achievements & dedicated service to protecting the rights of American Indians.

GREENE, EUGENE, JR. (Wasco)
(former tribal chairperson)
Affiliation & Address: Former Chairperson, Confederated Tribes of the Warm Springs Reservation, 1233 Veterans St.., Warm Springs, OR 97761; Agency District Representative.

GREENE, JEANIE (Upayok) (Inupiat Eskimo) 1951-
(president/CEO; television host, director, producer)
Born August 31, 1951, Sitka, Alaska. *Education*: University of Alaska, Anchorage, BA, 1990. *Principal occupation*: Television host, director, producer; president/CEO. *Affiliation*: President/CEO, Jeanie Greene Productions, Inc., Anchorage, AK (1992-present); executive producer, "Heartbeat Alaska", One Sky Productions, Anchorage, AK (907) 272-8111. *Memberships*: Native American Journalists Association; Alaska Press Club; Alaska Press Women. *Awards, honors*: Alaska Press Club Awards (1993-3rd Place, "Best Public Affairs"; 1994-2nd Place, "Best Feature Story," and 2nd Place, "Best Public Affairs' Citizen of the Year for 2010 by Alaska Federation of Natives' Board of Directors. *Interests*: "Heartbeat Alaska," focuses on the life and times of rural Alaska residents; "One Sky," which is a discussion style forum for rural issues, gets its name from the philosophy that all people are all members of the family of man and share the same hopes and dreams". Greene, an award-winning journalist and producer, distributes the show herself. "My professional research has focused on Alaska Natives, including topics related to pre-contact, historic & contemporary issues of the Tlingit & Haida, Aleut, Inupiat, Yupik, Athabascan & Tsimshian people."

GREENE, JEROME A.
(research historian, author-editor)
Affiliation: National Park Service, Denver, CO. *Published works*: Slim Buttes, 1876: An Episode of the Great Sioux War (University of Oklahoma Press); Battles & Skirmishes of the Great Sioux War, 1876-1877: The Military View (University of Oklahoma Press, 1993); Lakota & Cheyenne: Indian Views of the Great Sioux War, 1876-1877 (University of Oklahoma Press, 1994); Morning Star Dawn: The Powder River Expedition & the Northern Cheyenne, 1876 (University of Oklahoma Press, 2003); Washita: The U.S. Army & the Southern Cheyenne, 1867-1869 (University of Oklahoma Press, 2004).

GREENE, JUDITH (Seneca-Deer Clan) 1940-
(museum director)
Born January 2, 1940, Buffalo, N.Y. *Education*: Alfred University, BFA, 1984; University of Massachusetts at Dartmouth, MA, MFA, 1990. *Address & Affiliation*: Director, Seneca-Iroquois National Museum, Alleghany Indian Reservation, 794-814 Broad St., Salamanca, NY 14779 (716) 945-1738. *Other professional post*: Grant reviewer, New York State Foundation for the Arts. *Community activities*: Member, (Seneca Nation) Human Resource Oversight Committee, Higher Education Committee & the Bingo Advisory Committee.

GREENE, MARIE N. (*Kasannaaluk*) (Inupiaq Eskimo)
(Alaskan association president)
Born & raised in the Native Village of Deering, Alaska. Education: Masters degree in Rural Development. *Affiliation*: President & CEO, NANA Regional Corporation, Inc., P.O. Box 49, Kotzebue, AK 99752 (907) 442-3301. *Other professional posts*: Co-chair of the Northwest Arctic Workforce Development & Higher Education Consortium, and the Northwest Arctic Leadership Team (NWALT); an appointed member of the Alaska Redistricting Board.

GREENE, TIMOTHY J., SR. (Makah)
(former trbal chairperson)
Affiliation & Address: Former Chairperson, Makah Tribe, P.O. Box 115, Neah Bay, WA 98357 (360) 645-2201.

GREENE-SOTOMISH, SCHERRI (Nez Perce)
(marketing specialist, tribal board member)
Affiliation: Nez Perce Tribe Enterprise Board, Nez Perce Tribe, P.O. Box 161, Lapwai, ID 83540 (208) 843-5003. E-mail: riverrat@olynet.com. *Membership*: Americans for Indian Opportunity. Interests: Aquaculture, business.

GREENFEATHER, DON (Loyal Shawnee)
(tribal chairperson)
Address & Affiliation: Loyal Shawnee Tribe, P.O. Box 893, Tahlequah, OK 74465 (918) 456-0671 ext. 333.

GREENWOOD, BETH (Chickasaw)
(board vice president)
Affiliation: Vice President, Board of Directors, American Indian Chamber of Commerce of Texas (AICCT), 11245 Indian Trail, 2nd Fl., Dallas, TX 75229 (972) 241-6450. E-mail: bgreenwood@aicct.com. Website: www.aicct.com. *Other professional post*: President, The Greenwood Group.

GREENWOOD, MARGO (Cree)
(professor of First Nations Studies)
Affiliation & Address: Associate Professor, Department of First Nations Studies & Education, 3333 University Way, Admin 3060, Prince George, BC V2N 4Z9 Canada (250) 960-5239. E-mail: greenwom@unbc.ca. *Research Interests*: Structural impetus for the development & subsequent implementation of early childhood development programs & services in Canada; cross-cultural communication & children's transition from preschool to the formal education system.

GREETHAM, STEPHEN H.
(attorney; professor of American Indian law)
Affiliation & Address: Faculty, Center for the Study of American Indian Law & Policies, University of Oklahoma College of Law, 300 Timberdell Rd., Norman, OK 73019 (405) 325-4699. Stephen serves as Chief Counsel to the Chickasaw Nation Division of Commerce and as the Nation's Special Counsel on water & natural resources, where he works closely with tribal leadership in the management of complex litigation & resource protection & development strategies. *Past professional posts*: Partner with Nordhaus Law Firm in Albuquerque, where he served as water & general counsel to several American Indian tribes. He has taught Federal Indian tax, gaming, and water law at the University of New Mexico Law School & University of Oklahoma College of Law.

GREEVES, TERI (Kiowa-Comanche) 1970-
(beadwork artist)
Born in 1970 on the Wind River Reservation in Wyoming. *Education*: University of California, Santa Cruz, B.A., 1995. *Address*: Teri resides in Santa Fe, NM. *Artwork*: Greeves employs a variety of beadwork techniques in her art. She uses a loom for beaded bracelets. Her larger pictorial work involved beads stitched onto brain-tanned deerhide, which she often mounts onto wood or other structures. *Honors, awards*: Best of Show at the 1999 Indian Market; awards from the Heard Museum, Indian Market, and Eight Northern Pueblos Arts & Crafts Show. She was awarded the Eric & Barbara Dobkin Fellowship from the School of American Research in 2003. Her work is found in such public collections as the British Museum, Hear Museum, Montclair Art Museum, the Museum of Arts & Design, the Brooklyn Museum, the Denver Art Museum, the Haffenreffer Museum of Anthropology, the Hampton University Museum, the Joselyn Museum, the School of American Research, the National

Museum of the American Indian, the Museum of Fine Arts, Santa Fe, NM, and the Museum of Indian Arts & Culture. Teri is an enrolled member of the Kiowa Indian Tribe of Oklahoma.

GREGORY, ORVENA (Sac & Fox)
(former tribal 2nd chief)
Affiliation & Address: 2nd Chief, Sac & Fox Nation of Oklahoma, 920883 S. Hwy. 99 Bldg. A, Stroud, OK 74079 (918) 968-3526.

GRENIER, NICOLE
(Indian programs coordinator)
Affiliation & Address: Programs Coordinator, Harvard Project on American Indian Economic Development, Harvard University, 79 JFK St., Cambridge, MA 02138 (617) 495-1480. E-mail: Nicole_grenier@harvard.edu.

GRETZ, DAN (Anishinaabe)
(Indian college interim president)
Affiliation & Address: Interim President, Lac Courte Oreilles Ojibwa Community College, 13466 W. Trepania Rd., Hayward, WI 54843 (715) 634-4790. E-mail: dgretz@lco.edu.

GREYEYES, ALEX
(publisher; president of Indian centre)
Affiliation: Saskatchewan Indian, Saskatchewan Indian Media Corp., 2121 Airport Dr. #201A, Saskatoon, SK, Canada S7L 6W5 (306) 665-2175; Saskatchewan Indian Cultural Centre, Saskatoon.

GREYMORNING, STEPHEN (NEYOOOXET) (Arapaho)
(professor & co-chair of Native Ameriacn studies)
Education: University of Oklahoma, PhD (Political Anthropology), 1992. *Affiliation & Address*: Professor & Co-Chairperson, Dept. of Anthropology & Native American Studies, University of Montana, Soial Sciences 221, Native American Center 203F, Missoula, MT 59812 (406) 243-4409. E-mail: neyooxet.greymorning@ms0.umt.edu *Research interests*: Native American language maintenance & restoration, Indigenous sovereignty issues and contemporary Native American issues. *Past professional post*: From 1988 to 1992 he taught courses on Linguistics, Comparative Indian Legislation, & Aboriginal Self-Government at the University of Alberta in Canada; 1992-94, director of the Arapaho Language & Culture Project for the Wyoming Indian Schools. *Published work*: A Will to Survive: Indigenous Essays on the Politics of Culture, Language, & Identity (McGraw-Hill Pess, 2004); numerous articles.

GREYMOUNTAIN, MADELINE (Goshute)
(tribal vice chairperson)
Affiliation & Address: Vice Chairperson, Confederated Tribes of the Goshute Indian Reservation, P.O. Box 6104, Ibapah, UT 84034 (435) 234-1138. E-mail: mgreymountain@goshutetribe. com. *Past tribal post*: Chairperson & Administrator.

GRIBB, WILLIAM
(professor of geography & American Indian studies)
Affiliation & Address: Professor of Geography & American Indian Studies, Department of American Indian Studies, Arts & Sciences Bldg. 207, Laramie, WY 82071 (307) 766-3127. E-mail: planning@uwyo.edu. *Research Intersts*: Land Use & Natural Resource Management; American Indian Land Conflicts. Dr. Gribb's research has concentrated on the legal & spiritual definitions of land base and land use. *Interests*: The location & distribution of resources, and the management techniques used to utilize & conserve those resources within the cultural context of Native American heritage & spiritual perspectives.

GRIFFIN, BONNIE JO (Lenni Lenape)
(trbal assistant chief)
Affiliation & Address: Assistant Chief, Delaware Tribe of Indians, 170 NE Barbara, Bartlesville, OK 74006 (918) 337-6593. E-mail: bgriffin@delawaretribe.org

GRIJALVA, JAMES
(professor of law; project director)
Education: Northwestern School of Law of Lewis & Clark College, JD. *Affiliation & Address*: Lloyd & Ruth Friedman Professor of Law & Director, Tribal Environmental Law Project, University of North Dakota School of Law, Northern Plains Indian Law Center, 215 Centennial Dr. Stop 9003, Grand Forks, ND 58202 (701) 777-2104. E-mail: grijalva@law.und.edu. *Other professional post*: Summer Faculty, Vermont Law School. James writes & lectures on enviironmental law and federal Indian law, especially in the area of protection of the Indian country environment. *Past professional posts*: Clerkk to the Honorable Charles E. Wiggins of the U.S. Court of Appeals for the Ninth Circuit. He then practiced law in Seattle, Washington at Stoel Rives Boley Jones & Grey. Visiting lecturer at the University of Washington's Institute for Environmental Studies and a lecturer at the University of Puget Sound School of Law; a technical services contractor for the American Indian Environmental

Office of the U.S. EPA and an environmental law trainer for the EPA's Office of Environmental Justice. *Awards, honors*: Fulbright Scholar for Aboriginal Legal & Resource Rights at the University of Alberta in 2009. *Published works*: Tribal Sovereignty & Environmental Justice for Native America, in Tribes, Land & Environment (Ezra Rosser & Sarah Krakoff, eds., Ashgate Publishing, 2011; Closing the Circle: Emnvironmental Justice in Indian Country (Carolina Academic Press, 2008; numerous chapters in books, and articles in scholarly journals; Addresses & paper Presentationns

GRIM, CHARLES W., DR. (Cherokee of OK)
(dentist; former IHS director)
Education: University of Oklahoma, BS, DDS, 1983; University of Michigan, MMHSA (Health Services Administration), 1992; University of Oklahoma, College of Dentistry, D.D.S., 1983. *Affiliation & Address*: CEO, W.W. Hastings Indian Hospital, 100 S. Bliss Ave., Tahlequah, OK 74464 (918) 458-3100. *Past professional post*: Indian Health Service, Okmulgee, OK, 1983-89; director, Division of Oral Health in Albuquerque Area of IHS, 1992-95; director, Division of Clinical Services & Behavioral Health, Albuquerque Area Office of IHS, 1995-98; Assistant surgeon general and rear admiral in the Commissioned Corps of the U.S. Public Health Service; director, Indian Health Service (IHS), USD-HHS, 2003-07. *Awards, honors*: The first dentist to serve as director of the IHS; USPHS Commendation Medal (awarded twice), Achievement Medal (awarded twice), Citation, Unit Citation (awarded twice), & Outstanding Unit Citation; Outstanding Management & Superior Service awards by the Directors of three different IHS Areas; received the Jack D. Robertson Award, USPHS. *Memberships*: Society of American Indian Dentists; Commissioned Officers Association; American Association of Public Health Dentistry.

GRIMES, BARBARA FORNASERO (Cherokee) 1930-
(editor, bible translator, linguist)
Born August 19, 1930, San Diego, Calif. *Education*: Wheaton College, BA, 1952, Litt.D., 1993. *Address*: 84-664 Ala Mahiku, 191-B, Waianae, HI 96792 (808) 695-8402. Website: www.ethnologue.com. www.pidginbible.org. *Affiliations*: Summer Institute of Linguistics, 7500 W. Camp Wisdom Rd., Dallas, TX 75236 (member, 1951-; field investigator, Huichol language project, Mexico, 1952-67, 1979-80; field investigator, Hawaii Creole English (Pidgin) language project, 1987-). *Other professional post*: Editor, Ethnologue: Languages of the World, 1971-2000. *Awards, honors*: Scholastic Honor Society, Wheaton College. *Interests*: "Participated in linguistic workshops in 23 countries, from 2-6 months in each." *Published works*: Hawaiian Pidgin New Testament, with Joseph Grimes, 2000; numerous journal articles.

GRINDE, DONALD ANDREW, JR. (Yamasee) 1946-
(professor of American studies & history)
Born August 23, 1946, Savannah, Ga. *Education*: Georgia Southern College, Statesboro, BA, 1966; University of Delaware, MA, 1968, PhD (History), 1974. *Affiliation & Address*: Professor & Director of Graduate Studies, Dept. of Transnational Studies, Native American Studies Program, 732 Clemens Hall, Center for The Americas, SUNY Buffalo, Buffalo, NY 14260 (716) 645-2546 ext. 1217. E-mail: dgrinde@bufalo.edu. *Areas of specialization*: Native American Studies, Haudenosaunee/Iroquois history, Native American thought, U.S. Indian Policy since 1871, Environmental Studies and Native Americans, American Indian activism in the U.S. *Current Research*: Working on The Mission Indian Federation, 1920-1970 as well as a study of the ecological history of the Upper Susquehanna River Valley; collaborative work with the ecological scholars on Native American ecological perspective (National Science Foundation grant). *Other professional posts*: Editorial Board, American Indian Culture & Research Journal, 1990-present; Test Consultant, ACT (American College Testing), Iowa City, IA, 1994-present; historical & script consultant to WNED Public Television, "Iroquois Influence on American Government," 1998—2000; historical & script consultant with Jamie Redford for documentary entitled, "Native American Influences on American Society," 2010-present. *Past professional posts*: Assistant professor, Mercyhurst College, Erie, PA, 1971-73; assistant professor, SUNY at Buffalo, 1973-77; associate professor of history, California Polytechnic State University, San Luis Obispo, 1977-78, 1979-81, 1984-1998; visiting associate professor, UCLA, 1978-79; director, Native American Studies, University of Utah, Salt Lake City, 1981-84; professor of history & director of ALANA Studies at the University of Vermont, Burlington, VT; Instructor in Native American history, United Southeastern Tribes, Inc., and SUNY, College at Buffalo, Program for Indian Teacher Education at Allegany & Cattaraugus (Seneca) Reservations, 1974-75; Native American consultant, Buffalo City Schools, 1974-75; consultant, Smithsonian Institution, 1977; Native American consultant, Salt Lake City Schools, 1982-83; editor, Journal of Erie Studies, 1971-1973; editorial board, Indian Historian, 1976-. *Community activities*: Buffalo North American Indian Culture Center (corresponding secretary & board member, 1974-77); American Indian Historical Society (board member, 1976-); Central Coast Indian Council, Calif. (vice chairman, 1979-80); Salt Lake Indian Center (chairman of board, 1983-84). *Memberships*: National Indian Education Assn (member of Resolutions Committee, 1981-83); American Indian Historian's Assn (charter member); American Indian Historical Society; Organization of American

Historians (charter member); National Assn of American Indian Professors; American Indian Scholars Assn; Phi Alpha Theta; Smithsonian Institution. *Awards, honors*: Hagley Fellow, University of Delaware, 1966-70; Grant-in-Aid Scholar, Eleutherian Mills Historical Library, 1970-71; project historian & conservation consultant, Southern Railroad Restoration Project, National Park Service; Faculty Seed Grant, UCLA, American Indian Studies Center, 1978-79; Outstanding Professional Award (Education), 1984, from Wasatch Regional Minority Business and Professional Directory (Salt Lake City, Utah); Eugene Crawford Memorial Fellow, 1987-88; Rupert Costo Professor of American Indian History, University of California, Riverside, 1989-91; Co-PI, Western New York Stream Restoration, ERIE IGERT grant from National Science Foundation, 2007-2012;nco-principal investigator with Salish-Kootenai Tribal College from Kellogg Founation Research Project for Native American Curriculum Improvement, 2010-2013. *Interests*: American Indian history including: 20th century Indian policy, Native American science, American Indian political theory, history of American technology, museum administration; published testimony, "The Iroquois Roots of American Democracy," U.S. Senate Select Committee on Indian Affairs, Dec. 2, 1987. *Published works*: Has written over four dozen scholarly articles on American Indians; contributing editor, Readings in American History: Bicentennial Edition, II (Guilford, Conn., Dushkin Publishing, 1975); The Iroquois and the Founding of the American Indian (Indian Historian Press, 1977); Exemplar of Liberty: Native American and the Evolution of American Democracy, with Bruce E. Johansen (UCLA American Indian Studies, 1991); Exiles in the Land of the Free: Democracy, the Iroquois Nation and the U.S. Constitution, co-authored with Oren Lyons, John Mohawk, et al (Clearlight Publishers, 1992); The Unheard Voices: American Indian Responses to the Columbian Quincentennary, co-authored and co-edited with Carle Gentry (UC Press, 1994); Native America: Portrait of the Peoples, co-authored with Duane Champagne (Visible Ink Press, 1994); Ecocide of Native America, co-authored with Bruce Johansen (Clearlight Publishers, 1995; Co-author & editor, Encyclopedia of Native American Biography (Henry Holt, 1997, paper, Da Capo Press, 1998); Debaing Democracy: Native American Legacy of Freedom, with Bruce Johnsen & Barbara Mann (Clearlight Publishers, 1998); A Political History of Native Americans (CQ Press, 2002); The Mission Indian Federation, 1920-1970 (manuscript in progress).

GRINNELL, RANDY, M.P.H. (Sac & Fox Nation of Missouri)
(IHS former deputy director)
Education: East Central University, Ada, OK, BS (Environmental Science); University of Oklahoma Health Sciences Center, MPH. *Affiliation & Address*: Deputy Director (2006-12), Indian Health Service (IHS), DHH, The Reyes Bldg. 801 Thompson Ave., Suite 400, Rockville, MD 20852 (301) 443-1083. *Past professional posts*: Environmental Health Officer, Office of Environmental Health, Alaska, Albuquerque & Oklahoma Area Offices, Bureau of Indian Affairs, 1976-88; Assistant Director for Environmental Health & Engineering, 1988-92, 1998-2006; deputy Area Director, 1992-96; Acting Area Director, 1996-98. While serving as Acting Area Director, he provided overall management of clinical & administrative functions for a comprehensive health care system serving 300,000 American Indians & Alaska Natives in 44 tribes in Oklahoma, Kansas, & southern Texas. *Awards, honors*: HHH Secretary's Award for Distinguished Service, PHS Distinguished Service Medal, Meritorious Service Medal, two Outstanding Service Medals, Commendation Medal; numerous Service Awards.

GRINNELL, RICHIE K., RADM (Sac & Fox Nation of Missouri)
(IHS former deputy director)
Education: East Central University, Ada, OK, BS; University of Oklahoma Health Sciences Center, MPH. *Affiliation & Address*: Assistant Surgeon General & Deputy Director for Field Operations (20014-present), Indian Health Service (IHS), DHH, The Reyes Bldg. 801 Thompson Ave., Suite 400, Rockville, MD 20852 (301) 443-1083. *Past professional posts*: Served as the Area Director of the IHS Albuquerque Area Office, where he was responsible for providing leadership to 9 service units and 27 Pueblos and Tribes in New Mexico, Colorado, and Texas. During his career with the IHS, RADM Grinnell served field assignments as an environmental health sanitarian at Service Units in Oklahoma, Colorado, and New Mexico. He completed several management assignments with the IHS Albuquerque Area Office as the District Sanitarian; Director of the Division of Environmental Health; Associate Director, Office of Environmental Health and Engineering; Acting Area Executive Officer; and Acting Area Director. Starting in 1999, he served in the IHS Nashville Area as the Associate Director, Office of Environmental Health and Engineering. He also served as Acting Area Executive Officer and Acting Area Director while in Nashville before becoming the permanent Area Director in early 2004. Awards, honors: Received several public health service honors and awards, including an Exceptional Capability Promotion to Captain, the Outstanding Service Medal, two Commendation Medals, two Achievement Medals, one Citation, an Outstanding Unit Citation, three Unit Commendations, and the Crisis Response Service Award. He received the 2007 Flag Officer Award from the American Indian Alaska Native Commissioned Officer Advisory Committee for his continuous record of outstanding leadership.

GRISWOLD, THEODORE J.
(attorney-Native American law)
Education: San Diego State University, BS, 1985, MS, 1987; University of San Diego School of Law, JD, 1992. *Affiliation & Address*: Partner, Procopio, Cory, Hargreaves & Savitch LLP, 525 B St., Suite 2200, San Diego, CA 92101 (619) 515-3277 E-mail: ted.griswold@procopio.com. Mr. Griswold has counseled clients on Native American governance, intergovernmental agreements, natural & cultural resources, wetlands, habitat, environmental and land use matters. As the Chair of the Native American team, Ted's practice focuses on Native American governments & tribal land issues including self determination compacts and contracts, fee to trust applications, land and natural resource planning, tribal code and ordinance development, leasing, tribal property clean up, federal permitting, water supply development and protection, water quality, stormwater plans, and tribal cultural resource protections & policies. He regularly assists Tribal, public agency & private clients in negotiating & receiving permit approvals from all permitting agencies, including Tribal Governments, Bureau of Indian Affairs, California Dept. of Transportation, US Army Corps of Engineers, US Fish & Wildlife Service, US Environmental Protection Agency, California Regional Water Quality Control Board, California Department of Fish & Wildlife, California Coastal Commission & various municipalities. *Communty activities*: California Indian Legal Services – Pro Bono Co-Counsel Maataam NakaShin – Pro Bono Counsel American Indian Recruitment Program – Board Member Native American Environmental Protection Coalition – Pro Bono Counsel Ocean Discovery Institute – Board of Directors, Living Lab Design & Construction Committee Chair San Diego State University – College of Sciences Dean's Corporate Advisory Board Studio Earth Alliance (SEA) – Founding Member Tribal Tax Consortium (Development of multi-tribal think tank to discuss the interplay between tribal sovereignty and state and local taxing authority) American Bar Association – Native American Resources Committee. *Publications*: Editor & contributor. Blogging Circle. Creator & Producer. Indigenous San Diego mobile application, in partnership with the Southern California Tribal Chairmen's Association and Mataam Naka Shin, for the National Congress of American Indians 2015 Conference and Marketplace, San Diego, CA, October 18-23, 2015. Co-author. "AB 52: Protections for Native American culture," Daily Journal, January 21, 2015. Co-author with Eric D. Swenson. "The Internal Revenue Service Issues Important Final Guidance on the Application of the General Welfare Exclusion to Certain Tribal Government Programs," July 2, 2014. Co-author. "Possible Tax Benefits Relating to the Lease of Native American Tribal Land - An Important Clarification for All Parties Subject to a Lease on Tribal Land," January 16, 2014. Co-author with Andrea N. Jones in "Clarification Needed in the Affordable Care Act's 'Play or Pay' Rule & its Effect on Tribal Businesses," Indian Country Today Media Network, June 6, 2013. Numerous seminars on Native American issues.

GROBSMITH, ELIZABETH S. (*Anpo wicahpi*) 1946-
(Provost & vice president academic affairs; professor of anthropology)
Born May 27, 1946, Brooklyn, N.Y. *Education*: Ohio State University, BMus, 1968; University of Arizona, MA, 1970, PhD (Anthropology), 1976. *Affiliation & Address*: Provost & Vice President for Academic Affairs, (2002-present) Professor of Anthropology, Northern Arizona University, P.O. Box 4120, Flagstaff, AZ 86011 (928) 523-2230. E-mail: liz.grobsmith@nau.edu. *Past professional posts*: Dept. of Anthropology, University of Nebraska, Lincoln, NE (instructor & professor of anthropology, 1975-96); Assistant Vice Chancellor for Academic Affairs, Office of Academic Affairs, University of Nebraska, Lincoln, NE, 1991-96; Dean, College of Arts & Sciences, University of Colorado, 1996-2001. *Other professional posts*: Consultant, Association on American Indian Affairs, 1984-85; consultant, Indian Club, Nebraska State Penitentiary, and American Anthropological Association lecture series. *Memberships*: Plains Anthropological Society (board of directors, 1979-81; vice president, 1980-81); American Anthropological Association; University of Nebraska Graduate Faculty; Sigma Delta, Iota Chapter (Graduate Women's Scientific Fraternity); Association on American Indian Affairs; Society for Applied Anthropology. *Interests*: "My major professional interests are in studying & working with American Indian communities, with specific interests in helping them to design strategies & programs which alleviate reservation problems, be they juvenile justice concerns, alcoholism, curriculum development, legal or economic. When possible, I enjoy traveling to observe indigenous peoples to achieve a better understanding of native cultures (e.g. Alaska, Guatemala). Interested in Indian prisoners and their struggle to obtain religious freedom rights behind the walls. Serve as consultant/expert witness in numerous court cases involving Indian prisoners' efforts to practice their native culture and religion despite their incarceration. Served as expert witness for Northern Ponca tribal restoration, 1990. (I) Enjoy travel, particularly in Indian country and especially in Southwest U.S. Hobbies: choral music." *Published works*: Books: Lakota of the Rosebud, A Contemporary Ethnography (Holt, Rinehart & Winston, 1981); Indians in Prison: A Study of Incarcerated Native Americans in Nebraska (University of Nebraska Press, 1994). Chapters in books: "The Plains Culture Area", chapter in Native North Americans: An Ethno-historical Approach, edited by Daniel Boxberger (Kendall/Hunt, 1990); "Indian Prisoners", to appear in Encyclopedia on Native Americans in the 20th Century, Museum of the American Indian

(Garland, 1992). Articles: "The Relationship Between Substance Abuse and Crime Among Native Americans in the Nebraska Department of Corrections", Human Organization, Vol. 48, No. 4, Winter 1989; "The Impact of Litigation on the Religious Revitalization of Native American Inmates in the Nebraska Department of Corrections", Plains Anthropologist, Vol. 34, No. 124, Part I, 1989; "The Revolving Door: Substance Abuse Treatment & Criminal Sanctions for Native American Offenders", co-authored with Jennifer Dam, Journal of Substance Abuse, Vol. 2, No. 4, 1990; "Termination & Restoration of American Indian Tribes: The Northern Ponca Case", with Beth R. Ritter, Human Organization, Spring, 1992; "Inmates & Anthropologists: The Impact of Advocacy on the Expression of Native American Culture in Prison", High Plains Applied Anthropologist, Vol. II, No. 1, Spring, 1992; numerous book reviews.

GROENIG, NADINE (Laguna Pueblo)
(director of Indian education)
Education: Arizona State University, BA, 2001. *Affiliation & Address*: Director of Indian Education (2015-present), Office of Indian Education, Arizona State Department of Education, 1535 W. Jefferson, Phoenix, AZ 85007 (602) 542-5235. E-mail: Nadine.groenig@azed.gov. In her new role, Groenig will collaborate with Superintendent Douglas' Native American Education Action Committee to address issues affecting Native students. She will also help lead the Committee's efforts to integrate Native culture and history across academic subjects so that all Arizona children can develop an appreciation for their fellow students' unique backgrounds. *Past professional post*: Founder & CEO, Southwestern Institute for the Education of Native Americans (SIENA), 2007-15. *Community service*: She has served on the Committee for the National Forum on Dropout Prevention for Native and Tribal Communities, the American Indian Advisory Committee for the Heard Museum and various other committees and organizations related to Native American issues. She is also a member of the National Indian Education Association. "My vision for Arizona's Native American students is that they be well-educated, healthy, confident individuals with a strong sense of cultural identity, self-worth and the belief that their goals and dreams are attainable. By working closely with the Native American community, I believe we can help make that vision a reality."

GROUNDS, RICHARD A. (Yuchi)
(assistant professor)
Education: Princeton University, PhD (History of Religions). *Address & Affiliation*: Assistant Professor of Anthropology, University of Tulsa, Tulsa, OK 74104. *Other professional post*: Vice Chairperson, Cultural Survival's Program Council, Cambridge, MA., 2005-present; director, Euchee Langauge Project.

GROVE, DONALD
(attorney)
Education: University of Maryland, BS, 1993; American University, Washington College of Law, JD, 1997. *Address & Affiliation*: Managing Partner, Nordhaus Law Firm, LLP, 1401 K St. NW, Suite 801, Washington, DC 20005 (202) 530-1270. *Practice areas*: Co-chair of the Court of Federal Claims Bar Association's Indian Law Committee & Rules Committee; Mr. Grove represents tribal clients in timber management, tribal recognition, and legislative matters.

GRUBBE, JEFF L. (Agua Caliente Cahuilla)
(tribal chairperson)
Education: Haskell Indian Nations University, AA; University of Redlands, BA (Information Systems). *Affiliation & Address*: Chairperson, Agua Caliente Band of Cahuilla Indians, 5401 Dinah Shore Dr., Palm Springs, CA 92264 (760) 699-6800. *Other professional post*: Agua Caliente Development Authority (ACDA), (2003-present). He continues to serve as the Tribal Council Liaison. *Past professional posts*: Agua Caliente Resort & Spa tribal intern program where he worked in the casino as a table games shift manager; member, Agua Caliente Child Development Committee, Election Board, Gaming Commission, and Tribal Building Committee. *Honors & awards*: Recognized with a 40 Under 40 Award from The National Center for American Indian Enterprise Development. In addition, he was also recognized by Palm Springs Life Magazine with a 40 Under 40 Award for distinguished young professionals contributing to the success of the Coachella Valley.

GRUENIG, ROBERT
(attorney)
Education: Western Illinois University, BA & MA (Political Science); Governors State University (Master of Science in Environmental Biology), Southern Illinois University School of Law, JD; Master of Laws in Environmental Law, *magna cum laude*, from Vermont Law School. *Affiliation & Address*: Stetson & Jordan, P.C., 1305 Rio Grande Blvd. NW, Albuquerque, NM 87104 (505) 256-4911. E-mail: bgruenig@stetsonlaw.com. Bob has worked closely with Indian tribes since 2000, having been first employed by the Indian Country Environmental Justice Clinic at Vermont Law School & focusing on such matters as tribal water quality standards & solid waste issues. He subsequently joined the National Tribal Environmental Council (NTEC) in 2002 where he served the next nine years in a number of capacities including Air Program Director, Interim Executive Director and Senior Policy Analyst. In this latter position, Bob

provided legal, policy & technical support to tribes on a number of environmental and natural resources issues, with a particular focus on air quality, chemical & pesticide management. As part of these efforts, Bob regularly prepared policy materials & briefing documents, and also drafted comment letters on a number of administrative & legislative actions impacting Indian tribes. In addition, Bob spent a considerable amount of his time on climate change matters, working closely with members of Congress to improve domestic legislation to the benefit of tribes, & also actively engaging in international climate treaty negotiations on related matters. Bob has been a frequent speaker and writer on tribal environmental & natural resource issues. In addition to the many conferences and workshops to which Bob has been invited to speak, he has also served as a course instructor for the United States Environmental Protection Agency (EPA), Falmouth Institute, Law Seminars Int'l., & Rocky Mountain Mineral Law Foundation. Complementing these speaking engagements have been Bob's regular written contributions on a myriad of environmental issues facing Indian tribes, with such contributions made to weekly, monthly and quarterly publications. Bob has also served on a number of boards and committees in support of Indian tribes such as the Board of Directors for the Indian Law Section of the State Bar of New Mexico; the Native Dispute Resolution Network as a Provider in conjunction with the U.S. Institute for Environmental Conflict Resolution; the EPA's National Advisory Council for Environmental Policy and Technology, and the Agency's Clean Air Act Advisory Committee's Advanced Coal Technology Work Group; the Department of Energy's Transportation External Coordination Working Group; the Tribal Pesticide Program Council; and the Steering Committee for the Tribal Air Monitoring Support Center. Bob also currently serves as a Vice Chair for the Native American Resources Committee of the American Bar Association's Section on Environment, Energy, and Resources Committee, as well as a member of the Board of Directors for the Natural Resources, Energy and Environmental Law Section of the State Bar of New Mexico.

GRUMBLY, FRANCES (Mohawk)
(acting executive director)
Affiliation & Address: Acting Executive Director, American Indian Community House, 134 W. 29th St., 4th Fl., New York, NY 10001 (646) 357-6761.

GRUMMER, BRENDA KENNEDY (Citizen Band Potawatomi)
(professional artist)
Born in El Reno, Okla. *Address*: 11105 Coachman's Rd., Yukon, OK 73099. *Affiliation*: Grummer Art Studio, Yukon, OK, 1980-. *Memberships*: National League of American Pen Women; National Cowboy Hall of Fame; American Indian Arts & Crafts Assn. *Awards, honors*: Grand Award, Philbrook National Indian Artists Exhibition; First Place painting awards at Trail of Tears National Exhibition & Gallup Inter-Tribal Ceremonial; shown at Kennedy Center, Smithsonian Institution; Franco-American Union, Rennes, France, dozens of museums shows & awards. *Interests*: Professional writer as well as artist. *Biographical sources*: Mentioned in articles in "Southwest Art," "Art of the West," "Oklahoma Today," "Oklahoma Home and Garden."

GUEDEL, W. GREGORY
(attorney)
Affiliation & Address: Chair, Native American Practice, Foster Pepper LLP, 1111 Third Ave., Suite 3400, Seattle, WA 98101 (206) 447-8931. E-mail: guedw@foster.com. His litigation work includes all aspects of pre-trial, trial and appellate case management in state, federal and Tribal courts. He provides his clients with analysis, preparation, negotiation and resolution of contract claims, and drafts and interprets multi-party contracts. He regularly assists clients with business and construction planning and management, serving government, private and Tribal entities. Greg also serves as Editor of Foster Pepper's Native American legal blog: www.nativelegalupdate.com. *Activities*: National Chair for Native American Concerns, American Bar Association, 2010-present.

GUENTHER, JERRY D.
(attorney)
Education: University of Montana, BS, 1972; Washington State University, BS, 1977; University of Idaho, MS, 1978; University of Montana Law School, JD, 1981. *Affiliation & Address*: Assistant Attorney General (2008-present), Yavapai-Apache Nation, 2400 W. Datsi St., Camp Verde, AZ 85941 (928) 567-3649. *Other professional post*: Adjunct Faculty, The Falmouth Institute, Fairfax, VA. *Past professional posts*: In-House Counsel, Salt River Pima-Maricopa Indian Community, 2007-08. Jerry has more than 30 years of legal practice, serving as legal counsel for individuals & numerous tribal organizations. His Native American law practice has focused on matters involving contracts, contract & subcontract administration, procurement, economic development, natural resource law, tribal enterprise law gaming law & Native American government law.

GUERRERO, BRITTA (San Carlos Apache)
(chief executive officer)
Affiliation & Address: Chief Executive Officer, California Native Health Center, 2020 J St., Sacramento, CA 95811 (916) 341-0576 ext. 2205.

GUERRERO, JOYCE (Prairie Band Potawatomi)
(tribal vice chairperson)
Affiliation & Address: Vice Chair, Prairie Band Potawatomi Indian Tribe, 16281 Q Rd., Mayetta, KS 66509 (785) 966-4007. E-mail: lianao@pbpnation. org.

GUILLORY, JUSTIN P. (Nez Perce)
(tribal college president)
Education: Eastern Washington University, BA; Washington State University, MA (Educational Administration, 2000, PhD (Higher Education Administration), 2008. *Affiliation & Address*: President (2012-preent), Northwest Indian College, 2522 Kwina Rd., Bellingham, WA 98226 (360) 392-2772. Justin was appointed president after serving more than five years as NWIC's Dean of Academics & Distance Learning & Den of Extended Campus Sites. *Past professional posts*: Justin's previous professional experience includes serving as the Site Manager for the NWIC-Nez Perce Extended Campus site on the Nez Perce reservation in Lapwai, Idaho, and as the graduate assistant/mentor program coordinator for the Native American Student Center within the Office of Multicultural Student Services at Washington State University.

GUITIEREZ, BRANDON (Paiute)
(former tribal chairperson)
Brandon was born & raised in Susanville, California. His childhood was spent on the Lower & Upper Rancheria. *Affiliation & Address*: Former chairperson, Susanville Indian Rancheria, 745 Joaquin St., Susanville, CA 96130 (530) 257-4923. *Military service*: U.S. Marine Corps in 1998-2002. He earned various awards, commendations, & non-combat decorations. He achieved the rank of Sergeant, In 2003, Brandon enlisted in the United States Navy and served as an F/A-18 Plane Captain with Strike Fighter Squadron 81. In 2005 he was stationed aboard the USS Harry S. Truman CVN-75 as a Personnel Specialist. Brandon was honorably discharged from the Navy in 2007. After returning home to California, Brandon worked for the North Fork Rancheria of Mono Indians as a Maintenance Worker, Housing Specialist, and TANF Youth Coordinator. In 2010, Brandon returned home and served his community as a Legal Assistant to the Lassen County District Attorney's Office. In 2012, Brandon began work at the Lassen Indian Health Center where he worked in the Front Office and then as a Contract Health Specialist.

GUNN, BRIAN (Colville)
(attorney)
Address & Affiliation: Dorsey & Whitney LLP, 1001 Pennsylvania Ave., NW, Suite 300 South, Washington, DC 20004 (202) 824-8863. E-mail: gunn.brian@ dorseylaw.com. Associate attorney since 1999. Practice is in the areas of Federal Indian law and general litigation.

GURLEY, RON (Cherokee)
(consultant, education)
Education: BA (Education); MEd. *Affiliation & Address*: President, Gurley & Associates LLC. Website: www.rongurley.com. E-mail: rongurley@sbcglobal.et or ron@rongurley.com. (918) 884-8622. He is in his 46th year working with Native American families and youth. During his 22 years in public education he served as a Music Teacher, Indian Education Reading and Math Teacher, Counselor, Assistant Superintendent, Director of Curriculum, Special Education & Transportation & served as Superintendent of Schools. Following his career in education, four & one-half years were spent as a Case Manager Supervisor in a newly created Social Services Department within the Housing Authority of the Cherokee Nation. Ron served as founder & Chief Professional Officer of Boys & Girls Clubs of Green Country, Inc. located within the Cherokee Nation from 1997 to 2007. He served as Chairman of Boys & Girls Clubs of America's Native American National Advisory Committee (NANAC). Special recognitions include BGCA's Masters and Mentors Level of the Academy of Boys & Girls Clubs Professionals. For five years Ron served as the Projects Manager, Native American Program Specialist, FirstPic, Consulting. His work included Child Abduction Response Team Training, Internet Crimes Against Children & AMBER Alert in Indian Country training. Also Office of Justice Programs Boys & Girls Clubs of America Funding Initiative for Boys & Girls Clubs in Indian Country, Bureau of Justice's Methamphetamine Law Enforcement and Community Education Technical Assistance as well as Law Enforcement Investigative Technique Training. Ron also has experience in HUD's Office of Native American Program Training and Technical Assistance for Tribal Community Youth Programs. Ron teaches webinars for the Native Learning Center, Seminole Tribe of Florida and is consultant to the US Department of Justice AMBER Alert Training & Technical Assistance Program, where he acts as one of the national Liaison for Training & Technical Assistance to the AMBER Alert initiative for Indian Country. This is in conjunction with Fox Valley Technical College's National Criminal Justice Training Center.

GURNOE-SOULIER, ROSE (Red Cliff Ojibwe)
(former tribal chairperson)
Affiliation & Address: Red Cliff Band of Lake Superior Chippewa Indians of Wisconsin, 88385 Pike Rd., Hwy. 13, Bayfield, WI 54814 (715) 779-3700.

GUS, LARRY (Hopi-Navajo) 1954-
(photographer)
Born August 12, 1954, Keams Canyon, Ariz. *Education*: California Institute of the Arts (two years). *Principal occupation*: Photographer (self-employed). Resides in Los Angeles, Calif. *Memberships*: Native American Journalists Assn; Native Indian/Inuit Photographer's Assn; National Press Photographer's Assn; Advertising Photographers of America (APA) Crew Director, 1992/17th Ed.; ATLATL; Committee to Protect Journalists. *Awards, honors*: Finalist-Western Region-Leica Medal of Excellence, 1987. *Interests*: News photographer. "I try to photograph Indian people as they are in everyday life, not the way foreigners have convinced themselves that Indians should look & behave. As a photojournalist, my responsibility & obligation will remain with the subject being photographed--not with any organization or individual that has hired my services or expects me to produce images for their use and/or viewing."

GUSS, MARY E. (Pima-Maricopa)
(attorney)
Education: Reed College, BA (Philosophy), 1973; Lewis & Clark College, JD, 1976; University of Arizona, LLM (Indigenous Peoples Law & Policy), 2009. *Affiliation & Address*: Staff Attorney/Clinical Instructor, Native Peoples Technical Assistance Office, University of Arizona Law School, IPLP Program, Tucson, AZ. (520) 626-0236. E-mail: mguss@email.arizona.edu. *Past professional posts*: Owner, Law Office of Mary E. Guss, 1991-2008, Anchorage, AK; U.S. Magistrate Judge, U.S. District Court for the District of Alaska, 2000-08; Her current work is as staff attorney for the IPLP program & coordinator for University of Arizona NativeNet, and as an appellate judge for the Yavapai Apache Nation.

GUSTAFSON, CHARLES
(BIA education coordinator)
Affiliation: Aberdeen Area Office, Bureau of Indian Affairs, 115 4th Ave., SE, Federal Bldg., Aberdeen, SD 57401 (605) 226-7416. *Other professional posts*: Education coordinator, Fort Berthold Agency, New Town, ND, and Standing Rock Agency, Fort Yates, SD.

GUTIERREZ, DOROTHY (Navajo)
(craftsperson)
Address: P.O. Box 1441, Espanola, NM 87532 (505) 753-2890. *Products*: Pottery animals, mudheads, storytellers, mudhead storyteller, nativity sets.

GUY, ANDREW (Yup'ik Eskimo)
(corporation president & CEO)
Born & raised in Napaskiak, Alaska. *Education*: University of Alaska, Fairbanks, BS (Business Administration); University of Colorado School of Law, JD. *Affiliation & Address*: President & CEO (2010-present), Calista Corporation, 301 Calista Ct., Suite A, Anchorage, AK 99518 (907) 279-5516. He was General Counsel for the Corporation before being promoted to President & CEO. *Past professional post*: Vice President, Board of Directors, Yulista Management Services.

GUY, CARLA (Caddo)
(tribal vice chairperson)
Affiliation & Address: Vice Chairperson, Caddo Nation, P.O. Box 487, Binger, OK 73009 (405) 656-2344. E-mail: cguy@caddonation.org

GUY, ELMER (Navajo/Dine')
(Indian college president)
Education: University of Arizona, BA (Special Education), PhD (Rehabilitation); University of San Francisco, MRA (Rehabilitation Administration). *Affiliation & Address*: President, Navajo Technical College, P.O. Box 849, Crownpoint, NM 87313 (505) 786-4112. E-mail: eguy@navajotech.edu. *Other professional post*: Vice chairperson, American Indian College Fund, Denver, CO.

GUY, LYMON (Kiowa Apache)
(tribal chairperson)
Affiliation & Address: Chairperson, The Apache Tribe of Oklahoma, P.O. Box 1330, Anadarko, OK 73005 (405) 247-9493E-mail: chairman@apachetribe.org

GUZMAN, KATHLEEN R.
(attorney; associate dean; professor of law)
Education: University of Arkansas, JD; Law School; Yale Law School, LL.M. *Affiliation & Address*: Associate Dean for Academics, MAPCO/Williams Presidential Professor of Law, University of Oklahoma Law School, Center for the Study of American Indian Law & Policy, 300 Timberdell Rd., Norman, OK 73019. E-mail: kguzman@ou.edu. Kathleen teaches Property, Indian Land Titles & Wills & Trusts. She has researched the interplay between federal land consolidation policies & individual allotments, resulting in a published article in the Iowa Land Review (2000) entitled "Give & Take an Acre: Propety Norms and the Indian Land Consolidation Act."

GYORDA, LISA (Oglala Lakota)
(IHS director, Office of Human Resources)
University of Maryland, BS (Business & Management). *Affiliation & Address*: Acting Director, Office of Human Resources (OHR), Indian Health Service (IHS), DHH, 801 Thompson Ave., Rockville, MD 20852 (301) 443-1083. As the Director of OHR, Ms. Gyorda is responsible for providing strategic guidance & leadership for all aspects of the human resources function and establishing a vision and direction for the full complement of core human capital programs, policies and services. This includes providing leadership and direction in the development of HR policies that promote maximum effectiveness in the IHS workforce while supporting the IHS mission. Ms. Gyorda advises the IHS Principal Deputy Director and other senior agency officials on human capital management in support of the implementation and execution of key agency programs. *Past professional posts*: Ms. Gyorda has served in a leadership capacity overseeing the human resources office since joining IHS in 2012. In December 2014, Ms. Gyorda assumed the role of Acting Director for the newly established OHR at IHS Headquarters where she was instrumental in creating and launching the HR structure for the organization & also provided leadership and technical oversight to the five regional HR offices. Prior to joining IHS, Ms. Gyorda worked for the National Institutes of Health for 14 years where she gained valuable knowledge of federal HR and advised NIH leadership on human resources programs, including staffing and recruitment, classification, position management, employee relations and compensation policy. Awards, honors: Numerous awards from NIH and IHS, including an NIH Director's Award and an IHS Director's Award for customer service.

H

HACKER, PAUL (Choctaw-Cherokee) 1948-
(knife & flutemaker/player-recording artist, writer)
Born August 4, 1948, Oklahoma City, Okla. *Principal occupation*: Knife & flutemaker/player-recording artist, writer. Resides in Oklahoma (405) 787-8600. *Affiliation*: Owner, Paul Hacker Knives & Flutes, Bethany, OK. *Memberships*: Choctaw Tribe of Oklahoma; Kituwah; Indian Arts & Crafts Association; Gallup Intertribal Ceremonial; Southern Plains Association. *Awards, honors*: Over 80 awards in 15 years, including the 1992 2nd place & 1993 1st place Smithsonian Celebration of the American Indian. *Interests*: "My intention is to promote traditional & contemporary art. Most of my demonstrations are with young people and elementary schools. I enjoy doing concerts and lectures. I attend and show at Native American & Western Shows." *Published works*: Tapes: "Winds of the Past" Volumes I & II; "To Those Who've Gone Before Us," and "The Horses Still Cry" - flute music on cassette & compact discs - music composed and played by Paul Hacker. He's recorded music for several videos on domestic violence & recently "LaCrosse, the Creator's Game" by Ken Murch Productions (won 1st place Native American Film Festival for Documentaries. His music also on videos: "The Basketweavers" and The Woodcarvers" (available from Qualla Arts & Crafts, Cherokee, NC). He is currently working on a gospel album, "Healing Spirit."

HACKETT, DAVID KRAMER (*Woktela*) (Yuchi) 1948-
(professional engineer, writer)
Born November 11, 1948, Frankfort, Ind. Education: University of Tennessee, BS, 1972. *Principal occupation*: Professional engineer, writer. *Address*: 6500 Trousdale Rd., Knoxville, TN 37921 (615) 691-7835 (work). *Affiliations*: Engineer, Aztech Research Services, Knoxville, TN, 1975-77; welding engineer, Nuclear Div., Union Carbide, Oak Ridge, TN, 1977-81; owner, Aztech Research Services, Knoxville, TN, 1981-; CEO, Science Advocacy Pellissippi Science Enrichment Programs, Knoxville, TN, 1989-; consultant, Oak Ridge National Laboratory, Oak Ridge, TN, 1990-. *Community activities*: Science programs for the public: I.D. Day, Spaceweek, Astroweek, Earth Day, Science & Technician Week, Science Olympiad. *Memberships*: American Indian Science & Engineering Society; American Society for Metals; Dinosaur Society. *Awards, honors*: Numerous awards for photo documentation; Museum Replica Grants, 1987-89 for stone carving, American Indian Pipes; "Recently it has been my honor to rediscover the origin of the state name, Tennessee, in my Native tongue." Interests: "Forensic & failure science, science education, trickster path, critical thinking, paleontology, stone carver." *Biographical source*: Who's Who in the World (Marquis, 12th Ed.). *Published works*: Editor: Spruce Pine Mineral District (Aztech, 1979); Ambient Lighting Extremes (Aztech, 1984); Tales From the Red Earth & A Blue Planet (pending); numerous articles in professional journals.

HADLEY, FAYE
(Native American reference law librarian)
Affiliation & Address: Head Reference Librarian, Native American Resources, Mabee Legal Information Center, The University of Tulsa College of Law, 3120 East 4th Place, Tulsa, OK 74104 (918) 631-2457.

HAGEN, DOREEN (Mdewakanton Dakota)
(tribal council president)
Born on Prairie Island, Minn. *Address & Affiliation*: Tribal council president, Prairie Island Indian Community, 5636 Sturgeon Lake Rd., Welch, MN 55089 (651) 385-2554. *Past professional post*: Dept. of Mental Health, Atascadero, CA until 1994 *Military service*: U.S. Army.

HAGER, CLAY STEVEN (Cherokee) 1958-
(attorney)
Born February 25, 1958, Enid, Okla. *Education*: Phillips University, BA, 1981; University of Oklahoma, JD, 1987. *Address*: 2307 Ripple Creek Lane, Edmond, OK 73034 *Office address*: 4200 Perimeter Center Dr., Suite 222, Oklahoma City, OK 73112 (405) 943-6457. E-mail: hager@oilsonline.org. *Affiliation*: Staff attorney, 1990-2000; managing attorney, 2001-12; director of litigation, 2012-present), Oklahoma Indian Legal Services, Oklahoma City, OK. *Other professional post*: Supreme Court Justice, Kaw Nation, Kaw City, OK. *Past professional posts*: Professor, American Institute of Paralegal Studies, Oklahoma City, OK; served as the chair of the Indian Law Section of the Oklahoma Bar Association. *Memberships*: Oklahoma Bar Assn (Indian Law Section); Oklahoma Indian Bar Assn; 24 tribal bar associations. *Awards, honors*: 2008 Attorney of the Year Award by the Pawnee Court Appointed Special Advocate (CASA) program; guest lecturer, "Indian Housing Into the 90's" seminar, and "Sovereignty Symposium V - The Year of the Indian;" Who's Who in American Law. *Interests*: Indian Child Welfare Act expert. "I am currently rewriting our handbook on the subject." *Published works*: Editor, Oklahoma Indian Child Welfare Act Handbook (16 edtions) (Oklahoma Indian Legal Services, 1991-2012); Prodigal Son: The Existing Indian Family Exception (Clearinghouse Law Review, 1993); contributor, Sovereign Symposium VII (Oklahoma Sup. Ct., 1994); author of Transfer to Tribal Courts in Oklahoma Under the Indian Child Welfare Act, Feb. 2010 Oklahoma Bar Journal's Indian Law Issue; contributing author for the Greenwood Encyclopedia of American Indian Issues of Today (ABC-CLIO, 2012) .

HAIRE, WENONAH GEORGE (Catawba) 1953-
(dentist)
Born November 27, 1953, York County, Rock Hill, S.C. *Education*: Clemson University, BS, 1976; Medical University of SC, Charleston, D.MD, 1979. *Principal occupation*: Dentist. Address: 611 E. Main St., Rock Hill, SC 29730 (803) 324-5214. *Community activities*: Education committee, Career Development Center; chairman, Dental Health Month, 1985; Girl Scout Aid. *Memberships*: Tri-County Dental Society, Rock Hill, SC (secretary, 1985); U.S. Public Health Service (Lt., inactive reserve); Medical University Alumni Association; First Baptist Church. *Interests*: Enjoys travel vacations (Mexico and U.S.); collects Indian jewelry, paintings & pottery; enjoys pottery making (Catawba traditional coil method); enjoys canning. Only female dentist in Rock Hill, S.C.; just had her first child. *Biographical source*: Charlotte Observer article entitled Rock Hill Dentist Drills by Day, Fills by Night.

HALBRITTER, RAY (Oneida) 1953-
(newspaper publisher, tribal representative)
Born July 17, 1953, Oneida, N.Y. *Education*: Syracuse University, BA, 1985; Harvard University Law School, J.D., 1990; Honorary Doctorate of Humane Letters, SUNY Institute of Technology at Utica/Rome, NY. *Principal occupation*: Newspaper publisher, tribal representative. *Address*: P.O. Box 1, West Rd., Vernon, NY 13476 (315) 829-8900. *Affiliation & Address*: Nation Representative, Oneida Indian Nation, 5218 Patrick Rd., Oneida, NY 13421, 1975-present; CEO, Oneida Indian Nation Enterprises, 1990-present; president & CEO, Four Directions Media, Inc., Indian Country Today (newspaper), Canastota, NY. *Other professional posts*: Editorial Advisory Board, Indian Gaming News magazine; Adjunct Professor of Law at Benjamin Cardozo School of Law, New York University Law School, and Syracuse University College of Law. *Community activities*: Lecturer; Board of Directors, International Native American Center for the Performing & Visual Arts; member, Harvard University Native American Law Board; member, National Advisory Council for the American Indian Program at Cornell University. Halbritter has successfully negotiated a gaming compact with the State of New York that resulted in the development of Turning Stone Resort & Casino, the first legal casino in the state. In 2003, the Oneida Nation under Halbritter's leadership began a two-year, $300+ million expansion at Turning Stone. *Memberships*: National Congress of American Indian (Washington, DC); USET (Nashville, TN); Canadian Native Arts Foundation (Toronto); Economic Development & Planning Committee for City of Oneida, NY. *Awards, honors*: Man of the Year, by the Leatherstocking Country, NY; Grand Marshal, Rome (NY) America Days. *Biographical sources*: "Ray Halbritter," Central New Yorker Magazine, Nov. 12, 1993; "The Man Behind the Casino," Business Journal, Nov. 29 - Dec. 12, 1993; "A Salute to Those Who Came Before Us," Rome Observer, 7/20 1993; "Ray Halbritter," Syracuse New Times, 6/16, 1993.

HALE, ALBERT (Navajo)
(attorney; AZ State senator)
Affiliation & Address: AZ State Senate (2004-11) Representative (2013-14), Arizona House of Representative, Capitol Complex, Rm. 129, 1700 West Washington, Phoenix, AZ 85007 (602) 926-4323. E-mail: ahale@azleg.gov. Mr. Hale represents District 2 which spans a 300-mile width of Arizona from New Mexico to Nevada, including Flagstaff and the counties of Navajo, Apache, Coconino & Mohave with a population of 70,000 people and includes the Navajo, Hopi, Hualapai & Havasupai Nations. *Other professional post*: Hale Law Firm, .O. Box 40, St. Michaels, AZ 86511 (928) 871-4589. E-mail: ahalelaw@citlink.net. *Past professional posts*: Mr. Hale has been an attorney for 27 years specializing in federal Indian law & natural resource issues; president, Navajo Nation, Window Rock, AZ, 1994-98; served as assistant attorney general for the Navajo Nation; special counsel to the Navajo Nation Council. *Memberships*: Navajo Nation Bar Association (past president).

HALE, MICHELLE (Dine' Navajo)
(professor of American Indian studies)
Affiliation & Address: Assistant Professor, American Indian Studies, College of Liberal Arts & Sciences, MC: 4603, Arizona State University, Tempe, AZ 85287 (480) 965-3634. E-mail: michelle.hale@asu.edu.

HALFTOWN, CLINT (Cayuga)
(tribal representative)
Affiliation & Address: Federal Representative, Cayuga Indian Nation, P.O. Box 11, Versailles, NY 14168 (716) 337-4270.

HALL, KELLIE (Turtle Mountain Chippewa-Ojibwe)
(Indian college vice president)
Affiliation & Address: Vice President, Turtle Mountain Community College, P.O. Box 340, Belcourt, ND 58316 (701) 477-7822. E-mail: kmhall@tm.edu

HALL, MARY (Colville)
(tribal executive director)
Affiliation & Address: Executive Director, Confederated Tribes of the Colville Reservation, P.O. Box 150, Nespelem, WA 99155 (509) 634-2212. E-mail: mary.hall@colvilletribes.com.

HALL, McCLELLAN (Cherokee)
(founder & executive director)
Education: University of Washington, BA (Native American Teacher Education Program); Arizona State University, MA (American Indian Leadership Program). *Affiliation & Address*: Founder & executive director (1990-present), National Indian Youth Leadership Project, P.O. Box 2140, Gallup, NM 87305 (505) 722-9176. *Awards, honors*: Recipient of the Kurt Hahn Award; the Spirit of Crazy Horse Award; the E-Town Achievement Award from the National Public Radio & NIYLP's Project Venture. *Published work*: Co-author, Wisdom Teachings: Lessons Learned from Gatherings of Elders (2005); articles.

HALL, PATRICIA A. 1945-
(attorney)
Born November 18, 1945, Oak Park, Ill. *Education*: Arizona State University, BA, 1970; Arizona State University College of Law, JD, 1976. *Address*: 7859 County Road 203, Durango, CO 81301 (970) 247-1755. *Affiliations*: Partner, Maynes, Bradford, Shipps & Sheftel, Durango, CO, 1991-; General Counsel for the Southern Ute Indian Tribe. *Community activities*: La Plata County Judge, 1982-89; Southern Ute, Chief Judge, 1980-82; Ute Mountain Ute Judge, 1980-82; Jicarilla Apache Alt. Judge, 1982; Colorado Legal Board of Directors; Navajo Public Defender Commission. *Memberships*: Colorado Bar Association; Arizona State Bar; Navajo Nation Bar Association. *Awards, honors*: 1986 Judge of the Year, Colorado Dept. of Heath; 1988 Excellence in Criminal Justice Award, La Plata County Sheriff's Department. *Interests*: Indian law, criminal law; travel, music concerts, independent film, organic gardening.

HALL, TEX G. (*Ihbudah Hishi - Red Tipped Arrow*) (Hidatsa) 1956-
(tribal chairperson)
Born September 18, 1956, Watford, N.D. Education: University of South Dakota, MA, 1980. *Address*: Box 488, Mandaree, ND 58757 (701) 759-3311. Website: www.texghall.com; E-mail: chairman@mhanation.com. *Affiliations*: Chairperson (1998-present), Three Affiliated Tribes, 404 Frontage Rd., New Town, ND 58763 (701) 627-4781; president (2001-present), *Other professional posts*: Chairperson, Mandaree Day School, Mandaree, ND; chairperson, Native American Bancorporation Co.; president, Executive Board, NABI Foundation, Phoenix, AZ. *Memberships*: National Congress of American Indians (NCAI), Washington, DC.; North Dakota Indian Education Association; North Dakota Stockman's Association; National Indian Athletic Association; North Dakota & National Principals Association. *Awards, honors*: Outstanding Young Men of America, 1983, '86, '87. *Interests*: "Traveled to Europe, Canada, Soviet Union, Mexico, Puerto Rico & Western U.S., & most Indian reservations, instructing at basketball camps & playing basketball tournaments."

HALLMARK, CHARLOTE S. (Echota Cherokee)
(tribal vice chief)
Affiliation & Address: Vice Chief, Echota Cherokee Tribe of Alabama, 630
County Road 1281, Falkville, AL 35622 (256) 734-7337.

HALLORAN, JOSEPH A.
(attorney)
Education: Saint Joseph University (MN), BA, 1989; William Mitchell College of
Law (St. Paul, MN), JD, 1994. *Affiliation & Address*: Attorney & Shareholder,
The Jacobson Law Group, (651) 644-4710.
E-mail: jhalloran@thejacobsonlawgroup.com Throughout his career, Joe has
represented tribal gaming regulatory authorities in all aspects of tribal gaming
regulation, including internal governance and regulatory structure, compliance
& enforcement efforts, including litigation & administrative proceedings relating
to those activities, and intergovernmental affairs at the state and federal level.
He also represents tribes in real-property acquisition and trust-transfer efforts
involving bare land, land with housing, & land slated for housing & commercial
uses and involving exchanges, rights-of-way re-conveyances, interagency
transfers, & transfers of fractional interests. In addition, he represents tribes in
intellectual property protection, including service and trademarks and has been
active in enforcing client's rights against infringing users, including litigation
before the Trademark Trial & Appeal Board and the federal courts. Throughout
his career, he has also represented tribes in Indian child welfare proceedings
at the tribal, state and federal trial and appellate levels, both as parties and
as *amici curiae*. Joe has taught Indian law at William Mitchell College of Law
and has presented & lectured at numerous continuing legal education courses.
He is a special member of the Minnesota Indian Bar Association.

HALPERN, CHIA (Spirit Lake Dakota)
(tribal court specialist)
Affiliation & Address: The Tribal Law & Policy Institute, 8235 Santa Monica
Blvd., #211, West Hollywood, CA 90046 (323) 650-5467. E-mail: chia@tlpi.org.

HAMILL, CHAD (Spokan)
(professor of Indigenous studies)
Education: California Institute of the Arts, BFA, MFA; University of Colorado,
PhD, 2008. *Affiliation & Address*: Associate Professor (2007-present) &
Chairperson, Applied Indigenous Studies Department, SBS West Bldg. 70,
Room 9Bm Northern Arizona University, Flagstaff, AZ 86011 (928) 523-3849.
E-mail: chad.hamill@nau.edu. Chad specializes in music & sovereignty, music
& spirituality and cultural sustainability. Other professional post: Co-chair of the
Commission for Native Americans. *Published works*: Songs of Power & Prayer
in the Columbia Plateau; his next book will focus on the untold story of
American Indian musicians in the development of jazz.

HAMILTON, ANGE (*Aunko*) (Kiowa)
(attorney)
Born in Lawton, Okla. *Education*: University of Oklahoma, BA, 1980; Oklahoma
City University School of Law, JD, 1991. *Address*: 1326 S. 5th St., Aberdeen,
SD 57401-6810. *Affiliation*: Staff Attorney, Oklahoma Indian Legal Services,
Oklahoma City, OK, 1992-. *Other professional post*: General Counsel, Wichita
& Affiliated Tribes, Anadarko, OK, 1991-. *Community activities*: Children's
Review Board Commission; Campaign for Justice & Human Development
(board of directors); Oklahoma City Archdiocese. *Memberships*: Oklahoma Bar
Assn; American Bar Assn; Oklahoma Indian Bar Assn; Native American Bar
Assn; Native American Indian Bar Assn. *Awards, honors*: American Assn of
University Women Fellow, 1990-91; recipient of Oklahoma Bar Foundation
Scholarship, 1990; Assn of Business & Professional Women Scholarship,
1989-90; Daughters of American Revolution Scholarship. *Interests*: Federal
Indian law; tribal court development; Indian child welfare.

HAMILTON, ANNETTE (Kickapoo)
(chief operating officer)
Education: Washburn University (Topeka, KS), BS (Business Administration);
University of Minnesota, MBA. *Affiliation & Address*: Chief Financial Officer
(2001-04), Chief Operating Officer, 2004-present), Ho-Chunk, Inc., 1 Mission
Dr., Winnebago, NE 68071 (402) 878-2809. *Other professional posts*:
Chairperson, Native American Contractors Association, Washington, DC;
board member, Siouxland Human Investment Partnership; board member,
Mercy Medical Center. *Past professional post*: financial analyst & manager of
financial reporting, Gateway, Inc.

HAMILTON, D'ANNE MARIE (*Paaniikaaluk*) (Inupiat Eskimo) 1959-
(producer, host)
Born July 12, 1957, Kotzebue, Alaska. *Education*: Kauai Community College,
1978; University of Alaska, Fairbanks, 1979; Arizona State University, 1979-
81. *Affiliation & Address*: Producer/host, Alaska Public Radio Network, 810 E.
Ninth Ave., Anchorage, AK 99501 (907) 277-2776. *Past professional posts*:
Production assistant, Northwest Arctic Instructional Television Center,
Kotzebue (one year); reporter, K.O.T.Z. Radio Station, Kotzebue (one year);

producer/reporter, Alaska Public Radio Network, Anchorage, 1989-;
producer/reporter, National Native News, Anchorage, 1989-94; producer/host,
National Native News, 1994-. *Community activities*: Rural Alaska Television
Network Board, 1983; Inupiat Ilitqusiat Committee, 1983. *Membership*: Alaska
Press Club; Native American Journalists Association. *Awards, honors*: Alaska
Native Fellowship, Grotto Foundation. *Interests*: "I am interested in increasing
coverage of Native issues, particularly in the state of Alaska. I am also
interested in steps by Inuit towards political unity, and was part of a three-
person reporting team covering the Inuit Circumpolar Conference in July of
1989 in Greenland. I lived in Germany for nearly four years, and did a bit of
traveling in Europe. I speak some German and Spanish, and hope to begin
learning Russian this year." *Biographical sources*: Anchorage Daily News;
Tundra Times; Arctic Sounder.

HAMILTON, EDDIE (Cheyenne/Arapaho)
(tribal governor)
Affiliation & Address: Governor, Cheyenne & Arapaho Tribes, P.O. Box 38,
Concho, OK 73022 (405) 422-7430.

HAMILTON, MANUEL (Cahuilla)
(tribal vice chairperson)
Affiliation & Address: Vice Chairperson, Ramona Band of Mission Indians,
P.O. Box 391670, Anza, CA 92539 (959) 763-4105. E-mail:
mhamilton@ramonatribe.com

HAMLEY, JEFFREY (Turtle Mountain Ojibwe)
(BIE associate deputy director)
Born in North Dakota. *Education*: Western Washington University, BA
(Elementary Education), MA (Student Personnel Administration in Higher
Education); Harvard University, MA (Counseling & Consulting Psychology),
DEd (Administration, Planning & Social Policy). *Address & Affiliation*: Associate
Deputy Director (2009-present), Division of Performance & Accountability,
Bureaau of Indian Education, U.S. Department of the Interior, 1849 C St. NW
MS 3609-MIB, Washington, DC 20240 (202) 208-6123. E-mail:
Jeffrey.hamley@bie.edu. *Past professional post*: Director, Harvard Native
American Program, John F. Kennedy School of Government, Cambridge, MA,
2007-09). Before joining the BIE Senior Management Team, Dr. Hamley
served as the President of Southwestern Indian Polytechnic Institute (SIPI), a
BIE operated two-year college located in Albuquerque, New Mexico. He has
served in various leadership and administrative roles in higher education and
the tribal college movement. Prior to SIPI, he served as President of Saginaw
Chippewa Tribal College and he has worked at two of the nation's other tribal
colleges: the Institute of American Indian Arts & Northwest Indian College. At
Northwest Indian College, he directed a teacher preparation program for Native
students. He has served in other administrative roles at Harvard University,
Antioch University Seattle, and The Evergreen State College. He has held
teaching appointments at Harvard University & Walden University. He has a
longstanding interest in K-12 education & Indian Education. Early in his career,
he worked in Title IV (now Title VII) Indian education programs in the Seattle
Public Schools

HAMMETT, BRIAN (Gros Ventre)
(radio announcer, language instructor)
Affiliation: Announcer, KGVA 88.1 FM Radio, Fort Belknap Reservation, RR 1,
Box 66, Harlem, MT 59526; certified language instructor of White Clay
language and gives a daily language lesson on 88.1 FM radio.

HAMMOND, WYLIE
(Indian center director)
Affiliation: Director, Native American Cultural Awareness Center, Minot State
University, 500 University Ave. West, Minot, ND 58707 (701) 858-3112.

HAMMONS, DIANE (Cherokee)
(assistant professor of criminal justice)
Education: University of Oklahoma School of Law, JD, 1984. *Affiliation &
Address*: Assistant Professor of Criminal Justice, Legal Studies & Homeland
Security, Department of Cherokee & Indigenous Studies, Northeastern State
University, Seminary Hall 337, 609 N. Grand Ave., Tahlequah, OK 74464 (918)
444-3501; E-mail: hammonsa@nsuok.edu. *Past professional post*: Attorney
General of the Cherokee Nation, and was an Assistant Attorney General for
the State of Oklahoma for a number of years. *Awards, honors*: recipient of the
Cherokee Patriot Award.

HAMNER, DOROTHY (Colville)
(Indian education program director)
Address: Okanogan School District #105, P.O. Box 592, Okanogan, WA 98840
(509) 422-3770. *Affiliation*: Director, J.O.M./Title IX Native American Program
(serves the unique needs of federally recognized Indian students, Okanogan
School District #105, Okanogan, WA. *Community activities*: Inter-tribal student
club (parent committee).

HAMPSON, COLIN CLOUD (Winnebago/Chippewa)
(attorney)
Education: Stanford University, BA (American History), MA (International Policy Studies), 1991, Stanford Law School, JD, 1994. *Address & Affiliation*: Partner, Sonosky, Chambers, Sachse, Endreson & Perry, LLP, 600 West Broadway, Suite 700, San Diego, CA 92101 (619) 267-1306 E-mail: champson@sonosky.com. *Practice area*: Mr. Hampson joined the firm in 1994 and opened the firm's office in San Diego in 1999. He's engaged in all areas of the firm's Indian law practice, including Indian gaming, cultural resources, water, tax, & general counsel matters. *Memberships*: American Bar Association, California Bar Association; California Indian Law Assn (past president of board of directors).

HAMPTON, CAROL CUSSEN McDONALD (Caddo) 1935-
(clergy)
Born September 18, 1935, Oklahoma City, Okla. *Education*: H. Sophie Newcomb College, New Orleans, LA, 1953-54; University of Oklahoma, BA, 1957, MA, 1973, PhD, 1984; Certificate of Individual Theological Studies, Episcopal Theological Seminary of the Southwest, 1998; Master of Divinity, Phillips Theological Seminary, summa cum laude, 1999. *Principal occupation*: Clergy - ordained to priesthood (Episcopal Church) Dec. 1999, curate, 1999-2001; appointed Canon of St. Paul's Cathedral (Episcopal) Dec. 2001. *Address*: 1414 N. Hudson, Oklahoma City, OK 73103 (405) 235-1905. E-mail: hampton918@aol.com. *Affiliations*: Teaching assistant, University of Oklahoma, Norman, 1973-84; associate director & coordinator, Consortium for Graduate Opportunities for American Indians, University of California, Berkeley; Field Officer for Native American Ministry of the Episcopal Church, 1986-94; officer for multicultural ministry, 1994-98; ordained to diaconate (Episcopal Church) June, 1999; ordained to priesthood, Dec. 1999; curate, St. Pauls' Episcopal Church. *Community activities*: Caddo Indian Tribe of Oklahoma (tribal council, 1976-); Caddo Tribal Constitution Committee, 1975-76; Oklahoma City Area Indian Health Service (advisory board); Junior League of Oklahoma City, 1965-; National Committee on Indian Work, Episcopal Church (Co-chair, 1986); World Council of Churches (commissioner, Program to Combat Racism, 1985-91); Oklahoma State Regents for Higher Education on Social Justice (member, advisory board, 1984-86); Council of Native American Ministries (vice-chair, 1988-97); National Council of Church's (Racial Justice Working Group Co-convener, 1991-94); Oklahoma Conference of Churches (board member); Indigenous Theological Training Institute (board member); Central Oklahoma Human Rights Alliance; American Indian Graduate Center (Honorary Advisory Council of 100, 2003-present); University of Oklahoma, Native American Studies Board of Visitors, 2005-present. *Memberships*: National Indian Education Assn; National Historical Society; Oklahoma Historical Society; Western Historical Assn; Organization of American Historians; American Historical Assn; Oklahoma Foundation for the Humanities (Trustee, 1983-86). *Awards, honors*: Francis C. Allen Fellowship, D'Arcy McNickle Center for the History of the American Indian, Newberry Library, 1983; State of Oklahoma Human Rights Award, 1987; attendee, United Nations 4th World Conference on Women, Beijing, 1995. *Interests*: My interests are in history, philosophy and theology of American Indians as well as social and racial justice. Biographical sources: Who's Who Among American Women; Who's Who in the World; etc. *Published work*: Indian Colonization in the Cherokee Outlet & Western Indian Territory (Chronicles of Oklahoma, 1976). *Articles*: "Peyote and the Law", Between Two Worlds, Oklahoma Series, 1986; "Why Write History? A Caddo Grandmother's Perspective", The Creative Woman, Fall, 1987; "Opposition to Indian Diversity in the 20th Century", American Indian Policy and Cultural Values, UCLA, 1987; "Tribal Esteem and the American Indian Historian", An American Indian Identity, San Diego State University Publications, 1988; "A Heritage Denied: Racial Justice for American Indians", Sojourners, Jan. 1991; "Native American Church", Encyclopedia of North American Indian, 1996; editor, "When Caddos Came Upon the Earth," First Peoples Theology Journal, Vol. 2 No. 1, Sept. 2001.

HAMPTON, JAMES WILBURN, M.D. (*Sheko Okti Onna*)
(Chickasaw/Choctaw) 1931-
(physician & educator)
Born September 15, 1931, Durant, Okla. *Education*: University of Oklahoma, BA, 1952; University of Oklahoma, School of Medicine, MD, 1956. *Principal occupation*: Physician & educator. *Address*: 1414 N. Hudson, Oklahoma City, OK 73103. E-mail: james.hampton@usoncology.com. *Affiliations*: Medical Director, Troy & Dollie Smith Cancer Center, Baptist Medical Center, Oklahoma City; Clinical Professor of Medicine, University of Oklahoma Medical School, 1956-2010; hematologist/medical oncologist at Mercy Clinic, 2010-present. *Past professional posts*: Professor & Head, Hematology-Oncology, University of Oklahoma Medical School, 1971-77; head Hematology Research Laboratories, Oklahoma Medical Research Foundation, 1971-77; National Cancer Institute, Chairperson, Network for Cancer Control in American Indians/Alaska Natives, 1990-2000. *Community activities*: Oklahoma Indian Tumor Registry (Initiator); Oklahoma County Medical Society (member, board of directors, 1979-82, 1989-92; editor, The Bulletin, 1983-); Heritage Hills, Inc. (member, board of directors, 1973-90); Central Oklahoma American Indian

Health Council (board member, 1974-90); Faculty House (board member, 1974-75); Frontiers of Science Foundation of Oklahoma, Inc. (board member, 1974-78). *Memberships*: American Association for the Advancement of Science; American Assn for Cancer Research, Southwest Section; American Assn of University Professors; American Federation for Clinical Research; American Genetic Assn; American Medical Assn; American Physiological Society; American Psychosomatic Society; New York Academy of Sciences; Oklahoma County Medical Society; Oklahoma State Medical Assn; Assn of American Indian Physicians (president, 1979-80, 1989-90); National Institutes of Health; American Heart Assn; American Cancer Society (member of Committee on Cancer in the Socioeconomically Disadvantaged, Medicine & Scientific Committee; member at large, Board of Directors, 1990-95). *Consultations*: Consultant in Medicine, Tinker Air Force Base Hospital, Oklahoma City, Okla., 1965-; consultant for National Institutes of Health, National Cancer Institute, 1973-76, 1989-; National Heart & Lung Institute, 1971-92; consultant for Navajo Health Authority, 1974-76; consultant for Regional Breast Cancer Detection & Treatment Center, 1974-79. *Awards, honors*: NIH Career Development Award, 1965-75; Angiology Research Foundation Honors Achievement Award, 1967-68; Preservation & Restoration Award, Heritage Hills Assn, 1973; chairman, Planning Committee for Native American Medical School, sponsored by the Navajo Health Authority, 1974-76; associate editor, Journal of Laboratory & Clinical Medicine, 1974-76; Indian Physician of the Year Award, 1987 & 2000; Special Certificate of Appreciation from the National Cancer Prevention & Control Intervention Research Program for Special Populations, 1990; Special Recognition from National Indian Health Board; member, Minority Affairs Consortium, AMA, 1998-2000; member, Dialog on Concern (American Cancer Society), 1998-; The Humanitarian Award of the American Cancer Society, 1999. *Interests*: Cancer in American Indians/Alaska Natives.

HANEY, ENOCH KELLY (Seminole-Creek)
(tribal chief; artist, art gallery owner)
Affiliation: Principal Chief, Seminole Nation of Oklahoma, P.O. Box 1948, Wewoka, OK 74884 (405) 257-7276. Website: www.seminolenation.com. *Other professional post*: Owner, Kelly Haney Art Gallery, P.O. Box 3817, 723 E. Independence, Shawnee, OK 74801 (405) 275-2270. Gallery features original Indian paintings, sculpture, jewelry, baskets, pottery.

HANEY, WILLIAM M. "WILL" (Seminole of Oklahoma)
(attorney)
Education: University of Oklahoma, BA, 2010, UCLA School of Law, JD, 2014. *Affiliation & Address*: Associate, Berkey Williams LLP, 2030 Addison St. #410, Berkeley, CA 94704 (510) 548-7070. *Other professional posts*: Staff Attorney for the San Manuel Band of Mission Indians; Board Treasurer, California Indian Law Association. While at UCLA Law, Mr. Haney was a Staff Member and Associate Editor of the UCLA Law Review and served as Secretary and Alumni Chair of the UCLA Native American Law Students Association. His practice areas include Tribal governance, Tribal economic development, Tribal water rights, environmental law, intellectual property, religious rights, and the protection and promotion of Tribal sovereignty.

HANITCHAK, MICHAEL S. (Choctaw-Chickasaw)
(governing council chairperson)
Affiliation: Governing Council Executive Board Member, National Institute for Native Leadership in Higher Education (Website: www.ninlhe.unm.edu), University of Northern Colorado, Office of the Provost & Executive VP for Academic Affairs, Greeley, CO 80639 E-mail: mhanitchak@gmail.com. *Past professional post*: (Retired) Director of Native American Program, Dartmouth College.

HANS, BIRGIT
(professor of American Indian studies)
Education: University of Arizona Press, PhD (English), 1988. *Affiliation & Address*: Chester Fritz Distinguished Professor of English & American Indian Studies, College of Arts & Sciences, University of North Dakota, 221 Centennial Dr., Stop 7103, Grand Forks, ND 58202 (701) 777-4649. Email: birgit.hans@und.edu Her specialty is American Indian literature & oral traditions. *Past professional post*: She has conducted long-term field research on European perceptions of American Indian cultures. *Published works*: Dr. Hans has published extensively on D'Arcy McNickle, including a collection of his unpublished short stories called, "The Hawk is Hungry. Editor, D'Arcy McNickle's The Hungry Generation: The Evolution of a Novel (University of New Mexico Press, 2007) papers in Studies in American Indian Literatures, in the North Dakota Quarterly, et al.

HANSELL, TIMOTHY J. (Navajo-Dine')
(executive director & CEO)
Affiliation & Address: Executive Director & CEO, Cook Native American Ministries Foundation, 1414 W. Broadway Rd., Suite 122, Tempe, AZ 85282 (480) 968-9354

HANSEN, CECILE (Duwamish)
(tribal chairperson)
Affiliation & Address: Lifetime Chairperson, Duwamish Tribe of Indians, 4705 W. Marginal Way SW, Seattle, WA 98106 (206) 431-1582

HANSEN, ELIZABETH (Pomo)
(rancheria chairperson)
Affiliation & Address: Chairperson, Redwood Valley Band of Pomo Indians, 3250 Road I, Redwood Valley, CA 95470 (707) 485-0361.

HANSEN, EMMA I. (Pawnee) 1947-
(museum curator)
Born March 5, 1947, Oklahoma City, Okla. *Education*: Oklahoma State University, BA; University of Oklahoma, MAs (Sociology & Anthropology), A.B.D. - Anthropology. *Address*: 720 Sheridan Ave., Cody, WY 82414 (307) 587-4771. E-mail: emmah@blohc.org. *Affiliations*: Anthropology Dept., U. of Oklahoma, Norman, OK, 1978-80, 1985-89; Stovall Museum, U. of Oklahoma, Norman, OK, 1978-84; Oklahoma Museums Association, Oklahoma City, OK, 1990-91; curator, Plains Indian Museum, Buffalo Bill Historical Center, Cody, WY, 1991-; visiting curator, Hood Museum of Art, and Assistant Professor, Native American Studies, Dartmouth College, 1997; Associate Curator of Ethnology, Glenbow Museum, Calgary, Alberta, Canada, 1994-. *Other professional post*: Board member, Wyoming Council for the Humanities, 2003-06. *Community activities*: Programs presented at numerous museums & organizations, nationally & internationally; Powerful Images: Portrayals of Native America - exhibition touring major museums, 1998-2000; organizes annual Plains Indian Museum Powwow in Cody and Plains Indian Seminar. *Membership*: American Anthropological Association; American Association of Museums (board of curator's committee); Council for Museum Anthropology (officer); Native American Art Studies Association (board member, 1999-2006). *Awards, honors*: AASLH Award of Merit; Ford Foundation Fellowship; Newberry Library - Resident Research Fellowship; Sequoyah Graduate Award; American Philosophical Society, Phillips Fund Grant; several NEA and NEH grants, as well as grants from private foundations. *Interests*: Plains Indian culture & ethno-history; Pawnee history, contemporary art. *Published work*: The Artist and the Missionary - Intro. & edited, 1994; Powerful Images: Portrayals of Native America (University of Washington Press, 1998); Article, "People Without Borders: Natives of the North American Plains," in Voices from the West (Gibbs Smith Publishers, 1999); over 30 articles in journals.

HANSEN, JOAN LOUISE (Cherokee) 1945-
(reporter, photographer)
Born February 2, 1945, New Orleans, La. *Education*: Bacone College. Resides in Muskogee, OK. *Affiliation*: Reporter, photographer, Muskogee Daily Phoenix & Times Democrat. *Awards, honors*: Paintings shown at Philbrook Indian Annual, Tulsa; paintings shown at Department of the Interior, Washington, DC; numerous awards at local fairs. *Interests*: Reading of Plains Indian traditions and legends; art.

HANSEN, TERRI C. (Winnebago/Cherokee of Oklahoma) 1953-
(journalist-editor-storyteller)
Born October 18, 1953, Portland, Oreg. *Education*: Clark College (Vancouver, WA), 1990-92. *Address*: P.O. Box 972, Welches, OR 97067. E-Mail: info@terrihansen-journalist-storyteller.com. *Affiliation*: Regional/national correspondent, News From Indian Country, Hayward, WI, 1992-present. *Other professional post*: Founder/executive director, National American Indian Environmental Illness Foundation, a 501(c)3 non-profit educational organization. *Past professional posts*: Bureau Chief/editor, Pacific NW Bureau (OR, WA, ID, northern CA, B.C.), News From Indian Country, 1993-97; researcher/contributor, Encyclopedia of North American Indians, ten volumes plus appendix volume, edited by Water Buffalo Books, Milwaukee, WI, published by Marshall Cavendish, New York, NY, March 1997; journalism instructor, Swinomish Indian Reservation, LaConner, WA, 1999; national correspondent, Native American Smoke Signals, Meyer, AZ, 1993-95; contributor, The Circle, Minneapolis, MN, 1995; desktop publisher, journalist, Washington State editor, Portland Indian News, Portland, OR, 1992-94. *Community activities*: Speaker/storyteller, educational institutions & public libraries; Council of Better Business Bureau's National Panel of Consumer Arbitrators; volunteer/organizer, The American Indian Assn of Portland, Portland, OR; past-V.P., The Tillicum Indian Assn, Vancouver, WA; Local Indian Child Welfare Advisory Council; presented factual Native American historical education to elementary school audiences, & gives a variety of readings & Winnebago/Cherokee storytelling at local libraries and other audiences of significance. *Memberships*: Winnebago Tribe of Nebraska; Native American Journalist's Assn, 1990-; Wordcraft Circle of Native Writers, 1993-present; Society of Environmental Journalists, 1993-present (SEJ Fellow, 1993); Investigative Reporters & Editors, 2003-present. *Awards*: The Oregonian Publisher's Award of Excellence, 1990; The Wordcraft Circle of Native Writers & Storytellers, Writer of the Year, 1996-97; Native American

Journalist's Association. Honorable Mention, Best News Story 1997. She was the Native American representative & advisor for the Lewis & Clark End of the Oregon Trail Sesquicentennial Advisory Council, arranging opening presentation by Chinook Chief Cliff (Gray Wolf) Snider in addition to organizing the Native American display museum, Oregon City, OR, 1993. *Interests*: "Vocational - "As a reporter of regional & national Indian issues for several Native publications, I am particularly concerned with environmental and health issues as they pertain to American Indians and the general population, and enlightening a wider audience with reference to Native American historical events."

HANSON, BETH ROSE (Eastern Cherokee) 1957-
(administrator)
Born December 14, 1957, Biloxi, Miss. *Education*: University of Wisconsin, Stevens Point, BS, 1989; University of Wisconsin, Oshkosh, MBA (current). *Address*: 425 Front St., Stevens Point, WI 54481 (715) 342-1444. *Affiliations*: Program Manager, Las Vegas Indian Center, Las Vegas, NV, 1989-90; Coordinator, Weekend College Program for Native Americans, University of Wisconsin-Stevens Point, 1991-. *Other professional post*: Benefits administrator for Command Technologies of Virginia, 1993-. *Military service*: U.S. Army Journalist (enlisted member serving in Washington, DC). *Awards, honors*: Graduate Cum Laude from UW-SP; awarded the Chancellor's Leadership Award upon graduation in May 1989; State of Wisconsin Native American Leadership Award recipient; 1992 Mrs. North Carolina; 1992 National Mrs. U.S. Photogenic Winner, Las Vegas, NV. *Interests*: "Current primary career focus is developing education programs for Native Americans and transitional housing projects for homeless Native American families."

HAOZOUS, JEFF (Chiricahua Apache)
(tribal chairperson)
Education: University of Arkansas, BS (Business Administration); Duke University, MBA. *Affiliation & Address*: Chairperson (2002-present), Fort Sill Apache Tribe, Route 2 Box 121, Apache, OK 73507 (580) 588-2298. *Other professional posts*: Member, Board of Directors, Lawton Chamber of Commerce, the Oklahoma Academy for State Goals, the Seven Tribes of Southwest Oklahoma; member, Leadership Oklahoma, Class XXIII.

HAOZOUS, RICHARD "BOB" (Chiricahua Apache-Navajo) 1943-
(artist)
Born April 1, 1943, Los Angeles, Calif. *Education*: Utah State University; California College of Arts and Crafts. *Principal occupation*: Artist. Resides in Santa Fe, NM. *Exhibitions*: Scottsdale National Indian Arts Exhibition; Philbrook Art Center American Indian Artists Exhibitions; Oakland Museum Indian Show; Southwest Fine Arts Biennial-Museum of New Mexico. Permanent collections: Heard Museum; Southern Plains Indian Museum; Crafts Center, Anadarko, OK. *Awards*: First Prize, Sante Fe Indian Market, 1971; Gold Medal, Wood Sculpture I and II, Heard Museum, 1973, 1974; Grand Prize, Heard Museum National Sculpture Competition, 1975; et al.

HAPPY, RICHARD VICTOR (Paiute)
(tribal vice chairperson)
Affiliation & Address: Vice Chairperson, Lovelock Paiute Tribe, Fort Bidwell Reservation, P.O. Box 878, Lovelock, NV 89419 (775) 273-7861.

HAPUTA, ANDREW, MD (Cherokee) 1963-
(physician, association treasurer)
Education: Lenoir Rhyne College, BS (Magna Cum Laude-Biology), 1996; U. of North Carolina, Chapel Hill, School of Medicine, MD, 2000; Residency at University of Washington School of Medicine. *Affiliation & Address*: General Surgery, Surgery Associates, 16122 8th SW Ave., Suite D1, Burien, WA 98166. *Other professional post*: Treasurer, Association of American Indian Physicians, Oklahoma City, OK. *Military service*: U.S. Navy. *Awards, honors*: Healthgrades Honor Roll; The Muchiko Kuno Outstanding Research Award.

HARDACKER, WILLIAM
(attorney; staff counsel)
Education: University of Nebraska-Lincoln, BA (English), 1984; University of Minnesota Law School, JD, 1989. *Affiliation & Address*: Staff Counsel (1995-present) Shakopee Mdewankton Sioux Community, 2330 Sioux Trail, NW, Prior Lake, MN 55372 (952) 445-8900. *Past professional post*: attorney, BlueDog Law Office, 1990-95. *Community activities*: Member, Peace Corps, 1988-89.

HARDBARGER, TIFFANY DAWN (Cherokee)
(instructor in sociology)
Affiliation & Address: Instructor in Sociology, Department of Cherokee & Indigenous Studies, Northeastern State University, Seminary Hall 134, 609 N. Grand Ave., Tahlequah, OK 74464 (918) 444-3599; E-mail: ord@nsuok.edu

HARDEEN, GEORGE (Navajo)
(communications director-Navajo Nation)
Affiliation & Address: Communications Director, The Navajo Nation, Office of the President, P.O. Box 9000, Window Rock, AZ 86515 (928) 871-7917. E-mail: pressoffice@opvp.org.

HARE, CARLY (Pawnee/Yankton Sioux)
(executive director)
Affiliation & Address: Executive Director (2010-present), Native Americans in Philanthropy, 2801 21st Ave. #132D, Minneapolis, MN 55407 (612) 724-8798. E-mail: chare@nativephilanthropy.org. *Past professional posts*: Director of Development, Native American Rights Fund, Denver, CO; advisory committee, Denver Foundation's Inclusiveness Project & Chinook Fund Board; director of programs, The Community Foundation Serving Boulder County (five years). *Awards, honors*: 2006 Emerging Leader in International Philanthropy Fellow through the Center of Philanthropy & Civil Society at the City University of New York; Boulder County's Multicultural Award for Community Service in 2008.

HARE, JAN (Anishinaabe)
(professor of Language)
Education: BASc, BEd, MEd, PhD. *Address & Affiliation*: Associate professor, Dept. of Language & Literacy Education, University of British Columbia, Vancouver, BC, Canada V6T 1Z4 (604) 822-9329. E-mail: jan.hare@ubc.ca. *Research Interests*: Cultural studies; First Nations Education; Literacy. *Published works*: Book: Good Intentions Gone Awry: Emma Crosby & the Methodist Mission on the Northwest Coast (UBC Press, dist. by University of Washington Press, 2006) with Jean Barman; chapters in books: "Aboriginal Education Policy in Canada," et al. Journal articles, reports; presentations.

HARJO, JESSICA (San Carlos Apache)
(attorney)
Education: Mount Saint Mary's University, BS, MBA (Project Management). *Affiliation & Address*: Operations Director (2008-present), Tribal Law & Policy Institute (TLPI), 8235 Santa Monica Blvd. #211, West Hollywood, CA 90046 (323) 650-5467; E-mail: jessica@tlpi.org. Jessica serves as TLPI's Operations Director and has been with TLPI since 2008. She is responsible for the financial management, human resources and overall administrative operations of TLPI. She leads the TLPI Administrative team providing grants management and administrative support on all TLPI projects including: the OVC 11th, 12th, 13th and 14th National Indian Nations Conference; the OVC SANE-SART Training & Technical Assistance Initiative; the National Child Welfare Resource Center for Tribes, the OJJDP Attorney General's Task Force on American Indian/Alaska Native Children Exposed to Violence and the BJA Tribal Healing to Wellness Court program . She specializes in grant proposal submissions, semi-annual and quarterly grant reports, conference/training logistical coordination, budgeting and project management. Her background includes over 15 years of experience in the areas of administrative and executive assistance, office management, event coordination, corporate and tribal sponsorships, and ethnic marketing. Jessica received her B.S. in Film, Media, and Social Justice and minor in Business Administration from Mount Saint Mary's University and is currently an M.B.A. candidate at Mount Saint Mary's University where she is specializing in Project Management.

HARJO, JOY (Muscogee Creek) 1951-
(professor of American Indian studies; poet, musician)
Born in 1951, Tulsa, Okla. *Education*: Institute of American Indian Arts, 1968; University of New Mexico, BA, 1976; University of Iowa, MFA (Creative Writing), 1978; Anthropology Film Center (Santa Fe, NM). *Affiliation & Address*: Professor of American Indian Studies & English, College of Liberal Arts & Sciences, University of Illinois, 1204 W. Nevada St., MC-138, Urbana, IL 61801 (217) 265-9870. E-mail: jharjo@illinois.edu. Othe professional post: Founding board member of the Native Arts & Cultures Foundation, 2007-present. *Past professional posts*: Lecturer, Arizona State University, 1980-81; instructor, Santa Fe Community College, 1983-84; instructor, Institute of American Indian Arts, 1983-84 & 1978-79; assistant professor, University of Colorado, Boulder, 1985-88; associate professor, University of Arizona, Tucson, 1988-90; professor, Creative Writing Program, Dept. of English, University of New Mexico, Albuquerque, 1991-96; professor, UCLA, 2001-05; Joseph Russo Chair, Creative Writing Program, University of New Mexico, 2005-10. *Other professional posts*: Board Treasurer, Native Arts & Cultures Foundation, Vancouver, WA; member, Advisory Committee, Spirits of the Present, Native American Public Broadcasting Consortium and the Smithsonian; "High Plains Review" Poetry Advisor; Steering Committee of the En'owkin Centre International School of Writing (for Native American writers). *Past professional posts*: Editor, Americans Before Columbus, 1979-80; contributing editor; contributing editor, Tyuonyi, 1985-90; High Plains Literary Review (poetry editor, 1986-99. *Awards, honors*: Academy of American Poetry Award, University of New Mexico, 1st Place in Poetry, 1976; Writers Forum, University of Colorado, 1st Place in Poetry, 1977; National Endowment for the Arts Creative Writing Fellowship, 1978 & 1992; Santa Fe Festival for the Arts, 1st Place Poetry, 1980; Outstanding Young Women of America, 1978 & 1984; Pushcart Prize Poetry, 1988 & 1990; Recipient of 1989 Arizona Commission on the Arts - Creative Writing Fellowship, and two NEA Creative Writing Fellowships; 1990 American Indian Distinguished Achievement Award; 1991 William Carlos Williams Award from the Poetry Society of America; the Delmore Schwartz Award from New York University; The American Book Award, 1991; Poetry Award from the Mountains & Plains Booksellers Association, 1991; one of the winners of the Josephine Miles Award for Excellence in Literature from PEN Oakland, 1991; Delmore Schwartz Memorial Award, NYU, 1991; Honorary Doctorate, Benedictine College, 1992; Woodrow Wilson Fellowship, Green Mountain College, Poultney, VT, 1993; Witter Bynner Poetry Fellowship, 1994; Lifetime Achievement Award, Native Writers Circle of the Americas, 1995; Favorite Indian Writer & Musician, Oklahoma Indina Times Reader's Poll, 1997; New Mexico's Gvernor's Award for Excllence in the Arts, 1997; Eagle Spirit Achievement Award, American Indian Film Festival, November, 2002; Wordcraft Circle of Native Writers & Storytellers, Storyteller of the Year, 2004; New Mexico Music Awards, 2008-09; 2011 Artist of the Year from the Mvskoke Women's Leadership Initiative; Mvskoke Hall of Fame Induction, Okmulgee, Oklahoma, Oct. 11, 2012; awarded the 2013 PEN Center USA literary prize in creative nonfiction for "Crazy Brave." *Interests*: Travels extensively around the country giving readings & workshops; plays saxophone with her band, "Poetic Justice." Screen writing experience: Co-writer with Henry Greenberg, "The Gaan Story," one-hour dramatic story, produced by Silvercloud Video Productions; assistant screenwriter with Henry Greenberg, "The Beginning," half-hour dramatic story, produced by Native American Public Broadcasting Consortium (NAPBC), 1983-84; producer, "We Are One, Umonho," a series of eight 20-minute scripts for Nebraska Educational Television (NET), 1984; "Maiden of Deception Pass," a one-hour dramatic screenplay for NAPBC, 1984-85; "I Am Different From My Brother," rewrite of six half-hour scripts, NAPBC, 1986; "The Runaway," half-hour teleplay, NET, 1986; "Indians & AIDS," 20 & 30 second public service announcements for national television, Powhatan Renape Nation, 1988; "When We Used to Be Humans," in development (American Film Foundation); co-producer & writer, "The Sacred Revolt: The Red Sticks' Wars," full-length dramatic story. *Other film experience*: "American Indian Artist Series II" (composed poetry for narration & worked as production assistant, PBS, 1986); appeared on "Wildflowers," with Helen Hayes (KERA-TV documentary as a storyteller, PBS, 1992); reader for audio library recording, Circle of Nations, Voices & Visions of American Indians, edited by John Gattuso (Beyond Words, 1993); narrator, "Sand Creek," dramatic on-hour movie for Deborah Dennison (Santa Fe, 1994); narrator, the "Native Americans" 6-part series (Turner Broadcasting, 1994). *Biographical sources*: International Authors & Writers Who's Who; International Who's Who of Authors; World Who's Who of Women; Personalities of the West & Midwest; Foremost Women of the 20th Century; 5,000 Personalities of the World; The International Directory of Distinguished Leadership; Who's Who in U.S. Writers, Editors, & Poets; Contemporary American Writers; Poets & Writers. *Published works*: She has published four books of poetry including: She Had Some Horses (Thunder's Mouth Press, New York, NY); In Mad Love and War (Wesleyan University Press, 1990); anthology, Talking Leaves, Contemporary Native American Short Stories (Dell, 1991); collaborated with photographer/astronomer Stephen Strom to produce, Secrets From the Center of the World (University of Arizona Press); The Woman Who Fell From the Sky (W.W. Norton, 1994); co-wrote with Scott Garen, a filmscript, A Thousand Roads; also, an anthology of Native women's writing, Reinventing the Enemy's Language (U. of Arizona Press, 1997); A Map to the Next World (W.W. Norton, 2000); How We Became Human, New & Selected Poems, 2000; children's book, The GoodLuck Cat (Harcourt Brace, 2000); Soul Talk, Song Language, Conversations with Joy Harjo (Wesleyan University Press, 2012); Crazy Brave, a memoir (W.W. Norton, 2012. *Music releases*: CD with her band "Poetic Justice," Letter From the End of the 20th Century (Red Horses Records, 1996, Silver Wave Records, 1997; Native Joy for Real, solo (Mekko Productions, 2004); She Had Some Horses (Mekko Productions, 2006); Winding Through the Milky Way (Mekko Productions, 2009); Red Dreams, A Trail Beyond Tears (Mekko Productions, 2010). Joy is at work on a new show, commissioned by the Public Theater, "We Were There When Jazz Was Invented," a musical story that proves southeastern indigenous tribes are part of the origins of American music.

HARJO, LAURA (Muscogee Creek)
(professor of geography)
Education: University of Southern California, BA, Graduate Certificate in GIS, PhD (Geography). *Affiliation & Address*: Teaches geography & GIS, University of Southern California, Department of Geography, GIS Distance Learning Programs, 3616 Trousdale Pkwy., Suite B55, Los Angeles, CA 90089 (999) 907-0374. Laura has worked with her tribe and several others in conducting surveys & community development projects, has been the director of a tribal GIS center, & has coordinated land management activities. *Other professional post*: Board member, Indian Land Tenure Foundation, Little Canada, MN.

HARJO, LISA D. (Muscogee Creek)
(executive director)

Education: University of California, Davis, BS (Child Development & Native American Education & Counseling); University of Colorado, Denver, MA (Elementary Education, Curriculum & Instruction). *Affiliation & Address*: Executive Director, Native Amerian Cancer Research, 3110 S. Wadsworth, Suite 103, Denver, CO 80227 (303) 975-2449. Past professional posts: Director, Circle of Learning Early Childhood & Family Education Program, Denver Native Americans United, Denver Indian Center, Denver, CO; Adjunct Faculty, The Falmouth Institute, Fairfax, VA. Lisa has about 20 years experience in preschool education. She has administered a Head Start program in Denver and co-authored, "The Circle Never Ends," a multicultural American Indian based early childhood curriculum.

HARJO, LEONARD M. (Seminole of Oklahoma)
(tribal principal chief)

Education: Harvard University, BA (Economics), 1979. In 1986 he received a First Nations Fellowship to The Yale School of Organization & Management, graduated in 1988 with a Master's degree in Public & Private Management. *Affiliation & Address*: Principal Chief, Seminole Nation of Oklahoma, P.O. Box 1498, Wewoka, OK 74884 (405) 257-7205. *Past professional posts*: Oklahoma Indian Affairs Commission; the United Tribes of Western Oklahoma & Kansas, Inc.; Oklahoma Dept. of Commerce. In 1988, Chief Harjo entered employment with the Seminole Nation and for ten years he served in a variety of positions, including: Tribal Planner, Director of Economic Development, and first Director of the Seminole Nation Development Authority; executive director, Div. of Health Administration, Muscogee (Creek) Nation, 1998-2002; Since 2002, Mr. Harjo has provided project management & strategic planning services to tribes across western U.S. through his company, The Harjo Group, LLC. *Community services*: Regent for Seminole State College; member of the Board of Directors for Rural Enterprises, Inc.; member of various state committees; liaison to various tribal organizations & federal agencies, including the Oklahoma City area, National Indian Health Boards, and the IHS National Budget Formulation Team.

HARJO, RHONDA (Creek)
(attorney)

Affiliation & Address: Majority Senior Counsel, Senate Committee on Indian Affairs, 836 Hart Office Bldg., Washington, DC 20510 (202) 224-2251.

HARJO, SUZAN SHOWN (Cheyenne, Hodulgee Muscogee) 1945-
(writer, lecturer, curator, policy analyst)

Born June 2, 1945, El Reno, Okla. *Principal occupation*: Writer, poet, policy analyst, arts curator. *Affiliation & Address*: President & Executive Director, The Morning Star Institute, 403 15th St., SE, Washington, DC 20003 (202) 547-5531 1984-present. The Institute is a non-profit organization for Native American cultural rights & arts advocacy. *Other professional posts*: Founding Co-chair, Howard Simons Fund for Indian Journalists, 1989-present; columnist for Indian Country Today; board member, Native American Journalists Association; UNITY Journalists of Color, Inc., McLean, VA. *Past professional posts*: Special assistant for Indian Legislation, Carter Administration, 1978-79; co-founder & vice-president, Native Children's Survival; executive director, National Congress of American Indians, 1984-89; news director, American Indian Press Association; drama & literature director and "Seeing Red" producer for WBAI-FM Radio in New York City. *Community activities*: Common Cause (national governing board, 1982-88); National Museum of the American Indian, 1990-96 (Founding Trustee; member, executive committee, and collections committee; chair, program planning committee); lead negotiator of both the 1989 agreement with the Smithsonian Institution that led to the first repatriation law & the later agreement with the national museum community which resulted in the Native American Grave Protection & Repatriation Act of 1990, and was key to the development of the 1991 NMAI Trustees Policy Statement on Repatriation; Ms. Harjo served on the steering committee and as advocacy committee co-chair of a broad-based national coalition of Indian nations & organizations and environmental, human rights & religious groups to secure legal protections for Native Peoples' sacred places and passage of the Native American Free Exercise of Religion Act of 1993. She served as co-chair of the Indian organizing committee for the 1993 March on Washington, and is a charter member & organizer of Artists in Support of American Indian Religious Freedom, formed in 1992. She has helped Indian nations to recover nearly a million acres of land and to achieve appropriations & protections for sacred sites, natural resources, child welfare, health and other social services programs, hospitals, schools & cultural concerns. She has championed treaty rights and individual civil liberties cases, and has developed key federal Indian policy in Washington, DC for nearly two decades, conducting more than 350 successful legislative and appropriation efforts. On December 29, 1990, she participated in the 100-year commemoration of the Massacre of Lakota people at Wounded Knee. At the end of 1990, Congress passed a formal resolution apologizing tot he descendants of the victims of the 1890 Massacre. At the end of 1991, the legislation to establish a Little Big Horn Indian Memorial and to drop the name of Custer from the National Monument was signed into law; she

curated three journal gallery exhibits for the Cornell-based Native Americas: "Native Images in American Editorial Cartoons" (2001); "New Native Warrior Images in Art" (2001); & "Identity Perspectives by Native Artists" (2002). *Memberships*: Cheyenne-Arapaho Tribes of Oklahoma; Native American Journalists Association (board member); American Association of Museums (Committee on Museum & Native American Collaboration); Museum of the American Indian Heye Foundation (Trustee, 1983-90); National Congress of American Indians (executive director, 1984-89); The Association of American Cultures (board member, 1990-); National Commission on Libraries & Information Services Native American Task Force (board member, 1990-); American Indian Press Association (former news director). *Awards, honors*: The Keynote Speaker for the following events: California Indian Education Annual Conference, the University of South Dakota Law School's Indian Law Symposium on Sovereignty, the Ohio Arts Council's Native American Regional Conference, the Native North American Indian Women's Association's Annual Conference, the Federal Communication's Commission Heritage Symposium, the Tourism Conference of the Affiliated Tribes of Northwest Indians, and the Journalism & Women Symposium; Guest Speaker in the Getty Center for the History of Art in Los Angeles, at the "Red Nations Celebration of Native American Women" in Santa Fe, as well as the benefit concert for the "Sacred Run," introduced by Sacred Run Coordinator, Dennis Banks, at the El Ray Theatre in Albuquerque; 1998-99 Brain Trust Member for UNITY; Journalists of Color and a presenter at UNITY '99 in Seattle and UNITY '94 in Atlanta; the 1996 Stanford University Visiting Mentor; Special Guest Speaker at the 1995 All Apache Summit in Albuquerque; and 1992 Dartmouth Collect Montgomery Fellow. She was the first Native American selected for the honor by Stanford's Haas Center for Public Policy, and the first Native woman chosen for the Montgomery Fellowship Award. In 1993, she presented poetry readings at the Denver Art Museum, the Cleveland Public Theatre, and the Roxy Theatre in Los Angeles. She has appeared in poetry readings with Native American poets Joy Harjo & John Trudell, and with 20 American women writers including Nikki Giovanni and Alice Walker. She was a National Coordinator of the 1992 Alliance, which was the focal point for Native voices on the Columbus Quint-centennial, and was co-chair and coordinator of "Our Visions: The Next 500 Years," the historic gathering of Native artists, writers and wisdom-keepers (Taos Pueblo, 1992). Her policy & political writings have appeared in many magazines, journals, and newspapers. She has helped Native Peoples' recover more than one million acres of land. She also has developed the most important national policy advances in the modern era for the protection of Native American cultures & arts, including the 1996 Executive Order on Indian Sacred Sites, the 1990 Native American Graves Protection and Repatriation Act, the 1989 National Museum of the American Indian Act, and special assistant for Indian Legislation & Liaison in the Carter Administration and principal author of the 1979 President's Report to Congress on American Indian Religious Freedom. She has been profiled in the NY Times, Lear's, Fortune, High Times, UNITY Magazine, Glamour, Rocky Mountain News, and The Plains Dealer, and has been featured on the Oprah Winfrey Show, Larry King Live, CNN's World Day, Crier & Co., and Sonya Live, among others. In 1993, she wrote the Foreword for George Cantor's North American Indian Landmarks (Visible Ink Press, 1993). Ms. Harjo lectures throughout the U.S., including speeches for the past decade at the Harvard Law School, the Nieman Foundation for Journalism, and the Principal's Institute. She has presented poetry and/or lectures at various other universities and colleges. In 1991, she read with author, Michael Dorris from "The Crown of Columbus," at Chapters in Washington, DC. In 1992, she keynoted with Rev. Jesse Jackson the Multicultural Leadership Summit in January in Washington, DC, & shared a keynote address with California State Assemblyman Tom Hayden to open the "Seeds of Change" Conference in Sept. in Santa Fe, NM. Interests: At present, Ms. Harjo is developing Native Peoples' cultural property rights policy for the protection of such cultural property as tribal names, symbols, history and music building on the cultural patrimony provisions of the repatriation laws and policies. At the same time, she is addressing the issues of stereotyping, name-calling and the use of Indian imagery in popular culture through broad public awareness campaign, focusing on the sports media. *Published works*: Ms. Harjo's poetry has been published in journals, anthologies & textbooks. Her policy writings, arts criticism & social commentary have appeared in numerous newspapers & magazines. She has authored entries on Contemporary Native American arts: 1960-1995 for the "Encyclopedia of American Indians" (1996), and on the U.S. Senate Committee on Indian Affairs for "Native America in the Twentieth Century: An Encyclopedia." Her work is included in such books as "American Voices"; "Cast a Cold Eye: American Opinion Writing, 1990-91; "The Concise Guide to Writing"; "Elements of Writing"; "Exploring Ancient Native America"; "Family Ethnicity"; Native America: Portrait of the Peoples'; "Native North American Voices"; Rethinking Schools" among others.

HARJO, TIM (Muscogee Creek)
(acquisitions & programming manager)

Affiliation & Address: Acquisitions & Programming Manager, First Nation Experience (FNX), 701 S. Mt. Vernon Ave., San Bernardino, CA 92410 (909) 384-4444. FNX is the first television channel to broadcast only Native American & Indigenous peoples content. *Other professional post*: Chairperson,

Board of Directors, Prairie Band, LLC, Mayetta, KS. *Past professional post*: CEO, Earthstream Media, Santa Monica, CA.

HARJO, WILLIAM (Creek)
(flutemaker, musician, storyteller; board member)
Affiliation: American Indian Resource Center, 4914 Nuthatch, San Antonio, TX 78217 (210) 655-1300.

HARJU, PHILIP (Cowlitz)
(tribal vice chairperson; attorney)
Affiliation & Address: Cowlitz Indian Tribe, P.O. Box 2547, Longview, WA 98632 (360) 577-8140. E-mail: pharju@cowlitz.org. *Other tribal post*: Tribal attorney.

HARKIN, MICHAEL
(professor of anthropology & American Indian studies)
Education: University of Chicago, MA & PhD (Anthropology). *Affiliation & Address*: Professor of Anthropology & American Indian Studies, Department of American Indian Studies, Anthropology Bldg. 118, Laramie, WY 82071 (307) 766-3127. E-mail: harkin@uwyo.edu. *Research Interests*: Ethnohistory, the Northwest Coast, cultural theory, politics & power, and religious movements, transcultural representations. *Research areas*: Northwst Coast (Heiltsuk, Nuu-chah-nulth), Southeast (The Lost Colony), Wyoming (public lands ethnohistory. Michael teaches North American Indians for American Indian Studies.

HARKINS, AARON J.
(attorney)
Education: University of Wisconsin, BS, 1999; University of Wisconsin Law School, JD, 2002. *Affiliation & Address*: Partner, Faegre Baker Daniels, 2200 Wells Fargo Center, 90 S. Seventh St., Minneapolis, MN 55402 (612) 766-7442. E-mail: aaron.harkins@faegrebd.com. Aaron is on the firm's Indian tribes team and finance & restructuring practice group. He has an active Indian finance practice with experience representing both tribes & financial institutions in connection with bond offerings, bank loans and a broad range of other financing transactions. He represents clients throughout the United States on matters involving tribal, state and federal gaming laws, including management, development & consulting agreements for tribal gaming operations, gaming machine & equipment leases, tribal-state gaming compacts and matters before the National Indian Gaming Commission & tribal & state gaming commissions. Aaron's legal experience includes representing tribes and financial institutions in connection with all aspects of financing projects in Indian country. *Awards, honors*: Chambers USA: America's Leading Lawyers for Business — Native American Law, 2010-16; *Minnesota Super Lawyers* — Rising Stars, Native American Law, 2008, 2010 and 2012-16; *Global Game Business* — Emerging Leaders, 40 Under 40, 2013. Presentations; *The Best Lawyers in America* — Native American Law, 2017

HARLAN, MARSHA L. (Osage)
(attorney)
Education: Northeastern State University, BA/BS, 1991; University of Tulsa Law School, JD, 1999. *Affiliation & Address*: Partner, Legal Advocates for Indian Country, LLP, P.O. Bx 1434, Owasso, OK 74055 (918) 376-0630. Her practice concentrates in the areas of tribal governance, state-tribal relaions, tribal courts, tribal child support enforcement, domestic relations, children's rights advocacy, and mediation. *Other professional posts*: Founding partner in the consulting firm of Indian Collaborative Consultants, LLC; serves as a justice on the Pawnee Supreme Court & Miami Tribe of Oklahoma Supreme Court; district judge for the Kickapoo Tribe of Oklahoma & the Seminole Tribe of Oklahoma. *Past professional posts*: Solo-practitioner focusing on domestic relations, tribal law & children's rights advocacy; served as district judge for the Osage Nation.

HARMON, ALEXANDRIA "SASHA" 1945-
(professor of American Indian studies)
Education: Stanford University, BA, 1966; Yale Law School, JD, 1972; University of Washington, PhD (History), 1995. *Affiliation & Address*: Associate Professor, Department of American Indian Studies, Padelford Hall C-514, Box 354305, University of Washington, Seattle, WA 98195 (206) 543-7116. E-mail: aharmon@u.washington.edu. *Past professional post*: Advisor to Indian tribes in Washington State, 1972-1988. *Research Interests*: Examines histories of American Indians, with specific relations with non-Indians, to changing legal cultures, to ethnic, racial, and tribal identities, and to influences of and changes in economic cultures. *Awards, honors*: The 1999 Washington Governor's Writer's Award for book, Indians in the Making." *Published work*: Indians in the Making: Ethnic Relations & Indians Identities Around the Puget Sound (University of California Press, 1998); Rich Indians: Native People and the Problem of Wealth in American History (U. of North Carolina Press, 2013).

HARPER, CARL L. (Cherokee) 1950-
(IHS - ORAP director)
Education: Northeastern Oklahoma State University, BA, 1972; University of Kansas, MA, 1978; University of Oklahoma (training sessions). *Affiliation*: Director, Office of Resource Access & Partnerships (ORAP), Indian Health Service (IHS), DHH, Rm. 360, 12300 Twinbrook Parkway, Rockville, MD 20852 (301) 443-3216. *Past affiliations*: Senior Management Analyst, IHS, 1988-92; director, Office of Executive Management & executive officer, Office of Health programs, IHS, 1992-2004. *Awards, honors*: Numerous Superior Performance Awards; IHS National Council of Executive Officers Service Award; various IHS Director's Group Awards.

HARPER, KEITH M. (Cherokee) 1961-
(attorney)
Education: University of California, Berkeley, BA, 1990; New York University School of Law, JD, 1994. *Affiliation & Address*: Partner, Kilpatrick Townsend & Stockton, (Native American Affairs Team), 607 14th St., NW, Suite 900, Washington, DC 20005 (202) 508-5844. *Past professional posts*: U.S. Representative & Ambassador to the United Nations Human Rights Council (2014-17), Washington, DC. (Keith was the first ever member of a federally-recognized Indian Tribe to serve as a U.S. Ambassador); Senior Staff Attorney litigator at the Native American Rights Fund, Washington, DC, 1995-2006; adjunct professor of Federal Indian Law at the Catholic University Columbus School of Law & American University Washington College of Law, 1998-2001; appointed Appellate Justice on the highest court of the Mashantucket Pequot Tribal Nation, 2001-07; served on the Supreme Court of the Poarch Band of Creek Indians; Partner, Kilpatrick Townsend & Stockton, LLP, Washington, DC, 2007-13 (Partner & Chair of the Native Ameican Practice Group). In his previous legal practice, Mr. Harper focuses his practice on litigation & Native American affairs. He has represented tribes & individual Indians. *Awards, honors*: Keith served as a principal Advisor & Chair of the Native American Domestic Policy Committee for the Obama campaign and then as a member of the Obama-Biden Presidential Transition Team in the Energy & Environment Cluster. The National Law Journall selected Mr. Harper as one of 50 "Most Influential Minority Lawyers in America" in May 2008; 2010-13 editions of Chambers USA: America's Leading Lawyers for Business; recognized in "The Best Lawyers in America for Native American Law from 2008-13; listed in 2010, 2012 & 2013 Washington, DC "Super Lawyer" in Native American Law by Super Lawyers magazine; selected as a Leadership Conference on Civil Rights delegate to World Conference Aganst Racism in Durban, South Africa.

HARRELL, BEATRICE ORCUTT (Ohoyo Oti) (Choctaw/Creek)
(tutor)
Address: 13962 Hickory Place, Glenpool, OK 74033 (918) 291-3014. *Affiliation*: Indian education tutor, Sapupla Public Schools, Sapulpa, OK. *Community activities*: Cultural & fund raising activities for the Indian education program. Membership: Wordcraft Circle of Native American Writers & Storytellers. *Published work*: How Thunder & Lightning Came to Be.

HARRELL, RAY EVANS (*Nudvwiv Ani-noquisi*) (Keetoowah) 1941-
(artistic director, conductor, master teacher, performing artist)
Born December 3, 1941, Ada, Okla. *Education*: University of Tulsa, B. Mus., 1972; Manhattan School of Music, M. Mus., 1973; The Ilana Rubenfeld Center (New York, NY), RSM Certification, 1979. *Principal occupation*: Artistic director, conductor, master teacher, performing artist. *Address*: 200 West 70th St., #6C, New York, NY 10023 (212) 724-2398. *Affiliations*: Teacher, Manhattan School of Music, New York, NY, 1979-86; artistic director & developer of the Magic Circle Opera Repertory Ensemble, Inc. of New York, and the Magic Circle Training, New York, NY, 1978-. Harrell conducts the Magic Circle Ensemble in world premiere recordings of operas by Ned Rorem, "A Childhood Miracle & Three Sisters Who Are Not Sisters," as well as the Kurt Vonnegut/Edgar D. Grana Humanist Requiem, "Stones, Times & Elements." He is producer/artistic director/conductor for works like LaMama E.T.C.'s revolutionary "Flamenco Carmen" in New York City. A veteran performer and Metropolitan Opera Regional semi-finalist, Mr. Harrell is known for critically acclaimed performances and recitals across America in such venues as New York City's Weill Recital Hall and Lincoln Center's Alice Tully Hall, Carnegie Hall Main Stage and Avery Fisher Hall at Lincoln Center, Wolf Trap, and Constitution Hall in the Nation's Capital, among others. *Other professional posts*: Mr. Harrell writes, "a private teacher of illustrious singers in classical, contemporary and popular music, my students have performed in every major venue in New York City, across America, as well as in Europe and the Far East." Institutional Teaching & Lecture credentials include commissioned piano teacher & educational research (four years), University of Tulsa, OK; teacher of voice, Singers & Composer's Workshop and Vocal Anatomy at Manhattan School of Music, New York City (seven years); director of summer opera productions at Mannes College (two summers), New York City; guest lecturer on "Learning Organizations & Donald Schon" in Columbia U. Teacher's College PhD program (two years); lecturer on Somantics, the Arts and the Future of Work, Arts Economics, Culture & Diversity, e.g. at various schools and companies in

the New York City area, Auburn & Union Theological Seminary, Adelphi U., Manhattan School of Music, Mannes College, Lucent Technologies, New York City's Museum of Natural History, and conferences here and in Canada, and on the Internet. Opera singer in New York City & on London Records with Antol Dorati; conductor, MCORE Opera & Concert & Newport Classics Recordings; private voice teacher; former editor, The New York Singing Teacher's Bulletin; columnist, "Nuyagi Keetoowah Journal." *Military service*: U.S. Army Chorus, 1966-70 (staff sgt.); soloist, U.S. Army Field Band (touring) Fort Meade, Md., 1965-66. *Community activities*: Harrell is the Traditional Cherokee Proest (Didahnvwisgi) in New York's traditional Keetoowah community & speaks regularly on American Indian subjects in schools & companies as well as at the United Nations. *Memberships*: Nuyagi Keetoowah Society (council & columnist); New York Singing Teacher's Association (former editor & board of directors); Screen Actor's Guild; The American Guild of Musical Artists. *Awards, honors*: Harrell has convened a Blue Ribbon Roundtable of International Arts and Economics Experts on the Internet. In 2003, he will produce the Ned Rorem International Festival in New York City hosting performances of Rorem's work nationwide and in Europe. *Biographical source*: The International Who's Who in Music & Musicians' Directory, 11th (1988) and 20th (1996) editions.

HARRINGTON, SOPHIA (Creek)
(publisher)
Address & Affiliation: Owner, Semihoye-Shawnee Publishing, P.O. Box 5595, Norman, OK 73070 (405) 321-0900.

HARRIS, BARTLEY (Saulteaux-Cree from Peguis First Nation, (Manitoba/Dakota Plains Wahpeton Oyate)
Education: University of Lethbridge & Brigham Young University, B.Mgt. Finance); University of Manitoba, LLM (Indigenous jurisdiction over Gaming); ASU W.P. Carey School of Business, MBA; Arizona State University (ASU) Sandra Day O'Connor College of Law, JD. *Affiliation & Address*: Research Analyst, American Indian Policy Institute, Arizona State University, Box 872603, Tempe, AZ 85287(480) 965-1055. E-mail: bartley.harris@asu.edu. Bartley joins the American Indian Policy Institute from private practice of law in Arizona where he provided legal counsel to tribes & tribal corporations. Bartley's professional experience includes working for tribes in the United States & Canada. While in Canada, Bartley served as the Director of Gaming Development for a political organization representing the interests of 63 First Nations in Manitoba. In addition, Bartley worked for Canada's largest financial institution as a Senior Officer, Trust overseeing the management of First Nation trusts in the Manitoba and Ontario regions.

HARRIS, CURTIS (San Carlos Apache)
(project founder)
Resides in Montclair, NJ. Founder of the HIV/AIDS Project at the American Indian Community House. Established the Native American Leadership Commission on HIV/AIDS; also co-produced an education & prevention plan for Native American communities that resulted in the creation of four satellite clinics across the state. Board memberships: American Indian Community House, New York, NY; American Indian Law Alliance, New York, NY.

HARRIS, JASON (Catawba)
(tribal assistant chief)
Affiliation & Address: Assistant Chief, Catawba Indian Tribe, 996 Avenue of the Nations, Catawba, SC 29730 (803) 366-4792. *Past tribal post*: Former tribal secretary-treasurer.

HARRIS, LaDONNA (Comanche) 1931-
(organization founder/president)
Born February 15, 1931, Temple, Okla. *Affiliation & Address*: Founder & President, Americans for Indian Opportunity (1970-present), 1001 Marquette Ave., NW, Albuquerque, NM 87102 (505) 842-8677. E-Mail: aio@aio.org. Select Lectureships: Woodrow Wilson Fellow, 1982-; Aspen Institute; America Program Institute; Washington School of the Institute for Policy Studies. *Networking experience*: Launched a National American Indian leadership Program, The American Indian Ambassadors Program: "Medicine Pathways for the Future"; created the first Indian-owned & operated National Computer Network dedicated to provide information of interest to Native Americans & access to the National Information Highway; developed & implemented a series of four regional issue management forums for Indian tribes in overcoming barriers to working with environment protection agency; facilitated a series of governance forums with Poarch Creek, Winnebago, Comanche, Cheyenne-Arapaho, Pawnee, Apache & Menominee tribes; among others. *Community activities*: Oklahomans for Indian Opportunity, Inc. (founder/past president, 1965-70); founder, Council for Energy Resource Tribes, 1976. *Memberships*: Haskell Indian Junior College Foundation; National Indian Business Association; National Institute for Women of Color (advisory council); National Institute for the Environment (advisory council); Jacobson Foundation (honorary board); Native American Public Broadcasting Consortium; among others. *Awards, honors*: Outstanding American Citizen of 1965, Anadarko (OK)

American Indian Exposition and the Tulsa Indian Council, 1965; Woman of the Year, 1979, Ladies Home Journal; Lucy Covington Award for a Life of Leadership; Human Rights Award: Delta Sigma Theta Society, National Education Association; Outstanding Leadership in Advancing Public Support: 1990 Census; Honorary Doctor of Law, Dartmouth College; Honorary Doctor of Humanities, Marymount College; Honorary Doctor of Public Service, Westfield State College, MA; Honorary Doctor of Humanities, Northern Michigan University; Honorary West Virginian; adjunct professor, Te Wonanga O Aotearoa; in 1994, Vice President Gore recognized Harris as a leader in the area of telecommunications and was appointed by Sec. of Commerce Ron Brown to the Advisory Council on the National Information Infrastructure. *Interests*: Traveled extensively through Latin America, Russia & the former Soviet Union & Greece. Harris has spent many years training the executive branch of the federal government that tribes are an integral part of the political fabric of the U.S. She has held hundreds of forum on the issues surrounding the interaction between tribes & federal agencies. She applies much of her energy in reinforcing & strengthening tribal government. She has encouraged tribes to reweave traditional value based methods of consensus building into their governance systems. Harris was instrumental in the adoption of official Indian policies by the EPA, the Dept. of Energy, and Dept. of Agriculture. She still advocates for every federal department to create Indian policies that reaffirm a government-to-government relationship. In recent years, Harris has devoted much of her energies to her newest initiatives, the Americans for Indian Opportunity Ambassadors Program, which researches & demonstrates the innovations of Indigenous leadership development & identity. She believes that part of her own work as a leader must be mentoring & cultivating new leaders to take her place & the places of others like her. Consequently, the Ambassadors Program was designed to facilitate this trans-generational transition of leadership in Indian Country. This award-winning initiative is the only leadership program in the U.S. that encourages its participants to weave their respective traditional tribal values into a contemporary reality. *Published works*: LaDonna Harris: A Comanche Life, book edited by Henrietta Stockel (University of Nebraska Press, 2000); books & pamphlets published by the Americans for Indian Opportunity, including: A Resource Bibliography for Tribal Participation in Environmental Protection Activities, 1990; Tribal Governments in the U.S. Federal System, 1990; Designing the Future of the Comanche Tribe, 1990; To All My Comanche Relatives, 1990; Tribal Governments As Rural Health Providers; Designing the Economic Future of the Menominee People, 1991; Partnerships for the Protection of Tribal Environments, 1991; significant papers include: "To Govern or Be Governed: Indian Tribes at a Crossroads"; "Partnerships for the Protection of Tribal Environments"; "Indian Business Opportunities and the Defense Sector"; "Alternatives for Agriculture: Successful Tribal Farms"; "Hard Choices: Development of Non-Energy, Non-Replenishable Resources"; "Tribal Governments in the U.S. Federal System".

HARRIS, STUART G. (Confederated Tribes Umatilla Reservation)
(senior cultural risk associate)
Education: Eastern Oregon State University, BS; Oregon State University, BS. *Affiliation & Address*: Director, Department of Sciences & Engineering, Confederated Tribes of the Umatilla Indian Reservation (CTUIR), P.O. Box 638, Pendleton, OR 97801 (541) 966-2408. E-mail: stuartharris@ctuir.com.. He develops policy & technical guidance for and briefs tribal decision-makers on, CTUIR positions on risk-based cleanup levels & integration of Department of Energy oversight at Hanford. Stuart has written extensively on the tribal culture-risk interface. Among his latest writings with Dr. Barbara Harper are: Risk Assessment for Tribal Communities, and Risk Assessment for Native Americans.

HARRIS, WILLIAM "BILL" (Catawba)
(tribal chief)
Affiliation & Address: Chief, Catawba Indian Nation, 996 Avenue of the Nations, Rock Hill, SC 29730 (803) 366-4792.

HARRIS-TAYLOR, RHONDA LYNETTE (Choctaw of Oklahoma) 1951-
(library science educator)
Born April 24, 1951, Hugo, Okla. *Education*: North Texas State University, BS, 1974; Baylor University, Certificate for School Librarian, 1978; Texas Woman's University, MLS, 1980, PhD, 1985. *Affiliation & Address*: School of Library & Information Science, 401 W. Brooks, Room 120, University of Oklahoma, Norman, OK 73019 (405) 325-3921. *Past professional posts*: Assistant professor, 1992-99, associate professor, 1999-. *Other professional posts*: American Indian Library Association (AILA) (past president, 1984-90; editor, AILA Newsletter; member, Office of Admissions Native American Appeals Committee, 1995-; member, Planning & Budget Committee, College of Arts & Sciences, University of Oklahoma, 1999-2001. *Memberships*: American Indian Library Association; American Library Association; Association for Library & Information Science Education; Association of American Indian/Alaska Native Professors; Oklahoma Library Association; Popular Culture Association (area co-chair-with Judith Overmier-Libraries & Popular Culture (panel), 1995-). *Awards, honors*: Beta Phi Mu; Beta Lambda Chapter; Delta Kappa Gamma; Phi Kappa Phi.

HARRISON, DAVID C. (Osage-Cherokee) 1945-
(attorney; Indian program director)
Born July 28, 1945, Pawhuska, Okla. *Education*: Grinnell College, BA, 1967; Harvard Law School, JD, 1975. *Affiliation & Address*: Attorney (Mesothelioma Legal Experts), 1800 John F. Kennedy Blvd. #500, Philadelphia, PA 19103 (215) 665-1021. *Past professional posts*: Rights Protection Officer, BIA, Washington DC; director, Native American National Intern Program, American University, Washington, DC. *Military service*: U.S. Marine Corps, 1967-71 (Captain, Vietnamese Cross of Gallantry, Bronze Star, Purple Heart). *Memberships*: Osage Heloshka Society; Harvard Law School Association. *Awards, honors*: "I served as senior investigator and authored several chapters of report called by New York Times editorial, a magnificent document, sweeping in scope, meticulous in detail, unsparing in assessing blame." *Published work*: Attica, Official Report of the New York State Special Commission on Attica (Bantam, paper, Praeger, hardcover, 1972).

HARRISON, GARY (Aleut)
(Alaskan village chief)
Affiliation & Address: Chief, Chickaloon Native Village, P.O. Box 1105, Chickaloon, AK 99674 (907) 745-0749.

HARRISON, KATHRYN (Grand Ronde Molalla)
(Distinguished Fellow; former tribal chairperson)
Education: Chemawa Indian School (Oregon); Lane Community College, Eugene, OR (Nursing degree). *Affiliation & Address*: Distinguished Fellow, The Institute for Tribal Government, Portland State University, P.O. Box 751, Portland, OR 97207. As a founding member of the Policy Board of the Institute, she oversees the Great Tribal Leaders of Modern Times Interview Project," a video collection of the personal histories of contemporary tribal leaders. *Other professional post*: Serves as a governor's appointee to the Oregon Council for the Humanities. *Past professional posts*: Former chairperson, Confederated Tribes of the Grand Ronde Tribe, Grand Ronde, OR. She played a central role in obtaining federal recognition & restoration of the Grand Ronde Tribe in 1983, and represented her Tribe's interests in many organizations. *Awards, honors*: YWCA Woman of Achievement Award, 1995; Distinguished Service Award, League of Women Voters, 1995; American Indian Business leaders White Crown Award, 1999; Woman of Achievement Award, Oregon Commission for Women, 1999; Tom McCall Leadership Award from SOLV, 2001.

HARRY, DEBRA (Northern Paiute)
(executive director)
Education: New Hampshire College, MA (Community Economic Development), 1997; University of Aukland, School of Education, PhD. *Affiliation & Address*: Executive Director, Indigenous Peoples Council on Biocolonialism, P.O. Box 72, Nixon, NV 89424 (775) 574-0248. Website: www.ipcb.org. *Other professional post*: Founder & Director, Emerging Indigenous Leaders Institute. Resides in Pyramid Lake, Nevada. Dr. Harry has developed and teaches a 10-week online course titled, Protecting Cultural Property in the Biotech Age," offered through UCLA's Extension Tribal Learning courses. Debra is the producer of the documentary film, "The Leach & the Earthworm," an IPCB/Yeast Directions production, which examines the globalized hunt for genes within Indigenous territories and bodies & features Indigenous activities from around the world. *Awards, honors*: Received a Kellogg Foundation leadership fellowship in 1994 and studied the field of human genetic research & implications for Indigenous peoples. *Published works*: Authored a chapter entitled, "Acts of Self-Determination & Self-Defense: Indigenous Peoples Responses to Bio-colonialism" as contribution to a new book entitled, "Rights & Liberties in the Biotech Age" edited by Krimsky & Shorett (Rowmand & Littlefield, 2005); numerous articles in scholarly journals.

HART, ARIAN (Paiute)
(tribal vice chairperson)
Affiliation & Address: Vice Chairperson, Susanville Indian Rancheria, 745 Joaquin St., Susanville, CA 96130 (530) 257-4923.

HART, DANIEL
(professor of American Indian studies)
Education: Temple University School of Communication, MFA (Film & Television), 1984. *Affiliation & Address*: Professor (1999-present), Department of American Indian Studies, Padelford Hall Box 354305, Seattle, WA 98195 (206) 616-7752. E-mail: dhart@u.washington.edu. *Other professional posts*: Co-director, Native Voices Program, director, Canadian Studies Program, University of Washington. Professor Hart is an award-winning documentary producer & director, and has been working with Native American & First Nations educators, media producers, and youth for more than 20 years. He is involved with the development of Indigenous pedagogy & indigenous research methodologies. He is also involved in multipart project, which is developing health curricula for Native American schools. His films have been screened at the Sundance Film Festival, the Museum of Modern Art, the Vienna Film Festival. *Awards, honors*: Producer of the Year, by the National Native American Film Festival. *Films co-produced & directed*: A Return to Wellness,

produced in collaboration with The Indigenous Wellness Research Institute at UW (this film is about the effects that colonization has had upon the health of Native peoples & communities, and the ways in which indigenous peoples are reclaiming their health systems); *The Healthy Heart Video Series* produced with the U. of Washington School of Medicine. This series of instructional films deals with cardiovascular health for Native youth; *A Dream for Water*, a PBS/National Science Foundation film tells the stories about tribal peoples along the Missouri River Basin and *Schools Weren't Made to Separate*, which was part of an Annenberg/Corporation for Public Broadcasting funding series exploring innovations in the education of Native American students.

HART, JASON (Pit River)
(former tribal chairperson)
Affiliation & Address: Redding Rancheria, 2000 Redding Rancheria Rd., Redding, CA 96001 (530) 225-8979.

HART, NATHAN L. (Cheyenne)
(executive vice president)
Affiliation & Address: Raven Asset Management, 2013 Northgatewood, Oklahoma City, OK 73106 (405) 521-9035. E-mail: nathanhart@yahoo.com. *Other professional posts*: Board member (1999-present), The Chickasaw Foundation; woodturning & sculpture artist since 2002. Past professional posts: Director of Cash Management, The Chickasaw Nation; Executive Director, Oklahoma Indian Affairs Commission. *Interests*: Art, business. *Membership*: Americans for Indian Opportunity.

HART, PAULA L. (St. Regis Mohawk)
(director, Office of Indian Gaming – Indian Affairs, U.S. Dept. of the Interior)
Education: St. Larence University, BS (Political Science), 1984; University of Maryland School of Law, JD, 1990. *Affiliation & Address*: Director, Office of Indian Gaming – Indian Affairs, U.S. Dept. of the Interior, 1849 C St. NW, MS-3658-MIB, Washington, DC 20240 (202) 208-3710. Reporting to the Assistant Secretary-Indian Affairs, the OIG Director is responsible for, in addition to budget, personnel and administrative matters, overseeing the development of policies & procedures used to implement the Secretary's responsibilities under the Indian Gaming Regulatory Act of 1988 (IGRA) relating to land acquisition requests from federally recognized tribes for gaming purposes, tribal-state gaming compacts, tribal gaming per capita distribution plans, and gaming-related contracts and secretarial procedures for Class III casino-type gaming. *Past professional posts*: Prior to her appointment, Paula had served as the office's acting director since May 2008. She also served from May 2008 to May 2009 as acting Chief of Staff to the Assistant Secretary-Indian Affairs where she advised on matters relating to human resources, budget & administrative functions of IA offices and programs. She also worked on special projects concerning a variety of issues including federal acknowledgment, economic development, finance and tribal governanceMs. Hart's federal career began in March 1993 when she joined the Bureau of Indian Affairs' ranks as a Rights Protection Specialist in its Eastern Area Office (now Eastern Regional Office), then located in Arlington, Va., where she assisted federally recognized tribes with boundary disputes, treaty issues and tax rights. In June 1994, she joined the Interior Department's newly established office on tribal gaming as a Management Analyst where she was tasked with developing the initial national guidance for Indian Country on gaming matters – some of which is still being used today. From July 1997 to May 2005, Ms. Hart served as a Paralegal Specialist under the Director of the Office of Indian Gaming Management (now the Office of Indian Gaming). As such, she assisted the director and senior operating staff on all legal matters concerning tribal government operations & authorities relating to Indian gaming operations. In May 2005, Ms. Hart was promoted to Deputy Director of the Office of Indian Gaming Management. In that post she held supervisory responsibilities and served in an advisory capacity to the OIGM Director, the Assistant Secretary-Indian Affairs and senior IA officials on the formulation and development of the BIA's national gaming programs to ensure compliance with IGRA and DOI policies, regulations and guidelines.

HART, STEPHEN M
(attorney)
Education: Univesity opf California, Berkeley, BA (Economics), 1980; UC Berkeley School of Law, JD, 1985. *Affiliation & Address*: Practice Group Leader of the Tribal Affairs & Gaming Law section, Lewis Roca Rothgerber Christi, LLP, 201 East Washington St., Suite 1200, Phoenix, AZ 85004 (602) 262-5787. E-mail: shart@lrrc.com. Mr. Hart concentrates his practice on Indian law, gaming law & government relations. He represents Tribes & Tribal Gaming Commissions throughout the Western U.S. *Past professional post*: Partner, Burch & Cracchiolo where he also practiced in the areas of Indian law, gaming law, and corporate & government relations. In 1999, Stehen was appointed to Director of the Arizona Department of Gaming by former Arizona Governor, Jane Hull. He served through 2002. *Memberships*: American Bar Assn; International Masters of Gaming Law; Arizona Indian Gaming Assn; Indian Law Section of the State Bar of Arizona, Past Chairman; Intertribal

Court Bar; Shingle Springs Band of Miwok Indians Tribal Court; Native American Community Health Center, Inc. Advisory Board; Learn Yes, Chairman. *Bar Admissions*: Arizona State, 1985; Yavapai Apache Tribe, 2007; Yurok Tribe, 2009; Rincon Tribe, 2010; jamul Indian Village, 2013. *Awards, honors*: 2005-15 editions of Best Lawyers in America; "AV/Preeminent Attorney" rating with Martindale-Hubbell.

HARTLEY-KELSO, DEANNA (Chickasaw)
(attorney; executive officer)
Education: University of Texas, Arlington, BA (Political Science, minor in Business Administration), 1989; Tulsa University Law School, JD, 1993. *Affiliation & Address*: Attorney General & Executive Officer, Division of Justice, Chickasaw Nation, P.O. Box 1548, Ada, OK 74821 (580) 436-7280. Prior to serving in this capacity, Deanna served as general counsel for the Nations' Legal Division and was also the first legislative counsel for the Chickasaw Tribal Legislature. Her prior employment includes general corporate work as associate corporate counsel for Color Tile, Inc. in Fort Worth, Texas and general counsel for Marketing Investors Corp. in Dallas, Texas. Deanna is licensed to practice law by the states of Texas and Oklahoma as well as the tribal courts of the Chickasaw Nation. She is a member of the Oklahoma Indian Bar Association, Native American Bar Association, the Federal Bar Association and a fellow of The College of the State Bar of Texas. As for community activities, Deanna is the vice chairperson of the Chickasaw Foundation Board of Trustees, a citizen appointee to the Arkansas Riverbed Authority, an occasional adjunct professor at East Central University in Ada, Oklahoma, and a previous volunteer for North Texas Legal Services-American Indian Law Project. She also serves on numerous other boards and committees within the Chickasaw Nation as well as having represented the Chickasaw Nation at the United Nations Working Group on the Draft Declaration of the Rights of Indigenous Peoples, in Geneva, Switzerland.

HARTMAN, RUSSELL P. (Navajo)
(museum director/curator)
Affiliation & Address: Director/Curator, Navajo Tribal Museum, P.O. Box 308, Highway 264, Window Rock, AZ 86515 (602) 871-6673.

HARTZ, GARY J.
(IHS office director)
Education: University of North Dakota, BS (Civil Engineering), 1975; Stanford University, MS (Civil Engineering); He also has completed postgraduate studies at Syracuse University, Syracuse, New York, & continued management development at the Federal Executive Institute and the Senior Managers in Government program at the John F. Kennedy School of Government at Harvard University. *Affiliation & Address*: Director, Indian Health Service Office of Environmental Health & Engineering, Indian Health Service (IHS) Headquarters, The Reyes Bldg. (RB) 801 Thompson Ave., Suite 400, Rockville, MD 20852. Mr. Hartz oversees health care facilities & staff quarters construction, facility maintenance & operations, & realty. He also has responsibility for a comprehensive environmental health program including institutional environmental health, injury prevention, and sanitation facilities construction services throughout Indian Country. *Past professional posts*: Mr. Hartz began his career with the IHS in 1971. His first assignment as a PHS Commissioned Corps Officer and Field Engineer was with the IHS Navajo Area in Tohatchi, New Mexico, followed in 1974 with an assignment to the IHS Alaska Area in Ketchikan with responsibilities for sanitation facilities construction throughout Southeast Alaska. In 1977, he transferred to the IHS Headquarters in Rockville, Maryland, where he was subsequently promoted to positions of increasing responsibility within OEHE, including Chief of the Sanitation Facilities Construction Branch, Director for the Division of Environmental Health, and ultimately to his current position of Director, OEHE. He was promoted to Assistant Surgeon General in January 1996. In August 1998, Mr. Hartz was named Acting Director for the Office of Public Health. The Office of Public Health had responsibilities for a wide range of health activities related to health leadership, policy development, and advocacy for American Indian and Alaska Native public health issues. He managed a staff that assisted the agency on budget formulation and resource allocation regarding the operation and management of IHS direct, tribal, and urban public health programs; program evaluation and assessment; research agenda; and special public health initiatives for the agency. During the period of the IHS restructuring, Mr. Hartz held the position of Acting IHS Deputy Director from 8/2004 to 2/2005. He shared the responsibility for management of a national health care delivery program responsible for providing preventive, curative, and community care for approximately 1.8 million American Indians and Alaska Natives.

HARVIER, MARTIN (Pima-Maricopa) 1959-
(tribal vice president)
Born in Poston, Ariz. *Affiliation*: Vice President, Salt River Pima-Maricopa Indian Community, 10005 E. Osborn Rd., Scottsdale, AZ 85256. (480) 850-8000. *Other professional post*: Phoenix Area Representative, National Indian Health Board, Washington, DC.

HASKAYA, CARMEL LEWIS (Acoma Pueblo)
(artist)
Address: P.O. Box 35, San Fidel, NM 87049. *Artwork*: Traditional Acoma pottery made of native clays, painted with mineral paints in original Acoma and Anasazi designs.

HASKEW, DENNY (Citizen Band Potawatomi) 1948-
(artist/bronze sculptor)
Born March 15, 1949, Denver, Colo. *Education*: University of Utah, BA, 1971. *Principal occupation*: Artist/bronze sculptor. *Address*: 540 N. Grant, Loveland, CO 80537 (970) 663-6375. *Affiliation*: Owner, Haskew Studio's, Loveland, CO, 1986-. *Other professional posts*: Rafting guide - Idaho/Arizona; ski instructor - Utah/Idaho. *Military service*: U.S. Army, 1971-73 (PFC-4; Markmanship, Leadership, Honorable Discharge). *Memberships*: Indian Arts & Crafts Association; American Indian Cowboy Association. *Awards, honors*: Cheyenne Frontier Museum Regional Shows, Cheyenne, WY: 1987 & 1989 Sculpture Awards for, "Robed in Indigo" & "Courage to Lead" respectively; Red Earth Invitational, Oklahoma City, OK: 1988, 1990, 1992 & 1993 Sculpture Awards for, "Ancient Defender," "Moulding Our Future" monument; "Strength of the Maker," & "Courage to Lead" monument; Colorado Indian Market, Denver, CO: 1988 & 1989 Best of Class for "Trail of Prayers" & "At Eagles Glance"; Santa Fe Indian Market: 1989 1st Place Sculpture for, "At Eagles Glance"; 1989 presentation of "Courage to Lead" to W.K. Kellogg Foundation by the National Fellowship Program, Battlecreek, MI; Indian Arts & Crafts Association: "1991 Artist of the Year" Award for "Courage to Lead"; 1991 Judges Merit Award for "Trail of Prayers" from Wildlife and Western Art Exhibition; 1991, 1st, 2nd & 3rd Place for "Trail of Prayers," "He Who Fights With a Feather," & "Committed" from Odham Tosh, Casa Grande, AZ; 1991, 1st & 2nd Place for "Strength of the Maker" & "Committed;" 1s & 2nd Place, 1991 & 1992 Gallup Ceremonial Show; Smithsonian Institute (1992 Best of Show, 1st & 3rd Place, 1st Place Sculpture Award, "Courage to Lead" monument1992 Santa Fe Indian Market; 1993 "Western Heritage Award," Festival of Western Art. Finalist, Holocaust Memorial, Palm Desert, CA; finalist, City of Redwood, Public Art Competition pending. *Public Commissions*: Life Size Relief "John Yoder" - Minnoite School, 1987; "Youth in Crisis" - Dr. Thomas Barrett Counselor, 1987; "Judge Hatfield Chilson" Loveland, CO, 1988; "Crawford Follmer" Life Size - McKee Medical Center, Loveland, CO, 1990. *Shows*: 1989 Oklahoma Indian Artist Show, House of Representatives, Washington, DC; 1989 Kennedy Center for Performing Arts, Washington, DC, "Colorado Living Artists"; 1989 & 1990 Allied Artist of America Shows, New York, NY; 1991 Potawatomi Museum, Shawnee, OK, Permanent Display, "Trail of Prayers"; Franco American Exhibit at Rennes Institute, Paris France, 1992. *Permanent Exhibit*: National Museum of the American Indian. Biographical source: "Art of the West," May/June, 1992.

HASTINGS, JIM
(BIE acting associate deputy director of BIE operated schools)
Affiliation & Address: Acting Associate Deputy Director – Bureau Operated Schools, Bureau of Indian Education, 1011 Indian School Rd. NW, Albuquerque, NM 87104 (505) 563-5265

HATCHER, MYRA GAIL (Klamath)
(tribal vice chairperson)
Affiliation & Address: Vice Chairperson, Klamath Tribes of Oregon, P.O. Box 436, Chiloquin, OR 97624 (541) 783-2219. E-mail: myra.hatcher@klamathtribes.com

HAUTER, JASON TRAVIS (Pima-Maricopa)
(attorney)
Education: University of Washington, BA, 1999; University of New mexico School of Law, JD, 2002. *Affiliation & Address*: Counsel, Akin Gump Straus Hauer & Feld, LLP, Robert E. Straus Bldg., 1333 New Hampshire Ave. NW, Washington, DC 20036 (202) 887-4153; E-mail: jhauter@akingump.com. Jason advises clients regarding American Indian law & Policy. *Past professional post*: In-house counsel, Gila River Indian Community; represented the Wid Horse Pass Development Authority, a tribal enterprise responsible for managing the community's non-gaming hospitality & recreational ventures.

HAUXWELL, JON (Northern Cheyenne) 1948-
(MD physician)
Born July 31, 1948, Marysville, Kans. Education: University of Kansas, BA, 1970; University of Kansas, School of Medicine, Kansas City, MD, 1974. *Address*: 1335 Central, Hays, KS 67601. E-mail: hauxwell@ruraltel.net. *Affiliation*: President, Tobacco Free Kansas Coalition; Vice chair, Kansas Citizens' Committee on Alcohol & Other Drugs. *Past professional posts*: Clinical director, medical officer (retired), Northern Cheyenne Service Unit, Indian Health Service, Lame Deer, MT, 1977-2004; associate clinical professor, Family Medicine, University of Washington, School of Medicine; family nurse practitioner preceptor, University of North Dakota. *Military service*: Commissioned Corps, USPHS, 1977-04 (Outstanding Service Medal, 1989). *Community activities*: Member, Northern Cheyenne Gourd Dance Society; honorary member, Kit Fox Society (traditional Cheyenne military society).

Memberships: American College of Surgeons (Advanced Trauma Life Support Instructor, 1981-); Northern Cheyenne Multidisciplinary Chemical Dependence Team (chairman, 1986-). *Awards, honors*: National Indian Health Board, Certificate of Appreciation, 1982; National Outstanding Clinician Award - 1985, by National Council of Clinical Directors. Interests: Powwowing ("every member of family has been on powwow head staff & hosted giveaways on numerous occasions"). Photography; music (piano & vocal) gardening; teaching medical students; hiking; cooking; cross-cultural activities; track & field; football; reading; history; Native American art, especially beadwork. Iroquois ancestry. *Published work*: The Cheyenne (Children's Press, 1988).

HAVERKATE, RICK (Sault Ste. Marie Chippewa) 1965-
(university faculty)

Born October 2, 1965, Elmhurst, Ill. *Education*: Northern Michigan University, B.S., 1989; University of Hawaii-Manoa, MPH, 1993. *Affiliations & Address*: Coordinator (1992-present), American Indian Recruitment Program, University of Hawaii, Honolulu, 1890 East West Rd., Moore Hall 405, School of Public Health, Honolulu, HI 96822 (800) 927-3297; health education consultant, Inter Tribal Council of Michigan, Sault Ste. Marie, MI, 1991-. *Other professional post*: Community health educator, Sault Ste. Marie Tribe of Chippewa Indians. *Community activities*: V.P. American Heart Association, Upper Peninsula, 1991-92; Chippewa County AIDS Task Force, 1990-92; LifeGuard Hawaii -- AIDS Prevention/ Education Peer Program. *Memberships*: Society of Public Health Educators of Hawaii, 1992-; American Public Health Association, 1993- . *Awards, honors*: Health Educator of the Year, Bemidji Area IHS; Michigan Competitive Scholarship (4 years); Mortar Board Honor Society: Outstanding College Student of the Year; Student Commencement Speaker, 1989, Northern Michigan University. *Interests*: "Spent 8 weeks exploring the public health systems throughout Thailand during summer of 1993, I am interested in community development issues and how health care & politics relate."

HAVIER, MARTIN (Pima-Maricopa)
(tribal vice president)

Affiliation & Address: Vice President, Salt River Pima-Maricopa Indian Community, 10005 E. Osborn Rd., Scottsdale, AZ 85256 (480) 362-7465. Mr. Harvier supports improving education for Community members & creating opportunities for cultural preservation and promotion. He notes that the Pima were a peaceful people and believes these feelings could come back into the hearts of families if people know who they are. As Vice President, he will support educational and health-based programming that furthers theses goals.

HAWKINS, RUSSELL (Sisseton-Wahpeton Sioux)
(tribal chairperson)

Affiliation& Address: Sisseton Wahpeton Sioux Tribal Council, Route 2, Agency Village, Sisseton, SD 57262 (605) 698-3911. E-mail: russell.hawkins@bia.gov. *Awards, honors*: Superintendent Hawkins received the Bureau of Indian Affairs "Director's Award" for the effort in obtaining, posthumously the Congressional Medal of Honor for M/Sgt. Woodrow Keeble. Keeble, a WW2 & Korean combat veteran, a member of the Sisseton Wahpeton Oyate, a former BIA Employee, went far above & beyond the call of duty in the Korean War and was awarded the Congressional Medal of Honor.

HAWLEY, ERIC (Burns Paiute)
(former tribal vice chairperson)

Affiliation & Address: Former Vice Chairperson, Burns Paiute Tribe, 100 Pasigo St., Burns, OR 97720 (541) 573-1910

HAWLEY, VINTON (Paiute)
(tribal chairperson)

Affiliation & Address: Chairperson, Pyramid Lake Paiute Tribe, P.O. Box 256, Nixon, NV 89424 (775) 574-1000. E-mail: vhawley@plpt.bsn.us

HAWORTH, JOHN
(museum director)

Affiliation & Address: Director, National Museum of the American Indian, Smithsonian Institution, George Gustav Heye Center, New York, NY 10004 (212) 514-3772.

HAYES, DOUGLAS L. (Cocopah)
(artist)

Address: Cocopah Native Art Works, 9760 W. Hava St., Somerton, AZ 85350 (928) 627-8684. *Works*: Doug does hand-drawn Native American art work; Native American paintings, & hand-drawn reproductions of photos & portraits.

HAYES, JODI (Shawnee)
(tribal administrator)

Affiliation & Address: Administrator, Shawnee Tribe, P.O. Box 189, Miami, OK 74355 (918) 542-2441; or, P.O. Box 860114, Shawnee, KS 66286 (913) 284-6635.

HAYES, KATHERINE
(American Indian studies chair)

Affiliation & Address: Professor & Chair, Department of American Indian Studies, Department of History, 19 Scott Hall, 72 Pleasant St. SE, University of Minnesota, Twin Cities Campus, Minneapolis, MN 55455 (612) 626-5330. E-mail: kathayes@umn.edu. "My research, based in various North American colonial contexts, stems from a challenge to the dominant narratives about the inevitability of colonial outcomes. In particular I am interested in issues of agency, negotiation, resistance, & opportunistic power demonstrated by peoples who history once popularly regarded as having been totally powerless in contexts of European colonization, like indigenous communities & enslaved Africans and African Americans. I have pursued these issues, most recently at sites in New York and Minnesota, by examining the often silent materiality of social relations which were not controlled by European settlers. This arena has led me to work in the productive tension between history and archaeology, the curated and the abandoned, memory and forgetting, and most importantly in conflicting notions of heritage."

HAYES, W.A. "TONY" (Occaneechi Saponi)
(tribal chaireprson)

Affiliation & Address: Chairperson, Occaneechi Band of Saponi Nation (OBSN), P.O. Box 356, Mebane, NC 27302 (336) 421-1317. *Other professional post*: Chef Executive Officer, North Carolina Indian Economic Development Initiative, Inc., P.O. Box 58096, Raleigh, NC 27609 (919) 232-9414. E-mail: tony.hayes@nciedi.org.

HAYWARD, MICHELLE (Wintun)
(tribal secretary)

Affiliation & Address: Secretary, Redding Rancheria, 2000 Rancheria Rd., Redding, CA 96001 (916) 225-8979. *Other professional posts*: Chairperson, California Rural Indian Health Board, Sacramento, CA; California Area Representative, National Indian Health Board, Washington, DC.

HAYWARD, RICHARD A. "SKIP" (Mashantucket Pequot) 1948-
(tribal vice chairman)

Born November 28, 1948, Groton, Conn. *Address & Affiliation*: Mashantucket Pequot Tribal Council (Chairperson, 1975-98; vice-chairperson, 1998-), P.O. Box 160, Ledyard, CT 06339 (203) 536-2681. *Other professional posts*: Chairman, Board of Directors, Native American Rights Fund, Boulder, CO, 1988-94 (continues to serve on the executive board); chairman, Mashantucket Pequot Gaming Enterprise, 1991-; member, board of directors of Foxwoods Management Co. *Community activities*: Chairman, Mashantucket Pequot Indian Housing Authority; chairman, Economic Development & Planning Committee; member-Board of Directors, Mashantucket Pequot Museum & Research Center, set to open in late 1997; committee member, 1995 Special Olympics World Games, held in Connecticut, and to which the tribe donated $2 million (the largest single donation received by that organization). *Awards, honors*: Appointee of the Governor of Connecticut to the Legislative Task Force on Indian Affairs; received the National Historic Preservation Award, 1988; The Mashantucket reservation is designated a National Historic Landmark; honorary doctorate degrees (in 1994) from The University of Connecticut, Eastern Connecticut State University, and Roger Williams College in Rhode Island. In Sept. 1995, Mr. Hayward received the Jay Silverheels Award from the National Center for American Indian Enterprise Development in Los Angeles.

HEADLEY, LOUIS R. (Arapahoe) 1948-
(Indian school supt.)

Born February 25, 1948, Fort Washakie, Wyo. *Education*: University of Montana, Missoula, BA, 1974; University of South Dakota, Vermillion, MA, 1977; University of Wyoming, Laramie, EdS, 1986. *Home address*: Box 344, St. Stephens, WY 82524 (307) 856-4147. *Affiliations*: Teacher, Principal, St. Stephens Indian School, 1977-; minority counselor, special services, University of Wyoming, Laramie, 1984-. *Other professional posts*: Home-school coordinator, Lander (WY) Valley High School; field coordinator, Tri-State Tribes, Inc., Billings, MT. *Community activities*: Wind River Indian Education Assn, Wind River, Wyo. (past chair); Keepers of the Fire Indian Club, U. of Wyoming (advisor); Cub Scout volunteer, St. Stephens, WY; Head Start Policy Council, Ethete, WY (vice chairman). *Memberships*: Phi Delta Kappa; National Assn of Elementary School Principals; National Indian Education Assn (treasurer); Wyoming Assn for Bilingual-Bicultural Education (treasurer). *Awards, honors*: Wyoming Golden Gloves Championship Scholarship Award; Korean Temple Band, Casper, Wyo; Outstanding Young Men of America, U.S. Jaycees, 1978. *Interests*: "I was a member of the Arapahoe and Shoshone Indian Dance Troupe that danced in Switzerland. I was also selected to dance in Washington, D.C. during the 1976 Bicentennial. I have been chosen to be the head dancer in Denver, Steamboat Spring, Colorado & Rocky Boy Reservation."

HEADDRESS, CHARLES (Assiniboine & Sioux)
(tribal vice chairperson)
Affiliation & Address: Vice Chairperson, Fort Peck Asiniboine & Sioux Tribes, P.O. Box 1027, Poplar, MT 59255 (406) 768-5155. E-mail: cheaddress@fortpecktribes.net

HEAP OF BIRDS, EDGAR (*Hock E Aye Vi*) (Cheyenne/Arapaho) 1954-
(professor of Native American studies & Fine Arts)
Born November 22, 1954, in Wichta, Kans. *Education*: Haskell Indian Jr. College, 1972-74; University of Kansas, BFA, 1976; Temple University, Tyler School of Art, MFA, 1979; graduate studies at The Royal College of Art, London, England, 1976-77. *Affiliation & Address*: Professor, Native American Studies Program, Ellison Hall 208, University of Oklahoma, Norman, OK 73019 (405) 325-7908. E-mail: eheapofbirds@ou.edu. *Past professional posts*: Visiting professor at Yale University, Rhode Island School of Design, Michaelis School of Fine Art, University of Cape Town, South Africa. *Interests*: Contemporary Native American art: painting, drawing, printmaking, sculpture. *Published works*: Blasted Alegories, an Anthology of Artists Writings (New Museum-MIT Press, 1987); Makers (Point Riders Press, 1998); The Myth of the Primitive, Susan Hiller, ed. (Routledge Press, 1991); Completing The Circle: Artists' Book on the Environment (Minnesota Center for Book Arts, 1992); Visit Teepee Town, Native Writing After the Detours, with Dianne Glancy & Mark Nowak (Coffee House Press, 1999); Most Serene Republics (National Museum of the American Indian, 2002).

HEAPE, STEVEN R.
(executive producer)
Address & Affiliation: Executive Producer, Rich-Heape Films, Inc., 5952 Royal Lane, Suite 254, Dallas, TX 75230 (214) 696-6916. E-mail: steven@richheape. com. *Professional activities*: Producing Native American videos, films & movies dedicated to inform, educate and encourage the awareness of the history, cultures, languages, traditions and aspirations of Native Americans and other Native Peoples. Rich-Heape Films has been recognized as 1999 & 2003 American Indian Business of the Year by the American Indian Chamber of Commerce of Texas, and has received numerous awards. *Published works*: Videos: "Black Indians: An American Story," 60 mins. VHS & DVD; "How to Trace Your Native American Heritage," 35 mins. VHS & DVD; Tales of Wonder I & II, 60 mins. each. VHS & DVD, CD soundtrack; "Native American Healing in the 21st Century," 40 mins. VHS & DVD; "Walela-Live in Concert," DVD, VHS & audio CD (2004). *Book*: "American Indian Directory" -1999 (national listing of over 500 federally-recognized American Indian nations & tribes.

HEART, MANUEL (Ute Mountain Ute)
(former tribal chairperson)
Affiliation & Address: Former chairperson, Ute Mountain Ute Tribe, 124 Mike Wash Rd., Towaoc, CO 81334 (970) 565-3751. E-mail: mheart@utemountain.org.

HEATH, DELVIS (Warm Springs)
(tribal chief)
Affiliation & Address: Chief, Confederated Tribes of the Warm Springs Reservation, 1233 Veterans St., Warm Springs, OR 97761 (541) 553-1161. E-mail: delvis.heath@wstribes.org.

HEATH, MARGARET A. 1947-
(education program manager)
Born October 24, 1947, Boulder, Colo. *Education*: University of Colorado, BA, 1972, MA, 1979. *Principal occupation*: Manager of education program. *Address*: P.O. Box 758, Dolores, CO 81323 (970) 882-5637. E-mail: megg_heath@co.blm.gov. *Affiliations*: Administrator & teacher, Adams County School District No. 50, Westminster, CO, 1972-79; director, Ute Mountain Ute Tribal Youth Shelter, Towaoc, CO, 1988-; director of education, Crow Canyon Archaeological Center, Cortez, CO, 1986-92; manager, Heritage Education Program, Bureau of Land Management, Dolores, CO, 1992-. *Community activities*: Galloping Goose Historical Society. *Memberships*: Society for American Archaeology (Public Education Committee). *Interests*: "Heritage education & interesting the public in preserving & protecting historical places & cultural resources; K-12 education; experiential education, especially archaeology for all ages & designing curriculum about prehistory; curriculum development; motivating students; Native American crafts, past & present - learning how to do them; hiking and rafting canyons of the Southwest; writing." *Published works*: Co-authored, Crow Canyon Archaeological Center: Teacher's Guide to Archaeological Activities (Crow Canyon Archaeological Center, 1989); co-authored with Lewis Matis, Crow Canyon Archaeological Center: Windows Into the Past & Inquiries Into the Past (Crow Canyon Archaeological Center, 1989); "Why Archaeology" in Whole Language Catalog (McGraw-Hill, 1990); Editor of series: Discovering Archaeology in: Arizona (1994), Alaska (1996), Wyoming (1997), New Mexico (1998), Colorado (1999); Art & Archaeology: Conflict and Interpretation in a Museum Setting," in Ancient Muses:

Archaeology and the Arts (University of Alabama Press, 2003). History Mystery Series: The Mystery of Butch Cassidy and the Sundance Kid," (2003); The Mystery of the First Americans (2004); The Ghost Town Mysteries (2005).

HEATHE, DELVIS, SR. (Warm Springs) 1938-
(tribal hereditary chief)
Delvis was born on the family ranch near Simnasho on September 26, 1938. *Affiliation & Address*: Hereditary Chief (25 years), Confederated Tribes of the Warm Springs Reservation, 1233 Veterans St., Warm Springs, OR 97761 (541) 553-1161. E-mail: delvis.heath@wstribes.org Delvis became the Warm Springs Chief and took his place on Tribal Council on May 4, 1984. As the chief of the Sahaptin speaking people, he follows the teachings of the Washat religion. He is active in Longhouse, participating in spiritual dancing, drumming & singing. The Chief lives by traditional values taught to him as a child.

HEBB, VICKI (Cheyenne River Sioux)
(director of programs)
Education: Montana State University, BS (Animal Science-Feed & Health). *Affiliation & Address*: Marketing Specialist (2000-07), Director of Programs (2007-present), Intertribal Agriculture Council, 100 North 27th St., Suite 500, Billings, MT 59101 (406) 259-3525.

HEBBRING, MARGE (*Bibogonikwe*) (Lac Courte Oreilles Ojibwe) 1948-
(grant director)
Born January 13, 1948, Winter, Wisc. *Education*: MA (Educational Professional Development); EdD. *Principal occupation*: Grant director. *Address*: 7361 203rd St., Chippewa Falls, WI 54729 (715) 723-5278. E-mail: hebbrima@uwec.edu. Website: www.uwec.edu/gearup. *Affiliations*: Title IX Coordinator, Eau Claire Area School District, Eau Claire, WI, 1995-99; coordinator, American Indian Academic & Student Services; grant director, UW-Eau Claire, Eau Claire, WI, 1999-present. *Other professional posts*: Gear Up director, UW-Eau Claire & Lac du Flambeau Reservation; instructor, Wisconsin Indian Curriculum Development. *Membership*: Wisconsin Indian Education Association (board member); Wisconsin Charter Schools Association; Wisconsin Women in Higher Education Leadership. *Interests*: Fur trade re-enacting, American Indian history and culture; charter schools, education and learning.

HEDGPETH, DANA (Haliwa-Saponi)
(journalist-business reporter)
Born in Halifax, NC. Education: University of Maryland - College Park, BA (journalism). *Address*: c/o Native American Journalists Association (NAJA), 555 N. Dakota St., Vermillion, SD 57069 (866) 694-4264. E-mail: hedgpeth@ naja.com. *Affiliation*: Currently, Business Reporter, Washington Post, Washington, DC. *Other professional posts*: Member-board of directors, Native American Journalists Association; writing mentor for NAJA's Project Phoenix, which is a weeklong journalism boot camp for Native American youth.

HEELEY, STEVEN J. (Canadian Potawatomi)
(attorney; consultant)
Education: Arizona State University College of Law, JD. *Affiliation & Address*: Consultant, Akin Gump Straus Hauer & Feld, LLP, Robert E. Straus Bldg., 1333 New Hampshire Ave. NW, Washington, DC 20036 (202) 887-4051; E-mail: sheeley@akingump.com. Mr. Heeley advises Indian tribes on corporate, transactional & natural resources matters, as well as on tribal governance & jurisdictional issues. *Other professional posts*: Adjunct law professor, Arizona State University (ASU) College of Law, Tempe, AZ; Steven teaches seminars on economic development & applied business transactions in Indian Country; also serves as a member of the ASU's Advisory Committee for the Indian Law Program. *Community activities*: Member of the Board of Directors, Native American Bar Association of Arizona. *Past professional posts*: Partner (headed the firm's Indian law practice group), Law Firm, Phoenix, AZ; deputy geneal counsel, Gila River Indian Cmmunity (10+ years); From 1989-91, he served as Deputy Minority Counsel to Sen. McCain on the Senate Select Committee on Indian Affairs.

HEGWOOD, SUNNY (Comanche)
(Native American studies instructor)
Education: Oklahoma State University, BS (Sociology, with a Native American Certificate), 2004; University of Oklahoma, MA (Race & Ethnicity), 2006; University of Arizona, PhD (American Indian Studies), 2014. *Affiliation & Address*: Instructor, American Indian Studies, Comanche Nation College, 1608 SW 9th St., Lawton, OK 73501 (580) 699-7229. E-mail: shegwood@ cnc.cc.ok.edu. Sunny teaches Tribal Governance; Representation & Preservation of Cultural Heritage; American Indian Law & Sovereignty; Indigenous Perspectives; History of Indigenous Art; Sociological Perspectives of Indigenous Education. *Past professional posts*: Instructor, American Indian Studies, University of Arizona, Tucson, AZ, 2006-09; instructor, Pima Community College, 2010-12; Director of Education, Comanche National Museum & Cultural Center, Lawton, OK, 2012-13.

HEKIA, THOMAS (Choctaw)
   (artist, store owner)
Affiliation & Address: Artist/Owner, Iti-Hekia Cedar Boxes, P.O. Box 692, Wynona, OK 74084 (918) 846-2611 or 636-9619. Website: www.itihekiaco.com; E-mail: cedarboxes@itihekiaco.com. *Artwork*: Cedar feather boxes, jewelry boxes, bone chokers, necklaces, leather dance belts.

HELIN, CALVIN (Tsimishian)
   (author; speaker; attorney; entrepreneur; activist)
Born on the Northwest Coast of British Columbia; a member of the Tsimshian Nation of Lax Kw'alaams. *Address*: c/o Orca Spirit Publishing, 6520 Salish Dr., Vancouver, BC V6N 2C7 Canada (604) 275-6670. E-mail: info@spiritorca.com. *Affiliations*: President & CEO, Eagle Group of Companies, LLC; president, Native Investment & Trade Association. *Other professional posts*: Director, Vancouver Board of Trade, GeoScience BC, and the Canada-China Resource Development Foundation. *Community activities*: Ambassador for SOS Children's Village (founded in 2002), founded Shudokan Karate & Education Society; instructs Goju-Ru karate - providing free martial arts lessons to poor inner-city children. *Honors & awards*: Recipient of the top "40 Under 40" awards for both British Columbia and nationally for Canada; chairman of the Aboriginal trade delegation to China. *Published works*: Dances with Dependency: Indigenous Success Through Self-Reliance (Orca Spirit Publishing, 2006); The Economic Dependency Trap: Speaking Free to Self-Reliance (Orca Spirit Publishing, 2010).

HELTON, NORA (Mojave)
   (former tribal chairperson)
Affiliation: Fort Mojave Tribal Council, 500 Merriman Ave., Needles, CA 92363 (760) 629-4591.

HELTON, TAIAWAGI (Cherokee)
   (professor of law)
Education: Ohio State University, BA, 1995; University of Tulsa, JD, 1999; Yale Law School, LLM, 2001. *Affiliation & Address*: Professor of Law, Center for the Study of American Indian Law & Policy, University of Oklahoma College of Law, 300 Timberdell Rd., Norman, OK 73019 (405) 325-4699. E-mail: thelton@ou.edu. Professor Helton teaches environmental law, property, and Indian law. *Other professional posts*: Member, Board of Directors, Oklahoma Indian Legal Services; Special Justice for the Cheyenne & Arapaho Tribes Supreme Court. *Past professional post*: Editor-in-Chief, Tulsa Law Journal; clerk for the Honorable Robert H. Henry, U.S. Court of Appeals for the Tenth Circuit. *Memberships*: Oklahoma Bar in 1999; Cherokee Nation Bar in 2000. *Awards, honors*: Outstanding Law Student Class of 1999 by the OK Bar Association. Published work: "The Foundations of Federal Indian Law and Its Application in the Twentieth Century"*Beyond Red Power: American Indian Politics and Activism Since 1900*. (with Lindsay G. Robertson. Ed. Daniel M. Cobb & Loretta Fowler. SAR Press, 2008).

HEMSTED, ROBERT (Yurok)
   (rancheria vice chairperson)
Affiliation & Address: Vice Chairperson, Cher-Ae Heights Indian Community of the Trinidad Rancheria, P.O. Box 630, Trinidad, CA 95570 (707) 677-0211.

HENA, JAMES (Pueblo Tesuque-Zuni)
   (member of board of directors)
Affiliation & Address: Member, Board of Directors, Association on American Indian Affairs, P.O. Box 268, Sisseton, SD 57262 (605) 698-3998. *Past professional post*: Chairperson, All Indian Pueblo Council, Albuquerque, NM.

HENA, LOUIE (Tesuque Pueblo)
   (Pueblo lt. governor)
Affiliation & Address: Lt. Governor, Pueblo of Tesuque, Rt. 5 Box 360-T, Santa Fe, NM 87501 (505) 955-7732.

HENDERSON, EARL (Sioux/Cree/Metis)
   (professor of Fist Nations Studies)
Born in Manitoba, Canada. *Education*: Masters in First Nations, Anthropology, & Education, along with a Pre-BSW Diploma and a Metis Certificate. *Affiliation & Address*: Adjnuct Professor, Department of First Nations Studies, 3333 University Way, Prince George, BC V2N 4Z9 Canada (250) 960-5242. E-mail: earllzip@telus.net. Earl currently teaches Metis Studies/First Nations at UNBC.

HENRY, DALTON (Mississippi Choctaw)
   (BIA education specialist)
Education: Mississippi State University, M.A., 1983. *Affiliation*: Education specialist, Bureau of Indian Education, 1849 C St., NW - 3621MIB, Washington, DC 20240-0001 (202) 208-5820; E-mail: dhenry@bia.edu.

HENRY, DAVID (Santee Sioux)
   (tribal vice chairperson)
Affiliation & Address: Santee Sioux Tribal Council, 108 Spirit Lake Ave., Niobrara, NE 68760 (402) 857-2772.

HENRY, GORDON D., JR. (White Earth Chippewa) 1955-
   (institute director; professor of English; poet & novelist)
Born October 19, 1955, Philadelphia, Penna. *Education*: Michigan State University, MA, 1983; University of North Dakota, PhD, 1992. *Affiliation & Address*: Director, Native American Institute (NAI), Michigan State Univesity, Agricure Hall, 446 W. Circle Dr., 225B Morrill Hall, East Lansing, MI 48824 (517) 355-7570. E-mail: henryg@msu.edu. As director, Gordon will lead the NAI in providing training, technical assistance, research & educational assistance to Native American tribes & organizations in Michigan. *Past professional posts*: Senior Editor, American Indiann Studies, Michigan State University; Assistant professor, director of Creative Writing, Department of English, Michigan State University, E. Lansing, MI, 1992-95; Artist in the schools; North Dakota Arts Council, 1984-86; lecturer-storyteller, West Central Michigan Humanities Council. *Memberships*: Wordcraft Writing Circle; North American Native Writers Circle. *Awards, honors*: Thomas McGrath Award for Poetry, University of North Dakota. *Interests*: Fulbright, Lecture Award for Spain, 1995. Biographical source: Article in "Genre," by Kim Blaeser, 1994. *Published works*: Outside White Earth (Blue Cloud, 1985); The Light People (University of Oklahoma Press, 1994); co-editor, Stories Through Theories/Theories Through Stories: North American Indian Writing, Storytelling, & Critique (2009).

HENRY, JEANETTE
   (director-Indian society; editor)
Affiliation: American Indian Historical Society, 1451 Masonic Ave., San Francisco, CA 94117 (415) 626-5235. *Other professional post*: Editor, The Indian Historian.

HENRY, LEO R. (Haudenosaunee-Tuscarora)
   (tribal chief)
Affiliation & Address: Chief, Tuscarora Indian Nation, 2006 Mt. Hope Rd., Lewiston, NY 14092 (716) 622-7061.

HENRY, MELISSA (Navajo)
   (business president)
Education: Fort Lewis College, BA (English & Mass Communications), 2001; University of Maryland, MA (Comparative Literature - Visual Language and the Written Word), 2003. She is an alumnus of the WINS Program (Washington I nternships for Native Students), Summer 1999. *Address & Affiliation*: President & director, Red Ant Productions, P.O. Box 133, Rehoboth, NM 87322. Website: www.red-ant.net; E-mail: video@red-ant.net. Red Ant is a video production and web development business). After years of training, Melissa is using her education and professional expertise to serve the local Four Corners area's economy, cultural institutions and people.

HENRY, PHILIP NATHANIEL (Saginaw Chippewa)
   (Indian outreach worker)
Born June 7, 1933, Saginaw, Mich. *Education*: St. Clair Co. Community College. *Address*: 715 Summer St., Algonac, MI 48001 (810) 794-5413. *Affiliation*: Oakland County Family Independence Agency, Pontiac, MI, 1994-. *Other professional posts*: Home health care primary case manager; commissioner Region I, Michigan Commission on Indian Affairs. *Past professional posts*: Building Trades Roofer Local 149 (25 years); JTPA Indian Employment & Service Counselor (seven years); director of Indian education, Algonac Community Schools, Port Huron, MI, 1976-80. *Membership*: Saginaw Chippewa Indian Tribe of Michigan. *Community activities*: Board member, Down River Nutrition Center, Marine City, MI; past board member, Down River Community Services, Algonac, MI. *Military service*: U.S. Marine Corps, 1953-54. *Awards, honors*: Certificate of Recognition & Appointed by Governor Engler to Region I, Michigan Commission on Indian Affairs (Aug. 1992, reappointed, 1994-97); recognized as elder & Indian leader for Michigan Indian community; brother of Thelma Henry Shipman, former director of Urban Indian Affairs, Wayne County Mich. Dept. of Social Services.

HENRY, RONNIE (Navajo)
   (artist, shop owner)
Affiliation & Address: Owner, Contemporary Navajo/Dine Jeweler, P.O. Box 657, Crownpoint, NM 87313 (505) 786-5678 or 879-3030. E-mail: henry.ronnie @gmail.com. Artwork: Sterling silver & turquoise jewelry.

HENRY, RONNIE, SR. (Mississippi Choctaw)
   (tribal vice chief)
Affiliation & Address: Chief, Mississippi Band of Choctaw Indians, 101 Industrial Rd., Choctaw, MS 39350 (601) 656-5251.

HENRY, TERRI (Eastern Cherokee)
(organization founder & director)
Education: J.D. *Affiliation & Address*: Founder & Principal Director (2001-present), Clan Star, Inc., P.O. Box 1630, Cherokee, NC 28719 (828) 497-5507. *Other professional post*: Founding member, National Congress of American Indians Task Force on Violence Against Native Women. *Past professional posts*: Director of Policy, USDOJ Violence Against Women Office, 1996-99; found the Qualla Women's Justice Alliance. At the USDOJ, Terri formed the first native based federal programming to address violence against Native women; she initiated training for tribal judges, prosecutors, law enforcement officers & advocates to enhance tribal governmental efforts to address the safety of Native women. Programming under her direction recognized the sovereignty of Indian tribes and the principals of self-determination. Ms. Henry served The Eastern Band of Cherokee Indians as an Associate Justice of the Cherokee Supreme Court; worked with Sacred Circle, the National Council of Juvenile & Family Court Judges on the Green book project, and Mending the Sacred Hoop on violence against women initiatives. Terri worked at the Indian Law Resource Center in Washington, DC & Census Bureau in Suitland, MD.

HENRY, VIRGINIA
(Indian center director)
Affiliation & Address: American Indian Center of Arkansas, 235 N. Greenwood, Fort Smith, AR 72901 (501) 785-5149.

HENSLEY, JACQUE SECONDINE (Kaw)
(tribal chairperson)
Affiliation & Address: Chairperson/CEO (2017-), The Kaw Nation, 698 Grandview Dr., Drawer 50, Kaw City, OK 74641 (580) 269-2552. E-mail: jhensley@kawnation.coM

HENSLEY, WILLIAM L. (Eskimo) 1941-
(state senator)
Born 1941, Kotzebue, Alaska. *Education*: University of Alaska, 1960-1961; George Washington University, BA, 1966; University of Alaska, 1966; University of New Mexico Law School, 1967; UCLA Law School, 1968. *Principal occupation*: State Senator. *Address*: Kotzebue, Alaska. *Affiliations*: Alaska House of Representatives, 1966-70; Alaska State Senate, 1970-. *Community activities*: Rural Affairs Commission, 1968-1972 (chairman, 1972); Land Claims Task Force (chairman, 1968); Northwest Regional Educational Laboratory (board of directors, 1968-1969); Northwest Alaska Native Association Regional Corporation (board of directors). *Memberships*: Alaska Federation of Natives, 1966- (organizer, 1966; president, 1972); Northwest Alaska Native Association (organizer, 1966); National Council on Indian Opportunity, 1968-70. *Interests*: Land claims implementation; rural economic development; education facilities; old-age centers; bilingual programs.

HENSON, JIM (United Keetoowah Cherokee)
(tribal chief)
Address & Affiliation: United Keetoowah Band of Cherokees, P.O. Box 746, Tahlequah, OK 74465 (918) 456-5491.

HENSON, RICHARD ALLEN (Comanche) 1942-
(BIA employment assistance officer)
Born January 26, 1942, Pawnee, Okla. *Education*: Oklahoma State Tech, 1960-62; Minot State College, BA, 1976. *Affiliation & Address*: Employment Assistance Director, Bureau of Indian Affairs, 1951 Constitution Ave., NW, Rm. 331S, MS: 331SIB, Washington, DC 20245 (202) 343-1780. *Past professional posts*: Metropolitan Life Insurance Co., Ardmore, OK, 1967-71; guidance counselor, United Tribes Employment Training Center, Bismarck, ND, equal employment opportunity counselor, job developer and employment assistance officer, United Tribes Employment Training Center, Minot, ND, 1971-74, Fort Berthold Agency, BIA, New Town, N.D., 1974-76; area equal employment opportunity officer, BIA, Albuquerque, NM, 1976-77; director, equal employment opportunity, Indian Health Service, Rockville, MD; employment assistance officer, BIA, Washington, DC. *Military service*: U.S. Air Force, 1963-67. *Community activities*: Minot Indian Club (president, 1974); Minot Mayor's Human Rights Committee (member); Minot's Mental Health & Retardation Board (member). *Interests*: "To continue to work with Indian people in Indian affairs and to return to school to earn my master's degree in public health."

HEPFER, RUSSELL N. (Lower Elwha S'Klallam)
(tribal vice chairperson)
Affiliation & Address: Vice Chairperson, Lower Elwha Band of of S'Klallam Indians Tribal Council, 2851 Lower Elwha Rd., Port Angeles, WA 98362 (360) 452-8471.

HER MANY HORSES, CLEVE (Oglala Lakota)
(BIA agency supt.)
Affiliation & Address: Supt. Pine Ridge Agency, Bureau of Indian Affairs, P.O. Box 1203, Pine Ridge, SD 57770 (605) 867-5125.

HER MANY HORSES, DAWSON (Oglala Lakota)
(vice president, bank gaming group)
Education: Columbia University, BA; Tuck School of Business, Dartmouth College, MBA. *Affiliation & Address*: Vice President, Bank Gaming Group, Bank of America Merrill Lynch, 300 S. 4th St., Suite 200, Las Vegas, NV 89101. E-mail: dawson@nafoa.org. *Other professional post*: Secretary, Native American Finance Officers Assn, Washington, DC. *Past professional post*: Director of Native American Business Development, Merrill Lynch. In this role, Dawson launched Merrill Lynch Native American Banking & Financial Services. *Awards, honors*: 2011, one of "40 Native Americans under 40," nationally.

HER MANY HORSES, DANIELLE (Oglala Lakota)
(attorney; deputy executive director)
Education: University of New Mexico, BS (Finance), School of Law, JD. *Affiliation & Address*: Deputy Executive Director, National Indian Gaming Association, 224 Second St. SE, Washington, DC 20003 (202) 546-7711. E-mail: dhermanyhorses@indiangaming.org.

HER MANY HORSES, EMIL (Oglala Lakota)
(artist; associate curator)
Born & raised on the Rosebud Sioux Indian Reservation, S.D. *Education*: Augustana College, BA, 1979; Loyola University, Chicago, MA, 1995. *Affiliation & Address*: Associate Curator, National Museum of the American Indian (NMAI), Smithsonian Institution, Cultural Resources Section, 4220 Silver Hill Rd., Suitland, MD 20746 (301) 238-1436. His artwork is in contemporary beadwork & contemporary dolls, specializing in Northern & Southern Plains culture. *Other professional post*: Treasurer, Running Strong for American Indian Youth, Alexandria, VA. *Awards, honors*: Internship with the Smithsonian's Renwick Gallery in Washington, DC; 2001 Best of Show for his tribute to the Lakota Sioux Vietnam Veterans at the Northern Plains Tribal Arts Show.

HERBERT, LISA B. OTIPOBY (Comanche)
(attorney; tribal supreme court justice)
Education: Phillips University, Enid, OK, BS (Political Science), 1988; University of Kansas School of Law, JD, 1993; Oklahoma State University (Equine Studies); National Judicial College, Reno, NV, 2009. *Affiliation & Address*: Supreme Court Justice (2005-present), Kaw Nation, Drawer 50, Kaw City, OK 74641 (580) 269-2552. Justice Herbert presently serves the Te-Moak Tribe of Western Shoshone Indians of Nevada, the Otoe-Missouria Tribal Court (CFR), Southern Plains Area (CFR Court), Osage Nation, Iowa Tribe of Oklahoma, Kickapoo Tribe of Oklahoma as Trial Court and Associate Judge and CFR Appeals Magistrate. She also serves as the Children's Court Prosecutor for the Comanche Nation Children's Court and the Citizen Potawatomi Nation's Juvenile Division. Justice Herbert serves as a municipal judge for several Oklahoma municipalities including Kaw City (since 1998), Shidler (since 1999) and Fairfax, Oklahoma. She has been active with the Oklahoma Municipal Judges Association since 1998, serving as a board member from 2005 to 2010. Prior to returning to Oklahoma in 1998, Justice Herbert had a criminal & domestic practice in Lawrence, Kansas. Justice Herbert had the opportunity to work in gaming regulation and presently serves on the Pawnee Nation Gaming Commission, and has recently been appointed to serve on the Ponca Tribal Gaming Commission.

HERIARD, JACK B. 1948-
(editor/publisher)
Born July 26, 1948, New Orleans, LA. *Address*: 53236 Old Uneedus Rd., Folsom, LA 70437 (985) 796-5433. *Affiliation*: Editor/publisher, "Crafts: American Indian Past & Present," Written Heritage, Inc., Folsom, LA, 1967-. *Other professional post*: Managing editor, "Whispering Wind," Folsom, LA, 1967-. Military service: U.S. Air Force, 1969-72 (E7). *Memberships*: Louisiana Indian Heritage Association (president, 1967-72, 1978; secretary/treasurer, 1987-89, 1990-92). *Interests*: "American Indian culture; attending numerous powwows; dancing and singing."

HERMAN, SCOTT (Rosebud Lakota Sioux)
(tribal vice president)
Affiliation & Address: Vice President, Rosebud Sioux Tribal Council, P.O. Box 430, Rosebud, SD 57570 (605) 747-2381.

HERMOSILLO, PATRICIA (Pomo)
(tribal chairperson)
Affiliation & Address: Chairperson, Cloverdale Rancheria of Pomo Idians, 555 S. Cloverdale Blvd. #1, Cloverdale, CA 95425 (707) 894-5775.

HERNANDEZ-AVILA, INEZ (Nez Perce/Tejana) 1948-
(assistant professor)
Born in Texas, 1948. *Education*: University of Houston, BA, 1970, MA, 1972, PhD (English), 1984. *Address & Affiliation*: Professor, Dept. of Native American Studies, 2405 Hart Hall, University of California, One Shields Ave., Davis, CA 95616 (530) 752-4394. E-mail: ighernandez@ucdavis.edu. *Other professional post*: Editorial Advisory Board, "Hurricane Alice: A Feminist Quarterly."

Memberships: Modern Language Assn; MALCS (Mujeres Activas en Letras y Cambio Social); National Association of Chicano Studies; California Indian Education Assn. *Awards, honors*: Phi Kappa Phi Honor Society; Outstanding Chicana in the Arts (Literature) for the Austin community, 1977, award presented by the Mexican American Professional and Business Women of Austin; Outstanding Chicana faculty, 1977, award presented by the Minority Student Services, University of Texas, Austin; Outstanding Chicana faculty, 1978, award presented by the Center for Mexican American Studies, University of Texas, Austin; elected to Board of Directors of D-Q University, Davis, CA, June 1983, served through April 1986. *Interests*: "My mother is Nimipu (known as Nez Perce) Indian; I am an enrolled member of the Colville Confederated Tribes of Nespelem, Washington. My father is Texas-Tejana. I am Nimipu and Tejana. I am fluent in English & Spanish (reading, writing, speaking, translating)." Writer & director of the dramatic work "El Dia de Guadalupe," which featured eight women players focusing on the different forms of abuse that Chicanas encounter in contemporary society. *Published works*: Article - "Finding Our Way Back Home: Native American Women Writers," Dictionary of Native American Literature, edited by Andrew Wiget (Greenwood Press, 1991); among other articles and chapters & numerous poems in various publications.

HERNANDEZ, NAKOMIS (Chukchansi)
(tribal vice chairperson)
Affiliation & Address: Vice Chairperson, Picayune Rancheria of the Chukchansi Indians, 46575 Road 417, Coarsegold, CA 93614 (559) 683-6633 E-mail: nhernandez@tcouncil.com

HERNANDEZ, RUBEN (Rosebud Lakota)
(project officer)
Affiliation & Address: Project Officer, Research, Policy & Asset-Building Programs, First Nations Development Institute, 351 Coffman St., Suite 200, Longmont, CO 80501 (303) 774-7836. *Past professional post*: Database manager & project coordinator, American Indian College Fund, Denver, CO.

HERNANDEZ, SALLY A. (Laguna Pueblo)
(attorney)
Education: University of New Mexico, JD. *Address*: P.O. Box 66, Albuquerque, NM. *Affiliation*: U.S. Dept. of the Interior. *Memberships*: Native American Bar Association (Native American Legal Resource Center representative); American Bar Association.

HERNANDEZ, SARAH (Rosebud Lakota)
(program coordinator)
Education: Arizona State University, BA & MA (English); University of Colorado, Boulder,, PhD pending (English). *Affiliation & Address*: Program Coordinator (2012-present), First Nations Development Institute, 2432 Main St., 2nd Fl., Longmont, CO 80501 (303) 774-7836. *Past professional post*: Education Coordinator, Native American Finance Officer Assn, Phoenix, AZ.

HERNANDEZ, TED (Wiyot)
(tribal chairperson)
Affiliation & Address: Chairperson, Wiyot Tribe of the Table Bluff Rancheria, 1000 Wiyot Dr., Loleta, CA 95551 (707) 733-5055.

HERNE, SUSAN (Mohawk)
(museum giftshop manager)
Affiliation & Address: Manager, Sweetgrass Giftshop, Akwesasne Library & Museum, St. Regis Mohawk Nation, Rt. 37 RR 1, Box 14C, Hogansburg, NY 13655 (518) 358-2240. Website: www. akwesasne culture.org.

HERRERA, JOHN R. (Leech Lake Chippewa) 1952-
(attorney)
Born June 4, 1952, Milwaukee, Wisc. *Education*: University of Wisconsin, Milwaukee, BA, 1976; University of Minnesota, MBA, 1986; William Mitchell College of Law (St. Paul, MN), JD, 1992. *Address*: 27485 Chippewa Paws Lane, SE, Pennington, NM. *Affiliations*: Director of Economic Development, Minnesota Chippewa Tribe, Cass Lake, MN, 1978-80; director of business enterprises, Leech Lake Reservation, Cass Lake, MN, 1980-82; business finance representative, State of Minnesota, Prior Lake, MN, 1983-85; area credit officer/Indian services branch chief, Bureau of Indian Affairs, Minneapolis, MN, 1985-88 (managed implementation of Indian Finance Act for federally recognized Indian reservations in the four state area - provided loans & loan guarantees for business development); finance & planning consultant, Shakopee Sioux Community, Prior Lake, MN, 1988-90 (provided financial & developmental direction for the community which owns one of the largest and most successful Native American gaming ventures in the U.S.; president, First American Companies; Equipment Leasing & Securities, Minneapolis, MN, 1991- (provides consultant & equipment leasing services to a client base of Native American Tribes. *Other professional posts*: Judge, Leech Lake Reservation; associate judge, Minnesota Chippewa Tribe Appeals Court. Membership: Minnesota Indian Chamber of Commerce (founder/member).

HERRERA, MILTON (Tesuque Pueblo)
(Pueblo governor)
Affiliation & Address: Governor, Pueblo of Tesuque, Rt. 5 Box 360-T, Santa Fe, NM 87501 (505) 955-7732.

HERRERA, WILFRED, JR. (Laguna Pueblo)
(Pueblo Lt. governor)
Affiliation & Address: Lt. Governor, Pueblo of Laguna, P.O. Box 194, Laguna, NM 87026 (505) 552-6654.

HERRINGTON, JOHN BENNETT (Chickasaw)) 1958-
(retired NASA astronaut; special advisor)
Born Sept. 14, 1958, in Wetumka, Okla. *Education*: University of Colorado, BS (Applied mathematics), 1983; U.S. Naval Test Pilot School (Patuxent River, MD), 1990; U.S. Naval Postgraduate School, MS (Aeronautical Engineering), 1995. *Contact address*: c/o Sheri Berry, SRK Relations, P.O. Box 7871, Pasadena, TX 77508 (832) 875-8846. E-mail: speakerrequest@srkrelations. com. He resides in Colorado Springs, Colo. Affiliation: Currently, Herrington serves as a Special Advisor to the National Institute for Space, Science & Security Centers at the University of Colorado at Colorado Springs. *Other professional posts*: Chairperson of the Board for the American Indian Institute for Innovation (AIII) in Rapid City, SD. AIII is a non-profit organization dedicated to improving the opportunities for Native American students in Science, Technology, Engineering & Mathematics (STEM) education. Also, public speaking engagements & work with the Chickasaw Nation. *Past professional post*: Vice president & director of Flight Operations for Rocketplane Limited, Inc. (2005-07), where he served as the pilot of the XP Spaceplane. *Military service*: U.S. Naval Air, 1985-2005. *NASA Experience*: Selected by NASA in April 1996. He completed two years of training & evaluation, and was qualified for flight assignment as a mission specialist. In November 2002, he flew on STS-113 Endeavour (November 23-Dec. 7, 2002); it was the 16th Shuttle mission to visit the International Space Station. During the mission, Herrington performed three EVAs (Extravehicular Activities) totaling 19 hours & 55 minutes. On October 1, 2005, he retired from the U.S. Navy and left NASA to pursue a career in the commercial space industry. *Awards, honors*: Distinguished Naval Graduate from Aviation Officer Candidate School; awarded Legion of Merit, Defense Meritorious Service Medal, NASA Spaceflight Medal, Navy Commendation Medal & various other service awards; recipient of two honorary Doctorates of Science, one from the University of Colorado at Colorado Springs and the other from the South Dakota School of Mines & Technology. *Memberships*: Association of Naval Aviation, American Institute of Aeronautics & Astronautics; American Indian Sciences & Engineering Society (Sequoyah Fellow).

HERRON, MONTY (Grand Rondr)
(adjunct instructor in Indigenous Nations study)
Affiliation & Address: Adjunct Instructor of Indigenous Nations Studies, P.O. Box 751, Potland State University, Portland, OR 97207 (503) 725-9689.

HERSHEY, ROBERT A.
(attorney; professor of law)
Education: The University of Arizona, J.D., 1972. *Address & Affiliation*: Director, Tribal Law Clinic, Indigenous Peoples Law & Policy Program, James E. Rogers College of Law, The University of Arizona, Rountree Hall 207, P.O. Box 210176, Tucson, AZ 85721 (520) 621-5677. E-mail: hershey@law. arizona.edu. He teaches a Globalization & the Preservation & Transformation of Culture course. *Other professional posts*: Adjunct professor, American Indian Studies Program, The University of Arizona, Tucson, AZ; Special Litigation Counsel & Law Enforcement Legal Advisor to the White Mountain Apache Tribe, 1983-99; Judge Pro Tempore for the Tohono O'odham; and Deputy Judge Pro Tempore for the Colorado River Indian Community Tribal Courts, 2001-present. *Professional Interests*: Robert specializes in indigenous human rights focusing on economic development in Indian country, and the mechanics of criminal law in tribal courts and intellectual property rights. He has assisted tribes in forming & revising tribal constitutions & has conducted numerous training workshops for tribal judges & tribal court personnel. *Past professional posts*: Special Counsel to the Pascua Yaqui Tribe, 1994-96. *Memberships*: White Mountain Apache, Hopi, and Pascua Yaqui Tribal Courts, the Ninth Circuit Court of Appeals, the Federal District Court for the District of Arizona, and the Arizona & Montana State Bars. *Published work*: Globalization and the Transformation of Cultures & Humanity: A Curriculum & Toolkit for the Efflorescence of Ecological Literacy in Legal & Business School Education.

HERTEL, AMY LOCKLEAR (Lumbee)
(American Indian center director)
Education: University of North carolina, BA; Washington University, St. Louis, MSW, JD, PhD. *Affiliation & Address*: Director, American Indian center, University of North Carolina, 113A Abernathy Hall, CB 3457, Chapel Hill, NC 27599 (919) 962-4189. E-mail: amy_hertel@unc.edu. Amy also has an appointment as a Clinical Assistant Professor at the UNC School of Social Work. While at UNC, she served as president of the Carolina Indian Circle and

was inducted into the Order of the Golden Fleece. She was also one of the four founders of Alpha Pi Omega Sorority Inc., the country's first American Indian Greek letter organization. Previously, Amy served as a project manager at the Center for Social Development at Washington University in St. Louis, where she completed her doctoral studies. She also earned her master of social work and law degrees from Washington University in St. Louis. In her life as an attorney, she served as a corporate attorney for five years in St. Louis where she focused on mergers and acquisitions as well as securities filings. Her area of study is asset building in tribal communities as a means toward tribal self-determination. Amy has experience working in Indian Country with asset building, grassroots giving, capacity building, & community based participatory research. As a tribal citizen, professional, daughter, wife, and mother, Amy is dedicated to serving her communities. Amy serves on various boards and committees in North Carolina, as well as outside the state. Her service includes the G.A. Jr. & Kathryn M. Buder Charitable Foundation and the North Carolina American Indian Health Board. She also serves as a Co-Chair for the Chancellor's Task Force on UNC Chapel Hill History. Amy lives in Chapel Hill, NC with her husband, Johann, who is faculty at the UNC School of Medicine and works as a pathologist at UNC Hospitals, their 7 year old daughter Ava, and their 5 year old son Ahren.

HESTER, JAMES J. 1931-
(professor emeritus; senior consulting archaeologist; author)
Born September 21, 1931, Anthony, Kans. *Education*: University of New Mexico, BA, 1953; University of Arizona, PhD (Anthropology), 1961. *Principal occupation*: Anthropologist. *Address*: Dept. of Anthropology, CB233 University of Colorado, Boulder, CO 80309 (303) 492-7419. E-mail: james.hester@ colorado.edu. *Affiliations*: Department of Anthropology, University of Colorado, Boulder (professor, 1975-99; professor emeritus, 2000-present). *Other professional post*: Consulting Archaeologist, Walker Research Group, Ltd., Boulder, CO. *Past professional posts*: Assistant curator, Museum of New Mexico, 1959-64; adjunct professor, Southern Methodist University, 1964-65; scientist administrator, National Institute of Health, 1965-75; consultant, U.S. Army Corp. of Engineers, 1985-88 (directed a nationwide program in "in situ" site preservation). *Military service*: U.S. Air Force, 1954-56. *Awards, honors*: Served as Chief Archaeologist for the President's Advisory Council on Historic Preservation from 1978-79. *Memberships*: American Anthropological Assn (Fellow); Society for American Archaeology. *Interests*: "Archaeology of Navajo Indians; prehistory of Sahara desert; directed culture change; relationship of man to his environment. Currently writing fiction based on contemporary Native American issues - Sioux, Tlingit, Navajo, Hopi, Comanche." *Published works*: An Archaeological Survey of the Navajo Reservoir District, Northwestern New Mexico, with A.E. Dittert, Jr. & Frank W. Eddy (Museum of New Mexico, 1961); Early Navajo Migrations and Acculturation in the Southwest (Museum of New Mexico, 1962); Studies at Navajo Period Sites in the Navajo Reservoir District, with Joel Shiner (Museum of New Mexico, 1963); Rance Hood, Comanche Mystic Painter (University of New Mexico Press, 2005).

HESTER, THURMAN LEE, JR. (Oklahoma Choctaw) 1961-
(director of American Indian studies)
Born June 23, 1961, Oklahoma City, OK. *Education*: University of Oklahoma, BS (History), 1987, MS (Philosophy), 1991, & PhD (Philosophy), 1999. *Address*: 1353 Dorchester Dr., Norman, OK 73069; *Affiliation & Address*: Professor & Director of American Indian Studies Program, University of Science & Arts of Oklahoma, and Director, Meredith Indigenous Humanitites Center, 17th & Grand, Davis Hall, Rm. 229, Chickasha, OK 73018 (405) 574-1289. E-mail: fachesterl@usao.edu. Dr. Hester is the advisor to all American Indian Studies majors and is a faculty advisor to American Indian student organization on campus. He teaches Tribal Government and Law, History of Federal Indian Law, Contemporary American Indian Issues, American Indian Identity, Native American Philosophy, American Indian Art, American Indians in Film, American Indian Economics, Casino Management, Plains Indian Warfare, Removal, Native American Literature, & American Indian Education. *Other professional posts*: Director, Meredith Indigenous Humanities Center; advisor to all American Indian Studies majors; faculty advisor to American Indian student organization on campus; founding editor (along with Dennis McPherson) of Ayaangwagmizin: The International Journal of Indigenous Philosophy. *Past professional posts*: Taught at University of Oklahoma, 1988-94; Oklahoma City University, 1994-99; & Lakehead University (Canada). *Community activities*: Cultural Committee chair, Oklahoma Choctaw Tribal Alliance; founding board member for the Oklahoma Association for Healthcare Ethics. *Awards, honors*: Awarded the Presidential Award of Excellence for Environmental Protection Services in 1973 by President Richard M. Nixon. *Memberships*: Choctaw Code Talkers Assn; American Philosophical Assn, Wordcraft Circle of Native Writers & Storytellers; American Indian Philosophical Assn, APA Committee on the Status of American Indians. *Interests*: Indian law, philosophy. *Published work*: Political Principles & Indian Sovereignty (Routledge Press, 2001); numerous articles.

HETH, CHARLOTTE WILSON (Cherokee) 1937-
(retired museum professional)
Born October 29, 1937, Muskogee, Okla. *Education*: Oklahoma Baptist University, 1955-56; University of Tulsa, BA, 1959, MM, 1960; University of California, Los Angeles, PhD, 1975. *Affiliations*: The National Museum of the American Indian, Smithsonian, Washington, DC, 1995-2000; American Indian Studies Center, University of California, Los Angeles (Professor of ethnomusicology, 1974-87, 1989-95; director, 1976-87); director, American Indian Program, Cornell University, Ithaca, NY, 1987-89. *Community activities*: Panel Chair, Folk Arts Program, National Endowment for the Arts, 1981-83; Indian Centers, Inc., Los Angeles (board member). *Memberships*: Society for Ethnomusicology (council chair, 1981-82; president, 1993-95); National Indian Education Association; American Indian Historians' Association. *Awards, honors*: Senior Postdoctoral Fellowship, Center for the History of the American Indian, The Newberry Library, 1978-79; Southern Fellowships Fund, Postdoctoral Fellowship, 1978-79; National Research Council senior postdoctoral fellowship, 1984-85 (Ford Foundation Minority Fellowship). *Interests*: "American Indian music and dance; Cherokee language & culture; previously I was a Peace Corps volunteer in Ethiopia (1962-64) teaching English as a second language. I also was a high school teacher in OK, NM, and CA from 1960-72. I have traveled to Europe, the Middle East, East Africa, Mexico, Latin America, and Canada." *Published works*: General editor, "The Music of the American Indians", (Selected Reports in Ethnomusicology, 1982); general editor, "Music and the Expressive Arts", (American Indian Culture and Research Journal, 1982); Issues for the Future of American Indian Studies: A Needs Assessment & Program Guide, co-authored with Susan Guyette (American Indian Studies Center, UCLA, 1985); general editor, organizer, and contributor, Sharing a Heritage: American Indian Arts Conference, No. 3 in the Contemporary American Indian Issues Series (American Indian Studies Center, UCLA, 1984); editor/contributor, Native American Dance: Ceremonies & Social Traditions (American Indian Studies Center, UCLA, 1994).

HEYANO, ROBERT (Eskimo)
(Alaskan village president)
Affiliation & Address: President, Native Village of Ekuk, P.O. Box 530, Dillingham, AK 99576 (907) 842-3842. E-mail: ekuktrib@nushtel.com.

HIBBARD, JOSEPH (Dine'-Navajo)
(associate professor of law)
Education: University of Kansas, BS (Business Administration; Washburn University, JD. *Affiliation & Address*: Associate Professor of Law Advocate, School of Dine' & Law Studies, Navajo Technical University, P.O. Box 849, Crownpoint, NM 87313 (505) 786-4154. E-mail: jhibbard@ navajotech.edu

HIBBELER, PATRICIA (BARNES) (Salish & Kootenai)
(Indian center CEO)
Education: University of Montana, BA (Education, 1987; Hastings College, MA (Education), 1991. *Affiliation & Address*: Chief Executive Officer (2004-present), Phoenix Indian Center, 4520 N. Central Ave., Suite 250, Phoenix, AZ 85012 (602) 264-6768; E-mail: phibbeler@phxindcenter.org *Past professional posts*: Assistant Director, Arizona State University – Arizona Prevention Resource Center, 1991-2001; Research Coordinator, Washington University, 2001-04.

HIBBELER, TED (Rosebud Lakota) 1951-
(director of Native American education)
Born July 9, 1951, Rosebud, S.D. *Education*: Hastings College (Neb), MA, 1973. Principal occupation: Director of Native American education. *Address & Affiliation*: Phoenix Union High School District, 4502 N. Central Ave., Phoenix, AZ 85012 (602) 271-3514. E-mail: ted.hibbeler@qm.phxhs.k12.az.us. *Community activities*: Hoop of Learning Program - early bridge college program with Phoenix College, Phoenix, Ariz. *Interests*: "I am just a humble Native trying to help our own young Native people live in balance with the world around them. Are we not all trying to do the same thing?"

HIBBERT, JACK (Standing Rock Sioux)
(professional engineer)
Affiliation & Address: Engineer, JF Companies, LLC, 9145 E. Kenyon Ave., Suite 200, Denver, CO 80237 Jack, for more than 30 years, has directed local & national planning, management & development of water resources, water treatment & wastewater treatment systems. *Other professional posts*: Board of Directors, Denver Urban Ditch Company; secretary-treasurer, International Institute for Indigenous Resource Management, Denver, CO. *Past professional post*: Member, Board of Directors (ten years), Native American Multicultural Education School (NAMES), now defunct.

HICKS, LOUIS (Muscogee Creek)
(tribal 2nd chief)
Affiliation & Address: Principal Chief, Muscogee (Creek) Nation, P.O. Box 580, Okmulgee, OK 74447 (918) 732-7612.

HICKS, MITCHELL A. (Eastern Cherokee)
(former tribal principal chief)
Affiliation & Address: Principal Chief, Eastern Band of Cherokee Indians, Qualla Boundary, P.O. Box 455, Cherokee, NC 28719 (828) 497-7000.

HICKS, SARAH (Alutiiq)
(policy research center director)
Education: Goucher College, BA; George Warren Brown School of Social Work, Washington University, MA, PhD. *Affiliation*: National Congress of American Indians (Welfare Reform Program, 1997-2003; Founding Director, Policy Research Center, 2003-present), 1516 P St., NW, Washington, DC 20005 (202) 466-7767. E-mail: shicks@ncai.org. Website: www.ncai.org. She also serves as principle Investigator on a number of the Center's projects. *Past professional post*: Bureau of Indian Affairs, Washington, DC.

HIGH, ELLESA CLAY (Eastern Shawnee)
(professor of English; lecturer in Native American Studies)
Affiliation & Address: Associate Professor of nglish, Eberly College of Arts & Sciences, 229 Colson Hall, West Virginia University, P.O. Box 6296, Morgantown, WV 26506 (304) 293–9722. Email: ellesa.high@mail.wvu.edu. *Other professional posts*: Member, Native Amerian Studies Program Committee; lecturer in Native American Studies. Professor High teaches American Indian literature, film, & creative writing, as well as scholarly articles & chapters. Recently, she completed work focused on The indigenous history & cultures of West Virginia. *Published work*: West Virginia: Native America: A State-by-State Historical Encyclopedia, edited by Daniel S. Murphree. 3 vols. (ABC-CLIO, 2012).

HIGH TOWER, VALERIE (Mohawk)
(writer - children's literature)
Address: 430 S. Muskogee Ave., Tahlequah, OK 74464 (918) 456-7195.

HILDEN, PATRICIA PENN (Nez Perce) 1944-
(professor emerita)
Born May 31, 1944, Burbank, Calif. *Education*: University of California, Berkeley, BA, 1965; University of California, Davis, MA, 1977; University of Cambridge (England), MA, 1979, PhD, 1981. *Address & Affiliation*: Professor Emerita, Ethnic Studies Dept., College of Letters & Science, 542 Barrows Hall, Berkeley, CA 94720 (510) 642-6573. E-mail: hilden@berkeley.edu. *Research Interests*: Native American history. Past professional post: Associate professor, Emory University, Atlanta, GA, 1982-2009. *Other professional posts*: Fellow in History, Trinity Hall, Cambridge, England; coordinator, Special Action Tutoring Program, University of California, Davis (Office of Economic Opportunity). *Community activities*: New York University Talking Circle; Emory University Native America Awareness Month; Advisory Board, Mohawk Valley Project, 1993-94. *Memberships*: Wordcraft Circle of Native American Mentor & Apprentice Writers (regional coordinator, Northeast, 1992-93, board member, 1994-1995); American Historical Association, 1982-. *Awards, honors*: Best Article Prize, Berkshire Conference of Women Historians, 1992; Research awards from Fulbright Foundation, American Council of Learned Societies, National Endowment for the Humanities, British Academy, and Social Science Research Council. *Biographical sources*: Who's Who in the South & Southeast; Dictionary of International Biography; The Word Who's Who of Women. *Published works*: Working Women & Socialist Politics in France (Oxford University Press, 1986); Women, Work & Politics: Belgium 1830-1914 (Oxford University Press, 1993); When Nickels Were Indians: Growing Up Mixed Blood (Smithsonian Press, 1995); From A Red Zone: Critical Perspectives on Race, Politics & Culture (African World Press, 2006); Racing the West (collection of essays in progress); numerous articles & book chapters.

HILDEBRAND, JENNIFER
(American Indian studies coordinator)
Affiliation & Address: Coordinator, American Indian Studies Minr, State University of New York, Fredonia, E304 Thompson Hall, Fredonia, NY 14063 (716) 673-3274. E-mail: Jennifer.hildebrand@ferdonia.edu.

HILDERBRAND, NORMAN (Wyandotte)
(tribal 2nd chief)
Affiliation & Address: 2nd Chief, Wyandotte Nation of Oklahoma, P.O. Box 250, Wyandotte, OK 74370 (918) 678-2297.

HILDERMAN-SMITH, MARY
(museum executive director)
Affiliation: Marin Museum of the American Indian, P.O. Box 864, 2200 Novato Blvd., Novato, CA 94947 (510) 897-4064.

HILFIKER, MARY
(BIA special education coordinator)
Affiliation: Minneapolis Area Office, Bureau of Indian Affairs, 331 S. Second Ave., Minneapolis, MN 55401 (612) 373-1000.

HILL, BRENDA (Tuscarora)
(Native potter)
Affiliation: The Tomaquag Indian Memorial Museum, 390 Summit Rd., Exeter, RI 02822 (401) 491-9063. *Professional post*: Eastern Woodland pottery instructor.

HILL, BRYCE ANTHONY
(attorney)
Education: University of Tulsa College of Law, JD, 1985. *Affiliation & Address*: Founding Attorney, Office of Bryce A, Hill, 1511 S. Delaware Ave., Tlsa, OK 74104 (918) 584-2889 . *Practicing Area*: Native American Law. Practicing Jurisdictions: Cherokee Nation, 2006-present; Creek Nation, 2007-present; Oklahoma, 1985-present; 10th Curcuit, 1987-present; U.S. Supreme Court, 1994-present.

HILL, DANIEL C. (Cayuga)
(craftsperson)
Address: P.O. Box 22, Akron, NY 14001 (716) 542-3637. *Products*: Traditional carved flutes, Iroquois silverwork.

HILL, GERALD, M.D. (Klamath)
(Indian center director)
Education: University of Washington, MD; Robert Wood Johnson Clinical Scholars Program, Residency Training, UCSF/Stanford Program, 1986. *Affiliation*: Center of American Indian & Minority Health, School of Medicine, 10 University Dr., Duluth, MN 55812-2487 (218) 726-7235. Dr. Hill developed the nation's first Indian Health Pathway for Native American students, combining clinical experiences in Native communities all four years of medical school with courses & seminars in Indian health as well as education & experiences in Traditional Indian medicine and mentoring from Native physicians. He currently practices emergency Medicine in St. Paul, MN, and serves on the University of Minnesota's Medical School Admissions Committee. *Past professional posts*: Faculty, University of California, San Francisco Medical School 1986-90. *Community activities*: Chair, San Francisco Native American Health Board; member, Association on American Indian Physicians (former president (2008-09); health systems consultant & member of the Klamath Tribes' Health Committee.

HILL, GERALD L. (Oneida of Wisconsin)
(attorney, tribal judge)
Affiliation: Oneida Tribe of Wisconsin, P.O. Box 365, Oneida, WI 54155 (414) 869-2345; Prairie Band Potawatomi Nation Tribal Court, 15498 K Rd., Mayetta, KS 66509 (785) 966-2242. E-mail: tribalcourt@pbpnation.org. Website: www. pbpnation.org/tribalcourt. *Membership*: Wisconsin Indian Lawyers League.

HILL, GREGORY
(executive director)
Affiliation & Address: Executive Director, Indian Legal Program, Sandra Day O'Connor College of Law, LAW 230, Arizona State University, P.O. Box 877906, Tempe, AZ 85287 (480) 965-6204. E-mail: greg.hill@asu.edu.

HILL, GWENDOLYN A. (Chippewa/Cree) 1952-
(higher education administrator)
Born October 31, 1952, Ft. Belknap, Mont. *Education*: Northern Montana College, BS, 1976; University of South Dakota, MPA, 1989. *Principal occupation*: Higher education administrator. *Address*: RR 1, Box 1, Sisseton, SD 57262 (605) 698-3966. *Affiliations*: Teacher, BIA, Stewart Indian School, Stewart, NV, 1975-80; dean/president, Sisseton-Wahpeton Community College, Sisseton, SD, 1981-present. *Community activities*: Sisseton Public Schools (Parent Advisory Committee, Title IV, 1984-88); Native American Student Advisory Council, University of Minnesota, Morris, 1988-89. *Memberships*: American Indian Higher Education Consortium, 1988-; AACJC, 1989; National Association of Women Deans, Administrators & Counselors, 1987-89. *Interests*: "Extremely interested in promoting Indian higher education on the national, state and local level. As an administrator of a tribal college located on Lake Traverse Reservation where unemployment reaches 80%, it is imperative to ensure that our institution meets the unique educational needs of the Sisseton-Wahpeton Sioux Tribe." *Biographical source*: Carnegie Foundation for the Advancement of Teaching: Report on Tribal Colleges, 1989.

HILL, JANICE M. (Chilkoot)
(Alaskan association president)
Affiliation & Address: Chilkoot Indian Association, P.O. Box 490, Haines, AK 99827 (907) 766-2323. E-mail: chilkoot@wytbear.com. *Past professional post*: President, Klukwan Heritage Foundation, Haines, AK.

HILL, MARGO (Spokane)
(attorney)
Affiliation & Address: Attorney, Spokane Tribe, P.O. Box 100, Wellpinit, WA 99040 (509) 258-4581.

HILL, MEGAN MINOKA (Oneida of Wisconsin)
(director of Honoring Nations)

Education: University of Colorado, BA (International Affairs); Armand Hammer United World College of the American West, International Baccalaureate degree); University of Chicago, MA (Social Sciences). *Affiliation & Address*: Director of Honoring Nations Program, Harvard Project on American Indian Economic Development, John F. Kennedy School of Government, 79 JFK St., Cambridge, MA 02138 (617) 496-4229. E-mail: megan_hill@harvard.edu. *Other professional posts*: Vice-chair, Board of Directors, Rosa Minoka Hill Fund, which provides scholarship assistance to American Indian students; founder & president of Minoka Organics. *Past professional posts*: Treasurer on the Board of Native Americans in Philanthropy; director of development, University of New Mexico College of Arts & Sciences; senior program officer, Institute of American Indian Arts (IAIA), Santa Fe, NM. *Membership*: Americans for Indian Opportunity.

HILL, NORBERT S., JR. (Oneida) 1946-
(executive director)

Born November 26, 1946, Detroit, Mich. *Education*: University of Wisconsin, B.S., 1969, M.S., 1971; Cumberland College (Williamsburg, KY), Honorary Doctorate, 1994. *Affiliation & Address*: Advisory Trustee, Environmental Defense Fund, Inc., 257 Park Ave. South, New York, NY 10010 (212) 505-2100. *Past professional posts*: Director, Native American Educational Opportunity Program, University of Colorado, Boulder, 1977-83; executive director, American Indian Science & Engineering Society, Albuquerque, NM, 1983-; director, American Indian Graduate Center, Albuquerque, NM, 2000-08; chairperson, Oneida Tribal Education Committee, 1970-74; chairperson, Oneida Film Project, 1976; Chairman, Native American Career Exposition, Denver, CO, 1978-79; president, Dr. Rosa Minoka Hill Foundation, 1982-; publisher, "Winds of Change" magazine, 1986-99; Chairman, Smithsonian Institution's National Museum of the American Indian, 1991-99; Assistant Dean of Students, University of Wisconsin, Green Bay, 1972-77. *Community activities*: Colorado Endowment for the Humanities (board of directors); "Technos Quarterly," Editorial Advisory Board; Environmental Defense Fund (board of directors, 1992-); Women & Foundations/Corporate Philanthropy (board of directors, 1992-); National Science Foundation's "Project Mosaic," Advisory Committee, 1992-; George Bird Grinnell American Indian Children's Education Foundation (board of directors); National Action Council for Minorities in Engineering (NACME). *Awards, honors*: Indian Grant Scholarship, 1964-68; Education Policy Fellow, Institute for Educational Leadership, Washington, DC, 1980-81; Reginald H. Jones Distinguished Service Award, National Action Council for Minorities in Engineering, 1988; Chancellor's Award, University of Wisconsin, Oshkosh, 1988; member, Council of Advisors to President-Elect Clinton's Transition Team for Education, Dec. 1992; Honorary Doctorate, Cumberland College, 1994. *Published works*: Articles in "Smithsonian Handbook of American Indians," 1978; article in "The Indian Historian," Vol. II, No. 4, Dec. 1978; editor, "Changing America: The New Face to Science & Engineering," report (National Science Foundation, 1989); editor, "Education That Works: An Action Plan for the Education of Minorities," report (Quality Education for Minorities Project, 1990); editor, "Our Voices, Our Vision," report (The College Board/Charles Stewart Mott Foundation, 1990); editor, "Native American Repatriation of Cultural Patrimony Act & The Native American Grave & Burial Protection Act," testimony (AISES, 1990); publisher, "Winds of Change," magazine, 1985-; editor, "The Demographics of American Indians: One Percent of the People: Fifty Percent of the Diversity," report (Institute for Educational Leadership, Inc./Center for Demographic Study, 1990); Words of Power--Voices From Indian America (Fulcrum, 1994).

HILL, RICHARD G. (Tuscarora-Oneida)
(tribal chairperson)

Affiliations: Oneida Indian Nation Business Committee, P.O. Box 365, Oneida, WI 54155 (920) 869-2214. E-mail: rhill9@oneidanation.org. *Past professional posts*: Special assistant, National Museum of the American Indian, Smithsonian Institution; co-chair, Committee on Museum-Native American Collaboration, American Association of Museums; chairperson, National Indian Gaming Association, Washington, DC.

HILL, ROBERTA (Oneida of Wisconsin)
(professor of English & director of American Indian studies)

Affiliation & Address: Professor of English & Director, American Indian Studies (1995-present), University of Wisconsin, 318 Ingraham, 1155 Observatory Dr., Madison, WI 53706 (608) 262-6211. E-mail: rhill@wisc.edu

HILL, ROGER (Tonawanda Seneca)
(tribal chief)

Affiliation & Address: Chief, Tonawanda Band of Seneca Indians, 7027 Meadville Rd., Basom, NY 14013 (716) 542-4244

HILL, SID (Onondaga)
(former tribal chief)

Affiliation & Address: Onondaga Nation, RR 1 Box 270-A, Nedrow, NY 13120.

HILL, SUSAN (Mohawk)
(First Nations Studies program director)

Affiliation & Address: Director & Faculty, First Nations Studies Program, Social Science Centre, Rm. 3207A, The University of Western Ontario, Faculty of Social Science, London, ON N6A 5C2 (519) 661-2111 ext. 89285. E-mail: shill26@uwo.ca.

HILL, THOMAS VERNON (Seneca) 1943-
(museum director)

Born May 9, 1943, Ohsweken, Six Nations Reserve. *Education*: Ontario College of Art, Toronto, 1964-67 - A.O.C.A.; Carleton University, Ottawa, 1968; currently completing Ontario Museums Studies, Ontario Museums Association, 1985-89. *Address*: Box 129, Ohsweken P.O., Ontario, Canada N0A 1M0 (519) 759-2650. *Affiliations*: Director, Cultural Development, Indian & Northern Affairs, Ottawa, 1968-78; social development officer, 1979-81, native policy advisory, 1981-82, Secretary of State, Toronto, 1979-81; museum director, Woodland Cultural Centre, Brantford, 1982-. *Other professional post*: Vice-president, Visual Arts Ontario, Toronto, 1988-; chairman, Task Force on First Nations & Museums, Canadian Museums Association, 1989-; Editor, MUSE Magazine (Canadian Museums Association), 1989). *Community activities*: Six Nations Tourism; H.M. Chapel of the Mohawks Restoration; Ad Hoc Museum Committee, Brant County. *Memberships*: Visual Arts Ontario (vice-president); Canadian Museums Assn; Ontario Museums Association; Ontario Genealogical Assn; Society of Canadian Artists of Native Ancestry; Royal Ontario Museum; Ontario Assn of Art Galleries; Canadian Native Arts Foundation; Native Canadian Centre of Toronto; The Association of Cultural Executives; National Indian Arts Council. *Awards, honors*: H.R. Majesty Service Award, 1978; Certificate of Merit, Art Director, 1976; Public Service Commission Merit Award, 1974. *Interests*: First Nations and museums; Avocational: Filmmaking, painting, pottery, theatre & printmaking; Eskaneh singing. *Published works*: Editor, Indian Art in Canada (Government of Canada, 1972); Norval Morrisseau and the Emergence of the Image-Makers (Methuen Art Gallery of Ontario, 1984); Canadian Native Peoples, Vol. II (Heirloom Publishing, 1988); Beyond History (Vancouver Art Gallery, 1989).

HILL, VERNON (Shoshone)
(tribal co-chairperson)

Affiliation & Address: Co-Chairperson, Eastern Shoshone Tribe, P.O. Box 538, Fort Washakie, WY 82514; E-mail: vhill@e-shoshone.com (307) 332-3532

HILLABRANT, WALTER JOHN (Citizen Band Potawatomi) 1942-
(clinical psychologist)

Born December 17, 1942, Corsicana, Tex. *Education*: University of California, Berkeley, BA (Psychology), 1965; University of California, Riverside, PhD, 1972. *Principal occupation*: Psychologist. *Address*: 1927 38th St., NW, Washington, DC 20007. *Affiliations*: Assistant professor, Howard University, Washington, DC, 1970-80; psychologist, president, Support Services International, Inc., Silver Spring, MD, 1980-. *Other professional post*: Treasurer, Board of Directors, National Indian Youth Leadership Project, Albuquerque, NM. *Memberships*: American Psychological Assn; Washington Academy of Sciences; National Indian Education Assn. *Interests*: Indian education; cross-cultural psychology; application of computer & telecommunication technology to social problems. *Published work*: The Future Is Now (Peacock Press, 1974).

HILLER, JOSEPH G. (Lakota)
(professor of American Indian studies)

Education: University of Wyoming, PhD, 2000. Affiliation: Head, American Indian Studies Program, The University of Arizona, Harvill 216, Forbes 314, Tucson, AZ 85721 (520) 621-7201. E-mail: jghiller@cals.arizona.edu. *Other professional posts*: Assistant dean for American Indian programs, College of Agriculture & Life Sciences (CALS); associate director, Arizona Agricultural Experiment Station; assistant director, Arizona Cooperative Extension. *Past professional posts*: Chair, Watershed Management & Ecohydrology Program, 2004-07) in the CALS School of Natural Resources. He administers the budgeted research programs in CALS and in the principal investigator for the Federally Recognized Tribal Extension Program (FRTEP) (website: www.indiancountryextension.org). In addition, Joe serves on several national-level consultative panels & boards that interact with tribes and the U.S. Government, states & counties, including: The President's White House Advisory Board on Tribal Colleges & Universities, The Indian Land Tenure Foundation (website: www.indianlandtenure.org). *Interests*: Agriculture and natural resources technical & policy issues, especially water, in Indian country.

HILPERT, BRUCE
(professor of anthropology)

Affiliation & Address: Dept. of Anthropology, Emil Haury Anthropology Bldg., Rm. 221A, University of Arizona, Tucson, AZ 85721 (520) 621-2585. E-mail: bhilpert.@u.arizona.edu. *Interests*: American Indians of the Southwest.

HINTON, CHERYL M. 1953-
(museum director & chief curator)
Born October 24, 1953, New York, N.Y. Education: San Diego State University, BA & MA in Anthropology. *Affiliation & Address*: Director & Chief Curator (1999-present), Barona Cultural Center & Museum, 1095 Barona Rd., Lakeside, CA 92040 (619) 443-7003 ext. 2. E-mail: chinton@barona.org. *Past professional posts*: Anthropologist, Palm Springs Desert Museum, 1988-92; Curator, Agua Caliente (Band of Cahuilla Indians) Cultural Museum, 1992-96; Southwest Curator, Southwest Collections & NAGPRA (Repatriation) Coordinator, San Diego Museum of Man, 1996-99. *Other professional posts*: Adjunct Professor of Anthropology, University of San Diego, 1999-present; editor, Barona Spirits Speak, 2001-present. *Community activities*: Community liaison for local tribes for USD Indian Market & Festival; representative for Barona to Tribal Digital Village; Special Events Chair for Self Realization Fellowship, San Diego Temple; Indian Heritage Festival, Education Coordinator, 1993-96. *Memberships*: American Association of Museums: Tribal Museums Branch/Diversity Coalition; Western Museums Association; Society for Applied Anthropology; American Anthropology Association. *Interests*: Self-Image of stereotypes among Indians; NAGPRA (Native American Graves Protection & Repatriation; Yoga & Eastern religious philosophies. *Publications*: The Bear Shaman Tradition of Southern California Indians (Barona Cultural Center & Museum, Publication 2001-02).

HINTON, LEANNE
(professor emerita)
Affiliation: Dept. of Linguistics, U.C. Berkeley, Berkeley, CA 94720 (510) 643-7621. E-mail: hintonscot@aol.com. Dr. Hinton is a specialist on language revitalization. She consults with indigenous groups around the world on language maintenance & reclamation. As a founding member of "Advocates for Indigenous California Languages (AICLS), she is involved in their language programming. Leanne has published eight books, and written numerous articles and reports on the revitalization of indigenous languages.

HINTON, MICHAEL-COREY FRANCIS (Passamaquoddy)
(attorney)
Education: Colgate University, BA, 2008; Arizona State University College of Law, JD, 2011. *Affiliation & Address*: Associate, Akin Gump Straus Hauer & Feld, LLP, Robert E. Straus Bldg., 1333 New Hampshire Ave. NW, Washington, DC 20036 (202) 887-4415; E-mail: mhinton@akingump.com. Mr. Hinton advises clients regarding American Indian law & Policy. *Past professional posts*: Fellow for the Senate Committee on Indian Affairs, working with former Sen. Byron Dorgan (D. ND), in addressing problems & opportunities across Indian Country; policy analyst, American Indian practice at Akin Group in 2009; participated in the ASU Indan Legal Clinic

HIPP, JANIE SIMMS (Chickasaw)
(assistant professor)
Affiliation & Address: Director, Indigenous Food & Agriculture Initiative, University of Arkansas School of Law, 1045 W. Maple St., Fayetteville, AR 72701 (479) 575-4699; Email: jhipp@uark.edu. Ms. Hipp teaches agricultural law and is co-founder (with Professor Jennie Popp of the University of Arkansas), of the national organization, Native Women in Agriculture. The Initiative is the first of its kind nationally, with the following goals & objectives: To increase student enrollment in the land grant universities in food and agricultural related disciplines by supporting existing students and creating early pipeline programs for youth; To create new academic & executive education programs in food and agriculture, including law, policy, and tribal governance; To directly support Indian country by providing strategic planning and technical assistance, including research and publications in the following subject areas: Tribal Governance Infrastructure to Enhance Business & Economic Development Opportunities Financial Markets & Asset Management, including Banking, Risk Management, and Stewardship of Land and Natural Resources; Health and Nutrition Policy for Tribal Community Wellness; Intellectual Property Rights and Protection of Traditional Knowledge. Until 2004 there had never been a national organization for Indian women who owned & operated farms. There are currently about 12,000 Indian women operating farms in the U.S., according to the 2002 Census of Agriculture. With the help from a three-year, $200,000 grant from the Dept. of Agriculture, the two were able to start such a group. The group was formed in partnership with the Intertribal Agriculture Council in Billings, MT, which promotes the conservation and development of Indian farming among the 566 federally recognized tribal government & Alaskan villages. The operation of the Native Women in Agriculture will be turned over to the council in 2006.

HISA, CARLOS (Tigua)
(tribal governor)
Affiliation & Address: Governor, Ysleta Del Sur Pueblo, P.O. Box 17579, El Paso, TX 79907 (915) 859-8053. Website: www.ysletadelsurpueblo.org.

HITCHCOCK, RAYMOND (Wintun)
(Rancheria chairperson)
Affiliation & Address: Chairperson, Wilton Rancheria, 9728 Kent St., Elk Grove, CA 95624 (916) 683-6000; E-mall: rhitchock@wiltonrancheria-nsn.gov

HIX, VERONICA (Cherokee)
(executive director)
Affiliation & Address: Marketing & Entrepreneurial Services Manager (2012-13), Executive Director (2013-present), ONABEN, 53332 S. Memorial Dr., Suite 200, Tulsa, OK 74145 (918) 624-9176. E-mail: veronica@onaben.org. *Past professional post*: Entrepreneurial Services Manager, Cherokee Nation.

HOBENSHILED, SHARON (Gitxsan First Nations)
(director of aboriginal education)
Affiliation & Address: Director, Office of Aoriginal Education, Vancouver Island University, 900 5th St., Nanimo, BC V8R 5S5 (250) 740-6542. E-mail: Sharon.hobenshield@viu.ca.

HOBBS, CHARLES A.
(attorney)
Education: Yale University, BA, 1950; George Washington University, JD, 1957. *Principal occupation*: Attorney. *Address & Affiliation*: Senior Partner, Hobbs, Straus, Dean & Walker, LLP, 2120 L St., NW, Suite 700, Washington, DC 20037 (202) 822-8282. E-mail: chobbs@hsdwdc.com. *Past professional posts*: Clerk, Judge Warren F. Burger, U.S. Court of Appeals, DC Circuit, 1958-65; Wilkinson, Cragun & Barker, Washington, DC, 1968-82 (assisted tribal governments in all areas of Indian law, and prosecuted a large number of tribal land claims under the Indian Claims Commission Act; past chairperson, Committee on Indian Affairs, Administrative law Section, American Bar Association. In 1982 when Wilkinson, Cragun & Barker dissolved, Mr. Hobbs, along with Jerry Straus and Bobo Dean, formed the present firm, dedicated to advising and representing Indian tribes and Indian people. Mr. Hobbs has been a named attorney in over 100 litigations resulting in written decisions on Indian rights. He has argued five Indian cases before the U.S. Supreme Court, including United States v. Mitchell, 463 U.S. 206 (1983), which established that the U.S. must pay money damages when it breaches its trust duties to Indians, and Menominee Tribe v. United States, 391 U.S. 404 (1968), which held that when Congress terminates Indian tribes, the tribes retain their treaty rights unless specifically nullified. He also handled Rhode Island v. Narragansett Tribe, 19 F.3d 685 (1994), in which the First Circuit Court of Appeals held that the Tribe was entitled to operate gaming under the Indian Gaming Regulatory Act. Mr,. Hobbs and William Norman were the drafters of Chapter 2 of "Empowerment of Tribal Governments: Final Workgroup Report," developed by the Tribal Workgroup on Tribal Needs Assessments, May 1999. Mr. Hobbs' entire career has been spent working for Indian tribes & organizations, and individual Indians. He was honored in 1993 at the National Congress of American Indians' national convention for distinguished service to the Indian community.

HOBIA, JEREMIAH (Muscogee Creek)
(former tribal town king)
Affiliation & Address: Former Town King, Kialegee Tribal Town, P.O. Box 332, Wetumka, OK 74883 (405) 452-3262.

HOBIA, TIGER (Muscogee Creek)
(tribal town king)
Affiliation & Address: Town King, Kialegee Tribal Town, P.O. Box 332, Wetumka, OK 74883 (405) 452-3262.

HOBLET, CARLEEN (Eskimo)
(Alaskan village president)
Affiliation & Address: President, Native Village of False Pass, P.O. Box 29, False Pass, AK 99583 (907) 548-2227.

HOBOT, JOE (Hunk Papa Lakota)
(organization president & CEO)
Education: University of Minnesota, BA; University of St. Thomas, MA (Education); Hamline University (St. Paul, MN), EdD. *Affiliation & Address*: President & CEO, American Indian Opportunities Industrialization Center (OIC), 1845 East Franklin Ave., Minneapolis, MN 55404 (612) 341-3358 ext. 149; E-mail: joeh@aioic.org. Joe has served at the OIC since 2006, previously holding the position of Director of Education. He also served as the Lead Teacher of Takoda Prep with an emphasis on Social Studies and as an instructor at the Takoda Institute. *Other professional post*: Chair, Metropolitan Urban Indian Directors (MUID) group based in Minneapolis. *Awards, honors*: Recipient of the Minnesota Indian Chamber of Commerce's *Bear Award*.

HOBSON, BARBARA (*Torralba*) (Comanche) 1951-
(educator)
Born May 26, 1951, Lawton, Okla. *Education*: Oklahoma State University, BA, 1973; University of New Mexico, MA, 1978; University of Oklahoma, PhD, 1994. *Affiliation & Address*: Assistant Director, Native American Studies Program, Ellison Hall 212, University of Oklahoma, Norman, OK 73019 (405) 325-2324. E-mail: bhobsn@ou.edu. *Past professional posts*: Counselor, Southwestern Indian Polytechnic Institute, Albuquerque, NM, 1973-77; minority counselor, University of Albuquerque, 1978-80; coordinator, Native American Program, College of Engineering, University of Oklahoma, 1985-88; Returning the Gift Native Writers Project, 1990-92. *Awards, honors*: Foundations in Native Education Fellow, 1989-93, University of Oklahoma, College of Education; American Indian Education Fellow, Dept. of Indian Education, Washington, DC, 1990-93. *Interests*: "Special area of interests - American Indian retention." *Unpublished dissertation*: Cultural Values & Persistence Among Comanche College Students, University of Oklahoma, 1994. *Published work*: "Tribally Controlled Colleges: Meeting the Needs of American Indian Adults," monograph (Office of Indian Affairs, State of Oklahoma, 1991);

HOBSON, DOTTIE F. (Navaho) 1945-
(school principal)
Born March 9, 1945, Tohatchi, N.M. *Education*: University of Arizona, BA, 1972; University of New Mexico, MA, 1977; Northern Arizona University, MA, 1977. *Address & Affiliation*: Principal, Dilcon Boarding School, HC63, Box G, Winslow, AZ 86047 (602) 657-3211. *Other professional post*: Supt. for education, Chinle Agency, BIA, Chinle, AZ, 1978-90. *Community activities*: Boy Scouts of America (institutional representative); Gyro Scouts; Federal Women's Program Coordinator, Chinle Agency. *Memberships*: Navaho School Administrators Association; National Indian Education Assn. *Published works*: Kee's Grandfather (Rough Rock Demonstration School, Chinle, AZ, 1970).

HOBSON, GEARY (Cherokee-Quapaw/Chickasaw) 1941-
(professor, poet, writer/editor)
Born June 12, 1941, Chicot County, Ark. *Education*: Arizona State University, BA, 1968, MA, 1969; University of New Mexico, PhD, 1986. *Address & Affiliation*: Professor, Dept. of English, University of Oklahoma, 760 Van Vliet Oval, Room 113, Norman, OK 73019 (405) 325-6231 (work), 1988-. *Military service*: U.S. Marine Corps, 1959-65. *Community activities*: Project Director of Returning the Gift (now called Native Writers Circle of the Americas); co-organizer of the Arkansas Band of Quapaw Indians. *Awards, honors*: Rockefeller Fellowship for Minority Scholars, 1981-82; National Endowment of the Arts grant, 1982-83; Lifetime Achievement Award from the Native Writers' Circle of the Americas in 2003. *Biographical source*: Contemporary Authors, Vol. 122. *Published works*: Editor, The Remembered Earth: An Anthology of Contemporary Native American Literature (University of New Mexico Press, 1979); Deer Hunting & Other Poems (Point Riders Press, 1990); The Last of the Ofos (University of Arizona Press, 2000).

HODGE, FELICIA SCHANCHE (*Wailaki*) 1949-
(professor; primary care nursing)
Born January 3, 1949, Garberville, Calif. *Education*: University of California, Berkeley, MPH, 1976, Dr. P.H., 1987. *Address & Affiliation*: Director, Center for American Indian Research & Education (CAIRE), Chair, Graduate IDP, American Indian Studies, UCLA (1999-present), UCLA, 3101 Campbell Hall, Box 99999, Los Angeles, CA 90095 (310) 267-2255. E-mail: fhodge@sonnet.ucla.edu. *Other professional posts*: National Advisory Council for Nursing Research, NIH, 2005-2009; Peer Reviewer, National Cancer Institute, 1996-present. *Past professional posts*: Northwest Portland Area Indian Health Board, Portland, OR (evaluation coordinator, 1976-77; executive director, 1977-82); student research assistant, UC-Berkeley (while working on a doctoral degree); principal investigator, American Indian Cancer Control Project, Berkeley, CA, 1990-99; principal investigator, American Indian Women's Talking Circle, Berkeley, CA, 1993-99; director, Center for American Indian Research & Education, Western Consortium for Public Health, Berkeley, CA, 1994-1998. Consultant to agencies/projects, 1984-99; lecturer, School of Social Welfare, UC-Berkeley, 1989-99; director, American Indian Graduate Program, UC-Berkeley, 1989-99. *Community activities*: Chairman-Board of Directors, American Indian Child Resource Center, 1990-91, 1994; trustee, Administrative Board of the California Teen Nutritional & Fitness Program, Western Consortium for Public Health, Berkeley), 1993; Advisory Board, Rural Institute on Disabilities, University of Montana, 1994; Advisory Committee Member, American Indian Tobacco Education Network, 1995-99. *Membership*: National Network for Cancer Control Research Among American Indians & Alaska Native Populations; Native Researchers Network, 2000-present. Research & Scholarship: Dr. Hodge's research focuses on chronic health conditions & health beliefs & behaviors among American Indian & Alaskan Natives. Current Research Grants: Principle investigator, study based on "Reducing Symptoms Among American Indians," National Cancer Institute, 2005-2010; Principle investigator, Science of the Diabetes Wellness: American Indian Talking Circles Approach for Diabetes Prevention & Care in American Indian Communities, Centers for Disease Control (CDC) (2005-present);

Principle investigator, Native Nursing Careers Opportunity Program (NNCOP, U.S. Dept. of & Human Service, IHS, 2003-2008. *Interests*: Cultural diversity, health education, research methods, American Indian health & healthcare. *Awards, honors*: Duncan Neuhauser Award, UC-Berkeley, 1984; Kaiser Award, Golden State Minority Foundation, Los Angeles, 1984 & 1985; IHS Scholarship, 1985 & 1986; Ruth Muscrat Bronson Memorial Scholarship, Save the Children, Westport, CT, 1986; post-doctoral Fellowship, Alcohol Research Group, UC-Berkeley, 1987; Peer Reviewer, National Cancer Institute, 1996-present; 2005-2009 National Advisory Council for Nursing Research, NIH. *Published works*: Graduate Education & Employment, A Study of American Indian & Non-Indians in the School of Public Health, UC-Berkeley, 1971-85 (UC-Berkeley, 1986); The Socio-Cultural Aspects of Disability: A Survey of Disabled Adult American Indians, monograph, with R. Edmonds (University of Arizona, 1987); Creating an Agenda for American Indian Health in the Year 2000, monograph, with A. Williams & W. Whitehorse (State of California, 1992); "Contemporary U.S. Indian Health Care," in The Native North American Almanac (Gale Research, 1994); Papers submitted & accepted for publication: "Smoking Cessation for American Indians in Northern California," & "Tobacco Use Policies & Practices in Diverse Indian Settings" (Preventive Medicine, 1994); among other articles, and professional papers.

HODSON, CAMMERON (Wintun)
(Rancheria vice chairperson)
Affiliation & Address: Vice Chairperson, Wilton Rancheria, 9728 Kent St., Elk Grove, CA 95624 (916) 683-6000; E-mail: chodson@wiltonracnheria-nsn.gov

HOERIG, KARL A.
(museum director)
Affiliation & Address: Director, White Mountain Apache Cultural Center & Museum, P.O. Box 507, Fort Apache, AZ 85926 (928) 338-4625. E-mail: fortapachemuseum@hotmail. com.

HOFFMAN, ROSS
(professor of First Nations Studies program)
Born & raised in Ontario, Canada. *Education*: Trent University, BA (Native Studies), PhD (Native Studies); University of Victoria, M.Ed. *Affiliation & Address*: Assistant Professor & Program Chair, First Nations Studies Department, University of Northern British Columbia, 3333 University Way, Prince George, B.C. V2N 4Z9 Canada (250) 960-5242. E-mail: Hoffman@unbc.ca. *Other professional post*: Research Partner, Traditional Ecological Knowledge Stream. He has worked within Wet'suwet'en, Gitxsan & Cree communities on a variety of community-based research projects in the areas of education, language & culture, and health & wellness.

HOGEN, LINDA (Chickasaw) 1947-
(retired professor; writer)
Born July 16, 1947, Denver, Colo. Education: MA in English/Creative Writing. *Principal occupation*: Professor-retired, writer. *Address*: P.O. Box 141, Idledale, CO 80453 (303) 697-9097. E-mail: horsemustang@aol.com. *Past professional post*: Professor, University of Colorado, Boulder. *Awards, honors*: Native Writers Circle Lifetime Achievement Award; National Endowment for the Arts; Before Columbus American Book Award; Pulitzer Finalist; National Book Writers Finalist; Oklahoma Book Award; Colorado Book Award (2); Wordcraft Circle Lifetime Achievement Award. *Community activities*: Colorado Chickasaw Council. *Memberships*: Writers Guild; Authors Guild; PEN. *Interests*: Writing; horses (Indian horses); environment, Native science & indigenous knowledge. *Published works*: The Book of Medicines; Power; Solar Storms; Mean Spirit; Savings; Dwellings: A Spiritual History of the World; Red Clay; Seeing Through the Sun; Savings; Co-edit: Intimate Nature: The Bond between Woman & Animals (Farrar, Straus & Giroux); The Sweet Breathing of Plants: Women & The Green World (Farrar, Straus & Giroux); The Mysterious Journey of the Gray Whale (National Geographic); Woman Who Watches Over the World: A Native Memoir (Norton, 2001).

HOGEN, PHILIP N. (Oglala Lakota)
(attorney)
Education: Augustana College, BA, 1967; University of South Dakota, JD, 1970. *Affiliation & Address*: Of Counsel, Hogen Adams PLLP, 11312 N. High Meadows Dr., Black Hawk, SD 57718 (605) 787-6901. E-mail: phogen@hogenadams.com. A former Chairman of the National Indian Gaming Commission, Mr. Hogen specializes in intergovernmental relations, litigation, tribal gaming, gaming development, and gaming regulation. Before moving into private practice in 2009, Phil spent 25 years in the Federal government. That service began when he served as the first Administrative Assistant to then Congressman Jim Abdnor in 1973. Thereafter, he was appointed by President Ronald Reagan to serve as the United States Attorney for South Dakota, a position he held from 1981-1991. During his service as United States Attorney, Philip served as the Chairman of the Department of Justice, Indian Affairs Subcommittee of the Attorney General's Advisory Committee. In 1995, Interior Secretary Bruce Babbitt appointed Mr. Hogen to serve as an Associate Commissioner on the National Indian Gaming Commission. He served in that

position from 1995–1999. He returned to the private practice of law in Rapid City, only to be called on to serve as the Associate Solicitor for the United States Department of the Interior, in 2001, a position he held until he was again appointed to the National Indian Gaming Commission, this time by President George W. Bush and as the Commission's Chairman. Mr. Hogen served as the Chairman of the National Indian Gaming Commission for seven years, the longest serving Chairman of that body. During his service, Mr. Hogen oversaw the most dramatic sustained growth in Indian gaming in its history. During this period of change and growth, Mr. Hogen provided assistance to Tribes nationwide to ensure that the dramatic growth was accompanied by thorough and effective tribal regulation. Mr. Hogen has presented on topics relating to Indian Gaming regulation and governance for years and throughout Indian Country. He is active in his profession and in his community, serving as a founding incorporator and director of the South Dakota Indiann Country Bar Association. *Awards, honors*: Rising Star, Minnesota Super Lawyers Magazine (2005-2006, 2008- 2009, 2011-2013).

HOGEN, VANYA S. (Oglala Lakota)
(attorney)
Education: University of Minnesota, BA, 1990; University of Minnesota Law School, JD, 1993. *Affiliation & Address*: Hogen Adams PLLP, 1935 W. County Road B2, Suite 460, St. Paul, MN 55113 (651) 842-9103. E-mail: vhogen@ hogenadams.com. Vanya has practiced Indian law for almost 20 years, representing tribal governments and their business partners. Vanya maintains an active transactional practice, focusing primarily on Indian gaming, financing, and tribal economic development. She regularly assists clients with business transactions in Indian country, including advising them on appropriate business structures, guiding them through environmental & other regulatory-compliance issues, and negotiating and drafting contracts. She has worked closely with tribal governments to draft and enact tribal codes and ordinances involving a broad range of subjects, such as tribal-court systems, enrollment, family law, environmental laws, & secured transactions. She has also assisted with Secretarial elections and amending tribal constitutions. *Areas of Practice*: Civil Litigation, Environmental Law, Finance, Gaming Law, Indian/Tribal Law. She won a victory in the South Dakota Supreme Court that stopped South Dakota from imposing its motor-fuel tax on Indian reservations in the state. *Other professional posts*: Judge for the Shakopee Mdewakanton Sioux Community Tribal Court; member of the Board of Trustees for the Nature Conservancy (MN, SD & ND chapter); serves on the Board of Governors for the University of St. Thomas School of Law; frequent speaker at Indian-law seminars around the country. *Past professional post*: Partner, Jacobson, Buffalo, Magnuson, Anderson & Halloran, P.C., St. Paul, MN. *Awards, honors*: Vanya was named as "Lawyer of the Year" in Native American Law for Minneapolis in 2012, & has been named as a "Super Lawyer" in Minnesota 13 times, as a "Best Lawyer" in Native American law in 2009-2016, and is AV-rated by Martindale Hubbell. She is a frequent speaker at Indian-law seminars around the country and serves as a judge for the Shakopee Mdewakanton Sioux Community Tribal Court.

HOGUE, J. RENEE (Chickasaw)
(Indian academic services director)
Education: East Central University, BS (Mathematics), 1990, MS (Human Resources Administration), 2007. *Affiliation & Address*: Director, Native American Studient Services, East Central University (ECU), Horace Mann Bldg., Rm. 318B, Ada, OK 74820 (580) 559-5671. E-mail: rhogue@ecok.edu. *Past professional posts*: Project director, Native American Voices Project, ECU (a grant funded through the U.S. Dept. of Education); Recruitment & Retention coordinator for the Chickasaw Nation Division of Education on the ECU campus (four years); programmer & project manager for the Chickasaw Nation Information Technology Department (six years).

HOIG, STAN
(professor emeritus)
Affiliation: Professor Emeritus of Journalism, University of Central Oklahoma, Edmond, OK. *Published works*: The Sand Creek Massacre (University of Oklahoma Press, 1961); The Peace Chiefs of the Cheyenne (U. of Oklahoma Press, 1980); Tribal Wars of the Southern Plains (U. of Oklahoma Press, 1993); Beyond the Frontier: Exploring the Indian Country (U. of Oklahoma Press, 1998); The Western Odyssey of John Simpson Smith: Frontiersman & Indian Interpreter (U. of Oklahoma Press, 2004).

HOKOWHITU, BRENDAN (Metis)
(dean of Native studies)
Affiliation & Address: Dean, Department of Native Studies University of Alberta, 2031 Pembina Hall, Edmonton, AB T6G 2H8 (780) 492-2991. E-mail: nsdean@ualberta.ca.

HOLBROOK, KENNETH (Maidu)
(executive director)
Affiliation & Address: Executive Director, Maidu Summit Conservancy, 289 Main St., Chester, CA 96020 (916) 258-2299 E-mail: director@maidusummit. org

HOLLOW, WALTER B., M.D. (Assiniboine-Sioux)
(physician, family practitioner)
Education: University of Washington School of Medicine, MD. *Affiliation & Address*: Family Practitioner, Group Health Cooperative, 9800 4ᵗʰ Ave. NE, Seattle, WA 98115 (206) 302-1248. *Other professional post*: Dr. Hollow developed the Native American Center of Excellence in 1992 and served as director until 2001. He is now the director of faculty development and is an active instructor for the Indian Heath Pathway. *Community activities*: Board member of Seattle Indian Health Board and is presently working with the WWAMI Workforce Research Program at the University of Washington and studying workforce issues & higher education for Native American students. *Awards, honors*: Dr. Hollow was the first American Indian graduate from the UW School of Medicine.

HOLM, TOM (Creek/Cherokee)
(writer, professor)
Education: University of Oklahoma, PhD, 1978. *Affiliation & Address*: Professor (1980-present), American Indian Studies Program, The University of Arizona, Harvill 218, Box 210076, Tucson, AZ 85721 (520) 621-7108. E-mail: holm@email.arizona.edu. *Other professional posts*: Professor Holms is a reviewer for several academic presses & journals and is an advisory board member of Red Ink and Wicazo Sa Review. *Past professional posts*: In 1982, Professor Holm, Robert Thomas, Larry Evers, Vine Deloria, Jr., Emory Sekaquaptewa & N. Scott Momaday developed the M.A. program in American Indian Studies at the University of Arizona. Professor Holm has served on numerous Native American boards, panels, and working groups. In the 1980's he served as an advisor for the Readjustment Counseling Services and as a member of the Native American commission on veterans' affairs for the VA. *Military service*: U.S. Marine Corps (Vietnam Vet). *Awards, honors*: Twice the recipient of the Outstanding Native American faculty award, he has also been selected for an Excellence in Teaching Award during the U of A's "Year of the Undergraduate." In 2004, he was honored with the Graduate College's Outstanding Teaching & Mentoring Award. His book, Strong Hearts, Wounded Souls was a finalist for the Victor Turner Prize in ethnographic writing in Canada. In 2001, he was appointed to the Council of One Hundred Chiefs, Leaders, & Scholars for the American Indian Graduate Center in Albuquerque, NM, the organization that handles the Gates Millennium & American Indian Scholarship Fund scholarships. *Interests*: Federal Indian policy, colonization of Native peoples; Vietnam Era Veteran. *Published works*: Strong Hearts, Wounded Souls: Native American Veterans of the Vietnam War (University of Texas Press, 1996); The Great Confusion in Indian Affairs: Native American & White in the Progressive Era (University of Texas Press, 2005); children's book - Warriors & Code Talkers: Native Americans & World War II (Chelsea House/Facts on File), 2006); The Osage Rose (mystery) (University of Texas Press, 2008). Professor Holm has published over 50 articles, books, pamphlets, government reports, book reviews and essays, editorials and book chapters. His most recent articles & book chapters have dealt with the historical militarization of Native American peoples and the development of the "Peoplehood Matrix" as a theoretical construct for Native American/Indigenous Peoples Studies.

HOLMES, FRANCES KAY (Muscogee)
(professor of Native American & Indigenous studies)
Education: Arizona State University, BA, 1983; University of California, Davis, MA, 2006, PhD, 2013. *Affiliation & Address*: Assistant Professor, Dept. of Native American & Indigenous Studies, Fort Lewis College, 1000 Rim Dr., Durango, CO 81301 (970) 247-7227. E-mail: fkholmes@fortlewis.edu. *Expertise*: Contemporary Native Issues: Identity, Urban Issues, Art, Film, Native Thought, and Philosophy/Epistemology; Native American History: National contexts, California, Lakota, and Southeastern Tribes; Research Methodologies: Mixed (Indigenous) Methods, Oral History, Interview, Case Study, Ethnography, Participatory Action Research, and Narrative ; Education: Indigenous, Foundations/History, Critical Curriculum, Critical Pedagogy, and Social Justice

HOLMES, WALTER F. (Crow)
(consultant, paralegal)
Affiliation & Address: Consultant and paralegal, Albietz Law Corporation, 2001 N St., Suite 100, Sacramento, CA 95814 (916) 442-4241. Mr. Holmes was former chief of Lands & Minerals for the State of California's Bureau of Land management (BLM). He has 36 years of experience in minerals & lands adjudication with the BLM, and was responsible for program implementation as well as policy determination. *Awards, honors*: In 1983, Mr. Holmes received the U.S. Dept. of the Interior's highest honor for "Superior Service."

HOLSEY, SHANNON (Stockbridge-Munsee Mohican)
(tribal president)
Affiliation & Address: President, Stockbridge-Munsee Community Band of Mohican Indians, P.O. Box 70, Bowler, WI 54416 (715) 793-4111. E-mail: Shannon.holsey@mohican-nsn.gov.

HOLT, RONALD (Nez Perce) 1944-
(TV station director)
Born November 26, 1944, Orifino, Idaho. *Education*: Los Angeles Community College, 1970-72; Columbia College of Fine Arts, 1972-75. *Principal occupation*: TV station director. *Address & Affiliation*: Principal, KHMT - Channel 4, 445 S. 24th St. W., Suite 404, Billings, MT 59102 (406) 652-7366. *Past professional posts*: TV producer, National Education Association, Washington, DC; KOBL-TV, Dull Knife Memorial College, Lame Deer, MT. *Other professional post*: TV-host, TV writer; editorial board, "Native People" Magazine. *Memberships*: National Press Club; Native American Press Association; National Association of Broadcasters.

HOLTON, GARY
(professor of linguistics)
Education: University of Alaska, BS (Linguistics); University of California, Santa Barbara, PhD (Linguistics). *Affiliation & Address*: Professor of Linguistics, Alaska Native Language Center (Anchorage, AK) & Director, Alaska Native Language Archive, 306B Brooks/401 Brooks, University of Alaska, Fairbanks, Box 757680, Fairbanks, AK 99775 (907) 474-6585. E-mail: gmholton@alaska.edu. As a documentary linguist, his work focuses on the documentation & description of indigenous laguages, especially Dene (Athabascan) langages of Alaska, He is involved in geolinguistic research and is leading a project to revise the Alaska Native Languages map.

HOLTON, KERRY (*Welekishku*) (Delaware)
(former tribal president)
Affiliation & Address: Former President, Delaware Nation, P.O. Box 825, Anadarko, OK 73005 (405) 247-2448. E-mail: kholton@delawarenation.com.

HOLTSOI-ROBBINS, EUNICE (Navajo)
(registrar/student affairs)
Address & Affiliation: Cook College & Theological School, 708 S. Lindon Lane, Tempe, AZ 85281 (602) 968-9354. *Interests*: Give Native American presentation especially about the Navajo Tribe.

HOLY EAGLE, CLEM (*Wanbli Wakan*) (Oglala Lakota) 1969-
(dancer)
Born July 24, 1969, Pine Ridge, S.D. *Address*: P.O. Box 167, Wanblee, SD 57577 (605) 462-6724. Clem is a Hoop Dance performer, and a known expert on Lakota culture and heritage. Holy Eagle focuses on the deepening of Lakota values and Lakota customs in his performances.

HOMER, ELIZABETH LOHAN (Osage of Oklahoma)
(attorney-principal)
Education: University of Colorado, Boulder, BA, 1979; The University of New Mexico School of Law, JD, 1989. *Affiliation & Address*: Principal (2003-present). Homer Law, 1730 Rhode Island Ave., NW Suite 501, Washington, DC 20036 (202) 955-5601; E-mail: ehomer@homerlaw.com. *Past professional posts*: Vice Chairperson, National Indian Gaming Commission, 1999-2002; director, Office of American Indian Trust, 1994-99; Special Attorney, U.S. Department of Justice, 1992-94.

HOMER, PETE (Mojave/Shasta)
(president, CEO)
Affiliation & Address: President & CEO (1995-present), National Indian Business Association (NIBA), 1730 Rhode Island Ave. NW, Suite 501, Washington, DC 20036 (202) 223-3766. Website: www.nibanetwork.org. *Past professional posts*: From 1966 to 1975, he serves as executive director of the Inter-Tribal Council of Arizona; directed the Arizona' Governor's Employment & Training Program in Phoenix, and directed the Northern Arizona University's National Indian Business Development Program in Flagstaff, AZ. From 1975 to 1985, Mr. Homer implemented and served as director of the U.S. Dept. of Labor's Employment & Training Administration Program in Washington, DC. From 1985 to 1992, Pete founded & served as president & CEO of American Indian Business & Technologies, Inc. in Albuquerque, NM. From 1992-95, he implemented & served as the director of the Office of Native American Affairs, U.S. Small Business Administration, Washington, DC.

HONANIE, DELBRIDGE COOCHSIWUKIOMA (Hopi)
(artist)
Address: 1819 N. Turquoise Dr., Flagstaff, AZ 86001 (928) 779-5500. Mr. Honanie produces traditional Hopi cottonwood root sculptures, relief sculptural wall hangings, and paintings.

HONANIE, GILBERT, JR. (Hopi) 1941-
(architect, planner)
Born April 11, 1941, Tuba City, Ariz. *Education*: Pasadena City College, AA, 1969; Arizona State University, BA (Architecture), 1972. *Affiliation & Address*: President, owner, architect (1975-present), Gilbert Honanie, Jr., Inc., 6302 St. Albion Way, Suite B103, Mountlake Terrace, WA 98043 (425) 778-3988. E-mail: ggilhjr@yahoo.com. *Other professional posts*: National Council of

Architectural Registration Board; American Indian Council of Architects & Engineers; Western & Arizona Society of Architects. *Community activities*: Member of Hopi Tribe; member, Arizona Indian Chamber of Commerce; member. Central Arizona Chapter of Architects. *Biographical sources*: Articles in the Arizona Republic & Gazette, Arizona Builder, Progressive Architecture, and Architectural Journal.

HONANIE, HERMAN G. (Hopi)
(tribal council chairperson)
Affiliation & Address: Chairperson, Hopi Tribal Council, P.O. Box 123, Kykotsmovi, AZ 86039 (928) 734-2441.

HONANIE, WENDELL (Hopi)
(BIA agency supt.)
Affiliation & Address: Superintendent, Hopi Agency, Bureau of Indian Affairs, P.O. Box 158, Keams, Canyon, AZ 86034 (928) 738-2228.

HONER, JANELLE A. (Seminole) 1954-
(artist, gardener)
Born February 28, 1954, Hayward, Calif. *Education*: Humboldt State University, BA (Art, Native American Studies), 1976; Anderson Ranch, Snowmass Village, CO (seminars & workshops), 1978-82. *Principal occupation*: Artist, gardener. *Affiliations*: Owner operator, Doug & Janella's Garden, El Jebel, CO, 1981-; gallery artist, Janie Beggs Fine Arts Ltd., Aspen, Colo., 1986-. *Community activities*: Advisor, Aspen Dance Connection. *Memberships*: National Gardening Association; American Crafts Council; Aspen Art Museum; Colorado Council on the Arts; Carbondale Council on the Arts & Humanities. Art exhibitions & shows: Featured artist, Cohen Gallery, Denver, Colo., 1985; Roaring Fork Annual, Aspen Art Museum, 1985; Colorado Artists-Craftsmen Exhibit, Boulder, Colo., 1984; one-person show, Sioux National Museum, 1981; Roaring Fork Valley Art Show, Aspen Center for the Visual Arts, 1981. *Awards, honors*: Magna Cum Laude, Humboldt State University, Arcata, Calif., 1976; first & second place prizes, Women Art West, Grand Junction, Colo., 1982-1983; Craft Range Magazine award for Buy the Heartland, 1982; first place sculpture, Woman Art West, 1980; inclusion in Northern Plains, Southern Plains Indian Museum art collections; among others. *Interests*: Vocational: "We are organic farmers with a gourmet produce market garden. We teach people basic skills and give garden tours, sell produce. We educate about wild edibles, food storage; we both are chefs. I also do mixed media sculpture and ceramic sculpture, that is the art I show. We travel extensively. My goal is to help feed the hungry."

HONYOUTI, HARVEY A. (*Loma'oo yee*) (Hopi)
(teacher/coach)
Address: P.O. Box 998, Keams Canyon, AZ 86034 (520) 738-5285. *Affiliations*: Arizona Coaches Association, 1986-; Arizona Track Coaches Association, 1986-. Community activities: Local youth projects.

HOOBAN, HOMER, II "LOUIS" (*Flying Eagle*) (Bannock) 1943-
(publishing, writer)
Born June 21, 1943, Coeur d'Alene, Idaho. *Education*: Idaho State University, BA, 1966, MEd, 1969; University of Wyoming, EdS, PhD (Psychology), 1971. *Principal occupation*: Publishing, public speaker, educator. *Address*: 1572 Oakwood, P.O. Box 752, McCall, ID 83638 (208) 315-0916. *Affiliations*: CEO, Indian Heritage Council, McCall, ID. *Other professional posts*: Publisher, Native American Publishing, 1990-; board of directors, Native American University. *Community activities*: CEO, Books to Reservations; CEO, Plants to Reservations; CEO, Herbs to Reservations; sponsor of boy scout groups - national dance champions; B.P.O.E. - youth director; coach of all sports (25 years-never had a losing season as a head coach); sponsored first national powwows (1989-93) at Pigeon Forge, TN. Also sponsored numerous Native American events; involved in kayak & canoe instruction. *Awards, honors*: Poet Laureate of the Native Americans, 1988 - World's Fair Site of National Powwow - Knoxville, TN; Poet of the Year, Writer of the Year, Publisher of the Year; Indian Heritage Council Award for Literature; Eagle Award from Aniyonwiya Nation, a Native American think tank; Floating Feather Writing Award; Tennessee Coach of the Year, 1992; Tennessee Counselor of the Year, 2001. *Community activities*: Director of the Youth Indian League; National Powwow Coordinator. *Membership*: Native American Writers Guild; Indian Heritage Council; Native American Poets Association; National Education Association; Counselors & Coaches Association; Writers League; Publishers of America. *Interests*: Native Americans; writing, poetry, reading, travel, publishing, powwows & festivals; "have traveled around the world, to all major landmarks"; healing arts; "have always coached winning teams (all sports)." *Biographical sources*: Who's Who; Dictionary Biography of the West; Who's Who International Biography. *Published works*: Native American Play; The Vision Quest; Native American Drug Usage; Native American Coloring Book (Indian Heritage Publishing); The Scorched Earth (Scotway Press, 1988); editor - Great American Indian Bible (Indian Heritage Publishing, 1990); Indian Nation (three act play) (Indian Heritage Publishing, 1991); The Indian Anthology of Poetry (Indian Heritage Publishing, 1993); Poetry of Native

Americans (Indian Heritage Publishing, 2000); Crazy Horse's Philosophy of Riding Rainbows (Indian Heritage Publishing, 2001); The Vision: Native American Predictions (Indian Heritage Publishing, 2002).

HOOD, RANCE (Comanche)
(artist)

Address: Rance Hood Studio, P.O. Box 73, Denison, TX 75021 (903) 463-6020. *Art*: Original paintings, limited edition offset prints, serigraphs, and Giclee prints; posters and note cards. *Published work*: Rance Hood: Mystic Painter (University of New Mexico Press).

HOOK, JONATHAN B. (Cherokee)
(educator, author, speaker; board member)

Affiliation: Board member, American Indian Resource Center, 4914 Nuthatch, San Antonio, TX 78217 (210) 655-1300.

HOOVER, HERBERT T. (*Ta Chanunpa Ska*) 1930-
(professor of history)

Born March 9, 1930, Oakwood Township, Wabasha County, Minn. *Education*: New Mexico State University, BA, 1960, MA, 1961; University of Oklahoma, Norman, PhD, 1966. *Principal occupation*: Professor of history. *Address*: 401 Sunset Dr., Beresford, SD 57004 (605) 763-5323. *Office address*: Dept. of History, 414 E. Clark St., Dakota Hall, University of South Dakota, Vermillion, SD 57069 (605) 677-5218. E-mail: hhoover@usd.edu. *Affiliations*: Assistant professor of history, East Texas State University, 1965-67; professor of history, University of South Dakota, Vermillion, 1967-. *Other professional posts*: Director, Newberry Library Center for the History of the American Indian, Chicago, IL, 1981-83; director, South Dakota Oral History Center, 1967-; director, South Dakota Oral History Center, 1977-present; director, Indian Studies program, 1985-91. *Military service*: U.S. Navy, 1951-55 (Fleet Marine Corpsman with First Marine Division in Korean War). *Community activities*: SD Council of Humanists; SD Committee on the Humanities; National Endowment for the Humanities (review panels); SD Historical Society (board of trustees); SD Fairview Township Board of Control; SD Historical Publications & Records Commission; Augustana College, Center for Western Studies, National Council, 1984-present; Rhodes Scholar, SD State Selection Committee, 1991-96; chair, 1996-). *Memberships*: Western History Association, 1962- (chair, nominating board; local arrangements committee; program committee; membership committee; board of editors); Organization of American Historians, 1970- (nominating board; membership committee); Phi Alpha Theta, 1960- (international councilor; international board of advisors); SD Historical Society; Missouri Historical Society; Minnesota Wabasha County Historical Society. *Awards, honors*: Outstanding Educator of America Award, Washington, DC, 1975; Augustana College Center for Western Studies, 1985 Achievement Award, National Board of Advisors; National Endowment for the Humanities, Research Grant Award, 1978-81; Western America Award, 1984; National Teacher of the Year Award, 1985; 1990 Governor's Award for History (South Dakota); Professor of the Year, 2003, University of South Dakota Student Association. *Interests*: "Travel & recreation is tied to principal occupational interests: the history of Indian-white relations, & the preservation of natural life." *Biographical sources*: Who's Who in the Midwest, 1984; Who's Who in American Education, 2003; Who's Who in America, 2005. *Published works*: To Be An Indian (Holt, Rinehart & Winston, 1971); The Practice of Oral History (Microfilming Corp. of America, 1975); The Chitimacha People (Indian Tribal Series, 1975); The Sioux: A Critical Bibliography (Indiana University, 1979); Bibliography of the Sioux (Scarecrow Press, 1980); The Yankton Sioux (Chelsea House Publishers, 1988); Wildlife on the Cheyenne River & Lower Brule Reservations (University of South Dakota Press, 1992); co-author, Yanktonai Sioux Images; The Watercolors of John Saul (Center for Western Studies, Augustana College, 1993); co-author, South Dakota History: An Annotated Bibliography (Greenwood Press, 1993); The Sioux & Other Native American Cultures of the Dakotas: An Annotated Bibliography (Greenwood Press, 1993); co-author, Bon Homme County History (Pine Hill Press, 1994; Sioux Country: A History of Indian-White Relations, with Carol Goss Hoover (Center for Western Studies, Augustana College, 2000); A New South Dakota History (Center for Western Studies, Augustana College, 2004, 2005); numerous articles, book reviews, & consultations on publications.

HOPKINS, HARVEY (Pomo)
(rancheria chairperson)

Born in Santa Rosa, Calif. *Affiliation & Address*: Chairperson (2004-present), Dry Creek Rancheria Band of Pomo Indians, P.O. Box 607, Geyserville, CA 95441 (707) 431-2388. *Other professional posts*: Chair, River Rock Entertainment Authority Board of Directors, 2004-present.

HOPKINS, JAMES C. (Algonquin/Metis)
(associate clinical professor; attorney)

Education: University of Toronto, B.A., 1993, LL.B, 1996; Harvard Law School's joint Masters of Laws & International Tax Program (LL.M/ITP), June 2000. *Address & Affiliation*: Associate Clinical Professor, Indigenous Peoples Law & Policy Program, James E. Rogers College of Law, The University of Arizona, Rountree Hall 209, Tucson, AZ 85721 (520) 621-7669. E-mail: hopkins@law.arizona.edu. *Past professional post*: Assistant professor, Faculty of Law, University of Alberta; law clerk, Ontario Superior Court of Justice. *Awards, honors*: Recipient of the Harvard University International Tax Program's Award for Excellence in Research & Writing for his graduate thesis titled, "Democratization by Taxation: Democratic Experimentalism in Aboriginal Canada"; 1999 Massachusetts Indian Association Scholar. *Interests*: The intersection between trade, tax and Aboriginal law.

HOPKINS, JOHN CHRISTIAN (*Paukunnawaw Neepoush - Standing Bear*) (Narragansett) 1960-
(journalist/author)

Born July 6, 1960, Westerly, RI. *Education*: University of Rhode island, BA. *Principal occupation*: Journalist/author. *Address*: 59 John St., Westerly, RI 02891. E-mail: kngauthor@aol.com; Website: www.jchopkins.homestead.com. *Membership*: Native American Journalist Association (NAJA). Interest: Old West, Native Americana. *Awards, honors*: Won four 2003 NAJA awards: 1st newswriting, 1st feature writing, 2nd column writing, 3rd sports writing; 2000 RI Press Association, 3rd column writing. *Published articles*: "Carlomagno" (2003, IUniverse); "Nacogdoches", 2004, Publish America).

HOPKINS, SUE (*Jowanna*) (Cherokee) 1940-
(school secretary)

Born December 10, 1940, Durant, Okla. *Address*: Silo School, HC-62, Box 227, Durant, OK 74701 (405) 924-7000 (work). *Affiliation*: School secretary, Indian Education Director, Title V-C, JOM, Silo, OK, 1970-; pianist, Silo Baptist Church, 1970-. *Other professional post*: Piano teacher, 1964-. *Community activities*: Pianist for Memorial Day Services, Contatas, Plays, Rest Homes, Senior Citizens, Funerals, Weddings. *Memberships*: NAFIS, OASIS. *Interests*: "As Indian Education director, I travel to Washington, DC each year for meetings and visits with White House officials; JOM Meetings in Tulsa, OK, NAFIS Meetings in Yakima, WA. I am in the process of completing a journal which I am planning to put into a short story."

HORNBROOK, JOHN R. (*Anumpuli Shali Ossi*) (Choctaw of Oklahoma) 1943-
(associate professor)

Born May 17, 1943 in Lawton, Okla. Education: Oakland City University, B.A., 1964; B.S., 1965; M.A. (Teaching), 1968; Oklahoma City University, M.A.T., 1969; Nova University, D.Ed (Early Childhood Administration), 1986. *Address*: R1 Box 264EE, Francisco, IN 47149 (812) 782-9047. E-mail: hornbrook@oak.edu. *Affiliations*: Assistant director, Educational Extension Center, Evansville, IN, 1974-85; special concerns counselor, Student Services, E-VSC, 1985-88; assistant principal, Glenwood Middle School, Evansville, IN, 1988-89; principal, Howard Roosa Elementary School, Evansville, IN, 1989-2000; Associate Professor, Oakland City University, Oakland City, IN, 2000-. *Other professional post*: Director of Student Teaching, Oakland City University, 2000. *Military service*: U.S. Army, 1959-61. *Community activities*: Indiana Native American Council Board Member, 1992-present. *Memberships*: Choctaw Nation of Oklahoma; National Congress of American Indians; National Indian Education Association; Society for Early Childhood Development; Indiana Association for Counseling & Development; National Association for Counseling & Development; National Elementary School Principals Assn; Native American Indian Assn; Native American Law Enforcement Assn; Indians State Dept. of Education, Native American Curriculum Committee, 1993-present; Indiana American Indian Movement (state education director); Native American Inter-Tribal Council (president). *Awards, honors*: Indiana's Delegate - White House Conference on Indian Education, 1992; Awarded Sagamore of the Wabash by Indian's Governor, 1992; Who's Who Among Outstanding Americans, 1994-present; University of Evansville's Outstanding Administrator Award, 1995. *Interests*: "To educate the public about respect for all people & providing accurate information about American Indians. Indian storytelling & sharing about the Choctaw people to numerous civic groups as well as public and private schools. I feel honored along with my friend Nick Mejia to have been instrumental in changing the history of the U.S. through education. We started an educational process that eventually enlisted 125 Indian nations, the most profitable company in the U.S., and a vast general public audience. Through television & printed news medias, we presented the American Indian religious beliefs concerning respect for Indian graves & culture. After eight years of educating the public, the General Electric Corp. allowed Native Americans the honor of reburying our dead ancestors along with the funerary objects with which they were buried. This was the first time in the history of this country that valuable grave items were returned to graves instead of placing them in institutions. Through education, a precedence has been established that is changing the mentality of citizens about reburial issues for all races; especially Native Americans. We have changed one Indiana textbook that was insulting to Native Americans. By educating the editors of Silver-Burdette-Ginn, the company was apologetic and has revised the book. Thousands of students will benefit from this correction." *Published works*: You Are Somebody Special (Zoe Publications, 1980; The Miracle of Touching (Huntington House, 1985).

HORNETT, DANIELLE M. (Anishinaab, Ojibwe)
(educator, author)
Born & raised on the Bad River Reservationn in northern Wisconsin. *Past professional post*: Presient, Lac Courte Orielles Ojibwa Community College, Hayward, WI. *Publishd work*: Sage Dreams, Eagle Visions (American Indian Studies), (Michigan State University Press, 2004).

HORSE CAPTURE, GEORGE, JR. (A'ani Gros Ventre)
(tribal vice president)
Affiliation & Address: Vice President, Fort Belknap Indian Community, RR 1 Box 66, Harlem, MT 59526 (406) 353-8472.

HORSE, MICHAEL (Yaqui/Zuni/Mescalero)
(jeweler, artist, actor, activist)
Born near Tucson, Ariz. Website: www.michaelhorse.com. E-mail: michael@michaelhorse.com. His works of art have been shown in galleries throughout the world, and are currently available at the Southwest Museum in Los Angeles, the Autry Museum of Western Heritage in Los Angeles, the Eiteljorg Museum in Indiana, Kiva Fine Art Gallery in Santa Fe, and Gathering Tribes Gallery in Albany, California. As an actor, he has appeared in many movies and on television, including Twin Peaks, Passenger 57, Lakota Woman, and the CBC Canadian series, North of 60.

HORSE, PERRY G. (Kiowa)
(college president)
Born in Carnegie, Okla. *Education*: Harvard University Graduate School of Education, MEd; University of Arizona, PhD. *Address & Affiliation*: President, Institute of American Indian Arts, 83 Avan Nu Po Rd., Santa Fe, NM 87508 (505) 988-6463. *Past professional activities*: Has worked in Indian post secondary education for the past 24 years including management of community college development programs; has consulted on strategic & institutional planning & staff development for a number of tribal colleges across the country; was instrumental in developing the American Indian Higher Education Consortium; was an advisor to The MacArthur Foundation on funding for tribal colleges and the Albuquerque Public Schools on developing an American Indian cultural curriculum; has taught tribal government and Federal Indian Law for the Institute for Development of Indian Law, Oklahoma City, OK; and most recently, has been in charge of leadership & management development at Sandia National Laboratories in Albuquerque, NM.

HOSTLER, HEATHER (Hoopa)
(chief deputy-tribal advisor to the Governor)
Education: Humboldt State University, BA (American Indian/Native American Studies Law & Government), 2005. *Affiliation*: Chief Deputy-Tribal Advisor to Governor Gerry Brown (2012-present), c/o State Capitol, Suite 1173, Sacramento, CA 95814 (916) 445-2841. Under the direction of the tribal advisor, Cynthia Gomez, Heather works with state agencies and tribal governments to strengthen communication, collaboration and consultation. Covers all tribal issues in the state on behalf of the Governor with the exception of gaming. Active in areas of health, natural resources, fisheries, water, broadband, fee to trust and developing systems for tribes to navigate state government to work in better partnership. *Past professional posts*: Executive Administrator for Tribal Chairperson, Hoopa Valley Tribe, 2005-07; Program manager, Humboldt Area Foundation, 2007-12.

HOTCH, JANICE (Tlingit/Tsimshian)
(manager, office of diversity solutions)
Education: University of Washington, BA (Journalism). *Affiliation & Address*: Manager (2003-present), Office of Diversity Solutions, Sealaska Corporation, One Sealaska Plaza #400, Juneau, AK 99801 (907)586-1512. Began work for Sealaska in 1998 and is a Sealaska shareholder. *Other professional posts*: Secretary, Board of Directors, Native American Contractors Association, Washington, DC; member, Board of Directors, ANCSA village corporation, Klukwan, Inc.

HOTCH, JONES P., JR. (Tlingit/Tsimshian)
(AK village council president)
Affiliation & Address: Chilkat Indian Village of Klikwan, HC 60 Box 2207, Haines, AK 99827 (907) 767-5505.

HOUCK, DARCIE L. (Mohawk/Ottawa)
(attorney)
Education: University of California, Davis, BA, 1994, MS, 1998, JD, 1998. *Affiliation & Address*: Administrative Law Judge, California Public Utilities Commission, 770 L St., Sacramento, CA 95814. *Past professional post*: Staff Counsel (2000-05), California Energy Commission; Partner (2007-2016), Fredericks Peebles & Morgan, LLC, Sacramento, CA. *Practice areas*: Energy; environmental law; cultural resources; federal Indian law; litigation; federal, tribal & state regulatory law; land use & environmental planning; Indian child welfare; contracts; gaming law.

HOUSE, CARRIE H. (Navajo/Oneida) 1965-
(freelance film/video productions)
Born March 19, 1965, Winslow, Ariz. *Education*: Navajo Community College, 1982-83; University of Montana, BS (Natural Resource Conservation), 1987. *Principal occupation*: Freelance film/video productions. Resides in Santa Fe, NM. *Affiliations*: Native American Public Broadcasting Consortium, Lincoln, NE, 1985-90; National Center for Production of Native Images, Santa Fe, NM, 1991-. *Other professional post*: Engine Foreperson-fire fighter, USDA Coconino National Forest, Peaks Ranger District. *Community activities*: Navajo Nation, voluntarily assist in acquire/document history of our Oaksprings community for the Oaksprings Chapter House; presentations for educational institutions; presentations of Fire Behavior with Bureau of Land Management, USDI in Farmington, NM. *Awards, honors*: Public Affairs Production at the WGBH Educational Foundation as a WGBH - CPB Fellow in Feb. 1992; Award Fellow Recipient of Native American Public Broadcasting Consortium for Robert McKee's Story Structure Course in April 1991. *Interests*: Infinite travels for research/development of film/video and personal initiatives; yearly participant of the International Wildlife Film Festival in Missoula, MT, since 1985 to present. *Biographical sources*: Articles: "D-5 Sweeps CHIPA Muster," The Coconino Forest Pine Log, Sept. 1990; "Its a Jungle Out There," Los Angeles Times, Sect. F, April 11, 1991; and "House Completes Boston Workshop," Navajo Times, Vol. 23, No. 10, March 5, 1992.

HOUSE, ERNEST, JR. (Ute Mountain Ute)
(commission executive secretary)
Affiliation & Address: Executive Secretary, Colorado Commission of Indian Affairs, 130 State Capitol, Denver, CO 80202 (303) 866-5470. E-mail: ernest.house@state.co.us.

HOUTEN, MARGARET (Paiute) 1946-
(court administration)
Born October 2, 1946, Schurz, Nev. *Education*: High school. *Principal occupation*: Clerical. *Home address*: 14 Waterline Rd., P.O. Box 265, Nixon, NV 89424 (702) 574-0205. *Professional posts*: Court clerk; vice-president, National American Indian Court Clerks Association, Washington, DC. *Community activities*: Not as active as before, due to kidney failure. Assist with donation for fundraising such as Veteran's Memorial, church, senior citizens, when possible. *Memberships*: National American Indian Court Clerks Association; National Notary Public Association. *Interests*: "Vocation mostly geared toward legal matters, plan to do more traveling with arts & craft after retirement, possibly after a kidney transplant. Would like to get more into the legal aspect of Indian law in the future. I have had a lot of contact with Indian lawyers and judges, men and women, and it is exciting."

HOUTSMA, PETER C.
(attorney)
Affiliation & Address: Partner, Indian Law Practice Group, Holland & Hart LLP, 555 17th St., Suite 2700, Denver, CO 80202 (303) 295-8259. E-mail: phoutsma@hollandhart.com.

HOWARD, BRIAN (Akimel O'odham/Thono O'odham/Pi-Pash)
(research & policy analyst)
Education: University of New Mexico, BA (Native American Studies), 2009. Focused on Federal Indian Law & Policy with a minor in Political Science. *Affiliation & Address*: Research & Policy Analyst (2016-present), Tribal Economic Leadership Program at the American Indian Policy Institute, Ariizona State University, Box 872603, Tempe, AZ 85287 (480) 965-1055. Email: brian.howard@asu.edu. *Past professional posts*: Brian served over five years as a Legislative Associate with the National Congress of American Indians in Washington, DC. Working on behalf of American Indian and Alaska Native tribal governments, Brian's work included developing and advocating tribal policy initiatives in Congress and the Administration on issues such as Telecommunications, Government Contracting, & Cultural Protections (Sacred Places, Eagle Feather/Eagle Protections, NAGPRA, and Mascot issues). Brian's work experience has included numerous D.C.-based research and policy internships, as well as with the New Mexico House of Representatives and the Gila River Indian Community Council's Office.

HOWARD, GENA TIMBERMAN (Oklahoma Choctaw)
(attorney)
Education: Oklahoma State University, BA (English Literature), 1996; University of Oklahoma College of Law, JD, 1999. *Address & Affiliation*: Deputy Director, Native American Cultural & Educational Authority of Oklahoma, 900 N. Stiles, Oklahoma City, OK 73126-0980 (405) 815-5153. E-mail: gena_howard@odoc.state.ok.us. *Past professional post*: Associate, Holloway, Dobson, Hudson, Bachman & Jennings, Oklahoma City, OK., 1999-2004; her work in the Commercial Section of the law firm focused on the Economic Development of Native American businesses; editor, American Indian Law Review, 1997-99. *Community activities*: As a former Wings of America, Southern Plains runner, Gena has been active as a Facilitator and leader for the Wings of American Running & Fitness Camps. She has also been active in

United National Indian Tribal Youth (UNITY) as a Native Youth Leadership Development Facilitator. *Memberships*: American Bar Association, Oklahoma Bar Association, Oklahoma Indian Bar Association; Oklahoma City Chapter of the American Indian Chamber of Commerce (Board of Directors).

HOWARD, GERALD (Paiute)
(former tribal chairperson)
Affiliation & Address: Former chairperson, Bishop Paiute Tribe, 50 Tu Su Lane, Bishop, CA 93514 (760) 920-7168. E-mail: gerald.howard@bishoppaiute.org.

HOWARD, GREGG (Cherokee/Powhatan) 1934-
(writer, narrator, storyteller)
Born May 5, 1934, Central City, Kentucky. *Education*: Ohio State University, 1956-58. *Principal occupation*: Writer, narrator, Cherokee storyteller. Address & Affiliations: Executive Producer, V.I.P. (Various Indian Peoples) Publishing Co., 301 N. St. John's Dr., Richardson, TX 75081 (972) 671-3525. E-mail: VIPublish@aol.com., 1987-present. *Military service*: U.S. Marine Corps (Sgt.), 1953-57 (Korean Network). *Memberships*: Oklahoma Native Language Association; Wordcraft Circle of Native Writers & Storytellers; Texas Storytelling Association; Oklahoma Native Language Association; Cherokee Honor Society (spokesman); National Storytelling Association. *Awards, honors*: Wrangler Award, Cowboy Hall of Fame, 1966; IABC Golden Quill Award, 1984; Silver Mike Award, 1990; Native American Music Awards - Spoken Word Category, for "Tales of Wonder" - CD version. *Interests*: Formed Various Indian Peoples (V.I.P.) Publishing Co. in 1988 with Alfred Houser (brother of Alan Houser - the late Apache sculptor from Santa Fe, NM), and Rick Eby of Fayetteville, AR. The company is now owned by Lari Howard of Dallas, TX. VIP's mission was, and is, to record and publish American Indian language, legends, and cultural programs. They have produced language and legends programs for the Cherokee, Choctaw, Chickasaw, Muskogee (Creek), Kiowa & Western Delaware peoples. All of their language programs employ speakers who spoke their language first - English being their second language. A portion of every program is returned to the Nation, Tribe or individual who assisted in developing the program. Gregg has taught the Cherokee language since 1992 in and around Dallas at various colleges and through the continuing education program at Texas A&M in Commerce, Texas. He also teaches a weekly class at Stringbean Restaurant in Dallas. He is continuing to work with Indian Nations and Tribes as they work to reclaim their language and cultural past. *Published works*: Audiotapes: Authentic Indian Music of the Apache, Sioux, Navajo (Dine), Crow, Ute, and Shawnee; Cherokee, Choctaw, and Kiowa legend tapes; Introduction programs include Cherokee, Choctaw, Chickasaw, Muskogee (Creek), and Western Delaware. Language Samplers in Cherokee, Choctaw, Chickasaw, Muskogee (Creek), and Kiowa, Caddo; Cheyenne Legends (in English & Cheyenne); Cherokee Scary Stories - CD; Life With Little People - (Creek) in association with book, "Life With Little People." "Tales of Wonder" video & CD (winner of five awards), and "Tales of Wonder II" video (both now on DVD. A 9,500 word English to Cherokee/Cherokee to English glossary is currently a "work-in-progress."

HOWARD, HEATHER
(assistant professor of anthropology)
Affiliation & Address: Assistant Professor of Anthropology, Native American Institute, Agriculture Hall, 446 W. Circle Dr., Rm. 406 • East Lansing, MI 48824 (517) 353-6632. E-mail: howardh@msu.edu. She teaches cultural and medical anthropology courses, including Indigenous Peoples' Health. Her Native research interests include women and youth, the role of history in community and social service organizing, and transformations in community-based health knowledge and practice. She is currently developing research projects which examine Native experiences with and approaches to Type-2 Diabetes in Michigan, and in Toronto where she has worked with the Native community since 1995. She was a founder of the Toronto Native Community History Project and continues to work with Native youth in the city in connection with this program. Dr. Howard has also worked as a professional ethnohistorian for tribes in California and in the Great Lakes area on projects involving resource rights, tribal jurisdiction, federal acknowledgment & land claims. She is preparing publications of research she conducted on connections between Canadian boarding school & contemporary Native experiences of chronic illness, as well as on the impact of the vicissitudes in federal policy on Native people's health in early twentieth century central California. She has recently published an edited volume with Susan Applegate Krouse, *Keeping the Campfires Going: Native Women's Activism in Urban Communities* (2009, University of Nebraska Press), and has under review at Wilfrid Laurier University Press's Aboriginal Studies Series, another co-edited volume, *Aboriginal Peoples in Canadian Cities: Transformations and Continuities.*

HOWARD, LARRY (Seminole of Florida)
(tribal board of directors)
Affiliation & Address: Brighton Representative, Board of Directors, Seminole Tribe of Florida, 6300 Stirling Rd., Hollywood, FL 33024 (800) 683-7800.

HOWARD, LINDA (Paiute)
(former tribal chairperson)
Affiliation & Address: Former Chairperson, Yerington Paiute Tribe, 171 Campbell Lane, Yerrington, NV 89447 (775) 463-3301.

HOWE, CRAIG (Oglala Lakota)
(deputy director for cultural resources)
Education: University of Nebraska, MA; University of Michigan, PhD (Architecture & Anthropology). *Affiliation & Address*: Cultural Resources Center, 4220 Silver Hill Rd., Suitland, MD 20746 (301) 238-6624. *Past professional posts*: Director, D'Arcy McNickle Center for American Indian History, Chicago, IL, 1995-98; deputy assistant director for cultural resources, National Museum of the American Indian, 1999-present.

HOWE, EARL "TREY" S., III (Ponca)
(tribal chairperson)
Affiliation & Address: Chairperson, Ponca Tribe of Oklahoma, 20 White Eagle Dr., Ponca City, OK 74601 (580) 762-8104. E-mail: thowe@ponca.com.

HOWE, LEANNE (*Anolitubbee*) (Choctaw of Oklahoma) 1951-
(professor of American Indian studies; writer)
Born April 29, 1951, Edmond, Okla. *Education*: Vermont College, MFA (Creative Writing), 2000. *Principal occupation*: Professor, writer. *Address*: 626 West 9th, Ada, OK 74820. E-mail: lhowe1@aol.com. *Affiliations & Address*: Professor of English & American Indian Studies (2009-present), University of Illinois, College of the Arts & Sciences, Room 2003, 1204 W. Nevada St., Urbana, IL 61801 (217) 265-9870. E-mail: ileannehowe@gmail.com. Other professional post: Founder & director of WagonBurner Theater Troop. Her plays have been produced in Los Angeles, New York City, New Mexico, maine, Texas & Colorado. Her most recent one-act play, The Mascot Opera, A Minuet, was commissioned by Mixed Blood Theater in 2008, Minneapolis. She performed in a one-woman show titled, "Choctalking on Other Realities," for the Krannert Center for the performing Arts, Urbana, IL in Jan. 2009. *Past professional posts*: Lecturer, American Indian & Native Studies Program, University of Iowa, Iowa City, IA, 1992, 1994, 1995; visiting faculty, American Studies, English, Carleton College, Northfield, MN, 1996-97; Grinnell College, Grinnell, IA (visiting lecturer, 1997; assistant professor, 1997-2000); University of Cincinnati (OH) (visiting lecturer, Spring 2002; visiting professor, Fall 2002; Louis D. Rubin Writer-in-Residence, MFA graduate program, Hollins University, Roanoke, VA, 2003; Loft Mentor Series in Creative Prose & Poetry, Minneapolis, MN, 6/2003; professor of English, Department of American Indian Studies, University of Minnesota, Minneapolis, MN, 2003-08. *Awards, honors*: 2002 American Book Award from the Before Columbus Foundation for "Shell Shaker"; 2012 Lifetime Achievement Award, Native Writers' Circle of the Americas. Her book, "Reasoning Together," was named one of the most influential Native texts of the 21st century. Howe was screenwriter & on-camera narrator for the 90-minute PBS documentary, "Indian Country Diaries: Spiral of Fire" (2006); she was also writer & co-producer of "Playing Pastime: American Indian fast-Pitch Softball & Survival," both documentaries with James Fortier; Tulsa Library Trust's American Indian Words Award. *Memberships*: AWP (Associated Writing Programs); Wordcraft Circle, Native Writer Mentoring Program, Native Writers Circle of the Americas (an organization of North & South American indigenous writers, including the Arctic; American Studies Association; Native American Women's Playwrights Association (Miami University, Oxford, OH); Assn of American Indian & Alaska Professors; American Society for Ethnohistory; Choctaw Code Talkers Assn (Chickasha, OK); formerly part of Returning the Gift). *Published works*: Her prose essay, "My Mothers, My Uncles, Myself," appears in "Here First: Autobiographical Essays by Native Amercan Writers," 2001; Shell Shaker, novel (Aunt Lute Books, 2001); Coyote Papers (Wowapi Press); prose & poems, Evidence of Red (Salt Publishing); co-author, Clearing a Path: Theorizing a Past in Native American Studies (2001), Pre-Removed Choctaw History: Exploring New Paths (2008), and Reasoning Together: Native Critics Collective (2008); novel, Miko Kings (Aunt Lute Books, 2007); Seeing Red – Hollywood's Pixeled Skins: American Indians and Film," 36 essays on 36 films by leading American Indian scholars & filmmakers from the 1920s to the 21st century, edited with Harvey Markowitz & Denise Cummings (Michigan State U. Press, 2013).

HOWELL, CHRIS (Pawnee of Oklahoma)
(executive directr/tribal liaison)
Education: Emporia State University, BS (Business); Kansas Supreme Court Mediator in Civil Mediation. *Affiliation & Address*: Executive Director/Tribal Liaison, Kansas Native American Affairs Office, 900 SW Jackson St., Room 100, Topeka, KS 66612 (785) 296-1904. E-mail: knaa@ks.gov. *Past professional posts*: President, Lewis & Clark Trail Heritage Foundation; teacher for the Univefsity of Kansas, Osher Lifelong Learning Institute; speaker on Pawnee history for the Kansas Humanities Council; advor to the Committee commemorating the 150 years of statehood for Kansas; grant reviewer for the U.S. DHHS-Administration for Native Americans in Washington, DC; board member of the Governor's Interstate Indian Council.

HOWELL, GEORGE ELTON (Pawnee-Cheyenne) 1935-
(Indian college board chair)
Born December 30, 1935, Pawnee, Okla. Education: Westminster College, Salt Lake City, BS, 1978; University of Utah, MSW, 1980. *Affiliation & Address*: Chair, Board of Trustees (2013-present), Pawnee Nation College, P.O. Box 470, Pawnee, OK 74958 (918) 762-3621. *Past professional posts*: Health systems administrator, PHS Indian Health Center, Fort Thompson, SD, 1983-85; health systems administrator, PHS Indian Health Hospital, Wagner, SD, 1985-88; service unit director, PHS Indian Hospital, Pine Ridge, SD, 1988-92; director, Lawton PHS Indian Health Center, Lawton, OK, 1993-2007; director, Mental Health/Social Services, social worker, clinical instructor, University of Utah; president (two terms), 2008-12, Pawnee Nation of Oklahoma, P.O. Box 470, Pawnee, OK. *Military service*: U.S. Air Force, 1954-58 (A/1c). *Community activities*: Four Corners Gourd Dance Society (president); Alcohol Treatment Program (chair, board of directors); UNAC (chair, board of directors). *Memberships*: National Association of Social Workers; Native American-Alaska Native Social Workers Association. *Awards, honors*: CSWE Scholarship Grant; 4 consecutive years - "Outstanding Performance Awards" as Service Unit Director, for IHS. *Interests*: Accounting-computer programming; alcohol counseling, clinical instructor, social worker; administration, community planning; health systems administrator. Golfing, Indian dancing - Gourd dancer.

HOWELL, GORDON (Ute)
(former tribal chairperson)
Affiliation & Address: Former Chairperson, The Ute Indian Tribe, Uintah & Ouray Indian Reservation, P.O. Box 190, Fort Duchesne, UT 84026 (435) 722-5141.

HOWLAND, JOAN S.
(professor of American Indian law)
Education: University of California at Davis, BA; University of Texas, Austin, MA; California State Unicersity, MLS; University of Santa Clara, JD; University of Minnesota, MBA. Affiliation & Address: Roger F. Noreen Professor of Law, Associate Dean for Information & Technology, University of Minnesota Law School, Mondale Hall 120 B, 229 19th Ave.. South, Minneapolis, MN 55455 (612) 625-9036 E-mail: howla001@umn.edu. Professor Howland is recognized for her work in law and technology, American Indian law, legal education, legal research, and law librarianship. She teaches American Indian Legal History, Law in Cyberspace, and a seminar called Magna Carta and the Evolution of Anglo-American Law. She has held the Roger F. Noreen Chair at the Law School since 1996. She also has taught Law and Business at the Carlson School of Management at the University of Minnesota. *Past professional posts*: From 1975 to 1983, Professor Howland was associate public services librarian at the Stanford Law School Library. She then became associate librarian for public services at the Harvard University Law School Library. In 1986, she became deputy director of the Law Library at the University of California at Berkeley. Professor Howland also taught at the U.C. Berkeley School of Library & Information Sciences. Professor Howland joined the Law School faculty as a tenured professor and director of the Law Library in 1992. She also is the associate dean for information resources and technology. She is active in the American Bar Assn and served as a member of the ABA Accren Committee from 2001 to 2006. She has been a member of the Council of the ABA Section on Legal Education & Admissions to the Bar since 2007, and she served as the council's 2014-15 chair; she currently serves on the council as immediate past chair. She has served as chair of the ABA Committee on Libraries and as chair of the Association of American Law Schools Committee on Law Libraries and Technology. She is a member of the American Law Institute and serves on the ALI Advisory Group on Electronic Publishing. Professor Howland has served as a member of the editorial board of the American Journal of Legal History. She has been an appointed member of the American Library Association Committee on Accreditation since 2012 and is the current chair of the committee. She also serves on the ALA Task Force on Accreditation Process and Communications. She is co-chair of the Chinese and American Forum on Legal Information and Law Libraries. Professor Howland has chaired many American Association of Law Libraries committees, including the Diversity, Education, National Resources, Recruitment, & Scholarship Committees. She has been a member of the executive board of the American Indian Library Association, and served as its treasurer from 1992 to 2010. *Awards, honors*: In 2003, Professor Howland received the prestigious Spirit of Law Librarianship Award in recognition of her extensive volunteer efforts with a variety of legal aid programs serving the legal and technological needs of American Indians living in traditional communities. Professor Howland also received the University of Minnesota President's Award for Outstanding Service in 2010; 2017 AALS Law Library Section Award.

HOXIE, FREDERICK E. 1947-
(teacher)
Born April 22, 1947, Hoolehua, Molokai. Education: Amherst College, BA, 1969; Brandeis University, PhD, 1977. *Address*: 2717 Lincolnwood Ave., Evanston, IL 60201 (217) 333-8660. E-mail: hoxie@illinois.edu. *Affiliations*:

Director, D'Arcy McNickle Center for the History of the American Indian, Newberry Library, Chicago, IL, 1983-93; Academic Vice President, The Newberry Library, Chicago, IL, 1994-; Swanlund Professor, University of Illinois, Urbana Champaign, 1998-. *Other professional posts*: Adjunct professor of history, Northwestern University; Trustee, National Museum of the American Indian, 1990-95; Trustee, Amherst College, 2001-. *Memberships*: American Historical Association; Organization of American Historians; American Society of Ethnohistory. *Awards, honors*: Rockefeller Foundation Humanities Fellowship, 1983-84; NEH Fellowship, 1990-91; Doctor of Humane Letters, Amherst College, 1994. *Biographical source*: Who's Who in America; Who's Who in the Midwest. *Published works*: Editor, With the Nez Perce (University of Nebraska Press, 1981); author, A Final Promise (University of Nebraska Press, 1984); editor, Indians in American History (Harlan Davidson, 1988); author, The Crow (Chelsea House, 1989); author, Parading Through History: The Making of the Crow Nation in America, 1805-1935 (Cambridge Press, 1995); editor, Encyclopedia of the North American Indians (Houghton Mifflin, 1996); editor, Talking Back to Civilization: Indian Voices From the Progressive Era (Bedford Books, Boston), 2001); co-editor (with James Merrell & Peter Mancall) American Nations: Encounters in Indian Country, 1850-2000 (Routledge, 2001); co-author (with David Edmunds & Neal Salisbury) The People: A History of Native America (Houghton Mifflin, 2006); co-author (with Jay Nelson) Lewis & Clark and the Indian Country (University of Illinois Press, 2007); Co-author (with R. D. Edmunds, and Neal Salisbury) The People: A History of Native America (Houghton Mifflin, 2007).

HUBBARD, JOHN, JR. (Navajo-Dine')
(IHS area director)
Education: Sterling College (Sterling, Kans), BA (Sociology & Psychology); University of Texas in Houston, MA (Public Health Administration). *Affiliation & Address*: Area Director, Navajo Area IHS, P.O. Box 9020, Window Rock, AZ 86515 (602) 871-5811. E-mail: john.hubbard@ihs.gov. The Navajo Area provides a varied healthcare delivery program that consists of six hospitals, six health centers, 15 health stations, and multipleschool clinics. Mr. Hubbard was instrumental in coordinating efforts of the IHS with those of the Navajo Nation, the Centers for Disease Control and Prevention, and the health departments of the States of Arizona and New Mexico to investigate the mysterious respiratory illness now identified as a strain of Hantavirus that appeared in the area during 1993. His efforts in establishing the Navajo Area HantavirusTask Force, in association with the Navajo Nation, succeeded in calming and educating the public about the disease. This task force developed public health information materials that provided information andguidance in both the Navajo & English languages. *Awards, honors*: In FY 2002, Mr. Hubbard was selected as a recipient of the Presidential Rank award. These awards are presented annually to top federal managers for extended, exceptional performance in the federal government.

HUCK, DOUGLAS (Stockbridge-Munsee Mohican)
(tribal vice president)
Affiliation & Address: Vice President, Stockbridge-Munsee Community Band of Mohican Indians, P.O. Box 70, Bowler, WI 54416 (715) 793-4111. E-mail: douglas.huck@mohican-nsn.gov.

HUDETZ, MARY (Crow)
(journalist; editor)
Education: Fordham University, BFA (Dance); University of Montana, BA (Journalism), 2008; attended Freedom Forum's American Indian Journalism Institute, University of South Dakota. *Affiliation & Address*: Editor (2013-present), Native Peoples Magazine, 5333 N. 7th St., Suite C224, Phoenix, AZ 85014 (602) 265-4855. E-mail: maryhudetz@naja.com. *Other professional post*: Vice President (2012-13), Board President, Native American Journalists Association (NAJA), 2013-present. *Past professional posts*: Editor & West Regional Desk Editor, Associated Press, 2009-13.

HUDON, EILEEN (White Earth Ojibwe)
(director of advocacy training)
Affiliation & Address: Director, Advocacy Training, Southwest Center for Law & Policy, 475 S. Stone Ave., Tucson, AZ 85701 (520) 623-8192. E-mail: hudon@swclap.org

HUDSON, CHARLES M., JR. 1932-
(honorary director emeritus of INAS)
Born December 24, 1932, Monterey, Ky. *Education*: University of Kentucky, BA, 1958; University of North Carolina, MA, 1962, PhD, 1965. *Address*: 740 Floyd Rd., Danielsville, GA 30633 (706) 789-3329. *Affiliation & Address*: Honorary Director Emeritus, Institute for Native American Studies (INAS), Peabody Hall, University of Georgia, Athens, GA 30602 (706) 542-1492. E-mail: charleshudson@mindspring.com. Professor Hudson is a leading expert in the histories of the indigenous peoples of what is today the American Southeast. *Other professional post*: Member of Steering Committee, INAS. *Past professional posts*: Professor of anthropology, 1964-2000, Franklin professor emeritus, 2000-2010, University of Georgia, Athens. *Military service*:

U.S. Air Force, 1950-53 (Staff Sergeant). *Memberships*: American Anthropological Association; Southern Anthropological Society (president, 1973-74); American Society for Ethno-history (president, 1992-93). *Awards, honors*: Woodrow Wilson Fellow, 1959-60; senior fellow, Newberry Library, 1977-78; 1991 & 1995 James Mooney Prize, Southern Anthropological Society; Rembert W. Patrick Book Award, Florida Historical Society, 1994; Distinguished Alumnus Award, University of North Carolina, Chapel Hill, 2004. *Interests*: "My primary interest is in the historical anthropology of the Indians of the Southeastern U.S." *Biographical sources*: Joyce Rockwood Hudson, Looking for DeSoto (University of Georgia Press, 1993); Who's Who in the Southeast. *Published works*: The Catawba Nation (University of Georgia Press, 1970); editor, Four Centuries of Southern Indians (University of Georgia Press, 1975); The Southeastern Indians (University of Tennessee Press, 1976; editor, Black Drink: A Native American Tea (University of Georgia Press, 1978); editor, Ethnology of the Southeastern Indians (Garland Publishing, 1985); The Juan Pardo Expeditions (Smithsonian Institution Press, 1990); with Gerald Milanich, Hernando DeSoto and the Indians of Florida (University of Florida Press, 1993); co-editor, with Carmen Tesser, The Forgotten Centuries (University of Georgia Press, 1994); Knights of Spain, Warriors of the Sun (University of Georgia Press, 1997); co-editor, with Robbie Ethridge, The Transformation of the Southeastern Indians, 1540-1760 (U. Press of Mississippi, 2002); co-editor, with John C. Guilds, An Early and Strong Sympathy: The Indian Writings of William Gilmore Simms (U. of South Carolina Press, 2003); Conversations with the High Priest of Coosa (U. of North Carolina Press, 2003).

HUDSON, CLARISSA (Tlingit)
(artist)
Address: P.O. Box 2709, Pagosa Springs, CO 81147 (970) 264-2491. E-mail: ch@clarissahudson.com. Website: www.clarissahudson.com. Clarissa makes hand woven Chilkat & Ravenstail robes & regalia. Also, paintings, collages, beaded sculptures, carvings, silkscreened limited edition prints. She conducts apprenticeships and workshops.

HUDSON, DAVID (Hoh)
(tribal vice chairperson)
Affiliation & Address: Vice chairperson, Hoh Tribe, P.O. Box 2196, Forks, WA 98331 (360) 374-6582.

HUDSON, STEPHANIE (Kiowa)
(senior staff attorney)
Education: Oklahoma City University School of Law, JD, 1993. *Affiliation & Address*: Senior Staff Attorney (2000-present), Oklahoma Indian Legal Services, 4200 Perimeter Center Dr. #222, Oklahoma City, OK 73112 (405) 943-6457. E-mail: Hudson@oilsonline.org.

HUENEMANN, JUSTIN KII (Navajo)
(non-profit program officer)
Born & raised on the Navajo reservation in Arizona near the four corners. *Education*: University of Minnesota; Native Americans in Philanthropy Circle of Leaders Program, 2007. *Affiliation & Address*: Program Officer, Northwest Area Foundation, 60 Plato Blvd. E Suite 400, St. Paul, MN 55107 (651) 224-9635. *Other professional posts*: Vice chair, Indian Health Board, Minneapolis, MN, 2010-present; board member, Woodlands National Bank, 2009-present; board member, Neighborhood Development Center, Minneapolis, MN, 2009-present; board member, American Indian Community Development Corp., Minneapolis, MN, 2009-present; board chair, The Tiwahe Foundation, 2006-present. *Past professional posts*: President/CEO, Native American Community Development Institute (NACDI), Minneapolis, MN, 2007-12; director, American Indian Families project, Hennepin County, MN; 2003-07; Twin Cities Healthy Nations Program at Minneapolis American Indian Center, 2008-10.

HUGHES, KATHY (Oneida of Wisconsin)
(tribal vice chairperson)
Education: Fox Valley Technical College, A.A. *Affiliation*: Vice chairperson, Oneida Nation of Wisconsin, P.O. Box 365, Oneida, WI 54155 (920) 869-4428. E-mail: khughes@oneidanation.org. *Other professional posts*: Serves on the Indian Health Service Tribal Advisory Board, the U.S. Dept. of Health & Human Services Tribal Technical Advisory Group for CMS, the Wisconsin Council on Problem Gambling, and the Berlin College of Nursing Board of Trustees. *Past professional posts*: Treasurer, Oneida Business Committee (five terms). *Military service*: Women Army Corps (WAC) (Vietnam era veteran).

HUGHES, LAUREN (Cherokee/Muscogee Creek)
(program coordinator)
Affiliation & Address: Program Coordinator, California Indian Environmental Alliance, P.O. Box 2128, Berkeley, CA 94702 (510) 848-2043. E-mail: lauren@cieaweb.org. Lauren is Assistant to the Executive Director of CIEA & Program Coordinator. She is a pivotal part of CIEA's organizational development team & coordinates the Native Youth Environmental Leadership and college Fellowship Programs. Prior to joining CIEA she was the Assistant to Mary Trimble Norris, the Executive Director of the American Indian Child Resource Center in Oakland. At CRC she was Head Tutor, Case Manager, & Sustainability Educator. In this capacity, Lauren has worked to teach Native Youth about the importance of academics and environmental stewardship by creating a gardening program in which students learned how to grow crops native to the land and culturally significant to Indigenous peoples. Lauren has spent her career working to educate others about sustainability, renewable energy, energy efficiency, Permaculture, & Indigenous natural building practices. She graduated with her MSc in Sustainable Building Technology with Merit from the University of Nottingham, U.K.

HUGHES, RICHARD W.
(attorney)
Education: University of Virginia, BA, 1967; Yale Law School, JD, 1971. *Affiliation & Address*: Partner, Rothstein, Donatelli, Hughes, Dahlstrom, Schoenburg & Bienvenu, LLP, P.O. Box 8180, Santa Fe, NM 87504 (505) 988-8004. E-mail: rwhughes@rothsteinlaw.com. Richard started the firm's Indian law practice in 1988. His practice continues to focus on all areas of Indian law, including jurisdictional disputes, water law, natural resources, gaming, land recovery, transactions, and others. Richard and the firm's other partners were appointed Special Prosecutors by the Navajo Nation's Department of Justice in October 2011 and directed to investigate allegations related to the use of tribal funds. *Past professional posts*: Previously, he spent eight years providing legal services on the Navajo Reservation; and ten years in an Albuquerque law firm specializing in representation of Indian tribes and groups.

HUGHTE, PHIL (Zuni) 1954-
(artist - painter)
Born April 27, 1954, Zuni, N.M. *Education*: Northern Arizona University, BFA, 1980. *Principal occupation*: Artist - painter. *Address*: P.O. Box 151, Zuni, NM 87327 (505) 782-4920. *Affiliation*. Member, Pueblo of Zuni Higher Education Committee. *Membership*: Indian Arts & Crafts Association. *Award*: 1990 Best of Show, The Zuni Show, Flagstaff, AZ.

HUHNDORF, SHARI
(professor of Native American studies)
Education: University of Redlands, BA; New York University, MA & PhD (Comparative Literature). *Affiliation & Address*: Professor/Director-Chair, Native American Studies & Comparative Ethnic Studies, Ethnic Studies Department, University of California, Berkeley, 505 Barrows Hall, Berkeley, CA 94720 (510) 643-0796. E-mail: huhndorf@berkeley.edu. Shari is affiliated with the Joseph A. Myers Center for Research on Native American Issues. *Past professional post*: University of Oregon, Department of Ethnic Studies, and Associate Head of the Department of English. *Memberships*: Modern Language Association (former member & chair of the executive committee of the Division of Twentieth-Century American Literature; CIRI Foundation (board member). *Awards, honors*: She received a 2013 President's Award from the Alaska Federation of Natives for her contributions to Native education and a Distinguished Teaching Award from the Division of Social Sciences at UC Berkeley. *Published works*: Going Native: Indians in the American Cultural Imagination (Cornell Univerfsity Press, 2001); Mapping the Americas: The Transnational Politics of Contemporary Native Culture (Cornell University Press, 2009); co-editor, Indigenous Women & Feminism: Politics, Activism, Culture (University of British Columbia Press, 2010; winnr of the Canadian Women's Studies Association prize for Outstanding Scholarship); Co-editor, Sovereignty, Indigeneity, and the Law (Duke University Press, 2011), a special issue of *South Atlantic Quarterly*, won the Council of Editors of Learned Journals award for best special issue of a journal as well as the award for outstanding indigenous scholarship from the American Indian & Alaska Native Professors Association for 2011. Her work has also appeared in journals including *Critical Inquiry, PMLA, American Quarterly, American Anthropologist South Atlantic Quarterly, Social Identities*, and *Annals of Scholarship*. She has held major fellowships from the Woodrow Wilson Foundation, the Ford Foundation, and the American Association of University Women. Currently, she is working on a manuscript tentatively entitled "Indigeneity and the Politics of Space: Gender, Geography, Culture." At Berkeley, Professor Huhndorf is affiliated with the Center for Race & Gender, the Interdisciplinary Program in American Studies, the Designated Emphasis in Gender and Women's Studies, and the Joseph A. Myers Center for Research on Native American Issues. She previously taught at the University of Oregon, where she served as head of the Program in (now Department of) Ethnic Studies & associate head of the Department of English. She is a former member and chair of the executive committee of the Division of Twentieth-Century American Literature of the Modern Language Association. She also served for a decade on the board of the directors of the CIRI Foundation, which provides educational funding and supports cultural programs for Alaska Natives in her home community.

HUMBREE, TODD (Cherokee)
(tribal attorney general)
Affiliation & Address: Humbree Law Firm, 306 W. Choctaw St., Tahlequah, OK 74464 (918) 453-0101. *Other professional post*: Attorney General, Cherokee Nation, Tahlequah, OK.

HUMETEWA, DIANE J. (Hopi) 1965-
(professor of law)
Education: Arizona State University, BA, 1987; Sandra Day O'Connor College of Law, Arizona State University, JD, 1993. *Affiliation & Address*: Professor of Law, Sandra Day O'Connor College of Law, Arizona State University, P.O. Box 877906, Tempe, AZ 85287 (602) 528-4133. E-mail: diane.humetewa@ asu.edu. *Past professional posts*: Diane was Majority Senior Litigation Counsel, Senate Committee on Indian Affairs, Washington, DC; In 2001, she was promoted to Senior Litigation Counsel/Tribal Liaison where she fostered relationships between the office and Arizona's Indian tribes; U.S. Attorney for the District of Arizona, 2006-09. She was the first Native American woman to be presidentially appointed to that position. She also served as an Assistant U.S. Attorney, prosecuting a wide variety of federal crimes, including violent crimes in Indian Country, Native American cultural crimes & archaeological resource crimes.

HUME, GAYE (Potawatomi)
(attorney)
Address: 130 S. Woodrow St., Arlington, VA 22204. *Memberships*: Native American Bar Association (treasurer); American Bar Association.

HUMMINGBIRD, JESSE T. (Cherokee) 1952-
(self-employed fine artist)
Born February 12, 1952, Tahlequah, Okla. *Education*: Middle Tennessee State University, 1970-71; University of Tennessee, 1971-77; The American Academy of Art in Chicago. *Principal occupation*: Self-employed fine artist. *Address*: 102 Silver St., Bisbee, AZ 85603 (520) 432-7305. E-mail: jessehummingbird@cs.com. *Affiliations*: Printer, Peabody College, Nashville, TN, 1975-77; printer, FISI (Banking Institute), 1977-79; graphic artist, DLM (Chicago & Dallas), 1979-83; self-employed, 1983-. *Exhibits*: Featured artist at the Prescott Indian Market at Sharlot Hall Museum in 2002; poster artist for the West Valley Fine Arts Center Native American Marketplace and the St. George Fine Arts Festival in 2003; one-man show at the Brauer Museum of Art on the campus of Valparaiso University (IN) and was featured artist at their Native American Festival in October 2004. *Awards, honors*: Top awards for his paintings at the Five Civilized Tribes Museum (Muskogee, OK), Inter-Tribal Indian Ceremonial (Gallup, NM), The Heard Museum (Phoenix, AZ), Pueblo Grande Museum (Phoenix, AZ), and Santa Fe Indian Art Market. *Community activities*: Advisory Boards: Indian Artist Advisory Council, Sharlot Hall Museum, Prescott, AZ, 1999-current); Advisory Committee of Pueblo Grande Museum Indian Market, 2000-current; Artist Advisory Committee for Autry Southwest Museum Intertribal Indian Market, 2004-current. *Memberships*: Indian Arts & Crafts Association; Inter-tribal Indian Ceremonial Association; Southwestern Association for Indian Arts. *Interests*: As a successful printer, graphic artist, and commercial illustrator, Jesse pursues both Cherokee & Native American themes (in his acrylic paintings), especially legends of both Cherokee and other tribes passed to him. In addition to his original works, he has three full-color prints and publishes a new notecard/holiday card annually. "I am a traditionalist-both in spirit and art. I'm influenced by the nature that's around me. No matter how difficult, I want people to know I'm proud of my culture & traditions. I want to preserve what we have left as I create the new." *Published work*: Powwow Activity Book.

HUMPHREY, TIMOTHY J. (Blackfeet)
(attorney)
Education: New Mexico State University, BA; Worden School of Social Services, San Antonio, TX, MSW; University of Montana, JD, 1983. *Affiliation & Address*: Stetson & Jordan, P.C., 1305 Rio Grande Blvd. NW, Albuquerque, NM 87104 (505) 256-4911. E-mail: thumphrey@stetsonlaw.com. *Other professional post*: Adjunct Faculty, The Falmouth Institute, Fairfax, VA. *Past professional posts*: Court administrator, Blackfeet Tribal Court (two years); independent contractor with Gover, Stetson & Williams, P.C., Albuquerque, NM (six years) focusing on environmental issues, tribal corporations, code development, & gaming. Mr. Humphrey works extensively with tribal housing clients. He has been instrumental in the development of tribal environmental laws & regulations. Tim has had a wide range of experience with tribal courts, including employment as the Court Administrator to the Blackfeet Tribal Court for two years after graduating from law school. Tim worked as an independent contractor for six years with Kevin Gover at Gover, Stetson & Williams, P.C., focusing on environmental issues, tribal corporations, code development, and gaming before leaving to work for Stetson Law Offices, P.C. Tim brings important experience in the fields of cultural resources and environmental assessments and works extensively with our tribal housing clients. He has been instrumental in the development of tribal environmental laws and regulations, including solid waste management, and in the development of tribal-specific construction documents. Tim lectures nationally on Indian Housing issues. He was involved extensively with the negotiations that resulted in the first EPA approval of a tribal municipal solid waste facility permitting program. Tim served as Vice Chair of the American Bar Association's Section on Environment, Energy, and Resources Committee on

Native American Natural Resources for the 2009-10 ABA year. Tim is licensed in New Mexico and Montana.

HUNGRY WOLF, ADOLPH (*Natosina-Sun Chief*) (Blackfoot) 1944-
(writer)
Born February 16, 1944, Southern Germany. *Education*: California State University, Long Beach, BA. *Address*: Box 844, Skookumchuck, BC V0B 2E0, Canada. *Membership*: Blackfoot Crazy Dogs Society. *Published works*: Good Medicine book series; The Blood People - A Division of the Blackfoot Confederacy (Harper & Row, 1977); Shadows of the Buffalo - A Family Odyssey Among the Indians, with Beverly Hungry Wolf (William Morrow & Co., 1983); Canadian Railway Scenes, 5 Vols. (Canadian Caboose Press, 1983, '85, '86, '91, '97); Children of the Sun - Stories By and About Indian Kids, with Beverly Hungry Wolf (William Morrow & Co., 1987); Indian Tribes of the Northern Rockies, with Beverly Hungry Wolf (William Morrow & Co., 1987); Children of the Circle, with Star Hungry Wolf (Good Medicine Books, 1992).

HUNGRY WOLF, BEVERLY (Blood Blackfoot) 1950-
(writer)
Born on April 1, 1950 in Cardston, Alberta, Canada. *Address*: Box 844, Skookumchuck, BC V0B 2E0, Canada. *Published works*: The Ways of My Grandmother (William Morrow & Co., 1980); Shadows of the Buffalo - A Family Odyssey Among the Indians, with Adolph Hungry Wolf (William Morrow & Co., 1983); Children of the Sun - Stories by and about Indian Kids, with Adolph Hungry Wolf (William Morrow & Co., 1987); Indian Tribes of the Northern Rockies (William Morrow, 1991); Blackfoot Craft-workers Book (William Morrow, 1993); Daughters of the Buffalo Women: Maintaining the Tribal Faith (William Morrow, 1997).

HUNT, CHARLENE (Lumbee)
(executive director)
Education: Salem College, BA (Education). *Affiliation & Address*: Executive Director, North Carolina American Indian Health Board, Winston-Salem, NC 27157. *Other professional post*: Member, American Indian Heritage planning committee. *Community activities*: Selected to be part of the inaugural cohort for the 2013 North Carolina Native Leadership Institute.

HUNT, DEBORAH ESQUIBEL (Cherokee/Northeast Alabama)
(American Indian Student Services director)
Affiliation & Address: Director, American Indian Student Services, University of Colorado, Student Commons 2007C, 1200 Larimer St., P.O. Box 173364, Denver, CO 80217 (303) 315-1882; E-mail: deborah.hunt@ucdenver.edu

HUNTER, ANTHONY (Shinnecock) 1959-
(health director)
Born June 28, 1959, Queens, N.Y. *Education*: LaGuardia Community College, AAS, 1986; Hunter College, BS (Nursing), 1989. *Principal occupation*: Registered nurse. *Address & Affiliation*: Health Director (1992-present), American Indian Community House, 134 W. 29th St., 4th Floor, New York, NY 10001 (646) 357-6761. *Community activities*: Member, Board of Directors, American Indian Community House, 1982-. *Awards, honors*: Member of the United Nations NGO Committee for the 1993 International Year of Indigenous People. *Interests*: "Certified in psychiatric & mental health nursing by the American Nurses Association. Currently pursuing Master of Public Health (MPH) Degree in International Community Health Education at NYU. Hobby - genealogical research."

HUNTER, JULIUS ANDREW (*EagleHawk*) (Meherren) 1947-
(mortician)
Born December 25, 1947, Ahoskie, N.C. *Education*: North Carolina Central University, B.Sc., 1969; American Academy McAllister (New York City), MS, 1971. *Address*: P.O. Box 973, Ahoskie, NC 27910 (919) 332-4923. *Affiliations*: Owner, Hunter's Funeral Home, Ahoskie, NC & Rich Square, NC, 1974-; owner, Meherrin/Shinnecock Traders, Ahoskie, NC, 1992-. *Community activities*: Council Chairman, Meherrin Indian Tribe; Councilman, Town of Ahoskie; member, Board of Directors, United Tribes of North Carolina. *Memberships*: National Funeral Directors & Embalmers Association; North Carolina & Virginia Funeral Directors & Embalmers Association; Kappa Alpha Psi Frat. *Biographical sources*: Who's Who Among Outstanding Professionals; 2000 Notable American Men.

HUNTER, KARLENE (Oglala Lakota)
(business CEO & co-founder)
Education: Oglala Lakota College, MBA, *Affiliation & Address*: CEO & co-founder (with Mark Tilsen), Native American Natural Foods, 287 Water Tower Rd., Kyle, SD 57752 (605) 455-2187. Website: www.tankabar.com. *Other professional posts*: Co-founder (with Mark Tilsen), Lakota Express, a direct marketing & customer care management company, focused primarily on fundraising for nonprofit organizations. Ms. Hunter has led the direct marketing campaign for Oglala Lakota College for more than 21 years. Member, Board of

Directors, national Center for American Indian Enterprise Development, Mesa, AZ. *Past professional posts*: Member, Board of Directors, Native American Rights Fund, the National Indian Business Association, and the Pine Ridge Area Chamber of Commerce. *Awards, honors*: Recognized in 2003 as one of the 100 Best Minority Suppliers by the Minority Business Network; recipient of the 2006 National Director's Pioneer Award from the Department of Commerce; awarded the President Harry S. Truman Foundation Scholarship; Indian Business Woman of the Year from the National Indian Business Association; and the Rising Star Award from the Business Women's Network & Diversity Best Practices.

HUNTER, MICHAEL (Delaware)
  (tribal vice president)
Affiliation: Delaware Executive Committee, P.O. Box 825, Anadarko, OK 73005 (405) 247-2448.

HUNTER, PRISCILLA (Pomo)
  (tribal chairperson)
Affiliation & Address: Chairperson, Coyote Valley Reservation, P.O. Box 39, Redwood Valley, CA 95470 (707) 485-8723.

HUNTER, RAYMOND, (Kumeyaay Diegueno)
  (former tribal chairperson)
Affiliation & Address: Chairperson (1991-95; 2011-present), Jamul Indian Village, P.O. Box 612, Jamul, CA 91935 (619) 669-4785. *Other professional posts*: Secretary, Executive Board, Reservation Transportation Authority; board member, Southern California Tribal Chairman's Association. *Past professional post*: Service Technician, Pacific Bell, 1974-95. *Military service*: U.S. Marine Corps, 1968-69. *Memberships*: American Indian Veterans Association.

HUNTER, SALLY (White Earth Band Ojibwe)
  (professor)
Affiliation & Address: Professor, St. Thomas University, 2174 Berkley Ave., St. Paul, MN 55105. *Other professional post*: Vice Chair, American Indian Policy Center, St. Paul, MN.

HUNTER, TERRY
  (chief executive officer)
Affiliation & Address: Oklahoma City Indian Health Clinic, 4913 W. Reno, Oklahoma City, OK 73127 (405) 948-4900. *Past professional post*: Executive director, Association of American Indian Physicians, Oklahoma City, OK.

HUNTING, ERIKA (Little Traverse Bay Band Odawa)
  (attorney)
Education: Grand Valley State University, BA, 2011; Thomas Cooley Law School, Western Michigan University, JD, 2014. *Affiliation & Address*: Rosette, LLP, 25344 Red Arrow Hwy, Suite B, Mattawan, MI 49071 (269) 283-5005. E-mail: ehunting@rosettelaw.com. Ms. Hunting joined Rosette, LLP in June 2015. She brings with her extensive experience in commercial litigation and business law. Before joining Rosette, Ms. Hunting was an associate attorney at Talcott Franklin, P.C., where she practiced commercial litigation and business law with a focus on financial mortgage-backed securities litigation. Ms. Hunting has also served the Western Michigan Legal Aid Pro Bono program, where she represented low income clients with contract disputes. Currently, Ms. Hunting serves on the Board of Directors for Chandler Woods Charter School. She received her Juris Doctor magna cum laude from Thomas M. Cooley Law School. While in law school, Ms. Hunting focused on tribal law through a Self-Directed Concentration. She was also Senior Associate Editor of the Thomas M. Cooley Law Review & represented her class on the student bar association. Before law school, she obtained a B.A. in Management from Grand Valley State University. *Published works*: Contributing author, School Sexual Assault Policy Handbook (Penobscot 2015).

HUTCH, ELAINE (Kaw)
  (former tribal chairperson)
Affiliation & Address: Chairperson/CEO (2015-16), The Kaw Nation, 698 Grandview Dr., Drawer 50, Kaw City, OK 74641 (580) 269-2552. E-mail: ehuch@kawnation.com.

HUTCHINS, DEAN K. (*Yansv Gvnage-Black Buffalo*)
(Cherokee-Keetoowah) 1951-
  (management consultant; writer, poet, videographer)
Born November 1, 1951, Bronx, N.Y. Education: Queens College (Queens, NY); Manhattan College (New York, NY). *Principal occupation*: Writer, poet, videographer. *Address*: P.O. Box 462, Nyack, NY 10960 (845) 582-4020. E-mail: blackbuffalomc@aol.com. Website: www.deanhutchinsproductions.com. *Affiliations*: Writer & filmmaker, Black Buffalo Media, 1993-present; Independent Business Consultant, 1996-present; chairperson, Nuyagi Keetoowah Society, Inc., 2006-present; consultant & instructor, Rockland Community

College, 2008-12; president, Nighthawk Communications (video production company). *Past professional posts*: Producer, QPTV, 1993-2006; owner & CEO, Native Intelligence, Inc., 1986-2001; chief methodologist, IBM, 1995-1999; consultant, CGI Systems, 1993-99. *Community activities*: Served on the Board of the Native American Education Program of New York City, including two years as Chairperson; member, Rockland Coalition for Undoing Racism. He is active in New York's traditional Keetoowah community and produces television programs of interest to the Native community for cable television. *Memberships*: Wordcraft Circle; Native American Journalists Assn; Fellowship of Reconciliation. *Interests*: Hutchins worked in the computer industry for over 30 years, developing computer systems & methodologies for both government agencies and Fortune 500 corporations. He was the prime architect of systems methodologies for such companies as IBM & McDonald's. He has taught technical seminars at NYU and companies in the U.S., Canada, Mexico & Europe. His interest in communications gave him a second career as a writer. His poetry has been published in "Talking Stick" & "Native Realities." He has appeared at the biannual People's Poetry Gathering in New York City and has been a featured speaker at the American Museum of Natural History, the Native American Video Cultural Festival, the American Indian Community House in New York City, and the United Nations.

HUYSER, MICHELLE (Navajo-Dine')
  (physician)
Education: University of Minnesota School of Medicine, MD, 2014. *Affiliation*: Resident, University of California, San Francisco, East Bay Surgery Program, *Activities*: President (2013-14), Association of American Indian Medical Students.

I

IGNACE. LYLE A. (Menominee/Coeur D'Alene)
  (physician; executive director)
Education: Marquette University, BS, 1992; University of Minnesota, School of Medicine, MD, 1996; University of Wisconsin Medical College, Internal Medicine Residency Program, 1999; Harvard School of Public Health, MPH, 2010. Affiliation & Address: Executive Director, Gerald L. Ignace Indian Health Center, Inc., 1711 S. 11th St., Milwaukee, WI 53204 (414) 383-9526. E-mail: lignace@gliihc.net. *Past professional posts*: Ten years providing ambulatory & inpatient acut care for the Gallup Indian Medical Center and the Navajo Service Unit Indian Health Service. *Memberships*: Association of American Indian Physicians (executive board, 2003-03; 2007-08).

IGNACE, MARIANNE BOELSCHER (Skeetchestn Shuswap)
  (professor of linguistics & First Nations Studies)
Education: Simon Fraser University, PhD (Anthropology). Dissertation: The Curtain Within: Haida Social & Symbolic Discourse. *Affiliation & Address*: Professor of Linguistics & First Nations Studies, Simon Fraser University, 8888 University Dr., Burnaby, BC Canada V5A 1S6 (778) 782-4774. E-mail: ignace@sfu.ca. *Other professional posts*: Associate member in the Department of Sociology & Anthropology, Simon Fraser University; director, First Nations Language Centre, Simon Fraser University. *Research Interests*: Focuses her research on the Secwepemc (Shuswap) people of the Plateau, where her interests are aboriginal land use & occupancy, ethnobotany, traditional ecological knowledge, ethnohistory, & linguistic & anthropologiucal analysis of Aboriginal language discourse. Professor Ignace has worked with First Nations communities & elders on various language revitalization projects, including Secwepemctsin, St'at'imcets, Heiltsuk, Nuxalk, Haida & Sm'algyax. *Published works*: Papers in various journals & books on these topics, published in the "Handbook for Aboriginal Language Program Plannng in B.C." She has also published artcles on Haida oratory & Potlatching.

IGNACE, RONALD ERIC (Skeetchestn Shuswap)
  (Indian band chief)
Affiliations: Skeetchestn Indian Band, Box 178, Savona, B.C. Can. V0K 2J0 (604) 373-2493; co-chair, Simon Fraser U., Secwepeme Cultural Education Society, 345 Yellowhead Hwy., Kamloops, BC, Can. V2H 1H1 (604) 374-0616.

IGNACIO, MATT (Tohono O'odham)
  (capacity building liaison)
Education: University of California, Santa Barbara, BA (Sociology), 2000, MSW (Social Work), 2008; graduate of the Center for Progressive Leadership Fellowship Program, Colorado State office. *Affiliation & Address*: Capacity Building Liaison, National Native American AIDS Prevention Center (NNAAPC), 720 S. Colorado Blvd. #650, Denver, CO 80246 (720) 382-2244 x 313. E-mail: mignacio@nnaapc.org. Director of Training & Development, NNAAPC; AIDS Care & Support, Michael Palm Center, Gay Men's Health Crisis (GMHC), New York, NY; Harm Reduction Training Institute's National Training Coordinator.

IMPSON, J. LISA (Chickasaw)
(attorney; special counsel)
Education: East Central University (Ada, OK), BA; University of Tulsa Law School, JD; University of Oklahoma (Masters of Public Education–in progress). *Affiliation & Address*: Special Counsel (2009-present), Office of the Gaming Commissioner of the Chickasaw Nation, P.O. Box 1548 Ada, OK 74821. *Other professional post*: Vice President, Oklahoma Indian Bar Assn, Oklahoma City, OK. *Past professional posts*: Assistant Attorney General, Office of the Chickasaw Nation; private practice with Legal Advocates for Indian Country, Owasso, OK. *Memberships*: Oklahoma Bar Assn; Oklahoma Indian Bar Assn (present vice president); Chickasaw Bar Assn (chairperson, 2008).

IMPSON, ROBERT (Chickasaw)
(BIA agency supt.)
Affiliation & Address: Superintendent, Chickasaw Agency, Bureau of Indian Affairs, P.O. Box 2240, Ada, OK 74821 (405) 436-0784.

INGERSOLL, MARK (Lower Umpqua & Suislaw)
(tribal chairperson)
Affiliation & Address: Chairperson, Confederated Tribes of Coos, Lower Umpqua & Suislaw Indians, 1245 Fulton Ave., Coos Bay, OR 97420 (541) 290-4610. E-mail: mingersoll@ctclusa.org.

INGRAM, JERRY (Choctaw/Cherokee)
(artist, craftsman)
Address: P.O. Box 328, Rowe, NM 87562 (505) 421-2611. E-mail: ingrambead@plateautel.net. *Artwork*: Beadwork, porcupine quillwork, headdresses, clothing, bags, moccasins, accessories; original watercolor & acrylic paintings.

INNES, PAMELA (Creek)
(professor of Native American studies)
Affiliation & Address: Professor, American Indian Studies Program, University of Wyoming, College of Arts & Sciences, Ross Hall 114, 1000 E. University Ave. Laramie, WY 82071 (307) 766-6520

INNIS, ROBERT ALEXANDER (First Nations Plains Cree)
(professor of Native Studies)
Education: University of Toronto, BA (major in History & double minor in Aboriginal Studies), 1996; University of Saskatchewan, MA, 2000; University of Arizona, PhD (American Indian Studies), 2007. *Affiliation & Address*: Assistant Professor, Graduate Chair, Department of Native Studies, College of Arts & Sciences, Kirk Hall 130, University of Saskatchewan, Saskatoon, SK S7N 5C8 Canada (306) 966-2197. E-mail: rob.innes@usask.ca. *Research Interests*: Factors that lead to successful Aboriginal institutions, contemporary kinship roles & responsibilities, and Indigenous masculinities. *Published works*: Elder Brother and the Law of the People: Contemporary Kinship and Cowessess First Nation (University of Manitoba Press, 2013); numerous articles in scholarly journals.

INTERMILL, JESSICA
(attorney)
Education: University of Nebraska, BA, 2002; Hamline University School of Law, JD, 2005. *Affiliation & Address*: Attorney, Hogen Adams PLLP, 1935 W. County Road B2, Suite 460, St. Paul, MN 55113 (651) 842-9104. E-mail: jintermill@hogenadams.com. Jessica has made Indian law—particularly governance and litigation—the centerpiece of her career. She represents Indian tribes, tribal members, and businesses in matters involving sovereign immunity, tribal jurisdiction, commercial disputes, and taxation. She also assists tribes regarding governance issues, such as the drafting of tribal laws and the day-to-day administration of tribal constitutions and codes. After only one year on the *Rising Star* list, Jessica was selected to the *Super Lawyer* list for Minnesota Native American Law in 2013. She is a member of the Minnesota State Bar Association, and has published articles & book chapters on a variety of topics. Jessica is a past president of the Board of Directors of the nonprofit Family Tree Clinic.

IRON, PAMELA E. (Cherokee/Laguna Pueblo)
(executive director)
Affiliation & Address: Executive Director, American Indian Resource Center, Inc. & Institute for Native Justice, 110 W. Choctaw St., Tahlequah, OK 74464 (918) 456-5581. Pamela has forty (40) years of experience working in Indian country developing programs and assisting communities in discovering their needs and facilitating problem solving through guided community planning. She has served as Executive Director for two non-profits, one urban and one rural and was the Health Director and the Chief of Staff for the former Cherokee Chief Wilma Mankiller. During her tenure with these organizations she was able to develop cultural competency programs and co-author a book on cultural competency. Pamela has served on local, regional and national boards and committees. She was appointed by the Attorney General of the United States to sit on the National Advisory Committee on Violence against Women, 2006. Other committees and boards include the National Indian Women's Health Steering Committee for the Indian Health Service Director, and a founding board member of the National Indian Youth Leadership Project and the American Indian Theatre Company of Tulsa. She served as the Vice-President of the Oklahoma Health Care Authority when it was founded to assume Medicaid.

IRON CLOUD III, ED (Lakotah)
(state representative)
Affiliation & Address: Democrat, 27th District of the South Dakota State Legislature. *Address*: P.O. Box 172, Porcupine, SD 57772 (605) 773-3851.

IRON CLOUD, PATRICIA E. (Assiniboine & Sioux)
(former tribal vice chairperson)
Affiliation: Fort Peck Asiniboine & Sioux Tribes, P.O. Box 1027, Poplar, MT 59255 (406) 768-5155. E-mail: atstafne@fortpecktribes.net

IRWIN, KENNETH D. (*Two Mans*) (Mandan/Hidatsa/Arikara) 1946-
(electrician)
Born February 16, 1946, on the Fort Berthold Reservation, N.D. *Education*: Standing Rock Indian School, Wahpeton Indian School, White Shield Indian School, Flandreau Indian School. *Principal occupation*: Electrician. *Address & Affiliation*: CEO/Chair. Native American Indian Center of Central Ohio (NAICCO), P.O. Box 07705, Columbus, OH 43207 (614) 443-6120. *Other professional posts*: President, Ohio Council for Native American Burial Rights, Ohio Indian Movement, Columbus, OH; Irwin-Ruffini Committee (drafting bill for Ohio to coincide with Federal-Native American Grave Protection & Repatriation Act. *Community activities*: Coordinator of the Eastern Region of the American Indian Movement. Has hosted the last two Eastern Regional AIM Conferences in Columbus, OH. *Awards, honors*: Appointed by the Ohio Supreme Court and has served on the Ohio Commission on Racial Fairness as a Commission member. *Interests*: "Indian rights activist including protection of Indian religious freedom, Indian grave protection & repatriation, cultural protection & education. Reburial of ancient ancestors; spiritual rights of prisoners; Indian Child Welfare Act issues; sports mascot issue; issues relating to alcohol & substance abuse prevention & treatment. *Published works*: Contributed as a consultant to the development of a handbook used by the Ohio Dept. of Corrections in dealing with religious issues relating to prisoner population.

ISAAC, GORDON (Dine)
(development corporation president)
Affiliation & Address: President, Keya Earth, P.O. Box 2092, Flagstaff, AZ 86003. Website: www.keyaearth.com E-mail: g.isaac.az@gmail.com. Gordon is one of the key facilitators & educators of sustainable development.

ISAAC, NICK (Athapascan)
(AK village council president)
Affiliation: Native Village of Ohogamiut, Fortuna Ledge, AK 99585 (907) 679-6740.

ISHAM, MICHAEL "MIC" (Lac Courte Oreilles Ojibwe)
(tribal chairperson)
Affiliation & Address: Lac Courte Oreilles Band of Ojibwe, 13394 W. Trapania Rd., Hayward, WI 54843 (715) 634-8934. E-mail: misham@lco-nsn.gov.

ISHII, LOMAYUMTEWA (Hopi)
(associate professor & chair of Indigenous studies)
Education: Northern Arizona University, BS, MS, PhD. *Affiliation & Address*: Associate Professor (2004-present) & Chairperson, Applied Indigenous Studies Department, SBS West Bldg. 70, Northern Arizona University, P.O. Box 15020, Flagstaff, AZ 86011 (928) 523-6624; E-mail: lomayumtewa.ishii@nau.edu. Specializes in Native American history & historiography, the American West, and borderlands.

ISOM, DENISE
(professor of ethnic studies)
Affiliation & Address: Professor of Ethnic Studies & Department Chair, Ethic Studies Department, California Polytechnic State University, 1 Grand Ave., Bldg. 38 Rm. 136 • San Luis Obispo, CA 93407 (805) 756-7388) E-mail: disom@calpoly.edu

IVAN, IVAN M. (Yup'ik Eskimo)
(Alaskan village chief; state legislator)
Affiliation: Chief, Akiak Native Community, P.O. Box 52127, Akiak, AK 99552 (907) 765-7112. *Other professional post*: Member, Alaska State Legislature, Pouch V, Juneau, AK 99801.

IVERSON, PETER 1944-
(professor of history)
Born April 4, 1944, Whittier, Calif. *Education*: Carleton College, BA, 1967; University of Wisconsin-Madison, MA, 1969, PhD, 1975. *Affiliation & Address*: Professor, Dept. of History, Arizona State University (1988-present), Box

872501, Tempe, AZ 85287-2501 (480) 965-0032. E-mail: peter.iverson@asu.edu. *Community activities*: Advisory Board, American Indian Studies, Arizona State University; member of Heard Museum (Phoenix) and Museum of Northern Arizona (Flagstaff). *Memberships*: Western History Association; American Society for Ethno-history; Organization of American Historians. *Fellowships*: NEH Fellowship for Research, 1999-2000; John Simon Guggenheim Memorial Foundation for Research, May 2000 to Jan. 2001. *Awards, prizes*: Chief Manuelito Award for Contribution to Navajo Education, 1984; Carleton College Alumni Association Award for Distinguished Achievement, 1992; Winner of the Western Writers of America 2003 Spur Award for Nonfiction - Contemporary. *Published works*: The Navajos: A Critical Bibliography (Indiana University Press, 1976); Carlos Montezuma & the Changing World of American Indians (University of New Mexico Press, 1982); The Navajo Nation (University of New Mexico, 1983); edited, The Plains Indians of the 20th Century (University of Oklahoma Press, 1985); The Navajos (Chelsea House, 1990); The Plains Indians of the Twentieth Century (University of Oklahoma Press, 1992); When Indians Became Cowboys: Native Peoples & Cattle Ranching in the American West (University of Oklahoma Press, 1994); edited with Albert Hurtado, Major Problems in American Indian History (D.C. Heath, 1994); We Are Still Here: American Indians in the 20th Century (Harlan Davidson, 1998); edited with Frederick Hoxie, Indians in American History, 2nd Ed. (Harlan Davidson, 1998); Riders of the West: Portraits From Indian Rodeo (University of Washington Press, 1999); Dine: A History of the Navajos (University of New Mexico Press; Carlos Montezuma and the Changing World of American Indians (University of New Mexico Press, 2003) For Our Navajo People: Dine Letters, Speeches, and Petitions, 1900-1960 (University of New Mexico Press)

IVON, JERRY, SR. (Eskimo)
 (Alaskan village president)
Affiliation: Native Village of Kongiganak, P.O. Box 5069, Kongiganak, AK 99559 (907) 557-5226.

IVY, DONALD (Coquille)
 (tribal chief)
Affiliation & Address: Coquille Indian Tribe, P.O. Box 783, North Bend, OR 97459 (541) 756-0904; E-mail: donivy@coquilletribe.org

IYALL, CYNTHIA (Nisqually)
 (tribal chairperson)
Affiliation & Address: Chairperson, Nisqually Indian Tribe, 4820 SheNahNum Dr., SE, Olympia, WA98513 (360) 456-5221. E-mail: iyall.cynthia@nisqually-nsn.gov.

IYALL, WILLIAM "BILL" (Cowlitz)
 (tribal chairperson)
Education: Saint Martin's University (Lacey, WA), BS (Engineering), 1973. *Affiliation & Address*: Chairperson, Cowlitz Indian Tribe, P.O. Box 2547, Longview, WA 98632 (360) 577-8140. E-mail: wiyall@cowlitz.org. *Professional posts*: Elected to the tribal council in 1993, vice chairperson in 2006, chairperson in 2008, re-elected as chairperson in 2009; Economic Development Committee Chair; professional engineer. *Past professional post*: City of Tacoma – Civil Engineer 1975 – 2011. *Awards, honors*: Appointed by Governor Gary Locke to the Lewis & Clark 200 Year Commemoration Commission, representing Western Washington Tribes at the White House Celebration, July 4, 2002; 2004 Outstanding Civil Engineering Achievement – Thea Foss Waterway Redevelopment; attended Tribal White Conferences in 2009 & 2010, testified before Congress on Tribal Land Issues. *Past professional post*: City of Tacoma - Civil Engineer, 1975-2011.

JACK, ANTHONY (Pomo)
 (rancheria chairperson)
Affiliation & Address: Chairperson, Big Valley Rancheria, 2726 Mission Rancheria Rd., Lakeport, CA 95453 (707) 263-3924. E-mail: ajack@bvrancheria.com

JACK, MICHAEL (Quechen)
 (tribal vice president)
Affiliation & Address: Vice President, Quechen Tribe, Fort Yuma Reservation, P.O. Box 1899, Yuma, AZ 85366 (760) 572-0213.

JACKA, JERRY
 (photographer, illustrator)
Born & raised on ranches north of Phoenix, Ariz. *Address*: c/o Northland Publishing, P.O. Box 1389, Flagstaff, AZ 86002. Website: www.jerryjackaphotography.com. *Awards*: Western Heritage Award, best art book for 1988, "Beyond Traditions"; and, Emmy Award in Cultural Documentary for video version of "Beyond Traditions." *Published works*: Photographs for: "Beyond Tradition: Contemporary Indian Art and Its Evolution," with Lois Jacka (Northland Publishing, 1988); "David Johns; on the Trail of Beauty" (Snailspace Publication, 1991); "Enduring Traditions: Art of the Navajo," with Lois Jacka

(Northland Publishing, 1994); "Navajo Jewelry: A Legacy of Silver & Stone" (Northland Publishing, 1995). Illustrated seven books and four special issues of "Arizona Highway" on Native American art.

JACKA, LOIS ESSARY
 (writer)
Born & raised on ranches north of Phoenix, Ariz. *Address*: c/o Northland Publishing, P.O. Box 1389, Flagstaff, AZ 86002. *Awards*: Western Heritage Award, best art book for 1988, "Beyond Traditions"; and, Emmy Award in Cultural Documentary for video version of "Beyond Traditions." *Published works*: "Beyond Tradition: Contemporary Indian Art and Its Evolution," with Jerry Jacka (Northland Publishing, 1988); David Johns: On the Trail of Beauty (Snailspace Publication, 1991); Enduring Traditions: Art of the Navajo (with Jerry Jacka) (Northland Publishing, 1994); "Navajo Jewelry: A Legacy of Silver & Stone" (Northland Publishing, 1995). Articles for "Arizona Highway" and other magazines.

JACKSON, BRENT (Saginaw Chippewa)
 (tribal sub-chief)
Affiliation & Address: Sub-Chief, Saginaw Chippewa Indian Tribe, 7070 E. Broadway, Mount Pleasant, MI 48858 (989) 775-4000.

CHARLENE D. JACKSON (Navajo)
 (attorney; Of counsel)
Education: University of Arizona College of Law, JD. *Affiliation & Address*: Of Counel, Stetson & Jordan, P.C., 1305 Rio Grande Blvd. NW, Albuquerque, NM 87104 (505) 256-4911. Her practice has been dedicated almost exclusively to Indian Law, the representation of tribes, & the resolution of tribal issues. She has the unique experience of working internally in the legal offices of tribes as well as serving as a tribal court judge, tribal appellate court judge, and municipal court judge pro tem. While serving as a chief judge of a tribal court, Charlene oversaw the growth & development of a nationally recognized Tribal Healing to Wellness Court program, commonly known as a Drug Court. In addition, Charlene serves on the faculty at the National Tribal Justice Center at the National Judicial College and is a member of the Arizona Family Support Council. Raised on the Navajo reservation, Charlene is able to understand and appreciate the complexities of tribal governments & residing on the reservation. As a result, she is able to effectively work with tribal elders and assists with the development of modern tribal operations & contemporaneously working to protect tribal sovereignty. Charlene's family has long & continuous history of public service. Charlene's grandfather, Joseph McPherson, was a US Assistant Attorney General and attorney for the Navajo Nation. Her father, the late Dr. Dean C. Jackson, and her mother Stephanie were visionaries in Indian education. Her siblings each work for the advancement of Indian people, and her spouse, a combat veteran, continues his career in public service. In her spare time, Charlene enjoys horseback riding and competing in barrel racing.

JACKSON, CRAIG (Tlingit)
 (craftsperson)
Affiliation: Owner, Indian Arts, P.O. Box 85273, Las Vegas, NV 89185. *Products*: Jewelry semi-precious stones, dream catcher necklaces; baskets.

JACKSON, DANNA R. (Salish & Kootenai)
 (attorney)
Education: University of Montana, JD, 1996. *Affiliation*: Policy Counsel/Senior Consultant in the American Indian Law & Policy Practice Group of Akin Gump Strauss Hauer & Feld, Washington, DC. E-mail: danna_jackson@yahoo.com. Danna spends part of her time lobbying Congress on a broad range of tribal concerns including: federal rectification of the Crow water settlement, gaming issues, economic development issues n Indian lands, housing, education funding & transportation. *Other professional posts*: Visiting professor, University of Montana Indian Law Summer Program, teaching Indian Gaming, Contemporary Issues in Indian Policy & Indian Education Law; member, Board of Directors, American Indian Graduate Center, Albuquerque, NM. *Past professional posts*: Legislative Assistant to Senator Tim Johnson (D-SD) and advised the Senator on all legislative issues relevant to the Indian Affairs & Judiciary committees, & drafted legislation, Congressional Record Statements & oversaw the appropriations process for all tribal appropriations projects; worked with the National Indian Gaming Commission as advisor/ attorney regarding all Indian gaming issues.

JACKSON, DIXIE (Chukchansi)
 (rancheria treasurer)
Affiliation & Address: Treasurer, Picayune Rancheria of Chukchansi, 46575 Road 417, Coarsegold, CA 93614 (559) 683-6633.

JACKSON, DUANE (Sisseton-Wahpeton Sioux)
 (tribal vice chairperson)
Affiliation & Address: Vice chairperson, Spirit Lake Tribe, P.O. Box 359, Fort Totten, ND 58335 (701) 766-4221.

JACKSON, FARON, SR. (Ojibwe)
(tribal chairperson)
Affiliation & Address: Chairperson, Leech Lake Band of Ojibwe, 190 Sailstar Dr. NW, Cass Lake, MN 56633 (218) 335-8200.

JACKSON, GARY (Umpqua)
(tribal vice chairperson)
Affiliation & Address: Vice Chairperson, Cow Creek Band of Umpqua Tribe of Indians, 2371 N.E. Stevens, Roseburg, OR 97470 (541) 672-9405.

JACKSON, JACK C., JR. (Dine-Navajo)
(state senator)
Born & raised on the Navajo Reservation in Arizona. *Education*: Syracuse University, JD, 1989. *Affiliation & Address*: Senator, Arizona State Senate, 1700 W. Washington, Rm. 315, Phoenix, AZ 85007 (602) 926-5862. E-mail: jjackson@azleg.gov. Jack is a Democrat from District 2 in Northern Arizona that includes the city of Flagstaff, the Navajo Nation and the tribes of the Hopi, Havasupai, Hualapai, and San Juan Southern Paiute. He resides in Window Rock, AZ. *Other professional post*: Principal, Agassiz Group, a governmental affairs & public policy consulting firm that assists individuals, communities & businesses affected by governmental & regulatory actions in Arizona; senior strategist, Blue Stone Strategy Group, Phoenix, AZ. *Past professional posts*: Navajo Nation, Washington, DC office, 1989-2002; Arizona House of Representatives, 2003-05; served on the Arizona Commission on Indian Affairs, Phoenix, AZ, 2005-06; director of community relations & co-owner, AeroCare Medical Transport, Inc. (a Native majority-owned business), 2006-09; served on the Navajo Gaming Enterprise Board, 2007-09; In Feb. 2010, Jack was appointed to President Obama's Advisory Council on HIV/AIDS.

JACKSON, JASON BAIRD
(professor of folklore & anthropology)
Education: University of Florida, BA (Sociology), 1990; Indiana University, MA (Anthropology), 1995, MA (Folklore, 1996), PhD (Anthropology), 1998. *Affiliation & Address*: Assistant Professor of Folklore, Department of Folklore & Ethnomusicology, Indiana University, Bloomington, IN 47405. E-mail: jbj@indiana.edu. *Other professional post*: Adjunct Assistant Professor of Anthropology, American Indian Studies Research Institute, Indiana University, Bloomington, IN. *Past professional posts*: Professor of Anthropology, University of Oklahoma, Norman, OK; curator of ethnology, Sam Noble Oklahoma Museum of Natural History; curator of anthropology, Gilcrease Museum, Tulsa, OK. *Interests*: "My research centers on ethnographic collaboration (since 1993) with the Yuchi and other Woodland Indian communities living in eastern & central Oklahoma." *Published work*: Yuchi Ceremonial Life: Performance, Meaning & tradition in a Contemporary Native American Community (University of Nebraska Press, 2003).

JACKSON, KEN (Grey Eagle)
(storyteller)
Address: Sacred Circle Storytellers, 3810 Hubble Ct., Clinton, WA 98236 (206) 324-0071. He provides educational storytelling, cultural workshops and sharing circle ceremonies. Ken has performed in many countries and contexts. He also offers training in storytelling and theatre.

JACKSON, LARRY, SR. (Yavapai-Apache)
(tribal vice chairperson)
Affiliation & Address: Vice Chairperson, Yavapai-Apache Nation, 2400 W. Datsi St., Camp Verde, AZ 86322 (928) 567-3649.

JACKSON, MELVN (Koncow-Maidu)
(rancheria vice chairperson)
Affiliation & Address: Vice Chairperson, Mooretown Rancheria, 1 Alverda Dr., Oroville, CA 95965 (530) 533-3625.

JACKSON, MICHAEL, SR. (Quechen)
(former tribal president)
Affiliation & Address: Former president, Quechen Tribal Council, Fort Yuma Reservation, P.O. Box 1899, Yuma, AZ 85366 (760) 572-0213.

JACKSON, MIKE (Oglala Lakota)
(project manager)
Affiliation & Address: Project Manager (2010-present), First Peoples Fund, P.O. Box 2977, Rapid City, SD 57709 (605) 348-6594. *Past professional posts*: First Nations Oweesta Corporation, Rapid City, SD; ten years of grants administration, managed Indian self-determination grants for the Oglala Sioux tribe as a program director for Johnson O'Malley, and the Community Health Representatives (CHR) Program.

JACKSON, RYAN P. (Hoopa)
(tribal chairperson)
Affiliation & Address: Chairperson, Hoopa Valley Tribe, P.O. Box 1348, Hoopa, CA 95546 (530) 625-4211. E-mail: hupachair@hoopa-nsn.gov

JACKSON, WILLIAM (Rattlesnake) (Cherokee)
(tribal principal chief)
Affiliation & Address: Principal Chief, American Cherokee Confederacy, 619 Pine Cone Rd. • Albany, GA 31705-6906 (229) 787-5722

JACKSON CAMERON, SAMANTHA S. (Ojibwe)
(vice president of academic affairs)
Education: St. Clair County Community College, AB; Western Michigan University, BA; Michigan State University, MA. Affiliation & Address: Vice President of Academic Affairs, Bay Maill Community College, Mikanuk Hall, 12214 W. Lakeshore Dr. • Brimley, MI 49715 (906) 2483354 ext. 88429. E-mail: scameron@bmcc.edu.

JACOB, IGNATI (Eskimo)
(AK council president)
Affiliation: Oscarville Traditional Council, P.O. Box 1554, Oscarville, AK 99559 (907) 737-7321.

JACOB, MICHELLE M. (Yakama)
(professor of Ethnic Studies)
Affiliation & Address: Associate Professor of Ethnic Studies & Affiliated Faculty in Sociology, University of San Diego, San Diego, CA. E-mail: mjacob@sandiego.edu. She also serves as the Founding Director of the Center for Native Health & Culture at Heritage University on the Yakama Reservation. She engages in scholarly and activist work that seeks to understand and work toward a holistic sense of health and well-being within indigenous communities. *Published works*: Yakama Rising: Indigenous Cultural Revitalization, Activism, & Healing in paperback from the University of Arizona Press as part of the First Peoples: New Directions in Indigenous Studies Series; editor, On Indian Ground: The Northwest (Information Age Publishing).

JACOBS, ALEX A. (Karoniaktatie) (Mohawk) 1953-
(writer, artist, editor)
Born February 28, 1953, Akwesasne Reservation, via Rooseveltown, N.Y. *Education*: Institute of American Indian Arts, Santa Fe, N.M., AFA (sculpture, creative writing), 1977; Kansas City Art Institute, BFA (sculpture, creative writing), 1979. *Address*: Resides in Albuqueruqe, NM. *Affiliations*: Editor, Akwesasne Notes, via Rooseveltown, N.Y., 1979-1985; editor, Akwekon Literary Journal, Akwesasne Notes, Hogansburg, N.Y., 1985-91; instructor, University of New Mexico, Albuquerque, 1991-. *Other professional posts*: Board of directors, CKON-F, Radio Station, Mohawk Nation. *Awards, honors*: 1975 poetry award, Scottsdale National Indian Art Exhibit; 1979 honorable mention, Society of Western Art, Kansas City, Mo. *Interests*: Poetry, prose, short stories; graphic arts; sculpture; painting, printmaking; ceramics; video/audio/performance art; editor of Native American literature & journalism; networking national & international native peoples; poetry readings & workshops; travel U.S.A. with White Roots of Peace, 1973-74 (native touring group/communications). *Published works*: Native Colours (Akwesasne Notes, 1974); Landscape: Old and New Poems (Blue Cloud Quarterly, 1984); *Anthologies*: Come to Power, The Remembered Earth, The Next World, 3rd World Writers, and Songs From the Earth on Turtle's Back, in various literary magazines, 1972-1985; editor, Akwekon Literary Journal, 1985-91.

JACOBS, JOSEPH (Mohawk/Cherokee) 1947-
(NIH program director)
Born in 1947. Resides in Guilford, CT. *Education*: Yale Medical School, MD, 1974; Wharton School of Business, University of Pennsylvania, MBA, 1985. *Address & Affiliation*: Director, Office of Alternative Medicine, National Institutes of Health, Bethesda, MD, 1992-. *Past professional posts*: Pediatrician, Indian Medical Center, Gallup, NM; U.S. Public Health Service, Rockville, MD; Aetna Life Insurance Co., Hartford, CT.

JACOBS, MARY ANN (Lumbee)
(professor & chair of American Indian studies)
Affiliation & Address: Chair & Associate Professor of American Indian Studies, American Indian Studies Department, University of North Carolina, Pembroke, Old Main, Room 251, 308 Greenlaw Hall, CB 3520, Pembroke, NC 27599 (910) 775-4262. E-mail: mary.jacobs@uncp.edu.

JACOBSEN, WILLIAM H., JR. 1931-
(professor emeritus)
Born November 15, 1931, San Diego, Calif. *Education*: Harvard University, AB, 1953; University of California, Berkeley, PhD, 1964. *Affiliation*: Assistant Professor of English, 1965-68; associate professor, 1968-74; professor, 1974-present; professor of linguistics, 1989-present; Emeritus, 1994-present, University of Nevada, Reno. *Address*: 1411 Samuel Way, Reno, NV 89509 (775) 784-6689. E-mail: whj@scs.unr.edu. *Memberships*: Linguistic Society of America; International Linguistic Assn; Society for the Study of the Indigenous Languages of the Americas (vice-president, 1991, president, 1992); American Anthropological Assn; Society for Linguistic Anthropology; Great Basin Anthropological Conference. *Awards, honors*: Outstanding Researcher Award,

University of Nevada, Reno, 1983; Nevada Humanities Award, 2002. *Interests*: American Indian languages, primarily Washo & Makah, and the Hokan & Wakashan families; also, fieldwork or publication on Salinan, Yana, Nootka, Nez Perce, Numic, and Chimakuan. *Published works*: First Lessons in Makah (Makah Cultural & Research Center, revised ed. 1999); Beginning Washo (Nevada State Museum, 1996).

JACOBSON, CRAIG A.
(attorney)
Education: University of Oregon, BA; Northwestern School of Law of Lewis & Clark College, J.D., 1995; Certificate in Environmental & Natural Resources Law. *Address & Affiliation*: Attorney (1998-present), Hobbs, Straus, Dean & Walker, LLP, 806 SW Broadway Suite 900, Portland, OR 97205 (503) 242-1745. E-mail: caj_hsdwor@hotmail.com. *Past professional post*: Prior to joining HSDW, Mr. Jacobson was a sole practitioner focusing on environmental issues in Indian country, Title IV Self-governance (both BIA and non-BIA), and Indian Health Service related issues. Presently, he specializes in environmental and natural resources law and policy issues in Indian country.

JACOBSON, JOHN E.
(attorney)
Education: Carleton College, BA, 1968; University of Chicago Law School, JD, 1973. *Affiliation & Address*: General Partner & Of Counsel, The Jacobson Law Group, 335 Atrium Office Bldg., 1295 Bandana Blvd. • St. Paul, MN 55108 (651) 644-4710. E-mail: jjacobson@thejacobsonlawgroup.com. John began his work in Indian Country in 1973 with the United States Department of the Interior, Office of the Solicitor. In that capacity, he advised & represented the Department with respect to Indian treaty rights and land claims questions throughout the Midwest. After ten years with the Office of the Solicitor, he entered private practice in 1983, founding the firm that became The Jacobson Law Group, P.C. Since that time, John has devoted his career to representing Indian tribes, tribal entities, & persons having an interest in Indian-law matters. He directed litigation and conducted negotiations that led to the development of Indian gaming in Minnesota, Wisconsin, and Louisiana; he represented the only Indian tribal government that, following the passage of the Indian Gaming Regulatory Act of 1988, obtained Federal approval to operate gaming away from its reservation in a metropolitan area. John has extensive experience in on- and off-reservation financing. He served as principal adviser on Indian legal matters to publicly-held corporations extensively involved in Indian gaming, and as counsel to banks and institutions engaged in participating in financing development in Indian Country. In 1995, he served as special counsel to the underwriters of the first publicly traded bond issue by an Indian Tribe in the United States — the financing, by the Mohegan Tribe of Connecticut, of the Mohegan Sun Casino. John is an adjunct professor at William Mitchell College of Law, teaching Indian Law, and is a frequent lecturer throughout the United States to lawyers & business organizations on the subject of Indian law and Indian gaming. He has served as a Judge on the Tribal Court of the Shakopee Mdewakanton Sioux (Dakota) Community in Minnesota from 1988 to present. *Awards, honors*: Best Lawyers, Lawyer of the Year 2013 in Native American law in the Minneapolis Area. *Bar Admission*: Lac Courte Oreilles Tribal Court; Supreme Court of the U.S., et al.

JACOBSON, NAOMI (Quileute)
(tribal secretary & Operations Manager)
Affiliation & Address: Secretary & Operatins Manager, Quileute Nation, P.O. Box 279, LaPush, WA 98350 (374-6155). E-mail: naomi.jacobson @quileutenation.org *Past tribal post*: Tribal chairperson.

JAENEN, CORNELIUS J. 1927-
(emeritus professor)
Born February 21, 1927, Cannington Manor, Saskatchewan, Canada. *Education*: University of Manitoba, Winnipeg, BA, 1947, MA, 1950, BEd, 1958; University of Ottawa, Ontario, PhD, 1963; University of Winnipeg, LLD, 1982. *Address*: 9 Elma St., Gloucester, ON K1T 3W8 (613) 521-0167. *Affiliations*: Assistant & associate professor of history, United College (now University of Winnipeg), 1959-67; associate & full professor of history, 1967-92, professor emeritus, 1992-present, University of Ottawa. *Community activities*: Canadian Consultative Council on Multiculturalism; Native Awareness Program of Dept. of External Affairs (Ottawa). *Memberships*: American Society for Ethno-history; Canadian Historical Assn; Social Science Federation of Canada; Institut d'histoire de l'Amerique francaise; French Colonial Historical Society; Canadian Ethnic Studies Assn (founding president, 1971-73, councilor, 1971-). *Awards, honors*: Ste. Marie Prize in Canadian History, 1974, for Friend & Foe, awarded by Ministry of Culture, Government of Ontario; also Book Prize of the French Colonial Historical Society in 1976. LLD Honoris Causa from University of Winnipeg, 1981, in recognition of work on minorities, ethnic groups, Native peoples; J.B. Tyrell Medal in History, Royal Society of Canada, 1994; Distinguished Professor Award, Canadian Historical Assn, 1996; Officer of the Order of Leopold II (Belgium); Lifetime Achievement Award, Canadian Ethnic Studies Association, 2003. *Interests*: Visiting professor in Canada, India, France, Belgium, & Italy dealing with French colonization, Native peoples,

ethnicity. Participant in international congresses in Paris, Bucharest, Budapest, Brussels dealing with North American Indian issues. *Published works*: Friend & Foe: Aspects of French-Amerindian Cultural Contact in the Sixteenth and Seventeenth Centuries (Columbia U. Press, 1976); The French Relationship With the Native Peoples of New France (Indian & Northern Affairs, Canada, 1984); (in collaboration) Emerging Identities, Selected Problems & Interpretations in Canadian History (Prentice-Hall, Canada, 1986); (in collaboration) The American Indian & the Problem of History (1987); (in collaboration) Readings in Canadian Native History (1988); Canada, A North American Nation (McGraw-Hill-Ryerson, 1989); (in collaboration) Sweet promises: A Reader on Indian-White Relations (1991); (in collaboration) Les Hurons de Lorette (1996) The French Regime in the Upper Country in the Seventeenth Century (Toronto: Champlain Society, 1996); Material Memory: Vol. I (Addison Wesley, 1998); American Encounters. Natives & Newcomers (2000); (in collaboration) The Native North American Almanac (2001); First Contacts (Markham & Fitzhenry & Whiteside, 2002); Promoters, Planters, and Pioneers: The Course & Context of Belgium Settlement in Western Canada (U. Calgary Press, 2011); articles in journals on Canadian First Nations.

JAGER, MARY ELIZABETH (Citizen Potawatomi)
(research analyst)
Education: Carroll College, BA (Teaching English to Speakers of Other Languages; Washington University (St. Louis, MO), MSW (with emphasis on social & economic development in American Indian communities). *Affiliation & Address*: Research Analyst, Native Nations Institute for Leadership, Management & Policy, Udall Center for Studies in Public Policy, The University of Arizona, 803 East First St., Tucson, AZ 85719 (520) 626-0664. E-mail: jager@u.arizona.edu.

JAIME, ANGELA (Pit River/Maidu)
(professor of education & American Indian studies)
Education: California State University, Sacramento, BA (Ethnic Studies with concentration in American Indian studies); San Francisco State University, MA (Ethnic Studies); Purdue University, PhD (Curriculum Studies). *Affiliation & Address*: Associate Professor, Department of Educational Studies, College of Education, McWhinnie Hall 324, University of Wyoming, Laramie, WY 82071 (307) 766-3991. E-mail: jamiea@uwyo.edu. *Other professional post*: Associate professor, American Indian Studies Program. Angela specializes in American Indian education, the study of Native women and their experiences in higher education, multicultural education, & Women's Studies.

JAIME, JUSTIN "RIO" (Quileute)
(tribal vice chairperson)
Affiliation & Address: Vice Chairperson, Quileute Nation, P.O. Box 279, LaPush, WA 98350 (374-6155). E-mail: chas.woodruff@quileutenation.org.

JAMES, CHEEWA (Modoc)
(speaker, corporate trainer, author)
Affiliation & Address: Horizons, 3330 Union Springs Way, Sacramento, CA 95827 (916) 369-6616. E-mail: cheewa@cheewa.com. *Published work*: Catch the Whisper of the Wind: Inspiring Stories and Proverbs from Native Americans, revised edition. 1994.

JAMES, CORY (Cahto-Pomo)
(tribal vice chairperson)
Affiliation & Address: Vice Chairperson, Cahto Indian Tribe of the Laytonville Rancheria, P.O. Box 1239, Laytonville, CA 95454 (707) 984-6197. E-mail: vice-chair@cahto.org

JAMES, KEITH
(professor & program director)
Affiliation & Address: Professor & Director of Tribal Initiatives, American Indian Studies, American Indian Language Development Institute, The University of Arizona, Dept. of Language, Reading & Culture, Communication Bldg., Room 108B, 1430 E. Second St., P.O. Box 210069, Tucson, AZ 85721 (520) 621-8440. E-mail: keithjames@emai.arizona.edu.

JANDREAU, MICHAEL B. (Lower Brule Sioux)
(former tribal chairperson)
Affiliation & Address: Former Chairperson, Lower Brule Sioux Tribe, P.O. Box 187, Lower Brule, SD 57548 (605) 473-8000. E-mail: chairman@lbst.org.

JANIS, SANDRA (Oglala Lakota)
(director of finance & operations)
Affiliation & Address: Director of Finance & Operations, National Native American AIDS Prevention Center, 720 S. Colorado Blvd. #650, Denver, CO 80246 (720) 382-2244 ext. 307. E-mail: sjanis@nnaapc.org. *Past professional posts*: Grants specialist, accountant & program specialist for the Diabetes Prevention Program for the American Indian & Alaska Native Programs at the U. of Colorado at Denver. She provided guidance to 65 American Indian tribes in coordination with the National Indian Health, Indian Health Services

(NIH/HIS) contracts for prevention of diabetes; business manager/ accountant for Lakota Express, an American Indian, women-owned business on Pine Ridge Reservation; accountant (ten years), Native American Rights Fund.

JANIS, TERRY L. (Oglala Lakota)
(former college president)
Education: Macalester College, BA; Harvard University, MA (Education); University of Arizona College of Law, JD. *Affiliation & Address*: Former President, White Earth Tribal & Community College, P.O. Box 478, Mahnomen, MN 56557 (218) 935-0417. E-mail:n terry.janis@wetcc.edu. *Other professional post*: Board member of Two Feathers Endowment of the St. Paul Foundation. *Past professional post*: Program Officer (2004-12), Indian Land Tenure Foundation, Little Canada, MN. Over the years, he has worked extensively on Native American & international indigenous education & human rights issues. *Memberships*: Native Americans in Philanthropy, the National Indian Education Assn, the National Congress of American Indians, and State Bar of Arizona.

JARAMILLO, FRANCINE M. (Isleta Pueblo)
(staff attorney)
Education: University of Washington, BA; University of New Mexico School of Law, JD. *Affiliation & Address*: Staff Attorney, American Indian Law Center, P.O. Box 4456, Albuquerque, NM 87196 (505) 277-5462. E-mail: Jaramillo@ailc-inc.org. *Other professional posts*: Associate Justice for the Pueblo of Isleta Appellate Court; senior policy analyst for the New Mexico Indian Affairs Department (appointed by Governor Bill Richardson.)

JARBOE, MARK
(attorney)
Born August 19, 1951, Flint, Mich. *Education*: University of Michigan, BA, 1972; Harvard Law School, JD, 1975. *Affiliation*: Retired Partner & Chair (1978-2009), Indian Law Practice Group & the Indian & Gaming Dept., Dorsey & Whitney, LLP, Minneapolis, MN Mr. Jarboe joined Dorsey & Whitney in 1976 and as chair of the Indian Law Practice Group, represents Indian tribal governments, tribal business & entities doing business with tribes across the country in connection with financings of reservation infrastructure, economic development & other activities; contractual, regulatory, gaming, etc. *Other professional post*: Speaker at various conferences & workshops on the subject of business transactions in Indian country. *Memberships*: American Bar Association; Minnesota American Indian Bar Association. *Awards, honors*: Phi Beta Kappa; Best Lawyers in America - Gaming. *Biographical sources*: Who's Who in America; Who's Who in American Law; Who's Who in the Midwest. *Published works*: Regulating Indian Gaming; Fairness or Finagling? (Bench & Bar of Minnesota, 1993); The Nature of Tribal Sovereignty (The Legend, 1994); Fundamental Legal Principles Affecting Business Transactions in Indian Country (Hamline Law Review, 1994); Lending in Indian Country - The Principal Legal Issues (ABA Bank Compliance, 1995); Financing Alternatives for Tribal Gaming Facilities (Indian Gaming Magazine, 2003); Recourse & Limited Recourse in Casino Financing (Indian Gaming Magazine, 2004).

JARRATT-SNIDER, KAREN (Mississippi Choctaw)
(professor of Indigenous Studies)
Education: Northern Arizona Univesity, BS, MPA, PhD, 2006. *Affiliation & Address*: Chair & Associate Professor (2008-present), Applied Indigenous Studies Department, College of Social & Behavioral Sciences, Northern Arizna University, SBS West Bldg. 70, Room 100, Flagstaff, AZ 86011 (928) 523-6219. E-mail: Karen.jarratt-snyder@nau.edu. Karen specializes in Indgenous environmental justice, forestry policy & Inigenous people, tribal community participatory research models, federalism-American Indian intergovernmental relations, tribal administration, federal Indian policy & law, and Indigenous peoples rights in international law & policy.

JASTRZEMBSKI, JOSEPH C.
(coordinator of Native American studies)
Affiliation & Address: Coordinator, Native American Studies Program, Minot State University, 500 University Ave. West, Administration 355, Minot, ND 58707 (701) 858-3322. E-mail: joseph.jastrzembski@minotstateu.edu. *Other professional posts*: Co-director, with Calvin Grinnell of the Three Affiliated Tribes Cultural Preservation Office, of the Mandan Language & Oral Traditions Preservation Project; president of the Board of Directors, Lillian & Coleman Taube Museum of Art, Minot, ND. *Research Interests*: Native Language Documentation/Preservation. *Volunteer work*: Minot Area Council for International Visitors (vice executive director).

JEANOTTE, DARRELL F. (Turtle Mountain Chippewa))
(supt. of education)
Education: Penn State University, MA (Educational Administration), 1978. *Affiliation & Address*: Superintendent/Principal, Pierre Indian Learning Center, HC 31, Box 148, Pierre, SD 57501 (605) 224-8661. E-mail: jeanotte@dakota2k.net. *Past professional posts*: Principal, Ojibwa Indian School,

Belcourt, ND; assistant principal/federal programs administrator, Dnseith Public School District, ND.

JEANOTTE, LEIGH D. (Turtle Mountain Chippewa) 1948-
(higher education administrator)
Born November 1, 1948, Rolette, N.D. *Education*: University of North Dakota, EdD. *Address*: E-mail: leigh.jeanotte@und.nodak.edu. *Affiliation & Address*: Administrator, American Indian Student Services, Box 8274, University of North Dakota, Grand Forks, ND 58202 (701) 777-4291 (1972-present). *Other professional posts*: Treasurer, North Dakota Indian Education Association; Vice President, Higher Education Resource Organization for Students. *Awards, honors*: 1987 North Dakota Indian Educator of the Year; University of North Dakota Outstanding Meritorious Service, 1986; 1998 Friend of ASPIRE Award; 1999 International Honorary for Leaders in University Communities. *Community activities*: Evaluator of several tribal/federal education projects; Northeast Human Services Advisory Board. *Memberships*: North Dakota Indian Education Assn; Higher Education Resource Organization for Students; North Dakota College Personnel Assn; American College Personnel Assn. *Interests*: "Promotion of cultural sensitivity, educational evaluation & assessment, higher education, student support services."

JEFF, SANDRA D. (Navajo)
(NM state representative)
Address: Box 631, Crownpoint, NM 87313 (505) 786-4994. *Affiliation*: NM Legislature District 5 representative, 2009-present. *Committee Membership*: Indian Affairs Committee.

JEFFRIES, SHARN M. (Occaneechi Saponi)
(tribal vice chaireprson)
Affiliation & Address: Vice Chairperson, Occaneechi Band of Saponi Nation P.O. Box 356, Mebane, NC 27302 (336) 421-1317. E-mail: sharnjeffries@obsn.org

JEFFRIES, VICKIE (Occaneechi Saponi)
(tribal administrator; secretary/treasurer)
Affiliation & Address: Administrator, Secretary/treasurer, Occaneechi Band of Saponi Nation P.O. Box 356, Mebane, NC 27302 (336) 421-1317. E-mail: vickiejeffries@obsn.org

JEMISON, G. PETER (Seneca) 1945-
(professional artist; site manager)
Born January 18, 1945, Silver Creek, N.Y. *Education*: Buffalo State College, University of Buffalo. *Principal occupation*: Historic site manager. *Address*: P.O. Box 239, Victor, NY 14564 (585) 924-5848. E-mail: pjemison@frontiernet.net. *Affiliation*: Ganondagan State Historic Site, Victor, N.Y. *Other professional post*: Curator of Native American art exhibits consultant & lecturer on history & art. *Community activities*: Board of Trustees, Memorial Art Gallery of Rochester, NY; Native American Graves, Protection and Repatriation Act representative for the Seneca Nation of Indians. *Interests*: "I am a professional artist." *Published work*: Treaty of Canandaigua 1794: 200 Years of Treaty Relations Between the Iroquois Confederacy & U.S. (Clear Light Publishers).

JEMISON, NANCY L.
(BIA office director)
Affiliation & Address: Office of Economic Development, Bureau of Indian Affairs, Dept. of the Interior, MS-2061-MIB, Rm. 2529, 1849 C St., NW, Washington, DC 20240 (202) 208-5324.

JENKINS, DENNIS (Paucatuck Eastern Pequot)
(former tribal chairperson)
Affiliation & Address: Chairperson, Eastern Pequot Tribe, P.O. Box 370, North Stonington, CT 06359 (860) 535-1868.

JENKINS, SUSAN (OK Choctaw)
(executive director)
Education: University of Georgia, PhD (Sociology). *Affiliation & Address*: Cherokee Preservation Foundation (2002-present), 71 John Crowe Hill Rd., P.O. Box 504, Cherokee, NC 28719 (828) 497-5550. E-mail sjenkins@cpfdn.org.

JENSEN, JAMES (Sac & Fox of Missouri)
(tribal chairperson)
Affiliation & Address: Vice Chairperson, Sac & Fox Nation of Missouri in Kansas & Nebraska, 305 N. Main St., Reserve, KS 66434 (785) 742-0053. E-mail: jjensen@sacandfoxcasino.com

JENSVOLD, KEVIN (Dakota)
(tribal chairperson)
Affiliation & Address: Chairperson, Upper Sioux Community of Minnesota, P.O. Box 147, Granite Falls, MN 56241 (320) 564-2360.

JEROME, BERNARD (Maria Band of Micmacs)
(tribal cultural director)
Address: 50 Micmac Dr., Presque Isle, ME 04769; E-mail: bjerome@micmac.org. *Affiliation*: Cultural director, Aroostook Band of Micmacs, Presque Isle, ME. *Past professional post*: Chief, Maria Band of Micmac, PQ, Canada.

JERUE, CARL, JR. (Eskimo)
(Alaskan village chief)
Affiliation & Address: First Chief, Anvik Village, P.O. Box 10, Anvik, AK 99558 (907) 663-6322. E-mail: anviktribal@hotmail.com.

JIM, DANA GREY (Cherokee)
(attorney)
Education: Northeastern Oklahoma A&M College, AA, 1992; Oklahoma City University, BA, 1994; Oklahoma City University School of Law, JD, 1999. *Affiliation & Address*: Attorney-at-Law (2013-present), P.O. Box 1011, Vinita, OK 674301 (918) 457-6626. Past professional posts: Assistant Attorney General, Cherokee Nation, 2005-13.

JIM, REX LEE (Navajo-Dine')
(tribal vice president)
Born & raised in Rock Point, Ariz. Education: Princeton University, BA. *Affiliation & Address*: Vice President (2011-present), Navajo Nation, P.O. Box 7440, Window Rock, AZ 86515 (928) 871-7000. E-mail: vicepresident.rexleejim@navajo-nsn.gov. *Other professional post*: Board Treasurer & Navajo Area Representative, National Indian Health Board, Washington, DC. Rex served as a ranking member on the judiciary committee & chairperson of the Public Safety Committee within the 21st Navajo Nation Council. *Past professional posts*: Teacher, Rock Point Community School (teaching Navajo to K-12) He developed a curriculum for K-Graduate programs that was culturally & pedagogically appropriate for Navajo students. He played a key role in the drafting and final passage of the International Declaration on the Rights of Indigenous Peoples.

JIM, RUSSELL (Yakama)
(program director)
Affiliation & Address: Director, Environmental & Waste Management Program, Yakama Nation, P.O. Box 151, Toppenish, WA 98948 (509) 865-5121. *Interests*: To educate people about the Hanford Nuclear Reservation and its damage to the land and society. *Awards, honors*: 2002 Beeson Peace Award.

JOCKS, CHRISTOPHER P. (*Ronwanien:te*) (Kahnawake Mohawk) 1954-
(assistant professor; lecturer)
Born February 11, 1954, Omaha, Neb. *Education*: Lewis & Clark College, BA, 1985; University of California, Santa Barbara, MA, 1990; PhD, 1994. *Affiliation & Address*: Senior Lecturer, Applied Indigenous Studies Department, SBS West Bldg. 70, Suite 100, P.O. Box 15020, Flagstaff, AZ 86011 (928) 523-6140; E-mail: Christopher.jocks@nau.edu. Christopher devotes himself to the ongoing translation of Indigenous thought into action. He is especially interested in local, grassroots, community-based efforts to strengthen traditional social relations and decision-making in the midst of historical change, among Indigenous communities in Canada as well as the U.S. Language, religion or worldview, sovereignty, sustainability, and gender relations are all critical components of his work. *Past professional posts*: Consultant & Visiting Professor, Fort Lewis College, Dept. of Native American & Indigenous Studies, Durango, CO; University of California, Santa Barbara, CA, 1988-93; Assistant Professor of Native American Studies & Religion, Dartmouth College, Hanover, NH, 1993-2002. *Community activities*: Faculty advisor, Native American House at Dartmouth College. *Memberships*: American Academy of Religion; Society for the Study of Native American Religious Traditions. *Awards, honors*: Recipient of first annual (1993-94) Native American Dissertation Fellowship, Dartmouth College. *Interests*: "My academic work aims at describing & interpreting American Indian religious life in ways that do not intrude upon or exploit Indian communities; that use Indians' own languages & categories; and that expand our understanding of religion itself." *Published works*: "Native North American Environments as Webs of Relation-ship," chapter on World Religions and the Environment (Quo Vadis, 1994).

JOE, ANGELITA (Navajo)
(field office manager)
Affiliation & Address: Manager, Farmington Field Office, National Indian Youth Council, 653 West Broadway, Farmington, NM 87401 (505) 327-5341. E-mail: ajoe@niyc-alb.org.

JOE, JENNIE R. (Navajo-Dine')
(professor)
Born in New Mexico. *Education*: University of New Mexico, BS; University of California, Berkeley, MA, MPH, PhD, 1980. *Address*: 1642 E. Helen St., Tucson, AZ 85719 (520) 621-5076. E-mail: jrjoe@u.arizona.edu. *Affiliations*: Professor, Department of Family & Community Medicine (DFCM), College of

Medicine, The University of Arizona, Tucson, AZ; 1985-present; faculty, American Indian Studies Program. Dr. Joe also teaches in the American Indian Studies graduate program. *Other professional posts*: Director, Native American Research & Training Center (NARTC), University of Arizona, Tucson, AZ. Dr. Joe is a principal investigator in SEPTA, Special Education Program for Teachers & Administrators, University of Arizona, Tucson, AZ. She has & continues to conduct training & research projects collaboratively with a number of tribal & Native communities. Among one of her recent projects included coordinating a case study on the Office of Native Medicine in Chinle, Arizona, for the National Library of Medicine. The video illustrates the successes and challenges that traditional Navajo-Dine' practitioners (traditional healers) encounter as they collaborate with physicians and other health care providers in the clinical care arena. Also, she serves on the National Advisory Council for the National Heart, Lung, and Blood Institute. *Military service*: U.S. Navy - Lt. *Past professional posts*: American Indian Studies Center & Dept. of Anthropology, UCLA, 1981-85; *Community activities*: National Museum of the American Indian (Board of Trustees-Smithsonian Institution. *Memberships*: American Anthropological Assn; American Public Health Assn; Society for Medical Anthropology; The Congress of the Americanist. *Awards, honors*: 1994 National Katrin Lamon Scholar, Santa Fe, NM; 1995 Switzer Scholar, Washington, DC. *Interests*: American Indian health issues. *Published works*: 20 chapters in edited books; research reports, articles, and book reviews.

JOE, ROBERT (Dine'-Navajo)
(tribal chief operations office)
Affiliation & Address: Chief Operations Officer, The Navajo-Dine' Nation, 100 Parkway, P.O. Box 7440, Window Rock, AZ 86515 (928) 810-8505. E-mail: rjoe@navajo-nsn.gov

JOEST, PATTA LT (Choctaw)
(artist, designer)
Education: University of Oklahoma, BA (Fashion Arts, Clothing and Textiles), 1982. *Principal occupation*: Artist, designer of original contemporary Native influence clothing. *Address & Affiliations*: Owner, The Dancing Rabbit, 814 N. Jones, Norman, OK 73069 (405) 360-0512. *Shows*: Heard Museum, Phoenix, AZ; The Living Desert Museum, Palm Desert, CA; The Indian Art Market, Denver, CO; Indian Land, Scottsdale, AZ; The Inter-Tribal Indian Ceremonial in Gallup, NM; The Red earth Festival, Oklahoma City, OK; the Mulvane Museum of Fine Arts, Kansas City, MO. *Awards, honors*: Commissioned by Chief Wilma Mankiller of the Cherokee Nation of Oklahoma to create an ensemble for her and her Chief of Staff to wear to the Presidential Inaugural Gala in Washington, DC in January 1992; One of eight Native American artists selected to be highlighted in the "Goldbook," a nationally published book featuring the "Best of the Best"; honored by the Oklahoma Hospitality Club as one of eighteen "Ladies in the News"; special commission project to design Joseph's coat in the musical "Joseph and the Amazing Technicolor Dreamcoat," performed by a local company; 1993 "Best of Show" Artwear '93, Ft. Collins, CO; 1994 & 1995 "Best of Show" Embellishments IV & V, University of Tulsa School of Art; 1995. *Interests*: Patta frequently lectures around the country on how to design modern clothing using ancient tribal themes. "My artistic goal is to reach another dimension by using all elements of fiber, art, and textiles to develop my idea into wearable art."

JOHANNSEN-HANKS, CHRISTINA B. 1950-
(anthropologist; Indian museum board president)
Born October 29, 1950, Rahway, N.J. *Education*: Beloit College, BA, 1972; Brown University, PhD, 1984. *Address*: 139 Van Farm Rd., Warnerville, NY 12187 (518) 234-2841. E-mail: hankaero@midtel.net. *Affiliation*: Board President, Iroquois Indian Museum, Howes Cave, NY, 1980-present (vice-president & research associate, 1995-present). *Other professional post*: Lecturer, State University of New York at Albany. *Interests*: "Research and promotion of contemporary Iroquois art. Actively involved in educating the public about the contributions of Iroquois peoples today and to an understanding of their past. Concern in maintaining professional museological standards in small museums and delineating a museum's purposes and goals. Continued field research in Iroquois communities throughout the U.S. & Canada. Special interest in creatively photographing museum objects. Living part-time in South Africa. New interest in contemporary southern African arts." *Published works*: European Trade Goods and Wampanoag Culture in the Seventeenth Century in Burr's Hill: A 17th Century Wampanoag Burial Ground in Warren, Rhode Island (Haffenreffer Museum of Anthropology, Brown University, 1980); Iroquois Arts: A Directory of a People and Their Work, co-edited with Dr. John P. Ferguson (Association for the Advancement of Native North American Arts & Crafts, 1984); Efflorescence and Identity in Iroquois Art, Ph.D. Dissertation, Brown University, 1984.

JOHN, JENNIFER (Eskimo)
(Alaskan village president)
Affiliation & Address: President, Lime Village Traditional Council, P.O. Box LVD, Lime Village, McGrath, AK 99627 (907) 526-5236.

JOHN, JONATHON (Athapascan)
(Alaskan village president)
Affiliation & Address: President, Gwich'in Arctic Village, P.O. Box 22079, Arctic Village, AK 99722 (907) 587-5923.

JOHN, MAURICE A. (Seneca)
(Seneca Nation treasurer)
Address & Affiliation:, Treasurer, Seneca Nation of Indians, P.O. Box 231, Salamanca, NY 14779 (716) 945-1790. *Past professional post*: Former president, Seneca Nation.

JOHN, ROBERTA (Navajo) 1960-
(program & project specialist, writer, entrepreneur)
Born May 26, 1960, Monticello, Utah. Grew up on the Navajo Reservation. *Education*: Arizona State University, BS (Communications), 1982; Brigham Young University, MA (Communications), 1987. *Principal occupation*: Program & project specialist, writer, entrepreneur. *Address*: P.O. Box 2978, Window Rock, AZ 86515 (928) 871-7375. *Affiliation*: Navajo Nation Division of Economic Development, Window Rock, AZ, 1989-. "I send out press releases regarding economic development projects & activities within the Navajo Nation. I also send out an economic development newsletter." *Other professional post*: CEO, The Native American Distribution Co. (a small disadvantaged minority company). Membership: New Mexico Indian Tourism Association (board member). *Interests*: "Program & project specialist, marketing & public relations, promote the Navajo Nation and work on economic development projects & activities. *Published works*: Children's books: "Red Is Beautiful (Salina Bookshelf, 2003); and "Proud to be a Blacksheep" (Salina Bookshelf, 2005).

JOHN, THOMAS (Seneca)
(administrator for self-governance)
Affiliation & Address: Administrator for Self-Governance, Chickasaw Nation, P.O. Box 1548, Ada, OK 74821 (580) 436-7280. *Other professional post*: Treasurer, Oklahoma City Area Representative, National Indian Health Board, Washington, DC.

JOHNNY, RONALD EAGLEYE (Summit Lake Paiute)
(tribal administrator; environmental coordinator)
Education: University of New Mexico School of Law, JD. *Affiliation*: Administrator, Environmental Coordinator, Summit Lake Paiute Tribe, 1708 H St., Sparks, NV 89431 (775) 827-9670. E-mail: ron.johnny@summitlaketribe. org. *Past professional post*: President, Native American Law Students Association, American Indian Law Center, University of New Mexico School of Law, Albuquerque, NM.

JOHNNY, ZELDA (Goshute)
(former tribal vice chairperson)
Affiliation & Address: Former Vice Chairperson, Confederated Tribes of the Goshute Indian Reservation, P.O. Box 6104, Ibapah, UT 84034 (435) 234-1138. E-mail: mgreymountain@goshutetribe. com.

JOHNS, ALANA
(professor of linguistics & director of Abriginal Studies program)
Affiliation & Address: Professor of Linguistics & Director, Aboriginal Studies Program, University of Toronto, North Borden Bldg., 2nd Floor, 563 Spadina Ave., Toronto, ON M5S 2J7 (416) 978-2233. E-mail: director.aboriginal@ utoronto. ca.

JOHNS, AMY (Seminole of Florida)
(tribal associate chief justice)
Education: Arizona State University, BS (Social Work), MA (Public Administration). *Affiliation & Address*: Associate Chief Justice, Seminole Tribe, Brighton Reservation, 6300 Stirling Rd., Suite 320, Hollywood, FL 33024 Website: www. tribalcourt@semtribe.com (800) 683-7800; (954) 966-6300.

JOHNS, BOBBY THOMAS (Lower Muskogee Creek) 1936-
(artist/craftsman)
Born March 24, 1936, Dodge County, Ga. *Education*: College courses; Graphic Arts Certificate. *Principal occupation*: Artist/craftsman. *Address*: 12533 Polonious Pkwy., Pensacola, FL 32506 (904) 492-3593. *Affiliation*: Instructor & technical advisor for military training films & communications operations in a civilian capacity at Fort Gordon, GA (20 years). Disability retirement. *Military service*: U.S. navy (4 years) (Airman, sea/air rescue). *Community activities*: Museum of Commerce (volunteer); Northwest Florida Arts Council (Arts in Education Committee); Indian culture demonstrations for many events. *Memberships*: Pensacola Historical Society; National Woodcarvers Association; Arts Council of Northwest Florida; Historic Pensacola Village. *Awards, honors*: Artist Fellowship for folk art - Secretary of State, Cultural Affairs; Master Artist & Apprentice Program, Florida Folklife Division, Secretary of State. *Interests*: "Helping to keep alive the traditional attitudes & crafts/art of our Native American peoples. Visiting schools & powwows where interaction with others can take place to foster a better understanding of our people."

JOHNS, JOSEPH F. (*Cayoni*) (Eastern Creek) 1928-
(museum manager, artist)
Born January 31, 1928, Okefenokee Swamp, Ga. *Education*: High school (U.S. Armed Forces Institute). *Principal occupation*: Museum manager, artist. *Address*: 7 Russell St., West Peabody, MA 01960 (508) 535-2426. *Affiliation*: Indian Artist in Residence (sculpture & carving in any medium) & Building Manager, Peabody Museum Peabody Museum, Harvard University, Cambridge, MA, 1974-. "I maintain a small studio, at my home, for carving the eight traditional masks of the Creek people." *Military service*: U.S. Naval Amphibious Forces (Sniper), 1944-1946 (U.S. Navy P.O. 3; Asiatic Pacific Medal, Silver Star Medal); U.S. Coast Guard (retired), 1947-1965 (U.S.C.G. P.O. 1; Silver Life Saving Medal presented by President Harry S. Truman in Washington, D.C., 1947). *Community activities*: Masonic Shriner at Alleppo Temple, Wilmington, Mass. *Membership*: Boston Indian Council; Peabody Museum (Associate; member, Repatriation Committee). *Awards, honors*: "I was a crew member of the Coast Guard Cutter Westwind Expedition to the North Pole (Dew Line), 1953-1954; and a crew member of the Coast Guard's Cutter, Eastwind Expedition to the South Pole (Operation Deep Freeze, 1961-1962); (I am) holder of Antarctica Service Medal. A book about my life is now being written by Mitchell Wade."

JOHNS, MARY FRANCES (Florida Seminole) 1944-
(craft artist; shop owner)
Born October 7, 1944, Miami, Fla. *Education*: Edison Community College (Ft. Myers, FL), Nursing, 1979-1983. *Principal occupation*: Craft artist; shop owner. *Address*: Rt. 6, Box 595, Brighton Seminole Reservation, Okeechobee, FL 34974 (813) 467-7312. *Affiliation*: Owner, Arts & Crafts Shop, Brighton Reservation, 1984-. *Other professional posts*: Resource person for museums as arts & crafts demonstrator, storytelling & history of the Seminoles & Southeastern Indians. *Interests*: "I have demonstrated basketry, patchwork, doll making and Indian foods all over the State of Florida. I have given talks on our culture and its history throughout North & Central Florida. I was hired by the Tallahassee Junior Museum thru a State Dept. grant to be artist in resident. This is how I got started in this field. I am presently helping Charles Daniels with his Creek language classes and studying the Muskogean & Southeastern Indian culture thru Mr. Daniels classes. I speak Miccosukee, Creek & English fluently, and some Spanish. *Published works*: Co-author, with D. Alderson, "Muskogee Fires" (Muskogee Press, 1994); Muskogee Words & Ways-also Dictionary III, a Southeastern Reader V (7 part series).

JOHNS, WILLIE (Seminole of Florida) 1951-
(tribal chief justice)
Born March 23, 1951, Okeechobee, Fla. *Education*: Abraham Baldwin Agricultural College, A.A. (Animal Husbandry); Palm Beach Atlantic University, BA (History); University of Miami, MA (History). *Affiliation & Address*: Chief Justice, Seminole Tribe, Brighton Reservation, 6300 Stirling Rd., Suite 320, Hollywood, FL 33024 Website: www. tribalcourt@semtribe.com (800) 683-7800; (954) 966-6300. E-mail: wmjohns@ictransnet.com. *Affiliations*: Seminole Tribe, Okeechobee, FL; United South & Eastern Tribes. *Community activities*: President, E.I.R.A.; community adult education director. *Membership*: Eastern Indian Rodeo Assn (commissioner). *Past professional post*: Director of Education - Seminole Tribe.

JOHNSON, ALVIS (Karuk)
(tribal councilmember; health program director)
Affiliation & Address: Counsilmember, Karuk Tribe of California, P.O. Box 1016, Happy Camp, CA 96039 (530) 493-5305. *Other professional post*: Director, Karuk Tribal Health Program.

JOHNSON, CALVIN (Tonto Apache)
(tribal vice chairperson)
Affiliation & Address: Vice Chairperson, Tonto Apache Tribe, 18 Tonto Reservation, Payson, AZ 85541 (928) 474-3988.

JOHNSON, CAPT. BRIAN
(IHS acting area director)
Education: East Central University, Ada, Okla., BS (Environmental Science); University of North Carolina, MPH. *Affiliation & Address*: Acting Director, Navajo Area Indian Health Service, P.O. Box 9020, Window Rock, AZ 86515 (928) 871-4811. As the Acting Navajo Area Director, Capt. Johnson is responsible for ensuring the provision of comprehensive health care services to Tribes in the Four Corners area, comprising portions of the states of Arizona, New Mexico, Utah & Colorado. The Navajo Area Indian health service provides health care services through federally-operated facilities as well as through tribally managed programs assumed under the authority of the Indian Self-Determination & Education Assistance Act. *Past professional posts*: CAPT Johnson began his career with the IHS in 1993, serving with the IHS Bemidji Area White Earth Service Unit as an Environmental Health Specialist with the U.S. Public Health Service Commissioned Corps. He also worked as a supervisory environmental health specialist at the Whiteriver Service Unit in the Phoenix Area. In the Navajo Area, CAPT Johnson has served as Deputy

Director and Director of the Division of Environmental Health Services, in the Office of Environmental Health and Engineering (OEHE), Navajo Area. In 2010, he began serving as the Director of the Navajo Area OEHE, overseeing five professional divisions.

JOHNSON, DUSTIN OWL (Anishinaabe)
(program manager)
Education: University of Southern California, School of Cinematic Arts wth a focus on production). *Affiliation & Address*: Manager, Native American & Indigenous Program, Sundance Institute, 5900 Wilshire Blvd. #800, Los Angeles, CA 90036 (310) 360-1981 Fax 360-1969. He has written & directed seven short films, His latest film, The Tenth Day, was nominated for Best Live Action Short Filmm at the 2007 American Indian Film Fstival in San Francisco. One of his goals is to cast diverse talent so film & television will more accurately reflect the global society we live in today.

JOHNSON, EDWARD (Lower Elwha Klallam)
(tribal secretary/treasurer)
Affiliation & Address: Secretary/Treasurer, Lower Elwha Klallam Tribe, 2851 Lower Elwha Rd., Port Angeles, WA 98362 (360) 452-8471.

JOHNSON, GARY W. (Anishinabe)
(director of First Nations Center; professor of Fist Nations Studies)
Education: University of Wisconsin-Eau Claire, BS; University of Wisconsin-Superior, ME; University of Minnesota, ABD. *Affiliation & Address*: Director of Fist Nations Center & Assistant Professor, First Nations Studies Program, Human Behavior, Justice & Diversity Department, Swenson Hall 3103, Belknap & Catlin, Superior, WI 54880 (715) 394-8297. E-mail: gjohnson@uwsuper.edu. *Teaching Interests*; Native Studies; Education. *Research Interests*; Integration of Native culture into school curriculum; tribal mediation & conflict resolution.

JOHNSON, GERALDINE B. (Pomo)
(rancheria chairperson)
Affiliation: Elem Indian Colony of Pomo Indians, Sulphur Bank Rancheria, P.O. Box 757, Clearlake Oaks, CA 95423 (707) 998-3003.

JOHNSON, SKALAABA HERBERT (Alabama-Coushatta of Texas)
(tribal 2nd chief)
Affiliation & Address: 2nd Chief, Alabama-Coushatta Tribe of Texas, 571 State Park Rd., Livingston, TX 77351 (936) 563-1100.

JOHNSON, JACLYN "JACKIE" R. (Flathead)
(attorney)
Education: Dartmouth College, BA (Native American & Environmental Studies), 2005; University of Michigan Law School, JD, 2008. *Affiliation & Address*: Associate, Rothstein, Donatelli, Hughes, Dahlstrom, Schoenburg & Bienvenu, LLP, 80 E. Rio Salado Parkway, Suite 710, Tempe, AZ 85281 (480) 921-9296. E-mail: jrjohnson@rothsteinlaw.com. Jackie's Indian law experience includes drafting tribal ordinances, preparing & negotiating purchase & sale agreements, lease agreements & other real estte related agreements. She is admitted to practice in Arizona and the Navajo Nation.

JOHNSON, JAN
(American Indian Studies program coordinator)
Born & raised in Lewiston, Idaho. *Eduaction*: University of Washington, BA, 1990; Tulane University, PhD, 1999. *Affiliation & Address*: Clinical Assistant Professor, Department of English; coordinator, American Indian Studies Program, College of Letters, Arts & Social Sciences, University of Idaho, 875 Perimeter Dr., MS 1102, Brink Hall 224, Moscow, ID 883844. (208) 885-7743. E-mail: janjohn@uidaho.edu. Jan lectures on American Indian Literature and Native Americans in Popular Film.

JOHNSON, JO-ANNE (*Tilsma*) (Tahltan/Kaska) 1954-
(education)
Born April 30, 1954, Cassiar, B.C. Canada. *Education*: B.Ed. *Address & Affiliation*: Director, Yukon Native Language Centre, Yukon College, Box 2799, Whitehorse, Yukon, Canada Y1A 5K4 (867) 668-8820. E-mail: jjohnson@yukoncollege.yk.ca. *Other professional posts*: Council of Yukon First Nations; Yukon Department of Education. *Membership*: Yukon Teachers' Association. *Interests*: Native languages & education.

JOHNSON, JOE (Creek) 1950-
(executive vice president)
Born August 24, 1950, Council Hill, Okla. *Education*: Eastern Oklahoma State College (Wilburton, OK), AA; Oklahoma State University (two years). *Principal occupation*: Executive vice president, consulting. Resides in Texas. *Past professional posts*: Mayor, City of Eufaula, OK, 1975-99; chief justice, Muscogee Creek Nation, 1988-99; director, Native American Studies Program, Rose State College, Midwest City, OK 73110 (405) 733-7308. *Community activities*: Eastern OK Development District Board of Directors (three terms); Eufaula Municipal Hospital Board of Directors (chairperson, 1976-86); OK

Municipal League (president, vice-president & currently past president); McIntosh County Democratic Central Committee (past secretary-treasurer); OK Police Pension & Retirement Board (six years); State Higher Education Alumni of ESC. *Memberships*: National American Indian Court Judges Association (executive first vice president); OK Conference of Mayors; OK Conference of Regional Councils; Lions Club; Greater Eufaula Chamber of Commerce; Lake Eufaula Association (board member); serves on Development Council of Connors State College; serves on the Domestic Violence and Substance Abuse PAC Board; serves on the Board of Directors for Literacy Council, and OK Travel Industry Association. *Awards, honors*: Elected in 1975 as the youngest mayor in the state, at age of 24 years; selected to Who's Who in the South and Outstanding Young Men of America; George Nigh Mayor's Award. *Interests*: "Developed the local Posey Park, named after Alexander Posey, the most recognized Indian poet in Oklahoma's history; developed the Eufaula Community Center and the Eufaula Memorial Library; instrumental in the development & implementation of the Eufaula Main Street Program."

JOHNSON, LESLIE (Puyallup)
(tourism director)
Affiliation & Address: Tourism Director, Squaxin Island Tribe, 3591 Old Olympic Hwy., Shelton, WA 98584 (360) 432-3838.

JOHNSON, LEWIS (Micco) (Seminole of Oklahoma)
(tribal assistant chief)
Affiliation & Address: Assistant Chief, Seminole Nation of Oklahoma, P.O. Box 1498, Wewoka, OK 74884 (405) 257-7205. E-mail: Johnson.l@sno-nsn.gov. He was elected to two consecutive terms on the Seminole Nation General Council for the Tallahassee Band & served as Band Chief. Johnson was appointed to several boards & committees by four different Principal Chiefs of the Seminole Nation of Oklahoma and comes from a family with a tradition of service to the Seminole Nation and its members. *Past professional posts*: Seminole Nation Museum, Wewoka, OK. For nearly twenty years, he was selected to several fellowships with the Smithsonian Institution & specialized in Native Preservation programs; representative on tourism, Seminole Nation of Oklahoma. Prior to being elected Assistant Chief, Johnson served on the Administration Appeals Board, Revision Committee, Codification Committee, Arts & Culture Committee and Negotiation Committee for SNDA. He was also Commissioner of the Housing Authority of the Seminole Nation, Seminole Nation Development Authority Trustee, Tribal Liaison to the Congressional Code Talkers Medal the United States Mint and was selected by the General Council to be a speaker on behalf of the Seminole Nation of Oklahoma before the District Court of the United States in Washington, D.C. Johnson was a part of the authorship of many service oriented legislative laws during his tenure as council representative, and he is convinced that there are better days on the horizon. He has been featured in documentaries on Southeastern Native History televised on Discovery Channel, PBS & 60 minutes on CBS. Johnson worked for seven years in the tourism industry in South Florida and most recently as a Records Management Specialist for the Seminole Nation of Oklahoma prior to being elected Assistant Chief in August of 2013. He is also an ordained minister and serves as Associate Pastor of Indian Nations Baptist Church in Seminole. *Community activities*: Sorghum Day Festival grounds coordinator; Seminole Nation Day living history director; consultant for the National Park Service on Native American Projects. *Memberships*: Oklahoma Museum Assn; Oklahoma Historical Assn; Seminole Nation Historical Society. *Interests*: "I'm a Seminole Indian who makes and plays the Native flute. I also have an audio & video tape with recordings of Native flute music. I have worked with the Discovery Channel with the "How the West Was Lost" series. Time-Life magazine "The Southeastern Woodland Indians" project. Also made appearance at 1996 Olympic games in Atlanta."

JOHNSON, LYDIA (Battle Mountain Band of Te-Moak Western Shoshone)
(tribal chairperson)
Affiliation & Address: Chairperson, Te-Moak Band of Western Shoshone Indians of Nevada, 525 Sunset St., Elko, NV 89801 (775) 738-8889.

JOHNSON, MARYANNE (Eskimo)
(Alaskan village council president)
Affiliation & Address: President, Portage Creek Village Council, 1327 E. 72nd Ave., Unit B, Anchorage, AK 99515 (907)277-1105.

JOHNSON, MICHAEL R. (Umatilla)
(tribal council chairperson)
Affiliation & Address: Chair, Confederated Tribes of the Umatilla Indian Reservation, P.O. Box 638, Pendleton, OR 97801 (541) 276-3165. E-mail: michaelrjohnson@ctuir.com.

JOHNSON, PATRICIA LUCILLE PADDLETY (Kiowa) 1938-
(attorney)
Born October 22, 1938, Mountain View, Okla. *Education*: Oklahoma College of Liberal Arts, Chickasaw, BS, 1971; University of Oklahoma School of Law, JD, 1975. Resides in Oklahoma. *Affiliation*: Associate Magistrate, Bureau of Indian

Affairs, Code of Indian Offenses, Court, Anadarko, OK. *Community activities*: Indian Capital Baptist Church (member and teacher); Oklahoma Indian Rights Association; OK Indian Women Association. *Memberships*: OK Bar Association, 1975- (Minorities Law Committee, 1976); Federal Bar for the Western District of OK, 1975-. *Interests*: "I am interested in assisting young Indian people to achieve their life's goals, whether in Law or in any other field of training. I work extensively with our church in attempting to inspire and inform Indians in this area of the opportunities available to them. Alcoholism and drug related offenders make up the majority of my clients, and when I have the time, I counsel and encourage them."

JOHNSON, RENO (Apache)
(former tribal chairperson)
Affiliation: White Mountain Apache Tribal Council, P.O. Box 700, Whiteriver, AZ 85941 (602) 338-4346. *Other professional post*: Member, Council of Advisors, American Indian Heritage Foundation, Falls Church, VA.

JOHNSON, RONALD (Mdewankanton Sioux)
(former tribal president)
Affiliation & Address: Former President, Prarie Island Indian Community, 5636 Sturgeon Lake Rd., Welch, MN 55089 (651) 385-2554. E-mail: rjohnson@piic.org. Johnson has previously served as vice president & assistant secretary/treasurer of the Tribal Council. Serving as spokesperson for the tribe, he has testified before Congress on labor relations issues. Other professional post: Co-cair, National Congress of American Indian's Department of Homeland Security, Johnson also works with the State of Minnesota on Homeland Security to ensure that tribal concerns are recognized.

JOHNSON, SHEILA MEADOWS (Tsula Atsila)
(Southeastern Cherokee) 1949-
(arts-in-education teacher)
Born December 5, 1949, Collinsville, AL. *Education*: Jacksonville State University (AL), 1967-70 (major in art). *Principal occupation*: Arts-in-education teacher. *Address*: P.O. Box 227, Collinsville, AL 35961 (205) 524-2218. *Affiliation*: Alabama Arts Council, Dekalb County School System, Collinsville, AL. *Community activities*: North Alabama Cherokees (first vice-chief; tribal information & enrollment director; powwow & event coordinator); past president, Collinsville Business & Professional Association. *Memberships*: Indian Arts & Crafts Assn (member, Education & Enrollment Committee); Atlatl Native Arts Registry; Smithsonian National Museum of the American Indian (charter member). *Awards, honors*: Beloved Woman of the North Alabama Cherokees. *Interests*: "Serve as emcee of all tribal pow wows and events, and also emcee powwows for other tribes and groups in the Southeast. Coordinate may local festivals and school programs." *Biographical source*: Featured articles in "People & Places," published by Gadsden Times.

JOHNSON, SKALAABA HERBERT (Alabama-Coushatta of Texas)
(tribal second chief)
Affiliation & Address: Second Chief, Alabama Coushatta Tribe of Texas, 571 State Park Rd., Livingston, TX 77351 (936) 563-1100.

JOHNSON, SUSAN (Three Affiliated tribes/Aishinaabe)
(tribal relations program manager; field biologist)
Education: BS (Biology). Affiliation & Address: Regional Tribal Relations Manager, Forest Health Management, U.S. Forest Service, Rocky Mountain Region, 740 Simms St., Golden, CO 80401 (303) 275-5350. She works with tribal governments, tribal traditional & cultural practitioners, and Forest Service line and staff officers concerning natural & cultural resource management issues & opportunities in Colorado, Wyoming, South Dakota, Nebraska & Kansas. *Other professional post*: Chairperson, Society of Indian Government Employees (SAIGE), Washington, DC (board member, 2010-present).

JOHNSON, TADD (Bois Forte Ojibwe)
(director of department of American Indian studies)
Education: University of Minnesota Law School, JD, 1985. *Affiliation & Address*: Professor & Chair, Department of American Indian Studies, College of Liberal Arts, University of Minnesota, Duluth, 116 Cina Hall, 1123 University Dr., Duluth, MN 55812 (218) 726-6878. E-mail: tjohnson@d.umn.edu. *Other professional post*: Director, Master of Tribal Administration & Governance Program, Department of American Indian Studies, University of Minnsota, Duluth. *Past professional post*: He has served as a tribal administrator, a tribal attorney, a tribal court judge and has taught numerous courses on Federal Indian Law and American Indian History. From 1990-1995, he served as counsel & staff director to the United States House of Representatives Committee on Natural Resources in the Office of Indian Affairs and the Subcommittee on Native American Affairs. During the Clinton Administration, Professor Johnson was appointed by the President to chair the National Indian Gaming Commission. He has served as a faculty member of the National Judicial College, has served on the Board of the Minnesota Chamber of Commerce, and is co-producer & co-host of the PBS program "Native Report."

JOHNSON, TERROL DEW (Tohono O'odham)
(co-founder, president and CEO; artist)
Affiliation & Address: Co-Founder, President & CEO, Tohono O'odham Community Action, P.O. Box 1790, Sells, AZ 85634 (520) 383-4966. E-mail: tdewj@tocaonline.org. Terrol is a community leader, nationally recognized advocate for Native communities and a reknown artist. In 1996, he co-founded (with Tristan Reader) Tohono O'odham Community Action (TOCA), a grassroots community organization dedicated to creating positive programs based in the O'odham Himdag – the Desert People's Way. *Awards, honors*: In 1999, Terrol was named one of "America's top ten young community leaders" by the Do Something Foundation; In 2002, Terrol & Tristan were recognized as one of the Nation's top leadership teams when they received the Ford Foundation's Leadership for a Changing World Award. In 2009-10, he walked from Maine to Arizona as a part of The Walk Home: A Journey to Native Wellness, bringing awareness to the crisis of Diabetes in Native communiities and highlighting the ways in which communities have the capacity to create wellness by drawing upon their rich cultural traditions. As an artist, Terrol began learning to weave baskets in school when he was ten. He is now recognized as one of the top Native American Basketweavers in the U.S. His work is in the Smithsonian's National Museum of the American Indian and the Heard Museum. Today, he combines basketry with other media such as bronze castings & gourds. Terrol says, "My work reflects who I am as a person…my culture…my family…the desert."

JOHNSON, TONY (Chinook)
(tribal chairperson)
Affiliation & Address: Chairperson, Chinook Nation, P.O. Box 368, Bay Center, WA 98527 (360) 875-6670

JOHNSON, TROY R. 1940-
(professor, historian)
Born February 29, 1940, Wichita Falls, Tex. *Education*: San Diego State University, BA, 1986; UCLA, MA, 1989, PhD, 1993. *Principal occupation*: Professor, historian. *Address*: 555 Main Ave. #420, Long Beach, CA 90802 (310) 432-8721; 985-8703. *Affiliation*: Visiting professor, Native American Studies Program, University of California, Davis, Davis, CA, 1993-94; visiting research scholar, American Indian Studies Center, UCLA, Los Angeles, CA, 3/94-8/94; assistant professor, American Indian Studies Center, Dept. of History, California State University, Long Beach, CA, 1994-. *Military service*: U.S. Navy Retired (Lt. Commander), 1957-80 (Combat Action Ribbon, Vietnamese Service Medal; Vietnamese Presidential Citation; Navy Expeditionary Medal (Cuba). *Membership*: American Historical Society. *Interests*: American Indian history & culture, history of the American West, history of the 1960s. *Published works*: Master's Thesis, "Status of Adoption & Foster Home Placement of Indian Children Under the Indian Child Welfare Act (UCLA, 1988); book reviews, "American Indian Culture & Research Journal (UCLA, 1990-92); "Depression, Despair, and Death; Indian Youth Suicide," Looking Glass edited by Clifford Trafzer (San Diego University Press, 1991); editor, Proceedings of the First & Second Annual National Conference on Indian Child Welfare, "Indian Homes for Indian Children," & "Unto the Seventh Generation" (UCLA, 1991 & 1993); editor, Activism Poetry & Political Statements from Alcatraz: The Indian Voice (American Indian Studies Center, UCLA, 1994); associate editor, Native North American Almanac (Gale Research, 1993); associate editor, Chronology of the North American Indian (Gale Research, 1994); associate editor, Native American: A Portrait of a People (Visible Ink Press, 1994); article, with Joane Nagel, "The Indian Occupation of Alcatraz Island: Twenty-Five Years Later," in American Indian Culture & Research Journal, Nov. 1994); The Indian Occupation of Alcatraz Island and the Rise of Indian Activism (University of Illinois Press, 1995); editor, American Indian Activism: Alcatraz to the Longest Walk; editor, Contemporary Native American Political Issues; Red Power: The American Indians' Fight for Freedom, Second Edition, edited with Alvin M. Josephy, Jr. and Joane Nagel (University of Nebraska Press, 1999).

JOHNSON, VIRGIL W. (Goshute)
(tribal chairperson & administrator)
Affiliation & Address: Chairperson, Confederated Tribes of the Goshute Indian Reservation, P.O. Box 6104, Ibapah, UT 84034 (435) 234-1138. E-mail: goshutetribe@yahoo.com.

JOHNSON, WANDA (Paiute)
(former tribal chairperson)
Affiliation & Address: Chairperson, Burns Paiute Tribe, 100 Pasigo St., Burns, OR 97720 (541) 573-1910.

JOHNSON-JOCK, HEATHER (Jamestown S'Klallam)
(tribal secretary; traditional artist)
Affiliation: Jamestown S'klallam Tribe, 1033 Old Blyn Hwy., Sequim, WA 98382 (360) 683-1106. *Other professional posts*: Boeing Corp.; board member, Potlatch Fund in Seattle, WA; chair, JKT Art Board, Inc. *Past professional post*: Chair, Jamestown Community Network Board.

JOHNSTON, ROBERT (Comanche) 1953-
(lawyer)

Born January 28, 1953, Little Rock, Ark. *Education*: Wichita State University, BA, 1975; University of Oklahoma, College of Law, JD, 1978. *Principal occupation*: Lawyer. *Address*: 1330 Dorchester Dr., Norman, OK 73069. *Interests*: Indian law; oil & gas law; natural resources law. *Published work*: Whitehorn v. State: Peyote & Religious Freedom in Oklahoma (American Indian Law Review, Vol. V, No. 1, winter, 1977).

JOHNSTON, TYSON (Quinault)
(tribal vice chairperson)

Affiliation & Address: Vice Chairperson, Quinault Indian Nation, P.O. Box 189, Taholah, WA 98587 (360) 276-8211. E-mail: tjohnston@quinault.org.

JOJOLA, JOSEPH R. (*White Snow*) (Isleta Pueblo) 1945-
(electronics technician; craftsperson)

Born September 18, 1945, Albuquerque, N.M. *Education*: New Mexico State University, 1986-89; New York Regeants (New York, NY), BS, 1993. Principal occupation: Electronics technician. *Address*: P.O. Box A, White Sands M.R., NM 88002. *Affiliation*: Electronics technician, Army Research Laboratory, White Sands M.R., NM, 1989-. *Other professional posts*: Ammunition/explosives handler; owner of White Sands Photography; and craftsman of silversmithing & repair. *Military service*: U.S. Army Retired Master Sergeant/E-8 - 21 years active duty)12 years in Germany (Meritorious Service Medal; 7 Good Conduct Medals; 2 Army Commendation Medals: German & American Expert Marksmanship Badges; among others). *Community activities*: Mayor of White Sands Missile Range for two years. *Memberships*: Indian Arts & Crafts Association. *Awards, honors*: "I was honored in a Purification Ceremony in Dec. 1994 in the "Black Eye" clan. This consists of 4 days & 3 nights of total prayer & singing, no sleeping or eating (can drink). *Interests*: "I have traveled to approximately 17 countries in Europe and the Far East. I attend tribal functions when duty allows me to. I enjoy silversmithing and have taught all 5 of my children how to make Indian jewelry and they have successfully made themselves jewelry."

JOJOLA, TED (Isleta Pueblo) 1951-
(educator, administrator)

Born November 19, 1951, Isleta Pueblo, N.M. *Education*: University of New Mexico, BA; Massachusetts Institute of Technology, MA; University of Hawaii-Manoa, PhD (Political Science), 1982; University of Strasbourg, France, Certificate of International Human Rights Law, 1985. *Principal occupation*: Educator, administrator. *Address*: Route 6, Box 578, Albuquerque, NM 87105 (505) 277-3917. *Affiliations*: Internal planner, National Capital Planning Commission, Washington, DC, 1973; legal/historical researcher, Institute for the Development of Indian Law, Washington, DC, 1976; visiting research associate, Institute of Philippine Culture, Manila, 1977-78; visiting professor of urban planning, UCLA, 1984; professor of planning, University of New Mexico, Albuquerque, 1982-; director, Institute for Native American Development (INAD), Native American Studies Department, University of New Mexico, Albuquerque, 1982-95; Architecture Dept., University of New Mexico, Albuquerque, 1997-. *Other professional posts*: Consultant, Thurshun Consultants, Albuquerque, NM, 1980-; coordinator, Ethnic/Minority Directors' Coalition, 1983-; Apple Computer Corporation (Education Grants Program, 1986-); Museum of the American Indian Arts & Culture, State Museum of New Mexico, (Advisory Board, 1987-); New Mexico Architecture Foundation (advisory board, 1988-). *Major research*: Cohort Retention Study of Indian Students at UNM, 1973-84, 1985-; Preschool Computer Program in an Isolated American Indian Community, Education Grants Program, Apple Computer Corp., 1985-; On-site coordinator: "Headstart Classroom of the Future", U.S. Dept. of Health & Human Services, 1989 research involving the Isleta Pueblo Head Start Program along with two other sites in Michigan; Ethnographic Undercounts - 1990 Census, 1989, U.S. Census Bureau. Community activities: 9th Inter-American Indian Congress, Santa Fe, N.M. (U.S. organizing committee, 1985-); Zuni Tribal Museum, Zuni, NM (advisory board, 1985-); JOM/Indian Education Parent's Committee, Isleta Pueblo, N.M. (chair). *Memberships*: Native American Studies Assn. *Awards, honors*: Postdoctoral Fellow, American Indian Studies, UCLA, 1984; public grantee, Atherton Trust, Honolulu, 1976; recipient of Participant Award, East-West Center, Honolulu. *Interests*: My main interest lay in the notion of continued tribal survival, and the various and varying strategies that have ensued in the course of this struggle. Currently, I have been doing research in the notion of tribal (traditional) consensus making and its theoretical modeling toward the idea of using this mechanism for the integration of tribal policy in the regional development process. *Biographical source*: Who's Who in the West (Marquis, 1985-); (Marquis; Who's Who Among Young Emerging Leaders (Marquis, 1987). *Published works*: Memoirs of an American Indian House: The Impact of a Cross-National Housing Program on Two Reservations, 1976; Foreword and series editor, Irredeemable America: The Indians' Estate and Land Claims, Edited by Imre Sutton; Contributing editor, Wicazo sa Review (Eastern

Washington University, 1988-); foreword and series editor, Public Policy Impacts on American Indian Development; Modernization & Pueblo Lifeways: Isleta Pueblo, chapter in Pueblo Style & Regional Architecture (Van Nostrand Reinhold, 1989); many articles in various publications.

JOJOLA, TONY (*Thur-shun - Sunrise*) (Isleta Pueblo) 1958-
(artist, craftsperson)

Born August 11, 1958, Albuquerque, N.M. Education: Institute of American Indian Arts, AA, 1978; College of Santa Fe, BFA, 1983. *Principal occupation*: Artist, craftsperson. *Affiliation & Address*: Taos Glass Arts & Education, 1021 Salazar Rd., Taos, NM (505) 613-5848. Website: www.tonyjojola-tga.com. E-mail: tonyjojola-tga.com. *Other professional posts*: One/two day lectures/symposiums. Exhibitions: Indian Pueblo Cultural Center, Albuquerque, NM, 1979; Southern Plains Indian Museum, Anadarko, OK, 1988; Indian Pueblo Cultural Center, Albuquerque, NM, 1990; Milicent Rogers Museum, Taos, NM, 1993; numerous selected group exhibitions. *Awards, honors*: Most Innovative Artist, Red Cloud Indian Art Show, Browning, MT, 1984; Indian Market--SWAIA, Santa Fe, NM (Misc. Contemporary, 1985; Misc. Contemporary, 1st & 2nd Place, 1986; Misc. Contemporary, 3rd Place, 1988; Misc. Contemporary, 1989, Creative Excellence Award, 1991; 1st Place & Honorable Mention, 1992; 1st Place, Diversified Art Forms, 1993); among others. *Membership*: Southwestern Association of American Indian Affairs. Interests: Free-blown glass and cast sculptural work. *Biographical sources*: "Anthony Jojola," by Gail Bird, in Indian Market Magazine, August-1988; "Tony Jojola," by Suzanne Carmichael, in The Travelers Guide to American Craft, 1990; "Glass Artist Tony Jojola Looking for a Niche," by John Villani, in Pasa Tempo, Aug. 16, 1991; "Award Winning Glass Sculpture," by Irvin Borowsky, in Artists Confronting the Inconceivable, 1992; among others. Film: "Indian Market--A Winter Event," by Ms. Lena Carr, a SWAIA-sponsored Symposium filmed Dec. 9, 1988 (K-Karr Productions, Albuquerque, NM).

JOLIVETTE, ANDREW (Opelousa/Athakapa-Ishak; Choctaw)
(associate professor; writer, social/cultural critic)

Education: University of San Francisco, BA, MA (Ethnic Studies/American Indian Studies); University of California, Santa Cruz, MA, PhD (Sociology). *Affiliation & Address*: Associate Professor & former chair (2010-16), American Indian Studies Dept., Ethnic Studies & Psychology Bldg. 106, San Francisco State University, 1600 Holloway Ave., San Francisco, CA 94132 (415) 338-7062. E-mail: ajolivette@sfsu.edu. *Other professional posts*: Interim Executive Director, San Francisco American Indian Community Cultural Center for the Arts; adjunct professor, Dept. of Sociology, University of San Francisco; researcher, University of California, San Francisco on issues of racial violence; Board president of Speak Out – the Institute for Democratoc Education & Culture; board member of GLBT Historical Socety, San Francisco; and Board Vice Chair of the Data Center. Professor Jolivette serves as the tribal historian for the Atakapa-Ishak Nation located between southwest Louisiana and southeast Texas. He is a mixed-race studies specialist with a particular interest in Comparative Race Relations, the Urban Indian experience, Black-Indians, Creole studies, and mixed-race health disparities. *Awards, honors*: Recently completed a Ford Foundation Postdoctoral Fellowship through the National Academy of Sciences. *Published works*: Cultural Representation in Native America (AltaMira Press, 2006); Louisiana Creoles: Cultural Recovery & Mixed Race Native American Identity (Lexington Books, 2007); Obama and the Biracial Factor: The Battle for a New American Majority (University of Chicago Press, 2012); *Research Justice: Methodologies for Social Change (Policy Press July 2015); Indian Blood: HIV and Colonial Trauma in San Francisco's Two-Spirit Community (Indigenous Confluences Series, University of Washington Press, May 2016)*; recently edited a special volume of the American Indian Cultural & Research Journal (UCLA) entitled, "Indigenous Landscapes Post-Katrina: Beyond Invisibility & Disaster," which examines the state of Native American tribes & communities three years after Hurricane Katrina (8/08).

JONAITIS, ALDONA 1948-
(museum director)

Born Nov. 27, 1948. *Address & Affiliation*: Director, University of Alaska Museum (1993-present), 907 Yukon Dr., Fairbanks, AK 99775 (907) 474-7505. E-mail: ffaj@uaf.edu.; American Museum of Natural History, 1989-93; SUNY, Stony Brook, NY, 1977-89. *Memberships*: American Association of Museum, American Anthropological Association, NAASA. *Published works*: Art of the Northern Tlingit, 1986; From the Land of the Totem Poles, 1988; Chiefly Feasts: The Enduring Kwakiutl Potlatch, 1991; A Wealth of Thought: Franz Boas on Native American Art, 1995; Looking North, Art from the University of Alaska Museum, 1998; The Yuquot Whalers' Shrine, 1999.

JONES, BRANDON (Eastern Cherokee)
(tribal vice principal chief)

Affiliation & Address: Vice Principal Chief, Eastern Band of Cherokee Indians, Qualla Boundary, P.O. Box 455, Cherokee, NC 28719 (828) 497-7000.

JONES, CAROL FORBES (Cherokee)
(projects coordinator)
Education: University of Oklahoma, B.A. (Journalism). *Affiliation & Address*: Projects Coordinator (2004-present), Oklahoma Indian Affairs Commission, 4545 N. Lincoln Blvd., Suite 282, Oklahoma City, OK 73105 (405) 521-3828. Ms. Jones coordinates special projects such as OIAC's publications & events. *Past professional posts*: Indian Health Service; Dept. of Labor, Native American Employment & Training Programs; Administration for Native Americans; National Congress of American Indians; American Indian Institute, University of Oklahoma. While at the Institute, she wrote a training manual for Idaho State employees titled, "Native American Cultural Awareness of the Six Tribes of Idaho." *Awards, honors*: Two Outstanding Performance Awards for her service with Administration for Native Americans.

JONES, CARRIE (Ojibwe)
(former tribal chairperson)
Affiliation & Address: Former Chairperson, Leech Lake Band of Ojibwe, 190 Sailstar Dr. NW, Cass Lake, MN 56633 (218) 335-8200. E-mail: chairwoman.jones @llojibwe.org

JONES, DAN C. (Ponca)
(tribal chair; filmmaker & writer)
Affiliation & Address: Chairperson, Ponca Tribe of Oklahoma, 20 White Eagle Dr., Ponca City, OK 74601 (580) 762-8104. *Past professional post*: Director, Office of Environmental Management, Ponca Tribe. *Interests*: Filmmaker & writer; traditional straight dancer. Jones' television productions include "The World of American Indian Dance, which premiered on NBC in 2003. *Awards, honors*: In 2001, Dan was the co-host of The First Americans in the Arts awards ceremony, and produced the event's webcast; in 1993, he received the Museum Award from the Association of American Museums for a work produced by the new Smithsonian National Museum of the American Indian. *Published work*: Blood of Our Earth, his first book of poetry (University of New Mexico Press, 2005).

JONES, DENNIS PEBAAMIBINES (Ojibwe)
(Ojibwe language specialist)
Education: Lakehead University (Ontario, Canada), Native Teacher Education Program (NTEP) Teacher's Certificate, AA, 1982; Trent University (Ontario, Canada), BA, 1985; Master's of Indigenous Knowledge, Seven Generations Education Institute, MA, 2004. *Address & Affiliation*: American Indian Studies Department, University of Minnesota, Twin Cities Campus, College of Liberal Arts, 2 Scott Hall, 72 Pleasant St. SE, Minneapolis, MN 55455 (612) 624-1338. E-mail: jones112@umn.edu. *Interests*: Preservation & restoration of the Ojibwe language and culture. *Goal*: To develop & implement a total immersion Ojibwe Language program.

JONES, DORA (Timbisha Shoshone)
(tribal vice chairperson)
Affiliation & Address: Vice Chair, Timbisha Shoshone Tribe, 1349 Rocking W Dr., Bishop, CA 93514 (775) 572-3274. E-mail: dora.jones@timbisha.com.

JONES, GENEVIEVE "GINA" (Paiute)
(tribal chairperson)
Affiliation & Address: Chairperson, Big Pine Paiute Tribe of the Owens Valley, 825 S. Main St., P.O. Box 700, Big Pine, CA 93513 (760) 938-2003

JONES, GERALD J. (Port Gamble S'Klallam)
(tribal chairperson)
Affiliation: Port Gamble Business Committee, 31912 Little Boston Rd., NE, Kingston, WA 98346 (360) 297-2646.

JONES, HENRY G. (Haida)
(attorney)
Education: New Mexico State University, BA, 2001; SUNY Buffalo Law School, JD, 2004; Georgetown University Law Center, LLM, 2005. *Affiliation & Address*: Associate, Friedman Rubin, 1126 Highland Ave., Bremerton, WA 98337 (360) 782-4300. E-mail: hjones@friemanrubin.com

JONES, JAMES G. "JIM", MD (Lumbee) 1933-
(family physician)
Education: Wake Forest College, BS, 1955; Wake Forest College Bowman Gray School of Medicine, MD, 1958. Interns at Grady Hospital, Atlanta, GA. *Affiliation & Address*: (910) 259-5767; E-mail: drsjones@charter.net. *Past professional posts*: 1962, Begins practicing Family Medicine in Jacksonville, NC; 1974, Develops Family Medicine Program at East Carolina University's new medical school; 1976, Named chairman of the Department of Family Medicine at ECU; 1988, Named president of the American Academy of Family Physicians; 1994, Appointed the first executive director of the North Carolina Health Planning Commission; retires from ECU. Some of his most notable recognition is Past National Indian Physician of the Year & Past N.C. Family Physician of the Year. He is the Founding Chairman at the Department of Family Medicine ECU School of Medicine and Associate Dean of Rural Health ECU School of Medicine. He is Past President of both the N.C. and National Academy of Family Physicians, Past President AAFP Foundation, Past Member of American Board of Family Medicine, Professor of Family Medicine Emeritus UNC-CH School of Medicine, Honorary Doctorate UNC-Pembroke, Emeritus Member NCIOM & Former Director & member of the Board, N.C. Health Planning Commission.

JONES, JESSE E. (Wichita)
(tribal president)
Affiliation & Address: President, Wichita & Affiliated Tribes, P.O. Box 729, Anadarko, OK 73005 (405) 247-2425.

JONES, JIM L., JR. (Leech Lake Ojibwe)
(cultural resource director)
Affiliation & Address: Cultural Resource Director, Minnesota Indian Affairs Council, 3801 Bemidji Ave. NW, Suite 5, Bemidji, MN 56601 (218) 755-3223. E-mail: jim.jones@state.mn.us *Past professional post*: Part owner & business manager for All Nations Cultural Resource Preservation, Inc.

JONES, MRS. JAMES L. (Caddo)
(museum director)
Affiliation: Caddo Indian Museum, 701 Hardy St., Longview, TX 75604 (214) 759-5739.

JONES, JOHANNA
(Indian education coordinator)
Affiliation & Address: Coordinator, Office of Indian Education, Idaho State Department of Education, 650 W. State St., P.O. Box 83720, Boise, ID 83720 (208) 332-6968. E-mail: jjones@sde.idaho.gov. *Past professional post*: Professor & Director, Idaho State University, Native American Academic Services, Pocatello, ID.

JONES, JOHN PAUL (Choctaw/Cherokee) 1941-
(architect)
Born in Okmulgee, Oklahoma on July 24, 1941. *Education*: University of Oregon, BA (Architecture), 1967. *Affiliation & Address*: Partner, Jones & Jones Architects & Landscape Architects, 105 S. Main St., Suite 300, Seattle, WA 98104 (206) 624-5702. E-mail: info@jonesandjones.com. Mr. Jones' designs have won widespread acclaim for their reverence for the earth, for paying deep respect to regional architectural traditions & native landscapes, & for heightening understanding of indigenous people & cultures of North America. Johnpaul has led the design of numerous cultural centers and museums with tribes spanning the North American continent, culminating in his 12-year engagement as overall lead design consultant for the Smithsonian's National Museum of the American Indian on the Mall in Washington, D.C. *Awards, honors*: A Fellow in the American Institute of Architects, his designs have won a stream of local and national awards. In 2006, Johnpaul received the AIA Seattle Medal, conferred by the Seattle Chapter of the American Institute of Architects, for his leadership in design. He was also the recipient of the 2006 Executive Excellence Award from the American Indian Science & Engineering Society (AISES). In 2005, Johnpaul returned to receive the University of Oregon Distinguished Service Award from his alma mater for "not just designing buildings, but creating places that incorporate both the practical and the spiritual, and for heightening human sensitivity to cultural and environmental issues." *Presentations*: 2008, October 1. "Creating Places that Incorporate the Practical & the Spiritual Heightening Human Sensitivity to Cultural Environmental Issues. Speech presented at the Leading Change 2008: Blending Indigenous & Western Planning Tools, APA Indingenous Planning Conference, Anchorage, Alaska. 2008. "Stand in Our Ways & Beliefs." Presentation for Construction in Indian Country. Fort McDowell, AZ.

JONES, JUSTIN (Navajo)
(senior government affairs rep.)
Affiliation: BHP Billington, 300 W. Arrington St., Suite 200, Farmington, NM 87401 (505) 598-4337. E-mail: anccsb@hotmail.com. *Membership*: Americans for Indian Opportunity. *Interests*: Environment, legal issues, education, governance, language retention.

JONES, MIGUEL "LUKE" (Pamunkey/Chickahominy/Cherokee)
(U.S. EPA region director)
Education: Rutgers University, BA (Political Science), 1991; Junior Year Abroad at the University of Haifa, Israel, 1988-89; founded the Rutgers Organization for Native American Culture (1989-91), & was appointed to the Rutgers Organization for the Healing of Racial Prejudice, 1991; Indian University's School of Public & Environmental Affairs, MPA, 1996. *Affiliations*: Director, U.S. EPA Region 5 Indian Environmental Office, Chicago, IL, 2005-present, overseeing the delivery of EPA programs & services to 35 federally recognized tribal governments in the Great Lakes region; chair, American Society for Public Administration Section on Intergovernmental Administration & Management Tribal Relations Work Group. *Other professional post*: Board

member, SAIGE (Society for American Indian Governmental Employees), Washington, DC. *Past professional posts*: National Tribal Environmental Council, Albuquerque, NM, 1996-97; Native American Consultants, Washington, DC, 1997-99; U.S. EPA Office of Solid Waste (OSW) tribal program, 1999-2003; American Indian Environmental Office, 2003-2005. *Memberships*: National Congress of American Indians; member, American Political Science Assn's Indigenous Studies Network Coordinating Council.

JONES, MIKE (Zuni)
(tribal enterprise manager)
Affiliation: Pueblo fo Zuni Arts & Crafts, P.O. Box 425, Zuni, NM 87327 (505) 782-5531. *Products*: Zuni jewelry, pottery, fetishes; contemporary art.

JONES, PATRICK STANFIELD (Tsalagi {Cherokee}) 1957-
(musician, singer/songwriter, arranger/composer)
Born March 23, 1957, Teaneck, NJ. *Principal occupation*: Musician, singer/songwriter, arranger/composer. *Address*: 35 Main St., Nyack, NY 10960 (914) 348-0446. *Affiliation*: Performs with Sylvester Brothers & solo compositions. *Membership*: Nuyagi Keetoowah Society.

JONES, PETER B. (Onondaga-Seneca) 1947-
(potter/sculptor)
Born June 8, 1947, Cattaraugus Indian Reservation, N.Y. *Education*: Institute of American Indian Arts; Archie Bray Foundation (Helena, MT). *Principal occupation*: Potter/sculptor. *Address*: P.O. Box 174, Versailles-Plank Rd., Versailles, NY 14168 (716) 532-5993. *Exhibitions*: Peter B. Jones Retrospective Exhibition (1965-90), Iroquois Indian Museum, Schoharie, NY, 1990; Pottery Through the Ages: Traditions in Clay, Pueblo Grande Museum, Phoenix, AZ, 1990; Contemporary Native Ceramics, CN Gorman Museum, University of California, Davis, 1991; New Works in Ancient Traditions, Shoestring gallery, Rochester, NY, 1991; Creativity in Our Tradition: Three Decades of Contemporary Indian Art, Institute of American Indian Arts, Santa Fe, NM, 1992; Reflecting Contemporary Realities, Los Angeles, County Folk Art & Craft Museum, 1993; Art of First Nations, Brantford, Ontario, 1993; Area Artists Collection 1993 Members Gallery, Albright-Knox Art Gallery, Buffalo, NY, 1993. *Permanent collections*: Indian Arts & Crafts Board, U.S. Dept. of the Interior, Washington, DC; Institute of American Indian Arts, Santa Fe, NM; Heard Museum, Phoenix, AZ; Everson Museum, Syracuse, NY; Iroquois Indian Museum, Howes Cave, NY; Southern Plains Indian Museum, Anadarko, OK; Rochester Museum & Science Center, Rochester, NY; New York State Museum, Albany; Museum of Fine Arts Boston, MA. *Awards, honors*: Div. Award, Best of Class, Scottsdale (AZ) Native American Cultural Foundation, 1987 & 1988; Best of Show, Festival of Iroquois Arts, Cattaraugus Indian Reservation, NY, 1989; Excellence in Iroquois Arts, Iroquois Indian Museum, Howes Cave, NY, 1990; Best of Show, Quinnehtukqut Native American Festival, E. Hartford, CT, 1992. Works featured in the books & periodicals: Southwest Art, Sept. 1988, Vol. 18 No. 4, "Contemporary Native American Ceramics"; Beyond Tradition-Contemporary Indian Art and Its Evolution by Jerry & Lois Jacka (Northland Press, 1988); Peter B. Jones, Iroquois Art, Retrospective Catalogue, Iroquois Indian Museum, Howes Cave, NY; Winds of Change, Fall 1991, Vol. 6 No. 4, "Reflections of a Native Vision: American Indian Contemporary Art" by Ray Moisa.

JONES, ROSALIE (*Daystar*) (Pembina Chippewa)
(instructor in Indgenous studies)
Born on the Blackfeet Reservation in Montana. *Education*: Fort Wright College, BFA (Music major), 1964; University of Utah, MS (Music minor), 1968. Thesis: The Blackfeet Medicine Lodge Ceremony: Ritual & Dance. Postgraduate: Julliard Scool, New York City, 1969-70. *Affiliation & Address*: Music & Dance Instructor, Department of Indigenous Studies, Trent University, 1600 Westbank Dr., Peterborough, ON K9J 7B8, GC Room 324 (705) 748-1011 x7921. E-mail: rosaliejones@trentu.ca. Website: www.daystardance.com. *Production Film*: The Sun Dance, 1968.

JONES-FLOOD, DEIRDRE (Washoe)
(tribal vice chairperson)
Affiliation & Address: Vice Chairperson, The Washoe Tribe of Nevada & California, 919 U.S. Hwy. 395 South, Gardnerville, NV 89410 (775) 265-8600 E-mail: deirdre.flood@washoetribe.us..

JORDAN, DERRIL B. (Mattaponi) 1958-
(attorney)
Education: Temple University, BA (cum laude), 1979, MSW, 1980; Cornell Law School, JD, 1987 (Lawyers Cooperative Publisher's Award for Academic Achievement in American Indian Law). *Affiliation & Address*: Founder, Jordan Law Offices PLLC, 1730 Rhode Island Ave. NW, Suite 501, Washington, DC 20036 (202) 223-0893. Specializes in tribal government, tribal sovereignty & self-determination; gaming law, land-into-trust; land claims; tribal codes & economic development. Mr. Jordan has practiced Federal Indian law since 1987, working as an in-house attorney, Associate Solicitor for Indian Affairs, and in private practice. Mr. Jordan's career as a lawyer has been dedicated to

the representation of Indian tribes and tribal organizations and the promotion of tribal sovereignty. Mr. Jordan has served as an in-house tribal attorney for the Saginaw Chippewa Indian Tribe where he advised the Tribal Council and various tribal boards, committees, & staff on a variety of issues, including economic development activities, the Indian Gaming Regulatory Act ("IGRA"), and Constitution & Corporate Charter amendments. He also worked for the Seneca Nation of Indians, including as an Assistant Attorney General & then as Attorney General, serving as the primary legal adviser to the Nation's President and Council, and General Enterprises and Gaming Enterprises. He also represented the Nation before Nation Courts and Federal & State courts. His work in private practice focuses on the representation of Indian tribal governments & other Native American clients. Mr. Jordan regularly represents tribal clients before executive agencies of the Federal government, Congress and the courts. Mr. Jordan regularly represents tribal clients before the National Indian Gaming Commission on ordinance approvals, management and development contract issues, and Indian land determinations. He also advises tribes about class III gaming compact issues, questions regarding tribal jurisdiction over Indian country, land claims, historic & cultural preservation, and in many other areas. *Past professional posts*: Partner, Stetson & Jordan, P.C., Washington, DC; Of Counsel, Fredericks Peebles & Morgan, LLP, 2008-present; In-house tribal attorney for the Saginaw Chippewa Tribe; attorney general for the Seneca Nation of Indians; 1997-2000, Associate Solicitor for Indian Affairs, U.S. Dept. of the Interior, Bureau of Indian Affairs drafting legislation & testifying before congressional committees. He also provided legal advice to the Office of the Secretary and the Indian Water Rights Office. Mr. Jordan worked on tribal gaming matters under IGRA, including class III gaming compact approvals, off-reservation trust land acquisitions for gaming purposes & "Indian land" determinations under Section 20 of IGRA. Mr. Jordan also consulted with the Department of Justice on litigation strategy in Indian law cases pending in the federal courts, including the United States Supreme Court, & provided advocacy for Department of Interior and tribal interests with other Executive branch agencies (Agriculture, HUD, Commerce, and others).

JORDAN, KURT
(assistant professor)
Affiliation & Address: Dept. of Anthropology & American Indian Program - Cornell University, 210 McGraw Hall, Ithaca, NY 14853 (607) 255-3109. E-Mail: kj21@cornell.edu. *Interests*: Iroquois archaeology & history; 18th century Iroquois communities, political economy, colonialism & cultural entanglement.

JORDAN, SUE ZANN (Mescalero Apache) 1959-
(teacher)
Born December 17, 1959. *Education*: University of Illinois, BA, 1979; Sangamon State University, MA, 1983. *Address & Affiliation*: Teacher, Chapter I Coordinator (1984-present), Cibecue Community School, Cibecue, AZ, 85911 (602) 332-2444. *Other professional post*: Part-time teacher, Northern Pioneer College. *Membership*: Arizona Media Association. *Awards, honors*: State of South Dakota Poetry Award & money certificate; Golden Poet Award, World of Poetry. *Interests*: Poetry, art, music, education, earth science, literature, woodworking, graphic arts, ceramics, weaving, & horticulture. "(I) traveled extensively in North & South America and less extensively overseas." *Published works*: Poetry, too numerous to list.

JORGENSEN, MIRIAM R.
(research director)
Education: Swarthmore College, BA; University of Oxford, MA; Harvard University, MPP, PhD. *Affiliation & Address*: Research Director, Harvard Project on American Indian Economic Development (and its sister program, the Native Nations Institute at the University of Arizona), JFK School of Government, 79 JFK St., Cambridge, MA 02138 (617) 495-1480. E-mail: miriam_jorgensen@harvard.edu. *Other professional post*: Research director & instructor, Native Nations Institute for Leadership, Management & Policy, Udall Center for Studies in Public Policy, The University of Arizona, 803 E. First St., Tucson, AZ 85719 (520) 626-0664. E-mail: mjorgens@u.arizona.edu. *Research Interests*: Her areas of specialty are Indigenous governance & economic development, with a particular focus on the ways communities' social & cultural characteristics affect development. *Past professional posts*: Visiting scholar, Washington University Schools of Law & Social Work; instructor in economics at Harvard University & Washington University; former member, Swarthmore College Board of Managers. *Published works*: Editor & co-author, Rebuilding Native Nations: Strategies for Governance & Development (University of Arizona Press, 2007); co-author, The State of the Native Nations: Conditions Under U.S. Policies of Self-Determination (Oxford University Press, 2008); numerous articles & chapters.

JOSE, VERLON M. (Tohono O'odham)
(tribal vice chairperson)
Affiliation & Address: Vice Chairperson, Tohono O'odham Nation, P.O. Box 837, Sells, AZ 85634 (520) 383-2028.

JOSEPH, ANDREW C. (Colville)
(museum director/curator)
Affiliation & Address: Director/Curator, Colville Confederated Tribes Museum, P.O. Box 233, Coulee Dam, WA 99116 (509) 633-0751.

JOSEPH, ANDREW, JR. (Colville)
(tribal council member)
Affiliation & Address: Council member, Confederated Tribes of the Colville Reservation, P.O. Box 150, Nespelem, WA 99155 (509) 634-2208. E-mail: andy.joseph@colvilletribes.com. *Other professional posts*: Chairperson, Northwest Portland Area Indian Health Board, Portland Area Representative, National Indian Health Board, Washington, DC.

JOSEPH, DAROLD H. (Hopi)
(lecturer in Indigenous studies)
Education: Northern Arizona University, BS, M.Ed; University of Arizona, PhD. *Affiliation & Address*: Lecturer, Applied Indigenous Studies Department, SBS West Bldg. 70, Rm. 98, P.O. Box 15020, Flagstaff, AZ 86011 (928) 523-7179; E-mail: darold.joseph@nau.edu Mr. Joseph joined the Applied Indigenous Studies family in the Fall of 2014 and specializes in Disability & Psychoeducational Studies with an emphasis on Language, Reading, and Culture. Through a cultural, historical, and institutional lens, his current research explores concepts of resilience, persistence, and cultural identity, and their impact in the stories of American Indian Students pursuing higher education with and without Disabilities.

JOSEPH, FREDERICKA (*Evening Star*) (Kaw/Cherokee)
(BIA program manager)
Affiliation: Special Emphasis Program Manager (1998-present), BIA Equal Employment Opportunity, Washington, DC. *Other professional post*: Secretary, Society of American Indian Government Employees (SAIGE), P.O. Box 7715, Washington, DC 20044 (202) 564-0375. *Past professional post*: U.S. Dept. of Defense (1986-98), in the social service field. *Awards, honors*: Received several Meritorious Service Awards along with numerous Certificates of Appreciation, and was awarded an Army coin for her work with the Army in the performance of her duties as the Acting Family Advocacy Program Manager.

JOSEPH, JILLENE (Gros Ventre)
(executive director)
Education: BS (community health education). *Affiliation & Address*: Executive Director, Native Wellness Institute, 2830 SE Cleveland Dr., Gresham, OR 97080 (503) 666-7669. E-mail: jillene@nativewellness.com. *Other professional post*: Lead consultant trainer, National Indian Child Welfare Association's Positive Indian Parenting curriculum. *Past professional post*: Director, Northwest Portland Area Indian Health Board's Project Red Talon for ten years providing HIV prevention & health services to NW tribal communities.

JOURDAIN, FLOYD "BUCK", JR. (Ojibwe)
(former tribal chairperson)
Affiliation & Address: Red Lake Band of Ojibwe Indians, P.O. Box 550, Red Lake, MN 56671 (218) 679-3341.

JUAREZ, DEBORA G. (Blackfeet)
(attorney)
Education: Western Washington University, BA (Federal Indian Law/Tribal Law, with minor in Anthropology), 1983; University of Puget Sound School of Law, JD, 1987. *Address & Affiliation*: Of Counsel, Williams, Kastner & Gibbs, PLLC, Two Union Square, 601 Union St., Seattle, WA 98101-2380 (206) 628-6781. E-mail: djuarez@williamkastner.com. *Practice areas*: Education Indian Law & Gaming; Law Legislative & Government Affairs; Tribal Sports & Entertainment. Her practice focuses on providing legal & financial counsel to tribes in the areas of debt financing, corporate structure, economic development, natural resources, gaming, tribal-state inter-local agreements, among others. At the firm, she has created a Tribal Finance Group that provides financial advice & planning tailored to the needs of tribal governments & enterprises. *Other professional posts*: Extensive public speaking on Indian law & policy issues. *Past professional posts*: King County Public Defender; Evergreen Legal Services, Native American Project - where she represented a majority of Washington's 29 tribes in such areas as treaty rights, natural resources, Indian Child Welfare, & economic development; appointed a Judgeship to the King County Superior Court; Executive Director, Governor's Office of Indian Affairs, Olympia, WA. There she worked extensively with both state & tribal governments regarding economic diversity & initiated the Tribal Economic Vitality Initiative (TEVI). The TEVI Project culminated in a historic tribal-state economic development study entitled, "The Tiller Report." *Memberships*: Washington State Bar Assn (trustee, Indian Law Section); American Indian Bar Assn; Northwest Indian Bar Assn (founding member, vice-president); Washington State Hispanic Bar Assn (founding board member); United Indians All Tribes Foundation (board member); Alesek Institute, Native American Economic Development Corporation (Fellow). *Awards, honors*: Ms. Juarez was named to "Super Lawyers," by Washington

Law & Politics magazine; she was named one of the "Top Lawyers" of 2007 by Seattle Magazine; in June 2007, she was honored with the "Enduring Spirit Award" by the Native Action Network for her lifetime achievements in bettering Native American communities. In 2012, Debora was selected by her peers for inclusion in "The Best Lawyers in America," in the area of Native American Law; Also, she was awarded the Alumni Service Award by the Seattle University School of Law Alumni Association in 2013.

JUDD, CYNTHIA 1952-
(business owner)
Born August 19, 1952, Roswell, N.M. *Education*: Southwestern Business College, 1986. *Principal occupation*: Business owner. Resides in Albuquerque, NM (505) 271-1981. *Affiliation*: American Heritage Indian Arts, Albuquerque, NM, 1990- (owner of authentic Indian-made warbonnet factory). *Membership*: Indian Arts and Crafts Association. *Awards, honors*: "Warbonnets took 1st, 3rd & 4th prizes at the New Mexico State Fair - under Indian art. All of my employees are Native Americans."

JUDKINS, RUSSELL ALAN 1944-
(anthropologist)
Born August 8, 1944, Salt Lake City, Utah. *Education*: Brigham Young University, BS, 1966; Cornell University, PhD, 1973. *Address*: 142 W. Buffalo St., Warsaw, NY 14569 (716) 245-5277. *Affiliation*: Associate professor, Department of Anthropology (1972-), State University of New York, College, Geneseo, NY 14454 (716) 245-5277. *Memberships*: American Anthropological Association (Fellow); Northeastern Anthropological Association; Society for Medical Anthropology; American Folklife Society; New York Folklore Society; Rochester Academy of Science. *Interests*: Social & cultural anthropology; symbolism; medical anthropology; American Indians (Iroquois & Catawba); migration and resettlement; folklore & mythology; American Indian worldview; American Indian intellectuals. *Biographical source*: American Men & Women of Science. *Published works*: Iroquois Studies, 1987; First International Scholars Conference on Cambodia, 1988; Handbook for Archival Research in the Dr. Charles Bartlett Iroquois Collection, 1989 (all published by Papers in Anthropology, SUNY College at Geneseo); book: Lewis Henry Morgan's League of the Iroquois: the Ethnographic Core (Persimmon Press, 2004).

JUMPER, MOSES, JR. (*Shem pa he gee*) (Florida Seminole) 1950-
(tribal associate justice)
Born January 4, 1950, Fort Lauderdale, Fla. *Education*: Haskell Indian Jr. College, AA, 1971; University of Tampa; Bacone College; Oklahoma Panhandle State University. *Affiliation & Address*: Associate Justice, Seminole Tribe, Big Cypress Reservation, c/o 6300 Stirling Rd., Hollywood, FL 33024 (863) 983-9234. *Affiliation*: Recreation director, Seminole Tribe of Florida, Hollywood, FL. *Other professional posts*: Recreation director, coach; cattleman & writer. *Community activities*: Education Board of Florida. *Memberships*: President, Native American Sports Association; Native American Youth Organization. *Awards, honors*: Writers Award in Kansas from writers organization; Photo Award in Hollywood; Best Poem Award in Hollywood, FL; Who's Who in Poetry Award - numerous films & documentaries. *Biographical source*: Seminole Tribune. *Published work*: Echoes in the Wind: Seminole Indian Poetry (Seminole Tribe, 1990); Osceola, Patriot & Warrior (Raintree Steck-Vaugh, 1993).

JUMPER-THURMAN, PAMELA (Western Cherokee)
(senior research scientist, project director)
Affiliation & Address: Director, CA7AE: HIV/AIDS Prevention Project, Ethnic Studies Dept., 356 Aylesworth Hall SE, Colorado State University, Fort Collins, CO 80523 (303) 491-0251. E-mail: pamela.thurman@colostate.edu.

JUMPING EAGLE, SARA, M.D. (Oglala Lakota)
(pediatrician; assistant professor & instructor)
Born & raised in Kyle, SD. *Education*: Stanford University School of Medicine, M.D. Pediatrics Residency & Adolescent Medicine Fellowship at Denver Children's Hospital & The University of Colorado Health Sciences Center. *Affiliation*: Clinical Assistant Professor, Department of Pediatrics, University of North Dakota's School of Medicine, Bismarck, ND; Instructor, Center for American Indian & Alaska Native Health, University of Colorado's School of Public Health. *Other professional post*: Pediatrician & Clinical Director for the Standing Rock Indian Health Service in Fort Yates, North Dakota. *Medical interests*: Sexually transmitted infections, teen pregnancy prevention, & mental health issues among American Indian youth. Currently, she is conducting research on the prevention & screening for sexually transmitted infections among American Indian youth & young adults. Past professional post: Sara worked in the Adolescent & Pediatrics Departments at Denver Children's Hospital and served as a Pediatrician at Denver Indian Health and Family Services. She has conducted research with the University of Colorado. She formerly worked as a private practice pediatrician at the Mid Dakota Clinic and Saint Alexius Hospital in Bismarck, North Dakota. Her medical interests include adolescent medicine, reproductive health, behavioral health and the prevention of high-risk behaviors among youth.

JUNEAU, CAROL (Mandan & Hidatsa)
(association chairperson)
Education: Eastern Montana College, B.A. (Psychology); University of Montana, M.A. (Educational Administration), 1980. *Address*: Box 55, Browning, MT 59417. *Affiliation*: Chairperson, Montana Indian Education Association (MIEA), P.O. Box 848, Harlem, MT 59526 (406) 353-2205. *Other professional post*: Montana State Representative (D-Browning). She was active in the development of Tribal Colleges & served as the first president of Blackfeet Community College. *Awards, honors*: Recognized as one of six of the state's first National Milken Educators in 1993; received the Distinguished Alumni Award from MSU-Billings in 2000; Educator of the Year, MIEA; and a National Education Award from the NEA.

JUNEAU, DENISE (Hidatsa-Mandan/Blackfeet)
(Indian education specialist)
Born April 5th in Oakland, Calif. *Education*: Montana State University, BA; Harvard Graduate School of Education, EdM. *Principal occupation*: Indian education specialist. *Address & Affiliation*: Office of Public Instruction, P.O. Box 202501, Helena, MT 59620 (406) 444-3013. E-mail: djuneau@state.mt.us. *Memberships*: National Indian Education Assn; Montana Indian Education Assn; Montana Assn of Teachers of English & Language Arts; American Education Research Association.

JUSTICE, DANIEL HEATH (Cherokee; Canadian)
(professor of Aboriginal studies)
Education: University of Northern Colorado, BA; University of Nebraska, MA & PhD. *Affiliation & Address*: Associate Professor & Chair, First Nations Studies Program, The University of British Columbia, 1866 Main St., Buchanan E266, Vancouver, BC V6T 1Z1 Canada (604) 822-2905. E-mail: Daniel.justice@ubc.ca*Past professional posts*: Chairperson, First Nations Studies Program, University of British Columbia, Vancouver, BC Canada. Held the Canada Research Chair in Indigenous Literature & Expressive Culture. Professor of Aboriginal Literatures, Centre for Aboriginal Initiatives, University of Toronto, ON Canada. Website: *Published works*: Our Fire Survives the Storm: A Cherokee Literary History (University of Minnesota Press, 2005); The Way of Thorn & Thunder: The Kynship (2005), Wyrwood (2006), Dreyd (2007) Chronicles (Kegedonce Press, 2005-07) (revised & updated; University of New Mexico Press, 2011); co-editor with James H. Cox, The Oxford Handbook of Indigenous American Literature (forthcoming).

K

KAHN, FRANKLIN (Navajo) 1934-
(artist)
Born May 25, 1934, Pine Springs, Ariz. *Education*: Stewart Indian School. *Address*: 4 N. Leroux St., Flagstaff, AZ 86001 (602) 774-0174. *Affiliation*: Sketch artist & sign painter, Federal Sign and Signal Corp., Flagstaff; co-owner with Mary Jane Kahn, Turquoise Hogan, Flagstaff, AZ. *Membership*: American Indian Service Committee. *Awards, honors*: Second Prize, Scottsdale National Indian Art Show. *Interests*: Watercolor & oil painting; Indian designs & symbols. *Published work*: Illustrator, Going Away to School (BIA, 1951).

KAHN, KENNETH (Chumash)
(tribal chairperson)
Affiliation & Address: Chairperson, Santa Ynez Band of Chumash Indians, P.O. Box 517, Santa Ynez, CA 93440 (805) 688-7997. *Past professional post*: Secretary-Treasurer of Santa Ynez Band.

KALAFATIC, CAROL
(associate director-American Indian Program)
Affiliation: Associate Director, American Indian Program, Cornell University, 425 Caldwell Hall, Ithaca, NY 14853 (607) 255-4184. E-mail: cfk23@cornell.edu. *Interests*: Indigenous Peoples' rights advocacy & self-directed sustainable development, with a focus on strengthening our food & agriculture systems, our food sovereignty and our use of renewable energy resources; Indigenous People's film & video.

KALT, JOSEPH P.
(project co-director; professor emeritus)
Born in Tucson, Ariz. *Education*: Stanford University, BA (Economics), 1973; MA (1977) & PhD (1980) (Economics), UCLA. *Address & Affiliation*: Ford Foundation Professor of International Political Econmy, The John F. Kennedy School of Government, and co-director of The Harvard Project on American Indian Economic Development, Harvard University, Kennedy School of Government, 79 JFK St., Cambridge, MA 02138 (617) 495-4966. E-mail: joe_kalt@harvard.edu. *Other professional post*: Ford Foundation Professor of International Political Economy (Emeritus), Harvard Kennedy School, Harvard University, Cambridge, MA; visiting professor at The University of Arizona's Eller College of Management, 2005-present; faculty chair for nation building programs at the Native Nations Institute, The University of Arizona, Tucson,

AZ; Trustee of the White Mountain Apache Tribe's Fort Apache Heritage Foundation. *Past professional posts*: Advisor, Royal Commission on Aboriginal Peoples; mediator of disputes between tribes and the U.S. government; has testified on behalf of numerous tribes in federal & tribal courts and before the U.S. Senate Committee on Indian Affairs. *Published works*: Co-editor (with Stephen Cornell) of "What Can Tribes Do? Strategies & Institutions in American Indian Economic Development"; Harvard's Project, "The State of the Native Nations."

KAMKOFF, DAN (Eskimo)
(executive director)
Affiliation & Address: Executive Director, Northwest Intertribal Court System, 20818 44th Ave. West, Suite 120, Lynnwood, WA 98036 (425) 774-5808. E-mail: dank@nics.ws.

KAMPER, DAVID
(professor of American Indian Studies)
Education: UCLA, MS, 1998, PhD (Anthropology), 2003. *Affiliation & Address*: Associate Professor & Chair, Department of American Indian Studies, AL325, San Diego State University,, San Diego, CA 92182 (619) 594-8081. E-mail: dkamper@mail.sdsu.edu. *Past professional post*: Assistant Professor of Anthropology, Northeastern Illunois University. *Published works*: Indian Gaming: Who Wins?, with Angela Muliis (American Indian Studies Center, UCLA, 2000); American Indian Sovereignty & Law: An Annotated Bibliography (American Indian Studies Center, UCLA, 2000); The Work of Sovereignty: Tribal Labor Relations & Self-Determination at the Navajo Nation (School for Advanced Research Press, Santa Fe, NM, 2010).

KAN, SERGEI A. (Shaakunastoo & Gunaak'w) 1953-
(professor of anthropology & Native American Studies)
Born March 31, 1953, Moscow, Russia. *Education*: Moscow State University; Boston University, BA, 1976; University of Chicago, MA, 1978, PhD, 1982. *Affiliation & Address*: Professor of Anthropology & Native American Studies (1989-present), Native American Studies Program, Dartmouth College, 315 Silsby, Anthropology, 201 Sherman House HB 6047, Hanover, NH 03755 (603) 646-2550. E-mail: sergei.a.kan@dartmouth. Edu. *Past professional posts*: Assistant professor of anthropology, University of Michigan, Ann Arbor, 1983-89. *Other professional post*: Editorial Board, "Journal of Ethnohistory." Community activities: Native American Council, 1989-; Hood Museum of Art (acquisitions committee, 1989-93; director's advisory council, 1990-91); faculty advisory committee, Institute of Arctic Studies, 1989-; Dartmouth Fellow, Research Program for the Comparative Study of Intergroup Conflict in Multinational States, 1991-94; faculty representative, Foundation for Jewish Life at Dartmouth, 1992-; Alaska Native Brotherhood, 1979-. *Memberships*: American Anthropological Assn; American Ethnological Society; American Society for Ethnohistory; Alaska Anthropological Assn; American Assn for the Advancement of Slavic Studies; International Arctic Social Science Association. *Awards, honors*: Heizer Award for the Best Article in Ethnohistory by the American Society for Ethnohistory, 1987; American Book Award for "Symbolic Immortality," awarded by the Before Columbus Foundation, 1990. *Interests*: Ethnographic field research in southeastern Alaska since 1979 (intermittent); extensive archival research on Tlingit history & culture, since 1979; history of American & Russian anthropology; Russian anthropologists & the indigenous peoples of Siberia. *Published works*: Translated & edited, Tlingit Indians of Alaska, by Fr. A. Kamenskii (U. of Alaska Press, 1985); Symbolic Immortality: Tlingit Potlatch of the 19th Century (Smithsonian Press, 1989); Memory Eternal: Tlingit Culture & Russian Orthodox Christianity Through Two Centuries (U. of Washington Press, 1999); edited volume (that includes Dr. Kan's essay): Strangers to Relatives: Adoption and Naming of Anthropologists in Native North America (U. of Nebraska Press, 2001); numerous articles.

KANE EDWIN (White Mountain Apache)
(finance director)
Affiliations: Finance Director, Yavapai-Apache Nation, Camp Verde, AZ (520) 567-1007. E-mail: ya125@yavapai-apache-nation.com; First V.P.-Board of Directors, Native American Finance Officers Association, P.O. Box 12743, Green Bay, WI 54307.

KANJI, RIYAZ
(attorney)
Education: Harvard College, BA, 1986; Yale University Law School, 1991. *Affiliation & Address*: Founding Member, Kanjo & Katzen PLLC, 303 Detroit St. #400, Ann Arbor, MI 48104 (734) 769-5400. E-mail: rkanji@kanjikatzen.com. Riyaz's present practice encompasses a wide variety of issues of central importance to the preservation & enhancement of tribal sovereignty, including vindication of tribal jurisdictional & taxation authority, Indian gaming and other economic development matters, treaty hunting & fishing rights, land claims, and environmental protection. For example, Riyaz served as lead counsel for the Grand Traverse Band of Ottawa & Chippewa Indians in its successful trial and appellate efforts regarding the legality of its Turtle Creek Casino served as

lead litigator for the National Congress of American Indians and a coalition of Indian nations in successful efforts to require stricter federal regulation of mercury emissions by coal-fired power plants has served as lead counsel for the Seneca Nation in successful, ongoing efforts to protect the integrity of its court system from state interference, to preserve its sovereign immunity, and to vindicate its sovereign powers over its lands was the lead author of the amicus brief on tribal-state cooperation that NCAI, NIGA and tribes across the country filed in the Supreme Court in *Inyo County v Paiute-Shoshone Indians of the Bishop Community*, 538 U.S. 701 (2003) co-authored the brief filed by NCAI regarding Congress' ability to vindicate tribal sovereignty in *United States v. Lara*, 541 U.S. 193 (2004) has testified before both Houses of Congress on matters of vital importance to Indian nations across the country, including the land-into-trust process & efforts to legislate a *Carcieri* fix is actively involved in a variety of legislative discussions & efforts, including those directed at reducing the terrible epidemic of domestic violence in Indian country *Tribal Supreme Court Project*: In addition to significant trial successes on behalf of the firm's clients, Riyaz is frequently sought out as specialist counsel or as a consultant to Indian nations and their attorneys on matters of Supreme Court and appellate practice because of his special expertise in those areas. He is passionate about the work of the NCAI-NARF Tribal Supreme Court Project and its role in protecting tribal sovereignty. He played an active part in the formation of the Project and has devoted hundreds of hours of pro bono time to its work. He especially enjoys assisting Indian nations in defeating efforts by the federal government, States, & private parties to have the Supreme Court review lower court decisions favorable to tribal interests.

KAPAYOU, EVERETT (Mesquakie)
(singer)
Address: 713-320th St., Tama, IA 52339 (515) 484-2453. A member of the Mesquakie tribe in Iowa, Everett is respected as a distinguished tribal elder and religious devotee and for his commanding knowledge of Mesquakie history. He is a singer of traditional Mesquakie songs and a 1993 recipient of the National Heritage Fellowship from the Folk Arts Program of the National Endowment for the Arts.

KAPLAN, LAWRENCE
(professor of linguistics)
Affiliation & Address: Professor & Director, Alaska Native Language Center, 425 Brooks, University of Alaska, P.O. Box 757680, Fairbanks, AK 99775 (907) 474-6582. E-mail: ldkaplan@alaska.edu. Lawrence works as a linguist with the Inupiaq Eskimo language, spoken in northern Alaska. Dr. Kaplan is compiling dictionaries of Inupiaq as well as working on texts & grammatical explanations for the language. He is involved with training Inupiaq language & culture instructors.

KARNES, CHRISTOPHER A. (Tuscarora) 1969-
(attorney)
Born in 1969, Maryland. *Education*: Dartmouth College, BA, 1991; American University, JD, 1994. *Office Address*: Dorsey & Whitney LLP, 1001 Pennsylvania Ave., NW, Suite 300 South, Washington, DC 20004 (202) 824-8800. E-mail: karns.christopher@dorseylaw.com. *Affiliations*: U.S. Dept. of the Interior, Office of the Solicitor, Division of Indian Affairs, 1994-98; Attorney, Dorsey & Whitney LLP, 1998-. Associate in the Indian and Gaming Law practice group at Dorsey & Whitney since 1998. Practices in the areas of Federal Indian law, and gaming law.

KAROL, SUSAN V., M.D. (Tuscarora)
(physician; former IHS chief medical officer)
Education: Dartmouth College, BA (Biology); Medical College of Wisconsin, MD; Clinical Fellow in Surgery, Massachusetts General Hospital; Chief Resident & General Surgery Residency, University of Massachusetts Medical Center; General Surgery Resident, St. Mary's Hospital & Medical Center. *Past professional posts*: Lt. Commander, USPHS, IHS, & Chief of Surgery & Anesthesia, Shiprock Indian Hospital, Shiprock, NM, 1988-90; Medical Director, The Hunt Breast Center, Hunt Hospital, Danvers, MA, 1991-2008; founded Essex Surgical Associates, PC, Beverly, MA, 2004; Chief of Surgery, Beverly Hospital, Beverly, MA, 1996-2008. In 1988; Chief Medical Officer (2008-15), Indian Health Service, DHH, Rockville, MD. Dr. Karol provided medical advice & guidance to the Office of the Director & staff on American Indian & Alaska Native health care policies & issues. She served as the primary liaison & advocate for IHS field clinical programs & community-based health professionals. *Awards & honors*: Susan was the first woman of the Tuscarora Indian Nation to become a surgeon. In 1996, she was the first woman to be made chief of surgery at Beverly Hospital in Beverly, Mass.

KARSHMER, BARBARA
(attorney)
Education: UCLA School of Law, 1973. *Affiliation & Address*: Barbara Karshmer, P.C., 765 Market St., Suite 28F, San Francisco, CA 94103 (415) 615-0201. E-mail: barbara@karshmerindianlaw.com Barbara is committed to

Indian self-determination and to providing Indian tribes and tribal organizations with the highest quality of legal services. Ms. Karshmer has practiced exclusively in the area of Indian law for more than thirty-five years and has extensive Indian law experience. Since 1975, she has achieved substantial legal and legislative victories for her firm's clients in a broad range of cases and issues arising in Indian Country. Ms. Karshmer's experience involves representation of tribes & tribal organizations in Indian self-determination matters, self-governance, gaming, health law, water law, environmental issues, employment law, commercial and corporate matters, energy issues, jurisdictional conflicts, development of tribal constitutions and codes, and a wide variety of other matters involving tribes and tribal organizations. Ms. Karshmer is honored to be able to assist Indian tribes and tribal organizations in determining their own needs and in making educated decisions about their futures. In doing so, she strives to recommend the most practical and cost-effect solutions to any problems the clients may encounter. She plans to remain an effective advocate for the Indian community based on her experience of more than 35 years.

KASAYULIE, WILLIE (Akiachak Yup'ik Eskimo) 1951-
(administrator)
Born June 1, 1951, Fairbanks, Alaska. *Address*: P.O. Box 70, Akiachak, AK 99551 (907) 825-4813. *Affiliations*: Chairperson & CEO, Akiachak IRA Council, Akiachak, AK, 1984-; chairperson, Association of Village Council Presidents (AVCP), Box 219, Bethel, AK, 1985-. *Other professional posts*: Chair, Akiachak Limited, 1989-90; member, BIA Tribal Task Force, 1990-. *Military service*: Alaska Army National Guard (discharged in 1990 with the rank of 1st Lt.). *Community activities*: Chair, Yupiit School District, 1985-; Alaska Federation of Natives (Board member, 1991-). *Memberships*: Alaska Native Coalition (chairperson, 1985-); board member, Native American Rights Fund, 1990-. *Awards, honors*: 1985 AFN Citizen of the Year; 1987 CEDC Tribal Leadership Award. *Interests*: "I travel promoting self-sufficiency & self-determination for the Yup'ik Eskimo." *Biographical source*: Life Magazine (Feb. 1986).

KATCHENAGO, LINDA MOHAWK (Stockbridge-Munsee Mohican)
(tribal administrator)
Affiliation & Address: Executive Director, Stockbridge-Munsee Community Band of Mohican Indians, P.O. Box 70, Bowler, WI 54416 (715) 793-4355. E-mail: linda.katchenago@mohican-nsn.gov

KATZEN, PHIL
(attorney; Native American practice)
Education: University of California, Berkeley, BA (Political Science), 1970; UC Berkely School of Law, JD, 1977. *Affiliation & Address*: Founding member, Kanji & Katzen, PLLC, 401 2nd St. S., Suite 700, Seattle, WA 98104 (206) 344-8100. E-mail: pkatzen@kanjikatzen.com. Phil is a founding member of Kanji & Katzen and he serves as the firm's Managing Attorney. During law school he also served as a law clerk in the Oakland office of California Indian Legal Services. Past professional posts: Phil was a staff attorney with the Native American Project of Evergreen Legal Services (which became Columbia Legal Services) from 1978 through 1999; he was also the Project Director from 1986 to 1992. His primary responsibility with the Native American Project was representation of up to 13 Indian tribes in *United States v. Washington*, the long-running treaty fishing rights case, where he frequently served as a lead or coordinating counsel for the plaintiff tribes, including a leading role in vindicating the tribes' treaty rights to regulate salmon harvests, to a fair share of the salmon, to take a fair share of shellfish from public and private property, and to protect the habitat necessary to fulfill the tribes' treaty rights to take fish. He continued to represent many of the plaintiff tribes in the treaty fishing and shellfishing rights litigation when he left legal services and opened his own office in 1999, where he remained until founding Kanji & Katzen in 2000. *Areas of Concentration*: Phil continues his involvement in *United States v. Washington* and other treaty rights cases and he continues to be coordinating counsel in the ongoing litigation over implementation of the tribes' treaty shellfishing rights, including on privately owned property. Phil also represents and consults with tribes on matters related to tribal rights to fish, hunt and gather, protection of natural resources, taxation, & jurisdiction, both in litigation and before state and federal administrative agencies, including the Federal Energy Regulatory Commission, the Environmental Protection Agency, the Bonneville Power Administration, and the Army Corps of Engineers. *Community Service and Personal Interests*: Phil serves on the board of the non-profit Western Environmental Law Center and he serves as a guest lecturer at law schools and universities and as a speaker at continuing legal education seminars.

KAUFFMAN, CARLOTTA (*According to Coyote*)
(actress)
Address: P.O. Box 3085, Payson, AZ 85547. She tells Plains Indian Coyote stories in theatrical form...a combination of traditional storytelling and modern drama suitable for all ages. A one-person, one act play.

KAUFFMAN, HATTIE (Nez Perce) 1960-
(network television correspondent)
Education: University of Minnesota, B.S., 1981; Graduate School of Journalism, University of Minnesota, 1983. *Affiliations*: Reporter & weekend anchorwoman, KING TV, Seattle, Wash. (1981-87); reporter, Good Morning America, ABC-TV, New York, NY (1987-1990); correspondent, CBS This Morning, The Early Show, Los Angeles, CA (1990-present). *Awards, honors*: WCCO-TV Minorities in Broadcasting Scholarship for her graduate studies at the University of Minnesota; received four Emmy Awards for her reporting on KING-TV in Seattle. Ms. Kauffman is the only Native American correspondent featured on a national network, covering national issues.

KAVANAGH, THOMAS W.
(museum curator)
Affiliation & Address: Curator of Collections, William Hammond Mathers Museum, Indiana U., Bloomington, IN. *Published work*: The Comanches: A History, 1706-1875.

KAVASCH, MS. E. BARRIE (Cherokee/Creek/Powhatan)1942-
(author, artist, ethnobotanist, food historian)
Born December 31, 1942, Springfield, Ohio. *Education*: Western Connecticut University. *Address*: 324 Main St. South, Bridgewater, CT 06752 (860) 354-3128. *Affiliations*: President & Founder of The Medicine Wheel Wellness Center, Bridgewater, CT. *Other professional posts*: Guest lecturer on numerous college campuses and at museums; curator of the "Native Harvests: Plants in American Indian Life" Exhibition for SITES-Smithsonian, 1984-87. *Memberships*: Association on American Indian Affairs; Native American Rights Fund; Byelorussia American Society. *Awards, honors*: O'Connor Lecturer at Cornell Plantations, Cornell University, Ithaca, NY, Oct. 1992; Cullum Lecturer at Augusta College, Augusta, GA, Oct. 1992. *Interests*: Ms. Kavasch has traveled, researched, and lectured through much of North & Central America, and has worked with & written about numerous Native American Indian tribes & interest groups. She has done extensive ethno-botanical research, especially food & medicinal documentation. She writes, photographs & illustrates, as well as collects & presses plant specimens, while documenting diverse herbal/healing knowledge. "I have completed a new book on Native American Healing for a major publisher, as well as books on American Indian plants & people, along with several children's books for young readers. *Biographical sources*: American Indian Foods: A Harvest of American Indian Specialties" in Bon Appetite, Nov. 1987; "A Native Thanksgiving: American Indian Cooking" in Cooks Magazine, Nov. 1984; "My Grandmother's Hands" in Through the Kitchen Window (Beacon, 1997); and "Wild Things: Wild Foods" in Martha Stewart Living, March 1996. *Published works*: Native Harvests: Recipes & Botanicals of the American Indians (Random House, 1979); Herbal Traditions: Medicinal Plants in American Indian Life (SITES: Smithsonian Institution, 1984); Botanical Tapestry (Gunn Historical Museum, 1979); Guide to Eastern Mushrooms, 1982, Introducing Eastern Wildflowers, 1982, and Guide to Northeastern Wild Edibles, 1981 - full color photographic guide books - (Hancock House/Big Country Books); American Indian Cooking (Native Harvests, 1991); Earthmaker's Lodge: Native American Folklore, Activities, Foods (Cobblestone Press, 1994); Enduring Harvests: Native American Foods & Festivals for Every Season (IUniverse, 1995); "Native Northeastern Foods & Healing" (chapter) in Enduring Traditions (Greenwood Press, 1995); A Student's Guide to Native American Genealogy (Oryx Press, 1996); American Indian Earthsense: Herbaria, Ethnobotany & Ethnomycology (IAIS, 1996); American Indian Healing Arts (Bantam, 1999); The Medicine Wheel Garden (Bantam, 2002); The Mound Builders of North America (IUniverse, 2004); 2 books of poetry, "Hands of Time," and Ancestral Threads.".

KAWENNIIOSTA BOOTS (Onondaga-Iroquois)
(museum intern)
Affiliation & Address: School of American Research, P.O. Box 2188, Santa Fe, NM 87504 (505) 995-1924. E-Mail: boots@sar.com. *Other professional posts*: Intern, Iroquois Indian Museum, 1995; Carnegie Museum (Pittsburgh), 1995. *Memberships*: American Association of Museums; AIES; SWAIA.

KAZHE, CHRISTINA V. (Navajo/Mescalero Apache)
(attorney)
Education: University of California, Davis, BS, 1993; University of California, Berkeley, Boalt Hall School of Law, JD, 1996. *Address & Affiliation*: Monteau & Peebles, LLP, 1001 Second St., Sacramento, CA 95814 (916) 441-2700. E-mail: ckazhe@ndnlaw.com. *Practice areas*: Trial advocacy; tribal government; tribal sovereignty & self-determination; taxation; reservation economic development; ICWA; gaming law; environmental & cultural preservation; appellate advocacy. Past professional posts: Litigation Associate, Morrison & Foerster LLP, San Francisco, CA, 1997-2001. *Awards, honors*: UCD 2004 Young Alumni Award; Charles P. Gould Award for community service; UCD Outstanding Woman Graduate Class of 1993. *Memberships*: American Bar Association, Native American Bar Association, Sacramento County's Women Bar Association, Federal Bar Association. *Community activities*: Board of Directors, American Indian Child Resource Center, Oakland, CA.

KEAMS, GERALDINE (GERI) (*Yithaazbah'*) (Navajo) 1951-
(actress, storyteller, writer)
Born August 19, 1951, Winslow, Ariz. *Education*: University of Arizona, BFA, 1978. *Principal occupation*: Actress, storyteller, writer. *Address*: 2767 Butter Creek Dr., Pasadena, CA 91107. *Affiliation*: President, Hozhoni Productions, Hollywood, CA (film, video, theatre productions). *Other professional posts*: Navajo storyteller presents songs and stories of her people. Dramatizes legends and myths. She's on tour with Los Angeles Music Center on Tour. *Community activities*: Board of Advisors, ATLATL, a Native American arts organization, Native American Television; promoted Native Americans in film, video, media. *Memberships*: National Association for the Preservation & Perpetuation of Storytelling (NAPPS), 1989-; Screen Actors Guild, 1970-; American Indian Registry for the Performing Arts (board member, 1988-90; president, board of directors, 1990-91). *Awards, honors*: Bahti Award - Outstanding American Indian Student, University of Arizona; recipient of a Los Angeles Cultural Affairs Traditional Arts Grant. *Interests*: "Began performing at 7 years old; co-starred in, "Outaw Josie Wales," with Clint Eastwood; appearances in "Northern Exposure," "Twin Peaks." Storyteller featured at the National Storytelling Festival in Jonesborough, Tenn, St. Louis, Miami, and Smithsonian Discovery Theatre for Children Institute's, Washington, DC; San Francisco Storytellers on Tape Series, 1993. Featured on television shows, "Nickelodeon," & "Sesame Street": traveled as a storyteller throughout he U.S., Canada & Europe." *Published works*: Children's book - Grandmother Spider Steals the Sun (Northland Press, 1995); Poet Anthologies - "A Gathering of Spirits," 1985, "When Clouds Threw This Light," 1983, "Circle of the Moon."

KEESWOOD, LARRY (Dine-Navajo) 1954-
(silversmith)
Born January 26, 1954, Shiprock, N.M. *Education*: High school. *Principal occupation*: Silversmith. *Address*: P.O. Box 210, Kingston, MA 02364 (508) 830-1256. *Affiliation*: Native Expressions (Native fine arts store-jewelry smithing), Plymouth, MA. *Other professional post*: Machinist. *Interests*: Attends powwows; rodeos, basketball, fishing, reading, creating dream catchers, antique jewelry, Native American music, horses, dancing, and singing at the drum when invited to do so

KECKLER, KENTON (Cheyenne River Sioux)
(CPA, NAFOA secretary)
Affiliation: CPA, Kenton Keckler & Co., P.C., Santa Fe, NM 87505 (505) 955-0747. E-mail: cpaskk@cs.com. *Other professional post*: Secretary, Native American Finance Officers Assn, P.O. Box 12743, Green Bay, WI 54307.

KECKLER, KEVIN, SR. (Cheyenne River Sioux)
(tribal council memner)
Affiliation & Address: Council member, Cheyenne River Sioux Tribe, P.O. Box 590, Eagle Butte, SD 57625 (605) 964-4155. *Past tribal post*: Chairperson.

KEEL, JEFFERSON (Chickasaw)
(tribal lt. governor; NCAI president)
Affiliation & Address: Lieutenant Governor, Chickasaw Nation, P.O. Box 1548, Ada, OK 74821 (580) 436-2603. Mr. Keel often assists tribes & other groups in cultural & historic preservation activities. *Other professional posts*: Director of Social Services & Special Assistant for Cultural Affairs, Chickasaw Nation; Board President, National Congress of American Indians (NCAI), Washington, DC; commissioner, Tribal Law & Order Commission; member, Board Advisors of the Center for Native American Youth; member, Self-Governance Advisory Committee, the National Indian Child Welfare Association Board of Directors, and the Health Research Advisory Council for the Department of Health & Human Services' Office of Minority Health. *Past professional posts*: Chair, Indian Health Service Policy Advisory Committee; chair, Centers for Disease Control Tribal Consultation Advisory Committee; chair, Department of Justice Tribal Advisory Group. *Military service*: U.S. Army (20+ years active duty; Vietnam Vet, Airborne Ranger with two Purple Hearts, the Bronze Star with "V" for valor, and the Army Commendation Medal with valor; served as an instructor in the elite Army Rangers.)

KEELER, BRADFORD R. (Cherokee)
(treasurer, board of directors)
Affiliation & Address: Treasurer, Board of Directors, Association on American Indian Affairs, 966 Hungerford Dr., Suite 12-B, Rockville, MD 20850 (240) 314-7155.

KEELER, DONNA LC (Eastern Shoshoni)
(executive director)
Education: University of South Dakota, BS (Business/Journalism). *Affiliation & Address*: Executive Director (1978-81; 2002-present), South Dakota Urban Indian Health, Inc. , 711 N. Lake Ave., Sioux Falls, SD 57104 (605) 339-0420. *Past professional post*: SD Social Services (Medicaid/TANF), 1981-2002.

KEEN, TAYLOR R.M. (Cherokee)
(professor of Native American studies)
Education: Dartmouth College, BA; Harvard University, MBA, MPA. *Affiliation & Address*: Instructor, Native American Studies Program, Department of Sociology, Anthropology, and Social Work, College of Arts & Sciences, Creighton University, 2500 California Plaza, Room 437, Omaha, NE 68178 (402) 280-3587. E-mail: taylorkeen@creighton.edu. A member of the NAS Advisory Board, Taylor teaches a seminar entitled, Nation Building, focusing on tribal sovereignty & institutional development. A former member of the Council of the Cherokee Nation, he was Vice President of Cherokee Nation Enterprises, Inc., and was the project leader in the $80MM Phase 1 development of the Cherokee Casino and Resort near Tulsa, Oklahoma. *Past professional posts*: Mr. Keen has served as a Christian Johnson Fellow as a part of the Harvard Project on American Indian Chamber of Commerce of Olahoma. *Published work*: Co-author of the article, "Tribal Sovereignty & Economic Development," published recently for the Smithosonian Institution's Handbook of the American Indian.

KEGG, MATTHEW M. (Chippewa) 1953-
(teacher)
Born October 5, 1953, Brainerd, Minn. *Education*: Bemidji State University, BA, 1976. Resides in Minnesota. *Affiliations*: Graduate assistant, Indian Studies Program, Bemidji State University, 1980-81; teacher, Mille Lacs Indian Reservation, Onamia, MN, 1981-. *Awards, honors*: Recipient of Certificate of Appreciation from State Dept. of Education of Minnesota, 1980, for contributions to Indian education; Most Valuable Player award from hockey team, Bemidji Northland Icers, 1980. *Interests*: "Hockey; published several articles in magazines; poetry; outdoor activities - camping, backpacking, canoeing, biking."

KEHOE, ALICE BECK 1934-
(professor of anthropology)
Born September 18, 1934, New York, N.Y. *Education*: Barnard College, BA, 1956; Harvard University, PhD, 1964. *Address*: 3014 N. Shepard Ave., Milwaukee, WI 53211 (414) 962-5937. *Affiliations*: Assistant professor of anthropology, University of Nebraska, 1965-68; professor of anthropology, Marquette University, Milwaukee, WI, 1968-2000. *Memberships*: American Anthropological Association; Society for American Archaeology; American Society for Ethno-history. *Interests*: Cultural anthropology & archaeology; fieldwork among Blackfoot, Cree and Dakota tribes in the U.S. & Canada; archaeological fieldwork in Montana & Saskatchewan; ethnographic fieldwork in Montana, Alberta, Saskatchewan, and Bolivia. *Published works*: Hunters of the Buried Years (Regina, Sask. School Aids & Text Book Co., 1962); North American Indians (Prentice-Hall, 1981; 2nd ed. 1992; 3rd Ed. 2006); The Ghost Dance (Holt, Rinehart & Winston, 1989); Humans: An Introduction to Four-field Anthropology (Routledge, 1998); The Land of Prehistory: A Critical History of American Archaeology (Routledge, 1998); Shamans & Religion: An Anthropological Exploration in Critical Thinking (Waveland, 2000); America Before the European Invasions (Longman, 2002); The Kensington Rumestone: Approaching a Research Question Holistically (Waveland, 2005); The Ghost Dance: Ethno-history & Revitalization, 2nd Ed. (Waveland Press, 2006); Archaeology: Concise Introduction, 2007; Controversies in Archaeology, 2008.

KELIN, ZACKEREE S. (Caddo)
(attorney)
Education: School for International Traing (Melbourne, Australia), Multicultural Society Program, Fall 1999; Cornell College, BS (Political Science), 2001; Univesity of Iowa College of Law, JD, 2005. *Affiliation & Address*: Founder/Attorney, Kelin Law Firm, PC (2009-present), 1309 Rio Grande Blvd. NW, Albuquerque, NM 87104 (505) 507-9310. E-mail: z.kelin@kelinlaw.com. *Other professional post*: Of Counsel, Stetson & Jordan, P.C., Albuquerque, NM; member, Board of Directors, Tribal Business Opportunities, Inc., Albuquerque, NM. Kelin was a managing attorney for DNA-Peoples Legal Services, Inc. ("DNA"), the oldest & largest poverty law program in Indian Country. His work at DNA focused on representing indigent clients, tribes & non-profits before tribal, state, and federal courts and various administrative & legislative bodies in the areas of poverty law, Indian law, sacred sites protection, and environmental law. While in law school, Zackeree clerked for the Native American Rights Fund and the Winnebago Tribe of Nebraska. He is also a graduate of the Gerry Spence Trial Lawyers College, a member of the Board of Directors for the New Mexico Bar Association's Indian Law Section, and served as an advisor on the Native American Domestic Policy Committee for the Obama Campaign. He was recently awarded the National Center for American Indian Economic Development's "Native American 40 under 40," an award given to emerging & existing Native American leaders for their contributions to Indian Country. He is also "Of Counsel" for the Stetson Law Offices, P.C., www.stetsonlaw.com.

KELLER, LORRAINE (Paiute)
(former tribal chairperson)
Affiliation & Address: Chairperson, Reno-Sparks Indian Colony, 98 Colony Rd., Reno, NV 89502 (775) 329-2936. E-mail: lkeller@rsic.org.

KELLEY, ALAN (Ioway)
(tribal vice chairperson)
Affiliation & Address: Vice Chairperson, Iowa Tribe of Kansas & Nebraska, 3345 B Thrasher, White Cloud, KS 66094 (785) 595-3347. E-mail: akelley@iowas.org

KELLEY, JOSEPH E.
(executive director)
Affiliation & Address: Executive Director, Consortia of Administrators for Native American Rehabilitation (CANAR), 176 Martin Loop, Winnfield, LA 71483 (318) 413-7318. E-mail: jkelley@canar.org.

KELLY, BOB (Nooksack)
(tribal chairperson)
Affiliation & Address: Chairperson, Nooksack Tribe, P.O. Box 157, Deming, WA 98244 (360) 592-5176. E-mail: bkelly@nooksack-tribe.org.

KELTON, PAUL
(associate professor of history & department chair)
Education: University of Tulsa, BA, 1992; University of Oklahoma, PhD, 1998. *Affiliation & Address*: Associate Professor & Chairperson, Department of History, University of Kansas, Lawrence, KS 66045 (785) 864-9450. E-mail: pkelton@ku.edu. *Other professional post*: Adjunct Faculty, Global Indigenous Nations Studies, University of Kansas, Lawrence, KS. Professor Kelton's primary interests are indigenous peoples of North America, environmental, and Early American history. *Published works*: Chapter, The Great Southeastern Smallpox Epidemic, in Transformation of the Southeastern Indians, 1540-1760, ed. Ethridge & Hudson (U. of Mississippi Press, 2002); book, Epidemics & Enslavement: Biological Catastrophe in the Native Southeast (University of Nebraska Press, 2007); working title, Cherokee Medicine/ Colonial Germs: An Indigenous Nation and Introduced Diseases, 1518-1839 (forthcoming).

KENDALL-MILLER, HEATHER R. (Athabascan)
(attorney)
Education: University of Alaska, Fairbanks, BA (History), 1988; Harvard University Law School, MA & JD, 1991. *Affiliation & Address*: Staff Attorney (1994-present), Native American Rights Fund (NARF), 745 West 4th Ave. Suite 502, Anchorage, AK 99501 (907) 276-0680. Other professional post: She serves on the boards for Harvard University's Honoring Nations Program and The Wilderness Society. Kendall-Miller was lead counsel for both appeals (to the U.S. Circuit Court and to the U.S. Supreme Court) of the landmark cases State of Alaska v. Native Village of Venetie and Katie John v. Norton. Asked what the most important current challenges and issues faced by Native lawyers, she said, "Climate change presents a daunting challenge to Native Americans whose customary and traditional way of life is intimately connected to the land. We also face challenges preserving our rights in the courts in part because the current Supreme Court has little regard for tribal sovereignty, Indian canons of construction, or treaty rights." *Past professional posts*: Staff attorney, Sonosky, Chambers, Sasche & Miller in Anchorage, Alaska & Washingto, DC; from 1992-94, Heather was a Skadden Fellow working as a staff attorney for the Alaska Legal Services Corporation and also worked for NARF as a research attorney. Her civic activities include serving on the Honoring Nations Advisory Board of the Ford Foundation and a board member of the Alaska Conservation Foundation; former chair of the Indian Law Section of the Alaska Bar Association (1996-97) and served on the Alaska Supreme Court Committee on Fairness & Access to the Judicial System (1997).

KENNEDY, CHERYLE A. (Confederated Tribes of Grand Ronde)
(tribal councilperson)
Affiliation: Council member (former chairperson), Confederated Tribes of the Grand Ronde, 9615 Grand Ronde Rd., Grand Ronde, OR 97347 (503) 879-5211. E-mail: tribalcouncil@grandronde.org. *Other professional posts*: Grand Ronde health director for almost 15 years; executive director, Northwest Portland Area Indian Health Board; current commissioner on the State Commission on Indian Services; current member, Oregon Health Improvement Plan Board; currently active in tribal health, culture & royalty committees. *Memberships*: National Congress of American Indians; Affiliated Tribes of Northwest. *Awards, honors*: Health Administrator of the Year Award from the Indian Health Service's Dept. of Public Health; Outstanding Leader in Health Care Award from the Oregon State Dept. of Health.

KEOHANE, JEFFREY
(attorney)
Education: Stanford University law School, JD, 1997. *Affiliation & Address*: Associate, 4340 Redwood Hwy., Suite E352, San Rafael, CA 94903 (415) 491-

2310. E-mail: jeff@gformanlaw.com Jeff represents tribal governments & corporations in litigation, commercial, economic development, environmental, and tax law matters. *Past professional posts*: Associate, Holland & & Knight & Karshmer & Associates; EPA Office of General Counsel, Washington, DC During the six years at EPA, he was a designated national expert in Indian law, international indigenous rights, civil rights & environmental justice. *Awards, honors*: Gold Medal for Exceptional Service, EPA's highest honor.

KEPLIN, DEBBIE L. (Turtle Mountain Chippewa) 1956-
(general manager-radio station)
Born February 28, 1956, Belcourt, N.D. *Education*: Flandreau Indian School, 1974; University of North Dakota (two years liberal arts instruction). *Principal occupation*: Public radio station general manager. *Address*: P.O. Box 236, Belcourt, ND 58316. *Affiliation*: General manager, KEYA Radio Station, Belcourt, ND. *Other professional posts*: Occupied positions at KEYA radio of program director, news director, music director, and executive secretary. *Community activities*: Member, St. Ann's Society, Belcourt, ND; assistant-religious education, St. Anthony's Catholic Church, Belcourt; member, Turtle Mountain Musicians; member, Turtle Mountain Historical Society. *Memberships*: National Association of Female Executives, 1985-; Corporation for Public Broadcasting-National Public Radio (authorized representative). *Awards, honors*: Certificate of Native American Leadership Training by the Community Council of the Northern Plains Teacher Corps, Nov. 1979 & Feb. & April, 1980; Certificate of Training-Explosive Devices Training by the U.S. Dept. of the Interior, Sept., 1984; dedicated service to the KEYA Radio Station and the Belcourt community by Turtle Mountain Community School, Nov., 1985; for community service by Turtle Mountain Band of Chippewa Indians, Feb., 1985. *Interests*: "To promote and educate the local community and surrounding communities on the history and culture of the Turtle Mountain Band of Chippewa through the use of radio. To develop programs focusing on problems affecting the local community, such as alcoholism, unemployment, housing, recreation, etc. To encourage the training of high school students in the operation of broadcast facilities-radio." *Programs produced*: All Nations Music, 1980- (features traditional & contemporary Native American music, legends and stories); Memorial to James Henry, former chairman of Turtle Mountain Band of Chippewa, 5-minute piece aired nationally on radio series First Person Radio of Minn. in Sept., 1983; Music of the Turtle Mountains, 1985- (program features the talents & biographies of local artists, musicians and poets); the music of Floyd Westerman, Sr. Mary Anthony Rogers, many local fiddlers, Adella & Gilbert Kills Pretty Enemy, 1985- (program features biographical sketches of artists through interview and music selections).

KERN, JOHN A.
(attorney; chief judge)
Education: University of Michigan, BA, 1993; Vermont Law School, MS (Environmental Law), 1999, JD, 1999. *Affiliation & Address*: Chief Judge (2011-present), Grand Traverse Band of Ottawa & Chippewa Indians, 2605 N. West Bay Shore Dr., Peshawbestown, MI 49682 (231) 534-7050. *Past professional posts*: Senior Attorney, Navajo Nation Department of Justice, 1999-2003; Chief Judge, Laguna Pueblo, 2004-07; Presiding Judge, San Felipe Contemporary Tribal Court, 2008-11.

KESLER, LINC (Oglala Lakota)
(professor of First Nations studies)
Education: Yale University, BA; University of Toronto, MA & PhD. *Affiliation & Address*: Director (2009-present), First Nations House of Learning, Associate Professor of First Nations Studies, University of British Columbia, Buchanan E-255, 1866 Main Mall, Vancouver, BC V6T 1Z1 Canada (604) 822-3071. E-mail: linc.kesler@ubc.ca. *Other professional post*: Senior Advisor to the President on Aboriginal Affairs, University of British Columbia, Vancouver, BC. *Past professional posts*: Director, First Nations Studies, University of British Columbia, Vancouver, 2003-2012; Oregon State University (coordinated the Indian Education Office and the state's only Ethnic Studies Department). *Awards, honors*: Recipient of the Dean of Arts award, 2008-09.

KESSEL, WILLIAM B. (White Mountain Apache)
(professor of anthropology & sociology)
Born on the Fort Apache Reservation in Whiteriver, Ariz. *Education*: University of Arizona, PhD (Cultural Anthropology); Bethany Lutheran Theological Seminary, M Div. in Religious Studies. *Address & Affiliation*: Professor/Bolstad Chair, Bethany Lutheran College, Meyer Hall 308, 700 Luther Dr., Mankato, MN 56001 (507) 344-7786. Dr. Kessel teaches various courses on contemporary U.S. Indians especially Indian peoples of the southwestern U.S. *Past professional post*: Consultant to the White Mountain Apache tribe. *Field experience*: Extensive ethnographic research on the Apache Indians. *Published works*: Encyclopedia of Native American Wars & Warfare, edited with Robert Wooster; writings featured in books such as "Western Apache Material Culture: The Goodwin & Guenther Collections," & "The Apache Lutheran"; author in religious studies, two books and more than 50 articles; numerous articles & papers on Native American life.

KETCHER, MARTHA (Cherokee)
(IHS area director)
Education: Northeastern State University, BS (Accounting/Business); University of Phoenix, MS (Healthcare Administration). *Affiliation & Address*: Director, Nashville Area HIS, 711 Stewarts Ferry Pike • Nashville, TN 37214 (615) 467-1505. E-mail: Martha.ketcher@ihs.gov. Ms. Ketcher is responsible for providing leadership and partnering with 29 Tribes in 14 states for the overall administration of a health care system which includes ambulatory clinics, contracting & self-governance. *Past professional posts*: Acting Nashville Area Director from May 2010 to October 2012. During her career with IHS, Ms. Ketcher has served in several leadership roles in the Nashville Area office, including Director of Financial Management, Acting Executive Officer, and Deputy Area Director. In these positions, she has demonstrated a high level of management and business skills balanced with a commitment to the health care mission of the American Indian and Alaska Native people. *Awards, honors*: Recipient of numerous awards from HHS and IHS, including the HHS Secretary's Award for Distinguished Service recognition for dedication & expertise in self-governance contracting.

KETCHUM, DEE (Delaware)
(tribal chief & chairperson)
Address & Affiliation: Delaware Tribe of Indians, 220 NW Virginia Ave., Bartlesville, OK 74003 (918) 336-5272.

KETCHUM-HEAP OF BIRDS, SHANNA (Cheyenne/Arapaho)
(college instructor; Native American art historian/critic)
Affiliation & Address: Instructor, Native American Studies Program, Ellison Hall 208, University of Oklahoma, Norman, OK 73019 (405) 325-1422. E-mail: sheapofbirds@ou.edu. Shanna is a noted critic & art historian of contemporary Native American art. She lectures, both nationally & internationally, about contemporary issues in Native art. *Published works*: Articles in major publications across the globe.

KEWAYGOSHKUM, ROBERT (Ottawa)
(former tribal chairperson)
Affiliation: Grand Traverse Band of Ottawa & Chippewa Indians, Peshawbes-town Community Center, 2605 N.W. Bayshore Dr., Suttons Bay, MI 49682 (231) 271-3538.

KEYES, THERESA L.
(attorney)
Education: University of Washington, BA, 1991; Gonzaga University School of Law, JD, 1994. *Affiliation & Address*: Partner, K&L Gates LLP, 618 W. Riverside Ave., Suite 300, Spokane, WA 99201 (509) 241-1598. E-mail: Theresa.keyes@klgates.com Ms. Keyes' practice is focused on a broad spectrum of corporate & litigation work for clients who are involved in established on-reservation tribal businesses, as well as those seeking to partner in projects related to tribal economic development. Ms. Keyes has represented tribes directly, as well as triballylicensed entities which are not owned by the tribe, and off-reservation businesses working within Indian country. She provides general corporate advice to businesses including the nuanced issues associated with commercial contracts involving tribes, trust property, collateral, and other financing issues. Additional experience includes representation of clients on matters associated with servicing the emerging i-Gaming industry, and representation of Indian-owned businesses conducting business off-reservation into a myriad of marketplaces, including fuel distribution. Ms. Keyes has litigated federal and state taxation & regulation disputes that involve the manufacture, distribution, and sale of goods and services, both on and off-reservation, which involves legal advice on the interplay between treaty rights, state compacts, jurisdictional issues, and other federal tribal guarantees. Her experience also includes trademark litigation & employment law matters. *Awards, honors*: Named a "Rising Star" by Washington Law & Politics and was named one of Spokane's "20 Under 40 Rising Stars" by the Inland Business Catalyst. *Publication*: Supreme Court decides Match-E-be-Nash-She-Wish Band of Pottawatomi Indians v. Patchak, Indian Law (North America) Alert, July 11, 2012

KEYSER, DAVID (Miwok)
(former tribal chairperson)
Affiliation & Address: United Auburn Indian Community of the Auburn Rancheria, 10720 Indian Hill Rd., Auburn, CA 95603 (530) 883-2390. *Past tribal posts*: 3 terms as secretary, vice chairperson. David was instrumental in re-establishing federal recognition of the tribe & the development of Thunder Valley Casino.

KHERA, SUSHEILA
(executive director)
Affiliations: Fairbanks Native Association, Fairbanks, AK, 1983-92; executive director, Institute of Alaska Native Arts, P.O. Box 70769, Fairbanks, AK 99707 (907) 456-7491, 1996-. *Community activities*: Fairbanks North Star Borough Commission on Historic Preservation. *Membership*: Fairbanks Arts Assn.

KIANDOLI, JENNIFER (Micmac)
 (tribal vice chief)
Affiliation & Address: Vice Chief, Aroostook Band of Micmacs, P.O. Box 772, Presque Island, ME 04769 (207) 764-1972.

KICKINGBIRD, K. KIRKE (Kiowa) 1945-
 (attorney)
Education: University of Oklahoma, BA, 1966; University of Oklahoma School of Law, JD, 1969. *Affiliation & Address*: Owner (1984-present), Kickingbird Associates, 400 Hanover Dr., Edmond, OK 73034 (405) 340-5661. E-mail: info@kickingbirdassoicates.com. Website: www.kickingbirdassociates.com. *Other professional post*: Of Counsel, Hobbs, Straus, Dean & Walker, LLP, 101 Park Ave., Suite 700, Oklahoma City, OK73102 (405) 602-9425. E-mail: kkickingbird@hobbsstraus.com . *Past professional posts*: Executive Director, Institute for the Development of Indian Law, Oklahoma City, OK, 1971-83; director, Native American Legal Resource Center, Oklahoma City University, School of Law, professor, 1983-2000; Chief Justice of the Supreme Court of the Cheyenne & Arapaho Tribes of Oklahoma and as Chairman of the Oklahoma Indian Affairs Commission, 1992-95; appointed Special Counsel on Indian Affairs to the Governor of Oklahoma, 1995-2000. *Community activities*: Native American Asset Advisers (board member). *Memberships*: American Bar Association (Board of Governors, 1996-2000; chair, Native American Resource Committee, Section of Environment, Energy & Resources); Federal Bar Association; Native American Bar Association; Oklahoma Bar Association; Oklahoma Indian Bar Association. *Awards, honors*: 2012 Tulsa City-County Library's Circle of Honor; "One Hundred Million Acres," nominated to the Pulitzer Committee; "Indians & the U.S. Constitution: A Forgotten Legacy," honored by the U.S. Bicentennial Commission. *Published works*: One Hundred Million Acres (Macmillan, 1973); Indians & the U.S. Constitution: A Forgotten Legacy (1987); while executive director at the Institute for the Development of Indian Law, he and his staff wrote a set of books for tribal leaders which include: Indian Sovereignty, Indian Treaties, The Federal-Indian Trust Relationship, and Indian Jurisdiction; Youth for Tribal Government Curriculum Kit (Kickingbird Associates, 2001).

KICKINGBIRD, LYNN
 (editor)
Affiliation & Address: Editor, American Indian Journal, Institute for the Development of Indian Law, 2600 Summit Dr., Edmond, OK 73034

KICKINGBIRD, ROBIN (Kiowa)
 (librarian)
Has been involved in tribal libraries for several years and is currently working to set up a Tribal Library Association in Okla. She published "The Directory of Tribal Libraries" in 1991. She has worked in the Metropoltian Library System of Oklahoma City & in the Archives of the Oklahoma Historical Society, which is known for its extensive collection of documents related to Native American history. She was awarded the first Minority Fellowship for Librarian at the American Library Assn in 1991. She has worked as a law librarian and is now attending law school at the U. of Oklahoma - College of Law.

KIDWELL, CLARA SUE (Choctaw/Chippewa/Creek) 1941-
 (American Indian center director)
Born July 8, 1941, Tahlequah, Okla. *Education*: University of Oklahoma, BA, 1962; MA, 1966, PhD, 1970. *Principal occupation*: American Indian center director. *Affiliation*: Director, American Indian Center, University of North Carolina, Chapel Hill, NC (2007-present). E-mail: cskidwell@unc.edu. *Past professional posts*: Lecturer, Kansas City Art Institute, 1966-68; Instructor of Social Sciences, Haskell Indian Junior College, 1970-72; assistant professor, American Indian Studies Department, University of Minnesota, 1972-74; associate professor, Native American Studies, University of California, Berkeley, 1974-95; assistant director of cultural resources, National Museum of the American Indian, Smithsonian Institution, Washington, DC, 1993-95; director, Native American Studies Program, University of Oklahoma, OK, 1995-2007. *Teaching areas*: Native systems of knowledge, such as ethnobotany & archaeoastronomy. *Scholarly research*: The history of the Choctaw Indians in Mississippi. Also, Native American history, philosophy & medicine. *Memberships*: American Historical Association; Western History Association; American Society for Ethnohistory (president, 1991); History of Science Society; American Indian Science & Engineering Society. *Awards, honors*: Rockefeller Foundation Humanities Fellowship, 1976-77. *Published works*: The Choctaws: A Critical Bibliography (University of Indiana Press, 1981); Choctaws & Missionaries in Mississippi, 1818-1918 (University of Oklahoma Press, 1994); A Native American Theology, with Homer Noley & George E. Tinker (Orbis Books, 2001; Native American Studies, with Alan Velie (University of Edinburgh Press, 2005); The Choctaws in Oklahoma: From Tribe to Nation, 1855-1970, with Alan Velie (University of Oklahoma Press, 2007); numerous chapters in books & journal articles.

KIEVE, LOREN (Cherokee)
 (attorney)
Born & raised in New Mexico. *Education*: Stanford University, BA; Oxford University, JD; University of New Mexico, JD. *Affiliation & Address*: General Partner, Kieve Law Offices, Suite 5A Funston Ave., San Francisco, CA 94129 (415) 364-0060. E-mail: lk@kievelaw.com. His practice focuses on domestic & international disputes & legal problems. *Past professional posts*: Partner, Debevoise & Plimpton, Washington, DC & NYC; partner, Quinn Emanuel Urquhart & Sullivan, LLP, New York, NY. *Other professional posts*: Chair, Board of Trustees, Institute of American Indian Arts, Santa Fe, NM, 1994-present; member of board, audit & nominating committees of the National Lawyers' Committee for Civil Rights; member, National Advisory Board of Stanford's Center for Comparative Studies in Race & Ethnicity. *Membership*: American Bar Assn (Commission on Immigration, and its Section of Litigation.)

KIGER, STEPHANIE (*Pho-Poe*) (Santa Clara Pueblo)
 (attorney)
Education: American University, BA; University of Washington, JD. *Affiliation & Address*: General Counsel, State of New Mexico Indian Affairs Department, 347 E. Palace Ave., Santa Fe, NM 87501 (505) 983-7319. E-mail: skiger@nmlawgroup.com. She coordinates state policy with thte 22 New Mexico tribes and repreent the state on a wide variety of legal issues related to Indian law. Other professional post: Secretary, Southwestern Association of Indian Arts, Santa Fe, NM. *Past professional post*: Associate, Roth, VanAmberg, Rogers, Ortiz & Yepa, Santa Fe, NM.

KILLER, KEVIN (Oglala Lakotah)
 (state representative; student)
Affiliation: Democrat, 27th District, South Dakota State Legislature. *Address*: P.O. Box 322, Pine Ridge, SD 57770 (605) 454-8105 or 773-3851 (office).

KILLS SMALL, JEROME (Oglala Lakota)
 (college instructor/storyteller)
Born & raised on the Pine Ridge Reservation in Porcupine, S.D. *Education*: University of South Dakota, MA. *Affiliation*: Instructor/storyteller, Dept. of Native Studies, East Hall Rm. 309, The University of South Dakota, 414 E. Clark St., Vermillion, SD 57069 (605) 677-7251. E-mail: jerome.kills.small@usd.edu. Jerome teaches the Lakota language, American Indian Oratory & Argumentation, Siouan Tribal Culture, and Early American Indian History & Culture. Mr. Kills Small is also a storyteller & teacher of the Lakota language for the Head Start Program in Vermillion, SD. *Awards, honors*: Received the Distinguished Scholar Award in the Humanities for 2004; and the George Mickelson Reconciliation Award for 1994. He also has a CD of Sweatlodge songs entitled, "Inikagapi: Celebration of Life."

KILLS STAIGHT, BIRGIL (Oglala Lakota)
 (institute director)
Affiliation & Address: Executive Director, Oglala Sioux Parks & Recreation Authority, P.O. Box 2070, Pine Ridge, SD 57770. *Other professional post*: Co-Founder & Co-Director, Indigenous Law Institute, P.O. Box 127, Kyle, SD 57752. *Awards, honors*: The 2012 "Founders Award," The Seventh Generation Fund for Indian Development

KILLSBACK, DION (Northern Cheyenne)
 (attorney)
Education: Montana State University, BS, 2000; University of Montana School of Law, JD, 2003. *Affiliation & Address*: Associate Attorney, Rosette, LLP, 565 W. Chandler Blvd. #212, Chandler, AZ 85225 (480) 889-8990. E-mail: dkillsback@rosettelaw.com Before joining the Rosette team, Dion was hired as the first-ever General Counsel for the Jicarilla Apache Nation. As General Counsel, he established the Nation's in-house legal department to provide effective legal advice and representative at a substantially-reduced cost. In his short two years, Dion saved the Nation over four million dollars, with much of the savings going back to the Nation by funding 20 new job positions, overtime pay for Police, EMS and Fire Departments and providing COLA increases for more than 800 Nation employees. Dion also lead gaming compact negotiations with the State of New Mexico, which allowed the Nation to achieve a gaming compact that will be in place for the next twenty-two years while realizing reduced revenue sharing and administrative costs. Dion also negotiated oil and gas leases; worked with the Nation and federal agencies including the BIA, IHS, BLM, BOR on a myriad of issues ranging from water and labor rights, to administrative and business issues. Prior to serving as General Counsel for the Jicarilla Apache Nation, Dion served as Senior Counselor to the Principal Deputy Assistant Secretary- Indian Affairs, U.S. Department of the Interior. During his time in Washington, D.C., he worked on a variety of issues focusing on Indian water rights, economic and energy development, fee-to-trust issues, natural resource and cultural rights protection, sacred sites protection and Indian education. Before making the move to Washington, D.C., Dion was an Associate Attorney in the International Law Firm of Holland & Knight LLP Indian Law Practice Group. Dion represented Indian tribal governments in all aspects of the law including, but not limited to economic development, energy

development, water rights, oil & gas, taxation, corporate issues, child welfare, gaming, contracts, grant writing, federal BIA and IGRA compliance. Dion has also lead negotiations with state and federal governments on various funding and compliance issues, and has appeared before tribal, state and federal courts on a variety of matters concerning family law issues, contract and consumer protection issues, and criminal issues. He has also appeared before administrative tribunals on numerous occasions. Dion has served on the New Mexico State Bar Association - Indian Law Section Board of Directors and as a tribal appellate judge, and has taught Law & the American Indian as an adjunct professor at Chief Dull Knife College in Montana. Dion has provided training for judges, lawyers, tribal employees, social workers & tribal boards/commissions on a variety of topics, including criminal procedure, civil procedure, child welfare, appellate procedure, water rights, and secured transactions.

KILLSBACK, LAWRENCE JACE (*Voaxaa'e Nestoohe – Screaming Eagle*) (Northern Cheyenne)
(tribal president)

Education: University of California, Berkeley, BA (Native American Studies with a minor in Environmental Sciences). *Affiliation & Address:* President, Northern Cheyenne Tribe, P.O. Box 128, Lame Deer, MT 59043 (406) 477-6284. *Other professsional post:* Vice chairperson & Billings (MT) Area Representative, National Indian Health Board, Washington, DC. *Past professional posts:* Busby (MT) District Representative, Board member of the Native American Health Centers of Oakland & San Francisco; appointed as the Northern Cheyenne's delegate for the Montana & Wyoming Tribal Leaders Council (MT/WY-TLC) and the Council of Large Land-Based Tribes (CLLBT); former treasurer of the CLLBT and the past chairperson of the MT/WY-TLC. Served as the Billings Area Representative for the Direct Service Tribes Advisory Committee, IHS HP/DP Policy Advisory Committee, Tribal Consultation Advisory Committee for the Center for Disease Control & Prevention, and was a member of the U.S. Dept. of Health & Human Services Secretary's Tribal Advisory Commiittee now serving as an alternate.

KILLSBACK, LEO KEVIN (Northern Cheyenne)
(professor of American Indian studies))

Education: Montana State University, BS, 2003; University of Arizona, PhD (American Indian Studies), 2008. *Address & Affiliation:* Assistant Professor of American Indian Studies, College of Liberal Arts & Sciences, MC: 4603, Arizona State University, Tempe, AZ 85287 (480) 727-0061. E-mail: leo.killsback@asu.edu. *Past professional posts:* Professor, American Indian Studies Program, University of Arizona, Tucson, AZ; Tribal Report Editor, Northern Cheyenne Tribe, Lame Deer, MT. *Dissertation:* The Chiefs' Prophecy: The Destruction of Original Cheyenne Leadership During the Critical Era, 1876-1935; an epic of the history of Northern Cheyenne leaders, governance, and leadership systems.

KILPATRICK, JACQUELYN (Choctaw-Cherokee)
(professor of English)

Affiliations: Professor of English, Governor's State University, University Park, IL; Professor of English, California State University, Channel Islands. *Published works:* Celluloid Indians: Native Americans & Film (University of Nebraska Press, 1999) Louis Owens: Literary Reflections on His Life & Work (University of Oklahoma Press, 2004).

KIMBALL, CARLA REICHERT (Ottowah) 1949-
(Native American cultural heritage instructor)

Born May 8, 1949, Muskegon, Mich. *Education:* University of Alabama, MEd, 1987. *Principal occupation:* Native American cultural heritage instructor. *Affiliation & Address:* Head Official, Thurston T. Nelson Elementary School, 202 Ida Moody Rd., Scottsboro, AL 35769 (256) 218-2600. E-mail: ckimball@scottsboroschools.net. *Memberships:* National Indian Education Association; Alabama Indian Education Association. *Awards, honors:* Basic Education Grant Award, 1989 for research on Cherokee Treaties; resolution from Alabama Governor Guy Hunt - outstanding program. *Interests:* Native American studies; Native American art studies. Presentations at Anniston Army Depot (Anniston, AL), Birmingham Museum (Birmingham, AL), Russell Cave National Monument (Bridgeport, AL), Burritt Museum (Huntsville, AL); and Gadsden Graduate Center, University of Alabama (Gadsden, AL).

KIMBLE, GARY NILES (Gros Ventre)
(commissioner)

Born in 1944, Mont. Education: University of Montana, BA, 1966; University of Montana-College of Law, JD, 1972. *Affiliation & Address:* Commissioner (1994-present), Administration for Native Americans, U.S. Dept. of Health & Human Services, Humphrey Bldg., 200 Independence Ave., SW, Washington, DC 20201 (202) 690-7776. *Past professional posts:* Partner & General Counsel for Fort Belknap Indian Community, Kimble, Smith & Connors, Missoula, MT, 1972-75; assistant professor, Native American Studies, University of Montana, Missoula, 1974-79; chief counsel, U.S. Senate Select Committee on Indian Affairs, Washington, DC, 1979; delegate to U.S.-Canada Treaty Negotiations, U.S. Dept. of State, 1979-82; executive director, Columbia

River Intertribal Fish Commission, 1979-82; Advisor on Indian Affairs, State of Montana, Office of the Governor, 1983-89; adjunct professor of Federal Indian Law & director of Affirmative Action Program, Northwestern School of Law, Lewis & Clark College, 1987-89; executive director, Association on American Indian Affairs, New York, NY, 1989-93. *Other professional posts:* Kimball & Associates (consulting & economic development firm, 1982-) Major clients included: Qua-Qui Corp., Missoula, MT, 1982-84; Fort Peck Tribe, NAES College, Poplar, MT, 1984-87; Valley Industrial Park, Glasgow, MT, 1985-86; American Training & Technical Assistance, Albuquerque, NM, 1987-88; Tulalip Tribe, Marysville, WA, 1988; Multnomah Co. Risk Management Team, Portland, OR, 1988-90; Health & Human Services, Public Health Indian Health, Portland, OR, 1988-89. Aboriginal Public Policy Institute (member, Board of Directors & Advisory Board), 1990-. *Public service:* Northwest Communities Project, Portland, OR (chairperson, Board of Directors), 1986-89; Minority Education, Research & Training Institute, New York Medical College, New York, NY (co-principal investigator), 1990-93.

KIMELBERG, DAVID (Seneca)
(chief executive officer)

Affiliation & Address: Chief Executive Officer (CEO), Seneca Holdings LLC, 90 Oh:yo' Way, Seneca Nation (via NY) 14779 (716) 945-8142. *Other professional posts:* CEO, Seneca Broadcasting LLC (operates WGWE 105.9 FM); CEO, Seneca Imports LLC; Seneca Construction LLC; chairperson, Seneca Telecommunications LLC; treasurer, Native American Contractors Association, Washington, DC. *Past professional post:* Vice President & General Counsel, SoftBank Capital & SoftBank Holdings (venture capital & investment company).

KIMMERER, ROBIN WALL (Citizen Band Potawatomi)
(professor of Environmental Biology, Indian center director)

Education: SUNY College of Environmental Science & Forestry, BS, 1975; University of Wisconsin, Madison, MS, 1978, PhD (Botany), 1983. *Affiliation & Address:* Associate Professor, Environmental & Forest Biology; Founding Director, Center for Native Peoples & the Environment, SUNY College of Environmental Science & Forestry, 354 Ilick Hall, 1 Forestry Dr., Syracuse, NY 13210 (315) 470-6785. E-mail: rkimmer@esf.edu. *Other professional post:* Faculty member, Native American Studies Program, Syracuse University; Director, Native Earth Environmental Youth Camp (in collaboration with the Haudennosaunee Environmental Task Force). Dr. Kimmerer is active in efforts to broaden access to environmental science training for Native students, and to introduce the benefits of traditional ecological knowledge to the scientific community, in a way that respects & protects indigenous knowledge. *Past professional post:* Chair & co-founder of the Traditional Ecological Knowledge section of the Ecological Society of America. *Awards, honors:* 2005 John Burroughs Medal for outstanding nature writing for "Gathering Moss." *Published work:* Gathering Moss: A Natural & Cultural History of Mosses (Oregon State U. Press, 2003); Braiding Sweetgrass (Milkweed Editions, 2013); numerous book chapters & articles in scholarly journals..

KINDLE, WILLIAM "WILLIE" (Rosebud Lakota Sioux)
(tribal president)

Affiliation & Address: President, Rosebud Sioux Tribal Council, P.O. Box 430, Rosebud, SD 57570 (605) 747-2381.

KINEGAK-FRIDAY, KIRSTEN M. (Eskimo)
(attorney)

Education: Stanford University, BA, 2005; UCLA School of Law, JD, 2009. *Affiliation & Address:* Associate, Stoel Rives, LLP, 510 L St., Suite 500, Anchorage, AK 99501 (907) 263-8419. E-mail: kkfriday@stoel.com. Kirsten has experience in matters concerning Alaska Native Corporations & tribes, including drafting Village Corporation and tribal ordinances, resolutions & policies. *Past professional post:* Associate, Fortier & Mikko, P.C., 2009-11. *Community activities:* Vice chair, Secretary (2010-111), Board of Directors, Alaska Native Professional Association; member, Native Emering Leaders Forum Work Group.

KING, BARBARA (Ojibwe)
(American Indian studies chair)

Affiliation & Address: Chair, American Indian Studies Program, The College of St. Scholastica, School of Arts & Letters, Tower Hall, Room 4100, 1200 Kenwood Ave., Duluth, MN 55811 (218) 723-6170. E-mail: bking@css.edu.

KING. BRUCE (Choctaw of Oklahoma)
(interim executive director)

Education: East Central University, BA (English, MEd (Secondary Education); Texas A&M Uiversity-Commerce, EdD (Supervision, Curriculum & Instruction in Higher Education); University of Oklahoma for post-graduate studies in Native Studies, literacy & rhetoric.. *Affiliation & Address:* Interim Exexecutive Director, Native American Institute, Native American Center for Student Success, 1405 North 4th, PMB 2747, Durant, OK 74701-0609 (580) 745-3220. E-mail: bking@se.edu. Dr. King joined Southeastern in 1998 and has been the

McCurtain dean since 2011. Prior to this appointment, he served as associate dean, academic coordinator, and advisor. His areas of interest include school leadership, student retention issues, and teacher education training, especially in minority teacher recruitment. King is a member of The Choctaw Nation of Oklahoma and also teaches in the Native American Leadership master's degree program at Southeastern.

KING, DUANE H.
(museum director)

Education: University of Tennessee, BA (Anthropology); University of Georgia, MA & PhD. Dissertation: "A Grammar & Dictionary of the Cherokee Language." *Affiliation & Address*: Vice President for Museum Affairs & Director of Gilcrease Museum (2008-present), The University of Tulsa, 800 S. Tucker Rd., Tulsa, OK 74104 (918) 631-2000. *Other professional post*: Senior Advisor for Acadeic Research & Program Outreach, Smithsonian Institution's National Museum of the American Indian, Washington, DC (2012-present). *Past professional posts*: Executive Director, Southwest Museum of the American Indian/utry National Center, Los Angeles, CA (1995-2007); National Museum of the American Indian, Smithsonian Institution, George Gustav Heye Center, New York, NY; director (1985-95), Cherokee National Historical Society, Tahlequah, OK; director, Cherokee National Museum (TSA-LA-GI), Cherokee Heritage Center, Tahlequah, OK; director & editor (1975-85), "Journal of Cherokee Studies," Museum of the Cherokee Indian, Cherokee, NC; executive director, Middle Oregon Historical Society in Warm Springs, OR. *Awards, honors*: Sequoyah Distinguished Professor in Cherokee Studies, 1994-95. *Published works*: Numerous articles in scholarly journals.

KING, FARINA (Navajo-Dine')
(assistant professor of history)

Born on the Navajo Reservation. *Education*: Brigham Young University, BA (History); University of Wisconsin, MA (African History); Arizona State University, PhD (Indigenous studies). *Affiliation & Address*: Assistant Professor of History, Department of Cherokee & Indigenous Studies, Northeastern State University, Seminary Hall 313, 609 N. Grand Ave., Tahlequah, OK 74464 (918) 444-3500; E-mail: kingf@nsuok.edu She is currently preparing a book manuscript based on her doctoral study, "The Earth Memory Compass: Diné Educational Experiences in the Twentieth Century." She joins the History Department at Northeastern State University in August 2016. She is also The David J. Weber Fellow for the Study of Southwestern America (2016-2017) at the Southern Methodist University Clements Center. Learn more about Dr. King at farinaking.com.

KING, FRANK J., III (Rosebud Sioux)
(newspaper publisher & editor-in-chief)

Affiliation: The Native Voice, 2218 Jackson Blvd., Suite 7, Rapid City, SD 57702 (800) 449-8176; (605) 718-9141. E-mail: info@native-voice.com. Website: www.native-voice.com.

KING, JOHN I. (Navajo)
(shop owner)

Affiliation & Address: Owner, Mizhoni Spirit Horse, 1319 82nd St. SW, Albuquerque, NM 87121 (505) 830-1508 Website: www.nizhonispirithorse.com; E-mail: nizhonispirithorse@msn.com. *Artwork*: Native American tradition style watercolor prints & paintings.

KING, LAUREN J. (Muscogee Creek)
(attorney)

Affiliation & Address: Foster Pepper PLLC, 111 Third Ave., Suite 3400, Seattle, WA 98101 (206) 447-66286. E-mail: kingl@foster.com. *Practice areas*: Treaty rights protection; social gaming; sovereign immunity.

KING, LISE BALK (Oglala Lakota)
(newspaper publisher & executive editor)

Affiliation: Publisher & Editor, The Native Voice, 2218 Jackson Blvd., Suite 7, Rapid City, SD 57702 (800) 449-8176; (605) 718-9141. E-Mail: info@native-voice.com. Website: www.native-voice.com.

KING, PATRICIA (PATTI JO) (Cherokee)
(professor & Interim chair of American Indian studies)

Education: Northern Arizona University, BS (History), MS (American West & American Indian History); University of Oklahoma, PhD (American Indian, U.S. & British History). *Affiliation & Address*: Professor & Interim Division Chair, Native American Studies, Bacone College, & Director of the Center for American Indians (CAI), 2299 Old Bacone Rd., Muskogee, OK 74403 (918) 683-4581. E-mail: kingp@bacone.edu. *Other professional posts*: She is a Southwest & Northern Great Plains Correspondent, News & Lifestyle Feature writer, and Arts Reviewer with Indian Country Today News Media. She holds a number of fellowships including the Bruce Granger Literature Fellowship; the Browning Pipestem Fellowship; and she is a Francis Allen American Indian Fellow at the Newberry Library in Chicago. *Memberships*: Native American Journalist's Association as well as Online Journalist's Association, Professor

King turned her attention to History after a long career as a journalist, activist, and community organizer and has worked with numerous tribal and urban Indian communities across Indian country. She has over 40 years of experience working as a writer, editor & publisher for both mainstream & the Native press.

KING, RANDY (Shinnecock)
(former tribal trustee chairperson)

Affiliation & Address: Shinnecock Tribe, P.O. Box 5006, Southampton, NY 11968 (631) 283-6143.

KING, TIM (Samish)
(tribal vice chairperson)

Affiliation & Address: Vice Chairperson, Samish Indian Nation, P.O. Box 217, Anacortes, WA 98221 (360) 293-6404.

KING, TRACY C. (Assiniboine)
(former tribal president)

Affiliation & Address: President, Fort Belknap Community Council, RR 1, Box 66, Harlem, MT 59526 (406) 353-8303. E-mail: ching@ftbelknap-nsn-gov.

KING, WINDELL R. (St. Regis Mohawk) 1960-
(finance, construction & management)

Born February 9, 1960, Massena, N.Y. *Principal occupation*: Finance, construction & management of Green Energy Electric Power Generating Plants. *Address & Affiliation*: First NRG, Inc., 73 Indian Village Rd., Hogansburg, NY 13655 (613) 551-9022. E-Mail: firstnrginc@aol.com. *Interests*: Promoting economic development projects with Native American Indian tribes of the U.S. and First Nations Bands of Canada.

KING-TANTTU, MARGARET
(college dept. director)

Affiliation: Indian/Minority Services Dept., Mesabi Range Community & Technical College, 1001 Chestnut St. W., Virginia, MN 55792 (218) 749-7727. E-mail: m.king-tanttu@mailmr.mnscu.edu.

KINGEEKUK, KENNETH (Eskimo)
(Alaskan village president)

Affiliation: Native Village of Savoonga, P.O. Box 120, Savoonga, AK 99769 (907) 984-6414.

KINGMAN, A. GAY (Cheyenne River Sioux)
(educator)

Affiliation & Address: Lewis & Clark Graduate School of Education & Counseling, 0615 S.W. Palatine Hill Rd., Portland, OR 97219 (503) 805-4569. *Other professional post*: Consultant, Great Plains Chairman's Assn. *Past professional posts*: Executive director, National Congress of American Indians (NCAI), Washington, DC; Public Relations Director, National Indian Gaming Assn, Washington, DC; tribal college founder/president. *Awards, honors*: In 1991, the tribes of NCAI passed a resolution commending Kingman for her graciousness under pressure, her effectiveness in testifying before Congress, and her skill in coordinating lobbying campaigns.

KINGSBIRD, DENNIS (Shinnecock/Montauk/Mohegan) 1945-
(retired Inspector, Long Island Railroad)

Born December 19, 1945, Brooklyn, N.Y. *Address*: 425 Chapman Blvd., Manorville, NY 11949 (631) 878-4612. *Military service*: U.S. Army, Honorable Discharge, 1966). *Community activities*: Board member, Shinnecock Nation Cultural Center & Museum. *Interests*: "I'm a stone & wood sculptor."

KINNEY, JAVIER I. Yurok)
(attorney; self-governance director)

Education: University of Californa, Davis, BA (History & Native American Studies); Tufts University-Fletcher School of Law & Diplomacy, MA (Law Diplomacy, specializing in Development Economics & International Law; Suffolk Law School, JD. *Affiliation & Address*: Director, Office of Self-Governance, Yurok Tribe, P.O. Box 1027, Klamath, CA 95548 (707) 482-1350. Mr. Kinney has extensive experience working for Tribal governments specializing in areas of public policy, economic analysis, tribal governance, and protection of tribal cultural resources & strategic planning.

KINNEY, RODNEY P. (*Half Moon*) (Yup'ik Eskimo) 1932-
(engineer)

Born September 11, 1932, Nome, Alaska. *Education*: University of California, San Jose, B.S. (Civil Engineering), 1960; Graduate Studies at University of California, Berkeley & San Jose, and University of Alaska, Anchorage. *Affiliation & Address*: Principal & President, Rodney P. Kinney Associates, Inc., 16515 Centerfield Dr., Suite 101, Eagle River, AK 99577 (907) 694-2332. E-mail: rpka@rpka.net. *Past professional posts*: Geotechnical consultant, Woodward Clyde Consultants, Anchorage, AK, 1961-75; engineering coordinator, Alyeska Pipeline Service Co., 1975-79; manager of Engineering &

Planning Division, Anchorage Water & Wastewater Utility, 1979-1980; principal engineer, Rodney P. Kinney Associates, Eagle River, Alaska, 1980-. *Military service*: U.S. Navy, 1951-59. *Community activities*: Local Chamber of Commerce; Municipal Advisory Commission for Water & Wastewater; Founding Trustee of Alaska Southcentral Museum of Natural History; Vice-chair of Youth Club of Anchorage. *Memberships*: American Society of Civil Engineers; Bering Straits Native Association; American Indian Science & Engineering Society; American Water Works Association; American Public Works Association. *Interests*: Rodney P. Kinney Associates, a qualified Eskimo firm, was established October 2, 1980.

KINSEY, DANNA NICOLE (Axteca) 1970-
(historian, museum curator)
Born April 25, 1970, Santa Barbara, Calif. *Education*: BA in U.S. History, Native American Studies & Geography; Masters, Landscape Architecture. *Principal occupation*: Historian, museum curator. *Address*: P.O. Drawer 170, Moose, WY 83012 (307) 739-3591. *Affiliation*: National Park Service Historian; Curator, Colter Bay Indian Arts Museum, Grand Teton National Park, Moose, WY. *Community activities*: Grand Teton National Park Cultural Rendezvous, 1999; Mexican Independence Fiesta, 1999.

KINTER, JAMES (Yocha Dehe Wintun)
(tribal vice chairperson)
Affiliation & Address: Vice Chairperson, Yocha Dehe Wintun Nation, Rumsey Rancheria, P.O. Box 18, Brooks, CA 95606 (530) 796-3400.

KINTER, LELAND (Yocha Dehe Wintun)
(tribal chairperson)
Affiliation & Address: Chairperson, Yocha Dehe Wintun Nation, Rumsey Rancheria, P.O. Box 18, Brooks, CA 95606 (530) 796-3400.

KIOGIMA, FRED (Odawa)
(former tribal chairperson)
Affiliation & Address: Little Traverse Bay Bands of Odawa Indians, 7500 Odawa Circle, Harbor Springs, MI 49740 (231) 242-1418. *Military Service*: U.S. Marine Corps., 1980-2002.

KIPP, BILLIE JO (Blackfeet)
(Indian college president)
Affiliation & Address: President, Blackfet Community College, P.O. Box 819, Browning, MT 59417 (406) 338-5441. E-mail: drkipp@bbfcc.org

KIPP, ELIZABETH D. (Mono)
(tribal chairperson)
Affiliation & Address: Chairperson, Big Sandy Rancheria Band of Western Mono Indians, P.O. Box 337, Auberry, CA 93602 (559) 855-4003. E-mail: lkipp@bsrnation.com

KIPP, ILIFF "SCOTT" (Blackfeet)
(tribal vice chairperson)
Affiliation & Address: Blackfeet Reservation, 1 Agency Square, Browning, MT 59417 (406) 338-7521.

KIPP, WOODROW LOUIS (*Sun Chief*) (Blackfeet) 1945-
(English instructor; columnist)
Born October 5, 1945, Browning, Mont. (Blackfeet Reservation). *Education*: University of Montana, BA (Journalism), 1991. *Principal occupation*: Guidance counselor; journalism instructor & columnist. Resides in Missoula, MT (406) 243-5834 (work). *Affiliation*: English Instructor, Blackfeet Community College, Blackfeet Reservation, P.O. Box 819, Browning, MT 59417 (800) 549-7457; (406) 338-5441. *Past professional post*: Guidance counselor & journalism instructor, University of Montana, Missoula, MT, 1991-2000. *Other professional posts*: Columnist, Lakota Times (SD), Great Falls Tribune (MT), and Missoula Independent. *Military service*: U.S. Marine Corps, 1964-68 (Vietnam, 1965-67); Trail of Broken Treaties, Wounded Knee occupation. *Community activities*: Lecturer at school & civic organizations. *Memberships*: Native American Journalists Association; Blackfeet Medicine Pipe Society; Magpie Society. *Awards, honors*: Great Falls Tribune, Native American Scholarship Award. *Interests*: Powwow dancer; grass dance. *Published work*: Viet Cong at Wounded Knee: The Trail of a Blackfeet Activist (U. of Nebraska Press, 2004).

KIRK, RONALD (Wintun)
(rancheria chairperson)
Affiliation & Address: Chairperson, Grindstone Indian Rancheria, P.O. Box 63, Elk Creek, CA 95939 (530) 968-5365.

KIRK, WYMAN (Cherokee)
(board president)
Affiliation & Address: President, American Indian Resource Center, 110 W. Choctaw St., Tahlequah, OK 74464 (918) 456-5581.

KITCHEN, KAREN (Osage)
(educator, performance artist)
Education: University of Portland, MA (Teaching). *Affiliation*: Student Support Specialist, Title VII Indian Education Project, Portland Public Schools, Portland, OR. Address: 12565 SW Tremont, Portland, OR 97225 (503) 520-1822. E-mail: kkitchen@pps.k12.or.us. *Other professional post*: Member of the musical group, "Border Crossing." *Community activities*: Outreach Director (2004-present) for Panted Sky, a nonprofit organization whose mission is to honor Native American culture, performing music & dance by the North Star Dancers.

KITCHEYAN, KATHLEEN W. (San Carlos Apache)
(tribal chairperson)
Affiliation: San Carlos Apache Tribe, P.O. Box 1240, San Carlos, AZ 85550 (928) 475-2361.

KITKA, JULIA E. (Eskimo)
(association president; editor)
Affiliation & Address: President, Alaska Federation of Natives, 1577 C St. #300, Anchorage, AK 99501 (907) 276-7989. *Other professional posts*: Editor, "AFN News," monthly newsletter; member, Board of Directors, Chugack Alaska Corporation, Anchorage; chair, Chugach World Services, Inc.; director, Chugach Support Services, Inc.trste, Chugack Settlement Truse, Board of Trustees.

KITTSON, RONALD "SMILEY" (Blackfeet)
(Indian commission member)
Address: P.O. Box 850, Browning, MT 59417 (406) 338-7521. *Affiliation*: Member, State Tribal Economic Development Commission (STEDC), c/o Montana Dept. of Commerce, Helena, MT.

KIZER, DARRELL (Washoe)
(former tribal chairperson)
Affiliation: Stewart Community Council, 5258 Snyder Ave., Carson City, NV 89701 (702) 885-9115. E-mail: darrell.kizer@washoetribe.us

KIZER, L. MARK (Washoe)
(former tribal chairperson)
Affiliation: Washoe of the Dresslerville Indian Community, 919 US Hwy. 395 S., Gardnerville, NV 89410 (775) 265-4281. E-mail: mark.kizer@washoetribe.us.

KIZER, LENORA (Washoe)
(former tribal vice chairperson)
Address: 854 Amador Cr., Carson City, NV 89705 (702) 687-3111 (office). *Affiliation*: Washoe Tribal Council. E-mail: Lenora.kizer@washoetibe.us.

KLASKY, PHILIP M.
(writer, educator, oral historian, activist)
Education: San Francisco State University, BA (Environmental Studies), MA (Cultural Geography). *Affiliation & Address*: Lecturer, Department of American Indian Studies, College of Ethnic Studies, San Francisco State University (SFSU), 1600 Holloway Ave., San Francisco, CA 94132 (415) 338-7062. E-mail: pklasky@igc.org. *Other professional posts*: Coordinator, Ethnic Studies Student Resource & Empowerment Center, SFSU; director, The Storyscape Project, The Cultural Conservancy, P.O. Box 29044, Presidio of San Francisco, CA 94129 (415) 561-6594. He consults with indigenous peoples in the U.S. & abroad on the preservation & revitalization of their cultural resources and the protection of their ancestral lands.

KLEIDON, BERT HENRY (Ottawa of Oklahoma)
(former tribal secretray-treasurer & 2nd Chief)
Affiliation: Ottawa Tribe of Oklahoma, P.O. Box 110, Miami, OK 74355 (918) 540-1536. Website: www.ottawatribe.org.

KLEIN, BONITA (Menominee)
(school administrator)
Affiliation: Menominee Tribal School, P.O. Box 39, Neopit, WI 54150 (715) 756-2354.

KLIMIADES, MARIO NICK
(museum librarian/archivist)
Affiliation: The Heard Museum, 22 E. Monte Vista Rd., Phoeniz, AZ 85004 (602) 252-8840.

KNACK, MARTHA C. 1948-
(professor, anthropologist)
Born January 27, 1948, Orange, N.J. *Education*: University of Michigan, BA, 1969, PhD, 1975. *Principal occupation*: Professor, anthropologist. *Address & Affiliation*: Dept. of Anthropology & Ethnic Studies, University of Nevada, 4505 Maryland Pkwy., Las Vegas, NV 89154-5003 (702) 895-3590 (1977-present); chairperson, 1983-86). *Other professional posts*: Consulting for Native American Rights Fund, 1986-88; Pyramid Lake Paiute Tribe, 1984-87; Walker

River Paiute Tribe & U.S. Dept. of Justice, 1994-present; adjunct professor, Boyd School of Law, 2002. *Awards, honors*: Distinguished Professor, 2002; John C. Ewers Award for Ethno-history, 2002. *Memberships*: American Anthropological Assn; American Ethnological Society; American Society for Ethnohistory; Southwestern Anthropological Assn; Great Basin Anthropological Conference. *Awards, honors*: Barrick (U. of Nevada) Distinguished Research Scholar, 1991; Rockefeller Fellow, 1989-90. *Interests*: Great Basin Native American culture & history, Native American water rights & legal history, Native American women & social structures. *Published works*: "Life Is With People: Household Organization of the Contemporary Southern Paiute Indians of Utah" (Ballena Press, 1980); "Contemporary Southern Paiute Household Structure & Bilateral Kinship Clusters" (HRAF, 1982); "As Long As the River Shall Run: An Ethno-history of Pyramid Lake Reservation, Nevada," with Omer C. Stewart (U. of California Press, 1984); "Native Americans & Wage Labor: Ethno-historical Perspective," with Alice Littlefield (U. of Oklahoma Press, 1996); Boundaries Between: Southern Paiutes, 1775-1995 (U. of Nebraska Press, 2001).

KNICK, STANLEY (Lumbee)
(museum director/curator)
Affiliation & Address: Director & Curator, Native American Resource Center, Pembroke State University, Pembroke, NC 28372 (919) 521-6282. E-mail: stan.knick@uncp.edu. *Other professional post*: Asociate Professor of Research, American Indian Studies Department, Pembroke, NC.

KNIFE, TED, JR. (Cheyenne River Sioux)
(tribal council representative)
Affiliation & Address: Former Vice Chairperson, Cheyenne River Sioux Tribe, P.O. Box 590, Eagle Butte, SD 57625 (605) 964-4155. Past tribal post: Vice chairperson.

KNIGHT, HALE P. (Pomo)
(former tribal chairperson)
Affiliation: Hopland Band of Pomo Indians, P.O. Box 610, Hopland, CA 95449 (707) 744-1647.

KNIGHT, MARGARET (Laguna Pueblo)
(executive director)
Affiliation: Executive Director (1996-present), Association of American Indian Physicians, 1225 Sovereign Row #103, Oklahoma City, OK 73108 (405) 946-7072 ext. 103. E-mail: mknight@aaip.com. *Past professional post*: Native American Center, Oklahoma City, OK.

KNIGHT, MIKE (Pomo)
(rancheria chairperson)
Affiliation & Address: Chairperson, Sherwood Valley Rancheria, 190 Sherwood Hill Dr., Willits, CA 95490 (707) 459-9690.

KNIGHT, SANDRA (Mechoopda Maidu)
(tribal vice chairperson)
Affiliation & Address: Vice Chairperson, Mechoopda Maidu Indians of Chico Rancheria, 125 Mission Ranch Blvd., Chico, CA 95926 (530) 899-8922.

KNIGHT, STANFORD (Te-Moak Shoshone)
(tribal chairperson)
Affiliation: Battle Mountain Band Council, 37 Mountain View Dr. #C, Battle Mountain, NV 89820 (775) 635-2004.

KNIGHT, YVONNE T. (Ponca) 1942-
(attorney)
Born December 19, 1942, Pawnee, Okla. *Education*: University of Kansas, BS, 1965; University of New Mexico, School of Law, JD, 1971. *Address*: 1268 Westview Dr., Boulder, CO 80303 (303) 447-8760. *Affiliation*: Native American Rights Fund, Boulder, CO (staff attorney & member, Litigation Management Committee), 1972-. *Memberships*: Colorado Indian Bar Association; American Indian Bar Association; American Indian Policy Review Commission (Task Force on Law Consolidation, Revision, and Codification, 1975-76). *Awards, honors*: Pioneer Minority Women's Attorneys Award by Colorado Women's Bar Association, 1992; Reginald Haber Smith Fellowship, 1971-74.

KNIGHT-FRANK, JUDY (Ute)
(tribal chairperson)
Affiliation: Ute Mountain Ute Tribal Council, General Delivery, Towaoc, CO 81334 (970) 565-3751.

KNOCKWOOD, B.A. (Micmac) 1932-
(Indian center director)
Born July 18, 1932, Micmac Reservation, Nova Scotia, Canada. *Education*: St. Mary's University, 1977-84. *Address*: 2158 Goffingen St., Halifax, Nova Scotia, Canada B3K 3B4 (902) 420-0686. *Affiliations*: Instructor, Cambrian College, Sudbury, Dalhousie University; director, Micmac Learning Center, Halifax, N.S., 1988-. *Other professional posts*: Spiritual Indian Medicine Man. *Military*

service: Royal Canadian Artillery; served in Canada, USA, Japan & Korea (awarded the Korean Medal & U.N. Service Medal). *Community activities*: Involved in human rights at both provincial and national level; public speaker on Native rights & spirituality. *Memberships*: National Native Advisory Council, Connections Canada of the Solicitor General's Department; Spiritual Science fellowship; Assembly of First Nations; National Native Veterans Association; Canadian Legion; Korean Veterans Association. *Awards, honors*: Received a lifetime appointment to the Micmac Nation's Grand Council; given the title of the Micmac Spiritual Medicine Man by the Grand Chief. *Interests*: "I re-introduced the traditional Native beliefs, philosophy, holy ritual, and sacred ceremonies to Native Micmacs and others who are interested in traditional Indian beliefs. Teach and assist Native people in sacred fasting to receive a "vision" & spiritual purification through the Sweat Lodge Ceremony."

KNOWS GUN, ELLIS "RABBIT" (*Ba Sa' Goshe*) (Crow) 1948-
(administration, fine arts)
Born in Crow Agency, Mont. *Education*: Little Big Horn College (Crow Agency, MT), AA, 1988. *Principal occupation*: Administration, fine arts. *Address*: Box 133, Crow Agency, MT 59022 (406) 638-2922. *Affiliation*: Crow Tribe, Crow Agency, MT. *Other professional post*: Fine Arts & Advisory Board, Native American Cultural Institute, Billings, MT. *Military service*: U.S. Army, 1968-71; U.S. Army Reserves, 1983-86. His paintings portray Native American themes in an abstract manner. Knows Gun has been exhibiting his works since 1973, when he received the M.L. Woodrow Award at the 6th annual Red Cloud Indian Art Show in Pine Ridge, South Dakota. *Community activities*: Parish Council vice-president, St Dennis Parish, Crow Agency, MT; PAC Committee Chairman, School District 17H, Hardin, MT; Crow Tribe (secretary, 1976-78; chairman, Crow Air Quality Commission, 1992); past speaker on environmental issues affecting Crow Tribe; Carbon County Arts Guild, 1992. *Awards, honors*: Fine Arts awards; 1986 AIHEC basketball champs (Nationals.) *Biographical source*: Montana's Indians Yesterday & Today.

KNUTSON-KOLODZNE, JIM (Ottawa)
(American Indian center director)
Education: St. Cloud State University, PhD (Higher Education Leadership). *Affiliation & Address*: American Indian Center, Ethnic Studies Dept., 720 Fourth Ave. So., St. Cloud, MN 56301 (320) 308-5449. jkolodzne@ stcloudstate.edu.

KOHN, SAMUEL (Crow)
(attorney; member, public policy & regulation practice)
Education: Dartmouth College, BA, 2009; University of Wisconsin Law School, JD, 2012. *Affiliation & Address*: Associate, Dentons LLP, 525 Market St., 26th Floor, San Francisco, CA 94105 (415) 882-5031. E-mail: Samuel.kohn@ dentons.com. Sam is a member of Dentons' Public Policy & Regulation practice, where he is a member of the Firm's Tribal Litigation practice team and focuses on all matters related to American Indian lands. This includes trust acquisitions, *Carcieri v. Salazar* issues and land claim settlement matters. Sam also helps clients to navigate their concerns with federal agencies, with the United States Congress and throughout the tribal-state compacting process. *Prior and Present Employment*: Prior to law school, Sam worked for the United States Senate Committee on Finance in Washington, DC. His work there focused on Social Security, Indian health care, Indian tax matters and Montana tribes. During law school, Sam served as a managing editor for the *Wisconsin Law Review*. He also worked as a judicial extern to United States District Judge Charles N. Clevert Jr. of the United States District Court for the Eastern District of Wisconsin. Before joining Dentons, Sam acquired extensive experience working in the judiciary at both the trial court and appellate levels. He served as a law clerk to United States District Judge Brian Morris of the District of Montana, and as a law clerk to the Montana Supreme Court. He has also clerked for the Native American Rights Fund, where he worked on education, tribal-state compacting and water rights matters.

KOMALTY, MATTHEW M. (Kiowa)
(tribal chairperson)
Affiliation & Address: Chairperson, Kiowa Indian Tribe, P.O. Box 369, Carnegie, OK 73015 (580) 654-1729. E-mail: mkomalty@kiowatribe.org

KOOKESH, ALBERT (*KA ShAAN & YikdehHeIN*) (Tlingit)
(attorney; Inn owner; board chairperson)
Born & raised in Angoon, Alaska. Education: Alaska Methodist University, BA (History; University of Washington School of Law, JD. *Affiliation & Address*: Owner, Kootznahoo Inlet Lodge, Angoon, AK; board chairperson, Sealaska Corporation, One Sealaska Plaza, Suite 400, Juneau, AK 99801 (907) 586-1512; co-chair, Alaska Federation of Natives, Juneau, AK. Albert joined the Sealaska Board of Directors in 1976. He is an ex-officio ember of all board committees and serves on the Elders' Settlement Trust Board of Trustees. He also serves as a director for Sealaska Timber Corporation and Klawock Island Dock Co., Inc. *Past professional posts*: Served in the Alaska State Legislature as senator to District C; past secretary & grand president of the Alaska Native Brotherhood; special assistant to Alaska Governor, Tony Knowles..

KOOTENAY, CONWAY (Cree)
(singer, performer)
Born in Edmonton, Alberta, Can. *Address*: Red Power Squad, P.O. Box 3388, Morinville, Alberta, Canada (780) 266-2323. Website: www.redpowersquad. com. E-mail: rpsbooking@gmail.com. Founded "Red Power Squad," a Cree hip-hop group in 1998. Travels globally. *Awards, honors*: Winners of numerous Canadian Aboriginal Music Awards.

KOPPEN, JASON
(Indian college president)
Affiliaition & Address: President, Indian Bible College, P.O. Box 30880, F;agstaff, AZ 86003 (928) 774-3890.

KOTA, SHARON L.
(program coordinator; council president)
Education: Wayne State University, B.S.E.; graduate work at Oakland University. *Affiliation*: Coordinator, Indian Education & Gifted & Talented Programs, Port Huron Area School District, 1320 Washington St., Port Huron, MI 48061 (810) 989-2727. E-mail: skota@miec.org. *Other professional post*: President, Michigan Indian Education Council, Haslet, MI; chairperson, American Indian Communities Leadership Council (promotes cultural educational programming for Native students & community members in the southeastern Michigan area.) *Past professional post*: Sharon has worked with the U.S. Dept. of Education as field reader and served as a Michigan Delegate to the White House Conference on Indian education. *Interests*: Serves on many local boards in her community and is an advocate for Native issues.

KOTLA, SHARON (Leech lake Ojibwe)
(tribal college VP of operations)
Education: Metropolitan State University, B.S. (Business Administration), 1998. *Affiliation*: Vice President of Operations, Leech lake Tribal College, P.O. Box 180, Cass Lake, MN 56633 (218) 335-4200.

KOZEVNIKOFF, EILEEN (Athapascan)
(AK village council director)
Affiliations: Native Village of Tanacross, P.O. Box 77130, Tanacross, AK 99776 (907) 366-7160; health service director, Tanana Chiefs Conference Health Center, 122 First Ave., Fairbanks, AK 99701 (907) 452-8251.

KRACHT, BENJAMIN R.
(chair of Cherokee & Indigenous studies)
Education: Indiana University, BA (Anthropology/History), 1979; University of Nebraska, MA (Anthropology), 1982; Southern Methodist University, PhD (Anthropology), 1989. *Affiliation & Address*: Chairperson & Professor of American Indian Studies, Department of Cherokee & Indigenous Studies, Northeastern State University, Seminary Hall 313, 609 N. Grand Ave., Tahlequah, OK 74464 (918) 444-3500; E-mail: kracht@nsuok.edu. At SMU he studied medical anthropology and began researching urban Indian health. By the end of his first year of doctoral work, he began researching Kiowa culture, religion, and history. Most of his publications pertain to Kiowa religion, including coverage of the Ghost Dance, dancing and shamanic societies, & indigenized Christianity. A forthcoming book delineates aboriginal Kiowa religious beliefs (2016), & one in preparation pertains to Kiowa religious revitalization between 1875 and 1945. Dr. Kracht has also traveled to Central America with Dr. Erik Terdal to study Maya belief systems and the use of rainforest plant medicines. Each spring he teaches Field Methods in Ethnology and takes students to New Mexico during spring break to visit Acoma, Zuni, and Santo Domingo Pueblos. Dr. Kracht has published over 40 articles and book reviews, including entries in *American Indian Religious Traditions, American Indian Spirituality,Encyclopedia of Oklahoma History & Culture,* and*Encyclopedia of North American Indians.* His 2012 article in the *Chronicles of Oklahoma,* "'It Would Break Our Hearts Not to Have Our Kiowas': War Dancing, Tourism, and the Rise of Powwows in the Early Twentieth Century," won the Muriel Wright award for best article.

KRAFT, JOHN T.
(archaeologist/educator; museum curator)
Affiliation & Address: Curator, The Lenape Indian Museum & Village, Waterloo Village, Stanhope, NJ 07874 (973) 691-2316; director, Lenape Lifeways, Inc., P.O. Box 239, Stanhope, NJ 07874. John has presented thousands of programs on the Lenape or Delaware Indians of New Jersey. He has worked with the Lenape people, creating museum exhibits, consulting with editors for social studies textbooks, and lecturing for about 30 years. He has helped discover & excavate Lenape villages & artifacts, and has added much new information about their family life, dwellings, diet, spiritual beliefs & technology. *Publications*: "The Indians of Lenapehoking," with Herbert C. Kraft; illustrated, "The Lenape or Delaware Indians," et al.

KRAKOFF, SARAH
(professor of Indian law)
Education: Yale University, BA, 1986; University of California, Berkeley, JD, 1991. *Affiliation & Address*: Professor of Indian Law (1999-present), University of Colorado Law School, 407 Wolf Law Bldg. 401 UCB, Boulder, CO 80309. (303) 492-2641. E-mail: sarah.krakoff@colorado.edu. Sarah has been cited in several federal district court opinions, and has written about environmental ethics, public lands, and global warming. Her current projects include a new American Indian law casebook, co-authored, and a chapter in a book entitled "Parenting the Planet" about the different stages of the human relationship to nature, *Past professional posts*: Clerked on the Ninth Court of Appeals for Judge Warren J. Ferguson, 1992-93; director, Youth Law Project for DNA-people's Legal Services, Navajo Nation, 1993-95; director, American Indian Law Clinic, University of Colorado Law School, 1995-99. *Awards, honors*: Equal Justice Works Fellowship to work on the Navajo Nation, 1993; received the Jules Millstein faculty Writing Award at the University of Colorado Law School, 2006. *Published works*: "Tribal Sovereignty & Environmental Justice," book chapter in Justice & Natural Resources, by Bryner, Kenny & Mutz, Eds.), 2001; American Indian Law: Cases & Commentary, co-author with Anderson, Berger & Fricky, 1st, 2nd (2010) & 3rd (2015) Eds., and a Teacher's Manual to Accompany American Indian Law: Cases & Commentary (Thomson/West, 2008 & 2010); Radical Adaptation, Justice & American Indian Nations, (Environmental Justice, 2011); Editor (with Ezra Rosser) Tribes, Land & Environment (Ashgate Publishing, 2012); numerous articles.

KRAMER, PATTI (Kaw)
(former tribal chairperson)
Affiliation & Address: Former Chairperson/CEO (2016-), The Kaw Nation, 698 Grandview Dr., Drawer 50, Kaw City, OK 74641 (580) 269-2552. E-mail: tkramer@kawnation.com.

KREIPE de MONTANO, MARTHA (Prairie Band Potawatomi) 1944-
(museum professional)
Born November 9, 1944, Topeka, Kan. *Education*: Haskell Indian Junior College (Certificate, Welding), 1975; University of Kansas, Lawrence, BFA (Painting), 1978, MA (Special Studies-Anthropology-History). *Principal occupation*: Museum professional. *Work address*: National Museum of the American Indian/CRC, 4220 Silver Hill Rd., Suitland, MD 20746 (301) 238-6624 ext. 6422. E-mail: demontanom@si.edu. Website: www.conexus.si.edu. *Past Affiliation*: Manager, Indian Information Center, National Museum of the American Indian, New York, NY, 1984-2004. *Community activities*: Indian Center, Lawrence, KS (board of directors); Circle of Red Nations, New York, N.Y. (president, board of directors); Native American Education Program, New York, NY (parent's committee); Grupo Aymara Productions (board of directors); New York City Native American Heritage Month (committee). *Awards, honors*: HUD Minority Fellowship, University of Kansas. *Interests*: Contemporary North American Indian activities--cultural, social, artistic; Andean Indian life and music; Mayor's Ethnic New Yorker Award, 1986. *Published works*: 49's, A Pan Indian Mechanism for Boundary Maintenance and Social Cohesion (AAA meeting, 1980); Native American Conceptions of Time (Manhattan Laboratory Museum Symposium, 1983); Teacher's Kit: The Parfleche (Museum of the American Indian, Heye Foundation, 1985); Diplomacy In New England (Indians, Promises & Us, 1987); editor, Pachamama Project (Grupo Aymara, Inc., 1988); The Native American Almanac, with Arlene Hirschfelder (Macmillan, 1993); Coyote In Love With a Star; Harvest Ceremony, a play (George Gustav Heye Center, NY, 1996).

KREPPS, ETHEL CONSTANCE (*Kontameah*) (Kiowa/Miami) 1941-
(public health nurse III - R.N.; attorney)
Born October 31, 1941, Mt. View, Okla. *Education*: St. John's Medical Center, Tulsa, RN, 1971; University of Tulsa, BS, 1974; University of Tulsa, College of Law, JD, 1979. *Principal occupation*: Public Health Nurse III - R.N.; attorney. *Address*: 3000 N.W. 12th, Oklahoma City, OK 73107 (405) 942-7203. *Affiliations*: Lawyer, Native American Coalition of Tulsa, Inc., OK, 1981-88; Public Health Nurse III - R.N., Attorney, OK State Dept. of Health, Oklahoma City, OK, 1989-. *Other professional post*: Director, Oklahoma Indian Affairs Commission, Oklahoma City, OK, 1991-. *Community activities*: Kiowa Tribe of OK (secretary); Native American Chamber of Commerce (secretary); Tulsa Indian Affairs Commission; American Indian Toastmasters. *Memberships*: National Trial Lawyers Assn; American Bar Assn; Federal Bar Assn; OK Bar Assn; OK Indian Attorney's Association; Tulsa County Bar Assn; Tulsa Women Lawyers Assn; Women Lawyers Assn of OK; Phi Alpha Delta Legal Fraternity; National Indian Social Workers Assn (past president); OK Indian Child Welfare Assn (past president); American Indian/Alaskan Native Nurses Assn (past national vice-president); OK Indian Legal Assn (past board secretary) . *Awards, honors*: Indian Business Person of the Year Award, 1984; Outstanding Leadership Award, 1985, from International Indian Child Conference; Trial Lawyers Association National Essay Award; Tulsa Mayor's Appreciation Award. *Interests*: "Domestic law; Indian law; Writing, painting, photography; lap quilting; collection of unique indigenous cultural items from around the world; travel." Biographical sources: Who's Who in Finance and Industry; Who's Who

in the South and Southwest; Who's Who of American Law; Who's Who of American Women; Who's Who in the World of Women; Who's Who in Society; 1,000 Personalities of the World. *Published works*: A Strong Medicine Wind (Western Publications, 1981); Oklahoma Memories, chapter (U. of Oklahoma Press, 1982); Oklahoma Images, chapter (U. of Oklahoma Press, 1983).

KRISTOVICH, BROOK (Colville)
(executive director; board chairperson)
Affiliation & Address: Executive Director, Colville Indian Housing Authority, P.O. Box 528, Nespelem, WA 99155 (509) 634-4229. E-mail: bbkrist@msn.com. *Other professional posts*: Board Chairperson, Northwest Indian Housing Association, Seattle, WA, 1997-present); Independent Associate, Legal Shield, 2001-present); Secretary of Tribal Council, Native Village of Napaimute, AK, 2010-present. *Past professional post*: Executive Director, Spokane Indian Housing Authority, 1994-2005.

KROEBER, KARL
(professor in the humanities)
Affiliation & Address: Mellon Professor in the Humanities, Columbia University, New York, NY. *Other professional post*: Editor Emeritus of "Studies in American Indian Literature." *Published works*: Artistry in American Indian Myths, 1998; Ishi in Three Centuries, Ed. 2003; Native American Storytelling (Blackwell Publishing, 2004).

KROEBER, PAUL
(research associate)
Education: Harvard, BA (Linguistics); University of Chicago, PhD (Linguistics). He has held postdoctoral fellowships at the University of British Columbia (1993-94) and the Smithsonian Institution (1994-95), and has taught linguistics at Reed College (1990-92), in the Department of English at the Univrsity of North Texas (1992-93), and in the Departments of Anthropology of the Univesity of Wyoming (1995-96) and Indiana University (1996-97). *Affiliation & Address*: Research Associate, American Indian Studies Research Institute, Indiana University, 422 N. Indiana Ave., Bloomington, IN 47408 (812) 855-4086. E-mail: pkroeber@indiana.edu. Dr. Kroeber's interests include the descriptive & historical linguistics of the Salish language family, including relations between Salish languages and other languages of the Pacific Northwest (focusing especially on the Oregon coast). He has conducted fieldwork on two Salish languages & archival research on the Salish language Tillamook and its southern, non-Salish neighbor Alsea. He has been erratically involved with ongoing work on Lakota at the Institute. Published works: The Salish Language Family: Reconstructing Syntax: Studies in the Anthropology of North American Indians (University of Nebraska Press, 1999); numerous articles in scholarly journals.

KROHN, ELISE
(herbalist & natural foods specialist; educator)
Education: The Evergreen State College, BS (Ethnobotany & Pre-Medicine), 2001; Lesley University's Independent Study Degree Program, MA (Education in Traditional Foods & Medicines), 2007. *Affiliation & Address*: Instructor of Traditional Foods & Medicines, Educator & Program Coordinator of the Norhwest Indian College's Cooperative Extension's Traditional Plants & Foods Program and the Traditional Foods & Medicines Program at the Northwest Indian Drug & Alcohol Treatment Center; also, the principle nvestigator for the Buiding Tribal Community Health Through Education Project, Native culinary arts, growing plants & herbal medicine. These course are offered at the Northwest Indian College and through tribal education programs at the Northwest Indian College, 2522 Kwina Rd., Bellingham, WA 98226 (360) 676-2772. As a native food specialist, she empowers others in gathering and using wild foods & medicines. She has spent almost 20 years in medicine making, clinical practice, developing tribal community gardens, creatin curricula & teaching. *Published works*: Wild Rose & Western Red Cedar: The Gifts of the Northwest Plains (Northwest Indian College Cooperative Extension, Gorham Printing, 2007); co-author, Feeding the People, Feeding the Spirit: Revitalizing Northwest Coastal Indian Food Culture (Northwest Indian College Cooperative Extension, Gorham Printing, 2010); Contributed writing & recipes to, "Our Food, Our Right: Recipes for Food Justice (Community Alliance for Global Justice, 2012). *Radio program*: Guest Speaker (on the revitalization of native foods systems in the Northwest) Food Sovereignty on Tribal Lands," Think Out Loud Radio program, Oregon Public Broadcasting, aired, Nov. 1, 2013. *Film produced*: The Teachings of the Tree People, a one-hour film on the life of tribal elder and Skokomish cultural leader, Bruce Miller, 2006.

KRONK-WARNER, ELIZABETH A. (Sault Ste. Marie Chippewa)
(director of tribal law & government center; professor of law)
Education: Cornell University, BS, 2000; University of Micigan Law School, 2003. Affiliation & Address: Director, Tribal Law & Government Center, Associate Dean, Academic Affairs, Professor of Law, 406 Green Hall, Lawrence, KS 66045 (785) 864-1139; E-mail: Elizabeth.kronk@ku.edu Other professional posts: Chairperson, Kansas State Advisory Committee of the U.S. Commission on Civil Rights; She is an elected member of the board of

directors of the Federal Bar Association, and editor-in-chief of *The Federal Lawyer*. She has also chaired the Indian Law Section of the Federal Bar. Additionally, she is an appellate judge in Michigan for the Sault Ste. Marie Tribe of Chippewa Indians Court of Appeals. *Past professional post*: Faculty, Texas Tech University School of Law; Alexander Blewett III School of Law, University of Montana. *Published works*: With Randall Abate, she is the editor of the book *Climate Change and Indigenous Peoples: The Search for Legal Remedies* (Edward Elgar Publishing, 2013).

KROSKRITY, PAUL V.
(professor of anthropology)
Education: Indiana University, PhD (Linguistic Anthropology). *Address & Affiliation*: Professor of Anthropology, 329A Haines Hall, UCLA, Los Angeles, CA 90095 (310) 825-6237. *Other professional post*: Member, Faculty Advisory Committee, American Indian Studies Center, UCLA. E-mail: paulvk@ucla.edu. *Research interests*: Language & culture, language contact, language & identity, language ideologies, anthropology & verbal art, ethnography of communication, & American Indian language, especially the Kiowa-Tanoan & Uto-Aztecan families; the Pueblo Southwest, Central California. *Published works*: "Arizona Tewa Kiva Speech as Manifestation of a Dominant Language Ideology," In Language, Ideologies, Practice & Theory edited with Schieffelin & Woolard (Oxford University Press, 1998); "Language Ideologies in the Expression & Representation of Arizona Tewa Ethnic Identity," In (editor) Regimes of Language: Ideologies Politics & Identities (School of American Research, Santa Fe, NM, 2000).

KRULISH, ARLENE (Sisseton Wahpeton Sioux)
(chief executive officer-HIS)
Born & raised in Fort Totten, ND. *Education*: University of North Dakota, BSN (Nursing), 2001. *Affiliation & Address*: Chief Executive Officer, Indian Health Service, Spirit Lake Health Center, P.O. Box 359, Fort Totten, ND 58335 (701) 766-4221.

KRUPAT, ARNOLD
(professor of global studies-literature)
Education: New York University, BA; Columbia University, MA, PhD. *Address & Affiliation*: Sarah Lawrence College, 1 Mead Way, Bronxville, NY 10708 (914) 395-2309. E-mail: akrupat@slc.edu. *Special Interest*: Cultural studies and Native American literatures. *Published works*: For Those Who Come After: A Study of Native American Autobiography (University of California Press, 1985); I Tell You Now: Autobiographical Essays by Native American Writers, Edited with Brian Swann (University of Nebraska Press, 1987); 2nd Ed., 2005); Recovering the Word: Essays on Native American Literature, Edited with Brian Swann (University of California Press, 1987); The Voice In Margin: Native American Literature & the Canon (University of California Press, 1989); Ethnocriticism: Ethnography, History, Literature (University of California Press, 1992); New Voices in Native American Literary Criticism, Editor (The Smithsonian Institution Press, 1993); Native American Autobiography: An Anthology, Editor (University of Wisconsin Press, 1994; 2nd Ed., 1996); Woodsmen, or Thoreau & the Indians: A Novel (University of Oklahoma Press, 1994); The Turn to the Native: Studies in Criticism & Culture (University of Nebraska Press, 1996); Here First: Autobiographical Essays by Native American Writers, Edited with Brian Swann (Random House, 2000); Red Matters: Native American Studies (University of Pennsylvania Press, 2002); All That Remains: Native Studies (University of Nebraska Press, 2009); in progress, "That the People Might Live": A Theory of Native American Elegy.

KUKA, KING D. (Blackfeet) 1946-
(professional artist)
Born August 13, 1946, Blackfeet Reservation, Browning, Mt. *Education*: Institute of American Indian Arts, Diploma, 1965; University of Montana, BFA, 1973; Montana State University, M.A. *Principal occupation*: Artist (sculpture and painting); owner-operator, Blackwolf Gallery. *Address*: 907 Ave. C, NW, Great Falls, MT 59404 (406) 452-4449. *Military service*: U.S. Army, 1965-67. *Exhibits*: One-man shows: Reeder's Alley, Helena; University of Montana Center, Missoula; Museum of the Plains Indian, Browning; Rainbow Gallery, Great Falls; Flathead Lake Lookout, Lakeside. Painting & sculpture exhibits at Riverside Museum, New York, N.Y.; San Francisco; Philbrook Art Center, Tulsa, Okla.; Gallery of Indian Arts, Washington, D.C. *Awards, honors*: Numerous awards for art and creative writing; selected to exhibit and demonstrate in Kumamoto, Japan in 1992. *Membership*: Indian Arts & Crafts Association. *Interests*: Mr. Kuka's main interest is in the arts, Indian culture and outdoor life. *Published works*: Poetry: The Whispering Wind (Doubleday); Voices of the Rainbow (Viking Press); Anthologies: The First Skin Around Me (Territorial Press); The Remembered Earth (Red Earth Press); among others.

KUNESH, PATRICE H. (Standing Rock Sioux)
(professor of law; Indian studies director)
Education: University of Colorado School of Law, JD. *Affiliation*: Director (2008-present), Institute of American Indian Studies, The University of South Dakota, 414 E. Clark St., Dakota Hall Room 17, Vermillion, SD 57069 (605) 677-5208.

E-mail: pkunesh@usd.edu . Professor of Law, University of South Dakota School of Law, 2005-present. Patrice teaches in the areas of Children & the Law, Federal Indian Law, Legislation & Property Law. *Other professional post*: Visiting Professor of Law, Lewis & Cark Law School, Portland, OR. *Past professional posts*: Staff attorney, Native American Rights Fund, Boulder, CO, 1989-94; In-house counsel to the Mashantucket Pequot Tribe, 1994-2005. *Awards, honors*: Skadden Public Interest Fellow; Bush Leadership Fellowship. *Memberships*: Native American Bar Assn; Colorado Indian Bar Assn (secretary -treasurer). Professor Kunesh has widely lectured and published in the areas of Indian child welfare & tribal & federal Indian law. She is currently working on a book chapter entitled, "Maps as Legal Documents in Indian Affairs," as part of a project of the Smithsonian Institute on the Cartography of Indian Affairs.

KWAIL, DAVID (Yavapai-Apache)
(former tribal chairperson)
Affiliation: Yavapai-Apache Nation, P.O. Box 1188, Camp Verde, AZ 86322 (520) 567-3649.

LABAN, BRIAN (Hopi/Tewa)
(director of training & instruction)
Education: Westminster College, Northern Arizona University, BS; Yong in University (Korea); certified as a personal trainer by the Cooper Institute. *Affiliation*: Director of Training & Instruction & Co-Founder, Native American Fitness Council, P.O. Box K, Flagstaff, AZ 86002 (928) 774-3048. *Awards, honors*: Brian is a National Impact Award winner for his efforts in motivating Native American people to live active, healthy lifestyles. He served as martial arts coach for the North American Indigenous Games.

LaBELLE, MICHAEL JAMES (Sisseton-Wahpeton Sioux/
Turtle Mountain Chippewa) 1961-
(radio station manager)
Born July, 16, 1961, Chicago, Ill. *Address & Affiliation*: Station Manager, Dakota Nation Broadcasting Corp., KSWS 89.3 FM, P.O. Box 142, Sisseton, SD 57262 (605) 698-7972.

LACAPA-MORRISON, CAMILLE (Lac Courte Oreilles Ojibwe)
(radio station general manager)
Affiliation: WOJB-FM, Lac Courte Orielles Ojibwe Broadcasting Corp., Route 2, Box 2700, Hayward, Wisconsin 54843 (715) 634-2100.

LACHAPPA, CLIFFORD M. (Diegueno)
(former tribal chairperson)
Affiliation & Address: Former chairperson, Barona General Business Council, 1095 Barona Rd., Lakeside, CA 92040 (619) 443-6612.

LACHAPPA, MONIQUE (Kumeyaay Diegueno)
(former tribal chairperson)
Affiliation: Campo Kumeyaay Nation, 36190 Church Rd. #1, Campo, CA 91906 (619) 478-9046.

LaCOUNTE, CYNTHIA
(project manager)
Affiliation & Address: Project Manager, Office of American Indians & Alaskan Native & Native Hawaiian Programs, Administration on Aging (AoA), One Massachusetts Ave., Washington, DC 20201 (202) 357-0148. E-mail: cynthia. lacounte@aoa.hhs.gov.

LaCOUNTE, DARRYL
(BIA regional office director)
Affiliation & Address: Director, Bureau of Indiann Affairs, Rocky Mountain Regional Office, 2021 4th Ave. North, Billings, MT 59101 (406) 247-7943.

LaCOURT, JEANNE (Menominee)
(professor of American Indian studies)
Education: University of Wisconsin-Madison, PhD. *Affiliation & Address*: Professor of American Indian Studies (1999-present) & Chairperson of the Ethnic & Women's Studies Dept., St. Cloud State University, 720 4th Ave. South, B51 Rm. 210, St. Cloud, MN 56301 (320) 308-1048. E-mail: jalacourt@stclousstate.edu. *Research interest*: Her current work focuses on the intersections of indigenous & tribal ideologies with analytical psychology in the tradition of Carl Jung. *Published work*: Oral History & Native Youth: Strengthening Traditional American Indian Education (LAP Lambert Academic Publishing, 2010); numerous articles.

LaDUKE, WINONA (White Earth Chippewa)
(environmentalist)
Affiliations: Founder, White Earth Land Recovery Project, White Earth Reservation, Hwy. 224, P.O. Box 418, White Earth, MN 56591 (218) 983-3285. She founded the Recovery Project in 1989 with a $20,000 human-rights award from Reebok. *Other professional post*: President, Indigenous Women's Network, Lake Elmo, MN. *Past professional post*: Ran for Vice President of

the U.S. with Ralph Nader on the Green Party in 1996. *Interests*: She has quietly been buying back reservation land owned by non-Indians. The land is held in a conservation trust by the project, with the eventual goal of ceding the property to the tribal government. Winona supervises maple sugar & wild-rice processing operations, a stable of horses, an Anishinaabe language program, a wind-energy project, and a herd of buffalo. She is a devotee of coffee & imports beans harvested by peasants in Mexico.

LAFFERTY, GARI (Paiute)
(former tribal chairperson)
Affiliation & Address: Cedar Band of the Paiute Indian Tribe of Utah, P.O. Box 235, Cedar City, UT 84721 (435) 586-9433.

LaFONTAINE, CATHIE (Turtle Mountain Chippewa) 1957-
(school principal)
Born January 14, 1957, Rolla, N.D. *Education*: University of North Dakota, MA, 1983. *Address*: P.O. Box 564, Belcourt, ND 58316 (701) 477-3378. *Affiliation*: Principal, Ojibwa Indian School, Belcourt, ND, 1990-. *Community activities*: Chairperson for Twila Martin-Kekakbah - Tribal Council Campaign. *Memberships*: National Association of Elementary School Principals; North Dakota Association of Elementary School Principals. *Awards, honors*: Ojibwa Indian School - Service Award.

LaFRANCE, RON, JR. (Mohawk)
(former tribal chief)
Affiliation & Address: Former Chief, Saint Regis Mohawk Tribe, 412 State Route 37, Akwesasne, NY 13655 (518) 358-2272.

LAFROMBOISE, MEGAN (Sisseton Wahpeton Oyate)
(tribal attorney)
Education: University of North Dakota School of Law, JD. *Affiliation & Address*: Tribal Attorney (2013-present), Sisseton Wahpeton Oyate, Lake Traverse Reservation, P.O. Box 509, Agency Village, SD 57262 (605) 698-3911. E-mail: meganl@swo-nsn.gov

LaFROMBOISE, RICHARD (Turtle Mountain Sioux)
(tribal chairperson)
Affiliation: Turtle Mountain Tribal Council, P.O. Box 900, Belcourt, ND 58316 (701) 477-0470.

LaFROMBOISE, TERESA (Miami)
(director of Native American Studies; professor of education)
Affiliation & Address: Director of Native American Studies, Professor of Education, Stanford University, 450 Serra Mall, Bldg. 360, Stanford, CA 94305 (650) 723-1202. E-mail: lafrom@stanford.edu. *Professional Interests*: Teresa is a counseling psychologist with clinical & teaching experience in a wide variety of university & American Indian reservation settings, and well equipped to guide new professionals in school & community-based counseling interventions. She is the developer of the American Indian Life Skills Development Curriculum of problem-based lessons aimed at increasing social emotional competence & reducing the risk of suicide among American Indian adolescents. She is also investigating culture, social, and psychological indicators of adolescent risk behavior.

LaGARDE, MARY (Anishinabe)
(executive director)
Affiliation & Address: Executive Director, Minneapolis American Indian Center, 1530 E. Franklin Ave., Minneapolis, MN 55404 (612) 879-1750. E-mail: mlagarde@maicnet.org.

LAHREN, SYLVESTER (BUS)
(consultant in applied anthropology)
Education: University of Colorado, PhD (Anthropology). *Affiliation*: Research associate, Walker Research Group, Ltd., P.O. Box 4147, Boulder, CO 80306 (303) 492-6719. Website: www.walkerresearchgroup.com. Dr. Lahren has conducted applied research projects with American Indians, Hispanic populations, and Anglo-American populations of the Plains and Northwest in both Canada and the U.S. He is also trained and experienced in various aspects of cultural resource management throughout Western North America.

LALIBERTE, RON (Metis)
(professor of Native Studies)
Affiliation & Address: Professor of Native Studies, College of Arts & Sciences, Kirk Hall 129, University of Saskatchewan, Saskatoon, SK S7N 5C8 (306) 966-6211. E-mail: ron.laliberte@usask.ca. *Research Interests*: Metis issues & history, Aboriginal labour in Western Canada, the history of the sugar beet industry in southern Alberta and theoretical perspectives on migrant labour forces. Professor Laliberte writes, "I have recently been involved in a collaborative project on Fist Nations & Metis identities in Cities (a study of urban Aboriginal communities in Saskatoon). In the future, I hope to be involved in doing research on Metis rights in Saskatchewan." Published works:

Expressions in Canadian Native Studies Saskatoon (University of Saskatchewan Extension Press, 2000); numerous articles.

LAMB, JEFF (Gros Ventre)
(association president)
Affiliation: Native American Finance Officers Association, P.O. Box 50637, Phoenix, AZ 85076-0637 (602) 532-6295. E-mail: jlamb@millerschroeder.com.

LAMB-RICHARD, TRUDIE (Schaghticoke)
(storyteller & teacher)
Born & raised on the Schaghticoke Reservation in northwestern Connecticut. *Affiliation & Address*: Director of Public Programs, Mashantucket Pequot Museum & Research Center, P.O. Box 3180, Mashantucket, CT 06338 (800) 411-9671. *Past professional posts*: Director of Education for Public Programs (1988-93), Assistant Director ((1993-96), Institute for American Indian Studies, Washington, CT; Tribal Historian in Residence for 2011, University of Massachusetts, Amherst, MA.

LAMBERT, LORI (Mi'kmaq/Abenaki)
(medical ecologist/anthropologist; dept. head)
Education: Temple University, BS (Therapeutic Recreation). *Affiliation & Address*: Head, Native American Studies Department, Salish Kootenai College, P.O. Box 70, Pablo, MT 59855 (406) 675-4800. E-mail: lori_lambert@skc.edu. *Past professional posts*: E-learning Coordinator, Salish Kootenai College, 1995-2013; Assistant Education Director, Schuylkill Center for Environmental Education, 1984-94; Adjunct Faculty, Penn State University, 1984-94. *Awards, honors*: Received the prestigious Andrew W. Mellon Fellowship for Faculty Research from the American Indian College Fund.

LAMBERT, PATRICK (Eastern Cherokee)
(former tribal principal chief)
Affiliation & Address: Former Principal Chief, Eastern Band of Cherokee Indians, Qualla Boundary, P.O. Box 455, Cherokee, NC 28719 (828) 497-7000.

LAMBERT, VALERIE (Choctaw)
(professor of anthropology)
Affiliation & Address: Associate Professor, Department of Anthropology, University of North Carolina, Chapel Hill, NC 27599 (919) 962-4645. E-mail: vlambert@unc.edu. *Other professional post*: President, Association of Indigenous Anthropologists, section of American Anthropological Association, Arlington, VA. *Awards, honors*: Won the 2003 Edward Kidder Graham Award (for undergraduate teaching); winner of the 2006 North American Indian Prose Award for *Choctaw Nation*. *Membership*: President-elect, Association of Indigenous Anthropologists, 2008-Present. *Published work*: Native Spiritual Traditions and the Tribal State: The Oklahoma Choctaws in the Late Twentieth Century, in Niezen, Ronald. Spirit Wars: Native North American Religions in the Age of Nation-Building. (University of California Press, 2000); Choctaws in Oklahoma: Government. In Choctaw Language & Culture by Marcia Haag & Henry Willis. (University of Oklahoma Press, 2001); Contemporary Ritual Life. In Choctaw Language & Culture by Marcia Haag and Henry Willis. (University of Oklahoma Press, 2001); Choctaw Nation: A Story of American Indian Resurgence (University of Nebraska Press, 2007).

LA MERE, FRANK DEAN (Winnebago) 1950-
(executive director)
Born March 1, 1950, Sioux City, Iowa. *Education*: Nebraska Indian Community College, AA, 1989; Bellevue (NE) College, BS (Professional Studies), 1992. *Address*: 600 Pioneer Place, So. Sioux City, NE 68776 (402) 878-2242. *Affiliation & Address*: Executive Director, Nebraska Indian Inter-Tribal Development Corp., Rt. 1, Box 66A, Winnebago, NE 68071. *Other professional posts*: Chairperson, Nebraska Indian Commission; Board of Trustees of Nebraska Indian Community College, JTPA Indian & National Native American Advisory Commission; NE State Job Training Coordinating Council; NE Rural Development Commission; Board Member, National Rainbow Coalition; member, Winnebago Health Planning Committee. *Community activities*: Chairperson of National Indian Democrats; Associate Chairperson of NE Democratic Party; member of Democratic National Committee; Board of NE Wildlife Federation; Parents Advisory Council of University of Nebraska; Board of Counselors, NE Medical Center; Core Planning Committee-Dakota County Law Enforcement. *Interests*: Experienced motivational speaker & political activist. Also, founder of the NO Americans, the International Indian fast pitch softball team headquartered in Nebraska, 1991.

LAMOREAUX, LARRY (Ponca)
(tribal vice chairperson)
Affiliation & Address: Chairperson, Ponca Tribe of Nebraska, P.O. Box 288, Niobrara, NE 68760 (402) 857-3391. E-mail: poncapatrick@gmail.com

LANDIS, BARBARA 1951-
(biographer)
Born September 1, 1951, N. Tonawanda, N.Y. *Principal occupation*: Carlisle Indian School biographer. *Address & Affiliation*: Cumberland County Historical Society, P.O. Box 626, Carlisle, PA 17013 (717) 249-7610. E-Mail: blandis@epix.net. *Membership*: American Studies Association. *Interest*: Carlisle Indian School research.

LANDLORD, JAMES C (Yup'ik Eskimo)
(Alaskan tribal first chief)
Affiliation: First Chief, Asa'carsarmiut Tribe, P.O. Box 32249, Mountain Village, AK 99632 (907) 591-2814.

LANDLORD, TRINA (Yup'ik Eskimo)
(executive director)
Born in Bethel, grew up in Mountain Village & Anchorage, Alaska & Pennsylvania. *Affiliation & Address*: Executive Director, Alaska Native Arts Foundation, 500 West 6th Ave., Anchorage, AK 99501 (907) 258-2623. E-mail: trina@alaskanativearts.org. *Other professional posts*: Serves on the Boards for the Food Bank of Alaska & Alaska Native Heritage Month. *Past professional posts*: Liaison with the Alaska Humanities Forum; Communications Coordinator, Alaska Marketplace; she worked at the U.S. Department of the Interior; consulting & freelance writing with Alaska Native Tribal Health Consortium, First Alaskans Instsitute & Shell Exploration & Production Co. *Awards, honors*: 2006, Alaska's Top Forty Under 40.

LANDRETH, NATALIE A. (Chickasaw)
(attorney)
Education: Harvard College, BA, 1996; Harvard Law School, JD, 2001. *Affiliation & Address*: Staff Attorney (2003-present), Native American Rights Fund (NARF), 745 West 4th Ave. Suite 502, Anchorage, AK 99501 (907) 276-0680. While in law school, she served as vice president of the Harvard Native American Law Students Association ans as an Associate Editor for the Harvard Environmental Law Review, and clerked for the Supreme Court of the Navajo Nation. After graduation, she clerked for the Honorable Dana Fabe, then Chief Justice on the Alaska Supreme Court in Anchorage, Alaska. Natalie practices a broad range if Indian law from jurisdiction issues to fishing rights. She also works in the area of voting rights. She recently co-authored a report on the impact of the Voting Rights Act in Alaska called, "Voting Rights in Alaska 1982-2006." This report prompted her to be called to testify before U.. Senate Judiciary Committee in May of 2006. *Other professional posts*: Serves on the NARF's Litigation Management Committee, which manages the other attorneys and determines which cases to bring; chair of the Alaska Native Law Section of the Alaska Bar Association, and a board member on Alaska Dance Theatre and the Alaska Center for the Performing Arts.

LANE, ALFRED "BUD" III (Siletz)
(tribal vice chairperson)
Affiliation & Address: Vice Chairperson, Confederated Tribes of the Siletz Indian Reservation, P.O. Box 549, Siletz, OR 97380 (541) 444-2532. *Address*: P.O. Box 715, Siletz, OR 97380 (541) 444-1258. E-mail: budl@ctsi.nsn.us.

LANE, PHIL, JR. (Yankton Dakota/Chickasaw) 1944-
(hereditary chief)
Born at the Haskell Indian School in Lawrence, Kans. in 1944. *Affiliation & Address*: Chairperson, Four Directions International, P.O. Box 75028 Surrey, BC V4A 0B1 Canada (604) 542-8991. A Native American-owned company, which was incorporated in 1996 as Four Worlds' Economic Development Arm. *Past professional posts*: He served for 16 years as associate professor & founder & chairperson of the Four Worlds International Institute for Human & Community Development, University of Lethbridge, Alberta, Canada. Four Worlds became an independent Institute in 1995.

LANE, TRAVIS L. (Southern Ute/Navajo)
(outreach coordinator)
Education: WINS Program, Washington Internships for Native Students, American University, Washington, DC, Fall 2001; University of Arizona, BA (Political Science with a minor in American Indian Studies), 2002. *Affiliation & Address*: Outreach Coordinator, University of Arizona and Inter Tribal Council of Arizona, Inc. Indians Into Medicine (INMED) Program, Tucson, AZ 85721. He provides outreach & recruitment activities for K-12 American Indian students to enter into health professions as a career. In addition, he works on various health, education, & policy projects including coordinating voter outreach to tribes in Arizona.

LANG, RANDY D.
(attorney-Indian law)
Education: American College of Law, California, AA (Law & Business), BSL (Law), JD. *Affiliation & Address*: Integrated Legal Services & Associates (1989-present), P.O. Box 83958, Phoenix, AZ 85017 (623) 210-6166 Fax 537-7378. *Past professional posts*: Corporate Risk Officer, Oxford Health Network, 2013-

15; Assistant Prosecutor II, Office of the Prosecutor, San Carlos Apache Tribe, 2008-12. Awards, honors: American Jurisprudence Award for Academic Excelence in Law & Medicine & Appellate Advocacy.

LANKFORD, CAROLE (Salish & Kootenai)
  (former tribal vice chairperson)
Affiliation & Address: Former Vice Chair, Confederated Salish & Kootenai Tribes, P.O. Box 278, Pablo, MT 59855 (406) 675-2700. E-mail: clankford@cskt.org.

LANKFORD, DOUGLAS G. (Miami)
  (tribal chief)
Affiliation & Address: Chief, Miami Tribe of Oklahoma, P.O. Box 1326, Miami, OK 74355 (918) 542-1445.

LAPENA, FRANK (*Tauhindauli*) (Maidu/Wintu-Nomtipom) 1937-
  (teacher; poet & painter)
Born October 5, 1937, San Francisco, Calif. *Education*: Chico State College, BA; San Francisco State University, Secondary Life Credential; California State University, Sacramento, MA. *Principal occupation*: Teacher. *Address*: 1531 42nd St., Sacramento, CA 95819 (916) 278-6645. *Affiliation*: Professor, California State University, Sacramento, CA. *Other professional post*: Commissioner of California State Capitol. *Awards, honors*: 1988 Meritorious Performance & Professional Promise Award, California State University, Sacramento. *Interests*: Native American art: traditional & contemporary - emphasis on California; traditional dance & ceremony. *Published work*: World Is a Gift (Limestone Press, 1987).

LEROY "J.R." LaPLANTE (*Tasunke Waste*) (Cheyenne River Lakota)
  (attorney; secretary of tribal relations; tribal chief judge)
Born at Eagle Butte, S.D. *Education*: JD. J.R. is a practicing attorney in Vermillion (SD) and served as Chief Judge and Court Administrator for the Crow Creek Tribe in Fort Thompson (SD). *Affiliation & Address*: Secretary, South Dakota Department of Tribal Relations, 302 East Dakota, Pierre, SD 57501 (605) 773-3415. *Past professional posts*: Administative Officer, Cheyenne River Sioux Tribe; J.R. has an extensive background working for Native American human service organizations.

LaPLANTE, JAY (Blackfoot/Cree)
  (project director; tribal lisiason)
Born & raised on the Blackfeet Reservation in Montana. *Education*: Portland State University, BA (English). *Affiliation & Address*: Founding Board member & Project Director, Native Wellness Institute, 2830 SE Cleveland Dr., Gresham, OR 97080 (406) 450-3373. E-mail: jay@nativewellness.com. *Other professional post*: Tribal Liaison, Center for Clinical & Epidemiological Research, University of Washington's School of Medicine. For 19 years, Jay has provided training & technical assistance on community building approaches to prevent suicide, substance abuse, child abuse & neglect, HIV/STDs, and other social, health, education, and political issues.

LaPOINTE, DARLA (Winnebago)
  (tribal councilmember)
Affiliation & Address: Councilperson, Winnebago Tribal Council, P.O. Box 687, Winnebago, NE 68071 (402) 878-3129. E-mail: darla.lapointe@ winnebagotribe.com. *Past professional post*: Tribal Chairperson

LaPOINTE, JEROME (Winnebago)
  (tribal newspaper editor)
Affiliation: Winnebago Indian News, Winnebago Indian Tribe of Nebraska, P.O. Box 687, Winnebago, NE 68071 (402) 878-3220.

LaPOINTE, LaMOINE (Rosebud Sioux)
  (board vice chairperson)
Affiliation: Vice Chairperson, Board of Directors, American Indian Opportunities Industrialization Center (AIOIC), 1845 East Franklin Ave., Minneapolis, MN 55404 (612) 341-3358. E-mail: info@aioic.org

LaPOINTE, LAWRENCE W. (Puyallup)
  (tribal vice chairperson)
Affiliation & Address: Vice Chairperson, Puyallup Tribal Council, 2002 East 28th St., Tacoma, WA 98404 (253) 597-6200. Serving his 6th term on the council. *Military service*: U.S. Marine Corps (Vietnam Vet).

LaPOINTE, CAROL L. (Lake Superior Band of Chippewa)
  (tribal vice president)
Affiliation & Address: Vice President, L'Anse Reservation, Keweenaw Bay Indian Community of Michigan, 107 Beartown Rd., Baraga, MI 49908 (906) 353-6623.

LaPOINTE, TIMOTHY L.
  (BIA regional director)
Affiliation & Address: Director, Great Plains Regional Office, Bureau of Indian Affairs, 15 4th Ave. Southeast, Suite 400, Aberdeen, SD 57401 (605) 226-7343. E-mail: timothy.lapointe@bia.gov The Great Plains Regional Director is responsible for the direction & oversight of Bureau responsibilities & activities as they pertain to the mission and goals of the Department of Interior and the Bureau of Indian Affairs.

LARIMORE, COLLEEN K. (Comanche) 1963-
  (student support services)
Born March 3, 1963, Lakewood, N.J. *Education*: Dartmouth College, AB, 1985; Harvard University, EdM, 1990. *Principal occupation*: Director, Native American program. *Address*: Dartmouth College, Student Support Services, First Year Office, Hanover, NH 03755. *Affiliations*: Dartmouth College, Hanover, NH (assistant director, Native American Recruiter, 1985-88; Office of Admissions, acting director of Minority Recruitment, 1988-89; director, Native American Program, 1990-93; student support services, First Year Office, 2002-present); Harvard University, Cambridge, MA (administrative intern, American Indian Program, 1989-90). *Memberships*: National Indian Education Association, 1985-; National Association of Women Deans & Counselors, 1990-. *Interests*: "As a Comanche Indian & a first-generation college graduate, my interest in teaching & minority education stems from my own odyssey through the educational system and the history of my family, my tribe & Native peoples in general. My research interests include: cultural styles of learning evinced among Native American students; the diversification of teaching methods to address learning differences; the advent of the tribally controlled community colleges, & these institutions' growing success in establishing tribal culture as a viable & effective curriculum base for their students & the communities they serve."

LARIMORE, JAMES (Comanche)
  (college dean)
Affiliation & Address: Dean, Dartmouth College, The Sherman House, 37 N. Main St., Hanover, NH 03755 (603) 646-3530

LaROQUE, MIC, M.D. (Turtle Mountain Chippewa)
  (physician; association treasurer)
Affiliation: Treasurer, Association of American Indian Physicians, 1225 Sovereign Row #103, Oklahoma City, OK 73108 (405) 946-7072.

LaROSE, ARTHUR "ARCHIE" (Ojibwe)
  (tribal secretary-treasurer)
Affiliation & Address: Secretary-Treasurer, Leech Lake Band of Ojibwe, 190 Sailstar Dr. NW E, Cass Lake, MN 56633 (218) 335-8200. *Past tribal post*: Chairperson.

LARSEN, MIKE (Chickasaw) 1944-
  (artist, author)
Education: Amarillo Junior College, AA, 1964; University of Houston, BA, 1966; Arts Student League, New York, NY. *Address & Affiliation*: Larsen Studio, P.O. Box 160, Perkins, OK 74059 (405) 210-4945. E-mail: mike@larsenstudio.com. Commissioned by the State of Oklahoma to paint a 26 foot-long mural for the Capitol Rotunda; paint eight murals about local Native American History for the Oklahoma Art Institute; six murals for the University of Oklahoma Reynolds Performing Art Center & School of Dance. In 2008, Mike completed the two-year project of eight murals for the Pokagon Band Potawatomi Tribe in Michigan; the Chickasaw Nation's Living Elders project currently hanging in the Oklahoma Heritage Center; recently completed a public commission for a twice life sized sculpture for St. Joseph's Regional Health Center in Patterson, NJ; preparing a project on the Civil War in Oklahoma. *Awards, honors*: Created the 2007 Centennial U.S. postage stamp celebrating Oklahoma. *Published works*: They Know Who They Are: Elders of the Chickasaw Nation (Chickasaw Press, 2008); Proud to Be Chickasaw (Chickasaw Press, 2010).

LARSEN, ROBERT (Mdewakanton Sioux)
  (tribal chairperson)
Affiliation & Address: Chairperson, Lower Sioux Indian Community, P.O. Box 308, Morton, MN 56270 (507) 697-6185. E-mail: robert.larsen@lowersioux.com.

LARSON, CHRIS G. (Eskimo)
  (Alaskan village president)
Affiliation & Address: President, Native Village of Napaskiak, P.O. Box 6009, Napaskiak, AK 99559 (907) 737-7364.

LARSON, PETER A.
  (attorney)
Education: University of Washington, BA, 1996; Arizona State University Sandra Day O'Connor College of Law, JD, Indian Law Certificate, 2002; New York Univesity School of Law, LL.M Taxation, 2003. *Affiliation & Address*:

Partner, Trbal Affairs, Gaming & Public Fnance practice groups, Lewis Roca Rothgerber, LLP, 201 E. Washington St., Suite 1200, Phoenix, AZ 85004 (602) 262-5796. E-mail: plarson@lrrlaw.com Mr. Larson's transactional practice focuses on representing Indian tribes, tribal entities & those pursuing coomecial & economic development in Indian Country. He has considerable experience in all areas of Indian gaming, including Indian lands determinations, federal, state & tribal regulatory matters, and representations of tribal gaming agencies. *Memberships*: Indan Law Section of the State Bar of Arizona, Board Member; Indian Law Program at the O'Connor College of Law, Advisory Council Member; Intertribal Court of Southernn California Tribal Bar Association.

LATTY, THEODORE H.
(attorney; Native American practice)
Affiliation & Address: Partner, Gaming & Native American Practice, Hughes Hubbard & Reed LLP, 350 S. Grand Ave., Los Angeles, CA 90071 (213) 613-2808; E-mail: latty@hugheshubbard.com

LAUGHLIN, DON (Mojave)
(casino operator)
Affiliation & Address: Operator, Mojave Casino, 500 Merriman Ave., Needles, CA 92363 (619) 326-4591.

LAUGHLIN, SARAH
(Indian program coordinator)
Affiliation: Portal Program of the Palace of the Governors, P.O. Box 2087, Santa Fe, NM 87504 (505) 827-6474. *Products*: Traditional crafts of the 22 recognized New Mexico tribes and pueblos.

LAVELLE, JOHN P. (Santee Sioux)
(professor of law; attorney)
Education: Harvard University, BA, 1987; University of Caiforrnia, Berkeley, School of Law, JD, 1990. *Affiliation & Address*: Dickason Professor of Law, Director, Indian Law Program, University of New Mexico School of Law, 1117 Stanford NE, MSC11 6070, Albuquerque, NM 87131 (505) 277-0951. E-mail: lavelle@law.unm.edu. *Other professional posts*: Professor LaVelle is a member of the executive committee for *Cohen's Handbook of Federal Indian Law*, the preeminent treatise in the field of Indian law. In that capacity he helped author and edit the watershed 2005 edition of *Cohen's Handbook* as well as the treatise's 2007 supplemental update. *Past professional post*: He has also served as a co-chair and of the Federal Bar Association's annual Indian Law Conference, held each spring in Albuquerque, and as chair of the Association of American Law Schools Section on Indian Nations and Indigenous Peoples. *Memberships*: Co-chair of the Federal Bar Association's annual Indian Law Conference, held each Spring in Albuquerque; and as chair of the Association of American Law Schools Section on Indian Nations & Indigenous Peoples; Center for Support & Protection of Indian Religions & Indigenous Traditions, National Congress of American Indians, Washington, DC. *Awards, honors*: Dean's Award for Distinguished Law School Service. *Published works*: Professor LaVelle's publications address Indian people's involvement in the American political system, crosscurrents in the United States Supreme Court's Indian law and federalism jurisprudence, and collaboration between Indian tribes & conservation organizations for restoring tribal sacred lands, including the Black Hills of South Dakota.

LAVERDURE, DONALD "DEL" (Crow)
(attorney; consultant)
Education: University of Arizona, BS, 1995; University of Wisconsin Law School, JD, 1999. *Affiliation & Address*: Consulant, Akin Gump Straus Hauer & Feld, LLP, Robert E. Straus Bldg., 1333 New Hampshire Ave. NW, Washington, DC 20036 (202) 887-4000; E-mail: dlaverdure@akingump.com. Del is a strategic advisor advising Indian tribeson natural resources & tax matters, as well as on federal & tribal legislative matters. *Other professional post*: Senor advisor & counselor, Crow Nation Chairperson, Darrin Old Coyote. *Past professional posts*: Chief legal counsel for the executive branch of the Crow Tribe; held numerous judgeships; assistant professor of law. *Awards, honors*: In the fall of 2000, he was selected for President Clinton's White House Initiative on Tribal Colleges & Universities; appointed in 2009 by President Obama to serve at the Department of the Interior, and he served almost all of Obama's first term as acting assistant secretary, principal deputy assistant secretary, and deputy assistant secretary for Indian affairs in Washington, DC. Mr. Laverdure has written, testified (in U.S. & Canadian legislative bodies) and spoken extensively on a variety of Indian lw topics. He co-created & taught courses for the first four Crow Tribal Bar Exams.

LAWRENCE, WILLIAM J. (Red Lake Chippewa) 1939-
(publisher)
Born August 31, 1939, Red Lake Chippewa Reservation, Minn. *Education*: BA in Business Administration & JD. *Address*: 3501 Lakeside Dr. #2 NE, Bemidji, MN 56601 (218) 444-7800. E-mail: presson@isd.net. *Affiliation*: Publisher of the weekly newspaper Native American Press/Ojibwe News. *Community*

activities: President, Minnesota Minority Media Coalition. *Military service*: U.S. Marine Corps, 1962-66 (Commissioned Officer; served in Vietnam). *Membership*: National Rifle Association. *Published works*: "Tribal Justice: Red Lake Court of Indian Offenses," in the North Dakota Law Review, summer, 1972 (vol. 48, no. 4); "In Defense of Indian Right," essay in book on race entitled, Beyond Victimization (Hoover Institution Press, 2000).

LAWSON, ALLEN E. (Kumeyaay Diegueno)
(tribal chairperson; entrepreneur & businessman)
Affiliation & Address: Chairperson (1997-present), San Pasqual Band of Diegueno Indians, P.O. Box 365, Valley Center, CA 92082 (760) 749-3200. *Other professional posts*: Vice President, California Nevada Indian Gaming Commission; member, Southern California Tribal Chairman's Association.

LAWSON, MICHAEL
(historian)
Affiliations: Presently manages the office of Historical Research Associates (a consulting firm specializing in cultural & environmental resource management and litigation support) in Washington, DC; formerly the senior historian for the Bureau of Indian Affairs. *Published works*: Dammed Indians: The Pick-Sloan Plan and the Missouri River Sioux, 1944-1980 (University of Oklahoma Press, 1982).

LAWSON, SARAH (Miami)
(tribal secretary-treasurer)
Affiliation & Address: Secretary-Treasurer, Miami Tribe of Oklahoma, P.O. Box 1326, Miami, OK 74355 (918) 541-1300.

LAWSON, SARAH ROUBIDOUX (Iowa of Kansas & Nebraska)
(attorney)
Education: University of Michigan, BA, 1999; University of Wisconsin Law School, JD, 2004; University of Washington School of Law, MA of Law (in progress). *Affiliation & Address*: Of Counsel, Schwabe, Williamson & Wyatt, 1420 5th Ave., Suite 3400, Seattle, WA 98101 (206) 407-1507. E-mail: slawson@schwabe.com Lawson began her work in Indian Country as in intern with the Assembly of First Nations in Canada, where her research on Indian residential school abuse & impacts laid the groundwork for the Indian Residential Settlement Agreement (IRSSA). During law school she was a law clerk for the Oneida Indian Tribe of Wisconsin and the Native American Rights Fund in Washington D.C., where she worked on the Indian trust class action suit Cobell v. Salazar. Lawson serves as an appellate judge for the Northwest Intertribal Court System and has taught courses on the history of federal Indian policy, rights of tribes, Indian self-determination, & legal studies for Northwest Indian College. She is as a member of the boards of the Northwest Indian Bar Association, National Tribal Land Association, and is past president of the board of directors for Red Eagle Soaring Native Youth Theater. Prior to joining Schwabe, Lawson served as General Counsel for the Snoqualmie Indian Tribe, Trust Services Director for the Muckleshoot Indian Tribe, and Assistant Attorney General for the Tohono O'Odham Nation in Sells, Arizona. Lawson received her Juris Doctorate from the University of Wisconsin, and is admitted to practice in Washington, Wisconsin & Arizona. *Professional & Community Activities*: President Elect, Northwest Indian Bar Assn; Board of Directors, Tribal In-House Counsel Assn (the 's' was left off online); Board of Directors, National Tribal Land Assn; King County Bar Assn Diversity Committee; Lawyers Committee for Civil Rights, Washington State Judicial Diversity Program; Past President, Red Eagle Soaring Native Youth Theater Board of Directors; Leadership Tomorrow, Class of 2014. *Awards, honors*: National Native American Law Students Association Alumni of the Year

LEAKE, ROBIN
(research manager)
Education: State University of New York at Stony Brook, PhD (Social/Health Psychology). *Affiliation & Address*: Research Manager, Butler Institute for Families, University of Denver, Craig Hall, 2148 S. High St., Denver, CO 80208 (303) 871-6813. E-mail: robin.leake@du.edu. The Butler Institute serves as the Evaluation Partner for the National Child Welfare Resource Center for Tribes (NRC4Tribes). Robin is the primary author of the NRC4Tribes' National Needs Assessment of American Indian/Alaska Native Child Welfare Programs. Dr. Leake has authored several publications & presentations.

LE BEAU, RYMAN (Cheyenne River Sioux)
(tribal vice chairperson)
Affiliation & Address: Vice Chairperson, Cheyenne River Sioux Tribe, P.O. Box 590, Eagle Butte, SD 57625 (605) 964-6685.

LEAP, WILLIAM L. 1946-
(anthropologist)
Born November 28, 1946, Philadelphia, Pa. *Education*: Florida State University, BA, 1967; Southern Methodist University, PhD (Anthropology), 1970. Principal occupation: Anthropologist. *Affiliation & Address*: Professor of Anthropology, Department of Anthropology, American University, 4400

Massachusetts Ave., NW, Washington, DC 20016 (202) 885-1830 (work), 1970-. *Other professional post*: Director, Indian Education Program, Center for Applied Linguistics, Arlington, VA, 1974-79; director, Indian Education, National Congress of American Indians, Washington DC, 1980-83. *Awards, honors*: 1986 Finalist, Washington Association of Practicing Anthropologists' PRAXIS Award for outstanding achievement in anthropological problem-solving. *Interests*: "My vocational interests center on Indian self-determination through education. A major component of such a strategy is relevant education, and that means addressing the Indian (e.g. tribal or traditional) as well as the mainstream cultural components of the student's interests, lifestyle, and life-options. My work in the field has centered on assisting Tribal governments and Tribal agencies develop programs to provide Tribal members to take charge of and manage such programs without reliance on outside sources of support." *Published works*: Language Policies in Indian Education: Recommendations, 1973, and Handbook for Staff Development in Indian Education, 1976 (Center for Applied Linguistics); Studies in Southwestern Indian English (Trinity University Press, 1977); American Indian Language Education (National Bilingual Research Center, 1980); American Indian Language Renewal in Annual Review of Anthropology, 1981; Assumptions and strategies in Mathematics Problem-Solving by Ute Indian Students in Linguistic and Cultural Factors in Mathematics Education, edited by Rodney Cocking and Jose Metre (Erlbaum Press, 1987); Applied Linguistics and American Indian Language Renewal (Human Organization - Journal of the Society for Applied Anthropology,1989); Pathways & Barriers to Indian Language Literacy - Building on the Northern Ute Reservation (Anthropology & Education Quarterly, 1991); American Indian English (University of Utah Press, 1993).

LEASK, JANIE (Haida/Tsimshean) 1948-
(organization president)
Born September 17, 1948, Seattle, Wash. *Education*: East Anchorage High School, 1966. *Affiliation*: Alaska Federation of Natives, 411 W. 4th Ave., Suite 301, Anchorage, 1974- (vice president, 1977-82; president, 1982-). *Address*: 7021 Hunt Ave., Anchorage, AK 99504 (907) 274-3611 (work). *Community activities*: Enrolled in Cook Inlet Region (one of the 12 in-state Alaska Native Regional corporations); The State Board of Education; the Anchorage Organizing Committee for the 1992 Olympics; the Alaska Land Use Council; the ARCO Scholarship Committee. *Awards, honors*: Governor's Award in 1983 for work on behalf of Alaska Native people.

LEAVELLE, TRACY
(director of Native American studies; professor of history)
Education: Dartmouth College, BA (Anthropology & Native American Studies); Arizona State University, PhD (History). *Affiliation & Address*: Professor of History & Director (2003-present), Native American Studies Program, Creighton University, 2500 California Plaza, Admin. 437, Omaha, NE 68178 (402) 280-2652. E-mail: tracy.leavelle@creighton.edu. *Past professional post*: Smith College (Woodrow Wilson Foundation Postdoctoral Fellow in the Humanities, 2001-03. *Published works*: Encounters of Spirit: Religion, Culture, and Community in French & Indian North America (in progress).

LeBEAU, EDWARD A. (Cheyenne River Sioux) 1941-
(contracting specialist, public health advisor)
Born June 14, 1941, Cheyenne Agency, S.D. *Education*: Minot State University, BA, 1965. *Principal occupation*: Contracting specialist, public health advisor. *Address*: 1323 Minnesota Ave., Bemidji, MN 56601 (218) 751-7701. *Affiliations*: Tribal projects coordinator, Indian Health Service, Bemidji, MN, 1981-. *Military service*: U.S. Army, 1985-87. Northern Minnesota Indian Athletic Association (charter member, 1973-).

LeBEAU, MONTE
(former BIA agency supt.)
Affiliation & Address: Supt. Bureau of Indian Affairs, P.O. Box 270, Fort Totten, ND 58335 (701) 766-4545. E-mail: monte.lebeau@bia.gov

LeBEAU, R. REID, II (Cheyenne River Sioux)
(attorney)
Born & raised in Pierre, S.D. *Education*: University of Minnesota-Morris, BA, 2002; University of Minnesota, Minneapolis, Law School, JD (cum laude), 2005. He was the 2001 Truman Scholar from the State of South Dakota. *Affiliation & Address*: Staff Attorney (2005-present), The Jacobson Law Group, 1295 Bandana Blvd., St. Paul, MN 55108 (651) 644-4710. E-mail: rrlebeau@thejacobsonlawgroup.com. *Practice areas*: Campaign Finance, Election Law, Indian/Tribal Law. As a litigator, Mr. LeBeau practices in the areas of Indian Law & Campaign Finance & Election Law. As a lobbyist, he lobbies on behalf of tribes in Minnesota & South Dakota before both the state legislature and Congress. *Other professional posts*: Treasurer of the Indian Health Board of Minneapolis; founder of the Congressman Ben Reifel Memorial Scholarship.

LeCLAIR, LIONEL (Ponca)
(former tribal chairperson)
Address & Affiliation: Ponca Tribe, 20 White Eagle Dr., Ponca City, OK 74601 (580) 762-8104.

LEE, ALVINA (Navajo-Dine)
(attorney)
Education: University of Denver, BA, 2000. University of Colorado School of Law, JD, 2003. *Affiliation & Address*: Associate (2008-present), Fredericks Peebles & Morgan, LLP, 1900 Plaza Dr., Louisville, CO 80027 (303) 673-9600. *Practice areas*: Federal Indian Law; Tribal Government; Tribal Court & Federal Court Litigation; Legislative Law; Energy & Natural Resource Law; Environmental Law; Housing & Taxation Law. *Past professional posts*: Law clerk, Colorado Attorney General's Office, Denver, CO; law clerk, U.S. EPA, Air Enforcement Division, Lakewood, CO; law clerk, Fredericks, Pelcyger & Hester, LLC, Louisville, CO; prior to joining Fredericks Peebles & Morgan, Ms. Lee worked as a law clerk for Kamlet, Shepherd & Reichert, LLP, Denver, CO.

LEE, ANDREW J. (Seneca)
(director of research & policy analysis)
Born & raised in Connecticut. His extended family lives on the Seneca Nation's Cattaraugus Indian Reservation in western New York State. *Education*: Hamilton College, BA; Harvard's John F. Kennedy School of Government, MA. *Affiliation*: Director of Research & Policy Analysis, Aetna, Inc. He currently serves on the board of directors of the Smithsonian's Heye Center of the National Museum of the American Indian, the board of directors (vice-chair) of Indian Dispute Resolution Services, Inc.; the executive committee of the Harvard University Native American Program's faculty-advisory board; the advisory committee for Youth Build USA's Tribal Initiative; and the tribal policy board for The Institute of Tribal Government at Portland State University. *Past professional post*: Executive Director, Harvard Project on American Indian Economic Development, 1998-2004; founded "Honoring Nations," an annual awards program administered by the Harvard Project; prior to his appointment at Harvard in 1998, Mr. Lee worked in the Governance and Civil Society unit of the Ford Foundation's Peace & Social Justice Program

LEE, ANTHONY J. (White Mountain Apache)
(attorney; legal counsel)
Address: White Mountain Apache Tribe, P.O. Box 3931, Pinetop, AZ 85935 (928) 338-4346. *Affiliation*: Staff Attorney, American Indian Law Center, Inc., P.O. Box 4456, Albuquerque, NM 87196 (505) 277-5462. E-mail: lee@ailc-inc.org. *Other professional posts*: Chief Judge, San Manuel band of Mission Indians, Highland, CA; Legal counsel, Foxwoods Resort Casino, Mashantucket, CT; Board Secretary, Alzheimer's Association, Rochester, NY.

LEE, DARLENE (Ponca)
(tribal executive director)
Affiliation & Address: Ponca Tribe of Nebraska, P.O. Box 288, Niobrara, NE 68760 (402) 857-3391. E-mail: darlenel@poncatribe-ne.org

LEE, ISAIAH (Navajo-Dine)
(school principal)
Affiliation & Address: Cibecue Community School, P.O. Box 80068, Cibecue, AZ 85911 (520) 332-2480.

LEE, JEFFERY (Mono)
(tribal chairperson)
Affiliation & Address: Chairperson, Cold Springs Tribe of Mono Indians, P.O. Box 209, Tollhouse, CA 93667 (559) 855-5043. E-mail: csrancheriajeff@netptc.net.

LEE, JENNIE M. (Eskimo)
(Alaskan village president)
Affiliation & Address: Teller Traditional Council, P.O. Box 567, Teller, AK 99778 (907) 642-3381.

LEE, LLOYD (Navajo-Dine')
(professor of Native American studies)
Education: Dartmouth College, BA, 1994; Stanford University, MA (Education), 1995; University of New Mexico, PhD (American Studies), 2004. His dissertation titled, "21st Century Dine Cultural Identity: Defining & Practicing Sa'ah Naaghai Bik'eh Hozhoon," examined cultural identity among Navajo college graduates & college students. *Affiliation & Address*: Associate Professor, Native American Studies (NAS) Dept. (2007-present), University of New Mexico, Mesa Vista 3080, Albuquerque, NM 87131 (505) 277-3917; E-mail: nasinfo@unm.edu. His research focuses on American Indian identity, gender specifically Navajo masculinities, leadership, philosophies, transformative research, & American Indian community building. *Other professional post*: Book review editor, American Indian Quarterly. *Past professional posts*: Taught U.S. History & Native American Studies, Wingate High School (BIA), Gallup, NM; Arizona State University, Language, Culture &

History Dept., 2004-07. *Published works*: Dine' Masculinities: Conceptualizations & Reflections (2013) edited Dine' Perspectives: Reclaiming & Revitalizing Navajo Thought (2014); numerous articles in Wicazo Sa Review, Fall 2006, Spring 2007, Winter 2008.

LEE, KIMBERLI ANN
(associate professor of Native American languages & literature)
Education: Tarleton State University, MA (English), 197; University of Nebraska-Lincoln, PhD (English; Native American literature, history & Lakota language), 2003. *Affiliation & Address*: Associate Professor of Languages & Literature (2010-present), Department of Cherokee & Indigenous Studies, Northeastern State University, Seminary Hall 313, 609 N. Grand Ave., Tahlequah, OK 74464 (517) 775-1966; E-mail: lee36@nsuok.edu *Past professional posts*: Graduate Teaching Assistant Director. Aug 2010-2015. (Tenure granted May 2014) Visiting Assistant Professor. Michigan State University; Department of Writing, Rhetoric, and American Cultures. Core Faculty in Rhetoric and Writing; Faculty in American Indian Studies. August 2004-May 2010. Adjunct Instructor. Tarleton State University; Department of English and Languages. August 2003-May 2004. Adjunct Instructor. McLennan County College; Department of English and Communications. August 2001-December 2001. Adjunct Instructor. Central Texas College; Department of English and Communications. Department of Communications. January 1998-May 1998.

LEE, MOLLY (Inuit)
(professor of anthropology)
Affiliation & Address: Professor, Dept. of Anthropology, University of Alaska, 3211 Providence Dr., Anchorage, AK 99508 (907) 786-6840. *Interests*: Alaska Native & Inuit art of the historical & contemporary periods. E-mail: ffmcl@uaa.alaska.edu.

LEE, TIFFANY S. (*Dibe Lizhini - Blacksheep*) (Dine'/Lakota)
(asociate director & professor of Native American studies)
Born & raised in Crystal, N.M. on the Navajo Nation. *Education*: Stanford University, PhD (Sociology of Education). *Affiliation & Address*: Associate Director & Professor of Native American Studies, Native American Studies (NAS) Program, University of New Mexico, Mesa Vista 3080, Albuquerque, NM 87131 (505) 277-3917; E-mail: nasinfo@ unm.edu. *Other professional post*: Member, Executive Board, Independent Television Service (ITVS). *Research Interests*: Her research focuses on Indigenous education & language socialization experiences and the effects of competing language ideologies on Native students' commitment to (re)learning their heritage languages. *Awards, honors*: 2003 Postdoctoral fellowship from the American Educational Research Association. *Published works*: Indigenous Youth & Multilingualism: Language Identity, Idealogy, and Practice in Dynamic Cultural Worlds (Rutledge Press); Cultural Transformations: Youth & Pedagogies of ossibility (Harvard Education Press); Leadership & Accountability in American Indian Education: Voices from New Mexico, in American Journal of Education; Dineperspectives: Revitalizing & Reclaiming Navajo Thought (University of Arizona Press).

LEECY, KEVIN (Ojibwe)
(former tribal chairperson)
Affiliation & Address: Bois Forte Band of Ojibwe, P.O. Box 16, Nett Lake, MN 55772 (218) 757-3261. E-mail: kevin.leecy@boisforte-nsn.gov.

LEEDS, STACY (Cherokee)
(dean of law school & professor of law)
Affiliation & Address: Dean & Professor of Law,, University of Arkansas, School of Law, Waterman Hall, 1045 W. Maple St., Robert A. Lefler Law Center, Fayetteville, AR 72701 (479) 575-4504. E-mail: sleeds@uark.edu. Leeds, Cherokee, is the first American Indian woman to serve as dean of a law school (University of Arkansas). She has served on seven tribal courts, including as chief justice on the Cherokee Nation Supreme Court, as a director of the Tribal Law and Government Center at Kansas Law School, a director of the Northern Plains Indian Law Center at the University of North Dakota School of Law and a commissioner of the Secretarial Commission on Indian Trust Administration & Reform. Leeds co-authored, *Mastering American Indian Law*. One major legal issue facing Indian Country, Leeds says, "that we're fighting the battle of external legitimacy when it comes to both the federal government, the state and international forums recognizing the powers of our governments." She views her work on the trust reform commission as having "the potential to be the most impactful [she has done] because of the recommendations we [will] set forward to overhaul and reform the way our property system & the trust responsibility of the federal government play out."

LEFT HAND BULL, JACQUELINE (Sicangu Lakota)
(administrative officer)
Affiliation & Address: Executive Director, Northwest Portland Area Indian Health Board, 2121 SW Broadway #300, Portland, OR 97201 (503) 228-4185. E-mail: jlefthandbull@npaihb.org.

LEHI, CANDELORA (San Juan Southern Paiute)
(tribal administrative officer)
Address: P.O. Box 3700, Tuba City, AZ 86045 (928) 283-4587. *Affiliation*: Administrative Officer, San Juan Southern Paiute Tribe, Tuba City, AZ. *Other professional posts*: Tribal secretary & bookkeeper; powwow president; election president; member of enrollment committee. *Community activities*: Powwow in June; family gathering of the Paiute participants in Paiute Heritage Days. *Awards, honors*: Breast Cancer Sponsorship Award; Leadership Award; Volunteer Award; Traditional Knowledge Award; Writing Award; Creative Award. *Interests*: Teaching Paiute language & writing to children; Paiute history & stories; traditional foods.

LEIGH, ROVIANNE (Cherokee)
(attorney)
Education: University of California, Berkeley School of Law, JD, 2005. *Affiliation & Address*: Partner, Berkey Williams LLP, 2030 Addison St. #410, Berkeley, CA 94704 (510) 548-7070. E-mail: info@berkeywilliams.com. Ms. Leigh serves tribal clients in many areas of the law, including environmental and cultural resources protection, health, employment, Indian child welfare, Tribal TANF, general litigation, tribal code development, & tribal governance. Ms. Leigh has appeared in federal, state, and tribal courts on a number of issues affecting tribal rights and sovereignty. She regularly appears in tribal courts on Indian child welfare and employment matters. As a Partner, Ms. Leigh participates directly in serving tribal clients, specializing in the protection of tribal environmental & cultural resources, litigation, Indian child dependency, tribal TANF, employment & Indian health. Ms. Leigh successfully negotiated the first Memorandum of Understanding regarding Indian child welfare between an Indian tribe and the county's Child Welfare Services Department in Northern California. Along with Curtis Berkey & Scott Williams, Ms. Leigh teaches the Advanced Indian Law seminar at U.C. Berkeley School of Law. *Awards, honors*: Honorable Thelton E. Henderson Social Justice Prize by the U.C. Berkeley School of Law in 2012 for her dedication and commitment to the field of Indian law.

LEMIEUX, SUNSHINE (Bad River Ojibwe)
(attorney)
Education: University of Wisconsin-Superior, BA, 2000; University of Wisconsin Law School, JD, 2005. *Affiliation & Address*: Staff Attorney, Indian Law Office, Wisconsin Judicare, Inc., P.O. Box 6100, Wausau, WI 54402 (715) 842-1681. E-mail: slemieux@judicare.org. She is also a member of the Wisconsin State Bar and is admitted to practice in the Ho-Chunk, Menominee, and Sokaogon Tribal Courts. In her work at Wisconsin Judicare, aside from client casework, Attorney Lemieux presents on various legal topics at seminars, holds legal clinics at tribal health and disability fairs, and travels across the state to discuss health & income maintenance topics with Wisconsin tribal members under the NAEOP program. She also provides program management, legal backup, and training to the Tribal Elderly Benefit Specialists and Tribal Disability Benefit Specialists. Her casework and legal interests include: Family Law, Elder Law, Indian Law, Wills/Probate, Consumer Law, and Public Benefits.

LEMM, DANIEL (Mdewakanton Sioux)
(director of programs & finance)
Education: Iowa State University, BS (Business Finance). *Affiliation & Address*: Director of Programs & Finance (2008-present), Native Americans in Philanthropy, 2801 21st Ave. #132D, Minneapolis, MN 55407 (612) 724-8798. E-mail: dlemm@nativephilanthropy.org. *Other professional posts*: Board treasurer, Tiwahe Foundation, Ain Dah Yung Center, and Dakota Wicohan.

LENNIHAN, JOSEPH
(attorney-Native American law)
Education: Georgetown University Law Center, LLM, 1999. *Affiliation & Address*: P.O. Box 23136, Santa Fe, NM 87502 (505) 216-9300. *Practice area*: Native American lw.

LENO, REYNOLD L. (Confederated Tribes of Grand Ronde) 1950-
(tribal chairperson)
Affiliation & Address: Chairperson, Confederated Tribes of the Grand Ronde Community, 9615 Grand Ronde Rd., Grand Ronde, OR 97347 (503) 879-5211. *Other professional post*: Spirit Mountain Community Fund Board of Trustees; chairperson, Spirit Mountain Casino Board of Directors. *Past tribal posts*: Member of tribal council, 1996-present). *Military service*: U.S. Marine Corps (two years; Vietnam Vet).

LENOX, JACK (Coquille)
(tribal planning)
Affiliation & Address: Director, Planning, Realty & Community Services, P.O. Box 783, North Bend, OR 97459. Email: jacklenox@coquilletribe.org. *Other professional post*: Chairperson, Board of Directors, ONABEN, Tigard, OR.

LENTE, DAVID (Isleta Pueblo)
(substance abuse counselor)
Born & raised in Isleta Pueblo. *Affiliation & Address*: Board member, Native American Training Institute of New Mexico, 1208 San Pedro NE #126, Albuquerque, NM 87110 (505) 702-6524. He is the current Chair of the Albuquerque Area Inter-Tribal Council on Substance Abuse – Certification Board, that certifies Native American counselors working within tribal programs. He also holds credentials as National Certified Gambling Counselor (NCGC-II) and treats problem and compulsive gamblers and their family members. He is the co-founder of "Indigenous" the Native American Track in partner with The Evolution Group, Inc. He serves as a treatment provider for the Metropolitan Drug Court program in Albuquerque, New Mexico. The model includes a multi-disciplinary approach with treatment and judicial assemblies. He seeks to create a holistic approach to healing, offering a hierarchy of effective interventions, transforming a sense of balance in body, mind, and spirit to embrace true healing and restore life to integrity. *Past professional posts*: He has been in the field of addictions for 29 years working primarily with the Native American population in the Albuquerque area. He evolved a Paraprofessional direction in the field and has earned certification as Certified Alcohol & Drug Counselor (CADAC) since 1986 & Licensed Alcohol and Drug Counselor (LADAC) licensure as of 1997.

LENTE, MICHAEL ALLEN (Isleta Pueblo)
(Pueblo vice president)
Affiliation & Address: Vice President, Isleta Pueblo Council, P.O. Box 1270, Isleta, NM 87022

LEON, YOLANDA
(Indian program coordinator)
Education: University of California, Los Angeles, BA & MA. *Affiliation & Address*: Program Coordinator, American Indian Resource Program, University of California, Irvine, 407 Social Science Tower, Irvine, CA 92697 (949) 824-6251. E-mail: yleon@uci.edu. *Other professional post*: Director, American Indian Summer Institute in Computer Sciences summer residential program, UC, Irvine. She also coordinates various other projects such as Student Initiated Academic Preparation, Community College, & FIRE mentorship Program. Yolanda focuses on creating partnerships amongst tribes, universities, & community organizations in order to maximize efforts, resources & results. *Past professional posts*: Director, AIR Project at UCLA, 1999-2008.

LEONARD, LELAND (Dine-Navajo)
(program administrator)
Born in Chinle, Ariz. *Education*: MA in Education. *Principal occupation*: Program administrator. *Affiliation*: Executive Director, Division of Dine Education (2004-present), P.O. Box 9000, Window Rock, AZ 86515 (928) 871-6352. *Past professional post*: Executive Director, Phoenix Indian Center, Inc., Phoenix, AZ, 1998-2003.

LEONARD, MICHELE TINSLEY (Shinnecock) 1956-
(administrator)
Born October 26, 1956 in Southampton, N.Y. *Education*: Wellesley College, BA, 1977. *Address & Affiliation*: Executive director, United American Indians of Delaware Valley, 225 Chestnut St., Philadelphia, PA 19106 (215) 574-9020. *Other professional posts*: Assistant executive director, Council of Three Rivers American Indian Center, Pittsburgh (responsible for the Native American Elders Program, the Speaker's Bureau, and the Youth Group); coordinator of the Western Pennsylvania Native American Advisory Committee to the Carnegie Museum's new American Indian Hall that opened in 1996; developer and proprietor of a consulting firm called Spirit Guides (offers information on American Indian educational & cultural issues & is active in research & curriculum writing.) *Community activities*: Board of directors, Pennsylvania Small Business Education Scholarship Fund. *Interests*: She is a writer of American Indian curriculum & contemporary articles & is doing research with oral histories.

LEONARD, WESLEY (Miami of Oklahoma)
(associate professor of Native American studies)
Education: University of California, Berkeley, PhD (Linguistics). *Affiliation & Address*: Chair, Native American Studies Program, Southern Oregon University, Taylor Hall, Room 19b, 1250 Siskiyou, OR 97520 (541) 552-8256. E-mail: leonardw@sou.edu

LERMA, MICHAEL (*P'urhepecha*) (Navajo-Dine')
(professor of Applied Indigenous Studies)
Education: UCLA, BA (History), 2000; The University of Arizona, MA (Political Science), 2006, PhD (American Indian Studies), 2010. *Affiliation & Address*: Professor (2010-present), Applied Indigenous Studies Department, College of Social & Behavioral Sciences, Northern Arizna University, SBS West Bldg. 70, Room 100, Flagstaff, AZ 86011 (928) 523-3392. E-mail: Michael.lerma@nau.edu *Interests*: Native American politics, international relations, and applied indigenous studies. His recent research has explored the efficacy of traditional

Dine' institutions of governance. He also contributes to research conducted by Dine' Policy Institute (DPI).

LeSOURD, PHILIP S.
(professor of anthropology)
Education: Massachusetts Institute of Technology, BS, 1974, PhD, 1989. *Affiliation & Address*: Associate Professor of Anthropology, The American Indian Studies Research Institute, Indiana University, 422 N. Indiana Ave., Bloomington, IN 47408 (812) 855-4086. *Research Interests*: Linguistic theory and its application to the analysis of Native American languages, comparative Algonquian linguistics, Maliseet-Passamaquoddy, Wampanoag (Massachusetts), and Arapaho. *Past professional post*: Wabanaki Bilingual Education Program at Indian Township, Maine. In 1976, Philip set about organizing a Passamaquoddy dictionary project. A dictionary was published by the Micmac-Maliseet Institute in Fredericton in 1984. The results of his investigation of the phonological system of Passamaquoddy formed the basis for his dissertation, "Accent & Sylllable Structure in Passamaquoddy," completed in 1988. *Published works*: Translator & Editor, "Tales From Maliseet Country: The Maliseet Texts of Karl V. Teeter" (U. of Nebraska Press, 2007); numerous articles in selected publications.

LESTER, DARLENE
(Indian legal program coordinator)
Affiliation & Address: Program Coordinator (2002-present), Indian Legal Program, Sandra Day O'Connor College of Law, LAW 230, Arizona State University, P.O. Box 877906, Tempe, AZ 85287 (480) 965-7715. E-mail: Darlene.lester@asu.edu.

LESTER, JOAN 1937-
(museum curator; college lecturer)
Born July 4, 1937, New York, N.Y. *Education*: Brown University, BA, 1959; Sorbonne, Paris, France, Certificate of Studies, 1958; UCLA, MA (Primitive Art/American Indian Art), 1963; Union Institute for Graduate Study, PhD (Native American Art), 1998. *Address*: 2 Muster Ct., Lexington, MA 02173. E-mail: joanlester@aol.com. *Affiliations*: Curator, 1985-present, Boston Children's Museum; lecturer, 1987-present, Seminar: "Native American Issues: Politics of Representation," Dept. of American Studies, Tufts University, Medford, MA (617) 627-2311. *Other professional posts*: Chairperson, National Curator's Committee, 1982-; member-at-large, Council for Museum Anthropology, 1983-; principal investigator, American Indian Games, National Endowment for the Humanities Planning Grant, 1983-. *Past professional posts*: Coordinator of North American Indian resources & workshop (courses & workshops presenting Indian people in southern New England), co-developer of American Indian programs in Greater Boston area, 1971-74; museum coordinator-Native American Advisory Board, 1973-85; developer/curator, American Indian Collections & Programs, 1976-85, Boston Children's Museum. *Community activities*: Member, advisory boards: Phoenix School, Cambridge, Mass.; MIT Museum; Native American Studies Department of Plimoth Plantation, Mass.; Tomaquag Indian Memorial Museum, Exeter, R.I. MAP assessor, Museum Assessment Program. *Memberships*: American Assn. of Museums (curator's committee); International Council of Museums; New England Museum Assn; Native American Art Studies Assn.; Council for Museum Anthropology; Peabody Museum Assn. *Awards, honors*: Boston Indian Council Certificate of Merit, 1975; Bay State Historical League Award of Excellence, for Indians Who Met the Pilgrims, June, 1975; Award of Distinction, A.A.M. for "We're Still Here", catalog, 1987. *Interests*: "American Indian art; American Indian arts in New England as they continue today; cooking, bicycling, cross country skiing, theater, classical music, folk dancing, reading." *Published works*: The American Indian, A Museum's Eye View, in Indian Historian, summer, 1972; Indians Who Met the Pilgrims, the Match Program, American Science & Engineering, Boston, 1974; A Code of Ethics for Curator's, in Museum News, Jan/Feb., 1983; chapter I - The Production of Fancy Baskets in Maine (American Indian Archaeological Institute, 1986); American Indian Art in New England (Boston Children's Museum, 1986); The Art of Tomah Joseph, Passamaquoddy Artist (Turtle Quarterly, Spring 1988). Reports: American Indian Art Assn, Tomah Joseph, Passamaquoddy Artist, Sept., 1983; Metropolitan Museum of Art, The Northeast Native American Program at the Children's Museum, April, 1983; York Institute, Saco, Maine, Northeast Native American Baskets: A Continuing Tradition, Oct., 1982); Massachusetts Indian Association, The Significance of the Katherine Hall Newall Collection, Oct., 1982; American Indian Art Association, They're Still Here, Native American Art in New England, March, 1982.

LEVALDO,-GAYTON, RHONDA (Acoma Pueblo)
(freelance journalist; videographer; educator)
Affiliation & Address: Adjunct Faculty teaching video production, Haskell Indian Nations University, College of Arts & Sciences: Media Arts, 155 Indian Ave., Lawrence, KS (749-8442 ext. 442). E-mail: rhondalevaldo@gmail.com. *Research Interests*: Looks at how traditional knowledge integrated into a vast array of programs in myriad disciplines. *Past professional post*: President, Native American Journalists Association, 2012-13.

LEVI, HEATHER (Cheyenne-Kiowa)
(program director)
Education: University of Oklahoma Health Sciences Center, MPH, 2002. *Affiliation*: Director, HIV Aids Core Capacity Program, Association of American Indian Physicians, 1235 Sovereign Row, Suite C-7, Oklahoma City, OK 73108 (405) 946-7072. *Past professional post*: Oklahoma Indian Affairs Commission.

LEVIER, FRANCIS ANDREW (Citizen Band Potawatomi) 1950-
(tribal administrator, business committeeman)
Born November 13, 1950, Topeka, Kan. *Education*: Hofstra University, BA, 1973; University of Kansas, MS, 1975, EdD, 1979. *Principal occupation*: Tribal administrator & business committeeman. *Affiliation & Address*: Administrator, Citizen Band Potawatomi Tribe, 1901 S. Gordon Cooper Dr., Shawnee, OK 74801 (405) 275-3121. *Past professional posts*: Acting director, Supportive Educational Services, 1975-76, instructor, School of Social Welfare, 1977-79, assistant director of Minority Affairs, 1974-80, University of Kansas, Lawrence; director, Health Programs, Prairie Band Potawatomi Tribe, 1980-81; acting executive director, Prairie Band Potawatomi Tribe of Kansas, 1980-81; executive director, Region VI Indian Alcoholism Training Program, 1982-83; executive director, A proposal, Evaluation, Research, & Training consulting firm (P.E.R.T., Inc.), 1982-; director of economic development, Citizen Band Potawatomi Tribe, 1983-85; tribal administrator & business committeeman, Citizen Band Potawatomi Tribe, Shawnee, OK, 1983-. *Other professional post*: Member of the Board of Regents, Haskell Indian Jr. College, 1979-83; assistant director, Topeka (KS) Indian Center, 1977-78. *Community activities*: Affirmative Action, University of Kansas (board member, 1976-80); United Indian Recovery Association (board member, 1980-81); Emergency Services Council, City of Lawrence, KS (chairman, 1977-80). *Awards, honors*: Recipient of Ford Foundation Fellowship for American Indians, 1973-76; Elected to five-member Business Committee (governing body) of the Citizen Band Potawatomi Tribe in June, 1985. Was first business committee member ever named to the position of tribal administrator in the history of the 12,000-member tribe. *Published works*: A Brief History of the Pedigree Papers, 1983; editor, Using Indian Culture to Develop Alcohol & Drug Materials for Indian Adults and Youth, 1983; Overview of Inhalent Abuse Among American Indian Youth, 1981; An Attitude Survey of Urban Indians in N.E. Kansas Toward Higher Education, 1979; all published by the American Indian Institute, University of Oklahoma, 1983. The Need for Indian Student Organizations in Large Institutions of Higher Education, N.E.C.C.A. Conference Article, K.C., MO, 1979.

LEVINE, JEROME L.
(attorney; Native American law)
Education: University of California hastings College of the Law, JD. *Affiliation & Address*: Partner Holland & Knight, 400 S. Hope St., 8th Floor, Los Angeles, CA 99501 (213) 896-2565. E-mail: Jerome.levine@hklaw.com. Jerome is a business & litigation attorney who has been involved in all aspects of gaming, casino and Native American law for over 20 years. He has been particularly active in the development of the firm's Indian gaming practice, providing legal counsel in over a dozen major Tribal casino projects and as a leading Tribal representative in Tribal-State compact negotiations in several states, including California, Oklahoma and Washington State. Mr. Levine was lead counsel in State of Washington v. Chehalis, which resulted in making electronic gaming devices available to all tribes in that state. He has represented a number of Indian gaming organizations, including serving as corporate counsel to the National Indian Gaming Association (NIGA), the California Nations Indian Gaming Association (CNIGA) and the Washington Indian Gaming Association (WIGA). Mr. Levine was Chairman of the NIGA Task Force on IGRA Regulations and of NIGA's Law & Legislative Committee. He was also a member of the NIGA-National Congress of American Indians (NCAI) Tribal-State negotiating team which was formed several years ago to meet with the states' Governors & Attorneys General to examine critical issues under IGRA. Mr. Levine has organized, written and edited materials and been a speaker on numerous programs on gaming law, including national seminars on casino management, gaming regulation, casino employment and labor law, and gaming fraud. He has written several articles for Indian Gaming Magazine, International Gaming and Wagering Magazine, and is the Editor of the Indian Gaming Handbook, a popular four-volume reference set that has been distributed throughout the country and is in its sixth edition. Awards & honors: Chambers USA – America's Leading Business Lawyers guide, Native American Law, 2008-2016; The Best Lawyers in America guide, Native American Law, 2007-2017; Gaming Law, 2005-2017; The Best Lawyers in America guide, Los Angeles Native American Law Lawyer of the Year, 2013, 2017. *Memberships*: Federal Bar Association, Indian Law Section

LEVINE, VICTORIA LINDSAY 1954-
(ethnomusicologist; college professor)
Born September 8, 1954, Palo Alto, Calif. *Education*: San Francisco State University, BA (Anthropology), 1977, MA (Music History), 1980; University of Illinois at Urbana-Champaign, PhD (Musicology), 1990. *Principal occupation*: Ethnomusicologist; college professor. *Address*: 6265 Savannah Way, Colorado Springs, CO 80919. *Affiliation & Address*: Colorado College, 14 E. Cache la Poudre St., Colorado Springs, CO 80903 (719) 389-6183; (assistant professor, 1988-94; associate professor of ethnomusicology, 1994-present). *Other professional post*: W.M. Keck Foundation Director of the Hulbert Center for Southwestern Studies at Colorado College, 1999-present *Memberships*: Society for Ethnomusicology, 1980-; College Music Society, 1989-; Society for American Music, 1992-; The International Council for Traditional Music, 1995-. *Awards, honors*: John D. & Catherine T. MacArthur Professor, 1991-93, Colorado College; Jackson Fellow, 1991-92 (Colorado College); Ingolf Dahl Award in Musicology, 1979 (USC); Jackson Fellow, 19991-92, 1995-96, 1998-99; American Council of Learned Societies, Senior Fellowships, 1994-95; Ida Halpern Fellowship and Award, Society for Ethnomusicology, 1999. *Interests*: "Choctaw musical culture; musical cultures of Louisiana tribes; southeast Native American ethnomusicology; ethnomusicology of the Southwest." *Published work*: Choctaw Music and Dance (University of Oklahoma Press, 1990); Music in the Ruben Cobos Collection of Spanish New Mexican Folklore: A Descriptive Catalogue (Hulbert Center Press, 1999); Writing American Indian Music: Historic Transcriptions, Notations, & Arrangements (A-R Editions, American Musicology Society, 2002).

LEVINGS, MARCUS D. (Hidatsa) 1966-
(tribal chairperson)
Education: Bismarck State College, A.A., 1986; Dickinson (ND) State University, BS, 1988; University of Mary, MBA, 2002. *Affiliation*: Chairperson (2006-present), Three Affiliated Tribes of the Fort Berthold Reservation, 404 Frontage Rd., New Town, ND 58763 (701) 627-4781. E-mail: info@mhanation.com. *Past professional posts*: Three Affiliated Tribes, (director, Tribal Employment Rights Office, 1991-98; council member, 1998-2006).

LEWEY, ALISON (Passamaquoddy-Maliseet)
(company president, inventor)
Address: Lewey's Eco-Blends, Inc., 176 Amsden Rd., Corrina, ME 04928 (207) 278-5504. *Professional activities*: Started Lewey's Eco-Blends, Inc. and created a natural insect repellent, "Buzz-Off"...a soybean-based blend of natural oils that penetrates the skin and provides protection against more than 20 different kinds of insects. Ms. Lewey states, "...as a company we're committed to developing safe, natural products that people enjoy using." Lewey's other business focus is to expand on her company's mission of providing jobs and opportunity to Native people. She is currently working with groups in Maine and in Alaska to create economic opportunities.

LEWEY, JAMIE BISSONETTE (Abenaki)
(commission chair)
Affiliation & Address: Chairperson, Maine Indian Tribal-State Cmmission, P.O. Box 241, Stillwater, ME 04489 (207) 817-3799. E-mail: jbissonette@afsc.org. *Other professional posts*: Coordinator, Healing Justice Program, American Friends Service Committee in New England, Boston, MA; Board member, Northeast Community of Learning for Healing Justice; board member, Louis D. Brown Peace Institute.

LEWIS, CHUCK (Blackfeet)
(artist)
Address: Chuck Lewis Editions, P.O. Box 917, Questa, NM 87556 (505) 751-2158. *Products*: Monoprints, etchings, paper casts, lithographs, & original art.

LEWIS, FREDDIE (Choctaw of Oklahoma)
(Choctaw language instructor)
Affiliation & Address: Choctaw Language Instructor, Native American Language Program, Department of Anthropology, College of Arts & Sciences, The University of Oklahoma, 455 W. Lindsey, DHT 505, Norman, OK 73019 (405) 325-3729. E-mail:f.lewis-1@ou.edu.

LEWIS, GEORGE R. (Ho-Chunk)
(tribal president)
Education: BS in Public Administration. *Affiliation & Address*: President, Ho-Chunk Nation, P.O. Box 667, Black River Falls, WI 54615 (715) 284-9343. *Past professional posts*: Former Personal Director, District V Legislator, Ho-Chunk Nation; employed with Jackson County for 28 years; former Union President of American Federation of State, County & Municipal Employees (AFSCME).

LEWIS, HILDA (Passamaquoddy)
(tribal councilperson)
Education: Mercy Hospital Nursing School (Portland, Maine), RN, 1961. *Military service*: Air Force Reserve Nurse Corp. (Flight Nurse), 1973-95. *Address & Affiliation*: Member, Passamaquoddy Tribal Council at Sipayik (2004-present), P.O. Box 343, Perry ME 04667 (207) 853-2600. E-mail: flowers.bzbee@verizon.net. *Other professional post*: Owner of flower shop & seasonal restaurant; member, Maine Indian Tribal-State Commission.

LEWIS, JOAN MYRICK (Grand Traverse Ottawa & Chippewa) 1951-
(health project director)
Born June 30, 1951, Traverse City, Mich. *Education*: Western Michigan University, BS, 1973; University of Houston, 1981-83; Trinity University (San Antonio, TX), MS, 1987. *Principal occupation*: Health project director. Resides in Minneapolis-St. Paul, MN area. *Affiliations*: Medical technologist, Hospital Laboratory, Kalamazoo, MI, 1974-80; chief medical technologist, Physician Clinical Laboratory, Houston, TX, 1981-87; AIDS Project Director, American Indian Health Care Association, St. Paul, MN, 1988-. *Community activities*: Community advisors to the Executive Planning Committee for the National Minority AIDS Conference, Census Awareness Committee, Minority Recruitment Committee, and University of Minnesota. *Memberships*: National Minority AIDS Council; National AIDS Network. *Interests*: Culturally Sensitive AIDS presentations at regional and national meetings.

LEWIS, JOHN R. (Mojave/Pima/Tohono O'odham)
(executive director)
Education: University of Oklahoma, BA; University of Arizona, MA. *Affiliation & Address*: Executive Director (39 years), Inter Tribal Council of Arizona (ITCA), 2214 North Central Ave., Suite 100, Phoenix, AZ 85004 (602) 258-4822. E-mail: john.lewis@itcaonline.com. The ITCA has been a strong & effective advocate for tribal governments throughout Arizona on various federal, state legislative policies. John has maintained a focus on community development throughout his career and has served on multiple committees and boards of directors in order to advance this ideal. *Awards, honors*: Received the Community Service Award from the Native American Bar Associtaion of Arizona, for his work as an advocate for American Indian governments and in promoting intergovernmental cooperation between Indian nations and other government entities.

LEWIS, KIMBERLY R. (Pima-Maricopa)
(company president)
Education: Arizona State University, BA (Communications), University of Phoenix, MA (Organizational Management & Leadership). *Affiliation & Address*: President, KRL Partners LLC, 1663 S. Villas Lane, Chandler, AZ 85296. E-mail: k.roselewis@gmail.com. KRL Partners is a native-owned real estate development company focused on attracting business investment opportunities to Indian Country. *Other professional posts*: Executive Board Member, Gila River Indian Community, Wild Horse Pass Development Authority, 2013-present; board member, Native American Connections, Phoenix, AZ. *Past professional posts*: Real Estate Development Mnager, Foxwoods Development Co. LLC, Mashantucket Pequot Tribe, Ledyard, CT; general manager, Wild Horse Pass, Gila River Indian Community.

LEWIS, RODNEY B. (Gila River Pima)
(attorney; consultant)
Education: Arizona State University, MA, 1969; University of California, Los Angeles, School of Law, JD, 1972. *Affiliation & Address*: Consultant, Akin Gump Straus Hauer & Feld, LLP, Robert E. Straus Bldg., 1333 New Hampshire Ave. NW, Washington, DC 20036 (202) 255-4950; E-mail: rlewis@akingump.com. Rodney advises American Indian tribes on various federal & state public policy issues. *Past professional posts*: Arizona Bar Association (Indian Law Section-chairperson). *Membership*: Native American Bar Association. Mr. Lewis was the first member of an Arizona Indian tribe to become a member of the State Bar of Arizona and the first member of an Indian tribe to appear before the U.S. Supreme Court. Awards, honors: The Arizona State Bar Award of 2014..

LEWIS, STEPHEN ROE (Pima-Maricopa)
(tribal governor)
Affiliation & Address: Governor (2015-present), Gila River Indian Community Council, P.O. Box 97, Sacaton, AZ 85147 (520) 562-9840. E-mail: executive.mail@gric.nsn.us. Governor Lewis has long been an advocate for Native American issues nationally. In the area of Indian Education, Mr. Lewis was selected to serve as a Board member for the National Indian Education Association (NIEA), & Delegate to the White House Conference on Indian Education. He has served the Community as a Gaming Commissioner for the Gila River Gaming Commission, as a member of the Board of Directors for the Gila River Telecommunications, Inc., and as a member of the Board of Directors for the Gila River Healthcare Corporation. Governor Lewis was the first Native film curator for the Sundance Film Festival in Park City, Utah and was an Associate Producer for the groundbreaking and critically acclaimed TBS six-part feature documentary, "The Native Americans." He has worked on numerous political campaigns and organizing projects throughout Indian Country including Native voter organizing and Native voter protection in 2002 and selected as an Arizona delegate and Co-Chairing the Native American Caucus for the 2012 Democratic National Convention in Charlotte, North Carolina. Currently Governor Lewis serves on the Board of Directors for the Native American Rights Fund (NARF), the Executive Board for the National Indian Gaming Association (NIGA) and the Board of Trustee for the Heard Museum of Phoenix.

LIDMAN, ROGER W.
(museum director)
Born in Norfolk, Va. *Education*: Arizona State University, BA (Anthropology). *Affiliation & Address*: Director, Pueblo Grande Museum & Cultural Park, 4619 E Washington St., Phoenix, AZ 85034 (602) 495-0901. *Community activities*: Board Member, Artability; Papago Salado Association; State Library Advisory Council. *Memberships*: American Association of Museums; Western Museums Association (V.P.); Museum Association of Arizona (former president). *Interests*: Guitar, natural history.

LIGHT, STEVEN ANDREW
(associate vice president; professor of political science)
Education: Yale University, BA; Northwestern University, PhD. *Affiliation & Address*: Associate Vice President for Academic Affairs & Professor oof Political Science & Public Administration, University of North Dakta College of Business & Public Administration, Grand Forks, ND 58202. E-mail: steven_light@und.nodak.edu. *Other professional post*: Co-founder, Institute for the Study of Tribal Gaming Law & Policy, University of North Dakota, Grand Forks. Dr. Light is an internationally recognized expert on Indian Gaming. *Published works*: Co-authored with Kathryn Rand, Indian Gaming & Tribal Sovereignty: The Casino Compromise (University Press of Kansas, 2005); Indian Gaming Law & Policy (Carolina Academic Press, 2006); Indian Gaming Law: Cases & Materials (Carolina Academic Press, 2008).Kathryn Rand & Steven Light write a column, "Indian Gaming Today," that appears in Casino Lawyer magazine, and have written for Casino Enterprise Management & Indian Gaming magazine. They blog on Indian gaming and the legal, political, and public policy issues raised by the tribal gaming industry at their website, Indian Gaming Today, at www.indiangamingnow.com.

LIGHTFOOT, SHERYL (L'Anse Lake Superior Band Ojibwe)
(independent consultant)
Education: University of Minnesota, MA (Public Affairs), PhD (International Relations & Comparative Politics). *Affiliation & Address*: Canada Research Chair in Global Indigenous Rights & Politics & Assistant Professor of First Nations Studies Program, The University of British Columbia, Buchanan E-258, 1866 Main Mall, Vancouver, BC V6T 1Z1 Canada (604) 822-2905. E-mail: sheryl.lightfoot@ubc.ca. *Past professional post*: Chairperson, American Indian Policy Center, Minneapolis, MN.

LIGHTNING, GEORGINA LYNN (Cree)
(actor/singer & lyricist)
Born July 4 in Edmonton, Alberta, Can. *Education*: Concordia College (Edmonton, AB); American Academy of Dramatic Arts & UCLA. *Principal occupation*: Actor/singer & lyricist. Resides in California. *Community activities*: Volunteer to operations of American Indians in film and American Indian recognition of entertainers in media honored by the annual Kokopeli Awards and Concert Benefit. *Membership*: American Academy Alumni/Repertory Company. *Awards, honors*: Michael Toma Award by Concordia College for most progressed actor, first time ever awarded to a Canadian, not to mention first for an Indian graduate from the Academy; and first to be invited as a repertory actor. *Interests*: Performing arts/entertainment (music, 1977-; acting, 1988-); political activist willing to give her life for the rights and obligations the government owes to her people, the natives of this country. "I wish to travel the world as a performer who earns the public's appreciation and support for a native American point of view and deserved acceptance as an equal in art. I have written several songs which I hope to record soon." *Biographical source*: "Stars in the Desert," Navajo newspaper.

LIM, DAVID
(attorney)
Affiliation & Address: Staff attorney, National Indian Justice Center, 5250 Aero Dr., Santa Rosa, CA 95403 (707) 579-5507. E-mail: davidlim@nijc.org.

LIMAS, VICKIE J.
(professor of law; Indian law center co-director)
Affiliation & Address: Professor of Law & Co-director, Native American Law Center, University of Tulsa College of Law, 3120 E. 4th Place, Tulsa, OK 74104 (918) 631-2401. E-mail: Vickie-limas@utulsa.edu. Professor Limas is the leading national expert on labor and employment law in Indian country. She has published articles on the juxtaposition of tribal sovereign rights and individual civil rights in suits by employees and on the applicability of federal labor & employment laws to Indian nations. She is a contributing author to the 2005 Revisions of Cohen's Handbook of Federal Indian Law. She is an adjunct settlement judge in the U.S. District Court for the Northern District of Oklahoma and an arbitrator for the Financial Industry Regulatory Authority. Professor Limas teaches Employment Law, Employment Discrimination Law, Mediation & Introduction to Alternative Dispute Resolution.

LINCE, SARAH
(Native American Indian studies program academic coordinator)
Affiliation & Address: Academic Programs Coordinator, Five College Native American & Indigenous Studies, 97 Spring St., Amherst, MA 01004 (413) 542-4000.

LINCOLN, CAROL, CAPT. (Navajo/Pueblo)
(IHS chief of staff)
Education: University of New Mexico, BS (Nursing); University of Phoenix, MBA (Health Care management). *Affiliation & Address*: Chief of Staff, Indian Health Service (IHS), The Reyes Bldg., 801 Thompson Ave. #400, Rockville, MD 20852 (301) 443-1083. In her role as the Chief of Staff, CAPT Lincoln oversees the coordination of key Agency activitiesand works to improve overall Agency responsiveness. She provides operational & supervisory oversight for the Public Affairs Staff, Congressional & Legislative Affairs Staff, and Executive Secretariat Staff offices in the Office of the Director. CAPT Lincoln ensures the timely and accurate dissemination of internal and external communications on health care delivery & congressional activities. She works closely with HHS and supports the Office of the Director in abroad range of managerial duties related to the development & implementation of IHS initiatives and priorities. *Past professional posts*: CAPT Lincoln began her career with IHS in 1993 as a Commissioned Officer in the Nurse category. She has served in the Albuquerque Area at the Albuquerque Indian Hospital and the Santa Fe Indian Hospital, and in the Phoenix Area at the Phoenix Indian Medical Center. In 2005, she was deployed to the HHS Secretary's Emergency Response Team in Florida following Hurricanes Rita and Charlie. From August 2009 through October 2010, CAPT Lincoln served as the Deputy Director, Division of Acquisition Policy, Office of Management Services. In 2009, CAPT Lincoln returned to the IHS from her position as the Chief Nurse for the U.S. Marshals Service, where she also served as the Commissioned Corps Liaison to the Office of the Surgeon General (OSG), a role she continues for the IHS. She was appointed by the OSG to the Compensation Policy Advisory Board and is the IHS agency representative to the SurgeonmGeneral's Policy Advisory Council. CAPT Lincoln also continues to serve as the Director of themIHS Division of Commissioned Personnel Support. *Awards, honors*: Twice awarded the U.S. Public Health Service utstanding Service Medal.

LINCOLN, KENNETH
(professor of anthropology)
Born in Texas and raised in northwest Nebraska. *Education*: Stanford University, A.B. in American Literature; Indiana University, PhD, 1970 in British Literature. *Address & Affiliation*: American & Native American Studies, 240 Humanities Bldg., UCLA, Los Angeles, CA 90095 (310) 825-7420. E-mail: lincoln@humnet.ucla.edu. Prof. Lincoln has taught Contemporary & Native American Literature at UCLA for over 25 years. He developed the American Indian Studies curriculum, chaired the country's first interdisciplinary Master's Program in American Indian Studies. *Published works*: Native American Renaissance (University of California Press, 1983); The Good Red Road: Passages Into Native America (Harper & Row, 1987); UCLA Native American Poetry Series (nine titles, 1975-93); Indi'in Humor: Bicultural Play in Native America (Oxford University Press, 1993); Men Down West (Capra Press, 1997); Native Poetics, City of Indians (in production).

LINCOLN, SARA (Sisseton Wahpeton Oyate)
(former tribal vice chairperson)
Affiliation & Address: Former Vice Chairperson, Sisseton Wahpeton Oyate, Lake Traverse Reservation, P.O. Box 509, Agency Village, SD 57262 (605) 698-3911.

LIND, CYNTHIA H. (Aleut)
(executive director)
Born & raised on St. George Island, Alaska. *Affiliation & Address*: Executive Director, The Aleut Foundation, 703 W. Tudor Rd., Suite 102, Anchorage, AK 99503 (907) 646-1929. Cynthia is the first Aleut shareholder to go through the Aleut Management Services Mentorship Program. *Other professional posts*: President, Tanaq Foundation Board of Directors (member for 15 years). *Past professional posts*: President & COO, Aleut Northwest Services; served board member for St. George Tanaq Corporation & St. George Chadux Corporation; served as Regional Resource Council Member for the National center for Native Ameican Indian Economic Development; president & secretary/treasurer, Rocky Mountain Indian Chamber of Commerce. *Awards, honors*: 2007 Aleut Shareholder of the Year.

LINDALA, APRIL (Grand River Six Nations)
(professor & director of Native American studies)
Education: Northern Michigan University, BA (Speech Communications & Minor in Native American Studies), 1997, MA (English), 2003, MFA, 2006. *Affiliation & Address*: Director & Professor, Center for Native American Studies, 112 Whitman Hall, Northern Michigan University (NMU), 1401 Presque Isle Ave., Marquette, MI 49855 (906) 227-1397; E-mail: alindala@nmu.edu. *Other professional posts*: NMU Alumni Board; Women's Center of Marquette Board;

the Northern Options board; and the City of Marquette Arts & Culture committee. *Past professional posts*: Community Outreach Specialist, WNMU-TV13, 1993-98; Admissions Counselor, Center for Native American Studies, Northern Michigan University (NMU), 1998-2000; Assistant Director of Diversity Student Services, NMU, 2000-04. *Community service*: Board member: Native Americans of Marquette County, Inc., the MAPS Title VII Indian Education Parent Advisory Committee, and the Marquette Area Blues Society; she has taught beadwork classes and has been a part of a women's hand drum group. *Interests*: Dancing & singing at powwows in the Upper Great Lakes Region; Beadwork, cooking, films, and blues music.

LINDBERG, TRACY (Cree/Metis)
(director of Indigenous education; professor of Indigenous studies)
Education: University of Saskatchewan, College of Law, JD; Harvard Law School, graduate law degree. *Affiliation & Address*: Director, Indigenous Education & Associate Professor, Indigenous Studies, Athabasca University, Centre for World Indigenous Knowledge & Research, 1 University Dr., Athabasca, AB T9S 3A3 Canada (780) 428-2064. E-mail: traceyl@athabasca.ca. Tracy is the first Aboriginal woman in Canada to complete her graduate law degree at Harvard University; and she is thought to be the first Aboriginal woman to receive a doctorate in law from a Canadian University, as well, having received the Governor General's Award in 2007 upon convocation for her dissertation, "Critical Indigenous Legal Theory." Her work experience includes teaching at the Native Law Program, practicing law at Gauley & Co., and teaching in the University of Ottawa Common Law Faculty. She has written and/or taught courses on Critical Indigenous Legal Theory, Indigenous Wmen's Legal Advocacy, Aboriginal law & government, Aboriginal business law, Aborignal women and Aborignal dispute resolution. Dr. Lindberg works, upon request, with Indigenous nations & communities that require legal representation and research for the advancement of claims & suit.

LINDLEY, BRENDA (*Mahkoonsahkwa*) (Wea)
(herbalist, homeopathic practitioner, tribal administrator)
Affiliation: Wea Indian Tribe & Herbal Remedy Clinic, 715 Park Ave., Lafayette, IN 47904; E-mail: weatribe@wea-indian-tribe.com, or apilitasremedy@aol.com Website: www.wea-indian-tribe.com, or www.angelfire.com/in4/ herbal remedies. *Interests*: She specializes in Western & Native American Herbology, with knowledge in aromatherapy, homeopathy, surgical technology, and conventional medicines with over 16 years of experience. She studied under Master Herbalist, Michael Tierra, and is a licensed/certified herbalist. She also has 30 years of genealogical research experience. *Other professional post*: Administrator, genealogist & historian for the Wea Indian Tribe, and owns a Genealogy Service with an e-mail address, bloodlngenealogy@aol.com.

LINER-SANDERS, AUTUMN (Snoqualmie)
(attorney)
Education: University of Washngton, Tacoma, BA, 20005; Seattle University School of Law, JD, 2008. *Affiliation & Address*: Contract Attorney (2010-13); Associate Attorney (2013-present), Legal Advocates for Indian Country, LLP, 720 Third Ave., Suite 1900, Seattle, WA 98104 (206) 499-8684. HARLAN

LINDQUIST, CYNTHIA (*Pretty, Good Talk Woman*) (Sisseton-Wahpeton Sioux) 1951-
(tribal college president)
Born June 28, 1951, St. Paul, Minn. *Education*: University of North Dakota, BA, 1981; University of South Dakota, 1988; University of North Dakota, PhD. *Affiliation & Address*: President, Cankdeska Cikana Community College, P.O. Box, 269, Fort Totten, ND 58335 (701) 766-4055. E-mail: president@littlehoop.edu. *Other professional posts*: Chairperson, Board of Directors, American Indian Higher Education Consortium, Alexandria, VA; Adjunct, Assistant Professor of Community Medicine & Rural Health with UND School of Medicine, 1989-; consultant & advisor to the Kaiser Family Foundation. *Past professional posts*: Professional Services Director, Aberdeen Area Indian Health Service, Aberdeen, SD, 1987-89; Assistant Professor, Community Medicine & Rural Health & Associate Director, Center for Rural Health, University of North Dakota School of Medicine, Grand Forks, ND, 1989-91; executive director, Northern Plains Healthy Start, Aberdeen, SD, 1991-92; wrote and developed the Northern Plains Healthy Start Initiative; associate director, University of North Dakota's Center for Rural Health; Senior advisor to the Director, Indian Health Service, Rockville, MD, 1994-96; coordinator, Grand Forks Historic Preservation Commission, Grand Forks, ND 1997-98; executive director, North Dakota Indian Affairs Commission, Bismarck, ND, 1998-present. *Community activities*: Indian Women's Health Steering Committee; Foster parents Advisory Board. *Awards, honors*: Service/Appreciation Award, National Indian Health Board, 1995; TRIO Achiever Award for ASPIRE, University of North Dakota, 1995; Certificate of Appreciation, American Association of Indian Physicians, 1995; National TRIO Achiever Award, NCEOA, Washington, DC, 1996; Service Appreciation Award, IHS, 1996; Notable North Dakotan, Bismarck Tribune, 1998; Bush Leadership Fellowship, 1999; Good Housekeeping Award for Women in Government, 1999; 2012 Distinguished Alumnus Award from the University of North Dakota.

LINDSTROM, CHRIS (Luiseno)
(executive director)
Affiliation & Address: Executive Director, California Tribal Business Alliance (CTBA), 1530 J St., Suite 250, Sacramento, CA 95814 (916) 601-1969. Email: chris@ctba.org. *Past professional posts*: Field Representative, 1987-89, Administrative Assistant, 1989-94, California State Sentaor Alfred E. Alquist; Deputy Director of Legislation, California Gambling Control Commission, 2001-04; Chief Consutlant, California State Assembly Committee on Governmental Organization, 2004-07; principal Consultant, California Senate Committee on Governmental Organization, 2007-10.

LINER-SANDERS, AUTUMN
(attorney)
Education: Highine Community College, AA; University of Washington, Tacoma, BA (Political Science);Seattle University Shool of Law, 2008. *Affiliation & Address*: Associate Attorney (2009-present), Legal Advocates for Indian Country, LLP, 720 Third Ave., Suite 1900, Seattle, WA 98104 (206) 499-8684. Autumn focuses her practice on Native American law, Indian cild welfare, and advocates for the protection, promotion, and evolution of the rights of trbal nations and tribal people. While attending law school she served as president of the Native American Law Student Association.

LINGERFELT, WILLIAM D. (*Chief Medicine Wolf*) (Eastern Cherokee) 1949-
(construction contractor)
Born July 20, 1949, Atlanta, Ga. *Principal occupation*: Construction contractor. Resides in Canton, GA (404) 479-4627. *Military service*: U.S. Army, 1969-71 (Specialist 4th Class; Vietnam Vet - 1 Bronze Star, Vietnam Campaign Medal, Good Conduct Badge, several others). *Community service*: VFW member. *Interests*: "I am a lecturer and the voice of my people in the northern Georgia area. My family and I are active in the powwow trail. We are dancers and make Native American jewelry, costumes, beadwork, etc. I'm chief medicine man for Southeastern Cherokee Confederacy. I sit on the Chief's Council. My wife "Snow Deer" is chief of the Wolf Clan." *Biographical sources*: Paper which have done stories on Mr. Lingerfelt: The Atlanta Journal Constitution; The Cherokee Tribune; The Cleveland; Georgia Telegraph; Gainesville, GA Newspaper; The Indian Trader Magazine.

LINTINGER, BRENDA WAMBSEGANS (Tunica-Biloxi)
(tribal council member)
Education: University of New orleans, BA (English Literature with a minor in History & Linguistics), MBA (Finance), 2004. *Affiliation & Address*: Council member, Tunica-Biloxi Indian Tribe, 151 Melacon Dr., Marksville, LA 71351 (318) 253-9767. E-mail: lintingerbw@aol.com. Lintinger served her first term as a member of the Tunica-Biloxi Tribal Council in 1997. Her focus and main area of interests were Investments and Financial Markets and Institutions. She has served on the tribal POW WOW and Education committees, and she has represented her tribe on the United South and Eastern Tribes' Education as Secretary/Treasurer & Housing Committees. Mrs. Lintinger currently serves as the Secretary/Treasurer on the Tunica-Biloxi Economic Development Board and as CFO of the Economic Development Corporation. Lintinger has also been active in numerous organizations within & outside of her Native American community. She has worked with the Louisiana Office of Indian Affairs in conjunction with the Indian Education Advisory Board. She is currently employed as the Managing Editor of "News From the Tunica-Biloxi Tribe of Louisiana," a publication promoting education, information, and public relations on behalf of the tribe. She also functions as the liaison between the tribal government and JP Morgan/Chase as the Minors' Trust Program Coordinator.

LINTON, PAGE (Paiute)
(tribal chairperson)
Affiliation & Address: Chairperson, Summit Lake Paiute Tribe, 1708 H St., Sparks, NV 89431 (775) 827-9670. E-mail: page.linton@summitlaketribe.org

LINZER, ANNA (Lenape) 1950-
(writer)
Born February 10, 1950, Seattle, Wash. *Education*: University of Washington, Lewis & Clark College, Southern Oregon State College. *Principal occupation*: Writer. *Address*: P.O. Box 374, Indianola, WA 98342 (360) 297-8331. E-mail: linzer@centurytel.net. *Affiliation*: Richard & Anna Linzer, Facilitation & Consultation. *Memberships*: Native Writers Circle of the Americas; NW Native Writers Circle; PEN. *Awards, honors*: 1999 American Book Award for "Ghost Dancing." *Published works*: Ghost Dancing Picador (St. Martin's Press, 1998); numerous works of fiction, poetry & essays in literary magazines.

LITTLE, ANTHONY F. (Rosebud Sioux)
(attorney)
Address: P.O. Box 817, Bernalillo, NM 87004 (505) 867-3391. *Membership*: Native American Bar Association (board member).

LITTLE, DANA (Turtle Mountain & Rocky Boy Ojibwe)
(prosecuting attorney)
Education: University of Washington School of Law, JD, 2009. *Affiliation & Address*: Deputy Prosecuting Attorney (2009-present), Snohomish County Prosecutor's Office, 3000 Rockefeller, M/S 504, Everett, WA 98201 (425) 388-3333. *Other professional post*: Secretary (2012-13), Northwest Indian Bar Association, Edmonds, WA.

LITTLE BEAR, LEROY ROBERT (Blackfoot) 1941-
(professor of Native American studies)
Born November 11, 1941, Alberta, Can. *Education*: Wenatchee (WA) Valley College, AA, 1966; University of Lethbridge (Alberta, Can.), BA, 1971; University of Utah, School of Law, JD, 1975. *Principal occupation*: Professor of Native American studies. *Affiliations*: Native American Studies Department, University of Lethbridge, Alberta, Canada (associate professor, 1975-; chairperson, 1975-81) (403) 329-2733. *Other professional posts*: Consultant, National Indian Brotherhood, Lethbridge, AB, 1976-78; Department of Indian Affairs, Lethbridge, 1980-81; Blood Indian Tribe, Cardston, AB, 1980-; Indian Association of Alberta, Lethbridge, 1983-. *Community activities*: Blood Tribe Police Commission (volunteer), 1980-; Legal Aid Society of Alberta, Lethbridge (volunteer), 1981-82; Lethbridge Friendship Centre (volunteer), 1969-71. *Conferences*: Subcommission of Human Rights Commission (representative), 1984; United Nations' Conference (representative), 1984; attended Constitutional conventions on Native Rights, 1983, 1984 & 1985) as a legal advisor for Indian Association of Alberta. *Memberships*: Canadian Lawyers' Association; Indian Association of Alberta. *Interests*: Indian law; Native Canadian Government issues. Speak, read and write English & Blackfoot. *Published works*: Pathways to Self-Determination: Native Indian Leaders' Perspectives on Self-Government, and Quest for Justice: Aboriginal Rights in Canada, both with Nenno Boldt & J. Anthony Long. *Articles*: "Dispute Settlement Among the Nacirema," Journal of Contemporary Law; "A Concept of Native Title," presentation to MacKenzie Valley Pipeline Inquiry (Thomas Berger Commission Chairman).

LITTLE HAWK, KENNETH (Micmac/Mohawk) 1936-
(educator, lecturer, storyteller, musician, composer)
Born January 14, 1936, in New Jersey. *Address*: P.O. Box 107, Whiting, NJ 08759 (732) 716-0456. E-mail: littlehawk@kennethlittlehawk.com. Website: www.kennethlittlehawk.com. *Professional skills*: Little Hawk shares Native American culture, traditions, & musical instruments in a lecture, storytelling, and musical demonstration format. Little Hawk performs for a wide variety of audiences. His themes include Native American culture, cultural diversity, self-esteem, and respect for others & our environment. As a recording artist, Little Hawk composes, sings and plays Native American music on flutes, drums, rattles, and other traditional instruments for movies, plays, television, radio, and concerts. His music & singing are heard in the films, "The West," and "Lewis and Clark," both produced by Ken Burns. The soundtrack for "The West," produced by SONY, includes Little Hawk's original music and singing. "Wind, Sun and Stars," Helicon Records, was nominated for Best Children's Recording of 1998 by Native American Music Awards. Little Hawk's recordings include "First Light," "The Hawk Project," "From the Heart of Little Hawk," "In a Very Real Way," "In a Good Way," & "Brothers of the Wind." He has composed and performed music with the Westchester Philharmonic, New York. As an actor, Little Hawk appeared in "Black Elk Speaks" at the Denver Center Theatre Company and at the Mark Taper Forum in Los Angeles. He played Chief Joseph in "Indians" at the McCarter Theater Company in Princeton, NJ. He portrayed a Native American elder in "The Inheritance," a film directed by Mark Williams, NYU Dept. of Film & TV. He played an attorney in the film, "Petty Crimes," directed by Michael Ferry, and a storyteller in the film, "Campfire Stories," directed by Andrzej Krakowski & Jeff Mazzola. *Military service*: U.S. Army Paratrooper (honorable discharge-Good Conduct Medal. *Awards, honors*: Nominated twice by Native American Music Awards for "Best Storyteller" and "Best Spoken Word;" Has been on TV-PBS (Ken Burns' documentaries; Lewis & Clark, and Land of the Eagle. *Community activities*: Lecture and perform in public libraries & schools, colleges & universities, senior citizens' homes, and Veterans' hospitals. *Memberships*: Screen Actors Guild, Actors' Equity, Project Impact, BOCES, The Hawk Project, The Gatherers' Institute. *Interests*: Teaching respect for our Earth and all living things. Composing & playing Native music on traditional, natural instruments. Published CD's: "The Great Mystery," "In a Very Real Way," "In a Good Way," and "Wind, Sun, and Storm."

LITTLE THUNDER, KENNETH (Cheyenne River Sioux)
(tribal administrative officer)
Affiliation & Address: Administrative Officer, Cheyenne River Sioux Tribe, P.O. Box 590, Eagle Butte, SD 57625 (605) 964-4155.

LITTLEAXE, TROY (Shawnee)
(tribal attorney)
Education: University of Tulsa Law School, JD. *Affiliation & Address*: Founding Partner, Legal Advocates for Indian Country, LLP, P.O. Box 87, Miami, OK

74355 (918) 376-0630. *Other professional posts*: General Counsel, Modoc Tribe of Oklahoma, Miami, OK; serves other tribes as judge, gaming commissioner, health board member, & legal counsel. *Past professional post*: Assistant to legal counsel for Absentee Shawnee & Chickasaw Nation.

LITTLEBEAR, DR. RICHARD
(college president; Indian studies program coordinator)
Affiliation & Address: Chief Dull Knife College, P.O. Box 98, Lame Deer, MT 59043 (406) 477-6215. *Past professional posts*: Director, Multifunctional Resource Center, Anchorage, AK; chairperson, American Indian College Fund, Denver, CO.

LITTLEBIRD, LARRY
(writer)
Address: P.O. Box 2900, Santa Fe, NM 87501 (505) 455-3196.

LITTLECHILD, WILLIE (Wetaskiwin)
(Canadian parliament member)
Address: Parliament Bldgs., Ottawa, ON K1A 0A4 (613) 995-9364.

LITTLEFIELD, DANIEL F., JR. (Seminole of Florida)
(professor of English; research center director)
Affiliations & Address: Director, Sequoyah National Research Center, 500 University Plaza, University of Arkansas at Little Rock, 2801 S. University, Little Rock, AR 72204 (501) 569-8336. Email: dflittlefiel@uuair.edu. *Other professional post*: Director, American Native Press Archives. *Published work*: Africans & Seminoles: From Removal to Emancipation; editor with James W. Parins, Native American Writing in the Southeast: An Anthology.

LITTLELEAF, CHARLES (Confederated Tribes of Warm Springs)
(flutist, flute maker)
Born in Warm Springs, Oreg. *Affiliation & Address*: Littleleaf Native American Flutes & Music, P.O. Box 1225, Warm Springs, OR 97761 (541) 410-7803. Website: www.littleleaf.com; E-mail: littleleaf@centurylink.net. Charles was instructed by R. Carlos Nakai. In 1997, his first album (cassette) was released, titled "Whispers of Earth Medicine." In 2002, his album "Ancient Reflections" was released on CD.

LIVERMORE, EARL (Blackfeet)
(artist)
Address: Livermore Fine Arts & Design, P.O. Box 2173, Bellingham, WA 98227 (360) 647-9137. *Artwork*: Original artwork and limited edition prints.

LOBO, SUSAN
(cultural anthropologist; professor)
Education: University of Arizona, PhD (Cultural Anthropology), 1977. *Affiliation & Address*: Distinguished Visiting Professor, American Indian Studies Program, The University of Arizona, Harvill 226D, Tucson, AZ 85721. *Other professional posts*: Consultant emphasizing research, advocacy, project design & evaluation, working primarily for American Indian tribes & nations, and community-based NGOs in the U.S., Central & South America; visiting professor at La Universidad de la Republica in Uruguay and the Ilisilimatusarfic University in Greenland. *Interests*: Indigenous peoples worldwide, including urbanization, modernization, migration, & community development; American Indians with a focus on contemporary issues, urbanization, & social change; and current issues in Native American studies as an academic field of study. *Published works*: Urban Voices: The Bay Area American Indian Community; American Indian & the Urban Experience; Native American Voices: A Reader (three editions); numerous articles.

LOCHEN, ERIC M. (Ojibwe)
(attorney-Indian law)
Education: Miami University, BA, 1997; University of Wisconsin, MLS, 2004; William Mitchell College of Law, JD (Federal Indian Law), 2008. *Affiliation & Address*: Managing Partner, Lochen Thin Elk Denton, PLLC, 4124 Quebec Ave. North, Suite 307, Minneapolis, MN 55427 (2009-present). *Other professional post*: Board member, Wisconsin State Bar Association Indian Law Section, 2014-present. *Past professional posts*: Attorney General, Quinault Indian Nation, Taholah, WA, 2015-16; In-House Counsel, Leech Lake band of Ojibwe, 2008-10.

LOCKE, KEVIN (*Tokeya Inajin*) (Lakota-Anishinaabe) 1954-
(educator/performer)
Born in California. In 1954 and, raised in South Dakta. *Principal occupation*: Educator/performer (traditional Northern Plains flute player & hoop dancer) dba Lakota Performing Arts. *Affiliation & Address*: The Kevin Locke Native Dance Ensemble, c/o Lakota Performing Arts & Education, 47 N. Franklin St., Wilkes-Barre, PA 18701 (717) 319-8944. Robin Troup, contact. E-mail: rtroup@ ixtlanartists.com. *Awards & honors*: NEA National Heritage Award, 1990; delegate & featured performer at Earth Summit (Brazil 1992); 1993 Parent's Choice Gold Award, 1993 for "Wopila - A Giveaway," for outstanding material

for children ages 4-9; United Nations Habitat II Conference (Turkey 1996). *Interests*: Kevin not only performs & lectures in schools all across the Plains states, he has toured the world appearing in Canada, China, Spain, Australia, and Africa. *Published works*: Open Circle, 1996; Keepers of the Dream, 1994; Wopila-A Giveaway, 1993; Dream Catcher, 1992; The Flash of the Mirror, 1992; Make Me a Hollow Reed, 1990; Lakota Love Songs & Stories, 1990; The Seventh Direction, 1990; Love Songs of the Lakota, 1982. All cassettes & CDs produced & recorded at Meyer Creative Productions for Makoche Records (Bismarck), EarthBeat! Records (Redway), & Indian House Recordings (Taos).

LOCKEE, BARBARA B. (Cherokee)
(associate director & professor of education)
Education: Virginia Tech University, PhD (Curriculum & Instruction). *Affiliation & Address*: Associate Director & Professor of Education (specializing in Instructional Design & Technology), School of Education, 115 War Memorial Hall, Blacksburg, VA 24061 (540) 231-9193. E-mail: lockeebb@vt..edu. Research focuses on effective instructional design strategies for distance learning environments. *Awards, honors*: The Institute for Distance & Distributed Learning recognized her contributions to and achievements in E-Learning in 2006; 2002 Clifton Garvin Fellowship; XCaliber Award for Excellence in Courseware Development in 2000. *Published works*: Numerous journal articles, book chapters, columns & articles, & conference proceedings.

LOCKHART, GEMMA (Lakota)
(film producer)
Affiliation: Whirlwind Soldier, P.O. Box 154, Rosebud, SD 57570 (605) 747-2835.

LOCKLEAR, ARLINDA (Lumbee) 1951-
(professor of law)
Born September 9, 1951, at Fort Bragg, N.C. *Education*: Duke University School of Law, JD, 1976. Locklear holds honorary doctorates from The State University of New York at Oneonta (1990), North Carolina State University (2007) and The College of Charleston (2012), her alma mater. She began her career as an attorney at the Native American Rights Fund in Boulder, Co., and later transferred to the Washington D.C. office, serving as directing attorney. Arlinda has spent her career in Washington, D.C., working for American Indian rights. Among the tribes that Locklear has advocated for is her own Lumbee Tribe of North Carolina. She joined the Native American Rights Fund as a staff attorney at the Boulder, Colorado office in 1976. Then, in 1982, she became directing attorney of the Native American Rights Fund's Washington office. From 1988 to 2011, she represented the tribe's effort to win federal recognition. Locklear was described in American Bar Association publication as "a pioneering attorney in Native American law." In 1984, she became the first Native American woman to appear before the U.S. Supreme Court. As lead counsel in two cases, Locklear prepared the brief and presented the oral argument to the nation's highest court. In 1984, she successfully challenged South Dakota's authority to prosecute a member of the Cheyenne River Sioux Tribe for on-reservation conduct in Solem v. Bartlett. In 1985, Locklear represented the tribe in Oneida Indian Nation v. County of Oneida, in which she argued that tribes have a federal common law right to sue for possession of tribal lands taken in violation of federal law. The Oneida case is the seminal case upon which all other land claims litigation have since been based. In addition to her significant litigation experience, Locklear is a nationally recognized expert in the area of federal recognition of Indian tribes. She is well-versed in the legislative process as well, having successfully represented the Fort McDowell Yavapai Nation in the settlement of its water rights. Awards, honors: 2008 honor for her contributions to the American Indian community by the Conference of American Indian Women of Proud Nations; recipient of the Julian T. Pierce Award which recognizes an outstanding attorney & advocate of equal justice; recipient of the Margaret Brent Women Lawyers of Achievement Award from the American Bar Association in 2012; profiles in the following directories: Who's Who in the East (33rd-38th editions); Who's Who in American Politics (22nd & 23rd editions); Who's Who in American Law (14th-16th editions), and Who's Who in America (60th-64th editions).

LOCKLEAR, JUANITA O. (Lumbee)
(center director)
Affiliation: Native American Resource Center, Pembroke State University, Pembroke, NC 28372 (919) 521-4214.

LOCKLEAR, LINDA ROSE (Catawba/Lumbee)
(professor emeritus of American Indian studies)
Education: San Diego State University, BA (Sociology), MS (Counseling); University of California, San Diego, MA (Sociology). *Affiliation & Address*: Professor, American Indian Studies Program, American Studies Dept., Palomar Community College, 1140 W. Mission Rd., San Marcos, CA 92069 (619) 744-1150. E-mail: llocklear@palomar.edu She is a consultant & lecturer on contemporary American Indian issues for schools and organizations. Her research area is ethnographic and documentary film on American Indians.

LOCKLEAR, PATRICIA (Lumbee)
(playwright)
Address: P.O. Box 68-P, Pembroke, NC 28372 (910) 521-8602.

LOCKLEAR, RITA J. (Lumbee)
(director of Indian education)
Education: Campbell University, M.Ed. *Address & Affiliation*: Director, Title VII, Indian Education Program, Robeson County Schools, 957 Lonnie Farm Rd., Pembroke, NC 28372 (910) 521-2054. E-mail: locklearr.iea@robeson.k12. nc.us. *Other professional post*: Vice-president, Board of Directors, National Indian Education Association. *Past professional posts*: Teacher for 27 years with the Robeson County Schools; member of the North Carolina State Advisory Council on Indian Education for six years; National Trainer for the National Education Association.

LODGE, GLENN H. (Chemehuevi)
(tribal vce chairperson)
Affiliation & Address: Vice Chairperson, Chemehuevi Indian Tribe, P.O. Box 1976, Havasu Lake, CA 92363 (760) 858-4219. E-mail: vice.chair@cit-nsn.gov

LOERA, JAVIER (Tigua)
(tribal committeemember)
Affiliation & Address: Committeemember, Ysleta Del Sur Pueblo, P.O. Box 17579, El Paso, TX 79907 (915) 859-8053.

LOETHER, CHRISTOPHER
(director & professor of American Indian studies)
Affiliation & Address: Director, American Indian Studies Program, Dept. of Anthropology, Idaho State University, P.O. Box 8005, Pocatello, ID 83209 (208) 236-2629. E-mail: loetchri@isu.edu. Other professional posts: Director, Linguistics Program; co-director, Shoshoni Language Project. *Interests*: Linguistics, language; Indians of California. Dr. Loether has worked specifically with the Western Mono, Owens Valley Paiute, Shoshoni & Welsh languages.

LOEW, PATTY (*Waswaganokwe*) (Bad River Band-Ojibwe) 1952-
(assistant professor; public TV host)
Born May 15, 1952, Milwaukee, Wisc. *Education*: University of Wisconsin, LaCrosse, BS (Mass Communications), 1974; University of Wisconsin, Madison, MA (Broadcast Journalism), 1992, PhD in Mass Communications, 1998. *Address*: 7788 W. Old Sauk Rd., Verona, WI 53593. *Affiliation & Address*: Assistant professor, UW-Madison Dept. of Life Sciences Communication & Journalist, Wisconsin Public Television, University of Wisconsin, Madison, Dept. of Life Sciences Communication, Rm. 224A Ag Journalism, 440 Henry Mall, Madison, WI 53706 (608) 262-0654. E-Mail: paloew@wisc.edu. Website: www.lsc.wisc.edu/pattyloew.htm. *Other professional posts*: Affiliated Faculty, UW-Madison, American Indian Studies, UW-Madison School of Human Ecology, and UW-Madison Dept. of Family & Consumer Science. *Past professional posts*: Wisconsin Public Television, Madison, Wisc, 1993-present. WKOW-TV Madison, WI, 1975-79 and 1985-96. KHQ-TV, Spokane, WA, 1979-81. KATU-TV, Portland, OR, 1981-85. *Awards, honors*: Honorary Doctorate, Doctor of Humane Letters, Edgewood College, 2003; Women of Achievement Award, Wisconsin Woman of Color Network, 2003; Friend of Education, Wisconsin State School Superintendent's Award, 2003; Honorary Doctorate, Doctor of Public Service, Northland College, 2002; Outstanding Book Award, Wisconsin Library Association, 2001; Outstanding Service Award, Great Lakes Inter-Tribal Council, 1998; Frances C. Allen Fellowship, D'Arcy McNickle Center for American Indian History, Newberry Library, Chicago, IL, 1997; Anna Julia Cooper Fellow, UW History, 1996; Howard Simons Fellow, 1992. *Community activities*: UW Committee on Gender and Diversity, Wisc.; Advisory Board, Logan Museum of Anthropology, Beloit College; Advisory Board, Sequoyah Research Center, University of Arkansas at Little Rock. *Membership*: Native American Journalists Assn; Native American Public Telecommunications (former board member: Wisconsin Historical Society). *Interests*: American Indian treaty rights, Origin Stories, environmental justice issues, tribal & mainstream media. *Published work*: Books: Indian Nations of Wisconsin (Wisconsin Historical Society Press, 2001); Native People of Wisconsin (Wisconsin Historical Society Press, 2003); book chapter in, A Wisconsin Fifteen (Wisconsin Historical Society Press, 1998).

LOFTON, MARK Luiseno)
(tribal vice chairperson)
Affiliation & Address: Vice Chairperson, La Jolla Band of Luiseno Indians, 22000 Hwy. 76, Pauma Valley, CA92061 (760) 742-3771.

LOGAN, LINDA (Oklahoma Choctaw)
(executive director)
Affiliation & Address: Executive Director, Native American Children's Alliance, P.O. Box 18288, Cleveland, OH 44118 (216) 373-6862. E-mail: lindanative childalliance@gmail.com.

LOGAN, VINCENT G. (Osage)
(BIA Special Trustee for American Indians)
Born & raised in Norman, Oklahoma. *Education*: Oklahoma State University, BA; University of Oklahoma College of Law, JD; Oxford University & Columbia University School of International & Public Affairs. *Affiliation*: Special Trustee for American Indians (2014-present), Bureau of Indian Affairs, 1849 C St., NW, MS-4141-MIB • Washington, DC 20240 (202) 208-7163. He is the fourth person to be confirmed by the U.S. Senate for this position. Logan has been a mentor for Native American attorneys and is a founding member of the Native American Bar Association of Washington, D.C. An expert in debt financing and asset management, he has built a vast network of professional relationships within Indian Country. *Past professional posts*: Prior to joining the Department of the Interior as the Special Trustee, Logan was President of The Nations Group, LLC, an investment consulting firm in New York. The Nations Group works with tribal nations on asset management and investment strategies and is a leader in the financial education movement in Indian Country. Previously, Logan worked as a private banker at Merrill Lynch (NY), a corporate finance attorney at Schulte, Roth & Zabel in New York, and in the Antitrust Division of the U.S. Department of Justice. *Memberships*: Investment Management Consultants Association, the American Bar Association, the Federal Bar Association, the Oklahoma Bar Association, and the Global Association of Risk Professionals. In 2010, Logan was appointed to the Oklahoma State University Foundation Board of Governors.

LOHAH, ELIZABETH (Osage of Oklahoma)
(attorney)
Affiliation & Address: Director, Office of American Indian Trust, U.S. Dept. of the Interior, 1849 C St., NW, MS: 2471-MIB, Washington, DC 20240 (202) 208-3338. Website: www.doi.gove/indiantrust/

LOHSE, KYLE (Nomlaki) 1978-
(major league baseball player)
Born Oct. 4, 1978 in Chico, Calif. *Affiliation*: Pitcher, St. Louis Cardinals, St. Louis, MO, 2008-present. *Past affiliations*: Minnesota Twins, 2001-06; Cincinnati Reds, 2006-07; Philadelphia Phillies, 2007.

LOHSE, LESLIE (Nomlaki)
(tribal council treasurer)
Affiliation & Address: Treasurer (1998-present), Paskenta Band of Nomlaki Indians, P.O. Box 398, Orland, CA 95963 (530) 865-3119. Leslie was appointed by Governor Arnold Schwarzenneger as a commissioner to the Native American Heritage Commission in November 2007. *Other professional posts*: Chairperson, Bureau of Indian Affairs Central California Agency Policy Committee; Pacific Regional V.P. on the National Congress of American Indians Executive Committee; board V.P., California Tribal Business Alliance, Sacramento; board member, California Native American Heritage Commission, West Sacramento.

LOMAHAFTEWA, LINDA (Hopi) 1947-
(teacher, artist)
Born July 3, 1947, Phoenix, Ariz. *Education*: San Francisco Art Institute, BFA, 1970, MFA, 1971. *Principal occupation*: Teacher, artist. *Address*: Route 11, Box 20 SP 59, Santa Fe, NM 87501 (505) 424-2362. E-mail: llomahaftewa@ iaia.edu. *Affiliation*: Assistant professor of Native American Art, California State College, Rohnert Park, 1971-73; teacher, painting and drawing, Native American Studies, University of California, Berkeley, 1974-76; drawing and painting instructor, Center for Arts & Cultural Studies, Institute of American Indian Arts, Santa Fe, 1976-. *Exhibitions*: Festival of Native American Art, Aspen Institute at Baca, 1982; Contemporary Native American Art, Gardiner Art Gallery, Oklahoma State University, Stillwater, Okla., 1983; Contemporary Native American Photography, Southern Plains Indian Museum, Anadarko, Okla., 1984; Shadows Caught Images of Native Americans, Gilcrease Museum, Tulsa, 1984; 2nd Annual Heard Invitational, Heard Museum, Phoenix, 1985; One Woman Exhibit, American Indian Contemporary Arts, San Francisco, 1985; Women of Sweetgrass, Cedar and Sage, Gallery of the American Indian Community House, New York, N.Y., 1985; The Art of the Native American, Owensboro Museum of Fine Arts, KY, 1985; Native to Native, Alchemie Gallery, Boston, 1986. *Community activities*: City of Santa Fe Arts Board. *Memberships*: San Francisco Art Institute Alumni Association; Institute of American Indian Arts Alumni Association. *Awards, honors*: Indian Festival of Arts - First Place Painting, La Grande, Oregon, 1974; 61st Annual Indian Market - Third Place Painting, Santa Fe, 1982. Interests: "Art--displayed at the following permanent collections: Southern Plains Indian Museum, Anadarko, Okla.; Millicent Rogers Museum, Taos, N.M.; University of Lethbridge, Native American Studies Department, Alberta, Canada; Native American Center for the Living Arts, Inc., Niagara Falls, NY; American Indian Historical Society, San Francisco; Center for the Arts of Indian America, Washington, DC." *Biographical sources*: Who's Who in American Art, 1976; The Sweet Grass Lives on 50 Contemporary Native American Indian Artists, by Jamake Highwater (Lippincott, 1980); American Women Artists, by Charlotte Streifer Rubinstein (Avon, 1982); The World Who's Who of Women, Eighth

Edition, 1984; Bearing Witness Sobreviviendo, An Anthology of Writing and Art by Native American/Latina Women (Calyx: A Journal of Art and Literature by Women, Corvallis, Ore., 1984); The American West, The Modern Vision, by Patricia Janis Broder (Little, Brown, 1984).

LOMAKEMA, MILLAND, SR. (Hopi)
(Hopi craftsmen's coop guild manager)
Affiliation: Hopi Arts & Crafts/Silvercraft Cooperative Guild, P.O. Box 37, Second Mesa, AZ 86043 (520) 734-2463.

LOMAWAIMA, HARTMAN H. (Hopi)
(museum director)
Education: Harvard University, EdM, 1972. *Address & Affiliation*: Director, Arizona State Museum, Room 308B, University of Arizona, Tucson, AZ 85721 (520) 621-6281. E-Mail: hartman@email.arizona.edu. *Other professional post*: Affiliate faculty, American Indian Studies Program, University of Arizona, Tucson, AZ. *Affiliations*: Hearst Museum of Anthropology, UC Berkeley, CA, 1980-88; University of Washington, Seattle, 1988-94; Arizona State Museum, Tucson, AZ, 1994-present. *Community activities*: Hopi Foundation, Hotevilla, AZ (former president); trustee, Hopi Education Endowment Fund; trustee, National Museum of the American Indian, Smithsonian Institution (chair of the trustee's committee on research); Council, Adult Literacy Initiative, University of Arizona Press; locally, he serves as board member for the Tucson Pima Arts Council, The Arizona Town Hall and the Governor's Historical Advisory Commission that is planning Arizona's Centennial activities. *Memberships*: National Indian Education Association; American Association for State & Local History (National Council); American Association of Museums. *Interests*: Museology, ethnology. *Published works*: "I have authored articles & chapters that have been published in journals, readers & encyclopedias."

LOMAWAIMA, K. TSIANINA (Creek) 1955-
(professor of American Indian studies)
Born March 30, 1955, in Kansas. *Education*: Stanford University, MA, 1979, PhD, 1987. *Affiliation & Address*: Distinguished Scholar in Indigenous Education & Professor of Justice & Social Inquiry, School of Social Transformation, The Center for Indian Education, Arizona State University, Payne Hall 301, Wilson Hall, 373, Mail Code: 6403, Tempe, AZ 85287 (480) 965-3067. E-mail: k.tsianina.lomawaima@asu.edu. *Past professional posts*: Assistant Professor, Dept. of Anthropology, American Indian Studies, University of Washington, Seattle, 1988-94; University of Arizona, American Indian Studies, Tucson, AZ (associate professor, 1994-98; professor, 1998-2010; chair & interim director, 2006-10). *Memberships*: American Society for Ethnohistory; American Anthropological Assn; American Educational Research Assn; Native American & Indigenous Studies Assn (past president, 2012-13). *Awards, honors*: Ford Doctoral Fellow, 1977-79; Dorothy Danforth Compton Fellow, 1984; 1994 Native North American Prose Award & the 1995 American Indian Education Association's Critics' Choice Award; 1994 University of Washington Distinguished Teaching Award; 2003 University of Arizona Alumni Association Extraordinary Faculty Award. *Interests*: History of American Indian education, especially experiences of native people in federal boarding schools. Federal policy & practice to transform Native homes, and Native response. *Published works*: They Called It Prairie Light: The Story of Chilocco Indian School (University of Nebraska Press, 1994); Away From Home: American Indian Boarding School Experiences, 1878-2000, with M. Archuleta & B. Child (Heard Museum, 2000); Uneven Ground: American Indian Sovereignty and Federal Law, with D. Wilkins (University of Oklahoma Press, 2001); To Remain an Indian: Lessons in Democracy from a Century of Native American Education, with Prof. Teresa L. McCarty (Teachers College Press, 2006); articles.

LOMAX, WILLIAM (Gitxsan)
(financial advisor; director & Native American liaison)
Education: Columbia Business School, MBA; British Columbia (Canada) Law School, JD. *Affiliation & Address*: Director & Native American Liaison, Capital Dynamics, Inc., 645 Madison Ave., 19th Floor, New York, NY 10022 (917) 669-3309. E-mail: William@nafoa.org. *Other professional post*: President (2007-present), Board of Directors, Native American Finance Officers Association, Washington, DC. Bill has worked extensively with tribal governments for more than 13 years as a financial advisor on Wall Street. *Past professional post*: Portfolio Manager, San Manuel Band of Mission Indians.

LOMAYESVA, DEVON LEE (Iipay Nation of Santa Ysabel)
(executive director)
Education: San Diego State University (SDSU), BA, 1994; California Western School of Law, JD, 1999. *Affiliation*: Executive Director, California Indian Legal Services, 510 16th St. #301, Oakland, CA 94612 (510) 835-0284. Devon held positions from Law Clerk to Directing Attorney, 1998-2004. *Other professional post*: Co-founder & Board Chair, American Indian Recruitment (AIR) Program. *Past professional post*: Member, Santa Ysabel Tribal Council, 1998-2002. *Memberships*: Iipay Nation of Santa Ysabel; Native American Lawyers

Association of San Diego. *Interests*: Federal Indian Law, particularly the areas of ICWA, Cultural Resource protection, Gaming and Tribal Government issues. She enjoys attending & organizing local cultural events and spending quality time with her family.

LONE HILL, KAREN (Oglala Lakota)
(Lakota studies chairperson)
Affiliation & Address: Chair, Oglala Lakota Studies, Oglala Lakota College, P.O. Box 490, Kyle, SD 58852 (605) 455-6000. E-mail: kloneh@olc.edu

LONEWOLF, ROSEMARY "APPLE BLOSSOM" (Santa Clara Pueblo)
(business owner)
Affiliation & Address: Owner, Apple Blossom Accents, P.O. Box 850, Espanola, NM 87532 (505) 927-1827. E-mail: abaccents@aol.com. Website: www.abaccents.nativeart.net.

LONG, ALBERT E. (Blackfeet-Navajo) 1919-
(trader/craftsman)
Born September 9, 1919, Billings, Mont. *Education*: Los Angeles Art Center, 1946-48; received Graduate Gemologist diploma, 1967. *Principal occupation*: Trader/craftsman. *Address*: P.O. Box 40, Lake Havasu City, AZ 86405 (520) 453-5925. E-mail: allong@ctaz.com. Website: www.allong.com. *Military service*: U.S. Marine Corps, 1941-45 (First Marine Division-Communications Specialist; Guadalcanal and New Britain campaigns). *Membership*: Master Gemology Association. *Interests*: "Having worked both silver and gold, many times using non-traditional gemstones such as opals & diamonds. His work has appeared in "Arizona Highways" magazine and in numerous juried shows including the Scottsdale National and the Inter-Tribal Ceremonial in Gallup. Now, semi-retired, he plans to work on shows for his many trader friends and be involved with organizations such as the Inter-Tribal Ceremonial Association as well as other museums & foundations showing exclusive Native American arts & crafts. He's available for craft judging in juried shows of Native American crafts. He is no longer accepting commissions on his jewelry; however, he still offers his assistance to former customers & serious collectors."

LONG, KELVIN (Dine'-Navajo)
(executive director)
Affiliations: Executive director, ECHOES (Educating Communities While Healing & Offering Environmental Support), Flagstaff, AZ; co-owner, True Image World Marketing, Flagstaff, AZ; board member, Black Mesa Water Coalition (P.O. Box 613, Flagstaff, AZ 86002 (928) 213-5909). *Other professional posts*: Professional photographer; and professional speaker at area & national schools on his knowledge of Sacred Sited Protection, Environmental Justice & Indigenous Knowledge. *Membership*: Save the Peaks.

LONG FOX, DARWIN (Lakota)
(chief judge)
Affiliation & Address: Chief Judge, Puyallup Tribal Court, 1638 E. 29th St., Tacoma, WA 98404 (253) 680-5585.

LONG FOX, PAULA (Lakota)
(foundation chairperson)
Bornn & raised in rural South Dakota. *Education*: University of South Dakota, BA (History), MA (Social Administration & Counseling). *Address & Affiliation*: Chairperson, American Indian Education Foundation, P.O. Box 27491, Albuquerque, NM 87125 (866) 881-8694. Website: www.aiefprograms.org. *Other professional posts*: Paula has been a teacher and guidance counselor for 30+ years, primarily in schools with majority-native American enrollment.

LONGBOAT, DAN (Roronhiake:wen) (Mohawk)
(professor of Indigenous Studies; director, Indigenous
Environmental Studies)
Born & raised in Ohsweken – The Six Nations Grand River Territory. *Education*: Trent University, BA (Native Studies), 1973; University of Toronto, MS (Psychology), 1979; York University, MA & PhD (Environmental Studies), 1998. *Affiliation & Address*: Assistant Professor of Indigenous Studies (1995-present) Trent University; Designed & Developed (1996) the first program of its kind in North Ameica, Director (2004-present), Indigenous Enviironmental Studies, Trent University, Enweying Room 302, 1600 Westbank Dr., Peterborough, ON K9J 7B8 (705) 748- ext. 7844. E-mail: dlongboat@trentu.ca. Professor Longboat served as the first Director of Studies for the Native Studies PhD Program in 1998 at Trent University. *Other professional posts*: Board member, Haudenosaunee Environmental Task Force and cultural advisor & instructor for several programs at First Nations Technical Institute with St. Lawrence College, Sir Sandford Fleming College & Ryerson University. Areas of Research & Expertise: In Haudenosaunee cultural teachings, Kanyenn'keha language programs, Indigenous environmental knowledge systems with regard to: Indigenous peples health & the environment, traditional foods & medicines, natural resource & ecological restoration, Indigenous community sustainability & international Indigenous environmental networking.

LONGCOR, MEGAN (Lakota Sioux)
(marketing manager)
Education: University of California, Santa Barbara, BS (Microbiology). *Affiliation & Address*: Marketing Manager (2010-present), Society for Advancement of Chicanos & Native Americans in Science (SACNAS), P.O. Box 8526, Santa Cruz, CA 95061 (831) 459-0170.

LONGFISH, GEORGE C. (Iroquois-Seneca/Tuscarora) 1942-
(emeritus professor/artist)
Born August 22, 1942, Oshweken, Ontario, Can. *Education*: School of the Art Institute of Chicago, BFA (Painting, Sculpture), 1970; and MFA, (Filmmaking), 1972. *Affiliation & Address*: Emeritus Professor/artist, Native American Studies Dept., College of Letters & Science, 2401 Hart Hall, University of California, Davis, CA 95616 (530) 752-3237. E-mail: redbearlongfish@netscape.net. *Affiliations*: Director of the graduate program in American Indian Art, University of Montana, Missoula, 1972-73; professor in Native American Studies, University of California, Davis, 1973-2003. *Other professional post*: Director, Carl Nelson Gorman Museum, Native American Studies, University of California, Davis, CA. *Awards, honors*: Numerous awards & prizes throughout the years for his work. *Interests*: Contemporary Native American art; attended over 170 art exhibitions exhibiting paintings, sculpture & film; art lectures. *Publications*: Personal Symbols: Recent Paintings & Works on Paper (University of Northern Iowa, 1986); numerous articles. A faculty member for 30 years, Professor Longfish taught Modern Native American art, supported spiritual activities in the community, & developed the Carl N. Gorman Museum as a premier showplace, bringing renowned Native artists to the UC Davis campus. On the occasion of his retirement, his work was featured in a major retrospective exhibit at the John Natsoulas Gallery. He is currently living & painting in Maine. His current exhibition is at Zane Bennett Gallery in Santa Fe, NM. Website: http://www.zanebennettgallery.com/artist_galleries/longfish-g/longfishgallerynew.htm

LONGIE, ERICH (Sisseton-Wahpeton Sioux)
(college president)
Affiliation & Address: Cankdeska Cikana Community College (Little Hoop), P.O. Box 269, Fort Totten, ND 58335 (701) 766-4415.

LONGIE, KEITH (Turtle Mountain Chipewa)
(IHS Area Director)
Education: Southern Oregon State College, BS (Sociology); University of California, Berkeley, MPH. *Affiliation & Address*: Area Director, Bemidji Area HIS, 522 Minnesota Ave., NW, Bemidji, MN 56601 (218) 444-0452. Mr. Longie is responsible for providing leadership to the Bemidji Area and overseeing the delivery of health care to American Indians and Alaska Natives in Minnesota, Michigan, Wisconsin, and Illinois. *Past professional posts*: Mr. Longie began his federal career with the IHS in 1977 as a Commissioned Officer in the U.S. Public Health Service (USPHS). His first position was in the Facilities Construction Planning Branch in Rockville, Maryland. Mr. Longie then held multiple assignments in the IHS Portland Area, including Assistant Director of the Western Oregon Service Unit and Area Chief Management Information Officer. Mr. Longie transferred to the IHS Phoenix Area to serve as Director of the Office of Planning, Evaluation, and Information Resources. He then moved to IHS Headquarters to work as the IHS Chief Information Officer. In 2006, he returned to the Phoenix Area and served as the Deputy Area Director for Field Operations and as the Area Chief Information Officer. *Awards, honors*: Numerous awards during his service with the IHS. These include the USPHS Commendation and Achievement Medal, an IHS National Director's Award, and a Secretary's Award for Distinguished Service.

LONGIE, PHILLIP "SKIP" (Sisseton-Wahpeton Sioux)
(tribal chairperson)
Affiliation & Address: Spirit Lake Sioux Tribal Council, P.O. Box 359, Fort Totten, ND 58335 (701) 766-4221.

LOOKING ELK, ALEX (Standing Rock Sioux)
(radio project manager)
Affiliation & Address: KAEN - 89.5 FM, Standing Rock Sioux Radio Project, P.O. Box D, Fort Yates, ND 58538 (701) 854-7226.

LOONSFOOT, LELA
(program manager)
Affiliation & Address: Program Manager, American Indian Business Leaders (AIBL), Gallagher Business Bldg. #366, Missoula, MT 59812 (406) 243-4879.

LOPEMAN, DAVID (Squaxin Island)
(tribal chairperson)
Affiliation & Address: Chairperson, Squaxin Island Tribe, 10 SE Squaxin Lane, Shelton, WA 98584 (360) 426-9781. E-mail: dlopeman@squaxin.us

LOPEZ, CARMEN (Navajo)
(executive director)
Education: Dartmouth College, B.A. (History & Native American Studies); Harvard Graduate School of Education, Ed.M., 2000. *Address & Affiliation*: Executive Director, Native American Program, JFK School of Government, 79 JFK St., Cambridge, MA 02138 (617) 495-4923. E-mail: carmen.lopez@harvard.edu. Ms. Lopez oversees the operation of the University-wide interfaculty Initiative that focuses on American Indian, Alaska Native and Native Hawaiian recruitment and student support; interdisciplinary teaching & research projects on Native issues; & community outreach. *Past professional post*: Faculty, Native American Preparatory School, Rowe, NM.

LOPEZ, GEORGE (Klamath)
(tribal administration general manager)
Affiliation & Address: General Manager, Tribal Administration,, Klamath Tribes of Oregon, P.O. Box 436, Chiloquin, OR 97624 (541) 783-2219. E-mail: george.lopez@klamathtribes.com

LOPEZ, LOUISE (Tonto Apache)
(former tribal chairperson)
Affiliation & Address: Tonto Apache Tribe, 18 Tonto Reservation, Payson, AZ 85541 (928) 474-3988.

LOPEZ, MARIA (Hoh)
(tribal chairperson)
Affiliation & Address: Chairperson, Hoh Tribe, P.O. Box 2196, Forks, WA 98331 (360) 374-6582. E-mail: marial@hohtribe-nsn.gov

LOPEZ, NORMAN (Mountain Ute)
(traditional flute player)
Address: Ute Mountain Ute Tribe, Towaoc, CO 81334 (970) 565-3751. Lopez incorporates stories about the flute as well as stories about his tribe during his performances.

LOPEZ-KEIFER, MERRI (Luiseno)
(attorney; commissioner)
Education: Boston College School of Law, JD. *Affiliation & Address*: Commissioner (2015-present), California Native Ameican Heritage Commission (NAHC), 1550 Harbor Blvd. Suite 100, West Sacramento, CA 95691 (916) 373-3710. *Other professional post*: Chief Legal Counsel for the San Luis Rey Band of Mission ndians, 2010-present); assistant district attorney, San Francisco District Attorney's Office, 1999-2004.

LORENZ, CAROLL ANN
(director of Native American studies)
Education: Columbia University, PhD (Art History). *Affiliation & Address*: Associate Professor & Director, Native American Studies Program, Colgate University, 415 Alumni Hall, Hamilton, NY 13346 (315) 228-7184. E-mail: clorenz@colgate.edu. From Fall 1987 through Fall 2014, she served in various curatorial capacities in the Longyear Museum of Anthropology at Colgate, including Senior Curator from 2005-2014, while also teaching courses in her areas of expertise – Native American, Pre-Columbian, African, & Oceanic art primarily. Carol Ann has been the faculty mentor to the Native American Student Association since 2000, and has organized the annual Native American Arts and Culture Festival at Colgate since 2001. Research interests include the art and culture of Africa and the indigenous Americas, Southwest and Northeast Native American art, Haudenosaunee art & artists, Indigenous textiles and pottery. Lorenz currently teaches Native Art of North America, Art and Architecture of the Ancient Americas, Contemporary Issues in Native American Art, and Art of Africa. Because of the cultural content & approaches used in her courses, most are cross-listed in Anthropology and Art History, as well as in relevant multi-disciplinary programs, including Native American Studies, African Studies, and Latin American Studies. During her twenty-seven years of curatorship at Colgate, Lorenz researched & organized original exhibitions on a wide variety of topics, incuding eighty-one in the Longyear Museum gallery, twenty-five elsewhere on the Colgate campus, and another dozen that were shown in various museums and university galleries including the Munson-Williams-Proctor Arts Institute, Edith Barrett Gallery at Utica College, Rome Art and Community Center, Karpeles Museum in Buffalo, and Stone Quarry Hill Art Park in Cazenovia. For many of the exhibitions, Lorenz organized programming of various sorts, including lectures, performances, & symposia. Lorenz also developed the collections of the Longyear Museum, adding thousands of Native American & African objects that have given the museum known standing as a center for indigenous art in Central New York. Lorenz has authored or edited numerous exhibition catalogs & brochures in association with these exhibitions, as well as having contributed to journals & anthologies. Creation: Haudenosaunee Contemporary Art and Traditional Stories (2004) and African Shapes of the Sacred: Yoruba Religious Art (2006). Edited catalogs include Birds and Beast in Beads: 150 Years of Iroquois Beadwork (2011) and One Day, One Woman, One Child: The Holocaust in the

Art of Gabriella Nikolic (2013). She has given lectures at national conferences as well as public, gallery, docent training, and class lectures. *Awards, honors*: Received the ALANA Cultural Center faculty Award in 2014.

LORETTO, RAYMOND (Jemez Pueblo)
(former pueblo governor)
Affiliation & Address: Former Governor, Pueblo of Jemez, P.O. Box 100, Jemez, NM 87024 (505) 834-7359.

LORING, DONNA M. (Penobscot)
(tribal representative/coordinator)
Education: University of Maine at Orono, BA (Political Science); graduate of Maine Criminal Justice Academy; graduated Fleming Fellows Leadership Institute-Center for Policy Alternatives, 2001; recent graduate of the Eleanor Roosevelt Global Leadership Institute (leadership program). *Address*: 174 River Rd., Richmond, ME 04357 (207) 737-2608. E-mail: dmldab@wiscasset. net. *Affiliation*: Penobscot Nation's Representative to the Maine State Legislature, 10/97 to present. Note: Maine is the only state that has tribal representatives seated in it's legislature, representing tribal governments not districts; Penobscot Nation's Coordinator of Tribal, State and International Relations; president, Four Directions Development Corporation. *Military service*: U.S. Army, 1966-69 (Vietnam Veteran, 1967-68 - served in the communications center at Long Binh Army Base during the TET Offensive). *Past professional posts*: Police Chief for the Penobscot Nation, 1984-90; director of security, Bowdoin College, 1992-97. *Community activities*: Member and former chair, Commission on Women Veterans; member, Maine Advisory Committee to the U.S. Commission on Civil Rights; Joint Legislative standing committee on Judiciary; member, Chancellor's Diversity Task Force; member, Maine Community Foundation Board of Directors; Northeast Historic Film Board of Directors; Advisor to the Governor Angus King on woman veteran affairs; member, Coastal Enterprises, Inc. Capital Management LLC Advisory Board. *Awards, honors*: She was the first woman police academy graduate to become police chief in the State of Maine; appointed Aide de Camp to former Governor Angus King, March 1999; received the Mary Ann Hartman Award from the University of Maine's Women in Curriculum & Women's Studies Program; appointed House Chair of the Casino Study Task Force by the former Speaker of the House, Michael Saxl, Aug. 2002 (the first tribal representative to be appointed as the House Chair of any committee); as a recent graduate of the Eleanor Roosevelt Global Leadership Institute, she was one of 14 state legislators, selected from among more than 7,000 eligible state legislators from across the nation, to be sent to Chile to learn about the Chilean development process in the areas of social and economic development, and foreign trade; recently appointed by Governor Baldacci to serve on the New England Board of Higher Education. *Membership*: Maine Chiefs of Police; Commission on Women Veterans (former chair); Joint Legislative Standing Committee on the Judiciary; Chancellor's Diversity Task Force; Maine Community Foundation Board of Directors; Northeast Historic Film Board of Directors; Coastal Enterprises, Inc. Capital Management LLC Advisory Board.

LOUDNER, GODFREY, Jr. (Crow Creek Sioux) 1946-
(mathematics instructor)
Born September 30, 1946, Fort Thompson, S.D. *Education*: Black Hills State College, BS; South Dakota School of Mines & Technology, MS; University of Notre Dame, PhD (Mathematics), 1974. *Principal occupation*: Mathematics instructor, Sinte Gleska College, Rosebud, S.D. *Address*: Box 432, Mission, SD 57555. *Memberships*: American Mathematics Society. *Interests*: Working on monograph about Automonophic Forms With Applications."

LOUIS, ADRIAN C. (Lovelock Paiute) 1947-
(professor of English; writer/author)
Born & raised in northern Nevada on the Lovelock Paiute Reservation. *Education*: Brown University, MA (Creative Writing). *Affiliation & Address*: Professor of English (1999-present), Dept. of English, Southwest Minnesota State University, 1501 State St., Marshall, MN 56258. *Past professional posts*: Editor, The Lakota Times, Indian Country Today; instructor, Oglala Lakota College, Pine Ridge Reservation, SD, 1984-97; co-founder of Native American Journalists Association. *Publications*: Ten books of poetry; Fiction: "Wild Indians & Other Creatures" (short stories); "Skins" (novel) produced as a feature film directed by Chris Eyre. It premiered at the Sundance Film Festival and released in 2002; editor, Shedding Skins: Four Sioux Poets (Michigan State University Press, 2008). *Awards, honors*: Mr. Louis has won various awards including Pushcart Prizes & fellowships from the Bush Foundation, the National Endowment for the Arts, & the Lila Wallace-Reader's Digest Foundation. His 2006 collection of poems, "Logorrhea" (Northwestern University Press), was a finalist for the Los Angeles Times Book prize.

LOUIS, GEORGENE (Navajo-Dine')
(attorney; New Mexico State (D) representative)
Affiliation & Address: New Mexico State (D) Representative (2013-14), District 26, Capitol Room 203BN, P.O. Box 72123, Albuquerque, NM 87195 (505) 938-9144. E-mail: georgene.louis@nmlegis.gov.

LOW, DENISE 1949-
(professor & administrator)
Born May 9, 1949, Emporia, Kans. *Education*: University of Kansas, PhD (English). *Address & Affiliation*: Professor, English Dept. & American Indian Studies Dept., Haskell Indian Nations University, Lawrence, KS 66046 (785) 749-8431, 1984-present. E-mail: dlow@haskell.edu. *Memberships*: SAIL; Assoc. Writing Programs. *Interests*: American Indian literature; Cheyenne ledger art. *Published works*: New and Selected Poems, 1980-1999 (Lawrence: Penthe, 1999); Thailand Journal (Topeka-Woodley/Washburn U. Press, 2003); articles and reviews.

LOW, JOHN (Pokagon Band Potawatomi)
(professor of Comparative Studies)
Education: University of Minnesota, BA (American Indian Studies); University of Chicago, MA (Social Sciences); University of Michigan, Graduate Certificate (Museum Studies) & Law School JD. *Affiliation & Address*: Assistant Professor of Comparative Studies, The ohio State University, Newark Campus, 2057 Founders Hall, Newark, OH 43055 (740) 755-7857. E-mail: low.89@osu.edu. *Research Interests*: American Indian histories, literatures & cultures; Indigenous canoe cultures around the world; urban American Indians, museums, American Indian law & treaty rights, Indigenous cross-cultural connections, Native environmental perspectives & practices.

LOWAN-TRUDEAU, GREGORY (Metis)
(professor of First Nations Studies)
Born in southern Alberta, Canada. *Education*: University of Calgary, BS; Lakehead University, MS; University of Calgary, PhD. *Affiliation & Address*: Asistant Professor of First Nations Studies, University of Northern British Columbia, Admin 3020, 3333 University Way, Prince George, BC V2N 4Z9 Canada (250) 960-5434. E-mail: Gregory.lowan-trudeau@unbc.ca. *Research Interests*: Intercultural & Indigenous environmental studies & education; Indigenous resource & community planning; Metis history, culture, language, identity, and philosophy; and Japanese ecological knowledge & philosophy.

LOWE, PHYLLIS (St. Croix Ojibwe)
(former tribal vice chairperson)
Affiliation & Address: Former Vice Chairperson, St. Croix Chippewa Indians of Wisconsin, 24663 Angeline Ave., Webster, WI 54893 (715) 349-2195.

LOWE, SHELLY C. (*Bilagaana*) (Navajo-Dine')
(director of Native American program))
Born & raised in Ganada, Ariz. Education: University of Arizona, BA (Sociology), 1997, MA (American Indian Studies, 2005). *Affiliation & Address*: Executive Director (2009-present), Native American Program, Harvard University, 14 Story St., Cambridge, MA 02138 (617) 495-4923. E-mail: shelly_lowe@harvard.edu. *Other professional post*: Council Member, National Endowment for the Humanities, 2015-present. *Past professional posts*: Graduate Education Program Facilitator, American Indian Studies Program, The University of Arizona, Tucson, AZ (six years); Assistant Dean for Native American Affairs in the Yale College Deans Office & Director of the Native American Cultural Center at Yale University (two years). *Memberships*: National Indian Education Association (former board member); National Museum of the American Indian (former member, Board of Trustees).

LOWERY, ELWOOD (Paiute)
(former tribal chairperson)
Affiliation & Address: Chairperson, Pyramid Lake Paiute Tribe, P.O. Box 256, Nixon, NV 89424 (775) 574-1000. E-mail: elowery@plpt.bsn.us

LOWERY, JINNIE (Lumbee) 1953-
(health administrator)
Born February 21, 1953, Robeson County, N.C. *Education*: Pembroke State University, Pembroke, NC, B.A., 1978; UNC-Chapel Hill, NC, MSPH, 1982. *Affiliation & Address*: President & CEO (2010-present), Robeson Health Care Corp., 211 Wardell Rd., Pembroke, NC 28372 (910) 521-3066. *Past professional posts*: Associate director, 1986-91, executive director, 1991-2009, Robeson Health Care Corporation, Pembroke, NC; business manager, Lumbee Medical Center, Pembroke, NC, 1989-2009. *Community activities*: Founding member & past secretary of the Robeson County Dispute Resolution Center, 1988-; founding member and past president of the Robeson County Rape Crisis Center; past board member of the Lumbee Regional Development Association's Head Start Policy Council; member of Harper's Ferry Baptist Church; member of Steering Committee of the Health Access Coalition. *Memberships*: American Public Health Assn; North Carolina Primary Health Care Assn (past secretary, current vice-president of board of directors); National Assn of Community Health Centers; National Assn for Female Executives; National Geographic Society. *Awards, honors*: Graduated Magna Cum Laude - Pembroke State University, 1978; Recognized by Robeson County Rural Development Panel for Volunteer Service and Leadership in development of the Rape Crisis Center; Invited to be listed in the The World

Who's Who of Women; member of North Carolina Kappa Chapter of Alpha Chi Honor Society; recipient of the Indian Health Scholarship.

LOWERY, MALINDA MAYNOR
(professor of history & American Indian studies)

Education: Harvard University, BA, 1995; Stanford University, MA, 1997; University of North Carolina-Chapel Hill, PhD, 2005. *Affiliation & Address*: Associate Professor of History & American Indian Studies, 474 Hamilton Hall CB# 3195, University of North Carolina, Capel Hill, NC 27599 (919) 962-2924. E-mail: mmaynor@email.unc.edu. *Other professional posts*: Director, Honors Program; director, Southern Oral History Program, Univesity of North Carolina-Chapel Hill, NC. Lowery's interests include Native American history, southern history, nineteenth- & twentieth-century U.S. history, historical geography, race and ethnicity, identity, and Community-Engaged Research. *Published works*: Lumbee Indians in the Jim Crow South: Race, Identity, and the Making of a Nation (Univesity of North Carolina Press, 2010); *The Lumbee Indians: An American Struggle*, a book-length work in progress [under advance contract at University of North Carolina Press] as well as *Enterprising Indians: Labor and Capital in the Choctaw Nation, 1872–1948*, a book-length work in progress.

LUARKIE, RICHARD B. (Laguna Pueblo)
(former Pueblo governor)

Affiliation & Address: Former governor, Pueblo of Laguna, P.O. Box 194, Laguna, NM 87026 (505) 552-6654.

LUBENAU, CAROLYN (Snoqualmie Coast Salish)
(tribal chairperson)

Affiliation & Address: Chairperson, Snoqualmie Indian Tribe, P.O. Box 969, Snoqualmie, WA 98065 (425) 888-6551.

LUCAS, MERLE R. (Sioux) 1944-
(administrator)

Born June 9, 1944, Vanport City, Ore. *Education*: Northern Montana College, 1963-64. *Affiliation & Address*: Executive Director, Montana Inter-Tribal Policy Board, P.O. Box 850, Browning, MT 59417 (406) 652-3113. *Affiliations*: Director, Native American Studies, Carroll College, Helena, MT (one year); associate professor, Native American Studies, Blackfeet Community College, Browning, MT (two years); coordinator of Indian affairs, State of Montana, State Capitol, Helena, MT (nine years); associate planner, Department of Planning & Economic Development, State of MT (three years); executive director, Montana Inter-Tribal Policy Board, Browning, MT, 1983-. *Military service*: U.S. Army Airborne, 1965-68 (E-5; Bronze Star; Army Commendation Medal with one Oak Leaf; Purple Heart; National Defense Service Medal; Vietnam Service Medal with three Bronze Service Stars; Republic of Vietnam Campaign Medal). *Community activities*: Helena Indian Center (president, three years); MT United Indian Association, Helena (treasurer, two years). *Memberships*: Governor's Interstate Indian Council, 1973-82; MT Indian Education Association; MT Indian Education Advisory Board, 1985-. *Awards, honors*: Outstanding Vietnam Era Veteran (1977) of the Nation for outstanding contributions shown to the community, state, and nation since returning to civilian life, No Greater Love Organization, Washington, D.C. *Published works*: Profile of Montana Native American (State of Montana, 1974); Annual Report of the Governors' Interstate Indian Council Conference, 1979.

LUCAS, PHIL (Choctaw)
(film/video producer)

Affiliation & Address: Institute of American Indian Arts, Communications Arts Department, CSF Campus, St. Michael's Dr., Santa Fe, NM 87501 (505) 984-2365. An independent film/video producer for more than two decades, established his own production company in 1980. He has worked on productions with many tribes. His classic "Images of Indians" television series (1979) called to detailed account the damning misrepresentations of Indian character & tradition in American popular culture. He was honored for Lifetime Achievement at the October 1991 Two Rivers Native Film & Video Festival.

LUCERO, JOSEPH F. (Isleta Pueblo)
(IHS director of Division of Information Management)

Affiliation & Address: Director, Division of Information Management, Albuquerque Area Indian Health Service, 4101 Indian School Rd. NE, Albuquerque, NM 87110 (505) 256-6700. E-mail: joseph.lucero@ihs.gov.

LUCERO, LAWRENCE (Isleta Pueblo)
(pueblo chief judge)

Affiliation & Address: Chief Judge, Pueblo of Isleta, P.O. Box 1270, Isleta, NM 87022 (505) 869-3111.

LUCERO, RICHARD, JR. (*Morning Star*) (Mescalero Apache-Seminole) 1944-
(entrepreneur; minority business consultant, administration)

Born September 24, 1944, Billings, Mont. *Education*: University of Wyoming, 1963-66; Eastern Montana College, 1966-67; Rocky Mountain College (Billings), BA (Psychology), 1968. *Address*: 3733 Magnolia Dr., Grand Prairie, TX 75052 (972) 262-0939. E-mail: hungryhoss@aol.com. *Affiliations*: Executive director, Dallas Inter-Tribal Center, Dallas, TX 1980-89; director of Minority Affairs, Greater Dallas Chamber of Commerce, 1990-92; president, CEO, American International Materials (distribution for metal welding supplies), 1992-; vice-president, Capital Concepts (financial management/college scholarships), 1992-; president/CEO, Dialogue Resources (marketing-advertising-consulting to health care professionals attorneys), 1994-; president, Morning Star Consulting Services (develop contracts for small minority businesses with corporations in; provide diversity seminars to state institutions & businesses; help develop minority employment & minority vendor contracts for public & private businesses), 1994-; president/CEO, Finite Ventures Unlimited (marketing, product development, distribution, consulting services), 1994-98; director of Winfree Academy Alternative School in Dallas (services to high school students - academic, counseling, social, emotional, family counseling), 1998-present. *Other professional posts*: Currently on contract to Dallas Cowboys as consultant on minority contracting (developing Cowboy minority contracting & employment program), 1996-present; consultant to Elite Care Care Clinic, marketing concepts for car cleaning and waxing products, 1996-present. *Community activities*: Board member, Irving Together Town Organization, 1996-present; moderator, Black/Brown Dialogue in Dallas, 1995-96; consultant to Ross Perot and the John Sarota Group on Education issues at Dallas Independent School District, June 1998 to Nov. 1998. *Memberships*: American Indian Health Care Assn (chairman, Region VII, Health Directors Board, 1982-84; president, 1984-); Dallas Council on Alcoholism & Drug Abuse (board member, 1988-); Greater Dallas Community Relations Commission (board of directors, 1989, 1st vice-chair, chairperson-Health & Human Services Committee); Society for Advancement of Chicanos & Native Americans in Science; Texas American Indian Chamber of Commerce; National Minority Contractors Assn (charter board member, 1994); New Image Business Associates (advisory member). *Awards, honors*: Appointed by President Gerald Ford to serve on National Drug Abuse and Adolescents Task Force, 1977; "Leadership Dallas" Graduate 1988 - Dallas Chamber of Commerce Program for Selected Community Leaders; "Dallas Together" - committee member, selected by Dallas Mayor to recommend ways to diffuse racial tensions in Dallas, 1988-89; Outstanding Board Member Award for community contributions; 1989 Greater Dallas Community Relations Commission for "Outstanding Leadership"; 1989 1st Annual Leadership Awards sponsored by Dallas Chapter of American Muslim Commission; recipient, Community Service Award, 1991, Senator Eddie Bernice Johnson. *Interests*: "Minority business development, minority employment; political and economic enfranchisement in Dallas metro area; enhanced police/community relationship, access to college education for capable students of color." *Published works*: Minority Business Development Handbook, 1991 & Minority Personnel Enhancement Handbook, 1992 (Greater Dallas Chamber of Commerce).

LUJAN, BEN RAY (Nambe Pueblo)
(U.S. congressman)

Born & raised in Nambe, N.M. *Education*: New Mexico Highlands University, BS (Business Administration). *Affiliation & Address*: 3rd Congressional District (NM) Representative (112th Congress, 2010-present), U.S. Congress, 330 Cannon HOB, Washington, DC 20515 (202) 225-6190. *District offices*: 811 St. Michael's Dr., Suite 104, Santa Fe, NM 87505 (505) 984-8950; 903 University Ave., Las Vegas, NM 87701 (505) 454-3038. Rep. Lujan is a member of the Indian & Alaska Native Affairs Subcommittee. Together with co-chair Frank Wolf of Virginia, founded the Technology Transfer Caucus to bring together members who share the goal of strengthening the economy by helping move technological innovations that are occurring at New Mexico's national labs & universities into the marketplace. Rep. Lujan is also the 2nd Vice Chair of the Congressional Hispanic Caucus. Also, he is a member of the Committee on Natural Resources & the Water & Power Subcommittee. *Other professional post*: Member, board of trustees, Institute of American Indian Arts, Santa Fe, NM. *Past professional posts*: Chair, New Mexico Public Regulations Commission; director of administrative services & chief financial officer, New Mexico Cultural Affairs Dept.

LUJAN, CAROL CHIAGO (Dine')
(Emeritus professor of American Indian studies)

Education: University of New Mexico, BA, 1976; MA, 1979; PhD, 1986. *Affiliation & Address*: Emeritus Associate Professor (2004-present), American Indian Studies, College of Liberal Arts & Sciences, MC: 4603, Arizona State University, Tempe, AZ 85287 (480) 965-6977. E-mail: carol.lujan@asu.edu. *Past professional posts*: Director, American Indian Studies, Arizona State University, Tempe, AZ, 1997-2004; Special Assistant to Assistant Secretary of Indian Affairs, U.S. Dept. of the Interior, Washington, DC (leave of absence from AU, 1998-99; professor, School of Justice Studies, ASU, Tempe, AZ,

1987-2004. *Research Consultant activities*: Inter Tribal Council of Arizona, Researcher for the American Indian Childhood Obesity Study funded by the U.S. Dept. of Agriculture, 2000-03; among many others. *Memberships*: American Indian & Alaska Native professors Assn; American Sociological Assn; American Indian Studies Cnsortium; Native American Art Studies Assn; among others. *Awards, honors*: Featured artist, Southwest Indian Art Fair, Arizona State Museum, University of Arizona, Tucson, Feb. 2006; Bahti Indian Arts Award of Excellence in Figurative Clay, Southwest Indian Art Fair, Arizona State Museum, University of Arizona, Tucson, AZ, Feb. 2005. *Published works*: Monographs, articles, book chapters & reviews; numerous conference papers & professional presentations.

LUJAN, DEIDRE A. (Pueblo of Santa Ana)
(attorney)
Affiliation & Address: managing Partner, Nordhaus Law Firm, LLP, 6705 Academy Rd. NE, Albuquerque, NM 87109 (505) 243-4275 E-mail: dlujan@nordhauslaw.com. Ms. Lujan joined the Nordhaus Law Firm in April, 2002. During law school, Ms. Lujan clerked with the Nordhaus Law Firm for two summers. She also interned with the Public Defender's Office in Oklahoma County during her last year of law school. Prior to joining the Nordhaus Law Firm, Ms. Lujan gained extensive trial experience serving the public sector. Upon graduation from law school, she accepted a position to serve as an Assistant Public Defender for Oklahoma County. As an Assistant Public Defender she was court-appointed to represent indigent clients in all aspects of the criminal trial process. She conducted a number of jury trials in which she was appointed to defend individuals charged with felony crimes including white collar, property and violent offenses. In 2001, Ms. Lujan was asked to serve as an Assistant District Attorney for Oklahoma County. During her service as an Assistant District Attorney, Ms. Lujan had the opportunity to represent the citizens of the State of Oklahoma in the prosecution of numerous criminal cases including juvenile, misdemeanor & felony offenses. She was responsible for daily court appearances to conduct hearings and jury trials.

LUJAN, ERNEST (Tamaya Pueblo)
(former pueblo governor)
Affiliation & Address: Tamaya Pueblo, 2 Dove Rd., Pueblo of Santa Ana, NM 87004 (505) 867-3301.

LUJAN, FRANK E. (Pueblo of Isleta)
(Pueblo president)
Affiliation & Address: President, Isleta Pueblo Council, P.O. Box 1270, Isleta, NM 87022 (505) 869-3111.

LUJAN, FRED R. (Isleta Pueblo)
(former Pueblo governor)
Affiliation & Address: Isleta Pueblo Council, P.O. Box 1270, Isleta, NM 87022

LUJAN, ISAAC (Sandia Pueblo)
(former Sandia Pueblo governor)
Affiliation & Address: Former Governor, Pueblo of Sandia Pueblo, 481 Sandia Loop, Bernalillo, NM 87004 (505) 867-3317.

LUJAN, JAMES (Taos Pueblo)
(education administrator; board president)
Education: New Mexico State University, MA (Education), 1969. *Address*: P.O. Box 2534, Taos, NM 87571 (505) 301-5507. E-mail: jlujantaos@yahoo.com. *Affiliation*: Board President, Catching the Dream, Albuquerque, NM. *Past professional posts*: Retired president, Southwestern Indian Polytechnic Institute, Albuquerque, NM; former Governor, Taos Pueblo; former Agency Supt. for Education, Northern Pueblos Agency, BIA, Santa Fe, NM; director, San Juan School, San Juan Pueblo, NM.

LUJAN, LANCE (Pueblo)
(college dept. director)
Affiliation & Address: Director, Indian Resource Development Dept., New Mexico U., Box 30001, Dept. MSC, Las Cruces, NM 88003 (505) 646-1347.

LUJAN, VERNON G. (Taos Pueblo)
(program director)
University of New Mexico, BS (Southwest Studies), Masters in Public Administration. *Affiliation & Address*: Director & Tribal Historic Preservation Officer, Poeh Arts Program & Poeh Cultural Center & Museum, 78 Cities of Gold Rd., Santa Fe, NM 87506 (505) 455-3334. *Other professional post*: Adjunct faculty, The Falmouth Institute, Fairfax, VA; adjunct faculty, Native American Studies Department & Fine Arts Department, University of New Mexico, Albuquerque; grant writer & contributing author & editor for numerous publications such as the Taos County Historical Society, Santa Fe New Mexican, and various archaeological reports; tour guide & scholar for the Crow Canyon Archaeological Center. *Past professional posts*: Institute of American Indian Arts; Museums of New Mexico; Wheelwright Museum of the American Indian; Harwood Museum of the U. of New Mexico; Smithsonian Institution.

LUJAN-HAUER, PAM (Taos Pueblo)
(Taos potter)
Education: Institute of American Indian Arts, 1975-76. *Affiliation*: Artist Representative (Indian Arts & Crafts Assn), Santa Fe, NM. E-mail: pam@taosindianpottery.com Pam is a traditional Taos potter. Her contemporary pottery is made from various native clays which are al hand gathered and processed according to native tradition. The natural paints and slips are made from plants, clay and minerals. Her potery is pit or kiln fired and incorporates a silver inlay technique & sculptures.

LUKIN, SARAH L. (Alutiiq)
(native corporation vice president)
Education: University of Alaska, Anchorage, BA & MA. *Affiliation & Address*: Vice President of Corporate Affairs, Afognak Native Corporation, 215 Mission Rd., Suite 212, Kodiak, AK 99615 (907) 486-6014. *Other professional post*: Member, Board of Directors, Native American Contractors Association, Washington, DC. *Past professional posts*: Executive Director, Native American Contractors Association, Washington, DC, 2007-11; Community Development Director, Chugach Regional Resources Commission; member, Afognak Tribal Council (six years). Sarah is a shareholder of Afognak Native Corp. and Koniag, Inc. She is a tribal member of the Native Village of Afognak and Native Village of Port Lions, and served as the vice president of External Relations for Afognak & their wholly-owned government contracting subsidiary, Alutiiq, LLC.

LUMLEY, PAUL (Yakama)
(executive director)
Education: Western Washington University, BS (Mathematics), 1986. *Affiliation & Address*: Executive Director (2009-present), Columbia River Inter-Tribal Fish Commission (CRITFC), 729 NE Oregon St. #200, Portland, OR 97232 (503) 238-0667. *Past professional posts*: Senior Tribal Liaison within the Office of the Deputy Undersecretary of Defense's Installations & Environmentall Program, 2004-07. He was responsible for the Native American Lands Environmental Mitigation Program as well as working on policy issues affecting Native Americans, Alaska Natives, & Native Hawaiians; exec. Dir., National American Indian Housing Council, Washington, DC, 2007-09; CRITFC (1987-04).

LUNA-FIREBAUGH, EILEEN (Choctaw/Cherokee)
(associate professor)
Education: Peoples College of Law, University of San Diego, J.D., 1978; Harvard University, MPA, 1996. *Affiliation & Address*: Associate Head, American Indian Studies (AIS) Program, The University of Arizona, Harvill 214, Box 210076, Tucson, AZ 85721 (520) 621-2262. E-mail: eluna@email.arizona.edu. Associate professor, Luna-Firebaugh, teaches several courses in the law & policy concentration that are required in the MA, PhD & JD degree programs. *Other professional posts*: Member of the faculty of the National Tribal Trial College funded by the U.S. Dept. of Justice; in this capacity, she is a trainer of tribal judges, police & prosecutors; Justice of the Colorado River Indian Tribal Appellate Court; Member of the Board of Directors for the National Center for Responsible Gambling; member of the Advisory Boards for the Udall Center for Studies in Public Policy, the Harvard Medical School Division on Diversions Project on Pathological Gambling, and the Southwest Center on Law & Policy. *Community activities*: She serves on the Board of the University Human Subjects Protection Program, & is a member of the AIS Curriculum Committee, & the Colloquium Committee. *Interests*: Tribal governments; law enforcements on reservations; and federal Indian policy. She has received grants for research from American Philosophical Society, Phillips Fund for Native American Research, the University of Arizona, and the Bureau of Indian Affairs Law Enforcement Services. *Published work*: Tribal Policing: Asserting Sovereignty, Seeking Justice (University of Arizona Press, 2006).

LUNDY, PAUL A. (Lakota-*Mniconjou* (Cheyenne River Sioux) 1944-
(diaconal minister)
Born August 30, 1944, Sioux Falls, S.D. *Education*: South Dakota School of Mines & Technology, BS, 1967; Foundational Studies, Garrett Evangelical Theological Seminary, 2004. *Principal occupation*: Diaconal minister. *Address*: 4316 Phoenix St., Ames, IA 50014-3626 (515) 292-5255. E-Mail: mplundy@qwest.net. *Affiliations*: Project engineer, Iowa Department of Transportation, Ames, 1967-80; Environmental engineer, Iowa Dept. of Natural Resources, Des Moines, 1980-2004; Consecrated Diaconal Minister, 2004-present. *Military service*: U.S. Army, 1967-69; U.S. Army Reserve, 1969-87 (retired as Major; Humanitarian Service Medal, 1980; Army Achievement Medal, 1986). *Community activities*: Ames Council of PTAs (president, 1978); Ames Municipal Band, 1973-present (vice president, 1987-); Boy Scouts of America (assistant District Commissioner, Broken Arrow District, Mid-Iowa Council). *Membership*: American Indian Science & Engineering Society, 1982-; United Methodist Church, 1963-present (Lay Speaker, 1995-; candidate, diaconal minister, 1996-2004; minister, 2004-present; Certified Church Business Administrator, 2000-. *Awards, honors*: Distinguished Toastmaster, Toastmaster International, in 1974; Public Service Award by American Radio Relay League in 1972 & '79 for emergency communications handled. *Interests*: Amateur Radio; music (play sax & clarinet); railroading/model railroading

(charter member of the Kate Shelley Division, 1992) of the National Model Railroad Assn; history/genealogy. Vocational: Transportation & Environmental Engineering. *Biographical source*: Article in American Indian Scientist & Engineers, Vol. I, 1985.

LUPE, RONNIE (White Mountain Apache)
(tribal chairperson)
Affiliations & Address: Chairperson (2006-present), White Mountain Apache Tribe, Box 700, Whiteriver, AZ 85941 (520) 338-4346; E-mail: rupe@wmat.us.

LYONS, BETTY (Onondaga)
(president & executive director)
Education: Cazenovia College, ALA, 2013. *Affiliation & Address*: President & Executive Director, American Indian Law Alliance, P.O. Box 3036, Hoboken, NJ 07030

LYONS, OREN R. (Onondaga) 1930-
(traditional chief & faithkeeper)
Born & raised on the Seneca & Onondaga reservations in western & central New York State. Faithkeeper of the Turtle Clan Onondaga Council of Chiefs of the Haudenosaunee. *Education*: Syracuse University, BA (Fine Arts), 1958. *Affiliation & Address*: Chairperson of Honoring Nations Board of Governors & Traditional Chief & Faithkeeper, Onondaga Nation, RR 1, Box 319-B, Nedrow, NY 13120 (315) 492-4210. *Military service*: U.S. Army. *Other professional posts*: Professor of American Studies, SUNY Buffalo, where he directs the Native American Studies Program and teaches undergraduate courses; crisis-negotiator, coach, author & painter, Oren serves on the Executive Committee of the Global Forum of Spiritual & Parliamentary Leaders on Human Survival and is a principal figure in the Traditional Circle of Indian Elders, an annual council of traditional grassroots leadership of the major Indian nations of North America. *Awards, honors*: In 1990, he received the Ellis Island Congressional Medal of Honor &, that summer, was a negotiator between the Mohawk Indians and the overnments of Canada, Quebec & New York State in the crisis at Oka. On April 16, 1991 Chief Lyons led a delegaton of 17 American Indian leaders who met with President Bush in Washington. Later that same year, he was the subject of a one-hour BS television documentary. He is currently Honorary Chairman of the Iroquois National Lacrosse Team, which in 1990, at the World Games in Perth, Australia, became the first Indigenous national team in any sport to compete against the national teams of recognized nation states. In 1993, he was elected to the Lacrosse National Hall of Fame; named a distinguished professor at SUNY Buffalo in the Spring of 2007. *Interests*: Oren is an avid promoter of the Iroquois game of lacrosse and an educator on the international level about the environmental perils upon which human beings need to act. In 1982, Chief Lyons helped to establish the Working Group on Indigenous Populations, an advisory body to the Geneva-based U.N. Human Rights Commission & has been an active member in the Group.Through his educational efforts, the U.S. Senate passed a resolution in 1992 that formally acknowledged the contribution of the Iroquois Confederacy to the development of the U.S. Constitution. *Publlshed works*: Oren is co-editor with the late John Mohawk of Exiled in the Land of the Free: Democracy, Indian Nations, & the U.S. Constitution & publisher of Daybreak,National Native American magazine.

LYONS, SCOTT RICHARD (Leech Lake Ojibwe)
(professor & director of Native American studies)
Education: Miami University, PhD, 2000. *Affiliation & Address*: Associate Professor & Director of Native American Studies (NAS) (2011-present), Department of American Culture, 3527C Haven Hall, 505 State St., Ann Arbor, MI 48109 (734) 936-5902. E-mail: lyonssr@umich.edu. *Other professional post*: Undergraduate Advisor for the NAS minor. *Past professional posts*: Teacher, Syracuse University, Syracuse, NY & Leech Lake Tribal College, Cass Lake, MN. *Awards, honors*: 2011 Beatrice Medicine Award for Scholarship in Native American Studies; In 2014, he was a recipient of the University of Michigan's Henry Russel Award. *Published work*: X-Marks: Native Signatures of Assent (University of Minnesota Press, 2010) numerous articles.

M

MAAS, GARY (Iroquois/Ojibwe)
(stuntman, scriptwriter, filmmaker)
Affiliation & Address: c/o Dreamcatcher Films, Inc., 8251 Continental, Warren, MI 48089 (810) 756-6007.

MABEE, JANICE W. (Sauk-Suiattle)
(tribal chairperson)
Affiliation & Address: Sauk-Suiattle Indian Tribe, 5318 Chief Brown Lane, Darrington, WA 98241 (360) 436-0131.

MACARRO, HOLLY COOK (Red Lake Band Ojibwe)
(consultant; board president of Indian center)
Education: University of North Dakota, BBA; University of St. Thomas (St. Paul, MN), MBA. *Affiliation & Address*: Partner, Spirit Rock Consulting, Inc. (2017-present), 9 Forrest St., Alexandria, VA 22305 (202) 255-3220. E-mail: hmacarro@spiritrockinc.com. *Other professional post*: Board President, American Indian Graduate Center, Albuquerque, NM. *Post professional posts*: Partner, Letan Consulting, 2007-16; Sr. Public Affairs Advisor, Holland & Knight, LLP, 2001-07; Director, Office of Native American Affairs, Democratic National Commmittee, 1999-2001

MACARRO, MARK A. (Pechanga Luiseno) 1965-
(tribal chairperson)
Education: University of California, Santa Barbara, BA (Political Science). *Affiliation & Address*: Chairperson (1996-present), Pechanga Band of Mission Indians, P.O. Box 1477, Temecula, CA 92593 (951) 676-2768. *Other Tribal Posts*: Pechanga Tribal Council, 1992-present. Mark represents Pechanga in the National Congress of American Indians as an alternate area vice president of the Pacific region, 2007-09 & represents the Pacific region on the board of directors for the national Indian Gaming Association NIGA). *Past professional posts*: Program manager for the library & museum of the Rincon Reservation, 1992-95; director of youth education at Soboba Reservation's Noli School, 1990-92; grants/contracts administrator, Pechanga Reservation, 1988-90. Member of Boards: Native American Rights Fund, National Congress of Ameriacn Indians, National Indian Gaming Association, The Harvard Project on American Indian Economic Development. *Awards, honors*: He was a member of the Electoral College 2008 US Presidential Election, 2008 Platform Committee member of the Democratic Party, and a member of the Board of Governors, Harvard Honoring Nations; also, the 2008 Pathbreaker Award Honoree at 20th Annual IGRA Symposium.

MACAULAY, JENNA (Tuscarora)
(attorney)
Education: Syracuse University, BA, 2009, College of Law, JD, 2012. *Affiliation & Address*: Associate Attorney, Berkey Williams LLP, 2030 Addison St. #410, Berkeley, CA 94704 (510) 548-7070. E-mail: info@berkeywilliams.com While in law school, Ms. Macaulay clerked for the Seneca Nation of Indians in their Department of Justice where she conducted research on issues related to the tax-exempt status of sovereign Indian Nations & the application of international law on traditional Seneca territory. As a third year student at Syracuse University College of Law, Ms. Macaulay worked as a student attorney in the Securities Arbitration Consumer Law Clinic, where she assisted small investors and other consumers with problems in the financial and consumer markets. Ms. Macaulay also clerked for the Law Office of Joseph Heath, the General Counsel for the Onondaga Nation. During her clerkship, she worked on the Onondaga Land Rights Action, a historic case which calls for the healing between the Onondaga Nation and the Central New York region. Also during her clerkship, Ms. Macaulay worked on issues pertaining to the Superfund site at Onondaga Lake. She is a member of the Turtle Clan from the Tuscarora Nation where she grew up learning the traditional teachings of the Haudenosaunee. Her interest in law is derived from her family's long history as active traditional leaders in the community.

MacDONALD, BRIAN (Champagne & Aishinik First Nation)
(attorney; instructor)
Affiliation & Address: Instructor. The Institute of Tribal Government, Portland State University, P.O. Box 751, Portland, OR 97207. He has practiced law in Whitehorse Yukon since 1999 and has worked exclusively with First Nations & Aboriginal organizations on the implementation of land claims agreements. His practice has focused primarily on aboriginal rights law, environmental & corporate law.

MACK, LYNN (Aleut)
(Alaskan village president)
Affiliation & Address: President, Native Village of Belkofsky, P.O. Box 57, King Cove, AK 99612 (907) 497-3122.

MACK, THOMAS (Aleut)
(corporation president)
Education: University of Nevada, Las Vegas & University of Alaska, Anchorage, BS; Western Oregon University, MS. *Affiliation & Address*: President (2006-present), The Aleut Corporation, Anchorage, AK   *Other professional posts*: Board Representative, Alaska Federation of Natives, Association of ANSCA President & CEOs, The Aleut Foundation, and Aleutian Financial, Inc. Mr. Mack strives to help preserve the Alaka Native way of life, culture, & languages. He taught in the Ancorage School District for ten years.

MACLEAN, JENA A.
(attorney)
Education: Princeton University, BA, 1993; University of Virginia School of Law, JD, 2001. *Affiliation & Address*: Co-chair & Partner, Native American Law & Policy Group, Perkins Coie, 700 Thirteenth St., NW • Washington, DC 20005 (202) 434-1648. E-mail: jmaclean@perkinscoie.com. Jena has been counsel in

some of the most complex and controversial federal Indian law cases in the nation. Jena has advised both tribal & non-tribal clients nationwide on difficult Indian law questions relating to tribal acknowledgment, enrollment & governance, eligibility for trust land, gaming eligibility determinations, aboriginal land claims, gaming development, compact negotiations and treaty rights. She assists clients in navigating the regulatory review processes before the Bureau of Indian Affairs, U.S. Army Corps of Engineers, Bureau of Ocean Energy Management, U.S. Fish & Wildlife Service and other federal agencies. Additionally, she regularly litigates cases before administrative boards and in federal courts across the nation. Jena assists in developing comprehensive strategies to address the most intricate and challenging Indian law issues her clients face. She has extensive experience in issues arising under the Administrative Procedure Act (APA), Indian Reorganization Act (IRA), Indian Gaming Regulatory Act (IGRA), Indian Non-Intercourse Act (INIA), Indian Tribal Economic Development and Contract Encouragement Act of 2000, and principles of federal pre-emption and tax in Indian country.

MACRI, MARTHA JANE MITCHELL (*Tsoee*) (Cherokee) 1945-
(professor of Native American studies)
Born March 10, 1945, Lansing, Mich. *Education*: California State University, Fullerton, BA, 1968; University of California, Berkeley, MA (Linguistics), 1982, Ph.D. (Linguistics), 1988. *Address*: 2212 Whittier Dr., Davis, CA 95616 (530) 752-7086 (work); E-mail: mjmacri@ucdavis.edu. *Affiliations*: Endowed Chair, California Indian Studies & Director, Native American Language Center, Professor & Graduate Advisor, Department of Native American Studies, University of California, Davis, 2409 Hart Hall, Davis, CA 95616 (postgraduate researcher, 1985-88; lecturer, 1988-90; Postdoctoral Fellow, 1990-91; assistant & associate professor, 1991-1999; professor & Graduate Advisor, 2000-09). *Other professional posts*: Co-editor, Glyph Dwellers; Principal Investigator, J.P. Harrington Database Project, Maya Hieroglyphic Database Project. *Past professional posts*: Project coordinator, Art & Archaeology Database Project, Pre-Columbian Art Research Institute, San Francisco, CA, 1988-91; instructor, D-Q University, Davis, CA, 1990; New Faculty Research Grants, Tzeltal Language Project, 1991-94; Sr. Investigator, Maya Archival Database Project, Merle Greene Robertson, principal investigator, National Endowment for the Humanities, Reference Materials-Access, through the Pre-Columbian Art Research, San Francisco, CA; principal investigator, Maya Hieroglyphic Database Project, National Endowment for the Humanities, Reference Materials-Tools, 1992-94, 1994-96. *Community activities*: Group leader, La Leche League International (board of directors, N. Calif.); assistant chairperson, Leader Applicants for Northern California, 1976-78; volunteer teacher's aid, in programs for Gifted & Talented, ESL, and regular classroom, Fitch Mtn. Elementary School, Healdsburg, CA, 1978-80; volunteer caregiver, Home Hospice of Sonoma County, CA, 1990-91. *Memberships*: Pre-Columbian Art Research Institute (research associate); American Anthropological Association; California Indian Education Association; Linguistic Society of America; Society for the Study of the Indigenous Languages of the Americas. *Interests*: "I am committed to research & teaching about the world views of indigenous peoples of the Americas through study of their own writing systems. Areas of emphasis include Maya Hieroglyphic writing, Epi-Olmec writing & Micmac hieroglyphic writing (Canada), linguistic prehistory of the Americas, Native American language instruction, computers in linguistic research & electronic data archiving." *Published works*: A Glyphic Text from Naranjo, in Native American Text Series, Louanna Furbee, editor (Mouton, The Hague with James Brooks, The Maya Graphene Codes & Reference File (book) (U. of Oklahoma Press); Teaching & Learning Indian Languages; numerous articles in journals, and chapters in books.

MACY, ALYSSA (Wasco/Navajo/Hopi)
(foundation development specialist)
Affiliation & Address: Development Specialist, Native Arts & Cultures Foundation, Native Arts & Cultures Foundation, 11109 NE 14th St., Vancouver, WA 98684 (360) 314-2421. *Other professional posts*: Member, Global Coordinating Committee for the World Conference on Indigenous Peoples, scheduled for 2014. *Past professional posts*: Co-director & trainer with NVision, a national media justice initiative with the goal of developing Indigenous leadership & expression of media, art & culture. *Awards, honors*: Recipient of the Mark O. Hatfield Fellowship, sponsored by the Confederated Tribes of the Grand Ronde, where she served in the Office of Congresswoman Darlene Hooley. *Interests*: Writing, policy making, advocate; photographer, focusing on the exeriences of Indiegnous peoples, the hip-hop community, and architecture.

MADALENA, JAMES ROGER (Jemez Pueblo)
(NM state representative)
Address: 373 Buffalo Hill Rd., Jemez Pueblo, NM 87024 (575) 834-7005. E-mail: jmadalena@fsipinc.org. *Affiliation*: NM District 65 representative, 1985-present. Co-chair of Indian Affairs Committee.

MADALENA, JOSHUA (Jemez Pueblo)
(former pueblo governor)
Affiliation & Address: Pueblo of Jemez, P.O. Box 100, Jemez, NM 87024 (505) 834-7359.

MADDOX, JANICE (Delaware)
(tribal administrator)
Affiliation & Address: Administrator, The Delaware Nation, P.O. Box 825, Anadarko, OK 73005 (405) 247-2448.

MADDUX, MICHAEL THOMAS (*Red Hawk*) (N. Alabama Cherokee) 1955-
(tribal officer)
Born July 12, 1955, Albertville, Ala. *Address*: 203 West Don's Ave., Albertville, AL 35950 (205) 878-9602. *Affiliation*: Authorized tribal officer, Dist. #2 North Alabama Cherokees. "We have seven districts with enrollment of nearly 1,000 people. *Awards, honors*: Golden Arrowhead Society, North Alabama Cherokees, Creek Path-Williston Dist. *Interests*: Native American powwows in TN, GA, and AL.

MADISON, JEFFREY L. (Wampanoag of Gay Head (Aquinnah))
(tribal supreme court judge)
Education: Cambridge College; Massachusetts School of Law at Andover, JD. *Affiliation & Address*: Judge, Supreme Court, Mashpee Wampanoag Indian Tribe, P.O. Box 1048, Mashpee, MA 02649 (508) 477-0208.

MADRID, GEORGIA (Taos Pueblo/Navajo)
(EEO specialist)
Education: University of Colorado, Boulder, BS (Journalism). *Affiliation*: EEO Specialist, NOAA/Oceanic & Atmospheric Research EEO Office, Boulder, CO. *Other professional posts*: Board member, SAIGE (Society for American Indian Governmental Employees), P.O. Box 7715, Washington, DC 20044; current & founding member, Denver Federal Executive Board, American Indian Program Council; member & past chair, AISES, Government Relations Council & Sequoyah member; active committee member in the planning of the annual Boulder Valley School District, American Indian Youth Leadership Institute conference for high school students. *Awards, honors*: AISES Community Service Award in 2002; Boulder County Community Action Program Government Award in 2004; NOAA Administrator's Award in 2004.

MADRIL, EDWARDO (Pascua Yaqui)
(Hoop dancer, singer, teacher, playwright, filmmaker, artist, educator)
Affiliation: Founding member, *Four Winds American Indian Dance* Company He has been performed for more than 20 years. *Other professional post*: Board Vice President, Friendship House of San Francisco, CA. Among his achievements and contributions, he has researched and worked with tribal elders to preserve sacred, traditional ceremonial dance within tribal settings, taught American Indian music at San Francisco State University, served as Artist-In-Residence for the California Arts Council for 3 years, presented his plays, films and performances on stage, including at the Yerba Buena Center for the Arts and Brava Theatre, and his films have been accepted and featured in American Indian film festivals in San Francisco, Oklahoma and South Dakota. As a dancer, he has performed throughout the Western United States, including the San Francisco Ethnic Dance Festival, World Arts West's arts education program *People Like Me*, The Olympic Games and in Powwows across the nation. He is active and dedicated in his lifelong mission to pass along American Indian cultural riches and traditions to our American Indian youth, families, and communities.

MADSEN, LOIS
(Indian education program coordinator)
Affiliation & Address: Capistrano Unified School District, Indian Education Program, 24242 La Cresta Dr., Dana Point, CA 92629 (714) 248-7037.

MAGEE, DENNIS (Luiseno Band of Mission Indians) 1937-
(health administration)
Born October 9, 1937, Pala Indian Reservation, Calif. *Education*: San Diego City College, GE, 1957; San Diego State University, BS, 1962. *Address*: Pala Mission Rd., P.O. Box 86, Pala, CA 92059 (619) 749-1410 (work). *Affiliation*: Administrator, Indian Health Council, Inc., Pauma Valley, CA, 1970-. *Community activities*: Board of Directors, San Diego Council of Community Clinics; Citizens Equal Opportunity Commission, City of San Diego; United Way of San Diego (board of directors); Advisory policy panel, Indian Health Branch, State Department of Health Services; Native American Training Associates Institute (board chairman); National Social Workers Techno-culture Coalition (vice-president); Pauma Valley Community Assn; California Assn for Indian Health Administrators; Mental Health Assn in California (board member); National Indian Health Board (board of directors); California Rural Indian Health Board (chairman, board of directors); Masters in Public Health Program for Native Americans, University of California, Berkeley (advisory board). *Awards, honors*: Recipient of Robert F. Kennedy Memorial Fellowship, 1970; selected as one of the "Ten Outstanding Young Men of San Diego" by

the San Diego Junior Chamber of Commerce, 1971; selected as "San Diego North County Man of the Year" by the Northern San Diego County Associated Chamber of Commerce, 1971; awarded a "Resolution of Commendation" for outstanding community service by the California State Senate, 1972; awarded the "National Distinguished Community Service Award by the National Social Workers Techno-culture Coalition, 1973; Dedication by Indian Health Center, 1976; Letter of Commendation, 1980, by President Jimmy Carter; Luna Wessel Distinguished Service Award, California Rural Indian Health Board, 1986; Official Commendation, U.S. Senator Daniel K. Inouye, Chairperson of the Senate Select Committee on Indian Affairs, 1989. *Interests*: Testified before the Senate & House subcommittees on appropriations, Wash., D.C., 1971-.

MAGNUSON, MARY B.
(attorney)
Education: College of St. Benedict, BA,, 1980; J.D. William Mitchell College of Law, St Paul, MN), JD, 1984. *Affiliation & Address*: Partner (1992-present), Jacobson, Buffalo, Magnuson, Anderson & Hogen, LLP, 1295 Bandana Blvd., St. Paul, MN 55108 (651) 644-4710. E-mail: mmagnuson@ thejacobsonlawgroup.com. *Practice areas*: Administrative Law, Gaming Law, Government Relations & Regulatory Compliance, Indian/Tribal Law. Mary represents Indian & non-Indian entities involved in the development & operation of gaming activities throughout the U.S. & Canada. *Past professional post*: Chair of the Indian Gaming Committee of the North American Gaming Regulator's Association.

MAHKEE, WELLS, JR. (Zuni)
(managing editor)
Born in Zuni, N.M. *Education*: New Mexico Highlands University, B.A. (English). *Address & Affiliation*: Managing Editor, Navajo-Hopi Observer, 2224 E. Cedar Ave., Suite 2, Flagstaff, AZ 86001 (928) 226-9696. *Past professional posts*: Managing editor, The Shiwi Messenger, Zuni, NM. *Community activities*: Member, Indian Advisory Panel, Museum of Indian Arts & Culture, Santa Fe, NM. *Membership*: Zuni Pueblo Band. Mahkee is the first Native American managing editor of the Navajo-Hopi Observer.

MAHOOTY, DAVID (Pueblo of Zuni)
(banking; board president)
Education: University of New Mexico, BA (Economics), MA (Business Administration). *Affiliations & Address*: Senior Lender (2013-present), New Mexico Finance Authority, 207 Shelby St., Santa Fe, NM 87501 (505) 984-1454. *Past professional posts*: Assistant V.P. & Relationship Manager (2001-11), Wells Fargo New Mexico Commercial Banking, Albuquerque, NM; former board president, American Indian Graduate Center, Albuquerque, NM; member, Laguna Education Foundation Board; member, Advisory Council, Native American Initiative for Junior Achievement.

MAHSETKY, MICHAEL "MACK", JR. (Comanche)
(tribal vice chairperson)
Education: University of Oklahoma; University of Texas, BS; Antioch School of Law, Washington, DC., JD. *Affiliation & Address*: Vice Chairperson, Comanche Nation, P.O. Box 908, Lawton, OK 73502 (580) 492-3240. *Past professional posts*: Director, Legislative Affairs, Indian Health Service, Rockville, MD. Helped establish & served as director, Dallas Inter-Tribal Health Center, Dallas, TX, 1969-80; staff attorney with Senate Committee on Indian Affairs, Washington, DC, 1980-87; chief, Legislative Branch, Office of Planning, Evaluation, & legislation, IHS, Rockville, MD, 1988. *Awards, honors*: In 1978, he was recognized as one of ten outstanding citizens of Dallas for his contributions to improving the lives of Indian people; served on board of directors for the American Indian Health Care Association, Minneapolis, MN; presented testimony in Congress on the need for health care funding for urban Indians; helped establish and executive director, Dallas Minority Repertory Theatre, which promoted ethnic & minority actors, playwrights & stage technicians; numerous awards for his accomplishments, including recognition from his own tribe for his work with the Senate Indian Affairs Commission; acknowledged by the Governor of Maryland for his work in promoting cultural diversity in the State; received the Recognition Award from the University of Michigan School of Law for his work in the field of Indian law; and recognition awards for his work in the IHS. *Memberships*: Pi Sigma Epsilon Professional Marketing Fraternity, Native American Bar Association, American Bar Assn.

MAIN, ANDREA (ANGIE) (Gros Ventre)
(executive director; consultant)
Education: Montana State University-Northern, 1989-91. *Affiliation & Address*: Small Biz Specialist, 2005-11; Executive Director, 2011-present, Native American Community Development Corporation, P.O. Box 302, Browning, MT 59417 (406) 338-2992. *Past professional posts*: Executive director, Northcentral Montana Community Ventures Coalition; executive director, Montana Tribal Business Information Network; project coordinator, Native American Development & Finance Initiative, Rural Development & Finance Corp., 1999-2005;

MAINES, BILL J. (Aleut) 1954-
(radio station general manager)
Born October 30, 1954, Anchorage, AK. *Education*: Electronic Institute, Pittsburgh, AA, 1974. *Principal occupation*: General Manager. *Address*: P.O. Box 109, 4667 Okakok St., Barrow, AK 99723 (907) 852-6046. *Affiliations*: KDLG-AM, Dillingham, AK, 1977-88; KBRW-AM, Barrow, AK, 1988-. *Other professional posts*: Alaska Public Radio Network (board of directors); Alaska Native Communications Society (co-chair). *Community activities*: Choggiung Ltd., Dillingham Village corporation. *Memberships*: Bristol Bay Native Corporation - regional corp.; Alaska Federation of Natives.

MAJEL-DIXON, JUANA (Pauma Band Luiseno)
(tribal policy director; professor of American Indian studies)
Affiliation & Address: Policy Director (1997-present) & Tribal Legislative Councilperson (1974-present), Pauma Band of Luiseno Mission Indian, 110 Reservation Rd., P.O. Box 369, Pauma Valley, CA 92061. *Other professional post*: Adjunct Professor (1981-present), American Indian Studies Dept., Palomar College, San Marcos, CA 92069 (760) 744-1150.

MALDONADO, ROLAND (Paiute)
(tribal chairperson)
Affiliation & Address: Chairperson, Kaibab Paiute Tribal Council, #1 North Pipe Spring Rd., Fredonia, AZ 86022 (928) 643-8301. E-mail: rolandm@ kaibabpaiute-nsn.gov. Past professional post: Cultural Preservation Director, Kaibab Paiute Tribe.

MALERBA, MARILYN "LYNN" (Mohegan)
(lifetime chief)
Affiliation & Address: Lifetime Chief, Mohegan Indian Tribe, 5 Crow Hill Rd., Uncasville, CT 06382 (860) 862-6100. Former tribal chairperson.

MALLORY, KEN (Winnebago of Nebraska)
(tribal councilmember)
Affiliation & Address: Councilmember, Winnebago Tribe of Nebraska, P.O. Box 687, Winnebago, NE 68071 (402) 878-2272.

MALLOTT, BYRON (Tlingit) 1943-
(chief executive officer)
Born April 6, 1943, Yakutat, Alaska. *Education*: Western Washington University, BA. Honorary Doctorate in Humanities, University of Alaska. *Affiliation & Address*: Sealaska Corporation (chairman of the board, 1976-84; chief executive officer, 1982-present), One Sealaska Plaza, Suite 400, Juneau, AK 99801 (907) 586-1512 (work). *Other professional posts*: Director, Alaska Air Group & Alaska Communication Systems, Inc., 2008-present; member, Board of Trustees, National Museum of the American Indian, 2007-present. *Past professional posts*: Commissioner, Dept. of Community & Regional Affairs, State of Alaska, 1972-74; consultant, Alaska Natives Resources, Inc., 1974-78; president, Alaska Federation of Natives, 1977-78; board member, Colville Tribal Enterprise Corp., 1985-2005; board member, The Mediation Institute, 1985-2005. *Community service*: Rural Affairs Commission, State of Alaska, 1972-76; Alaska Native Foundation (vice chairman, 1975-79); Yak-Tat Kwaan, Inc. (Yakutat Village Corp.) (board of directors, 1974-78; chairman, 1976-77); B.M. Behrends Bank (director, 1975-84); White House Fellowship Selection Commission-Western Region, 1978-83; Commercial Fisheries & Agricultural Bank, State of Alaska (director, 1979); U. of Alaska Foundation (director, 1980-85). *Awards, honors*: Governor's Award for Service to Alaska, 1982; recipient of the Alaska Native Citizen of the Year Award from the Alaska Federation of Natives, 1982; Honorary Doctorate Degree in the Humanities by the U. of Alaska, 1984. *Published works*: Several articles: One Day in the Life of a Native Chief Executive, in 2 parts, AK Native Magazine, Sept. & Oct., 1985; Byron's Brew, AK Business Monthly, Oct., 1985; Sealaska: Soon to Rival Oil Companies in Power? an interview with Byron Mallott, AK Industry, 9/81.

MALONE, CHAD (Washoe)
(tribal vice chairperson)
Affiliation & Address: Washoe Tribe iof the Carson Indian Community, P.O. Box 3269, Carson City, NV 89703 (775) 221-0696. E-mail: cmalone@washoetribe.us.

MALOTKI, EKKEHART
(professor of languages)
Affiliation & Address: Dept. of Linguistics, Northern Arizona University, Flagstaff, AZ 86011. *Published works*: The Bedbugs' Night Dance & Other Hopi Tales of Sexual Encounter (University of Nebraska Press); Hopi Tales of Destruction (University of Nebraska Press); Kokopelli: The Making of an Icon (University of Nebraska Press, 2000).

MANAKAJA, LINCOLN (Havasupai)
(tribal committee member)
Affiliation & Address: Committee member Havasupai Tribe, P.O. Box 10, Supai, AZ 86435 (928) 448-2731.

MANATOWA-BAILEY, JACOB (Sauk, Sac and Fox of Oklahoma)
(Indian center director)
Affiliation & Address: Director, The Center for Tribal Languages, Bacone College, 2299 Old Bacone Rd., Muskogee, OK 74403 (918) 683-4581.

MANDAN, THOMASINA (Mandan/Hidatsa)
(director of Native Ameriacn studies)
Affiliation & Address: Online Education Director & Director, Native American Studies Program, Fort Berthold Community College, P.O. Box 490, New Towm ND 58763 (701) 627-4738 ext. 282.

MANDELL, KEITH ALAN (Paiute)
(tribal vice chairperson)
Affiliation & Address: Vice Chairperson, Pyramid Lake Paiute Tribal Council, P.O. Box 256, Nixon, NV 89424 (775) 574-1000.

MANDOKA, HOMER A. (Potawatomi)
(tribal sergeant-at-arms; former tribal chairperson)
Affiliation & Address: Sergeant-At-Arms, Nottawaseppi Huron Band of Potawatomi, 2221 - 1 1/2 Mile Rd., Fulton, MI 49052 (269) 729-5151. E-mail: mandokaha@nhbpi.com. *Past tribal affiliations*: Former chairperson, 2009-2015; Council member, 2002-2009.

MANDREGAN, CHRISTOPHER, JR. (Aleut)
(IHS area director)
Education: Washington State University, BS (Business Administration); University of Hawaii at Manoa, MPH. *Affiliation & Address*: Director, Alaska Area IHS, 4141 Ambassador Dr., Suite 300, Anchorage, AK 99508 (907) 729-3686. E-mail: chris.mandregan@ihs..gov. *Other professional posts*: Mr. Mandregan also serves on the Executive Committee of the Alaska Federal Health Care Partnership (AFHCP). The AFHCP is a collaboration of the IHS, Department of Defense (Air Force & Army), Veteran's Administration, and Coast Guard. *Past professional posts*: He began his career with the Indian Health Service (IHS), an agency of the Department of Health & Human Services (HHS), in 1986. In 1996, Mr. Mandregan was appointed as the Executive Officer for the Alaska Area IHS (AAIHS), responsible for administrative support services for the Area. In 1998 he accepted the position of Area Director for the AAIHS. As the Area Director, Mr. Mandregan is responsible for the federal portion of the health care system for Alaska Native people and for conducting government-to-government relationships with Alaska Native Tribes on behalf of the HHS Secretary. The AAIHS provides comprehensive health services to approximately 136,000 Alaska Native people (Eskimos, Aleuts, and Indians) and non-natives living in remote locations (non-native patients reimburse the IHS funded hospitals and clinics for the care they receive.). The AAIHS health care delivery system is linked to Alaska Native Tribes, tribal health organizations, & villages, and to state and local agencies. Field hospitals are located in the six rural communities of Barrow, Bethel, Dillingham, Kotzebue, Nome, & Sitka; and are operated by Alaska Native tribal organizations. Seven ambulatory health care centers are located in Juneau, Ketchikan, Metlakatla, Fairbanks, Tanana, Fort Yukon, and St. Paul Island. Over 170 additional clinics are located throughout Alaska. The Alaska Native Medical Center (ANMC), a 170-bed general medical and surgical hospital located in Anchorage, is the referral center for rural hospitals and clinics. In addition to serving as the Director of AAIHS, Mr. Mandregan also served as Acting Deputy Director of the IHS from October 1, 2007, through February 18, 2009. He also has served as Agency Lead Negotiator for the Alaska Tribal Health Compact & has been instrumental in implementing Indian Self Determination & Tribal Self-Governance in Alaska and through support he provides to other IHS Areas. *Awards, honors*: The AFHCP won Government Executive Magazine's 2002 Grace Hopper Government Technology Leadership Award for its implementation of a state-wide telemedicine system, deployed in over 200 health care facilities throughout Alaska. In 2004, Mr. Mandregan received the Presidential Rank Award for Meritorious Service. He is also a recipient of the Public Health Service Special Recognition Award for Productivity from the Assistant Secretary for Health, HHS. He was selected for this award for his efforts in securing lower rates for medical services purchased from private physicians & hospitals by the ANMC.

MANN, HENRIETTA (Cheyenne)
(founding college president; professor emeritus)
Education: Southwestern Oklahoma State University, BA, 1954, MA, 1970; University of New Mexico, PhD (American Studies), 1982. *Affiliation & Address*: Emeritus Professor, Department of Native American Studies, Montana State University, 2-179 Wilson Hall, P.O. Box 172340, Bozeman, MT 59717 (406) 994-3881 henrietta.mann@montana.edu. *Other professional post*: Professor Emeritus, Native American Studies Dept. & Special Assistant to the President, Montana State University, Bozeman, MT. *Past professional posts*: Professor/administrator, University of California, Berkeley, University of Montana, Missoula; Graduate School of Education, Harvard University; Haskell Indian Nations University, Lawrence, KS. *Awards, honors*: Founding President, Cheyenne & Arapaho Tribal College, Weatherford, OK; The first

Katz Endowed Chair in Native American Studies at Montana State University, Bozeman; 1991 one of the top ten professors in the nation from Rolling Stone Magazine; 1997 inductee to the Southwestern Oklahoma State U. Hall of Fame; 2008 recipient of the Bernard S. Rodey Award for her leadership in education; the 2008 National Indian Education Association Lifetime Achievement Award; 2012 recipient of the Ely S. Parker Award. *Interests*: American Indian religion.

MANN, MICHAEL (*Silver Cloud*) (Ramapough Lenape)
(tribal board president; nurse)
Born & raised in Hillburn, NY, the "Turtle Clan" community of Ramapough Lenape. *Education*: Passaic County Community College, Nursing degree, 1998. Michael, since 1998, has worked as an Operating Room nurse and most recently as Administrator of an Ambulatory Surgical Center. *Affiliation & Address*: Ramapough Lenape Indian Nation, P.O. Box 103, Hillburn, NY 10931 (201) 529-1171. *Interests*: "I am actively involved in the construction of the Long House on the Sacred Land in Mahwah. I look forward to working with our people in meeting the common goals of the Tribe."

MANN, VICTOR (Paiute)
(tribal chairperson)
Affiliation & Address: Chairperson, Lovelock Paiute Tribe, Fort Bidwell Reservation, P.O. Box 878, Lovelock, NV 89419 (775) 273-7861.

MANN, VINCENT (*Eagle Spirit*) (Ramapough Lenape)
(tribal chief)
Resides in Rhode Island within seven miles of the Pequot Mohegan & Narragansett Reservations. *Professional post*: Construction supervisor, Pequot Housing Dept. *Affiliation*: Turtle Clan Chief, Ramapough Lenape Indian Nation, Mahwah, NJ.

MANNING, JOHN W. "JACK" (Fort Peck Sioux) 1950-
(attorney)
Born March 8, 1950, Miles City, Mont. *Education*: Dartmouth College, AB, 1972; Stanford University Law School, JD, 1975. *Address*: 211 3rd Ave. N., Great Falls, MT 59401 (406) 727-3632 (work) *Affiliations*: Associate, Davis Polk & Wardwell, New York, NY 1975-80; Dorsey & Whitney Law Firm, Great Falls, MT (associate 1980-84; partner, 1984) *Community activities*: Board member of Neighborhood Housing Services & Great Falls Native American Center at various times.

MANNING, LINDSEY (Shoshone-Paiute)
(former tribal chairperson)
Affiliation & Address: Former chairperson, Shoshone Paiute Business Council, Duck Valley Reservation, P.O. Box 219, Owyhee, NV 89832 (702) 759-3100 ext. 1231. E-mail: manning.lindseyw@shopai.org.

MANNING-JOHN, LYNN (Shoshone Paiute)
(combined school principal)
Education: Smith College, BA (Education & Child Study); University of Nevada, Las Vegas, MA (Educational Leadership), 2004. *Affiliation & Address*: Principal, Owyhee Combined School, P.O. Box 100, Owyhee, NV 89832 (775) 757-3400. E-mail: lmanningjohn@ecsdnv.net. *Past professional posts*: Project Facilitator, Indian Education Opportunity Program in Clark Cuntry, Nevda (nine years), she worked for Title VII and Johnson O'Malley Program; Indian Education Coordinator for Washoe County (eight years). She facilitated Title VII and other funding for educational programs for WCSD in partnership with local tribes, including the Ren-Sparks Indian Colony, Pyramide Lake and the Nevada Urban Indian Commission, 2007-14.

MANRIQUEZ, L. FRANK (Tongva/Ajachmem)
(artist, tribal scholar, cartoonist, language advocate, singer)
Affiliation & Address: Trainer, The Cultural Conservancy, P.O. Box 29044, Presidio of San Francisco, CA 94129 (415) 561-6594. *Other professional post*: Co-founder, Advocates for Indigenous California Language Survival; board member of Neshkanukat; served as board member of the California Indian Basketweavers Association. *Interests*: She works to revitalize indigenous languages as a language trainer providing conferences & workshops with indigenous communities throughout the U.S. Ms. Manriquez is a Native California Indian artist, tribal scholar, cartoonist, language advocate, singer, and self-described "decolonizationist." She has exhibited her artwork in museums & galleries. *Published works*: Acorn Soup (Heyday Books); First Families: A Photographic History of California Indians (Heyday Books; articles to "News From Native California."

MANSON, SPERO M. (Pembina Chippewa) 1950-
(center director; medical anthropologist; distinguished professor)
Born May 2, 1950, Everett, Wash. *Education*: University of Washington, BA, 1972; University of Minnesota, MA, 1975, PhD (Anthropology), 1978. *Principal occupation*: Center director & mental health researcher. *Affiliation & Address*: Director, Centers for American Indian & Alaska Native Health, University of

Colorado Health Sciences Center, Dept. of Psychiatry, Nighthorse Campbell Native Health Bldg., 13055 E. 17th Pl., F800, Aurora, CO 80045 (303) 724-1444. E-mail: spero.manson@ucdenver.edu. *Past professional posts*: Professor & director, Institute on Aging, School of Urban & Public Affairs, Portland State University, 1982-86; associate professor & director, Social Psychiatric Research, Dept. of Psychiatry, School of Medicine, Oregon Health Sciences University, 1982-86; adjunct associate professor of anthropology, Portland State University, 1982-86; director, National Center for American Indian & Alaska Native Mental Health Research, University of Colorado Health Sciences Center, Denver, 1986-; associate professor, Dept. of Psychiatry, University of Colorado Health Sciences Center, Denver, 1986-; editor-in-chief, American Indian & Alaska Native Mental Health Research. *Other professional posts*: Program co-director, Robert Wood Johnson Foundation's Healthy Nations Initiative, a six-year, $16 million effort to assist 15 Indian and Native communities in their struggle to reduce harm due to substance abuse by promoting comprehensive intervention strategies that integrates resources across formal and informal sectors of the local citizenry; recently awarded a $1.2 million grant by the Administration on Aging to establish and direct the Native Elder Health Care Resource Center (NEHCRC). *Consultant ships*: Billings Area Office, Indian Health Service, MT, 1984-; Northwest Portland Area Indian Health Board, 1985-; Alaska Native Health Board, 1985-. *Community activities*: National Institute of Mental Health Epidemiology & Services Research Review Committee, 1983-87; NIDA Advisory Committee on Prevention, 1983-85; Oregon State Governor's Task Force on Alcohol & Drug Abuse, 1984-86; vice-chair, Denver Indian Health & Family Services; board of directors, Colorado Gerontological Society. *Memberships*: American Anthropological Association; Gerontological Society of America; Society for Applied Anthropology (Fellow); Society for Medical Anthropology. *Awards, honors*: 1984 Oregon State System of Higher Education, Faculty Excellence Award; Phi Beta Kappa; State of Oregon Excellence Award in Higher Education (1985); Fulbright-Hays Scholar; CIC Traveling Scholar; National Science Foundation Scholarship; 1994 Researcher of the Year, The Colorado Public Health Association; 1995 Beverly Visiting Professor at the University of Toronto (a national award honoring significant contributions to the mental health field); received the Indian Health Service's Distinguished Service Award, July, 1996. *Research Interests*: Substance abuse in Native Americans & Alaska Native populations; Native American & Alaska Native Mental Health. *Published works*: Co-editor, books in preparation: American Indian Youth: Seventy-five Years of Psychosocial Research (Greenwood Press); New Directions in Prevention (Oregon Health Sciences University, 1982); Psychosocial Research with American Indian & Alaska Native Youth (Greenwood Press, 1984); Health and Behavior: A Research Agenda for American Indians (University of Colorado Health Sciences Center, 1988); editor, Medical Anthropology: Implications for Stress Prevention Across Cultures (National Institute of Mental Health, GPO); numerous articles.

MANUEL, EDWARD D. (Tohono O'odham)
(tribal chairperson)
Affiliation & Address: Chairperson, Tohono O'odham Nation, P.O. Box 837, Sells, AZ 85634 (520) 383-2028. *Past professional post*: Legislative Vice Chairperson, Tohono O'odham Council,

MANUELITO, ETHEL M. (Navajo) 1954-
(associate director; consultant)
Born July 6, 1954, Fort Defiance, Ariz. *Education*: University of New Mexico, BS, 1977, MA, 1982; Western New Mexico University (Silver City), 3 years. Principal occupation: Associate director; consultant. *Address*: P.O. Box 51, Tohatchi, NM 87325 (505) 733-2200 (work). *Affiliation*: Associate director for Direct Services, Tohatchi Special Education & Training Center, 1978-. *Other professional post*: Consultant to Navajo Initiative Project. *Community activities*: Gallup McKinley County Schools (Board of Education, secretary); University of New Mexico-Gallup Branch (Advisory Board Member); New Mexico School Board (Region I President). *Memberships*: Council for Exceptional Children; National School Board Association; Navajo Nation Public School Board Association. *Awards, honors*: Navajo Tribal Scholarships. *Interests*: "Travel to various parts of the U.S.; beadwork, crochet, sewing Native American clothes."

MANYARROWS, VICTORIA LENA (Eastern Cherokee) 1956-
(social service/arts administrator; writer)
Born Aril 10, 1956, Des Moines, Iowa. *Education*: San Francisco State University, MSW, 1993. *Address*: Unknown. *Affiliation*: Support Service for the Arts, San Francisco, CA (administrator; co-director, 1981-). *Other professional post*: Counselor, administrator in various alcohol, substance abuse & homeless programs. Youth Empowerment Council member, United Indian Nations, Oakland, CA; volunteer, American Indian Contemporary Arts, San Francisco, & Indian Education Center, Oakland; volunteer, Brava! for Women in the Arts & Casa El Salvador (both in San Francisco). *Memberships*: ATLATL; National Service Organization for Native American Artists; Native Writer's Circle of the Americas; Wordcraft Circle of Native Writers & Apprentices; Indigenous Women's Network. *Awards, honors*: Graduate Honor Fellowship, San Francisco State University, 1991-92; Featured Poet (Summer, 1993), "Orphic

Lute" journal, Seattle, WA. *Interests*: "Creative writing (especially poetry & essays) & teaching creative writing to Native women and youth. Have traveled extensively in Mexico & Central America (speak Spanish) & speak out on international Indian issues; public health, environmental, and social psychological needs of Native women, children & communities; photography, video, and mixed media (poetry & visual art collaborative pieces)." *Published work*: Poetry, Songs From the Native Lands (Turtleland/Pajarta Press, 1995). Poems & essays published in various journals & anthologies in the U.S. & Canada, including: Without Discovery: A Native Response to Columbus (Broken Moon Press, 1992); The Colour of Resistance: A Contemporary Collection of Writing by Aboriginal Women (Sister Vision Press, Canada, 1993); Looking At the Words of Our People (Theytus Books, Canada, 1993); The Worlds Walking (New Rivers Press, 1994); Unsettling America: Race & Ethnicity in Contemporary American Poetry (Viking Penguin Press, 1994).

MANZO, KAREN
(lecturer in Native American Studies & Public Health)
Education: West Virginia Univesity, MPH & PhD ABD (Doctorate in Public Health Sciences). *Affiliation & Address*: Lecturer, Native American Studies Program & School of Public Health, Eberly College of Arts & Sciences, West Virginia University, P.O. Box 9190, Morgantown, WV 26506 (304) 293-8381. Email: kmanzo@hsc.wvu.edu. Other professional posts: Member, Native American Studies Committee; Ms Manzo is an evaluator with the Montana-Wyoming Tribal Leaders Councils Planting Seeds of Hope Youth Suicide Prevention Project. Her teachings & professional endeavors center on American Indian Health.

MAR, JOSE MATOS
(director of Inter-American Indian Institute)
Born November 1, Peru. *Education*: Universidad Nacional Mayor de San Marcos-Lima, Peru (Anthropology); Universidad de Paris (Ethnology), Postgraduate. *Affiliation & Address*: Director, Inter-American Indian Institute, #232, Colonia Pedregal de San Angel, Delegacion Alvaro Obregon C.P.01900, Mexico D.F.

MARACLE, THOMAS B. (Six Nations Iroquois-Mohawk) 1949-
(sculptor, musician; gallery owner)
Born in Belleville, Ontario in 1949. *Affiliation & Address*: Owner/artist, Native Renaissance II Gallery & Gift Shop, P.O. Box 61, Deseronto, ON K0K 1X0. Thomas is an acclaimed stone sculptor, images of his legendary people, animals & spirits of his native culture. He has won many awards across Canada & the U.S. Reproductions of many of his sculptures are available at art galleries & goft shops throughout North America including his own permanent gallery. *Music CDs*: Mixed Emotions, Catch the Dream, Different Vibes, Dancing Spirits, and Spirit Land Band which won the Best Instrumental Album & Best Contemporary Album at 2001-02 Canadian Aboriginal Music Awards.

MARCANO-QUINONES, MR. RENE (*Cibanacan*) (Taino) 1941-
(tribal organizer)
Born September 16, 1941, Santurce, San Juan, P.R. *Address*: 174 W. 107 St. #3E, New York, NY 10025 (212) 866-4573. *Affiliation*: Principal Cacike, Taino Nation of the Antilles (more than 4,000), P.O. Box 883, New York, NY 10025, Puerto Rico & abroad. *Other professional posts*: Editor of bimonthly, bilingual tribal newsletter, the "Boletin Informativo de la Nacion Taina de las Antillas"; lecturer on Taino history, culture, heritage an restoration. *Interests*: "Impart conferences regarding Taino restoration efforts regarding culture, history, music and art." Principal organizer of the Taino restoration movement that began in the late 1980s. 1990 organized the Taino Indigenous Association that gave way in 1992 to the Taino Nation of the Antilles found in Puerto Rico, eastern Cuba & U.S. diaspora. One of Native American leaders & consultants advising the National Museum of the American Indian on the propriety of exhibiting & publishing objects of great cultural & spiritual sensitivity, and a source of information on Taino people in the Smithsonian's publication, "Creation's Journey: Native American Identity & Belief," (Oct. 1994-Feb. 1997).

MARCHAND, ARNOLD N. (Colville)
(museum director)
Affiliation & Address: Director, Colville Confederated Tribes Museum, P.O. Box 150, Nespelem, WA 99155 (509) 634-4711.

MARCHAND, DOROTHY (Colville)
(school principal)
Affiliation & Address: Paschal Sherman Indian School, Omak Lake Rd., Omak, WA 98841 (509) 826-2097.

MARCHAND, MICHAEL (Colville)
(tribal chairperson)
Affiliation & Address: Chairperson & Omak District Rep., Confederated Tribes of the Colville Reservation, P.O. Box 150, Nespelem, WA 99155 (509) 634-2208. E-mail: michael.marchand@colvilletribes.com. *Other professional post*: President, ATNI Economic Development Corp., Affiliated Tribes of Northwest

Indians (ATNI), 18230 Frost Rd., Dallas, OR 97338 (503) 917-0550. *Past tribal post*: Tribal council member.

MARCUS. JOHN (Cahuilla)
(tribal vice chairperson)
Affiliation & Address: Vice Chairperson, Santa Rosa Band of Cahuilla Indians, P.O. Box 391820, Anza, CA 92539 (951) 659-2700. *Past professional posts*: Served as Chairperson from 2006-08, 2009-11 and 2011-2016; served on the Riverside-San Bernardino County Indian Health Clinic Board of Directors.

MAREK-MARTINEZ, ORA (Navajo/Nez Perce)
(Indian center executive director)
Affiliation & Address: Executive Director, Native American Cultural Center, Northern Arizona University, P.O. Box 4085, Flagstaff, AZ 86011 (928) 523-9557. E-mail: ora.marek-martinez.frank@nau.edu Before assuming the role of Executive Director of the Native American Cultural Center, Dr. Ora Marek-Martinez worked for the Navajo Nation as the Tribal Historic Preservation Officer and tribal archaeologist, conducting, reviewing, and approving cultural heritage work throughout the Navajo Nation. As Executive Director of the NACC, she is charged with programming, fundraising, strategic planning, development of the Office of Native American Initiatives newsletter, and budgetary oversight of the NACC. In addition, she is an Assistant Professor of Anthropology at NAU. Her research interests include Southwestern, Indigenous, and tribal archaeology, decolonizing methodologies, and epistemic injustice. She is focused on serving, supporting, and ensuring the success of NAU students through the programming and services provided at the Native American Cultural Center.

MARGOLIN, MALCOLM 1940-
(publisher, writer)
Born October 27, 1940, Boston, Mass. *Education*: Harvard University, BA, 1964. *Principal occupation*: Publisher, writer. *Address*: Heyday Books, P.O. Box 9145, Berkeley, CA 94709 (510) 549-3564. *Affiliation*: Executive Director, Heyday Books, Berkeley, CA, 1974-present; News From Native California, Berkeley, CA, 1987-present. *Other professional posts*: Serves on two boards of two organizations he helped found, Bay Nature Institute & Alliance for California Traditional Artists. *Interests*: "Writing and publishing has focused on the history and ongoing cultures of California Indian people. A major commitment of both Heyday Books & "News from Native California" has been to provide a vehicle by which Native Californians can describe their history & culture in their own voices." *Awards, honors*: The Fred Cody Award for Lifetime Achievement from the San Francisco Bay Area Book Reviewers Association; the 2008 Helen Crocker Russell Award for Community Leadership from the San Francisco Foundation; the Carey McWilliams Award for Lifetime Achievement from the California Studies Association; an Oscar Lewis Award for Western History from the Book Club of California; a Hubert Bancroft Award from the Friends of the Bancroft Library; a Cultural Freedom Award from the Lannan Foundation; Distinguished Service Award from the Society of Professional Journalists; and the Yosemite Foundation Minister of Beauty. *Published works*: Ohlone Way: Indian Life in San Francisco Area (Heyday Books, 1978); Way We Lived: California Indian Stories, Songs & Reminiscence (Heyday Books, 1981; revised ed. 1993); The Earth Manual: How to Work on Wild Land Without Taming It (Heyday Books, 1985 revised ed.); The East Bay Out: A personal Guide to the East Bay Regional Parks (Heyday Books, 1988 revised ed.); California Indians & the Environment, with Jeannine Gendar, Editor (Heyday Books, 1992); Living in a Well-Ordered World: Indian People of Northwestern California (Redwood National Park, 1994); Native Ways: California Indian Stories & Memories, with Yolanda Montijo, Eds. (Heyday Books, 1995); The Ohlone Way: Indian Life in the San Francisco-Monterey Bay Area (Heyday Books, 2003).

MARIELLA, PATRICIA 1952-
(institute director)
Education: University of Wisconsin, BA, 1973; Arizona State University, MA, 1976, PhD (Social Anthropology), 1983. *Affiliation*: Director, American Indian Policy Institute, Arizona State University, Discovery Hall, Rm. 272A, P.O. Box 872603, Tempe, AZ 85287 (480) 965-9005. E-mail: pat.mariella@asu.edu. *Past professional posts*: Executive director, Dept. of Environmental Quality, Gila River Indian Community, 1995-2006; Manager, Arizona Department of Environmental Quality, 1991-95; research specialist, 1981-83; research analyst, 1984-88; research director (1988-91), Inter-Tribal Council of Arizona, Phoenix, AZ. *Awards, honors*: Service to Tribes of Arizona, Inter Tribal Council of Arizona, 2000; Environmental Leadership Award, EPA, 1999. *Published works*: Numerous articles in journals.

MARION-KULAS, CHERYL (Oglala Lakota-Turtle Mountain Chippewa)
(director of Indian education)
Address: 325 Willow Lane, Bismarck, ND 58505-0440 (701) 328-2250. E-mail: ckulas@maihidpi.state.nd.us. *Affiliation*: Director of Indian Education, State Dept. of Public Instruction. Prior to current position, served as state's coordinator for Race & National Origin Equity; and Education Specialist to

United Tribes Technical College. *Memberships*: National Indian Education Association; University of Arizona Alumni; University of North Dakota Alumni.

MARKS, COLEEN KELLEY (Susquahana) 1951-
(museum curator, arts consultant)
Born January 12, 1951, Altoona, Pa. *Education*: College of the Redwoods (Eureka, CA), AA, 1978; Humboldt State University (Arcata, CA), two BA's, 1988. *Principal occupation*: Museum curator, American Indian arts consultant. *Address*: P.O. Box 295, Orick, CA 95555 (707) 488-3545. *Affiliations*: Curator, End of the Trail Museum, Klamath, CA, 1993-98; consultant of Native American arts, Orick, CA, 1979-. *Other professional posts*: Assistant director of California Indian Project, Lowie Museum of Anthropology (Berkeley, CA), 1988-89; director/curator, Clarke Memorial Museum, Eureka, CA (7 years); Redwood National Park, Patrick's Point State Park, and Del Norte County Historical Society - curated all collections (2 1/2 years). *Community activities*: Past vice president, YWCA; past member of Humboldt County Status of Women Commission; past president of Humboldt Open Door Clinic; past chair of Women's History Month for Humboldt County; past member, City of Arcata Design Assistance Committee; current member, Alice Spinas Basketry Collection Committee; board member, SPPLIA, Sumeg Yurok Indian Village. *Membership*: Phi Kappa Phi. Interests: "Collecting American Indian art & books; have traveled in Europe, Canada, Mexico, Caribbean & the USA. Have made numerous trips to Europe to view & study American Indian art in museum collections." Curated Exhibits: "Elizabeth Conrad Hickox: Baskets From the Center of the World," Reese Bullen Gallery, Humboldt State University, 1/90; "From Classic to Contemporary: The Basketry of Northwestern California," Muckenthaler Cultural Center, Fullerton, CA, 5-7/91; "From Women's Hands: The Basketry of Lena Reed McCovey and Ethel Jones Williams" Reese Bullen Gallery, Humboldt State University, 11/92; "Her Mind Made Up: Weaving Caps the Indian Way", Reese Bullen Gallery, Humboldt State University 4/97; among others. Published works: Editor, The Hover Collection of Karuk Baskets (Clarke Memorial Museum, 1985); co-authored with Ron Johnson, "From Women's Hands: The Basketry of Lena Reed McCovey and Ethel Jones Williams," (Humboldt State University, 1992); Her Mind Made Up: Weaving Caps the Indian Way," with Ron Johnson (Humboldt State University, 1997).

MARKS, IRVIN (Miwuk)
(former tribal chairperson)
Affiliation & Address: Jackson Rancheria Band of Miwuk Indians, P.O. Box 1090, Jackson, CA 95642 (209) 223-1935.

MARKS, PATRICIA ANN 1954-
(attorney, lobbyist, consultant)
Born March 2, 1954, Brockport, N.Y. Education: S.U.N.Y. at Brockport, BS, 1976; Georgetown University Law Center, JD, 1985. *Address*: 15992 AE Mullinix Rd., Woodbine, MD 21797. Partner, Fredericks Peebles & Morgan, LLP, 401 9th St. NW, Washington, DC 20004 (202) 450-4887. E-mail: pmarks@ndnlaw.com. *Affiliations*: Personal staff member, U.S. Senator James Abourezk, Washington, DC, 1975-76 (during this period, Sen. Abourezk was chairman of the Senate Indian Affairs Subcommittee of the Senate Interior and Insular Affairs Committee); professional staff member, American Indian Policy Review Commission, Washington, DC, 1976-77; legislative assistant, U.S. Senate Select Committee on Indian Affairs, Washington, DC, 1977-79; vice president & co-founder, Karl A. Funke & Associates, Inc., Washington, DC, 1979- (a lobbying & consulting firm which represents Indian tribes, national Indian organizations, business and local governments); Of Counsel, Fredericks Peebles & Morgan, LLP, 2009-present. *Practice areas*: Tribal Government; Tribal sovereignty & self-determination; Gaming law; Jurisdiction; Land-into-Trust; Federal grants & contracts; economic development & commercial transactions; legislative & administrative representation. As a tribal attorney, Ms. Marks has drafted numerous tribal codes & ordinances, negotiated a variety of types of funding agreements & self-determination contracts, worked with tribally owned companies on government contracting, negotiated state & tribal agreements, and drafted and secured the passage of federal legislation & amendments to existing law. She has a 25-year history of working with the Senate Indian Affairs Committee, the House Committee on Resources, the House & Senate Appropriations Committees & numerous other legislative bodies. *Other professional post*: Co-founder & officer, AAA Roofing Co. *Memberships*: National Congress of American Indians; ABA Student Bar Association. *Awards, honors*: National Indian Health Board Award for Service, 1983. *Interests*: "Indian health; Indian legislative specialist; Indian Child Welfare Act; national Indian budget issues; Indian economic development." *Published work*: American Indian Policy Review Commission Final Report, U.S. Congress.

MARKSTROM, CAROL A.
(professor of Native American Studies)
Education: University of Minnesota, BS (Family Relationships), 1981; North Dakota State University, MS (Child Development & Family Relations), 1985; Utah State University, PhD (Developmental Psychology), 1988. *Affiliation &*

Address: Professor (1993-present) of Child Development & Family Studies, Department of Technology, Learning, & Culture, College of Human Resources & Education, West Virginia University, 506G Allen Hall, Morgantown, WV 26506 (304) 293-3344. E-mail: carol.markstrom@mail.wvu.edu. *Other professional posts*: Professor of Native American Studies (NAS), WVU (former interim NAS Program Coordinator; member, Native American Studies Committee. *Professional Interests*: American Indian history, beliefs, and ritual practices; the study of indigenous models of human development and the roles of rituals as mechanisms designed to promote optimal outcomes across the life span, adolescence in particular. *Past professional posts*: Taught at the Sisseton-Wahpeton Tribal College, SD, 1982-85; academic appointment at the University of Gueph in Ontario, Canada, 1988-92. During her professional development leave in 1999, Carol stayed on the Navajo Nation in New Mexico and Arizona and did the same on the San Carlos Apache Nation in Arizona in 2007 where she consulted at the high school working with troubled youth. *Published works*: Empowerment of North American Indian Girls: Ritual Expressions at Puberty (University of Nebraska Press, 2012)

MARKWARDT, HOLLY JEAN (Ojibway) 1970- (American Indian admissions counselor)
Born October 27, 1970, Virginia, Minn. *Education*: St. Cloud State University, B.A., 1994; University of Minnesota, M.A., 1994. *Principal occupation*: American Indian admissions counselor. *Address*: 8748 Kilbirnie Ter., Brooklyn Park, MN 55443. *Affiliation*: University of Minnesota, Minneapolis, MN.

MARLEY, TENNILLE (White Mountain Apache)
(professor of American Indian studies)
Affiliation & Address: Assistant Professor, American Indian Studies Program, College of Liberal Arts & Sciences, MC: 4603, Arizona State University, Tempe, AZ 85287 (480) 965-8308. E-mail: tennille.marley@asu.edu.

MARNEY, MARGIE E. (Cherokee) 1948-
(educator)
Born February 25, 1948, Alva, Okla. *Education*: Phillips University (Enid, OK), B.S., 1970; University of Northwestern Oklahoma (Alva, OK), Masters of Reading & L.D. Educ., 1983; Oklahoma State University, Administrative Certificate, 1990. *Address*: Enid Public Schools, 2102 Beverly Dr., Enid, OK 73703 (580) 242-7185. E-mail: mmarney@ionet.net. *Affiliation*: Elementary Principal & Director of Indian Education, Enid Public Schools, Enid, OK, 1970-present. *Other professional posts*: Professor, Phillips University; Enid higher education instructor. *Community activities*: "Keeper of the Plains" scholarship officer & board member; president & board member, Cherokee Reading Council; Intertribal Club member. *Memberships*: National Education Assn; Oklahoma Education Assn; International Reading Assn; Oklahoma Reading Assn; Cherokee Strip Reading Council (president, 1985-); National Council on Indian Education; NIEA member; Oklahoma Indian Education Assn. *Interests*: "Avid reader and learner; parent of four active children in education; educator of kindergarten to college level."

MARQUES, ALVIN S. (Lemhi Shoshone)
(tribal chairperson)
Affiliation & Address: Chairperson, Ely Shoshone Tribe, 400 Newe View Dr., Ely, NV 89301 (775) 289-3013.

MARR, ALEXANDER BRIER
(Native American Collection curator)
Education: Beloit College, BA (Art History); Graduate degree in visual and cultural studies from the University of Rochester, He's completing his doctoral dissertation as a Ph.D. candidate at the University of Rochester *Affiliation & Address*: Assistant Curator for Native American Art (January 2016-present) St. Louis Art Museum, One Finne Arts Dr., Forest Park, St. Louis, MO 63110 (314) 721-0072; E-mail: orders@slam.org. *Other professional posts*: Board secretary, Native American Art Studies Association (2011-present), *Past professional posts*: Recently served as Mellon Pre-Doctoral Fellow in Native American Art at the Portland Art Museum in Oregon; and has participated in the Smithsonian Institution's Summer Institute in Museum Anthropology and the Otsego Institute for Native American Art. *Published works*: His article, "Scales of Vision: Kiowa Model Tipis and the Mooney Commission," was recently published in *Winterthur Portfolio* and he is finalizing an extensively revised edition of *Art of the North American Indians: The Thaw Collection at the Fenimore Museum* as co-editor. *Awards, honors*: He is the recipient of numerous awards, including those from the American Philosophical Society and the Center for the Advanced Study in the Visual Arts, National Gallery of Art.

MARSHALL, JOSEPH M., III (Sicangu Lakota) 1946-
(Lakota historian, educator, author, speaker/lecturer)
Born on the Rosebud Indian Reservation in S.D. *Affiliation*: Website: www.josephmarshall.com; www.thunderdreamers.com. E-mail: jmmail@ thunderdreamers.com. *Awards, honors*: One of the founders of Sinte Gleska University (1971) on the Rosebud Reservation He is one of the Charter Board

members; recipient of the 2008 PEN/Beyond Margins Award for "The Day the World Ended at Little Bighorn." *Published works*: Co-author, Soldiers Falling Into Camp: The Battles at the Rosebud & the Little Bighorn (Affiliated Writers of America, 1992); Winter of the Holy Iron (Red Crane Books, 1994); On Behalf of the Wolf and the First Peoples (Red Crane Books, 1995); The Dance House: Stories from Rosebud (Red Crane Books, 1998); The Lakota Way: Stories & Lessons for Living (Viking, 2002); The Journey of Crazy Horse: A Lakota History (Viking, 2004); Walking With Grandfather: The Wisdom of Lakota Elders (Sounds True, Inc., 2005); Keep Going: The Art of Perseverance (Sterling Publishing, 2006); The Day the World Ended at Little Bighorn: A Lakota History (Viking, 2007); Hundred in the Hand: A Novel (Fulcrum Publishing, 2008); The Long Knives Are Crying: A Novel (Fulcrum Publishing, 2009); The Power of Four: Leadership Lessons of Crazy Horse (Sterling Publishing, 2009); To You We Shall Return: Lessons About Our Planet from the Lakota (Sterling Ethos, 2010); Returning to the Lakota Way: Old Values to Save the Modern Work (Hay House, 2012), a sequel to The Lakota Way of Strength & Courage: Stories & Lessons for Living (Viking, 2002); Life Lessons from the Bow & Arrow (Sounds True); The Archer (online novel).

MARSHALL-BRINGS PLENTY, CARLA RAE (*Oyate Wowakiye Wi*)
(Cheyenne River Sioux) 1966-
(education, graphics)
Born May 7, 1966, Bitberg, Germany (USAF). *Education*: Black Hills State College (Spearfish, SD), Associate of Science, 1987. *Principal occupation*: Education, graphics. *Affiliation & Address*: Cultural Education Coordinator, The Intertribal Bison Cooperative, 1560 Concourse Dr., Rapid City, SD 57703 (605) 394-9730. Carla is currently coordinating the development of a comprehensive elementary & secondary education curriculum concerning all aspects of the North American buffalo. *Affiliations*: HP/DP Task Force Coordinator, Cheyenne River Sioux Tribe, Eagle Butte, SD, 1990-91; Indian Country Today/Lakota Times, Rapid City, SD (classified advertising representative, 1992-93; advertising sales director, 1993); administrative assistant, editor, education coordinator, Intertribal Bison Cooperative, Rapid City, SD, 1993-present. *Awards, honors*: Crazy Horse Memorial Scholarship; Kevin Whirlwind Horse Memorial. *Community activities*: "I was YMCA Chapter Coordinator for the Iron Lightning Community, located on the Cheyenne River Sioux Reservation. This volunteer work involved planning & coordinating activities for the youth in the community; also I was secretary for the two powwow committees, the Iron Lighting Community & Lakota Ominiciya at Black Hills State."

MARTIN, AURENE M. (Bad River Band Lake Suprior Chippewa)
(attorney)
Education: University of Wisconsin-Madison, BA, 1989; University of Wisconsin Law School, JD, 1993. *Affiliation & Address*: President, Spirit Rock Consuting, Inc., 9 Forrest St., Alexandria, VA 22305 (202) 255-3220 Fax (703) 535-7567. E-mail: amartin@spiritrockinc.com. Aurene has extensive experience in Federal Indian law & policy, having served in several tribal & Federal key government positions. She represents Indian tribes on Federal Indian law & policy issues, specializing in the areas of tribal land acquisition and the fee to trust process, tribal gaming & general tribal government issues. *Past professional posts*: Counselor to the Assistant Secretary of Indian Affairs; Principal Deputy Assistant Secretary; acting Assistant Secretary for Indian Affairs; Senior Counsel to the Senate Committee on Indian Affairs chaired by Senator Ben Nighthorse Campbell (R-CO), where she had a key role in developing legislation involving tribes, particularly in the areas of gaming health care; director of Congressional & Public Affairs for the National Indian Gaming Commission, Washington, DC; Aurene began her career as senior staff attorney of the Oneida Tribe of Indians of Wisconsnin (five years).

MARTIN, BRUCE W. (*Ta-ma-tet*) (Delaware of Oklahoma) 1962-
(Indian center executive director)
Born August 15, 1962, Webb City, Mo. *Education*: College High School, Bartlesville, OK. *Principal occupation*: Indian center executive director. *Address*: 1423 Haskell Ave., Lawrence, KS 66046 (785) 841-7202. E-mail: bmartin@pelathe.org. Website: www.pelathe.org. *Affiliation*: Executive director, Pelathe Community Resources Center, Lawrence, KS. *Other professional posts*: Director, Haskell Indian Nations University Upward Bound; director, New Dawn Native Dancers. *Awards, honors*: 1997 & 1999 Arena Director (3rd Favorite) in Oklahoma by Oklahoma Indian Times; 1999 Native American Parent of the Year (KANAE). *Community activities*: Co-sponsor, Lawrence High School, Native American Club; co-director, "Battle of the Plains" Youth Powwow Contest. *Memberships*: New Dawn Native Dancers; Intertribal Indian Club of Tulsa; Lenape Gourd Dance Society. *Interests*: "I have served on several pow-wow committees & enjoy traveling to powwow & stomp dances."

MARTIN, CONNIE SUE M.
(attorney)
Eduation: Ohio State University, BS, 1987; Rutgers University Institute of Animal Behavior, Graduate Fellow, 1987-88; University of Hawaii at Manoa, MA, 1993; Seattle University School of Law, JD, 1996. Affiliation: Attorney & Shareholder, Schwabe, Williamson & Wyatt, 1420 5th Ave., Suite 3400, Seattle,

WA 98101 (206) 407-1556. E-mail: csmartin@schwabe.com. Connie has 15 years of environmental law experience focusing on environmental and natural resource litigation. She has special expertise in matters involving Indian tribes, especially resource protection & natural resource damages claims, and is regarded as one of the leading oractitioners of environmental Indian law in Washington State. Ms. Martin has assisted tribes in addressing solid & hazardous waste cleanup. She has drafted & enforced tribal superfund ordinances for two tribes and assisted tribal govenments in managing public notice & comment on controversial projects, and prepared public comment on proposed action by federal agencies. In 2006, she worked with the National Tribal Environmental Council's Superfund Working Group to develop policies for enhancing the role of tribes in superfund and in managing environmental programs on Indian reservations, and assisted tribal governments in setting policy relating to the management of waste cleanup & disposal in areas where traditional practices are carried out. Ms. Martinn writes & speaks frequently on environmental & Indian law issues and is a frequent lecturer at the University of Washington School of Law & Seattle University School of Law, and has been adjunct professor at the University of Washington & Antioch University. Honors & awards: "Best Lawyers in America" – Environmental Law, 2010-11, Environmental Litigation, 2011; "Washington Law & Politics" Super Lawyer – Environmental Law, 2011.

MARTIN, DANIEL (Assiniboine Sioux)
(senior program associate)
Education: Haskell Indian Nations University, BS (Business Administration). *Affiliation & Address*: Senior Program Associate, Cherokee Preservation Foundation, 71 John Crowe Hill Rd., P.O. Box 504, Cherokee, NC 28719. (828) 497-5550. E-mail: dmartin@cpfdn.org. Daniel is responsible for the foudation's support of entrpreneurship & environmentl sustainability programs. *Past professional posts*: Vangent, Inc. & The World Company.

MARTIN, HELEN SMOKER (Eastern Cherokee)
(artist)
Address: 1663 Well Rd., Marble, NC 28905 (888) 527-1777. Website: www. artistsites.org/helensmokermartin/ E-mail: helensmokeremartin@yahoo.com. *Artwork*: Paintings; portraits, pen & ink, beadwork, porcupine quillwork; mural; crafts.

MARTIN, JACK B.
(associate professor)
Affiliation: Director of Linguistics & Associate Professor of English, College of William & Mary, VA. *Published works*: A Dictionary of Creek/Muskogee, co-author with Margaret Mauldin; Totkv Mocvse/New Fire: Creek Folktales, edited and trans. with Margaret Mauldin & Juanita McGirt.

MARTIN, JAMES T. (Poarch Band Creek)
(Indian tribal enterprises president & CEO))
Affiliation & Address: President & CEO, Creek Indian Enterprises Development Authority (CIEDA), Poarch Band Creek Indians,, 5811 Jack Springs Rd., Atmore, AL 36502 (251) 368-9136. E-mail: jmartin@pci-nsn.gov. Mr. Martin has held leadership positions for nearly 30 years beginning in 1986 as the tribal administrator for the Poarch Band of Creek Indians. Today his leadership continues as President/CEO of Creek Indian Enterprises Development Authority (CIEDA). In his current position, Mr. Martin provides CIEDA and its enterprises with executive direction and leadership to a staff of over two hundred. Reporting directly to the CIEDA Board of Directors and Tribal Council, Mr. Martin oversees high-level strategies and decision making, as well as, the overall operations and resources for CIEDA and its enterprises. *Past professional posts*: Tribal administrator, Poarch Creek Indians, Atmore, AL, 1986-95; Executive Director, United South & Eastern Tribes (USET), Inc., Nashville, TN; president, Calumet Development Corp., Nashville, TN. Served for 8 years as a member of the USET Board of Directors, representing the Poarch Creek Indians; current member of the Federal Advisory Committee for HHS/DOI; current member of Indian Health Service, Contract Support Work Group; current member of the 638 Re-Invention Lab for Self-Determination Contracts under both Indian Health Service and the Bureau of Indian Affairs.

MARTIN, JOYCE
(associate librarian; data center curator)
Education: Arizona State University, MA (Anthropology/Museum Studies), 1997; University of Arizona, MA (Information & Library Science), 2007. *Address* & *Affiliation*: Associate Librarian & Curator (2006-present), Labriola National American Indian Data Center (1999-present), ASU Libraries, Hayden Library, 2nd Floor, Box 871006, Tempe, AZ 85287 (480) 965-0298. E-mail: joyce.martin@asu.edu. As an advisor to the University of Arizona's School of Information Resources and Library Science (SIRLS) digital information management program, Joyce provides input on new directions for the library profession. She further contributes to the future of the profession by providing internship opportunities to emerging library professionals. Under Joyce's leadership the Labriola Center entered a formal partnership to provide internships for SIRLS Knowledge River Program students to foster understanding of library and information issues from the perspectives of Latino and Native American populations. The author of several successful grant proposals, Joyce recently collaborated with the ASU American Indian Policy Institute and the Inter Tribal Council of Arizona (ITCA) on a Library Services and Technology Act grant to document and preserve the legacy of ITCA, one of the most significant tribal organizations in the state. Joyce teaches in the areas of history of collecting and sociocultural anthropology. She speaks at national and regional conferences about the importance of diversity in libraries and archives, and recently authored chapters in *Library Services for Multicultural Patrons to Encourage Library Use* and *How to Thrive as a Solo Librarian*. Focused on outreach and relationship building, Joyce works with several ASU academic departments, American Indian programs, and the Heard Museum to coordinate the biannual *Simon Ortiz and Labriola Center Lecture on Indigenous Land, Culture, and Community*, which attracts world renowned speakers such as Wilma Mankiller and Leslie Marmon Silko to ASU. Joyce worked with Distinguished Foundation Professor of History Dr. Donald Fixico to establish the *Labriola Center American Indian National Book Award*, an award which encourages & rewards cross-disciplinary scholarship relevant to contemporary American Indian communities. *Other professional post*: Editor, Labriola National American Indian Data Center Newsletter, *Memberships*: Arizona Library Association; Society of Southwestern Archivists, where she is on the publications committee.

MARTIN, MICHAEL E. (Tonkawa)
(former tribal vice president)
Affiliation & Address: Former Vice President, Tonkawa Tribe of Oklahoma, 1 Rush Buffalo Rd., Tonkawa, OK 74653 (580) 628-2561.

MARTIN, PETER J. (White Earth Chippewa) 1937-
(federal government administrator)
Born July 21, 1937, White Earth Indian Reservation, White Earth, Minn. *Education*: University of New Mexico, BA, 1967. *Principal occupation*: Federal government administrator-Indian affairs. Resides in White Earth, MN. *Affiliations*: Administrative manager, Albuquerque Indian School, 1966-1969; administrative director, Institute of American Indian Arts, Santa Fe, 1969-70; executive assistant, 1970, chief, 1970-72, Plant Management Engineering Center, B.I.A., Denver, CO; chief, Indian Technical Assistance Center, Denver, 1972-77; program specialist, Muskogee Area Office, BIA, 1977-80; owner, Indian consultant business, American Indian Programs, White Earth, MN, 1980-. *Memberships*: Anishnabe Akeeng (The People's Land); National Congress of American Indians; Minnesota Indian Contactor's Association; Minnesota Democratic Farm Labor Party - National Roster of Buy Indian Contractor's. *Awards, honors*: Certificate of Superior Performance, Dept. of the Interior, BIA (for service in connection with the placement of 220 Job Corps employees, July, 1969); Dept. of the Interior, Bureau of Indian Affairs, 20-year Service Pin, April, 1978. *Interests*: Interested in and work for betterment of all American Indians; presently engaged as nationwide consultant in American Indian Programs (sole proprietorship enterprise); have visited over 200 Indian reservations and worked with respective tribal councils and program heads; research, writing articles and books, and study of American Indian tribes and involvement with Indian-Federal-State-Municipal programs and relationships.

MARTIN, ROBERT G. (Cherokee)
(college president)
Education: University of Kansas, EdD, 1994. Professor Martin is a graduate of the Dept. of Interior's Senior Executive Development Program, the John Heinz II School of Public Policy & Management, Carnegie-Mellon University, and the Center for Creative Leadership's Development Program. *Address & Affiliation*: President (2007-present), Institute of American Indian Arts, 83 Avan Nu Po Rd., Santa Fe, NM 87505 (505) 424-2301. E-mail: rmartin@iaia.edu. *Past professional posts*: President, Southwestern Polytechnic Institute, Albuquerque, NM, 1981-89; president, Haskell Indian Nations University, Lawrence, KS, 1989-99; professor, American Indian Studies (AIS) Program, The University of Arizona, Tucson, AZ, 1999-2008. *Other professional posts*: Member, Board of Trustees, American Indian College Fund, Denver, CO; member, Director's Council of Public Representatives for the National Institutes of Health. *Past professional posts*: Member of the Indian Nations At Risk Task Force and on the Advisory Board for the White House Conference on Indian Education.

MARTIN, ROBERT (Cahuilla)
(tribal chairperson)
Affiliation & Address: Chairperson, Morongo Band of Mission Indians, 12700 Pumarra Rd., Banning, CA 92220 (951) 849-4697.

MARTIN, RUSSELL (Tonkawa)
(tribal president)
Education: Northwestern Oklahoma State University, BS (Business Education), 1989. Affiliation & *Address*: President, Tonkawa Tribe of Oklahoma, 1 Rush Buffalo Rd., Tonkawa, OK 74653 (580) 628-2561. *Past professional posts*: Russell has worked as the CEO Seminole Nation Gaming, General Manager of

Native Lights Casino, Chairman Tonkawa Tribal Gaming Commission, and as a school teacher/coach for 18 years.

MARTIN, STEVEN
(director of Native American student affairs)
Affiliation & Address: Director, Native American Student Affairs Center, The University of Arizona, 1439 E. Helen St., Robert L. Nugent Bldg., Rm. 203, P.O. Box 210040, Tucson, AZ 85721 (520) 621-3835 E-mail: stevenm1@email.arizona.edu. *Past professional post*: Director, Native American Student Center College of Letters, Arts & Social Sciences, University of Idaho, Moscow, ID

MARTIN, VARENE (Muscogee Creek)
(senior vice president marketing)
Education: Oklahoma State University (BS (Finance). *Affiliation & Address*: Senior Vice President Marketing, Pacific American Securities LLC, 9191 Towne Centre Dr., San Diego, CA 92122 (619) 322-9285. E-mail: varene@nafoa.org. *Other professional post*: 1ˢᵗ Vice President, Native American Finance Officers Association, Washington, DC.

MARTIN, WILLIAM "BILL" (Tlingit)
(Alaskan tribal council president)
Affiliation: Central Council of Tlingit & Haida Indian Tribes of Alaska, 320 W. Willoughby Ave., #300, Juneau, AK 99801 (800) 344-1432; (907) 586-1432. E-mail: bmartin@ccthita.org

MARTINE, CYNTHIA "CINDY" (Jicarilla Apache/Navajo) 1964-
(manufacturing engineer)
Born November 3, 1964, Gallup, N.M. *Education*: New Mexico State University, BS, 1987. *Principal occupation*: Manufacturing engineer. *Address*: 685 N. Greece Rd., Rochester, NY 14626 (716) 392-8397. *Affiliation*: Eastman Kodak Co., Rochester, NY 1988-. *Community activities*: spokesman, Native American Council at Kodak; Native American Cultural Center, Rochester, NY; Friends of Ganodagan, Victor, NY (Board of Trustee member); co-chair, Native American Women's Recognition Event 1994. *Membership*: American Indian Science & Engineering Society (AISES) (board member, treasurer). *Interests*: "Very interested in helping young Indian students become interested in science, math, engineering. Have done numerous workshops on science projects for young students (grades K-8). Recently (I) did a workshop for young women (grades 6-8) in expanding Your Horizons in Science & Math. I strongly believe that our Indian people are becoming more prominent in their communities; reaching out to the young people and introducing opportunities for our young people in all arenas. I truly enjoy speaking to young people about opportunities in science & engineering and doing science projects with young students. I believe our young people can make great strides in any fields they choose because they have support systems in place to help them, such as AISES."

MARTINE, DAVID BUNN (*Chee/Waukus*) (Shinnecock/Montauk (Algonquian)-Chiricahua Apache) 1960-
(artist, poet, wood carver; museum director/curator)
Born June 11, 1960, Southampton, N.Y. *Education*: University of Oklahoma, BFA, 1982; Institute of American Indian Arts, 1983; Central State University, MEd, 1984. *Address*: P.O. Box 1285, Shinnecock Reservation, Southampton, NY 11969 (631) 287-6931. E-mail: cswmartine@hotmail.com. Website: www.amerinda.org. *Affiliation*: Director, Shinnecock Nation Museum Cultural Center Complex; director, Channel 25 Cable Vision, "Voices of Native America," Shinnecock Indian Tribe, Southampton, NY. *Other professional posts*: Professional artist - oil paintings - wood carvings; chairperson, American Indian Artists (Amerinda), New York, NY; Museum curator/exhibit designer, Shinnecock Nation Cultural Center & Museum, 2001; Book Illustrations: The Montaukett Indians of Eastern Long Island, Syracuse University, 2001; Fine artist; lecturer, Cooper Union, New York, NY, 1989-92. *Exhibits*: Rogers Memorial Library, Southampton, NY, 2001; "Whaling: A Cultural Odyssey", Sag Harbor Whaling & Historical Museum, NY, 2001; "Rider With No Horse," Artists Collective, Native Americans of New York City Area; The Native American Experience: Long Island, New York & Beyond, "We Are All Connected" - New York, NY, 1997. *Selected Commissions*: Children's Mural, Challenge America Grant joint project, Family Preservation Center, Shinnecock Reservation, Southampton, NY 2002; "The Peaceful People and the First Nations Mural," American Friends Service Committee, c/o Amerinda, Inc., New York, NY 2001; Shinnecock Indian Wigwam Replica, full-size scale exhibit, "Treasures of Long Island" exhibition, Museums at Stony Brook, NY, 1998. *Community activities*: Member of the Governance Committee of the Shinnecock Indian Nation Tribal Council. *Membership*: North Sea Poetry Scene (poetry club); Suffolk County Archaeological Association. *Interests*: Playing piano; writing poetry; teaching; environmental preservation movement; civil rights issues of Native American community; host, "Voices of Native America" Cablevision, Channel 25, Riverhead, NY; proposal reader, evaluator, Administration for Native Americans, Dept. of HHS, Washington, DC, 1991. *Biographical source*: "The Shinnecock Indians: A Culture History," (Ginn, 1984).

MARTINE-ALONZO, NANCY R. (Navajo/Yaqui)
(Indian education)
Address & Affiliation: Director, Indian Education Program, Albuquerque Public Schools, 6400 Uptown Blvd., NE, Suite 460W, Albuquerque, NM 87110 (505) 884-6392. E-mail: alonzo_nm@aps.edu. *Other professional post*: Member, Board of Directors, National Indian Education Association.

MARTINEZ, CODY J. (Kumeyaay Diegueno)
(tribal chairperson)
Born and raised on the Sycuan Indian Reservation *Affiliation & Address*: Chairperson, Sycuan Band of Kumeyaay Diegueno, 5459 Sycuan Rd., El Cajon, CA 92019 (619) 445-6002. Prior to his election as Chairman, Martinez worked for the tribal community development department. He played an instrumental role in developing new & improved infrastructure for the residents of the reservation by guiding an $18 million capital project and securing federal grant funds. With conservation and the protection of natural resources being close to his heart, Martinez helped create a first-in-the-nation Natural Resource Management Plan for nearly 1500 acres of land acquired by the Sycuan Band. Through this plan, Sycuan entered into unique and one-of-a-kind partnerships with the County of San Diego, US Fish & Wildlife Service, and the state of California to preserve and protect sensitive wildlife habitat while ensuring the tribe's future stability by providing room for future economic development and protection of cultural & archaeological resources. Chairman Martinez also served as Tribal Treasurer from 2007-2010. Prior to his service on the tribal council as Treasurer, Chairman Martinez served on the Sycuan Gaming Commission. As the primary regulator of the gaming operations, Chairman Martinez helped ensure strict compliance with tribal ordinances, the tribal-state compact & federal rules & regulations. Protecting the assets of the tribe while preserving the integrity of the gaming experience for customers was always front and center. Chairman Martinez is a fourth generation descendent of Soloman Paipa, an original allottee when the Sycuan reservation was established in 1875.,

MARTINEZ, DAVID (Gila River Pima)
(professor of American Indian studies)
Education: University of Rhode Island, BA; University of Arizona, MA (American Indian Studies); SUNY, New York, PhD (Philosophy), 1997. *Address & Affiliation*: Associate Professor of American Indian Studies, College of Liberal Arts & Sciences, Arizona State University, MC: 4603, Tempe, AZ 85287 (480) 727-9818. E-mail: david.martinez.3@asu.edu. His areas of concentration are American Indian intellectual history, art & aesthetics, and folklore studies. *Past professional post*: Assistant Professor of Philosophy & American Indian Religions, American Indian Studies Department, College of Liberal Arts, University of Minnesota, Minneapolis, MN. *Published works*: Dakota Philosopher: Charles Eastman & American Indian Thought (Minnesota Historical Society, 2009); editor, The American Indian Intellectual Tradition: An Anthology of Writings from 1772 to 1972 (Cornell University Pressm 2011) numerous articles in scholarly journals.

MARTINEZ, DONNA (Cherokee)
(professor & chair of ethnic studies)
Ediucation: PhD (Ethnic Studies). *Affiliation & Address*: Chairperson & Professor of Ethnic Studies, Department of Ethnic Studies, University of Colorado, Campus Box 134, P.O. Box 173364, Denver, CO 80217 (303) 315-7209; E-mail: donna.martinez@ucdenver.edu *Published works*: co-author with Jennifer Williams Bordeaux, 50 Events That Shaped American Indian History: An Encyclopedia of the American Mosaic, 2 Vols. (ABC-CLIO, 2017).

MARTINEZ, RODGER (Navajo)
(former tribal president)
Affiliation & Address: Former President, Ramah Navajo Chapter, HCR61 Box 13, Ramah, NM 87321 (505) 775-7140.

MARTINEZ, SONIA (Pascua Yaqui)
Sonia Martinez was recognized as NABA-AZ's Member of the Year. The Member of the Year Award is given to a member with a significant history of service and dedication to NABA-AZ and its goals. A member of the Pascua Yaqui Tribe of Arizona, Ms. Martinez is the owner of her own law firm in Mesa, Arizona. She works primarily in Indian Country, with a focus on family law, criminal justice, and dependency. Ms. Martinez graduated magna cum laude from Southwestern Law School as a John J. Schumacher Minority Leader Scholar and earned special United States Congressional recognition for "Outstanding and Invaluable Public Service to the Community" in 2004. Ms. Martinez began her career in California practicing complex environmental litigation before moving to Arizona, where she worked as a Special Prosecutor for the Ak-Chin Nation and as a Litigation Associate at Jones Skelton & Hochuli P.L.C. in Phoenix. Ms. Martinez is active in the Arizona State Bar, where she has co-chaired the Committee on Women and Minorities in the Law, served as Chair of 2013 Minority Bar Convention, and graduated from the State Bar Leadership Institute. Ms. Martinez currently serves as President of NABA-AZ.

MASAYESVA, VERNON (Hopi)
(executive director)
Affiliation & Address: Executive Director, Black Mesa Trust, P.O. Box 33, Kykotsmovi, AZ 86039. Website: www.blackmesatrust.org. E-mail: kuuyl@aol.com. *Past professional post*: Former chairperson, Hopi Tribe.

MASAYESVA, VICTOR, JR. (Hopi) 1951-
(film producer/director)
Born in Hotevilla, Ariz. IN 1951. *Education*: Princeton University, BA, 1973; University of Arizona (graduate studies). *Principal occupation*: Film producer/director. *Address*: P.O. Box 747, Hotevilla, AZ 86030. Victor has created a body of video & photographic work that represents the culture & traditions of Native Americans - particularly the Hopi of Southwest Arizona - through poetic visualizations. He employs high tech computer animation & graphics in lyrical translations of Hopi myths, rituals & history. Articulating the richness of his heritage in his own language, he allows the Hopi voice to be heard. *Videos produced, directed & photographed*: "Hopiit" (lyrical work observing Hopi cultural activities through the cycle of the seasons), 15 mins, 1982; "Itam Hakim, Hopiit" (poetic visualization of Hopi philosophy & prophesy - myths, religion, legends & history of the Hopi people), 58 mins, 1985; "Ritual Clowns" (the traditions & myths of their emergence in the plazas of Southwest Native American communities), 18 mins, 1988; "Pot Starr" (addresses ceramic designs, computer analysis & interpretation), 6 mins, 1990; "Siskyavi - The Place of Chasms" (presents the ceramic traditions of Native Americans), 28 mins, 1991. *Awards, honors*: His numerous awards include fellowships from the Ford Foundation, the Rockefeller Foundation, and the Southwest Association on Indian Affairs; and grants from the National Endowment for the Arts, and the Arizona Commission on the Arts; he was guest artist and artist-in-residence at the School of the Art Institute of Chicago, Princeton University, & the Yellowstone Summer Film/Video Institute, Montana State University. His videotapes have been exhibited internationally at festivals & institutions including the Native American Film & Video Festival, New York; the Museum of Modern Art, New York; World Wide Video Festival, The Hague, Netherlands; Whitney Museum of American Art Biennial, New York; San Francisco Art Institute; and the American Indian Contemporary Arts "Festival 2000," San Francisco.

MASHONEE, JANA (Lumbee)
(singer)
Address: Jana, Inc., P.O. Box 4866, Greenwich, CT 06830. CDs - New Moon Born; American Indian Christmas; American Indian Story (2006, Grammy nomination); Flash of a Firefly. Jana Poster available, $5 plus $2. shipping. *Community activities*: Jana's Kids Scholarships, established in 2002, benefits Native American youth. Jana's Native Youth Motivational Presentation. Her blend of music, dance & motivational speaking. *Awards, honors*: Best Pop Artist for 2001-2002; Song of the Year for the 2002-2003; Female Artist of the Year, 2003-2004; Album of the Year, 2006-2007 & Best Producer (Stephan Galfas & Alex Salzman) for 2006-07). Nammy (Native American Music Award) Winner for Song of the Year & video, "A Change Is Gonna Come." Jana was the first Native American female to land on the Billboard dance charts.

MASIEL, ANDREW, SR. (Luiseno)
(organization chairperson)
Education: University of California, Davis, BS (Environmental Planning & Business Development). *Affiliation & Address*: Council Member, Pechanga Band of Luiseno Indians, P.O. Box 1477, Temecula, CA 92593 (951) 676-2768. *Other professional post*: Chairperson, Native American Caucus of the California Democratic Party, 1401 21st St., Suite 100, Sacramento, CA 95814. Mr. Masiel was first elected to the Pechanga Tribal Council in 1982 and served until 1986. He then erved on the council from 1996-2000. In February 2009, he was elected once again, in a Special Election, to the Council. He is a regular speaker about tribal gaming, education, economic development, and social development at forums hosted by the UCLA School of Law, San Francisco State University, UC Riverside, San Diego State University and the University of Southern California. *Past professional posts*: Tribal Administrator, Soboba Band of Luiseno Indians, the Pauma Band of Mission Indians, and the Pechanga Tribe. Andrew also served as a Business Manager of the Pala Indian Tribe, & Planning Director for the Reservation Transportation Authority (RTA), a consortium of 22 Southern California Tribes. In 1998, Mr. Masiel co-founded & chaired the first Native American Caucua for the California Democratic Party. In 1987, he was appointed by Governor George Deukmejian to the California Public Utilities Commission. He was treasurer to the California Nations Indian Gaming Association, and chaired the IDRS' Advisory Committee to the Youth Caucus; served on the Board of Directors of California Indian Legal Services for eleven years; served with the National Center for American Indians Enterprise Development for 11 years.

MASSE, CHRISTINE M.
(attorney; partner)
Education: University of Illinois, BA (Business Administration), 1996; University of Washington School of Law, JD, 1999) *Affiliation & Address*: Miller Nash Graham & Dunn LLP, 2801 Alaskan Way, Suite 300, Seattle, WA 98121 (206) 777-7427. E-mail: Christine.masse@millerdunn.com. She Joined Miller Nash Graham & Dunn in 1999. She is the leader of the government and regulatory affairs practice group & specializes in representing businesses in highly regulated industries with their transactional, regulatory, & public policy needs. Chris also leads Miller Nash Graham & Dunn's tribal team, providing counsel to various Northwest Native American tribes and organizations on gaming, regulatory, real property, construction, financing, tax, liquor, marijuana, & economic development issues. She maintains a practice before the Washington State Gambling Commission relating to licensing issues and the approval and ongoing regulatory oversight of casino properties and before the Washington State Liquor Control Board on liquor & marijuana matters. Chris also has experience in governmental affairs. She is a registered lobbyist in Washington State and has successfully lobbied for the passage of legislation in various areas. Before joining the firm, Chris was a judicial extern for the Honorable Thomas S. Zilly, U.S. District Court, Seattle, Washington. In 1997, she clerked for the Department of Justice, U.S. Attorney, in Springfield, Illinois.

MASTEN, GREGORY J. (Hoopa)
(education director)
Education: BA (Native American Studies with minor in American Indian Education; MA (Education). *Affiliation & Address*: Director of Education, Hoopa Valley Tribe, P.O. Box 1348, Hoopa, CA 95546 (530) 625-4211. Mr. Masten is responsible for eleven comprehensive grant-funded education programs & six other tribal education programs & projects that span the entire education process. *Other professional posts*: President, Tribal Education Departments National Assembly (TEDNA); interim board member of the University of Indigenous Nations, Humboldt State University's American Indian Advisory Board; member of the Klamath Trinity Joint U.S.D. Strategic Planning Team; board member, Indian Policies & Procedures Task Force; member, Humboldt/ Del Norte P-16 Council. *Membership*: CA Indian Education Directors Assn.

MASTEN, SUSAN (Yurok)
(founder/president of Indian organization; former tribal vice chair)
Education: Oregon State University, BA. *Affiliation & Address*: Founder & co-president, Women Empowering Women for Indian Nations (WEWIN) Website: www.wewin04.org, P.O. Box 699, Hooper, CA 95546. E-mail: susanmasten04 @gmail.com; E-mail: *Other professional posts*: Vice Chairperson, National Center for Ameican Indian Enterprise Development, Mesa, AZ; vice president, Union Bank of California's Native Market Division; founding member, Klamath River Early College of the Redwoods High School. *Past professional posts*: Vice Chairperson, Yurok Tribe, Klamath, CA; Vice President, American Indian Film Institute, San Francisco, CA; chairperson, Indian Law Resource Center, Helena, MT; chairperson, Yurok Tribe.

MATHA, TODD (Ho-Chunk)
(adjunct law professor; tribal solicitor general)
Education: Dickinson College, BA; University of Minnesota Law School, JD. *Affiliation & Address*: Adjunct Law Professor, University of Minnesota Law School, Mondale Hall, 229 19th Ave. South, Minneapolis, MN 55455 (320) 412-6179. E-mail: math0066@umn.edu Adjunct Professor Matha currently serves as Solicitor General of the Mille Lacs Band of Ojibwe. As chief legal counsel since 2011, he advises both executive and legislative branches of tribal government; litigates in federal, state, and tribal courts; supervises eleven attorneys; and oversees a Police Department of twenty officers. He simultaneously occupies the elected position of Chief Justice on the Ho-Chunk Nation Supreme Court. Adjunct Professor Matha ascended to this role following five (5) consecutive terms within the Ho-Chunk Judiciary beginning in 1999. Additionally, Adjunct Professor Matha has adjudicated multiple cases in a *pro tempore* capacity for tribes throughout Wisconsin and Michigan. Adjunct Professor

MATHEWS, THOMAS (Quapaw)
(tribal vice chairperson)
Affiliation & Address: Vice Chairperson, Quapaw Tribe of Oklahoma, P.O. Box 765, Quapaw, OK 74363 (918) 542-4694. E-mail: crawfish74354@yahoo.com.

MATHEWS, DEREK (Cherokee) 1951-
(educator; events promoter; media specialist)
Born September 10, 1951, Chicago, Ill. *Education*: College of Santa Fe, BA, 1974; Governors State University, MA, 1977; University of New Mexico (Graduate work), 1979-85. *Principal occupation*: Educator; events promoter; media specialist. *Address & Affiliation*: Director, Gathering of Nations, 3301 Coors Rd., NW, Suite R-300, Albuquerque, NM 87120 (505) 836-2810. E-mail: derekmathews@gatheringofnations.com; Website: www.gatheringofnations. com (work). *Other professional post*: Dean of Students, University of New Mexico, Albuquerque, 1979-84. *Awards, honors*: Recipient of Media Grant, National Endowment for the Humanities, 1980. *Interests*: Traveled Europe, South Central America, Canada, and Asia.

MATHIESON, LLOYD (Me-wuk)
(rancheria chairperson)
Affiliation: Chicken Ranch Band of Me-wuk Indians, P.O. Box 1159, Jamestown, CA 95327 (209) 984-3057.

MATHIS, KATHRYN J. BEGAY (Navajo)
(artist)
Address: HC 63, Box 6061, Winslow, AZ 86047 (928) 657-3650.
E-mail: katimat@localnet.com. Kathryn makes traditional Navajo clothing.

MATRIOUS, SUSAN (Ojibwe)
(editor)
Affiliation: "Win-Awaenen-Nisitotung," Saulte Ste. Marie Tribe of Chippewa Indians, 2218 Shunk Rd., Saulte Ste. Marie, MI 49783 (906) 635-6050.

MATT, DUANE (Confederated Salish & Kootenai)
(technology coordinator)
Education: University of Montana, BS (Geology & English), MS (Geology). *Affiliation*: Technology Coordinator, Office of Surface Mining Reclamation & Enforcement (OSMRE), U.S. Dept. of the Interior, Denver, CO. *Other professional post*: Board member, SAIGE (Society for American Indian Governmental Employees, Washington, DC. *Past professional posts*: Schoolteacher, Laguna-Acoma Reservation, NM; Bureau of Land Management; field geologist, Scientific Applications International Corp.; geological intern, Bureau of Reclamation; smokejumper, U.S. Dept. of Agriculture.

MATT, FRED (Confederated Salish & Kootenai)
(executive director; former tribal chairperson)
Affiliation & Address: Executive Director, Native American Fish & Wildlife Society, 8333 Greenwood Blvd., Suite 260, Denver, CO 80221 (303) 466-1725. E-mail: fmatt@nafws.org, *Past professional post*: Former Chairperson, Confederated Salish & Kootenai Tribes, Pablo, MT.

MATTERN, PHYLLIS (Brotherton)
(tribal vice chairperson)
Affiliation: Brotherton Indians of Wisconsin, AV2848 Witches Lake Rd., Woodruff, WI 54568 (715) 542-3913.

MATTHEW, MARY (Eskimo)
(Alaskan village president)
Affiliation: President, Village of Chefornak, P.O. Box 110, Chefornak, AK 99561 (907) 867-8850.

MATTHEWS, ALEX (Pawnee)
(former tribal chairperson)
Affiliation: Pawnee Business Committee, P.O. Box 470, White Eagle, Pawnee, OK 74058 (405) 762-3624.

MATTSON, MATT (Snoqualmie Coast Salish)
(tribal administrator)
Affiliation: Snoqualmie Indian Tribe, P.O. Box 969, Snoqualmie, WA 98065. (425) 888-6551.

MATTWAOSHSHE, GALILA
(BIA agency supt.)
Affiliation: Concho Agency, Bureau of Indian Affairs, P.O. Box 68, El Reno, OK 73005 (405) 262-7481.

MATTZ, MICHAEL (Tolowa/Yurok)
(rancheria vice chairperson)
Affiliation & Address: Vice Chairperson, Elk Valley Rancheria, 2332 Howland Hill Rd., Crescent City, CA 95531 (707) 464-4680. E-mail: mmattz@elk-valley.com.

MAUCHAHTY-WARE, TOM (Kiowa/Comanche) 1949-
(musician, entertainer, educator)
Born March 21, 1949, Lawton, Okla. *Education*: Brookhaven College, Farmers Branch, TX (two years); UCLA (30 hours). *Principal occupation*: Musician, entertainer, educator. *Address*: P.O. Box 1771, Anadarko, OK 73005 (405) 588-2392. Titles: Indian Flute Player; Lead Singer of the all Indian Blues Band, "Tom Ware & Blues Nation"; Indian Dance Champion; Traditional & Contemporary Vocalist; Accomplished public speaker & educator; traditional artist (painter, sculptor, flute maker, beadworker & featherworker.) *Shows*: Colorado Indian Market - Western Art Roundup, Annual in Jan.; Texas Indian Market & Southwest Showcase, Annual in March; Kansas City Indian market & Southwest Showcase, Annual in April; Native American Days - Angel Mounds Historical Site, Evansville, IN, Annual in September; Inter-tribal Indian Ceremonials, Gallup, NM, Annual in August. *Other professional post*: Arts & crafts dealer. *Community activities*: Charter member, Optimist International; member, Toastmasters International. *Membership*: Kiowa Tribal Employment Association (vice-president, 1983-84). *Awards, honors*: "Best Counselor

Award," National Indian Youth Vocational Association, *Interests*: Former Oklahoma Friendship Force Ambassador to Ireland and Wales, Oct. 1979. *Biographical sources*: Listed in numerous newspapers, magazines, etc. Three movie soundtracks: "Last of the Caddos," HBO - 1980; "Son of the Morning Star," 1991 ABC Mini-Series; "Circle of Life, American Cancer Society - 1992.

MAULDIN, MARGARET (Muscogee-CreeK)
(Creek language instructor)
Affiliation & Address: Creek Language Instructor, Native American Language Program, Department of Anthropology, College of Arts & Sciences, The University of Oklahoma, 455 W. Lindsey, Cate 4 Room 206, Norman, OK 73019 (405) 325-2690. E-mail: mvhayv@ou.edu.

MAULSON, THOMAS (Lake Superior Ojibwe)
(former tribal president)
Affiliation & Address: Lac du Flambeau Band of Lake Superior Chippewa Indians, P.O. Box 67, Lac du Flambeau, WI 54538 (715) 588-3303.

MAXCY, HOWARD (*Kayetanto*) (Pala Band of Mission Indians)
(tribal vice chairperson)
Born August 22, 1945. *Education*: AA Fire Science. **(Luiseno-Cupa)**
Affiliation & Address: Vice Chairperson, Pala Band of Luiseno Indians, P.O. Box 50, Pala, CA 92059 (760) 891-3500. *Other professional posts*: Fire Captain, California Dept. of Forestry & Fire (30 years). *Past professional post*: Consultant to reservation fire service. *Membership*: Southern California Tribal Chairman's Association.

MAXCY, REBECCA (Diegueno)
(tribal chairperson)
Affiliation: Inaja-Cosmit Band of Mission Indians, 1040 E. Valley Pkwy., Unit A, Escondido, CA 92025 (760) 747-8581.

MAY, CHERYL (Cherokee) 1949-
(journalism)
Born February 22, 1949, Kansas City, Mo. *Education*: University of Missouri, BA, 1974; Kansas State University, MS, 1985. *Address*: 2005 Somerset Square, Manhattan, KS 66503 (785) 532-6415. E-mail: may@ksu.edu. *Affiliations*: Communications director, American Maine-Anjou Association, Kansas City, MO, 1975-76; deputy managing editor/research editor, University Relations, 1979-87, general news editor, 1987-88, director, Media Relations and Marketing, 1988-, Kansas State University (KSU), Manhattan, KS. *Other professional post*: Elected to KSU Faculty Senate, 1991-97. *Community activities*: United Way, KSU publicity chair, 1985; Riley County Historical Society volunteer (organized Celebrate American Indian Heritage); 4-H project leader; helped organize Kansas State's first Native American Heritage Month activities for March 1990; panel moderator, "People Making a Difference: People Keeping the King Tradition Alive," KSU Martin Luther King Week, Jan. 24, 1991; served on several search committees; volunteer with Flint Hills Breadbasket; co-founder & president, two terms, Heartland Dog Training Club. *Memberships*: Phi Kappa Phi; National Association of Science Writers; Council for Advancement & Support of Education (CASE); Kansas Association for Native American Education. *Awards, honors*: Grants and gifts for Native American Heritage Month, 1990-91; Best in Show photography award, K-State Union Program Council, 1990; Award of Excellence for "Perspectives" magazine, CASE, editor, 1987; Special Merit Award for Cattle Research in Kansas, Council for Advancement and Support of Education CASE, writer, 1984; scholarship winner, Communicating University Research, CASE, 1983; selected for listing in Ohoyo 1000, 1982, and for the Resource Directory of Alaskan and Native American Indian Women, 1980; Award for Merit for Artificial Insemination of Beef & Dairy Cattle, slide script, Society for Technical Communication, 1980; Award for Achievement for Safety in Handling Livestock, slide script, Society for Technical Communication, 1980; Award for Outstanding News Reporting, Carlsbad, Calif. Chamber of Commerce, 1969. *Interests*: "Since I have been director of News Services and later Media Relations and Marketing at Kansas State University. I supervise science reporting; radio-television news; and campus news as well as the faculty-staff newsletter. I am interested in photography and use it in my professional and private life. I have won numerous awards for photography and for writing." *Published works*: Cattle Management (Reston-Prentice-Hall, 1981); Legacy, Engineering at Kansas State University (KSU Press, 1983).

MAYER, RENEE J. (Mandan, Hidatsa, Arikara)
(artist)
Address: 500 5th St. N., New Town, ND 58763 (701) 627-4861. E-mail: reneem@mhanation.com. *Artwork*: Contemporary beadwork, leather items, embroidery, traditional clothing.

MAYER, TERRY "HAWK" (Ojibwe)
(school administrator)
Affiliation: Lac Courte Oreilles Ojibwe School, P.O. Box 2800, Hayward, WI 54843 (715) 634-1442.

MAYNAHONAH, LOUIS (Apache of Oklahoma)
(former tribal chairperson)
Affiliation: Apache Tribe of Oklahoma, P.O. Box 1330, Anadarko, OK 73005

MAYNOR, ELIZABETH (Coharie)
(tribal executive director)
Affiliation: Coharie Indian Tribe, 7531 N. US Hwy. 421, Clinton, NC 28328
(910) 564-6909. E-mail: emaynor@intrstar.net.

MAYNOR, GERALD
(Indian education)
Affiliation: North Carolina Advisory Council on Indian Education, NC Dept.
of Public Instruction, c/o Pembroke State University, Pembroke, NC 28372.

MAYO, DEE (Lac du Flambeau Ojibwe)
(tribal council vice president)
Affiliation: Lac du Flambeau Band of Lake Superior Chippewa,
P.O. Box 67, Lac du Flambeau, WI 54538 (715) 588-3303.

MAYO, WILL
(center president)
Affiliation: Tanana Chiefs Conference Health Center, 12 First Ave.,
Fairbanks, AK 99701 (907) 452-8251.

MAZZA, PAMELA J.
(attorney)
Education: Indiana University of Pennsylvania, BA, 1980; George Washington
University National Law Center, JD, 1984. *Affiliation*: Senior partner, Piliero,
Mazza & Pargament, PLLC, Farragut Square, 888 17th St., NW, Suite 1100,
Washington, DC 20005 (202) 857-1000. E-mail: pmazza@pmplawfirm.com.
Ms. Mazza practices in the areas of corporate counseling, government
contracts, government relations & Native American law. She represents Indian
tribes and Alaska Native Corporations and related entities on a variety of
issues pertaining to sovereignty, economic development, land issues, housing
& establishing tribal enterprises & subsidiaries to participate in commercial
business and government contracts. She is an editor of the firm's newsletters,
"Legal Advisor," & "Tribal Advocate," and a guest columnist for the
"Government Contract Audit Report."

MAZZETTI, BO (Luiseno)
(tribal chairperson)
Education: California Polytechnic University, BS (Behravioral Science).
Affiliation & Address: Chairperson (2007-present), Rincon Nation of Luiseno
Indians, P.O. Box 68, Valley Center, CA 92082 (760) 749-1051. E-mail:
bomazzetti@aol.com. *Other professional posts*: Founder and active member of
the Southernn California Trial Chairman's Association (SCTCA); serves on the
Governor's Drought Task Force, and as a chief organizer of Indian Day in
Sacramento. *Past professional posts*: Burea of Indian Affairs, Southern
California Agency in Riverside; served as first Indian Community Affairs &
Citizen Assistance Officer for San Diego County. Awards, honors: California
Indian Chamber of Commerce "Warrior Award," and the "Anna Sandoval
Ladership Award" from the California Nations Indian Gaming Association.

McADAMS, GARY (Wichita)
(tribal president)
Affiliation: Wichita & Affiliated Tribes, P.O. Box 729, Anadarko, OK 73005
(405) 247-2425.

McALISTER, DIANE
(editor)
Affiliation: "Native American Connection," Spotted Horse Tribal Gifts,
P.O. Box 414, Coos Bay, OR 97420.

McARTHUR, EUGENE, JR. (Chippewa)
(tribal chairperson)
Affiliation: White Earth Reservation Tribal Council, P.O. Box 418, White Earth,
MN 56591 (218) 983-3285.

McAULIFFE, DENNY (Osage) 1951-
(professor of journalism)
Born in 1951, Philadelphia, PA. *Principal occupation*: Associate professor of
journalism. *Address & Affiliation*: School of Journalism, University of Montana,
Missoula, MT 59812. E-mail: dmcauliffe@reznetnews.org. *Other professional
post*: Editor of Reznet, a native online student newspaper (www.reznetnews.
org). *Past professional post*: The night Foreign Editor of The Washington Post,
Washington, DC (16 years). At The Post, he also reported on Native American
issues and, for a while, was the Foreign Desk's Africa Editor and area
specialist; write sports for the Washington (D.C.) Daily News; former secretary,
Native American Journalists Association. *Military service*: U.S. Army. Awards,
honors: 1968 Grantland Rice Memorial Scholarship for Sports Writing; 1995
Oklahoma Book Award for Non-Fiction; One of four Freedom Forum Diversity

Fellows, who traveled across the country to colleges, universities & junior
colleges with high minority enrollments to identify talented students of color for
careers in print journalism. The position was a key part of the Freedom
Forum's national effort to increase diversity in newspaper newsrooms. Denny
focused on recruitment of Native Americans. A Freedom Forum grant brought
him to the University of Montana, School of Journalism in the Spring Semester
1999 as the Native American Journalist-in-Residence to direct the school's
American Indian program. *Published work*: "The Deaths of Sybil Bolton: An
American History," an account of the murder of his Osage grandmother during
the Reign of Terror against the Osage Indians in the 1920s (republished in
paperback as "Bloodland: A Family Story of Oil, Greed and Murder on the
Osage Reservation").

McBRIDE, BUNNY 1950-
(writer)
Born April 9, 1950, Washington, D.C. *Education*: Michigan State University,
BA, 1972; Boston University, MFA courses, 1973-75; Columbia University, MA
(Anthropology), 1980. *Principal occupation*: Writer. *Address*: 3301 Buffalo,
Manhattan, KS 66503 (785) 776-3876. E-mail: bmcb@ksu.edu. Website:
www.personal.ksu.edu/~bmcb/. *Affiliations*: Adjunct lecturer in anthropology,
Prncipia College, Elsah, IL, 1981-2002; Adjunct lecturer in anthropology,
Kansas State University, Manhattan, KS, 1996-; CO-PI Acadia National Park
ethno-history Project (in cooperation with Maine's four tribal groups). *Other
professional posts*: Consultant, Aroostook Band of Micmacs, Presque Isle, ME,
1982-91; Member, Advisory Committee on Exhibits & Programming, Abbe
Museum, Bar Harbor, ME, 1998-present; Curator of the Abbe's 2002 exhibit,
"Four Mollys: Women of the Dawn," chronicling the lives of four Native
American women whose combined lives spanned four centuries. *Community
activities*: Manhattan Habitat for Humanity (Development Board), 1996-; Martin
Luther King Task Force, Manhattan, KS, 1997-; Oral History Advisor, Kansas
Humanities Council, 1997-; Reader, Christian Science Church, Manhattan, KS,
1997-. *Awards, honors*: Pulitzer nominee for Molly Spotted Elk: A Penobscot
in Paris; Friends of American Writers Literary Award in 2000; special
commendation from Maine State Legislature for "tremendous contribution" as
the first author to research & write books about the history of Native American
women in Maine -- initiated by the Penobscot & Passamaquoddy tribal
representative to the legislature. Membership: Board member, Women's World
Summit Foundation, Geneva, Switzerland. *Biographical sources*:
Contemporary Authors; Globe Sunday Magazine 6/3/01. *Selected published
works*: Our Lives in Our Hands: Micmac Indian Basketmakers (photos by
Donald Sanipass, Aroostook Mimac); National Audubon Society Field Guide to
African Wildlife, with Peter Alden, Richard Estes & Donald Schlitter (Knopf,
1995); Molly Spotted Elk: A Penobscot in Paris (U. of Oklahoma Press, 1995);
Women of the Dawn (University of Nebraska Press, 1999); Lucy Nicolar: The
Artful Activism of a Penobscot Performer" in Sifters: Native American Women's
Lives, ed. by Theda Perdue (Oxford U. Press, 2001).

McBRIDE, D. MICHAEL
(attorney; Indian law & gaming practice group chair)
Education: Trinity University (San Antonio, TX), BA, 1989; University of
Oklahoma College of Law, JD (American Indian Law Review), 1993. *Affiliation
& Address*: Chairperson, Indian Law & Gaming Practice Group, Crowe &
Dunlevy LLP, 500 Kennedy Bldg., 321 S. Boston Ave., Tulsa, OK 74103 (918)
592-9824. E-mail: Michael.mcbride@crowedunlevy.com. Michael is an
experienced trial, appellate & business lawyer with two decades of experience.
He is a sought-after and trusted advisor with particular expertise in gaming,
federal Indian law, litigation & complex transactions. He has tried more than 50
cases to conclusion in federal, tribal and state courts including numerous jury
trials; as a Judge and Justice, he has adjudicated scores more and authored
many published decisions. He excels in gaming regulatory matters, "bet the
tribe" litigation, tribal government matters, economic development & regulatory
matters. Corporations, investment funds & individuals have hired him as an
expert consultant and as an expert witness in multiple federal state court cases
to testify on Indian gaming matters. *Other professional posts*: Member of the
Board of Trustees, Pawnee Nation College, Pawnee, OK. Michael is a regular
speaker at conferences around the country, and has had over 35 articles and
papers published on Indian law and gaming issues. *Awards, honors*: Mike's
professional peers have recognized him Chamber's U.S.A. (2009-present) in
"Band 1" for "Native American Law" and was named a 2013 "Star Individual",
the highest individual ranking awarded by Chambers, as a "Super Lawyer" in
Oklahoma Super Lawyers for Indian Law, Gaming, Political Law and Business
Litigation. He is also recognized by "Best Lawyers in America" for Native
American & Gaming Law and as "A-V" rated by Martindale-Hubbell. He is one
of only two Oklahoma "General Members" of the International Masters of
Gaming Law. He serves IMGL's Membership Chair. IMGL President Tony
Coles of London recognized Mike's outstanding accomplishments with the
President's Cup Award in Vienna, Austria in September 2011; The FBA has
recognized Mike with a number of awards including an Indian Law Section
Distinguished Service Award in 2009, an Outstanding Section Chair Award in
2007 & 2008 as well as several service awards over the last decade. The three
Inns in Tulsa of the American Inns of Court has also honored Mike with the

"John S. Athens Award" for Leadership and Ethics. *Past professional posts*: Mike served as Justice of the Pawnee Nation Supreme Court from 2003 until 2012. He formerly served as Attorney General to the Seminole Nation and the Sac & Fox Nation. He has represented over 20 Indian tribal governments or their entities and numerous corporations and individuals doing business with tribes. Mike is completing a three year term on the Federal Bar Association (FBA) national board of Directors and is Chair of its Audit Committee. He was Chair of the FBA's Indian Law Section, the largest Indian law organization in the country from 2006 to 2008. In September 2008, the Federal Bar Association named Mike as the General Counsel on the organization's National Board of Directors. Mike regularly speaks at conferences and symposia around the country (and outside the United States) and has had over fifty articles and papers published on Indian law and gaming issues. He has served as an Adjunct Professor of Law at the University of Tulsa and as an Adjunct Settlement Judge for the United States District Court for the Northern District of Oklahoma. He has also served in various American Bar Association leadership roles.

McBRIDE, MARY (San Felipe Pueblo) 1948-
(high school principal)
Born June 3, 1948, Albuquerque, N.M. *Education*: Eastern New Mexico University, Portales, BS, 1971; New Mexico Highlands University, Las Vegas, MA, 1982. *Address*: P.O. Box 751, Algodones, NM 87001 (505) 867-4766; 867-2388 (work). *Affiliations*: Elementary school principal, B.I.A., Isleta Pueblo, NM, 1984-86; high school principal, Bernalillo School District, Bernalillo, NM, 1986-. *Memberships*: Phi Delta Kappa, 1987-; Delta Kappa Gamma Society International, 1988-; National Education Association, 1990-. *Awards, honors*: Graduate Professional Opportunity Program. *Interests*: "I will be on leave of absence for a year to work on a MA in counseling for AT RISK youth."

McBRIDE, MIMI (*W'o okihi o'ta yua' win*) (Standing Rock Lakota)
(company president, editor)
Education: University of Montana, BA (Elementary Education), M.L.S., M. Ed. (all specializing in music & library science). *Address & Affiliation*: President, Oyate Views International, Inc. (music & education publishing & production company), PMB 268, 1840 E. Warner Rd., Suite A105, Tempe, AZ 85284 (480) 839-8355. Website: worldviewsintl.com. E-mail: wvi@worldviewsintl.com. *Other professional post*: Editor, The Independent American Indian Review (triannual journal of music & educational reviews of books, CDs, and other multi-media. Mimi is a recording & performing artist and educator specialist who writes & records contemporary, original music. She performs concerts mostly in the Southwest U.S. & motivational concert/school assembly programs for all ages K-University level) sharing her positive musical messages, stressing "belief in self" & "the importance of education" (staying in school). *Awards, honors*: Mimi was selected to participate in the Arizona Governor's "Business Breakthrough for Minorities & Women."

McCABE, MELVINA, M.D. (Navajo)
(MD; board president)
Education: University of New Mexico, BS; University of New Mexico School of Medicine, MD. *Affiliation*: Geriatrician & board certified Family Physician, University of New Mexico School of Medicine, Dept. of Family & Community Medicine, Albuquerque, NM. *Other professional posts*: Member, University of New Mexico Mosaic Committee to advise on the recruitment & retention of under-represented students. Her research includes issues regarding Hantavirus, alcohol abuse, diabetes, and geriatric education. Dr. McCabe is active in several key committees, including the Minority Affairs Consortium of the American Medical Association and the National Institutes of Health Advisory Council on Minority Health & Health Disparities. *Memberships*: American Medical Association; Association of American Indian Physicians, Oklahoma City, OK (president, 2000; 2009-2010). *Awards, honors*: She served as a Presidential appointee to the bipartisan advisory committee to the White House Conference on Aging in 2006. Mevina also served New Mexico's Gov. Bill Richardson as a member of the health Policy Committee.

McCAFFERY, AUGUSTINE (Comanche)
(senior academic program specialist)
Education: Ed.C. *Affiliation*: Senior Academic Program Specialist, The Graduate School - Office of Academic Affairs & Planning, Box 353770, University of Washington, Seattle, WA 98195 (206) 221-3628. E-mail: amccaf@u.washington.edu. *Other professional post*: Governing Council Executive Board Member, National Institute for Native Leadership in Higher Education, University of Northern Colorado, Greeley, CO.

McCAFFERTY, MICHAEL
(college president)
Affiliation: Cheyenne River Community College, P.O. Box 220, Eagle Butte, SD 57625 (605) 964-8635.

McCALEB, NEAL
(assistant secretary-BIA)
Affiliation: Assistant Secretary, Bureau of Indian Affairs, Dept. of the Interior, 1849 C St., NW - MS 4140-MIB, Washington, DC 20240 (202) 208-7163.

McCARTAN, KATHLEEN (Mohawk/Oneida) 1963-
(naval flight officer)
Born in 1963, Clarence, N.Y. *Education*: U.S. Naval Academy, BS, 1985. *Principal occupation*: Naval flight officer, U.S. Navy. At the Academy, she was editor of a literary magazine, president of the Bicycle Racing Club; san in the Glee Club and Choir and the Messiah Church group; she rowed on the crew team for two years. She is a qualified navigator and an Airborne Communications Officer. She has flown the T-34 C, and T-43. She currently flies the EC-130, an aircraft from Oahu, Hawaii.

McCARTHY, JOAN DOLORES (*Sun Dancer*) (Blackfoot-Bear Clan) 1935-
(shop owner)
Born January 14, 1935, Easton, Penna. *Principal occupation*: Reservation trader. *Address*: 1500 Eddy St., Merritt Island, FL 32952 (407) 631-0092. *Affiliation*: Family owns four shops: "This N' That," Cocoa Village, FL, 1975-; "Rags to Riches," Cocoa Village, FL--authentic Native American jewelry and crafts; "Sundancer Gallery, Cocoa Village, FL; and "Spare Time Hobby Shop," Cocoa Village, FL. "I'm known as Sun Dancer woman who keeps spirits together & bright, and bringer of light (lightening the soul or spiritual healing). (I) started business on my own as a single parent with three children to raise-- no outside help or child support." *Community activities*: Counsel Native Americans on their rights, on or off the reservation, the business or schooling open to them, water rights, etc.; give speeches to youth groups, all sorts of organizations; display in libraries, schools, and banks; guidance counselor - troubled teens of Brevard County; swimming instructor for handicapped & retarded citizens; and water safety instructor for American Red Cross, Miami, FL; crisis home/assisted Brevard Sheriff Rollin Zimmerman with benefits for teens, runaways-delinquents, etc.; assisted aid to several emergency charities. *Memberships*: Brevard County, Merritt Island, FL Chamber of Commerce; Big Mountain Legal Fund, Flagstaff, AZ; Kuwaiti Legal Fund, Cocoa Village, FL; Pioneer Women of Brevard Co. *Awards, honors*: Art awards in silver-smithing, pen & ink, watercolors, copper and enamel work, and sketching; Pioneer Women of Brevard - Entrepreneur in six businesses; Brevard County Board of Education Award for donations to local high schools. *Interests*: "Native American Rights including helping young artists to merchandise their products; helping young artists to seek grants; water rights on several reserves: Taos, Zuni, Ft. McDowell Apache Reservation; Big Mountain Legal Aid for displaced Native Americans (land disputes-Navajo, Mohawk). My desire is to give back the pride to the Native American encouraging them to protect their culture; travel to all the Southwestern reservations."

McCARTHY, PATRICK (Athapascan)
(Alakan tribal chief)
Affiliation: Ruby Tribal Council, P.O. Box 210, Ruby, AK 99768 (907) 468-4479.

McCARTHY, THERESA (Onondaga)
(professor of Native American Studies)
Education: McMaster University, PhD (Anthropology). Affiliation & Address: Co-Investigator, Indigenous Health Research Development Program, Six Nations Polytechnic, Box 700, 2160 Fourth Line Rd., Ohsweken, ON N0A 1M0 Canada (519) 445-0023 ext. 236. *Other professional post*: Professor of Native American Studies, Dept. of American Studies, U. of Buffalo, Buffalo, NY.

McCARTY, GLORIA (Muscogee-Creek)
(Creek language instructor)
Affiliation & Address: Creek Language Instructor, Native American Language Program, Department of Anthropology, College of Arts & Sciences, The University of Oklahoma, 455 W. Lindsey, Cate 4 Room 206, Norman, OK 73019 (405) 325-2690. E-mail: gmccarty@ou.edu.

McCARTY, MICAH (Makah)
(former trbal chairperson)
Affiliation & Address: Makah Tribe, P.O. Box 115, Neah Bay, WA 98357 (360) 645-2201. *Other professional post*: Advisor to Makah council's marine policy & fisheries. President Obama appointed Micah to the National Oceans Council's newly formed Governance Coordinating Committee.

McCARTY, TERESA L.
(educational anthropologist & professor of applied linguistics)
Affiliation & Address: Alice Wiley Snell Professor of Education Policy Studies, Professor of Applied Linguistics, & Co-director of the Center for Indian Education, Arizona State University, School of Social Transformation, MC: 4902, ED 144E, P.O. Box 874902, Tempe, AZ 85287 (480) 965-7483. E-mail: teresa.mccarty@asu.edu. Ms. McCarty is an affiliate faculty in American Indian Studies & the Mary Lou Fulton Teachers College. *Other professional posts*:

Co-editor, Journal of American Indian Education, and associate editor for Language Policy & the American Educational Research Journal. *Past professional posts*: Curriculum developer, teacher, & coordinator of American Indian education programs; professor & head, Dept. of Language Reading & Culture, interim dean of College of Education, and co-director of the American Indian Language Development, all at the University of Arizona, Tucson. She recently directed a U.S. Dept. of Education study of the Impacts of native language loss & retention on American Indian students' school achievement and, with the Fort Mojave Language Recovery Program, is directing a NSF-funded project to document endangered Mojave bird songs. *Awards, honors*: The 2010 George & Louise Spindler Award from the Council on Anthropology & Education for distinguished & inspirational contributions to the anthropology of education; 2011-12 academic year SAR's National Endowment for the Humanities Resident Scholar at the School for Advanced Research (SAR) in Santa Fe, NM. *Published works*: A Place to Be Navajo - Rough Rock & the Struggle for Self-Determination in Indigenous Schooling (Erlbaum, 2002); Language, Literacy, & Power In Schooling (Erlbaum, 2005); One Voice, Many Voices - Recreating Indigenous Language Communities, with O. Zepeda (Center for Indian Education, 2006); To Remain An Indian: Lessons In Democracy From A Century of Native American Education, with K.T. Lomawaima (Teachers College Press, 2006); Ethnography & Language Policy (Routledge, 2011).

McCLAIN, BRAD (Standing Rock Sioux)
(chief financial officer)
Education: University of Wisconsin-Platteville, BS (Accounting & Finance). Chief Financial Officer (CFO), University of Wisconsin Credit Union, P.O. Box 44963, Madison, WI 53744 (608) 232-5000. Website: www.uwcu.org. *Other professional post*: Board Member, Potawatomi Business Development Corp, Milwaukee, WI. *Past professional posts*: CFO, Potawatomi Bingo Casino, Milwaukee, WI; member, Forest County Potawatomi Investment Committee.

McLAUGHLIN STEVEN
(BIA agency supt.)
Affiliation: Crow Creek Agency, Bureau of Indian Affairs, P.O. Box 139, Fort Thompson, SD 57339 (605) 245-2311.

McLANE, MICHAEL (Delaware)
(tribal vice president)
Affiliation & Address: Vice President, Delaware Nation, P.O. Box 825, Anadarko, OK 73005 (405) 247-2448. E-mail: mmclane@delawarenation.com.

McCLEARY, TIMOTHY (Crow)
(speaker, teacher, author)
Address: Box 2116, Star Route, Hardin, MT 59034. *Interests*: Crow speaker; teacher at Crow Community College; active in Native American church.

McCLELLAND. JOHN
(organization chairperson)
Affiliation: Native American Coalition of Tulsa, Inc., 1740 West 41st St., Tulsa, OK 74107 (918) 446-8432.

McCLOUD, FARRON (Nisqually)
(tribal chairperson)
Affiliation & Address: Chairperson, Nisqually Indian Tribe, 4820 SheNahNum Dr., SE, Olympia, WA98513 (360) 456-5221. E-mail: mccloud.farron@nisqually-nsn.gov.

McCLOUD, RICHARD Turtle Mountain Chippewa)
(tribal chairperson)
Affiliation & Address: Chairperson, Turtle Mountain Band of Chippewa Indians, 4180 Hwy. 281, Belcourt, ND 58316 (701) 477-2600.

McCLURE, MIKE (Paiute)
(tribal enterprise manager)
Affiliation: Moapa Tribal Enterprises, P.O. Box 340, Moapa, NV 89025 (702) 864-2600.

McCLURE, RUSSELL J. (Sioux)
(BIA agency supt.)
Affiliation: Cheyenne River Agency, Bureau of Indian Affairs, P.O. Box 325, Eagle Butte, SD 57625 (605) 964-6611.

McCONNELL, DEBORAH (Yurok/Quinault/Hoopa)
(basketweaver; field director)
Education: Humboldt State University, B.A. (Art). *Address & Affiliation*: Northwest California Field Director (2000-present), California Indian Basket-weavers Association, P.O. Box 1147, Valley Center, CA 92082 (760) 749-1386. E-mail: demcconell@ciba.org. Ms. McConnell is responsible for implementing CIBAs programs on behalf of basketweavers in the region. *Past professional post*: Director, Hoopa Valley Tribe's Adult Vocational Program.

McCONNELL, JOSEPH F. (Gros Ventre)
(tribal president)
Address & Affiliation: Fort Belknap Community Council, RR 1, Box 66, Harlem, MT 59526 (406) 353-2205.

McCOOL, DANIEL
(center director)
Education: University of Arizona, PhD, 1983. *Address & Affiliation*: Director, The American West Center, University of Utah, 1901 E. South Campus Dr., Rm. 1023, Salt Lake City, UT 84112-8922 (801) 581-7611. *Publications*: Command of the Waters: Iron Triangles, Federal Water Development, and Indian Water Rights (University of California Press, 1987; University of Arizona Press, 1994); Waters of Good Faith: Indian Water Settlements and the Second Treaty Era (University of Arizona Press, 2001).

McCOVEY, DONALD (Yurok)
(former tribal chairperson)
Affiliation & Address: Resighini Rancheria Coast Indian Community, P.O. Box 529, Klamath, CA 95548 (707) 482-2431.

McCOY, DARWIN "JOE" (Sault Ste. Marie Chippewa)
(tribal chairperson)
Affiliation: Sault Ste. Marie Tribe of Chippewa Indians, 523 Ashmun St., Sault Ste. Marie, MI 49783 (906) 635-6050.

McCOY, MELODY (Cherokee)
(staff attorney)
Education: Harvard University, BA, 1981; University of Michigan Law School, JD, 1986. *Affiliation & Address*: Staff Attorney (1986-present), Native American Rights Fund, 1506 Broadway, Boulder, CO 80302 (303) 447-8760. Melody works primarily in the areas of tribal jurisdiction tribal education rights, tribal trust funds, and tribal intellectual property rights. *Past professional post*: Co-chair, Federal Bar Association's Indian Law Conference, 1990-92; member, NARF's Litigation Management Committee, 1992-95. *Membership*: Colorado Indian Bar Association (president).

McCOY, PADRAIC I. (Quechan/Cherokee)
(attorney; law firm partner)
Education: University of California, Irvine, BA (Criminology, Law & Society); University of California, Los Angeles, MA (American Indian Studies; UCLA School of Law, JD. *Affiliation & Address*: Partner, Tilden McCoy & Dilweg LLP, 2500 30th St., #207, Boulder, CO 80301 (303) 323-1922. E-mail: pmccoy@tildenmccoy.com. *Other professional posts*: Since 2012, Padraic has served on the law faculty at the University of Denver, Sturm College of Law, where he teaches federal-Indian law, and he also regularly guest lectures at the University of Colorado, School of Law. Padraic is President of the Colorado Indian Bar Association, Boulder, CO. Mr. McCoy represents Indian tribes and Indian country developers and investors on a variety of topics with an emphasis on transactional and regulatory matters, Indian gaming, Indian lands, and tribal finance. Padraic began his legal career in Washington, D.C., and has several years of experience with the Department of the Interior and the National Indian Gaming Commission. Padraic has been nationally recognized for his work, including from *Super Lawyers*, Native American Law, & Chambers USA, *America's Leading Lawyers for Business*, Native American Law (National). Padraic's practice also involves land-into-trust, Indian land determinations, leases, management and development agreements, gaming compacts, energy transactions, environmental law/NEPA, Oklahoma Indian issues, and over $1.0 billion in tribal financings. Padraic also represents clients in litigation matters in federal courts and before federal agencies. Padraic has worked as an attorney for large law firms in Washington, D.C., Los Angeles, and Denver/Boulder, including Sonosky Chambers; Holland & Knight; and Faegre & Benson. Padraic served as extern to a U.S. District Court and 9th Circuit Court of Appeals Judge, completed his Juris Doctor and Masters Degree in American Indian Studies at UCLA. *Memberships*: Admitted to practice before several federal, state, and tribal courts. e.g. Colorado & California. *Published works*: Numerous articles in legal journals.

McCOY, ROBERT R.
(professor of history)
Affiliation & Address: Associate Professor of History, Department of History, Washington State University, Box 641046 • PULLMAN, WA 99164 (509) 335-8618; E-mail: rmccoy@wsu.edu. *Published works*: Chief Joseph, Yellow Wolf, and the Creation of Nez Perce History in the Pacific Northwest (Routledge Press); Co-author with Clifford Trafzer, Forgotten Voices: Death Records of the Yakama 1888—1964 (Scarecrow Press, 2004); Co-author with Steven Fountain, History of American Indians (ABC-CLIO, 2017).

McCRACKEN, SAM (Sioux/Assiniboine)
(Nike program manager)
Born in Mont. Grew up on the Fort Peck Assiniboine/Sioux Reservation in Montana. *Education*: High School, Wolf Point, Mont. *Affiliation & Address*:

Manager, Nike Native American Business Program, Nike, Inc., One Bowerman Dr., Beaverton, OR 97005 (800) 344-6453. *Past affiliation*: Coached high school basketball in Oregon & California for 20 years. Started his Nike career in 1997 as a warehouse worker. In 2000, Sam became the manager of Nike's Native American Business Program. He wrote a business plan focusing on building relationships between Nike and the 250 Indian tribes that have received grants for diabetes education, plus 188 schools that are enrolled in the Office of Indian Education Programs (OIEP). As a result, Sam helped establish Nike's Native American Diabetes Program. He is also working in conjunction with Indian Health Service (IHS) and the National Indian Health Board (NIHB) on their "Just Move It" program, an alliance that promotes physical fitness on Indian Reservations. *Awards, honors*: In July 2004, Sam received Nike's Bowerman Award, the company's most prestigious form of employee recognition.

McDADE, MARVIN (Te-Moak Western Shoshone)
  (former Indian colony chairperson)
Affiliation: South Fork Band Council, Box B-13, Lee, NV 89829 (702) 744-4273.

McDADE, SHAROL (Paiute)
  (tribal administrator)
Affiliation: Fallon Paiute & Shoshone Tribe, 565 Rio Vista Rd., Fallon, NV 89406 (775) 423-6075.

McDANIEL, SHANNON (Choctaw)
  (health clinic director)
Affiliation & Address: Choctaw Nation Health Clinic, 205 E. 3rd St., Broken Bow, OK 74728 (405) 584-2740.

McDANIELS, PAUL, JR. (Kiowa-Oglala Sioux)
  (artisan)
Address: P.O. Box 1144, Anadarko, OK 73005. *Artwork*: Kiowa/Southern Plains style beadwork. *Membership*: Indian Arts & Crafts Board.

McDANIELS, TODD (Comanche)
  (professor of linguistics, dean of academic affairs)
Education: State University of New York, Buffalo, BFA, 1990, MA (Linguistics), 1996, PhD (Linguistics), 2005. Thesis: Establishing Perspective in Comanche Narrative. *Affiliation & Address*: Professor of Linguistics & Dean of Academic Affairs, Comanche Nation College, 1608 SW 9th St., Lawton, OK 73501 (580) 591-0203. E-mail: tmcdaniels@cnc.cc.o.us. *Linguistic Fieldwork*: Comanche fieldwork from 1996 to present, conducted typically in the greater Lawton region of Oklahoma. My commitment to this research stretches to seventeen years and continuing. I am the leading authority on the language from a linguistic standpoint. In addition to a thorough structural knowledge of the language I also currently enjoy an intermediate level speaking ability. *Awards, honors*: 2008 Comanche nation College's Outstanding Faculty Award.

McDARMENT, CHARMAINE (Yokut)
  (tribal general counsel)
Education: University of California, Santa Cruz, BA (Philosophy); University of New Mexico School of Law, JD. *Affiliation & Address*: General Counsel, Tule River Tribal Council, P.O. Box 589, Porterville, CA 93258 (559) 781-4271 ext. 1210. *Past professional posts*: Law Clerk, California Indian Legal Services, Eureka, CA; Law Clerk, C.A. Bowerman Esq, Albuquerque, NM, 2002; research assistant to Professor Christine Zuni-Cruz, UNM School of Law, Albuquerque, NM, 2001; tutor, American Indian Law Center, UNM School of Law, 2001.

McDARMENT, KENNETH (Yokut) 1975-
  (tribal vice chairperson)
Affiliation & Address: Vice Chairperson, Tule River Tribal Council, P.O. Box 589, Porterville, CA 93258 (559) 781-4271. E-mail: kenneth.mcdarment@ tulerivertribe-nsn.gov

McDERMOTT, BILL (Sault Ste. Marie Chippewa)
  (program director)
Affiliation & Address: Indian youth education & activities program director, Sault Ste. Marie Tribe of Chippewa Indians, 174 Zhigag, Manistique, MI 49854.

McDONALD, ARTHUR LEROY (Sioux) 1934-
  (research consultant)
Born December 26, 1934, Martin, S.D. *Education*: University of South Dakota, AB, 1962, MA, 1963, PhD, 1966. *Address*: Box 326, Lame Deer, MT 59043. *Affiliation*: Owner, Cheyenne Consulting Service. *Past professional posts*: Psychology Dept., Central College, 1963-64; Psychology Dept., Montana State University, 1968-71. *Military service*: U.S. Marine Corps, 1953-56 (Sergeant). Memberships: Pine Ridge Sioux Tribe; American Psychological Association; Sigma Xi; American Association for the Advancement of Science; American

Quarter Horse Association. *Interests*: Indian research in mental health, education, alcohol, & evaluation; raising quality American quarter horses. *Published works*: Psychology & Contemporary Problems (Brooks-Cole, 1974); co-authored, Schooling of Native America, 1977; Cheyenne Journey, 1977; numerous articles in scientific journals.

McDONALD, JOHN
  (radio station manager)
Affiliation: KYUK - 640 AM, Bethel Broadcasting, Inc., P.O. Box 468, Bethel, AK 99559 (907) 543-3131.

McDONALD, JOSEPH (Salish)
  (college president)
Education: Western Montana College, Teaching Certificate; University of Montana, B.S., M.S., EdD (Educational Administration). *Affiliation*: Salish Kootenai College, P.O. Box 117, Pablo, MT 59855 (406) 675-4800. E-mail: joe_mcdonald@skc.edu. *Other professional post*: Treasurer, American Indian Business Leaders (AIBL), University of Montana, Missoula, MT. Awards, honors: 1996 Montana's Governor's Humanity Award; 1989 National Indian Educator of the Year; Honorary Jurist Doctorate.

McDONALD, JUSTIN DOUGLAS (Oglala Lakota)
  (professor of clinical psychology; psychologist)
Born in Lame Deer, Mont. on the Northern Cheyenne Indian Reservation. *Education*: University of South Dakota, PhD (Clinical Psyhcology), 1992. *Affiliation & Address*: Professor of Psychology, Dept., of Psychology, University of North Dakota, Corwin-Larimore Hall, 319 Harvard St., P.O. Box 8380, Grand Forks, ND 58202 (701) 777-3451. E-mail: Justin.mcdonald@email.und.edu. *Other professional post*: Director, UND Indians Into Psychology Doctoral Education (InPsyDE) Program. *Research experience & interests*: Native American assessment & treatment issues with focus is on cross-cultural psychology issues, including psychological scale development, and the effects of biculturalism as predictor of functional behavior - particularly among American Indians. *Military service*: U.S. Navy (submarine veteran). *Memberships*: Society of Indian Psychologists (served two terms as president); American Psychological Association's (APA's) (served on the Board for the Advancement of Psychology in the Pubic Interest & the APA's Board of Educational Affairs); currently on Council of Representatives).

McDONALD, LEANDER "RUSS" (SissetonWahpeton Sioux)
  (former tribal chairperson)
Affiliation & Address: Spirit Lake Tribe, P.O. Box 359, Fort Totten, ND 58335 (701) 766-4221.

McDOWELL-ANTONE, NORA (Mojave)
  (former trial chairperson)
Affiliation: Fort Mojave Indian Tribe, Needles, CA.

McDOWELL-LOUDAN, ELLIS
  (co-coordinator of Native American studies program)
Affiliation & Address: Co-coordinator, Native American Studies Program, SUNY, Cortland, School of Arts & Sciences – Sociology-Anthropology Department, Old Main, Rm. 122, P.O. Box 2000, Cortland, NY 13045 (607) 753-5784; E-mail: ellie.mcdowell-loudan@cortland.edu

McELROY, DAVID "RON" (Arapaho)
  (tribal co-chairperson)
Affiliation & Address: Co-Chairperson, Northern Arapaho Tribe, P.O. Box 396, Fort Washakie, WY 82514 (307) 332-6120.

McELROY, DAVID W. (Oklahoma Choctaw)
  (attorney)
Education: Tufts University, BA, 1992; American University, JD, 1996. *Address & Affiliation*: Attorney, Travelers Express Co., Inc. & Money Gram Payment Systems, Inc., 1550 Utica Ave. S., M/S 8020, Minneapolis, MN. *Past professional post*: Attorney, Dorsey & Whitney LLP, Minneapolis, MN.

McELROY, SCOTT B.
  (attorney)
Education: Washington & Lee University, BA, 1970; University of Toedo College of Law, JD, 1974. *Affiliation & Address*: Partner, McElroy, Meyer, Walker & Condon, P.C., 1007 Pearl St., Suite 220, Boulder, CO 80302 (303) 442-2021. E-mail: s,celroy@mmwcclaw.com. His practice is limited to the representation of Indian tribes and their members, concentrating on the litigation & negotiation of natural resource & jurisdicatioal disputes. *Past professional posts*: Attorney, U.S. Deartment of Justice & Department of the Interior, and Native Ameriacn Rights Fund. *Awards, honors*: Fellow of the American College of Trial Lawyers; 2007 edition of The Best Lawyers in America, in the specialty of Native American law.

McGEE, HAROLD FRANKLIN, JR. 1945-
 (professor of anthropology)
Born June 5, 1945, Miami, Fla. *Education*: Florida State University, BA, 1966, MA, 1967; Southern Illinois University, PhD, 1974. *Principal occupation*: Professor of anthropology. *Address*: Dept. of Anthropology, Saint Mary's U., Halifax, Nova Scotia, Can. B3H 3C3 (902) 420-5628. *Affiliations*: Professor, Dept. of Anthropology, Saint Mary's U., Halifax, Nova Scotia, Can. *Other professional post*: Consultant to museums and other institutions. *Memberships*: Royal Anthropological Institute of Great Britain & Ireland (Fellow). *Interests*: Mr. McGee writes, "(My) major area of interest and expertise is with contemporary and historic Micmac and Malecite peoples of Atlantic Canada. In addition to standard ethnological concerns as an academic, I am interested in getting the non-native population to understand the reasons for similarity and difference of the native peoples' life ways to their own so that they will encourage governments to allow for greater local autonomy by the native people. Academically, I am particularly interested in native world view, politics, aesthetics, and reconstruction of aboriginal society and culture." *Published works*: Native Peoples of Atlantic Canada (McClelland and Stewart, 1974); The Micmac Indians: The First Migrants in Banked Fires-The Ethnics of Nova Scotia, ed. D. Campbell (Scribbler's Press, 1978); journal articles and papers.

McGERTT, CHARLIE (Creek)
 (tribal town king)
Affiliation: Thlopthlocco Tribal Town, Box 706, Okemah, OK 74859 (918) 623-2620.

McGESHICK, CHRIS. (Mole Lake Ojibwe)
 (tribal chairperson)
Affiliation & Address: Chairperson, Sokaogon (Mole Lake) Band of Lake Superior Chippewa, 3051 Sand Lake Rd., Crandon, WI 54520 (715) 478-7500.

McGESHICK, GARLAND T. (Mole Lake Ojibwe)
 (former tribal chairperson)
Affiliation: Sokaogon (Mole Lake) Band of Lake Superior Chippewa, 3051 Sand Lake Rd., Crandon, WI 54520 (715) 478-7500.

McGESHICK, JOHN (Chippewa)
 (tribal chairperson)
Affiliation: Lac Vieux Desert Band of Chippewa Indians, P.O. Box 249, Choate Rd., Watersmeet, MI 49969 (906) 358-4577.

McGHEE, DANIEL (Poarch Band Creek)
 (former tribal secretary)
Education: University of Alabama, Tuscaloosa, B.A. (Phi Kappa Phi). *Address & Affiliation*: Tribal Secretary (2000-09), Poarch Band of Creek Indians, 5811 Jack Springs Rd., Atmore, AL 36502 (251) 368-9136. E-mail: dmcghee@pci-nsn.gov. *Other professional posts*: Tribe's Powwow Committee; Recreation Committee; Chairperson, Education Committee; Site Manager, Creek Entertainment Center. He is an alumni of the Leadership Atmore Program & V.P. of Huxford Elementary P.T.O. He is an accomplished artist & graphic designer. *Past professional posts*: Community Relations Director, Tribal Administrator of the Tribe's Gaming Regulatory & Compliance Commission, 1996-2000.

McGHEE, ROBERT (Poarch Band Creek)
 (tribal vice chair)
Education: University of South Alabama, BA; University of Alabama, BSW; Washington University, MA; Georgetown Executive Leadership Program, Washington, DC; University of Tennessee, Knoxville, MBA. *Affiliation & Address*: Vice Chair (2014-present), Poarch Band of Creek Indians, 5811 Jack Springs Rd., Atmore, AL 36502 (251) 368-9136. E-mail: rmcghee@pci-nsn.gov. *Other professional post*: Secretary, Creek Indian Enterprises Board of Directors. *Past professional posts*: Dept. of the Interior, Bureau of Indian Affairs; U.S. Senate Committee on Indian Affairs, and Troutman Sanders LLP-Indian Law Practice Group, 2005-2009; Tribal Administrator (2000-04), Treasurer (2009-14), Poarch Band of Creek Indians; president & CEO, Creek Indian Enterprises, 1995-1999. *Community activities*: Vice president, Atmore Chamber of Commerce; vice chairman of the Episcopal Council of Indigenous Ministries.

McGINNIS, DAKOTA (Wiyot)
 (tribal vice chairperson & economic development director)
Affiliation & Address: Vice Chairperson & Economic Development Director, Bear River Band of the Rohnerville Rancheria, 27 Bear River Rd., Loleta, CA 95551 (707) 733-1900. E-mail: dakotamcginnis@brb-nsn.gov

McGINNIS, HELEN
 (museum director)
Affiliation: Tsut'ina K'osa (Sarcee), 3700 Anderson Rd., S.W., P.O. Box 67, Calgary, AB, Canada T2W 3C4 (403) 238-2676/7.

McGOVRAN, MARYANN (Mono)
 (former tribal chairperson)
Affiliation & Address: Former chairperson, North Fork Rancheria of Mono Indians, P.O. Box 929, North Fork, CA 93643 (559) 877-2461.

McGREGOR, DEBORAH (Anishnabe First Nation)
 (professor & director in Aboriginal Studies & Geography)
Affiliation & Address: Assistant Professor & Interim Director, Aboriginal Studies & Geography, University of Toronto, Toronto, ON M5S 2J7 (416) 978-2234. E-mail: Deborah.mcgregor@utoronto.ca. Professor McGregor focus is on Indigenus knowledge in relation to the environment. She is also an environmental consultant for various Ontario First Nations organizations.

McGUIRE, BETSY (Athabascan)
 (radio station manager)
Affiliation: KSKO - 870 AM, P.O. Box 195, McGrath, AK 99627 (907) 524-3001.

McGUIRE, KYLE (Umatilla)
 (triball vice chairperson)
Affiliation & Address: Confederated Tribes of the Umatilla Indian Reservation, Nixyaawii Governance Center, 46411 Timine Way, Pendleton, OR 97801 (541) 429-7379; E-mail: kylemcguire@ctuir.org

McHORSE, JOEL C. (Navajo/Taos Pueblo)
 (artist)
Address: P.O. Box 1711 • Santa Fe, NM 87504 (505) 989-7716. E-mail: McHorse@ix.netcom.com. *Artwork*: Pottery, silver jewelry & silverwork.

McINTYRE, ALLAN J.
 (museum curator)
Affiliation: The Amerind Foundation Museum, P.O. Box 248, Dragoon, AZ 86509 (602) 586-3666.

McKAY, ALEX (Anishnabe First Nation)
 (lecturer in Aboriginal studies)
Born & raised in northern Ontario, Canada. *Affiliation & Address*: Coordinator, Ojibwa Language Program, Aboriginal Studies, University of Toronto, Toronto, ON M5S 2J7 (416) 978-2233. E-mail: alex.mckay@utoronto.ca. Alex teaches courses in Language & Culrture, Aboriginal Teaching & Legends, and the Indian Act. He has recently been involved in a research project in which he has collected autobiographies from elder women in the northern Ontario community that he comes from. These are being transcribed.

McKAY, GINA
 (program centre head)
Affiliation: West Region Tribal Council, Indian Cultural Education Program, 21-4th Ave., N.W., Dauphin, MB, Canada R7N 1H9 (204) 638-8225.

McKAY, MARSHALL (Yocha Dehe Wintun)
 (former tribal chairperson)
Born in Colusa, California and grew up in Brooks nar his present-day home in Yocha Dehe tribal community. *Affiliation & Address*: Yocha Dehe Wintun Nation, Rumsey Rancheria, P.O. Box 18, Brooks, CA 95606 (530) 796-3400. Chairperson McKay oversees the day-to-day operations of the tribal government and the tribe's Cache Creek Casino Resort. *Other professional posts*: Commissioner, California Native American Heritage Commission, West Sacramento, CA; Board Chair-person, Native Arts & Cultures Foundation, Vancouver, WA; Chair of the Cultural Committee & Community Fund Committee; member of the Fire Commission, Property, Farm & Ranch Committee, Health & Wellness Committee, and the Yocha Dehe Wintun Academy Board; member, Board of Directors, Cache Creek Casino Resort; president, Board of Trustees of the Yocha-De-He Preparatory; Involved with the California Indian Project, University of California, Berkeley, the Institute of American Indian Arts, Santa Fe, NM, and Autry National Center and Southwest Museum of the American Indian. *Past professional post*: Treasurer & secretary, Rumsey Band of Wintun Indians. *Awards, honors*: Appointed by Governor Arnold Schwarzenneger November 2007 as commissioner to the Native American Heritage Commission, Sacramento, CA; appointed in 2009 to the Board of Trustees for the Smithsonian's National Museum of American Indians (NMAI); founding member of the Native Arts & Cultures Foundation; 2010 appointment to the board of the Native American Rights Fund (NARF).

McKAY, NEIL CANTEMAZZA (Spirit Lake Dakota/Turtle Mountain Ojibwe)
 (Dakota language specialist)
Education: University of Minnesota, BA (American Indian Studies), 1997. *Address & Affiliation*: American Indian Studies Department, University of Minnesota, Twin Cities Campus, College of Liberal Arts, 2 Scott Hall, 72 Pleasant St. SE, Minneapolis, MN 55455 (612) 624-1338. E-mail: mckay020@umn.edu. *Community activities*: Dakota Language Talking Table; advisor, to the student based Dakota Language Society. *Interests*: The preservation and

restoration of the Dakota language & culture; new curriculum & texts for the Dakota language

McKAY, WALLY (Ojibwe)
(member-board of directors)
Affiliation: Intertribal Christian Communications, P.O. Box 3765, Station B, Winnipeg, MB, Canada R2W 3R6 (204) 661-9333.

McKEE, RICHARD
(Indian education program counselor)
Affiliation: Milburn Public School, Indian Education Program, P.O. Box 429, Milburn, OK 73450 (405) 443-5522.

McKEE, WILLIAM
(BIA agency supt.)
Affiliation & Address: Supt., Bureau of Indian Affairs, Fort Totten Agency, P.O. Box 270, Fort Totten, ND 58335 (701) 766-4545.

McKENZIE, KENNETH (Eastern Creek)
(tribal chairperson)
Affiliation: Florida Tribe of Eastern Creek Indians, P.O. Box 3028, Bruce, FL 32455 (904) 835-2078.

McKINN, JOHN (Gila River Maricopa)
(associate director of American Indian studies)
Affiliation & Address: Associate Director, American Indian Studies, 1204 W. Nevada St. MC-138, Urbana, IL 61801 (217) 265-9878; E-mail: mckinn@illinois.edu. *Research Interests*: American Indian literature after 1850.

McKINNEY, ROGER (*Sinnagwin*) (Kickapoo) 1957-
(educator; artist)
Born February 24, 1957, Kansas City, Mo. *Education*: Graceland College (Lamoni, IA), BA, 1982; The American University (Washington, DC), MFA (Painting), 1986. *Affiliation & Address*: Program Advisor, 1996-2000; Interim Director, American Indian Programs, 2001-01; Residential Art Faculty (2002-present), Scottsdale Community College, 9000 E. Chaparral Rd., Scottsdale, AZ 85256 (480) 423-6000. *Past professional posts*: Art instructor/guidance counselor, Kickapoo Nation School, Horton, KS (acting supt./principal), 1982-83; associate/trainer, ORBIS Associates, Washington, DC, 1986-88; coordinator, Youth Leadership Program, Zuni School District, Zuni, NM, 1988-89; program management & design specialist, Southwest Resource and Evaluation Center IV, Tempe, AZ, 1989-91; educator, The Heard Museum, Phoenix, AZ, 1991-96. *Other professional post*: Professional artist. *Exhibitions*: Ha-Pa-Nyi Fine Arts Gallery, Santa Barbara, CA, 1988; Native American Arts Exhibition, UCSB, 1988; 68th Inter-Tribal Indian Ceremonial, Gallup, NM, 1989; Second Annual Lawrence Indian Arts Show, University of Kansas, 1990; Cultural Reality or Cultural Fantasy, Institute of American Indian Arts, Santa Fe, NM, 1991-92; Santa Fe Indian Market, 1991; among others. *Works in Public Collection/Places*: Graceland College Art Collection, Lamoni, IA; Kickapoo Nation School, Powhattan, KS; Watkins Gallery Collection, The American University, Washington, DC; among others. *Awards, honors*: Guitano Capasso Award, All Dept. Shoe, Graceland College, 1982; Second Premium Watercolor, Fairfax Co. Parks, Burke, VA, 1984; Wolpoff Award, Works on Paper, The American University, Watkins Collection, 1986; Honorable Mention, 68th Annual Inter-Tribal Indian Ceremonial, 1989; DeGrazia, Artist in Residence, The Heard Museum, 1990; Merit Award, Lawrence Indian Arts Show, 1990. *Biographical sources*: Public TV Broadcasting - Kickapoo Nation, Return to Sovereignty (University of Kansas, PBS, 1983); Twenty First Century Native American (CBS, Phoenix, AZ).

McKINNEY, THOMAS R., Sr. (*Gentgeen-Dancer*) (Seneca) 1951-
(fire fighter, museum director)
Born October 27, 1951, Butler Co., Penna. *Education*: Bacone Junior College, AA, 1974. *Address*: 323 Lawrence St., Muskogee, OK 74403 (918) 682-9138. *Affiliations*: Museum director, Bacone College, Muskogee, OK, 1990-; fire fighter, Muskogee Fire Dept., Muskogee, OK, 1979-. *Other professional posts*: Dancer of traditional Native American origin; Post Master of Boy Scouts, explorer post, specializing in Native American culture. *Community activities*: Inspector for district election board, member, Chamber of Commerce; member, Muskogee antique collector's guild. *Membership*: Muskogee Fire Fighters local #57. *Awards, honors*: Instructor I professional Fire Fighters; Honorable mention and work in the permanent collection of the Black Hills art competition; Eagle Scout; Vigil member of The Order of the Arrow; DAR achievement award. *Interests*: Native American studies, professional fire fighting skills, anthropology & ethnology; Native American dancing & the making of traditional clothing.

McKNIGHT, CINDY
(editor)
Affiliation: "Smoke Signals," Dallas Inter-Tribal Center, 209 E. Jefferson Blvd., Dallas, TX 75203 (214) 941-1050.

McKOSATO, HARLAN (Sac & Fox Nation of OK)
(radio host & producer)
Grew up on the Iowa Reservation in north central Oklahoma. *Education*: University of Oklahoma, BS (Journalism & Mass Communications), 1988. *Affiliation & Address*: Host/Producer, Native America Calling (NAC), P.O. Box 40164, Albuquerque, NM 87196 (505) 277-5201. E-mail: harlan@native americacalling.com. *Other professional posts*: Columnist, Santa Fe New Mexican magazine, 1999-present; special contributor, New Mexico Business Weekly magazine; commentator for the National Public Radio's talk show "All Things Considered"; serves on the screening committee for the Grammy's "Best Native American Album" category. *Awards, honors*: In 2002, he was appointed Chairman of the Albuquerque Mayor's Commission on Indian Affairs; 2003 Reader's Choice for "Best Radio Personality in New Mexico" by the statewide-circulated "Crosswinds Weekly magazine; 2005 Distinguished Alumnus, Gaylord College of Journalism, University of Oklahoma.

McLANE, MICHAEL (Lenni Lenape-Delaware)
(tribal vice president)
Affiliation & Address: Vice President, Delaware Nation, P.O. Box 825, Anadarko, OK 73005 (405) 247-2448.

McLAUGHLIN, JESSE B.J. (Standing Rock Sioux)
(tribal vice chairperson)
Affiliation & Address: Vice Chairperson (2013-present), Standing Rock Sioux Tribe, P.O. Box D, Fort Yates, ND 58538 (701) 854-8500.

McLAUGHLIN, MICHAEL (*Kaga shoga*) (Winnebago of Nebraska) 1951-
(librarian)
Born in 1951, Sioux City, Iowa. *Education*: University of California, Los Angeles, MLIS, 1995, MA (American Indian Studies-History & Law), 1999. *Affiliation & Address*: Librarian, American Indian Resource Center, Huntington Park Public Library, 6518 Miles Ave., Huntington Park, CA 90255 (323) 583-2794. E-mail: airc@gw.colapl.org. *Past professional posts*: Los Angeles Public Library Municipal Reference, 1989-95; UCLA-American Indian Studies Center - American Indian Terminology Project, 1995-99; American Indian Resource Center, Huntington Park, CA, 1999-present. *Community activities*: Member, American Indian Children's Council (Los Angeles County). *Membership*: American Indian Library Association. *Interests*: Urban American Indian topics; tribal sovereignty & relations with U.S. Government; developing library materials on American Indian subjects beyond standard library classification practices and systems.

McLAUGHLIN, STEVE
(BIA agency supt.)
Affiliation: Crow Creek Agency, BIA, P.O. Box 616, Ft. Thompson, SD 57339 (605) 245-2311.

McLEOD, LINDA (Wabanaki)
(Indian school principal)
Affiliation & Address: Principal, Indian Island School, 10 Wabanaki Way, Indian Island, ME 04468 (207) 827-4285. E-mail: linda.mcleod@bie.edu.

McLEOD, NEAL (Cree)
(professor of Indigenous studies)
Education: University of Saskatchewan, BA & MA; University of Regina, PhD. *Affiliation & Address*: Professor, Department of Indigenous Studies, Trent University, 1600 Westbank Dr., Peterborough, ON K9J 7B8 (705) 748-1011, E-mail: nealmcleod@trentu.ca. *Primary Research Areas*: Cree culture & history; Western Canadian Indigenous history; Indigenous, knowledge, political history, art & poetry. *Published works*: Songs to Kill a Wihtikow (Hagios Press, 2005); Gabriel's Beach (Hagios Press, 2008); numerous articles & book chapters.

McMASTER, GERALD R. (Plains Cree-Nehiyawuk) 1953-
(deputy assistant director for cultural resources)
Born March 9, 1953, North Battleford, Saskatchewan, Can. *Education*: Institute of American Indian Art (Santa Fe, 1973-75); Minneapolis College of Art & Design, BFA, 1977; Banff School of Fine Arts (Banff, Alberta), 1986; Carleton University (Ottawa, ON), MA, 1994. *Affiliation & Address*: Deputy Assistant Director for Cultural Resources (2001-present), National Museum of the American Indian, Smithsonian Institution, 470 L'Enfant Plaza, SW, Suite 7103, Washington, DC 20560 (202) 287-2525. *Past professional posts*: Head of the Indian Art Program, Saskatchewan Indian Federated College, Regina, Sask., 1977-81; curator, Canadian Museum of Civilization, Ottawa, Ont., 1981-2001. *Other professional posts*: Adjunct Research Professor, Carleton University, 1992-95; self-employed visual artist, 1977-; artistic coordinator for Plains Indian Dancers & Singers, the Holland Festival, Amsterdam, the Netherlands,

1984-85; program coordinator, Native Art Studies Group of Ottawa, 1984-85. *Solo exhibitions*: The Cowboy/Indian Show - Ufundi Gallery, Ottawa, Ontario, 1990; McMichael Canadian Gallery, Kleinburg, Ontario, 1991. Savage Graces: "afterimages by Gerald McMaster - UBC-Museum of Anthropology, Vancouver, BC, 1992; Winnipeg Art Gallery, 12/94-1/95; Windsor Art Gallery, 1994; Southern Alberta Art Gallery, 1994; Ottawa Art Gallery, 1994; Edmonton Art Gallery, 1995; Memorial Art Gallery, St. Johns, Newfoundland, 1995; numerous group exhibitions. *Collections represented*: Carleton University, Canadian Museum of Civilization, Dept. of Indian Affairs (Ottawa, ON), University of Regina, Canada Council Art Bank, City of Ottawa, City of Regina, Institute of American Indian Arts (Santa Fe, NM), Gettysburg College (Gettysburg, PA), Guilford Native American Art Gallery (Greensboro, NC). Commissions: Metro-Toronto, 1992; City of Ottawa, 1991; Canadian Museum of Civilization, Ottawa, 1988; among others. *Membership*: Native Art Studies Association of Canada (vice-president, 1987, president, 1988-92; editor, NASAC Newsletter); Ontario Arts Council (board member, 1991-); ICOM Canada (board member, 1992-). *Awards, honors*: Canada Council Travel Grants, to travel and present papers at various conference & workshops, 1989, '90, '93; Honorable Mention, National Educational Film Festival/Certificate for Creative Excellence, U.S. Industrial Film Festival, Firearms Safety Series, Indian Hunting Traditions, 1983; First Prize, "Byron and His Balloon, La Roche, Saskatchewan, 1981; Second Prize, wood sculpture, Scottsdale Annual Indian Art Competition, 1976. *Interests*: Travel; art exhibitions. From 1986 to 1989 developed concept for a National Indian & Inuit Art Gallery in the new Canadian Museum of Civilization. *Reviews on artist*: "Punning Artist Uses Native Wit," by Robin Laurence (The Georgia Straight, Aug 14-21, 1992); "Native Painter's Criticism Packs Strong Punchline," by Christopher Hume (The Toronto Star, Feb. 8, 1991; "Native Artist Throws Comic Curves But With a Serious Twist," by Nancy Baele (Ottawa Citizen, Feb. 24, 1991; "Indian Lore," by Nancy Baele (Ottawa Citizen, June 15, 1989; "Public Servant-Painter Wants to Help Native Artists," by Nancy Baele (Ottawa Citizen, Nov. 11, 1988); "Teacher-Artist's Commitment Extends Beyond Work As Curator," by Bill White (Echo-National Museums of Canada, Vol. 4, No. 7, Oct/Nov., 1984); among others. *Published works*: Indigena: Contemporary Native Perspectives, edited with Lee-Ann Martin (Douglas & McIntyre, Vancouver, 1992); First American Art: The Charles & Valerie Diker Collection of American Indian Art (University of Washington Press, 2004); Native Universe: Voices of Native America, edited with Clifford Trafzer (National Geographic Books, 2004); numerous articles. Recordings: "Songs from Bismarck," Indian Records, Taos, N.M (sang with the Red Earth Singers), 1976.

McMASTER, LAVERNA
(director-Indian centre)
Affiliation: Calgary Native Friendship Centre, 140 - 2nd Ave., S.W., Calgary, AB, Canada T2P 0B9 (403) 264-1155.

McMULLEN, Patrick
(administrator)
Affiliation: Majority Professional Staff, Senate Committee on Indian Affairs, 836 Hart Office Bldg., Washington, DC 20510 (202) 224-2251. Website: www.senate.gov/~scia/

McNAMARA, DEXTER (Odawa)
(former tribal chairperson)
Affiliation & Address: Chairperson, Little Traverse Bay Bands of Odawa Indians, 7500 Odawa Circle, Harbor Springs, MI 49740 (231) 242-1418.

McNEELY, KATHLEEN (Sault Ste. Marie Chippewa) 1951-
(librarian/director of library services)
Born February 19, 1951, Petoskey, Mich. *Education*: Lake Superior University, Sault Ste. Marie, MI (4 years); University of Southwestern Louisiana, Lafayette (1 year). *Principal occupation*: Librarian/Director of Library Services, Hannahville School-Community Library (Nah Tah Wahsh Library), Hannahville Reservation, Wilson, MI, 1985-. *Address*: W1971 Isaacson Dr., Menominee, MI 49858 (906) 466-2556 (work). *Other professional posts*: Lifestyle editor, Sault Evening News, Sault Ste. Marie, MI; managing editor, Franklin Banner, Franklin, LA. *Community activities*: St. Ignace Powwow Committee, St. Ignace, MI; Menominee County Library (board of trustees); Michinemackinong Powwow Committee (chairperson). *Memberships*: Bay De Noc Culture Association (board of directors); American Library Association (Minorities Round Table). *Awards, honors*: 1980 Outstanding Citizens of the Year - West St. Mary Parish Chamber of Commerce, Franklin, LA; 1991 Candidate for Medal of Honor, Michigan Daughters of the American Revolution. *Interests*: "Traditional & jingle dress dancer promoting traditional ways to our youth as alternatives to substance abuse."

McNEIL, CHRIS E., JR. (*Shaakakooni*) (Tlingit)
(president & CEO)
Born in Juneau, Alaska. *Education*: Stanford University, BA (Political Science); Yale University, MA (Political Science); Stanford Law School, JD. *Affiliation & Address*: President & CEO (2001-present), Sealaska Corporation, One

Sealaska Plaza, Suite 400, Juneau, AK 99801 (907) 586-1512. Mr. McNeil has worked for Sealaska Corporation since 1978, holding various positions, including two terms as executive vice president & general council and one term on the board of directors. Other professional post: Blue Stone Tribal Advisor, Phoenix, AZ. *Past professional posts*: Washington representative & counsel to the Mashantucket Pequot Tribal Nation in Connecticut; chairperson of the Native American Rights Fund; director, American Indian Programs at Stanford University; director, Goldbelt, Inc.; director, American Indian National Bank; president of the JuneauTlingit & Haida Community Council; chairperson of the Tlingit & Haida Regional Housing Authority; second vice president of the Tlingit & Haida Indians of Alaska.

McNEIL, RONALD S. (*His Horse Is Thunder*) (Hunkpapa Lakota) 1958-
(college president)
Born March 19, 1958, Rapid City, S.D. *Education*: Standing Rock College, AA, 1982; Black Hills State College, BS, 1985; University of South Dakota Law School, JD, 1988. *Principal occupation*: College president. *Address*: P.O. Box 67, Fort Yates, ND 58538 (701) 854-3861. *Affiliation*: President, Sitting Bull (Standing Rock) College, 1341 92nd St., Fort Yates, ND 58538, 1991-present. *Past professional posts*: Indian Law Instructor & Federal Grants Administrator, University of South Dakota Law School, 1989-91; president, American Indian College Fund, Denver, CO, 1993-1995. *Community activities*: Participates in tribal government & cultural activities. *Memberships*: SD Indian Education Association; American Indian Higher Education Consortium. *Interests*: Vocational: Native American higher education. In his two-year term as president of the American Indian College Fund, he hopes to help the Fund broaden its outreach and greatly increase its funding. "This is a very exciting time in the Indian-college movement. The older colleges are maturing and starting to offer bachelor's and master's programs, while new colleges are emerging all the time. Indian colleges are vital to the cultural survival of our people. I want to do all I can to help them grow."

McNELEY, DR. JAMES K.
(college vice president)
Affiliation: Dine (Navajo) College, P.O. Box 126, Tsaile, AZ 86556 (520) 724-6671.

McNICHOLS, ROBERT R.
(Indian affairs)
Born October 16, 1950, Columbus, Ohio. *Education*: BS (Gneral Studies/Forestry). *Address*: 2175 Seneca St., Kingman, AZ 86401. E-mail: bobmcnichols@rezbuilders.com. *Affiliation*: Superintendent, Truxton Canon Agency, Bureau of Indian Affairs, P.O. Box 37, Valentine, AZ 86437 (928) 769-2286. *Other professional post*: Certified Economic Developer. *Memberships*: American Economic Development Council; Society of American Foresters. *Interests*: Native American economic and community development.

McPEAK, JERRY (Muscogee Creek)
(D - Warner, OK state representative)
Affiliation: Co-chair, Native American Caucus of the Oklahoma House of Representatives, c/o Oklahoma Indian Affairs Commission, 4545 N. Lincoln Blvd., Suite 282, Oklahoma City, OK 73105 (405) 521-3828; Website: www.ok.gov/oiac/. Rep. McPeak is the Assistant Democratic Floor Leader of the House. He serves as member of the General Government & Transportation Committee; Economic Development & Financial Services Committee; Energy Subcommittee; and Transportation Subcommittee.

McPETERS, ANTHONY STEPHEN (*Walks in Two Worlds*) (Lumbee) 1944-
(drum builder)
Born July 26, 1944, Griffin, GA. *Address*: 117 Milling Rd., Poulan, GA 31781-2020 (912) 776-4292. *Affiliation*: Owner, Two Worlds Arts & Crafts, Poulan, GA, 1986-. *Military service*: U.S. Navy, 1959-63.

McPHERSON, DENNIS (First Nation Ojibwa)
(chair & professor of Indigenous Learning)
A member of the Couchiching First Nation at Fort Frances, Ontario, Canada. *Education*: BA (Arts), HBSW (Social Work), HBA-Phil (Philosophy), LLB & LLM (Law). *Affiliation & Address*: Chairperson & Associate Professor, Department of Indigenous Learning, RB 3020, 955 Oliver Rd., Thunder Bay, ON P7B 5E1 (807) 343-8984. E-mail: dennis.mcpherson@lakeheadu.ca. *Other professional post*: Coordinator & Co-Director, Native Philosophy Project, Lakehead University. *Published work*: Indian From the Inside: A Study in Ethno-Metaphysics, with Douglas Rabb, as a textbook in the delivery of Philosophy 2805, Native Canadain Worldviews, the first course in Native philosophy to be offered in a Canadian university. *Awards, honors*: Professor McPherson presented a paper on "Heteronomy & Autonomy in Canadian Native Policy" written with Duglas Rabb. It was the first time that a Native Canadian has presented a paper on Native philosophy at the Ontario Phiosophical Association Conference. He was instrumental in the development of the Department of Indigenous Learning within Lakehead University and the Master's Program in Native Philosophy.

McQUEEN, VICTOR, JR. (Lemhi Shoshone)
(tribal vice chairperson)
Affiliation & Address: Vice Chairperson, Ely Shoshone Tribe, 400 Newe View Dr., Ely, NV 89301 (775) 289-3013.

McSWAIN, ROBERT G. (North Fork Rancheria of Mono Indians of Calif.)
(director - IHS Office of Management Services)
Education: California State University-Fresno, BS (Business Administration), 1969; University of Southern California, M.P.A. (Public Administration), 1986. *Affiliation & Address*: Director (2017-present), Office of management Services, Indian Health Service (IHS), U.S. Dept. HHS, The Reyes Bldg., 801 Thompson Ave. #400, Rockville, MD 20852 (301) 443-1083. *Past professional posts*: Executive director, California Rural Indian Health Board, Clovis, CA, 1974-76; director, IHS California Area Office, 1976-84; special assistant to the director, IHS, 1984-92; acting associate director, IHS Office of Human Resources, 1992-97; director, IHS Office of Management Support, 1997-2004; acting deputy director of IHS Office of Management Operations, 2004-05; IHS deputy director, 2005-07 where he supervised the 12 IHS Area Directors; acting director, IHS, 2007-09; IHS Deputy Director for Management Operations (2009-12); Acting Director, IHS, 2013-14, Principal Deputy Director, 2014-16). *Awards, honors*: President's Rank Award for Meritorious Service in 2002 and Distinguished Service in 2006.

McTAGGART, FRED
(author)
McTaggart was a postdoctoral fellow in the Newberry Library's Center for the History of the American Indian, Chicago. *Published works*: Wolf That I Am: In Search of the Red Earth People (University of Oklahoma Press, 1985).

MEAD, BRIAN (Wiyot)
(tribal vice chairperson & administrator)
Affiliation & Address: Vice Chairperson & Tribal Administrator, Wiyot Tribe of the Table Bluff Rancheria, 1000 Wiyot Dr., Loleta, CA 95551 (707) 733-5055.

MEADE, BRENDA (Coquille)
(tribal chairperson)
Affiliation & Address: Chairperson, Coquille Indian Tribe, P.O. Box 783, North Bend, OR 97549 (541) 756-0904. E-mail: brendameade@coquilletribe.org.

MEANS, DAVID (Oglala Lakota)
(health director)
Affiliation: Northern Cheyenne PHS Indian Health Center, P.O. Box 70, Lame Deer, MT 59043 (406) 477-6201.

MEANS, JEFFREY D. (Oglala Lakota)
(historian, professor of American Indian studies)
Education: PhD (History). *Affiliation & Address*: Assistant professor, American Indian Studies Program, History Room 255, College of Arts & Sciences, University of Wyoming, 1000 E. University Ave., Laramie, WY 82071 (307) 766-3198. E-mail: jmeans4@uwyo.edu. *Research & teaching interests*: Identifying Great Plains Indian cultures, specifically the Oglala Lakota culture. Jeff is currently studying the spiritual & economic relationship developed between the Oglala Lakota and cattle during the 19th & early 20th century. *Awards, honors*: Power-Tanner Fellowship in American Indian Studies at the Newberry Library; the Burlingame O'Toole Award from the Montana Historical Society for the best graduate student article for 2003; the Phillips Fund Gant from the American Philosophical Society.

MEANS, WILLIAM A. (Oglala Lakota)
(organization council member)
Affiliations & Address: Co-founder & board member, American Indian Movement (AIM), P.O. Box 13521, Minneapolis, MN 55414 (612) 721-3914; founder & board member, International Indian Treaty Council (IITC). *Past professional post*: Executive director, Heart of the Earth Survival School.

MECHELS, DONALD (Chinook)
(tribal chairperson)
Affiliation: Chinook Indian Tribe, P.O. Box 228, Chinook, WA 98614 (360) 777-8303.

MEDFORD, CLAUDE, JR. (Choctaw) 1941-
(artist)
Born April 14, 1941, Lufkin, Tex. *Education*: University of New Mexico, BA, 1964; Oklahoma State University, 1969. *Principal occupation*: Artist. *Address*: Coushatta Indian Tribe, P.O. Box 818, Elton, LA 70532 (318) 584-2261. *Affiliations*: Museum director, Alabama-Coushatta Indian Reservation; manager of the Coushatta Cultural Center, Elton, LA; taught classes and workshops at the American Indian Archaeological Institute in Washington, CT in 1979, and the Clifton Choctaw Indian Community west of Alexandria, LA, in 1981; received a folk arts apprenticeship fellowship from the Louisiana State Arts Council, Division of the Arts, and now teachers basketry to any interested Indian among the five surviving tribes of Louisiana. Mr. Medford is a gifted craftsman and practitioner of Southeast Indian arts, including basketry, pottery, woodworking, metalworking, beadwork, featherwork, horn & hoofwork, brain tanning of deer hides, leatherworking & gourd work. His baskets are in numerous private collections as well as several public collections, that of the Southern Plains Indian Museum, the Museum of the Red River in Idabel, OK, Tantaquidgeon Mohegan Museum in Uncasville, CT and a traveling exhibit to be circulated by the Smithsonian Institution Traveling Exhibition Service. Since 1972, he has shown his work each year at the New Orleans Jazz and Heritage Festival. *Interests*: To perpetuate the arts & culture of the Southeastern Indian tribes. *Published works*: Numerous articles for various publications.

MEDICINE-EAGLE, BROOKE (*Daughter of the Rainbow*)
(Crow/Lakota/Nez Perce) 1943-
(international educator-catalyst for wholeness)
Born April 24, 1943, Crow Reservation, Mont. *Education*: University of Denver, BA; Mankato State University, MS; Humanistic Psychology Institute, ABD in Body Therapy and Native American Systems of Wholeness. *Address*: P.O. Box C401, One 2nd Ave. East, Polson, MT 59860 (406) 883-4686. E-mail: brooke@medicine-eagle.com. *Affiliations*: Self-employed via Earth Mages, Unlimited; Singing Eagle Music; Eagle Song Camps; also teaching affiliate with Feathered Pipe Foundation. *Community activities*: Serves a global community of those interested in healing themselves and Mother Earth. *Interests*: Her dedication is to bring forward the ancient truths concerning how to live a fully human life in harmony with All Our Relations. Brooke's primary interest is in the renewal of ancient ritual forms for creating a beautiful path upon Mother Earth, today and for the future. To this end she is creating an in-depth training, Wakantia, to awaken and challenge participants to the next level of being human, as Earth Mages living in harmony and grace upon a renewed Earth. She and Feathered Pipe Foundation produce "Song of the Nations" -- a blending of the finest teachers of Celtic, native and other traditions to open a path of beauty into the future. *Published works*: Buffalo Woman Comes Singing, a spiritual autobiography, 1991; The Last Ghost Dance: A Guide for Earth Mages 2000.

MEDICINEBULL, ORIE (*Hugaitha*) (Western Mono)
(executive director)
Born December 6 in Madera County, Calif. *Education*: UCLA, MFA, 1981; UC-Berkeley, MPH, 1983. *Principal occupation*: Administrator, artist-filmmaker, professor. *Address*: American Indian Center of Central California, P.O. Box 607, Auberry, CA 93602 (209) 855-2705. E-Mail: omedicinebull@telis.org. *Affiliations*: Executive director, American Indian Center of Central California, Auberry, CA; professor, Fresno City College, Fresno, CA. *Other professional posts*: Coordinator, Indian Education, Title V, Oakhurst, CA; coordinator, Sierra Children's Center, Oakhurst, CA. *Community activities*: Fresno American Indian Council (manpower director); Communication Committee (chairperson). *Memberships*: American Indian Women's Association (chairperson); Sierra Mono Museum; American Film Institute; UCLA & UC-Berkeley Alumni. *Awards, honors*: American Independent Filmmaker Award-Best Documentary, American Indian Film Festival; Best Documentary, Brockman International Gallery; Best Documentary Short, People's Film Festival (Italy); Carny Award, Golden Hills School District. *Interests*: "Major area of interest is outdoor, physical endurance hiking workout in Sierra Nevada Mountains as a team, ethnographic film study of Central California Indians of Central California (Numa)." *Published works*: Documentaries: "Colliding Worlds," 1980); Visions of Youth," 1991; and Success for American Indian Children," 1993 (all produced by Hugaitha Productions).

MEDINA, MAGDELENA "MENA" (Chehalis)
(former tribal chairperson)
Affiliation: Chehalis Community Council, P.O. Box 536, Oakville, WA 98568 (206) 273-5911.

MEDINA, MARCELLUS (Zia Pueblo)
(Pueblo governor)
Affiliation: Pueblo of Zia, 135 Capitol Square Dr., Zia Pueblo, NM 87053 (505) 867-3304.

MEDRANO, ANGELA M. (Cahuilla)
(attorney; community services coordinator)
Education: University of Southern California, BA, 2000; University of San Diego, JD, 2003. *Affiliation & Address*: TANF Community Services Coordinator, Pechanga Band of Luiseno Indians, P.O. Box 1477, Temecula, CA 92593 (951) 676-2768. *Other professional posts*: President, Native American Lawyers Association of San Diego County; board member, California Indian Law Association. *Past professional posts*: Staff Attorney, California Indian Legal Services (seven years); Lead Gaming Commissioner for the Cahuilla Band of Indians (two years).

MEEK, TERESA (Pomo)
(tribal vice chairperson)
Affiliation: Vice Chairperson, Habematolel Pomo of Upper Lake Rancheria, P.O. Box 516, Upper Lake, CA 95485 (707) 275-0737. *Past tribal positions*: Tribal Administrator, 2001-2003.

MEEKS, ELSIE (Oglala Lakota)
(SD USDA state director)
Affiliation & Address: South Dakota State Director (2009-present), U.S. Department of Agriculture Rural Development, 200 4th St. SW, Federal Bldg. Room 210, Huron, SD 57350 (605) 352-1100. E-mail: emeeks@usda.gov. *Past professional posts*: Chairperson, Native Financial Education Coalition (Oweesta serves as lead organization); member, International Advisory Council, Native Nations Institute; member, Board of Governors for the Honoring Nations Program of the Harvard Project on American Indian Economic Development; president/CEO, First Nations Oweesta Corp., Longmont, CO; chair & executive director (20 years), The Lakota Fund, Kyle, SD.; Federal Reserve Board's Consumer Advisory Council (three years); U.S. Commission on Civil Rights (three years); chair, Native Financial Education Coalition. *Awards, honors*: First Native American to serve on the U.S. Commission on Civil Rights.

MEEKS, KEVIN D., RADM (Chickasaw)
(IHS area director)
Education: East Central University, Ada, OK, BS; Oklahoma University Health Services Center. *Affiliation & Address*: Acting Deputy Director of Field Operations, Indian Health Service, Dept. of Health & Human Services, The Reyes Bldg., 801 Thompson Ave. #400, Rockville, MD 20852. E-mail: kevin.meeks@ihs.gov. *Past professional posts*: Director, Oklahoma City Area IHS, Oklahoma City, OK. RADM Kevin was responsible for the provision of comprehensive healthcare services to one of the largest and most diverse IHS service populations. RADM Meeks began his IHS career as a Commissioned Corps Officer in 1987. From 1987 through 1995, he served in a variety of Sanitarian/Environmental Health Officer positions in South Dakota, Oklahoma, and Alaska. From 1995 to 2009, he served in various management positions in the Oklahoma City Area Office. From 1995 to 2000, he served as the Assistant Associate Director for the Office of Environmental Health and Engineering (OEHE). From 2000 to 2006 he served as the Chief, Division of Environmental Health Service, and then from 2006 to 2007 he was the Associate Director, OEHE. In 2007 he was selected as the SE Regional Commissioned Corps Liaison, providing service to officers assigned to the Oklahoma City, Nashville, and Albuquerque Areas.

MEGGESTO, JAMES T. (Onondaga)
(attorney)
Education: State University of New York Colege at Brockport, BS, 1993; Albany Law School, Union University, JD, 1997. *Affiliation & Address*: Partner, Akin Gump Straus Hauer & Feld, LLP, Robert E. Straus Bldg., 1333 New Hampshire Ave. NW, Washington, DC 20036 (202) 887-4147; E-mail: jmeggesto@akingump.com. James advises clients regarding American Indian law & policy. He has represented Native American tribes & tribal entities in all regions of the country in areas such as Indian gaming law, land into trust matters, economic development and federal treaty rights litigation. *Community activities*: Member, Board of Diectors, Notah Begay III Foundation.

MEJIA, MARJORIE (Yurok)
(rancheria chairperson)
Affiliation & Address: Chairpeson, Lytton Rancheria, 1250 Coddingtown Center #1, Santa Rosa, CA 95401 (707) 575-5917.

MEJCHAR, GARY E.
(organization program director)
Education: University of Wisconsin, Madison, MS (Community Resource Development). *Affiliation & Address*: Program director, American Indian Chamber of Commerce of Wisconsin (AICCW), 10809 W. Lincoln Ave. #201, West Allis, WI 53227 (414) 604-2044. E-mail: gary.aiccw@gmail.com. *Past professional posts*: University of Wisconsin Extension (UWEX) working with the UW-Stevens Point Native American Center of Economic Development on Wisconsin Reservations Project & managing the UWEX Wisconsin American Indian Economic Development (WAIED) Program; management consultant specializing in business planning, project management, and assisting clients secure/administer project funding; assisted in the launch of the AICCW, Community Development Finance Institute.

MELAND, CARTER (White Earth Ojibwe)
(lecturer)
Affiliation & Address: American Indian Studies Department, University of Minnesota, Twin Cities Campus, College of Liberal Arts, 215 Scott Hall, 72 Pleasant St. SE, Minneapolis, MN 55455 (612) 625-3821. E-mail: melan002@umn.edu. *Interests*: American Indian writing; Ojibwe culture & philosophy. *Published work*: The Trickster is History (University of Oklahoma Press).

MELENDEZ, ARLAN D. (Paiute)
(tribal chairperson)
Affiliation & Address: Chairperson (1991-2010; 2015-present), Reno-Sparks Indian Colony, 98 Colony Rd., Reno, NV 89502 (775) 329-2936. E-mail: amelendez@rsic.org. *Other professional posts*: Chair, Taxation Subcommittee of the National Congress of American Indians; V.P., Inter-Tribal Council of Nevada. *Awards, honors*: Arlan was recently appointed to the U.S. Commission on Civil Rights by the Democratic Majority Leader of the U.S. Senate, Harry Reid (NV). Mr. Melendez is only the second Native American to serve on the Commission. *Past affiliations*: Treasurer & vice chairperson, Reno-Sparks Indian Colony, 1987-91; past president of the Inter-Tribal Council of Nevada; Western Region V.P. of the National Congress of American Indians.

MELENDEZ, RANDY
(Indian school principal)
Affiliation: Pyramid Lake High School, P.O. Box 256, Nixon, NV 89424 (702) 574-1016.

MELKILD, MARTIN A.
(museum curator)
Affiliation: Indian Drum Lodge Museum, 2308 N. US 31, Traverse City, MI 49684.

MELLICK, PETER (Athapascan)
(Alaskan village president)
Affiliation: Sleetmute Council, Box 109, Sleetmute, AK 99668 (907) 449-4205.

MELODY, MICHAEL E. 1947-
(professor; author)
Born October 14, 1947, Philadelphia, Penna. *Education*: University of Notre Dame, PhD, 1976. *Affiliation & Address*: Professor (1979-present), Barry University, 11300 N.E. 2nd Ave, Miami Shores, FL 33161 (305) 758-3391. *Other professional post*: Director & editor, Native American Policy Network & Newsletter. Published works: The Apache (Chelsea House, 2005); Indians of North America Heritage Edition (Chelsea House, 2005).

MELONI, ALBERTO C. 1946-
(executive director-Indian organization)
Born July 14, 1946, Lucca, Italy. *Education*: Marquette University, BA, MA; Harvard University, MA; University of Minnesota, Ph.D. *Affiliation & Address*: Executive Director, The Institute for American Indian Studies, P.O. Box 1260, Washington, CT 06793 (203) 868-0518. *Other professional posts*: Chief curator of collections & research; director of education; chief development officer, university instructor. *Community activities*: Hospice volunteer.

MENDOZA, GREGORY (Pima-Maricopa)
(tribal governor)
Education: Scottsdale Community College, AA, 1986; Arizona State University (Political Science & Government), 1986-88; University of Phoenix, BS (Business Administration & Management), 2004. *Affiliation & Address*: Governor (2012-present), Gila River Indian Community Council, P.O. Box 97, Sacaton, AZ 85147 (520) 562-9841. *Past professional posts*: Gila River Indian Community (Director of Youth Council, 1988-2005; Chief of Staff, 2006-11; Councilperson, 2011).

MENDOZA, PAULA (Ponca)
(tribal secretary-treasurer)
Affiliation & Address: Secretary/TreasurerPonca Tribe of Oklahoma, 20 White Eagle Dr., Ponca City, OK 74601 (580) 762-8104. E-mail: pmendoza@ponca.com.

MENDOZA, ZOLLA S.
(chair & director of Native American studies department)
Affiliation & Address: Department Chair & Professor, Department of Native American Studies, University of California, One Shields Ave., 2401 Hart Hall, Davis, CA 95616 (530) 752-9283. E-mail: zmendoza@ucdavis.edu.

MENINICK, JERRY (Yakama)
(tribal chairperson)
Affiliation: Yakama Tribal Council, P.O. Box 151, Toppenish, WA 98948 (509) 865-5121.

MENUSAN, FRANC (*Nookoosilichapko*) (Creek/Metis) 1954-
(artist/educator, storyteller/lecturer; musician)
Born May 17, 1954, New York, N.Y. *Education*: New York University, MA, 1984. Resides in New York City. *Affiliation*: Board of Education of the City of New York, 1982-; Museum of Natural History, New York, NY (Museum Teacher Associate Program); National Museum of the American Indian, Smithsonian, New York, NY (cultural interpreter, artist in residence). *Other professional posts*: Musician (Native American Flutes); composer of music

(using Native American instruments of Meso-America); speaker & consultant on Native American cultures; writer. *Community activities*: "I work with the American Indian Community House (New York City) as one of their artists on file," co-producing "Giving of Thanks to the First Peoples" Cathedral of St. John the Divine (Ann Rockefeller Roberts, 11/93); Committee (working/advisory), "Cry of the Earth-Legacy of the First Nations" (United Nations, 11/93); board trustee of the American Indian Ritual Object Repatriation Foundation. *Membership*: New York University Alumni. *Interests*: "Travels to collect indigenous musical instruments from Mexico, USA, and Canada. I share Native stories & music." *Published works*: Two curriculum guides for the Westchester Philharmonic, "Native American Music" & "Native Iroquois Culture", both for elementary & secondary schools; Fiddlesticks "Pre Columbian Music of the Americas - What Columbus Might Have Heard," 1992; New Orchestra of Westchester - "American Indigenous People - Contact Period to Present," 1992-93; Cobblestones - "Rock of the Ages Pre-Columbian American Music" p. 24 (Vol. 14) 1993; recorded double album, "The Divine Sound of Rudra Vina."

MERCER, BILL 1960-
(Native American arts administrator)
Born May 14, 1960, Anaheim, Calif. *Education*: Texas Tech University, M.A., 1986; University of New Mexico (PhD candidate). *Affiliations*: Texas Tech University Museum, Lubbock, TX, 1984-85; Plains Indian Museum, Cody, WY, 1985-86; National Park Service, 1988-93; curator, Cincinnati Art Museum, Cincinnati, OH, 1993-97; Native American Art Curator, The Portland (Oregon) Art Museum, Portland, OR, 1998-2007; director & curator of ethnology, Montana Historical Society, 2007-10; executive director, Sangre de Cristo Arts & Conference Center, 210 N. Santa Fe Ave., Pueblo, CO 81003 (719) 295-7200. *Memberships*: American Association of Museums; Midwest Museums Association; Ohio Museums Association; Native American Art Studies Association (secretary/treasurer, 1995-97). *Interests*: "I am especially interested in powwows & contemporary traditional Native American art. My PhD dissertation is a study of contemporary powwow clothing and how it communicates the identity of the wearer. I am currently developing a traveling exhibition of Pueblo pottery entitles, "Singing the Clay: Pueblo Pottery of the Southwest Yesterday & Today." *Published work*: "Singing the Clay: Pueblo Pottery of the Southwest Yesterday and Today," exhibition catalog (Cincinnati Art Museum, 1995).

MERCER, JACKIE
(chief executive officer-NARA)
Affiliation & Address: Native American Rehabilitation Association (NARA) of the Northwest, 1776 SW Madison, Portland, OR 97205 (503) 224-1044. E-mail: jmercer@naranorthwest.org. *Other professional post*: Secretary, NCUIH Board of Directors for Region 5. Dedicated to providing quality & culturally appropriate care to American Indians & Alaska Natives in Portland, OR area.

MERCER, MARY JO (Osage)
(store owner)
Affiliation: Bison Bison-The Buffalo Store, 129 E. Main, Pawhuska, OK 74056 (918) 287-3510 Website: www.bisonbison.gpg.com; E-mail: cyberbison2002@yahoo.com. *Products*: American bison products; jewelry, gift baskets, and authentic Osage arts & crafts.

MERCIER, MARK (Grande Ronde Confederated Tribes)
(tribal chairperson)
Affiliation: Confederated Tribe of the Grande Ronde Tribal Council, 9615 Grand Ronde Rd., Grande Ronde, OR 97347 (503) 879-5211.

MERCULIEF, CHRISTOPHER (Aleut)
(Alaskan village council president)
Affiliation: St. George Traditional Council, P.O. Box 940, George Island, AK 99591 (907) 859-2205.

MEREDITH, MARY ELLEN (MILAM) (Cherokee) 1946-
(society board president)
Born October 3, 1946. *Address*: 623 Culbertson Dr., Suite A, Oklahoma City, OK 73105 (405) 524-2615. E-mail: noksi@aol.com. *Affiliation*: Board President, Cherokee National Historical Society; Interim Executive Director, Cherokee Heritage Center, 1999-2003. *Other professional posts*: Cherokee Nation Enterprises (secretary of board); Noksi Press, Oklahoma City, OK (present). *Community activities*: Board member, Red Earth, Inc.; member, Junior League of Oklahoma City; Trail of Tears Advisory Commission, National Park Service. *Membership*: Pocahontas Club. *Interests*: Fiction writing. *Published work*: Edited with Howard Meredith, "Of the Earth: Oklahoma Architectural History" (Oklahoma Historical Society, 1980); B.D. Eddie (Bio); George Shirk (Bio); Cherokee Humanities Course Text; Cherokee Literary Perspectives (2003).

MERICLE, MICHAEL N.
(health center director)
Affiliation: Ignacio PHS Indian Health Center, P.O. Box 889, Ignacio, CO 81137 (303) 563-4581.

MERMEJO, RICHARD (Picuris Pueblo)
(former pueblo governor)
Affiliation & Address: Former Governor, Picuris Pueblo, P.O. Box 127, Penasco, NM 87553 (505) 587-2519.

MERRELL, JAMES H. 1953-
(professor of history)
Born October 19, 1953, Minneapolis, Minn. *Education*: Lawrence University, BA, 1975; Oxford University, England, BA, 1977; Johns Hopkins University, MA, 1979, PhD, 1982. *Address*: Vassar College, Poughkeepsie, NY 12604-0432. *Affiliation*: Professor of History, Vassar College, Poughkeepsie, NY, 1984-. *Memberships*: American Historical Association; Organization of American Historians; Society of American Historians; Omohundro Institute of Early American History & Culture. *Awards, honors*: Rhodes Scholarship; Danforth Fellowship; Predoctoral Fellowship, Newberry Library; Postdoctoral Fellowship, Institute of Early American History & Culture; America: History & Life Award; Robert F. Heizer Award, Douglass Adair Prize, Frederick Jackson Turner Award, Merle Curtis Award, and Bancroft Prize for book, "The Indians' New World"; Fellowships from American Council of Learned Societies, Guggenheim Foundation, & National Endowment for the Humanities; Bancroft Prize for "Into the American Woods". *Published works*: Co-editor, Beyond the Covenant Chain: The Iroquois & Their Neighbors in Indian North America, 1600-1800 (Syracuse University Press, 1987); The Indians' New World: Catawbas and Their Neighbors from European Contact Through the Era of Removal (University of North Carolina Press, 1989); The Catawbas (Chelsea House, 1989); Into the American Woods (W.W. Norton, 1999); co-editor, American Encounters: Natives & Newcomers from European Contact to Indian Removal, 1500-1850 (Routledge, 2000); co-editor, American Nations: Encounters in Indian Country, 1850 to the Present (Routledge, 2001).

MERRILL, DAVID (St. Croix Chippewa)
(former tribal chairperson)
Affiliation: St. Croix Tribal Mental-AODA, 4404 State Rd. 70,Webster, WI54893

MERRILL, HAMP
(American Indian studies)
Affiliation & Address: Special assistant to the Director, American Indian Studies Program, Harvill Bldg., Rm. 430, P.O. Box 210076, University of Arizona, Tucson, AZ 85721 (520) 621-7108. E-mail: hmerrill@u.arizona.edu.

MERRYWEATHER, ERIN (Oklahoma Choctaw)
(director of museum educational programs)
Education: Oklahoma Christian University, BS (Marketing). *Affiliation & Address*: Director of Programs, Red Earth Museum (Website: www.redearth.org), Red Earth, Inc., 6 Santa Fe Plaza, Oklahoma City, OK 73102 (405) 427-5228. E-mail: erin@redearth.org. Erin oversees museum, special event & educational programs. She recently participated in the Smithsonian National Museum of the American Indian, curatorial certification program and the National Institute for Tribal Archives, Libraries & Museums training program. *Memberships*: Oklahoma State Arts Council; Leadership Arts Class of 2009.

MESHIGUAD, ELAINE (Potawatomi)
(tribal vice chairperson)
Affiliation & Address: Vice Chairperson, Hannahville Indian Community, N-14911 Hannahville B-1 Rd., Wilson, MI 49896 (906) 466-0306.

MESHIGUAD, KENNETH (Potawatomi)
(tribal chairperson)
Affiliation & Address: Chairperson, Hannahville Indian Community, N-14911 Hannahville B-1 Rd., Wilson, MI 49896 (906) 466-0306.

MESHORER, HANK
(chief-Indian resources)
Affiliation & Address: U.S. Dept. of Justice, Indian Resources Section, Land & Natural Resources Division, Rm. 624, 10th & Constitution Ave., NW, Washington, DC 20530 (202) 724-7156.

MESSINGER, CARLA J.S. (Lenni Lenape Delaware) 1949-
(cultural educator/consultant)
Born May 20, 1949, Allentown, Pa. Education: Lehigh County Community College, AA, 1969; Kutztown University, BA, 1971; Lehigh University, MA (Elementary/Special Education), 1973. *Address*: 1819 1/2 Linden St., Allentown, PA 18104 (610) 434-6819. E-mail: palenape@enter.net. *Past professional posts*: Substitute teacher of elementary education & special education (12 years); special consultant, presents multi-media programs on Lenape culture to other organizations, such as Philadelphia school district;

leads in service programs on "Unstereotyping Indians" for school districts, colleges, and church groups; consultant & speaker for "Native Culture for Senior Citizens," St. Francis de Salles College, and Agape project "Lenni Lenape Indians, 1981-84; Founder & executive director, Lenni Lenape Historical Society & Museum, Allentown, PA, 1978-2002; consultant, 1978-present. Recognized nationally & internationally for her pioneering work as a Native American cultural educator. Speaker for Pennsylvania Humanities Council "Commonwealth Speakers Bureau," 2004-2007. *Memberships*: Pennsylvania Federation of Museums & Historical Societies. *Awards, honors*: 1985 President's Volunteer Action Award, Citation by the House of Representatives, PA; Keystone Award of Merit, Governor's Private Sector Initiatives Task Force for Lenni Lenape Historical Society; 1986 Award of Merit to the Society from the Pennsylvania Federation of Historical Societies for "Continuing Achievement in Public Education under Carla Messinger"; 1987 Jefferson Award from KYW-TV3; 1989 Letter of Commendation to the Society from the Pennsylvania Federation of Historical Societies for the publication of a new flyer (editor, Susanne Jeffries-Fox); 1989 Allentown Human Relations Award for creating & operating the Lenni Lenape Historical Society/Museum; appointed to the Advisory Council for constructing and Institute for Native American Studies at Mansfield University, 1990; 1991 Executive Leadership Award for two weeks at the Smithsonian Institution; chosen to participate in the 1991, two-week "Archaeology & Ethnography Collection Care & Maintenance Course" offered through the U.S. Dept. of the Interior, National Park Service; provided Lenape cultural programs to audiences in Scotland and England through the British North American Indian Association (Scotland in 1992 & 1996); in July 1993, she was a representative to the 9th European Conference on Indian Questions held in Trondheim, Norway, and then went to Stockholm, Sweden to meet with support groups and museum representatives; The Museum of Indian Culture/Lenni Lenape Historical Society was one of ten American organizations chosen to exhibit its crafts at the National Crafts Center in Washington, DC for 1993, International Year of the Indigenous People & the American Year of Handicrafts; provided educational, multi-media cultural programs in former East Germany in 1994, and the United Kingdom in 1996; received a scholarship from the Yakama Nation to attend the American Association of State & Local Historical Societies conference in Denver, 1997; panelist for the Smithsonian Institutions workshop titled, "Making a Difference in American Indian/Museum Relationships in Rochester, NY, 1997; attended the ATLATL conference in San Francisco, 1998; attended the Smithsonian Institution's Exhibits Development for Tribal Museums Conference in Ft. Lauderdale, Florida, 1999; received a scholarship to participate in the American Association for State & Local History & Mid-Atlantic Association of Museums' Annual Meeting, 1999; scholarship to attend National Trust for Historic Preservation Conference, 1999, in Washington, DC; scholarship, American Indian Women with Disabilities Conference, Mohave Reservation, Nevada, 2000; scholarship, Pennsylvania Federation of Museums & Historical Societies Conference, Penn State, State College, PA, 2000; attended Museums & Historical Societies Conference in Pittsburgh, PA, 2001; scholarship from National Museum of the American Indian to attend one-week "Preservation & Collection Methods" workshop in California, 2002; scholarship to attend conference on "Tribal Archives, Libraries & Museums: Preserving Our Languages, Memory & Lifeways" in Arizona, 2002. Carla was a representative to the United Kingdom in July, 2001, presenting Lenape cultural programs and environmental programs in England. *Interests*: Lenni Lenape history & culture.

MESTES, BEVERLY
(BIA supt. for education)
Affiliation & Address: Pima Agency, Bureau of Indian Affairs, P.O. Box 8, Sacaton, AZ 85247 (602) 562-3557.

METCALF, EDWARD L. (Coquille)
(former tribal chairperson)
Affiliation: Coquille Indian Tribe, P.O. Box 783, North Bend, OR 97549 (541) 756-0904. E-mail: edmetcalf@coquilletribe.org.

METCALF, JOAN (Coquille)
(tribal secretary-treasurer)
Affiliation: Coquille Indian Tribe, P.O. Box 783, North Bend, OR 97549 (541) 756-0904. E-mail: joanmetclaf@coquilletribe.org

METOXEN, KIRBY (Oneida)
(tribal tourism)
Born in Milwaukee, Wisc. *Affiliation & Address*: Director, Oneida Tourism Department, Oneida Tribe of Wisconsin, P.O. Box 365, Oneida, WI 54155. E-mail: kmetox@oneidanation.org. *Other professional posts*: Member, Native American Tourism of Wisconsin (NATOW); member, Green Bay Multi-Cultural Center Board; member, Oneida Tribal Elections Board; member, Oneida Appeals Commission; Midwest Region Representative, American Indian/Alaska Native Tourism Association, Albuquerque, NM. *Interests*: Kirby is a traditional dancer & has been singing with the Oneida Hymn Singers for More than 30 years.

METOXEN, LORETTA
(organization president)
Affiliation: Coalition for Indian Education, 8200 Mountain Rd., NE, Suite 203, Albuquerque, NM 87110 (505) 262-2351.

METOYER, CHERYL A. (Cherokee) 1947-
(adjunct associate professor of American Indian Studies)
Born February 18, 1947, Los Angeles, Calif. *Education*: Indiana University, PhD (Library & Information Science), 1976. *Affiliation & Address*: Adjunct Associate Professor, The Information School, University of Washington (UW), Seattle, 98195 (206) 685-9612. E-mail: metoyer@u.washington.edu. *Other professional post*: Adjunct Professor of American Indian Studies, UW, 2008-present. *Research Interests*: Management, design & evaluation of information services provided to American Indians and the information seeking behavior of culturally diverse groups. *Past professional posts*: Director, Mashantucket Pequot Thesaurus Project, American Indian Studies Center, UCLA, 2004-08; Graduate School of Library & Information Science, University of California, Los Angeles, CA, 1977-81, 1988-93, Assistant Dean, 1989-92; Rupert Costo Professorship in American Indian History, University of California, 1993-97; Mashantucket Pequot Tribal Nation; Director of Information Resources, Mashantucket Pequot Museum & Research Center, Mashantucket, CT, 1997-2004; UCLA Graduate School of Library & Information Studies, Los Angeles, CA, 2004-08. *Community activities*: Lector, St. Eugene Catholic Church, Southwest Museum. *Memberships*: American Indian & Alaska Native Professors Association; American Library Association (Library Research Round Table, Subcommittee on Library Services to American Indian People, Minority Recruitment Subcommittee); American Society for Information Science; Association of College & Research Libraries; Native American Professors Association; Kateri Circle. *Awards, honors*: 2006 Rockefeller Fellowship in the Humanities for her research on Native American Systems of Knowledge; Rupert Costo Professorship in American Indian History, University of California, Riverside, 1993-97; "American Indian Research Literature as Reflected through Citation Analysis." Paper selected for presentation at the ALA, LRRT Research Forums, Miami, Florida, June 26, 1994; Honoree, Association of College & Research Libraries, Racial & Ethnic Diversity Committee. Honored for research monograph, "Gatekeepers in Ethno-linguistic Communities"; K.G. Saur Award for Best Article in College & Research Libraries in 1992. *Article*: "Literature Reviews & Innacurate Referencing: An Exploratory Study of Academic Librarians." *Published work*: Gatekeepers in Ethno-linguistic Communities (Ablex Publishing Corp., 1993).

METZGER, KENAN (Cherokee/Ho-Chunk)
(assistant professor of English-Native American studies)
Education: University of Missouri (Kansas City) BA, 1993, MA, 1998; University of Kansas, PhD (English), 2004. *Affiliation & Address*: Assistant Professor of English Education (2005-present), Ball State University, English Dept., RB 380, Muncie, IN 47306 (765) 285-2679. E-mail: klmetzger@bsu.edu. *Other professional posts*: Member, Native American Studies committee, Ball State University. *Past professional posts*: English teacher, Lee's Summit High School, 1995-2002; Graduate teaching Assistant, University of Kansas, 2002-04; Instructor, Haskell Indian Nations University, 2003-05.

MEYA, WILHELM K. (Lakota)
(anthropologist; executive director)
Born in Vienna, Austria and grew up in the U.S. *Education*: Oglala Lakota College, B.A.; University of Arizona, M.A.; Indiana University, PhD. His dissertation focused on proto-historical Lakota writing & historical documents. His area of specializations are: Indians of North America, Plains ethno-history & ethnology, Siouan historical linguistics, native language revitalization, pictography, semiotics, the development of writing systems, and culture theory. *Affiliation & Address*: Executive Director, Chairperson & Founding Member, Lakota Language Consortium, 2620 N. Walnut St., Suite 825, Bloomington, IN 47404 (888) 525-6828. E-mail: meya@lakhota.org. *Past professional posts*: Associate instructor of Anthropology at Indiana University & Research Fellow at the American Indian Studies Research Institute. He has conducted fieldwork on the Lakota reservations of North & South Dakota, and the Zuni Indian Reservation of New Mexico. He has taught courses on the Indians of North America, anthropology, research design, Zuni history, and ethno-botany. *Awards, honors*: He has been an invited speaker and consultant for numerous organizations and is the recipient of many prestigious fellowships and prizes including: The SSILA ken Hale Prize, the John H. Edwards Fellowship, the David C. Skomp Fellowship, the Jacobs Grant, the National Endowment for the Humanities Research Institute Fellowship, the Arizona Graduate Project First Prize and the American Philosophical Society Phillips Fund Grant.

MEYER, ELIZABETH
(attorney)
Education: University of South Dakota, BA, 1968; University of Minnesota, MA, 1970; University of Colorado Law School, JD, 1976. *Affiliation & Address*: Senior Partner, McEroy, Meyer, Walker & Condon, 1007 Pearl St., Suite 220, Boulder, CO 80302 (303) 442-2021. E-mail: emeyer@mmwclaw.com. Ms.

Meyer has extensive litigation experience in Indian Child Welfare Act cases. She represents the Navajo Nation and previously represented the Cheyenne River Sioux Tribe in cases in Colorado, South Dakota, and South Carolina. She began her career at the Native American Rights Fund researching Indian law issues of concern to attorneys throughout the country employed by Legal Services Corporation funded programs on various Indian reservations. *Membership*: CoLorado Indian bar Assocaition. She has been actively involved in the Bar Association's efforts to directly incorporate the Indian Child Welfare Act into the Colorado Children's Code.

MEYER, MELISSA (Eastern Cherokee)
(associate professor of history)
Born in Cincinnati. *Affiliation & Address*: Dept. of History, 6296 Bunche Hall, UCLA, Los Angeles, CA 90095 (310) 825-4601. E-mail: meyer@history.ucla. edu. *Research Interests*: Centers on issues of American Indian identity particularly on "blood quantum" requirements for tribal enrollment & recognition as American Indians, and on intermarriage and the historical experiences of individuals of mixed descent. Dr. Meyer is tracing the history of tribal enrollment, a policy originated by the colonial U.S. Government but maintained by most tribes. She teaches a specialized courses dealing with sources, methods & interpretation in American Indian history, the interpretation in American Indian autobiographies, contemporary American Indian issues in historical perspective, ethno-historic methods, American Indian social history, and interdisciplinary methods in history. *Published works*: The White Earth Tragedy: Ethnicity & Dispossession at Minnesota Anishanaabe Reservations, 1889-1920 (University of Nebraska Press, 1994); "American Indian Blood Quantum Requirements: Blood Is Thicker Than Family," in Over the Edge: Remapping the American West, by Matsumoto & Allmedinger, Eds. (University of California Press, 1999)

MEYERS, JOSEPH
(executive director)
Affiliation: National Indian Justice Center, 7 Fourth St., Suite 46, Petaluma, CA 94952 (707) 762-8113.

MEYERS, RICHARD "RICHIE" (Oglala Lakota)
(tribal relations director)
Education: Amherst College, BA (Anthropology), 1997; Arizona State University, MA (Cultural Anthropology), 2004; PhD (Anthropology), 2008; Middlebury College (VT), MA (English), 2004. His dissertation within the anthropology department at the Smithsonian Institution in Washington, D.C. 2008. *Affiliation & Address*: Tribal Relations Director, SDSU; Program Coordinator, American Indian Studies, & Assistant Professor in Journalism & Mass Communication, South Dakota State University (SDSU), Brookings, SD 57007 (605) 688-6416; E-mail: Richard.meyers@sdstate.edu In 2012, he developed the American Indian Studies program at SDSU. *Other professional post*: President, Assn of Indigenous Anthropologists, American Anthropological Association. *Past professional post*: U.S. Department of Interior's Office of the Assistant Secretary for Indian Affairs as a writer & editor, 2008-12.

MEZA, KENNETH A. (*Misquish*) (Kumeyaay Diegueno) 1945-
(tribal chairperson)
Born December 3, 1945, Monte Vista Ranch, Calif. *Affiliation & Address*: Chairperson, Jamul Indian Village, P.O. Box 612, Jamul, CA 91935 (619) 669-4785. *Military service*: U.S. Marines (Vietnam Vet). *Memberships*: National Indian Gaming Association; National Congress of American Indians; California Nations Indian Gaming Association; California Indian Manpower Consortium. Mr. Meza is one of the original signers of the Jamul Indian Village Constitution of 1981. He served as the chairperson in the 1980s.

MICCO, MELINDA (Seminole of Oklahoma)
(associate professor of ethnic studies)
Education: University of California, Berkeley, BA (Native American Studies), MA (Ethnic Studies), 1992, PhD (Ethnic Studies), 1995. *Affiliation & Address*: Associate Professor (1993-present), Ethnic Studies, Dept., Mills College, Mills Hall 341. 5000 MacArthur Blvd., Oakland, CA 94613 (510) 430-3324. E-mail: melinda@mills.edu. *Research Interests*: American Indian history; ethnic identity in tribal communities; indigenous women, nationally & internationally; film studies & literature.

MICHAEL, ENOCH (Eskimo)
(Alaskan village president)
Affiliation: Native Village of Noatak, P.O. Box 89, Noatak, AK 99761 (907) 485-2173.

MICHAEL, NICKY KAY (Delaware) 1972-
(professor of Native American studies)
Education: Stanford University, BA (American Studies), 1994; Oklahoma State University, MA (History), 1999; University of Oklahoma, PhD (History), 2010. *Affiliations*: Owner, Nicky Kay Michael Consultancy, LLC (Grant writer), 2001-Present; Certified Facilitator, Institute of Cultural Affairs, 1991-Present;

Founder/CEO, Lenapeowski, 2005-Present; Professor, Rogers State University, 2011-Present; Trust Board, Education Chair, Delaware Tribe of Indians, 2013-Present; member, Tribal Council, Delaware Tribe of Indians, 2013-Present; Visiting Professor, Native American Studies, University of Wyoming, 2015-Present. *Other professional posts*: Historian, 2010-Present. "My Doctorate is in History with a focus on Native Americans; Consultant, Oklahoma Center for Nonprofits, 2012-Present. *Past professional posts*: Language manager, Delaware Nation, 2012-2014; Grant Writing Instructor, Tri-County Technology Center, 2009-2012; Consultant, First Nations Development Institute, 2010-2011; Board Member, North American Indian Legal Services, 1999-2006; Self-Governance Specialist, Iowa Tribe of Oklahoma, 1997-1998.

MICHAELS, MARK A. 1959-
(attorney, writer)
Born August 2, 1959, New York, N.Y. *Education*: University of Michigan, BA, 1980; New York University School of Law, JD, 1985. *Address*: 11 Broadway, 2nd Floor, New York, NY 10004 (212) 598-0100. *Affiliations*: Staff attorney, American Indian Alliance, New York, NY 1990- (established to address all issues affecting Indian survival); deputy director, Native American Council of New York City for 1992, New York, NY, 1991- (administrator for and advisor to a coalition of the three most active Native American organizations in New York City). *Other professional posts*: Literary manager, Roundabout Theatre, 1988-90, and Double Image Theatre, 1989-91. *Speeches, Lectures & Panels*: Native American Council Summit, Jan. 1991; Columbus Indians and 1992, The Learning Alliance, Columbia University School of Law, Dec. 1991; The Impact of the James Bay II Hydropower Project on Indigenous People, Sarah Lawrence College, Dec. 1991; The Continuing Impact of Columbus' Arrival on Native Americans, Northern Westchester Society for Ethical Culture, Dec. 1991. *Memberships*: American Bar Assn; Dramatist Guild. *Published works*: Articles - "Native American Council Update," American Indian Community House Bulletin, regular column in newsletter; "Native Americans and Free Exercise: Double Standard at Work," with Tonya Gonnella Frichner, National Bar Assn Magazine, Vol. 8, No. 1, 1/1991; "War Declared on Religious Freedom," with Tonya Gonnella Frichner, Native Nations, Vol. 1, No. 2, 2/1991.

MICHEL, KAREN LINCOLN (Wisconsin Winnebago)
(journalist; association president)
Education: Marquette University, MA. *Affiliation & Address*: President, Native American Journalists Association (NAJA), 1433 E. Franklin Ave., Suite 11, Minneapolis, MN 55404 (612) 874-8833. *Other professional posts*: Reporter, LaCross Tribune & Dallas Morning News; business partner & board member of Indian Country Communications, Hayward, WI, publishers of News From Indian Country. *Awards & honors*: Ms. Michel is the first woman to head NAJA.

MICHEL, PAUL (Shuswap First Nations)
(director of First Nations Centre; professor of First Nations studies)
Education: Simon Fraser University, BA (Sociology), M.Ed. *Affiliation & Address*: Director, First Nations Centre; Adjunct Professor, Department of First Nations Studies, University of Northern British Columbia, 333 University Way, Prince George, BC V2N 4Z9 Canada. E-mail: michelp@unbc.ca. *Past professional posts*: Principal, First Nations Elementary School in Fort St. James; taught for the Prince George Native Friendship Centre; Insstructed for the College of New Caledonia. Paul drums & sings traditional songs, and instructs & plays Lahal (First Nations game).

MIDDLETON, BETH ROSE
(assistant professor)
Education: University of California, Davis, BA); UC Berkeley, PhD. *Affiliation & Address*: Assistant professor, Dept. of Native American Studies, University of California, Davis, 2421 Hart Hall, One Shields Ave., Davis, CA 95616 (530) 754-4802. E-mail: brmiddleton@ucdavis.edu. Beth has developed courses on Native public health, Native environmental policy, and Federal Indian law. *Published works*: Trust in the Land: New Directions in Tribal Conservation (University of Arizona Press, 2011); articles in Economic Development Quarterly, the Journal of Political Ecology, Ethno-history, and News from Native California.

MIGUEL, ROBERT (Ak Chin)
(tribal chairperson)
Affiliation & Address: Chairperson, Ak Chin Indian Community, 42507 West Peters & Nall Rd., Maricopa, AZ 85139 (520) 568-1000. Website: www.ak-chin.nsn.us.

MIHESUAH, DEVON ABBOTT (Choctaw of Oklahoma) 1957-
(professor of history; editor, writer)
Born June 6, 1957, Wichita Falls, Tex. *Education*: Texas Christian University, BS, 1981, MEd, 1982, MA, 1986, PhD (History), 1989. *Dissertation*: "History of the Cherokee Female Seminary: 1851-1909." *Affiliations & Address*: Professor of Applied Indigenous Studies & History, College of Social & Behavioral Sciences (2000-present), Northern Arizona University, P.O. Box 15020, Flagstaff, AZ 86011 (928) 523-5159. E-mail: devon.mihesuah@nau.edu;

professor of history, College of Arts & Sciences, Northern Arizona University, Flagstaff, AZ, 1999-present. *Other professional posts*: "American Indian Quarterly" (associate editor of history, 1993-98; editor, 1998-present); Editor, University of Nebraska Press Book Series: Contemporary American Indigenous Issues, 2000-2005; member, Board of Trustees, Museum of Northern Arizona, Flagstaff, AZ, 1999-2003; consultant and reviewer: "Western Social Science Journal," "American Indian Culture & Research Journal," "Choice," "The Historian," "Frontiers," "Signs," 1990-present. *Awards, honors*: Won Phi Alpha Theta/Westerners International Award for Best Dissertation in Western History, directed by Donald E. Worcester; Winner of the 1995 & 1998 American Educational Studies Association Critics' Choice Awards for "Cultivating the Rosebuds: The Education of Women at the Cherokee Female Seminary, 1851-1909" & "Natives and Academics: Researching and Writing About American Indians" respectively; 1996-97 Ford Foundation Postdoctoral Fellowship; Winner of the The Oklahoma Writers' Federation Trophy Award for the Best Fiction Book of 2000 for "The Roads of My Relations"; Wordcraft Circle of Native Writers' 2001 Journal Editing Award for the "American Indian Quarterly," 2001. *Membership*: American Indian & Alaskan Native Professors' Association; American Society for Ethno-history; Oklahoma Historical Society; Phi Alpha Theta; Western History Association; Wordcraft Circle of Native Writers. *Interests*: Recovering indigenous knowledge; methodologies of studying Natives; activism. *Published works*: Cultivating the Rosebuds: The Education of Women at the Cherokee Female Seminary, 1851-1909 (University of Illinois Press, 1993, 1996); American Indians: Stereotypes & Realities (Clarity Press, 1996/1997); Natives & Academics: Researching & Writing About American Indians (University of Nebraska Press, 1998); Editor, Repatriation: Social and Political Dialogues (University of Nebraska Press, 1999); The Roads of My Relations (University of Arizona Press, 2000); "First to Fight": Henry Mihesuah, Nu Mu Nuu (Comanche) (University of Nebraska Press, 2002); American Indigenous Women: Decolonization, Empowerment, Activism (University of Nebraska Press, 2003); Indigenizing the Academy: Native Academics Sharpening the Edge (the sequel to "Natives and Academics: Researching & Writing About American Indians") with Angela Cavender Wilson (University of Nebraska Press, 2004); So You Want to Write About American Indians? A Guide for Writers, Students, and Scholars (University of Nebraska Press, 2005).

MIKE, DARRELL (Luiseno)
(tribal chairperson)
Affiliation & Address: Chairperson, Twenty-Nine Palms Band of Mission Indians, 46-200 Harrison St., Coachella, CA 92236 (760) 863-2444.

MIKE, JEFFREY (Navajo)
(association administrator)
Affiliation & Address: Administrator, Native American Grant School Association, P.O. Box 726, Flagstaff, AZ 86002 (928) 429-0505.

MIKE, JOSEPH P. (Eskimo)
(Alaskan village president)
Affiliation: Village of Kotlik, P.O. Box 20210, Kotlik, AK 99620 (907) 899-4326.

MIKE, JUNE (Luiseno)
(tribal chairperson)
Address: 555 Sunrise Hwy. #200, Palm Springs, CA 92264. *Affiliation*: Twenty Nine Palms Band of Mission Indians, Palm Springs, CA (619) 322-0559.

MIKE, LORNA J. (Elwha S'Klallam)
(former tribal chairperson)
Affiliation: Elwha S'Klallam Tribe, 2851 Lower Elwha Rd., Port Angeles, WA 98362 (360) 452-8471.

MIKE, RICHARD (Navajo)
(association president)
Affiliation: Navajo Nation Business Association, P.O. Box 1217, Kayenta, AZ 86033 (520) 697-3534.

MIKE, RODNEY (Shoshone)
(tribal chairperson)
Affiliation & Address: Duckwater Shoshone Tribal Council, P.O. Box 140068, Duckwater, NV 89832 (702) 863-0227.

MIKE, ROSALYN (Southern Paiute)
(tribal chairperson)
Affiliation: Moapa Business Council, P.O. Box 340, Las Vegas, NV 89025 (702) 865-2787.

MIKKANEN, ARVO Q. (Kiowa/Comanche) 1961-
(assistant U.S. attorney)
Born in Denver, Colo. in 1961. Education: Dartmouth College, BA (Government), 1983; Yale Law School, JD, 1986. Resides in Norman, Oklahoma. *Affiliation*: Assistant U.S. Attorney with the U.S. Attorney's Office

for the Western District of Oklahoma, 1994-present. *Other professional posts*: President, Oklahoma Indian Bar Association (OIBA), Oklahoma City, OK; lecturer & instructor in federal criminal investigations, prosecution issues & Indian affairs law. *Past professional posts*: Judge of the Court of Indian Offenses for the Anadarko Area Tribes, 1988-94; associate attorney & litigator with the Andrews Davis law firm in Oklahoma City, 1988-94; Chief Justice of the Supreme Court of the Cheyenne Arapaho Tribes, 1991-94; adjunct professor of law, Oklahoma City University School of Law, 1988-2000. *Memberships*: Oklahoma Indian Bar Association (president); National Native American Bar Association (two time past president, 1991 & 1995); Native American Alumni Association of Dartmouth College (president). *Awards, honors*: Recipient of the Gold U.S. Congressional Award from the U.S. Congress in 1985; Class Marshal for the Class of 1986, Yale Law School and received the Beinecke Award in 1986; received the Oklahoma Bar Association's Outstanding Pro Bono Service Award in 1992; recipient of the American Bar Association's Spirit of Excellence Award in 2004.

MILES, MARILYN
(attorney)
Affiliation: California Indian Legal Services, 324 F St., Suite A, Eureka, CA 95501 (707) 443-8397.

MILES, MARY JANE (Nez Perce)
(tribal chairperson)
Affiliation & Address: Chairperson, Nez Pece Tribe, P.O. Box 305, Lapwai, ID 83540 (208) 843-7342. E-mail: maryjanem@nezperce.org

MILES, REBECCA A. (Nez Perce)
(tribal vice chairperson)
Education: Washington, State University, B.A.; Gonzaga University, M.A. *Address & Affiliation*: Vice Chairperson, Nez Perce Tribe, P.O. Box 305, Lapwai, ID 83540 (208) 843-2253. E-mail: nptec@nezperce.org. Ms. Miles was the first woman to be elected to the position of chairperson.

MILES, TIYA
(professor of Native American studies)
Education: University of Minnesota, PhD, 2000. *Affiliation & Address*: Professor, Native American Studies Program, Department of American Culture, 4773 Haven Hall, 505 State St., Ann Arbr, MI 48109 (734) 764-5513. E-mail: tiya@umich.edu. *Other affiliations*: Chair, Department of Afroamerican & African Studies; Department of History; Department of Women's Study. *Fields of Study*: African American & Native American interrelated & comparative histories, especially 19th-century African American women's history & literature, Native American women's history & literature, and U.S. women's history. *Published works*: Ties That Bind: The Story of an Afro-Cherokee Family in Slavery & Freedom (2005); co-editor with Sharon P. Holland, Crossing Waters, Crossing Worlds: The African Diaspora in Indian Country (2006); House on Diamond Hill: A Cherokee Plantation Story (2010); numerous articles.

MILES, WILLIAM P. (*Swift Water*) (Pamunkey) 1943-
(director of administration; former tribal chief)
Born November 28, 1943, New Jersey. *Address*: Rt. 1, Box 987, King William, VA 23086 (804) 843-2851. *Affiliation*: Director of administration, U.S. Dept. of HUD, Richmond, VA, 1985-. *Past professional posts*: Chief (1993-2008), Pamunkey Indian Tribe, King William, VA; *Military service*: U.S. Army, 1962-65 (E-4). *Community activities*: Vice Chair, United Indians of Virginia; board member, Mattaponi, Pamunkey, Monacan, Inc.

MILHISER, G. MICHAEL (Cahuilla)
(tribal chief administrative officer)
Affiliation & Address: Chief Administrative Officer (2007-present), Morongo Band of Mission Indians Tribal Government Administration & Enterprise Operations, 12700 Pumarra Rd., Banning, CA 02220 (951) 849-4425. *Past professional posts*: Interim Executive Director, Tri-City Medical Center, 2005-07; Manager, City of Upland, California, 1996-2005; City Manager & Redevelopment Agency Executive Director, City of Ontario, California. *Community service*: Board member, Monte Vista Water District, James L. White Foundation, the George Chaffey Trust, and the West End YMCA.

MILLER, ANDREW, JR. (Eskimo)
(village president)
Affiliation: Nome Eskimo Community, P.O. Box 1090, Nome, AK 99762 (907) 443-2246.

MILLER, BEVERLY (Cherokee)
(HIS Area Director)
Education: University of Southern California, MHA; Golden Gate University, MBA. She is also a Certified Public Accountant. *Affiliation & Address*: Area Director, Indian Health Setrvice (HIS), 650 Capital Mall, Suite 7-100, Sacramento, CA 95814 (916) 930-3981. E-mail: Beverly.miller@ihs..gov. Ms.

Miller manages a unique health care program provided primarily through contracts recognized by the Indian Self-Determination & Education Assistance Act, Public Law 93-638, where Tribes establish and maintain responsibility for the development & operation of their health facilities, programs, and services. The California Area serves 104 tribal communities through 44 rural health care operating units, eight Urban Indian Health programs, and 2 alcohol treatment programs. Ms. Miller began her IHS career in 1993 with the California Area office as a financial management officer. She has served in various senior management positions in the California Area including Acting Area Director, Deputy Area Director, Associate Director of Office Management and Services, and Area Executive Officer.

MILLER, BOYD (Choctaw)
(organization president)
Education: Southeastern Oklahoma State University; Oral Roberts University Tulsa; Bishop State in Mobile, AL. *Affiliation & Address*: President, The American Indian Chamber of Commerce of Oklahoma, P.O. Box 141424, Broken Arrow, OK 74014 (918) 624-9382.

MILLER, CARY (Ojibwe)
(professor of history & coordinator, American Indian Studies)
Education: University of North Carolina-Chapel Hill, PhD (Histry). *Affiliation & Address*: Associate Professor of History & Coordinator, American Indian Studies Program, Department of History, Holton 365, University of Wisconsin-Milwaukee, 2442 E. Hartford Ave., Milwaukee, WI 53201 (414) 229-6251. E-mail: carym@uwm.edu. *Teaching/Research Interests*: Anishinaabe leadership in the early 19th century, Anishinaabe women's history; treaties & sovereignty, Wisconsin Indian history.

MILLER, CAROL (Cherokee)
(professor emerita)
Born in Muskogee, Okla. *Education*: University of Oklahoma, PhD (American Literature), 1980. *Address & Affiliation*: American Indian Studies Department, College of Liberal Arts, 206 Scott Hall, 72 Pleasant St. SE, University of Minnesota, Twin Cities Campus, Minneapolis, MN 55455 (612) 625-0112. E-mail: mille004@umn.edu. Carol is Professor Emerita of American Studies & American Indian Studies (Contemporary American Indian Literature & Multicultural Pedigogy). She is a Morse Alumni Distinguished Professor of Teaching in American Indian Studies. Her recent research focuses on American Indian literatures, particularly fiction by American Indian women writers, and is currently working on a book-length study, "Shifting Shapes: Convergence Authority in Fiction by American Indian Women." which examines how converging themes & narrative strategies in the work of writers like Leslie Marmo Silko, Louise Erdrich, Anna Lee Walters, Ella Deloria, Ignatia Broker, and others link that body of writing to the traditional functionality of ancestral storytelling.

MILLER, CHARLES "GUY" (Skokomish)
(tribal chairperson)
Affiliation & Address: Chair, Skokomish Tribal Nation, 80 N. Tribal Center Rd., Skokomish, WA 98584. (360) 426-4232. E-mail: gmiller@skokomish.org

MILLER, DALE A. (Tolowa/Yurok)
(tribal chairperson)
Affiliation & Address: Chairperson, Elk Valley Rancheria, 2332 Howland Hill Rd., Crescent City, CA 95531 (707) 464-4680. E-mail: dmiller@elk-valley.com.

MILLER, DONNA
(Indian education program director)
Affiliation: Bowler Public Schools, Indian Education Program, P.O. Box 8, Bowler, WI 54416 (715) 793-4101. E-mail: millerd@bowler.k12.wi.us.

MILLER, GLENN (Menominee)
(tribal chairperson)
Affiliation: Menominee Indian Tribe of Wisconsin, P.O. Box 910, Keshena, WI 54135 (715) 799-5100.

MILLER, GREGORY L. (Stockbridge-Munsee Mohican)
(former tribal vice president)
Affiliation & Address: Former Vice President, Stockbridge-Munsee Community Band of Mohican Indians, P.O. Box 70, Bowler, WI 54416 (715) 793-4111. E-mail: gregory.miller@mohican-nsn.gov.

MILLER, HAROLD (Crow Creek Sioux)
(tribal chairperson)
Affiliation: Crow Creek Sioux Tribal Council, P.O. Box 50, Fort Thompson, SD 57339 (605) 245-2221.

MILLER, JARED
(attorney)
Education: University of Montana, BA (Journalism); University of Wyoming College of Law, JD. *Affiliation & Address*: Galanda Broadman PLLC, 8606 35th Ave. NE, Suite L1, Seattle, WA 98115 (206) 919-5044. E-mail: jared@galandabroadman.com*Practice*: Tribal Law, Federal Indian Law, Civil Litigation. Jared's practice focuses on tribal court litigation & representing businesses & tribal governments in public affairs. Jared is licensed in more than a dozen tribal jurisdictions, where he litigates civil matters. A former newspaper reporter, Jared is skilled at assisting organizations in responding to public and private crises. *Memebership*: Washington State Bar Association, Indian Law Section, 2012-Present.

MILLER, JAY (Delaware) 1947-
(Native Americanist)
Born April 7, 1947. *Education*: University of New Mexico, BA, 1969; Rutgers University, PhD, 1972. *Principal occupation*: Native Americanist. *Affiliation & Address*: Executive Committee (1975-present), Dept. of American Indian Studies, Box 354305, University of Washington, Seattle, WA 98195 (206) 543-9082. *Past professional posts*: Teaching assistant, lecturer, instructor of anthropology, Rutgers University at Livingston & Newark, 1969-72; assistant professor of anthropology, Montclair State College. *Other professional posts*: Adjunct curator, North American Ethnology, Washington State Memorial Thomas Burke Museum; consultant, San Juan County Archaeological Research Project, 1973-; contributor, Smithsonian Handbook of North American Indians. *Memberships*: American Anthropological Association (Fellow); Society for American Archaeology. *Awards, honors*: National Science Foundation Predoctoral Fellowship, 1969; grant-in-aid for research in New Jersey history from the New Jersey Historical Commission, 1973; Summer Salary Award, University of Washington Graduate Research Fund, 1974; Delaware Indian Music, University of Washington Graduate Research Fund, Interdisciplinary Grant, 1975-76; Social Context of Southern Tsimshian, Jacobs Research Fund, Whatcom County Museum, 1977; among others. *Field research*: Archaeology, Anasazi Origins Project (summers, 1966-67); ethnography, Southwestern Pueblos, 1966-69; ethnography, Unami Delaware, 1972-; Southern Tsimshian: new language and ethnography at Hartley Bay, 1976 and Kelmtu, 1977, British Columbia; Colville Reservation: conceptual landscape, 1977-. *Dissertation*: The Anthropology of Keres Identity (A Structural Study of the Ethnographic and Archaeological Record of the Keres Pueblos). *Published works*: Shamanic Odyssey, Mourning Dove, Tsimshian and Their Neighbors. Numerous papers & articles.

MILLER, JEANETTE
(Indian education program director)
Affiliation: Rush-Henrietta Central School District, Indian Education Project, 2034 Lehigh Station Rd., Henrietta, NY 14467 (716) 359-5047.

MILLER, JEFF (Omaha)
(tribal chairperson)
Affiliation & Address: Chairperson, Omaha Tribal Council, P.O. Box 368, Macy, NE 68039 (402) 837-5391.

MILLER, JOHN (Potawatomi)
(tribal chairperson)
Affiliation: Pokagon Band of Potawatomi Indians, P.O. Box 180, Dowagiac, MI 49047 (616) 782-8998.

MILLER, KAREN L. (Tolowa)
(rancheria chairperson)
Affiliation: Smith River Rancheria, 250 N. Indian Rd., Smith River, CA 95567 (707) 487-9255.

MILLER, LATISHA (Paskenta Nomlaki)
(tribal vice chairperson)
Affiliation & Address: Vice Chairperson, Paskenta Band of Nomlaki Indians, 2625 Everett Freeman Way, P.O. Box 709 • Corning, CA 96021, CA 95963 (530) 528-3538 Fax 865-1870; E-mail: lmiller@paskenta.org

MILLER, LESLIE (Pomo)
(tribal co-chairperson)
Affiliation: Scotts Valley Band of Pomo Indians, 149 N. Main #200, Lakeport, CA 95453 (707) 263-4771.

MILLER, LLOYD B.
(attorney; Alaska Native law)
Education: Yale University, BA, 1975; University of Virginia School of Law, JD, 1978. *Affiliation & Address*: Partner, Sonosky, Chambers, Sachse, Endreson & Perry, LLP, 900 W. Fifth Ave., Suite 700, Anchorage, AK 99501 (907) 258-6377. E-mail: lloyd@sonosky.net. Lloyd joined the firm in 1979 and opened the firm's Alaska offices in 1984. Mr. Miller specializes in appellate and trial litigation, as well as congressional advocacy, for tribal governments, inter-tribal

organizations, Native American health and social service providers and Native American-owned profit and non-profit corporations. Mr. Miller's practice involves Indian Self-Determination Act health and social service matters, labor law issues, gaming issues, ICWA matters, environmental issues, and a wide range of additional Indian and general law matters. Mr. Miller also regularly assists clients in such diverse matters as government contract negotiations, labor law, fishing and hunting rights, child welfare matters, federal recognition, tribal constitutional law, environmental law, trust land acquisitions, land claims and corporate law. A significant portion of Mr. Miller's career has been devoted to litigation against the federal government on behalf of Tribes and tribal organizations contracting with the United States under the Indian Self-Determination Act, together with related legislative and appropriations work in Congress. Mr. Miller was counsel for the Cherokee Nation and the Shoshone-Paiute Tribes in the leading Supreme Court case setting the Government's liability for contract support cost underpayments, *Cherokee Nation v. Leavitt*, 543 U.S. 631 (2005). His successes also include the 2012 follow-on victory against the Indian Health Service in *Arctic Slope Native Ass'n*, v. *Sebelius*, 133 S. Ct. 22 (2012), *on remand ASNA* v. *Sebelius*, 501 Fed. Appx. 957 (Fed. Cir. 2012), and the successful *Ramah* litigation, *Salazar v. Ramah Navajo Chapter*, 132 S. Ct. 2181 (2012) (co-counsel to a class of over 600 Tribes and tribal organizations seeking damages against the Bureau of Indian Affairs for contract support cost underpayments). Mr. Miller has led the firm's successes in recovering over $750 million against the Indian Health Service for our tribal clients, & continues to press nationwide class damages against the BIA. More recently, he successfully litigated *Southcentral Foundation v. Roubideaux*, No. 13-164, Dkt. 77 (D. Alaska Sept 23, 2014) to further enforce tribal contracting rights with the federal government. He was a law clerk to the late James M. Fitzgerald of the United States District Court for the District of Alaska, and for whom the Alaska federal courthouse is named. He has served on the boards of several non-profit organizations & on the Conference Executive Committee for the Ninth Circuit Court of Appeals. He has also been honored by the National Indian Health Board, the Alaska Legislature and the Healthy Alaska Natives Foundation, all for his work to advance Native American health and tribal self-determination.

MILLER, MICHAEL R. (Chippewa-Stockbridge Munsee) 1946-
(Native American programs director)
Born April 26, 1946, Minneapolis, Minn. *Education*: Appalachian State University, Boone, N.C., BS, 1968; University of Minnesota, Duluth, MSW, 1984. *Principal occupation*: Native American programs director. *Address*: University of Wisconsin, River Falls, WI 54022. *Affiliations*: Indian education coordinator-supervisor, Title IV-A, Superior Public Schools, WI, 1974-81; Native American Outreach Coordinator, Northland College, 1981-84; director of Native American programs, international student advisor, University of Wisconsin, River Falls, WI, 1984-. Memberships: Wisconsin Indian Education Association, 1985-; National Association for Foreign Student Affairs, 1985-. *Interests*: My main areas of interest include Native education, the social aspects of education, improving the image of Native Americans as this image relates to alcoholism, and learning more about international problems and how they relate to the U.S. and Native American experience.

MILLER, RAYNELL (Paiute)
(tribal chairperson)
Affiliation: Walker River Paiute Tribe, P.O. Box 220, Schurz, NV 89427 (775) 773-2306.

MILLER, ROBERT J. (Eastern Shawnee)
(attorney; associate professor of law)
Education: Northwestern School of Law, Lewis & Clark College, JD, 1991. *Affiliation & Address*: Professor of Indian Law, University of Arizona Sandra Day O'Connor College of Law, McAllister & Orange Sts., Box 877906, Tempe, AZ 85287 (480) 965-6181; E-mail: Robert.miller@asu.edu*Other professional posts*: Visiting Associate Professor of Law, Indian Law Program, Lewis & Clark College of Law, Portland, OR. He teaches Indian law, Cultural Resources Protection, and other subjects. He serves on the board of National Indian Child Welfare Association, Oregon Native American Business Entrepreneurial Network, the Eastern Oregon University Foundation, and as a past Chair of the Oregon State Bar Indian Law Section. He has presented numerous federal & state training sessions on Indian law at various conferences, law schools & colleges. *Past professional posts*: He served as tribal appellate judge for various Northwestern tribes since 1995; Adjunct professor of Law, Northwestern School of Law, Lewis & Clark College, 1993-98; practiced Indian law with Hobbs, Straus, Dean & Walker, 1995-99; Associate Professor of Law (1999-2013), The Institute for Tribal Government, The Hatfield School of Government, College of Urban & Public Affairs, Portland State University. *Awards, honors*: His tribe appointed him to the Circle of Tribal Advisors (COTA), which worked with the National Committee of the Lewis & Clark Bicentennial in 2006. *Publication*: Native America, Discovered & Conquered: Thomas Jefferson, Lewis & Clark, and Manifest Destiny. Mr. Miller has published numerous articles on Indian law including

fishing & hunting rights, economic develop-ment, Federal Indian alcohol policies, & tribal government court systems.

MILLER, RODNEY (Assiniboine)
(WIA director; commission member)
Address: P.O. Box 901, Wolf Point, MT 59201. *Affiliation*: Director, Workforce Investment Act (WIA), Fort Peck Tribe, P.O. Box 102, Poplar, MT 59225 (406) 768-5805; member, State Tribal Economic Development Commission (STEDC), c/o Montana Dept. of Commerce, Helena, MT.

MILLER, THOMAS G.
(school administrator)
Affiliation: Hannahville Indian School, N14911 Hannahville B1 Rd., Wilson, MI 49896 (906) 466-2952.

MILLER, VERNON (Omaha)
(former tribal chairperson)
Affiliation & Address: Former chairperson, Omaha Tribe, P.O. Box 368, Macy, NE 68039 (402) 837-5391.

MILLER, VIRGINIA P. 1940-
(professor of anthropology)
Born October 28, 1940, Paterson, N.J. *Education*: Smith College, 1958-60; University of California, Berkeley, BA, 1962; University of California, Davis, MA, 1967, PhD, 1973. *Address & Affiliation*: Professor of anthropology, Dept. of Sociology & Anthropology, Dalhousie University, Halifax, Nova Scotia B3H 1T2, Can., 1974-. E-mail: vpmiller@ns.sympatico.ca. *Memberships*: American Anthropological Assn; American Society for Ethnohistory; Canadian Anthropology Society; Canadian Historical Assn (Native History Study Group, 1989-). *Interests*: Ethnohistory of North America, especially California and Eastern Canada; historical demography. *Published work*: Ukomno'm: The Yuki Indians of Northern California (Ballena Press, 1979); articles on Micmac & Yuki ethno-history and demography.

MILLER, YVONNE (Miwok)
(tribal chairperson)
Affiliation & Address: Chairperson, Ione Band of Miwok Indians. P.O. Box 699, Plymouth, CA 95669 (209) 245-5800.

MILLER, WALLACE A. (Stockbridge-Munsee Mohican)
(former tribal president)
Affiliation & Address: Former President, Stockbridge-Munsee Community Band of Mohican Indians, P.O. Box 70, Bowler, WI 54416 (715) 793-4111. E-mail: wally.miller@mohican-nsn.gov.

MILLION, DIAN (Tanana Athabascan)
(Professor of American Indian studies)
Education: University of California, Berkeley, MA & PhD (Ethnic Studies). *Affiliation & Address*: Assistant Professor, Dept. of American Indian Studies, Padelford Hall, Box 354305, University of Washington, Seattle, WA 98195 (206) 616-8032. E-mail: dianm@u.washington.edu. *Research Interests*: Politics of knowledge & intellectual production for Native & indigenous peoples; community mental health issues in Indian Country. *Other professional posts*: Co-founder of Northwest Native American Writers, with Gloria Bird, Elizabeth Woody, Ed Edmo & Vincent Wannassay, producing publications such as "Dancing on the Rim of the World: An Anthology of Contemporary Northwest Native American Writing." *Published works*: Articles, essays & poetry.

MILLS, ANTONIA
(professor of First Nations Studies)
Education: Radcliff College, BA; Harvard, PhD. *Affiliation & Address*: Professor, Department of Fist Nations Studies, admin. 3079, 3333 University Way, Prince George BC V2N 4Z9 Canada (250) 960-6690. E-mail: millsa@unbc.ca. *Research Interests*: First Nations land claims, religion & law, and reincarnation beliefs & cases. She has conducted field work with the Beaver Indians since 1964. *Past professional post*: Research Assistant Professor & Lecturer, University of Virginia. *Awards, honors*: Awarded a Shastri Indo-Canadian Instituted Felowship for "A Longitudian Study of Young Adults who were said to Remember a Previous Life." *Published works*: Co-editor with Richard Slobodin, Amerindian Rebirth: Reincarnation Belief Among North Ameican Indians & Inuit (1994); Eagle Down Is Our Law: Witsutit'en Feasts, Laws & Land Clais (UBC Press, 1994); Hang Onn To Those Words: Johnny David's Delgamuukw Testimony (University of Toronto Press, 2005); numerous articles in scholarly journals.

MILLS, BARBARA J.
(professor of American Indian Studies; anthropologist/archaeologist)
Education: University of Pennsylvania, BA, 1976; University of New Mexico, MA, 1983, PhD, 1989. *Affiliation & Address*: University of Arizona, Emil W. Haury Bldg., Room 408E, Tucson, AZ 85721 (520) 621-9671. E-mail: bmills@email.arizona.edu. She is also an interdisciplinary faculty member with

the American Indian Studies Program (1991-present). *Research Interests*: Ceramic analysis,, archaeologies of inequality, migration, colonialism, memory & Materiality, heritage preservation, Southwest archaeology. *Past professional post*: Director, University of Arizona Archaeological Field School, where she worked on collaborative heritage projects with the White Mountain Apache Tribe, the Hopi Tribe, and the Apache Sitgeaves National Forest. She also worked closely with the Pueblo of Zuni on a recent NEH-funded exhibit, "Hawikku: Echos of Our Past" for their tribal museum. *Interests*: Southwestern archaeology; Native American ceramics; Native American gender & archaeology; materials culture. *Published works*: Edited "Alternative Leadership Strategies in the Prehispanic Southwest" (University of Arizona Press, 2000); and edited "Identity, Feasting & the Archaeology of the Greater Southwest" (University of Colorado Press, 2004); currently writing a book about migration & ethnogenesis in the Western Pueblo area that focuses on the effects of the demographic upheavals of the thirteenth century for Ancestral Pueblo populations; numerous articles in scholarly journals.

MILLS, KATHRYN
(organization co-founder & vice president)
Affiliation & Address: Vice President, (2012-present) Creating Stronger Nations, Inc., P.O. Box 859, Hanover, NH 03755 (603) 643-6066 E-mail: kmills@dciamerica.com. *Past professional posts*: Founder & CEO, Creating Stronger Nations, 1992-2012.

MILLS, MONTE
(Indian law clinic co-director)
Education: Lewis & Clark College, BA, 1999; University of Colorado, JD, 2003. *Affiliation & Address*: Assistant Professor & Co-Director, Margery Hunter Brown Indian Law Clinic, Alexander Blewett III School of Law, University of Montana, 32 Campus Dr. #6552, Missoula, MT 59812 (406) 243-4311. E-mail: monte.mills@umontana.edu. He teaches a variety of Indian law courses & works with clinical students on a range of legal matters in the Indian Law Clinic. *Past professional post*: Director, Legal Department, Southern Ute Indian Tribe (2005-2015); *Associate/In-House Attorney Trainee*, Maynes, Bradford, Shipps & Sheftel, Durango, Colorado (2003-2005); *Research Assistant*, Professor Charles F. Wilkinson (2001-2003); as director of the legal department for the Southern Ute Indian Tribe in Colorado, an in-house counsel department that he helped organize & implement in 2005 following completion of a unique two-year in-house attorney training program. Monte represented and counseled the Tribe on a broad array of issues, including litigation in tribal, state & federal courts, legislative matters before the Colorado General Assembly and the United States Congress, and internal tribal matters such as contracting, code-drafting, and gaming issues.

MILLS, ROBERT (Mashpee Wampanoag)
(tribal supreme court judge)
Education: Boston College Law School, JD. *Affiliation & Address*: Judge, Supreme Court, Mashpee Wampanoag Indian Tribe, P.O. Box 1048, Mashpee, MA 02649 (508) 477-0208. *Memberships*: Massachusetts & Pennsylvania bar associations.

MINER, DYLAN AT (Metis)
(director of American Indian & Indigenous Studies program; artist, activist, scholar)
Education: University of New Mexico, PhD. *Affiliation & Address*: Director, American Indian & Indigenous Studies Program, College of Arts & Sciences; Association professor Residential College in the Arts & Humanities, Michigan State Univefrsity, 362 Bogue St., Rm. C210, East Lansing, MI 48825 (517) 884-1323. E-mail: dminer@msu.edu. *Other professional posts*: Adjunct Curator of Indigenous art, MSU Museum; founding member of the Justseeds artists collective; on The Board of the Michigan Indian Education Council. *Awards, honors*: In 2010, he was granted an Artist Leadership Fellowship from the National Museum of the American Indian (Smithsonian Institution). Miner has been featured in more than 20 solo exhibitions. Published works: Creating Aztlan: Chicago Art, Indigenous Sovereignty, and Lowriding Acros Turtle Island (University of Arizona Press, 2014).

MINHAS, JASJIT
(college president)
Affiliation & Address: Lac Courte Oreilles Ojibwa Community College, RR 2, Box 2357, Hayward, WI 54843 (715) 634-4790.

MINTHORN, ANTONE C. (Cayuse)
(tribal board chairperson)
Education: Gonzaga University; Eastern Oregon State College, BA. *Affiliation*: Chairman, Tribe's General Council, 1983-97; Chairman of the Board of Trustees, Dec. 1997 to Dec. 2001, 2003-present), Confederated Tribes of the Umatilla Indian Reservation, P.O. Box 638, Pendleton, OR 97801 (541) 276-3165. *Past professional post*: Served on the board of the Affiliated Tribes of Northwest Indians. *Military service*: U.S. Marine Corps, 1957-60.

MINTHORN, ROBIN (Kiowa/Apache/Nez Perce/Umatilla/Assiniboine)
(professor in Educational Leadership & Native American studies)
Education: University of Oklahoma BA (Psychology & Native American Studies), 2002, MA (Human Relations; Oklahoma State University, MA (Adult & Higher Education), 2007, PhD (Higher Education & Public Policy), 2012. *Affiliation & Address*: Assistant Professor in Educational Leadership & Native American Studies; Director (2012-present), Native American Leadership Program, Department of Native American Studies, University of New Mexico, 2500 Campus Blvd. NE, 3rd Floor Rm 377, Albuquerque, NM 87131 (505) 277-3917. Robin's research interests include indigenous leadership perspectives & experiences of Native college students, Indigenous female leaders, and multigenerational perspectives within tribal communities. *Other professional posts*: Elected to the National Indian Education Association's board of directors, 2012-present; member (2013-present), board of directors of the National Indian Youth Council. *Past professional posts*: Teacher, Comanche Nation College; Coordinator of Native American Affairs (2007-12), Office of Multicultural Affairs, Oklahoma State University, Stillwater, OK; teacher, Pawnee Nation College (two years).

MIRABAL, ERNEST L. (Nambe Pueblo)
(Pueblo governor)
Affiliation & Address: Pueblo of Nambe, Rt. 1 Box 117-BB 8, Nambe Pueblo, NM 87747 (505) 455-2036.

MIRANDA, JENNIE (Luiseno)
(tribal spokesperson)
Affiliation & Address: Pechanga Band of Mission Indians, P.O. Box 1477, Temecula, CA 92390 (714) 676-2768.

MIRANDA, LAURA (Luiseno)
(attorney)
Education: UCLA, B.A. (Philosophy); Cornell Law School, J.D. *Address & Affiliation & Address*: Deputy General Counsel, Pechanga Band of Luiseno Indians, P.O. Box 1477, Temecula, CA 92593 (909) 676-2768. *Other professional post*: Appointed by Governor Schwarzenneger as a commissioner to the Native American Heritage Commission in November 2007; vice chairperson, 2013-present. Board member, Riverside County Tribal Traditional Resources Advisory Committee; elected representative to the Luiseno/Cupeno Inter-Tribal NAGPRA Coalition (LINC). *Past professional posts*: Founding partner of Miranda, Tomaras & Ogas, LLP; Directing Attorney, California Indian Legal Services. She focused on assisting tribes with protection & preservation of their cultural resources, sacred resources & Native American human remains utilizing federal & state environmental laws, & historic preservation laws. *Interests*: Presentations on cultural resources protection to tribes, government organizations, universities, and interested organizations. She has testified on cultural resources protection.

MIRANDA, LORETTA L. (Morongo Band Mission Indians)
(attorney, Indian Law Fellow)
Education: California State University, Northridge, BA, 2008; Lewis & Clark Law School, JD, 2016. *Affiliation & Address*: Indian Law Fellow (2016-17), Berkey Williams LLP, 2030 Addison St., Suite 410, Berkeley, CA 94704 (510) 548-7070. While at Lewis & Clark Law School, Ms. Miranda served as Vice-President of the Native American Law Student Association (NALSA) and participated in the 2015 National NALSA moot court competition. Ms. Miranda was also a recipient of the Nelson D. Terry Scholarship, which is funded by the Quinault Indian Allottees Association. Ms. Miranda has clerked for the Department of the Interior, the Office of the Regional Solicitor in Portland, Oregon, the Native American Rights Fund (NARF) in Alaska, and for the Yurok Tribal Court. As a Fellow at Berkey Williams LLP, Ms. Miranda will lend her considerable talents to work on behalf of tribal clients in all of the firm's practice areas, including land rights, water rights, environmental and cultural resources, health care, Indian child welfare, and employment.

MISEGAN, JENNIFER (Lake Superior Ojibwe)
(tribal vice president)
Affiliation & Address: Vice President, Keweenah Bay Indian Community, 16429 Beartown Rd., Baraga, MI 49908 (906) 353-6623. E-mail: jmisegan@kbic-nsn.gov

MISIKIN, ALICIA (Aleut)
(radio station manager)
Affiliation: KUHB - FM, Pribiloff School, St. Paul, AK 99660 (907) 546-2254.

MISQUEZ, SARA (Mescalero Apache)
(tribal president)
Affiliation: Mescalero Apache Tribal Council, P.O. Box 227, Mescalero, NM 88340 (505) 464-4494.

MITCHELL, FRANCIS (Penobscot)
(former tribal governor)
Affiliation: Penobscot Indian Nation, Community Bldg., Indian Island,
6 River Rd., Old Town, ME 04468 (207) 827-7776.

MITCHELL, GARY E. (Prairie Potawatomi)
(former tribal chairperson)
Affiliation: Prairie Band Potawatomi Tribal Council, 14880 K. Rd.,
Mayetta, KS 66509 (913) 966-2255.

MITCHELL, JEFF (Klamath)
(tribal chairperson)
Affiliation: Klamath Tribe, P.O. Box 436, Chiloquin, OR 97624 (541) 783-2219.

MITCHELL, JOHN BEAR (Penobscot)
(lecturer in Wabanaki studies)
Education: University of Maine, BA (Elementary Education), MA (Educational
Leadership). *Affiliation & Address*: Wabanaki Center Outreach & Student
Development Coordinator, Native American Waiver Coordinator, Lecturer of
Wabanaki Studies, Native American Studies Program, Department of
Anthropology, 5773 S. Stevens Hall, Orono, ME 04469 (207) 581-1801. E-mail:
john.mitchell@umit.maine.edu. *Other professional post*: Teaches Introductory
to Wabanaki History & Contemporary Issues, Multicultural and Diversity, and
team teaches an Ethnomath class. *Past professional posts*: Native Studies
teacher at the Indian Island School; served on numerous museum &
educational boards throughout the state with missions based on Maine's
Wabanaki people. *Awards, honors*: Appointed by his tribal council to serve as
a member of the Wabanaki Education Committee. *Interests*: Singing &
storytelling, production of triball sponsored awareness viseos, and other
documentaries with topics on Maine's Native people.

MITCHELL, SR. KATERI
(center director)
Affiliation & Address: Tekakwitha Conference National Center, P.O. Box 6768,
Great Falls, MT 59406-6768 (800) 842-9635; (406) 727-0147. E-mail:
sisterkateri@worldnet.att.net.

MITCHELL, RON (Cherokee)
(artist; gallery owner)
Affiliation: Cherokee Artist Studio-Gallery, Rt. 1, Box 263, Prague, OK 74864
(405) 567-2856.

MITCHELL, RUDI L. (Omaha)
(former tribal chairperson)
Affiliation: Omaha Tribe, P.O. Box 368, Macy, NE 68039 (402) 837-5391.

MITCHELL, TERRY (Waccamaw Siouan)
(tribal vice chairperson)
Affiliation: Waccamaw Siouan Tribe, P.O. Box 69, Bolton, NC 28423
(910) 655-8778. E-mail: terry.mitchell@waccamaw-siouan.com.
Website: www.waccamaw-siouan.com.

MITCHELL, THEODORE N.
(Indian center director)
Address & Affiliation: Wabanaki Center, University of Maine, Rm. 314, 5724
Dunn Hall, Orono, ME 04469 (207) 581-1417; E-mail: tedm@maine.maine.edu

MITCHELL, WAYNE LEE (Santee Sioux-Mandan) 1937-
(health administrator)
Born March 25, 1937, Rapid City, S.D. *Education*: University of Redlands, BA,
1960; Arizona State University, MSW, 1970, EdD, 1979. Principal occupation:
Health administrator. *Address*: P.O. Box 9592, Phoenix, AZ 85068. *Affiliations*:
Professional social worker, various county, state & federal agencies, 1962-70;
social worker, BIA, Phoenix, AZ, 1970-77; assistant professor, Arizona State
University, Tempe, AZ, 1977-84; supervisor, 1984-88, program director of
social services, 1988-2003, U.S. Public Health Service, Indian Health Service,
Phoenix, AZ. *Other professional post*: Assistant professor, Arizona State
University. *Military service*: U.S. Coast Guard, 1960-66. *Community activities*:
Phoenix Indian Community School (board of directors); Phoenix Indian Center
(board of directors); Phoenix Area Health Advisory Board, 1975; Community
Behavioral Mental Health Board, 1976; Council on Foreign Relations; Heard
Museum (board of trustees). *Memberships*: National Congress of American
Indians; National Association of Social Workers; Association of American
Indian Social Workers. *Awards, honors*: Delegate to White House Conference
on Poverty, 1964; nominated, Outstanding Young Men of America, 1977;
Phoenix Indian Center: Community Service Award, 1977; Temple of Islam
Community Service Award, 1980; Arizona State University: Community
Service Award, 1996; Phoenix Area Indian Health Service: Professional
Employee of the Year Award, 2000; NASW: Lifetime Achievement Award,
2003; Arizona State University: Outstanding Native American Alumnus, 2003;

Combined Federal Campaign Award: Outstanding Volunteer, 2003. *Interests*:
World traveler. Biographical sources: Who's Who in the West; Who's Who in
America; Men of Achieve-ment. *Published works*: The Inside-Outside School
Concept As Observed in Educational Institutions in the People's Republic of
China; A Study of Cultural Identification on the Educational Objectives of Hopi
Indian High School Seniors (master's thesis), (Arizona State University, 1970);
Native American Substance Abuse (Arizona State University Press, 1983);
American Indian Families: Developmental Strategies & Community Health
(Arizona State U. Press, 1983).

MITCHELL, WAYNE T. (Penobscot)
(tribal representative)
Affiliation: Penobscot Indian Nation, 12 Wabanaki Way, Indian Island, ME
04468 (207) 827-7771.

MITCHELSON, MICHAEL
(attorney; professor of law; board chairperson)
Education: Columbia University School of Law, JD. *Affiliation & Address*:
Assistant Professor of Law (1999-present), Oklahoma City University School of
Law, 2501 N. Blackwelder, Oklahoma City, OK 73106 (405) 208-5337. *Past
professional posts*: Administrative Law Judge for the State of Oklahoma;
private attorney for Kornfeld Franklin Renegar & Randall.

MITCHUM, MARIA (Maidu)
(study skills specialist)
Affiliation: Learning Skills Center, University of California, Davis, Basement,
South Hall, Davis, CA 95616 (916) 752-2013.

MITCHUM, WAYNE R. (Cachil De-He Wintun)
(tribal chairperson)
Affiliation: Cachel De-He Band of Wintun Indians of the Colusa Indian
Community, 3730 Hwy. 45, Colusa, CA 95932 (530) 458-8231.

MITHUN, MARIANNE 1946-
(linguist, professor of linguistics)
Born April 8, 1946, Bremerton, Wash. Education: Pomona College, BA, 1969;
Yale University, MA, M.Phil., PhD, 1969-1974. *Affiliation & Address*: Professor
of Linguistics (1986-present), Dept. of Linguistics, University of California,
Santa Barbara, CA 93106; E-Mail: mithun@linguistics.ucsb.edu. *Past
professional posts*: Assistant/associate professor of linguistics, SUNY at
Albany, 1973-81; professor of linguistics, University of California, Berkeley,
1981-86. *Community activities*: Organizer, Iroquois Conference, 1973-85.
Memberships: Society for Linguistic Anthropology (president); American
Anthropological Association (executive committee, board of directors,
administrative advisory committee); Society for the Study of the Indigenous
Languages of the Americas (president, vice-president, executive board);
Linguistics Society of America (executive board). *Interests*: American Indian
languages and linguistics, especially Iroquoian (Mohawk, Oneida, Onondaga,
Cayuga, Seneca, Tuscarora, Huron), Pomo (Central Pomo), Siouan (Dakota,
Lakota, Tutelo), Algonquian (Cree); Yu'pik Eskimo; Navajo. *Published works*: A
Grammar of Tuscarora (Garland Press, 1976); Kanien'keha'Okara'shon:'a
(Mohawk Stories) & Iontenwennaweienstahkhwa' (Mohawk Spelling Dictionary)
(New York State Museum Bulletin, 1976,1977); The Languages of Native
America (University of Texas Press, 1979); Watewayestanih: A Grammar of
Cayuga (Woodland Indian Culture & Education Centre, 1982); Extending the
Rafters: An Interdisciplinary Approach to the Iroquois (SUNY Press, 1984);
The Native Languages of North America (Cambridge University Press, 1999);
numerous articles in "International Journal of American Linguistics."

MITRE, ALFRED L. (Paiute)
(tribal vice chairperson)
Affiliation: Las Vegas Paiute Tribe, 1 Paiute Dr., Las Vegas, NV 89106
(702) 386-3926.

MITTEN, LISA A. (Mohawk)
(librarian)
Education: University of Pittsburgh, BA, MLS. *Address*: 32 Stewart St., New
BrItain, CT 06053 (860) 347-6933. E-mail: mohawk6nations@yahoo.com.
Affiliation & Address: CHOICE, American Library Association, 575 Main St.,
Suite 300, Middletown, CT 06457. E-mail: lmitten@ala-choice.org. Website:
http://www.nativeculturelinks.com/indians.html. *Other professional posts*: Jury
Chairperson, American Indian Youth Literature Awards by the American Indian
Library Association. *Community activities*: Consultant, Alcoa Hall of Native
Americans, Carnegie Museum of Natural History, Pittsburgh, PA; board
member, Oyate, Berkeley, CA; Board of Directors, Council of Three Rivers
American Indian Center, Pittsburgh, PA, 1998-. *Memberships*: American
Library Association; American Indian Library Association (Member-at-Large);
National Museum of the American Indian; Native American Rights Fund
(NARF). *Published work*: Assistant editor, "Native America in the Twentieth
Century: An Encyclopedia" (Garland Publishing, 1994).

MNN, VICTOR (Paiute)
(tribal chairperson)
Affiliation & Address: Lovelock Paiute Tribe, P.O. Box 878, Lovelock, NV 89419 (775) 273-7861.

MODUGNO, REV. THOMAS A.
(director)
Affiliation: Marquette League for Catholic Indian Missions, 1011 First Ave., New York, NY 10022 (212) 371-1000.

MOE, ANGELA (Forest County Potawatomi)
(tribal vice chairperson)
Affiliation & Address: Forest County Potawatomi Community, P.O. Box 340, Crandon, WI 54520 (715) 478-2903.

MOFFETT, ELLIOT (Nez Perce)
(BIA agency supt.)
Affiliation: Northern Idaho Agency, BIA, P.O. Box 277, Lapwai, ID 83540 (208) 843-2300.

MOFSIE, LOUIS (*Greenrainbow*) (Hopi/Winnebago) 1936-
(teacher; founder, Thunderbird Dancers)
Born May 3, 1936, Brooklyn, N.Y. *Education*: Buffalo State Teachers College, BS, 1958; Hofstra University, MA, 1973. *Address*: 204 W. Central Ave., Maywood, NJ 07607 (201) 587-9633. E-mail: louismofsie@gmail.com. *Affiliation*: Director, Thunderbird American Indian Dancers, New York, NY; *Other professional post*: Art teacher, East Meadow Board of Education, East Meadow, NY (36 years); consultant, National Museum of the American Indian, 1991. *Community activities*: Chairman of the Board, American Indian Community House, New York, NY; president, International Council of McBurney YMCA. *Memberships*: New York State Art Teachers Association; Classroom Teachers Association. *Awards, honors*: Association of Southwestern Indians Award for painting submitted to the Annual Indian Artists Exhibition, Santa Fe Art Museum; New York City Indian of the Year, 1984; 1986 Calumet Award for Outstanding Achievement by the American Indian Community House, New York, NY; 1987 Ethnic New York Award; 1990 Outstanding Achievement Award by the New York State Council of the Disabled; 1991 Outstanding Achievement Award by the New York City Lawyers Local; Ellis Island Congressional Medal of Honor, 1993. *Interests*: American Indian dance - "as a dance company, we have traveled all over the U.S., Canada, Israel and Mexico. I am currently teaching dance at Brooklyn College and the YMCA." *Biographical sources*: "Indians of Today," by Marion Gridley; "American Indian Painters," by Joanne Snodgrass; "Dance Annuals," by John Mills. *Published work*: Co-author & illustrator, The Hopi Way (J.B. Lippincott, 1970); illustrator, Coyote Tales, and Teepee Tales (Holt, Rinehart & Winston).

MOLASH, CHARLENE
(IHS-executive officer)
Affiliation: Bemidji IHS Area Office, 127 Federal Bldg., Bemidji, MN 56601 (218) 759-3413.

MOLIN, PAULETTE FAIRBANKS (White Earth Chippewa)
(educator, writer)
Address: 102 Willis Church Yard, Hampton, VA 23669. E-Mail: pfmolin@ aol.com. *Affiliations*: Director, American Indian Educational Opportunities Program, Hampton University, Hampton, VA, 1991-99; assistant dean, Graduate College, Hampton University, 1991-94; director, Indian Elementary Curriculum Project, Minneapolis Public Schools. *Memberships*: American Indian Science & Engineering Society; Indigenous Women's Network; National Indian Education Association; Wordcraft Circle of Native Writers & Storytellers (board officer). *Published works*: Co-author, "To Lead and To Serve: American Indian Education at Hampton Institute, 1878-1923" (Hampton University & Virginia Foundation for the Humanities & Public Policy, 1989); co-author, "Unanswered Questions: Native Americans and Euro-Americans in Minnesota" for an exhibition & publication entitled "Minnesota 1900: Art & Life on the Upper Mississippi 1890-1915" (Associated University Press, 1994); Additional writings have included co-authorship of biographical booklets (historic Hampton students from Fort Berthold and Standing Rock), co-authorship of an encyclopedia; authorship of encyclopedia entries, curricula units, journal articles, and other publications. Guest co-editor of "Callaloo" (a special issue, Native American Literature, Winter, 1994); coedited, American Indian Stereotypes in the World of Children, 2nd Ed. (Scarecrow Press, 1999).

MOLINE, VANYA HOGEN (Oglala Lakota)
(attorney)
Education: University of Minnesota, BA, 1990; University of Minnesota Law School, JD, 1993. *Affiliation & Address*: Founding Partner, Hogen Adams PLLP, 1935 W. County Road B2, Suite 460, St. Paul, MN 55113 (651) 842-9100. E-mail: vhogenmoline@hogenadams.com. Vanya has practiced Indian law for 20 years, representing tribal governments and their business partners.

Vanya is an experienced litigator in federal, state, and tribal courts, and has successfully handled multi-million-dollar litigation and arbitration matters over key aspects of the Indian Gaming Regulatory Act. Meanwhile, she maintains an active transactional practice, focusing primarily on Indian gaming and tribal financing. Vanya won an important victory in the South Dakota Supreme Court that stopped South Dakota from imposing its motor-fuel taxes on Indian reservations in the state. And she has won both federal- and tribal-court victories in disputes over tribal rights to control reservation land use. *Awards, honors*: "Lawyer of the Year" in Native American Law for Minneapolis in 2012, and has been named as a "Super Lawyer" in Minnesota 11 times, as a "Best Lawyer" in Native American law in 2009-2014, and is AV-rated by Martindale Hubbell. She is a frequent speaker at Indian-law seminars around the country. Vanya is also a judge for the Shakopee Mdewakanton Sioux Community Tribal Court. Outside the office, Vanya has served on the boards of the Minnesota Center for Environmental Advocacy, the Nature Conservancy (Minnesota, South Dakota, & North Dakota Chapter), and the University of St. Thomas Law School. Vanya and her husband Jim have four children, Cora, Vincent, Mira, and Asha. In addition to spending time with her family, Vanya enjoys reading, playing piano, and going to movies.

MOMADAY, NAVARRE SCOTT (Kiowa-Cherokee) 1934-
(writer, painter, educator)
Born February 27, 1934, Lawton, Okla. *Education*: University of New Mexico, BA, 1958; Stanford University, MA, 1960, PhD, 1963. *Principal occupation*: Writer, educator, painter. *Address*: The University of Arizona, American Indian Studies Program, Harvill Bldg., Rm. 430, P.O. Box 210076, Tucson, AZ 85721 (520) 621-7108. *Affiliations*: Assistant professor, associate professor of English, University of California, Santa Barbara, 1962-69; professor of English & Comparative Literature, University of California, Berkeley, 1969-72; professor of English, Stanford University, 1972-80; professor of English & American Literature, University of Arizona, Tucson, AZ, 1981-. *Other professional posts*: Consultant, National Endowment for the Humanities, 1970-; trustee, Museum of the American Indian, 1978-; currently Regents Professor of the Humanities, University of Arizona, he directs projects which focus upon Native American oral tradition & Native American concepts of the sacred. Memberships: American Studies Association; MLA. *Awards, honors*: Guggenheim Fellowship, 1966; Recipient of the Pulitzer Prize for fiction, 1969; an award from the National Institute of Arts & Letters; the Golden Plate Award from the American Academy of Achievement; and the Premio Letterario Internazionale Mondello, Italy, 1979 (Italy's highest literary award); Fellow of the American Academy of Arts & Sciences; his paintings, drawings, and prints have been exhibited in the U.S. and abroad. A one-man, 20-year retrospective was mounted at the Wheelwright, Santa Fe, NM, in 1992-93. He holds 12 honorary degrees from American colleges & universities, including Yale, University of Massachusetts, and the University of Wisconsin. *Biographical source*: Who's Who in America; N. Scott Momaday: Remembering Ancestors, Earth, and Traditions; An Annotated Bio-Bibliography. *Published works*: The Complete Poems of Frederick Goddard Tuckerman (Oxford University Press, 1965); House Made of Dawn (Harper & Row, 1968); The Way to Rainy Mountain (University of New Mexico Press, 1969); Angle of Geese and Other Poems (David R. Godine, 1973); The Gourd Dancer (Harper & Row, 1976); The Names (Harper & Row, 1976); The Ancient Child (Doubleday); In the Presence of the Sun (St. Martin's Press); Circle of Wonder (St. Martin's Press; The Storyteller and His Art (Oxford University Press); A Dark, Indifferent Rage (Doubleday); and The Blind Astrologers (St. Martin's Press); Three Plays: The Indolent Boys, Children of the Sun, and The Moon In Two Windows (University of Oklahoma Press, 2007); his articles have appeared in "Natural History," "American West," "The New York Review of Books," "New York Newsday," "The New York Times Book Review," "The New York Times Magazine," etc.

MONCOOYEA, CHARLES J. (Otoe-Missouria)
(tribal vice chairperson)
Affiliation: Otoe-Missouria Tribe, 8151 Hwy. 177, Red Rock, OK 74651 (580) 723-4466.

MONETTE, GERALD (Turtle Mountain Chippewa)
(college president)
Affiliation: Turtle Mountain Community College, P.O. Box 340, Belcourt, ND 58316 (701) 477-5605. *Other professional post*: NSF-TCUP Technical Assistance Project Director, American Indian Higher Education Consortium, Alexandria, VA. E-mail: gmonette@aihec.org.

MONETTE, MELVIN E. (Turtle Mountain Chippewa)
(special programs director)
Education: University of North Dakota, BS (Elementary Education), MS (Education); working on Doctorate of Education, St. Mary's University (Twin Cities, MN). *Affiliation & Address*: Director, Graduate Fellowship & Special Programs, American Indian Graduate Center, 3701 San Mateo Blvd. NE #200, Albuquerque, NM 87110 (800) 628-1920 (505) 881-4584 ext. 116. E-mail: melvin@aigcs.org. *Other professional posts*: Two Feathers Endowment, St. Paul Foundation Spectrum Trust; works with local high schools to address

American Indian higher education issues & providing HIV prevention education through the Minnesota Aids Project & American Red Cross; ambassador of the Gates Millennium Scholars Program & Read Trainer. *Past professional posts*: Director for Student Recruitment for the University of Minnesota School of Public Health; member of executive board of the Midwest Center for Lifelong Learning in Public Health; chairperson, Scholarship Task Force; assistant for a RWJF National Quality Improvement Research Project.

MONETTE, RICHARD A. (Turtle Mountain Chippewa)
(associate professor of law; law center director)
Education: University of Oregon, JD; University of Wisconsin Law School, LL.M. *Affiliation & Address*: Associate Professor of Law & Director, Great Lakes Indian Law Center, UW Law School, Law Bldg., 975 Bascom Mall, Rm. 6112, Madison, WI 53706 (608) 263-7409. E-mail: monettee@facstaff. wisc.edu. Teaches torts, water law, & Federal Indian law including jurisdiction, taxation, and gaming. *Other professional posts*: "Of Counsel" with law firm, Brown & LaCounte, Madison, WI, a firm spcializing in Indian law. Monette specializes in drafting provisions for constitutions and codes for Indian tribes. *Past professional posts*: Chairman & CEO, Turtle Mountain Chippewa Tribe, Belcourt, ND, 2000-2003; staff attorney with U.S. Senate Committee on Indian Affairs; faculty advisor for the Great Lakes Indian Law Center, UW Law School, Madison; director, Office of Congressional & Legislative Affairs, BIA, U.S. Dept. of the Interior, Washington, DC.; past president, National Native American Bar Association; member of EPAs National Environmental Justice Advisory Council's Indigenous Peoples' Subcommittee; served as Chief Justice for Pascua Yaqui Tribe, Special Judge for Ho Chunk Nation, Special Judge for the Trial Court of the Turtle Mountain Band of Chippewa. *Publications*: Has written several law review articles, book reviews, and essays for edited collections.

MONONGYE, JESSE L. (Navajo)
(artist/jeweler)
Address: 6102 E. Charter Oak Rd., Scottsdale, AZ 85254 (480) 991-8159. Makes gold & silver jewelry. Membership: Indian Arts & Crafts Association.

MONTANO, FRANCIS (Ojibwe)
(museum director)
Affiliation: Red Cliff Tribal Museum, Arts & Crafts Cultural Center, P.O. Box 529, Bayfield, WI 54814 (715) 779-5609.

MONTEAU, CYNTHIA (Standing Rock Sioux)
(office manager)
Affiliation: National Indian Health Board, 1385 S. Colorado Blvd., Suite A708, Denver, CO 80221 (303) 759-3075.

MONTEAU, HAROLD A. (Chippewa-Cree)
(attorney)
Education: Northern Montana College, BS, 1975; University of South Dakota, MA, 1977; University of New Mexico School of Law, JD, 1986. *Address & Affiliation*: Partner, 1997-present, Monteau & Peebles, LLP, 815 E. Front St. #3, Missoula, MT 59802 (406) 829-3554. E-mail: hmonteau@ndnlaw.com. *Practice areas*: Reservation economic development & finance, tribal gaming commissions & regulations, tribal-state compacts, tribal government & sovereignty, self-determination, self-governance, SBA minority business contracting & taxation issues, inter-tribal trade & commerce, Indian housing, environmental & cultural preservation, et al. *Other professional post*: Appointed as a judge to the Spokane Tribal Court of Appeals, 2004. *Past professional posts*: Appointed to Montana Gaming Advisory Council, 1989-90; National Tribal Coordinator, Joint Tribal, Dept. of Interior; BIA Task Force on BIA Reorganization: appointed by national tribal leaders, 1991-94; Montana/ Wyoming Tribal Representative, U.S. Senate Committee on Indian Affairs Joint State-Tribal Task Force on amendments to the Indian Gaming Regulatory Act, 1992-94; chairman, National Indian Gaming Commission, Dept. of the Interior, 1994-97. *Memberships*: Montana Bar Assn; Native American Bar Assn (board member); Federal Bar Assn; National Congress of American Indian; various tribal courts.

MONTES, JAMES (Chippewa Cree)
(BIA field rep.)
Affiliation & Address: Rocky Boy's Agency Rep., Bureau of Indian Affairs, RR 1 Box 542, Box Elder, MT 59521 (406) 395-4476.

MONTES-HELU, MARIO (Tohono O'odham)
(Indian college academic chair)
Affiliation & Address: Academic Chairperson, Tohono O'odam Community College, P.O. Box 3129, Sells, AZ 85634 (520) 383-8401

MONTGOMERY, CHRISTOPHER (*Quiet Bear*) (Nipmuc)
(state Indian commission member)
Born in Boston, Mass. & resides in Revere, Mass. *Education*: Northeastern University, BA (Criminal Justice); Anna Marie College, MA (Criminal Justice).

Affiliation: On June 3, 2009, Chris was appointed by Governor Patrick for a 3-year term to the Massachusetts Commission on Indian Affairs. He will represent the Nipmuc Nation & cover Worcester & Middlesex counties. *Other professional posts*: Nipmuc Nation representative on the Boston Harbor Islands national Park Advisory Council; member, Native American Memorial Committee on Deer Island; chairperson, Nipmuc Nation Investigative Committee & the Activities Committee; member, Massachusetts Center for Native American Awareness. *Past professional post*: Member of Massachusetts State Police, 1957-91. *Military service*: U.S. Naval Reserves as a Seaman First Class during World War II.

MONTGOMERY, JANNEY
(executive officer)
Affiliation: Indian Rights Association, 1801 Market St., 10th Floor, Philadelphia, PA 19103 (215) 665-4523. *Other professional post*: Editor, Indian Truth," bi-monthly news journal of the Indian Rights Association.

MONTGOMERY-ANDERSON, BRAD
(associate professor of languages)
Born & raised in Boulder, Colo. *Education*: University of Kansas, MA (Indigenous Studies), PhD (Linguistics). *Affiliation & Address*: Assistant Professor of American Indian Studies, Department of Cherokee & Indigenous Studies, Northeastern State University, Seminary Hall 365, 609 N. Grand Ave., Tahlequah, OK 74464 (918) 444-3610; E-mail: montgomb@nsuok.edu He specializes in Cherokee language, Mayan languages, and language revitalization. Dr. Montgomery-Anderson is currently preparing for publication a Cherokee reference grammar as well as a dictionary of the Chontal Mayan language of Mexico. He has published papers in Southwest Journal of Linguistics, International Journal of Applied Linguistics, & Journal of Language Contact.

MONTIEL, ANYA
(NMAI cultural arts program specialist)
Affiliation: National Museum of the American Indian (NMAI), Smithsonian Institution, Cultural Resources Section, 4220 Silver Hill Rd., Suitland, MD 20746 (301) 238-1436.

MONTOYA, DAVID J., III (Ohkay Owingeh Pueblo)
(attorney; research analyst)
Education: Uniersity of California, Irvine, BA (Political Science with a minor in Philosophy); University of California, Los Angeles, JD (Federal Indian Law joint-degree program) & MA (American Indian Studies), 2009. *Affiliation & Address*: In-house attorney, Soboba Band of Luiseno Indians, Box 487, San Jacinto, CA 92583 (951) 654-5544. E-mail: montoya2008@lawnet.ucla.edu. *Other professional post*: Treasurer, California Indian Law Association, Sacramento, CA. *Past professional posts*: Research Analyst, UCLA's American Indian Studies Center and conducted legal research for the Tribal Law & Order Commission. *Community activities*: David works with another non-profit organization to educate younger Native Americans on our elder's experiences in boarding schools.

MONTOYA, GEORGE M. (Tamaya Pueblo)
(former Pueblo governor)
Affiliation & Address: Tamaya Pueblo, 2 Dove Rd., Pueblo of Santa Ana, NM 87004 (505) 867-3301.

MONTOYA, GERONIMA CRUZ (*P'otsunu*) (Ohkay Owingeh Pueblo) 1915-
(retired artist, teacher)
Born September 22, 1915, San Juan Pueblo, N.M. *Education*: St. Joseph's College, BS, 1958; University of New Mexico; Claremont College. *Principal occupation*: Art teacher, Santa Fe, NM. *Address*: 1008 Calle de Suenos, Santa Fe, NM 87505 (505) 471-5480. *Affiliation*: Co-founder, lifetime board chairperson, San Juan Pueblo Arts & Crafts Cooperative, 1973-. *Community activities*: Community Concert Association (captain); San Juan Pueblo Choir (secretary-treasurer); SWAIA - Southwest Association of American Indian Arts (board member); on Advisory Panel with Indian Art & Culture Museum. *Awards, honors*: School of American Research Purchase Award; Museum of New Mexico Special Category Prize, Inter-Tribal Indian Ceremonial, Gallup, N.M.; Special Prize, Philbrook Art Center, Tulsa, Okla.; DeYoung Museum Purchase Prize; 2010 Indian Market poster artist; among others.

MONTOYA, JOSEPH (Pueblo)
(administrative officer)
Affiliation: Santa Fe PHS Indian Hospital, 1700 Cerrillos Rd., Santa Fe, NM 87501 (505) 988-9821.

MONTOYA, LAWRENCE (Pueblo of Tamaya-Santa Ana)
(Pueblo governor)
Affiliation & Address: Pueblo of Tamaya (Santa Ana), 2 Dove Rd., Bernalillo, NM 87004 (505) 867-3301.

MONTOYA, MALCOLM (Sandia Pueblo)
(Pueblo governor)
Affiliation: Governor, Pueblo of Sandia, 481 Sandia Loop, Bernalillo, NM 87004. (505) 867-3317

MONTOYA, PAUL T. (Povi Ta') (Sandia/San Juan Pueblo), 1950-
(artist)
Address: Resides in Santa Fe, NM.

MONTOYA, ROBERT (Sandia/San Juan Pueblo) 1947-
(architect; artist)
Education: University of New Mexico, BA (Architecture); University of Oklahoma, MA. *Affiliation & Address*: Architect & artist. Resides in Albuquerque.

MONTOYA, RON (Santa Ana Pueblo)
(former Pueblo governor)
Affiliation: Pueblo of Tamaya (Santa Ana), 2 Dove Rd., Bernalillo, NM 87004 (505) 867-3301.

MONTOYA, TIMOTHY IKOSHY (Lipan Apache) 1956-
(artist)
Born in 1956 in Corpus Christi, Tex. *Education*: College of the Redwoods (Native American Studies Program). *Address*: P.O. Box 4060, Yankee Hill, CA 95965 (530) 533-1673. *Website*: www.ikoshy.com. *E-mail*: ikoshy.art@gmail.com. Mr. Montoya's art represents the evolution of immersion in native teachings as it traces it's way through ceremonies and the everyday part of his own personal life. "I was born with my artistic abilities and my elders, the sweat lodge and related ceremonies have been my art instructors." His art has been featured in documentary videos on Native America, in various periodicals, on book covers, CD jackets & cassettes. *Artwork*: Timoteo Ikoshy Montoya: Indigenous American Art; Notecards, Magnets.

MONTOYA, VINCE (*Pubsay*) (Isleta Pueblo) 1939-
(civil engineer)
Born July 19, 1939, Tohatchi, N.M. (Navajo Reservation). *Education*: University of New Mexico, BS, 1964; St. Mary's University (San Antonio, TX), MA, 1978. *Address*: Montoya, 3306 Carrngton Way, Bellingham, WA 98226 (505) 291-8402; 846-7904 (work). *Affiliations*: Project Manager, 542d Civil Engineering Squadron, Kirtland AFB, NM, 1986-. *Other professional post*: American Indian Employment Programs Manager, Kirtland AFB, NM, 1986-. *Military service*: U.S. Air Force, 1964-84 (Major {0-4}-retired; Missile Engineer (Minuteman) at Vandenberg AFB, CA; Site Civil Engineer at Hopedale Air Station, Labrador; Civil Engineering Chief of Operations at Torrejon AB & Zaragoza AB, Spain; and Korat Royal Thai Air Base, Thailand; Chief Civil Engineer Inspector, HQ 9th Air Force, Shaw AFB, SC; Chief Maintenance Mgmt. Division, DCS Engineering, HQ Air Training Command, Randolph AFB, TX; and as Base Civil Engineer, Zaragoza AB, Spain & RAF Chicksands, U.K.). *Community activities*: Persian Gulf Support Groups at various Indian communities; work with all Indian organizations in the Albuquerque area; conduct various activities at annual American Indian Heritage Week, Kirtland, NM. *Memberships*: Air Force Association; Disabled American Veterans Association; Society of American Military Engineers. *Awards, honors*: His military decorations and awards include: The Meritorious Service Medal with four oak leaf clusters; the Air Force Commendation Medal; the Air Force Outstanding Unit Award with Valor; Small Arms Marksmanship Ribbon; National Defense Service Ribbon; Republic of Vietnam Gallantry Cross with Palm; and the USAF Missile Man Badge. His civilian awards include the USAF Performance Award for each year he has been assigned at Kirtland. He was awarded a Quality Step Increase for 1991. He also received the Air Force Distinguished Equal Employment Opportunity Award for the American Indian/Alaskan Native Employment Program for 1991.

MONTOYA-LEWIS, RAQUEL (Isleta & Laguna Pueblo)
(attorney; associate professor)
Education: University of New Mexico, BA, 1992; University of Washington School of Law, JD, 1995; University of Washington Graduate School of Social Work, MSW, 1996. *Affiliation & Address*: Associate Professor, Center for Law, Diversity & Justice, Fairhaven College of Interdisciplinary Studies, Western Washington University, 516 High St., FA 328, Bellingham, WA 98225 (360) 650-2328. *E-mail*: raquel.montoya-lewis@wwu.edu. She teaches courses on the U.S. legal system, including Property Law & Federal Indian Law, as well as courses on cultural & gender identity. *Other professional posts*: Chief judge for the Upper Skagit Indian Tribe; acting chief judge for the Lummi Nation; appellate judge for the Northwest Intertribal Court System & Nisqually Indian Tribe. *Awards, honors*: "Community Building" award for 2009 from the Whatcom Family & Community Network. *Membership*: Washington State Bar Association (Law Clerk board for the northwest region of Washington).

MOODY, ROBERT, JR. (Potawatomi)
(tribal vice chairperson)
Affiliation & Address: Vice Chairperson, Pokagon Band of Potawatomi Indians, P.O. Box 180, Dowagiac, MI 49047 (616) 782-8998.

MOON, JAMES W., JR. (Wiyot)
(rancheria chairperson)
Affiliation: Bear River Band of Rohnerville Rancheria, 32 Bear River Dr., Loleta, CA 95551 (888) 733-1900.

MOORE, ARDINA REVARD (*Ma-shro-gita*) (Quapaw-Osage) 1930-
(business owner; designer-Indian clothes; teacher)
Born December 1, 1930, Belton, Tex. *Education*: Northeastern State University (Tahlequah, OK), BS (Education), 1957. *Principal occupation*: Business owner; designer-Indian clothing; teacher. *Address*: 1204 Sky Lane, Miami, OK 74354; *Office address*: P.O. Box 1556, Miami, OK 74355 (918) 542-8870 (office). *Affiliations*: Owner, Buffalo Sun, Miami, OK, 1982- (specialty Indian clothing business); instructor, Indian Studies Program, Northeastern Oklahoma Jr. College, Miami, OK, 1989-. *Community activities*: Chamber of Commerce, Miami, OK; Promenade Indian Club (president, 1992); Keepers of the Treasures; Quapaw Tribal Business Committee (secretary-treasurer (two years). *Memberships*: Oklahoma Federation of Indian Women; National Congress of American Indians; Indian & Western Arts Association; American Indian Designers Association (president, 1989). *Awards, honors*: Mother of the Year, 1992, Oklahoma Federation of Indian Women; Artistic Awards - 2nd Place, Creek Council House, Okmulgee, OK, 1989; 1st & 2nd Place, Indian Summer Art Show, Bartlesville, OK, 1990, 1991; 2011 Oklahoma Women's Hall of Fame Inductee. *Interests*: Genealogy research, Federal Archives; Indian Dance Troupe and fashion shows around the country.

MOORE, BRIAN
(executive director)
Affiliation & Address: Executive Director, North American Indian Association, 22720 Plymouth Rd., Detroit, MI 48239 (313) 535-2966. *E-mail*: bmoore@naiadetroit.org.

MOORE, DAVID J.
(college president)
Education: Evangel University, BA (Anthropology); Assemblies of God Theological Seminary, (Cross Cultural Communication & Doctor of Ministry in Leadership); University of Arizona, PhD (Higher Education Administration). *Affiliation & Address*: President, SAGU American Indian College, 10020 N. 15th Ave., Phoenix, AZ 85021 (602) 944-3335 ext 231. *E-mail*: dmoore@sagu.edu. President Moore returned in June, 2013 to serve for the second time as AIC president after a 19-year leave of absence.

MOORE, DONALD W. (Bad River Band of Lake Superior Ojibwe)
(former tribal chairperson)
Affiliation: Bad River Tribal Council, P.O. Box 39, Odanah, WI 54861 (715) 682-7111.

MOORE, FREDERICK, III (Passamaquoddy)
(former tribal chief)
Affiliation & Address: Former Chief, Passamaquoddy Tribe – Pleasant Point, 9 Sakom Rd., P.O. Box 343 • Perry, ME 04667 (207) 853-2600.

MOORE, GENE
(museum manager)
Affiliation: Kotzebue Museum, P.O. Box 46, Kotzebue, AK 99752 (907) 442-3401.

MOORE, JOHN H. (Nokoshutke-Muskogee Creek) 1939-
(anthropologist)
Born February 27, 1939, Williston, N.D. *Education*: New York University, PhD, 1974. *Address*: 3328 NW 18th Ave., Gainesville, FL 32605 (352) 846-0263 (work). *E-mail*: moojohn@anthro.ufl.edu. *Affiliations*: Chair & professor, Dept. of Anthropology, University of Oklahoma, Norman, OK, 1977-93; chair & professor, Anthropology Dept., University of Florida, Gainesville, FL 32611 (chair, 1993-98; professor, 1998-present). *Past professional post*: Consultant, Sand Creek Descendants Association, Muskogee Creek Tribal Towns, Inc. Military service: U.S. Army, 1962-64 (lieutenant). *Memberships*: American Anthropological Association; American Ethnological Society; American Association for the Advancement of Science. *Awards, honors*: Received title of Emafanaka from Muskogee Tribal Towns Organization; Certificate of Achievement from Cheyenne Sand Creek Descendants, "Most Helpful Faculty Member, American Indian Students Association, University of Oklahoma; Oklahoma Governor's Community Service Award for work with Creek communities; Fellow, American Association for the Advancement of Science. *Interests*: Treaty rights; health; demography. Presently working on Sand Creek Massacre Claim, the Twin case in Canada involving band sovereignty. Biographical source: Search for the Sand Creek Descendants, Sooner

Magazine, Spring, 1983; Who's Who in the South & Southwest, 1985-; Who's Who in America, 2003. *Published works*: Ethnology in Oklahoma (Papers in Anthropology, 1980); The Cheyennes in Moxtavhohona (Northern Cheyenne Tribe, Inc., 1981); The Cheyenne Nation (University of Nebraska Press, 1986); Political Economy of North American Indians (University of Oklahoma Press, 1993); The Cheyenne (Blackwell, 1996).

MOORE, KELLY R. (Creek) 1955-
(pediatrician; associate professor)
Born May 24, 1955, Tahlequah, Okla. *Education*: University of Oklahoma, BA, 1977; University of Oklahoma, Health Science Center, MD, 1983, Pediatric residency, 1986. *Affiliation & Address*: Associate Professor, University of Colorado Denver School of Public Health, 13055 E. 17th Ave., Suite F800, Nighthorse Campbell Native Health Bldg., Rm. 324, Anschutz Medical Campus, Aurora, CO 80045 (303) 724-1445. E-mail: Kelly.moore@ucdenver.edu. *Past professional posts*: Women's counselor, University of Oklahoma Health Sciences Center, Headlands Indian Health Careers Program, Mackinac City, MI, 1978-80; clinical director, Kayenta PHS, Indian Health Center, Kayenta, AZ on Navajo Reservation, 1987-89; clinical director, USPHS, Indian Health Service Clinic, Taholah, WA, 1989-91; clinical director, Sacaton PHS Indian Hospital, Sacaton, AZ, 1991-95; clinical director, PHS-Indian Health Service, Fort Duchesne, UT, 1995-99; clinical director, PHS, Albuquerque, NM, 2000-06. *Military service*: Commissioned Officer, USPHS, 1987-2006 (Commander; received Isolated Hardship Duty Ribbon & Achievement Medal. *Interests*: Health & healthcare disparities of urban Native Americans; adult & childhood type 2 diabetes in Native Americans; childhood obesity. *Memberships*: American Academy of Pediatrics (Fellow); Association of American Indian Physicians; Commissioned Officers Association. *Awards, honors*: Ungerman Scholarship Recipient, University of Oklahoma Health Sciences Center, 1982-83; University Scholar, University of Oklahoma, 1973-74. *Interests*: Child advocacy issues - child sexual/physical abuse; sex/AIDS education; fetal alcohol syndrome prevention; children's diabetes.

MOORE, LEE (Standing Bear) 1937-
(spiritual elder; historian, storyteller; keeper of Manataka)
Education: LaSalle University (Chicago), BS (Business Administration), 1974. *Affiliation & Address*: Founder (1989-present), Manataka American Indian Council, P.O. Box 476, Hot Springs Reservation, AR 71902 (501) 627-0555. E-mail: manataka@sbcglobal.net. Lee states, "The council exists to preserve & protect this sacred place." Manataka supports various funds & institutes. *Military service*: U.S. Army (awarded Silver Star, Bronze Star, Two Purple Hearts, Presidential & Unit Citations; Vietnam Vet). *Publication*: Manataka Smoke Signal News. Trading Post.

MOORE, MARIJO (Eastern Cherokee) 1952-
(writer, lecturer, publisher, artist)
Born August 24, 1952, Tenn. *Education*: Tennessee State University; Lancashire Polytechnic (Preston, England) BA Literature. *Principal occupation*: Writer, lecturer, publisher, artist. *Address*: P.O. Box 2493, Chandler, NC 28715 (828) 665-7630. E-mail: marijo@aol.com. Website: www.marijomoore.com. *Affiliation*: Owner, Renegade Planets Publishing, NC (only American Indian-owned publishing company in NC). *Other professional posts*: Contributing editor to An Anthology of 20th Century North Carolina Poets, Points of Entry: Cross-Currents in Storytelling; she has presented over 300 literary readings, lectures & creative writing workshops at numerous literary gatherings & educational institutions. *Community activities*: Board member, North Carolina Humanities Council. *Membership*: Wordcraft Circle of Native American Writers & Storytellers (National Caucus). *Awards, honors*: North Carolina's Distinguished Woman of the Year in the Arts in 1998; Ms. Moore was chosen by "Native Peoples" magazine as one of the top five American Indian writers of the new century (June/July 2000 issue). *Interests*: Working with unpublished Native authors. *Published/produced works*: Play: "Your Story," was produced at Lancashire Community Theatre in Preston, England, in 1991; books: Crow Quotes, Desert Quotes, Spirit Voices of Bones, Tree Quotes, Feeding the Ancient Fires: A Collection of Writings by North Carolina American Indians (editor), Ice Man, The First Fire, Red Woman with Backward Eyes & Other Stories (all published by Renegade Planets Publishing); The Cherokee Little People (children's books, published by Rigby Education); a bilingual edition (Dutch/English) Woestijnwoorden ("Desert Words" published by Uitgeverij, Kamat, Belgium); The Diamond Door Knob, a novel (Renegade Planets Publishing); editor, Genocide of the Mind (Nation Books/Thunder's Mouth Press); her work has appeared in numerous publications

MOORE, PATRICK EDWARD (*Totkv Vfvstv*) (Creek) 1942-
(attorney)
Born May 16, 1942, Wewoka, Okla. *Education*: University of Oklahoma, BS, 1972; Oklahoma City University School of Law, JD, 1977; University of Houston (Post Graduate Law); National Judicial College, University of Nevada. *Address*: 1 Edgevale Rd., Okmulgee, OK 74447 (918) 756-3391. *Affiliations*: Attorney, Moore & Moore (law firm), Okmulgee, OK, 1975-; Assistant District Attorney, Okmulgee, OK, 1983-1995. *Other professional posts*: District Judge,

Muscogee (Creek) Nation; District Judge, Devils Lake Sioux Nation; Board of Directors, CASA; instructor, Oklahoma Council on Law Enforcement & Training; member, State-Federal-Tribal Judicial Council, Five Civilized Tribes Council. *Military service*: U.S. Air Force, 1963-67 (E-5; Presidential Unit Citation, DSM, Good Conduct, Fairchild Trophy, Standboard). *Community activities*: President, Okmulgee County Shrine Bedovin A.A.N.O.M.S. *Memberships*: Oklahoma Tribal Judges Association (president); Okmulgee County Bar Association (past president); Creek Indian Memorial Association (Board of Trustees; U.S. Supreme Court, 10th Circuit Court of Appeals; U.S. District Courts for Western, Northern & Eastern Districts of Oklahoma; Supreme Court of Oklahoma; Supreme Court of the Muscogee (Creek) Nation; National Association of District Attorneys; Federal Bar Association; Oklahoma Association of District Attorneys; National Association of Tribal Court Judges; American Judicature Society. *Awards, honors*: Graduate, National Judicial College; U.S. Inspector General-Outstanding Prosecution Award; Governor's Commission on Law Enforcement.

MOORE, RICK DANE
(attorney-Native American law)
Education: University of Oklahoma, BA, 1984; University of Oklahoma College of Law, JD, 1986. *Affiliation & Address*: Owner, Rick Dane Moore & Associates Law Firm, PLLC (1987-present), 30630 S. Western Ave., Norman, OK 73070 E-mail: info@okmoorelawfirm.com (405) 366-0373. Prior to starting his own practice, he was a law clerk for Justice Marion Opala of the Oklahoma Supreme Court, and was an Assistant Public Defender with the Oklahoma County Public Defender's Office. He is admitted to practice in numerous jurisdictions, including: Oklahoma state courts Federal courts, including the United States District Court for the Eastern District of Oklahoma (Muskogee), United States District Court for the Western District of Oklahoma (Oklahoma City), the Tenth Circuit Court of Appeals (Denver), the Federal Circuit Court of Appeals (Washington, D.C.), & the United States Court of Claims (Washington, D.C.) Numerous tribal courts, including the Sac & Fox, Pottawottamie, Absentee Shawnee, and Court of Indian Offenses. Rick is a member of the Oklahoma Bar Association and the Oklahoma Indian Bar Association. He has spoken on various aspects of Native American Law & economic development at the Oklahoma Sovereignty Symposium. He also received a service award from the Executive Committee of the Sierra Club. He has served on the Advisory Board for Buddha Mind Monastery and as an Officer in Public Advocacy. Before starting his career as an attorney, *Military service*: U.S. Army Special Forces on HALO-SCUBA teams from 1972 - 1981, and was a member of the Green Berets.

MOORE, TRACEY ANN (*E-ne-opp-e - Protected One*)
(Pawnee/Otoe-Missouria/Osage/Sac & Fox) 1964-
(office clerk)
Born August 14, 1964, Fairfax, Okla. *Education*: Northern Oklahoma College, 1982-84; University of Oklahoma, 1984-87. *Address*: 511 Mason, Fairfax, OK 74637 (918) 287-4491. *Affiliations*: American Indian Student Service, University of Oklahoma, Norman, 1986-88; Claremore Indian Hospital, Claremore, OK, 1988-89. *Other professional posts*: CETA Summer Youth Program, The Osage Nation, 1981-. *Awards, honors*: Nominated twice for Outstanding Young Women of America, 1985; Osage Nation representative for Miss National Congress of American Indians Pageant, 1985; University of Oklahoma, American Indian Student Association Princess, 1985-1986; Tulsa Powwow Princess, 1984; Miss Indian Oklahoma, 1st runner-up-most talented; National Viet Nam Veterans Powwow Princess & Association Princess, 1982-84; Osage Tribal Princess, 1980 & 1983; 1st Place Women's Fancy Shawl, University of Oklahoma, American Indian Student Association Powwow, March 19, 1994; 2nd Place Women's Fancy Shawl, Red Earth Celebration, Oklahoma City, June 1994; 4th Place Gathering of Nations, Albuquerque; 5th Place Women's Fancy Shawl, 1993, Denver March Powwow; 1st Place Women's Fancy Shawl, Potawatomi Days Powwow, June 1993 in Shawnee, OK; 2nd Place Women's Fancy Shawl, Aspen, CO, July 1993 powwow to benefit the new Smithsonian Institution, National Museum of the American Indian; "I danced at the National Governors Association Convention in Sand Springs, OK, Aug. 1993 - President Clinton was an honored guest"; "Me and my gramma, Mary Osage Green (full blooded Osage) are painted in the Osage Council Chambers with other prominent Osages." *Interests*: "I am applying for IHS scholarship to further my education in business and/or public administration. I plan to document the elders of my tribe. I feel my elders are cherishable because they are our history, they lived in the beginning of the 1900's. Their stories are true compared to history books. I want to preserve our heritage. I enjoy traveling across the U.S. to Native American celebrations of every kind. I have represented my tribe at powwows, state & national organizations that involved me traveling to all 4 directions. My parents are Ted Moore, Sr., a former champion fancy dancer for a number of consecutive years at the American Indian Exposition in Anadarko, Okla., and Thomasine Moore, a former Osage princess and current Osage Tribal Director at the American Indian Exposition. My great-grandfather was See-Haw, a great leader of the Osage Nation."

MOOREHEAD, VIRGIL (Yurok)
(rancheria chairperson)
Affiliation: Chairperson, Big Lagoon Rancheria, 708 9th St., Arcadia, CA 95521 (707) 826-2079. E-mail: vmoorehead@earthlink.net.

MOOSE, VIRGIL (Paiute)
(former tribal chairperson)
Affiliation: Big Pine Paiute Tribe of the Owens Valley, Big Pine, CA.

MORALES, ANTHONY (Gabrielino/Tongva Mission Indians)
(tribal chairperson)
Affiliation: Gabrielino/Tongva Band of Mission Indians of San Gabriel, P.O. Box 693, San Gabriel, CA 91778 (626) 286-1632.

MORALES, SUMMER (La Jolla Band Mission Indians)
(executive assistant)
Affiliation & Address: Executive Assistant, California Indian Legal Services (CILS), 510 16th St. #301, Oakland, CA 94612 (510) 835-0284. She supports CILS principal office staff & the executive director with program administration. Summer currently lives on the San Pasqual Reservation.

MORAN, DAVID
(attorney-advisor)
Education: Georgetown University Law School, JD. *Affiliation & Address*: Attorney-Advisor, Division of Indian Affairs, Office of Solicitor, U.S. Department of the Interior, 1849 C St., NW, MS 6513, Washington, DC 20240.

MORAN, ERNEST T. "BUD" (Confederated Salish & Kootenai/Chippewa Cree) 1939-
(tribal chairperson)
Born August 27, 1939, Harlem, Mont. *Education*: Oceanside Junior College, 1960; Santa Ana Junior College, 1962-63; completed training courses in administration & management while in the USMC & working for the BIA. *Affiliation & Address*: Chairperson, Confederated Salish & Kootenai Tribes, P.O. Box 278, Pablo, MT 59855 (406) 675-2700. E-mail: budm@cskt.org. *Other professional post*: Alternate Vice-chairperson, Montana State Tribal Economic Development Commission, Helena, MT. *Past professional posts*: Credit & business development officer & director, Economic Development Program, Confederated Salish & Kootenai Tribes; Indian Community Action Program, University of Montana, Missoula; Bureau of Indian Affairs: housing officer, Rocky Boy, MT; reservation programs officer, Lame Deer, MT; credit & business development, Jicarilla Agency, Dulce, NM; tribal operations officer, Western Nevada Agency, Stewart, NV; field representative in Klamath, CA; supt., Northern Cheyenne Agency, Lame Deer, MT, 1980-85; supt., Northern Idaho Agency, Lapwai, ID, 1985-86; supt., Crow Agency, MT, 1986-89; supt., Colorado River Agency, Parker, AZ, 1989-91; supt., Flathead Agency, BIA, Pablo, MT, 1991-2002. *Military service*: U.S. Marine Corps, 1958-67 (Navy Unit Citation; Vietnam Unit Citation with Star; Vietnam Service Medal with Star; National Defense Service Medal with Star; Armed Forces Expeditionary Medal with 2 Stars). *Community activities*: Active Corps of Executives (member); Aide de Camp to Governor of New Mexico. Memberships: Confederated Salish & Kootenai Tribe; tribal affiliations with Chippewa Cree Tribe & Rocky Boy Tribe. *Awards, honors*: Special Achievement Award from Bureau of Indian Affairs; Letter of Appreciation from Jicarilla Apache Tribe & Northern Cheyenne Tribe; guest speaker (at Dull Knife Memorial College) on government and their relations with tribes.

MORAN, GEORGE F.
(museum director & executive V.P.)
Affiliation: Indian City, U.S.A., P.O. Box 695, Anadarko, OK 73005 (405) 247-5661. E-mail: info@indianncityusa.com.

MORAN, TONY (Chippewa)
(former tribal chairperson)
Affiliation: Trenton Indian Service Area, P.O. Box 210, Trenton, ND 58853 (701) 774-0461.

MORATTO, MICHAEL J.
(archaeologist)
Education: San Francisco State University, BA (Anthropology), 1966; University of Oregon, MA (Anthropology), 1969, PhD (Anthropology), 1972. *Affiliation & Address*: Principal Archaeologist, Native American Consultation, (2006-present), Applied Earthworks, Inc., P.O. Box 3215, Thousand Oaks, CA 91359 (805) 497-8493. E-mail: mmoratto@appliedearthworks.com. *Professional Interests*: Cultural Ecology; Historic Preservation Law; Prehistory of Western North America; Archaeological Theory & Methods; California History, 1540-1870; Indians of California. *Past professional posts*: Professor, Department of Anthropology, San Francisco State University, 1969-78; President/CEO, INFOTEC Research, Inc., Fresno, CA, 1984-97; Archaeologist/Lecturer, Department of Anthropology, Fresno State University, Fresno, 1995-2005.

MORAZA, ELENA (Chichimeca of Mexico)
(dancer)
Address: 11 Esta Rd., Plymouth, MA 02360 (508) 830-1256. Elena is a Northern traditional woman dancer who specializes in dance demonstrations with lectures & discussions. Proficient in various art forms including beadwork, jewelry, ribbon applique & dance outfits. Performances presented in full dance regalia to educate others about Native American culture.

MORGAN, KATIE (Ponca)
(attorney)
Education: University of Nebraska, BA, 2001; Columbia University School of Law, JD, 2005. *Affiliation & Address*: Counsel, Akin Gump Straus Hauer & Feld, LLP, Robert E. Straus Bldg., 1333 New Hampshire Ave. NW, Washington, DC 20036 (202) 255-4950; E-mail: kamorgan@akingump.com. Ms. Morgan's practice focuses on representation of Indian tribes, tribal governmental instrumentalities & tribally owned enterprises.

MORGAN, LANCE G. (Winnebago of Nebraska)
(attorney)
Education: University of Nebraska, BS, 1990; Harvard Law School, JD, 1993. *Address & Affiliation*: Of Counsel (2003-2007; partner, 2007-present), Fredericks Peebles & Morgan, LLP, 3610 North 163rd Plaza, Omaha, NE 68116-3966 (402) 878-2809. E-mail: lmorgan.ndnlaw.com. *Practice areas*: Economic development; Indian law; corporate & finance law. *Other professional posts*: President & CEO, Ho-Chunk, Inc., 1995-present); instructor, Little Priest Tribal College, 1997-present). *Past professional posts*: Attorney, Dorsey & Whitney, 1993-95; Monteau & Peebles, 1995-03. *Awards, honors*: 1999 Effective Economic Development Practices awarded by the National Congress of American Indians; 2000 Honoring Nations Award sponsored by the Harvard Project on American Indian Economic Development recognizing excellence in tribal governments; 2001 Innovations in Government Award, $100,000 prize sponsored by Harvard University and the Ford Foundation; 2002 Bureau of Indian Affairs, Indian Entrepreneur Spirit Award; 2003 Distinguished Alumni Speaker, Harvard Law School; featured in People Magazine, April 8, 2002 & December 30, 2002. *Community activities*: Board of Trustees, Little Priest Tribal College; Board of Directors: Dynamic Homes; Liberty Bank & Liberty Financial Services, Inc.; Fort Peck, Inc.; Winnebago Tribe of Nebraska Gaming Board; Forest County Potawatomi Corporation. *Memberships*: Minnesota State Bar; Winnebago Tribe of Nebraska.

MORGAN, LAWRENCE T. (Navajo)
(speaker-Navajo Nation Council)
Born in Pinedale, N.M. *Education*: University of New Mexico, Gallup; Dine College. *Address & Affiliation*: Speaker (2003-present), Navajo Nation Council, P.O. Box 3390, Window Rock, AZ 86515 (928) 871-7160. *Past professional posts*: Pinedale Chapter (Navajo Nation), Pinedale, NM (Manager, 1981-83, Secretary/Treasurer, 1983-85; President, 1985-90. Navajo Nation Council (Government Services Committee, 1991-95; chairperson, Transportation & Community Development Committee, 1995-2003.

MORGAN, MINDY
(professor of anthropology; American Indian studies & languages)
Affiliation & Address: Assistant Professor of Anthropology, Native American Institute, Agriculture Hall, 446 W. Circle Dr., Rm. 406 • East Lansing, MI 48824 (517) 353-6723. E-mail: morgan37@msu.edu. Research & teaching specialization includes North American Indian languages, language pedagogy, literacy and ideology and ethnohistory. Morgan works extensively with the Anishnabemowin (Ojibwe Language) projects on campus and is active in issues of Language revitalization and preservation among Native Peoples. Dr. Morgan teaches courses in Native North American Ethnography, Language and Culture, and special topics in Native North American languages. She hopes to develop more courses regarding both contemporary Native American communities and topics such as literacy and language endangerment. *Past professional posts*: In 2009, she served as the interim director of the American Indian Studies Program at MSU; during the 2010-2011 academic year, she served as the interim director of the CIC-American Indian Studies Graduate Consortium. She was selected as a Fulbright Scholar during the 2011-12 academic year and spent one semester teaching at the University of Zadar, Croatia. *Publihed works*: "The Bearer of This Letter": Language Ideologies, Literacy Practices, and the Fort Belknap Indian Community (Nebraska, 2009). Her book examines how literacy functioned as both a cultural practice and cultural symbol for the Assiniboine and Gros Ventre communities of Fort Belknap reservation during the late nineteenth and twentieth centuries. This work emerged from her experience as the curriculum coordinator for a collaborative Nakoda language project at Fort Belknap College, Montana.

MORGAN, PHILLIP CARROLL (Choctaw/Chickasaw
(poet; author)
Education: University of Oklahoma, PhD (Native Literature), 2009. Resides on his family farm in the Chickasaw Nation, in Oklahoma. *Affiliation*: A bi-lingual

poet who has a 25-year artistic collaboration with his painter-sculptor wife, Kate Arnott Morgan. *Published works*: The Fork-in-the-Road Indian Poetry Store (Salt Publishing, 2006); contributor to "Reasoning Together: The Native Critics Collective," 2008. Chickasaw Renaissance (Chickasaw Press, 2010); Who Shall Gainsay Our Decision? Choctaw Literary Nationalism in the Nineteenth Century (Chickasaw Press, 2011. *Awards, honors*: 2006 Native Writers Circle of the Americas First Book for Poetry.

MORGAN, RONALD J. (*Whitewolf*) (Blackfoot) 1940-
(writer, photographer, jeweler)

Born October 4, 1940, Seattle, Wash. *Education*: Universal Life Church (Modesto, CA), BA (History), 1974; McGraw-Hill Paralegal School, Washington, DC, 1990. *Principal occupation*: Writer, photographer, jeweler. *Address*: P.O. Box 297, Redwater, TX 75573. *Occupational activities*: "I'm a public speaker, lecturer and dancer. I give talks on the Old West and Indians, also have slide shows and relic displays using artifacts from my collections. As a dancer, I've demonstrated Indian dances for tourists, school and youth groups. I have appeared in three video movies, filmed on the Alabama-Coushatta Reservation, Livingston, Texas. I speak the Dakota Sioux language, sign language and Spanish." *Memberships*: Smithsonian Institution; National Archives. *Awards, honors*: Awarded honorary title, Special Consultant-American Indian Affairs, 1969; "I have been consulted by writers, U.S. Senators and many Indian organizations over the years. *Interests*: "Research is one of my main interests. I'm an Indian historian and always try to learn the old ways. My interests are many: archaeology, linguistics, publishing and law. I'm especially interested in state and federal law books relating Indian court cases. Collecting Indian artifacts; documents, photographs & original historical newspapers are just some of my interests, As a professional photographer, I'm busy recording western and Indian historical sites, graves of famous Indians and Indian powwows. My photographs are now in the permanent collections of three major museums: U.S. Dept. of the Interior, National Park Service, Fort Bowie, AZ; North American Indian Heritage Center, in WY; and the Amon Carter Museum, Fort Worth, TX. I'm a part-time jeweler, casting in both gold & silver. My future plans are to produce video movie documentaries pertaining to Indian ceremonies and wild life. I'm currently working on fictional book about intertribal wars. The University of South Dakota, Institute of Indian Studies, has expressed an interest in using my photographs in a future publication, Who's Who Among the Sioux; I now paint acrylic and oil paintings of my Indian people; I have made over 30 Indian videos (Indian dancing), filmed all over Texas and Tulsa, OK; I am learning to speak the Kiowa language, because of my close association with them." *Biographical sources*: Source Directory (U.S. Dept. of the Interior, BIA, 1985-87); The American Indian Index: A Directory of Indian Country (Arrowstar Publishing, 1986-87). *Published works*: Articles: I Fought With Geronimo by Jason Betzinez as told to Ronald Morgan (The Westerner, Stagecoach Publishing, 1971); series, The Indian Side, in The Frontier, Real West, True West, & American West Magazines; among others.

MORGAN, VANESSA (*Paukeigope*) (Cherokee)
(dancer, traditional crafts demonstrator)

Address: P.O. Box 1101, Anadarko, OK 73005 (405) 643-5075. Vanessa is a traditional Southern Plains dancer and performs in cloth or buckskin regalia. She lectures and provides slide presentations, and has a strong background as a cultural arts demonstrator.

MORGAN, WAYNE (Eskimo)
(Alaskan village president)

Affiliation: President, Village of Aniak, P.O. Box 176, Aniak, AK 99557 (907) 675-4349.

MORGAN-GIBSON, REGLA (*Winter Flower*) (Ramapough-Mohawk) 1951-
(computer specialist, health educator)

Born November 23, 1951, Bronx, N.Y. *Education*: York College, B.S. (Community Health Education, Summa Cum Laude). *Address*: 198-04 120th Ave. St. Albans, NY 11412 (718) 978-7057. *Affiliations*: Clanmother of the Northeastern Native American Assn, P.O. Box 266, Hollis, NY 11423. Community health educator; HIV/AIDS educator; primary care consultant; counselor. *Community activities*: AIDS Center of Queens County; American Red Cross; American Indian Community House; Planned Parenthood; emergency medical services; Mary Immaculate Hospital; St. Albans Extended Care Facility; Queen of Peace Nursing Home. *Memberships*: Pan-American India Association; American Indian Community House; Native American Leadership Commission on Health & AIDS. Native American Writers & Artists Association. *Awards, honors*: American Red Cross; AIDS Center for Queens County. *Interests*: "Educate the health care sector that Native American people are still here. Because Native Americans are usually racially mixed, they suffer two fold when it comes to health issues, I want to come up with a program that addresses their specific needs. Implement a comprehensive health program for my organization (Northeastern Native American Association). It's mission is to reach out into the Native American community and provide social services. Promote cultural programs & educate the public about Native American issues and concerns. I want to follow the spiritual path of my ancestors in a humble

and quiet way. To counsel, to teach, to grow." *Published works*: Notes; Pan-American Indian Newspaper; Mary Immaculate Newsletter; Smoke Signals.

MORIGEAU, MICHAEL A.
(BIA field representative)

Affiliation: Plummer Field Office, Bureau of Indian Affairs, c/o Coeur D'Alene Tribe, P.O. Box 408, Plummer, ID 83851 (208) 686-1887.

MORILLO, ROSEMARY (Luiseno)
(former tribal chairperson)

Affiliation & Address: Soboba Band of Luiseno Indians, P.O. Box 487, San Jacinto, CA 92583 (951) 654-2765.

MORIN, LYMAN
(school principal/supt.)

Affiliation: Cheyenne-Eagle Butte School, P.O. Box 672, Eagle Butte, SD 57625 (605) 964-8744.

MORNING OWL, THOMAS (Umatilla)
(tribal interpreter)

Affiliations: Confederated Tribes of the Umatilla Indian Reservation, P.O. Box 638, Pendleton, OR 97801 (541) 276-3165.

MORNINGSONG, SHELLEY
(singer, songwriter)

Address: c/o Silver Wave Records, P.O. Box 7943, Boulder, CO 80306 (800) 745-9283 (303) 443-5617. E-mail: info@silverwave.com. *Awards, honors*: Debut Artist of the Year, NAMMY Awards, 2007; Best Rock Album, Indian Summer Music Awards, 2007; Best Native American Record, New Mexico Music Awards, 2007.

MORRIN, JOHN (Ojibwe)
(tribal vice chairperson)

Affiliations & Address: Vice Chairperson, Grand Portage Band of Lake Superior Chippewa, P.O. Box 428, Grand Portage, MN 55605 (218) 475-2277.

MORRIN, LARRY
(BIA regional director)

Affiliation: Midwest Regional Office, BIA, One Federal Dr., Rm. 550, Fort Snelling, MN 55111 (612) 713-4400.

MORRIS, CAROLEE (Cowlitz)
(tribal administrator)

Affiliation & Address: Cowlitz Indian Tribe, P.O. Box 2547, Longview, WA 98632 (360) 577-8140. E-mail: cmorris@cowlitz.org

MORRIS, DANIEL (Anishinabe)
(attorney; executive director)

Affiliation & Address: Staff Attorney (2013-present), Anishinabe Legal Services, P.O. Box 157, Cass Lake, MN 56633 (218) 335-2223. Daniel is a licensed attorney in the State of Minnesota, as well as the tribal courts of White Earth and Leech Lake.

MORRISON, DAVID, SR. (Bois Forte Ojibwe)
(tribal secretary-treasurer)

Affiliation & Address: Secretary-Treasurer, Boise Forte Band of Ojibwe, P.O. Box 16, Nett Lake, MN 55772 (218) 757-3261. E-mail: david.morrison@boisforte-nsn.gov

MORRIS, DORAN L. (Omaha)
(former tribal vice chairperson)

Affiliation: Omaha Tribe, P.O. Box 368, Macy, NE 68039 (402) 837-5391.

MORRIS, GLENN T.
(executive director)

Affiliation: Fourth World Center for the Study of Indigenous Law & Politics, University of Colorado, Dept. of Political Science, Campus Box 190, P.O. Box 173364, Denver, CO 80217 (303) 556-2850.

MORRIS, TRACI L. (Chickasaw)
(American Indian Policy Institute director)

Education: Colorado State University, BA; University of Arizona's American Indian Studies, MA, PhD. *Affiliation & Address*: Director, American Indian Policy Institute, 250 E. Lemon St., Discovery Hall #272, Tempe, AZ 85287 (480) 965-9005. E-mail: t.moris@asu.edu. Morris has a diverse professional background, which includes academia; university teaching; book, article, and white paper researcher and author; and is a nationally acclaimed speaker. She has worked with Native American tribes; Tribal businesses; Native American non-profits; Native media makers, artists & galleries; written a college accredited curriculum in Native American new media; and has advocated for digital inclusion at the Federal Communications Commission and on Capitol

Hill. A member of the Chickasaw Nation of Oklahoma, Morris maintains a strong working relationship with her community and her passion for art, media, policy and advocacy emerged from these strong ties and her own tribal roots. Her book, *Native American Voices: A Reader,* continues to be a primary teaching tool in colleges throughout the country. Morris's research and publications on Native American media & the digital divide is focused on Internet use, digital inclusion, network neutrality, digital & new media curriculums, digital inclusion and development of broadband networks in Indian Country. As an entrepreneur prior to her ASU appointment, Morris founded *Homahota Consulting LLC* a national Native American woman-owned professional services firm working in policy analysis, telecommunications, education, & research assisting tribes in their nation-building efforts & working with Native Nations, tribal businesses & those businesses working with tribes.

MORRIS, WYNEMA (Omaha of Nebraska)
(instructor of Native American studies; board member)
Affiliation & Address: Instructor (2002-present), Native American Studies, Nebraska Indian Community College, P.O. Box 428, Macy, NE 68039 (402) 494-2311. E-mail: wmorris@thenicc.edu. *Other professional posts*: Member, Board of Directors of Nebraska Indian Community College. Her area of expertise is Omaha Tribal History, Culture & Tradition; Native American Philosophy; U.S.-American Indian Relations; Tribal Government. She serves as a cultural consultant to the Minnesota Humanities Center. She is an Associate Fellow with the Study of the Great Plains center at th e University of Nebraska at Lincoln.

MORRISON, EDDIE (Cherokee) 1946-
(artist-sculptor)
Born September 29, 1946, Claremore, Okla. *Education*: Northeastern State College (four years); Institute of American Indian Art (two years). *Principal occupation*: Artist-sculptor. *Address*: P.O. Box 148, Caldwell, KS 67022-0148 (316) 845-2259. *Affiliation*: Owner, Eddie Morrison Studio & Gallery, Caldwell, KS. Specializes with wood & stone sculpture in a contemporary traditional style. "Besides my own feelings & interpretations, my ideas & themes come from the philosophies of Indians about life, spirituality, respect for life, animals, and all that is around us, and the Great Creator." *Exhibits*: Annual Santa Fe Indian Market; Red Cloud Art Show, Pine Ridge, SD; Trail of Tears Art Show, Tahlequah, OK; Museum of the Cherokee, Cherokee, NC; America Indian Arts Council Art Show, Dallas, TX; Annual Indian Arts & Crafts Association, Denver, CO; Lawrence Indian Arts Show, Lawrence, KS; The Five Civilized Tribes Museum Show, Muskogee, OK; Scottsdale (AZ) Native American Indian Cultural Foundation; and Southwest American Indian Annual Indian Market, Santa Fe, NM. *Military service*: U.S. Army Reserve, 1964-69. *Community activities*: Caldwell Chamber of Commerce. *Memberships*: Indian Arts & Crafts Association; Southwest Association on Indian Affairs; Art Student League of Denver. *Awards, honors*: Faculty Departmental Award for Outstanding Student in Three Dimensional Arts, Institute of American Indian Art; 2 Honorable Mention Awards for wood sculpture at Santa Fe Indian Market, 1991; Best of Wood & Stone Category, 1st Place, 1994 Indian Arts & Crafts Association, Phoenix, AZ; his work has been featured in: Contemporary Native American Art in Kansas" Show; Smokey Hill Museum, Salina, KS, 1990; also numerous private collections and several galleries throughout the U.S.

MORRISON, NEVA (Eastern Cherokee/Skokomish)
(managing director)
Affiliation & Address: Managing Director, First Peoples Worldwide, 857 Leeland Rd., Fredericksburg, VA 22405 (540) 899-6545. E-mail: info@firstpeoples.org. She and her mother, Rebecca Adamson grew First Peoples Worldwide into the only Indigenous led organization that works at a grassroots, national & international level for Indigenous communities. She began her career as an advocate for American Indian Gaming tribes but following in her mother's footsteps is now an advocate for Indigenous peoples globally.

MORRISON, ROBERT (North Alabama Cherokees) 1938-
(maintenance)
Born October 27, 1938 in Alabama. *Affiliation*: Owner, Cherokee Indian Records, P.O. Box 41, Boaz, AL 35957 (205) 593-7336. Cherokee national Indian search; some Seminole, Choctaw & Chickasaw research; individual and family charts. Charges: $10/name, $20/family.

MORROW, PHYLLIS 1950-
(professor of anthropology & cross-cultural communications)
Education: Harvard University, BA (summa cum laude, Social/Cultural Anthropology) 1972; Cornell University, MA, 1976, PhD, 1987. *Principal occupation*: Associate Professor of Anthropology & Cross-cultural Communications. *Affiliation & Address*: Assistant professor, Dept. of Alaskan Native Studies, Dept. of Anthropology, Box 757720, 310 Eielson Bldg., University of Alaska, Fairbanks, AK 99775 (907) 474-6608 (office), (907) 479-5911 (home). E-mail: ffpm@uaf.edu. *Past professional posts*: Graduate teaching assistant, Cornell University, 1973-76; courses/workshops in Yup'ik Eskimo culture/history and language/linguistics, Kuskokwim College, Bethel

(University of Alaska), 1977-86; director, Yup'ik Eskimo Language Center, Kuskokwim College, 1979-81; assistant professor of anthropology & cross-cultural communications, University of Alaska, Fairbanks, 1987-. *Other professional posts*: Field coordinator for cross-cultural Education Development Program teaching B.Ed. students in rural Alaskan village sites, 1978; material development and teacher training for the Lower Kuskokwim School District in Bethel, AK, 1981-86; consulting services-law, education, & oral history/literature' conference/workshop presentations, 1981-. *Community activities*: Museum Collections Advisory Committee, Alaska State Museums (vice-chair); Alaska Organizing Committee member and conference chair, 1990 Conference on Hunting & Gathering Societies. *Memberships*: American Anthropological Association; Alaska Anthropological Association; Commission on Folk Law & Legal Pluralism; Society for Applied Anthropology. *Awards, honors*: Phi Beta Kappa (Harvard-Radcliffe), 1971; Andrew White Graduate Fellowship, 1973-74; National Institute of Mental Health Predoctoral Fellowship for ethnographic fieldwork in Southwestern Alaska, 1976; Alaska Historical Commission Grant for publication of Cauyarnariuq, 1985; Alaska Humanities Forum Grant for "The Writing of Cultural & Culture of Writing," 1988; Spencer Foundation Grant for "Yup'ik Eskimo Ceremonialism: Traditional Religion in Contemporary Education, 1989. *Published works*: Co-author, Qaneryaurci Yup'igtun: Learn to Speak Yup'ik, 1981; "It Is Time for Drumming: A Summary of Recent Research on Traditional Yup'ik Ceremonies," Etudes/Inuit/Studies, Vol. 8 The Central Yup'ik Eskimos, 1984; editor, Cauyarnariuq ('it is time for drumming", high school text: reconstructs & discusses the traditional ceremonial round of Yup'ik Eskimos In Yup'ik Eskimo (author, Elsie P. Mather); co-author, Teacher's Guide: Secondary Yup'ik Language & Culture Program for the Lower Kuskokwim School District (LKSD, Bethel), 1987; "Competing Realities: The Negotiation of Ethnic Identity & Public Policy in Rural Alaska" in Cross-Cultural Issues in Alaskan Education, V. III, Ray Barnhardt, Ed. (Center for Cross-cultural Studies, Fairbanks, AK, 1989; "Oral Literature of the Alaskan Inuit," in Dictionary of Native North American Literature, Andrew Wiget, Ed. (Greenwood Press, 1990); "The Woman Who Returned from the Dead," in Coming to Light (Brian Swam, ed. Random House); National Science Foundation 1991 cross-cultural legal encounters in western Alaska; When Our Words Return: Hearing, Writing, and Remembering Oral Traditions of Alaska and the Yukon (Utah State U Press, 1995); "Yup'ik Eskimo Agents & American Legal Agencies: Perspectives on Compliance & Resistance (Journal of the Royal Anthropology Institute, 1996).

MORROW, RYAN (Muskogee Creek)
(tribal town king)
Affiliation & Address: Thlopthlocco Creek Tribal Town, P.O. Box 188, Okemah, OK 74859 (918) 560-6198

MORSETTE, BILLI ANNE (*Raining Bird*) (Chippewa Cree)
(chief operating officer)
Affiliation & Address: Chief Operating Officer, National Tribal Development Association, RR 1 Box 1080, Box Elder, MT 59521 (406) 395-4095. E-mail: bmorsette@ntda.info.

MORSETTE, JOSEPH (Chippewa Cree)
(instructor/director of Native American law program)
Education: University of North Dakota, JD; University of Arizona, LL.M (Indigenous Law). *Affiliation & Address*: Instrictor/Director, School of Law, Native American Into Law (NAIL) program; instructor, American Indian Studies, University of North Dakota, 221 Centennial Dr., Stop 7103, Grand Forks, ND 58202. E-mail: joseph.morsette@email.und.edu. *Other professional post*: Tribal judge; faculty fellow at the Northern Plains Indian Law Center. *Past professional posts*: Milotary police officer; tribal law enforcement.

MORSETTE, RICK (Chippewa Cree)
(former tribal chairperson)
Affiliation & Address: Chairperson, Chippewa-Cree Indian Tribe, RR 1 Box 544, Box Elder, MT 59521 (406) 395-4282.

MORTIMER, NEIL (Washoe)
(tribal chairperson)
Affiliation & Address: Chairperson, The Washoe Tribe of Nevada & California, 919 U.S. Hwy. 395 South • Gardnerville, NV 89410 (775) 265-8600 E-mail: neil.mortimer@washoetribe.us. *Past professional post*: Vice Chairperson, The Washoe Tribe.

MORTON, NEIL
(center director)
Affiliation & Address: Director, Native American Center for Excellence, Center for Tribal Studies, Tahlequah, OK 74464 (918) 456-5511 ext. 3690.

MOSE, ELWOOD (Te-Moak Shoshone)
(former tribal chairperson)
Affiliation: Te-Moak Tribe of Western Shoshone Indians of Nevada, 525 Sunset St., Elko, NV 89801 (775) 738-9251.

MOSE-TEMOKE, CHERYL (Te-Moak Shoshone)
(former tribal chairperson)
Affiliation & Address: Te-Moak Tribe of Western Shoshone, 525 Sunset St., Elko, NV 89801 (775) 738-9251.

MOSES, JR., HARVEY (Colville)
(tribal vice chairperson; committee chair)
Affiliation: Confederated Tribes of the Colville Reservation, P.O. Box 150, Nespelem, WA 99155 (509) 634-2218. E-mail: harvey.moses@colvilletribes.com. *Other tribal post*: Chair, Management & Budget Committee. *Other professional post*: 2nd Vice President, Affiliated Tribes of Northwest Indians (ATNI), Portland, OR.

MOSES, JOHNNY
(storyteller)
Address: 6515 15th Ave., NE, Seattle, WA 98115 (206) 325-4280. Johnny is a traditional Northwest Coast storyteller in eight Native languages, English, and sign language.

MOSES, JOSEPH (Paiute)
(tribal chief)
Affiliation: Confederated Tribes of the Warm Springs Reservation, 1233 Veterans St., Warm Springs, OR 97761 (541) 553-1161. E-mail: josephmoses @wstribes.org.

MOSES, LILLY L. (Nez Perce) 1949-
(economic development planner)
Born November 8, 1949, Seattle, Wash. *Education*: Oregon State University, BS (Education), 1976; University of Idaho, College of Law, 1979-80. *Principal occupation*: Economic development planner. *Address*: Nez Perce Tribe, P.O. Box 365, Lapwai, ID 83540. *Affiliations*: Cooperative education coordinator, American Indian Higher Education Consortium, Denver, CO, 1973-74; teacher intern, Madras Public Schools, Madras, OR, 1975-76; grants/contracts specialist, Planning Department, Warm Springs Confederated Tribes, Warm Springs, OR, 1976-77; community service manager, Nez Perce Tribe, Lapwai, Idaho, 1977-79; researcher, Cobe Consultants, Portland, OR, 1980-81; economic development planner/manager, Limestone Enterprise, Nez Perce Tribe, Lapwai, ID 83540. *Community activities*: Kamiah Revitalization Committee, Kamiah, ID (member, 1983-); elected to Housing Board of Commissioners, Nez Perce Tribal Housing Authority, 1985-89. *Memberships*: Association for the Humanities in Idaho, 1978-81. *Awards, honors*: 1971 After Dinner Speech Award; All-Indian Debate Tournament, Dartmouth College. *Interests*: "To gain a professionally gratifying position in the federal government that assists American Indian tribes in achieving self-sufficiency; camping, hunting, fishing, beadwork, dancing."

MOSES, SHARON (Apache)
(administrator, part-time college faculty)
Address & Affiliations: Coordinator, Native American/Multicultural Affairs Department, Flathead Valley Community College, 777 Grandview Dr., Kalispel, MT 59901 (406) 756-3945. *Community activities*: Native American cultural liaison for Montana State Dept. of Commerce and state: Kumamoto, Japan and Taiwan. *Membership*: Native American Journalist's Association.

MOSS, MARGARET P. (*Kapi'olani*) (Hidatsa/Fort Peck Sioux)
(associate professor of nursing)
Education: University of Texas at Houston, Health Sciences Center, PhD (Nursing), 2000 and subsequently received a distinguished alumni award in 2002; She completed a two-year post-doctorate fellowship at the University of Colorado's Native Elder Research Center, a resource center for minority aging research. Concurrently, she entered and completed law school and received her Juris Doctorate from Hamline University School of Law, Saint Paul, Minn.. *Affiliation & Address*: Associate Professor of Nursing, Native American Cultural Center, Yale University, 26 High St., New Haven, CT 06520 (203) 432-2900. She is one of only 16 doctorally-prepared American Indian nurses in the country and the only one to focus solely on aging. She is the first and only American Indian to hold both nursing and juris doctorates. In 2008-2009, Dr. Moss was named a Robert Wood Johnson Health Policy Fellow, & staffed the Senate Special Committee on Aging under the ranking Senators Martinez and then Corker. She was inducted as a Fellow into the American Academy of Nursing in 2008. Dr. Moss' phenomena of interest include aging (long-term care, functional disability and related policy) & health disparity. Her population of interest is largely American Indians with a special focus on reservation based research.

MOSS, MYRNA
(executive director)
Affiliation: Cherokee National Historical Society, P.O. Box 515, Tahlequah, OK 74465 (918) 456-6007. *Other professional post*: Editor, "The Columns," quarterly newsletter.

MOSSETT, KANDI (Mandan, Hidatsa, Arikara)
(Native energy & climate campaign organizer)
Education: University of North Dakota, BS (Natural Resources & Park Management), MS (Environmental Management). *Affiliation & Address*: Native Energy & Climate Campaign Organizer (2007-present), Indigenous Environmental Network, P.O. Box 485, Bemidji, MN 56619 (218) 214-1389. E-mail: iencampusclimate@igc.org.

MOTHERSHED, ARTHUR (Poarch Band Creek)
(tribal treasurer & CFO)
Born & raised in the Poarch Tribal community. *Education*: Faulkner University, B.A.; University of Alabama, MBA (Business Administration). *Address & Affiliation*: Tribal Treasurer & CFO of PCI Gaming (2005-present), Poarch Band of Creek Indians, 5811 Jack Springs Rd., Atmore, AL 36502 (251) 368-9136. E-mail: amothershed@pci-nsn.gov. *Other professional posts*: Creek Indian Enterprises Board of Directors and is actively involved in the development of all tribal economic enterprises. *Interests*: Cultural awareness, assisted living for Tribal elders, universal healthcare for tribal members, & economic development beyond gaming. Arthur is the Property Manager for Wind Creek Casino and Hotel, a business enterprise of the Poarch Band of Creek Indians. In this position, Mothershed is responsible for all aspects of management of the Tribe's four diamond hotel and Class II gaming facility. In addition to overseeing day-to-day functions, Mothershed also works strategically toward building partnerships and managing future growth. He currently serves on the Creek Indian Enterprises Development Authority Board of Directors, and is actively involved in the development of all Tribal economic enterprises. Mothershed also serves on the Health/Family Services and Budget/Finance Legislative Committees, and formerly served as a member of the Housing Authority.

MOTLOW, SHIRLEY M. (Seminole)
(Indian store owner)
Address: North American Native Arts & Crafts, P.O. Box 15112, Baton Rouge, LA 70895.

MOTO, EMERSON (Eskimo)
(Alaskan village president)
Affiliation: Native Village of Deering, P.O. Box 89, Deering, AK 99736 (907) 363-2138. E-mail: rjmoto@maniilaq.org

MOUNT, HARLAN K. (Gros Ventre)
(former tribal chairperson)
Affiliation: Fort Belknap Community Council, RR 1, Box 66, Harlem, MT 59526 (406) 353-2205.

MT. PLEASANT, ALYSSA (Tuscarora)
(professor of American Studies & History)
Education: Barnard College, BA; Cornell University, PhD (History & American Indian Studies). *Affiliation & Address*: Assistant Professor, Dept. of American Studies & History, P.O. Box 208236, Yale University, New Haven, CT 06520 (203) 432-1186. *Other professional post*: Faculty representative (2006-present), Yale University, Native American Cultural Center, New Haven, CT. *Published works*: After the Whirlwind: Haudenosaunee People at Buffalo Creek, 1780-1825 (in progress).

MT. PLEASANT, JANE (Tuscarora)
(associate professor of horticulture)
Education: Cornell University, BA/BS, 1980, MS, 1982; North Carolina State University, PhD, 1987. *Affiliation & Address*: Associate Professor, American Indian Program, Cornell University, 450 Caldwell Hall, Ithaca, NY 14853 (607) 255-6470. E-Mail: jm21@cornell.edu. *Interests*: Plants & human well being; traditional & Iroquois agriculture, indigenous ecological knowledge. Dr. Mt. Pleasant's research focuses on Indigenous cropping systems, plants, and human well-being. She lectures frequently on Indigenous agriculture and its links to contemporary agricultural sustainability, and is considered a national expert in Iroquois agriculture. Dr. Mt. Pleasant has been exploring Iroquois agriculture from a multi-disciplinary perspective that includes history, archaeology, paleobotany, and cultural /social anthropology in order to provide a critically needed bridge between scholars in the humanities and social sciences who work in Iroquois Studies.

MOUNTAIN, JAMES (San Ildefonso Tewa)
(Pueblo governor)
Affiliation & Address: Governor, San Ildefonso Pueblo Council, Rt. 5 Box 315-A, Santa Fe, NM 87501 (505) 455-2273.

MOUSSEAU, SHARON A. (Oneida)
(school administrator)
Affiliation: Oneida Tribal School, P.O. Box 365, Oneida, WI 54155 (414) 869-2795.

MOWLES, STEPHANIE A.L.
(Native American studies program director)
Affiliation & Address: Director, Native American Studies Program, Community College of Baltimore County, College of the Humanities & Social Studies, 800 S. Rolling Rd., A 303, Baltimore, MD 21228 (443) 840-5916 E-mail: smowles@ccbcmd.edu.

MOWRER, JEFFREY (Cheyenne River Sioux) 1957-
(mental health counselor)
Born March 25, 1957, Mobridge, S.D. *Education*: South Dakota State University, BS, 1979; University of Wyoming, MS, 1987. *Principal occupation*: Mental health counselor. *Address*: 701 E. 6th St., P.O. Box 879, McLaughlin, SD 57642 (605) 823-4458. *Affiliation*: Private practice, Counseling psychologist. *Past professional post*: Psychologist, Oklahoma City Indian Clinic, Oklahoma City, OK, 1990-2002. *Awards, honors*: Indian Education Fellowship, U.S. Dept. of Education. *Interests*: "To professionally integrate mental health concerns & issues, in a culturally sensitive manner to our Indian people."

MOYA, CHRISTA (Dine')
(director-student services & financial aid)
Education: University of New Mexico, BA (Psychology & Criminology), MA (Community & Regional Planning). *Affiliations & Address*: Director of Student Services & Financial Aid, American Indian Graduate Center, 3701 San Mateo Blvd. NE #200, Albuquerque, NM 87110 (505) 881-4584 ext. 110. E-mail: christa@aigcs.org. *Other professional posts*: Supervises Outreach, Academic Empowerment, Leadership & Alumni Relations programs of the American Indian Graduate Center Scholars (AIGCS) and the Gates Millennium Scholars Program (GMSP), as well as assisting scholars with exploring positive educational experiences through program support, outreach & advocacy.

MOYA, ROBERT (Tesuque Pueblo)
(Pueblo governor)
Affiliation & Address: Governor, Pueblo of Tesuque, Rt. 5 Box 360-T, Santa Fe, NM 87501 (505) 955-7732.

MOYLE, ALVIN (Paiute)
(tribal chairperson)
Affiliation & Address: Fallon Paiute & Shoshone Tribe, 565 Rio Vista Rd., Fallon, NV 89406 (775) 423-6075. E-mail: chairman@fpst.org.

MUELLER, LIZ (Jamestown S'klallam)
(tribal vice chairperson)
Affiliation & Address: Jamestown S'Klallam Tribe, 1033 Old Blyn Hwy., Sequim, WA 98382 (360) 808-3103. E-mail: lmueller@jamestowntribe.org
Other tribal post: Chair, Washington Indian Policy Advisory Committee.

MULL, RAQUEL (Dine') 1953-
(ordained deacon-pastor)
Education: University of New Mexico; Perkins School of Theology, Southern Methodist University, Duke University (seminary work completed in 2000). *Principal occupation*: Ordained deacon-pastor in the United Methodist Church (UMC). *Address*: 2220 Utah St. NE, Albuquerque, NM 87110 (505) 298-5138. E-mail: bideezhi1@aol.com. *Affiliations*: Co-pastor (with Craig Mull), Grandfalls Union Church, Grandfalls, TX, and Imperial UMC, Imperial, TX, 1996-2002; Appointed as Funding pastor of First nations UMC (a church for urban Native Americans), Albuquerque, NM, 2002-present. Ordained deacon in the UMC, under appointment in the New Mexico Conference for eight years. Currently, a probationary member, anticipating ordination as Elder, May 2005. *Community activities*: Within the UMC - Chair for the Conference Ethnic Minority Local Church Task Force; member, South Central Jurisdiction American Indian Ministries; past chair of the South Central Region, Native American International Caucus of the UMC (NAIC); board member, General Commission on Role and Status of Women. Locally - President, Albuquerque Indian Center, Community Development Board; member, Albuquerque Navajo Club; member, Trustees, University Heights UMC; member, Albuquerque Indian Chamber of Commerce. *Membership*: National American Indian Women's Association.

MULLEN, DOUGLAS
(rancheria chairperson)
Affiliation: Greenville Rancheria, 645 Antelope Blvd. #15, Red Bluff, CA 96080 (916) 528-9000.

MULLEN, JOSEPH (Snoqualmie)
(tribal chairperson)
Affiliation: Chairperson, Snoqualmie Indian Tribe, P.O. Box 969, Snoqualmie, WA 98065. (425) 888-6551.

MULLIN, MARKWAYNE (Cherokee)
(U.S. congressman)
Born & raised in Westville, Okla. *Affiliation*: Republican, elected to the 113th Congress from the 2nd Congressional District in Oklahoma. *Past professional post*: Owner, Mullin Plumbing, Mullin Farms, Mullin Properties & Services.

MULLON, DAVID
(attorney)
Affiliation: Majority General Counsel, Senate Committee on Indian Affairs, 836 Hart Office Bldg., Washington, DC 20510 (202) 224-2251.

MUMFORD, MARRIE
(professor of Indigenous Studies; Canada Research Chair)
Education: University of Alberta, BA (Theatre); Brandeis University, MFA. *Affiliation & Address*: Assistant Professor (2004-present), Indigenous Studies Department, Enweying Room 326, Trent University, Peterborough, ON K9J 7B8 Canada (705) 748-1011 ext. 7310. E-mail: marriemumford@trentu.ca. *Other professional posts*: Canada Reseach Chair, Aboriginal Arts & Literature; Director, Nozhem, First Peoples Performance Space, Trent University, Peterboroigh, ON. *Past professional post*: Artistic Director, Aboriginal Arts Program, Banff Centre, Alberta. Professor Mumford works in Canada & the U.S. in professional theatre.

MUNGARY, WILLIAM (BILL) (Paiute/Apache)
(retired-community development)
Education: University of California, Los Angeles, B.A. (International Relations), MS (Business Administration). *Address & Affiliation*: Commissioner, Native American heritage Commission, Sacramento, CA.. *Past professional post*: Director (30 years - retired), Planning & Community Development Program, Resource Management Agency of Kern County, Bakersfield, CA. Mr. Mungary retired as the Director of the Community Development Program, Resource Management Agency of Kern County, a position he held for over 30 years. He received his Bachelor of Arts degree in International Relations Curriculum and Masters in Business Administration in General Management from the University of California at Los Angeles. He served in the US Air Force and achieved the rank of Captain. Mr. Mungary is on the Board of Directors of the National Association for County Community and Economic Development and founding member of the American Indian Council of Central California, Inc., California Association for Local Economic Development, and the Native American Heritage Preservation Council of Kern County, where he served on the Board of Directors from 1991-1995. He was a member of the Cultural Resources and Economic Development Committees of the Federal Advisory Council of California Indian Policy and the Committee on Native American Graves Protection and Repatriation Act Implementation for the California Department of Parks and Recreation. In March of 1995, Governor Wilson appointed Mr. Mungary to serve as a member of the California Rural Development Council. Governor George Deukmejian appointed Commissioner William (Bill) Mungary of Bakersfield to the Native American Heritage Commission on December 17, 1987. Mr. Mungary served as the NAHC Chairperson from 1990-2008. *Military service*: U.S. Air Force (Captain).

MINICH, SOPHIE (Athabascan)
(president & CEO)
Born & raised in Seward, Alaska. *Education*: University of Alaska, Anchorage, BS (Finance). *Affiliation & Address*: President & CEO (2013-present), Cook Inlet Region, Inc. (CIRI), P.O. Box 93330, Anchorage, AK 99503 (907) 274-8638. Sophie joned CIRI in 1993 and has served as chief operating officer, senior vice president of business development, chief financial officer, etc. *Other professional posts*: Director Anchorage Economic Development Corp. board of directors; trustee of Alaska Regional Hospital & CIRI's Elders' Settlement Trust. *Awards, honors*: Chaired the 2010 United Way of Anchorage community giving campaign; inducted into the thena Society in 2008 and is a 2011 YWCA Woman of Achievement award recipient.

MUNOZ, VINCE, JR. (Ysleta Del Sur Pueblo)
(former Pueblo governor)
Affiliation: Ysleta Del Sur Pueblo, P.O. Box 17579, Ysleta Sta., El Paso, TX 79917 (915) 859-7913.

MUNRO, PAMELA
(professor of linguistics)
Address & Affiliation: Dept. of Linguistics, 3125 Campbell Hall, UCLA, Los Angeles, CA 90095 (310) 749-0056. E-mail: munroe@ucla.edu. Prof. Munro's current research involves the study of all aspects of the grammar of a number of different American Indian languages (currently focusing on Chickasaw, Lakhota, Yavapai, Gabrielino, among others) & language families (especially Muskogean, Uto-Aztecan, Yuman, & Zapotecan) -- syntax, phonology, lexicon, history -- both through fieldwork with Native speakers & through comparative research & analysis of descriptions. She works with both undergraduate & graduate students in Linguistics, and graduate students in Applied Linguistics and American Indian Studies. *Published works*: Mojave Syntax (Garland

Publishing, 1976); Chem'ivillu (Let's Speak Cahuilla), with Katherine Siva Sauvel (UCLA American Indian Studies Center & Malki Museum Press, 1981); Chickasaw: An Analytical Dictionary (U. of Oklahoma Press, 1994)

MUNROE, GUY GENE (Kaw)
(former tribal chairperson)
Born in Old Washunga, Okla. *Education*: Wichita State University; Northern Oklahoma College. *Affiliation & Address*: Chairperson/CEO (2002-14), The Kaw Nation, 698 Grandview Dr., Drawer 50, Kaw City, OK 74641 (580) 269-2552. E-mail: gmunroe@kawnation.com. *Military Service*: U.S. Army, 1964-66.

MUNSON, CATHERINE F.
(attorney)
Education: Vanderbilt University, BA, 1995; Emory University School of Law, JD, 1999. *Affiliation & Address*: Managing Partner & Co-leader of the Native American Affairs practice, Kilpatrick Townsend & Stockton, LLP, 607 14th St., NW, Suite 900, Washington, DC 20005 (202) 824-1435. E-mail: cmunson@kilpatricktownsend.com. Ms. Munson is part of the Litigation Department of Kilpatrick Townsend, & focuses her practice on Native American affairs. She represents tribes & individual Indians in federal courts & before administrative agencies in matters involving the enforcement of the federal governments trust responsibility & the protection of tribal land & resources. *Awards, honors*: Recognized as a 2013 Washington, DC "Rising Star" in the area of General Litigation by Super Lawyers magazine.

MUNSON, MYRA
(attorney; Alaska Native law)
Education: University of Denver, MSW & JD, 1980. *Affiliation & Address*: Partner, Sonosky, Chambers, Sachse, Endreson & Perry, LLP, 302 Gold St. Suite 201, Juneau, AK 99801 (907) 586-5880. E-mail: myra@sonosky.net. *Myra M. Munson* founded the Juneau office of our firm in 1990, after serving as Commissioner of the Alaska Department of Health and Social Services from 1986 to 1990. Her nationwide practice emphasizes self-determination and self-governance, the Indian Health Care Improvement Act (IHCIA), Medicaid and other third-party reimbursement issues, and other tribal health program operations issues. Ms. Munson has represented tribes in planning and assuming programs and negotiating Title I and Title V agreements with the Indian Health Service (IHS) in more than half of the IHS Areas. She served on the negotiated rule making committees for the Title IV and Title V regulations. She was a technical advisor to the IHCIA National Steering Committee from its inception; assisted in drafting and editing substantial sections of the reauthorization; and testified before the Senate Committee on Indian Affairs. Since its adoption as part of the Affordable Care Act, she has conducted innumerable training programs at national and regional conferences and for individual tribes and tribal organizations, as well as assisting tribal health programs to implement various provisions of the IHCIA and ACA. Ms. Munson is also a member of the NIHB Medicare & Medicaid Policy Committee, and a technical advisor to the CMS Tribal Technical Advisory Group since their inception. She actively serves on a number of subcommittees, including ACA Policy, Tribal Consultation, and Regulation Review. In other areas of practice, Ms. Munson worked with Alaska Tribal Health Programs to draft the Community Health Aide Program Standards, including the standards for Dental Health Aide Therapists, and now assists tribes and organizations considering expansion of these services in other locations. She has worked on state redistricting matters with Donald Simon of our DC office. Ms. Munson was born in Juneau, Alaska and grew up in Fairbanks, Alaska. She earned her bachelor's degree at University of Alaska Fairbanks in 1972, and her law degree and master's degree in social work at the University of Denver in 1980 – both with distinction. Ms. Munson is currently serving on the Board of Alaska Legal Services Corporation. *Awards, honors*: In 2003 Ms. Munson was awarded the Alaska Federation of Native's Denali Award, and in 2011, the Healthy Alaska Natives Foundation awarded her its President's Award for promoting public understanding of Alaska Native health and wellness issues.

MUNSON, THOMAS A.
(monument supt.)
Affiliation: Effigy Mounds National Monument, RR 1, Box 25A, Harpers Ferry, IA 52146 (319) 873-3491.

MUNYAN, GEORGE F. (*Little Turtle*) (Nipmuc)
(author-illustrator; medicine person)
Born July 23rd in Putnam, Conn. *Education*: High school; various courses in art and related subjects, University of Connecticut, Worcester Art Museum, et al. *Principal occupation*: Author-illustrator-Indian subjects. Resides in East Douglas, MA. *Community activities*: Medicine person, past secretary, and tribal roll genealogist, Chaubunagungamaug Nipmuck Tribal Council. *Memberships*: New England Antiquities Research Association (contributing writer, Native American consultant). *Awards, honors*: Several awards from Nipmuck and other tribal groups for educational & cultural projects contributed to or

participated in. *Interests*: "Pre-Columbian American history, Native American & primitive art particularly in a spiritual context, herbal medicinal uses & propagation, environmental issues, inter-cultural understanding." *Published works*: Contributing writer/illustrator, Native American Sourcebook (Concord Museum, 1987); resource person, Legends of the New England Indians (Mohawk Arts, 1988); contributor-poetry: The Coming of Dawn (National Library of Poetry, Oct. 1993); All My Tomorrows (Quill Books, Feb. 1994).

MURIE, ROBERT (Chippewa Cree/Pawnee)
(Cree language instructor)
Education: Northern Montana College, BS (Elementary Education), 1981; Montana State University-Bozeman, MEd (School Administration), 1983. *Affiliation & Address*: Cree language instructor (1988-present), Native American Studies, Stone Child College, 8294 Upper Box Elder Rd., Box Elder, MT 59521 (406) 395-4875. E-mail: rmurie@stonechild.edu.

MURPHY, AMOS (Goshute)
(tribal vice chairperson)
Affiliation: Confederated Tribes of the Goshute Indian Reservation, P.O. Box 6104, Ibapah, UT 84034 (435) 234-1138. amosmurphy@goshutetribe.com.

MURPHY, CHARLES W. (Standing Rock Sioux) 1948-
(former tribal chairperson)
Born December 27, 1948, Fort Yates, N.D. *Education*: Saint Benedict College, 1968-69. *Address*: P.O. Box D, Fort Yates, ND 58538 (701) 854-8500. *Past tribal affiliations*: Police Officer, BIA, Fort Yates, ND, 1970-72; Range Technician, BIA, Standing Rock Sioux Tribe, 1972-76; agricultural director, 1976-79, economic development planner, 1979-81, vice chairperson & councilperson, 1981-83, chairperson, 1983-95. *Military service*: U.S. Army, 1969-70 (Vietnam Veteran; Army Commendation Medal; Bronze Star). *Community activities*: Standing Rock Sioux Tribe (chairperson, 1981-); United Tribes Educational Technical Center, Bismarck, ND (board of directors, 1983-); Aberdeen Tribal Chairman's Assn (chairman, 1986-); Theodore Jamerson Elementary School, Bismarck, ND (school board, 1984-); Saint Alexius Medical Center, Bismarck, ND (board of directors, 1985-). *Memberships*: National Tribal Chairman's Assn; United Sioux Tribes, Pierre, SD (chairperson, 1985-). *Awards, honors*: Certificate of Special Achievement, Dept. of the Interior, 1980. *Interests*: "Elected by the enrolled members of the Tribe (Standing Rock Sioux), (I) serve as the chair of the Tribal Council & the chief executive officer of the tribal government. Specialized experience or other related background in personnel management, administration, planning & budgeting, and land & resource management. Responsible for implementation of tribal law; & represent the tribe before Congress & government agencies."

MURPHY, HENRY R. (Kumeyaay Diegueno)
(tribal vice chairperson)
Affiliation & Address: Vice Chairperson, Sycuan Band of Kumeyaay Diegueno, 5459 Sycuan Rd., El Cajon, CA 92019 (619) 445-2613.

MURPHY, LUCY
(professor of American Indian studies)
Affiliation & Address: Associate Professor of History, The Ohio State University, Department of History, 1179 University Dr., Newark, OH 43055 (740) 366-3321. E-mail: murphy.500@osu.edu. *Published works*: A Gathering of Rivers: Indians, Metis, and Mining in the Western Great Lakes, 1737-1832 (University of Nebraska Press, 2000); co-editor with Rebecca Kugel, Native Women's History in Eastern North America Before 1900: A Guide to Research & Writing (University of Nebraska Press, 2007). Lucy helped create Oho State's Newark Earthworks Center and is a member of its Faculty Oversight Committee.

MURPHY, PATT (Iowa/Sauk)
(Indian art center owner)
Affiliation: American Indian Art Center, 206 S. Buckeye Ave., Abilene, KS 67410 (913) 263-0090. Specializes in Woodland and Prairie Indian items

MURPHY, RACHEL
(storyteller)
Address: 7 Hilda Rd., Bedford, MA 01730 (617) 275-6824. Rachel is a Native American storyteller & educator, & focuses on the importance of Native American awareness. Presentations include stories about the circle, the four directions, and dispelling the myths and misconceptions of Native American people. Rachel has performed in elementary schools, churches, civic organizations as well as ethnic folk festivals.

MURPHY, VIRGIL (Stockbridge-Munsee Mohican)
(tribal chairperson)
Affiliation: Stockbridge-Munsee Tribal Council, N 8476 Mo He Con Nuck Rd., Bowler, WI 54416 (715) 793-4111.

MURPHY-BRAZILL, KASSANDRA (Salish)
(institute principal)
Affiliation & Address: Principal, Nkwusm Salish Language Institute, P.O. Box 5, Arlee, MT 59821 (406) 726-5050. E-mail: kmurphybrazill@salishworld.com.

MURRAY, ARTHUR E. (Kaweah)
(mayor)
Address: 28 Sunnydell, South Hutchinson, KS 67505 (316) 662-7410. *Affiliations*: Mayor, South Hutchinson, KS; National Tribal Chairman, Kaweah Indian Nation of Western USA & Mexico. *Other professional post*: Deacon in local Southern Baptist Church.

MURRAY, CHRISTINA, M.D. (Saginaw Chippewa)
(medical doctor)
Address: 321 N.W. 14th St., Oklahoma City, OK 73103.

MURRAY, FRANK (Iowa)
(tribal enterprise manager)
Affiliation: Bah-Kho-Je Art Gallery (Iowa Tribe of Oklahoma enterprise), 103 S. 2nd St., Guthrie, OK 73044 (405) 282-7282.

MURRAY, L. ROBERT (Shoshone)
(attorney)
Affiliation: Holland & Hart, 2515 Warren Ave., Suite 450, Cheyenne, WY 82001 (307) 778-4225. *Membership*: Native American Bar Assn. (board member).

MURRAY, LAWRENCE P. (Ioway)
(tribal chairperson)
Affiliation: Iowa Tribe of Oklahoma Business Committee, Rt. 1, Box 721, Perkins, OK 74059 (405) 547-2402.

MURRAY, LINDA J. (Gila River Pima)
(board chairperson)
Affiliation & Address: Board Chairperson, American Indian Health & Services Corporation, 4141 State St., Santa Barbara, CA 93110 (805) 681-7356. Past professional post: Retired, University of California, Santa Barbara.

MURRAY, ROBERT T. (Metis Cherokee)
(tribal chief)
Affiliation: Tennessee River Band of Chickamauga Cherokee located near Flintstone, GA.

MURRY, LARRY (Shoshone)
(association president)
Affiliation: Wyoming Indian Education Association, P.O. Box 248, Fort Washakie, WY 82514 (307) 332-2681.

MURRY, W. DAVID (Mewuk)
(rancheria chairperson)
Affiliation: Shingle Springs Rancheria, P.O. Box 1340, Shingle Springs, CA 95682 (619) 676-8010.

MUSICK, JACK (Luiseno)
(former tribal chairperson)
Affiliation: La Jolla Band of Luiseno Indians, 22000 Hwy. 76, Pauma Valley, CA 92061 (760) 742-3771.

MUSKETT, MILFORD (Navajo)
(professor)
Education: Calvin College (Michigan), BA in Geography; Western Michigan University, MA in Geography; University of Wisconsin-Madison, PhD in Land Resources. *Affiliation*: Professor, Intra-American Studies & Social Sciences, Shoreline Community College, Rm. 5385, 16101 Greenwood Ave. North, Shoreline, WA 98133 (206) 546-4571 (2007-present). E-Mail: mmuskett@shoreline.edu. *Past professional posts*: Dept. of Natural Resources & American Indian Program, Cornell University, Ithaca, NY (2004-07). *Interests*: American Indian Studies; Environmental issues & Indigenous Peoples; History of Environmental Sciences; Native American Environmental Policies.

MUSSATO-ALLEN, CRISTALA
(executive director)
Affiliation & Address: Executive Director, Native Workplace, Inc., P.O. Box 136757, Fort Worth, TX 76136 (512) 462-9056. cristala@nativeworkplace.com.

MUSSER, RHODA (Eskimo)
(Alaskan tribal chief)
Affiliation: Evansville Native Village, P.O. Box 26087, Bettles Field, AK 99726 (907) 692-5005. E-mail: evansville@aitc.org.

MYER, CANDACE (Tonkawa)
(tribal secretary-treasurer)
Affiliation: Tonkawa Tribe of Oklahoma, 1 Rush Buffalo Rd., Tonkawa, OK 74653 (580) 628-2561.

MYERS, BRANDY (*Weeasayha*) (Cherokee)
(chaplain, councilor)
Affiliation: Native American Indian Community, Rd. 2 Box 247A, Kittanning, PA 16201 (724) 548-7335.

MYERS, CHARLIE (Eastern Cherokee)
(associate director for strategic initiatives & planning)
Education: Western Carolina University, BS (Finance & Economics). *Affiliation & Address*: Associate Director, Cherokee Preservation Foundation, P.O. Box 504, Cherokee, NC 28719. (828) 497-5550. E-mail: cmyers@cpfdn.org. In addition to his responsibilities for strategic initiatives & planning, Charlie is responsible for the Foundation's support of language revitalization & cultural tourism initiatives. *Past professional posts*: Director of Operations, Cherokee Casino & Hotel; headed Economic Development, Eastern Band of Cherokee Indians (EBCI); vice chairperson of the Board of Advisors for (EBCI) Tribal Casino Gaming & Bingo Enterprises; board member, Cherokee Preservaction Foundation.

MYERS, DAVID G.
(non-profit organization president)
Address & Affiliation: Native American Heritage Association, P.O. Box 512, Rapid City, SD 57709 (605) 341-9110. E-mail: dmyers@naha-inc.org.

MYERS, JOSEPH A. (Pomo)
(attorney; executive director)
Education: University of California, Berkeley School of Law, JD. *Affiliation*: Executive Director (1983-present), National Indian Justice Center, 5250 Aero Dr., Santa Rosa, CA 95403 (707) 762-8113. Email: josephmyers@nijc.org. Center creates & conducts legal education, research & technical assistance programs aimed at improving the administration of justice in Indian country. *Other professional posts*: Commissioner, Native American Heritage Commission, Sacrammento, CA (2015-present); co-chair, Joseph A. Myers Center for Research on Native American Issues, Institute for the Study of Societal Issues, University of California, Berkeley, (2002-present); lecturer, Native American Studies, UC Bekeley (15 years); founder & board member, California Indian Museum & Cultural Center; chairperson, CALTRANS Native American Advisory Committee. *Past professional post*: Associate Director, American Indian Lawyer Training Program, 1976-83. *Awards, honors*: Mr. Myers received national recognition from Attorney General Janet Reno for his work on behalf of victims of crime in Indian country. He has received numerous awards, including the 2002 California Peace Prize from The California Wellness Foundation, & 2010 Peter E. Haas Public Service Award from UC Berkeley.

MYERS, LARRY (Pomo)
(executive secretary)
Education: San Jose State College, B.A.; University of Utah, M.A. (Management). Affiliation: Native American Heritage Commission (NAHC), 915 Capitol Mall, Rm. 364, Sacramento, CA 95814 (916) 653-4082. Website: www.nahc.ca.gov. Appointed to the NAHC in July 1987. *Past professional posts*: Member, Dept. of Forestry's Native American Advisory Council; He assisted in the development of the Federal Oversight Hearing on Native American Legislation; *Awards, honors*: Appointed by California ex-Governor Pete Wilson to the Susquicentennial Commission. *Membership*: Committee on Native American Graves Protection & Repatriation Act (NAGPRA). Mr. Myers is a member of the Commemorative Seal Advisory Committee that is working on a commemorative seal to be placed on the west steps of the State Capitol that will memorialize California Indians. *Military service*: U.S. Army.

MYERS, LINDA (Navajo)
(program founder)
Affiliation: Founder, Adopt-A-Native-Elder Program, P.O. Box 3401, Park City, UT 84060 (435) 649-0535. Website: www.anelder.org.

MYERS, LUCINDA (Mvskoke)
(program director)
Education: University of Oklahoma, MSW, 2002. *Affiliation*: Program Director, National Native American Youth Initiative (NNAYI), Association of American Indian Physicians, 1235 Sovereign Row, Suite C-7, Oklahoma City, OK 73108 (405) 946-7072. E-mail: lmyers@aaip.org.

MYERS, PAXTON (Eastern Cherokee)
(tribal administrator)
Affiliation: Eastern Band of Cherokee Indians, Qualla Boundary, P.O. Box 455, Cherokee, NC 28719 (828) 497-7000.

MYERS, RAQUELLE (Pomo)
(attorney)
Affiliation & Address: Staff attorney, National Indian Justice Center, 5250 Aero Dr., Santa Rosa, CA 95403 (707) 579-5507. E-mail: nijc@aol.com.

MYERS, WASSILLIE (Eskimo)
(Alaskan village council president)
Affiliation: Pilot Station Traditional Village, P.O. Box 5119, Pilot Station, AK 99650 (907) 549-3373.

MYERS-LIM, NICOLE (Pomo)
(attorney)
Affiliation & Address: Staff attorney, National Indian Justice Center, 5250 Aero Dr., Santa Rosa, CA 95403 (707) 579-5507. E-mail: nicoleim@nijc.org.

MYLER, MICHAEL (Waccamaw-Siouan)
(tribal chairperson)
Affiliation: Waccamaw-Siouan Indians of SC, Gallivant's Ferry, SC 29544 (803) 248-9843.

N

NAAB, MICHAEL
(museum director)
Affiliation: Totem Heritage Center Museum & Library, 629 Dock St., Ketchikan, AK 99901 (907) 225-5900.

NABOKOV, PETER 1940-
(professor of anthropology, author)
Born October 11, 1940. *Education*: Columbia University, BS, 1965; Goddard College, MA (Ethnic Studies & Language Arts), 1972; University of California, Berkeley, PhD (Anthropology), 1988. *Affiliation & Address*: Professor of anthropology, Department of World Arts & Cultures, UCLA, Kaufman 130C, Box 951608, Los Angeles, CA 90095 (310) 825-3089. E-mail: pnabakov@arts.ucla.edu. *Other professional post*: Faculty Advisory Committee Chair, American Indian Studies Center, UCLA. *Past professional posts*: Research associate, Museum of the American Indian, Heye Foundation, New York, NY, 1962-85; University of California, Dept. of Native American Studies (instructor, Fall 1979 & 1980, Winter 1981, Spring 1982, Spring/Fall 1984, Spring 1985; lecturer, Fall 1989); Resident Fellow, D'Arcy McNickle Center for the History of the American Indian, Newberry Library, Chicago, IL, 1986-87; lecturer, Ethnic Studies, California State University, Hayward, Spring 1989; Dept. of Anthropology, University of Wisconsin-Madison, 1991-96; consulting & lecturing; manuscript & grant reviewing. Workshop Developer & Coordinator: The Blood of Things: American Indian Culture & History, D'Arcy McNickle Center Workshop series, Aug. 1991; consultant, Educational Broadcasting Corp./WNET-Thirteen, script critique for series on American environmental history entitled Nature: Land of the Eagle, 1989-91; member, The National Faculty of Humanities, Arts & Sciences; member, Little Big Horn College Library & Advisory Board; Alabama-Coushatta Indian Reservation, Livingston, TX (for book profiling four contemporary Native American communities); Summer 1985-87: Three Affiliated Tribes, Newtown, ND (for film, "Peoples of the Earthlodge"); Winter/Summer 1985-86: Crow Indian Reservation (conducting field research on history of the Crow Tobacco Society toward PhD dissertation, "Cultivating Themselves: The Inter-Play of Crow Indian Religion and History." *Awards, honors*: Awards for Native American Testimony: American Library Association Best Book for Young Adults, 1978; Library School Journal Best Book, 1978; National Council for the Social Studies, Carter G. Woodson Book Award, 1979. Awards for Native American Architecture: 9th Annual Bay Area Book Reviewers Association Awards, 1989; The American Institute of Architects, "Institute Honor" award, AIA National Annual Convention, Washington, DC, 1991. *Published works*: Two Leggings: The Making of a Crow Warrior (Thomas Y. Crowell, 1967); Apollo Books (paperback), 1970; University of Nebraska Press, Bison Books, 1981); Native American Testimony: An Anthology of Indian & White Relations, Vol. I: First Encounter to Dispossession (Thomas Y. Crowell, 1978; Harper & Row (paperback), 1979); Indian Running (Capra Press, 1981; Ancient City Press edition, 1987); Architecture of Acoma Pueblo (Ancient City Press, 1986); Native American Architecture, with Robert Easton (Oxford University Press, 1989); Native American Testimony: From Prophecy to the Present, 1492-1992 (including complete text of Native American Testimony, 1978, plus second unpublished sequel volume, "Reservation to Resurgence" (Viking Penguin, 1991); Native American Testimony: From Prophecy to the Present, 1492-2000, Revised Edition (Viking Penguin, 1999); A Forest of Time: American Indian Ways of History (Cambridge University Press, 2002); among others, as well as book chapters, introductions, research reports, papers, lectures and numerous articles and reviews.

NAGANASHE, PATRICK
(organization president)
Affiliation: South Eastern Michigan Indians, Inc., 26641 Lawrence St., Center Line, MI 48090 (810) 956-1350.

NAGARUK, LUTHER (Eskimo)
(village president)
Affiliation: Native Village of Elim, P.O. Box 39070, Elim, AK 99739 (907) 890-3741.

NAGEAK, BANJAMIN (Eskimo)
(Alaska State (D) representative)
Affiliation & Address: Alaska State Representative (2013-14), District 40, State Capitol, Room 428, Juneau, AK 99801 (907) 465-3473. *Committees*: Co-chair, Community & Regional Affairs Committee; Health & Social Services Committee; Energy Special Commiittee.

NAGEL, JOANE
(professor of sociology)
Address & Affiliation: Chairperson, Dept. of Sociology, University of Kansas, Lawrence, KS. *Published works*: American Indian Ethnic Renewal: Red Power and the Resurgence of Identity & Culture; Red Power: The American Indians' Fight for Freedom, Second Edition, edited with Alvin M. Josephy, Jr. and Troy Johnson (University of Nebraska Press, 1999).

NAHWEGAHBOW, BARBARA
(director-Indian centre)
Affiliation: Native Canadian Centre of Toronto, 16 Spadina Rd., Toronto, Ontario, Canada (416) 964-9087.

NAICHE-PALMER, CARLETON (Mescalero Apache)
(former tribal president)
Affiliation & Address: President (2008-14), Mescalero Apache Tribal Council, P.O. Box 227, Mescalero, NM 88340 (505) 671-4494.

NAILOR, GERALD (Picuris Pueblo)
(former pueblo governor)
Affiliation: Picuris Pueblo Council, P.O. Box 127, Penasco, NM 87553 (505) 587-2519.

NAIZE, JOHNNY (Navajo-Dine')
(tribal council speaker)
Affiliation & Address: Speaker, Navajo-Dine' Nation, P.O. Box 3390, Window Rock, AZ 86515 (928) 871-7160. E-mail: johnnynaize@navajo.org.

NAKAI, KATOSHA (Navajo-Dine')
(tribal affairs & policy development manager)
Education: Oklahoma City University, BA (Mass Communications), 1994; Arizona State University College of Law, JD, 2003. *Affiliation & Address*: Tribal Affairs & Policy Development Manager (2011-present), Central Arizona Project, P.O. Box 43020, Phoenix, AZ 85080 (623) 869-2333. knakai@cap-az.com. The Project is designed to bring about 1.5 million acre-feet of Colorado River water per year to Pima, Pinal & Maricopa counties. *Past professional posts*: Policy Advisor on Tribal Affairs, Office of AZ Governor, Janice Brewer, 2009-2011; attorney, Lewis & Rocca LLP, 2004-09; Communications & Public Education Director, American Indian College Fund, 1999-2000; Communications Diector, Minnesota Department of Children, Families & learning, 1998-2000; Media Coordinator, national marrow Donor Program, 1996-98; Associate Producer/Reporter, KSTP-TV, 1994-96; Associate Producer/Update Anchor/Assignment Editor, KFOR-TV, 1992-94.

NAKAI, ORLANDO (Navajo-Dine')
(executive Director)
Affiliation & Address: Executive Director, Friendship House Association of American Indians of San Francisco, 56 Julian Ave., San Francisco, CA 94103 (415) 865-0964.

NAKAI, R. (RAYMOND) CARLOS (Navajo-Ute) 1946-
(artisan, musician, lecturer)
Born April 16, 1946, Flagstaff, Ariz. *Education*: Northern Arizona University, BS, 1979, Honorary Doctorate, 1994; University of Arizona, MA (American Indian Studies), 1992.. *Address*: Native American Flute Music/A'mp, P.O. Box 86477, Tucson, AZ 85754 (320) 743-9902. E-mail: atoka1@cox.net. Affiliations: Canyon Records Productions, Phoenix, AZ (artist, 1984-); Arizona Commission on the Arts, Phoenix, AZ (artist/consultant, 1982-). *Other professional posts*: Touring Artist, Western States Arts Foundation, 1991-93; Certified Secondary teacher in Graphic Communications, State of Arizona; co-founder of the ethnic jazz ensemble Jackalope. Jackalope has released two albums, Jackalope and Weavings. History: In 1973, after earlier music studies on the classical trumpet at Northern Arizona University, Nakai began playing the wooden Native American flute. He learned the traditional flute melodies

and music forms of the Plains and Woodlands Indians and soon began to adapt these ideas to fit a style of his own. Nakai has recorded 12 albums for Canyon Records, including Earth Spirit, Canyon Trilogy, Carry the Gift, and most recently, Spirit Horses, a classically-oriented release featuring a concerto written for Nakai's Native American flute and chamber ensemble. Spirit Horses was chosen by Pulse music magazine as one of the top albums of 1991. Nakai's albums of solo flute music on the Canyon Records label include Changes, Journeys, Earth Spirit & Canyon Trilogy. On Cycles, Nakai uses the traditional flute with synthesizer accompaniment to create a dramatic work that serves as the music track for the multimedia presentation "Our Voices, Our Land" at The Heard Museum in Phoenix, AZ. Nakai has brought the Native American flute, traditionally a solo instrument used for courting and healing, into the realm of ensemble performance. In March 1993, he will appear as a soloist with the Phoenix Symphony in the world premiere of a new concerto for the cedar flute and orchestra composed by James DeMars. Nakai has collaborated with guitarist and luthier William Eaton on two albums, Carry the Gift and Winter Dreams. A new album by the duo will be released in 1992. Naka has performed at the World Music Seminar in Woodstock, NY, in concert, at schools, and at music festivals including the Telluride Bluegrass Festival, the Magic Flute Festival and throughout Europe & Japan. He has written & performed scores for film and TV, including selections for WGBH-TV, the National Park Service, the National Geographic Society, Fox TV, as well as many commercial productions. In October 1988, the Martha Graham Dance Co. premiered a dance set to five selections from nakai's album, Cycles. Since 1990, Nakai has collaborated and toured with pianist Peter Kater. Together they've recorded two albums, "Natives and Migration." He has recorded "Sundance Season and Desert Dance" for the Celestial Harmonies label. Nakai continues to tour extensively throughout the U.S., Canada, Europe & Japan, performing and lecturing on Native American culture & philosophy. Military service: U.S. Navy, 1966-71 (E-4, Radioman). *Community activities*: Panelist, The National Endowment for the Arts, Tucson Community Foundation, Phoenix Arts Commission; director, Arts Genesis, Arizona Ethno-botanical Research Association. *Memberships*: Cheyenne-Arapaho Gourd Society; National Flute Association; Blue Star Society. *Awards, honors*: Arizona State Governor's Arts Award, 1992, for individual achievement; has received two gold records and numerous Grammy nominations; inducted into the Arizona Music & Entertainment Hall of Fame, 2005. *Interests*: "While I am engaged in the study of indigenous North American Native culture & music, my goals will include but are not limited to the following: research the historical traditions & technology of Native American music and oral traditions; compose, arrange & perform new music for the Native American flute; demonstrate and lecture on aboriginal & contemporary Native American culture, music, spirituality & philosophies of self-awareness & survival, & most importantly, to express ideas, observations, & thoughts in a positive, non-rhetorical & unbiased manner, to educate rather than castigate. My objective is to communicate a perspective based upon the future oriented and on-going, living oral traditions of the Dine' and other aboriginal native peoples of North America that are uncoached in romantic and/or stereotypical idealism. I will utilize contemporary teaching methods to develop a creative learning atmosphere in which to share awareness." Nakai, while cognizant of the traditional use of the flute as a solo instrument, began finding new settings for it, especially in the genres of jazz & classical. He founded the ethnic jazz ensemble, the R. Carlos Nakai Quartet, to explore the intersection of ethnic & jazz idioms. *Published Albums*: "Changes" (Canyon Records, 1983); "Cycles" (Canyon Records, 1985); Canyon Trilogy & Earth Spirit; "Ancestral Voices" (Canyon Records, 1994) – won 1994 Best Traditional Folk Album; "Inner Voices and Inside Monument Valley" Canyon Records) - 2000 Best New Age Album; 'In a Distant Place' -2001 Best New Age Album; "Fourth World" - 2002 Best New Age Album; "Sanctuary" - 2003 Best Native American Album; and "People of the Peace" - 2004 Best New Age Album; @ 30 other albums. *Published book*: "The Art of the Native American Flute," with composer James DeMars - a guide to performing the traditional cedar flute.

NANENG, MYRON P.
 (association president)
Affiliation: Association of Village Council Presidents, Inc., P.O. Box 219, Bethel, AK 99559 (907) 543-3521.

NANEPASHEMET
 (program manager)
Affiliation: Plimoth Plantation, Wampanoag Indian Program, P.O. Box 1620, Plymouth, MA 02360 (617) 746-1622.

NAPEAHI, MISTY (Tulalip)
 (tribal general manager)
Affiliation & Address: General Manager, Tulalip Tribes, 6406 Marine Dr., Tulalip, WA 98271 (360) 651-4000.

NAPIER, L.A.
 (center director)
Affiliation: American Indian Education Policy Center, Pennsylvania State University, 320 Rackley Bldg., University Park, PA 16803 (814) 865-1489.

NAPOLEON, FRANKLIN D. (Eskimo)
 (Alaskan village president)
Affiliation: Native Village of Paimiut, P.O. Box 230, Hooper Bay, AK 99604 (907) 561-9878.

NAQUIN, ALBERT P. (Biloxi-Chitimacha Muskogees)
 (tribal chief)
Affiliation: Biloxi-Chitimacha Confederation of Muskogees, Grand Isle de Jean Charles Band, 100 Dennis St., Montegut, LA 70377 (985) 594-3725. E-mail: whitebuffalo@netscape.net.

NARANJO, ED (Goshute)
 (former tribal chairperson & administrator)
Affiliation: Confederated Tribes of the Goshute Indian Reservation, Box 6104, Ibapah, UT 84034 (435) 234-1138. E-mail: ednaranjo@goshutetribe. com.

NARANJO, MAKOWA KO (Santa Clara Pueblo)
 (artist, shop owner)
Address: 364 Ridge Circle, Waynesboro, VA 22980 (540) 946-7357. E-mail: nccrone@ntelos.net. *Artwork*: Traditional Santa Clara pottery; paintings & prints.

NARANJO, MARY L. (Santa Clara Pueblo)
 (school principal/teacher)
Affiliation: San Ildefonso Day School, Route 5, Box 308, Santa Fe, NM 87501 (505) 455-2366.

NARANJO, MICHAEL A. (Mountain Meadows)
(Tewa-Santa Clara Pueblo) 1944-
 (sculptor)
Born August 28, 1944, Santa Fe, N.M. *Education*: Highlands University (2 years). Principal occupation. Sculptor. *Address*: P.O. Box 5803, Santa Fe, NM 87502. E-mail: naranjostudio@hotmail.com. *Military service*: U.S. Army, 1967-68 (PFC; Accommodation Medal; Purple Heart in Vietnam). *Exhibits*: "My work has been shown in both one-man and group shows across the country, one of the latest being, at the Governor's Galleries in Santa Fe, NM, 7/04-8/04. *Permanent collections*: Albuquerque Museum; Museum of Fine Arts, Santa Fe, NM; State Capitol, Santa Fe, NM; Heard Museum, Phoenix, AZ; The White House, Washington, DC; Magee Women's Hospital, Pittsburgh, PA; The Vatican, Italy; among other places. Commissions: "Kokopelli," custom estate home, "Indian Springs Estates, Chatsworth, CA, 1985; "Yes, I Can" Award, Foundation for Exceptional Children, Reston, VA, 1988; "The Dancer," The Albuquerque Museum, 1989; "Justice," the Dennis Chavez Federal Bldg., Albuquerque, NM, 1993; "Spirit Mother," Yale Park, University of New Mexico, Albuquerque, 1996; "Emergence" monumental, Capitol Arts Board, State Capitol, Santa Fe, NM, 2000; "The Gift" - New Mexico State Library, Records & Archives, Santa Fe, NM; "Inner Visions - The Sculpture of Michael Naranjo," one person show at the Heard Museum, Phoenix, AZ, 9/00 to 2/01. *Awards, honors*: Appointed board member of the New Mexico State Arts Commission, 1971; Catlin Peace Pipe Award, 1973; "Governor's Award" for sculpture by Governor of New Mexico, Jerry Apodaca, 1976; presented with the 1982 "Profiles in Courage Award," by the New Mexico Vietnam Veteran's Association; presented sculpture to Pope John Paul II, at papal audience, Vatican City, Italy, 1983; chosen as "New Mexico Veteran of the Year," 1986; 1990 "Distinguished Achievement Award," by the American Indian Resources Institute, National Press Club, Washington, DC; 1991 recipient of the 1st Clinton King Purchase Award, Museum of Fine Arts, Santa Fe, NM; First prize, Southwest Art Exhibition '92, Del Rio Council of the Arts, Del Rio, TX; numerous prizes and medals at exhibits and shows. Nominated in 1996 by President Bill Clinton to serve on the Board of Trustees of the Institute of American Indian & Alaskan Native Culture and Arts Development. 1999 "Outstanding Disabled Veteran of the Year," by the Disabled American Veterans & LIFE Foundation"; "Presidential Unsung Hero Award"; 2004: Santa Fe Rotary Foundation, "Distinguished Artist of the Year," *Interests*: Sculpturing mainly in bronze, but has begun experimenting in stone. Biographical sources: Michael Naranjo, The Story of an American Indian (Dillon Press, 1975); Art and Indian Individualists (Northland Press, 1976); The Sweet Grass Lives On - 36 Contemporary American Indian Artists, by Jamake Highwater (Thomas Crowell, Co., 1980); Contemporary Western Artists (Southwest Art Publishing, 1982; In Pursuit of the American Dream (Atheneum, 1985); "The Spirit of Michael Naranjo," a biographical short story by Mary Carroll Nelson, in Time Was (Scott, Forsman Reading, 1986); featured in Beyond Tradition: Contemporary Indian Art and Its Evolution (Northland Press, 1988); featured in the 1988 CBS's Special, "Bodywatching," produced by New Screen Concepts, Louis H. Gorfain, Producer; feature article in "Southwest Art Magazine", Oct. 1989 issue; featured on PBS's "Colores" in 1992; "Motion in Bronze and Stone: The Sculpture of Michael Naranjo," in Kaleidoscope Magazine (Summer/Fall Issue, 1992); "A very Special Arts Story...Freedom of Expression," a syndicated television special, produced by Very Special Arts Production, Washington, DC, 1992 - Kara Kennedy, Producer; Santa Fe Indian Market: Showcase of Native American Art, by Sheila Tryk (Tierra Publications, 1993);

"Michael Naranjo: An Evolving Union," in Pasatiempo magazine of Santa Fe, NM, by Gussie Fauntleroy, Sept. 13, 1996; "A Touch of Genius," by Patricia Millman (Highlights for Children Magazine, 11/00); "An Artist's Visions," by David Kirby, (Modern maturity Magazine, March-April, 2000 issue; The Price of Their Blood, by Jesse Brown & Daniel Paisner (Bonus Books). Michael is currently listed in Who's Who in the West, and Who's Who in American Art.

NARANJO, ROBERT (Santa Clara Pueblo)
(craftsman; gallery owner)
Address & Affiliation: Gallery, P.O. Box 4599, Fairview, NM 87532 (505) 753-9239. *Artwork*: Traditional Santa Clara Pottery.

NARANJO, TESSIE (Tewa-Santa Clara Pueblo) 1941-
(cultural preservationist/consultant, Pueblo culture)
Born January 16, 1941, Santa Clara Pueblo, N.M. *Education*: Loma Linda (CA) University, MPH, 1977; University of New Mexico, PhD, 1992. *Principal occupation*: Cultural preservationist/consultant, Pueblo culture. *Address*: P.O. Box 1807, Espanola, NM 87532 (505) 753-3736. *Affiliation*: Santa Clara Pueblo, Espanola, NM, 1990-. *Memberships*: Rio Grande Institute, 1982- (vice-president); chairperson, Native American Graves Protection & Repatriation Act. *Interests*: Culture of the Southwest Pueblos. PhD Dissertation: Social Change & Pottery-Making at Santa Clara Pueblo, 1992.

NARANJO, TITO E. (*T'amu P'iin-Morning Mountain*)
(Tewa-Santa Clara Pueblo) 1937-
(professor emeritus, sculptor, writer, consultant)
Born August 6, 1937, Santa Clara Pueblo, N.M. *Education*: Baylor University, 1956-58; Hardin-Simmons University, 1958-59; New Mexico Highlands University, BA, 1962, MA, 1963; University of Utah, MSW, 1967. *Address*: P.O. Box 516, Mora, NM 87732 (505) 387-5658. *Affiliation*: New Mexico Highlands University, Las Vegas, NM (associate professor of social work, 1976-90, professor emeritus-part time professor, writer, sculptor, 1990-present). Other *professional posts*: Sculptor, writer, consultant; Mora Valley Health Services, Inc. (board of directors). *Past professional posts*: Community organizer, State of New Mexico, Taos, NM, 1964-65, 1967-69; state of Alaska director, Bristol Bay Social Services, Dillingham, AK, 1969-70; director of social services, Mora County, N.M., 1970-71; assistant professor, College of Santa Fe, NM, 1972-75. *Community activities*: Intermountain Centers for Human Development (board member); tribal secretary for Santa Clara Pueblo, 1976. *Memberships*: American Indian Higher Education (board of directors). *Interests*: "I am a part time rancher, part-time artist & writer. I enjoy hunting, fishing and photography. I am a distance runner in the masters category and I also love to canoe, hike and adventure in Alaska and Mexico." *Biographical source*: A Conversation With Tito Naranjo, in (Confluencia, summer, 1980); "Running on the Edge of Time," in Early Winters 10th Anniversary Catalogue, 1982. *Published work*: Native Americans of the Southwest - A Journey of Discovery (Running Press, 1993); A Pueblo (Runestone Press, 1999); Critical Neurophilosophy & Indigenous Wisdom (Sense Publishing, 2009).

NAREDO, PATRICK (Pomo)
(tribal vice chairperson)
Affiliation & Address: Vice Chairperson, Coyote Valley Reservation, P.O. Box 39, Redwood Valley, CA 95470 (707) 485-8723.

NARSISIAN, MARK (Akwesasne Mohawk)
(publisher)
Affiliation: Akwesasne Notes, P.O. Box 196, Mohawk Nation, Rooseveltown, NY 13655 (518) 358-9531.

NASH, ALICE
(associate professor of history; director of
Native American Indian Studies)
Education: Columbia University, PhD, 1997. *Affiliation & Address*: Director, Certificate Progrm in Native American & Indigenous Studies & Undergraduate Program Director in the Department of History, University of Massachusetts, Anthropology Department, Herter Hall 611, Amherst, MA 01003 (413) 545-6790. E-mail: anash@history.umass.edu. She is also a member of the Advisory Board of the American Indian Law Alliance. She is a co-editor with Josef Raab & Stefan Rinke of Rethinking the Americas: Historical Foundations to 1900, volume 1 of a 5-volume reference work: the Inter-American Key Topics Series Rethinking the Americas, edited by the Center for Inter-American Studies (CIAS) Bielefeld University (Germany) (Ashgate Publishing, 2017). She has published numerous articles on northeastern Native American history including three in French translation in the leading Quebec journal Recherches amérindiennes au Québec. With Christoph Strobel, she co-authored Daily Life of Native Americans from Post-Columbian through Nineteenth Century America (Greenwood, 2006). In 2003-2004 she held the first Fulbright-Université de Montréal Distinguished Chair, during which time she taught a course on the Deerfield Raid of 1704 to Canadian students and brought them to Deerfield for the Tercentenary of the Raid on February 29, 2004. She has worked with K-12 teachers since her arrival at UMass Amherst in 1999, including as co-director with Neal Salisbury of the 2013 NEH Summer Institute for K-12 Teachers, *Native Americans of New England: A Historical Overview*.

NASH, DOUGLAS R. (Nez Perce)
(attorney; adjunct professor of law; Indian center director)
Education: University of New Mexico School of Law, JD. *Affiliation & Address*: Director (2005-present), Center for Indian Law & Policy, Seattle University School of Law, 901 12th Ave., Sullivan Hall, P.O. Box 222000, Seattle, WA 98122 (206) 398-4284. E-mail: dnash@seattleu.edu. *Other professional post*: Judge, Tulalip Tribes' Court of Appeals and as Judicial Advisor to the Warm Springs Tribal Court of Appeals. *Past professional posts*: Staff attorney, Native American Rights Fund; 14 years in private, solo practice in Pendleton, OR, where he represented the Confederated Tribes of the Umatilla Indian Reservation; Chief Counsel, Nez Perce Tribe, 1989-99; head of the Indian Law Practice Group at Holland & Hart, LLP, 1999-2005. He served as Associate Professor of Law & James E. Rogers Fellow in American Indian Law at the University of Idaho, College of Law. He is the past Secretary & President and present Board Member of the National Native American Bar Association; past Board Member of the Northwest Indian Bar Association; and Secretary-Treasurer of the Indian Land Tenure Foundation Board until 2005.

NASH, GARY
(professor of history)
Education: Princeton University, B.A., 1955, PhD, 1964. *Address & Affiliation*: Dept. of History, 6265 Bunche, UCLA, Los Angeles, CA 90095 (310) 825-4702. E-mail: gnash@ucla.edu. *Other professional post*: Professor of American Indian Studies, UCLA; Director, National Center for History in the Schools. *Published works*: Red, White & Black: The Peoples of Early America, 1974; Forbidden Love: The Secret History of Mixed-Race America, 1999.

NASON, DORY (Anishinaabe-Leech Lake Band of Chippewa)
(professor of First Nations studies)
Education: University of California, Berkeley, PhD (Indigenous Feminism & Literature). *Affiliation & Address*: Assistant Professor (2008-present), First Nations Studies Program, Buchanan E-261, The University of British Columbia (UBC), 1866 Main Mall, Vancouver, BC V6T 1Z1 Canada (604) 827-5688. E-mail: dory.nason@ubc.ca. Dory holds a joint position with the UBC Department of English. Her areas of research include contemporary indigenous Feminisms and related Native women's intellectual history & literature. Professor Nason teaches on the subjects of Native Literature & Critcism; Indigenous Theory & Research Methods; and Wirting & Representation on Indgenous toics in advanced research. Awards, honors: Killam Teaching Prize in recognition of her contributions to teaching at UBC.

NASON, JAMES D. (Comanche) 1942-
(museum curator, social anthropologist)
Born July 19, 1942, Los Angeles, Calif. *Education*: University of California, Riverside, BA, 1964; University of Washington, MA, 1967, PhD, 1970. *Affiliation & Address*: Museum curator, social anthropologist, Thomas Burke Memorial Washington State Museum, Box 353010, University of Washington, Seattle, WA 98195 (206) 543-9680. E-mail: jnason@u.washington.edu. *Other professional posts*: Professor, Dept. of Anthropology, Curator of New World Ethnology, 1991-; director of Museology Program, Graduate School, 1993-; faculty associate, American Indian Studies Center, 1995-; faculty associate, Canadian Studies Program, Jackson School of International Studies, 1989-; University of Washington, Seattle, WA. *Other professional posts*: Member, Ethics & Standards Committee, American Assn for State & Local History, 1997-; co-founder & member, Executive Committee, American Indian Museum Association, 1997-. *Community activities*: People's Lodge design and EIS work, United Indians of All Tribes, Seattle, WA, 1994-; member, Circle of Advisors, National Museum of the American Indian Master Exhibition Plan, the Mall and New York, Phase 1, Smithsonian Institution, 1997-. *Memberships*: American Anthropological Assn, 1970 (Fellow); American Assn for the Advancement of Science, 1970- (Fellow); American Ethnological Society, 1970- (Fellow); Royal Anthropological Institute (Fellow); International Council of Museums; Assn for Social Anthropology in Oceana, 1971- (Fellow); American Assn of Museums (member); Canadian Museums Assn (member); Western Museums Assn; Washington State Museums Assn; British Columbia Museums Assn; Council for Museum Anthropology; International Council of Museums; Pacific Conservation Group. *Interests*: Museology; cultural heritage policy & law; intellectual property rights; socio-cultural change; curatorial conservation; museum architectural and operational design; Native North America; Micronesia. *Published works*: Edited with Mac Marshall, Micronesia, 1944-1974 (Human Relations Area Files Press, 1976); Museums and Indians. In, "Native American in the Twentieth Century: An Encyclopedia," ed. by Mary Davis (Garland, 1994); Beyond Repatriation: Issues of Cultural Policy and Practice for the 21st Century. In, "Borrowed Power: Essyas on Cultural Appropriation," Part 5, ed. by Bruce Ziff and P.V. Rao (Rutgers University Press, 1997); Native American Intellectual Property Rights: Issues in the Control of Esoteric Knowledge. In, "Borrowed Power: Essays on Cultural

Appropriation," Part 6, ed. by Bruce Ziff and P.V. Rao (Rutgers University Press, 1997); Our Indians: The Unidimensional Indian in the Disembodied Local Past. In, "Changing Presentations of the American Indian in Exhibits," ed. by George Horse Capture (Smithsonian Institution Press, 1999).

NATALIA, AILEEN (Navajo)
(dancer)
Address: 701 Airport Rd. #3, Santa Fe, NM 87505 (505) 473-4346. Aileen has over 20 years of dance experience. A former junior soloist with the Los Angeles Ballet, Aileen was granted a full scholarship to study with the Joffrey Ballet in New York City. She has won the Best of New Mexico dance choreographers showcase and has performed in several major productions.

NATAY, ED LEE (Navajo)
(singer)
Address: c/o Canyon Records Productions, 4143 North 16th St., Suite 6, Phoenix, AZ 85016 (602) 266-7835.

NATHANIEL, LARRY (Athapascan)
(Alaskan village chief)
Affiliation: Circle Native Community, P.O. Box 89, Circle, AK 99733 (907) 773-2822.

NATIVIDAD, RAY (Diegueno)
(former rancheria chairperson)
Affiliation: San Pasqual General Council, P.O. Box 365, Valley Center, CA 92082 (619) 749-3200.

NATSEWAY, THOMAS (Laguna Pueblo)
(craftsperson)
Address: P.O. Box 15, Acoma Pueblo, NM 87034 (505) 552-7225. *Products*: Traditional miniatures & replicas of old pottery circa late 1700s and earlier Mimbres.

NAUMAN, H. JANE 1929-
(filmmaker)
Born May 4, 1929, Grinnell, Iowa. *Education*: University of Iowa, BA, 1950; University of Heidelberg, Germany, advanced studies, 1955-56. *Address*: Box 232, Custer, SD 57730 (605) 673-4065. E-mail: hjane232@aol.com. *Affiliation*: President, Sun Dog Films, Custer, SD, 1989-present. *Other professional posts*: Free-lance photojournalist specializing in articles on Native American culture (published in Indian Trader, Native Peoples magazine, Dakota Heritage Magazine, Four Winds, and many others), 1955-present. *Past professional posts*: Executive vice-president, producer-editor, Nauman Films, Custer, SD, 1955-89; location manager for NBC's "Chi Chi Hoo Hoo Bogey Man," a film based on a story written by Sioux author Virginia Driving Hawk Sneve; location manager, Kevin Costner 1989 film "Dances With Wolves" about the Sioux in 1860; Indian historian & location manager for "Son of the Morning Star," an ABC-TV Special Feature (1990) regarding Native American involvement in the last ten years of General Custer's life; location manager for "Thunderheart," a Tri-Star Tribecca Production feature film filmed ion Pine Ridge Reservation & S.D. Badlands, involving Indians and the FBI; screenwriter of historic feature "Jesse Moran." including the first Native American graduate of Harvard in a major role; research, historian & set decorator coordinator for "Lakota Woman," a TV Feature Special for TBS, based on book by Mary Crow Dog, regarding the AIM uprising at Wounded Knee, 1972; humanities lectures on the seven Indian reservations in South Dakota on films dealing with Plains Indians, as well as at Harvard, Dartmouth, University of South Dakota, and many other universities, museums, etc.; 1998-2000, Regional Technician for the U.S. Census Bureau with primary emphasis to ensure an exact count of First Americans in the 92 tribal governments in the 2000 Census in the ten states of the Denver Regional Census Center. *Awards, honors*: Fulbright Scholarship Award; Cine "Golden Eagle" Award (twice); American Film Festival Blue Ribbon (three times); American Indian Film Festival; UCLA Film & Folklore (best film on folklore); Governor's Award in the Arts, 1989; Festival of American Folklife Ethnographic Film; (all of the above awards for films on Native Americans). *Interests*: Native American Indian Culture; travel; interested in any world travel involving filmmaking or other positive involvement with cultures; expedition into canyons of Sierra Madre Occidental of Mexico to film Tarahumara Indian culture and Easter festival; have planned and executed many film festivals dealing with Native American films. *Films produced*: Johnny Vik, 35mm full length feature film, 1971; produced & edited Sioux Legends (16mm documentary of Plains Indians culture, 1972 (Cine Golden Eagle Award; Martin Luther King, Jr. Award); wrote, directed, produced, edited and narrated, "Lakota Quillwork-Art & Legend" (honored at the 10th Annual American Indian Film Festival, San Francisco; best film on folklore in the UCLA Film & Folklore Festival; honored at the Smithsonian Institution's Festival of American Folklife Ethnographic Film; among other honors); assistant director, editor & producer of "Tahtonka," (a Cine "Golden Eagle" award winner; among 100 best educational films; best film of the week on BBC; Brussells International Film Festival, San Francisco International Festival, American Film

Festival award winners, among many others); produced and edited "They Are Coming to Norogachic" about the Tarahumara Indians of the Sierra Madre canyons in Mexico. *Published works*: Have written more than 300 stories about Native Americans & Native American culture, published in national and regional publications, such as Native Arts West, American West, The Homemaker Magazine, Dakota West, etc.; and written & produced educational slide films about Hopi, Navajo, Southwest Pueblos, and Plains Indians, Mandans, and Cliff Dwellers, and the Sioux sweat lodge and Sioux women.

NAVA, DOUGLAS A. (Taos-Apache) 1951-
(gold & silversmith; jewelry designer)
Born July 14, 1951, Montrose, Colo. *Education*: University of Colorado, 1969-71; Western State College (Gunnison, CO), BA, 1978. *Principal occupation*: Gold & silversmith; jewelry designer. *Address*: 61336 Hwy. 90, Montrose, CO 81401 (303) 249-8131. *Affiliation*: Owner, Nava Southwest, Ouray, CO, 1979- (retail-Native American arts). *Other professional posts*: Board member & chairperson, Atlatl, 1982-84; appointed to State Arts Agency Panel, National Endowment for the Arts, 1985-88. *Community activities*: Appointed to Governor's Colorado Council on the Arts & Humanities, 1979-83. *Memberships*: Indian Arts & Crafts Association; Friends of the Ute Indian Museum. *Awards, honors*: Appointed to Who's Who in American Colleges & Universities, 1978; 1985 - 2nd Place Ribbon, Lapidary, Gallup Indian Intertribal Ceremonials; 1986 - Ribbon for Jewelry at Pasadena (CA) American Indian & Western Relic Show; 1987 - 1st, 2nd & 3rd Place Ribbons for jewelry, O'odham Tash Indian Festival, Casa Grande, AZ; 1988 - 1st Place Ribbons for necklace and bracelet, Lapidary, Gallup Intertribal Ceremonials. *Interests*: "Jewelry design, painting (both oil and acrylic), sculpture-alabaster, marble, fiberglass resin. Also own and operate Nava Southwest, Ouray, Colo."

NAVARRO, IRENE A. (Eskimo)
(Alaskan village president)
Affiliation: Chinik Eskimo Community (aka Golovin), P.O. Box 62020, Golovin, AK 99762 (907) 779-2214.

NAYLOR, ISRAEL (Paiute)
(former tribal chairperson)
Affiliation & Address: Fort Independence Paiute Tribe, P.O. Box 67, Independence, CA 93526 (760) 878-2126.

NAYOKPUK, KARLA (Eskimo)
(Alaskan village president)
Affiliation: Native Village of Shishmaref, P.O. Box 72110, Shishmaref, AK 99772 (907) 649-3821.

NEEGANAGWEDGIN, ERICA (Taino)
(professor of Indigenous studies & academic coordiantor)
Education: Ontario Institute for Studies in Education, University of Toronto, MA, PhD (Sociology & Equity Studies in Education). *Affiliation & Address*: Assistant Professor of Indigenous Studies & Academic Coordinator, Centre for World Indigenous Knoowledge & Research, Athabasca University, 1 University Dr., Athabasca, AB T9S 3A3 (780) 675-6100. E-mail: erican@athabascau.ca.

NEELY, NORMA (Potawatomi)
(executive director)
Affiliation & Address: Executive Director, American Indian Institute, The University of Oklahoma, 1639 Cross Center Dr., Norman, OK 73019 (405) 325-4127. E-mail: nneely@ou.edu.

NEELY, SHARLOTTE K. (Lumbee) 1948-
(professor of anthropology; director/founder Native American studies)
Born August 13, 1948, Savannah, Ga. *Education*: Georgia State University, BA, 1970; University of North Carolina, MA, 1971, PhD, 1976. *Affiliation & Address*: Professor & coordinator of anthropology (1974-present), director/ founder, Native American Studies, Northern Kentucky University, Landrum 230, Dept. of Sociology/Anthropology/Philosophy, Highland Heights, KY 41099 (859) 572-5258. E-mail: neelys@nku.edu. *Research & Teaching Interests*: Cultural anthropology; North American Indians (especially Cherokees, Shawnee & Navajo); Native Hawaiians; Fourth World Peoples; ethno-history; the environment; social organization; kinship; gender roles; ethnicity. Most of her research has been on the Cherokee Indians of North Carolina, especially the previously unstudied Snowbird Community. Most recently, she has researched Black Cherokees, people of African & Cherokee descent, who were forced off Cherokee rolls despite having more than minimal Cherokee blood degree. *Memberships*: American Anthropological Association (Fellow); Southern Anthropological Association; Anthropologists & Sociologists of Kentucky (past president); American Society for Ethnohistory. *Awards, honors*: Predoctoral Research Fellowship, National Institutes of Mental Health, 1974; Alternate for Post-doctoral Fellowship, (D'Arcy McNickle) Center for the History of the American Indian, Newberry Library, Chicago, Ill., 1974; NKU Outstanding Professor Award, 1994; Strongest Influence Award, NKU Alumni Assn., 1996; Dr. Martin Luther King, Jr. Service Award, NKU Student

Government, 1998. Unpublished PhD dissertation, "Ethnicity in a Native American Community," & unpublished MA thesis, "The Role of Formal Education Among the Eastern Cherokee Indians, 1880-1971," University of North Carolina, Chapel Hill. *Published works*: Snowbird Cherokees (University of Georgia Press, 1991; VHS/DVD documentary film version in 1995); The Land Was Theirs: A Study of North American Indians, with Wendell H. Oswalt (Mayfield Publishing, 1996 & 1999 edition); Kasker: Anthropological Science Fiction (Airleaf Publishing, 2005); Black Cherokees: People of Persistence (Freedom Chronicle {online journal Fall 2006); numerous articles & papers.

NEGONSOTT, EMERY (Kickapoo)
  (former tribal chairperson)
Affiliation: Kickapoo of Kansas Tribal Council, P.O. Box 271, Horton, KS 66439 (913) 486-2131.

NELSON, CAPTAIN (*Chaawanta*) (Rappahannock)
  (tribal chief)
Affiliation: United Rappahannock Tribe, Indian Neck, VA 23077 (804) 769-3128.

NELSON, CASEY
  (community mayor)
Affiliation: Metlakatla Indian Community Council, P.O. Box 8, Metlakatla, AK 99926 (907) 886-4441.

NELSON, CHARLENE (Shoalwater Bay)
  (tribal chairperson)
Affiliation & Address: Chairperson, Shoalwater Bay Indian Tribe, P.O. Box 130, Tokeland, WA 98590 (360) 267-6766. E-mail: cnelson@shoalwaterbay-nsn.gov.

NELSON, CLAUDIA E.
  (technical assistance office director)
Education: University of Arizona, BS (Business Administration), 1993, MA (American Indian Studies, 2004. *Affiliation & Address*: Director, Native Peoples Technical Assistance Office, The University of Arizona, Rogers Rountree Hall, Suite 206, P.O. Box 210176, Tucson, AZ 85721 (520) 626-9181. E-mail: cen@email.arizona.edu. Ms. Nelson has worked in the field of American Indian economic & community development for over 20 years. *Past professional posts*: Legal assistant to the attorney for the White Mountain Apache Tribe's insurance defense litigation counsel office; program coordinator, U. of Arizona's American Indian Studies Program Office of Community Development

NELSON, CODY (Anishinabe)
  (attorney; executive Director)
Education: University of St. Thomas School of Law, JD, 2006. *Affiliation & Address*: Staff Attorney & Co-Executive Director (2006-present), Anishinabe Legal Services, P.O. Box 157, Cass Lake, MN 56633 (218) 335-2223. Cody is a licensed attorney in the State of Minnesota, as well as the tribal courts of White Earth, Leech Lake, and Red Lake.

NELSON, GLENDA (Maidu)
  (rancheria chairperson)
Affiliation & Address: Chairperson, Enterprise Rancheria Band of Maidu Indians, 2133 Monte Vista Ave., Oroville, CA 95966 (530) 532-9214. E-mail: glendan@enterpriserancheria.org

NELSON, HERMAN, SR. (Aleut)
  (Alaskan village president)
Affiliation: New Koliganek Village Council, P.O. Box 5057, Koliganek, AK 99576 (907) 593-3434.

NELSON, IRVING
  (library system manager)
Affiliation: Navajo Nation Library System, Window Rock Public Library, P.O. Box 9040, Window Rock, AZ 86515 (520) 871-6376.

NELSON, JOHN, JR. (Aleut)
  (Alaskan village president)
Affiliation: Kokhanok Village, P.O. Box 1007, Kokhanok, AK 99606 (907) 282-2202.

NELSON, MARY (Eskimo)
  (Alaskan tribal president)
Affiliation: Larsen Bay Tribal Council, P.O. Box 50, Larsen Bay, AK 99624 (907) 847-2207.

NELSON, MELISSA KAYE (Turtle Mountain Chippewa)
  (associate professor; cultural ecologist, writer,
  media-maker; indigenous scholar-activist)
Education: University of California, Santa Cruz, BA; University of California, Davis, PhD (Ecology & Native American studies), 2000. *Affiliation & Address*: Associate Professor, American Indian Studies, Ethnic Studies & Psychology Bldg., San Francisco State University, 1600 Holloway Ave., San Ortiz CA 94132 (415) 338-6422. E-mail: mknelson@sfsu.edu or mknelson@nativeland. org. *Other professional post*: President & Executive Director (1993-present), The Cultural Conservancy, P.O. Box 29044, Presidio of San Francisco, CA 94129 (415) 561-6594. Melissa's work is dedicated to indigenous revitalization, environ-mental restoration, intercultural understanding, and the renewal & celebration of community health & cultural arts. *Other professional posts*: Board member, Collective Heritage Institute/Bioneers, and the Center for Whole Communities; advisory board of the Alfonso Ortiz Center for Intercultural Studies. *Awards, honors*: In 2010-11, she served as the Anne Ray Resident Scholar at the School for Advanced Research, Santa Fe, NM; Visiting Scholar at the American Indian Studies Center, University of California, Los Angeles, 2006-07; In 2005, Melissa was the co-producer of the award-winning documentary film, "The Salt Song Trail: Bringing Creation Back Together. *Published work*: Edited anthology, "Original Instructions - Indigenous Teachings For A Sustainable Future" (Bear & Co., 2008), features three of her essays & focuses on the persistence of traditional ecological knowledge by contemporary Native communities; anthology, "The Hydromythology of the Anishinaabeg: Will the Infamous Water Spirit Mishipizhu Survive Climate Change?" in Centering Anishinaabeg Studies: Understanding the World Through Stories," edited by Heidi Kiiwetinepinesiik Stark & Niigonwedon James Sinclair (Michigan State U. Press, 2012); and "Indigenous Science – The Resilience of Place-Making" for World of Indigenous North America, edited by Robert Warrior (Routledge, 2012); numerous articles & essays.

NELSON, ROBERT M.
  (association director; editor)
Affiliation: Association for the Study of American Indian Literatures, Box 112, University of Richmond, Richmond, VA 23173 (804) 289-8311; editor, "Studies in American Indian Literatures."

NELSON, SCOTT H. 1940-
  (psychiatrist)
Born July 31, 1940, Cleveland, Ohio. *Education*: Yale University, BA, 1962; Harvard University, MD, 1966; Harvard School of Public Health, M.P.H., 1970. *Principal occupation*: Psychiatrist. *Address*: 1881 Conejo Dr., Santa Fe, NM 87505 (55300 Homestead Rd. NE, Albuquerque, NM 87110 *Other professional post*: Psychiatric consultant, Santa Fe Indian Hospital. *Military service*: USPHS (Captain, 1970-). *Past professional post*: Chief, Mental Health Programs, Indian Health Service, Albuquerque, NM, 1987-2005. *Membership*: American Psychiatric Association (Fellow, 1970-); National Association of State Mental Health Program Directors, (president & chairperson of the board, 1981-83); American Art Pottery Association (president, 1983-85). *Interests*: "Extensive travel to Indian tribes as part of work responsibility; interested in tribal arts." *Published works*: More than 30 publications in various mental health & government journals & documents.

NELSON, WILLIAM (Comanche)
  (tribal administrator)
Affiliation & Address: Chairperson, Comanche Nation, P.O. Box 908, Lawton, OK 73502 (580) 492-3251. E-mail: williamn@comanchenation.com

NELSON-BARBER, SHARON
  (Native American studies lecturer)
Education: Mount Holyoke College, BA; Harvard University, PhD (Human Development), 1985; Stanford University, postdoctoral (Spencer Fellow). *Affiliation & Address*: Lecturer, Stanford University, 450 Serra Mall, Bldg. 360, Stanford, CA 94305 (650) 725-6944. E-mail: snelson@wested.org; Director, Center for the Study of Cultural & Language in Education. Presently, she is researching culturally responsive math & science education for indigenous students. *Awards, honors*: Received the Paul D. Hood Award for distinguished contribution to the field from WestEd in 2006.

CHIEF NEMATTANEW "ROY CRAZY HORSE" (Powhatan Renape)
  (tribal chief)
Affiliation: Powhatan Renape Nation, P.O. Box 225, Roincocas, NJ 08073 (609) 261-4747.

NEMECEK, DIANE (Choctaw/Cherokee)
  (educator)
Address: P.O. Box 430, Allen, OK 74825 (405) 857-2419.

NENEMA, GLEN (Kalispel)
(tribal chairperson)
Affiliation & Address: Chairperson, Kalispel Tribe, P.O. Box 39, Usk, WA 99180 (509) 445-1147 (509) 445-1147.

NEPTUNE, STAN (Penobscot) 1949-
(master woodcarver, artist)
Born April 1, 1949, Indian Island, ME. *Education*: Old Town High School. Principal occupation: Master woodcarver, artist. *Address*: P.O. Box 128, Old Town, ME 04468 (207) 827-2847. *Affiliation*: Traditional Native American woodcarver, 1972-present. *Other professional post*: Indian arts & crafts director, Indian Island, ME. *Military service*: U.S. Army, 1969-71 (SP-5; Honorable Discharge). *Awards, honors*: Connecticut River Powwow & Rendezvous, 1990 & 1991, and 1st Annual Indian Market, Dayton, OH, 1990; He and his son, Petakisis ("Little Thunder') are the 1997 recipients of the Maine Arts Commission Apprenticeship Training Award as well as numerous awards of excellence for Stan's 25 years of carving. Annual Demonstrations/Presentations: Indian Summer Festival, Milwaukee, WI (Sept.); Boston Children's Museum (April); Tufts University, Medford, MA (April); Common Ground Fair, Unity, ME (Sept.); various Indian powwows - east & midwest U.S. *Interests*: Traditional Penobscot woodcarver, Stan specializes in hand carved ceremonial war clubs and walking sticks from birch, poplar & cedar, while some may be inlaid with various stones. This traditional art form is being done only by the Wabanaki people of the northeast woodlands. He also carves totem poles from poplar and cedar. Most of his carvings are in private collections, but some go to galleries, gift shops, and museums all over the country, such as the Abbe Museum, Bar Harbor, ME; Mashantucket PequotMuseum, Ledyard, CT; Penobscot nation Museum, Indian Island, ME; Boston Children's Museum; and American Indian Archaeological Institution. Stan is available for carving demonstrations. He is a private pilot, currently working on a commercial/instrument rating. *Awards, honors*: Received Letter of Recognition from the Maine State House of Representatives and the members of the Senate for his work as a master artist in the preservation of the Penobscot Indian practice of carving traditional birch root clubs (Augusta, ME, April 7, 1997); among others. *Artist/Work in Publications*: We're Still Here, Joan A. Lester (Children's Museum, Boston, 1987); Turtle Quarterly, Native American Center for the Living Arts, Spring, 1988; Artists of the Dawn, Lee Ann Konrad with Christine Nicholas (Northeast Folklore Society, 1987); ATLATL Directory of Native American Performing Artists (ATLATL, Phoenix, AZ, 1990); Eagle Wing Press, Winter 1984; March-April 1991; Colonial Homes, Hearst Corp. (Vol. 15, No. 5, Oct. 1989); American Indian Healing Arts, by E. Barrie Kavasch & Karen Baat, 1999; Stanley Neptune - Penobscot Artist/Carver, by Henry Bird, "The Northeast," Vol. 126, No. 9 (Advent, 1998); Spirits in the Wood, by Joyce Butler (Maine Historical Society, Portland, ME), 1997; Artifacts, American Indian Archaeological Institute (various issues); Wabanaki Guide to Maine (Maine Indian Basketmakers Alliance, 2001); among others.

NERBURN, KENT
(author)
Resides in Bemidji, Minn. *Address*: c/o New World Library, 14 Pamaron Way, Novato, CA 94949 (415) 472-2100. *Professional posts*: Directed "Project Preserve", an award-winning education program in oral history on the Red Lake Ojibwe Reservation. *Published works*: Neither Wolf Nor Dog: On Forgotten Roads With An Indian Elder, 1994; Native American Wisdom, book and audiocassette; The Wisdom of the Chief (published by New World Library).

NESBITT, HEIDI
(law institute director)
Education: Westminster College (Salt Lake City), BA; University of New Mexico, MBA. *Affiliation & Address*: Director, Pre-Law Summer Institute & Assistant Director, American Indian Law Center, Inc., P.O. Box 4456, Albuquerque, NM 87196 (505) 277-5462. E-mail: nesbitt@ailc-inc.org. *Other professional post*: Heidi works with other projects at the AILC overseeing the administrative & statistical portions of the projects. She joined the staff of the AILC in 1984, when she directed the Special Scholarship Program in Law for American Indians.

NESPER, LARRY
(professor of cultural anthropology & American Indian studies)
Education: University of Chicago, PhD, 1994. *Affiliation & Address*: Associate Professor of Cultural Anthropology & American Indian Studies (2002-present), Dept. of Anthropology, 5317 W.H. Sewell Social Science Bldg., 1180 Observatory Dr., University of Wisconsin-Madison, WI 53706 (608) 265-1992. E-mail: inesper@wisc.edu. *Research Interests*: "My research is in the area of Great Lakes Indian law & politics, largely in the federal Indian policy era of self-determination (post-1960's), but I also have ethno-historical interests in the region. I am generally interested in institutional development and am currently working on a research project on the development of the tribal courts in Wisconsin." *Published work*: The Walleye War: The Struggle for Ojibwe Spearfishing & Treaty Rights University of Nebraska Press, 2002); chapter:

"The Politics of Intercultural Resource Management," with James Schlender, in Native Americans & the Environment: Perspectives on Ecological Indian, ed., Michael Harkin & David Rich Lewis (University of Nebraska Press, 2007); Tribal Words, with Brian Hosmer (SUNY Press, 2013); numerous articles.

NESSE, ANNETTE (Jamestown S'Klallam)
(tribal chief of operations)
Affiliation & Address: Chief Operations Officer, Jamestown S'Klallam Tribe, 1033 Old Blyn Highway, Sequim, WA 98382 (360) 683-1109. E-mail: anesse@jamestowntribe.org

NETZ, TOM (*Soft Shell Turtle-Ah-koot-yah*) (Lumbee) 1960-
(pebbles oxide operator)
Born August 15, 1960, Elmore, Ohio. *Education*: High school. *Principal occupation*: Metal casting operator. *Address*: 201 Harrison St., Walbridge, OH 43465 (419) 666-3257. *Affiliations*: Museum consultant, president, Woodland Indian Alliance, 1989-96; pebbles oxide operator, Brush Wellman Engineering Materials, Elmore, OH, 1986-. *Other professional posts*: Traditional storyteller & lead singer, powwow drum, Blue Heron Singers. *Memberships*: NRA, Sandusky Co. Sportsmans Club, National Gourd Society. *Interests*: "I teach educational programs on Native American culture from pre-contact to removal period; instructor on many types of traditional work shops, flintknapping, basketry, rattles, drums, traditional clothing, beading, Native herbs. (I) enjoy Native flute, old songs, dancing and being with all my Native brothers & sisters from the Four Winds."

NEVILLES-SORELL, JEREMY (White Earth Ojibwe)
(organization co-director)
Affiliation & Address: Co-Director (1998-present), Mending the Sacred Hoop, 202 W. 2nd St., Duluth, MN 55802 (218) 623-HOOP. Jeremy provides training & technical assistance and conducts groups with teenage boys & girls on abusive relationships, and facilitates groups for Native men who have battered. He speaks locally and nationally on his firsthand knowledge of the dynamics children experience in violent homes, community organizing & education, and working with men who batter.

NEW HOLY, ANDREA
(college professor)
Affiliation: Native American Studies Dept., Montana State University, 2-179 Wilson Hall, P.O. Box 172340, Bozeman, MT 59717 (406) 994-3881. *Interests*: Federal Indian policy & law; Native Americans and the cinema.

NEWAGO, GEORGE P. (Red Cliff Lake Superior Ojibwe)
(former tribal chairperson)
Affiliation: Red Cliff Tribal Council, P.O. Box 529, Bayfield, WI 54814 (715) 779-3700.

NEWCOMB, STEVEN T. (Shawnee/Lenape)
(research coordinator)
Affiliations & Address: Co-founder & co-director, Indigenous Law Institute, P.O. Box 188, Alpine, CA 91903 (619) 618-9346. E-mal: stv4newcomb@yahoo.com. *Other professional posts*: Columnist, Indian Country Today, 2002-present; International Research Coordinator, American Indian Law Alliance (AILA), New York, NY. Newcomb has been a national & international speaker on American Indian issues since the early 1990's. He was the principal author of the "Preliminary Study of the Impact on Indigenous Peoples of the International Legal Construct Known as the Doctrine of Discover," submitted by Ms. Tonya Gonnella Frichtner to the 9th Session of the UN Permanent Forumm on Indigenous Issues in her capacity as the North American Regional Representative to the UN Permanent Frum. *Past professional post*: Indigenous Law Research Coordinator, Kumeyaay Community College, Sycuan Band of Kumeyaay Nation, El Cajon, CA. *Published works*: Pagans in the Promised Land: A Matter of Religious Freedom (self-published in 1992); Pagans in the Promised Land: Decoding the Doctrine of Christian Discovery (Fulcrum, 2008); Law Review articles published at NYU Law School & UCLA Law School.

NEWCOMBE, ROBERT
(health director)
Affiliation: Pine Hill PHS Indian Health Center, P.O. Box 310, Pine Hill, NM 87357 (505) 775-3271.

NEWELL, WAYNE (Passamaquoddy)
(educator)
Address: P.O. Box 271, Princeton, ME 04668.

NEWHOUSE, DAVID (Onondaga)
(professor of Indigenous studies)
Education: University of Western Ontario, BS & MBA. *Affiliation & Address*: Associate Professor & Chairperson, Department of Indigenous Studies & Business Administration Program, Enweying Rm. 301, Trent University, 1600

Westbank Dr., Peterborough, ON K9J 7B8 (705) 748-1011 ext. 7497. E-mail: dnewhouse@trentu.ca. *Other professional post*: Principle, First Peoples House of Learning, Gzowski College, Trent University.

NEWLIN, GORDON (Eskimo)
(village president)
Affiliation: Noorvik Community, Box 71, Noorvik, AK 99763 (907) 636-2144.

NEWMAN, CLAIRE
(attorney)
Education: Carleton College, BA (Political Science), 2005; University of Washington School of Law, JD, 2012. *Affiliation & Address*: Associate, Kilpatrick Townsend & Stockton, LLP, 1420 Fifth Ave., Suite 3700, Seattle, WA 98101 (206) 516-3097. *Services*: Claire focuses her practice on Native American Litigaton & Affairs. *Past professional posts*: Prior to joining the firm, Ms. Newman served as a law clerk to the Honorable Louis J. Menendez at the Juneau Superior Court and as a judicial extern to the Honorable John Coughenour at the United States District Court for the Western District of Washington. While in law school, Ms. Newman was the Managing Editor of the *Washington Journal of Environmental Law & Policy*. She was also the University of Washington Fellow for Senator Maria Cantwell and a law clerk at the Native American Rights Fund in Boulder, Colorado. Prior to attending law school, Ms. Newman worked at a non-profit law office assisting families and tribes in South Dakota to assert their rights under the Indian Child Welfare Act and to build capacity within tribal child welfare systems. Additionally after her undergraduate studies, Ms. Newman taught middle school on the Pine Ridge Indian Reservation in South Dakota.

NEWSOM, BONNIE (Penobscot)
(tribal historic preservation officer)
Education: University of Maine, B.A. (Anthropology), M.S. (Quaternary Studies); PhD candidate in Anthropology at the University of Massachusetts at Amherst. *Affiliation & Address*: Tribal Historic Preservation Officer, Penobscot Nation, 6 River Rd., Indian Island, ME 04468 (207) 817-7332. E-mail: bnewsom@penobscotnation.org. Bonnie ensures tribal compliance with the National Historic Preservation Act. Identifies & manages historic properties on tribal lands, consults with Federal & state agencies relative to historic site protection, participates in public education initiatives and serves as the tribal point of contact for all archaeological issues. *Past professional post*: Assistant Director, Wabanaki Center of the University of Maine. Board member: United South & Eastern Tribes Culture & Heritage Committee; Forest Society of Maine. *Military service*: U.S. Army; U.S. Army National Guard (instructor).

NEWTON, JIMMY R., JR. (Southern Ute)
(former tribal chairperson)
Affiliation & Address: Southern Ute Tribe, P.O. Box 737, Ignacio, CO 81137 (970) 563-0100.

NEWTON, WAYNE (Powatan)
(singer, entertainer)
Address: 6629 S. Pecos, Las Vegas, NV 89120.

NEZ, JONATHAN (Navajo-Dine')
(tribal vice president)
Affiliation & Address: 100 Parkway, P.O. Box 7440, Window Rock, AZ 86515 (928) 871-7000.   E-mail: jonathannez@navajo-nsn.gov

NEZ, PHOEBE (White Mountain Apache)
(radio station manager)
Affiliation: KNNB - 88.1 FM, White Mountain Apache Tribe, P.O. Box 310, Whiteriver, AZ 85941 (602) 338-5229.

NICELY, MARILYN K.
(law librarian)
Affiliation & Address: American Indian Law Subject Specialist, University of Oklahoma Law Library, 300 W. Timberdell Rd., Norman, OK 73072 (405) 325-4699. E-mail: mnicely@ou.edu. *Published works*: Annotated Bibliography of Federal & Tribal Law: Print & Internet Sources (U. of Oklahoma Press, 2010.

NICHOLAS, ELSIE (Eskimo)
(Alaskan village president)
Affiliation: Native Village of Kasigluk, P.O. Box 19, Kasigluk, AK 99609 (907) 477-6405

NICHOLAS, GRAYDON
(association president)
Affiliation: Union of New Brunswick Indians, 35 Dedam St., Fredericton, New Brunswick, Canada E3A 2V2 (506) 458-9444.

NICHOLAS, LESLIE (Passamaquoddy)
(tribal vice chief)
Affiliation & Address: Vice Chief, Passamaquoddy Tribe of Indians, P.O. Box 301, Princeton, ME 04668 (207) 796-2301.

NICHOLAS, SHEILAH (Hopi)
(assistant professor; Indian program coordinator)
Education: University of Arizona, PhD, 2008. Dissertation: "Becoming 'Fully' Hopi: The Role of the Hopi Language in the Contemporary Lives of Hopi Youth - A Hopi Case Study of Language Shift & Vitality." *Affiliations & Address*: Assistant professor, College of Education, Dept. of Teaching, Learning & Sociocultural Studies (TLSS), Language, Reading & Culture (LRC) Program, The U. of Arizona; Affiliate Faculty, American Indian Studies Program & Second Language Acquisition Teaching (SLAT), The U. of Arizona, Education 521, Tucson, AZ 85721 (520) 621-1311. E-mail: sheilahn@email. arizona.edu. Her work focuses on Indigenous/Hopi language maintenance & revitalization. *Published work*: Article - "I Live Hopi, I Just Don't Speak It; The Critical Intersection of Language, Culture, & Identity in the Lives of Contemporary Hopi Youth," Journal of Language Identity & Education, 2009.

NICHOLAS, VERONICA (Athapascan)
(Alaskan village president)
Affiliation: President, Native Village of Cantwell, P.O. Box 94, Cantwell, AK 99729 (907) 768-2591. E-mail:hallvc@mtaonlin.net

NICHOLAS, WILLIAM J. (Passamaquoddy)
(tribal chief)
Affiliation & Address: Chief, Passamaquoddy Tribe of Indians, P.O. Box 301, Princeton, ME 04668 (207) 796-2301.

NICHOLS, BRIAN K.
(attorney)
Education: Earlham College, BA, 1993; Georgia State University College of Law, JD, 2003. *Affiliation & Address*: Co-Chair Native American Law Practice Group, Modrall Sperling Lawyers, P.O. Box 2168, Albuqueque, NM 87103 (505) 848-1852. E-mail: brian.nichols@modrall.com. Brian's practice is primarily in litigation, with focuses on energy, natural resources & Indian Law. His experience includes labor law, federal compliance including Mine Safety & Health Administration (MSHA), contracts, employment law, personal injury, premises liability and royalty claims. He has advised clients including BHP Navajo Coal Company, San Juan Coal Company, Sempra Energy, BNSF Railway Company, Peabody Energy, Central Consolidated School District, Chevron USA, El Paso Natural Gas, Nacogdoches Oil & Gas, Siemens IT and Four Corners Giant (Western). As a member of the Navajo Nation Bar, Brian consults with businesses doing or considering commerce on the Navajo Nation. He advises clients regarding employment (the Navajo Preference in Employment Act), property (the Navajo Nation Civil Trespass Act), vendor preferences and procurement (the Navajo Business Opportunity Act), and worker health & safety (the Navajo Occupational Safety & Health Act). *Awards, honors*: Brian has achieved an AV® rating from *Martindale-Hubbell* based on peer review. He is recognized by *Best Lawyers in America*® in Native American Law & named Southwest Rising Star by *Southwest Super Lawyers*®.

NICHOLS, JOHN D.
(professor of American Indian studies)
Education: Hamilton College, BA (History); Harvard University, MA (Linguistics), PhD (Linguistics. *Address & Affiliation*: Professor, American Indian Studies Dept., College of Liberal Arts, 24 Scott Hall, 72 Pleasant St. SE, University of Minnesota, Twin Cities Campus, Minneapolis, MN 55455 (612) 625-2065. E-mail: jdn@umn.edu. *Interests*: American Indian language planning, oral literature & folklore, ethno-history & traditional arts, anthropological linguistics, indigenous languages of North America, et al. *Other professional post*: Editor, Algonquian & Iroquoiann Linguistics (newsletter).

NICHOLS, MARY (New River Metis)
(tribal vice chief)
Affiliation: New River Tribe of Metis, P.O. Box 1126, Laurel Springs, NC 28644 (910) 657-8891.

NICHOLS, ROGER L. 1933-
(professor of history)
Born June 13, 1933, Racine Wisc. *Education*: Wisconsin State College, BS, 1956; University of Wisconsin, Madison, MS, 1959, PhD, 1964. *Affiliation & Address*: Professor of history (1969-present), Dept. of History, 119 Social Sciences, The University of Arizona, Tucson, AZ 85721 (520) 621-4684. E-mail: nichols@email.arizona.edu. *Past professional post*: Professor, History Department, Wisconsin State University, Oshkosh, 1963-65; Professor, History Department, University of Georgia, Athens, 1965-69. *Community activities*: Board of Directors, Arizona Humanities Council. *Memberships*: American

Society for Ethno-history; Immigration & Ethnic History Society; American Historical Association; Organization of American Historians; Western History Association; Society for Historians of the Early Republic. *Awards, honors*: Huntington Library Fellowship; director, National Endowment for the Humanities, Summer Seminar for College Teachers, 1981, 1988, 1993; Fulbright Senior Lecturer, Martin Luther University, Germany, 1996-97; Senior Fulbright Scholar, University of Cologne, Germany, 2003-04. *Interests*: "History of the American frontier and West; American Indian relations; comparative history -- U.S.A. & Canada. *Biographical sources*: Contemporary Authors; Directory of American Scholars -- History. *Published works*: General Henry Atkinson (U. of Oklahoma Press, 1965); editor, The Missouri Expedition (U. of Oklahoma Press, 1969); Stephen Long & American Frontier Exploration (U. of Delaware, 1980); editor, American Frontier & Western Issues (Greenwood Press, 1986); editor, The American Indian: Past & Present (Alfred Knopf, 5 editions); co-author, Natives & Strangers: A History of Ethnic Americans (Oxford U. Press, 5 editions); Black Hawk's Autobiography and the Warrior's Path (Harlan Davidson, 1992); Indians in the U.S. & Canada: A Comparative History (U. of Nebraska, 1998); editor, The American Indian: Past & Present (U. of Oklahoma Press 6th Ed., 2010; 5th Ed. University of Arizona Press, 2008); Black Hawk's Autobiography (Iowa State U. Press, 1999); American Indians in U.S. History (U. of Oklahoma Press, 2003).

NICHOLS, BANTU (Eskimo)
(Alaskan Eskimo community president)
Affiliation: Nome Eskimo Community, P.O. Box 1090, Nome, AK 99762 (907) 443-2246.

NICK, OSCAR
(AK village president)
Affiliation: Village of Atmautluak, P.O. Box ATT, Atmautluak, AK 99559 (907) 553-5610.

NICKLIE, DAVID (Athapascan)
(AK village president)
Affiliation: Native Village of Cantwell, P.O. Box 94, Cantwell, AK 99729 (907) 768-2151.

NICOLAI, STEVEN D. (Eskimo)
(AK village chief)
Affiliation: Telida Native Village, P.O. Box 32, McGrath, AK 99627 (907) 843-8115.

NIELSEN, ROCHELLE (Shoshone/Bannock)
(adjunct instructor in Indigenous Nations Studies)
Affiliation & Address: Adjunct Instructor of Indigenous Nations Studies, P.O. Box 751, Potland State University, Portland, OR 97207 (503) 725-9689.

NIELSON, DONALD F. (Eskimo)
(Alaskan village president)
Affiliation: Native Village of South Naknek, P.O. Box 70029, South Naknek, AK 99670 (907) 246-8614.

NIETFELD, PATRICK
(NMAI collections manager)
Affiliation: National Museum of the American Indian (NMAI), Smithsonian Institution, Cultural Resources Section, 4220 Silver Hill Rd., Suitland, MD 20746 (301) 238-1454.

NIGHT PIPE, ORVILLE
(hospital director)
Affiliation: Eagle Butte PHS Indian Hospital, P.O. Box 1012, Eagle Butte, SD 57625 (605) 964-7030.

NIGHT SHIELD, EUSTACE
(home living specialist)
Affiliation: Rosebud Dormitories, P.O. Box 669, Mission, SD 57555 (605) 856-4486.

NISSEN, BRIAN (Colville)
(tribal council member, committee chair)
Affiliation: Member, Business Council, Confederated Tribes of the Colville Reservation, P.O. Box 150, Nespelem, WA 99155 (509) 634-2208. E-mail: brian.nissen@colvilletribes.com. *Other tribal post*: Chair, Employment & Education Committee.

NNEAKOK, WILLARD P. (Eskimo)
(Alaskan village president)
Affiliation & Address: President, Native Village of Point Lay, P.O. Box 59031, Point Lay, AK 99759 (907) 833-2575.

NOLAN, DAVID
(Indian program director)
Affiliation: Escambia County Middle School, Indian Education Program, P.O. Drawer 1236, Atmore, AL 36504 (205) 368-9105.

NOLAN-RENDE, HELEN (*Kanaiehson*) (Kahnawake Mohawk)
(administrator & lecturer)
Born on Kahnawake Mohawk Reserve, Canada. *Education*: Rutgers University, Newark, MA in Public Administration; Kennedy-Western University (WY), PhD in Public Administration. Certificates in Gerontology and Volunteer Management, pursuing certificates in Human Service Management & Train the Trainer from Rutgers School of Social Work. Continuing Education in Piscataway, NJ. *Principal occupation*: Director of social services. *Address*: 21 Village Rd., Morganville, NJ 07751. *Affiliations*: Assistant Director of Social Services & Director, Office on Aging, Township of Old Bridge, Old Bridge, NJ, 1982-; Commissioner, New Jersey State Commission on American Indian Affairs, 1996-present. *Community activities*: Old Bridge Community School Advisory Board (past member); Old Bridge Management Association; Old Bridge Emergency Food Bank Coordinator; Old Bridge Employee Trip Reduction Coordinator; Inter-Tribal American Indians of New Jersey (council member, past president); Middlesex County Older Adult Service Providers; Notary Public of New Jersey; New Jersey Affirmative Action Referral Contact. *Memberships*: New Jersey Assn of Senior Citizen Center Directors; American Society on Aging; National American Indian Council on Aging; National Council on Aging; National Institute of Senior Centers; American Assn of Public Administrators; National Honor Society, Pi Alpha Alpha. *Awards, honors*: Honorary member - National React/Pacers (police activated citizens Emergency Response Service) NJ Council; New Jersey Division on Civil Rights, 1986 Award for Outstanding Contribution; "Sentinel Newspaper, East Brunswick, NJ, 1987 Outstanding People Award; Society of St. Anthony of Padua, 1990 Padua Award; New Jersey General Assembly Citation 1990, Outstanding Commitment to Community; appointed (by Governor Whitman) commissioner of newly created New Jersey State Commission on American Indian Affairs, 1996; Indo-American Senior Citizens of New Jersey, 2000 Certificate of Commendation; United Way of Central New Jersey, 2000 Hometown Hero Nominee.. *Interests*: "Advocate for problems and concerns of aging population, accomplished lecturer & published writer on American Indian issues & concerns. Appeared on New Jersey network & radio stations on interviews regarding these issues."

NOLEY, GRAYSON B. (Choctaw) 1943-
(professor of educational leadership)
Born September 4, 1943, Talihina, Okla. *Education*: Southeastern Oklahoma State University, BA, 1969; Penn State University, University Park, MEd, 1975, PhD, 1979. *Affiliation & Address*: Academic Chair & Associate Professor of Educational Leadership & Policy Studies (2008-present), University of Oklahoma, Oklahoma City, OK 73104. E-mail: gnoley@ou.edu. *Other professional posts*: Project Director, American Leadership in School Administration; headed the Oklahoma Native Education Network; president, Midwest History of Education Society; board president, American Indian Graduate Center, Albuquerque, NM; president, Midwest History of Education Society; chair, Governing Board for National Native American Families Together. *Past professional posts*: Director, American Indian Leadership Program, Penn State University, Education Policy Studies, University Park, PA, 1979-88; administrator, Sequoyah High School, Tahlequah, OK, 1988-99; assistant professor of education; assistant director, American Indian Special Education Teacher Training Program; director, American Indian Education Policy Center, Penn State University, 2000-08. *Military service*: U.S. Army, 1961-64. *Community activities*: Partnership Coordinating Committee; Committee for Understanding Others (local school district). *Memberships*: American Educational Research Assn; Comparative & International Education Society; National Indian Education Assn. *Awards, honors*: Kellogg Foundation, National Fellowship Program, 1984-87; American Indian Leadership Program Fellowship, Penn State U., 1974-79. *Interests*: Federal policies on Native American education; drug & alcohol abuse in adolescent Native Americans; travel. *Published work*: Two chapters in The Choctaw Before Removal (Mississippi University Press, 1985); articles in American Indian journals.

NOLLNER, PADDY (Athapascan)
(village chief)
Affiliation: Galena Village, P.O. Box 182, Galena, AK 99741 (907) 656-1366.

NOMEE, ALFRED
(tribal school chairperson)
Affiliation: Coeur d'Alene Tribal School, P.O. Box A, DeSmet, ID 83824 (208) 274-6921.

NOMEE, CLARA (Crow)
(tribal chairperson)
Affiliation: Crow Tribal Council, P.O. Box 159, Crow Agency, MT 59022 (406) 638-2601.

NOMEE, MILTON (Kalispel)
(chief judge)
Affiliation & Address: Chief Judge, Kalispel Tribal Court, P.O. Box 96, Usk, WA 99180 (509) 445-1664.

NOMEE-HURLEY, MARIANNE A. (Coeur d' Alene)
(storyteller)
Address: P.O. Box 87, Tensed, ID 83870 (208) 274-5050. Marianne is a storyteller & performer of traditional songs of the Coeur d' Alene people of Northern Utah. She is an educator specializing in Native American arts & crafts, and focuses on Native American cultural values.

NOODIN, MARGARET (Anishinaabe)
(professor of English & Indigenous literature & culture)
Education: University of Minnesota, MFA, PhD. *Affiliation & Address*: Assistant Professor, Department of English, University of Wisconsin-Milwaukee, Curtin Hall 576, P.O. Box 413, Milwaukee, WI 53201 (414) 229-4511. E-mail: noodin@uwm.edu. *Other professional posts*: Faculty, American Indian Studies Program, University of Wisconsin-Milwaukee; member, Editorial Board, Studies in American Indian Literatures Journal; president, Studies in American Indian Literatures Association. *Teaching and Research Interests*: Indigenous & American Indian Literature and Culture; Indigenous Socio-Linguistics & Language Revitalization; Anishinaabe (Ojibwe) Language & poetry. *Published works*: Editor, Ogimaakwe Mitigwaki (Queen of the Woods): A Novel by Simon Pokagon (Michigan State University Press, 2011); Bawaajimo: A Dialect of Dreams in Anishinaabe Language & Literature (Michigan State University Press, 2014).

NOORI, MARGARET (Ojibwe)
(Ojibwe language & literature; Native American studies)
Education: University of Minnesota, BA (English), BS (Education), 1987; MA (Creative Writing), 1990: PhD (English), 2001. *Fields of Study*: Anishinaabe literature, poetry & drama; Native American linguistics & literature; teaching Ojibwe as a second language. *Affiliation & Address*: Director, Comprehensive Studies Program; Faculty, Program in American Culture (Ojibwe Language & Literature) & Native American Studies Program, University of Michigan, 3732 Haven Hall, 505 S. State St., Ann Arbor, MI 48109 (734) 615-8904. E-mail: mnoori@umich.edu.

NORDER, JOHN)Turtle Mountain Band of Chippewa)
(director of Native American Institute)
Education: University of Wisconsin, BS (Anthropology); University of Michigan, PhD. *Affiliation & Address*: Director, Native American Institute, Justin S. Morrill Hall of Agriculture, Michigan State University, 446 W. Circle Dr., Rm. 406, East Lansing, MI 48824 (517) 353-6632. E-mail: norder@nai.msu.edu. He has research & teaching interests on topics relevant to Native American & First Nations archaeology/ethnohistory/anthropology, particularly in the Great Lakes region of North America. Current and ongoing work has focused on the ways in which traditional Indigenous knowledge is used as a tool of mediation between issues of identity, cultural & natural resource heritages, & economic development in the context of local & state level political negotiations. In addition, he continues to examine the ways in which hunter-gatherer landscapes during the Woodland period of northwestern Ontario were created & maintained through the use of material markers such as rock-art sites, natural landmarks, habitation sites, etc. for purposes of structuring information exchange, regional population mobility, subsistence activities, and social organization.

NORDSTRAND, POLLYANNA
(education & repatriation coordinator)
Affiliations: American Indian Ritual Object Repatriation Foundation, 463 East 57 St., New York, NY 10128 (212) 980-9441.

NORDSTRUM, FRANK
(school principal)
Affiliation: Santa Clara Day School, P.O. Box 2183, Espanola, NM 87532 (505) 753-4406.

NORDWALL, WAYNE
(BIA regional director)
Affiliation: Western Regional Office, Bureau of Indian Affairs, P.O. Box 10, Phoenix, AZ 85001 (602) 379-6600.

NORGREN, JILL
(professor emerita, author)
Affiliations: Professor Emerita of Government & Legal Studies, John Jay College of Criminal Justice and the Graduate Center, The City University of New York. *Published works*: Coauthor of "Partial Justice: Federal Indian Law in a Liberal-Constitutional System," and "American Cultural Pluralism and Law"; The Cherokee Cases: Two Landmark Federal Decisions in the Fight for Sovereignty (U. of Oklahoma Press, 2004); biography of Belva Lockwood.

NORMAN, DARRELL (Blackfeet)
(artisan, shop owner)
Address: Manager/Owner, Lodgepole Gallery & Tipi Village, P.O. Box 1832, Browning, MT 59417 (406) 338-2787. E-mail: tipicamp@3rivers.net. .

NORMAN, DENNIS (Southern Cheyenne)
(chief of psychology; faculty chair)
Education: Tufts University, M.A. (Child Development); Harvard University, Ed.D. (Human Development, Counseling, & Consulting Psychology). *Address & Affiliation*: Chief of Psychology (1989-present), Massachusetts General Hospital, 55 Fruit St., Boston, MA 02114. Dr. Norman is Board Certified in Clinical & Child & Adolescent Psychology. *Other professional posts*: Faculty Chair (2005-present), Indian Health Initiative, Harvard University Native American Program, Cambridge, MA (E-mail: dennis_norman@harvard. edu); associate professor of psychology, Harvard Medical School. Dr. Dennis Norman has served as Faculty Chair of the Harvard University Native American Program since 2005. He is the chair for the Harvard University Native American Program and Health Initiative and teaches field research for Native communities at the Kennedy School of Government and the Harvard Graduate School of Education. His background is in clinical psychology with a special interest in culturally appropriate health care services. Dr. Norman is board certified in clinical and child and adolescent psychology. He received his doctorate in human development (cross cultural psychology), counselling, and consulting psychology from Harvard University and also has an MA in child development from Tufts University. Dr. Norman has been the Chief of Psychology at Massachusetts General Hospital since 1989. His research interests include personality structure & functioning, psychosocial adjustment to chronic illness & trauma, and intellectual and neuropsychological correlates of ADHD and provision of culturally appropriate health care services. He is a past chair of the Board of Registration for Psychology, Commonwealth of Massachusetts. *Past professional post*: Chair of the Board of Registration for Psychology, Commonwealth of Massachusetts. *Research Interests*: Personality structure & functioning, psychosocial adjustment to chronic illness & trauma, and the intellectual & neuropsychological correlates of ADHD. Also, healing & providing meaningful psychological consultation in differing cultural contexts.

NORMAN, MARGARET JANE (Seminole of Oklahoma)
(museum curator)
Affiliation: Seminole Nation Museum, 524 S. Wewoka, Box 1532, Wewoka, OK 74884 (405) 257-5580.

NORMAN, PATRICK N. (Eskimo)
(Alaskan village council chief)
Affiliation: Portage Graham Village Council, P.O. Box 5510, Port Graham, AK 99603 (907) 284-2227.

NORMAN, WILLIAM R., JR. (Muscogee Creek)
(attorney)
Education: University of Central Oklahoma, BBA, 1989; University of Oklahoma, J.D., 1992. *Address & Affiliation*: Partner, Hobbs, Straus, Dean & Walker, LLP, 117 Park Ave., 2nd Floor, Oklahoma City, OK 73102 (405) 602-9425. E-mail: wnorman@hobbsstraus.com. Mr. Norman joined the Washington, DC office in 1994 and in 1996 opened the Oklahoma office; Partner, 2000-present. William's varied practice includes advocating for tribal interests in federal & state legislation and rulemaking, and with agency decision-makers, in areas such as gaming, taxation, and transportation. His efforts as lead negotiator on the Oklahoma tribal gaming compact and the recent groundbreaking Oklahoma tobacco tax compact have secured for the Firm's clients and other Oklahoma tribes a foundation for economic success and stability. William concentrates considerable time in advising elected tribal leaders and agency officials on the development, operation, and regulation of tribal governmental infrastructure and economic development ventures, from drafting tribal laws & regulations to negotiating complex financing and business transactions. In addition, William's litigation work at the tribal, state, and federal level has resulted in the successful protection of tribal sovereignty and assets against numerous claims. William is a regular presenter on a range of Indian law topics and served on the Board of the Oklahoma Indian Legal Services from 2004 to 2008. He was a primary author, along with Charles Hobbs, of Chapter Two of *Empowerment of Tribal Governments: Final Workgroup Report*, developed by the Tribal Workgroup on Tribal Needs Assessments in May 1999. The chapter details the legal, historic, and moral obligations of the United States to tribes and the manner in which these responsibilities are fulfilled through today's tribal priority allocation programs. He also received the Salem Civil Rights Award for the note entitled "Native American Inmates and Prison Grooming Regulations: Today's Justified Scalps," *18 American Indian Law Review 191* (1993). *Memberships*: American Bar Assn; Oklahoma Indian Bar Assn; American Indian Chamber of Commerce of Oklahoma. *Areas of concentration*: Indian Self-Determination & Education Assistance Act; taxation, transportation, gaming, tribal sovereignty, & administrative & federal litigation resulting from disputes in such matters. Mr. Norman was primary author of

Chapter 2 of "Empowerment of Tribal Governments: Final Workgroup Report" developed by the Tribal Workgroup on Tribal Needs Assessments in May 1999. *Awards, honors*: Received the Salem Civil Rights Award for the note entitled, "Native American Inmates and Prison Grooming Regulations: Today's Justified Scalps," 18 Am. Indian L. Rev. 191 (1993).

NORRGARD, PHILIP (Fond du Lac Ojibwe)
  (director of human services)
Affiliation: Director of Human Services, Fond du Lac Band of Lake Superior Ojibwe, 105 University Rd., Cloquet, MN 55720 (218) 879-4593. *Past professional post*: Director, Min-No-Aya-Win Human Service Center, Cloquet, MN.

NORRIS, CHRISTINE (Jena Choctaw)
  (tribal principal chief)
Affiliation: Jena Band of Choctaw Indians, P.O. Box 14, Jena, LA 71342 (318) 992-2717. E-mail: chief@jenachoctaw.org.

NORRIS, DEBORA (Navajo-Dine')
  (education director)
Born & raised in Sells, Arizona on the Tohono O'odham Nation Reservation. *Education*: Stanford University, BA (History, minor in Education), 1993; Grand Canyon University, Phoenix, MA (Education Administration), 2006. *Affiliation & Address*: Director, Arizona Department of Education, Office of Indian Education, 1535 W. Jefferson, Phoenix, AZ 85007 (602) 542-2784. E-mail: dnorris@ade.az.gov. *Past professional posts*: Arizona House of Representatives, 1997-2002. She is one of the first two Native American women elected at the same time to serve in the Arizona Legislature in 1996 (the other one is Sally Gonzales from the Pascua Yaqui Tribe.)

NORRIS, LEONARD
  (organization director)
Affiliation: Organization of the Forgotten American, P.O. Box 1257, Klamath Falls, OR 97601 (503) 882-4441.

NORRIS, MARY TRIMBLE (Oglala Lakota)
  (executive director)
Affiliation & Address: Executive Director, American Indian Child Resource Center, 522 Grand Ave., Oakland, CA 94610 (510) 208-1870 ext. 305. E-mail: mary@aicrc.org. *Past professional post*: Deputy Director, California Indian Legal Services.

NORRIS, NED, JR. (Tohono O'odham)
  (former tribal chairperson)
Affiliation: Tohono O'odham Nation, P.O. Box 837, Sells, AZ 85634 (520) 383-2028.

NORRIS, SHERRI (Osage)
  (executive director)
Affiliation & Address: Executive Director, California Indian Environmental Alliance, P.O. Box 2128, Berkeley, CA 94702 (510) 848-2043. E-mail: sherri@cieaweb.org. Sherri has eleven years of experience working as a Tribal health and environmental advocate at the local level and at international fora and has given hundreds of presentations and trainings on the cycle and health effects of mercury on environmental health, exposure-reduction strategies, solution development and opportunities for advocacy related to mining issues in California. She coordinates CIEA's Tribal Self-Advocacy Program and is the primary contact for CIEA's Tribal Engagement responsibility under the North Coast Resource Partnership. Sherri is a graduate of the Hopa Mountain Foundation, a Rockridge Graduate and a member of the Sierra Fund's Blue Ribbon Panel of mercury experts. She is additionally a recipient of the Mills College Brave-Hearted Women Award, Sierra-Funds' Sierra Crest Award and the Davis-Putter Scholarship Award for Young Activists.

NORRIS, TAMMY (Seminole of Oklahoma)
  (organization president)
Affiliation & Address: President, National Native American Purchasing Association, P.O. Box 1498, Wewoka, OK 74884 (405) 257-7233. E-mail: tnorris@seminolenation.com. Tammy has been involved in tribal programs for the past 20 years. In 1988, she began her career at the Housing Authority of the Seminole Nation as an Administrative Assistant for the Rehabilitation & Development Program. The next year she became the program director. In 1996, Tammy moved to the Tribal Office and has worked in several areas for the Nation.

NORRIS, TERESA (Ojibwe)
  (executive director)
Affiliation & Address: Executive Director, Sacred Circle, P.O. Box 21451, Keizer, OR 97307 (971) 239-5697. E-mail: twinklestar2003@comcast.net.

NORTH, CHARLES, M.D.
  (clinical director)
Affiliation: Albuquerque PHS Indian Hospital, 801 Vassar Dr, NE, Albuquerque, NM 87106 (505) 254-4000.

NORTHBIRD, LOUIS (Leech Lake Ojibwe)
  (college instructor)
Affiliation: Leech Lake Tribal College, 6530 U.S. Hwy. 2 NW, Cass Lake, MN 56633 (218) 335-4220.

NORTHRUP, JIM (*Gi Gi Kunaw a magawinini*)
(Fond du Lac Lake Superior Chippewa) 1943-
  (writer, basketmaker)
Born April 28, 1943, Fond du Lac Reservation, Minn. *Principal occupation*: Writer, basketmaker. *Address*: 266 Northrup Rd., Sawyer, MN 55780 (218) 879-1691. *Professional posts*: Writes syndicated columns, "Fond du Lac Follies" in three Indian newspapers, 1989-; and "Commentaries," in Duluth News Tribune, 1993-. *Military service*: U.S. Marine Corps, 1961-66 (Sgt. - Vietnam Campaign). Video accomplishments: Warriors (PPTV - Fargo, ND, 1988); Diaries (KTCA - St. Paul, MN, 1991); Zero Street (Weapon of Choice, 1993); With Reservations (C.I.E., St. Paul, MN, 1994). *Radio accomplishments*: Commentaries - Superior Radio Network, 1992; Fresh Air Radio - NPR, 1994. *Awards, honors*: Lake Superior Contemporary Writers, 1986; Best Feature Story, Native American Journalists Association, 1987; Minnesota Book Award, Augsburg College, 1993; Northeast Minnesota Book Award 1994, University of Minnesota, Duluth. *Biographical sources*: Lake Superior Magazine, Oct. 1993; St. Paul Pioneer Press, 1993. *Published works*: "Touchwood" (New Rivers Press, 1987); "Stillers Pond" (New Rivers Press, 1988); "North Writers" (University of Minnesota Press, 1990); "Frags & Fragments"- Vietnam poetry (self published, 1990); "Three More" (Minnesota Center for the Book Arts, 1992); "Walking the Rez Road" (Voyageur Press, 1993); "Days of Obsidian, Days of Grace" (Poetry Harbor, 1994).

NORTON, BEATRICE Hopi)
  (community health representative; tribal board chairperson)
Affiliation & Address: Director, Hopi Community Health Representatives, Kykotsmovi, AZ. Beatrice helps provide at-home & transitional care for the elderly & the disabled. *Other professional post*: Chairperson, Board of Trustees, The Hopi Foundation,, P.O. Box 301, Kykotsmovi, AZ 86039 (928) 734-2380. *Past professional posts*: The Hopi Women's Coalition; Hopi Girl Power, a outh leadership program fr young women; cultural advisor, Hopi Leadership Program, 2006-07.

NORTON, GREGORY (Umpqua & Suislaw)
  (former tribal chairperson)
Affiliation: Confederated Tribes of Coos Lower Umpqua & Suislaw Indians, 338 Wallace Ave., Coos Bay, OR 97420 (503) 267-5454.

NORTON, JOSEPH TOKWIRO (Mohawk)
  (Indian band chief)
Affiliation: Mohawk Nation, Box 720, Kahnawake, Quebec, Canada J01 1B0 (514) 638-6790.

NORTON, MARY (Wintun)
  (rancheria chairperson)
Affiliation: Cortina Rancheria, Box 1630, Williams, CA 95987 (916) 726-7118.

NORTON, SANDRA H. (Eastern Cherokee)
  (executive director)
Affiliation & Address: Executive Director, Cumbeland County Association for Indian People, 2173 Downing Rd., Fayetteville, NC 28312 (910) 483-8442. E-mail: norton3034@aol.com.

NOSIE, WENDSLER (San Carlos Apache)
  (tribal chairperson)
Affiliation: Chairperson, San Carlos Apache Tribe, P.O. Box 0, San Carlos, AZ 85550 (928) 475-2361. *Past tribal affiliation*: Co-chair, Apaches for Cultural Preservation, San Carlos Apache Reservation, San Carlos, AZ.

NOT AFRAID, ALFRED, JR. (Crow)
  (tribal chairperson)
Born on the Crow Reservation in St. Xavier, Mont. *Afiliation & Address*: Chairperson, Crow Nation, P.O. Box 129, Crow Agency, MT 59022 (306) 638-3708.

NOTAH, GLORIA (San Carlos Apache)
  (tribal department director)
Affiliation: San Carlos Recreation & Wildlife Dept., P.O. Box 97, San Carlos, AZ 85550 (520) 475-2343.

NOTAH, NATHAN (Dine')
(program manager)
Born & raised on the Navajo Indian Reservation in Tohatchi, N.M. *Education*: New Mexico State University, BS (Animal Science). *Affiliation & Address*: Director, American Indian Foods International Export Program (2006-present), Intertribal Agriculture Council (IAC), 100 North 27th St., Suite 500, Billings, MT 59101 (406) 259-3525. Nathan's duties include working with tribal businesses & American Indian owned businesses by providing them export education, resources & opportunities that can facilitate global market penetration by increasing sales of their products. He has been employed with IAC since 1998 serving in the Southeast U.S. region. *Past professional posts*: Department of Agriculture for the Navajo Nation in Window Rock, AZ, 1987-91; agent, Cooperative Extension Service with the University of California-Davis, 1991-98; served as an advisor to the Oklahoma & Texas tribal Conservation Advisory Councils, the Oklahoma Food Policy Advisory Council, & Southeast Regional NYCS Native American workgroup. *Interests*: Production agriculture & working with Native communities..

NOVAK, YVONNE
(association president)
Affiliation: National Indian Education Association, 121 Oronoco St., Alexandria, VA 22314 (703) 838-2870.

NOVAS, AMERICA
(Indian school principal)
Affiliation: Miccosukee Indian School, Box 440021, Tamiami Station, Miami, FL 33144 (305) 223-8380.

NUCKOLLS, LARRY (Absentee-Shawnee)
(tribal governor)
Affiliation: Absentee-Shawnee Executive Committee, 2025 S. Gordon Cooper Dr., Shawnee, OK 74801 (405) 275-4030.

NUMKENA, WILFRED (*Tsung-Aya*) (Hopi) 1943-
(education)
Born December 24, 1943, Moencopi, Ariz. Education: Brigham Young University, BS, 1973; Pennsylvania State University, MEd., 1979. Principal occupation: Education. Resides in Flagstaff, AZ area. *Affiliation*: Executive director, Utah Division of Indian Affairs, Salt Lake City, UT, 1991-98. *Military service*: U.S. Army, 1965-67 (Sergeant E-5; Honorable Discharge). *Community activities*: Utah Columbus Quincentennary Commission; Utah Interagency Task Force. *Memberships*: National Indian Education Association; Natioal Congress of American Indians; Utah Federation for Indian Education. *Awards, honors*: Ute Indian Education Award; University of Utah Intertribal Student Association Leadership Recognition.

NUNNERY, BETTY D.
(program coordinator)
Affiliation: American Indian Professional Training Program in Speech-Language Pathology & Audiology, University of Arizona, Dept. of Speech & Hearing Sciences, Tucson, AZ 85721 (520) 621-1969. *Published works*: Editor, "Desert Connections"; Directory of Native Americans in Speech-Language Pathology & Audiology.

NUSKE, VIRGINIA (Menominee)
(association director)
Affiliation: Wisconsin Indian Education Association, Menominee Indian Tribe, P.O. Box 910, Keshena, WI 54135 (715) 799-5110.

NUSS, ROBERT (BOB) 1941-
(business owner)
Born in 1941, Ohio. *Education*: Marietta (OH) College, BA, 1963; University of Arizona, 1963-65, 1969-71. *Affiliation & Address*: Owner, Drumbeat Indian Arts, 4143 N. 16th St., Phoenix, AZ 85016 (602) 266-4823 (manager, 1972-83; owner, 1984-). Website: www.drumbeatindianarts.com. *Military service*: U.S. Army, 1966-68. *Community activities*: Board of Directors, ATLATL & Pueblo Grande Museum; Phoenix Indian Center (benefit dinner committee); Sun-N-Sand Model Railroad Club. *Awards, honors*: Outstanding Business for Service to the American Indian Community, Phoenix Indian Center, 1993. *Interests*: Drumbeat Indian Arts (until 1997 it was named Canyon Records & Indian Arts) is the largest distributors of American Indian recordings (cassettes, CDs, videos) - over 2,500 titles.

NUTTER, DELBERT
(health director)
Affiliation: W.W. Hastings Indian Hospital, 100 S. Bliss, Tahlequah, OK 74464 (918) 458-3100.

NUTTLE, MISTY M. (Pawnee)
(former tribal president)
Affiliation & Address: Former President, Pawnee Nation of Oklahoma,

P.O. Box 470, Pawnee, OK 74058 (918) 762-3621. E-mail: mnuttle@pawneenation.org

NUVAMSA, BENJAMIN H. (Hopi)
(BIA agency supt.)
Affiliation: Fort Apache Agency, Bureau of Indian Affairs, P.O. Box 560, Whiteriver, AZ 85941 (928) 338-5353.

NUVAMSA, MONICA (Hopi)
(executive director; tribal radio general manager)
Education: University of Arizona, BA (Psychology) & American Indian Studies), 1997. *Affiliation & Address*: Associate Director/Director of Programs, The Hopi Foundation, P.O. Box 301, Kykotsmovi, AZ 86039 (928) 734-2380. *Other professional post*: Geneal Manager, KUYI Hopi Radio; board member, Hopi Education Endowment Fund (2004-present), Native Americans in Philanthropy (2010-present), Native Public Media (2012-present).

NUVAYESTEWA, LEON (Hopi)
(school principal)
Affiliation: Principal, Hopi High School, P.O. Box 37, Keams Canyon, AZ 86034 (602) 738-5111.

NUVAYESTEWA, MARISSA (Hopi)
(capacity building director)
Education: Washington University, St. Louis, MO, MSW (Social Work & Economic Development in Native American Communities). *Affiliation & Address*: Capacity Building Director, The Hopi Foundation, P.O. Box 301, Kykotsmovi, AZ 86039 (928) 734-2380. *Past professional post*: Program officer, Fist Nations Development Institute, Longmont, CO.

NYE, DORIS R.
(council president)
Affiliation: National Urban Indian Council, 100068 University Park Station, Denver, CO 80210 (303) 750-2695.

NYE, VALERIE
(library director)
Affiliation & Address: Director, Institute of American Indian Arts Library, 83 Avan Nu Po Rd., Santa Fe, NM 87503 (505) 424-2397. E-mail: vnye@iaia.edu

NYGAARD, ROBERT WAYNE (Sault Ste. Marie Chippewa) 1953-
(director-planning & development)
Born September 5, 1953, Gaylord, Mich. *Education*: Bay de Noc Community College (Escanaba, MI), AA, 1972; Central Michigan University, BA, 1974. *Address*: 1829 Chestnut, Sault Ste. Marie, MI 49783. *Office address*: 5232 Ashmun, Sault Ste. Marie, MI 49783 (906) 635-6050. *Affiliation*: Director-Planning & Development, Sault Ste. Marie Tribe of Chippewa Indians, Sault Ste. Marie, MI, 1978-. *Other professional posts*: Adjunct professor, Bay Mills (MI) Community College 1991-present; member, Management Board, Kentwood Holdings (LLC), 1996-present. *Community activities*: member, Census Advisory Committee on the African American, American Indian & Alaskan Native, Pacific Islander, and Hispanic Populations, Washington, DC, 1994-; board of directors, Inter-tribal Bison Cooperative, Rapid City, SD, 1995-. *Membership*: Sault Ste. Marie Tribe of Chippewa Indians. *Awards, honors*: 15 Year Service Award, Sault Ste. Marie Tribe, 1993; Outstanding State Leadership Recognition Award, Circle of Life Conference, 1984.

O

OATMAN, McCOY (Nez Perce)
(tribal vice chairperson)
Affiliation & Address: Vice Chairperson, Nez Perce Tribe, P.O. Box 305, Lapwai, ID 83540 (208) 843-2253. E-mail: mccoyo@nezperce.org. Mr. Oatman is serving his first term on NPTEC. Mr. Oatman is a second generation NPTEC Member – his father, Kenneth, also served as a NPTEC Member. Mr. Oatman was recently elected to the position of Treasurer for NPTEC. Mr. Oatman Serves as Chairman for the Budget & Finance Subcomittee, and is a member of the Natural Resource and Land Commission Subcomittees.

OATMAN-WAK WAK, MARY JANE (Nez Perce)
(Indian association president)
Education: Lewis & Clark State College, B.S. (Justice Studies & minor in Nez Perce Language). *Affiliation & Address*: President, National Indian Education Association, 110 Maryland Ave., NE #104, Washington, DC 20002 (202) 544-7290. *Other professional post*: Indian Education Coordinator, Idaho State Dept. of Education, P.O. Box 83720, Boise, ID 83720 (208) 332-6968. E-mail: mowakwak@sde.idaho.gov. Appointed as Idaho's first Indian Education Coordinator by Idaho's Supt. of Public Instruction. Her role was to serve as a liaison between Indian tribes and the state. *Awards, honors*: 2008 Outstanding Nontraditional Student Award.

OBAGO-NICOLAR, LINDA (Lakota)
  (chief finanial officer)
Affiliation: CFO, Sisseton Wahpeton College, P.O. Box 689,
Agency Village, SD 57262 (605) 698-3966.

OBERLE, JASON D.
  (BIA agency supt.)
Affiliation & Address: Supt., BIA, Michigan Agency, 2845 Ashmun St.,
Sault Ste. Marie, MI 49783 (906) 632-6809 E-mail: jason.oberle@bia.gov

OBERLY, JR., ACEY (Yakama)
  (BIA agency supt.)
Affiliation: Yakama Agency, Bureau of Indian Affairs, P.O. Box 632,
Toppenish, WA 98948 (509) 865-2255.

OBERLY, JENNIFER (Iowa)
  (tribal administrator)
Affiliation & Address: Tribal Administrator, Iowa Tribe of Oklahoma, Rt. 1 Box
721, Perkins, OK 74059 (405) 547-2402. E-mail: joberly@iowanation.org

OBERLY, JOHN
  (administrative officer)
Affiliations: Wind River PHS Indian Health Center, Fort Washakie, WY 82514
(307) 332-9416; Arapaho PHS Indian Health Center, Arapaho, WY 82510
(307) 856-9281.

OBERLY, STACEY (Southern Ute)
  (Southern Ute language professor)
Education: College of Santa Fe, MA (Bilingual/Multicultural Education);
University of Arizona, MA & PhD (Linguistics), 2008. *Affiliation*: Professor
(Southern Ute Language), American Indian Language Development Institute
(AILDI), University of Arizona, Dept. of Language, Reading & Culture, College
of Education, Douglass 200; assistant professor, American Indian Studies
Program, University of Arizona, Harvill 320A, Tucson, AZ 85721 (520) 621-
0812. E-mail: soberly@email.arizona.edu. She specializes in Southern Ute
linguistics, Native American language immersion, language documentation &
revitalization, Native American education & instrumental phonetics.

OBOMSAWIN, TOMAS (Abenaki)
  (musician)
Address: c/o Abenaki Tribal Office, P.O. Box 276, Missisquoi, VT 05488 (802)
868-7146. Tomas plays contemporary & traditional Native American theme
music. Lyrics are of American Indian struggles and situations.

O'BONSAWIN, CHRISTINE
  (director of Indigenous Studies)
Education: Brock Univesity, BA (Sport Management), 1999; University of
Western Ontario, MA, 2002, PhD (Sport History), 2006. *Affiliation & Address*:
Professor (2007-present) and Director, Indigenous Studies Department,
Department of Anthropology, Cle B303, University of Victoria, 3800 Finnerty
Rd., Victoria, BC V8W 2Y2 Canada (250) 853-3807. E-mail: cobonsaw@
uvic.ca. Her research areas include Olympic history, indigenous sport history,
Canadian sport history as well as indigenous/Indian policy.

O'BRIEN, ARLENE (Tohono O'odham)
  (program manager)
Affiliation & Address: Program Manager, Southwest Center for Law & Policy,
475 S. Stone Ave., Tucson, AZ 85701 (520) 623-8192. E-mail:
obrien@swclap.org.

O'BRIEN, JEAN M. (White Earth Ojibwe)
  (professor of history)
Education: University of Chicago, PhD (History), 1990. *Address & Affiliation*:
Professor of History & former chair, Department of American Indian Studies,
Department of History, 1041 Heller Hall, 271 19th Ave. So., University of
Minnesota, Twin Cities Campus, Minneapolis, MN 55455 (612) 626-5330. E-
mail: obrien002@umn.edu. *Specialties*: Native American Representations;
State & Federal Recognition; Indians of the Northeast; and is especially
interested in social & cultural history in early New England & American Indian
women's history. *Other professional post*: Co-editor, Native American &
Indigenous Studies Journal. *Membership*: Native American & Indigenous
Studies Association (past president). *Published works*: Dispossession by
Degrees: Indian Land & Identity in Natick, Massachusetts, 1650-1790
(Cambridge University Press, 1997); Firsting & Lasting: Writing Indians Out of
Existence in New England (about the construction of the myth of Indian
extinction in 19th century New England) (University of Minnesota Press, 2010).

OCHOA, CARMEN (Cahto-Pomo)
  (rancheria chairperson)
Affiliation: Laytonville Rancheria, P.O. Box 1102, Laytonville, CA 95454
(707) 984-6197.

O'CONNELL, STEVE
  (Indian center director)
Affiliation: Director, Roundhouse Council, Inc., P.O. Box 217, Greenville, CA
95947 (916) 284-6866.

O'CONNOR, NANCY (Shawnee/Crow)
  (artist & producer)
Education: University of Montana, BA (Journalism). *Affiliations & Address*:
Director, Fred E. Miller Collection; vice president, UGO Productions, 30822
Broad Beach Rd., Malibu, CA 90265 (310) 457-1518. Nancy is founder/
chairperson of the John Wayne Cancer Clinic at UCLA; and a member of the
International Founders Council for the Smithsonian's National Museum of the
American Indian. Mrs. O'Connor and her late husband, the actor carroll
O'Connor, have been active spokespersons and philanthropists on social &
health issues related to addiction. Mrs. O'Connor lends continued support to
the University of Montana through the Ralph & Gulda Fields Scholarships
(named in honor of Mrs. O'Connor's parents), as well as endowment support to
the University's O'Connor Center for the Rocky Mountain EWest (CRMW). The
Fields Scholarships are awarded each year to Native American students
choosing to major in journalism, forestry, law or pharmacy, & Mrs. O'Connor's
particular interest is in the CRMW's work on tribal issues.

ODEN, HOLLY (Anishinaabe)
  (project resource & information specialist; theatrical artist)
Education: University of Minnesota, Duluth, BA, 1991; Purdue University, MFA,
1994. *Affiliation & Address*: Technical Assistance Project Resource &
Information Specialist, Mending the Sacred Hoop, 202 W. 2nd St., Duluth, MN
55802 (218) 623-HOOP. Holly began working with the Peroject in 2002 as an
editor & writer of mending the Sacred Hoop manuals, such as "Addressing
Domestice Violence in Native Communities," and the "Sexual Assault
Advocacy Guide." She provides training & technical assistance to tribes
nationally on addressing violence against Native women in their communities.
Her experience growing up with domestic violence have informed her work as
a theatrical artist; she has used theatre as a means of bringing violence
against women issues to the forefront of community awareness.

O'DONNELL, JIM
  (museum director)
Affiliation: Akta Lakota Museum, St. Joseph Indian School, P.O. Box 89,
Chamberlain, SD 57325 (605) 734-3455.

OESTREICHER, DAVID M. 1959-
  (anthropologist, writer, lecturer)
Born December 5, 1959, New York, N.Y. *Education*: SUNY at Purchase, BA,
1981; New York University, MA, 1985; Rutgers University, MA, PhD
(Anthropology). *Address*: 235 Mamaroneck Ave., White Plains, NY 10605
(914) 632-1928. *Affiliations*: Curator of the award-winning traveling exhibition,
"In Search of the Lenape: The Delaware Indians, Past & Present," Mr.
Ostreicher organized and is principal curator of the traveling exhibit "Touching
Leaves and Her People: The Lenape", initially funded in part by a grant from
the New York Council for the Humanities speaker at schools, New York
Botanical Garden; consultant for Native American Heritage Committee of New
York; Scarsdale Audubon Society (board of directors). *Other professional
posts*: Consultant for four books, a number of articles, and two films on the
Lenape, including Lenape: The Original People, by Thomas Agnello, which he
helped conceive & produce. David Oestreicher is recognized as a leading
authority on the Lenape and related Algonkian tribes. His research has taken
him from remote areas of Wisconsin & Canada to Oklahoma. For seven years
until her death in November of 1984, his principal work was conducted with the
late "Touching Leaves Woman", or Nora Thompson Dean, one of the few
remaining full blooded Lenape, one of the last speakers of her language and
the last person fully raised in the traditions of her ancestors. Much of this
information is recorded on tapes, notes and video and is a major contribution
to the Delaware Indian Resource Center at Ward Pound Ridge Reservation,
Cross River, NY. He has appeared as a guest on WOR radio in New York with
Ed & Pegeen Fitzgerald; has taught government sponsored Title IV (Native
American Indian Education) programs (his students, members of the Ramapo
Mountain Indian Tribe, studied Delaware language & culture with him) and has
taken part in and helped arrange various Delaware Indian symposiums and
programs at Yale University, Tulsa University, Seton Hall University, SUNY
Purchase, New York City Hall, the New Jersey Highlands Historical Society,
the Archaeological Society of New Jersey, and elsewhere. Oestreicher has
been a consultant for films & book in connection with the Delaware Indians.
Published works: Surviving Historic Traditions of the Unami Delaware and,
Monograph - The Munsee and Northern Unami Today: A Study of Traditional
Ways at Moraviantown, in The Archaeology & Ethnohistory of the Lower
Hudson Valley & Neighboring Regions (1991), marked the first ethnographic
account of the Hudson River Lenape since the work of M.R. Harrington (1908,
1913, 1921) and Frank G. Speck (1945); he completed the final portion of the
late Herbert C. Kraft's, "The Lenape-Delaware Indian Heritage: 10,000 B.C. -
2000 A.D."; The Algonquian of New York (Powerkids Press, 2003).

OHRE, MARK D.
(attorney)
Education: Arizona State University, BS, 1992; University of California School of Law, JD, 1996. *Affiliation & Address*: Snell & Wilmer, L.L.P., One Arizona Center, 400 E. Van Buren St., Suite 1900, Phoenix, AZ 85004-2202 (602) 382-6394 Fax 382-6070. E-mail: mohre@swlaw.com. *Awards, honors*: Wiley W. Manuel Award for Pro Bono Legal Srvices, Stte Bar of California; Volunteer of the Year Award, National Center for American Indian Enterprise Development, 1999; The Best Lawyers in America, Native American Law (2009-2013); Phoenix Native American Law Lawyer of the Year, 2013. *Presentation*: "Business Development in Indian Country," March 2010.

O'JAY, BETTY (Navajo)
(school director)
Affiliation: Navajo Preparatory School, 1200 W. Apache, Farmington, NM 87401 (505) 326-6571.

OJIBWAY, FR. PAUL
(commissioner)
Affiliation: Los Angeles City/County Native American Indian Commission, 500 W. Temple St., Room 780, Los Angeles, CA 90012 (213) 974-7554.

OKITKUN, MARK
(tribal chairperson)
Affiliation: Native Village of Bill Moore's Slough, P.O. Box 20037, Kotlik, AK 99620 (907) 899-4712.

OKLEASIK, TOM (Eskimo)
(Alaskan village executive director)
Affiliation & Address: Executive Director, Native Village of Kotzebue, P.O. Box 296, Kotzebue, AK 99752 (907) 442-3467.

OKSOKTARUK, PATTI (Inupiaq)
(village outreach coordinator)
Education: Master's degree in Higher, Adult, and Lifelong Education from Michigan State University (2010) and a BA in English from University of Alaska Fairbanks. *Affiliation & Address*: She works at UAF Northwest Campus in Nome, Alaska, as a village outreach coordinator. In this role she works with tribal and municipal governments, and other community leaders to identify and organize adult learning opportunities in 15 remote, primarily Alaska Native communities in the Northwest Campus service area. Prior to attending graduate school, Patti worked at UAF Northwest Campus as a student services coordinator for five years, providing outreach and support to new and continuing college students in these villages who were working toward their degrees via distance delivery. Her motivation for becoming, and then returning to UAF Northwest Campus is to serve her region in appreciation for the social and economic support she received while in college. Her professional interests include creating social and economic opportunities via local course design and delivery; promoting economic development in remote, rural, and predominantly indigenous communities in the Arctic; promoting greater understanding of how historic trauma in Alaska affects indigenous peoples' engagement in educational endeavors; and working with other educators to integrate cultural knowledge & place-based subjects of study into the K-12 curriculum. *Published works*: Editor, On Indian Ground: Alaska (Information Age Publishing, in prep).

OLANIO, HERMO (Miwok)
(tribal chairperson)
Affiliation & Address: Vice Chairperson, Shingle Springs Band of Miwok Indians, P.O. Box 1340, Shingle Springs, CA 95682 (530) 676-6281. E-mail: holanio@ssband.org

OLANNA, MICHAEL (Eskimo)
(Alaskan village president)
Affiliation: President, Native Village of Brevig Mission, P.O. Box 85039, Brevig Mission, AK 99785 (907) 642-4301. E-mail: tc.kts@kawerak.org.

OLBY, PATRICIA
(BIA agency supt.)
Affiliation & Address: Supt., Bureau of Indian Affairs, Minnesota Agency, Federal Bldg., Rm. 418, 522 Minnesota Ave., NW, Bemidji, MN 56601 (218) 751-2011; E-mail: patty.olby@bia.gov

OLD BEAR, DAVID, SR. (Sac & Fox)
(former tribal chief)
Affiliation: Sac & Fox Tribe of the Mississippi in Iowa, 349 Meskwaki Rd., Tama, IA 52339 (515) 484-4678

OLD COYOTE, DARRIN N. (Crow)
(former tribal chairperson)
Born on the Crow Reservation in St. Xavier, Mont. *Afiliation & Address*: Chairperson, Crow Nation, P.O. Box 129, Crow Agency, MT 59022 (306) 638-3708.

OLD COYOTE, JACKIE (Crow/Ho-Chunk)
(director of education & outreach)
Education: Montana State University, BA, 2003; Harvard Graduate School of Education, EdM, 2004. *Affiliation & Address*: Director of Education & Outreach, Harvard Project on American Indian Economic Development, John F. Kennedy School of Government, 79 JFK St., Cambridge, MA 02138 (617) 496-9446. E-mail: jackie_old_coyote@harvard.edu. *Other professional post*: Faculty member, Native Nations Institute (Tucson, AZ) & the Little Big Horn College (Montana); serves on the Board of Trustees for the National Museum of the American Indian. She is certified to teach "Indianpreneurship," and has assisted Harvard College professors with their course syllabi & construction through her appointment as a Community Liaison for the Native Voices, Native Homelands pilot project. *Awards, honors*: 2005 recipient of the Native Americans at Harvard College Role Model of the Year award. *Past professional posts*: Jackie enjoyed a career as an international fashion model & actress before her return to her educational path in 2000. She taught drama at her tribal college in Montana, Little Big Horn College, and has continued her drama career as both actress & writer. She was selected playwright for the Native Voices at the Autry Retreat in 2005; appeared in the 2003 movie, The Last Samurai; & her radio drama, Round Ball, aired on National Public Radio.

OLD PERSON, CHIEF EARL (Blackfeet)
(former tribal chief; councilman & spiritual leader)
Affiliation & Address: Councilman, Blackfeet Tribal Business Council, P.O. Box 850, Browning, MT 59417 (406) 338-7276. *Other professional post*: Member, Board of Regents, American Indian Heritage Foundation, Falls Church, VA. *Awards, honors*: The 1998 Jeanette Rankin Civil Liberties Award from the American Civil Liberties Union of Montana.

OLDMAN, GERALD (Athapascan)
(AK village chief)
Affiliation: Hughes Village Council, P.O. Box 45010, Hughes, AK 99745 (907) 899-2206.

OLDMAN, RONALD K. (Arapaho)
(former tribal co-chairperson)
Affiliation & Address: Former Co-Chairperson, Northern Arapaho Tribe, P.O. Box 396, Fort Washakie, WY 82514 (307) 332-6120.

OLDS, DUSTIN (Miami)
(tribal second chief)
Affiliation & Address: Second Chief, Miami Tribe of Oklahoma, P.O. Box 1326, Miami, OK 74355 (918) 542-1445.

OLDS, JULIE (Miami of Oklahoma)
(artist, studio owner)
Address: Alamooni Studio, 49900 E. 20 Road, Miami, OK 74354 (918) 541-3131. Website: www.joldsart.com. E-mail: jolds@miamination.com. *Artwork*: Original paintings in oil, acrylic, watercolor, gouache; original drawings in graphite, pastel; pottery, jewelry, sculpture.

OLEMAUN, THOMAS (Inupiat)
(Alaskan tribal president)
Affiliation: President, Inupiat Traditional Government, Native Village of Barrow, P.O. Box 1130, Barrow, AK 99723 (907) 852-4411.

OLIN, CHRIS (Nisqually)
(tribal vice chairperson)
Affiliation & Address: Vice Chairperson, Nisqually Indian Tribe, 4820 She-Nah-Num Dr., SE, Olympia, WA 98513 (360) 456-5221. E-mail: olin.chris@nisqually-nsn.gov

OLINGER, LARRY N. (Agua Caliente Cahuilla)
(tribal vice chairperson)
Affiliation & Address: Vice Chairperson, Agua Caliente Band of Cahuilla Indians, 5401 Dinah Shore Dr., Palm Springs, CA 92264 (760) 699-6800.

OLIVER, ELEANOR J. (Navajo)
(craftsperson)
Address: Ellie's Southwestern Arts & Crafts, 32 Sisson Dr., Rochester, NY 14623 (716) 334-5335.

OLIVER, MARVIN (Quinault/Isleta Pueblo)
  (professor of American Indian studies; adjunct curator)
Education: San Francisco State University, BA; University of Washington, MFA, 1973. *Affiliation & Address*: Professor, Dept. of American Indian Studies, Box 354305, University of Washington, Seattle, WA 98195 (206) 616-9508. E-mail: moliver@u.washington.edu. Website: www.marvinoliver.com. Professor Oliver is one of the Northwest Coast's foremost contemporary sculptors & printmakers with a career spanning over 40 years. His monumental sculptures in cedar, bronze & enameled steel have established Professor Oliver as an internally acclaimed contemporary sculptor & have been installed throughout Washington State and other parts of the US, as well as in Canada, Japan and Italy. Professor Oliver is the first non-Italian artist to be commissioned for a public art piece in Perugia, Italy, Seattle's sister city. His artwork & sculptures have won numerous awards. In 2006 his sculpture was the first glass piece to win the Best of Classification award at the Santa Fe Indian Market. In the same year his piece "Window to the Past" won the Best of Division award at the Heard Museum Fair and Market. The latest period of Professor Oliver's work has been characterized by mixed-media pieces such as his blown glass "Salish Basket" and "Spirit Board" series with etched photographs and bronze ravens. He is also renowned for the grand size of his sculptures such as the 26 foot-long suspended steel & glass piece "Mystical Journey" at the Seattle Children's hospital. Professor Oliver has been teaching Northwest coast art, graphics & design at the UW since 1974. Emphasizing traditional techniques, he is the only professor in the U.S. teaching Northwest coast graphics & wood design as a technical approach in studio courses.

OLIVERA, SHAWN (Kanatak)
  (Alaskan village president)
Affiliation: Native Village of Kanatak, P.O. Box 872231, Wasilla, AK 99687 (907) 357-5991. Website: www.kanatak.org.

OLSEN, POLLY (Yakama)
  (trabl liaison, Burke Museum)
Education: University of Washington, BA (Cultural Anthropology), 1994. *Affiliation & Address*: Tribal Liaison, Burke Museum, Washington State Museum of Natural History & Culture, Box 353010, University of Washington, Seattle, WA 98195 (206) 543-7907. E-mail: polly@uw.edu. Past professional post: Director, Native American Center of Excellence, University of Washington, School of Medicine, 2001-07; Director (2007-15), Community Relations & Development Core, Indigenous Wellness Research Institute, School of Social Work, University of Washington; Executive Director, Association of American Indian Physicians, 2015-17.

OLSON, ALLAN (Swinomish)
  (tribal general manager)
Affiliation: Swinomish Indian Tribal Community, P.O. Box 817, LaConnor, WA 98257 (360) 466-3163.

OLSON, APRIL ERIN (Ojibwe)
  (attorney)
Education: Eastern New Mexico University, BS, 2000; Arizona State University, Sandra Day O'Connor College of Law, JD (Certificate in ndian Law from Indian Legal Program), 2006. *Affiliation & Address*: Associate (2010-present), Rothstein, Donatelli, Hughes, Dahlstrom, Schoenburg & Bienvenu, LLP, 80 E. Rio Salado Parkway, Suite 710, Tempe, AZ 85281 (480) 921-9296. E-mail: aeolson@roothsteinlaw.com. April's law experience includes a variety of practice areas, including: criminal law, civil litigation, water law and Indian Child Welfare Act matters. *Past professional post*: Attorney (2006-09), Gila River Indian Community.

OLSON, BEVERLY
  (outreach)
Affiliation: Native American Coalition of Programs, P.O. Box 1914, Fargo, ND 58107 (701) 235-3124.

OLSON, DENNIS W., JR. (Fond du Lac Ojibwe)
  (director of Indian education)
Education: University of Minnesota Twin Cities, BA (American Indian Studies, Sociology, & Communications; MA (Liberal Studies (MLS) & Education (M.Ed.) from the University of Minnesota Duluth, both with a focus on Federal Indian policy and American Indian education. *Affiliation & Address*: Executive Director, Minnesota Indian Affairs Council, 161 St. Anthony St., Suite 919, St. Paul, MN 55155 (651) 296-0132. E-mail: deniis.w.olson@state.mn.us. *Past professional posts*: Director, Indian Education, Minnesota Department of Education, Roseville, MN. He served as the agency's chief liaison in working with the 11 Minnesota Tribal Nations & Twin Cities American Indian communities, and worked in collaboration with multiple agencies on issues impacting Indian Education in Minnesota. Before joining state government, Dennis served as Commissioner of Education for the Mille Lacs Band of Ojibwe, overseeing operations of the Tribal education department. He also

worked nearly 10 years in various capacties for the University of Minnesota – Institute on Community Integration, coordinating federally funded grant programs working directly with all eleven tribal communities in Minnesota, focussing on postsecondary transition for American Indian high school students, students with disabilities, and at-risk youth.

OLSON, MS. JOEL C.
  (Indian organization president)
Affiliation: American Indian Arts Council, 725 Preston Forest Shopping Center, Suite B, Dallas, TX 75230 (214) 891-9640.

OLSON, MIRIAM (Athapascan)
  (Alaskan village president)
Affiliation: Native Village of Aleknagik, P.O. Box 115, Aleknagik, AK 99555 (907) 842-2080. E-mail: alnilutsik@hotmail.com.

OLSON, TINA (Yaqui)
  (organization founding member)
Affiliation & Address: Founding member, Mending the Sacred Hoop, 202 W. 2nd St., Duluth, MN 55802 (218) 623-HOOP. Tina has worked on isues surrounding domestic violence for over 20 years. She has organized such domestic violence trainings as Law Enforcement, Building a Coordinated Response, Creating a Process of Change for Men Who Batter, and In Our Best Interest, a women's grop facilitator curriculum. She has served on the Board of Directors for American Indian Housing program, Dabinoo'lgan Shelter for Native Women; and on the board of Women in Construction, an economic justice project developed to provide livable wages to women by training low-income women to work in the building trades.

OLSON, TRACY (Confederated Tribes)
  (newsletter director)
Affiliation: "Smoke Signals," Confederated Tribes of Grand Ronde Community of Oregon, 9615 Grand Ronde Rd., Grand Ronde, OR 97347 (503) 879-5211.

OLSZESKI, KAREN
  (genealogist)
Address: 674 Chicago Dr., Howell, MI 48843 (517) 546-1557. E-mail: klapko@comcast.net. Specializes in Native American research.

OLTROGGE, MICHAEL (Winnebago)
  (college president)
Education: Nebraska Indian Community College, AA, 1997; Bellevue University, BS; Capella University, MS (Educational Administration), PhD (Leadership for Higher Education). *Affiliation & Address*: President (2004-present), Nebraska Indian Community College, 1111 Hwy. 75, Macy, NE 68039 (402) 837-5078. E-mail: moltrogge@thenicc.edu. *Other professional post*: Member, Board of Trustees, American Indian College Fund, Denver, CO.

OMIAK, PATRICK F. (Eskimo)
  (Alaskan village president)
Affiliation: Native Village of Diomede, P.O. Box 7079, Diomede, AK 99762 (907) 686-2175.

OMOTTO, LOREN
  (executive director)
Affiliation: Native American Journalists Association, 3359 36th Ave. S., Minneapolis, MN 55406 (612) 729-9244. E-Mail: omotto@naja.com.

ONCO, DIANA (Navajo-Dine')
  (Indian program coordinator)
Affiliation & Address: Coordinator, Native American Student Services, Northern Arizona University, Native American Cultural Center (Bldg. 14, Rm. 100), P.O. Box 5653, Flagstaff, AZ 86011 (928) 523-3147. E-mail: diana.onco@nau.edu

ONDOLA, GEORGE (Athapascan)
  (AK village president)
Affiliation: Eklutna Native Village, 26339 Eklutna Village Rd., Chugiak, AK 99567 (907) 688-6020.

ONE BEAR-HOLT, MURIEL (Crow & Northern Cheyenne)
  (TV station principal)
Address & Affiliation: Principal, KHMT-Channel 4 (American Indian-owned TV station), 445 S. 24th St. W., Suite 404, Billings, MT 59102 (406) 652-7366.

O'NEAL, DARRELL, SR. (Arapaho)
  (former tribal co-chairperson)
Affiliation & Address: Co-Chairperson, Northern Arapaho Tribe, P.O. Box 396, Fort Washakie, WY 82514 (307) 332-6120.

O'NEILL, GLORIA (Yupik-Irish)
(president & CEO)
Born in Soldotna, Alaska. *Education*: University of Alaska, Anchorage, BA (Sociology); Alaska Pacific University, MBA, 2000. *Affiliation & Address*: President & CEO (1998-present), Cook Inlet Tribal Council, Inc. (CITCI), 3600 San Jeronimo Dr., Anchorage, AK 99508 (907) 793-3278; E-mail: goneill@citci.org. *Other professional post*: Board Chairperson, University of Alaska, Nome. *Community activities*: Board member of Alaska Federation of Natives, Cook Inlet Housing Authority, BP Exploration (Alaska), Inc. Board of Community Advisors, Anchorage Museum Building Committee, University of Alaska - Anchorage Advisory Board, Alaska Mental Health Board & the U.S. Census Bureau Advisory Committee on Race & Ethnicity for American Indian & Alaska Native Populations. *Awards, honors*: Light of Hope, 2003; 2003 Woman of Achievement by BP & YWCA of Anchorage.

ONETTA, KATHRYN
(editorial director)
Affiliation: "Daybreak Star Indian Reader," Bernie Whitebear, P.O. Box 99100, Seattle, WA 98199 (206) 285-4425.

ONEY, RAYMOND D.
(AK village president)
Affiliation: Village of Alakanuk, Box 167, Alakanuk, AK 99554 (907) 238-3313.

ONNEN, LIANA (Prairie Band Potawatomi)
(tribal chairperson)
Affiliation & Address: Chair, Prairie Band Potawatomi Indian Tribe, 16281 Q Rd., Mayetta, KS 66509 (785) 966-4007. E-mail: lianao@pbpnation. org.

OPIKOKEW, BRIAN
(dean of students)
Affiliation: Saskatchewan Indian Federated College, University of Regina, 118 College West, Regina, SK, Canada S4S 0A2 (306) 584-8333.

OQUILLUK, LUCY H. (Eskimo)
(Alaskan village president)
Affiliation: Mary's Igloo Traditional Council, P.O. Box 546, Teller, AK 99778 (907) 642-3731.

ORECHIA, GWEN
(association president)
Affiliation: New Brunswick Native Indian Women's Council, 65 Brunswick St., Rm. 258, Fredericton, New Brunswick, Canada E3B 1G5 (506) 458-1114.

ORGANICK, ALIZA (Dine' Nation)
(attorney; professor of law)
Affiliation & Address: Professor of Law, University of New Mexico School of Law, 1117 Stanford NE, MSC11 6070, 1 University of New Mexico, Albuquerque, NM 87131. E-mail: organick@law.unm.edu.

OROPEZA, JOSE (Pomo)
(rancheria chairperson)
Affiliation: Manchester - Port Arena Rancheria, P.O. Box 623, Point Arena, CA 95468 (707) 882-2788.

O'ROURKE, THOMAS P., SR. (Yurok)
(tribal chairperson)
Affiliation & Address: Chairperson, Yurok Tribe, P.O. Box 1027, Klamath, CA 95548 (707) 482-1350. E-mail: torourke@yuroktribe.org.

ORR, DELILAH (Dine-Navajo)
(professor of English)
Affiliation & Address: Professor (1990-present), Department of English, 1000 Rim Dr., Fort Lewis College, Durango, CO 81301 (970) 247-7627. E-mail: orr_r@fortlewis.edu; Affiliated Faculty, Department of Native American & Indigenous Studies, Fort Lewis College. *Past professional post*: Navajo Community College, Tsaile, AZ, 1980-90. *Awards, honors*: Newberry Library Summer Fellow, 1990, 1991; Ford Fellowship Recipient, 1993-present.

ORTEGA, A. PAUL (Mescalero Apache)
(tribal president; singer, songwriter)
Affiliation & Address: Mescalero Apache Tribal Council, P.O. Box 176, Mescalero, NM 88340 (505) 671-4494. *Other professional posts*: Singer & songwriter for Canyon Records Productions, Phoenix, AZ. *Awards, honors*: Lifetime Achievement Award from the First Americans in the Arts for Outstanding Musical Achievement, February 1996.

ORTEGA, RUDY, JR. (Fernandeno Tataviam Mission Indian)
(tribal president)
Affiliation & Address: President, Fernandeno Tataviam Mission Indians, 1019 Second St. #1 • San Fernando, CA 91340 (818) 837-0794

ORTEZ, JOAN K. (Steilacoom)
(tribal chairperson)
Affiliation & Address: Steilacoom Indian Tribe, P.O. Box 88419, Steilacoom, WA 98388 (206) 584-6308; director, Steilacoom Tribal Cultural Center and Museum.

ORTIZ, ANNABEL
(program manager)
Education: University of California, Davis, BS. *Affiliation & Address*: Program Manager of American Indian Affairs (2010-present), Society for Advancement of Chicanos & Native Americans in Science (SACNAS), P.O. Box 8526, Santa Cruz, CA 95061 (831) 459-0170. She is the administrative coordinator & organizes the SYNAPSE Program & Native American confrence activities.

ORTIZ, ANTHONY (San Felipe Pueblo)
(former pueblo governor)
Affiliation & Address: Governor, Pueblo of San Felipe, P.O. Box 4339, San Felipe Pueblo, NM 87001

ORTIZ, MS. HANKIE (Kiowa/Caddo/Comanche)
(deputy Bureau of Indian Affairs director of Indian services)
Education: University of Oklahoma, BA (Psychology), 1991; University of Montana School of Law, JD, 1995. *Affiliation & Address*: Deputy Bureau of Indian Affairs Director of Indian Services, 1849 C St., NW, Washington, DC 20240. *Past professional posts*: Director, Office of Tribal Self-Governance (2007-12), Indian Health Service (IHS). She is responsible for advancing the positions & interests of self-governance tribes & providing policy analysis & development support to tribal governments & the IHS Director. Director, Division of Regulatory Affairs, deputy director, IHS Office of Management Services, 2006-2010; practicing attorney for 12 years before joining IHS. She worked for two private American Indian law firms in Oklahoma, representing tribes & individual American Indian clients & for the Native American Rights Fund in Washington, DC. Ms. Ortiz was an attorney with the DHH, Office of the General Counsel in the Public Health Division in Rockville, MD and in Region IX, San Francisco, California. She is regarded as an expert on Indian health law and Public Law 93-638 issues and is often asked to be a presenter, speaker, or instructor on related topics. *Awards, honors*: Founding member, treasurer & president-elect of the Native American Bar Assn of Washington, DC; founding board member of the California Indian Legal Assn; vice-chair on the Maryland Commission of Indian Affairs; co-chair of the Inaugural Washington, DC Indian Law Conference; & selected to serve as an Americans for Indian Opportunity Ambassador; three National Director's Awards for her outstanding perfor-mance, dedication & commitment to the mission of the IHS.

ORTIZ, JUAN
(Indian education program director)
Affiliation: Mt. Baker School District, Indian Education Program, P.O. Box 45, Deming, WA 98244 (360) 383-2015 ext. 4511.

ORTIZ, RAHO (Navajo-Dine'/Acoma Pueblo)
(IHS acting director Office of Urban Indian Health Programs)
Education: University of Notre Dame, BA (Government); University of Arizona College of Law, JD. *Affiliation & Address*: Acting Director, Office of Urban Indian Health Programs, Indian Health Service, 5600 Fishers Lane, Rockville, MD 20857. As Acting Director, Mr. Ortiz provides oversight of functions and operations related to Title V of the Indian Health Care Improvement Act (IHCIA) & health care services provided to American Indian and Alaska Native (AI/AN) beneficiaries who reside in urban areas across the nation. Mr. Ortiz is responsible for planning, developing and executing a federal health program that serves urban AI/AN people through programs that include direct medical services, dental services, pharmacy services, alcohol/substance abuse services, behavioral health, HIV/AIDS, health promotion & disease prevention services. Mr. Ortiz makes recommendations & provides key advice as a subject matter expert on methods of improving health care access & delivery to the urban AI/AN people through collaborative efforts with Indian tribes and tribal organizations; federal, state & local governments; public & private foundations; & other entities. Mr. Ortiz serves as principal advisor in the performance of national policy analysis, recommendation & implementation regarding legislative activities related to the Affordable Care Act (ACA), the IHCIA and the impact on urban AI/AN people and the Indian health system. *Past professional posts*: Mr. Ortiz joined IHS in 2007 as the Director of the Division of Regulatory Affairs. Most recently, he served as Director of the Division of Business Office Enhancement in the Office of Resource Access and Partnerships. He brings over 20 years of work experience in the field of Federal Indian law & policy. Served as Environmental Director for the Tohono O'odham Nation, Tribal Attorney for the Pascua Yaqui Tribe, Counsel to the U.S. Senate Committee on Indian Affairs, Tribal Liaison with the U.S. Environmental Protection Agency and as Development Director for the Friendship House Association of American Indians, Inc. of San Francisco, a residential substance abuse treatment facility for American Indians and Alaska Natives.

ORTIZ, ROBERT (Pueblo of Tamaya-Santa Ana)
 (Pueblo administrator)
Affiliation & Address: Administrator, Pueblo of Tamaya (Santa Ana), 2 Dove Rd., Bernalillo, NM 87004 (505) 867-3301.

ORTIZ, ROXANNE DUNBAR (Southern Cheyenne) 1938-
 (feminist, historian; professor of Native American studies)
Born September 10, 1938, Oklahoma. *Education*: San Francisco State University, BA, 1963; UC Berkeley, MA, 1965, UCLA, PhD (History), 1974. *Affiliation & Address*: Professor of Native Americann Studies, Dept. of Ethnic Studies. California State University, Hayward, CA 1974-present. E-mail: rdunbaro@pacbell.net. *Community activities*: Staff member, International Indian Treaty Council (non-governmental organization in consultative status with U.N.). *Published works*: The Great Sioux Nation (Random House, 1977); Roots of Resistance: A History of Land Tenure in New Mexico, 1680-1980 (UCLA, 1980; paper, University of Oklahoma Press, 2007); Outlaw Woman: A Memoir of the War Years, 1960-1975 (2002); Red Dirt: Growing Up Okie (paper, University of Oklahoma Press, 2005); Indians of the America: Human Rights & Self-Determination; Blood on the Border: A Memoir of the Contra War (2005).

ORTIZ, SIMON J. (Acoma Pueblo) 1941-
 (writer, poet, professor)
Born May 27, 1941, Albuquerque, N.M. *Education*: Fort Lewis College, 1961-62; University of New Mexico, Albuquerque, 1966-68; University of Iowa, Iowa City, 1968-69; Dr. of Letters, University of New Mexico (Honorary). *Affiliation & Address*: Regents Professor, Dept. of English, & American Indian Studies Program, College of Liberal Arts & Sciences, MC: 0302, Tempe, AZ 85287. (480) 965-7999. E-mail: simon.ortiz@asu.edu. Dr. Ortiz is an Indigenous poet & writer of Acoma Pueblo heritage who specializes in Indienous literature. *Other professional posts*: Founder & coordinator of the Indigenous Speakers Series sponsored by the ASU Dept. of English & American Indian Studies. *Past professional posts*: Instructor & co-director, Creative Writing Program, Sinte Gleska College, Mission, SD; consulting editor to Pueblo of Acoma, Institute of American Indian Arts Press, and Navajo Community College Press. *Military service*: U.S. Army, 1963-66. *Memberships*: Americans Before Columbus Foundation (board of directors, 1978-); American PEN, 1980-. *Awards, honors*: Discovery Award (Creative Writing, 1970), Fellowship (Creative Writing, 1981), National Endowment for the Arts. *Interests*: "Avocational interests include listening to music, long distance running, travel. Places I've traveled include all of the areas of the U.S., including Alaska in 1979, 1981, and 1984; I traveled to Europe, including Holland, Belgium, & Germany." *Published works*: Naked In The Wind (Quetzal-Vihio Press, 1971); Going For The Rain (Harper & Row, 1976); A Good Journey (Turtle Island Press, 1977); Howbah Indians (Blue Moon Press, 1978); The People Shall Continue (Children's Press Books, 1978); Fight Back (INAD-University of New Mexico, 1980); From Sand Creek (Thunder's Mouth Press, 1981); A Poem Is A Journey (Pternandon Press, 1982); Fightin' (Thunder's Mouth Press, 1983); Blue and Red (Acoma Pueblo Press, 1983); The Importance of Childhood (Acoma Pueblo Press, 1983); Woven Stone (University of Arizona Press, 1992); After and Before the Lightning (University of Arizona Press, 1994); Speaking for the Generations (U. of Arizona Press, 1998); Men on the Moon (U. of Arizona Press, 1999); From Sand Creek (U. of Arizona Press, 2000); Out There Somewhere (University of Arizona Press, 2002); The Good Rainbow Road (University of Arizona Press, 2004); numerous poetry collections and chapters in books.

ORTIZ, STEVE (Prairie Band Potawatomi)
 (former tribal chairperson)
Affiliation & Address: Prairie Band Potawatomi Indian Tribe, 16281 Q Rd., Mayetta, KS 66509 (785) 966-4007. E-mail: steveo@pbpnation. org

OSAWA, SANDY
 (film producer/director)
Affiliation: Upstream Productions, 420 First Ave. W., Seattle, WA 98119 (206) 524-8879.

OSBORNE, MARVIN
 (tribal chairperson)
Affiliation: Fort Hall Business Council, P.O. Box 306, Fort Hall, ID 83203 (208) 238-3700.

OSBURN-BIGFEATHER, JOANNA (Western Cherokee)
 (artist, curator)
Address & Affiliation: American Indian Community House Gallery & Museum, 11 Broadway, 2nd Floor, New York, NY 10004 (212) 598-0100.

OSCEOLA, CHRISTOPHER (Seminole of Florida)
 (tribal board of directors)
Affiliation & Address: Hollywood Reservation Representative, Board of Directors, Seminole Tribe of Florida, 6300 Stirling Rd., Hollywood, FL 33024 (800) 683-7800.

OSCEOLA, M. STEVE (Seminole of Florida)
 (tribal member of board of directors)
Affiliation & Address: Hollywood Representative, Board of Directors, Seminole Tribe of Florida, 6300 Stirling Rd., Hollywood, FL 33024 (800) 683-7800.

OSCEOLA, MARCELLUS W., JR. (Seminole of Florida)
 (tribal council representative)
Affiliation & Address: Hollywood Representative, Tribal Council, Seminole Tribe of Florida, 6300 Stirling Rd., Hollywood, FL 33024 (800) 683-7800.

OSCEOLA, TINA (Seminole of Florida)
 (former association president)
Affiliation: American Indian & Alaska Native Tourism Association (AIANTA), 2401 12th St., NW, Albuquerque, NM 87104 (505) 724-3592.

OSCEOLA-BRANCH, MARIE (Miccosukee/Seminole)
 (legislative specialist)
Education: University of Miami, BA (Elementary Education), 1975. Florida International University, MS (Educational Leadership), 1988. *Principal occupation*: Legislative specialist. *Address & Affiliation*: Hobbs, Straus, Dean & Walker, LLP, 2120 L St., NW, Suite 700, Washington, DC 20037 (202) 822-8282, 1994-present. E-mail: mosceola-branch@hsdwdc.com. *Past professional post*: Miccosukee Tribe, 1980-94, as health education coordinator, tribal school principal, & government programs manager. Firm responsibilities: Monitoring and advocacy on various legislative & appropriations issues, including Indian Self-Determination and housing as well as the BIA and HUD budgets. She closely follows legislation related to gaming and transportation.

OSKOLKOFF, D.L. (Kenaitse)
 (executive director)
Affiliation: Ninilchik Traditional Council Health Clinic, P.O. Box 39070, Ninilchik, AK 99762 (907) 567-3313.

OSKOLKOFF, GASSIM (Kenaitse)
 (association president)
Affiliation: Ninilchik Native Association, Inc., P.O. Box 282, Ninilchik, AK 99639 (907) 567-3313.

OSKOLKOFF, PAT (Kenaitse)
 (health director)
Affiliation: Ninilchik Traditional Council Health Clinic, P.O. Box 39070, Ninilchik, AK 99762 (907) 567-3313.

OSTERBACK, DAVID O. (Aleut)
 (Alaskan tribal president)
Affiliation: Qagan Tayagungin Tribe of Sand Point Village, P.O. Box 447, Sand Point, AK 99661 (907) 383-5616.

OSUNA, REBECCA M. (Kumeyaay Diegueno)
 (tribal chairperson)
Affiliation: Chairperson, Inaja-Cosmit Band of Mission Indians, 2005 S. Escondido Blvd., Escondido, CA 92025 (760) 737-7628.

OTHERBULL, DELEANA (Crow-Northern Cheyenne)
 (executive director)
Education: Institute of American Indian & Alaska Native Culture, BFA, 2006; University of Arizona, BA (Psychology), 2008; The University of New Mexico, MA (Health Policy & Administration), 2015. *Affiliation & Address*: Executive Director (2014-present), Coalition to Sop Violence Against Native Women, The University of New Mexico, Albuquerque, NM. *Past professional posts*: Director, Native American Education Program, Amphitheater Unified School District, 2007-09; Program Manager/Training & Development Manager, National Indian Council on Aging, 2009-12; Programs Officer, AISES, 2012-13. *Awards, honors*: New Ventures in Leadership Partner, Ameican Society on Aging, 2012; Native American Political Leadership Program, George Washington University, 2014; 2017 Emerge Co-hort, 2017; 2017 Albuquerque Professional Business Woman of the Year.

OTTERSON, JONATHAN (Miwok)
 (tribal executive director)
Affiliation & Address: Executive Director, Tuolumne Band of Me-wuk Indians, P.O. Box 699, Tuolumne, CA 95379 (209) 928-5300.

OWEN, CRYSTAL (Sisseton Wahpeton Oyate)
(tribal secretary)
Affiliation & Address: Secretary, Sisseton Wahpeton Oyate, Lake Traverse Reservation, P.O. Box 509, Agency Village, SD 57262 (605) 698-3911. E-mail: chairman@swo-nsn.gov.

OWENS, WILLIAM (Comanche)
(tribal administrator)
Affiliation & Address: Administrator, Comanche Nation, P.O. Box 908, Lawton, OK 73502 (580) 492-3240. E-mail: williamo@comanchenation.com

OWLE, DEB (Eastern Cherokee)
(program operations & grants manager)
Montreat College, BS (Buiness Administration). *Affiliation & Address*: Program Operations & Grants Manager (2002-present), Cherokee Preservation Foundation, P.O. Box 504, Cherokee, NC 28719. (828) 497-5550. E-mail: dmintz@cpfdn.org. *Other professional post*: Foundation's community liaison for the Cherokee Day of Caring. *Past professional post*: Eastern Band Cherokee Tribal Travel & Promotion Program (17 years).

OWLE, JIM (Eastern Cherokee)
(former tribal chairperson)
Affiliation & Address: Chairperson, Eastern Band of Cherokee Indians, Qualla Boundary, P.O. Box 455, Cherokee, NC 28719 (828) 497-7000.

OWLIJOOT, THOMAS (Inuit)
(director-Institute)
Affiliation: Inuit Cultural Institute, Eskimo Point, N.W.T., Canada X0C 0E0 (819) 857-2803.

OXENDINE, DARLENE (Lumbee)
(BIA area office director)
Affiliation: Director, Minneapolis Area Office, Bureau of Indian Affairs, 331 Second Ave. S., Minneapolis, MN 55401 (612) 373-1000.

OXENDINE, LINDA E. (Lumbee)
(Indian studies professor emeritus)
Affiliation & Address: Professor Emeritus, Department of American Indian Studies, University of North Carolina at Pembroke, P.O. Box 1510, Pembroke, NC 28372 (910) 521-6266. E-mail: linda.oxendine@uncp.edu

OXENDINE, RICK (Lumbee)
(executive director)
Affiliation & Address: Executive Director, Guilford Native American Association, Inc., P.O. Box 5623, Greensboro, NC 27435 (336) 273-8686. E-mail: rox12@windstream.net.

P

PACE, GARY (Chumash)
(tribal secretary-treasurer)
Born & raised on the Santa Ynez Reservation and attended local schools. *Affiliation & Address*: Secretary-Treasurer, Business Committee, Santa Ynez Band of Mission Indians, P.O. Box 317, Santa Ynez, CA 93460 (805) 688-7997. As a skilled welder, he worked in Santa Ynez for many years until recently retiring from the welding business. He continues to work on special welding projects creating unique signs and art for family and friends. Gary comes from a family of tribal leaders. His parents served on the tribal leadership team for many years and his two sisters have been involved on various tribal committees.

PACHECO, DAVID, JR. (Kickapoo)
(tribal chairperson)
Affiliation & Address: Chairperson, Kickapoo Tribe, P.O. Box 70, McLoud, OK 74851 (405) 964-2075. E-mail: dpacheco@kickapootribeofoklahoma.com

PACHECO, TOMMY (Shoshoni)
(tribal chairperson)
Affiliation: Northwestern Band of Shoshoni Nation, P.O. Box 637, Blackfoot, ID 83221 (208) 785-7401.

PACHITO, SASHA (Soboba Band of Luiseno)
(institute program coordinator)
Education: Cornell University, BS (Rural Sociology with concentrations in American Indian Studies & Latino Studies; Arizona State University, MA (Urban & Environmental Planning) & recently completed a graduate certificate in Public Administration from ASU. *Affiliation & Address*: Program Manager, Tribal Economic Leadership Program at the American Indian Policy Institute,

Ariizona State University, Box 872603, Tempe, AZ 85287 (480) 965-1055. Email: sasha.pachito@asu.edu. *Past professional post*: Prior to joining ASU, she was the Transportation Planning Manager for the Gila River Indian Community. While at Gila River, she was successful in obtaining several grants to improve the Community's infrastructure, represented Western Region tribes on transportation matters while serving on a Federal transportation policy committee, & was responsible for the creation & administration of the new Community transit service.

PACKINEAU, JASON (Mandan/Hidatsa/Arikara; Jemez/Laguna Pueblo)
(community coordinator)
Affiliation & Address: Community Coordiantor, Harvard University Native American Program, 14 Story St., 4th Floor, Cambridge, MA 02138 (617) 495-4923; E-mail: jason_packineau@harvard.edu. Prior to joining the HUNAP office, Jason helped build the Student Development Program for Native American students enrolled at the University of New Mexico's Health Sciences Center. During his time at the University of New Mexico he conducted outreach to tribal communities on behalf of the university and served as the Staff Advisor for two graduate Native American student groups. Mr. Packineau made the shift from K-12 education to higher education after spending seven years in Washington, DC as a teacher in DC Public Schools.

PACKINEAU, JESSICA (Mandan/Hidatsa/Arikara)
(assistant director of Honoring Nations)
Education: University of New Mexico School of Law, JD (Indian Law Ceritifate). *Affiliation & Address*: Visiting Administrative Fellow Assistant Director of Honoring Nations, The Harvard Project on American Indian Economic Development, 79 JFK St., Cambridge, MA 02138 (617) 495-8998. E-mail: Jessica_packineau@hks.harvard.edu. *Other professional post*: Serves as the Northeast Region Editor for the Federal Bar Association's Indian Law Section Newsletter. *Past professional posts*: Taught family law in Indian Country at Lewis & Clark Law School; spent two years living & teaching on the Rosebud Reservation.

PACKINEAU, MERVIN (Mandan, Hidatsa, Arikara)
(tribal vice chairperson)
Affiliation: Three Affiliated Tribes of the Fort Berthold Reservation, 404 Frontage Rd., New Town, ND 58763 (701) 627-4781.

PADI, SHAWN (Pomo)
(former tribal chairperson)
Affiliation & Address: Chairperson, Hopland Band of Pomo Indians, 3000 Shanei Rd., Hopland, CA 95449 (707) 472-2111. E-mail: spadi@hoplandtribe.com.

PADGETTE, DENISE (Tolowa)
(tribal vice chairperson)
Affiliation & Address: Vice Chairperson, Tolowa Tribe of the Smith River Rancheria, 140 Rowdy Creek Rd., Smith River, CA 95567 (707) 218-7723. dpadgette@tolowa. com.

PADILLA, HELEN B. (Isleta Pueblo)
(attorney; Indian law center director)
Education: University of New Mexico, BA, MBA, JD (Certificate in Indian Law). *Affiliation*: Director (2007-present), American Indian Law Center, Inc., P.O. Box 4456, Albuquerque, NM 87196 (505) 277-5462. E-mail: padilla@ailc-inc.org. *Other professional posts*: Member, Board of Directors, Indian Law Section of the New Mexico State Bar; vice chairperson, Laguna Pueblo Gaming Control Board. *Past professional posts*: Tax administrator & general counsel for the Pueblo of Tesuque (NM). In 2004, Gov. Bill Richardson (D-NM) appointed Helen to the General Counsel position for the New Mexico Indian Affairs Dept. She was also a senior staff attorney for the Mohegan Tribe of Indians in Connecticut; assistant counsel for the Social Security Administration in Denver and a legal intern with the National Indian Gaming Commission in Wash., DC.

PADDYAKER, DAREN (Comanche-Cherokee) 1964-
(adolescent counselor)
Born November 18, 1964, Oklahoma City, Okla. *Education*: University of Oklahoma, BA (Psychology), 1989. *Affiliation & Address*: Adolescent counselor, 14301 S. Rockwell, Oklahoma City, OK 73173 (405) 232-0736 (work). Oklahoma City Indian Clinic, Oklahoma City, OK (Adolescent Counselor, 1991-). *Past professional post*: Worked with repeat juvenile offenders for 3 years in an inpatient setting. *Community activities*: Member, Oklahoma City Public Schools Task Force on Reducing Gang Involvement in Oklahoma City Public Schools; speak with public school Title V programs and parent committees about street gangs & gang-related activities in the urban Indian community. *Membership*: University of Oklahoma American Indian Alumni Society. *Interests*: "working with "at-risk" urban Indian youth and helping them to find traditional as well as non-traditional support bases."

PADILLA, FERNANDO, JR. (San Felipe Pueblo-Navajo) 1958-
  (artist-painter)
Born July 29, 1958, Los Angeles, Calif. *Education*: Indian Bible College, Albuquerque; Bethany (OK) Southern Nazarene University. *Principal occupation*: Artist-painter. *Address*: 4632 SE 20th, Del City, OK 73115 (405) 672-9724. *Membership*: Indian Arts & Crafts Assn. *Awards, honors*: "Judges Best of Show," 1981-OK Indian Youth Art Festival; "Second Place - Sculpture," 1985-Native American Art & Craft Show, Rose State College, Midwest City, OK; Annual Trail of Tears Art Show, Tahlequah, OK (1985 "Newcomers Award,"; 1986 "Special Merit Award;" & 1989 "Special Merit Award"); Intertribal Ceremonial, Gallup, NM (1987-"First Place-Painting" & First Place-Miniatures; 1988-"Second Place-Watercolors; 1990-First Place Watercolors; 1991-"First Place-Mixed Media and "Third Place-Acrylics"; among others.

PADILLA, HELEN B. (Isleta Pueblo)
  (attorney; director of Indian law center)
Education: University of New Mexico, BS & MBA (Business Administration), PhD, with a Certificate in Indian Law. *Affiliation & Address*: Director, American Indian Law Center, Inc., P.O. Box 4456, Albuquerque, NM 87131 (505) 277-5462. E-mail: padilla@ailc-inc.org. *Other professional posts*: Board member for the Indian Law Section of the New Mexico State Bar; vice chair, Laguna Pueblo Gaming Control Board. *Past professional posts*: Tax administrator & general counsel for the Pueblo of Tesuque; senior staff attorney, Mohegan Tribe of Indians in Connecticut; assistant regional counsel for the Social Security Administration in Denver, CO; legal intern, National Indian Gaming Commission, Washington, DC. *Awards, honors*: In 2004, Governor Richardson appointed Helen to the General Counsel position for the New Mexico Indian Affairs Department. *Memberships*: New Mexico State Bar, Colorado State Bar, Connecticut State Bar.

PADILLA, JERRY (Penobscot)
  (former tribal governor)
Affiliation: Penobscot Tribal Council, Community Bldg., Indian Island, Old Town, ME 04468 (207) 827-7776.

PADILLA, RANDOLPH (Jemez Pueblo)
  (former pueblo governor)
Affiliation: Jemez Pueblo, P.O. Box 100, Jemez, NM 87024 (505) 834-7359.

PADILLA, SOLOMON, JR. (Pueblo)
  (school principal)
Affiliation: Santa Clara Day School, P.O. Box HHH, Espanola, NM 87532 (505) 753-4406.

PAHDOPONY, JUANITA (*Puh-Nah-Vet-Tha - the only daughter*)
(Comanche) 1947-
  (professor; gallery owner-visual artist)
Born January 18, 1947, Portland, Oreg. *Education*: Southwest Oklahoma State University, BA, 1970; Oklahoma City University, M.Ed., 1989; She was a tribal college fellow in the MDP at Harvard University. *Affiliations & Address*: Artist/Owner, Pahdopony Gallery, 209 NW Mamosa Lane, Lawton, OK 73507 (580) 591-0203; professor, Dept. of Education, Cameron University, Lawton, OK, 1994-present. *Other professional post*: National Advisory Board of Native Writers, Wordcraft Circle; professional artist. *Community activities*: Board member, Institute of the Great Plains; board member, Jacobson Foundation; Comanche Gourd Dancer. *Memberships*: Oklahoma Art Therapists Assn; Wordcraft Circle (National Advisory Board, 1992-96). *Past professional posts*: She has taught at Elgin Public Schools, Oklahoma City University, University of Science and Arts of Oklahoma, Cameron University, and Comanche Nation College. She is a member of the Southern Plains Indian Museum Association, Wordcraft Circle of Native Writers and Storytellers, National Advisory Caucus and the Jacobson Foundation. She has given numerous presentations related to art and has exhibited her own works at galleries throughout Oklahoma. *Awards, honors*: McMahon Foundation, 1985; "Outstanding Teacher of the Gifted" Jolene Grantham Award, Oklahoma City University, 1989; "Moving Murals" 2 year traveling tip show (State Arts Council, Jacobson Foundation), 1994. *Interests*: Professional painter, visual artist; cradlemaker. storyteller, lecturer, educator, writer, poet. *Biographical sources*: Artist cover: Callaloo, Vol. 17 #1, by Native American Literatures, Johns Hopkins University Press); designed logo of the National Indian Policy Center, Washington, DC. Published works: two poems - "Poetry Nebraska English Journal," 1994, & Returning the Gift, 1994; two published scholarly papers - "Creative Perspectives," 1990, & "Native American Art Therapy," 1985.

PAHMAHMIE, ZACH (Prairie Band Potawatomi)
  (tribal chairperson)
Affiliation: Prairie Band Potawatomi Tribe, 16281 Q Rd., Mayetta, KS 66509 (785) 966-4000.

PAILES, RICHARD
  (professor emeritus-Native American studies)
Affiliation & Address: Professor Emeritus, Native American Studies Program, University of Oklahoma, 455 W. Lindsey, Dale Hall Tower 521, Norman, OK 73019 (405) 325-2504. E-mail: rapailes@ou.edu. *Research Interests*: Method & theory in prehistoric anthropology, human ecology, greater Southwest, Mesoamerica.

PAINTE, DEBORAH A. (*Red Prairie Rose*) (Arikara, Hidatsa)
  (insitute director)
Born in Stanley, N.D. *Education*: Haskell Indian Jr. College, AA, 1977, AAS, 1978; Central State University (Edmond, OK), BBA, 1984; Montana State University, MPA, 1992. *Affiliation*: Director, Native American Training Institute (NATI) (Website: www.nativeinstitute.org), 3333 E. Broadway Ave. #1210, Bismarck, ND 58501 (701) 255-6374. E-mail: debp@nativeinstite.org. *Other professional post*: Chairperson-Board of Directors, Three Affiliated Tribes Museum. *Past professional posts*: Fort Berthold Community College, Newtown, ND (three years); director, Sacred Child Project (a graduated (SAMHSA) Center for Mental Health system of care (SOC) site (nine years) in developing "Wraparound in Indian Country: A CD-ROM Guide to Wraparound Meetings"; executive director (7 years), ND Indian Affairs Commission, Bismarck, ND.

PAINTER, CLARENCE (Athapascan)
  (Alaskan village president)
Affiliation: Shageluk Native Village, P.O. Box 109, Shageluk, AK 99665 (907) 473-8239.

PAINTER, WILLIAM (Eskimo)
  (Alaskan village president)
Affiliation: Organized Village of Grayling, P.O. Box 49, Grayling, AK 99590 (907) 453-5116.

PAISANO, E. SCOTT (Sandia Pueblo)
  (former Pueblo lt. governor)
Affiliation: Pueblo of Sandia Pueblo, 481 Sandia Loop, Bernalillo, NM 87004 (505) 867-3317.

PAISANO, EDNA
  (liaison)
Affiliation: Liaison for American Indian & Alaska Natives, Bureau of the Census, Federal Center, Suitland, MD 20233 (301) 763-2607.

PAISANO, STUART (Sandia Pueblo)
  (Pueblo lt. governor)
Affiliation & Address: Lt. Governor, Sandia Pueblo Tribal Council, P.O. Box 6008, Bernalillo, NM 87004 (505) 867-3317.

PAISANO, WALLY (Western Shoshone)
  (health director)
Affiliation: Owyhee Community Health Facility, P.O. Box 364, Owyhee, NV 89832 (702) 757-2415.

PAIVA, JAMES (Shoshone)
  (tribal chairperson)
Affiliation: Shoshone Paiute Business Council, Duck Valley Reservation, P.O. Box 219, Owyhee, NV 89832 (775) 757-3161.

PAIZ, FRANK (Tigua)
  (former tribal governor)
Affiliation & Address: Ysleta Del Sur Pueblo, P.O. Box 17579, El Paso, TX.

PAKOOTAS, JOSEPH (Confederated Tribes)
  (former tribal chairperson)
Affiliation: Colville Business Committee, P.O. Box 150, Nespelem, WA 98568 (360) 273-5911.

PALE MOON, PRINCESS (*Win Yon Sa Han We*) (Cherokee/Ojibwa)
  (performing author, concert recording artist; foundation executive)
Born April 15th in Asheville, N.C. *Education*: Sonoma State College, Sonoma, CA (Liberal Arts). *Principal occupation*: Performing author, concert recording artist; and foundation executive. *Address*: P.O. Box 750, Pigeon Forge, TN 37868. *Affiliation*: Founder, president & chairman of the Board, American Indian Heritage Foundation, Falls Church, VA, 1973-2005; Pigeon Forge, TN, 2005-present. *Memberships*: National Congress of American Indians (life member); Native American Advisory Committee; Boy Scouts of America; American Pen Women; Business & Professional Women's Association; International Platform Association. *Awards, honors*: Many outstanding achievement awards & other awards from colleges, independent organizations and service clubs, including: Sertoma International, "Humanitarian of the Year"; American Hostess at the International Olympics; concert performer at the Kennedy Center; featured on four vocal albums; Ambassador of Friendship

representative for USO shows in Europe; hostess of annual Children's Shows at the Kennedy Center. *Interests*: Has represented the U.S. & the American Indian people in numerous countries, both as spokesperson and as a performing artist. Has special interest in building better understanding between the tribes and people of the world. Many articles have been written about Palo Moon, and the Foundation, including the Style Section of the Washington Post, Decision Magazine, the Los Angeles, Times, the Fairfax Journal and many radio and TV interviews. *Published work*: Pale Moon: The Story of an Indian Princess (Tyndale, 1975).

PALMENTEER, EDDIE, JR. (Colville)
(former tribal chairperson)
Affiliation: Colville Business Committee, P.O. Box 150, Nespelem, WA 99155 (509) 634-4711.

PALMER, DIXON (Kiowa)
(craftsperson, store owner)
Affiliation: Artisan/Owner, Dixon Palmer Headdresses and Tipis, Rt. 3 Box 189, Anadarko, OK 73005 (405) 247-3983. *Artwork*: Headdresses of imitation eagle feathers; painted or plain tipi covers.

PALMER, GUS, JR. (*Panthaide*) (Kiowa)
(professor of anthropology; Interim Director, Native American Studies)
Education: Univesity of Oklahoma, PhD, 2000. *Affiliation & Address*: Associate Professor of Anthropology & Interim Director of Native American Studies, 455 West Lindsey, DHT 505C, University of Oklahoma (OU), Norman, OK (405) 325-8786. E-mail: gpalmer@ou.edu. *Research Interests*: Kiowa language database & dictionary, Kiowa texts documentation, and general storytelling & oral tradition. *Other professional posts*: Serves as an advisor to "Vocal & Oral Verbal Arts" (VOVA), based at the University of North Carolina. Dr. Palmer writes, "I will be contributing mainly to verse analysis, performance models for language revitalization programs, and some song lyrics editing. I have contributed chapters to books on American Indian texts (published in 2011, transcribed & translated both, one at the OU Press, edited by Paul Kroskrity, and the other at the University of Nebraska Press, edited by David Kozak. I have a recent publication in journals, "Oral Traditions" and "American Indina Quarterly." I am also editing a volume, "Great Plains Verbal Arts", in the Native American Literature Series, the University of Nebraska Press. I am also the co-author of an indigenous cultural geography & oral narrative book to be published by SUNY Press. My work continues as a speaker and translator contributor in new films & videos by Kiowa filmmaker, Jeffrey P. Palmer."

PALMER, JIM L. (Miami/Peoria of Oklahoma) 1943-
(founder/director-cultural center)
Born July 29, 1943, Oklahoma City, Okla. *Education*: Oklahoma University (2 years); Tulsa Technical College. *Address & Affiliation*: Founder-director, Native American Cultural Center, Fort Dodge, IA (515) 576-3867. *Military service*: U.S. Marine Corps (Cpl. - Received Heroism Award, 1983, Kiwanis-Las Vegas, NV). *Community activities*: Protection Advocacy Program of Iowa (board member), Des Moines; Pilot Parents of Iowa, Fort Dodge; Iowa Job Service, Fort Dodge; teach classes to college, high school & elementary levels, on culture, language & legends at request of teachers. *Interests*: "We research Indian languages on the verge of extinction (to reproduce, teach & put in libraries for posterity). We educate the general public about Native peoples customs, legends, languages, etc. We have craft classes for the general public, and had our 1st Annual Indian Powwow in Aug. 1994." *Biographical source*: "Fort Dodge Messenger," front-page articles, Dec., 1993 & May, 1994.

PALMER, TRACY L. (Creek/Seminole/Cherokee) 1958-
(director of Indian education)
Born December 31, 1958, Tulsa, Okla. *Education*: University of Tulsa, BFA, 1983, Oklahoma City University, MEd, 1991. *Principal occupation*: Training specialist/Indian educator. *Affiliation & Address*: Specialist, American Indian Education Program (2005-present), Dallas ISD, 3434 So. RL Thornton Freeway, Rm. 124, Dallas, TX 75224 (214) 932-5300. E-mail: tpalmer@dallasisd.org. *Past professional posts*: American Indian Research & Development, Inc., Norman, OK, 1991-95; director, Indian Education Program, Jones Public Schools, Jones, OK, 1995-2005. *Community activities*: Educational & Cultural Association for Indian Youth; volunteer, Democratic Party of Oklahoma. *Memberships*: National Association for Gifted Children; Oklahoma Federation of Indian Women. *Awards, honors*: Nominee for Leadership Tulsa, 1988; selected to do a presentation in Kansas City, MO, at the National Convention for Gifted Children, November, 1991; also gave same presentation at the State of Oklahoma Association for Gifted & Talented Children on cross-cultural development integrating art into mathematics for gifted & talented Native American students. *Interests*: Travel throughout Oklahoma & Texas giving presentations on self-esteem & motivation along with leadership, primarily targeting junior and senior high Indian students."

PALMER, VERA BAUER (Tuscarora-Six Nations)
(lecturer of Native American studies)
Education: Bryn Mawr College, B.A., M.A.; Cornell University, M.A. (English Language & Literature); PhD candidate. *Affiliation & Address*: Senior lecturer (1999-present), Dartmouth College, Native American Studies Program, 37 N. Main St., The Sherman House, Hanover, NH 03755 (603) 646-3530. E-mail: vera.b.palmer@dartmouth.edu. Vera teaches Contemporary Native American Oral Traditions Literature. *Awards, honors*: Dartmouth's Eastman Dissertation Fellowship in April 2000. Her dissertation, "Bringing Kateri Home: Restoring a Cultural Narrative of an Iroquoian Saint," considers the Jesuit hagiography of Mohawk Christian ascetic, Kateri Tekakwitha. Her work proposes an indigenous account of loss & historical grief employing perspectives & principles of the Iroquoian Condolence tradition. At Cornell, she created the Native American Indian Prisoners' Support Program within two New York State maximum-facilities. In recognition of her work on this project, she was awarded in 1999 the Robinson-Appel Humanitarian Award. Ms. Palmer began work to establish cultural outreach program at Dartmouth to benefit Native prisoners in New England correctional facilities. She initiated the Native Women's Song Circle at Dartmouth, and a Quilt Project at the NAD House. She serves as the Faculty Advisor for the Alpha Pi Omega Native American women's sorority.

PANEAK, RAYMOND (Eskimo)
(village council president)
Affiliation: Village of Anaktuvuk Pass, Anaktuvuk, AK 99721 (907) 661-3113.

PANTEAH, VAL (Zuni Pueblo)
(Pueblo governor)
Affiliation & Address: Governor, Pueblo of Zuni, P.O. Box 339, Zuni, NM 87327 (505) 782-7022.

PAPINEAU, IRVING (Mohawk)
(school principal)
Affiliation: St. Regis Mohawk School, Gowanda Central School District, Hogansburg, NY 13655.

PAQUIN, DANIEL GERARD (Chippewa) 1953-
(mechanical engineer)
Born January 4, 1953, Grand Rapids, Mich. *Education*: University of Hawaii, BS, 1980, MS, 1984. *Address*: 650 Ainapo St., Honolulu, HI 96825 (808) 395-2175. *Affiliation*: Dept. of Agricultural Engineering, University of Hawaii, Honolulu, 1986-present. *Other professional post*: President, American Society of Agricultural Engineers, Hawaii Section. *Military service*: U.S. Navy, 1972-75; Reserves, 1976-80 (E-4). *Memberships*: American Indian Science & Engineering Society; Sierra Club. *Interests*: "Science-by-mail "scientist" for Museum of the Rockies."

PAQUIN, RONALD J. (Sault Ste. Marie Chippewa)
(self-employed artist)
Born September 4, 1942, St. Ignace, Mich. *Address*: 1200 E. 11th Ave., Sault Ste. Marie, MI 49783 (906) 635-8158. E-Mail: ramp@lighthouse.net. *Affiliation*: Marquette Mission Park & Museum of Ojibwa Culture, St. Ignace, MI, 1985-2001. *Awards, honors*: 2003 Michigan Heritage Award. *Membership*: Sault Ste. Marie Tribe of Chippewa Indians. *Interests*: Birch bark canoe maker. *Published work*: Not First In Nobody's Heart: The Life Story of a Contemporary Chippewa, with Robert Doherty (RJP Press, St. Ignace, MI).

PARADA, GWENDOLYN (Diegueno)
(tribal chairperson)
Affiliation & Address: Chairperson, La Posta Band of Mission Indians, P.O. Box 1120, Boulevard, CA 91905 (619) 478-2113.

PARASHONTS, TRAVIS N. (Southern Paiute) 1953-
(tribal chief executive officer)
Born October 10, 1953, Cedar City, Utah. *Education*: Southern Utah State College, BA, 1979; University of Utah (Masters of Social Work candidate). *Affiliation & Address*: Chief Executive Officer, Nottawaseppi Huron Band of Potawatomi, 2221 - 1 1/2 Mile Rd., Fulton, MI 49052 (269) 704-8493. E-mail: tparashonts@nhbpi.com. *Past professional posts*: Director, Utah Division of Indian Affairs, Salt Lake City, UT; former tribal chairman, Paiute Tribe; American Indian Service, Brigham Young University, Provo, Utah (board member); American Indian Cultural Foundation, Page, AZ (board member); Indian Affiliates, Orem, UT (board member). *Awards, honors*: Spencer W. Kimball Award for working with Indian people; Paiute Tribal Award for service as tribal chairman; Cedar City Chamber of Commerce Award. *Interests*: "I assisted the Paiute Tribe in getting federal recognition in 1980 and helped them get back 5,000 acres of land and established a $2.5 million irrevocable trust fund for economic development." *Published work*: Paiute Language--For Beginner (Southern Utah State College, 1980).

PARCEAUD, JUDY
(Indian centre director)
Affiliation: Cree Indian Centre, 95 rue Jaculet, Chibougamau, Quebec, Canada G8P 2G1 (418) 748-7667.

PARDILLA, JERRY
(executive director)
Affiliation: National Tribal Environmental Council, 2221 Rio Grande NW, Albuquerque, NM 87104 (505) 242-2175.

PAREDES, J. ANTHONY 1939-
(professor of anthropology)
Born September 29, 1939, New York, N.Y. *Education*: Oglethorpe University (Atlanta, GA), AB, 1961; University of New Mexico, MA, 1964, PhD, 1969. *Affiliation & Address*: Professor Emeritus, Department of Anthropology, Tallahassee, FL 32306 (850) 644-4281 (work). E-mail: janthonyparedes@belsouth.net. FL, 1969-present. *Other professional posts*: Consultants to various federal & state agencies & private firms; editorial board, American Indian Culture & Research Journal. Past professional posts: *Affiliations*: Upper Mississippi Mental Health Center, Bemidji, MN, 1964-66; Bemidji State College (acting director, American Indian Studies), University of Minnesota, Bemidji, MN, 1967-69. *Community activities*: Member, Scientific & Statistical Committee, Gulf of Mexico Fishery Management Council (1978-88; task force on Federal Recognition, Association on American Indian Affairs, 1987-88. *Memberships*: Society for Applied Anthropology (president, 1993-95); Southern Anthropological Society (president, 1988-89); American Anthropological Association (Fellow); Sigma Xi, the Scientific Research Society. *Awards, honors*: Woodrow Wilson Fellow, 1961-62; National Institute of Mental Health Predoctoral Fellow, 1968-69; Poarch Creek Indian Service Award, 1990. *Interests*: Ethnographic fieldwork in Minnesota (non-Indians & Chippewa), Alabama (Creek Indians), Mexico (small town residents); Florida (commercial fisherman); travel in Southwestern U.S. & Spain. *Biographical sources*: American Men and Women of Science, Social and Behavioral Sciences (12th Edition); Who's Who in America, 48th Ed. *Published works*: Anishinaabe: Six Studies of Modern Chippewa (University Presses of Florida, 1980); editor, Indians of the Southeastern U.S. in the Late 20th Century (University of Alabama Press, 1992); numerous articles, chapters, reviews, etc. in scholarly books and journals.

PARENT, ELIZABETH ANNE (*Wa Su Win*) (Athabascan) 1941-
(professor of Native American studies)
Born January 12, 1941, Bethel, Alaska. *Education*: University of Alaska, BA (Anthropology); Harvard Graduate School of Education, MEd & CAS, 1973; Stanford University, PhD, 1984. *Principal occupation*: Professor of American Indian Studies. *Address*: 715-13 One Appian Way, So. San Francisco, CA 94080 (650) 589-4041. *Affiliation*: San Francisco State University, 1600 Holloway Ave., San Francisco, CA 94132, 1980-. *Other professional post*: Information & Technology Committee, National Museum of the American Indian, Smithsonian Institution. *Memberships*: American Indian Science & Engineering Society; Stanford Indian Alumni Association; American Indian Education Association. *Awards, honors*: Postdoctoral Fellow, American Indian Studies Center, U.C.L.A., 1985-1986; Ford Fellow; Danforth Fellow; Meritorious Professional Promise Awards, San Francisco State University, 1987 & 1989. *Interests*: American Indian education, and women's rights. *Published work*: The Educational Experiences of the Residents of Bethel, Alaska, Ph.D. dissertation (Stanford University); "Betty Parent - Woman With a Mission" in Winds of Change; & "Native Ability" in Spring Alumni SFSU, 1991.

PAREZO, NANCY J.
(professor of anthropology)
Education: University of Arizona, PhD, 1981. *Address & Affiliation*: American Indian Studies Program, University of Arizona, Harvill 235C, Box 210076, Tucson, AZ 85721 (520) 626-4057. E-mail: parezo@email.arizona.edu. (1998-present). *Other professional posts*: Arizona State Museum (1998-present); research associate, Field Museum of Natural History; she serves on the University of Arizona's Institutional Review Board in Medicine. *Interests*: Cultural/social anthropology; ethno-history southwest, especially Navajo. *Published works*: Paths of Life: American Indians of the Southwest & Northern Mexico (U. of Arizona Press); article: "Selling the Indian: Commercializing & Appropriating American Indian Cultures," & "Blackwell Companion to Native American History," A Companion to American Indian History.

PARISH, MICHAEL C. (Bay Mills Ojibwe)
(community college president)
Education: Lake Superior State University, BA; Thomas M. Cooley Law School, JD. *Affiliation & Address*: President, Bay Mills Community College, 12214 W. Lakeshore Dr., Administration Bldg., Brimley, MI 49715 (906) 248-3354 ext. 8400; E-mail: mparish@bmcc.edu. *Other professional post*: Treasurer, Board of Directors, American Indian Higher Education Consortium, Alexandria, VA.

PARISIAN, DEAN T. (White Earth Chippewa) 1953-
(investment advisor)
Born December 20, 1953, Morris, Minn. *Education*: U.S. Military Academy at West Point; University of Minnesota, Morris, BA, 1976; Hamline University School of Law. *Principal occupation*: Investment management. *Address & Affiliation*: Chairperson & founder, Chippewa Partners-Native American Advisors, Inc., 801 N. Brookshade Pkwy., Alpharetta, GA 30004 (770) 772-1621. E-Mail: thechippewafund@aol.com. *Other professional post*: Co-investment advisor to the Four Winds Fund; arbitrator, National Association of Securities Dealers & the New York Stock Exchange. *Past professional posts*: Kidder, Peabody, 1982; Drexel Burnham & First Union prior to founding Chippewa Partners in 1995. *Memberships*: Association of Investment Management & Research; Atlanta Society of Financial Analysts; President's Club of the University of Minnesota; Georgia Ornithological Society; Southeastern Hedge Fund Association. *Awards, honors*: While living on the Yankton Sioux Reservation, he received the South Dakota Outstanding Indian Athlete Award. After receiving an appointment to West Point & playing football there for a year, Dean transferred to the University of Minnesota. He has funded a $25,000 scholarship for Native American students for the President's Club of the University of Minnesota. Mr. Parisian was named one of the "Top Alumni Entrepreneurs" of 1996 from the University of Minnesota.; He was the first Native American licensed with the U.S. Securities & Exchange Commission as a mutual fund manager.

PARISIEN, ROBERT J.
(Indian education program administrator)
Affiliation: North Dakota Indian Affairs Commission, 600 E. Boulevard Ave. Room 117, Bismarck, ND 58505 (701) 328-2443. E-mail: bparisien@nd.gov.

PARK, PATINA (Cheyenne River Sioux)
(attorney)
Education: Arizona State University, BA; Hamline University School of Law, JD. *Affiliation & Address*: Tribal attorney, Ho-Chunk Nation, P.O. Box 667, Black River Falls, WI 54615 (715) 284-9343. E-mail: patina.park@ho-chunk.com. Ms. Park focuses her work on the statewide implementation of the Wisconsin Indian Child Welfare Act. Patina has developed Indian Child Welfare curriculums and has significant experience leading advanced ICWA trainings. *Other professional posts*: Appellate Court Justice for the Prairie Island Indian Community of Minnesota; board member of the Minnesota Indian Women's Resource Center.

PARKER, ALAN (Chippewa Cree)
(attorney; professor & director)
Education: University of California, Los Angeles School of Law, JD, 1977. *Affiliation & Address*: Professor & Director (1997-present), Northwest Indian Applied Research Institute, Evergreen College, Olympia, WA 98505 (206) 866-6000. E-mail: parkeral@evergreen.edu. *Other professional post*: Instructor, The Institute for Tribal Govern-ment, Portland State University, Portland, OR. *Past professional posts*: Practiced law in Washington, DC for over 20 years where he directed the Tribal Government Task Force of the American Indian Policy Review Commission, 1975-77; he was the first Native American to serve as Chief Counsel to the U.S. Senate Committee on Indian Affairs and was appointed to Staff Director in 1987-91. During his service on the Senate Committee, he was involved in the development of the following legislative initiatives: The Indian Child Welfare Act, the Indian Religious Freedom Act, the Native American Graves Protection & Repatriation Act, the Tribal Self-Governance Act, and the American Indian Development Finance Corporation Act. He also served as president of the American Indian National Bank in Washington, DC. In May of 2000, Prof. Parker was appointed, by then Governor Gary Locke, as the first Native American attorney to serve on the Washington State Gaming Commission.

PARKER, ANGELA K. (Mandan, Hidatsa, Cree)
(assistant professor of Native American studies)
Education: Stanford University, BA, 2001; University of Michigan, PhD (History), 2011. *Affiliations*: Native American Studies Program, Dartmouth College, 37 N. Main St., The Sherman House, Hanover, NH 03755 (603) 646-3530. E-mail: angela.k.parker@dartmouth.edu. Angela is an enrolled member of the Fort Berthold Indian Reservation (Mandan, Hidatsa) in North Dakota, and participates at her father's reservation, Rocky Boy (Cree) in Montana. *Research interests*: Focus is on the Northern Plains tribal communities and the lived experience of the federal-tribal relationship during the first half of the 20th century, particularly around questions of indigenous citizenship and tribal activism as building blocks to later claims of tribal sovereignty. Her dissertation examined the years from the Indian Reorganization Act to the early 1960s on the Fort Berthold Indian Reservation. The project focused on the interrelation of land and identity. Her courses focus on the 20th century Native American history & environmental issues in indigenous communities.

PARKER, BERNIE (Seneca)
(tribal chief)
Affiliation: Chief (lifetime), Tonawanda Band of Senecas Council of Chiefs, 7027 Meadville Rd., Basom, NY 14013 (716) 542-4244.

PARKER, JEFFREY D. (Chippewa)
(tribal chairperson)
Affiliation: Bay Mills Indian Community of Michigan, 12140 W. Lakeshore Dr., Brimley, MI 49715 (906) 248-3241.

PARKER, LARRY
(education administrator)
Affiliation: Billings Area Office, Bureau of Indian Affairs, 316 North 26th St., Billings, MT 59101 (406) 657-6375.

PARKER, LaRUE (Caddo)
(tribal chairperson)
Address & Affiliation: Caddo Tribe, P.O. Box 487, Binger, OK 73009 (405) 656-2344.

PARKER, MIKE (Eastern Cherokee)
(tribal chairperson)
Affiliation: Eastern Band of Cherokee Indians, Qualla Boundary, P.O. Box 455, Cherokee, NC 28719 (828) 497-7000.

PARKER, MITCHELL (Omaha)
(tribal chairperson)
Affiliation & Address: Chairperson, Omaha Tribe, P.O. Box 368, Macy, NE 68039 (402) 837-5391.

PARKER, PATRICIA K. (Choctaw of Oklahoma)
(business executive)
Education: University of Oklahoma (Journalism & Public Relations); University of Tulsa School of Dramatic Arts (Theatre); University of Maryland. *Affiliation & Address*: Co-founder, President & CEO (1992-present), Native American Management Services, Inc. (NAMS), 12110 Sunset Hills Rd., Suite 450, Reston, VA 20190 (571) 323-5635. *Other professional posts*: Member, Board of Directors, American Indian Business Leaders, Inc., Missoula, MT; chair, member, Board of Directors, National Center for American Indian Enterprise Development, Mesa, AZ; member, Board of Directors, Native American Women's Business Council; member, Board of Directors, National Indian Business Association (NIBA); founding partner, Women Impacting Public Policy (WIPP); founding member, Women Empowering Women for Indian Nations (WEWIN). *Past professional post*: Communications Director, Indian Health Service. *Awards, honors*: 2007 Artemus Award from the Euro-American Women's Council; 2006 Volunteer of the Year, Native American Business Leaders Award; 2001 Business Women's Network Entrepreneur of the Year & Diversity Best Practices Association Leader Award; 1998 National Native Woman of the Year, National Indian Business Association; et al.

PARKER, PAULINE A. (Pechanga Luiseno) 1947-
(Indian education)
Born May 23, 1947, Escondido, Calif. *Education*: Palomar College (two years). *Principal occupation*: Indian education. *Address*: 2116 Cook Place, Ramona, CA 92065 (619) 789-1624. *Affiliation*: Project coordinator, Indian Education, Ramona Unified Schools, Ramona, CA (619) 788-5010, 1982-present. *Other professional post*: Member, American Indian Education Council, Escondido, CA. *Community activities*: No. County American Indian Education Council; Ramona Unified School District (district advisory committee); past president, Chapter One Parent's Council. *Memberships*: San Diego No. County American Indian Education Council; League of American Pen Women. *Awards, honors*: Showcase Writers Guild Awards (1st Place - Poetry, 1991; 1st Place - Short Story, 1992 & 1993; 2nd Place Children's Story, 1992; 1st Place Article, 1993; 2nd Place - Short Story, 1993); National League of American Pen Women, 1992; San Diego Writer's Showcase, 1994-95 (fiction, non-fiction, poetry). *Interests*: "My main goal is to instill in my students a sense of pride and honor in their heritage. Each and every child should know their history, learn from it and grow into adulthood strong, proud men and women who will face the future with dignity and hope."

PARKER, RAYMOND "JAKE" JR. (Chippewa Cree)
(former tribal chairperson)
Affiliation: Chippewa-Cree Indian Tribe, RR 1 Box 544, Box Elder, MT 59521 (406) 395-4282.

PARKER, TASSY (Seneca)
(institute director; assistant dean of academic affairs)
Education: University of New Mexico-Gallup, AA (Nursing); University of New Mexico, BA (Sociology), MA (Sociology), PhD (Medical Sociology). *Affiliation & Address*: Director & Associate Professor of Family & Community Medicine, Institute of Indigenous Knowledge & Development, University of New Mexico,

Bldg. #044A, 717 Encino Place NE #9, Albuquerque, NM 87102 (505) 925-0776. E-mail: taparker@salud.unm.edu. Dr. Parker, an enrolled member of the Seneca Nation (Beaver clan), is a tenured Associate Professor of Family and Community Medicine, and Associate Professor of Nursing at the UNM HSC School of Medicine. She is director and co-founder of the UNM HSC's IIKD. Previously, she directed the UNM Center for Native American Health. Dr. Parker is also Assistant Dean of Academic Affairs and a fellow in the 2013-2014 Drexel University Executive Leadership in Academic Medicine (ELAM) program. Her research addresses American Indian (AI) depression, substance use, historical trauma, the role of maternal stressors in pediatric obesity prevention, & youth incarceration. Dr. Parker's research also includes integrated health care, including traditional healing. Her priority approach is AI health beliefs/practices as foundation for interventions development. She is co-founder of the All Nations Wellness and Healing Center (ANWHC) for the Albuquerque urban AI community. Dr. Parker mentors a number of junior faculty, and AI medical, doctoral and health professions students. She teaches a Community-Based Participatory Research and Indigenous Knowledge Summer Institute. Dr. Parker and the IIKD team deliver community health assessment education to AI communities nationally that emphasizes core cultural values, sovereignty, self-determination and health workforce development. Another innovation includes a Telehealth Connections for AI Education initiative to close curriculum gaps, create a bi-directional teaching bridge between traditional healers and health sciences students, and connect students from community to campus.

PARKER, TONYA (Choctaw of Oklahoma)
(business executive)
Education: University of Oklahoma (Journalism & Public Relations). *Affiliation & Address*: Co-founder & Vice President, Native American Management Services, Inc. (NAMS), 12110 Sunset Hills Rd., Suite 450, Reston, VA 20190 (571) 323-5635. *Past professional posts*: Health & Social Services Director & Program Administrator, Choctaw Nation of Oklahoma; Indian Health Service (Acting Director of the Community Health Representative (CHR), 1979-90.

PARKER-JOHNSON, TONI (*Seeing Hawk*) (Mashantucket Pequot-Cherokee) 1950-
(tribal public relations)
Born in 1950, Bronx, N.Y. *Education*: Associates degree in retail fashion merchandising & employment from the California Mart, Los Angeles. *Principal occupation*: Tribal public relations. *Address*: P.O. Box 3130, Mashantucket, CT 06338 (860) 396-6572. E-mail: tjohnson15@snet.net. *Affiliation*: Mashantucket Pequot Nation (Manager of Tribal Communication, 1998-99; director, Tribal Public Relations, 1999-present). Her tasks have included photography, interviewing tribal citizens on the Foxwoods News Network, performing in cultural presentations for new employee orientation, receiving & presenting awards on behalf of the tribe, giving tours of the casino, museum & reservation, attending seminars & conferences, and keeping council & tribal citizens informed of current events through written, oral & telephonic communications. She has also appeared in the commercial "The Wonder of It All" for Foxwoods. *Community activities*: Founding member, National Campaign for Tolerance; founding member, National Museum for Women; board member, Friends & Neighbors Community Organization (where she has trained for and facilitated study circles on race relations and spoken at community meetings). *Membership*: Native American Journalist Association. Interests: Photography, gaming, poetry; mentoring for younger tribal citizens.

PARKS, DOUGLAS R. (*Kaakaataaka-White Crow*) 1942-
(research institute co-director; professor of linguistics)
Born August 28, 1942, Long Beach, Calif. *Education*: University of California, Berkeley, BA, 1964, PhD, 1972. *Address*: 8275 East State Road 46, Bloomington, IN 47401. *Affiliation & Address*: Co-director, American Indian Studies Research Institute, Indiana University, 422 N. Indiana Ave., Bloomington, IN 47408 (812) 855-4086. E-mail: aisri@indiana.edu; research associate, Dept. of Anthropology, Indiana University, Bloomington, 1983-present. *Other professional post*: Editor, "Anthropological Linguistics"; Associate director, American Indian Studies Research Institute, Indiana University. *Past professional post*: Director, Title VII Program, White Shield School District, Roseglen, ND (three years). *Interests*: "At present, I am working with another team that includes Professor DeMallie & Mindy Morgan to develop a program for teaching Assiniboine on the Fort Belknap Reservation in Montana. For it, we are also producing materials in both printed & multimedia formats. Another dimension of my career is Native North American philology, the study of older linguistic records of American Indian languages, and the combination of American Indian language research with the writing & interpretation of history." *Memberships*: Plains Anthropological Society (board of directors, 1980-82; president, 1982); American Anthropological Association; American Society for Ethno-history. *Awards, honors*: American Council of Learned Societies Fellow, 1982-83; Smithsonian Fellow (Smithsonian Institution, 1973-74). *Published works*: A Grammar of Pawnee (Garland Publishing, 1976); An Introduction to the Arikara Language (Title VII Materials Development Center, Anchorage, Alaska, 1979); Ceremonies of the Pawnee, 2

Vols. (Smithsonian Institution Press, 1981); Arikara Coyote Tales: A Bilingual Reader (White Shield School, 1984); An English-Arikara Student Dictionary (White Shield School, 1986); Traditional Narratives of the Arikara Indians, 4 Vols. (University of Nebraska Press, 1991); An Introduction to the Arikara Language, two vols. co-authored with Janet Beltran & Ella Waters (American Indian Studies Institute, 1998 & 2001); An Introduction to the Pawnee Language, co-authored with Janet Beltran, Nora Pratt, Nicole Evans. (American Indian Studies Institute, 2001); A Dictionary of Skiri Pawnee, co-authored with Lulu Nora Pratt (University of Nebraska Press, 2005.); The Roaming Scout Narratives: Reminiscences of a Skiri Pawnee Priest, 2 vols. (University of Nebraska Press, 2007).

PARMAN, DONALD L. (Navajo) 1932-
(retired historian; author)
Born October 10, 1932, New Point, MO. *Education*: Central Missouri State College, BS, 1958; Ohio University, MA, 1963; University of Oklahoma, PhD, 1967. Principal occupation: Historian. *Address*: 614 Rose St., West Lafayette, IN 47906 (317) 743-3514. *Affiliation*: Retired Professor, Dept. of History, Purdue University, West Lafayette, IN, 1966-2001. *Military service*: U.S. Army, 1953-55 (Corporal). *Memberships*: Indiana Historical Society; Western History Association; Indiana Association of Historians. *Interests*: Main research interests are Navajo Indian history and twentieth century Indian affairs; main travels are in the Southwest & elsewhere in "Indian Country." *Biographical sources*: Directory of American Scholars, Vol. 1; Dictionary of International Biography; Contemporary Authors. *Published works*: Co-editor, American Search, 2 Vols. (Forum Press, 1974); Navajos & the New Deal (Yale University Press, 1976); Indians and the American West in the Twentieth Century (Indiana University Press, 1994); editor, Window to a Changed World: The Personal Memoirs of William Graham (Indiana Historical Society, 1998).

PARMENTER, JON W.
(assistant professor)
Affiliation: Professor of History & Native American Studies, Dept. of History & American Indian Program, Cornell University, 304 McGraw Hall, Ithaca, NY 14853 (607) 254-1876. E-Mail: jwp35@cornell.edu. *Interests*: Iroquois social & political history, Northwestern Algonquians, governance, settler relations.

PARRA, DONNA C. (Navajo) 1941-
(counseling services)
Born September 7, 1941, Rehoboth, N.M. *Education*: University of New Mexico, BA, 1970, MA, 1974. *Principal occupation*: Counseling services. *Address*: 819 Gonzales Rd., Santa Fe, NM 87501. *Affiliations*: Medical secretary, USPHS Indian Hospital, Gallup, NM, 1961-63, 1965; research assistant, National Institutes of Mental Health (Alcoholism Project: A Community Treatment Plan for Navajo Problem Drinkers), Family Service Agency, 1966-68; director of counseling services, Institute of American Indian Arts, Santa Fe, NM, 1976-. *Other professional posts*: Instructor of English, counselor, Gallup High School, 1970-75; consultant to teach workshops on ethnic literature, 1973-75, consultant, Curriculum Development, Native American Literature, 1974-75; Gallup-McKinley County Schools; consultant, University of New Mexico Cultural Awareness Center, Albuquerque, NM, 1975. *Community activities*: Santa Fe Public Schools Title IV Indian Education Parent Committee (officer); New Mexico Human Rights Commission Film Project (scholar & advisor); Ford Canyon Youth Center, Gallup, N.M. (advisory board); Gallup Inter-Agency Alcoholism Coordinating Committee (member); New Mexico International Women's Year Convention, June, 1977 (workshop leader on Indian Women). *Memberships*: League of Women Voters; New Mexico Association of Women Deans & Counselors; National Indian Education Association. *Awards, honors*: Four-year Navajo Tribal Scholarship recipient; Charles S. Owens Future Teachers of America Scholarship (Gallup High School, 1959); Sequoyah Indian Fellowship, University of New Mexico, 1970. *Interests*: Ms. Parra writes, "I have great interest in the field of human rights, specifically issues of Indian sovereignty, because I feel that this whole issue relates directly to the survival of the American Indian as a group. I also have great interest in Native American literature and have developed a curriculum on this that has been adopted by the Gallup-McKinley County School district. I have been involved in alcohol research among the American Indian in a National Institutes of Mental Health Project in Gallup, A Community Treatment Plan for Indian Problem Drinkers (1966-68), & am presently directing a program I designed with students and staff of our educational facility."

PARRISH, RAIN (Navajo) 1944-
(museum curator)
Born February 8, 1944, Tuba City, Ariz. *Education*: University of Arizona, BA (Anthropology), 1967. *Address*: 704 Kathryn Ave., Santa Fe, NM 87501 (505) 982-4636. *Affiliation*: Curator of American Indian Collections, Wheelwright Museum of the American Indian, Santa Fe, NM, 1979-. *Membership*: New Mexico Museum Association. *Awards, honors*: Navajo Woman of the Year in the Arts, 1985; 10 Who Made a Difference, 1985 The New Mexican Newspaper). *Interests*: Travel, art history, anthropology, sports, skiing, hiking, reading, writing. *Published works*: The Stylistic Development of Navajo Jewelry

(Minneapolis Institute of the Arts, 1982); Woven Holy People (Wheelwright Museum, 1983); The Pottery of Margaret Tafoya (Wheelwright Museum, 1984).

PARRY, BRUCE (Northwestern Shoshone)
(former tribal chairperson & CEO)
Education: University of Utah, B.A. (Education) M.A. (Science in Management). *Affiliations*: Northwestern Band of Shoshone Nation, 707 N. Main St., Brigham City, UT 84302; CEO, Northwestern Band of Shoshone Economic Development Corporation. Mr. Parry has held several leadership & education positions including member of the Davis County School Board and executive director for State of Utah, Division of Indian Affairs (under two Utah Governors for 14 years). He founded Shoshone Tooling and is the founder of the Tribe's economic ventures, emulating the Harvard Project on American Indian Economic Development's model that separates politics from tribal business.

PARRY, DARREN (Northwestern Shoshone)
(tribal vice chairperson)
Affiliation & Address: Vice Chairperson, Northwestern Band of Shoshone Nation, 707 N. Main St., Brigham City, UT 84302 (435) 734-2286. E-mail: dparry@arrowpoint.us

PARTON, TERRI (Wichita)
(tribal president)
Affiliation & Address: President, Wichita & Affiliated Tribes, P.O. Box 729, Anadarko, OK 73005 (405) 247-2425.

PATA, JACQUELINE L. JOHNSON (*Kus ees*) (Tlingit)
(NCAI executive director)
Affiliation & Address: Executive director (2001-present), National Congress of American Indians (NCAI), 1516 P St., NW, Washington, DC 20005 (202) 466-7767. *Other professional posts*: Member, Central Council of the Tlingit-Haida Indian Tribes of Alaska; board member Leadership Conference on Civil Rights; member, executive board, George Gustav Heye Center of the National Museum of the American Indian; board member, Sealaska Corporation; member, Native American Advisory Council for the Boys & Girls Clubs of America. *Past professional posts*: Executive Director, Tlingit-Haida Regional Housing Authority, Juneau, AK; vice chair, Alaska Housing Finance Corporation; executive director, Oneida Riders Association, Seymour, WI; director, Native Youth Culture Camp (13 summers); Deputy Assistant Secretary for Native American programs, U.S. Department of Housing & Urban Development (HUD); chairperson, National American Indian Housing Council, Washington, DC; liaison to Native America for the Clinton Administration.

PATCH, DENNIS (Mohave-Chemehuevi)
(tribal chairperson; education director)
Affiliation & Address: Chairperson & Education Director, Colorado River Indian Tribes, 26600 Mohave Rd., Parker, AZ 85344 (928) 669-9211.

PATKOTAK, CRAWFORD (*Ahkivgak*) (Inupiat)
(corporation chairperson)
Affiliation & Address: Chairperson, Arctic Slope Regional Corporation (ASRC), P.O. Box 129, Barrow, AK 99723 (907) 852-8633. *Other professional posts*: ASRC Corporate Treasurer, Sr. V.P. of Shareholder & Community Programs; ASRC Executive Committee, 2000-present; current Board President of Eskimo's, Inc.; ASRC Investment Committee, 2003-06, 2008-present; erctic Education Foundation Board Member, 2006-present; Barrow Utilities Electric Cooperative, Inc., Board of Directors, 1997-present; elected as a Board Member of the Barrow Whaling Captains Association. *Past professional posts*: Board member, Oetro Star, Inc., 1999-2005; Council member for the City of Barrow, Board of Trustees for Ilisagvik College.

PATKOTAK, HOWARD (Eskimo)
(Alaskan village president)
Affiliation & Address: Village of Wainwright, P.O. Box 184, Wainwright, AK 99782 (907) 763-2726. E-mail: hpatkotak@ain.olgoonik.com

PATRICIO, ANTHONY (Comanche)
(organization president)
Affiliation & Address: President, American Indian Chamber of Commerce of Texas (AICCT), 7457 Harwin, Suite 307 • Houston, TX 77036 (713) 614-1272

PATT, EVALINE (Wasco)
(tribal vice chairperson)
Affiliation & Address: Vice Chairperson, Confederated Tribes of the Warm Springs Reservation, 1233 Veterans St.., Warm Springs, OR 97761 (541) 553-1161. E-mail: epatt@wstribes.org

PATTEA, SANDRA, RADM (Yavapai/Hopi)
(IHS deputy director)
Education: Scottsdale Community College, AA; Arizona State University, BS (Nursing); Arizona State University, MS (Nursing Administration). *Affiliation &*

Address: Deputy Director for Intergovernmental Affairs, Indian Health Service (IHS), The Reyes Bldg., 801 Thompson Ave. #400, Rockville, MD 20852 (301) 443-1083. RADM Pattea advises the IHS Director & provides oversight on tribal & urban Indian health activities & communications, as well as public, legislative, and Congressional relations within the Office of the Director. *Past professional posts*: Nurse officer in the Commissioned Corps of the USPHS with 30 years of active duty; Dept. of Orthopedics, Gallup Indian Medical Center, Gallup, NM; Health Division Director, Fort McDowell Yavapai Nation (eight years); Phoenix Indian Medical Center, Intensive Care & Outpatient Surgery Units, 1985-96; Phoenix Area Integrated Services Delivery Network Coordinator. She formerly worked with the Phoenix Area tribes, service units, and urban programs of Arizona, Nevada, and Utah.

PATTERSON, BRIAN (Oneida)
(tribal representative; organization president; senior strategist)
Affiliation & Address: Bear Clan Representative (20 years), Oneida Indian Nation's Men's Council & Clan Mothers, 5218 Patrick Rd., Oneida, NY 13421 (315) 829-8900. Brian is dedicated to the cultural & historical revitalization of the Oneida people. He has created numerous economic & social opportunities for his people, including health & community programs, including an Oneida language program to ensure the Oneida language. *Other professional posts*: President (3 terms), United South & Eastern Tribes, Inc. (USET), Nashville, TN - serves on the National Tribal Natural Resources Strategy Group that has united more than ten tribal organizations to focus on developing a national natural resource strategy that will unite 566 federal recognized tribes...through his efforts, USET signed a covenant with Affiliated Tribes of the Northwest Indians (ATNI), uniting the voice of 80 tribes, and working to achieve common goals & priorities; senior strategist, Blue Stone Strategy Group, Irvine, CA/Phoenix, AZ. *Tribal community service*: Chairperson, Community Policing Committee, Oneida Nation; chairperson, Oneida Indian Nation Athletic Commission. Patterson has played an integral role in efforts to repatriate ancient Oneida artifacts, including wampum. He is the tribal liaison for issues related to the Federal Native American Graves Protection & Repatriation Act. In November 2010, Brian was nominated by his Nation and selected to serve on the board of trustees of the National Museum of the American Indian, Smithsonian Institution, and currently co-chairs the Dept. of the Interior (DOI) Tribal Consultation Team. He is a well-known authority on contemporary American Indian cultural issues and has spoken on the topic at several conferences.

PATTERSON, DONALD L. (Tonkawa)
(former tribal president)
Affiliation & Address: Former President, Tonkawa Tribe of Oklahoma, 1 Rush Buffalo Rd., Tonkawa, OK 74653 (580) 628-2561.

PATTERSON, JEREMY J. (Cheyenne River Sioux)
(attorney)
Education: Black Hills State University, BS (American Indian Studies), 1999; University of Wisconsin Law School, JD, 2002; University of Tulsa, LLM (American Indian & Indigenous Law), 2004. *Affiliation*: Senior Associate (2006-present), Fredericks Peebles & Morgan, LLP, 1900 Plaza Dr., Louisville, CO 80027 (303) 673-9600. E-mail: jpatterson@ndnlaw.com. *Practice areas*: Federal Indian law; economic development; energy & natural resource law; international indigenous law. *Past professional post*: Native American Rights Fund & the Native American Program of Oregon Legal Services, 2004-06, providing legal services to tribes on issues relating to tribal cultural preservation & natural resource development. *Awards, honors*: 2000-2001 Don A Olson Outstanding Native American Law Student award for academic & scholastic achievement.

PATTERSON, KENNETH (Tuscarora)
(tribal chief's council)
Affiliation & Address: Chief's Councilmember, Tuscarora Indian Nation, 2006 Mt. Hope Rd., Lewiston, NY 14092 (716) 297-1148.

PATTERSON, KERRY K. (Seneca)
(attorney)
Education: SUNY, Fredonia, BA, 1997; Arizona State University, Sandra Day O'Connor College of Law (Certificate in Indian Law), JD, 2001. *Affiliation & Address*: Partner, Lewis Rocca Rothgerber Christi, 201 E. Washington St., Suite 1200, Phoenix, AZ 85004 (602) 262-5717. E-mail: kpatterson@lrrc.com. Kerry is a tribal attorney focusing on real estate & gaming development and is a member of the firm's Tribal Affairs and Real Estate practice groups. She strives to create a winning situation for all sides in real estate transactions where Indian lands are concerned. Her clients include tribes, developers, lenders, manufacturers and other landowners. Kerry has worked on several multimillion dollar real estate projects involving Native American lands. Recently, she helped close a real estate deal for the Navajo Nation to build Twin Arrows Casino – a $120 million gaming facility, golf course and resort on 405 acres 20 miles east of Flagstaff. For development projects like these,

Kerry helps place land into trust for tribes and then handles real estate issues related to developing the land. Her work includes infrastructure design, road development, telecommunications, water, access (including IRR roads), wastewater disposal, due diligence, easements and encumbrances. Kerry also has experience identifying environmental issues and then working with the right professionals to mitigate any real or perceived concerns. Many of Kerry's real estate deals require her to interface with state and federal agencies such as the Department of the Interior, California Department of Transportation, and Arizona State Land Department. Her experience also includes preparing purchase and sale, development, lease, and licensing agreements and other related documents. Her gaming work covers the full range of issues including negotiation of tribal-state gaming compacts, related county agreements and development of tribal gaming ordinances and regulations. *Awards, honors*: 2009 *Arizona Business Journal* 40 Under 40 Honoree. She was also the recipient of the 2009 Arizona State University President's Medal for Social Embeddedness for Arizona Native Vote - Election Protection Project. Ms. Patterson was a Native American 40 Under 40 award winner, as presented by the National Center for American Indian Enterprise Development in 2009.

PATTERSON, LOTSEE (Comanche) 1931-
(professor emeritus of library & information studies)
Born December 3, 1931, Indian land near Apache, Okla. *Education*: Oklahoma College for Women, BS, 1959; University of Oklahoma, MLS, 1969, PhD, 1979. *Address*: 1705 Pembroke Dr., Norman, OK 73072 (405) 325-3921. *Affiliations*: Professor emeritus, University of Oklahoma, School of Library & Information Studies, 2009-present. *Other professional post*: Board member, National Museum of Library Sciences. *Past professional posts*: University of New Mexico, Albuquerque, 1972-78; Texas Woman's University, Denton, TX, 1978-85; director, Trails (Training & Assistance for Indian Library Service, University of Oklahoma, Norman, OK, 1985-87; director, Library Media Services, Oklahoma City Public Schools, 1989-91; editor, American Indian Libraries Newsletter, American Indian Library Association, 1992-97. *Other professional posts*: Advisory Committee, Brodart Foundation, Williamsport, PA, 1971-; White House Conference on Libraries & Information Services Taskforce, 1982- (Awards Committee, 1992-); National Archives & Records Administration, National Historical Publications & Records Commission (field advisory committee; review grant proposals under the Native American Institute), 1985-; National Commission on Libraries & Information Science (consultant to the Commission's Native American Task Force, Washington, DC, 1989-93); Admission Committee, School of Library & Information Studies, University of Oklahoma, 1991-; Western History Associates, University of Oklahoma, Board of Trustees (vice president, 1992-; chair, Acquisitions Committee, 1990-); member, Board of Directors, Native American Library & Museum Project, Washington, DC, 1994-; numerous conference presentations & invited formal lectures, 1985-. *Memberships*: American Library Association (council member, 1984-88); American Indian Library Association (president, 1981-84, 1984-87, 1991-); American Association of School Librarians (board member, 1980-83); Oklahoma Library Association. *Awards, honors*: Expert witness, Senate Select Committee on Indian Affairs: Hearing; Equality Award 1994, American Library Association; Silver Award 1996, National Commission on Libraries & Information Science; 1997 Distinguished Service Award from Oklahoma Library Association; Beta Phi Mu Award, American Library Association, 2001; Honorary Member, American Library Association, 2005. *Published works*: Contributor to Pathways to Excellence: A Report on Improving Library & Information Services for Native American Peoples (USGPO, 1992); "History & Status of Native Americans in Librarianship." Library Trends 49(1) 182-193; Comanche," in Native America in the Twentieth Century: An Encyclopedia, edited by Mary B. Davis (Garland Publishing, 1994); co-authored with Mary Ellen Snodgrass, Indian Terms of the Americas (Libraries Unlimited, 1994); Native Americans & Native American Resources, Guide to Multicultural Resources, 1995-96, 1997-98, edited with Alex Boyd (Highsmith Press, 1997); Native American Videos - Culturally Diverse Media Collections for Youth, 1997, edited with Irene Wood (Neal-Schuman, 1997); "Historical Overview of Tribal Libraries in the Lower Forty Eight States." in Bringing Libraries to People (McFarland, 2002). Book chapter: "Native American Resources: A Model for Collection Development," in Selecting Materials for Library Collections, (Haworth, 2004); book chapter: "Reflections on a Passion," in Contemporary Librarianship (Scarecrow, 2005).

PAUKAN, MOSES (Eskimo)
(village council president)
Affiliation & Address: President, Native Village of Algaaciq, P.O. Box 48, St. Mary's, AK 99658 (907) 438-2932.

PAUL, ALICE (Tohono O'odham)
(professor emeritus)
Education: University of Arizona, PhD, 1978. *Affiliation*: American Indian Studies Program, The University of Arizona, Harvill Bldg., Room 430, P.O. Box 210076, Tucson, AZ 85721 (520) 621-7108. E-mail: aisp@email.arizona.edu.

PAUL, BENOIT (Pabineau)
(chief/director-Indian band/centre)
Affiliation: Pabineau Indian Band, Cultural/Educational Centre, R.R. #5, Box 1, Site 26, Bathurst, New Brunswick, Can. E2A 3Y8 (506) 548-9211.

PAUL, BLAIR F. (Tlingit) 1943-
(attorney)
Born July 5, 1943, Juneau, Alaska. *Education*: Western Washington State College, BA, 1966; University of Washington Law School, JD, 1970. *Principal occupation*: Attorney. Address: 8010 Fairway Dr. NE, Seattle, WA 98115 (206) 527-3334. *Community activities*: Pioneer Square Historic Preservation Board, 1974-; Washington Trust for Historic Preservation (president, 1976-77); United Indians of All Tribes (board member, 1969-71): Seattle Indian Health Board, 1970-73; Seattle Indian Services Commission, 1972-73. *Memberships*: American Trial Lawyers; Washington Trial Lawyers; Seattle-Kings County Bar.

PAUL, EUGENE (Eskimo)
(Alaskan village chief)
Affiliation & Address: First Chief, Holy Cross Village, P.O. Box 89, Holy Cross, AK 99602 (907) 476-7124.

PAUL, FRANK E. (Navajo)
(tribal vice president)
Affiliation & Address: Vice President, Ramah Navajo Chapter, HCR61 Box 13, Ramah, NM 87321 (505) 775-7140.

PAUL, JIMMIE
(village president)
Affiliation & Address: President, Native Village of Kipnuk, P.O. Box 57, Kipnuk, AK 99614 (907) 896-5515.

PAUL, MONICA (*Kahen Ten Hawi*) (Kahnawake Mohawk)
(educator, council member)
Born in Kahnawake, Canada. *Address*: 21 Village Rd., Morganville, NJ 07751. *Community activities*: After retiring from NJ Bell, Monica has been working as a crossing guard since 1986. She is an active member of the Old Bridge Senior Choral Group that travels extensively throughout the area performing; she also volunteers for the Old Bridge Office on Aging as a commodity distribution helper. *Membership*: Inter-Tribal Indians of New Jersey (heads the Sunshine Committee), a non-profit cultural & educational organization dedicated to preserving & continuing American Indian heritage. Monica is one of the organization's educators that provide cultural/educational services at various institutions, such as the New Jersey State Museum, Newark Museum, schools and colleges. *Awards, honors*: Winner of the "Young at Heart" Award from the U.S. Health Core; elected as one of seven council members of the Inter-Tribal Indians of New Jersey; an award recognizing people who inspire community by activities and attitude. *Interests*: Ms. Paul instructs Mohawk language classes and traditional clothing and beadwork; she is a member of the Inter-Tribal Dance Group, & participates in all performances, explaining her regalia; writing - Monica compiled a book of memoirs for her family and is writing a second book that will contain the family tree with historical sketches on her ancestors.

PAUL, PATRICK (Cree-Kootnay) 1942-
(educator; consultant-human development)
Born January 24, 1942, Cranbrook, B.C. Can. *Education*: The Evergreen State College (Olympia, WA), MA, 1980; Antioch University (Seattle, WA), MA, 1984. *Principal occupation*: Educator; consultant-human development. Resides in Bellingham, WA. *Affiliations*: Assistant professor & coordinator, Native American Chemical Dependency Studies, Northwest Indian College, Bellingham, WA, 1984-; youth & family counselor, Chemical Dependency, United Indians, Seattle, 1984-88. *Other professional posts*: Trainer & consultant, 1982-; secretary/treasurer of the Northwest Indian Council on Chemical Dependency and the Northwest Indian Alcohol/Drug Specialist Certification Board. *Awards, honors*: National Indian Board on Alcoholism & Drug Abuse, for providing excellent Alcohol/drug education to the Indian people of the Pacific Northwest, 1980-90.

PAUL, SYLVANUS (Navajo-Dine)
(collections assistant)
Born & raised on the Ramah Navajo Reservation. *Education*: Dine College, AA (Dine Studies); Fort Lewis College, BA (American Indian Studies & Southwest History). *Affiliation & Address*: Collections Assistant (2007-present), Indian Arts Research Center, School for Advanced Research, P.O. Box 2188, Santa Fe, NM 87504 (505) 954-7205. Mr. Paul works with the Southwest Native textiles, where his knowledge in Dine Studies & Southwest History, as well as Native American Studies, benefits the care & interpretation of the collections.

PAULK, ANJELICA (Miwok)
(tribal vice chairperson)
Affiliation & Address: Vice Chairperson, California Valley Miwok Tribe of the Sheep Ranch Rancheria, 4620 Shippee Lane, Stockton, CA 95212 (209) 931-4567. E-mail: jelica@cvmt.net

PAULSON, GREG S.
(attorney)
Education: Augsburg College, BA, 1991; William Mitchell College of Law, JD, 1994. *Affiliation & Address*: Associate (1994-02), Partner (2002-present), BlueDog, Paulson & Small, PLLP, Southgate Office Plaza, Suite 500, 5001 West 80th, Bloomington, MN 55437 (952) 893-1813. Greg has experience in gaming law, employment law, including Tribal Employment Rights laws and Indian preference, drafting tribal legislation, health, environmental, and other tribal government concerns. His practice also includes assisting non-profit organizations aiding the Indian community, & individual criminal representation of Native American people. *Practice admissions*: Sisseton-Wahpeton Tribal Court of the Lake Traverse Reservation; the Court of the Shakopee Mdewakanton Sioux (Dakota) Community. *Membership*: Minnesota State Bar Associationn.

PAVEL, JOSEPH (Skokomish)
(former tribal vice chairperson)
Affiliation & Address: Former Vice Chairperson, Skokomish Tribal Nation, 80 N. Tribal Center Rd., Skokomish, WA 98584. (360) 426-4232. E-mail: jpavel@ skokomish.org

PAVEL, MARY J. (Skokomish)
(attorney; Indian law firm partner)
Education: Dartmouth College, BA, 1989; University of Washington School of Law, JD, 1992. *Affiliation & Address*: Partner, Sonosky, Chambers, Sachse, Endreson & Perry, LLP, 1425 K St., NW, Suite 600, Washington, DC 20005 (202) 682-0240. E-mail: mpavel@sonosky.com. Mary rejoined the firm in 2015 after serving as Staff Director and Chief Counsel for the United States Senate Committee on Indian Affairs. During her tenure, she served two Chairs: Senator Maria Cantwell (D-WA) and Senator Jon Tester (D-MT). As Staff Director and Chief Counsel, Ms. Pavel directed the Senate Committee on Indian Affairs agenda through the Senate. In this capacity, Ms. Pavel played a vital role in the enactment of the reauthorization of the Violence Against Women Act (VAWA), as well as critical legislation that restored tribal land rights, affirmed tribal water rights, and protected tribal health and veterans programs. Ms. Pavel initially joined the firm in 1992 and became a partner in 1999. She focuses her practice on working with congressional staff and the firm's legislative clients. Her work involves all aspects of legislative practice, including developing legislative strategies, meeting with tribal & congressional delegations and developing testimony. Ms. Pavel has extensive knowledge of the budget & appropriations process & has developed strong relationships with appropriations and other Hill staff. She has worked on some of the largest tribal settlements that Congress has enacted, including the Colville Tribes' Grand Coulee Dam Settlement Act and the Pueblo of Isleta Settlement and Natural Resources Restoration Act. Mary was also the lead lobbyist on the Fort Peck Reservation Rural Water System Act, which authorized the construction & operation of a $193 million domestic water system to provide safe drinking water to the 30,000 residents of the Fort Peck Indian Reservation and surrounding communities. She leads the firm's work on appropriations matters, where she has successfully worked with tribal clients to secure over $100 million in funding for vitally needed projects in their communities including roads, schools, & hospitals. She has also worked with a number of Tribes to address their land issues in Congress, including having land taken into trust for gaming purposes, restoring land to a Tribe because of its religious and cultural significance, and expanding tribal leasing authority. She has also worked on a number of national initiatives including amendments to the Federal Unemployment Tax Act, which secured Tribes parity to be treated as governments under this Act; reauthorization of the Indian Healthcare Improvement Act; the Tribal Law and Order Act, and the Violence Against Women Act. In addition, she actively worked to resist Congressional efforts to tax tribal revenues, abrogate tribal sovereign immunity, and impose State taxes for retail sales on tribal lands.

PAYMENT, AARON (Sault Ste. Marie Ojibwe)
(tribal chairperson)
Affiliation & Address: Chairperson, Sault Ste. Marie Tribe of Chippewa Indians, 523 Ashmun St., Sault Ste. Marie, MI 49783 (906) 635-6050. E-mail: aaronpayment@saulttribe.net.

PEACH, WILLIAM (Quileute)
(tribal executive director)
Affiliation: Quileute Indian Tribe, P.O. Box 279, LaPush, WA 98350 (360) 374-6163. E-mail: bill.peach@quileutenation.org.

PEACHES, DANIEL (Navajo) 1940-
(administrator, cultural consultant)

Born September 2, 1940, Kayenta (Navajo County) Ariz. *Education*: Northern Arizona University, BS, 1967; University of New Mexico, 1968-69 (Indian Law); American University, 1969 (Internship). *Principal occupation*: Navajo Tribal Administrator. *Address*: P.O. Box 1801, Kayenta, AZ 86033 (928) 697-5523. *Affiliations*: Navajo Peace Maker Court, 1990-; Dineh Spiritual & Cultural Society, 1985-; Board of Regents, Northland Pioneer College, Holbrook, AZ, 1985-; Board of Regents, Navajo Community College, Tsaile, AZ, 1988-. *Other professional posts*: Elected, Navajo Nation Council, 1998-2003; member, Ethics & Rules Committee, Navajo Nation, 1999-2003; Navajo Mountain Soil & Water Conservation District, 1984-; Arizona Town Hall Council, 1974-; National Indian Education Advisory Council, 1972-76. *Community activities*: Navajo Environmental Protection Commission, 1976-85; Governor's Commission on Arizona Indian Affairs, 1974; Kayenta Boarding School, 1985-; Arizona Town Hall. *Memberships*: Native American Grant School Association; Navajo Area School Board Association. *Awards, honors*: Presidential appointment to National Indian Education Advisory Council, 1972 by President Nixon; Honorary Degree in Law, Navajo Community College, 1978; Council Delegate of the Year, 2000. *Interests*: Elected to Arizona State Legislature, House of Representatives from Legislative Dist. 3, 1974-85. *Biographical sources*: Newsweek Magazine, 1981; Arizona Republic, Sunday Magazine, 1982; Time Magazine, 1984; Who's Who in the West, 1985-; Who's Who in America, 1986-

PEACOCK, MICHAEL D. (*Milky Way*) (Pueblo of Laguna/Seneca/Mohawk) 1957-
(American Indian entrepreneur)

Born March 27, 1957, Albuquerque, N.M. *Education*: University of New Mexico, AAS, 1986; College of Santa Fe, BA, 1989. *Affiliation & Address*: President/CEO, Southwest Business Development Consultants, 2401 12th St., NW 214-N, Albuquerque, NM 87104 (505) 342-8046. *Goal*: To assist in the development & expansion of American Indian tribes, tribal enterprises, tribal colleges, tribal institutions, organizations & government agencies; and American Indian-owned businesses which seek comprehensive assistance in business, economic, and community development. *Other professional posts*: Associate Director, New Mexico Native American Business Development Center, Albuquerque, NM, 1991-present; CEO/President, Southwest Business Development Consultants, LLC, Albuquerque, NM, 1999-present; CEO/President, Southwest Product Specialties, Albuquerque, NM, 2010-present.

PEAKE-RAYMOND, MARGARET (Oklahoma Cherokee) 1941-
(development director)

Born June 22, 1941, Tahlequah, Okla. *Education*: Northeastern State College (Tahlequah, OK), BS, 1963; University of Oklahoma, MSW, 1974. *Affiliation & Address*: Development Director, Cherokee Nation & Cherokee Nation education, Corp., P.O. Box 948, Tahlequah, OK 74465 (915) 453-5420. E-mail: margaret-raymond@cherokee.org. *Past professional posts*: Owner, First Phoenix American Corp., Minneapolis, 1978-84; Special assistant to the director, Minnesota Alcohol & Drug Authority, St. Paul, MN, 1974-77; tribal planner, Cherokee Nation of Oklahoma, 1976-77; National Advisory Council on Drug Abuse, 1980-84; founder, Minnesota Indian Women's Resource Center, Minneapolis, MN, 1984-2002; Field instructor, University of Minnesota, School of Social Work, 1990-2002. *Community activities*: United Way of Minneapolis Area. *Memberships*: Child Welfare League of America (Chemical Dependency Commission); Minnesota Board of Social Workers; American Indian Business Development Corporation; Hennepin County Foster Care Re-Design Commission; Healthy Nations Advisory Committee to Robert Woods Johnson Foundation; Minnesota Women's Economic Roundtable, 1994; Governor's Task Force on Housing, 1994. *Awards, honors*: "Resourceful Women's Award 1992; Jesse Bernard Award, Center for Women Policy Studies, 1992; Minneapolis Leadership Award, 1992; People of Phillips Leadership, 1994."

PEARCE, EILEEN (*Little Axe*) (Absentee Shawnee) 1961-
(journalism, mid-management)

Born June 8, 1961, Oklahoma City, Okla. *Education*: Rose State College (Midwest City, OK), AA, 1982, AAS, 1993; Central State University (Edmond, OK), BA, 1984. *Principal occupation*: Journalism, Mid-Management. Home address: 5225 S. Foster Rd., Oklahoma City, OK 73129 (405) 677-2560. E-mail: lapearce@aol.com. *Affiliation*: Former Treasurer, Shawnee Tribe of Oklahoma, 1988-2000. *Community activities*: Former member of Miss Indian Oklahoma Pageant. *Membership*: Native American Journalists Association. *Awards, honors*: Golden Touch Award, Wix/Dana Corp., 1993, 1994. *Published work*: Author of a small pamphlet, "Consumer Over-the-Counter Drug Pocketbook" (1997).

PEARSON, J. DIANE
(lecturer in Native American Studies)

Education: University of Arizona, MA, 1997, PhD (American Indian Studies), 2001. *Address & Affiliation*: Lecturer, Ethnic Studies Dept., American Studies Program, College of Letters & Science, 548 Barrows Hall, Berkeley, CA 94720 (510) 642-0236. E-mail: jdp@berkeley.edu. Research *Interests*: Peoplehood, indigenous survival & revised post-colonial histories, guide my critical contributions to Native American studies as a core discipline essential to the study of North America. My selected courses & lectures focus on comparative aspects of Native American survival. Courses instructed at the University of Arizona: Introduction to American Indian Studies; The Many Nations of North America; Learning Skills & Strategies; Public Policy & Native Nations. *Awards, honors*: Phillips-Fund, American Philosophical Society scholar; recipient of one of the first Professional Development Fund Grants for UCB lecturers; book, The Nez Perce in the Indian Territory: Nimiipuu Suvival, finalist for the Oklahoma Book of the Year Award. *Published works*: The Nez Perce In the Indian Territory: Nimiipuu Survival (University of Oklahoma Press, 2008); Imperial Medicine & the American Indian 1797-1928: The Politics of Disease (University of Oklahoma Press, 2011); numerous articles.

PEARSON, MARIA D. (*Hamichia Ianko-Running Moccasins*) (Yankton Sioux) 1932-
(consultant-Indian affairs)

Born July 12, 1932, Springfield, S.D. Education: Marty Indian School, Marty, SD, 1938-49; Iowa Western Community College, Council Bluffs, IA. Resides in Ames, Iowa. *Affiliation*: Owner, Maria Pearson, Consultant, Ames, IA. *Community activities*: Commis-sioner, Iowa Substance Abuse Commission; chair, State Archaeologist's Advisory Committee; chair, Iowa Governors Indian Advisory Council. *Awards, honors*: Governor's Award for Volunteer Work, Iowa Governor. *Membership*: Native American Advisory Council on Substance Abuse (treasurer). *Interests*: "Maria Pearson is generally regarded as the person who initiated the movement for protection of Indian burials & reburial of remains in universities, museums & private collections. Got first law on this subject passed in this area; initiated substance abuse treatment for Indians in Omaha, Neb. (CARE Program), one of the first such treatment programs. Funding member of Indian substance abuse group which got national programs initiated on reservations and in cities though Indian Health Service; has given many talks on both these subjects to professional society groups and national or state conferences. Very active as advisor to Iowa Governor & Iowa government agencies on these and other topics."

PEARSON, MYRA S. (Sisseton-Wahpeton Sioux)
(tribal chairperson)

Affiliation & Address: Chairperson, Spirit Lake Dakota Sioux Tribe, P.O. Box 359, Fort Totten, ND 58335 (701) 766-4221.

PEASLEY, SYLVIA (Colville)
(tribal secretary; committee chair)

Affiliation: Confederated Tribes Colville Reservation, P.O. Box 150, Nespelem, WA 99155 (509) 634-2214. E-mail: sylvia.peasley@colvilletribes. com. *Other tribal post*: Chair, Cultural Committee.

PECHONICK, PAULA (Lenni Lenape)
(tribal chief)

Affiliation & Address: Chief, Delaware Tribe of Indians, 170 NE Barbara, Bartlesville, OK 74006 (918) 337-6590. E-mail: ppechonick@delawaretribe.org

PECK, LAVONNE (Luiseno)
(former tribal chairperson)

Affiliation & Address: La Jolla Band of Luiseno Indians, 22000 Hwy. 76, Pauma Valley, CA 92061 (760) 742-3771.

PECKHAM, TOM
(attorney)

Address & Affiliation: Managing Partner (1998-present), Nordhaus Law Firm, LLP, 6705 Academy Rd. NE • Albuquerque, NM 87109 (505) 243-4275. He has represented tribes & tribal corporations in litigation in federal, state, and tribal courts regarding tribal sovereignty & jurisdiction, taxation, timber management, tribal trust funds, trust asset management, natural resources, oil & gas, Indian Gaming Regulatory Act, Indian Self-Determination Act, and other matters. *Past professional post*: Associate, Indian Law Dept., Dorsey & Whitney, LL., Minneapolis, MN, 1996-98. *Bar Admissions*: New Mexico, California, Minnesota, and the Jicarilla Apache Nation. He is admitted to practice before the Tenth and Eighth Circuits, the Pueblo of Laguna, the United States Court of Federal Claims, and the United States District Courts for the following districts: New Mexico, Minnesota, the Northern District of California, and the Western District of Michigan.

PECOS, REGIS (Cochiti Pueblo)
(former pueblo governor)

Born & raised at Cochiti Pueblo. *Education*: Princeton University, BA (History & Political Science), 1977; PhD candidate at the University of California, Berkeley. Regis is a lifetime member of the Traditional Tribal Council. He has been a Council member since 1978 and has served terms as Governor as well as Lt. Governor. *Affiliation & Address*: Chief of Staff, Speaker of the House of Representatives, W. Ken Martinez, Santa Fe, NM. *Other professional post*: Director & co-founder of the New Mexico Leadership Institute. *Past professional posts:* Executive Director, New Mexico Office of Indian Affairs (16 years); Economic Development Specialist & Director of Research for American for Indian Opprtunity & Instructor at the Institute for the Development of Indian Law; governor, Cochiti Pueblo, Cochiti, NM; executive director, New Mexico Office on Indian Affairs, Santa Fe, NM. Mr. Pecos has served on the Bernalillio Public School Board of Education and the Sana Fe Indian School Board, which he served as Chair for 12 years; he served the state of New Mexico and U.S. Government as a member of the Governor's Council of Policy Advisors on Rural Economic Development, the Planning Committee for the National Indian Policy Institute, the National Task Force on Cultural Resource & Rights Protection and the National EPA Pollution Prevention Environmental Education Task Force. *Awards, honors:* In 1996, Regis became the first American Indian to be appointed a s a member of the Board of Trustees for Princeton University. In 1999, he received New Mexico's highest honor, as he was named New Mexico's Distinguished Public Servant.

PEDWAYDON, ALVIN (Grand Traverse Ottawa/Chippewa)
(former tribal chairperson)
Affiliation & Address: Grand Traverse Band of Ottawa & Chippewa Indians, 1605 N West Bay Shore Dr., Peshawbestown, MI 49682 (231) 534-7103. E-mail: alvin.pedwaydon@gtbindians.com

PEEBLES, JOHN
(tribal lawyer)
Affiliation & Address: Tribal Attorney, Flandreau Santee Sioux Tribe, P.O. Box 283, Flandreau, SD 57028 (605) 997-3891.

PEGO, DAVID PAUL (*Anungons - Little Star*) (Saginaw Chippewa) 1954-
(journalist, writer)
Born February 1, 1954, Mt. Pleasant, Mich. Education: Central Oklahoma State University, 1972-74. *Address:* 320 10th St. W., Brookings, SD 57006-1164. E-Mail: NIE77@aol.com. *Affiliations:* The Daily Oklahoman & The Oklahoma City Times, 1974-84; The Dallas Times Herald, 1984-88; The Associated Press, Dallas, TX, 1988-90; Journalist, writer, The Austin American Statesman, Austin, TX, 1990-. *Other professional posts:* Founded Great Promise, 1992- (a non-profit organization that publishes educational materials for young American Indians). *Community activities:* Founding co-chair of the Austin Powwow & American Indian Art Festival; founding co-chair, First Americans of Central Texas; member, Texas Education Agency Technology Task Force; Rising Star Foundation Board; chair, Austin Independent School District's Community Involvement and Parenting Committee; workshop panelist, 1992 & 1993, Austin Women in Media seminar for non-profit organizations; workshop panelist, 1992 Texas Conference on Indian Education; Austin Independent School District's Native American Parents Committee (founding chairman); Conference on Minority Health (organizing committee for 1994); member of the Greater Austin Chamber of Commerce (community Issues & action committee - wrote special section on crime); presented more than 200 school lectures & performances on American Indians, and about 40 lectures on journalism; served on leadership Austin communications & diversity committees; performed storytelling and poetry, Texas Culture Bash, 1996; performer, Texas Minority Health Conference, 1996. *Awards, honors:* Oklahoma City YMCA Service Awards in 1982, 1983; 1988 minority fellowships for American Newspapers Publishers Workshop for Editors; 1991 University of Oklahoma Visiting Professor in Residence; guest lecturer at various colleges & universities; selected by President Bush in 1992 as delegate to the White House Conference on Indian Education; invited to appear on local television & radio shows; designed & coordinated production of special newspaper on AIDS that was approved for use by the Dallas Independent School District; appointed by Gov. George W. Bush as member of Goals 2000 Committee for Texas; Texas State Indian Education Conference Award, 1996; NIE Information Service Bright Ideas Award. *Memberships:* Leadership Austin, Native American Journalists Association; Southern Newspaper Publishers Association (literacy committee member); Texas Newspapers in Education (board member); Wordcraft Circle of Native Writers and Storytellers (national caucus member, 1996); Capital Area Social Studies Council; American Indian Resources & Educational Coalition. *Published work:* Short story, "Indian Medicine" in literacy quarterly published by Johns Hopkins University in 1994.)

PEGO, STEVEN (Saginaw Chippewa)
(former tribal chief)
Affiliation & Address: Chief, Saginaw Chippewa Indian Tribe, 7070 E. Broadway, Mount Pleasant, MI 48858 (989) 775-4000.

PELLETIER, JULIE A. (Wesget Sipu Band)
(professor & Indigenous studies chair)
Education: Michigan State University, MA & PhD (Cultural Anthropology). *Affiliation & Address:* Associate Professor & Chairperson, Department of Indigenous Studies, University of Winnipeg, 515 Portage Ave., Winnipeg, MB R3B 2E5 (204) 786-9305. E-mail: ju.pelletier@uwinnipeg.ca. *Research Interests:* Her dissertation involved applied anthropological research in an Ojibwa community in the Upper Peninsula of Michigan. This research, which

focused on tribal identity and its relationship to ceremony and ritual, was funded by the Sault Ste. Marie Tribe of Chippewa Indians. Her interest in tribal identity includes recent research on Indian casino gaming, a site of contestation about the "Noble Savage" conflict with the new stereotype of the "Rich Indian" who has given up his identity to be a capitalist. Dr. Pelletier is also interested in the economic impact of Indian casinos on surrounding communities and is compiling longitudinal data on perceptions of American Indians in those communities. As an award-winning teacher, Dr. Pelletier has published on decolonized pedagogy with Dr. Becca Gercken who also helped found the American Indian Studies program at the University of Minnesota – Morris, a former Indian boarding school. Dr. Pelletier has done fieldwork in Aotearoa/New Zealand that influenced her understanding & application of decolonized methodologies, and she has written on the linkages between Indigenous & feminist methodologies with sociologist Dr. Jennifer Rothchild.

PELTIER, LEONARD (*Gwarth-ee-las*) (Anishinabe - Turtle Mountain) 1944-
(artist, human rights worker)
Born September 12, 1944, Grand Forks, N.D. *Education:* St. Mary's (Leavenworth, KS), 1990-91. *Address:* Prisoner #89637-132, USP Box 1000, Leavenworth, KS 66048. *Affiliation:* Leonard Peltier Defense Committee, P.O. Box 583, Lawrence, KS 66044 (785) 842-5774, 1976-. E-mail: lpdc@idir.net Military service: U.S. Marine Corps, 1960. *Community activities:* AIM activist; food & clothing drives for reservations & public awareness regarding issues facing prisoners, Native peoples, and basic civil/human rights. *Memberships:* Leonard Peltier Defense Committee, 1977-; Rosenburg Fund for Children; Walk Across Europe (1994). *Awards, honors:* Frederick Douglass Award, Spanish Human Rights Award; Sacco & Vanzetti Award; Humanitarian Award; Nobel Prize nominee. *Interests:* Art, specifically oil painting; working on cars, gardening. *Biographical sources:* Spirit of Crazy Horse, by Peter Matthiessen; Agents of Repression, by Ward Churchill; Trial of Leonard Peltier, by Jim Messerschmidt; (documentary) "Incident at Oglala," by Robert Redford; (video) Freedom by Rage Against the Machine, MTI. *Published work:* Prison Writings: My Life Is My Sundance (St. Martin's Press).

PEMBER, MARY ANNETTE (Red Cliff Ojibwe)
(freelance photojournalist, writer)
Education: University of Wisconsin-Madison, School of Journalism, BA (Editorial Journals), 1985. Resides in Cincinnati, Ohio (513) 484-3015. *Website:* www.mapember.com *E-mail:* mpember@fuse.net. *Past professional post:* President, Board of Directors, Native American Journalists Assn (NAJA) (retired); coordinates NAJA's annual Photo-Shoot-out competition sponsored by The New York Times, USA Today; staff photojournalist at the Green Bay Press-Gazette, The Oregonian and the Arizona Republic; photo editor of the The Lexington Heald-Leader. Her photojournalism has dealt primarily with social issues, such as homelessness, drug abuse, youth gangs, as well as women's and indigenous people's issues in the U.S., Nepal & India. Currently, she is focusing exclusively on Native topics. *Awards, honors:* In 1995 traveled to Beijing as a representative of both NAJA and UNITY: Journalists of Color, Inc., as part of the United Nations' World Conference on Women; served on the Visual Task Force of UNITY '99; won several awards from the National Press Photographers Association, The Kentucky Newspaper Association, The Ohio Press Photographers Association; The Arizona Press Club; The Associated Press, and the Oregon Newspaper Association, as well as the Ralph Nafsiger Alumni Achievement Award from the University of Wisconsin-Madison School of Journalism; NAJA names her Best Photographer in 2000; she is a current recipient of a University of Maryland Child & Family Policy Journalism Fellowship. *Memberships:* National Press Photographers Association; Ohio Press Photographers Association; Native American Journalists Association. *Published works:* She has been published in Life, Time, Newsweek, The New York Times, USA Today, Ms., Indian Country Today, Aboriginal Voices, Winds of Change, News From Indian Country, Native Peoples, Indigenous Woman, The Discover Channel.com, The National Museum of the American Indian Magazine, and others. Her essays on Native American history & culture have just been published in the book, "America, The Complete Story."

PENDLETON, BRIAN (Mdewakanton Sioux)
(tribal vice chairperson)
Affiliation & Address: Vice Chairperson, Lower Sioux Indian Community, P.O. Box 308, Morton, MN 56270 (507) 697-6185. E-mail: brianpendleton@lowersioux.com

PENN, SAMUEL H., SR. (*Mountain Wolf*) (Cherokee of Virginia)
(tribal chief)
Affiliation & Address: Chief United Cherokee Indian Tribe of Virginia, P.O. Box 1104, Madison Heights, VA 24572 (434) 847-4104 Website: www.ucitova.org

PENN, W.S. (Nez Perce/Osage) 1949-
(writer, teacher)
Born March 21, 1949, Los Angeles, Calif. *Education:* University of California, Davis, AB, 1970; Syracuse University, DArts, 1979. *Address:* 963 Lantern Hill

Dr., East Lansing, MI 48823-2831 (517) 337-0694. E-mail: penn@pilot.msu. edu. *Affiliations*: Professor, Michigan State University (MSU), E. Lansing, MI, 1986-; Wordcraft Circle of Native Writers & Storytellers, Albuquerque, NM (mentor, 8 years). *Other professional post*: Director, Creative Writing Program, MSU (2004-present). *Memberships*: Wordcraft Circle (regional coordinator, member of National Advisory Council on Native American Writing); Associated Writing Programs; Modern Language Association. Awards, honors: 1994 North American Indian Prose Award for "All My Sins are Relatives" (narrative essays) from the University of Nebraska Press; Michigan Council on the Arts Award & New York Foundation on the Arts Grant for "The Absence of Angels" (novel); American Book Award, 2001 for "Killing Time With Strangers (novel); Choice Award for Most Significant Books, 2001, for "This Is the World (stories); Distinguished Faculty Award, MSU (2003). *Interests*: Writing (novels, essays); teaching/mentoring; giving back to the community; travel; reading. *Published works*: Novel - "The Absence of Angels" (The Permanent Press - hardcover, 1994; paperback, University of Oklahoma American Indian Lit. Series), 1995); Killing Time With Strangers (University of Arizona Press, 2000); narrative essays. "All My Sins Are Relatives" (University of Nebraska Press, 1995); The Telling of the World; As We Are Now: Essays on Race and Identity; editor, Native American Literatures (The Johns Hopkins University Press, 1994) a special anthology; Feathering Custer - essays (University of Arizona Press, 2000); This Is the World - stories (Michigan State University Press, 2000); editor, Michigan State University Press, American Indian Literature Series.

PENNEY, DAVID W.
(curator; association president)
Affiliations & Address: Associate Director of Museum Scholarship (2011-present), National Museum of the American Indian, 4th St. & Independence Ave., SW, P.O. Box 23473, Washington, DC 20026-3473 (202) 633-1000 *Past professional posts*: Vice President of Exhibitions & Collections Strategies & Curator of Native American Art, 1980-2011, President, Native American Arts Studies Association, Detroit Institute of the Arts; Adjunct Professor of Art History, Wayne State University, Detroit, MI 1989-2000. *Published work*: Native American Art (Universe, 1999).

PENNEY, SAMUEL N. (Nez Perce) 1955-
(policy board member)
Born & raised in Kamiah, Idaho. *Education*: University of Idaho (2003 honorary doctorate degree of Doctor of Administrative Science). Born & raised in Kamiah, Idaho. *Affiliation & Address*: Policy board member, Portland State University, Hatfield School of Government, Institute for Tribal Leadership Forum, P.O. Box 610, North Plains, OR 97133. *Other professional posts*: Tribal Advisor, Blue Stone Strategy Group, Irvine, CA; tribal advisory boards to the presidents of Washington State University, University of Idaho & Lewis & Clark State College. *Past professional posts*: Nez Perce Tribal Executive Committee, Lapwai, ID, 1989-2010 (chairperson, 10 years; vice chairperson, 3 years). Samuel served on the executive boards of the Intertribal Monitoring Association on Indian Trust Funds, Northwest Region delegate to the National Indian Gaming Association Board of Directors, National Trbal Environmental Council Executive Committee and the Affiliated Tribes of Northwest Indians Executive Board of Directors. He has provided testimony before Congress and worked with members of Congress in advocating on behalf of the Nez Perce Tribe regarding federal authorization/appropriations and the protection of Nez Perce treaty rights. *Awards, honors*: In 1999, the Idaho Statesman Newspaper featured Mr. Penney in an article entitled the "Idahoans Changing Idaho - 10 Who Make a Difference." 2003 President's Medallion from Lewis-Clark State College, Lewiston, Idaho. Also in 2003, The University of Iaho in recognition of a lifetime of contributions to the state of Idaho conferred upon him an honorary doctorate degree of Doctor of Administrative Scince.

PENSONEAU, SHAWN (Kickapoo)
(director of governmental affairs)
Affiliation & Address: Director of Governmental Affairs, National American Indian Housing Council, 900 2nd St., NE Suite 107, Washington, DC 20002 (202) 789-1754.

PEONE, RUDY (Spokane)
(former tribal chairperson)
Affiliation & Address: Former Chairperson, Spokane Business Council, P.O. Box 100, Wellpinit, WA 99040 (509) 258-4581. E-mail: rudy@spokanetribe.com

PEOPLES, LEE
(library director)
Education: University of Oklahoma, BA, MLIS, JD. *Affiliation & Address*: Director, Chickasaw Nation Law Library, Oklahoma City University School of Law, 2501 N. Blackwelder, Oklahoma City, OK 73106 (405) 208-5337; E-mail: lpeoples@okcu.edu *Other professional post*: Professor of Law, Oklahoma City University School of Law Professor Peoples' research and scholarship is focused on the impact of technology on legal research, the judiciary, and the law. He has published articles, books, and book chapters on these topics. He

is a co-founding editor of the *Legal Information and Technology* eJournal on SSRN. He teaches advanced legal research classes and is a frequent lecturer in law school classes. Professor Peoples is active in professional organizations including the American Association of Law Libraries and Association of American Law Schools. He is past president of the Mid-American Association of Law Libraries and recent past president of the Mid-American Law Libraries Consortium. He served as the Director of International Programs for the School of Law from 2007-2010. In that position, he developed the innovative Certificate in American Law Program. Prior to his appointment as Law Library Director in 2010, he served as Associate Director, Associate Director for Faculty and Research Services, and Head of Reference Services. Before joining the faculty, Professor Peoples practiced law in Oklahoma City. He is admitted to practice in the State of Oklahoma, Western District of Oklahoma, and Tenth Circuit Court of Appeals.

PEPION, DONALD D.
(professor of Native Ameriacn studies)
Education: New Mexico State University, BS (Business Management & Sociology), Montana State University, MEd & EdD, 1999. *Affiliation & Address*: Associate Professor of Anthropology specialzing in Native American Studies (2007-present), New Mexico State University, Breland Hall 303, Las Cruces, NM (575) 646-3610; E-mail: dpepion@nmsu.edu. *Research Interests*: Ethnohistory of the Indigenous Blackfoot peoples (Canada & U.S.). Dr. Pepion's general area of interest is in Native American studies. He has done much research on the culture and ethnohistory of the indigenous Blackfoot peoples of Canada and the United States. He has spent several years directing programs and teaching at the community college level. His research experience includes fellowships at Newberry Library in Chicago and the Smithsonian Museum of Natural History in Washington D.C. *Past professional posts*: Director, American Indian Program,& Assiatnt Profesor of Native American Studies, New Mexico State University, 2000-07; Blackfeet Community College, Browning, MT (Instructor/Counseor, 1993-97; Administrator, Blackfeet Tribal Health Department, Browning, MT, 1987-93; President, Blackfet Community College, 1983-86.

PEPION, LORETTA F. (Blackfeet) 1942-
(museum curator)
Born May 11, 1942, Mont. *Address & Affiliation*: Museum of the Plains Indian, Box 398, Browning, MT 59417 (406) 338-2230.

PEPPERS, PATRICIA RAE (Northern Cheyenne)
(Montana State representative)
Affiliation & Address: Montana State Representative (D) District 41 (2013-14), P.O. Box 200400, Helena, MT 59620; P.O. Box 497, Lame Deer, MT 59043 (406) 697-0565. E-mail: peppers@rangeweb.net.

PERATROVICH, ROY, JR. (Tlingit) 1934-
(sculptor, artist)
Born May 17, 1934, Klawock, Alaska. *Education*: University of Washington, BS, 1957. *Affiliation & Address*: 2122 47th St. Ct. NW, Gig Harbor, WA 98335 (253) 514-8190. E-mail: roy@ravenworksart.com. Roy's art is bronze sculpture. *Past professional posts*: Engineer, Seattle Engineering Dept., 1957-61; bridge designer, AK Dept. of Highways, 1961-72; supervisor of activities, R&M Consultants, Inc., 1972-77; first director, State of Alaska, Div. of Facility Procurement Policy, 1977-79; president, Peratrovich Consultants, Inc., Anchorage, 1979-; Sr. Vice President, Peratrovich, Nottingham & Drage, Inc. - Consulting Engineers, Anchorage, 1979-1999. *Memberships*: State of AK Board of Registration for Engineers, Architects, and Land Surveyors; American Society of Civil Engineers; The Society of American Military Engineers. *Awards, honors*: Five awards from James & Lincoln Arc Welding Foundation for design of welded structures; and numerous awards from Municipality of Anchorage Urban Design Awards Program, among others; first Alaska Native to become licensed as a professional engineer in the state of Alaska. *Interests*: "Son of prominent Alaskan civil rights activists, Roy & Elizabeth Peratrovich. Over 30 years experience in structural & civil engineering, facility planning, and engineering management, working in both government and private sector. Primary work emphasis has been in the fields of bridge & marine structural design & management of major planning agencies." *Published work*: Co-author, Guide to Maintenance and Operations of Small Craft Harbors, 1988, the first manual of its kind in the U.S.; articles on bridge design and construction, with Dennis Nottingham.

PERDASOFPY, ROGER V. (Kiowa, Apache, Comanche) 1959-
(drum maker, singer)
Born November 1, 1959, Lawton, Okla. Principal occupation: Drum maker. *Address*: P.O. Box 932, Midlothian, TX 76065 (972) 723-2984. E-mail: perdasofpy@cnbcom.net. *Affiliation*: Perdasofpy Crafts, 1990-present. *Other professional posts*: Employed as tour guide, singer, dancer, Village builder, Indian City U.S.A., Anadarko, OK, 1984-present. He has run dance shows, sung and danced professionally since the age of 10. *Military service*: U.S. Army, 1977-81 (Corporal or E-4). *Memberships*: Indian Arts & Crafts Assn,

IACA (Albuquerque); American Indian Art Council (Dallas); American Indian Chamber of Commerce of Texas; Native American Church. *Awards, honors*: He's won numerous First Place awards in national competition for his drums at Indian Markets around the country & National Champion Fancy Dancer; he has appeared on television and in many newspaper articles. *Interests*: He creates men's dance regalia and other cultural items, as well as jewelry and beadwork, along with his wife, Sharon. Roger is primarily a drum maker, in the Southern Plains Tradition. He is a southern singer and it is from his traditional background he creates hand drums to large powwow drums, using cedar and a variety of other wood and hide. Roger has lectured on his culture, hide and drum making at various art councils, and the Native American educational organization JOM (Johnson O'Malley), also included in some of this lecture is demonstration. He makes other cultural items but drum making is his specialty. He runs dance shows, teepee exhibitions, lectures, workshops, demonstrations & cultural programs. He enjoys fishing, being around water, camping, their many dogs and cats, watching wrestling, sports, movies & visiting with friends. "It's my wish that people when they hear the drum (the heartbeat of Mother Earth) that they feel good." *Biographical sources*: Texas Touring Arts Program Company & Artist Roster for the Texas Commission on the Arts.

PERDASOFPY, SHARON (Comanche, Cherokee)
(jeweler)
Born in San Antonio, Tex. *Address*: P.O. Box 932, Midlothian, TX 76065 (972) 723-2984. E-mail: perdasofpy@flash.net. *Affiliation*: Perdasofpy Crafts, 1990-present. *Memberships*: Indian Arts & Crafts Association, IACA (Albuquerque); American Indian Chamber of Commerce of Texas; American Indian Art Council, Inc. (Dallas); Arlington (TX) Gem & Mineral Club; Native American Church; American Indian Methodist Church. *Awards, honors*: Numerous awards for her jewelry. Her award winning jewelry is with collectors internationally, including Loretta Lynn & Family, Dr. Menninger, The Art Institute of Chicago & about 40 other museums around the country. Featured artist at Macy's, set an emerald from the Nuestra de Atocha (which sank in 1617). *Interests*: Sharon, besides beadworking, making small shields and a variety of jewelry, specializes in custom work, hand-sculptured wire jewelry (a 3,300 year old art form), silversmithing & repairs. "I love making jewelry with gifts from Mother Earth. It's my wish that people feel this flow from these gifts and that of The Creator. I love working with stones hand-sculpting them with sterling silver wire, or gold wire; with fossils, with carvings and sometimes in combination with woods, bone, etc. I love the outdoors: hiking, camping, working in the yard, our dogs & cats, visiting with friends, and watching true story movies and comedy. My wish is that people feel the flow of the Creator (thru my created jewelry pieces, and how we are all inter-related brothers and sisters.")

PERDUE, DAVID G., M.D. (Chickasaw)
(physician, gastroenterologist, medical director)
Born & raised in Spokane, Wash. *Education*: Washington State University, Honors College, BS; University of Colorado, MSPHA; University of Washington School of Medicine, MD; At UW, he participated in the Native American Health Pathway, He externed with the Seattle Indian Health Board, spent several months traveling with a traditional healer, and conducted research with Alaska Native population through the CDC's Arctic Investigation Program in Anchorage. He concluded his internal medicine residency & gastroenterology fellowship at the University of Minnesota, where he subsequently spent three years on the faculty. Dr. Perdue is the first American Indian gastroenterologist. *Affiliation & Address*: Gastroenterologist, Minnesota Gastroenterology, 5705 W. Old Shakopee Rd. #150, Minneapolis, MN 55437 (612) 871-1145. E-mail: perdu001@umn.edu. *Other professional post*: Medical Director, American Indian Cancer Foundation, Minneapolis, MN. E-mail: dperdue@aicaf.org; co-chairs the Minnesota Intertribal Colorectal Cancer Council and the Minnesota Colon Cancer Task Force. *Memberships*: Mayo Clinic's Spirit of Eagles Cancer Research Network. *Published works*: Numerous articles in journals.

PERDUE, THEDA
(professor of history)
Affiliation & Address: Professor of History, University of North Carolina, Chapel Hill, NC. *Published works*: Slavery and the Evolution of Cherokee Society, 1540-1866 (University of Tennessee Press, 1979); Native Carolinians: The Indians of North Carolina (North Carolina Division of Archives & Cherokee Publications, 1985); Cherokee Women (University of Nebraska Press, 1988); The Cherokee (Chelsea House, 1988); The Columbia Guide to American Indians in the Southeast (Columbia University Press, 2001); Mixed Blood Indians: Racial Construction in the Early South (U. of Georgia Press, 2002).

PEREA, JACOB (Mescalero Apache)
(college dean)
Affiliation & Address: Dean, College of Education, San Francisco State University, 1600 Holloway, San Francisco, CA 94132.

PEREA, JOHN-CARLOS (Mescalero Apache) 1975-
(musician)
Born March 7, 1975, Dulce, N.M. *Education*: San Francisco State University, BA (Music). *Address*: 149 Gonzalez Dr., San Francisco, CA 94132 (415) 452-8421. E-mail: pereajc@yahoo.com. *Community activities*: Co-leader, Sweetwater Singers, powwow drum. *Membership*: Wordcraft Circle of Native Writers and Storytellers. *Interests*: "Finding a musical language where powwow music & jazz can co-exist respectfully." *Published works*: Jazz CDs: Gathering of Ancestors (Asian Improv Arts, 1999); First Dance (Aerep Music, 2001).

PEREZ, DAVID A. (Nambe Pueblo)
(Pueblo governor)
Affiliation & Address: Governor, Nambe Pueblo Council, Rt. 1 Box 117-BB, Santa Fe, NM 87501 (505) 455-2036.

PEREZ, PHILLIP A. (Nambe Pueblo)
(Pueblo governor)
Affiliation & Address: Governor, Pueblo of Nambe, Rt. 1 Box 117-BB 8, Nambe Pueblo, NM 87747 (505) 455-2036.

PEREZ, ROBERT C.
(assistant professor)
Education: University of California, San Diego, BA; Universite de Pau et des Pays de l'Adour, MA; University of California, Riverside, PhD (History). *Affiliation*: Instructor, Native American Studies Program, Dept. of Ethnic Studies, INTS 4049, College of Humanities, Arts & Social Sciences, Riverside, CA 92521 (951) 827-1828. E-mail: perezr@ucr.edu. *Interests*: His work is focused on American Indian history with an emphasis on that region of the hemisphere that includes California, U.S. southwest, Texas & northern Mexico.

PEREZ, VIRGIL (Iipay-Diegueno)
(tribal chairperson)
Affiliation & Address: Chairperson, Iipay Nation of Santa Ysabel, P.O. Box 130, Santa Ysabel, CA 92070 (760) 765-0846.

PERKINS, TOBY (Chickasaw)
(tribal legislature representative)
Education: Oklahoma State University, BS. *Affiliation & Address*: Pontotoc District (Seat #1) Representative, The Chickasaw Nation, 15810 CR 1569, Ada, OK 74820 (580) 332-7073. E-mail: toby.perkins@chickasaw.net.

PERRY, DWAINE C. (*Sachem Maqua*) (Ramapough Lenape)
(tribal chief)
Born & raised in Hillburn, NY, the "Deer Clan" community of Ramapough Lenape. *Education*: Rockland Community College, AA; Pace University, BS; Southern New Hampshire University, MSCED (Community Economic Development). *Affiliation & Address*: Ramapough Lenape Indian Nation, P.O. Box 103, Hillburn, NY 10931 (201) 529-1171. *Military service*: U.S. Army (Vietnam Vet).

PERRY, GAYE BUMSTED (Tohono O'odham)
(Indian curriculum coordinator)
Affiliation & Address: Curriculum Coordinator, Tohono O'odham Studies, Tohono O'odam Community College, P.O. Box 3129, Sells, AZ 85634 (520) 383-8401

PERRY, ROBERT (Chickasaw) 1936-
(former tribal administrator)
Born in 1936. *Address*: Resides in Ada, OK. *Affiliations*: Chickasaw Advisory Council (secretary & chair, 1965-78; chair, Chickasaw Industrial Development Board, 1993-2001; Chickasaw Historical Society (eight years; currently an emeritus member); represented the Chickasaw Nation on the Five Civilized Tribes Inter-Tribal Council; Chickasaw Council of Elders, 2004-present). currently serves on the National Board of Directors of the Wordcraft Circle of Native Writers & Storytellers. *Awards, honors*: 2011 Inductee to the Chickasaw Nation Hall of Fame. *Published works*: Mr. Perry published three books, one of which is displayed in the exhibit center of the Chickasaw Cultural Center.

PERRY, SHAWN MICHAEL (Salish/Mayan)
(singer, songwriter, actor, educator, activist)
Born April 27, 1966 in San Diego, Calif. *Facebook*: www.facebook/shawn.m.perry. *Credits*: Music Video: "Forever" produced & directed by Perry, this video accompanies the track on full-length CD, "Shawn Michael Perry & Only the Brave." Sundance Film Festival asked Shawn to perform & show this video. *Bookings contact*: Belinda Corcovelos (928) 284-4736. Website: www.onlythebraveentertainment.com E-mail: belinda@otbentertainment.com

PERRY, WILLIAM R.
(attorney; Indian law)
Education: Brown University, BA, 1975; Georgetown University Law Center, JD, 1978. *Affiliation & Address*: Partner, Sonosky, Chambers, Sachse, Endreson & Perry, LLP, 1425 K St., NW, Suite 600, Washington, DC 20005

(202) 682-0240. E-mail: wperry@sonosky.com. Mr. Perry has represented Indian tribes on a broad range of matters for over thirty years. While he has represented many tribes during this time, he takes particular satisfaction in having had the opportunity to serve the Standing Rock Sioux Tribe continuously throughout his legal career. He has handled significant federal and state court litigation, as well as federal administrative appeals, regarding a variety of federal Indian law matters, including jurisdictional disputes, reservation boundary matters, state efforts to tax transactions in Indian country, Public Law 280 disputes, claims for damages for wrongs committed by the federal government, cases arising under the Indian Child Welfare Act, the American Indian Probate Reform Act and many others. Many of the cases he has handled have involved the intersection between Tribal history and Federal Indian law, an area of special emphasis in his practice. Mr. Perry has broad experience regarding tribal gaming under the Indian Gaming Regulatory Act (IGRA), including litigation to protect tribal authority to continue gaming in the face of a legal challenge based on a state constitutional amendment that broadly prohibited gaming under state law. He has negotiated compacts and management agreements, developed tribal gaming ordinances, assisted tribes win connection with various gaming investigations and personnel disputes, and advised tribal gaming commissions regarding their regulatory duties. He has addressed matters before the NIGC, including obtaining favorable Indian lands decisions for tribes under section 20 of IGRA. He has worked extensively on Tribal environmental matters, including successfully assisting tribes in securing Treatment as a State status, which enables Tribes to develop and implement their own environmental standards to protect their reservations. He also has substantial expertise on the trust land acquisition process – including both the nuts and bolts of the process and the legal issues associated with the frequent challenges to trust land acquisitions. He has also represented tribes before Congress.

PESANTUBBEE, MICHELENE E. (Choctaw)
(professor of Native American studies)
Affiliation & Address: Associate Professor of Native American Religious Traditions, American Indian & Native Studies Program, University of Iowa, 404 Jefferson Bldg., Iowa City, IA 52242 (319) 335-1980. E-mail: michelene-pesantubbe@uiowa.edu. She specializes in Southeastern Native American religious movements, & teaches courses in Native American environmentalism & Native American women & religious change. Her research program focuses on Native American religious change spanning the period from the eighteenth to the twentieth century. She is particularly interested in how contact experiences with European & European Americans affected Native American religious practices and Native women's lives. Her published articles and book chapters examine Native American religious movements that arise in response to colonization. *Published work*: Choctaw Woman in a Chaotic World (University of New Mexico Press, 2005); chapter, "Wounded Knee: Symboll of Resistance & Recovery, in Recovering Memory: Exposing Religion, Violence, and the Remembrance of Place," edited by Oren Baruch Stier & J.Landres (University of Indiana Press, 2006); chapter, "Beyond Domesticity: Choctaw Women Negotiating the Tension Between Choctaw Culture & Protestantism with new Introduction," in Native Women's History in Eastern North America Before 1900," edited by Rebecca Kugel & Lucy E. Murphy (U. of Nebraska Pr, 2007),

PESATA, LEVI (Jicarilla Apache)
(former tribal president)
Affiliation & Address: Jicarilla Apache Tribe, P.O. Box 507, Dulce, NM 87528

PESHEWA, MACAKI (Shawnee; Shaman) 1941-
(priest-Native American Church)
Born May 23, 1941, Spartanburg, S.C. *Education*: Spartanburg Junior College, AA, 1966; Wofford College, BA, 1968; Furman University, 1969; University of South Carolina, 1971-73; University of Tennessee, Knoxville, MS, 1974, 1976-77; Auburn University, 1974-75; Native Americas University (Doctorate-Human Development, 1975; Doctorate-System Theory of Life Science, 1976). *Affiliation & Address*: Priest, Native American Church, P.O. Box 53, Strawberry Plains, TN 37871. *Affiliations*: Regional coordinator, Catawba Labor Program; Chairman, Tennessee Indian Council, Knoxville, TN; chairperson & founder, Native American Indians in Media Corporation, Knoxville, TN; chairman, Indian Historical Society of the Americas, Knoxville, Tenn. *Other professional post*: Founder & publisher of the National Indian Reader Newspaper; founder of the Peace Park-Valley of the Totems; business developer in Indian Bingo. *Military service*: U.S. Air Force. *Community activities*: Work with off-reservation Indians; Tennessee Band of Cherokees (medicine man, business advisor); The American Indian Movement (urban Indian, Shawnee Nation); Native American Church of the Southeast (incorporator & head); National Lenape Band of Indians (medicine man); Consciousness Expansion Movement of Native Americans (president, chairman); Tuskegee Alumni Foundation, Knoxville, Tenn. (advisory board); Knoxville Communications Cooperative (advisory board); Native Americas University (Southeast regional coordinator; board of regents; Indian Voters League. *Memberships*: Assn of Humanistic

Psychology; XAT-American Indian Medicine Society; International Minority Business Council/Assn. *Awards, honors*: Notary-at-Large, Tennessee; Key-to-City Certificate of Appreciation, Knoxville, TN. Governor Recognitions: Appreciation Certificate, and Colonel-past & present administration. *Interests*: Archives of living elders in America today; art collector for Native American Church collection. Parapsychology; existential philosophy; existential phenomenology; altered states of consciousness & metaphysics; herbal medicine; yoga; handball; travel. *Published work*: Film produced: Amonita Sequoyah (Native American Media, 1982); *Archives*: Longest Walk for Survival, 1981; Archives: Black Elk, Sun Bear, Amy Lee, Simon Brasquepe.

PESHLAKAI, JAMESCITA (Navajo-Dine')
(Arizona State representative)
Affiliation & Address: Representatie (D) (2013-14), District 7, Arizona State Legislature, 1700 W. Washingtonn, Room 323, Phoenix, AZ 85007 (602) 926-5160. E-mail: jpeshlakai@azleg.gov.

PETAGO, ERNEST (Jicarilla Apache)
(tribal vice president)
Affiliation & Address: Vice President, Jicarilla Apache Tribe, P.O. Box 507, Dulce, NM 87528 (505) 759-3242.

PETE, JAMES E. (*Guyaushk*) (Red Cliff Lake Superior Chippewa)
(professor of Native American Studies; company owner)
Education: BS (Business Administration); MS (Organizational Management); PhD (Business Administration). Dr. Pete's doctoral project, entitled, "Native American/Indian Tribal Organization & Leadership: Understanding the Past, Living in the Present, Designing the Future for Tribal Organizations & Leadership." *Affiliation & Address*: Director of Native American & Indigenous Culture Center & Associate Professor of Native American Studies, Mead 123, 1411 Ellis Ave., Ashland, WI 54806 (715) 682-1366. E-mail: jpete@northland.edu. *Other professional post*: Guyaushk & Associates, 88225 State Hwy. 13, Bayfield, WI 54814 (715) 779-5782. A firm that concentrates on a variety of tribal management issues, organizational assessments, training & technical assistance services. E-mail: guyaushk@aol.com. *Past professional post*: Director, IHS-Rhinelander Field Office, Rhinelander, WI.

PETE, LYNDA TELLER (Navajo)
(artist)
Address: 2142 Irving St., Denver, CO 80211 (303) 561-1582. E-mail: ltellerpete @yahoo.com. Navajo weaving & beadwork.

PETE-BALDWIN, JOETTE (Lake Superior Chippewa)
(tribal vice president)
Affiliation & Address: Vice Presient, Lac Viex Desert Band of Lake Superior Chippea, P.O. Box 249, Watersmeet, MI 49969 (906) 358-4577.

PETER, EVON (Neetsaii Gwich'in)
(executive director)
Affiliation & Address: Executive director, Native Movement, Indigenous Leadership Institute, P.O. Box 834367, Fairbanks, AK 99708 (907) 388-8787. Website: www.evonpeter.net; E-mail: evonpeter@mac.com. *Other professional posts*: Speaker & writer. *Essays published*: "Undermining Alaska Native Nations," "The Colonization of Alaska Natives," "An Indigenous Vision to Heal America," and "We Must Stop the Violence."

PETER, MICHAEL (Athapascan)
(Alaskan village chief)
Affiliation: Native Village of Fort Yukon, P.O. Box 126, Fort Yukon, AK 99740 (907) 662-2581.

PETER-PAUL, EDWARD (Micmac)
(tribal chief)
Affiliation & Address: Chief, Aroostook Band of Micmacs, P.O. Box 772, Presque Island, ME 04769 (207) 764-1972.

PETERS, AARON (Karuk)
(former tribal chairperson)
Affiliation: Quartz Valley Indian Reservation, P.O. Box 24, Fort Jones, CA.

PETERS, CHRISTOPHER (Karuk)
(president & CEO)
Affiliation & Address: President & CEO, Seventh Generation Fund for Indian Development, Inc., P.O. Box 4569, Arcata, CA 95518 (707) 825-7640.

PETERS, DORY (Navajo)
(president & CEO)
Affiliation & Address: President & CEO, Big Navajo Energy, 2462 Charleston Ave., Harrisville, UT 84414. (928) 235-1997. dory@bignavajoenergy.com. A Navajo owned renewable energy business.

PETERS, ELAINE F.
(museum director)
Affiliation & Address: Director, Ak Chin Indian Him-Dak Museum/Archives, 42507 W. Peters & Nall Rd., Maricopa, AZ 85239 (520) 568-9480.

PETERS, JOHN A.
(executive director)
Affiliation & Address: Executive Director, Massachusetts Commission on Indian Affairs, 100 Cambridge St. #300, Boston, MA 02114 (617) 573-1291. E-mail: john.peters@state.ma.us.

PETERS, KURT (Blackfeet/Powhatan)
(professor of Native American studies)
Education: University of California, Berkeley, PhD. *Affiliation & Address*: Professor of Native American & Comparative Ethnic Studies, Ethnic Studies Dept., 230 Strand Ag, Oregon State University, Corvallis, OR 97331 (541) 737-5668. E-mail: kpeters@oregonstate.edu. *Research Interests*: 20th-century Native American experience & Native American wage labor. *Other professional posts*: Director, Native American Collaborative Institute, Oregon State U.; member, executive committee of the Sustainable Rural Communities Initiative. *Published work*: Visions & Voices: American Indian Activism & the Civil Rights Movement, edited with Terry Straus (Albatross Press, 2009).

PETERS, PHILLIP, SR. (Yup'ik Eskimo)
(Alaska native community president)
Affiliation & Address: President, Akiachak Native Community, P.O. Box 70, Akiachak, AK 99551 (907) 825-4626. E-mail: akiachak@aitc.org

PETERS, RAMONA (*Nosapocket*) (Mashpee Wampanoag) 1952-
(repatriation consultant, artist)
Born July 22, 1952. *Principal occupation*: Wampanoag Confederation Repatriation Project consultant, artist. *Address*: P.O. Box 244, Mashpee, MA 02649 (508) 477-1361. E-mail: nosap@cape.com. *Community activities*: Mentor for Tribal Girls (28 girls), teach Wampanoag traditional pottery to interested tribal members, conduct cultural sensitivity workshops, ceremonial duties/responsibilities. *Memberships*: Mashpee Women's Medicine Society (board member); Mashpee Domestic Violence Prevention Project; Wampanoag Nation Singers & Dancers Troupe.

PETERS, CHIEF RUSSELL (Mashpee Wampanoag)
(tribal chief)
Affiliation & Address: Mashpee Wampanoag Indian Tribal Council, P.O. Box 1048, Mashpee, MA 02649.

PETERS, TIA OROS (Zuni)
(executive director)
Education: Universit of California, Santa Barbara, BA (Law & Society); Antioch University, Los Angeles, Calif. MFA (Creative Writing). *Affiliation & Address*: Executive Director (2005-present), Seventh Generation Fund for Indigenous Peoples, Inc., P.O. Box 4569, Arcata, CA 95518 (707) 825-7640. E-mail: tia@7genfund.org.

PETERSON, CRYSTAL (St. Croix Ojibwe)
(tribal vice chairperson)
Affiliation & Address: Vice Chairperson, St. Croix Chippewa Indians of Wisconsin & Danbury Community Representative,, 24663 Angeline Ave., Webster, WI 54893 (715) 349-2195.

PETERSON, GARY W. (Skokomish)
(professor of Native studies; board treasurer)
Affiliation & Address: Tenure Track Professor, Native Studies, Native American Program, Evergreen College, 2700 Evergreen Parkway NW, Olympia, WA 98505 (360) 867-6286. Gary's strengths include cross-cultural communication, intergovernmental relations, and experiential teaching. *Other professional post*: Board treasurer, National Indian Child Welfare Association, Portland, OR. *Past professional posts*: Chairperson, Child & Family Welfare Committee; chair, Affiliated Tribes of Northwest Indians.

PETERSON, PATRICK, JR. (Aleut)
(Alaskan village president)
Affiliation & Address: President, Naknek Native Village, Box 106, Naknek, AK 99663 (907) 246-4210.

PETERSON, RICHARD J. (Tlingit)
(central council president)
Affiliation & Address: President (2014-present), Central Council of Tlingit & Haida (2014-present), 320 W. Willoughby Ave., Suite 300, Juneau, AK 99801 (907) 586-1432. E-mail: rpeterson@ccthita.org. *Past professional posts*: President, Administrator & Director of Economic Development, Organized Village of Kasaan, Kasaan, AK (1996-2008); CEO, POWTEC, LLC, 2008-2014.

PETERSON, RICHARD "RICK" (Red Cliff Ojibwe)
(tribal chairperson)
Affiliation & Address: Chairperson, Red Cliff Band of Lake Superior Chippewa Indians of Wisconsin, 88385 Pike Rd., Hwy. 13, Bayfield, WI 54814 (715) 779-3700.

PETOSKEY, JOHN F. (Grand Traverse Ottawa & Chippewa) 1954-
(attorney)
Born in 1954 on the Grand Traverse Band of Ottawa & Chippewa Indians Reservation in Peshawbestown, Mich. *Education*: Western Michigan University, BA, 1976; University of New Mexico School of Law, JD, 1979. *Affiliation & Address*: Partner (2010-present), Fredericks Peebles & Morgan, LLC, 2848 Setterbo Rd., Peshawbestown, MI 49682 (231) 631-8558. E-mail: jpetoskey@ndnlaw.com. *Practice areas*: Tribal government; self-determination & self-governance; gaming law & development; reservation economic develop-ment; tribal code development; Indian housing; Indian reservation roads; Indian commercial development; and taxation in Indian Country. Past professional post: General Counsel for Grand Traverse Band of Ottawa & Chippewa Indians for 23 years. *Publication*: Essay, "Indians and the First Amendment," Vine Deloria, Jr., Editor (essays in American Indian Policy in the 20th Century.)

PETRUSKA, SELINA (Athapascan)
(Alaskan village chief)
Affiliation: Chief, Beaver Village (Eskimo, Athapascan, Indian), P.O. Box 24029, Beaver, AK 99724 (907) 628-6126.

PETTIGREW, DAWN KARIMA (Creek/Chickasaw/Cherokee) 1970-
(author & novelist)
Born May 13, 1970, Columbus, Ohio. *Education*: Harvard University, BA, 1992; Ohio State University, MFA, 1996. *Principal occupation*: Author & novelist. *Address*: P.O. Box 1748, Qualla Boundary Reservation, Cherokee, NC 28719. *Affiliation*: Writer, 1979-present; instructor/researcher, Ohio State University, Columbus, OH, 1993-96; freelance correspondent for News from Indian Country, 1995-present; correspondent, "Whispering Wind" Magazine (current); writer-in-residence, Western Carolina University (current). *Community activities*: The Northeasterners, Inc.; Member, Cherokee United Methodist Church; singing, poetry & literary readings, mentoring. *Memberships*: Wordcraft Circle of Native Writers & Storytellers; Native American Journalists' Association; Native Writers Circle of the Americas. *Awards, honors*: Her novel, "The Way We Make Sense," was a finalist for the North American Native First Book Award; a first runner-up in Kent State's Southern Regional Education Board Doctoral Scholar, 1998-2001; 2000-2001, Miss Native American Worldwide Achievement; finalist - Woodford Reserve Literary Competition. *Interests*: Beadwork, traditional arts & dance, film. *Published works*: The Way We Make Sense (Aunt Lute Books-San Francisco, 2002) Website: www.auntlute.com; The Marriage of Saints (play).

PEWEWARDY, CORNEL (*Oyate Omp Moni*) (Comanche/Kiowa) 1952-
(retired director & professor of Indigenous studies)
Born January 20, 1952, Lawton, Okla. *Education*: Northeastern State University, BS, 1976, MEd, 1977; University of New Mexico, EdS, 1986; Penn State University, DEd, 1989; Postdoctoral Fellow, University of Oklahoma, 1989-91. *Affiliation & Address*: Retired Director & Professor of Indigenous Nations Studies, P.O. Box 751, Potland State University, Portland, OR 97207 (503) 725-9689. E-mail: cornelp@pdx.edu. *Past professional post*: Principal, Mounds Park All-Nations Magnet School, St. Paul, MN. *Community activities*: Board Director, Dayton's Bluff/Dist. 4; Afrocentric Academy; Minnesota Institute of Arts; St. Paul Indians in Unity; Kirkpatrick Center; Minnesota Technical College System. *Memberships*: National Association for Multicultural Education (founding member); American Education Research Association; National Association of American Indian Professors; PDK; Pi Lambda Theta; National Council of Teachers of English; National Indian Education Association; Oklahoma Council for Indian Education; Association of Institute Research. *Awards, honors*: John C. Rouillard Scholarship; Outstanding Young Men of America, 1988; Kozak Memorial Award, 1989; 1991 National "Indian Educator of the Year," by the National Indian Education Assn; Minnesota Transformational Leadership Award, 1991; served on tribal advisory councils, state textbook review committees, & national special interest groups in multicultural education. *Interests*: To promote & perpetuate the songs & dances of the Southern Plains' tribes; singing & playing the American Indian flute; teaches Native American song & dance. Dr. Cornel is a descendent of Chief Wild Horse. *Biographical sources*: Native American Mascots & Imagery; Medicine Wheel Circle; Indian Aerobics; Perceptions of American Indian High School Students Attending Public School. *Published works*: Culturally Responsible Pedagogy (National Education Services, 1992); American Indian Stereotypes in the World of Children (Scarecrow, 1992); Spirit Journey - cassette, CD (Meyer Creative Productions, 1993).

PEYRON, NEIL (Yokut) 1975-
(tribal chairperson)
Born & raised on the Tule River Reservation in 1975. *Affiliation & Address*: Chairperson, Tule River Tribal Council, P.O. Box 589, Porterville, CA 93258 (559) 781-4271. E-mail: neil.peyron@tulerivertribe-nsn.gov. Council member since 2006. *Military service*: U.S. Army, 1994-2005. *Awards, honors*: Numerous Army medals, badges, citations & ribbons; also, the Afghanistan Campaign Medal.

PFEFFER, MICHAEL S. 1949-
(attorney)
Born October 14, 1949, New York, N.Y. *Education*: Cornell University, BA, 1971; University of California, Berkeley, JD, 1979. *Affiliations & Address*: Executive director (1982-present), California Indian Legal Services, 510 16th St., 4th Floor, Oakland, CA 94612 (510) 835-0284. E-mail: mikepfeffer@ calindian.org. Website: www.calindian.org. *Membership*: State Bar of Calif.

PFIEFFER, TAMARAH (Navajo-Dine')
(BIE associate deputy director-Navajo schools)
Education: University of New mexico, BA (Education), 1990; Breadloaf School of English, MA (Engiish), 1999; Pennsylvania State University, DEd (Educational Administration & American Indians), 2006.) *Affiliation & Address*: Associate Deputy Director – Navajo Schools, P.O. Box 1449, Window Rock, AZ 86515 (928) 871-5932. E-mail: tamarah.pfieffer@bie.edu. Past professional posts: She served since 2010 as Superintendent of the Alamo Navajo Community School, a BIE-funded, tribally controlled K-12 day school in Magdalena,New Mexico on the Navajo Nation Reservation. Dr. Pfeiffer's career as an educator encompasses more than 35 years as a teacher and administrator in public, grant, and contract schools. Prior to working at Alamo Navajo Community School, Dr. Pfeiffer served from 2006-2009 as Associate Superintendent of the Rough Rock Community School on the Navajo Nation Reservation in Chinle, AZ. In addition, Dr. Pfeiffer has held faculty positions in education at Arizona State University, Dine College, Northern Pioneer College, and Northern Arizona University. She has served as an English Department Chair at Ganado Unified School District in Ganado, AZ and To'hajillee Community School in To'hajillee, NM and taught English and Navajo culture at Rock Point Community High School in Rock Point, AZ and Navajo Academy in Farmington, NM. Dr. Pfeiffer has been the recipient of numerous awards for her educational leadership & academic research, including Principal of the Year for Rough Rock Community School, Newberry Scholar Fellow, Who's Who Among American Teachers and Youth Development Inc. Teacher of the Year. *Published works*: Authored and served as editor of several publications including, Ethical Leadership and Decision Making in Education: Applying Theoretical Perspectives to Complex Dilemmas. Chapter 4: Ethics of Religion in Education, & Manette Kape'ahiokalani Nee-Benham Indigenous Educational Models for Contemporary Practice: Our Mother's Voices: Navajo Stories of student success (2007).

PHELAN, RANDY (Mandan)
(tribal vice chairperson)
Affiliation & Addresss: Chairperson, MHA Nation, Three Affiliated Tribes, 404 Frontage Rd., New Town, ND 58763 (701) 627-4781. E-mail: chairmanfox@mhanation.com

PHELPS, REBECCA BERMAN
(attorney)
Education: Brandeis University, BA, 1989; University of Colorado School of Law, JD, 1992. *Address & Affiliation*: Attorney, Albietz Law Corporation, 2001 N St. #100, Sacramento, CA 95814-4222 (916) 442-4241. Ms. Phelps practices in American Indian law and civil rights, among other areas.

PHELPS, RICHARD
(chief executive officer)
Affiliation & Address: CEO, The Falmouth Institute, 3702 Pender Dr. #300, Fairfax, VA 22030 (703) 352-2250. Richard has conducted hundreds of workshops for Alaska Native & American Indian tribal government. His areas of expertise include self-determination contracting, indirect cost issues, budgeting, finance & acquisition. He provides technical assistance to tribal organizations on matters such as business development & financial management. *Past professional post*: Senior trainer at Sterling Institute.

PHILEMONOF, DEMITRI (Aleut)
(president & CEO)
Born & raised on St. George Island, Alaska. *Affiliation & Address*: President & CEO (1985-present), Aleutian/Pribilof Islands Assn, 401 E. Fireweed Lane, Suite 201, Anchorage, AK 99503 (907) 276-2700. *Other professional posts*: Board Representative on St. George Village Corporation (TANAQ) Services, Aleutian Housing Authority, Alaska Federation of Natives, The Aleut Corp., Gold Cache Bingo, Lucky Strike Bingo, the Aleut League, and St. Hermanis Seminary Board. He was co-producer of "The Untold Story," an Aleut documentary, nominated for 1993 Emmy & received 1994 Bronz Telly Award.

PHILLIP, BEN (Eskimo)
(Alaskan village president)
Affiliation & Address: President, Native Village of Alakanuk, P.O. Box 149, Alakanuk, AK 99554 (907) 238-3419.

PHILLIPS, MELVINA PRITCHETT (Echota Cherokee) 1948-
(literacy practitioner; educator)
Born September 1, 1948, New Hope, Ala. Education: University of Montevallo (AL), BS, 1970; Alabama A&M University (Huntsville), MEd., 1976; UAB/VA, Ed.D. *Address*: 2279 Oak Grove Rd., New Hope, AL 35760 (256) 723-2256. E-mail: phillipsm@ principals.org. Website: www.principals.org. *Affiliations*: Madison County Board of Education, Huntsville, AL (teacher/principal, 1982-2003; Indian education, Title IX coordinator, 1989-2003); Literacy Practitioner, NASSP, Reston, VA. *Other professional post*: Board member, North Alabama Education Credit Union; Board member, FEMA (distribute funds to organizations that work with needy individuals). *Community activities*: Burritt Museum; Early Works Children's Museum; Education Committee, Huntsville Botanical Gardens. *Memberships*: Alabama Indian Education Assn (secretary); National Indian Education Assn; Alabama Environmental Education Association; Tennessee Valley Genealogical Assn. *Awards, honors*: Madison County Title IV/IX Projects recognized as Exemplary Projects by USDOE, was selected as Showcase Project by the U.S. Department of Education in 1987 & 1993; Outstanding Governor's Awards (two); Exemplary School Recognition; delegate to the White House Conference on Indian Education; education consultant to the Smithsonian's new Museum of the American Indian; Certificate of Recognition from Gov. Guy Hunt and the Alabama Environmental Education Association for Best Environmental Education Curriculum Guide for 1991. *Interests*: "Literacy, Native American education, & historical preservation of historical sites, environmental issues. Established two science camps for minority students. Involved with environmental concerns and organizations."

PIATOTE, BETH H.
(professor of Native American Studies)
Education: Bethel College, BA; University of Oregon, MA; Stanford University, PhD. *Address & Affiliation*: Assistant Professor of Native American Studies, College of Letters & Science, Ethnic Studies Dept., 582 Barrows Hall, Berkeley, CA 94720 (510) 642-0775. E-mail: piatote@berkeley.edu. *Research Interests*: Native American literature, history, law & culture; Native American/ Aboriginal literature & federal Indian law in the U.S. & Canada; Ni:mi:pu (Nez Perce) language & literature. *Awards, honors*: Ford Foundation Predoctoral Fellowship, 2001-03; Whiting Dissertation Fellowship in the Humanities, 2006-07; Ford Foundation Postdoctoral Fellowship, 2009-10; Hellman Family Faculty Fund Award, 2009. *Published works*: Domestic Subjects: Gender, Citizenship, and Law in Native American Literature (Yale University Press, 2013); Beading Lesson & Other Short Stories (fiction manuscript in progress). "I also continue to work on translations of Ni:mi:pu (Nez Perce) literary texts and am collaborating with Berkeley's department of Linguistics to create an audio dictionary of the Nez Perce language that will be available to academics and community members working on indigenous language study, continuity, and rejuvenation." *Research interests*: Native Ameican literature, history, law & culture in the U.S. & Canada; Nez Perce language & literature.

PICO, ANTHONY R. (Viejas Kumeyaay Diegueno)
(former tribal chairperson)
Education: Grossmont College (El Cajon, CA), AA; Long Island University (NY), Honorary Doctor of Humane Letters. *Affiliation & Address*: Chairperson (25+ years), Viejas Tribal Council, P.O. Box 908, Alpine, CA 91903 (619) 445-3810. *Accomplishment*: Helped to start the "Scholarship Fund" for every child on the reservation for higher education or for doctorate. *Activities*: Helped to establish the tribal casino. Anthony is a nationally recognized authority and leader on American Indian sovereignty and self-governance, Indian gaming and tribal economic development. For more than two decades he has been a strong voice for Indian self-reliance, economic development and diversification. Mr. Pico served for most of the past two decades as the elected leader of his tribe, the Viejas Band of Kumeyaay Indians of Alpine, Calif. In January 2011, Mr. Pico again assumed the title and responsibilities of Viejas Tribal Chairman, following a tribal election. *Past professional posts*: Mr. Pico recently served as a director of the Native American Rights Fund (NARF), a nonprofit law firm dedicated to asserting & defending the rights of Indian tribes, organizations, and individuals nationwide. In 2007, Mr. Pico was appointed to the Board of Trustees for the Gene Autry Center. Based in Los Angeles, the Center celebrates the American West through three important institutions: the Southwest Museum of the American Indian, Museum of the West and the Institute for the Study of the American West. He is also a director for Borrego Springs Bank, one of the first American Indian owned banks in the United States. *Awards, honors*: Mr. Pico was named the National Indian Gaming Association (NIGA) Man of the Year in 1997 and received the organization's 2007 John Kieffer Award demonstrating a lifetime of achievement and commitment to Indian Gaming. Pico is also a recipient of the prestigious 2008 Award for Public Service from the Woodrow Wilson International Center for Scholars of the Smithsonian Institution. He was a driving force and spokesman

in the landmark California ballot initiatives in 1998-2000 that brought economic growth to many of the 107 federally recognized tribes in the state and San Diego County. Pico served as co-chair of the Proposition 1A initiative to amend the California Constitution, enabling tribes to engage in gaming on tribal land.

PIERITE, MARSHAL (Tunica-Biloxi)
(former tribal chairperson)
Affiliation & Address: Chairperson (2014-16), Tunica-Biloxi Indian Tribe, 151 Melacon Dr., Marksville, LA 71351 (318) 253-9767.

PIERRE III, RAYMOND (Kalispel)
(tribal vice chairperson)
Affiliation & Address: Kalispel Indian Community, P.O. Box 39, Usk, WA 99180 (509) 445-1147.

PIFFERO, LYNETTE (Elko Band Te-Moak Western Shoshone)
(tribal chairperson)
Affiliation & Address: Elko Band Colony, P.O. Box 748, Elko, NV 89801 (775) 738-8889.

PIGEON, ED (Pottawatomi)
(tribal vice chairperson)
Affiliation & Address: Vice Chairperson, Match-e-be-nash-she-wish Band of Pottawatomi Indians, 2872 Mission Dr., Dorr, MI 49344 (269) 397-1780. Ed is has been on the Tribal Council since 1999. He is a member of the Pigeon Family, Heritage award winners known for their Black Ash Basketry, and has over ten years of involvement in cultural presentations & teaching activities throughout Michigan. *Other professional posts*: Gun Lake Language & Cultural Coordinator, providing language instruction through formal classes and in cultural workshops integrating language components. He has helped shape the direction & growth of the Tribal Government during his time on the Tribal Council. Sits on Health & Human Services, Emergency Preparedness, Environmental, Tax Agreement, Tribal Roads, Public Safety, & Development Board for our casino project. He is also a board member for the Kalamazoo Poverty Reduction Initiative & represents the Salem voting district. Interests: "As a member of the Match-E-Be-Nash-She-Wish Band of Pottawatomi Indians I feel it is all of our duty to maintain our traditions, language and culture. Each one of us must do our part to preserve these things for future generations as they are at the core of what defines us as Anishnabek people."

PIGSLEY, DELORES (Siletz)
(tribal chairperson)
Affiliation & Address: Chairperson, Confederated Tribes of the Siletz Indian Reservation, Tribal Council, P.O. Box 549, Siletz, OR 97380 (541) 444-2532. *Address*: 1322 N. Larchwood, Salem, OR 97303 (503) 393-6516. E-mail: dpigsley@msn.com.

PIKYYAVIT, TONI (Paiute)
(tribal band chairperson)
Affiliation & Address: Koosharem Band of the Paiute Indian Tribe of Utah, P.O. Box 205, Richfield, UT 84701 (435) 893-8432.

PINKHAM, BROOKE (Nez Perce)
(Indian law center staff director)
Education: University of Washington School of Law, JD, 2007. *Affiliation & Address*: Staff Director, Center for Indian Law & Policy, Seattle University School of Law, Sullivan Hall 115, 901 12th Ave., P.O. Box 222000, Seattle, WA 98122 (206) 398-4284; E-mail: pinkhamb@seattleu.edu. *Past professional posts*: Staff Attorney (2007-16), Northwest Justice Project, Seattle, WA Provides civil legal aid to individual tribal members. The Project provided direct representation and advocacy on behalf of tribal members throughout Washington State. Brooke is Nez Perce and grew up within the community of the Confederated Tribes & Bands of the Yakama Nation. Brooke most recently served as a guest-lecturer for the Law School's Incarcerated Parents Advocacy Clinic on the topic of the Indian Child Welfare Act. Brooke has particular expertise in Indian estate planning & probate, enforcing application of the Indian Child Welfare Act, protecting the rights to secure housing, tribal and non-tribal public benefits, and the education rights of Native American students. Brooke is a University of Washington School of Law graduate; has served on the Boards for the National Native American Law Students Association, the Washington State Bar Association Indian Law Section, and the Northwest Indian Bar Association.

PINKHAM, JAIME A. (Nez Perce)
(consultant)
Education: Portland State University & Peninsula College (degrees in Forestry); Graduate of the Washington Agriculture & Forestry Leadership Program. *Affiliation & Address*: Consultant, The Institute for Tribal Government, The Hatfield School of Government, College of Urban & Public Affairs, Portland State University, P.O. Box 751, Portland, OR 97207 (503) 725-9000. *Other professional posts*: Serves on various boards including the Governing Council

of the Wilderness Society, the Native Nations Institute for Leadership, Management & Policy through the Udall Center of the University of Arizona, et al. *Past professional posts*: Director, National Tribal Lands Program for the Trust for Public Land (TPL), Portland, OR; twice elected as treasurer to the Nez Perce Tribal Executive Committee; he also worked for the Bureau of Indian Affairs, the Washington State Dept. of Natural Resources, the U.S. Forest Service, et al. Chairperson, American Indian Science & Engineering Society; president, Inter-Tribal Timber Council; chairperson, Tribal Lands Advisory Council for TPL. *Awards, honors*: Earl Wilcox National Award from the Intertribal Timber Council; Chief Sealth Award from the Native American Fish & Wildlife Society. *Interests*: Sings with the Nez Perce Nation Drum.

PINKHAM, SCOTT (Nez Perce)
(lecturer in American Indian studies)
Education: University of Washington, BA, 1987, MA (Educational Leadership & Policy Studies) (in progress). *Affiliation & Address*: Lecturer (2000-present), Department of American Indian Studies, University of Washington (UW), Seattle, WA 98195 (206) 543-1770. E-mail: spinkham@u.washington.edu. *Other professional posts*: Currently he works for the College of Engineering as a full-time Counseling Services Coordinator in the Engineering Advising and Diversity Center where he heads the Minority Scholars Engineering Program. Mr. Pinkham also serves as the advisor to the UW's American Indian Science & Engineering Society student chapter. *Past professional posts*: American Indian Science & Engineering Society national office, the Nez Perce Tribe's Environmental Restoration & Waste Management Program, Yakima Valley Community College & Washington State's Dept. of Natural Resources. He served as the U. of Washington's Native American Recruiter until 1999.

PINOLA, NELSON (Pomo)
(rancheria chairperson)
Affiliation & Address: Chairperson, Manchester - Port Arena Rancheria, P.O. Box 623, Point Arena, CA 95468 (707) 882-2788.

PINTO, ERICA (Kumeyaay Diegueno)
(tribal chairperson)
Affiliation & Address: Chairperson, Jamul Indian Village, P.O. Box 612, Jamul, CA 91935 (619) 669-4785.

PINTO, JOHN (Pueblo)
(NM State senator)
Address: 509 W. Morgan Ave., Gallup, NM 87301 (505) 371-8342. *Affiliation*: New Mexico State Senator, District 3 (1977-present) Indian Affairs Committee.

PINTO, JUDY (Laguna Pueblo) 1953-
(substance abuse counselor)
Born June 6, 1953, Colorado Springs, Colo. *Education*: GED, Grants Branch College, 1979. *Affiliation & Address*: Substance abuse counselor (1989-present), Southwest Indian Polytechnic Institute, Albuquerque, NM (505) 766-8418. *Past professional posts*: Counselor, Santa Clara Rehabilitation Center, Santa Clara Pueblo, NM, 1980-84; counselor, 1984-87, supervisor, 1987-88. *Membership*: New Mexico Alcohol and Drug Counseling Association.

PINTO, ROBERT (Cuyapaipe Kumeyaay)
(tribal chairperson)
Affiliation & Address: Chairperson, Cuyapaipe Band of Kumeyaay Indians, P.O. Box 2250, Alpine, CA 91903 (619) 455-6315.

PINTO, SHARON
(BIA regional office director)
Affiliation & Address: Bureau of Indian Affairs, 301 West Hill St., P.O. Box 1060, Gallup, NM 87305 (505) 863-8314; E-mail: Sharon.pinto@bia.gov

PION, CONNOR
(coordinator of Indigenous language initiative)
Affiliation & Address: Professor of Linguistics & Coordinator, Indigenus Language Initiative, Aboriginal Studies Program, University of Toronto, North Borden Bldg., 2nd Fl, 563 Spadina Ave., Toronto, ON M5S 2J7 (416) 978-2233.

PIPER, AURELIUS H., JR. (*Chief Quiet Hawk*) (Golden Hill Paugussett)
(tribal council chief)
Affiliation: Golden Hill Indian Reservation, 95 Stanavage Rd., Trumbull, CT 06611 (203) 377-4410.

PIPER, KENNETH (*Moonface Bear*) (Golden Hill Paugussett) 1960-
(warchief)
Born September 9, 1960, Bridgeport, Conn. *Principal occupation*: Warchief of the Golden Hill Paugussetts. *Address*: Golden Hill Reservation, Trumbull, CT 06415 (203) 537-0390. *Community activities*: American Indians for Development (ex-Board member); Connecticut Indian Task Force of the Legislature Sovereignty Committee; Native American Heritage Advisory Council on Reburrials. *Membership*: Connecticut Indian Affairs Council.

PIPESTEM, WILSON K. (Otoe-Missouria)
(attorney; managing partner)
Education: Oklahoma State University, BA. Stanford University Law School, JD. *Affiliation & Address*: Managing Partner & Co-founder (2001-present), Ietan Consulting, LLC, 1333 New Hampshire Ave., NW, Washington, DC 20036 (202) 419-3527. Ieten Consulting is a federal government relations firm specializing in the representation of tribal governments & tribal business enterprises. *Other professional posts*: Speaker on developments in federal law & policy and has taught Federal Indian Law as a lecturer at Columbus School of Law at the Catholic University of America; adjunct professor at Washington College of Law at American University; chairperson, Notah Begay III Foundation; board member, Nike N7 Fund and the Close-Up Foundation, not-for-profit organizations that provide opportunities for Native youth. *Past professional posts*: Associate, Swidler Berlin Shereff Friedman, LLP, Washington, DC; Sr. VP, Wheat & Associates, LLC, Washington, DC, 1999-2001. *Practice interests*: Wilson has assisted tribal clients with expanding & strengthening their sovereign rights through federal actions that have returned former tribal lands to the tribal land base, given tribes more flexibility to exercise tribal authority on their lands and adjacent federal lands, and directly reaffirmed core sovereign rights.

PIRNER, ROBERT "BOB" (Rosebud Lakota)
(lecturer in Native American Studies)
Affiliation & Address: Lecturer, Native American Studies Program, Eberly College of Arts & Sciences, P.O. Box 6284, Morgantown, WV 26506 (304) 293-4626. facebok.com/yokipi. Mr. Pirner teaches about the art, politics, history, religion, social problems, and culture of the Lakota people of the Northern Plains. He was a 30-year resident of the Rosebud Lakota Reservation in South Dakota and a tribal college administrator. He is one of an estimated 6,000 living speakers of the Lakota language.

PITAWANAKWAT, KENN (Wikwemikong First Nations, Canada)
(Instructor of Native American studies)
Education: York University, BA (honors graduate); Lakehead University, (Native Language Instructor's Program); Ryerson University. *Affiliation & Address*: Anishinaabe Instructor (2007-present), Center for Native American Studies, 112D Whitman Hall,, Northern Michigan University, Marquette, MI 49855 (906) 227-1397. E-mail: kpitawan@nmu.edu. E-mail: kennpitawanakwat @gmail.com. Website: www.kennpitawanakwat.com. Kenn is a story teller. He is a cultural and Nishinaabe fluent teacher, presenter, and radio personality. *Published works*: When My Son Died (2015).

PITCHLYNN, GARY S. (Choctaw of Oklahoma)
(attorney; adjunct professor of law)
Education: University of Oklahoma, BA (Journalism), 1972; Oklahoma City University School of Law, JD, 1977. *Affiliation & Address*: Senior Partner & Counsel, Pitchlynn & Williams, P.O. Box 427, Norman, OK 73070 (405) 360-9600. E-mail: gspitchlynn@pitchlynnlaw.com. *Professional interests*: Gary is a criminal & civil trial lawyer who advises & represents tribes & Indian organizations in their dealings with state & federal government agencies as well as congressional staff. *Other professional post*: Adjunct professor of Tribal Gaming Law at the University of Oklahoma School of Law, 2011-present; guest speaker on U.S./Tribal relations & Tribal Gaming Law. He serves on a variety of professional panels & advisory committees and is active in advising & directing the efforts of state & national trade organizations. *Memberships*: Federal Bar Assn; Oklahoma Bar Assn; Oklahoma Indian Bar Assn; Absentee Shawnee Tribal Bar; Muscogee/Creek Nation Bar Assn; Potawatomi Tribe Bar Assn; Miccosukee Tribe of Florida Bar Association; Osage Nation Bar Assn.

PITKA, RHONDA (Athapascan)
(village chief)
Affiliation & Address: Chief, Beaver Village, P.O. Box 24029, Beaver, AK 99724 (907) 628-6126.

PITRE, JOSH (Houma)
(managing director of Native American law & policy practice)
Education: Louisiana tate University, BA (Political Science), 2002; University of Arizona, MA (American Indian Studies), 2007. *Affiliation & Address*: Managing Director, Native American Law & Policy Practice, Dentons LLP, 1301 K St., NW, Washington, DC 20005 (202) 408-3954. E-mail: josh.pitre@dentons.com Josh helps clients successfully navigate the federal legislative process by preparing oral and written testimony, arranging visits with Members and key staff members, tracking the progress of legislation important to these clients and advocating on policy issues of interest to Native Americans in general. Josh also helps clients understand the federal appropriations process and identify federal funding opportunities. He can call on a depth of resources to supplement his extensive familiarity from previously working with Members and the staff on the Senate Indian Affairs Committee and the House Natural Resources Committee, the committees most concerned with Indian issues. *Past professional posts*: Prior to joining Dentons, Josh worked at the Senate Committee on Indian Affairs under Chairman Daniel K. Akaka. He also worked for the House Committee on Natural Resources, Office of Indian Affairs, under Chairman Nick J. Rahall. During his Congressional service, Josh managed tribal issues and legislation related to federal recognition, cultural & sacred sites protection, natural resources, fee-to-trust, technical amendments, Indian gaming, Indian health care, and veterans affairs. *Awards, honors*: National Council on Urban Indian Health National Impact Award, 2012; George Washington University Native American Political Leadership Program, 2007; Morris K. Udall Native American Congressional Internship Program, 2005. *Memberships*: Thunder Hill -- a Southern-style PowWow drum group

PLAINFEATHER, MARDELL HOGAN (*Baahin'naaje*) (Crow) 1945-
(park ranger, Plains Indian historian)
Born September 28, 1945, Billings, Mont. *Education*: Maricopa County Junior College, 1967-68; Rocky Mountain College, BA, 1979. *Affiliation & Address*: Plains Indian historian, Little Bighorn National Monument, P.O. Box 38, Crow Agency, MT 59022 (406) 638-2621, 1980-. *Other professional post*: Part-time instructor (U.S. History & Montana State History): Crow Tribal Junior College, Little Big Horn College, Crow Agency, MT. *Community activities*: Fort Phil Kearny/ Bozeman Trail History Assn (board member); Crow Tribal Archives (board member). *Memberships*: Custer Battlefield Historical & Museum Assn; Jailhouse Gallery; Big Horn County Historical Assn; Montana State Oral History Assn; Montana Committee for the Humanities (speaker's bureau); Yellowstone County History Assn (honorary member); Yellowstone Coral of Westerners. *Awards, honors*: History Department Award, Rocky Mountain College, 1979; prize for Performance Achievement, Custer Battlefield National Monument, 1982; award from St. Augustine Preservation of Indian Culture, Chicago, IL in 1987. *Interests*: "My interest is in the cultural history of the Plains Indians, specifically from prehistory to 1880's. I enjoy visiting battlefields and making sure that the history is told correctly from the Indian viewpoint. I am also interested in exhibits in museums and their labeling. I am interested in oral history and the preservation of all sacred sites of Native peoples." *Published works*: A Personal Look at Curly After the Little Big Horn (Custer Battlefield Historical & Museum Association, in The Greasy Grass, annual publication, 1987); The Apsaalooke: Warriors of the Big Horns (Fort Phil Kearny/Bozeman Trail History Association, 1989).

PLATERIO, DAVID LOUIS (*Tosa-Wi-e*) (Shoshone) 1960-
(Native American consultant)
Born January 24, 1960, Elko, Nev. *Address*: P.O. Box 822, Elko, NV 89803 (702) 738-3618 (work). *Affiliations*: Native American Consultant, Shoshone Information Network, Elko, NV, 1992-; political consultant for the European Parliament. *Other professional posts*: Historian, Native American Consultant, Western Shoshoni National Council, Elko, NV. *Community activities*: Founding member, Western Shoshone Historic Preservation Society; board member, Citizen's Alert (environmental watchdog for Nevada); member, Cultural Commission of Northern Nevada; member, Alliance of Native Americans; citizen/lobbyist training from Military Production Network; registered researcher, National Archives & Library of Congress. *Memberships*: National Environmental Coalition of Native Americans; member of the Congress of the Global Anti-Nuclear Alliance (International); Rural Alliance for Military Accountability (SkyGuard); The International Declaration & Inquiry Commission. *Awards, honors*: Received diploma on completion of training in reading of nuclear waste documents from the "Institute for Energy & Environmental Research." *Interests*: "I take a real hard stand on cultural protection, burial grounds, culturally significant sites, battlegrounds, white chart quarries (Tosa-Wi) across our aboriginal territory. I'm also an alternate for the Western Shoshone National Council, which I speak on behalf of Western Shoshones. I'm currently in the process of (working on) a chronology of events concerning the Western Shoshoni - fur trapper, expeditions, explorations, wars & depredations, conditions, placement of names on a map, etc. (I was) a featured speaker at the 1991 Indian Survival Summit held at California State University, Los Angeles; speaker at 9th annual European Meeting of Indian Support Group in Trondheim, Norway, July, 1993; speaker at the National Lawyers Committee on Civil Rights Under Law, March, 1993.

PLATERO, PAUL (Dine'-Navajo)
(professor of linguistics & Navajo language; dept. chair)
Education: Massachusetts Institute of Technology, MS (Linguistics), PhD (Linguistics. *Affiliation & Address*: Professor of Linguistics & Navajo Language/ Dept. Chair for School of Dine' & Law Studies, Navajo Technical University, P.O. Box 849, Crownpoint, NM 87313 (505) 786-4100. E-mail: pplatero@ navajotech.edu

PLATERO, SANDRA (Mescalero Apache)
(tribal councilmember)
Affiliation & Address: Councilmember, Mescalero Apache Tribe, P.O. Box 227, Mescalero, NM 88340 (575) 464-4494.

PLENTYHOLES, JUANITA (Ute Mountain Ute)
 (tribal vice chairperson)
Affiliation & Address: Vice Chairperson, Ute Mountain Ute Tribe, P.O. Box 109, Towaoc, CO 81334 (970) 565-3751. E-mail: jplentyholes@utemountain.org

POE, DOUGLAS (Cherokee)
 (executive director)
Affiliation & Address: Executive Director, American Indian Center of Indiana, 2236 E. 10th St., Indianapolis, IN 46201 (317) 917-8000. E-mail: dpoe@americanindiancenter.org.

POITRA, KRYSTIN (Turtle Mountain Ojibwe)
 (training & technical assistance program coordinator)
Affiliation & Address: Training & TA Program Coordinator, National American Indian Housing Council, 900 2nd St. NE #107, Washington, DC 20002 (202) 789-1754.

POITRA, TAMMIE (Turtle Mountain Ojibwe)
 (BIA deputy regional director – trust services)
Affiliation & Address: Deputy Director – Trust Services, Midwest Region Office, Bureau of Indian Affairs, Norman Pointe II Bldg., 5600 W. American Blvd., Suite 500, Bloomington, MN 55437 (612) 713-4400.

POLACCA, BENNY (Hopi/Havasupai/Pima/Tohono O'odham)
 (tribal news reporter)
Education: Arizona State University (English); University of South Dakota, American Indian Journalism Institute (News Writing). *Affiliation & Address*: Reporter, Osage Nation News, 619 Kihekah, Pawhuska, OK 74056 (918) 287-5668. E-mail: bpolacca@osagetribe.org. *Past professional posts*: Reporter, Reznetnews.org, an online newspaper; wrote for the Native American Journalists Association's 2006 convention newspaper in Tulsa, OK.

POLEQUAPTEWA, NIKIISHNA NUMKINA (Hopi)
 (chief technology officer; senior strategist)
Education: Sherman Indian High School; University of California, Irvine, BA (Environmental Analysis & Design), 2005; Central Washington University, MA (Resource Management), 2007; Northern Arizona University, PhD (Earth Science & Environmental Sustainability), 2017. *Affiliation & Address*: Chief Technology Officer & Senior Strategist, Blue Stone Strategy Group (2014-present), Irvine, CA (949) 476-8828. *Past professional post*: Former Founding Director (2007-14), American Indian Resource Program, University of California (UC), Irvine, Irvine, CA; Chair, American Indian Counselors & Recruiters Assn, 2007-14; Vice Chair & Chairperson, The Nakwatsvewat Institute, Inc., 2008-11. *Awards, honors*: The UC Chancellor's 2008 "Living Our Values" award; National Center for American Indian Enterprise Development's 2009 "Native American 40 & Under 40" award; American Indian Science & Engineering Society's 2009 Sequoyah Fellowship Medal; National Indian Gaming Association's 2010 Chairman's Leadership Award; Hopi Leadership Fellow, The Hopi Foundation, 2010; Professional of the Year Award, University of California systemwide, Nov. 2012.. *Interests*: "Helping students believe in and achieve their dreams is my greatest goal."

POLER OMAR (Sokaogan Chippewa)
 (outreach specialist in continuing education)
Education: University of Wisconsin-Madison, MLS (Library & Information Science), 2010. *Affiliation & Address*: Outreach Specialist, Contnuing Education, University of Wisconsin-Madison, School of Library & Information Studies, Madison, WI 53715. Poler tries to provide the same opportunity for research & connection through the Tribal Libraries, Archives, & Museums (TLAM) Project, which he created to incorporate American Indian topics into LIS education. It's one of the few such programs in the United States. Among TLAM's initiatives are a graduate course cotaught by Poler, in which students learn about American Indian information issues, including indigenous languages, tribal histories, colonization, & cultural sovereignty; the Convening Culture Keepers professional development miniconference for Wisconsin tribal librarians, archivists, and museum curators; and a student group that brings students to tribal cultural institutions for service-learning projects. "It's not enough to study tribal institutions; you have to experience the living part of them," Poler says. "The TLAM Project has become the model both for library schools that want to teach students how to provide service for underserved populations like American Indian communities, as well as for states that want to create networks of tribal information and cultural professionals," says Robin Amado, a school librarian at Madison's Memorial High School who as a graduate student in 2012 was Poler's student assistant for Convening Culture Keepers. She continues to help organize the conference. So far seven conferences have been held, each attended by 50–60 people. In May 2013, the project received an Institute of Museum and Library Services grant to take the conference regional for 75 tribal librarians, archivists, & museum curators from Michigan, Minnesota, and Wisconsin.

POLSTON, JOANN (Eskimo)
 (Alaskan village president)
Affiliation & Address: President, Mendas Cha-ag Tribe of Healy Lake, P.O. Box 74090, Fairbanks, AK 99706 (907) 479-0638.

POMEROY, CHRISTINE (Chehalis)
 (chief judge)
Affiliation & Address: Chief Judge, Chehalis Tribal Court, P.O. Box 536, Oakville, WA 98568 (360) 709-1615.

POMMERSHEIM, FRANK (Rosebud Sioux)
 (professor of Indian law; author)
Affiliation & Address: Professor of Indian Law (1984-present), University of South Dakota School of Law, 414 E. Clark St., Vermillion, SD 57069 (605) 677-5209. *Other professional posts*: Visiting Professor of Law, Indian Law Program, Lewis & Clark College of Law, Portland, OR. Serves on a number of tribal appellate courts throughout Indian country including Chief Justice for the Cheyenne River Sioux Tribal Court of Appeals & Associate Justice for the Rosebud Sioux Supreme Court. *Past professional post*: Lived & worked on the Rosebud Sioux Reservation (ten years). *Awards, honors*: Received the University of South Dakota Belbas-Larson Award for Excellence in Teaching; the South Dakota Peace & Justice Center Reconciliation Award; contributor to the 2005 edition of Felix Cohen's, "Handbok of Federal Indian Law"; 2006 John Wesley Jackson Award as the Outstanding Professor of Law. *Published works*: Braid of Feathers (American Indian Law & Contemporary Tribal Life); East of the River: Poems Ancient and New; Broken Landscape: Indians, Indian Tribes, and the Constitution (Oxford U. Press, 2012); numerous scholarly articles.

PONCHO, BRIAN (Paiute)
 (Interim tribal chairperson; vice-chairperson)
Affiliation & Address: Interim chairperson, Bishop Paiute Tribe, 50 Tu Su Lane, Bishop, CA 93514 (760) 920-7168. E-mail: brian.poncho@bishoppaiute.org

PONCHO, ROLAND (Alabama-Coushatta of Texas)
 (tribal councilmember)
Affiliation & Address: Councilmember, Alabama-Coushatta Tribal Enterprise, Rt. 3, Box 640, Livingston, TX 77351 (409) 563-4391. *Past professional post*: Former tribal chairperson, Alabama-Coushatta Tribe, Livingston, TX.

POND, RONALD JAMES (*Itxutwin*) (Umatilla, Palouse) 1939-
 (cultural consultant)
Born December 6, 1939, McKay Creek, Oregon. *Education*: Blue Mountain Community College, Pendleton, OR, 1966-67; Eastern Oregon State College, BA, 1974; Oregon State University, Teaching Certificate, 1977, MA, 1992. *Address*: 45398 Lloyd Rd., Pendleton, OR 97801. *Affiliation*: Teacher, School District 16-R, Pendleton, OR, 1977-79; elected leader/education director, Umatilla Tribe, Mission, OR, 1981; archaeology technician/assistant, U.S. Forest Service, Pendleton, 1985-; co-curator, "Plateau Exhibit," Washington State U., Pullman, WA. *Other professional posts*: Firefighter, U.S. Forest Service, 1963-69; general council chairperson, governing body member, 1979-80, education director, 1981, Umatilla Confederated Tribes, Pendleton, OR; research consultant, elder/oral traditions. *Community activities*: Umatilla Tribe Cultural Committee, 1968-; Blue Mountain Equestrian Trail Ride, 1992-93. *Awards, honors*: Best All Around Indian Dancer/Indian Festival of Arts, LaGrange, OR, 1970; Smoke Jumper: Silver Wings, 1966; Seven Drums Religion, 1974-94; Annual Spring "First Food Feast": Singer, Lead Hunter, Lead Server; coordinator: 1976 Bi-Centennial Exposition, Umatilla cultural group to Wash., DC; 2007 Distinguished Alumni Award, Eastern OR State U.

PONGRACE, DONALD R.
 (attorney)
Education: Bates College, BA, 1979; American University, JD, 1985. *Affiliation & Address*: Partner & Head, American Indian Law & Policy Group, Akin Gump Straus Hauer & Feld, LLP, Robert E. Straus Bldg., 1333 New Hampshire Ave. NW, Washington, DC 20036 (202) 887-4466; E-mail: dpongrace@akingump.com. Donald has served as the chief counsel & advisor on a number of highly significant tribal issues, including the largest Indian water settlement in U.S. history, and one of the largest trust management claims n US. History. His work on the federal aspects of tribal policies in the United States includes serving as lead counsel on the two largest Indian water settlements in U.S. history and one of the largest trust mismanagement claims in U.S. history. Mr. Pongrace's public law & policy and American Indian law & policy practices are both ranked Band 1 by *Chambers* under the Nationwide Native American Law and Nationwide Government Relations categories, respectively. He is also personally ranked Band 1 in the *Chambers* Nationwide Native American Law category. *Awards, honors*: Chambers USA: America's Leading Lawyers for Business in the area of Native American law.

POOL, NATALIE
(Indian program coordinator)
Affiliation & Address: Program Coordinator, Department of Family & Community Medicine, University of Arizona; Native American Research & Training Center (NARTC), 1642 E. Helen St., Tucson, AZ 85719 (520) 626-1123. E-mail: nataliepool@email.arizona.edu

POOLAW, DANE (Kiowa)
(Kiowa language instructor)
Affiliation & Address: Kiowa Language Instructor, Native American Language Program, Department of Anthropology, College of Arts & Sciences, The University of Oklahoma, 455 W. Lindsey, DHT 505, Norman, OK 73019 (405) 325-3729. E-mail: dpoolaw@ou.edu.

POOLAW, LINDA S. (*Lees-seet-teen*) (Delaware-Kiowa) 1942-
(health research)
Born April 8, 1942, Lawton, Okla. *Education*: University of Sciences & Arts of Oklahoma, BA, 1974; University of Oklahoma, Masters work in Communications (two years). *Principal occupation*: Tribal cultural consultant, Delaware Tribe of Western Oklahoma, Anadarko, OK. *Address*: P.O. Box 986, Anadarko, OK 73005 (405) 247-7059. *Community activities*: Salvation Army, Caddo County (chairperson); Delaware Tribe of Western Oklahoma (treasurer); Riverside Indian School Board (vice president); American Indian Exposition (vice president). *Memberships*: Indian & Western Arts Association (vice president). *Interests*: "Writing fiction & history about American Indians. (I) have traveled coast to coast to develop relationships with tribes. In 1986, I plan to research & write a book on my deceased father's work in photography, 50 Years of Life on the Southern Plains, (Horace Poolaw)." Plays: "Skins", 1974; "Happiness Is Being Married to a White Woman", & "Written, Spoken & Unspoken Word" (University of Oklahoma Press, 1982); "The Day the Tree Fell", children's play (American Indian Institute, Norman, Okla. 1983).

POOLAW, MARTHA (Kiowa)
(Kiowa language instructior)
Affiliation & Address: Kiowa Language Instructor, Native American Language Program, Department of Anthropology, College of Arts & Sciences, The University of Oklahoma, 455 W. Lindsey, DHT 505, Norman, OK 73019 (405) 325-3729. E-mail: mpoolaw@ou.edu.

POOLAW, SANDRA (Kiowa/Choctaw)
(project director)
Affiliation & Address: Project Director, American Indian Institute, College of Continuing Education, University of Oklahoma, 555 Constitution Ave., Suite 237, Norman, OK 73072-7820 (405) 325-4127. E-mail: spoolaw@ou.edu.

POOLEY, ALBERT (Navajo/Hopi)
(association president & founder)
Education: University of Utah, MSW; University of Denver, MPA. *Affiliation & Address*: Founder & President, Native American Fatherhood & Families Association, 1215 E. Brown Rd., Mesa, AZ 85203 (480) 833-5007. E-mail: info@aznaffa@org. *Programs*: Fatherhood Is Sacred & Motherhood Is Sacred - created to specifically meet the needs of Native American fathers & mothers. Albert has worked & served 300 Native Tribes across North America and many urban Indian agencies. His special interest is on working with Native nen.

POOLHECO, WALTER L. (Southern Ute)
(tribal health director)
Affiliation: Southern Colorado Ute Health Center, P.O. Box 778, Ignacio, CO 81137 (303) 563-9443.

POON, ALYSIA
(program coordinator)
Education: University of California-San Diego, BA (Art History); University of New Mexico, MA (Art History). *Affiliation & Address*: Program Coord., Indian Arts Research Center (IARC), School for Advanced Research, P.O. Box 2188, Santa Fe, NM 87504 (505) 954-7205. Her responsibilities include IARC public programming, education, & overseeing the Native artist, intern, and volunteer programs. *Past professional posts*: J. Paul Getty Museum, Autry National Center, Los Angeles, CA; Museum of Indian Arts & Culture, Santa Fe, NM.

POOR BEAR, THOMAS (Oglala Lakota)
(tribal vice president)
Affiliation & Address: Vice President, Oglala Sioux Tribal Executive Committee, P.O. Box 2070, Pine Ridge, SD 57770 (605) 867-4009. E-mail: tommpb@oglala.org.

POOWEGUP, FRANCIS (Ute)
(tribal vice chairperson)
Affiliation: The Ute Indian Tribe, P.O. Box 190, Fort Duchesne, UT 84026 (435) 722-5141.

POPE, JERRY L. (Shawnee) 1941-
(artist)
Born April 26, 1941, Greenfield, Ind. *Education*: John Heron School of Art; Indiana University, B.F.A., 1964. *Principal occupation*: Artist. *Address*: 2911 Elmo Pl., Middletown, OH 45042. *Affiliations*: Curator, American Indian People's Museum, Indianapolis, IN; editor, Tosan, American Indian People's News, Indianapolis, IN; principal chief, United Remnant Band, Shawnee Nation of Indiana, Ohio, Kentucky & Pennsylvania; director, Three Feather Society (Native-professional-social organization). *Other professional post*: Assisted in the compilation of Smithsonian Institution's list of native publications. *Memberships*: League of Nations, Pan-American Indians; National Assn of Metis Indians; Three Feather Society (director); Mide Widjig, Grand Medicine Lodge Brotherhood, Albuquerque, NM. *Awards, honors*: First Prize, national Exhibition of Small Paintings; selected to preside over & organize dedication of world's largest collection of Cuna Indian art, Denison University, Granville, OH, 1972; among others. *Interests*: Mr. Pope writes, "1. Professional Native artist, by vocation; 2. editing & publishing of the Inter-Tribal Native publication, Tosan; 3. rebuilding the United Remnant Band of the Shawnee Nation, beginning in 1970 with seven persons; we now have re-established all twelve clans; 4. re-education of my people in traditional ways, instilling due pride in knowledge of their birthright; 5. work with in-prison Native groups." *Published work*: Native Publications in the U.S. & Canada (Smithsonian Institution, 1972).

POPE, RHONDA L. MORNINGSTAR (MeWuk)
(tribal chairperson)
Education: Sacramento City College, (Business & Native American Studies). *Affiliation & Address*: Chairperson, Buena Vista Rancheria of Me-Wuk Indians1418 20th St., Suite 200, Sacramento, CA 95816 (916) 491-0011. During her leadership of the Tribe, she has established a strong tribal government and infrastructure for ongoing Tribal programs. She established a Tribal office in Sacramento and on the reservation for ongoing Tribal and environmental affairs. In March 2008, Chairwoman Pope opened the Buena Vista Child Development Center, which serves low income Native American families. The school is the first of its kind offering an experience focusing on the traditions, culture and language, with a strong emphasis on California Indians. Some of the programs established under her leadership include Tribal Member Services, which provides education, social services, and child care services for Tribal members. She has established an Environmental Department, hiring a director to handle environmental, cultural, and NAGPRA related issues. She formed the Jesse Flyingcloud Pope Foundation in 2007 in honor of her father. Resources from the Foundation are used to support charitable programs designed to assist local community members and offer educational opportunities, specifically promoting & enhancing Tribal traditions, cultural awareness and community support. Her passion is promoting & strengthening culture through outreach programs and sponsorships.

PORTER, BRIAN (Swinomish)
(tribal chairperson)
Affiliation & Address: Vice Chairperson (2011-present), Swinomish Indian Tribal Community, P.O. Box 817, LaConnor, WA 98257 (360) 466-7314.

PORTER, FRANK W., III
(institute director)
Affiliation: American Indian Research and Resource Institute, Gettysburg College, P.O. Box 576, Gettysburg, PA 17325 (717) 337-6265.

PORTER, JENNIFER (Kootenai)
(former tribal chairperson)
Affiliation & Address: Kootenai Tribe of Idaho, P.O. Box 1269, Bonners Ferry, ID 83805 (208) 267-3519.

PORTER, ROBERT ODAWI (Seneca)
(attorney, American Indian law; former tribal president)
Education: Syracuse University, BA; Harvard Law School, JD, 1989. *Affiliation & Address*: Counsel, Dentons LLP, Public Policy and Regulation & Native American Law & Policy Practice, 1301 K St., NW, Washington, DC 20005 (202) 408-6348. E-mail: robert.porter@dentons.com, Robert is an expert in the field of American Indian law and has dedicated his 20-year legal career to protecting and expanding the rights of indigenous nations and peoples. He joined the firm on January 1, 2013, following the completion of his term as the 67th president of the Seneca Nation of Indians. Robert also served the Seneca Nation for nine years as its chief legal counsel, holding the position of attorney general and later acting as senior policy advisor and counsel. During his career, Robert has represented both private Indian-owned businesses and Fortune 500 corporations. Focusing on complex legal and policy matters, his practice at the firm represents Indian nations, individual Indians and Indian-owned businesses, as well as companies doing business in Indian Country.Robert is a recognized expert in federal Indian law and has worked to protect Indian treaty rights throughout his career as a practicing attorney. Before serving as Seneca Nation president, Robert spent more than 10 years as a tenured law professor at the University of Kansas, the University of Iowa

& Syracuse University. He is the author of numerous scholarly publications focusing on indigenous law and governance, tribal sovereignty, and the cultural, political and legal impacts of Euro-American colonization on indigenous peoples. Robert has lectured widely at universities, professional conferences and tribal events. He has also been an active media contributor, and served as a consulting expert and expert witness in matters pending before US and Indian tribal courts. *Past professional posts*: Dickstein, Shapiro & Morin, Washington, DC, 1989-91; appointed as first Attorney General, Seneca Nation, 1991-95; assistant professor, University of Tulsa College of Law, 1993-95; associate professor of law, University of Kansas, adjunct professor, Haskell Indian Nations University, 1995-2002 (at KU, founded the Tribal Law & Government Center); faculty, University of Iowa, 2002-2005; Justice of the Supreme Court of the Sac & Fox Nation of Missouri since 1997; counsel to several Indian Nations & Indian organizations; former president, Seneca Nation of Indians, Salamanca, NY; Professor of Law, Dean's Research Scholar of Indigenous Nations Law, Director, Center for Indigenous Law, Governance & Citizenship, College of Law, Syracuse University, Syracuse, NY

PORTRA, TERRY
(BIA education administrator)
Affiliation: Minneapolis Area Office, Bureau of Indian Affairs, 331 S. Second Ave., Minneapolis, MN 55401 (612) 373-1000.

POSEY, IVAN D. (Eastern Shoshone)
(tribal chairperson)
Affiliation: Wind River Eastern Shoshone Tribe, P.O. Box 538, Fort Washakie, WY 82514 (307) 332-3532.

POSEY, TIMOTHY S. (Cherokee/Muscogee Creek)
(attorney)
Education: University of Oklahoma, BA, 1986, College of Law, JD, 1989. *Affiliation & Address*: Staff Attorney (2005-present), Hall Estill, Attorneys at Law, Indian Law Program, 320 S. Boston Ave., Suite 200, Tulsa, OK 74103 (918) 594-0669. E-mail: tposey@hallestill.com. Mr. Posey is ranked Band 1 by Chambers USA as one of the best Native American lawyers in the state of Oklahoma; Best Lawyer in America in Native American Law; he is a frequent speaker on Indian law issues.

POSTON, L. STEPHINE (Sandia Pueblo)
(community, public & government relations)
Education: University of New Mexico, BS (Business Administration), 1990; University of Phoenix, Masters in Organizational Management, 1998; 1998 Ambassador for Americans for Indian Opportunity (Leadership Program); 2000 Leadership Sandoval County Graduate. *Affiliation & Address*: Owner, Poston & Associates (2004-present), 54 Morning Star Dr., Sandia Pueblo, NM 87004 (505) 379-6172. E-mail: stephposton@msn.com. Her company is a public and governmental relations firm with a focus on Native American entities. *Other professional posts*: Consulting editor for the American Indian Graduate magazine; member, Board of Directors, Tribal Business Opportunities, Inc., Albuqueque, NM. *Past professional posts*: Public Affairs Officer, U.S. Forest Service, NM & AZ, 1990-93; Tribal Planner, Pueblo of Sandia, NM, 1993-96; Health/Safety/Education Director, Pueblo of Sandia, NM, 1996-99; Public Relations Analyst, Puebl of Sandia, NM, 1999-2004.

POTTER, JACK, JR. (Pit River)
(rancheria chairperson)
Affiliation & Address: Chairperson, Redding Rancheria, 2000 Redding Rancheria Rd., Redding, CA 96001 (530) 225-8979.

POTTS, DONNA MARIE (Mewuk)
(rancheria spokesperson)
Affiliation: Buena Vista Rancheria, 4650 Coalmine Rd., Ione, CA 95640 (209) 274-6512.

POULEY, MARK W. (Sauk-Suiattle)
(tribal chief judge)
Affiliation & Address: Chief Judge, Sauk-Suiattle Tribal Court, 5318 Chief Brown Lane, Darrington, WA 98241 (360) 436-0131; chief judge, Swinomish Tribal Court, 17337 Reservation Rd., LaConnor, WA 98257 (360) 466-7217.

POULIOT, PAUL W. (Cowasuck Pennacook Abenaki)
(tribal chief & president)
Affiliation: Cowasuck Band of the Pennacook Abenaki People, P.O. Box 54, Forestdale, MA 02644 (508) 477-1772. E-mail: paulp@cowasuck.org.

POUPART, JOHN (Lac du Flambeau Band Lake Superior Anishinaabe)
(organization president)
Affiliation & Address: President, American Indian Policy Center, 1463 Hewitt Ave., St. Paul, MN 55104 (651) 644-1728.
Website: www.americanindianpolicycenter.org.

POUPART, LISA M. (Lac du Flambeau Band of Lake Superior Anishinabe)
(professor of First Nations studies; chairperson/advisor)
Education: University of Wisconsin-Milwaukee, BS & MS; Arizona State University, PhD (with concentration in American Indian law & Federal Indian policy). *Affiliation & Address*: Associate Professor of Humanistic Studies & Ojibwe Language, First Nation Studies (chairperson & advisor) & Women's Studies, University of Wisconsin-Green Bay, WH 420 Nicolet Dr., Green Bay, WI 54311 (920) 465-2185. E-mail: poupartl@uwegb.edu. *Interests*: "My scholarly publications & research are concerned with social problems in American Indian reservation & urban communities, and my primary research interest is concerned with internalized oppression in American Indian communities & the social problems that stem from this phenomenon including domestic violence, childhood sexual abuse, addictions, & juvenile delinquency; currently involved with a number of state & national initiatives to standardize First Nation Studies curriculum & core knowledge." *Other professional posts*: Consultant on issues concerning American Indian domestic violence & juvenile delinquency with the Department of Justice & National Institute of Justice.

POURIER, ERNEST F. (Winnebago)
(acting BIA agency supt.)
Affiliation & Address: Acting Supt., Bureau of Indian Affairs, Winnebago Agency, P.O. Box 18, Winnebago, NE 68071 (402) 878-2502. E-mail: ernest.pourier@bia.gov.

POURIER, LORI (Oglala Lakota)
(philanthropy; organization president)
Education: Southern New Hampshire University, Graduate School of Business, MS. *Affiliation & Address*: President (1999-present), First Peoples Fund, P.O. Box 2977, Rapid City, SD 57709 (605) 348-0324. *Other professional posts*: Serves on the Board of Directors for Grantmakers in the Arts; co-chair, Indigenous Resource Network; board member of the Native Americans in Philanthropy, and Red Cloud Indian School. *Past professional posts*: Associate Marketing Director, First Nations Development Institute, Fredericksburg, VA; marketing consultant specializing in developing marketing strategies for nonprofit American Indian organizations & tribal communities; served on the Board of Directors of the Western States Arts Federation, the Honor the Earth Fund, the Chinook Fund, and the National Indian Business Association. *Awards, honors*: In 1993, she participated in AIO's American Indian Ambassadors Leadership Program funded by the Kellogg Foundation; Ms. Pourier was selected for the Center for Social Innovation (CSI) fellowship at the Stanford Graduate School of Business. The Executive Program for Nonprofit Leaders - Arts honors 50 outstanding arts & culture leaders by selecting them to receive CSI fellowship for the program.

POUST, TERESA E. (Poarch Band Creek)
(attorney)
Education: California State University-Fullerton, BA, 1989; University of New Mexico, American Indian Law Center, Pre-Law Summer Institute, Indian Law, Summer 1989; Catholic University of America, Columbus School of Law, JD, 1992. *Affiliation & Address*: Owner/Attorney (2011-present)), Poust Law, 8732 Skyline Dr., Los Angeles, CA 90046 (323) 919-1800. E-mail: teri.poust@poustlaw.com. Teri is a member of the Board of Directors, Wind Creek Hospitality, 2015 – present. The Poarch Band of Creek Indians created Wind Creek Hospitality to serve as the principle gaming and hospitality business entity for the Tribe. The Board of Directors is responsible for establishing overall policies & objectives for the management of the affairs and assets of Wind Creek Hospitality. The company operates six properties throughout the state of Alabama & the Florida Panhandle; Chitimacha Gaming Commission, 2016 – present; Serve as the Chair of the Gaming Commission for the Chitimacha Tribe of Louisiana. *Past professional post*: Interim Gaming Commissioner, San Manuel Band of Mission Indians gaming Commission, 2013 – 2015; served as the sole Gaming Commissioner supervising all Gaming Commission staff, including Surveillance, Audit, Licensing and Compliance. Provides counsel on a broad range of Indian issues, with a particular emphasis on gaming facility regulation and operation. *Other professional posts*: Interim Gaming Commissioner, San Manuel Band of Mission Indians Gaming Commission, 2013-present); Founder & President, Doggne Crazy Animal Rescue, Inc., Los Angeles, CA, 2013-present. *Past professional posts*: Poarch Band of Creek Indians, Atmore, AL (Tribal Attorney, 1992-95; Tribal Administrator, 1995-99; Commissioner, National Indian Gaming Commission, Washington, DC, 1999-2002; Partner, Holland & Knight, LLP, Washington, DC, Los Angeles, CA, 2003-10). *Community activities*: Volunteer, Tails of the City Animal Rescue, 2010-present.

POWELL, LEONARD K. (Hopland Pomo)
(attorney; community preservation manager)
Affiliation & Address: Community Preservation Manager, City of Fremont, 39550 Liberty St., Fremont, CA 94538 (510) 494-4430.E-mail: lnrdpwll@gmail.com. *Other professional post*: President, Board of Directors, California Indian Law Association, Sacramento, CA. Leonard helped California Tribes establish the foundations & framework for effective gaming regulations

in California by co-founding & helping facilitate the California Tribal Gaming Commissioners/Regulators Networking Group.

POWELL, MALEA (Indiana Miami/Eastern Band Shawnee) 1962-
(associate professor)
Born December 7, 1962, Kokomo, Ind. *Education*: Indiana University, BA, 1992; Miami University, MA, 1994; PhD, 1998. *Principal occupation*: Associate Professor of Writing, Rhetoric & American Cultures. *Address & Address*: Professor, American Thought & Language, Michigan State University, 273 Bessey Hall, East Lansing, MI 48824-1033 (517) 432-2577. E-mail: powell37@ msu.edu; sail2@msu.edu. *Past professional posts*: Miami University (Ohio), 1992-98; University of Nebraska, 1998-2002. *Other professional post*: Editor, Studies in American Indian Literatures. *Community activities*: Member, Board of Directors, Center for the Study of Great Lakes Native American Culture. *Memberships*: American Assn of University Professors, American Assn of University Women, American Literature Assn, American Studies Assn, Association for American Indian & Alaskan Native Professors, Association for Studies in American Indian Literatures, Coalition of Women Scholars in the History of Rhetoric, International Society for the History of Rhetoric, MLA Division on American Indian Literatures, National Assn for Native American Studies, National Indian Education Assn, Wordcraft Circle of Native Writers, Native Writers Circle of the Americas, et al. *Grants & Awards*: Recipient, National Council for Teachers of English Scholars for the Dream Award Recipient, 1994; Certificate of Recognition for Contributions to Students, The Parents' Association & the Teaching Council of the University of Nebraska, January 2000; Recipient, University of Nebraska Research Council Grant-in-Aid, January 2001; Nominee, U. of Nebraska College of Arts & Sciences Distinguished Teaching Award, 2001-2002; Wordcraft Circle Writer's Award (Scholarly Editing), 2002. *Interests*: American Indian rhetoric & literature. *Articles Published*: "Imagining a New Indian: Listening to the Rhetoric of Survivance in Charles Eastman's From the Deep Woods to Civilization." (Paradoxa, August 2001); "Rhetoric of Survivance: How American Indians Use Writing." (College Composition & Communication 53.3 February 2002; "Real Indians," (Native Realities 3:2 Spring, 2003); "Extending the Hand of Empire: Women and Indians in the Indian Reform Movement, a Beginning," (American Ethnic Rhetorics, March 2003); Princess Sarah, the Civilized Indian: The Rhetoric of Cultural Literacies in Sarah Winnemucca-Hopkins' Life Among the Paiutes," in book, Rhetorical "Woman:" Fragmented Traces, Roles, Representations, edited by Bridwell-Bowles & Miller (U. of Alabama Press, 2004); "Down by the River, or How Susan LaFlesche Can Teach Us About Alliance as a Practice of Survivance" (College English, Sept. 2004); "Dear Simon, A Response to Simon Ortiz," in Writing Environments: Rhetoric, Texts, and the Construction of Nature, by Dobrin & Keller (SUNY Press, 2005). *Projects in Process*: Editor, Of Color: Native American Literature, an anthology with a rhetoric apparatus, under contract with Prentice Hall; book project in process.

POWELL, MELISSA (Sierra Me-Wuk)
(tribal chairperson)
Affiliation & Address: Chairperson, Chicken Ranch Band of Me-Wuk Indians, P.O. Box 159, Jamestown, CA 95327 (209) 984-4806.

POWER, SUSAN (Standing Rock Sioux)
(writer)
Address: c/o G.P. Putnam's Sons, 200 Madison Ave, New York, NY 10016. *Published work*: The Grass Dancer.

POWERS, MARLA N. 1938-
(anthropologist; publisher; writer)
Born January 8, 1938, Cranston, R.I. *Education*: Brooklyn College, C.U.N.Y., BA, 1973; Rutgers University, MA, 1979, PhD (Anthropology; dissertation: Oglala Women in Myth, Ritual, and Reality), 1982. *Principal occupation*: Anthropologist. *Address*: 74 Stillwell Rd., Kendall Park, NJ 08824. *Affiliation*: Visiting research associate, Institute for Research on Women, Rutgers University, New Brunswick, N.J., 1983-. *Other professional posts*: Owns & operates with husband, William K. Powers, Lakota Books. Founded in 1990 for the purpose of writing, publishig, and distributing monographs and books about Lakota & Dakota culture, history, and language. *Past professional posts*: Associate editor, Powwow Trails: American Indians, Past & Present, Somerset, NJ, 1964-66; consultant, Title IV Bilingual Health Program, Pine Ridge Indian Reservation, Summer, 1976; consultant, Psychiatric Nursing Program, University of South Dakota & USPHS satellite program, Oglala Sioux Community, Pine Ridge Reservation, Summer, 1976; consultant, Lakota Culture Camp (program evaluation for Dept. of Special Education, State of SD), Pine Ridge Indian Reservation, Summer, 1980; member of thesis committee in Psychiatric Nursing, Rutgers University--thesis title: An Exploratory Study of Mentoring Relationships Among Indian Women in the Profession of Nursing, 1982; also thesis committee in anthropology--Ph.D. thesis entitled: Comanche Belief & Ritual, 1985; professor of anthropology, Seton Hall University. *Memberships*: American Anthropological Association; Society for Medical Anthropology; Society for Visual Anthropology; American Folklore Society; American Ethnological Society; Philadelphia Anthropological

Society; Society for Ethnomusicology; Nebraska State Historical Society; American Dance Therapist Association; American Craftsman's Council; Actor's Equity; American Federation of Television & Radio Artists. *Fieldwork*: Pine Ridge, South Dakota, Oglala (Sioux), also various tribes of New Mexico, Arizona, Oklahoma & Wyoming; urban U.S. "I have done extensive anthropological research among the Oglala Lakota on the Pine Ridge Indian Reservation in South Dakota. A major part of the research focused on Native subsistence, food procurement, preparation, storage, distribution, and nutrition. I also studied Native therapeutic techniques, particularly treatment of psychosomatic disorders." *Awards, honors*: Wenner-Gren Foundation Grant-in-aid, Summer, 1980 (field research on the relationship of Oglala traditional women's roles to social structure); National Endowment for the Humanities, Research Assistant on Oglala Music & Dance, Sept. 1980 - Aug. 1982, Jan. 1983 - Dec. 1983; Douglass Fellows Grant for Research on photographs of American Indian women, Spring, 1983 & 1984; National Endowment for the Humanities, Planning Grant: principal investigator, Lakota Women: A Photographic Retrospective, Jan. 1985 - Dec. 1985; Minnesota Historical Society, grant for field research on Lakota medicine, Summer, 1985. *Interests*: "American Indians, particularly Northern Plains, urban U.S.; intercultural health care systems; anthropology of gender, medicine, art, and dance. *Dance*: have appeared in numerous Broadway and off-Broadway shows; on major network television shows; taught dance. *American Indian art*: "I have studied traditional crafts among the Sioux & Comanches and I'm proficient in various techniques of American Indian beadwork, quillwork, and ribbonwork." *Papers presented*: Images of American Indian Women: Myth and Reality, Rome, Italy, 1984, tour in West Germany-1985; Symbols in Contemporary Oglala Art, Vienna, Austria; Workshop on American Indian Music & Dance (with William K. Powers), Budapest, Hungary, 1985; Stereotyping American Indians, Cologne, West Germany, 1985; Native American Motherhood: A View From the Plains, Rutgers University, 1985; among others. *Published works*: Co-editor, Lakota Wicozanni-Ehank'ehan na Lehanl (Lakota Health Traditional & Modern), three volumes plus teacher's guide (Oglala Sioux Community College, 1977); Metaphysical Aspects of an Oglala Food System, in Food and the Social Order (Russell Sage Foundation, 1984); Oglala Women: Myth, Ritual, and Reality (University of Chicago Press, 1986); Putting on the Dog: Ceremoniousness in an Oglala Stew, with William K. Powers, in Natural History (American Museum of Natural History); Lakota Foods, with William K. Powers & Lakota Medicine (Minnesota Historical Society Press).

POWERS, W. ROGERS
(professor, dept. head)
Affiliation: Dept. of Alaskan Native Studies, University of Alaska, Dept. of Anthropology, 310 Eielson Bldg., Fairbanks, AK 99775 (907) 474-7288.

POWERS, WILLIAM K. 1934-
(anthropologist; journalist; publisher & writer)
Born July 31, 1934, St. Louis, Mo. *Education*: Brooklyn College, BA, 1971; Wesleyan University, MA (Anthropology; thesis: Yuwipi Music in Cultural Context), 1972; University of Pennsylvania, PhD (Anthropology; dissertation: Continuity & Change in Oglala Religion). *Address*: 74 Stillwell Rd., Kendall Park, NJ 08824. *Other professional posts*: Owns & operates with wife, Marla N. Powers, Lakota Books. Founded in 1990 for the purpose of writing, publishig, and distributing monographs and books about Lakota & Dakota culture, history, and language. *Past professional posts*: Associate editor, American Indian Tradition, 1960-62; editor & publisher, Powwow Trails, 1964-66; consulting editor, American Indians Then and Now Series (G.P. Putnam's Sons), 1968-; instructor, North American Indian music & dance, Wesleyan University, 1971-72; teaching fellow, 1972-73, lecturer, 1973-77, (North American Indians), University of Pennsylvania; distinguished professor, Dept. of Anthropology, Rutgers University, New Brunswick, NJ, 1974-96. *Fieldwork*: Primarily among the Oglala Sioux, Pine Ridge, South Dakota, 1966-; also various tribes in NM, AZ, OK and WY. Grants & Fellowships: Research in American Indian religion, linguistics & music, American Philosophical Society, 1966, '67, '77; among others. *Awards, honors*: Award of Excellence in Juvenile Literature, NJ State Teachers of English, 1972, '73; Faculty Merit Award, Rutgers University, 1977. *Memberships*: American Anthropological Assn; Society for Ethnomusicology; Indian Rights Assn. *Interests*: "North American Indian studies - historical & contemporary Indian affairs; urban U.S.; social organization; comparative religion; history of anthropology; sociolinguistics; ethnomusicology; culture change." *Published works*: Indian Dancing & Costumes (G.P. Putnam's Sons, 1966); Young Brave (For Children, Inc., 1967); Crazy Horse and Custer (For Children, Inc., 1968); Indians of the Northern Plains (G.P. Putnam's Sons, 1969); The Modern Sioux: Reservation Systems & Social Change (University of Nebraska Press, 1970); Indians of the Southern Plains (G.P. Putnam's Sons, 1971); Continuity & Change in the American Family, with Marla N. Powers (Dept. of HEW); Indians of the Great Lakes (G.P. Putnam's Sons, 1976); co-author, Lakota Wicozani - Ehank'ehan na Lehanl (Indian Health - Traditional & Modern), 1976; Oglala Religion (University of Nebraska Press, 1977); Lakota Foods, with Marla N. Powers (in preparation); numerous papers, articles in scholarly journals, notes, book reviews, abstracts, etc.

**POWLESS, DAVID (*Lani Kuhlaha'wis*) (Oneida) 1943-
(business executive)**
Born May 29, 1943, Ottawa, Ill. *Education*: University of Oklahoma, 1961-62; University of Illinois, BS, 1966. *Address*: 161 Sagebrush Dr., Corrales, NM 87048 (505) 897-9445. *Affiliations*: Owner & founder, Oneida Materials Co., Colorado Springs, CO., 1976-85; president & founder, ORTEK (Environmental Laboratory), Oneida Tribe, Green Bay, WI, 1987-92; V.P. Marketing-Western Regional, Arctic Slope Regional Corp., 1992- (owned by Inupiat Eskimos); also maintains a business interest in Bear Paw, Inc. which provides insurance benefits to tribes. Bear Paw is a joint venture with Dick Butkis (NFL Hall of Fame & former football team mate). *Memberships*: Oneida Tribe; American Indian Science & Engineering Society (board of directors, 1986-90). *Awards, honors*: University of Illinois Rose Bowl Team, 1963; professional football, NY Giants, 1965, Washington Redskins, 1966; National Science grant in 1977 to research, at the Colorado School of Mines, methods for recycling iron oxide wastes produced by steel mills. This was the first NSF Grant given to an individual Native American; 1981 - SBA Award "National Innovation Advocate of the Year". *Interests*: "Training Indians to be scientists to work in tribally-owned environmental laboratories; mediation training of groups. He is committed to caring for the environment. It is his belief that this commitment is one of the duties the creator has given to all Native Americans. Currently involved with tribal economic development with Arctic Slope Joint Ventures With Tribes."

**POWLESS, DONNA (Oneida)
(professor of psychology)**
Education: Black Hawk College (Moline, IL), AA (Liberal Studies), 1976 University of Wisconsin, Madison, BS (Behavior Disabilities), 1985, MA (Educational Psychology), 1990; PhD (Educational Psychology), 1995. She has worked in the Educational field for 20 years, starting as a Teacher's Aid, Special Education Teacher, & School Psychologist. Her counseling licensure has enabled her to provide Mental Health therapeutic services to native people. More recently, Donna has taken on roles of Administration at the Oneida Nations Schools, and Menominee Tribal School. *Affiliation & Address*: Professor of Psychology (2005-present), College of Menominee Nation, P.O. Box 1179, Keshena, WI 54135 (715) 799-4921. E-mail: dpowless@menominee.edu. *Past professional post*: Vice President of Academic Affairs, College of Menominee nation.

**POWLESS, IRVING, JR. (Oneida)
(tribal chief)**
Affiliation & Address: Chief, Onondaga Indian Nation, RR 1, Box 319-B, Nedrow, NY 13120 (315) 492-1922.

**POWVAL, SAMUEL (Luiseno)
(former tribal chairperson)**
Affiliation: Pauma Band of Mission Indians, P.O. Box 86, Pauma Valley, CA 92061 (619) 742-1289.

**POYNTER, KEN (Passamaquoddy)
(tribal lt. governor)**
Affiliation & Address: Lt. Governor (2010-present), Passamaquoddy Tribe, Pleasant Point, P.O. Box 343, Perry, ME 04667 (207) 853-2600. *Past professional post*: Executive director, Native American Fish & Wildlife Society, Denver, CO.

**PRATT, GARY (*Ahu Thaway – Black Wing*) (Iowa)
(former tribal chairperson)**
Affiliation & Address: Former Chairperson (2013-2015), Iowa Nation of Oklahoma, Rt. 1 Box 721, Perkins, OK 74059 (405) 547-2402. E-mail: gpratt@iowanation.org.

**PRATT, HARVEY (Cheyenne Arapaho)
(artist; board commission chair)**
Affiliation: Chairperson, Indian Arts & Crats Board Commission, Washington, DC. Harvey is a master artist who uses a variety of media, including oil, acrylic, watercolor, metal, clay, and wood. An award-winning artist, including being named The Honored One in 2005 by the Red Earth Festival, Oklahoma City, Okla., his paintings & sculpture include themes of tradition, warriors, the Cheyenne people; He has served as a consultant on Native American art & culture to many organiations in the State of Oklahoma, and has been inducted into the Southern Cheyenne Chief's Lodge as one of their traditional Peace Chiefs. He is currently employed as the police forensic artist by the Oklahoma State Bureau of Investigation. *Past professional post*: Assistant Director & nterim Director for the OK State Bureau of Investigation in Oklahoma City.

**PRATT, MICHAEL E. (*Wat-Si-Mori*) (Osage) 1947-
(professor/administrator)**
Born March 3, 1947, Hominy, Okla. *Education*: Utah State University, Logan, BS, 1971, MS, 1977; University of Oklahoma, PhD, 1986. *Address*: 702 N.

Katy Ave., Hominy, OK 74035 (918) 287-2587. *Affiliations*: Coach/instructor, Pratt College, KS; instructor, University of Oklahoma, 1982-. *Community activities*: Arkansas Museum of Natural History & Science (advisor, Indians of Arkansas exhibit). *Awards, honors*: Award from Administration for Native Americans. *Interests*: "White Hair Memorial, Oklahoma Historical Society; developed curriculum for preservation of Osage language, cultural retention courses for Osage people." *Published works*: Stereotyping of the American Indian (Utah State, 1978); Osage Kinship (University of Oklahoma Press, 1986).

**PRATT, W. BRUCE (Pawnee)
(tribal president)**
Affiliation & Address: President, Pawnee Nation of Oklahoma, P.O. Box 470, Pawnee, OK 74958 (918) 762-3621. *Past tribal post*: Vice president.

**PRATTE, CLARA (Navajo)
(government administrator)**
Education: University of Arizona, BS; Carnegie Mellon University, MA. *Affiliation*: National Director, Office of Native American Affairs, Small Business Administration, U.S. Dept. of Commerce, Washington, DC 20230 (202) 401-3059. *Past affiliations*: Policy Analyst & Legislative Liaison for the Navajo Nation focusing on economic & community development, housing, and education issues. Before that, she was with the U.S. Dept. of Commerce at the International Trade Administration as a trade specialist in the U.S. Foreign & Commercial Service. Pratte counseled small-to-medium sized U.S. companies on exporting. After, she joined the Office of the Chief Information Officer, where she oversaw information technology projects for the U.S. Foreign & Commercial Service and the Import Administration. *Awards, honors*: Former Udall Foundation Congressional Fellow & a Presidential Management Fellow.

**PRESCOTT, DENNY (Mdewakanton Sioux)
(tribal president)**
Affiliation & Address: President, Lower Sioux Indian Community, P.O. Box 308, Morton, MN 56270 (507) 697-6185. E-mail: denny.prescott@lowersioux.com

**PRESCOTT, GABE (Mdewakanton Sioux)
(former tribal president)**
Affiliation: Lower Sioux Indian Community of Minnesota, P.O. Box 308, Morton, MN 56270 E-mail: gprescott@lowersioux.com

**PRESCOTT, LEONARD (Mdewakanton Sioux)
(casino/bingo hall CEO)**
Affiliation: Mystic Lake Casino & Bingo Hall, 2400 Mystic Lake Blvd., Prior Lake, MN 55372 (800) 262-7799.

**PRESCOTT, ROGER (Mdewakanton Sioux)
(former tribal chairperson)**
Affiliation: Lower Sioux Indian Community Council, Rt. 1, Box 308, Morton, MN 56270 (507) 697-6185.

**PRESS, DANIEL S.
(attorney; Indian law)**
Affiliation & Address: Partner, Van Ness Feldman, 1050 Thomas Jefferson St., NW 7th Floor, Washington, DC 20007 (202) 298-1882. E-mail: dsp@vnf.com
For more than 40 years, Dan Press has provided legal & Washington representation assistance to Indian tribes, Indian organizations, & companies doing business with tribes. Dan assists tribes with strengthening their tribal governments by helping them develop and implement ordinances that exercise the tribe's sovereign authority in such areas as employment rights and labor relations. He has helped to establish a range of entities designed to promote economic development in Indian country, including creative use of the special 8(a) rights Congress has provided to tribes and the first multi-tribally owned financial institution. He has also counseled tribes to obtain legislation awarding them hundreds of millions of dollars in land claims settlements, new health facilities, and new authority to promote employment on their reservations. He has special knowledge of Indian land issues, including rights of ways and leases on Indian land and the unique legal issues that arise when doing business on reservations & assisted companies negotiate various agreements with tribes regarding land use. Dan has used his years of experience working with tribes and private sector companies to assist his clients develop productive business partnerships with tribes so that their projects can move forward quickly and cooperatively. He is also adept in the application of the Affordable Care Act to Indians and how tribal and other reservation health care facilities can use the Act to greatly expand the resources available to them to treat the underlying problems responsible for the serious health issues on many reservations. Dan has litigated in tribal and Federal courts on behalf of tribes and Indian business. Through his extensive knowledge of federal procurement law, he has advised tribes and businesses on contract issues & represented them on such issues in the Court of Federal Claims.

PRESTON, DREW (Navajo)
(dentist; dental clinic manager)
Education: University of California, Santa Barbara, BS 9 Biology), 2006; UCLA School of Dentistry, DDS, 2010. *Affiliation & Address*: Dentist & Dental Clinic Manager, American Indian Health & Services, Indian Health Service, 4141 State St., Santa Barbara, CA 93110 (805) 696-1002. *Other professional post*: Vice President, Society of American Indian Dentists (SAID), Menifee, CA. *Memberships*: California Dental Association; American Dental Association; Santa Barbara-Ventura Dental Society; SAID.

PRESTON, VICTOR (Paiute)
(former rancheria chairperson)
Affiliation: Susanville Indian Rancheria, P.O. Drawer U, Susanville, CA 06130 (530) 257-6264.

PRETTY ON TOP, BURTON (*Flirts With Women/Two Mornings*)
(Crow) 1946-
(spiritual leader; public speaker, teacher)
Born September 17, 1946, Crow Agency, Mont. *Education*: Rocky Mt. College (Billings, MT), 1965-67; Eastern Mt. College (Billings, MT), 1969-70. *Principal occupation*: Native American spiritual leader; public speaker, teacher. *Affiliations*: Crow Tribal Council Public Relations Director, Crow Agency, MT, 1991-97; spiritual leader for Crow Catholic Parishes, 1991-; executive director, Crow Tribal Housing Authority. *Community activities*: Traveled for 13 years giving talks & presentations on Native spirituality, nationally & internationally; involved with social justice issues, & protection of human rights. *Memberships*: Tekakwitha Conference (board of directors, 1988-93); Thanksgiving Square (Dallas, TX). *Awards, honors*: "I was one of two Native American spiritual leaders selected to represent the Native American traditions from the Western Hemisphere, at the "World Day of Prayer for Peace" held at Assisi, Italy (October, 1986); I was asked to sign a World Thanksgiving Document along with 11 other religious leaders from across the world, in 1987, at Dallas, TX; I was among 100 religious leaders honored at the "Thanksgiving Square" in Dallas (Sept., 1989); I was one of seven Native spiritual leaders asked to attend & give a presentation at the "Parliament of Worlds Religions" gathering in Chicago, IL (Sept./Oct., 1993)." *Interests*: "I am a member of the Whistling Water and Bad War Deed Clans of the Crow Nation. I am a child of the Big Lodge Clan. Among the Crow people today, we are blessed by our Creator "Akbaadaadia" in a way that is very unique; we all speak the Crow language, practice our Native spirituality, customs and traditions. We still follow and respect the 'clan' system." *Biographical sources*: Time Magazine, 5/10/93; Lily of the Mohawks magazine, Fall/Winter 1993; among others. Newspaper articles: The New York Times - Sunday, 8/9/92; The Dallas Morning News - Sunday, 10/4/92; Billings Gazette - Saturday, 4/17/93.

PRINDLE, TARA
(organization director)
Education: University of Connecticut, BA (Anthropology), 1988; University of Vermont, MA (Anthropology), 1989. *Affiliation & Address*: Director, Native American Technology & Art, P.O. Box 73, Storrs, CT 06268. E-mail: tprindle@nativetech.org.

PRINGLE, ROBERT
(education administrator)
Affiliation: Anchorage Education Field Office, Bureau of Indian Affairs, 3601 C St., Suite 1100, Anchorage, AK 99503 (907) 271-4115.

PRINS, HARALD E.L. 1951-
(professor)
Born September 7, 1951, Alphen a/d Rijn, The Netherlands. *Education*: University of Nijmegen, The Netherlands, 1971-76 (Doctoral-Anthropology/History); New School for Social Research (New York, NY), PhD, 1988. *Address*: 3301 Buffalo Rd., Manhattan, KS 66502 (785) 776-3876; 532-6865 (office); E-mail: prins@ksu.edu. *Affiliations*: University Distinguished Professor of Cultural Anthropology & American Ethnic Studies, Kansas State University, Manhattan, KS, 1990-present. *Other professional posts*: Research Associate at the Smithsonian Institution, Washington, DC, 2008-present; tribal researcher, Aroostook Band of Micmacs, Presque Island, ME, 1981-present; Miawpukek First Nation of Mi'kmaqs, Newfoundland, Canada, 1996-present. *Past professional posts*: Consultant on ethno-history, ethnographic film, Native rights; Visual Anthropology Editor, American Anthropologist, 1998-2002; guest curator, National Museum of Natural History, Smithsonian Institution, Washington, DC, 2003-07; principal investigator, Acadia National Parks Ethnographic Research, National Parks Services, 2003-06. *Community activities*: Aroostook Micmac Indian Community; Apache Tribe of Oklahoma (Culture Committee); Miawpukek Band of Micmacs, Newfoundland (Land Claims Team). *Memberships*: American Anthropological Assn; American Society for Ethno-history; Society for Visual Anthropology (board of directors; president, 1999-2001); Native American Rights Fund; National Museum of the American Indian (charter member); Current Anthropologist (Associate, 2002-present). *Awards, honors*: Aroostook Micmac Council Service Award, 1982;

Expert Witness on Tribal Rights, U.S. Congress, 1990; Jury Baxter Award, Maine Historical Society, 1991-; Margaret Mead Award Finalist, 1992 & 1997; Program Chair, Visual Anthropology, 1996; Honorable mention, Society for Visual Anthropology for film, "Wabanaki: A New Dawn, 1996; Vera G. List Fellowship; Criterion Foundation Award; Maine Humanities Council Film Award; Maine Arts Commission Award; National Endowment for the Humanities Award; Columbian Quincentennial Fellowship; Presidential Award for Outstanding Teaching, KSU, 1999; Distinguished Lecturer & Keynote Speaker, 2002-2003; John Culkin Award for Outstanding Praxis in the Field of Media Ecology, Media Ecology Assn, 2004; University Chair of Distinguished Teaching Scholars, Kansas State University, 2004-2005; Carnegie Foundation (CASE) Professor of the Year, KSU Provost's Nominee, 2005; 2010 AAA/Oxford University Press Award for Excellence in Undergraduate Teaching by the American Anthropological Assn. *Interests*: Canadian Maritimes, New England, Great Plains, Upper Amazon, Andean Highlands, Patagonia. "As a cultural anthropologist/ethno-historian/filmmaker, I have served the Aroostook Band of Micmacs in their quest for native rights in Maine since 1981. In 1990, I testified as expert witness in U.S. Congress, and November 26, 1991, the Band was officially recognized by the Federal Government and was awarded funding to purchase 5,000 acres of land that will serve as a land base. The federal recognition was based on ethnographic and historical documentation that I researched & presented as tribal anthropologist for the Micmacs. My documentary film "Our Lives in Our Hands," which aired on public television and featured at numerous national & international film festivals, portrays this Micmac Indian community in northern Maine in their quest for survival." *Published works*: Video - "Our Lives in Our Hands," 49 min., color 16mm/video (Documentary Educational Resources, 1985); "Oh, What a Blow that Phantom Gave Me!, 50 min. video/DVD (Documentary Educational Resources, 2004). Books - Tribulations of a Border Tribe (U. of Michigan Press, 1989); American Beginnings: Exploration, Culture, & Cartography in the Land of Norumbega, co-edited with E Baker et al. (U of Nebraska Press, 1994); The Mi'kmaq: Resistance, Accommodation, & Cultural Survival (Harcourt Brace, 1996).

PRITCHARD, EVAN (*Abachbahamedtch - chipmunk*) (Micmac)
(professor of Native American history, speaker/lecturer)
Affiliation & Address: Founder, The Center for Algonquin Culture, P.O. Box 1028, Woodstock, NY 12498; Resonance Communications (212) 714-7151; Council Oaks Books (800) 247-8850; E-mail: rezman@ulster.net. Website: www.algonquinculture.org; professor of Native American history, Marist College, Poughkeepsie, NY. *Community activities*: "Native New Yorker" walking tours of lower Manhattan for the Smithsonian Institution, The Open Center, South Street Seaport, and other institutions; shared his findings on Native American life in manhattann on Leonard Lopate's "New York & Company" show, on WBAI/Pacific Radio, ABC news, etc. He was the organizer of the North American Friendship Circle gathering on Columbus Day, 1992; also the founder of the Red Willow Society, Resonance Communications, & Roads to Awareness Seminars. *Interests*: His work helping Algonquin elders and brining their message to the media has helped thousands of people gain a better understanding of Native American civilization and its teachings. He lectures frequently around the U.S., sharing storytelling, traditional & contemporary songs, & bilingual poetry. *Biographical sources*: Feature article on Native New Yorkers in the November/December 2002 issue of Native Peoples Magazine; cover article in 2003 in the "Village Voice" by Erik Baard. *Published works*: Native New Yorkers, The Legacy of the Algonquin People of New York, No Word for Time; The Way of the Algonquin People; Introductory Guide to Micmac Words & Phrases; Aunt Helens Little Herb Book (A Miramichi Indian Woman's World of Herbs); Secrets of Wholehearted Thinking; Take the Red Road (poetry); Eagle Song: An Honor Roll of Great Algonquins. In the works: A Lenape Phrase Book is nearing completion, and Penobscot & Shinnecock language projects are being planned.

PRITCHARD, LARRY
(anthropologist, research associate)
Education: University of Colorado, MA (Anthropology), 1995. *Affiliation*: Research associate, Walker Research Group, Ltd., P.O. Box 4147, Boulder, CO 80306 (303) 492-6719. Website: www.walkerresearchgroup.com. Mr. Pritchard has worked with Dr. Deward Walker of Walker Research Group since 2000 and has been an integral part of a variety of research projects including an assessment of socioeconomic and housing conditions for the Rosebud Sioux Tribe, analysis of census methodology on Native American reservations, and socioeconomic and demographic analyses for a number of other Native American tribes. Also, he conducts research in the area of human health and the environment.

PROCELL, JOHN W. (Choctaw & Lipan Apache)
(tribal chief/chairperson)
Affiliation: Chair/Chief (2005-present), Choctaw-Apache Community of Ebarb Tribe, Box 1428, Zwolle, LA 71486 (318) 645-2588. *Military service*: U.S. Army

PROPHET, SU ZANNA K. (Shawnee/Delaware) 1951-
  (city management)
Born in 1951 in Tulsa, Okla. *Education*: Oklahoma State University, BA, 1973; Haskell Indian Junior College, AA (Art), 1978; University of Kansas, MA, 1979, MPA, 1985; University of Bridgeport, CT, BFA (Painting), 1981. *Principal occupation*: City Management. *Address*: RR 1, Box 137, Firth, NE 68358 (402) 791-5898. *Affiliations*: Budget Research Analyst, Odessa, TX, 1983-89; Administrative Assistant to City Manager, Urbandale, IA, 1989-98; Assistant City Manager, Urbandale, IA, 1998-.

PROUDFIT, JOELY (LUISENO)
  (director of Native studies)
Affiliation & Address: Director, California Indian Culture & Sovereignty Center (CICSC) at California State University, San Marcos and Director of Native Studies, 333 S. Twin Oaks Valley Rd., San Marcos, CA 992096 (760) 750-3535. E-mail: jpproudfit@csusm.edu. *Other professional posts*: Dr. Proudfit Wwas appointed a member of President Obama's national Advisory Council on Indian Education, for 2016; she is the owner of Naqmayam Communications, an independent, full-service, California Indian-owned & -operated public relations, marketing and advertising agency *Past professional post*: Associate professor of public administration and the director of the Tribal Government, Management & Leadership Master of Public Administration (MPA) program at CSU San Bernardino and also served as department chair of American Indian Studies at San Francisco State University. *Awards, honors*: Joely was the first special advisor to the Honorable Cruz M. Bustamante, lieutenant governor of California, for California Indian Sovereign Nations in 2002. She was the 2013 Recipient, American Indian Educator of the Year, 36th Annual California Conference on American Indian Education. *Published works*: Editor, 2015 On Indian Ground: California: A Return to Indigenous Knowledge: Generating Hope, Leadership, & Sovereignty Through Education (Information Age Publishing, 2015).

PRUSIA, SHIRLEY (Concow Maidu)
  (rancheria chairperson)
Affiliation: Mooretown Rancheria, 1 Alverda Dr., Oroville, CA 95966 (530) 533-3625.

PRYOR, NATHAN (Navajo – Dine')
  (policy coordinator; commission chair)
Education: University of Arizona, BS (Regional Development), MA (Public Administration). *Affiliation & Address*: Intergvernmental Policy Coordinator, Maricopa Association of Governments, 302 North 1ˢᵗ Ave., Suite 300, Phoenix, AZ 85003 (602) 254-6300 Fax 254-6490. *Other professional post*: Chair, Arizona Commission of Indain Affairs, Phoenix, AZ. *Past professional posts*: Research Assistant & Program Coordinator, Native Nations Institute for Leadership, Management & Policy, Udall Center, Tucson, AZ (examined Indigenous governance & economic development in the U.S. & Canada); worked for the Pascua Yaqui Tribe near Tucson.

PULLAR, GORDON L. (Koniag) 1944-
  (associate professor)
Born January 22, 1944, Bellingham, Wash. *Education*: Western Washington University, BA, 1973; University of Washington, MPA (Tribal Administration Program - Native American issues and programs), 1983; The Union Institute, PhD, 1997. *Affiliations*: Associate professor, College of Rural & Community Development (CRCD), Dept. of Alaska Native Studies & Rural Development (DANSRD), University of Alaska, Fairbanks, 2221 E. Northern Lights Blvd. #200, Anchorage, AK 99508 (907) 279-2706. E-mail: g.pullar@uaf.edu. *Past professional posts*: Rewind operator/ supervisor, Georgia Pacific Corp., Bellingham, WA, 1963-79; assistant editor, business editor, The Indian Voice (Small Tribes Organization of Western Wash.), 1979-81; associate editor, Nations magazine (National Communications, Inc., Seattle, 1981; owner/ publisher, Kodiak Times, Kodiak, AK 1983-85; president & CEO, Kodiak Area Native Association, 1983-89; president, Lesnoi Village, Woody Island Tribal Council, Kodiak, AK, 2007-11. *Community activities*: Volunteer work in social programs involving Native Americans: Washington State Dept. of Social & Health Services, Whatcom County Detoxification Center, and Whatcom County Juvenile Probation Dept.; Northwest Indian News Association (board of directors, 1979-81); Governor's Minority & Women's Business Development Advisory Council (appointed by Governor of State of Washington, 1980-81); Native American Business Alliance (board of directors, vice president-publicity chairman, 1981-83); Alaska Regional Energy Association (board of directors, 1984-85); Kodiak Area State Parks Advisory Board, 1983; Alaska Federation of Natives (board of directors, 1983-90); while a member of the Board of Alaska Federation of Natives, he served on the Legislative Committee that worked with Congress to secure the important "1991 Amendments" to ANCSA. *Awards, honors*: First recipient of the Anayuquq Oscar Kawagley Educators Award in 2013. *Memberships*: Koniag (regional Native Corporation); National Congress of American Indians; American Society for Public Administration (South Central AK Chapter).

PURDY, JOHN LLOYD 1949-
  (professor of American literature)
Born January 6, 1949, Salem, Oreg. *Education*: Western Oregon State College (Monmouth, OR), BA, 1978; University of Idaho, MA, 1980; Arizona State University, PhD, 1986. *Address*: 5334 Mosquito Lake Rd., Deming, WA 98244 (360) 650-3243 (work). *Affiliation*: Professor, Western Washington University, Bellingham, WA, 1991-. *Other professional post*: Associate editor (for fiction and Native American poetry) from Calapooya College, 1988-. *Military service*: U.S. Naval Air, 1968-72. *Memberships*: Assn for the Study of American Indian Literatures (editor of newsletter, 1988-; executive board, 1990-); American Literature Association; Modern Language Association. *Awards, honors*: Fulbright Lecturer, Universitat Mannheim, West Germany, 1989-90; Fulbright Lecturer, University of Canterbury, New Zealand, Fall 1993; Director, National Endowment for the Humanities. *Interests*: Degrees in American Literature, with emphasis in Native American Literatures. *Published works*: Riding Shotgun Into the Promised Land River Canyon Press, 2011). *Biographical source*: Word Ways: The Novels of D'Arcy McNickle (University of Arizona Press, 1990).

PURICH, DONALD J.
  (centre director/instructor)
Affiliation: University of Saskatchewan, Native Law Centre, Diefenbaker Centre, Saskatoon, Sask., Canada S7N 3S9 (306) 966-6189.

PUSHETONEQUA, ADRIAN (Meskwaki)
  (tribal chairperson)
Affiliation: Sac & Fox Tribe of the Mississippi in Iowa Meskwaki Nation, 349 Meskwaki Rd., Tama, IA 52339 (641) 484-4678.

PYEATTE, SHARON 1949-
  (Indian education program director)
Born March 11, 1949, Fayette, Mo. *Education*: University of Missouri, BS, 1972; University of Colorado, MA, 1987. *Principal occupation*: Counselor; Indian Education Program Director. *Address*: 9352 E. Arbor Dr., Englewood, CO 80111-5263. *Affiliations*: Assistant program director, College Board, Denver, CO, 1989-91; Director, Indian Education Program, Jenks Public School, 205 East "B" St., Jenks, OK, 74037, 1993-present. *Military service*: U.S. Naval Reserve, 1967-71.

PYLE, GREGORY E. (Choctaw of Oklahoma)
  (former tribal chief)
Affiliation & Address: Chief (1997-2014), Choctaw Nation of Oklahoma, P.O. Drawer 1210, Durant, OK 74702 (580) 924-8280. *Past professional posts*: Served several terms as a member on the National Indian Health Board; appointed to serve on a Task Force created to reorganize the Bureau of Indian Affairs. *Awards, honors*: Distinguished Alumni & Benefactor for Southeast Oklahoma State University; honorary member of the Oklahoma State Troopers Association; 2007 honoree inducted into the Oklahoma Hall of Fame.

PYNE, GARY (Picuris Pueblo)
  (pueblo LT. governor)
Affiliation & Address: Lt. Governor, Picuris Pueblo, P.O. Box 127, Penasco, NM 87553 (505) 587-2519.

Q

QITSUALIK, RACHEL A. (Inuit)
  (columnist)
Address & Affiliation: Columnist, Indian Country Today, 3059 Seneca Turnpike, Canastota, NY 13032 (315) 829-8355. Website: www.indiancountry.com. Rachel was born into a traditional Igloolik Inuit lifestyle. She has worked in Inuit sociopolitical issues for the last 25 years, and has witnessed the full transition of her culture into the modern world.

QOYAWAYMA, ALFRED Q. COLTON (Hopi) 1938-
  (potter & sculptor; consultant)
Born Feb. 26, 1938, Los Angeles, Calif. *Education*: California State Polytechnic University, BSME, 1961; University of Southern California, MSME, 1966; Arizona State University, 1979-85 (Graduate Studies in archaeological ceramic materials, painting passim); Scottsdale Artists School, 1990 & 1991 (Sculptural Studies); Scottsdale Community College, 1981-91 (Studies in Drawing, passim). *Address*: 1585 Majestic Way, Prescott, AZ 86301 (928) 443-1518. E-mail: alqoy@cableone.net; for pottery inquiries, alq@alqpottery.com. *Affiliations*: Project engineer, Litton Systems, Woodland Hills, CA, 1961-71; Manager, Environmental Services Dept., Salt River Project, Phoenix, AZ, 1971-90; investigator, Smithsonian Institute, 1982-present (with a four-man research group identifying original clay sources & pottery migration for ancient Hopi Sikyatki potter); political & technical consultant, Hopi Tribe, Kykotsmovi, AZ, 1989-91. *Community activities*: Board of Directors, The Heard Museum, Phoenix, AZ; Publication Board of Directors, "Winds of Change," American Indian Science & Engineering Society, 1986-; judge at various art shows.

Memberships: American Indian Science & Engineering Society (co-founder & first chairperson); Institute of American Indian & Alaska Native Culture & Arts (Board of Trustees, 1988-; vice-chairperson of the Board; chairperson, Presidential Search Committee, 1989; member, Developmental Committee); Institute of Electrical & Electronic Engineers. *Awards, honors*: First Place Popovi Da Award, Memorial Award, Scottsdale National Indian Arts Exhibition, 1976; Scottsdale National Indian Arts Exhibition; two blue ribbon awards, 1976, one blue ribbon, 1977, Heard Museum Indian Arts Exhibition, Phoenix, AZ; pottery work featured at 1977 Arizona Kidney Foundation Auction, Numkena Studio of Indian Art, Phoenix; individual showing at Santa East, Austin, Texas; 1st place and special award at the Museum of Northern Arizona's 1977 Hopi Show; 2nd & 3rd place at Gallup Ceremonial; holds patents in engineering work in the U.S. and several foreign countries. recipient, AISES, Ely S. Parker Award for Engineering Achievement & Service to the American Indian Community, 1986; University of Colorado, Regents' Honorary Degree of Doctor of Humane Letters, Boulder, May 1986; California Polytechnic University, San Luis Obispo, Alumnus of the Year, 1989; G.B. Grinnell American Indian Children's Education Foundation: Annual Al Qoyawayma Award for Excellence in Science & Engineering and the Arts or Cultural Contribution, established 1990; One of twenty "vision makers" invited, "A Vision for the Third Millennium," United Nations-The Club of Rome and UN Environmental Program, New York, NY 1991; appointed (by the Arizona Governor) Commissioner, Arizona Commission on the Arts, 1991; chairperson - Arizona Design/Public Art Panel, 1991. *Interests*: Al is an artist-potter in the tradition of his Hopi culture. He attributes his pottery training to working with his aunt Polingaysi E. Qoyawayma (aka Elizabeth Q. White), a noted Hopi potter, educator, and writer, who died in 1990. His pottery is known and collected throughout the U.S. Since 1989, he has produced five bronze sculpture series. In June of 1990, Al left his management position in the utility industry to pursue his art career full time. Enjoys travel & research. Selected *Exhibits*: ACA American Indian Art, New York, One-Man Show, 1982; "Night of the First Americans," Kennedy Center, Washington, DC, 1982; Smithsonian Institute of Natural History, Washington, DC, First Showing of Contemporary American Indian Art, 1982-83; Gallery 10, Scottsdale, annual exhibits, 1980-88; "Al Qoyawayma: A Retrospective," Taylor Museum, Colorado Springs, CO, Feb.- April 1985; Santa Fe Indian Market, 1978-93; Arizona State Museum, University of Arizona, Tucson, "Yellow Ware Road," 1990-94. Selected *Publications*: Generations in Clay - Pueblo Pottery of the American Southwest, by Dittert & Plog (Northlands Press, 1980); Santa Fe Design, by Baca & Deats (Crown Publishing, 1990 (3 color photos & story); "Recipient of Tradition," by Barbara Cortright, in Southwest Profile, Aug. 1985 (critical essay, photos); Art of Clay, by Lee M. Cohen, pp. 78-85 (Clearlight Publishers, 1993). Selected Videos: 1980 - Generations in Clay - Pueblo Pottery of the American Southwest, voice-over by Al Qoyawayma; 1985 - 30 minute Interview, Charles Loloma & Al Qoyawayma, PBS, Santa Fe, NM; 1988 - "Taking Tradition to Tomorrow," segment, in AISES Video; 1988 - Victor Masayesva, director & producer: Hopi film on ancient Hopi ceramics project, Smithsonian Institute, Washington, DC; 1989 - Jerry and Lois Jacka, "Beyond Tradition," four segments (video won two Rocky Mountain Emmy Awards; 1991 - contract for video consulting: Media Resource Associates; future video segment on "Indian America," PBS TV, Washington, DC, anticipated release, 1992. *Lectures*: Phoenix Art Museum, 1981; Arizona State University, 1985; Taylor Museum, 1985; University of Colorado, 1987; Scottsdale Historic Society, 1987; Museum of Northern Arizona, Flagstaff, 1988; Heard Museum, Phoenix, AZ ("Between Two Worlds: Native American Professional Today,", 1991; Maori and South Pacific Arts Commission, Fullbright Fellowship, cultural exchange (one month), New Zealand, May 1991.

QUANCHELLO, CRAIG (Picuris Pueblo)
(pueblo governor)
Affiliation & Address: GovernorPicuris Pueblo Council, P.O. Box 127, Penasco, NM 87553 (505) 587-2519.

QUANNIE, EMERSON H (Hopi)
(artist, shop owner)
Affiliation: Artist/Owner, Southwest Native American Promotions, 844 E. 8th St., Mesa, AZ 85203 (480) 834-3791. E-mail: ehquannie@swnap.org. Website: www.swnap.org. *Activities*: Emerson makes & sells Hopi jewelry; conducts workshops, gives lectures and classroom instruction. He's a promoter of local and national Native American art shows featuring top Native American artists and entertainers; provides consulting services.

QUANNIE, KEVIN H. (Hopi/Navajo)
(artist, shop owner)
Address: Artist/Owner, Waterbird Studio, 3723 E. Taylor, Phoenix, AZ 85008 (602) 244-9161. E-mail: kquannie@yahoo.com. *Art mediums*: Kevin does contemporary Hopi paintings, katsina sculptures, bronze sculptures & jewelry. *Activities*: Conducts workshops & gives lectures on contemporary Hopi art mediums.

QUARTZ, KATHERINE MARIE (*Cloud Woman*) (Walker River Paiute) 1963-
(writer, volunteer, floral designer)
Born January 14, 1963, Portland, Oregon. *Education*: Western Nevada Community College (Fallon, NV) (two years); Clackamas Community College (Oregon City, OR) (one year). *Principal occupation*: Writer, volunteer, floral designer. *Address*: Resides in OR. *Community activities*: Chairperson, Native American Intergroup, Schurz, NV, 1992-; volunteer, Native American Youth Conference, Portland State University, 1994; volunteer, Clackamas County Gang Task Force, 1994. *Memberships*: Native Writers Circle; National Alcoholic Anonymous for Native Americans, Las Vegas, NV (committee). *Awards, honors*: Award from Canada Drug Strategy, Nechi Institute for campaign in U.S. for National Addictions Awareness Week; speaker/ presentation on cultural roots and adoption search at the 1992 Healing Our Spirit Worldwide Conference for Indigenous People, Edmonton, Alberta, Canada; speaker on cultural values, presentation entitled, "The Healing Journey Within," at the Women's InterTribal Conference, Reno, NV, 1993. *Interests*: "I feel by volunteering I can devote my time & services to the youth, and also be a role model so they may follow. Speaking & making presentation.

QUASULA, TED
(BIA division director)
Affiliation: Bureau of Indian Affairs, Division of Law Enforcement, 1849 C St., NW, MS: 4140-MIB, Washington, DC 20240 (202) 208-5786.

QUERRY, RON (Choctaw of Oklahoma) 1943-
(writer/novelist)
Born March 22, 1943, Washington, D.C. *Education*: University of New Mexico PhD, 1975. *Address*: PMB 76-A, 2415 E. Musser, Laredo, TX 78043-2434 (524) 152-3524 (Mexico). E-mail: ronquerry@mpsnet.com.mx. *Past professional post*: Former professor, University of Oklahoma. *Military service*: U.S. Marine Corps, 1961-63. *Memberships*: Native Writers Circle of the Americas; PEN; Tucson Pima County Arts Commission (board of directors, 1994-97). *Awards, honors*: Mountains & Plains Booksellers Award & Border Regional Library Association Southwest Book Award (both for The Death of Bernadette Lefthand); Writer-in-Residence, Amerind Foundation (Dragoon, AZ). *Published works*: Growing Old At Willie Nelson's Picnic (Texas A&M University Press, 1987); Native Americans Struggle for Equality (Rourke, 1993); I See By My Get-Up (University of Oklahoma Press, 1994); The Death of Bernadette Lefthand (Bantam Books, 1995; German translation, Kruger Verlag, 1996); Le Dernier Powwow (Editions du Rocher, France, 1996); Bad Medicine (Bantam Books, 1997).

QUESENBERRY, STEPHEN V.
(attorney)
Education: California State University, BA, 1967; Loyola University School of Law, JD, 1974. *Affiliation & Address*: Partner, Hobbs, Straus, Dean & Walker, LLP, 1903 21st St., 3rd Floor, Sacramento, CA 95811 (510) 280-5135. E-mail: squesenberry@hobbsstraus.com From his early experience working with Washington tribes, which were asserting their treaty fishing rights in the face of fierce resistance by the State of Washington, Stephen developed a deep commitment to tribal sovereignty and the federally protected rights inherent in that status. Since then, he has represented numerous tribes and individual Indians on a wide range of issues in a practice that has spanned three decades and involved work on Indian reservations in the States of Washington and California. After a long career in Indian legal services, including 15 years as the Director of Litigation for California Indian Legal Services (1985-2000), Stephen entered private practice with the law firm of Karshmer & Associates in 2003, where he continued his representation of tribes. Stephen recently joined Hobbs Straus. Stephen has represented Indian tribal governments and individual Indians in federal agency proceedings and at federal and state trial and appellate court levels. His advocacy has encompassed a broad range of Indian law issues, including tribal licensing and regulatory authority, protection of Native American cultural and sacred sites, eligibility for and allocation of Indian education grant funds, tribal sovereign immunity, tribal and individual Indian immunity from state taxation, restoration of terminated tribes, and protection of federally reserved water & fishing rights. He has extensive experience in the area of legislative advocacy, having drafted and successfully advocated for passage of federal legislation providing for transfer of Bureau of Land Management lands to eight California tribes and for restoration of two terminated California tribes. His experience regarding issues of federal acknowledgment and individual Indian status spans more than two decades, including legal consultant to the Advisory Council on California Indian Policy in submitting its 1997 reports and recommendations to the United States Congress on the unique status problems of the California tribes. He has served as an adjunct professor at Santa Clara University School of Law and the University of San Francisco School of Law, teaching courses and seminars in Federal Indian Law and the Rights of Indigenous Peoples. He has also represented indigenous interests at the United Nations Commission on Human Rights in Geneva and completed the summer course in human rights law at the International Institute of Human Rights in Strasbourg, France.

QUETAWKI, ARLEN P. (Zuni Pueblo)
(former Pueblo governor)
Affiliation & Address: Pueblo of Zuni, P.O. Box 339, Zuni, NM 87327 (505) 782-7022.

QUETONE, JOE A.
(executive director)
Affiliation: Florida Governor's Council on Indian Affairs, Inc., 1341 Cross Creek Cir., Tallahassee, FL 32301 (850) 488-0730.

QUIGLEY, KAREN M.
(executive director)
Affiliation & Address: Executive Director, Oregon Legislative Commission on Indian Services, 900 Court St. NE, Room 167, Salem, OR 97301 (503) 986-1067. E-mail: Karen.m.quigley@state.or.us. Ms. Quigley has served as Executive Director for almost 20 years. This statutory commission considers matters regarding Oregon tribal-state relations, serves as a clearinghouse for information on Oregon tribes and Oregon's Indian population, and is the advisory body to the Executive and Legislative Branches on Indian issues. She has spoken or provided training to tribal governments, state agencies, organizations, associations, & universities on tribal-state government-to-government relations, consultation with tribal governments, and other topics. She authored a chapter in *Inside the Minds: Emerging Issues in State Tribal Relations,* Aspatore (Thomson-Reuters, 2009)

QUIROGA, ERNESTO
(college instructor)
Education: M.A. Affiliation: History/American Indian Studies, Pima County Community College, Tucson, AZ 85709 (520) 206-6094. E-mail: ernest.quiroga @pima.edu. *Membership*: National Association of Native American Studies (member, Nominations Committee) serves as coordinator for Native American tribes in Alabama, Louisiana, Mississippi and Texas.

QWETAWKI, ARLEN P., SR. (Zuni)
(Pueblo governor)
Affiliation & Address: Governor (2002-06; 2011-present), Pueblo of Zuni, P.O. Box 339, Zuni, NM 87327 (505) 782-700.

R

RABBIT, BILL (Cherokee)
(artist; gallery co-owner)
Affiliation: Rabbit Studio Gallery, P.O. Box 34, 583 S. Mill, Pryor, OK 74362 (800) 613-3716; (918) 825-3788 or 825-3716. *Products*: Original paintings, limited edition prints and posters; sculpture, knives, baskets, pottery.

RABBIT, TRACI (Cherokee)
(artist; gallery co-owner)
Affiliation: Rabbit Studio Gallery, P.O. Box 34, 583 S. Mill, Pryor, OK 74362 (800) 613-3716; (918) 825-3788 or 825-3716.

RABIDEAUX, MICHAEL
(Indian education program director)
Affiliation: Fond du Lac Ojibway School, 105 University Rd., Cloquet, MN 55720 (218) 878-4648.

RACHAL, SANDRA L. (Mole Lake Chippewa)
(tribal vice chairperson)
Affiliation: Sokaogon (Mole Lake) Chippewa Community, 3086 State Hwy. 55, Crandon, WI 54520 (715) 478-7500.

RACHO, MICHAEL (Pomo)
(rancheria chairperson)
Affiliation: Dry Creek Rancheria, P.O. Box 607, Geyserville, CA 95441 (707) 431-2388.

RACINE, HARLAW E. (Blackfeet)
(artist, shop owner)
Address: P.O. Box 92, Heart Butte, MT 59448 (406) 338-7082.
Art work: Wood & stone carvings of animals in Blackfeet culture.

RACINE, ROSS R. (Blackfeet)
(executive director)
Education: Montana State University, BS (Agriculture/Animal Science), 1982. *Affiliation & Address*: Natural Resource Director (1991-99), Director of Programs (1999-2001), Executive Director (2001-present), Intertribal Agriculture Council, 100 N. 27th St., #500, Billings, MT 59101 (406) 259-3525. Ross works with Indian farmers & ranchers in the development & management of their resources; he has been active in assisting USDA in bringing services to Indian producers. *Past professional posts*: Soil conservationist, Bureau of Indian Affairs, Blackfeet Reservation, Montana; soil conservationist, Warm Springs Indian Reservation, Oregon; Range & Agriculture Coordinator, Warm Springs Indian Reservation, Oregon. *Awards, honors*: Northwest Regional Award of the Intertribal Timber Council. *Military service*: U.S. Marine Corps.

RADEMACHER, PETER J.
(attorney, American Indian law)
Education: University of Minnesota, BS, 2006; North Dakota State University, M.Arch, 2009; William Mitchell College of Law, JD, 2014. *Affiliation & Address*: Associate Attorney, Hogen Adams PLLP, 1935 W. County Road B2, Suite 460, St. Paul, MN 55113 (763) 762-8292;. E-mail: prademacher@hogenadams.com Peter represents Indian tribes in high-profile litigation involving treaty rights, reservation boundaries, jurisdiction, sovereign immunity, and federal law. He also serves as a member of the Minnesota Tribal Court/State Court Forum, where he uses education, research, & advocacy to foster cooperation between the many judiciaries within Minnesota's borders. Before he entered private practice, Peter served as a law clerk to the Honorable Heidi S. Schellhas with the Minnesota Court of Appeals. He compliments the skills he gained in that position with a passion for tribal sovereignty & self-determination

RADULOVICH, MARY LOU FOX
(foundation director)
Affiliation: Ojibwe Cultural Foundation, Excelsior Post Office, West Bay, ON, Canada P0P 1G0 (705) 377-4902.

RAEL, JOSEPH (*Tslew-teh-koyeh - Beautiful Painted Arrow*)
(Ute-Tiwa Pueblo) 1935-
(Native American ceremonial dancer, shaman, artist; author)
Born on the Southern Ute Indian Reservation, Colorado. *Education*: Santa Fe Indian School; U. of New Mexico, BA; U. of Wisconsin-Madison, MA. *Address & Affiliation*: c/o Council Oak Books, 2 W. 6th St., #262, Tulsa, OK 74119 (800) 247-8850. In 1983, Joseph conceived the idea of building a kiva-like structure, which he called a "Sound Peace Chamber," "where people of all races might gather to chant and sing for world peace and to purify the earth & oceans." He built the first one in Bernalillo, NM. There are now chambers across the U.S. and around the world. For 25+ years, Mr. Rael has led spiritual dances in the Native American mode, workshops, and mystery schools all over the world. His portal art paintings have been displayed in galleries in Colorado, New Mexico, Texas, and San Francisco. As a Native American elder, Joseph has spoken before the U.N. & addresses a conference of military officers at the Pentagon on the role of the warrior in the modern world. *Published works*: Beautiful Painted Arrow: Stories & Teachings From the Native American Tradition (Element Books, 1992); Tracks of Dancing Light: A Native Approach To Understanding Your Name (Element Books, 1994); Being & Vibration; Beautiful Painted Arrow; Way of Inspiration; Ceremonies of the Living Spirit; House of Shattering Light; Sound: Native Teachings & Visionary Art. All published by Council Oak Books.

RAFEK, MAHILLAH
(First Nations studies program coordinator)
Affiliation & Address: Program Coordinator, First Nations Studies Program, Social Sciences Centre, Room 3207, The University of Western Ontario, London, ON N6A 5C2 (519) 661-2111 ext. 86429.

RAHEJA, MICHELLE (Seneca)
(assistant professor of English; center director)
Education: University of Chicago, PhD (English), 2002; University of California, Berkeley (Ethnic Studies) two years. *Affiliation & Address*: Associate Professor of English & Director, California Center for Native Nations (CCNN), College of Humanities, Arts & Social Sciences, 4033 CHASS Interdisciplinary North, Riverside, CA 92521 (951) 827-1799. E-mail: michelle.raheja@ucr.edu. *Area of Research*: Native American literature, with special interest in autobiography & film and visual culture. In 2005-06, she was invited to Oberlin College as part of the Indigenous Women's Series to present a lecture entitled, "Molly Spotted Elk Is a Dancer...But She Also Knows How to Punch a Typewriter: Gender, Biography, Race & Performance." *Community service*: Serves on the executive committee of the Film & Visual Culture Program and has co-organized two major conferences, Filmmaking @ the Margins: A Film Symposium & Red Rhythms: Contemporary Methodologies in American Indian Dance. *Published works*: Reservation Reelism: Redfacing, Visual Sovereignty, & Representations of Native Americans in Film (University of Nebraska Press, 2012).

RAINIE, STEPHANIE CARROLL (Ahtna Athabascan)
(tribal health program manager & researcher)
Affiliation & Address: Manager of Tribal Health Program & Senior Researcher at the Native Nations Institute (NNI), Udall Center for Studies in Public Policy, The University of Arizona, 803 E. First St., Tucson, AZ 85719 (520) 626-2969. E-mail: scrainie@u.arizona.edu. Rainie's research program, ongoing for over a decade, explores the links between governance, health care, & community wellness. Her current project, "Beyond Health Care: Community, Governance,

and Culture in the Health & Wellness of Native Nations," was awarded $731,573 in support by the W.K. Kellogg foundation. She is collaboratively engaged with a community of researchers at NNI, whose projects span the United States, Canada, Australia, et al. Rainie functions as the Center's liaison to the University's Human Subjects Protection Program, monitoring implementation of the guidelines in Center research projects. Rainie is a doctoral candidate at the University of Arizona's (UA) Mel and Enid Zuckerman College of Public Health (MEZCOPH), where she is also a long-standing teaching assistant for a graduate-level Public Health Research & Evaluation course. She is active in the UAs American Indian and Indigenous Health Alliance Club, working to support the recruitment & retention of Indigenous students and faculty in the health sciences. Annually, she facilitates a week-long, intensive service learning course that familiarizes public health graduate students with the Tucson community. *Published works*: Rainie, S.C., J. Arsenault, S. Cornell, and M. Jorgensen. "Health Care Access in American Indian Communities: A Brief History of American Indian Health & Health Management."

RAINES, BOBBY (Eastern Cherokee)
(program director)
Education: Haskell Indian Nations University, BA (American Indian Studies with emphasis on Interdisciplinary Leadership). *Affiliation & Address*: Program Director (2005-present), Cherokee Preservation Foundation, P.O. Box 504, Cherokee, NC 28719. (828) 497-5550. E-mail: braines@cpfdn.org. Bobby's responsibilities include its culture-based leadership program. *Past professional posts*: Harrah's Cherokee Casino; Cherokee Forestry.

RAMBEAU, JAMES (Paiute)
(tribal vice chairperson)
Affiliation & Address: Vice Chairperson, Big Pinee Paiute Tribe of the Owens Valley, 825 S. Main St., P.O. Box 700, Big Pine, CA 93513 (760) 938-2003; E-mail : j.rambeau@bigpinepaiute.org

RAMBLER, TERRY (San Carlos Apache)
(tribal chairperson; educator)
Born & raised in San Carlos, Ariz. Education: University of Phoenix, BS (Business Management). *Affiliation & Address*: Chairperson (2010-present), San Carlos Apache Tribe, 1 San Carlos Ave., P.O. Box 0, San Carlos, AZ 85550 (928) 475-2361. *Other professional post*: Chairman, Arizona Indian Gaming Association (AIGA), Tempe, AZ; president, Inter Tribal Council of Arizona (ITCA). *Past professional posts*: Educator, Arizona Public Schools (31 years); 14 years as superintendent; he was elected to the San Carlos Apache Tribal Council, 2004-10; from 2004 to 2012, Terry served on the Fort Thomas Unified School District Board. As a member of that board, he helped build a new learning center which led to the formation of an Alternative School. The board also initiated a new elementary school in the Bylas Community; In 2002, he served as executive assistant to Chairwoman Kathy W. Kitcheyan. From 1980 to 1990, Rambler worked for the San Carlos Forestry Program as a Southwest Fire Fighter. He helped fight forest fires in Arizona, Nevada, California, Idaho, Washington and New Mexico. He also was employed by the Tohono O'odham Nation in 1991 as a contract administrator.

RAMEY, KATHY (Miwok)
(tribal band chairperson)
Affiliation: Ione Band of Miwok Indians, P.O. Box 1190, Ione, CA 95640 (209) 274-6753.

RAMIREZ, DENNIS (Mechoopda Maidu)
(tribal chairperson)
Affiliation: Mechoopda Maidu Indians of Chico Rancheria, 125 Mission Ranch Blvd., Chico, CA 95926 (530) 899-8922.

RAMIREZ, LOUISE J. MIRANDA (Ohlone/Costanoan Esselen)
(tribal chairperson)
Affiliation: Ohlone/Costanoan Esselen Nation, P.O. Box 1301, Monterey, CA 93942 (408) 629-5189. ramirez.louise@ohlonecostanoanesselennation.org.

RAMIREZ, RION (Turtle Mountain Chippewa) 1972-
(attorney)
Born in Granada Hills, Calif. in 1972. *Education*: *Address & Affiliation*: Associate Attorney, Dorsey & Whitney LLP, U.S. Bank Centre, 1420 Fifth Ave., Suite 3400, Seattle, WA 98101. E-mail: ramirez.rion@dorseylaw.com. He practices in the areas of Indian law, tribal finance, business law, and gaming law. *Other professional posts*: General counsel, Port Madison Enterprises, Suquamish Tribe; General Counsel, Quinault Indian Nation Enterprise Board; president, Northwest Indian Bar Association, 2003-present.

RAMOS, DIANA S. (Yaqui/Cherokee) 1949-
(secretary)
Born June 5, 1949, Corpus Christi, Tex. *Address*: 6407 Starstreak Dr., Austin, TX 78745 (512) 444-6451. *Community activities*: American Indian Resource &

Education Coalition (treasurer); Native American Parent Committee; Boy Scouts of America; Girl Scouts of America; PTA.

RAMOS, JAMES (Serrano/Cahuilla)
(commission chairperson)
Affiliation & Address: Chairperson (2007-present), California Native American Heritage Commission, 915 Capitol Mall #288, Sacramento, CA 95814 (916) 322-7791. *Past professional posts*: Chairperson, San Manuel Band of Serrano Mission Indians, Highland, CA; San Bernardino Community College District Board of Trustees. *Past tribal posts*: Coordinator, cultural awareness program, treasurer & business committee member, and chairperson of the San Manuel Gaming Commission.

RAMSEY, ANDREW (Florida Eastern Creek)
(tribal chief)
Affiliation: Florida Tribe of Eastern Creek, P.O. Box 3028, Bruce, FL 32455 (904) 835-2078.

RAMSEY, ARLA (Blue Lake Rancheria Tribe)
(tribal vice chairperson & administrator)
Education: Humboldt State University; Pepperdine University; College of the Redwoods; The Falmouth Institute. *Affiliation*: Vice chairperson, Blue Lake Rancheria Tribe, P.O. Box 428, Blue Lake, CA 95525 (707) 668-5101. Arla's duties include oversight of the Business Council and the Blue Lake Economic Development Corporation. *Past professional posts*: U.S. Forest Service; HUD Grant Coordinator; owned & operated a children's daycare business for eight years for tribal & Blue Lake community residents. Arla has served as project manager for the following Tribal economic development initiatives: a 55,000 Sq. Ft. Casino (with 800+ slot machines), 100-Room Hotel/Pool Complex. Along with former chairperson, Sylvia Daniels, Arla led the 25-year political & legal fight for successful reinstatement in 1983 of Blue Lake Rancheria as a federally recognized tribe.

RAMSEY, STEPHANIE (Iowa)
(former tribal administrator)
Affiliation: Iowa Tribe of Oklahoma, Rt. 1 Box 721, Perkins, OK 74059 (405) 547-2402. E-mail: sramsey@iowanation.org.

RANCO, DARREN (Penobscot)
(professor of Native American studies)
Education: Dartmouth College, BA, 1993; Vermont Law School, MSEL, 1998; Harvard University, PhD, 2000. *Affiliation & Address*: Chair, Wabanaki Center & Coordinator of Native American Research; Associate Professor of Anthropology, University of Maine, 5717 Corbett Hall, Room 208, Orono, ME 04469 (207) 581-1417. E-mail: darren.ranco@maine.edu. Professor Ranco's research focuses on the ways in which indigenous communities in the U.S. resist environmental destruction by using indigenous diplomacies & critiques of liberalism to protect cultural resources & the continual exposures of indigenous peoples to an inordinate amount of environmental risk. "I am particularly interested in how better research relationships can be made between universities, Native & non-Native researchers, and indigenous communities."

RAND, KATHRYN R.L. (Menominee)
(college dean; professor of law; attorney)
Education: University of North Dakota, BA (Anthropology), 1990; University of Michigan Law School, JD, 1993. *Affiliation & Address*: Dean & Floyd B. Sperry Professor of Law; Co-Director (2002-present) (with Steven Light), Institute for the Study of Tribal Gaming Law & Policy, University of North Dakota School of Law, 215 Centennial Dr. Stop 9003, Grand Forks, ND 58202 (701) 777-2104. E-mail: rand@law.und.edu. The Institute is the first university-affiliated research institute dedicated to the study of Indian gaming. Dean Rand writes a regular column on tribal gaming in "Casino Lawyer," with Steven Light, blogs on Indian gaming at "Indian Gaming Now," *Past professional posts*: Clerked for Justice Beryl Levine of the North Dakota Supreme Court and Chief Judge J.P. Stadtmueller of the U.S. District Court for the Eastern District of Wisconsin; and served as a tribal liaison to the Menominee Nation. *Published works*: Co-author with Steven Andrew Light, Indian Gaming & Tribal Sovereignty: The Casino Compromise (University of Kansas Press, 2005); Indian Gaming Law & Policy (Carolina Academic Press, 2006); Indian Gaming Law: Cases & Materials (Carolina Academic Press, 2008); Newspaper articles; Conferences & Presentations; Book chapters & essays; Congressional testimony.

RANDALL, LESTER (Kickapoo)
(tribal chairperson)
Affiliation & Address: Chairperson, Kickapoo Tribe of Kansas, P.O. Box 271, Horton, KS 66439 (785) 486-2131. E-mail: lester.randall@kktc-nsn.gov

RANDALL, VINCENT (Yavapai-Apache)
(tribal chief)
Affiliation: Yavapai-Apache Community Council, Camp Verde, AZ 86322 (520) 567-3649.

RANDOLPH, PEPI (Potawatomi)
(chief executive officer)
Education: University of Wisconsin, BA (Journalism & History); University of Wisconsin, School of Law, JD. *Affiliation & Address*: CEO, Potawatomi Business Development Corporation, 320 E. Buffalo St., Suite 607, Milwaukee, WI 53202 (414) 727-2041. *Past professional posts*: PBDCs VP, National Sales & Marketing; president, Forward Wisconsin; assistant vice president, M&I Bank; assistant general counsel for the Milwaukee Brewers baseball club. *Community service*: Board of directors for Delta Dental, Visit Milwaukee Convention & Visitors Bureau, & the Marcus Center for Performing Arts.

RANDOLPH, RICHARD (Wampanoag)
(tribal vice chairperson)
Affiliation & Address: Vice Chairperson, Wampanoag Tribe of Gay Head, 20 Black Brook Rd., Aquinnah, MA 02535 (508) 645-9265.

RANKIN, DENISE M. (Aleut)
(Alaskan tribal president)
Affiliation & Address: President, Qawalangin Tribe of Unalaska, P.O. Box 334, Unalaska, AK 99685 (907) 581-2920. E-mail: robin.qawalangin@gmail.com

RANSOM, ALMA (St. Regis Mohawk)
(former tribal chief)
Born & raised on the Akwesasne Mohawk Reservation. *Education*: St. Lawrence University, BA. *Affiliation*: Chief (1995-2003), St. Regis Mohawk Tribe, 412 State Route 37, Akwesasne, NY 13655. *Past professional posts*: Served as vice president & treasurer of the National Congress of American Indians. Community activities: Hosted the Kateri Tekakwitha Conference in 2012. For the last 32 years, Alma has hosted the conference. She went to The Vatican in the Fall of 2012 to witness Tekakwitha's Canonization.

RAPHAEL, JOSEPH C. (Chippewa)
(tribal council member)
Education: Grand Rapids Jr. College (two years); Grand Rapids Bible College (1 year). *Affiliation*: Council member, Grand Traverse Band of Ottawa & Chippewa Indians (Chairperson 1980-96), 2605 N. West Bayshore Dr., Peshawbestown, MI 49682 (231) 534-7750. Website: www.gtbindians.org. *Military service*: U.S. Army, 1959. *Community service*: Board member, Michigan Indian Child Welfare Agency; State of MI Foster Parents (15 years).

RATION, NORMAN (Laguna-Navajo)
(executive director)
Affiliation & Address: Exec. director, National Indian Youth Council, 318 Elm, SE, Albuquerque, NM 87102 (505) 247-2251. Email: nration@niyc-alb.org.

RAVE, AUSTIN JERALD (Minneconjou Sioux) 1946-
(artist)
Born August 5, 1946, Cheyenne River Sioux Reservation, S.D. *Education*: Institute of American Indian Arts, Santa Fe, NM, 1964-66; San Francisco Art Institute, 1966-67; Engineering Drafting School, Denver, CO, 1970-72. *Address*: P.O. Box 356, Eagle Butte, SD 57625. *Other professional posts*: Draftsman, technical illustrator. *Awards, honors*: Numerous awards for art. *Biographical source*: Dictionary of International Biography.

RAVE, JODI (Mandan, Hidatsa, Arikara)
(reporter)
Affiliation: Reporter, "The Native Voice," "The Gazette," "Journal Star" (Lincoln, Neb.) among others, Lee Enterprises, Missoula, MT, 1998 to the present. Contact: E-mail: jodi.rave@lee.net (406) 523-5299. *Awards, honors*: One of 25 Nieman Fellows, Harvard University, 2003-04.

RAWLEY, MICHAEL E. (Tsimshian)
(corporation chairperson & treasurer)
Education: Northwest Indian College, AA; Western Washington University, BS; American Institute of Banking (certificate). *Affiliation & Address*: Chairperson & treasurer, 13th Regional Corporation, 13215-C8 Mill Plain, #393, Vancouver, WA 98684 (206) 254-0688. *Other professional posts*: CEO, National Tribal Development Association, Box Elder, MT; senior strategist, Blue Stone Strategy Group, Irvine, CA. *Memberships*: Western Coalition of Alaska Natives; Alaska Federation of Natives; Ho'oulu Lahui Hawaiian Charter School (advisory board). *Military service*: U.S. Marine Corps. *Interests*: For the past five years, Rawley has specialized in Native Entrepreneurship Development and the establishment of a Community Development Financial Institute (CDFI) to provide Native business people with access to start-up & expansion capital.

RAWLS, ROB (Inupiaq Eskimo)
(radio station manager)
Affiliation: KOTZ - 720 AM, P.O. Box 78, Kotzebue, AK 99752 (907) 442-3435.

RAY, ANITA (Shawnee/Cherokee)
(vice chairperson; fundraiser)
Affiliation & Address: Vice Chairperson, American Indian Center of Indiana, 2236 E. 10th St., Indianapolis, IN 46201 (317) 917-8000.

RAY, DELBERT (Pima-Maricopa)
(tribal president; attorney)
Affiliation & Address: President, Salt River Pima-Maricopa Indian Community, 10005 E. Osborn Rd., Scottsdale, AZ 85256 (480) 362-7465.

RAY, DONALD (Pomo) 1951-
(senior vice president)
Born February 27, 1951, Ukiah, Calif. *Education*: Mendocino Community College, 1972-73; American River College, 1974; Sacramento State University; Sacramento State University (two years). *Affiliation & Address*: Senior vice president, Hopland Tribe Economic Development Corp., 1999-present (707) 472-2100. E-mail: donr@pacific.net. *Affiliations*: Payroll clerk, Inter Tribal Council of California, Sacramento, CA, 1973-78; controller/director, Eagle Child, Indian Child Welfare Project, 1978-81; executive director, "Six Tribal Nations" (Indian child welfare program), Mendocino County, CA, 1981-82; Hopland Band of Pomo Indians, Hopland, CA (tribal council, 1982-92; chair, 1984-92; rep. for California tribes on the BIA, Tribal Reorganization Act, 1988-92; consultant - advised tribes on gaming contracts and found investors for gaming and/or other economic development ventures, 1992-94; accountant, Shodakai Coyote Valley Casino, Redwood Valley, CA, 1994-99; worked on (Proposition 5) legislation to approve gaming in California; also worked on Proposition 1-A until passed by the voters of California & amended to the California State Constitution. Presently working on new casino expansion for Hopland Tribe. *Other professional posts*: Central California Policy Committee, BIA, Sacramento, CA, 1976-80; Consolidated Tribal Health, Inc., Ukiah, CA, 1980-84; finance officer, Lake County Tribal Health, Inc. (first health clinic in lake County for Indian people), 1981-82; regional rep to the Central California Advisory Board for BIA services & Health Care Services), 1981-82; chairman, Mendocino County Tribal Chairman's Association, 1988-92; League of Indian Voters, 1990-92 (wrote the overall plan & design of this organization for the Indian people within California. *Military service*: U.S. Army, 1970-72 (Sergeant, Vietnam Era Veteran; Service Medal, Marksman Award-Firearms, Missile Special Training Award). *Community activities*: Board member on the Regional and Statewide "Indian Health Services" policy committee, 1986-91; Mendocino County Development Corporation, 1988-91; board member of Northern Circle Indian Housing Authority, 1985-91; chairman of board for Consolidated Tribal Health Clinic, Inc., 1985-92; 1990-92 implemented the area wide policy committee of the BIA. *Interests*: "I travel extensively throughout the U.S. on tribal business & represent California tribes in congressional hearings and other representatives as appropriate for Indian people. Now, I am working fulltime and helping local Indian people understand how the gaming business can be a benefit for their future, but not the answer to all." Also, computer programming.

RAY, GABRIEL (Pomo)
(tribal chairperson)
Affiliation & Address: Cairperson, Scotts Valley band of Pomo Indians, 2727 Systron Dr. #100, Concord, CA 94518 (925) 363-4778.

RAY, MARVIN (Mdewakanton Sioux)
(tribal administrator)
Affiliation: Prairie Island Indian Community, 5636 Sturgeon Lake Rd., Welch, MN 55089 (651) 385-2554. E-mail: mray@piic.org.

RAY-HODGE, VANESSA L. (Pueblo of Acoma)
(attorney; Indian law)
Education: Wellesley College, BA, 2000; Columbia Univesity Law School, JD, 2003. *Affiliation & Address*: Partner, Sonosky, Chambers, Sachse, Endreson & Perry, LLP, 500 Marquette Ave., NW, Suite 1310, Albuquerque, NM 87102 (505) 247-0147. E-mail: vrayhodge@abqsonosky.com. Prior to rejoining Sonosky, Vanessa served as the Senior Counselor to Solicitor Hilary Tompkins at the Department of the Interior. At Interior, Ms. Ray-Hodge advised the Solicitor on Indian Affairs issues & was integral in a multitude of decisions. Some of her key efforts included: Addressing, in part, the Supreme Court's decision in *Carcieri v. United States*, to continue to take land into trust for tribes, culminating in the Solicitor's M-Opinion 37029 (March 12, 2014), The Meaning of "Under Federal Jurisdiction" for Purposes of the Indian Reorganization Act. However, until a congressional fix is done the decision will continue to take up Interior resources. Advising the Assistant Secretary for Indian Affairs, the Office of Indian Gaming and National Indian Gaming Commission on Indian lands determinations, compact approvals and off reservation gaming issues, including looking critically at prior Indian gaming decisions. United States *Amicus* briefing of *Brown v. Rincon,* before the Supreme Court to support the Tribe on compact negotiation issues. Advising the Secretary's Indian Water Rights Office and Working Group on Indian Water Rights Settlements, including participation in numerous negotiation teams.

RAYMOND, LINDA (Maliseet)
 (tribal council member)
Address & Affiliation: Houlton Band of Maliseet Indians, 88 Bell Rd., Littleton, ME 04730 (207) 532-4273. E-mail: tribal.clerk@maliseet.com. Linda has worked as the Administrative Receptionist for almost 20 years and is currently a tribal council member. She has served five different terms as a council member and has also served numerous terms as the Tribe's Housing Authority commissioner; she chairs the Tribe's Constitution Committee and sits on the board of the Tribe's Tribal business venture. *Other professional post*: Member, Maine Indian Tribal-State Commission.

REAL BIRD, HENRY LEE (*Timber Leader*) (Crow) 1948-
 (educator)
Born July 24, 1948, Crow Agency, Mont. *Education*: Montana State University, BS, 1971; Eastern Montana College, MEd. *Principal occupation*: Educator. *Address*: P.O. Box 5, Garryowen, MT 59031 (406) 638-7211. *Other professional post*: Boss of a cow camp. *Memberships*: American Indian Higher Education Consortium; Crow Tobacco Society; Native American Church. Interests: "I've taught on the Navajo, Cheyenne, and Crow Reservations. I've been asked to read my poetry from Texas, New Mexico, Colorado, Nevada & Montana. I rodeoed when I was young from amateur-pro." *Published work*: Where Shadows Are Born (Guildhall, 1990).

REAL BIRD, SHAWN (Crow)
 (commission chairperson)
Address: P.O. Box 159, Crow Agency, MT 59022 (406) 638-3766. *Affiliation*: Chairperson, State Tribal Economic Development Commission (STEDC), c/o Montana Dept. of Commerce, Helena, MT.

REAL BIRD, THOMASINA (Sicangu Lakota)
 (attorney)
Education: Stanford University, BA (Native American Studies), 2002, MA (Sociology), 2003; Columbia University School of Law, JD, 2007. *Affiliation*: Associate (2007-present), Fredericks Peebles & Morgan, LLP, 1900 Plaza Dr., Louisville, CO 80027 (303) 673-9600. *Practice areas*: Federal Indian Law; Tribal Inter-Governmental Law; Tribal Court & Federal Court Litigation; Administrative Law; Legislation & Code Drafting; Wills, Trusts & Estates; Probate Law; Legal Ethics & Professional Responsibility.

REASON, JAMIE (Southeastern Cherokee) 1947-
 (traditional carver)
Born March 11, 1947, Muncie, Ind. *Principal occupation*: Owner/manager, Sacred Earth Studio, Mastic Beach, NY, 1980- (Native American art studio). *Address*: 197 Longfellow Dr., Mastic Beach, NY 11951 (516) 399-4539. Website: www.jamiereason.com. *Affiliation*: Journeys Into American Indian Territory, Fall 2003 to present. *Military service*: U.S. Air Force, 1966 (A/3/C; Vietnam Era Veteran; National Defense Expert Marksman; Air Police). *Memberships*: Indian Arts & Crafts Association; Vietnam Era Veterans Inter-Tribal Association; Ani-Yvwiya Association of New York. *Awards, honors*: 1988 Gallup Inter-Tribal 1st & 3rd prizes), 1989 Gallup Inter-Tribal (best in category peyote box); first place-Div. II Carved Cedar Box, Sinte Gleska Native American Art Show, 1987; 1987 Recipient of the "Elkus Award" at Gallup; designated "Master Artist" of the Southeastern Cherokee Confederacy 1992; Symposium, 10/30/04, "The Reemergence of Charles Bunn, America's Greatest Shorebird Carver," Shinnecock Nation Culture Center & Museum, Jamie Reason, Speaker, Southampton, NY. *Interests*: "Even though I am self taught, I attribute my ability to my grandfather, George Reason, who was a carver. He has been an inspiration and great influence on my art and in my life. Mr. Reason is probably best known for his solid carved cedar feather boxes. Since 1990, "most of my production of carvings were decoys, a traditional Native American art form indigenous to the Americas. Also, since 1990, "have operated Seatuck Gallery (14 years) in Eastport, NY (since 1995, formerly in Moriches, NY)." *Exhibitions*: Art work exhibited at the Museum of the American Indian, The Gallery of the American Indian Community House (New York City), Red Cloud Indian Art Show, Dartmouth College; Native American Symposium at Old Westbury College (N.Y.); Rhode Island Indian Council; Red Earth, Oklahoma City; The Ceremonial, Gallup Inter-Tribal, 1986-89; Sinte Gleska Native American Art Show (Cherokee Heritage Center, Tahlequah, OK); Scottsdale All-Indian Art Show (Scottsdale, AZ); and many galleries; The Five Civilized Tribes Museum, OK; Mashantucket Pequot Museum & Research Center, CT. *Biographical sources*: Southeastern Native American Arts Directory, by Nadema Agard-Smith; "Jamie Reason, Born to Carve," in Decoy Magazine, July-Aug. 2000, March-April 2002, Nov. Dec. 2003, & Jan. Feb. 2004; Southampton Press, April 18, 2002, Nov. 21, '02, Oct. 28, '04, Nov. 4, '04, Nov. 18, '04; NY Times Metro LI, Feb. 24, '01, Aug. 8, '03, Feb. 13, 2005.

REBAR, JOAN (Sac & Fox of Missouri)
 (former tribal chairperson)
Affiliation: Sac & Fox of Missouri Tribe, Rte. 1, Box 60, Reserve, KS 66434 (913) 742-7471.

RECK, PAT (Pueblo)
 (museum curator)
Affiliation: Indian Pueblo Cultural Center, 2401 12th St., NW, Albuquerque, NM 87102 (505) 843-7270.

RED BEAR, CHARLES (Sioux)
 (school chairperson)
Affiliation: Rock Creek Day School, Bullhead, SD 57621 (605) 823-4971.

RED EAGLE, JOHN D. (Osage)
 (former tribal principal chief)
Born and raised in Pawhuska, Okla. *Affiliation*: Osage Nation of Oklahoma, P.O. Box 779, Pawhuska, OK 74056 (918) 287-5555. *Past tribal post*: Assistant principal chief, 2002-2006

RED ELK, BONNIE (Asiniboine Sioux)
 (editor)
Affiliation: Wotanin Wowapi, Fort Peck Assiniboine & Sioux Tribes, P.O. Box 1027, Poplar, MT 59255 (406) 768-5155 Ext. 2370.

RED ELK, LOIS (Yankton Sioux)
 (poet)
Address: P.O. Box 371, Wolf Point, MT 59201 (406) 653-3300.

RED ELK, MICHELLE (Comanche-Kiowa)
 (artist)
Address: 2924 Urwiler Ave., Cincinnati, OH 45208 (513) 389-1919. E-mail: nokoni@cinci.rr.com. Artwork: Beadwork, pencil drawings.

REDELK, RONALD (Comanche)
 (former organization president)
Affiliation: Comanche Language & Cultural Preservation Committee, 1375 N.E. Cline Rd., Elgin, OK 73538.

RED HORSE, JOHN
 (professor & director of Indian center)
Affiliation: American Indian Studies Center, University of California, Los Angeles, 3220 Campbell Hall, Los Angeles, CA 90024 (213) 825-7315.

RED-HORSE, VALERIE (Eastern Cherokee/ Cheyenne River Sioux) 1959-
 (actress, writer, spokesperson)
Born August 24, 1959, in Calif. *Education*: UCLA, BA - Theater Arts (cum laude), 1981; Lee Strasberg Theater Institute/Professional Master Class (acting). *Address*: 6028 Calvin Ave., Tarzana, CA 91356 (818) 705-6972; 705-4905 (work). *Television credits*: The Dennis Miller Show; Unsolved Mysteries, Anything But Love; Santa Barbara; Divorce Court; Perry Mason; Buck James; Murder, She Wrote; among others. *Film credits*: Powwow Highway (voiceover); First & Ten (chore-ography); Return to the Country (lead dancer). Talk show hosting/ spokesperson: First Americans (talk show hostess); Walking In Both Worlds (keynote speaker & featured performer); Trail of Tears Youth Conference (keynote speaker & featured performer); Native Americans in the Media (celebrity panelist); Women of Color: Invisible On Screen (celebrity panelist). Theater: Love's Labour's Lost (Rosaline-lead); Uncommon Women & Others (Kate-lead); Dreams (Lisa-lead); A Hotel Chain (Rose-lead); From Broadway With Love (lead dancer/singer). Other professional posts: Co-owner (with husband, Curt Mohl), Executive Specialties (a promotional advertising retail business) and Maverick Outdoor Media Group, Inc. (a corporation specializing in outdoor signage for real estate developers); lead dancer & choreographer for the Bel Air Presbyterian Liturgical Dance Co. *Memberships*: Women in Film; Sacred Dance Guild; First Americans In the Arts; Native Writers Circle: Multicultural Minority Motion Picture Awards Board. *Awards, honors*: Keynote addresses to such organizations as The California Indian Manpower Assn, and California American Indian Women's Assn; Honoring voting committee member of the Minority Motion Picture Awards Assn; recently selected to testify for a Senate Committee reviewing minorities & females in the Film & Television industry. *Interests*: Writing - recently completed original screenplay, "Lozen," which chronicles the life of a historical Apache woman warrior and the women who fought alongside her. Valerie hopes that her script will "dispel some of the stereotypical images of the Native American female which television and film have created. As a Native American actress & writer, I am dedicated to improving and furthering the portrayal of Native American women in the media." *Biographical source*: Featured article in "Today's Christian Woman (July/Aug. 1993 issue).

RED SHE BEAR (DEANNA BARNES) (Ute) 1938-
 (teacher, craftswoman)
Born June 25, 1938, Boise, Idaho. *Education*: College of the Redwoods; Humboldt State University. *Principal occupation*: Founder/manager, Red Bear Creations, Bandon, OR. *Address*: 358 N. Lexington Ave., Bandon, OR 97411 (541) 347-9560. *Affiliations*: Founder, Indian Survival Society, Brandon, OR; founder & president, Women's Center. *Community activities*: American Red

Cross (provider and secretary); Coos & Curry Area Agency on Aging (provider); Intertribal Sweat Lodge Board (officer); District 7 Sub-Area Health Advisory Council (provider); Women's Crisis Service (advisory board). *Membership*: National Indian Health Care Assn (spokeswoman). *Interests*: "Making traditional quilts & blankets. Preserving our old culture & traditions is very important to me. I am an elder, pipe carrier, sweatleader, storyteller in the winter, tech survival skills in the woods, lecture on traditional uses of indigenous plants as food and medicine, and on Indian women's roles in society. I'm currently writing book, Crystal Wind Warrior, about a crystal who became a human to help the people (manuscript, 1986)."

RED SHIRT, DELPHINE (Lakota)
  (writer)
Publications: Bead on the Anthill: A Lakota Childhood (U. of Nebraska Press, 1997); Turtle Lung Woman's Granddaughter (U. of Nebraska Press, 2002);

RED STAR, WENDY (Crow)
  (professor of art & Indigenous Nations Studies; cultural archivist)
Born in Billings, Mont. just outside the Crow Indian reservation where she was raised. *Education*: Montana State University, BA; University of California, MFA (Sculptor). *Affiliation & Address*: Adjunct professor of Art, Portland State University, Indigenous Nations Studies, P.O. Box 751, Portland, OR 97201 (503) 725-5920. E-mail: redstar@pdx.edu. Website: www.wredstar.com. *Sculptor exhibits*: Her Helen E. Copeland Gallery, Bozeman, MT, The LA Municipal Art Gallery, Los Angeles, CA; The Plush Gallery, Dallas, TX; The Luckman Gallery, Los Angeles; The Volitant Gallery, Austin, TX; et al. and some galleries overseas.

REDCORN, RAYMOND (Osage)
  (tribal assistant principal chief)
Affiliation & Address: Assistant Principal Chief, Osage Nation of Oklahoma, P.O. Box 1449, Pawhuska, OK 74056 (918) 287-5555.

REDDICK, GINGER (Comanche)
  (craftsperson, shop owner)
Address & Affiliation: Co-owner (with husband Rex Reddick), Crazy Crow Trading Post, P.O. Box 847, 1801 N. Airport Rd., Pottsboro, TX 75076 (800) 786-6210; (903) 786-2287. E-Mail: crazycrow@texoma.com; Website: www.crazycrow.com.

REDER, DEANNA (Cree/Metis)
  (professor of First Nations Studies)
Education: Concordia, BA; York University, MA; University of British Columbia, PhD. *Affiliation & Address*: Assistant Professor of Indigenous Literature in Canada, Department of First Nations Studies, Saywell Hall 9081, Simon Fraser U., Burnaby, BC V5A 1S6 (778) 782-8192. E-mail: Deanna_reder@sfu.ca. *Awards, honors*: Recently appointed Series Editor of the Indigenous Studies Series at Wilfrid Laurier University Press. *Published works*: Co-editor with Linda Morra, Troubling Tricksters: Revisioning Critical Conversations (2010); she is working on a monograph on Cree and Metis autobiography in Canada.

REDWING, RAY (Santee Sioux)
  (pipemaker/carver)
Address: P.O. Box 283, Flandreau, SD 57028. *Affiliations*: Ray is one of three of the Flandreau Santee Sioux Tribe's Cultural Preservation Officers & Repatriation Officers, and a member of the Eastern Dakota Treaty Committee. *Past affiliations*: Pipestone National Monument (22 years); Flandreau Santee Sioux Tribe's Executive Committee as Trustee IV, 2000-08.

REED, EVA SILVER STAR (United Lumbee/Cherokee/Choctaw) 1929-
  (former national chieftain)
Born November 29, 1929, Vanita, Okla. *Address*: P.O. Box 512, Fall River Mills, CA 96028 (530) 336-6701. *Affiliation*: Former National Chieftain, United Lumbee Nation of N.C. and America, 1982-2007. *Other professional posts*: Parent committee of Title IV and Johnson O'Malley Indian Education Program, Tulare-Kings Counties, CA, 1978-1980; National Secretary, 1979-82, Head Chief, 1982-2007, and Grand Council member, 1979-2007, United Lumbee Nation of N.C. & America. *Memberships*: Native American Wolf Clan (secretary, 1977-); Chapel of Our Lord Jesus (church) (secretary, 1974-2001; president, 2001-present); United Lumbee Nation's Hawk Society, 1996-. *Awards, honors*: Numerous 1st & 2nd prizes for Indian beadwork at the Inter-Mountain Fair, McArthur, CA; 1991 Silver Eagle Award, United Lumbee Nation. *Interests*: "I teach an Indian Beading Class each year since 1980 -- I am editor of the United Lumbee Nation Times since 1981. I do sewing, leather crafts, painting and bead work, and write articles for the paper and books. Caring for my people the United Lumbees." *Biographical sources*: Articles in the United Lumbee Nation Times. *Published works*: Compiler, Over the Cooking Fires, featuring traditional Lumbee recipes (United Lumbee Nation, 1982); Lumbee Indian Ceremonies (United Lumbee Nation, 1982); United Lumbee Nation's Deer Clan Cook Book (United Lumbee Nation, 1988); co-author with Frank Chilcote, A Message to Our People (United Lumbee Nation, 1989).

REED-CRUM, ANNETTE
  (Native American Studies instructor)
Affiliation: Native American Studies Dept., College of Letters & Science, 2401 Hart Hall, University of California, Davis, CA 95616 (530) 752-3237.

REEDE, DAVID (San Carlos Apache)
  (tribal vice chairperson)
Education: Northern Arizona University (NAU), BA (Education); graduate of the Central Arizona College Police Academy. *Affiliation*: Vice Chairperson, San Carlos Apache Tribe, P.O. Box 0, San Carlos, AZ 85550 (928) 475-2361. *Other professional post*: Member, San Carlos School Board. *Past tribal posts*: Member of the Council, 2005-present; Mr. Reede has worked to improve the lives of Apache people by directing the Recreation Dept., the Alcohol & Substance Abuse Program, and the Wellness Center of the tribe.

REEDY-MASCHNER, KATHERINE
  (professor of anthropology)
Born & raised in Idaho. *Education*: University of Wisconsin, BA, 1977; University of Cambridge, PhD, 2004. *Affiliation & Address*: Professor of Anthropology & American Indian Studies, Department of Anthropology, College of Arts and Letters • Idaho State University, 921 S. 8th Avenue, Stop 8005, Pocatello, ID 83209-8005 (208) 282-2629. E-mail: reedkath@isu.edu. Katherine conducted anthropological fieldwork all over Alaska, from Nome to the Aleutians & Prince William Sound. She has been an affiliate faculty in the Anthropology Department since 2000, Since 2000, she has worked in Aleut villages of Alaska mapping socioeconomic relations around commercial & subsistence fisheries, including identity and status, economic development, fisheries permit access and policies, the globalization of fisheries, Aleut social life, & Russian & Scandinavian heritages on the North Pacific. Her dissertation investigated the role of traditional commercial and subsistence economies in the construction of Aleut identity. Her research interests include socio-ecological and applied anthropology, social anthropology of northern peoples, subsistence and commercial fishing practices, indigenous rights and representations of identity, Aleut culture & history, globalization, human relationships to endangered species, & environmental policymaking. *Ongoing Research*: She was awarded a U.S. Department of Interior Bureau of Ocean Energy Management, Regulation & Enforcement contract to conduct a subsistence harvest & local land use study in four Alaska Peninsula/Aleutian Island communities most proximate to the proposed offshore North Aleutian Basin oil and gas development project. This project provides an assessment of individual and community subsistence use and resilience in the context of changes or disruptions associated with the development in the Aleut and Alutiiq villages of Akutan, False Pass, Nelson Lagoon, & Port Heiden, Alaska. Katherine is working on a book based upon a NSF-funded fisheries policy project on the role of Alaska Native people in the structuring of fisheries policies, looking specifically at how people use elements of tradition, culture, the language of rights, scientific data and history, for example, in order to recover, preserve and expand fishing rights in front of the Alaska Board of Fisheries. Salmons' migratory ranges cross numerous cultural boundaries, and each society lays claim to the fish in dynamic ways. The goals of this project are to test the link between indigenous people's testimony at the Board of Fisheries level in order to understand indigenous relations with one another and with governmental entities, how they shape fisheries policies, and to understand the effects of past and current regulations on village life.

REELS, KENNETH M. (Mashantucket Pequot)
  (tribal chairperson)
Address: Mashantucket Pequot Tribal Nation, P.O. Box 3060, 1 Matts Path, Mashantucket, CT 06339 (860) 396-6572. *Affiliations*: Mashantucket Pequot Tribe (member, tribal council, 1991-; vice chairperson (three terms); chairperson, 1999-present). *Other professional posts*: Mashantucket Pequot Tribe (property purchasing & contracting officer, 1987-95; director, Centraliz-ation Project, 1995-98. *Military service*: U.S. Army.

REESER, RALPH R. 1932-
  (research; attorney)
Born November 26, 1932, Fairbanks, Alaska. *Education*: Seattle University, 1952-55; University of Washington, BA, 1956; George Washington University Law School, JD, 1960. *Address*: 3702 Spruell Dr., Wheaton, MD 20902; E-mail: r.reeser@comcast.net. *Affiliations*: Attorney-advisor, Public Housing Administration, Washington, DC, 1961-66; director, Housing, B.I.A., Washington, DC, 1966-70; deputy director, HUD, Washington, DC, 1970-72; director, Congressional & Legislative Affairs, B.I.A., Washington, DC, 1972-89; consultant, 1989-. *Other professional post*: Teaching course, "Indian Land & the Law" for Falmouth Institute, 1991-92. *Military service*: U.S. Air Force, 1951-52 (S/Sgt.). *Community activities*: Montgomery County, MD Advisory Committee on Cable Communications (member, 1991-96). *Membership*: D.C. Bar Assn. *Published work*: Manual of Indian Gaming Law (Falmouth Institute, 1992); A Complete Guide to P.L. 93-638: Contracting Through the Indian Self-Determination Act (Native American Technologies, 1996).

REEVES, ERNA F. (Cherokee)
(training & technical assistance specialist)
Affiliation & Address: Lead Training & Technical Assistance Specialist, National American Indian Indian Housing Council, Oklahoma Field Office, P.O. Box 145, Peggs, OK 74452 (918) 598-3331. E-mail: ereeves@naihc.net.

REEVES, JANET
(executive director)
Affiliation: Nevada Urban Indians, 1190 Bible Way, Reno, NV 89502 (775) 788-7600.

REFT, ALICIA (Aleut)
(Alaskan village president)
Affiliation: Native Village of Karluk, P.O. Box 22, Karluk, AK 99608 (907) 241-2218.

REGGUINTI, GORDON (Ojibway) 1954-
(company president)
Born February 10, 1954, in Minnesota. *Education*: University of Minnesota, BA (Indian Studies), 1987. *Principal occupation*: Company president. *Address*: 1008 Russell Ave. No., Minneapolis, MN 55411 (612) 287-9104. *Affiliations*: Currently, President, Native News & Entertainment Television, Minneapolis, MN; former executive director, Native American Journalists Association, Minneapolis, MN. *Other professional posts*: Newsletter instructor, Migizi Communications, Minneapolis, MN, 1988-; series editor, Lerner Publications, Minneapolis, MN, 1990-. *Published work*: The Sacred Harvest, Ojibway Wild Rice Gathering (Lerner Publications, 1992).

REID, JOSH R.
(Native American & Indigenouse studies program director)
Affiliation & Address: Assistant Professor of History & Director, Native American & Indigenous Studies Program, University of Massachusetts, Boston, College of Liberal Arts, McCormack Hall, Fl. 4, Rm. 631, Boston, MA 02125 (617) 287-68819.

REID, MORRIS (Chuckchansi)
(rancheria chairperson)
Affiliation: Picayune Rancheria of the Chuckchansi Indians, 46575 Road 417, Coursegold, CA 93614 (559) 683-6633. E-mail: mreid@tcouncil.com.

REID-ALANIZ, MICHELLE (*Raven Moon*) (Wampanoag/Mic Mac) 1954-
(native village director)
Born October 27, 1954, Taunton, Mass. *Education*: Johnson & Wales, Providence, RI, Fashion Merchandising (two years). *Principal occupation*: Native village director. *Address*: P.O. Box 296, Grantham, NH 03753-0296. *Affiliation*: Director, Moon Shadow Native Village, Lowell, VT. *Other professional post*: La Leche League leader; childbirth educator. *Community activities*: Birthright counselor/teen pregnancy; Coalition for Teen Pregnancy, Falmouth, MA; volunteer in public schools; help single moms. *Memberships*: Pan American Indians, 1991; Connecticut River Powwow Society, 1992-; Seneca Wolf Clan, 1991-; Indigenous Women's Network, 1992-; Good Medicine Society, 1993-. *Award*: Merit Award for work in public schools in Falmouth, MA. *Interests*: "My work involves sending boxes to those in need on the reservations. I have visited Akwesasne Reservation in New York, & Rosebud Reservation in South Dakota. (I am) presently helping two Navajo elders through Adopt a Native Elder Program. I have studied with Grandmother Alloday of the Good Medicine Society; studying with Spider about Moon Lodge Women's Cycle. Spider is of Seneca Wolf Clan; I use herbs for healing, making medicines & salves. Also homeopathy."

REIDER, ANTHONY (Santee Sioux)
(tribal president)
Affiliation & Address: President, Flandreau Santee Sioux Tribe, P.O. Box 283, Flandreau, SD 57028 (605) 997-3891.

REIDHEAD, CHARLES TY, RADM (Three Affiliated Tribes)
(IHS area director)
Education: 2009 Fellow with the Institute for Healthcare Improvement wherein he led the IPC program; Harvard School of Public Health, MPH, 2011. *Affiliation & Address*: Director, Phoenix Area Indian Health Service (IHS). Two Renaissance Square, 40 N. Central Ave., #600, Phoenix, AZ 85004 (602) 364-5039. He is the principal federal health care advocate and provider of health care services for American Indians & Alaska Natives. As Acting Director of the Phoenix Area, RADM Reidhead oversees the delivery of health care services to over 170,000 American Indians and Alaska Natives in Arizona, Nevada, & Utah. The Phoenix Area provides services ranging from inpatient & outpatient care to dental, behavioral health, public health nursing, health education, & environmental health. These services are provided through eight service units, two youth regional treatment centers, and three urban programs. The Phoenix Area works closely with 42 Tribes to provide health care and community health programs. As the Chief Medical Officer for the Phoenix Area, RADM Reidhead

served as the ranking officer for over 320 officers, & provided clinical leadership to over 200 medical providers delivering comprehensive care to over 170,000 American Indian and Alaska Natives. RADM Reidhead began his career with IHS in 1997 as a primary care internist at the Whiteriver Indian Hospital in Arizona. In 2004, the IHS Director appointed him to serve as the National Chief Clinical Consultant in Internal Medicine. He coordinated a national initiative to improve the care & prevention of chronic disease. His efforts to improve primary care across the Indian health system from 2006-2010 grew into the contemporary Improving Patient Care Program (IPC), which has brought more than 100 sites together from across the country to participate in innovative work, transforming the delivery of primary care. gained additional skills in improvement, and was exposed to large health care systems that are leading improvement around the world. He also assisted with the coordination of the National Hospital Consortium, a national initiative to improve hospital quality and safety.

REIFEL, NANCY, D.D.S, MPH (Rosebud Sioux)
(dentist; assistant researcher)
Address & Affiliation: Public Health & Community Dentistry, 63-087 CHS, University of California, Los Angeles, CA 90095 (310) 825-4320. E-mail: nancyr@dent.ucla.edu. *Other professional post*: Instructor, American Indian Studies, UCLA.

REILING, DENNIS L. (Potawatomi)
(tribal special judge)
Affiliation: Prairie Band Potawatomi Nation Tribal Court, 15498 K Rd., Mayetta, KS 66509 (866) 966-2242 or (785) 966-2242. E-mail: tribalcourt@pbpnation.org. Website: www.pbpnation.org/tribalcourt

REIMER, JOHN
(BIA education administrator)
Affiliation: Portland Area Office, Bureau of Indian Affairs, 911 N.E. 11th Ave., Portland, OR 97232 (503) 872-2743.

REIMER/YUMKS, RUDY (Squamish)
(archaeologist; professor of First Nations Studies)
Education: Simon Fraser University, BA, MA; McMaster University, PhD (Archaeology). *Affiliation & Address*: Professor of Archaeology, Department of Archaelogy, Simon Fraser University, Burnaby, BC Canada V5A 1S6 (778) 782-3594. E-mail: rudyr@sfu.ca.

REINHARDT, MARTIN (Anishinaabe Ojibway)
(assistant professor of Native American studies)
A citizen of the Sault Ste. Marie Tribe of Chippewa Indians from Mich. *Education*: BA & MA (Sociology); Penn State University, PhD (Educational Leadership). *Affiliation & Address*: Owner & CEO, Reinhardt & Associates, assistant professor of Native American Studies, Center for Native American Studies, Northern Michigan University, 1401 Presque Isle Ave., Marquette, MI 49855 (906) 227-1397. E-mail: mreinhardt@nmu.edu. *Past professional posts*: Research associate, Interwest Equity Assistance Center, Colorado State University; V.P. for Diversity & Research for Educational Options, Inc.; former director, Center for Native American Studies, Northern Michigan U.; former director, Native American Programs, Central Michigan U.. He has taught courses in American Indian education, tribal law & government, and sociology.

REINHART, YVONNE (Winnebago)
(education director)
Affiliation: Director, Education Dept., Winnebago Tribe of Nebraska, P.O. Box 687, Winnebago, NE 68701 (402) 878-3204.

RENICK, DORIS (Pomo)
(tribal chairperson)
Affiliation: Coyote Valley Reservation, P.O. Box 39, Redwood Valley, CA 95470-0039 (707) 485-8723.

RENTERIA, JOE (Cherokee)
(Indian center chairperson)
Affiliation: Indian Human Resource Center, 4040 30th St., Suite A, San Diego, CA 92104 (619) 281-5964.

REO, NICHOLAS JAMES (Sault Ste. Marie Chippewa)
(professor of environmental studies & Native American studies)
Education: University of Michigan, BS & MS (Natural Resources & Environment); Michigan State University, PhD, 2010). *Affiliation & Address*: Assistant Professor, Native American Studies & Environmental Studies, Dartmouth College, 104 Steele Hall HB 6152, Hanover, NH 03755 (603) 646-3530. E-mail: nicholas.j.reo@dartmouth.edu. Professor Reo works with American Indian Tribes in the U.S. and other Native peoples on applied research concerning the management and use of natural resources. He studies indigenous coupled human and natural systems. He is particularly interested in ways traditional ecological knowledge, ecosystem stewardship,

and socio-ecological adaptation contribute to sustainability in the context of rapid environmental change. Dr. Reo's recent work studies tribal participation in polycentric environmental governance & large-scale, indigenous led stewardship of riparian ecosystems.

RESSLER, KOREEN
(vice president of acadeimics)
Education: Moorhead State University, BS; University of Mary, MM; Capella University, PhD. *Affiliation & Address*: VP of Academics, Sitting Bull College, 1341 92nd St., Fort Yates, ND 58538 (701) 854-8001. E-mail: koreenr@ sbci.edu. She began her employment with Sitting Bull College in January of 1996 as Vocational Director. Prior to that she was employed with Fort Berthold Community College, New Town, North Dakota from 1982 to 1995. During her employment at Fort Berthold she served as the Business Faculty and for the last four years as Acting Academic Dean. During her employment with the Tribal Colleges, she has served as chairperson and member of various committees; curriculum development, faculty development, assessment, finance, facilities, & HLC/NCA Steering Committee. She has served as the HLC/NCA Self-Study Coordinator & participates in North Dakota Tribal College Deans Association. She is a certified Vocational Education Instructor/ Administrator in the State of North Dakota. Ressler has also served on the North Dakota Tech-Prep Council, State Vocational Education Curriculum Committee & panel for evaluation process of Vocational Programs for the State of North Dakota. In additions, Ressler has oversight for various grants including Department of Education Title III and Native American Career & Technical Education. She participated in the North Dakota Bush Fulbright Faculty Exchange Program in the summer of 1990. 1992-93 she was named the first time Fort Berthold Community College recipient of the Golden Apple award for Outstanding Teacher of the Year.

RESVALOSO, MARY L. (Cahuilla)
(former tribal chairperson)
Affiliation & Address: Former chairperson, Torres Martinez Desert Cahuilla Indians, P.O. Box 1160, Thermal, CA 92274 (760) 397-0300.
E-mail: tmchair@torresmartinez.org

RETASKET, TINA (Confederated Tribes Siletz)
(tribal council member)
Affiliation & Address: Tribal council member, Confederated Tribes of Siletz Indians, P.O. Box 549, Siletz, OR 97380. E-mail: retasket@hotmail.com. *Other professional post*: Board Vice Chairperson, ONABEN, Tigard, OR.

RETKA, LINDA LEE (White Earth Ojibwe)
(training & technical assistance specialist)
Affiliation & Address: Training & Technial Assistance Specialist, National American Indian Indian Housing Council, Minnesota Field Office, 20877 233rd St., Little Falls, MN 56345 (320) 745-2064. E-mail: lretka@naihc.net.

REVARD, CARTER C. (*Nompewathe*) (Osage) 1931-
(professor emeritus, writer)
Born March 25, 1931, Pawhuska, Okla. *Education*: University of Tulsa, BA, 1952; University of Oxford, BA/MA, 1958; Yale University, PhD, 1959. *Principal occupation*: Professor emeritus, writer. *Address*: 6638 Pershing Ave., St. Louis, MO 63130 (314) 727-9358. E-mail: ccrevard@artsci.wustl.edu. *Affiliations*: Washington University, St. Louis, MO, 1961-97; professor emeritus, 1997-). *Memberships*: Modern Language Association; Association of American Rhodes Scholars; American Indian Center of Mid-America. *Interests*: Writing, gourd dancing, medieval research & writing, poetry readings, talks. *Published works*: Ponca War Dancers! (poems) (Point Riders Press-Norman, OK, 1980); Cowboys and Indians, Christmas Shopping (poems) (Point Riders Press, 1992); An Eagle Nation (poems) (University of Arizona Press, 1993); Family Matters, Tribal Affairs (prose-scholarly essays and autobiography) (University of Arizona Press, 1998); Winning the Dust Bowl (poems & memoirs) (University of Arizona Press, 2001); How the Songs Come Down (new & selected poems) (Salt, Cambridge, England, 2005).

REXFORD, EDWARD (Eskimo)
(AK village council president)
Affiliation & Address: Kaktovik Village, P.O. Box 8, Kaktovik, AK 99747 (907) 640-6120.

REY-BEAR, DANIEL I.S.J. (Coushatta) 1969-
(attorney)
Born in London, England, January 11, 1969. *Education*: Rice University, BA, 1990, BS (Mechanical Egineering), 1992; University of Texas lw Schol, JD, 1995. *Affiliation & Address*: Partner, Nordhaus Law Firm, LLP, 421 W. Riverside Ave., Spokane, WA 99204 (509) 747-2502 E-mail: dreybear@ nordhauslaw.com. Mr. Rey-Bear is a Certified Specialist in Federal Indian Law by New Mexico Board of Legal Specialization. *Professional activities*: California Indian Law Association, Board member, 2005-present. *Professional Activities*: American Law Institute, Elected Member and appointed Advisor for inaugural

Restatement of American Indian Law, 2012 - present; *Past professional posts*: UNM Law School, Adjunct Professor - Indian Law Appellate Advocacy, 2008 – 2012; NALSA Moot Court Competition, 2004-13; California Indian Law Association, Board Member, 2005-11, President, 2010-11, & Vice-President, 2006-07; Federal Bar Association Indian Law Conference, Conference Co-Chair, 1998-2001; Staff attorney, U.S. Court of Appeals for the Eleventh Circuit, Atlanta, GA. Before joining the Nordhaus firm in April 1997, Mr. Rey-Bear served as a staff attorney for the U.S. Court of Appeals for the Eleventh Circuit, in Atlanta, Georgia. In that position, Mr. Rey-Bear worked on over 160 cases for various federal appellate judges and was recognized as the outstanding Eleventh Circuit Staff Attorney for the 1995-1996 term. During law school, Mr. Rey-Bear's work included experience with the Indian Law Resource Center, in Helena, Montana; the U.S. Environmental Protection Agency, Office of the General Counsel, and the U.S. Senate Indian Affairs Committee, both in Washington, D.C.; and the Texas Indian Bar Association and the Consumer Protection Division of the Texas Office of the Attorney General, both in Austin, Texas.

REYHNER, JON ALLAN 1944-
(professor of education)
Born April 29, 1944, Fountain Hill, Penna. *Education*: University of California, Davis, BA, 1966, MA, 1967; Northern Arizona University, MA, 1973, EdS, 1977; Montana State University, Bozeman, EdD, 1984. *Principal occupation*: Associate professor of education, Eastern Montana College. *Address*: Department of Education, Northern Arizona University, Flagstaff, AZ 86011. *Affiliations*: Principal, Rocky Boy Public School, Box Elder, MT, 1978-80; university supervisor of professional & student teachers, Dept. of Elementary Education, Montana State University, Bozeman, 1980-81; principal/federal projects director, Heart Butte Public School, MT, 1982-84; administrator/ principal, Havasupai School, Supai, AZ, 1984-85; academic coordinator & school administrator, Cibecue Community School, Cibecue, AZ, 1984-85; associate professor of education, Eastern Montana College, Billings, 1985-97; professor of education, Northern Arizona University, Flagstaff, AZ, 1997-present. *Memberships*: National Assn for Bilingual Education; American Educational Research Assn; International Reading Assn; American Assn of School Administrators; National Indian Education Assn; Council for Indian Education; Phi Delta Kappa; Phi Alpha Theta. *Interests*: Bilingual education; Indian education; photography; historical research on Western America. *Published works*: Heart Butte: A Blackfeet Indian Community, 1984; editor, Stories of Our Blackfeet Grandmothers, 1984; editor, The Story of Running Eagle, by James Willard Schultz, 1984; editor, Famine Winter, by James Willard Schultz, 1984; editor, The Loud Mouthed Gun, by James Willard Schultz, 1984; all published by Council for Indian Education; A History of Indian Education (Eastern Montana College, 1989); Effective Language Education Practices (NALI, 1990); Teaching American Indian Students (U. of Oklahoma Press, 1992); American Indian Education: A History, with Jeanne Eder (U. of Oklahoma Press, 2004); numerous articles.

REYNA, SHARON (*Dryflower*) (Taos Pueblo) 1949-
(artist-clay)
Born August 20, 1949, Taos, N.M. *Education*: Institute of American Indian Art, AFA (Museum Studies /three Dimensional Art), 1987. Santa Fe Community College (Painting/Business). *Principal occupation*: Artist-clay. *Address*: P.O. Box 3031, Taos, NM 87571 (505) 758-3790. 1991 *Open Shows*: Denver Indian Market; Native American Art Festival; Heard Museum; Scottsdale Native American Culture Foundation; Retrospective of Taos, 4-Man Show, Sables Art Center; Red Earth Fine Art Show; Eight Northern Indian Pueblos Art Show; Indian Market, Santa Fe. Collections: Denver Natural History Museum-Vernon Rickmeyer Collection; Millicent Rogers Museum; Institute of American Indian Arts, Santa Fe; Alll Indian Pueblo Culture Center, Albuquerque; Tony Reyna (private collection); Chicago Natural History Museum; Red Cloud Heritage Center, Rapid City, SD; among others. Memberships: Indian Arts and Crafts Association; The National Museum of Women in the Arts, Washington, DC; Stables Art Association; Spring Arts Board; TAA - Visual Arts Committee. *Awards, honors*: Best of Class, Ceramic Sculpture - 4th Annual Fine Art Show, Scottsdale Native American Indian Cultural Foundation; 1st, Pottery Division - Heard Museum Student Show; 2nd, Ceramic Division - Red Earth Fine Arts Show, Oklahoma City, OK; Thunderbird Scholarship, Hinsel Award & Purchase Award from the Red Cloud Heritage Center, Pine Ridge, SD; Gallup Ceremoial; Artist of the Year, Native American Fish & Wildlife Society. *Published works*: Taos Pueblo (Nancy Wood, 1988-89); Gold Book (Gold Book Pubs, 1992).

REYNA, TONY (Taos Pueblo)
(Indian shop owner)
Address: Tony Reyna Indian Shop, P.O. Box 1892, Taos Indian Pueblo, Taos, NM 87571 (505) 758-3835.

REYNOLDS, BRIAN (Maliseet)
(tribal education director)
Education: University of Maine, BS (Secondary Social Studies Education), 1994. *Address & Affiliation*: Education Director, Houlton Band of Maliseet

Indians, 88 Bell Rd., Littleton, ME 04730 (207) 532-4273. E-mail: education.director@maliseet.com. Mr. Reynolds serves on the Wabanaki Education Task Force; member, University of Maine at Presque Isle's "Project Compass" Community of Practice; tribal representative, United South & Eastern Tribes Education Committee; member, Wabanaki Education Steering Committee (U Maine); member, Wabanaki Studies Commission (State of Maine); member, Native American Progam Advisory Board (U Maine); member, Maine Indian Tribal-State Commission.

REYNOLDS, STEPHANIE
(professor of anthropology)
Address & Affiliation: School of Social Sciences, 3151 Social Science Plaza, University of California, Irvine, Irvine, CA 92697-5100 (714) 824-5894. *Activities*: Teaches lower & upper division social science courses pertaining to the Indians, Aleuts, and Eskimos of North America (past & present). Dr. Reynolds is a foremost authority on Native American dance; she offers a course on comparisons of dance among urban & reservation Utes, Shoshone, Eastern Pueblos, and Mixtecans, all groups she has conducted field research.

REYNOLDS, TYLER (Te-Moak Western Shoshone)
(tribal chairperson)
Affiliation & Address: Chairperson, Te-Moak Tribe of Western Shshone Indians, South Fork Reservation, 21 Lee Unit-13, Spring Creek, NV 89815 (775) 744-4273.

RHOADES, EVERETT RONALD (Kiowa) 1931-
(physician)
Born October 24, 1931, Lawton, Okla. *Education*: Lafayette College, 1949-1952; University of Oklahoma, College of Medicine, MD, 1956. *Affiliation & Address*: Physician, P.O. Box 26901, Oklahoma City, OK 73126 (405) 271-2330. Dr. Rhoades is the founding member & Board Chairperson for the Oklahoma City Indian Clinic. He was also the founding member of the Association of American Indian Physicians. *Past professional posts*: Chief, Infectious Diseases, Wilford Hall, U.S. Air Force Hospital, 1961-66; assistant professor of microbiology and associate professor of medicine, University of Oklahoma Medical Center, 1966-72; professor of medicine, Chief, Infectious Diseases, University of Oklahoma College of Medicine, Oklahoma City, OK, 1968-82; professor of medicine & adjunct professor of microbiology, University of Oklahoma, Health Sciences Center, 1972-82; Chief, Infectious Diseases Service University Hospital, 1975-82; director, Indian Health Service, Rockville, MD, 1982-93; Assistant Surgeon General, USPHS, 1982-93; associate dean, University of Oklahoma College of Medicine, 1993-; director of Education Initiatives, Center for American Indian/Alaska Native Health, Johns Hopkins School of Public Health, 1993-; director, Native American Prevention Research Center, University of Oklahoma College of Public Health, 1998-. *Military service*: U.S. Air Force, 1957-66 (Major; Certificate of Merit, 1967). *Community activities*: Task Force on Health of American Indian Policy Review Commission (chairman, 1975); National Advisory Allergy and Infectious Disease Council (NIH), 1971-75; Central Oklahoma Indian Health Project (board of directors; chairman, 1976); Kiowa Tribal Business Committee (1967-70, 1979-81; vice chairman, 1974-76); Kiowa Tribal Land Management Committee, 1967-70; National Congress of American Indians (health committee); founder & donor, Dorothy Rowell Rhoades Prize to outstanding graduating Indian student, Elgin High School, Okla. *Memberships*: American Thoracic Society, 1963-82; American Federation for Clinical Research, 1960-; American College of Physicians, 1963- (Fellow); American Society for Microbiology, 1970-; Association on American Indian Affairs (board of directors, 1967-82; vice president, 1978-82); Association of American Indian Physicians (founder, 1971; president, 1972, 1976); Sigma Xi; Phi Beta Kappa; Kiowa Gourd Clan, 1970-; Association of Military Surgeons, 1982-; Infectious Disease Society of America, 1974-. *Awards, honors*: Markle Scholar, Academic Medicine, 1967-72; John Hay Whitney Opportunity Fellow, 1952-56; Student Research Achievement Award, 1956; Outstanding Achievement, Veterans Administration Hospital, 1960, 1961; Recognition Award, Assn of American Indian Physicians, 1973, 1976; Breath of Life Award, Oklahoma Lung Assn, 1977; Public Health Service Recognition Award, 1977; National Honor Lecturer, Mid-America State Universities Assn, 1979; Assn of American Indian Physicians Award of Excellence, 1980; PHS Meritorious Service Medal, 1985; Richard Kern Lecture Award, 1988; Kiowa Tribe of Oklahoma, "Exemplary Contributions to Health of Native Americans, 1988; Kiowa Veterans Association & Auxiliary, "In Appreciation for Dedicated Service to the American Indian Health Service, 1988; PHS Chief of Staff's Special Commendation Award, 1989. *Published works*: Numerous articles in scientific journals relating to infectious diseases, microbiology, and Indian life; author of Kiowa Tribe for World Book Encyclopedia; edited Task Force Report to American Indian Policy Review Commission (Health), U.S. Government Printing Office, 1975.

RHOADS, KAY (Sac & Fox)
(tribal principal chief)
Affiliation & Address: Principal Chief, Sac & Fox Nation of Oklahoma, 920883 S. Hwy. 99 Bldg. A, Stroud, OK 74079 (918) 968-3526 E-mail: chief@

sacandfoxnation-nsn.gov. *Past professional post*: President, Medicine Creek Tribal College, Tacoma, WA

RHOAN, A. ROBERT (Choinumni/Creek)
(attorney)
Education: UCLA, BA, 1999; University of California, Hastings College of the Law, JD, 2003. *Affiliation*: Associate (2009-present), Fredericks Peebles & Morgan, LLP, 1001 Second St., Sacramento, CA 95814 (916) 441-2700. E-mail: rrhoan@ndnlaw.com. *Practice areas*: Federal Indian Law; Commercial Litigation. *Past professional posts*: Law clerk, California Indian Legal Services; judicial extern to Hon. Carlos R. Moreno of the California Supreme Court; prior to joining Fredericks Peebles & Morgan, Mr. Rhoan worked at Bingham McCutchen, LLP and McCormick Barstow, LLP as a commercial litigator.

RHODD, DOUGLAS G. (Ponca)
(former tribal chairperson)
Affiliation: Ponca Tribe of Okla., 20 White Eagle Dr., Ponca City, OK 74601

RHODD, HENRY (Ponca)
(former tribal vice chairperson)
Affiliation: Ponca Tribe of Indians of Oklahoma, 20 White Eagle Dr., Box 2, Ponca City, OK 74601 (580) 762-8104. E-mail: hrhodd@ponca.com.

RHODD, TIMOTHY (Ioway)
(tribal chairperson)
Affiliation & Address: Chairperson, Iowa Tribe of Kansas & Nebraska, 3345 B Thrasher, White Cloud, KS 66094 (785) 595-3347. E-mail: trhodd@iowas.org.

RHODES, CLARK (Paiute)
(former tribal chairperson)
Affiliation: Lovelock Paiute Tribe, Fort Bidwell Reservation, P.O. Box 878, Lovelock, NV 89419 (775) 273-7861.

RHODES, KRISTINE (Anishinaabe)
(executive director)
Born & raised on the Fond du Lac Indian Reservation. *Education*: University of Minnesota, BS (Community Health Education), MPH (Public Health Administration & Policy). *Affiliation & Address*: Executive Director (2010-present), American Indian Cancer Foundation, 800 IDS Center, 80 S. 8th St., Minneapolis, MN 55402 (612) 672-8668. E-mail: krhodes@aicaf.org. Kristine has worked on improving the health of American Indian communities for the past two decades. *Past professional posts*: Coordinator (2000-10), multiple research projects at the American Indian Community Tobacco projects at the University of Minnesota; health educator, Fond du Lac Indian Reservation.

RICE, ALEX (Mohawk of Quebec, Can.)
(actress)
Contact: Imparato Fay Management, Los Angeles, CA (3100 557-2112; Website: www.alexrice.biz. *Credits*: Films: "The Doe Boy," 2001; "Chasing Indigo," "The War Bride," "Thunderbird," and in "Lewis & Clark: Great Journey West." TV Guest Star appearances: "Spin City" (ABC); "Strong Medicine" (Lifetime); "CSI: Crime Scene Investigation" (CBS; "The Sopranos" (HBO); PBS mysteries, "Skinwalker," (2002); "Coyote Waits," (2003); and "Thief of Time," (2004); based on Tony Hillerman's novels; ABC miniseries, "Dreamkeeper." Awards: Nominated for Best Actress for, "Skinwalkers," 2002, and won Best Actress for "Coyote Waits," 2003, American Indian Motion Picture Awards.

RICE, G. WILLIAM (United Keetoowah Cherokee) 1951-2016 (deceased)
(attorney; associate professor of law; law center co-director)
Born August 3, 1951, Anadarko, Okla. *Education*: Phillips University (Enid, OK), BA, 1973; Lowell (MA) Technological Institute (MS degree program), 1973-75; University of Oklahoma College of Law, JD, 1978. *Affiliation & Address*: Associate Professor of Law (1995-2015) & Co-Director of the Native American Law Center, University of Tulsa College of Law, 3120 E. 4th Place, Tulsa, OK

RICE, STAN, JR. (Yavapai)
(tribal president)
Affiliation: Yavapai-Prescott Board of Directors, 530 E. Merritt St., Prescott, AZ 86301 (928) 445-8790.

RICEHILL, ERNEST (Winnebago/Omaha) 1948-
(administrator)
Born November 29, 1948, Winnebago, Neb. *Education*: Briar Cliff College (Sioux City, IA), 1976. Resides in Grand Junction, Colorado. *Affiliations*: Curator, Sioux City Art Center, 1973-79; director, Office of Indian Education, Sioux City Community Public Schools, 1979-84; personnel administrator, Omaha Tribe of Nebraska, 1984-88; executive director, Sioux City American Indian Center, Sioux City, IA, 1991-95; PSA at Lowes, Grand Junction, CO. *Community activities*: Sioux City Community Schools (member of Project

Awareness, the Curriculum Committee, Multicultural Committee, and Committee on Formulating Policy on Chronic Absenteeism; chairman of Sioux City Minority Coalition; board member, Native American Alcoholic Treatment Center; chairman of Siouxland Council of Agency Executives; member of Winnebago Tribe's Healthy Start Planning Committee; member of the Siouxland Housing Corporation; among others. *Memberships*: National Indian Education Association; National Indian Media Association; Iowa Museum Association. *Awards, honors*: Elected Delegate to the precinct, county, & state Democratic Conventions, 1972-80, 1984-85; appointed Chairman of Precinct 16, Democratic Party; elected National Delegate to the 1972, 1988 & 1992 National Democratic Conventions; appointed Iowa State Coordinator of the Native Americans for Clinton-Gore National Election Committee, Aug. 1992; member of the President Clinton's transition team of the Native Americans for Clinton-Gore National Election Committee, Nov. 1992; appointed member of the White House/Robert Wood Johnson Foundation panel on "Conversations on Health: A Dialogue with the American People, Amkeny, Iowa, March 1993; member/representative to the National Native American Listening Conference sponsored by the Dept. of Justice & Interior, Albuquerque, May 1994.

RICHARDS, EDWARD S. (Navajo)
(Navajo corporation secretary/treasurer)
Born & raised in Fort Defiance, Ariz. *Education*: Northern Arizona University (NAU), BS (Forestry). *Affiliation*: Secretary/treasurer, Dine Development Corporation, P.O. Box 307, Window Rock, AZ 86515 (505) 879-1533. *Other professional posts*: Member, Board of Directors, Navajo Times Publishing Co. & Nova Corporation. *Past professional posts*: CEO & General Manager, Navajo Forest Products Industries, 1969-1995; Director, Small Business Development Dept., Navajo Nation Division of Economic Development, 1995-2003. *Awards, honors*: Numerous honors & awards from NAU in recognition of his academic achievements, distinguished business career & positive impact on his community.

RICHARDS, THOMAS, JR. (*Aviaq*) (Inupiat Eskimo) 1949-
(writer/planner)
Born September 27, 1949, Kotzebue, Alaska. *Education*: University of Denver, 1967-68; University of Alaska, 1968; Armed Forces Air Intelligence Training Center, CO, 1969. *Principal occupation*: Writer/planner. Resides in Bethel, Alaska. *Affiliations*: Editor/publisher, Tundra Times (newspaper), 1973, 1977-80; vice-president, Association of Village Council Presidents, Bethel, AK, 1981-86; owner/operator, Thomas Richards, Jr. & Associates, Bethel, AK (current). *Other professional post*: Author. *Military service*: U.S. Navy, 1969-73 (Vietnam Service Vet, E-5; Photo-Intelligence Specialist. *Community activities*: Founding director, Institute of Alaska Native Arts (board of directors, 1975-76); member, Inuit Circumpolar Conference Communications & Broadcasting Commission, 1979-84. *Memberships*: Alaska Federation of Natives (Human Resources Board, 1980-86); American Legion, Post No. 11. *Awards, honors*: Congressional Intern, 1970-72, office of U.S. Rep. Nick Begich; Governor's Representative, State Committee, Alaska Humanities Forum (Chairperson & member, 1975-82); Committee on Arctic Cultural Development, UNESCO, United Nations (U.S. Representative, 1979-80, appointed by U.S. Dept. of State); Outstanding Young Man of America, U.S. Jaycees, nominated by the Office of the Governor, 1979; Howard Rock Award for Native community service, presented by the Board of Directors, Tundra Times, 1980. *Interests*: "After 20 years as a writer and administrator for Alaska Native organizations, my primary career interest now centers on economic & business development. Although I still write (mostly histories), most of my current work is in entrepreneurship training. I help rural Alaskans research & write business plans and start-up their own business ventures." *Published works*: Alaska Native Claims-Unit 4 (AK Native Foundation, 1976); Pribilof Progress...Pribilof Pace (Aleutian/Pibilof Islands Association, 1979); ANCSA and Related Studies - textbook history of Alaska Native land claims for Lower Kuskokwim School District, Bethel, AK (Lower Kuskokwim School District, 1992).

RICHARDS, WILLIAM H. (*Xus-x'a-yo*) (Smith River Rancheria-Tolowa)
(tribal chairperson)
Born March 17, 1936, Del Norte, Calif. *Education*: College of the Redwoods (2 years). *Address*: 301 N. Indian Rd., Smith River, CA 95567 (707) 487-9255 (work). *Affiliation*: Chairman, Smith River Rancheria, Smith River, CA, 1978-. *Military service*: 1955-58 (Sp. 4). *Community activities*: State Committee on Indian Juvenile Justice (member).

RICHARDSON, BARRY (Haliwa-Saponi) 1954-
(tribal administrator)
Born August 13, 1954, in Warren County, N.C. *Education*: Pembroke State University, BA (Political Science), 1976. *Principal occupation*: Tribal administrator. *Address*: P.O. Box 609, Hollister, NC 27844 (919) 586-4017 (work). *Affiliations*: Administrator, Haliwa-Saponi Indian Tribe, P.O. Box 99, Hollister, NC 27844. Website: www.haliwa-saponi.com; owner/operator, Powwow, Hollister, NC. *Other professional posts*: Founder & treasurer of the National American Indian Council; founded, in 1993, Native Opportunity Way

Community Development Corp., Hollister, NC; founder & president, Tuscarora, Occaneechee, Tuitelo Properties, a Land Development Co.; owner/president, BR & Associates (consulting firm specializing in writing proposals, strategic loans & financial management); field reader, Administration for Native Americans, Office of Indian Education & the Social Security Administration. He is a certified housing counselor. *Past professional posts*: Executive director, Baltimore American Indian Center, 1980-93; NC Commission of Indian Affairs, Housing Program, 1976-80. *Community activities*: Preserve Haliwa Now, Bethlehem Recreation. *Membership*: National Congress of American Indians. *Awards, honors*: City of Baltimore Citation, 1983; Distinguished Service Award, 1992; Haliwa-Saponi Business Person of the Year, 1996.

RICHARDSON, BRUCIE O. (Haliwa-Saponi)
(tribal chief)
Affiliation & Address: Chief, Haliwa-Saponi Indian Tribe, 39021 NC Hwy.561, P.O. Box 99, Hollister, NC 27844 (252) 586-4017

RICHARDSON, G. ANNE (Rappahannock)
(tribal chief)
Affiliation: Rappahannock Tribe, 5036 Indian Neck Rd., Indian Neck, VA 23148 (804) 769-0260.

RICHARDSON, GREGORY A. (Haliwa-Saponi)
(executive director)
Affiliation: Executive Director, North Carolina Commission of Indian Affairs, 116 West Jones St., 1317 Mail Service Center, Raleigh, NC 27699 (919) 807-4440. E-mail: greg.richardson@doa.nc.gov

RICHARDSON, JOSEPH O. (Haliwa-Saponi) 1941-
(former tribal chairperson)
Born January 27, 1941, in Washington, DC. *Education*: Appalachian State Teachers College, BS, 1963; MEd, (Principal's Certification & Educational Specialist's Degree in Educational Administration), EdS, Superintendent's Certification); Doctorate in Educational Administration, 1999. *Affiliation & Address*: Haliwa-Saponi Tribe (treasurer, 1998-2008, chair, 2008-present), P.O. Box 99, Hollister, NC 27844 (919) 586-4017. *Other professional posts*: Adjunct professor, North Carolina Wesleyan College, 1998-present. *Past professional posts*: Teacher, 1963-66; teacher, Warren County School System, 1969-81; principal, 1966-69, Haliwa Indian School; principal, 1981-91; director of transportation, 91-98, Hawkins Elementary School.

RICHARDSON, PATRICIA ROSE (BREWINGTON) (Coharie-Cherokee) 1933-
(crafts consultant)
Born July 21, 1933, Clinton, N.C. *Education*: East Carolina Indian School, 1952; Nash Technical College, AA, 1986. *Principal occupation*: American Indian crafts consultant/pottery and beadwork. *Address*: P.O. Box 130, Hollister, NC 27844. *Affiliations*: Instructor, Title IV Indian Education, Halifax Board of Education, N.C. (six years); crafts instructor, Haliwa-Supai Indian Tribe, Hollister, N.C. (five years). *Memberships*: North Carolina Crafts Association (board member); American Indian Heritage Foundation. *Awards, honors*: First Place Awards--Excellence in Beadwork, Schiele Museum Indian Festival, 1978/1986; Good Medicine Crafts Award, 1980/1986. *Interests*: Exhibitions at major Indian festivals: Grand Prairie, TX, Hunter Mountain, NY, Palm Beach, FL, NC Indian festivals, National Indian Festival, Wash., DC.

RICHARDSON, RONALD (Haliwa-Saponi)
(tribal chief)
Affiliation: Chief (2000-present), Haliwa-Saponi Tribe, P.O. Box 99, Hollister, NC 27844 (919) 586-4017. *Other professional posts*: Owns a Real Estate Investment Co.; pastor, Essex Community Church (1987-present).

RICHARDSON, TROY (Saponi/Tuscarora)
(professor of American Indian studies)
Education: University of Pennsylvania, BA, 1996; University of Utah, PhD, 2006. *Affiliation & Address*: Associate Professor, Cornell University, American Indian Program, 492 Caldwell Hall, Ithaca, NY 14853 (607) 255-4681. E-mail: tar37@cornell.edu. "As both a philosopher of education & scholar in American Indian and Indigenous Studies, my research, scholarship and pedagogical efforts center on the intellectual traditions of Indigenous and other minoritized communities. I draw particular attention to the epistemological and ontological dimensions of Indigeneity as it is revealed in literature, visual culture and non-fiction works by Indigenous peoples. More specifically, I theorize the nature of selfhood, ethics, gender, ecology and power from these Indigenous intellectual traditions to chart the alternative social & philosophical imaginaries of Indigenous peoples. Moreover, this work assists in revealing the precise operations of a still operative coloniality in Euro-centric intellectualism and knowledge production in research and academic settings. My scholarship seeks to contribute to philosophical and theoretical discourses developed by Indigenous peoples to advance forms of de-colonial education."

RICHEY, KENT E.
(attorney)
Education: Moorhead State University, BS, 1970; University of Minnesota Law School, JD, 1973. *Affiliation & Address*: Partner, Faegre Baker Daniels, 2200 Wells Fargo Center, 90 S. Seventh St., Minneapolis, MN 55402 (612) 766-7442. E-mail: kent.richey@faegrebd.com. Kent is one of the nation's leading Indian Country business and finance attorneys. He began this practice in 1994, drawing upon his extensive prior experience as a bond and underwriter's counsel for tax-exempt and taxable governmental financings and, prior to that, his experience as a business lawyer & litigator. With his practice now centered in Indian Country, Kent has represented a variety of clients, including banks, investment banks, broker-dealers, insurance companies, credit enhancers, equipment vendors, casino developers, consultants, managers & Indian tribes and their instrumentalities. More than 90 Indian tribes throughout the country have been involved in Kent's transactions. Relevant financings have taken a variety of forms – including bank loan & credit facilities (both syndicated and non-syndicated), leases (both financing and operating), and the offer and sale of indentured debt securities. Such financings have involved senior debt, subordinated debt, credit enhanced debt, so-called participating or continent interest debt, and transactions with interest rate protection or swaps. Not only has Kent been extensively involved in the issuance of new tribal debt, he can also speak authoritatively as to the restructuring of that debt, as a result of representation in connection with a number of defaulted tribal commercial loans & two bond issues presently undergoing restructuring efforts. In connection with his restructuring efforts, Kent has met personally with senior legal and other staff of the National Indian Gaming Commission to explore new approaches that might enable restructurings and restore investor and lender confidence in tribal financings. In the course of his practice, Kent is in almost continuous contact with the National Indian Gaming Commission or the Bureau of Indian Affairs. In the course of this practice, Kent has developed a comprehensive understanding of the various commercial considerations intrinsic in tribal financings, such as the effectiveness of tribal waivers of sovereign immunity, the availability and advisability of various forums for dispute resolution, and the specialized requirements for secured lending within tribal jurisdictions. The specialized interplay of Indian law, commercial law, and in the instances of securities offerings, securities law, is a challenge Kent is able to meet efficiently on a cost-effective basis through his broad practical-based knowledge and experience in Indian country. Furthermore, drawing on his public finance background, he recognizes the critical role tribal governments & their members can play in the negotiation of Indian commercial transactions. *Awards, honors*: The Best Lawyers in America — Gaming Law, Native American Law, 2005-14; Chambers USA: America's Leading Lawyers for Business — Gaming & Licensing and Native American Law, 2007-14.

RICHIE, CHIP
(film director; co-owner)
Address & Affiliation: Director, Rich-Heape Films, Inc., 5952 Royal Lane, Suite 254, Dallas, TX 75230 (888) 600-2922; (214) 696-6916. E-mail: chip@richheape.com; Website: www.richheape.com *Professional activities*: Director of Native American videos, films & movies dedicated to inform, educate and encourage the awareness of the history, cultures, languages, traditions and aspirations of Native Americans and other Native Peoples. Rich-Heape Films has been recognized as 1999 & 2003 American Indian Business of the Year by the American Indian Chamber of Commerce of Texas, and has received numerous awards. *Videos produced*: "Black Indians: An American Story," 60 mins. VHS & DVD; "How to Trace Your Native American Heritage," 35 mins. VHS & DVD; Tales of Wonder I & II, 60 mins. each. VHS & DVD, CD soundtrack; "Native American Healing in the 21st Century," 40 mins. VHS & DVD; "Walela-Live in Concert," DVD, VHS & audio CD (2004). Book: "American Indian Directory" -1999 (national listing of over 500 federally-recognized American Indian nations & tribes.

RICKARD, JOLENE (Tuscarora)
(visual historian, artist, curator; American Indian program director)
Education: State University of New York at Buffalo, PhD. *Affiliation & Address*: Associate Professor, Dept. of History of Art, Dept. of Art Visual Studies Program; Director (2011-present), American Indian & Indigenous Studies Program, G35 Goldwin Smith Hall, Cornell University, Ithaca, NY 14853 (607) 255-0570. E-mail: jkr33@cornell.edu. *Research Interests*: Indigenous issues within a global context. She is conducting research in the Americas, Europe, New Zealand & Australia culminating in a new journal on Indigenous Aesthetics, and has a forthcoming book on Visualizing Sovereignty. *Past professional post*: Interim Chair, Art Dept., Cornell University, 2009-10. *Award, honors*: Recipient of a Cornell University Society of Humanities Fellowship on the thematic topic of "Global Aesthetics."

RIDING IN, JAMES (Pawnee)
(associate professor; Indian studies Interim Director)
Education: Haskell Indian Junior College, AA, 1974; Fort Lewis College, BA (History), 1976; University of California, Los Angeles, MA (American Indian Studies), 1985, PhD (History), 1991. *Affiliation & Address*: Associate Professor

& Interim Director, Arizona State University (ASU), American Indian Studies, College of Liberal Arts & Sciences, MC: 4603, 250 E. Lemon St., P.O. Box 874603, Tempe, AZ 85287 (480) 965-9360. E-mail: pawnee1@asu.edu. *Other professional posts*: Editor, Wicazo Sa Review: A Journal of Native American Studies, 2003-present; affiliated faculty, School of Justice Studies, ASU, 2004-present; member, American Indian Academic Coucil, ASU, 1990-present; member, Board of Trustees, Pawnee Nation College (chair, 2005-2013); member, Native American Advisory Board & Historical Consultant of the Eiteljorg Museum, Indianapolis, IN, 1998-present; member, Genoa Indian School Scholarship Committee, Genoa, NE, 2004-present. *Past professional posts*: Associate Professor, School of Justice Studies, ASU, 1998-2004; director, American Indian Justice Studies, ASU,1993-99; lecturer & assistant professor, School of Justice Studies, ASU, 1990-98; social studies instructor, Zuni Learning Center, Zuni Pueblo, NM, 1979-83. *Memberships*: American Indian Studies Assn; Indigenous Professors Assn. *Activities*: Lectures; presentations; educational video participations; *Publications*: Co-editor, Native Historians Write Back (Texas Tech University Press, 2010); book chapters, journal articles, book reviews, research reports.

RIDINGTON, ROBIN 1939-
(anthropologist; professor emeritus)
Born November 1, 1939, Camden, N.J. *Education*: Swarthmore, BA, 1962; Harvard University, Ph.D., 1968. *Address*: RR 2, Site 44 C-16, Galiano, BC V0N 1P0 Canada (250) 539-3095. E-mail: ridington@gulfislands.com. *Affiliations*: Professor of anthropology, University of British Columbia, Vancouver, BC, 1967-95, professor emeritus, 1995-present; associate dean of graduate studies, University of Retreat Island. *Memberships*: Society for Humanistic Anthropology (Canadian representative); Canadian Ethnology Society; American Anthropological Association. *Award*: 1989 Hubert Evans Non-Fiction Book Prize of British Columbia. *Interests*: Field research among Beaver Indians, 1964-; writing about Omaha ceremony, 1985-. *Biographical source*: "A Sacred Object as Text: Reclaiming the Sacred Pole of the Omaha Tribe," American Indian Quarterly, 1993. *Published works*: Articles: "From Artifice to Artifact: Stages in the Industrialization of a Northern Native Community" (Journal of Canadian Studies, 1983); "Stories of the Vision Quest Among Dunne-za Women" (Atlantis, 1983); "Beaver Indians" (The Canadian Encyclopedia, Hurtig, 1985); "Native People, Subarctic" (The Canadian Encyclopedia, Hurtig, 1985); "Fox and Chicadee: The Writing of Indian White History" in volume edited by Calvin Martin; "The Northern Hunters" (Newberry Library volume, America in 1492, Alvin Josephy, Editor, 1990). Books: Swan People: A Study of the Dunne-za Prophet Dance (National Museums of Canada, 1978); co-author, People of the Trail: How the Northern Forest Indians Lived (Douglas & McIntyre, 1978); co-author, People of the Longhouse: How the Iroquoian People Lived (Douglas & McIntyre, 1982; Trail to Heaven: Knowledge & Narrative in a Northern Native Community (U. of Iowa Press, 1988); Little Bit Know Something: Stories in a Language of Anthropology (U. of Iowa Press, 1990); Blessing for a Long Time: The Sacred Pole of the Omaha Tribe, with Dennis Hastings (U. of Nebraska Press, 1997).

RIFKIN, MARK
(professor of English)
Education: Rutgers University, BA, 1996; University of Pennsylvania, MA, 1999, PhD, 2003. *Affiliation*: Professor of English (2008-present), Department of English, University of North Carolina, Greensboro, MHRA 3129, 1111 Spring Garden St., Greensboro, NC 26412 (336) 334-5311. E-mail: m_rifkin@uncg.edu. *Other professional post*: President (2014-15, Native American & Indigenous Studies Association, Website: www.naisa.org. Dr. Rifkin's research primarily focuses on Native American writing and politics from the eighteenth century onward, exploring the ways that Indigenous peoples have negotiated U.S. racial and imperial formations. In particular, he is interested in how U.S. law shapes the possibilities for representing Native political identity and the ways that Native writers have worked to inhabit, refunction, refuse, and displace dominant administrative formulations in order to open room for envisioning and enacting self-determination. More recently, he has been drawing on queer theory to rethink the role kinship systems have played in Native governance and internationalism and to address the ways U.S. imperialism can be thought of as a system of compulsory heterosexuality. *Publications*: Settler Common Sense: Queerness and Everyday Colonialism in the American Renaissance, (University of Minnesota Press, 2014); The Erotics of Sovereignty: Queer Native Writing in the Era of Self-Determination (U. of Minnesota Press, 2012); When Did Indians Become Straight?: Kinship, The History of Sexuality, and Native Sovereignty (Oxford University Press, 2011); Sexuality, Nationality, Indigeneity: Rethinking the State at the Intersection of Native American and Queer Studies (special issue of "GLQ: A Journal of Lesbian and Gay Studies," co-edited with Daniel Heath Justice and Bethany Schneider, 16.1-2, 2010); Manifesting America: The Imperial Construction of U.S. National Space (Oxford University Press, 2009). *Articles*: "The Silence of Ely S. Parker: The Emancipation Sublime and the Limits of Settler Memory," (*Native American and Indigenous Studies*, 2014); "Queering Indigenous Pasts, or Temporalities of Tradition & Settlement," *Oxford Companion to Indigenous American Literatures*. Eds. Daniel Heath Justice and James Cox. (New York:

Oxford University Press, 2014. 137-151); "Making Peoples into Populations: The Racial Limits of Tribal Sovereignty," *Theorizing Native Studies*, eds. (Audra Simpson and Andrea Smith, Duke University Press, 2014. 149-187); "The Frontier as (Movable) Space of Exception, " *Settler Colonial Studies* 4.2 (2014): 176-180; "Settler Common Sense," *Settler Colonial Studies* 3.4 (2013): 322-340); "Shadows of Mashantucket: William Apess and the Representation of Pequot Place," *American Literature* 84.4 (2012): 691-714; "The Transatlantic Indian Problem," *American Literary History* 24.2 (2012): 337-355; "Settler States of Feeling: National Belonging and the Erasure of Native American Presence,"*Blackwell Companion to American Literary Studies*, eds. Robert Levine and Caroline Levander. New York: Wiley-Blackwell, 2011. 342-355; "The Erotics of Sovereignty," in *Queer Indigenous Studies: Critical Interventions in Theory, Politics, and Literature*. Eds. Qwo-Li Driskill, Chris Finley, Brian Joseph Gilley, and Scott Morgensen. Tucson: University of Arizona Press, 2011. 172-189; "Remapping the Family of Nations: The Geopolitics of Kinship in Hendrick Aupaumut's 'A Short Narration'," *Studies in American Indian Literature* 22.4 (2010): 1-31. *Awards, honors*: Best Subsequent Book in Native American and Indigenous Studies for 2011 (for *When Did Indians Become Straight?*), Native American and Indigenous Studies Association, 2013; John Hope Franklin Prize for best book in American Studies for 2011 (for *When Did Indians Become Straight?*), American Studies Association, 2012.

RIGDON, PHILIP (Yakama)
  (deputy director)
Affiliation & Address: Deputy Director, Department of Natural Resources, Yakama Nation, P.O. Box 151, Toppenish, WA 98948   (509) 865-5121 ext. 4648. *Other professional post*: Board President, Intertribal Timber Council, Portland, OR.

RIGGINS, IDA (Pit River)
  (former tribal chairperson)
Affiliation & Address: Former chairperson, Pit River Tribe, 36970 Park Ave., Burney, CA 96013 (530) 335-5421. E-mail: ida.riggins@frontiernet.net.

RILEY, ANGELA R. (Citizen Potawatomi of Oklahoma)
  (professor of law; American Indian studies center director)
Education: University of Oklahoma, BA; Harvard Law School, JD. *Affiliations*: Director & Professor of Law, MA/JD Program of UCLA School of Law, Los Angeles, CA 90024 (310) 825-7315. E-mail: riley@law.ucla.edu. *Other professional posts*: Co-Director, Native Nations Law & Policy Center. Member (Justice, 2003-2010; Chief Justice, 2010-present), Supreme Court of the Citizen Potawatomi Nation of Oklahoma (the first & youngest woman justice). Angela teaches & writes in the area of indigenous peoples' rights, with a particular emphasis on cultural property & Native governance. Her work has been published in the Yale Law Journal, Columbia Law Review, California Law Review, Washington Law Review, et al. *Past professional post*: Director, American Indian Studies Center, UCLA, Los Angeles, CA, 2010-15. *Awards, honors*: In 2003, Angela was selected to serve on her tribe's Supreme Court, becoming the first woman & youngest Justice of the Supreme Court of the Citizen Potawatomi Nation of Oklahoma. In 2010, she was elected as Chief Justice. She was recently appointed to serve on the United Nations – Indigenous People's Partnership Policy Board. Ms. Riley is also an Evidentiary Hearing Officer for the Morongo Band of Mission Indians.

RILEY, KURT (Pueblo of Acoma)
  (Pueblo governor)
Affiliation & Address: Governor, Pueblo of Acoma, P.O. Box 309, Acomita, NM 87034. (505) 552-6604.

RINER, REED D. 1941-
  (anthropologist/futurist)
Born December 22, 1941, Mentone, Ind. *Education*: University of Colorado, Ph.D., 1977 (dissertation: A Study of Attitudes Toward Formal Education Among Indian Parents and Students in Six Communities. *Principal occupation*: Professor of anthropology, Northern Arizona State University, Flagstaff, 1975-. *Address*: 506 Charles Rd., Flagstaff, AZ 86001. *Military service*: U.S. Naval Reserve, 1963-68. *Memberships*: American Anthropological Association; Society for Applied Anthropology; High Plains Society for Applied Anthropology (past president); World Future Studies Federation; World Future Society - Professional Section; Contact Cultures of the Imagination (board of directors). *Interests*: "My primary professional interests are applied futures research; Native American Indian studies, especially Indian education; and the application of anthropology in the solution of--especially institutional--organizational problems such as the future of Native American Indians." *Published works*: Numerous articles in professional journals.

RIOS, CRYSTAL (Maidu)
  (tribal vice chairperson)
Affiliation & Address: Vice Chairperson, Greenville Rancheria, 1425 Montgomery Rd., Red Bluff, CA 96080 (530) 528-8600.

RIOS, DORIE (Potawatomi)
  (tribal vice chairperson)
Affiliation & Address: Vice Chairperson, Nottawaseppi Huron Band of Potawatomi, 2221 - 1 1/2 Mile Rd., Fulton, MI 49052 (269) 729-5151. E-mail: dorier@nhbpi.com

RISLING, DALE, SR. (Hoopa)
  (BIA agency deputy regional director)
Affiliation & Address: Deputy Director – Indian Services, Bureau of Indian Affairs, Pacific Regional Office, 2800 Cottage Way, Sacramento, CA 95825 (916) 978-6000; E-mail: dale.risling@bia.gov

RISLING, GARY (Hoopa)
  (former tribal vice chairperson)
Affiliation & Address: Hoopa Valley Tribe, P.O. Box 1348, Hoopa, CA 95546 (530) 625-4211. E-mail: gary.risling@hoopa-nsn.gov

RISLING, LOIS (Hupa)
  (center director)
Affiliation: Center for Indian Community Development, Humboldt University, Brero House 93, Arcata, CA 95521 (707) 826-3711.

RISLING, MARY
  (attorney)
Affiliation: California Indian Legal Services, 324 F St., Suite A, Eureka, CA 95501 (707) 443-8397.

RITCHIE, KIP (Forest County Potawatomi)
  (chief operations officer)
Education: University of Wisconsin-Madison, BA. *Affiliation & Address*: Founding member & Chief Operations Officer, Potawatomi Business Development Corporation (Sr. VP, 2005-10; COO, 2010-present), 320 E. Buffalo St., Suite 607, Milwaukee, WI 53202 (414) 727-2041. Through the corporation, Richie promotes the importance of investing in the Tribe's future by diversifying resources beyond gaming. *Other professional posts*: Chairperson, Forest County Potawatomi Community Foundation's Board of Directors, 2000-present; member, Board of Directors, Native American Contractors Assn, Washington, DC; board member, National Center for American Indian Enterprise Development; senior strategist, Blue Stone Strategy Group, Irvine, CA. *Past professional posts*: Director of Marketing & Assistant General Manager, Potawatomi Bingo Casino, 1997-2005. *Community service*: Children's Health Alliance Board of Directors; Froedtert Hospital Foundation Board of Directors; Native American Contractors Association Board; Native American Finance Conference Board; National Indian Gaming Association-Associate Member Board; American Indian Business Network Advisory Board. *Awards, honors*: Recognized by the Business Journal as one of Milwaukee's "40 under 40" in 2000.

RITTER, BETH R. 1961-
  (anthropologist, geographer)
Born June 21, 1961, Kearney, Neb. *Education*: University of Nebraska, MA, 1990, PhD, 1996. *Address*: 2725 S. 16th, Lincoln, NE 68502 (402) 472-9677. *Affiliations*: Anthropologist, National Park Service, Lincoln, NE, 1993-94; instructor, University of Nebraska, Lincoln, 1992-. *Other professional post*: Consultant, Ponca Tribe of Nebraska & Black Eagle Corp. *Memberships*: American Anthropological Association; Society for Applied Anthropology. *Interests*: "Primary interest is the Plains Indians & contemporary issues; Federal Indian policy; Native American political & legal systems; Indian gaming (consultant to Ponca Tribe of Nebraska during recent (1990) restoration of their federally-terminated status)." *Published works*: Articles: "The Ponca Tribe of Nebraska: The Process of Restoration of a Federally-Terminated Tribe," in Human Organization, 1992; "The Politics of Retribalization: The Northern Ponca Case," in Great Plains Research, 1994; "Will the House Win: Does Sovereignty Rule in Indian Casinos," in Great Plains Research, 1994.

RITZ, LAN BROOKES
  (writer/filmmaker)
Affiliation & Address: Writer/filmmaker, Brown Bird Productions, 1971 N. Curson Ave., Hollywood, CA 90046 (213) 851-8928. *Film produced*: Annie Mae - Brave Hearted Woman (written, produced & directed by Lan Brookes Ritz) this film is an account of recent Native American history told from the intimate perspective of a dedicated young Indian woman killed on a reservation in the aftermath of the human rights stand at Wounded Knee (16mm, 80 minutes, color). *Awards, honors*: Best Motion Picture, American Indian Film Festival; Award of Excellence, Film Advisory Board; Best in Category, San Francisco International Film Festival. Featured screenings: Museum of Modern Art, New York, NY; Kennedy Center, Washington, DC; London and Melbourne Film Festivals; Cinema du reel, France; etc. Interest: Visual design.

RIVERA, ANTHONY, JR. (Juaneno Mission Indians)
(former tribal chairperson)
Affiliation: Juaneno Band of Mission Indians (Acjachemen Nation), 31411-A La Matanza St., San Juan Capistrano, CA 92675 (949) 488-3484.

RIVERA, BARRY L. (Lenni Lenape)
(historical society secretary)
Address & Affiliation: Lenni Lenape Historical Society, 2825 Fish Hatchery Rd., Allentown, PA 18103 (610) 797-2121. E-mail: lenape@lenape.org.

RIVERA, GEORGE (Pojoaque Pueblo)
(Pueblo governor)
Affiliation & Address: Governor, Pueblo of Pojoaque, 78 Cities of Gold Rd., Santa Fe, NM 87506 (505) 455-3334.

RIVERA, J. CARLOS (Pomo/Mexican)
(executive director)
Affiliation & Address: Executive Director, Coyhis Publishing & White Bison, Inc., 6145 Lehman Dr., Suite 200, Colorado Springs, CO 80918 (719) 548-1000. Website: www.whitebison.org. E-mail: info@whitebison.org. He served as a substance abuse treatment provider for 10-years at the Sacramento Native American Health Center, Inc. providing services to adult men and women on parole, juvenile offenders and other referrals from the Department of Corrections. He continues to make a difference in Native Tribal communities serving as the Executive Director for White Bison, Inc. In his role he oversees daily operations and is also passionate about developing new curriculum to better meet the needs of Native American/Alaska Native communities. Carlos has also been an active committee member for the Juvenile Justice & Delinquency State Committee for California, appointed by Governor Jerry Brown.

RIVERA, PAULA (Taos Pueblo)
(Indian market manager/artist services)
Affiliation & Address: Indian Market Manager/Artist Services, Southwestern Association for Indian Arts, P.O. Box 969, Santa Fe, NM 87504 (505) 983-5220. E-mail: privera@swiai.org. *Past professional posts*: Curatorial Assistant, Wheelwright Museum of the American Indian; worked at the Millicent Rogers Museum, Museum of Indian Arts & Culture, & the Museum of Contemporary Native Art. Her professional experience ranges from Collections Care to Conservation & Preservation. As an independent researcher, she was able to curate exhibitions, & assist with publications about Native American artists.

RIVERS, THOMAS (Choctaw-Apache)
(tribal chief/chairperson)
Affiliation & Address: Chief, Choctaw-Apache Tribe of Ebarb, P.O. Box 1428, Zwolle, LA 71486 (318) 645-2588.

RIVES, CAPT. MARK (Crow Creek Sioux)
(IHS chief information officer)
Education: Oklahoma State University, BS (Economics); Oklahoma City University, MBA; University of Phoenix, MS (Comuter Information Systems); Robert Morris University (Pittsburgh, PA) School of Communications & Information Systems, DSc. *Affiliation & Address*: Chief Information Officer & Director of the Office of Information Technology, Indian Health Service (IHS), DHH, 801 Thompson Ave., Rockville, MD 20852 (301) 443-1083. Mark is responsible for advising senior IHS leadership on all aspects of information resource management & technology & ensures IHS compliance with information technology laws, regulations and policies. Under his leadership, OIT designs, develops, implements & maintains policies, budgets, standards, architecture & systems for IHS information technology, including the IHS information technology security program that protects HIS resources. OIT also participates in cross-government initiatives and collaborates with federal, tribal, state and other partners to serve American Indians and Alaska Natives. Rives began his career with the Indian Health Service in 2002 at the Claremore Indian Hospital in Claremore, Okla., as an Information Technology Specialist & subsequently became the manager of the Information Technology Department. In 2006, he joined the Oklahoma City Area Office as the Information Systems Security Officer. In 2008, Rives joined OIT, serving in numerous capacities, including, most recently, Deputy Chief Information Officer. *Awards, honors*: In 2013, CAPT Rives was selected as the Health Services Officer IT Specialist of the Year for the U.S. Public Health Service. In 2014, CAPT Rives received the IHS Director's Award for leadership in Health Information Technology.

ROBBINS, KENNETH (Standing Rock Sioux)
(organization president; co-publisher & writer)
Affiliations: National Center for American Indian Enterprise Development, 953 E. Juanita Ave., Mesa, AZ 85204 (480) 545-1298. Co-publisher & writer, with A. David Lester, of "RedEarth" Magazine, Council Publications, Denver, CO.

ROBBINS, REBECCA (Standing Rock Sioux)
(writer)
Education: PhD. *Affiliation*: Writer, "RedEarth" Magazine, Council Publications, 695 S. Colorado Blvd., Suite 10, Denver, CO 80246 (303) 282-7576.

ROBERTS, BARBARA (Lummi) 1955-
(college administrator)
Born June 14, 1955, Bellingham, Wash. *Education*: Walla Walla College, BA, 1977; University of Hawaii, MPH, 1980. *Address*: 2730 Cagey Rd., Bellingham, WA 98226-9287 (206) 676-2772. *Affiliations*: Dept. Head, Lummi Health & Human Services, Bellingham (ten years); Title III Director, Personnel Officer, Northwest Indian College, Bellingham, 1990-. *Interests*: Development of culturally relevant curriculum for college courses.

ROBERTS, CARLA A. (Delaware) 1957-
(consultant)
Born in 1957. *Education*: University of Alaska, Fairbanks, BFA, 1979; University of Iowa, MFA, 1981. *Principal occupation*: Consultant. *Address*: ATLATL, P.O. Box 34090, Phoenix, AZ 85067 (602) 277-3711. *Affiliations*: Coordinator, Univerity of Alaska, Rural Education, Fairbanks, AK, 1976-79; assistant director, Intermedia Arts-Minnesota, University of Minnesota, Minneapolis, 1982-86; executive director, Boston Film/Videl Foundation, Boston, MA, 1986-87; consultant, Art Management for Boston Conservatory, Indian Hill Arts, University of Lowell, Center for Native American Awareness, 1988-91; executive director, ATLATL, Phoenix, AZ. *Other professional posts*: Consultant, Tribal Museum Program, Arizona Commission on the Arts, Phoenix, AZ, 1991-; speaking engagements. *Community activities*: National Endowment for the Arts (panelist, Jan. 1992; advisory group, 1991-93) panelist, Arizona Commission on the Arts, Phoenix, AZ, 1991-; board member, Indian Hill Arts, Littleton, MA, 1991. *Published works*: ATLATL: Serving the Needs of Native American Artists, Art View (National Assembly of State Arts Agencies, Washington, DC, 1991).

ROBERTS, CHRIS 1948-
(photographer/writer; video/book distributor)
Born March 29, 1948, London, England. *Education*: Masters Degree in Interpersonal Communications. *Principal occupation*: Photographer/writer; video/book distributor. *Affiliation & Address*: Meadowlark Media, P.O. Box 7218, Missoula, MT 59807 (406) 728-2180. *Military service*: U.S. Army, 1966-70. *Community activities*: Powwow Committee; Boy Scouts of America. *Published works*: Powwow Country, 1993; People of the Circle, 1998.

ROBERTS, ALBERT (Paiute)
(tribal vice chairperson)
Affiliation & Address: Vice Chairperson, Yerington Paiute Tribe, 171 Campbell Lane, Yerrington, NV 89447 (775) 463-3301. E-mail: chairman@ypt-nsn.gov.

ROBERTS, KEITH (Cherokee)
(president; board secretary-treasurer)
Affiliation: President, Raincor, Inc., Colleyville, TX. (817) 858-0972. E-mail: keith.roberts@raincorinc.com. *Other professional post*: Secretary-treasurer, board of directors, American Indian Chamber of Commerce of Texas (AICCT), 11245 Indian Trail, 2nd Fl., Dallas, TX 75229 (972) 241-6450. E-mail: kroberts@aicct.com.

ROBERTS, LAWRENCE S. (Oneida of Wisconsin)
(Acting Assistant Secretary for Indian Affairs,
   U.S. Dept. of the Interior)
Education: University of Wisconsin-Madison, BS, 1992; University of Wisconsin Law School, JD, 1995. *Affiliation & Address*: Acting Assistant Secretary for Indian Affairs (2013-present), U.S. Department of the Interior, 1849 C St., NW, MS-3658-MIB, Washington, DC 20240 (202) 208-3710. *Past professional posts*: Trial Attorney, Indian Resources Section, U.S. Department of Justice; worked in private practice on federal Indian law and environmental matters; chair, Native American Resources Committee of the American Bar Association's Section of Environmental, Energy and Resources, 2003-05; General Counsel of the National Indian Gaming Commission, 2010-12. He served as the Deputy Ass't Secretary for Indian Affairs from 2012-13.

ROBERTS, MICHAEL E. (*Teix Shaach Tsin*) (Tlingit)
(institute president)
Education: University of Colorado, BS (Environmental Design in Architecture); University of Washington, MBA. *Affiliation & Address*: President (2006-present), First Nations Development Institute, 2432 Main St., 2nd Fl., Longmont, CO 80501 (303) 774-7836. E-mail: mroberts@firstnations.org. Mike is responsible for First Nation's overall vision & coordination for programmatic, administrative and grant making strategies & lead spokesman for the Institute. *Other professional post*: Founding board member & chairperson, First Nations' Oweesta Corp.; Member, Grants Review Committee, First Nations' Eagle Staff Fund; serves on the advisory council of the Center for Native American Public Radio (CNAPR), serves on the National Advisory Committee for the National

Center for Family Philanthropy, as well as on the advisory committee for the Lakota Fund. *Past professional posts*: Michael operated his own consulting firm, Camus Consulting, Denver CO; consultant, Heritage Private Equity Fund; past board member & treasurer, Association for Enterprise Opportunity (AEO).

ROBERTS, ROY (Eastern Cherokee)
(chamber of commerce president)
Affiliation & Address: President, American Indian Chamber of Commerce of North Carolina, 8200 Brownleigh Dr., Raleigh, NC 27617 (919) 247-4946.

ROBERTSON, DONALD
(Dakota studies program director)
Affiliation & Address: Director & Faculty, Indigenous Nations & Dakota Studies Program, Department of Social Sciences, SS103, Southwest Minnesota State University, 1501 State St., Marshall, MN 56258 (507) 537-6699. E-mail: don.robertson@smsu.edu.

ROBERTSON, ELLEN (Cherokee) 1945-
(reference librarian)
Born March 7, 1945, Washington, D.C. *Education*: University of California, Berkeley, B.A., 1973, M.L.S., 1974. *Address*: 3000 18th St., Boulder, CO 80304 (303) 939-9003. *Affiliation*: Reference librarian & online search service coordinator, University of Colorado, University Libraries, Boulder, 1984-present. *Past professional posts*: Librarian, American Indian Law Center, University of New Mexico School of Law, Albuquerque, N.M., 1975-77; reference librarian, University of New Mexico General Libraries, 1977-84. *Memberships*: American Library Association; Colorado Library Association.

ROBERTSON, KIMBERLY (Muscogee Creek)
(professor of American Indian studies)
Education: University of Northern Colorado, BA, 1999; University of Michigan, MA, 2001; University of California, Los Angeles, MA, 2008, PhD, 2012. *Affiliation & Address*: Assistant Professor, American Indian Studies Program, Jerome Richfield 219, 18111 Nordhoff St., University of California, Northridge, CA 91330 (818) 677-3418. E-mail: Kimberly.robertson@csun.edu. Her academic interests include the relationships between violence against Native women, construction of identity, urbanity, sovereignty, & indigienous feminism.

ROBERTSON, LINDSAY
(attorney; law professor; faculty director)
Education: Davidson College, AB, 1981; University of Virginia, MA, 1986; University of Virginia Law School, JD, 1986; University of Virginia, PhD, 1997. *Affiliation & Address*: Faculty Director, Center for the Study of American Indian Law & Policies, University of Oklahoma College of Law, 300 Timberdell Rd., Norman, OK 73019 (405) 325-4699. E-mail: lrobertson@ou.edu. Dr. Robertson teaches courses in Federal Indian Law, Comparative Indigenous Peoples Law, Constitutional Law & Legal History. *Other professional post*: Associate Director, Inter-American Center for Law & Culture, University of Oklahoma College of Law; special justice, Supreme Court of the Cheyenne-Arapaho Tribes; member, board of directors, Oklahoma Indian Legal Services, Oklahoma City, OK. *Membership*: Oklahoma Bar Assn. *Past professional posts*: Taught Federal Indian Law at the University of Virginia; judicial clerk at the U.S. District Court for the District of Delaware; Research & Visiting Fellow at the Philadelphia Center for Early American Studies, 1992-94. *Published works*: Conquest by Law (Oxford University Press, 2005); "The Foundations of Federal Indian Law and Its Application in the Twentieth Century" *Beyond Red Power: American Indian Politics and Activism Since 1900*. (with Tiawagi Helton. Ed. Daniel M. Cobb & Loretta Fowler. SAR Press, 2008).

ROBERTSON, PAUL M. (Tohono O'odham)
(college president)
Affiliation & Address: President, Tohono O'odam Community College, P.O. Box 3129, Sells, AZ 85634 (520) 383-8401

ROBIDEAU, BRIGETTE (Sac & Fox of Missouri)
(former tribal chairperson)
Affiliation & Address: Sac & Fox Nation of Missouri in Kansas & Nebraska, 305 N. Main St., Reserve, KS 66434 (785) 742-0053.
E-mail: brobidoux@sacandfoxcasino.com

ROBBINS, KIPPY (Coquille)
(tribal vice chairperson)
Affiliation & Address: Vice Chairperson, Coquille Indian Tribe, P.O. Box 783, North Bend, OR 97549 (541) 756-0904. E-mail: kippyrobbins@coquilletribe.org.

ROBINSON, AARON (Menominee of Wisconsin)
(physician)
Education: University of Wisconsin at Oshkosh, BS (Biology); University of Wisconsin School of Medicine & Public Health, MPH, MS IV, 2017. As the Technology & Social Media Coordinator, I hope to further strengthen the bond

that we all share & increase the networking capabilities and support networks of ANAMS, the Association of American Indian Physicians, and everyone else involved in the pursuit of better health care. Native communities face challenges that others don't in terms of health care, and I hope to help address these challenges as well as learn from others. *Activities*: President (2016-17), Association of Native American Medical Students.

ROBINSON, DENTEN D. (Dine'-Navajo)
(attorney)
Education: Southern Utah University, BA, 2001; Columbia Law School, JD, 2005. *Affiliation & Address*: Partner, Rothstein, Donatelli, Hughes, Dahlstrom, Schoenburg & Bienvenu, LLP, 80 E. Rio Salado Parkway, Suite 710, Tempe, AZ 85281 (480) 921-9296. E-mail: drobinson@rothsteinlaw.com. *Practice area*: Indian law. Denton specializes in representing Tribes & Tribal entities in various areas of the law including real estate, corporate, employment & gaming. *Other professional posts*: Native American Bar Association (director & treasurer, 2007-present). *Past professional post*: Associate, Quarles & Brady, LLP, Phoenix Branch. *Memberships*: State native American Bar Association (Director & Treasurer, 2007-present); State Bar of Arizona (Indian Law Section & Real Estate Section, 2006-present; Maricopa County Bar Association.

ROBINSON, GARY (Cherokee/Mississippi Choctaw) 1950-
(filmmaker, writer, producer, director)
Born January 12, 1950, Dallas, Tex. *Education*: University of Texas, Austin, BS, 1973; MA (Radio, TV, Film), 1978. *Affiliation & Address*: Writer, Producer, Director, Tribal Eye Productions (website: www.tribaleyepro.com), P.O. Box 1123, Santa Ynez, CA 93460 (855) 392-1803. E-mail: garyd1123@gmail.com. *Past professional posts*: Production assistant, Instructional Media Department, Tulsa Public Schools, Tulsa, OK 1973-74; media specialist, Texas Department of Mental Health/Mental Retardation, Austin, TX 1975-78; branch sales manager, Magnetic Media Corp., Austin, TX, 1978-1979; Writer, producer, director of video programs about the history, culture and current affairs of the Muscogee (Creek) Indian Nation, Okmulgee, OK, 1981-90; owner-producer, Pathfinder Communications (produced programs for other Indian organizations & clients), Okmulgee, OK, 1981-90; vice president, American Indian Media Services (planned & supervised projects, produced media programs for Indian tribal governments, Indian-owned businesses & Indian organizations; developed Oklahoma statewide American Indian newspaper called "Intertribal."); independent writer/producer/media consultant, Spirit World Productions, Santa Fe, NM, 1992-present. *Awards, honors*: "Dances for the New Generations" (director of photography) Emmy-nominated documentary & "Best Documentary" awards at film festivals - on the American Indian Dance Theater and the tribal roots of these dances. *Interests*: Robinson has been working on several film and video projects with his partner & wife Joanelle Nadine Romero (Apache) with their company "Spirit World Productions. He is co-creator & co-producer of "The Red Nation Celebration, an annual live performance of contemporary and traditional Native American Entertainment, and co-creator of "Red Blanket," a contemporary Native American TV series, which is currently being pitched to TV executives in Hollywood. He has also written two feature film screenplays which are available for production and is currently writing a novel. Robinson writes, "Throughout my adult life, one of my over-riding interests has always been, & continues to be, the promotion of understanding between diverse cultural and ethnic groups, to promote a better understanding of the roles that culture, history and the arts play in our daily lives, and to promote an ethnic & cultural diversity within the arts." *Avocational interests*: music, religion, movies, travel. *Video productions*: He has written, produced, directed, shot and/or edited more than 100 video /television programs about Native American history, culture, health, education, economic development and other contemporary issues affecting Native peoples. Recent project credits include: director of "Allan Houser: A Listing Vision"; writer/director, "Home, Home On the Rez"; a demo episode of "Red Blanket" series; director of photography on an international co-production, "Storytellers of the Pacific" for PBS; co-producer & director of photographer on Melvin & John, 1994, a segment on American Indians with AIDS for a PBS documentary series; and director of "Where the Red Road Meets the Information Superhighway, 1994, an introduction to telecommuni-cations technologies for tribal communities. *Published works*: Tribal Journey & Thunder on the Plains (young adult books) (Native Voices/Book Publishing Co., 2013); Native American Twelve Days of Christmas (children's book) (Clearlight Publishing, 2011); The Language of Victory, 2011; Native American Night Before Christmas (children's book) (Clearlight Publishing, 2010); From Warriors to Soldiers, 2008 Driving the Chumash Highway, 2008; Those Who Defend Us: Honoring Chumash Veterans & Active Duty Soldiers, 2009.

ROBINSON, MICHAEL A.
(attorney)
Education: Eastern Michigan University, BA, 1992; Ohio State University, MA (History), 1994; University of New Mexico School of Law, JD, 1999. *Address & Affiliation*: Associate (2003-present), Monteau & Peebles, LLP, 1001 Second St., Sacramento, CA 95814 (916) 441-2700. E-mail: mrobinson.ndnlaw.com. *Practice areas*: Gaming law; litigation; tribal sovereignty; natural resources &

environmental law. Mr. Robinson has a strong background in Indian, natural resource & environmental law. *Practice experience*: While attorney at Nevada Legal Services, he provided legal representation to individual Indian clients, as well as tribes in all areas of Indian law, including protection of tribal water rights. With the New Mexico Wilderness Alliance, Michael practiced extensively in the areas of natural resources & environmental law, working closely with New Mexico tribes on land claims issues. *Past professional posts*: Staff Attorney, Nevada Legal Services, 1999-2000; director of Wilderness Protection/staff attorney, New Mexico Wilderness Alliance, 2002-2003. *Membership*: California State Bar.

ROBINSON, PRENTICE (Cherokee) 1932-
(retired teacher; business owner)
Born September 25, 1932, Hominy, Okla. *Education*: Masters Degree in Education. *Address*: 4158 E. 48 Place, Tulsa, OK 74135 (918) 749-3082. E-mail: prenticewillena@aol.com. Website: www.cherokeemadeeasy.com. *Affiliation*: Owner (with wife Willena), Cherokee Language & Culture; president & secretary, Cherokee Heritage Indian Education Foundation (C.H.I.E.F.) (purpose is to preserve Cherokee history on video). *Military service*: U.S. Army, 1954-56. *Community activities*: Active in Church; on call for questions on Cherokee history and language. At present, working on a major monument/ memorial for Cherokee history. *Interests*: Recording and preserving Cherokee language. *Memberships*: First Methodist Church; National Woodcarvers Association. *Published works*: Cherokee Made Easy (booklet with three 60-minute tapes or CDs); Cherokee Language Workbook with tape; Out of the Flame (beliefs & practices of the ancients).

ROBINSON, WILLENA (Cherokee) 1938-
(retired teacher; business owner)
Born February 13, 1938, Peggs, Okla. *Education*: Teacher's Degree. Address: 4158 E. 48 Place, Tulsa, OK 74135 (918) 749-3082. E-mail: prenticewillena@aol.com. Website: www.cherokeemadeeasy.com. *Affiliation*: Owner (with husband Prentice), Cherokee Language & Culture, 1974-present; Cherokee Heritage Indian Education Foundation (C.H.I.E.F.), 1991-present. The purpose of the Foundation is to preserve Cherokee history on video. *Community activities*: Active in Church; on call for questions on Cherokee history and language. At present, working on a major monument/memorial for Cherokee history. *Interests*: Designing, writing, painting, Cherokee history & research. *Memberships*: First Methodist Church; C.H.I.E.F. *Published works*: Design artist and proof writer - Cherokee Made Easy (booklet with tapes); Cherokee Language Workbook/tape; Out of the Flame (beliefs & practices of ancients).

ROCHA, FELIX, JR. (United Lumbee) 1945-
(criminal investigator)
Born March 29, 1945, San Antonio, Tex. *Education*: Golden West College, 1999). *Principal occupation*: Criminal Investigator. *Address*: 9867 Sturgeon Ave., Fountain Valley, CA 92708 (714) 964-3939. *Affiliation*: U.S. Dept. of Justice/Immigration & Naturalization Service (primarily in the Investigation Division/Organized Crime Unit), 1967-. *Military service*: U.S. Air Force, 1966. *Community activities*: Elected to the Orange County Board of Education, 1992 & 1996 (four year terms); currently President of the Board of Education. *Memberships*: American Legion, 1972- (formerly post commander; currently Commissioner for Boys State). *Published works*: Screenplays: Snakeheads; For the Greater Good; and Diary of a Special Agent.

ROCHA, VICTOR
(Internet owner & editor)
Affiliation & Address: Owner, Victor Rocha Communications, LLC, P.O. Box 892559, Temecula, CA 92589. E-mail: victor@pechanga.net. Facebook: Victor Rocha @victorrocha1. Editor, Pechanga.net. Following politics & policy of Native American & commercial gambling since 1998. Victor is owner and editor of Pechanga.net. Rocha has been involved in the politics of Indian gaming since 1998. *Honors, awards*: National Indian Gaming Association's 2002 Outstanding Contribution to Indian Country, VCAT's 2001 Catalyst Award, Global Gaming Business Magazine's "40 Under 40," Raving's 2012 Casino Marketing Lifetime Achievement Award, & the AGA's Lifetime Achievment for Gaming Marketing.

ROCHE, ROBERT (Chirichau Apache)
(Indian center director)
Affiliation & Address: Executive Director (1992-present), American Indian Education Center, 2303 Brookpark Rd., Parma, OH 44102 (216) 351-4488. E-mail: aiecinc@aol.com.

ROCK, PATRICK, M.D. (Leech Lake Ojibwe)
(medical director)
Education: University of North Dakota School of Medicine, M.D.; Residency – Hennepin County Medical Center. *Affiliation*: CEO & Medical Director, Indian Health Board of Minneapolis, 1315 East 24th St., Minneapolis, MN 55404 (612) 721-9800. Dr. Rock is board certified in family practice. *Other*

professional posts: Regional representative for the Bemidji area and president (2010-2012) for the National Council of Urban Indian Health (NCUIH) Board.

ROCK, REX A. (*Kakianaaq*) (Inupiat)
(president & CEO)
Education: University of Alaka, Fairbanks, BS (Linguistics & Engineering). *Affiliation & Address*: President & CEO (2010-present), Arctic Slope Regional Corporation, P.O. Box 129, Barrow, AK 99723 (907) 852-8633. Rock has served on the ASRC board of directors since 1993. Served as president & CEO of Tikigaq Corporation and continues on the board of directors.

ROCKEFELLER, DOROTHY
(Indian education program director)
Affiliation & Address: Unified School Dist. #321, Kaw Valley Special Services, Indian Education Program, P.O. Box 578, Rossville, KS 66533 (913) 584-6731.

RODDA, TIMOTHY A. (Kaweah)
(tribal chief)
Affiliation: Cawis-California Kawweah Tribe, 23514 Archibald Ave., Carson, CA 90745.

RODEE, MARIAN E. 1940-
(museum curator; consultant-Native American art)
Born March 13, 1940, Philadelphia, Penna. *Education*: University of Pennsylvania, B.A., 1961; Columbia University, M.A., 1965. *Address*: 413 Camino de la Sierra N.E., Albuquerque, NM 87123 (505) 298-3105. *Affiliation*: Museum curator; consultant on Native American art, Maxwell Museum of Anthropology, University of New Mexico, Albuquerque, NM (registrar, 1970-73; associate curator, 1975-76; curator, 1977-. *Other professional posts*: Shows & brochures for Museum, 1972-; lecturer, Art Department, College of Fine Arts, University of New Mexico; seminars, exhibits & classes. *Memberships*: Smithsonian Institution; Textile Museum; Textile Society; New Mexico Association of Museums. *Awards, honors*: Smithsonian Fellowship for Studies in Conservation, 1978-79, 1981-82; Pasold Fellowship, 1982; Smithsonian Institution Visiting Fellowship, 1987 (study of the 19th century Zuni fetishes); New Mexico Humanities Council grant, 1989 (visit Zuni and do study of fetish carvers. Interests: "In the past 15 years, I have examined the collections of Native American & Spanish American weaving along with the storage, exhibition and conservation techniques of various museums." *Biographical sources*: Who's Who in American Women. *Published works*: One Hundred Years of Navajo Rugs (University of New Mexico Press, 1995); Fetish Carvers of Zuni, with James Ostler (Maxwell Museum of Anthropology, 1995).

RODERIQUE, CHARLOTTE (Burns Paiute)
(former tribal chairperson)
Affiliation & Address: Former Chairperson, Burns Paiute Tribe, 100 Pasigo St., Burns, OR 97720 (541) 573-1910.

RODEWALD, ROYETTA (Prairie Band Potawatomi)
(judicial administrator)
Affiliation: Prairie Band Potawatomi Nation Tribal Court, 15498 K Rd., Mayetta, KS 66509 (866) 966-2242 or (785) 966-2242. E-mail: tribalcourt@pbpnation. org. Website: www.pbpnation.org/tribalcourt

RODGERS, DONALD WAYNE (Catawba)
(tribal chief)
Affiliation: Catawba Indian Tribe, 996 Avenue of the Nations, Catawba, SC 29730 (803) 366-4792. E-mail: donaldr@comporium.net.

RODGERS, ED (Quapaw)
(tribal chairperson)
Address & Affiliation: Delaware Executive Committee, P.O. Box 765, Quapaw, OK 74363 (918) 542-1853.

RODGERS, JUANITA (Navajo)
(board secretary-treasurer)
Affiliation & Address: Sec.-treas., National Indian Youth Council, 318 Elm St. SE, Albuquerque, NM 87102 (505) 247-2251. E-mail: erodgers@niyc-alb.org.

RODGERS, WAYNE (*Guardian Bear*) (New River Metis)
(tribal chief)
Affiliation: New River Tribe of Metis, P.O. Box 1126, Laurel Springs, NC 28644 (910) 657-8891.

RODGERS, WILLIAM H., JR.
(professor of environmental law)
Education: Harvard University, BA, 1961; Columbia School of Law, JD, 1965. *Affiliation & Address*: Stimson Bullitt Endowed Professor of Environmental Law, University of Washington School of Law, William H. Gates Hall, Box 353020, Seattle, WA 98195 (206) 543-5182. E-mail: whr@uw.edu. *Published works*: Environmental Law in Indian Country, Vol. 1 of 2 (Thomson West, 2005); co-

author, The Si'lailo Way: Salmon, Indians & Law on the Columbia River (Carolina Academic Press, 2006).

RODRIGUEZ, STAN (Santa Ysabel Lipay)
  (chair of Indian college)
Affiliation & Address: Chairperson, D-Q University, 33250 County Road 31, P.O. Box 409, Davis, CA 95617 (530) 758-0470

RODRIGUEZ, THOMAS (Luiseno)
  (tribal chairperson)
Affiliation & Address: Chairperson, La Jolla Band of Luiseno Indians, 22000 Hwy. 76, Pauma Valley, CA 92061 (760) 742-3771.

ROEHL, IDA (Athapascan)
  (village president)
Affiliation: Dillingham Village Council, P.O. Box 216, Dillingham, AK 99576 (907) 842-2384.

ROEHL, PAT
  (Indian education program director)
Affiliation: Fresno Unified School District, Indian Education Program, 2348 Mariposa St., Fresno, CA 93726 (559) 457-3634.

ROELS, STARLA K.
  (attorney)
Education: Arizona State University, BA, 1992; Northwestern School of Law of Lewis & Clark College, J.D., 1996. *Affiliation & Address*: Associate, Hobbs, Straus, Dean & Walker, LLP (1999-present), 806 SW Broadway, Suite 900, Portland, OR 97205 (503) 242-1745. E-mail: sroels@hsdwor.com. *Professional activities*: Her work includes a wide range of issues, including salmon & natural resources, health care, employment & personnel, and matters under the Indian Self-Determination & Education Assistance Act. She also was actively involved in the reauthorization of the Indian Health Care Improvement Act by assisting the national Steering Committee of tribal leaders in developing legislative language and exploring policy issues relating to health facilities. Starla has made numerous presentations on tribal rights and the ESA. She also participated in a national dialog on HCPs (Habitat Conservation Plans) to address tribal participation in such ESA planning processes. *Past professional post*: Policy analyst with the Columbia River Inter-Tribal Fish Commission, focusing on treaty-reserved fishing rights and the impacts on those rights caused by hydroelectric dams. *Memberships*: Oregon State Bar Association (member, Environmental & Natural Resources Section; Chair, Executive Committee, Indian Section; editor, "The Arrow's Edge," newsletter).

ROEN, TODD M. (Ojibwe)
  (attorney)
Education: State University of New York, BA, 1992; University of Minnesota College of Law, JD, 1996. *Affiliation & Address*: Associate Attorney, BlueDog, Paulson & Small, PLLP, Southgate Office Plaza, Suite 500, 5001 West 80th, Bloomington, MN 55437 (952) 893-1813. Todd has practiced Indian law fpr more than ten years. He represents tribal governments, tribal governmental entities & tribal businesses. Mr. Roen has worked with tribal governments in the areas of gaming, housing, enrollment, environmental protection, tax law, education, construction law and child welfare. *Practice admissions*: Mille Lacs Band of Ojibwe Tribal Court; Bad River Band of Chippewa Tribal Court; Shakopee Mdwewakanton Sioux (Dakota) Community Tribal Court; Spirit Lake Tribal Court. *Memberships*: Minnesota American Indian Bar Association; American bar Association.

ROESSEL, CHARLES M. (Monty) (Navajo) 1961-
  (Indian college president)
Education: University of Northern Colorado, BS, 1984; Prescott College, MA (Journalism), 1995; Arizona State University, DEd (Administration & Supervision), 2007. *Address*: P.O. Box 3034, Kayenta, AZ 86033 (928) 697-3417. *Affiliation & Address*: President, Dine College, 1 Circle Dr., 3rd Floor, Ned Hatathlie Center, P.O. Box 126, Tsaile, AZ 86556 (928) 724-6600; E-mail: cmroessel@dinecollege.edu. *Past professional post*: Former Director, Bureau of Indian Education, Washington, DC, 2012-16. Before joining the BIE's headquarters staff in Washington, D.C. in 2012, Roessel had served since October 2011 as the Bureau's Associate Deputy Director for Navajo Schools, where he was responsible for overseeing 66 BIE-funded schools on the Navajo Nation reservation in Arizona, New Mexico and Utah. He became the associate deputy director after having served since 2007 as superintendent of Rough Rock Community School, a BIE-funded, tribally operated K-12 boarding school near Chinle, Ariz., on the Navajo Nation reservation. From 2010 to 2011, Roessel had served as chair of the Department of the Interior's No Child Left Behind Negotiated Rule Making Committee and on the Sovereignty in Navajo Education Reauthorization Task Force with the Navajo Education Department of Diné Education. Roessel has been a prominent figure in Indian education for many years. The Rough Rock Community School, at which he

served for more than a dozen years from 1998 to 2011, had been the first American Indian-operated, and the first Navajo-operated, school when it opened in 1966 within what was then the Bureau of Indian Affairs school system. Today that system is administered by the BIE, established in 2006. During his tenure as superintendent at Rough Rock, Roessel helped to oversee a major school replacement and improvement project funded under the American Recovery and Reinvestment Act of 2009 and carried out by the Indian Affairs Office of Facilities, Environmental & Cultural Resources. The official opening of the replacement school and facilities was held on August 15, 2011. Roessel started at Rough Rock in August 1998 as the director of community services, developing programs for teacher recruitment and student enrollment in addition to coaching baseball and teaching photography to students. In July 2000, he became the school's executive director, where he served until he was named superintendent in 2007. Before working for the Rough Rock Community School, Roessel served from September 1997 to December 2000 as director of the Navajo Nation Round Rock Chapter AmeriCorps program where he developed partnerships to improve education and housing within the Round Rock chapter community. Roessel also has worked as a photographer, writer and editor for various publications and projects including vice president/editor of the *Navajo Nation Today* newspaper (1990-1992), which he also co-owned; managing editor of the *Navajo Times Today* (1985-1987); a photojournalist with the *Greeley (Colo.) Tribune* (1985) & a photographer/writer with the Navajo View of Navajo Life Project (1984). In addition, he has worked since 1987 as an author and photographer on various projects, and has written extensively about Navajo life and culture. He also served on the Visual Task Force board for the first annual gathering of minority journalists associations, including the Native American Journalists Association (NAJA), known as the UNITY conference

ROFKAR, TERI (Tlingit)
  (craftsperson, art studio owner)
Affiliation: Raven Art Studio, 820 Charles St., Sitka, AK 99835 (907) 747-3641; E-mail: cuthbert@ptialaska.net

ROGERS, ED (Quapaw)
  (former tribal chairperson)
Affiliation: Quapaw Tribal Business Committee, P.O. Box 765, Quapaw, OK 74363 (918) 542-1853.

ROGERS, STEVE
  (library curator)
Affiliation: The Wheelwright of the American Indian, Mary Cabot Wheelwright Research Library, P.O. Box 5153, 704 Camino Lejo, Santa Fe, NM 87501 (505) 982-4636.

ROGERS, TIM (Paiute)
  (tribal chairperson)
Affiliation: Kaibab Paiute Tribe, 1 N. Pipe Spring Rd., Fredonia, AZ 86022 (928) 643-7245.

ROHRER, BARBARA
  (Indian education program director)
Affiliation: Vivian Banks Charter School, Pala Band of Mission Indians, P.O. Box 80, Pala, CA 92059 (760) 742-3300.

ROKWAHO (DAN THOMPSON) (Mohawk) 1953-
  (publications & graphic design consultant)
Born November 7, 1953, Akwesasne Territory. *Principal occupation*: Publications & graphic design consultant. *Address*: P.O. Box 166, Rooseveltown, NY 13683. *Affiliations*: Media specialist, St. Regis Mohawk Language Program, 1980-82; co-founder (with John Fadden) and production manager, Pictographics, P.O. Box 166, Rooseveltown, NY, 1977-. *Other professional posts*: Literary editor, artist and photographer, Akwesasne Notes, 1982-83; founding editor, Indian Time, an Akwesasne biweekly newspaper, 1983; art director for Indian Studies, Cornell University, Ithaca, N.Y., 1984; editor, Akwesasne Notes and Indian Time, 1984-85; co-founder of Akwekon, a literary & arts quarterly published by Akwekon/Akwesasne Notes; co-founder of Suntracks, a tracking & nature observation school in the Adirondack Mountains near Ochiota, N.Y. *Membership*: Association for the Advancement of Native North American Arts & Crafts (administrative executive; project, Iroquois Arts: A Directory of a People and Their Work, published, 1984). *Interests*: Music, literature, theatre, computer science, electronic & mechanical gadgetry, the sciences, and archaic Mohawk words & semantics (compiling a dictionary of terms). *Published works*: Editor & designer, Trail of Broken Treaties. B.I.A. I'm Not Your Indian Anymore (Akwesasne Notes, 1974); translator & illustrator, Teiohakwente, a Mohawk language textbook (Dept. of Indian Affairs, Ottawa, Can., 1977); author & artist, Covers (poetry, illustrations) (Strawberry Press, 1982); contributor of poetry to numerous anthologies; cover art and illustrations for many publications, as well as design production for Akwesasne Notes Calendars.

ROLIN, BUFORD L. (Poarch Band Creek)
 (former tribal chairperson)
Affiliation & Address: Chairperson (2006-14), Poarch Band of Creek Indians, 5811 Jack Springs Rd., Atmore, AL 36502 (251) 368-9136. He has served as secretary & vice-chairperson from 1991-99. *Other professional posts*: Co-Chair (1999-present), Tribal Leaders Diabetes Committee; member of the HIS Strategic Planning Committee; Nashville Area Representative, National Indian Health Board (NIHB); member, State of Alabama Public Health Advisory Board; member, USET Health Committee. *Community activities*: Co-Chair of Tribal Leaders Diabetes Committee; member, HIS Strategic Planning Committee. *Past community & professional posts*: National Congress of American Indians; Atmore Area Partnership for Youth Board of Directors; Florida's Governor's Council on Indian Affairs; Northwest Florida Creek Indian Council; National Committee on Indian Work; Creek Indian Arts Council. *Awards & honors*: 1989 Service Award for improving the Health of Indian People; 1993 Director's Award for Excellence by the Indian Health Service (IHS); 1996 Area Director's Special Commendation Award from the IHS. Mr. Rolin was appointed in 1998 by Dr. Michael Trujillo, Director, IHS, as Tribal Co-Chair of the National Steering Committee (NSC), Reauthorization of the Indian Health Care Improvement Act (HCIA); appointed in 1999 Tribal Co-Chair to the Tribal Leaders Diabetes Committee by Dr. Trujillo; In 2000, he was appointed to the White House Commission on Complimentary & Alternative Medicine Policy by President Bill Clinton; appointed to the NCAI Tribal Leaders Health Information Technology Task Force by Tex Hall, and elected Chair in 2001; In 2007, Mr. Rolin received the Jake Whitecrow Award from the National Indian Health Board for his work promoting Native healthcare issues. He was inducted in 2013 into the Atmore Hall of Fame.

ROLLER, TONI (Santa Clara Pueblo)
 (craftsperson)
Affiliation & Address: Toni Roller Indian Pottery Studio & Gallery, Box 171, Santa Clara Pueblo, Espanola, NM 87532 (505) 753-3003. *Product*: Hand-made traditional Santa Clara pottery of natural materials.

ROLLINS, DOUGLAS J.
 (BIA agency supt.)
Affiliation: Central California Agency, BIA, 1824 Tribute Rd., Suite J, Sacramento, CA 95815 (916) 566-7121.

ROLO, MARK ANTHONY (Lake Superior Ojibwe) 1962-
 (playwrite, producer, lecturer; consultant)
Born Dec. 11, 1962 in Milwaukee, Wisc. He is an enrolled member of the Bad River Band of Lake Superior Ojibwe. *Education*: University of Minnesota-Twin Cities, BS (Rhetoric & Journalism), 1991; Chatham University, MFA (Creative Writing), 2010. *E-mail*: mrolo@mail.com. Lecturer: School of Human Ecology, University of Wisconsin-Madison, 2005-present). *Past professional posts*: Journalist, "The Circle Newspaper," 1996-98; "Indian Country Today," 1999-2000; executive director, Native American Journalists Association, 2000-2002; editor, American Indian & the Media, 2000 National Conference for Community & Justice; wrote a collection of essays on covering Indian Country; Mark continues to write op-eds on American Indian issues for the "Progressive Media Project." He is a 1997 alum of the Sundance Screenwriters Lab, Play: "Indigging." He is host & co-writer of the PBS documentary, "A Seat at the Drum," which is a part of the "Indian Country Diaries" series. He has produced education videos and a short film, "Wicked Ancestors." In 2010, he produced the documentary, "Legend Lake: A Talking Circle" addressing land conflict issues on the Menominee Nation reservation in Wisconsin. Plays: "The Way Down Story," 1999; "Sweatlodge Pork," 2001; "Mama Earth Love's Lace," 2002; "What's an Indian Woman To Do?," 2005. Books: "Mama Earth Loves Lace," 1998; The Wonder Bull (2006 iUniverse); What's an Indian Woman To Do? and Other Plays, (2010 UCLA American Indian Studies); My Mother Is Now Earth (forthcoming) A Lyrical Memoir. Films: Co-writer & host, "A Seat at the Drum (Indian Country Diaries), 2006 Native American Public Telecommunications & Adanvdo Vision; executive producer, "Coloring the News: When Race Becomes the Story," 2006 SixOneFive Productions; writer & director, "Wicked Ancestors," producer, with Lauren Skinner, "American Indians at the University of Wisconsin-Madison," 2007 SkinRol Productions; 2008 Story Owl; producer, "Building Bridges: Community-Based Journalism Training in Mozambique," 2009 Terra Institute; producer & writer, "Legend Lake: A Talking Circle," 2010 Terra Institute; producer, Breaking the Circle: The Threat of Gangs in Indian Country (in production, Story Owl).

ROMAN NOSE, QUINTON (Cheyenne-Arapaho)
 (tribal education)
Education: Oklahoma City University, MEd (Gifted & Talented Education). *Address & Affiliation*: Director, Cheyenne & Arapaho Tribes of OK Education Dept., P.O. Box 30, Concho, OK (800) 247-4612. E-mail: qrn@lycos.com. *Other professional post*: Executive Director, Tribal Education Departments National Assembly (TEDNA), P.O. Box 18000, Boulder, CO 80308; *Membership*: National Indian Education Association (president, 2012).

ROMANELLI, LARRY (Ottawa)
 (tribal ogema)
Affiliation & Address: Ogema, Little River Band of Ottawa Indians, 375 River St., Manistee, MI 49660 (231) 723-8288.

ROMERO, CLYDE M. (Taos Pueblo)
 (former Pueblo governor)
Affiliation & Address: Pueblo of Taos, P.O. Box 1846, Taos, NM 87571 (575) 758-9593.

ROMERO, EDWIN "THORPE" (Diegueno)
 (former tribal chairperson)
Affiliation: Barona Band of Mission Indians, 1095 Barona Rd., Lakeside, CA 92040 (619) 443-6612.

ROMERO, JOHN, JR. (*Blue Lake Night Dancer*) (Taos Pueblo)
 (Indian education coordinator)
Affiliation & Address: Taos Municipal Schools, 213 Paseo del Canon, Taos, NM 87571 (505) 758-3884 ext 49. *Past professional posts*: Santa Fe Indian School, 1978-91; Taos Municipal Schools, Taos, NM, 1992-present. *Military service*: U.S. Army, 1968-72 (Vietnam, 1969-70). *Community activities*: Member, Community Education Program; member, Indian Education Committee. *Memberships*: National Coalition for Indian Education; National Indian Education Assn.

ROMERO, JOANELLE NADINE (*Redhawk*) (Apache/Cheyenne)
 (humanitarian, filmmaker-director/producer/writer,
 actress, singer/songwriter, public speaker)
Born in Albuquerque, N.M. *Address*: Red Nations Celebration, 9420 Reseda Blvd., P.O. Box 352, Northridge, CA 91324 (818) 904-9256. Website: www.rednation.com; E-mail: info@rednation.com. *Affiliations*: Founded Spirit World Productions - produces American Indian films, television & music (1991); founder, president, Red Nation Film Festival (RNFF) - annual concert series & educational out-reach programs (1995); founded Red Nation Records - American Indian record label (2001); launched in 2006, the first American Indian Internet Media Network Channel (all Native programming); also in 2006, launched & hosts Red Nation Radio Contemporary & Traditional American Indian Music, Northridge, CA. *Community activities*: Initiated, created and produced the launching of the "First Annual American Indian Heritage Month" in the City of Los Angeles. *Film & Video credits*: Romero, with seventeen films to her credit as a lead actress, is perhaps best known for her leading roles in such films as "A Girl Called Hatter Fox" and "Powwow Highway," a winner at a previous Sundance Film Festival. In 1992, she founded Spirit World Productions, an American Indian production company, dedicated to supporting Native American music, film and television projects. Spirit World's introductory project was Michael Jackson's Black or White music video. Then Romero began producing, directing, and writing her own film and video projects, the first of which was a documentary short film, "The Third Verse, 500 Years, Land of the Children. This film won a merit award at the Columbus International Film Festival in 1993, a first place trophy at the Red Earth Film Festival in 1994, and shown two years in a row at the American Indian Film Festival in San Francisco. In 1994, she produced an informational video for U.S. West Communications, "Where the Red Road Meets the Information Super Highway," 1st Place award winner at the Red Earth Film Festival in 1995. Also in 1994, she directed "Melvin and John," a documentary segment for a PBS series about people living with HIV/AIDS all across America...won 1st Place at Red Earth in 1995. In 1995, she co-created and co-produced the first "Red Nation Celebration" (contemporary Native American entertainment to Santa Fe's Indian Art Market each year) and was one of the featured performers. In 1996, Romero produced "Allan Houser: A Lasting Vision," a documentary on the early life of world renowned Apache Indian sculptor Allan Houser. Recently, she co-created and produced a contemporary American Indian dramatic TV series, "Red Blanket," currently being pitched to major networks & studios. She also produced "Home, Home on the Rez," a demo episode of this series. As a direct result of the demo, she and her production company were written up in Newsweek, appeared on the cover of the LA Times. Romero believes that the TV series, "Red Blanket" will begin shooting in 1997. Most recently, Romero co-created and co-wrote an American Indian children's program which will be produced in 1997; Directed, produced & wrote in 2000, "American Holocaust, When It's All Over, I'll Still Be Indian" a 30 minute documentary feature film. *Memberships*: Screen Actors Guild. *Awards, honors*: The 2005 Armin T. Wegner Humanitarian Award (Documentary); 2003 Fargo Film Festival Award (Documentary); 2002 Los Angeles Women's Theatre Integrity Award; 2000 American Indian Film Festival Award (Documentary); 2000 Oscar Consideration (Documentary); Joanelle is the longest standing American Indian member of the Screen Actors Guild and produced the only panel, "Where Are We in Film, Television & Radio" to date at the SAG in 2000 and in 2012 "Native Women in Film & Television. *Interests*: Ms. Romero has been a true activist against alcoholism among her American Indian people. Romero, fifteen years sober, promotes sobriety & healthy lifestyles within the American Indian community. She has traveled from reservation to reservation to speak

with youth on racism, alcoholism, and encouraging them to "Live Their Dream." She is writing her autobiography: Maybe I'm Not Crazy. She believes that there should be more stories by and about American Indian women.

ROMERO, LAUREANO B. (Taos Pueblo)
(former pueblo governor)
Affiliation & Address: Governor, Taos Pueblo, P.O. Box 1846, Taos, NM 87571 (575) 758-9593.

ROMERO, LUIS (Taos Pueblo)
(pueblo governor)
Affiliation & Address: Governor, Taos Pueblo, P.O. Box 1846, Taos, NM 87571 (575) 758-9593.

ROMERO, M. SUE (Hidatsa/Creek) 1955-
(administrative assistant)
Born August 11, 1955, Claremore, Okla. *Education*: University of New Mexico, 1985-86. *Principal occupation*: Administrative assistant. *Address*: Resides in Albuquerque, NM (505) 766-8418 (office). *Affiliations*: Clerical specialist, Albuquerque Public Schools, Indian Education Dept., 1977; administrative assistant: Santa Fe Indian School, 1977-85; All Indian Pueblo Council, Albuquerque, 1985-87; SW Indian Polytechnic Institute, Albuquerque, 1988-. *Community activities*: SW Indian Personnel Management, 1983-85. *Memberships*: Santa Fe Indian School Alumni Association; NONAW - National Organization of Native American Women, 1989-; Indian Bowling Association. *Awards, honors*: Nominated to Outstanding Women in America, 1984; SW Region Personnel Management Training Intern, 1984; 1985 Santa Fe Indian School Employee of the Year. *Interests*: "Over 12 years of extensive experience working with Native American Programs from a boarding school situation to a political entity to a substance abuse program."

ROMERO, MARK (Kumeyaay Diegueno)
(former tribal chairperson)
Affiliation & Address: Mesa Grande Band of Mission Indians, P.O. Box 270, Santa Ysabel, CA 92070 (760) 782-3818.

ROMERO, SHANNON (Paiute)
(former tribal chairperson)
Affiliation & Address: Former chairperson, Big Pinee Paiute Tribe of the Owens Valley, 825 S. Main St., P.O. Box 700 • Big Pine, CA 93513 (760) 938-2003; E-mail: s.romero@bigpinepaiute.org

ROMERO, TERESA M. (Juaneno Mission Indians)
(tribal chairperson)
Affiliation & Address: Juaneno Band of Mission Indians (Acjachemen Nation), 31411-A La Matanza St., San Juan Capistrano, CA 92675 (949) 488-3484.

ROMERO-LITTLE, EUNICE (Cochiti Pueblo)
(professor of American Indian studies)
Affiliation & Address: Associate Professor of Indigenous Language Education & Applied Linguistics, School of Social Transformation/American Indian Studies, Wilson Hall 376, Arizona State University, MC: 6403, Tempe, AZ 85287 (480) 965-3133. E-mail: m.eunice@asu.edu.

ROOD, DAVID S. (kiic'akwakhariw) 1940-
(professor of linguistics)
Born in 1940, Albany, N.Y. *Education*: University of California, Berkeley, PhD, 1969. *Affiliation & Address*: Professor of linguistics, 295 UCB, Dept. of Linguistics (1969-present), University of Colorado, Boulder, CO 80309-0295 (303) 492-2747. E-mail: rood@colorado.edu. *Published works*: Beginning Lakhota, 4 vols. with Allan Taylor, (Garland, 1976); Wichita Grammar (Garland, 1976). Dr. Rood is considered the leading Lakota linguist today.

ROOSEVELT, DAVID (Cabazon Cahuilla)
(tribal chairperson)
Affiliation & Address: Chairperson, Cabazon Band of Mission Indians, 84-245 Indio Spring Dr., Indio, CA 92201 (760) 342-2593.

ROQUENI, REUBEN TOMAS (Yaqui/Mexican)
(multimedia visual artist; program director)
Education: Evergreen State College, BFA. Graduate of the National Association of Latino Arts & Culture (NALAC) Leadership Institute and was one of eight selected for the NALAC Advocacy Institute in Washington D.C. *Affiliation & Address*: Program Director, Native Arts & Cultures Foundation, 11109 NE 14th St., Vancouver, WA 98684 (360) 314-2421. *Other professional posts*: Member, Board of Directors, The Association of American Cultures, a national arts advocacy organization convening artists & cultural workers reflective of our pluralistic society. *Past professional posts*: Grants Program Manager, Tucson Pima Arts Council, Tucson, Ariizona; board member, Access Tucson (public television) and was a founding board member of the Tucson Musicians & Artists Health Alliance; Old Pascua Youth Artists (six years).

ROSALES, SALVADOR (Pomo)
(tribal chairperson & administrator)
Affiliation & Address: Chairperson & Administrator, Potter Valley Tribe, 2251 S. State St., Ukiah, CA 95482 (707) 462-1213.

ROSE, AHNIWAKE (Cherokee)
(executive director)
Affiliation & Address: Executive Director, National Indian Education Association (NIEA), 1514 P St., NW, Suite 8, Washington, DC 20005 (202) 544-7290. E-mail: arose@niea.org. *Other professional post*: Member, Equity & Excellence Commission on addressing achievement gaps convened by the U.S. Secretary of Education. *Past professional post*: Policy Director, National Congress of American Indians, Washington, DC; consutant, U.S. Department of Education where she worked on implementation of Executive Order 1336, which aimed to ensure that Native students receive comprehensive, culturally-based education

ROSE, JOSEPH (Bad River Ojibwe)
(professor of Native American Studies)
Born & raised on the Bad River Indian Reservation. Education: Northland College, BA; Black Hills State College, M.Ed; University of Montana, MS. *Affiliation & Address*: Associate Professor of Native American Studies, Mead 123, 1411 Ellis Ave., Ashland, WI 54806 (715) 682-1204. E-mail: jrose@northland.edu. "Along with my time spent teaching, I am working on a Native American Museum project that includes three phases. Phase one involves designing a floor plan; designing display cases; budgeting, requisition & procurement of materials; & construction skills. Phase two involves displaying artifacts; researching, developing & writing text for exhibits with Ojibwe and English translations; & artifact security. The final phase will include teaching work-study students operational museum skills in conducting guided tours, assisting in sponsoring & coordinating cultural awareness activities related to the overall theme of the museum, & Anishinabe seasonal activities. Growing up on the Bad River Indian Reservation, I have always lived very close to nature and the teachings of tribal elders, which inspired me to choose Biology and Secondary Education as my undergraduate majors. Being raised in a native traditionalist family, I have been fortunate to have my grandfather and many other native elders as teachers.

ROSE, LAVERA M. (Rosebud Lakota))
(library director/archivist)
Education: Black Hills State College, BS (Political Science); University of Northern Arizona, MA (History); University of Wisconsin-Madison, MLIS. *Affiliation*: Director/Archivist, Oglala Lakota College, Academic/Public Library & Archives, 3 Mile Creek Rd., P.O. Box 310, Kyle, SD 57752 (605) 455-6064. E-mail: lrose@olc.edu. *Other professional post*: Adjunct History Instructor, Oglala Lakota College. *Past professional posts*: Internship, Oglala Lakota College Archives, 1988-89; archivist, South Dakota State Archives, 1989-2005; digital librarian, South Dakota State Library, 2005-08.

ROSE, PHYLLIS
(art/media consultant; business owner)
Education: California State University, Los Angeles, BA in Broadcast Communications. *Principal occupation*: Art/media consultant; business owner. *Address*: 47080 Pala Rd., Temecula, CA 92592. *Affiliations*: Photojournalist for "The Talking Leaf Publication"; hosted two radio shows while working as an independent radio producer for National Public Radio. Some of her interviews include: Native American political prisoner Leonard Peltier, U.S. Senator Ben Nighthorse Campbell, Rita Coolidge and Connie Stevens; Presently, she is owner of First People Communications so she could assist individuals and organizations as an art/media consultant in various aspects needed to obtain their goals. Most of Phyllis's experience has been working in film and television. She has worked in various aspects of production from on camera shows such as, "Crazy Horse," "Dances With Wolves," "Ninja Kids Knucke Up," and the children's show, "Romper Room." *Community activities*: California Indian Legal Services (committee member, board of directors); Pechanga Tribe (councilperson, youth program volunteer); speaker, Cal State Northridge Native American Student Group. Memberships: SAG, AFTRA. Interests: Phyllis says her legacy is to follow her grandmother's commitments for Native American concerns and love for their culture.

ROSEN, DIANE K. (Red Cliff/Lac Courte Oreilles Chippewa)
(BIA regional director)
Education: Northland College, BS (Management & Leadership - Magna Cum Laude), 2006. *Affiliation & Address*: Director (2009-present), Bureau of Indian Affairs (BIA), Midwest Regional Office, 5600 W. American Blvd., Suite 500, Bloomington, MN 55347 (612) 713-4400. *Past professional posts*: Realty Specialist, 1991-94; Tribal Operations Officer, 1994-2003, Supt, 2004-09, BIA-Great Lakes Agency, Ashland, WI.

ROSEN, LAWRENCE 1941-
(professor of anthropology)

Born December 9, 1941, Cincinnati, Ohio. *Education*: Brandeis University, BA, 1963; University of Chicago, MA, 1965, PhD, 1968, JD, 1974. Principal occupation: Professor of anthropology. *Address*: 435 Alexander St., Princeton, NJ 08540 (609) 258-5535. E-mail: lrosen@princeton.edu. *Affiliations*: Professor, 1977-, dept. chairperson, 1989-2001, Dept. of Anthropology, Princeton University, Princeton, NJ; adjunct professor of law, Columbia Law School, New York, NY, 1979-. *Community activities*: Volunteer legal work for the Native American Rights Fund. *Memberships*: American Anthropological Assn; Law and Society Assn (board of directors). *Awards, honors*: John D. & Catherine T. MacArthur Foundation Award; John Simon Guggenheim Foundation Fellow; National Science Foundation Fellow, 1990-92; Phi Beta Kappa Visiting Scholar. *Interests*: "Research on American Indian legal problems, especially the return of Indian skeletal remains, the furtherance of Indian religious rights, and the rights of indigenous peoples in international law; extensive research in North Africa, particularly on Islamic law." *Published work*: Editor, The American Indian and the Law (Transaction Books, 1976); Bargaining for Reality (University of Chicago Press, 1984); The Anthropology of Justice (Cambridge University Press, 1989); Other Intentions (School of American Research Press, 1994); The Justice of Islam (Oxford University Press, 2000); The Culture of Islam (University of Chicago Press, 2002); Law as Culture (Oxford University Press, 2004); The Rights of Indigenous Peoples (Oxford University Press, 2005).

ROSENFELD, MARGARET CROW
(attorney)

Education: Golden Gate University School of Law, JD, 1985. *Affiliation & Address*: Associate, Forman & Associates, 4340 Redwood Hwy., Suite E352, San Rafael, CA 94903 (415) 491-2310; E-mail: Margaret@gformanlaw.com *Past professional posts*: U.S. Departemnt of Justice, Indian Resources Section primarily handling water rights adjudications; California Indian Legal Services (five years); administrator of the externship program at U.C. Berkeley's Boalt Hall School of Law (eight years); Office of General Counsel for the U.S. Department of Health & Human Services (seven years) advising Indian Health Service on all matters related to the administration of their direct care facilities; taught Federal Indian Law at Boalt Hall, University of San Francisco School of Law, U.C. Davis School of Law, and Santa Clara University School of Law.

ROSENFELT, DANIEL M.
(attorney-Native American law)

Education: Johns Hopkins University, BA, 1963; Columbia Law School, LB, 1966. *Affiliation & Address*: Founder, Rosenfelt Law, P.C., 1418 Aliso Dr. NE, Albuquerque, NM 87110. Since 1982, I've been practicing law in New Mexico. For 21 years, I worked with a private law firm with offices in Albuquerque and the Navajo Nation and served as managing director. I have been an Assistant Solicitor with the U.S. Department of Interior, and now I work as a sole practitioner. Over the past 30 years I've represented hundreds of individuals in personal injury, family law, and employment cases. I served as school board attorney, general counsel for Indian tribes and counsel for small businesses. I've handled many tort claims against the federal government in the New Mexico and Arizona federal courts. My current areas of interest include litigation in Navajo, federal and state courts and school law, especially charter schools.

ROSENTHAL, LARRY
(attorney)

Affiliation & Address: Partner, Ietan Consulting, LLC, 1333 New Hampshire Ave., NW, Washington, DC 20036 (202) 419-3527. Ieten Consulting is a federal government relations firm specializing in the representation of tribal governments & tribal business enterprises. *Past professional posts*: Sr. V.P., Wheat Associates, LLC, Washington, DC; chief-of-staff, National Indian Gaming Commission; director, Congressional Native American Caucus & legislative director for Congressman Dale E. Kildee of Michigan (11 years). The Caucus was the first to voice support of sovereignty and Native American issues, and led efforts to improve funding for Indian education, housing, economic & community development, and Indian health services.

ROSETTE, ROBERT A. (Chippewa-Cree) 1971-
(attorney; law firm partner)

Education: University of New Mexico, BA, 1993; Arizona State University, College of Business, MBA, 1996; ASU College of Law, JD, 1996. *Affiliation & Address*: Founding Partner, Rosette LLP (2005-present), 565 W. Chandler Blvd. #212, Chandler, AZ 85225 (480) 889-8990. E-mail: rosette@rosettelaw.com. Mr. Rosette formed Rosette, LLP to exclusively represent Indian Tribal Governments in all facets of federal Indian law, including finance, commercial transactions, economic development, gaming and litigation. Having obtained a Masters of Business Administration in finance, Robert maintains a unique and keen understanding of financial transactions, which is evidenced by over $4 Billion in economic development and governmental infrastructure projects for over 30 tribes in eight States. He has raised such capital through various forms of financing, including direct bank loans, taxable & tax exempt bond financing, venture capital, development loans, and bridge financing for his Tribal clients. Mr. Rosette's extensive experience also includes all areas of gaming for both brick and mortar and Internet gambling ventures. Mr. Rosette has successfully negotiated dozens of gaming compacts and has overseen the development, management and financing of tribal casinos in several states throughout the country. Mr. Rosette works tirelessly to restore Indian lands and take land into trust for gaming purposes, and has done so for Tribes such as the Picayune Rancheria and the Habematolel Pomo of Upper Lake, both located in the State of California. Mr. Rosette has been involved with Internet gaming issues pursuant to the IGRA since 1997. He has represented Indian tribes with the successful launch of internet gaming websites for Class II bingo and poker. He brings legal ingenuity & creativity in developing and defending economic development diversification projects by utilizing Tribal sovereign attributes (e.g.: enabling legislation, regulation, value adding), which allows his Tribal clients to pursue opportunities in unique business ventures such as tribal government consumer lending, pharmaceutical distribution, gasoline distribution, & cigarette manufacturing & distribution. Mr. Rosette's litigation experience includes Indian tribal cases involving public interest and civil rights. For example, he successfully resolved a dispute between the Havasupai Tribe and the State of Arizona in a case whereby the Tribe alleged the illegal taking of its blood & genetic material. Mr. Rosette also successfully litigated a case saving the Pauma Band of Luiseno Mission Indians over $100 Million in Compact payments allegedly owed to the State of California against then Governor Schwarzenegger. He conducted the first arbitration regarding off-Reservation mitigation pursuant to a gaming compact, and received a victorious award against the County of San Diego on behalf of the La Posta Tribe of Mission Indians. Mr. Rosette has also successfully restored recognition of Tribal governments against United States' attempts to dissolve them, including the California Valley Miwok Tribe; the Lower Lake Rancheria, Koi Nation; and the Wilton Rancheria. Mr. Rosette has extensive federal lobbying experience. He frequently drafts tribal constitutions, ordinances and policies, and has negotiated thousands of business agreements between tribal governments and private corporations for economic development projects. *Past professional posts*: Clerk for Hon. Raymond Austin, Navajo Nation Supreme Court, 1994-95; managing partner, Monteau & Peebles, LLP, 1997-2005. Mr. Rosette's practice includes all facets of federal Indian law, including gaming, finance, economic development & commercial transactions. *Membership*: Chippewa-Cree Tribe of the Rocky Boys Indian Reservation.

ROSIER, KATHLEEN (Cmanche of Oklahoma)
(attorney; executive director)

Education: Capital University, BA, 1993; University of Utah S.J. Quinney College of Law, JD, 1998. *Affiliation & Address*: Executive Director & Faculty member, Indian Legal Program, Sandra Day O'Connor College of Law, Arizona State University, Box 877907, Tempe, AZ 85287 (480) 965-6181. *Past professional posts*: Assistant General Counsel, Fort McDowell Yavapai Nation, 2011-14; director, Indian Legal Program, Arizona State U. College of Law, 2000-11.

ROSIERE, RAMONA (Modoc)
(tribal secretary-treasurer)

Affiliation & Address: Modoc Tribe of Oklahoma, 515 G St. SE, Miami, OK 74354 (918) 542-1190.

ROSS, A. CHUCK (*Ehanamani-Walks Among*) (Santee Sioux) 1940-
(author, publisher; lecturer, international consultant)

Born October 25, 1940, Pipestone, Minn. *Education*: Black Hills State College, BS, 1967; Arizona State University, MA, 1971; University of Minnesota, ABD, 1973; Western Colorado University, EdD, 1980. *Address*: P.O. Box 480005, Denver, CO 80248 (303) 238-3420. E-mail: acrossehanamani@yahoo.com. *Affiliations*: Author, publisher, international consultant (Bear Publishing), 1991-present; lecturer, 'In Search of the Origins of the Red Man,' presented in 44 state & 6 Canadian provinces, 1975-; lecturer on topics including Lakota history & culture, psychology, holistic health & education, 1975-; primary investigator for various publications; and technical advisor for various film/TV broadcast. *Past professional posts*: Instructor (contract), Native American Studies, University of Colorado, Boulder, 1977-80; health & education consultant, Edgewater, CO, 1980-83; instructor (contract) - Native American Studies, Standing Rock College, Fort Yates, ND, Oglala Lakota College, Kyle, SD, & Fort Peck Community College, Poplar, MT, 1983-90; Agency Supt. for Education, Bureau of Indian Affairs, Fort Yates, ND; supt., Little Wound School, Kyle, SD, 1990-91. *Military service*: U.S. Army Airborne, 1962-65. *Memberships*: Dakota Astronomical Society; National Indian Education Association. *Awards, honors*: Friendship Award, White Buffalo Council, 1977; nominee, National Indian Educator of the Year, National Indian Education Association, 1980; Outstanding Volunteer Service Award, U.S. Dept. of Health & Human Services, 1982; Gubernatorial Appointment, North Dakota Teacher's Professional Practices Commission, 1985; Who's Who Among the Sioux - University of South Dakota, 1986; Participant, Effective Schools Team for BIA, 1988; Honoree, 'Top 50' Selection at International Book Fair, Frankfurt,

Germany, recognition for "Mitakuye Oyasin," 1992; Special Recognition Award for Contribution to Indian Education, National Indian Education Association, 1992; Mitakuye Oyasin approved for cinema film production by Osmond Productions (Pleasant Grove, UT), 1994. *Interests*: Lectures & presentations; Dr. Ross has worked for 30 years in the field of education as a teacher, principal, superintendent, college professor, and college department chairman. He has lectured on cultural understanding in 44 states in the U.S., 6 Canadian provinces, and 8 European countries and Japan. His book Mitakuye Oyasin was a bestseller. *Published works*: Biographies of Spotted Tail & Crow Dog for the Encyclopedia of the Indians of the Americas, 1975; Mitakuye Oyasin: We Are All Related (Bear Publishing, 1989); Ehanamani: Walks Among (Bear Publishing, 1992), a book that compares customs, languages, and spiritual beliefs of Indians with other peoples; Keeper of the Female Medicine Bundle (Bear Publishing, 1998).

ROSS, CAROL (Caddo)
(tribal vice chairperson)
Affiliation & Address: Vice Chairperson, Caddo Nation, P.O. Box 487, Binger, OK 73009 (405) 656-2344. E-mail: cross@caddonation.org

ROSS, DALLAS (Dakota)
(tribal chairperson)
Affiliation & Address: Upper Sioux Board of Trustees, P.O. Box 147, Granite Falls, MN 56241 (320) 564-2360.

ROSS, GYASI (Blackfeet)
(attorney)
Education: Evergreen State College, BA, 2000; Columbia University Law School, JD, 2003. *Affiliation & Address*: Associate (2010-present), Crowell Law Office, Tribal Advocacy Group, 10 N. Post, Suite 445, Spokane, WA 99201 (206) 261-0085. E-mail: gyasi.ross@gmail.com. Legislative Associate (2003-05), National Congress of American Indians, Washington, DC (worked with tribal leaders on economic development & voter empowerment issues. One of the coordinators of 2004 Native Vote effort); staff attorney (2005-06), The Defender Association, Seattle, WA; associate general counsel (2006-10), Port Madison Enterprises, Suquamish, WA.

ROSS, JACK (Eastern Shawnee)
(tribal 2nd chief)
Affiliation & Address: Eastern Shawnee Tribe of Oklahoma, P.O. Box 350, Seneca, MO 64865 (918) 666-2435.

ROSS, JACQUELYN (Pomo/Coast Mewuk)
(outreach coordinator)
Affiliation & Address: Relations with Schools/EOP Outreach Services, 2828 Chiles Rd. Hall, Davis, CA 95616 (916) 752-3124.

ROSS, JOHN (Cherokee)
(tribal chairperson)
Affiliation: United Keetoowah Band of Cherokee Indians, Box 746, Tahlequah, OK 74465 (918) 456-5491.

ROSS, LORELLE W.B. (Coast Miwok)
(tribal vice chairperson)
Affiliation & Address: Vice Chairperson, Federated Indians of the Graton Rancheria, 6400 Redwood Dr., Suite 300, Rohnert Park, CA 94928 (707) 566-2288. Lorelle Ross has served five elected terms as a member of the Tribal Council to further her commitment to building a healthy tribal community that values cultural and social development, health, education, and economic fortitude. Beginning when she was just nineteen, she has served as a Council Member, Treasurer, and currently is serving her second term as Vice-Chair. Lorelle's grandfather was one of Graton Rancheria's original distributees. After the Federated Indians of Graton Rancheria was illegally terminated in the late 1950's and early 1960's, her Grandfather maintained ownership of one acre on the original Rancheria. The one-acre parcel is currently owned and held in fee simple by Lorelle's mother Gloria Armstrong, who has lived on the land for over fifty years. Lorelle was also raised on this parcel and currently lives with her mother in the original wood frame house that was first constructed on the Rancheria approximately seventy years ago.

ROSS, LUANA (Salish & Kootenai)
(professor of American Indian studies)
Education: University of Montana, BA; University of Oregon, PhD (Sociology). *Affiliation & Address*: *Other professional posts*: Associate professor of Women Studies & American Indian Studies (1999-present), Padelford Hall C-514 Box 354305, Department of American Indian Studies, University of Washington (UW), Seattle, WA 98195 (206) 616-9375. E-mail: luana@u.washington.edu; Co-director, Native Voices, Graduate Program, University of Washington (UW), Seattle, WA. Since her tenure with Native Voices, Dr. Ross has produced several award winning films including: A Century of Genocide in the Americas: The Residential School Experience; White Shamans & Plastic Medicine; and

The Place of Falling Waters. *Past professional posts*: President, Salish Kootenai College, Pablo, MT; Professor, University of California, Berkeley & University of California, Davis; professor, University of Washington where she served as co-director of Native Voices, a graduate film program. *Research Interests*: Dr. Ross conducted extensive research on the experiences of women in prison, which resulted in many publications including a book, *Inventing the Savage*. This book was awarded the "Best Book of 1998" by the American Political Science Association. She was also awarded a Newberry Library Fellowship and a Ford Foundation Fellowship. She has published numerous articles including, *"Race, Gender, and Social Control: Voices of Imprisoned Native American and White Women"* in *Wicazo Sa Review*, and *"Native Women, Mean-Spirited Drugs, and Punishing Policies"* in *Social Justice*. She has also contributed chapters to important Native Studies & sociology texts including, *"Reading Native American Women, Native American Voices: A Reader*, and *States of Confinement: Policing, Detention, and Prisons."*

ROSS, MARGIE (Ottawa of Oklahoma)
(tribal administrator)
Affiliation: Ottawa Tribe of Oklahoma, P.O. Box 110, Miami, OK 74355 (918) 540-1536. Website: www.ottawatribe.org.

ROSS, NORMA (Lac Courte Oreilles Ojibwe)
(tribal secretary/treasurer)
Affiliation & Address: Secretary/Treasurer, Lac Courte Oreilles Band of Ojibwe Indians, 13394 W. Trapania Rd., Bldg. #1, Hayward, WI 54843 (715) 634-8934. E-mail: nross@lco-nsn.gov.

ROSS-PETHERICK, CASEY (Cherokee)
(attorney; clinical professor)
Education: Oklahoma City University, Meinders School of Business, BS, 2000, MBA, 203, School of Law, JD, 2003. *Affiliations & Address*: Staff Attorney, Hall Estill Attorneys at Law, 100 North Broadway, Chase Tower, Suite 2900, Oklahoma City, OK 73102 (405) 553-2309. crosspetherick@hallestill.com; Clinical Professor, American Indian Wills Clinic, Oklahoma City University School of Law, Oklahoma City, OK. Casey joined the staff at Oklahoma City University School of Law in 2005 and since 2009, has taught in the Indian Law program there. Casey focuses on American Indian land & property issues in Oklahoma. *Other professional posts*: Secretary, Cherokee Nation Foundation; board member, Oklahoma Indian Legal Services. *Memberships*: Oklahoma Bar Association; Oklahoma Indian Bar Association.

ROSSER, REBECCA HERNANDEZ
(Mescalero Apache/Mexican American)
(Indian studies assistant director; management services officer)
Education: California State University, Fullerton, MFA (Exhibition Design & Museum Studies); UCLA, MA (American Indian Studies); University of New Mexico, PhD (American Studies). *Affiliation & Address*: Assistant Director, UCLA American Indian Studies Center (2000-present), Campbell Hall 3220, Los Angeles, CA 90024 (310) 206-7506. E-mail: rhrosser@aisc.ucla.edu. Rebecca has worked in a variety of institutions, including universities, museums & archives such as the Center for Southwest Research, the Indian Pueblo Cultural Center, and the Southwest Museum in Los Angeles.

ROSSETTI, MICHAEL G.
(attorney, American Indian law)
Education: University of Buffalo, SUNY, BA, 1981; Cleveland State University, Cleveland-Marshall College of Law, JD, 1987. *Affiliation & Address*: Partner, Akin Gump Strauss Hauer & Feld, LLP, Robert S. Strauss Bldg., 1333 New Hampshire Ave., NW, Washington, DC 20036 (202) 887-4311. E-mail: mrossetti@akingump.com. *Areas of Experience*: American Indian Gaming & Compact Negotiation; American Indian Policy & Regulation; Ennvironmenta, Natural Resources & Land for American Indian Tribes; Litigation for Indian Tribes. Michael G. Rossetti advises tribal clients regarding economic development and Indian gaming, and tribal governance issues. Mr. Rossetti also lobbies on a broad range of tribal concerns, & works on litigation matters and the settlement of Indian water rights. In addition, Mr. Rossetti advises clients regarding land use & other issues before the Department of the Interior, including the Bureau of Land Management, the Fish & Wildlife Service and the National Park Service. Also, Mr. Rossetti advises clients regarding state attorneys general issues. *Past professional posts*: Immediately prior to joining Akin Gump, Mr. Rossetti served for three years as personal counselor to the secretary of the Department of the Interior in Washington, where he assisted the secretary in formulating & implementing policies regarding Indian economic development, Indian gaming, land acquisition, law enforcement & homeland security. Among the decisions made during his tenure are the approval of the gaming compacts submitted by Indian tribes in the states of New York, Arizona, New Mexico and Wisconsin & a positive two-part determination by the secretary regarding a gaming facility proposed by the Jena Band of the Choctaw Indians in Louisiana. He also served on the federal committee charged with negotiating the implementation of regulations for certain Indian

schools under the No Child Left Behind Act, a presidential educational initiative. *Awards, honors*: Chambers USA: America's Leading Lawyers for Business in the area of Native American law; Best Lawyers in America (2007-2015) for Native American law.

ROTH, GEOFFREY (Hunkpapa Standing Rock Sioux)
(council director)
Education: University of Oregon, B.S. (Educational Studies); graduate courses at Georgetown University. *Affiliation & Address*: Senior Advisor to the Director, Indian health Service, DHH, The Reyes Bldg., 801 Thompson Ave., Suite 400, Rockville, MD 20852 (301) 443-1083. *Other professional posts*: V.P. Board & chairperson of the Policy Advisory Committee, National Native American AIDS Prevention Center. *Past professional posts*: Team Leader, Education Program Specialist, Office of Indian Education, U.S. Dept. of Education; executive director, Native American Youth Assn, Portland, OR; Executive Director, National Council of Urban Indian Health (NCUIH), Wash., DC, 2006-2010.

ROTH, SUSAN
(executive director)
Affiliation & Address: Executive director, Native American Lifelines, 106 West Clay Ave., Baltimore, MD 21201 (410) 837-2258. E-mail: susan.nal@verizon. net. *Other professional post*: Board member, Region 1, National Council of Urban Indian Health (NCUIH), Washington, DC, 2006-present). Ms. Roth has worked in the Native American community for more than 15 years.

ROUBIDEAUX, NANETTE S. (Ioway of Kansas/Nebraska) 1940-
(museum professional)
Born July 20, 1940, Porcupine, S.D. *Education*: Haskell Indian Junior College, AAS, 1975; University of Kansas, B.A. (Honors), 1977, PhD candidate. Resides in Horton, Kans. *Affiliations*: Consultant, Haskell Indian Junior College; Museum of the American Indian; *Past professional posts*: Teaching assistant, research assistant, assistant instructor, graduate assistant, University of Kansas, Lawrence, Kan., 1977-83; co-director, Kansas Committee for the Humanities Project Change, Continuities, and Challenges, Haskell Indian Junior College, 1984-85; Intern Fellowship, The Gustav Heye Center, Museum of the American Indian, Smithsonian Institution, New York, NY, 1985-86; consultant: KANU Radio, University of Kansas; Women's Transitional Care, Lawrence, KS; chairperson, Grand Review Committee for Dept. of Health & Human Services, Office of Human Development Services, 1985-. *Memberships*: American Historical Assn; American Anthropological Assn; Phi Alpha Theta; Society for Values in Higher Education. *Awards, honors*: Danforth Foundation Fellowship, 1979-1982; Outstanding Americans Program, listed in Outstanding Young Women in America, 1977; American Indian Scholarship Program, 1977-80; Lawrence Professional & Business Women's Outstanding Haskell Indian Junior College Student, 1975; Merwlyn Foundation Research Grant, 1976; Commission of the Status for Women, Outstanding Student in Contributions to a Minority Culture, 1976; Minority Affairs Teaching Assistant Award, 1977; Graduate School, Dissertation Fellowship, 1984-85. *Interests*: Contemporary Native American activities. *Published works*: The Native American Woman: A Cross-Disciplinary Bibliography (in preparation); Up Before Dawn: A Study of the Family Farm, paper given at regional meeting of American Anthropological Association, Memphis, TN., 1979.

ROUBIDOUX, VIC (Iowa)
(tribal Aviary manager)
Affiliation: Office of Environmental Services, Iowa Tribe of Oklahoma, Rt. 1 Box 721, Perkins, OK 74059 (405) 547-2402. *Past tribal positions*: Treasurer for 13 years. Vic takes care of Bald Eagles & Golden Eagles that can be rehabilitated and released back into the wild, as well as eagles that are permanently injured and must have a lifelong home. *Past professional posts*: Chair, Repatriation & Sacred Sites Committee for the National Congress of American Indians; treasurer for Keeper of the Treasures.

ROUBIDEAUX, YVETTE (Rosebud Sioux)
(MD; IHS acting director)
Education: Harvard Medical School, MD, 1989; Harvard School of Public Health, MPH, 1997. *Affiliation & Address*: Director (2009-present), Indian Health Service (IHS), 5600 Fishers Lane, Rockville, MD 20857 (301) 443-1083. *Past professional posts*: Clinical director (three years), IHS - San Carlos Service Unit, San Carlos Apache Indian reservation in Arizona; medical officer, Hu Hu Kam Memorial Indian Hospital on the Gila River Indian reservation in Arizona; assistant professor of family & community medicine, University of Arizona College of Medicine; co-director of the Special Diabetes Program for Indians Demonstration Projects (66 American Indian & Alaska Native communities are implementing diabetes prevention & cardiovascular disease prevention initiatives); director of two University of Arizona programs designed to recruit American Indian & Alaska Native students into health & research professions. *Memberships*: Association of American Indian Physicians (past president). *Published works*: Co-editor, Promises to Keep: Public Health Policy for American Indians & Alaska Natives in the 21st Century; several mono-

graphs & peer-reviewed publications on American Indian/Alaska Native health issues, research, and policy.

ROUNTREE, HELEN C. 1944-
(anthropologist)
Born October 8, 1944, Camp Le Jeune, NC. *Education*: College of William & Mary, AB, 1966; University of Utah, MA, 1968; University of Wisconsin, Milwaukee, PhD, 1973. *Address*: 268 Harris Creek Rd., Hampton, VA 23669 (804) 683-3812. *Affiliation*: Professor Emerita of Anthropology, Old Dominion University, Norfolk, VA, 1968-. *Memberships*: American Anthropological Association, 1968-; Royal Anthropological Institute of Great Britain & Ireland, 1969-; Society for Applied Anthropology, 1981-; American Society for Ethnohistory, 1988-. *Interests*: North American Indian ethnology, especially Virginia Algonquians; ecological anthropology; political anthropology; anthropology of gender; Middle Eastern ethnology (ancient & modern), ethnicity. *Avocations*: music, textiles, embroidery-designing. *Published works*: The Powhatan Indians of Virginia: Their Traditional Culture (University of Oklahoma Press, 1989); Pocahontas' People: The Powhatan Indians of Virginia Through Four Centuries (University of Oklahoma Press, 1990); editor, Powhatan Foreign Relations, 1500-1722 (University Press of Virginia).

ROUSSEAU, GARRYL, SR. (Sisseton-Wahpeton Oyate)
(tribal vice chairperson)
Affiliation & Address: Vice Chairperson, Sisseton-Wahpeton Dakota Tribe, P.O. Box 509, Agency Village, SD 57262 (605) 698-3911. E-mail: vicechair@swo-nsn.gov.

ROUTEL, COLETTE
(attorney)
Education: Ithaca College, BM, 1998; University of Michigan Law School, JD, 2001. *Affiliation & Address*: Of Counsel, Hogen Adams PLLP, 1935 W. County Road B2, Suite 460, St. Paul, MN 55113 (651) 290-6327. E-mail: Colette.routel@mitchellhamline.edu. Colette is a tenured professor at the William Mitchell College of Law, where she is Co-Director of the Indian Law Program, and teaches Federal Indian Law, an Indian Law Clinic, Natural Resources Law and Property Law. She maintains an active pro bono practice in federal Indian law and wildlife law, and consults with the firm on its cases. Colette often testifies before Congressional committees concerning Indian law issues, and presents at symposia & legal-education seminars around the country. Before entering academia, Colette worked at Faegre & Benson (now Faegre Baker Daniels) and Jacobson, Buffalo, Magnuson, Anderson & Hogen, where her practice centered on the representation of Indian tribes and environmental organizations. *Experience includes*: Lac Courte Oreilles Indian Tribe et al. v. Wisconsin (W.D. Wis. 2012 – present). Providing *pro bono* representation, including completion of five-day trial as lead attorney to certain Wisconsin tribes seeking relief from 1991 judgment preventing them from hunting white-tailed deer at night due to purported safety concerns. *Adoptive Couple v. Baby Girl* (U.S. 2013). Drafted *pro bono* amicus brief to the U.S. Supreme Court on behalf of all Wisconsin Indian tribes, which supported the position of the Cherokee Nation & Cherokee birth father seeking to maintain custody of his daughter pursuant to the Indian Child Welfare Act. *Summit Lake Paiute Tribe v. FERC* (9th Cir. 2010-2012) and *Summit Lake Paiute Tribe v. BLM* (D.C. Cir. 2010-2012). Provided *pro bono* representation as lead attorney in cases challenging the federal government's authorization of an interstate natural gas pipeline that would destroy sacred sites, burial grounds, greater sage grouse habitat, and traditional plants and medicines in the Tribe's aboriginal territory. Obtained partial re-route of pipeline to avoid core areas of sacred site. *Saginaw Chippewa Tribe v. Michigan* (E.D. Mich. 2007-2010). Represented tribe in litigation against the State of Michigan, and obtained successful settlement acknowledging that the Isabella Indian Reservation was established through treaties with the United States in 1855 & 1864, & continues to exist. *Carcieri v. Kempthorne* (U.S. 2008). Drafted *pro bono* amicus brief to the U.S. Supreme Court on behalf of law professors who specialize in Federal Indian Law, which supported affirming the United States' decision to take land into trust for the Narragansett Indian Tribe pursuant to the Indian Reorganization Act of 1934. Amicus brief was cited by Justice Breyer in his concurring opinion. *Awards, honors*: Rising Star, Minnesota Super Lawyers Magazine (2005-2006, 2008- 2009, 2011-2013).

ROUWALK, ALYCE
(BIA agency supt.)
Affiliation: Shiprock Agency, Bureau of Indian Affairs, P.O. Box 966, Shiprock, NM 87420 (505) 368-4301.

ROWE, DAN (*First Scout*)
(professor of Native American studies)
Affiliation & Address: Professor, Native American Studies, Fairhaven College of Interdisciplinary Studies, 516 High St., Western Washington University, Bellingham, WA 98225 (360) 650-3620.

ROWE-KURAK, JANICE (Iowa)
(former tribal chairperson)
Affiliation: Iowa Tribe of Oklahoma, Rt. 1 Box 721, Perkins, OK 74059
(405) 547-2402. E-mail: rowe-kurak@iowanation.org.

ROWLEN, SHALAH (Sac & Fox-Pawnee)
(craftsperson; store owner)
Affiliation: American Indian Handicrafts, P.O. Box 358, Meeker, OK 74855
(405) 279-2896. *Products*: Ribbonwork, blankets & apparel, beadwork and
featherwork.

ROY, GEORGE (Saginaw Chippewa)
(instructor in Ojibwa language)
Education: Lansing Community College, AA, 1996-97; Ferris State University,
BA (Social Work), 2007. *Affiliation & Address*: Instructor, Ojibwa Language,
Saginaw Chippewa Tribal College, 2274 Enterprise Dr., Mount Pleasant, MI
48858 (989) 775-4123. E-mail: roy.george@sagchip.edu.

ROY, HELEN (Wikwemikong First Nations Band, Ontario - Canada)
(teaches Ojibwe language courses)
Affiliation & Address: Teacher, Ojibwe Language Courses, American Indian
Studies Department, Michigan State University, 8380 Wells, East Lansing, MI
48824 (517) 432-2193. E-mail: royh@mmsu.edu. Helen has worked for the
Lansing School District as a Language specialist, taught at Central Michigan
Univeristy,Western Michigan University, and at Bay Mills Community College.
Helen currently teaches Ojibwe Language courses on and off campus, while
organizing Anishnabemowin events such as the Ojibwe Language Quiz
Bowland Anishinaabemowin Pow Wow which combine community and the
university around the importance of language maintenance and revitalization.
Additionally, Helen is one half of the duet *Diiva miinwa Davis*, which performs
pop songs translated into Anishinaabemowin. This is another way in which
Helen works to revitalize the language.

ROY, LORIENE (White Earth Anishinabe) 1954-
(associate professor)
Born June 12, 1954. *Education*: Oregon Institute of Technology, AS, BT, 1977;
University of Arizona, MLS, 1980; University of Illinois at Urbana-Champaign,
PhD, 1987. *Address & Affiliation*: Associate Professor, Graduate School of
Library & Information Science, SZB 564, University of Texas at Austin, Austin,
TX 78712 (1987-present) (512) 471-3959. E-Mail: loriene@ischool.utexas.edu.
Other professional posts: Advisory board (2002-present), International
Children's Digital Library; advisory board (2002-present), WebJunction.org;
advisory board (2001-present), Sequoyah Research Center; advisory board
(2005-present), Texas State Library & Archives Commission. *Community
activities*: Austin Free Net volunteer. *Memberships*: American Library
Association (president, 2007-08); American Indian Library Association
(president, 1997-98); Public Library Association; Library & Information Science
Education; National Trust for Historic Preservation; Oral History Association;
Popular Culture Association; Texas Library Association. *Interests*: "Current
writing interest areas include: library service to Native American populations;
collection management; progressive era librarian education; creative fiction."
Published works: Over 40 professional papers, reports, chapters; over 60
presentations at professional conferences.

ROYBAL, EDWARD R., II (Piro/Manso/Tiwa)
(pueblo governor)
Affiliation & Address: Governor, Pueblo of San Juan de Guadalupe,
4048 Callede Estrellas, Las Cruces, NM 88012 (505) 647-5372

ROYER, BARBARA
(tribal library director)
Affiliations: Yavapai-Prescott Tribal Library, 530 E. Merritt, Prescott, AZ 86301
(928) 445-8790.

ROYSTER, JUDITH
(attorney; professor of law; Indian center/program co-director)
Education: University of Wisconsin-Madison, BA (History, 1973, MA (Library
Science), 1978, Law School, JD, 1986. *Affiliation & Address*: Director, Native
American Law Certificate Program & Co-Director, Native American Law
Center, University of Tulsa College of Law, John Roger Hall 2416, 3120 E. 4th
Pl., Tulsa, OK 74104 (918) 631-3191. E-mail: judith-royster@utulsa.edu.
Professor Royster is a nationally recognized expert in the areas of Indian
environmental law, water law, & mineraldevelopment; as such, she is regularly
sought after to speak at conferences. She co-authored the leading textbook on
Native American natural resources law and is published extensively on a
variety of Indian law topics. In addition to her role as a contributing author of
Felix S. Cohen's Handbook of Federal Indian Law, she also serves on the
editorial board for the treatise. She writes & lectures in the areas of federal
Indian environmental, natural resources and water law. She teaches civil
procedure, adminis-trative law, federal Indian law, and Native American natural
resources law. *Past professional posts*: Clerked for the Western District of

Wisconsin, was the Natural Resources Law Fellow at Northwestern School of
Law, Lewis & Clark College, and taught at Chicago Kent & Stetson University
law schools. *Awards, honors*: Her article in the Tulsa Law Review entitled
Mineral Development in Indian Country: The Evolution of Tribal Control Over
Mineral Resources was cited by Justice Souter in his dissent in the 2003 U.S.
Supreme Court case of *United States v. Navajo Nation*. *Published works*:
Editor of & contributing author to *Cohen's Handbook of Federal Indian Law*,
and the co-author of *Native American Natural Resources Law: Cases and
Materials*. Her article on tribal mineral development was cited by the U.S.
Supreme Court in the 2003 case of *United States v. Navajo Nation*.

ROZEMA, VICKI BELL (Cherokee)
(writer & photographer)
Education: University of Tennessee, Knoxville, PhD (Early American History &
Cherokee History). *Address*: 7500 Woodland Bay Dr., Harrison, TN 37341. E-
mail: vickirozema@comcast.net. *Awards, honors*: Award of Merit for
"Footsteps of the Cherokees," by the Tennessee Historical Commission.
Memberships: Tennessee Trail of Tears Association; Tennessee Writers
Association; Smithsonian National Museum of the American Indian. *Published
works*: Footsteps of the Cherokees: A Guide to the Eastern Homelands of the
Cherokee Nation (John F. Blair, Publisher, 1995); Cherokee Voices: Early
Accounts of Cherokee Life in the East (John F. Blair, Publisher; editor, Voices
From the Trail of Tears (John F. Blair, Publisher, 2002) Her articles appear in
the Blue Ridge Country & Country Extra. magazines.

ROZIE, LEE (*Mixashawn*) (Mohegan)
(musickeeper)
Born in Hartford, Conn. *Principal occupation*: Musickeeper. *Address*: 108
Sisson St., E. Hartford, CT 06118 (800) 949-MIXA. *Membership*: Executive
Director, Pequonawonk Canoe Society, E. Hartford, CT. *Interests*: "The
musical trio, "Afro-Algonquin" which derives its name from the ethnic
background of its two co-leaders, Rick & Lee Rozie. The idea behind the group
is to integrate American Indian folk music themes into modern Afro-American
jazz. Lee plays tenor and soprano saxophones, flutes, percussion, vocals.
"Maheekanew," is the traditional name of our people." Records & CDs: "Word,
Out" Music for the Next Century," "Plastic Champions," & "Maheekanew View
of Mixashawn," all produced by (Indian Runs Records, 1991-93).

RUBIN, JEANNE M.
(general counsel)
Education: Stanford University, JD. *Affiliation & Address*: General Counsel,
International Institute for Indigenous Resource Management, 444 S. Emerson
St., Denver, CO 80209 (303) 733-0481. E-mail: jeannerubin@iiirm.org. *Past
professional posts*: Private practice, Denver, CO (concentrated in Indian law
with an emphasis on gaming & general commercial concerns); served as
Special General Counsel to the Ute Mountain Ute Tribe from 1992-99 and in
that capacity advised & represented tribal officials on a full range of regulatory,
jurisdictional and commercial issues; several years as a policy analyst with the
Administration for Native Americans in the Department of Health & Human
Services; lectured at seminars sponsored by the National Indian Gaming
Association, National Congress of American Indians, the Council of Energy
Resource Tribes, CERT Tribal Environmental Institute, the Bureau of Indian
Affairs, et al. on a variety of tribal gaming, contract & environmental issues.

RUBIO, DARLENE (Yavapai-Apache)
(former tribal vice chairperson)
Affiliation & Address: Vice Chairperson, Yavapai-Apache Nation, 2400 W.
Datsi St., Camp Verde, AZ 86322 (928) 567-3649.

RUKOVISHNIKOFF, JESSICA (Aleut)
(Alaskan tribal president)
Affiliation: Aleut Community of St. Paul Island, P.O. Box 86, St. Paul Island, AK
99660 (907) 546-3200.

RULE, CHRIS A. (Chickasaw)
(attorney; member, tribal advocacy group)
Education: University of Oklahoma, BA, 1982; Cornell Law School, JD,
1985.*Affiliation & Address*: Member, Tribal Advocacy Group (2013-present),
Crowell Law Office, 1487 W. 89A, Suite 8, Sedona, AZ 86336 (425) 802-5369.
E-mail: crule@cotag.net As a member of Tribal Advocacy Group team, Chris
will continue his general representation of Tribal clients, and will focus on the
areas of gaming, including negotiation and documentation with consultants,
management companies, vendors and other entities in all aspects of the
gaming business; real estate, including real estate acquisition, maintenance,
financing, and fee-to-trust transfers; legislation & governmental relations,
including the preparation & negotiation of proposed legislation and dealing with
federal, state and local officials; and other contract preparation and negotiation
required for the protection of Tribal governmental and business interests. Other
professional posts: General Counsel, Alabama-Coushata Tribe of Texas,
2011-03; 2013-present. *Past professional posts*. Crowell Law Office, Attorney,
1999-2001 at its San Diego, California location, where in keeping with the

firm's mission, he represented Tribal clients exclusively. At Crowell, Chris had the opportunity to represent a variety of Tribal clients. Representative clients included the Tule River Tribe, the Shoalwater Bay Tribe, the Manzanita Tribe and the Alabama-Coushatta Tribe of Texas. While at Crowell Law Offices, Chris also had the opportunity to represent the Rincon Band of Luiseno Indians in its dealings with Harrah's Gaming, culminating in the development of the Harrah's Rincon Casino, currently one of the largest Tribal gaming operations in California; Shoshone-Bannock Tribes, General Counsel, 1996-1999 As General Counsel for Shoshone-Bannock, Chris worked on the Reservation and focused primarily on Tribal business matters, working directly with the Tribal Council and its individual members to promote & protect Tribal interests. Of particular note, Chris handled the negotiations between the Tribe & the U.S. Department of the Navy arising out the transportation of spent naval nuclear fuel across the Reservation; negotiations which resulted in a substantial settlement in favor of the Tribe. Chris also represented the Tribe in its gaming operations, which lead to his long-standing association with attorney Scott Crowell, and Chris and Scott worked together on the negotiation and finalization of a favorable gaming compact between the Tribe and the State of Idaho; American General Corp., Senior Counsel, 1993-1996 - senior counsel in the real estate group; Butler & Binion Law Firm, as Associate & Senior Associate, 1985-1993 - Chris worked in the firm's real estate section from 1985-1993. *Memberships*: Texas Bar Association, 1985-present (Member, Native American Law Section); Idaho Bar Association, 1997-present

RUNNELS, DENNIS M. (Colville Confederated Tribes) 1941-
(college instructor)
Born March 29, 1941, Bremerton, Wash. *Education*: University of Washington, PhD Candidate in Romance Language. *Address*: RR 1 Box 576, Sharon, VT 05065 (802) 763-7554. E-mail: dennis.runnels@dartmouth.edu. *Affiliation*: Instructor, Native American Studies Program, Dartmouth College, 1990-present (teaches courses on American Indian Autobiography, Native American Languages, American Indian Identity, Spanish, and Latin American Studies. *Military service*: U.S. Marine Military Academy, King's Point, 1959-63. Published works: Journal articles.

RUNNELS, TERESA WASHINGTON (Creek/Shawnee/Delaware)
(center coordinator)
Education: Oklahoma State University, MA; University of Oklahoma, MA (Library Information Studies). *Affiliation & Address*: Coordinator (2004-present), American Indian Resource Center, Tulsa City-County Library, 400 Civic Center, Tulsa, OK 7410 (918) 549-7323.

RUNNINGWATER, N. BIRD (Cheyenne/Mescalero Apache) 1973-
(program director)
Education: University of Oklahoma, BA (Journalism), 1994. *Affiliation & Address*: Director, Native American & Indigenous Program, Sundance Institute, 5900 Wilshire Blvd. #800, Los Angeles, CA 90036 (310) 360-1981 Fax 360-1969. Mr. Runnngwater scouts worldwide and across the U.S. for indigenous artists with projects that can be supported through the Institute's Feature Film Program, Docuemntary Program, Theatre Program, Independent Producers Conference, and Sundance Film Festival. He also oversees the Sundance Institute-Ford Foundation Film Fellowship established for emerging Native Americn filmmakers. *Past professional posts*: Executive Director, Fund of the Four Directions, the private philanthropy of a Rockefeller family member. The Fund focused on supporting the revitalization of the languages & lifeways of North America's indigenous peoples.

RUOFF, A. LaVONNE BROWN 1930-
(professor emerita of English)
Born April 10, 1930, Charleston, IL. *Education*: Northwestern University, B.S., 1953, M.A., 1954, Ph.D., 1966. *Affiliation & Address*: Professor Emerita of English; Interim director, D'Arcy McNickle Center for American Indian History, Newberry Library. 300 Forest Ave., Oak Park, IL 60302 (708) 848-9292; E-mail: lruoff@uic.edu. *Past professional post*: Dept. of English, University of Illinois, Chicago, 1966-94. *Community activities*: Chicago Indian Council Fire, 1980-89; Indian Business Associate Advisory Board, 1977-84. *Memberships*: Modern Language Association, 1966-; Association for the Study of American Indian Literature, 1977-; Discussion Group on American Indian Literature (MLA, 1978-; chair, 1978, 1990); Society for the Study of Multi-Ethnic Literature in the U.S.; American Studies Association; Native American Literature Symposium. *Awards, honors*: Achievement Award, Indian Council Fire, 1989; Distinguished Contribution to Ethnic Studies, Society for the Study of Multi-Ethnic Literature in the U.S., 1986; director, Summer Seminars for College Teachers on American Indian Literatures, 1979, 1983, 1989, 1994; National Endowment for the Humanities Fellowship, 1992-93; honored for contributions to American Indian literature by the Division of American Indian Literatures, Modern Language Association, and Association for Study of American Indian Literatures, 1993; American Book Awards, Before Columbus Association, 1998; Writer of the Year for Bibliography, Wordcraft Circle of Native Writers & Storytellers, 1998; Writer of the Year for Series Editing, Wordcraft Circle of Native Writers & Storytellers, 2002; Lifetime Scholarly Achievement Award,

Modern Language Association, 2002. *Interests*: History of American Indian literature written in English. *Biographical sources*: Directory of American Scholars; Who's Who in the Midwest; Who's Who in America (millennium edition); Writer's Directory. *Published works*: The Moccasin Maker, by E. Pauline Johnson, edited with intro. by Ruoff (University of Arizona Press, 1987; reprinted by University of Oklahoma Press, 1998); co-editor, Redefining American Literary History, with Jerry Ward (Modern Language Assn, 1990; American Indian Literatures (Modern Language Assn, 1990); Literatures of the American Indian (Chelsea House, 1990); Wynema: A Child of the Forest, by S. Alice Callahan, edited with intro. by Ruoff (University of Nebraska Press, 1997); Life Letters and Speeches, edited with intro. by Ruoff and biography by Donald Smith (University of Nebraska Press, 1997); editor, American Indian Lives Series (University of Nebraska Press); From the Deep Woods to Civilization with Excerpts from Indian Boyhood, by Charles A. Eastman, edited with an intro. by Ruoff, Lakeside Classic Series (Donnelley Press, 2001).

RUPERT, SHERRY L. (Paiute/Washoe)
(state commission executive director)
Born in Carson City & raised on the Washoe Reservation in Gardnerville, Nevada. *Education*: University of Nevada, Reno, BS (Business Administration). *Address & Affiliation*: Executive Director, Nevada Indian Commission (2005-present), 5366 Snyder Ave., Carson City, NV 89701 (775) 687-8333. E-mail: srupert@nic.nv.gov. *Other professional posts*: Chair, Nevada Commission on Tourism; Vice President (Nevada Indian Territory), American Indian Alaska Native Tourism Assn, Albuquerque, NM; Appointed by U.S. Deputy Secretary of Commerce, Rebecca Blank to the Travel & Tourism Advisory Board. *Past professional posts*: Served two terms as president of the Governor's Interstate Indian Council, formerly treasurer for two terms. *Community activities*: Past President, Native Alumni Chapter of the University of Nevada, Reno. *Awards, honors*: Awarded the 2007 & 2009 Excellence in Tourism Award from the Nevada Commission on Tourism for her success in promoting & advancing tourism in Indian Country; 2009 Human & Civil Rights Award from the Nevada State Education Assn. *Interests*: Women's Jingle dancer.

RUPPEL, KRISTIN T.
(professor of Native American Studies)
Education: Montana College of Mineral Science & Technology, BA, 1989; Idaho State University, MA, 1995; Columbia University, PhD, 2004. *Affiliation & Address*: Professor (2005-present), Department of Native American Studies, Montana State University, 2-186 Wilson Hall, P.O. Box 172340, Bozeman, MT 59717 (406) 994-5261. E-mail: ktruppel@montana.edu. Kristin currently teaches graduate & undergraduate courses in Federal Indian Policy & Law, Native Food Systems, Indigenous People & Film, and Critical Methodologies in Native American Studies. *Published works*: Unearthing Indian Land: Living With the Legacies of Allotment (University of Arizona Press, 2008).

RUSS, JAMES (Pomo)
(tribal president)
Affiliation & Address: President, Round Valley Indian Tribes, 77826 Covelo Rd., Covelo, CA 95428 (707) 983-6126. E-mail: president@rvit.org. *Past professional post*: Director, Round Valley Indian Tribes Education Center, Covelo, CA.

RUSS, JOSEPH A., SR. (Pomo)
(tribal president)
Affiliation: Covelo Indian Community Council, Round Valley Reservation, P.O. Box 448, Covelo, CA 95428 (707) 983-6126.

RUSSELL, BEVERLY (San Carlos Apache)
(tribal liaison)
Born & raised on the San Carlos Apache Reservation, Arizona. *Education*: Seton Hall University, BA. *Affiliation & Address*: Director, Tribal Affairs, First Thngs First, 4000 N. Central Ave., #800, Phoenix, AZ 85012 (602) 771-5100.

RUSSELL, CASKEY
(director of American Indian studies program)
Education: PhD (English). *Affiliation & Address*: Professor of English & Director, American Indian Studies Program, College of Arts & Sciences, University of Wyoming, Ross Hall 114, 1000 E. University Ave., Laramie, WY 82071 (307) 766-6520. E-mail: ccaskey@uwyo.edu. *Research Interests*: American Indian Literature & Film; Critical Race Theory; Rhetoric of American Indian Treaties & Sovereignty. *Published works*: Critical Race Theory Matters: Education & Ideoogy, with Margaret Zamudio, et al (Routledge, Taylor & Francis, 2010); numerous articles.

RUSSELL, JIM (*Chief Badger*) (Kaweah)
(vice principal chief, publisher)
Address: 2220 E 4500 S. Apt. 1, Salt Lake City, UT 84117. *Affiliations*: Vice principal chief, Kaweah Indian Nation of Western USA & Mexico; tribal chief, Kayenta Kaweah Tribe. *Other professional post*: Member, American Indian Defense of Americas.

RUSSELL, LUVETTE (Papago)
 (BIA special education coordinator)
Affiliation: Papago Agency, Bureau of Indian Affairs, P.O. Box 490, Sells, AZ 85634 (520) 383-3292.

RUSSELL, NEIL (Sioux)
 (secondary school principal)
Affiliation: Lower Brule Day School, P.O. Box 245, Lower Brule, SD 57548 (605) 473-5510.

RUSSELL, SCOTT C.
 (professor of anthropology)
Affiliation: Dept. of Anthropology, Box 872402, Arizona State University, Tempe, AZ 85287 (480) 965-6213. *Interests*: Native American studies. E-mail: scott.russell@asu.edu.

RUSSELL, SIERA (Yavapai)
 (program director)
Affiliation: Indian Legal Program, Arizona State University College of Law, Box 877906, Tempe, AZ 85287 (480) 965-6204.

RUSSELL, JUDGE STEVE (Cherokee) 1947-
 (associate professor of criminal justice)
Born February 10, 1947, Bristow, Okla. *Education*: University of Texas, B.S.Ed. (magna cum laude), 1972, J.D., 1975; University of Nevada, Reno, Masters of Judicial Studies, 1993. *Thesis*: "Ethnic Cleansing and Land Ownership: Why the Native American Graves Protection & Repatriation Act Does Not Protect Native American Graves in Texas." *Address & Affiliation*: Associate professor, Dept. of Criminal Justice, 1033 E. 3rd St., 302 Sycamore Hall, Indiana University, Bloomington, IN (812) 855-2601. E-mail: swrussell@indiana.edu. *Other professional post*: Visiting Judge, State of Texas, 1995-present. *Past professional posts*: Teaching - Instructor, University of Texas School of Law, 1985-90, 1992-93; Assistant Professor, Division of Social & Policy Sciences, The University of Texas at San Antonio, 1995-2000; Assistant Professor, Division of Criminal Justice, The University of Texas at San Antonio, 2000-2001; Professional - Simons, Cunningham, Coleman, Nelson & Howard, law clerk, 1974-75, associate, 1975-76; partner, Russell & Mahlab, 1976-78; Austin Municipal Court, Associate Judge, 1978-80, Presiding Judge, 1980-82; Judge, Travis County Court at Law No. Two, 1982-94. *Military service*: U.S. Air Force, 1964-68 (Top Secret Security Clearance). *Professional Training*: Numerous workshops, symposiums & seminars, including: "Sovereignty and the Right to Death," Cleveland-Marshall College of Law, Cleveland, OH, 2003; "International Indian Treaty Council Conference," Sac & Fox Nation, 2003; "Decolonizing American Indian Studies," The Newberry Library, Chicago, IL, 2003; "Honoring Nations," The Harvard Project on American Indian Economic Development, Santa Fe, NM 2002 (invited). *Memberships*: Academy of Criminal Justice Sciences (life); American Association of University Professors; American Society of Criminology (life); American Society of Criminology (life); American Indian Philosophy Association; Association of Trial Lawyers of America; Bristow Historical Society; Cherokee National Historical Society; Law & Society Association; Native Writers Circle of the Americas; Ninth Circuit Historical Society; State Bar of Texas; Texas Indian Bar Association (two term president); U.S. District Court Bar (Western District of Texas); U.S. Supreme Court Bar; Wordcraft Circle of Native American Writers & Storytellers. Published works: Numerous book chapters, book & film reviews; refereed and law review articles; non-refereed articles; poetry and fiction; and paper presentations.

RUSSELL, WINFIELD (Northern Cheyenne)
 (tribal vice president)
Affiliation & Address: Vice President, Northern Cheyenne Tribal Council, P.O. Box 128, Lame Deer, MT 59043 (406) 477-8284.

RUSSONIELLO-DAMASKOS, RUBY K. (Gros Ventre/Assiniboine) 1963-
 (teacher; Indian education facilitator)
Born June 19, 1963, Havre, Mont. *Education*: University of Montana, BA (Elementary Education), 1985; University of Washington (Med-At Risk Education). *Affiliation & Address*: Teacher; Indian education facilitator, Tacoma Public Schools District #10 (special education teacher; Dept. Chair, 1990-2001; Indian education facilitator, 2001-present), P.O. Box 1357, Tacoma, WA 98401 (253) 571-1139. E-mail: ruby_russoniello@hotmail.com or E-mail: rdamask@tacoma.k12.wa.us. *Past professional posts*: Chapter 1/special education teacher, Woodman School District #18, Lolo Creek, MT, 1987-89; special education teacher, Bonner, MT, 1989-90. *Community activities*: Parent Advisory Committee - Indian Education; Powwow Planning Committee - UPS - Tacoma, WA. *Memberships*: National Indian Education Association; Phi Delta Kappa; Teaching Tolerance; Council of Exceptional Children Foundation; National Education Association. *Interests*: History, ancestry, reading, poetry, animals, movies, hiking.

RYAN, ARNOLD R. (Sisseton-Wahpeton Sioux)
 (former tribal chairperson)
Affiliation: Sisseton-Wahpeton Sioux Tribe, Rt. 2 - Agency Village, Sisseton, SD 57262 (605) 698-3911.

RYAN, IRENE (Washoe)
 (Indian store owner)
Affiliation: The Teepee, 2500 E. 2nd St., Suite #38, Reno, NV 89595 (702) 322-5599.

RYAN, JESSICA L. (Brothertown)
 (attorney)
Education: Hamline University, BA, 1994; Hamline University School of Law, JD, 1997. *Affiliation & Address*: Associate Attorney, BlueDog, Paulson & Small, PLLP, Southgate Office Plaza, Suite 500, 5001 West 80th, Bloomington, MN 55437 (952) 893-1813. *Other professional posts*: Vice President, Board of Directors, Indian Child Welfare Law Center; secretary, American Indian Policy Center, Minneapolis, MN. Ms. Ryan has been appointed by the Minnesota Supreme Court to serve on the Imlementation Committee on Multi-Cultural Diversity & Racial Fairness in the Courts Task Force Committee; the Minnesota Tribal Court/State Court Judges Assn; and the Minnesota Supreme Court's Children's Justice Initiative. She continues to volunteer as a Guardian ad litem on the panel serving American Indian families in Hennepin County & recently assisted in preparation of a Petition for Federal Acknowledgment on behalf of a tribe. Practice admissions: The Court of the Sac & Fox Tribe of the Mississippi in Iowa, the hakopee Mdwekanton Sioux (Dakota) Community Tribal Court, the Sisseton-Wapeton Tribal Court of the Lake Traverse Reservation, and the Northern Plains Intertribal Court of Appeals. *Memberships*: Minnesota State Bar; Minnesota American Indian Bar Assn.

RYSER, RUDOLPH C. (Cowlitz)
 (center chairperson)
Education: Washington State University BA (Philosophy); UCLA, The Center for War/Peace Studies & Indian Education Administration, MA; The Union Institute Graduate School in Cincinnati, OH, PhD, 1996. *Affiliation & Address*: Chairperson (1984-present), Center for World Indigenous Studies, PMB 214, 1001 Cooper Point Rd. SW, Suite 140, Olympia, WA 98502-1107 (360) 450-5183. *Past professional posts*: Specialist on U.S. Government federal administration of Indian Affairs on the American Indian Policy Review Commission, 1975 where Dr. Ryser authored the Federal Administration Task Force Report in 1976; executive director, Small Tribes Organization of Western Washington, 1976-79; Special Assistant to President George Manuel (Canada) and the World Council of Indigenous Peoples, 1979-83; Acting Executive Director, National Congress of American Indians, 1983-84. *Interests*: Dr. Ryser has become a well-known essayist among indigenous peoples throughout the world and is a spokesperson for Fourth World political development, tribal/state conflict resolution & International cooperation between indigenous nations. *Published works*: Contributor to two anthologies on Indian Rights, "Indian Rights and the Great Lie," 1983, and "Fourth World Wars: The Emerging International Political Order," (University of Toronto Press, 1985); contributor & editor, "Indian Self-Government: Perspectives on the Political Status of Indian Nations in the USA (Center for World Indigenous Studies, 1989); contributor to the "Encyclopedia of Native Americans in the 20th Century (Garland, 1993); Resuming Self-Government in Indian Country (Murdoch University E-Law Review, Western Australia, 1995); article - "State Craft, Nations and Sharing Governmental Power," in Systems of Self-Government for Indigenous Peoples (International Work Group on Indigenous Affairs, Copenhagen, 1994).

S

SABATTIS, MR. CLAIR (Maliseet)
 (former tribal chief)
Affiliation: Houlton Band of Maliseet Indians, Rt. 3, Box 450, Houlton, ME 04730 (207) 532-4273.

SABATTIS, CLARISSA (Maliseet)
 (tribal chief)
Affiliation & Address: Chief, Houlton Band of Maliseet Indians, 88 Bell Rd., Littleton, ME 04730 (207) 532-4273. E-mail: tribal-chief@maliseet.com

SACHSE, HARRY R.
 (attorney)
Education: Louisiana State University, BA, 1955, JD, 1957; University of Paris, (diploma in comparative law). *Affiliation & Address*: Founding Partner, Sonosky, Chambers, Sachse, Endreson & Perry, LLP, 1425 K St., NW, Suite 600, Washington, DC 20005 (202) 682-0240. E-mail: hsachse@sonosky.com. *Harry*, a founding partner of the firm, specializes in litigation and negotiations concerning land claims, hydropower, fishing rights, water rights, oil and gas

issues, and gaming. He was the principal attorney in the Puyallup Land Settlement and the Colville Grand Coulee Settlement – two landmark settlements. From 1971 to 1976, Mr. Sachse was an Assistant to the Solicitor General of the United States, U.S. Department of Justice. In this role, he argued ten major cases in the Supreme Court including such historic cases as *McClanahan v. Arizona Tax Commission*, 411 U.S. 164 (1973) (state taxation of reservation income); *Washington Department of Game v. Puyallup Tribe*,414 U.S. 44 (1973) (Indian fishing and hunting rights); *United States v. Mazurie*, 419 U.S. 544 (1975) (tribal governmental powers); & *Morton v. Mancari*, 417 U.S. 535 (1974) (preference in hiring Native Americans.) Immediately before that, Mr. Sachse had been Assistant General Counsel of the U.S. Agency for International Development. Mr. Sachse, as an adjunct professor, has taught American Indian Law and Appellate Advocacy at the University of Virginia School of Law, American Indian Law at Harvard Law School, and the Rights of Indigenous Peoples in International and Comparative Law at The Georgetown University Law Center.

SACKLER, ELIZABETH
(public historian, arts activist, American Indian advocate)
Education: PhD. *Affiliations & Address*: Founder & President, American Indian Ritual Object Repatriation Foundation, 463 East 57 St., New York, NY 10128 (212) 980-9441; CEO & president, Board of Directors, Arthur M. Sackler Foundation, New York, NY; president, Elizabeth A. Sackler Foundation, New York, NY; member, National Advisory Board, National Museum of Women in the Arts (NMWA), Washington, DC; member, Board of Trustees, Brooklyn (NY) Museum. *Other professional post*: Lectures at universities & colleges in New York, NY. *Awards, honors*: Honored in 1999 by the Yurok Tribe; in 2002, the "Women in the Arts Award," from the Brooklyn Museum of Art Community Committee; in 293, she was named one of "21 Leaders of the 21st Century," from Women eNews; she received the "President's Award," from the Women's Caucus for Art; in 2005, she was named, "Native American of the Year," from Drums Along the Hudson; in 2006, "Distinguished Service to the Visual Arts Award," from ArtTable; in 2007, "Women of Power & Influence Award," from NOW-NYC, and the "Visionary Woman Award," from Moore College of Art in Philadelphia; and in 2008, "Art to Life Award," from A.I.R. Gallery and Art & Living magazine. *Published works*: Chapter - "Calling for a Code of Ethics in the Indian Art Market," in Ethics & the Visual Arts by Elaine A. King & Gail Levin, Editors (Allworth Press, 2006); delivered papers, " Raising the Bar Searching for an Ethical Morality," at the National Museum of the American Indian; ""Ethics, Morality, and the Cultural genocide of the American Indian Peoples," at the New School; and "The Museum's Role in the Repatriation of American Indian Cultural Material," at the Guggenheim Museum.

SACKS, EDDIE (Ketoowah Cherokee)
(tribal district representative)
Education: Bacone College, AA; Northeastern State University, BA. *Affiliation & Address*: Canadian District Representative (2001-present), United Keetoowah Band of Cherokee Indians of Oklahoma, P.O. Box 746, Tahlequah, OK 74465 (918) 431-1818. *Other tribal posts*: Vice-chairperson, Keetoowah Cherokee Economic Development Authority; vice-chairperson of the Gaming Board; serves on the Elders Committee & Education Committee.

SACKS, LINDA K. (Cherokee)
(organization vice president; member, board of directors)
Born in Tahlequah, Okla. *Education*: Oklahoma Christian Univesity, BS (Journalism and a minor in Biblical Studies); she also obtained credits from Harvard University, Laval University in Quebec City, Canada, & Manhattan Christian College & earned letterman awards in three collegiate sports: tennis, basketball, & soccer. Professionally, *Affiliations*: Vice President, American Indian Chamber of Commerce of Oklahoma, Broken Arrow, OK; member of Board of Directors for Goodwill Industries of Tulsa. *Other professional posts*: She serves as a member of the board of directors for Goodwill Industries of Tulsa and is an alumna of Leadership Tulsa's flagship program Class 54, whose mission is to identify, develop, and connect diverse leaders who impact the community through service. She is also a member of the Oklahoma Center for Community & Justice, Tulsa Cherokee Community Organization, and CN's Tulsa Career Services Group. As an employee of the Cherokee Nation (CN) she helps administer grants from the Department of Labor for workforce development creating area partnerships with the private and public sector, and strengthening relationships with the area workforce for all citizens via Cherokee Nation's successful Career Services' work programs. Linda has a background with the Walt Disney World Company in Orlando, FL, and the Salvation Army of Chicago Metropolitan Division working with at-risk urban youth. Upon returning to Oklahoma & the Cherokee Nation she engaged with Boulevard Christian Church, her home church, & helped establish a program for Muskogee's youth, The Landing of Muskogee. The faith-based after-school program is helping to break cycles of intergenerational dysfunction by helping teens build healthy relationships with one another & the community. During this time she served in the Muskogee public school system for Indian Education, teaching culture & identity to the 33 represented tribes in the school district.

SADONGEI, ALYCE (Kiowa/Tohono O'odham)
(project coordinator)
Affiliation & Address: Project Coordinator, American Indian Language Development Institute, The University of Arizona, Dept. of Teaching, Learning & Sociocultural Studies, College of Education, Rm. 517, P.O. Box 210069, Tucson, AZ 85721 (520) 621-1068. Alyce has a career history of working with Native Ameican arts & culture. *Past professional posts*: She worked at the Arizona State Museum at the University of Arizona. She served as principal investigator on numerous grants, the most primary being an eight year project that focused on tribal libraries, archives & museums and was implemented in partnership with the Arizona State Library. She was the co-project director of several grants related to repatriation, consultation & research regardin the use of pesticides on museum objects subject to repatriation. Previous to her work at ASM, she worked at the National Museum of the American Indian, Smthsonian Institution where she developed the internship progrram & other areas of outreach. She has also served on numberous boards & commissions.

SAENZ, DANIEL (Mescalero-Chiricahua Apache)
(business development specialist)
Affiliation & Address: Senior Strategist, Blue Stone Strategy Group, ITCA/El Canto Bldg., 2214 N. Central Ave., Suite 130, Phoenix, AZ 85004 (602) 307-1994. *Professional interests*: Mr. Saenz has developed relationships with prominent Native American tribal leaders & council members. He serves as an advisor to several tribes throughout the U.S. & Canada, for both businesses & governmental affairs. *Other professional post*: Principal & Managing Sales/ Marketing Director, Fire Mountain Wines (tribally owned & operated winery), Cottonwood, AZ (928) 649-9135. Website: www.firemountainwines.com. *Community service*: Serves on the Native American Council in San Diego, CA.

SAFFORD, GLEN
(administrative officer)
Affiliation: Peter Christiansen Health Center, 450 Old Abe Rd., Lac du Flambeau, WI 54538 (715) 588-3371.

SAHALI, ROY
(project manager; co-editor)
Affiliation & Address: Project Manager & Co-editor, Tribal Connections Project (TCP), National Network of Libraries of Medicine, University of Washington, P.O. Box 357155, Seattle, WA 98195 (206) 543-8262.

SAILORS, PAMELA
(Native American studies program administrator)
Affiliation & Address: Administrator, Native American Stdies Program, Missouri State University, 901 S. National Ave., Springfield, MO 65897 (417) 836-5529. E-mail: pamelasailors@missouristate.edu.

SAINTE-MARIE, BUFFY (Cree) 1941-
(folksinger, poet, author)
Born February 20, 1941, Craven, Saskatchewan, Can. *Education*: University of Massachusetts, BA (Philosophy), 1963. *Principal occupation*: Folksinger, poet. *Address*: c/o Paquin Entertainment, 468 Stradbrook Ave., Winnipeg, MB R3L 0J9 Canada (204) 988-1120. *Affiliations*: Recording artist, Vanguard Recording Society; president, Cradleboard Teaching Project (promotes multicultural education programs to grade schools around North America), Nihewan Foundationn for Native American Education, Beverly Hills, CA (808) 822-3111. *Other occupation*: Free-lance writer on Indian culture & affairs; associate editor, The Native Voice (Vancouver, B.C., Can.); teaches at York University, Indian Federated College in Saskatchewan, Evergreen State College in Washington State, and the Institute for American Indian Arts in Santa Fe, NM. *Other professional post*: Advisory Board member, National Leadership Council, Native Arts & Cultures Foundation, Vancouver, WA. *Awards, honors*: Wrote song, "Up Where We Belong," recorded by Joe Cocker and Jennifer Warens for the film, An Officer and a Gentleman, won an Academy Award in 1982; Lifetime Musical Achievement by the First Americans in the Arts. *Interests*: Lecturing on Indian affairs; composing, singing. Miss Sainte-Marie writes, "I am best known for songs & poems directly related to past & present American Indian affairs. (I have contributed) to The Native Voice, Thunderbird, American Indian Horizons, and Boston Broadside in the fields of North American Indian music and Indian affairs. Have lived on & visited reserves (reservations) in fifteen states & four provinces; have traveled, lectured and sung in England, France, Canada, Italy, and Mexico, and have given performances in concert and on television internationally and in all major American cities." *Published works*: She has contributed writings to "The Native Voice," "Thunderbird," "American Indian Horizons," & "Boston Broadside," in the field of North American Indian music and Indian affairs. Sainte-Marie is the author of Nokosis and the Magic Hat (1986), a children's adventure book set on an Indian reservation. *Recordings*: Confidence and Likely Stories (CD), 1993; Up Where We Belong, collection of new songs (CD), 1996.

ST. CLAIR, DARWIN, JR. (Shoshone)
(former tribal chairperson)
Affiliation & Address: Former Chairperson, Eastern Shoshone Tribe, P.O. Box 538, Fort Washakie, WY 82514; E-mail: darwin.stclair@e-shoshone.com (307) 332-3532

ST. CLAIR, KAREN (Bdewakantuwan Dakota)
(psychotherapist/social worker)
Education: Concordia College, BA; Simmons College, MSW, 1987. *Affiliation & Address*: Private Practice as Clinical Social Worker, 2625 SE Hawthorne Blvd., Portland, OR 97214 (503) 407-0421. Website: www.karenstclairpdx.com. *Other professional post*: Board member, Native American Youth & Family Center, Portland, OR. *Past professional posts*: Treatment, Native American Rehabilitation Association, Portland, OR, 2000-06; clinical director & grant project manager, Samaritan Counseling Centers, Portland, OR, 2007-09.

ST. CLAIRE, MERLE (Turtle Mountain Ojibwe)
(former tribal chairperson)
Affiliation: Turtle Mountain Band of Chippewa Indians, P.O. Box 900, Belcourt, ND 58316 (701) 477-2600. E-mail: merle.stclair@yahoo.com.

ST. CYR, DEE (Winnebago of Nebraska)
(enterprise president)
Address & Affiliation: President, Bear Woman Enterprises, 2760 West 5th Ave., Denver, CO 80204 (720) 443-8009. E-mail: dee@bearwomanenterprises.com *Other professional posts*: Chairperson, Denver Indian Center, 4407 Morrison Rd., Denver, CO 80219 (303) 936-2688. Board member, Rocky Mountain Indian Chamber of Commerce; board member, MGM Markets Advisory Council; board member, Native American Sports Council. Bear Woman is a Native American woman-owned small business providing turnkey environmental remediation & structural demolition services. *Past Professional post*: Chairperson, Denver Indian Center, Denver, CO; Director of Corporate Development, CADDO Design & Office Products, Denver, CO. *Awards, honors*: Recipient of the Martin Luther King Business Social Responsibility Awards for her unique contributions to Colorado's Indian community; Volunteer of the Year (2000), The Urban League of Metro Denver..

ST. CYR, WEHNONA (*Mi'-texi-Sacred Moon*, Buffalo Clan) (Omaha) 1957-
(health systems administrator)
Born December 6, 1957, Wichita, Kans. *Education*: High school (Riverside Indian School, Anadarko, OK); Morningside College, BS, 1981; University of Hawaii, MPH, 1987. *Principal occupation*: Health systems administrator. *Address*: Resides in NE. *Affiliations*: Omaha Tribe of Nebraska, Macy, NE (social worker-2 years; nursing home administrator-3 years; health systems administrator-2 years); currently employed by the Public Health Service, U.S. Government, Indian Health Service as a Service Unit Director at the Winnebago Indian Hospital in Winnebago, NE. *Community activities*: Member of the Dr. Susan Picotte Hospital restoration Committee in Walthill, NE. Dr. Picotte was the first Native American woman physician in the U.S. *Memberships*: American College of Healthcare Executives; Nebraska State Historical Foundation (board of trustees); "I am also the Service Unit Director Chairperson for 1990 in the Aberdeen Area." *Awards, honors*: Received an "Outstanding" EPMS rating for 1989 thru Indian Health Service, and was also nominated by the Winnebago Hospital staff for outstanding employee in the area of Administration for 1989. *Interests*: "I continue to be involved in the Native Hawaiian Rights issues, specifically in the area of Health Care. I did receive my MPH from the University of Hawaii in 1987 and have traveled there again in 1989 to try and keep current and lend my expertise to their struggle. I also am active in my culture and dance in the traditional style."

ST. FRANCIS-MERRILL, APRIL (Abenaki)
(tribal chief)
Affiliation: Abenaki Nation of Missisquoia, P.O. Box 276, Swanton, VT 05488 (802) 868-7146.

ST. GERMAINE, HENRY "BUTCH", SR. (Lake Superior Chippewa)
(tribal president)
Affiliation & Address: President, Lac du Flambeau Tribal Council, P.O. Box 67, Lac du Flambeau, WI 54538 (715) 588-3303.

ST. GERMAINE, RICHARD (Migisi) (Lac Courte Oreilles Ojibwa) 1947-
(associate professor)
Born March 4, 1947, Idabel, Okla. *Education*: University of Wisconsin, Eau Claire, BA, 1969; Arizona State University, MA (Education), 1972, PhD, 1975. *Affiliation & Address*: Associate professor, Foundations of Education Dept., University of Wisconsin, Eau Claire, WI 54701. *Affiliations*: Tribal chairperson, Lac Courte Oreilles Tribe, Hayward, WI, 1977-86; director of the American Indian Graduate Studies Program & lecturer, University of California, Berkeley, 1986-88; associate professor, University of Wisconsin, Eau Claire, 1989-. *Other professional posts*: President, American Indian Graduate Center, Albuquerque, NM; (appointed by President Clinton) member of the National Advisory Council on Indian Education, 1994-. *Memberships*: National Indian Education Association (president, 1975-77); National Tribal Chairmen's Association (treasurer, 1978-80); Phi Delta Kappa, 1972-75, 1990. *Awards, honors*: Ford Foundation Fellowship, 1971-75.

ST. MAURICE, HENRY (Ojibwe)
(Native American studies program coordinator)
Affiliation & Address: Coordinator, Native American Studies Program, College of Letters & Science, 464 College of Professional Studies, U. of Wisconsin, Stevens Point, WI 54481 (715) 346-3576. E-mail: hstmauri@uwsp.edu.

ST. PIERRE, NATHANIEL (Chippewa Cree) 1962-
(college president)
Born December 28, 1962, Fort Belknap, Mont. *Education*: Montana State University, MEd., 1989, EdD, 1996. *Affiliation & Address*: President, Stone Child College, 8294 Upper Box Elder Rd., Box Elder, MT 59521 (406) 395-4875. E-mail: nstpierre@stonechild.edu. *Past professional posts*: Stone Child College, adjunct instructor, 1986-87, 2003-06; Dean of Academics, 2003-06; director, Office of Tribal Service, Rocky Boy's Reservation, Chippewa-Cree Tribe, Box Elder, MT; faculty, administrator, Montana State University, Bozeman, MT, 1992-96. *Interests*: Adult education; Indian health education. *Published works*: "Educational Issues in Montana's Tribal Colleges," in Adult Literacy & Basic Education, 1990; "Multiculturalism: A Native American Perspective," in Journal of Lifelong Learning, 1993.

SAKAR, SOPHIE
(village chief)
Affiliation: Native Village of Chuathbaluk, P.O. Box 31, Chuathbaluk, AK 99557 (907) 467-4313.

SAKIM (Alleghenny Lenape)
(tribal chief)
Affiliation: Chief (lifetime), Alleghenny Tribal Council, Canton, OH 44705 (216) 453-6224.

SALAZAR, EARL (San Juan Pueblo)
(former pueblo governor)
Affiliation & Address: Former Governor, San Juan Pueblo, P.O. Box 1099, San Juan Pueblo, NM 87566 (505) 852-4400.

SALAZAR, GILBERT (Kickapoo)
(former tribal chairperson)
Affiliation & Address: Kickapoo Tribe, P.O. Box 70, McLoud, OK 74851 (405) 964-2075.

SALAZAR, NICK L. (Ohkay Owingeh San Juan Pueblo)
(NM state representative)
Address: Box 1076, Ohkay Owingeh, NM 87566 (505) 663-5849. *Affiliation*: New Mexico State Legislature, District 40 representative since 1973. *Committee memberships*: Co-chair, Interim Legislative Ethics Committee; advisory, Indian Affairs Committee.

SALAZAR-IVES, PATRICIA (Navjo-Dine')
(attorney; partner-Indian law program)
Affiliation & Address: Partner, Cuddy & McCarthy, LLP, P.O. Box 4160, Santa Fe, NM 87502 (505) 988-4476. Patricia is licensed to practice before all courts and agencies of the Navajo Nation. Ms. Ives regularly provides day-to-day advice to employers located on and/or doing business on the Navajo Nation on all aspects of Navajo law and regularly appears on their behalf before the Office of Navajo Labor Relations, the Navajo Nation Labor Commission and the Navajo Supreme Court. Ms. Ives also represents insurance companies and their insured before all Navajo Nation tribunals. The Firm advises clients regarding a wide scope of tribal, federal and state law and jurisdiction and we are experienced in drafting constitutions, agreements, codes, and other legal documents to ensure the protection and exercise of tribal sovereignty.

SALAZAR, STEPHANIE (Dine'-Navajo)
(Indian law center associate attorney)
Education: University of New Mexico, BA (Native American Studies & Political Science); University of New Mexico School of Law, JD (Certificate in Indian Law. *Affiliation & Address*: Associate Attorney, American Indian Law Center, University of New Mexico, 1117 Stanford Dr. NE, P.O. Box 4456, Albuquerque, NM 87131 (505) 277-5462. E-mail: salazar@ailc-inc.org

SALGADO, ERNEST C., JR. (Soboba-Cahuilla)
(Indian education executive director)
Affiliation & Address: Executive Director, Ahmium Education, Inc., 711 W. Esplanade Ave., Suite D, P.O. Box 366, San Jacinto, CA 92582 (951) 654-2781. E-mail: erniesalgado51@hotmail.com

SALGADO, LEE ANN (Cahuilla)
 (tribal spokesperson)
Affiliation & Address: Spokesperson, Cahuilla Band of Mission Indians, P.O. Box 391760, Anza, CA 92539 (909) 763-5549.

SALGADO, LUTHER, SR. (Cahuilla)
 (tribal chairperson)
Affiliation & Address: Chairperson, Cahuilla Band of Mission Indians, P.O. Box 391760, Anza, CA 92539 (909) 763-5549.

SALGADO, ROBERT J. (Luiseno)
 (tribal spokesman)
Affiliation & Address: Spokesman, Soboba Band of Mission Indians, P.O. Box 487, San Jacinto, CA 92381 (909) 654-2765.

SALGADO, ROSE (Luiseno)
 (tribal vice chairperson)
Affiliation & Address: Vice Chairperson, Soboba Band of Mission Indians, P.O. Box 487, San Jacinto, CA 92381 (909) 654-2765.

SALINAS, ELAINE J. (Ojibwe)
 (organization president)
Born in Minnesota. *Education*: Moorhead State University, B.A. (Education); University of Minnesota (Education Administration). *Affiliation & Address*: President, Migizi Communications, Inc., 3123 E. Lake St. #200, Minneapolis, MN 55406 (612) 721-6631 ext. 205. Website: www.migizi.org. *Past professional posts*: Director of Programs, Heart of the Earth Survival School, and Education Program Officer for the Urban Coalition, Director of Training & Development for the Oneida Nation of Wisconsin. She has developed & evaluated K-12 and adult education programs, conducted policy analysis and legislative advocacy in Minnesota for substantive education policy reforms including charter schools, American Indian Language & Culture Programs. Elaine has authored many reports and made numerous presentations related to the education of Indian children.

SALISBURY, NEAL 1940-
 (author, historian)
Born May 7, 1940, Los Angeles, Calif. *Education*: University of California, Los Angeles, BA, 1963, MA, 1966, PhD, 1972. *Principal occupation*: Historian. *Address & Affiliation*: Professor (1973-present), Dept. of History, Smith College, Northampton, MA 01063 (413) 585-3726. *Memberships*: American Historical Association; American Society for Ethno-history; Organization of American Historians. *Awards, honors*: Fellow, Smithsonian Institution, 1972-73; Fellow, Newberry Library Center for History of the American Indian, 1977-78; Fellow, National Endowment for the Humanities, 1984-85; Fellow, Charles Warren Center for Studies in American History, 1989; Fellow, National Humanities Center, 1991-92; Fellow, American Antiquarian Society, 1995-96; Fellow, American Council of Learned Societies, 2000-2001. *Published works*: Manitou and Providence: Indians, Europeans, and the Beginnings of New England, 1500-1643 (Oxford University Press, 1982); The Indians of New England: A Critical Bibliography (Indiana University Press, 1982); The Sovereignty & Goodness of God, by Mary Rowlandson, and Related Documents (1997); A Companion to American Indian History, with Philip J. Deloria (2002); The Enduring Vision: A History of the American People, 2nd Ed., with Paul S. Boyer, et al (D.C. Heath, 2002).

SALISBURY, RALPH (Eastern Cherokee) 1926-
 (writer, professor emeritus)
Born January 24, 1926, Arlington, Iowa. Education: University of Iowa, MFA, 1951. *Address*: 2377 Charnelton, Eugene, OR 97405 (541) 343-5101. *Affiliation*: Professor emeritus (1960-), English Dept., University of Oregon, Eugene, OR. *Military service*: U.S. Air Force, 1944-46. *Awards, honors*: Rockefeller Bellagio Award for novel; Chapelbrook Award, Short Story & Poetry. *Interests*: Writing fiction & poetry. *Published works*: Pointing At the Rainbow (Blue Cloud, 1980); Spirit Beast Chant (Blue Cloud, 1982); A Nation Within (Outrigger, 1983); Going to the Water (Pacific House, 1983); A White Rainbow (Blue Cloud, 1985); One Indian, Two Chiefs (Navajo Community College Press, 1993); Trekways of the Wind (University of Arizona, 1994); The Last Rattlesnake Throw (stories) (University of Oklahoma Press, 1997); Rainbows of Stone (University of Arizona Press, 1999); Light from a Bullet Hole: Poems New and Selected, 1950-2008 (Silverfish Review Press, 2009).

SALLEE, JACLYN (Inupiat Eskimo) 1964-
 (broadcasting president & CEO)
Born November 15, 1964, Anchorage, Alaska. *Education*: Western Washington University, 1983-85; University of Alaska, Anchorage, BA, 1988. *Affiliation & Address*: President & CEO, Koahnic Broadcasting Corporation, 3600 San Jeronimo Dr., Suite 480, Anchorage, AK 99508 (907) 793-5500. *Other professional posts*: Member, Foraker Operations Board; Task Force Chairperson, Native Broadcast Center, 1991-. *Community activities*: United Way (member, Allocation Committee). *Memberships*: Alaska Press Club

(board member, 1989-91); Alaska Native Communications Society (Steering Committee, 1988-). Interests: Art, Alaska Native issues, skiing. Awards, honors: Award for Media Excellence at the Eighth Annul Native Media Summit, July 2012, Santa Fe, NM.

SALMON, ALEXANNA (Eskimo)
 (Alaskan village president)
Affiliation: Igiugig Village, P.O. Box 4008, Iguigig, AK 99613 (907) 533-3211.

SALMON, ENRIQUE (Tarahumara)
 (associate professor & chair of department of ethnic studies)
Affiliation & Address: Associate Professor & Chair, Department of Ethnic Studies, 4094 Meiklejohn Hall, CSUEB • Hayward, CA 94542 (510) 885-3255 E-mail: Enrique.salmon@csueastbay.edu.

SALMON, WILLIAM, JR. (Eskimo)
 (Alaskan village chief)
Affiliation: Chief, Chalkyitsik Village, P.O. Box 57, Chalkyitsik, AK 99788 (907) 848-8117.

SALOIS, CHANE (Little Shell Chippewa) 1947-
 (civil engineer)
Born February 20, 1947, Kalispel, Mont. *Education*: Montana State University, BS (Math), 1970, BS (Civil Engineering), 1974. *Address*: 1330 Knight Hill Rd., Zilah, WA 98953 (509) 865-6146. *Affiliations*: Manager, Bureau of Indian Affairs (Roads Branch Manager, Lame Deer, MT, two years; Colville Agency, Nespelem, WA, six years; Flathead Agency, Pablo, MT, nine years; Flathead Agency, Irrigation Division, St. Ignatius, MT, 1992-99; Yakama Nation Engineering, Toppenish, WA, 2000-present. *Community activities*: Little Shell Tribe of Chippewa Indians of Montana (secretary/treasurer).

SALOIS, JOHN E. (Little Shell Chippewa)
 (college president)
Affiliation: President, Blackfeet Community College, P.O. Box 819, Browning, MT 59417 (406) 338-5441. *Other professional post*: Member, Board of Trustees, American Indian College Fund, Denver, CO.

SALTER, JOHN L., JR.
 (Indian studies chairperson)
Affiliation: University of North Dakota, Department of Indian Studies, Grand Forks, ND 58202 (701) 777-4314.

SALUSKIN, DELANO (Yakama)
 (tribal vice chairperson)
Affiliation & Address: Vice Chairperson, Yakama Nation, P.O. Box 151, Toppenish, WA 98948 (509) 865-5121.

SALVADOR, MARIA "LILLY" (*Dzaisratyaitsa*) (Acoma Pueblo) 1944-
 (craftsperson, potter, gallery owner/manager)
Born April 6, 1944, McCartys Village, Acoma Pueblo, N.M. *Education*: New Mexico State (one year). *Principal occupation*: Traditional Native American potter; craftsperson. *Address*: P.O. Box 342, 505 Acoma Rd., Acoma, NM 87034 (505) 552-9501. *Affiliations*: Pottery is displayed at the following museums & galleries: Boston Museum of Fine Arts; The Heard Museum, Phoenix; The Museum of Man, San Diego; Museum of Natural History, Los Angeles; The Whitehorse Gallery, Boulder, CO; Museum of Arizona, Tucson, AZ; Elitejorge Museum, Indiana. *Other institutional affiliation*: National Indian Council on Aging Catalogue. *Awards, honors*: Prize Awards for handcrafted pottery from Whitehorse Gallery, Boulder, CO; Prize Award Ribbons from New Mexico State Fair; Prize Awards for handcrafted/hand painted pottery from the Southwest American Indian Arts Assn; Awards from the Gallup InterTribal Indian Ceremonial; Special Award Ribbon from the Heard Museum, Phoenix, AZ; Southwestern Assn on Indian Affairs, Prize Ribbon for finest of Acoma Pueblo pottery; Prize Ribbons from Elitejorge Museum, IN; Best of Division in Miniatures at the Heard Museum. *Community activities*: Native needle embroidery instructor, Acoma Adult Education Programs; secretary, Sky City Community School; member, parent-student association of Saint Joseph School, San Fidel, NM; demonstrate pottery making to Acoma Sky City Elementary School & Cubero Elementary School. *Memberships*: Gallup Intertribal Ceremonial Assn; Southwest American Indian Arts Assn; National Indian Arts & Crafts Assn; Southwestern Assn on Indian Affairs; AICA; Smithsonian Institution. *Interests*: "To develop and expand my present pottery gallery (the first at the Pueblo Acoma) into a major showcase for collectors, tourists (who visit, annually, the oldest inhabited village in the U.S.) and discriminating curators of various museums throughout the U.S. With the private invitations extended by the above-mentioned museums & galleries, I have traversed the southwest and northwest region of the U.S. exhibiting my traditional hand-crafted/hand painted Acoma Pueblo pottery and figurines. I started working with oil paints. My gallery is open by appointment only." *Biographical sources*: American Indian Pottery, 2nd Edition; Amerika newsletter, Chicago, Ill.; National Indian Council on Aging Catalogue; Talking

With Clay - Pueblo Storytellers, by Barbara Babcock; Pueblo Pottery Families by William Peaster; The Potters Art by henry Glassic..

SALWAY, HAROLD D. (Oglala Lakotah)
  (former tribal president)
Affiliation: Oglala Lakotah Tribal Council, P.O. Box H #468, Pine Ridge, SD 57770 (605) 867-5821.

SALWAY-BLACK, SHERRY (Sioux)
  (vice president)
Affiliation: First Nations Development Institute, The Stores Bldg., 11917 Main St., Fredericksburg, VA 22408 (703) 371-5615. E-mail: ssblack@firstnations. org *Other professional post*: Vice-chairperson, American Indian Business Leaders (AIBL), University of Montana, Missoula, MT.

SALZANO, JOSEPH (Choctaw)
  (musician)
Born in 1958, Biloxi, Miss. & raised in Rochester, NY on Lake Ontario. Address: Unknown. Trained in the clarinet, sax and composition since age 8 and American Indian flute since 1985--on flute, Joe has studied with R. Carlos Nakai and Eddie Box, Sr. and learned from Kevin Locke and Tom Ware. He has performed live, and on radio & TV throughout the U.S. including schools, concerts and clubs. Recordings: "Turtle Island Flute, " & "Four Winds." Both distributed by Morning Star Music. A collection of traditional & contemporary Native American flute music. *Quote*: "Being half Italian & half Choctaw, a saxophonist & flute player, a performer of Jazz and Indian music, I seek to use my music as a way of bridging differences and affirming that we are all children of Mother Earth."

SALZMANN, ZDENEK 1925-
  (professor emeritus of anthropology)
Born October 18, 1925, Prague, Czech Republic. *Education*: Caroline University, Prague, 1945-47 (Absolutorium, 1948); Indiana University, MA, 1949, PhD, 1963. *Address*: 120 Highland Dr. So., Sedona, AZ 86351 (928) 284-0344. Adjunct professor & professor emeritus of anthropology, Northern Arizona University, Flagstaff, 1990-. E-mail: zdenek.salzmann@nau.edu. *Other professional posts*: Visiting professor, Yale University; consultant to Wind River Reservation schools on Arapaho language & culture curriculum, 1979-; visiting professor, Charles University, Prague, Czech Republic. *Past professional post*: Professor emeritus of anthropology, University of Massachusetts, Amherst, 1968-89; *Memberships*: Linguistic Society of America, 1949-; American Anthropological Association, 1954-. *Awards, honors*: Research grants from the following: American Philosophical Society; National Endowment for the Humanities; Senior Fulbright-Hays Scholar; International Research and Exchanges Board; American Council of Learned Societies. Given in a public ceremony with the approval of Arapaho elders, the name hinono'ei neecee (Arapaho Chief). *Interests*: Fieldwork among Northern Arapaho Indians, 1949-; numerous trips to the Wind River Reservation under various auspices. *Published works*: Dictionary of Contemporary Arapaho Usage (Arapaho Language & Culture Commission, 1983); The Arapaho Indians: A Research Guide and Bibliography (Greenwood Press, 1988); Language, Culture & Society: An Introduction to Linguistic Anthropology, 1st Ed. 1993, 2nd Ed. 1998, 3rd Ed. 2004, 4th Ed. 2007, 5th Ed. 2011 with Stanlaw & Adachi (Westview Press); Guide to Native Americans of the Southwest, with Joy Salzmann (Westview Press, 1997); among others; numerous articles.

SAMPLE,. GREGORY W.
  (attorney; founder, Indian law group)
Education: Washington University (St. Louis, MO), BA, 1969; University of Chicago Law School, JD, 1975. *Affiliation & Address*: Founder, Indian Law Group, Drummond Woodsum, 84 Marginal Way, Suite 600, Portland, ME 04101 (207) 772-1941. E-mail: gsample@dwmlaw.com. Gregory has had a full-time law practice in Maine for almost 20 years. *Professional interests*: He currently focuses his practice on tribal economic development, representing tribal businesses, and representing tribal Housing Authorities in financing & developing tribal housing. Merging his knowledge of Indian law with the firm's well-established Affordable Housing and Community Development practice, Greg has taken the firm into transactions using Low Income Housing Tax Credits for Indian Country housing development. He has represented tribal Housing Authorities in new construction & housing rehabilitation projects financed with Tax Credits, and has frequently spoken on the tribal use of Tax Credits at regional and national Indian housing programs. *Memberships*: Federal Bar Association, Indian Law Section; Maine Bar Association. *Awards, honors*: Listed in "Best Lawyers in America," in the category of Native American Law (2008-16).

SAMPSEL, ROY HUNTER (Choctaw/Wyandotte)
  (director of Institute on Tribal Government)
Education: Portland State University, BA (Political Science). *Affiliation & Address*: Director/instructor, The Institute for Tribal Government, The Hatfield School of Government, College of Urban & Public Affairs, Portland State

University, P.O. Box 751, Portland, OR 97207 (503) 725-9000. E-mail: rhsampsel@aol.com. Roy has worked for more than 30 years with tribal governments on inter-governmental relations, policy development & Implementation. *Other professional posts*: President, Global Resources, Inc. (a natural resources & management consulting firm), Portland, OR. *Past professional posts*: Special assistant to the Secretary of the Interior for the Pacific Northwest Region, 1971-76 (developing & implementing departmental policy for federal resources & liaison with tribal & state governments & federal agencies throughout the region); served as the first executive director of the Columbia River Inter-Tribal Fish Commission (Portland & Oregon); served as Deputy Assistant Secretary for Indian Affairs, U.S. Dept. of the Interior, Washington, DC, 1981-83. He worked on Indian rights protection and natural resources policy, and worked for the Bureau of Indian Affairs on implementtation of the Indian Self-Determination & Education Act.

SAMPSON, DONALD (Umatilla)
  (tribal leadership forum director)
Affiliation & Address: Director, Institute for Tribal Government – Tribal Leadership Forum, Hatfield School of Government, P.O. Box 751, Portland, OR 97207 (541) 215-2753; E-mail: d.sampson@pdx.edu. *Past professional post*: Chairperson, Umatilla Board of Trustees, Pendleton, OR.

SAMPSON, MARSHALL RAY, SR. (Tunica-Biloxi)
  (tribal vice chairperson)
Education: University of Louisiana at Lafayette, BS (Computer Science). *Affiliation & Address*: Vice Chairperson, Tunica-Biloxi Tribe of Louisiana, 150 Melacon Rd., Marksville, LA 71351 (318) 253-9767. He has served on the Tribal Council as a Council Member-at-Large since the spring of 1997. An employee of the Paragon Casino since its opening in June 1994, Sampson now holds the position of Assistant General Manager of Operations. A native of Avoyelles Parish,. He has served on numerous community and pan-Native American boards on local and regional levels.

SAMPSON, SKY (Eastern Cherokee)
  (Indian center director)
Education: Western Carolina University, BA (Communicationns/Public Relation), 2010; University of Alabama, MA (Human Environmental Sciences), 2014. *Affiliation & Address*: Director (2016-present), Cherokee Center, Western Carolina University, 1594 Acquoni Rd., Cherokee, NC 28719 (828) 497-7920. E-mail: ssampson@email.wcu.edu. Her goal is to prepare more Cherokees for college and to encourage them to attend. She has served as program manager for the Cherokee Youth Council of the Cherokee Boys Club since May 2011. As director of the Cherokee Center, Sampson will serve as a liaison between WCU and the Eastern Band of Cherokee Indians.

SAMPSON, ZORA (Choctaw)
  (library director)
Affiliation & Address: Director, Elton S. Karrmann Library, University of Wisconsin-Platteville, 1 University Plaza, Platteville, WI 53818 (608) 342-1668. E-mail: samsonz@uwplatt.edu. Other professional posts: Liiaison to American Library Association Diversity Council; vice president & president-elect (2014-15), American Indian Library Assocation. *Published works*: Articles in journals & newsletters; chapters in books..

SAN JUAN, SETH (Yaqui)
  (professor of American Indian studies)
Education: University of California, San Diego, BA (Political Science); University of Arizona, MA (American Indian Studies. *Affiliation & Address*: Professor, American Indian Studies Program, American Studies Dept., Palomar Community College, 1140 W. Mission Rd., San Marcos, CA 92069 (619) 744-1150. E-mail: ssanjuan@palomar.edu. He is currently writing his dissertation in Ethnic Studies at the University of California, San Diego. Some of his research interests include, Federal Indian Law, Borderlands, American Indian Education and Race and Ethnicity.

SANBORN, DAVID (Penobscot)
  (executive director)
Affiliation & Address: Executive Director, National American Indian Indian Housing Council, 900 1nd St. NE #107, Washington, DC 20002 (202) 789-1754.

SANCHEZ, BIRDENA (Zuni Pueblo)
  (Pueblo lt. governor)
Affiliation & Address: Lt. Governor, Pueblo of Zuni, P.O. Box 339, Zuni, NM 87327 (505) 782-7022.

SANCHEZ, BOBBY D. (Paiute)
  (tribal chairperson)
Affiliation & Address: Chairperson, Walker River Paiute Tribe, P.O. Box 220, Schurz, NV 89427 (775) 773-2306.

SANCHEZ, BRUCE (Santa Ana Pueblo)
  (Pueblo governor)
Affiliation: Pueblo of Santa Ana, 2 Dove Rd., Bernalillo, NM 87004
(505) 867-3301.

SANCHEZ, CHANDLER (Acoma Pueblo)
  (Pueblo council chair)
Affiliation & Address: Chairperson (2010-present), All Indian Pueblo Council, 2401 12th St. NW, Albuquerque, NM 87104 (505) 881-1992. E-mail: chairmansanchez@aipcnm.org. *Other professional post*: At-Large board member, National Indian Gaming Association. *Past professional post*: Governor, Pueblo of Acoma, Acomita, NM, 2008-10.

SANCHEZ, DELBERT (San Felipe Pueblo)
  (Pueblo lt. governor)
Affiliation & Address: Lt. Governor, Pueblo of San Felipe, P.O. Box 4339, San Felipe Pueblo, NM (505) 867-3381 Fax 867-3383.

SANCHEZ, MATEO L. (Mestizo)
  (Native American studies program coordinator)
Education: University of New Mexico, BA (Elementary Education with minor in Bilingual Education & Social Studies), MA (Elementary Education; Eduactional Leadership Administration licensure program at UNM. *Affiliation & Address*: Program Coordiantor, Native American Studies Program, University of New Mexico, Albuquerque, NM 87131 (505) 277-0111. Mateo has dedicated his career to teaching life skills to young people and leading community initiatives in Native Communities. He has been a teacher in BIA and Public Schools, Director of Education for the Pueblo of San Felipe, Director of Indian Education for the Bernalillo Public School District and most recently was a Wellness Teacher and Dean of Students for a charter school in Albuquerque, NM.

SANCHEZ, MERLENE (Pomo)
  (rancheria chairperson)
Affiliation & Address: Chairperson, Guidiville Rancheria, P.O. Box 339, Talmadge, CA 95481 (707) 462-3682.

SANCHEZ, RACHAEL (Cochiti/Santo Domingo Pueblo)
  (parent trainer/ liaison)
Education: University of New Mexico, BA (Elementary Education); Leadership Education in Neurodevelopmental Related Disabilities (LEND) Program at the University of New Mexico. *Affiliation & Address*: Parent Training Specialist, The Education for Parents With Indian Children With Special Needs, 1600 San Pedro Dr. NE, Albuquerque, NM 87110 (505) 767-6630. E-mail: rsanchez@epicsnm.org.

SANCHEZ-JANKOWSKI, MARTIN (Yaqui)
  (professor of sociology; co-chair, center for research)
Education: Massachusetts Institute of Technology, PhD (Political Science & Economics). *Affiliations & Address*: Professor of Sociology & Founder & Co-Chair of the Joseph A. Myers Center for Research on Native American Issues, Director of the Study of Societal Issues, and Director of ISSI's Center for Urban Ethnography, 2420 Bowditch St., University of California, Berkeley, CA 94720 (510) 643-7238. *Research Interests*: Focuses on inequality in advanced & developing societies and has been directed toward understanding the social arrangements & behavior of people living in poverty. He is currently engaged in comparative field research on poverty among indigenous groups within the U.S. & Fiji. *Published works*: Islands in the treet: Gangs & American Urban Society (1991); co-author, Inequality By Design: Cracking the Bell Curve Myth (1996); Cracks in the Pavement: Social Change & Resilience in Poor Neighborhoods (2008).

SAND, WILLIAM (Wiyot-Mattole)
  (former tribal chairperson)
Affiliation & Address: Bear River Band of the Rohnerville Rancheria, 27 Bear River Rd., Loleta, CA 95551 (707) 733-1900. E-mail: williamsand@brb-nsn.gov

SANDERS, CHERYL (Lummi)
  (tribal vice chairperson)
Affiliation & Address: Chairperson, Lummi Nation, 2616 Kwina Rd., Bellingham, WA 98226 (360) 384-1489.

SANDERS, JEFFREY M.
  (professor of Native American studies)
Affiliation & Address: Professor of Native American Studies, Montana State University, 1500 North 30th St., Billings, MT 59101 (406) 657-1674. E-mail: jsanders@msubillings.edu.

SANDERS, M. CAROLEEN "CAROL" (Catawba) 1944-
  (cosmotologist)
Born July 20, 1944. *Address & Affiliations*: Catawba Indian Pottery (Whispering Sage Collections), 2253 Indian Trail, Catawba Indian Nation, Rock Hill, SC 29730 (803) 329-2707; Hollywood Hair, Charlotte, NC (40 years). *Products*: Catawba Indian ceremonial pottery with ancient Catawba designs & motifs. *Awards, honors*: Master potter. *Community activities*: Catawba Cultural Center (board member). *Membership*: North Carolina Pottery Center.

SANDERS, WARREN (Catawba)
  (craftsperson; company owner)
Affiliation: Catawba Arts, 1822 Indian Trail, Rock Hill, SC 29730 (803) 325-2012. Products: Catawba pottery.

SANDERSON, PRISCILLA R. (Navajo-Dine') 1959-
  (professor of Applied Indigenous Studies & public health)
Born November 26, 1959, Shiprock, N.M. *Education*: Southwestern College (Winfield, KS), BA, 1983; Oklahoma State University, MS, 1984; University of Arizona, PhD, 2005. *Affiliation & Address*: Assistant Professor (2005-present) of Applied Indigenous Studies, Northern Arizona University, Health Sciences Bldg. 66, Room 231A, Flagstaff, AZ 86011 (928) 523-6741. E-mail: Priscilla.sanderson@nau.edu. She is co-principal investigator of a National Institute of Health, National Institute on Minority & Health Disparities grant entitled, Center for American Indian Resilience. Priscilla specialies in public health, rehabilitation and cancer prevention. Her research is in colorectal cancer screening knowledge, attitudes, and beliefs (KAB), cancer prevention, and resilience among American Indians. *Past professional posts*: Director, American Indian Rehabilitation Research & Training Center, Northern Arizona University, Flagstaff, AZ; vocational rehabilitation services specialist, Arizona Rehabilitation Services Administration, Flagstaff. *Memberships*: Consortia of Administrators for Native American Rehabilitation & Research (chairman, 1994); National Congress of American Indians; Rehabilitation Leadership Council. *Awards, honors*: Outstanding Young Women of America, Sonoma Club, 1984; Professional Worker of the Year," Flagstaff Mayor's Committee on Disability Awareness, 1989; "In recognition for your leadership in providing service to American Indians," Texas Rehabilitation Commission, 1994. *Published works*: "Needs of American Indians with Disabilities" (American Indian Rehabilitation Research & Training Center, 1993); "Response to Perspectives" (The Leading Edge. Focusing on Rehabilitation's Human Resources, 1993); "Needs Assessment Survey to the State Vocational Rehabilitation Agencies" (American Indian Rehabilitation Research & Training Center, 1994).

SANDERSON, ROBERT A., JR. (*Gu'usuwaa*) (Haida)
  (central council 1st vice president)
Affiliation & Address: 1st Vice President (2016-2018), Central Council of Tlingit & Haida, 320 W. Willoughby Ave., Suite 300, Juneau, AK 99801. *Past professional posts*: Rob has been a delegate since 2000. Hr has served on the Ketchikan Indian Community Tribal Council, the Alaska Inter-Tribal Council, and Alaska Federation of Naties Board of Directors as representative for Southeast Alaska villahge tribes & corporations.

SANDOVAL, ALVINO (Navajo)
  (early childhood training specialist)
Born in Ketchikan, Alaska and raised in Hydaburg, Alaska. *Affiliation & Address*: Early Childhood Training Specialist, The Education for Parents With Indian Children With Special Needs, 1600 San Pedro Dr. NE, Albuquerque, NM 87110 (505) 767-6630. E-mail: asandoval@epicsnm.org.

SANDOVAL, JOSEPH E. (San Felipe Pueblo)
  (Pueblo governor)
Affiliation & Address: Governor, Pueblo of San Felipe, P.O. Box 4339, San Felipe Pueblo, NM 87001 (505) 867-3381.

SANDOVAL, NANCY F. (Navajo)
  (physician-anesthesiologist)
Education: Stanford University School of Medicine, MD, 1992; Stanford University Hospital, Residency, 1996. *Affiliation & Address*: Children's Anesthesia Medical Group, 747 52nd St., Oakland, CA 94609 (510) 428-3070. *Affiliation*: Children's Hospital Research Center, Oakland, CA. *Other professional post*: Secretary, Assn. of American Indian Physicians, Oklahoma City, OK.

SANDOVAL, PATRICK (Navajo-Dine')
  (Indian college center director)
Education: University of New Mexico, BS. *Affiliation & Address*: Director, Dine' College, Window Rock Center, P.O. Box 1924, Window Rock, AZ 86515 (505) 786-7391. E-mail: psandoval@dinecollege.edu.

SANDVIK, HELVI (Eskimo)
  (president of Alaskan corporation)
Born & raised in the Village of Kiana, Alaska. *Education*: Kalamazoo College, BA (Economics); University of Alaska, Fairbanks, MBA. *Affiliation & Address*: President, NANA Development Corporation, P.O. Box 256, Kotzebue, AK 99752 (907) 442-3301. *Other professional post*: Member, Board of Directors,

Native American Contractors Association, Washington, DC. *Past professional post*: Transportation Planner, Director of Statewide Aviation, Deputy Commissioner, State of Alaska Dept. of Transportation & Public Facilities.

SANGREY, RICHARD (Chippewa-Cree)
(Indian commission member)
Address: RR #1, Box 544, Box Elder, MT 59521 (406) 395-5705. E-mail: richard@cct.rockyboy.org. *Affiliation*: Member, State Tribal Economic Development Commission (STEDC), c/o Montana Dept. of Commerce, Helena, MT.

SANKEY, CORNELL (Cheyenne/Arapaho)
(tribal lt. governor)
Affiliation & Address: Lt. Governor, Cheyenne & Arapaho Tribes, P.O. Box 38, Concho, OK 73022 (405) 422-7430.

SANTOSHAM, MATHURAM
(center director)
Affiliation & Address: Director, Health Systems Program; Director, Center for American Indian Health; Professor, International Health & Pediatrics, 621 N. Washington St., Baltimore, MD 21205 (410) 614-1419. msantosh@jhsph.edu. *Awards, honors*: Indian Health Service Awards for outstanding dedication & contribution to improving health of the White Mountain Apache people; 1988 Thrasher Research Fund Award "in recognition of excellence in research.".

SANTOS, STEVE C. (Mechoopda) 1957-
(tribal chairperson)
Born May 11, 1957, Chico, Calif. *Education*: Butte Community College, A.A. *Affiliation & Address*: Chairperson, Mechoopda Indian Tribe of the Chico Rancheria, 125 Mission Ranch Blvd., Chico, CA 95926 (530) 899-8922. E-mail: ssantos@mechoopda.nsn.us. *Military service*: U.S. Air Force, 1975-99 (Honorable Discharge).

SANYAL, GOVINDA (Creek/Seminole & Asian Indian) 1947-
(psychotherapist, special educator, Southeastern Native American historian, genealogist)
Born August 12, 1947. *Education*: Manhattan Community College, AAS, 1971; Hunter College (NY), BA, 1975; Long Island University, MS (Special Education), 1982, New York University, PD, 1984; MS (Educational Psychology), 1997; California Institute of Integral Studies, current PhD (Native Studies. *Principal occupation*: Special educator, New York City Board of Education. *Address*: 85 Regis Dr., Staten Island, NY 10314 (718) 761-5436. *Community activities*: Director of Mandala Nataka, a cultural center of Native American & Asian Indian philosophy and art. Presently serving as a researcher, historian and genealogist for Southeastern Native communities specializing in the Carolinas, Georgia and Florida. *Awards, honors*: Ford Foundation Award, 1982 - Social Studies. Interests: "My ambition is to assist in restoring the ancient historical tradition and knowledge of those descendants of indigenous populations of the Southeast."

SARABIA, EDWARD W., JR. (*Stockk-Waan*) (Tlingit) 1948-
(Indian affairs coordinator)
Born November 11, 1948. *Education*: Seattle University, BA (Rehabilitation). *Affiliation & Address*: Coordinator (2007-present), Connecticut Office of Indian Affairs, 79 Elm St., Hartford, CT 06106 (860) 424-3066. E-mail: edward.sarabia@po.state.ct. us. *Other professional posts*: Board member, Institute for American Indian Studies, Washington, CT; board member, Institute for Community Research, Hartford, CT; liaison between Connecticut Indian Affairs Council and Connecticut Dept. of Environmental Protection, the tribes and tribal members. *Community activities*: Volunteer for the Connecticut Dept. of Corrections, Native American religious services.

SARAYDAR, STEPHEN
(professor & chair, Dept. of Anthropology;
director of Native American studies program)
Education: Cornell University, PhD. *Affiliation & Address*: Professor & Chair, Department of Anthropology; Director of Native American Studies Program, State University of New York Oswego, 307A Mahar Hall, Oswego, NY 13126 (315) 312-4190. E-mail: Stephen.saraydar@oswego.edu.

SARGENT, ELVERA (Konwanaktotani) (Akwesasne Mohawk)
(manager)
Address: P.O. Box 290, Rooseveltown, NY 13683 (518) 358-2073. E-mail: bela@westelcom.com. *Affiliations*: Director, Native American Travelling College; director, Akwesasne Area Management Board. *Interests*: Native American education, language, and culture.

SARKOZY-BANOCZY, STEWART (Cheyenne River Lakota)
(director of training & technical assistance)
Affiliation & Address: First Nations Oweesta Corp., 1010 Ninth St., Suite 3, Rapid City, SD 57701 (605) 342-3770. E-mail: ssarcozy@oweesta.org. *Other professional post*: Member, Board of Directors, Cheyenne River Youth Project

(Running Strong for American Indian Youth, Eagle Butte, SD). *Past professional posts*: Executive director & co-founder, Four Bands Community Fund, Cheyenne River Reservation; director, Little Traverse Bay Band of Odawa Indians' economic development department. *Awards, honors*: 2004 Appel Prize for Entrepreneurial Vitality from the Price-Babson College Fellows Program as part of the Symposium for Entrepreneurship Educators.

SARRIS, GREG (Coast Miwok)
(tribal chairperson)
Education: Stanford University, PhD. *Affiliation & Address*: Chairperson (13 terms), Federated Indians of the Graton Rancheria, 6400 Redwood Dr., Suite 300, Rohnert Park, CA 94928 (707) 566-2288. Website: www.greg-sarris.com. Greg oversees all business negotiations and the daily operations of the tribe. In 1992, when Greg was beginning his teaching career at UCLA as a professor, he got word of another tribe attempting to establish a casino at Tomales Bay. This tribe was not Coast Miwok or Southern Pomo and was well out of its ancestral territory. Greg immediately notified and consulted with Tribal elders, and soon after called the first meeting to reorganize the Federated Indians of the Graton Rancheria. He led the push for restoration of the tribe as a federally recognized American Indian nation. It took years of gathering records, family histories and interviews of all who were descended from the original Tribal members, in order for this evidence to be submitted to the United States Department of the Interior. Finally, eight years later, Greg co-authored the Graton Rancheria Restoration Act, 25 U.S.C. §1300n (Act) with California Indian Legal Services. President Clinton signed the Act into law on December 27, 2000, officially granting the Tribe status as a federally recognized tribe. The Act mandated that the Secretary of the Interior take land in the Tribe's aboriginal territory of Marin or Sonoma Counties into trust as the Tribe's reservation. *Other professional posts*: 2005 to present, Greg has held the Graton Rancheria Endowed Chair in Writing and Native American Studies at Sonoma State University. He teaches Creative Writing & lecture-based classes on Native Cultures of Northern California. *Past professional post*: 2001-05, Fletcher Jones Endowed Professor of Creative Writing & Literature, Loyola Marymount University. *Past professional post*: Assistant professor at UCLA. *Awards, honors*: In the early 90's, Greg led the push for restoration of the tribe as a federally recognized American Indian nation on Dec. 27, 2000. *Published works*: Keeping Slug Woman Alive: A Holistic Approach to American Indian Texts (University of California Press, 1993); and six novels, the last of which was published by Viking/Penguin in 2005. An earlier book, "Grand Avenue," was made into an HBO miniseries, which Greg wrote & produced with Robert Redford.

SASAKAMOOSE, MURIEL
(museum director)
Affiliation: Secwepemc Cultural Education Society, 345 Yellowhead Hwy., Kamloops, BC, Canada V2H 1H1 (604) 374-1096.

SAZUE, BRANDON (Crow Creek Sioux)
(tribal chairperson)
Affiliation: Crow Creek Sioux Tribe, P.O. Box 50, Fort Thompson, SD 57339 (605) 245-2221

SATALA, TAYLOR J. (Yavapai-Apache/Hopi) 1945-
(health systems administrator)
Born August 25, 1945, Prescott, Ariz. Education: San Francisco City College, AA, 1966; Arizona State University, BS, 1976, MSW, 1978. *Affiliation & Address*: Administrator, Keams Canyon PHS-IHS Hospital, P.O. Box 98, Keams Canyon, AZ 86034 (602) 738-2211. *Affiliation*: Service unit director, USPHS, Indian Health Service, Keams Canyon, AZ, 1989-. *Other professional posts*: Health Center Director, IHS, Peach Springs, AZ; extension associate, University of Kansas, Lawrence, KS; social worker, MCH, Rapid City, SD. *Military service*: U.S. Air Force, 1966-70 (E-4 Sgt.; Vietnam Era Veteran-stationed at DaNang Air Base); USPHS Commission Corps, National Health Service, 1978-80. National Association of Social Workers (vice president, 1978-84); Black Hills Region of South Dakota State Chapter; Council on Social Work Education (member, House of Delegates, 1982-83); American Indian/Alaska Native Association of Social Workers, 1978-84. *Awards, honors*: Exceptional Performance Award, 1989, for Effective Management. *Published works*: Multi-Cultural Development in the Aging Network: "An Indian Perspective" "A Forgotten People" (University of Kansas, 1981); The Indian Experience: Special Topics in Social Welfare (University of Kansas, 1983).

SAUBEL, CATHERINE (Luiseno)
(Indian band spokesperson)
Affiliation: Los Coyotes Band of Mission Indians, P.O. Box 189, Warner Springs, CA 92086 (760) 782-0711.

SAULQUE, JOSEPH C. (Paiute) 1942-
(administration; college instructor)
Born October 20, 1942, Bishop, Calif. *Education*: West Valley Community College, Campbell, Calif., AA, 1970; Brigham Young University, BA, 1973;

University of California, Davis, 1978-80 (Graduate work on MA). *Affiliation & Address*: Administration; college instructor, Benton Paiute Reservation, Rt. 4, Box 56-A, Benton, CA 93512 (619) 933-2321. *Affiliation*: Instructor, Cerro Coso Community College, Bishop, CA (current). *Other professional posts*: Utu Utu Gwaitu Paiute Tribe, Benton Paiute Reservation, Benton, CA (chairperson, 1973-90; vice-chairperson, 1991-); chairperson, Toiyabe Indian Health Project (board of directors, 1977-); chairperson, California Rural Indian Health Board (board of directors, 1978-). *Military service*: U.S. Army, 1961-64 (E-4/Sp-4, 101st Airborne Division). *Community activities*: Grand Jury, County of Mono, CA; Tri-Valley Regional Planning and Advisory Commission to the Tri-Valley Water District, County of Mono, CA; Owens Valley Indian Water Commission (member). *Memberships*: National Congress of American Indians, 1974-; California Tribal Chairman's Association, Sacramento, Calif. (secretary-three years); California Indian Manpower Consortium, Inc. (past vice-chairperson, 1988-90). *Interests*: "Indian affairs, especially tribal government concepts; American Indian history; Indian health issues & operations; college instructor on American Indian studies; history and career opportunities."

SAULQUE, BILLIE G. "JAKE" (Utu Utu Gwaitu Paiute)
(former tribal chairperson)
Affiliation: Utu Utu Gwaitu Paiute Tribal Council, Benton Paiute Reservation, 567 Yellow Jacket Rd., Benton, CA 93512 (760) 933-2321.

SAULQUE, SHANE (Paiute)
(tribal vice chairperson)
Affiliation & Address: Vice Chairperson, Bentonn Paiute – Utu Utu Gwaitu Paiute Tribe, 555 Yellow Jacket Rd., Benton, CA 93512 (760) 933-2321. E-mail: s.saulque@bentonpaiutereservation.org

SAUNSOCI, ADRIANA (Omaha)
(tribal vice chairperson)
Affiliation & Address: Vice Chairperson, Omaha Tribe, P.O. Box 368, Macy, NE 68039 (402) 837-5391.

SAUNOOKE, CHARLOTTE (Eastern Cherokee)
(tribal executive secretary)
Affiliation: Eastern Band of Cherokee Indians, Qualla Boundary, P.O. Box 455, Cherokee, NC 28719 (828) 497-7000.

SAUNOOKE, OSLEY BIRD, JR. (Eastern Cherokee) 1943-
(attorney, business consultant)
Born April 6, 1943, Jacksonville, Fla. Education: East Tennessee State University, 1962-63; Brigham Young University, BS, 1965; University of New Mexico Law School, JD, 1972. *Principal occupation*: Attorney, business consultant. *Address*: 2435 Gulf Gate Dr., Sarasota, FL 34231 (813) 921-3297. *Affiliations*: Teacher-guidance counselor, Cleveland, Ohio, Chicago, Ill., 1965-69; executive director, United Southeastern Tribes, Inc., 1972-73; executive director, Florida Governor's Council on Indian Affairs, 1973-74. *Awards, honors*: 1987 Regional Minority Entrepreneur of the Year - Atlanta Region OMBE. *Memberships*: National Congress of American Indians (Southeast area vice president, 1972-73; first vice president, 1973-74; board member, American Indian Scholarships, 1974-).

SAUNOOKE, ROBERT OSLEY (Eastern Cherokee)
(attorney)
Affiliation & Address: Owner, Osley Law Firm, PA, 18620 SW 39th Court, Miramar, FL 33029 (561) 302-5297. *Other professional post*: Board member, National Native American Bar Association. *Past professional posts*: Robert has worked with a number of Tribal Governments throughout Indian Country assisting them in enacting legislation and codifying their own laws, including the Susanville Indian Rancheria (1994-95), the Eastern Band of Cherokee Indians serving as Legislative Counsel from 1997-99; the Seminole Tribe of Florida as General Counsel to Chairperson, James E. Billie, 2001-01. He served as juvenile defender in the Cherokee Tribal Court and assisted in the implementation of the Eastern Band of Cherokee Indians domestic violence and violence against children program. Awards, honors: Received the Shining Example of America Award for Acts of Heroism associated with his actions in saving the lives f eleven children.

SAUNT, CLAUDIO
(professor of history)
Education: Columbia University, BA, 1989; Duke University, MA, 1991, PhD, 1996. *Affiliation & Address*: Professor of History & member, Steering Committee, Institute for Native American Studies, Peabody Hall, University of Georgia, Athens, GA 30602 (706) 542-1492. E-mail: jweaver@uga.edu. *Interests*: Specializes in the history of Native Americans, particularly in the Southeast. *Awards, honors*: "A New Order of Tings" won the Charles S. Sydnor Award for the best book on Southern history from the Southern Historical Association & the Wheeler-Vogelin Award for the best book in ethnohistory from the American Society for Ethnohistory, both in 2000; "Black, White, and Indian" won the 2005 Clements Prize for the best non-fiction book

on Southwestern America from the Clements Center for Southwest Study at Southern Methodist University; his article, "The English Has Now a Mind to Make Slaves of Them All: Creeks, Seminoles, and the Problem of Slavery," (American Indian Quarterly 22: 1998) won the 1999 Bolton-Kinnaird Award for the best journal article on Spanish borderlands history. *Published works*: A New order of Things: Property, Power, and the Transformation of the Creek Indians, 1733-1816 (Cambridge University Press, 1999); Black, White, and Indian: Race & the Unmaking of an American Family (Oxford U. Press, 2005).

SAVAGE, JEFF (Fond du Lac Band of Lake Superior Chippewa) 1950-
(tribal artist)
Born November 28, 1950, Duluth, Minn. *Education*: College of St. Scholastica, 1974-76. *Principal occupation*: Tribal artist. *Address*: 1780 Blue Spruce Dr., Cloquet, MN 55720 (218) 879-0157. E-mail: jsavage730@aol.com. Website: www.savageart.com. *Affiliation*: Artist and Public Information Specialist, Fond du Lac Reservation, Cloquet, MN. For 25 years, Savage has sculpted Pipestone. A national, inter-tribally & internationally known pipemaker and sculptor, Savage's dedications with quarrying the pipestone himself. It is with this art form that Jeff has excelled into the class of artistic masters. Jeff is also an art educator and consultant, sharing his artistic talents in the classrooms of public & tribal schools and community and four year colleges. As an artist educator, Jeff's recent project endeavors include "Sculptor in the Schools," which brings tribal art and sculptor to all grade levels. *Community activities*: Currently vice-chairperson, Indian Advisory Board, Minnesota Historical Society; former tribal election judge for Fond du Lac Reservation. *Memberships*: Minnesota Historical Society (chairman of local Indian Education Committee). *Awards, honors*: 1981 Gallup Intertribal, Certificate of Merit, Blue Ribbon, and special exhibit awards; 1985 1st Place Sculpture Award in Ojibwe Art Expo; numerous basket & sculptor awards from the Eiteljorg Indian Market, Santa Fe Indian Market from 1998 to the present. Savage's work appears in various public & private collections including the collection of the Smithsonian Museum, & the Department of Interior Museum in Washington, DC. *Interests*: Personal interest in pursuing the perpetuating of endangered Ojibwe art forms, i.e., pipestone quarrying, pipe making, traditional Ojibwe sweet grass baskets and birch bark baskets, moccasins and beadwork of floral Ojibwe design done in hand tanned leather. Sweet Grass basketry is one of the traditional Chippewa art forms that Savage believes needs to be revived.

SAVAGE, MARILYN (Athabascan)
(radio station manager)
Affiliation: KZPA-AM, P.O. Box 126, Fort Yukon, AK 99740 (907) 662-2587.

SAVALA, MANUAL (Paiute)
(former tribal chairperson)
Affiliation & Address: Kaibab Paiute Tribal Council, #1 North Pipe Spring Rd., Fredonia, AZ 86022 (928) 643-8301. Email: msavala@kaibabpaiute-nsn.gov.

SAYERS, ANN-MARIE (Mutsun-Ohlone-Costanoan)
(tribal chairperson)
Affiliation: Indian Canyon Mutsun Band of Costanoan Indians, P.O. Box 28, Hollister, CA 95024.

SAZUE, BRANDON (Crow Creek Sioux)
(tribal chairperson)
Affiliation & Address: Chairperson, Crow Creek Sioux Tribe, P.O. Box 50, Fort Thompson, SD 57339 (605) 245-2221.

SAZUE, ROXANNE (Crow Creek Sioux)
(former tribal chairperson)
Affiliation & Address: Former Chairperson, Crow Creek Sioux Tribe, P.O. Box 50, Fort Thompson, SD 57339 (605) 245-2221.

SCERATO, BEN (Diegueno)
(former tribal chairperson)
Affiliation: Santa Ysabel Band of Mission Indians, P.O. Box 130, Santa Ysabel, CA 92070 (760) 765-0846.

SCHAAF, BILL (Mille Lacs Ojibwe)
(store owner)
Address: Owner, Keewadin Wild Rice, 9462 State Hwy. 27, Onamia, MN 56339 (320) 492-5686. Website: www.keewadinwildrice.com. E-mail: info@keewadinwildrice.com. *Product*: Birch bark crafts.

SCHAAF, GREGORY (Northern Cherokee) 1953-
(author; organization director)
Born July 24, 1953, Kansas City, MO. *Education*: University of California, Santa Barbara, BA, MA, PhD. *Affiliation & Address*: CIAC-Center for Indigenous Arts & Culture (director, 1994-present), P.O. Box 8627, Santa Fe, NM 87504 (505) 473-5375. E-mail: greg@indianartbooks.com. Website: www.indianartbooks.com, or www.indianartforsale.com. *Other professional*

posts: Co-founder, executive director & vice-chair, Tree of Peace Society, Inc., Washington, DC, 1984-present; secretary, Southwest Learning Center, Santa Fe, N, 1995-present; co-founder, Indian Art Collectors Circle, Santa Fe. *Past professional posts*: Visiting lecturer, Native American Studies, Dept. of ABS, University of California, Davis, 1986-87; assistant professor & acting coordinator of American Indian Studies, Dept. of Ethnic & Women's Studies, California State University, Chico, CA, 1988-90; associate professor & coordinator of American Indian Studies, Dept. of Ethnic Studies, Minnesota State University, Mankato, MN, 1990-93; Native American consultant, The Last of His Tribe, a movie for HBO starring John Voight & Graham Greene, 1992; overall contributing script consultant, 500 Nations (8-hour TV mini-series for CBS, produced by Kevin Costner, 1995). *Community activities*: "Southwest Indian Curricula: Our Visions for the 21st Century," World Conference on Indigenous Peoples Education, Albuquerque, NM 1996; "Symbols in Indian Art," Children's Indian Art Camp, Santa Fe, 1997; "Evaluating Indian Art," Elder Hostel, College of Santa Fe, 1998; "Preserving Indian Baskets," Museum of Indian Arts & Cultures, 1999; "Mesa Verde: Clan Stories Leading to Living Pueblo Descendants," Americas Quest for a million school children via www.classroom.com, 2000. *Published works*: The Iroquois Great Law of Peace and the U.S. Constitution (Canal Press, New York, 1987); Wampum Belts and Peace Trees: George Morgan, Native Americans and Revolutionary Diplomacy (Fulcrum, Inc., 1990); Ancient Ancestors of the Southwest (Graphic Arts Center Publishing Co., Portland, OR, 1996); Honoring the Weavers (Kiva Press, Santa Fe, 1996); Hopi-Tewa Pottery: 500 Artist Biographies (CIAC Press, Santa Fe, 1998); Pueblo Indian Pottery: 750 Artist Biographies (CIAC Press, Santa Fe, 2000); American Indian Textiles: 2,000 Artist Biographies (CIAC Press, Santa Fe, 2001); Southern Pueblo Pottery: 2,000 Artist Biographies (CIAC Press, Santa Fe, 2002); American Indian Jewelry: 1,200 Artist Biographies (CIAC Press, Santa Fe, 2003); American Indian Baskets: 1,200 Artist Biographies (CIAC Press, Santa Fe, 2004); Franklin, Jefferson, & Madison: On Religion & the State (CIAC Press, Santa Fe, 2004); Vol. 7 – Hopi Katsina: 1,600 Artist Biographies, $65; Vol. 8 – American Indian Jewelry II: A-L: 1,800 Artist Biographies, $70; Vol. 9 – American Indian Jewelry II: M-Z: 2,000 Artist Biographies, $70; Vol. 10 – Artists of Indian Market: 1922 to the present, coming 2013. Future volumes will profile sculptors, beadworkers, dollmakers, musical instrument makers, clothing designers and more. The last three volumes will be the Native artists of Mexico, Central & South America. Once completed the series will embrace over 30,000 artists throughout the Western Hemisphere.

SCHAEFFER, SUZANNE R.
(attorney)
Education: University of Virginia School of Law, 1990, JD; The College of William & Mary, 1985, BA. *Affiliation & Address*: Counsel, Dentons LLP, Public Policy and Regulation & Native American Law & Policy Practice, 1301 K St., NW, Washington, DC 20005 (202) 408-7097. She concentrates her practice on Indian lands and environmental compliance issues. Susi draws on her years of experience in both the federal government and the private sector working to resolve legal issues pertaining to Indian lands, natural resources and the federal environmental regulatory system. Susi advises clients in acquiring land in trust for both gaming and non-gaming purposes pursuant to the fee-to-trust authorities of the US Department of the Interior (DOI), and she has extensive experience working with the DOI to achieve clients' land acquisition objectives. She is also well versed in other Indian lands issues, including land claims, leasing and rights-of-way over Indian lands, and Section 81 approval requirements. Susi has particular experience in handling environmental compliance issues on Indian lands, and she regularly counsels clients regarding compliance with the National Environmental Policy Act (NEPA), as well as other environmental requirements in conjunction with acquiring land in trust. She also provides advice regarding environmental regulatory and jurisdictional issues, such as tribal environmental ordinances and the extent of state, tribal and federal permitting authority. She has participated at a number of conferences as an invited speaker on Indian land, energy and environmental matters. In addition, Susi is very familiar with the requirements of the Indian Gaming Regulatory Act. She has significant experience working with both the DOI and the National Indian Gaming Commission on gaming matters, and she has spoken at several conferences on Indian gaming issues. This experience serves as a foundation for providing strategic and practical advice to clients regarding tribal gaming ordinances, management contracts, Indian lands issues and other matters related to the development of Indian gaming facilities. She also advises clients regarding federal acknowledgment and federal funding issues. *Awards, honors*: Best Lawyers anking, 2013-15. Memberships: Federal Bar Association, Indian Law Section; Native American Bar Association. *Past affiliations*: Prior to going into private practice, Susi served in key positions at the DOI and the US Department of Justice (DOJ). At the DOI, she provided legal advice to the Bureau of Indian Affairs on a wide variety of environmental matters arising on Indian lands, and from 2000 to 2005 she served as the assistant solicitor for Environment, Land and Minerals. Her duties included providing legal advice and supervising legal work involving all aspects of the acquisition, sale, development, leasing, use & conservation of Indian lands & natural resources,

including fee-to-trust acquisitions, compliance with the NEPA, and the nature and extent of the federal government's trust obligations. During her tenure with the federal government, Susi received numerous awards and honors and developed excellent professional contacts and a unique perspective and understanding of the components of the federal government that make and influence Native American policy and legal positions.

SCHAFER, LORNA
(publisher)
Affiliation: Tsa'Aszi (The Yucca) Magazine of Navajo Culture, Tsa'Aszi Graphics Center, Ramah Navajo School Board, CPO Box 12, Pine Hill, NM 87321 (505) 783-5503.

SCHALLER, K.B. (Cherokee/Seminole)
(author, journalist)
Address: c/o OakTara Publishers, P.O. Box 8, Waterford, VA 20197 (540) 882-9062. Website: www.kbschaller.com. *Affiliations*: Schaller organized and served as playwright/director of an ensemble theater for Native American youths at the former Chickee Christian Academy on the Florida Seminole Indian Reservation. An independent journalist, she has contributed articles to "Indian Life" and the "Seminole Tribune" Native newspapers. She is also a poet whose poems appear in several anthologies. *Membership*: Native Christian Church. *Published work*: Gray Rainbow Journey (OakTara Publishers, 2008).

SCHEFFLER, LENOR A. (Lower Sioux Dakota)
(attorney)
Education: St. Olaf College, BA, 1979; William Mitchell College of Law, JD, 1988. *Affiliation & Address*: Attorney & Chair, Native American Law Section, Best & Flanagan LLP, 225 S. Sixth St., 40th Fl., Minneapolis, MN 55402 (612) 349-5687. Email: lscheffler@bestlaw.com. She practices in the areas of federal Indian law, tribal law, tax, governance, gaming law, gaming regulatory, tribal financing and business law. Born and raised on the Lower Sioux Reservation near Morton, Minnesota, Lenor is an enrolled member of the Lower Sioux Dakota Community in Minnesota and the first member of the Mdewakanton Dakota Community to become an attorney. In October 2001, she was sworn in as chief judge of the Upper Sioux Community Tribal Court, and served until 2006. In 2012, she was reappointed to the bench. Scheffler brings a wide range of experience in gaming and regulatory matters, complex business transactions, finance, tax, governance and other areas critical to tribal clients. These areas require special understanding of tribal immunity and law principles as applied to a sovereign nation. Along with the other members of the firm's Native American Law Section, she serves as general and special counsel to tribes and tribal entities, and provides advice and support to in-house counsel. Lenor and her partners have been on the cutting edge of obtaining favorable tax solutions for beneficiaries of tribal minors' trusts and for tribal members participating in tribal housing and other social benefit programs. In one significant case, Lenor and her partners successfully argued on behalf of a tribal minor's trust fund, receiving a very substantial monetary award. She also assisted in developing programs for investing tribal funds, educational assistance for tribal members and sophisticated financing for tribal projects. In 2003, Lenor was appointed to the Minnesota Commission on Judicial Selection as an at-large member and served for eight years. She is a frequent conference speaker on the topics of Indian taxation, economic development, governance, tribal court & jurisdiction issues across the country, including classes for tribal tax commissions, tribal councils, tribal enterprise boards, tribal management teams and other tribal government departments. In addition, the Internal Revenue Service appointed Lenor to its Advisory Committee for Tax Exempt and Government Entities for a term from 2004 to 2007. Lenor has also been named among the Best Lawyers in America. Lenor contributes her time and expertise to the community in multiple ways and was a recipient of the Turtle Award from the Minnesota American Indian Chamber of Commerce for volunteering time, energy and services to support & promote the American Indian business community. She also serves as an Associate Judge II with the Sisseton Wahpeton Oyate Tribal Court and a Justice of the Prairie Island Indian Community Appellate Court. *Memberships*: Minnesota State Bar Assn; Minnesota American Indian Bar Assn (founding member); Minnesota American Indian Chamber of Commerce. *Admissions*: Ho-Chunk Nation Tribal Court; Mille Lacs Band of Ojibwe Court of Central Jurisdiction; Prairire Island Dakota Community, Shhakopee Mdewekanton Dakota Community, and Stillaguamish Tribal Courts.

SCHENCK, THERESA M. (Ojibwe)
(professor of American Indian studies)
Education: Mount St. Mary's (Los Angeles, CA), BA; Catholic University of America, MA; Rutgers University, PhD (Anthropology). *Affiliation & Address*: Professor of American Indian Studies, American Indian Studies Program, 2414 Sterling Hall, University of Wisconsinn-Madison, Madison, WI 53706 (608) 262-4902. E-mail: schenck@wisc.edu. *Interests*: American Indians, Ojibwe history & culture; Blackfeet history & culture; travel. *Awards, honors*: Native American Fulbright Scholar to Canada, 1997-98. *Published works*: The Voice of the Crane Echoes Afar (Garland Publishing, 1997); My First Years in the Fur

Trade: The Journals of George Nelsonn, 1802-1804, with laura Peers (Minnesota Historical Society Press, 2002); William W. Warren: The Life, Lteers & Times of an Ojibwe Leader (University of Nebraska Press, 2007); All Our Relations: Chippewa Mixed Bloods & the Treaty of 1837 (Amik Press, 2009); History of the Ojibwe People, by William W. Warrenm 2nd Edition (Minnesota Historical Scoiety Press, 2009); The Ojibwe Journals of Edmund F. Ely, 1833-1849 (University of Nebraska Press, 2012).

SCHERER, JOANNA COHAN
(emeritus anthropologist)
Education: Syracuse University, BA, 1963; Hunter College, MA, 1968. *Affiliation & Address*: Emeritus Anthropologist, Department of Anthropology, Smithsonian Institution, Washington, DC 20013. E-mail: schererj@si.edu. Joanna is the former anthropologist/illustrations researcher for the 20-volume Handbookk of North American Indians (1978-2006) project, Smithsonian, where she created a collection of more than 100,000 images relating to American Indians currently housed in the Smithsonian, National Anthropologial Archives Curator of the Wrensted Exhibition, which traveled throughout the U.S. from 1994 to 1996, currently available on the Worldwide Web.

SCHERER, MARK R.
(attorney, adjunct instructor of history)
Address & Affiliation: Dept. of History, University of Nebraska, Lincoln, NE; instructor of law, College of St. Mary, Lincoln, NE; practicing attorney. *Published work*: Imperfect Victories: The Legal Tenacity of the Omaha Tribe, 1945-1995 (University of Nebraska Press, 1999).

SCHILL, VICTOR
(association president)
Affiliation & Address: President, American Indian Library Association (AILA), 620-U Hillman Library, University of Pittsburgh, Pittsburgh, PA 15260 (412) 648-7780. vschill@stic.lib.tx.us

SCHINDLER, CYRUS (Seneca)
(tribal council president)
Affiliation: Seneca Nation Tribal Council, 1490 Rt. 438, Irving, NY 14081 (716) 532-4900.

SCHINDLER, DUANE E. (Turtle Mountain Chippewa) 1944-
(educational administration)
Born April 22, 1944, Turtle Mountain Indian Reservation, Belcourt, N.D. *Education*: University of North Dakota; Valley City State College, ND; University of Wisconsin, Eau Claire; Arizona State University; University of South Dakota. *Affiliations*: Program development specialist, Eastern Montana State College, Billings (two years); program specialist, University of New Mexico; instructor, Adult Programs, Wenatchee Valley College, Omak, WA (two years); director, Adult Education, Colville Confederated Tribes, Nespelem, WA; director, American Indian Student Division, U. of Washington, Seattle, WA (one year); principal, Turtle Mountain Chippewa High School, Belcourt, ND. *Other professional posts*: Field reader, consultant: Logo language; computer applications, literacy, & office systems; curriculum development; program evaluation management. *Community activities*: American Indian Center, Spokane, WA (chairperson). *Memberships*: National Assn of Secondary School Principals; National Indian Education Assn; ASCD, NABE. *Awards, honors*: Outstanding Teacher, Oglala Community Schools, Pine Ridge, SD. *Interests*: Computers in classroom; research in mathematics. *Published works*: Concepts of American Indian Learners (Education, Tempe, Ariz.); Language, Culture & the Mathematics (Journal of the American Indian, 1986).

SCHINDLER, MICHAEL W. (Seneca)
(tribal council president)
Affiliation: Seneca Nation Tribal Council, P.O. Box 231, Salamanca, NY 14479 (716) 945-1790.

SCHLOSSER, THOMAS P.
(attorney; professor of Indian law)
Education: University of Washington, BA (Political Science), 1970; University of Virginia School of Law, JD, 1975. *Affiliation & Address*: Principal (1986-present), Morisset, Schlosser & Jozwiak, 801 Second Ave., Suite 1115, Seattle, WA 98104 (206) 386-5200. Represents Indian tribes & tribal organizations in federal litigation, natural resources, business development & Indian property issues. *Other professional post*: Part-time lecturer, Native American Law Center, UW School of Law, Seattle, WA *Past professional post*: Principal, 1982—1986; Associate 1979-1982, Zionntz, Pirtle, Morisset, Ernstoff, Chestnut & Anderson, Seattle, WA. Represented Indian tribes and tribal organizations in natural resource and tribal property issues, including continuing jurisdiction in United States v. Washington (treaty fishing rights); Columbia River hydropower, fisheries and cultural resources matters; Indian tribal enrollment and claims litigation. *Awards, honors*: Tom is the founding member of the Indian Law Section of the Washington State Bar Association

and also served on the WSBA Bar Examiners Committee. Tom is a frequent CLE speaker and moderates an American Indian Law discussion group for lawyers at http://forums.delphiforums.com/IndianLaw/messages.

SCHMIDT, MARSHA KOSTURA
(attorney)
Education: University of Pittsburgh, BA, 1981; George Washington University, J.D., 1984. *Address & Affiliation*: Hobbs, Straus, Dean & Walker, LLP (Associate, 1984-93; Partner, 1994-present), 2120 L St., NW, Suite 700, Washington, DC 20037 (202) 822-8282. E-mail: mkschmidt@hsdwdc.com. She represents tribal clients in diverse matters including gaming, contract disputes, tax, land acquisition, and the Indian Health Care Improvement Act. She also played a major role in Menominee Tribe v. United States, a case before the U.S. Court of Federal Claims that successfully sought money damages for the wrongful termination of the Tribe and mismanagement of tribal timber resources by the federal government.

SCHMIDT, TERRI (Arapaho)
(IHS acting director, Office of Resource Access & Partnerships)
Education: Southwestern Oklahoma State University, BS (Nursing). *Affiliation & Address*: Acting Director, Office of Resource Access & Partnerships, Indian Health Service (IHS), DHH, 801 Thompson Ave., Rockville, MD 20852 (301) 443-1083. As the Acting ORAP Director, Ms. Schmidt is responsible for providing direction and leadership in the areas of purchased/referred care, business office/third-party collections, and partnerships with other Agencies and organizations. The office deals with over $1 billion in collections and purchased/referred care funds. The Office focus is on supplementing IHS' appropriated funds with other Federal, state, and private sector resources through revenue generation and to enhance Federal & Tribal access to those resources. The office consists of the Division of Contract Care and the Division of Business Office Enhancement. Ms. Schmidt has a broad array of management experience, and her career progression includes both direct clinical care and service unit leadership experience. *Past professional posts*: She began her IHS career as a staff nurse in 1989, and through the years she served as the Chief Nurse Executive, Acting Contract Health Services Supervisor, Public Health Nurse, and Chief Executive Officer (CEO) for the Clinton Service Unit in the Oklahoma City Area IHS. In 2007, during her tenure as CEO, she partnered with the Cheyenne and Arapaho Tribes on the design, building, and move from the Clinton Indian Hospital to the Clinton Indian Health Center. In 2008, Ms. Schmidt became the Area Contract Health Service Officer for the Oklahoma City Area. In 2010, she moved to IHS Headquarters to work as a Management Analyst for ORAP. From October 2011 to December 2014, she served as the Director of the Division of Contract Care in ORAP. She most recently served from December 2014 to January 2016 as Acting Director of the IHS Office of Management Services. Terri Schmidt, R.N. Acting Director Office of Resource Access and Partnerships Indian Health Service January 2016 In September 2002, Ms. Schmidt completed an Executive Leadership Development Program. From 2007 to 2008 she served as the Secretary and Vice-Chair of the National Council of Chief Executive Officers and as faculty and a facilitator of the IHS National CEO Boot Camp. *Awards, honors*: Numerous awards during her professional career, including an IHS Director's Award for personal dedication, commitment, and accomplishments toward the mission of the Indian Health Service in 1999 and in 2011 for outstanding support of the Contract Health Services Workgroup. In 2005 and 2008 she received the National Council of Chief Executive Officers Managerial Excellence Award. In 2007, Ms. Schmidt received the Oklahoma City Area Superior Support Service award for successfully coordinating the design and construction of a new facility.

SCHONCHIN, JOLENE (Comanche)
(director of tribal information office)
Affiliation & Address: Director, Comanche Nation Public Information Office, P.O. Box 908, Lawton, OK 73502.

SCHREEN, JAMES E. (Tonkawa)
(tribal vice president)
Affiliation: Vice President, Tonkawa Tribe of Oklahoma, 1 Rush Buffalo Rd., Tonkawa, OK 74653 (580) 628-2561.

SCHREMS, MELISSANE
(coordinator of Native American studies)
Education: Boston University, PhD (History) with minor of Native American history. Dissertation explores the history of the Mashpee Wampanoag Indians of Cape Cod, 1754-1834. *Affiliation & Address*: Associate Professor of History & Coordinator, Native American Studies, Piskor Hall 112, St. Lawrence University, 23 Romoda Dr., Canton, NY 13617 (315) 229-5221. E-mail: mschrems@stlawu.edu. Dr. Schrems is a member of the Native American Studies Advisory board and teach courses focused on Native American & Colonial American history.

SCHUBERT, GAIL (Eskimo)
(chief executive officer)
Born & raised in Unalakleet, Alaska. *Education*: Stanford University, BS; Johnson School of Management, Cornell University, MBA; Cornell University Law School, JD. *Affiliation & Address*: Bering Straits Native Corp. (Board of Directors, 1992-present; Executive VP & General Counsel, 2003-09; President & CEO, 2009-present), P.O. Box 1008, Nome, AK 99762 (907) 443-5252. *Other professional posts*: Member, Board of Directors for the following: Alaska Federation of Natives (treasurer); the ANCSA Regional Association (vice president); Alaska Native Heritage Center (chairperson); the Alaska Retirement Management Board (chairperson); the Alaska Native Justice Center (vice chairperson); the Akeela Treatment Services (chairperson); Native American Contractors Association (former treasurer).

SCHULTE, CONLY J.
(attorney)
Education: University of Nebraska, BA, 1990; Creighton University, JD, 1993. *Affiliation & Address*: Partner (2000-present), Fredericks Peeles & Morgan LLP, Louisville, CO 80027 (303) 673-9600. E-mail: cschulte@ndnlaw.com. Conly serves as lead litigation counsel for American Indian tribes in judicial & administrative forums on a wide variety of issues, including Indian Gaming Regulatory Act litigation, federal Indian law and constitutional rights litigation. *Practice areas*: Trial & Appellate Advocacy; Tribal Governance; Tribal Sovereignty & Self-Determination, et al. *Membership*: Native American Bar Association.

SCHULTZ, MARILOU (Navajo)
(craftsperson)
Address: P.O. Box 882, Mesa, AZ 85211 (602) 964-3566.

SCHULTZ, MARK (Kumeyaay Diegueno)
(tribal chief operating officer)
Education: Drew University, BA (Economics & Political Science); The Naval War College, MA (National Security & Strategic Studies); California State University, Fullerton, MBA. *Affiliation & Address*: Chief Operating Officer, San Pasqual Band of Diegueno Indians, P.O. Box 365, Valley Center, CA 92082 (760) 749-3200. Past professional posts: Chief operating officer for two companies including a building products and LED light manufacturer. *Military service*: U.S. Marine Corps (achieved the rank of lieutenant colonel with highlights including commanding an aviation logistics squadron and serving as a Marine aircraft wing inspector general.)

SCHULTZ, MIKE (Snohomish)
(tribal chairperson)
Affiliation: Vice chairperson (2007-present), Snohomish Tribe, 11014 19th Ave. SE, Suite 8, PMB 101, Everett, WA 98208 (425) 744-1855. E-mail: vicechair@snohomishtribe.com. *Other tribal post*: Council member, 2003-2007). *Other professional post*: Electronic technician since 1980; with collateral duty as a Native American Outreach Program Manager under the EEO Office. *Military service*: U.S. Army. *Memberships*: ATNI (Affiliated Tribes of Northwest Indians); SAIGE (Society of American Indian Government Employees); NCAI (National Congress of American Indians).

SCHUMACHER, WILLIAM (Flandreau Santee Sioux)
(tribal executive committee president)
Affiliation: Flandreau Santee Sioux Executive Committee, P.O. Box 283, Flandreau, SD 57028 (605) 997-3891.

SCHUTT, AARON M. (Athabascan) 1973-
(attorney)
Born March 28, 1973, Anchorage, Alaska & raised in Tok, Alaska. *Education*: Washington State University, BS (Civil Engineering), 1996; Stanford University, MS (Civil Engineering), 1997, Stanford Law School, JD, 2000. *Address & Affiliation*: President & CE, Doyon, Limited, 1 Doyon Place, Suite 300, Farbanks, AK 99701 (907) 452-1648. *Other professional posts*: Adjunct professor, University of Alaska, Anchorage, Dept. of Engineering & Science Management; director, Anchorage Youth Court & Ekeela, Inc. *Past professional posts*: Judicial law clerk, Alaska Supreme Court - Juneau, AK, 2000-2001); Associate Attorney, Sonosky, Chambers, Sachse, Miller & Munson, LLP (2003-06) & Heller, Ehrman White & McAuliffe, Anchorage, AK, (2001-03). *Community activities*: Covenant House Alaska (board of directors). *Memberships*: American Bar Association; Alaska Bar Association. *Awards, honors*: Won Top 40 Under 40 Award in 2004.

SCHUTT, ETHAN G. (Athabascan) 1973-
(senior vice president; attorney)
Born March 28, 1973, Anchorage, Alaska & raised in Tok, Alaska. *Education*: Washington State University, BS (Mathematics), 1995; Stanford Law School, JD, 1999. *Affiliation & Address*: Senior Vice President, Cook Inlet Region, Inc., P.O. Box 93330, Anchorage, AK 99509 (907) 274-8638. Ethan oversees CIRI's land & energy development departments including their efforts in developing renewable & alternative energy projects. *Other professional posts*: Member, Boards of Covenant House Alaska & Resource Development Council. *Past professional posts*: General Counsel, Tanana Chiefs Conference in Fairbanks, AK; served on Doyon Ltd. Board of directors, 2003-06. *Awards, honors*: Won Top 40 Under 40 Award in 2004.

SCHUYLER, LINDA LAROQUE
(board president)
Affiliation & Address: Board President (2009-present), North American Indian Association, 22720 Plymouth Rd., Detroit, MI 48239 (313) 535-2966. E-mail: linda.schuyler@att.net.

SCHWENINGER, LEE
(coordinator of Native American studies)
Affiliation & Address: Native American Studies Minor coordinator, University of Noth Carolina, Wilmington, Department of English, 601 S. College Rd., Wilmington, NC 28403 (910) 962-3539. E-mail: schweningerl@uncw.edu. Lee teaches American Indian literature and his research interests include contemporary Native American novelists and poets.

SCOTT, ANTOINETTE (Seneca)
(business owner/manager)
Affiliation & Address: Owner/manager, Iroquois Doll Makers, 13853 Rt. 438, Gowanda, NY 14070 (716) 532-3117. Website: www.senecahuskdolls.com.

SCOTT, COLIN (*Kaa-uumaakiimishit*) 1952-
(professor of anthropology)
Born June 1, 1952, Indian Head, Sask. Can. *Education*: University of Regina, BA, 1972; McGill University (Montreal), MA, 1983, PhD, 1983. *Principal occupation*: Professor. Resides in Montreal, Quebec, Canada. *Affiliation*: Assistant professor of anthropology, McGill University, Montreal. *Other professional post*: Consultant to aboriginal and regional governments. *Memberships*: Canadian Anthropological Society; American Anthropological Association. *Awards, honors*: Social Sciences & Humanities Research Council of Canada, Strategic Research Grant, "Aboriginal Government, Resources & Development"; Australian National University, Visiting Fellowship, 1991. *Interests*: Knowledge construction among Cree hunters of James Bay; political discourse of aboriginal rights; development in the Subarctic. *Published works*: Books - section, "Ideology of Reciprocity Between the James Bay Cree and the Whiteman State" in P. Skalnik, ed. Outwitting the State (Transaction Publishers, 1989); Income Security for Cree Hunters, with H. Feit (M.A.S., 1992); article - "Knowledge Construction Among Cree Hunters" Journal de la Societe des Americanistes (LXXV: 193-208, 1989).

SCOTT, CYRIL L. (Rosebud Lakota Sioux) 1962-
(former tribal president)
Born in 1962 & raised on the Rosebud Indian Reservation. *Affiliation & Address*: Rosebud Sioux Tribe, Box 430, Rosebud, SD 57570 (605) 747-2381.

SCOTT, GEORGE (Muskogee Creek)
(former tribal town king)
Affiliation & Address: Former Town King, Thlopthlocco Tribal Town, P.O. Box 188, Okemah, OK 74859 (918) 560-6198.

SCOTT, JOSEPH C. (Siletz)
(artisan)
Address: 29733 Peoria Rd., Shedd, OR 97377 (541) 491-3984. *Products*: Shell & bead jewelry; Siletz regalia & sculpture

SCOTT, KENDALL (Kickapoo)
(tribal chairperson)
Address & Affiliation: Kickapoo Tribe, P.O. Box 70, McLoud, OK 74851 (405) 964-2075.

SCOTT, MARILYN M. (Skagit)
(tribal chairperson; health director)
Affiliations: Upper Skagit Indian Tribe, 25944 Community Plaza, Sedro Woolley, WA 98284 (360) 856-5501. *Other professional post*: Director, Lummi PHS Indian Health Center, Bellingham, WA.

SEABOURN, BERT D. (Cherokee-Chickasaw) 1931-
(artist)
Born July 9, 1931, Iraan, Tex. *Education*: Oklahoma City University, MFA, 1963; Central State University, Edmond, OK, 1973; University of Oklahoma, 1976. *Principal occupation*: Artist. *Address*: 6105 Covington Lane, Oklahoma City, OK 73132 (405) 722-1631. E-mail: seabournart@aol.com. *Military service*: U.S. Navy (Journalist, Third Class, 1951-55). *Community activities*: Oklahoma State Arts Council; Oklahoma City Arts Council. Memberships: Oklahoma Art Guild (past president); Oklahoma Art Directors Club (past president); Oklahoma Watercolor Association (past treasurer). *Awards, honors*: Best of Show (oil), Oklahoma Art Guild Annual, Oklahoma City, OK, 1966;

Grand Award (acrylic), Five Civilized Tribes Museum, Muskogee, OK, 1973; Best of Show (watercolor), Red Cloud National Indian Art Exhibition, Pine Ridge, SD, 1974; Governor's Award, presented by Governor George Nigh, Oklahoma State Capitol, Oklahoma City, OK 1981; Sculpture Commission (23 bronze), Southwestern Bell Corporate Headquarters, Oklahoma City, OK, 1986; Best of Show (watercolor), Master Artist Show, Five Civilized Tribes Museum, 1988; numerous Best of Show and First Prizes in watercolor, oil, graphics, acrylics, and drawings at above shows, et al. *Interests*: "In 1989, I had art shows in Taiwan in March, and in July shows in Singapore; two art shows in Germany, one in the 60's and one in the 70's. Works are exhibited in The Heard Museum, Phoenix; The Five Civilized Tribes Museum, Muskogee, OK; Oklahoma Art Center, Oklahoma City, OK; Red Cloud Indian School, Pine Ridge, SD; The Vatican Museum of Modern Religious Art, Italy; Inter-Tribal Indian Ceremonial Association, Gallup, NM; among others. Biographical sources: Who's Who in America; Who's Who in American Art; Who's Who in American Indian Art; Who's Who in the South and Southwest; Dictionary of International Biography; Artists of Reknown; Contemporary North American Indian Painters; Contemporary Southwest Painters; American Indian Painters; 100 Years of Native American Indian Painters; Southwest Art Magazine; Oklahoma Today Magazine, et al. *Published works*: Master Artists of the Five Civilized Tribes, 1976; Cherokee Artist, 1981; & Vanishing Americans, 1984 - both published by Seabourn Graphics.

SEABOURN, CONNIE (Cherokee) 1951-
(painter, printmaker)
Born September 20, 1951, Purcell, Okla. *Education*: University of Oklahoma, BFA, 1980. *Principal occupation*: Painter, printmaker. *Address*: P.O. Box 23795, Oklahoma City, OK 73123 (405) 728-3903. *Selected Exhibitions*: People, Places & Spirits, Adagio Gallery; Red Earth, Oklahoma City; Winter Art Show, Indian Paintbrush Gallery, Siloam Springs, AR; Color-Culture-Creed: Multi-Culturism in Oklahoma, City Arts Center, Oklahoma City; Connie & Bert Seabourne, El Taller, Austin, TX; Joan Cawley Gallery, Santa Fe, NM. Numerous other exhibitions. *Collections*: Museum of the American Indian, New York City; The Heard Museum, Phoenix; Center for Cherokee Heritage Museum, Cherokee, NC; Southern Plains Indian Museum, Anadarko, OK; Gilcrease Museum, Tulsa, OK; among many others. Recent Lectures & Public Speaking Engagements: Blind Embossment Printmaking Workshop, Johnson Atelier, Tulsa, OK; Demonstration, Bartlesville Art Guild, Bartlesville, OK; Demonstration, Mid-Del Art Guild, Midwest City, OK; Demonstration, Central Oklahoma Art Guild, Oklahoma City, OK; Lecture & Demonstration, Southeastern State College, Wilburton, OK; among many others. *Recent Awards*: Third Place, Watercolor, Gallup Intertribal Ceremonial, Gallup, NM, 1990; Third Place, Watercolor, Layers of Stories, Chisholm Trail Art Show, El Reno, OK, 1990; Special Merit Award, Painting, Annual Trail of Tears Show, Trail of Tears Museum, Tahlequah, OK; First Place, Graphics, Little Classic Art Show, for Winter Vision, Guthrie, OK; among many others.

SEAGLE, RUSS (Eastern Cherokee)
(executive director)
Affiliation & Address: Executive Diector, Seqouyah Fund, 810 Acquoni Rd., Cherokee, NC 28719 (828) 359-5003. E-mal: russseagle@seqouahfund.org.

SEALY, LeROY (Choctaw of Oklahoma)
(Choctaw language instructor)
Affiliation & Address: Kiowa Language Instructor, Native American Language Program, Department of Anthropology, College of Arts & Sciences, The University of Oklahoma, 455 W. Lindsey, Cate Center 4 Room 432, Norman, OK 73019 (405) 325-4894. E-mail: chahhtanakni@ou.edu.

SEAMAN, P. DAVID 1932-
(professor emeritus of linguistics)
Born January 31, 1932, Connellsville, PA. *Education*: Asbury College, AB, 1957; University of Kentucky, MA, 1958; Indiana University, PhD (Linguistics), 1965. *Principal occupation*: Professor of Linguistics, Dept. of Anthropology, Northern Arizona U., Flagstaff, AZ (1967-94); consultant, researcher, author, professor emeritus, 1994-present. *Address*: 4221 E. White Aster St., Phoenix, AZ 85044 (480) 759-0969. E-mail: pdseaman@asu.edu. *Past professional posts*: Bilingual/bicultural consulting for Zuni Tribal Council, 1970-72; linguistic consulting for Bureau of Indian Affairs, 1968-69, 1970-76; cross-cultural management consulting for Hopi Tribal Council, 1974-79; accounting & management consulting for Fort Mojave Tribal Council, 1977-80. *Military service*: U.S. Army, 1951-54 (Sergeant; U.S. Army Commendation Medal for efficient administration of U.S. Army field hospital in Korea, 1953). *Memberships*: Linguistic Society of America; Society for Study of Indigenous Languages in America; Society for Linguistic Anthropology; Friends of Uto-Aztecan. *Awards, honors*: Distinguished Faculty Award, Northern Arizona University, 1980. *Research*: Hopi dictionary project; traditional Havasupai culture; American Indian languages/cultures; H.C. Diehl Hopi Archives, 1976; Hopi Linguistics Articles - compiled by Mary & Dave Seaman in 1977; Helen M. Greene Indian Archives in 1985; Alfred F. Whiting Ethnographic Notes &

Papers: Southwest Indian tribes, 1993; P. David Seaman Hopi Archives (Hopi language materials relating to Seaman's 1974-1985 Hopi Dictionary project), 1993. *Interests*: American Indian languages & culture. *Paper delivered*: "Hopi Dictionary & Computers," joint meeting, Arizona Humanities Association & Arizona Alliance for Arts Education, Scottsdale Community College, 1983 (article--Arizona Humanities Association Journal, Feb. 1984). *Published works*: Co-editor, Havasupai Habitat: A.F. Whiting's Ethnography of a Traditional Indian Culture (U. of Arizona Press, 1985); Hopi Dictionary: Hopi-English, English-Hopi (Northern Arizona U., Anthropological Paper, 1985; revised ed. 1996); Born a Chief: The Nineteenth Century Hopi Boyhood of Edmund Nequatewa (U. of Arizona Press, 1993). *Article*: "Hopi Linguistics: An Annotated Bibliography" (Anthropological Linguistics, 1977); Bootstraps & Blessings: From Poverty to Success (Legend Express Publishers, 2004).

SEBASTIAN, ROY (Chief Hockeo) (Pequot)
(Hopi elder & cultural ambassador; artist & tribal chairperson)
Affiliation: Eastern Pequot Reservation, North Stonington, CT 06359.

SEBASTIAN-DRING, KATHERINE (Eastern Pequot)
(tribal chairperson)
Affiliation & Address: Chairperson, Eastern Pequot Tribe, P.O. Box 370, North Stonington, CT 06359 (860) 535-1868.

SECAKUKU, EDRED (Ute)
(tribal vice chairperson & band representative)
Affiliation & Address: White River Band Representative, The Ute Indian Tribe, P.O. Box 190, Fort Duchesne, UT 84026 (435) 722-5141.

SECAKUKU, KIM (Hopi)
(tribal consultant & advisor)
Affiliation & Address: Tribal Advisor, Blue Stone Strategy Group, ITCA/El Canto Bldg., 2214 N. Central Ave., Suite 130, Phoenix, AZ 85004 (602) 307-1994. *Professional interests*: Kim has worked for more than 20 years with tribes in the capacity of tribal government operations, policy development, and public relations. She has assisted tribal councils & executive offices in establishing policy for administrative operations for effective management & government operations. Kim assisted in the development of tribal legislative and federal appropriations for tribes, & organizing & developing lobbying strategies for tribes. As a member of the Hopi Tribe, she has played an important role in the development & updating of its strategic plan the "Hopi Potskwaniat. She has managed public relations efforts for the Hopi, Yavapai-Apache, & San Carlos Apache Tribes where she developed tribal communications plans for effective communications with tribal membership, the external public, and the media. Secakuku has also assisted tribal councils and executive offices in establishing policy for administrative operations for effective management and government operations. Her experience also includes assisting in the development of tribal legislative & federal appropriations for tribes, and organizing and developing lobbying strategies for tribes.

SECATERO, LESTER (Navajo)
(Indian health board chair)
Affiliation & Address: Chairperson, Albuquerque Area Indian Health Board, 5015 Prospect Ave. NE, Albuquerque, NM 87110 (505) 764-0036. *Other professional post*: Albuquerque Area Representative, National Indian Health Board, Washington, DC.

SECENA, DON (Chehalis)
(tribal chairperson)
Affiliation & Address: Chairperson, Confederated Tribes of the Chehalis Reservation, P.O. Box 536, Oakville, WA 98568 (360) 273-5911.

SEIDNER, CHERYL (Wiyot)
(former tribal chairperson)
Affiliations: Chairperson (1996-2008), Wiyot Tribe, Table Bluff Rancheria, Loleta, CA; Humboldt State University (staff member in the Educational Opportunity Program for 28 years). *Awards, honors*: Honorary degree of Doctor of Humane Letters from the Board of Trustees of the California State University & Humboldt State University.

S'EILTIN, TANIS (Tlingit)
(American Indian studies coordinator)
Education: University of Alaska, Fairbanks, BFA; University of Arizona, MFA. *Affiliation & Address*: Program Coordinator, American Indian Studies, Western Washington University, Fairhaven College of Interdisciplinary Studies, 516 High St. FA 309, Bellingham, WA 98225 (360) 650-6564. E-mail: Tanis.S'eiltin @wwu.edu (650-6564). *Art*: Videos, prints, series of non-functional handbags titled, "Savage Apparel. *Awards, honors*: 2005 Eiteljorg Fellowship, Eiteljorg Museum of American Indians & Western Art, Indianapolis, IN.

SEIM, JESSIE STOMSKI (Muscogee Creek)
  (attorney)
Education: University of Wisconsin-Madison, BA, 2002; William Mitchell College of Law, JD, 2008. *Affiliation & Address*: Attorney, Hogen Adams PLLP, 1935 W. County Road B2, Suite 460, St. Paul, MN 55113 (651) 842-9105. E-mail: jseim@hogennadams.com. Jessie has experience in all aspects of civil litigation in federal and state court, as well as in administrative proceedings and regulatory investigations. Jessie now focuses her practice on representing tribes in litigation & economic development. Her litigation experience includes first chairing a successful civil trial, and representing defendants in nationwide class-action disputes, state and federal appeals, FINRA arbitrations, employment litigation and counseling, and criminal matters. Minnesota *Super Lawyers* magazine named Jessie a Minnesota "Rising Star" in 2011, 2012 and 2013. Outside the office, Jessie serves on the board of directors for the Minnesota American Indian Bar Association, & is a delegate to the Minnesota State Bar Association Assembly. Jessie was a member of the University of Wisconsin-Madison's women's basketball team, and she was a professional basketball player for several years before she went to law school. The Charlotte Sting drafted Jessie into the WNBA, and she also completed seasons in France and Greece.

SEKAKUKU, LAUREL (Hopi)
  (program director)
Affiliation & Address: Program Director (2008-present), The Hopi Foundation, P.O. Box 301, Kykotsmovi, AZ 86039 (928) 734-2380. Laurel is a current participant in the 2012 Healthy Native Community Partnerships Fellows Program, Shiprock, NM.

SEKAQUAPTEWA, EMORY (Hopi)
  (professor)
Education: University of Arizona, J.D., 1970. *Address*: University of Arizona, Anthropology 308, Tucson, AZ 85721 (520) 621-6284. *Affiliation*: Professor, American Indian Studies Program, U. of Arizona. E-mail: esekaquaptewa@email.arizona.edu. His scholarly focus is on development of a comprehensive dictionary of the Hopi language. He teaches the course, "Hopi Language in Culture." *Interests*: Hopi language/lexography/culture.

SEKAQUAPTEWA, KEN (Hopi)
  (publisher)
Affiliation: Eagle's Eye, Brigham Young University, Office of Student Programs, 4th Floor, ELWC, Provo, UT 84602 (801) 378-6263.

SEKAQUAPTEWA, PAT (Hopi)
  (lecturer in law)
Education: Stanford University, B.A., 1990; U.C. Berkeley Law School, J.D., 1995. *Affiliation & Address*: Assistant Professor (2015-present), University of Alaska, Fairbanks, Department of Alaska Native & Rural Development, 3rd Floor Brooks Bldg., P.O. Box 756500, Fairbanks, AK 99775 (907) 474-1539 E-mail: pssekaquaptewa@alaska.edu. Her academic research & teaching areas include: rural and Native economic and community development, tribal sovereignty, governance, and management, and tribal courts and conflict transformation. She is also a nationally known presenter and trainer on tribal law, court development, and conflict resolution topics. She presently serves as a tribal judge, arbitrator, and mediator and sits as a justice on the Hopi Tribe's high court in Arizona. *Past professional post*: Formerly she served as the co-founder & Executive Director of the Nakwatsvewat Institute, a non-profit and tribal community mediation program on the Hopi Reservation. Prior to that she served as the director of the UCLA Native Nations Law & Policy Center & its Tribal Legal Development Clinic, part of the UCLA School of Law in Los Angeles, CA. As director of the law clinic she provided instruction in, and supervised legal clinical projects on, tribal constitution & statutory drafting, tribal judging and the development of tribal common law, and in tribal court development. She co-founded the Tribal Law & Policy Institute with Jerry Gardner in 1996, has served as TLPI's Associate Director, as an ongoing consultant, and she continues to serve on its board of directors. In 1998, she worked for the law firm of Alexander & Karshma, which represents American Indian tribes, Alaska Native villages, and inter-tribal organizations. She is co-founder & associate director of the Tribal Law & Policy Institute in West Hollywood, California. The Institute is committed to the development of tribal justice systems & coordinates conferences on national policy & law affecting tribal courts, tribal-federal & tribal-state relationships, & comparative tribal law. Provides on-site technical assistance to tribes setting up or enhancing their tribal courts & related systems.

SEKI, DARRELL G., SR. (Ojibwe)
  (tribal chairperson)
Born in Red Lake, Minn. Education: University of Minnesota (two years). *Affiliation & Address*: Chairperson (2014-present), Red Lake Band of Ojibwe Indians, P.O. Box 550, Red Lake, MN 56671 (218) 679-3341. Military service: Vietnam Veteran. He has worked for Red Lake Nation in various capacities for 40 years, including as Executive Administrator. Elected Treasurer of the Red Lake Tribal Council in 2002, he has remained in that position ever since, overseeing the finances of the Red Lake Nation. Darrell is also one of the longest-serving members of the Tribal Interior Budget Council, and has represented the Midwest Region for more than ten years.

SELAM, SR., LONNIE (Yakama)
  (tribal chairperson)
Affiliation: Yakama Tribal Council, P.O. Box 151, Toppenish, WA 98948 (509) 865-5121.

SELDEN, DAVID
  (law librarian)
Affiliation & Address: Librarian, National Indian law Library, Native American Legal Fund, 1522 Broadway, Boulder, CO 80302 (303) 447-8760. E-mail: dselden@narf.org.

SELF, GEORGE WESLEY (*Twin Eagles*) (Comanche, Cherokee-Ouachita Indian Confederation) 1941-
  (swap meet dealer of crystals)
Born April 1, 1941, Los Angeles, Calif. *Education*: San Diego State University, BA, 1977. *Address*: 7614 Pacific Ave., Lemon Grove, CA 91945 (619) 298-5248. *Military service*: U.S. Army (PFC). *Memberships*: San Diego Museum of Man (life member); Vice-President, San Diego Lapidary Society, 1993-; San Diego State University Alumni Association. *Awards, honors*: Council member, Ouachita Indian Confederation; *Interests*: "I enjoy gems & minerals (rock-hounding). I was an archaeologist."

SELF, KYLE (Maidu)
  (tribal chairperson)
Affiliation & Address: Chairperson, Greenville Rancheria, 1425 Montgomery Rd., Red Bluff, CA 96080 (530) 528-8600.

SELVAGE, MICHAEL (Sisseton-Wahpeton Oyate)
  (former tribal chairperson)
Affiliation: Sisseton-Wahpeton Dakota Tribe, P.O. Box 509, Agency Village, SD 57262. (605) 698-3911. Website: www.swo-nsn.gov.

SENA, CARLOS (Southern Ute)
  (radio station manager)
Affiliation: KSUT - 91.3 FM, Southern Ute Tribe, P.O. Box 737, Ignacio, CO 81137 (303) 563-0255.

SEOUTEWA, CLAYTON
  (BIA agency supt.)
Affiliation: Zuni Agency, Bureau of Indian Affairs, P.O. Box 369, Zuni, NM 87327 (505) 782-5591.

SEPPANEN, JOHN (Chippewa)
  (health director)
Affiliation: Keweenaw Bay Indian Community Health Clinic, Route 1, Baraga, MI 49908 (906) 353-6671.

SEPULVEDA, RALPH (Kashia Pomo)
  (former tribal chairperson)
Affiliation: Kashia-Stewarts Point Rancheria, 3535 Industrial Dr., Suite B-2, Santa Rosa, CA 95401 (707) 591-0580.

SEQUAPTEWA, ANDREA (Hopi)
  (program coordinator)
Education: Northern Arizona University, BGS (Business Administration), MEd (Educational Leadership). *Affiliation & Address*: Senior Program Coordinator, Native American Student Services, Northern Arizona University, P.O. Box 5653, Flagstaff, AZ 86011 (928) 523-5512. E-mail: andrea.sequaptewa@nau.edu.

SERO, THOMAS (Mohawk)
  (board member)
Affiliation: Intertribal Christian Communications, P.O. Box 3765, Station B, Winnipeg, Manitoba, Canada R2W 3R6 (204) 661-9333.

SETH, LEROY L. (*Pe-Nock-We-Ya-Tillupt*) (Nez Perce) 1936-
  (patient advocate)
Born December 23, 1936, Lewiston, Idaho. *Education*: University of Montana, MA. *Principal occupation*: Patient advocate. *Address*: 22641 Sandhill Lane, Lapwai, ID 83540 (208) 843-2982. E-mail: leroys@enterprise.nezperce.org. *Affiliation*: Indian Health Service, Lapwai, Idaho, Nez Pece Tribe. *Other professional posts*: Consultant, painter & dancer. *Military service*: U.S. Army (Paratrooper). *Community activities*: Works with Indian basketball tournaments; assist powwow committees; Indian advisory boards. Interests: Art, photography, old cars, Indian rugs.

SETSHWAELO, SARA DUTSCHKE (Ione Miwok)
(attorney; Native American law & practice)

Education: California State University, Chico, BS, 1999; University of California, Davis, MA (Native American Studies); University of the pacific, McGeorge School of Law, JD, 2006. *Affiliation & Address*: Counsel, Dentons LLP, 525 Market St., 26th Floor, San Francisco, CA 94105 (415) 882-5031. E-mail: sara.setshwaelo@dentons.com. Sara is a member of Dentons' Public Law practice, focusing on Native American Law & Policy. She has experience working on a myriad of issues involving tribal sovereignty, governance, government-to-government relations & economic development. She assists tribal clients with the federal land acquisition process (a.k.a. fee-to-trust), including gaming and non-gaming acquisitions. She drafts and reviews tribal governing documents and intergovernmental agreements. She has also represented tribal clients in Indian Child Welfare Act matters. Sara is a member of the firm's tribal litigation practice team. **Honors & Awards**: Witkin Award for Academic Excellence: International Advocacy; International Advocacy Honors Board; Traynor Honor Society. **Published works**: Co-author, "Branding the Band: Protecting Tribal Identities Through Trademark Law," *The Federal Lawyer*, April 2014. **Presentations**: Lecturer, Santa Clara Law, Federal Indian Law, Spring 2013; *Tribal Tax Exempt and Economic Development Bonds*, California Association of Tribal Government Council Fire, October 2011; *Tribal Rights Under ICWA*, Morongo Annual ICWA Conference, October 2009; *Tribal Disenrollment*, 19th Annual National Indian Justice Center For All My Relations Conference, July 2008. **Memberships**: Federal Bar Assn; National Native American Bar Assn, Board of Directors, 2013-2015; California Indian Law Assn. **Prior & Present Employment** Prior to and during law school, Sara worked for the US Department of the Interior, Bureau of Indian Affairs, Pacific Regional Office in Sacramento. Her work there focused on administration and federal land acquisitions. She spent two years working as a liaison between the Pacific Regional Office and the California Tribal Trust Reform Consortium, assisting in the development & execution of an operating agreement between the parties, which took a progressive approach to implementing the federal trust responsibility. During law school, Sara served as a comment writer & editor for the *McGeorge Law Review*. She also participated in the Geneva Institute on Indigenous Peoples Law and Human Rights in Geneva, Switzerland, completing courses in international social, cultural and political rights and attending the Working Group on Indigenous Peoples at the United Nations Office at Geneva.

SETTEE, PRISCILLA (First Nation Cree)
(professor of Native Studies)

Born & raised Cumberland House Cree First Nations from Northern Saskatchewan. *Education*: University of Guelph, BA (Sociology), 1974; University of Saskatchewan, B.Ed., 2002; University of Manitoba, M.Ed. (Curriculum Studies), 2004, PhD, 2007. *Affiliation & Address*: Associate Professor of Native Studies, Kirk Hall 134, University of Saskatchewan, Saskatoon, SK S7N 5C8 (306) 966-5556. E-mail: priscilla.settee@usask.ca. *Courses taught*: Native politics, Indigenous Women, Indigenous Food Sovereignty, et al. *Other professional posts*: Invited lectures & conference presentations; Keynote Speaker, "Food, Culture & Wellness, Federation of Saskatchewan Indian Nations Wellness Conference," March 2009; "A Brief History of Indigenous Food Sovereignty," North American Indigenous Food Symposium, June 2009. *Awards, honors*: Nominated – Excellence in Teaching Award, 2007-08 & 2010-11, University of Saskatchewan; Oxfam's Saskatoonn W8 Women of Distinction; University f Saskatchewn Provost Teaching Award for Excellence in Indigenous Education, June 2012; Queen Elizabeth Jubilee Award for contribution to Canada, by Governor General of Canada, April 2012. *Published works*: Editor, Akemeyimow, A Book of Women's Stories (Coteau Publishing, 2011); chapters in numerous boks; articles in refereed journals; papers in published conference proeedings & abstracts.

SEVIER, JACKIE (Northern Arapaho) 1953-
(artist, shop owner)

Born July 30, 1953, Riverton, Wyo. *Education*: Casper (WY) College, 1971-72. *Principal occupation*: Artist. *Address & Affiliation*: Northern Plains Studio, P.O. Box 86, Seneca, NE 69161 (308) 639-3227. *Membership*: Indian Arts & Crafts Association. *Awards, honors*: Red Earth, Oklahoma City; Northern Plains Tribal Arts, Sioux Falls, SD; Aspen Celebration for the American Indian; Smithsonian Institution, Museum of Anthropology; Twin Cities Indian Market, Minneapolis; Aplan Award & Diederich Award at Red Cloud Art Show, Pine Ridge, SD; Lawrence Indian Art Festival, Lawrence, KS. *Exhibits*: Stuhr Museum, Grand Island, NE; Sioux Indian Museum, Rapid City, SD; Buffalo Bill Historical Society, Cody, WY; and 1989 World Expo in Shizouka, Japan.

SEWARD, TIMOTHY C.
(attorney)

Education: Colgate University, BA, 1988; UCLA School of Law, JD, 1993. *Affiliation & Address*: Partner, Hobbs, Straus, Dean & Walker, LLP, 1903 21st St., 3rd Floor, Sacramento, CA 95811 (916) 442-9444. E-mail: tsteward@hobbsstraus.com Tim joined Hobbs Straus as partner in 2005 and opened the

Firm's newest office in Sacramento, California. Prior to joining Hobbs Straus, he served as general counsel for the Washoe Tribe of Nevada and California for seven years. Tim assists Indian tribes in their efforts to enhance, preserve, and protect their nationhood and to provide for the health, safety, & well-being of tribal citizens. He is devoted to developing strong tribal government institutions and economies. Through his experiences as in-house counsel, he has a thorough understanding of the challenges confronting tribal governments and has developed and implemented strategies to resolve these matters and advance the priorities of the tribal government. Tim is recognized for his knowledge of & experience in Public Law 280 Jurisdiction, tribal Temporary Assistance for Needy Families (TANF), the Indian Child Welfare Act (ICWA), & protection of tribal sacred sites. His extensive experience, particularly in California, includes the successful defense of tribal jurisdiction law enforcement authority & reassumed exclusive ICWA jurisdiction. Tim negotiated intergovernmental agreements with the California attorney general, Department of Social Services, & several counties. He negotiated and drafted numerous commercial contracts and a gaming compact. Additionally, he assisted tribes with real estate transactions, drafting and securing federal and state laws, and has testified before the California legislature on several occasions. Tim also worked with tribal clients to draft and implement a range of tribal laws, regulations, policies, and bylaws in the areas of environmental regulation, land use, housing, elections, child protection, and procurement. Among his many accomplishments, Tim played a central role in developing a successful tribal TANF program that provides services in 13 counties located in two states. This included funding negotiations, state and county agreements, and drafting of governing policies. In the area of cultural preservation, he secured federal protection of tribal cultural sites, including Cave Rock, filed an amicus brief with the 9th Circuit supporting this decision, and secured tribal acquisition of several sites. *Memberships*: California Indian Law Association, Board Member; Federal Indian Bar Association.

SEXTON, R. JOSEPH
(attorney)

Education: The Citadel, BA (English); University of Arizona College of Law, JD. *Affiliation & Address*: Attorney, Galanda Broadman, 8606 35th Ave. NE, # L1, P.O. Box 15146, Seattle, WA 98115 (509) 910-8842. Email: joe@galandabroadman.com. Joe focuses his practice on tribal sovereignty issues, primarily working on land & environmental matters, cultural resources protection cases, economic development for tribal governments & individuals, & complex Indian Country litigation. Joe has also successfully represented individual tribal members in situations involving catastrophic injuries. Before joining Galanda Broadman, Joe's work in-house for a tribal government resulted in the development and enhancement of tribal government programs. He also negotiated the purchase of tribal lands, & successfully fought in courts and administrative forums to protect his client's tribal sovereignty, the indigenous and human rights of his client's constituents, & his client's threatened cultural resources. Joe's experiences before practicing law—including service in the United States Marine Corps and working on property & human rights issues as an intern in Bosnia and Herzegovina—equipped Joe to thrive in diverse communities, work efficiently and effectively under pressure, relentlessly pursue his and his clients' objectives, and serve American indigenous communities.

SEYLER, DEAN (Warm Springs Spokane)
(IHS area director)

Education: University of Phoenix, BS (Healthcare Administrtion). *Affiliation & Address*: Director, Portland Area IHS, 1414 NW Northrup St., Suite 800, Portland, OR 97204 (503) 414-5555. E-mail: dean.seyler@ihs.gov. Mr. Seyler oversees a health care delivery system for more than 100,000 Native Americans, primarily members of the 43 federally recognized Tribes in Oregon, Washington, and Idaho. Dean consults with tribal leaders at local, state, and national levels & keeps the Tribes informed of new legislation, policy changes, management actions, and available resources. In addition, each service unit in the Portland Area maintains a close working relationship with the local tribal health board. *Past professional posts*: He started his health care career in 1976 as an emergency medical technician for the Warm Springs Tribes. Over the next 16 years, Mr. Seyler gained experience in emergency medicine and law enforcement with the Warm Springs Tribes and the city of Prineville, Oregon. From 1992 to 1995, Mr. Seyler held positions with the Bureau of Indian Affairs Great Plains Region and with his Tribe. Mr. Seyler began his career with IHS in 1995 as the Deputy Service Unit Director for the Portland Area Warm Springs Service Unit. In 2000, he transferred to the Whiteriver Indian Health Hospital to accept the position of Administrative Officer. He was named Acting Chief Executive Officer (CEO) in 2002 and was appointed CEO in 2004. During this time, Mr. Seyler was detailed for six months to the Phoenix Area Office as Deputy Director where he managed service unit operations. In 2006, Mr. Seyler returned to Portland Area as the Public Health Emergency Manager. He was selected as Portland Area Executive Officer in 2008.

SEYMOUR, TRYNTJE VAN NESS 1956-
(writer, lecturer)
Born July 2, 1956, New York, N.Y. *Education*: Smith College, BA, 1978. *Principal occupation*: Writer, lecturer. *Address*: P.O. Box 363, Salisbury, CT 06068 (203) 435-2236. *Affiliation*: Guest curator, The Heard Museum, Phoenix, 1985-87. Membership: The Author's Guild. *Interests*: Extensive travels in the Southwest since 1970. Conducted in-depth interviews of Native American artists. Served as assistant boatman and, recently, as archaeology guide on raft trips through the Grand Canyon. Judge of paintings at Santa Fe Indian Market, 1987. *Biographical source*: "Traditional India Art," by Paula Panich in Southwest Profile, Feb. 1987. *Published works*: Acoma (Lime Rock Press, 1980); When the Rainbow Touches Down: The Artists and Stories Behind the Apache, Navajo, Rio Grande Pueblo & Hopi Paintings in the William and Leslie Van Ness Denman Collection (The Heard Museum, Dist. by U. of Washington Press, 1989); The Gift of Changing Woman (Henry Holt & Co., 1993).

SHACKELFORD, ALAN
(professor of history & American Indian studies)
Education: Southwestern University, BA; University of Wyoming, MA (American History); Indiana Uniersity, PhD (American History). *Affiliation & Address*: Assistant Professor of History & American Indian Studies, College of Arts & Sciences, University of North Dakota, 221 Centennial Dr., Stop 7103, Grand Forks, ND 58202 (701) 777-4649. Email: alan.shackelford@email.und.edu *Teaching Interests*: American Indian History; PreColumbia & Early American History; Plains Indian history; ethnohistorical research & writing. His current book project is a study of PreColumbian and colonial Indian communities in the middle Mississippi Valley. It focuses on how a series of communities in the region responded to both their environment as well as to outsiders in constructing their identities. The study aims to help better integrate the PreColumbian past into our understandings of how American Indian identities have been constructed historically and to answer the question of why American Indians in the region initially embraced European and Euroamerican newcomers. In the future, Dr. Shackelford hopes to continue studying how localized environment as well as interactions with outsiders shaped indigenous equestrian cultures in the Americas.

SHADBURN, DONALD L.
(editor, author)
Education: Truett McConnell College; University of West Georgia (Carrollton). *Address & Affiliation*: The Cottonpatch Press, P.O. Box 762, Cumming, GA 30028 (770) 887-1626. E-mail: donshadburn@webtv.net. Don taught middle school for about 30 years in Forsyth County, GA. He began his historical & genealogical research in 1965. He published the county's first history in 1981. He was appointed Forsyth County historian in 1983. *Awards, honors*: Lilla Mills Hawes Award in 1995 by the Georgia Historical Society, for "Unhallowed Intrusion." *Published works*: Pioneer History of Forsyth County, Georgia, 1981;." Cherokee Planters in Georgia, 1832-1838 (Cottonpatch Press, 1989); Unhallowed Intrusion: A History of Cherokee Families in Forsyth County, Georgia (Cottonpatch Press, 1993); Cottonpatch Chronicles: Reflections on Cherokee History, People, Places, and the Events in Forsyth County, Georgia (Cottonpatch Press, 1996); Upon Our Ruins: A Study in Cherokee History & Genealogy (Cottonpatch Press, in progress)..

SHADOWWALKER, DUPREE (Mescalero Apache)
(language team founder)
Education: University of Arizona, MA (Education with emphasis in Learning Technology), PhD candidate at the University of Arizona. *Affiliation*: Founder, Red Pony Heritage Language Team (505) 491-3401. www.redpony.us; E-mail: rphlt@redpony.us. The Language Team will create language learning modules, electronic dictionaries, fonts, and spell-check facilities for tribes endeavoring to revitalize their language at a minimal cost.

SHADWICK, JACK (Modoc)
(tribal registrar & historian)
Affiliation & Address: Tribal Registrar Historian & Education Director, Modoc Tribe of Oklahoma, 418 G St. SE • Miami, OK 74354 (918) 542-1190

SHAFFER, SUSAN M. (Umpqua)
(former tribal chairperson)
Affiliation: Board of Directors (35 years; chairperson for 20 years), Cow Creek Band of Umpqua Indians, 2371 N.E. Stevens, #100, Roseburg, OR 97470 (541) 672-9405. *Other professional posts*: Board member, Advisory Board for the Institute for Tribal Government, Hatfield School of Government, Portland (OR) State University; Board member, Native American Rights Fund; Delegate, National Congress of American Indians; delegate, Affiliated Tribes of Northwest Indians; vice-chair, Oregon Commission on Indian Services; member of the cultural committee, Cow Creek Band of Umpqua Tribe; delegate, National Women's Leadership Conference (Heart of the American Indian Women's Network); delegate, Indian Women's Leadership, White House Conference; board of trustees, Umpqua Community College (17 years, retired

1999). *Community activities*: Lecturer and resource person for courses in sociology & anthropology at various colleges & institutions. *Awards, honors*: Eleanor Roosevelt Award, 2003; Woman of Achievement Award, 2000; 2000 Female Citizen of the Year Award; 1999 President's Award; Hall of Fame at Umpqua Community College, 1999; first woman to chair the Board of Trustees at Umpqua Community College; 1997 Dedicated Service Award for 16 years of service, Oregon Community College Association; Aubry R. Watzek Award, 1986. *Publications*: Author, "We Must Reach Out," paper on tribal & government state/federal relations, presented to the Harvard University School of Government in 1989; articles on Oregon Indian history & culture published in "Pioneer Days in South Umpqua Valley," the annual journal of the South Umpqua Historical Society.

SHAKESPEARE, JIM L. (Arapaho)
(former tribal co-chairperson)
Affiliation & Address: Northern Arapaho Tribe, P.O. Box 396, Fort Washakie, WY 82514 (307) 332-6120.

SHAKESPEARE, JUNE (*Singing Pipe*) (Arapaho)
(Indian education director; home school coordinator)
Address: Riverton High School, 2001 W. Sunset, Riverton, WY 82501 (307) 856-9491 ext. 13. *Affiliations*: Chair, Wind River Reservation Health Promotion Board of Directors, 1995-present. *Other professional posts*: Coalition of Families & Youth member, 1992-present; Wind River Reservation Youth Council Board member, 1996-present. *Community activities*: Region VI-HIV/AIDS Committee member; Region VI - Peer Mentors Advisor, 1995-present; Wind River Chapter, American Red Cross, 1995-present. *Memberships*: National Indian Education Association; American Indian Education Advisory Committee, Central Wyoming College (Riverton, WY); Institute of American Indian Arts Alumni Association (Santa Fe, NM).

SHALIFOE, RICHARD (Lake Superior Band of Chippewa)
(councilmember; former tribal president)
Affiliation & Address: Councilmember, L'Anse Reservation, Keweenaw Bay Indian Community of Michigan, 107 Beartown Rd., Baraga, MI 49908 (906) 353-6623. *Past tribal post*: President.

SHANGREAUX, LILY (Oglala Lakota)
(museum assistant)
Education: Princeton University, BA. Affiliation: Museum Assistant, Red Earth Museum (Website: www.redearth.org), Red Earth, Inc., 6 Santa Fe Plaza, Oklahoma City, OK 73102 (405) 427-5228. E-mail: lily@redearth.org. *Other professional post*: Co-owner (with husband, Dan Bigbee) of BIG Productions, Edmonds, OK. *Past professional posts*: Institute of American Indian Arts, Santa Fe, NM; Indian Center, Lincoln, Neb.

SHANIGAN, EDGAR (Eskimo)
(Alaskan village president)
Affiliation: Ivanof Bay Village Council, P.O. Box 500, Perryville, AK 99648 (907) 522-2263.

SHANIGAN, MARIANE (Kanatak)
(Alaskan village president)
Affiliation: Native Village of Kanatak, P.O. Box 693, Dillingham, AK 99576 (907) 842-4004.

SHANKS, LAURENCE "SWIFT TIDE" (Schagticoke)
(tribal chief)
Affiliation: New England Coastal Schagticoke Indian Association, P.O. Box 551, Avon, MA 02322 (617) 961-1346.

SHANLEY, JAMES E. (Fort Peck Assiniboine)
(retired college president)
Affiliation: Fort Peck Community College, P.O. Box 398, Poplar, MT 59255 (406) 768-5551. *Other professional post*: Chairperson, American Indian College Fund, Denver, CO.

SHANLEY, KATHRYN (Fort Peck Assiniboine)
(professor of Native American studies)
Born & raised on the Fort Peck Assiniboine (Nakoda) Reservation. *Education*: Moorehead State University, BA (English), 1980; University of Michigan, MA (Diaspora Literature) & PhD (English with a specialization in Native American Literature), 1987. *Affiliation & Address*: Professor & Speical Assistant to the Provost for N, University of Montana, Native American Studies, NAC 203C, Missoula, MT 59812 (406) 243-5832. E-mail: shanleykw@mso.umt.edu. *Past professional posts*: Held positions at Cornell University & the University of Washington. *Research Interests*: Includes the work of James Welch, Blackfeet/Gros Ventre writer, gender issues in Indigenous studies, Native American religious autobiography, and Indigenous Knowledge-based theory. *Interests*: She is the University of Montana project director (2008-present) for collaboration with the Sami Studies Center at the University of Tromso,

Norway, and also collaborates with faculty at Maori Studies, Victoria University, Wellington, New Zealand. Dr. Shanley has worked for numerous years to raise funds to build a new Native American Center at the University of Montana that is to be dedicated in the Spring 2011. *Community activities*: She serves as the Ford Foundation, Diversity Fellowship regional liaison and on boards for the National Academy of Sciences Fellowships, the executive committee of the Modern Language Association, Division of American Indian Literatures, and (for almost ten years) on the American Indian Graduate Center. *Biographical sources*: Notable Native Americans; Dictionary of American Indian Women. *Published works*: "Only An Indian": Reading James Welch (University of Oklahoma Press, 2004)

SHANNON, LEE K. (Salish; Cowichan of B.C., Canada)
(attorney)
Education: Seattle University, BS, 1986; University of Washington, J.D., 1993, MBA, 1994. *Affiliation & Address*: Of Counsel, Hobbs, Straus, Dean & Walker, LLP, (2001-present), 851 S.W. Sixth Ave., Suite 1650, Portland, OR 97204 (503) 242-1745. E-mail: lshannon@hsdwor.com. Mr. Shannon focuses on finance, tax, tribal gaming, tribal sovereignty, & economic development for Indian tribes. Lee assists tribes in the areas of Federal Indian law, tribal sovereignty, jurisdiction and intergovernmental relations and agreements, tribal constitutions and codes, land acquisitions, land use, tribal infrastructure, and election issues. *Past professional posts*: Staff attorney and acting executive director of the Native American Program of Oregon Legal Services where he concentrated on commercial, corporate, gaming, finance and tax issues on behalf of Oregon tribes, tribal enterprises and Indian non-profit corporations. *Community activities*: Board of directors, Legal Aid Services of Oregon; board of directors, Oregon Law Center; board of directors, Affiliated Tribes of Northwest Indians. *Memberships*: Oregon State Bar Assn (member and former chair of the Indian Law Section); Washington State Bar Assn (member and former secretary-treasurer of the Indian law Section); Northwest Indian Bar Assn; Federal Bar Assn; National Assn of Bond Lawyers; National Indian Gaming Association.

SHANNON, RALPH
(Indian school principal)
Affiliation: Indian Township School, Peter Dana Point, HC78, Box 1A, Princeton, ME 04668 (207) 796-2362.

SHARP, FAWN R. (Quinault) 1973-
(tribal chairperson)
Education: Gonzaga University, B.A.; University of Washington, J.D., 1995. *Affiliation & Address*: Chairperson, Quinault Indian Nation, P.O. Box 189, Taholah, WA 98587 (360) 276-8211. E-mail: fsharp@quinault.org. *Past professional posts*: Managing attorney & lead counsel, Quinault Indian Nation; administrative law judge, Washington State Dept. of Revenue - Tax Appeals Division; Quinault Tribal Court Associate Judge; Counsel for Phillips, Krause & Brown; vice president & founding member, National Intertribal Tax Alliance; director/secretary, Quinault Nation Enterprise Board. *Community activities*: Appointed, by Governor Gray Locke, Trustee for Grays Harbor College. *Membership*: Washington State Bar Assn (governor-Indian Law Section).

SHARP, JOHN W. (Eskimo)
(Alaskan village president)
Affiliation: Twin Hills Village Council, P.O. Box TWA, Twin Hills, AK 99576 (907) 525-4821.

SHARP, WILLIE, JR. (Blackfeet)
(former tribal chairperson)
Affiliation: Chairperson (2008-11), Blackfeet Nation, Browning, MT.

SHAW, FRANCES (Diegueno)
(tribal chairperson)
Affiliation: Manzanita General Council, P.O. Box 1302, Boulevard, CA 91905 (619) 766-4930; chairperson, Southern Indian Health Council, P.O. Box 20889, El Cajon, CA 92021.

SHAW-DUTY, SHANNON (Osage)
(tribal newspaper editor)
Education: University of Oklahoma, BA (Journalism & Mass Communications); graduate of the American Indian Journalism Institute, University of South Dakota. *Affiliation & Address*: Editor, Osage Nation News, 619 Kihellah, Pawhuska, OK 74056 (918) 287-5668. E-mail: sshaw@osagetribe.org. *Other professional post*: Member, Board of Directors, Native American Journalists Association, Norman, OK. *Past professional posts*: Assignment editor, Reznetnews.org, online Native American news; reporter, The Santa Fe New Mexican.

SHAY, DARRELL (Shoshone-Bannock)
(tribal vice chairperson)
Affiliation & Address: Vice Chairperson (2017-present), Shoshone-Bannock Tribes, P.O. Box 306, Fort Hall, ID 83203 (208) 478-3721; E-mail: dshay@sbtribes.com.

SHEARER, LEAH (Choctaw of Oklahoma)
(Indian studies research analyst)
Education: University of Houston, BA (History); UCLA, MA (American Indian Studies), 2011. *Affiliation & Address*: Research Analyst, UCLA American Indian Studies Center, Campbell Hall 3220, Los Angeles, CA 90024 (310) 206-4380. E-mail: lshearer@aisc.ucla.edu. Leah's undergraduate thesis, "The Crisis of Crow Dog," is an examination of the early shifts in criminal jurisdiction in Indian country in the late 19th century and its current impact on federal Indian law. Her graduate thesis, "Justice in Indian Country: A Case Study of the Tulalip Tribes," explores the goals & methods of the justice system of the Tulalip Reservation in Washington State. Her research continues to focus on those topics, with an emphasis on tribal sovereignty & cultural theory. In the summer of 2009, she participated in the Washington Internships for Native Students program (WINS), where she interned at the Dept. of Veterans Affairs.

SHEBALA, MARLEY (Navajo)
(reporter & photographer)
Affiliation: The Navajo Times, P.O. Box 310, Window Rock, AZ 86515 (520) 871-6641. *Other professional post*: Treasurer, Native American Journalists Association (NAJA), Vermillion, SD).

SHEDD, AARON
(educational administrator)
Affiliation: Director, Office of Indian Education, U.S. Department of Education, Rm. 2177, Federal Office Bldg. 6, 400 Maryland Ave., Washington, DC 20202 (202) 401-1887.

SHEGONEE, HARTFORD (Potawatomi) 1943-
(administrator; tribal vicechairperson)
Born October 27, 1943, Hayward, Wisc. *Education*: Nicolet College (Vocational Diploma-Auto Mechanics, 1986); Mt. Scenario College, 1987-88. *Principal occupation*: Administrator. Resides in Crandon, WI. *Affiliation & Address*: Vice Chairperson, Forest County Potawatomi Community, P.O. Box 340, Crandon, WI 54520 (715) 478-2903. Vice chairperson, Forest County Potawatomi Executive Council, Crandon, WI, 1987-91. *Community activities*: Great Lakes Inter-Tribal Council (sec/treasurer, 1987-); Inter-Tribal Timber Council, 1987-; also active in local chapter of Headstart program. National Congress of American Indians. *Awards, honors*: Honored with Plaque by the Canadian Potawatomi for assistance in quest for federal (U.S.) recognition of treaty. *Interests*: "Anything that will improve the lifestyle of the Forest Co. Potawatomi people. Instrumental in the Potawatomi having land in the City of Milwaukee placed into Trust for the Tribe in 1990. Restored political stability after BIA shutdown operations of the tribe in 1987."

SHELDON, MELVIN R., JR. (Tulalip)
(tribal chairperson)
Education: University of Washington, BA (Political Science). *Affiliation*: Tulalip Tribes, 6406 Marine Dr., Tulalip, WA 98271 (360) 651-4000. *Other professional posts*: 2nd Vice President, Affiliated Tribes of Northwest Indians (ATNI), Portland, OR; member of the Services Committee, NICS Advisory Board, and Citizen's Committee for Marysville Schools; co-chair of the Boys & Girls Club Yearly Auction. *Military service*: Vietnam Veteran. His accomplishments include helping to get Medicine Wheel tracking, contributing to business park & new casino development, & expanding the Veteran's Center.

SHELLY, BEN (Navajo-Dine')
(tribal president)
Born in Thoreau, New Mexico. *Affiliation & Address*: President (2011-15), Navajo Nation, P.O. Box 7440, Window Rock, AZ 86515 (928) 871-7000. E-mail: president.benshelly@navajo-nsn.gov. Ben served the Navajo people in 1991 as a council delegate representing Thoreau Chapter. He served as a mmber of the Transportation & Intergovernmental Relations Committee, and chairperson of the Budget & Finance Committee. President Shelly also served for 12 years as a McKinley County Commissioner. He also owned & operated a fleet maintenance & mechanic shop in Thoreau, NM before being elected.

SHENANDOAH, JOANNE (*Tekalihwakwa-She Sings*)
(Oneida-Iroquois) 1957-
(musician-composer)
Born June 23, 1957, Syracuse, N.Y. *Education*: Andrews University, 1975-76; Columbia Union College, 1976-78; Doctorate of Music, S.U., 2002. *Principal occupation*: Musician-composer. *Address*: Oneida Nation Territory, P.O. Box 450, Oneida, NY 13421 (315) 363-1655. E-mail: shenandoaj@aol.com. Website: www.joanneshenandoah.com. *Community activities*: Board member,

Hiawatha Institute for Indigenous Knowledge. *Memberships*: ASCAP; ACTRA; National Congress of American Indians; National American Indian Women's Association. *Interests*: "Music writing, performing, producing, composing; travels to Europe, throughout North America; sailing, canoeing; historical research. Round Dance Productions is a non-for-profit corporation formed specifically to assist in the preservation and development of indigenous North American language, history, music & art. Primary focus is on Haudenosaunee (Oneida, Mohawk, Onondaga, Seneca, Cayuga & Tuscarora Nations) although it encompasses other aboriginal cultures as well." *Awards, honors*: 1992 Special Award for dedicated service to Oneida Nation from U.S. Indian Health Service; "1993 Native Musician of the Year"; performed for first lady Hillary Clinton & V.P.'s wife, Tipper Gore in Washington, DC; 1994 & 1997 Outstanding Musical Achievement Awards; Native American Woman's Recognition Award, 1996; Native American Record of the Year, NAIRD 1997 INDIE Award; Native American Woman of Hope Award, 1997; 1998 Best Female Artist & Best Children's Album, Native American Music Awards; 1998 ASCAP, Popular Awards Recipient; 1998 Grammy Nominations for two albums: World Music - Matriarch and Children's Music - All Spirits Sing; Grammy nomination, 2005; Indian Summer Music Awards, Best Historical Recording, 2005. *Biographical source*: Who's Who in the East, 1991-92; feature story in, "The Turtle" magazine, Winter 1993. 1994 Who's Who Among Native Americans; Joanne has appeared on numerous television shows, radio broadcasts, and video documentaries. *Produced works*: She released her first album with Canyon Records in September 1989. She also recorded with NATO Records in France for the 2-CD album "Oyate" produced by Tony Hymas. Two of her compositions are featured on the Leonard Peltier album, "In the Spirit of Crazy Horse." "Loving Ways" is co-produced with a A. Paul Ortega, Canyon Records, Phoenix, AZ. "Nature Dance" with Sun Child Productions, distributed by Eye-Q Records, Warner of Germany was released June 1991 and made "Record of the Month." "Orenda" Native American Songs of Life, "Matriarch" Iroquois Women's Songs, & "Life Blood" all by Silver Wave Records. *Performances*: Shenandoah has performed thousands of concerts throughout North America and Europe. Some of the more recent include: Indian Time II, Winnipeg, Canada, - American Indian Music Festival, San Francisco, June 1991; National Canadian TV, Toronto Harbourfront Festival, July 1991; Earth Day, Washington, DC, May 1991; Woodstock 94, Special Olympics, 1996; 1997 Presidential Inaugural in Washington, DC; among others. Future Projects: TV Mini Series - Wampum Belts & Peace Trees, Author, Dr. Gregory Schaaf, Executive Producer, Sam Bottoms; European Tour, 1992 Spring "Indian Saga"; Planet Live - Earth Day, 1992. *Published work*: Skywoman - Legends of the Iroquois with co-writer Doug George (Clearlight Publishers).

SHENDO, BENNY, JR. (Jemez Pueblo)
(tribal administrator)
Born & raised in Jemez Pueblo, N.M. *Education*: Colorado College, 1982-83; University of Colorado, 1987, College of Law, 1988-89. *Affiliation & Address*: Tribal Administrator, Pueblo of Jemez, P.O. Box 100, Jemez, NM 87024 (575) 834-7359. *Past professional post*: New Mexico State Senator (D) (2013-14), District 22, New Mexico State Legislature, *Committees*: Chairperson, Behavioral Health Subcommittee; Indian Affairs Committee; Water & Natural Resources Committee. *Other professional post*: Vice President, Business Development, Notah Begay III Consulting, 2009-present. *Past professional posts*: Assistant Dean of Students, Stanford University, 1994-97; Senior Manager of Native American Programs, University of New Mexico, 2004-07; 2nd Lt. Governor, Pueblo of Jemez, 1998; 1st Lt. Governor, Pueblo of Jemez, 2002, 2009; Co-Founder, San Diego Riverside Charter School, Jemez Pueblo, 1999; Cabinet Secretary, Deartment of Indian Affairs, N.M., 2004-07. *Awards, honors*: Fellow, W.K. Kellogg National Leadership Program (1997); Mary G. Ross Award, Council of Energy Resource Tribes (2004); Public Advocate Award, National Center for American Indian Enterprises Development (2007).

SHEPHERD, ALEX (Paiute)
(tribal chairperson)
Affiliation: Paiute Indian Tribe of Utah Tribal Council, 600 N. 100 E. Paiute Dr., Cedar City, UT 84720 (801) 586-1121.

SHEPHERD, ROBERT (Sisseton Wahpeton Oyate)
(former tribal chairperson)
Education: University of North Dakota, BS (Recreation & Leisure Services), 2008; University of Mary (Bismarck, ND), MBA, 2010. *Affiliation & Address*: Native American Tribal Relations Officer, Monarch America, Inc., 9457 S. University Blvd., Suite 806, Highlands Ranch, CO 80126 (844) 852-1537. *Military service*: U.S. Army. *Past professional posts*: Former Chairperson, Sisseton Wahpeton Oyate, Lake Traverse Reservation, Agency Village, SD; secretary, National Congress of American Indians.

SHEPHERD, STACY (Choctaw-Chickasaw)
(tribal member services executive officer)
Education: Southeastern Oklahoma State University, BA (English & Elementary Education), 1980, MA (Secondary School Administration), 1987.

Affiliation & Address: Senior Executive Officer of Member Services, Choctaw Nation of Oklahoma, P.O. Box 1210, Durant, OK 74702 (580) 924-8280. E-mail: sshepherd@choctawnation.com. She was employed with the Choctaw Nation in 2010 with Career Development as an Academic Employment Specialist. In 2011 Stacy accepted the position as Executive Director of the Chahta Foundation, a 501(c)3 Nonprofit that supports Tribal members in reaching full potential and self-reliance. Stacy focus is on Haudenosaunee is the great granddaughter of Joseph H. Goforth, a Chickasaw who earned his law degree from Vanderbilt University School of Law in 1900 and became the first Native American judge in Indian Territory. She is the granddaughter of Jesse Goforth Clark, a Choctaw woman who attended Oklahoma Presbyterian College (OPC), and the daughter of Choctaw Nation Executive Director of Education, Joy Culbreath. Stacy represented Durant ISD as a top 12 finalist for Oklahoma Teacher of the Year in 2000 (Runner Up) and in 2010. She completed her teaching career after 30 years in Oklahoma Public Education. One of Stacy's accomplishments was to establish the Teacher Cadet program at Durant High School (DHS) for juniors and seniors who were considering education as a career and forming the Future Educators Association (FEA). Many students who participated in the Teacher Cadet program have grown into professional educators. She believes there is no greater accomplishment than to mentor and prepare teachers to continue a legacy of the most respected profession in the world - TEACHING. Her greatest privilege was facilitating the Choctaw Language classes at DHS where she studied along side her students. Stacy has completed 18 hours of Choctaw Language at SOSU.

SHEPPARD, LAVERNE (Shoshone-Bannock) 1960-
(association executive; editor)
Born April 17, 1960, Blackfoot, Idaho. *Education*: University of Arizona, 1982; Idaho State University, BA (Journalism), 1984. *Affiliations*: Editor, Sho-Ban News, Fort Hall, ID, 1984-89, National American Indian/Alaska Native Media Specialist, U.S. Census Bureau, Seattle, 1989-90; Executive Director, Native American Journalism Assn, U. of Colorado School of Journalism, Campus Box 287, Boulder, CO 80309 (303) 492-7397, 1990-. *Other professional post*: Co-chairperson, Native Communications Group, Lincoln, NE, 1990-.

SHERER, MARCIE (Eskimo)
(Alaskan village president)
Affiliation: Native Village of Napaimute, P.O. Box 1301, Bethel, AK 99559 (907) 543-2887.

SHERIDAN, AMEN (Omaha)
(former tribal chairperson)
Affiliation & Address: Omaha Tribe, P.O. Box 368, Macy, NE

SHERLOCK, LONNIE
(Indian education program coordinator)
Affiliation: Alliance Public Schools, Indian Education Program, 1604 Sweetwater, Alliance, NE 69301 (308) 762-1580.

SHERLOCK, SALINA (Muscogee Creek)
(board vice president)
Affiliation & Address: Board Vice President, Marin American Indian Alliance, P.O. Box 150565, San Rafael, CA 94915.

SHERMAN, DUANE, SR. (Hoopa)
(tribal chairperson)
Affiliation: Hoopa Valley Tribal Council, P.O. Box 1348, Hoopa, CA 95546 (530) 625-4211.

SHERMAN, GERALD J. (Oglala Sioux) 1949-
(company president)
Born July 17, 1949, Kyle, S.D. *Education*: Oglala Lakota College, BS, 1987. *Affiliation & Address*: President, Indian Land Capital Company (ILCC), P.O. Box 45, Roscoe, MT 59071 (406) 328-4622. The ILCC provides alternative loan options to Indian nations for tribal land acquisition. *Other professional posts*: Member of the International Advisory Council of the Native Nations Institute at the University of Arizona, affiliated with the Harvard Project on American Indian Economic Development; board member of Indian Dispute Resolution Services of Sacramento, CA; chair, Indian Nonprofit Alliance in Montana. *Past professional posts*: Founding chairman of the board & executive director. The Lakota Fund, Kyle, SD, 1987-91 (a community loan fund on the Pine Ridge Indian Reservation); Pine Ridge Area Director, Native American Economic Development Project, Business Opportunity Center - University of South Dakota, 1991-93 (provided business technical assistance to tribal members at Pine Ridge); manager, Norwest Bank Lower Brule (a new bank on the Lower Brule Indian Reservation), Lower Brule, SD, 1993-2007. *Community activities*: Board member, Habitat for Humanity, Ft. Thompson, SD; board member, Food Services of South Dakota. *Membership*: North Plains Tribal Arts Council. *Awards, honors*: Minority Small Business Advocate of the Year, 1993, for South Dakota & SBA Region VIII. *Interests*: Indian economic development, finance. As founding chairman of the board & executive director of the Lakota

Fund, Mr. Sherman played a principal role in developing the Fund & forging the relationships between the fund, its investors, funders, and clients. He traveled to Canada & Bangladesh to study the peer group lending method now in use by the Lakota Fund to make micro enterprise loans. Gerald has several years experience in television production but has been active in Indian economic development since 1986.

SHERMAN, GERALDINE (Sioux)
(craftsperson)
Affiliations: Contemporary Lakota Fashions by Geraldine Sherman, 714 Wambli Dr., Rapid City, SD 57701 (605) 341-7560.

SHERMAN, JILL (Hoopa)
(tribal environmental director)
Education: Humboldt State University, B.A. (minor in Native American Studies). *Address & Affiliation*: Environmental Director, Pechanga Band of Luiseno Mission Indians, P.O. Box 1477, Temecula, CA 92593 (909) 676-2768. *Other professional posts*: Governor Gray Davis appointed Ms. Sherman commissioner to the Native American Heritage Commission in May 2000. She is a member of the Hoopa Tribal Council; was elected representative to the EPA Regional Tribal Operations Committee (RTOC) for Southern California Tribes, and serves on the Native American Environmental Protection Coalition (NAEPC) Board. Jill has been a participant with the North County American Indian Education Group and an alternative board member of the Southern California Indian Human Resources Agency.

SHERMAN, MARION (Oglala Lakota)
(professor & chair of Native American studies)
Education: University of Colorado School of Law, JD, 1997. *Affiliation & Address*: Professor & Chair, Native American Studies Department, Humboldt State University, 1 Harpst St., Arcata, CA 95521 (707) 826-3821. E-mail: ms31@humboldt.edu Mr. Sherman specializes in indigenous and tribal law, justice, peacemaking, governance, environment, resource use, culture, history and philosophy. His poems were awarded the 2003 First Book Award for Poetry by the Native Writers' Circle of the Americas.

SHERMAN, PAULA (Algonquin)
(professor of Indigenous Studies)
Affiliation & Address: Assistant Professor of Indigenous Studies (2004-present), Department of Indigenous Studies, Enweying Room 307, Trent University, (705) 748-1011 ext. 7904. E-mail: psherman@trentu.ca. *Research Interests*: The Atlantic World, the fur trade & Indigenous theatre & performance.

SHERWOOD, NEVA (Rosebud Sioux)
(BIA education administrator)
Affiliation: Rosebud Agency, Office of Indian Affairs, P.O. Box 669, Rosebud, SD 57570. (605) 856-4478. E-mail: neva.sherwood@bie.edu.

SHEWANO, DON (Potawatomi)
(health director)
Affiliation: Forest County Potawatomi Community Clinic, P.O. Box 346, Crandon, WI 54520 (715) 478-3471.

SHIELDS, CALEB (Assiniboine Sioux)
(tribal chairperson)
Affiliation: Fort Peck Tribal Executive Board, P.O. Box 1027, Poplar, MT 59255 (406) 768-5155.

SHIELDS, RANDY (Crow Creek Sioux)
(tribal vice chairperson)
Affiliation: Vice Chairperson, Crow Creek Sioux Tribe, P.O. Box 50, Fort Thompson, SD 57339 (605) 245-2221.

SHIJE, AMADEO (Zia Pueblo)
(council chairperson)
Affiliation: All Indian Pueblo Council, P.O. Box 400, Albuquerque, NM 87190 (505) 881-1992.

SHIJE, HENRY (Zia Pueblo)
(former Pueblo governor)
Affiliation & Address: Pueblo of Zia, 135 Capital Square Dr., Zia Pueblo, NM 87053 (505) 867-3304.

SHIJE, JOHN, JR. (Santa Clara Pueblo)
(Pueblo lt. governor)
Affiliation & Address: Lt. Governor, Pueblo of Santa Clara, P.O. Box 580, Espanola, NM 87532 (505) 753-7330.

SHIJE, WILFRED (Zia Pueblo)
(former Puebo governor)
Affiliation: Pueblo of Zia, 135 Capital Square Dr., Zia Pueblo, NM 87053 (505) 867-3304.

SHINGOITEWA, LEROY N. (*Dawa yes va*) (Hopi) 1942-   (former tribal chairperson)
Born August 4, 1942, Keams Canyon, Ariz. *Education*: Northern Arizona University, BS, 1969; Pennsylvania State University, MEd, 1972. *Address*: P.O. Box 1258, Tuba City, AZ 86045 (928) 283-5623. *Affiliations*: Hotevilla Bacavi Community School, Hotevilla, AZ, 1990-93; executive assistant, Office of Hopi Tribal Chairman, Hopi Indian Tribe, Kykotsmovi, AZ, 1993-2007; chairperson, Hopi Tribe, 2008-13. E-mail: lshingoitewa@hopi-nsn.gov. *Other professional post*: Executive assistant, Navajo Nation Division of Health. Community activities: Member of Tuba City School Board; Arizona School Board Association (Legislative Committee, Resolution Committee, Chapter I Committee); White House Delegate for Indian Education; Indian Education Graduate Advisory Board, Berkeley, CA. *Memberships*: National Indian Education Association; Curriculum & Supervision Association; National School Board Association. *Awards, honors*: National Civic Award - Supermarkets Association; President Bush 1000 Points-of-Light Award; Hopi Man-of-the-Year (Hopi-Navajo Observer). *Interests*: "Work to help all Indian people throughout the U.S. in education & management areas."

SHIPLEY, PRISCILLA (Stillaguamish)
(tribal vice chairperson)
Affiliation: Stillaguamish Board of Directors, P.O. Box 277, Arlington, WA 98223 (360) 652-7362.

SHIPMAN, MIKE (Shoalwater Bay)
(tribal vice chairperson)
Affiliation: Shoalwater Bay Indian Tribe, P.O. Box 130, Tokeland, WA 98590 (360) 267-6766. E-mail: mshipman@shoalwaterbay-nsn.gov.

SHIPPS, THOMAS H. 1953-
(tribal attorney)
Born February 13, 1953, Hyannis, Mass. Education: Fort Lewis College, BA, 1976; University of Houston Law School, JD, 1979. *Address*: P.O. Box 2717, Durango, CO 81302 (970) 247-1755. *Affiliation*: Tribal attorney, Southern Ute Indian Tribe, Ignacio, CO, 1980-. *Memberships*: American Bar Assn; Colorado Bar Assn; Colorado Indian Bar Assn; National Indian Law Support Center (board of directors); Rocky Mountain Mineral Law Foundation. *Published works*: The American Indian and the Constitution (University of Houston Law Center, 1979); "Oil & Gas Lease Operation & Royalty Valuation on Indian Lands," Rocky Mountain Mineral Law Foundation, 1991.

SHIRLEY, JOE, JR. (Navajo) 1947-
(former president-Navajo (Dine') Nation)
Born December 4, 1947 in Chinle, AZ. *Education*: Magic Valley Christian College (Albion, Idaho), AA, 1968; Abilene (TX) Christian University, BS (Business), 1976; Arizona State University, MSW, 1978. *Affiliation & Address*: Supervisor, District I, Apache County, P.O. Box 428, St. Johns, AZ 85936 (928) 674-5664. *Other professional posts*: President, Navajo-Dine' Nation, Window Rock, AZ (2003-2011); 16 years to the social services field, 1978-84; executive director, Navajo Division of Social Services, 1983-84; Navajo Nation Council, 1986-99 where he was the Chairman of the Labor & Manpower Committee, 1987-91, Chairman of the Tax Commission, 1991-95, member of the Intergovernmental Relations Committee & Chairman of the Ethics & Rules Committee, 1995-98. *Awards, honors*: In 1996, he was appointed to the Board of Directors of the National Association of Counties (NACo), Washington, DC. He is also a member of the Economic & Community Development Committee & appointed to serve as a member of the Sustainable Leadership Team of NACo. In 1997, he served as a member of the Advisory Committee to the President's Commission on Sustainable Communities in Washington, DC, and from 1985 to 1991, a member of the Public Lands Committee. Appointed by Native American leaders to co-chair both BIA/Tribal Budget Advisory Council and the Sovereign Protection Initiative. *Interests*: Lecturing on the Navajo way of life for self-development. He enjoys playing basketball, running and spending time with his family.

SHIVELY, ALAN (Chippewa)
(former tribal chairperson)
Affiliation & Address: Lac Vieux Desert Band of Lake Superior Chippewa Indians, P.O. Box 249, Watersmeet, MI 49969 (906) 358-4577.

SHOEMAKE, BEN (Cherokee)
(coalition chairperson)
Affiliation: Native American Coalition of Tulsa, 1740 West 41st, Tulsa, OK 74107 (918) 446-8432.

SHOEMAKER, EDWARD C. (Cherokee of OK) 1943-
(director of research management)
Born July 20, 1943, Nowata, Okla. *Education*: Oklahoma State University, BA; University of Oklahoma, MLS. *Address*: 2331 Rockwood Lane, Norman, OK 73071. *Affiliation*: Director, Research Division (1980-present), Oklahoma Historical Society, 2100 North Lincoln Blvd., Oklahoma City, OK 73105 (405) 522-4025. E-mail: edshoemaker@ok-history.mus.ok.us. Website: www.ok-history.mus.ok.us. *Military service*: U.S. Navy, 1967-69 (Mobile Riverine Forces). *Military awards, honors*: Combat Action Ribbon, Good Conduct, Vietnam Campaign Medal, Republic of Vietnam Medal. *Community activities*: Member of Canticle Singers & Chair of Library Council, McFarlin Memorial United Methodist Church, Norman, OK. *Memberships*: Mobile Riverine Forces Assn; Navy MSO Association.

SHOEMAKER, MARY J. (Pueblo)
(school principal)
Affiliation: San Juan Day School, P.O. Box 1077, San Juan Pueblo, NM 87566 (505) 852-2154.

SHOLTON, JOHN R. (Otoe-Missouria)
(tribal council chairperson)
Affiliation: Otoe-Missouria Tribal Council, Rt. 1, Box 62, Red Rock, OK 74651 (405) 723-4466. E-mail: jshotton@omtribe.org

SHOPODOCK, PHILIP (Forest County Potawatomi)
(tribal chairperson)
Affiliation & Address: Forest County Potawatomi Executive Council, P.O. Box 340, Crandon, WI 54520 (715) 478-2903. *Other professional post*: Board member, Potawatomi Business Development Corporation, Milwaukee, WI.

SHOPTEESE, JOHN T. (*Washah*) (Prairie Band Potawatomi) 1938-
(freelance jeweler, designer, artist; photographer; tribal consultant)
Born February 28, 1938, Mayetta, Kan. *Education*: Haskell Indian Junior College, 1956-58. *Principal occupation*: freelance jeweler, designer, artist; photographer; tribal economic development consultant. *Address*: 14471 Kipling Ave. S., Savage, MN 55378 (612) 895-5207; E-mail: johnshop@gold.tc.umn.edu. *Affiliations*: Indian Health Service, Rockville, MD, 1958-86; National Indian Health Board, Denver, CO, 1992-94. *Military service*: U.S. Army Medical Corps, 1961-62. *Memberships*: Native Arts Circle, Minneapolis, MN; Southwest Association on Indian Affairs, Santa Fe, NM, 1980-. *Community activities*: Indian Parents Committee, School District 191, MN. *Awards, honors*: Several awards for achievement in the arts (I am a jeweler--gold/silver smith); sculpture in bronze, pewter, clay; received several juried art show awards throughout the Southwest; 1994 fellowship from the Jerome Foundation of Minnesota. *Interests*: Pursuing excellence in Native arts; to enhance cultural awareness and enact the trends of art through significant application of contemporary overtones. (I) "have displayed my arts/crafts at major art shows of Native American artists."

SHORE, NANCY (Sos'setv) (Creek/Seminole) 1947-
(education)
Born April 6, 1947, Glades County, Fla. *Education*: Barry University (Miami, FL), MSW, 1982. *Affiliation*: Seminole Tribe of Florida, Hollywood, FL, 1973-. *Community activities*: Seminole Higher Education Committee; Seminole Women's Club; Parent Advisory Committee; Okee Parent/Teacher; Seminole Education Advisory.

SHORES, TRENT (Choctaw of Oklahoma)
(deputy directory - Office of Tribal Justice)
Affiliations: Deputy Director, Office of Tribal Justice, U.S. Dept. of Justice, 950 Pennsylvania Ave., NW, Rm. 1000, Washington, DC 20530 (202) 514-8812. E-mail: trent.shores@usdoj.gov.

SHORT BULL, ARTHUR J. (Oglala Lakota)
(watercolorit artist; gallery owner)
Born & raised on the Pine Ridge Indian Reservation. *Affiliation & Address*: Artist/Owner, Dawnhawk Productions, 34420 Wabaunsee Rd., Alma, KS 66401. Website: www.dawnhawk.org; E-mail: wakinyan1@mac.com. *Awards, honors*: Recipient of 2006 First Peoples Fund Cultural Capital Program Fellowship Award; 2009 First Peoples Fund Business Leadership Fellowship Award.

SHORTBULL, THOMAS (Lakota)
(college president)
Affiliation & Address: President, Oglala Lakota College, P.O. Box 490, Kyle, SD 57752 (605) 455-2321.

SHOTTON, HEATHER (Wichita/Kiowa/Cheyenne)
(professor of Native American studies)
Education: University of Oklahoma, BA (Native American Studies), MA (Human Relations), PhD &Adult & Higher Education). *Affiliation & Address*: Visiting Assistant Professor of Native American Studies, University of Oklahoma, Department of Anthropology, 455 W. Lindsey, Norman, OK 73019 (405) 325-2312. E-mail: hshotton@ou.edu. Her research focuses on addressing issues of Native American student success & retention in secondary education. *Other professional posts*: National Chair, Indigenous People Knowledge Community of the National Association of Student Personnel Administrators; board member, Oklahoma City Indian Clinic.

SHOTTEN, JOHN R. (Otoe-Missouria)
(tribal chairperson)
Education: University of Oklahoma, BS (Business Administration), Master of Public Administration. *Affiliation & Address*: Chairperson, Otoe-Missouria Tribe, 8151 Hwy. 177, Red Rock, OK 74651 (580) 723-4466 ext. 107. E-mail: jshotton@omtribe.org. *Awards, honors*: In 2012, he was recognized as one of the "Native American 40 Under 40" by the National Center for American Indian Enterprise Development.

SHOW, T.J. (Blackfeet)
(tribal chairperson)
Affiliation & Address: Chairperson, Blackfeet Nation, P.O. Box 850, Browning, MT 59417 (406) 338-7521.

SHOYO, ARLEN (Eastern Shoshone)
(tribal vice chairperson)
Affiliation: Wind River Eastern Shoshone Tribe, P.O. Box 538, Fort Washakie, WY 82514 (307) 332-3532.

SHUCKAHOSEE, CORBIN (Sac & Fox of Missouri)
(tribal chairperson)
Affiliation: Sac & Fox of Missouri Tribal Council, Rt. 1, P.O. Box 60, Reserve, KS 66434 (913) 742-7471.

SHULTES, STEPHANIE E. (Iroquois)
(museum curator)
Affiliation: Iroquois Indian Museum, Box 7, Caverns Rd., Howes Cave, NY 12092 (518) 296-8949.

SHUNATONA, GWEN (Prairie Band Potawatomi/Pawnee/Otoe-Missouria)
(chair of fundraising committee)
Education: Sacred Heart College (now Newman University, Wichita, KS), BA; University of Minnsota, MA (Educational Administration). *Affiliation & Address*: Chairperson, Fundraising Committee. Pawnee Nation College, 861 Little Dee Dr., Pawnee, OK 740058 (918) 762-3343. *Other professional post*: Member, Board of Trustees, Pawnee Nation College (Interim President, 2013). *Past professional posts*: President, Orbis Associates, Washington, DC; director of planning & coordination, IAIA's Lifelong Learning Center; vice president, Native American Research Institute, Washington, DC; branch chief, Office of Indian Education, Department of Education, Washington, DC; assistant dean of student affairs, Stanford University, Palo Alto, CA; instructor, tutor, counselor, U. of Minnesota, Wichita State Univesity, Dept. of the Interior/BIA at Chilocco, and Renwick U.S.D. Andale, KS.

SHURR, JOHN CARTER (Oklahoma Cherokee) 1947-
(journalist, bureau chief-Associated Press)
Born March 15, 1947, Muskogee, Okla. *Education*: University of Oklahoma, BA (Journalism), 1973. *Principal occupation*: Bureau chief, Associated Press. *Address*: 116 Shallow Brook Dr., Columbia, SC 29223 (803) 788-1077. E-Mail: jshurr@ap.org. *Affiliation*: Chief of Bureau, The Associated Press, Columbia, SC, 1984-. *Other professional post*: Curriculum Advisory Committee, University of South Carolina, College of Journalism. *Military service*: U.S. Navy, 1966-70 (2nd Class Radioman, E-5; Vietnam, 1967-68; Vietnam Service Medal, Vietnam Campaign Medal-3 Bronze Stars; Presidential Unit Citation, Navy Unit Commendation, Combat Action Ribbon). *Memberships*: Reporters Committee for Freedom of the Press, 1991- (Steering Committee); First Amendment Congress (Trustee & Vice President, 1980-88); South Carolina Press Association Freedom of Information Committee, 1986-, Chairperson; Society of Professional Journalists; Native American Journalists Assn. *Awards, honors*: American Bar Assn Gavel Award, 1981; SC Press Assn Award, 1987 & 1994; several Associated Press Managing Editors Awards. *Interests*: Sailboat racer. *Published work*: Freedom of Information Guide (SC Press Assn, 1987-93).

SHUTIVA, RONALD (Acoma Pueblo)
(pueblo council governor)
Affiliation: Acoma Pueblo Council, P.O. Box 309, Acomita, NM 87034 (505) 552-6604.

SIBBISON, V. HEATHER
(attorney; chair of practice group)
Education: Tufts University, BA, 1983; Columbia Law School, JD, 1988. *Affiliation & Address*: Chairperson, Native American Law & Policy Practice, Dentons LLP, 1301 K St., NW, Washington, DC 20005 (202) 408-6439. E-mail: heather.sibbison@dentons.com. Heather serves clients on matters related to

American Indian, Alaska Native, and Native Hawaiian issues. Her practice is primarily focused on all matters related to Indian lands, including trust acquisitions, Indian lands opinions, *Carcieri v. Salazar* issues, land claim settlement issues, and related compliance with the Indian Gaming Regulatory Act (IGRA) and the Natural Environmental Policy Act (NEPA). Heather's long experience with the Indian Reorganization Act, IGRA, NEPA, various land and water rights settlements, and the legal issues that have been spawned by the Supreme Court's decision in Carcieri, enable her to assist clients in developing and implementing workable fee-to-trust & reservation proclamation strategies for tribes needing additional land for gaming, non-gaming economic development, housing or any other use. Her practice encompasses extensive representation of tribes in tribal-state compacting process, the development of inter-governmental services agreements and most matters for which federal administrative approval is required from either the Department of the Interior (Interior) or the National Indian Gaming Commission (NIGC). Heather also has been actively engaged in federal recognition issues, representing clients before the DOI. In all of these matters, Heather has assisted clients navigate their issues both with the federal agencies and with the United States Congress. *Past professional posts*: Before returning to private practice in 2001, Heather served in the Office of the Secretary at the Department of the Interior (Special Assistant to the Secretary, Counselor to the Deputy Secretary, and Director of the Secretary's Office of Indian Water Rights), and also at the Department of Justice (Counsel to the Assistant Attorney General for Environment and Natural Resources, focus on work with the Indian Resources Section). During her federal service, her duties included management of issues related to fee-to-trust and Indian gaming, and she was lead federal negotiator in various settlement negotiations involving Indian land claims, Indian water rights and treaty fishing rights. *Honors & awards*: *Best Lawyers* ranking, 2010-2014; Named Lawyer of the Year, Native American Law, 2013; Ranked, Chambers *USA: America's Leading Lawyers for Business*, Native American Law, National, 2007, 2014 & 2015; Band One Ranking, 2011-2012; Distinguished Service Award, Indian Arts and Crafts Board, US Department of the Interior, 2002; Pro Bono Partner of the Year Award, 2001; Commendation from US Attorney, Western District of Michigan, for work related to settlement of *U.S. v. Michigan* treaty rights dispute, 2000; US Department of Justice, Environment and Natural Resources Division, Special Commendation for work related to treaty-based land claim and fishing rights cases, 1999.

SICKEY, DAVID (Coushatta)
(tribal chairperson)
Affiliation & Address: Vice Chairperson, Coushatta Tribe of Louisiana, Box 818, Elton, LA 70532 (337) 584-2261.

SICKEY, ERNEST
(health center director)
Affiliation: Dallas Inter-Tribal Council Health Center, 209 E. Jefferson, Dallas, TX 75203 (214) 941-1050.

SICKEY, KEVIN (Coushatta)
(tribal chairperson)
Affiliation & Address: Chairperson, Coushatta Tribe of Louisiana, Box 818, Elton, LA 70532 (337) 584-2261.

SIDNEY, IVAN (Hopi)
(former tribal chairperson)
Affiliation: Hopi Tribal Council, P.O. Box 123, Kykotsmovi, AZ 86039 (602) 734-2445.

SIERRA, JOSE, JR. (Tigua)
(tribal Aguacil)
Affiliation: Ysleta Del Sur Pueblo, P.O. Box 17579, El Paso, TX 79907 (915) 859-8053. Website: www.ysletadelsurpueblo.org.

SIESTREEM, SARA (Hanis Coos) 1976-
(artist; Indian college instructor)
Born & raised in the Umpqua River Valley in South Western Oregon. *Education*: Phi Kappa Phi from Portland State University in 2005. She earned an MFA with distinction from Pratt Art Institute in 2007. She is a Master Artist, Educator, and Theorist. *Affiliation & Address*: Art Instructor, Natve American Studies, Indigenous Nations Studies, P.O. Box 751, Portland, OR 97207 (503) 725-9066. E-mail: ssiiiestreem@pdx.edu. Her art work is represented Augen Gallery in Portland. Her artwork has been on display in many museums around the country and is in many prestigious private and public collections. She now lives and works exclusively in the arts in Portland, Oregon.

SIGALA, SANDRA (Pomo)
(tribal chairperson)
Affiliation: Hopland Tribe, P.O. Box 610, Hopland, CA 95449 (707) 744-1647.

SIGO, CHARLES (Suquamish)
(museum curator)
Affiliation: Suquamish Museum, P.O. Box 498, Suquamish, WA 98392 (206) 598-3311.

SILAS, BERKMAN (Athapascan)
(village chief)
Affiliation: Minto Village Council, Box 26, Minto, AK 99758 (907) 798-7112.

SILAS, PAMELA M. (Menominee/Oneida of Wisconsin)
(executive director)
Affiliation & Address: Executive Director, Native American Journalists Association (NAJA), University of Oklahoma, Gaylord College, 395 W. Lindsey St., Norman, OK 73019 (405) 325-1649. E-mail: pamelasilas@naja.com. Pamela is a Certified Association Executive (CAE), a credential held by only 5% of the association management field. Prior to forming her own association management company, Pam was CEO of American Indian Science & Engineering Society's national operation and AISES Publishing, Inc.; served as executive director for Metropolitan Tenants Organization, Chicago, IL.

SILEX, EDGAR (Tiqua del Sur) 1958-
(creative writing instructor/poet, author)
Born March 31, 1958, El Paso, Tex. *Education*: University of Maryland, MFA, 1994. *Affiliation*: The Cafe Workshops, Baltimore, MD. *Membership*: Native American Student Union of U. of Maryland. *Biographical source*: Washington Post article, 6/15/93. *Published works*: Even the Dead Have Memories (New Sins Press); Through All the Displacements (Curbstone Press, 1995).

SILLIBOY, ROSELLA (Micmac)
(craftsperson)
Affiliation: Owner, Three Feathers Native baskets, P.O. Box 644, Houlton, ME 04730 (207) 532-0862. *Products*: Traditional brown ash utility and work baskets made by Micmac tribal members.

SILVAS, VICTOR (Yokut)
(tribal administrator)
Affiliation & Address: Administrator, Tule River Tribe, P.O. Box 589, Porterville, CA 93258 (559) 781-4271 ext. 1039.

SILVERBIRD, J. REUBEN (Nedhni Apache/Cherokee) 1940-
(musician, singer & performer; peace ambassador)
Born July 27, 1940, Placentia, Calif. Education: St. Michaels College (two years). Website: www.reubensilverbird.com. *Affiliation*: President, Silverbird Productions (Music, Film, Stage & TV), Orlando, FL, 1984-. *Other professional post*: He travels with The Universal Peace Federation. He is attached to the United Nations as an NGO (Non-Governmental Organization); he is only one of the countless women and men Ambassadors who speak on behalf of "Love and Peace throughout the world today." *Military service*: U.S. Army (two years) Special Services (Master Sergeant) taught electronics (produced & appeared in show that toured for Special Services). Certificate of Achievement for teaching electronics. *Community activities*: Assn on American Indian Affairs, NYC; American Indian College Fund, NYC; American Indian Community House, NYC. *Memberships*: American Society of Composers & Publishers; Screen Actors Guild; Actor's Equity Assn; New York Screen Writer's Assn. *Awards, honors*: Owned & operated NYC 1st Native American restaurant, 1984-87. *Interests*: Singing tour Asia (three times); lectures on Native America.

SILVERMAN, GREGORY (Mohegan)
(associate professor of law & faculty director)
Education: Vassar College, BA, 1978; Graduate Fellow Massachusetts Institute of Technology, 1978-79; Columbia University, MA, 1984, M.Phil, 1991, Columbia Law School, JD, 1987. *Affiliation & Address*: Associate Professor of Law & Faculty Director, Center for Indian Law & Policy, Seattle University School of Law, Sullivan Hall 115, 901 12th Ave., P.O. Box 222000, Seattle, WA 98122 (206) 398-4018; E-mail: gmsilver@seattleu.edu. He joined the faculty in 1999. In addition to being a tenured member of the law faculty, for the past 15 years, Professor Silverman has been an active tribal judge sitting as an appellate justice on tribal courts throughout the Pacific Northwest with the Northwest Intertribal Court System. Two judicial opinions authored by Judge Silverman have been included in the leading casebook on American Indian Tribal Law. One opinion concerned land use and zoning law, which he wrote while sitting as a justice on the Court of Appeals of the Tulalip Tribes of Washington. The second opinion, which he penned while sitting as a justice on the Court of Appeals of the Puyallup Tribe of Indians, dealt with the Tribal constitutional right of privacy in the context of drug testing Tribal shellfish divers. Since joining the faculty of Seattle University School of Law in 1999, Professor Silverman has taught courses on Property Law, Tribal Law, Intellectual Property, the Law of Trade Secrets, Video Game Law, and the Law of Electronic Commerce as well as seminars on various topics in jurisprudence and legal theory, including Game Theory & the Law, Neuroscience & the Law, Postmodern Legal Theory, and Rethinking Legal Responsibility in the Age of

Neuroscience. He has written two books on electronic commerce, intellectual property and the Internet as well as articles on technology, the law of privacy & the judicial system, jurisprudence, and legal education. *Past professional posts*: Professor Silverman was managing partner for the Cape Cod-area law firm of Kearney & Silverman from 1991-97, where he practiced admiralty defense, corporate, intellectual property, estate planning, and civil litigation, and played a significant role in the largest fisheries fraud litigation in American history, with a focus on land use, fisheries and environmental law He was a Bigelow Fellow and lecturer in law at the University of Chicago School of Law from 1997-99. A former Max Rheinstein Research Fellow and a visiting legal scholar for two years at the Universität Erlangen-Nürnberg in Germany, Professor Silverman was a summer associate for the Manhattan law firm of Cahill, Gordon & Reindel. He is an enrolled member of the Mohegan Tribe of Indians of Connecticut. *Published works*: Coauthored two books, *Internet Commerce, The Emerging Legal Framework*, and *Intellectual Property and the Internet*.

SILVERSMITH, SHIRLEE
 (educator; director)
Education: Brigham Young University, BS (Secondary Education); Arizona State University, MEd (Education). *Affiliation & Address*: Director (2011-present), Utah Division of Indian Affairs, 300 S. Rio Grande St., Salt Lake City, UT 84101 (801) 245-7209. E-mail: ssilversmith@utah.gov. *Past professional posts*: Learning For Life Director (2007-11), UT National Parks Council. A career development program for youth, which included outreach programs for Tribal Nations; Indian Education Specialist (1987-2007), UT State Office of Education. She directed outreach efforts & training for improved relations with Tribal Nations & educators.

SILVERTHORNE, JOYCE A. (Confederated Salish & Kootenai)
 (director of Indian education)
Education: University of Montana, BA, 1977, MA (Secondary Education), 1990; Gonzaga University, DEd, 2004. *Affiliation & Address*: Director (2011-present), Office of Indian Education, U.S. Department of Education, Rm. 3W200, Federal Office Bldg. 6, 400 Maryland Ave. SW, Washington, DC 20202 (202) 260-3774. *Past professional posts*: Taught at Two River Eagle School and taught & worked as a manager of the bilingual education personnel training program at Salish Kootenai College; Education Coordinator (1999-2007), Confederated Salish & Kootenai Tribes, Pablo, MT; Montana Education Superintendent, 2008-11. *Awards, honors*: 2008 Tribal Education Department National Assembly (TEDNA) Director of the Year; 2004 National Indian Education Association Educator (NIEA) of the Year.

SILVEY, LE ANNE E. (Little Traverse Bay Bands of Odawa)
 (associate professor of American Indian studies)
Education: Michigan State University, PhD, 1997. *Affiliation & Address*: Director of American Indian Studies Program & Associate Professor of Human Development & Family Studies, Dept. of Family & Child Ecology, Michigan State University, 414 Baker Hall, East Lansing, MI 48824 (517) 432-2193. E-mail: silveyle@msu.edu. *Research Interest*: Health disparities among American Indians, obesity & weight-related lifestyle issues with American Indian youth, beliefs & values of American Indians, individual & family development among American Indians, & Indian child welfare. *Past professional posts*: Executive director, Michigan Indian Child Welfare Agency, Sault Ste. Marie, MI.

SIMAS, ROSY (Seneca)
 (choreographer)
Affiliation & Address: Blue Heron Bodywork, 2721 East 42nd St., Minneapolis, MN 55406 (612) 719-9605. E-mail: dance@rosysimas.com. Dance workshops. *Other professional posts*: Rosy specializes in alignment/body re-education, massage, shiatsu, and global somatics.

SIMEON, TRACY (Eskimo)
 (Alaskan village chairperson)
Affiliation & Address: Chairperson, Native Village of Chuathbaluk, P.O. Box CHU, Chuathbaluk, AK 99557 (907) 467-4313.

SIMEONOFF, HELEN J. (Sugpiaq)
 (artist; art studio owner)
Born in Kodiak, AK. *Affiliation*: Alaska Watercolor, 3212 West 30th Ave., Anchorage, AK 99517 (907) 248-0454. Website: www.alaskawatercolor.com E-mail: helen.simeonoff@ak.net. Her prints and originals are sold at the Alaska Native heritage center in Anchorage, AK, and Alutiiq Museum in Kodiak. *Awards, honors*: Helen is an Alaskan Native holding a Silver Hand Certificate from the State of AK.

SIMMERMEYER, JOHN (Coharie Tuscarora)
 (legislative analyst for law firm)
Education: Cornell University, BA, 2007; Michigan State University College of Law, JD (Certificate in Indigenous Law and Policy), 2014. *Affiliation & Address*:

Legislative Analyst, Rosette, LLP, 1100 H St. NW, Suite 400, Washington, DC 20005 (202) 652-0579. E-mail: jsimermeyer@rosettelaw.com. John's focus at Rosette, LLP centers on assisting firm clients with Congressional and Agency outreach. His experience in navigating both the legislative process as well as agency procedures has helped clients to achieve success on a number of issues ranging from land into trust, protection of sacred sites, taxation, tribal healthcare, & the financial services sector. At Cornell John received a degree in City & Regional Planning, & focused his work on Community and Economic Development in Indian Country. John's federal work experience includes the Department of the Interior (DOI)-Office of the Solicitor General – Departmental Ethics and the National Indian Gaming Commission (NIGC) Office of General Counsel in Washington D.C. During his time at DOI, John researched federal ethics laws & gave analysis on their application & enforcement against the Department's ethics policy. Specifically John researched & gave analysis on issues involving the HATCH Act and employee political activities. While at the NIGC, John worked closely with the Chairman & senior attorneys to review amendments to tribal gaming ordinances and provided research and analysis on matters in tribal gaming that pertained to the Indian Gaming Regulatory Act & NIGC regulations. Prior to his legal studies, John worked with the Baltimore American Indian Center (BAIC) and the National Congress of American Indians (NCAI) in Washington D.C. At the BAIC John served as executive director of the organization. John managed the operation of the Center's community health outreach initiatives and acted as a community liaison to local, state, and private sector leadership. At NCAI John worked with the legislative staff and was an advocate to local, state, and federal lawmakers on behalf of tribal clients in the area of homeland security, public safety, law enforcement, & emergency management. He is nootlicensed to practice law.

SIMEROTH, BARBARA (*Little Star*) (Cherokee)
 (tribal chief)
Affiliation: Cherokees of California, P.O. Box 2372, Marysville, CA 95901 (530) 633-4038.

SIMMONS, JOHN (Nisqually)
 (tribal chairperson)
Affiliation: Nisqually Indian Community, 4820 She-Nah-Num Dr. SE, Olympia, WA 98513 (360) 456-5221.

SIMMONS, VICKIE (Southern Paiute)
 (tribal vice chairperson)
Affiliation & Address: Vice Chairperson, Moapa Band of Paiute Indians, P.O. Box 340, Moapa, NV 89025 (702) 865-2787. E-mail: vickiesimmons@gmail.com

SIMMS, RUSSELL
 (executive director)
Affiliation: Council of Three Rivers American Indian Center, Inc., Rt. 2, Box 247-A, Dorseyville, PA 15238 (412) 782-4457. *Other professional post*: Editor, The Singing Winds Newsletter.

SIMON, FRANKLIN (Huslia Athabascan)
 (AK village council chief)
Affiliation: Huslia Village Council, P.O. Box 45010, Hughes, AK 99745 (907) 899-2206.

SIMON, HAROLD (Athapascan)
 (Alaskan village president)
Affiliation: Native Village of Stevens, P.O. Box 74012, Stevens Village, AK 99774 (907) 478-7228.

SIMON, JENNIFER (Cheyenne River Lakota)
 (American Indian student services director)
Education: Augsburg College, BA & MA. *Affiliation & Address*: Director, American Indian Student Services Program, American Indian Studies Deparrment, CB 122, Minneapolis, MN 55454 (612) 330-1144. E-mail: simonj@augsburg.edu. Jennifer started with Augsburg College in 2007.

SIMON, JOSE, III (Pomo)
 (rancheria chairperson)
Affiliation & Address:: Chairperson, Middletown Rancheria, 22223 Hwy. 29, Middletown, CA 95461 (707) 987-3670.

SIMON, LUCAS (Pomo)
 (former tribal chairperson)
Affiliation: Middletown Rancheria, P.O. Box 292, Middletown, CA 95461.

SIMON, LINCOLN (Eskimo)
 (village president)
Affiliation: Native Village of White Mountain, P.O. Box 84082, White Mountain, AK 99784 (907) 638-3651.

SIMON, RALPH (Yurok)
(tribal executive director)
Education: University of Tulsa College of Law, J.D., 1981. *Address & Affiliation*: Yurok Tribe, P.O. Box 1027, Klamath, CA 95548 (707) 482-1350. *Past professional post*: Executive Director, California Nations Indian Gaming Association, Sacramento, CA.

SIMPSON, AUDRA (Mohawk) 1969-
(assistant professor)
Born July 12, 1969, Brooklyn, N.Y. *Education*: Concordia University, BA; McGill University, MA, PhD (Anthropology). *Principal occupation*: Assistant professor of Anthropology & American Indian Studies. *Address & Affiliation*: 208 McGraw, Dept. of Anthropology, Cornell University, Ithaca, NY 14853 (607) 255-6783. E-Mail: as447@cornell.edu. *Memberships*: American Anthropological Assn; Society for Cultural Anthropology; Assn for Political & Legal Anthropology; American Studies Assn; Canadian Anthropology Society; American Political Science Assn. *Published works*: Article - "Paths Toward a Mohawk Nation: Narratives of Citizenship & Nationhood in Kahnawake" Duncan Ivison, Paul Patton & Will Sanders (eds.). Political Theory & the Rights of Indigenous Peoples (Cambridge University Press, pp: 113-136, 2000).

SIMPSON, SCOTTY, JR. (Ponca)
(tribal vice chairperson)
Affiliation & Address: Vice Chairperson, Ponca Tribe of Oklahoma, 20 White Eagle Dr., Ponca City, OK 74601 (580) 762-8104. E-mail: ssimpson@ponca.com.

SINCLAIR, JOHN (Little Shell Chippewa)
(former tribal chairperson)
Affiliation & Address: Former Chairperson, Little Shell Tribe of Chippewa Indians, P.O. Box 1384, Great Falls, MT 59403 (406) 452-2892.

SINEWAY, CARLA (Ojibwa)
(Indian college president)
Education: Central Michigan University, BS (Sociology/Social Work), 1988, MS (Professional Counseling), 1995; Capella University, MS (Education), 2010. *Affiliation & Address*: President, Saginaw Chippewa Tribal College, 2274 Enterprise Dr., Mt. Pleasant, MI 48858 (989) 775-4123. E-mail: csineway@sagchip.org

SINGEL, WENONA T. (Little Traverse Bay Bands of Odawa)
(associate professor of law)
Education: Harvard University, BA, 1995, JD, 1999. *Affiliation & Address*: Associate Professor of Law, Michigan State University College of Law, 648 N. Shaw Lane Rm. 405A Law College Bldg., East Lansing, MI 48824 (517) 432-6915. E-mail: singel@law.msu.edu. *Other professional posts*: Associate director, Indigenous Law & Policy Center, Michigan State University College of Law, East Lansing, MI; Chief Appellate Judge, Little Traverse Bay Bands of Odawa Indians; Of Council, Kanji & Katzen, PLLC, Ann Arbor, MI (specializes in representing tribes in Indian law matters); In her time with Kanji & Katzen, Singel served as general counsel to the tribally-owned Grand Traverse Resort, participated in the Indian gaming litigation of *Grand Traverse Band of Ottawa and Chippewa Indians v. U.S. Attorney for the Western District of Michigan*, negotiated a tribal-state omnibus tax agreement & performed land claims research. Professor Singel has taught Federal Indian Law, Advanced Topics in Indian Law, Natural Resources Law and an experiential learning class in which students complete research and writing assignments for tribal governments and judiciaries. External Reviewer for the American Indian Law Review. *Past professional post*: Assistant Professor, University of North Dakota School of Law, Grand Forks, ND. *Membership*: Secretary, National Native American Bar Association. *Awards, honors*: Presidential appointee with the U.S. Senate Confirmation, Advisory Board of the St. Lawrence Seaway Develoment Corporation (confirmed on March 29, 2012); elected member of the American Law Institute (ALI). *Published works*: "Labor Relations & Tribal Self Governance," published in the *North Dakota Law Review* in 2004, "Power, Authority & Tribal Property" co-authored with Matthew L.M. Fletcher & published in the *Tulsa Law Review* in 2005, & "Cultural Sovereignty & Transplanted Law: Tensions in Indigenous Self-Rule," forthcoming in the *Kansas Journal of Law and Public Policy*.

SINGER, BEVERLY R. (Tewa/Dine')
(professor of anthropology & Native American studies)
Born in Santa Clara Pueblo, N.M. *Education*: College of Santa Fe, BA, 1975; University of Chicago, MA, 1977; The Anthropology Film Center, Santa Fe, NM (Documentary Filmmaking Certificate, 1984); University of New Mexico, PhD, 1996. *Dissertation*: "Film & Video Made By Native Americans: A Cultural Examination of Native American Participation in Film & Video Production." *Affiliations & Address*: Associate Professor of Anthropology & Native American Studies, University Regents Lecturer, Native American Studies (NAS) Dept., University of New Mexico, Mesa Vista 3080, Albuquerque, NM 87131 (505) 277-3027. E-mail: mesa@unm.edu; director, The Institute of American Indian

Research, University of New Mexico, Albuquerque, NM, 2000-present. *Other professional posts*: Executive board member, Independent Television Service (ITVS). *Research Interests*: Beverly is an award-winning documentary video producer whose concern is indigenous community wellness. She is active in producing & writing about indigenous films. Critical studies of images & narratives produced & written by indigenous peoples. *Video productions*: Oku P'in, Alfonso Ortiz, 1939-1997, 19-minute video (Alfonso Ortiz Center for Intercultural Studies, UNM, 2000); Desert Rainwater Harvesting, 24-minute video (UNM & Woodrow Wilson Foundation, 2002); Who We Are, ten min. orientation film for the National Museum of the American Indian, Smithsonian Institution, Washington, DC; The Unveiling of Po'Pay Statue, ten minute video (Po'Pay Commemoration Symposium, UNM, 2005); Decolonized Education at the University of New Mexico, 24-minute video (Native American Studies, UNM, 2006); The Answer Lie Within: The Institute of American Indian Arts in Southern Africa, 28-minute video (Kellogg Foundation & IAIA, 2007). *Published work*: Wiping the War Paint Off the Lens: Native American Film & Video (University of Minnesota Press, 2001).

SINGER, MICHELLE J. (Navajo-Dine')
(communications coordinator)
Education: University of Oregon, BS (Science). *Affiliation & Address*: Communication Coordinator, One Sky Center, Oregon Health Sciences University, 3181 SW Sam Jackson Park Rd., GH 151, Portland, OR 97239 (503) 494-3703. *Other professional post*: Instructor, member of Policy Board, The Institute for Tribal Government, Portland State U., Portland, OR. *Past professional post*: Michelle spent seven years in the U.S. Senate as a policy advisor to Senate Democratic Leader, Tom Daschle (DSD), Senate Committee on Indian Affairs Chairperson, Ben Nighthorse Campbell (R-CO), & Senator Ron Wyden (D-OR). She is one of the few American Indian professionals who have worked on Capitol Hill for both political parties. Michelle's professional and personal background is strongly rooted in Indian education, Indian health, and Indian affairs. She has worked with the American Indian Higher Education Consortium in Alexandria, Virginia; Northwest Indian College on the Lummi Indian Reservation in Bellingham, Washington; and, Salish Kootenai College on the Flathead Indian Reservation in Pablo, Montana. Michelle also worked for the Bureau of Indian Affairs at Chemawa Indian School, an off-reservation Bureau of Indian Affairs-operated boarding school, in Salem, Oregon.

SIROIS, JOHN E. (Okanagan/Wenatchi)
(former tribal chairperson; tribal councilmember)
Affiliation & Address: Councilmember, Colville Business Council, P.O. Box 150, Nespelem, WA 99155 E-mail: john.sirois@colvilletribes.com. *Other professional post*: Board Chair, Indian Land Tenure Foundation, Little Canada, MN. *Past professional posts*: Assistant director of Undergraduate Admissions & acting director of the Native American Program at Dartmouth College; research assistant for Gates Foundation library programs.

SISCO, DENNIS (Seneca-Cayuga of Oklahoma)
(tribal executive director)
Affiliation & Address: Executive Director, Seneca-Cayuga Tribe of Oklahoma, P.O. Box 1283, Miami, OK 74355 (918) 542-6609. *Past professional post*: Supt., Miami Agency, Bureau of Indian Affairs, Miami, OK.

SISTO, EARL DEAN (San Carlos Apache)
(education, artist)
Affiliation: Native American Student Programs, 224 Costo Hall, University of California, Riverside, CA 92521, 1977-present (909) 787-4143. E-Mail: sisto@ucracl.ucr.edu. *Other professional post*: Na Chee, 1995-present. *Community activities*: San Bernardino/Riverside American Indian Council.

SIXKILLER, JESSE (Cherokee)
(attorney; Indian gaming)
Education: Dartmouth College, BA, 2006; University of Arizona, JD, 2010. *Affiliation & Address*: Associate, Dorsey & Whitney LLP, Corporate Group & Indian & Gaming Practice, 50 S. Sixth St., Suite 1500, Minneapolis, MN 55402 (612) 492-6182. E-mail: sixkiller.jesse@dorsey.com, Jesse is a member of the Corporate group and is also an active member of the Indian & Gaming practice group where he provides counsel in connection with various matters involving Indian tribes, including business reorganizations, financings secured by casino & other business assets, and tribal & corporate governance matters. *Awards, honors*: MSBA North Star Lawyer, 2013 and 2014.

SKEETER, ANDREW (Yuchi)
(tribal chairperson)
Affiliation & Address: Chairperson, Euchee (Yuchi) Tribe of Indians, P.O. Box 10, Sapulpa, OK 74067 (918) 224-3605.

SKEETER, CARMELITA WAMEGO (Citizen Potawatomi)
(chief executive officer)
Affiliation & Address: Chief Executive Officer (1989-present), Indian Health Care Resource Center of Tulsa, 550 S. Peoria Ave., Tulsa, OK 74120 (918)

588-1900. Carmelita was hired by IHCRC in 1976 as one of four original employees, when she helped survey residents to assess health needs of the local urban Indian population. She was Clinic Adminsitrator until 1989.

SKELTON, JUDY BLUEHORSE (Nez Perce/Cherokee)
(senior instructor of education & Indigenous Nations Studies)
Education: Portland State University, MA (Educational Leadership and Policy's, Leadership in Ecology, Culture & Learning Program). *Affiliation & Address*: Senior Instructor, Educational Leadership & Policy, University Studies & School of Education (ELP), 504 ED Bldg., Room 145, Potland State University, Portland, OR 97207 (503) 725-4716. E-mail: judyblue@pdx.edu. *Other professional post*: Professor, Indigenous Nations Studies, Portland, OR. *Teaching Interests*: Environmental education through Native American lenses. *Past professional posts*: Judy worked with federal and state Indian Education programs throughout the Northwest for 18 years, creating cultural activities focusing on traditional & contemporary uses of native plants for food, medicine, ceremony, and healthy lifeways. Judy is author of six collections of essays for teachers, including Native America: A Sustainable Culture (1999), and Lewis & Clark Through Native American Eyes (2003); she wrote & recorded 24 segments on Health & Healing and Sacred Landscapes for Wisdom of the Elders radio programs, airing on Public Broadcasting and AIROS (American Indian Radio on Satellite). As Senior Instructor, Judy is full-time faculty in Indigenous Nations Studies at Portland State University, teaching Intro to Native American Studies, Environmental Sustainability – Indigenous Practices, Indigenous Gardens & Food Justice, and Indigenous Women Leaders. She received the Oregon Indian Education Association's Award for Outstanding Indian Educator in 2006 and serves on the boards of the Urban Greenspaces Institute, Portland Parks, and the Native American Community Advisory Council. Collaborative work includes the Confederated Tribes of Grand Ronde, the Confederated Tribes of Siletz Indians, the Native American Youth and Family Center (NAYA) & Wisdom of the Elders, Inc., integrating permaculture principles with traditional ecological knowledge to address Food Sovereignty/ Justice and reclaim the urban forest.

SKENANDORE, FRANCIS R. (Oneida)
(attorney)
Affiliation: Oneida Tribe, P.O. Box 129, Oneida, WI 54155; Associate Justice, Prairie Band Potawatomi Nation Appelate Court, 15498 K Rd., Mayetta, KS 66509 (866) 966-2242 or (785) 966-2242. E-mail: tribalcourt@pbpnation.org.

SKENANDORE, JUDY (Oneida)
(health center director)
Affiliation: Oneida Comunity Health Center, P.O. Box 365, Oneida, WI 54155 (414) 869-2711.

SKENANDORE-HOLTZ, KELLY (Oneida of Wisconsin)
(training & development manager)
Education: Holds a baccalaureate degree in Communicative Disorders and a Master's degree in Management & Organizational Behavior. *Affiliation & Address*: Training & Development Manager, Oneida Casino, 2100 Airport Dr., Green Bay, WI 54313 (920) 494-4500. *Other professional posts*: Member, National Strategy Management Team for the Oneida Nation; adjunct faculty, The Falmouth Institute, Fairfax, VA.

SKENANDORE, KEVIN (Navajo)
(BIA education administrator)
Affiliation: Northern Pueblos Agency, Bureau of Indian Affairs, P.O. Box 4269, Fairview Station, Espanola, NM 87533 (505) 753-1465.

SKENANDORE, PAUL A. (*Shenandoah*) (*Scan doa*) (Oneida) 1939-
(editor/publisher, bookstore owner)
Born January 21, 1939, Kaukauna, Wisc. *Education*: High school. Address: 736 W. Oklahoma St., Appleton, WI 54914 (920) 832-9525. *Affiliations*: Editor & publisher of "Shenandoah," the monthly Oneida newsletter, 1973-; owner/operator, Shenandoah Bookstore, Appleton, WI, 1983-. *Military service*: U.S. Army, 1962-1964 (E-4 Sergeant). *Interests*: "To educate Native peoples on their rights as independent nations and peoples; to educate all peoples of the world on the spiritual existence of all societies and our responsibility to said; to take the U.S. (Government) to World Court and charging them with trespass and genocide, and to have aboriginal nations assume their correct place on Great Turtle Island." *Published works*: Newsletter - Shenandoah; and other native newsletters. I have written by the name of Skenandoah, Shenandoah, or Scan doa."

SKIBINE, ALEXANDER TALLCHIEF (Osage)
(attorney; professor of law)
Education: Northwestern University, JD. *Affiliation & Address*: Professor of Law, University of Utah S.J. Quinney College of Law, Salt Lake City, UT 84112 (801) 581-4177. *Other professional post*: Visiting professor, Indian Law Summer Program, Lewis & Clark College Law School, Portland, OR. *Past professional post*: Attorney for the Institute for the Development of the Interior,

and deputy counsel for the congressional committee on Interior & Insular Affairs. *Membership*: Native American Bar Association (secretary).

SKIBINE, GEORGE (Osage)
(attorney)
Education: University of Minnesota Law School, 1977, JD; University of Chicago, 1974, BA, Economics. *Affiliation & Address*: Counsel, Dentons LLP, Public Policy and Regulation & Native American Law & Policy Practice, 1301 K St., NW, Washington, DC 20005 (202) 408-8665. E-mail: george.skibine@ dentons.com. George has extensive knowledge of all aspects of the Indian Gaming Regulatory Act, especially in the areas of class III gaming compacts, revenue allocation plans for the distribution of per capita payments and provisions pertaining to gaming on newly acquired lands. In addition, George has been extensively involved in the federal acknowledge-ment process, contracting under the Indian Self-Determination Act, compacting under the Tribal Self-Governance Act, the land-into-trust process & tribal government matters. *Past affiliations*: Prior to joining Dentons, he spent his career with the US Department of the Interior in various capacities, including serving as Deputy Associate Solicitor for Indian Affairs, Director of the Office of Indian Gaming, Deputy Assistant Secretary for Policy and Economic Development (Indian Affairs), Acting Assistant Secretary for Indian Affairs, Acting Chairman of the National Indian Gaming Commission & Acting Principal Deputy Assistant Secretary for Indian Affairs. Most recently he served as the Deputy Assistant Secretary–Management (Indian Affairs), where he was responsible for ensuring that all Indian Affairs organizations were in compliance with federal laws and regulations related to employment, and where he oversaw the development of the Indian Affairs yearly budget, audits, information technology, construction and facilities program, and financial management. *Awards, honors*: Meritorious Service Award, 2004; Silver Executive Leadership Award, 2008; Gold Executive Leadership Award, 2009; Best Lawyers ranking, 2014 & 2016; Ranked, *Chambers USA*, Native American Law, National, 2015

SKIBY, LORI BEAR (Goshute)
(tribal chairperson)
Affiliation & Address: Chairperson, Skull Valley Band of Goshute Indians, 1198 N. Main St., Tooele, UT 84029 (435) 882-4532.

SKIDMORE, ANN (White Mountain Apache)
(museum store manager)
Affiliation: Manager, Nohwike Bagoa: House of Our Footprints Museum Shop, P.O. Box 507, Fort Apache, AZ 85926 (928) 338-4625.

SKRELUNAS, TONY (Navajo)
(economic program director)
Education: Northern Arizona University, BA & MBA. *Affiliation & Address*: Native American Program Director (2003-present), Grand Canyon Trust, 2601 N. Fort Valley Rd., Flagstaff, AZ 86001 (928) 774-7488. E-mail: tonyskrelunas @gmail.com. *Other professional posts*: Partner, Southwest Tradition Log Homes; board president, Navajo Nation Shopping Centers, Inc. (realty management company); chairperson, Native American Bank, Denver, CO; chairperson, Native American Community Development Corporation; board member, Coconino County Sustainable Development Initiative. *Past professional posts*: Executive Director, Navajo Nation Economic Development Division & Government Development Office (12 years); partner, Horizon Springs Partnership.

SKYHAWK, SONNY
(executive director)
Affiliation: American Indians in Film, 65 N. Alien Ave., Suite 105, Pasadena, CA 91106 (818) 578-0344.

SLADE, LYNN H. 1948-
(attorney, Federal Indian law)
Born January 29, 1948, Santa Fe, N.M. *Education*: University of New Mexico, BA, 1973, Law School, JD, 1976. *Principal occupation*: Attorney with substantial experience in American Indian law. *Affiliation & Address*: Co-Shareholder & Co-Chairperson, Native American Law Practice Group, Modrall Sperling Lawyers, P.O. Box 2168, Albuquerque, NM 87103 (505) 848-1828. E-mail: lynn.slade@modrall.com. Lynn serves clients' needs addressing Federal Indian law and Native American law, energy, natural resources, environmental law, project development, complex litigation and transactions for over 30 years. In his Indian law practice, Lynn advises and counsels natural resource and energy developers, financial institutions, utilities, and other businesses in transactions & project development, including extensive involvement with renewable energy projects. He also leads litigation teams in disputes concerning resource development, environmental regulation and business activities on Indian lands. On the litigation side, he has been involved in federal, state, and tribal trial and appellate courts in numerous states, providing counsel in complex mediations & arbitrations. *Awards, honors*: He received national recognition "as a market leader in this field" from *Chambers USA* in Native American Law. For more than twenty-five years, he has been listed

by*Best Lawyers in America®,* and named Lawyer of the Year – Albuquerque in multiple areas: Oil and Gas Law, 2014; Native American Law, 2012; Natural Resources Law, 2012; Energy Law, 2011. In addition, he has received recognition from *Southwest Super Lawyers®,* selected as one of the Top 25 New Mexico Super Lawyers; from *Benchmark Litigation* as a local Litigation Star; and *New Mexico Business Weekly,* Best of the Bar in Native American Law, 2009. Lynn has an AV® rating from *Martindale-Hubbell,* based on a peer review. Lynn serves as Co-Chair of the firm's Native American/Federal Indian Law Practice and is a member of the Natural Resources and Environment; Oil, Gas & Midstream; and Renewable Energy Practice Groups. *Community activities*: Chairperson (1991-92), Committee on Native American Natural Resources, American Bar Association. *Memberships*: American Bar Association; American Indian Bar Association; State Bar of New Mexico (Natural Resource Section Chair); Indian Law Section (Board of Directors). *Awards, honors*: Best Lawyers in America, 1989-90, 1991-92 Editions. *Interests*: "Representation of businesses doing business on Indian lands; litigation & advice concerning Indian law and Indian lands law." Published work: article, "Coal Surface Mining on Indian Lands: Checkerboard or Crazy Quilt," (Rocky Mountain Mineral Law Foundation, 1989); article, "Puzzling Powers: Overlapping Jurisdictions of Indian Tribes, the Federal, State, & Local Governments in Development of Natural Resources in Indian Country," (42 Rocky Mountain Mineral Law Inst. 11-1 (1996).

SLATTERY, MICO (Saginaw Chippewa)
(professor of Native American studies)
Education: Colorado State University, BA, 1990; Univefrsity of Colorado-Boulder, MA (Religious Studies), 1994; Michigan State University, PhD (American Studies), 2008. *Affiliation & Address*: Professor of Native American Studies, Saginaw Chippewa Tribal College, 2274 Enterprise Dr., Mount Pleasant, MI 48858 (989) 775-4123. E-mail: slattery.mico@sagchip.edu.

SLEDD, JOHN
(attorney; Of counsel, Indian law)
Education: University of Montana, BS (Forestry), 1979; University of California, Berkeley, School of Law, JD, 1982. *Affiliation & Address*: Of Counsel, Kanji & Katzen, PLLC, 401 2ⁿᵈ St. S., Suite 700, Seattle, WA 98104 (206) 344-8100. E-mail: jsledd@kanjikatzen.com. *Areas of Concentration*: Federal litigation; Treaty rights; Allotted lands; Land use and environment. *Community Service*: Associate Justice, Tulalip Tribes Court of Appeals, 2004-present. *Past professional posts*: John was Director of Litigation, from 1986-1989, at DNA People's Legal Services, Inc., where he served as General Counsel to the nation's largest Indian legal services program and supervisor of attorney staff in eight offices in three states.Before becoming Director of Litigation at DNA, John served as Deputy Director of Litigation, Managing Attorney, and Attorney, from 1982-1986, where his practice emphasized consumer, disability, and land cases, including claims by Indian allotment owners for damages from uranium contamination and a class action to establish allotment owners' title to coal and other minerals under their land. John served as Tribal Attorney for the Suquamish Tribe, in Suquamish, Washington, from 1989-1999, where he was General Counsel, the supervisor of the legal department, the prosecutor and the ICW presenting officer. His practice emphasized litigation & negotiations over treaty rights, gaming, jurisdiction, and other matters. He also obtained a $950,000 judgment for BIA denial of a tribal 638 contract proposal & represented the Tribe in a $24 million settlement over pollution by Seattle city sewers. From 1999-2004, John was the Director of the Native American Project of Evergreen Legal Services in Seattle, Washington. As Director he supervised a statewide project that provided free civil legal services to low income Indian individuals. He also conducted litigation & Congressional & administrative advocacy that emphasized allotted land, Indian probate, and breach of trust claims. From 2004-2006, John was the Senior Attorney for the Native American Unit of the Northwest Justice Project in Seattle, Washington, a statewide project that provided free legal services to low income Indian individuals. John also developed tribal court public defender & Indian will drafting projects. Chair, Indian Law Section, Washington State Bar Association, 1994; Board Member, Indian Law Support Center at Native American Rights Fund, 1986-1989. *Awards & Honors*: President's Award, Northwest Indian Bar Association, 2009; Pierce-Hickerson Award, National Association of Indian Legal Services, 2004.

SLEEPER-SMITH, SUSAN
(professor of history; director, American Indian Studies Consortium)
Affiliation & Address: Associate Professor of History, American Indian Studies Program, Michigan State University & Director of the CIC-American Indian Studies Consortium, 343 Old Horticulture, East Lansing, MI 48824 (517) 432-2193. E-mail: sleepers@msu.edu. She received a 2002-2003 research fellowship at the Newberry Library in Chicago *Teaching interests*: 18th & 19th century U.S. History, Native American History & Women's History. Published works: Several recent publications on First Nations peoples and the fur trade in the Great Lakes areas and elsewhere. Her book *Indian Women and French Men: Rethinking Cultural Encounter in the Western Great Lakes,* published in 2002.

SLICKPOO, ALLEN, JR. (*Hodge*) Nez Perce)
(tribal general council chairperson)
Affiliation & Address: Secretary, Nez Perce Tribe, P.O. Box 305, Lapwai, ID 83540 (208) 843-2253. E-mail: allensgc@nezperce.org

SLICKPOO, ALLEN P. (Nez Perce-Walla Walla-Cayuse) 1929-
(former tribal administrator)
Born May 5, 1929, Slickpoo Mission, Culdesac, Idaho. *Education*: Chemawa Indian School, 1945-48; University of Idaho, 1953-55. *Affiliation*: Councilman, administrator, Nez Perce Tribal Executive Committee, Lapwai, ID, 1955- (chairperson, General Council, 1961-63, 1986-88; chairperson, Resolutions Committee, 1988-89; secretary, vice-chairperson, and chairperson, Executive Committee, 1955-86). *Address*: 809 Nez Perce Lane, Box 311, Kamiah, ID 83536 (208) 843-2253 (work). *Other professional posts*: Tribal historian & cultural consultant; consultant to the Northwest Regional Educational Laboratory on Indian education and curriculum; consultant to documentary movies including, "I'll Fight No More Forever" about Nez Perce War of 1877, etc. *Military service*: U.S. Army, 1948-1952 (Japanese Occupation/Korea/UN Service). *Community activities*: Served on the Governor's Indian Advisory Council, Idaho; Veterans of Foreign Wars (Kamiah, Idaho); 2nd Presbyterian Church of Kamiah; Mat'alym'a (Up-river Nez Perce) Culture Club. *Awards, honors*: Outstanding Achievement Award, Indian Child Welfare, 1983; Governor of Idaho Award for Promoter of the Week, 1961. *Interests*: "Have traveled to Mexico City and Canada to participate and/or speak at conference relating to the Indian of North America; also to Tokyo, Japan, to lecture on Native American history & culture; bilingual/bicultural activities; consultant on historical and cultural concerns (recognized as authority on the history and culture of the Nez Perce people); have lectured at major institutions, including Newberry Library, Chicago, University of Colorado, Oregon State University, Dartmouth College, University of Washington, Navajo Community College, etc.; has lectured in public schools, to students and organizations relative to American Indian history, culture, government, education, and economic status; has been a reader and/or panelist for the National Endowment for the Humanities; have participated on many panels, workshops, and conferences. Advocate to promote tribally-sponsored projects relating to the preservation of the knowledge and identity of the Nez Perce history and culture; developing plans for tribal archives." *Published works*: NuMeePoom Tit-Wah-tit (Pruitt Press, 1973); Noon Nee MePoo (Pruitt Press, 1974); Nez Perce Attitude Toward the Missionary Experience (Pruitt Press, 1987); wrote a paper for the Northwest Quarterly on Anthropology, on the Indian fishing rights controversy.

SLIGER, MICHAEL D.
(attorney; Of counsel, Indian law practice)
Education: Grand Valley State University, BA, 2005; Cornell Law School, JD, 2008. *Affiliation & Address*: Of Counsel, Jordan Law Offices PLLC, 1730 Rhode Island Ave. NW, Washington, DC 20036 (202) 223-0893. Since 2010, Mr. Sliger has served as counsel to Jordan Law Offices, where he has focused his work on matters relating to federal Indian law, including economic development, land claims, working with federal agencies, general business matters & matters relating to tribal gaming and the government-to-government relationship between tribes & the United States. Mr. Sliger has also represented non-profit entities primarily operating in Indian country, and often represents clients before federal agencies & courts. In addition to his representation of tribal clients, Michael specializes in corporate law, including advising companies at all stages of development, from initial company formation to financings & acquisition events. His broad-based experience spans several industries, including health care, waste management & technology. Mr. Sliger also assists his corporate clients in litigation, including trial preparation & the discovery process. In his free time, he regularly advocates for, & consults with, pro se litigants on matters related to consumer law, & has worked with the Kings County Civil Court in administering a consumer law advisory clinic.

SLY, GLORIA (Cherokee)
(education services; government relations officer; board president)
Education: Northeastern State Uiversity, EdD. *Affiliations & Address*: Director, Cherokee Nation Cultural Resource Center, P.o. Box 948, Tahlequah, OK 74465 (918) 207-0950; Board President, Tribal Education Department National Assembly (TEDNA), 309 NW 13ᵗʰ St., Oklahoma City, OK 73103 (405) 563-7912. Gloria works with Cherokee students & staff from Northeastern State University in Tahlequah teaching the Cherokee language.

SMALL, ANDREW M.
(attorney)
Affiliation & Address: Partner, BlueDog, Paulson & Small, PLLP, Southgate Office Plaza, Suite 500, 5001 West 80th, Bloomington, MN 55437 (952) 893-1813. *Past professional posts*: Associate, Gross Ventre & Assiniboine Tribes of the Fort Belknap Reservation in Montana, 1981-83; counsel, Blackfeet Nation, Rocky Boy's government; counsel, Crow Tribe. Mr. Small served as general counsel & special counsel for 13 tribes and is admitted to practice in 14 Tribal jurisdictions throughout Indian Country. He served as an Associate Judge for

the Lower Sioux Indian Community from 1995-2005; and Children's Court Judge for the Prairie Island Mdwekanton Dakota Community from 1994-2002. *Awards, honors*: Andrew was one of the principal drafters of the Iowa ICWA (Indian Child Welfare Act) law of 2003.

SMALL, CLAYTON (Northern Cheyenne)
(chief executive officer)
Affiliation & Address: Chief Executive Officer, Native P.R.I.D.E., P.O. Box 471, Corrales, NM 87048 (505) 321-2808. E-mail: clayton@nativeprideus.org. *Past professional posts*: School & University administrator; director of two non-profit organizations; administrator, Indian Health Services. He has developed training programs for the Bureau of Indian Affairs, Indian Health Srervicces, Department of Justice, and SAMHSA.

SMALL, NATHAN (Shoshone-Bannock)
(tribal chairperson)
Affiliation & Address: Chairperson (2009-15, 2017-present), Shoshone-Bannock Tribes, P.O. Box 306, Fort Hall, ID 83203 (208) 478-3805; E-mail: nsmall@sbtribes.com. *Other tribal posts*: Member of the Tribal Bar Association since 1980, and has held positions as both a prosecutor & public defender in the Tribal Court. *Past tribal posts*: Vice chair, Business Council, 2006-09; also worked in the Tribal Water Resources Dept.

SMALL, NORMAN (Eskimo)
(Alaskan village president)
Affiliation: Platinum Traditional Village Council, P.O. Box 8, Platinum, AK 99651 (907) 979-8220.

SMALL-RODRIGUEZ, DESI (*Bear Mint Woman*) (Northern Cheyenne)
(secretary, student board member)
Education: Stanford University, B.A. (Comparative Studies in Race & Ethnicity), 2007; M.S. *Affiliation*: Diversity Recruitment Associate, Stanford University, Stanford, CA. Secretary, Student Board member, NIEA, Washington, DC.

SMART, TILDON (Shoshone-Paiute)
(tribal chairperson)
Affiliation & Address: Chairperson, Fort McDermitt Paiute & Shoshone Tribe, P.O. Box 457, McDermitt, NV 89421 (775) 532-8259.

SMARTT, EDITH (Te-Moak Western Shoshone)
(tribal vice chairperson)
Affiliation & Address: Vice Chairperson, Te-Moak Tribe of Western Shoshone Indians, South Fork Reservation, 21 Lee Unit-13, Spring Creek, NV 89815 (775) 744-4273.

SMILEY, TAMARA (Quapaw)
(tribal secretary-treasurer)
Affiliation & Address: Secretary-Treasurer, Quapaw Tribe, P.O. Box 765, Quapaw, OK 74363 (918) 542-4694. E-mail: tsmiley@quapawtribe.com.

SMILEY-MARQUEZ, CAROLYNA (San Juan Pueblo) 1946-
(consultant)
Born in 1946 in N.M. *Education*: Indiana University, BA, 1973, MA, 1974; University of Colorado, PhD (Social and Multicultural Foundations of Education), 1985. *Principal occupation*: Consultant. *Address*: P.O. Box 211, Hygiene, CO 80533 (303) 772-1714; E-mail: carolyna@uconsultus.com. *Affiliations*: New Mexico State Dept. of Education (Cross Cultural, Title IX Education Specialist), 1974-79; Washington State University (Minority Recruitment Officer, Interim Assistant Director, Instructor-Bilingual Education Institute), 1976-81; University of Colorado, Health Sciences Center (Chief Curriculum Development Liaison, 1981-83; Director for Affirmative Action & Coordinator for Staff Development and Guest Relation, 1986-90); University of Colorado (Instructor & Lecturer), 1982-; professional consultant, C. Smiley-Marquez, dba, Smiley & Co., 1988-. *Other professional posts*: Adjunct professor, University of Northern Colorado, Greeley, 1992-. *Community activities*: Hope for the Children, Kempe National Center for the Prevention & Treatment to Child Abuse & Neglect (board member). Awards, honors: Outstanding Young Women of America, 1982-84; Outstanding Young Women in Colorado, 1986; President's Award, EEO/Affirmative Action Coalition (Regional Professional Association), 1991. *Membership*: National Association for Human Rights Workers (board member, 1988-90). Biographical source: Directory of American Indian & Native American Women, 1985-. *Published works*: Monographs, brochures & bibliographies published by the State Dept. of Education, State of New Mexico, 1975-80. Videotapes: Pieces of Life - Profiles of Minority Women in Longmont (documentary), 1982; New Indian Wars (documentary of the conflict for American Indians and those seeking rights over natural resources on reservations), 1983; Storyteller (video presenting Anah Nahtanaba, American Indian Storyteller maker in the tradition of the Cochiti), 1985; Know It When You See It: Sexual Harassment for Supervisors & Managers and the Rights & Responsibilities of Employees

(sexual harassment training), 1986; Cultural Awareness: Introduction, 1990; Mentoring: Special Issues of Women and Minorities in Organizations, 1990. Education training kits: Diversity Training Kit for Managers & Employees, and Diversity Training for Law Enforcement Officers.

SMILEY-REEVES, TAMARA (Quapaw)
(tribal sect=retary/treasurer)
Affiliation & Address: Secretary/Treasurer, Quapaw Tribe of Oklahoma, P.O. Box 765, Quapaw, OK 74363 (918) 542-4694. E-mail: tsmiley@quapawtribe.com

SMITH, BARBARA (Chickasaw)
(attorney; professor of Indian law; court justice for Chickasaw Nation)
Education: East Central State University, BS, 1971; University of Oklahomma, ME, 1987; Oklahoma City University, JD, 1991. *Affiliation & Address*: Adjunct Professor of Law, Center for the Study of American Indian Law & Policies, University of Oklahoma College of Law, 300 Timberdell Rd., Norman, OK 73019. Michael has taught courses on tribal courts & tribal sovereignty. *Other professional post*: Attorney/Principal, Smith & Smith Attorneys at Law, 765 Asp Ave., Norman, OK 73069 (405) 447-2224. *Other professional post*: Supreme Court Justice, Chickasaw Nation of Oklahoma, 2003-present); member, Board of Directors of the Native American Rights Fund, Boulder, CO; Advisory Council for the National Tribal Judicial Center at the National Judicial College in Reno, NV. *Past professional posts*: Formerly District Judge of the Chickasaw Nation; Special Judge for the Cheyenne & Arapaho Trbal Courts.

SMITH, BRADDEN (Shinnecock)
(tribal vice chaiperson)
Affiliation & Address: Vice Chairperson, Shinnecock Tribe, P.O. Box 59, Southampton, NY 11968 (516) 283-1643.

SMITH, CHADWICK (*Ugisata - Corntassel*) (Cherokee) 1950-
(former tribal principal chief)
Born December 17, 1950, Pontiac, Mich. *Education*: University of Georgia, BA (Education), 1973; University of Wisconsin, Madison, MS, 1975; University of Tulsa Law School, JD, 1980. *Principal occupation*: Attorney. *Affiliation & Address*: Chairperson (1999-present), Cherokee Nation, P.O. Box 948, Tahlequah, OK 74465 (918) 4563-500 ext. 5204; in OK (800) 256-0671 ext. 5204. E-mail: csmith@cherokee.org. *Affiliations*: Private practice, Tulsa, OK, 1982-; Cherokee Nation, Tahlequah, OK (director of tribal planning, legal historian, tribal attorney, prosecutor, director of justice and advisor to the tribal tax commission, 1984-99; principal chief, 1999-present). *Other professional posts*: Speaker, educator & constitutional scholar; taught college courses in Indian law & history around the country including Indian law as a visiting professor at Dartmouth College. *Memberships*: Oklahoma Bar Association; American Bar Association; 10th Circuit Federal District Court; Cherokee Nation; Creek Nation. *Interests*: Indian law; Cherokee legal history. *Published works*: Cherokee Nation Course Work (Cherokee Nation Press, 1993); Cherokee Case Book (Cherokee Nation Press, 1993).

SMITH, CHERYL (Choctaw)
(tribal principal chief)
Affiliation & Address: Principal Chief, Jena Band of Choctaw Indians, P.O. Box 14, Jena, LA 71342 (318) 992-2717. E-mail: csmith@jenachoctaw.org

SMITH, CINDY (Hoh)
(tribal judge)
Affiliation & Address: Judge, Hoh Tribal Court, P.O. Box 2156, Forks, WA 98331 (360) 374-7772.

SMITH, DANELLE J. (Winnebago of Nebraska)
(attorney)
Education: Wayne State College, NE, BS, 1998; University of Iowa School of Law, JD, 2003. *Affiliation*: Associate, 2006-09; Partner, 2009-present, Fredericks Peebles & Morgan, LLC, 3610 North 163rd Plaza, Omaha, NE 68116 (402) 878-4383. E-mail: dsmith@ndnlaw.com. *Other professional posts*: General Counsel, Winnebago Tribe of Nebraska & Ho-Chunk, Inc., 2003-present; adjunct instructor, Business & Federal Indian Law, Little Priest Tribal College, Winnebago, NE; vice chairperson, Thurston County Board of Supervisors, 2004-present. *Past professional posts*: Legal intern, Ho-Chunk, Inc., 2001, Native American Rights Fund, 2002; *Practice areas*: Tribal economic development & corporate law; finance; taxation; gaming; employment; education; tribal ordinance & code drafting; and tribal government. *Awards, honors*: 2009 "Native American 40 and under 40" Award from the National Center for American Indian Enterprise Development (NCAIED).

SMITH, DENNIS J. (Assiniboine) 1950-
(professor of history & director of Native American studies)
Born July 23, 1950, Helena, Mont. *Education*: Montana State University, BS, 1972; University of Iowa, Certificate (Physical Therapy), 1974; University of Montana, MA (History), 1983; University of Nebraska, Lincoln, PhD (History),

2001. *Address & Affiliation*: Associate Professor of History & Directr of Native American Studies Program (2002-present), 287C ASH, University of Nebraska, Omaha, 6001 Dodge St., Omaha, NE 68182-0213 (402) 554-3688. E-Mail: dennissmith@unomaha.edu. *Other professional posts*: Fellow, Center for Great Plains Studies, University of Nebraska-Lincoln, 2001-present. Dennis teaches courses on the Sioux Tribe, Northern Plains Tribes, Native American History, North American Indian cultures, and Federal Indian policy. *Past professional post*: Instructor/Dean of Instruction, Fort Peck Community College, Poplar, MT, 1981-85; director of American Indian Studies, Morningside College, Sioux City, IA, 1989-2001. *Community activities*: Guest speaker on tribal cultures. *Membership*: National Indian Education Association; Western History Association. *Interests*: North American Native cultures & history with specialization in Plains tribes; Federal Indian policy.

SMITH, EDWARD D. "TITO" (Chemehuevi)
(tribal chairperson)
Affiliation & Address: Chairman, Chemehuevi Indian Tribe, P.O. Box 1976, Havasu Lake, CA 92363 (760) 858-4301.

SMITH, FAITH (Chippewa)
(college president)
Affiliation: President, NAES (Native American Educational Services) College, 2838 W. Peterson Ave., Chicago, IL 60659 (773) 761-5000. *Other professional posts*: Chairperson, Native American Public Telecommunications, Lincoln, NE; editor, "Inter-Com Newsletter, NAES College, Chicago, IL.

SMITH, GEORGETTE PALMER (Kiowa)
(executive director)
Education: University of Science & Arts of Oklahoma, BA (Communications); Eli Broad Graduate School of Management, School of Hospitality Musiness, Michigan Sate University, CMM (Certificate in Meeting Management.) *Affiliation & Address*: Executive Director, Native Learning Center, Seminole Tribe of Florida, 6363 Taft St., Hollywood, FL 33024 (954) 985-2315; E-mail: GeorgetteSmith@semtribe.com. *Past professional posts*: Director of Member Engagement, Membership, Conferences, Communications & Marketing Department, BICSI; Director, Forum & Conference Services, University of Oklahoma; Director of Meetings, American Society for Therapeutic Radiology & Onclogy (ASTRO), Fairfax, VA; Senior Project Manager, William H. Natcher Conference Center, National Institutes of Health, Bethesda, MD; Director of Convention Services, National Congress of American Indians (NCAI), Washington, DC. *Awards, honors*: Served as White House Logistical Coordinator representing NCAI for the historic meeting between President Bill Clinton and all 545 Tribal Leaders at the White House on April 29, 1994; In October 2004, Georgette created the University of Oklahoma's (OU) first ever Meetings & Events Management Certificate Program and served as a member of the OU Outreach Continuing Education faculty; named "Meeting Professional to Watch in 2009" by ConventionSouth Magazine.

SMITH, GRACE A. (Muscogee Creek)
(adjunct professor of flute; musician/composer)
Affiliation: Adjunct professor of flute, Dept. of Music, University of Central Oklahoma, Edmond, OK, 1993-present. *Community activities*: Henderson Hills Baptist Church Orchestra; Oklahoma Iris Society. *Memberships*: National Flute Association; Oklahoma Flute Society; Edmond Sigma Alpha Iota Alumnae. *Published compositions*: "Whisper on the Land" for flute & piano (Medici Music Press) included in the National Flute Association Collection at the University of Arizona's Library & the "New Plains Review," University of Central Oklahoma, 1986; "A Distant Dream" for flute & piano (Harmon Richard Music) included in the Contemporary Anthology of Music by Women (Indiana University Press, 1996); "Legende" for alto flute (Harmon Richard Music) included in "New Plains Review," University of Central Oklahoma, 1989.

SMITH, H. SALLY (Yup'ik Eskimo)
(board chairperson)
Affiliation & Address:Chairperson, Board of Directors, Bristol Bay Area Health Corporation, P.O. Box 10235, Dillingham, AK 99576 (907) 842-5266. *Other professional posts*: Secretary & Alaska Area Representative, National Indian Health Board, Washington, DC; member, Health Research Advisory Committee, Centers for Disease Control & Prevention, State Territorial Local & Tribal Committee; member, Indian Health Service National Tribal Budget Formulation Wrokgroup; serves on the Centers for Medicare & Medicaid Services Tribal Technical Advisory Group; chair, NIHB's Medicare, Medicaid & Health Reform Advisory Committee; chair, Alaska Native Health Board, 1998-present; presides as the Chair for the Alaska Native Medical Center Joint Operating Board, the Bristol Bay Area Health Corporation; Sergeant-at-Arms for the Alaska Native Tribal Health Consortium; serves as 3rd Chief of the Native Village of Dillingham and was a Tribal Judge. *Awards, honors*; Received the 1998 National Indian Health Board's highest recognition, The Jake White Crow Award.

SMITH, JANE M. (Colville) 1954-
(chief justice; court administrator)
Born April 9, 1954, Colville, Wash. *Education*: University of Washington (two years). *Affiliation & Address*: Chief Justice, Tulalip Tribal Court of Apeals, 6103 31st Ave. NE, Tulalip, WA 98271 (425) 774-5808. *Other professional posts*: Magistrate & Court Administrator, Colville Tribal Court, Nespelem, WA, 1994-present; Instructor with DCI out of Albuquerque, NM, 1993-present. *Past professional posts*: Pro Tem and/or appellate judge: Spokane Tribal Court, Quinault Nation Tribal Court, Kalispel Tribal Court, Suquamish Appellate Court, Northwest Intertribal Court System, Coeur D'Alene Tribal Court & Puyallup Tribal Court. *Military service*: U.S. Naval Reserve (Legalman Second Class),1987-91). *Community activities*: On committee that designed & contributed photos for the "Time for Gathering" exhibit honoring Indian tribes in the State of Washington for Centennial in 1989; junior rodeo timer; tribal exhibit committee; University of Washington museum exhibit. *Membership*: National American Indian Court Clerks' Association (president, 1986-88; member, 1985-present). *Interests*: "On team that evaluated the Hopi Tribal Court in November, 1991. Traveled to the Hopi Reservation, interviewed tribal members & staff, made an evaluation with recommendations. It was very interesting to see the differences & similarities between the Hopi and the Colville Tribal Courts."

SMITH, KAIGHN, JR.
(attorney)
Education: University of California, Berkeley, BS, 1979; University of Sussex, MPhil, 1983; University of Maine School of Law, JD, 1986. *Affiliation & Address*: Chairperson & Counsel, Indian Nations Labor & Employment Group, Drummond Woodsum, 84 Marginal Way, Suite 600, Portland, ME 04101 (207) 263-0559. E-mail: ksmith@dwmlaw.com. In 2011, he published the leading treatise, *Labor & Employment Law in Indian Country*, with the Native American Rights Fund. Since 2012, he has served as associate reporter (with Professors Matthew L.M. Fletcher and Wenona Singel) on the *Restatement of American Indian Law* for the American Law Institute. *Other professional posts*: Adjunct Professor of American Indian Law, University of Maine School of Law. He's an established national speaker on Indian affairs. *Awards, honors*: Best Lawyers USA, Native American Law (2008-2016); New England Super Lawyers, Native American Law, Employment & Labor (2011-2016); Chambers USA, Nationwide, Native American Law; Martindale Hubbell, BV Distinguished. *Memberships*: American Law Institute; Maine Bar Foundation (Fellow). *Published work*: Labor & Employment Law in Indian Country (Drummond Woodsum & Native American Rights Fund, 2011).

SMITH, KEITH
(chair of department of First Nations studies)
Affiliation & Address: Chair, Department of First Nations Studies, Vancouver Island University, 900 5th St., Nanaimo, BC V8R 5S5 (250) 740-6194. E-mail: keith.smith@viu.ca.

SMITH, KEITH C.
(attorney; tribal & Federal Indian law)
Education: University of Colorado at Boulder, BA; Arizona State University Sandra Day O'Connor College of Law, JD, 1997. *Affiliation & Address*: Founding Partner (2004), Smith, Shellenberger & Salazar, LLC, 14694 Orchard Pkwy. A-210, Westminster, CO 80023 (303) 255-3588; E-mail: kcs@ssslawyers.com. Keith is the majority owner & managing partner and has been practicing Tribal & Federal Indian law since he received his juris doctorate degree. As such, his experience in in Tribal and Federal Indian law is unparalleled to many working in the field. In addition to practicing Tribal and Federal Indian law, Keith's practice also includes domestic relations, land issues, business law, employment matters, general civil litigation, and minor criminal offenses. *Past professional posts*: Prior to establishing the firm, Mr. Smith held a position as a visiting professor of law at the University of Denver Sturm College of Law, where he taught Federal Indian Law, Family Law, and Contracts, and as an adjunct professor at the University of Colorado at Boulder. He continues to present as a guest lecturer and speaker at numerous venues, such as the University of Colorado, University of Denver, Arizona State University, Metro State College, Colorado State University, American Indian College, Dine College, National Indian Education Association, National Conference, Indigenous Bar Association, British Columbia, & many others. Prior to serving as a professor, Keith served as in-house counsel & senior administration director for the American Indian College Fund ("AICF"). While serving as in-house counsel, Keith advised the AICF on all legal matters facing the AICF and was instrumental in the creation and establishment of employee and management procedures. He also provided contract supervision for construction projects for 31 tribal colleges and universities in the United States - an approximate $31 million project. Each year, Keith assisted the AICF in providing counsel for each of the colleges belonging to the American Indian Higher Education Consortium ("AIHEC"), during legislative hearings with the U.S. Congress, Washington, D.C. He later accepted a position as Director of the Indian Legal Program at the Arizona State University College of Law, where he worked to further develop the law school's Federal Indian Law

curriculum and helped nurture and maintain many relationships with American Indian tribal nations. In addition, he managed the school's recruitment efforts of enrolling native law students and was an active member of law school's admission's committee. Immediately following law school, Keith served as a staff attorney for the Navajo Nation's DNA Peoples' Legal Services firm in Farmington, New Mexico. While at DNA Peoples' Legal Service, he worked in the areas of family law, including the Indian Child Welfare Act, contracts, consumer law and landlord/tenant; he worked with issues regarding the Navajo Housing Authority, representing tenants. with honors. While in law school, Keith clerked for the Chief Justice of the Salt River Pima-Maricopa Indian Community where he drafted and wrote the Community's Domestic Violence Code. The Code was enacted in 1997. Keith served as the Vice President of the Native American Law Student Association while in law school. He also received the distinction of being named a Chief Manuelito Scholar throughout college and law school earned a nomination to the prestigious honor society Phi Theta Kappa.

SMITH, MARGUERITE (Shinnecock)
(attorney, educator, consultant)
Education: Smith College, BA; New York University School of Law, JD. Resides on the Shinnecock Indian Reservation on Long Island, New York. She's an arbitrator and a consultant in dispute resolution with special interests in human resources & Native American, multicultural, environmental & social justice issues. *Other professional post*: Vice Chair, First Nations Development Institute, Longmont, CO; board member, First Nations Oweesta Corporation. *Past professional posts*: Law clerk, New York Supreme Court, Suffolk County; associate attorney general, New York State Law Department; field attorney, National Labor Relations Board.

SMITH, MARY L. (Cherokee)
(attorney; principal deputy director of IHS)
Education: Loyola University (Chicago), BS; University of Chicago School of Law, JD (member of Law Review). *Address*: 17533 Maple Dr., Lansing, MI 60438. *Affiliation & Address*: Principal Deputy Director (2016-present), Indian Health Service (IHS), The Reyes Bldg. 801 Thompson Ave., Suite 400, Rockville, MD 20852 (301) 443-1083. *Past professional posts*: President-elect (2013-15), National Native American Bar Association, Tempe, AZ; member, Board of Directors (2011-13), National Native American Bar Assn. Partner, Chicago law firm; senior litigation counsel, Tyco International, Inc.; staff attorney, Skadden, Arps, Slate, Meagher & Flom, Washington, DC; served in the Clinton White House as associate counsel to President Clinton & associate director of Policy Planning. She was the highest-ranking Native American in the White House during the Clinton Administration; Smith served as a trial attorney for the U.S. Department of Justice Civil Division, 1994-96. *Awards, honors*: Mary was elected the first Native American woman to the American Bar Association's Board of Governors in the Association's over 130-year history; 2012 Spirit of Excellence award from the American Bar Association.

SMITH, MAUREEN (Oneida of Wisconsin)
(professor of Native American studies & history)
Education: University of Wisconsn, Oshkosh, MA (Counseling); University of Wisconsin, Milwaukee, PhD (Urban Education. *Affiliation & Address*: Associate Professor of Interdisciplinary Studies & Director, Native American Studies Program, University of Maine, 5724 Dunn Hall, Orono, ME 04469 (207) 581-1417. *Teaching areas*: American Indian Studies, American Indian Women, Research & Theory of Native Studies, and Multicultural Education. *Research areas*: Stereotyping of American Indians, American Indian education, culturally relevant assessments of Native children, and sovereignty, treaty rights & cultural appropriations in relation to American Indian nations. *Past professional posts*: Professor of Education, University of Wisconsin-Oshkosh, 1993-97; acting Associate Vice Chancellor for Multicultural Affairs, advisor to minority students, 1986-90; advisor to American Indian students, 1982-86; alcohol counselor at the Oneida Tribal Health Center, Oneida, Wisconsin & Fond du Lac County Mental Health Center; multicultural specialist on the National Advisory Committee on Multicultural Affairs & diversity trainer consultant with the Girl Scout Council of the Fox Valley and with Reed Elementary School in Oshkosh, Wisconsin.

SMITH, MAURICE "MO" (Navajo)
(former executive director)
Education: Regis University, BS (Business Administration), & MS (Nonprofit Management). *Past professional posts*: Executive director, Native American Sports Council, Colorado Springs, CO; executive director, American Indian Business Leaders, Missoula, MO.

SMITH, MAYLINN (Salish/Kootenai)
(professor & co-director of Indian law clinic)
Affiliation & Address: Clinical Supervisor & Co-Director, Margery Hunter Brown Indian Law Clinic, U. of Montana School of Law, Law 147, 32 Campus Dr., Missoula, MT 59812 (406) 243-5351. E-mail: maylinn.smith@umontana.edu. She teaches Federal Courts and, during the summer session, Indian Child

Welfare Act as part of the University's Summer Indian Law Program. Working under her guidance, law student interns in the Indian Law Clinic assist tribal governments & organizations dealing with Indian law issues. *Activities include*: drafting model codes; working on civil rights cases; practicing in tribal court; mediations; training on Indian law issues; and natural resource issues as well. Professor Smith's previous service as Chief Judge of the Southern Ute Indian Tribal Court, as Appellate Judge of the Southwest Intertribal Court of Appeals, as well as her experience as legal counsel for the Salish & Kootenai Tribal Court, benefit not only the tribes served by the Indian Law Clinic, but also the law students enrolled.

SMITH, MELANIE M. (Dakota – Santee Mdewankanton Band) 1943-
(alcohol/drug program director)
Born August 17, 1943, Wisconsin Rapids, Wisc. *Education*: Blackhawk College (Moline, IL), 1972-74. *Principal occupation*: Alcohol/drug program director. *Address*: 2350 Wallace Rd. NW, Salem, OR 97304 (503) 585-0564. E-Mail: tahana@open.org. *Affiliations*: Director, Tahana Whitecrow Foundation, Salem, OR, 1987-; Mid-Willamette Behavioral Care Network, Salem, OR, 1995-. *Community activities*: Preach sustainable development; client advocate; sustainable development; POW/MIA Float - Albany Vets Day Parade; member, Ladies Auxiliary Military Order of Purple Heart. *Memberships*: American Correctional Association; National Alcohol/Drug Counselors Association; AARP; Salem Chamber of Commerce; Greater Area Veterans Association; Native American Counselor II. *Interests*: Journalism, grant writing, substance abuse. *Published works*: Reflections; The Wall.

SMITH, MICHAEL COLBERT (Chickasaw)
(attorney; professor of American Indian law)
Education: University of Oklahoma, BA, 1983; Oklahoma City University Law Scool, JD, 1990. *Affiliation & Address*: Adjunct Professor of Law, Center for the Study of American Indian Law & Policies, University of Oklahoma College of Law, 300 Timberdell Rd., Norman, OK 73019. Michael has taught courses on tribal courts & tribal sovereignty. *Other professional post*: Attorney/Principal, Smith & Smith Attorneys at Law, 765 Asp Ave., Norman, OK 73069 (405) 447-2224. *Past professional posts*: Former District Judge of Sac & Fox Nation of Oklahoma; court advocate for the Judicial Branch, Chickasaw Nation.

SMITH, MICHAEL (Lakota)
(institute founder & president)
Affiliation: American Indian Film Institute, 333 Valencia St., Suite 322, San Francisco, CA 94103 (415) 554-0525. Website: www.aifisf.com.

SMITH, MICHAEL R.
(deputy director, Bureau of Indian Affairs – Field Operations)
Affiliation & Address: Deputy Bureau Director (2004-present) – Field Operations, Bureau of Indian Affairs, 1849 C St., NW – MS-4606-IB, Washington, DC 20240. E-mail: mike.smith@bia.gov. *Past professional posts*: He served in senior management positions as the Regional Director, Southern Plains Region in Anadarko, Okla. & Director of the Office of Tribal Services in Washington, D.C.

SMITH, MICHAEL R.
(attorney, Native American law)
Education: Tulane University, BA, 1976; Stanford Law School, JD, 1979. *Affiliation & Address*: Leads the Native American law practice, Zuckerman Spaeder, LLP, 1800 M St., NW, Suite 1000, Washington, DC 20036 (202) 778-1832. Practice focus is on American Indian law, litigation and political disputes with regard to land claims, trust land, gaming, governance, tax, & sovereignty issues. Represents the Oneida Nation of New York. *Awards, honors*: The Best Lawyers in America, Native Amerian Law, 2007-present.

SMITH, P. BENJAMIN (Navajo-Dine')
(IHS office director)
Education: Brigham Young University, BA; American University, MA (International Peace & Conflict Resolution); Georgetown University (post-graduate certificates in Senior Executive Leadership & Business); Johns Hopkins Bloomberg School of Public Health (graduate certificate in Epidemiology). *Affiliation & Address*: Deputy Director for Intergovernmental Affairs, Indian Health Service, USDHHS, The Reyes Bldg., 801 Thompson Ave., Rockville, MD 20852. *Past professional post*: Director, Office of Tribal Self-Governance, Indian Health Service, USDHHS, Rockville, MD. Specialist for the Choctaw Nation of Oklahoma performing research, advisory services, and consultation on health programs with national, state & local health departments. *Awards, honors*: HIS National Directors Awards for his Agency contributions to efforts; numerous HIS Superior Support Service Awards for his involvement on HIS/Tribal Workgroups & special projects.

SMITH, RAYMOND R. (Navajo)
(Navajo tribal enterprise manager)
Affiliation: Navajo Arts & Crafts Enterprise, P.O. Box 160, Window Rock, AZ 86515 (520) 871- 4090.

SMITH, RICHARD (Tlingit)
(Alaskan Native association president)
Affiliation: Klawock Cooperative Association, P.O. Box 430, Klawock, AK 99925 (907) 755-2265.

SMITH, RICHARD J. (Cahto-Pomo)
(former tribal chairperson)
Affiliation & Address: Former chairperson, Cahto Indian Tribe of the Laytonville Rancheria, P.O. Box 1239, Laytonville, CA 95454 (707) 984-6197

SMITH, RICK (Ojibwe)
(American Indian center director)
Affiliation & Address: Director, American Indian Learning Resource Center, University of Minnesota, Duluth, 315 Kirby Plaza, 1208 Kirby Dr., Duluth, MN 55812 (218) 726-6293. E-mail: rsmith1@d.umn.edu.

SMITH, ROB ROY EDWARD STUART
(attorney)
Education: College of the Holy Cross, BA, 1997; Northwestern School of Law of Lewis & Clark College, JD, 2000. *Affiliation & Address*: Partner, Kilptarick Townsend & Stockton, LLP, 1420 Fifth Ave., Suite 4400, Seattle, WA 98101 (206) 224-2868. Mr. Smith focuses his practice on federal Indian law. He advises Indian tribal clients on all aspects of federal, state, & tribal law, including economic development, natural & cultural resource protection, taxation, tribal sovereignty & gaming. *Other professional posts*: Mr. Smith is also an active member of the Indian Law Committee for the Northwestern School of Law, Lewis & Clark College. The committee's goals are to strengthen the school's Indian Law program and to secure funding to engage visiting professors to the school to teach Federal Indian law. Additionally, Mr. Smith serves as an adjunct professor at Seattle University School of Law. He is a frequent author and lecturer on various aspects of Indian law. Professional & Community activities: Animal Legal Defense Fund, Volunteer Attorney (2007 to Present); Idaho State Bar, Indian Law Section, Co-Founder and Past Chair; King County Bar Assn, Urban Indian Legal Clinic, Volunteer Attorney (2008 to Present); Lewis & Clark Law School, Alumni Board of Directors, Member (2007 to 2012); Marathon Maniac, Member; Northwestern School of Law Lewis & Clark College, Indian Law Committee, Member; Oregon State Bar, Indian Law Section, Member; Seattle University School of Law, Federal Indian Law, Adjunct Professor (2008 to Present); Washington State Bar, Indian Law Section, Member; Washington State BarBri, Federal Indian Law, Instructor (2009 to 2012). *Past professional posts*: Staff attorney & Policy Analyst for the Nez Perce Tribe Office of Legal Counsel in Lapwai, Idaho. *Awards, honors*: Rob Roy has been recognized as a "Rising Star" in the area of Native American Law by Washington Super Lawyers magazine; he was listed by "The Best Lawyers in America" for Native American Law in 2014.

SMITH, ROBERT H. (Luiseno-Cupa)
(tribal chairperson)
Affiliation & Address: Chairperson (1987-present), Pala Band of Luiseno Indians, Box 50, Pala, CA 92059 (760) 891-3500. E-mail: cupa@palatribe.com; Website: www.palatribe.com. Resides on the Pala Indian Reservation. Chairman Smith successfully negotiated the first Tribal-State compact in California with Governor Pete Wilson in 1996, and subsequently supervised the opening of the Pala Casino. In 2004, Robert was one of five tribal leaders to work side-by-side with Governor Schwartzenegger to come to agreement on a set of compacts that benefited both the tribes and the State of California. *Other professional posts*: Chairperson, California Indian Manpower Consortium; delegate, National Bureau of Indian Affairs Tribal Leaders Budget Committee; delegate, the National Indian Gaming Assn; delegate, National Congress of American Indians; chairperson, California Tribal Business Alliance, Sacramento, CA; chairperson, Southern California Tribal Chairmen Assn; board member, Indian Health Council for North San Diego County.

SMITH, SHEILA S. (Oneida of Wisconsin) 1962-
(artist)
Born September 19, 1962, Green Bay, Wisc. *Education*: University of Wisconsin, La Crosse. *Address & Affiliation*: Volunteer, Oneida (WI) Nation Museum, 1980-. *Awards, honors*: 1st Place, University of Wisconsin, Stevens Point, 1985 Woodlands Indian Arts Festival; proclaimed a master of my art by the U.S. Dept. of the Interior and the Wisconsin Arts Board. *Interests*: "I have brought back the last art of the Iroquois costume designs. I have sold four costumes to the U.S. Dept. of the Interior for their permanent collection of Indian artifacts. I had two costumes worn during President Reagan's Inaugural Festivities. I was also a selected artist from Wisconsin to be videotaped & exhibited by the National Endowment of the Arts & Wisconsin Arts Council as a national traveling exhibit. I have also had a cover of the Stevens Point Magazine published in Stevens Point, Wisconsin."

SMITH, TERESA (Ottawa of Oklahoma)
(tribal secretary-treasurer)
Affiliation & Address: Secretary-Treasurer, Ottawa Tribe of Oklahoma, P.O. Box 110, Miami, OK 74355 (918) 540-1536.

SMITH, THEODORE (Yavapai Apache)
(spiritual leader)
Affiliation: Yavapai-Apache Tribe, 2400 W. Datsi, Camp Verde, AZ 86322 (520) 567-3649. *Past professional post*: Former chairperson, Yavapai-Apache Tribal Council, Camp Verde, AZ.

SMITH, VICTORIA ANDERSON/OXENDINE (Cherokee/Delaware)
(professor of Native American studies; faculty advisor)
Education: University of Arizona, BA (History), 1992, MA (American Indian Studies), 1995; Arizona State University, PhD (History), 2002. *Affiliation & Address*: Professor of History, Native American Studies, Institute for Ethnic Studies, 303 Seaton Hall, University of Nebraska-Lincoln, 420 University Ter., Lincoln, NE 68588 (402) 471-1663. E-mail: vsmith4@unl.edu. *Other professional post*: Faculty Advisor, University of Nebraska Inter-Tribal Exchange (UNITE); Edgerton Junior Faculty Chair. *Published works*: Editor, with Hollis Stabler, No One Ever Asked Me: The World War II Memoirs of an Omaha Indian Soldier (University of Nebraska Press, 2005); Captive Arizona: Indian Captives & Captive Indians in Arizona Territory, 1850-1912 (University of Nebraska Press, 2009).

SMITH, VIRGIL S. (Quechan)
(tribal vice president)
Affiliation & Address: Vice President, Quechen Tribal Council, Fort Yuma Reservation, P.O. Box 1899, Yuma, AZ 85366 (760) 572-0213.

SNEED, RICHARD (Eastern Cherokee)
(tribal principal chief)
Affiliation & Address: Principal Chief, Eastern Band of Cherokee Indians, Qualla Boundary, P.O. Box 455, Cherokee, NC 28719 (828) 497-7000.

SNELL, LISA HICKS (Cherokee)
(publisher)
Education: University of Tulsa, BA (Communications), 1993; Art Institute of Dallas. *Affiliation & Address*: Publisher (2008-present), Native American Times, P.O. Box 411, Tahlequah, OK 74465 (918) 708-5838. E-mail: lisa@nativetimes.com. *Past professional posts*: Grahpic artist, Cherokee Nation, 2003-07; Native American Times, 2007-08; advertising manager/graphic artist, Cjerkee Phoenix, 2003-07; art director, Preview Magazine, 1998-2002; announcer/producer, KWGS-FM 89, 1991-1993.

SNEVE, SHIRLEY K. (Rosebud Sioux) 1956-
(education)
Born July 14, 1956, Rapid City, S.D. *Education*: South Dakota State University, BA, (Journalism) 1978; University of South Dakota & University of Massachusetts, Amherst (graduate work in public and arts administration), 1984-86. *Affiliation & Address*: Executive Director, Native American Public Telecommunications (NAPT), 1800 North 33 St., Lincoln, NE 68583 (402) 472-0208. E-mail: shirley.sneve@unl.edu. *Other professional posts*: Produer, South Dakota Public Radio, 1981-persent; board member, The Association of American Cultures, 2003-present. *Past professional posts*: Minority Affairs Producer, South Dakota Public Broadcasting, Vermillion, SD, 1981-87; executive director, Alliance of Tribal Tourism Advocates, a consortium of the nine tribes in South Dakota, 1995-97; contractual services for Native American Public Telecommunications, Lincoln NE, 1996-98; director, Visual Arts Center at the Washington Pavilion of Arts & Science, Sioux Falls, SD, 1998-2000; arts management consultant, Technical Assistance Group, South Dakotans for the Arts, Sioux Falls, SD, 2000-2001; executive director (2001-04), The Arts Extension Service, University of Massachusetts, Amherst, MA. *Community activities*: Project director, Native Arts Planning Effort, funded by NEA Locals program, 1991-present. Native American Advisory Committees, State Historical Society, Pierre, SD, 1993, and Siouxland Heritage Museums, Sioux Falls, 1992-present; University of Massachusetts Fine Arts Center Strategic Planning Committee, 2001-present; Steering Committee, Western Massachusetts Arts Alliance, 2001-present; Five College Native American Studies Committee. *Memberships*: Native American Journalism Association; New England Region of University Continuing Education Association (vice president); The National Community Arts Network (vice president).

SNEVE, VIRGINIA DRIVING HAWK (Rosebud Sioux) 1933-
(guidance counselor, writer)
Born February 21, 1933, Rosebud Reservation, S.D. *Education*: South Dakota State University, BS, 1954, MEd, 1969. Address: 1617 Debra Dr. #110, Rapid City, SD 57702 (605) 716-3877. E-mail: vsneve@rushmore.com. *Affiliations*: Teacher-counselor, Flandreau Indian School, Flandreau, SD, 1966-70; editor,

Brevet Press, Sioux Falls, SD, 1970-72; consultant, producer-writer, SD Public TV, Brooking, 1973-80; educational counselor, Flandreau Indian School, 1981-85; guidance counselor, Rapid City Central High School, 1986-present. *Other professional posts*: Part time English instructor, Oglala Community College, Rapid City Extension. *Community activities*: Rapid City Project 2,000 (drop out prevention coalition) Emanual Episcopal Church, Episcopal Diocese Commission on Racism. *Memberships*: SD Press Women (secretary, 1976-78); National Federation Press Women; SD Diocese of the Episcopal Church (historiographer, 1977-85); SD State University, Foundation Board, 1990-; enrolled member of Rosebud Sioux Tribe. *Awards, honors*: Council on Interracial Book Award for Jimmy Yellow Hawk, 1972; Western Writers of America Award for Betrayed, 1974; Special Contribution to Education, SD Indian Education Association, 1975; Honorary Doctorate of Letters, Dakota Wesleyan University, 1979; Distinguished Contribution to SD History, Dakota History Conference, 1982; 2nd Annual Native American Prose Award, University of Nebraska Press, 1992, for ms. "Completing the Circle. *Interests*: Indian education, art and literature. *Published works*: Jimmy Yellow Hawk (Holiday House, 1972); High Elk's Treasure (Holiday House, 1972); editor, South Dakota Geographic Names (Brevet Press, 1973); Betrayed (Holiday House, 1974); When Thunders Spoke (Holiday House, 1974); The Dakota's Heritage (Brevet Press, 1974); The Chichi Hoohoo Bogeyman, Ms. Sneve wrote the script for the screen play of the same title for the Vegetable Soup Children's TV series (Holiday House, 1975); They Led a Nation (Brevet Press, 1975); That They May Have Life: The Episcopal Church in South Dakota, 1859-1976 (Brevet Press, 1981); Dancing Teepees (Holiday House, 1989); The Navajos (Holiday House, 1993); When Thunders Spoke (University of Nebraska Press, 1993); The Nez Perce (Holiday House, 1994); The Seminoles (Holiday House, 1994); The Sioux (Holiday House, 1994); Completing the Circle (University of Nebraska Press, 1995); The Trickster and the Troll (University of Nebraska Press, 1997); Grandpa Was a Cowboy and an Indian and Other Stories (University of Nebraska Press, 2000); short stories and non-fiction articles.

SNIGAROFF, MARK (Eskimo)
(Alaskan village president)
Affiliation: President, Native Village of Atka, P.O. Box 47030, Atka, AK 99547 (907) 839-2229. E-mail: atka@aitc.org

SNIPP, C. MATTHEW (Choctaw/Cherokee)
(professor of sociology; program director)
Education: University of California, Davis, BA (Sociology), 1974; University of Wisconsin-Madison, MS (Sociology), 1976, PhD (Sociology), 1981. *Affiliation & Address*: Professor of Sociology, 1996-2008; Professor of Humanities & Sciences (2008-present), Department of Sociology; Bldg. 120, Room 138, Stanford University, Stanford, CA 94305 (650) 725-0414. E-mail: snipp@stanford.edu. *Other professional posts*: Director, native American Studies Program; Director, Institute for Research in the Social Science's Secure Data Center, Stanford University; serves as an appointed member of the Census Bureau's Racial & Ethnic Advisory Committee (10+ years); serves on the National Institute of Child Health & Development's Population Science Subcommittee. Professor Snipp has published three books and over 70 articles & book chapters on demography, economic development, poverty & unemployment. His current research & writing deals with the methodology of racial measurement, changes in the coial & economic well-being of American ethnic minorities, and American Indian education; addresses & presentations. *Past professional posts*: Professor of Sociology, University of Maryland, 1981-87; professor of Sociology, 1988-96 & director, American Indian Studies Program, University of Wisconsin, Madison, WI, 1992-96. Published works: Public Policy Impacts on American Indian Economic Development, Institute for Native American Development, University of New Mexico, 1988; American Indians: The First of the Land (Russell Sage Foundation, 1990) selected as an academic book of the year by CHOICE, 1990; edited with Carol Ward, Research in Human Capital & Development: American Indian Economic Development, vol. 10 (JAI Press, 1996); numerous chapters in books, articles in journals; contributed papers, reports & book reviews.

SNOOKS, PAUL (Te-Moak Western Shoshone)
(tribal chairperson)
Affiliation: Battle Mountain Band Council, 35 Mountain View Dr., #138-13, Battle Mountain, NV 89820 (702) 635-2004.

SNOOKS, KENNY (Shoshone)
(tribal vice chairperson)
Affiliation & Address: Vice Chairperson, Yomba Shoshone Tribe, HC61, Box 6275, Austin, NV 89310 (775) 964-2463.

SNYDER, BARRY E. (Seneca)
(former tribal president)
Affiliation & Address: Seneca Nation of Indians, 12837 Rt. 438, Irving, NY 14081 (716) 532-4900.

SNYDER, CHRISTINA
(associate professor of American studies & history)
Education: University of Georgia, BA (Anthropology), 2001; University of North Carolina at Chapel Hill, PhD (History), 2007. *Affiliation & Address*: Associate professor of American Studies & History, Native American & Indigenous Studies, Ballantine Hall 828, 1020 E. Kirkwood Ave., Bloomington, IN 47405 (812) 855-2287. E-mail: snyderch@indiana.edu. Currently working on a book on Choctaw Academy, the first national Indian oarding school in the U.S., open from 1825-48. *Awards, honors*: Won the best first book prize at the 2011 Berkshire Conference of Women Historians; won the James H. Broussard prize by the Society for Historians of the Early American Republic for the year's best first book; a finalist for the Frederick Douglass Prize from Yale University's Gilder Lehrman Center for the Study of Slavery. *Published work*: Slavery in Indian Country: The Changing Face of Captivity in Early America (Harvard University, 2010); working title, Race and Indian Removal: Perspectives from Choctaw Academy, in Oxford handbook on the History of Race, ed. Matthew Guterl (Oxford University Press (forthcoming); numerous articles.

SNYDER, DARWIN (Winnebago of Nebraska)
(tribal vice chairperson)
Affiliation & Address: Vice Chairperson, Winnebago Tribe of Nebraska, P.O. Box 687, Winnebago, NE 68071 (402) 878-3103. E-mail: darwin.snyder@winnebagotribe. com

SOBOTTA, BOB
(coordinator, elementary & Indian education)
Address & Affiliation: Coordinator, Elementary & Indian Education, Idaho Dept. of Education, P.O. Box 83720, Boise, ID 83720-0027 (208) 332-6942. E-Mail: bsobott@sde.state.id.us. *Past affiliations*: Supt. of Schools, Lapwai School District, Lapwai, ID; Assistant Supt. of Schools, Wapato School District, Wapato, WA.

SOCTOMAH, DONALD (Passaquoddy)
(tribal representative)
Affiliation: Passaquoddy Tribe, P.O. Box 343, Perry, ME 04667 (207) 853-2600. E-mail: soctomah@ainop.com. Representative to the Maine Legislature, 2002-present. Donald also serves as the Tribe's Tribal Historic Preservation Officer,

SOCKYMA, MICHAEL C., SR. (Mong-eu-ma-Young Corn) (Hopi) 1942-
(Hopi silver/gold smith)
Born June 4, 1942, Hotevilla, Ariz. *Education*: Phoenix Indian High School. *Principal occupation*: Hopi silver/gold smith. *Address*: P.O. Box 96, Kykotsmovi, AZ 86039 (928) 734-1050. *Affiliations*: Hopi Kiva Arts & Craft Shop (Sockyma's Hopicrafts), Kykotsmovi, AZ, 1975-. *Community activities*: Member of Hopi Tribal Council. *Awards, honors*: "(I) have won ribbons for jewelry at Jemez Indian Art Shows, and Gallup Indian Art Shows, New Mexico; Red Earth Art Craft Show, Oklahoma; Houston and Dallas Art Craft Shows, Texas; and Sedona, AZ Art Craft Show." *Interests*: "35 years in making Hopi overlay jewelry in silver & gold; custom jewelry in precious stones; artist in oil and acrylic; specialize in both men & women Concho belts; council member for the Hopi Tribe; active in traditional cultural activities." *Biographical source*: Government Directory of Indian Arts; Hopi Silver I & II, by Margaret Wright.

SOCOBASIN, JOSEPH (Passamaquoddy)
(former tribal chief)
Education: University of Maine at Orono, 1990-92. *Affiliation & Address*: Chief (2010-present), Passamaquoddy Tribe of Indian Township, P.O. Box 301, Princeton, ME 04668 (207) 796-2301. *Past professional post*: Tribal Lieutenant Governor, 2002-10; Game Warden, Indian Township, 2000-02; Public Safety Officer, Indian Township Police Department, 1991-2000.

SOCTOMAH, DONALD (Passamaquoddy)
(tribal historian & representative)
Address: P.O. Box 102, Princeton, ME 04668. E-mail: soctomah@ainop.com. *Affiliation*: Historian & Representative, Passamaquoddy Tribe. *Past professional post*: Tribal representative to the Maine State Legislature for the Passamaquoddy Tribe. He has authored several books.

SOEDER, PAMELA (Muscogee Creek) 1953-
(associate professor)
Born December 8, 1953. *Education*: Mt. Senario College, BS, 1977; University of Wisconsin, MA, 1981, PhD, 1985. *Principal occupation*: Associate professor. *Address*: Slippery Rock University, Early Childhood Education Dept., 112 McKay Education Bldg., Slippery Rock, PA 16057 (412) 738-2864. E-Mail: pamela.soeder@sru.edu. *Affiliations*: Madison Metropolitan School District, Madison, Wi (Elementary teacher, 1977-81; coordinator, American Indian Program, 1987-90); associate professor, Slippery Rock University, Slippery Rock, PA, 1990-present.

SOLIMON, RONALD J. (Laguna/Zuni Pueblo)
(president & CEO)
Education: New Mexico State University, BS (Business Administration), 1973; University of New Mexico School of Law, JD, 1976. *Affiliation & Address*: President & CEO, Indian Pueblo Cultural Center, Inc., 2401 12th St. NW, Albuquerque, NM 87104 (505) 843-7270. E-mail: rsolimon@indianpueblo.com. *Other professional posts*: President & CEO, Indian Pueblos Marketing, Inc., Albuquerque, NM; At-Large Representative & Vice President, American Indian Alaska Native Tourism Association, Albuquerque, NM; board member, National Center for American Indian Enterprise Development, Mesa, AZ; board member, Laguna Development Corporation; board member, Pueblo of Tesuque Development Corporation; board member, New Mexico Workforce Development Board. *Awards, honors*: Inducted into the New Mexico Business Hall of Fame in 2008; in 2009, The New Mexico Office of African American Affairs gave Ron an "Outstanding Achievement Award" for Educational Services Rendered Toward the Betterment of African Americans & Other Underserved Citizens of the State of New Mexico.

SOLOMON, CORA NICHOLASA (NICKY) (*Victory Walker or War Path Woman*) (Winnebago of Nebraska) 1933-
(former national director, CHR program)
Born February 11, 1933, Winnebago, Neb. *Affiliation*: Former national director, Community Health Representatives (CHR)) Program, Indian Health Service, Rockville, MD, 1983-95. Mrs. Solomon was the first national director of the CHR program. *Address*: P.O. Box 596, Winnebago, NE 68071 (402) 878-2521. *Other professional post*: Director, Winnebago Tribe of Nebraska Health Department; IHS Aberdeen Area Alcoholism Program Coordinator; Business Representative, Northwestern Bell Telephone Co.; former business partner in a trading post. *Community activities*: Former secretary, Winnebago Tribal Council; Winnebago Public School Board; Nebraska Indian Commission; Nebraska Indian Inter-Tribal Development Corporation; Goldenrod Hills Community Action Agency; Seven States Indian Health Association; American Indian Human Resource Center Board (Alcohol Program). *Memberships*: National Association of Community Health Representatives; National Congress of American Indians. *Awards, honors*: Membership in the California Scholarship Federation; Woman Pioneer Award (social services) from the Governor of Nebraska, Charles Thone; awards received from the Lakota Health Association and the CHR organizations throughout Indian country. In 1994, the Office of Inspector General presented their "Integrity" Award for work done for the CHR program. Mrs. Solomon is the first person in the history of Indian Health Service to receive this award. *Interests*: "Since 1969, my interest and occupation has been in tribal health. The CHR program was the forerunner to the concept of Indian self-determination. Tribes began to provide services of CHRs through contractual agreements with IHS in 1968. They are providers of health promotion & disease prevention services, as well as health care outreach workers, and are the epitome of commitment and dedication to serving American Indians and Alaska Natives. I am proud to be a part of this great movement and become filled with emotion just thinking of the great sacrifices CHRs make on a daily basis." Co-authored paper, "A Population-Based Assessment of Alcohol Abuse Using a Community Panel."

SOLOMON, GLENN W. (Cherokee) 1945-
(professor of research)
Born in 1945, Ochelata, Okla. *Education*: University of Oklahoma, BA, 1967, MA, 1972; U of OK Health Sciences Center, MPH, 1981, PhD, 1990. *Principal occupation*: Professor of research. *Address*: 1033 Leslie Lane, Norman, OK 73069 (405) 364-0308. *Affiliation*: University of Oklahoma Health Sciences Center, Dept. of Pediatrics, Adolescent Medicine, Oklahoma City, OK. *Other professional posts*: Editor, "Wassaja," (American Indian Historical Society, San Francisco, CA) the national newspaper of Indian America, 1971-86; founding member, Advisory Board, Jacobson Foundation for American Indian Art, Norman, OK, 1986-; health careers consultant, Northeastern State University, Tahlequah, OK, 1988-; Urban Indian Health Forum, Health Concerns, Oklahoma City, OK, 1990-; visiting assistant professor, University of Oklahoma, Human Relations, Norman, OK, 1992-. *Research activities*: Minority recruitment & retention policy development for State Regents of Higher Education & State Supt. of Instruction, 1971-; development of criteria & analysis of minority students in higher education including health professionals, 1971-; quality assurance for field aid stations - combat & non-combat conditions, U.S. Army Special Forces, Worldwide Multi-National Scope of Service, 1980-; cultural assessment in adolescent health behaviors, Oklahoma Youth Health Risks (funded), 1990-; women, infant & children nutritional program, State Health Dept., Wichita, Caddo, & Delaware WIC, Cherokee Nations, WIC, 1990-; Cherokee Nation baseline study of substance abuse (funded), Evaluator for Substance Abuse Program in Cherokee Nation, 1992-; Cheyenne & Arapaho Health Needs Assessment (funded), 1993-. Community activities: Advisor to Executive Council, American Indian Training & Employment Program, Oklahoma City, OK, 1980-; member, Board of Directors, Native American Center, Oklahoma City, 1978-81; member, Advisory Board, Central Tribes Health Manpower Project, IHS, Shawnee, OK, 1979-82; member, Advisory Board, State Dept. of Public Health, Child &

Maternal Care, Oklahoma City, OK, 1979-85; Native American Center for Excellence, University of Oklahoma Health Sciences Center, College of Medicine, 1991-93; producer & host, American Indian Magazine (weekly television program), 1984-89; president, American Indian/Alaskan Native Staff & Faculty, University of Oklahoma Health Sciences Center, Oklahoma City, 1989-90; sponsor, American Indian Science & Engineering Students, University of Oklahoma, Health Sciences Center, 1989-91. *Membership*: National Indian Education Association (presidential search committee, 1988). *Awards, honors*: Public Health Fellow, University of Oklahoma Health Sciences Center, Oklahoma City, 1976-77; Fellowship, U.S. Office of Indian Education, 1977-80; Outstanding Staff & Faculty Award, American Indian Women's Association, University of Oklahoma, Norman, 1984; Oklahoma Human Rights Award, Oklahoma City, OK, 1986; American Indian Scholarships, Albuquerque, NM, 1988-90; Oklahoma State Regents of Higher Education, Minority Doctoral Scholar, Oklahoma City, OK, 1988-90; Major Bass Academic Scholarship, University of Oklahoma Health Sciences Center, Oklahoma City, 1988. Published works: The Odyssey of Wassaja: Carlos Montezuma, MD; First American Indian Physician (1972 master's thesis - University of Oklahoma), currently being revised for submission to a university press; "American Indian Studies: A Status Report," paper presented at the Organization of American Historians, New Orleans, LA, 1974; "American Indian Advocate for the Campus," National Indian Education Association, 1980; "Status of American Indian Studies & Students," National Indian Education Association, 1982; AIDS: Prevention for Life Saving, a 1 hour video, Ft. Bragg, ND, 1987; "Cultural Involvements & Substance Abuse of Oklahoma Cherokee Adolescents," American Federation for Clinical Research, Carmel, CA, 1993; editor, et al, "Complexities of Ethnicity Among Oklahoma Native Americans: Health Behaviors of Rural Adolescents," in The Culture of Oklahoma (University of Oklahoma Press, 1993); "Nutritional Status of Obesity in Oklahoma Indians" (current).

SOLOMON, TESHIA G. ARAMBULA (Choctaw/Mexican-American)
(associate professor of family & community medicine)
Education: PhD (Family & Community Medicine). *Affiliation & Address*: Associate Professor, Department of Family & Community Medicine, University of Arizona; Director (2007-present), Native American Research & Training Center (NARTC), 1642 E. Helen St., Tucson, AZ 85719 (520) 626-1123. E-mail: solomont@email.arizona.edu. She has almost 20 years experience in health-related research & training involving Native American students in public health. *Other professional posts*: Principal investigator & Director of the Faculty & Student Research Development Program of the American Indian Research Centers for Health (AIRCH5) as well as Director of the Research Core; serves as Co-Investigator & Co-Director of the Native Ameican Cancer Program research training initiative and as co-Investigator on the Community Outreach component with the Arizona Cancer Center. As Co-Investgator for the Arizona Study Center of the National Children's Study (DHHS Eunice Kennedy Shriver National Institute of Child Health & Human Development), she is responsible for the Tribal community engagement component. *Past professional posts*: Founding member and past co-chair of the Native Research Network; served as the director of the Southern Plains Inter-Tribal Epidemiology Center at the Oklahoma City Area Inter-Tribal Health Board; Fellow at the Northwest Portland Indian Health Board, NARCH, and a National Center for Minority Health & Health Disparities Scholar.

SOMDAY, FRANCIS (Colville)
(tribal executive director)
Affiliation & Address: Executive Director, Confederated Tribes of the Colville Reservation, P.O. Box 150, Nespelem, WA 99155 (509) 634-2212. E-mail: francis.somday@colvilletribes.com

SORBEL, IVAN (Oglala Lakota)
(executive director; board president)
Education: Chadron State College, BA (Criminal Justice). *Affiliation & Address*: Executive Director, Pine Ridge Area Chamber of Commerce, P.O. Box 375, Kyle, SD 57752 (605) 455-2685. *Other professional post*: Board President, The Laota Fund, Kye, SD.

SORRELL, DARLENE A., DDS (Navajo) 1959-
(dentist)
Born October 8, 1959, Fort Defiance, Ariz. *Education*: DDS. *Principal occupation*: Dentist. *Address*: 704 Rio Vita Dr., Rio Rancho, NM 87144 (505) 892-3124. *Affiliations*: Clinical Director, Albuquerque Indian Health Service Dental Clinic, 1994-present; vice-president, Society of American Indian Dentists, 1991-present. *Military service*: Indian Health Service - Commissioned Officer, 1985-present). *Awards, honors*: First Navajo dentist. *Community activities*: High School Principal Selection Committee, 1996, Rio Rancho, NM, 1996; Board member of the Circle of Light, Navajo Educatinal Project, 2002-present; Board member of the Community Dental Board, 2005; Board member of New Mexico Oral Health Council, 2005. *Memberships*: American Dental Association (1985-present); Commissioned Officers Association (1985-present); Oregon Health Sciences, University Alumni Association, 1985-

present); National Society of American Indian Dentists (1990-present); Association of Military Surgeons of the U.S. (1995-present); University of Arizona, American Indian Alumni Association (1997-present); North American Indian Women's Association (2000-present).

SOTO, JACK (Navajo/Cocopah)
(independent consultant; project coordinator)
Education: American University, BA (Public Affairs), MS (Organizational Development). *Affiliation & Address*: Independent Consultant (2011-present), Soto Consulting, P.O. Box 416, Yuma, AZ 85366 (202) 445-5211 (mobile). E-mail: jack.soto@gmail.com. *Other professional post*: Project coordinator (2012-present), National Coalition for the Advancement of Natives in Higher Education, Washington, DC. *Past professional posts*: Director (2007-12), Washington Internships for Native Students (WINS) Program, American University; staff, American University's Graduate Horizons, 2008-10; co-founder, American University's iVoteNative, 2008-10; staff assistant, National Indian Education Association, 2006; volunteer, Museum of the American Indian, Sithsonian Institution, 2005-06. Jack is an alumnus of AU and the WINS program, and was president & co-founder of the Native Communities Policy Center within the AUs chapter of the Roosevelt Institute, a student operated think-tank. *Awards, honors*: DC American Indian Society's Distinguished Service Award; As an AU graduate, he was recognized for his efforts on bringing American Indian issues and culture to the fore when he received the Multicultural Affairs Ideas Into Action award.

SOTO, ROBERT (Lipan Apache)
(tribal vice chairperson)
Affiliation & Address: Vice Chairperson, Lipan Apache Tribe of Texas, P.O. Box 8888, Corpus Christi, TX 78468 (361) 215-5121. E-mail: robtsoto@aol.com. *Other tribal position*: Director of Communications; newsletter editor.

SOUCIE, CHARISSE (Burns Paiute)
(tribal vice chairperson)
Affiliation & Address: Vice Chairperson, Burns Paiute Tribe, 100 PaSiGo St., Burns, OR 97720 (541) 573-1910. Website: www.burnspaiute-nsn.gov.

SOUERS, TWILA
(association president; editor)
Affiliations: Editor, "Native News," School Dist. 4J Indian Education Program, 3411-A Willamette St., Eugene, OR, 97405; Oregon Indian Education Association (president), 720 Nantucket, Eugene, OR 97404 (541) 687-3489.

SOULIER, ERVIN (Lake Superior Ojibwe)
(tribal chief judge)
Address & Affiliation: Bad River Reservation Tribal Court, P.O. Box 39, Odanah, WI 54861 (715) 682-7102 ext. 113.

SOUTHARD, PEGGY ANN (DEE) (*Starfire*) (United Lumbee) 1969-
(sociologist & anthropologist)
Education: Central Oregon Community College, AA, 1989; Southern Oregon State College, BA, 1991; University of Oregon, MS (Sociology), 1993, PhD (Sociology), 1997. E-mail: southard@ oregon.uoregon.edu. *Tribal affiliation*: Head Chief of the Beaver Clan of the United Lumbee Nation. *Affiliations*: Administrative analyst, Proteus Adult Training, Visalia, CA, 1975-83; business consultant/owner, Yesterday's Gone Bookstore, Bend, OR, 1983-89, and Pageantry Book Co. (mail order), 1989-96; professor's assistant, Southern Oregon State College, Ashland, OR, 1989-91; administrative assistant & assistant editor, University of Colorado, Boulder, CO, 1991-92; National Science Foundation Research Fellow, University of Oregon, Eugene, OR, 1992-95; sociology instructor, University of Oregon, Eugene, OR, 1993-present; sociology instructor, Central Oregon Community College, Bend, OR, 1995-present. *Community activities*: Oregon Council for the Humanities, Chautauqua Lecture Series Presenter, 1994-98; member of the Homeless Leadership Council, Deschutes County, Bend, OR, 1995-present; director, Low Income Families Together (LIFT) for Central & Southern Oregon, 1995-present; coordinator of the Global Homeless Discussion List & Electronic Archives, 1994-present, located at: http://csf.colorado.edu/ homeless. *Memberships*: Beaver Clan of the United Lumbee Nation (head chief); American Sociological Assn; Pacific Sociological Assn; International Assn of Visual Sociologists for Women in Society; Central Oregon Archaeological Society; Sociologists for Women in Society; Qualitative Researchers Assn; National Coalition for the Homeless; Phi Kappa Phi; Omicron Delta Kappa. *Published works*: Shelters are for Scum, and I Ain't No Bum!: Homeless People Who Avoid the Shelters (California Anthropology Press, 1992).

SPANGLER, TERESA (Lower Umpqua & Suislaw)
(tribal vice chairperson)
Affiliation & Address: Vice Chairperson, Confederated Tribes of Coos, Lower Umpqua & Suislaw Indians, 1245 Fulton Ave., Coos Bay, OR 97420 (541) 297-1655. E-mail: wbrainard@ctclusi.org

SPANIOLA, CHERYL L. (*Ikwe Awesii Saiagiiwed*) (Eastern Cherokee) 1954-
(Indian education program director)
Born October 2, 1954, Flint, Mich. *Education*: Bay Mills Community College, Native Language & Instructors Institute, 1999. *Address*: 2166 S. Elms Rd./8354 Cappy Lane, Swartz Creek, MI 48473 (810) 591-2312 ext. 252. E-mail: ikweawesii@juno.com. *Affiliations*: Director, Swartz Creek Indian Education Program, 1980-present; Native Language Instructors Institute, Bay Mills College, MI, 1994-present. *Community activities*: University of Michigan, Flint, Native American Indian Student Organization (annual powwow committee member, secretary, chair, 1983-95). *Memberships*: Genesee Valley Indian Association (powwow committee member - secretary, chair, 1983-95; board of directors - secretary, vice-chair, chair, 1989-95); Genesee County Indian Education Committee; National Indian Education Association; Michigan Indian Education Association; Anishinaabemowin Teg, Inc., 1998-.

SPARKMAN, RON (Shawnee)
(tribal chief)
Affiliation & Address: Chief, Shawnee Tribe, P.O. Box 189, Miami, OK 74355 (918) 542-2441; or, P.O. Box 860114, Shawnee, KS 66286 (913) 284-6635. E-mail: rondede1@gmail.com

SPARKS-ROBINSON, LILLIAN A. (Oglala/Sicangu Lakota)
(attorney; executive director)
Born in Baltimore, MD. *Education*: Morgan State University, B.A. (Political Sciences); Georgetown University Law Center, J.D. *Address & Affiliation*: Commissioner (2010-present), Administration for Native Americans (ANA), Dept. of Health & Human Services, 330 C St., SW, Washington, DC 20201 (202) 401-9246. *Past professional posts*: Executive director, National Indian Education Association (NIEA), Washington, DC, 2004-2010; Staff attorney with the National Congress of American Indians where she worked on international indigenous rights, sacred sites & religious protection, and issues related to youth & healthcare; staff attorney, National Indian Gaming Commission, U.S. Dept. of the Interior, Washington, DC. *Awards, honors*: Miss Sparks was a former Miss Indian World and named as one of seven young leaders in Indian Country; In 2004, was named one of seven young Native American Leaders by USA Today Magazine. *Memberships*: National Congress of American Indians; Native American Bar Association (past chapter president).

SPEAKS, STANLEY M. (Oklahoma Chickasaw) 1933-
(BIA regional director)
Born November 2, 1933, Tishomingo, Okla. *Education*: Northeastern State College, Tahlequah, OK, BS, 1959, MEd, 1962. *Affiliation & Address*: Director, Northwest Regional Office, Bureau of Indian Affairs, 911 NE 11th Ave., Portland, OR 97232 (503) 231-6702. *Past professional posts*: Supt., Anadarko Agency, BIA, 1975-77; area director, Anadarko Area Office, BIA, Anadarko, OK, 1976-80; director, Portland Area Office, BIA, Portland, OR, 1980-. *Community activities*: Boy Scouts of America (member-American Indian Relations Committee); 16th American Indian Tribal Leader's Seminar on Scouting (chairman, 1972-73); Rotary International (member); Oklahoma Governor's Committee on Small Business (member). *Awards, honors*: 2002 Inductee to the Chickasaw Nation Hall of Fame. *Interests*: Boating, fishing, hunting, golf; Boy Scouts of America.

SPEARMAN, GRANT (Avingaluk-Inupiaq name) 1951-
(museum curator)
Born April 24, 1951, Seattle, Wash. *Education*: University of Washington, BA, 1975. *Address*: 3022 Main St., Anaktuvuk Pass, AK 99721 (907) 661-3413. *Affiliation*: Curator, Simon Paneak Memorial Museum, Anaktuvuk Pass, AK, 1986-. *Memberships*: Museums Alaska; Alaska Anthropological Association; International Association of Arctic Social Scientists. *Interests*: Archaeology, ethnography, ethnology, oral history, aviation history.

SPEAS, DAWN (Tomaquag)
(consultant/director)
Education: University of Rhode Island (Fine Arts/Native Studies), 2006-09. *Affiliation & Address*: Consultant/Director (2014-present), Northeast Indigenous Arts Alliance, *Other professional post*: Owner/Artist/Cpnsultant 1987-present), House of Two Fires Studio at NativeConnect, board member, Native Americans in Philanthropy, 2007-present). *Past professional posts*: Tribal Secretary, Narragansett Indian Tribe, 2008-12; Native Arts Program Manager, New England Foundation for the Arts, 2007-14.

SPEARS, LOREN M. (Tomaquag)
(museum director; adjunct professor)
Education: University of Rhode Island, BS (Elementary Education & Teaching), 1988; University of New England, MSED (Elementary Education & Teaching), 2002. *Affiliation & Address*: Executive Director (2002-present), The Tomaquag Indian Memorial Museum, 390 Summit Rd., Exeter, RI 02822 (401) 491-9063. E-mail: lorenspears@tomaquagmuseum.com. *Other professional posts*:

Adjunct Professor, University of Rhode Island, 2014-present). Teaching Honors Seminar in Literature: American Indian/Indigenous Representation in Literature; Executive director, Nuweetooun School. *Past professional post*: Elementary teacher, Newport Public Schools, 1990-2002. Awards, honors: "Women of Distinction," International Gallery for Heritage & Culture, 2014; Special Drum Honoring, Rhode Island College New Egland Native American Culture Week, 2014. *Published works*: Through Our Eyes: An Indigenous View of Mashapaug Pond (Tomaquag Museum, 2012); Dawnland Voices: An Anthology of Indigenous Writings of New England (University of New England Press, 2014).

SPEARS, MICHAEL (Sicangu Lakota) 1977-
(actor; dancer, singer, speaker)
Born December 28, 1977 on the Lower Brule Reservation in South Dakota. Website: www.michaelspearsactor.com. He first won hearts – and widespread acclaim – as Otter, in the Academy Award-winning epic, Dances With Wolves. Spears appeared in 2012's Winter in the Blood; and this year, as Bud "One Bull" Ward in The Activist, and as Tenkill in Angels in Stardust. When not onstage or onscreen, Spears is an expert horseman and marksman, as well as a champion Lakota Traditional and Grass Dancer, hand drum singer, Lakota language speaker, and lead vocalist for the Bad Nation Singers. Along with frequent co-star Tonantzin Carmelo, Spears returns as co-host of AIFF 38's American Indian Motion Picture Awards.

SPEAS, MARGARET
(professor of linguistics, author)
Education: University of Arizona, MA; Massachusetts Institute of Technology, PhD. *Address & Affiliation*: Professor of Linguistics, University of Massachusetts, Amherst, Dept. of Linguistics, South College 220, Amherst, MA 01003 (413) 545-6833. E-mail: pspeasatlinguist.umass.edu. Margaret studied Navajo Linguistics with Professor Ken Hale, & attended several workshops at Dine College. Her doctoral dissertation, 'Adjunctions & Projections in Syntax,' examined how Navajo verbal & sentence structures compare & contrast with the structures of other languages around the world. Dr. Speas has worked with Navajo linguists, and has led numerous workshops for Navajo linguists and Navajo teachers interested in linguistics. Her paper, "From Rules to Principles in the Study of Navajo Syntax' explains some of the reasons that linguists have been interested in studying Navajo. *Other professional posts*: Founding member of the Board of Directors of the Navajo Language Academy, the mission of which is to promote scholarship on the Navajo language & support Navajo teachers in their efforts to ensure that the Navajo language will continue to live in future generations. *Published works*: Dine Bizaad, Binahoo'aah: Rediscovering the Navajo Language (Salina Bookshelf, 2008); numerous papers on the grammar of Navajo & other languages.

SPENCE, JUSTIN
(professor & director of Native American language center)
Affiliation & Address: Assistant Professor & Director of Native American Language Center, Department of Native American Studies, University of California, One Shields Ave., 2401 Hart Hall, Davis, CA 95616 (530) 752-9283. E-mail: jspence@ucdavis.edu

SPICER, VALERIE
(executive director)
Affiliation & Address: Executive Director, Arizona Indian Gaming Association, 521 S. 48th St., Tempe, AZ 85281 (480) 284-4034. *Past professional posts*: 26 years of gaming experience to AIGA, having worked in the private and public sectors. Most recently she was CEO of Gaming Strategies Group where she promoted business development with Tribal enterprises, governments and consulted to tribal and individually-owned businesses. She has consulted to the Oklahoma Indian Gaming Assn, Casino Omaha, Global Gaming Group, Arizona Indian Gaming Assn & Dick Clark Signature Entertainment. She was also Vice President & General Manager Borrego Springs Bank and provided marketing and public relations services to Viejas Enterprises. In addition she has held management positions with companies including Travelers Express, Ceridian/Comdata Corporation, Service Data Corporation and American Express. *Awards, honors*: She was named as a Great Woman of Gaming, Proven Leader 2011 by Casino Enterprise Management magazine. In 2004 she was named as one of the "Top 25 People To Watch" by Global Gaming Magazine. Spicer has contributed both her time and her talents to Indian gaming. She was co-chair for the landmark, ten-year Harvard/National Indian Gaming Association (NIGA) National Census Data Impact Study and founder and co-chair of the American Indian Business Network. She also served as Founding Chair for NIGA Spirit of Sovereignty Scholarship Foundation.

SPIELMANN, ROGER (*Shaganash*) 1951-
(associate professor)
Born April 13, 1951, Chicago, Ill. *Education*: University of Texas, Arlington, MA, 1978; University of British Columbia, PhD, 1984. E-mail: rspielma@ nickel.laurentian.ca. *Affiliation & Address*: Associate professor, Dept. of Native Studies, Laurentian University, Sudbury, ON, 1990-. *Other professional post*:

Algonquian language consultant. *Past professional post*: From 1983-1990, Roger served as coordinator of the Algonquin Language & Culture Program at Amo Asowan School in the community of Winneway. *Community activities*: board of directors, University of Sudbury. *Memberships*: American Anthropological Association; Survival International. *Awards, honors*: Anishnaabe World, winner of the 2011 Ontario Library Services—North, Louise de Kiriline Lawrence Award for non-fiction. *Interests*: Algonquian languages & cultures; Native education; Algonquian Discourse Analysis; sociolinguistics, ethnomethodology. *Published works*: You're So Fat!: Exploring Ojibwe Discourse (University of Toronto Press, 1998); Anishnaabe World: A Survival Guide for Building Bridges Between Canada & First Nations (Scrivener Press, 2009); numerous articles on the Algonquian language in journals & books.

SPILBURY, DELAINE (Western Shoshone) 1937-
(Indian shop owner)
Born September 21, 1937, Ely, Nev. *Affiliation & Address*: Owner, Ms. Squaw Indian Art, Crafts, and Jewelry, 2429 Salt Lake St., N. Las Vegas, NV, 1973-present (866) 212-7774; (775) 235-7557. Website: www.mssquaw.com. A wholesale company offering sterling jewelry, crafts, fine arts, and traditional archery. *Community activities*: Director, Powwow of the 4 Winds. *Membership*: National Bowhunting Rights Organization. *Awards, honors*: National Field Archery Association - Big Game Awards. *Interests*: Bowhunting; traveling the West to promote Native craftsmen. *Biographical sources*: National Bowhunter magazine; Native Nevadan magazine; Indian Trader magazine.

SPILDE, KATHERINE
(institute chairperson)
Education: MBA, PhD. *Affiliation & Address*: Chairperson, Sycuan Institute on Tribal Gaming, San Diego State University, 5500 Campanile Dr., PSFA 430, San Diego, CA 92812 (619) 594-4443. E-mail: kspilde@mail.sdsu.edu. Dr. Spilde is a cultural anthropologist specializing in tribal government gaming. Her areas of research include the economic & social impacts of gambling and Indian gaming, responsible gaming & corporate social responsibility, needs assessment & program evaluation, federal recognition, and tribal governance. She has worked with 100 tribal governments in the United States on economic development & gaming issues & does applied work on inter-governmental relations, business development and mitigation. She is currently working on responsible gaming program developed by investigating the ways that casino operators & tribal governments can work together to develop comprehensive education & prevention programs for employees & casino guests.

SPINNIKEN, DAVE (Ottawa)
(editor)
Affiliatio & Addressn: GTB News, Grand Traverse Band of Ottawa & Chippewa Indians, 2605 N. West Bayshore Dr., Peshawbestown, MI 49682 (231) 271-7366. E-mail: dspinn@gtbindians.com

SPIVEY, TOWANA (Chickasaw) 1943-
(curator, archaeologist)
Born November 8, 1943, Madill, Okla. *Education*: Southeastern State University, BA, 1968; University of Oklahoma, 1970-71. *Principal occupation*: Curator, archaeologist. *Address*: 2101 Oak St., Duncan, OK 73533. *Affiliation*: Curator of anthropology, Museum of the Great Plains, Lawton, OK, 1974-. *Other professional posts*: Curator-archaeologist, Oklahoma Historical Society, 1974-; archaeologist, Oklahoma Archaeological Survey (two years). *Military service*: Army National Guard, 1960-68. *Memberships*: Oklahoma Anthropological Society, 1963- (board member); Oklahoma Museums Association, 1973- (council member); Society for Historic Archaeology, 1973-; Council on Abandoned Military Posts (vice president of Oklahoma Department, 1975-). *Interests*: Historic sites-restoration, archaeology, etc.; 19th century military forts & camps; fur trade & exploration of Trans-Mississippi West; conservation of cultural material or artifacts; wagon restoration! *Published works*: Co-author, An Archaeological Reconnaissance of the Salt Plains Areas of Northwest Oklahoma (Museum of the Great Plains, 1976); co-author, Archaeological Investigations Along the Waurika Pipeline (Museum of the Great Plains, 1977).

SPOONHUNTER, HARVEY (Northern Arapahoe)
(tribal co-chairperson)
Affiliation: Northern Arapahoe Tribe, P.O. Box 396, Fort Washakie, WY 82514 (307) 332-6120. Website: www.northernarapaho.com.

SPOONHUNTER, LEE (Northern Arapahoe)
(tribal co-chairperson)
Affiliation & Address: Co-Chairperson, Northern Arapahoe Tribe, P.O. Box 396, Fort Washakie, WY 82514 (307) 332-6120.

SPOONHUNTER, MARLIN (Northern Arapaho)
(Indian college president)
Affiliation & Address: President, Wind River Tribal College, P.O. Box 1190, Washakie, WY 82514 (307) 335-8243. E-mail: mspoonhunter@windrivertc.org.

SPOTTED BEAR, ALYCE (Mandan/Hidatsa)
(educator)
Education: Dickinson State College (ND), BS, 1970; Penn State University, MA in Education, 1978; Cornell University, PhD Candidate in Education. *Home address*: P.O. Box 86, Halliday, ND 58636. Affiliation & Address: Vice President, Native American Studies/Tribal Relations, Frt Berthod Community College, P.O. Box 490, New Town, ND 58763. (701) 627-4738. *Past professional posts*: Supt., Twin Buttes School District #37, 1993-96; President, Fort Berthold Community College, 1997; Visiting Instructor, Native American Studies, Dartmouth College, Hanover, NH, 1998-2013 (taught course entitled, "American Indian Women of the Plains: A Social History." *Community activities*: ND Committee to Prevent Child Abuse Advisory Committee, 1994-present. *Awards, honors*: Native American Women of Upstate NY Recognition "Hall of Fame," 1990-91; Anonymous Donor Fellowship, Cornell U., 1992-93; Educational; Leadership Award, TAT Tribal Education Dept., 1993; Educator of the Year, TAT Tribal Government, 1994; New York State Minority Fellowship, Cornell U., 1997-98; David L. Call Achievement Award, Cornell U., 1997.

SPOTTED EAGLE, CHRIS (Houma)
(documentary filmmaker; president-Indian society)
Address: 2524 Hennepin Ave., Minneapolis, MN 55401 (612) 377-4212. *Affiliation*: American Indian Talent Society, 2225 Cavell Ave. North, Golden Valley, MN 55427.

SPOTTED ELK, DAVINA (Navajo)
(project director)
Affiliation & Address: Project Director, The Four Corners Teacher Training Project, Center for Indian Education, Arizona State University, School of Social Transformation, MC: 4902, Payne 302 B, P.O. Box 874902, Tempe, AZ 85287 (480) 965-3264. E-mail: dspotted@asu.edu. *Published work*: Strong Marriages for Navajo Couples: Activity Book for Couples, Editor, et al (Utah State University, Cooperative Extension, 2007)

SPOTTEDBIRD, LAWRENCE (Kiowa)
(tribal manager; consultant)
Affiliation: Manager, Sitka Tribe of Alaska, Stka, AK. Spent 34 years working with tribes & Native American entrepreneurs on business & economic development. He currently runs a consulting firm, SpottedBird Development.

SPOTTEDEAGLE, CHRIST (Paiute)
(tribal vice chairperson)
Affiliation & Address: Vice Chairperson, Las Vegas Paiute Tribe, 1 Paiute Dr., Las Vegas, NV 89106 (702) 386-3926.

SPRAGUE, DAVID K. (Pottawatomi)
(former tribal chairperson)
Affiliation & Address: Former Chairperson (1992-2015), Match-e-be-nash-she-wish Band of Pottawatomi Indians, P.O. Box 218, Dorr, MI 49323 (616) 681-8830. *Military service*: U.S. Army (six years; Vietnam Veteran). David (D.K.) has served in the capacity of Tribal Chairperson since the Tribe began the federal acknowledgment process in 1992. His leadership was instrumental in achieving federal acknowledgment. He has been active in the Native American community for many years and is looked upon with admiration and respect. He is a veteran of the US Army and served six years of active duty and one tour in Vietnam. Our chairman has volunteered his services to the American Red Cross to assist in thirteen disasters worldwide. Chairman Sprague represents the Bradley voting district.

SPRAGUE, DONOVIN (Minnicoujou Lakota)
(university instructor, director of cultural center, author)
Born on the Cheyenne River Sioux Reservation, Dupree, S.D. *Education*: Black Hills State University, BS; University of South Dakota, MA. *Principal occupation*: University instructor & education director at Crazy Horse Memorial. *Address*: Crazy Horse Memorial, Ave. of the Chiefs, Rapid City, SD 57730 (605) 673-4681. E-mail: memorial@crazyhorse.org. Website: www.crazyhorse memorial.org. *Affiliations*: University instructor at the Indian University of North America, Crazy Horse Memorial, 1996-present; director, Native American Educational & Cultural Center, and assistant director of Indian Museum of North America, 1996-present. *Other professional posts*: Owner, Rock-N-Records, 1985-present; part-time instructor in Lakota Studies, Oglala Lakota College, 1988-; part-time instructor in American Indian Studies, Black Hills State University, 1990-present. *Past professional posts*: General manager-Lakota Radio (100,000 watts), KILI-FM, 1995-96; American Indian coordinator, Iowa Regents Universities (Iowa State, U. of Iowa, & U. of Northern Iowa), 1994-95. *Community activities*: Rapid City (SD) Indian/White Relations Committee (member & chairperson); Rapid City Human Relations Commission; Rapid City Minority Relations Committee; Rapid City Area Schools-Indian Education; Board President of Rapid City American Indian Development Corporation; Rapid City Office Manager of United Sioux Tribes, Choctaw Nation of OK, Citizen Potawatomi Nation, OK. *Memberships*: Cheyenne River Sioux Tribe (enrolled member); Wounded Knee Survivors Assn; American

Indian Science & Engineering Society (AISES); National Indian Education Assn (NIEA). *Awards, honors*: Donovin Sprague Day, March 23, 1994, proclaimed by Mayor of Rapid City, SD; received grandfather's name, "Hump," on Wounded Knee Day, Dec. 29, 2002, in a ceremony; award winning flutes in art shows; movie extra in the movie, "Lakota Woman." *Interests*: Musician: guitar/vocals - music productions; artist: Lakota flute maker; instructor in Lakota arts & crafts; historical field research. Mr. Sprague writes, "Lecturer in American Indian studies (through-out the U.S. & Canada), such as the warrior, Crazy Horse & the Battle of the Little Bighorn, Fetterman Fight, and Wagon Box Fight in which my Great, Great Grandfather, Chief Hump led his warriors. Hump's father was also named Hump and was the uncle of Chief Crazy Horse." *Published works*: *Books*: Cheyenne River Sioux, 2003; Standing Rock Sioux, 2004; Pine Ridge Reservation, 2004; & Rosebud Sioux, 2005. *Music*: CD producer of the band "Shakedown," 2002. The band features Brandon Sprague who was opening act on 2004 B.B. King northern U.S. tour.

SPRAGUE, SCOTT (Pottawatomi)
(tribal chairperson)
Affiliation & Address: Chairperson, Match-e-be-nash-she-wish Band of Pottawatomi Indians, 2872 Mission Dr., Dorr, MI 49344 (269) 397-1780. Scott represents the Bradley Voting District and has been a member of the Gun Lake Tribal Council since 2014. As a Tribal Elder, Scott is a family man – proud husband and father of four, with four amazing grandchildren. Since moving back to Michigan in 2012, Scott has made a commitment to expand his knowledge of the Pottawatomi culture while renewing old relationships and starting many new ones with fellow Gun Lake Tribal Citizens. Scott has been instrumental to the success of Gun Lake Casino as a member of the Executive Team and the Director of Facilities. He is dedicated to the success, viability and economic prosperity of the Gun Lake Tribe, Tribal Government and all enterprise endeavors. Scott has been a member of the Asset & Liability Committee, the Gun Lake Tribal Gaming Commission, Housing Committee and the Revenue Allocation Plan Committee. Even with that busy schedule, Scott is committed to making sure that all citizens know that he is always available to listen to any concerns, ideas, critiques or suggestions that they may have.

SPRINGER, MARION (Choctaw)
(Indian dollmaker)
Address: 720 Mirage Lake Rd., Adelanto, CA 92301 (760) 388-4002. E-mail: ddakota@earthlink.net. *Artwork*: Original handmade Indian dolls. Website: wwwauthameriindiandolls.com

SPURR, LAURA (Huron Potawatomi)
(tribal chairperson)
Education: University of Michigan, B.S. (Nursing), 1967; DePaul University, M.A. (Nursing Admin. & Education). *Affiliation*: Chairperson, Nottawaseppi Band of Huron Potawatomi, 2221 - 1.5 Mile Rd., Fulton, MI 49052 (616) 729-5151. E-mail: lspurr@nhbpi.com *Past professional posts*: Nursing posts for over 40 years; Laura has been a member of the tribal council since 1999 serving as chair of the Education & Health Committees and working with the elders group.

STAINBROOK, CRIS (Oglala Lakota)
(foundation president)
Education: University of Iowa, BS; Oregon State University, MS (Fisheries Science). *Affiliation & Address*: President, Indian Land Tenure Foundation, 151 E. County Road B2, Little Canada, MN 55117 (651) 766-8999. *Other professional post*: Board member of the Minnesota Community Foundation & the St. Paul Foundation. *Past professional posts*: Program Officer & Community Activities Lead, Northwest Area Foundation (13 years); founding member & board member for 11 years of Native Americans in Philanthropy; founder & advisory committee member of the Two Feathers Endowment of the St. Paul Foundation.

STALLINGS, STEVEN L.A. (Rincon Nation Luiseno) 1951-
(banking director; association president)
Born May 12, 1951, San Diego, Calif. *Education*: California State University, Long Beach, BS; University of Southern California, MBA. *Principal occupation*: Banking services director; association president. *Address*: National Center for American Indian Enterprise Development, 953 E. Juanita Ave., Mesa, AZ 85204 (800) 423-0452 or (602) 831-7524. *Affiliations*: President, National Center for American Indian Enterprise Development, Mesa, AZ, 1976-; Sr. V.P. & Director, Wells Fargo Native American Banking Services, Phoenix, AZ, 2002- present (responsible for the nationwide delivery of financial-services products to Native American communities & enterprises). *Other professional posts*: Council member, Rincon Nation of Luiseno Indians, Valley Center, CA; board member, "Native Peoples" magazine, Phoenix, AZ. *Past professional posts*: Prior to joining the National Center, Mr. Stallings was executive director of a consulting firm in San Francisco, & supervised a job creation program which trained 300 American Indians. *Community activities*: Coordinator for the National Congress of American Indians, a lobbying group; former member of the steering committee for the National Indian Education Association; member

of Board of Directors for a beginning Development Band directed at solving the domestic financing needs of American Indians; member of Advisory Committee for 1984 Olympics; served on Los Angeles Bicentennial Commission and the Los Angeles Private Industry Council; appointed to the Los Angeles City/County Indian Commission by Republican Supervisor Dean Dana. *Awards, honors*: Cited and recognized by the State Assembly of California for his contributions and efforts in small business & economic development; Session chairman, Fifth International Symposium on Small Business, 1978; delegate to the White House Conference on Small Business, 1978. *Interests*: The National Center assists over 600 businesses annually and has secured over $200 million in financing and contracts for its clients. Long interested in developing American Indian talent, an interest that has accelerated since the formation of UIDA's Management Institute that trains Indian managers, Mr. Stallings has conducted dozens of workshops & seminars. Two of his training books are used throughout America by Indians learning planning & manage-ment. *Biographical sources*: Who's Who in Finance and Industry, 1982-1983; Who's Who in the West, 1982-1983. *Published work*: Directory of American Indian Businesses (National Center for American Indian Enterprise Development).

STANDING BEAR, E. SEAN (Osage)
(oral historian, artist)
Affiliation: Osage Tribal Council, P.O. Box 779, Pawhuska, OK 74056 (918) 287-1085. *Published work*: "Art of the Osage," with Garrick Bailey, Daniel C. Swan, and John W. Nunley (University of Washington Press, 2004).

STANDING BEAR, GEOFFREY (Osage)
(tribal principal chief)
Affiliation & Address: Principal Chief, Osage Nation of Oklahoma, P.O. Box 1449, Pawhuska, OK 74056 (918) 287-5555.

STANDING BEAR, ZUG G. (Kompau*skwe)
(Kanienkehaka/Abenaki/Wampanoag/Metis) 1941-
(professor)
Born January 10, 1941, Boston, Mass. Education: University of Nebraska, BS; The George Washington University, MSFS; University of Southern California, MSEd; Jacksonville (AL) State University, MPA; Florida State University, PhD; Fellow in Forensic Medicine, The Armed Forces Institute of Pathology, Washington, DC. *Principal occupation*: Professor. *Address*: 514 Hopi Circle, Divide, CO 80814 (719) 687-8087. E-mail: mgspikers@aol.com. *Affiliation*: Valdosta State University, Dept. of Sociology, Valdosta, GA, 19086-95; Colorado State University, Dept. of Sociology, Fort Collins, CO, 1995-2001; Associate professor & coordinator of Forensic Health Science Programs, University of Colorado, Colorado Springs, CO, 2001-present. *Other professional posts*: Secretary (1987-88), chairman (1988-90), program co-chair (1995-96), General Section, American Academy of Forensic Sciences; program committee member, Academy of Criminal Justice Sciences (1996-97); chairman, Ethics Committee, International Assn of Forensic Nurses (1995-present); member, Commission on Gender Equality, Colorado State University (1997-2000); consultant in criminal justice, criminal investigation, and forensic science administration, organization, management, & curriculum design, 1981-; member, Governor's Criminal Justice Coordinating Council (State of Georgia, 1988-92). *Military service*: U.S. Army, 1958-81 - Special Agent, U.S. Army Criminal Investigation Command (Bronze Star, Vietnam, 1970; Meritorious Service Medals, oak leaf cluster; Army Commendation Medals, oak leaf cluster). *Community activities*: Lowndes Drug Action Council (member, Board of Directors, 1992-95); Valdosta Symphony Orchestra (member, Board of Directors, 1993-95); Black on Black Crime Committee, Valdosta (member); Community Policing Transition Project, Valdosta Police Dept. (member, Leadership Council, 1994-95); Readership Board, The Valdosta Daily Times, 1994-95; treasurer, Wolves Offered Life & Friendship, Inc., LaPorte, Colo., 1995-2000; administrator, The Flash & Thelma Memorial Hedgehog Rescue, Inc., Divide, Colo., 1997-present. *Memberships*: American Academy of Forensic Sciences (Fellow); American College of Forensic Examiners (Life Fellow); American Sociological Assn; American Society of Criminology; Academy of Criminal Justice Sciences (Life Member); National Congress of American Indians; Association on American Indian Affairs; Vietnam Veterans of America; Veterans for Peace; National Organization for Women; American Association of University Professors; International Association of Forensic Nurses (Distinguished Fellow). *Awards, honors*: Service Award & Distinguished Fellow Award, International Assn of Forensic Nurses, 1994, 1995; Meritorious Service Award, American Academy of Forensic Sciences, 1996; numerous military awards, 1960-81. *Biographical sources*: Who's Who in American Education (1992-97); Who's Who in America (1996-2002). *Published works*: Books: Law Enforcement (U. of Florida, Dept. of Continuing Education, 1985); Criminology (U. of Florida, Dept. of Continuing Education, 1985). Articles: "Crime Statistics in Nursing" (Journal of Psychosocial Nursing and Mental Health Services, Oct. 1996); "Will the Vision be Co-Opted: Forensic Nursing and Death Investigation (Journal of Psychosocial Nursing and Mental Health Services, Sept. 1995); "To Guard Against Invading Indians: Struggling for

Native Community in the Southeast" (American Indian Culture & Research Journal, Nov. 1994); "Crime Scene Responders: The Imperative Sequential Steps (Critical Care Nursing Quarterly, May 1999); numerous articles.

STANLEY, MICHELE (Saginaw Ojibwe)
(board president)
Affiiation & Address: Board President, Midwest Alliance of Sovereign Tribes (MAST), 1011 Main St., P.O. Box 265, Gresham, WI 54128 (715) 787-4494.

STANLEY, NATALIE T. 1963-
(museum interpreter)
Born December 4, 1963, Fort Riley, Kans. Education: Christopher Newport College, BA, 1985; William & Mary (continuing education courses in archaeology & Virginia Native American culture.) *Principal occupation*: Museum interpreter. *Address*: 81 Robinson Dr., Newport News, VA 23601 (804) 595-4931. *Affiliation*: Interpreter (conduct tours through Indian Village; presents slide show on the Eastern Woodland Indian culture), Syms-Eaton Museum & Kecoughtan Indian History Center, Hampton, VA, 1985-91. *Memberships*: The Lower James Chapter of the Archaeological Society of Virginia, (founder & president, 1988-; Kicotah Chapter of ASV (vice-president, 1986-87). *Interests*: "Apart from interpreter, I'm an active researcher of Native American cultures; work with Virginia & North Carolina tribal members. Assist other researchers; research & reconstruct native dwellings & implements; have working knowledge of Native American domestic skills; participate and attend Native American festivals; work with archaeologists - research & site work."

STARK, HEIDI (*Kiiwetinepineslik*) (Turtle Mountain Ojibwe)
(professor of Indigenous Governance)
Education: University of Minnesota, PhD (American Studies), 2008. *Affiliation & Address*: Assistant Professor & Director, Indigenous Governance Program, Faculty of Human & Social Development, University of Victoria, 3800 Finnerty Rd., HSD Bldg., Rm. A260, Victoria, BC V8W 2Y2 (250) 721-6438. *Current Research*: Indigenous Comparative Politics, Native Diplomacy & Treaty & Aboriginal Rights; Anishinaabe treaty-making with the U.S. & Canada. *Published works*: Co-author of third edition of American Indian Politics & the American Political System, with David E. Wilkins, 2010; Stealing Fire, Scattering Ashes: Anishinaabe Treaty-Relations & U.S. & Canada State Formation (University of Minnesota Press, 2012).

STARKS, RACHEL ROSE (Zuni/Navajo)
(research analyst & coordinator)
Born & raised in the Pueblo of Zuni, N.M. *Education*: Wheaton College, BA (Sociology); University of Arizona, MA (Sociology); NNI Graduate student. *Affiliation & Address*: Research Analyst & Coordinator, Native Nations Institute (NNI), The University of Arizona, 803 E. First St., Tucson, AZ 85719 (520) 626-5756. E-mail: rstarks@u.arizona.edu. She has participated in research on per capita distributions of tribal revenue, comparing the tribal economic changes from 1990-2000 using the U.S. Census, Native arts leadership, border tribes, asset building, tribal justice systems, and Indigenous rural development in Alberta. Rachel began work at NNI as a graduate student in 2000, and joined the staff in 2005. *Published works*: Starks, R.R., and A. Quijada-Mascarenas. 2012 (in press). Indigenous peoples and the U.S.-Mexico border wall. In *The Border Wall between Mexico and the United States. Venues, Mechanisms and Stakeholders for a Constructive Dialogue*, eds. A. Cùrdova, C.A. de la Parra, and E. Peters. Tlalpan, Mexico: SEMARNAT. Starks, R.R., J. McCormack, and S. Cornell. 2011. *Native Nations and U.S. Borders: Challenges to Indigenous Culture, Citizenship, and Security*. Tucson: Native Nations Institute. Cornell, S., R. Goldtooth, M. Jorgensen, R.R. Starks, and others. 2010. *Making First Nations Law: The Listuguj Mi'gmaq Fishery*. Tucson and Vancouver: Native Nations Institute and National Centre for First Nations Governance. Starks R.R., and A. Quijada-Mascarenas. 2009. Convergence of Borders: Indigenous Peoples and Environmental Conservation at the U.S.-Mexico Border. In *Conservation of Shared Environments: Learning from the United States and Mexico*, eds. Edited L. Lopez-Hoffman, E. McGovern, R.G. Varady, and K. Flessa. Tucson: University of Arizona Press. Jorgensen, M., and R. Starks. 2008. *Leadership Development in the Native Arts and Culture Sector*. New York: Ford Foundation. Subsumed in the 2010 Ford Foundation report, *Native Arts and Cultures: Research, Growth, and Opportunities for Philanthropic Support*, as "Supporting a Burgeoning Revival of Native Arts: Leaders Wanted," pp. 16-27. Jorgensen, M., M. Begay, N. Pryor, A. Sadongei, J. Snell, R. Starks, and J. Timeche. 2005. *Native Cultural Arts Organizations: Who They Are and What They Need*. Report prepared for Atlatl, Inc. Tucson: Native Nations Institute.

STARR, RACHEAL N. . (Tonkawa)
(former tribal president)
Affiliation & Address: Secretary/Treasurer, Tonkawa Tribe of Oklahoma, 1 Rush Buffalo Rd., Tonkawa, OK 74653 (580) 628-2561. Website: www.tonkawatribe.com.

STAUDENMMAIER, HEIDI McNEIL
(attorney)

Education: University of Iowa, BA (Journalism), 1981; University of Iowa, College of Law, JD, 1985. *Affiliation & Address*: Snell & Wilmer, Attorneys-at-Law, One Arizona Center, 400 E. Van Buren St., Suite 1900, Phoenix, AZ 85004-2202. (602) 382-6366. E-mail: hstaudenmaier@swlaw.com. Heidi is nationally recognized in the areas of Indian law, gaming law & business litigation. *Awards, honors*: First American Leadership Award, National Center for American Indian Enterprise Development, 2001; Top Ten Great Women of Gaming, 2006; Arizona's Finest Lawyers, 2011; Chambers Global: America's Leading Lawyers for Business, Gaming & Gambling, 2012-13; Chambers USA: rica's Leading Lawyers for Business, Native American Law (2009-2013); Gaming & Licensing, 2013; The Best Lawyers in America, Commercial Litigation, Gaming Lawm Native Ameican Law (2005-13); Phoenix Gaming Lawyer of the Year, 2011. *Memberships*: State Bar of Arizona, Indian Law Section, Founding Member & Past Chairperson; Native American Bar Association of Arizona, Founding Member. *Published works*: "Effect of Patchak on Tribal Trust Lands," Co-author, Casino Lawyer (Spring 2013).

STAUSS, JOSEPH H. "JAY" (Jamestown S'Klallam)
(professor)

Education: Washington State University, PhD, 1972. *Address & Affiliation*: American Indian Studies (AIS) Program (director, 1992-2002), University of Arizona, Harvill 226D, Box 210076, Tucson, AZ 85721 (520) 621-0812. E-mail: jstaus@email.arizona.edu. *Other professional post*: Co-administrator of a multi-year grant from The Economic Research Service, U.S. Dept. of Agriculture and AIS Program at UA to facilitate research on the impact of food assistance programs on American Indian reservations. *Areas of Interest*: American Indian Studies Program Development; Pacific Northwest tribes. Presently, he is focused on the Indian Shaker Church of the Pacific Northwest. *Published works*: Native American Studies in Higher Education (Alta Mira Press, 2002); text co-edited with Duane Champagne, The Jamestown S'Klallam Story: Rebuilding a Northwest Coast Indian Tribe (Jamestown S'Klallam Tribe, 2002).

STAVIN, BRETT (Mohawk)
(attorney)

Education: University of Miami, BA, 2008; O'Connor College of Law, Arizona State University, JD, 2013. *Affiliation & Address*: Associte Attorney, Rosette, LLP, 1100 H St. NW, Suite 400, Washington, DC 20005 (202) 652-0579. E-mail: bstavin@rosettelaw.com. Brett joined Rosette, LLP in 2013 after graduating from the Sandra Day O'Connor College of Law, where he focused his studies on federal Indian law. While in law school, he spent time as a law clerk for the Office of the General Counsel for the Salt River Pima–Maricopa Indian Community and was also a judicial extern at the Arizona Court of Appeals. He has experience working on matters pending in tribal, state, and federal courts. His practice has largely focused on issues involving e-commerce, business disputes, and internal tribal government matters. As a staff writer and Executive Managing Editor of the Arizona State Law Journal, he published an article on the federal trust responsibility to Indian tribes, titled Responsible Remedies: Suggestions for Indian Tribes in Trust Relationship Cases, 44 Ariz. St. L.J. 1743 (2012). The article examines jurisdictional problems that arise when tribes sue the federal government for breach of common law trust duties and how those problems might be avoided. Brett is a descendant of the Mohawk Tribe of the Kahnawake Reservation in Canada.

STEARNS, CHRISTOPHER T. (Navajo) 1964-
(attorney)

Born December 13, 1964 in Los Angeles, Calif. *Education*: Williams College, BA, 1986; Cornell Law School, JD, 1989. *Address & Affiliation*: Of Counsel, Hobbs, Straus, Dean & Walker, LLP (Associate, 1989-94; Partner, 2001-present), 2120 L St., NW, Suite 700, Washington, DC 20037 (202) 822-8282. E-mail: cstearns@hobbsstraus.com. He specializes in the practice of energy, health care, self-determination and self-governance, education, campaign and election law, and matters involving the U.S. Congress and federal agencies. *Other professional posts*: Chris is currently in his second term as Chairman of the Washington State Gambling Commission, the second oldest gambling regulatory agency in the nation. He was first appointed to the Commission by Governor Jay Inslee in 2013. In the past two years, the Commission has successfully renegotiated numerous tribal-state gaming compacts, including a major market-based class III machine increase. The Commission has been an international leader in the criminal investigation of unlawful internet gaming, and has taken on leading roles in policies surrounding fantasy sports, internet poker, and skill-based gaming. *Past professional posts*: In 1994, Mr. Stearns worked as Counsel to the House of Representatives Sub-committee on Native American Affairs for then Chairman, Bill Richardson (D-NM) where he helped secure passage of the 1994 Indian Self-Determination Act Amendments; from 1995-98, he served as Democratic Counsel to the U.S. House Committee on Resources where he handled Native American issues for Ranking Member, George Miller (D-CA). Among the issues for which he had direct oversight were Indian gaming, labor relations, health care, federal recognition, the original Title V Self-Governance legislation, amendments to the Indian Child Welfare Act, and California Indian Policy; between 1998 & 2000, he served as Director of Indian Affairs at the U.S. Dept. of Energy under Secretary Bill Richardson. He oversaw all national DOE tribal relations & policy initiatives. In 1998, he was appointed by President Bill Clinton as the first-ever Director of Indian Affairs for the U.S. Department of Energy where he helped Energy Secretary Bill Richards craft Indian energy policy & build tribal relations. Mr. Stearns served as the North Dakota state campaign director for former Vice-President Al Gore's campaign in the 2000 presidential campaign. He was the first-ever Native American appointed to such a senior position within a presidential campaign. Chris later spent four years as the political advisor to the President of the National Congress of American Indians. He also worked on Senator John Kerry's 2004 presidential campaign in New Mexico, on Governor Bill Richardson's 2002 campaign in New Mexico, & on President Barack Obama's 2008 campaigns in Washington State. *Awards, honors*: He is the first Native American appointed to the position of state director in presidential campaign history. He also served two terms as Chairman of the City of Seattle's Human Rights Commission where he led efforts on police accountability, on jobs assistance legislation for people with criminal records, and he also testified before the United Nations on indigenous rights. Chris helped establish Native Vote Washington, a nonpartisan, nonprofit corporation whose purpose is to increase Native American participation in elections. *Membership*: Native American Bar Assn (board member); District of Columbia Bar Assn.

STEBBINS, SUSAN ANN (Mohawk/Metis) 1951-
(professor of Native American studies)

Born March 15, 1951, Springfield, Mass. *Education*: Florida Atlantic University, BA; VCU, MA; SUNY Albany, Doctor of Arts. *Affiliation & Address*: Associate Professor (1992-present), Department of Anthropology, SUNY College at Potsdam, 246 MacVicar Hall, 44 Pierre Point Ave., Potsdam, NY 13676 (315) 267-2047; E-mail: stebbisa@potsdam.edu. *Past professional posts*: Richmond Public Schools, Richmond, VA, 1972-82; Girls Incorporated, Schenectady, NY, 1988-92. *Other professional post*: Director of Native American Studies, SUNY, Potsdam. *Community activities*: North Country Public Radio Advisory Board. *Membership*: American Society for Ethnohistory.

STEELE, DAVID (Pomo)
(tribal vice chairperson)

Affiliation & Address: Vice Chairperson, Hopland Band of Pomo Indians, 3000 Shanei Rd., Hopland, CA 95449 (707) 472-2111. E-mail: dsteele@hoplandtribe.com

STEELE, JOHN (*Yellow Bird*) (Oglala Sioux)
(former tribal president)

Affiliation & Address: Former President (1992-94, 1996-98, 2000-04, 2010-12), 2014-16), Oglala Sioux Tribal Executive Committee, Pine Ridge Indian Reservation, P.O. Box 2070, Pine Ridge, SD 57770 (605) 867-5326. E-mail: johns@oglala.org. *Other professional post*: Aberdeen (SD) Area Representative, National Indian Health Board, Washington, DC.

STEELE, LOIS G. (Fort Peck Assiniboine) 1939-
(physician; family practitioner)

Born November 27, 1939, Washington, D.C. *Education*: Colorado College, BA, 1961; University of Montana, MS, 1969; University of Minnesota Medical School, Duluth & Minneapolis, MD, 1978. *Affiliation & Addresses*: 100 Tilbury Dr., Kearny, AZ 85237 (520) 363-5573; 2360 W. Canada, Tucson, AZ 85746 (520) 578-0644; (520) 383-7211 (work); Continental Family Medical Center, 1260 S. Campbell Ave., Green Valley, AZ 85614 (520) 625-3691. *Past professional post*: Clinical Director, Sells Service Unit, USPHS-Indian Health Service, Tucson, AZ, 1980-2000; Clinical Director, Pascua Yaqui Health Dept., 1986-91; director, Indians Into Medicine Program (INMED), University of New Mexico. *Community activities*: Assistant Cub Scout Master, 1986, 1988-89; PTA, 1986-90; United Way, Tucson (board member); Holy Way Presbyterian Church, Tucson (Deacon, 1991); Theodore & Vivian Johnson Foundation (board member). *Memberships*: Association of American Indian Physicians; American Academy of Family Physicians; American Medical Association; Commissioned Officers of America; Arizona Academy of Family Physicians. *Awards, honors*: Faculty President, Dawson College, 1972; Outstanding Woman Medical Student, Lampson Award, U. of Minnesota Medical School, Duluth, 1976; Distinguished Achievement Award, Rocky Mountain College Alumni Assn, 1981; National Indian Health Board - Honoree, 1982; selected as Advisory Committee Member, FDA - Consumer Status, 1982-83; U. of North Dakota Indian Students Association, Time-Out Award, 1983; Wonder Women Foundation - Finalist, 1983; USPHS Unit Commendation, April 1988; American Indian Science & Engineering Society Eli Parker Award, 1989; Indian Health Service Award for Health Promotion, Disease Prevention Work, 1989; Pascua Yaqui Project Head Start Volunteer Award, 1991; AMA Physicians Recognition Award, 1991-1993; et al. *Interests*: Member, "Saturday Group" Sophisticated Dancers of Tucson - woman's tap dance performing group; numerous presentations, workshops, field readings & consulting positions over the years. *Research and Publications*: "(AIDS) Education Among Native Americans in

Arizona: The Pascua Yaqui, Navajo Nation & Urban Indian Experience". May 1990; Stone & Steele. Presented at the International AIDS Conference in Puerto Rico; "Leading Causes of Death Among Yaqui Indians, 1970-90" Sept. 1990 - Presented at American Public Health Associations Annual Meeting, New York; "Cardiovascular Risk Among the Pascua Yaqui" April 1991. Presented at the IHS National Research Conference, Tucson; among others.

STEELE, NANCY RICHARDSON (Karuk)
(language specialist & consultant)
Address: 381 Fern Lane, Crescent City, CA 95531 (707) 464-6365. E-mail: bnsteele@charter.net. *Affiliation*: Board member, Advocates for Indigenous California Languages, Vallejo, CA; board member, Karuk Language Restoration Board. Nancy is a language specialist & consultant, and is an accomplished storyteller, basket weaver and traditional singer.

STEELE, DAVID (Pomo)
(tribal vice chairperson)
Affiliation & Address: Vice Chairperson, Hopland Band of Pomo Indians, 3000 Shanei Rd., Hopland, CA 95449 (707) 472-2111.
E-mail: dsteele@hoplandtribe.com

STEELE, VICTORIA (Seneca/Mingo)
(Arizona State representative)
Affiliation & Address: Arizona State Representative (2013-14), District 9, House of Re[presentative, 1700 W. Washington, Room 318, Phoenix, AZ 85007 (602) 926-5683. E-mail: vsteele@azleg.edu. *Other professional post*: Teaches psychology & counseling at the University of Phoenix (at Tucson) and mentors students at Prescott College (Tucson Center).

STEEVES, PAULETTE (Cree-Metis)
(professor of anthropology)
Born & raised in Lillooet, British Columbia. *Education*: SUNY Binhmaton, PhD. *Affiliation & Address*: Interim Director, & Professor of Anthropology, University of Massachusetts, Amherst, Certificate Program in Native American Indian Studies, Anthropology Dept., 314 Machmer, Amherst, MA 01003 (577-3781) E-mail: psteeves@anthro.umass.edu Dr. Steeves, who grew up in Dr. Steeves is an Indigenous archaeologist with a focus on the Pleistocene history of the Western Hemisphere (the Americas). She has focused her research on decolonizing and rewriting Indigenous histories through indigenous method and theory. In her research Steeves argues that indigenous peoples were present in the Western Hemisphere as early as 60,000 years ago, and possibly much earlier. She has created a data base of hundreds of archaeology sites in both North and South America that date from 250,000 to 12,000 years before present.

STEIN, WAYNE J. (Turtle Mountain Chippewa) 1950-
(professor of Native American Studies)
Born September 17, 1950, Wolf Point, Mont. *Education*: Montana State University, BS, 1973; Penn State University, MEd., 1977; Washington State University, EdD, 1988. *Affiliation & Address*: Professor Emeritus (1991-present), Higher Education//Native American Studies, Department of Native American Studies, Montana State University, 2-188 Wilson Hall, P.O. Box 172340, Bozeman, MT 59717 (406) 994-3881. wstein@montana.edu. *Other professional posts*: Vice President, International College; President, Standing Rock College, AZ. *Past professional posts*: President, Sitting Bull College, 1981-85; Director, Office of Tribal Service, Center for Native American Studies, Montana State University, 1989-91; board member, National Museum of American Indian, Smithsonian Institution, 2002-07. *Memberships*: Montana Indian Education Association; National Indian Education Association. *Awards, honors*: Bush Leadership Award, 1985; Community College Educator of the Year, WSU, 1986. *Interests*: Rights and needs of the poor and working people of U.S.; rights of indigenous people of the world; world environment issues; economic development of State of Montana and its Indian reservations; reading, writing, fishing. *Published work*: Tribally Controlled College (Peter Lang, 1992); co-editor, American Indians & Alaska Natives in Postsecondary Education (U.S. Dept. of Education, 1998); co-edited with Maenette K.P.Benham, The Renaissance of American Indian Higher Education: Capturing the Dream (Lawrence Erlbaum Associates, 2002) numerous chapters in books & articles in scholarly journals; numerous reports & documents contributions; presentations.

STEINBRING, JOHN H. (JACK) 1929-
(adjunct scholar, anthropologist)
Born July 1, 1929, Oshkosh, Wisc. *Education*: University of Wisconsin, Oshkosh, BA, 1955, Madison, MA, 1959; University of Minnesota, PhD, 1975. *Affiliation & Address*: Adjunct Scholar (2006-present), Dept. of Anthropology, Ripon College, 300 Seward St., Ripon, WI 54971 (920) 748-8378. E-mail: steinbringj@ripon.edu. *Past professional post*: Professor of anthropology, University of Winnipeg, Manitoba, Canada, 1963-2006. *Military service*: Wisconsin National Guard/U.S. Army Reserve, 1949-62 (1st Lt.; Expert Rifle, Pistol, Carbine). *Community activities*: President, Assiniboine Senior Rifle

Club, 1978-90. *Memberships*: American Anthropological Association (Foreign Fellow); Society for American Archaeology; Society of Professional Archaeologists; Rock Art Association of Canada (president, 1990); Rock Art Association of Manitoba (president, 1993-); Australian Rock Art Research Association (vice president, 1988-92. *Interests*: "Extensive research into the impact of television among Algonkian populations resulting in several books, 1974-81; studies of alcohol among the Northern Ojibwa, 1964-82, resulting in one book and one professional paper; general ethnographic studies among the North Ojibwa, 1963-, resulting in numerous papers and a chapter in the Handbook of North American Indians (Vol. 6, Smithsonian); many years of research into Native North American rock art leading to many professional papers and the identification of two rock art styles and the discovery of Canada's oldest dated rock art." *Published works*: Television and the Canadian Indian (University of Winnipeg Press, 1979); Alcohol and the Native Peoples of the North (U. Press of America, 1980); An Introduction to Archaeology on the Winnipeg River (Manitoba Historic Resources Branch, 1980); Communications in Cross-Cultural Perspective (University of Winnipeg Press, 1980); General Guidelines in the Development of Native Television Programming (U. of Winnipeg Press, 1981); The Impact & Meaning of Television Among Native Communities in Northern Manitoba (Canadian Commission for UNESCO, 1984); numerous articles on rock art & archaeology.

STEINDORF, HARRY J. (*Keddy-Ju-Sa-Skagga, White Blackhawk*) (Ho-Chunk Nation) 1946-
(educational administrator)
Born February 20, 1946, Black River Falls, Wisc. *Education*: University of Wisconsin, Whitewater, BBA, 1973; University of Wisconsin, Madison Law School, 1973-75. *Principal occupation*: Educational administrator. *Address*: 460 Bonnie Rd., Cottage Grove, WI 53527 (608) 262-0314. E-mail: hsteindorf@hotmail.com. *Affiliation*: University of Wisconsin-Madison, Art Dept., 1988-present; Academic Advancement Program, 1974-80. *Past professional posts*: Vice-Chairman, Wisconsin Winnebago Business Committee, 1978-79; director of planning & economic development for Wisconsin Winnebago Tribe, 1980-83; Winnebago Research Center, Inc. (board of directors, 1980-83; sec/treas. of Wisconsin Winnebago Enterprises, Inc. (founding board of directors, 1980-83); executive director, Ho-Chunk Nation Business Dept., 1995; DJ Hosts Corp. (President & CEO, 1995-98). *Military service*: U.S. Marine Corps, 1964-70; Aviator, Captain (Distinguished Flying Cross; Sixteen Strike/Flight Air Medals; Vietnam Gallantry Cross; Vietnam Service Medal; Vietnam Campaign Medal; Naval Unit Citation; Meritorious Unit Citation). *Community activities*: Veterans of Foreign Wars #7591, Madison, WI; Disabled American Veterans, Post #2, Madison, WI; American Legion Post #442, Wisconsin Rapids, WI; Wisconsin Aviation Hall of Fame, Waunakee, WI, 1995-present. *Awards, honors*: "Top Gun" Award from 2nd Marine Air Wing, 1968, MCAS Cherry Point, NC; Outstanding Young Alumnus Award, University of Wisconsin, Whitewater, 1978; Outstanding Young Men of America, 1979; Commander VFW Post #7591, Madison, WI, 1996-97; Keynote Address Speaker, Veterans Day Ceremony, State Capitol Rotunda, Madison, WI, 1996. Interests: Fiction writing, pleasure flying, hunting & camping. *Published works*: In progress: "Seaworthy Injun."

STEINER, KERRY
(executive director)
Affiliation & Address: Executive Director, Indiana Native American Indian Affairs Commission, 100 N. Senate Avenue, Rm N103, Indiana Government Center, N. Indianapolis, IN 46204 317-234-4887. E-mail: info@inaiac.in.gov. As the Executive Director of INAIAC, Steiner is responsible for researching challenges and developing solutions to issues affecting the Native community in Indiana. Steiner began her duties on March 2, 2015. Kerry is a former U.S. Army Journalist who has served as a volunteer at The American Indian Center of Indiana since 2008. At the American Indian Center she manages the website and social media outlets (Facebook and Twitter), and is the Editor of both the monthly e-newsletter and quarterly print publications. It is both her hope and her goal that these communication channels will unify the Indigenous community of Indiana. In addition, Kerry is a professional genealogist and a member of the Association of Professional Genealogists.

STENSGAR, ERNEST L. (Coeur d'Alene) 1947-
(tribal vice chairperson)
Born on the Coeur d'Alene Indian Reservation. *Education*: Chilocco Indian School in Oklahoma, 1965. *Affiliation & Address*: Vice Chairperson (1986-present), Coeur d'Alene Tribe, P.O. Box 408, Plummer, ID 83851 (208) 686-1800. Website: www.cdatribe-nsn.gov. *Other professional posts*: President, Affiliated Tribes of Northwest Indians (representing 55 tribes), 1996-present; Chairperson, Alliance of Idaho Tribes; Portland Area Vice President for the National Congress of American Indians. *Military service*: U.S. Marine Corps, 1965-67 (Vietnam-Purple Heart). *Community activities*: Representative, Tribal Leaders Task Force; member, Tribal School Board; co-chair, Idaho Centennial Committee; Commander, Joseph R. Garry American Legion Post #5, Plummer, ID; also District Commander; created the Coeur d'Alene Warrior Society (veterans on the Coeur d'Alene Reservation). *Awards, honors*: First tribal

leader to be listed among Idaho's 100 most influential people; first tribal leader named to the Idaho Hall of Fame; first tribal leader to be honored with the Byard Rustin Award, for the advancement of human rights; first tribal leader to be awarded an honorary JD from Gonzaga University, Spokane, WA.

STENSGAR, JOHN (Colville)
(tribal council member, committee chair)
Affiliation: Member, Business Council, Confederated Tribes of the Colville Reservation, P.O. Box 150, Nespelem, WA 99155 (509) 634-2208. E-mail: john.stensgar@colvilletribes.com. *Other tribal post*: Chair, Natural Resources Committee.

STEORTS, DENNIS (Chief Red Eagle) (Kaweah)
(principal chief, minister)
Address & Affiliation: Principal chief, Kaweah Indian Nation of Western USA & Mexico, P.O. Box 642, Abilene, KS 67410. *Other professional posts*: Co-national chairman, American Indian Defense of the Americas, Hutchinson, KS; general secretary, Native American Church, P.O. Box 265, Hutchinson, KS 67501. *Community activities*: Board member, Congregational Bible Churches International; Minister of Native American Church/CBC Division.

STEPETIN, JACOB
(village president)
Affiliation: Native Village of Akutan, Box 89, Akutan, AK 99553 (907) 698-2301.

STEPHENS, Y. ELAINE 'ELLE' (Hopi/Cherokee)
(director of development & communications)
Affiliation & Address: Director of Development & Communications, Native Americans in Philanthropy, 2801 21st Ave. #132D, Minneapolis, MN 55407 (612) 724-8798. E-mail: ystephens@nativephilanthropy.org. *Other professional post*: Board member, Arts High Alumni Association,

STEPHENSON, DAVID
(attorney, consultant)
Education: University of Colorado, PhD (Anthropology), 1982; University of Denver, J.D., 1984. *Principal occupation*: Attorney, consultant. *Affiliations*: Attorney, Fairfield & Woods, P.C. (law firm); research associate, Walker Research Group, Ltd., P.O. Box 4147, Boulder, CO 80306 (303) 492-6719. Website: www.walkerresearchgroup.com. Mr. Stephenson performs consulting and legal work in areas of American Indian economic & business development, housing, complex business litigation, and American Indian intellectual property rights and licensing.

STERN, NICOLE (Mescalero Apache)
(physician; assistant professor of medicine)
Education: Stanford University, BA; University of Arizona College of Medicine, MD.; Fellowship in Primary Care Sports Medicine at the University of Oklahoma Health Sciences Center in Oklahoma City. *Affiliation & Address*: Assistant Professor of Medicine, Department of Internal Medicine, University of Arizona College of Medicine, P.O. Box 245017, Tucson, AZ 85724 (520) 626-4555. *Other professional posts*: In her outpatient practice, Nicole specializes in both general Internal Medicine & Sports Medicine; president (2012-13), Association of American Indian Physicians (AAIP), Oklahoma City, OK. *Research Interests*: Disease prevention through exercise, childhood obesity, and the prevention of other health disparities affecting American Indian communities. While living in Oklahoma City, she co-produced a documentary film with AAIP about a young man living with AIDS. This documentary was distributed to American Indian health clinics around the country.

STERN, WALTER E.
(attorney)
Education: University of California, Berkeley, BS, 1978; Boston College Law School, JD, 1982. *Affiliation & Address*: President & Chair of the Executive Committee, Modrall Sperling Lawyers, P.O. Box 2168, Albuquerque, NM 87103 (505) 848-1837. E-mail: walter.stern@modrall.com. Walter brings over thirty years of experience providing representation, advice and counsel to businesses and individuals in their dealings with Indian tribes and public land management agencies, like the U.S. Bureau of Land Management, the U.S. Forest Service and New Mexico State Land Office. Walter's practice is focused on natural resources, energy and environmental law. Clients throughout the west and across the country seek Walter's advice in matters involving transactions, disputes and consultations with Indian tribes and other Native American groups. In addition, clients look to Walter when pursuing federal lands leasing, development, and related permitting and environmental compliance efforts under the National Environmental Policy Act ("NEPA"), Section 106 of the National Historic Preservation Act, the Endangered Species Act, and related federal statutes. Walter also is actively involved in community & professional non-profit organizations. He has served as President of the Rocky Mountain Mineral Law Foundation, a world-class continuing education provider for professionals working in the areas of natural resources development and environmental law. In addition, Walter is Chair of the Board

of Trustees of the Albuquerque Academy, an independent day school. *Awards, honors*: Nationally recognized in Native American Law by *Chambers USA,* Walter has also received top recognition in the areas of Environment, Natural Resources & Regulated Industries in Chambers' New Mexico review. As reported in *Chambers,* clients highlight his "keen knowledge of day-today dealings with tribes and good perspective on previous deals." He has been listed by *Best Lawyers in America®* since 1995 and named Lawyer of the Year in Albuquerque three times: Energy Law, 2014; Oil and Gas Law, 2012; and Native American Law, 2011. In addition, Walter has achieved the AV® rating from *Martindale-Hubbell*, was selected as one of the Top 25 Super Lawyers in New Mexico by *Southwest Super Lawyers®*, and chosen as Best of the Bar in Native American Law by the *New Mexico Business Weekly.*

STERNER, MICHELE
(Dakota studies associate director & academic specialist/counselor)
Affiliation & Address: Associate Director, Academic Specialist, Counselor, Indigenous Nations & Dakota Studies Program, Department of Social Sciences, SS103, Southwest Minnesota State University, 1501 State St., Marshall, MN 56258 (507) 537-7382. E-mail: michele.sterner@smsu.edu.

STERUD, BILL (Puyallup)
(tribal chairperson)
Affiliation & Address: Chairperson, Puyallup Tribe, 3009 E. Portland Ave., Tacoma, WA 98404 (253) 573-7800.

STETSON, CATHERINE BAKER
(attorney)
Education: Vassar College, BA, 1971; Brown University, MA, 1972; University of New Mexico, PhD (Cultural Anthropology, Native American Studies), 1977; University of New Mexico Law School, JD, 1981. *Affiliation & Address*: Managing Partner & Attorney, Stetson Law Offices, P.C. (1997-present), 1305 Rio Grande Blvd. NW, Albuquerque, NM 87104 (505) 256-4911. E-mail: cbs@stetsonlaw.com. *Other professional post*: President, LEGI\X, Albuquerque, NM, 1986 to present. Indian law, housing, gaming, commercial transactions, and legislative consulting; member, Board of Directors, Tribal Business Opportunities, Inc., Albuquerque, NM. Catherine is a New Mexico Board Certiifed Specialist in Federal Indian Law. *Past professional posts*: Attorney, Ussery & Parrish, P.A., Albuquerque, NM, 1982-86; Managing Partner, Gover, Stetson & Williams, P.C., Albuquerque, NM, 1986-97 (Indian law, housing, lobbying). *Community activities*: Past director, Southwest Association for Indian Arts; member, New Mexico Women in the Arts Advisory Council; chair & board member for Bien Mur, Sandia Pueblo's arts & crafts enterprise; officer & regent of the Museum of New Mexico. *Professional Memberships*: U.S. Supreme Court; U.S. Court of Appeals, Tenth Circuit; D.C. Court of Appeals; U.S. District Court for the District of New Mexico; American Bar Association; State Bar of New Mexico (Indian Law Section, director, 1987-91, chair, 1989-90; chair, Indian Law Specialization Committee (2004-present); State Bars of Minnesota, Nebraska, New York, Washington; D.C. Bar. *Interests*: Native American art; jazz. *Biographical sources*: Who's Who in the World, 21st Ed.; Who's Who of American Women, 2002-present; Who's Who Among Executives & professionals, 2004-2005 Honors Edition; Who's Who in Executives & Businesses, Millennium Edition. *Published works*: Numerous articles in law journals, newsletters, bulletin.

STEVENS, BART
(BIE deputy bureau director)
Affiliation & Address: Deputy Bureau Director, School Operations Division, Bureau of Indian Education, Department of the Interior, 1849 C St., NW, MS-3609-MIB, Washington, DC 20240 (202) 208-3312. E-mail: bart.stevens@bie.edu.

STEVENS, BRIAN (*Tyo'glo'ta'kwa*) (Oneida of WI) 1954-
(Native American education coordinator)
Born April 25, 1954, Detroit, Mich. *Education*: University of Wisconsin, Oshkosh, BS (Social Work), 1976. *Principal occupation*: Native American education coordinator. *Address & Affiliation*: Pupil Services Dept., Howard/Suamico School District, 1935 Cardinal Lane, Green Bay, WI 54313 (920) 662-7886. E-mail: briastev@hssd.k12.wi.us. *Other professional post*: Vice-chairperson, United American Indian Center, Green Bay, WI (2002-present). *Awards, honors*: Received the Dutch Uncle Award from the Big Brothers organization while attending college; numerous youth awards for outstanding leadership. *Community activities*: Mr. Stevens writes, "Provides instructional activities within school systems & participates in on-going cultural workshops to share knowledge." *Interests*: he also writes, "Active in ceremonies within our Longhouse and spending quality time instructing my three children in traditional values."

STEVENS, BRUCE (Te-Moak Western Shoshone)
(former tribal chairperson)
Affiliation: Wells Indian Colony Band Council, P.O. Box 809, Wells, NV 89835

STEVENS, CONNIE (Iroquois-Cherokee) 1938-
(actress; executive director-foundation)
Born August 8, 1938, Brooklyn, N.Y. Resides in Beverly Hills, CA. *Affiliation*: Founder, president, executive director, Windfeather Foundation. *Memberships*: Screen Actors Guild, AFTRA, Actors Equity.

STEVENS, ERNIE, JR. (Oneida of Wisconsin)
(association chairperson)
Education: Haskell Indian Nations University, AA; Mount Scenario College (Ladysmith, Wisc.), BS (Criminal Justice). *Affiliation & Address*: Chairperson, National Indian Gaming Association (NIGA), 224 2nd St., SE, Washington, DC 20003 (202) 546-7711. E-mail: estevens@indiangaming.org. *Other professional posts*: Chairperson, American Indian Business Network, Washington, DC; member, Native American Rights Fund National Support Committee (NARF); board member, National Center for American Indian Child Welfare Association (NICWA); advisor, Blue Stone Strategy Group, Phoenix, AZ; serves on the Native American Advisory Board, Boys & Girls Club of America; vice president, Executive Board, NABI Foundation, Phoenix, AZ. Ernie is the co-founder of Dreamseekers Foundation of America, along with Hulk Hogan, which provide contributions to tribal nations, specifically focusing on efforts to improve health care & education for Native youth & their families. *Past professional posts*: Elected councilman for the Oneida Nation of Wisconsin, 1993-99; former V.P., National Congress of American Indians.

STEVENS, FERMINA (Te-Moak Western Shoshone)
(tribal chairperson)
Affiliation: Elko Band Council, 511 Sunset St., Elko, NV 89803 (775) 738-8889.

STEVENS, JOHN W. (Passamaquoddy) 1933-
(former tribal governor)
Born August 11, 1933, Washington Co., Maine. *Principal occupation*: Tribal governor, Indian Township-Passamaquoddy Tribal Council, Princeton, ME. *Address*: P.O. Box 407, Princeton, ME 04668. *Military service*: U.S. Marines, 1951-54 (Presidential Unit Citation; Korean Presidential Unit Citation; United Nations Medal). *Interests*: Mr. Stevens writes, "Being the chief of an Indian tribe of about a thousand members who are struggling in court and on all fronts to overcome local discrimination & poverty and to have our reservation treaty rights respected by the State of Maine is enough of a task, and doesn't leave much time for anything else."

STEVENS, JULIE (Te-Moak Western Shoshone)
(former tribal chairperson)
Affiliation & Address: Te-Moak Tribe of Western Shoshone Indians of Nevadad, Wells Band Colony, P.O. Box 809, Wells, NV 89835 (775) 752-3045.

STEVENS, NICHOLAI (Eskimo)
(Alaskan village president)
Affiliation: Oscarville Tribe, Box 6129, Oscarville, AK 99559 (907) 737-7099.

STEVENS, PHILIP (San Carlos Apache)
(director of American Indian studies program)
Affiliation & Address: Assistant Professor of Anthropology & Director, American Indian Studies Program, Department of Sociology & Anthropology, 875 Perimeter Dr. P.O. Box 1110, Moscow, ID 83844 (208) 885-6751; E-mail: pstevens@uidaho.edu *Research interests*: Apache mathematics, educational pedagogical disconnects between dominant cultures and Indian communities, "educational raiding", and the cultural values imparted through the educational process.

STEVENS, RICHARD (Passamaquoddy)
(tribal chairperson)
Affiliation: Indian Township Passamaquoddy Tribal Council, P.O. Box 301, Princeton, ME 04668 (207) 796-2301.

STEVENS, SCOTT MANNING (Mohawk)
(Native American studies program director)
Education: Dartmouth College, BA, 1985; Harvard University, MA (English), 1992, PhD (English), 1997. *Affiliation & Address*: Director, Native American Studies Program, Syracuse University, 314 Tolley Humanities Bldg., Syracuse, NY 13244 (315) 443-8785. E-mail: scsteven@syr.edu *Past professional posts*: Adjunct Professor of American Studies, University of Notre Dame, fall 2011; Director of Graduate Studies in English, University at Buffalo, 2003-2006; Assistant Professor of English, University at Buffalo, 2001-2007; Assistant Professor of English, Arizona State University, 1997-2000; 2009-2010; director (2009-present), D'Arcy McNickle Center for American Indian & Indigenous Studies, Newberry Library, Chicago, IL, 2010-13. Continued state curriculum review with members of the Committee on American Indian Language & Cultural Preservation - Selected as a speaker for the Illinois Humanities Council's "Road Scholar Programs." This program provides funding for speaking engagements at public libraries & historical societies throughout the state. I proposed three different lectures on historical topics relating to American Indians in Illinois. Co-founded the Committee on American Indian Language and Cultural Preservation with Ms. Jolene Aleck of the Chicago Public Schools Title VII Program for American Indian Education. This on-going committee will be hosted by the D'Arcy McNickle Center. Invited to be the Keynote Speaker for the 2008-2009 Achievement Award Celebration for Title VII American Indian Education Program. Delivered an invited lecture at the Sulzer Branch of the Chicago Public Library. The public lecture is titled, "American Indians in Chicago: Our Legacies, Our Communities." *Interests*: Stevens' research interests have revolved around the diplomatic & cultural strategies of resistance among North American Indians in the face of European & American settler colonialism, as well as the political & aesthetic issues that surround museums & the indigenous cultures they put on display. *Published works*: "The National Museum of the American Indian and the Politics of Display." American Indians & Popular Culture: Literature, Arts, and Resistance. Edited by Elizabeth DeLaney Hoffman (Praeger Publishers, 2012). Stevens is currently at work on a book-length research project entitled, "Indian Collectibles: Encounters, Appropriations, & Resistance in Native North America" (contracted with Cornell U Press); A View From Iroquoia," primary essay in a catalog for exhibit, "On the Trails of the Iroquois," opened March 2013 inn Bonn, Germany' Other Homes, Other Fronts: Native American During the Civil War," a 9,000 word essay in the exhibit catalog, "Home Front: Daily Life in the Civil War North," exhibited at The Newberry Library, November, 2013 (University of Chicago Press, 2013); Art of the American West: The Haub Family Collection at the Tacoma Art Museum (Yale University Press, 2014); Why You Can't Teach United States History without American Indians. (University of North Carolina Press - Chapel Hill, 2015).

STEVENS, TRACIE L. (Tulalip)
(gaming commission chairperson)
Education: University of Washington, BA (Social Sciences). *Affiliation & Address*: Chairperson (2010-present), National Indian Gaming Commission, 1441 L St., NW #9100, Washington, DC 20005 (202) 632-7003. *Past professional posts*: Legislative Policy Analyst (2003-06), Senior Policy Analyst, (2006-09), Tulalip Tribe. While working for the Tulalip Tribe, Tracie also served as the Chair of the Gaming Committee for the Affiliated Tribes of Northwest Indians, 2003-09; secretary of the board of directors for the Washington Indian Gaming Association, 2002-09; northwest delegate, National Indian Gaming Association, 2003-09; and prior to becoming Commission Chair, she was senior advisor to Assistant Secretary-Indian Affairs (2009-2010) providing policy guidance regarding tribal issues such as gaming, law enforcement, energy, consultation, economic development, land-into-trust, tribal government disputes, budget priorities, and treaty and natural resource rights.

STEVENSON, GELVIN (OK Cherokee) 1944-
(writer, consultant, teacher, mediator)
Born November 6, 1944, Chelsea, Okla. *Education*: Carleton College, BA; Washington University, MA, PhD. *Address*: 2160 Bolton St., Bronx, NY 10462 (718) 863-4156. E-mail: gelvins@earthlink.net. *Affiliations*: Investment consultant for Oneida Trust Committee; Adjunct professor, Urban Environmental Policy, New School University; independent writer & consultant. *Community activities*: Member, Board of Directors of American Indian Community House (NYC), First Nations Development Institute, & Cherokee National Historical Society. *Memberships*: Nuyagi Keetowah Society; Social Investment Forum; International String Figure Association. *Published work*: Indigenous Economics, co-authored with Rebecca Adamson (forthcoming).

STEWART, EVIE (Catawba)
(tribal administrator)
Affiliation: Catawba Indian Tribe, 996 Avenue of the Nations, Catawba, SC 29730 (803) 366-4792.

STEWART, LEO (Umatilla)
(tribal board vice chairperson)
Affiliations: Confederated Tribes of the Umatilla Indian Reservation, P.O. Box 638, Pendleton, OR 97801 (541) 276-3165.

STICKLAND, MICHAEL J. (Athapascan)
(Alaskan tribal chief)
Affiliation: Chief, Nulato Tribal Council, P.O. Box 65049, Nulato, AK 99765 (907) 898-2339.

STIFFARM, DENISE L. (Gros Ventre)
(attorney)
Education: Washington State University, BA, 1991; University of Washington School of Law, JD, 1996. *Affiliation & Address*: Patner, Pacific Law Group, 1191 2nd Ave., Suite 2000, Seattle, WA 98101 (206) 602-1203. E-mail: denise.stiffarm@pacificalawgroup.com. *Professional/Civic Activities*: Denise currently serves as the President of the Board of Directors of the Chief Seattle Club, a nonprofit organization serving homeless & low-income American Indian, First Nations & Alaskan Native people; she currently serves on the

Board of Directors for the YWCA (Seattle/King/ Snohomish). Denise previously served on the board of directors for YouthCare, Audubon Washington, and the Seward Park Environmental and Audubon Center. She also previously served two terms as a member of the Pioneer Square Preservation Board, as a trustee for the King County Bar Association Young Lawyers Division, and as a Law Alumni Ambassador for the University of Washington (conducting outreach to college, high school, and junior high school students of color). She is also a member of the Leadership Tomorrow class of 2001. *Past professional post*: Partner, K&L Gates LLP, Seattle, WA. *Memberships*: Northwest Indian Bar Assn; National Native American Bar Assn. *Awards, honors*: Named as one of the "Best Lawyers in America" in Education Law and Lawyer of the Year - Washington (Education Law) 2012 by Best Lawyers; Selected to the Washington Rising Stars List (2004-2009) and the Washington Super Lawyers List (2011-2013). *Published works*: Koontz: The Latest Chapter in Land Use Permitting & Takings (Environmental, Land & Natural Resources Alert, Nov. 22, 2013); numerous Alerts/Updates.

STIFFARM, LOREN "BUM" (Gros Ventre, Assiniboine)
(tribal chief administrative officer)
Address: P.O. Box 848, Harlem, MT 59526 (406) 353-8558. *Affiliation*: Fort Belknap Community Council, RR #1, Box 66, Harlem, MT 59526 (406) 353-2205. *Other professional post*: Alternate member, State Tribal Economic Development Commission (STEDC), c/o MT Dept. of Commerce, Helena, MT.

STILL, COREY (Cherokee/Keetoowah)
(adjunct professor of American Indian studies)
Education: University of Oklahoma, BA (Native American Studies with minor in Anthropology); Northeastern State University (OK), Graduate student. *Affiliation & Address*: Adjunct Professor, Bacone College, Center for American Indians, 2229 Old Bacone Rd., Muskogee, OK 74403 (918) 683-4581. E-mail: stillc@bacone.edu. His area of expertise is Higher Educational Leadership. His Education doctoral research will focus on cultural perspectives in learning styles and methods for Native youth. He has also served in a variety of leadership roles both within his tribe and the community at large. He currently serves as National Chairman for Sigma Nu Alpha Gamma, a Native fraternity founded at the University of Oklahoma. He also served as a Cultural Delegate of the 2012 Emissaries of Peace Trip to the United Kingdom, and as a Student Representative on the Board of Directors for the National Indian Education Association from 2012 to 2014.

STINE, WENDY (Paiute)
(former tribal chairperson)
Affiliation: Fort Independence Tribal Council, P.O. Box 67, Independence, CA 93526 (760) 878-2126.

STIX, AMY
(Indian program director)
Education: Colorado College, BA, 1991; University of Montana, MS (Environmental Studies, with a focus in community development), 2001. *Affiliation & Address*: Director, American Indian Research Opportunities (AIRO), Mntana State University, P.O. Box 173820, Bozeman, MT 59717 (406) 994-5567. E-mail: amy.stix@coe.montana.edu.

STOCK, MICHELE DEAN (Seneca-Iroquois)
(museum director)
Affiliation: Seneca-Iroquois National Museum, Allegany Indian Reservation, 794-814 Broad St., Salamanca, NY 14779 (716) 945-1738/3895.

STOFFLE, RICHARD W.
(research anthropologist; professor)
Education: University of Colorado, BA; University of Kentucky, MA, PhD, 1972. A Full Research Anthropologist, Bureau of Applied Research in Anthropology. *Affiliation*: American Indian Studies Program, University of Arizona, Haury 317A, Tucson, AZ 85721 (520) 621-2462. E-mail: rstoffle@email.arizona.edu. *Interests*: American Indian social impact assessment; American Indian natural resource policy. He has worked extensively with American Indians since 1972, particularly with the Kaibab Paiute of northern Arizona & southern Utah. He has written extensively on issues such as NAGPRA (Native American Graves Protection & Repatriation Act, resource management, cultural resource management, and other topics of interest in American Indian Studies.

STOGAN, WALKER (Salish)
(spiritual leader)
Address: 4035 Thallaiwhaltum Ave., Musqueam Reserve, Vancouver, B.C., Canada V6H 3V1. *Interests*: Salish elder/spiritual leader of Winter Spirit Dance ceremonial.

STONE, CRAIG
(director of American Indian Studies)
Affiliation & Address: Director, American Indian Studies Department, College of Liberal Arts, 1250 Bellflower Blvd., FO3-306, California State University, Long Beach, CA 90840 (562) 985-8203. E-mail: cstone@csulb.edu.

STONER, KELLY A. (Cherokee)
(attorney; instructor in American Indian law)
Education: Oklahoma Panhandle State University, BA; University of Oklahoma College of Law, JD. *Affiliation & Address*: Instructor & Director, Native American Legal Resource Center, Oklahoma City University, 2501 Blackwelder, Oklahoma City, OK 73106 (405) 208-5188. E-mail: kstoner@okcu.edu. Professor Stoner teaches in the areas of Indian Law, Tribal Law, Domestic Violence & Family Law. *Past professional post*: Instructor & director of the The Native American Law Project at the University of North Dakota Law School; Tribal Prosecutor, Spirit Lake Tribe in North Dakota. She has extensive experience in drafting law & order codes for tribal governments across the U.S. *Published works*: Sharing Our Stories of Survival: Native Women Surviving Violence, with Sarah Dee, Bonnie Clairmont, and Carrie A. Martell (AltaMira Press, 2008); The Indian Child Welfare Act Handbook: A Legal Guide to the Custody & Adoption of Native American Children, with B.J. Jones & Mark Tilden (AltaMira Press, 2009); numerous articles in journals.

STORY, CHARLENE TUCKALEECHE (Northeast Alabama Cherokee) 1939-
(medical communications director)
Born May 29, 1939, Moorpark, Calif. *Education*: Ventura (CA) College. *Principal occupation*: Customer relations manager. *Address*: 53 Buckworth Cir., Trafford, AL 35172 (205) 681-0080; 856-2544 (work). *Affiliation*: Commissioner for Alabama Indian Affairs, 1995-2001. *Community activities*: Principal Chief, Northeast Alabama Cherokee Tribe, 1998-present; representing Native Americans thru churches, schools, parades, and at powwows. *Interests*: Indian festivals, powwows, traditional southern cloth dancer, head lady dancer at powwows; collect Native American artist plates. *Biographical sources*: "I have been subject of several articles in "The Blount Countian" regarding tribal activities."

STOTT, MARGARET 1945-
(artist; anthropologist)
Born September 25, 1945, Vancouver, Can. *Education*: University of British Columbia, BA, 1966; McGill University, MA, 1969; London (England) School of Economics & Political Science, PhD (Anthropology), 1982. Resides in Vancouver, BC, Canada. E-mail: margaret.stott@vancouverartguild.com. *Affiliations*: Museum curator of ethnology, Museum of Anthropology, University of British Columbia, Vancouver, 1979-90. Since 1999 Margaret has worked less as an anthropologist and teacher, and has devoted more of her time to drawing & painting in Vancouver & abroad. *Memberships*: British Columbia Museums Association; Canadian Museums Association; American Association of Museums; Canadian Ethnology Society; Canadian Anthropology & Sociology Association; Mediterranean Institute; Council for Museum Anthropology. *Interests*: Northwest Coast Indian material culture and art with particular emphasis on the Bella Coola Indians; material culture studies; museum studies; Mediterranean ethnography with particular emphasis on modern Greece; tourism studies, particularly in the Mediterranean. Published works: Bella Coola Ceremony & Art (National Museums of Canada, 1975); Material Anthropology: Contemporary Approaches to Material Culture (University Press of America, in press). *Exhibitions*: Northwest Coast Indian Art, exhibition of contemporary Indian art (20 pieces), displayed in four cases at Air Canada Maple Leaf Lounge, Vancouver International Airport, 1980-; numerous other exhibitions in the past. Audio-visual productions: The Raven and the First Man, visuals of the sculpture carved by Haida artist Bill Reid, with the artist narrating the Haida origin myth depicted in the carvings; Salish Art & Culture, an interview with an anthropologist in the Museum exhibition Visions of Power, Symbols and Wealth; among others.

STRANGE OWL-RABIN, ANN (Medicine Eagle Feather Woman)
(Northern Cheyenne) 1936-
(gallery owner)
Born June 1, 1936, Birney Village, Mont. *Education*: University of Alaska (two years); Ames College, Greeley, CO (two years). *Principal occupation*: Gallery owner. *Address*: 9853 Hwy. 7, Allenspark, CO 80510 (303) 747-2861; Website: www.eagleplume.com. *Affiliation*: Owner/partner, Eagle Plume's, Allenspark, CO, 1976-. *Published work*: Four Great Rivers to Cross: Cheyenne History, Culture, and Traditions, with Patrick Mendoza & Nico Strange Owl.

STRANGE OWL, NICO (*Buffalo Appearing Woman*)
(Northern Cheyenne) 1963-
(gallery owner; American Indian art appraiser)
Born June 28, 1963, Bakersfield, Calif. *Education*: Colorado State University (5 years). Principal occupation: Gallery owner; appraiser, consultant. *Address*:

9853 Hwy. 7, Allenspark, CO 80510 (303) 747-2861 E-mail: strangeowl@ baol.com; Website: www.eagleplume.com. *Affiliations*: Manager, Squash Blossom, Vail. CO, 1986-89; managing director, Lone Mountain Gallery, Vail, CO; consultant, Denver Art Museum, 1991-93; partner, Eagle Plume's, Allenspark, 1993-. *Community activities*: Various lectures regarding American Indian art & culture; member, Douglas Society. *Memberships*: American Society of Appraisers (candidate member); Indian Arts & Crafts Association; Antique Tribal Arts Dealers Association; Southwestern Association on Indian Affairs; Douglas Society (Denver Art Museum). *Published work*: Four Great Rivers to Cross: Cheyenne History, Culture, and Traditions, with Patrick Mendoza & Ann Strange Owl-Rabin.

STRAUS, JERRY C.
(attorney)
Education: Columbia University, BA, 1958, LL.B., 1961; U.S. Attorney General's Honors Program. *Address & Affiliation*: Co-founder (with Charles Hobbs and Bobo Dean in 1982), Hobbs, Straus, Dean & Walker, LLP (1988-present), 2120 L St., NW, Suite 700, Washington, DC 20037 (202) 822-8282. E-mail: jstraus@hsdwdc.com. *Past professional posts*: Dept. of Justice, Washington, DC, 1961-63; Wilkinson, Cragun & Barker, Washington, DC, 1963-82. Mr. Straus has worked in the field of Indian law since 1963. He led the successful legislative efforts to return the 48,000-acre Blue Lake land to the Taos Pueblo in 1970, and the 26,000-acre Santa Cruz Spring Tract to the Pueblo de Cochiti in 1984. He assisted the Seminole Tribe of Florida in successfully negotiating a landmark water rights compact with the State of Florida. He led the firm's legislative efforts to secure congressional approval of a $32 million award to the Menominee Tribe of Wisconsin for damages the Tribe suffered as a result of the termination of its federal trust status in 1961. Presently, Mr. Straus specializes in representing tribes who conduct high stakes gaming, and assists those tribes in defining their rights under the Indian Gaming Regulatory Act (IGRA). He represented the Mohegan Tribe of Connecticut in its successful efforts to establish a major casino in that state. He was also co-counsel to the Seminole Tribe in the 1996 case of Seminole Tribe of Florida v. State of Florida, the first IGRA case to reach the U.S. Supreme Court. Mr. Straus is a major strategist in tribal opposition to federal legislation that would curtail Indian gaming rights.

STREITZ, MARY J.
(attorney)
Education: Carleton College, BA, 1980; New York University School of Law, 1984. *Affiliation & Address*: Co-chair, Indian Law Practice Group, Dorsey & Whitney LLP, 50 S. Sixth St., Suite 1500, Minneapolis, MN 55402 (612) 340-7813 E-mail: streitz.mary@dorsey.com. Mary is a Partner and Co-Chair of the Indian and Gaming practice group. She represents Indian tribes, tribal entities, tribal members, and entities doing business with tribes in all types of federal, state, & tribal tax matters, involving advice regarding available tax exemptions, business & investment tax planning, representation in tax controversies in the IRS, in the state taxing agencies, & in the courts, legislative and administrative lobbying on tax policy matters, and compliance with applicable federal and state tax laws involving employment taxes, income taxes, property taxes, sales and use taxes, and other excise and transaction taxes.

STREMLAU, ROSE
(professor of history & American Indian studies)
Affiliation & Address: Professor of History & American Indian studies, University of North Carolina at Pembroke, Native American Resource Center, Dept. of American Indian Studies, Old Main Rm. 231, P.O. Box 1510, Pembroke, NC 28372 (910) 521-6266. *Published works*: Sustaining the Cherokee Family: Kinship & The Allotment of an Indigenous Nation (University of North Carolina Press, 2011).

STRICKLAND, CALEB
(museum director)
Affiliations: Community Services Dept., National Museum of the American Indian, Smithsonian Institution, 4220 Silver Hill Rd., Suitland, MD 20746 (301) 238-6624.

STRICKLAND, JOHNYE E.
(secretary/treasurer)
Affiliation & Address: American Native Press Archives & Research Association, American Indian & Alaska Native Periodicals, Research Clearinghouse, 502 Stabler Hall, University of Arkansas, 33rd & University Ave., Little Rock, AR 72204 (501) 569-3160.

STRICKLAND, RENNARD JAMES (Cherokee, Osage) 1940-
(law professor; senior schlar in residence)
Born September 26, 1940, St. Louis, Mo. *Education*: Northeastern State College, BA, 1962; University of Virginia, JD, 1965, SJD, 1970; University of Arkansas, MA, 1966. *Affiliation & Address*: Senior Scholar in Residence, Center for the Study of American Indian Law, University of Oklahoma School of Law, Norman, OK (405) 325-4676. Other professional post: Distinguished

Professor E,eritus, University of Oregon School of Law, *Past professional posts*: Professor, University of Arkansas, 1965-69; professor of law, University of Tulsa, 1972-74; Acting Dean, School of Law, University of Tulsa, 1974-75; associate professor, University of Washington, 1975-76; supervising director, Shleppey Native American Collections, University of Tulsa, 1976-85; John W. Shleppey Research Professor of Law & History, University of Tulsa, 1976-85; dean & professor, School of Law, Southern Illinois University, 1985-88; professor of law, University of Wisconsin, Madison, 1988-90; professor of law & director, Center for the Study of American Indian Law, The University of Oklahoma, College of Law, Norman, OK, 1990-2012. Director, Indian Heritage Association, Muskogee, Okla., 1966-84; director, Oral History Project, University of Florida, 1969-1971; Site Inspector, American Bar Association, Section on Legal Education & Admission to the Bar, 1974-; chair, Indian Advisory Board, Philbrook Art Center, 1979-83; editor-in-chief, revision of Handbook of Federal Indian Law, Solicitor's Office, Dept. of the Interior, 1975-82; member, National Museum Advisory Board, Heard Museum, 1986-; board of directors, ATLATL, Native American Arts Service Organization, 1988-90; consultant, Panel for National Dialogue on Museums -- Native American Relations, Center for Cross-Cultural Communications, 1989-90; Law School Admissions Council, 1988-90; Smithsonian Institution, Planning Committee, 1990-91; American Bar Association, Affirmative Action Committee, 1988-91. Visiting professor at the following: Sylvan Lange Distinguished Visiting Professor, St. Mary's University, Summer 1973, University of New Mexico, Fall 1976, Summer, 1975-79, University of West Virginia (Reyer Distinguished), October 1982, University of Florida, Spring, 1983; University of Kansas (Langston Hughes Distinguished); Heard Museum of Native American and Primitive Art (Scholar-in-Residence), 1988-89; Arizona State University, 1988-89; public lectures. *Memberships*: Association of American Law Schools (Accreditation Committee, 1990-92; president, 1994); American Society of Legal History; Selden Society; Communications Association of America; Oklahoma Historical Society; American Society for Ethnohistory; American Association of Museums (member, Task Force-Reparations of Ceremonial Objects and Human Remains, 1987-88; American Bar Association (co-chair, Section on Legal Education and Admission to the Bar, Bicentennial Committee on the U.S. Constitution, 1984-87; member, Task Force on Minorities in the Legal Profession, 1987-89). *Awards, honors*: Sacred Sash of the Creeks for Preservation Tribal History; Fellow in Legal History, American Bar Association, 1970-1971; Fellow, American Council of Learned societies, 1972; Fellow, Doris Duke Foundation, 1970-73; Distinguished Service Award, Creek Indian Nation, 1972; Outstanding Faculty member, School of Law, University of Tulsa, 1975; Distinguished Alumnus Award, Northeastern State College, 1976; Society of American Law Teachers (SALT) Annual Award for Outstanding Teaching & Contribution to Law Reform, 1978; Award of Merit, Association for State & Local History, 1981 (editorial board member); Award of Excellence, Western Book Association, for A Trumpet of Out Own, 1982; Distinguished Service Citation, American Indian Coalition, Tulsa, OK, 1985; Chairman's Award, Contribution to Development of Indian Law in Oklahoma, presented by Chief Claude Cox, Chairman, Oklahoma Indian Affairs Commission, Tribal Summit, 1990; received the Spirit of Excellence Award from the American Bar Association Commssion on Minorities in the Profession in 1997. *Interests*: Indian law, Indian art, film & filmmaking. Mr. Strickland writes, "Primary interest (is in) law and the American Indian, including programs to attract Indian students to the law as a profession, and programs to make the law responsive to the needs of Indian citizens; culture of the American Indian, with primary emphasis upon myths and legends and upon the arts and crafts of native tribes; contemporary American Indian paintings, and the evolution of Indian culture as reflected in evolving styles; ethnohistory of specific tribes--the Cherokee, Creek. Seminole, Choctaw & Chickasaw; development of traditional legal systems among the tribes." *Published works*: Sam Houston With the Cherokees, 1829-1833, with Jack Gregory (University of Texas Press, 1967); Starr's History of the Cherokees (1968); Cherokee Spirit Tales (1969); Cherokee Cook Book (1969); Creek-Seminole Spirit Tales (1971); Choctaw Spirit Tales (1972); Hell on the Border (1971); Adventures of an Indian Boy (1973); American Indian Spirit Tales (1973); all with Jack Gregory, published by Indian Heritage Association; Cherokee Law Ways (University of Oklahoma Press, 1972); with Earl Boyd Pierce - The Cherokee People (Indian Tribal Series, 1973; How to Get Into Law School (Hawthorne Books, 1974, revised editions, 1975-77-79-82); Fire & Spirits: Cherokee Law From Clan to Court (University of Oklahoma Press, 1975); with William & Janet Phillips - Avoiding Teacher Malpractice (Hawthorne Books, 1976); The Prelaw Handbook (Assn. of American Law Schools, 1975, rev. eds. 1976-79); The Indians in Oklahoma (University of Oklahoma Press & Oklahoma Images Project, 1980); A Trumpet of Our Own: Yellow Bird on the American Indian (Book Club of California, 1981); Handbook of Federal Indian Law (Michie-Bobbs-Merrill, 3rd Ed., 1982); Magic Images: Contemporary Native American Art (University of Oklahoma Press, 1982); As In a Vision: Masterworks of American Indian Art (University of Oklahoma Press, 1983); Arizona Memories (University of Arizona Press, 1984: The Right Law School for You (Law School Admission Council, Newtown, PA, 1986, 1987); "Keeping Our Word: Indian Treaty Rights & Public Responsibilities," a report (with S.J. Herzberg & S.R. Owens) for the Senate Select Committee on Indian Affairs, 1990; Shared Visions: Native American

Painting & Sculpture (The Heard Museum, 1991); Trying a New Way: An Assessment of the Indian Self-Governance Demonstration Project, an analysis prepared for the BIA & Self-Governance Demonstration Tribes, 1992; Savages, Sinners, & Redskinned Redeemers: Images of the Native American (University of New Mexico Press); Indian Dilemma: Rhetoric & Reality of Cherokee Removal (University of Oklahoma Press); numerous edited books/studies, and articles/chapters/essays.

STROMMER, GEOFFREY D.
(attorney)
Education: University of California, Berkeley, BA, 1986; Georgetown University Law Center, J.D., 1990. *Address & Affiliation*: Managing Partner, Hobbs, Straus, Dean & Walker, LLP (1992-present), 851 S.W. Sixth Ave., Suite 1650, Portland, OR 97204 (503) 242-1745. E-mail: gstrommer@hsdwor.com. Represents tribal clients on a wide range of issues, specializing in the Indian Self-Determination and Education Assistance Act (ISDEAA). He was actively involved with the development of regulations to implement Title IV of the ISDEAA, & was a key member of the tribal team that drafted and successfully lobbied for the enactment of the Self-Governance Amendments of 2000. He's also an active participant in the negotiated rulemaking process to develop a new formula and regulations for the Indian Reservation Roads Program as well as the negotiated rulemaking process under Title V of the ISDEAA. *Past professional posts*: Adjunct professor of law, Northwestern School of Law at Lewis & Clark College, 1997, where he taught a course on federal Indian law instructor, Dept. of Health & Human Services Executive Leadership Program. Geoffrey has written several articles for legal publications on Indian law issues. Co-authored a law review article (with Craig Jacobson), "Indian Tribes & the Base Realignment & Closure Act: Recommendations for Future Trust Land Acquisitions," North Dakota Law Review, Sept. 1999.

STRONG, KIMBERLY (Klukwan)
(Alaskan village president)
Affiliation: Chilkat Indian Village (Klukwan), P.O. Box 210, Haines, AK 99827 (907) 767-5505.

STRONG, TED (Yakama)
(tribal chief judge)
Affiliation & Address: Chief Judge, Yakama Tribal Court, P.O. Box 151, Toppenish, WA 98948 (509) 865-5121.

STRONG STAND, CHIEF
(tribal chief)
Address: 106 Fox Chase Village, New Bern, NC 28562.

STROUD, VIRGINIA (Cherokee/Creek) 1951-
(artist, illustrator)
Born March 13, 1951, in Madera, Calif. *Education*: Bacone Jr. College, 1969-70; University of Oklahoma, 1971-73, 1976-77. "As an artist, I touch the human chord that erases the multicultural boundaries and ask the viewer to look for the familiar and not the differences of humanity. I paint for my people. Art is a way for our culture to survive…perhaps the only way. More than anything, I want to become an orator, to share with others the oldest of Indian traditions." Virginia began creating her painted furniture in 1988; dollmaking; and in the past few years has authored & illustrated four books for children. Her current projects include designing baby blankets and a baby journal for the American Indian College Fund. *Past professional posts*: Member, board of directors, Indian Arts & Crafts Association; 1999 candidate for Principal Chief of the Cherokee Nation; *Awards, honors*: Miss Cherokee Tribal Princess, 1969-1970; Miss National Congress of American Indian, 1970-71; Miss Indian America, 1971; The Woody Crumbo memorial award, Best of Show, Best Painting, and Best in the Traditional category at the 1992 Indian Market in Santa Fe, NM; her book, "Doesn't Fall Off His Horse," was recognized as NCSS=CBC Notable Children's Trade Book in the field of Social Studies, IRA-CBC Children's Choice, and received the IRA Distinguished Book Award. A large collection of Virginia's artwork was recently (2003) included in the Smithsonian's archives of living artists and the Fred Jones, Jr. Museum of Art at the University of Oklahoma. *Books illustrated*: Doesn't Fall Off His Horse, 1994; The Story of the Milky Way, 1995; A Walk to the Great Mystery, 1995; The Path of Quiet Elk: A Native American Alphabet Book, 1996.

STUART-RICHARD, GINA (Choctaw of Oklahoma)
(professor of Native American studies)
Education: University of ColoradoBA; University of Ariona, MA & PhD; Graduate Certificate in Geographic Information Science (GISc) from the University of Arizona's School of Natural Resources and the Environment. *Affiliation & Address*: Assistant Professor, Native American Studies Department, Montana State University, 2-179 Wilson Hall, P.O. Box 172340 • Bozeman, MT 59717 (406) 994-3883. E-mail: gina.richard@montana.edu. *Other professional post*: Teaching & Research Assistant and an Instructor since 2010. as Assistant NAGPRA Coordinator. Her research interests lie at

the intersections of Indigenous oral tradition & climate change, federal Indian law and policy, promoting access to ancestral heritage lands, and helping Native Nations build a legal-cartographic strategy for assertions of treaty rights and land claims via geospatial technology. In recent years, she has focused on developing a curriculum of theory and methodology unique to working with Indigenous communities, has collaborated with museums & Native Nations to ensure compliance with the Native American Graves Protection & Repatriation Act (NAGPRA) & has collaborated with other scholars & researchers in several other disciplines including natural resources, law, and archaeology. *Awards, honors*: She held the prestigious National Science Foundation Graduate Research Fellowship for her research on the connections between ancestral landscapes & Native American identity. She remains the only graduate student to have received this award in an American Indian Studies department. *Past professional posts*: In addition to her teaching and research, she held a position with the Arizona State Museum, the oldest & largest anthropology museum in the Southwest, Dr. Stuart-Richard has a body of work as a NAGPRA specialist and historic archaeologist that spans over two decades. After the passage of the Native American Graves Protection and Repatriation Act in 1990, she worked with the U. S. Army Corps of Engineers Center for Expertise to develop Standard Operating Procedures to ensure the U. S. Army's full compliance with this unique federal law. As a Native from Oklahoma, Dr. Stuart-Richard has performed significant research into the historical process of allotment in Indian Territory in the late 19th century, the after-effects of intergenerational trauma and historic grief, and the significant role that access to natural resources played in the allotment process. Her lecture When the Watchdogs Joined the Wolves: A Tricky Little Game of Indian Territory Land Fraud remains a popular & frequently requested presentation. She also performs in-depth research into topics such as Native Americans in the formation of the Early National (Colonial) period in U. S. history as well as the Civil War and Reconstruction eras.In her ever-vanishing spare time,

STUCK, JAMIE (Potawatomi)
(tribal chairperson)
Affiliation & Address: Chairperson, Nottawaseppi Huron Band of Potawatomi, 2221 - 1 1/2 Mile Rd., Fulton, MI 49052 (269) 729-5151. E-mail: jstuck@nhbpi.com

STULL, DONALD D.
(Emeritus-Sociocultural Anthropology)
Education: University of Colorado, PhD, 1973; University of California-Berkeley, MPH, 1975. *Affiliation*: University of Kansas, Dept. of Anthropology, 1415 Jayhawk Blvd., Lawrence, KS 66045 (785) 864-4103. E-mail: stull@ku.edu. Dr. Stull works closely with the Kansas Kickapoo.

STULL, WAYNE (Delaware Lenni Lenape)
(tribal assistant chief)
Education: Oklahoma State University; Northeastern State University. *Affiliation*: Delaware Tribe of Indians, 170 NE Barbara, Bartlesville, OK 74006 (918) 336-5272. E-mail: w_stull2006@yahoo.com. *Past professional posts*: Member, Tribal Trust Board & Tribal Council, 2002-present; chairperson, Economic Development Committee; chair, Delaware Enterprise Corp., Assistant Chair, Delaware Enterprise Authority.

SUAGEE, DEAN B. (Cherokee)
(attorney)
Education: University of Arizona, BA, 1972; University of North Carolina, J.D., 1976; American University, LL.M., 1989. *Affiliations & Address*: Attorney Of Counsel, Hobbs, Straus, Dean & Walker, LLP, 2120 L St., NW, Suite 700, Washington, DC 20037 (202) 822-8282 (Associate, 1988-93; Of Counsel, 1993-present); Director of the First Nations Environmental Law Program, Vermont Law School (VLS) (802) 763-8303, 1998-present, E-mail: dsuagee@vermontlaw.edu; also serves as the Director of VLS Indian Country Environmental Justice Clinic. Mr. Suagee specializes in environmental and natural resources law & cultural heritage preservation. He has taught courses in Indian country environmental law and federal Indian law at VLS and the Washington College of Law, American University. He frequently speaks at seminars on environmental law & federal Indian law, and has authored many law journal articles in these fields.

SUAZO, GILBERT (Taos Pueblo)
(pueblo lt. governor)
Affiliation & Address: Lt. Governor, Pueblo of Taos, P.O. Box 1846, Taos, NM 87571 (575) 758-9593.

SUEHEAD, JOHN (Miwok)
(tribal vice chairperson)
Affiliation & Address: Chairperson, United Auburn Indian Community, 10720 Indian Hill Rd., Auburn, CA 95603 (530) 883-2390. *Other professional post*: Tribal Historic Preservation Officer.

SUFFICOOL, SCOTT
   (BIA deputy regional director – Indian services)
Affiliation & Address: Deputy Director – Indian Services, Midwest Region Office, Bureau of Indian Affairs, Norman Pointe II Bldg., 5600 W. American Blvd., Suite 500, Bloomington, MN 55437 (612) 713-4400.

SUINA, JOSEPH H. (Cochiti Pueblo)
   (former Pueblo governor)
Affiliation & Address: Governor, Pueblo of Cochiti, P.O. Box 70, Cochiti Pueblo, NM 87072 (505) 465-2244.

SUINA, RAMOS (Cochiti Pueblo)
   (tribal relations specialist)
A full blood and fluent Keresan speaking tribal member in New Mexico. *Affiliation & Address*: Tribal Relations Specialist, Center for Lifelong Education (CLE) at the Institute of American Indian Arts (IAIA), 83 Avan Nu Po Rd., Santa Fe, NM 87508 (505) 424-2387. *Other professional post*: Board member, Native American Training Institute of New Mexico, Abuquerque, NM. *Past professional posts*: In 1987 he server as the Governor of Pueblo de Cochiti where he lead his people to regain thousands of acres of aboriginal land, resolved a longstanding seepage problems caused by a reservoir built by the U.S. Corp of Engineers and secured programs in heath, education, social and economic based programs. An Alumnus of IAIA, Ramus served as IAIA's Director of Enrollment Management/Admissions for more than 16 years and managed Student Financial Aid, Recruitment and Registrar's Office. During this time he served on numerous education committees for the state, local tribes and an advisory member to tribal community colleges. He also served as a part-time faculty, member of the faculty council and the curriculum committee. Each year during the state Legislative Sessions and for congressional appropriations, he was appointed a liaison to solicit and raise capital outlay, projects and operations funds on behalf of IAIA. As a longtime strong advocate for Indian education, he supported tribes to create and establish their own contract schools and help establish traditional language programs in their communities. He also served as the Head Start Director for Five Sandoval Indian Pueblos, Inc. a consortium of five New Mexico member tribes and served as Executive Director for the New Mexico Office of Indian Affairs (OIA). At OIA, he was an advisor to the State Department of Education, Indian Education Division and served on the Advisory Board for the State Cultural Affairs. In later years, he served as Chairman of the Five Sandoval Governing Board, Indian Pueblo Cultural Center Board (IPCC), Pueblo de Cochiti Economic Development Corporation and NM Pueblo Housing Authority. Mr. Suina has a BA degree in Psychology and Counseling and has served as a school counselor to high school students. In his current position, he continues to advocate excellence in Indian education, better health & wellness initiatives, community based economic development, leadership, language preservation and revitalization as well as built capacity to empower tribes & Indian communities to self determine for economic sufficiency.

SULLIVAN, DOROTHY (Oklahoma Cherokee) 1939-
   (artist)
Born January 8, 1939, Seminole, Okla. *Education*: East Central University, Ada, OK, BA in Art Education & History. *Principal occupation*: Artist. *Address & Affiliation*: Owner & Cherokee Master Artist, Memory Circle Studio, P.O. Box 732, Norman, OK 73070 (405) 360-0751. *Awards, honors*: Numerous awards fro her art. *Interests*: Exhibitions and One Woman Shows. *Collections*: Dorothy's art work is in the Museum of the Cherokee Indian & Cherokee Heritage Museum in Cherokee, NC; & in private art collections including Wilma Mankiller, Betty Ford, Wes Strudi, John Quinn, III, etc. *Memberships*: Indian Arts & crafts Association; National Penn Women (Artists, Writers, Musicians) for Art & Letters; Cherokee Historical Society. *Published work*: Cherokee Heritage Collection, 1994 (sold out edition) "seven years of my art & research;" Biographical Directory of Native American Painters (Oklahoma University Press, 1995); Illustrator, Winter Story Time (Children's Press, 1994); Illustrator, The Man Hunting for the Sun (McMillan Spotlight Books, 1996; The Woman's Way - She Speaks for Her Clan (Time Life Books, 1995). Calendars: Cherokee Heritage 1999; Native American People's 1997; American Indian Artists, 1995-92; Dorothy's Cherokee Heritage Collection, 1994.

SULLIVAN, JEROMY C. (Port Gamble S'Klallam)
   (tribal chairperson)
Affiliation & Address: Chairperson, Port Gamble S'Klallam Tribe, 31912 Little Boston Rd. NE, Kingston, WA 98346 (360) 297-2646.

SULLIVAN, MICHAEL (Ojibwe)
   (Ojibwe language studies chair)
Affiliation & Address: Chair, Global, Cultural & Language Studies Program, Ojibwe Language Studies, The College of St. Scholastica, School of Arts & Letters, Tower Hall, Room 4106A, 1200 Kenwood Ave., Duluth, MN 55811 (218) 625-4860. E-mail: msullivan@css.edu.

SULLIVAN, PATRICK
   (attorney)
Education: Reed College, BA, 2000; Portland State University School of Business Administration, MBA, 2005; Lewis & Clark Law School, JD, 2012. *Affiliation & Address*: Member, Dickinson Wright, Indian Law Section, 1875 Eye St., NW, Washington, DC 20006 (202) 659-6936. E-mail: psullivan@dickinsonwright.com. Mr. Sullivan represents clients in tribal, state and federal litigation, regulatory matters before various government agencies and negotiation of intergovernmental agreements between Indian tribes and state & local municipalities. Represented large California Indian tribe in development of casino resort. Advised tribal council and staff on government-to-government relations, negotiation of Class III Gaming Compact & intergovernmental agreements, real estate transactions, environmental compliance, construction & development contracts. Represented city government in major state court litigation involving two Indian tribes. Drafted motions, briefs, discovery requests and settlement agreement. Represented landowner in APA challenge to unlawful Indian lease termination in federal district court. Represented well-known franchise restaurant in negotiation of contract to place new location on Indian land. Memberships: Executive Committee, Oregon Bar Association Indian Law Section; Board Member, Native American Bar Association of D.C.

SULLIVAN, SCOTT D. (Tolowa)
   (tribal chairperson)
Affiliation & Address: Chairperson, Tolowa Tribe of the Smith River Rancheria, 140 Rowdy Creek Rd., Smith River, CA 95567 (707) 951-4864. E-mail: Scott.sullivan@tolowa. com.

SUMMERFIELD, HARRY B., JR. (Paiute)
   (former tribal chairperson)
Affiliation: Lovelock Tribal Council, P.O. Box 878, Lovelock, NV 89419 (702) 273-7861.

SUMMERFIELD, TAMARA R. (Quapaw)
   (tribal chairperson)
Affiliation: Quapaw Tribal Business Committee, P.O. Box 765, Quapaw, OK 74363 (918) 542-1853. E-mail: tsummerfield@chek.com.

SUMMERS, ALLEN (Paiute)
   (tribal chairperson)
Affiliation: Bishop Indian Tribal Council, P.O. Box 548, Bishop, CA 93514 (619) 873-3584.

SUMMERS-FITZGERALD, DIOSA (Mississippi Choctaw) 1945-
   (director of education, artist)
Born December 23, 1945, New York, N.Y. *Education*: State University College at Buffalo, BA, 1977; Northwestern University Archaeological Center, Kampsville, IL (Certificate), 1981; Harvard University Graduate School of Education, EdM, 1983. *Principal occupation*: Director of education, artist. Resides on Staten Island, NY. *Affiliations*: Instructor, History Dept. & Continuing Education Dept., State University College at Buffalo, NY, 1975-77; instructor, Haffenreffer Museum of Anthropology, Bristol, RI, 1979-80; acting tribal coordinator, Narragansett Tribal Education Project, Inc., 1980; administration, instructor, proposal writer, program coordinator, 1980-81, education director, instructor, 1982-85, Tomaquag Indian Memorial Museum, Exeter, RI; Native American historical and educational consultant, Plimoth Plantation, Plymouth, MA, 1981-82; artist in residence, Folk Arts Program, RI State Council on the Arts, Providence, 1982-85; artist, Native American Art Forms Nishnabeykwa Productions, Charlestown, RI, 1982-85; education director, Jamaica Arts Center, Jamaica, NY, 1985-. *Other professional post*: Owner, artist, consultant, Nishnabeykwa Productions, Staten Island, N.Y., 1982-. *Memberships*: Harvard Club of RI. *Awards, honors*: 1st Prize, Photography, Thomas Indian School Exhibit; Kappa Delta Pi, National Undergraduate Honor Society; Phi Alpha Theta, International History Honor Society. *Interests*: "Over the years, I have devoted most of life to Native American art, and a clear understanding of the roots of Native American tradition through art. I have also sought to develop a better understanding of the Native American through art as well as in the classroom initially as a teacher, and more recently a curriculum developer, & program developer. Other expertise: Cultural consultant & educational consultant; craft demonstrations; curator of exhibitions." *Published works*: Native American Foods; Fingerweaving, narrative and instruction; Ash Splint Basketry; Tomaquag Indian Museum brochures.

SUMNER, CLAUDE (Muscogee Creek)
   (tribal executive director)
Born in Talihina, Okla. *Education*: University of Kansas, BA with a double major in Speech & Drama & Sociology; University of Oklahoma, JD. *Affiliation*: Executive director, Muscogee Creek Nation, P.O. Box 580, Okmulgee, OK 74447 (918) 732-7612. *Past professional posts*: He served in other Muscogee

Creek Tribal administrative positions; taught college courses in Indian Law and Public Speech & Communications. *Military service*: U.S. Air Force; administrative officer for Avionics Maintenance Squadron, then as Squadron Commander in the Strategic Air Command (SAC); Vietnam Vet.

SUMNER, DELORES TITCHYWY (*Toos-z*) (Comanche) 1931-
(special collections librarian)
Born May 11, 1931, Lawton, Okla. *Education*: Northeastern State University, BS, 1964, MEd, 1967; University of Oklahoma, MLS, 1981. *Principal occupation*: Special collections librarian; assistant professor. *Address*: 405 N. Bliss, Tahlequah, OK 74464 (918) 456-5511, Ext. 3252. E-Mail: sumner@cherokee.nsuok.edu. *Affiliations*: Special Collections Librarian, John Vaughn Library, & assistant professor of Library Services, Northeastern State University, Tahlequah, OK, 1982-present; coordinator/director, Comanche Cultural Center, Comanche Complex, Lawton, OK. *Community activities*: Northeastern State University Symposium on the American Indian (appointed member, 1982-). *Memberships*: North American Indian Women's Association (president, Northeastern Oklahoma chapter, 1989-92); American Indian Libraries Association; Assn of College & Research Libraries; Tahlequah Area Arts & Humanities Council; Philbrook Museum Assn; Gilcrease Museum Association; North American Indian Museum Assn; Oklahoma Historical Society; Oklahoma Library Assn; American Library Assn; Delta Kappa Gamma (Research Committee Chairperson). *Awards, honors*: Certificate of Appreciation, Oklahoma Library Assn. *Interests*: "Supporting the traditional artists in Native American art by traveling to exhibits, showings, and galleries is one of my main interests. I am very much interested in the preservation of Native American culture and tradition through oral history, genealogy, artwork, and the retention of the native language, of which I have accomplished only a small portion while working for my tribe as their cultural director. Today, I am still working toward this goal by personally contacting elders to record their songs, stories, and memories. I also record Comanche hymns whenever possible." *Published works*: Numa-Nu: The Fort Sill Indian School Experience (Oklahoma Humanities Committee, 1980); Descendants of Titchywy, 2001; Descendants of Wis-sis-che, 2001.

SUNCHILD, JOHN (Chippewa-Cree)
(tribal chairperson)
Affiliation: Chippewa-Cree Business Committee, Rocky Boy's Reservation, Rocky Boy Route, Box 544, Box Elder, MT 59521 (406) 395-4282.

SUNDAY-ALLEN, ROBYN (Cherokee)
(health administrator)
Education: University of Oklahoma, BS, RN (Psychology & Nursing), MPH. *Affiliation & Address*: Chief Executive Officer, Oklahoma City Indian Clinic, 4913 W. Reno Ave., Oklahoma City, OK73127 (405) 948-4900. She and her staff of over 130 nurses, physicians and support staff provide comprehensive medical & behavioral health services to all tribal members in central Oklahoma. Robyn joined the Oklahoma City Indian Clinic in 1995 as a registered nurse. She was subsequently promoted to nurse manager of health services in 1997, to chief operating officer in 2001, and to chief executive officer in early 2009. She is a member of the Oklahoma Nurses Association and the Oklahoma Public Health Association.

SUNDBERG, GARTH (Yurok)
(rancheria chairperson)
Affiliation & Address: Chairperson, The Cher-Ae Heights Indian Community of the Trinidad Rancheria, P.O. Box 630, Trinidad, CA 95570 (707) 677-0211.

SUNDHEIM, JOYCE KASANOUKWAS (Penobscot-Mohawk)
(artist, shop owner)
Address: Owner, Indian Sun, Inc., 3831 Monica Pkwy., Sarasota, FL 34235 (941) 388-2975. Joyce does jewelry, rugs, and sandpaintings.

SUNDSTROM, LINEA
(consultant, author)
Affiliation: Private consultant in archaeology, historic resource management, and ethnohistory. *Published works*: Rock Art of the Southern Black Hills: A Contextual Approach; coauthor, Rock Art of Western South Dakota; Storied Stone: Indian Rock Art in the Black Hills Country (U. of Okla. Press, 2004).

SUPAHAN, SARAH
(Indian education program director)
Affiliation: Klamath-Trinity Joint U.S.D., Indian Education Program, P.O. Box 1308, Hoopa, CA 95546 (916) 625-4412. ssupahan@humboldt.k12.ca.us.

SUPER, ARCH (Karuk)
(former tribal chairperson)
Affiliation: Karuk Tribe of California, P.O. Box 1016, Happy Camp, CA 96039 (530) 493-1600.

SUPER , ROBERT (Karuk)
(tribal vice chairperson)
Affiliation & Address: Vice Chairperson, Karuk Tribe of California, P.O. Box 1016, Happy Camp, CA 996039 (530) 493-1600. E-mail: rsuper@karuk.us

SUPERNAW, KATHLEEN RAE (Creek/Munsee) 1949-
(attorney)
Born October 15, 1949, Hominy, Okla. *Education*: Northeastern Oklahoma A & M College, AA, 1969; Central State University, BS, 1971; Antioch University, MA, 1986; University of Oklahoma Law School, JD, 1992. *Address*: 7906 E. 33rd St., Tulsa, OK 74145 (918) 669-7730. *Affiliations*: Indian Tribes Community Development Association (past president), Oklahoma City, 1984-88; American Indian Law Review (editor-in-chief), Norman, OK, 1991-92; U.S. Dept. of the Interior, Office of the Field Solicitor, Tulsa, OK, 1993-. *Other professional posts*: Attorney, Pitchlynn, Odom, Morse & Ritter; Research Associate, University of Oklahoma - Center for American Indian Law & Policy; Rural Development Fellow, University of California, Davis, CA, 1985-86. *Community activities*: Recruitment of Indians to go to law school; work in Indian communities to encourage Indian kids to complete education and establish goals; support Indian arts & crafts fairs & promotions. *Memberships*: Oklahoma Indian Bar Assn; American Indian Bar Assn; American Indian Heritage Center. *Awards, honors*: Outstanding Second Year Editor, American Indian Law Review; recipient of the Gretchen Harris, Dean's, & Jones-Givens Scholarships; Joseph Rarick Outstanding Native American Student Award. *Interests*: Environmental & Indian law; Indian history & Indian studies; education in general; Indian tribal planning & development. Major employment before law school was working for several Indian tribes as the drafter of planning. *Published work*: Co-authored with Rennard Strickland, "Back to the Future: A Proposed Model Tribal Act to Protect Native Cultural Heritage (Arkansas Law Review, 1993).

SUPERNAW, KUGEE (Quapaw-Osage)
(craftsperson; business owner)
Affiliation: Supernaw's Oklahoma Indian Supply, 303 E. Rogers Blvd., P.O. Box 216, Skiatook, OK 74070 (918) 396-1713. Website: www.supernaw.com. *Artwork*: Featherwork, roaches, silver metalwork, women's accessories, beadwork, boxes, jewelry, shell-tempered Mississippian pottery.

SUPPAH, JAKE (Warm Springs)
(tribal secretary/treasurer)
Affiliation & Address: Secretary/Treasurer, Confederated Tribes of the Warm Springs Reservation, 1233 Veterans St., Warm Springs, OR 97761 (541) 553-1161. E-mail: jsuppah@wstribes.org

SUPPAH, RON (Warms Springs)
(former tribal chairperson)
Affiliation & Address: Confederated Tribes of the Warm Springs Reservation, 1233 Veterans St., Warm Springs, OR 97761 (541) 553-1161. E-mail: rsuppah@ wstribes.org.

SURVEYOR, CHARLES (Cheyenne-Arapaho)
(tribal chairperson)
Affiliation: Cheyenne-Arapaho Business Committee, 100 Red Moon Cir., Box 38, Concho, OK 73022 (405) 262-0345.

SUTEER-FENTON, BEVERLY S. (Ojibwe) 1950-
(American Indian advisor)
Born April 16, 1950, Cape Girardeau, Mo. *Education*: University of Illinois, 1968-69; Eastern Illinois University, BA, 1989, MS, 1991. *Principal occupation*: American Indian advisor. *Address*: 4130 Granby Ct., Fort Collins, CO 80526. *Affiliation*: University of Utah, Salt Lake City, UT, 1991-97. *Community activities*: Board of Directors, Indian Walk-In Center, Salt Lake City; Utah InterTribal Veterans Association Auxiliary; Heber Valley Powwow Committee. *Memberships*: Utah Coalition for the Advancement of Minorities in Higher Education; National Indian Education Society; American College Personnel Assn; Phi Delta Kappa Honorary Education Society. *Awards, honors*: Outstanding Community Service Award, Salt Lake City Indian Community, 1992. *Interests*: "Have participated in workshops & presentations which address recruitment & retention of American Indians in higher education."

SUTTEER, BARBARA A. (Northern Ute/Cherokee) 1940-
(American Indian liaison)
Born December 9, 1940, Roosevelt, Utah. *Education*: University of Utah, 1959-60. *Affiliation & Address*: Liaison, Office of American Indian Trust Responsibility, National Park Service, Rm. 550 (Rocky Mountain System Support Office), P.O. Box 25287, Lakewood, CO 80225 (303) 969-2511. E-mail: barbara_sutteer@nps.gov. 1993-present. *Other professional posts*: Supt., Little Bighorn Battlefield National Monument, Crow Agency, MT; Indian Allotment Coordinator, Bureau of Indian Affairs (Alaska). *Community activities*: Serves on the American Indian Task Force, Denver Art Museum & Colorado History Museum. *Awards, honors*: Special Achievement, BIA (Alaska).

Interests: Federal Indian Policy; interpretation of American Indian cultures/histories. *Biographical sources*: Chapter on Little Bighorn Battlefield (Name Change/Indian Memorial) in biography, "Ben Nighthorse Campbell."

SUTTON, VICTORIA
(attorney)
Education: North Carolina State University, BS (Zoology & Animal Science); Old Dominion University, MA (Public Administration); University of Texas, Dallas, PhD (Environmental Sciences); Washington College, American University, JD (magna cum laude). *Affiliations*: Robert H. Bean Professor of Law, Texas Tech University School of Law; director, Center for Biodefense, Law & Public Policy. *Other professional posts*: Member, Advisory Board, National Congress of American Indians Policy Research Center, 1301 Connecticut Ave. NW, Suite 200, Washington, DC 20036 (202) 466-7767. E-mail: vsutton@ncai.org; founding Chair, Federal Indian Law Committee of the Federal Circuit Bar Association. *Past professional posts*: Secretary, National Native American Bar Association, 2001-2002; chair-elect & chair, American Association of Law Schools, Nation Nations & Indigenous Peoples, 2005. She is the former Assistant Director in the White House Office of Science & Technology Policy in the Pres. George W. Bush Administration; appointed by Pres. George W. Bush as Chief Counsel, Research & Innovative Technology Administration, Department of Transportation. *Memberships*: American Indian Science & Engineering Society (AISES); & National Native American Bar Association. She ran for U.S. Congress in 2003 and is the first Republican Native American woman to run for Congress.

SUZACK, CHERYL (Batchewana First Nation)
(professor of English & Aboriginal Studies)
Affiliation & Address: Assistant Professor of English & Aboriginal Studies, Department of English, University of Toronto, Toronto, ON M5S 2J7. E-mail: cheryl.suzack@utoronto.ca. *Research & Teaching Interests*: Indigenous literatures, law & literature, indigenous feminism, feminist theory, postcolonial theory, and legal writing. *Past professional posts*: University of Alberta & University of Victoria. *Published work*: Co-editor (essay collection), Indigenous Women & Feminism: Politics, Activism, Culture (UBC Press, 2010).

SWAIN, PHILIBERT (Moapa Paiute)
(tribal chairperson)
Affiliation: Moapa Business Council, P.O. Box 340, Moapa, NV 89025 (702) 865-2787.

SWALLEY, LARRY (Oglala Lakota Sioux)
(radio station program director)
Affiliation: KILI - 90.1 FM, Oglala Lakota Sioux Tribe, P.O. Box 150, Porcupine, SD 57772 (605) 867-5002.

SWAMP, LAWRENCE (Mohawk)
(environmental health education specialist)
Education: St. Lawrence University, B.A. (Anthropology). *Address & Affiliation*: Environmental Health Education Specialist, St. Regis Mohawk Tribe, 412 State Rte. 37, Akwesasne, NY 13655 (518) 358-2272.

SWAMP, SKAHENDOWANEH (Mohawk)
(faithkeeper; artist; chair of Indigenous knowledge)
Affiliation & Address: Chairperson, Indigenous Knowledge, Department of Indigenous Studies, Enweying Rm. 306, Trent University, 1600 Westbank Dr., Peterborough, ON 9J 7B8 (705) 748-1011 ext. 7922. The first academic chair of its kind in Canada and all of North America to be awarded to a native Elder or traditional person. Mr. Swamp is an artist who paints & carves detailed figures out of stone.

SWAN, ANITA L. (Yakama)
(school supt.)
Affiliation: Yakama Tribal School, P.O. Box 151, Toppenish, WA 98948 (509) 865-5121.

SWAN, CLAIRE (Kenaitze)
(tribal chairperson; health director)
Affiliation: Kenaitze Indian Tribe Executive Committee/Tribal Council & Health Center, P.O. Box 988, Kenai, AK 99611 (907) 283-3633.

SWAN, DANIEL C. (Osage)
(curator of ethnology)
Affiliation & Address: Associate Curator of Ethnology, Sam Noble Museum of Natural History, 2401 Chautauqua Ave., Norman, OK 73072 (405) 325-1600. E-mail: dcswan@ou.edu. *Other professional post*: Associate professor, Department of Anthropology, Dale Hall Tower 804-D, University of Oklahoma, Norman, OK. Research Interests: Native North Ameica; Heritage Construction; History and expressive culture of the Peyote Religion; Museum Anthropology; Theories of Materiality..

SWAN, DAVID (Inupiat)
(AK village council president)
Affiliation: Native Village of Kivalina Council, P.O. Box 50051, Kivalina, AK 99750 (907) 645-2153.

SWAN, JAMES A. (Canadian Metis) 1943-
(author/events producer)
Born February 25, 1943, Trenton, Mich. *Education*: University of Michigan, BS, 1965; MS (Resource Planning), 1967; 1967-69 (Environmental Psychology). *Principal occupation*: Author/events producer. *Affiliations*: President, Institute for the Study of Natural Systems, Mill Valley, 1987-; associate professor, California Institute of Integrated Studies, San Francisco, CA, 1987-. *Membership*: American Bison Association. *Awards, honors*: Homer N. Calver Lecturer for American Public Health Association; California State Assembly Award of Recognition; Xi Sigma Forestry Honorary; Phi Sigma Biological Sciences Honorary. *Interests*: Cross-cultural psychology & applications to ecology; producer of concerts, symposiums, & conferences; actor/musician. *Biographical sources*: Who's Who in the West; "James Swan: On Aligning Oneself With Sacred Places" Wingspan. *Published works*: Sacred Places (Bear & Co., 1990); The Power of Place (Quest, 1991); Nature As Teacher and Healer (Villard-Random House, 1992).

SWAN, SR., JOSEPH (Inupiat)
(former Alaskan village president)
Affiliation: Native Village of Kivalina, P.O. Box 50051, Kivalina, AK 99750 (907) 645-2153.

SWANASET, GEORGE (Nooksack)
(tribal vice chairperson)
Affiliation: Nooksack Tribe, P.O. Box 157, Deming, WA 98244 (360) 592-5176. E-mail: gswanasetsr@nooksack-nsn.gov.

SWANBERG, KIM (*Bboon kwe*) (Sault Chippewa) 1953-
(Indian education program director)
Born July 4, 1953, Munising, Mich. *Principal occupation*: Coordinator/director-Indian education program. *Address*: 411 Elm St., Munising, MI 49862 (906) 387-3861. E-mail: kimswanberg@hotmail.com. *Community activities*: Powwow annual presentations. *Awards, honors*: AIGER County's "Women of Honor" Award of 1996.

SWANEY, RHONDA R. (Confederated Salish & Kootenai) 1952-
(tribal chairperson)
Born May 15, 1952, in St. Ignatius, Mont. *Education*: University of Montana, B.A. (Political Science, Honors), 1984. *Address*: P.O. Box 278, Pablo, MT 59855 (406) 675-2700. E-Mail: csktadmn@ronan.net. *Affiliations*: Bureau of Indian Affairs, Flathead Agency, Ronan, MT, 1974-80 (clerk typist, 1974-79, Rights of Way Specialist, 1979-80); Bureau of Indian Affairs, Portland Area Office, Portland, OR, 1984-87 (natural resources specialist, 1984-85; realty specialist, 1985-87); Chairperson, Tribal Council of the Confederated Salish & Kootenai Tribes, Pablo, MT, 1987-present (natural resources department head, 1987-94; vice-chairperson of tribal council, St. Ignatius District Rep., 1994-96, chairperson, St. Ignatius District Rep., 1996-present. *Community activities*: Self-governance & environmental protection committees. *Awards, honors*: Ms. Swaney became the first tribal chairwoman in 1996.

SWANICK, CHRISTINE L.
(attorney-partner)
Education: Boston College, BA, 1990; University of Arizona School of Law, JD, 1995. *Affiliation & Address*: Partner, Sheppard Mullin Richter & Hampton LLP, 30 Rockefeller Plaza, New York, 10112 (212) 634-3051. *Area of Practice*: Tribal & Indian Law; Co-Team Leader. Christine Swanick has practiced federal Indian law for 19 years. Christine advises clients in all aspects of federal Indian law and tribal law matters and represents tribes & entities doing business with tribes in complex contractual, gaming, regulatory & economic development matters. Christine began her Indian law career working as an in-house tribal attorney for three different federally recognized Indian tribes where she developed gaming ordinances & regulations necessary for start-up tribal gaming operations, advised tribal governments on Indian land status & matters, formed tribal instrumentalities & agencies, drafted employee handbooks and provided a broad range of legal advice and services to her tribal clients. In more recent years, Christine has negotiated on behalf of tribes and gaming developers gaming consulting & management agreements, advised on tribal energy matters and specialized in financing projects on tribal lands. Christine is a nationally recognized expert in tribal lending & restructuring transactions of all kinds and has worked on over 100 Native American and gaming credit transactions involving over 50 different Native American tribes.

SWANSON, JOANNE (Inupiaq Eskimo)
(artist)
Born July 7, 1952, in Shaktoolik, Alaska (Norton Sound Village). *Education*: Alaska Pacific University, BA (Elementary Education), 1985 *Address*: P.O. Box 53027, Koyuk, AK 99753 (907) 963-2450; E-mail: swanson@artnatam.com. *Awards, honors*: Honorable Mention, Inuit Circumpolar Conferences Logo Contest, 2002. *Professional interests*: Painting in watercolor of contemporary & traditional Eskimo village scenes, activities, & portraits. *Personal interests*: Reading, studying, beading, camping, berry picking, some travel.

SWARTZ, WARREN C. "CHRIS", JR. (Lake Superior Ojibwe)
(tribal president)
Affiliation & Address: President, Keweenah Bay Indian Community, 16429 Beartown Rd., Baraga, MI 49908 (906) 353-6623. E-mail: tcchris@kbic-nsn.gov

SWEENEY, THOMAS W. (Citizen Potawatomi)
(director of public affairs; editor)
Affiliation & Address: Director of Public Affairs, National Museum of the American Indian, Smithsonian Institution, 4th & Independence Ave., SW, Washington, DC 20024 (202) 633-6611. *Other professional post*: Editor, American Indian, publication of the National Museum. sweeneyt@si.edu.

SWEET, DENISE (White Earth Anishinaabe)
(associate professor of English)
Affiliation & Address: Associate Professor of English, Creative Writing Program, Humanistic Studies, University of Wisconsin-Green Bay, TH331B, Green Bay, WI 54311 (920) 465-2727. E-mail: sweetd@uwgb.edu. Denise teaches courses on the literary traditions of native peoples. *Awards, honors*: Wisconsin's 2nd Poet Laureate, 2004-08.

SWEET-GARCIA, LISA (Chickasaw)
(associate attorney)
Education: East Central (OK) University, BS (Legal Studies), 2005; University of Tulsa Law School, JD, 2009. *Affiliation & Address*: Associate Attorney, Legal Advocates for Indian Country, LLP, P.O. Box 973, Wagoner, OK 74477 (918) 485-1718. Ms. Sweet practices Indian law, family law & criminal law, and provides legal representation to victims of domestic violence. While in Law School, she worked with the Boesche Legal Clinic's Muskogee Creek Nation program providing legal representation for Muscogee Creek Nation citizens.

SWENSEN, THOMAS MICHAEL (Alutiiq)
(assistant professor of ethnic studies)
Education: University of Utah, BA (Literature & Art, 2000; University of Oregon, MA (Literature), 2002; University of California, Berkeley, PhD (Ethnic Studies) 2011. *Affiliation & Address*: Assistant Professor, Ethnic Studies Department, Colorado State University, 214 Willard O. Eddy Hall, Fort Collins, CO 80523 (303) 491-2418. E-mail: thomas.swensen@colostate.edu Other professional posts: In July 2017 he will be an assistant professor of ethnic studies at the University of Utah in Salt Lake City and, in September 2017, the Katrin H. Lamon Fellowship Scholar in residence at the School for Advanced Research in Santa Fe, New Mexico. Dr. Swensen produces scholarship at the crossroads of Native American studies & the environmental humanities. He's published articles on the Alaska Native Claims Settlement Act of 1971, Native publics & environmental disasters, the emergence of Alaska Native tribal governments, urban space and the John T. William's Memorial Pole, the cultural geographies of Native punx, and the distinctions between Alaska Native civil rights and Native title. He's finishing a draft of a book length manuscript, *The Great Land: Alaska Native assemblages of belonging and the environment*. Article wise, he's working on pieces exploring Native subsistence practices & animal studies, Alaska punx and the environment, the Indigenous urban, & as well as an essay on hemispheric transnational Native ecological art. Thomas was born and raised in the Kodiak Archipelago and graduated from S.A.V.E. II secondary school in Anchorage on the Alaska mainland. After enrolling at a community college at a non-traditional ageAn original shareholder in the Alaska Native Claims Settlement corporations Koniag, Inc., and Leisnoi, Inc., Thomas is also enrolled in the federally recognized Tangirnaq Native Village aka the Woody Island Tribe. With pride, he serves the Alutiiq community on the board of directors of the Koniag Education Foundation, an organization that promotes the educational goals and economy of the Koniag Alutiiq & their descendants. When he was still in graduate school the Western History Association awarded him with the Autry prize in Public History for his authorship of the "We Shall Remain: The Utah Indian Curriculum Project" in 2010, http://utahindians.org/Curriculum. The following year he was awarded the Chancellors Postdoctoral Fellowship in American Indian Studies at the University of Illinois, Urbana-Champaign. From 2012-2014 he worked as the assistant Professor of Native Arts & Culture at the Herberger Institute at Arizona State University. He consistently posts on the Alaska Native Studies Blog http://alaskanativestudies.blogspot.com. Blog Facebook at www.facebook.com/AlaskaNativeStudiesBlog & Tumblr at http://alaskanativestudies.tumblr.com.

SWENTZELL, ROXANNE (*Ojegepovi*) (Santa Clara Pueblo) 1962-
(artist)
Born December 9, 1962, Taos, N.M. *Education*: Institute of American Indian Arts (two years); Portland Museum Art School (one year). *Address*: P.O. Box 4154, Fairview, NM 87533 (505) 747-4827. Website: www.roxanneswentzell.net. *Artwork*: Contemporary and traditional pottery and clay sculpture.

SWETT, PURNELL (Lumbee)
(tribal chairperson)
Education: University of North Carolina, Pembroke, BS; Western Carolina University, MA (Education); post-graduate studies from North Carolina Institute of Law, the University of North Carolina, Chapel Hill, and Virginia Polytechnic Institute. *Affiliation*: Chair, Lumbee Tribe of North Carolina, P.O. Box 2709, Pembroke, NC 28372 (919) 521-7861. Website: www.lumbeetribe.com. *Past professional posts*: Chief of Program Operations, Program manager & Acting Deputy Commissioner, Dept. of Health, Education & Welfare, Office of Indian Education, Washington, DC, 1971-74; Associate Supt., 1975-77, Supt., 1977-89; Indian Vocational Education, University of North Carolina, Pembroke, 1990-93; Supt. of Robeson County Schools, 1993-97.

SWIFT ARROW, BERNADINE (Quechan)
(Indian education director)
Affiliation: Quechan Indian Tribe Education Dept., P.O. Box 1446, Winterhaven, CA 92283 (760) 572-0603

SWIMMER, JOHN S. (Cherokee) 1973-
(attorney)
Education: University of Oklahoma, BA (Communications), 1990; University of Wisconsin Law School, JD, 1998. *Affiliation & Address*: Owner-Attorney (2009-present), Swimmer Law Offices, 500 W. Silver Spring Dr. Suite K-200, Glendale, WI 53217 (414) 380-2433. Website: www.swimmerlaw.com. E-mail: jswimmer@swimmerlaw.com. *Other professional post*: General Council Attorney, Ho-Chunk Nation, 2015-present; Board member, First American Capital Corporation, 2006-present. *Past professional posts*: Tribal Attorney, Ho-Chunk Nation, 1998-2001; Solicitor General, Mille Lacs Band of Ojibwe, 2001-06; Attorney, Godfrey & Kahn, S.C., 2006-09. *Practice areas*: Federal Indian law, litigation, criminal law, ICWA. *Military service*: Staff Sergent, Tulsa Air National Guard, 1986-95. *Memberships*: American Bar Association; Wisconsin Bar Association; Minnesota American Indian Bar Association.

SWIMMER, MARGARET A. (Cherokee)
(attorney)
Affiliation & Address: Staff Attorney (2005-present), Hall Estill, Attorneys at Law, Indian Law Program, 320 S. Boston Ave., Suite 200, Tulsa, OK 74103 (918) 594-0669. E-mail: mswimmer@hallestill.com. Mr. Posey is ranked Band 2 by Chambers USA as one of the best Native American lawyers in the state of Oklahoma; Best Lawyer in America in Native American Law; he is a frequent author & speaker on Indian law issues.

SWIMMER, ROSS O. (Cherokee) 1943-
(president/CEO-Cherokee Nation Industries)
Born October 26, 1943, Oklahoma City, Okla. *Education*: University of Oklahoma, BA, 1965; University of Oklahoma School of Law, J.D., 1967. *Principal occupation*: President & CEO of Cherokee Nation Industries. *Affiliations*: Law partner, Hansen, Peterson & Thompkins, Oklahoma City, Okla., 1967-72; general counsel, 1972-75, principal chief, 1975-85, Cherokee Nation of Oklahoma, Tahlequah, OK; executive vice president, 1974-75, president, 1975-85, First National Bank in Tahlequah, OK; Co-chairman, Presidential Commission on Indian Reservation Economies (a panel of tribal leaders appointed to seek ways to help tribes improve economic conditions), 1983-84; assistant secretary, U.S. Department of the Interior, Bureau of Indian Affairs, 1951 Constitution Ave., NW, Washington, DC, 1985-89; developed an Indian law practice for law firm of Hall, Estill, Harswick, Gale, Golden and Nelson, Tulsa, OK, 1989-92; president/CEO of Cherokee Nation Industries, Inc., Stillwell, OK, 1992-. *Other professional posts*: Director on several boards, including the University of Tulsa, Gilcrease Museum and the Oklahoma Medical Research Foundation; counsel to Hall, Estill, Hardwick, Gable, Golden and Nelson. *Community activities*: Boy Scouts of America in Eastern Oklahoma (executive committee); Cherokee National Historical Society (past president); Tahlequah Planning and Zoning Commission (former chairman); Eastern Oklahoma Indian Health Advisory Board (secretary-treasurer); Inter-Tribal Council of the Five Civilized Tribes (advisory board, director). *Memberships*: Oklahoma Bar Assn; American Bar Assn; Oklahoma Historical Society; Oklahoma Industrial Development Commission. *Awards, honors*: Honorary Doctoral Degree, Phillips University, Enid, OK; Distinguished Service Award, University of Oklahoma, Norman; Distinguished Service Citation, U.S. Dept. of Interior, 1989. *Interests*: USIA sponsored speaking tour of 14 cities in Germany to discuss issues related to the American Indian. Interior Secretary Donald Hodel said of Swimmer, "He combines a solid knowledge of tribal & Indian affairs with understanding & skill in modern business management.

Swimmer has frequently expressed his views that Indian tribes should be less dependent on the federal government." When nominated for the position of Assistant Secretary, Swimmer said of President Reagan: "I know he is committed to an Indian policy that supports tribal self-determination, which is something I have worked for during my ten years at the Cherokee Nation."

SWISHER, KAREN GAYTON (Standing Rock Sioux) 1943-
(Indian college president.)

Born April 3, 1943, Fort Yates, N.D. *Education*: Northern State University, BS, 1964, MS, 1974; University of North Dakota, EdD, 1981. *Principal occupation*: College president. *Affiliation & Address*: President, Haskell Indian Nations University, 155 Indian Ave. #1305, Lawrence, KS 66046 (875) 749-8404. E-Mail: kswisher@ross1.cc.haskell.edu. *Past professional posts*: Teacher & principal, Bureau of Indian Affairs, 1967-77; assistant professor of education, University of Utah, Salt Lake City, 1982-85; associate professor/director of CIE, Arizona State University, Tempe, AZ, 1985-96; editor, "Journal of American Indian Education," Center for Indian Education, Arizona State University, Tempe, AZ, 1990-96; Haskell Indian Nations University, Lawrence, KS (chairperson, Teacher Education Department, 1996-2002; president, 2003-present). *Memberships*: American Educational Research Association (American Indian/Alaska Native Education Special Interest Group Chair, 1984-86, 1987-89); National Indian Education Association; Association for Supervision & Curriculum Development; American Anthropological Association; Council on Anthropology & Education. Awards, honors: Sioux Award, highest honor of University of North Dakota Alumni Association for professional career accomplishments, 1989; Early Contribution Award, AERA Committee on the Role and Status of Minorities in Educational Research & Development, 1990. *Interests*: "Enjoy travels to American Indian reservations in lower 48 states and desire to travel to other countries to study indigenous people's participation in educational systems." *Published works*: Co-editor, Special Issues on Learning Styles (Center for Indian Education, Arizona State University, 1989); co-editor, First American Firsts (Gale Research, 1997).

SYLESTINE, COLABE III CLEM (Alabama-Coushatta of Texas)
(tribal principal chief)

Affiliation & Address: Principal Chief, Alabama-Coushatta Tribe of Texas, 571 State Park Rd., Livingston, TX 77351 (936) 563-1100.

SYLESTINE, OSCOLA CLAYTON M. (Alabama-Coushatta of Texas)
(former tribal principal chief)

Affiliation: Alabama-Coushatta Tribe of Texas, 571 State Park Rd., Livingston, TX 77351 (936) 563-1100.

SYLVIA, TONY J. (Yurok/Narragansett)
(artist)

Address: Owner, Teewood Designs, P.O. Box 1409, Hoopa, CA 95546 (707) 499-1922. Makes wearable art (Native design only); paintings.

SYNDER, FRED (*Bi'son*) (Chippewa/Colville) 1951-
(consultant, editor/publisher)

Born March 8, 1951, Pennsylvania. *Education*: Rutgers University (three yrs.). *Principal occupation*: Director/consultant, National Native American Co-operative, San Carlos, AZ. *Address*: P.O. Box 27626, Tucson, AZ 85726 (520) 622-4900. Website: www.usaindianinfo.org. *Other professional posts*: Editor/publisher, Native American Directory--Alaska, Canada, U.S.; educator. *Community activities*: Sponsors American Indian powwows & arts & crafts markets, monthly, Phoenix, Ariz. (sponsor); powwow attender for North America. *Awards, honors*: Blue Ribbon (three years), Beadwork Competition, Heard Museum of Anthropology, Phoenix, AZ; numerous awards from Indian cultural programs, Title IV, Indian education, ethnic fairs. *Interests*: "Most of my time is shared between directing the Co-Op, distribution of Native American Directory, traveling extensively throughout North America to Indian powwows, rodeos, craft shows & conventions, and establishing the first Watts Line American Indian Information Center & Chamber of Commerce." *Published work*: Native American Directory--Alaska, Canada, U.S. (National Native American Co-Op, 1982 & 1996); On the Red Road: Powwows (National Native American Co-Op, 1993).

SZABO, LINDA (Sicangu Lakota)
(craftsperson)

Affiliations: Co-owner (with Paul Szabo), Szabo Studio, P.O. Box 906, Mission, SD 57555 (605) 856-4548. *Product*: Handmade Northern Plains style jewelry.

SZABO, PAUL (Rosebud Sioux) 1947-
(high school art teacher)

Born December 26, 1947, Burke, S.D. *Education*: Southern State, 1966-70; Dakota State College, Madison, SD, 1970-71. *Address*: P.O. Box 906, Mission, SD 57555 (605) 856-4548. *Affiliations*: Art teacher, Todd County High School, Mission, SD, 1985-; owner, Szabo Studio, Mission, SD 1975-. *Community activities*: Church leader; Boy Scouts. *Memberships*: National Education Association; South Dakota Education Association; TCEA. *Awards, honors*:

Northern Plains Art Show - 2nd place, 2 years, honorable mention; Cultural Heritage Art Show - 1st place, metal work; Renwick Collection at the Smithsonian, Washington, D.C. *Interests*: "Metalworking; travel."

SZOTKOWSKI, WILIAM A.
(attorney)

Education: University of Wisconsn, Eau Caire, BA, 1981; Hamline University School of Law, JD, 1984. *Affiliation & Address*: Attorney, Hogen Adams PPLP, 1935 W. County Road B2, Suite 460, St. Paul, MN 55113 (651) 842-9105. E-mail: bszotkowski@hogenadams.com. Mr. Szotkowski has extensive experience in Indian law issues. Since 2004, Bill has represented tribes and tribal members in governance mattes, complex federal-court litigation, contract negotiation and construction litigation. He was the lead attorney in a successful 2010 federal-court case brought by the Saginaw Chippewa Tribe of Michigan to gain permanent recognition of its Reservation Boundary, as defined by Executive Order and treaties in 1855 and 1864. The United States joined the Saginaw Tribe's efforts in the litigation against the State of Michigan & county and city governments. After five years of protracted litigation, the parties were able to reach a successful mediated settlement of the litigation. That settlement provided for permanent recognition of the Isabella Reservation, including all lands within the reservation as Indian Country. The settlement also provided for multifaceted agreements in areas relating to law enforcement, taxation, Indian Child welfare protection, and natural resource issues, as well as jurisdictional agreements relating to land use, local revenues, and local ordinances. It remains in place today and is a model for boundary disputes nationwide. Mr. Szotkowksi also has extensive experience in litigation involving the application of the National Labor Relations Act to tribes, both before the National Labor Relations Board and in the federal courts. Before he entered private practice, Bill spent several decades in service to the Minnesota Attorney General's Office. During that time, he gained significant litigation experience before state & federal courts, including the Supreme Court of the United States. Mr. Szotkowksi had principal responsibility for the State's major cases involving Indian-law issues, & handled litigation concerning jurisdictional disputes, class-action land claims, treaty rights, natural-resource issues, and Indian burial grounds. In addition to litigating cases, he coordinated settlement efforts in several cases, and was able to put in place solutions that included legislation at both the state and federal level. Mr. Szotkowski has lectured on Indian law, tribal sovereignty, and natural-resource issues.

TABOR, ROBERT (Cheyenne-Arapaho)
(tribal chairperson)

Affiliation: Cheyenne-Arapaho Tribal Business Committee, P.O. Box 38, Concho, OK 73022 (405) 262-0345.

TADGERSON, STACEY (Sault Ste. Marie Ojibwe)
(office of Native American Affairs director)

Education: University of Michigan-Dearborn, BA; Northern Michigan University, MPA. *Affiliation & Address*: Director (2008-present), Office of Native American Affairs, Michigan Dept. of Human Services, 333 S. Grand Ave., Box 30195, Lansing, MI 48909 (517) 335-7782; Website: www.michigan.gov/mdhhs. *Past professional posts*: Tadgerson worked with the Pomo Indian Nations in Northern California as the executive director for Consolidated Tribal Health Project, Inc. a rural ambulatory Indian health center providing medical, dental, behavioral health, and community outreach services. In addition, she has been employed with the Sault Ste. Marie Tribe of Chippewa Indians as a grant specialist; and Anishnabek Community & Family Services as special project assistant & as project facilitator (Safe Kids/Safe Streets initiative, Department of Justice, Office of Juvenile Justice & Delinquency Prevention).

TAH, ANDREW M. (Navajo)
(supt. of schools)

Affiliation: Navajo Nation Superintendent of Schools, Department of Dine Education, P.O. Box 670, Window Rock, AZ 86515 (928) 871-7475. *Past professional post*: Supt., Chinle Agency, Bureau of Indian Affairs, Chinle, AZ.

TAH, GLOREE (Otoe-Missouri)
(higher education director)

Affiliation: Director, Education Dept., Otoe-Missouria Tribe of Oklahoma, 8151 Hwy. 177 • Red Rock, OK 74651 (580) 723-4466 ext. 209

TAH-BONE, GEORGE (Kiowa)
(attorney)

Affiliation: Oklahoma Indian Bar Assn, Oklahoma City, OK (405) 521-5277. *Membership*: Oklahoma Indian Bar Assn (committee chairperson-tribal courts).

TAHDOOAHNIPPAH, FORREST (Comanche)
(attorney; Federal Indian law)

Education: Stanford University, BA (Public Policy), 2007; University of Minnesota Law School, JD, 2010. *Affiliation & Address*: Associate, Dorsey & Whitney LLP, Corporate Group & Indian & Gaming Practice, 50 S. Sixth St., Suite 1500, Minneapolis, MN 55402 (612) 492-6182. E-mail: forrest@dorsey.

com. An associate in Dorsey's Intellectual Property Litigation Group, Forrest helps clients through all stages of intellectual property litigation. Forrest also enjoys a robust practice in the area of federal Indian law. Forrest provides litigation and transactional advice to both Indian tribes and companies doing business in Indian Country.

TAHSEQUAH, JERRY (Comanche)
(tribal secretary/treasurer)

Affiliation & Address: Secretary/Treasurer, Comanche Nation, P.O. Box 908, Lawton, OK 73502 (580) 492-3240. E-mail: jerryt@comanchenation.com
Past professional post: Associate Director, Native American Center of Excellence Consortium, Univefrsity of Oklahoma Health Sciences Center, Oklahoma City, OK.

TAHSUDA, MAX (Kiowa)
(IHS-area tribal development)

Education: University of Oklahoma, BS (Business Administration), MPH (Health Administration), 1980. *Affiliation & Address*: Office of Tribal Development, Indian Health Service, Oklahoma Area Office, Indian Health Service, Five Corporate Plaza, 3625 NW 56th St., Oklahoma City, OK 73102 (405) 231-4796. E-mail: max.tahsuda@ihs.gov. *Past professional posts*: Mr. Tahsuda is the Director of the Office of Tribal Self-Determination in the Oklahoma City Area, a post he has held since 1992. He also serves as the Acting Director of Information Technology and Telecommunications for the Oklahoma Area. Mr. Tahsuda first joined the Oklahoma City Area Office in 1988 as a Health Systems Specialist in the Tribal Office. Previously he served as a Commissioned Officer of the Public Health Service with the IHS in Sacramento, California. He also worked on the Salt River reservation for the Pima-Maricopa Tribes as a Health Planner for four years.

TAKEN ALIVE, JESSE "JAY" (Standing Rock Sioux)
(tribal chairperson)

Affiliation: Standing Rock Sioux Tribe, P.O. Box D, Fort Yates, ND 58538 (701) 854-7202.

TALACHY, JOSEPH M. (Pojoaque Pueblo)
(pueblo governor)

Affiliation & Address: Governor, Pojoaque Pueblo Council, P.O. Box 127, Penasco, NM 87553 (505) 587-2519.

TALACHY, PEARL (Nambe Tewa)
(potter)

Address & Affiliation: Native American Heirlooms, 318 County Rd. 119 So., Nambe Pueblo, NM 87506 (505) 455-3429. Artwork: Pottery from native clay stone-polished and traditionally fired.

TALAHONGVA, PATTY (Hopi)
(multi-media journalist)

Born in Polacca (First Mesa), Ariz. *Principal occupation*: Independent multi-media journalist based in Tempe, AZ. She is a television news producer and produces newscasts, special projects & documentaries. Currently, she writes for several national magazines & newspapers. In addition, she is producing video documentaries on Native people; currently, she hosts & produces the radio programs, "National Native News," & "Native America Calling." *Past professional posts*: Board of Directors, Native American Journalists Assn (NAJA); Since 1994, Patty had been the lead mentor for NAJA students in the summer broadcast project, NAJA News 4board of directors, Radio & Television News Directors Association as an Ex-Officio representative for NAJA through the RTNDA/UNITY Covenant. *Interests*: Her goal is to bring more native & aboriginal people into careers with mainstream television news.

TALAKTE, BONNIE (Hopi)
(tribal affairs liaison)

Born in the Second Mesa Village of Shungopavi & raised at the Grand Canyon & Fagstaff. Education: Northern Arizona University, BA (Education), MA (Fine Arts; University of Arizona, PhD (Higher Education Administration). *Affiliation & Address*: Tribal Affairs Liaison, Office of the Director of AHCCCS in the Interdepartmental Affairs Division, AHHCCS American Indian Health, 801 E. Jefferson, MD 4100, Phoenix, AZ 85034 (602) 417-4610. E-mail: bonnie.talakte@azahcccs.gov. Bonnie is responsible for coordinating tribal consultation between AHCCS & American Indian Tribes in Arizona.

TALAKTE, CATHERINE (Hopi)
(Native American students services)

Education: B.A. in Psychology & M.A. in Counseling. *Address & Affiliation*: Director, Native American Student Services (NASS), Northern Arizona University, P.O. Box 653, Flagstaff, AZ 86011. (928) 523-9416. E-mail: catherine.talakte@nau.edu. Ms. Talakte has been at NAU for about 20 years, serving as a counselor for the Educational Talent Search Program, 1987-1990; project director for the Upward Bound Program, 1990-94; & assisted in developing a Native American College Retention Program which later developed into NASS and has been on NASS for more than ten years as a Retention Specialist and Assistant Director. Also, she has served on various committees focusing on Native American recruitment & retention issues.

TALAMANTEZ, INES M. (Mescalero Apache)
(associate professor)

Address & Affiliation: Associate Professor of Religious Studies, University of California at Santa Barbara, Santa Barbara, CA 93106.

TALBOT, F. MEDICINE STORY (*Manitonquat*) (Wampanoag) 1929-
(storyteller, teacher, author, lecturer)

Born July 17, 1929, Salem, Mass. *Education*: Cornell University, BA, 1954; MEd, 1974, PhD, 2002. *Principal occupation*: Storyteller, teacher, author, lecturer. *Address*: 167 Merriam Hill Rd., Greenville, NH 03048 (603) 878-2310. E-mail: medicinestory@yahoo.com. Website: www.circleway.org. *Affiliation*: Co-director, Another Place, Inc., Greenville, NH, 1980-; Mettanokit Outreach, Greenville, NH. *Other professional posts*: Editor, Native Liberation Journal: Heritage; editor, Talking Stick (newsletter), 1987-present. *Military service*: U.S. Army, 1951-53 (PFC). *Community activities*: Elder; Liberation Reference Person for Native American Counselors (Eastern Canada & U.S.); spiritual advisor to Native Prison Programs in New England (re-evaluation counselor & counseling teacher); Tribal Healing Council (co-founder); Massachusetts Center for Native American Awareness; Watuppa Wampanoag Reservation Improvement Committee; Indian Spiritual & Cultural Training Council, Inc. *Interests*: "Counselor & spiritual advisor to six Native Prison Circles in New England; storyteller; author/lecturer/workshop & seminar leader at schools, universities, religious, cultural, environmental, health, peace and other organizations throughout North America & Europe; former writer-poetry editor-illustrator - cartoonist with Akwesasne Notes; now edits The Talking Stick, newsletter of activities of Mettanokit Outreach, Prison Program & Assonet Wampanoag activities. *Published works*: Manitonquat (Medicine Story): Return to Creation (Bear Tribe, 1991); story in "Spinning Tales, Weaving Hope" (New Society, 1991); The Children of the Morning Light (Macmillan, 1994); Ending Violent Crime, a Report on a Prison Program That Is Working (Story Stone 1996); The Circle Way (Story Stone, 1997).

TALGO, HARRISON (Apache)
(former tribal chairperson)

Affiliation: San Carlos Apache Tribal Council, P.O. Box 0, San Carlos, AZ 85550 (602) 475-2361.

TALLCHIEF, GEORGE EVES (*Sa-toa-enza*) (Osage) 1916-
(president of Osage National Council)

Born November 16, 1916, Arkansas City, Kans. *Education*: Central State College (Edmond, OK), BA, 1952; Pacific University (Forest Grove, OR), MA, 1957. *Principal occupation*: President of the Osage National Council. *Address*: P.O. Box 14, Fairfax, OK 74637 (918) 642-5642. *Affiliations*: President of the Osage National Council (former chief); president of State Indian Health Board; president of the United Tribes of Kansas, Texas & Oklahoma; Board of Standing Bear Foundation posts: Supt. of Lodge Pole Schools, Hayes, MT; principal of Crescent & Fairfax Schools in Oklahoma; president, Indian Festival of Arts; coach & teacher (45 years in the field of education). *Community activities*: Rotary Club; Chamber of Commerce; Quarterback Club; volunteer fireman. *Membership*: National Tribal Chairman's Association (chairman, 1982; vice president-Sergeant at Arms, 1990). *Awards, honors*: Iron Eyes Cody Peace Medal; Golden Glove Champion of Oklahoma (in college); Little All-American Coach of the Year in Pacific Coast Wrestling Conference. *Interests*: "My interests at the present time is to better the lot of the American Indian; sports; raise cattle, Appaloosa Show horses, karakul sheep & Yorkshire Terrier dogs since retirement. In earlier years, I rodeod - riding bulls & horses; roughnecked in the oil fields."

TALLENT, REBECCA (Cherokee)
(professor of journalism & American Indian studies)

Education: University of Central Oklahoma, BA (Education), M.Ed (Journalism), 1977; Oklahoma State University, EdD (Higher Education, Classroom Teaching, Mass Communication), 1995. Affiliation & Address: Professor of Journalism (2006-present), School of Journalism & Mass Communications, College of Letters, Arts & Social Sciences, University of Idaho, 340 Administration Bldg., MS 3178, 875 Perimeter Dr., Moscow, ID 83844 (208) 885-8872. E-mail: rtallent@uidaho.edu. Other professional post: Affiliate Faculty, American Indian Studies Program, University of Idaho, Moscow, ID. Becky is an award-winning journalist & public relations specialist with more than 12 years experience as an energy, environmental and financial journalist plus an additional 18 years experience as a public relations specialist, primarily with state government agencies. In addition to her UI teaching, Becky was the ombudsman for the Spokane *Spokesman-Review* in 2008 and is a member of the UI American Indian Studies Faculty. Becky is a member of both the Society of Professional Journalists (SPJ) and the Native American Journalists Association (she is of Cherokee heritage), and she is the adviser to both students groups on campus. Becky is also a member of the

SPJ National Education and Diversity committees. In 2013 she was elected to the national SPJ Board of Directors as a Campus Advisor at Large. She earned both her Bachelor of Arts in Journalism and her Master of Education in Journalism from the University of Central Oklahoma, and her Doctor of Education in Classroom Teaching/Mass Communications from Oklahoma State University in 1995. As part of her continuing education, Becky attended the Poynter Institute for Media Studies in the summer of 2007 to learn more about teaching Diversity Across the Curriculum. In 2007-2008, she held a Diversity Leadership Fellowship with the Society of Professional Journalists. *Awards, honors*: SPJ Diversity Leadership Fellowship, 2007; Educational Diversity Fellowship, Poynter Institute for Media Studies, 2007; Faculty Member of the Year, Embry-Riddle Aeronautical U. Oklahoma City, 2002-2003.

TALLMADGE, BERNADINE W. MINER (*Sitting in the Moonlight*) (Wisconsin Winnebago) 1920-
(owner/curator-Indian museum)
Born April 6, 1920, Necedah, Wisc. *Address*: P.O. Box 441, 3889 N. River Rd., Wisconsin Dells, WI 53965 (608) 254-4006 or 254-2268. *Affiliation*: Owner/curator, Winnebago Indian Museum, Wisconsin Dells, WI, 1953-. *Community activities*: Organized Dells Area Indian Club; presently on State Council on Aging, Tribal Council on Aging, and Tribal Personnel Committee, Wisconsin Winnebago Tribe. *Awards, honors*: Attended Presidential Inaugural Parade in 1952 in full regalia; Mrs. Congeniality during competition in Mrs. Wisconsin Pageant, 1961. *Interests*: Master weaver of "needle loom," sash weaving and appliqué.

TANKERSLEY, JEANETTE (Yuchi)
(executive director)
Affiliation & Address: Native American Coalition of Tulsa, Inc., 4935 S. Union Ave., Tulsa, OK 74107 (918) 446-8432. E-mail: jtankersley@nacths.com.

TANNER, KENNETH (Coquille)
(former tribal chief)
Affiliation & Address: Chief, Coquille Indian Tribe, P.O. Box 783, North Bend, OR 97459 (541) 756-0904. E-mail: ktanner@coquilletribe.org.

TANO, MERVYN L.
(attorney; organization president)
Affiliation & Address: President, International Institute for Indigenous Resource Management, 444 S. Emerson St., Denver, CO 80209 (303) 733-0481. E-mail: mervtano@iiirm.org. Mr. Tano has been working on tribal & indigenous peoples' issues since the early 1970s as the director of planning & budget for the Administration for Native Americans, as a private consultant and as general counsel & director of environmental programs at the Council of Energy Resource Tribes. *Other professional post*: Member of the Siting & Waste Facilities Subcommittee of National Environmental Justice Advisory Council.

TAPAHE, EUGENE (Navajo-Dine' Nation)
(graphic design; web developer)
Education: Brigham Young University, BFA (Graphic Design), 1992, MA (Business Administration) in process. *Affiliation & Address*: Senior Designer & Web Developer, Bringham Young University, Office of Information Technology, 1388 University Ave., Provo, UT 84602 (801) 422-5075. Other professional post: Member, Board of Directors, Native American Journalists Association, Norman, OK.

TAPAHE, LOREN (Navajo-Dine' Nation) 1953-
(president & CEO)
Born September 17, 1953, Fort Defiance, Ariz. *Education*: Brigham Young University, AA, 1974. *Affiliation & Address*: President & CEO (2011-present), American Indian Chamber of Commerce of Arizona, P.O. Box 481, Tempe, AZ 86515. E-mail: ltapahe@aol.comOther professional posts: Co-founder & First Vice President, Native American Journalists Association, 2011-present; board member, National Indian Education Association. *Past professional post*: Owner, Arizona Native Scene (monthly newspaper), 1996-2011.

TAPAHONSO, LUCI (Navajo-Dine' Nation)
(professor of English)
Born in Shiprock, NM. *Education*: University of New Mexico, MA, 1983. *Address & Affiliation*: American Indian Studies Program, The University of Arizona, 226B Harvill Bldg., Box 210076, Tucson, AZ 85721 (520) 621-7149. E-mail: tapahons@email.arizona.edu. She teaches courses in American Indian Literature & Creative Writing. *Interests*: Contemporary poetry in American Indian literature. *Awards, honors*: 2002 American Indian Leadership Award from the University of Kansas for her role in establishing the Indigenous Nations Studies Graduate Program in 1998; her book, "Blue Horses Rush In," was awarded the Mountain & Plains Booksellers Association's 1998 Award for Poetry; awarded the 1999 Storyteller of the Year by The Wordcraft Circle of Native Writers; the Kansas Governor's Art Award in 1998; Distinguished Woman awards from the National Association of Women in Education and the Girl Scout Council of America; served twice as Grand Marshall of the Northern

Navajo Fair (Shiprock, NM) in 1991 & 1999. Professor Tapahonso's work has appeared in many print & media productions in the U.S. & internationally. Her poems have been translated into German, Italian & French. She was featured in Rhino Records' CD "In Their Own Voices: A Century of American Poetry" and in the films: "The Desert Is No Lady," "Art of the Wild," and "Woven by the Grandmothers: An Exhibition of 19th Century Navajo Textiles," which were all released on PBS stations. Her work was featured in Norton Anthology's "American Passages," (2002) which is a PBS video series focusing on contemporary American writers. Published work: A Breeze Swept Through: Poetry (University of New Mexico Press, 2005).

TARBELL, NORMAN (St. Regis Mohawk)
(tribal chief)
Affiliation: St. Regis Mohawk Council, Akwesasne Community Bldg., Rt. 37, RR 1, Box 8A, Hogansburg, NY 13655 (518) 358-2272.

TATUM, MELISSA L.
(research professor of law & associate director)
Education: Trinity University, BA, 1989; University of Michigan Law School, JD, 1992. *Address & Affiliation*: Research Professor of Law & Associate Director (2009-present), Indigenous Peoples Law & Policy Program, James E. Rogers College of Law, The University of Arizona, Rountree Hall 309, P.O. Box 210076, Tucson, AZ 85721 (520) 626-9762. E-mail: melissa.tatum@law.arizona.edu. Professor Tatum specializes in tribal jurisdiction & tribal courts, as well as in issues relating to cultural property. *Past professional posts*: Faculty member, University of Tulsa (13 years); taught at Wayne State University Law School, Michigan State University Law School, and the University of Detroit Mercy Law School; Melissa was Judge on the Southwest Intertribal Court of Appeals, 1999-2006. She has served on task forces in Michigan & New Mexico charged with developing procedures to facilitate cross-jurisdictional enforcement of protection orders, and has taught seminars on domestic violence & protection orders throughout the U.S. for judges, attorneys, law enforcement, & victim advocates, including the National Tribal Judicial Center. *Published works*: Contributing author to Felix Cohen's Handbook of Federal Indian Law.

TAVARES, JESSICA (Miwok)
(tribal chairperson)
Affiliation: Chairperson, United Auburn Indian Community, 10720 Indian Hill Rd., Auburn, CA 95603 (530) 883-2390. *Other professional post*: Chief executive officer, Thunder Valley Casino, Auburn, CA.

TAVENNER, TERRI (*Wabgoneese*) 1947-
(cultural curriculum developer)
Born January 23, 1947, Seattle, Wash. *Education*: Antioch University, BA, 1979. *Principal occupation*: Cultural curriculum developer. *Address*: 20532 S. Riverside Dr., Pickford, MI 49774 (906) 647-5807. *Affiliation*: Coordinate Language & Culture Program Development, Quileute Tribal School, LaPush, WA, 1974-95. *Community activities*: Various Indian education curriculum advisory boards, projects; Clallam County Heritage Advisory Board. *Membership*: Washington State Indian Education Association. *Awards, honors*: Indian Education Showcase of Excellence Award, U.S. Dept. of Education, 1989. *Interests*: "Personally and professionally committed to preservation and protection of indigenous sacred site and practices; and revival of the Northwest tribes; canoe tradition-embarked on a cedar dugout canoe journey from LaPush, Washington to Bella Bela, British Columbia, Canada in 1993. *Published works*: Editor, Manual for Building a Big House & Canoes, 1990, by David Forlines; co-authored with David Forlines & Joe Karchsey, Medicinal Plants of Northwest Indigenous Peoples (OSU Dept. of Forestry, 1992).

TAVUI, DOROTHY (Diegueno)
(tribal chairperson)
Affiliation: San Pasqual General Council, P.O. Box 365, Valley Center, CA 92082 (619) 749-3200.

TAYLOR, BANNING (Luiseno)
(tribal chairperson)
Affiliation: Los Coyotes Band of Mission Indians, P.O. Box 249, Warner Springs, CA 92086 (619) 782-3269.

TAYLOR, BILL (Eastern Cherokee)
(tribal chairperson)
Affiliation & Address: Chairperson, , Eastern Band of Cherokee Indians, Qualla Boundary, P.O. Box 455, Cherokee, NC 28719 (828) 497-7000.

TAYLOR, CARMAN CORNELIUS (Salish/Oneida)
(tribal college academic vice president)
Education: Montana State University, MA (Counseling). Address & Affiliation: Academic Vice President, Salish Kootenai College (SKC), P.O. Box 70, Pablo, MT 59855 (406) 675-4800. E-mail: carman_taylor@skc.edu. *Other professional post*: Member, Board for the SKC College Foundation (15 years).

Past professional posts: Program Director (24 years), National Indian School Board Association, Polson, Montana. Carmen directed an Upward Bound Program at the University of Montana and was a division chief in the Bureau of Indian Affairs Office of Indian Education programs in Washington, DC; she also worked for the Office of Public Instruction for the state of Montana; member of the Board of Advisors of the Close-Up Foundation, the National Indian Education Association, and the Office of Indian Education Programs Goals 2000. *Awards, honors*: NIEA's 1999 Indian Educator of the Year Award; she was one of 234 delegates to the White House Conference of Indian Education in 1992; won the Advancement of Native American People Award from Brigham Young University in 1990. In 2010, Montana's Gov. Brian Schweitzer appointed Carmen as one of six Commissioners representing Montana on the Education Commission of the States, a national policy organization; she also represented SKC in the Minority-Serving Institutions Fellows Program (2005) funded by the Kellogg Foundation.

TAYLOR, CRISTY (Cahto-Pomo)
(tribal chairperson)
Affiliation: Cahto Indian Tribe of the Laytonville Rancheria, P.O. Box 1239, Laytonville, CA 95454 (707) 984-6197.

TAYLOR, LOUIS (Lac Courte Oreilles Ojibwe)
(tribal chairperson)
Affiliation: Lac Courte Oreilles Band of Ojibwe Indians, 13394 W. Trapania Rd., Bldg. #1, Hayward, WI 54843 (715) 634-8934. E-mail: ltaylor@lco-nsn.gov.

TAYLOR, LEWIS (St. Croix Ojibwe)
(tribal chairperson)
Affiliation & Address: Chairperson, St. Croix Chippewa Indians of Wisconsin, 24663 Angeline Ave., Webster, WI 54893 (715) 349-2195.

TAYLOR, FRANK (Luiseno)
(school principal)
Affiliation: Shiprock Northwest High School, Shiprock Alternative Schools, P.O. Box 1799, Shiprock, NM 87420 (505) 368-2070.

TAYLOR, JASON (Flandreau Santee Sioux)
(tribal vice president)
Affiliation: Vice President, Flandreau Santee Sioux Executive Committee, P.O. Box 283, Flandreau, SD 57028 (888) 922-0016; (605) 997-3891. E-mail: info@fsst.org.

TAYLOR, JENNIFER (Shoalwater Bay)
(tribal vice chairperson)
Affiliation & Address: Vice Chairperson, Shoalwater Bay Indian Tribe, P.O. Box 130, Tokeland, WA 98590 (360) 267-6766. E-mail: jtaylor@shoalwaterbay-nsn.gov.

TAYLOR, JONATHAN L. (Eastern Cherokee)
(tribal chief)
Affiliation: Eastern Band of Cherokee Indians, P.O. Box 455, Cherokee, NC 28719 (704) 497-2771.

TAYLOR, RADM KELLY M. (Choctaw of Oklahoma)
(acting chief of staff-HIS)
Education: University of Arkansas, BS; Colorado State University, MS (Environmental Health). She completed the Office of Personnel Management's Federal Executive Institute, Leadership for a Democratic Society in 2013 and has been a registered environmental health specialist since 1992. *Affiliation & Address*: Acting Chief of Staff, Indian Health Service, USDHHS, The Reyes Bldg., 801 Thompson Ave. #240, Rockville, MD 20852. In this position, RADM Taylor oversees the coordination of key Agency activities and works to improve overall Agency responsiveness. She works closely with HHS and supports the Office of the Director in a broad range of managerial duties related to the development and implementation of IHS initiatives and priorities. RADM Taylor began her career with Indian Health Service in 1990 as a Service Unit Sanitarian in Pine Ridge, South Dakota. She also served as an Environmental Health Specialist in Albuquerque, New Mexico, and as the Director of the IHS Albuquerque Area Office Division of Environmental Health Services. RADM Taylor's most recent assignment was Acting Director, Office of Clinical and Preventive Services. Her position of record is Director of the IHS Division of Environmental Health Services, where she provided leadership and direction to the 12 IHS Area environmental health programs and technical expertise to IHS leadership on all environmental health issues affecting American Indians and Alaska Natives. RADM Taylor currently represents IHS on the Centers for Disease Control & Prevention's Board of Scientific Counselors, which advises the DHHS Secretary, CDC Director & the National Center for Injury Prevention and Control Director regarding policies, strategies, objectives, projects and priorities in injury prevention. She also served on two international workgroups between the U.S. Department of Health & Human Services & Health Canada, where she coordinated a multi-year staff exchange between U.S. & Canada.

TAYLOR, LEWIS (St. Croix Chippewa)
(tribal chairperson)
Affiliation & Address: Chairperson & Sand Lake Community Representative, St. Croix Council, P.O. Box 287, Hertel, WI 54845 (715) 349-2195.

TAYLOR, LINDA (Cherokee)
(tribal enterprise manager)
Affiliation: Cherokee Nation Gift Shops, P.O. Box 1037, Tahlequah, OK 74465 (800) 256-2123, (918) 456-2793. Website: www.cherokeegiftshop.com.

TAYLOR, LUCY (Mdewankanton Sioux)
(tribal vice president)
Affiliation & Address: Vice President, Prarie Island Indian Community, 5636 Sturgeon Lake Rd., Welch, MN 55089 (651) 385-2554. E-mail: ltaylor@piic.org.

TAYLOR, MELANIE B.
(chair of Native American studies program)
Education: Smith College, BA; Boston University, MA, PhD. Affiliation & Address: Chair & Associate Professor of Native American Studies, 302 Sherman House HB6152, Dartmouth College, Hanover, NH E-mail: Melanie.b.taylor@dartmouth.edu. *Other professional posts*: Co-Editor, Native South Journal; House Professor, North Park House. *Areas of Expertise*: Native American literature; cultural studies. *Published works*: Disturbing Calculations: The Economics of Identity in Postcolonial Southern Literature, 1912-2002 (University of Georgia Press, 2008); Reconstructing the Native South: American Indian Literature and the Lost Cause (University of Georgia Press, 2012). Doom and Deliverance: Faulkner's Indians and the Dialectics of Modernity (in preparation); Indian Killers: The Savage Economies of Contemporary American Literature (in preparation) Editor: The Cambridge History of Native American Literature (under contract with Cambridge University Press); I Am Where I Come From: Native American College Students and Graduates Tell Their Life Stories, eds. Andrew Garrod, Robert Kilkenny, and Melanie Benson Taylor (Cornell University Press, forthcoming 2016)

TAYLOR, RADM KELLY M. (Choctaw of Oklahoma)
(IHS acting chief of staff)
Education: University of Arkansas, BS; Colorado State University, MS (Environmental Health). She completed the Office of Personnel Management's Federal Executive Institute, Leadership for a Democratic Society in 2013 and has been a registered environmental health specialist since 1992. *Affiliation & Address*: Acting Chief of Staff, Indian Health Service, Dept. of Health & Human Services, The Reyes Bldg., 801 Thompson Ave. #400, Rockville, MD 20852. E-mail: kevin.meeks@ihs.gov. In this position, RADM Taylor oversees the coordination of key Agency activities and works to improve overall Agency responsiveness. She works closely with HHS and supports the Office of the Director in a broad range of managerial duties related to the development and implementation of IHS initiatives and priorities. *Past professional posts*: RADM Taylor began her career with Indian Health Service in 1990 as a Service Unit Sanitarian in Pine Ridge, South Dakota. She also served as an Environmental Health Specialist in Albuquerque, New Mexico, and as the Director of the IHS Albuquerque Area Office Division of Environmental Health Services. RADM Taylor's most recent assignment was Acting Director, Office of Clinical and Preventive Services. Her position of record is Director of the IHS Division of Environmental Health Services, where she provided leadership and direction to the 12 IHS Area environmental health programs and technical expertise to IHS leadership on all environmental health issues affecting American Indians and Alaska Natives. RADM Taylor currently represents IHS on the Centers for Disease Control & Prevention's Board of Scientific Counselors, which advises the DHHS Secretary, CDC Director & the National Center for Injury Prevention and Control Director regarding policies, strategies, objectives, projects and priorities in injury prevention. She also served on two international workgroups between the U.S. Dept. of Health & Human Services & Health Canada, where she coordinated a multi-year staff exchange between the U.S. & Canada.

TAYLOR, MELANIE B. (Herring Pond Wampanoag)
(professor & chair of Native American studies)
Education: Smith College, BA, 1998; Boston University, MA, 1999, PhD, 2005. Affiliation & Address: Chairperson & Associate Professor, Native American Studies Program, Dartmouth College, 302 Sherman House, HB 6152, 37 N. Main St., Hanover, NH 03755 (603) 646-3530. E-mail: melanie.b.taylor@ dartmouth. edu. *Other professional post*: Co-Editor, Native South Journal. Professor Taylor is a literary critic who specializes in U.S. Southern studies. She explored the intersection of Native, African American, white, & immigrant southern cultures. *Awards, honors*: John M. Manley Huntington Award for newly tenured faculty. *Published works*: Disturbing Calculations: Economics of Identity in Postcolonial Southern Literature, 1912-2002 (2008); Reconstructing the Native South: American Indian Literature and the Lost Cause (U. of Georgia Press, 2012).

TAYLOR, REBECCA T. (*Clear Sky*) (Lac Courte Oreilles Ojibwe)
(educator)
Born May 2, 1960, Chicago, Ill. *Education*: Lac Courte Oreilles Ojibwe Community College, Hayward, WI, A.A. Native American Studies. *Address*: 9664 N. County Rd., N., Hayward, WI 54843 (715) 634-8401. *Membership*: Honor the Earth Education Foundation (Board of Directors, 1980). *Awards, honors*: Inward Journey for Outstanding Service from L.C.D. College, 1991; Cultural Award in recognition of cultural contribution as a role model. *Biographical source*: "The Color of Our Song," educational video, 28 minutes, University of Eau Claire, WI.

TAYLOR, RHONDA HARRIS (Cherokee)
(associate professor of library & information studies)
Education: North Texas State University, BS, 1974; Baylor University, Certification for School Librarian, Dec. 1978; Texas Woman's University, MLS, 1980, PhD (Library & Information Studies), 1985. *Affiliation & Address*: Associate Professor, School of Library & Information Studies, University of Oklahoma, 401 West Brooks, Room 120, Norman, OK 73019 (405) 325-3921; E-mail: rtaylor@ou.edu. *Research Interests*: Multicultural Librarianship. *Past professional post*: Editor-Newsletter (1996-2012), American Indian Library Association.

TAYLOR, URSHEL (*Owl Ear*) (Pima-Ute) 1937-
(artist)
Born May 31, 1937, Phoenix, Ariz. *Address*: 2901 W. Sahuaro Divide, Tucson, AZ 85742 (520) 297-4456. E-Mail: urshel@artnatam.com; Website: www.artnatam.com/utaylor. *Affiliation*: Former owner, The Owl Ear Gallery, Tucson, AZ, 1990-95. *Other professional posts*: Consultant to Tucson Indian Center & LFC, Inc. *Past professional posts*: Bureau of Indian Affairs, Intermountain Inter-Tribal School (art teacher), 1963-79 (Director of Cultural Arts Program, 1971-79); art teacher, Utah State University; owner, Indian Craft Shop, Brigham City, Utah, 1979-89. *Military service*: U.S. Marine Corps (Sgt.) 1956-63. *Community activities*: Tucson International Mariachi Conference. *Memberships*: Pima Salt River Community Indian Tribe; Indian Arts & Crafts Association. *Awards, honors*: Nine first place awards from 1984-90, then stopped entering contests. *Interests*: Urshel's years of study & research into historical Indian culture & crafts has served to reinforce his dedication to the authentic presentation of the American Indian. He says, "I always try to capture the dignity & majesty of what my people have been and what they continue to be today." *Published works*: Writes a column for Smoke Signals, Native American paper; working on children's book, "The Weasel Clan."

TAYLOR, WAYNE, JR. (Hopi)
(tribal chairperson)
Affiliation: Hopi Tribal Council, P.O. Box 123, Kykotsmovi, AZ 86039 (928) 734-2441.

TAYLOR, WILFORD (*Longhair*) (Mowa Choctaw/Chickasaw) 1946-
(technician)
Born October 31, 1946, McIntosh, Ala. *Address & Affiliation*: Chief, Mowa Band of Choctaw Indians, 1080 West Red Fox Rd., Mt. Vernon, AL 36560 (251) 829-5500. E-mail: chieftaylor@mowachoctaw.com. *Other professional post*: Commissioner of Alabama Indian Affairs Commission. *Military service*: U.S. Army, 1967-68; Vietnam War Veteran. *Community activities*: Museum/Library Board of Advisory; Mowa Choctaw Housing Authority Commissioner; Chairman of Alabama Intertribal Council. *Interests*: "To eliminate poverty & substance abuse, and to provide sanitary living conditions for my people."

TCHIN (Blackfoot-Narragansett)
(musician, storyteller)
Born in New England. *Education*: Rhode Island School of Design. Tchin's performances illustrate the significance of music and dance in the lives of Native Americans. He has performed extensively throughout the U.S.

TEEMAN, DIANE (Burns Paiute)
(tribal chairperson)
Affiliation & Address: Former Chairperso, Burns Paiute Tribe, Burns Paiute Indian Colony, 100 Pasigo St., Burns, OR 97720 (541) 573-1910

TEEPLE, DWIGHT (Ojibwe)
(chairperson, Board of Regents)
Affiliation & Address: Chairperson, Board of Regents, Bay Mills Community College, 12214 W. Lakeshore Dr., Brimley, MI 49715.

TEHEE, CANDESSA (Cherokee)
(assistant professor of American Indian studies)
Education: University of Oklahoma, BA (American Indian Studies & Communications), 2000, MA (Education, 20003, PhD (Linguistic Anthropology), 2014. *Affiliation & Address*: Assistant Professor of American Indian Studies, Department of Cherokee & Indigenous Studies, Northeastern State University, Seminary Hall 313, 609 N. Grand Ave., Tahlequah, OK 74464 (918) 444-3500; E-mail: teheec@nsuok.edu Candessa's dissertation focuses on the experiences of second language users in endangered language communities. Other areas of focus in her studies are the link between language and culture, the social power of language, and the politics of indigeneity. In addition to her academic and career pursuits, Candessa also continues to carry on Cherokee artistic traditions and has been finger weaving since 2000. In 2011, she received instruction from Cherokee National Treasure Dorothy Dreadfulwater Ice in table top loom weaving which allows her to carry on the legacy of her paternal grandfather, Rogers McLemore, Cherokee National Treasure for loom weaving. Candessa continues producing work which carries on the tribal and family tradition of weaving.

TELACHY, JOSEPH M. (Pojoaque Pueblo)
(pueblo governor)
Affiliation & Address: Governor, Pojoaque Pueblo, 78 Cities of Gold Rd. Santa Fe, NM 87506 (505) 455-3334

TELLER, JOANNE (Navajo)
(company owner)
Address & Affiliation: Infinity Horn Publishing, P.O. Box 1999, Chinle, AZ 86503 (520) 674-5259.

TELLER, JOHN H. (Menominee)
(tribal chairperson)
Affiliation: Menominee Tribal Legislature, P.O. Box 910, Keshena, WI 54135 (715) 799-5100.

TENORIO, DARIENNE (Washoe)
(tribal vice chairperson)
Affiliation: Stewart Indian Community, 919 Hwy. 395 South, Gardnerville, NV 89410 (775) 883-7794.

TENORIO, RONALD (San Felipe Pueblo)
(Pueblo governor)
Affiliation & Address: Governor, Pueblo of San Felipe, P.O. Box 4339, San Felipe Pueblo, NM (505) 867-3381 Fax 867-3383.
E-mail: gov.rtenorio@sfpueblo.com

TEPP, ROSALIE A. (Kenaitze)
(Alaskan tribal vice chairperson)
Affiliation & Address: Vice Chairperson, Kenaitze Indian Tribe, P.O. Box 988, Kenai, AK 99611 (907) 283-3633.

TERRANCE, CINDY (St. Regis Mohawk)
(editor)
Affiliation: "The People's Voice," Kanienkehaka Territory, P.O. Box 216, Hogansburg, NY 13655 (518) 358-3022.

TeSAM, STEVEN (Diegueno)
(tribal chairperson)
Affiliation: Viejas Baron Long Capitan Grande Band of Mission Indians, P.O. Box 908, Alpine, CA 91903 (619) 445-3810.

TETER, LIANA CHAPMAN (Pawnee/Otoe)
(college board secretary & business council representative)
Education: Northeastern Oklahoma State University (Tahlequah, OK), BA & MA. *Affiliation & Address*: Secretary & Pawnee Business Council Representative, Pawnee Nation College Board of Trustees, 861 Little Dee Dr., Pawnee, OK 740058 (918) 762-3343. Ms. Teter was appointed to the Board in 2013. *Past professional posts*: In addition to having been a teacher in various Oklahoma public schools for she has also taught undergraduate coursework at Oklahoma State University in the College of Human Environmental Sciences. Her credentials include teaching certification by the OK State Department of Education as a 'Highly Qualified Teacher' of Early Childhood Education, along with Learning Disabilities, Mental Retardation, Multi-Handicapped, Music, and Social Studies as well the full spectrum in the elementary grades. She worked with the Pawnee Nation's "Pa<ee Pakoo<oo: Revitalizing Our Language, Strengthening Our Nation" Language Program, first, as Pre-school Curriculum Specialist, eventually becoming Program Director. Recently, she worked as the Education Specialist in the Education Department for the Iowa Tribe in Perkins, OK. This involved administering the daily operations of the tribe's Higher Education Scholarship Program, Adult Vocational Training, Adult Education, and Direct Employment Assistance.

TEUTON, CHRISTOPHER B. (Cherokee)
(coordinator of American Indian studies program)
Education: University of Colorado-Boulder, BA (English), 1994; University of Wisconsin-Madison, MA (English), 1995, PhD (English with Minor in American Indian Studies), 2003. *Affiliation & Address*: Professor & Chair, American Indian Studies Program, University of Washington, Seattle, WA (206) 616-2048. E-mail: teuton@uw.edu. Chris teaches Indigenous Textual & Cultural

Studies within the American Indian Studies curriculum of the American Studies Department. Before coming to Chapel Hill, Teuton taught Indigenous literature at the University of Victoria in British Columbia, the University of Denver, and Appalachian State University. He's honored to be living in the traditional homelands of the Shakori, Eno, & Sissipahaw, close to the Smoky Mountains & Cherokee country. Dr. Teuton's scholarship is in the forefront of developing Indigenous research methodologies within the study of Indigenous literature. Grounding his critical approach in the concept of praxis, a mutual commitment to theory & practice, Teuton's work engages decolonization through centering Indigenous knowledge systems in the study of Indigenous textuality, cultural practice, politics, & history. He has lectured nationally & internationally as a guest of the University of Sydney, University of Toronto, University of Wisconsin-Madison, University of Oklahoma, Colorado College, University of Manitoba, and Monash University. Teuton has worked as a consultant with the Cherokee Nation to create a Cherokee Nation K-12 educational curriculum. He is a former Katrin H. Lamon Fellow at the School for Advanced Research on the Human Experience in Santa Fe, New Mexico (2009-10). *Past professional posts*: Taught Indigenous Textural & Cultural Studies and Indigenous literature at the University of North Carolina at Chapel Hill (coordinator, 2012-14), the University of Victoria in British Columbia, the University of Denver, and Appalachian State University. Teuton has worked as a consultant with the Cherokee Nation to create a Cherokee Nation K-12 educational curriculum. He is a former Katrin H. Lamon Fellow at the School for Advanced Research on the Human Experience in Santa Fe, New Mexico (2009-10). *Published works*: Cherokee Stories of the Turtle Island Liars' Club (University of North Carolina Press, 2012), a collection of forty stories, conversations & teachings about Western Cherokee life, beliefs, & art of storytelling. *Cherokee Stories* was written collaboratively with Elders & traditionalists Hastings Shade, Sammy Still, Sequoyah Guess, and Woody Hansen; Deep Waters: The Textual Continuum in American Indian Literature (University of Nebraska Press, 2010) as well as co-editor and co-author of Reasoning Together: the Native Critics Collective (University of Oklahoma Press, 2008). *Awards, honors*: In 2011, *Reasoning Together* was voted one of the ten most influential books of the first ten years of the twenty-first century in Native American and Indigenous Studies by the members of the Native American & Indigenous Studies Association. Teuton's present book-length project offers a model for understanding the evolving narrative patterns that chart the literal and figurative movements of characters and plots in Indigenous literature. It builds on his recent article, "The Cycle of Removal & Return: A Symbolic Geography of Indigenous Literature."

TEUTON, SEAN (*Kicummah*) (Cheokee)
(professor of English & American Indian Studies)
Education: University of Colorado, BA, 1990; San Francisco State University, MA, 1994; Cornell University, MA, 1999, PhD, 2002. *Affiliation & Address*: Associate Professor of Engish & American Indian Studies, c/o English Department, 7167 Heen C. White Hall, 600 N. Park St., Madison, WI 53706 (608) 263-3448. E-mail: steuton@wisc.edu. On leave for academic year 2013-14 at the University of Arkansas. E-mail: steuton@uark.edu. *Teaching Interests*: Native American literature, Postcolonial/World literature, 20 & 21st-century American literature. *Published works*: Reasoning Together: Native Critics in Dialogue, edited with Daniel Justice, Chris Teuton, and Craig Womack (University of Oklahoma Press, 2008); Red Land, Red Power: Grounding Knowledge in the American Indian Novel (Duke University Press, 2008); American Indian Literature: A Very Short Introduction (Oxford University Press, 2014); working on a second monograph entitled "Cities of Refuge: Indigenous Cosmopolitan Writers and the International Imaginary"; numerous articles & essays in scholarly journals.

THAMES, MARIE
(administrator)
Affiliation & Address: Interim CEO, American Indian Science & Engineering Society (AISES), P.O. Box 9828, Albuquerque, NM 87119. (505) 765-1052. E-mail: mthames@aises.org.

THAYER, GORDON (Lac Courte Oreilles Ojibwe)
(former tribal chairperson)
Affiliation & Address: Lac Courte Oreilles Band of Ojibwe, 13394 W. Trapania Rd., Hayward, WI 54843 (715) 634-8934.

THEODOROU, CHRISTINA S. (Lumbee)
(Native project director)
Education: University of North Carolina-Pembroke, BA; University of North Carolina, Chapel Hill, MA. *Affiliation & Address*: Asset Coalition Project Director, Community Engagement Coordinator, American Indian Center, University of North Carolina, 113A Abernathy Hall, CB 3457, Chapel Hill, NC 27599 (919) 962-5528. E-mail: ctheo@email.unc.edu.

THEISZ, R.D. (*Wicuwa*) 1941-
(professor)
Born May 4, 1941, Yugoslavia. *Education*: Queens College, B.A., 1964; Middlebury College, MA, 1965; New York University, PhD, 1972. *Address*: Box 9033, Black Hills State University, Spearfish, SD 57799-9033 (605) 642-6247. E-Mail: ronniethiesz@bhsu.edu. *Affiliations*: Professor, Sinte Gleska College, Rosebud, SD, 1972-77; Center of Indian Studies, Black Hills State University, Spearfish, SD (associate professor, 1977-83, director, 1983-88); chair, Division of Humanities, Black Hills State University, Spearfish, SD, 1988-. *Memberships*: South Dakota Indian Education Association; MELUS (Multi-Ethnic Literary Society of the U.S.); Porcupine Singers (traditional Lakota singing group). *Awards, honors*: 1972 Excellence in Scholarship Award, NYU; 1981 Special Contribution to Education, South Dakota Indian Education Association. *Interests*: Comparative literature & education; Native American cultural history, especially Lakota culture: literature, music, dance & art; cross cultural education. *Published works*: Buckskin Tokens (Sinte Gleska College, 1974); Songs & Dances of the Lakota, with B. Black Bear (Sinte Gleska College, 1976); Perspectives on Teaching Indian Literature (Black Hills State University, 1977); Lakota Art Is An American Art: Readings in Traditional & Contemporary Sioux Art (Black Hills State University, 1985); Standing in the Light, with S. Young Bear (University of Nebraska Press, 1994); Raising Their Voices: Essays in Lakota Ethnomusicology, 1996; Sharing the Gift of Lakota Song (Dog Soldier Press, 2003).

THIEL, MARK G. 1950-
(archivist)
Born July 10, 1950, Milwaukee, Wisc. Education: University of Wisconsin, Stevens Point, MA in History, 1980. *Address*: 1500 Michigan Ave., Waukesha, WI 53188-4253. *Affiliation & Address*: Marquette University, Raynor Memorial Libraries, 1355 W. Wisconsin Ave., P.O. Box 3141, Milwaukee, WI 53201-3141 (414) 288-5904. E-mail: mark.thiel@marquette.edu. *Past professional posts*: Oglala Lakota College, Kyle, Pine Ridge Reservation, SD, 1983-86; archivist, Marquette University Libraries, Dept. of Special Collections, Milwaukee, WI, 1986-present. *Awards, honors*: Certified Archivist, 2002-present. *Community activities*: Reviewer of Native American Library Enhancement Grants for the Institute of Museum & Library Services (U.S. Federal Agency. *Membership*: Society of American Archivists, 1981-; Academy of Certified Archivists, 1989-; International Council on Archives, 1995-; Midwest Archives Conference. *Interests*: Manages collections on Catholic Church-Native American relationships from throughout North America, 16th century to present. A leading proponent/supporter of Native American archives. *Published works*: Co-author with Philip C. Bantin, "Guide to Catholic Indian Missions & School Records in Midwest Repositories," Marquette University, 1984) revised online, 2003, www.marquette.edu/library/collections/archives/index.html, as "Guide to Catholic - Related Native American Records in Midwest Repositories;" "Indian Way," an illustrated reference guide (Noc Bay Publishing, 2001, CD-ROM); co-editor with Christopher Vecsey & Sr. Marie Therese Archambault, OSF, The Crossing of Two Roads, Being Catholic & Native in the U.S.," (Orbis Books, 2003).

THIN ELK, SHANE (Sicangu Lakota)
(attorney)
Education: University of South Dakota, BS, 2000; University of South Dakota School of Law, JD, 2003. *Address & Affiliation*: Associate (2004-present), Monteau & Peebles, LLP, 12100 West Center Rd., Suite 202, Omaha, NE 68144-3966 (402) 333-4053. E-mail: sthinelk.ndnlaw.com. Admitted to practice in the U.S. District Court for the District of Nebraska. *Practice areas*: Federal Indian law; tribal sovereignty & self-determination; economic development; trial & appellate advocacy; gaming law; administrative law. *Past professional post*: Instructor, Dept. of Indian Studies/Political Science, University of South Dakota, 2003; law clerk to Chief Justice David Gilbertson of the South Dakota Supreme Court, 2003-2004. *Membership*: South Dakota State Bar Association.

THIRION, WINONA (Navajo)
(American Indian program advisor)
Affiliation & Address: Advisor, American Indian Program, Scottsdale Community College, 9000 E. Chaparral St., Scottsdale, AZ 85256 (480) 423-6531. E-mail: winona.thirion@sccmail.maricopa.edu.

THOM, LAURIE A. (Paiute)
(tribal chairperson)
Affiliation & Address: Chairperson, Yerington Paiute Tribe, 171 Campbell Lane, Yerington, NV 89447 (775) 463-3301. E-mail: chairman@ypt-nsn.gov.

THOMAS, EDWARD K. (Tlingit) 1941-
(council president emeritus)
Born September 21, 1941, Craig, Alaska. *Education*: University of Alaska, Fairbanks, B.S., 1963; Penn State University, M.A. Educational Administration, 1965. *Address*: 3450 Meander Way, Juneau, AK 99801 (907) 789-2929; 585-1432. *Affiliation*: President Emeritus (2014-present), Tlingit Haida Central Council, 320 W. Willoughby Ave. #300, Juneau, AK 99801, 1984-. He served

as president of the Central Council (1984-2007) and was re-elected president 2010-14 when he resumed as president emeritus. *Other professional posts*: Board member, Sealaska Board of Directors, 1993-present; board member of the Office of the Special Trustee for Indian Affairs – Dept. of the Interior, Juneau Area Representative for the Bureau of Indian Affairs Tribal Fair-Shares Task Force; Education counselor, teacher. *Past professional posts*: Former chairperson, president, member of various Indian corporations in Alaska; delegate, National Congress of American Indians (National Tribal Advocacy Organization); delegate, Alaska Federation of Natives (Statewide Native Representative Organization). *Awards, honors*: Alaska Teaching Certificate, Type A; Alaska School Administrator's Certificate; Ketchikan Native Citizen of the Year, 1978; T&H Citizen of the Year, 1991.

THOMAS, ELMER (Tachi Yokut)
(tribal vice chairperson)
Affiliation & Address: Chairperson, Tachi-Yokut Tribe of the Santa Rosa Rancheria, P.O. Box 8, Lemoore, CA 93245 (559) 924-1278. E-mail: ethomas@tachi-yokut.com

THOMAS, EVELYN (Athapascan)
(Alaskan village president)
Affiliation & Address: President, Native Village of Crooked Creek Council, P.O. Box 69, Crooked Creek, AK 99575 (907) 432-2200.

THOMAS, FREDERICK R. (Kickapoo) 1946-
(tribal vice chairperson)
Born February 21, 1946, Horton, Kan. *Education*: Haskell Indian Junior College, AA, 1966. *Affiliation & Address*: Vice Chairperson, Kickapoo Tribe of Kansas, P.O. Box 271, Horton, KS 66439 (785) 486-2131. E-mail: fred.thomas @ktik-nsn.gov *Other professional post*: Chairperson, Kansas Service Unit, Health Advisory Board. *Military service*: U.S. Army, 1966-68. *Community activities*: Powhatan Precinct (past board member); Kickapoo Housing Authority (past president); community fundraising projects; community food & clothing bank (founding member); Horton Chamber of Commerce; Horton City Commissioner for Economic Development. *Memberships*: National Tribal Chairman's Association; American Legion; Kickapoo Chapter, Lions International; National Indian Gaming Association (treasurer). *Awards, honors*: Goodyear--Tire Builder of the Year. *Interests*: Member of Delaware Singers; enjoys hunting and fishing, farming, traveling.

THOMAS, KIM M.
(Native American affairs specialist)
Affiliation: New York State Office of Children & Family Services, Native American Services, General Donovan State Office Bldg., 125 Main St., Rm. 475, Buffalo, NY 14203 (716) 847-3123.

THOMAS, KRISTINE (*FireThunder*) (Navajo/Hopi)
(executive director; policy advisor)
Education: Arizona State University, BS, MBA. *Affiliation & Address*: Executive Director Arizona Commission of Indian Affairs, 1700 W. Washington St. #430, Phoenix, AZ 85007 (602) 542-4421. E-mail: kfirethunder@az.gov. Kristine facilitates partnerships & educates the public & private sectors on the unique government-to-government relationship between tribal, state & federal entities. *Other professional post*: Policy Advisor on Tribal Affairs for the Office of (AZ) Governor Janice K. Brewer. *Past professional post*: Director, AZ Governor's Office of Equal Opportunity.

THOMAS, LEONARD, D., M.D. (Navajo)
(IHS area director)
Education: Fort Lewis College in Colorado BS (Cellular and Molecular Biology and Chemistry); University Of New Mexico School Of Medicine and completed a 3-year family practice residency at Saint Joseph's Medical Center in Indiana. *Affiliation & Address*: Director, Albuquerque Area IHS, 5300 Homestead Rd., NE, Albuquerque, NM 87109 (2005-present) (505) 248-4500. E-mail: leonard.thomas@ihs.gov. Dr. Thomas provides leadership to ten service units & 27 Pueblos & tribes in NM, CO, and TX that delivers services at the community level through a system of 4 hospitals, 12 health centers, 6 health stations, 2 urban Indian programs, one dental center, and one regional residential treatment center. *Past professional posts*: Dr. Thomas began his IHS career in the Billings Area at the Crow/Northern Cheyenne Service Unit where he served as a Family Practice Medical Officer, Chief Medical Officer, and Clinical Director from July 1999 to August 2002. In September 2002, he accepted the position of Taos/Picuris Service Unit Clinical Director in the IHS Albuquerque Area. Dr. Thomas completed the Executive Leadership Development Program in September 2001 and participated in the Department of Health & Human Services Primary Health Care Policy Fellowship in 2004 as an IHS representative. He served on the 2006 Director's Executive Council representing the National Council of Chief Medical Officers and the 2007 Director's Executive Council Steering Group. *Memberships*: American Academy of Family Physicians; & Association of American Indian Physicians.

THOMAS, MARJORIE (Navajo)
(author, storyteller, youth advocate)
Born in Chinle, Ariz. *Education*: Northern Arizona University, BA (Elementary Education); University of New Mexico, MA (Educational Leadership); honorary doctorate from Dine College. Resides in Chinle, Arizona. *Affiliations*: She has served as a teacher, bilingual coordinator, and principal in schools on the Navajo Nation and has worked with curriculum and school reform for over 30 years. Marjorie currently serves as a member of the Chinle Unified School District Governing Board and as the Summer Institute Director of the "Learn in Beauty Project" at Northern Arizona University. *Awards, honors*: She is known as "Grandma Thomas" to the youth of the Navajo Nation. *Community activities*: Founding member of the "Dine bi Olta Association," and president of the "Dine Language Teachers' Association." *Published works*: Bidii; White Nose the Sheep Dog; What Does "Died" Mean? (Salina Bookshelf).

THOMAS, MARY V. (Pima-Maricopa)
(tribal council governor)
Affiliation: Gila River Indian Community Council, P.O. Box 97, Sacaton, AZ 85247 (520) 562-6000.

THOMAS, MATTHEW (*Seventh Hawk*) (Narragansett)
(tribal chief sachem)
Affiliation & Address: Chief Sachem, Narragansett Indian Tribal Council, P.O. Box 268, Charleston, RI 02813 (401) 364-1100. E-mail: mattslawlaw61@ hotmail.com.

THOMAS, RONNIE (Alabama-Coushatta of Texas)
(tribal vice chairperson)
Affiliation & Address: Vice Chairperson, Alabama Coushatta Tribe of Texas, 571 State Park Rd., Livingston, TX 77351 (936) 563-1100.

THOMAS, SHERRI NICOLE (Tiwa-Taos Pueblo)
(law librarian; assistant professor of law librarianship)
Born & raised on the Dine' (Navajo) Reservation. *Education*: San Juan College, AAS; Fort Lewis College, BA; University of New Mexico School of Law, JD (Indian Law Certificate). *Affiliations & Address*: Law Librarian, Assistant Professor of Law Librarianship, and Chair, Native Peoples Law Caucus, Faculty & Public Service Department, University of New Mexico School of Law Library, 1117 Stanford NE, Albuquerque, NM 87131 (505) 277-2228. E-mail: thomas@law.unm.edu. Sherri is responsible for providing reference services to law school students, staff, faculty, and the public. She plays an integral role in the law library's outreach program. Ms. Thomas created & teaches the two-credit hour Indian Law Research course & leads legal research workshops. She's also responsible for collecting monographs in different legal subject areas. *Past professional posts*: Information Manager, Environmental Risk Analysis, San Mateo, CA; database specialist & cataloger, Wilson, Sonsini, Goodrich & Rosati, PC, Palo Alto, CA. *Published work*: How to Manage a Law School Library: Leading Librarians on Updating Resources, Managing Budgets, & Meeting Expectations (Inside the Minds), 2008.

THOMAS, WESLEY K. (Dine-Navajo)
(assistant professor)
Born in Crownpoint, NM. *Education*: AA, 1975; BA, 1994; MA, 1996; PhD, 1999. *Affiliation & Address*: Professor & Chair of School of Dine' & Law Studies, Navajo Technical University, P.O. Box 849, Crownpoint, NM 87313 (505) 786-4333. E-mail: wthomas@navajotech.edu. *Past professional posts*: University of Washington, Seattle, 1991-99; Idaho State University, Pocatello, ID, 1999-2001; Assistant professor, Dept. of Anthropology, Bloomington, IN 2001-14. *Community activities*: Annual Indian University Powwows; IU's First Nations Speaker Series. *Memberships*: American Anthropological Association (life member); American Ethnological Society; Anthropology Museum Society. *Interests*: Social-cultural anthropology; gender & ethnic identities; American Indian studies, Navajo culture & language.

THOMPSON, BETTY (Cherokee)
(artist, craftsperson)
Affiliation: Co-owner, Tah-Mels, P.O. Box 1123, Tahlequah, OK 74465 (918) 456-5461.

THOMPSON, BILL (Penobscot)
(tribal vice chief)
Affiliatio & Addressn: Vice Chief, Penobscot Indian Nation, 12 Wabanaki Way, Indian Island, ME 04468 (207) 817-7350.

THOMPSON, CHAD (*Xodaaw' Chwang'*) (Hupa) 1953-
(assistant professor of linguistics)
Education: University of Alaska, BA, 1975, MA, 1977; University of Oregon, PhD, 1989. *Principal occupation*: Assistant professor of linguistics. *Address*: 6108 Old Brook Dr., Fort Wayne, IN 46835 (219) 485-6775. *Affiliation*: Indiana University/Purdue University, Fort Wayne, IN, 1991-. *Memberships*: Society for the Study of Indigenous Languages of the Americas; Linguistic Society of

America; Hoosier Folklore Society. *Awards, honors*: 1990 Distinguished Service Award for dedication to and support of the teaching of Native American languages, Center for Community Development, Humboldt State University, Arcata, CA. *Interests*: Native American languages, literatures, and folklore, particularly those of Alaskan & Pacific Coast Athabaskan. *Published works*: 21 readers in the Alaskan Athabaskan Languages - Holikachuk & Deg Hit'an, mostly traditional stories (Yukon Koyukuk School District, 1983-87); co-author, "Dinaakk'a I" - Koyukon language for students in secondary grades & adults (Yukon Koyukuk School District, 1983); co-author, "Scope & Sequence for Teaching Koyukon Athabaskan" (Yukon Koyukuk School District, 1983); "Dinaakk'a for Children," Koyukon Athabaskan language for elementary grades (Yukon Koyukuk School District, 1984); "Athabaskan Languages & the Schools: A Handbook for Teachers" (Alaska Dept. of Education, 1984); "Denakenaga' for Children" - Tanana Athabaskan language for elementary grades (Yukon Koyukuk School District, 1987); "Dinaakk'a II" Second year Koyukon for secondary grades & adults (Yukon Koyukuk School District, 1987); "An Introduction to Athabaskan Languages" (Yukon Koyukuk School District, 1987); co-author, "Teachers Guide to Baakk'aatEgh Ts'EhEniy" (Alaska Native Language Center, 1989); co-editor, "Baakk'aatEgh Ts'EhEniy: Stories We Live By" (Alaska Native Language Center, 1989); "An Analysis of K'etetaalkkaanee" (Alaska Native Language Center, 1990).

THOMPSON, DONA K. (Caddo-Wichita) 1949-
(counselor/administrator)
Born August 31, 1949, Lawton, Okla. *Affiliations*: Counselor/Recruiter, University of Oklahoma Health Sciences Center, Oklahoma City, OK, 1981-87; Counselor for Native American Students, 1987-, Associate Director - Minority Affairs, 1991-, Washington State University, Pullman, WA. *Memberships*: National Indian Counselor's Association (president, 1987-89; treasurer, 1980-85, 1990-); Association of Faculty Women; National Association of Student Personnel Administrators; National Indian Education Association.

THOMPSON, ERIC *(Tehoroniathe)* (St. Regis Mohawk)
(tribal chief)
Affiliation & Address: Chief (2015-18), St. Regis Mowak Tribe, 3412 State Rt. 37, Akwesasne, NY 13655 (518) 358-2272.

THOMPSON, HEATHER DAWN (Cheyenne River Sioux)
(attorney)
Affiliation & Address: The Appleseed Foundation/Native Vote Election protection Project, 3245 Holmead Pl., NW, Washington, DC 20010 (202) 258-3767. E-mail: heather@heatherthompson.org. *Other professional post*: President, National Native American Bar Association.

THOMPSON, KERRY (Navajo)
(professor of Applied Indigenous Studies; archaeologist)
Education: University of Arizona, PhD (Anthropology & Archaelogy). *Affiliation & Address*: Professor of Anthropology & Archaeology, and Applied Indigenous Studies, Emerald City Bldg.. 98D #101A, Northern Ariona University, Flagstaff, AZ 86011 (928) 523-0712. E-mail: Kerry.thompson@nau.edu. Dr. Thompson's research interests revolve around Indgenous issues in Anthropology & archaeology. She is also a lithic analyst and has analyzed assemblages in the Ameriacn Southwest Peru.

THOMPSON, MARK (Acoma Pueblo)
(Pueblo 1st lt. governor)
Affiliation: Pueblo of Acoma, Box 310, Acomita, NM 87034 (505) 552-6604.

THOMPSON, PAM (Monacan)
(tribal assistant chief)
Affiliation & Address: Assistant Chief, Monacan Indian Nation, P.O. Box 1136, Madison Heights, VA 24572 (804) 946-0389.

THOMPSON, PERLINE (Shoshone)
(former tribal chairperson)
Affiliation & Address: Former chairperson, Duckwater Shoshone Tribe, P.O. Box 140068, Duckwater, NV 89314 (775) 863-0227.

THOMPSON, THOMAS (Cherokee)
(Deputy Assistant Secretary – Indian Affairs, Management U.S. Dept. of the Interior)
Education: Oklahoma State University School of Technical Training in Okmulgee, AA (Accounting), 1973; CPA licenses from the states of Oklahoma, Arkansas & Montana. *Affiliation & Address*: Deputy Assistant Secretary – Indian Affairs, Management, Office of Public Affair – Indian Affairs, U.S. Dept. of the Interior, 1849 C St. NW, MS-3658-MIB, Washington, DC 20240 (202) 208-3710. *Past professional posts*: Prior to his federal career, Thompson held from July 1975 to August 1995 several management positions with the Cherokee Nation including financial controller, executive director of tribal operations, president and CEO of gaming operations, & secretary & treasurer. From January 1992 until October 1997, Thomas owned and operated an accounting firm, Thompson & Company, in Stilwell, Okla., which provided management, audit, accounting, and tax planning and preparation services to public and private sector and tribal clients. Thompson has over 14 years of federal service, starting in October 1997 as superintendent of the Bureau of Indian Affairs Ft. Belknap Agency in Harlem, Mont. In December 2000, he became director of the IHS Phoenix Area Office's Division of Financial Management. In 2002, he joined the U.S. Department of Agriculture's National Center for Toxicological Research (NCTR) as Finance Director, where he served as senior advisor to the director on all matters related to resource and financial management. As such, he played a major role in efforts to modernize & update administrative support services & program accountability systems. In October 2003, Thompson returned to the IHS Phoenix Area Office as the financial management division director, a post he held until September 2005. While serving as senior financial advisor for health programs throughout the Phoenix Area he helped develop & implement a strategic plan to enhance patient services through increased revenues and more effective management practices. Thompson was promoted in September 2005 to Chief Financial Officer & Director of the Office of Finance & Accounting in IHS's headquarters in Rockville, Md., where he was responsible for a $4.1 billion health delivery network across Indian Country generating over $540 million in patient revenues. He oversaw the development of a performance-based budget formulation methodology to improve decision making for effective use of scarce resources and that linked budgets to performance to improve efficiency in program planning. In June 2010, he returned to the Phoenix Area as senior advisor to the area director, where he provided upper level program, operational, budgetary and financial analysis on special projects to senior management. *Memberships*: He is a member of the Oklahoma Society of Certified Public Accountants and the Arizona Society of Certified Public Accountants. *Community activities*: He also has served on various boards and committees including the Oklahoma Society of Certified Public Accountants Governmental Accounting Committee, the Tahlequah Chamber of Commerce, the Eastern Oklahoma Development District, the Cherokee Nation Outpost Corporation, the Cherokee Nation Trust Authority, Cherokee Nation Industries, and the Christian Children's Fund.

THRASHER, MICHAEL (*Ka-Whywa-Weet*) (Metis)
(teacher & consultant)
Address: 5470 Fowler Rd., Saanich, B.C. Canada V8Y 1Y3 (250) 658-6717. E-mail: turtleshell@telus.net. *Affiliation*: Turtle Island Intercultural Consulting - provides consulting services to First Nations, governments, industry, community organizations & educational institutions since 1977. He is a nationally recognized Metis teacher of Anishinabi First Nation's philosophy, tradition & culture. He uses traditional knowledge & viewpoints to address contemporary issues. *Awards, honors*: Michael was one of four traditional teachers and elders invited to conduct the sacred pipe ceremony at the opening of the Royal Commission on Aboriginal People. In addition, he was co-chair of the first Round Table Hearings for the Royal Commission in Edmonton.

THUNDER, CARA (Menominee)
(programs director)
Affiliation & Address: American Indian Science & Engineering Society (AISES), P.O. Box 9828, Albuquerque, NM 97119 (505) 765-1052. E-mail: cthunder@ aises.org.

THUNDER, GORDON (Winnebago)
(tribal chairperson)
Affiliation: Wisconsin Winnebago Business Committee, P.O. Box 667, Black River Falls, WI 54615 (715) 284-9343.

THUNDER, STACEY (Red Lake Ojibwe)
(attorney; senior deputy solicitor general/legislative counsel)
Education: Hamline University, BA (Psychology), 1994; William Mitchell College of Law, JD, 1998. *Affiliation & Address*: Senior Deputy Soliiicitor General/Legislative Counsel, (2015-present), Mille Lacs Band of Ojibwe Indians, 43408 Oodena Dr., Onamia, MN 56359 (320) 532-4181. *Past professional posts*: Legal Counsel, Red Lake Band of Chippewa Indians, Red Lake, MN, 2005-14; Staff Attorney, Mille lacs Band of Ojibwe Corporate Commission, 2001-05.

THUNDERCLOUD, ALEC (Ho-Chunk)
(director, Indian Health Service)
Education: University of Wisconsin-Madison, BS (Bacteriology); University of Minnesota-Minneapolis, MD; Pediatrics Residency at Georgetown University, Washington, DC; Fellowship in Community Pediatrics & Child Advocacy at Albert Einstein University-Montefiore Medical Center of New York City. *Affiliation & Address*: Director, Office of Clinical & Preventive Services, Indian Health Service (HIS), The Reyes Bldg. (RB) 801 Thompson Ave., Suite 400, Rockville, MD 20852 (301) 443-1083. In this position, Dr. Thundercloud is the principal advisor for policy development, budget development, and allocation for clinical, preventive, and public health programs throughout the IHS. The OCPS is responsible for national health professional recruitment, health

program implementation, emergency services, and the management of several grant programs. *Past professional posts*: Prior to assuming his role as the Director of OCPS, Dr. Thundercloud served as the Clinical Director of the White Earth Health Center in Minnesota. Dr. Thundercloud also formerly served as the Executive Director of Health for the Ho-Chunk Nation. During his tenure, he worked at the local, state, and federal levels to decrease health disparities in American Indians and Alaska Native communities.

THUNDERCLOUD, ANNE (Ho-Chunk)
(public relations officer)
Affiliation & Address: Public Relations Officer, Ho-Chunk Nation, P.O. Box 667, Black River Falls, WI 54615 (715) 284-9343. *Other professional post*: Adjunct faculty, The Falmouth Institute, Fairfax, VA.

THUNDERCLOUD, TRACY L. (Ho-Chunk)
(tribal executive director)
Affiliation & Address: Executive Director, Ho-Chunk Nation, Box 667, Black River Falls, WI 54615 (715) 284-3297. E-mail: tthundercloud@ho-chunk.com.

THUNDEREAGLE, DAVID (Karuk)
(tribal operations manager)
Education: Eastern Washington University, B.A. (Education). *Affiliation*: Tribal Operations Manager (2002-present), Nottawaseppi Huron Band of Potawatomi Indians, 2221 - 1 1/2 Mile Rd., Fulton, MI 49052 (269) 729-5151. *Past professional posts*: School teacher, Colville Indian Reservation in Washington State; manager, Indian Education, Spokane (WA) School District; executive director, American Indian Community Center, Spokane, WA; executive director, Kootenai Tribe of Idaho; vice president of programs, Cook Inlet (AK) Tribal Council, (17 years).

THUNDERHAWK, MADONNA (Dakota)
(field coordinator)
Affiliations: Dakota Women of All Red Nations, P.O. Box 69, Fort Yates, ND 58538; Women of All Red Nations, P.O. Box 2508, Rapid City, SD 57709.

THURMAN, GEORGE (Sac & Fox)
(former tribal principal chief)
Education: Southern Nazarene University, BS (Organizational Leadership). *Affiliation & Address*: Former Principal Chief, Sac & Fox Nation, 920883 S. Hwy. 99 Bldg. A, Stroud, OK 74079 (918) 968-3526. *Other professional posts*: Vice Chairperson, Self Governance Communication & Education Tribal Consortium Board, Bellingham, WA; representative to the seven member TTFSP tribal consortium of the Intertribal Monitoring Association, Albuquerque, NM; member of National Congress of American Indians; member, National Indian Education Association; Central Tribes Shawnee Area Board member; Inter-Tribal Monitoring Association Board Member; liaison to Sac & Fox Nation: Education Dept., Environmental Dept., Self-Governance Dept., Law & Order Committee & Rodeo Committee. *Past tribal positions*: Tribal secretary, 2001-05. *Memberships*: National Congress of American Indians; National Indian Education Association; Central Tribes Shawnee Area board member, Shawnee, OK; Inter-Tribal Monitoring Association Board, Albuquerque, NM.

TIAM, ELETTA (Nisqually)
(tribal chief executive officer)
Affiliation & Address: Chief Executive Officer, Nisqually Indian Tribe, 4820 SheNahNum Dr., SE, Olympia, WA98513 (360) 456-5221. E-mail: tiam.eletta@nisqually-nsn.gov.

TIBETS, TERRENCE "TERRY" (White Earth Ojibwe)
(tribal chairperson)
Affiliation & Address: Chairperson, Ojibwe of the White Earth Nation, P.O. Box 418, White Earth, MN 56591 (218) 983-3285.

TICKET, ALLEN (Eskimo)
(Alaskan village president)
Affiliation: Native Village of Selawik, 59 N. Tundra St., Selawik, AK 99770 (907) 484-2165.

TIGER, BUFFALO (Creek)
(BIA agency supt.)
Affiliation: Miccosukee Agency, Bureau of Indian Affairs, P.O. Box 44021, Tamiami Station, FL 33144 (305) 323-8380.

TIGER, DANA (Creek/Seminole-Cherokee) 1961-
(artist)
Born in 1961. *Address*: 26467 S. Peaceful Valley Lane, Park Hill, OK 74451 (918) 457-6035. *Awards, honors*: Served as the featured artist for the Indians in Medicine project, a scholarship program, in 1992; selected nationally as one of nine women to serve as a committee member for the National Organization for Women in the planning of the National Racial & Ethnic Diversity Conference. *Interests*: Painting in acrylics, watercolors and gouche.

TIGER, CORA (Sisseton-Wahpeton Sioux)
(tribal executive secretary)
Affiliation: Spirit Lake Dakota Sioux Tribe, P.O. Box 359, Fort Totten, ND 58335 (701) 766-4221.

TIGER, GEORGE P. (Muscogee Creek) 1950-
(former tribal chief)
Born March 22, 1950 in the rural Yardeka community near Henryetta, Okla. *Education*: Haskell Indian Nations University; Northeastern State University. *Affiliation & Address*: Principal Chief, Muscogee (Creek) Nation, P.O. Box 580, Okmulgee, OK 74447 (918) 732-7601. *Other professional post*: Member of Board of Regents of Haskell Indian Nations University. George has been a member of the Muscogee (Creek) National Council for 14 years and served as Speaker of the Council in 2006-07.

TIGER, JOHNNY, JR. (*Tony*) (Creek-Seminole) 1940-
(artist, sculptor; gallery owner)
Born February 13, 1940, Tahlequah, Okla. *Education*: Bacone College, 1959-60; Chilocco Indian School, 1960-61. *Principal occupation*: Artist-sculptor; gallery owner. *Address*: P.O. Box C, Muskogee, OK 74402 (918) 687-3505. *Affiliation*: Co-owner, Tiger Art Gallery, 2110 E. Shawnee St., Muskogee, OK 74403, 1982-. *Other professional post*: Design T-shirts for the Tiger Gallery (Indian themes). *Military service*: U.S. Air Force, 1963-65 (E-4). *Memberships*: Creek Tribe; Indian Arts & Crafts Association; Five Civilized Tribes Museum (Master Artist). *Awards, honors*: "I've won over 100 major awards all over the country (USA) in my 30 year span in painting & sculpture." *Interests*: "I've had art shows all over the country, and also London, England in 1987 (one man art shows)." Currently, Johnny's paintings and prints are in galleries across the nation. He has paintings on permanent display and the Russian Cultural Museum, Togliatle, Russia. *Biographical source*: Southwest Art magazine.

TIGER, LEE (Miccosukee/Florida Seminole)
(tourism marketer; website founder; musician)
Affiliation & Address: Founder, Discover Native America (website), 2461 SW 85th Terrace, Fort Lauderdale, FL 33324 (954) 370-3900. Website: www.discovernativeamerica.com. Lee brings expertise in the areas of American Indian relations and global marketing to the website project. He has promoted Native American & eco-heritage tourism for more than 30 years. He has marketed both the Seminole Tribe of Florida & The Miccosukee Tribe of Indians of Florida encouraging Indian cultural awareness & tourism development on a global scale. In the 1970's, Mr. Tiger established the Miccosukee Indian Village as a major Everglades tour; from 1986 to 1991, Lee promoted Discovery Cruise Lines and five other South Florida attractions. Recently, Lee has helped coordinate a coop among the Miccosukee, Seminole & Miami-Dade & Broward Counties, called "The Everglades Gateway." In 1992, he established Florida Seminole Tourism on behalf of the Seminole Tribe of Florida with marketing partnerships with the greater Ft. Lauderdale Convention & Visitor's Bureau and the City of Hollywood. Mr. Tiger has collaborated with Indian tourism efforts in worldwide capacities, including the American Indian Alaskan Native Tourism Association and with the Discover Native America promotion in conjunction with See America at the International Tourism Exchange ITB Berlin. He has been appointed to serve on Florida's Cultural Heritage Tourism Committee by two Florida Governors Bush & Crist. Lee and his brother Stephen are front men for the band, Tiger Tiger (website: www.tigertigermusic.com). CD: "Peace From the Everglades." receiving two Native American Music Award (NAMMY) nominations in 2005 for Best Pop/Rock Recording & Song/Single of the Year for "Heya".

TIGER, MANUEL M. (Miccosukee Seminole)
(former tribal representative)
Affiliation & Address: Former Big Cypress Representative, Seminole Tribe of Florida, 6300 Stiriing Rd., Hollywood, FL 33024 (954) 966-6300.

TIGER, MICHAEL D. (Creek)
(IHS-area deputy director)
Affiliation: Nashville Area IHS Office, 711 Stewarts Ferry Pike, Nashville, TN 37214 (615) 736-2400.

TIGERMAN, KATHLEEN (Ojibwe) 1948-
(professor of English, author)
Born July 4, 1948. *Affiliation & Address*: Associate Professor of English, 314 Warner Hall, University of Wisconsin-Platteville, Platteville, WI. (608) 342-1866. E-mail: tigerman@uwplatt.edu. She developed a course on Wisconsin Indian Literature, which is now a permanent course offering at UW-Platteville. *Published work*: Wisconsin Indian Literature: Anthology of Native Voices (University of Wisconsin Press, 2007).

TILDEN, MARK C. (Navajo-Dine')
(attorney; law firm founding partner)
Education: Creighton University, BS (Finance); University of Denver Law School, JD. Affiliation & Address: Funding Partner, Tilden McCoy & Dilweg

LLP, 2500 30th St., Suite 207, Boulder, CO 80301 (303) 323-1922. E-mail: mctilden@tildenmccoy.com. He represents tribal governments on federal acknowledgment, general counsel matters, administrative law, environmental law, Indian housing law, Indian gaming law and economic development, legislative advocacy at the state and federal level, Indian child welfare and protection services law and tribal governance. He writes, lectures and trains in some of these areas of federal Indian law. *Past professional posts*: Associate, Private law firm from September, -1990-94; Staff attorney (1994-2009), Native American Rights Fund (NARF). *Awards, honors*: Environmental Achievement Award by the U.S. Environmental Protection Agency for Outstanding Work with the Oglala Sioux Tribe on developing a Tribal Environmental Code. He was the Lead Attorney and Project Manager on the development and publication of "A Practical Guide to the Indian Child Welfare Act," as well as a contributing author. In April 2012, he was appointed by Colorado Governor John Hickenlooper to serve on the Colorado's Children's Trust Fund as a member of the Board of Directors. He has also been appointed to serve as a Trustee on Father Flanagan's Boys' Home National Board of Trustees, beginning in November 2012. *Published works*: author of a book titled "Tribal Constitution Handbook, A Practical Guide to Writing or Revising a Tribal Constitution" and co-author of "Indian Child Welfare Act Handbook: A Legal Guide to the Custody and Adoption of Native American Children" published by the American Bar Association. *Admitted to Practice*: In Colorado, New York and the District of Columbia, as well as several federal and tribal courts. He is a member of a number of legal associations, including former service on the American Bar Association's Presidential Advisory Council on Diversity in the Profession, the ABA Steering Committee on the Unmet Legal Needs of Children and the ABA Commission on Homelessness and Poverty.

TILDEN, THOMAS (Athapascan)
(Alaskan tribal chief)
Affiliation: Curyung Tribal Council, P.O. Box 216, Dillingham, AK 99576 (907) 842-2384. E-mail: curyung@nutshtel.com.

TILLER, JACQUELINE (Tlingit/Fiipino)
(grants & internship coordinator)
Born & raised in Southeast Alaska. *Affiliation & Address*: Office Coordinator (2007-10), Grants & Internship Coordinator (2010-present), First People Worldwide (2007-present), 857 Leeland Rd., Fredericksburg, VA 22405 (540) 899-6545. E-mail: info@firstpeoples.org.

TILLEY, CAREY (Cherokee)
(executive director)
Affiliation: Exec Director, Cherokee Heritage Center, P.O. Box 515, Tahlequah, OK 74465 (918) 456-6007. E-mail: carey.tilley@cherokeeheritage. org.

TILLMAN, CHARLES O., JR. (Otoe-Missouria)
(former tribal chairperson)
Affiliation: Otoe-Missouria Tribe, 8151 Hwy. 177, Red Rock, OK 74651 (580) 723-4466.

TILOUSI, REX (Havasupai)
(former tribal chairperson)
Affiliation: Havasupai Tribal Council, P.O. Box 10, Supai, AZ 86435 (602) 448-2961.

TIMBERMAN, GENA (Choctaw of Okla.)
(cultural center & museum director)
Education: Oklahoma State University, B.A. (English Lit.), 1996; University of Oklahoma College of Law, JD, 1999. *Affiliation & Address*: Native American Indian Cultural Center & Museum, 900 N. Broadway, #200, Oklahoma City, OK 73102 (405) 239-5500. Website: www.aiccm.org. Website: www.nacea.com (deputy director, 1999-2007; executive director, 2007-present). *Past professional posts*: Associate, Holloway, Dobson, Hudson, Bachman & Jennings, Oklahoma City (she focused on the economic development of Native American businesses); legal intern, Dept. of Justice, Washington, DC, Office of Tribal Justice and the Environment & Natural Resources Division, Indian Law Section (her efforts were in the research of Indian law issues affecting Indian country). *Community activities*: Facilitator & Leader for the Wings of American Running & Fitness Camps; member of Board of Directors, Oklahoma Chapter of the American Indian Chamber of Commerce. *Memberships*: Oklahoma Bar Assn, American Bar Assn; Oklahoma Indian Bar Assn. *Awards, honors*: As president of the Native American Student Association, she received the Outstanding Contribution to the Native American Community Award.

TIMECHE, JOAN (Hopi)
(executive director)
Education: Northern Arizona University, BS (Social Work), MBA. *Affiliation & Address*: Executive Director (2001-present), Native Nations Institute for Leadership, Management & Policy, Udall Center for Studies in Public Policy, The University of Arizona, 803 East First St., Tucson, AZ 85719 (520) 626-0664. E-mail: timechej@u.arizona.edu. *Other professional posts*: Board member, Arizona American Indian Tourism Association, the National Center for American Indian Enterprise Development, & the Economic Development Authority of the Tohono O'odham Nation. *Past professional posts*: Program director, Northern Arizona University Center for American Indian Economic Development (CAIED), 1992-2001; co-executive director, National Executive Education Program for Native American Leadership, CAIED & Harvard University, 1992-95; director of the Hopi Tribe's Department of Education (eight years); executive director, Arizona Native American Economic Coalition; chairperson, Hopi Tribe Economic Development Corporation. *Membership*: American Indian/Alaska Native Tourism Association (past president). *Interests*: Ms. Timeche is a regular speaker at both regional & national conferences on topics related to Indian economic development & tourism, and is a recognized expert on doing business on Indian lands. *Awards, honors*: Founded the Native American Youth Entrepreneur Camp, for which she & NNI received the 2006 Youth Entrepreneurship of the Year Award by the National Center for American Indian Enterprise Development; receive in 2009, the American Indian Business Leaders Advocate of the Advocate of the Year Award for her work in promoting & cultivating Native American entrepreneurship; 2010, Joan was named "Woman of the Year" by the Phoenix Indian Center. *Published works*: Native nations, the Environment, and the State of California: Tribal Relationships & Environmental Quality, with S.C. Rainie, K. Dickman & R. Meredith, editors (workshop proceedings – Udall Center for Studies in Public Policy, 2003); Native Cultural Arts Organizations: Who They Are & What They Need, with M. Jorgensen, M. Begay, N. Pryor, et al, eds. (report prepared for ATLATL, Inc. – Native Nations Institute, 2005); chapter, with S. Cornell, M. Jorgensen, and I. Record, "Citizen Entrepreneurship: An Underutilized Development Resource," in Rebuilding Native Nations: Strategies for Governance & Development, ed. Miriam Jorgensen (University of Arizona Press, 2007).

TIMME, WILLIAM H.
(attorney)
Education: Rice University, BA, 1965; Columbia University School of Law, LLB, 1968. *Affiliation & Address*: Of Counsel (2009-present), Stoel Rives, LLP, 510 L St., Suite 500, Anchorage, AK 99501(907) 263-8436. Email: bill.timme@ stoel.com Bill focuses his practice on business & transactional matters with emphasis on ANCSA corporation issues. He has spent more than 35 years counseling primarily Alaska native Corporation clients ona broad range of issues. *Past professional posts*: President & shareholder, Timme & Cainn, P.C., 2007-09; shareholder & partner, Middleton & Timme P.C., 1984-2007. *Awards, honors*: Native American Law Lawyer of the Year, 2013-16 by "Best Lawyers in America."

TIMOTHY, JOHN, II (*Yafke - Evening*) (Muscogee Creek)
(artist)
Address & Affiliation: Director/manager, Ataloa Lodge Museum Shop, Bacone College Campus, 2299 Old Bacone Rd., Muscogee, OK 74403 (918) 781-7283. Website: www.bacone.edu/ataloa. *Other professional post*: Staff artist, Five Civilized Tribes Museum, Agency Hill on Honor Heights Dr., Muskogee, OK 74401. Resident artist & tour guide for the museum. *Interests*: Traditional Indian art & history; study of traditional Southeastern cultures, symbolism & religious rites. Member of the Cherokee Dancers of Fire (Tommy Wildcat). Available for oral storytelling, flute playing, blowgun demonstrations, & stickball demonstrations.

TINGLE, TRICIA A. (Oklahoma Choctaw) 1955-
(attorney)
Born May 1, 1955, Wharton, Tex. Education: Southwest Texas State University (San Marcos), BS, 1978, Post-Graduate-Paralegal Certificate, 1985; Oklahoma City University School of Law, JD, 1990. *Principal occupation*: Attorney. *Affiliation & Address*: Assistant U.S. Attorney, Office of the U.S. Attorney, 300 S. 4th St., Suite 600, Minneapolis, MN 55415 (612) 664-5600; (888) 264-5107. *Past professional posts*: Teacher, Brazosport Independent School District, Freeport, TX, 1978-84; paralegal, Texas Railroad Commission, Austin, TX, 1985-87; Clinic Legal Aid for Native American Indians, Oklahoma Indian Legal Services, 1989; law clerk for Judge Tom Brett, Oklahoma Court of Criminal Appeals, Oklahoma City, 1989; General Practice, Leon Breeden & Associates, San Marcos, TX, 1990; self-employed, Law Office of Tricia A. Tingle, San Antonio, TX, 1991-2002. *Other professional posts*: Legal counsel to American Indian Resource & Education Coalition, Inc., Austin, TX; Redwood Community Center, Inc., Hays County, TX; Program Director and original Board Member of Great Promises, Inc. (children's newspaper dealing with Indian issues). *Memberships*: Texas Bar Association; Texas Indian Bar Association (president & original Board Member); Association of Trial Lawyers of America; Hays County Bar Association (director); Oklahoma Indian Bar Association; Native American Bar Association (president-elect). *Awards, honors*: Presidential Delegate to White House Conference on Indian Education, 1992.

TINKER, GEORGE (Osage) 1945-
(associate professor)
Born in 1945. *Education*: New Mexico Highlands University, BA, 1967; Pacific Lutheran Theological Seminary (Berkeley, CA), M.Div., 1972; Graduate

Theological Union (Berkeley, CA), PhD, 1983. *Principal occupation*: Associate professor of Cross-Cultural Ministries. *Address & Affiliation*: Iliff School of Theology, 2201 S. University Blvd., Denver, CO 80210 (303) 744-1283, 1985-. *Other professional post*: Pastor (part-time), Living Waters Indian Church, Denver, CO. *Community activities*: Director, Bay Area Native American Ministry (three years). *Memberships*: American Academy of Religion (co-chair, Native American Religious Traditions Group, 1991-93); American Indian Scholars Assn (corresponding secretary, 1991-); Native American Theological Assn (chairperson, 1985-87). *Awards, honors*: Recipient of a Lutheran Brotherhood Award for doctoral work & two Bacon Fellowships at the Graduate Theological Union. *Interests*: Native American studies; Native American Mission history; cross-cultural studies, including the study of "racism." *Published work*: Missionary Conquest & the Cultural Genocide of Native Americans (Fortress Press, 1993); numerous papers & articles.

TINKER, GEORGE (Eskimo)
(village president)
Affiliation: Native Village of Chignik, P.O. Box 11, Chignik Lake, AK 99563 (907) 749-2285.

TINKER, PHILIP (Osage)
(attorney)
Education: Trinity University, BA (Philosophy), 2003; University of Tulsa College of Law, 2011. *Affiliation & Address*: Attorney (2013-present), Kanji & Katzen PLLC, 303 Detroit St., Suite 400, Ann Arbor, MI48l04 (734) 769-5400. E-mail: ptinker@kanjikatzen.com. While in law school Philip was the Articles Research Editor & Symposium Coordinator for the Tulsa Law Review, President of the Native American Law Students Association, and he received the Award for Highest Academic Honors & Distinguished Service to the University and the Oklahoma Bar Association Outstanding Law School Senior Student Award. *Prior Experience*: Before joining Kanji & Katzen, Philip served for two years as a law clerk to Chief Judge William J. Riley of the United States Court of Appeals for the Eighth Circuit. While in law school, Philip also participated in the Udall Foundation Native American Congressional Internship Program at the White House Council on Environmental Quality and in the United States Justice Department Summer Law Internship Program at the Office of Civil Rights, where he worked on Native American policy issues. *Areas of Concentration*: Philip will initially focus his attention on matters affecting tribal sovereignty & jurisdiction, land claims, & environmental issues. *Community Service & Personal Interests*: Philip has actively supported grassroots, student-led efforts to increase cultural awareness and preserve traditional practices amongst Native American student groups and the broader community. He supports inherent tribal sovereign rights and the civil & cultural rights of Native peoples, through pro bono advocacy, scholarship, public speaking, and counseling tribal leaders and communities.

TINNO, KEITH (Shoshone-Bannock)
(former tribal chairperson)
Affiliation: Fort Hall Business Council, P.O. Box 306, Fort Hall, ID 83203

TIPPECONNIC, JOHN W. (Comanche/Cherokee)
(Emeritus professor of American Indian Studies Dept.)
Education: Oklahoma State University, BA (Secondary Education); Penn State University, MA & PhD.. Affiliation & *Address*: Emeritus faculty, American Indian Studies at Arizona State University, 250 E. Lemon St., Tempe, AZ 85287 (480) 727-0600. E-mail: john.tippeconnic@asu.edu. *Other professional post*: He currently serves on the editorial boards of the Journal of Diversity in Higher Education and the Journal of American Indian Education. He serviced two terms as president of the National Indian Education Association & chair of the American Educational Research Association American Indian Education Special Interest Group. He was a founding member of the Governing Board or Council of Comanche Nation College, the first tribal college in Oklahoma. In 2011 he was named a "Fellow" by the American Educational Research Association. In 2012 the National Indian Education Association awarded him a Lifetime Achievement Award for his work in the education of American Indians & Alaska Natives *Past professional posts*: Co-director, Center for the Study of Leadership in American Indian Education, Penn State University, University Park, PA; Instructor/Editor (Journal of American Indian Education), Center for Indian Education, Arizona State University, Tempe, AZ; He also was the Director of the Office of Indian Education (OIE) located in the U.S. Department of Education & served as vice president of Navajo Community College (now Dinè College. Published works: Co-editor, Next Steps: Research & Practice to Advance Indian Education, and The Dropout/Graduation Crisis among American Indian & Alaska Native Students. He co-edited a special issue of the Journal of American Indian Education on Culturally Responsive Education for American Indian, Alaskan Native and Native Hawaiian students; editor, On Indian Ground: The Southwest (Information Age Publishing (in preparation).

TIPPECONNIE, ROBERT (Comanche)
(tribal secretary-treasurer)
Affiliation: Comanche Nation, Box 908, Lawton, OK 73502 (580) 492-3251.

TISDALE, SHELBY
(director of Center Southwst Studies)
Education: University of Colorado-Boulder, BA (anthropology and southwestern archaeology); University of Washington, MA (social anthropology & museum studies); University of Arizona, PhD (cultural anthropology), 1997. Affiliation & Address: Director, Center of Southwest Studies, Fort Lewis College, 1000 Rim Dr., Durango, CO 81301 (970) 247-77456. E-mail: stisdale@fortlewis.edu. Dr. Shelby Tisdale has over thirty-five years of combined experience in museums; anthropological, tribal museum & cultural resource management consulting; and, university teaching. Dr. Tisdale is the former Director of the Museum of Indian Arts and Culture/Laboratory of Anthropology in Santa Fe, New Mexico and the Millicent Rogers Museum in Taos. More recently she served as Vice President of Curatorial & Exhibitions at the Autry Museum of the American West in Los Angeles. *Published works*: She has published forty articles & book chapters relating to American Indian art & culture, repatriation, and women in the West. She contributed to and directed the publication of the Oklahoma Book Award winning *Woven Worlds: Basketry from the Clark Field Collection*, for the Philbrook Museum of Art in Tulsa, Oklahoma. Her book, *Fine Indian Jewelry of the Southwest: The Millicent Rogers Museum Collection* (Museum of New Mexico Press, 2006) received the Ralph Emerson Twitchell Book Award from the Historical Society of New Mexico and the Southwest Book Award from the Border Regional Library Association. Her latest book, *Pablita Velarde: In Her Own Words* (Little Standing Spruce Publishing, 2012), is a full-length biography of this famous American Indian painter. Dr. Tisdale became interested in repatriation in the early 1980s while working on her master's thesis which resulted in a proposed repatriation policy for the School of American Research (now the School for Advanced Research). She reported on this at the Sacred Materials Conference held at the Buffalo Bill Historical Center in 1985 and has been actively involved in repatriation since. She currently serves on the Smithsonian Institution's Repatriation Review Committee for the National Museum of Natural History. She has also served on the boards of the Society for Applied Anthropology and the Mountain-Plains Museum Association.

TITLA, MARY KIM (San Carlos Apache)
(publisher)
Affiliation: Native Youth Magazine, online at www.nativeyouthmagazine.com. *Past affiliation*: Television reporter in Phoenix, AZ.

TITLA, PHILLIP, SR. (San Carlos Apache) 1943-
(artist)
Born September 17, 1943, Miami, Ariz. *Education*: Eastern Arizona College, AA, 1979. *Principal occupation*: Artist. *Address*: P.O. Box 497, San Carlos, AZ 85550. *Affiliations*: Director of development, San Carlos (AZ) Apache Tribe, 1967-81; director, Phillip Titla Apache Galleria, San Carlos, Ariz., 1981-. *Other professional post*: Board member, San Carlos Arts & Crafts Association, 1981-. *Community activities*: Bylas Recreation Program (chairman); San Carlos Powwow Association, 1980-; San Carlos Pageant Committee, 1978-; Cobke Valley Fine Arts Guild, Inc., 1985-86. *Awards, honors*: Sculpture Award, Best of Show, Pasadena (CA) Art Show. *Interests*: "My interest is to continue to grow in the art field; presently doing some gallery shows and lecture at various clubs on Apache culture; also sing Apache songs; shows at colleges, high schools and elementary schools of my work--for education." *Biographical source*: Art West, Sept./Oct., 1984.

TITUS, LEE (Athapascan)
(village president)
Affiliation: Northway Village Council, P.O. Box 516, Northway, AK 99764 (907) 778-2250.

TITUS, ROBERT J. (*Whitefeather*) (Cherokee) 1938-
(merchant; shaman)
Born December 17, 1938, Helena, Ark. *Education*: Phillips College, AA, 1969. *Principal occupation*: Merchant, shaman. Resides in Helena, Arkansas. (501) 338-7966. *Affiliations*: Helena Pawnshop, Helena, AR, 1978-; project director, Mid Delta Community Services, Helena, AR. *Other professional post*: Shaman, Circle of the Whitefeather, Helena, AR; regional chief, Free Cherokees. *Goals*: "To revive universal natural shamanism the world's original & true religious practice." *Community activities*: State Elector for Arkansas Green Party (environment); member of DEEP (Delta Environmental Ecology Project); advisor to USDA Forest Management - Ozark: St. Francis National Forests; storyteller for local schools & library; Blues Festival volunteer. *Memberships*: Arkansas Travelers Story Tellers Association; local library association & museum; Good Medicine Society of Arkansas; National Pawnbrokers Association (local board member). *Awards, honors*: Academic Excellence, Phi Theta Kappa (president); guest speaker, Lion's Club. *Interests*: Mescalero

customs; alcohol/drugs/crime problems of Sioux, Cheyenne & Navajo; spirituality of Hopi. Maintain a private collection of some spiritual artifacts: shaman's staffs, shaman's "Medicine Hats" & healing sticks & stones.
Published works: Miser's Muniment (Pine Hill Press, 1985); Book of Shaman (Conservatory of American Letters, 1988); The Complete Book of Natural Shamanism (Snowbird Publishing, 1993); articles for various magazines.

TOADECHEENIE, SHARON (Navajo/Dine')
(associate director of university branch)
Education: Arizona State University, MA (Educational Leadership). *Affiliation & Address*: Associate Director, Navajo Technical University, Chinle, (928) 674-5761. E-mail: stoadecheenie@navajotech.edu.

TOBEY, AARON, JR. (Mashpee Wampanoag)
(tribal vice chairperson)
Affiliation: Mashpee Wampanoag Indian tribe, P.O. Box 1048, Mashpee, MA 02649. (508) 477-0208.

TOELUPE, BRANDY K.M. (Hawaiian)
(attorney; Indian law practice)
Education: JD. *Affiliation & Address*: Associate, Tilden McCoy & Dilweg LLP, 2500 30th St., Suite 207, Boulder, CO 80301 (303) 323-1922 Brandy represents tribal governments on federal acknowledgment, general counsel matters, administrative law, legislative advocacy at the federal level, formation of non-profit and for-profit entities, tribal governance, and the Indian Child Welfare Act. In particular, Brandy assists tribal governments in the development, drafting and implementation or ordinances that exercise the tribe's sovereign authority in such areas as employment rights and practical counsel on labor and employment matters, helping them solve workplace problems and avoid employee claims and litigation. Brandy's practice has also included intellectual property protection, such as trademarking & copyrighting. During and after law school, before joining Tilden McCoy + Dilweg LLP, Brandy was a law clerk at the Native American Rights Fund, working on significant impact cases involving the Indian Child Welfare Act, tribal governance and federal acknowledgment. Brandy is a member of a number of legal associations, including the American Bar Assn, Colorado Bar Assn and the Native Hawaiian Bar Assn. In 2012, Brandy was appointed as the Vice Chair of Electric Communications for the ABA SEER Native American Resource Committee, she was later appointed to serve as Co-Chair for this committee, a position she continues to hold presently.

TOFOYA, GILBERT (Santa Clara Pueblo)
(pueblo governor)
Affiliation: Santa Clara Pueblo Council, P.O. Box 580, Espanola, NM 87532 (505) 753-7300.

TOFPI, CHERYL McCLELLAN (Sac & Fox of OK)
(tribal 2nd chief)
Education: University of Oklahoma, BS (Engineering). *Affiliation*: Second Chief (2007-present), Sac & Fox Nation of Oklahoma, Rt. 2 Box 246, Stroud, OK 74079 (918) 968-3526. E-mail: secondchief@sacandfoxnation-nsn.gov. *Past professional posts*: Engineer, Honeywell, Albuquerque, NM, 1983-2007. *Memberships*: American Indian Science & Engineering Society (AISES); Native American Church.

TOFPI, DONALD (Kiowa)
(tribal chairperson)
Affiliation: Kiowa Indian Tribe, P.O. Box 369, Carnegie, OK 73015 (580) 654-2300.

TOHE, LAURA (Dine-Navajo) 1952-
(associate professor, writer)
Born October 5, 1952, Ft. Defiance, Ariz. *Education*: University of New Mexico, BA, 1975; University of Nebraska, MA, 1985, PhD, 1993. *Principal occupation*: Associate professor, writer. *Address & Affiliation*: Professor of English (1994-present), Dept. of English, Arizona State University, P.O. Box 870302, Tempe, AZ 85287 (480) 965-5553. E-mail: l.tohe@asu.edu. *Other professional posts*: Affiliate faculty, ASU Women's Studies and American Indian Studies; writer. *Awards, honors*: Blue Mesa Review Poetry Prize Winner, University of New Mexico; Regents Fellowship & Minority Fellowship, University of Nebraska; Outstanding Young Women of America; University of Nebraska Teaching Assistantship & Reading Assistantship; University of Nebraska, Omaha Goodrich Program Award; National Sports Academy Prize Winner; 1999 Poetry of the Year Award, Wordcraft Circle of Native American Writers & Storytellers for "No Parole Today"; 2003 Minnesota Book Award nomination for "Sister Nations: Native American Women Writers on Community." *Community activities*: Board member, Dine College, Dine Teacher Education Program, Tsaile, AZ; consultant, ACT (American College Testing). *Memberships*: Wordcraft Circle (National Caucus Member); MLA (Modern Language Assn); American Poetry Assn; Academy of American Poets. *Interests*: Photography, film, poetry, travel, physical fitness training. *Published works*: Making Friends

With Water (Nosila Press, 1986); co-editor, Nebraska Humanities (Nebraska Humanities Council, 1994); No Parole Today; Sister Nations: Native American Women Writers on Community; Tseyi', Deep in the Rock.

TOINTIGH, JACKIE DALE (*Blackhorse*) (Kiowa-Apache of Oklahoma) 1949-
(artist)
Address: 511 E. Colorado, Anadarko, OK 73005 (405) 247-7695; Website: www.geocities.com/paris/8300. *Principal occupation*: Artist. *Community activities*: Culture program director, Apache Tribe of Oklahoma; chair, Cultural and Community Enrichment Task Force; Native American Graves Protection & Repatriation Act, and State Historical Preservation Office representative; Nine Nations of Apache, delegate from Oklahoma. *Awards, honors*: Mr. Tointigh has won numerous awards and his paintings and his works are in permanent collections of Oklahoma University's Stovall Museum of Natural History, the Shoshone Warm Springs Tribal Museum, Wichita Tribal Museum, Apache Tribal Museum, the Mid-America All-Indian Center Museum (Wichita, KS), as well as private collectors. *Interests*: He also makes presentations of his art and lectures at high schools and universities on the history and culture of his tribal background that is the Kiowa and Apache Tribe of Oklahoma.

TOLEDO, MICHAEL (Jemez Pueblo)
(former pueblo governor)
Affiliation: Jemez Pueblo, P.O. Box 10, Jemez, NM 87024.

TOLEDO, RICHARD (Navajo) 1951-
(school principal)
Born March 21, 1951, Crownpoint, N.M. *Education*: University of New Mexico, MEd (Administration, 1980 & MEd (Elementary Education, 1985). *Address*: *Affiliation & Address*: Principal, Bread Springs Day School (grades K-3), P.O. Box 1117, Gallup, NM 87305 (505) 778-5665.

TOLLIVER, MARIA (Makah)
(former trbal chairperson)
Affiliation & Address: Former Chairperson, Makah Tribe, P.O. Box 115, Neah Bay, WA 98357 (360) 645-2201.

TOM, ANTHONIA (Paiute)
(tribal band chairperson)
Affiliation & Address: Indian Peaks Band of the Paiute Indian Tribe of Utah, P.O. Box 973, Cedar City, UT 84721 (435) 586-1112.

TOM, CHRIS (Port Gamble S'Klallam)
(tribal vice chairperson)
Affiliation & Address: Vice Chairperson, Port Gamble S'Klallam Tribe, 31912 Little Boston Rd. NE, Kingston, WA 98346 (360) 297-2646.

TOM, EUGENE (Moapa Paiute)
(former tribal chairperson)
Affiliation & Address: Moapa Business Council, P.O. Box 340, Moapa, NV 89025 (7092) 865-2787.

TOM, KATHLEEN (Confederated Tribes of Grand Ronde)
(tribal secretary)
Education: Chemeketa Community College; Western Business College. *Affiliation & Address*: Secretary, Confederated Tribes of Grand Ronde, 9615 Grand Ronde Rd., Grand Ronde, OR 97347 (503) 879-5211. Member of the tribal council since 2005.

TOM, LORA E. (Paiute)
(tribal band chairperson)
Affiliation & Address: Cedar Band of the Paiute Indian Tribe of Utah, P.O. Box 235, Cedar City, UT 84721 (435) 586-9433.

TOM, ROBERT (Southern Paiute)
(former tribal chairperson)
Affiliation & Address: Former chairperson, Moapa Band of Paiute Indians, P.O. Box 340, Moapa, NV 89025 (702) 865-2787. E-mail: chair.mbop@mvdsl.com

TOM SHARON (Navajo)
(communications specialist)
Education: Marquette University, BA (Journalism); Arizona State University W.P. Carey College of Business, MBA. *Affiliation & Address*: Research Analyst, American Indian Policy Institute, Arizona State University, Box 872603, Tempe, AZ 85287 (480) 965-1055. E-mail: sltom@asu.edu. Sharon's primary role is to work on the communications and marketing efforts for the American Indian Policy Institute. Sharon has worked in the technology, non-profit & tribal government sectors. Previously, she worked as a Senior Technical Editor for Maxim Integrated Products and as a Community Relations Specialist with the Salt River Pima-Maricopa Indian Community.

TOM, VALERIE (Navajo-Dine')
(special assistant to Indian college president)
Affiliation & Address: Special Assistant to the President, Dine College, 1 Circle Dr., 3rd Floor, Ned Hatathlie Center, P.O. Box 126, Tsaile, AZ 86556 (928) 724-6600; E-mail: valtom@dinecollege.edu

TOMPKINS, JILL E. (Penobscot)
(director of Indian child welfare program)
Born June 20, 1963, Kingston, N.Y. *Education*: The King's College (NY), BA, 1985; University of Maine School of Law, JD, 1989. *Affiliation & Address*: Senior Director, Casey Family Programs Indian Child Welfare Program, 1999 Broadway, Suite 1415, Denver, CO 80202 (303) 871-8201. *Other professional posts*: President, Eastern Tribal Court Judges Association; Appellate Justice, Pokagon Band of Potawatomi Indians Court of Appeals, Dowagic, MI; Appellate Justice, Mashantucket Pequot Court of Appeals, Mashantucket, CT; Appellate Justice, Passamaquoddy Appellate Court, Sipayik & Motakmikut, ME. *Past professional posts*: Director & Clinical Professor of Law (Dec. 2001-10), American Indian Law Program, American Indian Law Clinic, University of Colorado Law School; executive director (2000-01), Board President (2011-12), National Tribal Justice Resource Center, Boulder, CO; chief judge, Mashantucket Pequot Tribal Court, 1994-2000; faculty, National Judicial College, Tribal Court Jurisdiction Course, 1993-97; chief judge, Passama-quoddy Tribal Court, 1992-95; Justice of the Peace, State of Maine, 1992-97; director, Penobscot Nation Judicial System, Indian Island, ME, 1990-94. *Awards, honors*: First woman to serve as president of Region 7 Northeast, 1997-99; national coordinator for the annual National Tribal Judicial Conference, 1995-99; represented the NAICJA on national tribal justice issues, including testifying before the U.S. Senate Committee on Indian Affairs and meetings with members of Congress & Attorney General, Janet Reno. *Community activities*: Penobscot Nation Election Appeals Commission, 1994-present; secretary & treasurer, Board of Director, Maine Indian Basket-makers Alliance, 1993-present; founding member, Connecticut Coordinating Council for State & Tribal Courts, 1996-present. *Memberships*: Penobscot Indian Nation; National American Indian Court Judges Assn (NAICJA), 1994-present; Maine Bar Assn, Colorado Indian Bar Assn; Connecticut Bar Assn. *Interests*: Traditional Penobscot baskets; numerous presentation & papers on tribal sovereignty & Indian law. *Published works*: A Summary of Income Tax and Other Reporting Requirements for Investors Doing Business in Maine (KPMG Peat Marwick, Portland, ME), 1989; Answers to Frequently Asked Questions About Native Americans in Maine (pamphlet), 2000; A Guide for Tribal Court Law Clerks & Judges, with Massey May Case (U. of Colorado Law School, 2007); Walking In Two Worlds: Tribal Judicial Ethics, Tribal Customs & Traditions (U. of Washington School of Law, 2009); numerous articles & book chapters. *Video Presentation*: Sovereignty Redefined: A Retrospective on the 1980 Maine Indian Land Claim Settlement (Maine Dept. of Education, 2009).

TOMPINS, JOSHUA L. (Lakota)
(concert pianist; adjunct professor; board chairperson)
Education: University of Minnesota, BM, MM, DMA (Music). *Affiliation & Address*: Teacher, Class Piano, Northwestern College, 3003 Snelling Ave. North, St. Paul, MN 55113 (651) 631-5218. E-mail: jltompkins@nwc.edu. *Other professional posts*: Chairperson, National Relief Charities, Sherman, TX; founder & general manager, JLT Productions, Minneapolis, MN; adjunct professor, Department of Music, North Central University, Minneapolis, MN. Dr. Tompkins is an active church musician, freelance pianist, and recording artist with CDs released under his own label, JLT Productions. He is also engaged in writing & arranging music for various Twin Cities musical artists.

TONASKET, MEL (Colville)
(tribal vice chairperson)
Affiliation & Address: Vice Chairperson & Omak District Rep., Confederated Tribes of the Colville Reservation, P.O. Box 150, Nespelem, WA 99155 (509) 634-2212; E-mail mel.tonasket@colvilletribes.com. *Past professional posts*: Director, PHS Indian Health Care, President, National Congress of American Indians (mobilized national support for major tribal legislation passed in the 1970's. With Ron Allen & the late Joe Delacruz (Quinault), Mel helped develop the Centennial Accord, which delineates the principles of government-to-government relationship between the tribes & the State of Washington. *Membership*: Confederated Tribes of the Colville Indian Reservation in Washington. *Awards, honors*: 2002 "Heroes of Healthcare" award from the Washington Health Foundation.

TONE-PAH-HOTE, JENNY (Kiowa)
(professor of American Inian studies)
Education: University of Missouri, BA, 2001; University of Minnesota, PhD, 2009. *Affiliation & Address*: Associate Professor of American Indian Studies, American Indian & Indigenous Studies Program, Department of American Studies, Greenlaw Hall 516 CB# 3520, University of North Carolina, Chapel Hill, NC 27500 (919) 843-7099. E-mail: tonepahh@email.unc.edu. *Research Interests*: American Indian history, material, & expressive culture. Her current project, a book manuscript based on her dissertation, entitled "Envisioning Nationhood: Kiowa Expressive Culture 1875-1939," argues that expressive culture (beadwork, metalwork, painting, and dance) is a vital location through which the Kiowa, a tribe in Oklahoma have created, maintained, and reformulated the boundaries and bonds of their nation. She has also done research on nineteenth century Plains ledger drawings examining intercultural interactions featured in Southern Plains pictorial art. Before joining the faculty in American Studies, she earned a Carolina Postdoctoral Fellowship for Faculty Diversity. She was also awarded a Doctoral Dissertation Fellowship from the University of Minnesota and the Charles A. Eastman Pre-Doctoral Fellowship in Native American Studies at Dartmouth College. *Teaching Interests*: American Indian cultural and political history. She has offered, "Twentieth Century Native America," a class that explored American Indian social history, sovereignty, and autonomy though an interdisciplinary lens. It also examined Native artists, cultural leaders, athletes, and others participated in the lives of their communities and American popular culture. She also teaches " The Kiowa in American Indian Studies," which considers the field through the lens of scholarship about the Kiowa and "American Indian Art and Material Culture."

TONEMAH, DARRYL (Kiowa/Comanche/Tuscarora)
(consultant; health psychologist; musician)
Born on the Tuscarora Reservation, N.Y. *Education*: University of Nebraska-Lincoln, BA (Psychology, Sociology & Gerontology), MA (Community Counseling), PhD (Counseling Psychology & Cultural Studies). *Affiliation & Address*: Director of Health Promotion Program, University of Oklahoma College of Continuing Education, 1700 Asp Ave., Norman, OK 73072 (405) 325-4414. *Other professional posts*: Consultant, American Indian Health & Management Policy, Phoenix, AZ; board member, American Diabetes Association, 2011-present). Darryl is an award-winning recording artist, having produced five CDs since 1992: Can You Hear Me? (1992), The Ghosts of St. Augustine (1997), Journals of My Misperceptions (2000), A Time Like Now (2002), One In Every Crowd (2004), Welcome to Your Rainy Day (2006), Ink Blots & Random Thoughts (2009). Awards, honors: 2008 Native American Music Award for Best Folk Recording (Welcome to Your Rainy Day); 2008 Silver Arrow Award for Contributions to Native American Music.

TONEMAH, DAVID (Kiowa)
(organization president)
Education: Oklahoma Baptist University, BS (Healthcare Administration); University of Phoenix, MBA. *Affiliation & Address*: President, American Indian Health & Management Policy, P.O. Box 42535, Phoenix, AZ 85080 (602) 999-5391. *Past professional posts*: Medical Services Director, Native American Community Health Center, Phoenix, AZ; Health Department Business Administrator, Wassaja Memorial Health Center, Fort McDowell Indian Community; budget officer, Phoenix Indian Medical Center.

TOPFI, CHERYL McCLELLAN (Sac & Fox of Oklahoma)
(tribal 2nd chief)
Affiliation: 2nd Chief, Sac & Fox Nation of Oklahoma, 920883 S. Hwy. 99 Bldg. A, Stroud, OK 74079 (918) 968-3526. Website: www.sacandfoxnation-nsn.gov.

TOPPAH, AMBER C. (Kiowa)
(former tribal chairperson)
Affiliation & Address: Former Chairperson, Kiowa Indian Tribe, P.O. Box 369, Carnegie, OK 73015 (580) 654-1729.

TOPPING, KYSTIE (Red Cliff Ojibwe)
(tribal treasurer & education director)
Affiliation & Address: Treasurer & Education Director, Red Cliff Band of Lake Superior Chippewa Indians of Wisconsin, 88385 Pike Rd., Hwy. 13, Bayfield, WI 54814 (715) 779-3700.

TOPSKY, ELIZABETH, MD (Chippewa Cree)
(physician)
Education: University of Montana (BS-Pre-Medicine); University of Washington School of Medicine, MD, 2003. *Affiliation & Address*: Staff Physician, Pueblo of Jemez (Walatowa), P.O. Box 100, Jemez, NM 87024 (575) 834-7359. *Other professional post*: Member-at-Large, Assn of American Indian Physicians, Oklahoma City, OK.

TORRES, AMBER (Paiute)
(tribal chairperson)
Affiliation & Address: Vice Chairperson, Walker River Paiute Tribe, P.O. Box 220, Schurz, NV 89427 (775) 773-2306.

TORRES, EDDIE PAUL, SR. (Pueblo of Isleta)
(Pueblo governor)
Affiliation & Address: Governor, Pueblo of Isleta, P.O. Box 1290, Isleta, NM 87022 (505) 869-3111.

TORRES, GERALD (Mexican American)
(professor of Indian law)
Education: Stanford University, BA, 1974; Yale University Law School, JD, 1977; University of Michigan-Ann Arbor Law School, LLM, 1980. *Affiliation & Address*: Jane M.G. Foster Professor of Law, Cornell Law School, 314 Myron Taylor Hall, Ithaca, NY 14853 (607) 254-1630; E-mail: gt276@cornell.edu. Gerald Torres is a leading figure in critical race theory, environmental law, and federal Indian Law. He served as the Bryant Smith Chair in Law at the University of Texas School of Law and taught at The University of Minnesota Law School, where he served as Associate Dean. He has been a visiting professor at Harvard, Stanford, and Yale law schools. A nationally recognized expert in Indian law who has taught and published on Indian law issues for many years, he developed his Indian jurisprudence course specifically for the summer program. Gerald is a leading figure in critical race theory, environmental law and federal Indian law. *Other professional posts*: Visiting Professor of Indian Law, Lewis & Clark College of Law, Portland, OR; He is currently Vice Chair of Earth Day Network & Board Chair of the Advancement Project as well as serving on the Board of the Natural Resources Defense Council and the Texas League of Conservation Voters. He is a member of the Council on Foreign Relations and the American Law Institute. *Past professional posts*: He previously served as the Bryant Smith Chair in Law at the University of Texas School of Law and taught at The University of Minnesota Law School, where he served as Associate Dean. He is also a former president of the Association of American Law Schools (AALS). Torres has served as deputy assistant attorney general for the Environment and Natural Resources Division of the U.S. Department of Justice in Washington, D.C., and as counsel to then U.S. attorney general Janet Reno. *Awards, honors*: Torres was honored with the 2004 Legal Service Award from the Mexican American Legal Defense & Educational Fund (MALDEF) for his work to advance the legal rights of Latinos. *Published works*: Coauthor, with Lani Guinier, of *The Miner's Canary: Enlisting Race, Resisting Power, Transforming Democracy*, a book recently nominated for a Pulitzer Prize. Torres' many articles include "Translation and Stories" (Harvard Law Review, 2002), "Who Owns the Sky?" (Pace Law Review, 2001) (Garrison Lecture),"Taking and Giving: Police Power, Public Value, and Private Right" (Environmental Law, 1996), and "Translating Yonnondio by Precedent & Evidence: The Mashpee Indian Case" (Duke Law Journal, 1990).

TORRES, GUADALUPE "LOU" (White Mountain Apache)
(engineer)
Principal occupation: Engineer. *Affiliations & Address*: Field engineer, Lockheed Corp., 1968-1986; president/owner, Systems Integration & Research, Inc., 1100 N. Glebe Rd. PH 1, Arlington, VA 22201 (703) 486-7933, 1986-. *Description*: The company's primary business is analyzing the life cycles of computer & technology systems & providing program management. A majority of its contract are with the Navy. Employs 150 people at eight offices across the country with two more planned for Sacramento and San Diego, California. Award: "Outstanding National Technologies Firm of the Year," by the U.S. Small Business Administration, Office of Native American Affairs.

TORRES, RAYMOND (Cahuilla)
(tribal vice chairperson)
Affiliation & Address: Vice Chairperson, Torres Martinez Desert Cahuilla Indians, P.O. Box 1160, Thermal, CA 92274 (760) 397-0300. E-mail: rtorres@torresmartinez.org

TORRES, REBECCA (Alabama-Quassarte)
(tribal chief)
Address & Affiliation: Alabama-Quassarte Tribal Town, 323 W. Broadway #300, Muskogee, OK 74401 (918) 683-2388.

TORRES, SHARON (Navajo-Dine')
(Indian program coordinator)
Affiliation & Address: Program Coordinator, American Indian Policy Institute, Arizona State University (ASU), Discovery Hall Rm. 272, 250 E. Lemon St., Tempe, AZ 85287 (480) 965-1306. E-mail: Sharon.torres@asu.edu.

TORRES-NEZ, JOHN (Dine')
(Native archaeologist; chief operating officer)
Affiliation & Address: Chief Operating Officer, Southwest Association for Indian Ats (SWAIA), P.O. Box 969, Santa Fe, NM 87504 (505) 983-5220. E-mail: jtorresnez@swaia.org. *Past professional posts*: For 15 years he worked in the cultural resource world of dozens of western tribes, but the longest was with his native tribe, the Navajo Nation; curator, Museum of Indian Arts & Culture, Santa Fe, NM, 2000-2006.

TORTALITA, TONY (Santo Domingo Pueblo)
(Pueblo governor)
Affiliation: Santo Domingo Pueblo Council, P.O. Box 99, Santo Domingo, NM 87052 (505) 465-2214.

TORTEZ, THOMAS (Cahuilla)
(tribal chairperson)
Affiliation & Address: Chairperson, Torres Martinez Desert Cahuilla Indians, P.O. Box 1160, Thermal, CA 92274 (760) 397-0300. E-mail: tmttortez@torresmartinez.org; E-mail: tmchair@torresmartinez.org

TOTEMOFF, CHARLES W. (Eskimo)
(Alaskan village chairperson)
Affiliation: Chair, Native Village of Chenega, P.O. Box 8079, Chenega Bay, AK 99574 (907) 573-5132.

TOTEMOFF, DAVID (Aleut)
(Alaskan village president)
Affiliation: Native Village of Tatitlek, P.O. Box 171, Tatitlek, AK 99677 (907) 325-2311.

TOUCHTONE, RANDY (Ojibwe)
(tribal vice chairperson)
Affiliation & Address: Vice Chairperson, Bay Mills Indian Community, 12140 W. Lakeshore Dr., Brimley, MI 49715 (906) 248-3241.

TOULOU, TRACY (Colville)
(director, DOJ-Office of Tribal Justice)
Education: University of New Mexico, JD. *Affiliation & Address*: Director, Office of Tribal Justice, U.S. Dept. of Justice, 950 Pennsylvania Ave., NW, Room 1000, Washington, DC 20530 (202) 514-8812. *Past professional posts*: Clerk for DNA Legal Services on the Navajo Nation & Laguna Pueblo Tribal Court; U.S. Agency for International Development & the U.S. Peace Corps in Africa, Central America and the Caribbean; Assistant U.S. Attorney for the District of Montana where his duties included tribal outreach and the prosecution of violent crime in Indian country.

TOVAR, MOLLY (Comanche/Hispanic)
(American Indian studies director)
Education: Oklahoma State University, PhD (Higher Education & Administration). *Affiliation & Address*: Director, Kathryn M. Buder Center for American Indian Studies, George Warren Brown School of Social Work, 336 Goldfarb, St. Louis, MO 63130 (314) 935-7767. E-mail: mtovar@wustl.edu. *Past professional posts*: Director of Student Academic Services, Graduate College, Oklahoma State University; director of leadership for the Bill & Melinda Gates Millennium Scholars Program, Fairfax, VA.

TOWNSEND, ANGELIQUE (*EagleWoman; Wambdi A. WasteWin*)
(Sisseton-Wahpeton)
(professor of law & American Indian studies)
Education: Stanford University, BA (Political Science); University of Noth Dakota School of Law, JD (with Distinction); University of Tulsa College of Law, LLM (American Indian & Indigenous Law, with honors). *Affiliation & Address*: Professor of Law, College of Law, University of Idaho & James E. Rogers Fellow in American Indian Law, Moscow, ID 883844 (208) 885-7634. E-mail: eaglewoman@uidaho.edu. Professor EagleWoman brought a diverse background that includes tribal economic development, legal code development, litigation, criminal law & scholarly interest in international indigenous law to the University of Idaho College of Law when she joined the faculty in 2008. Professor EagleWoman received her LL.M. in American Indian and Indigenous Studies in 2004 from the University of Tulsa College of Law. She teaches in the areas of Native American Law, Native Natural Resources Law, Tribal Economics & Law, & Civil Procedure. She has served several terms as a board member of the National Native American Bar Association & believes in staying firmly tied to the Native American legal field. She also maintains membership in the bar associations of the District of Columbia, Oklahoma, and South Dakota. Highlights of her legal career include serving as General Counsel to the Sisseton-Wahpeton (Dakota) Oyate of the Lake Traverse Reservation, working as an associate attorney with Sonosky, Chambers, Sachse & Endreson in Washington, D.C. and serving as Tribal Public Defender for the Kaw Nation and the Ponca Nation, both of Oklahoma. Angelique EagleWoman (Wambdi A. WasteWin) is a citizen of the Sisseton-Wahpeton Dakota Oyate of the Lake Traverse Reservation. Professor EagleWoman was formerly a member of the law faculty at Hamline University School of Law in St. Paul, Minnesota and held a visitorship position at the University of Kansas (KU) in the KU School of Law and the Indigenous Nations Program. In the spring of 2008, she was selected as the recipient of the KU Center for Indigenous Nation's Crystal Eagle Award for showing leadership & dedication toward helping community members or students within indigenous communities. She has been the recipient of numerous awards in legal academia including: recipient of the William F. & Joan L. Boyd Excellence in Teaching Award (January 2010); recognized as one of twelve national Emerging Scholars by Diverse Issues in Higher Education (January 7, 2010 edition); recognized as a Distinguished Alumni Scholar by Stanford University

(May 2010); recipient of the Inspirational Faculty Award by the University of Idaho Office of Alumni Relations (Dec. 2010); named the Allan G. Shepard Distinguished Professor at the College of Law for 2011-2012; and received the UI Athena Woman of the Year Award for Faculty April 2014. Angelique Townsend EagleWoman was featured in the article "9 Notable Women Who Rule American Indian Law"

TOYA, JOSEPH A. (Jemez Pueblo)
(Pueblo governor)
Affiliation & Address: Governor, Pueblo of Jemez, P.O. Box 100, Jemez, NM 87024 (575) 834-7359.

TOYA, RONALD GEORGE (Jemez Pueblo) 1948-
(BIA agency supt.)
Born March 8, 1948, Albuquerque, N.M. *Education*: Westmont College, BA (Economics), BS (Psychology), 1970. *Principal occupation*: B.I.A. agency supt. *Address*: BIA, P.O. Box 189, Mescalero, NM 88340 (505) 464-4202. *Affiliations*: Chief, Branch of Reservation Programs, Southern Pueblos Agency, BIA, Albuquerque, NM; chief, Branch of Self-Determination Services, assistant area director, BIA, Albuquerque Area Office; supt., Mescalero Agency, BIA, Mescalero, NM; supt., Southern Ute Agency, BIA, Ignacio, CO; special assistant to the Assistant Secretary of Interior for Indian Affairs, Washington, DC; special assistant to the Commissioner of Indian Affairs; chief, Branch of Tribal Government Services, U.S. Dept. of Interior, BIA, Albuquerque Area Office. *Other professional post*: Executive director & chairman of the board, Tribal Government Institute; Chairman of the Board, New Mexico Commission on Higher Education. *Community activities*: Conduct radio show on Indian affairs entitled Native American Perspective; involved in youth activities, including baseball & Special Olympics. *Memberships*: New Mexico Industrial Development (board of directors, 1975-1981; CEDAM - international scuba & archaeological association; Society for American Baseball Research. *Awards, honors*: Special & Superior Achievement Awards, BIA 1972, 1979, 1981, 1982; various letters/citations. *Interests*: "Management of tribal governments; economic development & preservation of Indian culture; travel; baseball; scuba diving; car racing; hang gliding; dancing." *Published work*: Pueblo Management Development (Southwest Indian Polytechnic Institute, 1976).

TOYA, VINCENT (Jemez Pueblo)
(Pueblo tribal administrator)
Affiliation & Address: Tribal Administrator, Jemez Pueblo Council, P.O. Box 100, Jemez, NM 87024 (505) 834-7359. *Past tribal position*: Jemez Pueblo governor.

TRACK, JOANN SOGIE (Sioux-Tiwa) 1949-
(clay artist/poet)
Born June 26, 1949, Taos, N.M. *Address*: P.O. Box 992, Taos, NM 87571. *Affiliation*: Assistant curator, Millicent Rogers Museum, Taos, NM, 1990-. *Other professional post*: Instructor in micaceous clay, Taos Institute of Art. Membership: American Association of Museums. *Published work*: Spider Woman's Granddaughters (Beacon Press, 1989).

TRAFZER, CLIFFORD E. (Wyandot) 1949-
(professor of history & Native American studies)
Born March 1, 1949, Mansfield, Ohio. *Education*: Northern Arizona University, BA (History), 1970, MA (History), 1971; Oklahoma State University, PhD (American History), 1973. *Principal occupation*: Professor of History & Costo Chair in Native American Indian History. *Address*: 34815 Olive Tree Lane, Yucaipa, CA 92399 (951) 827-1974. E-mail: clifford.trafzer@ucr.edu. *Affiliations*: Distinguished Professor of History, Dept. of History & Ethnic Studies, Professor of Native American Studies (1991-2003), Dept. of History & former director of Native American Studies, University of California, Riverside, 1991-present; director, Costo Native American Research Center, Riverside, CA, 2003-present. *Other professional post*: Vice Chairperson, California Native American Heritage Commission; Board, Sherman Indian Museum; Board, Cabazon Indian Cultural Commission; Board, Loma Linda University Indian Health Center; Native American Land Conservancy Board. *Past professional posts*: Museum curator, The Arizona Historical Society, 1973-76; instructor of history, Northern Arizona University, 1974-77; instructor, Navajo Community College, Tsaile, AZ, 1977-78; associate professor of history & Native American Studies, Washington State University, Pullman, 1977-82; professor & chair, Dept. of American Indian Studies, San Diego State University, 1982-91. *Awards, honors*: Oklahoma Heritage Association Doctoral Scholarship, $5,000; appointment by Gov. Raul Castro to the Arizona Historical Records Advisory Board, 1976-77; Eagle Feather Award for teaching Excellence and service to the American Indian community by the American Indian Student Organizations of Washington State University & San Diego State University, 1982 & 1986; Research and Teaching Awards, San Diego State University, 1984, '85, '88 & '89; 1986 Governor's Book Award for "Renegade Tribe: The Palouse Indians and the Invasion of the Inland Pacific Northwest," and for "Washington's Native American Communities, Peoples of Washington," 1991 - best historical works

in Northwestern history; Penn Oakland Literature Award, 1994, for "Earth Song, Sky Spirit"; Wordcraft Circle of Native Writers Book Award for "Death Stalks the Yakama"; appointment by Governor George Deukmajian to the California Native American Heritage Commission, 1988; Outstanding Faculty Award, Associated Students of San Diego State University, 1989-90; Academic Specialist Program Fellow, U.S. Information Agency, Sept. 1991, to Sweden lecturing on Native American History & Literature. *Memberships*: American Historical Association; American Association for Ethno-history; American Association for History of Medicine; Canadian Association of History of Medicine; California Historical Society; Organization of American Historians; Wordcraft Circle of Native American Writers; Phi Kappa Phi; California Indian Education Association; American & Canadian Association for the History of Medicine. *Interests*: Native American history, literature, and religion; writing, hiking, fishing, and camping. *Published works*: The Judge: The Life of Robert A. Hefner (University of Oklahoma Press, 1975); The Volga Germans: Pioneers of the Pacific Northwest, with Richard Scheuerman (University Press of Idaho, 1980); Yuma: Frontier Crossing of the Far Southwest (Western Heritage Press, 1980); The Kit Carson Campaign: The Last Navajo War (University of Oklahoma Press, 1982); editor, American Indian Identity: Todays Changing Perspectives (American Indian Studies, San Diego State, 1985); Northwestern Indians in Exile: Removal of the Modocs, Palouses & Nez Perces to the Indian Territory (Sierra Oaks Publishing Co., 1986); editor, Indians, Superintendents, and Councils: Northwestern Indian Policy, 1850-1855 (University Press of America, 1986); editor, Indian Prophets and Prophecy: An American Indian Tradition (Sierra Oaks Publishing Co., 1986 - reprint of special issue of American Indian Quarterly, Summer 1985); The Renegade Tribe: The Palouse Indians and the Invasion of the Inland Pacific Northwest, with Richard Scheuerman (Washington State University Press, 1986); Creation of a California Tribe: Grandfather's Maidu Indian Tales, 1988; California's Indians and the Gold Rush, 1989; American Indians as Cowboys, 1992; Chief Joseph's Allies, 1992 (all published by Sierra Oaks Publishing); also, The Chinook & The Nez Perce (Chelsea House, 1990 & 1992); editor, Looking Glass (San Diego State University Press, 1991); Yakama, Palouse, Cayuse, Umatilla, Walla Walla, and Wanapum Indians: An Historical Bibliography (Scarecrow Press, 1992); Earth Song, Sky Spirit: Short Stories of the Contemporary Native American Experience (Anchor/Doubleday, 1993). Anthologies: editor, Mourning Dove's Stories, with Richard Scheuerman (San Diego State University Press, 1991); editor, Looking Glass (San Diego State University Press, 1991); Death Stalks the Yakama: Epidemiological Transitions and Mortality on the Yakama Indian Reservation, 1888-1964, (Michigan State University Press, 1996); editor, Blue Dawn, Red Earth, (Anchor/Doubleday, 1996); Grandmother, Grandfather, and Old Wolf (Michigan State University Press, 1997); Chemehuevi People of the Coachilla Valley, with T. Madrigal and L. Madrigal (Chemehuevi Press, 1997); Exterminate Them!: Written Accounts of Murder, Rape, and Enslavement, with Joel Joel Hyer (Michigan State University, 1998); As Long As the Grass Shall Grow and Rivers Flow: A History of Native Americans (Harcourt, 2000); The People of San Manuel, (San Manuel Tribe, 2003); The Native Universe, with Gerald McMaster (National Museum of the American Indian, 2004).

TRAHAN, RODNEY (Northern Cheyenne)
(certified business coach; non-profit treasurer)
Education: University of Montana, BS (Business), 1990, MBA, 2007. *Affiliation & Address*: Founder & CEO (2007-present), ActionCoach, Streamline Enterprises, 641 Nottingham Circle, Apt. 5, Billings, MT 59105 (406) 248-8001. *Other professional post*: Board treasurer, National Relief Charities, Sherman, TX. Past professional post: Chief Planned Giving Officer, St. Labre Indian School, Busby, MT, 1995-2007.

TRAHAN, RON (Salish & Kootenai)
(tribal chairperson)
Affiliation & Address: Chairperson, Confederated Salish & Kootenai Tribes, P.O. Box 278, Pablo, MT 59855 (406) 675-2700. E-mail: rtrahan@cskt.org.

TRAHANT, MARK N. (Shoshone-Bannock) 1957-
(writer, speaker, twitter poet)
Born August 13, 1957, Fort Hall, Idaho. *Education*: Pasadena City College; Idaho State University. *Affiliation & Address*: Charles R. Johnson Endowed Professor of Journalism (2015-present), University of North Dakota, College of Arts & Sciences, O'Kelly Hall 202, 221 Centennial Dr., Stop 7103, Grand Forks, ND 58202. E-mail: mntrahant@me.com. *Other professional posts*: Blogger, journalist, content producer, speaker, Twitter Poet, 2010-present; Board member, Vision Maker Media, Lincoln, NE; Board Member, American Indian Law Center, Inc., Albuquerque, NM. *Past professional posts*: Editor-in-chief, The Sho-Ban News, Fort Hall, ID, 1976-86; editor & publisher, Navajo Nation Today, Window Rock, AZ, 1986-93; executive news editor, The Salt Lake Tribune, Salt Lake City, UT, 1993-95; editor & publisher, Moscow-Pullman Daily News, Moscow, ID, 1995-2002; Editor, Editorial pages, Seattle Post-Intelligencer, Seattle, WA, 2003-09. *Community activities*: Chair, Maynard Institute for Journalism Education; Trustee, The Freedom Forum. *Memberships*: Native American Journalists Assn (past president); American

Society of Newspaper Editors; Northwest Indian Press Assn. *Interests*: "I've spent the past year writing about health care reform and the implications for Indian Country. Now, I'm adding new topics to the mix: Indian Country & federal policy, economics, tribal governments, gaming, social media and, well, I think I'm interested in everything." *Published works*: "Pictures of Our Nobler Selves," 1995; "The Whole Salmon," 2002; Trahant Reports on Twitter (every Monday, Mark posts a new column about an issue facing Indian Country); writing about Henry Jackson, A U.S., Senator from Washington state whom he described as the primary sponsor for the golden era of Indian legislation. Trahant specifically wants to recognize the work of Forrest Gerard, a Blackfeet Indian who was one of Jackson's aides and the first Native to work on Capitol Hill.

TRANCOSA, JEANETTE (San Felipe Pueblo)
(executive director)
Education: University of New Mexico School of Medicine, BA (Community Services). *Affiliation & Address*: Executive Director & Director of Education, The Education for Parents of Indian Children With Special Needs (EPICS), 1600 San Pedro Dr. NE, Albuquerque, NM 87110 (505) 767-6630. E-mail: jtrancosa@epicsnm.org. *Interests*: Advocate of children, families and their progress; directing, coordinating & conducting trainings for diverse families.

TRAVARES, JESSICA (Miwok, Maidu)
(rancheria chairperson)
Affiliation: United Auburn Indian Community, 661 New Castle Rd. #1, New Castle, CA 95658 (916) 663-3720.

TREADWELL, HOWARD E. (Poospatuck)
(tribal chief)
Affiliation: Poospatuck Reservation, P.O. Box 86, Mastic, NY 11950 (516) 399-3843.

TREPPA, SHERRY (Habematolel Pomo)
(tribal chairperson)
Born in Lake County & raised in the San Francisco Bay area. *Education*: University of San Francisco, BS. *Affiliation & Address*: Chairperson (2008-present), Habematolel Pomo of Upper Lake Rancheria, P.O. Box 516, Upper Lake, CA 95485 (707) 275-0737. Sherry started her work for the tribe by volunteering for the Enrollment Committee in 2001; she also has served as a member of the Housing Committee, CILS (California Indian Legal Services) Board of Directors & Trine's NIGA & NCAI delegation. Sherry was elected Vice Chairperson of the Executive Council in June 2004, re-elected in 2006. *Past professional posts*: 15 years as Account Manager servicing a variety of Industries (Medical, Biotech, Wine, Welding & Pharmaceutical).

TREPPA-DIEGO, LEORA J. (Pomo)
(former rancheria chairperson)
Affiliation: Habematolel Pomo of Upper Lake Rancheria, P.O. Box 516, Upper Lake, CA 95485 (707) 275-0737.

TRETT, JENNY (Chickasaw)
(executive officer)
Education: East Central University (BS (Accounting), 1995; Oklahoma State University, MBA, 2009. *Affiliation & Address*: Executive Officer (2012-present), Chickasaw Nation Division of Organizational Planning & Support, P.O. Box 1548, Ada, OK 74821 (580) 436-7280. *Other professional posts*: Board member, The Chickasaw Foundation; member, Executive board, Chickasaw Nation Boys & Girls Club. *Past professional post*: Tribal accountant & treasury administrator, The Chickasaw Nation, 1997-2005.

TREUER, DAVID (Leech Lake Ojibwe)
(assistant professor)
Education: Princeton University, BA, 1992; University of Michigan, PhD, 1999. *Address & Affiliation*: University of Minnesota, Twin Cities Campus, 110L LindH, Minneapolis, MN 55455 (612) 626-7119. E-mail: treue003@umn.edu. *Other professional post*: Translator of many Ojibwe stories & texts and teaches Native American literature. *Awards, honors*: Recipient of a Fulbright Fellowship to Canada, a Pushcart Prize, the 1996 Minnesota Book Award, and was a finalist for the Pen West Prize in 1999. Has held a Bush Artist's Fellowship and a McNight Land-Grant Professorship. *Published works*: Novels: Little, 1995, Hiawatha, 1999.

TREVATHAN, LOUIS "BUZZ", JR. 1944-
(gallery owner)
Born October 9, 1944, in N.C. *Education*: U.S. Military Academy (West Point), BS, 1967. *Principal occupation*: Gallery owner. *Address*: P.O. Box 23597, Santa Fe, NM 87502-3597 (505) 985-1417 or 988-9881. E-mail: buzzart@cristofs.com. Website: www.cristofs.com. *Affiliation*: Co-owner, Cristof's, Santa Fe, NM 87501. *Military service*: U.S. Army, Captain-Vietnam Vet (Flying Cross, Bronze Star, Air Medals, etc.). *Published works*: Magazine articles (1993-04) on contemporary Navajo weaving, in "Focus/Santa Fe," & "Southwest Art."

TRIBBETT, NORMAN HENRY (Forest County Potawatomi) 1948-
(tribal librarian)
Born November 5, 1948, Hayward, Wisc. *Education*: University of Wisconsin, Oshkosh, BA, 1981; University of Wisconsin, Madison, MLS, 1983. *Address*: 801 Chelsea Way, Lake Placid, FL 33852. E-mail: nokmes@strat0.net. *Affiliation*: Library Director (1986-present), Seminole Tribe of Florida, Rt. 6, Box 668, Okeechobee, FL 34974 (941) 763-4236. *Memberships*: American Indian Library Association; National Congress of Native Americans. *Military service*: U.S. Army (pvt.), 1969-70. *Interests*: Forest County Potawatomi history; history of the treaties for Potawatomi, & history of natives who relocated to Canada.

TRICKEY, RAFE EDWARD, JR. (Comanche)
(president & chief executive officer)
Education: Modesto Junior College, AA (Social Sciences), 1983; University of Caiifornia, Santa Barbara, BA (Political Science & History), 1985; Columbia University, School of International & Public Affairs, 1986-88; University of Southern California, MS (Education, ABD (Philosophy), Educational Planning & Administration), 1990-95; Loyola Law School, Loyola Marymount University, JD, 2001; UCLA (Certificate, Fund Raiiising & Institutional Development, 2002-03; University of California, San Diego, EdD (Educational Leadership), 2010. *Affiliation & Address*: President & CEO (2010-present), Principal, 1988-present), Greater Pacific Planning & Effectiveness Group, Foundation for College Access Services, Oceanside, CA *Other professional posts*: Past *professional posts*: President (2014-15), Comanche Nation College, Lawton, OK. President, Sisseton Wahpeton College, 2012-13; vice-president of Planning & Institutional Development & vice-presient of Student Services, College of the Marshall Islands, 2011-12; executive director of Development & External Relations, Citrus Community College, Glendora, CA, 2009-10; president & CEO, California Highway Patrol 11-99 Foundation, 2003-09; University of Southern California (director of student services, The Law School, 2000-02; Interim Dean & Assistant to V.P. for Student Affairs, 1992-96;counselor, Office of Admission & Financial Aid, 1990-92); economist, Federal Reserve Bank of New York, 1988-89; editor, Journal of Intenational Affairs, Columbia University, New York, NY, 1986-88.

TRIMBLE, CHARLES E. (Oglala Lakota)
(organization president)
Affiliation: Red Willow Institute, Omaha, NE. *Past professional posts*: Principal founder, American Indian Press Association, 1970; executive director, National Congress of American Indians, 1972-78.

TRIPP, CHARLES H. (Cherokee)
(attorney; tribal judge)
Education: Univesity of Tulsa, BA, 1988, JD, 1993; MBA, 1995. *Affiliation & Address*: Founding Partner, Legal Advocates for Indian Country LLP & Indian Collabrative Consultants, LLC, P.O. Box 1434, Owasso, OK 74055 (918) 376-0630. *Other professional posts*: Chief Supreme Court Justice, Kaw Nation, Kaw City, Oklahoma; District Judge, Miami Tribe of Oklahoma, Sac & Fox Tribe of Missouri, and the Iowa Tribe of Kansas & Nebraska.

TRITT, LINCOLN (*Shigin*) (Gwich'in Athabaskan) 1946-
(writer, speaker, musician)
Born October 18, 1946, Salmon River, AK. *Education*: Mt. Edgecumbe High School; University of Alaska, Fairbanks, 1984-86. *Principal occupation*: Writer, speaker. *Address*: P.O. Box 22016, Arctic Village, AK 99722 (907) 587-5010 (messages only). *Affiliation*: 2nd Chief, Arctic Village Traditional Council, Arctic Village, AK. *Other professional posts*: Write articles for local newspapers; lobbyist, tribal judge. *Past professional posts*: Instructor, College of Rural Alaska, Interior Campus, Fort Yukon Center, Fort Yukon, AK; consulting in education, alcohol & drugs; teach Native pre-contact history in psychology, sociology, philosophy, spirituality, etc. *Military service*: U.S. Navy, 1966-70 (Radioman 3rd Class; Vietnam Vet). *Community activities*: Native Village of Venetie Tribal Government; Neets'aii Corp.; Arctic Village School Advisory Committee' Tanana Chiefs Conference; Interior Education Committee; Council for Athabaskan Tribal Government; Gwitch'in Niintsyaa Coordinator. *Interests*: "Teach Native pre-contact human value system and why they lived the way they did and still do." *Biographical source*: "The County's Monthly" in Santa Cruz Magazine, Dec. 1991. Published works: Raven Tell Stories (Anthology) (The Greenfield Review Literary Center, 1991); Coyote Bark/Poetic Art (Harrison Publishers, 1991).

TRONCOSA, LAWRENCE (San Felipe Pueblo)
(former pueblo governor)
Affiliation: San Felipe Pueblo Council, P.O. Box 4339, San Felipe, NM 87001 (505) 867-3381.

TROPE, JACK F.
(executive director)
Education: Harvard Law School, JD. *Affiliation*: Executive Director, Association on American Indian Affairs, 966 Hungerford Dr., Suite 12-B, Rockville, MD 20850 (240) 314-7155. E-mail: general.aaia@verizon.net.

TROSPER, RONALD L.
(professor of director of graduate studies)
Education: Harvard University, BA, 1967, MA, 1970, PhD (Economics), 1974. *Address & Affiliation*: Professor & Director of Graduate Studies, American Indian Studies Program, The University of Arizona, Harvill 216, Tucson, AZ 85721 (520) 621-7108. E-mail: rltrosper@email.arizona.edu. *Other professional post*: Faculty Fellow, Native American Student Affairs Center, The University of Arizona, Nugent Bldg. Rm 203, Tucson, AZ. *Past professional posts*: Assistant professor of Economics & Public Affairs, University of Washington, Seattle, WA, 1973-77; assistant professor, Boston College, 1977-80; tribal economist, Confederated Salish & Kootenai Tribes of the Flathead Indian Reservation, Pablo, MT, 1983-89; associate professor, Native American Forestry program, School of Forestry, Northern Arizona University (NAU), Flagstaff, AZ, 1989-2004; acting director, National Indian Policy Center, The George Washington University, Washington, DC, 1994; Interim director, Institute for Native Americans, NAU, 1995-96; Interim chair, Dept. of Applied Indigenous Studies, NAU, 2000-2001; associate professor, Dept. of Forest Resources, Management, Faculty of Forestry, U. of British Columbia, 2004-2005. *Areas of Interest*: Indigenous economic theory; traditional ecological knowledge; aboriginal forestry; American Indian economic development; ecological & environmental economics. *Published works*: Earnings & Labor Supply: A Microeconomic Comparison of American Indians & Alaskan Natives to American Whites & Blacks (NTUS, 1980); Resilience, Reciprocity & Ecological Economics: Northwest Coast Sustainability (Routledge, 2009); Traditional Forest Knowledge: Sustaining Communities, Ecosystems & Biocultural Diversity, co-edited with John Parrotta (Springer, 2011); numerous articles.

TROUSDALE, D. WAYNE (Citizen Potawatomi)
(tribal secretary-treasurer)
Affiliation & Address: Secretary-Treasurer, Citizen Potawatomi Nation, 1601 Gordon Cooper Dr., Shawnee, OK 74801 (405) 275-3121. E-mail: dtrousdale@potawatomi.org.

TRUDELL, RICHARD (Santee Sioux)
(executive director)
Education: San Jose State University, BS; Catholic University, JD. *Affiliation & Address*: Founder & Executive Director, American Indian Lawyer Training Program, Inc. (AILTP), 1025 W. Vine St., Stockton, CA 95203 (209) 460-0924. In 1980, he helped establish the American Indian Resources Institute (AIRI). He has played a major role in convening intergovernmental forums & meetings to address issues & challenges facing Indian Country. In the 1990s, he worked closely with the U.S. Senate Committee on Indian Affairs on Indian leadership forums and the U.S. Publish Health Service and the Indian Health Service on regional & national meetings that addresses Indian healthcare reform. *Other professional post*: Advisor, Blue Stone Strategy Group, Irvine, CA.

TRUDELL, ROGER (Santee Sioux)
(tribal chairperson)
Affiliation & Address: Chairperson, Santee Sioux Tribal Council, 425 Frazier Ave. N. Suite 2, Niobrara, NE 68760 (402) 857-2302.

TRUJILLO, EVELYN C. (Acoma Pueblo)
(IHS-administrative officer)
Affiliation: Indian Health Service (Headquarters West), 300 San Mateo, NE, Suite 500, Albuquerque, NM 87102 (505) 766-6215.

TRUJILLO, JIM (Taos Pueblo)
(Indian arts & gallery co-owner)
Affiliation: Co-owner, Bear Paw Indian Arts & Gallery, 326 San Felipe, NW, Historic Old Town, Albuquerque, NM 87104 (505) 843-9337.

TRUJILLO, JOSEPH G. (Taos Pueblo)
(IHS-property management chief)
Affiliation: Indian Health Service (Headquarters West), 2401 12th St., NW, Albuquerque, NM 87102 (505) 766-5557.

TRUJILLO, MARIAN (Taos-Acoma Pueblo)
(Indian arts & gallery co-owner)
Affiliation: Bear Paw Indian Arts & Gallery, 326 San Felipe, NW, Historic Old Town, Albuquerque, NM 87104 (505) 843-9337.

TRUJILLO, MARY A. (Acoma Pueblo)
(Indian arts & gallery co-owner)
Affiliation: Co-owner, Bear Paw Indian Arts & Gallery, 326 San Felipe, NW, Historic Old Town, Albuquerque, NM 87104 (505) 843-9337.

TRUJILLO, MICHAEL H. (Laguna Pueblo)
(physician; associate professor)
Education: University of New Mexico Medical School, MD. *Address & Affiliation*: Associate Professor of Family & Community Medicine, University of New Mexico, School of Medicine, Albuquerque, NM. *Past professional post*: Former Director (1994-2002) & Assistant Surgeon General, Indian Health Service (IHS), U.S. Dept. of Health & Human Services, Rockville, MD. *Awards, honors*: The first American Indian to graduate Mr. Trujillo had a 30-year career in IHS, and he was the first full-blooded American Indian to serve as Director.

TRUJILLO, OVTAVIANA (Yaqui)
(professor of Indigenous studies)
Education: Northern Arizona University, PhD. *Affiliation & Address*: Professor, Applied Indigenous Studies Department, SBS West Bldg. 70, Rm. 212, P.O. Box 15020, Flagstaff, AZ 86011 (928) 523-6140; E-mail: octaviana.trujillo@nau.edu. She is founding chair and professor of the department of Applied Indigenous Studies at Northern Arizona University (NAU) and teaches courses on Tribal Nation Building. A primary focus of her work as a former tribal leader has been developing programs that take advantage of her academic and professional experience. Dr. Trujillo is the Co-PI (outreach) on the National Cancer Institute, U54- funded Partnership for Native American Cancer Prevention. The major goal of this project is to alleviate the unequal burden of cancer among Native Americans of the Southwest through research, training and outreach programs that are collaborative with the communities they serve. Her recent publication, "A Perspective on Diabetes from Indigenous Views" in *Fourth World Journal* was collaboration between university scholars and traditional-knowledge scholars. Dr. Trujillo is also the NAU research, education and training co-director of the Center for American Indian Resilience (CAIR). CAIR NIH R25 is a partnership with University of Arizona, College of Public Health, to explore resiliency to reduce American Indian health disparities. Throughout her professional career she has been involved with education, health, social services, and cultural enhancement programs in conjunction with the communities themselves, the tribal government entities, & higher education institutions. Professor Trujillo, the National Council for Science and Environment and American Indian Higher Education Consortium have partnered to develop and augment Tribal Colleges and Universities (TCU) faculty knowledge and skills in climate research, education, and community engagement through increased awareness of climate change learning materials and enhance student learning in TCU science courses and academic programs. Additionally, she is the Co-PI on her recent National Science Foundation TUES grant "Southwest Native Lands Integrated Curriculum." The aims of the project is to increase the success rate of Native American students majoring in the social sciences in applications of math and science concepts to understand and identify solutions to authentic problems. Dr. Trujillo has extended this professional focus into the international arena; with the National Institutes of Health funded P37 "Native Americans Exploring Global Health Disparities" project. NAU proposes to provide short-term global research training opportunities for qualified Native American students and others who are underrepresented in the life, social, and health sciences. The results of this project will not only increase Native American participation in health sciences, but provide these students with a broad global perspective on potential solutions to health disparities that they can apply to their future careers in the United States. Professor Trujillo serves on local, national and international governing boards, including the Environmental Protection Agency (EPA), Governmental Advisory Committee (GAC). The committee helps shape U.S. policies that improve the environment and health conditions of the United States, Canada, and Mexico.

TRUJILLO, PATRICK S. (Cochiti Pueblo) 1954-
(president & executive director)
Born March 5, 1954, Albuquerque, N.M. *Education*: University of New Mexico Continuing Education (1 year), Certificate of Completion (288 hours of Alcohol & Drug Abuse Studies Institute). *Address*: P.O. Box 1500, Pena Blanca, NM 87041 (505) 766-8418 (office) 465-9992 (home). *Affiliation & Address*: Board President & Eexutive Director, Native American Training Institute of New mexico, 1208 San Pedro NE #126, Albuquerque, NM 87110 (505) 702-6524. *Past professional posts*: Substance Abuse Counselor, Five Sandoval Indian Pueblos, Inc., Bernalillo, NM, 1985-88; substance abuse counselor, Southwestern Indian Polytechnic Institute, Albuquerque, NM, 1989-92; counselor, All Indian Pueblo Council, Inc., Albuquerque, NM, 1992-2010. *Memberships*: New Mexico Alcoholism & Drug Abuse Counselors Association. *Awards, honors*: Outstanding Academic Achievement Award in the Drug/Alcohol Studies, University of New Mexico; Certified Alcoholism Counselor. *Interests*: "Enjoy working with youths in prevention & I like to implement seminars/training for communities, public service agencies. I have great interest in implementing cultural awareness, a holistic spiritual approach to wellness for both youths and adults. I am also a trainer for fetal alcohol syndrome prevention."

TRUJILLO, RAYMOND H. (Pueblo)
(tribal scholarship officer)
Affiliation: Zuni Scholarship Program, P.O. Box 339, Zuni, NM 87327 (505) 782-4481 Ext. 482/9.

TSABETSAYE, ROGER JOHN (*Eagle's Tail*) (Zuni) 1941-
  (artist, jeweler & businessman)
Born October 29, 1941, Zuni Pueblo, N.M. *Education*: Institute of American Indian Arts, 1962-63; School for American Craftsmen, Rochester Institute of Technology, 1963-65; University of Arizona, 1960-63. *Principal occupation*: Artist, jeweler & businessman. Resides in Albuquerque, NM. *Affiliation*: Owner-founder, Tsabetsaye Enterprises, Zuni, NM (Zuni jewelry--wholesale/retail), 1970-88; Wright's Indian Art, 1988-99; Santa Ana Casino, Santa Ana Pueblo, NM. Self-employed artist-designed & produced original pieces of jewelry in gold, silver, precious & semi-precious gems to create both traditional & contemporary style pieces. *Community activities*: Zuni Pueblo (head councilman, tribal treasurer); board of directors, New Mexico State Office of Indian Affairs. *Membership*: Zuni Craftsmen's Coop Association. *Awards, honors*: Numerous awards from various exhibitions and shows, 1968-.

TSATOKE, TONI LEE (Kiowa)
  (adjunct lecturer)
Education: Haskell Indian Nations University, BA; University of Oklahoma, MEd & PhD (Educational Leadership & Policy Studies). *Affiliation & Address*: Adjunct Lecturer, Native American Language Program, Department of Anthropology, College of Arts & Sciences, The University of Oklahoma, 455 W. Lindsey, DAHT 505, Norman, OK 73019 (405) 325-3729. E-mail: tsatoke@ou.edu. *Research Interests*: Kiowa language & culture; traditional roles of American Indian women; the history and impact of cultural hegemony on American Indian educational experiences.

TSINAJINNIE, VERONICA (*Tachiinii*) (Navajo-Dine')
  (editor, author, educator)
Born in Ganado & Birdsprings, Ariz. *Education*: Dine College, Tsaile, AZ, AA (Elementary Education); University of New Mexico, BA (Psychology). *Address & Affiliation*: Editor, author, Salina Bookshelf, Inc., 3120 N. Caden Ct. #4, Flagstaff, AZ 86004. *Published work*: Johanaa'ei: Bringer of Dawn (Salina Bookshelf, 2007).

TSINHNAHJINNIE, HULLEAH J. (Seminole/Muscogee/Dine')
  (associate professor)
Education: Institute of American Indian Arts, Santa Fe, NM; California College of Arts & Crafts, Oakland, CA (B.F.A., Painting); Studio Arts, UC Irvine (M.F.A., 2002). *Affiliation & Address*: Associate Professor, Dept. of Native American Studies (2004-present), UC Davis, 2411 Hart Hall, Davis, CA 95616 (530) 752-0568. E-mail: tsinhnahjinnie@ucdavis.edu. *Other professional post*: Director, C.N. Gorman Museum, 1316 Hart Hall, UC Davis (530) 752-6567. *Awards, honors*: Principle Investigator for the April 2009 "Visual Sovereignty: International Indigenous Photographers Conference & Exhibition," hosted by the C.N. Gorman Museum. *Published works*: Our People, Our Land, Our Images: International Indigenous Photography, Ed. with V. Passalacqua (Heyday Books, 2007); Visual Currencies: Native American Photography (National Museums of Scotland, Edinburgh, 2009; numerous articles & exhibitions.

TSINNIE, ORVILLE Z. (Navajo-Dine')
  (artison, shop owner)
Affiliation: Owner Tsinnie's Gallery, Box 537 · Shiprock, NM 87410 (505) 368-5936. *Products*: Navajo-made jewelry; buckles, squash blossoms, bracelets, earrings, rings, conchos.

TSO, BENNY (Paiute)
  (tribal chairperson)
Affiliation & Address: Chairperson, Las Vegas Paiute Tribe, 1 Paiute Dr., Las Vegas, NV 89106 (702) 386-3926.

TSO, EMMETT (Navajo-Dine')
  (school chairperson)
Affiliation: Greyhills High School, P.O. Box 160, Tuba City, AZ 86045 (602) 283-6271.

TSO, MATTHEW (Navajo-Dine')
  (legislative analyst)
Affiliation & Address: Legislative Analyst, Department of Dine' Education, P.O. Box 670, Window Rock, AZ 86515 (928) 871-7469.

TSO, RON (Navajo-Dine')
  (health director)
Affiliation: Chinle Comprehensive Health Care Facility, P.O. Drawer PH, Chinle, AZ 86503 (602) 674-5282.

TSO, ROSELYN (Navajo-Dine')
  (IHS acting director, Office of Direct Services & Contracting Tribes)
Education: Marylhurst University, BA (Arts), MA (Organizational management). *Affiliation & Address*: Acting Director, Office of Direct Services & Contracting Tribes (ODSCT), Indian Health Service (IHS), DHH, 801 Thompson Ave.,
Rockville, MD 20852 (301) 443-1083. Ms. Tso is responsible for policy development & technical assistance concerning Title I Indian Self-Determination contracting; management of the approximately $400 million contract support cost program. *Past professional posts*: She began her career with the IHS in 1984, previously serving in various roles in the Portland, (OR) Area. In 2005, Roselyn assumed the role of Director, Office of Tribal & Service Unit Operations for the Portland Area. She was responsible for the implementation of the Indian Self-Determination and Education Act and worked directly with the Tribes. Ms. Tso also worked with the three urban programs in the Portland Area that provide services ranging from community health to comprehensive primary health care services. She previously served in the role of Acting Director for ODSCT in 2010.

TSO, SAMUEL (Navajo-Dine')
  (school chairperson)
Affiliation: Lukachukai Boarding School, Navajo Route 12, Lukachukai, AZ 86507 (520) 787-2301; Many Farms High School, P.O. Box 307, Many Farms, AZ 86532 (520) 781-6226.

TSO, WILLIAM (Navajo)
  (school chairperson)
Affiliation: Navajo Preparatory School, 1200 West Apache, Farmington, NM 87401 (505) 326-6571.

TSOSIE, CALVIN (Navajo-Dine")
  (school chairperson)
Affiliation: Chinle Boarding School, P.O. Box 70, Many Farms, AZ 86538 (520) 781-6221.

TSOSIE, DEBRA (Navajo-Dine')
  (director)
Affiliation: Winds of Change, P.O. Box 1213, Middlebury, CT 06762.

TSOSIE, DENNISON (Navajo-Dine')
  (artist, business owner)
Address: Owner, The Navajo Silversmith, P.O. Box 394, Alpine, AZ 85920 (928) 339-1948. Website: www.navajosilversmith.com. E-mail: silversmith@3pmc.com. Mr. Tsosie features custom jewelry and other fine artwork

TSOSIE, KENNETH (Navajo-Dine')
  (executive director)
Affiliation: National Indian Youth Council, 318 Elm St., S.E., Albuquerque, NM 87102 (505) 247-2251.

TSOSIE, LARRY, SR. (Navajo-Dine')
  (school principal)
Affiliation: Shiprock Reservation Dormitory, Shiprock, NM 87420 (505) 368-5070.

TSOSIE, LESTER (Navajo-Dine')
  (BIA agency supt.)
Affiliation & Address: Supt., Bureau of Indian Affairs, Eastern Navajo Agency,, P.O. Box 328, Crownpoint, NM 87313 (505) 786-6032 E-mail: lester.tsosie@bia.gov

TSOSIE, LORETTA A.W. (*Ke'hanibaa*) (Navajo-Dine') 1943-
  (administration)
Born March 13, 1943, Morenci, Ariz. *Education*: University of New Mexico, BS, 1971, MA (Educational Administration), 1976. *Address*: P.O. Box 112, Window Rock, AZ 86515 (520) 831-3957. *Affiliations*: Instructor, Navajo Community College, Tsaile, AZ, 1972-86; special liaison officer, Alamo-Canoncito Liaison Office, Bureau of Indian Affairs, Canoncito, NM, 1987-. *Other professional post*: Chairperson, Career Education Division, Navajo Community College.

TSOSIE, MICHAEL (Navajo-Dine')
  (executive director)
Affiliation: Director, Colorado River Indian Tribes Museum, Rt. 1, Box 23-B, Parker, AZ 85344 (928) 669-1339.

TSOSIE, MONIQUE (Navajo-Dine')
  (program coordinator)
Affiliation & Address: Coordinator, Native American Research & Training Center, University of Arizona, 1642 E. Helen St., Tucson, AZ 85719 (520) 621-5075. E-mail: moniquet@email.arizona.edu.

TSOSIE, NATHANIA (Navajo-Dine')
  (associate director of Indian institute; health planner)
Education: University of New Mexico, BS (Anthropology), 2003, MA (Community & Regional Planning), 2011. *Affiliation & Address*: Associate Director & Health Planner, Istitute for Indigenous Knowledge & Development, MSC07 4255, 1 University of New Mexicom Albuquerque, NM 87131(505) 925-

4377. E-mail: nttoosie@unm.edu. Nathania Tsosie is one of the co-founders for the Institute for Indigenous Knowledge & Development (IIKD) at the University of New Mexico Health Sciences Center. Her master's thesis is titled "Native Artists Youth Suicide in an Indigenous Community" which she completed (with distinction) at the UNM School of Architecture & Planning. As an advocate for Indigenous Planning, Nathania has been active in community health assessment since 2005. She was the project manager responsible for organizing the first Community Health Assessment (CHA) Workshop series, which engaged representatives from off-reservation communities, tribes, Pueblos and Nations across New Mexico and Arizona in developing unique and innovative planning strategies for CHA.

TSOSIE, NELSON (Navajo-Dine') 1961-
(stone & bronze sculptor, painter)
Born July 1, 1961, Shiprock, N.M. *Education*: Yavapai Community College (Prescott, AZ), AA, 1981; University of Arizona, Studio Arts major, 1981-82. *Principal occupation*: Stone & bronze sculptor, painter. Resides in Santa Fe, NM. "Nelson's work remains steep in tradition, with a historical accuracy that can only come from a comprehensive love of one's own culture, and the people that represent it with such pride and dignity. He places great emphasis on his desire to portray the positive aspects of Navajo life rather than the harsher, more negative aspects that are so often over-exploited." *Professional post*: Co-owner, Free A.I.R. Fine Art, a Santa Fe-based promotional private art business that aids other artists as well. *Memberships*: Indian Arts & Crafts Association; Gallup Inter-Tribal Ceremonial Association (contributing member). *Awards, honors*: Numerous shows & awards, including: Santa Fe Indian Market, Inter-Tribal Indian Ceremonial (Church Rock, NM); Lovena Ohl Gallery, Scottsdale, AZ; Navajo Nation Fair Fine Art Show, Red Earth Art Show, Indian Arts & Crafts Association Show & Sale. *Interests*: "Travels frequently, participating in community activities, and works with his wife to promote the talents of other promising artists as well." Biographical source: Enduring Traditions, by Jerry & Lois Jacka.

TSOSIE, RAYMOND (Navajo-Dine')
(employment supervisor)
Affiliation: BHP Minerals, P.O. Box 155, Fruitland, NM 87416.

TSOSIE, REBECCA ANITA (Yaqui)
(professor of law)
Education: University of California, Los Angeles, BA, 1987; JD, 1990. *Address & Affiliation*: Regents' Professor of Law; Special Advisor to the Provost for Diversity & Inclusion (2015-present), Indigenous Peoples Law & Policy (IPLP) Tribal Justice Clinic, Law 221, James E. Roger College of Law, Box 210176, Tucson, AZ 85721 (520) 621-0121. E-mail: rebeccatsosie@email.arizona.edu. *Past professional posts*: Executive Director, Indian Legal Program, Sandra Day O'Connor College of Law, Arizona State University, Tempe, AZ; Professor of Law (1993-2015); Willard H. Pedrick Distinguished Research Scholar (2005-2015), Faculty Fellow, Center for Law & Global Affairs, ASU, Tempe, AZ; & Affiliate Professor, American Indian Studies Program, ASU, Tempe, AZ; Supreme Court Justice for the Fort McDowell Yavapai Nation. *Awards, honors*: She was awarded a Woodrow Wilson Fellowship; 2002 Spirit of Excellence Award, American Bar Association; 2006 recipient of the "Judge Learned Hand Award" for Public Service. *Published works*: Co-authored with Carole Goldberg, Kevin Washburn & Elizabeth Rodke Washburn, a federal Indian law casebook, American Indian Law: Native Nations & Federal System.

TSOSIE, WALLACE (Navajo-Dine')
(BIA agency chairperson)
Affiliation: Fort Defiance Agency, BIA, P.O. Box 110, Fort Defiance, NM 86504 (602) 729-5041.

TUCCIARONE, ALEXANDER J. (A:rek) (Blackfoot)
(chief plumbing inspector)
Address: P.O. Box 662, Old Bridge, NJ 08857 (908) 591-8335. *Affiliations*: Chair, New Jersey Commission on Plumbing - Sub Code Committee; certified instructor in plumbing & pipefitting. *Community activities*: Inter-tribal advisor on Native Affairs. *Awards, honors*: 1996 New Jersey Plumbing Inspector of the Year. *Membership*: New Jersey State Plumbing Inspectors Assn (president).

TUCKER, DANIEL J. (Kumeyaay Diegueno)
(tribl advisor & Indian association chair)
Address: Resides on the Sycuan Reservation, El Cajon, CA. *Affiliations*: Chairperson, California Nations Indian Gaming Association, Sacramento, CA (vice chairperson & chairperson, 1992-present); Vice Chairperson, National Indian Gaming Association. *Other professional posts*: Director, Borrego Springs Bank, National Association, 2000-present; Tribal Advisor, Blue Stone Stategy Group, Irvine, CA. *Past professional posts*: Chairperson, Sycuan Band of Kumeyaay Diegueno, El Cajon, CA. Daniel is a renowned & respected Native American leader as well as one of the Nation's leading advocates for tribal gaming rights. He currently serves as Chairman of the California Nations Indian Gaming Association (CNIGA), and as Vice Chairman of the National

Indian Gaming Association (NIGA). Tucker's dedication has been the driving force in making Native American gaming an essential component of local economies. Tucker led more than 70 California tribes in a quest to protect tribal gaming rights and pioneered the first successful tribal gaming legislation in California history to win bi-partisan support. The National Indian Gaming Association (NIGA) has recognized him with the John Keefer Award for his tireless dedication to protecting tribal gaming. Tucker also played a vital role in the successful passage of Proposition 1A, which created an amendment to the California Constitution, ensuring Indian self-reliance in the state. He has worked with the White House & members of congress to achieve collaboration for tribal government gaming.

TUCKER, LIBBY (Cherokee)
(professor of English)
Born Nov. 29, 1948, Bethesda, Md. *Education*: Indiana University, PhD. *Address*: 500 Magnolia Dr., Vestal, NY 13850. *Affiliation*: Professor, Dept. of English, Binghamton University, Binghamton, NY 13902, 1977-present (607) 777-6402. E-mail: ltucker@binghamton.edu. *Other professional post*: Editorial Board of "Voices: Journal of the New York Folklore Society." *Military service*: Peace Corps, 1972-74. *Community activities*: Vestal High School Parent-Teacher Association; speaker at community events related to folklore; organizer of poetry readings. *Memberships*: Wordcraft Circle of native Writers & Storytellers; American Folklore Society; New York Folklore Society; Hoosier Folklore Society; International Society for Folk Narrative Research. *Interests*: Children's & college students' folklore; ghost stories; Native American literature; poetry & memoir. *Published works*: "Campus Legends" (Greenwood Press, 2005); poetry & memoir pieces in Long Shot & Paterson Literary Review; folklore articles in Children's Folklore Review, International Folklore Review, Western Folklore, others.

TUELL, LORETTA A. (Nez Perce) 1967-
(attorney; company president)
Education: Washington State University, BA, 1988; Univesity of California, Los Angeles, College of Law, JD, 1992; Senior Executive Program, JFK School of Government, Harvard University, 1999. *Address & Affiliation*: President (2001-present), iNative Consuting, LLC, Washington, DC area. Website: www.inativeconsulting.com. Email: info@inativeconsulting.com. Loetta repesents a nation-wide base of Native American governments. pursuing legal strategies to advance the core Indian law principles of self-determination and self-governance, and advocating Tribal interests before the U.S. Congress, the White House and various federal agencies. *Practice areas*: Tribal government; legislative analysis/ reporting; legislative advocacy/lobbying; land into trust; gaming law; environmental law; administrative procedures; acknowledgement & recognition. *Past professional posts*: Counsel, U.S. Senate Committee on Indian Affairs, Senator Daniel Inouye (D-Hawaii, 1993-98; Special Assistant & Counselor to the Assistant Secretary-Indian Affairs, U.S. Dept. of the Interior (appointed by President Clinton, 1998-99) acting director, Office of Tribal Services, BIA-DOI, 6/99-12/99; director, Office of American Indian Trust, U.S. Dept. of the Interior (appointed by President Clinton, 2000-2001); partner, Monteau & Peebles, Washington, DC; In 2011-12, rejoined the Senate Committee on Indian Affairs in the 112th Congress to work for then Chair, Senatoor Daniel K. Akaka as the Majority Staff Director & Chief Counsel. *Memberships*: American Bar Association; Federal Bar Association; National Native American Bar Association; (UNITY) United National Indian Tribal Youth (Board of Trustees, 1998-present; Chair, 2002-present). *Awards, honor*: Recognized in 2009 as one of five women – and the first American Indian woman in history – to receive the Margaret Brent Women Lawyers of Achievement Award from the American Bar Asociation.

TUGATUCK, WASSILLE (Eskimo)
(Alaskan village president)
Affiliation: Manokotak Village, P.O. Box 169, Manokotak, AK 99628 (907) 289-2067.

TULEE, MIKE (*Koosheyi*) (Yakama) 1961-
(Indian education program manager)
Born April 11, 1961, Grand Coulee Dam, Wash. *Education*: University of Washington, BA, 1991, MEd, 1993. *Address & Affiliation*: Indian education program manager, Seattle School District, 1330 N. 90th St., Seattle, WA 98103 (206) 298-7945. E-mail: mtulee@is.ssd.k12.wa.us. *Military service*: U.S. Air Force, 1983-87. *Membership*: Yakama Nation.

TULIK, PAUL (Eskimo)
(Alaskan village president)
Affiliation: Nightmute Traditional Council, P.O. Box 90021, Nightmute, AK 99690 (907) 647-6215.

TULLIS, EDDIE (Poarch Band Creek) 1938-
(tribal councilman)
Education: Faulkner State College, Bay Minette, AL, 1975. *Affiliation*: Tribal councilman (chairperson (1978-2005) Poarch Band of Creek Indians, 5811

Jack Springs Rd., Atmore, AL 36502 (251) 368-9136. Website: www. poarchcreek indians.org. He serves as Chief Executive of the Officer of Tribal Administration & oversees the grants and contracts funded through federal, state & local governments. Chairperson of the Board for Creek Indian Enterprises that is the economic development branch of the Tribe. *Other professional posts*: Area V.P., National Congress of American Indians; member, Indian Advisory Council, Trust for Public Lands; appointed to the Alabama State Incentive Grant Advisory Committee and the Alabama Archives & History Foundation Board; secretary, former V.P., United South & Eastern Tribes, 1990-present; former V.P., Americans for Indian Opportunities, 1986-present; advisory council member, Trail of Tears National Historic Trail, 1988-.

TULLIUS, TREVOR J. (Chickasaw)
(attorney)
Affiliation & Address: Squire Patton Boggs, 2550 M St., NW, Washington, DC 20037 (202) 457-5108. E-mail: trevor.tullius@squirepb.com
Trevor focuses his practice on prvate investment funds, public finance, and Native American affairs. He also advises tribal business enterprises and Alaska Native corporations in a wide range of Federal Indian law matters, including government contracting, tribal governance, drafting tribal ordinances, transactional, and regulatory matters. Memberships: American Bar Association, Native American Bar Association, Chickasaw Bar.

TULLY, JAMES
(distinguished professor of Indigenous Govenance & Philosophy)
Education: University of British Columbia, BA; University of Cambridge, PhD. *Affiliation & Address*: Distinguished Professor of Political Science, Law, Indigenous Governance & Philosophy; Founding Member, IGOV program), University of Victoria, Faculty of Human & Social Development, P.O. Box 1700 STN CSC, Victoria, BC V8W 2Y2 Canada (250) 721-6438. *Other professional post*: Consulting editor of the journals of political journals Political Theory & Gobal Constitutionalism; co-editor of the Clarendon Works of John Locke. *Past professional posts*: Professor of Philosophy & Political Science, McGill University, 1977-96; professor & chair, Department of Political Science, University of Victoria, 1996-2001; Jackman Distinguished Professor in Philosophical Studies, University of Toronto, 2001-03. *Awards, honors*: Killam Prize in the Humanities for outstanding contrubition to scholarship & Canadian public life; awarded the C.B. Macpherson Prize by the Canadian Political cience Association for best book in political theory written in English or French in Canada, 2008-10. *Published works*: Public Philosophy in a New Key (Cambridge University Press, 2008); numerous chapters & articles on political theory and Indigenous politics.

TUMAMAIT-STENSLIE, JULIE (Chumash)
(tribal chairperson; artist)
Affiliation & Address: Chairperson, Barbareno/Ventureno Band of Mission Indians (Ojai). *Other professional post*: Secretary, Native American Heritage Commission, Sacramento, CA. Commissioner Tumamait-Stenslie is the chairperson of the Barbareno /Ventureno Band of Mission Indians. Commissioner Tumamait-Stenslie is a respected elder, singer, storyteller, and Cultural Resource Consultant/Advisor. Commissioner Tumamait-Stenslie a member of the Board of Trustees for the Ojai Valley Historical Society and Museum, the Board of Trustees and California Indian Advisory Committee for the Santa Barbara Museum of Natural History, and the University of California at Santa Barbara's Committee on the "Repatriation" of Native American ceremonial artifacts. Commissioner Tumamait-Stenslie currently serves on the Ojai Valley Museum Board of Trustees as well as the Oakbrook Chumash Interpretative Center Board. Commissioner Tumamait-Stenslie has served as a consultant for Chumash Cultural Services since 1985. Commissioner Tumamait-Stenslie is an artist that uses native materials to create her jewelry, musical instruments, and basketry. Commissioner Tumamait-Stenslie continues to practice and teach her native language. *Governor Arnold Schwarzenegger appointed Commissioner Tumamait-Stenslie to the Native American Heritage Commission on November 14, 2007.*

TURMELL, MARY ELLEN
(trustee emeritus; board vice chairperson)
Education: University of Montana, BA. *Affiliations*: American Indian Business Leaders (AIBL), Gallagher Business Bldg., Suite 366, Missoula, MT 59812 (406) 243-4879. E-mail: maurice.smith@aibl.org. *Other professional posts*: Trustee Emeritus, University of Montana Foundation; president, University of Montana Alumni Association; member of board, Flathead Lakers.

TURNER, DALE A. (Teme-Augama Anishnabai) 1960-
(professor of Native American studies)
Born December 22, 1960, Sept-Iles, Quebec. Education: PhD in Philosophy. *Address*: 135 Drum Heller, Sharon, VT 05175. *Address & Affiliation*: Associate Professor of Government & Native American Studies (1997-present), Dartmouth College, 37 N. Main St., The Sherman House, Hanover, NH 03755 (603) 646-0324. E-mail: dale.turner@dartmouth.edu. *Past professional post*: Professor, McGill University, 1992-97. *Interests*: The importance of asserting

and protecting tribal sovereignty in Indian Country. He teaches courses in government, indigenous philosophy & contemporary Native American issues. *Military service*: Canadian Navy, 1979-85. *Memberships*: American Philosophical Association; American Political Science Association; Canadian Philosophical Association.

TURNER, DOYLE I. (Ojibwe)
(tribal chairperson)
Affiliation: White Earth Reservation Business Committee, P.O. Box 418, White Earth, MN 56591 (218) 983-3285.

TURNER, ELIZABETH ROBERTS 1957-
(gallery owner)
Born September 1, 1957, Newark, OH. *Education*: Ohio Wesleyan University, 1975-76; Denison University, BA, 1980. *Principal occupation*: Art gallery owner. Resides in Vermont (802) 645-9975. *Affiliation*: Owner, Long Ago & Far Away (Native American art gallery), Manchester Center, VT, 1986-. *Memberships*: Indian Arts & Crafts Association; Southwestern Association of Indian Affairs; Manchester and the Mountains Chamber of Commerce.

TURNER, LOWELL KEVIN (*Skypainter*) (Choctaw) 1958-
(sign painter, designer)
Born October 1, 1958, St. Louis, Mo. Education: National Beauty Academy, St. Louis, MO (Diploma-Manicuring & Nail Sculpturing), 1992. *Address*: P.O. Box 166, Valles Mines, MO 63087-0166 (636) 337-4105. E-mail: skypntr58@aol.com. Website: www.profiles.yahoo.com/librame58. *Affiliation*: Self-employed, Lowell Turner & Son Sign Co., De Soto, MO, 1973-. *Other professional posts*: Native American Indian painter & jeweler; historian & archivist on family genealogy, public speaker; licensed manicurist. *Community activities*: Mastodon Museum, Imperial, MO; Jefferson Memorial History Museum, St. Louis, MO. *Memberships*: S.A.R. Sons of the American Revolution, Delaware Chapter), Jefferson Co., MO; St. Louis Hobby Association; Warbirds of the Royal Air Force, West Palm Beach, FL. *Awards, honors*: Honorable Mention Certificate, and 3 Master Division Award Plaques for (my) model making realism. *Published work*: Artwork in "Native American Art & Folklore, edited by David Campbell (Crescent Books, 1993) and in Contemporary Native American Artists," by Dawn Reno (Alliance Pubg, 1995).

TUTTLE, ROCHELLE (Round Valley Nomilacki/Wylacki)
(consultant; strategist)
Education: University of California, Irvine, BA (Publisc Health Policy), with a minor in Native American Studies), 2009; Loma Linda University, MPH, 2012. *Affiliation & Address*: Junior Strategist, Blue Stone Strategy Group, 19900 MacArthur Blvd., Suite 658, Irvine, CA 92612 (949) 476-8828. *Past professional post*: U.S. Dept. of Agriculture, Outreach, Employee Education & Training, and State Outreach & technical Assistance Division. *Professional interests*: The development of policies aimed at increasing economic development for tribal governments & enterprises.

TUZROYLUKE, SHIRLEY (Tlingit)
(tribal educator)
Address & Affiliation: Cook Inlet Tribal Council, Educational Services System Community Liaison, 3600 San Jeronimo Dr., Anchorage, AK 99508 (907) 793-3274. E-mail: stuzroyluke@citci.com. *Other professional post*: Board member, National Indian Education Association, Washington, DC.

TWIDDY-BUTLER, TERRI (Skokomish)
(tribal vice chairperson)
Affiliation & Address: Vice Chairperson, Skokomish Tribal Council, N. 80 Tribal Center Rd., Shelton, WA 98584 (206) 426-4232..

TWO BULLS, JAMES (Lower Brule Sioux)
(BIA superintendent)
Affiliation & Address: Supt., Bureau of Indian Affairs, 190 Oyate Circle, Lower Brule, SD 57548 (605) 473-5512. E-mail: james.twobulls@bia.gov

TWO BULLS, THERESA (Oglala Sioux)
(former tribal president)
Affiliation: President (2008-2010), Oglala Sioux Tribe, P.O. Box 2070, Pine Ridge, SD 57770 (605) 867-5821. *Past tribal posts*: Secretary, 1990-98; vice-president, 2000-2002. *Past professional post*: State Senator, South Dakota State Senate, State Capitol, Pierre, SD, 2003-07.

TWO EAGLES, ROBERT (Oglala Lakota)
(poet, author)
Address: 15150 S. Golden Rd. #1002, Golden, CO 80401 (303) 271-9233.

TWO EAGLES, VINCE (*Choka Opi*) (Yankton Sioux) 1953-
(entertainer, songwriter, recording artist)
Born January 26, 1953, Yankton, S.D. *Education*: Dakota State College (two years); Black Hills State College (one year). *Principal occupation*: Entertainer,

writer, recording artist. *Address*: P.O. Box 9, Wagner, SD 57380 (605) 384-3814. *Affiliation*: Trainer, Institute of Reality Therapy, Los Angeles, CA (ten years). *Other professional posts*: Entertainer, songwriter, recording artist, lecturer on traditional Dakota culture & the impact of alcoholism/drug abuse. Trainer - intervention teams, protective services programs (tribal); coordinator, Yankton Sioux Tribe Radio Project, KONA, Inc., Marty School, Marty, SD. *Community activities*: Marty Indian School's Advisory Committee on Alcohol & Drug Free Policy to the school's Board of Directors; member, Action Committee (designed to intervene in sexual, physical & emotional abuse of children); Yankton Sioux Tribe's representative on the "Lakota Camp Courage" Planning Board; Ad-Hoc Committee, Yankton Sioux Tribe's General Council. *Membership*: South Dakota Indian Counselors Association. *Awards, honors*: Currently an applicant for a Touring Arts and Artists Fellowship grant from SD Arts Council. Interests: "I have traveled throughout the U.S., Canada & Italy along with my backup musical group called, "People of the Earth," spreading a message of healing & support for local sobriety efforts & environmental issues and calling attention to the need for all races of people to come together in a spiritual manner toward reconciliation between the Native and non-Native communities as a means to fulfill the true teachings of our traditional elders & spiritual leaders." *Published songs*: "People of the Earth," 1990 & "In the Night," 1992 by Max Records; "In America," 1994 & 1996 by Sound of America Records.

TWO HAWKS, WEBSTER
(IHS-tribal health management)
Affiliation: Indian Health Service, Aberdeen Area Office, Federal Bldg., 115 4th Ave., S.E., Aberdeen, SD 57401 (605) 226-7591.

TWO RIVERS/BROEFFLE, E. DONALD
(performer)
Two-Rivers specializes in performance poetry relating to the urban experience of many Native Americans. He has appeared at the Center Theatre in Chicago as well as other area community theatres. He can be contacted at phone number 1-312-728-6756.

TWOGUNS, TIM (Cayuga)
(tribal representative)
Affiliation & Address: Alt. Federal Representative, Cayuga Indian Nation, P.O. Box 11, Versailles, NY 14168 (716) 337-4270.

TWOTEETH, LEONARD (Salish & Kootenai)
(tribal vice chairperson)
Affiliation & Address: Vice Chairperson, Confederated Salish & Kootenai Tribes, P.O. Box 278, Pablo, MT 59855 (406) 675-2700.

TYBO, ALICE (Te-Moak Western Shoshone)
(tribal chairperson)
Affiliation & Addess: Chairperson, Te-Moak Tribe of Western Shoshone Indians of Nevada (South Fork Band), P.O. Box B-13, Lee, NV 89829 (775) 744-4273.

TYLER, LEEJUAN (Shoshone-Bannock)
(former tribal vice chairperson)
Affiliation & Address: Vice Chairperson (2015-present), Shoshone-Bannock Tribes, P.O. Box 306, Fort Hall, ID 83203 (208) 478-3805. E-mail: ltyler@sbtribes.com

U

ULLRICH, JAN F.
(linguistic director)
Education: University of Ostrava, MS (Education & Linguistics). *Affiliation & Address*: Linguistic Director & Founding member of the Board, Lakota Language Consortium, 2620 N. Walnut St., Suite 825, Bloomington, IN 47404 (888) 525-6828. E-mail: jfu@lakhota.org. He is a fluent speaker of Lakota & specializes in Siouan linguistics, language pedagogy, & language revitalization. *Past professional posts*: Project Associate, Lakota & Dakota Language Documentation Project, Dept. of Linguistics, University of Colorado, Boulder, CO, 1998-2001; English instructor of English as a second language, language teaching methodology instructor, research assistant, and exhibit curator at various academic institutions. Mr. Ullrich has been undertaking linguistic fieldwork on the Indian reservations of South Dakota since 1992. He has amassed one of the largest collections of Lakota texts in the world and has published numerous books & articles on Lakota language & mythology.

UNDERWOOD, GINNY (Comanche/Kiowa)
(communications director)
Affiliation & Address: Communications Director, Indian Law Resource Center, 602 N. Ewing St., Helena, MT 59601 (406) 449-2006.

UNGARO, LOUIE (Muckleshoot)
(tribal councilperson)
Affiliation & Address: Councilperson, Muckleshoot Indian Tribe, 39015 172nd St., SE, Auburn, WA 98002 (253) 939-3311. *Past tribal post*: Vice Chairperson.

UTSEY, BRIAN (Pima-Maricopa)
(tribal attorney)
Education: University of Tulsa College of Law, JD, 2005, LL.M., 2006. *Affiliation & Address*: Staff attorney, Salt River Pima-Maricopa Indian Community Legal Services, 10005 E. Osborn Rd., Sacaton, AZ 85258 (480) 362-7400.

V

VAINIO, ARNE (Mille Lacs Ojibwe) 1958-
(physician)
Education: University of Minnesota Medical School, MD, 1994. *Affiliation & Address*: Family Medicine, Min-No-Aya-Win Human Services Clinic, Fond du Lac Ojibwe Reservation, 927 Trettel Lane, Cloquet, MI 55720 (218) 879-1227. *Hospital Affiliations*: St. Lukes Hospital of Duluth; Community Memorial Hospital. *Columnist*: News From Indian Country. *Video produced*: Documentary, "Walking Into the Unknown,"

VALANDRA, EDWARD CHARLES (Sicangu Lakota)
(associate professor, dept. chair)
Born & raised on the Rosebud Reservation in Rosebud, S.D. *Education*: Minnesota State University, BA; University of Colorado, MA (Political Science); State University of New York, Buffalo, PhD (American Studies). *Affiliation*: Associate professor & Chair, Dept. of Native Studies, East Hall Rm. 311, The University of South Dakota, 414 E. Clark St., Vermillion, SD 57069 (605) 677-7253. E-mail: edward.valandra@usd.edu. Dr. Valandra's current research interests focus on the national revitalization of the Oceti Sakowin Oyate (People of Seven Fires). *Past professional posts*: He has taught at the University of California, Davis & Metropolitan State University in St. Paul, MN. *Membership*: Native Research & Advocacy Collaborative. *Published works*: Not Without Our Consent: Lakota Resistance to Termination, 1950-1959 (University of Illinois Press, 2006); currently working on a follow-up book, entitled, "The 1964 Plebiscite: A Nation Is Coming."

VALBUENA, LYNN (*Nay*) San Manuel Band of Serrano Mission Indians)
(tribal chairperson)
Affiliation & Address: Chairperson, San Manuel Band of Serrano Mission Indians, 26569 Community Center Dr., Highland, CA 92346 (909) 864-8933. *Other professional posts*: Chairperson, Tribal Alliance of Sovereign Indian Nations (TASIN), 1995-present; executive secretary, National Indian Gaming Association, Washington, DC (1997-present); member, Board of Trustees, Autry National Center, Los Angeles, CA, 2007-present; member, Advisory Council to the Board of Directors for the American Indian Chamber of Commerce of California, 1999-present). *Past professional posts*: San Bernardino Indian Center, 1974-77; San Bernardino Police Department, 1977-93; San Manuel's tribal delegate to the National Congress of American Indians (NCAI), 1991-2007; executive secretary of the Board of Directors for the San Bernardino Valley Lighthouse for the Blind, 1994-2006; chairperson, Native American Advisory Committee, University of California at Riverside, 1994-2000; secretary & vice chairperson, California Nations Indian Gaming Association, 1996-2000; member, board of directors, Riverside-San Bernardino County Indian Health, Inc., 1998-2006. *Awards, honors*: March 2005, "Woman Making History," Lynn was honored by California Assemblyman, Joe Baca, Jr.; speaker at the UC Irvine Distinguished American Indian Lecture Series, 2010-2011.

VALDEZ-SINGLETON, HEATHER
(program director)
Affiliation & Address: The Tribal Law & Policy Institute, 8235 Santa Monica Blvd., Suite 211, West Hollywood, CA 90046 (323) 650-5467. E-mail: heather@tlpi.org.

VALENCIA, ROBERT (Pascua Yaqui)
(tribal chairperson)
Affiliation & Address: Chairperson, Pascua Yaqui Tribe, 7474 S. Camino De Oeste, Tucson, AZ 85746 (520) 883-5000. E-mail: robert.valencia@ pascuayaqui-nsn.gov

VALENCIA-WEBER, GLORIA (Mexican Indian)
(attorney; emerita professor of law)
Education: Oklahoma State University, BA, 1970, MA, 1974; Harvard University, JD, 1986. *Affiliation & Address*: Emerita Professor of Law, University of New Mexico School of Law, 1117 Stanford NE, MSC11 6070, Albuquerque, NM 87131 (505) 277-4101. E-mail: valenciaweber@law.unm.edu Gloria established the Indian Law Certificate Program at UNM School of Law in 1994. *Past professional post*: She established the country's first Indian Law cer

Valencia-Weber, a bilingual child of Mexican Indian heritage, enrolled in Harvard Law School after a career that included working for the American Civil Liberties Union, coordinating a diversified students program and teaching psychology at Oklahoma State University. Because Indian Law offerings were scarce at Harvard, she learned much about that area of law on her own. After two federal judicial clerkships (in district court and for the chief judge of the 10th Circuit), in 1990 Valencia-Weber established the country's first Indian Law certificate program at the University of Tulsa College of Law. Since Valencia-Weber arrived at UNM, the number of Indian Law course offerings has increased significantly and Indian Law is woven throughout the law-school curriculum. Her research focuses on the evolution of American Indian Law that includes the customary principles of tribal sovereigns. She has contributed the section on the Indian Child Welfare Act for a revision of the Felix Cohen Handbook of Federal Indian Law. In 2000, she studied the legal experience of the indigenous Maori culture in New Zealand. In 2002, she stepped down as director of the Indian Law Certificate Program. *Awards, honors:* Appointed in 2010 by President Obama to serve on the National Legal Services Corp. Board of Directors. *Membership:* Southwest Intertribal Court of Appeals.

VALENTINE, RAND (Ojibwe)
(professor of linguistics; director of native American studies)
Education: University of Texas, PhD (Linguistcs, Ojibwe dialect), 1994. *Affiliation & Address:* Professor of Linguistics (former director), American Indian Studies (1995-present), University of Wisconsin, 318 Ingraham, 1155 Observatory Dr., Madison, WI 53706 (608) 263-3448. E-mail: jrvalent@wisc.edu. *Other professional post:* Lecturer in Algonquian Linguistics, Lakehead University (Thunder Bay, Ontario), 1983-present. Rand specializes in Algonquian languages & linguistics, field methods & documentation of endangered languages, morphology.

VALENZUELA, DONALD D. (Yurok)
(tribal vice chairperson & administrator)
Affiliation & Address: Vice Chairperson, Resighini Rancheria Coast Indian Community, P.O. Box 529, Klamath, CA 95548 (707) 482-2431. E-mail: valenzuela.don@gmail.com

VALLIE, LAURA (Chippewa)
(craftsperson; company co-owner)
Affiliation & Address: La Ray Turquoise Co., P.O. Box 83, Cody, WY 82414 (307) 587-9564. *Products:* Navajo, Zuni, Chippewa, Hopi, and Santo Domingo silver & beadwork; Navajo rugs.

VALLIE, RAY (Chippewa)
(craftsperson; company co-owner)
Affiliation & Address: La Ray Turquoise Co., P.O. Box 83, Cody, WY 82414 (307) 587-9564. *Products:* Navajo, Zuni, Chippewa, Hopi, and Santo Domingo silver & beadwork; Navajo rugs.

VAN MECHELEN, NADINE (Yurok-Karok-Tolowa)
(craftswoman; gallery owner)
Address: Rt. 1, Box 270, Pendleton, OR 97801 (503) 276-2566. *Affiliation:* Owner, Nadine's Native Dolls & Wind Song Gallery, 7 SE Court, Pendleton, OR 97801 (541) 276-7993. *Product:* Native dolls dressed in authentic Indian clothing for collectors.

VAN ALST, THEODORE
(associate professor & co-chair of Native American studies)
Education: University of Connecticut, PhD (Comparative Literary & Cultural Studies). *Affiliation & Address:* Associate Professor & Co-Chair of Native American Studies at the University of Montana, 32 Campus Dr., Missoula, MT 59812 (406) 243-5831. E-mail: neyooxet.greymorning@mso.umt.edu
Past professional post: Assistant Dean & Director of the Native American Cultural Center at Yale University, 2010-14; Assistant Professor & Co-Chair of the Program in Comparative Literary and Cultural Studies at the University of Connecticut, 2006-08. He has worked as a consultant on multiple projects for the Disney Channel as well as on NPR's *All Things Considered*, and has recently appeared in multiple segments of the History Channel series *Mankind the Story of All of Us*. He has been interviewed by *The Washington Post*, Canadian Broadcast Corporation, *Native America Calling*, *Smithsonian Magazine*, and Al-Jazeera America Television on a variety of subjects, from Native representation & Tonto to Spaghetti Westerners, headdresses, & Twilight. *Published works:* "Lapin Noir: To Del Rio It Went" in *A Critical Companion to the Fiction of Stephen Graham Jones*, ed. Billy J. Stratton from the University of New Mexico Press as well as the chapters "Navajo Joe," & "The Savage Innocents," in *Seeing Red—Hollywood's Pixeled Skins: American Indians and Film* (Michigan State University Press, 2013). His current book-length project is *Spaghetti and Sauerkraut with a Side of Frybread*, and he edited volume *The Faster Redder Road: The Best UnAmerican Stories of Stephen Graham Jones* (University of New Mexico Press, 2015).

VAN HALL, DAWN
(co-cordinator of Native American studies program)
Affiliation & Address: Co-coordinator, Native American Studies Program, SUNY, Cortland, School of Arts & Sciences – Sociology-Anthropology Department, Old Main, Rm. 122, P.O. Box 2000, Cortland, NY 13045 (607) 753-5784; E-mail: ellie.mcdowell-loudan@cortland.edu

VAN NORMAN, SARA K.
(attorney)
Education: University of Minnesota, BA, 1999; University of Minnesota, Minneapolis, Law School, JD, 2004. *Affiliation & Address:* Staff Attorney (2007-present), Jacobson, Buffalo, Magnuson, Anderson & Hogen, LLP, 1295 Bandana Blvd., St. Paul, MN 55108 (651) 644-4710. E-mail: svannorman@jacobsonbuffalo.com. *Practice areas:* Civil Litigation, Construction Law, Indian Child Welfare Act, Environmental Law, Indian/Tribal Law. Sara regularly drafts & negotiates construction contracts for tribal casino developments and other Indian Country projects; serves as vice president of the Indian Child Welfare Law Center in Minneapolis and as a special member of the Minnesota American Indian Bar Assn. She has written various articles & book chapters on construction law & other topics, and regularly lectures on Indian law issues.

VAN NORMAN, THOMAS (Cheyenne River Sioux)
(attorney; state representative)
Affiliation: Tribal attorney, Cheyenne River Sioux Tribal Council, P.O. Box 590, Eagle Butte, SD 57625 (605) 964-4155. *Other professional post:* South Dakota State Representative.

VAN ZANT, BOB (Cherokee)
(board chairperson)
Affiliation: Chairperson, Board of Directors, American Indian Opportunities Industrialization Center (AIOIC), 1845 East Franklin Ave., Minneapolis, MN 55404 (612) 341-3358. E-mail: info@aioic.org

VANCE, AMANDA (Cahuilla)
(tribal chairperson)
Affiliation & Address: Augustine Band of Cahuilla Indians, P.O. Box 846, Coachella, CA 92236 (760) 398-4722

VANDERHOOP, TOBIAS (Wampanoag)
(former tribal chairperson)
Affiliation & Address: Former chairperson, Wampanoag Tribe of Gay Head, 20 Black Brook Rd., Aquinnah, MA 02535 (508) 645-9265.

VANDERPOOL, CAROLYN J. (Athapascan)
(Alaskan village president)
Affiliation: McGrath Native Village, P.O. Box 134, McGrath, AK 99627 (907) 524-3024.

VANDERWAGEN, W. CRAIG, M.D.
(IHS-director/clinical services)
Affiliation: Office of Health Programs, Div. of Clinical Services, Indian Health Service, Rm. 6A-55, 5600 Fishers Lane, Rockville, MD 20857 (301) 443-4644.

VANN, DONALD (*Q-A Na Da-Ga-Do-Ga*) (Cherokee) 1949-
(artist, publisher)
Born October 22, 1949, Adar County, Okla. *Address & Affiliation:* Partner, Native American Images (publishing co. that has worked with many renowned artists over the past 20 years), P.O. Box 746, Austin, TX 78767 (512) 472-3049. *Military service:* U.S. Army, 1969-71 (First Calvary in Vietnam, helicopter gunman). *Awards, honors:* His original watercolors have won scores of ribbons across the country. Includes a half-dozen First Place & Grand Awards from the Five Civilized Tribes Museum; his paintings, lithographs & prints have been featured at exhibits across the U.S. More than 50 limited edition releases of his works have sold out and now command collector values many times their original issue price. The Smithsonian Institution's Museum of the American Indian has presented him with their highest honor. He has also been proclaimed "on of the best known Indian artists working in this century" by the Cherokee Historical Society. His paintings have been exhibited at the Smithsonian. *Interests:* Backpacking, camping, canoeing, skiing, heli-skiing, running, and video-photography.

VANN, MICHAEL V. (Turtle Mountain Chippewa)
(radio station president)
Affiliation: KEYA - 88.5 FM, Turtle Mountain Chippewa Tribe, P.O. Box 190, Belcourt, ND 58316 (701) 477-5686.

VARESE, STEFANO 1939-

(professor of Native American studies)
Born July 27, 1939, Genova, Italy. *Education*: Catholic University (Lima, Peru) Diplomas (History & Anthropology), 1963 & 1964, BS (Ethnology), 1966, PhD (Anthropology), 1967. *Principal occupation*: Professor of Native American studies. *Affiliation & Address*: Professor, Dept. of Native American Studies (1990-present), UC Davis, 2419 Hart Hall, Davis, CA 95616 (530) 752-0357. E-mail: svarese@ucdavis.edu. *Address*: 1309 Monarch Lane, Davis, CA 95616 (916) 753-9508; 752-0357. *Other professional post*: Director, Indigenous Research Center of the Americas, affiliated center of the Dept. of Native American Studies, UC Davis, 1994-present). *Past professional posts*: Director, Unidad Regional de Oaxaca, Direccion General de Culturas Populares, Secretaria de Educacion Publica de Mexico, 1981-86; Native American Studies, U. of California, Davis (visiting professor, 1988-90). *Memberships*: American Anthropological Association; Latin American Studies Association; Society for Applied Anthropology; Cultural Survival, Cambridge, MA (Advisory Board). *Awards, honors*: Tinker Visiting Scholar, Stanford University, 1986-87; Ford Foundation Fellow at the Humanities Center, Stanford University, 1987-88; Co-Chair-elect of Society for Latin American Anthropology (American Anthropological Association), 1989-90. *Interests*: Indians of the Americas. *Published works*: Numerous books & monographs, chapters in edited books.

VARGO, KIMBERLY (Grand Traverse Ottawa/Chippewa)
(tribal vice chairperson)
Affiliation & Address: Vice Chairperson, Grand Traverse Band of Ottawa & Chippewa Indians, 1605 N West Bay Shore Dr., Peshawbestown, MI 49682 (231) 534-7103. E-mail: alvin.pedwaydon@gtbindians.com

VASKA, RUTH B. (Eskimo)
(AK village president)
Affiliation: Village of Aniak, P.O. Box 176, Aniak, AK 99557 (907) 675-4349.

VASQUEZ, REUBEN (Washoe)
(tribal chairperson)
Affiliation & Address: Washoe Tribe of the Dresslerville Colony, 1585 Watasheamu, Gardnerville, NV 89460 (775) 265-5645 E-mail: reuben.vasquez@washoetribe.us

VASQUEZ, VERONICA (Santa Clara Chumash)
(equal opportunity specialist)
Affiliations: Equal Opportunity Specialist (1986-present), U.S. Dept. of the Navy, Naval Air Warfare Center Weapons Division at Point Magu, CA; manager/committee member (15 years), Native American/Alaskan Native (NA/AN) Program; diversity chair, NAVAIR System Command Professional Recruitment Board; trains Federal managers on equal employment regulations & programs, analyzes activities & employment efforts, and identifies and implements initiatives to eradicate discrimination in the workforce. *Other professional post*: Board member, SAIGE (Society of American Indian Government Employees, Washington, DC. *Awards, honors*: Veronica designed & implemented the SAIGE Award & Scholarship Program, and served as SAIGE 2009 Conference Chair.

VAUGHN, CHRISTINA M.
(attorney; director of Indian law & gaming practice group)
Education: Northeastern State University, BBA (International Business), 2002; University of Tulsa College of Law, JD, 2006. Affiliation & Address: Director, Indian Law & Gaming Practice Group, Crowe & Dunlevy LLP, 500 Kennedy Bldg., 321 S. Boston Ave. • Tulsa, OK 74103 (918) 592-9800; E-mail: Christina.vaughn@crowedunlevy.com. Christina is a also director in the firm's Litigation & Trial & Energy, Environment & Natural Resources practice groups. She represents both plaintiffs & defendants in commercial litigation, business torts, oil and gas, environmental & Native American law, and currently serves as attorney general for one of the largest Indian tribes in Oklahoma. An experienced attorney, Vaughn's practice highlights include: Representing a major pipeline company with obtaining rights-of-way on Indian lands on a 600-mile interstate crude oil pipeline project; Obtaining dismissal of an appeal in the Interior Board of Indian Appeals lodged by the Cherokee Nation of Oklahoma—a landmark decision by the Bureau of Indian Affairs to take into trust 76 acres of land for the benefit of the previously landless tribe under its corporate charter; btaining a permanent injunctive relief to protect rights of an oil company in a producing oil lease from interference by an entity claiming rights in the lease; Representing a public entity in prisoner civil rights lawsuits and in discrimination suits brought by employees; Serving as coordinating counsel for a group of potentially responsible parts (PRPs) in a Superfund action in Oklahoma City, including an appeal before the Tenth Circuit Court of Appeals. An extensive portion of Vaughn's practice is dedicated to Native American law. She is admitted to practice in the following courts: United Keetoowah Band of Cherokee Indians in Oklahoma, Muscogee (Creek) Nation, Pawnee Nation of Oklahoma, Seminole Nation of Oklahoma and the United States Court of Indian Offenses. Vaughn is also licensed to practice in Oklahoma and several of its district courts. In addition to her substantial Native American practice, Vaughn's clients vary in industry and range from small

businesses to corporate and commercial clients. She represents plaintiffs and defendants in transactional matters such as commercial contracts, Uniform Commercial Code (UCC) issues, class actions, management agreements and joint partnership agreements. *Awards, honors*: Vaughn was honored with the Tulsa County Bar Association's Outstanding Young Lawyer Award and Outstanding Community Service Award. She's been named one of Oklahoma Super Lawyers' top 25 women & selected as a Rising Star in the areas of Native American Law, civil litigation defense & environmental litigation. Vaughn was also selected for inclusion in Chambers USA for Native American law and Tulsa Business & Legal News' Tulsa 40.

VELASQUEZ, KASEY (White Mountain Apache)
(tribal vice chairperson)
Education: BA (Criminal Justice; MA (Educational Psychology Counseling); MA (Educational Leadership). Affiliations & Address: Vice Chairperson (2014-present), White Mountain Apache Tribe, Box 700, Whiteriver, AZ 85941 (520) 338-4346.

VELASQUEZ, ROBERT (San Felipe Pueblo)
(former Pueblo governor)
Affiliation: San Felipe Pueblo Council, P.O. Box A4339, San Felipe Pueblo, NM 87001 (505) 867-3381.

VELE, KIMBERLY (Stockbridge-Munsee Mohican)
(tribal council president)
Affiliation: Stockbridge-Munsee Community of Wisconsin, P.O. Box 70, Bowler, WI 54416 (715) 793-4111. Website: www.mohican-nsn.gov.

VELE, SCOTT R. (Stockbridge-Munsee Mohican)
(executive director)
Affiiation & Address: Executive Director, Midwest Alliance of Sovereign Tribes (MAST), 1011 Main St., P.O. Box 265, Gresham, WI 54128 (715) 787-4494.

VELKY, RICHARD L. (Schaghticoke)
(tribal chief)
Affiliation & Address: Chief, Schaghticoke Tribeal Nation 101 Elizabeth St., 2nd Fl. • Derby, CT 06418 (203) 736-0782. E-mail: chiefvelkystn@aol.com

VENDIOLA, MICHELE "SHELLY" (Swinomish-Visayan)
(mediator, peacemaker consultant)
Address & Affiliation: Indian Dispute Resolution Services, Sacramento, CA 95814 (916) 447-4800. E-Mail: idrs@tomatoweb.net. *Other professional post*: Adjunct Professor, D-Q University. *Community activities*: Community Boards Peacemaker Program; Student Council of Intertribal Nations, SFSU; American Indian Education Conference Planning Committee. *Memberships*: California Association of Community Mediation Program; National Association of Dispute Resolution Programs; Indigenous Women's Network; Greenpeace.

VENT, GILBERT (Athapascan)
(village first chief)
Affiliation: Allakaket Community, Box 30, Allakaket, AK 99720 (907) 968-2241.

VENT, WARNER (Athapascan)
(village chief)
Affiliation: Huslia Village Council, P.O. Box 32, Huslia, AK 99746 (907) 829-2202.

VERDIN, CHARLES (Pointe au Chien)
(tribal chairperson)
Affiliation & Address: Chairperson, Pointe au Chien Indian Tribe, P.O. Box 416, Montegut, LA 70377 (985) 594-6250. E-mail: verdin1504@yahoo.com.

VERDUN, RANDY P. (Biloxi-Chitimacha)
(tribal chairperson)
Affiliation: Biloxi-Chitimacha Confederation of Muskogees, Bayou Lafourche Band, Box 856, Zachary, LA 70791 (225) 359-2476. E-mail: chiefrandyverdun @biloxi-chitimacha.com.

VERMILLION, EDWARD (Hopi)
(school principal)
Affiliation: Hopi Day School, P.O. Box 42, Kykotsmovi, AZ 86039 (520) 734-2468.

VERMILLION, LAUREL (Hunkpapa-Lakota)
(tribal college president)
Education: Sitting Bull College (Standing Rock Community College), AA; University of North Dakota, BA (Education), 1980, MA (Education Administration), 1992, EdD (Teaching & Learning, Higher Education), 2005. *Affiliation & Address*: President, Sitting Bull College, 1341 92nd St., Fort Yates, ND 58538 (701) 854-8014. E-mail: laurelv@sbci.edu. *Other professional post*: She is an active board member for numerous non-profit and community service

groups, including Bear Soldier Horizons, the Standing Rock Education Consortium, Standing Rock Education Leaders, the North Dakota Association of Tribal Colleges (NDATC), Recruiting American Indian Nurses (RAIN) program, Quality Education for Minorities (QEM), American Indian College Fund (A*CF), and the American Indian Higher Education Consortium (AIHEC). *Past professional posts*: Teacher, Fort Yates BIA Elementary School (14 years); principal, Marty Indian School; vice president of Academic Affairs, Sitting Bull College, 1995-99, VP of Operations, 1999-2006. *Community service*: Board member, for Bear Soldier Horizons, the Standing Rock Education Consortium, Standing Rock Education Leaders, the North Dakota Association of Tribal Colleges (NDATC), Recruiting American Indian Nurses (RAIN) Program, Quality Education for Minorities (QEM), American Indian College Fund, and the American Indian Higher Education Consortium (AIHEC).

VERMILLION, SARAH ECHOHAWK (Pawnee)
(acting V.P. - grantmaking & development)
Education: Metro State College, P.S. (Political Science & Native American Studies); Regis University, M.N.M. (Masters of Nonprofit Management). *Address & Affiliation*: Director of Development & Communications & Acting V.P. (2007-present), First Nations Development Institute, 703 3rd Ave., Suite B, Longmont, CO 80501 (303) 774-7836. E-mail: svermillion@firstnations.org. *Past professional post*: American Indian College Fund, 2002-2007. Sarah worked in program management, communications, foundation relations & individual giving. *Other professional post*: Consultant (2003-present) offering training seminars/services to Native American Indian & nonprofit organizations.

VERNON, IRENE (Mescalero-Apache, Yaqui & Mexicana)
(professor & chair of ethnic studies dept.)
Education: University of California, Berkeley, BA (Native American Studies), 1983 & PhD (Ethnic Studies), 1994; University of New Mexico, MA (History), 1992. *Affiliation & Address*: Professor & Chairperson, Ethnic Studies Dept., 356 Aylesworth Hall SE, CD 1790, Fort Collins, CO 80523 (970) 491-2418. E-mail: irene.vernon@colostate.edu. *Other professional posts*: Assistant Dean, College of Liberal Arts, Colorado State University; member, affiliated staff, Materials Review, CA7AE: Dr. Vernon is a Full Professor at Colorado State University, Chair of the Ethnic Studies Department and the Assistant to the Dean of the College of Liberal Arts. *Research*: Native American Studies, Ethnic Studies, Health Disparities, Native American Health, HIV/AID. *Teaching*: ETST 510 Ethnicity, Race, and Health Disparities in the U.S., ETST 438 Native American Literature, ETST 240 Native American Cultural Experience. She was appointed for the Fall 2009 term as the Associate Provost of Special Projects where she worked on a number of projects including developing family friendly resources and RAMS for Diversity activities. She is also committed to the discipline of Ethnic Studies and is an Executive Board member of the National Association for Ethnic Studies. Dr. Vernon has trained in Native American Studies & Ethnic Studies and throughout the years has engaged in ethnic studies program reviews & serves as a manuscript reviewer for a number of journals & presses. As well, Dr. Vernon has membership in several professional health societies such as the National Association of Ethnic Studies, Racial and Ethnic Populations Ad Hoc Committee, National Institute of Health, & Indigenous HIV/AIDS Research Training Council. She was appointed by Department of Health and Human Services Secretary Kathleen Sebelius to the Office of AIDS Research Advisory Council from 2010-2012 and has recently been appointed by CO Governor John Hickenlooper to the Colorado HIV/AIDS Care & Prevention Coalition. She has been actively involved in the field of health for eighteen years and is the author of *Killing Us Quietly: Native Americans and HIV/AIDS* (2001) & several other journal articles. Her research area is Native American health, particularly HIV/AIDS with other sub interests in health disparities. Dr. Vernon also provides capacity building assistance aimed at mobilizing communities around HIV/AIDS prevention in Native communities throughout the U.S. HIV/AIDS Prevention Project, Colorado State University, Fort Collins, CO. *Research Interests*: Native American Studies; Ethnic Studies; Health Disparities; Native American Health, HIV/AIDS. *Memberships*: National Assn of Ethnic Studies; National Minority AIDS Council (NMAC); Colorado Public Health Assn; National Institute of Health, Indigenous HIV/AIDS Research Training Council. *Awards, honors*: Recently nominated to the Office of AIDS Research Advisory Council. *Published works*: Killing Us Quietly: Native Americans & HIV/AIDS (University of Nebraska Press, 2001); Co-authored with Roe Bubar, Social Life & Issues, Contemporary Native American Issues Series, (Chelsea Publishing, 2006); numerous journal articles; book chapters; book/technical reports & video reviews.

VERNON, RACHEL (Yaqui/Mescalero Apache)
(program officer)
Education: Stanford University, BA; Colorado State University, MA pending (Ethnic Studies). *Affiliation & Address*: Program Officer, First Nations Development Institute, 2432 Main St., 2nd Fl., Longmont, CO 80501 (303) 774-7836. *Other professional posts*: Native American Cultural Center at CSU, CA7AE: HIV/AIDS Prevention Project; board member, Northside Aztlan Community Center, Fort Collins, CO. *Past professional post*: Development Associate, Asian Pacific Environmenal Network, Okaland, CA.

VERRET, C.A. KIRBY (Houma) 1947-
(coordinator of Indian education)
Born June 26, 1947, Duharge, La. *Education*: College. *Principal occupation*: Supportive coordinator of Indian education. *Affiliation & Address*: Coordinator, Terrebonne Parish School District, Indian Education Program, 301 Academy St., Houma, LA 70360 (504) 851-1553. *Affiliations*: Terrebonne Parish Indian Education, 1980-; pastor, Native American United Methodist Church. *Community activities*: Member & past chair of United Houma Nation Tribal Council; vice-chair, Salvation Army; member, Coastal Zone management Committee; member, Alcohol Drug Abuse Council Advisory Committee.

VERRI, VANESSA 1983-
(attorney; law firm associate)
Education: Colby College, BA (Anthropology), 2004; Arizona State University, Sandra Day O'Connor College of Law, JD, cum laude, 2008; ASU Sandra Day O'Connor College of Law, LL.M. Tribal Policy, Law, & Government, graduated with High Pro Bono Distinction, 2009. *Affiliation*: Associate, Rosette & Associates, PC, 565 W. Chandler Blvd. #212, Chandler, AZ 85225 (480) 889-8990. E-mail: vverri@rosettelaw.com. Ms. Verri has specialized training in Indian law as well as tribal law & government, water law, environmental law, natural resources & cultural resources law. She also participated in ASU law school's Indian Legal Clinic where she drafted federal legislation for tribes, appeared before tribal courts, and assisted in the submission of oral & written testimony before the Senate Committee on Indian Affairs regarding reform recommendations for the federal acknowledgement process. *Memberships*: American Bar Association; Native American Bar Association of Arizona; Ak-Chin Community Court, 2009. *Awards, honors*: Named Willard H. Pedrick Scholar in 2006 & 2007; recipient of numerous CALI Awards in 2007 & 2008 for excellence achieved by law students in their studies in the areas of Federal Indian Law, Cultural Resources Law, Sustainable Development, Human Rights, and Law & the Arts.

VICENTI, CAREY (Jicarilla Apache)
(professor of sociology)
Education: J.D. *Affiliation & Address*: Professor, Department of Sociology, Fort Lewis College, 1000 Rim Dr., Durango, CO 81301 (970) 247-7639. E-mail: vicenti_c@fortlewis.edu. Affiliated Faculty, Department of Native American & Indigenous Studies, Fort Lewis College.

VICENTI, TY (Jicarilla Apache)
(tribal president)
Affiliation & Address: President, Jicarilla Apache Tribe, P.O. Box 507, Dulce, NM 87528 (505) 759-3242.

VICKERS, WALTER (Nipmuc)
(tribal chief)
Affiliation & Address: Chief, Nipmuc Nation, 25 Main St., South Grafton, MA 01560 (774) 317-9138.

VIG, CHARLIE (Mdewakanton Sioux-Dakota)
(tribal chairperson)
Affiliation & Address: Chairperson, Shakopee Mdewakanton Sioux (Dakota) Community, 2330 Sioux Trail NW, Prior Lake, MN 55372 (952) 445-8900.

VIGIL, B. THOMAS (Jicarilla Apache/Jemez Pueblo)
(institute chairperson)
Education: New Mexico Highlands University, BS (Economics); University of Southern California, MA (Management). *Affiliation & Address*: Chairman of the Board, First Nations Development Institute, 2432 Main St., 2nd Fl., Longmont, CO 80501 (303) 774-7836. Maintains extensive experience in economic development issues and in the hotel & hospitality industry. *Past professional posts*: Chair, New Mexico Association of Commerce & Industry; Chair, Northern Arizona University School of Hotel & Restaurant Management. Founder & past president of the Apache Indian Development, Inc. He was appointed to the New Mexico Economic Development Committee; and was policy advisor to two Assistant Secretaries for Indian Affairs, U.S. Dept. of the Interior; associate commissioner for the Administration for Native Americans, U.S. Dept. of Health & Human Services. *Awards, honors*: An award "For Outstanding Success in Indian Business Community," presented by the U.S. Dept. of Commerce, Minority Business Development Agency.

VIGIL-MASTEN, DANIELLE (Hoopa)
(former tribal chairperson)
Affiliation & Address: Hoopa Valley Tribe, P.O. Box 1348, Hoopa, CA 95546 (530) 625-4211. E-mail: hupachair@hoopa-nsn.gov

VIGIL-MUNIZ, CLAUDIA J. (Jicarilla Apache)
(tribal president; education program counselor)
Affiliations & Address: President, Jicarilla Apache Tribal Council, P.O. Box 507, Dulce, NM 87528 (505) 759-3242; counselor, Jicarilla Apache Higher Education Program, P.O. Box 507, Dulce, NM 87528 (505) 759-3615.

VILLA, GLEN, SR. (Miwok)
(tribal vice chairperson)
Affiliation & Address: Vice Chairperson, Ione Band of Miwok Indians. P.O. Box 699, Plymouth, CA 95669 (209) 245-5800.

VINCENT, JOYCE W. (Cherokee/Blackfoot)
(assistant director of Native American studies)
Affiliation & Address: Assistant Director, Certificate Program in Native American Studies & Director, Dr. Josephine White Eagle Cultural Center, Chadbourne House OH/C, University of Massachusetts, Amherst, MA 01003 (413) 545-4932. E-mail: dvincent@acad.umass.edu.

VIOLA, HERMAN J. 1938-
(historian; curator emeritus)
Born February 24, 1938, Chicago, Ill. *Education*: Marquette University, BA, 1962, MA, 1964; Indiana University, PhD, 1970. *Principal occupation*: Historian-specialist on the history of the American West, specifically American Indian history; curator emeritus. *Address*: 7307 Pinewood St., Falls Church, VA 22046. *Affiliations*: Staff, National Archives, 1968-72; director, National Anthropological Archives, Smithsonian Institution, Washington, DC, 1972-87; curator emeritus, Smithsonian's National Museum of Natural History. *Other professional posts*: Founder and first editor of Prologue, The Journal of the National Archives, 1968-72; consultant to numerous scholarly and educational organizations, including, the Galef Institute, Randam House, The Library of the American West, and the Library of the American Indian. *Military service*: U.S. Navy, 1960-62. *Memberships*: Society of American Archivists; Western History Association; Organization of American Historians; Phi Beta Kappa. *Awards, honors*: 1984 Merit Award for "Distinguished Professional Achievement," from Marquette University; in 1987, he was one of three finalists for the position of Archivist of the U.S., which is a presidential appointment; in June 1988, he received an honorary doctor of letters degree from Wittenberg University. *Interests*: Research specialties are the American West and the American Indian. Biographical source: Who's Who in America. *Published works*: Thomas L. McKinney, Architect of America's Early Indian Policy, 1816-1830 (Swallow Press, 1972); The Indian Legacy of Charles Bird King (Smithsonian Institution Press & Doubleday, 1976); Diplomats in Buckskin (Smithsonian Institution Press, 1981); The National Archives of the U.S. (Harry N. Abrams, 1984); Magnificent Voyagers: The U.S. Exploring Expedition, 1838-1841 (Smithsonian Institution Press, 1986); Exploring the West (Smithsonian Exposition Books, 1987); After Columbus: The Smithsonian's Chronicle of the Indians of North America Since 1492 (Smithsonian Institution Press, 1990); editor, Seeds of Change, A Quincentennial Commemoration (Smithsonian Institution Press, 1991).

VISBEEK, SARAH STEPHENS
(attorney; Indian law practice)
Education: Seattle pacific University, BA, 2005; Seattle University School of Law, JD, 2011. *Affiliation & Address*: Associate, Williams, Kastner & Gibbs, PLLC, Two Union Square, 601 Union St. #4100, Seattle, WA 98101 (206) 233-2873. E-mail: svisbeek@williamskastner.com Ms. Visbeek has experience defending various Washington Tribes in employment and personal injury, and premises liability claims. *Awards, honors*: Cali Award For Excellence In Federal Indian Law (2010)

VIT, LINDA C. (Karuk/Cree) 1947-
(jewelry designer-traditional)
Born November 28, 1947, Yreka, Calif. *Principal occupation*: Jewelry designer-traditional. *Address*: 326 2nd St., Eureka, CA 95501 (707) 442-3042. E-mail: indianwest@yahoo.com. *Website*: www.indianwest.com. *Affiliation*: Generations by Linda Vit; Indian West Emporium, Eureka, CA, 1977-present. *Other professional post*: Marketing developer, Northern California Development Council. *Membership*: Indian Arts & Crafts Association (1980-present). *Interests*: Owner of two retail American Indian & special occasion clothing boutique; fictional writing.

VIVANCO, ISAIAH (Luiseno)
(tribal vice chairperson)
Affiliation & Address: Vice Chairperson, Soboba Band of Luiseno Indians, P.O. Box 487, San Jacinto, CA 92583 (951) 654-2765.

VIZENOR, ERMA J. (White Earth Ojibwe)
(former tribal chairperson; former Indian college president)
Affiliation & Address: Former Chairperson, Ojibwe of the White Earth Nation, P.O. Box 418, White Earth, MN 56591 (218) 983-3285. Former Presisent, Leech lake Tribal College, Cass Lake, MN.

VIZENOR, GERALD
(Native American studies instructor)
Affiliation & Address: Professor, Native American Studies Dept., University of California, Dwinelle Hall, #3415, Berkeley, CA 94720 (510) 642-6717.

VOIGHT, THOMAS F. 1947-
(publisher)
Born March 8, 1947, Milwaukee, Wisc. *Education*: University of Wisconsin, Milwaukee, BA, 1972, MA, 1976. *Principal occupation*: Publisher. *Address*: P.O. Box 889, New Castle, CO 81647 (303) 984-3685. *Affiliation*: President (owner/founder), Wintercount (art, prose & poetry of the American Indian), New Castle, CO, 1984-. *Other professional post*: Instructor, Colorado Mountain College, Glenwood Springs, CO. *Community activities*: Member, Chamber of Commerce, New Castle; member & volunteer, Public Radio Station, KDNK, Carbondale, CO; board member, Rural Fire District; sponsor Ute Legacy Juried Art Show. *Memberships*: National Indian Youth Council; American Indian Arts & Crafts Association; National Museum of the American Indian (charter member); Hollywood Stuntman Hall of Fame, Moab, UT (charter member); Appaloosa Horse Club. *Awards, honors*: Certificate of Excellence, Colorado Mountain College. *Interests*: "Extensive art collection of American Indian paintings & crafts. Have traveled to numerous Indian reservations & archaeological sites and have participated in the discovery and restoration of archaeological areas."

VOLBORTH, JUDITH ANN (*Mountain-Leaf*) (Blackfeet) 1956-
(writer, poet, speaker)
Born October 23, 1956, New York, N.Y. *Education*: Los Angeles Pierce College, AA, 1975; University of California, Los Angeles, BA, 1986. Principal occupation: Writer, poet. *Other professional posts*: Educator, public speaker. *Community activities*: Emergency medical technician (volunteer); Community Emergency Response Team (search & rescue, firefighting, triage); Disaster Service Worker (volunteer); volunteer working with homeless & mentally ill adults. *Memberships*: Native Writer's Circle of the Americas; Wordcraft: Circle of Native American Mentor & Apprentice Writers; Association for the Study of American Indian Literature. *Awards, honors*: Ina Coolbrith Memorial Prize for Poetry; Shirley Dorothy Robbins Creative Writing Award; The May Merrill Miller Award for Poetry; Academy of American Poets Award (honorable mention). *Biographical sources*: "Portrait of a Mentor," by Lee Francis, in Native American Renaissance, by Ken Lincoln; Indian Humor: Bicultural Play in Native America, by Ken Lincoln; Native American Lesbian & Gay Literature, by Will Roscoe. *Published work*: Thunder-Root: Traditional & Contemporary Native American Verse (American Indian Studies Center, UCLA, 1978).

VON FICKENSTEIN, MARIA 1942-
(curator of Inuit art)
Born March 10, 1942, in Germany. *Education*: BA in Art History; MA in Art Therapy. *Principal occupation*: Curator of Inuit art. *Address*: 521 Chapel St., Ottawa, ON K1N 8A1, Canada (819) 776-8433. E-mail: maria.vonfinckenstein @civilization.ca. *Affiliations*: Indian & Northern Affairs Canada, Ottawa, ON, 1980-93; curator of Inuit art, Canadian Museum of Civilization, Hull, ON, 1997-present. *Interests*: Gardening, yoga, reading, films, meditation. *Published works*: Celebrating Inuit Art, 1948-1970 (Key Porter Books, 1999); Nuvisavik: The Place Where We Weave (McGill/Queen's University Press, 2002).

W

WABAUNSEE, JOHN (Potawatomi)
(tribal chief justice)
Affiliation: Prairie Band Potawatomi Nation Appellate Court, 15498 K Rd., Mayetta, KS 66509 (785) 966-2242. E-mail: tribalcourt@pbpnation.org.

WACHSMUTH, GINA (Paiute)
(tribal council member)
Affiliation & Address: Council Member, Walker River Paiute Tribe, P.O. Box 220, Schurz, NV 89427 (775) 773-2306. *Past tribal post*: Vice Chairperson.

WADE, CLAUDIA ANN (Washoe)
(tribal chairperson)
Affiliation: Woodfords Washoe Community Council, Alpine Washoe Reservation, 2111 Carson River Rd., Markleeville, CA 96120.

WADE, KEN
(librarian)
Affiliation: UCLA American Indian Studies Center Library, 3220 Campbell Hall, Box 951548, Los Angeles, CA 90095-1548 (310) 206-7510.

WADENA, DARRELL (Chippewa)
(tribal president/chairperson)
Affiliation & Address: President, Minnesota Chippewa Tribal Executive Committee, P.O. Box 217C, Cass Lake, MN 56633 (218) 335-2252; chairperson, White Earth Reservation Business Committee, P.O. Box 418, White Earth, MN 56591 (218) 983-3285; Circle of Life Survival School, White Earth, MN.

WADZINSKI, KEVIN J. (Stockbridge/Munsee-Mohican) 1966-
(attorney)
Born May 3, 1966, Oconto Falls, Wisc. *Education*: University of Wisconsin, BA, 1988; University of Wisconsin Law School, JD, 1993. *Address & Affiliation*: Staff Attorney, Dorsey & Whitney LLP, Indian Law Dept., 1001 Pennsylvania Ave., NW, Suite 300 So., Washington, DC 20004 (202) 824-8863, 1993-. *Memberships*: Minnesota American Indian Bar Association; Native American Bar Association; Wisconsin Bar Association - Indian Law Section.

WAFFLE, JOSH (Tonkawa)
(tribal administrator)
Affiliation: Administrator, Tonkawa Tribe of Oklahoma, 1 Rush Buffalo Rd., Tonkawa, OK 74653 (580) 628-2561.

WAGON, CLINT (Shoshone)
(tribal chairperson)
Affiliation & Address: Chairperson, Eastern Shoshone Tribe, P.O. Box 538, Fort Washakie, WY 82514; E-mail: cdwagon@e-shoshone.com
(307) 332-3532

WAHKINNEY-KEELY, COLLINE (Comanche)
(attorney; executive director)
Education: University of Oklahoma College of Law, JD, 1987. *Affiliation & Address*: Staff Attorney (1989-2000), Executive Director (2000-present), Oklahoma Indian Legal Services (OILS), 4200 Perimeter Center Dr., Suite 222, Oklahoma City, OK 73112 (405) 943-6457. E-mail: keely@oilsonline.org. Colline is an expert on Indian Land Titles, Probates and Wills & Estates. *Other professional post*: Member, Steering Committee of the National Association of Indian Legal Services and on the Respect Diversity Committee of the Oklahoma Bar Association. *Past professional post*: Treasurer, Oklahoma Indian Bar Association; chair, Indian Law Section, Oklahoma Bar Association. *Published works*: Editor of several editions of The Indian Child Welfare Act: Case & Analysis; author of an article, "The Need for Indian Legal Aid" (Feb. 2010 Oklahoma Bar Journal's Indian Law Issue).

WAHNEE, BEVERLY (Hopi)
(BIA special education coordinator)
Affiliation: Hopi Agency, Bureau of Indian Affairs, P.O. Box 568, Keams Canyon, AZ 86034 (520) 738-2262.

WAHNEE, JOHN D. (Hopi)
(BIA education administrator)
Affiliation: Hopi Agency, Bureau of Indian Affairs, P.O. Box 568, Keams Canyon, AZ 86034 (520) 738-2262.

WAHNEE, ROBBIE (Comanche)
(Indian college president)
Affiliation & Address: President, Comanche Nation College, 1608 S.W. 9th St., Lawton, OK 73501 (580) 591-0203. E-mail: rwahnee@cnc.cc.ok.us

WAHPEPAH, CAROL (Ojibway)
(Indian center director)
Affiliation & Address: Executive Director, Intertribal Friendship House, 523 East 14th St., Oakland, CA 94606 (510) 452-1235. *Past professional post*: Director, American Indian Child Resource Center, Oakland, CA.

WAHPEPAH, WILDA (Winnebago of Nebraska/Kickapoo)
(attorney)
Education: University of Oklahoma, BA; University of Notre Dame, JD, 2000. *Address & Affiliation*: Special Counsel, Finance & Bankruptcy Practice Group, Sheppard, Mullenn, Richter & Hampton LLP, 1300 I St., NW, 11th Floor East, Washington, DC 20005 (202) 218-0022. Wilda represents tribal governments, businesses & entities doing business with tribes across the country. Her areas of emphasis include regulatory counseling & advice related to tribal jurisdiction & governmental matters, gaming, financing & business development, natural resources, & environmental law. Ms. Wahpepah represents tribal governments in state, federal, & tribal courts. *Past professional post*: Staff Attorney, Dorsey & Whitney LLP, Minneapolis, MN. *Awards, honors*: 'Rising Star' named by Minnesota Law & Politics, 2005. *Community activities*: Board member, Minnesota American Indian Bar Assn; board member, U. of Notre Dame Native American Alumni.

WAKEMAN, RICHARD K. (Flandreau Santee Sioux) 1923-
(former tribal president)
Born February 9, 1923, Flandreau, S.D. Education: Haskell Institute. *Address*: R.R. 1, Box 59A, Flandreau, SD 57028. *Affiliation*: Former president, Flandreau Santee Sioux Business Council. *Military service*: U.S. Marine Corps, 1942-45; U.S. Army, 1951-53 (Presidential Unit Citation; Commendation; Asiatic Pacific Award). Community activities: South Dakota Indian Commission; South Dakota Letter Carriers (president); Dakota Presbytery (moderator); Masonic Lodge. *Interests*: Tribal history.

WALDEN, HENRY ALTON, JR. (Pima) 1950-
(health systems management)
Born November 29, 1950, Albuquerque, N.M. Education: Phoenix City College, AA, 1976; Arizona State University, BS, 1978; University of Hawaii, MPH, 1982. *Principal occupation*: Health systems management). *Address*: Resides in Maricopa County, Arizona. *Affiliations*: Community Health Education, Scottsdale, AZ, 1982-84; Public Health Education, Parker, AZ, 1984-88; hospital administrator, Indian Health Service, USPHS, Fort Yuma, AZ, 1988-2000; director, Gila River Health Care, 2001-present. E-mail: henry.walden.jr@gric.nsn.us. *Military service*: U.S. Navy, Dental Corps. (Petty Officer-Third Class, National Defense, Viet Nam Service, Viet Nam Campaign Good Conduct); Lt. Commissioned Corps, U.S. Public Health Service. *Community activities*: Board of directors, Behavioral Health Agency of Central Arizona. *Interests*: "Native American culture, social inter-actions between Native peoples & mainstream America, health & social problems and their resolutions. *Hobbies*: Automobile restoration, silversmithing, painting, musical instruments and my children." *Published works*: "A Second Opinion on Zuni Diabetes" (U.S. Public Health Reports, April 1983); "Are We Overlooking Some Winning Strategies (IHS Provider, June 1988).

WALDRAM, JAMES B. 1955-
(professor)
Born August 20, 1955, Oshawa, Ontario, Can. *Education*: University of Waterloo, BA, 1978; University of Manitoba, MA, 1980; University of Connecticut, PhD, 1983. *Address*: 247 Sylvian Way, Saskatoon, SK, Can. *Affiliation*: Assistant professor, Dept. of Native American Studies, University of Saskatchewan, Saskatoon, Sask., Canada, 1983-. *Other professional post*: Associate editor, Native Studies Review. *Memberships*: Canadian Ethnology Society; Canadian Indian/Native Studies Association; Canadian Association for Medical Anthropology; American Anthropological Association; Society for Applied Anthropology. *Awards, honors*: Social Sciences & Humanities Research Council of Canada Doctoral Fellowship. Interests: "The impact of hydroelectric development of northern Canadian Native communities. Dietary change in the Canadian north; education needs assessment of urban Native people; health and health care delivery of urban Native people." *Published work*: 1885 and After: Native Society in Transition (Canadian Plains Research Center, Regina, 1986).

WALDRON, DARRELL
(executive director)
Affiliation & Address: Executive Director, of the Rhode Island Indian Council, 807 Broad St., Providence, RI 02907 (401) 781-1098. E-mail: dwaldron@rhodeislandindiancouncil.org Also executive director of the Connecticut, New Jersey & Delaware Indian Councils; an acknowledged national authority in employment, technical training & economic development for Native American programs. Of the 35 years that the Council has been in existence Darrell is now entering his 28th year. His current federal appointments are: Chairperson of the US Department of Labor's Native American Economic Development Business Relations Committee, Region I of the Native American Employment & Training Council & Advisory Board Member of the US Civil Rights Commission forRhode Island. Darrell has served on the Urban Indian Policy Coalition at the US White House assisting the Office of Management and Budget on policy design for urban-based Indian communities in theUnited States. He was also a founding board member of the Minority Investment Development Corporation. Additional memberships include: Past Chairman for the National Indian/Native American Employment Training Conference (NINAETC), Workforce Partnership of Greater RI Board Member, Providence/Cranston Workforce Investment Board Member and President of Harbor Heritage Museum Board of Directors. Affiliations include: Civil Rights Roundtable, Providence Chapter of the NAACP and the Rhode Island Coalition for Affirmative Action. In 1990 Darrell created the first Urban Indian Housing Authority in the United States. Today there are many US agencies that provide safe, sanitary housing for urban-based Indians. One of Darrell's most recent accomplishments is the establishment of Algonquin House, a major renovation of the former Steere House on Broad Street in Providence, RI. Besides serving as the home to the RI Indian Council, the Algonquin House offers low monthly rental office space to nonprofit organizations, and is approximately 90% occupied by social service based agencies. Its progression into becoming the hub of the surrounding community is the realization of Darrell's strategic vision. The US Department of Labor awarded Darrell the prestigious "Chief's Award" for his outstanding work in the Division of Indian & Native American Programs, federally funded employment & training program Darrell's leadership and direction have brought numerous awards of excellence to the RI Indian Council. His expertise has been repeatedly recognized by his peers on a national level as the five-time elected Chairman of NINAETC.In addition to Darrell's executive responsibilities, he has also served as a panelist, guest speaker and lecturer at many of Rhode Island's institutions of higher learning, including Brown University. A graduate of Leadership Rhode Island, Darrell has received numerous citations from RI Governors, Mayors and Chambers of Commerce.

WALDROUP, PATRICK (Tonkawa)
(tribal vice president)
Education: Seminole State College. *Affiliation & Address*: Vice President, Tonkawa Tribe of Oklahoma, 1 Rush Buffalo Rd., Tonkawa, OK 74653 (580) 628-2561. Military service: U.S. Navy. Past professional posts: Compliance Manager for the Tonkawa Tribal Gaming Commission, and the General Manager for Tonkawa Indian Casino East and Tonkawa Indian Casino West.

WALHOVD, GERALD
(BIA regional deputy supt.)
Affiliation & Address: Deputy Supt. – Trust Services, Bureau of Indian Affairs, Great Lakes Agency, 916 W. Lake Shore Dr., Ashland, WI 54806 (800) 495-4655; (715) 682-4527. E-mail: Gerald.walhovd@bia.gov.

WALKER, ALICE E.
(attorney)
Education: Earlham College, BA, 1987; Georgetown University School of Foreign Service, MS, 1989; Georgetown University Law Center, JD, 1992. *Affiliation & Address*: Managing Partner, McEroy, Meyer, Walker & Condon, 1007 Pearl St., Suite 220, Boulder, CO 80302 (303) 442-2021. E-mail: awalker@mmwclaw.com. Her practice is limited to the representation of Indian tribes and their members, concentrating primarily on the litigation & negotiations of natural resource disputes, Indian gaming matters, federal tribal acknowledgement, taxation, and jurisdictional & regulatory issues. Includes the representation of Indian tribes in all aspects of federal Indian law.

WALKER, DEWARD E., JR. 1935-
(research associate, anthropologist)
Born August 3, 1935, Johnson, Tenn. *Education*: University of Oregon, BA, 1961, PhD (Anthropology), 1964. *Address & Affiliation*: Vice President, Walker Research Group, Ltd., P.O. Box 4147, Boulder, CO 80306 (303) 492-6719. E-mail: walkerde@colorado.edu. Website: www.walkerresearchgroup.com. Mr. Walker has conducted research among tribal and non-tribal populations of the Columbia Basin, Western Plains, Northern Great Basin & Southwest. He is frequently retained by tribal governments & agencies to conduct demographics, legal, housing, health, education, and economic research relating to planning, program development, risk assessment, legal defense of treaty rights, and various tribal environmental initiatives concerning water, fish, mining, nuclear waste, logging, etc. *Military service*: U.S. Army, 1954-62. *Community activities*: Advisory Board member, High Desert Museum Fellowship Program. *Awards, honors*: Invited Keynote Addresses: "The American Indian in Transition--Past as Prologue," Idaho State University, Pocatello, 1972; "Legal & Political History of the Indians of Idaho," Idaho State legislature, Boise, 1982; Northwestern Anthropological Conference, "Anthropology & the Law: American Indians & Cultural Resource Management," Moscow, Idaho, 1986; Newberry Library Conference on American Indian Religious Freedom, Chicago, 1988. Invited Testimony on "Amending the American Indian Religious Freedom Act," before the U.S. Senate Select Committee on Indian Affairs, Washington, DC, 1988. Nominee for various teaching awards from the University of Colorado, Boulder, 1989-1995. Acknowledgement by the Nez Perce Tribal Executive Committee for Successful Efforts to Protect & Preserve the Sacred Sovereignty of the Nez Perce Tribe, 2001. Invited member of EPA Region's 8 October Native American Sacred Lands Forum, 2001. Nomination for membership to the Technical Recovery Team for the Interior Columbia Basin Salmon Recovery Domain by the Shoshone-Paiute Tribes of the Duck Valley Indian Reservation, 2001. Invited Presenter at session "Trouble in Paradise: Violence and Conflict Among the Indigenous Peoples of the Americas" at the AAA meeting in Chicago, Nov. 19-23, 2003. *Memberships*: American Anthropological Association, 1966-present; Society for Applied Anthropology, 1965-present; American Indian Development, 1969-present (Academic advisor, 1980-82); Northwest Anthropological Conference, 1970-present; High Plains Society for Applied Anthropology, Albuquerque, 1980-present. *Interests*: Acculturation & cultural change; natural & cultural resources; applied anthropology; ethnographic reconstruction & description; ethnography & ethnology of Northwestern North America; ethno-history; religion, folklore, and language; cultures of the Southwest: Hispanic, Hopi, and Navajo. *Published works*: The Chinook Indians; Nez Perce Coyote Tales, 2nd Ed. (University of Oklahoma Press, 1998; "The Nez Perce," in American Indians of the Pacific Northwest Website (University of Washington & Library of Congress, 2000); Sacred Geography in Native North America (Encyclopedia of Religion & Nature, 2003); Paiute Culture, Religion & Nature (Encyclopedia of Religion & Nature, 2003); Western Shoshone Culture, Religion & Nature (Encyclopedia of Religion & Nature, 2003; Nez Perce (The Greenwood Encyclopedia of World Folklore, 2005); numerous articles and reviews.

WALKER, GARY (Mono)
(tribal chairperson)
Affiliation & Address: Chairperson, North Fork Rancheria of Mono Indians, P.O. Box 929, North Fork, CA 93643 (559) 877-2461.

WALKER, HANS, JR. (Mandan/Hidatsa) 1936-
(attorney)
Education: University of North Dakota, Ph.B., 1957, LL.B., 1960. *Address & Affiliation*: Partner, Hobbs, Straus, Dean & Walker, LLP (1988-present), 2120 L St., NW, Suite 700, Washington, DC 20037 (202) 822-8282. E-mail: hwalker@hsdwdc.com. *Past professional posts*: General counsel for the Three Affiliated Tribes of the Fort Berthold Reservation of North Dakota, 1960-65; U.S. Dept. of the Interior (Assistant & Associate Solicitor for Indian Affairs, Director of the Office of Indian Water Rights), 1965-82. Presently, Mr. Walker is counsel for the St. Regis Mohawk Tribe in its suit for the return of thousands of acres of land taken by the State of New York early in the last century in violation of the Non-Intercourse Act. He has prepared manuals on taxation & gaming that are widely used in Indian country. *Areas of concentration*: Tribal sovereignty, taxation, Indian gaming, jurisdiction, trust & restricted Indian lands, water rights.

WALKER, JANA LYNN (Cherokee/Delaware/Shawnee) 1954-
(attorney)
Born October 2, 1954, Tulsa, Okla. *Education*: University of Oklahoma, BS, 1977; University of New Mexico School of Law, JD, 1987. *Address*: P.O. Box 121, Placitas, NM 87043 (505) 867-0579. *Affiliation*: Formerly, Junior partner, Gover, Stetson & Williams (an Indian-owned law firm), Albuquerque, NM, 1989-93; solo practitioner, Placitas, NM, 1993-97; Associate, Stetson & Jordan, Albuquerque, NM, 1998-present. Jana represents Indian tribes & tribal agencies & organizations in the areas of taxation, environmental regulation, economic development, reservation business transactions, code development, gaming, and organization & maintenance of business associations. She is a well-known speaker on Indian law issues, and is widely published on Indian environmental issues. *Other professional post*: Senior Attorney, Indian Law Resource Center, Helena, MT. *Memberships*: American Bar Association - Section of Natural Resources, Energy & Environmental Law (council member, 1991-94; secretary, 1994-96); Committee on Native American Natural Resources (chair, 1991-92, vice-chair, 1988-90); Standing Committee on Environmental Law (member, 1992-95); Section on General Practice, Solo, and Small Firms, Indian Law Committee (vice-chair, 1996); New Mexico Bar Association - Indian Law Section (chair, 1992-93; board member, 1989-94); Indian Bar Assn of New Mexico; Arizona Bar Association - Indian Law Section; Native American Bar Association. *Biographical sources*: Who's Who Among Rising Young Americans, 1992; Who's Who in American Law, 1992-93, 7th Ed, 1993-94, 8th Ed. *Published works*: Articles - "On-Reservation Treaty Hunting Rights" (26 Natural Resources Journal 187, 1986); "Tribal Environmental Regulation" with B. Kevin Gover (36 Federal Bar Journal No. 9, Nov. 1989); "Tribal Civil Regulatory Jurisdiction to Enforce Environmental Laws," with B. Kevin Gover (Institute on Mineral Development on Indian Lands, Paper No. 14, Rocky Mountain Mineral Law Foundation, 1989); "Native American Study Draws Poor Conclusions From Poor Conditions" with W. Richard West, Jr. (Legal Times, June 4, 1990; Texas Lawyer, July 2, 1990); "Indian Reserved Water Rights" with Susan M. Williams (5 Natural Resources & Environment No. 4, Spring 1991); "Commercial Solid & Hazardous Waste Disposal Projects on Indian Lands," (10 Yale J. on Reg. 229 (Winter 1993), with Kevin Gover; "Tribal Jurisdiction Over Reservation Water Quality and Quantity," (43 S.D. L. Rev. 315, 1998), with Jane Marx & Susan M. Williams; "A Closer Look at Environmental Injustice in Indian Country," with Jennifer Bradley & Timothy Humphrey, Sr. (Seattle Journal for Social Justice 379, 2002).

WALKER, JASON S. (Shoshone)
(former tribal chairperson; tribal corp. CEO)
Education: Haskell Indian Nations University, AA (Natural Science; Idaho State University, BS (Business Management with emphasis in Native American Business). *Affiliations & Addresses*: Chairperson (2011-present), Northwestern Band of Shoshone Nation, 427 N. Main, Suite 101, Blackfoot, ID 83204 (208) 478-5712. E-mail: jwalker@nwbshoshone-nsn.gov. *Other professional post*: CEO, Tribal Economic Development Corp., 1177 E. South Temple, Salt Lake City, UT 84102 (877) 777-2327.

WALKER, JOE (Delaware of Western Okla.)
(Indian initiative evaluator)
Education: University of Mary, MA (Management). *Affiliation*: Evaluator, Medicine Moon Initiative (MMI), Native American Training Institute (NATI) (Website: www.nativeinstitute.org), 3333 E. Broadway Ave. #1210, Bismarck, ND 58501 (701) 255-6374. E-mail: joew@nativeinstite.org. Joe is currently providing evaluation services for the Mountain & Plains Child Welfare Implementation Center, Western Workforce Initiative, and the National Resource for Indian Child Welfare. *Past professional posts*: Research associate, MMI; Development Specialist & Evaluator, Sacred Child Project.

WALKER, JOHNNA R. (Chickasaw)
(executive director)
Affiliation & Address: Executive Director, The Chickasaw Foundation, P.O. Box 1726, Ada, OK 74821 (580) 421-9030. *Other professional post*: Board member, Native Americans in Philanthropy, Mineapolis, MN.

WALKER, MIRANNE (Yankton Sioux)
(program officer)
Affiliation & Address: Program Officer (2004-present), First Peoples Fund, P.O. Box 2977, Rapid City, SD 57709 (605) 348-6594. Miranne's goal is to provide eligible Native artists & community spirit treasurers the means to share & deepen the native art experience.

WALKER, PATRICIA SILK (Cherokee)
(community mental health instructor)
Education: University of Oklahoma, BSN (Nursing), 1970; Wayne State University, MSN (Child Psychiatric Nursing & Community Mental Health), 1973; University of Washington, PhD (Nursing & Epidemiology), 1993. *Affiliation & Address*: Child Psychiatric Clinical Specialist, One Sky Center, Oregon Health & Science University, 3181 SW Sam Jackson Park Rd., GH 151, Portland, OR 97239 (503) 494-3703. Dr. Silk Walker's focus is community mental health & American Indians. Her research includes assessment of risk factors associated with alcohol, drug and other mental health problems.

WALKER, R. DALE (Cherokee)
(physician; professor of psychiatry)
Education: University of Oklahoma, BS (Microbiology), 1968; University of Oklahoma, College of Medicine, MD, 1972. Residency, Psychiatry, University of Oklahoma College of Medicine, 1972-73; Residency, Psychiatry, University of California, San Diego, 1975-77. *Affiliations & Address*: Professor of Psychiatry, Professor of Public Health & Preventive Medicine, Director of the Center for American Indian Health Education & Research, and Director, One Sky Center for American Indian/Alaska Native Health, Education & Research (2004-present), Oregon Health & Science University, 3181 SW Sam Jackson Park Rd, GH 151, Portland, OR 97239. E-mail: onesky@ohsu.edu. (503) 494-3703. Dr Walker has served nationally and locally as an advocate and activist for access to healthcare and the elimination of the stigma of mental illness and substance use disorders. A major focus of his research has been on addictions and mental health issues of American Indians. Over the past 25 years the American Indian Research Group has studied the prevalence and natural history of addiction disorders, risk and protective factors relating to addiction disorders, the relationship between mental and addictive disorders, and treatment strategies. He and his colleagues have consulted and lectured throughout North America on American Indian issues. *Past professional post*: Dr. Walker led the development of the first National Center of Excellence for Treatment of Alcohol & Drug Problems within the national VA Medical Center system. This work & focus began at the Seattle VA Medical Center & the University of Washington School of Medicine. *Awards, honors*: 1995 VA Service Award; 1996, Mental Health Excellence Award, Indian Health Service; 1998 APA Presidential Commendation, Strategic Planning Committee; 1999 Outstanding Service, Oregon Indian Council; 1999-2000; 1996-present, Best Doctors in the Pacific Northwest, Woodward White Publications. *Membership*: American Psychiatric Assn (Chair, Nominating Committee; 1996-present).

WALKER-GRANT, LEANNE (Yokut)
(tribal chairperson)
Affiliation & Address: Chairperson, Table Mountain Rancheria, P.O. Box 410, Friant, CA 93626 (559) 822-2587.

WALKING BULL, GILBERT C. (Oglala Sioux) 1930-
(spiritual teacher, artist)
Born June 18, 1930, Hot Springs, S.D. *Education*: Oregon College of Education (2 years). *Principal occupation*: Spiritual teacher, artist. *Address*: P.O. Box 200, Wanblee, SD 57577 (605) 462-6544. *Affiliation*: Co-director, Ti Ospaye, Wanblee, SD, 1991-; editor, "Wolf Songs (quarterly newsletter). *Community activities*: Member, Pine Ridge Reservation, Oglala Sioux Tribe; Gilbert, while residing in Oregon from the early 1970s through 1990, was instrumental in starting Native American clubs, & played an important role in bringing powwows to the Pacific Northwest. *Memberships*: Inter-Tribal Council, Portland, OR; National Indian Education Assn (Project Media evaluation team); Independent Indian Arts & Crafts Persons Assn (helped to organize). *Awards, honors*: Award for Distinction for Art, La Grande Indian Arts Festival, 1974; First Prize Award for Traditional Sioux Fancy Dance, Siletz, OR, 1973; First Prize Award for Traditional Sioux Painting, 1976, '77, La Grande Indian Arts Festival. *Interests*: "Do traditional Sioux geometrical designs on canvas in oil and acrylics; do Sioux crafts in beadwork & leather. (I am a) soloist, singing in the Lakota language with guitar and drum in public performance. Fancy dancer and participator in Indian gatherings since youth, winning many awards. At present, I am concentrating on traditional Sioux art, translating the legends of my people. I am traditional & bilingual. In my books, I am recording tales from the reservation, writing original poetry, translating songs and scoring songs." His grandfather was Move Camp (spiritual leader), his great grandfather was the prophet, Sitting Bull, and his great uncle was Crazy Horse. *Biographical source*: Who's Who Among the Lakotas. *Published works*: O-hu-kah-kan (Poetry, Songs, Legends, Stories), 1975; Wo ya-ka-pi (Telling Stories of the Past & Present), 1976; Mi ta-ku-ye (About Our People), 1977; all books co-authored with Montana H.R. Walking Bull, printed by the Itemizer Observer, Dallas, OR, may be purchased from the Walking Bulls at their home address.

WALKINGSTICK, DAVID (Cherokee) 1980-
(public school Federal programs' director; Cherokee Nation tribal councilor;)
Education: University of Central Oklahoma, BA; East Central Univesity, Ada, OK, MA (School Administration). *Affiliation & Address*: Federal Programs Director, Muskogee Public Schools, 202 W. Broadway, Muskogee, OK 74401 (918) 456-4256. *Other professional posts*: Cherokee Nation Tribal Councilor (District 3) (2011-present), Tahlequah, OK; member, Oklahoma Advisory Council on Indian Education; chair, Cherkee Nation Tribal Council Education Committee; former teacher & athletic director for Bell Elementary School in Adair County, OK. *Awards, honors*: The first All-State basketball player (1999) in Sequoyah High School history; named a 2013 "Native American 40 Under 40" recipient by National Center for American Indian Enterprise Development.

WALKUP, BOBBY (Iowa)
(tribal chairperson)
Affiliation & Address: Chairperson (2016-), Iowa Nation of Oklahoma, Rt. 1 Box 721, Perkins, OK 74059 (405) 547-2402. E-mail: bwalkup@iowanation.org

WALL, STEPHEN (Minnesota Ojibwe)
(attorney; artist; chairperson)
Education: Fort Lewis College, BA (Anthropology); University of New Mexico, JD, 1975. *Affiliation & Address*: Department Chairperson (2006-present), Indigenous Liberal Studies Program, Institute of American Indian Arts, 83 Avan Nu Po Rd., Santa Fe, NM 87503 (505) 424-2302. *Past professional posts*: Research Analyst, American Indian Law Center, Albuquerque, NM; community development specialist, Albuquerque Area Indian Health Board; behavioral health coordinator, Tohono O'odham Health Department, Sells, AZ; prosecutor & chief judge, Mescalero Apache Tribal Court, Mescalero, NM (11 years).

WALLACE, BONNIE (*Gida-gaa-bines-ikwe*) (Lake Superior Chippewa) 1946-
(program administrator)
Born December 4, 1946, Fond du Lac Reservation, Cloquet, Minn. Education: University of Minnesota, BA, 1974, Graduate Work, 1982. *Address*: 2211 Riverside Ave., Minneapolis, MN 55454 (612) 330-1138. *Affiliations*: Community program assistant, University of Minnesota, 1970-74; education specialist, Minnesota Chippewa Tribe, 1974-78; program administrator, Augsburg College, Minneapolis, MN, 1978- (director, American Indian Support Program, Minnesota Indian Teacher Training Project, American Indian Studies Minor, Woodland Anishinaabe Library). *Other professional posts*: Fond du Lac Urban Representative; Minnesota Chippewa Tribe's Executive Committee; Fond du Lac Tribal College, Cloquet, MN (chair, board of regents); planner, Annual Ojibwe Art Expo; grants evaluator; advisory board of numerous organizations, including: American Indian Business Development Corp. *Community activities*: Grants reviewer, Minnesota State Department of Corrections; Victim Services Programs; member, Minnesota Indian State Scholarship Committee; member, Mixed Blood Theatre; member, Urban Advisory Council-State of Minnesota; member, Minnesota Minority Education Partnership; former chairperson, American Indian Business Development Corp. *Memberships*: Minnesota Chippewa Tribe; Minnesota Indian Education Association (advisory board); National Indian Education Association; Museum of the American Indian/Smithsonian. *Awards, honors*: Contributions to Community United Way of Minneapolis, 1984; Contributions to Elders Award, American Indian Family Services, 1986; Contributions to Youth Award, Minneapolis Youth Diversion Project, 1986; Counselor of the Year, Minnesota Indian Education Association, 1987; Award of Merit, National Women of Color Day, 1990. *Published works*: Battering and the Indian Women, State Dept. of Corrections, 1980); Case Study, Ojibwe Women, Minority Women (Women's Institute of S.E. Atlanta, 1981); Touchwood, A Collection of Ojibwe Prose (Two Rivers Press, 1987); article - "Great Strides, Great Strides" in Private College Magazine, 1988).

WALLACE, GLENNA J. (Eastern Shawnee)
(tribal chief)
Education: Pittsburg State University, BA, MA, EDS. *Affiliation & Address*: Chief, Eastern Shawnee Tribe of Oklahoma, P.O. Box 350, Seneca, MO 64865 (918) 666-2435. E-mail: chief@estoo.net. *Past professional posts*: At Crowder College, she was employed for 38 years in various capacities including: director of Adult Basic Education; director of International Travel; Title III Director; Grant writer; instructor of Communications; Dept. Chair of Communications; Div. Chair of Communications of Fine Arts/Design; Interim Academic Dean. *Community Service*: Eastern Shawnee Tribal Business Committee (18 years); Seneca Chamber of Commerce & School Board; Neosho Area Habitat for Humanity; Chautauqua Performer. *Awards, honors*: Governor's Award for Outstanding Teacher; Business & Professional Woman of the Year; DAR Heritage Award; Soroptimist Woman of Distinction; 2006

Eastern Shawnee Senior Princess; 2007 Woman Tribal Leader of the Year by Engage Life Program; 2007 Ten Most Influential Woman in the Tri-State Region; 2009 Participant Colonial Williamsburg Foundation "American Indian Initiative."

WALLACE, HARRY B. (*Keytaiki-Chief*) (Unkechaug-Poospatuck) 1953-
(tribal principal chief; attorney)
Born December 11, 1953 in New York. *Education*: Dartmouth College, BA; New York Law School, J.D. *Affiliation & Address*: Attorney, tribal chief, Unkechaug Indian Nation, P.O. Box 86, Mastic, NY 11950 (631) 281-4143. E-mail: hwall@aol.com. *Other professional post*: Founder, Poospetuck Trading Co., Mastic, NY; chief, Unkechaug Nation, Mastic, NY. *Community activities*: Sponsor, Wampum Magic; member, Intertribal Hospice Preservation Task Force. *Awards, honors*: Commendations-Language Study Abroad. *Memberships*: Trial Lawyers Assn; Native American Music Assn. *Interests*: History, language, music, education. *Published work*: Eastern Indian Land Claims.

WALLACE, LEE (Tlingit)
(Alaskan village president)
Affiliation & Address: President, Organized Village of Saxman, Rt. 2, Box 2, Saxman, Ketchikan, AK 99901 (907) 247-2502.

WALLACE, MARLEITA (Tlingit-Tsimshian)
(craftsperson)
Address: Mardina Dolls, P.O. Box 611 Wrangell, AK 99929 (907) 874-3854

WALLULATUM, NELSON (Wasco)
(chief)
Affiliation & Address: Confederated Tribes of the Warm Springs Reservation, P.O. Box C, Warm Springs, OR 97761 (541) 553-1161. *Other professional post*: Member, Confederated Tribes Tribal Council, for over 40 years. Nelson was the driving force in the establishment of the Warm Springs Museum. *Interests*: Witness to the devastating episodes of the Columbia River over the past 70 years.

WALSTEDTER, ELAYNE (Navajo) 1959-
(academic librarian, assistant professor)
Born July 1, 1959. *Address*: Reed Library Fort Lewis College, 1000 Rim Dr., Durango, CO 81301 (970) 247-7662; E-Mail: walstedter_e@fortlewis.edu. *Affiliations*: Education program liaison, Futures for Children, Albuquerque, NM, 1989-90; information specialist, Native American Studies, University of New Mexico, Albuquerque, 1990-91; homemaker & school/community library volunteer, Chuska School, Tohatchi, NM, 1991-96; librarian & assistant professor, Reed Library, Fort Lewis College, 1996-present. *Memberships*: American Indian Library Association; Taa Dine (Navajo) Library Association; American Library Association; Association of College and Research Libraries, New Mexico & Colorado Library Association.

WALTERS, ANNA LEE (Pawnee/Otoe)
(English teacher; writer-editor)
Address: P.O. Box 276, Tsaile, AZ 86566. *Affiliation*: Navajo Community College, Tsaile, AZ. *Other professional post*: National Advisory Caucus for Wordcraft Circle of Native American Mentor & Apprentice Writers. *Published works*: Talking Indian: Reflections on Writing & Survival; Neon Powwow: New Native American Voices of the Southwest.

WALTERS, FONDA (Navajo-Dine')
(senior research analyst)
Education: Arizona State University, PhD (Entrpreneurial Education). *Affiliation & Address*: Senior Research Analyst, American Indian Policy Institute, Arizona State University, 250 E. Lemon St., Discovery Hall, Room 272, Box 872603, Tempe, AZ 85287 (480) 965-1055. E-mail: fonda.walters@asu.edu. *Past professional posts*: Director, Multicultural Engineering Program, Northern Arizona University, Institute for Tribal Environmental Professionals.

WALTERS, KARINA L. (Choctaw of OK)
(Indigenous Wellness Research Institute director)
Born in Glendale, Calif. *Education*: University of California, Los Angeles, BA (Sociology), 1987, MSW (Social Welfare), 1990, PhD (Social Welfare), 1995. *Address*: 18808 39th Ave. N.E., Lake Forest Park, WA 98155 (206) 440-9326; *Affiliation & Address*: Director, Indigenous Wellness Research Institute, University of Washington, 4101 15th Ave. NE, Box 354900, Seattle, WA 98105 (206) 543-5647) E-mail: kw5@uw.edu. *Other professional posts*: Associate Dean for Research & Professor (2001-present), University of Washington (UW) School of Social Work, Seattle, WA; Research Affiliate, Socio-behavioral & Prevention Research Core, UW Center for AIDS Research, 2004-present; Adjunct Faculty, Women's Studies, UW; founder & director (2005-present; co-director, 2002-05), Indigenous Wellness Research Institute (website: www.iwri.org), School of Social Work-UW; Endowed Professor, William B. & Ruth Gerberding University Professorship, UW, 2005-present; Research Fellow, Maramatanga National Institute for Research

Excellence in Maori Development & Advancement, University of Auckland, New Zealand, 2007-present; Adjunct Associate Professor, Dept. of Global Health, School of Public Health, UW, 2008-present. *Past professional posts*: Faculty Affiliate, 1997-2000, Center for the Study for Social Work Practice, Columbia University School of Social Work (CUSSW, NY; Associate Professor, CUSSW, NY, 2000-2001; Director, Doctoral program, UW School of Social Work, 2003-05; Teaching/Research Assistant, UCLA School of Social Welfare, Women's Studies Program, American Indian Studies Program, 1990-95. *Awards, honors*: Dukepoo Award for promoting integrity, respect, and excellence in Native health research, Native Research Network Annual Health Conference, August, 2009; Distinguished Contribution to Ethnic Minority Issues for 2009 Award, Society for the Psychological Study of Lesbian, Gay, Bisexual & Transgender Issues; Fulbright U.S. Senior Scholar Award, New Zealand 2007-08; Curve Magazine selection as on of the top 20 lesbian academics in the world; 2008 "Heart of Wellness" IWRI Film selected to show at the American Indian Film Festival, SF, CA2007 Selected Samuel E. Kelly Distinguished Faculty Lecture, UW; 2006 Honoree for Women of Color Empowered: Excellence in Science, Seattle, WA; 2006 Selected speaker for UW Global Health Lecture Series & UW Television; Association for Women in Psychology 2002 Women of Color Psychologies Award (APA). Funded Research & Training Grants As Principal Investigator: "Indigenous HIV/AIDS Research Training (IHART) Program, 2009-14"; "Healthy Hearts Across Generations," 2006-11; "Health Survey of Two-Spirited Native Americans," 2002-08; "Trauma, Coping, and Health Options Among HIV+ Native Americans, 2002-07; "Urban American Indian Identity, Alcohol Use, & HIV Risk," 1999-2004. *Published works*: Book (in preparation) with C. Aspin, "The Impact of Chronic Illnesses on Indigenous People"; numerous peer-reviewed journal articles, book chapters & reports. *Films*: Co-producer, "The Heart of Wellness," Indigenous Wellness Institute (UW), in collaboration with UW Native Forces (Dan Hart) produced and developed a 12 minute film on indigenous health and wellness. Selected to be shown at the American Indian Film Festival in San Francisco (2008) and to be shown at the National Museum of the American Indian (2009); 2005 "Looking Towards Home," a PBS documentary on Urban American Indians. Consulted and Kalyn was filmed for this documentary.

WAMPLER, NINA (Eastern Cherokee)
(professor)
Education: Boston University, MPH (Environmental Health & Epidemiology/ Biostatistics); PhD (Epidemiology). *Affiliation & Address*: Affiliate Faculty, Native American Research & Training Center, University of Arizona, 1624 Helen St., Tucson, AZ 85719 (720) 933-8402. E-mail: nwampler@email. arizona.edu. She is currently funded through a Research Supplement to Promote Diversity in Health-Related Research from the National Cancer Institute under the tutelage of University of Arizona/Arizona Cancer Center faculty member, Dr. Scott Leischow. Dr. Wampler is specializing in social network analysis and tobacco control.

WANASSAY, VINCENT (Umatilla)
(poet)
Address: 1828 SE Tibbets, Portland, OR 97202 (503) 236-3029.

WANATEE, GAILEY
(former tribal chief)
Affiliation: Sac & Fox Tribal Council, 3137 F Ave., Tama, IA 52339 (515) 484-4678.

WANATEE, TROY (Meskwaki Sac & Fox)
(tribal chairperson)
Affiliation & Address: Chairperson, Sac & Fox of the Mississippi in Iowa Meswaki Nation, 349 Meskwaki Rd.,Tama, IA 52339 (641) 484-4678.

WANCHENA, MATTHEW JOHN (Blackfeet) 1951-
(tribal building official)
Born March 9, 1951, Tacoma, Wash. *Education*: Washington State University, BS (Architecture), 1974; City University (Bellevue, WA), 1984-89, MBA, MPA. *Principal occupation*: Tribal building official. *Address*: 4529 Tacoma Ave. South, Tacoma, WA 98408 (253) 472-4011. E-mail: tacbac2380@aol.com. *Affiliations*: Building inspector/plans examiner for different local governments, 1979-; self-employed building code consultant, Tacoma, WA. 1993-2003; building official, Muckleshoot Indian Tribe, Auburn, WA, 2004-present. *Military service*: U.S. Army (Army Commendation, National Defense Army Reserves Overseas Medal, Army Reserve Components Achievement Medal, Overseas Service Medal, Army Service Medal, Southwest Asia Service Medal); rank LTC in U.S. Army Reserves, Corps of Engineers (retired 2003). *Community activities*: Currently helping with establishing WSU ROTC Alumni Association & Steering Committee member; Co-chairperson of Pierce County Native American Indian Advisory Council for Minority Commission; Pierce County Ethnic Commission (vice president, 1993); vice-president of the "Arts Together," an ethnic association in the Pierce County & Tacoma area; do job fairs at local schools. *Memberships*: American Institute of Architects, Tacoma,

WA; International Conference of Building Officials, Whittier, CA; American Indian Science & Engineering Society; National Fire Protection Association; Society of American Military Engineers. *Awards, honors*: Saudi Arabia Joint Support Medal from the Saudi Government for Desert Storm, 1991-92. *Interests*: "Architectural history, Native American architecture in the U.S.; visited Italy, Yugoslavia, Portugal and Spain. Have been through the Southwest and in my own Northwest to see the types of architecture that is out there. Currently helping the University of Puget Sound with setting up an American Indian Association, mentoring to junior high school & college students in the Tacoma & Pierce County area. Knowledgeable in computers & helping the local school districts with Indian students that need help." *Biographical source*: American Association of the Army, 1982 article by a soldier on me.

WAPATO, S. TIMOTHY (Colville)
(executive director)
Affiliation & Address: Colville Confederated Tribes, P.O. Box 150, Nespelem, WA 99155 (509) 634-2200. *Past professional posts*: Commissioner, Administration for Native Americans, Dept. of Health & Human Services, Washington, DC, 1990-92; executive director, National Indian Gaming Association, Washington, DC, 1993-1997; executive director, Columbia River Inter-tribal Fish Commission, Portland, OR, 1998-2002; director, Tribal Bison Cooperative. *Membership*: Colville Confederated Tribes (Pacific Northwest & national leader in tribal issues. *Awards, honors*: President Reagan & Bush Sr. appointed Mr. Wapato as the U.S. Commissioner for the Pacific Salmon Commission.

WARD, WILLIAM (BILL) (White Mountain Apache)
(board chairperson)
Born & raised on the White Mountain Apache Indian Reservation. *Affiliation & Address*: Chairperson, Board of Directors, Native People's Circle of Hope, 9770 SW Ventura Ct., Tigard, OR 97223 (503) 970-8004. Bill is a prostate cancer survivor diagnosed in October 2004. *Other professional posts*: Founding member, NPCOH-Eagle Feather Men's Chapter; serves on the Prostate Program Advisory Council, Spirit of Eagles-Mayo Clinic and is affiliated with and support by Intercultural Council ICC) in Houston, TX. *Past professional post*: High Voltage Electrical Power District Operations Manager, Bonneville Power Administration, Portland, OR; member, Oregon Governor's Veterans' Advisory Board (eight years); former City Councilman for the city of The Dalles, OR. *Military service*: U.S. Army (Vietnam Vet).

WARE, LORI GOODAY (Chiricahua Apache)
(tribal vice chairperson)
Education: University of Science & Arts of Oklahoma, BS (Business Administration). *Affiliation & Address*: Vice Chairperson (2005-present), Fort Sill Apache Tribe, Route 2, Box 121, Apache, OK 73507 (580) 588-2298. *Other tribal post*: Human Resource Coordinator for the Gold River Casino, 2007-present. *Past tribal posts*: Secretary-Treasurer, 1989-2002, Housing Commission, 1997-2003; Program Director & Human Resource Manager, 1988-2007.

WARE, SUE (Modoc) 1944-
(forensic anthropologist; artist, teacher)
Born September 24, 1994, St. Joseph, Mo. *Education*: University of Northern Colorado, MA, 1977; University of Colorado, MA, 1990. *Principal occupation*: Forensic anthropologist, teacher. *Address*: 307 Clermont St., Denver, CO 80202 (303) 320-4566. *Affiliation*: Earth Gypsy, Denver, CO. E-mail: info@earthgypsy.com; Denver Museum of Natural History (part time). *Memberships*: American Institute of Archaeology; American Association of Physical Anthropology; Egyptian Study Society; Western Interior Paleontological Society; American Research Center in Egypt; American Indian Science & Engineering Society; Friends of Earth Sciences. *Interests*: "I travel extensively throughout the U.S., Egypt, and pursue an avid paraprofessional paleontology area of study interest."

WARITO-TOME, RONALDA (Navajo)
(parent training specialist)
Education: University of New Mexico (Athletic Training & Anthropology); University of Northern Colorado (Special Education). *Affiliation & Address*: Parent Training Specialist, The Education for Parents With Indian Children With Special Needs, 1600 San Pedro Dr. NE, Albuquerque, NM 87110 (505) 767-6630. E-mail: ronwartome@hotmail.com.

WARNE, JIM E. (Oglala Lakota) 1964-
(Indian center director)
Born November 27, 1964, Phoenix, Ariz. *Education*: Arizona State University, BS, 1987; San Diego State University, MS, 1993. *Principal occupation*: Human resource development specialist; Indian center director. *Address & Affiliation*: Interwork Institute, College of Education (1993-present), San Diego State University, 3950 Camino del Rio North, San Diego, CA 92108 (619) 594-6163, E-mail: jwarne@interwork.sdsu.edu. *Other professional posts*: Coordinator,

Post Employment Training - American Indian Rehabilitation (PET-AIR) Project and working as a trainer for TACE IX at SDSU; consultant trainer, through SDSU, for the American Indian Disability Technical Assistance Center (AIDTAC) administered through the U. of Montana; vice president, Southern California Chapter, California Indian Education Assn, San Diego, CA, 1994-present; training coordinator, TVR CIRLE (Training Vocational Rehabilitation Continuous Improvement of Rehabilitation Counselors, Leaders, and Educators); motivational speaker. *Past professional posts*: Former vice president, Consortia of Administrators for Native American Rehabilitation (CANAR); Former co-director, Sycuan Inter-Tribal Vocational Rehabilitation program; worked with the Navajo Nation coordinating a Disability Needs Assessment Project through a contract with the Navajo Nation; coordinator, Circle of Support Project, American Indian Rehabilitation Research & Training Center, Northern Arizona University (NAU); Football player, National Football League (Cincinnati Bengals, Detroit Lions, Tampa Bay Buccaneers, San Francisco 49ers), 1987-89; football player, World League of American Football, New York, NY, 1991; football player, Arena Football League, Albany, NY, 1992; extra/actor, Segal Productions, "Silk Stalkings" & "Renegade," one episode each. *Community activities*: Member, Consortium of Administrators for Native American Rehabilitation (chair, Professional Standards Committee), 1993-; member, San Diego East County Native American Education Council, San Diego, CA, 1993-; board member, American Indian Health Council, San Diego, CA, 1993-. *Awards, honors*: Keynote speaker, American Indian Empowerment Conference, San Diego State University, Nov. 1994; nominated for vice president for the Southern Chapter of the California Indian Education Association, San Diego, May 1994; conducted Cultural Diversity Training for various groups in 1994; keynote speaker, Arizona State U., American Indian Institute "Feast-n-Fest celebration for Native American students, Tempe, AZ, Nov. 1993; speaker at numerous events. *Interests*: Rehabilitation counseling with an emphasis on education enhancement of Native American youth, multicultural issues, & Native American health, social, and rehabilitation issues.

WARNER, BARBARA A. (*The-Za'Teh*) (Ponca) 1949-
(executive director)
Born January 3, 1949, Pawnee, Okla. *Education*: BA in Sociology & English; MBA in Management. *Address*: Oklahoma Indian Affairs Commission, 4545 N. Lincoln Blvd., Suite 282, Oklahoma City, OK 73105 (405) 521-3828. E-mail: bwarner@oklaosf.state.ok.us. *Affiliations*: Cheyenne-Arapaho Tribe Manpower Program, Concho, OK, 1979-83; American Indian Institute, College of Continuing Education, University of Oklahoma, Norman, OK 1987-91, 92-93; executive director, Oklahoma Indian Affairs Commission, Oklahoma City, OK, 1993-present. *Community activities*: American Indian Business Legislative Day; Sovereignty Symposium (co-sponsor). *Memberships*: National Congress of American Indians; Governors' Interstate Indian Council; National Indian Education Association; Haskell Indian Nations University; Native American Preparatory School.

WARNER, ELIZABETH A. KRONK (Sault Ste. Marie Chippewa) 1979-
(professor of law; associate dean; Indian center director)
Education: Cornell University, BS, 2000; University of Michigan Law School, JD, 2003. *Affiliation & Address*: Professor of Law; Associate Dean, Academic Affairs; Director, Tribal Law & Government Center; Affiliated Professor, Indigenous Studies; Courtesy Faculty, Environmental Studies Program, University of Kansas, School of Law, 406 Greenn Hall, Lawrence, KS 66045 (785) 864-1139. E-mail: elizabeth.kronk@ku.edu. Elizabeth joined the KU Law faculty in June 2012. Couses taught: Federal Indian Law; Native American Natural Resources; Property; Tribal Law. *Past professional posts*: Prior to her arrival at KU, Warner served on the law faculties at Texas Tech University and the University of Montana. In 2010, Warner was selected to serve as an Environmental Justice Young Fellow through the Woodrow Wilson International Center for Scholars and U.S.-China Partnership for Environmental Law at Vermont Law School. She has also served as a visiting professor at Xiamen University in Xiamen, China, and Bahcesehir University in Istanbul, Turkey. In 2014, Community activities: In addition to teaching, Warner serves as an appellate judge for the Sault Ste. Marie Tribe of Chippewa Indians Court of Appeals in Michigan and as a district judge for the Prairie Band Potawatomi Nation in Kansas. Before entering academia, Warner practiced environmental, Indian, and energy law as an associate in the Washington, D.C. offices of Latham & Watkins LLP and Troutman Sanders LLP. Warner previously served as chair of the Federal Bar Association Indian Law Section and was elected to the Association's national board of directors in 2011. She currently serves as chairwoman of the Kansas Advisory Committee to the U.S. Civil Rights Commission. *Awards, honors*: Warner received the Immel Award for Excellence in Teaching, and in 2016 she received the Dean Frederick J. Moreau teaching and mentoring award from the graduating class. *Published works*: She is also co-author of the casebook Native American Natural Resources, and she co-edited "Climate Change & Indigenous People: The Search for Legal Remedies." Her scholarship, which focuses primarily on the intersection of Indian Law & Environmental Law, is published in several prominent journals, including the Arizona Law Review, Colorado Law Review & Columbia Journal of Environmental Law.

WARNER, LINDA SUE (Comanche)
(Special Assistant on Tribal affairs)
Education: University of Oklahoma, PhD (General Administration). *Affiliation & Address*: Special Assistant to the President on Tribal Affairs at Northeastern A & M College in Oklahoma, 2001 I St. NE, Miami, OK 74354 (918) 542-8441. She has over forty years' experience working with American Indian/Alaska Native/Native Hawaiian peoples working as both administrator and professor. Dr. Warner is extensively published with over two hundred articles, presentations, technical reports, books & book chapters that explore processes linked to cultural knowledge bases and pedagogy and leadership. *Published works*: Series co-editor, On Indian Ground: California (Information Age Publising, 2015).

WARNER, RICHARD (Tolowa-Yurok)
(rancheria councilmember)
Affiliation & Address: Councilmember, Elk Valley Rancheria Tribal Council, P.O. Box 1042, Crescent City, CA 95531 (707) 464-4680.

WARNER, SHANE (Shoshone)
(tribal chairperson)
Affiliations & Addresses: Chairperson (2015-present), Northwestern Band of Shoshone Nation, 505 Pershing Ave. #200, Pocatello, ID 83201 (208) 478-5712. E-mail: swarner@nwbshoshone.com

WARREN, ALVIN HARLYN (Santa Clara Pueblo)
(Pueblo lt. governor)
Education: Dartmouth College, BA (History & Certification in Native American Studies). *Affiliation & Address*: Partner/executive vice president, Blue Stone Strategy Group, ITCA/El Encanto Bldg., 2214 N. Central Ave., Suite 130, Phoenix, AZ 85004 (602) 307-1994. *Other professional posts*: Tribal council member, Santa Clara Pueblo, NM; chairperson, Native American Democratic Caucus of New Mexico; board member, Native Public Media and the Curriculum Committee for Leadership New Mexico. *Past professional posts*: Cabinet Secretary of Indian Affairs, State of New Mexico, 2008-2010, appointed by former Governor Bill Richardson, Alvin worked closely with the tribal leaders of the 22 Indian Pueblos, Tribes and Nations in New Mexico. He played a key role in the enactment of permanent funding for the New Mexico Tribal Infrastructure Fund in 2010, which will yield $110 million in funding to tribes in the first ten years alone; Lt. Governor, Pueblo of Santa Clara, (two terms); elected and appointed to serve a total of nine terms in various positions in Santa Clara's tribal government, including Tribal Treasurer. *Awards, honors*: 2010 Excellence in Leadership Award from the American Indian Chamber of Commerce of New Mexico.

WARREN, ANDREA (Cherokee)
(attorney)
Education: Indiana University, BA; Indiana University Mauer School of Law, JD. *Affiliation & Address*: Staff attorney, Barnes & Thornburg, 11 S. Meridian St., Indianapolis, IN 46204 (317) 236-1313. *Other professional post*: Secretary, American Indian Center of Indiana, Indianapolis, IN.

WARREN, JOHN (Potawatomi)
(tribal chairperson)
Born & raised in South Bend, Ind. *Education*: Ivy Tech Community College, AA. *Affiliation & Address*: Chairperson, Pokagon Band of Potawatomi Indians, P.O. Box 180, Dowagiac, MI 49047 (269) 782-6323. E-mail: john.warren@pokagonband-nsn.gov. *Other professional post*: Chairperson & CEO, Pokagon Gaming Authority Board. *Past professional posts*: Council member (2006-11), treasurer (2011-14), Pokagon Band of Potawatomi Indians. *Military service*: U.S. Army & Indiana National Guard.

WARRINGTON, BURTON W. (Menominee/Prairie Band Potawatomi/Ho-Chunk)
(chief executive officer)
Born & raised in the Land of the Menominee, in northern Wisconsin. *Education*: Haskell Indian Nations University, BS (Business Administration); University of Kansas School of Law, JD. *Affiliation & Address*: President & Chief Executive Officer, Prairie Band, LLC, 16281 Q Rd., Mayetta, KS 66509 (785) 966-0130. *Other professional post*: Board member, Native American Contractors Association, Washington, DC. *Past professional post*: Counselor to the Assistant Secretary of Indian Affairs, U.S. Department of the Interior, Washington, DC; attorney, Prairie Band Potawatomi Entertainment Corporation, Prairie Band Casino & Resort.

WARRIOR, DELLA C. (Otoe-Missouria)
(organization vice chairperson)
Affiliation & Address: Vice Chairperson, Wings of America, The Earth Circle Foundation, Inc., 901 W. San Mateo, Suite M • Santa Fe, NM 87505 (505) 982-6761. Past professional post: Institute of American Indian Arts, Santa Fe, NM

WARRIOR, ROBERT ALLEN (Osage) 1963-
(professor of American Indian studies, English & History)
Born July 25, 1963, Marion County, Kans. *Education*: Pepperdine University, BA (Speech Communication); Yale University, MA, 1988, Union Theological Seminary (New York, NY), PhD, 1992. *Affiliation & Address*: Professor of American Indian Studies, English & History (2010-present), American Indian Studies Program, University of Illinois at Urbana-Champaign, Room 1003, 1204 W. Nevada St., MC-139, Urbana, IL 61801 (217) 265-9870. E-mail: rwarrior@illinois.edu. *Other professional post*: Co-editor, Native American & Indigenous Studies Journal. *Past professional post*: Dept. of English, Stanford University, Stanford, CA, 1992-2002; Professor of Native American Studies & English, University of Oklahoma, Norman, OK, 2002-2010. *Memberships*: American Studies Association; Native American Journalists Association; Native American & Indigenous Studies Association (founding president). *Awards, honors*: Annenberg Fellowship for outstanding junior faculty, Stanford University, 1993-95; won (with Jace Weaver & Craig Womack) the 2007 Bea Medicine Award for Best Book in American Indian Studies from the Charles Redd Center for Western Studies & the Native American Literature Symposium for "American Indian Literary Nationalism." *Published works*: Co-author with Paul Chaat Smith, Like a Hurricane: The Indian Movement from Alacatraz to Wounded Knee (University of Minnesota Press, 1994); Tribal Secrets; Recovering American Indian Intellectual Traditions (University of Minnesota Press, 1995); The People & the Word: Reading Native Nonfiction (University of Minnesota Press, 2005); co-author, American Indian Literary Nationalism (University of New Mexico Press, 2006). His academic & journalistic writing has appeared in a wide variety of publications, including American Quarterly, World Literature Today, News From Indian Country, Lakota Times, Village Voice, UTNE Reader, Guardian, and High Times. Professor Warrior has lectured in a wide variety of places, including Guatemala, Mexico, France, Malaysia, Yale University, Harvard University, the University of Wisconsin-Madison, University of Chicago, the University of California-Berkeley, and the University of Miami.

WASHBURN, FRANCES L.
(professor)
Education: University of New Mexico, BA, MA (English), PhD American Studies), 2003. *Address & Affiliation*: Director of Graduate Studies (2004-present); American Indian Studies Program, The University of Arizona, Harvill 226B, Box 210076, Tucson, AZ 85721 (520) 626-8581. E-mail: washburn@email.arizona.edu. She writes poetry, short fiction and novels, and has published articles in Indigenous Nations Studies Journal, American Indian Quarterly, & Studies in American Indian Literature. *Interests*: American Indian literature, creative writing, poetry & fiction; Lakota culture, history & politics; literary theory; American Indian art, particularly American Indian beadwork. *Published works*: Novel, Elsie's Business (University of Nebraska Press, 2006); The Sacred White Turkey (University of Nebraska Press, 2010); James R. Walker and the Lakota Creation Story (in production).

WASHBURN, KEVIN K. (Chickasaw of Oklahoma)
(Assiatnt Secretary - Indian Affairs, U.S. Dept. of the Interior)
Education: University of Oklahoma, BA (Economics), 1989; Yale University Law School, JD, 1993. *Address & Affiliation*: Assistant Secretary – Indian Affairs, U.S. Department of the Interior, 1849 C St., NW, MS-3658-MIB, Washington, DC 20240 (202) 208-3710. *Past professional posts*: Clerked for judge on the U.S. Court of Appeals, Ninth Circuit; Attorney General's Honors Program, U.S. Dept. of Justice, 1993-94; Assistant U.S. Attorney, Albuquerque, NM, 1997-2000 General Counsel, National Indian Gaming Commission, 2000-02; Associate Professor of Law, University of Minnesota Law School, Minneapolis, MN (2002-08); Visiting Oneida Nation Professor at Harvard Law School, 2007-08; Rosentiel Distinguished Profssor of Law, U. of Arizona James E. Rogers College of Law, 2008-09; Professor of Law & Dean, 2009-12, University of New Mexico School of Law, Albuquerque, NM. *Awards, honors*: Special Commendation for Outstanding Service from the Justice Department, 1997, 1998; Environmental Protection Agency's Bronze Medal for Commendable Service, 2000. Mr. Washburn writes in the area of Federal Indian law, Federal criminal justice, and administrative law property.

WASHINAWATOK, JAMES (Menomniee)
(attorney)
Education: University of Wisconsin, Madison, BA, 2000, /JD, 2003. *Affiliation & Address*: Attorney (2010-present), Southern Ute Tribe, 356 Ouray Dr., P.O. Box 737, Ignacio, CO 81137 (970) 563-0100. *Past professional posts*: Associate, Nordhaus Law Firm, 2005-07; Ambassador, Americans for Indian Opportunity, 2009-10.

WASHINGTON, JENNIFER (Upper Skagit)
(tribal chairperson)
Affiliation & Address: Chairperson, Upper Skagit Tribe, 25944 Community Plaza, Sedro Woolley, WA 98284 (360) 854-7004. E-mail: jenniferw@upperskagit.com.

WASHINGTON, PAULA S. (Elewei Ditlihi Agehya) (Cherokee) 1952-
(teacher of orchestral music)
Born March 2, 1952, Frankfurt, Germany. *Education*: Smith College, BA, 1974; New York University, MA, 1976, PhD, 1993. *Address*: 9 Oak Ridge Rd., Pomona, NY 10970 (845) 354-7452. *Affiliation*: Fiorello H. LaGuardia High School of Music & Art & Performing Arts, New York, NY, 1981-. *Community activities*: Nuyagi Keetoowah Society/Cherokee Scribe Society. *Memberships*: Phi Delta Kappa; New York Viola Society; The Broadway Bach Ensemble; The Bergen Philharmonic.

WASHUTA, ELISSA (Cowlitz)
(advisor in American Indian studies)
Education: University of Maryland, BA (English), 2007 University of Washington, MFA (Creative Writing), 2009. *Affiliation & Address*: Advisor, Department of American Indian Studies, University of Washington, Seattle, WA 98195 (206) 543-9082. E-mail: elissaw@u.washington.edu. Elissa has been a part of the American Indian Studies Department since 2007, and in 2010, she became the department's academic counselor. Previously, she worked as an office assistant for AIS in while studying Creative Writing at the University of Washington. After receiving her M.F.A. in 2009, she began working as an assistant teacher for AIS 102 (Intro to AIS) & AIS 360 (Indians in Cinema), and taught AIS 377 (American Indian Memoir & Autobiography) in the summer of 2010. *Community activities*: Active in the Seattle literary community, Ms. Washuta has served as organizer of a monthly open mic at Richard Hugo House; served as a curator for Castalia, the literary series of the UW M.F.A. program in Creative Writing; and worked as Richard Hugo House's volunteer web editor, blogger and Facebook czar. She has performed her writing at many venues around (and beyond) Seattle, including Bumbershoot. *Published work*: My Body Is a Book of Rules (Red Hen Press, 2014).

WATAHOMIGIE, DON E. (Havasupai)
(tribal chairperson)
Affiliation & Address: Chairperson, Havasupai Tribe, P.O. Box 10, Supai, AZ 86435 (602) 448-2961. E-mail: htchair@havasupai-nsn.gov

WATAHOMIGIE, LUCILLE J. (Hualapai)
(tribal director of education)
Education: Northern Arizona University, BA (Eduation); University of Arizona, MA (Education). *Affiliation & Address*: Director, Hualapai Education & Training Department, Hualapai Tribe, P.O. Box 179, Peach Springs, AZ 86434 (928) 769-2216. Since her retirement, she has been working with the Hualapai Education Dept. and is in the process of applying for an Administration of Native Americans grant for a community language program. *Past professional posts*: 30 years in language education in public schools (retired); co-founder & instructor, American Indian Language Development Institute (AILDI), University of Arizona, Dept. of Language, Reading & Culture, College of Education, Tucson, AZ. Lucille continues to work in the revitalization of the Hualapai language using culture, traditions, spirituality, songs stories. *Published works*: Co-editor, Spirit Mountain: A Yuman Anthology; Hualapai Reference Grammar; articles on Native American linguistic & language issues.

WATAN, STERLING (Cheyenee-Arapaho)
(broadcaster; co-chair, AIM)
Affiliation: Crow Tribal Council, Crow Agency, MT 59022 (406) 638-2316. *Other professional post*: Co-chair, American Indian Movement; owner, former KKUL-AM, Hardin, MT.

WATCHMAN, DERRICK (Dine'-Navajo)
(chief financial officer)
Born & raised on the Navajo Reservation. *Education*: University of Arizona, BS; University of California, MBA. *Affiliation & Address*: Chief Financial Officer, Navajo Nation Gaming Enterprise, 249 East NM State Hwy. 118, P.O. Box 1700, Church Rock, NM 87311 (505) 905-7100. *Other professional posts*: Owner, Watchman & Associates, Window Rock, AZ (provides business advisory & development services); chief of staff, Navajo Nation; director of Indian Affairs, U.S. Dept. of Energy; chief Operating Officer & General Manager, Navajo Nation's Dine Power Authority; director, Navajo Tax Commission; Chairperson, National Center for American Indian Enterprise Development, Mesa AZ. *Past professional posts*: Vice president & Senior Relationship Manager, J.P. Morgan Chase Bank's Native American Banking Group.

WATERS, MICHAEL R.
(professor of anthropology & geography)
Education: University of Arizona, BS, 1977, MS, 1980, PhD (Geosciences), 1983. *Affiliation & Address*: Professor of Anthropology & Geography (1986-present), Texas A&M University, 4352 TAMU, College Station, TX 77843 (979) 845-4046. E-mail: mwaters@tamu.edu. *Other professional posts*: Holder of the Endowed Chair in First Americans Studies, director, Center for the Study of the First Americans, TAMU; executive director, North Star Archaeological Research Program, Texas A & M University, 2002-present). *Research &*

Teaching Interests: Peopling of the Americas, Late Quaternary history, Geoarchaeology, North America. *Awards, honors*: Evans B. Mayo Award for outstanding performance in field geology, University of Arizona, Dept. of Geosciences, 1977; Kirk Bryan Award, Geological Society of America, 2003; Fellow, Geological Society of America, 2004; Rip Rapp Archaeological Geology Award, 2004. *Published works*: Numerous journal articles, book chapters, technical reports, monographs, research grants, book reviews, lectures & presentations

WATKINS, C.J. (Lenni Lenape-Delaware)
(former tribal vice president; former acting president)
Affiliation & Address: Former Acting President & Vice President, Delaware Nation, P.O. Box 825, Anadarko, OK 73005 (405) 247-2448.

WATKINS, JOE (Choctaw)
(Native American studies program director)
Education: University of Oklahoma, BA (Anthropology); Southern Methodist University, MA & PhD (Anthropology). *Affiliation & Address*: Director, Native American Studies Program (2007-present), University of Oklahoma, 633 Elm Ave., Ellison Hall 204, Norman, OK 73019 (405) 325-2312. E-mail: jwatkins@ou.edu. Dr. Watkins serves as a mediator between various academic disciplines & members of Indigenous groups. *Past professional post*: Associate Professor of Anthropology, University of New Mexico, 2003-07. *Study interests*: Includes the ethical practice of anthropology & the study of anthropology's relationships with descendant communities & aboriginal populations. *Publications*: Indigenous Archaeology: American Indian Values & Scientific Practice (AltaMira Press, 2000); Reclaiming Physical Heritage: Repatriation & Sacred Sites (Chelsea House Publishers, 2005).

WATKINS, SHERRIN (Shawnee/Cherokee)
(attorney; title agent)
Education: University of Tulsa College of Law, JD. *Affiliation & Address*: Title Agent, Universal Field Services, 6666 S. Sheridan Ave., Suite 230, Tulsa, OK 74133. *Other professional posts*: Attorney, Muscogee (Creek) Nation, 1983-88; private practice, 1988-present; D.C. Phillips & Associates, P.C.; Loyal Shawnee Business Committee, 1995-present; Sac & Fox Supreme Court (Justice), 1995-present. *Community activities*: Haskell Pa-a-linn, General Federation of Women's Clubs. *Memberships*: Oklahoma Bar Association; U.S. District Court Northern District of Oklahoma & Eastern District of Oklahoma; U.S. Court of Appeals, 10th Circuit and D.C. Circuit; Cherokee Nation Bar; Creek Nation Bar. *Published works*: Native American History: A Pocket Reference Guide (Myles Publishing, Los Angeles, CA, 1992); White Bead Ceremony (Council Oak Books, Tulsa, OK, 1994); Green Snake Ceremony (Council Oak Books, 1995); Headstart (Council Oaks Books, 1997); Different Prayers (Council Oaks Books, 1997).

WATSO (Wabanaki, Odanak Band) 1954-
(financial services)
Born May 4, 1954, Buffalo, N.Y. *Education*: Concordia University, BA-Business. *Principal occupation*: Investment executive for Dain Rauscher Financial Services, Minneapolis, MN (working with Native bands, tribes and organizations. *Address*: P.O. Box 7103, Minneapolis, MN 55407 (612) 371-7964. E-mail: watso@dainrauscher.com. *Affiliations*: Owner "Singing Spirit", Native American Works, Dayton, OH, 1985-88; cultural director, Minneapolis American Indian Center, & curator, Two Rivers Gallery, Minneapolis, MN, 1988-99; planning consultant, National Indian AIDS Media Consortium & National Native American AIDS Prevention, Oakland, CA, 1993-; AFTRA (on camera print and voice overs). *Other professional posts*: National Advisor, Shooting Back Project, Washington, DC, 1991-; author of "Artline," in Circle Newspaper; curator for various art exhibits. *Community activities*: Public speaker - art, culture, issues; design consultant; actor; Metropolitan Regional Arts Council (board member, 1990-91; review panel, 93-94); Northern Plains Tribal Arts (advisory committee, 1990-91); Minneapolis American Red Cross (board member, 1989-91. *Membership*: Minnesota Assn of Museums (steering committee, 1990-91); AFTRA. *Awards, honors*: Recipient of 1991-92 Arts Midwest Arts Administrative Fellowship. *Interests*: "To utilize resources, skills and experience to help Native people achieve financial security and growth."

WATSON, LARRY S. (Brothertown) 1941-
(editor, writer)
Born May 3, 1941, Oklahoma City, Okla. *Education*: Oklahoma State University, BA, 1963; Central Missouri State University, MA, 1964. *Principal occupation*: Editor, writer. Resides in Calif. *Affiliation*: Co-owner, Histree (genealogical research & publishing organization), Laguna Hills, CA, 1978-. *Other professional posts*: Active genealogical researcher for better than 40 years: Southern States & Native American; genealogical teacher for 20+ years; consultant: Riverside Indian Center, Saddleback College, Sac River Cherokee Indians & several other genealogical & Native American groups; editor of The Journal of American Indian Research (monthly newsletter of Histree). *Military service*: U.S. Army, 1959-78. *Community activities*: Organizing President of Southwest Oklahoma Genealogical Society; charter member, Stars & Bars,

Lawton, OK. Memberships: California Genealogical Alliance. Speaker at: World Conference on Genealogical Research, New Orleans, LA, 1975, 1976, 1977; Cherokee Indian Descendants of the A-niyun-wiya, Inc., 1992; numerous other genealogical & historical societies, 1974-. *Awards, honors*: Named Fellow of the Ark-La-Tex Genealogical Society, Shreveport, LA, 1976; Certificate of Acknowledge from The Richstone Family Center, Hawthorne, CA for "his time & expertise, assisting our Native American clients research their heritage," 1994. *Published works*: Family History of the Brothertown Indians (Histree, 1986); Finding our Metis Ancestors (Histree); General editor of a reprint of Senate Document 512, 23rd Cong. 1st Sess. concerning Indian removal with comments and index; general editor of Series on Indian Treaties (28 volumes plus guide book); author/editor of several other records on Indians & books of historical & genealogical importance about Indian Territory & Oklahoma; numerous articles in various journal publications.

WATSON, LORIN (Shoshone)
(tribal vice chairperson)
Affiliation & Address: Vice Chairperson, Duckwater Shoshone Tribe, P.O. Box 140068, Duckwater, NV 89314 (775) 863-0227.

WATTS, JOHN
(program director)
Affiliation & Address: Program Director, American Indian Research Opportunities (AIRO), Montana State University, 312 Roberts Hall, P.O. Box 173925, Bozeman, MT 59717 (406) 994-5567. E-mail: jwatts@montana.edu

WATTS, STEVEN M. 1947-
(museum educator)
Born July 25, 1947, Lincoln County, N.C. Education: Appalachian State University, Boone, NC, BA, 1969; Duke University, M.Div., 1972. Principal occupation: Museum educator. *Address*: 207 W. Fourth Ave., Gastonia, NC 28052 (704) 866-6912. *Affiliation*: Director, Southeastern Native American Studies Program, Schiele Museum, Gastonia, NC, 1984-present. *Other professional posts*: Director, "Abo-Tech", providing instruction in aboriginal/primitive skills & prehistoric tool replicas for museums and functional experiments. *Past work experience*: Minister, school counselor, classroom teacher, camp director, and substance abuse educator. *Community activities*: Commission on the Status of Women; Southeastern Indian Culture Study Group (director); American Indian Cultural Association (past director); Mental Health Association; volunteer work with schools, churches, scout groups, etc. *Memberships*: Center for the Study of Early Man; The Archaeological Society of North Carolina; Society of Prehistoric Technology; International ATLATL Association. *Awards, honors*: Statewide speaker for N.C. Mental Health Association (1984); Master of ceremonies, NC Commission of Indian Affairs--Unity Conference Intertribal Dance (1981); Outstanding Service Award, Mental Health Association, 1985. *Interests*: "Major interests is replication and experimental use of Native American tools, weapons, utensils, etc.--with the goal of (through educational programs) increasing the appreciation of primitive survival/subsistence skills & lifestyles among participants -- helping to rediscover & preserve Native technologies for generations to come; ethnology, archaeology. Most spare time is spent visiting native communities in the Southeast and historic & prehistoric Native sites to increase the understanding & collection of knowledge." *Biographical sources*: Approximately a dozen newspaper articles in local and statewide newspapers (copies available upon request). *Published works*: The Old Bearskin Report, journal (Schiele Museum, 1985); Southeastern Craft Articles, series (The Backwoodsman, Tex., 1984 & 1985).

WAUKAU, JERRY L. (Keneahetim) (Menominee) 1956-
(health administrator)
Education: Ripon College, 1974-78; University of Minnesota, Independent Study Program for Ambulatory Care Administration, 1987-88. *Address*: P.O. Box 970, W3275 Wolf River Dr., Keshena, WI 54135 (715) 799-5482. *Affiliation*: Administrator, Menominee Indian Tribe of Wisconsin, Keshena, WI, 1981-85; health Administrator, Menominee Tribal Center, Keshena, WI, 1985-present. *Community activities*: Council on American Indian Health, Chairperson, 1994-97; secretary, Northern Wisconsin Area Health Education Center, Inc., 1990-96; St. Anthony's Parish Council, 2001-present. *Memberships*: Wisconsin Tribal Health Director's Association (1991-present); Red Cross, Lakeland Chapter (board of directors, 1987-92); American College of Healthcare Executives. *Awards, honors*: American Heart Association of Wisconsin Volunteer Recognition Award, 1987; Indian Health Service (IHS) Exceptional Performance Award, 1988; IHS Citation for Exemplary Group Performance, Menominee Tribal Clinic Management Team, 1990; IHS Citation for Exemplary Group Performance, Wisconsin Health Director's Association (chairperson, 1991-2004); Great Lakers Inter-Tribal Council, Inc. Award in recognition of Outstanding Service & Commitment, 1996 & 2003; Bemidji Area Director's Outstanding Health Administrator Award, Sept. 1998; Minority Health Leadership 2003. *Interests*: Enjoys fishing, committed to providing quality patient care to the Menominee people and reducing health disparities in the State and Indian Country.

WAUKAZOO, HELEN DEVORE (Navajo-Dine')
(chief executive officer)
Affiliation & Address: Chief Executive Officer, Friendship House Association of American Indians of San Francisco, 56 Julian Ave., San Francisco, CA 94103 (415) 865-0964.

WAUKAZOO, MARTIN (Rosebud Lakota)
(health director)
Born in Rapid City, S.D. *Education*: Black Hills State University, BA. *Affiliation & Address*: Chief Executive Officer, Native American Health Center, 3124 International Blvd., Oakland, CA 94601 (510) 535-4400. *Past professional posts*: Urban Indian Health Board, Oakland, CA; Native American Health Clinic, San Francisco, CA.

WAUPOOSE, JANET (Menominee)
(association president)
Affiliation: National Tribal Court Clerks Association, 1000 Connecticut Ave., NW, Suite 1206, Washington, DC 20036 (202) 296-0685.

WAUPOOSE, RUTH (Menominee)
(tribal vice chairperson)
Affiliation & Address: Vice Chairpeson, Menominee Indian Tribe of Wisconsin, P.O. Box 910, Keshena, WI 54135 (715) 799-5100.

WAUQUA, JOHNNY C. (Comanche)
(tribal administrator)
Affiliation: Administrator, Comanche Tribe, P.O. Box 908, Lawton, OK 73502 (580) 492-3240. E-mail: johnnyw@comanchenation.com. *Past tribal post*: Chairperson.

WAY, J. EDSON 1947-
(museum administration)
Born May 18, 1947, Chicago, Ill. *Education*: Beloit College, BA, 1968; University of Toronto, M.A., 1970, PhD, 1972. *Principal occupation*: Museum administration. Resides in New Mexico. *Affiliations*: Associate professor of anthropology, Beloit College, 1972-85; director, Logan Museum of Anthropology, Beloit, WI, 1980-85; director, Wheelwright Museum of the American Indian, 1985-89; acting director, New Mexico Museum of Natural History, Albuquerque, 1990-91; executive director, International Space Hall of Fame, Alamogordo, NM, 1991-. *Community activities*: Public speaker, Native American arts & history; Society of Friends (Quakers); Southeast Asian Refugee Resettlement; Rotary; chair, Tourism Committee, Alamogordo (NM) Chamber of Commerce; vice-president, Apache Trails Tourism Promotions, Ruidoso, NM. *Memberships*: American Assn of Museums; New Mexico Museum Assn; American Assn of Physical Anthropologists; Society for American Archaeology; Plains Anthropological Society. *Interests*: Archaeological fieldwork in Labrador, and Ellesmere Island, N.W.T., Canada; northern Wisconsin; northeast New Mexico; Native American arts; music; horsemanship; cross-country skiing; camping; fishing; Western history; & cattle ranching.

WAYNEE, ROBERT D. (*Lone Eagle*) (Saginaw Chippewa) 1939-
(sculptor in wood)
Born July 8, 1939, Bay City, Mich. *Address*: 1101 McCulloch Blvd. S., Lake Havasu, AZ 86404. *Principal occupation*: Sculptor in wood. *Other professional posts*: Carpenter, photographer, welder, furniture maker, artist. *Memberships*: Southwest Association for Indian Arts (Santa Fe Indian Market). *Awards, honors*: "Gate Keepers" Award by Country Home Magazine, 1989 at the National Christmas Show, Washington, DC; a pictorial in the early American Home Magazine Directory, Aug. 1996; received first place and division awards at Santa Fe Indian Market, 1995 & 1996; solo exhibit at the Southern Plains Indian Museum, Anadarko, OK, 1996; numerous other awards. He is featured in galleries and collections throughout the U.S.

WAZIYATAWIN (Wahetounwan Dakota)
(associate professor of Indigenous Governance)
Education: Cornell University, PhD American History). *Affiliation & Address*: Associate Professor & Indigenous Peoples Research Chair, Indigenous Governance Program, Faculty of Human & Social Development, University of Victoria, 3800 Finnerty Rd., HSD Bldg., Rm. A260, Victoria, BC V8W 2Y2 (250) 721-6438. *Current Research*: Indigenous decolonization strategies such as truth-telling & reparative justice, indigenous women & resistance, the recovery of indigenous knowledge, and the development of liberation ideology in indigenous communities. *Published works*: Author & editor of five volumes including: Remember This!: Dakota Decolonization & the Eli Taylor Narratives; Indigenizing the Academy: Transforming Scholarship & Empowerment Communities; For Indigenous Eyes Only: A Decolonization Handbook; In the Footsteps of Our Ancestors: The Dakota Commemorative Marches of the 21st Century; and What Does Justice Look Like? The Struggle for Liberation in Dakota Homeland.

WEAHKEE, ROSE (Navajo)
(former acting IHS area director)
Education: Loyola Marymount University, BA (Psychology), 2014; California School of Professional Psychology, MA (Clinical Psychology). *Affiliation & Address*: Acting Director, Phoenix Area IHS, Two Renaissance Square, 40 N. Central Ave., Suite 600, Phoenix, AZ 85004 (602) 364-5039. E-mail: rose.weahkee@ihs.gov. Dr. Weahkee helps oversee the delivery of health care services to about 160,000 American Indians & Alaska Natives in Arizona, Nevada, and Utah. *Past professional posts*: Director for Field Operations for the Phoenix Area and worked with the health facilities and youth regional treatment centers to ensure accreditation, quality & safe patient care, implementation of the Patient-Centered Medical Home concept, budget management, improved business practices, & tribal partnerships & collaboration. Dr. Weahkee has extensive experience working with IHS, tribal, and urban leadership on a range of health and behavioral health issues. Dr. Weahkee previously served as the Director of the Division of Behavioral Health at IHS headquarters. In this position, she provided leadership, direction, and expert knowledge in the planning, development, implementation, & evaluation of behavioral health programs throughout the Indian health system. She also previously served as the Area Behavioral Health Consultant for the IHS California Area Office and provided behavioral health leadership to 31 tribal and 8 urban Indian health programs in California. Awards, honors: In 2006, recipient of the American Psychological Association's Early Career Award in the Public Interest. In 2011 and 2012, she was recognized by the IHS Director for her leadership in behavioral health with a National Director's Award. In 2011, Dr. Weahkee was recognized for her professional leadership and community involvement as the recipient of the prestigious Luana Reyes Leadership Award. Also in 2011, Dr. Weahkee was awarded a Presidential Citation by the American Psychological Association's for her lifelong commitment to multicultural issues and her work in psychology.

WEATHERFORD, ELIZABETH 1945-
(head of film & video center)
Born July 30, 1945, Anson County, N.C. Education: Duke University, BA, 1966; The New School for Social Research, MA, 1970. *Principal occupation*: Head of film & video center. *Affiliation & Address*: National Museum of the American Indian-Smithsonian Institution, George Gustav Heye Center, One Bowling Green, New York, NY 10004 (212) 514-3730. E-mail: wford@ic.si.edu. *Affiliations*: Research Associate, Dept. of Anthropology, New York University, New York, NY; department head, Film & Video Center, National Museum of the American Indian, New York, NY, 1981-. *Community activities*: Board Member, Human Studies Film Archives; Media Alliance. *Memberships*: National Association for Media Culture; Association of Moving Image Archivists; American Anthropological Association; Association for Independent Video and Film Makers; Media Alliance; Society on Visual Anthropology; Cultural Survival. Interests: Recent and archival films and videotapes about Native Americans. *Published works*: Native Americans on Film & Video (Museum of the American Indian, 1981); Native Americans on Film and Video II (Museum of the American Indians, 1986); "Starting Fire with Gunpowder" in Film Comment (June 1992); To End & Begin Again: Victor Masayesva in Art Journal (Winter 1995).

WEATHERS, THOMAS (Aleut) 1968-
(attorney)
Education: McGeorge School of Law, JD, 1993. *Affiliation & Address*: Founding Partner (2003-present), Alexander, Berkey, Williams & Weathers, 2000 Center St., Suite 308, Berkeley, CA 94704 (510) 548-7070. His practice is devoted primarily to Indian law & business law. He advises tribal & non-tribal on a range of matters including, land use & development, gaming, tribal governance, Indian health care, Indian child welfare, Indian probate, and crisis management. *Past professional posts*: Long & Levit, San Francisco; Crosby, Heafey, Roach & May (now Reed Smith); past board president, national Native American Bar Association. *Awards, honors*: Mr. Weathers has participated on several conference panels in relation to Indian law and published on many topics; he has repeatedly been named by "Super Lawyers" magazine as one of the top attorneys in Northern California.

WEAVEL, TONIA (Cherokee)
(education director)
Affiliation & Address: Education Director, Cherokee National Historical Society, Cherokee Heritage Center, P.O. Box 515, Tahlequah, OK 74465 (918) 456-6007.

WEAVER, FRAMON (Mowa Choctaw)
(tribal chief)
Affiliation: Mowa Band of Choctaw Indians, Rte. 1, Box 330-A, Reservation Rd., Mt. Vernon, AL 36560 (205) 829-5500.

WEAVER, JACE
(professor of religion, adjunct professor of law)
Education: Union Theological Seminary (New York), PhD; Columbia University Law School, JD. *Affiliation & Address*: Professor of Religion & Director, Institute for Native American Studies, Peabody Hall, University of Georgia, Athens, GA 30602 (706) 542-1492. E-mail: jweaver@uga.edu. *Interests*: Dr. Weaver's work in Native American Studies focuses primarily on religious traditions, literature, and law. *Awards, honors*: In 1999, Jace won the Portfolio Award for excellence in teaching resources from the Journal Media & Methods for his book on CD-ROM, American Journey: The Native American Experience; In 2003, he won the Wordcraft Award for Best Creative Non-Fiction for Other Words; Dr. Weaver won the 2007 Bea Medicine Award for Best Book in American Indian Studies from the Charles Redd Center for Western Studies & the Native American Literature Symposium for American Indian Literary Nationalism. *Published works*: American Journey: The Native American Experience; That the People Might Live: Native American Literatures & Native American Community; Other Words: American Indian Literature, Law, and Culture; Turtle Goes to War: Of Military Commissions, the Constitution & American Indian Memory; American Indian Literary Nationalism (written with Warrior, Womack & Ortiz) (University of New Mexico Press).

WEAVER, KESLER (Mowa Choctaw)
(tribal chairperson)
Affiliation: Council Chairperson, Mowa Band of Choctaw Indians, 1080 West Red Fox Rd., Mt. Vernon, AL 36560 (251) 829-5500. E-mail: kweaver@mowachoctaw.com.

WEAVER, PRISCILLA (Navajo-Dine')
(Dine' College, Shiprock Branch director)
Education: New Mexico State University, MA. *Affiliation & Address*: Director, Shiprock Branch, Dine' College, P.O. Box 580, Shiprock, NM 87420 (505) 368-3522. E-mail: pweaver@dinecollege.edu.

WEAVER, ROBERT (Quapaw)
(health consulting services)
Affiliation & Address: Founder, Native Health & Insurance Network, 1027 S. Main St., Suite 318, Joplin, MO 64801. www.facebook.com/NHandIN.

WEAVER, TIM 1944-
(trial lawyer; Yakama Nation litigation attorney)
Born November 28, 1944, Fort Lewis, Wash. *Education*: University of Washington, BA, 1967; Willamette University, JD, 1970. *Address*: 402 E. Yakima Ave. #190, Yakima, WA 98801 (509) 575-1500. E-mail: weavertimatty@qwest.net. *Affiliation*: Litigation attorney (handling all aspects of their legal matters), Yakama Nation, Toppenish, WA, 1971-present. *Other professional posts*: Legal representation of numerous tribal members & businesses. *Past professional posts*: Former president of the Litigation Section Executive Committee of the Washington State Bar Assn; former cleric, Washington State Supreme Court; editor of the Willamette Law Journal. *Community activities*: Yakama Rotary Club; Habitat for Humanity (volunteer). *Memberships*: Washington State Bar Assn (WSBA); Federal Bar Assn (FBA); American Trial Lawyers Assn (ATLA); Washington Trial Lawyers Assn.

WEBBER, CHIEF THUNDERBIRD IV (Kaweah Shoshone)
(tribal grand chief)
Affiliation & Address: Grand Chief, Kaweah Indian Nation of America, P.O. Box 48003, Wichita, KS 67201 (316) 303-1275

WEBKAMIGAD, HOWARD (Ojibwe)
(director of Ojibwe language program)
Education: Laurentian University, BA, BEd (Native Languages); Michigan State University, MA (Linguistics);. *Affiliation & Address*: Program Director & Assistant Professor of the jibwe Language, Algoma University, 1520 Quen St. East, Sault Ste. Marie, ON P6A 2G4 Canada (705) 949-2301. E-mail: howard.webkamigad@algomau.ca.

WECKEAH (BILL BRADLEY) (Comanche)
(storyteller)
Address: Bill Bradley, Rt. 1, Box 128-A, Lawton, OK 73501. Weckeah tells traditional Comanche stories, Comanche oral history, & original oral tales.

WEDDELL, CYNDI (Santee Sioux)
(tribal vice president)
Affiliation & Address: Vice President, Flandreau Santee Sioux Tribe, P.O. Box 283, Flandreau, SD 57028 (605) 997-3891.

WEDDLE, JENNIFER HARVEY (Northern Cheyenne/Cree)
(attorney; co-chair, Indian law practice)
Education: University of Michigan, BA, 1997; Harvard Law School, JD, 2000. *Affiliation & Address*: Co-chair, National American Indian Law Practice,

Greenberg Traurig, LLP, 1200 Seventeenth St., Suite 2400, Denver, CO 80202 (303) 572-6565. E-mail: weddlej@gtlaw.com. *Past professional post*: Manager, Indian Law Practice Group (2000-10), Holland & Hart LLP, Denver, CO. *Practice area*: Indian law; litigation; oil & gas. *Practice expertise*: Tribal jurisdiction & natural resources development on tribal lands. Ms. Weddle also has U.S. Supreme Court experience, serving as on of the attorneys for respondent in the Indian Law case of Nevada vs. Hicks (2001). Jennifer is a frequent speaker on tribal rights, Indian law matters & Native Americans' unique racial & political perspective on legal diversity issues. *Membership*: National Native American Bar Association. *Awards, honors*: Listed, The Best Lawyers in America, Native American Law, 2010-2013; listed, "Top Women Lawyers," Law Week Colorado, 2012; listed, Super Lawyers magazine, Colorado Super Lawyers, "Rising Star," 2010-2012; listed, Chambers USA Guide, 2010-12; listed, "Forty Under 40," Denver Business Journal, 2010.

WEDDLE, STAR TEHEE (Oklahoma Cherokee)
(artist)
Born February 24 in Okla. *Education*: Southern Methodist University, 1973-75; Trinity University (San Antonio, TX), BA, 1977). *Principal occupation*: Artist. *Address*: 806 Jefferson St., Bastrop, TX 78602 (512) 321-3733. *Affiliation*: Full time artist, 1984- (emphasis on easel art with Indian subject matter). *Community activities*: Judge of student art; art committee of Houston Livestock Show & Rodeo; office & director of InterTribal Council. *Memberships*: Indian Arts & Crafts Assn; Southwestern Assn for Indian Arts; Descendants of Cherokee Seminaries' Students; National Museum of the American Indian, Smithsonian Institution. *Awards, honors*: Santa Fe Indian Market: First Place in Painting, 1990; Third Place in Miniature Paintings, 1990; Honorable Mention, Contemporary Painting, 1990 & 1991; Third Place in Drawing, 1991; First Place in Miniature Paintings, 1991 & 1992. Gallup Inter-Tribal Ceremonial: Second Place in Miniature Painting, 1990. Ohio Inter-Tribal Experience: Honorable Mention in Painting, 1991. *Interest*: Featured artist at the State Capitol of Texas; participant in juried & invitational shows; numerous gallery exhibits and shows. Co-author of educational book in progress.

WEEDEN, ANNAWON S., SR. (Mashpee Wampanoag) 1973-
(museum Native American program developer)
Born October 19, 1973, Westerly, R.I. *Education*: GED. *Principal occupation*: Museum Native American program developer. *Address*: 99 David St., Apt. 1E, New Bedford, MA 02744 (508) 979-4171. E-mail: weeden@bostonkids.org. *Affiliations*: Museum teacher/artisan/speaker/interpreter, Plimoth Plantation, 1992-99; Native American program developer, The Children's Museum, Boston, MA, 1999-present. *Other professional posts*: Lectures, school visits (programs); wood/carving demonstrations; curriculum consultant; actor. *Community activities*: Helped develop a seven house village for Mashpee Wampanoag Tribe; American Indian Day Coordinator, Boston Powwow, 2002; drummer & singer, public speaker; mentor. *Membership*: Mashpee Wampanoag Tribe (Mashpee, MA). *Interests*: Preservation of Wampanoag culture, heritage, traditions, oral history, songs, language, society, youth, etc.

WEEDEN, EVERETT G., JR. (*Tall Oak*) (Mashantucket Pequot, Wampanoag) 1936-
(educational consultant; storyteller)
Born September 4, 1936, Providence, R.I. Education: Rhode Island School of Design, 1955-56. *Principal occupation*: Educational consultant. *Address*: 4600 S. County Trail, Charlestown, RI 02813-3426 (401) 364-8859. *Affiliations*: Boston Children's Museum, Boston, Mass., 1973-; Haffenreffer Museum of Anthropology, Brown University, Bristol, RI, 1992-. *Military service*: U.S. Army Reserves, 1957-63. *Memberships*: Charlestown Historical Society (charter member since 1970); Connecticut Society of Genealogists, 1981-; Indian & Colonial Research Center, Old Mystic, CT, 1992-; Rhode Island Historical Society; Mashantucket Pequot Museum Research Center (charter member); American Indian Friends Coalition (advisory board). *Awards, honors*: Helped develop the concept of the "National Day of Mourning" Observance at Plymouth Rock on Thanksgiving Day 1970. *Interests*: Tall Oak is a specialist in New England Native American histories & traditions. His lecture/demonstration programs are available using songs and dance of the New England Native Americans. "Always seeking to generate a more accurate and honest image of our people has led to my participation in several videos including Kevin Kostner's, "500 Nations" production in 1994, & "Mystic Voices" a documentary video on the Pequot War, now in production.

WEIDNER, KEZBAH (Navajo)
(actress, playwright)
Born in Indian Wells, Ariz. *Education*: Arizona State University. Resides in Flagstaff, Arizona. *Affiliation*: Owner, KEZ Productions. She has written & produced short plays & children's programs. She has appeared in numerous movies and has been a Navajo language consultant to various projects. *Film*: Bodies, Rest & Motion (Dine Woman, character), 1993;

WELBURN, RON (Gingaskin Assateague/Cherokee) 1944-
(professor of English)
Born April 30, 1944, Berwyn, Penna. *Education*: Lincoln University (PA), BA; University of Arizona, MA; New York University, PhD (American Studies). *Affiliation & Address*: Professor (1992-present), English Department, Bartlett Hall, University of Massachusetts, E463 South College, Amherst, MA 01003 (413) 545-5518. E-mail: rwelburn@english.umass.edu. *Past professional posts*: Ron served as director of the department's American Studies Graduate Concentration, and co-founded and directed the Certificate Program in Native American Indian Studies (Anthropology). He has led teacher workshops and book discussions for the Five College Public School Partnership, state arts and humanities councils in New York, Connecticut, and Massachusetts, and for the Mashantucket Pequot Library and Research Center. His book reviews have appeared in *CHOICE, American Indian Culture and Research Journal*, and elsewhere. *Community activities*: Massachusetts Foundation for the Humanities; Southern Connecticut Library Council; consultant & discussion leader, Five Colleges Public School Partnership, Amherst, MA 1995-; Massachusetts Foundation for the Humanities *Memberships*: Assn for American Indian & Alaskan Professors; Greenfield Review Literary Center (Board of Directors); Wordcraft Circle of Native Writers & Storytellers (Mentor). *Interests*: Hiking; "attending selected powwows with my wife where we occasionally vend for the Native Authors Project and/or dance." *Published works*: Poetry: Peripheries, 1972; Heartland; The Look in the Night Sky; Brownup; Council Decision, 1990; Roanoke and Wampum: Topics in Native American Heritage & Literatures, (Peter Lang, 2001) 2002 co-winner of the Wordcraft Circle of the Americas Creative Prose Nonfiction Award.; Coming Through Smoke and the Dreaming: Selected Poems, 2001; *Hartford's Ann Plato and the Native Borders of Identity* (SUNY Press, 2015).

WELCH, KAMAILI (*Smiles*) (Mohawk)
(special education teacher)
Education: Western Maryland College, BA in Psychology; Johns Hopkins University, MS (Special Education). *Principal occupation*: Special education teacher. *Address*: 4911 42nd Ave., Hyattsville, MD 20781. E-mail: kamaili_welch@fc.mcpps.k12.md.us. *Community activities*: Volunteer with animal rescue organizations.

WELCH, MARVEL ANDREA (Eastern Cherokee)
(social worker)
Education: University of Tennessee, Knoxville, MSW (Clinical Social Work), 2005; PhD candidate in Public Health at Walden University. Her concentration is on Community Health promotions. *Affiliation & Address*: Cherokee Center of Native Health Board, Cherokee, NC 28719. She began working with the Eastern Band of Cherokee Nations Mental Health & Substance Abuse program as a Child and Family Therapist, and Clinical Supervisor for the Child Team. To date Marvel affiliations consist of the following: Cherokee Center of Native Health Board North Carolina Commission of Indian Affairs: Executive Committee; Indian Child Welfare Committee (Chairwoman); Legislative Committee; Recognition North Carolina Indian Health Board; North Carolina Minority Focus Group North Carolina Native Leadership Institute; North Carolina State Cooperative Extension Advisory Board; Marvel believes that it is an honor and privilege to be a member of the Eastern; Band of Cherokee's and a fluent speaker of her language. She is proud of her rich and unique culture and tradition.

WELCH, RICHARD (Eastern Cherokee)
(editor)
Affiliation: Cherokee One Feather, Eastern Band of Cherokee Indians, P.O. Box 501, Cherokee, NC 28719 (704) 497-5513.

WELCH, ROBERT J. (Viejas Kumeyaay Diegueno)
(tribal chairperson)
Affiliation & Address: Chairperson, Viejas Band of Kumeyaay Indians, 1 Viejas Grade Rd., Alpine, CA 91901 (619) 445-3810. E-mail: apico@viejas-nsn.gov. Elected in 2015 as chairman, Robert "Cita" Welch, Jr. is now serving his fourth term in office. Having previously serviced as vice chairman, Welch is well aware of the responsibilities placed upon him as chairman & leader of his Tribe. In order to pursue public & political administration, Welch left an 18 year career with Viejas Casino. Being one of Viejas' original employees, Welch held various roles and responsibilities within the casino and has a full understanding of tribal business. Throughout his scope of work, Welch held high-level positions in the Security, Off-Track Betting and Controller departments. At one time, Welch worked as the vice president of Tribal Enterprise Business Development. Politically, Welch has served as a lobbyist for the Tribe, building relationships and gaining support with state and federal elected officials during the campaign for Propositions 5 and 1-A in 2001, which successfully granted tribes across the state the exclusive right to tribal gaming. He gives presentations on Kumeyaay history & culture throughout the community.

WELLS, BERT (Caddo/Cherokee)
  (board president)
Affiliation: President, Board of Directors, American Indian Chamber of Commerce of Texas (AICCT), 11245 Indian Trail, 2nd Fl., Dallas, TX 75229 (972) 241-6450. E-mail: bwells@aicct.com. Website: www.aicct.com. *Other professional post*: Beard Mechanical, Inc., Dallas, TX.

WELLS, ELIZABETH A. (Sh-ush) (Mescalero Apache) 1940-
  (program director/founder)
Born March 12, 1940, Mescalero, N.M. *Address*: 6541 Baby Bear Dr., Anchorage, AK 99507 (907) 243-5561. *Affiliation*: Director & founder, Orre Drumrite Walking Heritage, Anchorage, AK (non-profit program to contact the Indian nation, thus to dedicate annually, an additional; thousand drums to sound at the same moment across all time zones. 1991: 1,000 drums; 1992: 2,000 drums; 1993: 3,000 drums, etc.) *Other professional post*: Editor, "Dancing Prayers," quarterly publication of Orre Drumrite Walking Heritage. Community activities: Coordinating international drum ceremonies, "Parade of the Spirits," "World Drum: Secrets of Life," "Drums of the Whispering Moon," "Standing Sun-calls-drums." Interests: "To meet with and visit all indigenous people around the world."

WELLS, LYNDEE (Gros Ventre/Chippewa Cree)
  (attorney)
Address & Affiliation: Dorsey & Whitney LLP, U.S. Bank Centre, 1420 Fifth Ave., Suite 3400, Seattle, WA 98101. E-mail: wells.lyndee@dorseylaw.com.

WELLS, WAYNE A. (Cheyenne River Lakota Sioux)
  (Indian center vice-chair)
Education: University of Colorado, BS (Management & Information Systems, 1995; Regis University, MS (Computer Information Systems), 2000. *Address & Affiliation*: Vice-chair, Denver Indian Center, 4407 Morrison Rd., Denver, CO 80219 (303) 936-2688. *Past professional post*: Mountain Bell/U.S. West, 1973-96. *Community activities*: Denver & Aurora Jaycees; vice-chair, Denver Indian Center. *Membership*: Masons. *Interests*: Indian education; "I am a Northern Traditional Dancer, and have participated in many powwows in Colorado, New Mexico & South Dakota. I practice my spirituality by being involved in the sweat lodge & other ceremonies."

WELTER, CHRISTINE
  (coordinator of Indigenous studies department)
Affiliation & Address: Academic Program Coordinator, Department of Inigenous Studies, Trent University, 1600 Westbank Dt., Peterborough, ON K9J 7B8 (705) 748-1011. E-mail: cwelter@trentu.ca.

WELSCH, ROGER
  (professor of anthropology)
Affiliation & Address: Adjunct Professor, Department of Anthropology, University of Nebraska, Lincoln, NE 68588. *Published works*: The Relunctant Pilgrim: A Skeptics Journey Into Native Mysteries (University of Nebraska Press, 2015); Touchng the Fire: Buffalo Dancers, The Sky Bundle, and Other Tales (Bison Books); My Nebraska (Bison Books); Embracing Fry Bread: Confessions of a Wanabe (the story of his lifelong relationship with Native American culture) (Bison Books, 2012).

WELSH, CAROL L. (*Zitkana Ho Waste Wi*) (Sisseton-Wahpeton) 1957-
  (Indian center director)
Born April 5, 1957, Calif. *Education*: BS degree. *Affiliation & Address*: Executive director, Native American Indian Center of Central Ohio, 67 E. Innis Ave., P.O. Box 07705, Columbus, OH 43207-0705 (614) 443-6120. E-mail: naicco@aol.com. *Interests*: Traditional music, dance, and crafts.

WELSH, RUSSELL (Mohave)
  (tribal vice chairperson)
Affiliation: Colorado River Indian Tribal Council, Route 1, Box 23-B, Parker, AZ 85344 (928) 669-9211.

WERCHOUSKI, KATRINA (Red Cliff lake Superior Ojibwe)
  (cultural center director)
Education: Northland College, BS (Environmental Studies), BA (Native American Studies; Green Mountain College, MS (Environmental Studies). *Affiliation & Address*: Director, Native American & Indigenous Culture Center, Northland College, Mead 116, 1411 Ellis Ave., Ashland, WI 54806 (715) 682-1344. E-mail: kwerchouski@northland.edu.

WESBERRY, CHRIS (Chickasaw)
  (coordinator of Native American studies program)
Affiliation & Address: Coordinator, Native American Studies Program, Native American Center for Student Success, Southeastern Oklahoma State University, 1405 North 4th, PMB 2747, Durant, OK 74701 (580) 745-3220. E-mail: cwesberry@se.edu.

WESLEY, LOWELL (Kialagee)
  (tribal town king)
Affiliation: Kialagee Tribal Town, P.O. Box 332, Wetumka, OK 74883 (405) 452-3262.

WESO, JEREMY (Menominee)
  (tribal vice chairperson)
Affiliation: Menominee Indian Tribe of Wisconsin, P.O. Box 910, Keshena, WI 54135 (715) 799-5100.

WESO, THOMAS F. PECORE (Menominee) 1953-
  (college instructor)
Born July 16, 1953, Keshena, Wisc. *Education*: University of Kansas, BS (Indigenous Nations Studies). *Address*: 1916 Stratford Rd., Lawrence, KS 66044 (913) 841-5757. E-Mail: tomweso@mmsn.com. *Affiliations*: University of Missouri, Kansas City - U.S. Archives Research Project, 1994-95; Instructor, Avila College, 1997; G.T.A., University of Kansas Dept. of Biological Science, 1998-99; temporary instructor, Haskell Indian Nations University, 2001-03; Instructor, Longview Community College, Kansas City, MO. *Membership*: Kansas Folklore Society; Native American Rights Fund. *Publication*: Langston Hughes in Lawrence.

WESSELS, WILLIAM (Chippewa)
  (school administrator)
Affiliation: Circle of Life Survival School, P.O. Box 447, White Earth, MN 56591 (218) 983-3285 ext. 269.

WEST, DAVID (Citizen Potawatomi)
  (Native American Studies & program director & instructor)
Education: University of Oregon, BA (Sociology), 1981; University of Alaska, Fairbanks, MA (Community Psychology), 1990. *Affiliation & Address*: Director Emeritus, Native American Studies Program, Southern Oregon University, Taylor Hall, Room 18b, 1250 Siskiyou, OR 97520 (541) 552-6751. E-mail: dwest@sou.edu. David serves as an advisor to the Native American student body and is faculty advisor for the Native American Student Union on campus.He actively participates in the Spring Powwow, often joining the drumming, singing & dancing in his traditional regalia; also assists at the annual Spring salmn bake during the Native American month in April. *Past professional posts*: David was the Native American Studies coordinator at Southern Oregon University until his retirement in 2015; Instiuional representative for the Southern Region with the Oregon Indian Coalition on Post Secondary Education; program director, Konaway Nika Tillicum, a residential Native American youth summer academy held on the univesity campus. David taught the Core courses in N.A. Studies at Southern Oregon University offering insight into both the historical perspectives as well contemporary Native American issues. His advocacy efforts for Native American Indian education in Oregon is evidenced by the success of Konaway Nika Tillicum, a residential Native American youth summer academy held on the University campus . This academy is a stand alone unique model program in Oregon and the West Coast. David is a member of the Oregon Indian Education Association, the National Indian Education Association, The National Congress of American Indians and serves as the institutional representative for the Southern Region with the Oregon Indian Coalition on Post Secondary Education.

WEST, JAMES L. (Cheyenne)
  (former president/CEO)
Education: University of Redlands, BA, 1968; Andover Newton Theological School, MDiv., 1971. *Past Affiliation*: President/CEO (1997-2012), Futures for Children, Albuquerque, NM. Mr. West became president/CEO of Futures for Children in 1997 after serving on its Board of Directors for more than eight years. *Past professional posts*: President, Jim West Financial Group, Inc.; president, Okom Enterprises, Inc.; vice-president, American Indian National Bank of Albuquerque.

WEST, W. RICHARD, JR. (Cheyenne/Arapaho) 1943-
  (former founding museum director)
Born January 6, 1943, San Bernardino, Calif. *Education*: University of Redlands (CA), BA, 1965 (Magna Cum Laude-Phi Beta Kappa); Harvard University, MA (American History), 1968; Stanford University School of Law, JD, 1971. *Affiliation & Address*: President/CEO, Autry National Center of the American West, 4700 Western Heritage Way, Los Angeles, CA 90027 (323) 667-2000. *Other professional posts*: Of Counsel Attorney, Stetson & Jordan, P.C., Albuquerque, NM; Founding Director & (Director Emeritus, 2007-present), National Museum of the American Indian, Smithsonian Institution, Washington, DC.; board member, Native Arts & Cultures Foundation, Vancouver, WA; member, Board of Directors, Tribal Business Opportunities, Inc., Albuquerque, NM. Mr. West was responsible for guiding the successful opening of the three facilities that comprises the National Museum. He oversaw the creation & completion of the George Gustav Heye Center, a museum exhibition facility, which opened in New York City on Oct. 30, 1994.

He supervised the overall planning of the Museum's Cultural Resources Center, which houses its vast 800,000-object collection, and is located in Suitland, MD. West oversees the fund-raising campaign of the museum, which also provides for an endowment & ongoing educational & outreach programs. *Past professional post*: Formerly a partner in the Washington, DC law firm of Fried, Frank, Harris, Shriver & Jacobson, and the Indian-owned, Albuquerque, NM law firm of Gover, Stetson, Williams & West, P.C. He served as general counsel & special counsel to numerous Indian tribes & organizations. *Community activities*: Stanford University, 2002-present; Ford Foundation, 1999-present; member, National Support Committee, Native American Rights Fund, 1990-; board member, National Support Committee of the Native American Rights Fund, 1990-present; American Indian Resources Institute, 1973-present. *Memberships*: American Association of Museums/ International Council of Museums (vice-chairman of the Board of Directors); National Parks & Conservation Assn; Cheyenne-Arapaho Tribe of Oklahoma; Bar of the State of California; Bar of the District of Columbia; Bar of the U.S. Supreme Court; Bar of the U.S. Court of Appeals for Eighth District; American Bar Assn (former chairperson, Committee on Problems of the American Indian, Section of Individual Rights & Responsibilities); Federal Bar Assn (Indian Section); Indian Bar Assn of New Mexico; *Awards, honors*: Recipient, Career Achievement Award, University of Redlands, 1987; Hilmer Oehlmann, Jr. Prize for excellence in legal writing at Stanford University Law School and served as an editor & note editor of the Stanford Law Review. *Interests*: As director of the National Museum of the American Indian, West is responsible for guiding the successful opening of the three facilities that will comprise the museum. He oversaw the completion of the George Gustav Heye Center, the museum's exhibition facility which opened in New York City on October 30, 1994, and continues to supervise the overall planning of the museum's Cultural Resources Center, which will house the NMAI's vast one-million object collection, scheduled to be completed in Suitland, MD, in 1999. West's philosophy & vision for the museum have been critical in guiding the architectural planning of the Mall museum, which is scheduled to open on the last available site on the National Mall in Washington, DC, in 2002. West has devoted his professional life and much of his personal life to working with American Indians on cultural, educational, legal, and governmental issues. West will continue to oversee the fund-raising campaign of the museum, which will provide for an endowment and ongoing educational & outreach programs. *Published works*: Articles - "Chief Justice Traynor and the Parol Evidence Rule (22 Stanford Law Review 547, 1970); co-author, "Healing v. Jones: Mandate for Another Trail of Tears" (N.D. Law Review 73, 1974); co-author, "The Alaska Native Claims Settlement Act: A Flawed Victory" (40 Law & Contemporary Problems 132, 1976); author, "The Source and Scope of Tribal Powers" (Manual of Indian Law, 1977); co-author, "The Struggle for Indian Civil Rights" (Indians in American History, 1988).

WESTERMAN, GWEN N.
(symposium director)
Affiliation & Address: Director, Native American Literature Symposium, Minnesota State University, Mankato, P.O. Box 541, Mankato, MN 56002 (507) 389-5508. E-mail: gwen.westerman@mnsu.edu.

WESTERMEYER, JOSEPH JOHN, MD 1937-
(physician, psychiatrist)
Born April 8, 1937, Chicago, Ill. *Education*: University of Minnesota, BS, 1959, MD, 1961; MA, 1969, MPH & PhD, 1970. *Address*: 1935 Summit Ave., St. Paul, MN 55105 (612) 725-2037. E-mail: weste010@umn.edu. *Affiliations*: University of Minnesota Hospitals & Clinics (UMHC), Minneapolis, MN, 1970-89, 1992-present; professor & chair, Dept. of Psychiatry & Behavioral Sciences, University of Oklahoma Health Sciences Center, 1989-92; director of Mental & Behavioral Health Patient Service Line at Minneapolis VAMC, 1992-present. *Other professional posts*: Director, Alcohol-Drug Dependence Program, (UMHC), 1982-; director, International Clinic (UMHC), 1984-. *Community activities*: Indian Guest House (halfway house for Indian alcoholics), Minneapolis, MN (board member, 1969-72); Juel Fairbanks House (halfway house for Indian alcoholics), St. Paul, Minn. (board member, 1970-73); South Side Receiving Center (a detoxification unit for American Indian alcoholics), Minneapolis, Minn. (consultant, 1974-75); Association of American Indian Affairs, including Senate subcommittee hearing on American Indian child welfare, 1973-76. *Memberships*: American Psychiatric Assn (Fellow); American Anthropological Assn (Fellow); American Public Health Assn; American Assn of Family Practice (Fellow); Assn of Academic Psychiatrists; Minnesota Psychiatric Society (president); National Assn of V.A. Psychiatric Administrators & Leaders (past president) Society for the Study of Psychiatry & Culture; American Assn of Addiction Psychiatry; et al. *Biographical sources*: Who's Who in America; International Who's Who in Medicine (Cambridge, UK); International Who's Who of Professionals (Jacksonville, NC); *Awards, honors*: The Best Doctors in America, Alcoholism-Addictions Psychiatry, 1993 & 1998; numerous research grants. *Published works*: Chapters in books & monographs: "The Ravage of Indian Families in Crisis," in The Destruction of Indian Family Life, S. Unger, ed. (Assn of American Indian Affairs, 1976); edited with J. Baker, "Alcoholism & American Indian Alcoholism," in Alcoholism

Development, Intervention & Consequences (E. Heinman, 1986); Alcoholism & Comorbid Psychiatric Disorder Among Native Americans (University of Arizona Press, 2002). Also, wrote & co-wrote numerous journal articles on mental health care & issues pertaining to alcohol use & gambling among American Indians & Hispanics; book reviews.

WESTON, TROY "SCOTT" (Oglala Sioux)
(tribal president)
Affiliation & Address: President (2017-present), Oglala Sioux Tribal Executive Committee, Pine Ridge Indian Reservation, P.O. Box 2070, Pine Ridge, SD 57770 (605) 867-4021. E-mail: tsweston@gwtc.net

WESTON, WENDY (Navajo)
(arts administrator)
Education: Arizona State University, BS (Political Science). *Address*: 2301 N. Central Ave., Phoenix, AZ 85004 (602) 251-0284. E-mail: wweston@heard.org. *Affiliations*: Education Programs Specialist, Heard Museum, Phoenix, AZ; co-curator: Horse exhibition, WE ARE! Exhibition, Sharing Ancestral Creations, City of Phoenix Art Collection, Phoenix, AZ; museum's editor, Native Peoples Magazine. *Community activities*: Native American Recognition Days Committee, Phoenix, AZ; Phoenix Dine Incorporated, Phoenix, AZ. *Publications*: Editor, Directory of Native American Performing Artists (ATLATL, Phoenix, AZ).

WETSIT, DEBORAH
(dean of instruction)
Education: Ed.D. Affiliation: Haskell Indian Nations University, 155 Indian Ave. #1305, Lawrence, KS 66046 (875) 749-8404. dwetsit@rossl.cc.haskell.edu

WETZEL, DON (*Flying Eagle*) (Blackfeet) 1948-
(administrator)
Born August 1, 1948, Cut Bank, Mont. *Education*: University of Montana, BA, 1972, MA, 1981. *Affiliation & Address*: Coordinator (1989-present), Governor's Office of Indian Affairs, 1218 E. 6th Ave., Helena, MT 59620 (406) 444-3702. *Past professional posts*: Teacher/coach in Browning, MT (eight years); High School Principal in Browning, MT (3 years); Supt. of Schools, Corvallis, MT (four years); teacher/coach, Haskell Indian Junior College, 1982-83. *Awards, honors*: Nominated National Coach of the Year, 1980; Coach of the Year, Blackfeet Reservation, 1980; Jefferson Award-outstanding public service Administrator of the Year, State of Montana Library Association, 1988. *Interests*: "All on my own time - used vacation time & received the Jefferson Award for my crusade against drug and alcohol use among our young Indian People. I traveled 12,000 miles and talked with 10,000 students in Montana in a 2 1/2 year span." *Biographical sources*: Article on crusade, "Indian Life"; Missoula and Great Falls Tribune, and Billings Gazette.

WEXLER, LISA MARIN
(associate professor & program head, community health education)
Education: University of West Florida, BA, 1991; Florida State University, MSW, 1996; University of Minnesota, PhD, 2005. *Affiliation & Address*: Associate Professor & Program Head, Community Health Education, School of Public Health & Health Sciences, 313 Arnold House, University of Massachusetts, Amherst, MA 01003 (413) 545-2248. E-mail: lwexler@schoolph.umass.edu. *Other professional post*: Affiliated Faculty, Five College Native American & Indigenous Studies. *Areas of Specialization*: American Indian/Alaska Native Suicide Prevention; Indigenous Youth Resilience; Culturally-Specific Behavioral Health Services; Digitally-Enhanced Participatory Research.

WHEAT, SCOTT (Choctaw of Oklahoma)
(attorney)
Education: The Evergreen State College, BA; Seattle University School of Law, JD, 1995. *Affiliation & Address*: Of Counsel, Galanda Broadman, 1403 S. Grand Blvd., Suite 101, North #11, Spokane, WA 99203 (509) 954-6557. E-mail: scott@galandabroadmann.com (2013-present), Scott's practice focuses on tribal sovereignty issues, including land & environmental issues, economic development matters, & complex Indian Country litigation. Scott's broad, multi-state litigation experience includes representing tribal governments and enterprises in tribal, state & federal courts in matters involving gaming, taxation, jurisdiction, sovereign immunity, Treaty fishing rights, natural resource protection, land use, federal recognition, ancient land claims, commercial agreements, and PL 638 contracts. Scott has served tribal governments in various capacities, including as general counsel, in-house associate counsel, and special gaming counsel. He has negotiated Class III gaming compacts, federal Secretarial procedures in lieu of compacts, & state/tribal cigarette, tobacco & fuel taxation agreements. Scott has substantial experience representing tribes throughout the West in all areas of tobacco commerce. He is also a leading practitioner in the area of after-acquired Indian lands for gaming, under the Indian Gaming Regulatory Act. Scott, a sole proprietor, currently serves as General Counsel and Special Gaming Counsel for the Spokane

Tribe. Prior to associating with Galanda Broadman as Of Counsel, Scott was an attorney for Crowell Law Offices from 2007-2013, where he focused on complex litigation on behalf of tribes. Scott has also served as in-house counsel for the Office of the Spokane Tribal Attorney (2005-2007) and for the Office of the Suquamish Tribal Attorney (1996-2002). Over the course of his career, he has also served tribes as a tribal prosecutor, public defender, judge, or appellate justice.

WHEELER, GARY (Cayuga)
(tribal representative)
Affiliation & Address: Representative, Cayuga Indian Nation, P.O. Box 11, Versailles, NY 14168 (716) 337-4270.

WHEELER, MARGARET ROACH (Chickasaw-Choctaw) 1944-
(fashion designer, weaver; lecturer, teacher)
E-mail: margaret@margaretroachwheeler.com. *Affiliations*: Wheeler has merged her fine arts education with her Native American heritage to weave contemporary garments based on American Indian costumes. She has also created "the Mahotans" an imaginary tribe of totemic structures and spirit figures, where each member is adorned in hand woven robes. Her hand woven garments are shown at the major Indian Markets in North America and exhibited in museums in Oklahoma, New Mexico, New York, Colorado, Indiana & Arizona and in Handweavers Guilds of America's "Convergence" fashion shows. She lectures, and teaches workshops & seminars on Native American fibers and her unique style of weaving. *Awards, honors*: Margaret was one of four Native American fashion designers chosen to speak at the Smithsonian's National Museum of the American Indian in New York. She was also one of the recipients of the Artist-in-Residence program National Museum of the American Indian in New York; President's Award at Red Earth Festival; textile awards at the 2009 Southeastern Art Show & Market. Her work was exhibited in "Changing Hands II" at the Museum of Art & Design in New York. Wheeler is a 2010 Inductee into the Chickasaw Nation Hall of Fame.

WHEELER, WINONA (Cree/Assiniboine/Salteaux)
(professor of Native Studies)
Education: University of Manitoba, BA, 1986; University of British Columbia, MA, 1988; University of California, Berkeley, PhD, 2000. *Affiliation & Address*: Associate Professor & Head, Department of Native Studies, Kirk Hall 127, University of Saskatchewan, 117 Science Place, Saskatoon, SK S7N Canada (306) 966-6210. E-mail: winona.wheeler@usask.ca. *Other professional post*: Presient-Elect (2014-15), Native American & Indigenous Studies Association. Winona has been a professional historian & a professor of Indigenous Studies since 1988. She is a member of the Fisher River Cree Nation in Treaty No. 5 (Manitoba). *Other professional post*: Regular columnist "Introspection" in Eaglefeather News. *Published works*: Numerous articles in scholarly journals.

WHEELOCK, RICHARD M. (Oneida of Wisconsin) 1950-
(associate professor)
Born April 30, 1950, Yakima, Wash. *Education*: Fort Lewis College, BA (English and teaching certification); University of Arizona, MA (American Indian Studies); University of New Mexico, PhD (American Studies). *Address*: P.O. Box 524, Ignacio, CO 81137. *Office address*: 284 Center of Southwest Studies, Fort Lewis College, Durango, CO 81301 (970) 247-7227; E-Mail: wheelock_r@fortlewis.edu. *Affiliation*: Associate Professor, Dept. of Southwest Studies, Fort Lewis College, Durango, CO. *Other professional post*: Faculty sponsor for the "Intertribal News," a bi-weekly student publication of Fort Lewis College. *Memberships*: Native American Journalists Assn; Western Social Sciences Assn (executive board member). *Interests*: Communications issues in Indian country; tribal sovereignty issues; tribal-state relations; Indian education issues. *Published works*: The Ute Legacy: A Study Guide, with Farren Webb, provides activities for public high schools in their classes about the Ute Indian Tribe (Southern Ute Tribe, 1989); The Ute Circle of Life, edited with Farren Webb, an elementary school teaching unit (includes over 20 activities, and many games & photographs for classroom use) about the history and modern culture of the Southern Ute Tribe (Southern Ute Tribe, 1990); "Indian Self-Determination: The Charge to Indian Journalists," article in The Social Science Journal, Vol. 32, No. 3, 1995); "The Value of the Concepts of 'Tribalism' and 'Mass Society' in Tribal Communications Research," section in A Good Cherokee, A Good Anthropologist: Papers in Honor of Robert K. Thomas, ed. by Steve Pavlik (American Indian Studies Center, UCLA, 1998).

WHEELOCK, SARAH I. (Meskwaki "Sac & Fox Tribe of the MS in IA")
Education: University of Iowa, BA (Honors & Distinction), College of Law, JD (with Distinction). *Affiliation & Address*: Of Counsel, Tilden McCoy & Dilweg LLP, 5006 Sergeant Rd. #263, Sioux City, IA 51106 (612) 280-8851. E-mail: swheelock@tildenmccoy.com. Sarah represents Indian tribes, tribal organizations, tribal colleges, and entities doing business with tribes in a variety of matters, including: tribal economic development, finance & project lending, New Markets Tax Credit transactions, corporate law (including creating holding companies and setting up corporate structures for tribally owned businesses), employment law, contracts and contractual disputes, tribal

governance & code drafting, administrative proceedings, environmental law, and general & appellate litigation. She has represented tribes in closing approximately $54 Million of New Market Tax Credits in the last few years. Sarah's pro bono practice includes Indian Child Welfare Act (ICWA) and general guardianship matters. Sarah has spoken at a number of professional events on topics including how to use tax credits to fund tribal projects, diversity in the legal profession, and the need to test federal Indian law on state bar exams. Prior to joining Tilden McCoy + Dilweg LLP in April 2015, Sarah began her legal career at a large law firm in Minneapolis, Minnesota, before returning to her home state of Iowa. After two years with a local Iowa firm, she spent three years at a nationally recognized boutique Indian law firm. During her career, Sarah has been selected as a Super Lawyers Rising Star in Native American Law on four occasions (Minnesota Rising Stars in 2008 and 2009 and Great Plains Rising Stars in 2013 and 2014). She was also recognized as the Outstanding Alumni of the Year in 2007 by the National Native American Law Students Association. Sarah is admitted to practice law in Iowa, Minnesota, and various tribal & federal courts. Sarah has been active in professional organizations, including the Iowa State Bar Assn; Minnesota State Bar Assn (Council Member 2007-2008 and Alternate Council Member 2006-2007); Federal Bar Assn, Indian Law Section (Development of Federal Indian Law Committee Member 2010-2013); Minnesota American Indian Bar Assn (Vice President 2006-2008, Secretary 2005-2006, and Board Member, 2005-2009).

WHIPPLE, CRYSTAL M. (Pequot)
(former tribal vice chairperson)
Education: University of New Haven, A.A. (Business Administration). *Affiliation & Address*: Vice Chairperson (2010-15), Mashantuckett Pequot Tribal Nation, 2 Matts Path, P.O. Box 3060, Mashantucket, CT 06338 (860) 396-6100.

WHITAKER, KATHLEEN 1945-
(research center director)
Born October 10, 1945, Los Angeles, Calif. *Education*: Northern Arizona University, BA, 1976; University of California, Los Angeles, MA, 1982, PhD, 1986. *Principal occupation*: Research center director. *Address*: 2501 Kerwin Pl., Los Angeles, CA 90065. E-mail: whitaker@sarsf.org. *Affiliations*: San Diego Museum of Man, 1976-79; chief curator, Southwest Museum, Los Angeles, CA, 1979-98; director, Indian Arts Research Center, School of American Research, Santa Fe, NM, 1998-present. *Other professional posts*: Former editor, Council for Museum of Anthropology; Research Associate, Los Angeles County Museum of Natural History. *Membership*: American Association of Museums; New Mexico Association of Museums; Native American Arts Studies Association; American Anthropological Association. *Published works*: Common Threads: Navajo & Pueblo Textiles in the Southwest Museum; Southwest Textiles: Weavings of the Navajo & Pueblo.

WHITE, ALBERT (Mohawk) 1950-
(artist)
Born January 25, 1950, Binghamton, N.Y. *Education*: Maryland Art Institute (Baltimore, MD), BA; attended San Francisco Institute of Art; post graduate student of Master Ann Schuler, disciple of the maroger technique. *Principal occupation*: Artist. *Address*: 386 Loughlin Rd., Binghamton, NY 13904 (607) 775-2453. E-mail: familycs@spectra.net. *Affiliations*: Otsiningo Powwow, Binghamton, NY, 1980-; affiliate artist, The Iroquois Museum, Howes Cave, NY, 1985-. *Other professional posts*: Commissioned portrait artist; consultant for A&E presentation, "How the West Was Lost," 1995. *Community activities*: Teacher & storyteller in the Iroquois tradition; school presentations. *Memberships*: A.I.M.; World Wildlife Foundation. *Published works*: Skunnywundy Stories, 1996; The Albert White Cookbook: YoWago "It Tastes Good!" 1999.

WHITE, BETTY JANE (*Usdi agehya*) (Cherokee) 1943-
(professional nurse)
Born July 2, 1943, Holton, Kans. *Education*: Haskell Indian Jr. College, AA, 1991; Baker University/Stormont Vail School of Nursing (Baldwin City, KS), BS (Nursing), 1993; University of Kansas, MS (Nursing); *Principal occupation*: Professional nurse. *Address*: P.O. Box 906, Wagner, SD 57380-0906. *Affiliation*: St. Francis Hospital & Medical Center, Topeka, KS (Oncology Nursing; Clinical Caring for AIDS patients & other acute medical disease/illnesses), 1989-. *Community activities*: Topeka Railroad Days (chairperson for Native Americans); director of Native American Dance Troupe; lecturer of Native American history & legends. *Memberships*: American Nurses Assn; Kansas Student Nurses Association; Native American Journalism Society; American Indian Science & Engineering Society (vice-president, local chapter, 1990-91; member, 1992-); Native American Cultural Society (chairperson, 1992). *Awards, honors*: Haskell Scholastic Excellence Award from Bess Spiva Timmons Foundation; Darby Scholarship Award for most active in Native American culture; Scholastic Excellence Award, Haskell Indian Jr. College; Selectee for Truman Award, Baker University; Kansas Nurse Foundation Award. *Interests*: "Areas I am most interested in are the protection & rights of children from all forms of abuse & neglect. I am involved in the beginning stages of organizing a chapter in Jefferson County for the prevention of child

abuse. Health care to the elderly & disabled – longterm care facilities are needed on our reservations, run by the tribal members, for tribal members. Educating the public regarding misconceived ideas about Native Americans. Until the schools and media begin educating the public of the true history of the U.S., the public will always need educating. Holistic healing - the body, mind, and spirit needs to be in balance for healing to occur. If one is ill, the other two will be affected also. I have initiated and started up a Native American Dance Troupe to perform at various functions. The goal for this troupe is to perform nationwide and in foreign countries. Telling a story while the dancing is taking place and the dancing tells the story, is another way to educate the public about Native Americans." *Biographical sources*: Numerous articles relating to health care in "Nursing News," "Sunflower Times," & "Professional Journal"; and a weekly article entitled, "The Fun Side of Life," in Oskaloosa Independent Newspaper.

WHITE, BONNIE L. 1953-
(Indian education program director)
Born October 31, 1953, Tampa, Fla. *Education*: BA in Secondary Education & Foreign Languages (French & German). *Principal occupation*: Indian education program director. *Address*: 312 Oswego St., Syracuse, NY 13204 (315) 435-4288. E-mail: blwhite315@aol.com. *Affiliations*: Syracuse City School District (Substance Abuse Prevention Counselor/Educator, 1988-95; Title IX Indian Education Program Director, 1995-present); Consultant & Interpreter, Ste. Marie Among the Iroquois Living History Museum, 1995-present. *Community activities*: Board member, North American Indian Project; Trainer & Facilitator for Community-Wide Dialogue on Race & Racism; advisory board member, AICH Outreach programs - Wish, Generations. *Memberships*: National Indian Education Association; NANACOA.

WHITE, CAROL
(cultural center director)
Address & Affiliation: Akwesasne Cultural Center - Akwesasne Library & Museum, St. Regis Mohawk Nation, Rt. 37 RR 1, Box 14C, Hogansburg, NY 13655 (518) 358-2240. *Other professional post*: Editor, "Kariwenhawi Newsletter," St. Regis Mohawk Reservation, Hogansburg, NY.

WHITE, DOUGLAS (Snuneymuxw First Nation)
(First Nation chief)
Education: Vancouver Island University, BA (First Nations Studies); University of Victoria, JD. *Affiliation*: Chief, Snuneymuxw First Nation, Nanaimo, BC, Canada. *Address*: 630 Shoreline Dr., Nanaimo, BC V0R 5A1 Canada (250) 740-2300. E-mail: douglaswhite@snuneymuxw.ca. *Other professional posts*: Lecturer at universities on legal issues regarding Aboriginal peoples; board member of many boards & committees including: Snuneymuxw First Nation Economic Development Corporation, the University of Victoria's School of Public Administrations Advisory Board, and a past executive member of the Indigenous Bar Association of Canada. *Past professional post*: Practicing lawyer at an Aboriginal law firm in Vancouver representing First Nations & Aboriginal organizations on a range of legal issues.

WHITE, ERIC (Stillaguamish)
(tribal vice chairperson)
Affiliation & Address: Vice Chairperson, Stillaguamish Tribe of Indians, P.O. Box 277, Arlington, WA 98223 (360) 652-7362.

WHITE, FRANK (Winnebago of Nebraska)
(tribal chairperson)
Affiliation & Address: Chairperson, P.O. Box 687, Winnebago, NE 68071 (402) 878-3110; E-mail: frank.white@winnebagotribe.com

WHITE, HALLIE BONGAR
(executive director)
Affiliation & Address: Executive Director, Southwest Center for Law & Policy, 475 S. Stone Ave., Tucson, AZ 85701 (520) 623-8192. E-mail: bongarwhite@ swclap.org.

WHITE, JACKIE (Cherokee)
(executive director of federal programs)
Education: Northeastern State University, BA (Special Education), 1972; University of Tulsa, MA (Public School Administration), 1979. *Affiliation & Address*: Executive Director of Federal Programs (2012-present), Johnson-O'Malley Board of Directors, Union Public Schools, Indian Education Programs, 8506 E. 61st St., Tulsa, OK 74133 (918) 357-4321. *Other professional post*: Appointed to the National Johnson-O'Malley Board of Directors

WHITE, JAMES M. (Mdewakanton Sioux)
(tribal council president)
Affiliation: Prairie Island Community Council, 5750 Sturgeon Lake Rd., Welch, MN 55089 (612) 385-2536.

WHITE, KALVIN (Dine' Navajo)
(education administrator; CEO & founder)
Born & raised in White Cone, Arizona. *Education*: University of Utah, PhD (Counseling Psychology), 1998. *Affiliation & Address*: Principal Investigator, Navajo Nation Rural Systemic Initiative (NN-RSI), Navajo Nation, Department of Dine Education, P.O. Box 670, Window Rock, AZ 86515 (928) 871-7448. E-mail: kalvinwhite@nndode.org (NN-RSI is a National Science Foundation grant awarded to the Navajo Nation with emphasis on closing the academic achievement gap between Navajo & non-Navajo students). *Other professional post*: CEO & Founder, Native Wholistic Specialists, Inc., P.O. Box 3297, Window Rock, AZ 86515 (928) 871-5726.

WHITE, KEVIN
(director of Native American studies program)
Affiliation & Address: Department Chair & Program Director, SUNY-Oswego, Native Studies Program, Anthropology Department, 307A Mahar Hall, Oswego, NY 13126 (315) 341-3290; E-mail: kevin.white@oswego.edu

WHITE, LINCOLN C. (Mohawk)
(tribal chief)
Affiliation: St. Regis Mohawk Council Chiefs, Akwesasne-Community Bldg., Hogansburg, NY 13655 (518) 358-2272. *Past professional post*: Director, National Advisory Council on Indian Education, Washington, DC.

WHITE, MARILYN J. (Dine-Navajo)
(storyteller, writer, poet)
Address: 3023 W. Brenda Loop, Flagstaff, AZ 86001 (520) 774-2613.

WHITE, MINERVA
(program coordinator)
Affiliation: New York State Education Dept., Native American Program, 543 Education Bldg. Annex, Washington Ave., Albany, NY 12234 (518) 474-0537.

WHITE, SAMMY (Tone-kei) (Kiowa)
(storyteller, advisor)
Tone-kei has had extensive experience sharing traditional stories of his people with many groups of people including school age children and tour groups in the Southwest. He can be contacted at 1-602-946-7407 or the Arizona Commission on the Arts at 1-602-255-5882. *Affiliation*: Council of Advisors, American Indian Heritage Foundation, Falls Church, VA.

WHITE, THOMAS R. (Pima-Maricopa)
(tribal governor)
Affiliation: Gila River Indian Community Council, P.O. Box 97, Sacaton, AZ 85247 (520) 562-3311.

WHITE EAGLE, CATHY (Eastern Cherokee) 1960-
(executive director)
Born July 14, 1960, Merced, Calif. *Education*: Santa Clara University, BS, 1982. Address unknown. *Affiliation*: Executive Director (1992-present), Eagle Vision, Granite Bay, CA (916) 791-7910. *Other professional posts*: Director, AIM, Sacramento Region; committee member, Multicultural Affairs, Sacramento Access. *Memberships*: American Indian Women's Association; National Organization for Women; American Indian Movement (AIM); Multi-Cultural Women's Network. *Awards, honors*: Honorary Award for community service, Sacramento State University; delegate to the United Nation on behalf of the American Indian Movement for the purpose of working on the basic human rights issues for American Indian people & children. *Interests*: "Sovereignty & treaty rights; currently working on the Native American Biography Series for Paramount's Modern Press, a series of six books for teachers to be released for 1995 school year.

WHITE EAGLE, LARRY (Nez Perce)
(craftsperson)
Affiliation & Address: Co-owner, White Eagle's Nez Perce Indian Arts, P.O. Box 4, Orofino, ID 83544 (208) 476-7753.

WHITE EAGLE, PAM (Nez Perce)
(craftsperson)
Address: Co-owner, White Eagle's Nez Perce Indian Arts, P.O. Box 4, Orofino, ID 83544 (208) 476-7753.

WHITE EAGLE, TOM (Oglala-Hunkpapa Sioux) 1941-
(artist; owner/curator)
Born October 26, 1941, Rapid City, S.D. *Education*: California Polytechnic University, BA; University of California, Davis, MS. *Principal occupation*: Artist. *Address & Affiliation*: Owner/curator, White Eagle Creations, P.O. Box 615, Elkron, OR 97436 (541) 584-2176. *Military service*: U.S. Air Force. *Interests*: "Restoration & study of Plains artifacts, primarily Lakota; work with youths & adults to promote Native culture; traditional dancer."

WHITE HAT, ALBERT H. (Rosebud Sioux) 1938-
(Lakota studies instructor)
Born November 18, 1938, St. Francis, S.D. *Education*: Sinte Gleska College, AA (Lakota Studies), 1986. *Principal occupation*: Lakota studies instructor. *Address*: P.O. Box 168, St. Francis, SD 57572 (605) 747-2711. *Affiliations*: Teacher, Indian Studies Program, St. Francis Indian School, 1974-80; part-time teacher, Lakota Medicine, 1979-85, Lakota studies instructor, Sinte Gleska College, Rosebud, SD, 1983-. *Other professional posts*: Tribal council (Rosebud Sioux) representative and committee work, 1979-81; president, Board of Directors, Sinte Gleska College, 1981-83. *Community activities*: Rosebud Community Action Program, 1967-70; Rosebud Ambulance Service, 1970-72; St. Francis Indian School (chairman of the board). *Memberships*: National Assn for Bilingual Education; SD Assn for Bilingual Education; SD Indian Education Assn. *Awards, honors*: Fellowship Award in 1978 to research Native American History for high school history course at Newberry Library, Chicago, IL; Voted in to serve on the Board of Trustees at Proctor Academy in Andover, NH (trustee, 3 years; corporate member, 5 years). *Interests*: "Carpentry, woodwork and construction; horse training; cultural and traditional activities. Presently, I am coordinating three instructional pamphlets in the areas of Lakota kinship--early childhood development, bilingual science, and bilingual language arts; I have done lectures on the philosophy of the Lakota, oral history & traditions in different colleges & organization, civic groups, pastoral groups, & church organizations." *Published work*: Co-editor, Lakota Ceremonial Songs (song book with cassette tape) (Sinte Gleska College).

WHITE HAT, EMILY (Sicangu Lakota)
(attorney; program manager)
Born & raised on the Rosebud Reservation in S.D. *Education*: Sinte Gleska University, AA (Lakota History & Culture); Colorado State University, BS (Forestry); University of New Mexico, JD & Natural Resources Law Certificate, 2007. *Affiliation*: Program Manager, National Congress of American Indians Policy Research Center, 1301 Connecticut Ave. NW, Suite 200, Washington, DC 20036 (202) 466-7767. *Past professional posts*: Assistant prosecutor, Rosebud Reservation; taught Environmental Law & Land Tenure, Sinte Gleska University; deputy director of Policy & Research for the Tribal Land Enterprise; policy analyst for Smith, Shelton & Ragona, LLC; legal researcher for the Utton Transboundary Resource Center and the Skokomish Indian Nation.

WHITE HORSE, SHEILA (Sicangu Lakota)
(operations manager)
Education: Southwestern Indian Polytechnic Institute, Certificate in Business Administration & Office Management. *Affiliation & Address*: Operations Manager (2011-present), First Peoples Fund, P.O. Box 2977, Rapid City, SD 57709 (605) 348-0324. *Past professional posts*: Office Manager, First Nations Oweesta Corporation, Rapid City, SD; administrative positions (11 years) at Intertribal Bison Cooperative & Rapid City Indian Health Board; regional program director, Childfund International, (five years).

WHITE MOUNTAIN, SHEILA (Standing Rock Sioux)
(BIA regional supt.)
Affiliation & Address: Supt., Bureau of Indian Affairs, Standing Rock Agency, P.O. Box E, Fort Yates, ND 58538 (701) 854-3433 E-mail:

WHITE TAIL FEATHER, ALEXANDER (Assiniboine Sioux)
(president & CEO)
Affiliation & Address: President & CEO, National Native American Aids Prevention Center, 720 S. Colorado Blvd., #650-S, Denver, CO 80246 (720) 382-2244. E-mail: awhitetailfeather@nnaapc.org.

WHITE TEMPLE, EMMET
(BIA education administrator)
Affiliation: Standing Rock Agency, Bureau of Indian Affairs, Agency Ave., P.O. Box E, Fort Yates, ND 58538 (701) 854-3497.

WHITEBIRD, III, ROBERT (Quapaw)
(family wellness program director)
Education: University of Oklahoma, B.A. (Political Science), BS (Business Administration). *Affiliation & Address*: Director, Family Wellness & Youth in Distress Program, Association of American Indian Physicians, 1235 Sovereign Row, Suite C-7, Oklahoma City, OK 73108 (405) 946-7072. *Past professional posts*: Coordinator of Native American Recruitment, University of Oklahoma; director of higher education, Comanche Nation.

WHITEFEATHER, BOBBY (Red Lake Ojibwe)
(former tribal chairperson)
Affiliation: Red Lake Band of Ojibwe Indians, P.O. Box 550, Red Lake, MN 56671 (employment & training program, 1975-86; tribal treasurer, 1986-90; tribal secretary, 1990-94, chairperson, 1994-98).

WHITEFISH, EUGENE L. (Forest County Potawatomi)
(tribal chief judge)
Address & Affiliation: Chief Judge, Forest County Potawatomi Tribal Court, P.O. Box 340, Crandon, WI 54520 (715) 478-5850.

WHITEFOOT, PATRICIA (Yakama/Dine)
(Indian education program director)
Born & raised on the Yakama Indian Nation tribal lands in Washington State. *Education*: Central Washington University, BA with Teaching Certificate in Education; Fort Wright College (Spokane, Wash.), M.A. in Education. *Affiliation & Address*: Director, Indian Education Program, Toppenish School District, 306 Bolin Dr., Toppenish, WA 98948 (509) 865-8293. E-mail: pwhitefoot@toppenish.wednet.edu. *Other professional posts*: President, Washington Indian Education Association, 2008-presnt; chairperson, ATNI (Affiliated Tribes of Northwest Indians) Education Committee; chair, University of Washington Native American Advisory Board, Seattle, WA, 2009-present; appointed by Secretary Sennellius, U.S. Department of Health & Human Services to the Substance Abuse & Mental Health Services Administration Prevention Advisory Council, Rockville, MD, 2010-present; appointed by President Obama to the National Advisory Council on Indian Education, U.S. Department of Eucation, Washington, DC, 2010-present; board member, Tribal Education Departments National Assembly (TEDNA), Boulder, CO. *Community activities*: Founded the Tribal Leaders' Diabetes Committee; she was a tribal leader at the Reauthorization of the Indian Health Care and Improvement Act and the Indian Education Executive Order; Patricia was involved in the creation of the Gathering of Native America, a curriculum team used widely in Indian country to address multigenerational trauma & healing. Past professional posts: President, National Indian Education Association, Washington, DC, 2010-11.

WHITEHOUSE, GENE (Miwok)
(tribal chairperson)
Affiliation & Address: Chairperson (2013-present), United Auburn Indian Community of the Auburn Rancheria, 10720 Indian Hill Rd., Auburn, CA 95603 (530) 883-2390. *Other professional post*: Board Chairperson, Thunder Valley Casino Resort, Auburn Rancheria. *Past professional posts*: Served two years as Tribal Secretary & six years as Council Member at Large. During his tenure, Chairman Whitehouse has been actively involved in advancing the academic success of his Tribe's youth by serving as a member of the United Auburn Indian Community School Board. He has also been a dedicated advocate of the Tribe's Elder Center and the preservation of cultural resources. Chairman Whitehouse has traveled to Washington, DC & throughout California to promote cooperative & constructive relationships between tribal governments & California State & local governments. He is known for his advocacy for the preservation of Native American cultural sites and his opposition to off-reservation casinos. Under his leadership, the United Auburn Indian Community has diversified its investments beyond casino gaming in order to protect the long term interests of the Tribal members. Prior to joining the UAIC Tribal Council, Chairman Whitehouse was employed with AT&T Corporation and Lucent Technologies for 25 years and served as Warehouse Manager for Thunder Valley Casino Resort. Chairman Whitehouse is a member of the Sheridan Municipal Advisory Council.

WHITEKILLER, VIRGINIA DRYWATER (Cherokee)
(professor of social work & American Indian studies)
Education: Northeastern State University, BS (Social Work); Washington University, St. Louis, MSW; Oklahoma State University, EdD (Higher Education Administration). *Affiliation & Address*: Professor of Social Work & American Indian Studies, Department of Cherokee & Indigenous Studies, Northeastern State University, Seminary Hall 326, 609 N. Grand Ave., Tahlequah, OK 74464 (918) 444-3517; E-mail: longvs@nsuok.edu Her academic administrative experience includes having chaired Northeastern State University's social work and criminal justice departments, coordinating the Title IV-E program, directing the social work practicum program, and writing the self-study for the Council on Social Work Education re-affirmation. Along with extensive work in direct and macro social work practice with Native populations in health care, education, juvenile offenders, and child welfare, she has 20 years' experience in teaching undergraduate & graduate level social work courses. She has served as an external program evaluator for various tribal social service projects & currently is the principal investigator for a university partnership with the National Child Welfare Workforce Initiative, one of twelve in the nation. The NSU program is designed to promote workforce diversity through the recruitment, entry & retention of Native Americans in child welfare & child welfare specialization curriculum development. She has published on topics pertaining to Native American cultural diversity, social work, & higher education retention. Her current research interests include furthering the development of cultural resilience theory regarding Native populations, tribal child welfare & gerontological workforce development, & Native Americans coping with microaggressions.

WHITELAW, SHEILA (Colville)
(editor)
Affiliation & Address: Editor, "Tribal Tribune," Colville Confederated Tribes, P.O. Box 150, Nespelem, WA 99155 (509) 634-8835.

WHITEMAN, ERNEST M., III (Northern Arapaho)
(film & video festival director)
Affiliation & Address: Coordinator (2005-08), Director (2011-present), First Nations Film & Video Festival, Inc. Website: www.fnfvf.org. (847) 863-8693. E-mail: ernest-3@fnfvf.org.

WHITEMAN RUNS HIM, HEATHER (Crow)
(attorney)
Born & raised on the Crow Reservation, Montana. *Education*: Institute of American Indian Arts, AFA; University of New Mexico, BAFA (Art History); Harvard Law School, JD. *Affiliation & Address*: Staff Attorney, Native American Rights Fund (NARF), 1506 Broadway, Boulder, CO 80302 (303) 447-8760. She focuses on tribal water rights & natural resource issues. *Past professional posts*: Served as Joint Lead Counsel for the Crow Tribe of Montana; practiced in New Mexico as an Assistant Public Defender and associate attorney in private practice, serving tribal governmental clients on a wide variety of issues.

WHITENER, RON J. (Nisqually)
(assistant professor of law)
Education: Evergreen State College, BA, 1991; University of Washington School of Law, JD, 1994. *Affiliation & Address*: Assistant Professor of Law & Director, Tribal Court Public Defense Clinic (2002-present), Assistant Director, University of Washington School of Law, Native American Law Center, W.H. Gates Hall 265, Box 353020, Seattle, WA 98195 (206) 543-4099 Fax 685-2861. E-mail: ronw@uw.edu. *Other professional posts*: Chief Judge, Tulalip Tribe, Tulalip, WA; Executive Director, Native American Law Center, Senior Law Lecturer, UW School of Law, Seattle, WA; Associate Justice of the Northwest Intertribal Court of Appeals; Chief judge of the Confederated Tribes of the Chehalis Reservation; Of Counsel with Foster Pepper PLLC. *Past professional posts*: Tribal attorney for Squaxin Island Tribe (of which he's a member), 1994-2000; Northwest Justice Project, Native American Unit, Seattle, WA, 2000-2002; Fellow of the University of Colorado, Health Sciences Center, Native Elder Research Center, 2006-07. *Research Interests*: Jurisdictional and ethical issues of public defense in courts of American Indian & Alaska Native tribal courts. Legal, ethical & societal implications of research among American Indian & Alaska Native communities The effect of fetal alcohol syndrome/effect, post traumatic stress disorder, traumatic brain injury and mental illness on American Indians/Alaska Natives compliance with probationary requirements in tribal, state & federal criminal systems. Jurisdictional authority of federally recognized tribes and villages to regulate and control data collected by outside researchers and institutions. *Awards, honors*: 2008 MacArthur Foundationn Models for Change grant to identify strong programs & areas of need for Washington State tribal juvelile justice programs; 2009 American Association of Law Schools Section on Clinical Education's Shanara Gilbert Emerging Clinician Award; was honored by the White House as a "Champion of Change." The award features lawyers "who dedicate their professional lives to closing the justice gap in America" and is given to a small group of people who are "Winning the Future." This honor was presented to Whitener at the White House on October 13, 2011.

WHITEROCK, JUNIOR (Navajo-Dine')
(artist, shop owner)
Affiliation & Address: owner, Traditions & Innovations Navajo Sandpainting, P.O. Box 154, Tonalea, AZ 86044 (928) 283-8820. Junior makes Navajo handmade pottery and sandpainting

WHITETHORNE, BAJE, SR. (Navajo)
(author, illustrator)
Born in Shonto, Ariz. *Address & Affiliation*: Author/illustrator, Salina Bookshelf, Inc., 3120 N. Caden Ct. #4, Flagstaff, AZ 86004. *Awards, honors*: 1998 Outstanding Contributor to Children's Literature by the Arizona Library Association. His watercolor paintings appear at the Heard Museum, The Smithsonian Museum. The Field Museum, the Gallup Indian Ceremonial, and Museum of Northern Arizona. *Published works*: Sunpainters: Eclipse of the Navajo Sun, Father's Boots, & Beauty Beside Me: Stories of My Grandmother's Skirts. *Illustrated works*: Native American legends including Monster Birds, Monster Slayer, and Sika and the Raven.

WHITEWOLF, CELESTE (Umatilla)
(organization director)
Education: JD. *Affiliation & Address*: Director, Native People's Circle of Hope, 9770 SW Ventura Ct., Tigard, OR 97223 (503) 970-8004. E-mail: admin@nativepeoplescoh.org. Celeste is a Stage III breast cancer survivor diagnosed in August 1998. She is a non-practicing attorney and a volunteer director of the Native People's Circle of Hope, a coalition of native cancer survivors & supporters. Ms. Whitewolf is the northwest representative to the

Inter-Cultural Cancer Coalition. She is a past member of the National Cancer Institute/Director's Consumer Liaison Group, the American Indian/Alaska Native Advisory Council to the Susan G. Koman Foundation and Oregon Partnership for Cancer Control. Celeste is a national advocate for Native American cancer survivors.

WHITFORD, LEA (Blackfeet)
(Montana State representative)
Born & raised in Browning, MT. *Affiliation & Address*: Montana State Representative, (2013-14), District 16, Montana House of Representatives, P.O. Box 200400, Helena, MT 59620. *Home address*: 221 Ed Williams Rd., Cut Bank, MT 59427 (406) 873-2582. *Other professional post*: Charperson & Instructor, Blackfeet Studies Department, Blackfeet Community College, Browning, MT. E-mail: lea@bfcc.edu.

WHITING, BERNARD (Rosebud Lakota Sioux)
(radio station manager)
Affiliation: KINI - 96.1 FM, Rosebud Lakota Sioux Tribe, P.O. Box 146, St. Francis, SD 57572 (605) 747-2291.

WHITING, MARSHA (Chippewa Cree/Sicangu Lakota)
(senior program officer)
Affiliation & Address: Senior Projects Coordinator (2009-present), First Nations Development Institute, 301 Coffman St., Suite 200, Longmont, CO 80501 (303) 774-7836. *Past professional post*: Grants administrator, American Indian College Fund, Denver, CO. *Awards, honors*: 2008-09 Leadership & Entrepreneurial Apprenticeship Development (LEAD) Program Fellow.

WHITING-SORRELL, ANNA (Confederated Salish & Kootenai)
(public health & human services director)
Education: University of Montana, BA (Political Science & Education) & MPA (Masters of Public Administration). Resides on the Flathead Reservation in Ronan, Mont. *Affiliation*: Director, Montana State Department of Public Health & Human Services, Helena, MT 59620. *Past professional posts*: Tribal administrator, Confederated Salish & Kootenai Tribes, Pablo, MT (Anna developed & implemented a nationally recognized substance abuse prevention & treatment program for nearly ten years); president, National Association for Native American Children of Alcoholics, Seattle, WA; policy advisor on families, Montana Governor's Office of Indian Affairs, Helena, MT, 2005-2010.

WHITMAN, KATHY (*Elk Woman*) (Manadan-Hidatsa-Arikara) 1952-
(artist, sculptor, painter)
Born August 12, 1952, Bismarck, N.D. *Education*: University of South Dakota; Sinte Gleska College, Rosebud, SD; Standing Rock Community College, Ft. Yates, ND. *Principal occupation*: Artist, sculptor, painter. Address: Resides in Arizona. *Affiliations*: Owner, Nux-Baga Lodge, New Town, N.D., 1981-1985; owner, Recreation Center, New Town, N.D., 1985. *Other professional post*: Art instructor, Standing Rock Community College & Sinte Gleska College. Community activities: Parent representative-Headstart, Fort Yates, N.D.; Fort Berthold Community College, New Town, N.D. (board of directors); Pow-Wow, Canonball, N.D. (president, committee member). *Memberships*: Indian Arts & Crafts Association; Gallup Intertribal Ceremonial; Southwest Association on Indian Affairs. *Awards, honors*: Best Craftsman/Special Award, BuKllock's Santa Monica Indian Ceremonial, 1986; 1st Place, San Juan Bautista Indian Arts and Crafts Show, 1986; 1st Place, 1986, 2nd Place, 1987, 1st Place, 1990, Eight Northern Pueblos Arts & Crafts Show; Special Merit Award, Trail of Tears Arts Show, 1987; 3rd Place, Gallup Indian Ceremonial; Best of Fine Arts/Split Best of Show, Northern Plains Tribal Arts Show, 1988; 1989 Poster Artist, Southwest Association on Indian Affairs; 1990 One Woman Exhibition in Nurnberg, Germany; 1991 Best of Show, Pasadena Western Relic & Indian Arts & Crafts Show; Governors Award, Directors and Choice Merit Award, United Tribes Educational Training Center, Bismarck, N.D. *Interests*: "Demonstrated and exhibited paintings and sculpture in numerous galleries; danced and exhibited artwork in Charleroi, Belgium, Dijon, France, and Nurnberg, Germany; started a recreation center on Ft. Berthold Reservation for the youth and sponsored an alternative camp for youth. I believe that all things of the Sacred Mother Earth are special & holy. I want people to see and feel, the pride, the unity, the happiness, and the spiritual strength that is so close to us. There is serenity in having a strong relationship with the Great Spirit and all His Sacred Beings." *Biographical sources*: Article - "People, Faces of the 90's: A Closeup Look at Valley Newsmakers," Valley of the Sun Times, June 1991; articles in The Desert Leaf, July 1989; Antiques & the Arts Weekly, Sept. 1989; Santa Fe Reporter, Aug. 1990; Indian Trader, Aug. 1990; New York Times, Sept. 1991 ad. 1989 Video - Beyond Tradition, by Jerry and Lois Jacka (one of featured artists).

WHITMAN, ROBERT K. (Navajo) 1954-
(electrical engineer)
Born February 25, 1954, Fort Defiance, Ariz. *Education*: University of New Mexico, BS, 1977; Colorado State University, MS, 1986; University of Colorado, PhD (Electrical Engineering), 1990. Resides in Boulder, Colorado.

Affiliations: Engineer, IBM Corp., San Jose, CA & Boulder, CO, 1977-90; deputy director, American Indian Science & Engineering Society, Boulder, CO, 1991-. *Past professional post*: Industrial Development Specialist, Navajo Nation Economic Development Dept., Window Rock, AZ, (3 months) 1987-88. *Community activities*: AISES student chapter advisor at University of Colorado, Boulder; member, University of Colorado Graduate School Advisory Council; member, Science Service International, Science & Engineering Fair Advisory Council; member, Committee on Feasibility of a National Scholars Program, National Research Council. *Memberships*: Institute of Electrical & Electronics Engineers (IEEE); American Indian Science & Engineering Society (AISES) (board of directors, 1983-87, board secretary, 1984-85, board chairperson, 1985-87, chair of Scholarship Committee, 1988-92). *Awards, honors*: NASA Minority Fellowship, 1975-77; Outstanding Achievement Award, Navajo Nation, 1980; Information Systems Division Achievement Award, IBM Corp., 1981; Information Products Division Achievement Award, IBM Corp., 1984; AISES/GE Fellowship, 1993. *Interests*: "Doctoral dissertation on human speech synthesis, non-linear methods of sound reconstruction. Outside activities include: reading history of American Indians, learning about Navajo traditional ways and about my ancestors; giving presentations to high school & college students on technical careers & importance of traditions. Judge science fair projects at high school level; traveled to Europe 4 times." *Biographical source*: "New Mexico Professional Engineer," 9/78; "Graduate Engineer," 10/81; "Minority Engineer," Summer 1984; "Winds of Change," 2/86.

WHITMAN, SILAS C. (Nez Perce) 1942-
  (former tribal chairperson)
Education: Portland Business College (Certificate); University of Idaho. *Affiliation & Address*: Nez Pece Tribe, P.O. Box 305, Lapwai, ID 83540 (208) 843-7342. *Other professional post*: Vice Chair, Idaho Council on Indian Affairs, Boise, ID. "I have accumulated over 50 years of work experience with 43 yrs in administration & management in both public & private sectors throughout Indian Country USA. I've spent considerable time working in various capacities with the Nez Perce Tribe and would welcome to provide the effort needed to represent the best interests of the Nez Perce people and their tribal government in the demanding policy issues the tribe deals with on a day to day basis. It is in the interests of our Executive Committee to forge enhanced communications between employees, Committee members, Boards and Commissions within the General Council to represent the best interests of our tribal membership. A most important element I would impress on all concerned is the need for Policy Management coordination in the interests of health & human services, employment/training/education & economic opportunities, natural & cultural resources support, & the strengthening of public consultation and coordination between agencies and the general public with the Nez Perce Tribe."

WHITMORE, ANNETTE CHAVEZ (Comanche)
  (board president)
Affiliation & Address: Board President, Marin American Indian Alliance, P.O. Box 150565, San Rafael, CA 94915.

WHITTLESEY, DENNIS J.
  (attorney)
Education: University of Oklahoma, BA, 1964; Georgetown University Law School, JD, 1967, LLM, 1973. *Affiliation & Address*: Member, Dickinson Wright, Indian Law Section, 1875 Eye St., NW, Washington, DC 20006 (202) 659-6928. E-mail: dwhittlesey@dickinsonwright.com. Expertise in development of economic projects, including casinos, for Indian tribes in America & Canada. Served as legal counsel to both unrecognized & federally recognized Indian tribes, providing counsel on Indian gaming law and Indian lands as well as a wide range of state & federal taxation issues unique to Indian tribes, individuals & lands. Served as Special Counsel for Gaming to the cities of Detroit; Buffalo, NY; Battle Creek, MI; Lima, OH; Middleborough, MA; and Barstow, CA as well as Calhoun County, MI, DeKalb County, IL, and seven California counties. Represented developers in their dealings with Indian tribes, including Trump Entertainment Resorts, Inc. & Delaware Casino Development & Management Co., LLC

WHITWORTH, DACIA (Confederated Salish Kootenai)
  (artist, shop owner)
Address: Native American Art Sales, 51761 Hillside Rd., Charlo, MT 59824 (406) 644-3046. Website: www.nativeamericanartsales.com. *Artwork*: Beadwork, jewelry, clothing, carvings, hangings, art.

WHYTE, KYLE POWYS (Citizen Potawatomi)
  (professor of philosophy)
Affiliation & Address: Associate Professor of Philosophy, Michigan State University, Department of Philosophy, Professor of American Indian Studies, 535 S. Kedzie, East Lansing, MI 48825 (517) 432-3325. E-mail: kwhyte@msu.edu. He is affiliated faculty for Peace & Justice Studies, Environmental Science & Policy, the Center for Regional Food Systems,

Animal Studies and American Indian StudiesKyle writes primarily on environmental justice & American Indian philosophy. His most recent research addresses moral and political issues concerning climate change impacts on Indigenous peoples. *Other professional post*: He serves on the U.S. Department of Interior's Advisory Committee on Climate Change and Natural Resource Science and is involved in the Climate and Traditional Knowledges Workgroup, Menominee Sustainable Development Institute, Tribal Climate Camp, Michigan Environmental Justice Coalition, Everybody Eats: Cultivating Food Democracy, Humanities for the Environment, and the Consortium for Socially Relevant Philosophy of/in Science. His articles have appeared in journals such as Climatic Change, Environmental Justice, Hypatia, Ecological Processes, Synthese, Human Ecology, Journal of Global Ethics, American Journal of Bioethics, Journal of Agricultural & Environmental Ethics, Ethics, Policy & Environment, and Ethics & the Environment. Kyle's work has been funded by the National Science Foundation, Bureau of Indian Affairs, U.S. Fish and Wildlife Service, Northeast Climate Science Center, Great Lakes Integrated Sciences & Assessments Center, the Sustainable Michigan Endowed Program and Spencer Foundation. He is involved in the Michigan Environmental Justice Coalition, Everybody Eats: Cultivating Food Democracy, Networking the Global Humanities: Humanities & the Environment (Mellon), the Consortium for Socially Relevant Philosophy of/in Science and the American Philosophical Association Committee on Status of Indigenous Philosophers.

WICHTMAN, KARRIE S. (Sault Ste. Marie Chippewa) 1989-
  (attorney; law firm associate)
Education: Davenport University, BS (Paralegal Studies), 2001; Western Michigan University, Master of Public Administration, 2006; Michigan State University College of Law, JD, 2009. *Affiliation*: Associate, 2010-present), Rosette & Associates, 112 E. Allegan St. #600, Lansing, MI 48933 (517) 367-7040. E-mail: kwichtman@rosettelaw.com.

WICKER, SUSAN M. (Poarch Creek)
  (executive director)
Affiliation & Address: Executive Director, Poarch Creek Indian Housing Dept., 5811 Jack Springs Rd., Atmore, AL 36502 (251) 368-9136 ext. 2255. *Other professional post*: Member, Board of Directors for Region 1, AMERIND Risk Management Corporation, Santa Ana Pueblo, NM.

WICKLIFFE, GEORGE G. (United Keetoowah Cherokee)
  (former tribal chief)
Education: Oklahoma Military Academy Junior College, AA; Northeastern Oklahoma State University, BS; University of Tulsa, MS (Secondary School Administration); Pittsburgh State University, MBA. *Affiliation & Address*: Former Chief (2005-present), United Keetoowah Band of Cherokee Indians, P.O. Box 746, Tahlequah, OK 74465 (918) 431-1818. *Past professional posts*: Catoosa Public Schools, Principal, 1973-78; White Oak Public Schools, Supt., 1977-99; Northeastern State University, Cherokee Language Instructor; Rogers State University, Cherokee Language Instructor; 20 years experience in UKB tribal administration. *Awards, honors*: Inducted into the Sequoyah Hall of Fame of the Sequoyah Alumni Association, 2012.

WIDMARK, LAWRENCE (Sitka)
  (tribal chairperson)
Affiliation & Address: Chairperson, Sitka Tribe of Alaska, 456 Katlian St., Sitka, AK 99835 (907) 747-3207.

WIEHLE, SCOTT (Osage/Kaw)
  (attorney)
Affiliation & Address: Vinson & Elkins LLP, 2001 Ross Ave., Suite 3700, Dallas, TX (214) 220-7913. E-mail: swiehl@velaw.org. *Other professional post*: Board Member, National Native American Bar Association.

WIGGINS, ARMSTRONG A. (Miskito)
  (attorney)
Affiliation & Address: Director, Indian Law Resource Center (Washington Office), 601 E St., SE, Washington, DC 20003 (202) 547-2800. Email: dcoffice@indianlaw.org.

WIGGINS, MICHAEL, JR. (Bad River Ojibwe)
  (former tribal chairperson)
Affiliation & Address: Former Chairperson, Bad River Band of Lake Superior Chippewa Tribe, P.O. Box 39, Odanah, WI 54861 (715) 682-7111.

WILBUR, MARY
  (school district supervisor; consortium president)
Affiliation & Address: Supervisor, Eastside Native American Education Program, Lake Washington School District, P.O. Box 97039, Redmond, WA 98073 (425) 936-1402. E-mail: mwilbur@lwsd.org. *Other professional post*: President, Western Washington Native American Education Consortium, Port Orchard, WA.

WILCOX, MICHAEL (Yuma)
(assistant professor of anthropology)

Education: Harvard University, PhD. *Affiliation & Address*: Assistant Professor, Dept. of Cultural & Social Anthropology, Stanford University, 450 Serra Mall, Bldg. 50, Stanford, CA 94305 (650) 736-1255. E-mail: mwilcox@stanford.edu. *Other professional post*: Instructor, Native American Studies, Stanford University. His dissertation, entitled, "The Pueblo Revolt of 1680: Communities of Resistance, Ethnic Conflict & Alliance Formation Among Upper Rio Grande Pueblos," articulates the social consequences of subordination, and explores the processes of boundary maintenance at both regional & communal levels. During his graduate studies at Harvard, he was involved in strengthening the Harvard Native American Program and in designing & teaching award-winning courses in Native American Studies. *Research Interests*: Postcolonial approaches to archaeology, ethnic identity & conflict, and political & historical relationships between Native Americans & anthropologists & archaeologists. *Published works*: Dialogue or Diatribe? Indians & Archaeologists in the Post-NAGPRA Era (2000); Now the God of the Spaniards Is Dead: Ethno-genesis & Community Formation in the Aftermath of the Pueblo Revolt of 1680 (2000).

WILD CAT, ALVIN (Meskwaki Sac & Fox)
(tribal vice chairperson)

Affiliation & Address: Vice Chairperson, Sac & Fox of the Mississippi in Iowa Meswaki Nation, 349 Meskwaki Rd.,Tama, IA 52339 (641) 484-4678.

WILDCAT, DARRELL (Pawnee)
(tribal vice president)

Affiliation & Address: Vice President, Pawnee Nation of Oklahoma, P.O. Box 470, Pawnee, OK 74958 (918) 762-3621.

WILDCATT, LISA ANNE FRANCESCHINI, MD (Choctaw of Oklahoma) 1970 -
(pediatrician)

Born August 5, 1970, Fort Lauderdale, Fla. *Education*: University of North Dakota, B.S., 1995, M.D., 2000; Medical College of Georgia, Pediatric Residency. *Principal occupation*: Pediatrician. *Address & Affiliation*: Cherokee Hospital, Box C-268, Hospital Rd., Cherokee, NC 28719 (828) 497-9163. E-mail: lisa.wildcatt@mail.ihs.gov. "I chose University of North Dakota because of the Native American Program (NAP) and the Indians Into Medicine Program (InMed)." *Memberships*: American Medical Association; Academy of American Family Physicians; American Academy of Pediatrics. *Interests*: Family; outdoors; biking, computers, reading, cooking, photography.

WILDER, NORM (Paiute)
(tribal chairperson)

Affiliation & Address: Chairperson, Fort Independence Paiute Tribe, P.O. Box 67, Independence, CA 93526 (760) 878-2126.

WILKINS, DAVID E. (Lumbee) 1954-
(professor of American Indian studies)

Born September 18, 1954, Fort Bragg, N.C. *Education*: Pembroke State University, BA, 1976; University of Arizona, MA, 1982; University of North Carolina, Chapel Hill, PhD, 1990. *Affiliation & Address*: Assistant professor (2000-present), American Indian Studies Dept., University of Minnesota, 330 Scott Hall, 72 Pleasant St. SE, Minneapolis, MN 55455 (612) 624-1634. E-mail: wilkinsd@umn.edu. *Past professional posts*: Assistant Professor of Political Science & Indian Law & Policy, University of Arizona, Tucson, AZ, 1990-97; Assistant Professor of Political Science & American Indian Studies, University of Colorado, Boulder, CO., 1993-99. *Other professional post*: Columnist, Indian Country Today, Canastota, NY. *Membership*: American Political Science Association. *Awards, honors*: Ford Foundation Dissertation Fellowship, 1989-90; Ford Foundation Post-Doctoral Fellowship, 1993-94; Center for Advanced Study in the Behavioral Sciences Post Doctoral Fellowship; Minnesota Humanities Commission Grant, 2002; McKnight Research Award, University of Minnesota Arts & Humanities Endowment Fund, 2000-2003. *Research interests*: Federal Indian policy & law, comparative indigenous peoples, tribal governments, judicial politics, and tribal-state relations. *Published works*: Dine Bib eehaz'aanii: A Handbook of Navajo Government (Navajo Community College Press, 1987); American Indian Sovereignty and the U.S. Supreme Court: The masking of Justice (U. of Texas Press, 1997); Uneven Ground: American Indian Sovereignty & Federal Law, with Tsianina Lomawaima (University of Oklahoma Press, 2001); The Navajo Political Experience (Rowman & Littlefield, 2003); Native Voices: American Indian Identity & Resistance, co-edited with Richard Grounds & George Tinker (University Press of Kansas, 2003); On the Drafting of Tribal Constitutions (University of Oklahoma Press, 2006); American Indian Politics & the American Political System (Rowman & Littlefield, 2007); Documents of Native American Political Development: 1500s to 1933 (Oxford University Press, 2009); The Hank Adams Reader (Fulcrum Publishing, 2011); The Legal Universe, with Vine Deloria, Jr. (Fulcrum Publishing, 2011); Hollow Hope: Indigenous Claims Against the U.S. (Yale University Press, 2013); numerous academic journal articles.

WILKINSON, CHARLES
(attorney; Indian law scholar & professor)

Education: Denison University, BA, 1963; Stanford University Law School, JD, 1966. *Affiliation & Address*: Moses Lasky Professor of Law, University of Colorado Law School, 405 Wolf Law Bldg. 401 UCB, Boulder, CO 80309 (303) 492-8262; E-mail: charles.wilkinson@colorado.edu. *Other professional post*: Serves as mediator in negotiations between the City of Seattle and the Muckleshoot Indian Tribe. His primary specialties are federal public land law and Indian law. In addition to his many articles in law reviews, popular journals, and newspapers, his fourteen books include the standard law texts on public land law and on Indian law. He also served as managing editor of Felix S. Cohen's *Handbook of Federal Indian Law*, the leading treatise on Indian law. The books he has written in recent years, such as 1992's *The Eagle Bird*, are aimed for a general audience, and they discuss society, history, and land in the American West. He won the Colorado Book Award for *Messages From Frank's Landing*, a profile of Billy Frank, Jr. of the Nisqually Tribe of western Washington. In his book, *Blood Struggle: The Rise of Modern Indian Nations*, he poses what he calls "the most fundamental question of all: Can the Indian voice endure?" Listen to an interview on Colorado Public Radio conducted by Dan Drayer about *Blood Struggle*. In his latest book *The People Are Dancing Again: The History of the Siletz Tribe of Western Oregon*, Professor Wilkinson writes about how the history of the Siletz Tribe is in many ways the history of many Indian tribes: a story of heartache, perseverance, survival, and revival.*Past professional posts*: Prior to joining the faculty of Colorado Law School, Charles Wilkinson practiced law with private firms in Phoenix and San Francisco and then with the Native American Rights Fund. In 1975, he became a law professor, teaching at the law schools of the University of Oregon, Michigan and Minnesota before moving to Colorado in 1987. Native American Rights Fund; Special Counsel to the Interior Department for the drafting of the Presidential Proclamation, signed by President Clinton in Sept. 1996, establishing the Grand Staircase-Escalante National Monument Zion National Park, Utah; acted as facilitator in negotiations between the National Park Service and the Timbisha Shoshone Tribe concerning tribal land base in Death Valley National Park in 2000. *Awards, honors*: University of Colorado's Distinguished University Professor; Professor Wilkinson has received teaching awards from his students at all three law schools where he has taught, and the Universities of Colorado and Oregon have given him their highest awards for leadership, scholarship, and teaching. He has also won acclamation from non-academic organizations. The National Wildlife Federation presented him with its National Conservation Award, and in its 10-year anniversary issue, Outside Magazine named him one of 15 "People to Watch," calling him "the West's leading authority on natural resources law." He has served on several boards, including The Wilderness Society, the Grand Canyon Trust, and the Center of the American West at the University of Colorado. Over the years, Professor Wilkinson has taken on many special assignments for the Departments of Interior, Agriculture, and Justice. He was a member of the tribal team that negotiated the 1997 Joint Secretarial Order of the Interior and Commerce Departments concerning tribal rights under the Endangered Species Act. He served as special counsel to the Interior Department for the drafting of the Presidential Proclamation, signed by President Clinton in September 1996, establishing the Grand Staircase-Escalante National Monument in Utah. In December 1997 Agriculture Secretary Glickman appointed him a member of the Committee of Scientists, charged with reviewing the Forest Service planning regulations. Professor Wilkinson acted as facilitator in negotiations between the National Park Service and the Timbisha Shoshone Tribe concerning a tribal land base in Death Valley National Park; in 2000 Congress enacted legislation ratifying the resulting agreement. He also served as facilitator in far-ranging negotiations between the City of Seattle and the Muckleshoot Indian Tribe. *Published works*: The Eagle Bird (1992); Crossing the Next Meridian (1992); Fire on the Plateau (1999); Messages From Frank's Landing: A Story of Salmon, Treaties, and the Indian Way; Blood Struggle: The Rise of Modern Indian Nations (W.W. Norton & Co., 2005); The People Are Dancing Again: The Siletz Tribe of Western Oregon (U. of Washington Press, 2010); Editor, et al. Cases & Materials on Federal Indian Law, 6th Ed. 2011; numerous articles & book chapters.

WILLETO, ANGELA (Navajo)
(associate professor)

Education: University of North Carolina, M.A. (Sociology), 1990; Ph.D., 1996. *Address & Affiliation*: Associate professor, Dept. of Sociology & Social Work (1995-present), College of Social & Behavioral Sciences, Northern Arizona University (NAU), P.O. Box 15020, Flagstaff, AZ 86011 (928) 523-6624. E-mail: angela.willeto@nau.edu. *Other professional post*: Member, Commission for Native Americans, NAU.

WILLIAMS, CHRISTINE (Yurok)
(attorney; tribal judge)

Education: Arizona State University, JD, 2000. *Affiliations*: Christine is a judge for several tribes in Northern California; she also provides training & education on various areas of Indian law & history; Board Vice President, California Indian Law Association, Sacramento. Website: www.calindianlaw.org. Judge

Williams career has focused on representing Tribes in a broad spectrum of tribal legal matters primarily Indian child welfare, tribal court development and cultural resource protection.

WILLIAMS, DEANNA M. (Choctaw of Oklahoma)
(professor of Native Studies & program coordinator)
Education: Southeastern Oklahoma State University, BA (Psychology), 1996, MA (Counseling Psychology), 2001; Oklahoma State University, PhD (Counseling Psychology). *Affiliation & Address*: Professor & Program Coordinator, Native Studies Program, Department of Behavioral Sciences, 1405 North 4th Durant, OK 74701 (580) 745-2000. E-mail: *Professional Interests*: Psychological assessment and cultural diversity.

WILLIAMS, DONYA (Miami)
(tribal first councilperson)
Affiliation & Address: Miami Tribe of Oklahoma, 3410 P St., NW, P.O. Box 1326 • Miami, OK 74355 (918) 541-1300

WILLIAMS, JAMES, JR. (Lake Superior Chippewa)
(tribal chairperson)
Affiliation & Address: Chairperson, Lac Vieux Desert Band of Lake Superior Chippewa Indians, P.O. Box 249, Watersmeet, MI 49969 (906) 358-4577.

WILLIAMS BORDEAUX, JENNIFER (Lakota)
(program assistant in ethnic studies)
Education: University of CoLorado, Denver, MA (Political Science & Indigenous Peoples, 2009. *Affiliation & Address*: Program Assistant in Ethnic Studies (2004-present), Department of Ethnic Studies, University of Colorado, Campus Box 134, P.O. Box 173364, Denver, CO 80217 (303) 315-7209; E-mail: Jennifer.williams@ucdenver. edu *Other professional post*: Board Member, Denver Metro Fair Housing Center, 20014-present. *Past professional post*: Former Co-Chair, Denver American Indian Commission, 2010-14. *Published works*: Co-author with Donna Martinez, 50 Events That Shaped American Indian History: An Encyclopedia of the American Mosaic, 2 Vols. (ABC-CLIO, 2017).

WILLIAMS, JOHN (Miwok)
(tribal vice chairperson)
Affiliation & Address: Vice Chairperson (2013-present), United Auburn Indian Community of the Auburn Rancheria, 10720 Indian Hill Rd., Auburn, CA 95603 (530) 883-2390.

WILLIAMS, JOSH
(attorney)
Education: Northwst Missouri State University, BS; Seattle University School of Law, JD. *Affiliation & Address*: Associate Attorney (2009-present), Legal Advocates for Indian Country, LLP, 720 Third Ave., Suite 1900, Seattle, WA 98104 (206) 499-8684. Mr. Williams is licensed to practice in the State of Washington and within the Chehalis, Port Gamble, and Tulalip Tribal Courts.

WILLIAMS, LEONA (Pomo)
(rancheria chairperson)
Affiliation & Address: Chairperson, Pinoleville Indian Rancheria of Pomo Indians, 500B Pinoleville Dr., Ukiah, CA 95482 (707) 463-1454.

WILLIAMS, MARIA (Tlingit)
(associate professor of music & Native American Studies)
Education: UCLA, PhD (Music-Ethnomusicology), 1996. *Affiliation*: Associate Professor of Music & Native American Studies, Native American Studies (NAS) Dept., University of New Mexico, Mesa Vista 3080, Albuquerque, NM 87131. Her main area of research is on Alaska Native indigenous cultural practices. She recently produced a documentary called, "Nilgaq: 5th Annual Kinigikmiut Dance Festival, June 25-27, 2004," working in partnership with the Native Village of Wales & Alaska's National Park Service. Maria also completed a major project working with the King Island Inupiat community of Alaska in which their entire music/dance repertoire was documented via audio//video recordings to establish a tribally controlled archive.

WILLIAMS, MIKE (Yupiaq)
(mental health counselor; council chairperson)
Affiliation: Chairperson, Alaska Inter-Tribal Council. Address: 1569 S. Bragaw St., Suite 102, Anchorage, AK 99508 (907) 563-9334. E-mail: aitc@aitc.org. *Other professional posts*: Vice-chair, Alaska State Board of Education; board member, Alaska Humanities Forum & the Native American Rights Fund. *Awards, honors*: Honor for Sobriety Advocacy Award from the Alaska State Legislature. Interests: Iditarod Dog Sled Racing, sobriety.

WILLIAMS, O. JOSEPH (Mississippi Choctaw)
(attorney)
Education: Murray State College, AAS, 1994; Southeastern Oklahoma State University, BS, 1995; Oklahoma City University, MBA, 1998; Oklahoma City University School of Law, JD, 2001. *Affiliation & Address*: Partner Attorney

(2001-present), Pitchlynn & Wiliams, 1717 S. Cheyenne Ave., Tulsa, OK 74119 (918) 582-9292. E-mail: jwilliams@pitchlynnlaw.com. *Other professional post*: Justice on the Supreme Court for the Sac & Fox Nation. *Memberships*: Oklahoma Indian Bar Association (secretary); Oklahoma Bar Association-Indian Law Section (past chair); Oklahoma Indian Legal Services (board member); Federal Bar Association; Muscogee (Creek) Nation Bar Association.

WILLIAMS, PERRY (Alabama-Coushatta of Texas)
(tribal chairperson)
Affiliation: Alabama-Coushatta Tribe of Texas, Rt. 3 Box 659, Livingston, TX 77351 (409) 563-4391.

WILLIAMS, RICHARD B. (Oglala Lakotah)
(educator, advocate, historian; advisor)
Born in Crawford, Neb. *Education*: University of Nebraska, Lincoln, BA (University Studies); University of Wyoming, MA (Education Administration). *Address*: 13028 Julian Court, Denver, CO 80221 (303) 492-5474. *Affiliations*: University of Denver, Denver, CO (teaches American Indian history for the graduate program in Indian Studies); president, & CEO (1997-2012), senior advisor, 2012-2014, American Indian College Fund, Denver, CO., 1997-2012; senior advisor. The College Fund raises private support for scholarships, endowments, programs, and public awareness efforts on behalf of 32 tribally chartered colleges. *Other professional post*: Lecturer & presenter on Native American history & education. *Past professional posts*: Director, Student Academic Service Center, University of Colorado, Boulder, CO; director of Minority Student Affairs and director of the American Indian Upward Bound Program; consulting editor for the Discovery Channel series, "How the West Was Lost"; also worked with other programs targeting Indian youth & serving Indian reservation populations. *Awards, honors*: 2007 Honorary Doctorate of Humane Letters from Roger Williams University, RI; 2005 Educator of the Year award, National Indian Education Association; 1999 University of Nebraska-Distinguished Alumni Award; Mr. Williams was the first American Indian student ever to have earned a bachelor's degree from University of Nebraska, Lincoln. *Interests*: Working with American Indian and other youth promoting Indian education & the success of tribal peoples, & furthering the public's understanding of contemporary and historical Indian issues.

WILLIAMS, ROBERT, JR. (Lumbee)
(professor of law & American Indian studies)
Education: Loyola College (Baltimore, MD), BA, 1977; Harvard Law School, JD, 1980. *Affiliation & Address*: E. Thomas Sullivan Professor of Law & American Indian Studies & Founding Director & Faculty Chair, Indigenous Law & Policy (IPLP) Program, James E. Rogers College of Law, RH 308, Box 210176, Tucson, AZ 85721 (520) 621-5622. E-mail: williams@law.arizona.edu. *Other professional posts*: Affiliated faculty, American Indian Studies Program, The University of Arizona, Tucson, AZ; principal investigator for the establishment of the "IPLP/NNI (Native Nations Institute) Collaborative Project" at the University of Arizona; serves as Chief Justice of the Yavapai-Prescott Apache Tribe Court of Appeals and the Court of Appeals, Pascua Yaqui Indian Reservation; serves as judge pro tempore for the Tohono O'odham Nation. *Past professional posts*: Served as Chief Justice for the Court of Appeals, Pascua Yaqui Indian Reservation, and as Justice for the Court of Appeals & trial judge pro tem for the Tohono O'odham Nation. *Awards, honors*: Served as Bennet Boskey Distinguished Visiting Lecturer of Law at Harvard University, 2000-01, the first Oneida Indian Nation Visiting Professor of Law at Harvard Law School, 2003-04; Gustavus Meyers Human Rights Center Award for the book, The American Indian in Western Legal Thought; 2006 recipient of the University of Arizona Henry & Phyllis Koffler Prize for Outstanding Accomplishments in Public Service; has received numerous grants & awards; has represented tribal groups before the Inter-American Court of Human Rights and the UN Working Group on Indigenous Peoples. Interests: Energy/natural resource management; Indian law & policy. *Published works*: The American Indian in Western Legal Thought: The Discourses of Conquest (Oxford University Press, 1990); Linking Arms Together: American Indian Treaty Visions of Law & Peace, 1600-1800 (Oxford University Press, 1997); co-author of Federal Indian Law: Cases & Materials, 5th & 6th Eds. with David Getches & Charles Wilkinson (West, 2004 & 2011); "Like a Loaded Weapon:" The Rehnquist Court, Indian Rights & the Legal History of Racism in America (University of Minnesota Press, 2005); Savage Anxieties: The Invention of Western Civilization (Oxford U. Press, 2012).

WILLIAMS, SCOTT
(Indian law partner)
Education: Stanford University, BA, 1970; Boston College Law School, JD, 1974. *Affiliation & Address*: Partner, Berkey Williams LLP, 2030 Addison St., Suite 410, Berkeley, CA 94704 (510) 548-7070. Mr. Williams began an affiliation with his current partners in 1997, working on select Indian law employment & litigation matters. He has an extensive background in complex litigation. In addition, he also provides ongoing advice & consultation on water rights and natural resources, cultural site protection, employment relations, healthcare, and governmental and corporate affairs. In the field of employment

relations, he provides ongoing advice and consultation on employment issues as they arise, assists tribes and tribal organizations in the development of policies & procedures, & works with tribal leaders to achieve stability in a highly competent work force. Illustrative work includes representation of a Tribe in negotiating agreements to remove dams and restore the Klamath River in California and Oregon, protection of Tribal access to significant off-reservation cultural sites, Indian health programs in all aspects of health care delivery, and protection of water resources in New Mexico. Along with his partners, Curtis Berkey & Rovianne Leigh, Mr. Williams teaches the Advanced Indian Law seminar at Berkeley Law (Boalt Hall) at the University of California, Berkeley

WILLIAMS, SHARI (Choctaw)
 (education)
Education: Arizona State University, MA (Education). *Affiliation & Address*: Assistant Director, Choctaw Nation Interlocal Alternative High School, Choctaw Nation of Oklahoma, P.O. Box 602, Durant, OK 74701 (580) 931-0691. E-mail: swilliams@choctawnation.com. Shari works with Choctaw Nation Language Program in areas of language acquisition; Board member, National Indian Education Association, Washington, DC (vice-president, 2007-2008).

WILLIAMS, SHERRIE (Karuk)
 (tribal vice chairperson)
Affiliation & Address: Vice Chairperson, Quartz Valley Indian Reservation, 13601 Quartz Valley Rd., P.O. Box 24, Fort Jones, CA 96032 (530) 468-5907. E-mail: tribalvice@qvir-nsn.gov

WILLIAMS, SHIRLEY I. (*Migizi ow Kwe*) (Ojibway/Odawa First Nations)
 (professor emeritus of Indigenous Studies)
Born & raised at Wikwemikong, Manitoulin Island. *Education*: Trent University, BA (Native Studies); Lakehead University Thunder Bay), Native Language Instructors Program diploma; York University, MS (Environmental Studies). *Affiliation & Address*: Professor Emeritus, Department of Indigenous Studies, Trent University, Enweying 315, 1600 Westbank Dr., Peterborough, ON K9J 7B8 (705) 748-1011 ext. 7477. E-mail: siwilliams@trentu.ca.

WILLIAMS, STEPHANIE (Alabama-Coushatta of Texas)
 (tribal administrator)
Affiliation & Address: Tribal Administrator, Alabama-Coushatta Tribe of Texas, 571 State Park Rd., Livingston, TX 77351 (936) 563-1100.

WILLIAMS, STRATFORD (Wichita)
 (tribal vice president)
Affiliation: Wichita & Affiliated Tribes, P.O. Box 729, Anadarko, OK 73005 (405) 247-2425. Website: www.wichitatribe.com.

WILLIAMS, SUSAN M. (Sisseton-Wahpeton Dakota)
 (attorney)
Education: Radcliff College, BA, 1976; Harvard Law School, JD, 1981. *Affiliation & Address*: Partner, Williams & Works, P.A., 565 W. Ella Dr., Corrales, NM 87048 (505) 899-7994. An Indian-owned and woman-owned law firm. As a lead lobbyist in several successful Indian legislative efforts, Ms. Williams has impacted amendments such as one to treat Indian tribes as states under the Safe Drinking Water Act, the Clean Water Act, and the Indian Tribal Government Tax Status Act. In April of 1989, she successfully argued the Big Horn case before the U.S. Supreme Court. She represents numerous Indian tribes on their water rights and other matters. *Other professional posts*: She serves on several Boards of Directors and National Advisory Committees on state-tribal relations, resource development & environmental protection, including the World Wildlife Fund, the American Bar Association, Water Resources Committee, the American Indian Resources Institute, St. Michaels Indian School, Indian Law Resource Center and the Grand Canyn Trust.; also the Harvard Alumni Association. *Past professional posts*: Fried, Frank, Harris, Shriver & Kampelman; executive director & chairperson, Navajo Tax Commissionn, Window Rock, AZ; lecturer, Harvard Law School, in Indian Law (five years), Stanford University (one year).

WILLIAMS, TIMOTHY (Mojave)
 (tribal chairperson)
Affiliation & Address: Chairperson, Fort Mojave Indian Tribe, 500 Merriman Ave., Needles, CA 92363 (760) 629-4591.

WILLIAMS, WALTER L. 1948-
 (professor of gender studies)
Born November 3, 1948, Durham, N.C. *Education*: Georgia State University, BA, 1970; University of North Carolina, Chapel Hill, MA, 1972, PhD, 1974. *Affiliation*: Professor of Anthropology, History & Gender Studies, (Teaches classes on gender & sexuality and on American Indian studies) Gender Studies Program, Anthropology Dept., University of Southern California, Los Angeles, CA, 1985-. *Address*: 2319 Portland St., Los Angeles, CA 90007.

Other professional post: Founding Editor, International Gay & Lesbian Review. Website: www.gaybookreviews.info. Consultant, American Indian Studies Center, UCLA. Dr. Williams has done fieldwork research living on the Eastern Cherokee and Pine Ridge Sioux reservations, and also among several other Native American groups from the Yup'ik in Alaska to the Maya in Yucatan, Mexico. *Community activities*: Gay American Indians, Inc. (consultant); Museum of the Cherokee Indians (consultant); International Gay & Lesbian Archives (president, board of directors). *Military service*: U.S. Army, 1973 (Captain). *Awards, honors*: Woodrow Wilson Fellow, 1970; American Council of Learned Societies grant awards, 1977, 1983; UCLA American Indian Studies Center Fellow, 1980, 1982; Newberry Library Fellow, 1978; Ruth Benedict Prize Book Award, 1986, for The Spirit and the Flesh. *Interests*: "Homosexuality & gender variance in American Indian cultures; Indian sexuality; 19th century Indian legal status; Southeastern Indian ethno-history, 1830-present." *Published works*: Editor, Southeastern Indians Since the Removal Era (University of Georgia Press, 1979); editor, Indian Leadership (Sunflower University Press, 1984); The Spirit and the Flesh: American Indian Sexual Diversity in American Indian Culture (Beacon Press, 1986); Two Spirits: A Story of Life With the Navajo, with Toby Johnson (Lethe Press, White Crane Books), 2006. Articles, and book reviews on Southeastern Indians in Ethno-history, North Carolina Historical Review, American Indian Journal, and Journal of Southern History.

WILLIAMSON, BILLY TALAKO (*Grey Eagle*) (Oklahoma Choctaw) 1948-
 (film director/producer)
Born February 2, 1948, Okla. Education: CSU (Edmond, OK), BA, 1973; UCLA, MFA (Film), 1977. *Principal occupation*: Film director/producer. Address unknown. *Affiliation*: Director, I.T.I. Film & Video, Oklahoma City, OK, 1980-. *Memberships*: National Association of American Indian Social Workers; Directors Guild of America; Screen Actors Guild; A.C.S. *Awards, honors*: 4 ADDY Awards; 6 Telly Awards. *Interests*: Zuni Pueblo.

WILLIAMSON, JIM (Chippewa) 1949-
 (energy research management)
Born November 30, 1949, Williston, N.D. Education: Montana State University, BS, 1971; University of California, Berkeley, MS (Math), 1974. *Address*: 5025 Garton Rd., Castle Rock, CO 80104. *Affiliations*: Project Manager, U.S. Atomic Energy Commission, Oakland, CA (seven years); Director-International Solar Programs, Midwest Research Institute, Kansas City, MO (eight years); Associate Partner, Meridian Corporation, Alexandria, VA, 1988-; Manager, National Renewable Energy Laboratory, Washington, DC, 1989-. *Membership*: American Indian Science & Engineering Society. *Awards, honors*: Project Achievement, King Abdul-Aziz Center for Science & Technology; Project Management, Atomic Energy Commission; Spacecraft Support Team Award, Energy Research & Development Administration. *Interests*: "Extensive international travel to energy research centers including an around-the-world trip in 1987. Raising horses in Virginia." *Published works*: Co-editor - Solar Cooling, April 1980; Solar Water Desalination, March 1981; Solar Storage, April, 1982; Solar Thermal Collectors, April 1983; Solar Buildings, May 1984; Solar for Remote Applications, April 1985 (published by U.S. Dept. of Energy).

WILLIE, MARY ANN (Dine'-Navajo) 1951-
 (professor)
Born April 11, 1951, Tolani Lake, Ariz. *Education*: University of Arizona, PhD (Linguistics), 1991. *Affiliation & Address*: Associate Professor of Linguistics & American Indian Studies, The University of Arizona, American Indian Language Development Institute, Linguistics Department (1994-present), Communications 108A, P.O. Box 210028, Tucson, AZ 85721 (520) 621-9726. E-mail: mwillie@email.arizona.edu. Professor Willie is head of the Native American Linguistics Master's Program with a shared appointment in American Indian Studies. *Interests*: Navajo syntax; Athabaskan linguistics. She focuses on psyche verbs in Navajo, the expression of modality in Navajo, and number and person in Dine. She is developing a major proposal to NSF to study morphological knowledge of Navajo speakers.

WILLIE, MELLOR (Dine'-Navajo)
 (executive director)
Affiliation & Address: Executive Director, National American Indian Housing Council (NAIHC), 900 2nd St., NE, Suite 107, Washington, DC 20002 (202) 789-1754.

WILLIFORD, WANDA L. (Umpqua & Suislaw)
 (president/CEO)
Affiliation: Native American Technology Corp. (NATECH), 377 Laclaire St., Coos Bay, OR 97420 (541) 888-8100. E-mail: contact@natechcop.com. Website: www.natechcorp.com. NATECH is a Native American woman-owned firm specializing in environmental & safety compliance, professional & administrative support services; full service engineering; base operations support; and OSHA/EPA training.

WILLIS, GEORGE "SHUKATA" (Choctaw)
(artist & inventor)
Trained at the Southern California College of Jewelry Design & The Starline Jewelry in Los Angeles, California. He has been a professional jeweler since 1964. He operated his own jewelry shop until 1990. *Past professional posts*: Executive director, Indian Arts & Crafts Association, Albuquerque, NM. *Awards, honors*: Top award at the Indian Arts & Crafts Association annual Market; Artist of the Year (2000) Indian Arts & Crafts Association.

WILLIS, MICHAEL (Ojibwe)
(Native American studies department chair)
Education: A.A.S.. & Diploma, Nishnaabemwin Language Instructors Institute, Bay Mills Community College, Northern Michigan University & Lake Superior State University. *Affiliation & Address*: Chairperson, Native American Studies Deparrment, Bay Mills Community College, Mikanuk Hall, 12214 W. Lakeshore Dr., Brimley, MI 49715 (906) 248-3354 ext. 8447. E-mail: mlwillis@bmcc.edu.

WILLIS-ESQUEDA, CYNTHIA (Cherokee)
(professsor of Psychology & Native American studies)
Education: Washburn University, BA; University of Kansas, MA & PhD (Social Psychology). *Affiliation & Address*: Professor, Department of Psychology & Native American Studies, Institute of Ethnic Studies, University of Nebraska, Lincoln, 420 University Ter., Lincoln, NE 68588 (402) 471-1663. E-mail: cwillis-esqueda1@unl.edu. *Other professional posts*: Chair, Department of Psychology's Sarata Diversity Enhancement Committee, 2001-present; Advisor for Graduate Minor in Diversity for the Psychology Department and administers the Psychology Department's annual Levine Diversity Research Award. *Past professional post*: Purdue University (five years); . *Interests*: American Indian domestic violence, as well as the ways in which stereotypes about American Indians can impact governmental resource allocations. *Published works*: Numerous articles in academic journals.

WILLOW, NORMAN (Northern Arapaho)
(tribal co-chairperson)
Affiliation & Address: Northern Arapahoe Tribe, P.O. Box 396, Fort Washakie, WY 82514 (307) 332-6120. Website: www.northernarapaho.com.

WILNOTY, JOHN JULIUS (Cherokee) 1940-
(stone carver)
Born April 10, 1940, Cherokee, N.C. *Principal occupation*: Stone carver. *Address*: P.O. Box 517, Cherokee, NC 28719. *Membership*: The Qualla Indian Arts & Crafts Cooperative. *Interests*: "Building toys for children; rebuilding and designing machinery." Mr. Wilnoty's work is displayed at the Smithsonian Institution and the Museum of the American Indian.

WILSON, CANDICE (Lummi)
(tribal vice chairperson)
Affiliation & Address: Vice Chairperson, Lummi Nation, 2616 Kwina Rd., Bellingham, WA 98226 (360) 384-1489.

WILSON, CATHERINE E. (Nez Perce)
(attorney)
Membership: Native American Bar Association; Native American Alumni Association of Dartmouth College.

WILSON, CHESLEY GOSEYUN (*White Eagle*) (San Carlos Apache) 1932-
(singer, painter, woodcarver, silversmith, storyteller, actor, model)
Born July 31, 1932, Bylas Village on the San Carlos Reservation, Ariz. *Address*: 333 S. Alvernon Way, #60, Tucson, AZ 85711 (520) 881-4842. *Affiliations*: Comstock Silversmiths, Carson City, NV1960-80; artist, San Carlos Apache Tribe Cultural Center; Pinkerton Security Corp., Tucson, AZ, 1987-. *Other professional posts*: Various TV, film, stage & music productions; numerous television appearances over the years as free lance performer in the arts, music & dance; numerous live performances throughout the U.S. *Military service*: U.S. Army, 1950-52 (Corporal; Korea). *Community activities*: Tucson Indian Center - Powwow; president, Arco-Iris (Indian arts organization), Tucson, AZ. *Memberships*: San Carlos Apache Tribe; Gene Autry Western Heritage Museum (Los Angeles, CA). *Awards, honors*: 1st Place Award for silver work at the Tohono O'odham Spring Fair, 1987; 1989 Heritage Fellowship Award, National Endowment for the Arts-Folk Arts for his traditional Apache violin; An Apache violin made by Chesley is in the musical instruments collection of the Smithsonian Institution, Washington, DC; Chesley was commissioned by the Arizona Commission on the Arts to make a traditional Apache violin for the Governor's Arts Awards in March 1991; he played the role of "Singer of Songs" in the TNT production of Geronimo. Interests: Chesley is a singer, maker and player of traditional Apache violins & flutes which he handcrafts, woodcarver, storyteller & silversmith. He is the great-grandson of Aravaipa Apache Chief Eskiminzin and the great-great grandson of White Mountain Apache Chiefs Hashkedasila and Santo as well as the famous Chiricahua Apache Chief Cochise. He learned the arts of Apache musical

instruments making from his uncles Albert Goseyun & Amos Gustina. He is considered an authority on Ga'an (Mountain Spirit or Crown Dancers) ceremonies. He regularly takes part in religious ceremonies on Apache reservations in Arizona as singer. *Published work*: When the Earth Was Like New, with CD & cassette tape (songs and stories of the Apache, with Ruth Longcor Harnisch Wilson; edited/published by Judith Cook Tucker; CD & cassette by World Music Press, Danbury, CT, 1994). Roles in Films: Buffalo Soldiers (role: Chief Nana), 1997; South of Heaven West of Hell (role: Chief Nathan), 1999.

WILSON, CLARA (Pomo)
(rancheria chairperson)
Affiliation & Address: Robinson Rancheria, 1545 E. Hwy. 20, Nice, CA 95464 (707) 275-0527.

WILSON, DANA (Crow)
(tribal vice chairperson)
Afiliation & Address: Vice Chairperson, Crow Nation, P.O. Box 129, Crow Agency, MT 59022 (306) 638-3708.

WILSON, DAVID R. (Navajo-Dine' Nation)
(director of American Indian affairs & policy)
Education: Arizona State University, PhD (Biology). *Affiliation & Address*: Director of American Indian Affairs & Policy (2010-present), Society for Advancement of Chicanos & Native Americans in Science (SACNAS), 1155 16th St., NW, Washington, DC 20036 (877) 722-6271. E-mail: dave@sacnas.org. His work with SACNAS is aimed at encouraging & supporting Native American students in their pursuit of higher education.

WILSON, DEBRA J. (Ojibwe)
(dean of student services)
Education: Bay Mills Community College, AA, AAS; Central Michigan University, BS. *Affiliation & Address*: Dean of Student Services, Bay Mills Community College, Administration Bldg., 12214 W. Lakeshore Dr., Brimley, MI 49715 (906) 248-3354 ext. 8442. E-mail: dwilson@bmcc.edu.

WILSON, EDWARD P. (*White Bear*) (Southern Cheyenne)
(economic development specialist, administrator)
Born August 2, 1943, Clinton, Okla. *Education*: Haskell Institute, Northern Oklahoma College, Oklahoma State University. *Address*: 1811 Shelby Court, Norman, OK 73071 (405) 329-4597. *Affiliation*: Chairman, Cheyenne-Arapaho Tribe, 1980-81. *Other professional posts*: Vice-president & secretary of Reserve Industrial Authority; director, Citizen Band Potawatomi's Tax Program; administrator, Sac & Fox Tribe of Missouri; director, National Indian Activities Association. *Military service*: U.S. Army Airborne, 1965-67, E-4 (Vietnam-Bronze Star & Purple Heart). *Community activities*: Parent Teachers Organization; Vietnam Era Veterans Organization; active in support of tribal ceremonial preservation; NAC (Church). *Memberships*: Board Member, Native Americans Veterans Services Access (model since mid 1993); board member, Oklahoma Indian Affairs Commission (appointed by Governor, 1992, reappointed 1993 to full term. *Interests*: "Reservation/tribal economies; financing for individuals, groups, tribes, corporations; develop sources of capital to enhance development & employment; raise educational levels of groups or communities; develop entrepreneurship."

WILSON, JERRY (Muscogee Creek)
(former tribal administrator)
Affiliation & Address: Administrator, Muscogee (Creek) Nation, P.O. Box 580, Okmulgee, OK 74447 (918) 732-7620. E-mail: jwilson@mcn-nsn.gov

WILSON, KRISTEN (Kickapoo)
(tribal executive director)
Affiliation: Kickapoo Tribe, P.O. Box 70, McLoud, OK 74851 (405) 964-2075.

WILSON, LARRY (Cree)
(member-board of directors)
Affiliation: Intertribal Christian Communications, P.O. Box 3765, Station B, Winnipeg, Manitoba, Canada R2W 3R6 (204) 661-9333.

WILSON, LENA R. (Navajo)
(school principal)
Affiliation: Crystal Boarding School, Navajo, NM 887328 (505) 777-2385.

WILSON, RYAN (Inupiaq from White Mountain, Alaska)
(physician)
Education: Dartmouth Medical School, MD, 2015. Affiliation & Address: Intern, Dartmouth Hitchcock Medical Center, Lebanon, NH. "I have been all over the world, from Dartmouth to Red Cliff to my current location, Minnesota, to expand my knowledge & cultural horizon. A Neuroscience major in undergrad, I hope to enter ophthalmology as I return to Alaska to provide eye care for Alaska Native people. Through working with other ANAMS students and

different AAIP mentors, I've found a huge wealth of knowledge and wisdom from which to draw inspiration. I'm looking forward to the new heights we're achieving as a group, and am excited to be a part of shaping the future of Indigenous healthcare in America." *Activities*: President (2014-15), Association of Native American Medical Students.

WILSON, MICHAEL D (Choctaw)
(Native American literary critic, educator & writer)
Education: Oklahoma State Univesity, BA (Literary Studies; Cornell University, MA & PhD (English Language & Literature). *Affiliation & Address*: Professor of English & American Indian Literature, American Indian Studies Program, Univeristy of Wisconsin, Milwaukee, College of Letters & Sciences, Holton Hall, Rm. 365, P.O. Box 413, 2442 E. Hartford Ave., Milwaukee, WI 53201. E-mail: Michael@uwm.edu. is a Native American literary critic, educator, and writer. *Published works*: He is the author of the monograph, Writing Home: Indigenous Narratives of Resistance; editor, On Indian Ground: Northern Woodlands (Information Age Publishing (in preparation).

WILSON. NORMAN G. (Rosebud Sioux)
(former tribal president)
Affiliation: Rosebud Sioux Tribal Council, P.O. Box 430, Rosebud, SD 57570 (605) 747-2381.

WILSON, RAYMOND 1945-
(professor of history)
Born April 11, 1945, New Kensington, Penna. *Education*: Fort Lewis College, BA, 1967; University of Nebraska, Omaha, MA, 1972; University of New Mexico, PhD, 1977. *Principal occupation*: Professor of history, Fort Hays State University, Hays, KS, 1979-. *Address*: 500 W. 30th, Hays, KS 67601. *Other professional post*: History instructor, Sam Houston State University, 1977-79. *Memberships*: Western History Association; Indian Rights Association; Kansas Council for the Social Studies; Kansas Corral of the Westerners; Phi Alpha Theta; Pi Gamma Mu; Phi Delta Kappa; Phi Kappa Phi. *Interests*: "My major area of study is the American West with an emphasis on 19th & 20th century American Indian history. I enjoy playing the guitar, playing golf and traveling throughout western America." *Published works*: Administrative History, Canyon de Chelly National Monument, Arizona, co-authored with David M. Brugge (U.S. Dept. of the Interior/National Park Service, 1976); Ohiyesa: Charles A. Eastman, Santee Sioux (University of Illinois Press, 1983, paperback edition, 1999); Native Americans in the Twentieth Century (Brigham Young University Press, 1984), co-author, James S. Olson; Indian Lives: Essays on 19th & 20th Century Native American Leaders (University of New Mexico Press, 1985; Second Edition, 1993), co-author, L.G. Moses; Kansas Land (Gibbs M. Smith, Publisher, 1988; Second Edition, 1993), co-author, Thomas D. Isern.

WILSON, ROLLIE
(attorney)
Education: Miami University, Oxford, OH, B.Phil, 1992; University of Wisconsin Institute for Environmental Studies, MS, 1999; Uniersity of Wisconsin law School, JD, 1999. *Affiliation & Address*: Partner (2011-present), Fredericks Peebles & Morgan, LLP, 401 9th St. NW, Washington, DC 20004 (202) 450-4887. E-mail: rwilson@ndnlaw.com. *Practice Areas*: Trribal Sovereignty & Jurisdiction; Energy, Water, Natural & Cultural Resources, Enerygy. *Past professional posts*: In-House Counsel for the Menominee Indian Tribe of Wisconsin; U.S. Department of the Interior, Washington, DC; U.S. Senate Committee on Indian Affairs, Senior Counsel for the Majority, 2008-11. Mr. Wilson staffed development of the Indian Energy Parity Act of 2010 for introduction by Senator Dorgan in the 111th Congress. He also developed legislation on Indian energy taxation, water rights, and cultural & natural resources.

WILSON, RYAN (*Tatanka Wasaka*) (Oglala Lakota)
(organization president)
Affiliation & Address: President, National Alliance to Save Native Languages, 1455 Pennsylvania Ave, NW, Washington, DC 20004. *Other professional posts*: Board member, National Indian Education Association (NIEA), Washington, DC; staff, Cultural Survival; board member, Native American Children's Alliance, Cleveland, OH.

WILSON, SAUNIE K. (Oglala Lakota)
(tribal judge)
Education: University of South Dakota, MA (Public Administration), *Address*: P.O. Box 167, Pine Ridge, SD 57770. (605) 867-5041. *Affiliation*: Youth & Family Court Judge, Oglala Lakota Tribe, Pine Ridge, SD. *Other professional post*: Vice President, Native American Children's Alliance, Muskogee, OK; board member, South Dakota Voices for Children; member of the sub-committee task force Tribal Advisory Group; adjunct faculty member at Oglala Lakota College; president of the Great Plains Tribal Judges Association. "Saunie has a strong belief that the only way our young tribal members are going to be productive tribal members is through the the re-establishment of the Lakota culture and the strong values associated through the Lakota

language." *Past professional posts*: Executive secretary for the Oglala Sioux Tribal Gaming Commission (13 years); secretary of the Great Plains Indian Gaming Association. Interests: Saunie is a sundancer and offers many cultural alternatives through the Youth & Family Court in reuniting & healing families.

WILSON, STEVEN (Muscogee Creek)
(chairperson)
Affiliation/Address: Chairperson, National Society of American Indian Elderly, P.O. Box 50070, Phoenix, AZ 85076 (602) 424-0542 E-mail: swilson@nsaie.org. *Past professional posts*: Worked with the elderly nutrition program for the Muscogee Nation since the 1980's. *Awards, honors*: The Betsy D. Smith award for his efforts working on behalf of the Oklahoma Elder Programs.

WILSON, TERRY P.
(professor of Native American studies)
Affiliation: Native American Studies Department, University of California, Dwinelle Hall, Suite 3415, Berkeley, CA 94720 (510) 642-6717.

WILSON, TIM (Ottawa of Oklahoma)
(tribal 2nd chief)
Affiliation & Address: 2nd Chief, Ottawa Tribe of Oklahoma, P.O. Box 110, Miami, OK 74355 (918) 540-1536.

WIND DAUGHTER (Muskogee Creek)
(medicine chief)
Affiliation: Panther Tribe Medicine Society, P.O. Box 2388, Mountain View, AR 72560 (870) 368-7877. E-mail: wdwinddaughter@gmail.com.

WINDCHIEF, ROBERTA DENNY (*Black Hawk Woman*) (Assiniboine) 1941-
(health administrator)
Born January 16, 1941, Fort Belknap, Mont. *Education*: College of Great Falls, MT, BS; University of Oklahoma, MPH; University of Minnesota (Amb. Care). *Address*: P.O. Box 118, Neola, UT 84053. *Affiliations*: Public health educator, 1973-83, health systems administrator, 1983-85, Rocky Boy, MT; health system administrator, Fort Duchesne PHS Indian Health Center, Ft. Duchesne, UT, 1985-. *Membership*: American College of Health Care Professionals. *Interests*: Beading; traveling; intercultural communications.

WINDER, NATHAN W., JR. (*Strong Elk, Blue Fox*) (Southern Ute) 1960-
(training coordinator)
Born October 2, 1960, Albuquerque, N.M. *Education*: Stanford University, BA, 1983; University of Oregon, School of Law, 1984-1985, 1986. *Principal occupation*: Training coordinator. *Address*: P.O. Box 227, Ignacio, CO 81137 (800) 262-7623 (work). *Affiliations*: Counselor, Nevada Urban Indians, Inc., Reno; counselor, grants/contracts administrator, Pyramid Lake Paiute Tribal Council, Nixon, Nev., 1985-88; planning director, Southern Ute Indian Tribe, Ignacio, CO, 1988-; training coordinator, Colorado State University, Fort Collins, CO, 1993-. *Other professional posts*: Southern Ute Indian Tribal Council; 190 Tribal Liaison Representative, U.S. Department of Commerce, Bureau of Census, Economic Development Administrator; Housing & Urban Development, Office of Indian Programs, Region VIII; *Community activities*: Colorado Association of Non-Profit Organizations; Native American Church (vice president, Pyramid Lake chapter); Save the Children Committee (chairman); chairman, Southern Ute Indian Housing Authority, 1989-91 (term); Leadership la Plata (participant); Southern Ute Language & Cultural Committee; Community Development Block Grant Administrator, Southern Ute Indian Tribe. *Membership*: InterTribal Transportation Association (Albuquerque Area Representative). *Awards, honors*: Housing & Urban Development, Office of Indian Programs, Region VIII, Excellence in Maintenance; certified as an Economic Development Finance Professional by the National Development Council, Oct. 1990; Merit Award from Southern Ute Indian Tribe recognizing dedication and commitment to tribe. *Interests*: Administration for Native Americans Grant Reader; Colorado Dept. of Corrections, Native American Spiritual Facilitator; Western Colorado Grassroots Leadership Development Program, 1992, Community Resources Center, Denver, CO. "I am interested in traveling to historical & spiritual areas across the Western Hemisphere. I would like to find an American Indian woman who is interested and will participate in Sweat Lodge ceremonies and spiritually support me and my family during Sun Dance." *Published works*: Narrow Gauge Scenic Road *HNTB Corp., Dec. 1993; Southern Ute Transportation Study Update (Nurwoso, Dec. 1993).

WINDLE, LORI (White Earth Ojibwe)
(society vice chairperson)
Born & raised in the Denver, Colo. area. *Education*: Metropolitan State College, Denver, CO, BA. University of Colorado, MFA. Lori was the first to graduate with an advanced degree in Media Arts in their Arts Dept. *Affiliation*: Co-founder & vice chairperson, Society of American Indian Government Employees (SAIGE), P.O. Box 7715, Washington, DC 20044 (202) 564-0375. Website: www.saige.org. She was instrumental in the development of SAIGE from an idea to a working organization, and was the first elected Chairperson of the founding Board of Directors. *Other professional posts*: Audio Visual

Production Specialist, U.S. Dept. of the Interior's Office of Surface Mining, and has been their American Indian Special Emphasis Program Manager, 1992-present; chair, Valmont Butte Heritage Alliance, dedicated to the protection & preservation of this sacred place in Colorado. *Awards, honors*: Secretary of the Interior's Equal Opportunity Award (1996), and an Excellence in Government Award (1998) from the Denver Federal Executive Board. Lori helped to produce three joint interagency & tribal conferences on Sacred Sites issues in 2001-2004. Lori is an award-winning independent documentary videographer who has shown her work nationally & internationally. In 2004, she organized the Native Peoples Political Alliance (NPPA), a volunteer non-partisan get-out-the-vote effort to increase the voter registration & election participation of Indians in the Denver/Boulder area. In 2006, Ms. Windle received the Inspiration Award from Boulder's Safehouse Alliance for Non-Violence.

WINDWALKER, JIM (Cherokee/Choctaw)
  (project director & founder)
Born in northern Alabama. *Affiliation*: Founder & Executive Director, First Nations Outreach Project, Wolf Gardens Wildlife Center. Website: www.wolfgardens.org. *Activities*: Annual Spirit of the Wolf powwow & annual Kiowa Gourd Dance in late May.

WINDY BOY, ALVIN (Chippewa-Cree)
  (former tribal chairperson)
Affiliations: Rocky Boy's Reservation, Chippewa-Cree Business Committee, RR 1, Box 544, Box Elder, MT 59521 (406) 395-4282. *Other professional posts*: Chairperson of the following organizations: Montana-Wyoming Area Indian Health Board, Rocky Boy's Health Board, National Tribal leaders Diabetes Committee, & the National Tribal Diabetes Council; Vice-chairperson, National Tribal Self-Governance Advisory Committee; president, Montana-Wyoming Indian Stockgrowers Assn; secretary, Intertribal Agriculture Council.

WINDY BOY, JONATHAN (Chippewa-Cree)
  (state senator)
Affiliations: Democrat SD16, Representative, HD32 Montana House of Representatives, Helena, MT, 2016-present; Senator Emeritus, Montana State Senator, 2008-present. *Address*: P.O. Box 269, Box Elder, MT 59521 (406) 444-4800. Serving my second four (4) year term. I will be termed out after the next session in 2015, and I will no longer be eligible to run because of the State of Montana's term limits. Unless a new Constitution Initiative that the people of Montana will be voting on in the 2014 election. This bill/referendum was passed during this last session. If it passes, then the term limits will be extended to 16 year terms in either Chamber, making it a total of thirty two (32) years total. Also served 6 years, 3 two-year terms in the Montana House of Representativves from 2002-2008. Also served 12 years on the Chippewa Cree Tribal Council from 1998-2010. Two of those years serve has been in the position of the Vice Chairman for the Tribe. The 2013 Montana Senate Committee Appointments have been posted. My appointments are to the Montana Senate Finance and Claims Committee for my Class I committee. Along with that appointment I've been appointed to the Senate Finance/House Appropriations Joint Subcommittee for Education. My Class II Committee is the Senate Education and Cultural Affairs Committee. The 63rd Montana Legislature (2013) is over. I was fortunate to get passed "Senate Bill 342, Native Language Preservation Pilot Program." The bill that got passed this session has a $2 million dollar price tag. It is the first of it's kind to be passed in state statute in any state in the US. Also passed in this session was Senate Joint Resolution 9, A resolution to support the "Idle No More (INM) movement", that has become a global movement that recently occured.. The Interim Committee assignments have appointed, and I was fortunate to be appointed to three (3) committees, 1) The State/Tribal Relations Interim committee, which will oversee the newly passed Senate Bill 342. 2) Children, Families, Health & Human Services Interim Committee, and 3) The Education, Local Government Interim Committees.

WINFREY, VICTORIA (Mdewakanton Sioux)
  (tribal vice president)
Affiliation & Address: Vice President, Prairie Island Indian Community, 5636 Sturgeon Lake Rd., Welch, MN 55089 (651) 385-2554. E-mail: vwinfrey@piic.org.

WING, RANDALL E. (Gros Ventre)
  (tribal council member)
Affiliation & Address: Fort Belknap Community Council, P.O. Box 1019, Harlem, MT 59526.

WINIECKI, JANE RUSSELL (Yavapai-Apache)
  (tribal chairperson)
Affiliation & Address: Chairperson, Yavapai-Apache Nation, 2400 W. Datsi St., Camp Verde, AZ 86322 (928) 567-3649.

WINN, ANGEL (Pit River)
  (tribal council chairperson)
Affiliation & Address: Chairperson, Pit River Tribal Council, 37014 Main St., Burney, CA 96013 (530) 335-5421.

WINNE, BRUCE (Spokane)
  (former tribal chairperson)
Affiliation: Spokane Business Council, P.O. Box 100, Wellpinit, WA 99040 (509) 258-4581.

WINSHIP, ONEIDA (Choctaw of Oklahoma)
  (secretary/treasurer)
Affiliation & Address: Secretary/Treasurer, National Society of American Indian Elderly, 200 East Fillmore St. #151, Phoenix, AZ 85004 (602) 424-0542. E-mail: owinship@nsaie.org. *Other professional posts*: Member, Choctaw Nation Healthy Lifestyles Task Force, 2001-present; member, Wellness Program for the Choctaw Nation.

WINSTON, AARON (Meherrin)
  (tribal chairperson)
Affiliation: Meherrin Indian Tribe, P.O. Box 508, Winton, NC 27986 (252) 398-3321.

WINTERS, CARL (Standing Rock Sioux)
  (artist)
Born in S.D. Well-known Lakota artist, Mr. Winters has won many awards for hist paintings on canvas, drums & hides. His works are in numerous galleries & private collections worldwide, and a commissioned mural of his work is in the Denver International Airport, CNN's "Across America" & Southwest Art Magazine featured him. "I strive to communicate the validity of the Indian experience," Winters has said, "in hopes that my work will serve as a vehicle for cross-cultural understanding and respect."

WINTON, BEN (Yaqui)
  (editor)
Address & Affiliation: Editor, Native Peoples Magazine, 5333 N. 7th St. #224C, Phoenix, AZ 85014 (602) 265-4855.

WIRICK, NOWETAH (*Nowetah*) (St. Francis Abenaki-Paugussett) 1947-
  (owner/curator of store & museum; teacher, craftswoman;
    Indian dancer; author)
Born February 21, 1947, New Haven, Conn. *Address & Affiliation*: Founder/owner/curator, Nowetah's Indian Museum & Store (1969-present), 2 Colegrove Rd. (Route 27), New Portland, ME 04961-3821 (207) 628-4981. *Other professional posts*: "Currently teaching American Indian history, Indian dancing, and Indian crafts to school children; as a museum curator - researching, cataloging & labeling museum pieces I purchase." *Memberships*: Connecticut Archaeological Society; Audubon; National & International Wildlife Federation; Connecticut Herpetological Society; Maine Archives & Museums; Maine Tourism Association. *Awards, honors*: Community Leaders & Noteworthy Americans Award, 1975-76, by the American Biographical Institute. *Interests*: "To start my museum and store, I traveled all over the U.S. & Canada to make contacts with other Indian people, so I could purchase direct from them instead of buying crafts through big companies. I would be called an amateur archaeologist. Of course my major interest is naturally American Indian culture & writing about it. But, another interest is herpetology (giving nature talks on frogs, toads, salamanders, snakes & an interest in birds. Have done nature studies in remote Ontario, Canada & Everglades Park in Florida for Audubon & Wildlife (photographing & studies of habitat). Also, I teach classes on wild plants/herbs as medicine & food. I'm a glass blower and make glass animal figurines, hand weaving wool Indian rugs, hand crafting Indian beadwork, porcupine quill jewelry, fancy dream catchers, dolls, leather products, bone jewelry, birchbark products; also, basketry, pottery, etc." Mail order available. *Biographical source*: "Nowetah's Indian Museum & Store," chapter in Profiles: Directory of Women Entrepreneurs (Wind River Publishing, 1991). *Published works*: Writer of small booklets with illustrations on past Indian life including, "History of Indian Wampum" (shell beads), "Brain Tanning Hides & Pelts," How to Weave an Indian Rug," "The Drum," "The Sacred Pipe," The Ancient Wisdoms & Knowledge of the Abenaki Indians"; The Medicine Wheel; The Abenaki Indian Massacree with Fr. Rasle at Narrantsauak (Aug. 23, 1724); Indian Legends, Recipes & Names.

WIRTA-KOSOBUSKI, ANNA (Bois Forte Ojibwe)
  (assistant director)
Affiliation & Address: Assistant Director, Center for American Indian & Minority Health, 185A SMed, 1035 University Dr., Duluth, MN 55812 (218) 726-7235. E-mail: awirta1@umn.edu.

WISE OWL, CHIEF (Tuscarora)
(tribal chief)
Affiliation: Tuscarora Indian Tribe, Drowning Creek Reservation, Maxton, NC 28364 (919) 844-3827.

WISEMAN, FREDERICK M. (Abenaki) 1948-
(chair & professor of humanities)
Born March 15, 1948, Baltimore, Md. *Education*: University of Arizona, PhD (Geosciences), 1978. *Principal occupation*: Professor of humanities. *Address*: 17 Spring St., Swanton, VT 05488 (802) 868-3808. *Affiliations*: Center for Materials Research in Archaeology & Ethnology, M.I.T., Cambridge, MA, 1983-87; chair & professor, Dept. of Humanities, Johnson State College, Johnson, UT, 1987-present. *Other professional posts*: Director, Abenaki Tribal Museum & Cultural Center, Swanton, VT; Governor's (VT) Advisory Commission on Native American Affairs. *Community activities*: Guest curator, Abenaki Museum, Odanak, Quebec; "Champlain Zoo" Commission (VT); lobbying for state recognition of Vermont Abenakis. *Interests*: Paleo environment & Native peoples; ethnic revitalization, Wabanaki studies; digital video in teaching. *Published works*: Voice of the Dawn (University Press of New England, 2001); Reclaiming the Ancestors (University Press of New England, 2005).

WISEMAN, JOSEPH J.
(attorney)
Education: UCLA, BA, 1978; University of Oregon School of Law, JD, 1982. *Affiliation & Address*: Principal, Wiseman Law Corporation, 431 I St., Suite 201, Sacramento, CA 95814 (916) 668-7353. Mr. Wiseman has more than 30 years experience as a federal criminal trial and appellate lawyer, which gives me a unique perspective on what works and does not work with defending serious, complex federal charges. I prepare each case for trial, since a good result is only attainable if the lawyer is prepared and willing to go to trial. And I expect my clients to be actively involved in participating in their defense. I also have specialized expertise in American Indian Law and a law professor and Tribal Court Judge. *Other professional posts*: Professor of Law, Empire College of Law, 1996-present; Tribal Court Judge, Dry Creek Rancheria Band of Pomo Indians, 2012-present; Chief Justice, Round Valey Indian Tribes, Court of Appeals, 2015-present; Chief Judge, Northern California Intertribal Court System, 2015-present. *Professional Associations*: National American Indian Court Judges Association member, 2012-present; Vice-chair, California Tribal Court Judges Association, 2016-present. *Awards, honors*: Super Lawyer, White Collar Crime, 2014, 2015 & 2016; Invited member, National Association of Distinguished Counsel, 2015; Invited member, Rue's Rating of Best Attorneys in America, 2013.

WISNER-FOLEY, GERI (Muscogee Creek)
(attorney; chief of staff)
Education: Oklahoma State University, BA (Political Science and American Indian Studies Certificate, 2001; University of Tulsa Law School, JD and Native American Law Certificate), 2003. *Affiliation & Address*: Chief-of-Staff, Native American Children's Alliance, 101 West Broadway, Muskogee, OK 74401 (918) 683-5291. Geri trains law enforcement, prosecutors, advocates and allied professionals responding to child maltreatment & domestic violence issues, as well as criminal investigation & prosecution issues specific to Indian Country. She has developed many tribal criminal codes, family codes, child support & enforcement codes, as well as many amending language to existing codes to Include laws to protect tribal elders. *Past professional posts*: Senior Tribal Attorney, National Center for Prosecution of Child Abuse at the National District Attorneys Association (NDAA); Attorney General for the Kickapoo Tribe of Oklahoma; prosecutor for the Iowa Tribe of Oklahoma, the Citizen Potawatomi Nation of Oklahoma, the Absentee Shawnee Tribe, the Kickapoo Traditional Tribe of Texas, and the Seminle Nation of Oklahoma; served as the first Muscogee (Creek) Nation Ambassador the the U.N. in Geneva, Switzerland and New York City. *Military service*: U.S. Marines.

WITCRAFT, JULIE (Miami)
(tribal secretary-treasurer)
Affiliation: Miami Tribe of Oklahoma, P.O. Box 1326, Miami, OK 74355 (918) 542-1445.

WITGEN, MICHAEL (Red Cliff Ojibwe)
(director of Native American studies)
Education: University of Washington, PhD, 2004. *Affiliation & Address*: Director, Associate Professor & Undergraduate Advisor, Native American Studies Program, Department of American Culture, Department of History, 505 S. State St., University of Michigan, Ann Arbor, MI 48109 (734) 647-5419. E-mail: mwitgen@umich.edu. *Published work*: An Infinity of Nations: How the Native New World Shaped Early North America (University of Pennsylvania Press, 2012); several articles.

WITHERSPOON, GARY J.
(professor of American Indian studies)
Education: Ohio State University, BA; Brigham Young University, MA; University of Chicago, PhD, 1970. *Affiliation & Address*: Professor, Department of American Indian Studies, University of Washington, Seattle, WA 98195 (206) 616-9508. E-mail: gjspoon@u.washington.edu. Website: www.garywitherspoon.com. *Past professional posts*: Head Start teacher on the Navajo reservation, at the Rough Rock Demonstration School and at the Navajo Community College; assistant professor at Yale; an associate and full professor at the University of Michigan, 1971-1982; Director, Navajo Language Institute at the Navajo Academy in Farmington, NM, 1982-87. *Published works*: Six books and 40+ articles in journals & chapters in books. *Awards, honors*: Language & Art in the Navajo Universe won numerous awards including Book of the Year Award at the University of Michigan in 1977; also nominated for a Pulitzer Prize and was selected by the NY Times Book Review section as one of the top 50 books published in the field of anthropology in the 20th century. The American Anthropologist selected one of Dr. Witherspoon's articles for inclusion in its centennial edition, describing it as one of the best and most representative article published by the journal in its first hundred years. Dr. Witherspoon has also worked on four ethnographic films & recently has been working with friends & colleagues in producing films for educational purposes.

WITTSTOCK, LAURA WATERMAN (Seneca) 1937-
(administrator)
Born September 11, 1937, Cattaraugus Indian Reservation, N.Y. *Education*: University of Minnesota, BS. *Principal occupation*: Non-profit administrator. *Affiliation & Address*: Endowment Chair (2011-present), Tiwahe Foundation, 2801 21st Ave. South, Suite 132F, Minneapolis, MN 55407 (612) 722-0999. *Other professional post*: President & CEO (2005-present), Wittstock & Associates, Minneapolis, MN; board member (2010-present), American Indian Cancer Foundation, Minneapolis, MN; producer (2009-present), First Person Radio, Minneapolis, MN; board vice chair (2006-present), Native American Public Telecommunications (NAPT), Minneapolis, MN; board member (1994-present), Greater Metropolitan Housing Corporation, Minneapolis, MN. *Past professional posts*: Rosy Simas Dance, Minneapolis, MN Website: www.laurawatermanwittstock.com; Migizi Communications, Inc., Minneapolis, MN (director, curriculum project, 1986-99; president, 2000-09); chairperson (1995-2011), SEARCH Minneapolis; vice chair (2005-10), Minnesota Planetarium Society; board member (2008-11), Civic Media Minnesota; chairperson, editor, Legislative Review, 1971-73; executive director, American Indian Press Association, Washington, DC, 1975; associate director, Red School House, St. Paul, MN, 1975-77; director, Project Media, National Indian Education, Minneapolis, 1973-75; administrator, Heart of the Earth Survival School, Minneapolis, 1982-85. *Community activities*: Minnesota Governor's Job Training Council (vice chair, 1983-); Minneapolis Community Business Employment Alliance (vice chair, 1983-present); United Way Planning & Priorities Committee (member); Christian Sharing Fund, Minneapolis-St. Paul Archdiocese (chair, 1981-86); Minnesota Women's Fund (executive committee, 1983-); Children's Theatre & School, Minneapolis (board member, 1984-). *Awards, honors*: 2001 Frank Premack Award: The Farr Award for Public Affairs Journalism; 2007 University of Minnesota, Indian Studies Department Honored American Indian Women; 2006 Institute for Educational Leadership Distinguished IEL Service Award; 2005 Committee for Indian College Graduation American Indian Honored Educator; 1992 8th Annual Human Rights Award, Minnesota Lawyers International Human Rights Committee; 1992 Minneapolis/St. Paul Magazine: 1992 Twin Citiian Volunteer Hall of Fame; 1992 National Headliner Award for Outstanding Documentary by a Network, Executive Producer. *Interests*: "Journalism, writing; American Indian education --program designer, evaluator, administrator; American Indian alcoholism & related problems; employment-program designer, board member, policy-maker; American Indian urban studies." *Published works*: Indian Alcoholism in St. Paul, study with Michael Miller (U. of Minnesota, 1981); Native American Women: Twilight of a Long Maidenhood, Comparative Perspectives of Third World Women, Beverly Lindsay, editor (Praeger Publishers, 1980); On Women's Rights for Native Peoples (Akwesasne Notes, 1975); editor, Indian Education, National Indian Education Assn, 1973-74; The Federal Indian Relationship, Civil Rights Digest, Oct., 1973; ed., Legislative Review, 1971-73.

WOESTEHOFF, MICHAEL (Navajo)
(communications coordinator)
Born in Tuba City, Ariz. *Education*: Northern Arizona University, B.A. (Political Science). *Affiliation*: Membership & Communications Coordinator, National Indian Education Association, 110 Maryland Ave., N.E., Suite 104, Washington, DC 20002 (202) 544-7290. E-mail: woesterhoff@nniea.org. *Past affiliations*: Michael interned at the National Museum of the American Indian in 2004 and U.S. Dept. of Agriculture in 2003 at their Office of Public Affairs. *Interests*: Passionate about uniting all Native peoples through education.

WOLF, CHIPA & RUBY (*Chipa*, Cherokee; *Ruby*, Rosebud Lakota)
(cultural affairs producer)
Affiliation & Address: Rolling Thunder Enterprise & The H.O.M.E. Organization, 34 Rolling Thunder Dr., Jasper, GA 30143 (770) 735-6275. E-mail: rte@rthunder.com; Website: www.rthunder.com. Producers of the annual Cherokee County Mother's Day Powwow in Canton, GA (The H.O.M.E. Organization); producers of special events - powwows, rodeos, environmental expo's, wildlife rehab-animal handler; casting agents for motion pictures & television (Rolling Thunder Enterprise); Native American & Indigenous Peoples Talent Network. *Community activities*: School Program - dance, primitive skills, etc.; also H.O.M.E. Help Our Mother Earth (Stewardship Development Program). *Interests*: Bringing a better understanding between humans and those they share the Earth with. Wildlife rehabilitation & education - diversity programming.

WOLF, ERICA L.
(Indian law center senior attorney)
Education: Seattle University School of Law, JD, *2005*. *Affiliation & Address*: Associate Professor of Law & Faculty Director, Center for Indian Law & Policy, Seattle University School of Law, Sullivan Hall 115, 901 12th Ave., P.O. Box 222000, Seattle, WA 98122 (206) 398-4018; E-mail: wolfer@seattleu.edu She is the Director of Graduate Programs for the law school, as well as an Adjunct Professor of Law at the Ronald A. Peterson Law Clinic, where she teaches a clinical course in Indian Trusts & Estates. Ms. Wolf has served as the Center's managing attorney and a supervising attorney of the Indian Estate Planning Project since 2006. *Past professional posts*: Prior to joining Seattle University School of Law, Ms. Wolf worked in private practice. Her practiced involved litigation, business law, and estate planning. She is a member of the state bars of Washington, California, and Alaska, and is a member of the federal bar in the Western District of Washington.

WOLF, JAMES H. (Hidatsa)
(trading post owner)
Affiliation: Owner, Wolf's Trading Post, P.O. Box 877, New Town, ND 58763 (800) 735-6957; (701) 627-3393. Products: Handmade American Indian crafts: beadwork, quilts, dance regalia, pow wow supplies, blankets.

WOLFE, CHIPA (Lakota 'Rosebud Sioux')
(traditional dancer, lecturer, event producer)
Address: Rolling Thunder Enterprises/American Indian Market, 34 Rolling Thunder Dr., Jasper, GA 30143. (770) 735-6275. Website: www.rthunder.com. E-mail: aim68@earthlink.net, chipa1@earthlink.net.

WOLFE, CLIFFORD, JR. (Omaha)
(tribal concilmember)
Affiliation & Address: Council member, Omaha Tribal Council, P.O. Box 368, Macy, NE 68039 (402) 837-5391. *Past tribal post*: Chairperson.

WOLFE, DAVID MICHAEL (*Wahya*) (Eastern Cherokee) 1948-
(administrator officer)
Born August 27, 1948, Huntington, W.V. *Education*: School of Visual Arts (New York, NY), 1968-70; Art Institute of Pittsburgh, 1978-79; LaRoche College, 1993-94. *Principal occupation*: Administrator officer; artist, historian, cultural consultant. *Address*: 2 Hazy Morn Ct., Apt. L, Timonium, MD 21093 (410) 683-8895; E--mail: aniwahya1@earthlink.net. *Affiliation*: Administrative officer, Maryland State Dept. of Health & Mental Hygiene, Office of Minority Health & health Disparities, Baltimore, MD. *Other professional posts*: American Indian artist & historian; cultural consultant; instructor of American Indian history, Goucher College, Towson, MD. *Past professional posts*: Young American Indian Council, New York, NY, 1968-70 (investigated racial & legal problems affecting urban & rural Indigenous communities nationally; participated in the establishment of the American Indian Community House in New York City; advocate for self-reliant & traditional governance); coordinator, American Indian Movement, South Eastern Community, Robeson County, NC, 1972-74 (Tuscarora Indian community of Robeson County); The American Indian Community House, New York, NY, 1974-76 (involved with the development of community based & oriented programs such as vocational counseling & programs, job training programs, cultural programs, summer youth-adult activities, and development of the Art Gallery); Veterans Administration Hospital, East Orange, NJ, 1976-77 (contract from New Jersey American Indian Center to the Visual Media Dept. - VA Hospital, 1978-79; consultant, Long Island Affirmative Action Program, Melville, NY (established Native American liaison within L.I.A.A.P); Snelling & Snelling, Melville, NY, 1980-82; Ewing Technical Designs, Melville, NY, 1982-83; Huntington Personnel, Huntington, NY, 1983-84; Wolfe Consultants, Long Island, NY & Pittsburgh, PA, 1984-91; cultural consultant to original indigenous communities of the Virginia's & Carolina's; co-operated in cross cultural-historic exchange with the Tirona of Columbia, S.A., 1997. Exhibits (for contemporary & traditional, fine art & illustration): Five Civilized Tribes Gallery/Museum, Muskogee, OK (awarded prize in graphics), 1990; U.S. Postage Stamp Commission - Regional Contest (awarded 2nd Place), 1991; Cherokee National Museum,

Tahlequah, OK, annual Trail of Tears Art Show (awarded prize in graphics), 1992; among others. *Community activities*: Kalanuh - (Raven) Sun Rise Mountain Keetoowah Fire - Nyagi Keetoowah Society; consultant/historian of Eastern Indigenous communities. Memberships: Eastern Cherokee Georgia Tribe - Echota Fire; Indian Nationalist Movement of North America. *Interests*: Traditional indigenous history/iconography. "As an advocate for the survival of traditional Indigenous people of the Americas since 1968, my primary involvement addresses social, legal & cultural concerns of rural and urban Indigenous communities. I have researched & documented a variety of previously ignored original eastern tribal histories addressing their cultural, legal & social issues within public & secular forums. As an artist, I continue to produce contemporary wildlife, country & rural community life as well as, traditional Indigenous Iconography of the AniYunwiya. My mediums are oil and canvas, with additional work in Acrylic, water color and pen & ink." *Published works*: The People of the Red Bird; Daksi; Appalachian Mountain AniYunwiya (updated 2nd ed.); The Original Cherokee-Souian Alliance of the Central Appalachians and the Pocahontas Myth; People of the Red Bird, the Taeys Valley Cherokee; A Chronicle of the Cherokee and Souian Record of Ouscioto and Winginia; Daksi (in progress); Bibliographic-Iconographic Time Line of the Original People with Cultural, Social, Traditional, Geologic, Scientific & Ethnologic Comparative Analysis.

WOLFE, MIKE (Omaha)
(tribal chairperson)
Affiliation & Address: Chairperson, Omaha Tribe, P.O. Box 368, Macy, NE 68039 (402) 837-5391.

WOLFE, PHYLLIS S. (Choctaw)
(director, IHS office)
Education: American University, BA. *Affiliation*: Director, Office of Urban Indian Health Programs, Indian Health Service (IHS), DHH, 801 Thompson Ave., Rockville, MD 20852 (301) 443-1083. Ms. Wolfe is responsible for planning, developing & executing a government health-related program that serves American Indian & Alaska Native people now residing in urban areas throughout the U.S. *Past Professional posts*: Grants Management Specialist and as acting chief of the IHS Grants Management Branch, 1980-99; special assistant & senior advisor to the Director of Field Operations, IHS, 1999-2005.

WOLFLEY, JEANETTE (Shoshone Bannock)
(assistant professor of law)
Education: University of Minesota, BA, 19979; University of New Mexico, JD, 1982. *Affiliation & Address*: Assistant Professor of Law, Law & Indigenous Peoples Program, University of New Mexico School of Law, 1117 Stanford NE, MSC11 3415, Albuquerque, NM 87131 (505) 277-0951. E-mail: wolfley@law.unm.edu. She teaches federal Indian law, Indian water rights, federal jurisdiction and Tribal natural and cultural resources courses. Beginning in Spring 2017, Professor Wolfley will teach in the new Natural Resources and Environmental Law Clinic, providing students with a wide array of natural resources administrative and judicial matters. Prior to joining the School of Law faculty, Professor Wolfley practiced law for over 30 years representing exclusively Tribal clients' interests in a wide variety of matters including, federal Indian law issues, tribal law, water law adjudications and implementations of water settlement agreements, environmental and land use regulation, hunting and fishing treaty rights, gaming law, taxation, employment rights, and natural -cultural resource protection. She has a wealth of litigation experience before federal, tribal & state courts, legislation work before Congress and state legislatures, and administrative law practice before federal administrative agencies. Wolfley served as General Counsel for the Shoshone-Bannock Tribes from 1988 to 1996 before serving as special counsel. Prior to her general counsel work she worked with the Native American Rights Fund in Boulder, Colorado where she served as Staff Attorney and Deputy Director for six years, 1982 - 1988. Just prior to joining the law school she was in private practice representing tribal clients, 1996 – 2013. Professor Wolfley serves and appellate judge on the Southwestern Intertribal Court of Appeals. Her academic interests include a variety of Indian law issues, Indian voting rights and natural and cultural resource protection matters. *Membership*: American Bar Association (Committee on Opportunities for Minorities in the Profession).

WOLFSON, EVELYN
(author)
E-mail: ewolfson@comcast.net. *Published works*: American Indian Habitats, American Indian Utensils. American Indian Tools & Ornaments (David McKay Co., 1978, 1979, 1981, respectively); From Abenaki to Zuni: A Dictionary of Native American Tribes (Walker & Co., 1988); The Teton Sioux (The Millbrook Press, 1992); The Iroquois (The Millbrook Press, 1992); From the Earth to Beyond the Sky: Native American Medicine (Houghton Mifflin, 1993); Growing Up Indian (Walker & Co., 1997); American Indian Mythology (Enslow Publishers, 2001); American Indian Mythology (Enslow Publishers, 2001); Inuit Mythology (Enslow Publishers, 2001); A First Look at History: Native Americans (Gareth Stevens Publishing, 2004); Wayland A-Z: A Dictionary of Then & Now (McNaughton & Gunn, 2004).

WOMACK, CRAIG S.
(professor of English)
Affiliation & Address: Associate professor of English & Native American Studies, 633 Elm Ave., Rm. 216, University of Oklahoma, Norman, OK 73019 (405) 325-2312. *Published works*: Drowning in Fire: Red on Red: Native American Literary Separatism; co-author, American Indian Literary Nationalism (University of New Mexico)

WOOD, CHARLES F. (Chemehuevi)
(tribal chairperson)
Affiliation & Address: Chairperson, Chemehuevi Indian Tribe, P.O. Box 1976, Havasu Lake, CA 92363 (760) 858-4219. E-mail: chairman@cit-nsn.gov

WOODRUFF, CHARLES (Quileute)
(tribal chairperson)
Affiliation & Address: Chairperson, Quileute Nation, P.O. Box 279, LaPush, WA 98350 (374-6155). E-mail: chas.woodruff@quileutenation.org.

WOODS, ANTHONY (Omaha of Nebraska)
(communications director)
Affiliation & Address: Communications Director, National Tribal Development Association, RR 1 Box 1080, Box Elder, MT 59521 (406) 395-4095. E-mail: tonywoods@ntda.info.

WOODS, J. CEDRIC (Lumbee)
(director of Native American studies)
Education: University of Connecticut, PhD. *Affiliation & Address*: Director, Institute for New England Native American Studies, University of Massachusetts, Boston, 100 Morrissey Blvd., Boston, MA 02125 (617) 287-5784. E-mail: cedric.woods@umb.edu. Cedric is working on projects with tribes in the areas of tribal government capacity building, Indian education, economic development, and chronic disease prevention. *Other professional post*: Member, Board of Trustees of Plimoth Plantation, Plymouth, MA. *Past professional posts*: Mashantucket Pequot Tribal Nation (director of career development, research analyst, tribal government spokesman & deputy chief operating officer); consultant, National Museum of the American Indian, the Haliwa Saponi Indian Tribe of North Carolina, and the Mashantucket Pequot Museum & Research Center. Prior to arriving at UMass Boston, Cedric completed a study on the evolution of tribal government among the Mashpee Wampanoag Tribe and the Mashantucket Pequot Tribal Nation. While pursuing his doctoral studies at the University of Connecticut, Cedric served in a variety of capacities for the Mashantucket Pequot Tribal Nation. *Published work*: Essay, "A Different Path Forward: The Institute for New England Native American Studies at UMass," in the New England Journal of Higher Education, Winter 2010; essay "Native Tribal Scholars: Building an Academic Community" by J. Cedric Woods that appeared in *The New England Journal of Higher Education* in January 2012.

WOODS, PAT (Chickasaw)
(tribal administrator)
Affiliation & Address: Director of Operations/Administrator, Chickasaw Nation, P.O. Box 1548, Ada, OK 74821 (580) 436-7280.

WOODS, STEVEN (Chickasaw)
(tribal legislature representative)
Affiliation & Address: Tishomingo District (Seat #3) Representative, The Chickasaw Nation, 4736 Chickasaw Trail, Sulphur, OK 73086 (580) 622-3523. E-mail: steven.woods@chickasaw.net. *Other tribal posts*: Chairperson, Human Resources Committee; Chairperson, Election Rules & Regulations Ad Hoc Committee; member, Education Committee; member, Land Committee. *Past tribal posts*: Justice, Chickasaw Nation Supreme Court, 1991-2002; Chickasaw Housing Authority, 1980-85.

WOODS, VICTOR E. (Viejas Kumeyaay Diegueno)
(tribal vice chairperson)
Affiliation & Address: Vice Chairperson, Viejas Band of Kumeyaay Indians, 1 Viejas Grade Rd., Alpine, CA 91901 (619) 445-3810.

WOODWARD, DENNI DIANE
(Indian program administrator)
Affiliation: American Indian & Alaska Native Program, Stanford University, Old Union Clubhouse #12, Stanford, CA 94305 (415) 725-6944. E-mail: denni.woodward@forsyth.stanford.edu.

WOOLSTON, KRISTINA (Yup'ik)
(vice president for government relations)
Education: Dartmouth College, BA (Political Science, with minor in Native American studies). *Affiliation & Address*: Vice President of Government Relations, Chenega Corporation, 3000 C St., Suite 301, Anchorage, AK 99503 (907) 277-5706. *Other professional post*: Board member, Native American Contractors Association, Washington, DC.

WOOTEN, THOMAS (Samish)
(tribal chairperson)
Affiliation & Address: Chairperson, Samish Indian Nation, P.O. Box 217, Anacortes, WA 98221 (360) 293-6404.

WOPSOCK, RON (Ute)
(tribal representative)
Affiliation & Address: Uintah Band Representative, The Ute Indian Tribe, P.O. Box 190, Fort Duchesne, UT 84026 (435) 722-5141. *Past tribal post*: Vice Chairperson.

WORDEN, DENNIS (Coeur d'Alene)
(legislative director)
Education: University of Oregon, JD. *Affiliation & Address*: Legislative Director, Native American Contractors Association (NACA), 1514 P St. NW #2, Washington, DC 20005. (202) 758-2676. Dennis is responsible for advocacy of the Native program, and responsible for monitoring legislative developments pertaining to the NACA program. *Past professional posts*: Legislative Assistant & Mark O. Hatfield Fellow, U.S. House of Representatives; advocated for the improved health care for American Indians & Alaska Natives at the National Indian Health Board. *Awards, honors*: Received the National Center for American Indian Enterprise Development "40 Under 40."

WORL, ROSITA (Tlingit)
(organization president)
Education: Alaska Methodist University, BA; Harvard University, MS & PhD (Anthropology); University of Alaska, Anchorage, Honorary Doctor of Sciences). *Affiliation & Address*: Assistant Professor of Anthropology, University of Alaska Southeast. *Other professional post*: President, Sealaska Heritage Institute, Juneau, AK. (907) 463-4844. E-mail: Rosita.worl@sealaska.com.

WORLEY, CHARLENE (Qualla Cherokee/Tahitian)
(director of research & evaluation)
Education: University of Santa Cruz, BA (Medical Anthropology), 1991; Harvard University, MA, 1995, ScD, 2003. *Affiliation & Address*: Director of Research & Evaluation, National Native American AIDS Prevention Center, 436-14th St., Suite 1020, Oakland, CA 94612 (510) 444-2051. E-mail: cworley@nnaapc.org.

WRIGHT, ALLEN (Pomo)
(rancheria chairperson)
Affiliation: Sherwood Valley Rancheria, 190 Sherwood Hill Dr., Willits, CA 95490 (707) 459-9690.

WRIGHT, BEVERLY M. (Soaring Feather) (Wampanoag Aquinnah)
(tribal chairperson)
Born on Martha's Vineyard Island, Mass. *Education*: New York School of Design, 1962-65; Continuing Education, University of Massachusetts. *Address*: 146 Lighthouse Rd., Aquinnah, MA 02535 (508) 645-2018. *Office address*: Wampanoag Tribe of Gay Head/Aquinnah, 20 Black Brook Rd., Aquinnah, MA 02535 (508) 645-9265. E-mail: chairprs@wampanoagtribe.net. *Affiliations*: Chairperson, Wampanoag Tribe of Gay Head/Aquinnah, Aquinnah, MA, 1991-present. *Past professional posts*: Owner of "The Wright Place" Restaurant, 1974-2001; administrative assistant, Dukes County Commissioners, 1982-91; treasurer, Town of Aquinnah, 1975-1982; office manager, Elder Services of Cape Cod & Islands, 1976-82. *Memberships*: United South & Eastern Tribes (USET) (vice-president & secretary); National Congress of American Indians (board member); BIA tribal Self-Governance Advisory Council (board member); IHS Tribal Self-Governance Advisory Council (board member); Native Nations Institute (NNI), University of Arizona, Morris Udall Center (board member); Massachusetts Commission on Indian Affairs (board member); Female Tribal Leaders (board member); All Islands Selectmen Assn (tribal representative); Harvard Project on American Indian Economic Development (board member); NCAI Chairman's Health Information Task Force (board member).

WRIGHT, BOBBY (Chippewa-Cree) 1950-
(research associate, assistant professor)
Born December 28, 1950, Tacoma, Wash. *Education*: University of San Francisco, BS, 1973; SUNY, Buffalo, MA, 1977; Montana State University, Bozeman, EdD, 1985. *Principal occupation*: Research associate, assistant professor. Resides in State College, PA (814) 865-6346 (office). *Affiliations*: Director, Montana State University, Bozeman, 1983-89; faculty, Penn State University, University Park, 1990-. *Memberships*: National Indian Education Association; American Society for Ethno-history. *Awards, honors*: 1986 Distinguished Dissertation Award, Association for the Study of Higher Education; 1986 Montana State University Endowment and Alumni Foundation Award for Outstanding Graduate Performance.

WRIGHT, CHARLIE (Wintun)
  (rancheria chairperson)
Affiliation & Address: Chairperson, Cortina Indian Rancheria, 570 6th St., P.O. Box 1630 • Williams, CA 95987 (530) 473-3274

WRIGHT, CHRIS (Pomo)
  (tribal chairperson)
Affiliation & Address: Chairperson, Dry Creek Rancheria Band of Pomo Indians, P.O. Box 1607, Geyserville, CA 95441 (707) 431-4090.

WRIGHT, KENNETH (Pomo)
  (former tribal president)
Affiliation & Address: Round Valley Indian Tribes, 77826 Covelo Rd., Covelo, CA 95428 (707) 983-6126. E-mail: president@rvit.org.

WRIGHT, LARRY, JR. (Ponca)
  (tribal chairperson)
Affiliation & Address: Chairperson, Ponca Tribe of Nebraska, P.O. Box 288, Niobrara, NE 68760 (402) 857-3391. E-mail: ldwrightjr@gmail.com

WRIGHT, LISA (Hoh)
  (tribal vice chairperson)
Affiliation & Address: Vice Chairperson, Hoh Tribe, P.O. Box 2196, Forks, WA 98331 (360) 374-6582. E-mail: lisaw@hohtribe-nsn.gov

WRIGHT, MARY C.
  (lecturer in American Indian studies)
Education: Portland State University, BS (History, Journalism), MA (istory); Rutgers University, PhD (History), 1996. *Affiliation & Address*: Senior lecturer, Department of American Indian Studies, University of Washington, Seattle, WA 98195 (206) 543-7894. E-mail: wrightm@u.washington.edu. *Research Interests*: Dr. Wright's research interests began with her dissertation "The Circle, Broken: Gender, Kinship and The Construction of Difference in the Pacific Northwest, 1811-1850," an examination of cross-cultural relations in the context of colonialism. Her research interests expanded into 20th and 21st century. She has explored the cultural continuance & symbolic importance of the "Tule Mat Lodge" for the Plateau peoples and is currently researching the history of Indian gaming & casinos in Washington State. *Published works*: Dr. Wright has published numerous articles and papers that became part of collections & anthologies such as "Re-Claiming Space, Creating Change: The American Indian Women's Service League & the Seattle Indian Center, 1958-1978" in the forthcoming *Keeping the Campfires Going: Native Women's Activism in Urban Communities* by Susan Applegate Krouse & Heather A. Howard; "The Women's Lodge: Constructing Gender on the Pacific Northwest Plateau" in Mary-Ellen Kelm & Lorna Townsend's 2006 *In the Days of Our Grandmothers: a Reader in Aboriginal Women's History in Canada*; and an early "Economic Development & Native American Women in the Early Nineteenth Century" appeared in the 3rd & 4th editions of *The American Indian, Past and Present* by Roger Nichols. Wright also organized & edited *More Voices, New Stories: King County, Washington's First 150 Years*, a volume on local history.

WRIGHT, MERVIN (Paiute)
  (tribal councilmember)
Affiliation & Address: Councilmember, Pyramid Lake Paiute Tribe, P.O. Box 256, Nixon, NV 89424 (775) 574-1000.

WRIGHT, MIRANDA (Koyukon Athabascan)
  (professor of Alaska Native studies)
Born in Nulato, Alaska. *Education*: University of Alaska, Fairbanks, BA, 1992, MA (Anthropology), 1995; PhD in Interdisciplinary Studies (in progress). *Affiliation & Address*: Assistant Professor (2002-present), & Director (2010-present), Department of Alaska Native Studies & Rural Development, University of Alaska, Fairbanks, 323 Brooks Bldg., P.O. Box 756500, Fairbanks, AK 99775 (907) 474-6433. E-mail: m.wright@uaf.edu. *Other professional posts*: Co-owner, Wright Aurora Kennel, 1967-present; Vice President, W.A., Inc., 1970-present. *Past professional posts*: Owner, Miranda Wright, Furs, 1981-85; co-owner, Wright Aurora Construction, 1967-90; executive director, Doyon Founation, 1995-2002. *Community activities*: Board of Dictors, Doyon, Ltd., 1995-present; treasurer, Doyon, Ltd., 2002-present; Board of Directors, Doyon Communications, Inc., 2000-present; Chancellors Advisory Committee on Native Education, 1995-present; Advisory Committee, Arctic Studies Center, Smithsonian Institution, 1994-present; Community Advisory Board, Holland America Westours, 2001-present; volunteer, World Indiann Eskimo Olympics, 1972-present. *Published works*: Numerous articles in scholarly journals.

WRIGHT, NADINE (Coharie)
  (tribal chairperson)
Affiliation: Chair (2010-present), Coharie Indian Tribe, 7531 N. US Hwy. 421, Clinton, NC 28328 (910) 564-6909. Website: www.coharietribe.org.

WRIGHT, REBECCA (Ponca)
  (former tribal chairperson)
Affiliation & Address: Ponca Tribe of Nebraska, P.O. Box 288, Niobrara, NE 68760 (402) 857-3391. E-mail: white.house@cox.net

WRIGHT, RICK (Ponca)
  (tribal vice chairperson)
Affiliation: Ponca Tribe of Nebraska, P.O. Box 288, Niobrara, NE 68760 (402) 857-3391.

WRIGHT, ROBIN K. 1949-
  (curator & professor)
Born September 10, 1949, Mankato, Minn. *Education*: University of Washington, BA, 1971, MA, 1977, PhD (Art History), 1985. *Principal occupation*: Curator & professor. *Address & Affiliation*: Curator of Native American Art (1985-), Burke Museum, Box 353010, University of Washington, Seattle, WA 98195 (206) 543-5595. E-mail: wright@u.washington.edu. *Other professional post*: Professor, School of Art, University of Washington, Seattle, 1990-present; director, Bill Holm Center for the Study of Northwest Coast Art. *Memberships*: American Association of Museums; College Art Association; Native American Art Studies Association (board member, 1989-93; president, 1999-2003). *Awards, honors*: Phi Beta Kappa. *Interests*: Northwest Coast Indian art: Haida art, specifically Haida argillite carving, and Washington State Native art. Travel to museums to do research in Canada, Europe and the U.S. *Published works*: A Time of Gathering - An Intertribal Welcome: Statements from 36 Washington Tribes, with Roberta Haines (eds.) (Burke Museum 1990); A Time for Gathering: Native Heritage in Washington State (Burke Museum & U. of Washington Press, 1991); Northern Haida Master Carvers (U. of Washington Press, 2001); numerous articles in American Indian Art Magazine.

WRIGHT, WILLIAM (Nottoway of Virginia)
  (tribal war chief & vice chairperson)
Affiliation & Address: War Chief/Vice Charperson, Nottoway Indiann Tribe of Virginia, P.O. Box 246, Capron, VA 23829 (434) 658-4454.

WUESTER, MARY (Paiute-Shoshone)
  (tribal chairperson)
Affiliation & Address: Chairperson, Lone Pine Paiute-Shoshone Tribe, P.O. Box 747, Lone Pine, CA 93545 (760) 876-1034. E-mail: chair@lppsr.org.

WYATT, APRIL C. (Chitimacha)
  (tribal vice chairperson)
Affiliation & Address: Vice Chairperson (2016-present), Chitimacha Tribal Council, P.O. Box 661, Charenton, LA 70523 (337) 924-4973. E-mail:

WYATT, JANE E. (*Ishilee*) (Chuckchansi) 1943-
  (tribal chairperson)
Born December 21, 1943, Madera, Calif. *Education*: Galen College (Fresno, CA), RDA, 1987. *Principal occupation*: Tribal chairperson. *Address*: P.O. Box 1661, Coarsegold, CA 93614 (559) 658-3951. *Affiliation*: Chairperson, Provisional Tribal Council, Picayune Rancheria, Coarsegold, CA, 1983-. *Other professional posts*: BIA Policy Task Force Representative; Sierra Tribal Consortium (board member); California Indian Manpower Co. (board member); CRIHB Representative; Central Valley Indian Health, Inc. (member-life); Table Mountain Rancheria (Special Player-life). *Community activities*: Master teacher, Chuckchansi Language; basket weaving classes; basket material gathering classes.

WYATT, KATHIE (Washoe)
  (former tribal chairperson)
Affiliation: Dresslerville Indian Colony Community Council, 1585 Watasheamu Rd., Gardnerville, NV 89410 (702) 883-1446.

WYMAN, LEISY
  (assistant professor)
Education: Stanford University, PhD, 2004. *Affiliation & Address*: Assistant professor, Dept. of Language Reading & Culture, Education 527, The University of Arizona, Tucson, AZ 85721 (520) 626-8787. E-mail: lwyman@email.arizona.edu. *Other professional post*: Affiliated faculty, American Indian Studies Program, The University of Arizona, Tucson, AZ. *Areas of Interest*: How identities, ideologies & patterns of community bilingualism intersect in formal & informal education; specializes in Indigenous education.

Y

YACKESCHI (WALTERS), WINIFRED "BUD" (Comanche)
  (organization president)
Affiliation & Address: President, Comanche Language & Cultural Preservation Committee, 1375 N.E. Cline Rd., Elgin, OK 73538 (580) 492-4988

YAIVA, GABRIEL (Dineh-Hopi)
(marketing specialist; rapper/music producer)
Born in Pinon, Ariz. & raised in Shiprock, N.M. *Education*: Northern Arizona University, BS (Applied Indigenous Studies; minor in Economic Development). *Affiliations & Address*: Marketing Specialist, Native Green Leadership Academy, c/o Native Movement, P.O. Box 896, Flagstaff, AZ 86002 (928) 699-9601. E-mail: yaiva101@gmail.com or yaiva@4went.com; director, Peace & Balance Project (substance abuse prevention & violence awareness program), Native Movement. *Other professional posts*: Founder & owner of 4th World Entertainment (www.4went.com) an independent record label; co-founder of Native Renaissance & True Image World Marketing; member, KEYA Earth (focuses on violence prevention & actively does the "Education & Healing Through Hip-Hop Tours" where Yaiva has performed at many venues & released his past 3 cd's thru this program, "The Speaking & Listening Tours" Yaiva has spoken to over 50 schools and 15,000 students; he is planning the building of a youth retreat center on the Navajo reservation.

YALLUP, WILLIAM "BILL" (Yakama)
(former tribal chairperson)
Affiliation: Yakama Tribal Council, P.O. Box 151, Toppenish, WA 98948 (509) 865-5121.

YANITY, SHAWN (Stillaguamish)
(tribal chairperson)
Affiliation & Address: Chairperson, Stillaguamish Tribe of Indians, P.O. Box 277, Arlington, WA 98223 (360) 652-7362.

YANKTON, DOUGLAS, SR. (Sisseton-Wahpeton Sioux)
(tribal vice chairperson)
Affiliation & Address: Vice Chairperson, Spirit Lake Dakota Sioux Tribe, P.O. Box 359, Fort Totten, ND 58335 (701) 766-4221.

YANKTON, ROGER (Sisseton-Wahpeton Sioux)
(former tribal chairperson)
Affiliation: Spirit Lake Tribe, P.O. Box 359, Fort Totten, ND 58335

YANTZ, MICKEL (Cherokee)
(museum curator)
Affiliation & Address: Museum Curator, Cherokee National Historical Society, Cherokee Heritage Center, Box 515, Tahlequah, OK 74465 (918) 456-6007.

YARGEE, TARPIE (Alabama & Quassarte)
(tribal chief)
Affiliation & Address: Chief, Alabama Quassarte Tribal Town, 101 E. Broadway, Wetumka, OK 74437 (405) 452-3987.

YARLOTT, CURTIS (*Isaluutshiile - Yellow Arrows*) (Crow)
(executive director)
Affiliation: St. Labre Indian School, Ashland, MT 59004 (406) 784-2347. Website: www.stlabre.org.

YARLOTT, DAVID, JR. (Crow)
(tribal college president)
Affiliation & Address: President, Little Bighorn College, P.O. Box 370, Crow Agency, MT 59022 (406) 638-3104. *Other professional post*: Member, Board of Trustees, American Indian College Fund, Denver, CO. *Other professional post*: Member-at-Large, Board of Directors, American Indian Higher Education Consortium, Alexandria, VA.

YATES, HERBERT (Nambe Pueblo)
(former pueblo governor)
Affiliation: Nambe Pueblo Council, Rte. 1, Box 117-BB, Santa Fe, NM 87501 (505) 455-2036.

YATES, PAUL (Miami)
(BIA Agency Supt.)
Affiliation & Address: Superintendent, Miami Agency, Bureau of Indian Affairs, P.O. Box 391, Miami, OK 74355 (918) 542-3396.

YAZZI, BERTA (Navajo)
(shop owner)
Affiliation & Address: Owner, Navajo Sandpainters, P.O. Box 1849, Sheepsprings, NM 87364 (505) 732-4542. *Artwork*: Navajo sandpaintings.

YAZZIE, EVANGELINE PARSONS (Navajo)
(professor, author)
Born on the Navajo Reservation. *Education*: Northern Arizona University, M.A. (Bilingual Multicultural Educational Leadership, PhD (Educational Leadership). *Address & Affiliation*: Author, Salina Bookshelf, Inc., 3120 N. Caden Ct. #4, Flagstaff, AZ 86004; Professor of Navajo, Northern Arizona University,

Flagstaff, AZ. Dr. Yazzie teaches and writes on the behalf of elders, and encourages others to honor their elders. *Past affiliations*: Director of Navajo Treaty Project, 1997-99. *Published works*: Dzani Yazhi Naazba': Litle Woman Warrior Who Came Home (2007 Lacapa Spirit Prize for Narrative; 2007 Storytelling World Award; 2006 Notable Children's Social Studies Trade Book); Dine Bizaad, Binahoo'aah: Rediscovering the Navajo Language.

YAZZI, HERBERT (Navajo)
(attorney; chief justice)
Education: Arizona State University, BA, 1973, JD, 1976. *Affiliation & Address*: Chief Justice, Supreme Court, Navajo Nation, P.O. Box 520, Window Rock, AZ 86515. *Membership*: Navajo Nation Bar Association (president); Native American Bar Association.

YAZZI, KEE IKE (Navajo)
(senior planner)
Affiliation & Address: Senior Planner, Department of Dine' Education, P.O. Box 670, Window Rock, AZ 86515 (928) 871-7274.

YAZZI, MELANIE (Navajo)
(assistant professor)
Education: University of Colorado, MFA, 1993. *Affiliation*: School of Art, c/o American Indian Studies Program, The University of Arizona, Harvill Bldg., Rm 430, P.O. Box 210076, Tucson, AZ 85721 (520) 621-7108. E-mail: aisp@ email.arizona.edu. *Interests*: Special focus in printmaking & contemporary indigenous artists.

YAZZI, ROBERT (Navajo)
(institute director; tribal chief justice emeritus)
Education: Oberlin College, BA; University of New Mexico, JD. *Affiliation*: Director, Dine Policy Institute, P.O. Box 96, Tsaile, AZ 86556 (928) 724-6946. E-mail: robertyazzi@dinecollege.edu. *Other professional post*: Chief Justice Emeritus, Navajo Nation Supreme Court; chief justice (1992-2003), Navajo Nation. He has been a powerful force in integrating traditional Navajo law & peacemaking techniques into the Nation's court system. Mr. Yazzi will devote his retirement years to the education of Indian youth and the concerns of indigenous peoples of other countries.

YAZZI-BALLENGER, VIRGINIA (Navajo)
(designer)
Affiliation: Owner, Navajo Spirit Southwestern Wear, American Indian Fashions (1984-present), 815 E. Coal Ave., Gallup, NM 87301 (505) 722-6837; (800) 377-6837. Website: www.navajospirit.com. *Product*: Contemporary western wear & traditional Navajo clothing; women's clothing.

YAZZI-KING, ELA M. (Navajo) 1955-
(rehabilitation specialist/counselor)
Born May 31, 1955, Fort Defiance, Ariz. *Education*: Virginia Intermount College (Bristol), BA, 1977; University of New Mexico, MA (Rehabilitation Counseling), 1981. Address unknown. *Affiliations*: Director, Spinal Cord Injury Follow-up Project, 1979-81; director, IHS Medical Management Project, 1981-82; director, Learn to Earn, Ltd., 1983-84; director, Navajo Undergraduate Rehabilitation Training Project, 1984-86; Navajo Evaluation of Existing Disability Services, 1986-87; executive director, Chinle Valley School for Exceptional Children, 1988-90; coordinator, Indian Children's Program, Utah State University, Logan, UT, 1991-. *Professional presentations*: Multi-Cultural Successes: The Navajo Nation," at the National Association of Developmental Disabilities Councils, Orlando, FL, 1992; "Beyond Rhetoric-A Blueprint for Action" & "A Native American Perspective on Disability & Self-Determination," at the ADD Commissioner's Institute on Cultural Diversity, Washington, DC, 1992 & 1993; "Self-Determination-The Road to Personal Freedom," at NM Protection & Advocacy System Mini Conference, Albuquerque, 1993. *Other professional posts*: Adjunct Facility with Navajo Community College, 1984-87 (produced: "Rehabilitation Practicum Manual," 1984; "Job Development/Job Placement Manual," 1985; "Navajo Evaluation of Existing Disability Research Study" (unpublished), 1987. *Community activities*: Assistive technology; Independent Living Center. *Advisory/Councils*: Chairperson, Navajo Nation Advisory Council on the Handi-Capable, 1979-93; Native American Research & Training Center, Northern Arizona University, Flagstaff (advisory council, 1990-93; advisory board, 1987-); New Mexico Independent Living Advisory Council, 1990-; advisory council, American Indians with Disabilities Public Awareness Campaign, Anchorage, AK, 1991-93; Administration on Developmental Disabilities, Multi-Cultural Task Force, Washington, DC, 1992-; Developmental; Disabilities Advisory Council, Phoenix, AZ, 1992-95; National Council on Disabilities; Development Disabilities Advisory Council; Administration on Development Disabilities Advisory Council; Administration on Developmental Disabilities-Multi-Cultural Task Force; New Mexico Independent Living Advisory Council. *Awards, honors*: "Citizen of the Year," Arizona Governor's Council on Disabilities, Phoenix, 1985; "Outstanding Volunteer," Navajo Nation Council on the Handicapped, 1986.

YELLOW EAGLE, LISA (Navajo/Lakota)
(attorney; program officer)
Education: University of Colorado, BA (English Literature, minor in Ethnic Studies), 2002; University of Colorado Law Scool, JD, 2008. *Affiliation & Address*: Program Officer (2012-present), First Nations Development Institute, 2432 Main St., 2nd Floor, Lngmont, CO 80501 (303) 774-7836. Lisa manages projects focused on strengthening tribal economies through education, strengthening tribal and Native institutions through peer learning & model development, and projects that provide technical assistance to various groups throughout the U.S. *Other professional post*: Treasurer, Colorado Indian Bar Association, Boulder, CO.

YELLOW ROBE, KIMBERLY (Rosebud Sioux)
(SSA public affairs; Lakota storyteller)
Education: BA & MBA (Political Science). *Affiliation*: Social Security Administration (SSA), Regional Public Affairs Office, San Francisco, CA, 2000-present. *Other professional posts*: Board member, SAIGE (Society of American Indian Governmental Employees, Washington, DC; Lakota Storyteller sharing history, heritage & culture of her Oyate/People. *Awards, honors*: Co-founder of the National Society of American Indian MBAs; received awards from SSA for the Outreach conducted throughout Indian Country, and Region IX.

YELLOW ROBE, WILLIAM S., JR. (Assiniboine) 1960-
(playwright, director, actor, lecturer, instructor)
Born February 2, 1960, Poplar, MT. *Education*: High school. *Affiliation & Address*: Playwright, director, actor, lecturer, instructor, English Dept., University of Maine, Orono, ME (teaches Native American literature & drama). *Past professional posts*: Former literary manager of Seattle Group Theater; regional vice president, Literary Managers & Dramaturgs of America, New York, NY, 1990-91. *Works: Plays*: "The Council," for Honolulu Theater for Youth, 1992; "Taking Aunty to the Wake, Northern Montana College, Havre, MT, 1991; "The Independence of Eddie Rose," The Seattle Group Theater, 1990. Directing: "The Council," & "The Magic Flute," an opera, San Antonio (TX) Festival. Acting: Norman Bulanski, "The Boys Next Door"; & Donny Dubrow, "American Buffalo." Lecturer: 'Watermark reading series', University of Washington, Seattle; '10th Anniversary', New World Theater, University of Mass. Instructor: Playwriting & writing, Fort Peck Community College, Poplar, MT; acting, St. Paul (MN) Central High School. Community activities: Advisory Board, Red Eagle Soaring Theater, Seattle, WA. *Memberships*: Dramatists Guild of America (associate member, 1988-). *Awards, honors*: Jerome Fellowship, 1989; Princess Grace Fellowship, 1989; NEA Playwright's Fellowship, 1991; James Baldwin Honorable Mention. *Published works*: Sneaky, a one-act play, "SlantSix" an anthology (New Rivers Press, 1990); The Burning of Uncle, a short story, "Dancing on the Rim of the World," an anthology (University of Arizona Press, 1991); The Pavement Ends: Five Native American Plays (University of Oklahoma Press, 2009).

YELLOWHAMMER, TERRI (Standing Rock Sioux/Ojibwe)
(tribal supreme court judge)
Resides in Mineapolis, Minn. *Affiliation & Address*: Judge, Supreme Court, Mashpee Wampanoag Indian Tribe, P.O. Box 1048, Mashpee, MA 02649 (508) 477-0208.*Other professional post*: Appellate Justice for the White Earth Band of Ojobwe.

YELLOWHAWK, SANDRA (Navajo)
(health director)
Affiliation: Peach Springs PHS Indian Health Center, Peach Springs, AZ 86434 (520) 769-2204.

YELLOWHORN, ELDON (Peigan Blackfoot)
(archaeologist; professor & chair of First Nations Studies)
Education: University of Calgary, BA, BSc; Simng Fraser University, MA; McGill University, PhD. *Affiiation & Address*: Associate Professor of Archaeology, Department of Archaeology, Simon Fraser University, 8888 University Dr., Burnaby, BC Canada V5A 1S6 (778) 782-6669. E-mail: ecy@sfu.ca. *Other professional post*: Chair, Department of First Nations Studies, Simon Fraser University. *Research Interests*: Paleoindian research, and the interaction occurring between Indians & archaeology, and the emerging field of indigenous archaeology. Research in Native Studies focus on examining the experience of aboriginal people in the modern world and their struggle to promote cultural diversity in homogeneous society. Professor Yellowhorn writes, "I am presently working toward defining the tenets and objectives of indigenous archaeology & examining its contributions to archaeological theory. I have strong interest in traditional knowledge and I look for its meaning & significance to better understand the archaeological record. *Published works*: First Peoples in Canada, with Alan McMillan (Douglas & McIntyre, Vancouver, BC), 2004; articles & book reviews.

YELLOWTAIL, JACKIE (Crow, Apsaalooke Nation)
(treasurer, Plains region representative)
Born & raised on the Crow Reservation. *Affiliation & Address*: Treasurer, Plains Region Representative, American Indian Alaska Native Tourism Association (AIANTA), 2401 12th St. NW, Albuquerque, NM 87104 (505) 724-3592. *Past professional posts*: Tourism Coordinator for the Apsaalooke Tours, Little Big Horn College; coordinator; Montana Tribal Tourism Alliance; director of Apsaalooke Nation Tourism for the Crow Tribe, 2008; representative of the Crow Tribe in Governor Schweitzer's.

YELLOWTAIL, WILLIAM P. (Crow)
(EPA administrator)
Born in Crow Agency, Mont. *Education*: Dartmouth College, BA, 1971. *Principal occupation*: EPA administrator. *Address & Affiliation*: Katz Endowed Chair in Native American Studies, Montana State University, P.O. Box 172220, Bozeman, MT 59717 (406) 994-2721. E-mail: wyellowtail@montana.edu. Yellowtail said he will develop curriculum & leadership activities that will center on the "personal Indian sovereignty," as well as the future of Native peoples in the West. *Past professional posts*: Wyoming State Senator, 1985-1993 (chairman-State Judiciary Committee & the Legislature's Environmental Quality Council); regional director, EPA Region 8, Denver, CO, 1994-2005. *Membership*: Native American Alumni Association of Dartmouth College (national steering committee).

YEPA, DAVID R. (Jemez Pueblo)
(former Pueblo governor)
Affiliation & Address: Former Governor, Pueblo of Jemez, P.O. Box 100, Jemez, NM 87024 (575) 834-7359.

YORK, LAURENE L.
(trading post owner)
Address & Affiliation: Owner, Mohawk Trading Post, 874 Mohawk Trail, Shelburne, MA 01370 (413) 625-2412. E-mail: lyork@mohawk-trading-post.com. Web site: www.mohawk-trading-post.com. *Membership*: Indian Arts & Crafts Association.

YOST, PAULA M.
(attorney)
Education: School of Law, University of Texas, 1991, JD, with honors, Iowa State University, 1985, BS, Journalism & Political Science, *Affiliation & Address*: Counsel, Dentons LLP, Public Policy and Regulation & Native American Law & Policy Practice, 525 Market St., 26th Floor, San Francisco, CA 94105 (415) 882-5009. E-mail: paula.yost#dentons.com. Paula is dedicated to representing Indian tribal governments & their businesses in varied contexts, providing general advice & counsel on matters of governance & commerce, representing tribes in their dealings & negotiations with other governments and third parties & protecting or defending tribal sovereignty and general tribal interests through litigation. She acts in a general counsel capacity for two of the Firm's tribal clients. In representations that reach from California to Washington, DC, Paula has worked closely with tribal clients in their project development and gaming efforts, securing the needed federal approvals and then defending those approvals in litigation. In the same vein, she has negotiated Class III gaming compacts with the state of California on behalf of several tribal clients. She has a deep background in federal Indian law and gaming law, including the Indian Gaming Regulatory Act & the Unlawful Internet Gambling Enforcement Act. She regularly handles matters involving regulatory & environmental compliance & cultural resource protection. Paula's litigation work for tribal governments is wide-ranging, from the dismissal of litigation on sovereignty & related jurisdictional grounds to the representation of an Indian tribe in its effort to secure water and access rights for its reservation. For one tribal client in particular, she has defeated every one of the nearly dozen lawsuits she has handled. For another client, she secured a permanent injunction barring an individual's misappropriation of the tribe's name and identity under a novel theory involving federal trademark law. Her particular experience in the doctrine of tribal sovereign immunity, and has secured dismissal of high-stakes contract litigation on immunity & related jurisdictional grounds, even though the contracts at issue contained provisions purporting to waive the tribe's sovereign immunity. Prior to dismissal on immunity grounds, the case generated new Ninth Circuit precedent holding that Indian tribes may not be sued in federal district court on "diversity of citizenship" grounds. Paula presently works as general counsel for the California Tribal College, a nonprofit corporation governed by federally recognized tribal governments in California, & first institution dedicated to providing secondary educational opportunities for Native Americans, a largely underserved population in the state that is home to more recognized tribes than any other state save Alaska. She has successfully defended the Table Mountain Rancheria, an Indian tribe that owns & operates a casino outside Fresno, CA, in lawsuits; has represented the Shingle Springs Band of Miwok Indians in a series of lawsuits challenging the tribe's economic development efforts; negotiated for the Yocha Dehe Wintun Nation the first ever cultural easement to be held by a federally- recognized tribal government over public lands in the state of California. The cultural easement, to be held in

perpetuity, gives Yocha Dehe exclusive control over sacred sites and cultural resources located in a public park that is within the Tribe's ancestral territory and that is now owned by the City of Vallejo. She has negotiated tribal-state compacts on behalf of tribal clients vis-a-vis the state of Calif.

YOUCKTON, DAVID (Chehalis)
(tribal enterprise executive director)
Affiliation: Confederated Tribes of the Chehalis Reservation, P.O. Box 536, Oakville, WA 98568 (360) 273-5911.

YOUNG, ED 1906-
(Indian arts & crafts trader)
Born April 14, 1906, New York, N.Y. *Education*: City College of New York, BA, 1930. *Principal occupation*: Indian arts & crafts trader. *Address & Affiliation*: President (1947-present), The Ed Young's, Inc., 2323 Krogh Ct. NW, Albuquerque, NM 87104-2508 (505) 864-1242. *Interests*: "Trading & traveling the U.S." *Biographical source*: Indian Jewelry - Fact or Fantasy by Marsha Lund.

YOUNG MAN, ALFRED (*Eagle Chief*) (Cree) 1948-
(professor & chair of Native American studies)
Born in 1948, Browning, Montana on the Blackfeet Indian Reservation. Paternal & maternal Cree grandparent's were from the Duck Lake Reserve in Saskatchewan, the Erminiskin and Cold Lake reserves in Alberta, respectively. *Education*: Slade School of Fine Arts, University of London, England, BA, 1972; University of Montana, MA, 1974; Rutgers University, PhD (Anthropology), 1997. His thesis has been called "a history, an economic treatise, a political exercise, & cultural disquisition" - entitled, "The Socialization and Art-Politics of Native Art." *Principal occupation*: Professor & Chair of Native American Studies. *Address & Affiliation*: Professor, Native American Studies Dept., University of Lethbridge, A410 University Hall, 4401 University Dr., Lethbridge, Alberta, Can T1K 3M4 (403) 329-2721 (1977-present) E-mail: youngman@uleth.ca. *Other professional posts*: Art instructor and reading specialist among his own people on the Chippewa-Cree reservation, Rocky Boy, and later on the Blackfeet reservation. In addition, he worked as media/TV specialist at Flathead Valley Community College in Kalispell, MT. He is writing a doctoral thesis on North American Indian Art for Rutgers University. *Memberships*: Member of the Chippewa/Cree Rocky Boy Indian Reservation, Box Elder, MT; Society of Canadian Artists of Native Ancestry, Department of Indian & Northern Development, Ottawa, Ontario. *Awards, honors*: Numerous scholarships, fellowships, awards, contracts. *Biographical sources*: The Sweetgrass Lives On: 50 Contemporary North American Indian Artists, by Jamake Highwater (Lippincott & Crowell, 1980); Native Writers Circle of the Americas - A Directory 1993; American Indian Quarterly, Vol. 17, No. 4, by University of Nebraska Press, Fall 1993; *Published works*: "Token and Taboo - Academia vs. Native Art," (article) in Fuse Magazine, Vol. II, No. 6 (July, 1988); "Issues and Trends in Contemporary Indian Art," (article) in Parallelogram, Vol. 3, No. 3 (Feb./March, 1988); editor, Networking - National Native Indian Artists Symposium IV (Graphcom Printer, Lethbridge, 1988); "Visions of Power: Contemporary Art by First Nations, Inuit and Japanese Canadians," (article) in Earth Spirit Festival catalogue (Toronto, 1991); "The Metaphysics of North American Indian Art," (article) in Indigena: Contemporary Native Perspectives, Vancouver/Toronto: Douglas & McIntyre, 1992; "Kiskayetum: Allen Sapp, a Retrospective," Regina: The Mackenzie Art Gallery, 1994; "First Nations Art, 'Canada", and the CIA: A Short Non-Fiction Story," in Studies in Critical Practices, Calgary: Canadian/Communications Research Group, University of Calgary, 1994; "Native Arts in Canada: The State, Academia, and the Cultural Establishment," (article) in Beyond Quebec: Taking Stock of Canada, McGill-Queen's University Press, 1995; "Lawrence Abbot Interview with Alfred Young Man," co-authored and published by the Canadian Journal of Native Studies, Brandon, Manitoba, Spring 1997; North American Indian Art: It's a Question of Integrity, published by Kamloops Art Gallery, Kamloops, B.C., 1998; Indian Reality Today: Contemporary Indian Art of North America, published by the Westphalian State Museum of Natural History, Muenster, Germany, 1999. Latest manuscript: "You Are On Indian Land: A Native Perspective on Native Art/Politics," a major critique of the issues and problems faced by Native artists today in North America; among many other published & unpublished articles, essays & books reviewed & published in many learned magazines, newspapers, and refereed journals over 25 years; produced and/or directed numerous videos.

YOUNKER, JASON (Coquille)
(department of anthropology chair)
Education: Cameron University (Lawton, OK), BA (Communications), 1990; Oklahoma City University, MEd (Special Education), 1994; University of Oregon, MS (Anthropology), 1997, PhD (Anthropology), 2003. *Affiliation & Address*: Associate Professor of Anthropology (tenured 2010) & Chair, Department of Sociology & Anthropology, Rochester Institute of Technology, 18 Lomb Memorial Dr., Rochester, NY 14623 (585) 475-5549. E-mail: jtygla@rit.edu. *Other professional posts*: President (2011-present), Association

of Indigenous Anthropologists, American Anthropological Association; Assistant to the Provist for Native American Relations, Rochester Institute of Technology; Assistant Vice President & Advisor to the President on Sovereignty & Government-to-Government Relations, University of Oregon, Eugene, OR. During his studies in Oregon, he was a leader in the Southwest Oregon Research Project at the Smithsonian Institution & in the subsequent Potlatches (traditional native gifting) that returned documents relating to their cultural heritage to the nine federally recognized tribes and the historic 54 bands and tribes that occupied the land that is now known as the state of Oregon.

YUCUPICIO, PETER (Pascua Yaqui)
(tribal vice chairperson)
Affiliation & Address: Vice Chairperson, Pascua Yaqui Tribe, 7474 S. Camino De Oeste, Tucson, AZ 85746 (520) 883-5000. E-mail: peter.yucupicio@pascuayaqui-nsn.gov

Z

ZACKUSE, MARIE (Tulalip)
(tribal vice chairperson)
Affiliation & Address: Vice Chairperson, Tulalip Tribes, 6406 Marine Dr., Tulalip, WA 98271 (360) 651-4000.

ZAH, PETERSON (Navajo) 1937-
(consultant, advisor)
Born December 2, 1937, on the Navajo Reservation at remote Low Mountain, Ariz. *Education*: Phoenix Community College, AA, 1960; Arizona State University, BA, 1963. *Affiliation & Address*: Advisor on American Indian Affairs, Office of the President, Arizona State University, Tempe, AZ 85287. *Other professional post*: Emeritus Board member, Friendship House of San Francisco. *Past professional post*: Chairperson (1983-87), First President (1990-94), Navajo Nation, Window Rock, AZ. *Community activities*: Wide Public School Association; Window Rock School Board (past president); National Association of the Indian Legal Services (founder); AZ State Advisory Committee to the U.S. Civil Rights Commission (member). *Memberships*: Navajo Education & Scholarship Foundation; National Tribal Chairmen's Assn; Council of Energy Resource Tribes. *Awards, honors*: Humanitarian Award, City of Albuquerque, NM--Mayor Harry Kinney; Honorary Doctorate (Humanitarian), Santa Fe College. Zah is considered on of the 100 most important Native Americans in the 20th century and a key leader in Native American government & education. He received an Honorary Doctoral Degree of Humane Letters from Arizona State University in 2005. He is also the recipient of the 2008 Martin Luther King, Jr. Servant Leadership Award. *Published works*: We Will Secure Our Future: Emowering the Navajo Nation (University of Ariona Press).

ZAH-BAHE, LORENA (Navajo)
(former association president)
Affiliation: National Indian Education Association, 700 N. Fairfax, Suite 210, Alexandria, VA 22314 (703) 838-2870.

ZAHARLICK, ANN MARIE, 1947-
(professor emerita of anthropology)
Born March 24, 1947, Scranton, Penna. *Education*: Cedar Crest College, BA, 1969; Lehigh University, MA, 1973; The American University, PhD, 1977 (Dissertation: Picuris Syntax). *Principal occupation*: Professor of anthropology. *Address*: Dept. of Anthropology, Ohio State University, 124 W. 17th Ave., Columbus, OH 43214 (614) 292-4149. E-mail: zaharlick.1@osu.edu. *Affiliations*: Instructor & curriculum development specialist, Bilingual/Multicultural Teacher Training Program for Native Americans, The University of Albuquerque, NM, 1975-77; assistant professor and language development specialist, Native American Bilingual Teacher Education Program, The University of Albuquerque, 1977-79; professor, Dept. of Anthropology, The Ohio State University, Columbus, Ohio, 1979-. *Past professional posts*: Instructor, Acoma Pueblo Bilingual Education Program, 1978; instructor, Sandia Pueblo Language Program. *Research/ Fieldwork*: Research on the Picuris language, Picuris Pueblo, NM, 1973; research on Picuris syntax, Picuris and Taos, NM, 1974-76; development of Keresan language spoken by the pueblos of Acoma, Cochiti, Santo Domingo, Laguna, Zia, Santa Ana, and San Felipe, and development of curriculum guides and bilingual education materials in Keres and Picuris; analysis of Picuris syntax & semology--updating of John P. Harrington's Picuris Children's Stories & preparation of a dictionary and grammar for use in the Picuris bilingual education program, 1976-; linguistic research on passive construction and tone in Picuris, Picuris, NM, 1980-81. *Community activities*: Assisted in the establishment of bilingual education programs at Acoma, Laguna, Cochiti, Santa Ana, and Picuris Pueblos, 1975-79; produced teaching guides & materials for the Picuris Bilingual Education Programs (10 stories & booklets in Picuris, 1975-); presentations on American Indians to 4th & 5th grade students in the Albuquerque and Columbus Public Schools, 1978-82. *Memberships*: American

Anthropological Assn (Fellow); American Assn for the Advancement of Science; American Ethnological Society; Linguistic Assn of the Southwest; Linguistic Society of America; New Mexico Assn for Bilingual Education; Society for Applied Anthropology (Fellow), Society for the Study of the Indigenous Languages of the Americas; Southwestern Anthropological Assn; The Southwest Circle; Southwest Journal of Linguistics (editorial board, 1985-87); et al. *Published works*: Picuris Syntax (University Microfilms, 1977); A Picuris/English Dictionary; Picuris Grammar; editor, Native Languages of the Americas (special issue of the Journal of the Linguistic Assn of the Southwest, 1981); numerous book chapters, articles, book reviews, papers & presentation.

ZASTROW, PHILIP (Hoopa)
  (ITEPP director)
Address & Affiliation: Director (2007-present), Indian Teacher & Educational Personnel Program (ITEPP), 1 Harpst St., Spidell House #85, Arcata, CA 95521 (707) 826-3672 E-Mail: philip.zastrow@humboldt.edu. *Past professional post*: Student services coordinator, ITEPP, 1996-2007. As coordinator, Phil was responsible for recruiting & retention services; and as director, he does some of the same duties as well as liaison with the Native community. The majority of time spent as director is with administration of ITEPP.

ZAUKAR, JANE (Athapascan)
  (village president)
Affiliation: Native Village of Sleetmute, P.O. Box 21, Sleetmute, AK 99668 (907) 449-9901.

ZEDENO, MARIA NIEVES
  (professor of anthropology)
Education: Southern Methodist University, PhD, 1995. *Affiliation*: Dept. of Anthropology, Emil Haury Anthropology Bldg., Rm. 221A, University of Arizona, Tucson, AZ 85721 (520) 621-2585. E-mail: mzedeno@u.arizona.edu. *Interests*: American Indian cultural resource preservation.

ZELL, PATRICIA M. (Navajo/Arapaho)
  (attorney)
Education: Georgetown University Law School, JD, 1981. *Affiliation & Address*: Partner (2005-present), Zell & Cox Law, PC, 1210 Hundy Place, Alexandria, VA 22307 (703) 660-6697. Patricia is a partner in Zell & Cox Law, P.C., a law firm that specializes in laws affecting American Indians, Alaska Natives and Native Hawaiians. She joined the staff of the U.S. Senate Select Committee on Indian Affairs in 1978 as a professional staff member, becoming Chief Counsel to the Committee in 1986 and Staff Director in 1990. During her 18 year tenure, she worked on major legislative initiatives developed by the Committee in conjunction with tribal leaders, including the Indian Health Care Improvement Act, the Indian Self-Determination and Education Assistance Act, the Indian Education Act, and the Native American Graves Protection and Repatriation Act. She retired from public service in March 2005. For nearly 30 years, she also served as Editor of the Indian Law Reporter. *Awards, honors*: She received the 1992 Distinguished Service Award from the American Indian Resources Institute. She has been recognized by numerous organizations for her career-long dedication to Native nations and issues.

ZENDEJAS, EDOUARDO (Omaha)
  (professor & director of Native American studies)
Address & Affiliation: Professor of Native American Studies (2002-present), 307 ASH, University of Nebraska, Omaha, 6001 Dodge St., Omaha, NE 68182-0213 (402) 554-2624. E-mail: ezendejas@unomaha.edu. Teaches courses on Native American mascots Native American law.

ZEPEDA, GAYLE (Pomo)
  (rancheria chairperson)
Affiliation: Redwood Valley Rancheria, P.O. Box 499, Redwood Valley, CA 95470 (707) 485-0361.

ZEPEDA, OFELIA (Tohono O'odham)
  (Regents professor of linguistics, poet, editor)
Education: University of Arizona, PhD, 1984. *Affiliation & Address*: Regents Professor of Linguistics & Director, American Indian Studies, American Indian Language Development Institute, The University of Arizona, Dept. of Language, Reading & Culture, Communication Bldg., Room 108B, 1430 E. Second St., P.O. Box 210069, Tucson, AZ 85721 (520) 621-8294. E-mail: ofelia@email.arizona.edu. Dr. Zepeda specializes in writing English & Tohono O'odham languages. She teaches Toono O'odham language courses and survey courses on American Indian languages. Her research areas include language variation, language policy, and issues of endangered languages. Her writing is concerned with the American Southwest, environment, history, and culture. She is the series editor of the Native American literacy publication series, "Sun Tracks," focusing on Native American authors, University of Arizona Press. *Other professional post*: Affiliate Faculty, American Indian Studies (director, 1986-91), University of Arizona, Tucson, AZ. *Awards, honors*: 1996 Tanner Award for significant contributions to the American Indian

Community awarded by the UA Indian Alumni Association; recipient of award from the UA Graduate College for service to graduate students. In 1999, Dr. Zepeda was recognized with a prestigious MacArthur Fellowship from the MacArthur Foundation for her life long work on American Indian language issues; Principal Investigator & Director of the Ford Foundation project on Training Native American Language Immersion Teachers. *Published works*: A Papago Grammar (University of Arizona Press), the first book on the grammar of Tohono O'odham language; Tohono O'odham Grammar; Ocean Power: Poems from the Desert (University of Arizona Press); Jewed 'I-Hoi/Earth Movements, bilingual collection with CD (Kore Press). Her poetry appears in various anthologies and collections.

ZEPHIER, JODY (Yankton Sioux)
  (tribal vice chairperson)
Affiliation & Address: Vice Chairperson, Yankton Sioux Tribe, Box 248, Marty, SD 57361 (605) 384-3804.

ZEPHIER, MITCHELL C. (*Cetan Ho Waste*) (Lower Brule Lakota) 1952-
  (Plains Indian jeweler; shop owner)
Born July 5, 1952, Pine Ridge, S.D. *Education*: High school. *Principal occupation*: Plains Indian jeweler. *Address & Affiliation*: Artisan/Owner, Whispering Thunder, 2107 Oak Ave., Rapid City, SD 57701 (605) 716-7552. *Exhibits/Shows*: Intertribal Missouri River Arts Festival, Lakota Council, Chamberlain, SD, July 1986 (won 1st Place Ribbon & cash award); American Indian Gallery, Steamboat Springs, CO, Feb. 1987; Northern Plains Tribal Arts 88, Sioux Falls, SD, Sept. 1988 (won 1st Place; White Buffalo Winter---Opulence Jewelers, Breckenridge, CO, Feb. 1989; among others. *Interests*: "I've developed a singular and totally original style of jewelry that is a combination of artistry and craftsmanship. I define my work as 'Lakota Jewelry Visions' because there is a visionary aspect to it as well as an expressionistic aspect that describes many ideas, legends, wintercounts, and Lakota cultural concepts. I work in sterling silver, brass, jeweler's gold, copper, Geman silver and have just recently begun to work in 14 karat gold. I incorporate stones and materials from the Northern Plains area. My work can be summed up as an honoring or a dedication to the heritage & spiritual values of my Lakota ancestors. My work is displayed in numerous private & public collections." *Biographical sources*: "Indian Trader" magazine article by Jane Nauman, Jan. 1980; "Dakota West" magazine article by James Aplan, Summer 1981; "Four Winds" magazine article by Rosemary Webb, Summer 1982; "Rapid City Journal" - two part article by Jane Nauman, Sept. 1984; Lost and Found Traditions, book by Ralph T. Coe (University of Washington Press, 1986); Crafts in America, book by Constance Stapleton (Harper & Row, 1988).

ZEPHIER, RICHARD (Oglala Lakota)
  (tribal executive director)
Education: Northern State University, BA; Penn State University, MA & PhD (Educational Administration); University of Phoenix, MBA. *Affiliation & Address*: Executive Director, Oglala Lakota Nation, P.O. Box 2070, Pine Ridge, SD 57770 (605) 867-8429. E-mail: rzephier@oglala.org.

ZEPHIER, TRACEY FISCHER (Cheyenne River Sioux)
  (attorney)
Education: Yale law School, JD, 1999. *Affiliation & Address*: Associate, 2008-10, Partner, 2010-present, Fredericks Peebles & Morgan, LLC, 2040 Main #102, Rapid City, SD 57702 (605) 347-1265. E-mail: tfischer@ndnlaw.com. *Other professsional posts*: Member, Board of Directors, Partnership With Native Americans; President, Wind Energy Tribes United (WETU); adjunct professor, U. of South Dakota School of Law, (Indian Country economic development); Oglala Lakota College, on tribal governance issues. *Practice areas*: Tribal/ state relations; tribal legal & physical infrastructure; tribal financial & real estate transactions. Ms. Fischer has done extensive legal work for Cheyenne River Sioux Tribe & other tribes in Northern Plains region. *Past professional post*: President & CEO of First Nations Oweesta Corp. in Rapid City, SD developing community development financial institutions (CDFIs), tribal enterprises & tribal citizen entrepreneurship systems in Native communities throughout the U.S.

ZIBELL, WILLIAM (Eskimo)
  (village president)
Affiliation: Noorvik Native Community, P.O. Box 71, Noorvik, AK 99763 (907) 636-2144.

ZIEGLER, WILLIAM 'BILL' (Lower Brule Sioux)
  (president & CEO)
Affiliation & Address: President & CEO, Little Earth of United Tribes, 2495 18th Avenue South, Minneapolis, MN 55404 (612) 724-0023 Fax 724-1703. Website: www.littleearth.org. *Program*: Homeownership Iniiative (LEUTHI).

ZIMMERMAN, LARRY JOHN 1947-
(professor of anthropology & museum studies)
Born May 24, 1947, Anamosa, Iowa. *Education*: University of Iowa, BA, 1969, MA, 1971; University of Kansas, PhD, 1976. *Affiliations & Address*: Professor of Anthropology, University of South Dakota, Vermillion, SD, 1974-96; University of Iowa, Iowa City (American Indian & Native Studies, 1996-2001; Dept. of Anthropology, 2002); Minnesota Historical Society, Dept. of Archaeology, 2003-0; professor of anthropology & museum studies, Dept. of Anthropology & Museum Studies, 433 Cavanaugh, Indiana University-Purdue University-Indianapolis, 425 University Blvd., Indianapolis, IN 46202 (317) 274-2383. E-mail: larzimme@iupui.edu. Dr. Zimmerman is a public scholar of Native American Representation. Website: www.larryjzimmerman.com. *Past professional posts*: Editor, South Dakota Archaeology, 1977-79; editor, Plains Anthropologist, 1987-89; editor, World Archaeological Bulletin, 1990-94; secretary, World Archaeological Congress, 1990-94; chairman, Dept. of Social Behavior, 1988-. *Military service*: U.S. Air Force, 1965-69, 2nd Lt. *Community activities*: Vermillion Chamber of Commerce (Board of Directors, 1983-84); Friends of the W.H. Over Museum (vice president, Board of Directors); consultant for Native American Rights Fund, American Indian Movement, American Indians Against Desecration, Pawnee Tribe of Oklahoma, and other groups; Friends of Grand Portage (director); Minnesota Archaeological Society (director). *Awards, honors*: Presidential Fellow (USD), 1985; Burlington Northern Award for Meritorious Teaching, 1986; Burlington Northern Award for Meritorious Scholar, 1990; Distinguished Regents Professor, 1990. *Interests*: "Primary interest is in the prehistory of North America, especially the Great Plains, others are ethical treatment of the dead, public education in archaeology, Native American rights." *Published works*: Prehistoric Locational Behavior (University of Iowa Press, 1977); The Crow Creek Massacre (Corps of Engineers-Omaha, 1981); The Future of South Dakota's Past (South Dakota Archaeological Society, 1981); People of Prehistoric South Dakota (University of Nebraska Press, 1985); South Dakota Leaders (University of South Dakota Press, 1989); Idea to Institution: Higher Education in South Dakota (University of South Dakota Press, 1989); Native North America (Little Brown, 1996); Indians & Anthropology (University of Arizona Press, 1997); Ethical Issues in Archaeology (Alta Mira Press, 2003); The Archaeologist's Toolkit (Alta Mira Press, 2003); Native North American Indian/First Nations: Myth, Life, and Art (Duncan Baird, 2003); Exploring the Life, Myth & Art of Native Americans (Rosen Publishing, 2010); numerous articles.

ZIOLKOWSKI, ANNE
(foundation/museum director)
Affiliation & Address: Crazy Horse Memorial Foundation & Museum, Ave. of the Chiefs, The Black Hills, Crazy Horse, SD 57730 (605) 673-4681.

ZOBEL, MELISSA TANTAQUIDGEON (Mohegan)
(tribal historian)
Affiliation & Address: Tribal Historian (1991-present), Executive Director of the Department of Cultural & Community Programs, Mohegan Tribe, 5 Crow Hill Rd., Uncasville, CT 06382 (860) 862-6100. *Community activities*: Mohegan Medicine Woman in 2008, following in the footsteps of her great aunt Gladys Tantaquidgeon who taught her the traditional herbs & remedies of the Mohegan & Delaware tribes; Editorial Board, NI Ya Yo (tribal newspaper). *Past professional post*: Tribal Historian in Residence for 2012, U. of Massachusetts, Amherst. *Awards, honors*: She received the first annual Chief Little Hatchet Awad in 1996, granted for contributions to the success & survival of the Mohegan people. *Published works*: The Lasting of the Mohegans (1995); Makiawisug: The Gift of the Little People (1997); Medicine Trail: The Life & Lessons of Gladys Tantaquidgeon (2000); Oracles: A Novel (2004); Fire Hollow (2010).

ZOGRY, MICHAEL J.
(associate professor of religious studies)
Education: University of California, Santa Barbara, PhD, 2003. *Affiliation & Address*: Director, Indigenous Studies Program, College of Liberal Arts & Sciences, University of Kansas, Lippincott, Rm. 6, 1410 Jayhawk Blvd., Lawrence, KS 66045 (785) 864-5271. E-mail: mzogry@ku.edu. *Other professional post*: Associate professor, Religious Studies Dept. University of Kansas (2003-present). *Research Interests*: Native American/First Nations religions; theory & method in the study of religions; ritual studies; U.S. religious history; performance & play in the study of religions. His area of specialty is Native American/First Nations religions. *Published work*: Anetso, the Cherokee Ball Game: At the Center of Ceremony & Identity (University of North Carolina Press, 2010).

ZOLBROD, PAUL G.
(adjunct professor of humanities)
Affiliation & Address: Adjunct Professor of Humanities, Dine College, P.O. Box 849, Crownpoint, NM 87313 (505) 786-4100. *Past professional post*: Senior Curator, Museum of Indian Arts & Culture, Museum of New Mexico, 1994-97. *Published works*: Dine Bahane: The Navajo Creation Story (University of New Mexico Press, 1984).

ZOTIGH, DENNIS W. (*T'don-say*) (Kiowa/Santee Dakota/San Juan Pueblo)
(research historian)
Born in Lawton, Okla. *Education*: University of Oklahoma, BA (Journalism/Public Relations). *Affiliation & Address*: American Indian Research Historian, American Indian Culture & Preservation Office, Oklahoma History Center, Oklahoma Historical Society, 800 Nazih Zuhdi Dr., Oklahoma City, OK 73105 (405) 521-2491. E-mail: dzotigh@ok-history.mus.ok.us. *Other professional posts*: National speaker on Indian culture and issues, American Speakers Bureau; Executive board of directors, American Indian Broadcasting, Inc.; Smithsonian Museum Affiliates Program, Washington, DC, 2002-present. *Awards, honors*: Powwow awards for powwow dancing & singing competition; emcee for the Miss Indian World Pageant, Gathering of Nations, Albuquerque, NM, 1993, 1994, 1995; co-founder of the World Hoop Dance Championships, Heard Museum, Phoenix, AZ; consultant/cultural advisor for Hallmark Miniseries, "Dream Keepers," ABC TV, 2003; consultant/history advisor for "World of American Indian Dance," NBC TV, 2002. *Community activities*: Board member, Oklahoma Folk Life Council. *Memberships*: Mountain Plains Museums Association (Little, CO, 2001-present); Oklahoma Museums Association (Oklahoma City, 2001-present).

ZUMIGA, ARTHUR W. (Lakota)
(Indian education program director)
Affiliation: Rapid City School District, Indian Education Program, 300 Sixth St., Rapid City, SD 57701 (605) 394-4071. E-mail: arthur.zumiga@csac.rcas.org.

ZUNI, CHRISTINE (Isleta Pueblo)
(attorney)
Address: P.O. Box 402, Isleta Pueblo, NM 87022 (505) 869-3421. *Membership*: United Indian Pueblo Lawyers Association.

ZUNI, MAX (Isleta Pueblo)
(pueblo 1st lt. governor)
Affiliations: Pueblo of Isleta, P.O. Box 1290, Isleta, NM 87022 (505) 869-3111.

ZUNI, WILLARD (Zuni Pueblo)
(Pueblo lt. governor)
Affiliation: Pueblo of Zuni, P.O. Box 339, Zuni, NM 87327 (505) 782-7000.

ZUNI CRUZ, CHRISTINE (Isleta Pueblo)
(professor of law)
Education: Stanford University, BA, 1980; University of New Mexico School of Law, JD, 1982. *Affiliation & Address*: Professor of Law, Associate Dean for the Indian Law Program, University of New Mexico School of Law, 1117 Stanford NE, MSC11 1123, Albuquerque, NM 87131 (505) 277-1007. E-mail: zunicruz@law.unm.edu. Christine went to the UNM law school in 1993 to establish the Southwest Indian Law Clinic. In her research and teaching, Zuni Cruz, a member of Isleta Pueblo, explores law and culture, including the impact of law on Indian families, the practice of Indian Law and lawyering for native communities and the internal traditional and modern law of indigenous peoples domestically and internationally. In 2001, she traveled to Greenland where she helped teach an intensive course on international indigenous human rights at the International Training Center of Indigenous Peoples. *Other professional posts*: She currently serves as an associate justice on the Isleta Appellate Court; editor-in-chief of the Tribal Law Journal, an online law journal dedicated to the internal law of indigenous peoples. *Past professional posts*: Served as tribal judge for the Pueblo of Laguna and the Pueblo of Taos., a tribal gaming commissioner and been in provate practice for ten years. Awards, honors: The first Pueblo woman to earn tenure as a law professor.

ZUNIGA, GLORIA (Cheyenne)
(program director)
Education: University of Oklahoma, BSN/RN. *Affiliation*: Director, RN/HIV AIDS Education & Awareness Program, Association of American Indian Physicians, 1235 Sovereign Row, Suite C-7, Oklahoma City, OK 73108 (405) 946-7072. Gloria has been with AAIP since 1999. She has worked in the field of HIV/AIDS for more than 20 years and is considered one of the pioneers of prevention & education on HIV/AIDS for Native American peoples having won numerous awards for her accomplishments.

ZUNIGHA, CURTIS (Lenni Lenape)
(tribal manager)
Affiliation & Address: Manager, Delaware Tribe of Indians, 170 NE Barbara, Bartlesville, OK 74006 (918) 337-6573. E-mail: czunigha@delawaretribe.org. *Past tribal post*: Chief, Delaware Tribe, 1994-98; two terms tribal council; Housing Director & Election Chair. *Military service*: U.S. Air Force. *Past professional post*: Manager, American Indian/Alaska Native program for the 2010 Census in Washington, DC, 2009-11. *Awards, honors*: 2011 Gold Medal from the U.S. Department of Commerce for distinguished performance.

$195.00   10-30-17

LONGWOOD PUBLIC LIBRARY
800 Middle Country Road
Middle Island, NY 11953
(631) 924-6400
longwoodlibrary.org

LIBRARY HOURS

Monday-Friday	9:30 a.m. - 9:00 p.m.
Saturday	9:30 a.m. - 5:00 p.m.
Sunday (Sept-June)	1:00 p.m. - 5:00 p.m.